THE NEW NATURAL HISTORY OF
MADAGASCAR

VOLUME 1

THE NEW NATURAL HISTORY OF MADAGASCAR

VOLUME 1

EDITED BY STEVEN M. GOODMAN

SUBJECT EDITORS
Aristide Andrianarimisa, Amanda H. Armstrong, Andrew Cooke, Maarten De Wit, Jörg U. Ganzhorn, Laurent Gautier, Steven M. Goodman, Julia P. G. Jones, William L. Jungers, David W. Krause, Olivier Langrand, Porter Peter Lowry III, Paul A. Racey, Achille P. Raselimanana, Roger J. Safford, John S. Sparks, Melanie L. J. Stiassny, Pablo Tortosa, and Miguel Vences

PRINCETON UNIVERSITY PRESS
PRINCETON AND OXFORD

Published by Princeton University Press
41 William Street, Princeton, New Jersey 08540
6 Oxford Street, Woodstock, Oxfordshire OX20 1TR

press.princeton.edu

Library of Congress Cataloging-in-Publication Data
Names: Goodman, Steven M., editor. | Andrianarimisa, Aristide, editor.
Title: The new natural history of Madagascar / edited by Steven M. Goodman ; subject editors: Aristide Andrianarimisa [and sixteen others].
Description: Princeton : Princeton University Press, 2022. | Includes bibliographical references and index. | Contents: History of Scientific Exploration—Geology—Climate—Forest and Grassland Ecology—Human Ecology—Diversity, Evolutionary History, Transmission of Zoonotic Pathogens, and Other Infectious Microbes—Marine and Coastal Ecosystems—Plants—Invertebrates—Freshwater Fishes—Amphibians—Reptiles—Birds—Mammals—Conservation.
Identifiers: LCCN 2021048337 (print) | LCCN 2021048338 (ebook) | ISBN 9780691222622 (hardback) | ISBN 9780691229409 (ebook)
Subjects: LCSH: Natural history—Madagascar. | Biodiversity—Madagascar. | Biodiversity conservation—Madagascar.
Classification: LCC QH195.M2 N395 2022 (print) | LCC QH195.M2 (ebook) | DDC 508.691–dc23
LC record available at https://lccn.loc.gov/2021048337
LC ebook record available at https://lccn.loc.gov/2021048338

British Library Cataloging-in-Publication Data is available

Editorial: Robert Kirk and Megan Mendonça
Production Editorial: Kathleen Cioffi
Jacket Design: Wanda España
Production: Steven Sears
Publicity: Matthew Taylor and Caitlyn Robinson
Copyeditors: Amy K. Hughes, Laurel Anderton, Frances Cooper, Patricia Fogarty, Judith Hoffman, and Maia Vaswani
Typeset and Design: D & N Publishing, Wiltshire, UK

Jacket images:
Front of jacket: © Harald Schütz
Back of jacket: (Top left) V. Soarimalala; (top right) WWF; (bottom left) F. Rasambainarivo; (bottom right) Matthew S. Leslie/WCS Ocean Giants; (center) L. Dinraths

Publication of this book has been aided by Bioculture (Mauritius) Ltd., Ellis Goodman Family Foundation, Field Museum of Natural History (FMNH), Fondation pour les Aires Protégées et la Biodiversité de Madagascar (FAPBM), and Programme des Nations Unies pour le Développement (PNUD)

This book has been composed in Garamond Premier Pro and Brandon Grotesque
Printed on acid-free paper. ∞

Printed in Italy

10 9 8 7 6 5 4 3 2 1

CONTENTS

For chapters 10–15, list of contributors, and indexes see Volume 2

FOREWORD

By Chantal Radimilahy

Two decades have elapsed since the beginning of the third millennium CE, and in 2020 Madagascar celebrated its 60th anniversary since the return of political independence. And it was about two decades ago that *The Natural History of Madagascar* (University of Chicago Press, 2003) was published. That book was a hitherto unparalleled synthesis, the first since the 40-volume series of Alfred Grandidier and collaborators, *Histoire physique, naturelle et politique de Madagascar* (1875–1954), on the multiple facets of the island's natural history. The 2003 book also heralded a turning point for many Malagasy scientists publishing in the Anglophone world. The completely revised *New Natural History of Madagascar* presented herein attests to the advances over the past 20 years in multiple fields of research, including those related to biodiversity in a broad sense and the history of humans on the island.

Indeed, the study of people cannot be separated from their environment, and many mysteries remain to be resolved. Both natural and cultural heritage define the specificity and identity of a country, which is most notably the case for the island nation of Madagascar. The academic world is informed often of new revelations on the island, such as the discovery of a fossil that forces revision of past axioms on the ancestry of prehistoric animals, or evidence that the first human colonization of the island reaches deeper into prehistory than was thought.

The study of Madagascar's flora and fauna is progressing rapidly, and the results published herein bear witness to this. At the same time, points of human history remain to be resolved, and the uncovering of evidence to establish when, who, and following what pathways people originally settled the island in turn allows historians to shed previously imposed hypotheses and form a coherent general synthesis of these critical questions. Eminent scientists and academics, or simple travelers of past centuries, have also been interested in solving what Hubert Deschamps (1960: 13) called, in his *Histoire générale de Madagascar* and in reference to the origin and complex history of the Malagasy people, "the most beautiful enigma in the world."

In 1960, with the beginning of the Madagascar university system, French archaeologist Pierre Vérin was convinced that the human settlement of Madagascar began earlier than the 14th or15th century, the proposed dating in that era, and launched the study of archaeology on the island. The results of the first surveys provided dates around the 10th century, further strengthening Vérin's conviction. This pioneering work was continued by Jean-Aimé Rakotoarisoa and myself, then and today as president of the African Archaeology Network Association, which provided assistance to strengthen the institutional framework of research by bringing together colleagues from the African continent. Before 1970, apprentice archaeologists were initiated into different research, and important results on various aspects were produced. The real succession of training seasoned national archaeologists began in earnest in the late 1970s and early 1980s. These individuals produced theses and hypotheses, building upon one another, that made it possible to better understand and bring to light aspects until then unknown about Malagasy culture.

The Institut de Civilisations Musée d'Art et d'Archéologie (ICMAA), a cultural research institution at the University of Antananarivo, established in 1970, has been from the start a benevolet crossroads for research groups, bringing together nationals and international students and academics. These researchers have made significant contributions based on considerable efforts to improve our knowledge of the past. At first, questions revolved around the timing and identification of Madagascar's first human colonizers. The debates for several decades focused on the origins of the island's settlement and were dominated by studies of the Malagasy language compared mainly to those of southeastern Asia. Subsequently, archaeologists were able to obtain substantial new results and insights by broadening their fields of investigation with other disciplines, including paleontology, paleoecology, and genetics. Currently, the study of genetics is becoming an essential tool in understanding human settlement of the island and the three-part question of when, who, and following what pathway people arrived. However, the contributions of different disciplines are not always consistent.

Different aspects of the cultural history of Madagascar have been brought to light during the past couple of decades. The diversification of research partnerships and priorities, under the direction of national archaeologists and in collaboration with international groups, has made it possible to reorient study themes and associated methodologies. This period has seen the importance of Malagasy students and scholars being recognized as they are incorporated into networks of researchers working in the southwestern region of the Indian Ocean, with results that have been rather astonishing. During this period, the date of the first human presence has been pushed back in time, as the discoveries include a rock-shelter site with microlithic tools in the far north that was occupied by humans about 2500 BCE. There is also a provocative report from paleontologists in the central south of subfossil animal bones with perimortem incision marks dating to around 10,000 BCE. First analyses and publications of rock paintings include symbols similar to those from Borneo, the place of origin for a portion of the Malagasy people. Hence, extraordinary strides have been made since the discoveries of Pierre Vérin and his colleagues, who used classical archaeological techniques, and these new dates, which are not without considerable debate, push deeper into time the first evidence of humans on the island. Many questions remain unanswered, including those about the sequence and origin of the establishment of human settlement on the island and its material culture.

We must maintain hope that in the future, despite climatic change and environmental perturbations, the most important archaeological sites on Madagascar will be preserved. It is also hoped that sites buried or erased from collective memory, including those underwater, will be rediscovered, and that the results will provide interesting elements for progressively improving our knowledge and promotion of the Malagasy heritage. Arriving in 2020, the global Covid-19 pandemic is also likely to impact the natural environment and the manner in which people interact with and exploit it. This will certainly affect investigations currently underway and those that remain to be carried out. Malagasy national institutions will have to redefine policies to support research in disciplines ranging from the humanities and social sciences to the biological and geological sciences.

The synthetic book presented herein, *The New Natural History of Madagascar*, should be the point of departure and contribute to the advancement of hypotheses and research programs related to the history of the human presence on the island, as well as aspects related to its fauna and flora, and, the most critical point, the conservation of both Malagasy culture and biodiversity. I take this opportunity to warmly thank all those who have contributed to this book for sharing their knowledge and the results of their research.

Chantal Radimilahy, Archaeologist and Past Director of the ICMAA (2007–2015)
Antananarivo, August 2020

FOREWORD

By Peter H. Raven

The biodiversity of Madagascar, perhaps the richest and most interesting of any part of the world, is incredibly diverse, with many ancient evolutionary lineages represented. Beautifully illuminating many of its features, this book's valuable and highly informative collection of contributions was organized by Steve Goodman of the Field Museum in Chicago; the first iteration of this project (2003) was coedited with Jonathan Benstead. The first week Steve joined the staff of the Field Museum in 1989, he took off for Madagascar, and he has never looked back. Deeply devoted to the study and conservation of Madagascar's biological and human riches, he has personally contributed a great deal to our understanding and conservation of the region and has recruited hundreds of others to join the effort. During the relatively short span since the 2003 book appeared, our knowledge of the island's biodiversity has increased greatly; the protected areas have been expanded substantially; and, most important, the number of active, trained Malagasy biologists has grown rapidly to its current impressive level.

Madagascar gained its independence from France in 1960. At the time, there were very few trained Malagasy biologists, whereas now there are hundreds, most of them engaged in research, teaching, or conservation activities. Madagascar's population has grown from 5.1 million at independence to about 28 million now and is projected to increase substantially. Rural agriculturists, the great majority of the population, depend directly on the forests not only for watershed protection but for fuel, some of their food, and most of the medicines on which they depend. However, a substantial portion of forests still standing in 1960 have been destroyed in the ensuing 60 years. Globally, Madagascar is one of the five poorest countries. Even after 60 years without war, it is the only country in which the national GDP has fallen behind the level of 1960. It is important to note that the modern "biological" crisis facing Madagascar is a direct result of its long-term "social-economic" crisis. So let us consider why its biodiversity remains so important; briefly review the efforts to understand and conserve it; and discuss some of the socioeconomic and other steps that will be necessary if much natural vegetation and animal life is to survive beyond the next few decades.

Madagascar is less than 10% larger than France, about 1120 km from north to south and 570 km across at its widest point; its higher mountains reach over 2500 m in elevation. The island lies mostly in the tropics; if it were placed along the west coast of the American tropics, it would extend from the latitude of central Mexico south to Nicaragua. Although the island lies only about 420 km off the coast of Mozambique, Madagascar has not been joined with Africa for about 160 million years, well before the origin of most modern groups of plants and animals. After separating from Africa, the island remained joined to India until about 88 million years ago, when India began its northward displacement to collide far to the north with the mainland of Asia. As is generally accepted, there have been no geologically recent opportunities for overland migration between Madagascar and any other landmass, so that virtually all of the native plants and animals there now have clearly reached the island over water. For example, lemurs originated 53–62 million years ago; their ancestors probably reached Madagascar by rafting from continental Africa.

Humans have been actively sailing around the coasts of Madagascar for millennia and formed permanent settlements there from at least 450 CE onward. Various cultural groups have colonized the island over the years. Based on the modern Malagasy population, these settlers included Austronesian people from the east and Bantu people from the African mainland, the populations of which subsequently expanded into different portions of the island. Some of the island's grasslands are, without any doubt, natural features of the island, including some of the Central Highlands, while others were formed as agriculturists spread inland from their original coastal settlements.

After some centuries of European coastal exploration and periodic onshore forays, Britain and France emerged as the two nations competing for control of Madagascar. In 1882, they agreed that it would become a French protectorate, and in 1897, it was reclassified as a French colony, which it remained for 63 years. The French added cities and institutions, including universities, to those that already existed when they arrived. In addition, they instituted large-scale agriculture to produce export products. Meanwhile, the rapidly growing rural population caused extensive degradation of most of the island's forests, a process that, augmented by growing commercial exploitation, continues rapidly today. Under such circumstances, the destruction of virtually all of Madagascar's native ecosystems is assured unless large-scale, well-directed funding, necessarily mostly foreign aid, is somehow soon coupled with a stable government and social justice.

A wonderful feature of Madagascar is that there is probably no place in the world that has a richer or more interesting set of plants and animals. For example, the island is estimated to be home to about 14,000 species of vascular plants, perhaps 95% of them found nowhere else; they amount to more than a fifth of the plant species in the entire Afrotropical region, an area 40 times as large. Prior to independence and through the 1960s, the biodiversity of Madagascar was studied mostly by French scientists, based either on the island or in France. By the 1970s, Malagasy universities—especially the Université d'Antananarivo and other scholarly institutions—were enrolling substantially increased numbers of Malagasy students. An important conference on conservation was organized under the leadership of the late Joseph Andianampianina in 1970, as the need for reversing some of the destructive trends became obvious.

In 1972, the political situation in Madagascar abruptly swung from an almost complete reliance on France to an exclusive and growing relationship with the Soviet Union and other Soviet bloc countries, a transition that rapidly led to a highly destructive economic collapse. When Alison Jolly and Alison Richard began their lemur studies on Madagascar in about 1964 and 1970, respectively, they found biological research there still being conducted almost exclusively by French professors and other scientists; they had very few Malagasy counterparts at the time. From this period, the transition over the years to today's Madagascar—with a wonderful, talented, dedicated cadre of biologists and conservationists—has been remarkable. In different manners, these two primatologists set the stage for what would unfold over the course of many decades, and many of the advances presented herein stem from their vibrant interest in the natural history of Madagascar, needed conservation actions, and the island's future.

Like Alison Jolly and Alison Richard, a few other scientists from abroad began, during the 1970s, to visit Madagascar and to accept Malagasy students at their European and American universities. Starting in 1972, though, the foreigners were greatly restricted in their activities and eventually were prohibited from even visiting the country. In an attempt to find a way out of this dilemma, a group of those who had begun research and training activities earlier, including Alison Jolly, Alison Richard, Bob Martin, Elwyn Simons, Yves Rumpler, Bob Sussman, and myself, convened in early 1983 on the island of Jersey; the Jersey Wildlife Preservation Trust (now the Durrell Wildlife Conservation Trust) had been active in Madagascar for a number of years. Following her marriage to Gerald Durrell four years earlier, Lee Durrell had taken up an active conservation and training role on Madagascar. Significantly, the Jersey meeting was also attended by Madame Berthe Rakotosamimanana and Voara Randrianasolo from Madagascar, who attended at some personal political risk. Madame Berthe (a name universally used as an expression of both respect and affection) was head of the Department of Paleontology at the Université d'Antananarivo, and she also held one of the leading positions in Madagascar's Ministry of Higher Education and Research. At the same time, Madagascar politically was moving slowly back toward a relationship with France and a general opening to other countries. The Jersey meeting stressed cooperative research and training, which proved to be a very successful formula over the years to come.

From the early 1980s onward, Madagascar has welcomed many foreign researchers interested in forging relationships for conservation, research, and training. For example, the World Wildlife Fund (WWF), which had begun working on the island in the 1960s, resumed both biodiversity and conservation activities there; it established a permanent program in 1986, and in 1989, under the helm of the late Martin Nicoll and Olivier Langrand, published a critical review of the island's protected-area system. In 1984, Russ Mittermeier established a WWF–US program that was initially centered on Alison Richard's Bezà-Mahafaly project in the south but grew from that point onward. In 1985, the WWF, the World Bank, and the United States Agency for International Development (USAID) together organized a conference on development and conservation that became a real turning point for conservation activities on the island and that, in several different ways, has led to major advances in a range of programs.

Russ Mittermeier moved to Conservation International (CI) in 1989, establishing a major and enduring emphasis on Madagascar, which continues to the present day. In 2017, Russ moved to Global Wildlife Conservation and again established a presence on Madagascar for that organization. The WWF–Madagascar Ecology Training Program (ETP) was initiated in 1991 at WWF by Martin Nicoll, Sheila O'Connor, and Olivier Langrand under the highly effective and dedicated supervision of Steve Goodman. Both the ETP and its Malagasy derivative Association Vahatra, cofounded by Steve Goodman and several Malagasy field biologists in 2005 (it became independent from the ETP in 2007), have been active in the education and advancement of Malagasy scientists, particularly in zoology and ecology. Together, they have trained over 500 Malagasy students, many of them working in fields related to conservation and the advancement of science.

In 1984, the Missouri Botanical Garden, which had initiated collecting trips to the island in the 1970s, established a permanent presence and, in 1986, a headquarters. The garden recruited a largely self-directed staff of between 100 and 150 Malagasy citizens for its research, conservation, and education programs there. Largely as a result of their continuing efforts, as well as those of a number of national and international botanical institutions, the estimated number of flowering plant species on Madagascar (more than 95% of them endemic) has been increased by two-thirds from the 8500 thought to occur on the island in the 1970s to an estimated 14,000 today. The garden's conservation efforts, which have resulted in the protection of 44,504 ha of land, centered on a dozen villages in which livelihoods have been enhanced and many inhabitants employed for conservation purposes. In addition, the garden has trained or helped train more than 150 Malagasy students, mainly through cooperative programs with local universities and a few abroad. Some 85% of these students are engaged in careers that make full use of their training. In addition, several hundred university students have been brought from overseas to study and work at the garden's conservation sites in country.

The British Royal Botanic Gardens, Kew, initiated a robust research program on Madagascar in 1986. Over the following three decades, Kew has effectively emphasized revisionary work on important plant groups, such as palms, legumes, and orchids, and currently employs about 40 Malagasy collaborators. Kew helped establish the Itremo protected area and several others, and has trained a number of graduate students.

In addition to specific training programs, Malagasy scientists and students have, since the 1980s, been appropriately involved in virtually every foreign-based effort that has taken place in the country.

In 1990, the Peregrine Fund, for example, began an effort in Madagascar that is now under the leadership of Lily-Arison Rene de Roland, an outstanding Malagasy field biologist, who has led the group to great success. The Peregrine Fund has worked to preserve local biodiversity, with an emphasis on raptors and waterbirds. It now supports a network of 11 local institutions in this effort, which includes ample opportunities for training.

In 1993, the Wildlife Conservation Society (WCS) established an important, site-based conservation program on Madagascar, starting with organization's participation in the preservation of forest on the Masoala Peninsula. Subsequently, it has emphasized forest carbon storage and eventually the community management of dozens of terrestrial and marine areas. With over 100 Malagasy staff members, WCS has played an important role in lowering deforestation rates, especially in and around the critically important Makira and Masoala protected areas. The Madagascar Fauna Group, a consortium of zoos, botanical gardens, aquariums, and universities, with its training center at Parc Ivoloina (north of Toamasina), has prepared numerous Malagasy students for roles in similar institutions locally.

In 1996, BirdLife International convened a workshop in Antananarivo on priority sites for bird conservation, which also led to the creation of an all-Malagasy conservation association, Asity. The two organizations worked together until 2008, when the association, renamed Asity Madagascar and with its own staff, was appointed as the full partner of the BirdLife International network. Asity Madagascar manages four conservation areas, having led in the creation of three of them. Most of the association's work takes place at these remote rural areas, which together encompass nearly 800,000 ha.

As for research and training in Madagascar's marine and coastal habitats, the Institut Halieutique et des Sciences Marines at the Université de Toliara has been an outstanding contributor for many years. And Blue Ventures, founded on Madagascar in 2003, has actively conducted efforts to conserve Madagascar's many local fisheries, greatly improving the sustainability of commercial fishing resources in many coastal areas.

An emphasis on the local value of tourism provided by the protected area system has, in some instances, proved a powerful incentive for maintaining such areas intact. A particularly good example is Ranomafana National Park, established in 1991 through the efforts of Patricia Wright of Stony Brook University and numerous colleagues. From the start, local infrastructure included housing for tourists, who provide income for maintenance and increase enthusiasm for conservation; in recent years, there have been more than 20,000 paying visitors annually. In 2003, Pat Wright established an outstanding research facility, the Centre ValBio, near the park.

As for international understanding of the conservation situation on Madagascar, the online weekly *Mongabay*, global in scope and published since 1999, has effectively called attention to the many opportunities and problems connected with conservation on the island. Within the *Mongabay* organization, founder Rhett Butler has established WildMadagascar.org, a site that highlights Madagascar and its environmental news. The *Mongabay* series, as of late 2020, had published nearly 100 articles; it constitutes a valuable resource for anyone concerned with conservation on the island.

While the number of trained Malagasy and other residents concerned with conservation and possessing the skills to do something about it has grown substantially since the publication of *The Natural History of Madagascar* in 2003, the country has remained one of the poorest on earth, and it has been racked with persistent corruption. In its 2019 report, the group Transparency International rates Madagascar 158th of the 180 ranked countries, based on its "corruption perceptions index," and the trend is described as downward. Medical care is very poor by global standards; most people living in rural areas have no access to any such services. Some 92% of Malagasy people survive on less than US$2 per day. Particularly in rural areas, very few people have access to electricity or clean drinking water. The many coups d'état and changes in government, along with considerable corruption, have left the country in an unfortunate state.

Given this background, development aid has not been particularly effective in helping resolve socioeconomic problems on the island. Around US$200 billion of such aid has been granted since independence, but there has been relatively little sustained improvement in roads, education, or other infrastructure. There have been a few clearly successful programs, but overall little progress. In recent years, China has become a major consumer of the country's resources, especially timber, but also gold, precious stones, rare earths and minerals, and, increasingly, cattle. The terms of the pertinent contracts are not made public.

Where, in the coming years, the rapidly growing numbers of Malagasy people will find food, fuel, water, and other essential commodities is difficult to say; the possibility of sustainability seems to recede ever further into the future. Madagascar's current population of about 28 million is projected to grow by 1.1 million per year and reach 61 million by mid-century. Unfortunately, the local situation reflects that of sub-Saharan Africa in general, and Madagascar certainly faces some of the worst problems of any country on earth. As a result of these factors, which together might lead to the rapid destruction of substantial proportions of all natural habitats on the island, Madagascar could easily lose more than half of its species during the remainder of this century. More than 90% of the ones lost would be unique, found nowhere else.

What can slow down or reverse this permanent loss? Conservation depends on many factors, some of the most important of them external to Madagascar. The world is already using some 175% of its potentially sustainable productivity each year (www.footprintnetwork.org), with the rich nations appropriating far more than their share. For example, if everyone lived at the level of consumption of the United States or western Europe, sustainability would require five planets like Earth; that reality leaves little room for poor nations to improve their situation. Social justice must come to prevail both globally and in every country, whether concerning class hierarchies or the rights of women, which are improving on Madagascar. Nations will need to support one another not only by providing aid but by working steadily and cooperatively to improve conditions. In a country where so many people depend directly on natural vegetation and various forest resources for fuel, medicine, building materials, and food, the future of conservation does not seem particularly bright. Improving conservation prospects would require major changes in the lives of people, the current economic structure, and the way they are governed. Not only are hungry people exploiting resources from protected areas, but wealthy ones are illegally harvesting other resources and exporting them to enrich themselves further. Only social justice practiced at national and global levels can ultimately make it possible for poor countries to attain sustainability.

In attaining this goal, the inhabitants of wealthy countries ultimately have no option but to help the developing ones; only through such caring collaboration will we have a chance to build and maintain global sustainability. It is both a matter of enlightened self-interest and of simple social justice. Much outstanding work has been done, especially over the past four decades, to train Malagasy nationals to be effective students and caretakers of their unique and incredibly diverse biodiversity. In order for this island nation to carry these efforts into the future effectively, we must help the people to avoid being victims of poverty and find ways to strengthen different sectors of society, including law enforcement. This will be a difficult task as the island's population doubles over the next 30 years, but it is one that we must undertake together for our common benefit and that of future generations. The opportunity to save this priceless biodiversity will never be greater and more pressing than it is now. By caring enough about this problem to act, we will give the future a priceless gift and live up to our responsibilities as world citizens concerned about our planetary home.

Peter H. Raven, President Emeritus, Missouri Botanical Garden
Saint Louis, Missouri, USA, July 2020

PREFACE

By Steve Goodman

The fauna and flora of Madagascar have intrigued natural historians and biologists for centuries and continue to attract ever-increasing interest. In 2003, a large-scale synthesis was published on different aspects of the island's natural history (Goodman and Benstead 2003), defined in the broad Victorian sense of the expression, which comprised a single, large-format (28 × 21.5 cm) volume of over 1700 pages, and in many ways, the book and its contents heralded a new era of documenting what is known about Madagascar. These aspects included fascinating results and new information from several decades of biological exploration of the island and from projects addressing a variety of research themes. This was also the period of the first leaps forward in understanding the evolutionary history of a range of organisms, based on molecular genetics and the Malagasy scientific community taking its rightful place in progressing scientific and conservation advances in their island nation.

The period during which the 2003 book, *The Natural History of Madagascar*, was put together marked the start of email as a widespread form of communication and provided the means of passing manuscript and figure files across the world within a few seconds, rather than weeks of waiting for uncertain-to-arrive postal packets shared between the two editors, one based in Madagascar (myself) and the other (Jonathan P. Benstead) in the United States, and among 281 contributors scattered around the globe. Without the extremely efficient means of email to send, edit, and transfer manuscripts and associated illustrations, the 2003 book project, which took about 16 months from when invitations went out to contributors to the submission of the manuscript to the University of Chicago Press, would have taken place over many additional years rather than being published in a timely fashion.

In the editorial procedure for the 2003 book, the two editors commented jointly on each submitted manuscript, taking the lead for editorial annotations on each contribution based on knowledge of the subject, making a range of suggestions and edits, as well as verifying the format, then returning the edited manuscript to the author for revision. Depending on the contribution and level of comments, this process was repeated in one to five iterations before the contribution was accepted. In order to be certain that any given authority would not be deterred in submitting their work for a book to be published in English, we accepted manuscripts in any European language, which in the end included many in French and others in German, Italian, Spanish, and so on. This language aspect and the associated translation and verification of texts added time-consuming steps to the process of putting together about 10% of the final manuscripts, but helped to assist non-Anglophone authors or those not comfortable using English.

Fast-forward to about two decades later. Even though the 2003 book was cited as "a scientific milestone and by far the largest synthesis of tropical biology research ever" (Bohannan 2003: 1836), progress in more recent years has gone beyond the most enthusiastic expectations and certainly has been greater in terms of scientific research and conservation actions on Madagascar than in the 20-year period before the 2003 book. In order to highlight this astounding progress, it was decided to completely revamp the 2003 book and produce, in as expedited a manner as possible, a new synthesis of what is known about the island's natural history.

The New Natural History of Madagascar was put together in a different fashion from the *The Natural History of Madagascar*. First, rather than two overall editors giving comments on manuscripts (in some cases, out of their fields of specialty), a group of subject editors was engaged to comment on and revise contributions falling within their expertise. The role of these subject editors cannot be sufficiently emphasized in ensuring the scientific integrity of the current volumes; their names appear on the title page of the book. In short, the expansion of information related to the natural history of Madagascar, once again defined in a broad manner, over the past two decades, is, in our opinion, simply astonishing. This new book—to be published in two volumes totaling 2296 pages and encompassing, for a number of disciplines and associated subjects, the state of knowledge a couple of months before the manuscript was completed—was sent to Princeton University Press.

Another critical advancement has been the role of Malagasy biologists and conservationists in this new adventure. The 2003 book had 281 contributors, of which 60 were Malagasy; in this current book, these figures are 539 and 157, respectively (see Table P.1 for a more detailed breakdown of these figures by chapter). Further, only two of the contributions in the new book were translated into English, both from French, and this clearly highlights the integration of Malagasy national biologists into the international scientific community, which in general uses English as the language of communication. In other words, the fact that nearly all of the contributions from Malagasy authors were submitted in English shows remarkable progress

TABLE P.1. **Contributions, total contributors, and number and percentage of Malagasy contributors herein, by chapter**

	NUMBER OF CONTRIBUTIONS	NUMBER OF CONTRIBUTORS	NUMBER OF MALAGASY CONTRIBUTORS	PERCENTAGE OF MALAGASY AUTHORS
Chapter 1. History of Scientific Exploration	1	2	1	50%
Chapter 2. Geology	6	27	3	11%
Chapter 3. Climate	1	1	0	0%
Chapter 4. Forest and Grassland Ecology	8	28	9	32%
Chapter 5. Human Ecology	8	27	9	33%
Chapter 6. Zoonotic Pathogens and Other Infectious Microbes: Diversity, Evolutionary History, and Transmission	7	30	10	33%
Chapter 7. Marine and Coastal Ecosystems	10	44	15	34%
Chapter 8. Plants	50	165	47	28%
Chapter 9. Invertebrates	47	89	9	10%
Chapter 10. Freshwater Fishes	18	35	2	6%
Chapter 11. Amphibians	24	105	28	27%
Chapter 12. Reptiles	19	90	28	31%
Chapter 13. Birds	22	55	19	35%
Chapter 14. Mammals	51	162	35	22%
Chapter 15. Conservation	7	24	18	75%
Totals	279	884	233	26%

Note: In total, 539 contributors authored or coauthored contributions in this book, of which 157 (29.1%) are Malagasy. In many cases, an individual authored multiple contributions; the tally of "number of contributors" presented in this table is based on the total contributions.

during the course of about 18 years, which is about a generation on Madagascar.

When deciding who to invite to author contributions for this new book and the subjects they would cover, the 19 principal subject editors were directly involved. Decisions on topics were made based on the group's comprehensive knowledge of advancements in the study of the island's natural history over the past two decades and of the individuals who would be most appropriate to take on these new subjects or revise those that appeared in the 2003 book. The general procedure was to send to the proposed author an invitation to submit a manuscript for a given contribution and, once the invitation was accepted, to pass on details associated with format, style, and length. It was left largely up to the corresponding author to pick their co-contributors; the principal editor and subject editors refrained from micromanaging aspects of how the accepting author handled coauthorship. At the end of each contribution herein, the subject editors for the text are named, in some cases along with additional individuals who helped with the editing.

A considerable number of contributors to the 2003 book were also contacted to take part in this new project. The critical first question asked during these exchanges was whether knowledge on their subject group had sufficiently advanced to warrant a revision. When the reply was not a clear yes, these authors were not invited to revise their texts; the subject editor or editors also had input on this decision. When the response was that important advances had taken place in the intervening years, either the previous first author or a new designated corresponding author received the final text file from the 2003 book for large-scale revision. These revisions took three different paths: 1) the 2003 author or authors took on the modifications, 2) new authors revised the former text and maintained the previous author or authors, or 3) the previous text was not used, and the revision was written from scratch. In a few cases, the original author had retired or passed away, a new author came forward to lead the revision, and the original contributor is maintained in the author line. In short, no contribution from the 2003 book is simply reprinted herein, and the current work is not a revised edition but a completely new book—hence, the title: *The New Natural History of Madagascar*.

Given the breadth of organisms occurring on Madagascar and the multitude of researchers working on the island, it is certain that some reasonably well-known taxonomic groups or subjects have not been included in this book when they arguably should have been. We apologize to those who were not contacted to contribute to this volume or to those scientists who were unable to take part in the project because of its relatively rapid production schedule and other impediments. In a few cases, the leading authorities on certain groups have passed away over the last two decades, and we knew of no other specialist who could rework the subject text; hence, a new text herein could not be produced. A list of contributors to this book, with their postal and email addresses, is presented (see pp. 2147–71).

In general, the resolution of contribution subject coverage within a chapter is directly related to the number of researchers working with a taxonomic group, species diversity, and the level of available information. For example, many mammal systematic contributions are presented at the level of genera and, in some cases, even species, while those for invertebrates are at higher taxonomic levels, such as order, family, or subfamily. It was not possible to strike a balance in the book's coverage, but this is the direct result of research activity and taxonomic complexity. More important, in general, we considered it best, within any given chapter, to allow authors to explore the subjects of their research interest as expressed in their contributions, rather than imposing a fixed format and topics to be covered. There are some exceptions to this; for example, in the Plants chapter, a series of topics was provided to authors to follow, a scheme that was largely adhered to. The Conservation chapter in the 2003 book was much more detailed than the one herein, with a series of site-specific contributions. Given the recent large-scale review of terrestrial protected areas on Madagascar (Goodman et al. 2018), we decided to reduce redundancy with that book and to focus in the Conservation chapter herein on different types of advances over the past couple of decades and a broad synthetic contribution.

This leads us to one of the strange twists associated with the massively expanded amount of information on different facets associated with what is known about Madagascar. On one hand, the collective knowledge of the island's biota and its natural history increased colossally over a few decades before the publication of the 2003 book and, then again, at an even heightened level in the intervening years before this current book. On the other hand, our knowledge of many groups, particularly those that are forest-dwelling or living in particular nonforested habitats, remains very incomplete, and this is cast against continued high levels of natural habitat degradation on the island. In attempting to put this current book together, often much to the chagrin of many contributors, we have strived to edit and publish the book as quickly as possible to minimize its obsolescence the moment it is printed. However, this is the eventual destiny, if not the goal, of such a book.

Our ability to produce this two-volume set, including a considerable number of color illustrations, with colleagues at Princeton University Press at such a reasonable price, is based on the financial support of numerous individuals and organizations, listed in the Acknowledgments. This project would not have been possible without their help, and as a group of researchers/authors working with the Malagasy biota, as well as for the future of the natural patrimony of the island nation, we are indebted to them for their generosity.

Steve Goodman
Antsiranana, Madagascar, 27 December 2020

REFERENCES

Bohannan, J. 2003. A biological bible for Madagascar. *Science* 301: 1836.

Goodman, S. M., and Benstead, J. P. 2003. *The Natural History of Madagascar*. Chicago: University of Chicago Press.

Goodman, S. M., Raherilalao, M. J., and Wohlhauser, S. (eds.) 2018. *Les aires protégées terrestres de Madagascar: Leur histoire, description et biote/The Terrestrial Protected Areas of Madagascar: Their History, Description, and Biota.* Association Vahatra, Antananarivo.

ACKNOWLEDGMENTS

Approximately 17 months elapsed between inviting people to contribute to this book and the submission of the manuscript to Princeton University Press. Clearly, the task of putting together this book was an enormous effort on the part of many subject editors and authors. We are grateful to all those who have taken part in one way or another. We apologize to those contributors who felt pressure in different manners, including manuscript submission or revision, and sincerely hope that they are satisfied with the resulting book. Jonathan P. Benstead played a major role in the 2003 book as coeditor, and we are grateful to him for all his efforts with the previous book.

The period when the book was put together coincided with the Covid-19 epidemic, which continued in January 2021, when the manuscript was submitted. In many areas of the world, lockdowns or other forms of restriction were in place, with both positive and negative impacts on advancing this book project. Most of the contributors to this book were unable to be in the field or traveling in general, which provided more time than usual for most to devote to writing their contributions and revising after editorial comments. On the other hand, many individuals needed computer files and publications housed in their work offices, which for many were inaccessible during periods of confinement, and this produced some delays in finalizing texts and figures. Finally, the virus itself directly touched the lives of individuals associated with this project and their families and close associates, which naturally changed a range of different work-related priorities.

In establishing the first-round lists of possible contributors, particularly those that did not take part in the 2003 book, we are grateful to the following individuals, many of them subject editors: Aristide Andrianarimisa, Amanda H. Armstrong, Martin Callmander, Andrew Cooke, Brian Fisher, Jörg U. Ganzhorn, Laurent Gautier, David W. Krause, Olivier Langrand, Pete Lowry, Marie Jeanne Raherilalao, Achille P. Raselimanana, Roger J. Safford, John S. Sparks, Voahangy Soarimalala, Melanie L. J. Stiassny, Pablo Tortosa, and Miguel Vences. Two manuscripts were submitted in French, and we thank Fanja Andriamialisoa for her fine translations into English. We thank Chantal Radimilahy and Peter Raven for their forewords that open this book. Olivier Langrand and Russ Mittermeier kindly commented on a previous version of the foreword by Peter Raven.

It should be emphasized that the extraordinary expansion of new information on several different fronts and the number of national and foreign researchers working on Madagascar is due, in the most fundamental manner, to the openness and considerable interest of the Malagasy authorities. With considerable pleasure, we acknowledge the ongoing role of several governmental and para-governmental organizations in the progression of information on the natural history of the organisms living on their island nation and associated aspects related to conservation: Ministère de l'Environnement et du Développement Durable; Madagascar National Parks; Centre National de Formation, d'Etudes et de Recherche en Environnement et Forestier; Centre National de la Recherche sur l'Environnement; several universities, including, at the Université d'Antananarivo, Mention Zoologie et Biodiversité Animale and Mention Biologie et Ecologie Végétales, and the Département des Eaux et Forêts de l'Ecole Supérieure Agronomique; as well as Université de Fianarantsoa, Université de Mahajanga, Université d'Antsiranana, and Université de Toliara; Office National pour l'Environnement; and Parc Botanique et Zoologique de Tsimbazaza. We sincerely hope that these organizations understand their critical role in the advances underlined in this book and will continue to support various forms of research in the future, helping to ensure the needed documentation to advance the conservation of the island's biodiversity and the secure future of the Malagasy people.

The remarkable and numerous photographs that grace the pages of this book and make it come alive include those of the following individuals (those with 10 or more images used, in order of the number used): F. Andreone, P. Antilahimena, K. Behrens, C. Birkinshaw, C. Boluda, M. Callmander, L. R. de Roland, Z. Farris, B. Fisher, P.-S. Gehring, F. Glaw, G. Gustafson, C. R. Hutter, S. Hugel, K. Kainulainen, D. Lees, P. V. Loiselle, Porter P. Lowry II, N. Manjato, M. Manuel, E. Mertz, A. Miralles, P. B. Phillipson, C. Rakotovao, G. M. Rosa, G. Schatz, M. D. Scherz, H. Schütz, F. Schumm, V. Simeonovski, C. Skema, J. S. Sparks, V. Soarimalala, A. Stroiński, M. Tuttle, M. Vences, and M. S. Vorontsova. We are grateful to Tolotra Ranarilalatiana for his help with Malagasy invertebrate names.

I would like to add some personal acknowledgments. Three mentors guided me in different ways over the years to view and interpret aspects of the natural world, each in a very different manner—the late Robert W. Storer, the late Jean Parsons, and Michel Chamberlin—and I owe them a great debt. My position at the Field Museum of Natural History as MacArthur Field Biologist has provided the means and freedom for me to explore Madagascar for more than three decades and to assist with the advancement on the island of the natural sciences and national scientists. Without this liberty and the confidence of colleagues at the Field Museum, these explorations and associated advances would have not happened, and neither the 2003 book nor this one would have been published. For encouragement and aid in numerous ways, I wish to thank individuals currently or formerly at the Field Museum (in alphabetic order): Mark Alvey, John Bates, John Fitzpatrick, Shannon Hackett, Larry Heaney, Richard Lariviere, Meganne Lube, Thorsten Lumbsch, John McCarter, Debra Moskovits, Bruce Patterson, Julian Siggers, and Dave Willard.

In many ways, the launchpad for my work on Madagascar was associated with the Ecology Training Program at WWF–Madagascar, where I was based from 1992 to 2007, and I extend my heartfelt thanks to Olivier Langrand, Sheila O'Connor, Jean-Paul Paddack, Achille P. Raselimanana, Malalarisoa Razafimpahanana, and "Ledada" Rachel Razafindravao. Much administrative aid in the early years, as well as different forms of collaboration, were received from Prof. Daniel Rakotondravony and the late Madame Berthe Rakotosamimanana at the Université d'Antananarivo. For more than a decade, my colleagues at Association Vahatra, including Malalarisoa Razafimpahanana and scientists Marie Jeanne Raherilalao, Achille P. Raselimanana, and Voahangy Soarimalala (all cofounding members), have helped to advance a wide range of programs and acted as an inspiration for the future of research and the advancement of science on the island. To help put our joint work into a greater perspective, between the four scientific founding members of Association Vahatra, including myself, we have been working in the forests of Madagascar for what will soon be a cumulative total of 120 years. Further, I would like to thank Sabrina Raharinirina of Association Vahatra for her help in many ways in putting this book together, including assembling a considerable number of photo montages, and Mbola Rakotondratsimba for help with certain figures. Generations of Malagasy students and researchers have been involved in our field and laboratory activities, and we are grateful for their interest, in some cases devoted passion, and participation.

A number of organizations have financially supported our research on Madagascar (in alphabetic order by first word in the organization's name): Alexander von Humboldt Foundation, Conservation International, Critical Ecosystem Partnership Fund (CEPF), Field Museum of Natural History, Institut Français de la Biodiversité, John D. and Catherine T. MacArthur Foundation, Leona M. and Harry B. Helmsley Charitable Trust, Liz Claiborne and Art Ortenberg Foundation, Ministère des Affaires Etrangères (France), National Geographic Society, National Science Foundation (USA), Schlinger Foundation, Volkswagen Foundation, Vontobel Foundation, World Wide Fund for Nature–Madagascar, and World Wildlife Fund–United States. The Critical Ecosystem Partnership Fund is a joint initiative of l'Agence Française de Développement, Conservation International, the European Union, the Global Environment Facility, the Government of Japan, and the World Bank. A fundamental goal is to ensure that civil society is engaged in biodiversity conservation.

For financially supporting the publication of this book, which clearly shows their interest in and dedication to the advancement of science and conservation on Madagascar, we thank the following private donors (arranged alphabetically by family name): Joyce Chelberg, Paul Goodman, Mary-Ann and Owen Griffiths, Gail and Bob Loveman, Tanya and Michael Polsky, Shaw Family Supporting Organization, and Adele Simmons; and the following companies, foundations, and organizations: Bioculture (Mauritius) Ltd., Ellis Goodman Family Foundation, Field Museum of Natural History (FMNH), Fondation pour les Aires Protégées et la Biodiversité de Madagascar (FAPBM), and Programme des Nations Unies pour le Développement (PNUD).

It has been a pleasure to work with several colleagues at Princeton University Press. First, we thank Christie Henry, who was the editor for the 2003 book when she was at the University of Chicago Press and is now Director, Princeton University Press. Also at Princeton University Press, we are grateful to Robert Kirk, Publisher (Princeton Field Guides and Natural History), for taking this book under his helm and guiding it through different stages in a very efficient manner. We are grateful to the production group at Princeton University Press for making this adventure such a positive experience, specifically Kathleen Cioffi, Senior Production Editor; Dimitri Karetnikov, Illustration Manager; and Jaden Young, Diversify Publishing Fellow. The large endeavor to put this book together benefited from the acumen of the copyediting team which included Amy K. Hughes (team leader, to whom we are indebted), Laurel Anderton, Frances Cooper, Patricia Fogarty, Judith Hoffman, and Maia Vaswani. Illustration work was done by Jan Troutt, Troutt Visual Services. The book has been typeset and designed by Namrita and David Price-Goodfellow, D & N Publishing, and we cannot sufficiently express our gratitude for the detail and precision they devoted to this herculean project.

I am grateful to my immediate family, Asmina Gandie and Hesham Goodman, for their patience over the years, when I have frequently been away from home and working in the field, often for extended periods, and have been absorbed in various tasks related to putting this book together; they have been very supportive of my activities, and I am indebted to them.

Steve Goodman
Antsiranana, Madagascar, 27 December 2020

ABBREVIATIONS AND ACRONYMS

Over the years, there has been a remarkable—perhaps *daunting* is the correct word—proliferation of acronyms and abbreviations associated with governmental and nongovernmental organizations, projects and programs, protected areas, technical terms, and so forth, related to the natural history and conservation of the remaining natural habitats of Madagascar. Within each contribution, we have attempted to define these at first usage. To help uninitiated readers navigate through this near Babylon of acronyms and abbreviations, we present below a listing of the terms used in this book, including translations when appropriate from French and Malagasy to English.

ABC approximate Bayesian computation
ABFMP Antongil Bay Fisheries Co-Management Plan
ACAP Amphibian Conservation Action Plan
ACEP African Coelacanth Ecosystem Programme
ACLME Agulhas Current Large Marine Ecosystem
α-CoV *Alphacoronavirus*
ACSAM A Conservation Strategy for the Amphibians of Madagascar
AFD Agence Française de Développement
AFLP amplified fragment-length polymorphism
AFOLU Agriculture, Forestry, and Other Land Use
AFR100 African Forest Landscape Restoration Initiative
AFS allele frequency spectrum
AGERAS Appui à la Gestion Régionalisée et à l'Approche Spatiale (Support to Decentralized Management and the Ecoregional Approach)
ALD abbreviated larval development
ALOs *Arsenophonus*-like organisms
AMNH American Museum of Natural History
APMCs *aires protégées marines et côtières* (protected marine and coastal areas)
AMS accelerator mass spectrometry
AMT annual mean temperature
ANAE Association Nationale pour l'Action Environnementale (National Association for Environmental Action)
ANGAP Association Nationale pour la Gestion des Aires Protégées (National Association for the Management of Protected Areas; now **MNP**)
AOO area of occupancy
APG Angiosperm Phylogeny Group
APN Agents de Protection de la Nature (Nature Protection Agents)
ARDRA amplified ribosomal DNA restriction analysis; see **DNA**
ASCLME Agulhas and Somali Current Large Marine Ecosystems
ASE Association de Sauvegarde de l'Environnement (Association to Save the Environment)
AstVs astroviruses
AVHRR Advanced Very High Resolution Radiometer
AWG Angiosperm Working Group
AZA Association of Zoos and Aquariums
AZE Alliance for Zero Extinction

BCE before the Common Era
BCM Biodiversity Conservation Madagascar
β-CoV *Betacoronavirus*
Bd *Batrachochytrium dendrobatidis*
BIN barcode index number
BIOPAT Patrons for Biodiversity
BMNH British Museum (Natural History); now Natural History Museum, London (**NHMUK**)
BN-CCCREDD+ Bureau National des Changements Climatiques, du Carbone et de la REDD+ (National Office for Climate Change, Carbon, and Reduction of Emissions from Deforestation and Forest Degradation)
BNS basic necessity surveys
BOLD Barcode of Life Data System
BP years before present ("present" is taken to be the year 1950)
bp base pairs
BRD bycatch reduction devices
BS breeding stock
BSP Bayesian skyline plots
Bsal *Batrachochytrium salamandrivorans*

C3 Community Centered Conservation
CABI Centre for Agricultural Bioscience International
CAF Cadre d'Appui Forestier (Forestry Support Units)
CAFF/CORE Comité Ad Hoc pour la Faune et la Flore/Comité Organisationel pour la Recherche Environnementale (Ad Hoc Committee for Fauna and Flora/ Organizational Committee for Environmental Research)
cal BP calibrated years before present
CAM crassulacean acid metabolism
CAMP Conservation Assessment and Management Plan (Evaluation et Plans de Gestion pour la Conservation)
CAS California Academy of Sciences
CAZ Corridor Ankeniheny-Zahamena (Ankeniheny-Zahamena Forested Corridor)
CBD Convention on Biological Diversity
CBOL Consortium for the Barcode of Life
CCBA Climate Community and Biodiversity Alliance
CCC Coelacanth Conservation Council (Conseil pour la Conservation du Cœlacanthe)
CCHFV Crimean-Congo Hemorrhagic Fever Virus
CDC Centers for Disease Control (USA)
CE Common Era
CEC Chytrid Emergency Cell (Cellule d'Urgence Chytride)
CEMES Cercle d'Etudes Multidisciplinaires pour l'Environnement et la Santé (Circle of Multidisciplinary Research for Environment and Health)
CEPF Critical Ecosystem Partnership Fund
CF constant frequency

CFM Community Forest Management (Gestion Communautaire des Forêts; see **TGRN**)
CFPF Centre de Formation Professionnelle Forestière (Professional Forestry Training Center; now **CNFEREF**)
CGP Comité de Gestion de la Pêche aux Poulpes (Octopus Fishing Management Committee)
CHIKV Chikungunya Virus
CHIRPS Climate Hazards InfraRed Precipitation with Station
CI Conservation International
CIBIO-InBIO Centro de Investigação em Biodiversidade e Recursos Genéticos (Research Centre in Biodiversity and Genetic Resources)
CIRAD Centre de Coopération Internationale en Recherche Agronomique pour le Développement (Agricultural Research Center for International Development)
CITES Convention on International Trade in Endangered Species of Wild Fauna and Flora (Convention sur le Commerce International des Espèces de Faune et de Flore Sauvages Menacées d'Extinction)
CJB Conservatoire et Jardin botaniques de la Ville de Genève
CM causal modeling
CMR capture-mark-recapture
CMS Convention on Migratory Species
CMU Crocodile Management Unit
CNA Conservation Needs Assessment
CNARP Centre National d'Application des Recherches Pharmaceutiques (National Center for the Application of Pharmaceutical Research)
CNFEREF Centre National de Formation, d'Etudes et de Recherche en Environnement et Foresterie (formerly **CFPF**) (National Center for Training, Studies, and Research in Environment and Forestry)
CNGIM Commission Nationale de Gestion Intégrée des Mangroves (National Integrated Mangrove Management Commission)
CNGIZC Comité National de la Gestion Intégrée des Zones Côtières (National Committee for Integrated Coastal Zone Management)
CNRE Centre National de Recherches sur l'Environnement (National Center for Environmental Research)
CNRO Centre National de Recherches Océanographiques (National Center for Oceanographic Research)
CNRS Centre National de la Recherche Scientifique (National Center for Scientific Research)
COGAP Code de Gestion des Aires Protégées (Protected Areas Management Code)
CoBa *communauté de base* (community-based association)
COFAV Corridor Forestier Fandriana–Ambositra–Vondrozo (Fandriana–Ambositra–Vondrozo Forested Corridor)
COGAP Code de Gestion des Aires Protégées (Protected Areas Management Code)
COI Commission de l'Océan Indien (Indian Ocean Commission)
COI cytochrome oxidase I
COMATSA Nord Corridor Marojejy–Anjanaharibe-Sud–Tsaratanàna Nord (Northern Corridor Marojejy–Anjanaharibe-Sud–Tsaratanàna)
COMATSA Sud Corridor Marojejy–Anjanaharibe-Sud–Tsaratanàna Sud (Southern Corridor Marojejy–Anjanaharibe-Sud–Tsaratanàna)
Copefrito Compagnie de Peche Frigorifique de Toliara
CORDIO Coastal Oceans Research and Development–Indian Ocean
CoVs coronaviruses
CPUE catch per unit of effort
CR Critically Endangered (IUCN Red List status)
CRESICA Consortium for Research, Higher Education, and Innovation in New Caledonia
CRISPR Clustered Regularly Interspaced Short Palindromic Repeat
CSIC Consejo Superior de Investigaciones Científicas (Spanish National Research Council)
CSP Centre de Surveillance des Pêches (Fisheries Monitoring Center)
CSPN Conseil Supérieur pour la Protection de la Nature (High Council for Nature Protection)
CTFT Centre Technique Forestier Tropical (Technical Center for Tropical Forestry)

DAPTF Declining Amphibian Populations Task Force
DBA Département de Biologie Animale, Université d'Antananarivo (**UADBA**) (see also **MZBA**)
DBC/SAP Biodiversity Conservation/Protected Area System Directorate
DBEV Département de Biologie et Ecologie Végétales, Université d'Antananarivo (see also **MBEV**)
dbh diameter at breast height
DBV Dakar Bat Virus
δ-CoV *Deltacoronavirus*
DD Data Deficient (IUCN Red List status)
ddRAD double-digest restriction-site-associated sequencing
DEA *diplôme d'études approfondies*
DEAP Droit d'Entrée dans les Aires Protégées (protected area entry fee)
DEF Département des Eaux et Forêts (Department of Water and Forest)
DELC Development and Environmental Law Center
DENV Dengue Virus
DFN Domaine Forestier National (National Forest Lands)
DGEF Direction Générale des Eaux et Forêts (General Directorate of Water and Forests)
DGF Direction Générale des Forêts (General Directorate of Forests)
DGGE denaturing gradient gel electrophoresis
DIANA Region Diego–Ambilobe–Nosy Be–Ambanja region
DLC Duke Lemur Center
D-loop displacement-loop
DNA deoxyribonucleic acid
DPZ Deutsches Primatenzentrum (German Primate Center)
DREDD Direction Régionale de l'Environnement et du Développement Durable (Regional Department of Environment and Sustainable Development)
DREEF Direction Régionale de l'Environnement, de l'Ecologie et des Forêts (Regional Department of Environment, Ecology, and Forests)
DRFP/FOFIFA Département des Recherches Forestières et Piscicoles (Forestry and Pisciculture Research Department)
DUPC Duke University Primate Center (now **DLC**)
DWCT Durrell Wildlife Conservation Trust
DWFN distant water fishing nation

E herbarium code for Royal Botanic Garden Edinburgh
EAZA European Association of Zoos and Aquaria
EBSA Ecologically or Biologically Significant Area
EBSP Extended Bayesian skyline plots
EC European Community
ECH energy conservation hypothesis
ECMWF European Centre for Medium-Range Weather Forecasts
ED evolutionary distinctiveness
EDEN Ecole Doctorale Ecosystèmes Naturels, Université de Mahajanga
EDGE Evolutionarily Distinct and Globally Endangered
eDNA environmental DNA; see **DNA**
EEP European Endangered Species Programme
EEZ exclusive economic zone
EGP extra-group paternity
EIA environmental impact assessment (*étude d'impact environnemental*)
EL ear (pinna) length
ELD extended larval development
ELISA enzyme-linked immunosorbent assay
EN Endangered (IUCN Red List status)
EOT Eocene–Oligocene transition
EP1, 2, 3 National Environmental Action Plan, first, second, and third phases
ER-PA Emission Reductions Purchase Agreements

ESBL-E extended-spectrum-beta-lactamase-producing Enterobacteriaceae
ESSA-Forêts Etablissement de l'Enseignement Supérieur des Sciences Agronomiques, Département des Eaux et Forêts, Université d'Antananarivo (School of Agronomical Sciences, Department of Water and Forest, University of Antananarivo)
ETP Ecology Training Program
EVI Enhanced Vegetation Index
EX Extinct (IUCN Red List status)

FAO Food and Agriculture Organization of the United Nations
FAPBM Fondation pour les Aires Protégées et la Biodiversité de Madagascar (Madagascar Biodiversity and Protected Areas Fund)
FBM Fikambanana Bongolava Maitso (Association for a Green Bongolava)
FC Forêt Classée (classified forest)
FCPF Forest Carbon Partnership Facility
FFEM Fonds Français pour l'Environnement Mondial (French Funds for Global Environment)
FIPs fishery improvement plans
FLR Forest Landscape Restoration
FM frequency modulated
FMG *franc malgache* (Malagasy franc; now Malagasy ariary, **MGA**)
FMNH Field Museum of Natural History
FMTF Fikambanana Miaro ny Trozona sy Fesotra (Association for the Protection of Whales and Dolphins)
FOFIFA Foibem-pirenena momba ny Fikarohana ampiharina amin'ny Fampandrosoana ny eny Ambanivohitra (Centre National de la Recherche Appliquée au Développement Rural; National Center for Applied Research on Rural Development)
FTM Foiben-Taosarintanin'i Madagasikara (Institut Géographique et Hydrographique de Madagascar, or National Institute of Survey and Cartography)

G herbarium code for the Conservatoire et Jardin botaniques de la Ville de Genève, Switzerland
GAA Global Amphibian Assessment
GAPCM Groupement des Aquaculteurs et Pêcheurs de Crevettes à Madagascar (Association of Aquaculturists and Shrimp Fishers in Madagascar)
GBIF Global Biodiversity Information Facility
GBSSI granule-bound starch synthase
GCF Gestion Contractualisée des Forêts (contractualized forest management)
γ-CoV *Gammacoronavirus*
GDP gross domestic product
GE global endangerment
GEE Google Earth Engine
GEF Global Environment Facility
GELOSE Gestion Locale des Ressources Naturelles Renouvelables, or Gestion Locale Sécurisée (Local Management of Renewable Natural Resources, or Secure Local Management)
GERP Groupe d'Etude et de Recherche sur les Primates de Madagascar (Group for the Study and Research on Madagascar Primates)
GHG greenhouse gas
GHR growth-hormone receptor
GIS geographic information system
GLAD Global Land Analysis and Discovery alerts
GMYC General Mixed Yule-Coalescent
GPL Global Pandemic Lineage
GPP gross primary productivity
GPS global positioning system
GRENE Gestion de Ressources Naturelles et Environnement; now Institut Supérieur de Sciences, Environnement et Développement Durable, Université de Toamasina (see **ISSEDD**)
GSAF global shark attack files
GTZ Deutsche Gesellschaft für Technische Zusammenarbeit (German Technical Cooperation)

HBL head-and-body length
HCPS hantavirus cardiopulmonary syndrome
HD-CF high duty–constant frequency
HDR *habilitation à diriger des recherches*
HEV Hepatitis E Virus
HF hindfoot length
HFRS hemorrhagic fever with renal syndrome
hPa hectopascal
HPD highest probability density
HWE Hardy-Weinberg equilibrium

IBA Important Bird and Biodiversity Area
IBD isolation by distance
IBE isolation by environment or by ecology
IBR isolation by resistance
ICDP integrated conservation and development project
ICMAA Institut de Civilisations Musée d'Art et d'Archéologie (Institute of Civilizations and Museum of Art and Archeology)
ICTE Institute for the Conservation of Tropical Environments
ICTV International Committee on Taxonomy of Viruses
ICZM integrated coastal zone management
iDNA invertebrate DNA
IEFN Inventaire Ecologique Forestier National (National Ecological Forestry Inventory)
IgG immunoglobulin G
IgM immunoglobulin M
IHSM Institut Halieutique et des Sciences Marines (Institute of Fisheries and Marine Sciences)
IMMA Important Marine Mammal Area
IMRA Institut Malgache de Recherches Appliquées (Malagasy Institute of Applied Research)
INDC intended nationally determined contribution
ind/ha individuals per hectare
ind/km² individuals per square kilometer
INR Integrated Nature Reserve (Réserve Spéciale Intégrale)
IOC Indian Ocean Commission
IOTC Indian Ocean Tuna Commission
IPCC Intergovernmental Panel on Climate Change
IPM Institut Pasteur de Madagascar (Institute Pasteur of Madagascar)
IPSIO Insects and People of the Southwest Indian Ocean
IRBP interphotoreceptor retinoid-binding protein
IRD Institut de Recherche pour le Développement (Institute of Research for Development); formerly Office de la Recherche Scientifique et Technique Outre-Mer (**ORSTOM**)
IRSM Institut de Recherche Scientifique de Madagascar (Institute of Scientific Research of Madagascar)
ISAF international shark attack files
ISSEDD Institut Supérieur de Sciences, Environnement et Développement Durable, Université de Toamasina (Higher Institute of Sciences, Environment and Sustainable Development, University of Toamasina)
ISSG Invasive Species Specialist Group
ISTE Institut des Sciences et Techniques de l'Environnement, Université de Fianarantsoa
ITCZ Intertropical Convergence Zone
IUCN International Union for the Conservation of Nature and Natural Resources
IWC International Whaling Commission

JEV Japanese Encephalitis Virus

K herbarium code for Royal Botanic Gardens, Kew
KBA Key Biodiversity Areas
Kbp kilobase pair
KfW Kreditanstalt für Wiederaufbau
kHz kilohertz
K–Pg Cretaceous–Paleogene extinction event
Kya thousand years ago

L liter
LC Least Concern (IUCN Red List status)
LD-CF low-duty cycle, constant frequency
LD-QCF low-duty cycle, quasi-constant
LGM Last Glacial Maximum
LMD *licence-master-doctorat*
LMMA locally managed marine area
LPWG Legume Phylogeny Working Group

LRSAE Laboratoire de Recherche sur les Systèmes Aquatique et Leur Environnement (Research Laboratory on Aquatic Systems and their Environment)

MAB Man and Biosphere Reserve
MAEE Ministère et Affaires Etrangères et Européennes de France (Ministry and Foreign and European Affairs of France)
MAEP Ministère de l'Agriculture, de l'Elevage et de la Pêche (Ministry of Agriculture, Livestock and Fisheries)
MAHERY Madagascar Health and Environmental Research
MAP mean annual temperature
MAT microscopic-agglutination test
MaVoa Madagasikara Voakajy
MBEV Mention de Biologie et Ecologie Végétales, Université d'Antananarivo (formerly Département de Biologie et Ecologie Végétales, Université d'Antananarivo, **DBEV**)
MBG Missouri Botanical Garden
MBP Madagascar Biodiversity Partnership
Mbp megabase pairs (1 million base pairs)
MCCSUP Madagascar Crocodile Conservation and Sustainable Use Program
MCP minimum convex polygon
MCSN Museo Civico di Storia Naturale, Comiso, Italy
MECIE Mise en Compatibilité des Investissements avec l'Environnement (Compatibility of Investments with the Environment)
MEDD Ministère de l'Environnement et du Développement Durable (Ministry of the Environment and Sustainable Development; formerly **MEF**, then **MEEF**)
MEEF Ministère de l'Environnement, de l'Ecologie et des Forêts (Ministry of the Environment, Ecology, and Forests)
MEF Ministère des Eaux et Forêts (Ministry of Waters and Forests)
MERS Middle East respiratory syndrome
MFG Madagascar Fauna and Flora Group
MGA Malagasy ariary (monetary unit)
MHC major histocompatibility complex
MICET Malagasy Institut pour la Conservation des Ecosystèmes Tropicaux (Malagasy Institute for the Conservation of Tropical Environments)
MinSup Ministère de l'Enseignement Supérieur (Ministry of Higher Education)
MISA Miaro Ny Sahona
MLE maximum likelihood estimate
MMPATF Marine Mammal Protected Areas Task Force
MNHN Muséum National d'Histoire Naturelle, Paris
MNHU Museum für Naturkunde Humboldt-Universtät, Berlin
MNP Madagascar National Parks (formerly **ANGAP**)
MO herbarium code for Missouri Botanical Garden
MODIS Moderate Resolution Imaging Spectroradiometer
MoU memorandum of understanding
MPA marine protected area
MPRH Ministère de la Pêche et des Ressources Halieutiques (Ministry of Fisheries and Fishery Resources)
MRCA most recent common ancestor
Ms milliseconds
MSC Marine Stewardship Council
MSY maximum sustainable yield
Mt megaton
mtDNA mitochondrial DNA
MWSP Madagascar Whale Shark Project
Mya million years ago
MZBA Mention Zoologie et Biodiversité Animale, Université d'Antananarivo (formerly Département de Biologie Animale, Université d'Antananarivo, or **UADBA**)

NAP *nouvelle aire protégée* (new protected area)
NASA National Aeronautics and Space Administration, USA
NATO North Atlantic Treaty Organization
NCAR CESM1 National Center for Atmospheric Research Community Earth System Model, USA
NCEP National Centers for Environmental Prediction
NDV Newcastle Disease Virus
NDVI Normalized Difference Vegetation Index
NE nephropathia epidemica
NE Not Evaluated (IUCN Red List status)
NEAP National Environmental Action Plan
NEMC Northern East Madagascar Current
NGO nongovernmental organization (*organisation non-gouvernementale*)
NGS next-generation sequencing
NHMUK Natural History Museum, London
NJ neighbor joining
NMP National Monitoring Plan
NOAA National Oceanic and Atmospheric Administration, USA
NP National Park
NPFWs nonpollinating fig wasps
NRGT natural resource governance tools
NSAP New Sahonagasy Action Plan
NSF National Science Foundation
NTAC National Toad Advisory Committee
NT Near Threatened (IUCN Red List status)

ODK Open Data Kit
OMNIS Office des Mines Nationales et des Industries Stratégiques de Madagascar (Office of National Mines and Strategic Industries of Madagascar)
ONE Office National pour l'Environnement (National Office for the Environment)
ONG SEDIM Sauvegarde de l'Environnement et pour le Développement Intégré de Madagascar (NGO for the Protection of the Environment and for the Integrated Development of Madagascar)
OPJ Officier de Police Judiciaire (Judicial Police Officer)
ORSTOM Office de la Recherche Scientifique et Technique Outre-Mer (Overseas Office of Scientific and Technical Research), now Institut de Recherche pour le Développement (**IRD**) (Research Institute for Development)
OSL optically stimulated luminescence

P herbarium code for Muséum National d'Histoire Naturelle, Paris
PA protected area
PADAP Projet Agriculture Durable par une Approche Paysage (Sustainable Agriculture Project through a Landscape Approach)
PAE Plan d'Action Environnementale (Environmental Action Plan)
PAMELA Passive Margins Exploration Laboratories
PANA Programme d'Action National d'Adaptation au Changement Climatique (National Adaptation Program of Action on Climate Change)
PAP *plan d'aménagement des pêches* (fisheries management plan)
PBI Planetary Biodiversity Inventory
PBZT Parc Botanique et Zoologique de Tsimbazaza (Botanical and Zoological Park of Tsimbazaza)
PC principal component
PCD Pêche Côtière Durable (Sustainable Coastal Fisheries)
PCR polymerase chain reaction
PERR-FH Programme Eco-Régional REDD+ des Forêts Humides (Eco-Regional REDD+ Program for Humid Forests); see **REDD +**
PES payment for ecosystem services
PF peak frequency
PHVA population and habitat viability analysis
PIT passive integrated transponder
PIMIT Processus Infectieux en Milieu Insulaire Tropical
PK *point kilométrique* (kilometer point)
PlanGRAP Plan Stratégique de Gestion du Réseau des Aires Protégées (Protected Area Network Management Plan)
PMVs paramyxoviruses
PN Parc National (National Park)
POWO Plants of the World Online
ppb parts per billion
ppt parts per thousand
PRISM Projet Récif Ile Sainte Marie (Sainte Marie Island Reef Project)
PRU Polyaquaculture Research Unit
PSMC pairwise sequentially Markovian coalescent
PVA population viability analysis

QMM QIT Madagascar Minerals (Rio Tinto)

RABV Rabies Lyssavirus
RAD-seq restriction-site-associated DNA sequencing
RAI relative abundance index
RAP rapid assessment program
RAPD random amplification of polymorphic DNA
RB Réserve de Biosphère (Biosphere Reserve)
RBG or **RBG-Kew** Royal Botanic Gardens, Kew
RCP Recherche Coopérative sur Programme (Cooperative Program Research)
REBIOMA Réseau de la Biodiversité de Madagascar (Madagascar Biodiversity Network)
REDD+ Reducing Emissions from Deforestation and Forest Degradation
RLE Red List of Ecosystems
RLE reference level of emissions
REMMOA Recensement des Mammifères Marins et Autre Mégafaune Pélagique par Observation Aérienne (Census of Marine Mammals and other Pelagic Megafauna by Aerial Observation)
RF Réserve Forestière (Forestry Reserve)
RFLP restriction fragment-length polymorphism
RMCA Royal Museum for Central Africa, Tervuren, Belgium
RMR resting metabolic rate
RNA ribonucleic acid
RNI Réserve Naturelle Intégrale (Strict Nature Reserve)
RoC rate of change
RPP Readiness Preparation Proposal
R/R regurgitation and reingestion
rRNA ribosomal RNA
RS Réserve Spéciale (Special Reserve)
RVF Rift Valley fever
RVFV Rift Valley Fever Virus

SAGE Service d'Appui à la Gestion de l'Environnement (Support Service for Environmental Management)
SANBI South African National Biodiversity Institute
SAP Sahonagasy Action Plan
SAPM Système des Aires Protégées de Madagascar (Madagascar Protected Areas Network/System)
SARS severe acute respiratory syndrome
SAVA Region Sambava–Antalaha–Vohemar–Andapa region
SD standard deviation
SDM species distribution modeling
SEED-Madagascar Sustainable Environment, Education and Development in Madagascar
SEMC Southern East Madagascar Current
SF Station Forestière (Forestry Station)
SFS site frequency spectrum
SMACC Southwest Madagascar Coastal Current
SMART Spatial Monitoring and Reporting Tool
SNP single-nucleotide polymorphism
SODA Simple Ocean Data Assimilation
SOPTOM Station for the Observation and Protection of Tortoises and Their Environment
SPAGeDI Spatial Pattern Analysis of Genetic Diversity
SRI System of Rice Intensification
SROV Station de Recherches Océanographiques de Vangaindrano (Vangaindrano Oceanographic Research Station)
SSC Species Survival Commission
SSP Species Survival Program
SST sea surface temperature
STM seasonal trend model
STs sequence types
SVL snout-to-vent length
SWIO southwest Indian Ocean

t ton
TAMIA Tahosoa Alandriake Mitambatse Ianantsono Andatabo
TAN herbarium code for Parc Botanique et Zoologique de Tsimbazaza
TCI Temperature Condition Index
TEAM Tropical Ecology and Assessment Monitoring
TEDs turtle excluder devices
TEF herbarium code for Foibem-pirenena momba ny Fikarohana ampiharina amin'ny Fampandrosoana ny eny Ambanivohitra (see **FOFIFA**)
TGRH Transfert de Gestion des Ressources Halieutiques (Aquatic Resource Management Transfer)
TGRN Transfert de Gestion des Ressources Naturelles (Natural Resource Management Transfer)
TL tail length
TL total length
TPF The Peregrine Fund

UADBA Département de Biologie Animale, Université d'Antananarivo
UAVS unmanned aerial vehicles
UCE ultraconserved genetic element
UMRVs Unclassified Morbilli-related paramyoxoviruses
UNA Université d'Antananarivo
UNDP United Nations Development Programme
UNEP United Nations Environmental Programme
UNESCO United Nations Educational, Scientific and Cultural Organization (Organisation des Nations unies pour l'Education, la Science et la Culture)
UNFCCC United Nations Framework Convention on Climate Change
URL Unité de Recherche Langoustière (Lobster Research Unit)
USAID United States Agency for International Development
USDA United States Department of Agriculture
USGS United States Geological Survey
USNM United States National Museum; now National Museum of Natural History, Washington, DC
USTA Unité Statistique Thonière d'Antsiranana (Statistical Unit of Antsiranana Tuna Fisheries)

VCI Vegetation Condition Index
VH vegetation health
VHI Vegetation Health Index
VIF Vondrona Ivon'ny Fampandrosoana (Association for Local Development)
VOCs volatile organic compounds
VOI Vondron Olona Ifotony
VSF Vétérinaires Sans Frontières (Veterinarians Without Borders)
VU Vulnerable (IUCN Red List status)

WCMC World Conservation Monitoring Centre
WCS Wildlife Conservation Society
WCSP World Checklist of Selected Plant Families
WFO World Flora Online
WGD whole-genome duplication
WGS whole-genome sequencing
WHO World Health Organization
WIKTROP Weed Identification and Knowledge in the Tropical and Mediterranean Areas
WIKWIO Weed Identification and Knowledge in the Western Indian Ocean
WIOMER Western Indian Ocean Marine Ecoregion
WNV West Nile Virus
WSC World Spider Catalog
WSLV Wesselsbron Virus
WWF World Wide Fund for Nature, or World Wildlife Fund

YFV Yellow Fever Virus

ZICOMA Les Zones d'Importance pour la Conservation des Oiseaux à Madagascar
ZIKAV Zika Virus
ZMUH Zoologisches Institut und Museum der Universität, Hamburg, Germany
ZPC Zone Prioritaire de Conservation (Priority Zone for Conservation)
ZSM Zoologische Staatssammlung München

FORMAT AND PRESENTATION

GENERAL

Although information presented in this book is in the form of discrete chapters, each composed of up to 51 separate contributions, many of the covered subjects are interconnected. In order to guide readers between contributions, we have included, when appropriate, cross-references to link together different portions of the book. In some cases, certain points that are critical for context or detail are repeated between chapters.

As is natural for the diversity of subjects treated herein, not all authors agree on certain points. For example, there are several systems proposed for vegetation types on Madagascar, particularly for the mesic forest formations, and it was considered inappropriate to impose on authors a single system, although we have generally used the vegetation-type terms proposed by Gautier et al. (2018). In order to help navigate the names used for vegetation types between the different published systems, we have included in the introduction to the Plants chapter a summary of terms used in the literature and their equivalent names or synonyms (see Gautier et al., pp. 452–64, Table 8.1). Other points of disagreement include, for example, interpretations of the phylogenetic relationships between certain organisms, the role of human versus natural environmental changes associated with the disappearance of different ecosystems and now-extinct organisms, and points on the geological history of the island.

GEOGRAPHIC NAMES AND DEFINITIONS

For certain localities on Madagascar, two parallel systems of geographic place names exist, one associated with the former colonial system and the other employing more standard Malagasy designations. We have generally followed Malagasy names used on recent maps published by Foiben-Taosarintanin'i Madagasikara (FTM, or National Institute of Survey and Cartography). In many cases, names dating from the colonial era have been added in parentheses at first use within a contribution—e.g., Tolagnaro (Fort Dauphin) ; many of these are more widely employed than the Malagasy names in local daily use on the island. On the other hand, certain authors preferred to use place names from the colonial system, and we decided not to impose a single system but, in such cases, to provide the FTM name in parentheses at first use within a contribution.

All references to elevation in the text are given in meters above sea level. The use of the term "region" also poses some complications. Other than as a reference to a general geographical area, the term has additional specific meanings. One is associated with recognized biogeographical areas, such as Afrotropical region, or a specific vegetational type, such as Sambirano Region. For a definition of the term *Malagasy Region*, see below. Another meaning has an administrative context: formerly, Madagascar was divided into administrative provinces (*faritany* in Malagasy); in October 2009, this system was changed to one of regions (*faritra* in Malagasy), which includes 22 administrative units, such as the Sofia Region.

There have been changes in the past years to categories of Malagasy protected areas; for example, several preexisting reserves have been reclassified as national parks, new categories have been designated, and many protected areas have been named (see Goodman et al., pp. 2091–107). In Table 15.1, we present a listing of the definitive protected areas of the island as of November 2020, including both marine (see Figure 7.10) and terrestrial sites (see Figure 15.1), and the most recent statute governing each site. The spelling of protected-area site names varies in the literature; we have used those from Goodman et al. (2018), which are, for the most part, based on official governmental decrees.

SCIENTIFIC VERSUS VERNACULAR NAMES

With a few exceptions, mostly notably for birds and mammals, we have generally shied away from the use of English vernacular names when referring to a specific organism, which can create a certain level of ambiguity; we prefer the use of scientific names. In many chapters, particularly those for land vertebrates, at first mention of a species in a given contribution, the scientific name is given, followed by the generally accepted English vernacular name with initial capital letters. Further, while we mention them in some cases for a given organism or group, we tend not to use Malagasy common names, which can show considerable regional and dialectal differences.

PUBLISHED VERSUS UNPUBLISHED WORK

Given the diversity of researchers working on Madagascar, as well as many conservation, development, and aid projects, a considerable number of unpublished reports are available. We have generally asked authors, when possible, to refrain from using this "gray literature." However, in certain cases, the citation of this unpublished literature was necessary, and authors have indicated in the associated reference citation where these unpublished documents can be obtained, often with a web addresses where they can be downloaded. In other cases, unpublished data are referred to and the name of the individual(s) or organization are provided. The existence of published literature, gray literature, and unpublished documents (some broadly circulated and others not widely diffused) is problematic with regard to access and quality control via the peer-review process.

OTHER TERMS AND DEFINITIONS

Highland areas: In general, Madagascar is geographically divided into two broad zones, lowland areas and highland areas, the latter often defined as the inland portion of the island situated at 800 or 900 m above sea level, herein referred to as the **Central Highlands** and with a range of alternative terms (e.g., Central Plateau, Hautes Terres Centrales, etc.). Finer analyses, such as in Betsch (2000), have shown that there are northern and southern biogeographic breaks, specifically, to the north of the Mandritsara Valley and another to the south of the Menaharaka Valley, which separates the Central Highlands into two additional zones, the **Northern Highlands** and **Southern Highlands**, respectively. These latter two terms and this biogeographic classification are used herein by certain authors.

IUCN Red List categories: The conservation statutes extracted from the IUCN Red List are widely cited. Those falling in the "threatened" category include Critically Endangered (CR), Endangered (EN), and Vulnerable (VU). Other categories, including Near Threatened (NT), Least Concern (LC), and Data Deficient (DD), indicate lower or poorly known conservation threats. Not Evaluated (NE) indicates that a taxon has not yet been evaluated against the IUCN criteria.

Malagasy language: In the text, words, names, and expressions from the Malagasy are in italics and generally lowercase, with the exception of proper names.

Malagasy Region: We use this term in a biogeographic sense to include Madagascar and neighboring archipelagoes, which comprise the Comoros (Mayotte and the three islands of the Union of the Comoros), the Mascarenes (La Réunion, Mauritius, and Rodrigues), and the Seychelles (over 110 islands and islets that range across a distance of about 1120 km from Aldabra in the west to Coëtivy Island in the east).

Malagasy versus Madagascan: Throughout the book, we use the term Malagasy as a noun and adjective, not Madagascan, to refer to the people, culture, and other animate and inanimate objects of Madagascar. See Voarintsoa et al. (2019) for further details.

Megafauna: This term has been widely used in the literature to denote the large-bodied animals that have gone extinct on the island in the past few millennia. Herein, we generally follow Martin's (1984) use of the term to denote animals of at least an estimated body mass of 44 kg (100 lb.); for those that are smaller, other descriptive terms (e.g., extinct large-bodied mammals) are used.

REFERENCES

Betsch, J.-M. 2000. Types of spéciation chez quelques collemboles Symphypleones Sminthuridae (Aptérygotes) de Madagascar. In *Diversité et endémisme à Madagascar*, eds. W. R. Lourenço and S. M. Goodman, pp. 295–306. Paris: Mémoires de la Société de Biogéographie.

Gautier, L., Tahinarivony, J. A., Ranirison, P., and Wohlhauser, S. 2018. Végétation/Vegetation. In *Les aires protégées terrestres de Madagascar: Leur histoire, description et biote/The Terrestrial Protected Areas of Madagascar: Their History, Description, and Biota*, eds. S. M. Goodman, M. J. Raherilalao, and S. Wohlhauser, pp. 207–242. Antananarivo: Association Vahatra.

Martin, P. S. 1984. Prehistoric overkill: The global model. In *Quaternary Extinctions: A Prehistoric Revolution*, eds. P. S. Martin and R. G. Klein, pp. 354–403. Tucson: University of Arizona Press.

Voarintsoa, N.R.G., Raveloson, A., Barimalala, R., and Razafindratsima, O. H. 2019. "Malagasy" or "Madagascan"? Which English term best reflects the people, the culture, and other things from Madagascar? *Scientific African* 4: e00091.

CHAPTER 1

HISTORY OF SCIENTIFIC EXPLORATION

THE HISTORY OF ZOOLOGICAL EXPLORATION OF MADAGASCAR

F. Andriamialisoa and O. Langrand

THE FIRST ACCOUNT ON THE FAUNA OF MADAGASCAR

The natural history chapter in *L'Histoire de la grande isle Madagascar* (Flacourt 1658, 1991) by Etienne de Flacourt (1607–1660) begins with a statement praising the considerable diversity of animals, including birds and fishes and rare animals, as well as plants on the island. In 1648, Flacourt became the governor of the French commercial enclave of Fort Dauphin (Tolagnaro) and, through his first detailed accounts of the natural history of the island, pioneered the era of explorers and discoverers of Madagascar's fauna and flora.

The modern phase of human settlement of the island started in an earnest manner in the seventh century (see Wright and Rakotoarisoa, pp. 181–90), and until the 16th century the links with the outside world were most likely dominated by Arabian sailors and merchants whose trading routes passed by Madagascar's coasts (Brown 1995). Those early visitors brought home tales of fantastic Malagasy animals that became characters of legend and fable. The rokh, a bird found in the accounts of Sinbad's travels in *A Thousand and One Nights*, is believed by some authors to have been a monstrous version of an elephant bird (family Aepyornithidae) (Decary 1937; Allibert 1992).

From the 16th century, Portuguese, Dutch, and English vessels often berthed off the Malagasy coasts, particularly around Toliara, including the Saint Augustin Bay. Their passengers were mostly transient traders and did not settle in a permanent manner on the island. They left little testimony of their passage with regard to the wildlife, except for a few anecdotes and illustrations. William Finch (d. 1613), a member of the East India Company of London's 1608 expedition, noticed the abundance of lizards and chameleons on the island. He also had a glimpse of an ash-colored, white-and-black-tailed creature near the Onilahy River, which was undoubtedly a *Lemur catta* (Ring-tailed Lemur) (Mittermeier et al. 2010).

In 17th century Europe, dreams of conquest of faraway lands gave rise to one commercial company after the other. France created the Compagnie Française des Indes Orientales in 1643. Flacourt was an official envoy of France and an employee of this company

FIGURE 1.1 ***Isle de Madagascar—Isle St. Laurens*, early map of Madagascar, dating from 1658 (Flacourt).** (SOURCE: Bibliothèque Nationale de France.)

when he arrived on the island on 15 December 1648. His mission was to revitalize the tiny trading post of Fort Dauphin. His commercial efforts failed, but his writings were a different form of success. He remained on Madagascar until 1655 and visited the southern and eastern areas, studying the geography, anthropology, arts, traditions and customs, flora, and fauna (Figure 1.1). When introducing his book to Nicolas Fouquet, King Louis XIV's representative, Flacourt "offered the island" to the French kingdom.

Flacourt depicted three groups of Malagasy fauna—terrestrial animals and insects, birds, and aquatic life—using local names with phonetic translation. This was before the use of binomial scientific names, which Swedish naturalist Carolus Linnaeus (1707–1778) would not develop until 1758. For the first time, a publication contained descriptions, though in some cases rudimentary, of lemur species ("monkeys" according to Flacourt). *L'Histoire de la grande isle Madagascar* enables the identification of lemur genera such as *Varecia* and *Propithecus* and some lemur species, such as *Hapalemur griseus* (Gray Bamboo Lemur). Flacourt also described a species of mouse lemur in the genus *Microcebus* ("some sort of gray squirrel") and *Cryptoprocta ferox* (Fosa, "an animal related to the badger") and made reference to the existence of mammals now extinct and known only from the subfossil record (see Godfrey and Douglass, pp. 191–97), such as giant lemurs and dwarf hippopotamuses.

Flacourt's bird list comprises 50 species, either "forest birds" or "night birds." His text presents a most valuable mention of the existence of elephant birds. On the basis of his writings, Flacourt never saw an elephant bird but reported stories from local people: the "vouron patra" haunted the Ampatres (almost certainly the area known today as Androy), had nesting habits similar to those of an ostrich, was hard to catch, and sought the most remote areas. Flacourt's accounts were far from scientific but presented Madagascar's mythic fauna to the outside world. The writer Ruelle, one of Flacourt's contemporaries, had his own imaginary way of describing the "vouron patra" (*vorompatra* in Malagasy and perhaps best translated as "the bird of the southern plains"). He wrote about a "flying dragon" that he had killed in order to have its skin (Allibert and Vérin 1993).

THE ENGAGEMENT OF THE FIRST TRUE NATURALISTS

The 18th century was a favorable time for scientific discoveries, intellectual novelties, and curiosities in Europe. Natural history societies, public or private collectors, botanical and zoological gardens, and curiosity cabinets gathered specimens from all around the world. In 1703, James Petiver (1665–1718), a London apothecary, first illustrated a lemur specimen, *Eulemur mongoz* (Mongoose Lemur) (Mittermeier et al. 2010).

The increasing sophistication of navigational techniques ushered in the dawn of a new category of voyagers: naturalist travelers. Formal natural exploration expeditions were organized. In 1766, Philibert Commerson (1727–1773) joined Antoine de Bougainville (1729–1811) on his trip around the world. Pierre Poivre (1719–1786), the French representative in the Isles de France et de Bourbon (Mauritius and La Réunion), asked Commerson to study the flora and fauna of the Indian Ocean region. Commerson soon realized how unique and fascinating Madagascar's nature was and collected mammals, birds, and insects. A large insectivorous bat (*Macronycteris commersoni*) named by the naturalist Etienne Geoffroy Saint-Hilaire (1772–1844) reminds us today of Commerson's visit to Madagascar. Poivre himself traveled to the island and collected birds and lemurs, and in 1768, he invited his nephew Pierre Sonnerat (1748–1814) to come to Madagascar. Sonnerat was a colonial administrator and a keen naturalist. During his exploration of the eastern part of the island, he recorded and illustrated *Indri indri* (Indri) and *Daubentonia madagascariensis* (Aye-aye). Johann Friedrich Gmelin (1748–1804), a student of Linnaeus, used Sonnerat's plates to name these two lemur species (Viette 1981).

In herpetology, Briton James Parson (1705–1770) was the first to describe, in 1768, a species of Malagasy chameleon, which he named *Cameleonis rarissima*. This was subsequently, in 1824, renamed *Calumma parsonii* in his honor by Georges Cuvier (1769–1832) (Brygoo 1971). French naturalists Alphonse Charles Joseph Bernier (1802–1858)—to whom *Anas bernieri* (Madagascar Teal), *Oriolia bernieri* (Bernier's Vanga), and a recently described bird family, the Bernieridae (Cibois et al. 2010), are dedicated—Jules Goudot (1803–1858?), Louis Rousseau (1811–1874), and Charles Coquerel (1822–1867) visited the eastern and northeastern parts of Madagascar. A bird species, *Coua coquereli* (Coquerel's Coua), and two lemur species, *Propithecus coquereli* (Coquerel's Sifaka) and *Mirza coquereli* (Coquerel's Giant Mouse Lemur), are named after Coquerel, a beetle specialist. Goudot's contributions are honored in the names of several animals (see Box 1).

The Dutchmen François Pollen (1842–1886) and Douwe van Dam (1827–1898), the Frenchman Etienne Geoffroy Saint-Hilaire, and the Briton Alfred Crossley (1842–1877) were other famous leaders of naturalist expeditions on Madagascar. Crossley gathered a large collection of mammals, birds, and insects for the Natural History Museum in London (see Box 2).

Pollen and van Dam collected numerous specimens on Madagascar and neighboring islands in 1864 and 1865. They summarized their discoveries in a report, which includes chapters on mammals, birds, reptiles, fishes, and insects. Pollen and van Dam's collection of lemurs formed a central resource for the study of Malagasy primates. Pollen was the first to contract German collector Josef-Peter Audebert (1848–1933) to collect in the eastern parts of the island for the Leiden Museum (Carleton et al. 2014). Audebert arrived on Madagascar in 1876 and traveled and collected specimens extensively over the next seven years. An endemic rodent, *Nesomys audeberti* (Lowland Red Forest Rat), is named after him.

Pollen and van Dam's ornithological work was particularly remarkable and pioneered a new era of bird studies on the island. Two species are named after these early naturalists: *Xenopirostris polleni* (Pollen's Vanga) and *X. damii* (Van Dam's Vanga). They are also honored with two freshwater fish species (*Paratilapia polleni* and *Paretroplus damii*) and a reptile (*Madascincus polleni*). Pollen and Hermann Schlegel (1804–1884), a German ornithologist (Figure 1.2) for whom *Philepitta schlegeli* (Schlegel's Asity) is named, compiled a list of 190 birds species known from Madagascar (Schlegel and Pollen 1868).

Another famous ornithologist of the same period was the German Gustav Hartlaub (1814–1900), who, although he never

BOX 1 JULES PROSPER GOUDOT (1803–1858?), FRENCH NATURALIST AND COLLECTOR, ON MADAGASCAR BETWEEN 1829 AND 1857

F. ANDRIAMIALISOA AND O. LANGRAND

JULES PROSPER GOUDOT was born on 12 December 1803 in Lons-le-Saunier, France. Very little is known about his family and education. He probably attended the Ecole des Voyageurs, created in 1819 by the Muséum National d'Histoire Naturelle in Paris to promote the collection by travelers of plants and animals across the world. Goudot collected flora and fauna specimens on Madagascar and La Réunion between 1829 and 1857, while his older brother Justin Marie did the same in the northern part of South America (specifically in Colombia) (Brygoo 1981).

While Goudot's extensive collections largely benefited the French national museum, his name appears neither on the list of the museum's correspondents from the period 1708–1909 nor on the list of travelers who contributed to the collections of the museum or the Jardin du Roi (Blanchard 1872; Frémy 1889; Anonyme 1909). In 1828, with a grant obtained from the museum, Goudot left France on the vessel *La Zélée* and arrived five months later on La Réunion; he spent three months there before leaving for Madagascar, disembarking in Toamasina in May 1829. He stayed a few months on the east coast, visiting Tintingue and Ile Sainte Marie. The Hova authorities did not allow him to visit the Central Highlands. He was forced to leave Toamasina at the end of 1829 and went back to La Réunion, then to France in 1830.

With another grant from the museum, Goudot returned to Madagascar, arriving in Toamasina in October 1831, and visited the Sihanaka region, to the east of Lake Alaotra. In 1833, he traveled to the north, up to Antsiranana, aboard the vessel *La Nièvre*. He returned to France the same year with many specimens. In 1834, out of 4023 specimens Goudot collected on Madagascar, the museum received 1641.

In 1834, Goudot sailed back to Madagascar after obtaining a three-year grant from the museum and the official title of "Voyageur Naturaliste." In 1835, he went back to the Sihanaka region, and in 1838, he visited the Central Highlands for the first time, spending six months in Antananarivo. He decided to base himself in the capital city and married a Malagasy woman named Augustine Jolicoeur (Boudou 1940).

In 1839, he went back to France with his wife, apparently to buy fabrics and jewelry for Madagascar's Queen Ranavalona I. In 1842, he collected in the region of Toamasina, in 1852 in the region of Nosy Be, and in 1856 near Toamasina. In 1857, Goudot lived in Antananarivo, in a location southeast of Mahamasina, and inventoried plants in an area known today as Tsimbazaza, which at that time was on the outskirts of the capital city and the private property of the Rafaralahiberonga Radaody-Rainidaorodina family, with whom Goudot was acquainted from the time he spent in Toamasina. While Goudot's activities were purely nature-related, some people, including his friend Rainidaorodina, believed he was a spy for the French government (Radaody-Ralarosy 1966). In 1857, Joseph Lambert, a French resident in Antananarivo, and a few high-ranking officers planned a coup to overthrow Queen Ranavolona I, with the support of her son, Prince Rakoto. The coup failed, and Queen Ranavalona I ordered the trial of the Malagasy involved in the plot and the deportation of several Europeans, including Lambert, Jean Laborde, his son Clément Laborde, Marius Arnaud, and Austrian traveler Ida Pfeiffer (Pfeiffer 1861; Brown 1995). Forced to leave Madagascar with these French personalities, Goudot settled on La Réunion. He sent several letters in 1858 asking Queen Ranavalona I authorization to return to Madagascar but was denied.

In 1861, Queen Ranavalona I died, and many Europeans went back to Madagascar. It is possible that Jules Goudot was among them, but there is no proof. The French government, eager to find out what had happened to the relatively famous traveler and naturalist, asked Jean Laborde, who had returned to Madagascar as the first French consul, to locate Goudot. He was not found, and his notes and last collections were forever lost. The date and location of his death are unknown. The Malagasy nicknamed Goudot "Mose Bibikely" or "Monsieur [or Mister] Small Animals/Insects." Some also called him "Rafaralahy-Bibikely" (Boudou 1940).

During his time in Madagascar, Goudot lived in very modest conditions. He walked barefoot and dressed as a Malagasy peasant, in a *lamba jabo* made of raffia and cotton, a shirt known as an *akanjo ketrom-bozona*, and a straw hat on which he pinned various insects and other small animals. His passion for nature took him to remote parts of Madagascar, where he ignored risks associated with safety, health, and comfort. Because of his appearance and lifestyle, Goudot was not appreciated by some of his French compatriots and was often a target of defamation (Brygoo 1981).

The specimens of plants and animals Goudot collected on Madagascar gave many scientists opportunities to describe new species (Poisson 1948). Among the vertebrates, were the first fragments of elephant bird eggs studied by Paul Gervais in 1841; a specimen of *Geobiastes squamiger* (Scaly Ground-roller) that led to the description of this species by Frédéric de Lafresnaye in 1838; some freshwater fishes, such as *Mesopristes elongatus*, described by Alphonse Guichenot in 1866; and several species of lemurs, such as *Phaner furcifer* (Masoala Fork-marked Lemur), described by Henri de Blanville in 1839, and *Lepilemur mustelinus* (Weasel Sportive Lemur), described by Isidore Geoffroy Saint-Hilaire in 1851.

MALAGASY VERTEBRATE SPECIES NAMED AFTER J. P. GOUDOT

1. ***Boophis goudotii*** **(Goudot's Bright-eyed Frog), described by Tschudi (1838)**
2. ***Ithycyphus goudoti*****, a snake, described by Schlegel (1837)**
3. ***Myotis goudoti*** **(Malagasy Mouse-eared Bat), described by Smith (1834)**
4. ***Eupleres goudotii*** **(Falanouc), a carnivoran described by Doyère (1835)**

BOX 2 ALFRED CROSSLEY (1842–1877), BRITISH NATURALIST AND COLLECTOR, ON MADAGASCAR BETWEEN 1869 AND 1877

F. ANDRIAMIALISOA AND O. LANGRAND

ALFRED CROSSLEY was born in 1842 and lived in Halifax, West Yorkshire, United Kingdom. Nothing is known about his academic or professional background. During the late 1800s, when the trade in natural specimens was thriving, Crossley worked as a specimen collector and for this purpose went to Madagascar, Cameroon, and today's Zimbabwe (Thomas 1906). On Madagascar, Crossley collected specimens of plants, insects, birds, and mammals, which he sold to individuals and museums through natural history agents and dealers, such as William D. Cutter and Edward Gerrard Jr. (of Edward Gerrard & Sons), both located in Bloomsbury, London (Sharpe 1870a; Dorr 1997; Morris 2004; Carleton et al. 2014).

Crossley conducted three expeditions to Madagascar between 1869 and 1877. His trips to the island were financed by Christopher Ward (1836–1900), a lepidopterist and naturalist from Halifax, United Kingdom. Crossley visited localities in the northeast, the central east, and the west (Sharpe 1870a, 1871, 1875; Grandidier 1892). He was assisted in the eastern region by local hunters who used blowpipes to kill birds (Sharpe 1871). Crossley did not systematically record information related to the collected specimens. However, his notes regularly mentioned the locality and the local name of bird species, as well as the date and sometimes other details such as stomach contents or eye color. Crossley had the habit of sending accompanying notes with the specimens, but these documents did not always reach the agent, as was the case with the 1875 shipment to Cutter (Sharpe 1875). In addition, when specimens were sold by the agents, this information was not always transmitted to the buyers.

In 1869 and 1870, Crossley visited Iharana (also known as Vohémar, recorded on specimen labels as "Vohima," presumably derived from the locality name Vohimarina), as well as Antalaha, Maroantsetra, and Toamasina. From Toamasina, he went to Mahambo and Fenoarivo Atsinanana and to Nosivola (mentioned as "Nossi Vola"), southeast of Lake Alaotra. Specimen labels mention a place called "Saralalan," located 12 km from Nosivola and presumably in close vicinity of today's Zahamena protected area, referred to in Grandidier (1892) as "Pays de l'Antsihanaka" (also see Box 3, on Charles Herschell-Chauvin for details concerning the "Sihanaka Forest"). From there, he reached the Imerina region and collected in a place he referred to as "Vodirat," 40 km northwest of Antananarivo. In London, Cutter made a collection of Crossley's bird specimens available for inspection by Richard Bowdler Sharpe (1847–1909), the curator of the bird collections at the British Museum (now the Natural History Museum) (Sharpe 1870a). From this consignment, Sharpe described two new bird genera, *Oxylabes* and *Mystacornis*, and two new bird species, *Sarothrura insularis* (Madagascar Flufftail) and *Pseudobias wardi* (Ward's Vanga), the latter named in honor of Christopher Ward, the sponsor of Crossley's expeditions to Madagascar (Sharpe 1870a, 1870b).

In 1870, British zoologist Michael Rogers Oldfield Thomas (1858–1929) received a shipment of 133 mammal specimens obtained by Crossley. German zoologist Wilhelm Carl Hartwig Peters (1815–1883), from the Museum für Naturkunde, Berlin, described one rodent specimen as a new species, *Nesomys rufus* (Red Forest Rat), in 1870 (Peters 1870; Thomas 1906; Carleton et al. 2014). Peters (1874) also described a new bat species, *Paremballonura atrata* (Peter's Sheath-tailed Bat) (originally named *Emballonura atrata*), from a specimen collected by Crossley (Goodman et al. 2006).

Crossley also provided specimens, collected in 1869, to Alfred Grandidier (1836–1921), who described a new species of bird, *Mystacornis crossleyi* (Crossley's Vanga) originally described as *Bernieria crossleyi*), and a new species of lemur, *Cheirogaleus crossleyi* (Crossley's Dwarf Lemur). The specimen for the latter was collected in the vicinity of today's Zahamena protected area; Grandidier (1870) recorded its origin as "Forêts est Antsianak."

Toward the end of 1870, Crossley went back to England. In 1871, Sharpe looked at a second consignment of natural history specimens from Crossley, collected in the central-eastern part of Madagascar. This did not lead to the description of any new species (Sharpe 1871). These specimens had been transported in Crossley's personal luggage, while the greater part of his collection had been sent to Paris, where the siege by Prussian forces had just started. However, no damage occurred to any of the specimens in Paris.

In 1871 and 1872, back in Madagascar, Crossley traveled from Maroantsetra to Toamasina, Mahanoro to Masindrano, and Masindrano to Ambohimanga Atsimo. The same year, he spent time in the western part of the country and went from Ankavandra to Mahajanga (Grandidier 1892). In 1872, Sharpe studied a third shipment of Crossley's specimens, collected southeast of Antananarivo, in which he did not find any taxonomic novelty (Sharpe 1872). Between 1873 and 1875, Crossley went to Antongil Bay and then from Toamasina to Morondava (Tattersall 1986). Specimens of lemurs attest to his collecting activities in the eastern part of the country (Schlegel 1876; Jentink 1887).

In 1875, Sharpe studied a fourth consignment sent by Crossley, which contained some rare species and novelties. Unfortunately, the usual accompanying notes were missing from the collection, which complicated efforts to pinpoint the collecting sites. In 1875, Sharpe described *Eutriorchis astur* (Madagascar Serpent-eagle), a new genus and species of raptor; *Atelornis crossleyi* (Rufous-headed Ground-roller), a new ground-roller species collected in Ampasimaneva (mentioned as "Ampasmonhavo"); *Neodrepanis coruscans* (Common Sunbird-asity), a new genus and species of asity; and finally, *Crossleyia xanthophrys* (Madagascar Yellowbrow) and *Xanthomixis zosterops* (Spectacled Tetraka), two species of the family Bernieridae. It is worth noting that Sharpe first described *Crossleyia xanthophrys* as *Oxylabes xanthorphys*, and the genus *Crossleyia* was created by German medical doctor, ornithologist, and zoologist Karel Johan Gustav Hartlaub (1814–1900) in 1877. Hartlaub was associated with the natural history museum of the city of Bremen. Crossley also sent a collection of mammals to Albert Günther (1830–1914) of the British Museum, including a specimen of a new lemur species, *Allocebus trichotis* (Hairy-eared Dwarf Lemur) (Günther 1875).

Crossley, like many other collectors, was overshadowed by the museum-based scientists who described species using the specimens he collected on Madagascar. However, his fieldwork significantly contributed to the advancement of knowledge on the island's plants, insects, birds, small mammals, and lemurs (Sharpe 1906; Dorr 1997; Carleton et al. 2014). Sharpe (1875) summarized this well: "I have been permitted to examine a very fine collection recently sent home by my old correspondent Mr. Crossley, whose investigations in the wonderful island of Madagascar will forever connect his name with the natural history of this part of the world."

Crossley left Madagascar in June 1875, returning to England via Mauritius, but was back in Madagascar in 1876. According to German naturalist and collector Josef-Peter Audebert (1848–1933), who arrived on the island in 1876, Crossley had died in 1877 (letter from Audebert to François Pollen, January 1878, Leiden Museum). Tattersall (1986), based on information reported in *Ny Diary Malagasy*, indicates that Crossley died in Madagascar on 28 February 1877. Crossley's death was confirmed by Sharpe, who referred to "the late Mr. Crossley" in a publication dated February 1879 (Sharpe 1879).

MALAGASY VERTEBRATE SPECIES NAMED AFTER A. CROSSLEY

1. ***Atelornis crossleyi*** **(Rufous-headed Ground-roller), described by Sharpe (1875)**
2. ***Mystacornis crossleyi*** **(Crossley's Vanga), described by Grandidier (1870)**
3. ***Crossleyia xanthophrys*** **(Madagascar Yellowbrow), described by Hartlaub (1877)**
4. ***Crossleyia tenebrosa*** **(Dusky Tetraka), described by Stresemann (1925)**
5. ***Cheirogaleus crossleyi*** **(Crossley's Dwarf Lemur), described by Grandidier (1870)**

FIGURE 1.2 **Portrait of Hermann Schlegel by Johan Heinrich Neuman, dated 1882. Schlegel, the second director of the Leiden Museum, Netherlands, encouraged the Dutch naturalist François Pollen to conduct a zoological mission to Madagascar.** (SOURCE: Naturalis Biodiversity Center, Leiden, Netherlands.)

visited Madagascar, compiled and updated lists of the island's birds based on specimens in the collections of various museums, such as those in Paris, Leiden, Vienna, and Stuttgart. The collections in Vienna were examined for Hartlaub by Austrian ornithologist August von Pelzeln (1875–1891), to whom Hartlaub dedicated *Tachybaptus pelzelnii* (Madagascar Grebe). Hartlaub published a book on the birds of Madagascar and the Mascarenes, covering 214 Malagasy species (Hartlaub 1877).

THE STATE OF EXPLORATION AND KNOWLEDGE BEFORE THE COLONIAL PERIOD (PRE-1896)

Africa was the scene of fierce struggle for religious and political influence between the British and the French during the 19th century, and this extended to Madagascar. To counterbalance the French influence, the London Missionary Society sent several envoys to the island. Many of those missionaries traveled to different areas and left some valuable testimonies of their observations of nature.

Among them, the Reverend William Deans Cowan (1844–1923) was clearly a keen observer and wrote about Malagasy lemurs and birds. His name is remembered today with a species of shrew tenrec (*Microgale cowani*) and three amphibians (*Mantella cowanii*, *Mantidactylus cowanii*, and *Platypelis cowanii*). The photographs made by Reverend William Ellis (1794–1872) (Figure 1.3) are among the first taken on Madagascar and remain his most precious legacy (Peers 1995). He traveled to Madagascar three times (1853, 1854, and 1856), passing from Toamasina to Antananarivo via Andasibe, and took an interest in natural history, collecting specimens

FIGURE 1.3 **Portrait of William Ellis engraved by W. Holl from a photograph by T. R. Williams. In his book *Three Visits to Madagascar* (1859), Ellis included notes on the natural history of Madagascar recorded during the three visits he made in 1853, 1854, and 1856.** (SOURCE: Ellis 1859.)

of flora and fauna, specifically mammals for the London natural history cabinet of Richard Owen (1804–1892) (Ellis 1859).

The Reverend James Sibree (1836–1929), also associated with the London Missionary Society, spent time on Madagascar between 1863 and 1915. Competition between France and Great Britain is illustrated by Sibree's criticism of one of his French contemporaries, Alfred Grandidier (1836–1921), who authored some of the most monumental publications on Madagascar. In his book *A Naturalist in Madagascar*, Sibree (1915) admitted that Grandidier's work was impressive but regretted that the volumes were in French, which he felt diminished their potential to advance scientific knowledge, and found their price exorbitant for the general public.

Sibree's major contribution to the knowledge of the fauna was through his work as the editor, between 1875 and 1900, of a naturalist journal, the *Antananarivo Annual and Madagascar Magazine*, which he published with his friend the Reverend Richard Baron (1847–1907). Aimed at the general public, the magazine presented information on the topography, natural history, and customs and traditions of Madagascar. Although it may seem surprising that topographic data was available at such an early date, rudimentary mapping of the island had commenced in 1871. Baron was a missionary on the island for 35 years, during which he collected many plants and published a significant synthesis of the island's phytogeography, the study of the geographic distribution of plants (Baron 1890). Some species of plants and animals are named after him, including a frog (*Mantella baroni*).

THE GRANDIDIER LEGACY: AN ERA OF MAJOR ADVANCEMENTS

Alfred Grandidier played a role of paramount importance in the exploration of Madagascar, and his name remains forever linked to the island. His interests included geography, nature, exploration, and ethnology. He traveled to Madagascar for the first time in 1865 with Jean Auguste Lantz (1828–1893), the first curator of the Muséum d'Histoire Naturelle de Saint-Denis de La Réunion (Dorr 1997). In 1866, Grandidier explored the southern and southwestern parts of the island, and in 1868 he visited the west and the Central Highlands. He obtained important collections of mammals, birds, reptiles, fishes, invertebrates, plants, fossils, minerals, and ethnographic objects, which are still used today by scientists. Lantz also visited Madagascar several times, collecting birds and lemurs for his museum, and met Pollen and van Dam on Nosy Be.

After he returned to France in 1870, Grandidier devoted the rest of his career to Madagascar (Figure 1.4) and in part worked on his collections in collaboration with Alphonse Milne Edwards (1835–1900), a zoologist from the Muséum National d'Histoire Naturelle in Paris. They pioneered the classification and systematic study of virtually all aspects of the fauna and flora of the island known at that time, publishing their work in the monumental *Histoire physique, naturelle et politique de Madagascar*, initially planned to be a 60-volume series. Toward the end of his life, Grandidier delegated the editorial task of continuing the series to his son Guillaume (1873–1957), an accomplished geographer, ethnologist, and zoologist. The series, ultimately comprising 39 volumes, was published over the course of 80 years and included volumes dedicated to the island's meteorology, ethnography, politics and history, mosses, plants, mammals, birds, fishes, reptiles, and some families of insects and other invertebrates, and even today represents an important reference work.

Alfred Grandidier and Milne Edwards were the principal authors for the volumes on mammals (in collaboration with French physician and zoologist Henri Filhol [1843–1903] and Guillaume Grandidier). They also wrote the volume on birds, to which Louis Lavauden (1881–1935), an engineer for the Département des Eaux et Forêts, added a supplement (Lavauden 1937). French paleontologist and ichthyologist Henri Emile Sauvage (1842–1917) contributed to the volume on fishes. French herpetologist and ornithologist Léon Louis Vaillant (1834–1914) and Guillaume Grandidier wrote the only volume on reptiles, which covered crocodiles and turtles (Vaillant and Grandidier 1910).

Alfred Grandidier's contribution to the history and natural science knowledge of Madagascar is unparalleled. He was one of the founders of the Comité de Madagascar and edited the journal *La Revue de Madagascar*. He also published the *Collection des ouvrages anciens concernant Madagascar*, a compilation of works written between 1500 and 1800—mostly French publications, plus translations of virtually

FIGURE 1.4 **Alfred Grandidier's bookplate, or ex libris. Alfred Grandidier was not only a very prolific author; he amassed a personal library of over 17,000 references covering various subjects on Madagascar, which was bequeathed to the Académie Malgache.** (PHOTO by O. Langrand, courtesy of the Académie Malgache.)

all foreign-language publications—concerning the exploration of Madagascar. Grandidier was a role model for numerous scientists, including his son Guillaume. Guillaume Grandidier made several visits to the western and eastern coasts and to the extreme south of the island and continued to collect birds, insects, plants, and fossils.

Alfred Grandidier described a great number of animal species, and his major contribution to the advancement of natural history of the island is immortalized in the names of a skink genus (*Grandidierina*) and nine faunal species: a fish (*Ptychochromis grandidieri*); a frog (*Mantidactylus grandidieri*); two snakes (*Liopholidophis grandidieri* and *Xenotyphlops grandidieri*); one iguanid (*Oplurus grandidieri*); one bird, the Madagascar Spinetail (*Zoonavena grandidieri*); one shrew tenrec (*Microgale grandidieri*); and a rodent (*Eliurus grandidieri*). With *Megaladapis grandidieri*, a giant lemur, and *Aldabrachelys grandidieri*, a giant tortoise, Grandidier also left his mark on the subfossil fauna. Alphonse Milne Edwards is remembered through two giant subfossil lemurs (*Archaeolemur edwardsi* and *Megaladapis edwardsi*), the nocturnal *Lepilemur edwardsi* (Milne-Edwards' Sportive Lemur), and the diurnal *Propithecus edwardsi* (Milne-Edwards' Sifaka) (Figures 1.5a and b).

FIGURE 1.5 **Plates of *Propithecus edwardsi* (Milne-Edwards' Sifaka) from the volume dedicated to lemurs in the monumental *Histoire physique, naturelle et politique de Madagascar*. A) Species depicted in the wild. B) Craniums, mandibles, and teeth. Alfred Grandidier described this species in 1871 and named it after his coauthor Alphonse Milne Edwards.** (SOURCE: Grandidier 1875.)

OTHER EXPLORERS ON THE EVE OF THE 20th CENTURY

Other major collectors at the end of the 19th century, many of whom were contemporaries of Alfred Grandidier, included Charles Immanuel Forsyth Major (1843–1923), of British Swiss origin, and Johann Maria Hildebrandt (1847–1881), of Germany. Forsyth Major collected intensively on an extended expedition to the island from 1894 to 1896. His work provided a comprehensive and systematic knowledge of the mammal fauna of the central east. He described three new genera and 13 new species of mammals, and his collections led to the description of seven other mammal species (Jenkins and Carleton 2005). Five vertebrate species are named in his honor: two frogs (*Boophis majori* and *Mantidactylus majori*), one shrew tenrec (*Microgale majori*), one rodent (*Eliurus majori*), and one bat (*Miniopterus majori*).

FIGURE 1.6 **Carl Ebenau, a zoologist who lived on Madagascar from 1880 to 1890, collected specimens of amphibians and reptiles, and sent them to Oskar Boettger at the Senckenberg Museum in Frankfurt, Germany. In 1879, Boettger described a new species of leaf-tailed lizard of the genus *Uroplatus*, and named it after Ebenau. The type specimen of *U. ebenaui* is housed in the Senckenberg Museum.** (PHOTO by O. Langrand, courtesy of the Senckenberg Museum.)

Hildebrandt, a collector for the Berlin Museum, now known as Museum für Naturkunde, spent two years on the island in 1879–1881. He mostly collected plants but also participated in the discovery of an extinct dwarf hippopotamus. He died at the age of 34 in Antananarivo and is buried in the Norwegian cemetery of Ambatovinaky (Beentje 1998). One reptile species (*Paracontias hildebrandti*) and one extinct elephant bird species (*Aepyornis hildebrandti*) honor him (Goodman and Jungers 2014).

The Frenchman Léon Humblot (1852–1914) collected specimens while on missions to Madagascar between 1878 and 1883. Humblot worked in the northern and eastern parts of the island, and his specimens were sent to Alfred Grandidier. The localities where Humblot collected specimens, at least for bats, were in some cases confused (Goodman and Ranivo 2009). One endemic species of bird is named after him, *Ardea humbloti* (Madagascar Heron).

Collections from Madagascar were sent to European museums, where eminent scholars studied the specimens. Individuals participating in the description of new vertebrate species from Madagascar toward the end of the 19th century included André Marie Constant Duméril (1774–1860), François Mocquard (1834–1917), and Pieter Bleeker (1819–1878) at the Muséum National d'Histoire Naturelle, Paris; Wilhelm Carl Hartwig Peters (1815–1883) at the Museum für Naturkunde, Berlin; John Edward Gray (1800–1875), Albert Günther (1830–1914), Richard Bowdler Sharpe (1847–1909), and George Albert Boulenger (1858–1937) at the British Museum (now the Natural History Museum), London; Oskar Boettger (1844–1910) at the Senckenberg Museum, Frankfurt (Figure 1.6); and Mario Giacinto Perraca (1861–1923) at the Museo Regionale di Scienze Naturali, Turin.

RESEARCH EFFORTS DURING THE COLONIAL PERIOD

In 1896, the French parliament passed an annexation law, and Madagascar officially became a colony of France. In 1902, General Joseph Galliéni, the governor of Madagascar, created a new colonial institution, the Académie Malgache, with the intent to merge in one structure research efforts on the island conducted by scholars from France as well as Madagascar and other nations. For several decades, researchers associated with the Académie Malgache and with the Muséum National d'Histoire Naturelle in Paris published monographs and articles in the *Bulletin de l'Académie Malgache* and in the *Mémoires de l'Académie Malgache*. Jacques Pellegrin (1873–1944) published through the Académie Malgache a monograph on freshwater fishes (Pellegrin 1933), and a monograph on lizards by Fernand Angel followed (Angel 1942).

Important advancements occurred in the first portion of the 20th century, specifically in 1929 with the launch of the Mission Zoologique Franco-Anglo-Américaine, which ended in 1931. Jean Delacour (1890–1985) from the Muséum National d'Histoire Naturelle, Paris; Willoughby Prescott Lowe (1872–1949) from the British Museum (Natural History Museum), London; and Leland C. Sanford (1868–1950) from the American Museum of Natural History, New York, were its initiators. Members of the expedition included Delacour, Lowe, Richard Archbold (mammal collector, 1907–1976), Austin L. Rand (ornithologist, 1905–1982), James Cowan Greenway (ornithologist, 1903–1989), Errol White (paleontologist, 1901–1985), and Cecil Stanley Webb (live animal collector, 1898–1964). Raymond Decary (1891–1973), the director of the Recherche Scientifique Coloniale, replaced Delacour as the expedition leader in 1930. Philip A. DuMont (1903–1996) from the American Museum of Natural History joined the team in January 1930. The mission gathered an impressive quantity of specimens, including about 12,000 birds and hundreds of mammal, reptile, amphibian, and fish samples. Further, collections bought from Charles Herschell-Chauvin (1875–1959), a French trader, augmented the collection (see Box 3).

Reporting on the mission was the responsibility of Delacour, who published the systematic part of the ornithological work (Delacour 1932a, 1932b). Rand also wrote two publications on birds (Rand 1932, 1936) and another on mammals (Rand 1935). The mission's results included descriptions of 13 new forms of birds: 10 new subspecies, two new species (Figure 1.7), and one new genus (Rand 1936). Reports provided details on habitats, behavior, distribution, and migration patterns. Decary published a considerable amount on the mission and on his own collections. He left a collection of 4300 publications on Madagascar to the Académie des Sciences d'Outre Mer in Paris (Decary 1946, 1947; Balard 2003).

Several species of birds and other vertebrates were named after the expedition members. Rand was honored with *Randia pseudozosterops* (Rand's Warbler), representing the new genus discovered during the mission and now placed in the endemic family Bernieridae (see Reddy and Schulenberg, pp. 1621–26). Archbold left his name to a new species of passerine, *Newtonia archboldi* (Archbold's Newtonia), and Decary to three reptile species, including the dwarf chameleon *Brookesia decaryi*, and an amphibian, *Gephyromantis decaryi*. Archbold (1932) described a new subspecies of brown lemur from the island's extreme north, subsequently elevated to a full species, *Eulemur sanfordi* (Sanford's Brown Lemur), which he dedicated to one of the mission's organizers, Leland C. Sanford.

FIGURE 1.7 **In 1932, Jean Delacour described a new species of grebe, *Tachybaptus rufolavatus*, from Lake Alaotra, Madagascar. The type specimen of this endemic species, collected on 7 June 1929 at Andreba, is deposited in the Muséum National d'Histoire Naturelle (MNHN) in Paris, France. The Alaotra Grebe is now considered extinct.** (PHOTO by O. Langrand, courtesy of the MNHN.)

Post–World War II until the end of the 1960s, the Académie Malgache and the Institut de Recherche Scientifique de Madagascar (IRSM)—an affiliate institute of the Office de la Recherche Scientifique et Technique Outre-Mer (ORSTOM), which was renamed subsequently the Institut de Recherche pour le Développement (IRD)—supported frequent zoological expeditions. French researchers, with occasional collaborators from other countries, collected specimens in the fields of entomology, ichthyology, herpetology, ornithology, and mammalogy. Researchers were from the IRSM, the Institut Pasteur de Madagascar (IPM), the Centre National de la Recherche Scientifique (CNRS), and the Centre Technique Forestier Tropical (CTFT). Specimens collected during this period, which was one of hegemony for French research institutions, augmented the holdings of the Muséum National d'Histoire Naturelle, Paris, and the Académie Malgache, Antananarivo.

The results of hundreds of missions and field projects, particularly in many cases the associated scientific specimens, have been incorporated in the *Faune de Madagascar*, a monograph series created by Renaud Paulian (1913–2003), an entomologist and deputy director of IRSM from 1947 to 1961. The first volume in the series came out in 1956. Since 2003, the series has been published by three research institutions: the Centre de Coopération Internationale en Recherche Agronomique pour le Développement (CIRAD), the IRD, and the Muséum National d'Histoire Naturelle, Paris. Nearly 90 monographs on vertebrates and invertebrates were published in the series. Publications from this same period also appeared in the *Bulletin de l'Académie Malgache*, *Le Naturaliste Malgache*, and the *Mémoires de l'Institut Scientifique de Madagascar*. Jacques Millot (1897–1980), a zoologist and director of IRSM, published a monograph on Malagasy arachnids (Millot 1948).

In ichthyology, Jacques Arnoult (1914–1995), the director of the vivarium at the Parc de Tsimbazaza between 1959 and 1963,

BOX 3 CHARLES HERSCHELL-CHAUVIN (1875–1959), FRENCH GENERAL TRADER, WILDLIFE SPECIMEN TRADER, PHOTOGRAPHER, ON MADAGASCAR BETWEEN 18?? AND 1959

F. ANDRIAMIALISOA AND O. LANGRAND

CHARLES HERSCHELL-CHAUVIN was born on 14 August 1875 at Grand Port, Mauritius. He settled in Toamasina, where he operated a general store. The 1905 *Guide annuaire de Madagascar et Dépendances* (République Française 1905) described his business as: "Grand assortiment d'articles de ménage. Épicerie, quincaillerie, literie, vins fins. Photographies, vues, cartes postales et curiosités du pays [Large assortment of household items. Groceries, hardware, bedding, fine wines. Photographs, postcards, and curiosities of the country]."

A friend of Herschell-Chauvin, Edouard Perrot (1863–1903), a naturalist and professional photographer, was also born on Mauritius and settled in Toamasina, arriving in 1894. Perrot appeared as the witness on the birth certificate of Conrad Herschell-Chauvin (1902–1985), the first of Herschell-Chauvin's five children. Charles Herschell-Chauvin, in turn, was the witness on Perrot's death certificate. It is very likely that Perrot had a strong influence on the professional orientation of Herschell-Chauvin, both as a wildlife specimen trader and as a photographer.

Herschell-Chauvin published postcards based on his own images depicting landscapes, infrastructure, and daily scenes of people from eastern Madagascar (Figure 1.8). He also documented the devastating impacts of the cyclone of 3 March 1927 in Toamasina.

Until World War II, Herschell-Chauvin sold wildlife specimens, mostly birds but also insects, amphibians, reptiles, and probably mammals, to scientists and museums of the world. Herschell-Chauvin also collected specimens himself, as he did from May to December 1911, when he accompanied Paul Methuen (1886–1974) on a mission to different parts of southern and eastern Madagascar associated with work on reptiles. Their collections yielded the description of a new gecko, *Phelsuma standingi* (Methuen and Hewitt 1913a). As a general procedure, Herschell-Chauvin established camps in the forest, particularly in the central east, and had hunters work with him (Lamberton 1927). The specimens from the Herschell-Chauvin collections are labeled, for example, "Folohy" (Ivoloina), "Maroantsetra," "Sihanaka Forest," "Vokarakaro," or simply "Eastern Region." Rand (1936) indicated that to augment the series of birds from the eastern forest obtained during the large-scale Franco-Anglo-Américaine mission (1929–1931), he bought bird skins from Herschell-Chauvin collected in the Sihanaka Forest. Rand noted that the colors of some specimens were altered as they were dried above a fire or handled in areas saturated with smoke.

The Swedish Royal Museum of Natural History in Stockholm purchased a small collection of bird skins from Herschell-Chauvin. Among those was a specimen Herschell-Chauvin collected in December 1931 in Fanovana that was described by Nils Gyldenstolpe (1886–1961) as a species new to science, *Newtonia fanovanae* (Red-tailed Newtonia) (Gyldenstolpe 1933). Philippe Milon (1908–1993), the first author of the bird volume in the series *Faune de Madagascar* (Milon et al. 1973), also bought many bird skins from Herschell-Chauvin, which he later deposited in the Muséum National d'Histoire Naturelle, Paris. Methuen bought specimens of amphibians and reptiles from Herschell-Chauvin that led to the description of three species new to science (Methuen and Hewitt 1913b).

Through the specimens collected, Herschell-Chauvin's commercial activities contributed significantly to the discovery of a range of different Malagasy organisms (Lamberton 1927; Paulian 1954). Despite his contributions, no species of vertebrates recognized today are named after him. *Chameleon chauvini*, described by Methuen and Hewitt (1913a), was subsequently considered a synonym of *Calumma furcifer* (Gehring et al. 2010); and *Asio chauvini*, described by Lamberton (1927), turned out to be an aberrant form of *Asio madagascariensis* (Madagascar Long-eared Owl) (Delacour 1932b). Herschell-Chauvin later left Toamasina, resettling in Ankadifotsy in Antananarivo. He died in the capital on 7 September 1959.

FIGURE 1.8 **Charles Herschell-Chauvin was a collector and dealer of faunal specimens, many of which ended up in different European and American museum collections. He was also a photographer and published postcards capturing scenes typical of the beginning of the 20th century, such as transport in a sedan chair, or *filanzana*, as it is known locally.** (PHOTO by C. Herschell-Chauvin, 1909.)

published a monograph on freshwater fishes in the *Faune de Madagascar* series (Arnoult 1959). Other ichthyologists active in that period included Yves Thérézien (1925–2015), an inspector in the Département des Eaux et Forêts between 1960 and 1966; André Kiener (1920–2009), the conservator of the Département des Eaux et Forêts and chief of the fish-breeding research division in the early 1960s; and André Maugé (1922–2008), the general secretary of IRSM in 1958. Two fishes are named after Arnoult (*Gobitrichinotus arnoulti* and *Pachypanchax arnoulti*), one after Thérézien (*Acentrogobius therezieni*), and two after Kiener (*Paretroplus kieneri* and *Teramulus kieneri*).

A number of researchers and scientific institutions focused their attention on reptiles and amphibians: Charles Blanc, Edouard-Raoul Brygoo (1920–2016), Charles Domergue (1914–2008), Paul Griveaud (1907–1980), Jean Guibé (1910–1999), Harald Meier (1922–2007), Georges Pasteur (1930–2015), and André Peyriéras (1927–2018). Guibé published a systematic revision of Malagasy snakes followed by the first monograph on the frogs of Madagascar (Guibé 1958, 1978). Roland Albignac, Arnoult, René Capuron (1921–1971), Paulian, Jean-Jacques Petter (1927–2002), Thérézien, and Jean Vadon (1904–1970) were among the field scientists and often collectors who contributed significantly to the advancement of knowledge of amphibians and reptiles. Several species of reptiles and amphibians bear the names of this generation of scientists. Guibé is honored with a genus of amphibian (*Guibemantis*), two frog species (*Spinomantis guibei* and *Boophis guibei*), and two reptiles (*Lygodactylus guibei* and *Calumma guibei*); Domergue with one amphibian (*Blommersia domerguei*) and one reptile (*Madatyphlops domerguei*). One dwarf chameleon is named after Griveaud (*Brookesia griveaudi*), one after Vadon (*B. vadoni*), and one after Thérézien (*B. therezieni*), who also left his name to a snake (*Liophidium therezieni*). Two reptiles (*B. brygooi* and *Zonosaurus brygooi*) are dedicated to Brygoo. A frog (*Mantella haraldmeieri*) and a lizard (*Z. haraldmeieri*) are named in recognition of Meier. The botanist Capuron and the zoologist Petter left their names to two chameleons, *Calumma capuroni* and *Furcifer petteri*, respectively. The ichthyologist Arnoult is honored with a gecko (*Lygodactylus arnoulti*), and the entomologist Paulian with a gecko (*L. pauliani*) and two amphibians (*Boophis pauliani* and *Mantidactylus pauliani*). A snake (*Ithycyphus blanci*), a gecko (*Lygodactylus blanci*), and a frog (*Gephyromantis blanci*) inherited Blanc's name. A bat (*Miniopterus griveaudi*) is named in honor of Griveaud.

POST-INDEPENDENCE ZOOLOGICAL EXPLORATION

Before Madagascar gained independence, scientific research was under the tutelage of France, as the colonial power, and therefore dominated by French institutions. Madagascar became independent on 26 June 1960, and for a transitional period, research occurred under French-Malagasy joint supervision, with gradual transfer of capacity and authority. From 1960 to 1972, reduced financing had major consequences on research activities, but French researchers remained strongly involved and organized numerous expeditions and surveys. The year 1972 saw great political changes on Madagascar with the proclamation of the Second Republic. Cooperation agreements were revised, and Malagasy authorities made clear their wish to operate national research structures without the contribution of foreign specialists (Menu and Roederer 2010). The period saw an exodus of foreign scientists and few avenues for international collaboration in scientific research. The number of expatriate staff at ORSTOM dropped from 76 in 1972 to seven in 1975, and by 1976 the office's only remaining activity was hydrology. Virtually no visas for foreign researchers were granted between 1975 and 1985 (Jolly and Sussman 2007).

Paulian left Madagascar in 1961 after a postindependence change of leadership at ORSTOM. However, he pursued his involvement through the continued supervision of the publication of *Faune de Madagascar* and, in the 1960s and early 1970s, by coordinating and initiating the Recherche Coopérative sur Programme (RCP) no. 225 under the CNRS, which conducted field missions to several high-mountain areas on the island. Sites surveyed by a multidisciplinary group of geologists, botanists, and zoologists included Tsaratanàna, Marojejy, Itremo, Ibity, Analavelona, and Andohahela (Paulian et al. 1971, 1973; Guillaumet et al. 1975).

The taxonomy of fishes saw little progress from the 1960s through the 1980s, with only a few descriptions by established ichthyologists such as Kiener, Arnoult, and Maugé. In contrast, herpetology was a much more dynamic field during this period, with the continuation of work by scientists such as Brygoo, Domergue, and Guibé. Domergue, an ornithologist and herpetologist by passion, worked on the island from 1959 to 1971 as a geologist in the national hydrology department and was involved in the installation of wells and boreholes in numerous remote areas of the south. He pursued research on snake taxonomy, which led to the description of about 20 new species between 1983 and 1986 (Domergue 1983, 1984a, 1984b, 1986).

Brygoo was a physician by trade and a naturalist by passion, and his research program was a rather remarkable mixture of these two aspects. He was deputy director and then director of the Institut Pasteur de Madagascar from 1954 to 1974. He conducted many faunal surveys with Blanc and Domergue. Brygoo described 25 new species of reptiles, mostly chameleons, between 1966 and 1981 and wrote two monographs on this group published in the *Faune de Madagascar* series (Brygoo 1971, 1978).

In the postindependence period, for the first time, a Malagasy scientist, Guy Ramanantsoa, played a major role in taxonomic research. Ramanantsoa described the chameleons *Calumma ambreense* (Ramanantsoa 1974) and *Brookesia bonsi* (Ramanantsoa 1980). The head of the Département des Eaux et Forêts at the Ecole Supérieure des Sciences Agronomiques (Water and Forest Department, School of Agronomy, known as ESSA-Forêts), Université d'Antananarivo, Ramanantsoa was instrumental in the identification, creation, and subsequent management of the Bezà-Mahafaly protected area, in collaboration with primatologists Alison Richard and Robert W. Sussman (1941–2016). A species of chameleon, *B. ramanantsoai*, is named after him.

During the reign of the French institutions (i.e., before independence), little work was devoted to ornithology. Perhaps this is because the Mission Zoologique Franco-Anglo-Américaine of 1929–1931 was such a success for ornithology that scientists felt there was little left to discover. Three naturalists working in the field of ornithology, Philippe Milon (1908–1993), Petter, and Georges Randrianasolo (c. 1930–1989), continued collecting information on Malagasy birds and compiled a volume for *Faune de Madagascar* (Milon et al. 1973) (Figure 1.9). Randrianasolo started out as an assistant to Milon in 1947, at the age of 17, and was trained to prepare specimens. An important scientific career awaited Randrianasolo (see Box 4).

Petter, Albignac, Yves Rumpler, and Peyriéras worked on mammals during the period before and after independence. They authored monographs in the *Faune de Madagascar* series on Malagasy carnivorans (Albignac 1973) and lemurs (Petter et al. 1977). Petter, a veterinarian and primatologist, started his work on Madagascar in 1956 in collaboration with his wife, Arlette Petter-Rousseaux. They undertook a mission around the country to survey lemur species and study their social behavior and reproduction. The mission was sponsored by Millot, then director of IRSM. Petter and Petter-Rousseaux published numerous scientific articles on their fieldwork and other aspects of their studies, considerably improving the state of knowledge on lemurs. They also described the genus *Allocebus* (Petter-Rousseaux and Petter 1967). Petter-Rousseaux is the only woman to have described a genus of Malagasy primate. Petter's work stimulated much subsequent research. Genetic and karyological research took off under the supervision of Rumpler, from the Faculté de Médecine, Université de Strasbourg, France. Albignac, associated with ORSTOM, brought to mammal research a combination of scientific training and fieldwork experience. Researchers active in mammal fieldwork during this period also included Randrianasolo (see Box 4), Peyriéras (see Box 5), and Eugène Ursch (1882–1962), and nonresident researchers such as Pierre Charles-Dominique, Annette Hladik, Claude Marcel Hladik, and Georges Pariente (1937–1976).

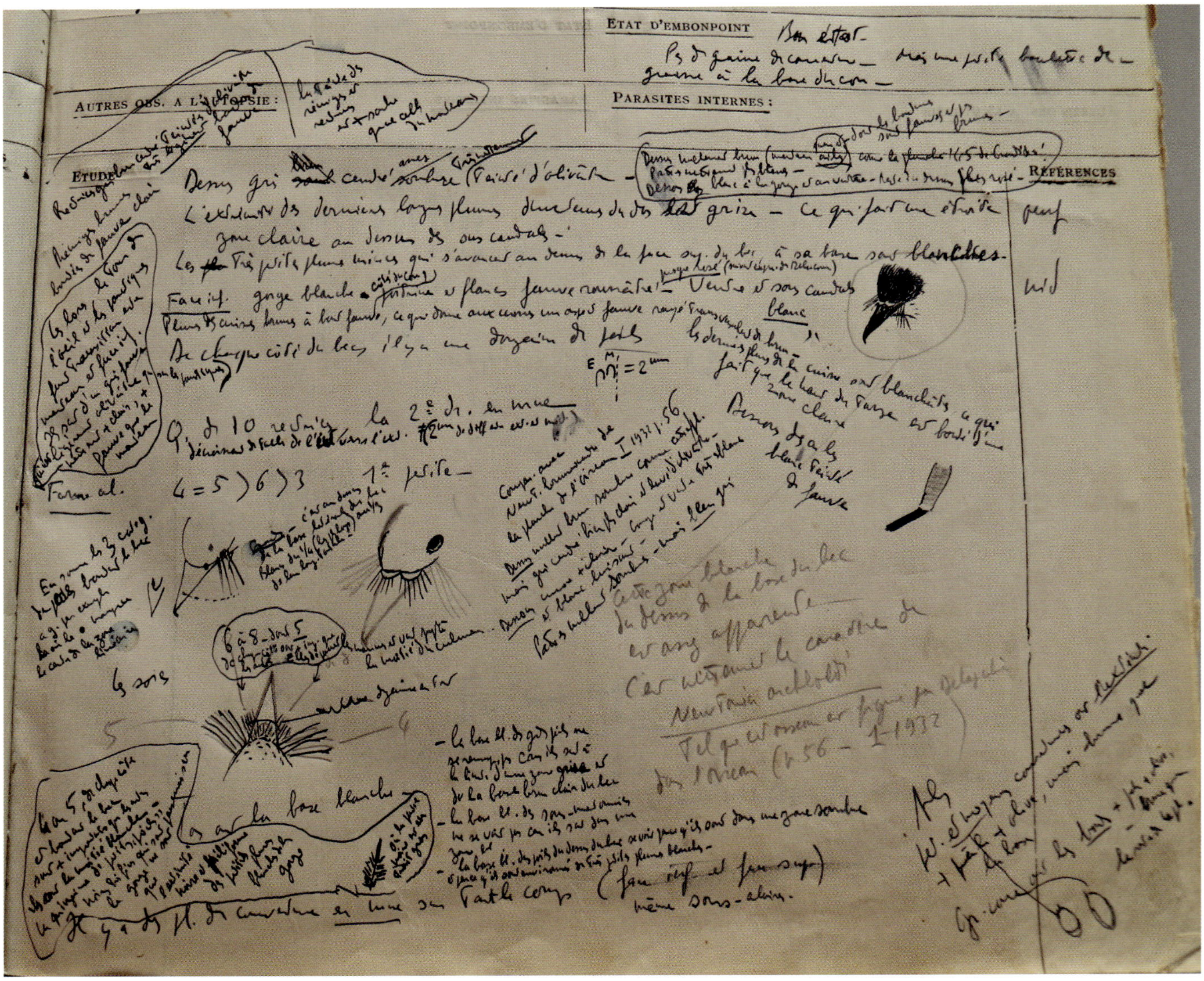

FIGURE 1.9 **Philippe Milon was an officer of the French army stationed on Madagascar. He was a passionate ornithologist who observed and collected birds in various parts of the island. He wrote very precise notes associated with the specimens he collected and deposited in the Muséum National d'Histoire Naturelle (MNHN), in Paris, France. The notes from Milon's specimen catalog presented here refer to a specimen of *Newtonia brunneicauda* (Common Newtonia) collected at Orangea (Oronjia) on 25 March 1947.** (PHOTO by O. Langrand, courtesy of the MNHN.)

BOX 4 GEORGES RANDRIANASOLO (C. 1930–1989), MALAGASY BOTANIST, ENTOMOLOGIST, ORNITHOLOGIST, MAMMOLOGIST, NATURALIST

F. ANDRIAMIALISOA AND O. LANGRAND

THE EXACT DATE when and the location where Georges Randrianasolo was born are not known. From October 1947, starting when he was about 17 years old, to September 1948, Randrianasolo was an ornithological research assistant to Philippe Milon (1908–1993), who was a squadron commander for the French Army based in Toliara and an accomplished ornithologist. This was the beginning of a collaboration that culminated with the publication of a volume on the birds in the series *Faune de Madagascar* (Milon et al. 1973). In 1952, Randrianasolo worked as a forestry auxiliary guard with the Service des Eaux et Forêts, based in Farafangana, and was registered as plant collector no. 208 of the Service Forestier.

He frequently accompanied visiting scientists, naturalists, and filmmakers. In 1960, while employed by the Institut de Recherche Scientifique de Madagascar (IRSM), Randrianasolo spent four months traveling around Madagascar with Sir David Attenborough (Figure 1.10) and cameraman Geoffrey Mulligan for the BBC TV series *Zoo Quest to Madagascar*, broadcast in 1961 (Attenborough 1961). In 1966, he accompanied Ike and Jean Russell, Paul Martin, and Alan Walker to Ampasambazimba in the Central Highlands and to Lake Alaotra to look for fossils (Walker 2010). In 1973, he led Dafila Scott and Joanna Lubbock, from Slimbridge Wildfowl Trust in the United Kingdom, to the island's west, as a guide and interpreter (Scott and Lubbock 1974). In 1985, he accompanied primatologist Alison Jolly (1937–2014) and photographer Frans Lanting, who were preparing an article on nature conservation for *National Geographic* magazine (Jolly 1988). Lanting considered Randrianasolo one of the country's greatest naturalists (Jolly 2015). They worked together in Beroboka, north of Morondava, to document local endemics that had rarely been photographed.

Between 1970 and 1977, Randrianasolo collected *Lepilemur* specimens in the region of Antsalova, including some distant localities, which would subsequently be used in a taxonomic revision of this genus (Andriaholinirina et al. 2006). He worked for the Office de la Recherche Scientifique et Technique Outre-Mer (ORSTOM) as a zoologist, caring for the lemurs in the Parc Botanique et Zoologique de Tsimbazaza. In 1978, he became the director of the Tsimbazaza park and occupied this post until 1986, when he retired. He continued to live in a house on the park premises with his family. He died in Antananarivo in 1989.

During his career, Randrianasolo worked with many scientists including Roland Albignac, Paul Griveaud, Philippe Milon, Renaud Paulian, Jean-Jacques Petter, André Peyriéras (see Box 5), and Yves Rumpler. The specimens of plants, invertebrates, and vertebrates he collected in different portions of the island led to the discovery of several species new to science, but he was never associated with these formal scientific descriptions. Only Milon and Petter gave him coauthorship, for their monograph on the birds of Madagascar (Milon et al. 1973).

FIGURE 1.10 **Georges Randrianasolo was trained as an ornithologist by Philippe Milon. He was an excellent field naturalist who worked with many scientists on Madagascar. In 1960, he accompanied Sir David Attenborough to document the unique biodiversity of Madagascar for the BBC. The photo, taken in November 1960, shows Randrianasolo dismantling an illegal lemur trap set in the Ankarafantsika Forest Reserve.** (PHOTO by Sir D. Attenborough.)

MALAGASY VERTEBRATE SPECIES NAMED AFTER G. RANDRIANASOLO

1. *Cryptosylvicola randrianasoloi* (Cryptic Warbler), described by Goodman et al. (1996)
2. *Lepilemur randrianasoloi* (Bemaraha Sportive Lemur), described by Andriaholinirina et al. (2006)

BOX 5 ANDRÉ PEYRIÉRAS (1927–2018), FRENCH ENTOMOLOGIST, NATURALIST, PRIMATOLOGIST, AND HERPETOLOGIST, ON MADAGASCAR BETWEEN 1954 AND 2005

F. ANDRIAMIALISOA AND O. LANGRAND

ANDRÉ PEYRIÉRAS was born on 11 December 1927 in Saint-Moreil, France, and died on 24 December 2018 in Limoges, France. He showed an interest in insects at an early age, starting his first collections at seven years old, for his teacher in his home village of Bujaleuf (Compère 2014). A self-taught scientist, he became an expert entomologist and had extensive knowledge on primates, carnivorans, reptiles, amphibians, and birds.

He started as a carpenter in Paris and came to Madagascar in 1954 to work for a forester based in Maroantsetra, in the northeast. There, he met Jean Vadon (1904–1970), the local school director and a keen entomologist. Vadon mentored Peyriéras, who started collecting and studying Malagasy Coleoptera. Peyriéras presented his PhD thesis, on the Scaratinae, a subfamily of ground beetles, at the Université de Montpellier, France, in 1974. A portion of his thesis was published in 1976 as volume 41 in *Faune de Madagascar* (Peyriéras and Basilewski 1976).

As a naturalist, Peyriéras acquired significant knowledge on a variety of Malagasy faunal groups other than insects. He traveled extensively around the island, spending extended periods of time in the field and in remote areas. He established a network of insect collectors who also acquired information on land vertebrates. His knowledge of and personal experience with Madagascar biodiversity were exceptional. He acquired detailed information on the high level of specificity in the plants that different butterfly species use at various stages of their development.

In the late 1970s, Peyriéras met Dominique Halleux (see Box 8), who had just been appointed by the French Ministère de la Coopération as an agronomist in charge of the development of coffee production in the region of Maroantsetra. A keen naturalist and birdwatcher in his home country, Halleux was very appreciative of Peyriéras's mentorship and started looking for rare birds and mammals around Maroantsetra and on the Masoala Peninsula.

Peyriéras worked closely with many entomologists and other scientists living in or visiting Madagascar, including Roland Albignac, Edouard-Raoul Brygoo, Charles Blanc, Charles Domergue, Paul Griveaud, Jean-Jacques Petter, Georges Randrianasolo (see Box 4), and Yves Rumpler. Peyriéras was for many years closely associated with the Office de la Recherche Scientifique et Technique Outre-Mer (ORSTOM), at its main office in Antananarivo. In 1972, Peyriéras was contracted by ORSTOM and slated to replace Griveaud, who was planning to retire in 1973, but his career in this organization was abruptly halted by the nationalization program initiated by the Malagasy authorities in the context of the move toward socialism (Brown 1995; Lacroix 1998).

In the 1980s, Peyriéras resettled in Antananarivo in a large house next to Lake Mandroseza. He established there a facility for captive rearing of butterflies for exportation. This project was successful thanks to Peyriéras's considerable knowledge of the relationships between certain butterfly species and their specific food plants, acquired over the many years he spent observing these interactions in the wild. Later, he moved this facility to a large estate in Marozevo later known as the Mandraka Nature Farm, halfway between Antananarivo and Andasibe. There, he had more space to grow the plants he needed to continue rearing butterflies in captivity (Figure 1.11). Finally, he started breeding some Malagasy reptile and amphibian species in captivity and made the Mandraka Nature Farm a tourist attraction, where visitors could see and photograph many endemic species of insects, amphibians, reptiles, and mammals, some unusual and rare.

MALAGASY VERTEBRATE SPECIES NAMED AFTER A. PEYRIÉRAS

1. *Avahi peyrierasi* (Peyriéras' Woolly Lemur), described by Zaramody et al. (2006)
2. *Calumma peyrierasi*, a chameleon, described by Brygoo et al. (1974)
3. *Brookesia peyrierasi*, a dwarf chameleon, described by Brygoo and Domergue (1974)

FIGURE 1.11 **André Peyriéras was an accomplished naturalist and an expert entomologist who spent 50 years on Madagascar. In his own facilities in Antananarivo and Marozevo, Peyriéras, photographed here in 1985, raised a number of endemic vertebrate and invertebrate species, such as the iconic Comet Moth (*Argema mitrei*).** (PHOTO by Frans Lanting/Lanting.com.)

Between 1972 and 1985, a period of difficult political transition on Madagascar, a few researchers, such as American primatologist Alison Jolly (1937–2014) and British primatologist Alison Richard, maintained their research programs. These two scientists conducted studies on lemur behavior and biology in the south, the former at Berenty and the latter in the Bezà-Mahafaly protected area. British American primatologist Ian Tattersall, from the American Museum of Natural History, started studying lemurs on Madagascar in 1969 but was forced to leave in 1975 because of the political situation.

THE MODERN PERIOD: INTERNATIONAL COOPERATION, ENGAGEMENT OF MALAGASY SCIENTISTS, AND EXPANSION OF ZOOLOGICAL EXPLORATION

Key individuals from various foreign and national institutes, museums, and universities have played important roles in a very active period of biodiversity data collection since the 1980s. In numerous cases, field scientists have systematically applied standardized collection methods, optimizing the utilization of specimens. Researchers with different expertise often participate in field expeditions, and through this period there has been an ever-increasing integration of Malagasy students and researchers, who also have been involved in the subsequent analyses and publications. This has been an important step in ensuring a truly international scientific collaboration and provided practical training opportunities for Malagasy scientists.

Nature conservation organizations have and continue to play an important role, through their research and education programs, in augmenting the knowledge of the fauna and flora of Madagascar and training national scientists. The World Wildlife Fund for Nature (WWF) started its research program in the 1980s, followed by Conservation International (CI) and the Wildlife Conservation Society (WCS) in the 1990s. Three members of the WWF program on Madagascar had a key role in stimulating biodiversity research, training, and international collaboration. All three arrived on Madagascar in 1980 and before joining WWF were involved in independent research projects: Olivier Langrand worked on birds, Martin E. Nicoll (1954–2020) studied tenrecs (see Box 6), and Sheila M. O'Connor investigated lemurs.

Steven M. Goodman arrived on the island in 1989 (Figure 1.12). He initiated an ambitious multidisciplinary research program, launched under the auspices of the WWF in the context of the Ecology Training Program, started by Nicoll (see Box 6), which focused on training of Malagasy graduate students and biological inventories of poorly known or unknown forested areas. Subsequently, this program became an independent Malagasy nongovernmental organization called Association Vahatra, dedicated to the study of the terrestrial biodiversity of Madagascar. Founded with three Malagasy scientists, all of whom conducted their graduate studies in the context of the Ecology Training Program—herpetologist Achille P. Raselimanana, ornithologist Marie Jeanne Raherilalao, and mammologist Voahangy Soarimalala—Vahatra put a great emphasis on the training of Malagasy researchers to acquire excellent academic credentials and strong field experience. Many Malagasy scientists and students have taken part in field inventories conducted at over 820 sites across Madagascar (Figure 1.14). In addition, efforts have also been put into formal training, in collaboration with different national universities, particularly the Université d'Antananarivo. The focus of the four scientific members of Association Vahatra, both in support of Malagasy students and in collaboration with national and foreign scientists, has been mostly associated with land vertebrates. Vahatra scientists and students have published many scientific papers, considerably advancing knowledge on the vertebrates of Madagascar and in many cases associating Malagasy and foreign scientists, who participated in the research, analysis, and different forms of intellectual input. In addition, Vahatra has published a number of books (in French or bilingual French-English) on various Malagasy animal groups (ants, frogs, small mammals, carnivorans, bats, and birds), a three-volume set on the protected areas of Madagascar, and a remarkable account of the Holocene ecosystems of Madagascar (Goodman 2011, 2012; Raherilalao and Goodman 2011; Soarimalala and Goodman 2011; Goodman and Jungers 2013; Goodman and Raherilalao 2013; Andreone et al. 2014, 2018; Goodman et al. 2018; Fisher and Peeters 2019).

FIGURE 1.12 **Steven M. Goodman, together with many Malagasy and foreign scientists as well as national students, inventoried the biodiversity of over 820 sites on Madagascar, providing a clear picture of the distribution of vertebrate taxa. Goodman is photographed here in December 1999, in front of a pitfall trap line set at 1600 m in a marsh area in the Manambolo Valley, during a survey to assess the biological importance of the forest corridor linking Ranomafana and Andringitra.** (PHOTO by H. Schütz.)

BOX 6 MARTIN EDWIN NICOLL (1954–2020), BRITISH NATURALIST, MAMMOLOGIST, CONSERVATIONIST, ON MADAGASCAR FROM 1980 TO 2020

F. ANDRIAMIALISOA AND O. LANGRAND

MARTIN NICOLL was born on 17 April 1954 in Devizes, Wiltshire, United Kingdom. His father was in the Royal Air Force (RAF) and his mother a homemaker. The family, which included two older sisters, lived in RAF Compton Bassett, Wiltshire. At a young age, Nicoll showed an interest in nature and explored small neighboring streams looking for all types of tiny creatures. From 1962 to 1964, Nicoll's family lived in Gibraltar, where he scoured the seashore for crabs and shellfish. When the family lived in Pitreavie, Fife, Scotland, from 1964 to 1966, Nicoll spent extensive time exploring the area and developed his interest in birds and small mammals, such as dormice and bats. In 1970, after residing in Aden, Yemen (1966–1967); Northern Ireland (1968); and Cyprus (1969–1970), the family returned to Rosyth, Scotland, and Nicoll finished high school in Kirkcaldy. He attended the University of Aberdeen and obtained a bachelor of science with honors in zoology in 1976.

According to Paul Racey, Regius Professor Emeritus of Natural History at the University of Aberdeen and a world expert on bats, Nicoll was a keen observer and stood out among his peers for the originality of his mind. In the mid-1970s, Nicoll participated in an undergraduate expedition to the Seychelles, where his fascination for fruit bats and tenrecs led him to select the latter as the subject of his PhD dissertation. Nicoll undertook his graduate studies under the supervision of Racey, was one of Racey's first PhD students, and introduced his supervisor to the Seychelles and later to Madagascar. Nicoll secured a highly competitive Leverhulme Overseas Studentship and a North Atlantic Treaty Organization (NATO) Studentship to work on Praslin Island, Seychelles, for three years, from August 1977 to September 1980, studying the reproductive ecology of *Tenrec ecaudatus* (Tailless Tenrec), a member of the family Tenrecidae. He also completed a survey of the roosting sites of the Seychelles endemic *Coleura seychellensis* (Seychelles Sheath-tailed Bat) (Nicoll and Suttie 1982) and the regional endemic *Pteropus seychellensis* (Seychelles Flying Fox) (Nicoll and Racey 1981). After completing his field research, Nicoll visited Madagascar for the first time in October 1980, before returning to Scotland. He obtained his PhD in zoology from the University of Aberdeen (Nicoll 1982).

Subsequently, Nicoll was awarded a Harkness Fellowship to the United States. He started a postdoctoral program at the National Zoological Park, Smithsonian Institution, in Washington, DC, to work with Edwin Gould and John Eisenberg, both pioneers of tenrec biology. From 1982 to 1985, Nicoll conducted field research on Madagascar on the reproductive energetics of the Malagasy Tenrecidae and on the niche partitioning among small mammals in moist evergreen forests of Madagascar (Thompson and Nicoll 1986). His field study site was the Analamazaotra Forest near Andasibe (Périnet). He was based at the Hôtel de la Gare, the only hotel in Andasibe at that time, where he was one of the very few clients. Monsieur Joseph, the hotel manager, assisted Nicoll with the logistics at a time when supplies were scarce on the island. In 1985, Nicoll crossed paths with Alison Jolly and wildlife photographer Frans Lanting, who were on Madagascar for a National Geographic Society assignment (Figure 1.13). The article, published in 1987, featured Nicoll and his work on tenrecs and showed the magazine's readers the uniqueness of Madagascar's biodiversity as well as threats to its survival (Jolly 1987). In Antananarivo, Nicoll worked with Felix Rakotondraparany, who from 1982 to 2003 was the curator of reptiles and small mammals at the Parc Botanique et Zoologique de Tsimbazaza. It was at Tsimbazaza in 1985 that Nicoll first met Peter J. (PJ) Stephenson, who had just returned from surveying small mammals in Zahamena as part of a student expedition.

FIGURE 1.13 **During the 30 years he spent on Madagascar, Martin E. Nicoll, a tenrec specialist and conservationist, actively promoted the training of Malagasy scientists in biodiversity research and conservation and their involvement in field project implementation. Nicoll is photographed here in 1985 while conducting field research on the reproductive energetics of Tenrecidae in the Analamazaotra protected area.** (PHOTO by Frans Lanting/Lanting.com.)

In April 1986, WWF International planned to establish a new conservation initiative on the island, the Biodiversity and Protected Area Program. WWF selected Nicoll as the principal technical adviser and Olivier Langrand as technical adviser. As the process of getting signed approval from the Malagasy government took more time than anticipated, WWF decided in May 1986 to send Nicoll and Langrand to Gabon to undertake an assessment of the conservation of the country's forest ecosystems, including a management plan for the Lope Reserve (Nicoll and Langrand 1987). It was also a way for Jeff Sayer, their International Union for the Conservation of Nature (IUCN) supervisor, working on behalf of WWF International, to test how well the pair worked together. The approval process by the Malagasy authorities was further delayed, as the paperwork for the establishment of the new WWF program and the formal appointment of both advisers was in the hands of Rear Admiral Guy Sibon, Madagascar's minister of defense, who died in a plane crash on 24 May 1986.

Nicoll and Langrand finally arrived in Antananarivo in September 1986. They established the office of the WWF Programme Biodiversité et Aires Protégées at the Direction des Eaux et Forêts (DEF) in Nanisana, Antananarivo, under the direction of Philémon Randrianarijoana. For two years, Nicoll and Langrand, together with Malagasy DEF staff, including Jean-Prosper Abraham (a field botanist) and Joël Ratsirarson (a wildlife specialist trained at the Ecole de Faune de Garoua, Cameroon), visited all the protected areas existing in Madagascar at that time and some classified forests. This two-year island-wide survey was concluded with the publication of a large-scale review of Malagasy biodiversity and was a critical turning point for the advancement of a national conservation strategy and action plan for the island (Nicoll and Langrand 1989). Nicoll led the WWF Programme Biodiversité et Aires Protégées until 1992, and management plans for the protected areas of Ankarana, Montagne d'Ambre, and Marojejy and a strategic document for Andohahela were prepared under his supervision.

In parallel to his responsibilities at WWF, Nicoll held an honorary position at the University of Aberdeen between 1988 and 1992, as senior research associate, and became the assistant PhD supervisor of Stephenson, who studied tenrecs in the country from 1988 to 1990, building on Nicoll's early work on tenrec physiology and ecology. Nicoll helped ensure that the two students who acted as field assistants for Stephenson's tenrec work, Nasolo Hubert Neomane Rakotoarison (1961–1996) and Herilala Randriamahazo, were also able to benefit from training offered by Professor Racey's research lab in Aberdeen.

Nicoll promoted the participation and training of Malagasy students in field biodiversity work, leading to the creation, in 1991, at his initiative, of the WWF Madagascar Ecology Training Program. Nicoll selected promising students for training overseas, including Rakotondraparany, Randriamahazo, Rakotoarison, and Jeannot Randrianasy, who all went to the United Kingdom for six months of training at the Jersey Zoo and the University of Aberdeen, funded by the British Council. Rakotondraparany, a small-mammal specialist, would subsequently become Maître de Conférences and researcher in the Département de Biologie Animale (subsequently called Mention Zoologie et Biodiversité Animale), Université d'Antananarivo. Randriamahazo, a herpetologist, obtained his PhD at the University of Kyoto, Japan, and after several years as coordinator of the Turtle Survival Alliance on Madagascar, is now the marine program director at the Wildlife Conservation Society in Antananarivo. Rakotoarison, a primatologist, obtained a master's degree in 1992 and worked as curator of small mammals at the Parc Botanique et Zoologique de Tsimbazaza. Subsequently, he started work on his PhD, concerning nocturnal lemurs, but unfortunately died in a car accident. In 1992, the WWF's Ecology Training Program was placed under the technical supervision of Steven M. Goodman of the Field Museum of Natural History, Chicago.

On account of his work as one of the pioneers of research on tenrecs, from 1986 to 1994, Nicoll was appointed chairman of the IUCN Species Survival Commission (SSC) Insectivore, Tree-shrew, and Elephant-shrew Specialist Group. He coproduced the first conservation action plan for tenrecs (Nicoll and Rathbun 1990), and three decades later, based on his continued interest in these animals, coauthored an update on their status and conservation priorities (Stephenson et al. 2019).

In 1992, Nicoll left Madagascar for Nairobi to work as senior conservation adviser for the WWF Africa continent-wide program on strategic development and project design, support, and evaluation. In 1997, he returned to Madagascar to serve as a technical assistant for WWF, based in Antananarivo, to provide assistance for the protected area network. For six years, Nicoll provided support to newly created interregional offices and individual protected areas under the authority of ANGAP (Association Nationale pour la Gestion des Aires Protégées and now known as Madagascar National Parks) and offered his expertise on conservation management and national system planning.

In 2004, Nicoll became senior conservation adviser for the WWF Madagascar and Western Indian Ocean Programme office. This position involved different responsibilities, among them providing support to the Madagascar protected area system with respect to developing protected area management plans, assessing management effectiveness, conducting ecological monitoring, implementing the work program on protected areas of the United Nations Convention on Biological Diversity, supporting the Madagascar Foundation for Protected Areas and Biodiversity, and developing World Heritage Sites in collaboration with UNESCO. Nicoll was involved in the implementation of the Durban Vision, which had been formulated to operationalize the declaration made in 2003 by former president Ravalomanana to triple the surface size of the protected areas of Madagascar (Gardner et al. 2018; Langrand and Rene de Roland 2018).

Nicoll was a passionate and knowledgeable scientist and conservationist with an excellent knowledge of Madagascar's protected areas and biodiversity. He inspired, advised, and mentored many individuals who have dedicated their careers to documenting and conserving the biodiversity of Madagascar. Nicoll died in Toliara on 1 January 2020.

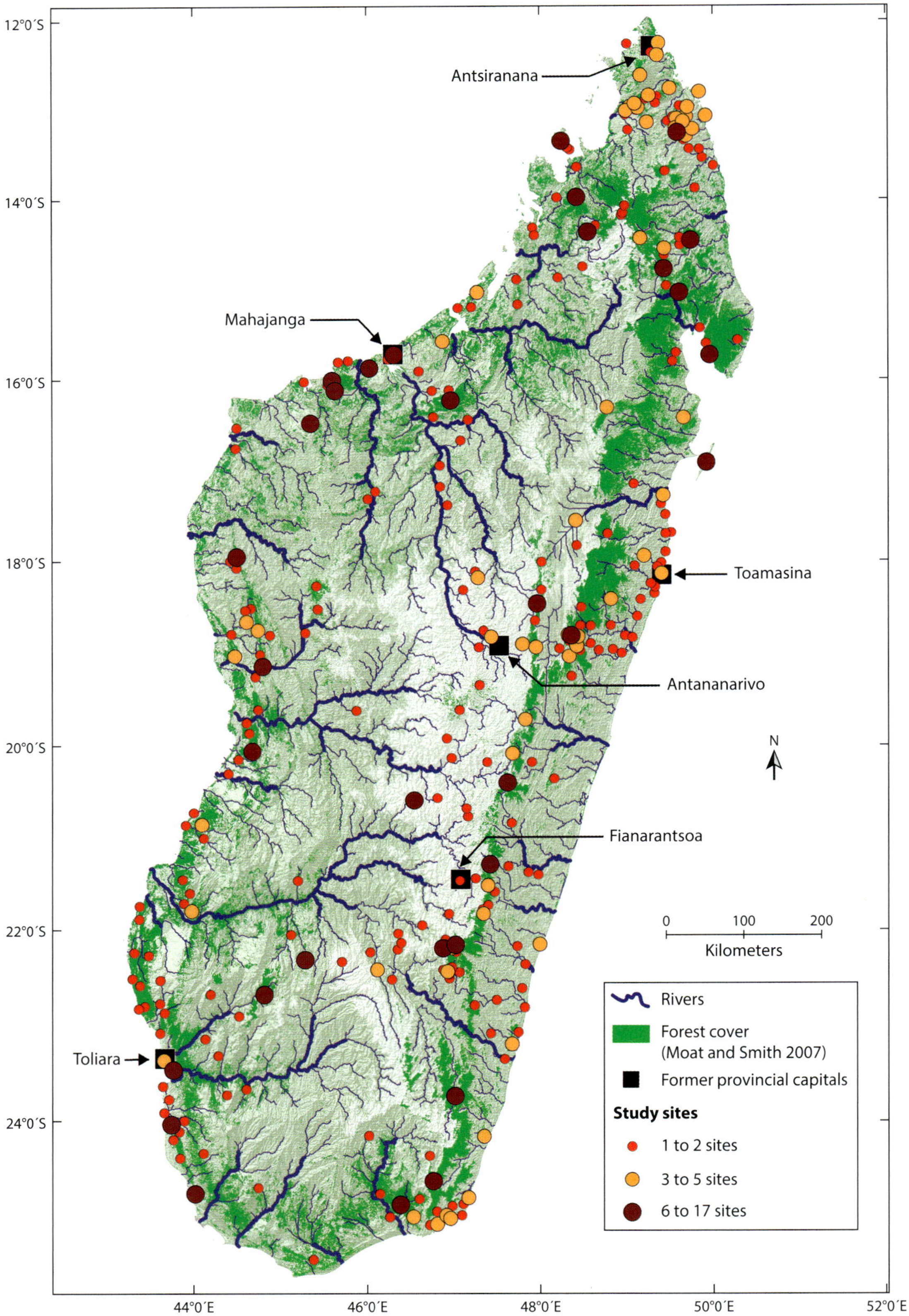

FIGURE 1.14 **Since the late 1990s, a research team of field biologists, associated Malagasy graduate students, and collaborators from numerous national and international institutions have conducted biological inventories on Madagascar, mostly on land vertebrates. This was first done under the auspices of the WWF Madagascar Ecology Training Program (ETP), until 2007, when the program was turned over to Association Vahatra, a direct product of the ETP. The inventories were done under the direction of Achille P. Raselimanana and Steven M. Goodman, and as of June 2020, over 820 sites (indicated on map) have been visited by the team. Many of the points on the map are sites of large-scale multidisciplinary surveys of many weeks to months, often along mountain elevational transects, while others are site inventories of a single taxonomic group.** (FIGURE created by H. M. Rakotondratsimba.)

For the past 30 years, the field of herpetology has seen a sharp increase in research intensity and collaboration, leading to remarkable results and advances. It has also witnessed the emergence of highly qualified national scientists and remarkable capacity building in fields associated with research and conservation. This is due to the work over the years of active leaders and mentors such as Franco Andreone, from the Museo Regionale di Scienze Naturali, Turin, Italy; Frank Glaw, from the Zoologische Staatssammlung München, Germany; Noromalala Raminosoa, from the Université d'Antananarivo; Achille P. Raselimanana, from the Université d'Antananarivo and Association Vahatra; Christopher J. Raxworthy, from the American Museum of Natural History, New York; and Miguel Vences from the Technische Universität Braunschweig, Germany. The two German institutions, Zoologische Staatssammlung München and Technische Universität Braunschweig, are currently hotspots of research on the amphibians and reptiles of Madagascar, benefiting from modern technology such as molecular labs and a strong pool of experts, including Malagasy scientists, affiliated or closely collaborating with Glaw and Vences.

Primatology has made spectacular progress since the beginning of the 21st century thanks to different individuals, including Edward E. Louis Jr. from Omaha's Henry Doorly Zoo and Aquarium, Nebraska, United States, who supervised many Malagasy students in the field and in his US laboratory. He also established the Madagascar Biodiversity Partnership, incorporating research, education, and community involvement for biodiversity conservation. Louis and his colleagues have inventoried lemurs in numerous sites, leading to the description of many species new to science (Figure 1.15).

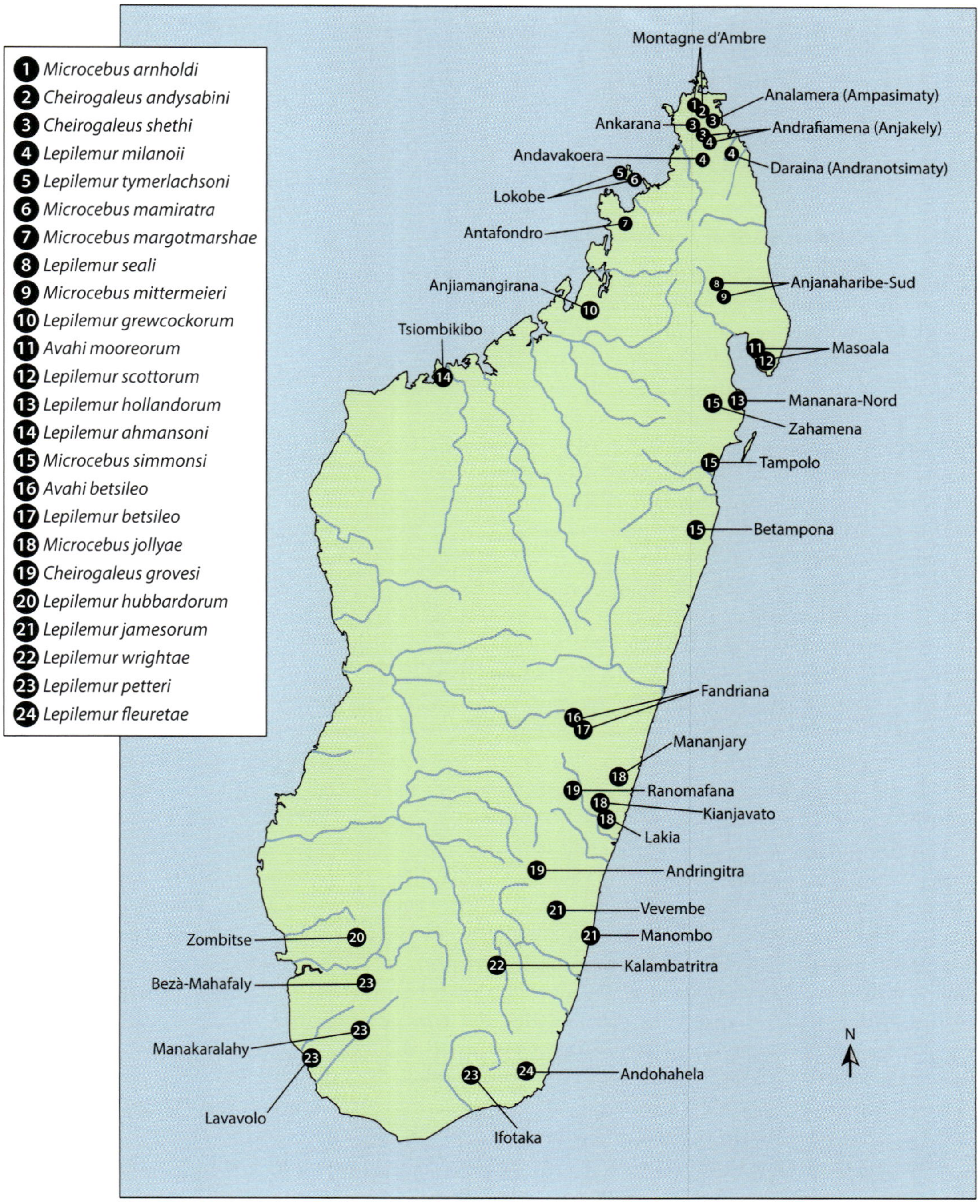

FIGURE 1.15 **Edward E. Louis Jr. and his team inventoried lemurs at over 250 sites across Madagascar, collecting genetic material and morphometric data from 7000-plus individual animals. The information generated subsequently led to the discovery of 24 species new to science at 37 of the inventoried sites.** (FIGURE created by B. Robertson and C. Bailey.)

In 2003, Centre ValBio, a biodiversity research and training station located just outside Ranomafana National Park and overlooking the Namorona River, was established by Patricia C. Wright from the State University of New York at Stony Brook, in partnership with the Université d'Antananarivo, the Université de Fianarantsoa, and the University of Helsinki. This biological research center was established based on previous fieldwork at a field station within this protected area that started in 1986. Many Malagasy and foreign students and scientists have benefited from this research facility to study lemurs and other biota but also to examine a wide range of other topics associated with zoonotic diseases and conservation issues.

Other organizations have contributed to improve the knowledge of the vertebrates of Madagascar. The Peregrine Fund, a US-based NGO dedicated to raptor conservation, started working on Madagascar in 1991, when Rick Watson established a bird and habitat conservation program, focusing on the Masoala Peninsula. The organization has made significant investment to build the capacity of Malagasy field biologists. Today, under the leadership of its national director, Lily-Arison Rene de Roland, the Peregrine Fund Madagascar is participating in the active management of protected areas and studying and conserving rare, endangered, and endemic bird species.

The Role of International Zoo Associations

Scientific and conservation-related advances on Malagasy land vertebrates have been linked for several decades and based on the generosity of a range of sponsors. In the early days, institutions or wealthy individuals financed naturalists and collectors to obtain specimens to enrich the holdings of museums or private collectors: Léon Humblot was sent to Madagascar by the Muséum National d'Histoire Naturelle, Paris; Alfred Crossley's expeditions (see Box 2) were funded by British lepidopterist Christopher Ward; and some individuals, including Alfred Grandidier and Richard Archbold, used their personal wealth to plan and carry out their own zoological explorations.

During the colonial period, institutions were established to support exploration and research on vertebrates, mostly by French researchers: the Académie Malgache in 1902 and the Institut de Recherche Scientifique de Madagascar (IRSM) in 1946. The socialist revolution that coincided with the beginning of the Second Republic (1975–1992) of the Malagasy government focused on the progress of the rural economy; biodiversity research and conservation for many years were not the focus of efforts, although a few scientists continued their studies.

In 1983, Gerald Durrell (1925–1995) and Lee Durrell from the Jersey Wildlife Preservation Trust (now the Durrell Wildlife Conservation Trust) organized a meeting on the island of Jersey concerning research and nature conservation on Madagascar. Berthe Rakotosamimanana (1938–2005), then permanent secretary of the Ministère de l'Enseignement Supérieur, was appointed head of the Malagasy delegation. During this important meeting, the terms of the collaboration between foreign and Malagasy researchers and students were redefined, which in turn, allowed for the possibility of issuing research permits. It was a turning point in the modern era of research and conservation of Malagasy biodiversity.

Another important meeting took place in 1987, at Saint Catherine's Island, Georgia, United States (Figure 1.16), when the IUCN Species Survival Commission (SSC) Primate Specialist Group, the Conservation Breeding Specialist Group, the New York Zoological Society, and the Los Angeles Zoo brought together Malagasy government representatives of the Ministère des Eaux et Forêts, the Ministère de l'Enseignement Supérieur, and the Ministère de la Recherche Scientifique, and international zoo professionals and scientists. The participants discussed how zoos could assist the Malagasy government to conserve endangered species through research, conservation, capacity building, and captive breeding.

In 1988, the Madagascar Fauna and Flora Group (MFG) was created. One of its initial projects was research and captive breeding at Parc d'Ivoloina near Toamasina, first with the support of the Duke University Primate Center (subsequently renamed the Duke Lemur Center), Durham, North Carolina, United States, and later the American Association of Zoos and Aquariums (AZA). In the period from 1988 until 2004, under the leadership of Andrea Katz and Charlie Welsh, MFG carried out activities in Ivoloina and Betampona, contributed to improve the facilities at the Parc Botanique et Zoologique de Tsimbazaza, and developed many partnerships with research institutions and zoos. In 2005, MFG established the Ivoloina Conservation Training Center. The organization has pursued its research and conservation activities under the successive leadership of Karen Freeman, An Bollen, Maya Moore, and Virginia Rodriguez Ponga. MFG has played an important role in uniting zoos and aquaria worldwide to conserve the wildlife of Madagascar. Additional American zoos, such as the Houston Zoo, the Indianapolis Zoo, and Omaha's Henry Doorly Zoo and Aquarium, and European zoos, through the European Association of Zoos and Aquaria (EAZA), joined forces to support research and conservation of species and sites on Madagascar.

Some European zoos had an early involvement in species conservation on Madagascar. One important example is the Durrell Wildlife Conservation Trust, which for more than 30 years has implemented in situ and ex situ conservation programs focused on threatened species such as *Astrochelys yniphora* (Ploughshare Tortoise), *Hapalemur alaotrensis* (Lake Alaotra Bamboo Lemur), and *Aythya innotata* (Madagascar Pochard), the lattermost in partnership with the Wildfowl and Wetlands Trust (see Rene de Roland and Young, pp. 1650–53).

In 2006, EAZA launched a two-year campaign focusing on Madagascar under the leadership of the Zoological Society of London, Zürich Zoo, and Durrell Wildlife Conservation Trust. The Berlin Zoological Park, the Duisburg Zoo, the Münster Zoo, and Weltvogelpark Walsrode created a consortium to focus on waterbirds from Bombetoka. Several EAZA and AZA members launched concerted efforts to conserve lemurs; among the early players were the Parc Zoologique et Botanique de Mulhouse, France; the Parc Zoologique de Paris; the Duke Lemur Center; and the Durrell Wildlife Conservation Trust, Jersey. Others established comprehensive research and conservation programs integrated into the Malagasy scientific and conservation community. In the past 15 years, Chester Zoo, United Kingdom, in partnership with Madagasikara Voakajy, has implemented projects on amphibian conservation around Moramanga and on lemur preservation in the Nosy Mangabe protected area. Bristol Zoo Gardens, United Kingdom, under the leadership of Christoph Schwitzer, deputy chair of the IUCN SSC Primate Specialist Group, has supported lemur conservation in the

FIGURE 1.16 **Group photo from meeting on Saint Catherine's Island, Georgia, United States, in May 1987. From left to right: Louise Emmons (Smithsonian Institution); Patricia C. Wright (then at Duke University Primate Center, now Duke Lemur Center); Joël Ratsirarson (Direction des Eaux et Forêts, Madagascar); Barthélémy Vaohita (WWF Madagascar); Ken Creighton (Smithsonian Institution); Berthe Rakotosamimanana (Ministère de l'Enseignement Supérieur, Madagascar); Mario Gagnon (Duke University, Department of Biological Anthropology); Elwyn Simons (Duke University Primate Center); Russ Mittermeier (then at WWF US; IUCN Species Survival Commission Primate Specialist Group); Alison Jolly (Rockefeller University); Joseph Randrianasolo (Ministère de la Production Animale et des Eaux et Forêts, Madagascar); Joseph Andriamampianina (Département des Eaux et Forêts, Ecole Supérieure des Sciences Agronomiques, Université d'Antananarivo); Voara Randrianasolo (Parc Botanique et Zoologique de Tsimbazaza); and John Hartley (Jersey Wildlife Preservation Trust).** (PHOTO by R. A. Mittermeier.)

FIGURE 1.17 **Edward E. Louis Jr. holding a newly captured male *Daubentonia madagascariensis* (Aye-aye) (see Sterling et al., pp. 1975–78), and the Madagascar Biodiversity Partnership (MBP) organization immobilization team and Aye-aye monitoring field assistants, in Kianjavato, Madagascar, on 17 May 2013. The Kianjavato project has intensively monitored the regional Aye-aye population, conducting nightly follows of multiple individuals since 2011. Pictured from left to right: Stéphane Justin Randriambololona and Elyse Fortinand Razafindrazefa, MBP Aye-aye field assistants; Jean Boniface Andrianjafinirina Ramampiandra, MBP logistical and driver supervisor; Richard Randriamampionona, MBP immobilization team leader; Edward E. Louis Jr., MBP director general; and Jeannot Miandrisoa Rakotomalala, MBP immobilization field assistant. The male Aye-aye was given the name Dera, after a former Malagasy graduate student, and since this initial capture has been monitored with telemetry equipment that collects habitat use and home territorial range data.** (PHOTO by MBP.)

northwestern part of Madagascar. Omaha's Henry Doorly Zoo and Aquarium started its involvement on the island in 1998. Edward E. Louis Jr., director of the zoo's Conservation Genetics Department, transformed this initial scientific interest into a major research and conservation program that gave birth to a Malagasy organization, Madagascar Biodiversity Partnership (Figure 1.17).

SCIENTIFIC ADVANCES BY FAUNAL GROUP

Freshwater Fish Exploration

Ichthyology on Madagascar has never initiated much excitement compared to research on other vertebrate groups, despite the 122 endemic species, including 35 undescribed taxa (see Sparks and Stiassny, pp. 1245–60), among the 178 known freshwater and euryhaline fish species. A long period of inactivity followed the work of Jacques Arnoult in the 1950s, André Kiener in the 1960s, and René Catala (1901–1988) in the 1970s. By the 1990s, researchers including the Swiss Patrick de Rham and the Frenchman Jean-Claude Nourissat (1942–2003) (de Rham 1996), the American Paul Loiselle, the Briton Mark Pidgeon (Pidgeon 1996), and the Frenchman Jean-Marc Elouard from the Institut de Recherche pour le Développement (IRD) conducted fieldwork on this group associated with taxonomy and geographic distribution (Elouard and Gibon 2001). The research of Melanie Stiassny and Peter Reinthal, ichthyologists from the American Museum of Natural History, in association with Noromalala Raminosoa, from the Université d'Antananarivo (Reinthal and Stiassny 1991; Stiassny and Raminosoa 1994), produced important advances. In 1996, de Rham estimated that, based on the knowledge of fish species and the studies underway at the time, the number of endemic species would exceed 50 (de Rham 1996). Subsequent research by Stiassny, Reinthal, and John Sparks, also from the American Museum of Natural History, showed that de Rham's prediction, which seemed rather optimistic to some researchers, was actually an underestimate of the island's fish fauna (see Sparks and Stiassny, pp. 1245–60).

The start of the 21st century saw some work on the revision of catfishes. Heok Hee Ng from the Museum of Zoology at the University of Michigan, United States, and Sparks described two new species of Ariidae (Ng and Sparks 2003). A remarkable addition was the description in 2005 of a new genus, *Gogo*, including one reassigned and two new species, and a third new species in a closely related genus, *Ancharius griseus* (Ng and Sparks 2005), followed by a fourth *Gogo* in 2008 (Ng et al. 2008; see Ng and Sparks, pp. 1260–62). At approximately the same time, Paul Loiselle reviewed the

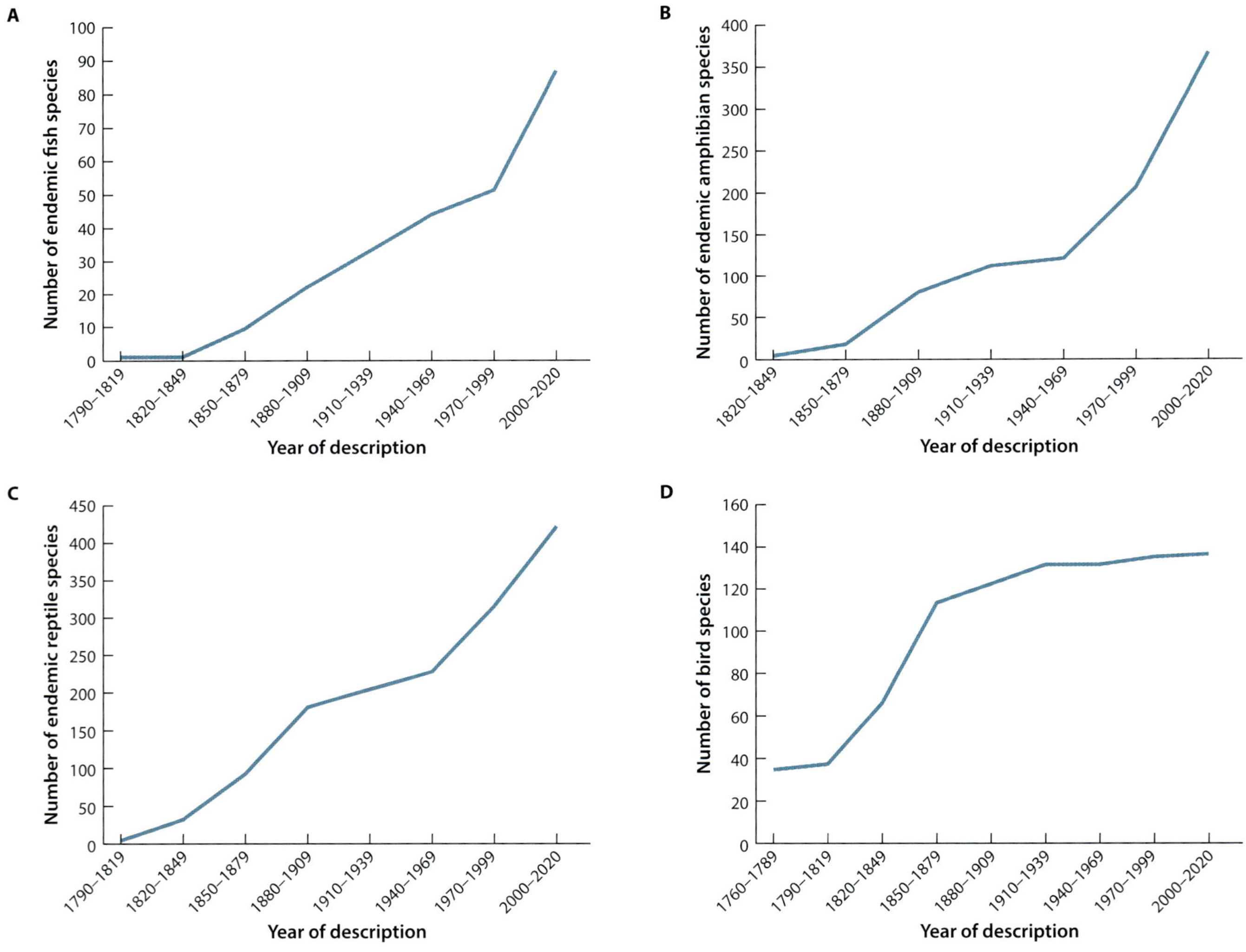

FIGURE 1.18 **Rates of description of different Malagasy vertebrate groups over time and by 30-year periods. Data used in these tabulations extend to May 2020. A) Endemic freshwater fish described between 1790 and 2020. B) Endemic amphibian species, between 1820 and 2020. C) Endemic reptile species, between 1790 and 2020. D) Bird species endemic to the Malagasy Region, between 1760 and 2020.**

genus *Pachypanchax* and described four new species (Loiselle 2006; see Loiselle and de Rham, pp. 1268–70). Among those, *P. sparksorum* was named after Sparks and his wife, Karen Riseng Sparks, and *P. arnoulti* honored Jacques Arnoult.

The genus *Bedotia* (Bedotiidae) gained an additional five new species in the past 20 years (see Stiassny et al., pp. 1273–76). Two new species in the genus *Rheocles* (Bedotiidae), both restricted to the northeastern part of Madagascar, were described in the early 2000s, *R. derhami* (Stiassny and Rodriguez 2001), dedicated to de Rham, and *R. vatosoa* (Stiassny et al. 2002; see Stiassny et al., pp. 1273–76).

The Cichlidae dominates the freshwater fish fauna of Madagascar. Some members of this family (*Coptodon rendalli*, *C. zillii*, *Oreochromis macrochir*, *O. mossambicus*, *O. niloticus*, and *O. spirulus*) originally introduced to Madagascar from Africa for fish farming have escaped and subsequently invaded many Malagasy freshwater ecosystems. A total of 40 endemic cichlids, regrouped in six genera, are found on the island. A notable proportion of these have been described since 2000: five species in the genus *Paretroplus* and eight species in the genus *Ptychochromis*. In each of these two genera, a species is named in honor of American ichthyologist Paul Loiselle (Sparks and Schelly 2011; Stiassny and Sparks 2006).

Today, 87 described endemic freshwater species are recognized, a growth of 82% from the end of the 20th century (Figure 1.18a). This number is certain to increase as many small river basins and watersheds are explored that have not been thoroughly inventoried and numerous confirmed candidate species are formally described. The slow progress compared to the other groups of vertebrates can best be explained by two factors. First, because none of the few active international ichthyologists working on Malagasy fish are permanently based on the island, they conduct irregular field missions and do not have steady contact with Malagasy students. Second, only one Malagasy university scientist, Noromalala Raminosoa from the Université d'Antananarivo, has been engaged in recent decades in the field of ichthyology. In addition, Raminosoa, now retired, has been more involved in herpetological research in recent years, associated with international researchers such as Miguel Vences, Frank Glaw, and Franco Andreone.

Amphibian Exploration

In the field of herpetology, Rose Blommers-Schlösser from the University of Amsterdam in many ways started the modern era by initiating comprehensive research on the amphibians of Madagascar and describing numerous new species. Blommers-Schlösser was the first to integrate karyotype, bioacoustics, and behavior in the delimitation of amphibian species (Vences and Raselimanana 2018). In collaboration with Charles Blanc, she published in the *Faune de Madagascar* series a comprehensive monograph on amphibians in two volumes (Blommers-Schlösser and Blanc 1991, 1993), in which a species, *Spinomantis guibei*, was dedicated to Jean Guibé. Blommers-Schlösser's pioneering role in the modern knowledge of the batrachofauna of the island is recognized with the naming of a genus, *Blommersia* (Dubois 1992), and two species, *B. blommersae* (Guibé 1975) and *Boophis blommersae* (Glaw and Vences 1994), in her honor.

Italian herpetologist Franco Andreone, who started working on Madagascar in the early 1990s, made major contributions to the study and conservation of Malagasy frogs. Hailing from the Museo Regionale di Scienze Naturali, Turin, he undertook during that decade numerous field missions, associated with Malagasy biologists Jasmin Randrianirina and Herilala Randriamahazo from the Parc Botanique et Zoologique de Tsimbazaza. He and his colleagues published some of the initial studies on the amphibian and reptile diversity of the Ranomafana moist evergreen forest (Andreone 1994), the Andohahela moist evergreen forest (Andreone and Randriamahazo 1997), and the forest corridor between the massifs of Marojejy and Anjanaharibe-Sud (Andreone et al. 2000). Andreone has contributed to the description of close to 80 new species of Malagasy amphibians and reptiles, including 21 as first author. A species from the Sambirano Region, *Boophis andreonei* is dedicated to him (Glaw and Vences 1994). With fellow scientists, Andreone published two reference field guides on Malagasy amphibians, one on the arid portions of the island (Andreone et al. 2014) and another on the north (Andreone et al. 2018), aimed at field researchers, students, conservation experts, and naturalists. These books contain succinct details on identification, calls, tadpoles, distribution, habitat, and conservation status.

Beyond his work on taxonomy, Andreone has taken a lead role in the conservation of the threatened amphibian biodiversity of Madagascar (see Crottini et al., pp. 1326–30). As cochair—with Malagasy herpetologist Andolalao Rakotoarison—of the IUCN SSC Amphibian Specialist Group Madagascar, he launched the ACSAM program (A Conservation Strategy for the Amphibians of Madagascar) in 2006 (Andreone 2008). Further, he has been one of the leaders in different aspects of monitoring the chytrid fungus *Batrachochytrium dendrobatidis* on the island (see Bletz et al., pp. 1342–49).

Among the experts involved in the description of new amphibian taxa at the dawn of the 21st century were scientists associated with the Zoologisches Forschungsmuseum Alexander Koenig in Bonn, Germany—Thomas Pintak, Klaus Busse, and Wolfgang Böhme. *Boophis boehmei* (Glaw and Vences 1992) honors Böhme, curator of herpetology at the museum for nearly four decades and author of several new species of Malagasy amphibians and reptiles. Other important figures from this period include the American John Cadle, attached at the start of his research on Madagascar to the Museum of Comparative Zoology at Harvard University and then associated with the Centre ValBio at Ranomafana, who described five new species of reptiles; and Italian biologist Angelica Crottini, from CIBIO-InBIO (Research Centre in Biodiversity and Genetic Resources) at the University of Porto, Portugal, and a member of the IUCN SSC Amphibian Specialist Group Madagascar.

The Swiss Denis Vallan, from the University of Bern, Switzerland, described two species of frogs: *Boophis lichenoides*, from Andasibe (Vallan et al. 1998), and *Anilany helenae*, from Ambohitantely (Vallan 2000). In recognition of his extensive work at Ambohitantely, Vallan was honored in 2010 in the name of a new species of microhylid frog from that forest, *Anodonthyla vallani* (Vences et al. 2010).

Without question, the Germans Frank Glaw, now curator at Zoologische Staatssammlung München, and Miguel Vences, professor of evolutionary biology and zoology at the Technische Universität Braunschweig, have had the longest—over 30 years each—and most significant impact on the development of herpetology on the island; they are authors and coauthors of over 200 species descriptions of Malagasy amphibians and reptiles (Figure 1.19). Each has a chameleon named for him, *Calumma glawi* (Böhme 1997) and *C. vencesi* (Andreone et al. 2001).

Vences and Glaw's fruitful collaboration started at the end of the 1980s, in the framework of their respective PhD projects under the supervision of Böhme. Together, they produced the essential field guide to the reptiles and amphibians of Madagascar, now in its third edition (Glaw and Vences 1992, 1994, 2007). Their joint work and collaborations with other scientists, including many Malagasy graduate students, ushered in a new era of field research in herpetology, resulting in the description of 46 species of amphibians between 1990 and 1999, an unmatched figure in any other land vertebrate group. In 2000, Glaw and Vences estimated that this research effort would have to continue with the same intensity for the next 20 years in order to document in its near entirety the diversity of Malagasy frogs (Glaw and Vences 2000). Fast-forward to 2020 (see Glaw et al., pp. 1305–22), and the results are well beyond their original expectations.

FIGURE 1.19 **The involvement of Frank Glaw (right) and Miguel Vences (center) in Malagasy herpetology started in the late 1980s. The photo was taken in 2005 at Andasibe during pitfall trapping of leaf-litter skinks with Alimarisy Sam Alain (left), a guide from Association Mitsinjo, a local organization focused on ecotourism, conservation, and research. Glaw and Vences have conducted herpetological inventories in all major terrestrial ecosystems of Madagascar, described dozens of new species of amphibians and reptiles, trained Malagasy herpetologists in field and laboratory techniques, and promoted herpetology as a citizen science through the publication of their field guide to the amphibians and reptiles of Madagascar, first published in 1992 and constantly improved through new editions.** (PHOTO by M. Vences.)

Starting in the first decade of 2000, there was a steep and continuous increase in the number of recognized amphibian species on the island (Figure 1.18b), and this was associated with the integration of molecular, osteological, and bioacoustic characters, as well as a dramatic increase in field research and collecting intensity (Vences et al. 2008). An analysis of herpetological work on the island counted that, between 2000 and 2007, 22 herpetological surveys (amphibians and reptiles) were conducted at 20 different sites, among which 11 were outside of protected areas (D'Cruze et al. 2009).

Among the 51 new amphibian species described after 2000, the family Microhylidae was enriched with 12 new species. However, the greatest taxonomic advances occurred in another endemic family, the Mantellidae, which gained 16 new species of the bright-eyed frogs of the genus *Boophis* (see Hutter et al., pp. 1357–60): intensive survey work led by Vences and Glaw in the eastern part of Madagascar produced two species from Andasibe in 2002 (Vences and Glaw 2002) and one species from Ranomafana (Glaw and Vences 2002). Morphological and genetic analyses of specimens yielded two other species from Andasibe in 2003 (Vallan et al. 2003) and another from Tsaratanàna (Vences et al. 2005). New species were identified from the Manongarivo Massif (Vences and Glaw 2005), Tsingy de Bemaraha (Köhler et al. 2007), and Masoala (Wollenberg et al. 2008). Fieldwork carried out in 2006 and 2007 led to the description of *B. baetkei* from Forêt d'Ambre and *B. lilianae* from Ifanadiana (Ranomafana), the latter dedicated to Malagasy herpetologist Liliane Raharivololoniaina (Köhler et al. 2008).

The mantellid family also underwent a novel classification (see the 10 different contributions on this family in the amphibians chapter), based on phylogenetic information and new analysis of molecular data, and several genera were formally recognized or established: *Boehmantis*, *Spinomantis*, and *Wakea* (Glaw and Vences 2006). The newly described species of *Spinomantis* included *S. nussbaumi*, named after American herpetologist Ronald A. Nussbaum, who conducted numerous field surveys of amphibians and reptiles on Madagascar (Cramer et al. 2008). Finally, in a rare event, as the discovery of new frog genera is exceptional, surveys in the Ankarana protected area in 2003 and 2004 produced four specimens not referable to a known amphibian genus, leading to the description of a new genus and species, *Tsingymantis antitra* (Glaw et al. 2006; see also Glaw et al., p. 1381).

The first decade of 2000 saw the continuation or intensification of the work by established scientists such as Andreone, Achille P. Raselimanana, Vallan, and, of course, Vences and Glaw, and the emergence of several prominent Malagasy amphibian specialists. Jörn Köhler, from the Hessisches Landesmuseum Darmstadt, Germany, started his involvement on the island at that time. His main research focus is on taxonomy, systematics, phylogeny, biogeography, and ecology of tropical amphibians and reptiles. Köhler is the designer with Glaw of the BIOPAT (Patrons for Biodiversity) initiative, launched in 1999 to raise funds for taxonomic research through individual sponsorships for newly discovered animal and plant species. Several new species of Malagasy amphibians and reptiles are named after BIOPAT donors.

The end of the decade saw also the participation in taxonomic work of the first generation of what would be a long and productive sequence of doctoral and postdoctoral students supervised by Vences and Glaw. Among the first ones were Julian Glos, who worked on the amphibian fauna of western dry deciduous forests, particularly Kirindy Forest CNFEREF (Centre National de Formation, d'Etudes et de Recherche en Environnement et Foresterie); and Katharina Wollenberg, who focused on the radiations of endemic Malagasy amphibians.

While the participation of Malagasy scientists in biodiversity exploration and publications was marginal in the past, notable progress was registered starting in the 1990s with a stronger cohort of Malagasy researchers in herpetology (Vences et al. 2008). Some of the major herpetological expeditions were led or co-led by Malagasy scientists such as Raselimanana, Domoina Rakotomalala, Jean-Baptiste Ramanamanjato, Nirhy Rabibisoa, and Parfait Bora, and about a third of the herpetological survey-based manuscripts included Malagasy scientists either as the first author or among the coauthors (D'Cruze et al. 2009).

The progress in molecular techniques, including greater and more affordable acquisition of DNA sequences, fostered a major boom in the systematics of Malagasy frogs. In 2009, a thorough assessment of the morphological, bioacoustic, and genetic variation of the amphibians of Madagascar, using the DNA sequences of 2850 specimens, concluded that the amphibian diversity of the country had been vastly underestimated and that there were an estimated 221 undescribed candidate species (Vieites et al. 2009). The lead author of the study, David Vieites, from the Spanish National Research Council (Consejo Superior de Investigaciones Científicas, or CSIC), has worked on the speciation and diversification of Malagasy herpetofauna since 2000, in frequent collaboration with Glaw and Vences and his CSIC colleague Ignacio de la Riva. A subsequent publication, led by Bina Perl from the Technische Universität Braunschweig, identified 14 additional undescribed candidate species (Perl et al. 2014). Intensive efforts to investigate these candidate species, coupled with regular fieldwork to gather more material and associated tissue samples, have led to the description since 2010 of 101 endemic species of amphibians—an extraordinary number.

Taxonomic revision of the mantellid genus *Aglyptodactylus* in 2015 resulted in the description of two species and the resurrection of a third from synonymy (Köhler et al. 2015). Significant investigative work was also devoted to the mantellid genus *Gephyromantis*, resulting in a systematic revision (Wollenberg et al. 2012) and the description of 10 species new to science from 2010 to 2019. Among those, *G. saturnini* was dedicated to Alain Dubois, retired director of the Laboratoire Reptiles et Amphibiens, Muséum National d'Histoire Naturelle, Paris, who used the pseudonym Saturnin Pojarski as a radio presenter. The Malagasy subgenus *Duboimantis* (Glaw and Vences 2006) is also named after him. *Gephyromantis grosjeani* honors Stéphane Grosjean, now at the Muséum National d'Histoire Naturelle, who completed his PhD under the mentorship of Dubois and provided valuable contribution to the knowledge of tadpoles of Madagascar (Scherz et al. 2018).

Richard Lehtinen, from the College of Wooster, Ohio, United States, who completed his PhD at the University of Michigan under the supervision of Ronald A. Nussbaum, is at the forefront of ecological and taxonomic work on the genus *Guibemantis*, using DNA and morphology data (Lehtinen et al. 2007). Subsequently, seven new species of this genus have been described by Lehtinen and others (see Lehtinen et al., pp. 1374–78).

In the family Microhylidae, the cophyline frogs were identified as rich in species and genera (Vieites et al. 2009; Perl et al. 2014) and have been the subject of detailed investigation. Mark Scherz, then a doctoral student at Ludwig-Maximilians Universität München and Technische Universität Braunschweig, supervised by Vences and Glaw, and colleagues resurrected the genera *Stumpffia* and *Platypelis* and described a new genus, *Anilany* (Scherz et al. 2016). A remarkable 2019 paper, led by Scherz, described five new species of frogs, including a new genus, *Mini*, containing three minute species (Scherz et al. 2019a). Since around 2010, Scherz has been one of the most productive and prolific researchers on the Cophylinae of Madagascar (Scherz et al., pp. 1382–90), contributing to the description of over 40 new species, as well as other aspects of the island's herpetofauna.

Andolalao Rakotoarison started working with Vences as a student researcher at Tsaratanàna. This work led to her first taxonomic description, a new *Platypelis* (Rakotoarison et al. 2012). She pursued a PhD at the Technische Universität Braunschweig on a taxonomic revision of microhylid cophyline frogs. Her work on the genus *Cophyla* resulted in the description of three new species (Rakotoarison et al. 2015), including *C. noromalalae* dedicated to Noromalala Raminosoa, professor at the Université d'Antananarivo. Rakotoarison applied CT-scanning technology and integrative taxonomy methods on Malagasy specimens of the genus *Stumpffia*, which led to the description of 26 new species of *Stumpffia* in a single paper (Rakotoarison et al. 2017). Rakotoarison's valuable contribution to the field of herpetology was recognized with the naming of a new species of arboreal frog, *Platypelis ando*, in her honor in 2019 (Scherz et al. 2019b).

The increasing rate and volume of taxonomic descriptions have been made possible by considerable technological advances, the availability of specimens from different areas of Madagascar, DNA barcodes, and the tireless work of scientists. The Technische Universität Braunschweig has to be mentioned as the great research hub on the amphibians of Madagascar, its slate of scientists including Vences, Scherz, and Rakotoarison. In addition, research in this domain has benefited from the valuable contributions of Molly Bletz, Bora, Crottini, Glos, Olga Jovanovic, Johannes Klages, Maciej Pabijan, Joana Sabino-Pinto, Axel Strauss, and Wollenberg, who were all affiliated at one point with the institution.

Other scientists involved in taxonomy work included Neil D'Cruze, from the World Society for the Protection of Animals; Dante Fenolio, now at San Antonio Zoo, in Texas; Carl Hutter, University of Kansas, who worked with Shea Lambert, now at University of Arizona, on the molecular phylogeny of the genus *Boophis*; and Gonçalo Rosa from the Zoological Society of London, who is Andreone's former student and works on different aspects of amphibian and reptile conservation, in collaboration with, among others, Samuel Penny from the Bristol Zoological Society.

Last but not least, the 2010s saw the strong and increasing participation of highly qualified Malagasy herpetologists in taxonomy. An undisputed leader in the field is veteran herpetologist Achille P. Raselimanana, professor in the Mention Zoologie et Biodiversité Animale, Université d'Antananarivo, and president of Association Vahatra. A new species in 2017, *Stumpffia achillei*, recognized his leadership (Rakotoarison et al. 2017). Parfait Bora, another PhD student supervised by Vences, took part in numerous field expeditions. A reptile, *Phelsuma borai*, for which he captured the holotype, is named after him (Glaw et al. 2009). Accomplished and mostly self-taught herpetologist Jean Noël, head conservation agent for Madagascar Fauna and Flora Group at the Betampona protected area, who participated in numerous surveys and publications, was honored with the species *S. jeannoeli* (Rakotoarison et al. 2017).

The discovery of new taxa on the island would not be possible without the essential knowledge of local guides and naturalists. Some have, year after year and over decades, contributed to the success of numerous field projects and expeditions. A few species of amphibians have been named to recognize their hard work and commitment: *Anodonthyla emilei* and *A. theoi* are dedicated to brothers Emile Rajeriarison and Theophilus Rajoafiarison, working at Ranomafana National Park (Vences et al. 2010); and *Stumpffia angeluc* honors Angeluc Razafimanantsoa (see Box 7), an expert guide to the north of Madagascar (Rakotoarison et al. 2017).

See chapter 11, on amphibians, for further details on remarkable advances in knowledge and measures of species diversity in this group. New taxa of amphibians have been discovered at a rate that exceeds the capacity for the small but prodigious group of active amphibian specialists to describe them. In 2007, it was already predicted that the taxonomic work in herpetology on the island would not be completed for at least 20 years (Glaw and Vences 2007). Therefore, it is foreseen that the description of new amphibian species over the coming years will continue on its nearly exponential curve.

Reptile Exploration

In the 1990s, research on reptiles uncovered 51 new species for Madagascar. One of the most active groups throughout much of that decade and beyond was composed of Ronald A. Nussbaum from the University of Michigan; Christopher J. Raxworthy from the American Museum of Natural History, who was Nussbaum's postdoctoral student; and Achille P. Raselimanana and Jean-Baptiste Ramanamanjato, both students then at the Université d'Antananarivo. They conducted inventories in numerous sites, including remote areas such as Tsaratanàna (Raxworthy and Nussbaum 1996a), Anjanaharibe-Sud (Raxworthy et al. 1998), Andringitra (Raxworthy and Nussbaum 1996b), and Andohahela (Nussbaum et al. 1999).

Ronald Nussbaum started working on Madagascar in 1989 and was involved in numerous studies on the distribution, ecology, and systematics of amphibians and reptiles. Christopher Raxworthy started studying the amphibians and reptiles of Madagascar in 1985. He has contributed to over 60 descriptions of new taxa of reptiles and amphibians, including 22 as first author, and also to a few on small mammals. Raxworthy conducted herpetological surveys across the island between 1991 and 2001, working closely with two local guides who would become among the most skilled in the country, twin brothers Angelin and Angeluc Razafimanantsoa (see Box 7 and Figure 1.21).

Achille P. Raselimanana (Figure 1.20), for whom Nussbaum was a doctoral supervisor, is now one of the foremost herpetological experts of Madagascar and has published close to 100 scientific papers on Malagasy amphibians and reptiles, including descriptions of four new species of *Zonosaurus* (of the lizard family Gerrhosauridae) and the rediscovery of a species thought to be extinct (Raselimanana et al. 2000, 2006).

Malgasy herpetologist Jean-Baptiste Ramanamanjato, an active field researcher, named two species of skinks (Scincidae), *Trachylepis tavaratra* and *T. vezo* (Ramanamanjato et al. 1999a, 1999b). A frog species, *Anodonthyla jeanbai* (Vences et al. 2010), recognizes his long-lasting participation in advancing herpetological studies on the island.

FIGURE 1.20 **Achille P. Raselimanana in the herpetology collection at the Field Museum of Natural History, Chicago, in June 2001, with a specimen of *Flexiseps meva*, collected in the Ambohijanahary Special Reserve by Domoina Rakotomalala in 1999. Raselimanana identified the skink as a probable new species in 2001; in 2009, Aurélien Miralles, postdoctoral student of Miguel Vences, confirmed it as a species new to science using molecular analysis and additional material from Marotandrano and Makira (Miralles et al. 2011).** (PHOTO by O. Langrand.)

BOX 7 ANGELIN RAZAFIMANANTSOA AND ANGELUC RAZAFIMANANTSOA, MALAGASY HERPETOLOGISTS, MAMMOLOGISTS, NATURALISTS

C. J. RAXWORTHY

ANGELIN AND ANGELUC RAZAFIMANANTSOA are identical twins (Figure 1.21) who grew up in their family's house at the edge of the Montagne d'Ambre National Park, above the town of Joffreville. During their childhood, the road barrier to the park was positioned outside their house, and their older brother, René, worked as a forest guard for the park, while their father frequently was engaged by visiting scientists as a porter and camp assistant. After successfully evading the Madagascar national military draft (by failing the medical test through adding salt to their urine samples!), the twins worked in 1989–1991 as camp and research assistants with Ben Freed, who was conducting research for his PhD on *Eulemur coronatus* (Crowned Lemur) in the park. After this, they also gained experience working with local tourism operators and local caving guides, serving as naturalists in Montagne d'Ambre, Ankarana, and other regional sites such as Montagne des Français and Oronjia.

FIGURE 1.21 **In 1993, Christopher Raxworthy and his team conducted an inventory of the amphibians and reptiles of the Tsaratanàna Massif. This photo was taken on 28 March at the Maromokotro summit (2876 m). Top row (left to right): Pierre Soga (Service des Eaux et Forêts), Angelin Razafimanantsoa (field assistant); middle row: Jean-Baptiste Ramanamanjato (herpetologist), Angeluc Razafimanantsoa (field assistant); bottom row: Christopher Raxworthy (expedition leader, University of Michigan) and two local guides.** (PHOTO by A. P. Raselimanana.)

Between 1991 and 2001, they worked closely with Chris Raxworthy (University of Michigan and subsequently American Museum of Natural History), conducting herpetological surveys throughout Madagascar. The first survey, at Montagne d'Ambre in 1991, was immediately followed by surveys in Ankarana and Manongarivo in 1992. Subsequently, they participated in surveys in tens of sites. They also worked occasionally with other herpetologists, such as Ronald Nussbaum in the south, and Miguel Vences and Frank Glaw in the north; and in different areas, principally Montagne d'Ambre and Ankarana, with different Malagasy students and collaborators. The two brothers were able to work under the toughest of field conditions and became highly skilled at finding amphibians and reptiles, including very cryptic species such as fossorial skinks and lizards, and tiny *Brookesia* dwarf chameleons. They helped collect many important amphibian and reptile specimens, including some newly described species (Nussbaum and Raxworthy 1995; Rakotoarison et al. 2017).

Thanks to their natural history skills and extensive knowledge of reserves and research methods, they also became highly sought-after guides for natural history television programs (including BBC productions and the PBS series *Nova*). Good accounts of their personalities are captured in Tyson (2000), which describes them working with Chris Raxworthy's survey team in the Lokobe protected area, and Heying (2002). Angelin and Angeluc continue to work as biodiversity tourism guides throughout Madagascar. Both are married with children and live in Antsiranana and Joffreville.

MALAGASY VERTEBRATE SPECIES NAMED AFTER THE TWO RAZAFIMANANTSOA BROTHERS

1. *Pseudoacontias angelorum*, a skink known from moist evergreen forests in the Marojejy region, was described and named in a plural form after both Angelin and Angeluc by Nussbaum and Raxworthy (1995).
2. *Stumpffia angeluci*, a microhylid frog known from moist evergreen forest in Montagne d'Ambre, was named after Angeluc by Rakotoarison et al. (2017).

Other contributors of the 1990s included American John Cadle, from the Museum of Comparative Zoology at Harvard, who revised several groups of snakes and described five new species. German researchers, including Wolfgang Böhme and Mathias Lang from the Zoologisches Forschungsmuseum Alexander Koenig in Bonn, Herbert Rösler from the Staatliche Naturhistorische Sammlungen in Dresden, and Robert Seipp from the Senckenberg Museum in Frankfurt, named several taxa of reptiles. The Italians Riccardo Jesu, Fabio Mattioli, and Giovanni Schimmenti worked on Madagascar from 1995 to the early 2000s, under a cooperation agreement between the Acquario di Genova, Italy, and the Université d'Antananarivo, authoring or contributing to descriptions of new species, including two new chameleons with Franco Andreone (Andreone et al. 2001).

In 2002, Andreone and Allen Greer, the latter from the Australian Museum, Sydney, completed a comprehensive taxonomic revision of 33 species of scincid lizards, resulting in the description of nine new species (Andreone and Greer 2002). The Malagasy skinks were further enriched with two other species, described by Japanese researchers Shuichi Sakata and Tsutomu Hikida from Kyoto University, including *Voeltzkowia yamagishii*, named after Satoshi Yamagishi, the project leader of an ecological survey at Ankarafantsika (Sakata and Hikida 2003). The collaboration between Kyoto University and the Université d'Antananarivo started in 1997 and led to important joint zoological discoveries in the fields of ethology and ecology. Further knowledge on the skinks of Madagascar was acquired through several studies of their phylogeny and systematics, including by Jörn Köhler from the Hessisches Landesmuseum Darmstadt, Germany, who rediscovered two species and named two new species of the limbless genus *Paracontias* (Köhler et al. 2009, 2010).

Aurélien Miralles, a French expert in the systematics of the Scincidae, was an important driver to advances in knowledge of this family on Madagascar (see Miralles et al., pp. 1494–502). After receiving a doctorate at the Muséum National d'Histoire Naturelle, Paris, Miralles pursued his postdoctoral research at the Centre National de la Recherche Scientifique (CNRS) and at the Technische Universität Braunschweig with Miguel Vences. Finally, Miralles led the publication of the only Malagasy taxonomic novelty in the family Iguanidae since 1900 (see Cadle et al., pp. 1502–5).

In total, 21 new species in the family Scincidae have been described since 2000 on Madagascar. Comprehensive taxonomic reviews and molecular and morphological data have indicated that numerous widespread Malagasy reptile species actually represent species complexes and require further investigation (Glaw and Raselimanana 2018). In 2012, a DNA barcoding study led by Zoltán Nagy, a researcher at the Institut Royal des Sciences Naturelles de Belgique, Brussels, revealed a substantial number of unrecognized genetic lineages and many potential undescribed reptile species (Nagy et al. 2012). This approach has been particularly useful for the emblematic chameleons of Madagascar, as intensive fieldwork and taxonomic revisions have identified 26 new species in the family Chamaeleonidae since 2000 (see Scherz et al., pp. 1506–16).

For his PhD at the Zoological Institute of the Technische Universität Braunschweig, German herpetologist Philip-Sebastian Gehring worked on the phylogeny and phylogeography of different amphibian and reptile species of Madagascar, including a phylogenetic assessment of species in the genus *Calumma*, identifying 33 potential new species (Gehring et al. 2012). David Prötzel, from the Zoologische Staatssammlung München, focused his PhD on the taxonomy of *Calumma*, leading to the revalidation and description of eight new species since 2017, including *C. gehringi* (Prötzel et al. 2017), dedicated to Gehring for his comprehensive and fundamental molecular study. The latest development for this group was a further revision using an integrative taxonomic approach, leading to the resurrection of one species and the description of three new species in 2020 (Prötzel et al. 2020). See Scherz et al. (pp. 1506–16) for a review of taxonomical work on Malagasy chameleons.

The geckos of Madagascar have been one of the most researched groups of reptiles over the past 20 years, involving experts from all over the world and resulting in the description of 39 new species. Gecko specialists Aaron Bauer from Villanova University, Pennsylvania, United States; Ivan Ineich from the Muséum National d'Histoire Naturelle, Paris; and Teppei Jono from Kyoto University, Japan, worked on the genus *Blaesodactylus* (see Bauer et al., pp. 1474–79). Oliver Hawlitschek carried out the taxonomic revision of the genus *Ebenavia* and described two new species during his postdoctoral research at the Zoologische Staatssammlung München (Hawlitschek et al. 2018). Mark Scherz and colleagues from the United States and Germany discovered the first new species of *Geckolepis* in 75 years, *G. megalepis* (Scherz et al. 2017). Marta Puente from the Universidade de Vigo, Spain, in collaboration with Vences, David Vieites, and Frank Glaw, reviewed the systematics of the genus *Lygodactylus*. A species of lamprophiid snake from Madagascar, *Thamnosophis martae*, was named to recognize Puente's work (Glaw et al. 2005). Angelica Crottini focused on the morphological and genetic research of the gecko genera *Paragehyra* and *Phelsuma*.

Malagasy herpetologist Fanomezana Ratsoavina pursued a doctorate on the taxonomy, phylogeny, and phylogeography of leaf-tailed geckos, genus *Uroplatus*, at the Technische Universität Braunschweig. She conducted molecular studies to define species boundaries, candidate species, and geographic distribution (Ratsoavina et al. 2013) and was the lead author for descriptions of six new *Uroplatus* species since around 2010 (see Gehring et al., pp. 1480–85).

The snakes of Madagascar have been enriched with a few novelties, including 16 new species described since 2000 and significant generic and specific rearrangements (see Cadle et al., pp. 1525–31). Vences and Glaw described a subspecies of *Sanzinia* boa (Vences and Glaw 2003) that was subsequently elevated to species level, *S. volontany* (Reynolds et al. 2014; see Raxworthy and Glaw, pp. 1522–25). A molecular phylogenetic study revealed that Malagasy blind snakes are a distinct lineage, leading to the creation of a new subfamily, Madatyphlopinae, and a new genus, *Madatyphlops* (Hedges et al. 2014). Among the 11 species transferred into this new genus were two discovered after the start of the 21st century (see Raxworthy, pp. 1532–34), including *M. rajeryi*, dedicated to Emile Rajeriarison, an expert guide from Ranomafana National Park (Renoult and Raselimanana 2009).

Scientists from the Zoologische Staatssammlung München have been among the most active in the field of molecular phylogeny and systematics studies of Malagasy snakes over the past 20 years, working under the leadership of Glaw, who participated in the description of 11 new species, including seven as first author. Affiliated with the same research institution, Michael Franzen described a new species of *Liophidium* and contributed to numerous research papers on the reptiles of Madagascar (Franzen et al. 2009).

Sara Ruane, then a postdoctoral researcher at the American Museum of Natural History and now at the Field Museum of Natural History, collaborated with Raxworthy on the phylogenetics of Malagasy snakes and described one species of *Madagascarophis* in 2016 (Ruane et al. 2016). While at Rutgers University, New Jersey, United States, Ruane continued her research on the herpetofauna of Madagascar and applied an integrative taxonomy approach to the then monotypic snake genus *Mimophis*, to conclude the existence of two distinct taxa (Ruane et al. 2018).

The taxonomic research on reptiles has greatly benefited from the strong involvement of a great diversity of international researchers and institutions over the past 20 years, particularly the German research centers Zoologische Staatssammlung München and Technische Universität Braunschweig. The increasing and critical participation of Malagasy scientists must also be highlighted in the productivity that led to the description of 107 new species of reptiles since 2000 (see Figure 1.18c). In addition to veteran specialists such as Raselimanana, the past decade saw the emergence of new scientists such as Ratsoavina, an active contributor to countless projects on herpetological taxonomy, phylogeny, phylogeography, distribution, and conservation assessment, and the leader of her own research team at the Université d'Antananarivo. Other Malagasy experts actively involved in the research on reptiles since about 2010 included Christian Randrianantoandro; Roger Daniel Randrianiaina, another doctoral student of Miguel Vences; and Herilala Randriamahazo, now at the Wildlife Conservation Society, Antananarivo.

Bird Exploration

The alpha-taxonomy of Madagascar birds was well documented before the 1980s and based on classical museum studies. Publications by a number of authors—starting with Karel Johan Gustav Hartlaub (1877) and Milne Edwards and Grandidier (1876–1885), then Delacour (1932a, 1932b) and Rand (1936), and until a few decades ago Benson et al. (1976, 1977)—summarized information on most species. After the considerable work of the Mission Zoologique Franco-Anglo-Américaine from 1929 to 1931, almost no bird species were described from the island for several decades. The single exception was *Xanthomixis apperti* (Appert's Tetraka), named after Otto Appert (1930–2012), who lived for years in Manja, where he was a Catholic priest, and discovered this bird in the 1970s in the Zombitse Forest near Sakaraha (Colston 1972).

Between 1980 and 2000, ornithological research focused mostly on bird distribution and ecology and to a lesser extent on phylogeny. Important ornithologists during this period include Aristide Andrianarimisa, Appert, Steven M. Goodman, Dominique Halleux (see Box 8), Frank Hawkins, Olivier Langrand, Richard Lewis, Raoul Mulder, Mark Pidgeon, Michael Putnam, Georges Randrianasolo (see Box 4), Mamy Ravokatra, Jean-Claude Razafimahaimodison, Lily-Arison Rene de Roland, Thomas S. Schulenberg, Russell Thorstrom, Lucienne Wilmé, Satoshi Yamagishi, and Steve Zack, among others.

Langrand spent 12 years on Madagascar between 1980 and 1996, and his fieldwork, largely within the WWF program, led to the publication of numerous scientific articles. He also published four field guides on Madagascar birds that promoted birdwatching and ornithology nationally and internationally. The first, published first in English (Langrand 1990) and later in French (Langrand 1995), fostered the interest of foreign and Malagasy ornithologists in the birds of the island. This was followed by a guide to the birds of Madagascar and the neighboring islands, coauthored with Ian Sinclair, in English, including a revised edition (Sinclair and Langrand 1998, 2013), and in French (Sinclair and Langrand 2014).

Interest in Malagasy birds was further reinforced by the publication of a photographic guide (Morris and Hawkins 1998) and more recently by the comprehensive and exceptional encyclopedic accounts in the volume on the birds of western Indian Ocean islands in the series *Handbook of the Birds of Africa* (Safford and Hawkins 2013).

Goodman's first fieldwork on Madagascar was to conduct an ornithological survey in the Tolagnaro region, in 1989, in collaboration with Schulenberg, then a PhD student (and both from the Field Museum of Natural History, Chicago). This first contact marked for Goodman the beginning of a deep involvement in the study of Malagasy biodiversity. He truly catalyzed the scientific community and imposed a rigorous and systematic approach to surveys and data collection. He ignited a common effort among the international scientific community to document the fauna of Madagascar, and ornithology was one of his priorities.

Goodman's scientific missions have led him all over the country. As of June 2020, he and his colleagues and associated students had visited over 820 sites on the island (see Figure 1.14). Numerous monographs in *Fieldiana: Zoology*, a series published by the Field Museum of Natural History; scientific publications in a range of international journals; and chapters in a number of books reflect this great dynamism. For close to three decades, capacity building for Malagasy scientists has been one of his priorities: he and colleagues have published 16 monographs in French within the series Centre d'Information et de Documentation Scientifique et Technique d'Antananarivo. Furthermore, Goodman, along with Langrand and Wilmé, founded in 1992 the Working Group on Birds in the Madagascar Region, which until 2002 published a bulletin with the objective of informing regional ornithologists on publications and giving them the opportunity to publish their own information.

In 1993, Schulenberg, Goodman, and Jean-Claude Razafimahaimodison, now of Centre ValBio, Ranomafana National Park, reevaluated the taxonomic status of one subspecies of *Nesillas typica* (Madagascar Brush-warbler) and elevated it to a full species, *N. lantzii* (Subdesert Brush-warbler) (Schulenberg et al. 1993), named after French zoologist Jean Auguste Lantz, who collaborated with Alfred Grandidier. A few years later, Goodman was the lead author of a new genus and species of bird described in collaboration with Langrand and Brett Whitney, *Cryptosylvicola randrianasoloi* (Cryptic Warbler) (Goodman et al. 1996), named in honor of the first Malagasy ornithologist, Georges Randrianasolo (see Box 4). In 1997, Goodman, Hawkins, and Charles Domergue described a new species of vanga, *Calicalicus rufocarpalis* (Red-shouldered Vanga), located in the region south of Toliara (Goodman et al. 1997). Domergue's observations and photos from the 1980s and specimens from the Muséum National d'Histoire Naturelle, Paris, formed the basis for the description.

BOX 8 DOMINIQUE HALLEUX (B. 1953), FRENCH AGRONOMIST, ORNITHOLOGIST, NATURALIST, PHOTOGRAPHER, ON MADAGASCAR BETWEEN 1978 AND 1998

F. ANDRIAMIALISOA AND O. LANGRAND

DOMINIQUE HALLEUX was born in Mulhouse, France, on 21 August 1953, and spent his childhood there. His father held a position of research director in a large textile factory in Mulhouse. His grandfather and father both hunted in the Ardennes, France, the family's home region. Halleux started birdwatching at the age of nine, first with his father and later with a local NGO called Les Jeunes Amis des Animaux of Mulhouse. As part of this organization, he actively participated each winter in the waterfowl census on the Rhine River.

Halleux moved to Paris in 1971, where he obtained his baccalaureate in 1972 in a scientific section. In 1973–1974, he completed the first two preparatory years at the Institut Supérieur Agricole de Beauvais, France. In 1974, when it was time for completing his mandatory military service, he opted to serve abroad and was sent to Madagascar.

He set foot on the island in September 1974, as a member of the French Navy, and was posted in Antsiranana (Diégo Suarez) but assigned as school supervisor at the Lycée Français de Diégo Suarez. With this posting, Halleux had his first exposure to the extraordinary richness and diversity of species of the flora and the fauna of Madagascar. He not only explored the surroundings of Antsiranana but also went to the Masoala Peninsula and to the region of Toliara. Once his military service was completed in August 1975, he returned to France and resumed his studies at the agronomy school of the Institut Supérieur Agricole de Beauvais. He graduated as agronomy engineer in 1978 and was hired by the Ministère de la Coopération of the French government.

Halleux left for Madagascar in May 1979 to take the position of technical assistant of a national program promoting coffee, pepper, clove, and cacao production (Opération Café, Poivre, Girofle, Cacao). He was in charge of the northeastern sector and was based in Maroantsetra, where he lived from May 1979 to January 1984. In Maroantsetra, he rented one of the few concrete houses in town from André Peyriéras (see Box 5), who by that time had largely left Maroantsetra to live in Antananarivo. Peyriéras introduced Halleux to one of his favorite sites on the Masoala Peninsula, the small village of Hiaraka, where Peyriéras had observed and collected endemic species of insects, reptiles, birds, and mammals. Halleux started exploring this site on his own, as well as other parts of the region. He rapidly became familiar with the flora, in particular orchids, and the local fauna. At that time, the Masoala Peninsula was poorly known and was still covered with extensive areas of forest. Halleux's knowledge of the biota of the region became known internationally, and some birdwatchers started knocking at his door to be guided in the region.

In August 1980, Halleux welcomed Olivier Langrand in Maroantsetra during Langrand's first visit to Madagascar. They had been introduced to each other by Michel Gunther, a naturalist, birdwatcher, and photographer, as all three had grown up in Alsace. Extensive discussions between Halleux and Langrand influenced the latter's decision to come back to Madagascar to work on the first field guide to the birds of the island.

In October 1980, Halleux guided French ornithologist Jean-Marc Thiollay, from the Laboratoire d'Ecologie, Ecole Normale Supérieure, Paris, and German plastic surgeon Berndt-Ulrich Meyburg, based in West Berlin, the chairman of the World Working Group on Birds of Prey. Both were interested in finding *Eutriorchis astur* (Madagascar Serpent-eagle) and *Falco zoniventris* (Banded Kestrel) (Thiollay and Meyburg 1981). In February 1981, Gunther came to visit Halleux in Maroantsetra; together they explored the regional forests.

In January 1982, Langrand returned to Madagascar and, with Lucienne Wilmé, spent four months in Maroantsetra and benefited immensely from Halleux's knowledge and generosity. They were joined in April 1982 by Vincent Bretagnolle, who had just graduated from the Institut National Agronomique Paris-Grignon, France, and was preparing the illustrations for Langrand's field guide to the birds of Madagascar (Langrand 1990). Other naturalists, including French nature photographer Roland Seitre, who visited Halleux in Maroantsetra in 1982, benefited from Halleux's knowledge of the region and the logistic means at his disposal to explore the region.

American Mardy Darian (1933–2015), a passionate palm collector, relied on the support of Halleux and of one of his employees, Jean Gérard, to track down rare species of palm trees in the Maroantsetra region. Darian and Gérard's first survey led to the discovery of a new species of palm, *Marojejya dariani*, honoring Darian, described in 1984. Halleux and Gérard continued to work on palms, mainly by collecting information from local people, who proved to have a very fine knowledge of large species of palm trees and their different uses. Botanist John Dransfield, of the Royal Botanic Gardens, Kew, United Kingdom, described a new genus and species of palm from Masoala, *Voanioala gerardii*, dedicating it to Gérard (Dransfield 1989), who was the first to locate the trees and provide the seeds. Two years later, Dransfield described another new genus and species of palm tree, *Lemurophoenix halleuxii*, discovered on the foothills of Masoala by Gérard and Halleux in 1987, and named it after Halleux (Dransfield 1991). Swiss ornithologist Otto Appert visited Halleux in February 1983 with the hope of seeing the forest bird *Mesitornis unicolor* (Brown Mesite), which they did not chance to find.

In 1985, Halleux was transferred to Manakara, for the Opération de Développement Agricole du Sud-Est, to continue promoting coffee culture. While traveling to his new posting, he drove through an intact block of forest and immediately suspected its conservation value. This forest is today Ranomafana National Park.

Halleux stopped by a small forest village called Ambatolahy and asked a young man standing there if he knew something about the birds of the area. The young man ran back to his house to pick up feathers of a bird he had killed that day. The feathers belonged to *Brachypteracias leptosomus* (Short-legged Ground-roller), which at that time was a species that had been rarely seen by scientists or birdwatchers. The young man was Emile Rajeriarison, also known as Rajery. Rajery and his brother-in-law Loret Rasabo became Halleux's guides in Ranomafana and worked with him until 1988 (Figure 1.22).

With the creation of Ranomafana National Park in 1991, ecotourism came to Madagascar, and Rajery and Loret became nature guides, and quickly were sought after by anyone interested in the local rare endemic birds. Both are still highly valued tour guides and live in Ranomafana. They are closely associated with the Centre ValBio, a research and conservation institution established by the State University of New York at Stony Brook under the leadership of American primatologist Patricia C. Wright. Rajery and Loret's photos are featured in the historical section at the Ranomafana National Park interpretation center, where they are credited as leaders in establishing the park. Wright considers Rajery the best natural historian alive today on Madagascar. Rajery's son is pursuing a college degree in environmental studies, partially supported by Wright, and Loret's children are tour guides in Ranomafana National Park.

Halleux was the first to reveal Rajery and Loret as outstanding naturalists. The collaboration of Halleux, Rajery, and Loret led to the first descriptions of the reproductive behavior of some cryptic forest bird species, such as *Mesitornis unicolor* (Appert 1995), and improved the knowledge of the vernacular names of bird species. An amphibian species described in 2010 (*Anodonthyla emilei*) and a reptile species described in 2009 (*Madatyphlops rajeryi*) were named after Rajery to acknowledge his engagement in the documentation of the biota of Ranomafana.

In 1986, Halleux informed Corinne Dague, a primatologist working under the supervision of Jean-Jacques Petter (1927–2002), from the Muséum National d'Histoire Naturelle, Paris, of the presence in Ranomafana of a population of *Eulemur rubriventer* (Red-bellied Lemur) that was easy to observe. Dague came to Ranomafana to study the species' behavior (Dague and Petter 1988) and hired Rajery and Loret to assist with her fieldwork. Dague reported to Petter the observation of *Prolemur simus* (Greater Bamboo Lemur), a species considered extinct in the early 1970s, which Petter and Peyriéras had found in Kianjavato in the mid-1970s, but that had not been observed in the intervening years. Petter then sent a German researcher, Bernhard Meier, to look for *Prolemur* in Ranomafana. For the purpose of his study, Meier established a field camp in the middle of the forest on the right bank of the Namorona River and recruited Rajery and Loret as field assistants. The associated collaboration led to the discovery of a new species, *Hapalemur aureus* (Golden Bamboo Lemur), which Meier and collaborators described in 1987 (Meier and Rumpler 1987; Meier et al. 1987).

Halleux left Madagascar in 1988 for a post in Guinea but came back in 1993 and, based in Andapa, in the north, was hired by the WWF as a technical adviser in charge of the conservation of the Marojejy and the Anjanaharibe-Sud protected areas. There, he helped orchestrate the large-scale biological inventories in these zones. Halleux continued documenting the birds and the mammals of the region, including the rediscovery of *Tyto soumagnei* (Red Owl), which had not been seen in 20 years (Halleux and Goodman 1994). He also explored the region of Daraina and the wetlands located north of Iharana (Vohémar).

In 1996, while based in Antsiranana, Halleux worked for the WWF to advance the conservation of Montagne d'Ambre, and during his regional exploration, he discovered a new location for the rare endemic *Anas bernieri* (Madagascar Teal), near Ambanja, a site located very far north of its previously known distribution area (Halleux 1998). Halleux left Madagascar in 1998 and now lives in Brittany, France, where he monitors migrant shorebirds and photographs and participates in the regional inventory of moths of the region (Boudet 2019).

FIGURE 1.22 **Dominique Halleux was among the first naturalists to highlight the biological importance of the Ranomafana forest. This photo, taken in November 1988 at the entrance to the village of Ambatolahy near Ranomafana, shows Halleux (center) with Loret Rasabo (left) and Emile Rajeriarison (right) coming back from a photographic hide that had been established to document the nesting habit of *Atelornis pittoides* (Pitta-like Ground-roller). For several years Halleux worked closely with Rajeriarison and Rasabo, who quickly became very skilled naturalists and are still working today at the Ranomafana National Park. Together, they photographed the first nests of *Mesitornis unicolor* (Brown Mesite), *Bradypterus brunneus* (Brown Emutail), and *Crossleyia xanthophrys* (Madagascar Yellowbrow).** (PHOTO by C. Deulofeu.)

BirdLife International conducted a project from 1997 to 1999 entitled Les Zones d'Importance pour la Conservation des Oiseaux à Madagascar (ZICOMA), under the technical coordination of Hawkins and Peter Robertson. Marc Nestor Rabenandrasana led teams of ornithologists, often 100% Malagasy, including Rado Hanitriniaina Andriamasimanana, Narisoa Andriamboavonjy Ramanitra, Isidore Ranaritsito, Mihajamanana Randrianarisoa, The Seing Sam, Zefania Sama, and Marie Clémentine Virginie, to conduct numerous ornithological surveys across Madagascar and nearshore islands, including terrestrial, saltwater, and freshwater species. The results of this fieldwork were presented in a long series of reports, and the synthesis as a book (Projet ZICOMA 1999).

ZICOMA constituted the incubator from which emerged a cadre of Malagasy field ornithologists. Asity Madagascar, an organization born in 1996, became in 2008 the conservation partner representing Madagascar in the BirdLife International network. With its staff composed of only Malagasy ornithologists and conservation experts, Asity, under the leadership of chairman of the board Aristide Andrianarimisa and director Vony Raminoarisoa, is actively involved in conservation and is responsible for the management of four protected areas: Complexe Mahavavy Kinkony, Complexe Mangoky Ihotry, Tsitongambarika, and Torotorofotsy.

Between 2000 and 2019, ornithological fieldwork continued and led to the discovery of a new species of rail, *Mentocrex beankaensis* (Tsingy Wood-rail) (Goodman et al. 2011a), restricted to limestone areas in central-western Madagascar, specifically the Bemaraha and Beanka protected areas. In the past 40 years, only five species of birds have been discovered on Madagascar that are new to science (see Figure 1.18d).

Like other groups of vertebrates, birds have been the focus of phylogenetic and phylogeographic studies (see Reddy and Schulenberg, pp. 1621–26), and significant efforts were initiated in the early 2000s (Cruaud et al. 2011; Goodman et al. 2011a; Block et al. 2015; Fuchs et al. 2016). Molecular phylogeny studies of Malagasy birds first started with the Vangidae (see Schulenberg, pp. 1694–99), highlighting one of the most spectacular cases of adaptive radiation among the birds of the world. Studies were also carried out on the Sylviidae (Cibois et al. 1999, 2001). Genetic work led to the identification of a new endemic family of birds, the Bernieridae (Cibois et al. 2010), unveiling a previously unrecognized adaptative radiation. Today, a total of 13 species placed in eight genera are known, including one that remains undescribed (see Safford et al., pp. 1553–602). The family name Bernieridae honors Alphonse Charles Joseph Bernier, a French physician, naval surgeon, and botanist, who collected flora and fauna specimens (insects, birds, and lemurs) on Madagascar between 1822 and 1848 (Dorr 1997).

Additional genetic analysis coupled with morphological information applied to the genus *Newtonia* led to the identification of a new species, *N. lavarambo* (Lavarambo Newtonia) (Younger et al. 2018). Molecular research also led to the elevation of some endemic subspecies to full species, such as *Circus macrosceles* (Madagascar Harrier) (Oatley et al. 2015) and *Apus balstoni* (Madagascar Swift) (Päckert et al. 2012). Conversely, some recent taxonomic splits that relied on morphological characters were reconsidered based on the results of molecular analysis. *Otus madagascariensis*, described by Rasmussen et al. (2000), was shown not to be distinct from *O. rutilus* (Madagascar Scops-owl) (Fuchs et al. 2007).

Finally, the genus *Monticola* (rock-thrushes) was revised based on molecular work. The analysis concluded that the forms previously referred to as *M. erythronotus*, from Montagne d'Ambre, and *M. bensoni*, from Isalo Massif, are best considered within *M. sharpei* (Forest Rock-thrush). However, the study indicated that these isolated populations of *M. sharpei* were going through a nascent speciation process (Zuccon and Erickson 2010; Cruaud et al. 2011).

The avifauna of Madagascar includes 110 endemic species (see Safford et al., pp. 1553–602). It is almost certain that the list of island endemics will grow in the near future, as has been the case with other groups, based on additional genetic analysis demonstrating, with previously unrecognized cryptic speciation, that certain geographic forms (subspecies) are best elevated to full species rank. Further, previously unrecorded vagrants, or migratory species unknown from the island, are certain to be recorded, as occurred with the first observation of *Ichthyaetus hemprichii* (Sooty Gull) on Madagascar in 2007 (Renoult 2009) and a considerable number of other seabirds (see Le Corre et al., pp. 1637–50).

New species of fossil birds have been discovered thanks to the paleontological work on Quaternary fossils carried out by Goodman. These include a coua (*Coua berthae*) (Goodman and Ravoavy 1993), dedicated to the late Berthe Rakotosamimanana, professor at the Université d'Antananarivo; an eagle (*Stephanoaetus mahery*) (Goodman 1994); a lapwing (*Vanellus madagascariensis*) (Goodman 1996); and a ground-roller (*Brachypteracias langrandi*) (Goodman 2000), named after Langrand.

In the past 20 years, ornithology has attracted fewer Malagasy scientists than the fields of primatology or herpetology. However, in addition to the people mentioned above, a few others need to be mentioned. Marie Jeanne Raherilalao (Université d'Antananarivo and Association Vahatra) has been involved in fieldwork around the island and associated with recent laboratory molecular analysis conducted on Malagasy birds. She also has been a mentor in the form of director or committee member for a considerable number of Malagasy graduate students. Another remarkable national ornithologist is Rivo Rabarisoa, who obtained his higher degree (DEA) from the Université d'Antananarivo in 1985. Since 2005, he has worked for Asity Madagascar, where he has been responsible for the wetland program and has completed important waterbird surveys, including those on rare and threatened species such as the *Haliaeetus vociferoides* (Madagascar Fish-eagle), and *Anas bernieri* (Madagascar Teal).

Lily-Arison Rene de Roland is one of Madagascar's leading conservationists and field ornithologists. Trained as a field biologist and presented his DEA and PhD degrees in the Département de Biologie Animale, Université d'Antananarivo, Rene de Roland has an excellent knowledge of the moist evergreen forest and wetland ecosystems of Madagascar. In 2004, he became the national director of the Peregrine Fund Madagascar, working on bird and habitat conservation (Figure 1.23). Under his leadership, the Peregrine Fund Madagascar has reinforced its position as an important player in the conservation of the island. Rene de Roland has focused his energy on the survey of rare bird species and in a few years has managed to collect considerable information on species that were considered rare or even extinct, including *H. vociferoides*, *Eutriorchis astur*

FIGURE 1.23 **The Peregrine Fund Madagascar has been instrumental in documenting the natural history of rare and elusive bird species such as *Aythya innotata* (Madagascar Pochard), *Eutriorchis astur* (Madagascar Serpent-eagle), and *Tyto soumagnei* (Red Owl). The photo, taken on 9 June 2018 at the field camp of the Peregrine Fund Madagascar at Bemanevika, shows the organization's national director, Lily-Arison Rene de Roland (far right), with the field team responsible for the radio tracking of *E. astur*, from left to right: Monesy, Moise, Be Berthin, and Eugène Ladoany.** (PHOTO by O. Langrand.)

(Madagascar Serpent-eagle), *Tyto soumagnei* (Red Owl), *Sarothrura watersi* (Slender-billed Flufftail), and *Aythya innotata*. The last of these species, the Madagascar Pochard, was considered extinct until Rene de Roland and The Seing Sam rediscovered a small population in the north (see Rene de Roland and Young, pp. 1650–53).

Small-Mammal Exploration

Knowledge of Madagascar's small mammals increased substantially in the 1990s, a period during which several genera and species of rodents (subfamily Nesomyinae) and tenrecs (family Tenrecidae) new to science were described. This trend has continued steadily, thanks to the systematic fieldwork and collections made by Steven M. Goodman, Voahangy Soarimalala (Université de Fianarantsoa and Association Vahatra), and a range of international and national researchers and students. These studies focus on small-mammal distribution, including along elevational gradients of different massifs. A considerable number of new species of tenrecs and rodents have been discovered, even at some previously "well-known" sites (see Figure 1.24a).

Identification of small mammals often requires detailed museum-based work as well as molecular analyses. Collaboration of Goodman and Soarimalala with Paulina D. Jenkins from the Natural History Museum, London; Michael D. Carleton from the Smithsonian Institution, Washington, DC; Link E. Olson from the University of Alaska Museum, Fairbanks; and Sharon A. Jansa from the University of Minnesota, led to the description of seven species of tenrecs and 10 species of rodents (including two new genera) (see Goodman and Soarimalala, pp. 1737–69). *Microgale jenkinsae* (Jenkins's Shrew Tenrec) was named after Jenkins for her important contribution to the systematics of the Tenrecidae (Goodman and Soarimalala 2004). *Microgale nasoloi* (Nasolo's Shrew Tenrec) was named by Jenkins and Goodman (1999) after field biologist Nasolo Hubert Neomane Rakotoarison, who died in a car accident in 1996. *Eliurus petteri* (Petter's Tufted-tail Rat) (Carleton 1994) was dedicated to Francis Petter (1923–2012), a rodent specialist from the Muséum National d'Histoire Naturelle, Paris, brother of primatologist Jean-Jacques Petter. Francis Petter described *Macrotarsomys ingens* (Long-tailed Big-footed Mouse) in 1959 and *Brachytarsomys albicauda villosa* (now *B. villosa*, Hairy-tailed Tree Rat) in 1962. *Eliurus danieli* (Daniel's Tufted-tail Rat) discovered in the Isalo protected area, was named in honor of Daniel Rakotondravony (Carleton and Goodman 2007), professor, now retired, from the Département de Biologie Animale,

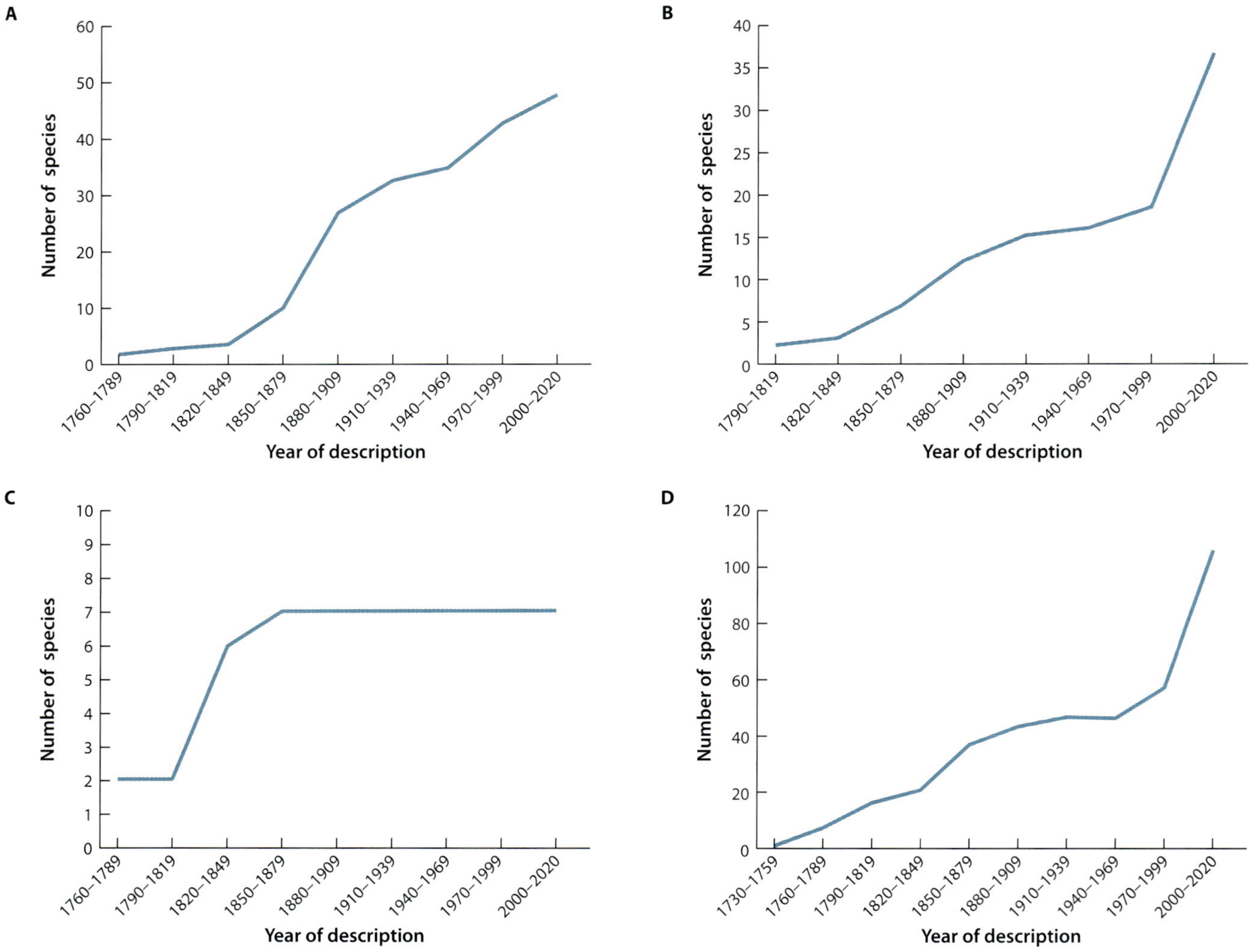

FIGURE 1.24 **Description of different Malagasy mammal groups over time and by 30-year periods. Data used in these tabulations extend to May 2020. A) Endemic small mammals (rodents and tenrecs combined) described between 1760 and 2020. B) Endemic bat species, between 1790 and 2020. C) Endemic carnivoran species, between 1760 and 2020. D) Endemic lemur species, between 1730 and 2020.**

Université d'Antananarivo. Rakotondravony's contribution to field research and to the training of Malagasy and foreign students alike contributed greatly to the advancement of knowledge of the small mammals of Madagascar. *Eliurus carletoni* (Carleton's Tufted-tail Rat) was named for Carleton in honor of his extensive museum-based work on the systematic and morphological evolution of Malagasy rodents (Goodman et al. 2009a). *Monticolomys koopmani* (Koopman's Mountain-dwelling Mouse) (see Carleton et al., pp. 2031–32), a rodent found in montane forests of the Central Highlands, was named after mammologist Karl Koopman (1920–1997), of the American Museum of Natural History.

Jenkins has collaborated with herpetologists, as they use the same pitfall traps as mammalogists to catch reptiles, amphibians, and small tenrecs. She described a new species in 1997, *Microgale fotsifotsy* (Pale Shrew Tenrec), with herpetologists Christopher J. Raxworthy and Ronald A. Nussbaum (Jenkins et al. 1997). Specimens collected by Raxworthy were used to describe *M. dryas* and *M. soricoides* (Dryad Shrew Tenrec and Shrew-toothed Shrew Tenrec, respectively) (Jenkins 1992, 1993). Jenkins named a new species, *M. pulla* (Jenkins 1988), now a synonym of *M. parvula* (Jenkins et al. 1997), from a specimen collected by Peter J. Stephenson, who in an early phase of his career, based at the University of Aberdeen, Scotland, conducted studies on the physiology of the Tenrecidae (Stephenson 1991).

Since the late 1990s, different scientists, such as Goodman, Rakotondravony, and Soarimalala, involved in different aspects of fieldwork on rodents and tenrecs, promoted the advancement of Malagasy graduate students working with these animals, including, to name a few, Claudette P. Maminirina (Université d'Antananarivo and WWF), who would become professor at the Institut Supérieur de Technologie d'Ambositra; Zafimahery Rakotomalala (Association Vahatra), who would be given a professorship and would be named head of Mention Zoologie et Biodiversité Animale, Université d'Antananarivo; and Beza Ramasindrazana (Association Vahatra), who would get a postdoctoral degree at Processus Infectieux en Milieu Insulaire Tropical (PIMIT), associated with the Université de La Réunion, and then obtain a research post at Institut Pasteur de Madagascar.

Bat Exploration

Until the early 2000s, bats had been the least-studied group of mammals on the island from either ecological or taxonomic perspectives. In 1995, three Canadians, Randolph L. Peterson (1920–1989), Judith Eger, and Lorelie Mitchell, all associated with the Royal Ontario Museum, Toronto, published an important monograph on the bats of Madagascar (Peterson et al. 1995). Published after Peterson's death, the monograph was based largely on fieldwork he had conducted several decades earlier and in collaboration with Office de la Recherche Scientifique et Technique Outre-Mer (ORSTOM).

Starting in the late 1990s, a project was initiated by several researchers associated with the University of Aberdeen and Malagasy students on the fruit bats of Madagascar (MacKinnon et al. 2003). This project subsequently led to the creation of Madagasikara Voakajy, a Malagasy organization that would concentrate on research concerning the island's land vertebrates and a range of different conservation projects. Starting in the early 2000s, Goodman, associated with different scientists and students from Malagasy and foreign research institutions, conducted work on the taxonomy and ecology of bats. This countrywide research effort led to the description of 16 new species between 2004 and 2016 and clarified the taxonomic status of many bat species endemic to Madagascar, as well as species found on neighboring islands, such as the Comoros, and on the eastern part of the African continent (Foley et al. 2015; see Goodman et al., pp. 1894–911).

Among these new discoveries was a new species in the endemic family Myzopodidae (see Ralisata et al., pp. 1917–22), *Myzopoda schliemanni* (Schliemann's Sucker-footed Bat), described in 2007 and named after Harald Schliemann, retired from the University of Hamburg, Germany, who conducted important anatomical studies, including the sucker structures of *Myzopoda*, and was Goodman's PhD thesis director in Hamburg. *Pipistrellus raceyi* (Racey's Pipistrelle) (Bates et al. 2006) was dedicated to Paul A. Racey from the University of Aberdeen, who has been associated with research on bats and tenrecs of Madagascar since 1986, directly through fieldwork and the supervision of Malagasy and foreign students, including doctoral and postdoctoral students like the late Martin E. Nicoll (see Box 6) and Peter J. Stephenson. Goodman et al. (2012) described a new bat species found in medium-altitude moist evergreen forest areas of the central east, *Neoromicia robertsi*, subsequently transferred to the genus *Laephotis*, named after Austin Roberts (1883–1948), a zoologist from South Africa who dedicated part of his career to African bat studies.

The taxonomy of the family Miniopteridae has been well studied on the basis of molecular and morphological evidence. Between 2005 and 2019, seven species new to science were identified in the genus *Miniopterus* from Madagascar, plus two shared with the Comoros. These include *M. petersoni* (Peterson's Long-fingered Bat) (Goodman et al. 2008), dedicated to Randolph Peterson; *M. griffithsi* (Griffiths' Long-fingered Bat) (Goodman et al. 2010), named after Owen Griffiths, a regional terrestrial snail specialist and founding director of Biodiversity Conservation Madagascar; *M. egeri* (Eger's Long-fingered Bat) (Goodman et al. 2011b), dedicated to Judith Eger; and *M. aelleni* (Aellen's Long-fingered Bat) (Goodman et al. 2009b), memorializing Swiss zoologist Villy Aellen, who worked extensively on African bats and was curator at Muséum d'Histoire Naturelle de Genève.

Recent inventory of the island's bat fauna accounts for 46 species, 36 of which are endemic and nine shared between Madagascar, Africa, and the Comoros (Goodman et al., pp. 1894–911; see Figure 1.24b). Of the 18 species new to science identified in the past 15 years, 17 were described by Goodman and colleagues, in all cases associated with Malagasy students and scientists, including Ramasindrazana, Maminirina, and Fanja Ratrimomanarivo (Association Vahatra, Université d'Antananarivo, and now professor at the Université de Toliara).

Carnivora Exploration

At the species level, the vast majority of Malagasy members of the order Carnivora were described early in the timeline of Malagasy zoological description, but significant changes have taken place in their higher-level systematics, and today all native species are placed in an endemic family, the Eupleridae (Yoder et al. 2003; see Veron et al., pp. 1863–65). Recent developments included the description by Chris Wozencraft of a new species of euplerid from Lake Tsimanampesotse (*Galidictis grandidieri*) (Wozencraft 1986, 1987). More recent molecular work demonstrated that the genetic divergence between *G. grandidieri* and *G. fasciata* (Broad-striped Vontsira), occurring in moist evergreen forest, was not at the species level, and *G. grandidieri* is best considered a subspecies, *G. f. grandidieri* (Veron et al. 2017).

In 2010, based mostly on morphological characters, a new species, *Salanoia durrelli*, was described from Lake Alaotra (Durbin et al. 2010). Recent genetic research showed that this taxon was not genetically distinct from *S. concolor* (Brown-tailed Vontsira) (Veron et al. 2017). Goodman and Helgen (2010), based on morphological characters, proposed to elevate the subspecies *Eupleres goudotii major* to a full species. However, more recent genetic analysis showed little variation in members of the genus, and it was determined that only *E. goudotii* (Falanouc) should be recognized (Veron and Goodman 2018). This species is named after the early French naturalist and explorer Jules Prosper Goudot (see Box 1).

No new species of Eupleridae carnivoran considered valid today has been described since 1839 (see Figure 1.24c). Genetic analyses have permitted scientists to clarify the taxonomy of the genera *Eupleres*, *Galidia*, *Galidictis*, and *Salanoia* (Veron et al. 2017; Veron and Goodman 2018). The native carnivoran fauna of Madagascar has seven species belonging to seven monotypic genera, all endemic.

Lemur Exploration

The primary focus of mammal studies on Madagascar has always been lemurs, as these unique primates are truly the island's flagship species. Between 1980 and 2000, an extraordinary amount of behavioral and ecological research was conducted on this group. Much of this work was done in the context of research at natural history museums, university science departments, and other institutions, such as the Deutsches Primatenzentrum in Göttingen, Germany, and Kirindy Forest CNFEREF, Madagascar (Claudia Fichtel, Jörg U. Ganzhorn, Peter Kappeler, Rodin Rasoloarison, and others);

Ruhr University Bochum, Germany (Bernhard Meier); Duke University, Department of Anthropology and Primate Center, which would later be renamed Duke Lemur Center (David Meyers, Elwyn Simons [1930–2016], Patricia C. Wright, and Anne D. Yoder, to name a few); Yale University (Alison Richard, Hilary Simons-Morland, and Eleanor Sterling); University of Tokyo (Chiaki Iwakawa and Taizo Iwano); Kyoto University (Naoki Koyama); Jersey Wildlife Preservation Trust, which would later be renamed Durrell Wildlife Conservation Trust (Anna Feistner); Washington University (Robert W. Sussman); Field Museum of Natural History (Steve Goodman and Robert D. Martin); University of Zürich (Robert D. Martin, Thomas Mutschler, and Urs Thalmann); American Museum of Natural History (Ian Tattersall and Eleanor Sterling); Université d'Antananarivo (Nasolo Rakotoarison [1961–1996], Pothin Rakotomanga [1936–1999], Daniel Rakotondravony, Berthe Rakotosamimanana, and Rodin Rasoloarison, among others); State University of New York at Stony Brook (William L. Jungers, Patricia C. Wright, and others); University of Hamburg (Katherin Dausmann, Jörg U. Ganzhorn, and Simon Sommer); and Université Louis Pasteur Strasbourg (Ludo Koenders and Yves Rumpler) (Figure 1.25). By no means is this list exhaustive.

A number of primatologists and molecular biologists study lemur phylogenetics and systematics. Field and laboratory work have led to discovery of new species, the rediscovery of poorly known species, and better knowledge of the distribution of different lemur species. The level of discovery among the lemurs of the island, the vertebrate group that until a few decades ago was thought to be the best known, is simply extraordinary (see Figure 1.24d). One such discovery, which commenced the wave, took place in Ranomafana in 1986, when Meier found a new species, *Hapalemur aureus* (Golden Bamboo Lemur), that would subsequently be described by five primatologists—Meier, Albignac, Peyriéras, Rumpler, and Wright (Meier et al. 1987; see Box 8).

An even more stunning discovery, given its large size and diurnal habit, followed in 1988: a new *Propithecus*, *P. tattersalli* (Tattersall's Sifaka), found in Loky Manambato in the Daraina region in the northeast. Elwyn Simons from Duke University described the species, which was dedicated to Tattersall (Simons 1988).

The publication in 2000 of three articles on the taxonomy of lemurs, all in the same issue of the *International Journal of Primatology*, marked the beginning of a remarkable increase in the number of new species in the subsequent two decades. The first

FIGURE 1.25 **Primatologists have played an important role in biodiversity conservation through the creation of protected areas. This photo was taken in 1985 at the occasion of the inauguration of the Bezà-Mahafaly Special Reserve. From left to right: Joseph Andriamampianina (Département des Eaux et Forêts, Ecole Supérieure des Sciences Agronomiques [ESSA-Forêts], Université d'Antananarivo), Gilbert Ravelojaona (president of ESSA-Forêts, Université d'Antananarivo), Alison Richard (Yale University), Pothin Rakotomanga (ESSA-Forêts, Université d'Antananarivo), Robert W. Sussman (Washington University, Saint Louis, Missouri), and Behaligno (from near Ejeda). Son of a Mahafaly king, Behaligno was the founding member of the monitoring team and worked with Richard as chief darter when she began a sifaka capture-and-release program in 1984.** (PHOTO by A. Jolly.)

involved a reassessment of western *Avahi* species and the description of a new species, *A. unicolor* (Sambirano Woolly Lemur) (Thalmann and Geissmann 2000; see Donati et al., pp. 1963–66). The second article, a systematic revision of the genus *Cheirogaleus* across Madagascar, resulted in the description of two new dwarf lemurs, *C. minusculus* and *C. ravus* (Groves 2000). The recognition of *C. minusculus* as a distinct species is uncertain, and *C. ravus* is now considered a synonym of *C. major* (see Blanco, pp. 1922–26). Several new species of *Cheirogaleus* were subsequently described (Lei et al. 2015; Frasier et al. 2016; McLain et al. 2017), including *C. grovesi* (Groves' Dwarf Lemur), named for the late British Australian biological anthropologist Colin Groves (1942–2017); see Blanco (pp. 1922–26) for a review of the taxonomy of this genus. Finally, the third article involved a reassessment of the forms of western *Microcebus* (Rasoloarison et al. 2000); its authors redefined the species *M. myoxinus* (Peters' Mouse Lemur), described two species new to science, and resurrected another species from synonymy; see Kappeler et al. (pp. 1927–32) for a review of the taxonomy of this genus.

In 2005, Samuel Furrer and Robert Zingg from the Zürich Zoo obtained nine live *Microcebus* mouse lemurs in the forest of Andasibe, a prime ecotourist destination and one of the biologically best-known sites on the island. Studies by primatologists Christian Roos and Peter Kappeler from the Deutsches Primatenzentrum in Göttingen showed that these mouse lemurs were genetically different from *M. rufus* (Rufous Mouse Lemur), believed at that time to be distributed across the eastern part of Madagascar. They named the new species after Steven M. Goodman, to recognize his major contribution to the advancement of knowledge on the vertebrate fauna of Madagascar. The common name of this new species is Goodman's Mouse Lemur, and the scientific name is *M. lehilahytsara*—in Malagasy, *lehilahy* means "man" and *tsara* means "good" (Kappeler et al. 2005).

The discovery by Kappeler et al. (2005) of a new species of *Microcebus* slightly preceded a major revision of the genus (Louis et al. 2006a), during which three new species were described, which included *M. mittermeieri* (Mittermeier's Mouse Lemur) and *M. jollyae* (Jolly's Mouse Lemur), recognizing the lifetime contributions to lemur research and conservation by Russell A. Mittermeier and Alison Jolly, as well as *M. simmonsi* (Simmons' Mouse Lemur). Additional studies of *Microcebus* from northern, northwestern, and eastern Madagascar generated 12 new species (see Kappeler et al., pp. 1927–32 for a summary), including *M. ganzhorni* (Ganzhorn's Mouse Lemur), named after German primatologist and ecologist Jörg U. Ganzhorn, who has been associated with research on the island for more than 30 years (Hotaling et al. 2016). In total, 16 new species of mouse lemurs and one new species of *Mirza*, *M. zaza* (Northern Giant Mouse Lemur) (Kappeler et al. 2005), have been discovered in the past 15 years.

Among the world's primates, *Lepilemur* is the genus that has seen the greatest increase in recognized forms in the past 15 years, with 18 new species described between 2006 and 2009 (Mittermeier and Rylands 2020; see Radespiel et al., pp. 1935–40, for a review). Molecular and morphological analyses of the genus *Lepilemur* have shown the existence of 11 previously unrecognized species, all published in a single scientific paper (Louis et al. 2006b), including *L. petteri* (Petter's Sportive Lemur), named in honor of French primatologist Jean-Jacques Petter, the first author of the lemur volume in the *Faune de Madagascar* series (Petter et al. 1977), and *L. wrightae* (Wright's Sportive Lemur), honoring American primatologist Patricia C. Wright of the State University of New York at Stony Brook.

The genus *Avahi* also saw a significant growth, as six new species were described between 2005 and 2008 (see Donati et al., pp. 1963–66). These include a new species from Ranomafana, *A. peyrierasi* (Peyriéras' Woolly Lemur), named after French entomologist and primatologist André Peyriéras (see Box 5), who was active on Madagascar until the 1990s and involved in the discovery of *Hapalemur aureus* (Golden Bamboo Lemur) (see Box 8).

The years since 2005 have seen the emergence of many Malagasy primatologists, who have described or contributed to papers naming new species of lemurs and done a range of other types of field and laboratory research. This was in particular the result of major efforts dedicated by individual scientists such as Edward E. Louis Jr. from the Omaha's Henry Doorly Zoo and Aquarium, and Wright from the State University of New York at Stony Brook. Not only have Louis and Wright supervised many Malagasy students involved in lemur research, they have also promoted the establishment of Malagasy NGOs focusing on research closely associated with conservation: respectively, Madagascar Biodiversity Partnership, which has its main office in Antananarivo, and Centre ValBio in Ranomafana. Partnerships between academic institutions around the world—from Canada (University of Calgary, University of Toronto, University of Victoria), France (Université Louis Pasteur de Strasbourg), Italy (University of Turin), Germany (University of Göttingen, University of Hamburg, University of Hannover), Switzerland (Zürich University), and the United States (Duke University, State University of New York at Stony Brook, University of Boulder [Colorado], University of Kentucky, University of Nebraska, to name a few)—and Malagasy institutions (Groupe d'Etude et de Recherche sur les Primates de Madagascar [GERP], Parc Botanique et Zoologique de Tsimbazaza, Université d'Antananarivo, Université de Mahajanga, Université d'Antsiranana, Université de Fianarantsoa, Université de Toliara) created opportunities for researchers to be trained and to access laboratories, to resolve taxonomic relationships of the various genera of lemurs based on genetic evidence, and to undertake a wide range of behavioral and ecological studies.

GERP deserves a special mention. This Malagasy association was founded in 1994 by Malagasy primatologists, among them the late Berthe Rakotosamimanana. Under the leadership of Jonah Ratsimbazafy since 2003, this organization, originally focused on lemurs, has put an emphasis since around 2015 on primate conservation and environmental education. Ratsimbazafy, who obtained his PhD from the State University of New York at Stony Brook, is currently adjunct professor at the Département de Paléontologie et d'Anthropologie, Université d'Antananarivo, and the vice chair of the Madagascar section of the IUCN SSC Primate Specialist Group. In the past years, Ratsimbazafy has often been a spokesperson for Malagasy conservation NGOs in dialogues with the Malagasy government and international institutions supporting nature conservation on the island.

A total of 15 lemur species have been described by Malagasy scientists as first authors. Nicole Andriaholinirina, affiliated with the

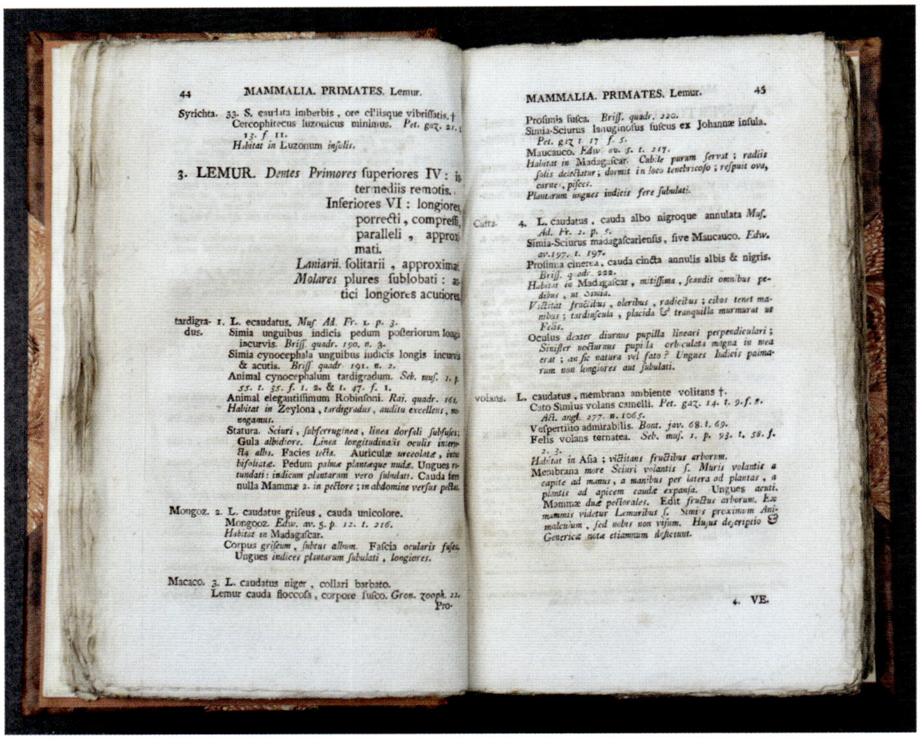

44 MAMMALIA. PRIMATES. Lemur.

Syrichta. 33. S. caudata imberbis, ore ciliisque vibrissatis. †
Cercophitecus luzonicus minimus. *Pet. gaz. 21. t. 13. f. 11.*
Habitat in Luzonum *insulis.*

3. LEMUR. *Dentes Primores* superiores IV: intermediis remotis.
Inferiores VI: longiores, porrecti, compressi, paralleli, approximati.
Laniarii. solitarii, approximati.
Molares plures sublobati: antici longiores acutiores.

tardigradus. 1. L. ecaudatus. *Mus. Ad. Fr. 1. p. 3.*
Simia unguibus indicis pedum posteriorum longis incurvis. *Briss. quadr. 190. n. 3.*
Simia cynocephala unguibus indicis longis incurvis & acutis. *Briss. quadr. 191. n. 2.*
Animal cynocephalum tardigradum. *Seb. mus. 1. p. 55. t. 35. f. 1. 2. & t. 47. f. 1.*
Animal elegantissimum Robinsoni. *Raj. quadr. 161.*
Habitat in Zeylona, *tardigradus, auditu excellens, monogamus.*
Statura. *Sciuri, subferruginea, linea dorsali subfusca;* Gula *albidiore. Linea longitudinalis oculis interjecta albi.* Facies *tecta.* Auriculæ *urceolatæ, intus bifoliatæ.* Pedum *palmæ plantæque nudæ.* Ungues *rotundati: indicum plantarum vero subulati.* Cauda fere nulla Mammæ 2. *in pectore; in abdomine versus pectus.*

Mongoz. 2. L. caudatus griseus, cauda unicolore.
Mongooz. *Edw. av. 5. p. 12. t. 216.*
Habitat in Madagascar.
Corpus *griseum, subtus album.* Fascia *ocularis fusca.* Ungues *indices plantarum subulati, longiores.*

Macaco. 3. L. caudatus niger, collari barbato.
Lemur cauda floccosa, corpore fusco. *Gron. zooph. 22.*
Pro-

MAMMALIA. PRIMATES. Lemur. 45

Prosimia fusca. *Briss. quadr. 220.*
Simia-Sciurus lanuginosus fuscus ex Johannæ insula. *Pet. gaz. t. 17. f. 5.*
Maucauco. *Edw. av. 5. t. 217.*
Habitat in Madagascar. *Cubile purum servat; radiis solis delectatur; dormit in loco tenebricoso; respuit ova, carnes, pisces.*
Plantarum ungues indicis fere subulati.

Catta. 4. L. caudatus, cauda albo nigroque annulata *Mus. Ad. Fr. 2. p. 5.*
Simia-Sciurus madagascariensis, sive Maucauco. *Edw. av. 197. t. 197.*
Prosimia cinerea, cauda cincta annulis albis & nigris. *Briss. quadr. 222.*
Habitat in Madagascar, *mitissima, scandit omnibus pedibus, ut Simia.*
Victitat fructibus, oleribus, radicibus; cibos tenet manibus; tardiuscula, placida & tranquilla murmurat ut Felis.
Oculus *dexter diurnus pupilla lineari perpendiculari; Sinister nocturnus pupilla orbiculata magna in mea erat; an sic natura vel fato? Ungues Indicis palmarum non longiores aut subulati.*

volans. L. caudatus, membrana ambiente volitans †.
Cato Simius volans camelli. *Pet. gaz. 14. t. 9. f. 8. Act. angl. 277. n. 1065.*
Vespertilio admirabilis. *Bont. jav. 68. t. 69.*
Felis volans ternatea. *Seb. mus. 1. p. 93. t. 58. f. 2. 3.*
Habitat in Asia; *victitans fructibus arborum.*
Membrana *more Sciuri volantis s. Muris volantis a capite ad manus, a manibus per latera ad plantas, a plantis ad apicem caudæ expansa.* Ungues *acuti.* Mammæ *duæ pectorales.* Edit *fructus arborum. Ex mammis videtur Lemuribus s. Simiis proximum Animalculum, sed nobis non visum. Hujus descriptio & Genericæ notæ etiamnum desiciunt.*

4. VE.

FIGURE 1.26 **In 1758, Carolus Linnaeus provided the first scientific description of a lemur: *Lemur catta* (Ring-tailed Lemur). In 1766, he described two more species: *Eulemur mongoz* (Mongoose Lemur) and *E. macaco* (Black Lemur).** (PHOTO by O. Langrand, Linnaeus 1767.)

Université d'Antananarivo and Université de Mahajanga, described three new species of sportive lemurs (Andriaholinirina et al. 2006, 2017), including *Lepilemur randrianasoloi* named after Georges Randrianasolo (see Box 4). Rambinintsoa Andriantompohavana, from the Université d'Antananarivo, described a new species of mouse lemur (Andriantompohavana et al. 2006) and a new species of woolly lemur (Andriantompohavana et al. 2007), while Clément Rabarivola, from the Université de Mahajanga, is the first author of the description of *L. mittermeieri* (Rabarivola et al. 2006). Boromé Ramaromilanto, from the Parc Botanique et Zoologique de Tsimbazaza, also described a new species of sportive lemur (Ramaromilanto et al. 2009). Rodin Rasoloarison, from the Université d'Antananarivo, who for many years has worked with with the Deutsches Primatenzentrum in the Kirindy Forest CNFEREF, in 2013 described two species of mouse lemur new to science (Rasoloarison et al. 2013). Alphonse Zaramody, from the Université de Mahajanga, described three new species of woolly lemur (Zaramody et al. 2006).

A total of 49 new species of primates have been described from Madagascar since 2000, representing 46% of all the primate species known from the island today, an inventory that started more than 250 years ago when Linnaeus (1758) described *Lemur catta* (Ring-tailed Lemur) (Figure 1.26).

CONCLUSION

Challenges for future nature conservation on Madagascar will require active participation from the national and international scientific community in research on, and documentation of, the island's biota. The priorities of scientists include studies of the least-known vertebrate groups and surveys of unknown or poorly documented sites in order to advance knowledge of species delimitations and distributions. Knowledge is critical, as Madagascar's natural ecosystems have been facing severe degradation for centuries, and in a more acute way in recent decades. This situation leads to the risk of extinction of some species even before they become known to science. To advance the conservation of the remaining natural ecosystems of the island, there is a critical need for any measures to be based on concrete information of species distribution and other aspects of natural history, most of which are derived from inventory-based research.

Biological exploration by outsiders has taken place on Madagascar for four centuries—since the time of those first chasing the myth of the monster bird—resulting in the current extensive knowledge of its rich biodiversity and high levels of endemism. The early travelers went on long journeys to discover unexplored lands. The clock is ticking for today's scientists. Exploration still serves the advancement of knowledge; most important, however, it contributes to the conservation of plant and animal species, indispensable elements of life on earth and precious parts of our world patrimony.

Subject editor: Steven M. Goodman

REFERENCES

Albignac, R. 1973. Mammifères carnivores. *Faune de Madagascar* 36: 1–206.

Allibert, C. 1992. Le monde austronésien et la civilisation du bambou: Une plume qui pèse lourd: L'Oiseau Rokh des auteurs arabes. *Taloha* 11: 167–181.

Allibert, C., and Vérin, P. 1993. Les Comores et Madagascar: Le premier peuplement. *Archeologia* 290: 64–77.

Andreone, F. 1994. The amphibians of Ranomafana rain forest, Madagascar—preliminary community analysis and conservation considerations. *Oryx* 28: 207–214.

———, ed. 2008. *A Conservation Strategy for the Amphibians of Madagascar.* Monografie 45. Turin: Museo Regionale di Scienze Naturali.

Andreone, F., and Greer, A. E. 2002. Malagasy scincid lizards: Descriptions of nine new species, with notes on the morphology, reproduction and taxonomy of some previously described species (Reptilia, Squamata: Scincidae). *Journal of Zoology* 258: 139–181.

Andreone, F., and Randriamahazo, H. 1997. Ecological and taxonomic observations on the amphibians and reptiles of the Andohahela low altitude rainforest, S. Madagascar. *Revue Française Aquariologie* 24: 95–129.

Andreone, F., Randrianirina, J. E., Jenkins, P. D., and Aprea, G. 2000. Species diversity of Amphibia, Reptilia and Lipotyphla (Mammalia) at Ambolokopatrika, a rainforest between the Anjanaharibe-Sud and Marojejy massifs, NE Madagascar. *Biodiversity and Conservation* 9: 1587–1622.

Andreone, F., Mattioli, F., Jesu, R., and Randrianirina, J. E. 2001. Two new chameleons of the genus *Calumma* from north-east Madagascar, with observations on hemipenial morphology in the *Calumma furcifer* group (Reptilia, Squamata, Chamaeleonidae). *Herpetological Journal* 11: 53–68.

Andreone, F., Rosa, G. M., and Raselimanana, A. P. 2014. *Les amphibiens des zones arides de l'ouest et du sud de Madagascar.* Antananarivo: Association Vahatra.

Andreone, F., Crottini, A., Rosa, G. M., Rakotoarison, A., Scherz, M. D., and Raselimanana, A. P. 2018. *Les amphibiens du nord de Madagascar.* Antananarivo: Association Vahatra.

Andriaholinirina, N., Fausser, J.-L., Roos, C., Zinner, D., Thalmann, U., et al. 2006. Molecular phylogeny and taxonomic revision of the sportive lemurs (*Lepilemur*, Primates). *BMC Evolutionary Biology* 6: 17–29.

———. 2017. Corrective paper concerning three new species of the genus *Lepilemur* Geoffroy, 1851 (Mammalia). *Dumerilia* 7: 62–71.

Andriantompohavana, R., Zaonarivelo, J. R., Engberg, S. E., Randriamampionona, R., McGuire, S. M., Shore, G. D., Rakotonomenjanahary, R., Brenneman, R. A., and Louis, E. E., Jr. 2006. Mouse lemurs of northwestern Madagascar with a description of a new species at Lokobe Special Reserve. *Occasional Papers, Museum of Texas Tech University* 259: 1–24.

Andriantompohavana, R., Lei, R., Zaonarivelo, J. R., Engberg, S. E., Nalanirina, G., et al. 2007. Molecular phylogeny and taxonomic revision of the woolly lemurs, genus *Avahi* (Primates: Lemuriformes). *Special Publications, Museum of Texas Tech University* 51: 1–59.

Angel, F. 1942. Les lézards de Madagascar. *Mémoires de l'Académie Malgache* 36: 1–193.

Anonyme. 1909. Liste des correspondants du Muséum national d'Histoire naturelle nommés de 1798 à 1909. Liste des correspondants existant en 1910. *Bulletin du Muséum National d'Histoire Naturelle* 8: 559.

Appert, O. 1995. Zum Dunenkleid des Nakas (Mesitornithiformes) von Madagaskar. *Der Ornithologische Beobachter* 92: 455–458.

Archbold, R. 1932. A new lemur from Madagascar. *American Museum Novitates* 518: 1.

Arnoult, J. 1959. Poissons des eaux douces. *Faune de Madagascar* 10: 1–155.

Attenborough, D. 1961. *Zoo Quest to Madagascar*. London: Lutterworth Press.

Balard, M. 2003. *Madagascar 1916–1945: Les regards d'un administrateur ethnographe, Raymond Decary*. Sainte-Marie, La Réunion: Azalées Editions.

Baron, R. 1890. The flora of Madagascar. *Journal of the Linnean Society* 25: 246–350.

Bates, P.J.J., Ratrimomanarivo, F. H., Harrison, D. L., and Goodman, S. M. 2006. A description of a new species of *Pipistrellus* (Chiroptera: Vespertilionidae) from Madagascar, with a review of related Vespertilioninae from the island. *Acta Chiropterologica* 8: 299–324.

Beentje, H. J. 1998. J. M. Hildebrandt (1847–1881): Notes on his travels and his plant collections. *Kew Bulletin* 4: 835–856.

Benson, C. W., Colebrook-Robjent, J.F.R., and Williams, A. 1976. Contribution à l'ornithologie de Madagascar. *L'Oiseau et la Revue Française d'Ornithologie* 46: 209–242.

———. 1977. Contribution à l'ornithologie de Madagascar. *L'Oiseau et la Revue Française d'Ornithologie* 47: 41–64.

Blanchard, E. 1872. L'Ile de Madagascar: Les tentatives de colonisation—La nature du pays—Un récent voyage scientifique. *Revue des Deux Mondes* 100: 596–637.

Block, N. L., Goodman, S. M., Hackett, S. J., Bates, J. M., and Raherilalao, M. J. 2015. Potential merger of ancient lineages in a passerine bird discovered based on evidence from host-specific ectoparasites. *Ecology and Evolution* 5: 3743–3755.

Blommers-Schlösser, R.M.A., and Blanc, C. 1991. Amphibiens, pt. 1. *Faune de Madagascar* 75(1): 1–384.

———. 1993. Amphibiens, pt. 2. *Faune de Madagascar* 75(2): 385–530.

Böhme, W. 1997. Eine neue Chamäleonart aus der *Calumma gastrotaenia*-Verwandtschaft Ost-Madagaskars. *Herpetofauna* 19: 5–10.

Boudet, V. 2019. Patrimoine naturel briochin: L'Insondable monde des papillons nocturnes. *Le Télégramme*, 1 Aug. 2019.

Boudou, A. (R. P.). 1940. Petites notes d'histoire malgache: Le naturaliste Goudot. *Bulletin de l'Académie Malgache*, nouvelle série, 23: 66–68.

Brown, M. 1995. *A History of Madagascar*. Ipswich: Damien Tunnacliffe.

Brygoo, E. R. 1971. Reptiles Sauriens Chamaeleonidae—Genre *Chamaeleo. Faune de Madagascar* 33: 1–318.

———. 1978. Reptiles Sauriens Chamaeleonidae—Genre *Brookesia* et complément pour le genre *Chamaeleo. Faune de Madagascar* 47: 1–173.

———. 1981. Les Goudot, des voyageurs naturalistes bien mal connus. *Histoire et Nature* 17–18: 33–47.

Brygoo, E. R., and Domergue, C. A. 1974. Notes sur les *Brookesia* de Madagascar IX. Observations sur *B. tuberculata* Mocquard, 1894, *B. ramanantsoai* sp. nov. et *B. peyrierasi* nom. nov. (Reptilia, Squamata, Chamaeleontidae). *Bulletin du Muséum National d'Histoire Naturelle*, série 3, no. 267, *Zoologie* 189: 1769–1782.

Brygoo, E. R., Blanc, C. P., and Domergue, C. A. 1974. Notes sur les *Chamaeleo* de Madagascar XII. Caméléons du Marojejy. *C. peyrierasi* sp. nov. et *C. gastrotaenia guillaumeti* nov. subsp. *Bulletin de l'Académie Malgache* 51: 151–166.

Carleton, M. D. 1994. Systematic studies of Madagascar's endemic rodents (Muroidea: Nesomyinae): Revision of the genus *Eliurus*. *American Museum Novitates* 3087: 1–55.

Carleton, M. D., and Goodman, S. M. 2007. A new species of the *Eliurus majori* complex (Rodentia: Muroidea: Nesomydae) from south-central Madagascar, with remarks on emergent species groupings in the genus *Eliurus*. *American Museum Novitates* 3547: 1–21.

Carleton, M. D., Smeenk, C., Angermann, R., and Goodman, S. M. 2014. Taxonomy of nesomyine rodents (Muroidea: Nesomyidae: Nesomyinae): Designation of lectotypes and restriction of type localities for species-group taxa in the genus *Nesomys* Peters. *Proceedings of the Biological Society of Washington* 126(4): 414–455.

Cibois, A., Pasquet, E., and Schulenberg, T. S. 1999. Molecular systematics of the Malagasy babblers (Passeriformes: Timaliidae) and warblers (Passeriformes: Sylviidae), based on cytochrome b and 16S rRNA sequences. *Molecular Phylogenetics and Evolution* 13: 581–595.

Cibois, A., Slikas, B., Schulenberg, T. S., and Pasquet, E. 2001. An endemic radiation of Malagasy songbirds is revealed by mitochondrial DNA sequence data. *Evolution* 55: 1198–1206.

Cibois, A., David, N., Gregory, S.M.S., and Pasquet, E. 2010. Bernieridae (Aves: Passeriformes): A family group name for the Malagasy sylvioid radiation. *Zootaxa* 2554: 65–68.

Colston, P. R. 1972. A new bulbul from southwestern Madagascar. *Ibis* 114: 89–92.

Compère, S. 2014. Collectant les insectes de Saint Moreil à Tananarive, André Peyriéras est devenu une référence. *Le Populaire du Centre*, 13 Oct. 2014.

Cramer, A. F., Rabibisoa, N.H.C., and Raxworthy, C. J. 2008. Descriptions of two new *Spinomantis* frogs from Madagascar (Amphibia, Mantellidae), and new morphological data for *S. brunae* and *S. massorum*. *American Museum Novitates* 3618: 1–22.

Cruaud, A., Raherilalao, M. J., Pasquet, E., and Goodman, S. M. 2011. Phylogeography and systematics of the Malagasy rock-thrushes (Muscicapidae, *Monticola*). *Zoologica Scripta* 40: 544–566.

Dague, C., and Petter, J.-J. 1988. Observations de *Lemur rubriventer* dans son milieu naturel. In *L'Equilibre des ecosystèmes forestiers à Madagascar: Actes d'un séminaire international*, eds. L. Rakotovao, V. Barre, and J. Sayer, pp. 78–89. Gland: IUCN.

D'Cruze, N. C., Henson, D., Olsson, A., and Emmett, D. A. 2009. The importance of herpetological survey work in conserving Malagasy biodiversity: Are we doing enough? *Herpetological Review* 40: 19–25.

Decary, R. 1937. La légende du Rokh et l'Aepyornis. *Bulletin de l'Académie Malgache* 20: 107–114.

———. 1946. Animaux de Madagascar. *Annales du Musée Colonial de Marseille* 6(4): 234

———. 1947. *La faune malgache*. Paris: Payot.

Delacour, J. 1932a. La mission zoologique Franco-Anglo-Américaine à Madagascar. *Bulletin du Muséum d'Histoire Naturelle* 4: 212–221.

———. 1932b. Les oiseaux de la mission zoologique Franco-Anglo-Américaine à Madagascar. *L'Oiseau et Revue Française d'Ornithologie* 2: 1–96.

de Rham, P. H. 1996. Poissons des eaux intérieures de Madagascar. In *Biogéographie de Madagascar*, ed. W. R. Lourenço, pp. 423–440. Paris: ORSTOM.

Domergue, C. A. 1983. Notes sur les serpents de la région malgache. III. Description de trois espèces nouvelles apportées au genre *Liophidium* Boulenger, 1896. *Bulletin du Muséum National d'Histoire Naturelle* 5: 1109–1122.

———. 1984a. Notes sur les serpents de la région malgache. IV. Le genre *Pararhadianea* Boettger, 1898. Descriptions d'une espèce et d'une sous-espèce nouvelles. *Bulletin du Muséum National d'Histoire Naturelle* 6: 149–157.

———. 1984b. Notes sur les serpents de la région malgache. V. Le genre *Alluaudina* Mocquard 1891. *Bulletin du Muséum National d'Histoire Naturelle* 6: 537–549.

———. 1986. Notes sur les serpents de la région malgache. VI. Le genre *Ithycyphus* Günther 1873. Description de deux espèces nouvelles. *Bulletin du Muséum National d'Histoire Naturelle* 8: 409–434.

Dorr, L. J. 1997. *Plant Collectors in Madagascar and the Comoro Islands*. Kew: Royal Botanic Gardens.

Doyère, M. 1835. Notice sur un mammifère de Madagascar formant le type d'un nouveau genre de la famille des carnassiers insectivores de M. Cuvier. *Annales des Sciences Naturelles* 2(4): 270–283

Dransfield, J. 1989. *Voanioala* (Arecoideae: Cocoeae: Butiinae), a new palm genus from Madagascar. *Kew Bulletin* 44(2): 191–198.

———. 1991. *Lemurophoenix* (Palmae: Arecoideae), a new genus from Madagascar. *Kew Bulletin* 46(1): 61–68.

Dubois, A. 1992. Notes sur la classification des Ranidae (Amphibiens anoures). *Bulletin Mensuel de la Société Linnéenne de Lyon* 61: 305–352.

Durbin, J., Funk, S. M., Hawkins, F., Hills, D. M., Jenkins, P. D., Moncrieff, C. B., and Ralainasolo, F. B. 2010. Investigations into the status of a new taxon of *Salanoia* (Mammalia: Carnivora: Eupleridae) from the marshes of Lac Alaotra, Madagascar. *Systematics and Biodiversity* 8: 341–355.

Ellis, W. 1859. *Three Visits to Madagascar*. London: John Murray.

Elouard, J.-M., and Gibon F.-M. 2001. *Biodivesité et typologie des eaux continentales de Madagascar*. Antananarivo: IRD, CNRE, LRSAE.

Fisher, B. L., and Peeters, C. 2019. *Fourmis de Madagascar: Une guide pour les 62 genres / Ants of Madagascar: A Guide to the 62 Genera*. Antananarivo: Association Vahatra.

Flacourt, E. de. 1658. *L'Histoire de la grande isle Madagascar*. Paris: Pierre L'Amy.

———. 1991. *L'Histoire de la grande isle Madagascar*. Facsimile of 1658 ed. La Réunion: A.R.S. Terres Créoles.

Foley, N. M., Thong, V. D., Soisook, P., Goodman, S. M., Armstrong, K. N., Jacobs, D. S., Puechmaille, S. J., and Teeling, E. C. 2015. How and why overcome the impediments to resolution: Lessons from rhinolophid and hipposiderid bats. *Molecular Biology and Evolution* 32: 313–333.

Franzen, M., Jones, J., Raselimanana, A. P., Nagy, Z. T., D'Cruze, N., Glaw, F., and Vences, M. 2009. A new black-bellied snake (Pseudoxyrhophiinae: *Liophidium*) from western Madagascar, with notes on the genus *Pararhadinaea*. *Amphibia-Reptilia* 30: 173–183.

Frasier, C. L., Lei, R., McLain, A. T., Taylor, J. M., Bailey, C. A., et al. 2016. A new species of dwarf lemur (Cheirogaleidae: *Cheirogaleus medius* group) from the Ankarana and Andrafiamena-Andavakoera Massifs, Madagascar. *Primate Conservation* 30: 59–72.

Frémy, E. 1889. *Muséum d'Histoire naturelle: Inauguration des nouvelles galeries de zoologie*. Paris: Imprimeries Réunies.

Fuchs, J., Pons, J.-M., Pasquet, E., Raherilalao, M. J., and Goodman, S. M. 2007. Geographical structure of the genetic variation in the Malagasy scops-owl (*Otus rutilus* s.l.) inferred from mitochondrial sequence data. *Condor* 109: 409–418.

Fuchs, J., Lemoine, D., Parra, J. L., Pons, J.-M., Raherilalao, M. J., Prys-Jones, R., Thebaud, C., Warren, B. H., and Goodman, S. M. 2016. Long-distance dispersal and inter-island colonization across the western Malagasy Region explain diversification in brush-warblers (Passeriformes: *Nesillas*). *Biological Journal of the Linnean Society* 119: 873–889.

Gardner, C. J., Nicoll, M. E., Birkinshaw, C., Harris, A., Lewis, R. E., Rakotomalala, D., and Ratsifandrihamanana, A. N. 2018. The rapid expansion of Madagascar's protected area system. *Biological Conservation* 220: 29–36.

Gehring, P.-S., Pabijan, M., Ratsoavina, F. M., Köhler, J., Vences, M., and Glaw, F. 2010. A Tarzan yell for conservation: A new chameleon, *Calumma tarzan* sp. n., proposed as a flagship species for the creation of new nature reserves in Madagascar. *Salamandra* 46(3): 167–179.

Gehring, P.-S., Tolley, K. A., Eckhardt, F. S., Townsend, T. M., Ziegler, T., Ratsoavina, F. M., Glaw, F., and Vences, M. 2012. Hiding deep in the trees: Discovery of divergent mitochondrial lineages in Malagasy chameleons of the *Calumma nasutum* group. *Ecology and Evolution* 2: 1468–1479.

Glaw, F., and Raselimanana, A. P. 2018. Systématique des reptiles terrestres malgaches (Ordre: Squamata, Testudines, Crocodylia / Systematics terrestrial Malagasy reptiles (Ordre: Squamata, Testudines, Crocodylia). In *Les aires protégées terrestres de Madagascar: Leur histoire, description et biote / The Terrestrial Protected Areas of Madagascar: Their History, Description, and Biota*, eds. S. M. Goodman, M. J. Raherilalao, and S. Wohlhauser, pp. 289–327. Antananarivo: Association Vahatra.

Glaw, F., and Vences, M. 1992. *A Fieldguide to the Amphibians and Reptiles of Madagascar*. Köln: Moos Druck.

———. 1994. *A Fieldguide to the Amphibians and Reptiles of Madagascar*. 2nd ed. Bonn: Zoologisches Forschungsinstitut und Museum Koenig.

———. 2000. Current counts of species diversity and endemism of Malagasy amphibians and reptiles. In *Diversité et endémisme à Madagascar*, eds. W. R. Lourenço and S. M. Goodman, pp. 243–248. Paris: Mémoires de la Société de Biogéographie.

———. 2002. A new cryptic treefrog species of the *Boophis luteus* group from Madagascar: Bioacoustic and genetic evidence. *Spixiana* 25: 173–181.

———. 2006. Phylogeny and genus-level classification of mantellid frogs. *Organisms Diversity and Evolution* 6: 236–253.

———. 2007. *A Field Guide to the Amphibians and Reptiles of Madagascar*. 3rd ed. Cologne: Vences and Glaw Verlag.

Glaw, F., Franzen, M., and Vences, M. 2005. A new species of colubrid snake (*Liopholidophis*) from northern Madagascar. *Salamandra* 41: 83–90.

Glaw, F., Hoegg, S., and Vences, M. 2006. Discovery of a new basal relict lineage of Madagascan frogs and its implications for mantellid evolution. *Zootaxa* 1334: 27–43.

Glaw, F., Köhler, J., and Vences, M. 2009. A new species of cryptically coloured day gecko (*Phelsuma*) from the Tsingy de Bemaraha National Park in western Madagascar. *Zootaxa* 2195: 61–68.

Goodman, S. M. 1994. Description of a new species of subfossil eagle from Madagascar: *Stephanoaetus* (Aves: Falconiformes) from the deposits of Ampasambazimba. *Proceedings of the Biological Society of Washington* 107: 421–428.

———. 1996. Description of a new species of subfossil lapwing (Aves: Charadriiformes, Charadriidae, Vanellinae) from Madagascar. *Bulletin du Muséum National d'Histoire Naturelle*, série 4, 18: 607–614.

———. 2000. A description of a new species of *Brachypteracias* (family Brachypteraciidae) from the Holocene of Madagascar. *Ostrich* 71: 318–322.

———. 2011. *Les chauves-souris de Madagascar: Guide de leur distribution, biologie et identification*. Antananarivo: Association Vahatra.

———. 2012. *Les Carnivora de Madagascar*. Antananarivo: Association Vahatra.

Goodman, S. M., and Helgen, K. 2010. Species limits and distribution of the Malagasy carnivoran genus *Eupleres* (Family Eupleridae). *Mammalia* 74: 177–185.

Goodman, S. M., and Jungers, W. L. 2013. *Les animaux et écosystèmes de l'Holocène disparus de Madagascar*. Antananarivo: Association Vahatra.

———. 2014. *Extinct Madagascar: Picturing the Island's Past*. Chicago: University of Chicago Press.

Goodman, S. M., and Raherilalao, M. J., eds. 2013. *Atlas d'une sélection de vertébrés terrestres de Madagascar / Atlas of Selected Land Vertebrates of Madagascar*. Antananarivo: Association Vahatra.

Goodman, S. M., and Ranivo, J. 2009. The geographical origin of the type specimen of *Triaenops humbloti* and *T. rufus* (Chiroptera: Hipposideridae) reputed to be from Madagascar and the description of a replacement species name. *Mammalia* 73: 47–55.

Goodman, S. M., and Ravoavy, F. 1993. Identification of bird subfossils from cave surface deposits at Anjohibe, Madagascar, with a description of a new giant coua (Cuculidae: Couinae). *Proceedings of the Biological Society of Washington* 106: 24–33.

Goodman, S. M., and Soarimalala, V. 2004. A new species of *Microgale* (Lipotyphla: Tenrecidae: Oryzorictinae) from the Forêt des Mikea of southwestern Madagascar. *Proceedings of the Biological Society of Washington* 117(3): 251–265.

Goodman, S. M., Langrand, O., and Whitney, B. M. 1996. A new genus and species of passerine from the eastern rain forest of Madagascar. *Ibis* 138: 153–159.

Goodman, S. M., Hawkins, A.F.A., and Domergue, C. A. 1997. A new species of vanga (Vangidae, *Calicalicus*) from southwestern Madagascar. *Bulletin of the British Ornithologists' Club* 117: 5–11.

Goodman, S. M., Cardiff, S. G., Ranivo, J., Russell, A. L., and Yoder, A. D. 2006. A new species of *Emballonura* (Chiroptera: Emballonuridae) from the dry regions of Madagascar. *American Museum Novitates* 3538: 1–24.

Goodman, S. M., Bradman, H. M., Maminirina, C. P., Ryan, K. E., Christidis, L., and Appleton B. 2008. A new species of *Miniopterus* (Chiroptera: Vespertilionidae) from lowland southeastern Madagascar. *Mammalian Biology* 73: 199–213.

Goodman, S. M., Raheriarisena, M., and Jansa, S. A. 2009a. A new species of *Eliurus* Milne Edwards, 1885 (Rodentia: Nesomyinae) from the Réserve Spéciale d'Ankarana, northern Madagascar. *Bonner Zoologische Beiträge* 56: 133–149.

Goodman, S. M., Maminirina, C. P., Weyeneth, N., Bradman, H. M., Christidis, L., Ruedi, M., and Appleton, B. 2009b. The use of molecular and morphological characters to resolve the taxonomic identity of cryptic species: The case of *Miniopterus manavi* (Chiroptera, Miniopteridae). *Zoologica Scripta* 38: 339–362.

Goodman, S. M., Maminirina, C. P., Bradman, H. M., Christidis, L., and Appleton, B. 2010. Patterns of morphological and genetic variation in the endemic Malagasy bat *Miniopterus gleni* (Chiroptera: Miniopteridae) with the description of a new species, *M. griffithsi*. *Journal of Zoological Systematics and Evolutionary Research* 48: 75–86.

Goodman, S. M., Raherilalao, M. J., and Block, N. L. 2011a. Patterns of morphological and genetic variation in the *Mentocrex kioloides* complex (Aves: Gruiformes: Rallidae) from Madagascar, with the description of a new species. *Zootaxa* 2776: 49–60.

Goodman, S. M., Ramasindrazana, B., Maminirina, C. P., Schoeman, M. C., and Appleton, B. 2011b. Morphological, bioacoustical, and genetic variation in *Miniopterus* bats from eastern Madagascar, with description of a new species. *Zootaxa* 2880: 1–19.

Goodman, S. M., Taylor, P. J., Ratrimomanarivo, F., and Hoofer, S. R. 2012. The genus *Neoromicia* (Family Vespertilionidae) in Madagascar, with the description of a new species. *Zootaxa* 3250: 1–25.

Goodman, S. M., Raherilalao, M. J., and Wohlhauser, S., eds. 2018. *Les aires protégées terrestres de Madagascar: Leur histoire, description et biote / The Terrestrial Protected Areas of Madagascar: Their History, Description, and Biota*. Antananarivo: Association Vahatra.

Grandidier, A. 1870. Description de quelques animaux nouveaux découverts à Madagascar en novembre 1869. *Revue et Magasin de Zoologie Pure et Appliquée et de Sériciculture Comparée* 22(2): 49–50.

———. 1892. *Histoire physique, naturelle et politique de Madagascar*. Vol. 1, *Histoire de la géographie*. 2nd ed. Paris: Imprimerie Nationale.

Groves, C. P. 2000. The genus *Cheirogaleus*: Unrecognized biodiversity in dwarf lemurs. *International Journal of Primatology* 21: 943–962.

Guibé, J. 1958. Les serpents de Madagascar. *Mémoires de l'Institut Scientifique de Madagascar* 12: 189–260.

———. 1975. Batraciens nouveaux de Madagascar. *Bulletin du Muséum National d'Histoire Naturelle*, série 3, *Zoologie*, 323: 1081–1089.

———. 1978. Les batraciens de Madagascar. *Bonner Zoologische Monographien* 11: 1–140.

Guillaumet, J.-L., Betsch, J.-M., Blanc, C., Morat, P., and Peyriéras, A. 1975. Etude des écosystèmes montagnards dans la région malgache. III. Le Marojejy. IV. L'Itremo et l'Ibity. Géomorphologie, climatologie, faune et flore (campagne RCP 225, 1972–1973). *Bulletin du Muséum National d'Histoire Naturelle*, série 3, *Ecologie générale*, 25: 29–67.

Günther, A. 1875. Note on some mammals of Madagascar. *Proceedings of the Zoological Society of London* 1875: 78–80.

Gyldenstolpe, N. 1933. A remarkable new flycatcher from Madagascar. *Arkiv för Zoologi* 25B(2): 1–3.

Halleux, D. 1998. Un nouveau site pour la Sarcelle de Bernier *Anas bernieri*. *Working Group on Birds in the Madagascar Region Newsletter* 8(1): 8.

Halleux, D., and Goodman, S. M. 1994. Rediscovery of the Madagascar Red Owl *Tyto soumagnei* (Grandidier 1878). *Bird Conservation International* 4: 305–311.

Hartlaub, C.J.G. 1877. *Die Vögel Madagascars und der benachbarten Inselgruppen*. Halle: H. W. Schmidt.

Hawlitschek, O., Scherz, M. D., Ruthensteiner, B., Crottini, A., and Glaw, F. 2018. Computational molecular species delimitation and taxonomic revision of the gecko genus *Ebenavia* Boettger, 1878. *Science of Nature* 105: 49.

Hedges, S. B., Marion, A. B., Lipp, K. M., Marin, J., and Vidal, N. 2014. A taxonomic framework for typhlopid snakes from the Caribbean and other regions (Reptilia, Squamata). *Caribbean Herpetology* 49: 1–61.

Heying, H. E. 2002. *Antipodes: Seasons with the Extraordinary Wildlife and Culture of Madagascar.* New York: Saint Martin's Press.

Hotaling, S., Foley, M. E., Lawrence, N. M., Bocanegra, J., Blanco, M. B., Rasoloarison, R., Kappeler, P. M., Barrett, M. A., Yoder, A. D., and Weisrock, D. W. 2016. Species discovery and validation in a cryptic radiation of endangered primates: Coalescent-based delimitation in Madagascar's mouse lemurs. *Molecular Ecology* 25: 2029–2045.

Jenkins, P. D. 1988. A new species of *Microgale* (Insectivora: Tenrecidae) from northeastern Madagascar. *American Museum Novitates* 2910: 1–7.

———. 1992. A new species of *Microgale* (Insectivora: Tenrecidae) from eastern Madagascar. *Bulletin of the British Museum of Natural History (Zoology)* 58(1): 53–59.

———. 1993. A new species of *Microgale* (Insectivora: Tenrecidae) from eastern Madagascar with an unusual dentition. *American Museum Novitates* 3067: 1–11.

Jenkins, P. D., and Carleton, M. D. 2005. Charles Immanuel Forsyth Major's expedition to Madagascar, 1894 to 1896: Beginnings of modern systematic study of the island's mammalian fauna. *Journal of Natural History* 39: 1779–1818.

Jenkins, P. D., and Goodman, S. M. 1999. A new species of *Microgale* (Lipotyphla, Tenrecidae) from isolated forest in southwestern Madagascar. *Bulletin of the Natural History Museum*, London, *Zoology* 65: 155–164.

Jenkins, P. D., Raxworthy, C. J., and Nussbaum, R. A. 1997. A new species of *Microgale* (Insectivora: Tenrecidae) with comments on the status of four other taxa of shrew tenrec. *Bulletin of the Natural History Museum*, London, *Zoology* 63: 1–12.

Jentink, F. A. 1887. *Muséum d'Histoire naturelle des Pays-Bas: Catalogue ostéologique des mammifères*. Bk. 9. Leiden: E. J. Brill.

Jolly, A. 1987. Madagascar: A world apart. *National Geographic* 171: 148–183.

———. 1988. Madagascar lemurs: On the edge of survival. *National Geographic* 174: 132–161.

———. 2015. *Thank You, Madagascar: The Conservation Diaries of Alison Jolly*. London: Zed Books.

Jolly, A., and Sussman, R. W. 2007. Notes on the history of ecological studies of Malagasy lemurs. In *Lemurs: Ecology and Adaptation*, eds. L. Gould and M. L. Sauther, pp. 9–39. New York: Springer.

Kappeler, P. M., Rasoloarison, R. M. Razafimanantsoa, L, Walter, L., and Roos, C. 2005. Morphology, behaviour and molecular evolution of giant mouse lemurs (*Mirza* spp.) Gray, 1970, with description of new species. *Primate Report* 71: 3–26.

Köhler, J., Glaw, F., and Vences, M. 2007. A new green treefrog, genus *Boophis* Tschudi 1838 (Anura Mantellidae), from arid western Madagascar: Phylogenetic relationships and biogeographic implications. *Tropical Zoology* 20: 215–227.

———. 2008. Two additional treefrogs of the *Boophis ulftunni* species group (Anura: Mantellidae) discovered in rainforests of northern and south-eastern Madagascar. *Zootaxa* 1814: 37–48.

Köhler, J., Vieites, D. R., Glaw, F., Kaffenberger, N., and Vences, M. 2009. A further new species of limbless skink, genus *Paracontias*, from eastern Madagascar. *African Journal of Herpetology* 58: 98–105.

Köhler, J., Vences, M., Erbacher, M., and Glaw, F. 2010. Systematics of limbless scincid lizards from northern Madagascar: Morphology, phylogenetic relationships and implications for classification (Squamata: Scincidae). *Organisms Diversity and Evolution* 10: 147–159.

Köhler, J., Glaw, F., Pabijan, M., and Vences, M. 2015. Integrative taxonomic revision of mantellid frogs of the genus *Aglyptodactylus* (Anura: Mantellidae). *Zootaxa* 4006: 401–438.

Lacroix, M. 1998. Insectes Coléoptères Hopliidae (pt. 2): Notices sur les récolteurs malgaches Melolonthidae et Hopliidae (Comores-Madagascar-Mascareignes) avec la participation de Pierre Viette. *Faune de Madagascar* 88(2): 657–691.

Lamberton, C. 1927. Notes d'ornithologie malgache. *Bulletin Trimestriel de l'Académie Malgache*, nouvelle série, 10: 40–42.

Langrand, O. 1990. *Guide to the Birds of Madagascar*. New Haven: Yale University Press.

———. 1995. *Guide des oiseaux de Madagascar*. Neuchâtel: Delachaux et Niestlé.

Langrand, O., and Rene de Roland, L. A. 2018. Histoire des aires protégées de Madagascar / History of Madagascar protected areas. In *Les aires protégées terrestres de Madagascar: Leur histoire, description et biote / The Terrestrial Protected Areas of Madagascar: Their History, Description, and Biota*, eds. S. M. Goodman, M. J. Raherilalao, and S. Wohlhauser, pp. 79–104. Antananarivo: Association Vahatra.

Lavauden, L. 1937. *Histoire physique, naturelle et politique de Madagascar*. Vol. 12, *Oiseaux*, supplement. Paris: Société d'Editions Géographiques, Maritimes et Coloniales.

Lehtinen, R. M., Nussbaum, R. A., Richards, C. M., Cannatella, D. C., and Vences M. 2007. Mitochondrial genes reveal cryptic diversity in plant-breeding frogs from Madagascar (Anura, Mantellidae, *Guibemantis*). *Molecular Phylogenetics and Evolution* 44: 1121–1129.

Lei, R., McLain, A. T., Frasier C. L., Taylor, J. M., Bailey, C. A., et al. 2015. A new species in the genus *Cheirogaleus* (Cheirogaleidae). *Primate Conservation* 29: 43–54.

Linnaeus, C. 1758. *Systema naturae per regna tria naturae, secundum classes, ordines, genera, species, cum characteribus, differentiis, synonymis, locis*. Bk. 1. 10th ed. Stockholm: Laurentius Salvus.

———. 1767. *Systema naturae, per regna tria naturae, secundum classes, ordines, genera, species cum characteribus, differentiis, synonymis, locis*. Bk 1. 13th ed. Vienna: Johann Thomas von Trattner.

Loiselle, P. V. 2006. A review of the Malagasy *Pachypanchax* (Teleostei: Cyprinodontiformes, Aplocheilidae), with descriptions of four new species. *Zootaxa* 1366: 1–44.

Louis, E. E., Jr., Coles, M. S., Andriantompohavana, R., Sommer, J. A., Engberg, S. E., Zaonarivelo, J. R., Mayor, M. I., and Brenneman, R. A. 2006a. Revision of the mouse lemurs (*Microcebus*) of eastern Madagascar. *International Journal of Primatology* 27: 347–389.

Louis, E. E., Jr., Engberg, S. E., Lei, R., Geng, H., Sommer, J. A., et al. 2006b. Molecular and morphological analyses of the sportive lemurs (family Megaladapidae: genus *Lepilemur*) reveals 11 previously unrecognized species. *Special Publications, Museum of Texas Tech University* 49: 1–47.

MacKinnon, J. L., Hawkins, C. E., and Racey, P. A. 2003. Pteropodidae, fruit bats, *fanihy, angavo*. In *The Natural History of Madagascar*, eds. S. M. Goodman and J. P. Benstead, pp. 1299–1302. Chicago: University of Chicago Press.

McLain, A. T., Lei, R., Frasier C. L., Taylor, J. M., Bailey, C. A., Robertson, B.A.D., Nash, S. D., Randriamanana, J. C., Mittermeier, R. A., and Louis, E. E., Jr. 2017. A new *Cheirogaleus* (Cheirogaleidae: *Cheirogaleus crossleyi* group) species from southeastern Madagascar. *Primate Conservation* 31: 27–36.

Meier, B., and Rumpler, Y. 1987. Preliminary survey of *Hapalemur simus* (Primates) and of a new species of *Hapalemur* in eastern Betsileo, Madagascar. *Primate Conservation* 8: 40–43.

Meier, B., Albignac, R., Peyriéras, A., Rumpler, Y., and Wright, P. 1987. A new species of *Hapalemur* (Primates) from southeast Madagascar. *Folia Primatologica* 48: 211–215.

Menu, R., and Roederer, P. 2010. Histoire institutionnelle de l'ORSTOM-IRD à Madagascar. In *Parcours de recherche à Madagascar. L'IRD-ORSTOM et ses partenaires*, eds. C. Feller and F. Sandron, pp. 45–69. Marseille: IRD Editions.

Methuen, P. A., and Hewitt, J. 1913a. On a collection of reptiles from Madagascar made during the year 1911. *Annals of the Transvaal Museum* 3(4): 183–193.

———. 1913b. On a collection of Batrachia from Madagascar made during the year 1911. *Annals of the Transvaal Museum* 4(2): 49–64.

Millot, J. 1948. Revue générale des Arachnides de Madagascar. *Mémoires de l'Institut Scientifique de Madagascar*, série A, 1: 137–155.

Milne Edwards, A., and Grandidier, A. 1875. *Histoire physique, naturelle et politique de Madagascar*. Vol. 9, *Histoire naturelle des mammifères*. Tome IV, Atlas I. Paris: Imprimerie Nationale.

———. 1876–1885. *Histoire physique, naturelle et politique de Madagascar*. Vols. 12–15, *Histoire naturelle des oiseaux*. (1 vol. of text: 1879; 3 vols. of plates.) Paris: Imprimerie Nationale.

Milon, P., Petter, J.-J., and Randrianasolo, G. 1973. Oiseaux. *Faune de Madagascar* 35: 1–263.

Miralles, A., Köhler, J., Glaw, F., and Vences, M. 2011. A molecular phylogeny of the "*Madascincus polleni* species complex," with description of a new species of scincid lizard from the coastal dune area of northern Madagascar. *Zootaxa* 2876: 1–16.

Mittermeier, R. A., and Rylands, A. B. 2020. New primate species described from 1 January 1990 to 1 February 2020. Global Wildlife Conservation–IUCN/SSC Primate Specialist Group. http://www.primate-sg.org/new_species/.

Mittermeier, R. A., Louis, E. E., Jr., Richardson, M., Schwitzer, C., Langrand, O., et al. 2010. *Lemurs of Madagascar*. 3rd ed. Arlington: Conservation International.

Moat, J., and Smith, P. 2007. *Atlas of the Vegetation of Madagascar*. Kew: Royal Botanic Gardens.

Morris, P. A. 2004. *Edward Gerrard and Sons: A Taxidermy Memoir*. Ascot: MPM Publishing.

Morris, P., and Hawkins, F. 1998. *Birds of Madagascar. A Photographic Guide*. New Haven: Yale University Press.

Nagy, Z. T., Sonet, G., Glaw, F., and Vences, M. 2012. First large-scale DNA barcoding assessment of reptiles in the biodiversity hotspot of Madagascar, based on newly designed COI primers. *PLoS One* 7: e34506.

Ng, H. H., and Sparks, J. S. 2003. The ariid catfishes (Teleostei: Siluriformes: Ariidae) of Madagascar, with the description of two new species. *Occasional Papers, Museum of Zoology, University of Michigan* 735: 1–21.

———. 2005. Revision of the endemic Malagasy catfish family Anchariidae (Teleostei: Siluriformes), with descriptions of a new genus and three new species. *Ichthyological Exploration of Freshwaters* 16(4): 303–323.

Ng, H. H., Sparks, J. S., and Loiselle, P. V. 2008. A new species of catfish of the genus *Gogo* from northeastern Madagascar (Siluriformes: Anchariidae). *Copeia* 2008(2): 395–400.

Nicoll, M. E. 1982. Reproductive ecology of the tenrec, *Tenrec ecaudatus* (Insectivora: Tenrecidae) in the Seychelles. PhD thesis, University of Aberdeen.

Nicoll, M. E., and Langrand, O. 1987. *Conservation et utilisation rationnelle des ecosystèmes forestiers du Gabon*. Gland: WWF/IUCN.

———. 1989. *Madagascar: Revue de la conservation et des aires protégées*. Gland: WWF.

Nicoll, M. E., and Racey, P. A. 1981. The Seychelles fruit bat *Pteropus seychellensis seychellensis*. *African Journal of Ecology* 19: 361–364.

Nicoll, M. E., and Rathbun, G. B. 1990. *African Insectivora and Elephant-Shrews. An Action Plan for Their Conservation*. Gland: IUCN.

Nicoll, M. E., and Suttie J. M. 1982. The sheath-tailed bat *Coleura seychellensis* (Chiroptera: Emballonuriodae) in the Seychelles islands. *Journal of Zoology* 197(3): 421–426.

Nussbaum, R. A., and Raxworthy, C. J. 1995. Review of the scincine genus *Pseudoacontias* Barboza du Bocage (Reptilia: Squamata: Scincidae) of Madagascar. *Herpetologica* 51: 91–99.

Nussbaum, R. A., Raxworthy, C. J., Raselimanana, A. P., and Ramanamanjato, J.-B. 1999. Amphibians and reptiles of the Réserve Naturelle Intégrale d'Andohahela, Madagascar. In A floral and faunal inventory of the Réserve Naturelle Intégrale d'Andohahela, Madagascar, with reference to elevational variation, ed. S. M. Goodman. *Fieldiana: Zoology*, new series, 94: 155–175.

Oatley, G., Simmons, R. E., and Fuchs, J. 2015. A molecular phylogeny of the harriers (*Circus*, Accipitridae) indicate the role of long-distance dispersal and migration in diversification. *Open Ornithology Journal* 5: 42–56.

Päckert, M., Martens, J., Wink, M., Feigl, A., and Tietze, D. T. 2012. Molecular phylogeny of Old World swift (Aves: Apodiformes, Apodidae, *Apus* and *Tachymarptis*) based on mitochondrial and nuclear markers. *Molecular Phylogenetics and Evolution* 63: 606–616.

Paulian, R. 1954. Cinquante années d'entomologie générale à Madagascar. *Bulletin de l'Académie Malgache*, numéro spécial du cinquantenaire: 65–70.

Paulian, R., Betsch, J.-M., Guillaumet, J.-L., Blanc, C., and Griveaud, P. 1971. Etude des écosystèmes montagnards dans la région malgache. I. Le massif de l'Andringitra. 1970–1971. Géomorphologie, climatologie et groupements végétaux. *Bulletin de la Société d'Ecologie* 2: 189–266.

Paulian, R., Blanc, C., Guillaumet, J.-L., Betsch, J.-M., Griveaud, P., and Peyriéras, A. 1973. Etude des écosystèmes montagnards dans la région malgache. II. Les chaînes Anosyennes. Géomorphologie, climatologie et groupements végétaux (campagne RCP 225, 1971–1972). *Bulletin du Muséum National d'Histoire Naturelle*, série 3, *Ecologie Générale* 118: 1–40.

Peers, S. 1995. *The Working of Miracles: William Ellis; Photography in Madagascar 1853–1865*. London: British Council.

Pellegrin, J. 1933. Les poissons des eaux douces de Madagascar et des îles voisines. *Mémoires de l'Académie Malgache* 14: 1–224.

Perl, R.G.B., Nagy, Z. T., Sonet, G., Glaw, F., Wollenberg, K. C., and Vences, M. 2014. DNA barcoding Madagascar's amphibian fauna. *Amphibia-Reptilia* 35: 197–206.

Peters, W.C.H. 1870. Über Nesomys rufus, eine neue Gattung und Art madagascarischer Nager. *Sitzungs-berichte der Gesellschaft Naturforschender Freunde, Berlin* 1870: 54–55.

———. 1874. Über eine neue Gattung und zwei neue Arten von Säugethieren aus Madagascar. *Monatsberichte der Akademie der Wissenschaften zu Berlin* 1874: 690–694.

Peterson, R. L., Eger, J. L., and Mitchell, L. 1995. Chiroptères. *Faune de Madagascar* 84: 1–204.

Petter, J.-J., Albignac, R., and Rumpler, Y. 1977. Mammifères lémuriens (Primates Prosimiens). *Faune de Madagascar* 44: 1–513.

Petter-Rousseaux, A., and Petter, J.-J. 1967. Contribution à la systématique des Cheirogaleidae (lémuriens malgaches). *Allocebus*, gen. nov., pour *Cheirogaleus trichotis* Günther 1875. *Mammalia* 31(4): 574–582.

Peyriéras, A., and Basilewski, P. 1976. Insectes Coléoptères Carabidae Scaritinae. *Faune de Madagascar* 41: 1–222.

Pfeiffer, I. 1861. *The Last Travels of Ida Pfeiffer: Inclusive of a Visit to Madagascar*. New York: Harper and Brothers Publishers.

Pidgeon, M. 1996. An ecological survey of Lake Alaotra and wetlands of central and eastern Madagascar in analyzing the demise of Madagascar Pochard *Aythya innotata*, ed. L. Wilmé. Antananarivo: WWF–Missouri Botanical Garden.

Poisson, H. 1948. A propos d'un manuscrit du naturaliste Goudot et considérations sur les travaux de ce voyageur. *Bulletin de l'Académie Malgache*, nouvelle série, 28: 18–20.

Projet ZICOMA. 1999. *Zones d'importance pour la conservation des oiseaux à Madagascar*. Antananarivo: Projet ZICOMA.

Prötzel, D., Vences, M., Scherz, M. D., Vieites, D. R., and Glaw, F. 2017. Splitting and lumping: An integrative taxonomic assessment of Malagasy chameleons in the *Calumma guibei* complex results in the new species *C. gehringi* sp. nov. *Vertebrate Zoology* 67: 231–249.

Prötzel, D., Scherz, M. D., Ratsoavina, F. M., Vences, M., and Glaw F. 2020. Untangling the trees: Revision of the *Calumma nasutum* complex (Squamata: Chamaeleonidae). *Vertebrate Zoology* 70: 23–59.

Rabarivola, C., Zaramody, A., Fausser, J. L., Andriaholonirina, N., Roos, C., Zinner, D., Hauwy, M., and Rumpler, Y. 2006. Cytogenetic and molecular characteristics of a new species of sportive lemur from northern Madagascar. *Lemur News* 11: 45–49.

Radaody-Ralarosy, P. 1966. "Mose Bibikely" (Le naturaliste Goudot) à Tsimbazaza. *Bulletin de l'Académie Malgache*, nouvelle série, 42: 15–17.

Raherilalao, M. J., and Goodman, S. M. 2011. *Histoire naturelle des familles et sous-familles endémiques d'oiseaux de Madagascar*. Antananarivo: Association Vahatra.

Rakotoarison, A., Glaw, F., Vieites, D. R., Raminosoa, N. R., and Vences, M. 2012. Taxonomy and natural history of arboreal microhylid frogs (*Platypelis*) from the Tsaratanàna Massif in northern Madagascar with description of a new species. *Zootaxa* 3563: 1–25.

Rakotoarison, A., Crottini, A., Müller, J., Rödel, M.-O., Glaw, F., and Vences, M. 2015. Revision and phylogeny of narrow-mouthed treefrogs (*Cophyla*) from northern Madagascar: Integration of molecular, osteological, and bioacoustic data reveals three new species. *Zootaxa* 3937: 61–89.

Rakotoarison, A., Scherz, M. D., Glaw, F., Köhler, J., Andreone, F., et al. 2017. Describing the smaller majority: Integrative taxonomy reveals twenty-six new species of tiny microhylid frogs (genus *Stumpffia*) from Madagascar. *Vertebrate Zoology* 67: 271–398.

Ramanamanjato, J.-B., Nussbaum, R. A., and Raxworthy, C. J. 1999a. A new species of *Mabuya* Fitzinger (Squamata: Scincidae: Lygosominae) from northern Madagascar. *Occasional Papers, Museum of Zoology, University of Michigan* 728: 1–22.

———. 1999b. A new species of *Mabuya* Fitzinger (Reptilia: Squamata: Scincidae) from the Onilahy River of south-west Madagascar. *Herpetological Journal* 9: 65–72.

Ramanantsoa, G. A. 1974. Contribution à la connaissance des Caméléonidés de Madagascar. Description d'une sous-espèce nouvelle: *Chamaeleo oshaughnessyi ambreensis* n. subsp. *Terre Malgache* 16: 239–249.

———. 1980. Description de deux nouvelles espèces de *Brookesia* (Reptilia, Squamata, Chamaeleonidae): *B. legendrei* et *B. bonsi*. *Bulletin du Muséum National d'Histoire Naturelle* 4: 685–693.

Ramaromilanto, B., Lei, R. H., Engberg, S. E., Johnson, S. E., Stizmann, B. D., Louis, E. E., Jr. 2009. Sportive lemur diversity at Mananara-Nord Biosphere Reserve, Madagascar. *Occasional Papers, Museum of Texas Tech University* 286: 1–22.

Rand, A. L. 1932. Mission Franco-Anglo-Américaine à Madagascar. Notes de voyages. *L'Oiseau et la Revue Française d'Ornithologie* 2: 227–282.

———. 1935. On the habits of some Madagascar mammals. *Journal of Mammalogy* 16: 89–104.

———. 1936. The distribution and habits of Madagascar birds. Summary of the field notes of the Mission Zoologique Franco-Anglo-Américaine à Madagascar. *Bulletin of the American Museum of Natural History* 72: 143–499.

Raselimanana, A. P., Raxworthy, C. J., and Nussbaum, R. A. 2000. A revision of the dwarf *Zonosaurus* Boulenger (Reptilia: Squamata: Cordylidae) from Madagascar, including descriptions of three new species. *Scientific Papers, Natural History Museum, University of Kansas* 18: 1–16.

Raselimanana, A. P., Nussbaum, R. A., and Raxworthy, C. J. 2006. Observations and re-description of *Zonosaurus boettgeri* Steindachner 1891 and description of a second species of long-tailed *Zonosaurus* from western Madagascar. *Occasional Papers, Museum of Zoology, University of Michigan* 739: 1–16.

Rasmussen, P. C., Schulenberg, T. S., Hawkins, F., and Voninavoka, R. 2000. Geographic variation in the Malagasy scops-owl (*Otus rutilus* auct.): The existence of an unrecognized species on Madagascar and the taxonomy of other Indian Ocean taxa. *Bulletin of the British Ornithologists' Club* 120: 75–102.

Rasoloarison, R. M., Goodman, S. M., and Ganzhorn, J. U. 2000. Taxonomic revision of mouse lemurs (*Microcebus*) in the western portions of Madagascar. *International Journal of Primatology* 21: 963–1019.

Rasoloarison, R. M., Weisrock, D. W., Yoder, A. D., Rakotondravony, D., and Kappeler, P. M. 2013. Two new species of mouse lemurs (Cheirogaleidae: *Microcebus*) from eastern Madagascar. *International Journal of Primatology* 34: 455–469.

Ratsoavina, F. M., Raminosoa, N. R., Louis, E. E., Jr., Raselimanana, A. P., Glaw, F., and Vences, M. 2013. An overview of Madagascar's leaf tailed geckos (genus *Uroplatus*): Species boundaries, candidate species and review of geographical distribution based on molecular data. *Salamandra* 49: 115–148.

Raxworthy, C. J., and Nussbaum, R. A. 1996a. Montane amphibian and reptile communities in Madagascar. *Conservation Biology* 10: 750–756.

———. 1996b. Amphibians and reptiles of the Réserve Naturelle Intégrale d'Andringitra, Madagascar: A study of the elevational distribution and local endemicity. In A floral and faunal inventory of the eastern slopes of the Réserve Naturelle Intégrale d'Andringitra, Madagascar: With reference to elevational variation, ed. S. M. Goodman. *Fieldiana: Zoology*, new series, 85: 158–171.

Raxworthy, C. J., Andreone, F., Nussbaum, R. A., Rabibisoa, N., and Randriamahazo, H. 1998. Amphibians and reptiles of the Anjanaharibe-Sud Massif, Madagascar: Elevational distribution and regional endemicity. In A floral and faunal inventory of the Réserve Spéciale d'Anjanaharibe-Sud, Madagascar: With reference to elevational variation, ed. S. M. Goodman. *Fieldiana: Zoology*, new series, 90: 79–93.

Reinthal, P. N., and Stiassny, M.L.J. 1991. The freshwater fishes of Madagascar: A study of an endangered fauna with recommendations for a conservation strategy. *Conservation Biology* 5: 231–243.

Renoult, J. 2009. The sooty gull, *Larus hemprichii* (Aves: Laridae), on Nosy Ve: First records for Madagascar. *Malagasy Nature* 2: 174–176.

Renoult, J., and Raselimanana, A. P. 2009. A new species of Malagasy blind snake of the genus *Typhlops* Oppel (Serpentes: Typhlopidae). *Zootaxa* 2290: 65–68.

République Française. 1905. *Guide annuaire de Madagascar et dépendances à l'usage des colons, planteurs, commerçants, industriels, fonctionnaires et voyageurs: Année 1905*. Tananarive: Imprimerie Officielle.

Reynolds, R. G., Niemiller, M. L., and Revell, L. J. 2014. Toward a tree-of-life for the boas and pythons: Multilocus species-level phylogeny with unprecedented taxon sampling. *Molecular Phylogenetics and Evolution* 71: 201–213.

Ruane, S., Burbrink, F. T., Randriamahatantsoa, B., and Raxworthy, C. J. 2016. The cat-eyed snakes of Madagascar: Phylogeny and description of a new species of *Madagascarophis* (Serpentes: Lamprophiidae) from the Tsingy of Ankarana. *Copeia* 104: 712–721.

Ruane, S., Myers, E. A., Lo, K., Yuen, S., Welt, R. S., et al. 2018. Unrecognized species diversity and new insights into color pattern polymorphism within the widespread Malagasy snake *Mimophis* (Serpentes: Lamprophiidae). *Systematics and Biodiversity* 16: 229–244.

Safford, R. J., and Hawkins, A.F.A., eds. 2013. *The Birds of Africa*. Vol. 8, *The Malagasy Region*. London: Christopher Helm.

Sakata, S., and Hikida, T. 2003. A fossorial lizard with forelimbs only: Description of a new genus and species of Malagasy skink (Reptilia: Squamata: Scincidae). *Current Herpetology* 22: 9–15.

Scherz, M. D., Vences, M., Rakotoarison, A., Andreone, F., Köhler, J., Glaw, F., and Crottini, A. 2016. Reconciling molecular phylogeny, morphological divergence and classification of Madagascan narrow-mouthed frogs (Amphibia: Microhylidae). *Molecular Phylogenetics and Evolution* 100: 372–381.

Scherz, M. D., Daza, J. D., Köhler, J., Vences, M., and Glaw, F. 2017. Off the scale: A new species of fish-scale gecko (Squamata: Gekkonidae: *Geckolepis*) with exceptionally large scales. *PeerJ* 5: e2955.

Scherz, M. D., Rakotoarison, A., Ratsoavina, F. M., Hawlitschek, O., Vences, M., and Glaw, F. 2018. Two new Madagascan frog species of the *Gephyromantis* (*Duboimantis*) *tandroka* complex from northern Madagascar. *Alytes* 36: 130–158.

Scherz, M. D., Hutter, C. R., Rakotoarison, A., Riemann, J. C., Rödel, M.-O., et al. 2019a. Morphological and ecological convergence at the lower size limit for vertebrates highlighted by five new miniaturised microhylid frog species from three different Madagascan genera. *PLoS One* 14: e0213314.

Scherz, M. D., Köhler, J., Vences, M., and Glaw, F. 2019b. A new yellow-toed *Platypelis* species (Anura, Microhylidae, Cophylinae) from the Maroantsetra region, northeastern Madagascar. *Evolutionary Systematics* 3: 75–83.

Schlegel, H. 1837. *Essai sur la physionomie des serpents*. Amsterdam: M. H. Schonekat.

———. 1876. *Monographie des singes*. Leiden: E. J. Brill.

Schlegel, H., and Pollen, P. L. 1868. Mammifères et oiseaux. In *Recherches sur la faune de Madagascar et de ses dépendances d'après les découvertes de François P. L. Pollen et D. C. Van Dam*. Pt. 2. Leiden: J. K. Steenhoff.

Schulenberg, T. S., Goodman, S. M., and Razafimahaimodison, J.-C. 1993. Genetic variation in two subspecies of *Nesillas typica* (Sylviinae) in south-east Madagascar. In Birds and the African environment: Proceedings of the eighth Pan-African Ornithological Congress, ed. R. T. Wilson. *Annales Musée Royal de l'Afrique Centrale (Zoologie)* 268: 173–177.

Scott, D., and Lubbock, J. 1974. Preliminary observations on waterfowl in western Madagascar. *Wildfowl* 25: 117–120.

Sharpe, R. B. 1870a. Contributions to the ornithology of Madagascar. Pt. 1. *Proceedings of the Zoological Society of London* 1870: 384–400.
———. 1870b. *Pseudobias wardi*. *Ibis* 6: 498.
———. 1871. Contributions to the ornithology of Madagascar. Pt. 2. *Proceedings of the Zoological Society of London* 1871: 313–320.
———. 1872. Contributions to the ornithology of Madagascar. Pt. 3. *Proceedings of the Zoological Society of London* 1872: 866–869.
———. 1875. Contributions to the ornithology of Madagascar. Pt. 4. *Proceedings of the Zoological Society of London* 1875: 70–78.
———. 1879. On a second species of *Dromaeocercus* from Madagascar. *Proceedings of the Zoological Society of London* 1879: 177.
———. 1906. 3. Birds. In *The History of the Collections Contained in the Natural History Departments of the British Museum*, vol. 2, ed. E. R. Lankester, pp. 79–515. London: Trustees of the British Museum.
Sibree, J. 1915. *A Naturalist in Madagascar*. London: Seeley, Service and Co.
Simons, E. L. 1988. A new species of *Propithecus* (Primates) from northeast Madagascar. *Folia Primatologica* 50: 143–151.
Sinclair, J. C., and Langrand, O. 1998. *Guide to the Birds of the Indian Ocean Islands*. 1st ed. Cape Town: Struik.
———. 2013. *Guide to the Birds of the Indian Ocean Islands*. 3rd ed. Cape Town: Struik.
———. 2014. *Oiseaux des îles de l'océan Indien: Madagascar, Maurice, Réunion, Rodrigues, Seychelles, Comores*. Paris: Delachaux et Niestlé.
Smith, A. 1834. An epitome of African zoology; or, A concise description of the objects of the animal kingdom inhabiting Africa, its islands and seas. *South African Quarterly Journal* 2: 244.
Soarimalala, V., and Goodman, S. M. 2011. *Les petits mammifères de Madagascar: Guide de leur distribution, biologie et identification*. Antananarivo: Association Vahatra.
Sparks, J. S., and Schelly, R. C. 2011. A new species of *Paretroplus* (Teleostei: Cichlidae: Etroplinae) from northeastern Madagascar, with a phylogeny and revised diagnosis for the *P. damii* clade. *Zootaxa* 2768: 55–68.
Stephenson, P. J. 1991. Reproductive energetics of the Tenrecidae (Mammalia: Insectivora). PhD thesis, University of Aberdeen.
Stephenson, P. J., Soarimalala, V., Goodman, S. M., Nicoll, M. E., Andrianjakarivelo, V., et al. 2019. Review of the status and conservation of tenrecs (Mammalia: Afrotheria: Tenrecidae). *Oryx* 1–10. doi.org/10.1017/S0030605318001205.
Stiassny, M.L.J., and Raminosoa, N. 1994. The fishes of the inland waters of Madagascar. In Biological diversity in African fresh and brackish water fishes, eds. G. G. Teugels, J. F. Guegan, and J. J. Albaret. *Annales du Musée Royal d'Afrique Centrale, Zoologie*, 275: 133–149.
Stiassny, M.L.J., and Rodriguez, D. M. 2001. *Rheocles derhami*, a new species of freshwater rainbowfish (Atherinomorpha: Bedotiidae) from the Ambomboa River in northeastern Madagascar. *Ichthyological Exploration of Freshwaters* 12(2): 97–104.
Stiassny M.L.J., and Sparks, J. S. 2006. Phylogeny and taxonomic revision of the endemic Malagasy genus *Ptychochromis* (Teleostei: Cichlidae), with the description of five new species and a diagnosis for *Katria*, new genus. *American Museum Novitates* 3535: 1–55.
Stiassny, M.L.J., Rodriguez, D. M., and Loiselle, P. V. 2002. *Rheocles vatosoa*, a new species of freshwater rainbowfish (Atherinomorpha: Bedotiidae) from the Lokoho River basin in northeastern Madagascar. *Cybium* 26: 71–77.
Tattersall, I. 1986. Alfred Crossley. *Archives of Natural History* 13(2): 216–217.
Thalmann, U., and Geissmann, T. 2000. Distribution and geographic variation in the western woolly lemur (*Avahi occidentalis*) with description of a new species (*Avahi unicolor*). *International Journal of Primatology* 21: 915–41.
Thiollay, J.-M., and Meyburg, B. U. 1981. Remarques sur l'organisation d'un peuplement insulaire de rapaces: Madagascar. *Alauda* 49(3): 216–226.
Thomas, O. 1906. *The History of the Collections Contained in the Natural History Departments of the British Museum*. Vol. 2, *Mammals*. London: Trustees of the British Museum.
Thompson, S. D., and Nicoll, M. E. 1986. Basal metabolic rate and energetics of reproduction in therian mammals. *Nature* 321(6071): 690–693.
Tschudi, J. J. von. 1838. *Classification der Batrachier mit Berücksichtigung der fossilen Thiere dieser Abtheilung der Reptilien*. Neuchâtel: Petitpierre.
Tyson, P. 2000. *The Eighth Continent: Life, Death, and Discovery in the Lost World of Madagascar*. New York: Harper Collins Publishers.
Vaillant, L., and Grandidier, G. 1910. Histoire naturelle des reptiles, pt. 1: Crocodiles et Tortues. In *Histoire physique, naturelle et politique de Madagascar*, vol. 17: 1–86. Paris: Imprimerie Nationale.
Vallan, D. 2000. A new species of the genus *Stumpffia* (Amphibia: Anura: Microhylidae) from a small forest remnant of the central high plateau of Madagascar. *Revue Suisse de Zoologie* 107: 835–841.
Vallan, D., Glaw, F., Andreone, F., and Cadle, J. E. 1998. A new treefrog species of the genus *Boophis* (Anura: Ranidae: Rhacophorinae) with dermal fringes from Madagascar. *Amphibia-Reptilia* 19: 357–368.
Vallan, D., Vences, M., and Glaw, F. 2003. Two new species of the *Boophis mandraka* complex (Anura, Mantellidae) from the Andasibe region in eastern Madagascar. *Amphibia-Reptilia* 24: 305–319.
Vences, M., and Glaw, F. 2002. Two new treefrogs of the *Boophis rappiodes* group from eastern Madagascar. *Tropical Zoology* 15: 141–163.
———. 2003. Phylogeography, systematics and conservation status of boid snakes from Madagascar (*Sanzinia* and *Acrantophis*). *Salamandra* 39: 181–206.
———. 2005. A new cryptic frog of the genus *Boophis* from the north-western rainforests of Madagascar. *African Journal of Herpetology* 54: 77–84.
Vences, M., and Raselimanana, A. P. 2018. Systématique des amphibiens malgaches (Amphibia: Anura) / Systematics of Malagasy amphibians (Amphibia: Anura). In *Les aires protégées terrestres de Madagascar: Leur histoire, description et biote / The Terrestrial Protected Areas of Madagascar: Their History, Description, and Biota*, eds. S. M. Goodman, M. J. Raherilalao, and S. Wohlhauser, pp. 257–288. Antananarivo: Association Vahatra.
Vences, M., Andreone, F., and Vieites, D. R. 2005. New treefrog of the genus *Boophis* Tschudi 1838 from the northwestern rainforests of Madagascar. *Tropical Zoology* 18: 237–249.
Vences, M., Jovanovic, O., and Glaw, F. 2008. Historical analysis of amphibian studies in Madagascar: An example for increasing research intensity and international collaboration. In *A Conservation Strategy for the Amphibians of Madagascar*, ed. F. Andreone, pp. 47–58. Monografie 45. Turin: Museo Regionale di Scienze Naturali.
Vences, M., Glaw, F., Köhler J., and Wollenberg, K. C. 2010. Molecular phylogeny, morphology and bioacoustics reveal five additional species of arboreal microhylids of the genus *Anodonthyla* from Madagascar. *Contributions to Zoology* 79: 1–32.
Veron, G., and Goodman, S. M. 2018. One or two species of the rare Malagasy carnivoran *Eupleres* (Eupleridae)? New insight from molecular data. *Mammalia* 82: 107–112.
Veron, G., Dupré, D., Jennings, A. P., Woolaver, L., Hassanin, A., Gardiner, C., and Goodman, S. M. 2017. New insights into the systematics of Malagasy mongoose-like carnivorans (Carnivora, Eupleridae, Galidiinae) based on mitochondrial and nuclear DNA sequences. *Journal of Zoological Research and Evolutionary Systematics* 55: 250–264.
Vieites, D. R., Wollenberg, K. C., Andreone, F., Köhler, J., Glaw, F., and Vences, M. 2009. Vast underestimation of Madagascar's biodiversity evidenced by an integrative amphibian inventory. *Proceedings of the National Academy of Sciences of the USA* 106: 8267–8272.
Viette, P. 1981. Les naturalistes à Madagascar. In *Madagascar: Un sanctuaire de la nature*, ed. P. Oberlé, pp. 98–104. Paris: Lechevalier.
Walker, A. 2010. Looking for lemurs on the great Red Island. In *Backcountry Pilot: Flying Adventures with Ike Russell*, ed. T. Bowen, pp. 99–104. Tucson: University of Arizona Press.
Wollenberg, K. C., Andreone, F., Glaw, F., and Vences, M. 2008. Pretty in pink: A new treefrog species of the genus *Boophis* from north-eastern Madagascar. *Zootaxa* 1684: 58–68.
Wollenberg, K. C., Glaw, F., and Vences, M. 2012. Revision of the little brown frogs in the *Gephyromantis decaryi* complex with description of a new species. *Zootaxa* 342: 32–60.
Wozencraft, W. C. 1986. A new species of striped mongoose from Madagascar. *Journal of Mammalogy* 67: 561–571.
———. 1987. Emendation of species name. *Journal of Mammalogy* 68: 168.
Yoder, A. D., Burns, M. M., Zehr, S., Delefosse, T., Veron, G., Goodman, S. M., and Flynn, J. J. 2003. Single origin of Malagasy Carnivora from an African ancestor. *Nature* 421: 734–737.
Younger, J. L., Stroezier, L., Maddox, J. D., Nyári, A. S., Bonfitto, M. T., Raherilalao, M. J., Goodman, S. M., and Reddy, S. 2018. Hidden diversity of forest birds in Madagascar revealed using integrative taxonomy. *Molecular Phylogenetics and Evolution* 124: 16–26.
Zaramody, A., Fausser, J. L., Roos, C., Zinner, D., Andriaholonirina, N., Rabarivola, C., Norscia, I., Tattersall, I., and Rumpler, Y. 2006. Molecular phylogeny and taxonomic revision of the Eastern Woolly Lemur (*Avahi laniger*). *Primate Report* 74: 9–23.
Zuccon, D., and Erickson, P.G.P. 2010. The *Monticola* rock-thrushes: Phylogeny and biogeography revisited. *Molecular Phylogenetics and Evolution* 55: 901–910.

CHAPTER 2

GEOLOGY

INTRODUCTION TO THE GEOLOGY OF MADAGASCAR

A. S. Collins, J. R. Ali, and T. Razakamanana

Madagascar's geological record extends back over more than 3 billion years. In that time, its constituent domains have experienced repeated periods of continental breakup, plate convergence, and subsequent continental collisions—each leaving their mark in the rocks of the island. Much of the ancient center and eastern region of Madagascar comprise rocks that at one point or another were deeply buried in the earth's crust. These are key for deciphering the island's long-term geotectonic development, and much research effort since the late 20th century has gone into deciphering them.

Breakup of the southern supercontinent, Gondwana, dating to roughly 170–85 million years ago (Mya), isolated Madagascar in the southwest Indian Ocean. The geology of the western and northern parts of the island is made up of young sedimentary basins that formed on Gondwana or later as the supercontinent split apart. Their lack of deep burial means that they preserve fossil evidence of the past life that proliferated on ancient Madagascar or in the shallow seas that lapped upon the island.

THE GEOLOGICAL FRAMEWORK OF MADAGASCAR

Over two-thirds of Madagascar's bedrock dates from before the explosion of complex life marked by the start of the Cambrian (~541 Mya; Walker et al. 2018). The basement to Madagascar underlies north, east, central, and southern parts of the island (Figure 2.1), along the east coast from north of Iharana (Vohémar), south through the Masoala Peninsula, Nosy Boraha (Ile Sainte Marie) and the eastern escarpments, down to the south coast at Tolagnaro. These ancient rocks underlie the Central Highlands from the Tsaratanàna Massif through Imerina, the headwaters of the Mania and Matsiatra Rivers, and the Andringitra Massif to the dry spiny thicket near Bekily. The basement rocks do not form a single entity but instead comprise a series of domains, each with a unique history and geological development. Notably, the domains are separated by large faults, along which they were juxtaposed at various times in the 3 billion years prior to the Cambrian. Some of these boundaries mark sites of ancient oceans, long destroyed by the forces of plate tectonics. Others represent immense fractures that cut through earth's crust and along which packages of rocks were thrust over other rocks, or slid alongside them, just as today the San Andreas Fault of California and the Alpine Fault of New Zealand juxtapose unrelated terranes.

The Basement Domains of Madagascar

Considerable advances in the understanding of the mapped geology of Madagascar were gained through the collection of isotopic, structural, and mapping data during a World Bank–sponsored project on the island (BGS-USGS-GLW 2008). This resulted in several publications (e.g., Thomas et al. 2009; Goodenough et al. 2010; Schofield et al. 2010; De Waele et al. 2011) and an updated 1:1,000,000 map for the entire country (Figure 2.1; Roig et al. 2012). This literature provides a foundation for understanding the age and nature of the major domains of Madagascar.

The Antananarivo Domain underlies much of central Madagascar and is made up of ~2500-million-year-old magmatic gneisses of the Betsiboka Suite (Kröner et al. 2000; Collins and Windley 2002). The Antongil and Masora Domains are present in eastern Madagascar and contain ~3100-million-year-old rocks that were originally contiguous with the Dharwar Craton of southern India (Tucker et al. 1999; Schofield et al. 2010; Armistead et al. 2018); their separation dates from the Late Cretaceous. The Itremo Group lies to the southwest of, and overlies, the Antananarivo Domain. This package of metamorphosed sedimentary rocks forms the rugged Ibity Massif, which dominates the view south from Antsirabe, and the mountains of the Ambatofinandrahana region. To the southwest of the Itremo Group lies the Ikalamavony Domain.

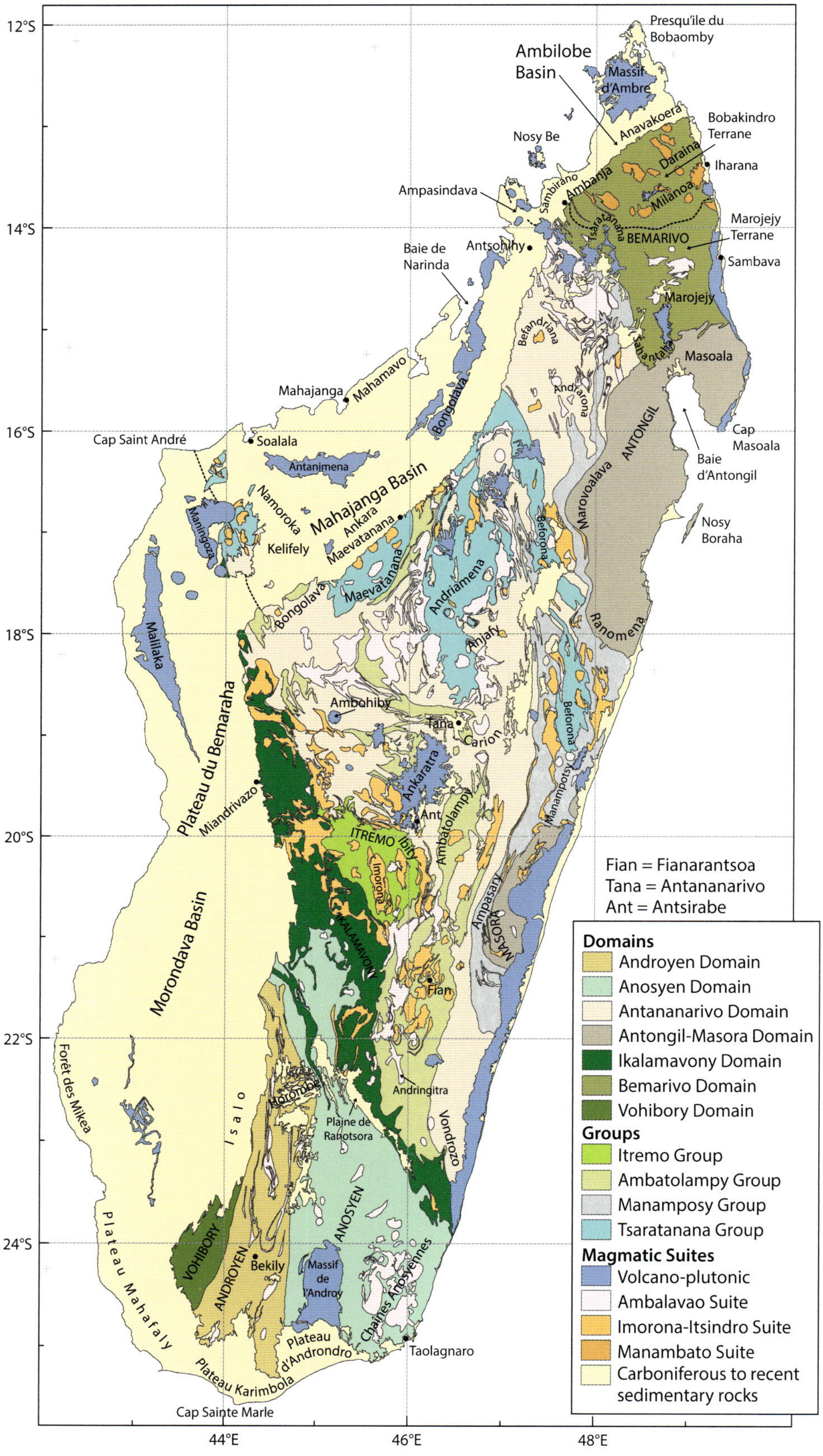

FIGURE 2.1 **Geological map of Madagascar, modified from Roig et al. (2012).**

Like the rocks of the Itremo Group, it comprises quartzites, schists, and marbles, but they are thought to be considerably younger (Archibald et al. 2017). To the south of these metamorphosed sedimentary domains, and to the south of the Ranotsara Valley, are the Proterozoic Anosyen, Androyen, and Vohibory Domains (Emmel et al. 2008; Jöns and Schenk 2008; Boger et al. 2014). On the northern end of the island, including the coast from Sambava to Iharana, the basement is known as the Bemarivo Domain. It is anomalously young (~800–600 Mya) and is conspicuous for truncating the old domains (Figure 2.1) (Armistead et al. 2019).

Madagascar lacks Cambrian to Devonian (541–359 Mya) sedimentary rocks, reflecting its location at the time at the heart of an immense mountain range. In fact, evidence from rocks that formed in contemporary oceans suggests that this was the planet's largest mountain chain of the last billion years (Collins et al., forthcoming). Only the modern Himalaya rivals it for the impact it had on the global ocean's chemistry and climate (Halverson et al. 2009). Stretching through central Gondwana, it ran across what is today the Middle East, Arabia, East Africa, Madagascar, South India, Sri Lanka, and East Antarctica; it is known as the East African Orogen (Stern 1994; Merdith et al. 2017). The vast mountains have long since eroded away—their detritus is now found in the Paleozoic basins of Africa, India, and even Europe, Antarctica, and Australia. The now-exposed surfaces of the basement terranes of Madagascar then lay tens of kilometers beneath the East African Orogen and were exhumed as the mountains were worn down by wind, rain, and glacial action. The growth and destruction of this mountain chain occurred at the same time as life on earth proliferated and developed large multicellular body plans and hard parts to support increasing body size and defend against newly evolved predators. In fact, it is likely that the East African Orogen had a major role in this biological innovation. Erosion of the deeply formed silicate rocks in this mountain chain would have modulated the climate by scrubbing CO_2 from the atmosphere, just as erosion of the Himalaya does today (Kasting 2019). Also like the Himalaya, elements released by weathering of these fresh mountainous rocks fertilized the primordial oceans, providing nutrients for evolving life to use (Halverson et al. 2009).

The Younger Sedimentary Basins of Madagascar

Two large sedimentary basins occupy much of the dry western and northwestern parts of the island that slope toward the Mozambique Channel. The Morondava Basin lies in the west and has a broad eastward-convex boundary with the basement along a line linking Faux Cap in the south, to Isalo, Miandrivazo, and Cap Saint André in the north (Figure 2.1). The Mahajanga Basin underlies much of the northwest of the island, with the basement boundary hitting the coast west of Soalala and tracing a line directly west of the Tsingy de Namoroka to Maevatanana, Boriziny, and Antsohihy to Ambanja, where it connects via a narrow neck to the smaller Ambilobe Basin, which forms the northernmost part of Madagascar, underlying the Ankarana Massif and Antsiranana. The successions that have accumulated in all three basins preserve a key suite of fossils detailing the past life-forms that once inhabited the country and which are described in contributions elsewhere in the chapter.

Volcanic Regions of Madagascar

Upper Cretaceous volcanic rocks crop out in both the Morondava and Mahajanga Basins, but also form much of the thin coastal strip between Iharana and Cap Masoala in the northeast, and along the east coast between Nosy Varika and Manantenina. They are also present in a 4000 km^2 elliptical exposure in the south of the island, known as the Massif de l'Androy, centered on the peak of Vohitsimbe. Isolated lava flows that are thought to be the same age overlie some of the highest parts of Madagascar and form the flat-topped *tampoketsa* in the northern Andriamena region. Their presence indicates that at least the northern half of the island was blanketed with basaltic lava around 92–84 Mya (Storey et al. 1997).

Two more recent volcanic fields make up the geology of Madagascar. In central Madagascar, the Ankaratra and Itasy Massifs contain volcanic rocks that have been dated from the Miocene epoch, ~18 Mya (Cucciniello et al. 2017) to ~20,000 years ago (Rufer et al. 2014).

MADAGASCAR IN DEEP TIME: A DIVIDED LAND (3400–1000 MYA)

The oldest rock units of Madagascar lie in the northeast, in Nosy Boraha, in the Antongil Peninsula, and south along the east coast. They make up the Nosy Boraha Suite and are exclusive to the Antongil-Masora Domain (Hottin 1976; Caen-Vachette and Hottin 1979; Windley et al. 1994). Some of the oldest suites may have formed over 3300 Mya, in the Paleoarchean (Tucker et al. 2014). These ancient rocks form a series of granite plutons and related rocks that were deformed by mountain-building forces prior to the intrusion of a voluminous suite of rocks at the end of the Archean eon. The Antongil-Masora Domain has been linked with rocks of southwestern India (Tucker et al. 1999, 2011a; Armistead et al. 2018)—an area known as the Dharwar Craton.

The Antananarivo Domain of central Madagascar also contains Archean rocks that are approximately the same age as the younger granites of the Antongil-Masora Domain. Known as the Betsiboka Suite, they form much of the basement of central portions of the island. They are highly deformed and interleaved with metamorphosed sedimentary rocks (rocks that originated as quartz-rich sandstones and mudstones) of the Ambatolampy Group. Structurally above these rocks is a series of highly metamorphosed Neoarchaean rocks that form three north–south elongate outcrop belts above the Antananarivo Domain and also overlie younger metasedimentary rocks that separate the Antananarivo Domain from the Antongil-Masora Domain (the Manampotsy Group). In a similar vein, the Antananarivo Domain has been argued as being an extension of the Archean Indian Dharwar Craton (Tucker et al. 2011a, 2011b). Other authors, however, point out that the Manampotsy Group that separates the Antananarivo Domain from undisputed Dharwar-affinity rocks likely represents the site of a much younger, but still Precambrian, ocean basin (Collins and Windley 2002; Archibald et al. 2016). This ocean was subducted just before the formation of Gondwana in the Neoproterozoic era (Windley et al. 1994; Kröner et al. 2000; Collins and Windley 2002; Collins et al. 2003; Cox et al. 2004; Fitzsimons and Hulscher 2005; Armistead et al. 2018).

The Itremo Group and the likely correlative sequences of the Sahantaha Group in northern Madagascar, the Maha Group in the central east, and the Anosyen Group of the far southeast (De Waele et al. 2011; Armistead et al. 2019; Boger et al. 2019), have become key sequences for establishing the origin of the oldest parts of the island. They form a sequence of variably metamorphosed quartz-rich sandstones, mudrocks, and carbonates (Moine 1967, 1974; Cox et al. 1998) that locally contain microbialites. Their depositional age is imprecisely constrained (1800–850 Mya), but they preserve carbon isotope values consistent with those of Mesoproterozoic (1600–1000 Mya) sea water (Cox et al. 1998). The sandstones contain many detrital sand grains that originate from a region rich in felsic rocks dating from 2000–1800 Mya (Cox et al. 2004; Fitzsimons and Hulscher 2005). Rocks of these ages are rare in the Dharwar Craton of southern India, yet common in eastern Africa (where there are also similar sedimentary sequences, such as the Muva Group in Zambia (Alessio et al. 2019). Collins and Pisarevsky (2005) argued for an African (rather than Indian) origin for the Antananarivo Domain and the Itremo Group.

There are two hypotheses explaining archaic Madagascar. One suggests it formed an extension of the nucleus of southern India—the Greater Dharwar Craton of Tucker et al. (2011a). The other suggests that the island was an extension of the Indian Dharwar Craton (Antongil-Masoala Domain), with the remainder belonging to the Congo Craton of central Africa (Collins and Windley 2002). According to the second model, the African part of what is now Madagascar separated from Africa (possibly in the Mesoproterozoic, 1600–1000 Mya) to form a separate continent, which Collins and Pisarevsky (2005) called Azania, after the name used in antiquity for the East African coast (Huntingford 1980).

MADAGASCAR AMALGAMATES: CLOSING AN OCEAN AND FORMING A SUPERCONTINENT (1000–200 MYA)

Many of the prominent rocks that form the landmarks of central Madagascar formed in the half billion years of the Neoproterozoic era (1000–541 Mya) and the first half of the succeeding Cambrian period. These include the suites beneath the royal palaces at Ambohimanga and Antananarivo, the mountains that frame Fianarantsoa, and the vast Marojejy and Andringitra Massifs. Globally, eukaroyte cells took over from prokaryotes as the dominant lifeform at this time (Brocks et al. 2017), oxygen levels in the atmosphere finally reached levels similar to today's (Och and Shields-Zhou 2012; Ward et al. 2019), metazoans evolved and rapidly radiated (Shu et al. 2014), and the planet experienced two extreme glacial events during which ice covered most of the planet (Hoffman et al. 2017). This period also marked the breakup of a continental grouping known as Rodinia and the later amalgamation of Gondwana (Merdith et al. 2017). The components of basement Madagascar found themselves at the edges of large continents (see Figure 2.2). The preceding section summarized the controversy over exactly what continent(s) parts of Madagascar were attached to when they formed, but there is no controversy associated with the evidence that all extant Madagascar lay close to a major ocean that separated Neoproterozoic India from the kernel of Africa throughout the Neoproterozoic.

Three large parts of basement Madagascar formed within this ocean. The Ikalamavony, Vohibory, and Bemarivo Domains are relative newcomers in the basement of Madagascar. Unlike the archaic Antongil-Masoala and Antananarivo Domains (and the associated Itremo Group) these domains contain no known rocks older than about 1100 million years. They are all thought to have formed as volcanic arcs above subduction zones within this long-lost ocean—the Mozambique Ocean—in a similar way to Tonga or Vanuatu today, in the southwest Pacific (Jöns and Schenk 2008; Thomas et al. 2009; Collins et al. 2012; Armistead et al. 2019). The

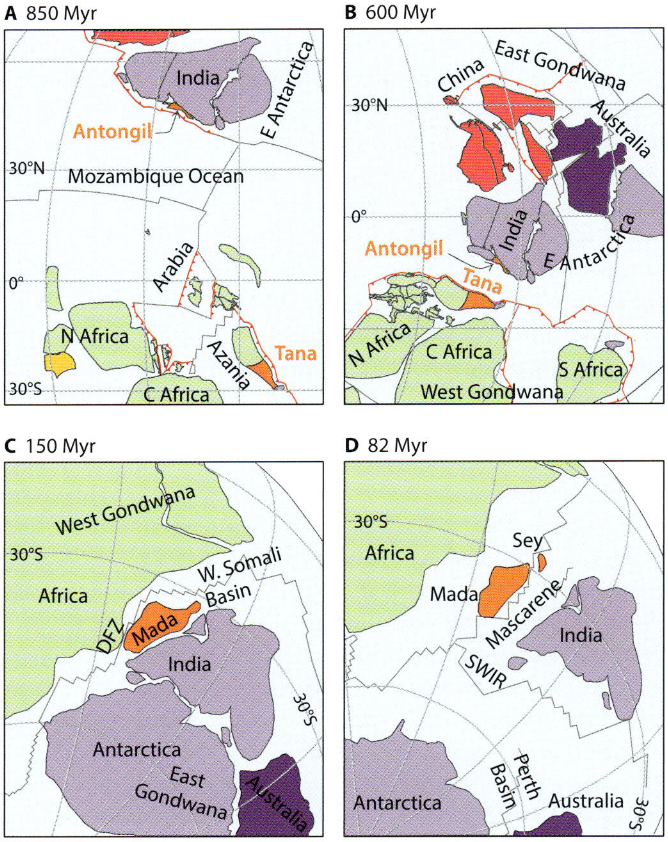

FIGURE 2.2 **Plate tectonic reconstructions of the environs of Madagascar (and its various predecessor components). A) 850 Mya, in the Neoproterozoic, when the Antongil-Masora Domain (labeled "Antongil") formed part of western India and the Antananarivo Domain (labeled "Tana") formed a part of a larger African-derived continent with parts of Arabia, northeast Africa, and southernmost India that has been called Azania (Collins and Pisarevsky 2005). These parts of ancestral Madagascar were separated by the Mozambique Ocean. B) 600 Mya, also in the Neoproterozoic, when the Mozambique Ocean had nearly closed. It closed more than 520 Mya, in the Cambrian, forming the supercontinent Gondwana. C) 150 Mya, in the Jurassic, when mid-ocean ridge spreading started in the western Somali basin separating East and West Gondwana. D) 82 Mya, in the Late Cretaceous, with spreading from the Mascarene Basin, Madagascar was left on its own. A and B modified from Collins et al. (2021); C and D are modified from Reeves (2018). DFZ, Davie Fracture Zone; Mada, Madagascar; Mascarene, Mascarene Basin, Sey, Seychelles; SWIR, Southwest Indian Ridge. The colors refer to parts of the continental crust that form much of modern East Asia (red), Australia (purple), India and east Antarctica (mauve), South America (yellow), Africa (green), and Madagascar and the Seychelles (orange).**

Ikalamavony Domain is the oldest of the three, with rocks dating back to ~1080 Mya. It has many gold-rich igneous intrusions (for example the rocks exploited by many artisanal miners at Dabolava), separated by expanses of volcano-derived sedimentary rocks. The Vohibory Domain in the far southwest is the next oldest of these volcanic arc domains, and contains rocks that formed about 900 Mya (Collins et al. 2012); these are similar to rocks found in southeastern Kenya (Hauzenberger et al. 2004; Fritz et al. 2013). The youngest of these so-called juvenile terranes is the northern half of the Bemarivo Domain, recently called the Bobakindro Terrane by Armistead et al. (2019). This region dates to ~850 Mya and is thought to be a Malagasy remnant of a larger chain of igneous rocks that are now dispersed in the Seychelles, northwestern India, and Oman (Armistead et al. 2019).

By about 650 Mya, parts of Madagascar were colliding with each other as they were caught up in the gargantuan collision between Neoproterozoic India and the core of what was to become Africa (Figure 2.2). This plate-tectonic tumult closed the Mozambique Ocean and as the basement components of Madagascar either formed within this ocean or lay along its edges they bore the full brunt of the collision. Madagascar at the beginning of the Phanerozoic eon—the eon of complex life—would have topographically resembled the Himalaya and Tibet. The mountains rose in the east of the island to form a high plateau that extended through Madagascar to what is now eastern Africa. This entire mountain surface is long gone, eroded away and deposited in the surrounding oceans and river basins, but the rocks now found in basement Madagascar preserve evidence of the 20–30 km depth of burial they experienced. When the elements in them reconfigured to grow the garnets and other metamorphic minerals common in these rocks, huge mountains 6–8 km high sat above them. The rocks heated up and partially melted forming the granites that dot the Central Highlands today. This vast mountain range was the product of the forming of Gondwana and the domains of basement Madagascar came together in the center of this supercontinent. Madagascar was to stay in this location, within the heart of Gondwana, for 300 million years.

MADAGASCAR'S TECTONIC "DISROBING": EMERGENCE AS THE WORLD'S OLDEST ISLAND (200 MYA–PRESENT)

Since the start of the Jurassic (201.3 Mya; Walker et al. 2018) Madagascar has transitioned from an unremarkable patch of ground within the interior of Gondwana to the world's oldest island, surrounded by the deep seas of the southwestern Indian Ocean (Figure 2.3). The process of isolation started ~180 Mya in the Early Jurassic and was completed ~89 Mya in the Late Cretaceous (Figure 2.4). This "disrobing" was a consequence of three separate plate-rifting events: the first to the north and the west, the second to the south, and the third to the east. The basic story has been explored in many publications (e.g., Norton and Sclater 1979; Reeves 2018) following the groundbreaking work of McKenzie and Sclater (1971). Here, we draw upon the plate-modeling scenario of Tuck-Martin et al. (2018). It should be noted, however, that their reconstructions adopt a fixed-Africa reference frame and are purely tectonic. Hence, they do not reflect the ancient paleogeographical positioning (e.g., Reeves 2018), nor the former land-sea boundaries (Ali and Aitchison 2008), the latter having considerable relevance for the understanding of Madagascar's flora and fauna through geological time.

Episode one involved the formation of a rifting-spreading system off eastern Africa in what are now the West Somali and Mozambique Basins (Figure 2.2c). Between ~180 and 133 Mya, East Gondwana (Madagascar-Seychelles-India-Australia-Antarctica) was, relative to West Gondwana (Africa-South America), displaced south (modern coordinates) along the Davie Fracture Zone/Ridge (a right-lateral transform fault; Figures 2.2c and 2.3). The long-held view was that this movement ended ~120 Mya (e.g., Rabinowitz et al. 1983; Reeves 2018); the newer opinion of Tuck-Martin et al. (2018) is thus a significant change. The second episode resulted in Australia-Antarctica rifting-drifting from Madagascar-Seychelles-India starting ~133 Mya. At this time, oceanic crust formed synchronously in the Perth Basin (west of Australia) and at the Southwest Indian Ridge. It should be noted that the latter still operates today, although the rate of separation between Madagascar and Antarctica is extremely slow, at around a millimeter or two per year (Argus et al. 2011). Isolation was completed when the Mascarene Basin began opening between eastern Madagascar and western India-Seychelles ~88 Mya (Figure 2.2d). Although only indirectly relevant, it is worth pointing out that the split between the Seychelles and the Indian subcontinent, along the Carlsberg Ridge (Figure 2.3), started in the early Paleocene, ~63 Mya (Collier et al. 2008). This was shortly after the Cretaceous–Paleocene

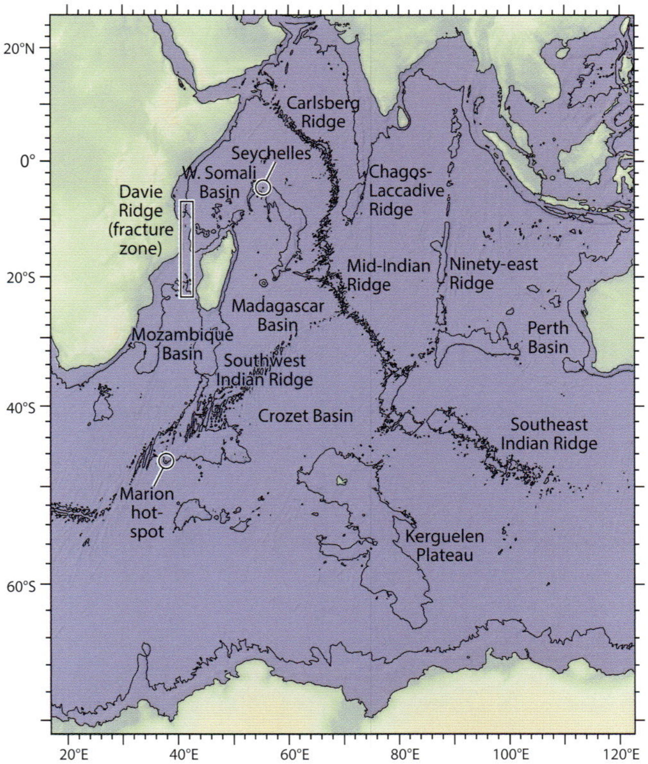

FIGURE 2.3 **Map showing some of the key physiographical features in the Indian Ocean. The image was generated using GeoMapApp (Ryan et al. 2009). The bathymetric contour is at 3000 m below sea level.**

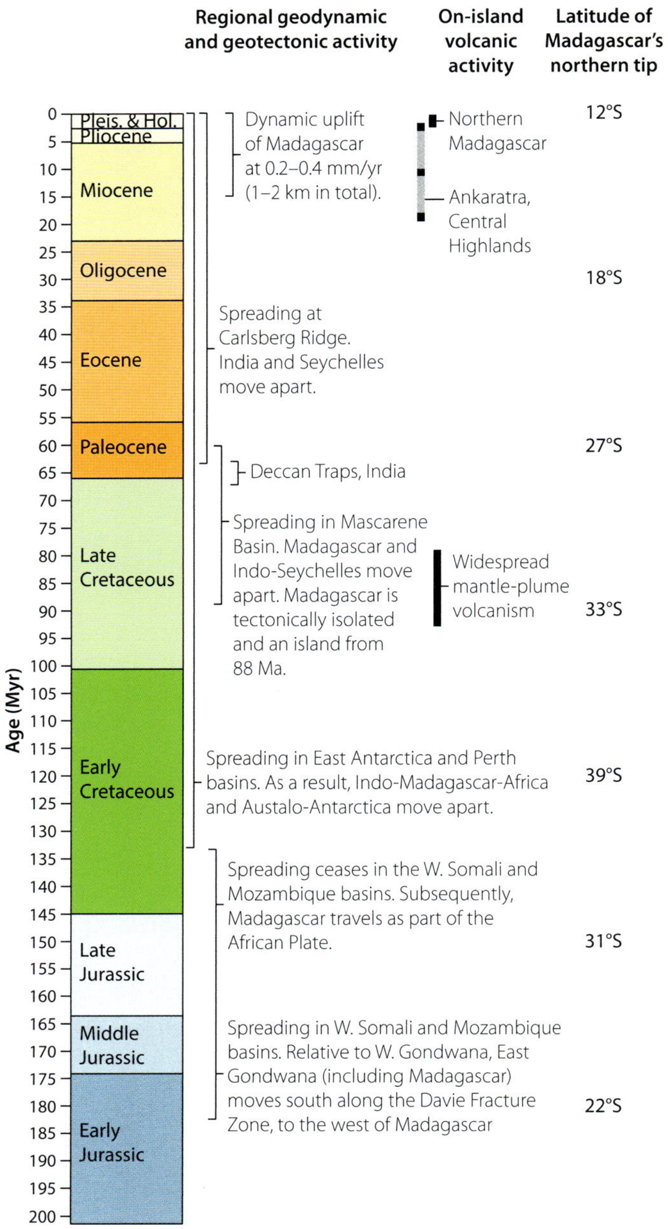

FIGURE 2.4 **Timescale showing a chronology for key events on Madagascar and elsewhere. The numerical scale is from Walker et al. (2018). Vertical lines delineate the time range of geological events.**

boundary, ~66 Mya, when the main Deccan Traps were erupted onto the western part of the subcontinent. It should be noted that the large igneous province's emplacement has on many occasions been implicated as the causal mechanism behind the mass extinction at the end of the Cretaceous (Schoene et al. 2015). If correct, then Madagascar's relative proximity (~1100 km) presumably resulted in a considerable impact on its biota.

In terms of Madagascar's paleolatitude, the data presented in Figure 2.2 (based on Schettino and Scotese 2005; Reeves 2018; associated reconstructions are shown in Ali and Aitchison 2008) for the northern tip of the island (12°S) indicate a steady north–south and then south–north migration (Figures 2.2 and 2.4): 180 Mya: 22°S; 150 Mya: 31°S; 120 Mya: 39°S; 90 Mya: 33°S; 60 Mya: 27°S; and 30 Mya: 18°S.

SUBSTANTIAL BUOYING-UP OF MADAGASCAR FROM THE MIDDLE MIOCENE TO THE PRESENT

A feature of Madagascar, as well as southern Africa, is that it is conspicuously elevated (Dixey 1960; de Wit 2003). This uplift is unrelated to a tectonic plate collision, as is the case for the Alps, Himalaya, and Taiwan; nor is it due to the building of a volcanic arc/accretion complex above a subduction system, as with the Andes. Instead, it is caused by the lithosphere of the southwestern Indian Ocean region sitting above an anomalously warm underlying mantle, and is thus akin to a thermal blister elevating the crust. Three lines of evidence support the idea. First, in northern Madagascar there are localized outcrops of horizontally bedded Eocene marine limestones at elevations of 300–500 m (Stephenson et al. 2019). Second, the ocean basins on either side of Madagascar, as well as the island itself, are not at their natural heights—under normal circumstances their depths should be fairly predictable based on their ages and a simple cooling-with-time subsidence model (Winterbourne et al. 2014). In the southwestern Indian Ocean, the basement part of the oceanic crust in the Mozambique Basin is ≤1 km too deep; in the Mascarene Basin it is too shallow by 1–2 km (Roberts et al. 2012; Winterbourne et al. 2014). Third, seismic waves passing through the region's sub-lithospheric mantle have lower than anticipated velocities indicating that the material is less dense than normal (Simmons et al. 2007). This low-gravity mass thus elevates the overriding lithospheric mantle and crust. The geomorphological study of Roberts et al. (2012), which focused on river profiles and their drainage basins, located across Madagascar, argued for the up-warping to have begun ~15 Mya (middle Miocene). The peak rates were estimated to be 200–400 m/million years, with total displacements of 1–2 km. Significantly, the uplift, plus localized tilting, is ongoing as evidenced by unevenly raised Pleistocene reef terraces on the northern tip of the island (Stephenson et al. 2019).

Accumulation of Sedimentary Rocks

One of the consequences of Madagascar's Neogene to present uplift is that it is possible to inspect directly, or via on-land boreholes, the sedimentary rocks that have accumulated on Madagascar from the Jurassic to the present. These are preserved in a broad arc of deposits along the west, northwest, and northern flanks of the island in the Morondava, Mahajanga, and Ambilobe Basins (Figure 2.1; de Wit 2003; Wu et al. 2019). Predominantly, they comprise fine-grained clastic rocks and limestones that accumulated in shallow marine-shelf settings. The sequences also include hiatuses, for instance at the cusp of the Early to Middle Jurassic and Middle to Late Jurassic (Wu et al. 2019), but none were especially long. Also preserved are some low-elevation terrestrial accumulations that can be traced laterally into marine units. Due to Madagascar's isolation, many of the vertebrate fossils (land and marine) that have been recovered from its sedimentary rocks provide globally significant data for unraveling the history of life. These works are described elsewhere and summarized in the following contributions in this chapter.

Latest Cretaceous to Neogene times saw global sea levels reach some of the highest levels known in the last 300 million years (Miller et al. 2005) due to high global temperatures and the lack of terrestrial icecaps. This resulted in a marine transgression across coastal Madagascar and a dearth of Paleogene terrestrial deposits, which has led to much uncertainty about the origins of much of Madagascar's living fauna. Significant marine vertebrate finds have been made in Mahajanga Basin (e.g., Samonds et al. 2019a), but significant scope exists in further exploration of these and similar-aged rocks in the southern Morondava Basin. By the time global sea levels dropped in the late Cenozoic, the island had experienced the uplift described in the previous section. This led to erosion and a lack of preservation of any late Cenozoic deposits. Limited Pliocene to recent deposits have been recorded from the Morondava Basin (Coffin and Rabinowitz 1992), but little more is known about these.

Volcanic Activity

Since the start of the Jurassic, volcanic activity on Madagascar has occurred in two main phases. The earliest was a fairly sharp pulse in the middle of the Late Cretaceous triggered by the Marion mantle-plume hot-spot, which today sits 2450 km south of the island and a short distance south of the Southwest Indian Ridge on the Antarctic Plate (Figure 2.3). As a consequence, large volumes of associated basaltic rocks were erupted onto the island, and these have radiometric age dates of about 92–84 Mya (e.g., Cucciniello et al. 2013). The arrival of the plume's head was also the trigger for opening of the Mascarene Basin between Madagascar and the Indian subcontinent (Storey et al. 1995). A more protracted, less voluminous magmatic phase has affected Madagascar since the Miocene, with the activity mainly in the center and north (Bardintzeff et al. 2010). The eruptions are thought to be related to the regional uplifting described earlier.

ACKNOWLEDGMENTS

The government of the Republic of Madagascar is thanked for supporting our research activities on the island. Alan S. Collins is grateful for funding from the Geological Society of London (through a Fermor Fellowship 1997–1999), then the Australian Research Council (through the award of an Australian Postgraduate Fellowship and a Future Fellowship), which funded work in Madagascar over the last 23 years.

Subject editors: David W. Krause and Steven M. Goodman

LATEST PALEOZOIC TO MESOZOIC TERRESTRIAL VERTEBRATE FAUNAS OF MADAGASCAR: BIOTIC HISTORY DURING THE BREAKUP OF GONDWANA

J. J. Flynn, L. Ranivoharimanana, and A. R. Wyss

Madagascar hosts one of earth's most unusual biotas, yet the origins and history of the island's remarkable biological diversity remain poorly understood. The fossil record of Madagascar's terrestrial lifeforms also was woefully incomplete until the mid-1990s, particularly for pre-Holocene (last Ice Age) times. Thus, many aspects of the island's biological heritage, particularly that of its vertebrates, had been highly speculative. Plate tectonics undoubtedly helped shape this fauna, but so too must have Mesozoic and Cenozoic climate changes, global extinctions at the Cretaceous-Paleogene boundary 66 million years ago (Mya), and chance biogeographic dispersal events from larger landmasses. The phylogeny and geographic distributions of the living biota provide important insights, but the most direct evidence of Madagascar's faunal history resides in the fossil record. While the Cenozoic terrestrial fossil record remains poorly known, some advances have been made (see Samonds, pp. 69–73). The terrestrial fossil record for the Mesozoic, in contrast, has improved markedly since our last synthesis of this subject (Flynn and Wyss 2003, and references therein), with new fossil discoveries opening several new windows into the deeper history of Madagascar's terrestrial vertebrates. This contribution, therefore, summarizes recent progress in illuminating the Mesozoic record, complementing Krause et al.'s (1997a, 2019; see also Krause et al., pp. 59–68) treatment of the island's Late Cretaceous plate tectonic history and vertebrate diversity.

At the end of the 20th century, little was known about the terrestrial vertebrates that inhabited Madagascar between Early Triassic and Pleistocene times—a span of some 240 million years, despite abundant stratified rocks of this age within three main basins along the western side of the island, ranging in age from Carboniferous to recent (Figure 2.5). These deposits were carefully studied and mapped by Henri Besairie and colleagues from the 1920s (e.g., compilations of Besairie 1936, 1972; see also references in Flynn and Wyss 2003). Their work revealed, among other things, a thick and geographically widespread succession of Mesozoic strata along the western two-thirds of the island, much of it clearly deposited in terrestrial environments (Figure 2.6). For a variety of reasons,

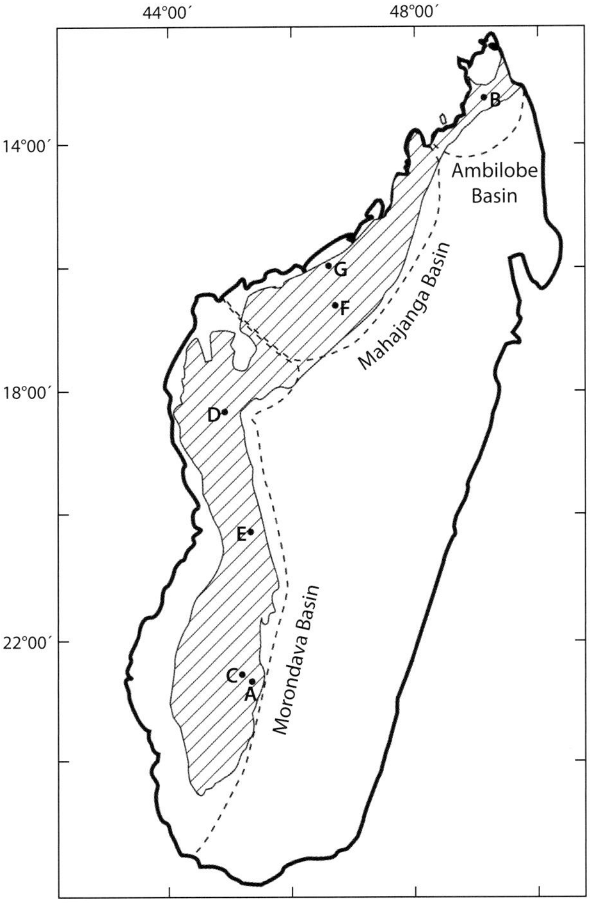

FIGURE 2.5 **Simplified map of Madagascar showing distribution of Mesozoic strata (hatched) in the Morondava, Mahajanga, and Ambilobe Basins of western and northern Madagascar. Letters and black dots indicate approximate regions of stratigraphic units yielding fossil vertebrates discussed in the text and shown in Figure 2.6: A) Sakamena Group, southern Morondava Basin; B) Sakamena Group, Ambilobe Basin; C) Isalo Group, Isalo II, southern Morondava Basin; D) Isalo Group, Isalo II and III, northern Morondava Basin, Folakara and northern Miandrivazo District; E) Isalo Group, Isalo II and III, central Morondava Basin, Poamay locality; F) Isalo Group, Isalo III, Mahajanga Basin, Ambondromamy and area localities; G) Maevarano Formation, Mahajanga Basin.**

including poor exposures and difficult logistics, the paleontological potential of these rocks long remained untapped. Besairie's work also revealed that younger sedimentary deposits, although broadly distributed, are almost entirely of marine origin, implying that a pre-Pleistocene Cenozoic (66–2.6 Mya) record of land animals would be exceedingly difficult to recover.

Madagascar has been geographically isolated since before the extinction of non-avian dinosaurs (end of the Cretaceous, 66 Mya; see Collins et al., pp. 45–51). The island was last broadly connected to another major landmass (India) 80–90 Mya, as the Gondwanan supercontinent was in the final stages of fragmenting tectonically, sending the southern landmasses toward their current positions. As detailed by Krause et al. (2019; see also Geiger et al. 2004; Ali and Aitchison 2008; Klimke et al. 2018; and references in Flynn and Wyss 2003), at the end of the Paleozoic era, 252 Mya, Madagascar was embedded within the supercontinent of Pangea (Gondwana plus Laurasia). Early phases of extensional basin development and rifting of Madagascar (and other still-associated Gondwanan continents) from the east African margin began prior to 230 Mya (e.g., Schandelmeier et al. 2004) during the Triassic. Breakup occurred as early as ~183 Mya (judging from strata in the Morondava Basin; Geiger et al. 2004; Alberti et al. 2019), but Madagascar did not split completely from eastern Africa (modern Somalia area) until the Middle Jurassic, some 165 Mya, as reflected in the post-rift or drift phase sediments of the Bemaraha/Sakaraha Formation or Isalo IIIb deposits (Geiger et al. 2004). Madagascar moved rapidly southward to its current position (relative to the African mainland) by ~120–136 Mya (Rabinowitz and Woods 2006; Samonds et al. 2013), maintaining its connection to India during this time, and through it to Antarctica, Australia, and South America. Madagascar plus India cleaved from Antarctica (and all other major landmasses) sometime thereafter; estimates of the isolation of Indo-Madagascar from other landmasses range between 120 and 85 Mya, with more recent analyses placing it near 115 Mya (Ali and Aitchison 2008; Ali and Krause 2011; Samonds et al. 2013; Krause et al. 2019). Madagascar and India finally rifted apart by ~88 Mya (Krause et al. 2019) and completely separated from each other well before the latest Cretaceous, as India shot northward en route to colliding with Asia during the early Cenozoic.

LATE PALEOZOIC TO CENOZOIC (PRE-PLEISTOCENE) TERRESTRIAL FOSSIL RECORD OF MADAGASCAR

In the late 1990s, Krause et al. (1997a, 1998, 1999) summarized the rapidly expanding Cretaceous record for Madagascar, commented on other aspects of the island's terrestrial vertebrate record, and inferred temporal spans of the major taxonomic groups involved. Several conclusions emerging from those early analyses still hold, while others have been overturned by more recent discoveries and analyses. First, the fossil record of Malagasy vertebrates over the past 66 million years is poorly known, owing to the persisting lack of any definitive pre-Pleistocene Cenozoic terrestrial deposits (see Samonds, pp. 69–73). Second, the latest Cretaceous record provides the youngest clear glimpse of an ancient, pre-Pleistocene Malagasy vertebrate community available. Krause and colleagues have revolutionized our understanding of this fauna, which now constitutes one of the most comprehensive and intensively studied records of Late Cretaceous vertebrate life on the planet. New fossils from two Late Cretaceous intervals have more than quadrupled the species richness known for this time (e.g., Krause et al. 1999; Krause 2003; see Krause et al., pp. 59–68 and discussion here). Findings included the first records of many major vertebrate clades in Madagascar, some indicating unexpected biogeographic relationships with other regions. Intriguingly, Krause et al. (1999) noted very early on that none of the major endemic vertebrate lineages currently living on Madagascar were represented in the Cretaceous record, a finding confirmed by the discovery of dozens of new taxa over the following 20 years, none of which represent extant groups. Instead,

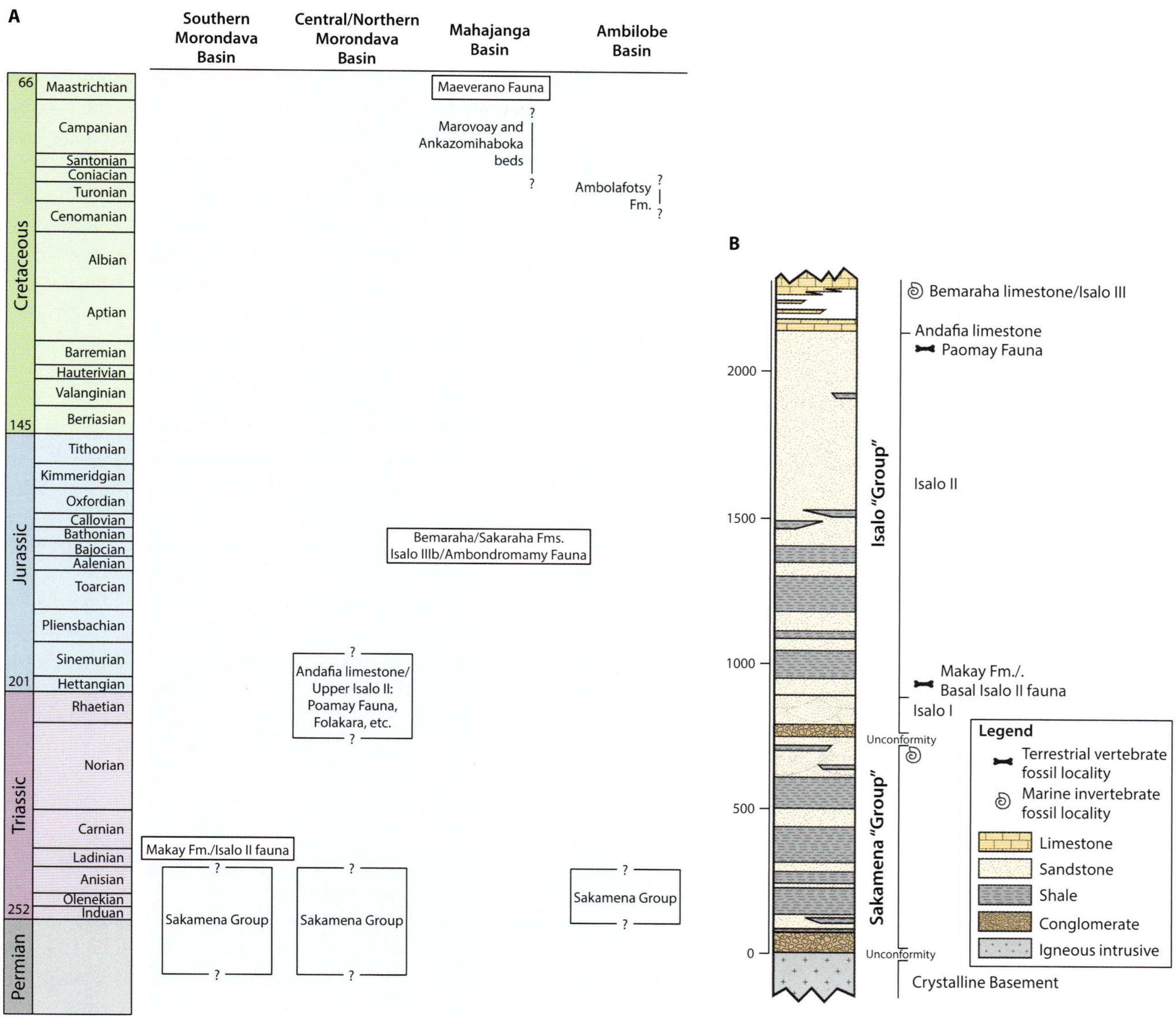

FIGURE 2.6 **Mesozoic timescale, spanning the Triassic to Cretaceous, indicating the temporal placement of Madagascar's major terrestrial vertebrate-bearing strata and faunas. Key: Fm., formation; scale on left side of B is in meters.**

all Late Cretaceous taxa identified to date represent a combination of lineages that are unique to Madagascar (implying possible in situ origin and diversification) or occur in the Mesozoic record elsewhere in Gondwana. All of these lineages became extinct on Madagascar sometime during the substantial latest Cretaceous–Pleistocene gap in the fossil record, which has only begun to be ameliorated by a few tantalizing discoveries in Cenozoic coastal marine-terrestrial interface strata (Mahajanga Basin, Samonds et al. 2009; southern Morondava Basin, J. Flynn et al., unpublished data). Third, no Early Cretaceous (or early Late Cretaceous) faunas were known at the time, representing another gap of about 65 million years. Fourth, the late Permian (latest Paleozoic)/Early Triassic through middle Mesozoic (Jurassic) terrestrial vertebrate record was very incomplete, represented by only a few horizons with generally meager taxonomic sampling. This part of the record has been augmented dramatically by our own research since the 1990s, including new faunas from a series of key temporal intervals in the late Middle to early Late Triassic, Late Triassic to Early Jurassic, and Middle Jurassic. Key finds include exquisitely preserved specimens of synapsids, archosaurs, and other major vertebrate groups.

With regard to the latest Permian, Triassic, and Jurassic record, diverse vertebrate faunas have been reported from the Sakamena Group in the west and southwest of the island (Morondava Basin), and in the north (Ambilobe Basin, following the terminology of, e.g., Lalaharisaina and Ferrand 1994 and Krause et al. 1999, which is equivalent to the various terms used for this basin, such as Diego, Diego-Suarez, Ankitohazo, or Majunga North, by other authors).

Late Permian to Early–Middle Triassic Record: The Sakamena Group

The Sakamena Group in the southern Morondava Basin (Figure 2.5a) is generally considered to be continental in origin, primarily deep-water lacustrine to sub-lacustrine deltaic (Smith 2000) with possible minor interbeds of marine strata reflecting short incursions of the sea (Nichols and Daly 1989), and mostly of late Permian age (e.g., Carroll 1978; Currie 1981; Smith 2000) although its upper horizons may be as young as Early Triassic or Early and Middle Triassic in age (Razafimbelo 1987; Ketchum and Barrett 2004). The Sakamena Group within the Mahajanga Basin is much thinner than in the Morondava Basin, and unconformably overlies basement (e.g., the Sakoa Group in the Morondava Basin, which is absent in the north). Here the Sakamena Group also is largely continental, although marine intercalations become more common to the northeast, and ranges in age from late Permian (Lower Sakamena, age based on a continental flora) to Early Triassic (Middle and Upper Sakamena, age based on unstated criteria). In the Ambilobe Basin (Figures 2.5b and 2.6), the Sakamena has been considered Early Triassic in age, and its faunas to derive from either the lower (e.g., Lehman 1966) or middle (e.g., Beltan 1993; Ketchum and Barrett 2004; Falconnet et al. 2012) part of the unit. These faunas, primarily marine and freshwater aquatic species (Ketchum and Barrett 2004), include a diverse ichthyofauna (36 taxa) and temnospondyls, including the stem anuran *Triadobatrachus*.

More recent discoveries from Sakamena horizons include new material of previously known taxa, and new aquatic procolophonid and tangasaurid younginiform eosuchian reptiles (Ketchum and Barrett 2004; Falconnet et al. 2012). Clearly the Sakamena Group is time-transgressive across these broad areas, and direct and reliable lithostratigraphic correlations of subdivisions (e.g., lower, middle, upper) of the unit are virtually impossible between basins. Overall, the late Permian–Triassic sequence of Sakoa, Sakamena, and overlying Isalo strata are believed to reflect continental rifting, sedimentation, and local marine incursions (e.g., Smith 2000; Scheyer et al. 2014). Battail et al. (1987) provided an early summary of correlations of Permian to Early Triassic Malagasy vertebrate faunas from these units to those from the African mainland, while Steyer (2002), Maganuco et al. (2009), Scheyer et al. (2014), and Yabumoto et al. (2019) summarize paleoenvironmental and paleobiogeographic implications of these faunas.

Late Permian to Early Triassic Record: Lower Sakamena Group

The oldest assemblages from the Sakamena Group, from the southern Morondava Basin, are dominated by a variety of putatively aquatic and terrestrial diapsids (Piveteau 1926a; Carroll 1978; Currie 1981). Currie (1981: Appendix 1) provided a list of the plant, invertebrate, and vertebrate taxa known at that time from the Lower Sakamena of this area. This late Permian assemblage is now considered to originate from the Lower Sakamena (Carroll 1978; Currie 1981; Smith 2000; Ketchum and Barrett 2004). Piveteau (1926a), on the other hand, considered most of this fauna to derive from the Upper (superieur) Sakamena, while Martin (1981) reported Triassic fishes as occurring in the Middle (moyen) Sakamena.

The late Permian Sakamena assemblage includes: 1) the rare atherstoniid/paleoniscid fish *Atherstonia*; 2) the temnospondyl "amphibian" *Rhinesuchus* (questionably referred to this genus) and possibly labyrinthodont basal tetrapods (Currie 1981); 3) a series of terrestrial, aquatic, semiaquatic, and gliding reptiles, including *Barasaurus* (procolophonid parareptile), *Acerodontosaurus* (basal younginiform), *Claudiosaurus* (aquatic basal neodiapsid), *Hovasaurus* (aquatic tangasaurid younginiform), *Thadeosaurus* (semiaquatic tangasaurid younginiform), and the gliding basal neodiapsids *Coelurosauravus* and *Daedolosaurus*; 4) a typical Gondwanan *Glossopteris* flora (including *Glossopteris* and *Thinnfeldia*); and 5) the oldest synapsid reported from Madagascar, a single relatively complete but crushed therapsid skull (*Oudenodon*; Mazin and King 1991), and possibly other therapsids (Ketchum and Barrett 2004).

In contrast, contemporaneous South African faunas are therapsid dominated, suggesting some degree of faunal provinciality at this time relative to Madagascar, despite the geographic proximity and presumably similar paleoclimates of these two areas. As the Malagasy assemblage includes many presumed aquatic or semiaquatic neodiapsid reptiles, which are rare or absent in equivalent South African faunas, Mazin and King (1991) suggested that paleoenvironmental sampling differences may be the dominant explanation for the marked contrast between the Malagasy (more aquatic) and South African (more terrestrial) late Permian faunas. From this perspective, more fully terrestrial taxa (such as dicynodonts) may have been more common in Madagascar but typically lived in habitats far removed from the depositional environments that produced the lower levels of the Sakamena Group.

Recent studies suggest that the Lower Sakamena Group in the Morondava Basin extends into the Early Triassic, from which an articulated skeleton of the trematosaur temnospondyl *Wantzosaurus elongatus* has been recovered (Steyer 2002). A new capitosaur temnospondyl from this interval, *Watsonisuchus madagascariensis*, was recognized on the basis of an unusually complete growth series of material originally referred to two distinct taxa, *Benthosuchus madagascariensis* and *Wetlugasurus milloti* (Steyer 2003).

Early to Middle Triassic Record: Middle Sakamena Group

The diverse vertebrate faunas from the Sakamena Group in the Ambilobe Basin, recently summarized by Ketchum and Barrett (2004), are from dominantly marine (Piveteau 1936, 1937; Beltan 1993) or lagoonal environments, suggesting a major marine incursion. The Middle Sakamena Group of the Ambilobe Basin has produced at least 36 species of actinopterygian and sarcopterygian fishes (for a list of taxa, references, and discussion, see Beltan 1993; Ketchum and Barrett 2004; Kogan and Romano 2016; Marramà et al. 2017) and at least 10 tetrapod taxa (Lehman 1979; Janvier 1992; Ketchum and Barrett 2004; and references cited herein), such as: 1) abundant material of the stem anuran *Triadobatrachus* (e.g., Rage and Rocek 1989; Gardner and Rage 2016; = "*Protobatrachus*" of Piveteau 1936, 1937); 2) *Mahavisaurus dentatus* (a rhytidosteid [*sensu lato*] short-faced stereospondyl, including "*Lyrosaurus australis*," which is now recognized to represent juvenile stages of this taxon; Maganuco et al. 2014); 3) the capitosaur temnospondyls *Wetlugasaurus* and *Edingerella* (Steyer 2003; Maganuco et al. 2009; Fortuny et al. 2019); 4) the enigmatic trematosaur or mastondonsaur stereospondyl *Benthosuchus* (questionably assigned by Lehman 1966); 5) the trematosaur temnospondyls *Deltacephalus* (near outgroup to short-faced stereospondyls in Maganuco et al. 2014), *Aphaneramma* (Fortuny et al. 2018), *Tertrema*, *Tertremoides* (and cf. *T. madagascariensis* of Maganuco and Pasini 2009), *Trematosaurus*, and *Wantzasaurus* (including *Ifasaurus*; Steyer 2002); 6) the new procolophonid parareptile *Lasasaurus* (Falconnet et al. 2012); and 7) indeterminate eosuchian reptiles. The stereospondyl questionably referred to *Benthosuchus* by Lehman (1966) was considered to be referable to *Parotosuchus* by Warren and Hutchinson (1988); *Parotosuchus*, and not *Benthosuchus*, was reported by Ketchum and Barrett (2004) for the Early Triassic Sakamena Group of the Ambilobe Basin; and *Benthosuchus* was considered a trematosaur in Maganuco et al. (2014). Beltan (1993: Figure 11) mentioned the occurrence of at least five species of vascular land plants.

Middle to Late Triassic Record: The Isalo Group, Isalo I and II

Prior to the 1990s, the rhynchosaur *Isalorhynchus* was the lone terrestrial vertebrate known from the Middle to Late Triassic of Madagascar (Buffetaut 1983). Fragmentary remains of two aquatic taxa had been reported from the island: an unnamed metoposaur temnospondyl (recovered near Folakara, in the northern Morondava Basin) (Dutuit 1978; see Fortuny et al. 2019) and phytosaurs (crocodile-like archosaurian reptiles). The phyotosaur material was reported from both the northern (also near Folakara) (Guth 1963) and southern (Dutuit 1978) Morondava Basin, although the provenance and taxonomic assignment of the latter occurrence have been questioned (Westphal 1970).

Beginning in 1996, joint expeditions with the Université d'Antananarivo have recovered an extensive and exceptionally well-preserved fauna from the basal Isalo II strata in the island's southwestern portion (see Figures 2.5c, 2.6, and 2.7b–e). It is almost certain that the holotype (Buffetaut 1983) and later referred material (Langer et al. 2000) of *Isalorhynchus genofevae* also originates from this lithostratigraphic unit and region, contra Langer et al. (2000). Flynn et al. (1998, 1999a, 2000a) provided preliminary faunal lists and discussions of the significance of this remarkable fauna; a series of more recent studies (Flynn and Wyss 2003; Goswami et al. 2005; Whatley 2005; Ranivoharimanana 2007, 2011, 2012; Kammerer et al. 2008, 2010, 2012, 2020; Flynn et al. 2010; Ranivoharimanana et al. 2011; Nesbitt et al. 2015) and others in progress will continue to more fully elucidate its taxonomic breadth and significance. At least eight to 10 taxa are known from this fauna (Flynn et al. 1999a, 2000a; Nesbitt et al. 2015), including one of the best-preserved assemblages of Triassic eucynodonts globally. It contains at least three eucynodonts, including the traversodontids *Menadon besairei* and *Dadadon isaloi* (Flynn et al. 2000a; Kammerer et al. 2012; see Figures 2.7d and e), and a chinquodontid probainognathian *Chiniquodon kalanoro* (Kammerer et al. 2010). In addition, the fauna includes a kannemeyerid dicynodont; two rhynchosaurs, including two almost-complete skeletons and abundant additional material of *Isalorhynchus genofevae* (Flynn et al. 1999a; Whatley 2005); a tiny new lagerpetid ornithodiran archosaur, *Kogonaphon kely*, which indicates an episode of miniaturization early in the history of this group (Kammerer et al. 2020); and other taxa still being prepared and studied. *Azendohsaurus madagaskarensis* (Flynn et al. 2010; Nesbitt et al. 2015; see Figures 2.7b and c), the first archosauromorph described from this fauna, is closely related to *A. laroussi* from Morocco. Both taxa originally were considered prosauropod dinosaurs (see Flynn et al. 1999a) based on the striking similarities of their teeth and jaws. Phylogenetic analyses of *A. madagaskarensis*, following the recovery of more complete material, showed that its craniodental resemblances to prosauropods are convergent. Broader comparisons, moreover, revealed that the convergent acquisition of such herbivorously related specializations is much more pervasive in archosauromorph reptiles than previously recognized, appearing to have occurred at least six to eight times independently (Flynn et al. 2010; Nesbitt et al. 2015). Phytosaurs and aetosaurs (stagonolepids), armored basal archosaurs, are common in most Late Triassic (Carnian–Norian) assemblages around the world, but curiously remain unrecorded in the basal Isalo II fauna. The sole armored archosaur in this fauna, as yet unnamed, may represent the earliest-diverging avemetatarsalian (Patellos et al. 2019).

The precise dating of and temporal correlation among terrestrial vertebrate assemblages dating from the Middle to Late Triassic is hindered by sparse independent age control from radioisotopic dating (few horizons associated with fossiliferous terrestrial Ladinian- and Carnian-aged strata have been dated globally; see Flynn et al. 1999a; Marsicano et al. 2016) and the general lack of associated marine strata of known ages. Based on a variety of biostratigraphic evidence (the only available method for time correlation over this interval), this basal Isalo II fauna is considered late Middle Triassic to early Late Triassic (late Ladinian or earliest Carnian) in age, roughly 235 million years old (Flynn et al. 1999a; Kammerer et al. 2010; Nesbitt et al. 2015). Contrary to an earlier suggestion (Langer et al. 2000), this fauna clearly pre-dates that from the Ischigualasto Formation of Argentina and instead more closely correlates temporally to the Chañares Formation of northwestern Argentina and the Santa Maria Formation of Brazil, based on the shared presence of *Menadon besairiei* on Madagascar and in the Ladinian *Santacruzodon* Assemblage Zone of Brazil. The *Santacruzodon* Assemblage Zone is in turn correlated to the Chañares deposits, which are late Middle Triassic to early Late Triassic in age (see Desojo et al. 2011; Marsicano et al. 2016 for South American dating and correlations; see Flynn et al. 1999a, 2000a; Nesbitt et al. 2015 for Madagascar correlations). The probainoganthian *Chiniquodon* co-occurs with members of the traversodontid clade Massetognathinae on Madagascar (*Dadadon*), in the *Santacruzodon* Assemblage Zone of the Santa Maria Formation of Brazil (*Santacruzodon* and *Massetognathus*), and in the Chañares Formation of Argentina (*Massetognathus*), further supporting the temporal correlation of these faunas and the widespread biogeographic connectivity of Gondwanan faunas at this time.

Jurassic Record: The Isalo Group, Isalo III—Mahajanga Basin

The Malagasy record of Jurassic terrestrial vertebrates was equally scanty until recently, consisting of fragmentary remains of the sauropod dinosaur *Bothriospondylus madagascariensis* (genus level assignment questioned by McIntosh 1990; perhaps assignable to the new taxon *Lapparentosaurus madagascariensis* erected by Bonaparte 1986a for juvenile sauropod material from this area), plus isolated marine reptile teeth from the Isalo III formation of the Mahajanga Basin (Figures 2.5f and 2.6). Later work in this region, from sites near Ambondromamy, vastly improved the sampling of vertebrates from this period (Flynn et al. 1998, 2000b, 2006). New material from this area consists largely of isolated teeth, bones, and jaws. Initial analyses of fossils picked from part of more than 7 metric tons of sediment, yielding about 1 metric ton of screen-washed

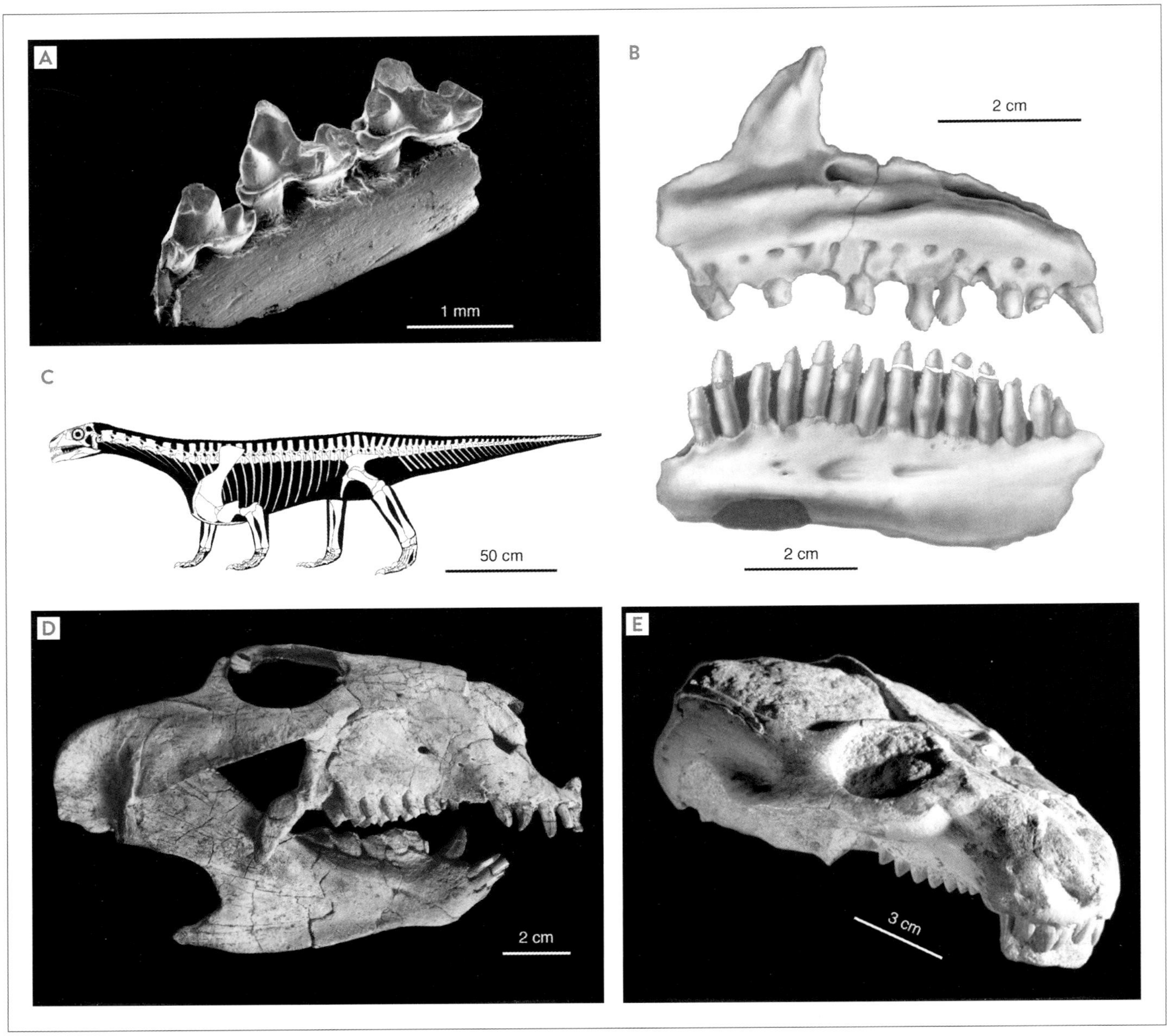

FIGURE 2.7 **Representative vertebrate fossils from the Triassic and Jurassic of Madagascar: A) oblique view of the lower jaw portion with three teeth of the early tribosphenic mammal *Ambondro mahabo* (Middle Jurassic); B) medial view of a maxilla (top) and lateral view of a mandible (bottom) of the basal archosauromorph reptile *Azendohsaurus madagaskarensis* (Middle–Late Triassic)** (ILLUSTRATIONS by M. Donnelly, Field Museum of Natural History, Chicago)**; C) skeletal reconstruction of *A. madagaskarensis* (from Nesbitt et al. 2015); D) lateral view of the skull of the traversodontid eucynodont *Menadon besairei* (Middle–Late Triassic); E) oblique view of a skull of the traversodontid eucynodont *Dadadon isaloi* (Middle–Late Triassic). Approximate scale bars included in each part (A–E).**

concentrate, from 19 separate Isalo IIIb (Sakaraha/Bemaraha Formation) localities in the region, yielded more than 5000 specimens, representing at least 13 vertebrate taxa (Flynn et al. 2000b, 2006). This Ambondromamy fauna includes a wide diversity of actinopterygian, chondrichthyan, and sarcopterygian fishes; a urodele amphibian; turtles; atoposaurid crocodyliforms; pterosaurs (see also Dal Sasso and Pasini 2003); sauropod, theropod, and ornithischian dinosaurs; and at least one mammal (Flynn et al. 1999b, 2000b, 2006). Continued sorting of large volumes of screen-washed sediment concentrate collected over several field seasons and additional field discoveries should yield further significant finds, as rarefaction analyses by Flynn et al. (2006) suggested that some less intensively sampled localities may ultimately yield even more taxa than those with the highest known diversity.

Among the most striking of the initial discoveries from this fauna were the oldest theropod dinosaurs known from Madagascar, and the likely first occurrence of ornithischian dinosaurs known from the island. Flynn et al. (2006) and Mannion (2010) recognized three sauropod dinosaurs from these deposits: a taxon with prosauropod-like teeth *Archaeodontosaurus descouensi* (named by

Buffetaut 2005), "*Bothriospondylus madagascariensis*," and *Lapparentosaurus* (a titanosauriform mentioned in Mannion 2010). More recently, Bindellini and Dal Sasso (2019) tentatively referred eight sauropod tooth morphotypes from this region to these three taxa, a possibly new diplodocoid sauropod (which would be the first from Madagascar, and the first Bathonian diplodocoid known), and an indeterminate titanosauriform sauropod. Maganuco et al. (2006) described *Razanandrongobe sakalavae* (see also Dal Sasso et al. 2017), which they originally identified as an indeterminate archosaur but subsequently considered a large-bodied mesoeucrocodylian, based on more complete craniodental material. Maganuco et al. (2005, 2007) referred isolated teeth and a vertebra to three unnamed theropod dinosaur taxa—argued to include the oldest records of Abelisauridae and Coelurosauria in Gondwana—and a phalanx to an indeterminate non-abelisauroid ceratosaur.

Wagensommer et al. (2010) reported the first dinosaur footprint trackways from Madagascar in the Middle Jurassic Bemaraha Formation (limestones) of the northern Morondava Basin between Bekopaka and Antsalova; the first represented a quadrupedal dinosaur (probably sauropod) and the second included more than 50 theropod footprints in multiple trackways.

Careful reconsideration of the identification of this array of theropod material from the Isalo III formation is warranted given its potential biogeographic implications. If current assessments are substantiated, the Malagasy Jurassic theropod fauna differs from that of its Late Cretaceous counterpart in not being composed exclusively of abelisauroids (Sampson et al. 1998, 2001; Krause et al. 2019, Krause et al., pp. 59–68). Instead it more closely resembles contemporaneous faunas from mainland Africa in its broader mix of theropod clades.

A Middle Jurassic Mammal from Isalo III Strata of the Mahajanga Basin

A key fossil recovered from this Middle Jurassic interval near Ambondromamy is a mammalian jaw bearing three teeth (Flynn et al. 1999b; Figure 2.7a). This taxon, *Ambondro mahabo*, represents the earliest (by 25 million years) documented global occurrence of an advanced (tribosphenic) type of dentition, conventionally regarded as characteristic of the clade including marsupials and placental mammals. Since its original interpretation as a member of Tribosphenida (Flynn et al. 1999b), *Ambondro* has been suggested to be allied with disparate mammalian clades (see summary in Bininda-Emonds et al. 2012). These include: 1) inclusion within a subsequently proposed, dominantly austral group (Australosphenida), with Australosphenida either: a) nested deeply within the Eutheria (Woodburne et al. 2003) or b) related to monotremes and convergently tribosphenic (Luo et al. 2001, 2007, 2015; Rougier et al. 2007); or 2) inclusion within a large basal polytomy encompassing other tribosphenic mammals (e.g., metatherians, eutherians, and other Theriiformes) (Rowe et al. 2008). While its precise phylogenetic affinities remain uncertain, as does the related issue of whether a tribosphenic dentition arose only once or multiple times within Mammalia, *Ambondro* nonetheless provides a pivotal test of molecular clock-based predictions for diversification of ages of major mammalian clades and related biogeographic hypotheses (Flynn et al. 1999b; Archibald 2003; Bininda-Emonds et al. 2012; Springer et al. 2017). If *Ambondro* is indeed a member of Tribosphenida (Flynn et al. 1999b; Woodburne et al. 2003; Rowe et al. 2008), as that group is traditionally conceived, then Tribosphenida appeared some 25 million years earlier in the southern hemisphere than in Laurasia. *Ambondro* thus would invert conventional views that Laurasian and Gondwanan mammal faunas were isolated during much of the late Mesozoic (e.g., Bonaparte 1986b), and that tribosphenic mammals reached Gondwanan landmasses only very late in the Cretaceous or in the early Cenozoic. Instead, Tribosphenida may have originated in the south and later dispersed to the north, or faunal interchange was more widespread than previously thought. In contrast, Luo et al. (2001, 2007) and Rougier et al. (2007) have argued that Gondwanan mammals with tribosphenic dentition (Australosphenida) are not closely connected to Laurasian tribosphenidans, and are instead linked to monotremes, a view requiring the independent origin of tribosphenic dentitions in geographically and phylogenetically disparate mammals (see also Davis 2011). Discovering new fossils offers perhaps the most promising avenue for reconciling the disparity between current hypotheses.

Isalo III: Geological Dating

In contrast to the poor age control for lower portions of the Isalo Group sequence, most Jurassic terrestrial fossils from the Mahajanga Basin are well dated by bracketing marine strata. They occur within the Bathonian Faciès Mixte Dinosauriens of the Isalo IIIb—this unit's marine intertongues containing a rich Bathonian-age invertebrate fauna, capped by ammonite-bearing strata of Callovian age (Besairie 1972; Flynn et al. 1999b, 2006).

Jurassic Record: The Isalo Group, Isalo II and III—Northern Morondava Basin

We have recovered new terrestrial vertebrate assemblages at two sets of localities (Flynn et al. 1998; Burmeister et al. 2006) from the Isalo Group in the northern Morondava Basin, in the west-central part of the country (Figure 2.5d and e). These include currently undescribed material related to fishes, stereospondyl temnospondyls, and a diverse suite of reptiles from likely Late Triassic–age deposits in the northern Miandrivazo District (Figure 2.5d), and a substantial assemblage from the Poamay locality in the Malaimbandy area (Figure 2.5e). Guth (1963) reported phytosaur material from Late Triassic Isalo II deposits in the Folakara area (Figure 2.5d), from which Fortuny et al. (2019) also (re)described temnospondyl material (previously ascribed to the poorly known "*Metoposaurus hoffmani*," but now referred to Metoposauridae indet.), which suggests a close relationship to taxa from India. The fauna from Poamay includes isolated elements of an acrodontid elasmobranch (*Asterocanthus*); semionotid and colobodontid osteichtyan fishes; a crocodyliform; possible sauropod and theropod fossils (which would represent records of the earliest dinosaurs from each of those groups on Madagascar); potential cynodont teeth; crocodylotarsan material of uncertain affinities (questionably representing aetosaur, phytosaur, or some other enigmatic crocodylotarsan taxa); various indeterminate vertebrate skeletal elements; and abundant coprolites, some including microvertebrates or bone fragments (Burmeister et al. 2006). The Poamay locality appears to be Early Jurassic in age, based on its vertebrate fauna and the age of marine strata immediately overlying the deposits (Andafia limestone,

Upper Isalo II), although an age at the very end of the Triassic cannot be excluded (Figure 2.6; see also Burmeister et al. 2006). Further study of the faunas from Poamay and the Miandrivazo District noted above will further illuminate the Late Triassic to Early Jurassic fossil record in Madagascar.

Cretaceous Record: Maevarano Formation—Mahajanga Basin

Cretaceous-aged faunas from the Mahajanga Basin have been known for more than 100 years (Lydekker 1895; Depéret 1896). Work in the Maevarano Formation (Figure 2.5g) by D. Krause and colleagues, beginning in the early 1990s, has vastly improved the record of fossil vertebrates from this region, with more than 40 species now known (Krause et al. 1997a, 1998, 1999, 2019; Krause 2003; see also Krause et al., pp. 59–68). Collectively, these finds have greatly clarified understanding of the biogeographic history of the Malagasy fauna. The remarkable Maastrichtian-aged (latest Cretaceous) fauna from the Maevarano Formation now includes the first Cretaceous mammals from Madagascar—a metatherian (marsupial relative), a multituberculate, an indeterminate mammal, and three gondwanatheres, a peculiar clade otherwise recorded only from South America and India. The avifauna includes at least six taxa, some of which are close outgroups to crown clade birds (Forster et al. 1996; O'Connor and Forster 2010), representing one of the most taxonomically diverse, and wide-ranging in body size, Mesozoic avifaunas known from Gondwana. The fauna also includes the oldest and first definitive record of a Mesozoic lizard on the island (a cordyliform scincomorph) (Krause et al. 2003); one of the most diverse crocodyliform assemblages known globally (at least seven taxa, ranging from tiny to giant) (Krause et al. 2019); and a rich array of fishes, frogs, turtles, snakes, a titanosaurian sauropod dinosaur, and two abelosauroid theropod dinosaurs. Farke and Sertich (2013) reported a slightly older (Turonian, early Late Cretaceous) small abelosaurid theropod, *Dahalokely*, from the Ambolafotsy Formation of the Ambilobe Basin (Figure 2.6).

As mentioned, even after more than 25 years of exploration and study, very few of the living vertebrate lineages or higher taxa (e.g., traditional families or orders) occurring on Madagascar today are represented in the Late Cretaceous record, nor in older Triassic to Jurassic strata, suggesting that virtually all extant clades dispersed to, or at least diversified within, Madagascar during the latest Cretaceous or Cenozoic. Gottfried et al. (1998) reported that of the 14 living major clades of freshwater fishes in Madagascar, only one (the catfish clade Ariidae) may have a Cretaceous representative. Available phylogenetic and biogeographic analyses (e.g., a review of crocodyliforms, sauropod and nonavian theropod dinosaurs, and mammals by Krause et al. 2019; see also: anuran amphibians, Asher and Krause 1998; cordyliform lizard, Krause et al. 2003; gondwanathere mammals, Krause et al. 1997b and Krause 2014; abelisauroid theropod dinosaurs, Sampson et al. 1998, 2001, and Sampson and Krause 2007; and crocodyliforms, Buckley and Brochu 1999 and Krause and Kley 2010) support Gondwana breakup vicariance models for explaining the biogeography of Malagasy vertebrates, although interpretation of the history of some lineages remains ambiguous and equally compatible with dispersal (from mainland Africa, for example) during the late Mesozoic (Samonds et al. 2012, 2013).

BIOGEOGRAPHIC AFFINITIES OF MALAGASY TERRESTRIAL VERTEBRATE ASSEMBLAGES THROUGH TIME

Shubin et al. (1991) suggested that broad faunal cosmopolitanism of Mesozoic faunas persisted from the Triassic through at least the Early Jurassic, and that the initial phases of Pangean/Gondwanan rifting yielded no corresponding provinciality of terrestrial vertebrates. Lucas and Hunt (1994) endorsed this view on the basis of Late Triassic traversodontid distributions, while Battail (1991) argued for greater provinciality. Our work (Flynn et al. 1999a, 2000a, 2010; Kammerer et al. 2010; Nesbitt et al. 2015) helps resolve debate over whether biotic provinciality was already established by the Triassic. Comparisons to the Lower Santa Maria Formation of Brazil (e.g., Abdala et al. 2001, 2009) and Chañares Formation of Argentina, which have yielded cynodonts very similar to but differing at the species to genus level relative to those from the basal Isalo II, suggest contemporaneity but at least some degree of provinciality among these sites. For example, *Chiniquodon* (Kammerer et al. 2010) and *Menadon* differ at the species level and *Dadadon* differs at the genus level from near relatives in South America (Flynn et al. 2000a). In contrast to the species-level similarities of cynodonts in late Early to early Middle Triassic Gondwanan faunas, late Middle to early Late Triassic–age (Ladinian–Carnian) cynodonts exhibit greater degrees of continental provinciality, potentially representing "additional evidence for climate-controlled endemism in synapsids, which seem to have been rare in extremely arid paleoenvironments" (Kammerer et al. 2010).

Breakup of Pangea is hypothesized to have increased levels of endemism and provinciality of terrestrial vertebrates as landmasses became progressively more isolated during the Mesozoic (see Krause et al. 1997a, 1999, 2019, pp. 59–68; Masters et al. 2006). The phylogeny and distribution of proximal outgroups for many Cretaceous vertebrates from Madagascar indicate that some degree of isolation and provincialism had developed among former Gondwanan landmasses during the late Mesozoic, in concert with the breakup of these areas as inferred from geophysical studies. Gondwanatheres provided one of the first recognized exceptions to this pattern, as their cosmopolitanism led Krause et al. (1997b) to hypothesize that Antarctica was an important biogeographic link between South America and Indo-Madagascar during the Late Cretaceous. As reviewed and detailed by Krause (2003), Masters et al. (2006), and Krause et al. (2019), theropods parallel the gondwanathere pattern (Sampson et al. 1998, 2001; Sampson and Krause 2007) as do crocodyliforms (Buckley and Brochu 1999; Krause and Kley 2010), again indicating close biogeographic affinities between Madagascar and India during the Late Cretaceous, slightly weaker ties between Indo-Madagascar and South America, and much weaker links between these areas and mainland Africa. At the same time, geological evidence and stratigraphically calibrated phylogenies (Ali and Krause 2011; see also Samonds et al. 2013) argue against an uninterrupted connection between Antarctica and Madagascar (e.g., across a long and continuous Gunnerus Ridge "causeway") during the Late Cretaceous, implying that terrestrial vertebrates of moderate to large body size, such as abelisauroid theropods, titanosaurian sauropods, and notosuchian crocodyliforms (all presumably poor dispersers, particularly over oceanic barriers) must have been more widespread across Gondwana earlier, becoming isolated on Indo-Madagascar during the Early Cretaceous, a time interval not currently represented in the Malagasy vertebrate fossil record.

CONCLUSION

While Mesozoic vertebrate fossils have been known from Madagascar for over a century, discoveries since the late 20th century have greatly enriched our understanding of the history of terrestrial vertebrate diversity and assemblage composition over key intervals of Triassic, Jurassic, and Cretaceous time. These recent finds shed light on the phylogeny and biogeography of Madagascar's ancient vertebrate communities, the relationships of the Mesozoic Malagasy fauna to those from other landmasses, and the responses of these assemblages to global and local tectonic, climatic, and environmental changes. Against the backdrop of this remarkable progress, with continuing exploration for new sites, application of novel analytical methods, recent and ongoing comprehensive descriptions and analyses of taxa and faunas, and the growing cadre of Malagasy scientists being trained in vertebrate paleontology, this upward trajectory in understanding Madagascar's Mesozoic history can only be expected to continue into the future.

Subject editor: Steven M. Goodman

LATE CRETACEOUS VERTEBRATES OF MADAGASCAR: A WINDOW INTO GONDWANAN BIOGEOGRAPHY

D. W. Krause, P. M. O'Connor, J. J. W. Sertich, K. Curry Rogers, R. R. Rogers, and B. Rakotozafy

Madagascar became an island during the Late Cretaceous, approximately 88 million years ago (Mya). Once lying at the core of the southern supercontinent Gondwana, the "Great Red Island" now sits physically and biotically isolated from its former neighbors in the vast expanse of the western Indian Ocean. The island lies at a minimum distance of 430 km from mainland Africa, the closest point being the Nampula Province of Mozambique, and approximately 4000 km from India, 4500 km from Antarctica, and 6500 km from Australia. The highly endemic and taxonomically imbalanced extant nonmarine vertebrate fauna of Madagascar owes its uniqueness to a long history of geographic isolation, with only occasional immigrants colonizing the island via rare, but consequential, sweepstakes dispersal events from other landmasses, primarily Africa (Yoder and Nowak 2006; Samonds et al. 2012, 2013; see Samonds et al., pp. 73–78). This contribution reviews the rapidly expanding record of Late Cretaceous fossil vertebrates from Madagascar and what it is beginning to reveal about the biogeographic history of the island in particular and Gondwana in general.

Complementing this summary of Late Cretaceous (100–66 Mya) discoveries of vertebrate fossils in the context of the plate tectonic and biogeographic history of the island is an extensive review of the late Permian, Triassic, and Jurassic vertebrate fossil records of Madagascar (see Flynn et al., pp. 51–59). Vertebrate fossils have not been described from the Early Cretaceous (145–100 Mya) of Madagascar. The pre–late Pleistocene Cenozoic record of fossil vertebrates is frustratingly sparse, but K. Samonds and colleagues have made several significant discoveries in the last two decades, which are reviewed herein (see Samonds, pp. 69–73). By contrast, vertebrate fossils and subfossils of late Pleistocene and Holocene age are quite well known and the record has recently been extended back ~80,000 years (Samonds 2007; also see Godfrey and Douglass, pp. 191–97. Given that the fossil records of vertebrates both before and after the Late Cretaceous are reviewed in other contributions, we will restrict our consideration here to the record from the Late Cretaceous epoch.

THE LATE CRETACEOUS RECORD OF MALAGASY FOSSIL VERTEBRATES

Historical and Geological Context

Sedimentary rock records of Mesozoic age are preserved in three large sedimentary depocenters along the western coast of Madagascar: the Morondava Basin to the south, the Mahajanga Basin to the north, and the smaller Ambilobe Basin at the northern tip of the island (Figure 2.8). The record of Late Cretaceous vertebrate fossils from the Morondava Basin is limited to preliminary reports of Coniacian-aged (~87 Mya) titanosaurian sauropods (Marshall et al. 2015) and Campanian-aged (~78 Mya) pterosaurs (Burch and Sertich 2011). The Late Cretaceous record from the Ambilobe Basin is limited to a single specimen, a partial skeleton of a new genus and species of abelisauroid theropod dinosaur, *Dahalokely tokana*, which was recovered from Turonian-aged (~92 Mya) strata (Farke and Sertich 2013).

The vast majority of Late Cretaceous vertebrate fossils from Madagascar have been recovered from the Mahajanga Basin. Terrestrial and freshwater vertebrates of Late Cretaceous age are

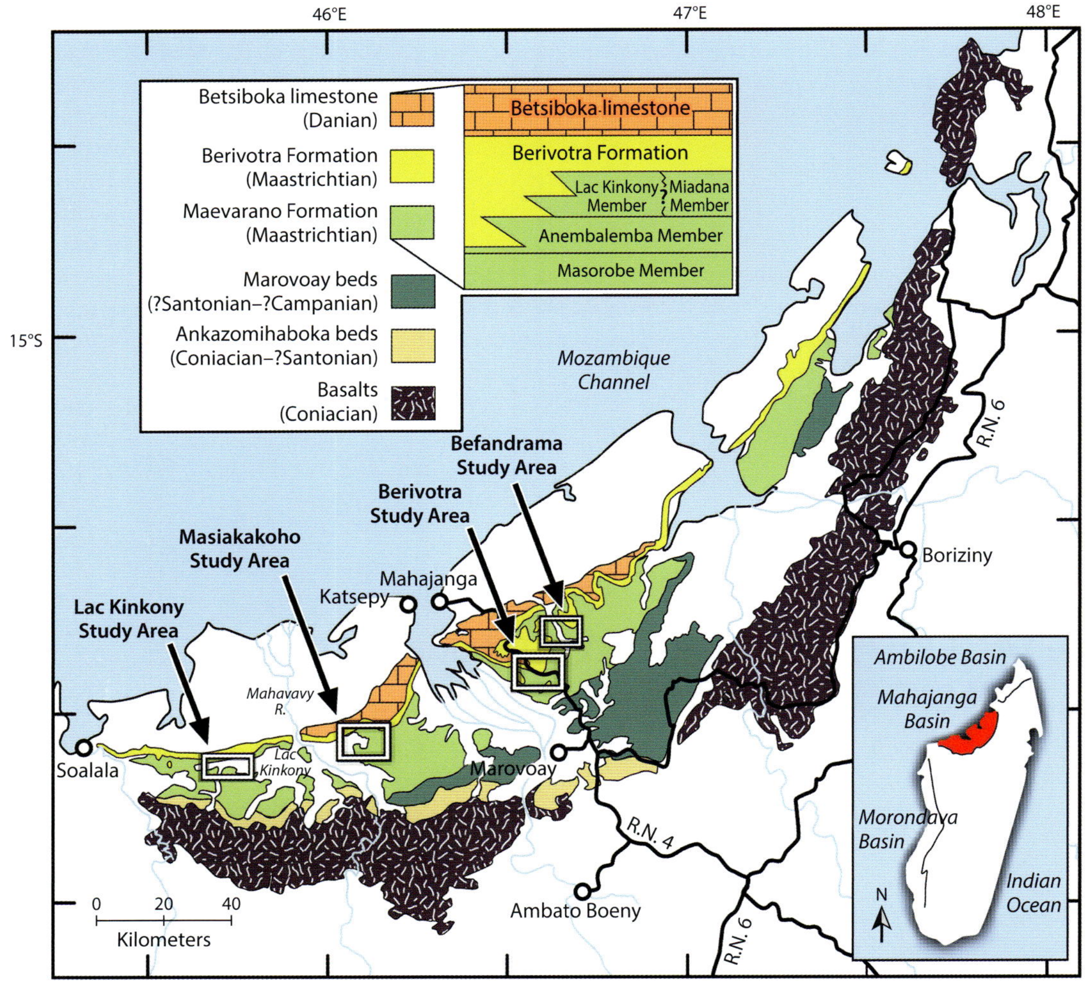

FIGURE 2.8 **Geological map of Upper Cretaceous (Coniacian through Maastrichtian) and Paleocene (Danian) strata of the Mahajanga Basin, northwestern Madagascar, including four main study areas. Top left key depicts stratigraphic relationships of four members of Maevarano Formation and marine facies of Berivotra Formation. Bottom right inset map depicts three major sedimentary basins along western coast of island. From Rogers et al. (2013).**

known from three nonmarine rock units in the Mahajanga Basin: the Ankazomihaboka beds, the Marovoay beds, and the Maevarano Formation (Figure 2.8), all of which occur stratigraphically above Coniacian-age flood basalts dated at ~88 Mya (Storey et al. 1995, 1997). Fossil vertebrates from the Ankazomihaboka and Marovoay units are still very poorly known (e.g., Martin 1981; Curry 1997) but explorations over the last 25-plus years in the uppermost reaches of the Maevarano Formation have resulted in the discovery of approximately 20,000 specimens representing a diverse assemblage of taxa (see updated faunal list in Krause et al. 2020: Table S2). These discoveries are the product of 13 expeditions, from 1993 onwards, and all part of the ongoing Mahajanga Basin Project.

Stratigraphic analysis of the Maevarano Formation and associated units, in four separate field areas, by Rogers et al. (2000, 2013) has revealed that the most richly fossiliferous horizon (the Anembalemba Member) correlates with the marine Berivotra Formation (Figure 2.8). Abundant invertebrate and microfossil evidence in the Berivotra Formation, which has also yielded a moderately diverse fauna of chondrichthyan fishes, including the first-known fossil of recent sawsharks (Gottfried and Rabarison 1997) and rays (Gottfried et al. 2001) from the island, indicates that it is Maastrichtian, probably late Maastrichtian (i.e., latest Cretaceous), in age (Rogers et al. 2000). The Maevarano Formation is, therefore, roughly the same age as the Deccan basalt volcano-sedimentary sequence of India, which has also produced a diverse Maastrichtian vertebrate fauna (e.g., Khosla and Verma 2015; Kapur and Khosla 2018).

From a paleoenvironmental perspective, the Maevarano Formation represents an ancient semiarid ecosystem that was characterized by shallow ephemeral streams and dryland soils that developed on a low-relief alluvial plain under a strongly seasonal rainfall regime. The ancient river deposits of the Anembalemba Member exhibit striking evidence of variable discharge (Rogers 2005), and the oxidized paleosols of the underlying Masorobe Member preserve abundant indication of seasonal dryland conditions, with vertical tap roots, slickensides, and pedogenic carbonate accumulations, including nodules and root encrustations. The taphonomy of the Maevarano vertebrate assemblage is consistent with this seasonal, semiarid paleoenvironmental reconstruction. Indeed, the Maevarano vertebrate fossil record is punctuated by numerous multitaxic bonebeds that have been interpreted as drought-related mass kills. The spectacular quality of the fossils preserved in these bonebeds has been attributed to burial by fine-grained debris flows that were triggered when seasonal rains returned to the Mahajanga Basin (Rogers 2005; Rogers et al. 2007).

The Maevarano vertebrate assemblage is one of the richest and best preserved yet known from the Mesozoic of Gondwana. Approximately 50 species of terrestrial and freshwater vertebrates have been recovered as part of the Mahajanga Basin Project, septupling the previously known (pre-1993) species richness from the Late Cretaceous of Madagascar (Krause et al. 2020: Table S2). To date, complementing three species described prior to 1993 (the snake *Madtsoia madagascariensis*, the crocodyliform *Miadanasuchus oblita*, and the theropod dinosaur *Majungasaurus crenatissimus*), 19 new genera and species have been named: one frog, two turtles, one lizard, four snakes, three crocodyliforms, four non-avian dinosaurs, one bird, and three mammals. Most of these taxa are now represented by complete, or nearly complete, exquisitely preserved skulls and/or skeletons that are, in many cases, the best specimens for entire clades known from other Gondwanan landmasses. Concerning fossil representatives of extant higher taxa of vertebrates in Madagascar, the Mahajanga Basin Project has provided the first pre–late Pleistocene records of frogs, lizards, birds, and mammals.

Fishes

Fishes are represented by at least 11 species. A taxonomically indeterminate dipnoan is known from a large series of estivation burrows, the first to be documented from the Gondwanan rock record (Marshall and Rogers 2012). The presence of these burrows is consistent with the paleoclimatic interpretation of marked seasonality. The ray-finned fishes (actinopterygians) include at least two holosteans (*Lepisosteus* and *Coelodus*) and eight teleosteans (*Albula*, *Egertonia*, *Paralbula*, *Enchodus*, and four indeterminate ostarioclupeomorphans), all of which are represented by only isolated elements that are currently unidentified below the genus rank (Gottfried and Krause 1998; Ostrowski 2012).

Anurans

Frogs are represented by a small, indeterminate form, based on a few isolated bones, and the massive ceratophryid *Beelzebufo ampinga*, described from a partial cranium and numerous isolated elements (Figure 2.9; Evans et al. 2008, 2014). Ceratophryids are voracious ambush predators otherwise known only from South America. *Beelzebufo ampinga* is particularly noteworthy because it is the only described pre-Holocene frog from Madagascar but also because of its large size (body length 232 mm; skull width 154 mm) and the presence of heavy cranial and dorsal body armor. It also had an impressive bite force, purported to be equivalent to that of medium- to large-size mammalian carnivorans (Lappin et al. 2017).

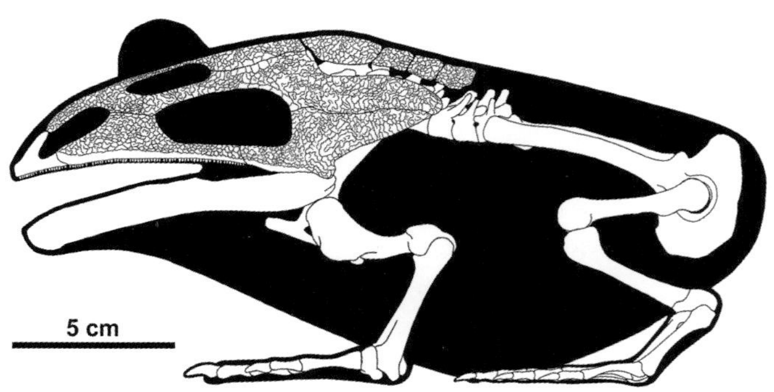

FIGURE 2.9 **Reconstructed skeleton of the ceratophryid frog *Beelzebufo ampinga* from the Late Cretaceous of Madagascar, in left lateral view.**

Turtles

Turtle specimens have been known from the Maevarano Formation for well over a century (Depéret 1896; Russell et al. 1976) but none were complete enough to be diagnostic. The Mahajanga Basin Project has recovered the remains of at least five species of turtles, only two of which have been named and described to date. All are side-necked pleurodirans. The two new species are *Sokatra antitra* (see Gaffney and Krause 2011), an early branching podocnemideran (sister taxon to Euraxemydidae + Podocnemidoidea), and *Kinkonychelys rogersi* (see Gaffney et al. 2009), a bothremydid. Both species are represented only by skull remains and associating isolated postcranial material of these different turtles must await the recovery of more complete specimens. *Kinkonychelys rogersi*, however, is significant in that it was phylogenetically resolved to be nested within the Kurmademydini, a clade otherwise only known from the Maastrichtian of India and thus supporting a relatively recent biogeographic connection. A lower jaw previously referred to cf. *Erymnochelys* (Gaffney and Forster 2003) may not be closely related to *Erymnochelys* (W. Joyce, unpublished data), an extant, monotypic genus endemic to Madagascar (see Kuchling et al., pp. 1469–74). The fifth taxon, represented by a recently discovered, complete, and exquisitely preserved skeleton, will soon be described (W. Joyce et al., unpublished data).

Squamates

Squamates are represented by one lizard and six snake species, consistent with the disproportion generally present in Late Cretaceous vertebrate faunas of Gondwana and the opposite of those in Laurasia (Krause et al. 2003; Evans and Jones 2010). An earlier report that lizards were present in the Maevarano fauna (Russell et al. 1976) has not been confirmed but a single partial skeleton of a cordyliform lizard, tentatively identified as a cordylid, has since been described and named *Konkasaurus mahalana* by Krause et al. (2003). Stanley (2013) reassessed the affinities of *Konkasaurus* and suggested possible gerrhosaurid affinities. Cordyliforms, the girdled (Cordylidae) and plated (Gerrhosauridae) lizards, are otherwise only known from the Cenozoic of Europe and as extant forms restricted to sub-Saharan Africa and Madagascar.

The largest of the snake species is the madtsoiid *Madtsoia madagascariensis*, a sit-and-wait ambush constrictor estimated to have reached body lengths of nearly 8 m and a body mass of at least 50 kg; it is the largest known snake from the Mesozoic (Hoffstetter 1961; LaDuke et al. 2010). In addition to *M. madagascariensis*, the snake fauna includes two other madtsoiids: 1) *Menarana nosymena*, estimated to have been ~2.5 m long and a head-first terrestrial burrower related to a species, *M. laurasiae*, from Europe (LaDuke et al. 2010); and 2) *Adinophis fisaka*, the smallest of the madtsoiid species, with an estimated length of ~1.5 m (Pritchard et al. 2014). The remaining snakes are all smaller still. These include the nigerophiids *Kelyophis hechti* (see LaDuke et al. 2010), with an estimated length of ~1 m, and *Indophis fanambinana* (see Pritchard et al. 2014), the smallest snake in the assemblage with an estimated length of 50 cm. Nigerophiids are generally thought to have been semiaquatic or aquatic. *Indophis* is elsewhere only known from India, represented by the penecontemporaneous *I. sahnii* (see

Rage and Prasad 1992), again indicating a strong biogeographic link between Madagascar and the Indian subcontinent earlier in the Late Cretaceous. The sixth snake species identified in the Maevarano assemblage is known only from a single fragmentary vertebra and has not been named (Pritchard et al. 2014). With the exception of a braincase fragment of *Menarana nosymena*, all of the snake taxa are represented by only vertebrae and, in two cases (*Madtsoia madagascariensis* and *Menarana nosymena*), ribs. Finally, in light of the large sample and diversity of snakes from the Late Cretaceous of Madagascar, it is notable that there is no evidence of any of the extant Malagasy families (Sanziniidae, Pseudoxyrophiidae, Psammophiidae, Typhlopidae, and Xenotyphlopidae) (see Glaw et al., pp. 1423–42).

Crocodyliforms

The Maevarano Formation crocodyliforms are among the most phylogenetically, ecologically, and morphologically diverse in any known Gondwanan assemblage, and represented by six taxa. Particularly noteworthy are four notosuchian taxa: the small, gracile *Araripesuchus* (Figure 2.10d and 2.10d'), the bizarre, herbivorous *Simosuchus* (Figure 2.10c), the terrestrial carnivore *Miadanasuchus* (Figure 2.10b), and the large, semiaquatic *Mahajangasuchus* (Figure 2.10a).

The first described crocodyliform material from the Maevarano Formation was a partial mandible assigned to a new species, "*Trematochampsa*" *oblita*, and a taxon that provided early insights into possible biotic links with the African mainland (Buffetaut and Taquet 1979). New materials from the Maevarano Formation that included a more complete mandible were used to assign the species to a new genus, *Miadanasuchus* (Rasmusson Simons and Buckley 2009). Many additional specimens, including nearly complete cranial remains from an ontogenetic range of specimens, from hatchling to large adult, will establish *Miadanasuchus* as one of the best-represented peirosaurid crocodyliforms, a clade widespread in the Cretaceous of Africa and South America (J.J.W Sertich, unpublished data).

To date, *Araripesuchus tsangatsangana* is known primarily from a single, densely packed block of multiple associated/articulated skeletons (Turner 2006). This small-bodied crocodyiform is a late-surviving member of a genus that was widespread in middle and early Late Cretaceous assemblages from North Africa and South America. Its small size, sharp teeth, and likely terrestrial habit indicate that *Araripesuchus* probably preyed upon small vertebrates and invertebrates.

The large-bodied crocodyliform *Mahajangasuchus insignis*, initially described on the basis of a partial postcranial skeleton and associated mandible (Buckley and Brochu 1999), is now known from a number of nearly complete skulls and partial skeletons (Turner and Buckley 2008). The species is notable for its wide, dorsoventrally flattened rostrum and narrow, U-shaped mandibular ramus. Despite its phylogenetic links to the more terrestrial peirosaurids, *Mahajangasuchus* shows adaptations, including dorsally positioned orbits and nares, consistent with a semiaquatic, ambush predator habit similar to that of extant crocodylians.

The fourth, and most unusual, of the notosuchians is *Simosuchus clarki*, a pug-nosed and heavily armored, terrestrial crocodyliform. Its palmate, multi-cusped teeth, similar to those of extant iguanids, suggests a largely herbivorous diet (Buckley et al. 2000; Kley et al. 2010). A monographic treatment of *Simosuchus* (Krause and Kley 2010) described nearly every aspect of its osteology based upon exquisitely preserved cranial and postcranial remains.

Two additional, undescribed taxa, both of them neosuchians, are represented by abundant, disarticulated remains. One, a small-bodied, semiaquatic form similar in general appearance to extant alligatorids, represents an early branching neosuchian similar to other Gondwanan forms such as *Isisfordia* and *Susisuchus*. The second, a long-snouted eusuchian, likely represents a Gondwanan radiation of gavial-like crocodyliforms, including *Dolicochampsa* and *Ocepesuchus*. Given the semiaquatic habit of both forms, they represent lineages that potentially could have dispersed to Madagascar following its isolation, in contrast to the largely terrestrial notosuchian taxa that are likely relics of lineages that pre-date the segregation of Madagascar from the rest of Gondwana (Ali and Krause 2011).

Non-Avian Dinosaurs

The first dinosaurian remains from Madagascar were described in 1896 by Charles Depéret, and included several postcranial elements designated as the sauropod *Titanosaurus madagascariensis* and both teeth and postcranial remains used to erect the non-avian theropod *Majungasaurus* (= *Megalosaurus*) *crenatissimus*. Dinosaur material has since been found in abundance but remains limited to the Saurischia. Despite many thousands of person-hours of collecting from the surface, quarrying, and screen-washing from the Maevarano Formation since 1993, no ornithischian material has been found. This calls into question an earlier report by Piveteau (1926b) of the presence of ornithischians, purportedly from the same formation, based on two isolated teeth (now apparently lost, Sues 1980).

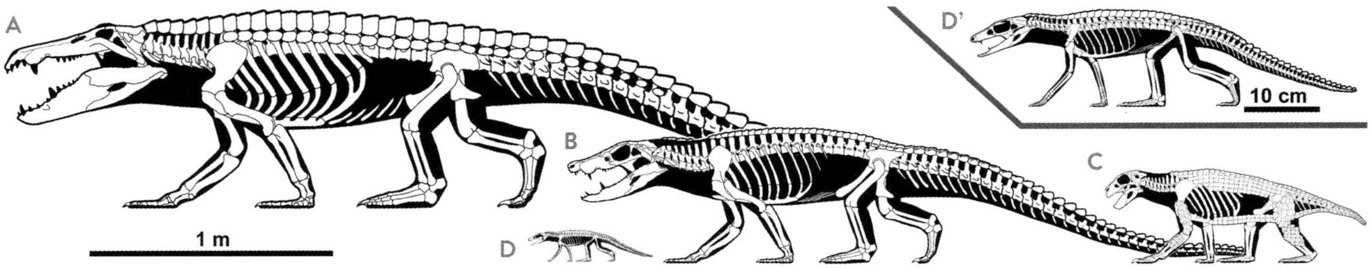

FIGURE 2.10 Reconstructed skeletons of crocodyliforms from the Late Cretaceous of Madagascar, in left lateral view: A) the mahajangasuchid *Mahajangasuchus insignis*, B) the peirosaurid *Miadanasuchus oblita*, C) the libycosuchid *Simosuchus clarki*, and D) the uruguaysuchid *Araripesuchus tsangatsangana*, enlarged in D'. Drawings from Krause et al. (2019).

Regarding sauropod material, the two caudal vertebrae, one osteoderm, and fragment of humerus described by Depéret (1896) represented only the second named titanosaurian known to science. Curry Rogers and Forster (2001) reevaluated these specimens and concluded that they were insufficient to defend the taxonomic uniqueness of *Titanosaurus madagascariensis*. Since then, hundreds of additional titanosaurian elements have been collected from the Maevarano Formation and provide evidence for two valid species, *Rapetosaurus krausei* and *Vahiny depereti*. *Rapetosaurus* (Figure 2.11a) is known from well-preserved, associated, and articulated cranial and postcranial remains representing ontogenetic stages from neonate to large subadult (Curry Rogers and Forster 2004; Curry Rogers 2009; Curry Rogers et al. 2016). *Rapetosaurus* has proven pivotal to ongoing revisions of titanosaurian anatomy and phylogeny (e.g., Curry Rogers 2005; Wilson et al. 2016 and references therein), refining our understanding of the distribution and potential functions of titanosaurian osteoderms (e.g., Curry Rogers et al. 2011; Vidal et al. 2014) and highlighting the growth strategies in these large-bodied vertebrates (e.g., Curry Rogers and Kulik 2018; González et al. 2020). *Vahiny depereti*, named and described by Curry Rogers and Wilson (2014), is much less common than *R. krausei* and, although the two forms coexisted on the island, they are not closely related. Whereas resolution of the phylogenetic affinities of *Rapetosaurus* has proven difficult, *Vahiny* appears to be closely related to Indian and South American taxa (Curry Rogers and Wilson 2014).

Non-avian theropods are represented by three taxa, two abelisauroids (*Majungasaurus crenatissimus* and *Masiakasaurus knopfleri*; Figure 2.11b, c, and c') and an enigmatic unenlagiine dromaeosaurid (*Rahonavis ostromi*; Figure 2.11d and d'). *Majungasaurus* is a midsize (~5.5 m long) abelisaurid, once thought to be a pachycephalosaurid (a "dome-headed" dinosaur named *Majungatholus*) based on fragmentary material (Sues and Taquet 1979; Sues 1980). *Masiakasaurus* is a noasaurid and much smaller (~2 m long). The feathered *Rahonavis* is the smallest (~80 cm long) non-avian theropod in the fauna, and is phylogenetically distinct from the abelisauroids, being affiliated with the small-bodied raptors, near the split between non-avian and avian (i.e., birds) dinosaurs.

Majungasaurus represents one of the best preserved (e.g., Sampson et al. 1998) and best documented of all Gondwanan predatory dinosaurs, with several skulls and skeletons known. A monographic treatment detailed virtually all aspects of the osteology of *Majungasaurus* based on discoveries through 1999 (Sampson and Krause 2007). Since that time, several additional skulls and skeletons have been recovered, allowing for broad insights into the paleobiology of this animal, including ontogenetic changes in craniomandibular shape (Ratsimbaholison et al. 2016), tooth replacement rate and patterning (D'Emic et al. 2019), and paleopathology (Gutherz et al. 2020). Several additional ongoing studies are addressing a multitude of topics related to intraspecific variation in growth patterns and skeletal size and shape variation.

Masiakasaurus, although much less completely known, is now represented by isolated skull and postcranial bones in addition to partially articulated postcranial skeletons (Sampson et al. 2001; Carrano et al. 2002, 2011). This taxon is unique among Dinosauria

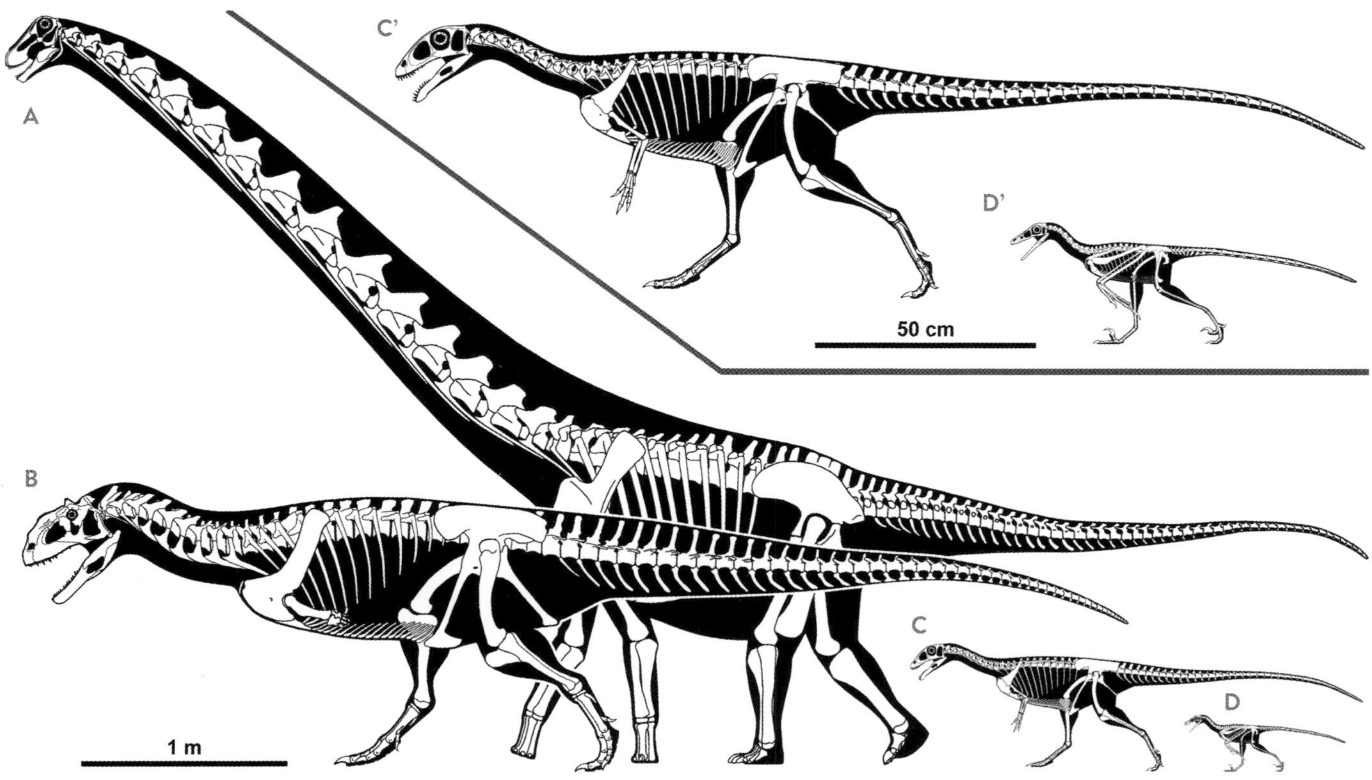

FIGURE 2.11 **Reconstructed skeletons of non-avian dinosaurs from the Late Cretaceous of Madagascar, in left lateral view: A) the titanosaurian sauropod *Rapetosaurus krausei*, B) the abelisaurid theropod *Majungasaurus crenatissimus*, C) the noasaurid theropod *Masiakasaurus knopfleri*, enlarged in C', and D) the dromaeosaurid theropod *Rahonavis ostromi*, enlarged in D'. Drawings from Krause et al. (2019).**

in having procumbent teeth anteriorly. The recovery of postcranial materials of individuals representing different size classes has allowed for the generation of the first growth curve for any abelisauroid, revealing that *Masiakasaurus* matured (skeletally) at a relatively a slow rate when compared with other non-avian dinosaurs (Lee and O'Connor 2013).

Originally described as a bird, and one closely related to the Late Jurassic icon *Archaeopteryx* (Forster et al. 1998), the crow-size *Rahonavis* has more recently been affiliated with a Gondwanan-restricted clade of unenlagiine dromaeosaurids (Makovicky et al. 2005; Turner et al. 2012). Nonetheless, controversy concerning its affinities continues. The most complete specimen is a partial skeleton that exhibits a mosaic of non-avian theropod (e.g., an enlarged, hyperextendible "killing claw" on the second toe) and avian-like (e.g., quill knobs on the forearm bones) features. A recent monographic treatment of *Rahonavis* (Forster et al. 2020) provides extensive description and illustration, including 3D digital models.

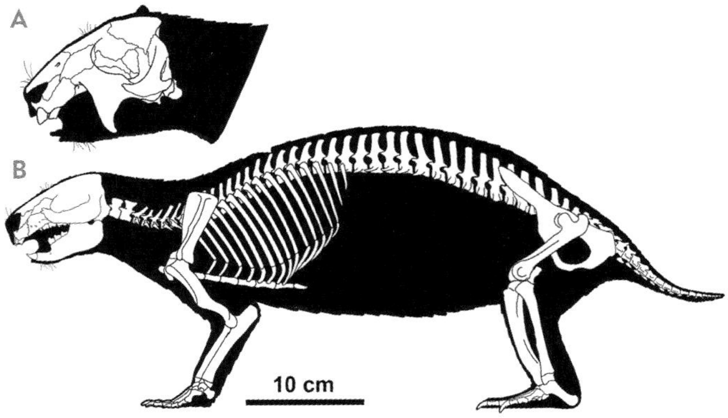

FIGURE 2.12 **Reconstructions of gondwanatherian mammals from the Late Cretaceous of Madagascar, in left lateral view: A) cranium of *Vintana sertichi* and B) skeleton of *Adalatherium hui*. Drawing of *V. sertichi* from Krause et al. (2014) and drawing of *A. hui* from Krause et al. (2020).**

Birds

The raven-size *Vorona berivotrensis* was described based on two partial hind limbs and represents the first bird named from the Maevarano Formation (Forster et al. 1996, 2002). Continuing efforts, particularly the discovery of an exceptionally bird-rich locality (MAD 05–42), have resulted in the recovery of over 100 additional specimens that substantiate an unexpected avian diversity, including four more non-neornithine (i.e., non-modern) taxa (O'Connor and Forster 2010).

With the new material, *Vorona* is now represented by most parts of the skeleton, including spectactular examples of soft tissue preservation (e.g., keratinous claw sheaths, tendons). Recent phylogenetic analyses strongly link this taxon with the early branching, flightless *Patagopteryx* from the Late Cretaceous of South America (e.g., O'Connor et al. 2016). Perhaps most significant is the recovery of two partial avian skulls, including one associated with a significant portion of the postcranial skeleton of a new enantornithine bird and a second form with a long, tall rostral morphology unknown among Mesozoic birds altogether (O'Connor et al. 2019, 2020). Mechanical and digital preparation are now nearly complete on a plethora of new bird fossils, offering great potential for further expanding the Gondwanan avian record at the close of the Cretaceous, a time when most Mesozoic avian groups went extinct, while modern (neornithine) birds were establishing a foothold in advance of their great diversification during the Cenozoic.

Mammals

Whereas the rest of the vertebrate fauna from the Late Cretaceous of Madagascar is now known from approximately 20,000 identifiable specimens, the mammalian fauna is represented by only 12 specimens, listed here in order of description: 1) a fragmentary tooth not identifiable beyond Mammalia *incertae sedis* (Krause et al. 1994); 2) two isolated teeth of the gondwanatherian *Lavanify miolaka* (see Krause et al. 1997b); 3) a fragmentary lower molar tentatively identified as that of a marsupial (Krause 2001; but see Averianov et al. 2003); 4) four isolated teeth, only one of them complete, tentatively assigned to Sudamericidae gen. et sp. indet. (Krause 2013); 5) a molar fragment of a possible multituberculate (Krause 2013); 6) a complete and well-preserved cranium of the gondwanatherian *Vintana sertichi* (Figure 2.12a; Krause 2014; Krause et al. 2014); 7) a fragmentary femur confidently identified as that of a multituberculate (Krause et al. 2017); and 8) a complete and well-preserved skeleton of the gondwanatherian *Adalatherium hui* (Figure 2.12b; Krause and Hoffmann 2020; Krause et al. 2020).

Despite the paucity of these remains, they represent the greatest diversity of Late Cretaceous Gondwanan mammals outside of Argentina. The fauna appears to have been dominated by gondwanatherians, a poorly known group previously recorded from Late Cretaceous to Eocene horizons of South America, Africa, India, and the Antarctic Peninsula, in addition to Madagascar (see summary in Goin et al. 2020). Gondwanatherians, prior to the recovery of the holotype specimens of *V. sertichi* and *A. hui*, were only known from isolated teeth and fragmentary lower jaws. *Vintana sertichi* is noteworthy for being the second-largest known Mesozoic mammal represented by relatively complete material (the largest being *Repenomamus giganticus* from China, Hu et al. 2005) and the skeleton of *A. hui* is noteworthy for being the most complete for any mammaliaform from the entire Mesozoic of Gondwana.

PLATE TECTONIC HISTORY OF MADAGASCAR

The timing and sequence of Gondwanan fragmentation (see Figure 2.13) (detailed reviews in de Wit 2003; Reeves 2014; Krause et al. 2019, 2020) had profound consequences for the biogeographic history of Malagasy vertebrates. Prior to fragmentation, Madagascar lay sandwiched between Somalia, Kenya, and Tanzania to the west, the Seychelles island group and the Indian subcontinent to the east, and Antarcto-Australia to the south. Madagascar, with the Indian subcontinent and the Seychelles still attached to its eastern margin and Antarcto-Australia to the south, physically sundered from Africa in the Early to Middle Jurassic, over 165 Mya. Madagascar moved south-southeastward relative to the African coast along the Davie Fracture Zone and came to rest off Mozambique approximately

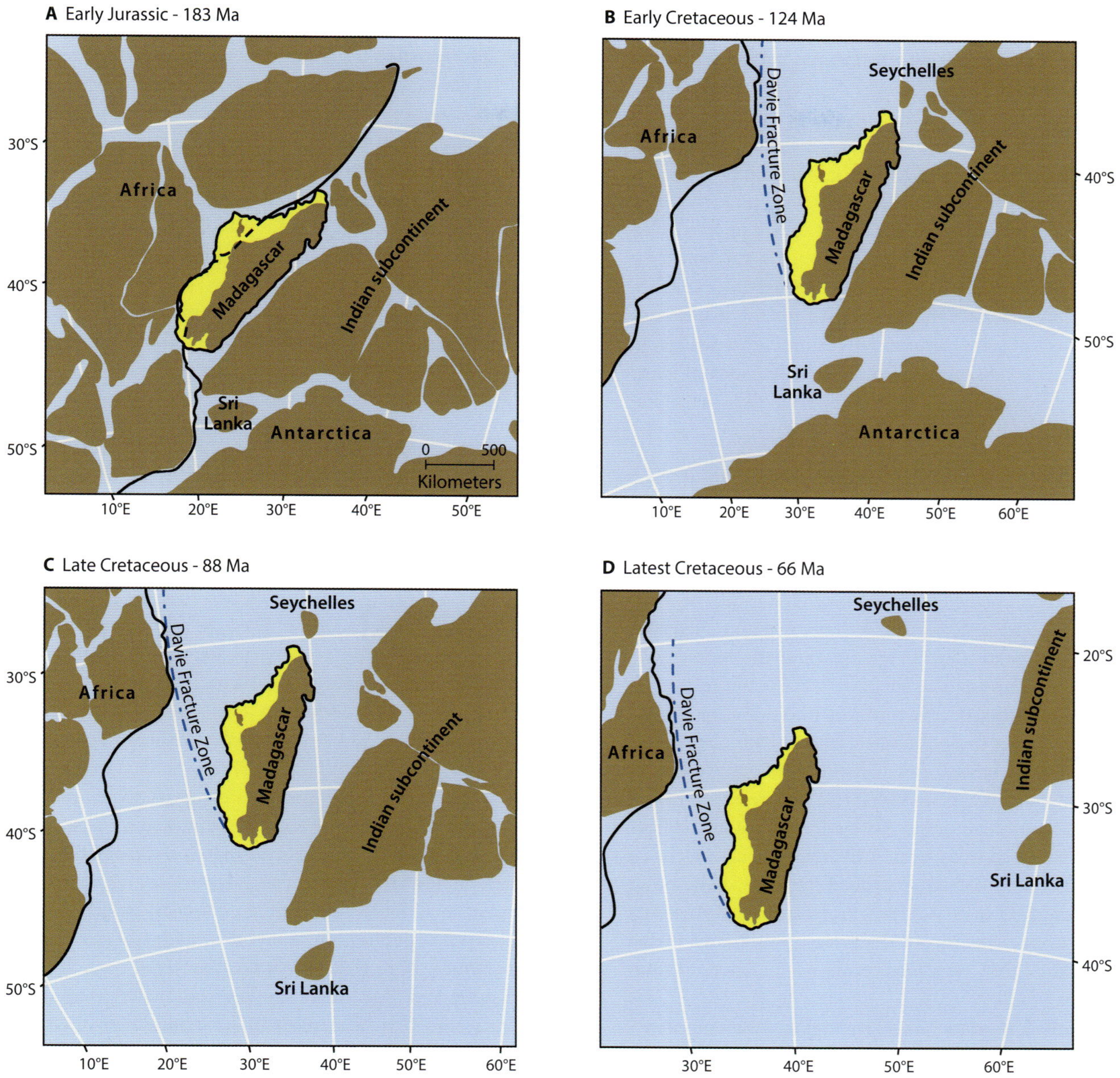

FIGURE 2.13 **Key stages in the plate tectonic history of Madagascar: A) position of Madagascar prior to rifting between West Gondwana (South America-Africa) and East Gondwana (Madagascar-Seychelles-Indian subcontinent-Sri Lanka-Antarctica-Australia) at 183 Mya (Early Jurassic); B) separation of Indo-Madagascar from Antarctica-Australia at 124 Mya (mid–Early Cretaceous); C) separation of Indian subcontinent from Madagascar at 88 Mya (mid–Late Cretaceous); and D) approximate time of deposition of Maevarano Formation at 66 Mya (latest Cretaceous). Solid black lines indicate current coastlines of Madagascar and east Africa; brown represents Precambrian terranes; yellow indicates sedimentary basins along west coast of Madagascar. Modified from Krause et al. (2020). Maps adapted from Earthworks (2021).**

120 Mya (or even earlier, by 133 Mya) (Tuck-Martin et al. 2018; see also Collins et al., pp. 45–51), well before the beginning of the Late Cretaceous, a position it has maintained ever since. It was at approximately this time that a profound plate reorganization event resutured Madagascar with the African plate while a schism developed and expanded between Indo-Madagascar and Antarcto-Australia. The Indian subcontinent-Seychelles block detached from Madagascar approximately 88 Mya, as signaled by the eruption of massive amounts of basaltic lava (e.g., Storey et al. 1995, 1997), and migrated rapidly northeastward toward Eurasia.

The rifting event between Africa and Madagascar created the three large sedimentary basins (Ambilobe, Mahajanga, and Morondava) along the island's west coast (Figure 2.8), which has been a tectonically passive margin since relative movement between the two landmasses ceased in the Early Cretaceous (Obrist-Farner et al. 2017). Nonmarine sediments of Permo-Triassic age were laid down in the marginal basins during the earliest stages of rifting, followed by marine conditions in the developing rift zone in the Early–Middle Jurassic, and then transgressive-regressive cyclicity until the end of the Cretaceous. Fully marine conditions were established in the basins by the terminal Cretaceous, when Madagascar lay approximately 15° farther south than it does today, and persisted through the Paleogene and into the Neogene.

BIOGEOGRAPHIC HISTORY REVEALED

A densely sampled fossil record coupled with well-supported phylogenetic hypotheses and accurate paleogeographic reconstructions provide the building blocks for sound biogeographic analysis. These building blocks are still in short supply for the majority of Gondwanan biotas but some patterns are beginning to emerge, in part the result of recent discoveries from Mesozoic strata in many areas of the former supercontinent, including from the Late Cretaceous of Madagascar.

Biogeography of the Late Cretaceous Vertebrate Fauna of Madagascar

Our research group has written extensively about the general similarities of the vertebrate fauna from the Late Cretaceous of Madagascar with penecontemporaneous vertebrate faunas in other parts of Gondwana, particularly Argentina and the Indian subcontinent (e.g., see Krause et al. 2006, 2019, 2020 and references therein), including in the precursor of this book (Krause 2003). We inferred a level of cosmopolitanism among Late Cretaceous Gondwanan vertebrate faunas that had not been recognized to such an extent previously. Several vertebrate taxa recovered from the Upper Cretaceous Maevarano Formation appeared to have their most closely related sister taxa in the Late Cretaceous of either Argentina or the Indian subcontinent, or both. How other Gondwanan landmasses such as Africa, Antarctica, and Australia (and southern Europe) were involved was largely unknown owing to the paucity of the Late Cretaceous vertebrate fossil record from those areas at that time.

We regarded the close relationships among penecontemporaneous vertebrates from the latest Cretaceous of Madagascar, India, and Argentina to be consistent with an alternative paleogeographic reconstruction of Gondwana that posited a lingering connection between these landmasses through Antarctica (Hay et al. 1999). This reconstruction contrasted rather sharply with earlier paleogeographic reconstructions (e.g., Smith et al. 1994; Scotese 1998) in which Indo-Madagascar was viewed as having been isolated from all other Gondwanan landmasses by ~120 Mya (see Figure 2.17 in Krause 2003). In other words, the purported Late Cretaceous physical connections between Indo-Madagascar and South America through Antarctica were employed to help explain the unexpected cosmopolitanism among those vertebrate faunas.

A great deal of progress has been made since the review in the precursor of this book (Krause 2003). First, the hypothesis of Late Cretaceous Gondwanan cosmopolitanism spurred closer inspection of the potential viability of physical connections at that time between Indo-Madagascar and Antarctica. The Hay et al. (1999) paper hypothesized a connection from Antarctica to Indo-Madagascar across the Kerguelen Plateau until as late as 80 Mya; this was effectively refuted by Ali and Aitchison (2009), who established that only small portions of the Kerguelen Plateau were subaerially exposed at the beginning of the Campanian (~83 Mya) in an ocean expanse of approximately 2100 km between India and Antarctica. Similarly, the geological evidence for a connection between Antarctica and Madagascar across the Gunnerus Ridge, proposed by Case (2002), was found wanting by Ali and Krause (2011). The evidence for such a causeway simply does not exist; indeed, 83 Mya Antarctica and Madagascar were separated by a distance of ~3000 km. Furthermore, Ali and Krause (2011) discounted Late Cretaceous land connections between Madagascar and South America through Africa.

Second, Ali and Krause (2011) also examined the relationships of the relatively large vertebrate taxa from the Late Cretaceous of Gondwanan landmasses that are inferred to be obligatorily terrestrial (abelisauroid theropods, titanosaurian sauropods, and notosuchian crocodyliforms) in a stratigraphically calibrated (i.e., temporal) context. The authors concluded that the closely related forms from Madagascar, the Indian subcontinent, and South America had long ghost lineages (hypothesized earlier lines of descent that are not represented in the fossil record), most of them extending back to near, or even well before, the Early-Late Cretaceous boundary at 100 Mya. In other words, the ancestry of these taxa appeared to extend back to a time when the landmasses involved were either contiguous or still relatively close to one another, thus indicating a distribution based on vicariance.

Third, the record of Gondwanan fossil vertebrates from the 34-million-year span of the Late Cretaceous has improved considerably since 2003, although it is still very uneven. It is well beyond the scope of this overview to provide a comprehensive review of these discoveries, but a recently compiled list of newly discovered crocodyliform, sauropod, non-avian theropod, and mammaliaform genera from Gondwanan landmasses is instructive (Krause et al. 2019: supplemental Tables 1–4 therein). Table 2.1, which summarizes data from that publication, shows the number of new generic records for these groups that have been discovered from 2003 to 2019 inclusively, and reveals that, for these four major groups, 60% of Late Cretaceous Gondwanan genera have been discovered during that interval, despite the fact that the earliest records commenced in the late 1800s. The greatest gains, by far, have been in South America but important discoveries in Africa and Arabia, the Indian subcontinent, and Madagascar have also been made. Despite the recent recovery of new non-avian dinosaur taxa from Australia (e.g., Poropat et al. 2016, and references therein) and both non-avian (Lamanna et al. 2019, and references therein) and avian (Cordes-Person et al. 2020, and references therein) dinosaur taxa from Antarctica, the Late Cretaceous vertebrate record from those two continents remains extremely incomplete. The Late Cretaceous diversity of vertebrates from Australia, however, is significantly enhanced if the Lightning Ridge fauna (Griman Creek Formation) is Cenomanian (earliest Late Cretaceous) in age, rather than Albian (latest Early Cretaceous), as concluded by Bell et al. (2019: Table 1).

Fourth, the discoveries of new Late Cretaceous taxa from other Gondwanan landmasses have resulted in new opportunities to test phylogenetic and biogeographic hypotheses. Consistent with a plate tectonic history indicating most recent physical connections with the Indian subcontinent, sister taxon relationships of several Late Cretaceous vertebrates from Madagascar are with those

TABLE 2.1. **Discoveries of Late Cretaceous crocodyliforms, sauropod dinosaurs, non-avian theropod dinosaurs, and mammaliaforms from the major Gondwanan landmasses**

MAJOR GONDWANAN LANDMASSES	CROCODYLIFORMS	SAUROPODS	NON-AVIAN THEROPODS	MAMMALIAFORMS	TOTALS
Africa and Arabia	6/11 = 55%	4/6 = 67%	1/5 = 20%	0/0 = 0%	11/22 = 50%
Antarctica	0/0 = 0%	0/0 = 0%	0/0 = 0%	0/0 = 0%	0/0 = 0%
Australia	0/0 = 0%	3/3 = 100%	0/0 = 0%	0/0 = 0%	3/3 = 100%
Indian subcontinent	0/1 = 0%	4/7 = 57%	3/6 = 50%	4/5 = 80%	11/19 = 58%
Madagascar	1/4 = 25%	1/2 = 50%	1/4 = 25%	1/2 = 50%	4/12 = 33%
South America	24/38 = 63%	33/46 = 72%	23/38 = 61%	5/11 = 45%	85/133 = 64%
TOTALS	31/54 = 57%	45/64 = 70%	28/53 = 53%	10/18 = 56%	114/189 = 60%

Notes: Numerator indicates number of genera identified 2003–2019. Denominator indicates number of total genera known through all time. Numbers extracted from Krause et al. (2019).

recovered from India. These are summarized in Krause et al. (2019) but are witnessed among several taxa, including bothremydid turtles (Kurmademydini), nigerophiid snakes (*Indophis*), notosuchian crocodyliforms (*Simosuchus*), non-avian theropods, and gondwanatherian mammals. Similarly, relatively recent discoveries in the Late Cretaceous of mainland Africa have led to new phylogenetic analyses that have revealed some important biogeographic signals. For instance, the terrestrial notosuchian crocodyliforms *Kaprosuchus* from the Cenomanian of Niger and *Libycosuchus* from the Cenomanian of Egypt were resolved as sister taxa of *Mahajangasuchus* and *Simosuchus*, respectively, from the Maastrichtian of Madagascar (Sereno and Larsson 2009; Turner and Sertich 2010). Similarly, *Araripesuchus*, known from the Aptian of Niger, and the Aptian to Turonian of South America, is represented in the Maastrichtian of Madagascar (Turner 2006). Neosuchian remains from the Late Cretaceous of Africa hint at endemic or Tethyan distributions (e.g., Jouve et al. 2008; Saber et al. 2018). The titanosaurian sauropod story remains complicated by lack of a comprehensive phylogenetic analysis for the group, but some interesting patterns are emerging that suggest an early, widespread distribution. In particular, new titanosaurians from the Cretaceous of Africa have revealed possible connections to faunas in Europe and South America (e.g., Gorscak et al. 2017; Sallam et al. 2018). Localized extinctions appear to explain some geographic restrictions, and hypothesized long ghost lineages for some taxa indicate distributions driven by vicariance (e.g, Gorscak and O'Connor 2016; Poropat et al. 2016).

Finally, an outgrowth of these phylogenetic analyses is that, as each vertebrate taxon from the Late Cretaceous of Madagascar is described and analyzed in a phylogenetic context, we find a consistent pattern: the Malagasy taxa exhibit an unusually high number of unique features, or autapomorphies. This has not yet been rigorously quantified across the fauna but there is a general sense that these autapomorphies are reflective of a long period of isolation, which is consistent with current knowledge that, in the late Maastrichtian, Madagascar had already been an island for ~20 million years (~88–66 Mya) and, before that, was a part of Indo-Madagascar, which itself was isolated from other Gondwanan landmasses for ~30 million years (~120–88 Mya). Perhaps the most notable examples of morphological uniqueness are found in the frog *Beelzebufo* (Evans et al. 2008, 2014), the crocodyliform *Simosuchus* (Buckley et al. 2000; Turner and Sertich 2010), selected birds (O'Connor et al. 2020), and the gondwanatherian mammals *Vintana* and *Adalatherium* (Krause et al. 2014, 2020).

What Became of the Late Cretaceous Vertebrates of Madagascar?

In light of the dearth of information from the pre–late Pleistocene Cenozoic vertebrate fossil record of Madagascar, it is impossible to know precisely what became of the island's Late Cretaceous vertebrate fauna. What we do know is that there are no extant, Holocene, or late Pleistocene taxa on Madagascar that are clearly descended from any of the known Late Cretaceous taxa of terrestrial or freshwater vertebrates. This line of evidence suggests that the Late Cretaceous taxa went extinct sometime between the Maastrichtian and the late Pleistocene. Although there were pronounced warming and cooling intervals during that time span that indubitably affected patterns of vertebrate evolution and diversity (e.g., Figueirido et al. 2012; Samuels and Hopkins 2017), some more rapid than others (Zachos et al. 2008), we also know of a truly major cataclysmic event that occurred—the asteroid impact at the Cretaceous–Paleogene boundary. The impact eradicated 75–80% of life on the planet (Jablonski 1994; Khosla and Lucas 2020). There is no reason to believe that Madagascar was immune to this global scourge (Agnarsson and Kuntner 2012). We also know of the massive eruptions and associated intrusive magmatism now preserved as the Deccan Traps, in India, which, at the end of the Cretaceous, was much closer to Madagascar than it is today (Figure 2.13d). It is impossible to know how much of vertebrate life in the Late Cretaceous of Madagascar was affected by one as opposed to the other of these events, but they likely both had devastating effects resulting in ecosystem collapse on the island, as they did globally (e.g., Samonds et al. 2013; Schoene et al. 2019). Whether some Malagasy vertebrate taxa passed through the Cretaceous–Paleogene boundary, as they did elsewhere (see summary in Khosla and Lucas 2020), and became extinct later will only be known with a more complete fossil record.

Biogeographic Origins of the Extant Vertebrate Fauna of Madagascar

The Maevarano Formation assemblage yields substantial, though negative, evidence with regard to the biogeographic origins of the highly endemic and taxonomically imbalanced extant vertebrate fauna of Madagascar. Unfortunately, the oldest undisputed terrestrial and freshwater vertebrates recorded from the 66-million-year post-Cretaceous Cenozoic era are only some 80,000 years old, of late Pleistocene age (Samonds 2007). The huge temporal gap in the Late Cretaceous to late Pleistocene record of nonmarine fossil vertebrates is largely the consequence of the overwhelming predominance of marine rocks on Madagascar during this interval (Besairie 1972; Krause et al. 1997a; Obrist-Farner et al. 2017). The late Pleistocene and Holocene record only increases the level of endemism so characteristic of the extant fauna. It includes an array of extinct lemurs (some as large as a modern-day gorilla), pygmy hippopotamuses, the aardvark-like *Plesiorycteropus*, giant tortoises and crocodiles, enormous flightless birds, and several other taxa unique to the island (Godfrey and Douglass, pp. 191–97).

None of the fish, frog, turtle, snake, lizard, crocodyliform, bird, or mammal taxa now known from the Maevarano Formation appears closely related to the higher taxa of vertebrates on the island today, or those that existed during the late Pleistocene and earlier in the Holocene. The progenitors of the later vertebrate taxa therefore appear to have been absent from the island in the Late Cretaceous (Krause 2010; Krause et al. 2019), thus casting considerable doubt on speculation that the ancestral stocks were isolated on the island when it separated from other parts of Gondwana, including Africa, in the Jurassic (e.g., Masters et al. 1995; see reviews in Krause et al. 1997a and Agnarsson and Kuntner 2012). Direct testing is not possible because of the virtual absence of a Paleogene and Neogene nonmarine vertebrate fossil record on Madagascar, but the negative evidence from the Late Cretaceous Maevarano assemblage suggests that the ancestors of the extant Malagasy fauna must have arrived sometime during the Cenozoic, presumably by crossing a significant marine barrier. This possibility, as unlikely as it might seem, is made more feasible in light of inferences concerning the physiology of the ancestors of some extant Malagasy vertebrates (e.g., Kappeler 2000; Dausmann et al. 2009), demonstration that even relatively salt-intolerant species crossed large marine gaps (e.g., Vences et al. 2003; Pyron 2014; da Fonte et al. 2019), first-hand observations of terrestrial vertebrates traversing marine barriers (e.g., Censky et al. 1998; Van Duzer 2004), and examples of inferred marine crossings in the past that were much greater in distance than those across the Mozambique Channel (e.g., Seiffert et al. 2020). Also supporting this assessment is the computer modeling of paleo-ocean surface currents by Ali and Huber (2010), which is consistent with the possibility of west-to-east rafting of small vertebrates from Africa across the Mozambique Channel in the Cenozoic prior to the mid-Miocene. Although it appears that certain Malagasy taxa (e.g., some birds, bats, and frogs) may be of Indo-Malaysian origin, a consensus is emerging that most taxa did indeed arrive by sweepstakes dispersal (rafting, swimming, and/or island hopping) across the minimum 430 km span of the Mozambique Channel from Africa (Yoder and Nowak 2006; Samonds et al. 2012). This included the signature group of extant Malagasy vertebrates on the island, the lemurs, which appear to have made the crossing at least twice during the middle of the Cenozoic (Gunnell et al. 2018; see Yoder, pp. 1821–24, for further discussion on this point).

McCall (1997: 664) suggested that "large areas of the Mozambique Channel were dry land" during the Paleogene as a result of uplift along the Davie Ridge, a north–south feature deep on the Indian Ocean floor that marks the track along which Madagascar moved during the Middle Jurassic to Early Cretaceous as it separated from Africa. McCall speculated that the Davie Ridge served as a land bridge for mammalian colonization of Madagascar from Africa. The extreme dissimilarity of the modern-day African and Malagasy terrestrial faunas refutes this contention (e.g., Simpson 1952), as does the lack of compelling geological evidence to support the notion that the Mozambique Channel, which is currently 2 km deep in most areas and over 3 km deep in others, was largely dry land at certain times during the Cenozoic (Rabinowitz and Woods 2006; Krause 2010). Although seamounts along the Davie Ridge may have been emergent during sea level lowstands, the evidence for them being emergent islands is inconclusive and, furthermore, they would have been but small dots of land in a channel 430–1000 km wide (Rabinowitz and Woods 2006). Furthermore, the Comoro islands, though larger than the seamounts along the Davie Ridge, at most served as recent stepping-stones for dispersal since they are volcanic in origin and were emplaced less than 8 Mya (Nougier et al. 1986). Based on currently available biological, paleontological, and geological evidence, it appears that the ancestors of the extant vertebrate fauna of Madagascar did indeed survive the rigors of crossing formidable marine barriers surrounding the island sometime after the Late Cretaceous, thus refuting a vicariance hypothesis for the biogeographic origins of the extant vertebrate fauna (Samonds et al. 2012, 2013).

ACKNOWLEDGMENTS

We are deeply grateful to the government of the Republic of Madagascar for the ability to conduct research on the island. We also thank our colleagues at the Université d'Antananarivo; B. Andriamihaja and the staff of the Madagascar Institute for the Conservation of Tropical Environments; and the villagers living in our study areas of northwestern Madagascar for the last quarter of a century of collaboration and logistical support; J. Ali for helpful comments on the manuscript; L. Betti-Nash for Figures 2.8 and 2.13 and S. Hartman for skeletal drawings in Figures 2.9 to 2.12; all expedition members for their hard work, long hours, and good humor in the field; and the US National Science Foundation and the National Geographic Society for funding.

Subject editor: Steven M. Goodman

CENOZOIC FOSSILS OF MADAGASCAR

K. E. Samonds

Madagascar has been isolated for more than 80 million years, meaning that its separation happened well before the origin of most of its endemic modern biota that lives on the island today. The critical question is: if most of the ancestors of these groups were not stranded when Madagascar separated from other landmasses, how did it acquire such unusual animals and plants, especially those with close relatives on distant modern continents? How, when, and from where did they cross such a formidable marine barrier?

The Phanerozoic is divided into three major eras: the Paleozoic, Mesozoic, and Cenozoic, but Madagascar's fossil record of terrestrial vertebrates contains major gaps. Fossils are described from the Mesozoic spanning the period 259–66 million years ago (Mya) (late Permian, Triassic, Early to Middle Jurassic, and Late Cretaceous), and then the record jumps to recent geological time, extending back only ~80,000 years to the Late Quaternary (see Samonds 2007; Krause et al., pp. 59–68; Flynn et al., pp. 51–59; Godfrey and Douglass, pp. 191–97). As such, this major gap of 66 million years, nearly the entire span of the Cenozoic era, means that we know very little about this critical interval when the ancestral stocks of many extant clades are thought to have colonized and established themselves on the island (Samonds et al. 2012, 2013; Samonds et al., pp. 73–78).

Fossils deposited during the Cenozoic remain our best direct source of information to test different biogeographic hypotheses associated with the history of colonization of extant organisms, yet due to the low representation of fossiliferous Cenozoic terrestrial deposits, this critical time period is virtually unrepresented in Madagascar's fossil record. This contribution reviews our current understanding of the island's pre–late Pleistocene Cenozoic fossil record, highlighting recent discoveries, and interprets these findings in the context of the origin and evolution of Madagascar's modern groups.

GEOLOGICAL CONTEXT

Madagascar's Cenozoic sediments are primarily concentrated along the northwest coast within the Mahajanga sedimentary basin, along a northeast–southwest arch parallel to the Mozambique Channel shoreline (Figure 2.14). These rocks are largely Eocene to Pliocene in age, and overlay thick Cretaceous siliciclastic, carbonate, and volcanic units (Besairie 1956, 1969; Samonds et al. 2009). Until relatively recently, the only comprehensive description of this region's fossils was the reconnaissance work done in the early part of the last century (Collignon and Cottreau 1927). Like most of the island's mapped Cenozoic sediments, those in the Mahajanga Basin are primarily marine, so their potential to elucidate the origin of the modern terrestrial groups was previously thought to be limited. As a result, many potential fossil-bearing beds remained unexplored until relatively recently.

Eocene

The Eocene of Madagascar is represented by two main fossil sites: Ampazony and Katsepy (Samonds et al. 2001, 2009, 2019a). Ampazony is a nearshore marine site, 15 km northeast of the city of Mahajanga (Figure 2.14). This locality includes both Eocene and Pliocene deposits; fossil-bearing rocks were previously mapped as Pliocene (Besairie 1969) but have since been reinterpreted as middle to late Eocene (Samonds et al. 2009). Sediments consist of interbedded sandy claystones, mudstones, siltstones, and marly limestones formed in low-lying coastal and shallow marine environments. Nearby underlying exposures display large-scale mud cracks consistent with subaerial exposure, likely on peritidal mudflats. Fossiliferous beds at Ampazony have produced invertebrates (including bivalves and gastropods), selachians, fragmentary remains of bony fishes and reptiles, and sirenians (Samonds et al. 2009, 2019a). Ampazony is the type locality for the primitive endemic pygmy seacow *Eotheroides lambondrano*, a member of a genus that was broadly distributed within shallow marine waters of the Tethyan region during the middle and late Eocene (Samonds et al. 2009).

The site of Katsepy is located on the western side of the Betsiboka River, west of Mahajanga (Figure 2.14). Sediments are exposed on the shore face of the Mozambique Channel as cliffs and large overturned blocks of carbonate units, and have been interpreted as Eocene in age (Besairie 1956). Sedimentary facies consist largely of nummulitic limestones with numerous other foraminiferans (mostly alveolinids), crinoids, echinoids, bivalves, gastropods, crabs, and occasionally vertebrate fossils (bony fishes, sharks, and rays) (Samonds et al. 2019a).

Miocene

The most complete marine Miocene sedimentary sequence reported from Madagascar is Nosy Makamby (also known as Mahakamby), a small (~1.6 km × 0.4 km) offshore island located near the Mahavavy River delta in the northwest, about 50 km west of Mahajanga (Figure 2.14). This site is recognized for having produced a partial sirenian braincase attributed to the genus *Halitherium* nearly a century ago (Collignon and Cottreau 1927; but see discussion and reinterpretation in Samonds et al. 2019b). Nearshore sandy limestone deposits have yielded a diverse assemblage of benthic foraminiferans, crabs (Crustacea, Decapoda, Brachyura), bivalves, gastropods, echinoids, sharks, rays, bony fish, reptiles (including crocodyliform teeth and large pieces of turtle carapace and plastron), dolphins, and sirenians (Collignon and Cottreau 1927; Besairie and Collignon 1972; Charbonnier et al. 2012; Ramihangihajason et al. 2014; Andrianavalona et al. 2015; Gottfried et al. 2017; Samonds and Fordyce 2019; Samonds et al. 2019b, 2019c).

Based on the fossil mollusks, Collignon and Cottreau (1927) originally interpreted the age of nearshore marine deposits of Nosy Makamby as early Miocene (younger than Aquitanian), ranging

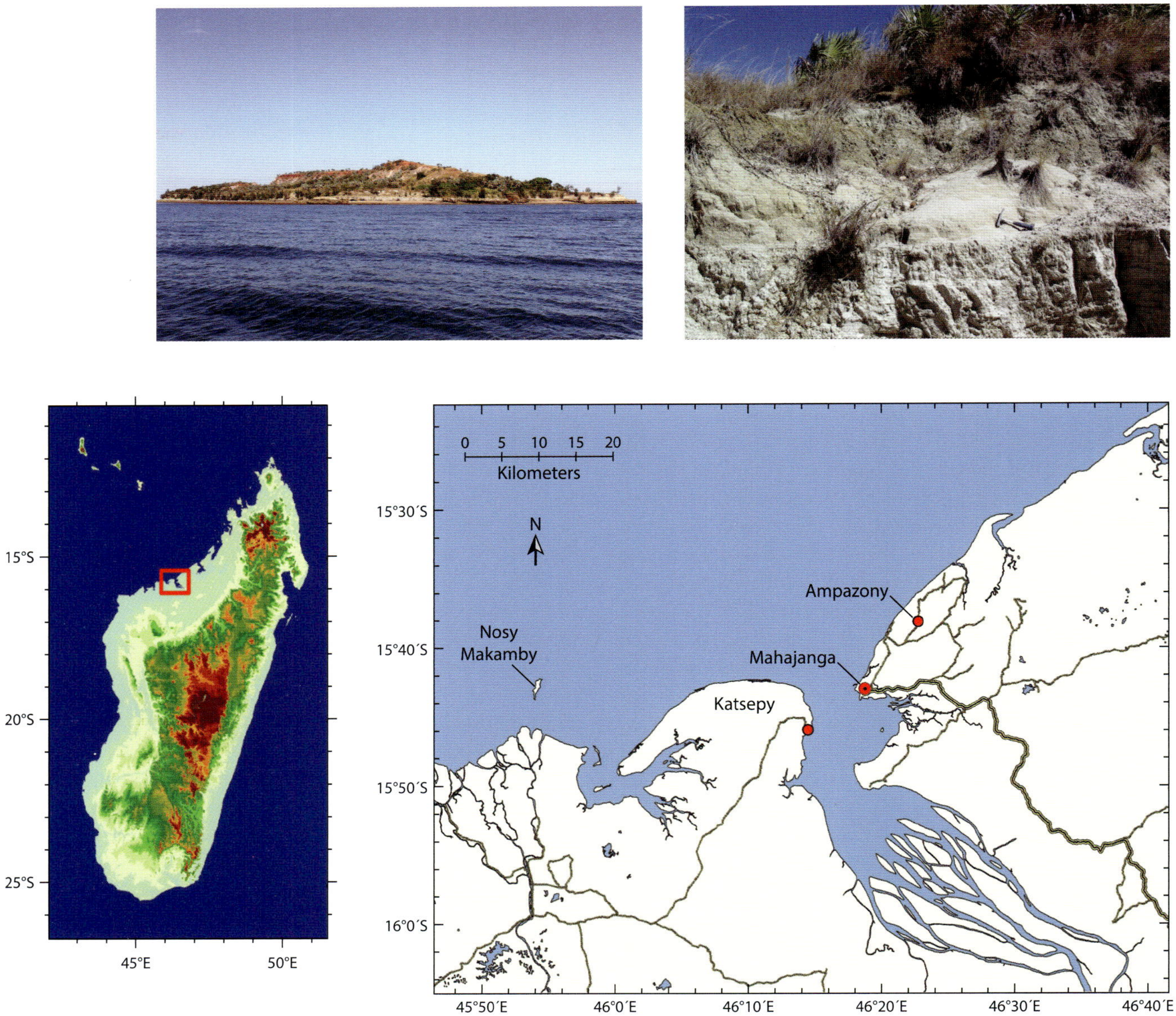

FIGURE 2.14 **Map showing location of study localities, as well as photographs of sites at Nosy Makamby (top left) and Ampazony (top right); also indicated is the city of Mahajanga. Elevation model (bottom left) from Jet Propulsion Laboratory (2004).**

between the Burdigalian and Helvetian (the older term Helvetian approximately equates to the Langhian–Serravallian interval). Miliolid foraminiferans are abundant in nearly all of the deposits of Makamby and support a Miocene tropical nearshore paleoenvironment (Lavocat et al. 1960; Ramihangihajason et al. 2014). Recent work on strontium isotopes suggests that some of the sediments may be as late as early Tortonian in age (~10 Mya) (Samonds and Fordyce 2019). Limited exploration has also been conducted in the lateral extensions of these Miocene sedimentary sequences in the regions of Cap Tanjona, Cap Sada, and Amparafaka to the west (Collignon and Cottreau 1927; K. Samonds, unpublished data); invertebrate and vertebrate fossils (sharks, turtles, and sirenians) have been discovered.

Other Deposits

It is worth noting that there are also lacustrine sedimentary basins in the Central Highlands of Madagascar, mapped as Pliocene in age (Lenoble 1949). These basins are surrounded by basaltic formations (including the Ankaratra Massif and associated flows) and gneissic massifs, and include clays, cinerites, sandstones, marls, diatomites, marls, and lignites. Early expeditions by scientists reported the presence of vertebrate fossils (hippopotamus, herons, crocodiles, and fishes), as well as gastropods, diatoms and plants, but the age and exact location of these deposits has never been verified (Lenoble 1949).

REPRESENTED GROUPS

Cenozoic invertebrate fossils tend to be well preserved and recovered in high density in Eocene and Miocene deposits, in contrast to the relative paucity of vertebrate fossils. Groups reported include echinoderms, foraminiferans, gastropods, bivalves, crinoids, bryozoans, and crabs (Collignon and Cottreau 1927; Charbonnier et al. 2012; Ramihangihajason et al. 2014). Miocene benthic foraminiferans include 25 genera; and on the basis of the groups recovered the local environment is presumed to have had warm, shallow water (Ramihangihajason et al. 2014). Marine bivalve mollusks of the genus *Kuphus* (family Teredinidae) are shipworms that secrete calcareous tubes and are frequently fossilized. They are preserved in exceedingly high numbers at Nosy Makamby but are currently understudied and remain poorly known.

Selachians, a type of elasmobranch, have been described from both the Eocene and Miocene record of Madagascar (Andrianavalona et al. 2015; Samonds et al. 2019a; Figure 2.15a–c). The Eocene record includes eight sharks: *Nebrius blankenhorni*, *Brachycarcharias koerti*, *Galeocerdo eaglesomei*, two species of *Carcharhinus* (including locality for the type of *C. underwoodi*), *Physogaleus*, *Rhizoprionodon*, and *Sphyrna* (Samonds et al. 2019a). Three rays have also been reported (*Pristis*, *Myliobatis*, and an undetermined dasyatid ray). The species diversity of this site is low, but the age and taxa recovered are similar to genera from Congo, west Africa, Arabia, Asia, Europe, and North, Central, and South America, suggesting that these genera were broadly distributed and diverse within the shallow marine settings of the Tethyan and southern provinces during the middle and late Eocene. Miocene selachians from Madagascar include *Otodus*, *Carcharhinus*, *Galeocerdo*, *Rhizoprionodon*, *Sphyrna*, *Hemipristis*, *Squatina*, *Rostroraja*, *Himantura*, and Myliobatidae (Andrianavalona et al. 2015).

Bony fish fossils span both the Eocene and Miocene but are generally poorly known. Preliminary work on Miocene fishes reported a large sample of barracuda teeth (*Sphyraena* sp.; Figure 2.15d).

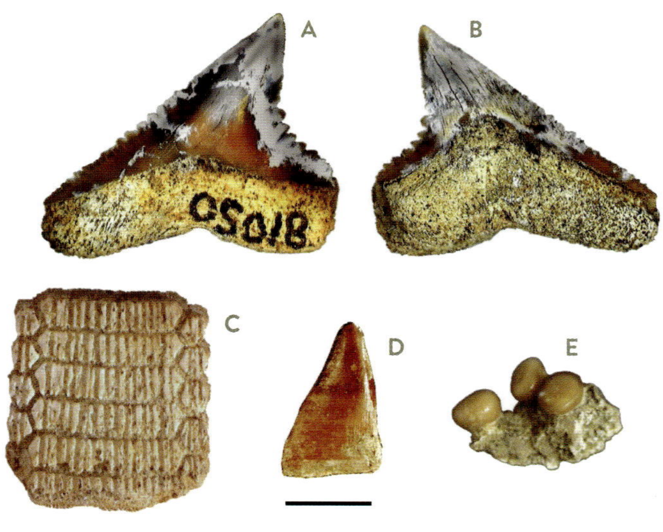

FIGURE 2.15 **Fossil selachians and bony fishes from northwestern Madagascar. A) and B) paratype of Eocene shark *Carcharhinus underwoodi* from Ampazony (UAP 05.018), upper anterolateral tooth in labial and lingual views, respectively; C) Eocene ray (*Myliobatis* sp.) from Ampazony (UAP 03.738a) partial lower dentition in basal view; D) Miocene barracuda tooth (*Sphyraena* sp.) from Nosy Makamby; and E) Eocene pycnodont fish jaw (UAP 037.61) from Ampazony. Scale bar = 5 mm. UAP, Université d'Antananarivo Paléontologie, Antananarivo, Madagascar.**

These barracuda appear to have inhabited environments that also included coral reefs (based on fossil scleractinians) and seagrass beds (evidenced by the epiphytic benthic foraminifera *Elphidium* sp.). The relatively common occurrence of barracuda in Miocene deposits at Nosy Makamby corroborates the presence of a tropical marine ecosystem encircling Madagascar by the Miocene, likely similar to the environment found there today. In addition to *Sphyraena*, isolated pycnodont teeth are also common (Figure 2.15e).

Sirenians represent the best-studied and most diverse mammals from Madagascar's Cenozoic fossil record. *Eotheroides lambondrano* was first named from the Eocene nearshore marine deposits of Ampazony (Figure 2.16a). Referred material consists of a nearly complete adult skull (including the first complete rostrum known for *Eotheroides*) and several portions of pachyosteosclerotic ribs. The cranium shares similarities to *E. aegyptiacum* from the middle Eocene of Egypt, but the age and relatively primitive morphology makes it a potential candidate for a basal member of the genus, implying that it may represent the ancestral form from which more northerly species were derived (Samonds et al. 2009). The naming of this species also demonstrates a much larger geographic range of *Eotheroides* than previously appreciated—Ampazony is about 5000 km from both Egypt and India, the location of other species within this genus.

Miocene dugongid sirenians from Nosy Makamby include four contemporaneous forms: *Rytiodus heali* (subfamily Dugonginae), *Norosiren zazavavindrano* and *Metaxytherium* cf. *krahuletzi* (subfamily Halitheriinae), and one additional form that is a probable dugongine but not yet matched with any named genus (Samonds et al. 2019b). The occurrence of a shallow nearshore marine environment harboring multiple contemporaneous sirenians is a pattern seen elsewhere in the world over the past approximately 26 million years (e.g., Vélez-Juarbe et al. 2012). Surprisingly, the sirenian fauna from Nosy Makamby appears to share no genera in common with the roughly contemporaneous Kutch, western India.

Metaxytherium cf. *krahuletzi* marks the first Neogene occurrence from the Indian Ocean, not only of this genus but of the subfamily Halitheriinae; this supports the hypothesis that both taxa were more widely distributed during the Miocene than previously thought. The occurrence of *Rytiodus heali* on Madagascar (Samonds et al. 2019b) also demonstrates a much larger geographic and possibly temporal range for this genus (Domning and Sorbi 2011) as Nosy Makamby is about 6000 km from the only other known locality of this species (Jabal Zaltan, Libya) and 8500 km from the only other species recognized within this genus (*R. capgrandi*, known from France).

Nosy Makamby is the type locality for *Norosiren zazavavindrano* (gen. et. sp. nov.), interpreted as a primitive relative of *Xenosiren* (subfamily Dugonginae; Figure 2.16c). *Norosiren* appears to have closest affinities to the Mexican genus *Xenosiren*; the fact that each of these two genera is known from only a single fragmentary specimen suggests that there is still a lot to learn about dugongine relationships and diversity.

Other mammals recovered include a single lumbar vertebra from a small Miocene dolphin (Cetacea: Odontoceti); this specimen represents the first cetacean fossil reported from Madagascar (Samonds and Fordyce 2019; Figure 2.16b). There are no close matches with extant genera representing the major clades of Odontoceti (Physeteridae, Kogiidae, Ziphiidae, Platanistidae, Inioidea, and Delphinoidea), but there is some similarity with the much larger stem-platanistid

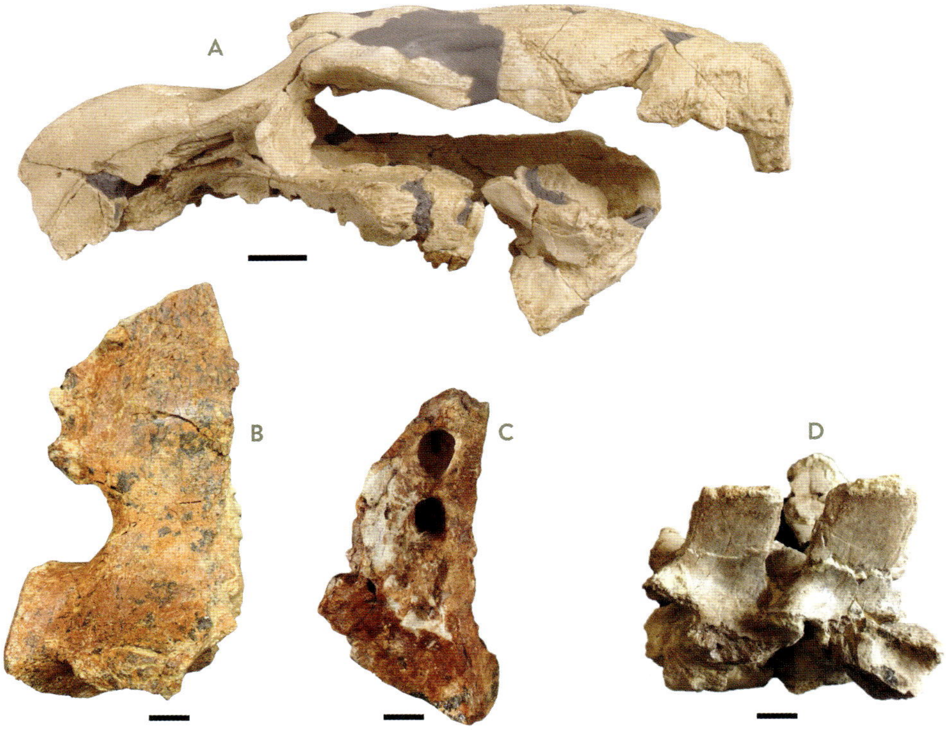

FIGURE 2.16 **Fossil marine mammals and reptiles from northwestern Madagascar. A) cast of the type specimen of Eocene sirenian *Eotheroides lambondrano* (UA 9046) in left lateral view, scale bar = 2 cm; B) fossil dolphin lumbar vertebra (UA 10.528) from Nosy Makamby in lateral view, scale bar = 1 cm; C) type specimen of Miocene sirenian *Norosiren zazavavindrano* (UA 14.139) maxilla in ventral view, scale bar = 1 cm; and D) pair of articulated crocodyliform sacral vertebrae (UA 13.001), scale bar = 1 cm. UA, Université d'Antananarivo, Antananarivo, Madagascar.**

Zarhachis flagellator (marine middle Miocene, Maryland). This specimen is one of few cetacean fossils reported from around the Indian Ocean, beyond India, Pakistan, and Sri Lanka.

Fossil reptiles include both turtles and crocodyliforms. Turtles are poorly known in Eocene deposits with none complete enough to be diagnostic, and are represented by large pieces of plastron and carapace, isolated vertebrae, and limb bones. Crocodyliforms are poorly represented in the Eocene of Madagascar (e.g., isolated teeth, osteoderms, fragmentary lower jaw, and vertebrae) but better known in the Miocene, including osteoderms, vertebrae, a partial lower jaw, and an anterior snout (Samonds et al. 2019c; Figure 2.16d). The Miocene form preserves a combination of character states inconsistent with any previously described Malagasy crocodyliform (e.g., procoelous vertebrae), and is broadly similar to slender-snouted crocodylians from the Cenozoic of Africa (e.g., *Eogavialis*).

Recent efforts to screen Miocene nearshore marine sediments from Nosy Makamby have also produced the oldest nonmarine fossils from within the island's approximately 65-million-year fossil gap (Samonds et al., 2019c). These include partial skulls, isolated teeth, and postcranial elements of bats (see Samonds et al., pp. 1859–62), an isolated rodent tooth, and fragmentary remains of a frog and scincoid lizard. As these fossils represent our first glimpse into this unknown time period, ongoing work on these groups will continue to help refine our understanding of the timing of specific biogeographic events.

IMPLICATIONS FOR INTERPRETING BIOGEOGRAPHIC HISTORY

The island's patchy Cenozoic fossil record makes it difficult to fully resolve the biogeographic origins of the extant fauna, but has great potential to inform some contentious issues, often where the more ancient fossil record (e.g., the giant frog *Beelzebufo*; Evans et al. 2014) is in strong conflict with scenarios implied by molecular clock data. For certain other groups, such as crocodyliforms, the Late Cretaceous forms (i.e., basal meseoeucrocodylians) are not considered ancestral to those of the Quaternary (*Voay robustus* and modern *Crocodylus niloticus*); the near lack of Cenozoic vertebrate fossils obscures the origin and early evolution these groups (Buckley and Brochu 1999; Turner 2006; Brochu 2007). Malagasy turtles may also have a surprising biogeographic history as they have been suggested to contain the sole example of a Late Cretaceous fossil taxon (cf. *Erymnochelys*) closely related to the extant, monotypic genus endemic to Madagascar (Gaffney and Forster 2003; but see Krause et al., pp. 59–68). Whether these Cenozoic fossils represent descendants of the Cretaceous forms, ancestors of the modern/subfossil species, or something not yet reported from Madagascar is as yet unclear. As new material becomes available and specimens in hand are studied in more detail, they will certainly yield important information needed for reconstructing the biogeographic history of these groups.

Despite the fact that these Cenozoic deposits are marine, the presence of sirenians, crocodiles, and turtles are indicators that the sediments were deposited close to shore (nearshore marine). These types of mixed deposits can occur through catastrophic events or proximity to where rivers and streams empty into the ocean, carrying terrestrial animal remains. Therefore, these kinds of deposits represent our best opportunity to date to find terrestrial and freshwater vertebrates, which are well-documented to occur in these types of mixed facies at other sites (e.g., Gingerich 1977; Cunningham et al. 1993; Rogers and Kidwell 2000)—though clearly with a bias towards sampling groups and species found near the coast. Future discoveries will surely continue to help reconstruct aspects of how, when, and from where the basal stocks of Madagascar's extant clades arrived on the island.

ACKNOWLEDGMENTS

Special thanks to the government of the Republic of Madagascar for permission to conduct this research and the Domaine des Sciences et Technologies, Mention Bassins Sédimentaires Evolution Conservation, Université d'Antananarivo for the opportunity to collaborate. Fieldwork was performed under collaborative accords with the Université d'Antananarivo by Stony Brook University (USA), McGill University (Canada), and Northern Illinois University (USA). Thanks are due to J. Groenke, J. Mathews, and K. Ababio, all of whom prepared fossils described in this contribution. Special thanks to J.-L. Raharison and Sadabe Madagascar for logistical support, as well as to M. Irwin, J. Ali, C. Botou (Ramiaramila), D. Branch, M. Gottfried, S. Ostrowski, J. Mathews, T. N. Ramihangihajason, L. Raharivony, Z. Rakotomalala, N. Rasolofomanana, and I. Zalmout for their hard work in the field. I would also like to thank the late Prince of Ampazony (M. Philibert Tsiaraso) and the local villagers who received our teams with immeasurable hospitality. Thanks to M. Irwin for Figure 2.14. This research was supported by grants from the National Geographic Society Committee for Research and Exploration to KES (#9662–15, #8667–09, #8125–06, and #7687–04). Thanks to D. Krause for helpful comments.

Subject editor: Steven M. Goodman

HISTORY OF ANIMAL AND PLANT COLONIZATION: A SYNOPSIS

K. E. Samonds, J. R. Ali, M. Huber, M. Vences, G. P. Tiley, and A. D. Yoder

Deducing how, when, and from where Madagascar's land and freshwater vertebrates arrived on the island is a challenging puzzle hampered by the incompleteness of the Cenozoic fossil record. The island's long isolation for nearly 90 million years has resulted in a fauna that is highly endemic and is taxonomically imbalanced, yet is not typically "African," as might be expected if the ancestors of these groups arrived by a land bridge across the Mozambique Channel (McCall 1997). Additionally, many species occupy phylogenetic positions that are basal relative to off-island members of their group.

Madagascar's endemic vertebrate assemblage has been strongly shaped by the island's paleogeographic history. A small number of the extant groups appear to be "stranded relicts" with ancient biogeographic links resulting from vicariance related to Madagascar's shared plate tectonic history with Gondwana (Ali and Aitchison 2008). These include oplurid lizards, podocnemidid turtles, the endemic family of blind snakes, Xenotyphlopidae Aepyornithidae), as well, possibly, as actinopterygian fishes, some amphibian groups, and sanziniid snakes (Ali and Aitchison 2008; Vidal et al. 2010; Samonds et al. 2013). It should be noted, however, that some clades (e.g., elephant birds, hippopotamuses [*Hippopotamus* and *Hexaprotodon*], and crocodiles [*Voay*]) survived into the Quaternary but are now extinct, at least in part due to human activities.

The colonizing ancestors for most vertebrate clades are thought to have rafted, swum, or flown to Madagascar after the island finally became isolated following its breakup with India-Seychelles ~88 million years ago (Mya), as this separation occurred long before these groups evolved on other landmasses. This includes, for example, the Testudines (turtles and tortoises), colubrid snakes, plated lizards, most birds, and all of the endemic mammals (Raselimanana et al. 2009; Samonds et al. 2012; Yoder et al. 1996, 2003). Molecular data suggests that for the vast majority of groups the ancestral source area was Africa, thus requiring passage across the Mozambique Channel. Madagascar's four extant nonvolant native land mammal groups—lemuroids, carnivorans, tenrecs, and nesomyine rodents—arrived during the Cenozoic through independent colonization events (Poux et al. 2005). Among volant vertebrates, bats show a different pattern by being highly nested within distantly related families with wide distributions, suggesting multiple colonization events within each family, frequently from Africa.

Madagascar's temporally patchy fossil record makes it very difficult to fully resolve the biogeographic origins of the extant fauna. Fossils are largely constrained to three geological intervals—the Late Triassic to Middle Jurassic, Late Cretaceous, and late Pleistocene to Holocene (extending back only ~80,000 years). The "missing" Cenozoic period creates a major problem as it is when many of the extant groups are thought to have both arrived and subsequently evolved (see Samonds, pp. 69–73). The fact that so few of the Late Cretaceous vertebrate clades are represented in Madagascar's modern fauna has been interpreted as additional support for a mass extinction on the island at the Cretaceous–Paleogene (K–Pg) boundary (Krause et al. 1997a). It is worth noting that there is also little to no record of Late Cretaceous precursors for modern African vertebrates, but this is more likely a result of the fact that the Late Cretaceous record of vertebrates there is poorer than that from Madagascar (but see Ibrahim et al. 2020).

GLOBAL CONTEXT

The Middle Jurassic (165 Mya) to present geophysical development of Madagascar and the once-adjacent landmasses of Africa, Seychelles, India, and Antarctica, is summarized in Ali and Aitchison

(2008), Samonds et al. (2012), and Reeves (2018). The island currently forms part of the African Plate and has done so since ~120 Mya (mid–Early Cretaceous); for 45–50 million years prior to that it belonged to east Gondwana, which rifted and moved away from west Gondwana (Africa-Arabia-South America). Since Madagascar became isolated from all of the other Gondwana blocks ~85 Mya (mid–Late Cretaceous), the Madagascar unit has largely drifted northward. Importantly, since the start of the Cenozoic, ~66 Mya (Walker et al. 2018), the island has moved some 1550 km (14°) toward the equator. At this juncture it is worth noting that the ancestors of practically all of Madagascar's modern and recently extirpated faunal components colonized the landmass after that time; much of the island's earlier biota was lost during the end-Cretaceous mass extinction. This movement combined with the steady opening up of the Indian Ocean basin would have profoundly impacted the island and its biota, with large-scale changes in the configuration of the ocean currents and prevailing winds. Paleoclimatic modelling for the K–Pg boundary period (Ohba et al. 2016) suggests that temperatures and precipitation rates were then very different to the modern conditions, but often in a localized manner. The early Eocene paleoclimate model results suggest a mean average temperature of 27–33°C, summer 33–37°C, and winter 20–28°C; and mean average precipitation ~2.5 mm/day, summer 4–6 mm/day, and winter 0.2–0.5 mm/day (Huber and Caballero 2011).

From a biogeographic perspective, it is important to note that the land-locked animals (derived mainly from Africa) that colonized the island during the Cenozoic had to have rafted in. A key problem, though, is that the regional surface-water flows (e.g., Schott et al. 2009; Lutjeharms et al. 2012) presently inhibit the transfer of vegetation mats and uprooted trees and such like from traversing the Mozambique Channel to the island (those washing off Africa would tend to get entrained in eddies 100–200 km wide that migrate southward along the coast). However, paleo-oceanographic modeling studies involving massive computer-power simulations indicate that in the early and middle Cenozoic (66–20 Mya), the conditions were more conducive as the island sat somewhat further to the south within the vast gyre that sweeps counterclockwise around the Indian Ocean south of the equator. Critically, every ~100 years there would have been several-week periods when flows were directed across the northern Mozambique Channel (Ali and Huber 2010). Notably, since 15–20 Mya there have not been any mammal colonization events that would have required rafts; hippopotamuses, which arrived more recently, are buoyant in saltwater, and likely floated over unaided (Ali and Vences 2019a). Interestingly, the tipping point that led to the modern flow configuration might have resulted from Madagascar's northern tip breaching the northern (east to west direction) sector of the gyre (South Equatorial Current). Disruption of the flows would have had a regional ripple effect, which would have intensified as Madagascar (and Africa) continued on the journey northward.

Computer simulations of the fully coupled ocean-atmosphere model (National Center for Atmospheric Research Community Earth System Model [NCAR CESM1]; University Cooperation for Atmospheric Research 2020) were carried out for two intervals, the early to mid-Eocene (56–37.8 Mya, nominally ~45 Mya) (as described in Cramwinckel et al. 2018); and the early to mid-Miocene (23–11.6 Mya, nominally ~15 Mya) (Zhou et al. 2018). Following the approach described in Ali and Huber (2010), Figure 2.17 (45 Mya, mid- middle Eocene) shows the surface-ocean currents and depict the major Indian Ocean gyres as indicated by the barotropic streamfunction (vertical integral of the horizontal velocities). These circulations vary seasonally, but one for the Eocene austral summer configuration (January–March) is notable in that it produces flows from Africa to Madagascar (Figure 2.18). In such circumstances, journey times to Madagascar from the coast of northern Mozambique would have been ~30–35 days. Importantly, in the Miocene, no season that provides a direct transport path is evident.

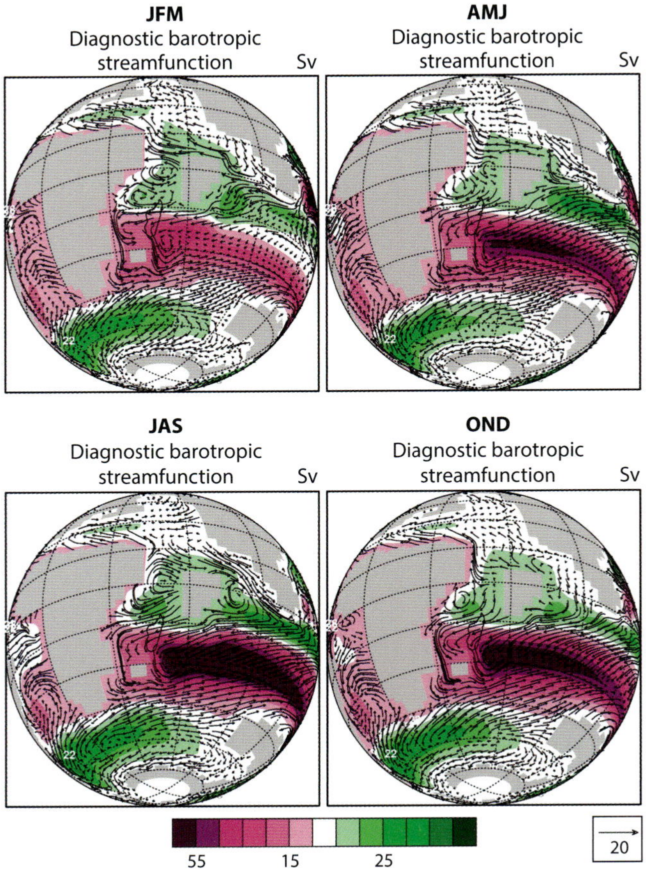

FIGURE 2.17 **Computer simulations of ocean circulation for the southwest Indian Ocean at 45 Mya (mid–middle Eocene) for each of the four quarters: January–March (JFM; austral summer), April–June (AMJ), July–September (JAS), and October–December (OND). The thin arrows show the surface-water flow speeds and directions (note the reference velocity arrow, bottom right. The colored patches indicate the bulk, vertically integrated gyre transport through the water column (positive/green shows clockwise flows; negative/purple shows counterclockwise flows; flux units in svedrups (Sv), with 1 Sv being 1 km^3 per second). As a consequence of the discrete numerical grid used in modeling, the land-sea boundaries have a pixelated appearance and Madagascar is portrayed as a squat rectangle. For reference, the outline of modern-day Madagascar is added to the plot. Also, note the slow northward drift of Africa-Madagascar and the more rapid transit of India, the latter having a major effect on flows across the equatorial Indian Ocean.**

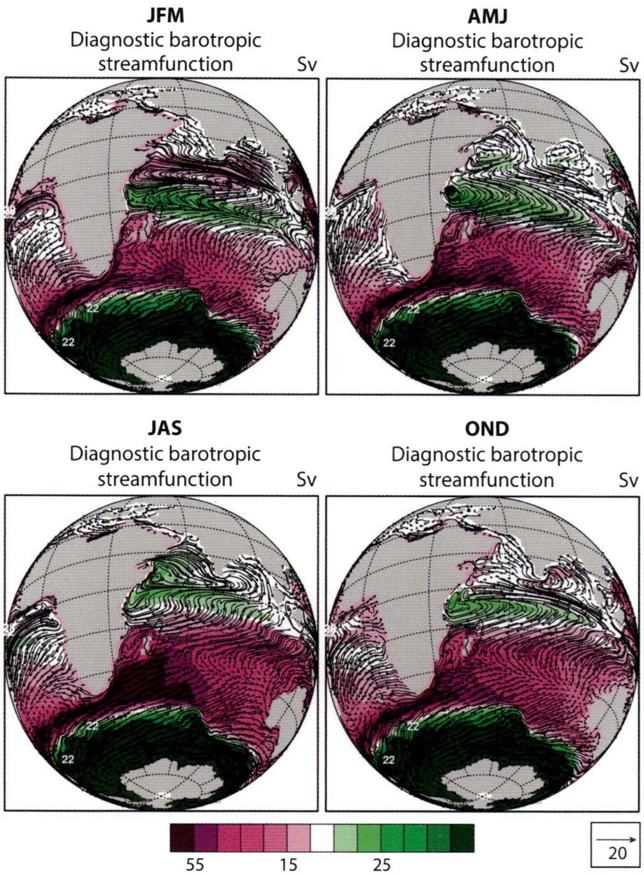

FIGURE 2.18 **Computer simulations of ocean circulation for the southwest Indian Ocean at 15 Mya (early middle Miocene). See Figure 2.17 for an explanation of the various elements.**

GENERAL DIVERGENCE TIME PATTERNS FOR MALAGASY VERTEBRATE CLADES

The accurate reconstruction of the colonization of Madagascar by different groups of vertebrates is hampered by the incompleteness of the Cenozoic fossil record. We are therefore reliant on molecular dating (Yoder and Nowak 2006), but it should be noted that there are phylogenetic uncertainties in several groups such as chameleons and geckos, plus methodological issues inherent to any such timing estimates. In an attempt to include all Malagasy nonvolant terrestrial and freshwater vertebrate clades in a single timetree, Crottini et al. (2012) relied on two protein-coding nuclear genes and various well-established calibrations, which yielded relatively congruent time estimates in cross-validations. In the preferred scenario, eight vertebrate clades were estimated to have arrived on Madagascar between the present and 30 Mya, all from Africa; 21 clades colonized the island 40–80 Mya, most of which were from Africa but with 4–8 from Asia; and two clades showing South American/African affinities (iguanas and podocnemid turtles) may already have been in place 90–120 Mya. The timetree also reconstructed various out-of-Madagascar colonization events to the Comoro and Seychelles archipelagoes, and in three cases probably to Africa or Asia, all up to 40 Mya. While each of the single estimates may be in need of revision as new evidence accumulates (for instance in lemurs and freshwater fishes), it is unlikely that the overall pattern will change: the ancestors of many Malagasy nonvolant vertebrate clades clearly arrived by overseas rafting from Africa, while some of the older clades (60–80 Mya) with Asian affinities may have benefited from stepping-stone dispersal over parts of the Greater India block, which at this time may not yet have fully completed its drift toward the Asian plate (Figure 2.19). The period of arrival on Madagascar had a weak influence on the success of the respective clade, with an overall trend of older clades having diversified into more species; however, the essential factor for a clade's species diversity was adaptation to moist evergreen forest, with those clades that colonized this forest type being dramatically more species rich (Crottini et al. 2012).

Although moist evergreen forest has been important for the diversification of some clades, this forest type is relatively young in Madagascar with origins near the Eocene-Oligocene boundary c. 34 Mya (Wells 2003). Dryer forest types like those observed in western Madagascar or central Madagascar west of the escarpment were present at least during the K-Pg boundary c. 66 Mya (Ohba et al. 2016). There has also been vegetative turnover since the late Miocene c. 8 Mya that coincides with an increase of monsoon intensity. For example, C_4 grasses that are typically adapted to dry and open habitats diversified at this time (Hackel et al. 2018). Although it remains unclear to what extent the Central Highlands separating eastern moist forest and western dry forest were composed of C_4 grasslands throughout the Miocene, the Central Highlands have likely been a mosaic of grassland and forests (Vorontsova et al. 2016), which has allowed some dispersal between eastern and western forests through time (Yoder et al. 2016).

A number of studies in different vertebrate groups have used timetrees to investigate patterns of diversification in eastern moist forests versus western dry forests. For instance, tenrecs have diversified with very little dispersal to western forests (Everson et al. 2016). Similarly, ancestral area reconstructions imply eastern origins of *Boophis* tree frogs (Hutter et al. 2018) but with repeated dispersal to more arid habitats. Additionally, Madagascar's gemsnakes show higher species richness in the eastern forests compared with western dry deciduous forests (Burbrink et al. 2019). However, dispersal between habitat types may have played a larger role in speciation for certain groups such as vangas (Reddy et al. 2012; Younger et al. 2019).

ORIGINS AND DIVERGENCE TIMES OF MALAGASY INVERTEBRATES

Traditionally, for the majority of invertebrate groups studied, their present distribution has been attributed to the vicariant event of the splitting of Gondwana during the Mesozoic, as indicated by the presence of endemic families or subfamilies presumably representing ancient phylogenetic splits (see Paulian and Viette 2003; for more general view see Ali and Vences 2019b).

A recent, comprehensive review of the biogeography of Madagascar's invertebrates is lacking and is beyond the scope of this contribution. Molecular studies have usually found evidence for post-Gondwanan dispersal to Madagascar, for example, in termites (Nobre et al. 2010), carpenter bees (Rehan et al. 2010), orb spiders (Kuntner and Agnarsson 2011), dung beetles (Sole et al. 2011), pierid

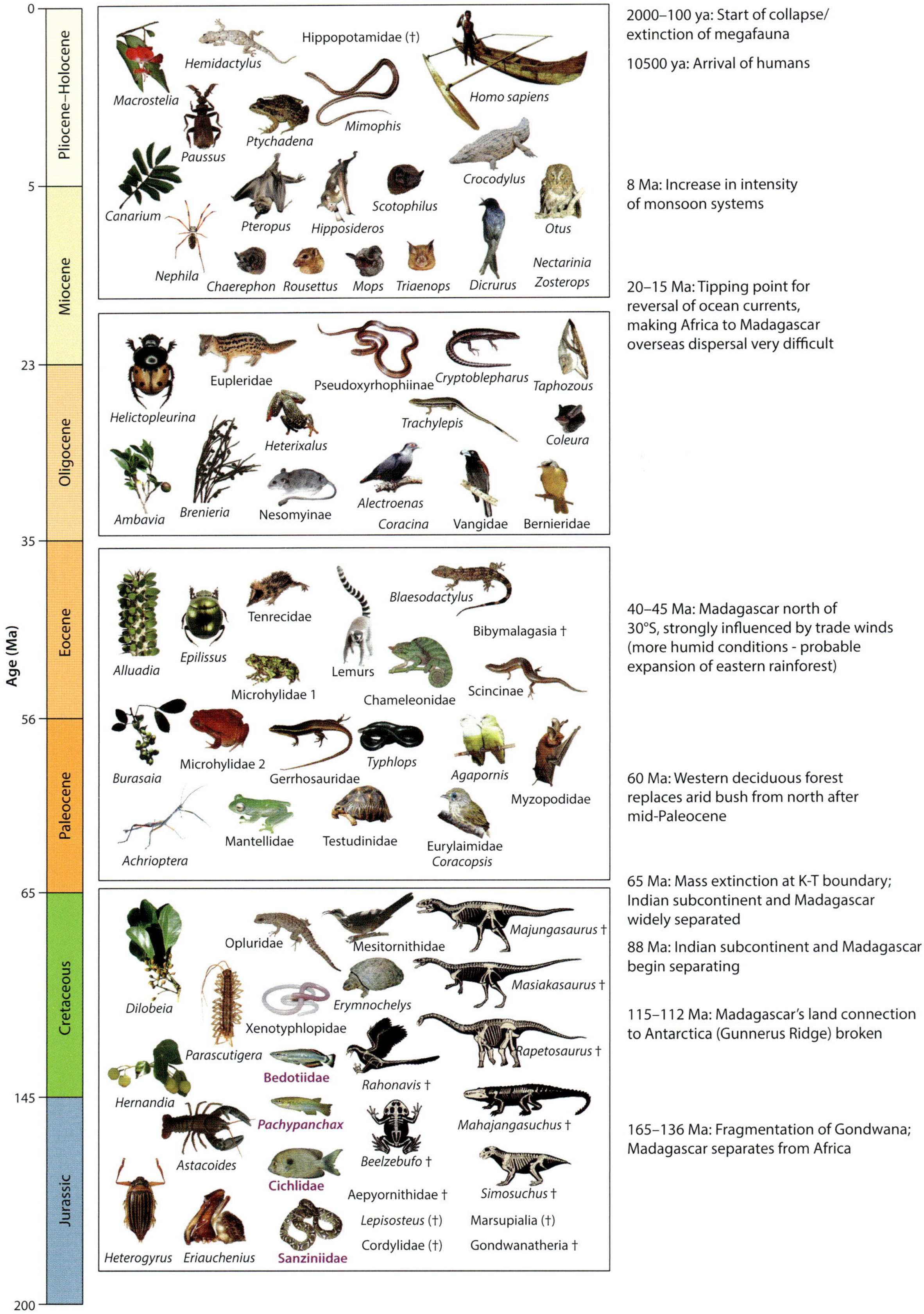

FIGURE 2.19 **Timetable summarizing major paleogeographic and paleoclimatic events relevant to the biogeographic history of Madagascar, modified after Samonds et al. (2013). Table includes a nonexhaustive summary of vertebrate taxa that arrived or were present on the island. The box for the Jurassic–Cretaceous shows extinct fossil taxa that were present on Madagascar in the Late Cretaceous, plus extant taxa reconstructed to have existed during this time. Subsequent boxes show taxa that are estimated to have arrived on the island during the respective interval, with each image representing one (or rarely two) endemic Malagasy clades. Extinct taxa are marked with † (in parentheses if taxon is extinct on Madagascar but surviving elsewhere). Text in purple marks taxa for which current evidence is controversial and new studies suggest might be of younger origin. K–T, Cretaceous–Tertiary boundary.**

and satyrine butterflies (Nazari et al. 2011; Aduse-Poku et al. 2015), mayflies (Vuataz et al. 2013), ant-nest beetles (Moore and Robertson 2014), diving beetles (Bukontaite et al. 2015), and stick insects (Simon et al. 2019). Stick insects comprise a Malagasy radiation that separated from its sister group around 57 Mya and started to diverge around 46 Mya (Simon et al. 2019); also dung beetles, mayflies, and termites comprise Madagascar-endemic radiations (Nobre et al. 2010; Sole et al. 2011; Vuataz et al. 2013). In several other groups, the Malagasy representatives do not form monophyletic groups, suggesting multiple post-Gondwanan dispersals into Madagascar (Kuntner and Agnarsson 2011; Nazari et al. 2011), and possibly also out of Madagascar, as it has been postulated for Hydaticini diving beetles (Bukontaite et al. 2015; see Bergsten et al., pp. 1024–34).

However, some Malagasy invertebrate clades have also been reconstructed as ancient, for instance the beetle *Heterogyrus*, which is currently the oldest known clade in Madagascar, with a Late Triassic to Early Jurassic origin (Gustafson et al. 2017; see Gustafson et al., pp. 1034–41). Other groups of Cretaceous to Jurassic age, and thus probably Gondwanan origin, are crayfish, scutigeromorph centipedes, and pelican spiders (Toon et al. 2010; Giribet and Edgecombe 2013; Wood et al. 2015; Gustafson et al. 2017).

ORIGINS AND DIVERGENCE TIMES OF MALAGASY PLANTS

As is true for virtually all of Madagascar's biota, the flora shows high levels of endemism with estimates in the order of 84% for indigenous angiosperms and 82% for all indigenous vascular plants (Callmander et al. 2011). It is generally agreed that both the vicariance resulting from the breakup of Gondwana and the action of long-distance dispersal contributed to the development of the Malagasy flora, but the exact relative magnitude of these two mechanisms is contended. Schatz (1996) was the first to put an emphasis on long-distance dispersal as a mechanism of origin for many elements of the island's plants. He considered the Malagasy flora to be strongly influenced by the arrival of Australian, Indian, and southeast Asian floras, and at the time of writing, no studies have been produced to verify the influence of Gondwanan vicariance that has been posited by other authorities (e.g., Leroy 1978; Grubb 2003). This is not to say that these vicariant patterns do not exist, but rather they must be rare or expressed at deep taxonomic scales (e.g., familial or ordinal levels). Rather, with virtually all recent phylogenetic work conducted on Madagascar's flora, the signal is revealed to be dispersal from either Africa (e.g., Hong-Wa and Besnard 2014) or Asia (e.g., Federman et al. 2015). And, indeed, relevant to the hypothesis of ease of dispersal, there are several cases where the initial ancestral radiation appears to have occurred within Madagascar with subsequent dispersal to surrounding islands (e.g., Strijk et al. 2012, 2014; Nowak et al. 2014). Thus, it is increasingly evident that dispersal, rather than vicariance, has been the dominant force shaping Madagascar's highly endemic flora.

ONGOING DISCUSSIONS AND DISPUTES

Given the poor Cenozoic fossil record from Madagascar, and the uncertainties inherent in any approach to estimate divergence times from molecular data, it is unsurprising that the origins of many components of Madagascar's biota have not been fully resolved. For instance, the (extinct) giant frog *Beelzebufo* from the Late Cretaceous has been related to the South American ceratophryid frogs (Evans et al. 2008, 2014), which is in strong conflict with molecular clock data (Ruane et al. 2011), and a relationship with other more ancient frog lineages has been suggested (Agnolín 2012).

More relevant for the analysis of Madagascar's current vertebrate assemblage is the recent study of Gunnell et al. (2018) that identified the extinct African *Propotto* as sister taxon to the Malagasy Aye-aye (*Daubentonia madagascariensis*). This finding, if confirmed, not only implies that Madagascar has been colonized twice by lemurs, but also that these colonizations were younger than previously assumed: contemporary lemur timetrees (e.g., Herrera and Dávalos 2016) estimate a divergence of Malagasy lemurs from their non-Malagasy ancestors at 55 Mya, while the timetree including *Propotto* (Gunnell et al. 2018) estimates the divergence of *Daubentonia* from *Propotto* to be ~28 Mya, and maximum age of the divergence of the remaining Malagasy lemurs from their sister group at ~41 Mya (see Yoder, pp. 1821–24, for further discussion on this point).

One of the groups with most disputed divergence times—and by implication, origins on Madagascar—is ray-finned fishes (Actinopterygii). Four main groups of freshwater fishes occurring on the island—cichlids, rainbow fishes, killifishes, and gobies—belong, within actinopterygians, to the spiny-finned fishes (acanthomorphs), and within these to the percomorph clade. Percomorphs represent about half of the extant fish species, including many that are intimately associated with tropical coral reefs. Various comprehensive studies have inferred a recent origin of percomorphs (e.g., Near et al. 2012, 2013; Betancur-R et al. 2017) in agreement with the fossil record, dated to about the Early Cretaceous, which implies that all extant families within percomorphs are distinctly younger. Accordingly, several studies focusing on cichlids placed their origin in the early Cenozoic, long after Gondwanan rifting (Vences et al. 2001; Friedman et al. 2013; Matschiner et al. 2017), and the same is true also for the rainbow fish and killifish clade (Crottini et al. 2012).

Conversely, though, other recent timetree studies reported Mesozoic ages for the Malagasy gobies (Chakrabarty et al. 2012) and cichlids (Irisarri et al. 2018). In the case of milyeringid gobies, this disagreement can potentially be explained by the use of only mitochondrial genes as this often leads to significant overestimation of divergence times (Near et al. 2012), and in the case of cichlids by the use of only internal calibration points. The main problem with assuming old Gondwanan ages for Malagasy freshwater fishes is that this implies that the origin of the deep splits within ray-finned fishes was well into the Paleozoic ages, which is in conflict with the fossil record. On the other hand, although all Malagasy freshwater fish clades contain species with some tolerance of salinity, it is hard to imagine them crossing the open ocean, even if traveling in lenses of superficial low-salinity water originating from the discharges of large rivers (Measey et al. 2007); such oceanic dispersal appears especially implausible in milyeringids for which both the Malagasy *Typhleotris* and its Australian sister group, *Milyeringia*, are highly specialized, blind freshwater cave fish (Chakrabarty et al. 2012). While mechanistic explanations and experimental evidence for transocean voyages of freshwater fishes are pending, we can only conclude at this time that vicariant Gondwanan origins of Madagascar's freshwater fishes would require substantial assumptions on very erratic molecular substitution rates or an extremely incomplete fossil record, and at present the majority of recent studies point to post-Gondwanan dispersal to explain their origins.

Many of these uncertainties will ultimately be resolved given the extraordinary pace at which methods for divergence time estimation are being developed and tested (e.g., Alvarez-Carretero et al. 2019; Anisimova 2019; Jones 2019; Marshall 2019). Additionally, new discoveries related to Madagascar's Cenozoic fossil record have great potential to fill in many gaps in our knowledge of the origin and evolution of the modern Malagasy fauna (see Samonds, pp. 69–73).

ACKNOWLEDGMENTS

Computer simulations were generated at the Climate Dynamics Prediction Laboratory at Purdue University. Research support includes the National Geographic Society (K. E. Samonds), Duke University, Guggenheim Foundation, and the Alexander von Humboldt Foundation (A. D. Yoder), Deutsche Forschungsgemeinschaft and Deutscher Akademischer Austauschdienst (M. Vences), and the National Science Foundation. A. D. Yoder thanks the National Science Foundation (NSF) for support throughout her career; M. Huber acknowledges NSF grant #1602905. Special thanks to Henner Brinkmann, Angelica Crottini, Iker Irisarri, Ole Madsen, Axel Meyer, Thomas J. Near, Hervé Philippe, Celine Poux, and Walter Salzburger for fruitful, often controversial discussions over timetrees.

Subject editors: †Maarten de Wit and Steven M. Goodman

† Deceased (1947–2020)

GEODISPERSAL AS A BIOGEOGRAPHIC MECHANISM FOR CENOZOIC EXCHANGES BETWEEN MADAGASCAR AND AFRICA

J. C. Masters, F. Génin, R. Pellen, P. P. A. Mazza, Y. Zhang, T. Huck, M. Rabineau, and D. Aslanian

Islands are a natural consequence of earth's dynamic nature, and hundreds of thousands occur in our oceans. Most are classified as either continental (subaerial parts of continental shelves, connected to the mainland during sea level lowstands, and often inhabited by elements of the mainland biota) or oceanic (formed over oceanic plates and never connected to a continent, so their biota arrives by dispersal) (Whittaker and Fernández-Palacios 2007). Madagascar comprises a large continental fragment (587,041 km^2) that shares attributes with both continental and oceanic islands. Today it has an oceanic level of isolation, separated by the Mozambique Channel from Africa's eastern shore by 420 km at its closest point. The channel is an extraordinarily ancient and formidable biogeographic barrier to the migration of terrestrial vertebrates, marking the first major rupture in the fragmentation of the Gondwana supercontinent (Reeves and de Wit 2000), 157–120 million years ago (Mya). For most of its extent, its depth reaches 2000–3000 m; eustatic sea level changes of one to several hundred meters could not moderate its effectiveness by very much. The Agulhas Current, which flows down this channel, is one of the fastest-flowing currents in the world.

Prior to this fragmentation in deep geological time, Madagascar was connected on all sides to the Gondwanan supercontinent, and undoubtedly hosted an ancient Gondwanan flora and fauna. With equal certainty, Madagascar's biotic composition has altered repeatedly in response to the tectonic and climatological upheavals that accompanied geological and organismal evolution on earth. A comprehensive study of phylogenetic relationships among 188 living taxa of Malagasy vertebrates led Crottini et al. (2012) to reconstruct a complex scenario of biogeographic origins, including ancient (Cretaceous) elements, as well as a majority of Cenozoic (66 Mya–10,000 years ago) colonists that have their closest relatives in either Africa or Asia. Phylogeographic investigations of the Malagasy flora show similar patterns (Buerki et al. 2013).

Biogeographic mechanisms are often viewed through a binary filter: either the organisms were in place before the landmasses sundered, or they arrived by dispersal. In the case of Madagascar, all organisms with African affinities that arrived after 120 Mya and all those with Indian/Asian affinities that arrived after 83 Mya are hence assumed to be products of long-distance dispersal; and dispersal is equated with "flying, swimming or rafting ... across considerable marine barriers" (Krause et al. 2020). Comparable methods of dispersal are proposed for Madagascar's Cenozoic flora (Yoder and Nowak 2006; Buerki et al. 2013), although eolian transport has also been shown to be an effective long-distance dispersal agent to faraway islands for a number of plants (Nathan 2006). There is a third alternative that has received insufficient consideration, in our view: geodispersal, or the expansion of floral and faunal ranges in response to the elimination of a prior biogeographic barrier (Lieberman 2000; Upchurch 2008). For Madagascar, this process implies the presence of episodic Cenozoic land connections between the island and eastern Africa, the elevation and submersion of which would yield a pattern of alternating periods of colonization and in situ diversification (Upchurch 2008).

The possibility of land bridges connecting Africa and Madagascar has been rejected repeatedly by scientists for a variety of reasons, primary among which is the limited and "unbalanced" higher-taxonomic composition of the island's biota relative to that of the mainland. In 1940, George Gaylord Simpson published a renowned and much-cited paper on mechanisms of insular colonization by mammals, proposing that they involve three potential migration routes: 1) corridors, 2) filter-bridges, and 3) sweepstakes. Corridors are pathways devoid of any physical or ecological barriers; filter-bridges are perennially open to some species and not to others; and sweepstakes are routes of sporadic, accidental, and highly selective dispersal from continent to island by means of either stepping-stones or natural rafts. Simpson (1940) explained the fact that Madagascar's mammal fauna comprises only four terrestrial lineages with links to Africa (lemurs, tenrecs, euplerid carnivorans, and nesomyine rodents) in terms of sweepstakes dispersal. Because Simpson worked within a framework of fixed continents, the only way he could envisage for animals to cross the Mozambique Channel was by floating on rafts of vegetation. Late Miocene taxa including large carnivores, paenungulates (chiefly elephants), apes, and ungulates (other than hippopotamuses) were considered nonstarters as colonists, whereas a major contributing factor to successful dispersal for earlier and smaller mammals was chance: being in the right place at the right time. Small-bodied canids and felids, monkeys, shrews, and most rodents were simply unlucky and missed the raft. This argument continues to be cited (e.g., Krause et al. 2020): If there had been a land bridge then, "a greater variety of animals would have crossed" (Ali and Huber 2010) as, "all clades of that antiquity would have had equally probable chances of colonizing Madagascar" (Yoder and Nowak 2006), and "large-scale invasions [would] almost certainly have ensued" (Ali and Vences 2019a).

These predictions place a high value on taxonomic filtering but fail to acknowledge the significance the habitat filtering; in other words, colonizers can only establish viable populations in habitats to which they are at least partially adapted. Habitat filtering may impose more restrictions on biogeography than dispersal, even on remote oceanic islands (Carvajal-Endara et al. 2017). Land bridges provide not only causeways but habitats as well. This means that, while rafting must occur within an individual's lifetime, geodispersal can occur over several generations. Another biological aspect that needs to be considered is the vulnerability of island biotas to extinction. The limited number of Malagasy clades alive today is unlikely to represent all of the lineages that ever colonized the island, but the absence of any Cenozoic fossils older than 26,000 years renders them invisible to modern research.

TEMPORAL (IN)CONGRUENCE

Despite the age and depth of the Mozambique Channel, bathymetric studies have revealed the presence of seamounts and submarine ridges comprising continental material topped by carbonates, which were probably exposed periodically during the Cenozoic (Courgeon et al. 2017). McCall (1997) proposed that the Davie Fracture Zone, the submarine ridge that marks the fault line that led to the Africa-Madagascar separation, was at least partially emergent 45–26 Mya, and could, therefore, have assisted Cenozoic dispersal events. Poux et al. (2005) tested this hypothesis by estimating the colonization dates of Madagascar's four terrestrial mammal lineages, and although their data, with its broad confidence intervals, could not refute the proposal, they demonstrated no particular pattern of congruence between the dates proposed for the land bridge and the separation ages of the African and Malagasy lineages. Furthermore, the colonization dates for lemurs and tenrecs differed by tens of millions of years from those estimated for the arrival of carnivorans and rodents (Yoder et al. 1996, 2003; Poux et al. 2005), and this asynchrony was also viewed as evidence in favor of sweepstakes dispersal (Yoder and Nowak 2006).

LOOKING MORE DEEPLY INTO THE MOZAMBIQUE CHANNEL

Past geological studies of the Mozambique Channel have focused on horizontal movements, which form the crux of plate tectonics, whereas vertical movements—or the connection between deep (magmatic) and surface processes (subsidence, uplifts)—have largely been neglected. A major French-led project, PAMELA (Passive Margins Exploration Laboratories), has conducted sedimentary, tectonic, kinematic, and paleoenvironmental studies of the history of the Mozambique Channel, involving eight oceanographic cruises (for a total of 224 days at sea) between 2014 and 2017, and three onshore geological surveys (for 50 land days) in 2017 and 2018. The results obtained from this intensive and extensive study, involving more than 100 researchers, present a much more complex and dynamic picture of the channel's bathymetric topography (Courgeon et al. 2016, 2017, 2018; Delaunay 2018; Ponte 2018; Leroux et al. 2018, 2020; Ponte et al. 2019; Thompson et al. 2019; Moulin et al. 2020). We conducted a cross-disciplinary study of Madagascar's Cenozoic biogeography using these new data (Masters et al. 2020) and concluded that there is strong evidence that geodispersal has contributed significantly to Madagascar's standing (and recently extinct) biotas. Paleosedimentological maps (Figure 2.20) indicate three phases of regional uplift that affected connectivity between Africa and Madagascar during the Cenozoic.

A. Early Paleocene (66–60 Mya; exposure of the Sakalaves platform, Glorieuses and Juan de Nova Islands, and Leven-Castor highs);
B. Late Eocene to early Oligocene (36–30 Mya; exposure of Bassas da India, and Hall Bank);
C. Late Miocene (12–5 Mya; worldwide Messinian crisis and origin of the Comoro archipelago).

These three periods reflect the three phases of uplift that led to Madagascar's modern topography (Delaunay 2018). They coincided with episodes of marked tectonic and climatic change: global cooling leading to droughts in Madagascar and sub-Saharan Africa, associated with mass extinctions and subsequent radiations, and low sea level stands. The fact that similar conditions are likely to have prevailed on both sides of the Mozambique Channel would

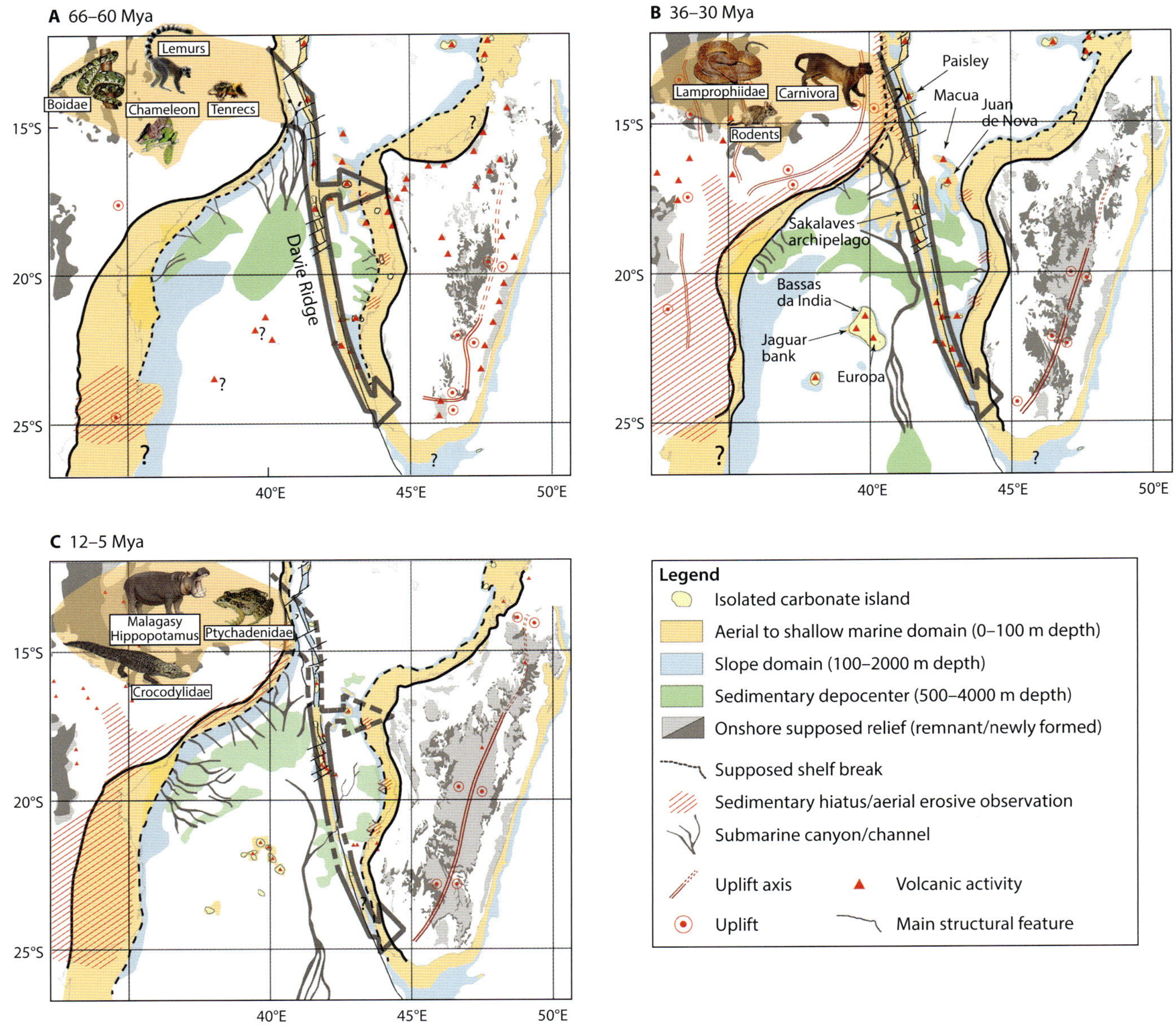

FIGURE 2.20 **Paleosedimentological maps representing possible land bridges during three Cenozoic time frames, concomitant with the three phases of uplift of Madagascar's highlands: A) early Paleocene, B) late Eocene to early Oligocene, and C) late Miocene.**

have facilitated faunal and floral exchanges. This also suggests that some colonization events may have proceeded from Madagascar to Africa, as was recently proposed for *Croton* species (Euphorbiaceae; Ngumbau et al. 2020).

Latest Cretaceous to Early Paleocene (66–60 Mya): Widespread Continental Uplift

This period is coincident with a global mass extinction and several major magmatic events, including the outpouring of the Deccan flood basalts and the collision of India with Asia; the first episode of uplift of the South African plateau (Baby et al. 2018); and volcanism in the Mozambique Channel and Madagascar (Bardintzeff et al. 2010; Delaunay 2018; Ponte 2018). A sedimentary hiatus on Madagascar's west coast 66–60 Mya (Delaunay 2018) corresponds to a hiatus along the Mozambican coast (Ponte 2018), indicating a general exposure of coastal land on both sides of the channel, and subaerial exposure of the Davie Ridge (Figure 2.20a). Faunal studies based on extinct and extant taxa link this period to a major biotic turnover on Madagascar, coincident with the worldwide Cretaceous–Paleogene mass extinction: While some ancient reptilian taxa (iguanas, river turtles, boas) survived the environmental catastrophe (Noonan and Chippendale 2006; Crottini et al. 2012), forms known only from fossils (mammaliaform gondwanatheres, dinosaurs, and early birds; Krause et al. 1997c, 2020; Sampson et al. 1998) succumbed.

At this time, both Madagascar and Africa were 10–15° (1100–1650 km) south of their present position. At such high latitude, Madagascar's landscape was probably dominated by lowland woodland, with only a few Cretaceous angiosperm families (Proteaceae,

Hernandiaceae, and Winteraceae) (Schatz 2001; Buerki et al. 2013). The two older mammal clades, lemurs and tenrecs, are likely to have dispersed during this period (Yoder et al. 1996; Poux et al. 2005). Other potential Paleogene colonists include angiosperm families (Fabaceae, Meliaceae, and Menispermaceae) (Buerki et al. 2013), freshwater fishes (Bedotiidae, Aplocheilidae, and Cichlidae), amphibians (Mantellidae, Microhylidae, and Hyperoliidae), and reptiles (Chamaeleonidae, Gekkonidae, Gerrhosauridae, and Scincidae) (Crottini et al. 2012).

Late Eocene to Early Oligocene (36–30 Mya): Very Shallow Marine Corridors

The Eocene–Oligocene transition (EOT) (Figure 2.20b) is an extinction event well-known among students of lemur biology as it caused the near-extinction of the Eocene relatives of modern tooth-combed primates (Fleagle 2013). Its devastation of Paleogene biotas led to it being termed "la Grande Coupure" ("the great cut"), and it marked a major shift in global climates, related to the first occurrence of ephemeral ice sheets in Antarctica (Zachos et al. 2001). The initiation and growth of ice sheets locked down water on land, causing a drop in global sea levels, and exposing coastal land. This was a dynamic time for Africa, coincident with the initiation of the East African rift system (Ebinger 1989; de Wit 2003; Chorowicz 2005; Macgregor 2015), and the second uplift of the southern Africa plateau (38–16 Mya; Mougenot et al. 1986; Baby et al. 2018). It also marked the second phase of uplift in Madagascar and affected the physiography of the Mozambique Channel leading to the reemergence of the carbonate platforms on the western and eastern shores, the Davie Ridge, the Sakalaves archipelago, and Juan de Nova volcanic island, west of Cap Saint André. Other isolated islands (Bassas da India, Europa, Jaguar Bank, Macua, and Paisley) were also mostly subaerial 36–30 Mya, before being weathered and eroded through wave activity during the late Oligocene and Miocene (Courgeon et al. 2017). While connections between the Davie Ridge, Rovuma, and Madagascar may not have been continuous throughout this period, hiatuses between topographic highs would have consisted of short (<50 km) and shallow marine corridors (1–100 m).

The EOT land bridge would have enabled the colonization of Madagascar by carnivorans, rodents, and the endemic snake family Lamprophidae. Comparison with continental-shelf islands on Africa's east coast, such as Zanzibar and Pemba (which do not have elephants, giraffes, or lions but do have primates, carnivorans, and rodents), suggests that this land bridge was probably dominated by mangroves, which were dispersed throughout the Indian Ocean (Ellison et al. 1999). Important plant colonists would have included Euphorbiaceae and the ancestors of the Didiereaceae, which form the matrix of Madagascar's dry spiny thicket biome. Today, this vegetation type is endemic to southern Madagascar, but xerophytic relicts in the north and the west suggest that it once occupied the entire western region. The many plant families that probably colonized Madagascar at this time include Arecaceae (palms) and the speciose Rubiaceae (coffee family).

Late Miocene (12—5 Mya): Noncontinuous Connections

Volcanism is recorded for 12 Mya ago, south of the Sakalaves archipelago (Figure 2.20) in the northern part of the Davie Ridge, coeval with the final uplift of Madagascar (Delaunay 2018) and exposure of the Madagascar continental platform. Courgeon et al. (2017) identified late Miocene to early Pliocene subaerial volcanism covering previous carbonate platforms and extensional tectonic deformation, which led to the post-tectonic Pliocene drowning of the platforms, and to their present-day setting largely below sea level. Drowning of the southern part of the Davie Ridge occurred from the mid-Miocene onward, with deep-sea channels originating in the Morondava Basin and reaching the deep turbiditic system south of the Mozambique Channel (Delaunay 2018). This north–south inundation is also attested by very low sedimentary accumulation (<100 m) in the north of the Morondava Basin, and a mean sedimentary accumulation increasing 300–800 m below the main river outlets and deltas in the central and southern parts.

We infer that this third bridge offered a noncontinuous connection interrupted by small, shallow marine corridors between the Davie Ridge and the northern part of the Morondava Basin (Figure 2.20). Two major deltas faced each other across the Mozambique Channel, separated by a narrow remnant of the old land bridge. The narrow marine corridors are likely to have included various stepping-stones, such as shallow reefs and small volcanic islands; hence, this connection would have facilitated the dispersal of aquatic animals (crocodiles, hippopotamuses, and one family of frogs, Ptychadenidae), but not of terrestrial forms. The spread of grasses (Poaceae) was limited to wetlands, forests, and some high summits (Paulian 1961; Bosser 1969). The only ungulate grazers to follow them across the channel were hippopotamuses, which subsequently evolved dwarf forms. This last bridge was followed by a general drowning of the Mozambique Channel during the late Miocene and early Pliocene.

CONCLUSIONS

Recent research indicates that invoking geodispersal by means of short-lived land bridges to account for Madagascar's extant biota provides a new framework for understanding the evolution of life on the island.

Subject editor: Steven M. Goodman

REFERENCES

Abdala, F., Ribeiro, A. M., and Schultz, C. L. 2001. A rich cynodont fauna from Santa Cruz do Sul, Santa Maria Formation (Middle–Late Triassic), southern Brazil. *Neues Jahrbuch fur Geologie und Paläontologie* 11: 669–687.

Abdala, F., Martinelli, A. G., Soares, M. B., de la Fuente, M., and Ribeiro, A. M. 2009. South American Middle Triassic continental faunas with amniotes: Biostratigraphy and correlation. *Palaeontologia Africana* 44: 83–87.

Aduse-Poku, K., Brattström, O., Kodandaramaiah, U., Lees, D. C., Brakefield, P. M., and Wahlberg, N. 2015. Systematics and historical biogeography of the Old World butterfly subtribe Mycalesina (Lepidoptera: Nymphalidae: Satyrinae). *BMC Evolutionary Biology* 15: 167.

Agnarsson, I., and Kuntner, M. 2012. The generation of a biodiversity hotspot: Biogeography and phylogeography of the Western Indian Ocean islands. In *Current Topics in Phylogenetics and Phylogeography of Terrestrial and Aquatic Systems*, ed. K Anamthawat-Jónsson, pp. 33–82. Rijeka: InTech Europe.

Agnolín, F. L. 2012. New Calyptocephalellidae (Anura, Neobatrachia) from the Upper Cretaceous of Patagonia, Argentina, with comments on its systematic position. *Studia Geologica Salmanticensia* 48: 129–178.

Alberti, M., Arabas, A., Fürsich, F. T., Andersen, N., and Ziółkowski, P. 2019. The Middle to Upper Jurassic stable isotope record of Madagascar: Linking temperature changes with plate tectonics during the break-up of Gondwana. *Gondwana Research* 73: 1–15.

Alessio, B. L., Collins, A. S., Siegfried, P., Glorie, S., De Waele, B., Payne, J., and Archibald, D. B. 2019. Neoproterozoic tectonic geography of the south-east Congo Craton in Zambia as deduced from the age and composition of detrital zircons. *Geoscience Frontiers* 10: 2045–2061.

Ali, J. R., and Aitchison, J. C. 2008. Gondwana to Asia: Plate tectonics, paleogeography and the biological connectivity of the Indian sub-continent from the Middle Jurassic through latest Eocene (166–35 Ma). *Earth-Science Reviews* 88: 145–166.

———. 2009. Kerguelen Plateau and the Late Cretaceous southern-continent bioconnection hypothesis: Tales from a topographical ocean. *Journal of Biogeography* 36: 1778–1784.

Ali, J. R., and Huber, M. 2010. Mammalian biodiversity on Madagascar controlled by ocean currents. *Nature* 463: 653–656.

Ali, J. R., and Krause, D. W. 2011. Late Cretaceous bioconnections between Indo-Madagascar and Antarctica: Refutation of the Gunnerus Ridge causeway hypothesis. *Journal of Biogeography* 38: 1855–1872.

Ali, J. R., and Vences, M. 2019a. Mammals and long-distance over-water colonization: The case for rafting dispersal; the case against phantom causeways. *Journal of Biogeography* 46: 2632–2636.

———. 2019b. Novel summary metrics for insular biotic assemblages based on taxonomy and phylogeny: Biogeographical, palaeogeographical and possible conservational applications. *Journal of Biogeography* 46: 2735–2751.

Alvarez-Carretero, S., Goswami, A., Yang, Z., and Dos Reis, M. 2019. Bayesian estimation of species divergence times using correlated quantitative characters. *Systematic Biology* 68: 967–986.

Andrianavalona, T. H., Ramihangihajason, T. N., Rasoamiaramanana, A., Ward, D. J., Ali, J. R., and Samonds, K. E. 2015. Miocene shark and batoid fauna from Nosy Makamby (Mahajanga Basin, Northwestern Madagascar). *PLoS One* 10: e0129444.

Anisimova, M., ed. 2019. *Evolutionary Genomics: Statistical and Computational Methods*. New York: Humana Press.

Archibald, D. B., Collins, A. S., Foden, J. D., Payne, J. L., Holden, P., Razakamanana, T., De Waele, B., Thomas, R. J., and Pitfield, P. E. 2016. Genesis of the Tonian Imorona-Itsindro Magmatic Suite in central Madagascar: Insights from U-Pb, oxygen and hafnium isotopes in zircon. *Precambrian Research* 281: 312–337.

Archibald, D. B., Collins, A. S, Foden, J. D., Payne, J. L., Macey, P. H., Holden, P., and Razakamanana, T. 2017. Genesis of the Stenian–Tonian Dabolava Suite of west central Madagascar: Implications for the evolution of the Mozambique Ocean and the formation of Rodinia. *Journal of the Geological Society,* London 175: 111–129.

Archibald, J. D. 2003. Timing and biogeography of the eutherian radiation: Fossils and molecules compared. *Molecular Phylogenetics and Evolution* 28: 350–359.

Argus, D. F., Gordon R. G., and DeMets, C. 2011. Geologically current motion of 56 plates relative to the no-net-rotation reference frame. *Geochemistry, Geophysics, Geosystems* 12: Art. No. Q11001.

Armistead, S. E., Collins, A. S., Payne, J. L., Foden, J. D., De Waele, B., Shaji, E., and Santosh, M. 2018. A re-evaluation of the Kumta Suture in western peninsular India and its extension into Madagascar. *Journal of Asian Earth Sciences* 157: 317–328.

Armistead, S. E., Collins, A. S., Merdith, A. S., Payne, J. L., Cox, G. M., Foden, J. D., Razakamanana, T., and De Waele, B. 2019. Evolving marginal terranes during Neoproterozoic supercontinent reorganization: Constraints from the Bemarivo Domain in northern Madagascar. *Tectonics* 38: 2019–2035.

Asher, R. J., and Krause, D. W. 1998. The first pre-Holocene (Cretaceous) record of Anura from Madagascar. *Journal of Vertebrate Paleontology* 18: 696–699.

Averianov, A. O., Archibald, J. D., and Martin, T. 2003. Placental nature of the alleged marsupial from the Cretaceous of Madagascar. *Acta Palaeontologica Polonica* 48: 149–151.

Baby, G., Guillocheau, F., Morin, J., Ressouche, J., Robin, C., Broucke, O., and Dall'Asta, M. 2018. Post-rift stratigraphic evolution of the Atlantic margin of Namibia and South Africa: Implications for the vertical movements of the margin and the uplift history of the South African Plateau. *Marine and Petroleum Geology* 97: 169–191.

Bardintzeff, J. M., Liégeois, J.-P., Bonin, B., Bellon H., and Rasamimanana, G. 2010. Madagascar volcanic provinces linked to the Gondwana break-up: Geochemical and isotopic evidences for contrasting mantle sources. *Gondwana Research* 18: 295–314.

Battail, B. 1991. Triassic terrestrial ecosystems and the biogeography of the Triassic. In *Fifth Symposium on Mesozoic Terrestrial Ecosystems and Biota* (extended abstracts), eds. Z. Kielan-Jaworowska, N. Heintz, and H. A. Nakrem, pp. 3–4. Oslo: University of Oslo Palaeontological Museum.

Battail, B., Beltan, L., and Dutuit, J.-M. 1987. Africa and Madagascar during Permo-Triassic time. The evidence of the vertebrate faunas. In Gondwana six: Stratigraphy, sedimentology, and paleontology, ed. G. D. McKenzie. *Geophysical Monograph* 41: 147–155.

Bell, P. R., Fanti, F., Hart, L. J., Milan, L. A., Craven, S. J., Brougham, T., and Smith, E. 2019. Revised geology, age, and vertebrate diversity of the dinosaur-bearing Griman Creek Formation (Cenomanian), Lightning Ridge, New South Wales, Australia. *Palaeogeography, Palaeoclimatology, Palaeoecology* 514: 655–671.

Beltan, L. 1993. Overview of systematics, paleobiology, and paleoecology of Triassic fishes of northwestern Madagascar. In *Mesozoic Fishes: Systematics and Paleoecology*, eds. G. Arratia and G. Viohl, pp. 479–500. Munich: Dr. Friedrich Pfeil.

Besairie, H. 1936. Recherches géologiques à Madagascar, première suite; la géologie du nord-ouest. *Mémoires de l'Académie Malgache* 21: 1–259.

———. 1956. Carte géologique [Majunga, No. 2], 1:500,000. Antananarivo: Service Géologique de Madagasikara.

———. 1969. Carte géologique [Majunga, No. 3], 1:500,000. Antananarivo: Service Géologique de Madagasikara.

———.1972 (also dated 1971). Géologie de Madagascar, 1. Les Terrains Sédimentaires. *Annales Géologiques de Madagascar* 35: 1–463.

Besairie, H., and Collignon, M. 1972. Géologie de Madagascar—les terraines sédimentaires. *Annales Géologiques de Madagascar* 35: 1–553.

Betancur-R, R., Wiley, E. O., Arratia, G., Acero, A., Bailly, N., Miya, M., Lecointre, G., and Ortí, G. 2017. Phylogenetic classification of bony fishes. *BMC Evolutionary Biology* 17: 162.

BGS-USGS-GLW. 2008. République de Madagascar Ministère de l'éngergie et des Mines (MEM/SG/DG/UCP/PGRM). British Geological Survey Research Report.

Bindellini, G., and Dal Sasso, C. 2019. Sauropod teeth from the Middle Jurassic of Madagascar, and the oldest record of Titanosauriformes. *Papers in Palaeontology* 2019: 1–25. doi:10.1002/spp2.1282.

Bininda-Emonds, O.R.P., Beck, R.M.D., and MacPhee, R.D.E. 2012. Rocking clocks and clocking rocks: A critical look at divergence time estimation in mammals. In *From Clone to Bone: The Synergy of Morphological and Molecular Tools in Palaeobiology*, eds. R. J. Asher and J. Müller, pp. 38–82. Cambridge: Cambridge University Press.

Boger, S. D., Hirdes, W., Ferreira, C.A.M., Schulte, B., Jenett, T., and Fanning, C. M. 2014. From passive margin to volcano-sedimentary forearc: The Tonian to Cryogenian evolution of the Anosyen Domain of southeastern Madagascar. *Precambrian Research* 247: 159–186.

Boger, S. D., Maas, R., Pastuhov, M., Macey, P. H., Hirdes, W., Schulte, B., Fanning, C. M., Ferreira, C.A.M., Jenett, T., and Dallwig, R. 2019. The tectonic domains of southern and western Madagascar. *Precambrian Research* 327: 144–175.

Bonaparte, J. F. 1986a. The early radiation and phylogenetic relationships of the Jurassic sauropod dinosaurs, based on vertebral anatomy. In *The Beginning of the Age of Dinosaurs*, ed. K. Padian, pp. 247–258. Cambridge: Cambridge University Press.

———. 1986b. History of the terrestrial Cretaceous vertebrates of Gondwana. *IV Congreso Argentino Paleontología Bioestratigrafía* 2: 63–95.

Bosser, J. 1969. *Graminées des pâturages et des cultures à Madagascar*. Antananarivo: ORSTOM.

Brochu, C. A. 2007. Morphology, relationships, and biogeographical significance of an extinct horned crocodile (Crocodylia, Crocodylidae) from the Quaternary of Madagascar. *Zoological Journal of the Linnean Society* 150: 835–863.

Brocks, J. J., Jarrett, A.J.M., Sirantoine, E., Hallmann, C., Hoshino, Y., and Liyanage, T. 2017. The rise of algae in Cryogenian oceans and the emergence of animals. *Nature* 548: 578–581.

Buckley, G. A., and Brochu, C. A. 1999. An enigmatic new crocodile from the Upper Cretaceous of Madagascar. In *Cretaceous Fossil Vertebrates*, ed. D. Unwin. Special Papers in Palaeontology 60: 147–155.

Buckley, G. A., Brochu, C. A., Krause, D. W., and Pol, D. 2000. A pug-nosed crocodyliform from the Late Cretaceous of Madagascar. *Nature* 405: 941–944.

Buerki, S., Devey, D. S., Callmander, M. W., Phillipson, P. B., and Forest, F. 2013. Spatio-temporal history of the endemic genera of Madagascar. *Botanical Journal of the Linnean Society* 171: 304–329.

Buffetaut, E. 1983. *Isalorhynchus genovefae*, n. g. n. sp. (Reptilia, Rhynchocephalia), un nouveau Rhynchosaure du Trias de Madagascar. *Neues Jahrbuch für Geologie und Paläontologie, Monatschefte* 1983: 465–480.

———. 2005. A new sauropod dinosaur with prosauropod-like teeth from the Middle Jurassic of Madagascar. *Bulletin de la Société Géologique de France* 176: 483–489.

Buffetaut, E., and Taquet, P. 1979. Un nouveau Crocodilien mésosuchien dans le Campanien de Madagascar: *Trematochampsa oblita*, n. sp. *Bulletin de la Société Géologique de France* S7-XXI(2): 183–188.

Bukontaite, R., Ranarilalatiana, T., Randriamihaja, J. H., and Bergsten, J. 2015. In or out-of-Madagascar?—Colonization patterns for large-bodied diving beetles (Coleoptera: Dytiscidae). *PLoS One* 10: e0120777.

Burbrink, F. T., Ruane, S., Kuhn, A., Rabibisoa, N., Randriamahatantsoa, B et al. 2019. The origins and diversification of the exceptionally rich gemsnakes (Colubroidea: Lamprophiidae: Pseudoxyrhophiinae) in Madagascar. *Systematic Biology* 68: 918–936.

Burch, S., and Sertich, J.J.W. 2011. Giant pterosaur remains from the Campanian of the Morondava Basin, western Madagascar. *Journal of Vertebrate Paleontology*, Program and Abstracts 31: 80.

Burmeister, K. C., Flynn, J. J., Parrish, J. M., and Wyss, A. R. 2006. Paleogeographic and biostratigraphic implications of new early Mesozoic terrestrial vertebrate fossils from Poamay, central Morondava Basin, Madagascar. *Bulletin of the New Mexico Museum of Natural History* 37: 457–475.

Caen-Vachette, M., and Hottin, G. 1979. The Precambrian of Madagascar through whole-rock Rb/Sr isochron data. In *Histoire du Gondwana vue de Madagascar*, pp. 1–19. Antananarivo.

Callmander, M. W., Phillipson, P. B., Schatz, G. E., Andriambololonera, S., Rabarimanarivo, M., Rakotonirina, N., Raharimampionona, J., Chatelain, C., Gautier, L., and Lowry, P. P. 2011. The endemic and non-endemic vascular flora of Madagascar updated. *Plant Ecology and Evolution* 144: 121–125.

Carrano, M. T., Sampson, S. D., and Forster, C. A. 2002. The osteology of *Masiakasaurus knopfleri*, a small abelisauroid (Dinosauria: Theropoda) from the Late Cretaceous of Madagascar. *Journal of Vertebrate Paleontology* 22: 510–534.

Carrano, M. T., Loewen, M. A., and Sertich, J.J.W. 2011. New materials of *Masiakasaurus knopfleri* Sampson, Carrano, and Forster, 2001 and implications for the morphology of the Noasauridae (Theropoda: Ceratosauria). *Smithsonian Contributions to Paleobiology* 95: 1–53.

Carroll, R. L. 1978. Permo-Triassic "lizards" from the Karoo System. Pt. 2. A gliding reptile from the Upper Permian of Madagascar. *Palaeontologia Africana* 21: 143–159.

Carvajal-Endara, S., Hendry, A. P., Emery, N. C., and Davies, T. J. 2017. Habitat filtering not dispersal limitation shapes oceanic island floras: Species assembly of the Galápagos archipelago. *Ecological Letters* 20: 495–504.

Case, J. 2002. A new biogeographic model for dispersal of Late Cretaceous vertebrates into Madagascar and India. *Journal of Vertebrate Paleontology* 22, supplement 3: 42A.

Censky, E. J., Hodge, K., and Dudley, J. 1998. Over-water dispersal of lizards due to hurricanes. *Nature* 395: 556.

Chakrabarty, P., Davis, M. P., and Sparks, J. S. 2012. The first record of a trans-oceanic sister-group relationship between obligate vertebrate troglobites. *PLoS One* 7: e44083.

Charbonnier, S., Garassino, A., and Pasini, G. 2012. Review of the crabs (Crustacea, Decapoda, Brachyura) from the Miocene of the Mahakamby Island (Mahajanga, NW Madagascar) collected during the Waterlot's Mission (1922). *Geodiversitas* 34: 873–881.

Chorowicz, J. 2005. The East African rift system. *Journal of African Earth Sciences* 43: 379–410.

Coffin, M. F., and Rabinowitz, P. D. 1992. The Mesozoic East African and Madagascan conjugate continental margins; stratigraphy and tectonics. In *Geology and Geophysics of Continental Margins*, eds. J. S. Watkins, F. Zhiqiang and K. J. McMillen. *American Association of Petroleum Geologists Memoir* 53: 207–240.

Collier, J. S., Sansom, V., Ishizuka, O., Taylor, R. N., Minshull, T. A., and Whitmarsh, R. B. 2008. Age of Seychelles–India break-up. *Earth and Planetary Science Letters* 272: 264–277.

Collignon, M., and Cottreau, J. 1927. Paléontologie de Madagascar: Fossiles du Miocène marin. *Annales de Paléontologie* 16: 135–170.

Collins, A. S., and Pisarevsky, S. 2005. Amalgamating eastern Gondwana: The evolution of the Circum-Indian Orogens. *Earth-Science Reviews* 71: 229–270.

Collins, A. S., and Windley, B. 2002. The tectonic evolution of central and northern Madagascar and its place in the final assembly of Gondwana. *Journal of Geology* 110: 325–339.

Collins, A. S., Kroner, A., Fitzsimons, I., and Razakamanana, T. 2003. Detrital footprint of the Mozambique ocean: U-Pb SHRIMP and Pb evaporation zircon geochronology of metasedimentary gneisses in eastern Madagascar. *Tectonophysics* 375: 77–99.

Collins, A. S., Kinny, P. D., and Razakamanana, T. 2012. Depositional age, provenance and metamorphic age of metasedimentary rocks from southern Madagascar. *Gondwana Research* 21: 353–361.

Collins, A. S., Blades, M. L., Merdith, A. S., and Foden, J. D. 2021. Closure of the Proterozoic Mozambique Ocean was instigated by a late Tonian plate reorganization event. *Communications Earth and Environment* 2: 75.

Collins, A. S., Kröner, A., Blades, M. L., Razakamanana, T., Merdith, A. S., et al. Forthcoming. The largest mountain belt of the last billion years: The East African Orogen of Africa, Madagascar, India, Sri Lanka and Antarctica. *Precambrian Research.*

Cordes-Person, A., Hospitaleche, C. A., Case, J., and Martin, J. 2020. An enigmatic bird from the lower Maastrichtian of Vega Island, Antarctica. *Cretaceous Research* 108: 104314.

Courgeon, S., Jorry, S. J., Camoin, G. F., BouDagher-Fadel, M. K., Jouet, G., et al. 2016. Growth and demise of Cenozoic isolated carbonate platforms: New insights from the Mozambique Channel seamounts (SW Indian Ocean). *Marine Geology* 380: 90–105.

Courgeon, S., Jorry, S. J., Jouet, G., Camoin, G., BouDagher-Fadel, M. K., et al. 2017. Impact of tectonic and volcanism on the Neogene evolution of isolated carbonate platforms (S W Indian Ocean). *Sedimentary Geology* 355: 114–131.

Courgeon, S., Bachelery, P., Jouet, G., Jorry, S. J., Bou, E., BouDagher-Fadel, M. K., Révillon, S., Camoin, G., and Poli, E. 2018. The offshore East African rift system: New insights from the Sakalaves seamounts (Davie Ridge, SW Indian Ocean). *Terra Nova* 30: 380–388.

Cox, R., Armstrong, R. A., and Ashwal, L. D. 1998. Sedimentology, geochronology and provenance of the Proterozoic Itremo Group, central Madagascar, and implications for pre-Gondwana palaeogeography. *Journal of the Geological Society*, London 155: 1009–1024.

Cox, R., Coleman, D., Chokel, C., DeOreo, S., Wooden, J., Collins, A., De Waele, B., and Kroner, A. 2004. Proterozoic tectonostratigraphy and paleogeography of central Madagascar derived from detrital zircon U-Pb age populations. *Journal of Geology* 112: 379–399.

Cramwinckel, M. J., Huber, M., Kocken, I. J., Agnini, C., Bijl, P. K., et al. 2018. Synchronous tropical and polar temperature evolution in the Eocene. *Nature* 559: 382–386.

Crottini, A., Madsen, O., Poux, C., Strauß, A., Vieites, D. R., and Vences, M. 2012. Vertebrate time-tree elucidates the biogeographic pattern of a major biotic change around the K-T boundary in Madagascar. *Proceedings of the National Academy of Sciences of the USA* 109: 5358–5363.

Cucciniello, C., Melluso, L., Jourdan, F., Mahoney, J. J., Meisel, T., and Morra, V. 2013. ^{40}Ar–^{39}Ar ages and isotope geochemistry of Cretaceous basalts in northern Madagascar: Refining eruption ages, extent of crustal contamination and parental magmas in a flood basalt province. *Geological Magazine* 150: 1–17.

Cucciniello, C., Melluso, L., le Roex, A. P., Jourdan, F., Morra, V., Gennaroa, R. de, and Grifa, C. 2017. From olivine nephelinite, basanite and basalt to peralkaline trachyphonolite and comendite in the Ankaratra volcanic complex, Madagascar: $^{40}Ar/^{39}Ar$ ages, phase compositions and bulk-rock geochemical and isotopic evolution. *Lithos* 274–275: 363–382.

Cunningham, C., Feldman, H., Franseen, E., Gastalso, R., Mapes, G., Maples, C., and Schultze, H. 1993. The Upper Carboniferous Hamilton fossil-lagerstatte in Kansas—a valley-fill, tidally influenced deposit. *Lethaia* 26: 225–236.

Currie, P. J. 1981. *Hovasaurus boulei*, an aquatic eosuchian from the Upper Permian of Madagascar. *Palaeontologia Africana* 24: 99–168.

Curry, K. A. 1997. Vertebrate fossils from the Upper Cretaceous Ankazomihaboka sandstones, Mahajanga Basin, Madagascar. *Journal of Vertebrate Paleontology* 17: 40A.

Curry Rogers, K. A. 2005. Titanosauria: A phylogenetic overview. In *The Sauropods: Evolution and Paleobiology*, eds. K. Curry Rogers and J. A. Wilson, pp. 50–103. Berkeley: University of California Press.

———. 2009. The postcranial osteology of *Rapetosaurus krausei* (Sauropoda: Titanosauria) from the Late Cretaceous of Madagascar. *Journal of Vertebrate Paleontology* 29: 1046–1086.

Curry Rogers, K. A., and Forster, C. A. 2001. The last of the dinosaur titans: A new sauropod from Madagascar. *Nature* 412: 530–534.

———. 2004. The skull of *Rapetosaurus krausei* (Sauropoda: Titanosauria) from the Late Cretaceous of Madagascar. *Journal of Vertebrate Paleontology* 24: 121–144.

Curry Rogers, K. A., and Kulik, A. 2018. Osteohistology of *Rapetosaurus krausei* (Sauropoda: Titanosauria) from the Upper Cretaceous of Madagascar. *Journal of Vertebrate Paleontology* 38: 1–24.

Curry Rogers, K. A., and Wilson, J. A. 2014. *Vahiny depereti*, gen. et sp. nov., a new titanosaur (Dinosauria, Sauropoda) from the Upper Cretaceous Maevarano Formation, Madagascar. *Journal of Vertebrate Paleontology* 34: 606–617.

Curry Rogers, K. [A.], D'Emic, M. D., Rogers, R. Vickaryous, M., and Cagan, A. 2011. Sauropod dinosaur osteoderms from the Late Cretaceous of Madagascar. *Nature Communications* 2: 564.

Curry Rogers, K. A., Whitney, M., D'Emic, M., and Bagley, B. 2016. Precocity in a tiny titanosaur from the Cretaceous of Madagascar. *Science* 352: 450–453.

da Fonte, L.F.M., Mayer, M., and Lötters, S. 2019. Long-distance dispersal in amphibians. *Frontiers of Biogeography* 11: e44577.

Dal Sasso, C., and Pasini, G. 2003. First record of pterosaurs (Pterosauria, Diapsida, Archosauromorpha) in the Middle Jurassic of Madagascar. *Atti della Società Italiana di Scienze Naturali e del Museo Civico di Storia Naturale di Milano* 144 (2): 281–296.

Dal Sasso, C., Pasini, G., Fleury, G., and Maganuco, S. 2017. *Razanandrongobe sakalavae*, a gigantic mesoeucrocodylian from the Middle Jurassic of Madagascar, is the oldest known notosuchian. *PeerJ* 5: e3481.

Dausmann, K. H., Glos, J., and Heldmaier, G. 2009. Energetics of tropical hibernation. *Journal of Comparative Physiology B* 179: 345–357.

Davis, B. M. 2011. Evolution of the tribosphenic molar pattern in early mammals, with comments on the "Dual-Origin" Hypothesis. *Journal of Mammalian Evolution* 18: 227–244.

D'Emic, M. D., O'Connor, P. M., Pascucci, T. R., Gavras, J. N., Mardakhayava, E., and Lund, E. K. 2019. Evolution of high tooth replacement rates in theropod dinosaurs. *PLoS One* 14: e0224734.

Delaunay, A. 2018. Les mouvements verticaux de Madagascar (90–0 Ma): Une analyse couplée des formes du relief et de l'enregistrement sédimentaire des marges ouest malgaches. PhD thesis, Université de Rennes 1. doi:10.13140/RG.2.2.35631.69283.

Depéret, C. 1896. Note sur les dinosauriens sauropodes et théropodes du Crétacé supérieur de Madagascar. *Bulletin de la Société Géologique de France*, série 3, 24: 176–194.

Desojo, J. B., Ezcurra, M. D., and Schultz, C. L. 2011. An unusual new archosauriform from the Middle–Late Triassic of southern Brazil and the monophyly of Doswelliidae. *Zoological Journal of the Linnean Society* 161: 839–871.

De Waele, B., Thomas, R. J., Macey, P. H., Horstwood, M.S.A., Tucker, R. D., et al. 2011. Provenance and tectonic significance of the Palaeoproterozoic metasedimentary successions of central and northern Madagascar. *Precambrian Research* 189: 18–42.

de Wit, M. J. 2003. Madagascar: Heads it's a continent, tails it's an island. *Annual Review of Earth and Planetary Sciences* 31: 213–248.

Dixey, F. 1960. The geology and geomorphology of Madagascar, and a comparison with eastern Africa. *Quarterly Journal of the Geological Society of London* 116: 255–268.

Domning, D., and Sorbi, S. 2011. *Rytiodus heali*, sp. nov., a new sirenian (Mammalia, Dugonginae) from the Miocene of Libya. *Journal of Vertebrate Paleontology* 31:1338–1355.

Dutuit, J. M. 1978. Description de quelques fragments osseux provenant de la region de Folakara (Trias supérieur malagache). *Bulletin du Muséum National d'Histoire naturelle* 516(69): 79–89.

Earthworks. 2021. Gondwana. http://www.reeves.nl/gond.com.

Ebinger, C. 1989. Tectonic development of the western branch of the East African rift system. *Geological Society of America Bulletin* 101: 885–903.

Ellison, A. M., Farnsworth, E. J., and Merkt, R. E. 1999. Origins of mangrove ecosystems and the mangrove biodiversity anomaly. *Global Ecology and Biogeography* 8: 95–115.

Emmel, B., Jöns, N., Kröner, A., Jacobs, J., Wartho, J.-A., Schenk, V., Razakamanana, T., and Austegard, A. 2008. From closure of the Mozambique Ocean to Gondwana breakup: New evidence from geochronological data of the Vohibory Terrane, southwest Madagascar. *Journal of Geology* 116: 21–38.

Evans, S. E., and Jones, M.E.H. 2010. The origins, early history and diversification of lepidosauromorph reptiles. In *New Aspects of Mesozoic Biodiversity*, ed. S. Bandyopadhyay. Lecture Notes in Earth Sciences, 132: 27–44.

Evans, S. E., Jones, M.E.H., and Krause, D. W. 2008. A giant frog with South American affinities from the Late Cretaceous of Madagascar. *Proceedings of the National Academy of Sciences of the USA.* 105: 2951–2956.

Evans, S. E., Groenke, J. R., Jones, M. E., Turner, A. H., and Krause, D. W. 2014. New material of *Beelzebufo*, a hyperossified frog (Amphibia: Anura) from the Late Cretaceous of Madagascar. *PLoS One* 9: e87236.

Everson, K. M., Soarimalala, V., Goodman, S. M., and Olson, L. E. 2016. Multiple loci and complete taxonomic sampling resolve the phylogeny and biogeographic history of tenrecs (Mammalia: Tenrecidae) and reveal higher speciation rates in Madagascar's humid forests. *Systematic Biology* 65: 890–909.

Falconnet, J., Andriamihaja, M., Läng, E., and Steyer, J.-S. 2012. First procolophonid (Reptilia, Parareptilia) from the Lower Triassic of Madagascar. *Comptes Rendus Palevol* 11: 357–369.

Farke, A. A., and Sertich, J.J.W. 2013. An abelisauroid theropod dinosaur from the Turonian of Madagascar. *PLoS One* 8(4): e62047.

Federman, S., Dornburg, A., Downie, A., Richard, A. F., Daly, D. C., and Donoghue, M. J. 2015. The biogeographic origin of a radiation of trees in Madagascar: Implications for the assembly of a tropical forest biome. *BMC Evolutionary Biology* 15: 216.

Figueirido, B., Janis, C. M., Pérez-Claros, J. A., De Renzi, M., and Palmqvist, P. 2012. Cenozoic climate change influences mammalian evolutionary dynamics. *Proceedings of the National Academy of Sciences of the USA.* 109: 722–727.

Fitzsimons, I.C.W., and Hulscher, B. 2005. Out of Africa: Detrital zircon provenance of central Madagascar and Neoproterozoic terrane transfer across the Mozambique Ocean. *Terra Nova* 17: 224–235.

Fleagle, J. G. 2013. *Primate Adaptation and Evolution*. 3rd ed. New York: Academic Press.

Flynn, J. J., and Wyss, A. R. 2003. Mesozoic terrestrial vertebrate faunas: The early history of Madagascar's vertebrate diversity. In *The Natural History of Madagascar*, eds. S. M. Goodman and J. P. Benstead, pp. 34–40. Chicago: University of Chicago Press.

Flynn, J. [J.], Parrish, J. M., Wyss, A., and Simpson, W. 1998. New Triassic and Jurassic vertebrates from Madagascar. *Journal of Vertebrate Paleontology* 18: 42A.

Flynn, J. J., Parrish, J. M., Rakotosamimanana, B., Simpson, W. F., Whatley, R. L., and Wyss, A. R. 1999a. A Triassic fauna from Madagascar, including early dinosaurs. *Science* 286: 763–765.

Flynn, J. J., Parrish, J. M., Rakotosamimanana, B., Simpson, W. F., and Wyss, A. R. 1999b. A Middle Jurassic mammal from Madagascar. *Nature* 401: 57–60.

Flynn, J. J., Parrish, J. M., Rakotosamimanana, B., Ranivoharimanana, L., Simpson, W. F., and Wyss, A. R. 2000a. New traversodontids (Synapsida: Eucynodontia) from the Triassic of Madagascar. *Journal of Vertebrate Paleontology* 20: 422–427.

Flynn, J. J., Parrish, J. M., Ranivoharimanana, L., Simpson, W. F., and Wyss, A. R. 2000b. New traversodontid eucynodonts from the Middle or Late Triassic of Madagascar. *Journal of Vertebrate Paleontology* 20, supplement 3: 41A.

Flynn, J. J., Fox, S., Parrish, J. M., Ranivoharimanana, L., and Wyss, A. R. 2006. Assessing diversity and paleoecology of a Middle Jurassic microvertebrate assemblage from Madagascar. *Bulletin of the New Mexico Museum of Natural History* 37: 476–489.

Flynn, J. J., Nesbitt, S. J., Parrish, J. M., Ranivoharimanana, L., and Wyss, A. R. 2010. A new species of *Azendohsaurus* (Diapsida: Archosauromorpha) from the Triassic Isalo Group of southwestern Madagascar: Cranium and mandible. *Palaeontology* 53(3): 669–688.

Forster, C. A., Chiappe, L. M., Krause, D. W., and Sampson, S. D. 1996. The first Cretaceous bird from Madagascar. *Nature* 382: 532–534.

Forster, C. A., Sampson, S. D., Chiappe, L. M., and Krause, D. W. 1998. The theropod ancestry of birds: New evidence from the Late Cretaceous of Madagascar. *Science* 279: 1915–1919.

Forster, C. A., Chiappe, L. M., Krause, D. W., and Sampson, S. D. 2002. *Vorona berivotrensis*, a primitive bird from the Late Cretaceous of Madagascar. In *Mesozoic Birds: Above the Heads of Dinosaurs*, eds. L. M. Chiappe and L. M. Witmer, pp. 268–280. Berkeley: University of California Press.

Forster, C. A., O'Connor, P. M., Chiappe, L. M., and Turner, A. H. 2020. The osteology of the Late Cretaceous paravian *Rahonavis ostromi* from Madagascar. *Palaeontologia Electronica* 23(2): a29.

Fortuny, J., Gastou, S., Escuillé, F., Ranivoharimanana, L., and Steyer, J.-S. 2018. A new extreme longirostrine temnospondyl from the Triassic of Madagascar: Phylogenetic and palaeobiogeographical implications for trematosaurids. *Journal of Systematic Palaeontology* 16(8): 675–688.

Fortuny, J., Arbez, T., Mujal, E., and Steyer, J. S. 2019. Reappraisal of "*Metoposaurus hoffmani*" Dutuit, 1978, and description of new temnospondyl specimens from the Middle–Late Triassic of Madagascar (Morondava Basin). *Journal of Vertebrate Paleontology* 39: 1, e1576701.

Friedman, M., Keck, B. P., Dornburg, A., Eytan, R. I., Martin, C. H., Hulsey, C. D., Wainwright, P. C., and Near, T. J. 2013. Molecular and fossil evidence place the origin of cichlid fishes long after Gondwanan rifting. *Proceedings of the Royal Society of London B: Biological Sciences* 280: 20131733.

Fritz, H., Abdelsalam, M., Ali, K. A., Bingen, B., Collins, A. S., et al. 2013. Orogen styles in the East Africa Orogens: A review of the Neoproterozoic to Cambrian tectonic evolution. *Journal of African Earth Sciences* 86: 65–106.

Gaffney, E. S., and Forster, C. A. 2003. Side-necked turtle lower jaws (Podocnemididae, Bothremydidae) from the Late Cretaceous Maevarano Formation of Madagascar. *American Museum Novitates* 3397: 1–13.

Gaffney, E. S., and Krause, D. W. 2011. *Sokatra*, a new side-necked turtle (Late Cretaceous, Madagascar) and the diversification of the main groups of Pelomedusoides. *American Museum Novitates* 3728: 1–28.

Gaffney, E. S., Krause, D. W., and Zalmout, I. 2009. *Kinkonychelys*, a new side-necked turtle (Pelomedusoides: Bothremydidae) from the Late Cretaceous of Madagascar. *American Museum Novitates* 3662: 1–25.

Gardner, J. D., and Rage, J.-C. 2016. The fossil record of lissamphibians from Africa, Madagascar, and the Arabian Plate. *Palaeobiodiversity and Palaeoenvironments* 96: 169–220.

Geiger, M., Clark, D. N., and Mette, W. 2004. Reappraisal of the timing of the breakup of Gondwana based on sedimentological and seismic evidence from the Morondava Basin, Madagascar. *Journal of African Earth Sciences* 38: 363–381.

Gingerich, P. 1977. A small collection of fossil vertebrates from the Middle Eocene Kuldana and Kohot formations of Punjab (Pakistan). *Contributions from the Museum of Paleontology, University of Michigan* 24: 190–203.

Giribet, G., and Edgecombe, G. D. 2013. Stable phylogenetic patterns in scutigeromorph centipedes (Myriapoda: Chilopoda: Scutigeromorpha): Dating the diversification of an ancient lineage of terrestrial arthropods. *Invertebrate Systematics* 27: 485–501.

Goin, F. J., Martinelli, A. G., Soto-Acuña, S., Vieytes, E. C., Manríquez, L.M.E., et al. 2020. First Mesozoic mammal from Chile: The southernmost record of a Late Cretaceous gondwanatherian. *Boletín del Museo Nacional de Historia Natural* 69: 5–31.

González, R., Cerda, I. A., Filippi, L. S., and Salgado, L. 2020. Early growth dynamics of titanosaur sauropods inferred from bone histology. *Palaeogeography, Palaeoclimatology, Palaeoecology* 537: 109404.

Goodenough, K. M., Thomas, R. J., De Waele, B., Key, R. M., Schofield, D. I., et al. 2010. Post-collisional magmatism in the central East African Orogen: The Maevarano Suite of north Madagascar. *Lithos* 116: 18–34.

Gorscak, E., and O'Connor, P. M. 2016. Time-calibrated models support congruency between Cretaceous continental rifting and titanosaurian evolutionary history. *Biology Letters* 12: 20151047.

Gorscak, E., O'Connor, P. M., Roberts, E. M., and Stevens, N. J. 2017. The second titanosaurian (Dinosauria: Sauropoda) from the middle Cretaceous Galula Formation, southwestern Tanzania, with remarks on African titanosaurian diversity. *Journal of Vertebrate Paleontology* 37: e1343250.

Goswami, A., Flynn, J. J., Ranivoharimanana, L., and Wyss, A. R. 2005. Dental microwear in Triassic amniotes: Implications for paleoecology and masticatory mechanics. *Journal of Vertebrate Paleontology* 25(2): 320–329.

Gottfried, M. D., and Krause, D. W. 1998. First record of gars (Ginglymodi, Actinopterygii) on Madagascar: Late Cretaceous remains from the Mahajanga Basin. *Journal of Vertebrate Paleontology* 18: 275–279.

Gottfried, M. D., and Rabarison, J. A. 1997. First Mesozoic Gondwanan record of a sawshark (Chondrichthyes, Pristiophoriformes), from the Late Cretaceous of Madagascar. *Journal of Vertebrate Paleontology* 17: 750–751.

Gottfried, M. D., Randriamiarimanana, L. L., Rabarison, J. A., and Krause, D. W. 1998. Late Cretaceous fish from Madagascar: Implications for Gondwanan biogeography. *Journal of African Earth Sciences* 27: 91–92.

Gottfried, M. D., Rabarison, J. A., and Randriamiaramanana, L. L. 2001. Late Cretaceous elasmobranchs from the Mahajanga Basin of Madagascar. *Cretaceous Research* 22: 491–496.

Gottfried, M. D., Samonds, K. E., Ostrowski, S. A., Andrianavalona, T. H., and Ramihangihajason, T. N. 2017. New evidence indicates the presence of barracuda (Sphyraenidae) and supports a tropical marine environment in the Miocene of Madagascar. *PLoS One* 12: e0176553.

Grubb, P. J. 2003. Interpreting some outstanding features of the flora and vegetation of Madagascar. *Perspectives in Plant Ecology, Evolution and Systematics* 6: 125–146.

Gunnell, G. F., Boyer, D. M., Friscia, A. R., Heritage, S., Manthi, F. K., Miller, E. R., Sallam, H. M., Simmons, N. B., Stevens, N. J., and Seiffert, E. R. 2018. Fossil lemurs from Egypt and Kenya suggest an African origin for Madagascar's aye-aye. *Nature Communications* 9: 3193.

Gustafson, G. T., Prokin, A. A., Bukontaite, R., Bergsten, J., and Miller, K. B. 2017. Tip-dated phylogeny of whirligig beetles reveals ancient lineage surviving on Madagascar. *Scientific Reports* 7: 8619.

Guth, C. 1963. Au sujet de restes de Reptiles de Madagascar. *Comptes Rendus Académie Sciences*, Paris, 256: 2661–2663.

Gutherz, S. B., Groenke, J. R., Sertich, J.J.W., Burch, S. H., and O'Connor, P. M. 2020. Paleopathology in a nearly complete skeleton of *Majungasaurus crenatissimus* (Theropoda: Abelisauridae). *Cretaceous Research* 115: 104553.

Hackel, J., Vorontsova, M. S., Nanjarisoa, O. P., Hall, R. C., Razanatsoa, J., Malakasi, P., and Besnard, G. 2018. Grass diversification in Madagascar: In situ radiation of two large C_3 shade clades and support for a Miocene to Pliocene origin of C_4 grassy biomes. *Journal of Biogeography* 45: 750–761.

Halverson, G. P., Hurtgen, M. T., Porter, S. M., and Collins, A. S. 2009. Neoproterozoic-Cambrian biogeochemical evolution. In *Neoproterozoic-Cambrian Tectonics, Global Change and Evolution: A Focus on Southwestern Gondwana*, eds. C. Gaucher, A. N. Sial, G. P. Halverson, and H. E. Frimmel. Developments in Precambrian Geology 16: 351–365.

Hauzenberger, C. A., Bauernhofer, A. H., Hoinkes, G., Wallbrecher, E., and Mathu, E. M. 2004. Pan-African high pressure granulites from SE-Kenya: Petrological and geothermobarometric evidence for a polycyclic evolution in the Mozambique belt. *Journal of African Earth Sciences* 40: 245–268.

Hay, W. W., DeConto, R. M., Wold, C. N., Willson, K. M., Voigt, S., et al. 1999. An alternative global Cretaceous paleogeography. In Evolution of Cretaceous ocean/climate systems, eds. E. Berrera and C. Johnson. *Geological Society of America*, Special Papers, 332: 1–48.

Herrera, J. P., and Dávalos, L. M. 2016. Phylogeny and divergence times of lemurs inferred with recent and ancient fossils in the tree. *Systematic Biology* 65: 772–791.

Hoffman, P. F., Abbot, D. S., Ashkenazy, Y., Benn, D. I., Brocks, J. J., et al. 2017. Snowball Earth climate dynamics and Cryogenian geology-geobiology. *Scientific Advances* 3: e1600983.

Hoffstetter, R. 1961. Nouveaux restes d'un serpent Boïdé (*Madtsoïa madagascariensis* nov. sp.) dans le Crétacé supérieur de Madagascar. *Bulletin du Muséum National d'Histoire Naturelle*, Paris, 33: 152–160.

Hong-Wa, C., and Besnard, G. 2014. Species limits and diversification in the Madagascar olive (*Noronhia*, Oleaceae). *Botanical Journal of the Linnean Society* 174: 141–161.

Hottin, G. 1976. Présentation et essai d'interprétation du Précambrien de Madagascar. *Bulletin du Bureau de Recherches Géologiques et Minières,* section 4, 2: 117–153.

Hu, Y., Meng, J., Wang, Y., and Li, C.-K. 2005. Large Mesozoic mammals fed on young dinosaurs. *Nature* 433: 149–152.

Huber, M., and Caballero, R. 2011. The early Eocene equable climate problem revisited. *Climate of the Past* 7: 603–633.

Huntingford, G.W.B. 1980. *The Periplus of the Erythraean Sea by an unknown author with some extracts from Agatharkides "On the Erythaean Sea"*. London: The Hakluyt Society.

Hutter, C. R., Lambert, S. M., Andriampenomanana, Z. F., Glaw, F., and Vences, M. 2018. Molecular phylogeny and diversification of Malagasy bright-eyed frogs (Mantellidae: *Boophis*). *Molecular Phylogenetics and Evolution* 127: 568–578.

Ibrahim, N., Sereno, P. C., Varricchio, D. J., Martill, D. M., Dutheil, D. B., Unwin, D. M., Baidder, L., Larsson, H.C.E., Zouhri, S., and Kaoukaya, A. 2020. Geology and paleontology of the Upper Cretaceous Kem Kem Group of eastern Morocco. *ZooKeys* 928: 1–216. https://doi.org/10.3897/zookeys.928.47517.

Irisarri, I., Singh, P., Koblmüller, S., Torres-Dowdall, J., Henning, F., et al. 2018. Phylogenomics uncovers early hybridization and adaptive loci shaping the radiation of Lake Tanganyika cichlid fishes. *Nature Communications* 9: 3159.

Jablonski, D. 1994. Extinctions in the fossil record. *Philosophical Transactions of the Royal Society of London B: Biological Sciences* 344: 11–17.

Janvier, P. 1992. Les écailles des Trématosaures (Tetrapoda, Temnospondyli): nouvelles données sur les Trématosaures du Trias inférieur de Madagascar. *Bulletin Muséum National d'Histoire Naturelle*, Paris, série 4, 14 (Section C, no. 1): 3–13.

Jet Propulsion Laboratory. 2004. Aster Global Digital Elevation Model. https://asterweb.jpl.nasa.gov/gdem.asp.

Jones, G. R. 2019. Divergence estimation in the presence of incomplete lineage sorting and migration. *Systematic Biology* 68: 19–31.

Jöns, N., and Schenk, V. 2008. Relics of the Mozambique Ocean in the central East African Orogen: Evidence from the Vohibory Block of southern Madagascar. *Journal of Metamorphic Geology* 26: 17–28.

Jouve, S., Bardet, N., Jalil, N.-E., Suberbiola, X. P., Bouya, B., and Amaghzaz, M. 2008. The oldest African crocodylian: Phylogeny, paleobiogeography, and differential survivorship of marine reptiles through the Cretaceous-Tertiary boundary. *Journal of Vertebrate Paleontology* 28: 409–421.

Kammerer, C. F., Flynn, J. J., Ranivoharimanana, L., and Wyss, A. R. 2008. New material of *Menadon besairiei* (Cynodontia: Traversodontidae) from the Triassic of Madagascar. *Journal of Vertebrate Paleontology* 28(2): 445–462.

———. 2010. The first record of a probainognathian (Cynodontia: Chiniquodontidae) from the Triassic of Madagascar. *Journal of Vertebrate Paleontology* 30(6): 1889–1894.

———. 2012. Ontogeny in the traversodontid *Dadadon isaloi* and a reconsideration of its phylogenetic relationships. *Fieldiana Life and Earth Sciences* 5: 112–125.

Kammerer, C. F., Nesbitt, S. J., Flynn, J. J., Ranivoharimanana, L., and Wyss, A. R. 2020. A tiny ornithodiran archosaur from the Triassic of Madagascar and the role of miniaturization in dinosaur and pterosaur ancestry. *Proceedings of the National Academy of Sciences of the USA*. 117(30): 17932–17936.

Kappeler, P. M. 2000. Lemur origins: Rafting by groups of hibernators? *Folia Primatologica* 71: 422–425.

Kapur, V. V., and Khosla, A. 2018. Faunal elements from the Deccan volcano-sedimentary sequences of India: A reappraisal of biostratigraphic, palaeoecologic, and palaeobiogeographic aspects. *Geological Journal* 54: 2797–2828.

Kasting, J. F. 2019. The goldilocks planet? How silicate weathering maintains earth "just right". *Elements* 15: 235–240.

Ketchum, H. F., and Barrett, P. M. 2004. New reptile material from the Lower Triassic of Madagascar: Implications for the Permian–Triassic extinction event. *Canadian Journal of Earth Sciences* 41: 1–8.

Khosla, A., and Lucas, S. G. 2020. End-Cretaceous extinctions. *Encyclopedia of Geology*, 2nd ed., eds. S. Elias and D. Alderton. Amsterdam: Elsevier. doi.org/10.1016/B978-0-12-409548-9.12473-X.

Khosla, A., and Verma, O. 2015. Paleobiota from the Deccan volcano-sedimentary sequences of India: Paleoenvironments, age and paleobiogeographic implications. *Historical Biology* 27: 898–914.

Kley, N. J., Sertich, J.J.W., Turner, A. H., Krause, D. W., O'Connor, P. M., and Georgi, J. A. 2010. Craniofacial morphology of *Simosuchus clarki* (Crocodyliformes: Notosuchia) from the Late Cretaceous of Madagascar. *Journal of Vertebrate Paleontology* 30, supplement 1: 13–98.

Klimke, J., Franke, D., Mahanjane, E. S., and Leitchenkov, G. 2018. Tie points for Gondwana reconstructions from a structural interpretation of the Mozambique Basin, East Africa and the Riiser-Larsen Sea, Antarctica. *Solid Earth* 9: 25–37.

Kogan, I., and Romano, C. 2016. Redescription of *Saurichthys madagascariensis* Piveteau, 1945 (Actinopterygii, Early Triassic), with implications for the early saurichthyid morphotype. *Journal of Vertebrate Paleontology* 36(4): e1151886.

Krause, D. W. 2001. Marsupial from the Late Cretaceous of Madagascar. *Nature* 412: 497–498.

———. 2003. Late Cretaceous vertebrates from Madagascar: A window into Gondwanan biogeography at the end of the Age of Dinosaurs. In *The Natural History of Madagascar*, eds. S. M. Goodman and J. P. Benstead, pp. 40–47. Chicago: University of Chicago Press.

———. 2010. Washed up in Madagascar. *Nature* 463: 613–614.

———. 2013. Gondwanatheria and ?Multituberculata (Mammalia) from the Late Cretaceous of Madagascar. *Canadian Journal of Earth Sciences* 50: 324–340.

———, ed. 2014. *Vintana sertichi* (Mammalia, Gondwanatheria) from the Late Cretaceous of Madagascar. *Society of Vertebrate Paleontology Memoir* 14: 1–222.

Krause, D. W., and Hoffmann, S., eds. 2020. *Adalatherium hui* (Mammalia, Gondwanatheria) from the Late Cretaceous of Madagascar. *Society of Vertebrate Paleontology* 40, supplement 1: 1–234.

Krause, D. W., and Kley, N. J., eds. 2010. *Simosuchus clarki* (Crocodyliformes: Notosuchia) from the Late Cretaceous of Madagascar. *Society of Vertebrate Paleontology Memoir* 10: 1–236.

Krause, D. W., Hartman, J. H., Wells, N. A., Buckley, G. A., Lockwood, C. A., Wall, C. E., Wunderlich, R. E., Rabarison, J. A., and Randriamiaramanana, L. L. 1994. Late Cretaceous mammals. *Nature* 368: 298.

Krause, D. W., Hartman, J. H., and Wells, N. A. 1997a. Late Cretaceous vertebrates from Madagascar: Implications for biotic change in deep time. In *Natural Change and Human Impact in Madagascar*, eds. S. M. Goodman and B. D. Patterson, pp. 3–43. Washington, DC: Smithsonian Institution Press.

Krause, D. W., Prasad, G.V.R., Koenigswald, W. von, Sahni, A., and Grine, F. E. 1997b. Cosmopolitanism among Gondwanan Late Cretaceous mammals. *Nature* 390: 504–507.

Krause, D. W., Rogers, R. R., Forster, C. A., Hartman, J. H., Buckley, G. A., and Sampson, S. D. 1997c. The Late Cretaceous vertebrate fauna of Madagascar: Implications for Gondwanan paleobiogeography. *GSA Today* 9(8): 1–7.

Krause, D. W., Forster, C. A., Sampson, S. D., Buckley, G. A., and Gottfried, M. 1998. Vertebrate fossils from the Late Cretaceous of Madagascar: Implications for Gondwanan plate tectonics and biogeography. *Journal of African Earth Sciences* 27(1A): 128–129.

Krause, D. W., Rogers, R. R., Forster, C. A., Hartman, J. H., Buckley, G. A., and Sampson, S. D. 1999. The Late Cretaceous vertebrate fauna of Madagascar: Implications for Gondwanan paleobiogeography. *GSA Today* 9(8): 1–7.

Krause, D. W., Evans, S. E., and Gao, K.-Q. 2003. First definitive record of Mesozoic lizards from Madagascar. *Journal of Vertebrate Paleontology* 23: 842–856.

Krause, D. W., O'Connor, P. M., Curry Rogers, K., Sampson, S. D., Buckley, G. A., and Rogers R. R. 2006. Late Cretaceous terrestrial vertebrates from Madagascar: Implications for Latin American biogeography. *Annals of the Missouri Botanical Garden* 93: 178–208.

Krause, D. W., Hoffmann, S., Wible, J. R., Kirk, E. C., Schultz, J. A., et al. 2014. First cranial remains of gondwanatherian mammal reveal remarkable mosaicism. *Nature* 515: 512–517.

Krause, D. W., Hoffmann, S., and Werning, S. 2017. First postcranial remains of Multituberculata (Allotheria, Mammalia) from Gondwana. *Cretaceous Research* 80: 91–100.

Krause, D. W., Sertich, J.J.W., O'Connor, P. M., Curry Rogers, K., and Rogers, R. R. 2019. The Mesozoic biogeographic history of Gondwanan terrestrial vertebrates: Insights from Madagascar's fossil record. *Annual Review of Earth and Planetary Sciences* 47: 519–553.

Krause, D. W., Hoffmann, S., Hu, Y., Wible, J. R., Rougier, G. W., et al. 2020. Skeleton of a Cretaceous mammal from Madagascar reflects long-term insularity. *Nature* 581: 421–427. https://doi.org/10.1038/s41586-020-2234-8.

Kröner, A., Hegner, E., Collins, A., Windley, B., Brewer, T., Razakamanana, T., and Pidgeon, R. 2000. Age and magmatic history of the Antananarivo Block, central Madagascar, as derived from zircon geochronology and Nd isotopic systematics. *American Journal of Science* 300: 251–288.

Kuntner, M., and Agnarsson, I. 2011. Phylogeography of a successful aerial disperser: The golden orb spider *Nephila* on Indian Ocean islands. *BMC Evolutionary Biology* 11: 119.

LaDuke, T. C., Krause, D. W., Scanlon, J. D., and Kley N. J. 2010. A Late Cretaceous (Maastrichtian) snake assemblage from the Maevarano Formation, Mahajanga Basin, Madagascar. *Journal of Vertebrate Paleontology* 30: 109–138.

Lalaharisaina, J. V., and Ferrand, N. J. 1994. Cretaceous may hold promise in Majunga Basin, Madagascar. *Oil and Gas Journal* 1: 54–58.

Lamanna, M. C., Case, J. A., Roberts, E. M., Arbour, V. M., Ely, R. C., Salisbury, S. W., Clarke, J. A., Malinzak, D. E., West, A. R., and O'Connor, P. M. 2019. Late Cretaceous non-avian dinosaurs from the James Ross Basin, Antarctica: Description of new material, updated synthesis, biostratigraphy and paleobiogeography. *Advances in Polar Sciences* 30: 228–250.

Langer, M., Boniface, B., Cuny, G., and Barbieri, L. 2000. The phylogenetic position of *Isalorhynchus genovefae*, a Late Triassic rhynchosaur from Madagascar. *Annals of Paleontology* 86(2): 101–127.

Lappin, A. K., Wilcox, S. C., Moriarty, D. J., Stoeppler, S.A.R., Evans, S. E., and Jones M.E.H. 2017. Bite force in the horned frog (*Ceratophrys cranwelli*) with implications for extinct giant frogs. *Scientific Reports* 7: 11963.

Lavocat, R., Marie, P., and Sigal, J. 1960. La faune de foraminifères du Miocène de l'ile Mahakamby (Madagascar). *Compte Rendu Sommaire des Séances de la Société Géologique de France* 11: 211–213.

Lee, A. H., and O'Connor, P. M. 2013. Bone histology confirms determinate growth and small body size in the noasaurid theropod *Masiakasaurus knopfleri*. *Journal of Vertebrate Paleontology* 33: 865–876.

Lehman, J.-P. 1966. Nouveaux stégocéphales de Madagascar. *Annales de Paléontologie Vertébrés* 52: 115–139.

———. 1979. Nouveaux trématosaures de Madagascar: les stégocéphales Malgaches et leur paléoécologie. *Annales de Paléontologie Vertébrés* 65: 35–53.

Lenoble, A. 1949. Les dépôts lacustres Pliocène-Pléistocène de l'Ankararatra. *Annales Géologique du Service des Mines* 18: 2–73.

Leroux, E., Aslanian, D., Rabineau, M., Pellen, R., and Moulin, M. 2018. The late Messinian event: A worldwide tectonic revolution. *Terra Nova* 30 (2–3): 1–8. doi: 10.1111/ter.12327.

Leroux, E., Counts, J., Jorry, S., Jouet, G., Révillon, S., et al. 2020. Evolution of the Glorieuses seamount in the SW Indian Ocean and surrounding deep Somali Basin since the Cretaceous. *Marine Geology* 427: 106202.

Leroy, J.-F. 1978. Composition, origin, and affinities of the Madagascan vascular flora. *Annals of the Missouri Botanical Garden* 65: 535–589.

Lieberman, B. S. 2000. *Palaeobiogeography: Using Fossils to Study Global Change, Plate Tectonics, and Evolution*. New York: Kluwer Academic/Plenum Press.

Lucas, S. G., and Hunt, A. P. 1994. The chronology and paleobiogeography of mammalian origins. In *In the Shadow of the Dinosaurs: Early Mesozoic Tetrapods*, eds. N. C. Fraser and H.-D. Sues, pp. 335–351. Cambridge: Cambridge University Press.

Luo, Z.-X., Cifelli, R. L., and Kielan-Jaworowska, Z. 2001. Dual origin of tribosphenic mammals. *Nature* 409: 53–57.

Luo, Z.-X., Chen, P., Li, G., and Chen, M. 2007. A new eutriconodont mammal and evolutionary development in early mammals. *Nature* 446: 288–293.

Luo, Z.-X., Gatesy, S. M., Jenkins, F. A., Amaral, W. W., and Shubin, N. H. 2015. Mandibular and dental characteristics of Late Triassic mammaliaform *Haramiyavia* and their ramifications for basal mammal evolution. *Proceedings of the National Academy of Sciences of the USA* 112: E7101-E7109.

Lutjeharms, J.R.E., Biastoch, A., Van der Werf, P. M., Ridderinkhof, H., and De Ruijter, W.P.M. 2012. On the discontinuous nature of the Mozambique Current. *South African Journal of Science* 108: 428.

Lydekker, R. 1895. On bones of a sauropodous dinosaur from Madagascar. *Quarterly Journal of the Geological Society of London* 51: 329–336.

Macgregor, D. 2015. History of the development of the East African Rift System: A series of interpreted maps through time. *Journal of African Earth Sciences* 101: 232–252.

Maganuco, S., and Pasini, G. 2009. A new specimen of trematosaurian temnospondyl from the Lower Triassic of NW Madagascar, with remarks on palatal anatomy and taxonomic affinities. *Atti della Società Italiana di Scienze Naturali e del Museo Civico di Storia Naturale di Milano* 150: 91–112.

Maganuco, S., Cau, A., and Pasini, G. 2005. First description of theropod remains from the Middle Jurassic (Bathonian) of Madagascar. *Atti della Società Italiana di Scienze Naturali e del Museo Civico di Storia Naturale di Milano* 146(2): 165–202.

Maganuco, S., Dal Sasso, C., and Pasini, G. 2006. A new large predatory archosaur from the Middle Jurassic of Madagascar. *Atti della Società Italiana di Scienze Naturali e del Museo Civico di Storia Naturale di Milano* 147(I): 19–51.

Maganuco, S., Cau, A., and Dal Sasso, C. 2007. Evidence of large theropods from the Middle Jurassic of the Mahajanga Basin, NW Madagascar, with implications for ceratosaurian pedal ungual evolution. *Atti della Società Italiana di Scienze Naturali e del Museo Civico di Storia Naturale di Milano* 148 (2): 261–271.

Maganuco, S., Steyer, J.-S., Pasini, G., Boulay, M., Lorrain, S., Beneteau, A., and Auditore, M. 2009. Osteology of *Edingerella madagascariensis* (Temnospondyli) from the Triassic of Madagascar, phylogeny and reconstruction of the stereospondyls. *Memorie della Società Italiana di Scienze Naturali e del Museo Civico di Storia Naturale di Milano* 36: 1–72.

Maganuco, S., Pasini, G., and Auditore, M. 2014. A revision of the short-faced stereospondyls *Mahavisaurus dentatus* and *Lyrosaurus australis* from the Lower Triassic of Madagascar: Cranial anatomy, ontogenetic remarks, palaeoecology and rhytidosteid phylogeny. *Memorie della Società Italiana di Scienze Naturali e del Museo Civico di Storia Naturale di Milano* 39: 1–64.

Makovicky, P. J., Apesteguía, S., and Agnolín, F. L. 2005. The earliest dromaeosaurid theropod from South America. *Nature* 437: 1007–1011.

Mannion, P. D. 2010. A revision of the sauropod dinosaur genus "*Bothriospondylus*" with a redescription of the type material of the Middle Jurassic form "*B. madagascariensis*". *Palaeontology* 53: 277–296.

Marramà, G., Lombardo, C., Tintori, A., and Carnevale, G. 2017. Redescription of "*Perleidus*" (Osteichthyes, Actinopterygii) from the Early Triassic of northwestern Madagascar. *Rivista Italiana di Paleontologia e Stratigrafia* 123(2): 219–242.

Marshall, C. R. 2019. Using the fossil record to evaluate timetree timescales. *Frontiers in Genetics* 10: 1049.

Marshall, M. S., and Rogers, R. R. 2012. Lungfish burrows from the Upper Cretaceous Maevarano Formation, Mahajanga Basin, northwestern Madagascar. *Palaios* 27: 857–866.

Marshall, M. S., Sertich, J.J.W., Miller, I. M., and Andrianarivo, M. 2015. Stratigraphy and paleontology of a new nearshore dinosaur-bearing succession from the Late Cretaceous of the Morondava Basin, western Madagascar. *Geological Society of America*, Abstracts with Programs 47: 566.

Marsicano, C. A., Irmis, R. B., Mancuso, A. C., Mundil, R., and Chemale, F. 2016. The precise temporal calibration of dinosaur origins. *Proceedings of the National Academy of Sciences of the USA* 113(3): 509–513.

Martin, M. 1981. Les Dipneustes mésozoïques malgaches, leurs affinités et leur intérêt paléobiogéographique. *Bulletin de la Société Géologique de France* 23: 579–585.

Masters, J. C., Rayner, R. J., and Tattersall, I. 1995. Pattern and process in strepsirhine phylogeny. In *Creatures of the Dark: The Nocturnal Prosimians*, eds. L. Alterman, G. A. Doyle, and M. K. Izard, pp. 31–44. New York: Plenum Press.

Masters, J. C., de Wit, M. J., and Asher, R. J. 2006. Reconciling the origins of Africa, India and Madagascar with vertebrate dispersal scenarios. *Folia Primatologica* 77: 399–418.

Masters, J. C., Génin, F., Zhang, Y., Pellen, R., Huck, T., Mazza, P.P.A., Rabineau, M., Doucouré, M., and Aslanian, D. 2020. Biogeographic mechanisms involved in the colonization of Madagascar by African vertebrates: Rifting, rafting and runways. *Journal of Biogeography* 48(3): 492–510. doi: 10.1111/jbi.14032.

Matschiner, M., Musilová, Z., Barth, J. M., Starostová, Z., Salzburger, W., Steel, M., and Bouckaert, R. 2017. Bayesian phylogenetic estimation of clade ages supports trans-Atlantic dispersal of cichlid fishes. *Systematic Biology* 66: 3–22.

Mazin, J. M., and King, G. M. 1991. The first dicynodont from the Late Permian of Malagasy. *Palaeontology* 34: 837–842.

McCall, R. A. 1997. Implications of recent geological investigations of the Mozambique Channel for the mammalian colonization of Madagascar. *Proceedings of the Royal Society of London B: Biological Sciences* 264: 663–665.

McIntosh, J. S. 1990. Sauropoda. In *The Dinosauria*, eds. D. B. Weishampel, P. Dodson, and H. Osmólska, pp. 345–401. Berkeley: University of California Press.

McKenzie, D., and Sclater, J. G. 1971. The evolution of the Indian Ocean since the Late Cretaceous. *Geophysical Journal of the Royal Astronomical Society* 25: 437–528.

Measey, G. J., Vences, M., Drewes, R. C., Chiari, Y., Melo, M., and Bourles, B. 2007. Freshwater paths across the ocean: Molecular phylogeny of the frog *Ptychadena newtoni* gives insights into amphibian colonization of oceanic islands. *Journal of Biogeography* 34: 7–20.

Merdith, A. S., Collins, A. S., Williams, S. E., Pisarevsky, S., Foden, J. D., et al. 2017. A full-plate global reconstruction of the Neoproterozoic. *Gondwana Research* 50: 84–134.

Miller, K. G., Kominz, M. A., Browning, J. V., Wright, J. D., Mountain, G. S., Katz, M. E., Sugarman, P. J., Cramer, B. S., Christie-Blick, N., and Pekar, S. F. 2005. The Phanerozoic record of global sea-level change. *Science* 310: 1293–1298.

Moine, B. 1967. *Etudes complémentaires dans le massif "schisto-quartzo-calcaire" (région d'Ambatofinandrahana)*. Rapport Annuel du Service Géologique pour 1967, pp. 69–81. Tananarive: Service Géologique de Madagascar.

———. 1974. Caractères de sédimentation et de métamorphisme des séries précambriennes épizonales à catazonales du centre de Madagascar (Région d'Ambatofinandrahana): approche structurale, pétrographique et spécialement géochimique. *Sciences de la Terre*, série mémoires, 31: 1–293.

Moore, W., and Robertson, J. A. 2014. Explosive adaptive radiation and extreme phenotypic diversity within ant-nest beetles. *Current Biology* 24: 2435–2439.

Mougenot, D., Recq, M., Virlogeux, P., and Lepvrier, C. 1986. Seaward extension of the East African rift. *Nature* 321: 599–603.

Moulin, M., Aslanian, D., Evain, M., Leprêtre, A., Schnurle, P., Verrier, F., Thompson, J., De Clarens, P., Dias, and PAMELA-MOZ35 team. 2020. Gondwana breakup and passive margin genesis: Messages from the Natal Valley. *Terra Nova* 32(3): 205–214. https://doi.org/10.1111/ter.12448.

Nathan, R. 2006. Long-distance dispersal of plants. *Science* 313(5788): 786–788.

Nazari, V., Larsen, T. B., Lees, D. C., Brattström, O., Bouyer, T., Van de Poel, G., and Hebert, P.D.N. 2011. Phylogenetic systematics of *Colotis* and associated genera (Lepidoptera: Pieridae): Evolutionary and taxonomic implications. *Journal of Zoological Systematics and Evolutionary Research* 49: 204–215.

Near, T. J., Eytan, R. I., Dornburg, A., Kuhn, K. L., Moore, J. A., Davis, M. P., Wainwright, P. C., Friedman, M., and Smith, L. 2012. Resolution of ray-finned fish phylogeny and timing of diversification. *Proceedings of the National Academy of Sciences of the USA* 109: 13698–13703.

Near, T. J., Dornburg, A., Eytan, R. I., Keck, B. P., Smith, W. L., et al. 2013. Phylogeny and tempo of diversification in the superradiation of spiny-rayed fishes. *Proceedings of the National Academy of Sciences of the USA* 101: 12738–21743.

Nesbitt, S. J., Flynn, J. J., Pritchard, A. C., Parrish, J. M., Ranivoharimanana, L., and Wyss, A. R. 2015. Postcranial osteology of *Azendohsaurus madagaskarensis* (?Middle to Upper Triassic, Isalo Group, Madagascar) and its systematic position among stem archosaur reptiles. *Bulletin of the American Museum of Natural History* 398: 1–126.

Ngumbau, V. M., Nyange, M., Wei, N., van Ee, B. W., Berry, P. E., Malombe, I., Hu, G., and Wang, Q. 2020. A new species of *Croton* (Euphorbiaceae) from a Madagascan lineage discovered in coastal Kenya. *Systematic Botany* 45: 242–248.

Nichols, G. J., and Daly, M. C. 1989. Sedimentation in an intracratonic extensional basin: The Karoo of the central Morondava Basin, Madagascar. *Geological Magazine* 126: 339–354.

Nobre, T., Eggleton, P., and Aanen, D. K. 2010. Vertical transmission as the key to the colonization of Madagascar by fungus-growing termites? *Proceedings of the Royal Society of London B: Biological Sciences* 277: 359–365.

Noonan, B., and Chippindale, P. T. 2006. Vicariant origin of Malagasy reptiles supports Late Cretaceous Antarctic landbridge. *The American Naturalist* 168: 730–741.

Norton, I. O., and Sclater, J. G. 1979. A model for the evolution of the Indian Ocean and the breakup of Gondwanaland. *Journal of Geophysical Research, Solid Earth*, 84B: 6803–6830.

Nougier, J., Cantagrel, J. M., and Karche, J. P. 1986. The Comores Archipelago in the western Indian Ocean: Volcanology, geochronology, and geodynamic setting. *Journal of African Earth Sciences* 5: 135–145.

Nowak, M. D., Haller, B. C., and Yoder, A. D. 2014. The founding of Mauritian endemic coffee trees by a synchronous long-distance dispersal event. *Journal of Evolutionary Biology* 27: 1229–1239.

Obrist-Farner, J., Ball, P. J., McGilvery, T. A., and Rogers, R. R. 2017. A prograding margin during global sea-level maxima: An example from Mahajanga Basin, northwest Madagascar. *Basin Research* 30: 671–687.

Och, L. M., and Shields-Zhou, G. A. 2012. The Neoproterozoic oxygenation event: Environmental perturbations and biogeochemical cycling. *Earth-Science Reviews* 110: 26–57.

O'Connor, P. M., and Forster, C. A. 2010. A Late Cretaceous (Maastrichtian) avifauna from the Maevarano Formation, Madagascar. *Journal of Vertebrate Paleontology* 30: 1178–1201.

O'Connor, P. M., Turner, A. H., and Groenke, J. R. 2016. New avialans from the Upper Cretaceous Maevarano Formation, Mahajanga Basin, northwestern Madagascar. *Journal of Vertebrate Paleontology*, Program and Abstracts, 2016: 53.

O'Connor, P. M., Turner, A. H., Groenke, J. R., Felice, R. N., and Rogers, R. R. 2019. New avialan fossil from the Maevarano Formation, Mahajanga Basin, NW Madagascar expands cranial shape disparity among Mesozoic birds via an expanded maxilla contributing to enhanced rostralization. *Journal Vertebrate Paleontology*, Program and Abstracts, 2019: 162–163.

O'Connor, P. M., Turner, A. H., Groenke, J. R., Felice, R. N., Rogers, R. R., Krause, D. W., and Rahantarisoa, L. J. 2020. Late Cretaceous bird from Madagascar reveals unique development of beaks. *Nature* 588: 272–276.

Ohba, M., Samonds, K. E., LaFleur, M., Ali, J. R., and Godfrey, L. R. 2016. Madagascar's climate at the K/P boundary and its impact on the island's biotic suite. *Palaeogeography, Palaeoclimatology, Palaeoecology* 441: 688–695.

Ostrowski, S. 2012. Fossil teleost fishes of the Late Cretaceous of Madagascar: Systematics, distribution, and implications for Gondwanan biogeography. PhD thesis, Michigan State University, East Lansing, Michigan.

Patellos, E. A., Nesbitt, S. J., Kammerer, C. F., Wyss, A. R., Flynn, J. J., and Ranivoharimanana, L. 2019. A new reptile from the ?Middle Triassic of Madagascar may represent the earliest-diverging avemetatarsalian (Archosauria). *Journal of Vertebrate Paleontology*, Program and Abstracts, 2019: 167.

Paulian, R. 1961. La zoogéographie de Madagascar et des iles voisines. *Faune de Madagascar* 13: 1–475.

Paulian, R., and Viette, P. 2003. An introduction to terrestrial and freshwater invertebrates. In *The Natural History of Madagascar*, eds. S. M. Goodman and J. P. Benstead, pp. 503–511. Chicago: University of Chicago Press.

Piveteau, J. 1926a. Le Permien du Sud de Madagascar et sa faune de Vertébrés. Thesis. Faculté des Sciences de Paris, A, 1061: 55–179.

———. 1926b. Contribution à l'étude des formations lagunaires du Nord-Ouest de Madagascar. *Bulletin de la Société Géologique de France* 26: 33–38.

———. 1936. Une forme ancestrale des Amphibiens Anoures dans le Trias inférieur de Madagascar. *Comptes Rendus des Séances de l'Académie des Sciences* 202: 1607–1608.

———. 1937. Paléontologie de Madagascar. XXIII.—un amphibien du Trias inférieur. *Annales de Paléontologie* 26: 135–177.

Ponte, J.-P. 2018. La marge africaine du canal du Mozambique (le système turbiditique du Zambèze) : Une approche "Source to Sink" au Méso-Cénozoïque. PhD thesis, Université de Bretagne Loire. https://hal-insu.archives-ouvertes.fr/tel-01865479.

Ponte, J.-P., Robin, C., Guillocheau, F., Popescu, S.-M., Suc, J.-P., Dall'Asta, M., Melinte-Dobrinescu, M. C., Bubik, M., Dupont, G., and Gaillot, J. 2019. The Zambezi delta (Mozambique Channel, East Africa): High resolution dating combining bio-orbital and seismic stratigraphies to determine climate (palaeoprecipitation) and tectonic controls on a passive margin. *Marine and Petroleum Geology* 105: 293–312.

Poropat, S. F., Mannion, P. D., Upchurch, P., Hocknull, S. A., Kear, B. P., et al. 2016. New Australian sauropods shed light on Cretaceous dinosaur palaeobiogeography. *Scientific Reports* 6: 34467.

Poux, C., Madsen, O., Marquard, E., Vieites, D. R., de Jong, W. W., and Vences, M. 2005. Asynchronous colonization of Madagascar by the four endemic clades of primates, tenrecs, carnivores, and rodents as inferred from nuclear genes. *Systematic Biology* 54: 719–730.

Pritchard, A. C., McCartney, J. A., Krause, D. W., and Kley, N. J. 2014. New snakes from the Upper Cretaceous (Maastrichtian) Maevarano Formation, Mahajanga Basin, Madagascar. *Journal of Vertebrate Paleontology* 34: 1080–1093.

Pyron, R. A. 2014. Biogeographic analysis reveals ancient continental vicariance and recent oceanic dispersal in amphibians. *Systematic Biology* 63: 779–797.

Rabinowitz, P. D., and Woods, S. 2006. The Africa–Madagascar connection and mammalian migrations. *Journal of African Earth Sciences* 44: 270–276.

Rabinowitz, P. D., Coffin, M., and Falvey, D. 1983. The separation of Madagascar and Africa. *Science* 220: 67–69.

Rage, J.-C., and Prasad, G.V.R. 1992. New snakes from the Late Cretaceous (Maastrichtian) of Naskal, India. *Neues Jahrbuch für Geologie und Paläontologie, Abhandlungen* 187: 83–97.

Rage, J.-C., and Rocek, Z. 1989. Redescription of *Triadobatrachus massinoti* (Piveteau 1936) an anuran amphibian from the Early Triassic. *Palaeontographica, Abteilung A*, 206: 1–16.

Ramihangihajason, T., Andrianavalona, T., Razafimbelo, R., Rahantarisoa, L. J., Ali, J., and Samonds, K. E. 2014. Miocene benthic foraminifera from Nosy Makamby and Amparafaka, Mahajanga Basin, northwestern Madagascar. *Journal of African Earth Sciences* 100: 409–417.

Ranivoharimanana, L. 2007. Structure cranio-dentairs: Implication biomecanique de la mandibule de deux nouveaux traversodontides eucynodontes, ("reptiles-mammaliens"), du Trias de Madagascar. PhD thesis, Université d'Antananarivo.

———. 2011. Structure dentaire: Implication pour la Paléoécologie des Traversodontidae (Eucynodontia) du Trias de Madagascar. *Malagasy Nature* 5: 1–13.

———. 2012. Analyse biomécanique masticatrice chez des traversodontidés eucynodontes du Trias de Madagascar. *Geodiversitas* 34(3): 505–515.

Ranivoharimanana, L., Kammerer, C. F., Flynn, J. J., and Wyss, A. R. 2011. New material of *Dadadon isaloi* (Cynodontia: Traversodontidae) from the Triassic of Madagascar. *Journal of Vertebrate Paleontology* 31(6): 1292–1302.

Raselimanana, A. P., Noonan, B., Karanth, K. P., Gauthier, J., and Yoder, A. D. 2009. Phylogeny and evolution of Malagasy plated lizards. *Molecular Phylogenetics and Evolution* 50: 336–344.

Rasmusson Simons, E.L.R., and Buckley, G. A. 2009. New material of "*Trematochampsa*" *oblita* (Crocodyliformes, Trematochampsidae) from the Late Cretaceous of Madagascar. *Journal of Vertebrate Paleontology* 29: 599–604.

Ratsimbaholison, N. O., Felice, R. N., and O'Connor, P. M. 2016. Ontogenetic changes in the craniomandibular skeleton of the abelisaurid dinosaur *Majungasaurus crenatissimus* from the Late Cretaceous of Madagascar. *Acta Palaeontologica Polonica* 61: 281–292.

Razafimbelo, E. 1987. Le basin de Morondava (Madagascar). Synthèse géologique et structurale. PhD thesis, Université de Louis Pasteur, Strasbourg.

Reddy, S., Driskell A., Rabosky, D. L., Hackett, S. J., and Schulenberg, T. S. 2012. Diversification and the adaptive radiation of the vangas of Madagascar. *Proceedings of the Royal Society of London B: Biological Sciences* 279: 2062–2071.

Reeves, C. [V.] 2014. The position of Madagascar within Gondwana and its movements during Gondwana dispersal. *Journal of African Earth Sciences* 94: 45–57.

———. 2018. The development of the East Africa margin during Jurassic and Lower Cretaceous times: A perspective from global tectonics. *Petroleum Geoscience* 24: 41–56.

Reeves, C. [V.], and de Wit, M. 2000. Making ends meet in Gondwana: Retracing the transforms of the Indian Ocean and reconnecting continental shear zones. *Terra Nova* 12: 272–280.

Rehan, S. M., Chapman, T. W., Craigie, A. I., Richards, M. H., Cooper, S.J.B., and Schwarz, M. P. 2010. Molecular phylogeny of the small carpenter bees (Hymenoptera: Apidae: Ceratinini) indicates early and rapid global dispersal. *Molecular Phylogenetics and Evolution* 55: 1042–1054.

Roberts, G. G., Paul, J. D., White, N. J., and Winterbourne, J. 2012. Temporal and spatial evolution of dynamic support from river profiles: A framework for Madagascar. *Geochemistry, Geophysics, Geosystems* 13: Art. No. Q04004.

Rogers, R. R. 2005. Fine-grained debris flows and extraordinary vertebrate burials in the Late Cretaceous of Madagascar. *Geology* 33: 297–300.

Rogers, R. R., and Kidwell, S. 2000. Associations of vertebrate skeletal concentrations and discontinuity surfaces in terrestrial and shallow marine records: A test in the Cretaceous of Montana. *Journal of Geology* 108: 131–154.

Rogers, R. R., Hartman, J. H., and Krause, D. W. 2000. Stratigraphic analysis of Upper Cretaceous rocks in the Mahajanga Basin, northwestern Madagascar: Implications for ancient and modern faunas. *Journal of Geology* 108: 275–301.

Rogers, R. R., Krause, D. W., Curry Rogers, K., Rasoamiaramanana, A., and Rahantarisoa, L. 2007. Paleoenvironment and paleoecology of *Majungasaurus crenatissimus* (Theropoda: Abelisauridae) from the Late Cretaceous of Madagascar. *Society of Vertebrate Paleontology Memoir* 8: 21–31.

Rogers, R. R., Krause, D. W., Kast, S. C., Marshall, M. S., Rahantarisoa, L., Robins, C. R., and Sertich, J.J.W. 2013. A new, richly fossiliferous member comprised of tidal deposits in the Upper Cretaceous Maevarano Formation, northwestern Madagascar. *Cretaceous Research* 44: 12–29.

Roig, J., Tucker, R., Delor, C., Peters, S., and Théveniaut, H. 2012. Carte géologique de la République de Madagascar à 1/1 000 000. Programme de gouvernance des ressources minérales (PGRM). Antananarivo: Ministère des Mines.

Rougier, G. W., Martinelli, A. G., Forasiepi, A. M., and Novacek, M. J. 2007. New Jurassic mammals from Patagonia, Argentina: A reappraisal of australosphenidan morphology and interrelationships. *American Museum Novitates* 3566: 1–54.

Rowe, T., Rich, T. H., Vickers-Rich, P., Springer, M., and Woodburne, M. O. 2008. The oldest platypus and its bearing on divergence timing of the platypus and echidna clades. *Proceedings of the National Academy of Sciences of the USA* 105: 1238–1242.

Ruane, S., Pyron, R. A., and Burbrink, F. T. 2011. Phylogenetic relationships of the Cretaceous frog *Beelzebufo* from Madagascar and the placement of fossil constraints based on temporal and phylogenetic evidence. *Journal of Evolutionary Biology* 24: 274–285.

Rufer, D., Preusser, F., Schreurs, G., Gnos, E., and Berger, A. 2014. Late Quaternary history of the Vakinankaratra volcanic field (central Madagascar): Insights from luminescence dating of phreatomagmatic eruption deposits. *Bulletin of Volcanology* 76: 817–837.

Russell, D., Russell, D., Taquet, P., and Thomas, H. 1976. Nouvelles récoltes de vertébrés dans les terrains continentaux du Crétacé supérieur de la région de Majunga (Madagascar). *Comptes Rendus Sommaires de la Société Géologique de France* 5: 204–207.

Ryan, W.B.F., Carbotte, S. M., Coplan, J. O., O'Hara, S., Melkonian, A., et al. 2009. Global multi-resolution topography synthesis. *Geochemistry, Geophysics, Geosystems* 10: Art. No. Q03014.

Saber, S., Sertich, J.J.W., Sallam, H. M., Ouda, K. A., O'Connor, P. M., and Seiffert, E. R. 2018. An enigmatic crocodyliform from the Upper Cretaceous Quseir Formation, central Egypt. *Cretaceous Research* 90: 174–184.

Sallam, H. M., Gorscak, E., O'Connor, P. M., El-Dawoudi, I. A., El-Sayed, S., Saber, S., Kora, M. A., Sertich, J.J.W., Seiffert, E. R., and Lamanna, M. C. 2018. New Egyptian sauropod reveals Late Cretaceous dinosaur dispersal between Europe and Africa. *Nature Ecology and Evolution* 2: 445–451.

Samonds, K. E. 2007. Late Pleistocene bat fossils from Anjohibe Cave, northwestern Madagascar. *Acta Chiropterologica* 9: 39–65.

Samonds, K. E., and Fordyce, R. E. 2019. The first pre-Pleistocene cetacean from Madagascar, western Indian Ocean. *Journal of African Earth Sciences* 151: 184–188.

Samonds, K. E., Loewen, M., Buckley, G., and Whatley, R. 2001. Vertebrate fossils from the Cenozoic of Madagascar. *Geological Society of America Bulletin* 33, supplement 6: 389A.

Samonds, K. E., Zalmout, I. S., Irwin, M. T., Krause, D. W., Rogers, R. R., and Raharivony, L. L. 2009. *Eotheroides lambondrano*, new middle Eocene seacow (Mammalia, Sirenia) from the Mahajanga Basin, northwestern Madagascar. *Journal of Vertebrate Paleontology* 29(4): 1–11.

Samonds, K. E., Godfrey, L. R., Ali, J. R., Goodman, S. M., Vences, M., Sutherland, M. R., Irwin, M. T., and Krause, D. W. 2012. Spatial and temporal arrival patterns of Madagascar's vertebrate fauna explained by distance, ocean currents, and ancestor type. *Proceedings of the National Academy of Sciences of the USA* 109: 5352–5357.

———. 2013. Imperfect isolation: Factors and filters shaping Madagascar's extant vertebrate fauna. *PLoS One* 8(4) e62086.

Samonds, K. E., Andrianavalona, T., Wallett, L., Zalmout, I., and Ward, D. 2019a. A middle–late Eocene neoselachian assemblage from nearshore marine deposits, Mahajanga Basin, northwestern Madagascar. *PLoS One* 14: e0211789.

Samonds, K. E., Ernat, R. A., Andrianavalona, T., and Domning, D. P. 2019b. New Miocene sirenians from Nosy Makamby, northwestern Madagascar. *Journal of Vertebrate Paleontology* 39: e1570223.

Samonds, K. E., Brochu, C., Adams, A., and Rakotozandry, R. 2019c. A new Miocene crocodyliform from the island of Nosy Makamby, northwestern Madagascar. *Journal of Vertebrate Paleontology*, Program and Abstracts, 2019: 185.

Sampson, S. D., and Krause, D. W., eds. 2007. *Majungasaurus crenatissimus* (Theropoda: Abelisauridae) from the Late Cretaceous of Madagascar. *Society of Vertebrate Paleontology Memoir* 8: 1–184.

Sampson, S. D., Witmer, L. M., Forster, C. A., Krause, D. W., O'Connor, P. M., Dodson, P., and Ravoavy, F. 1998. Predatory dinosaur remains from Madagascar: Implications for the Cretaceous Biogeography of Gondwana. *Science* 280: 1048–1051.

Sampson, S. D., Carrano, M. T., and Forster, C. A. 2001. A bizarre predatory dinosaur from the Late Cretaceous of Madagascar. *Nature* 409: 504–506.

Samuels, J. X., and Hopkins, S.S.B. 2017. The impacts of Cenozoic climate and habitat changes on small mammal diversity of North America. *Global and Planetary Change* 149: 36–52.

Schandelmeier, H., Bremer, F., and Holl, H.-G. 2004. Kinematic evolution of the Morondava rift basin of SW Madagascar—from wrench tectonics to normal extension. *Journal of African Earth Sciences* 38: 321–330.

Schatz, G. E. 1996. Malagasy/Indo-australo-malesian phytogeographic connections. In *Biogéographie de Madagascar*, ed. W. R. Lourenço, pp. 73–84. Paris: Editions ORSTOM.

———. 2001. *Generic Flora of Madagascar*. Kew: Royal Botanic Gardens, and Missouri Botanical Garden.

Schettino, A., and Scotese C. R. 2005. Apparent polar wander paths for the major continents (200 Ma to the present day): A palaeomagnetic reference frame for global plate tectonic reconstructions. *Geophysical Journal International* 163: 727–759.

Scheyer, T. M., Romano, C., Jenks, J., and Bucher, H. 2014. Early Triassic marine biotic recovery: The predators' perspective. *PLoS One* 9(3): e88987.

Schoene, B., Samperton, K. M., Eddy, M., Keller, G., Adatte, T., Bowring, S. A., Khadri, S. F. R., and Gertsch, B. 2015. U-Pb geochronology of the Deccan Traps and relation to the end-Cretaceous mass extinction. *Science* 347: 182–184.

Schoene, B., Eddy, M. P., Samperton, K. M., Keller, C. B., Keller, G., Adatte, T., and Khadri, S. F. R. 2019. U-Pb constraints on pulsed eruption of the Deccan Traps across the end-Cretaceous mass extinction. *Science* 363: 862–866.

Schofield, D. I., Thomas, R. J., Goodenough, K. M., De Waele, B., Pitfield, P.E.J., et al. 2010. Geological evolution of the Antongil Craton, NE Madagascar. *Precambrian Research* 182: 187–203.

Schott, F. A., Xie, S. P., and McCreary, J. P. 2009. Indian Ocean circulation and climate variability. *Reviews of Geophysics* 47: RG1002.

Scotese, C. R. 1998. Continental drift (0–750 million years), a quicktime computer animation: PALEOMAP Project, University of Texas at Arlington, Arlington, Texas.

Seiffert, E. R., Tejedor, M. F., Fleagle, J. F., Novo, N. M., Cornejo, F. M., Bond, M., de Vries, D., and Campbell, K. E., Jr. 2020. A parapithecid stem anthropoid of African origin in the Paleogene of South America. *Science* 368: 194–197.

Sereno, P., and Larsson, H.C.E. 2009. Cretaceous crocodyliforms from the Sahara. *ZooKeys* 28: 1–143.

Shu, D. G., Isozaki, Y., Zhang, X. L., Han, J., and Maruyama, S. 2014. Birth and early evolution of metazoans. *Gondwana Research* 25: 884–895.

Shubin, N. H., Crompton, A. W., Sues, H.-D., and Olsen, P. E. 1991. New fossil evidence on the sister-group of mammals and Early Mesozoic faunal distributions. *Science* 251: 1063–1065.

Simmons, N. A., Forte, A. M., and Grand, S. P. 2007. Thermochemical structure and dynamics of the African superplume. *Geophysical Research Letters* 34: Art. No. L02301.

Simon, S., Letsch, H., Bank, S., Buckley, T. R., Donath, A., et al. 2019. Old World and New World Phasmatodea: Phylogenomics resolve the evolutionary history of stick and leaf insects. *Frontiers in Ecology and Evolution* 7: 345.

Simpson, G. G. 1940. Mammals and land bridges. *Journal of the Washington Academy of Sciences* 30: 137–163.

———. 1952. Probabilities of dispersal in geologic time. *Bulletin of the American Museum of Natural History* 99: 163–176.

Smith, A. G., Smith, D. G., and Funnell, B. M. 1994. *Atlas of Mesozoic and Cenozoic Coastlines*. Cambridge: Cambridge University Press.

Smith, R.M.H. 2000. Sedimentology and taphonomy of Late Permian vertebrate fossil localities in southwestern Madagascar. *Palaeontologia Africana* 36: 25–41.

Sole, C. L., Wirta, H., Forgie, S. A., and Scholtz, C. H. 2011. Origin of Madagascan Scarabaeini dung beetles (Coleoptera: Scarabaeidae): Dispersal from Africa. *Insect Systematics and Evolution* 42. https://doi.org/10.1163/187631211X552800.

Springer, M. S., Emerling, C. A., Meredith. R. W., Janečka, J. E., Eizirik, E., and Murphy, W. J. 2017. Waking the undead: Implications of a soft explosive model for the timing of placental mammal diversification. *Molecular Phylogenetics and Evolution* 106: 86–102.

Stanley, E. L. 2013. Systematics and morphological diversification of the Cordylidae (Squamata). PhD thesis, American Museum of Natural History, New York.

Stephenson, S. N., White, N. J., Li, T., and Robinson, L. F. 2019. Disentangling interglacial sea level and global dynamic topography: Analysis of Madagascar. *Earth and Planetary Science Letters* 519: 61–69.

Stern, R. J. 1994. Arc Assembly and continental collision in the Neoproterozoic East African orogeny-implications for the consolidation of Gondwana. *Annual Review of Earth and Planetary Sciences* 22: 319–351.

Steyer, J.-S. 2002. The first articulated trematosaur "amphibian" from the lower Triassic of Madagascar: Implications for the phylogeny of the group. *Palaeontology* 45: 771–793.

———. 2003. A revision of the Early Triassic "capitosaurs" (Stegocephali, Stereospondyli) from Madagascar, with remarks on their comparative ontogeny. *Journal of Vertebrate Paleontology* 23: 544–555.

Storey, M., Mahoney J. J., Saunders A. D., Duncan R. A., Kelley S. P., and Coffin M. F. 1995. Timing of hot spot–related volcanism and the breakup of Madagascar and India. *Science* 267: 852–855.

Storey, M., Mahoney, J. J., and Saunders, A. D. 1997. Cretaceous basalts in Madagascar and the transition between plume and continental lithosphere mantle sources. In *Large Igneous Provinces: Continental, Oceanic and Planetary Flood Volcanism*, eds. J. J. Mahoney and M. F. Coffin. Monograph series, vol. 100, pp. 95–122. Washington DC: American Geophysical Union.

Strijk, J. S., Noyes, R. D., Strasberg, D., Cruaud, C., Gavory, F., Chase, M. W., Abbott, R. J., and Thebaud, C. 2012. In and out of Madagascar: Dispersal to peripheral islands, insular speciation and diversification of Indian Ocean daisy trees (*Psiadia*, Asteraceae). *PLoS One* 7: e42932.

Strijk, J. S., Bone, R. E., Thébaud, C., Buerki, S., Fritsch, P. W., Hodkinson, T. R., Strasberg, D., and Richardson, J. 2014. Timing and tempo of evolutionary diversification in a biodiversity hotspot: Primulaceae on Indian Ocean islands. *Journal of Biogeography* 41: 810–822.

Sues, H.-D. 1980. A pachycephalosaurid dinosaur from the Upper Cretaceous of Madagascar and its paleobiogeographical implications: *Journal of Paleontology* 54: 954–962.

Sues, H.-D., and P. Taquet, P. 1979. A pachycephalosaurid dinosaur from Madagascar and a Laurasia-Gondwanaland connection in the Cretaceous. *Nature* 279: 633–635.

Thomas, R. J., De Waele, B., Schofield, D. I., Goodenough, K. M., Horstwood, M., et al. 2009. Geological evolution of the Neoproterozoic Bemarivo Belt, northern Madagascar. *Precambrian Research* 172: 279–300.

Thompson, J. O., Moulin, M., Aslanian, D., de Clarens, P., and Guillocheau, F. 2019. New starting point for the Indian Ocean: Second phase of breakup for Gondwana. *Earth-Science Reviews* 191: 26–56.

Toon, A., Pérez-Losada, M., Schweitzer, C. E., Feldmann, R. M., Carlson, M., and Crandall, K. A. 2010. Gondwanan radiation of the Southern Hemisphere crayfishes (Decapoda: Parastacidae): Evidence from fossils and molecules. *Journal of Biogeography* 37: 2275–2290.

Tucker, R. D., Ashwal, L. D., Handke, M. J., Hamilton, M. A., Le Grange, M., and Rambeloson, R. A. 1999. U-Pb geochronology and isotope geochemistry of the Archean and Proterozoic rocks of north-central Madagascar. *Journal of Geology* 107: 135–153.

Tucker, R. D., Amelin, Y., Belcher, R. W., Delor, C., Goncalves, P., Rabarimanana, M. H., and Ralison, A. V. 2011a. Neoproterozoic extension in the Greater Dharwar Craton: A reevaluation of the "Betsimisaraka suture" in Madagascar. *Canadian Journal of Earth Sciences* 48: 389–417.

Tucker, R. D., Roig, J. Y., Macey, P. H., Delor, C., Amelin, Y., Armstrong, R. A., Rabarimanana, M. H., and Ralison, A. V. 2011b. A new geological framework for south-central Madagascar, and its relevance to the "out-of-Africa" hypothesis. *Precambrian Research* 185: 109–130.

Tucker, R. D., Roig, J. Y., Moine, B., Delor, C., and Peters, S. G. 2014. A geological synthesis of the Precambrian shield in Madagascar. *Journal of African Earth Sciences* 94: 9–30.

Tuck-Martin, A., Adam, J., and Eagles G. 2018. New plate kinematic model and tectono-stratigraphic history of the East African and West Madagascan margins. *Basin Research* 30: 1118–1140.

Turner, A. H. 2006. Osteology and phylogeny of a new species of *Araripesuchus* (Crocodyliformes: Mesoeucrocodylia) from the Late Cretaceous of Madagascar. *Historical Biology* 18: 255–369.

———. 2012. A review of dromaeosaurid systematics and paravian phylogeny. *Bulletin of the American Museum of Natural History* 371: 1–206.

Turner, A. H., and Buckley, G. A. 2008. *Mahajangasuchus insignis* (Crocodyliformes: Mesoeucrocodylia): Cranial anatomy and new data on the origin of the eusuchian-style palate. *Journal of Vertebrate Paleontology* 28(2): 382–408.

Turner, A. H., and Sertich, J.J.W. 2010. Phylogenetic history of *Simosuchus clarki* (Crocodyliformes: Notosuchia) from the Late Cretaceous of Madagascar. *Society of Vertebrate Paleontology Memoir* 10: 177–236.

University Cooperation for Atmospheric Research. 2020. CESM models. http://www.cesm.ucar.edu/models/cesm1.0.

Upchurch, P. 2008. Gondwanan break-up: Legacies of a lost world? *Trends in Ecology and Evolution* 23: 229–236.

Van Duzer, C. 2004. *Floating Islands: A Global Bibliography.* Los Altos Hills: Cantor Press.

Vélez-Juarbe, J., Domning, D. P., and Pyenson, N. D. 2012. Iterative evolution of sympatric seacow (Dugongidae, Sirenia) assemblages during the past ~26 million years. *PLoS One* 7: e31294.

Vences, M., Freyhof, J., Sonnenberg, R., Kosuch, J., and Veith, M. 2001. Reconciling fossils and molecules: Cenozoic divergence of cichlid fishes and the biogeography of Madagascar. *Journal of Biogeography* 28: 1091–1099.

Vences, M., Vieites, D. R., Glaw, F., Brinkmann, H., Kosuch, J., Veith, M., and Meyer, A. 2003. Multiple overseas dispersal in amphibians. *Proceedings of the Royal Society of London of London B: Biological Sciences* 270: 2435–2442.

Vidal, D., Ortega, F., and Sanz, J. L. 2014. Titanosaur osteoderms from the Upper Cretaceous of Lo Hueco (Spain) and their implications on the armor of Laurasian titanosaurs. *PLoS One* 9: e102488.

Vidal, N., Marin, J., Morini, M., Donnellan, S., Branch, W., Thomas, R., Vences, M., Wynn, A., Cruaud, C., and Hedges, S. B. 2010. Blindsnake evolutionary tree reveals long history on Gondwana. *Biology Letters*. doi: 10.1098/rsbl.2010.0220.

Vorontsova, M. S., Besnard, G., Forest, F., Malakasi, P., Moat, J., et al. 2016. Madagascar's grasses and grasslands: Anthropogenic or natural? *Proceedings of the Royal Society of London B: Biological Sciences* 283: http://doi.org/10.1098/rspb.2015.2262.

Vuataz, L., Sartori, M., Gattolliat, J.-L., and Monaghan, M. T. 2013. Endemism and diversification in freshwater insects of Madagascar revealed by coalescent and phylogenetic analysis of museum and field collections. *Molecular Phylogenetics and Evolution* 66: 979–991.

Wagensommer, A., Latiano, M., and Nicosia, U. 2010. First report of dinosaur footprints from Madagascar: Two tracksites from the Middle Jurassic Bemaraha Formation. *Ichnos* 17: 127–136.

Walker, J. D., Geissman, J. W., Bowring, S. A., and Babcock, L. E. (compilers). 2018. Geologic time scale v. 5.0. Geological Society of America. doi: 10.1130/2018.CTS005R3C.

Ward, J. F., Verdel, C., Campbell, M. J., Leonard, N., and Nguyen, A. D. 2019. Rare earth element geochemistry of Australian Neoproterozoic carbonate: Constraints on the Neoproterozoic oxygenation events. *Precambrian Research* 335: 105471.

Warren, A. A., and Hutchinson, M. N. 1988. The Madagascar capitosaurs. *Bulletin Muséum National d'Histoire Naturelle*, Paris, série 4, 10 (Section C, no. 1): 23–30.

Wells, N. A. 2003. Some hypotheses on the Mesozoic and Cenozoic paleoenvironmental history of Madagascar. In *The Natural History of Madagascar*, eds. S. M. Goodman and J. P. Benstead, pp. 16–34. Chicago: University of Chicago Press.

Westphal, F. 1970. Phytosaurier-Hautplatten aus der Trias von Madagaskar—ein Beitrag zur Gondwana-Paläogeographie. *Neues Jahrbuch für Geologie und Paläontologie Monatshefte* 1970(10): 632–638.

Whatley, R. L. 2005. Phylogenetic relationships of *Isalorhynchus genovefae*, the rhynchosaur (Reptilia, Archosauromorpha) from Madagascar. PhD thesis, University of California, Santa Barbara.

Whittaker, R. J., and Fernández-Palacios, J. M. 2007. *Island Biogeography*, 2nd ed. Oxford: Oxford University Press.

Wilson, J. A., Pol, D., Carvalho, A. B., and Zaher, H. 2016. The skull of the titanosaur *Tapuiasaurus macedoi* (Dinosauria: Sauropoda), a basal titanosaur from the Lower Cretaceous of Brazil. *Zoological Journal of the Linnean Society* 178: 611–662.

Windley, B. F., Razafiniparany, A., Razakamanana, T., and Ackermand, D. 1994. Tectonic framework of the Precambrian of Madagascar and its Gondwana connections: A review and reappraisal. *Geologische Rundschau* 83: 642–659.

Winterbourne, J., White, N. J., and Crosby, A. 2014. Accurate measurements of residual topography from the oceanic realm. *Tectonics* 33: 982–1015.

Wood, H. M., Gillespie, R. G., Griswold, C. E., and Wainwright, P. C. 2015. Why is Madagascar special? The extraordinarily slow evolution of pelican spiders (Araneae, Archaeidae). *Evolution* 69: 462–481.

Woodburne, M. O., Rich, T. H., and Springer, M. 2003. The evolution of tribospheny in Mesozoic mammals. *Molecular Phylogenetics and Evolution* 28: 360–385.

Wu, D. T., Ramaniraka, J. I., Xu, F. M., Shao, J. B., Zhou, Y. H., Zhao, Y. D., and Ralison, B. 2019. Characteristics and potential analysis of Madagascar hydrocarbon-bearing basins. *China Geology* 1: 56–66.

Yabumoto, Y., Brito, P. M., Iwata, M., and Abe, Y. 2019. A new Triassic coelacanth, *Whiteia uyenoteruyai* (Sarcopterygii, Actinistia) from Madagascar and paleobiogeography of the family Whiteiidae. *Bulletin Kitakyushu Museum Natural History and Human History*, series A, 17: 15–27.

Yoder, A. D., and Nowak, M. D. 2006. Has vicariance or dispersal been the predominant biogeographic force in Madagascar? Only time will tell. *Annual Review of Ecology, Evolution, and Systematics* 37: 405–431.

Yoder, A. D., Cartmill, M., Ruvolo, M., Smith, K., and Vilgalys, R. 1996. Ancient single origin for Malagasy primates. *Proceedings of the National Academy of Sciences of the USA* 93: 5122–5126.

Yoder, A. D., Burns, M. M., Zehr, S., Delefosse, T., Veron, G., Goodman, S. M., and Flynn, J. J. 2003. Single origin of Malagasy Carnivora from an African ancestor. *Nature* 421: 734–737.

Yoder, A. D., Campbell, C. R., Blanco, M. B., dos Reis, M., Ganzhorn, J. U., et al. 2016. Geogenetic patterns in mouse lemurs (genus *Microcebus*) reveal the ghosts of Madagascar's forests past. *Proceedings of the National Academy of Sciences of the USA* 113: 8049–8056.

Younger, J. L., Dempster, P., Nyári, A. S., Helms O., Raherilahao, M. J., Goodman, S. M., and Reddy, S. 2019. Phylogeography of the Rufous Vanga and the role of bioclimatic transition zones in promoting speciation within Madagascar. *Molecular Phylogenetics and Evolution* 139: 106535.

Zachos, J. C., Pagani, M., Sloan, L., Thomas, E., and Billups, K. 2001. Trends, rhythms, and aberrations in global climate 65 Ma to present. *Science* 292: 686–693.

Zachos, J. C., Dickens, G. R., and Zeebe, R. E. 2008. An early Cenozoic perspective on greenhouse warming and carbon-cycle dynamics. *Nature* 451: 279–283.

Zhou, H., Helliker, B. R., Huber, M., Dicks, A., and Akçay, E. 2018. C_4 photosynthesis and climate through the lens of optimality. *Proceedings of the National Academy of Sciences of the USA* 115: 12057–12062. doi: 10.1073/pnas.1718988115.

CHAPTER 3

CLIMATE

THE CLIMATE OF MADAGASCAR

M. R. Jury

The local climate depends on sun angle (and thus latitude), as well as response to the earth's ocean-atmosphere circulation. Whereas easterly trade winds prevail in latitudes 20–30°S, in the tropics, winds can blow across latitudes because of thermal differences between continents and oceans.

Climate is an average of daily weather events, often expressed as cumulative monthly values over many years. Its characteristics may be illustrated spatially with maps or temporally with graphs. Climatic attributes are locally altered by surface factors such as elevation, proximity to the coast, topographic roughness, vegetation cover, and nearby marine conditions. Climate affects our lives and economic well-being through food production and the extraction of water and energy resources. In this chapter, the climate of Madagascar is described using historical observations averaged into months or seasons.

OVERVIEW OF MADAGASCAR'S CLIMATE

The island of Madagascar extends some 1650 km from 12°S to 26°S and is located off the southeast coast of Africa from longitude 43°E to 51°E. A 1200 m mountain ridge with massifs above 2600 m runs north–south through the entire length of the island and disproportionately on the eastern side, creating important topographic asymmetry. Warm sea surface temperatures surround the island because of the tropical ocean currents that supply humid air (Sengupta et al. 2001; Halkides and Lee 2011). The geography and wind regimes induce a seasonally varying climate (Donque 1972; Griffiths and Ranaivoson 1972), evident in the maps in Figures 3.1a–c. The Indian Ocean monsoon diverts the trade winds in austral winter (June–August), but during austral summer (December–February) easterly winds cross the island and bring rainfall (Jury et al. 1995; Nassor and Jury 1998a).

Donque (1972), a half century ago, described the regional weather elements, land-atmosphere exchanges, and local climate regimes. The island's northern and southern extremities are windy, and the east coast is often cloudy, but the Central Highlands experience a mild continental climate. Another perennial feature is the Indian Ocean anticyclone to the southeast of the island. Tropical cyclones often strike Madagascar between December and March and can bring wind gusts up to 200 km/hr as well as multiday floods near points of landfall.

This background knowledge is a valuable point of reference for an in-depth description using contemporary data, based on measurements from surface stations blended with satellite observations. These are listed in Table 3.1 and include rainfall (Funk et al. 2014), temperature, wind, humidity, vegetation, and ocean conditions (Carton and Giese 2008). Seasonal mean patterns are calculated over 1990–2018, and the annual cycle is studied by averaging over the island of Madagascar (12–26°S, 43–50.5°E). Tropical cyclone tracks and intensities since 1990 are mapped around Madagascar using data from Météo France and the US National Oceanic and Atmospheric Administration (NOAA). Correlations are performed between the Pacific Southern Oscillation Index and regional sea surface temperatures, cloudiness, and wind. Climate change impacts are analyzed using European Centre for Medium-Range Weather Forecasts (ECMWF) observations and model projections, and US National Aeronautics and Space Administration (NASA) satellite air-chemistry measurements. Numerical data assimilation products such as those employed here use sophisticated weather models coupled to the sea and land surface. They blend hourly observations from surface stations, satellite radiometers, profiling systems, and maritime ships and buoys to accurately interpolate the climate to a high resolution.

THE SOUTHWESTERN INDIAN OCEAN

Madagascar's climate is affected by a monsoon circulation (Figure 3.1a) because of the seasonally reversing thermal contrasts between the southern Indian Ocean and Asia to the north. Inflow (outflow) occurs from December to February (June to August) and provides an unusual setting for tropical air-sea interactions.

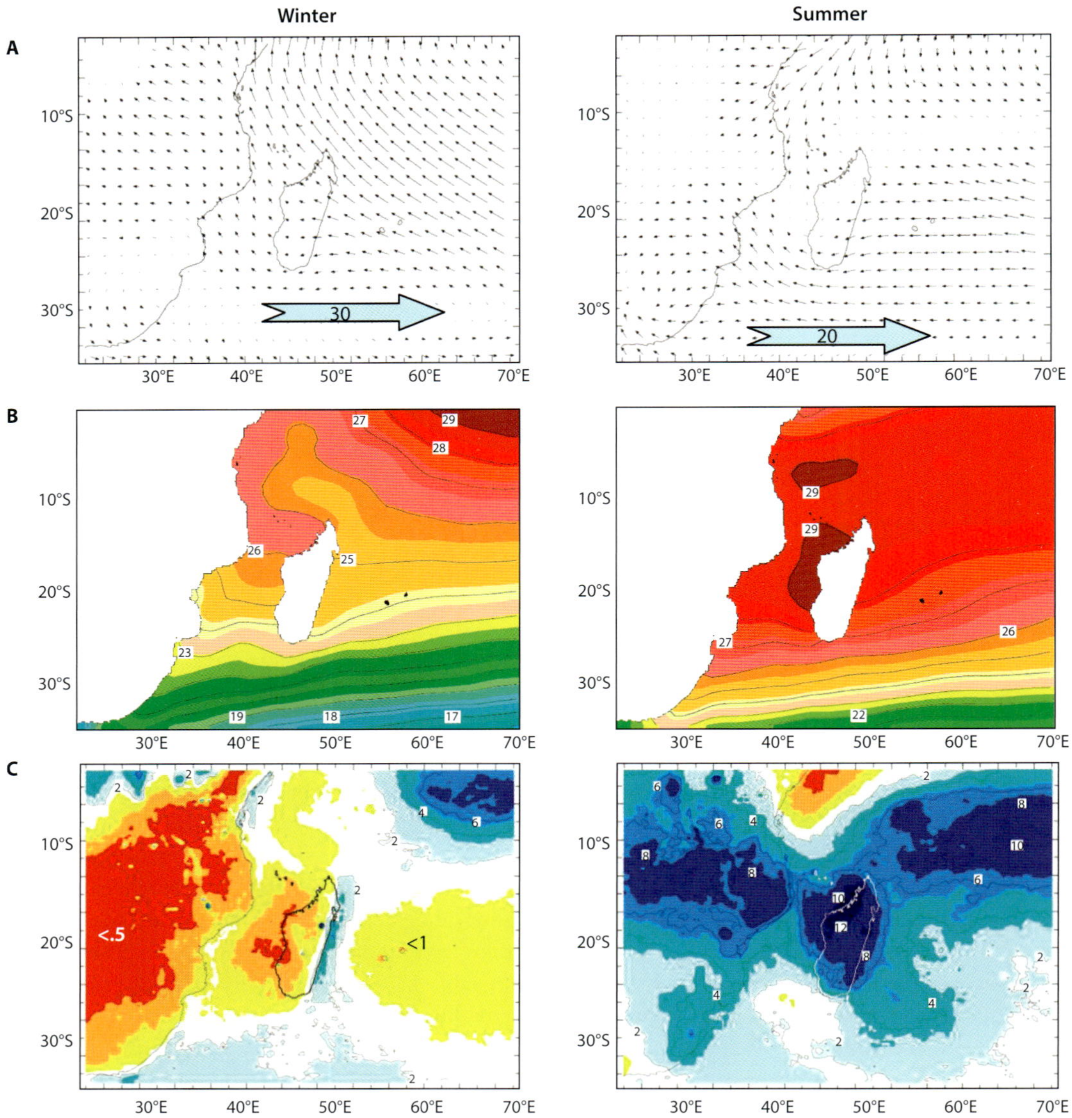

FIGURE 3.1 **Seasonal averaged A) surface winds (vectors, largest is 10 m/s), B) sea surface temperatures, and C) rainfall for winter (left column, June–August) and summer (right column, December–February). Blue arrow in A) shows the axis and speed (inset, m/s) of the upper westerly winds.**

TABLE 3.1 **Acronyms and descriptions of data sets**

ACRONYM	NAME	RESOLUTION
CHIRPS	Climate Hazards InfraRed Precipitation with Station (satellite-gauge blended)	5 km
ECMWF	European Centre for Medium-Range Weather Forecasts (observations and projections)	50–100 km
MODIS	Moderate Resolution Imaging Spectroradiometer (visible and infrared satellite measurements)	1 km
NASA	US National Aeronautics and Space Administration (satellite air chemistry measurements)	100 km
NCEP	National Centers for Environmental Prediction (winds, air pressure, humidity data)	50–100 km
NOAA	US National Oceanic and Atmospheric Administration (hurricane and sea surface temperature data)	25 km
SODA	Simple Ocean Data Assimilation (marine currents, upwelling, and salinity)	50 km

Note: Web sources are listed in the acknowledgments.

Sea surface temperatures over the southwestern Indian Ocean remain high throughout the year (Figure 3.1b), as sun-warmed currents sweep westward across the basin. Evaporative cooling maintains sea surface temperatures near 25°C in winter, when there is little rainfall (Figure 3.1c). With the advent of summer, solar radiation and lighter winds induce a warmer upper ocean (28°C), which promotes tropical thunderstorms. A zone of heavy rainfall forms over Madagascar during summer (Figure 3.1c) and replenishes water resources; it is located at 15°S to the west and at 10°S to the east of the island. Throughout most of the year, subtropical trade winds impinge on the southeast coast (Figure 3.1a).

LOCAL PATTERNS IN AUSTRAL SUMMER CLIMATE

The mountains along the east side of Madagascar (Figure 3.2a) partially trap the moisture there, imparting a pronounced east-to-west gradient in vegetation and rainfall (Figures 3.2b and c). Moist evergreen forests form along the eastern escarpment. The northern half of the island experiences mean summer rainfall above 12 mm/day, as seen by the blue shading in Figure 3.2c. These values are in the upper 1% of rainfall intensities worldwide. Leeward areas in the southwest receive a paltry 2 mm/day.

In the nearby ocean, Madagascar's wind shadow ensures that waters in the Mozambique Channel to the west (Figure 3.2d) are warmer (29.5°C) than in the Indian Ocean to the east (28°C). A poleward boundary current flows along the east coast (Figure 3.2e), characterized by cool upwelling at Tolagnaro. The salinity (Figure 3.2f) reflects a tropical influx of fresh water off the northern half of the island, creating a stable surface layer that traps heat. River runoff along the west coast near Mahajanga is particularly heavy at the end of summer, and salinity there drops below 34.8 parts per thousand (ppt).

Madagascar experiences a variety of temperatures because of the expanse of latitudes covered by the island and its mountains. The summer daytime land temperature, illustrated in Figure 3.3a, reaches only 20°C along the eastern escarpment but climbs to 44°C in the southwestern plains, where water resources are scarce. The local wind and air pressure map (Figure 3.3b) shows that incoming easterly flow is turned southward during summer to form a cyclonic vortex at 20°S, 43°E that draws humid air from the north (Nassor and Jury 1998a, 1998b). This "west coast trough" tends to steer tropical cyclones poleward as they transit the island. In contrast, the rain shadow over southern Madagascar extends south of Toliara.

The subtropical westerlies during winter (June–August) bring dry air and cold fronts from southern Africa that can reduce Central Highlands air temperatures below freezing. An example of that phenomenon is illustrated in Figures 3.3c and d for 16–17 July 2018, when the area around the Andringitra Massif experienced frost. During the austral winter, hail, sleet, and snow are recorded from different portions of the Central Highlands (Figure 3.4).

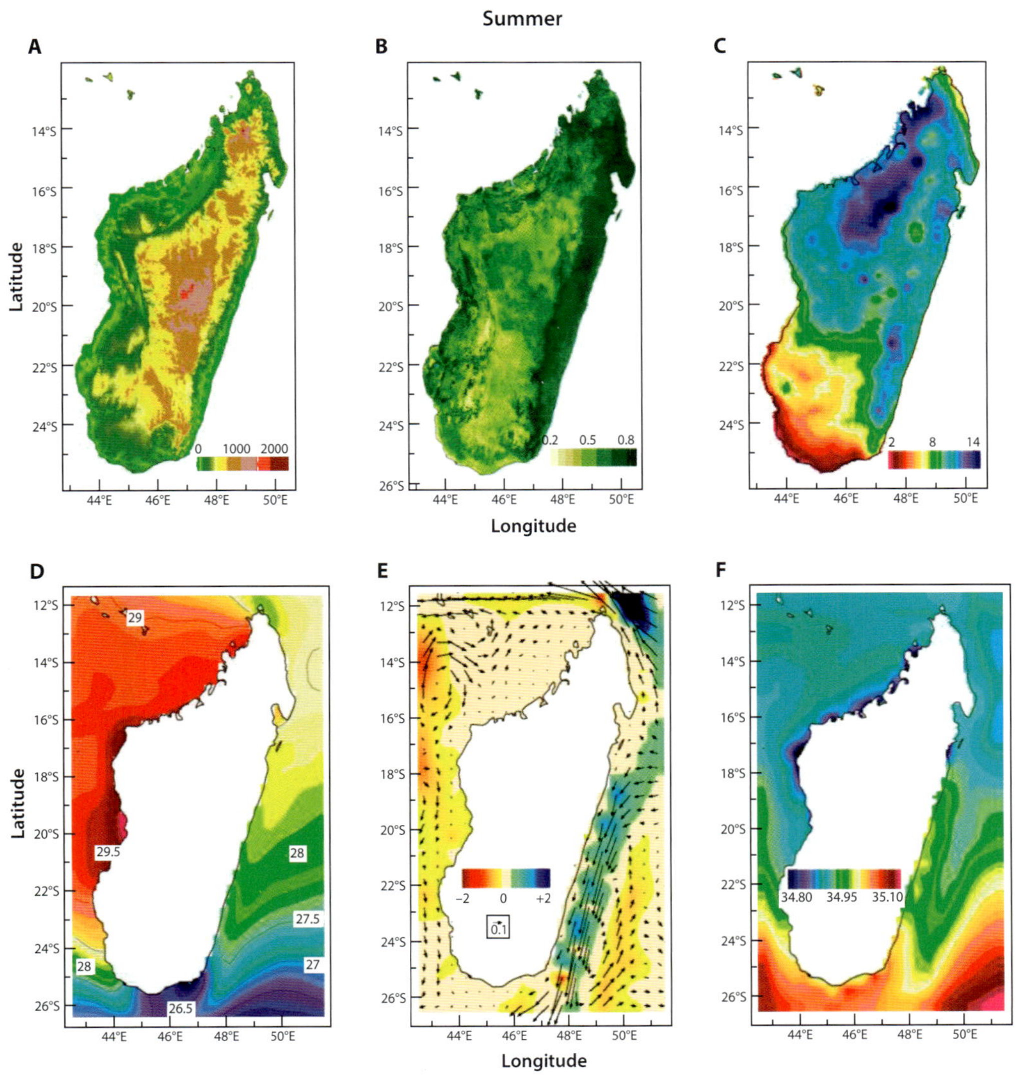

FIGURE 3.2 **Mean summer (December–February) climate of Madagascar: A) topography, B) vegetation fraction, C) land rainfall (mm/day), D) satellite sea surface temperature, E) upper ocean currents (vectors, m/s) and vertical motion (m/day; blue indicates upwelling), and F) upper ocean salinity (ppt).** (SOURCE: modified from Jury 2016.)

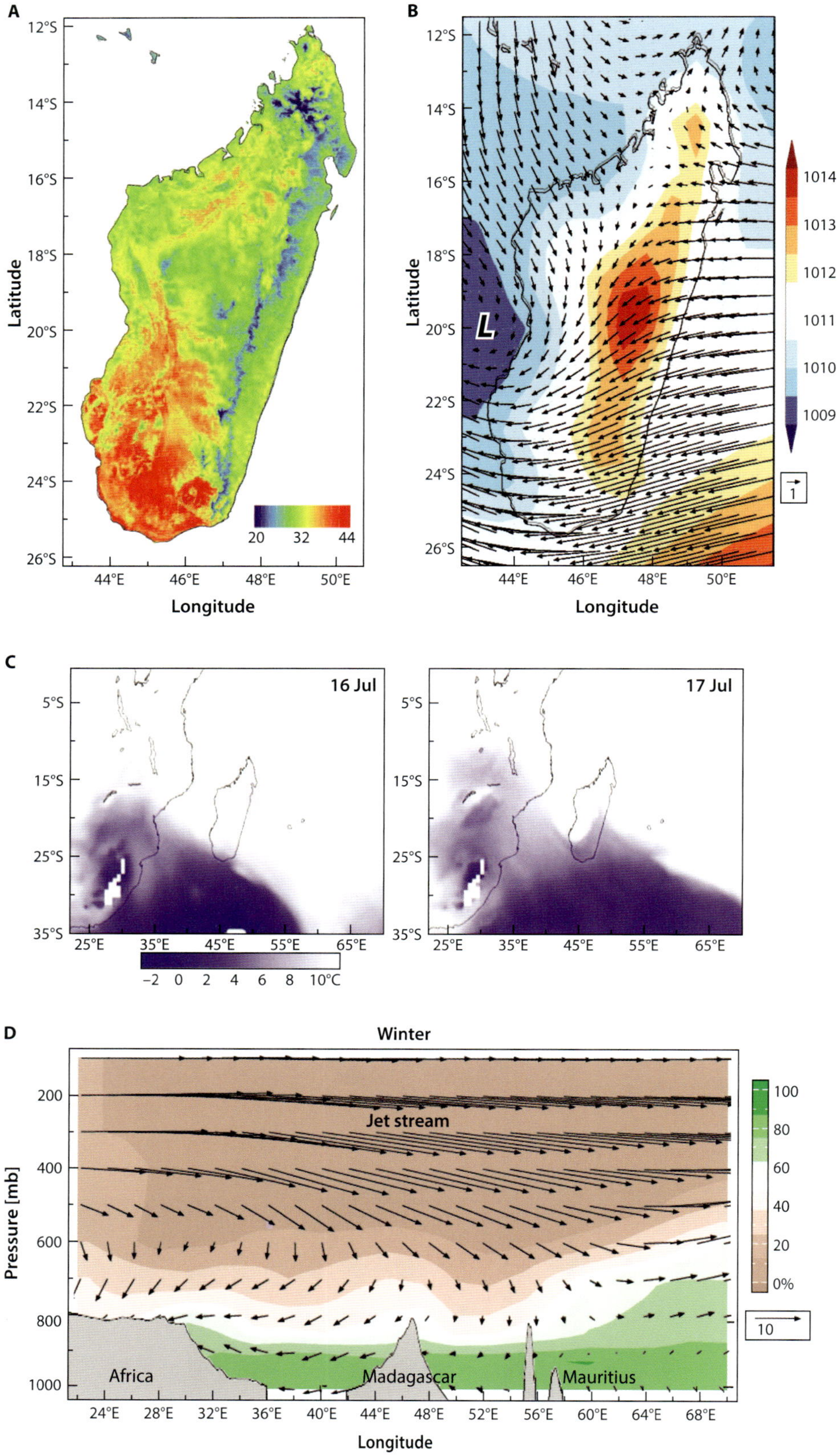

FIGURE 3.3 **Mean summer A) MODIS satellite daytime land temperature, and B) surface winds and sea-level air pressure (modified from Jury 2016). C) Air temperatures at 850 hPa (1.5 km), shaded blue below 10°C, illustrating cold air advancing between 16 and 17 July 2018. D) West–east slice at 20–25°S of winds and relative humidity (shaded) averaged from 16 and 17 July 2018, showing upper westerlies and dry air sinking over Madagascar.**

THE ANNUAL CLIMATE CYCLE

Seasonal changes in climate, which are known to be amplified by the Indian Ocean monsoon (Riehl 1979; Hastenrath 1985; Williams 1990; Jury and Pathack 1991), are studied using graphs of the annual cycle, shown in Figures 3.5a and b. The September–November spring season is very warm and dry: all-island averaged land temperatures reach 38°C, and the fraction of green vegetation

FIGURE 3.4 **Historical image from November 1899 of hail and sleet covering the ground near Antananarivo.** (PHOTO by A. Grandidier, from the collection of the Académie Malgache.)

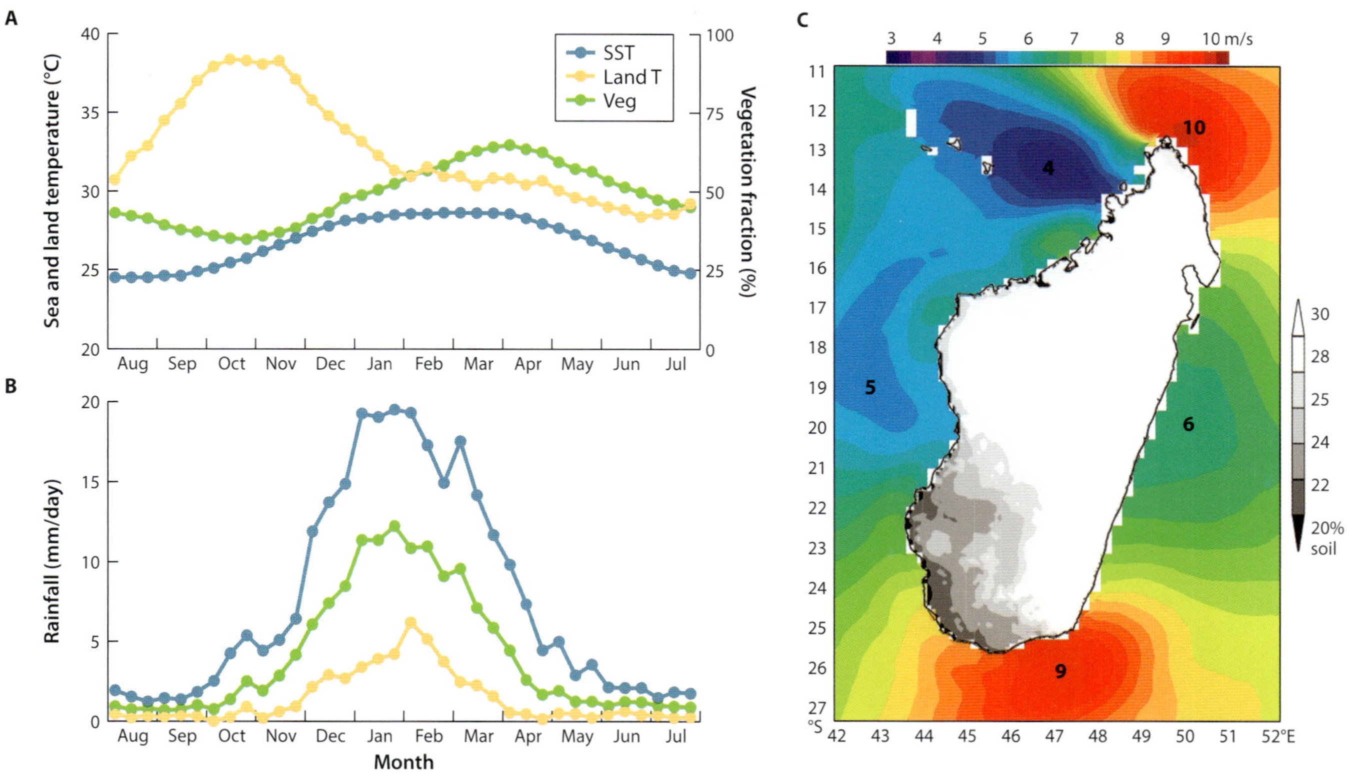

FIGURE 3.5 **Mean annual cycle of Madagascar area-averaged climate variables: A) land and sea surface temperature (SST) and vegetation fraction, B) rainfall and upper/lower quintiles, plotted at 10-day intervals, and C) all-year average marine wind speed (m/s), revealing hotspots at the northern and southern edges, and the leeward shadow. Interior gray-scale shading refers to soil moisture fraction below 30%.**

cover declines to 43%. Together these promote agricultural burning and greenhouse gas emissions, as discussed below. With the onset of summer, sea surface temperatures and vegetation fraction climb to a peak in March (28°C, 67%), while daytime land temperatures hover near 30°C. Rainfall is nearly absent between June and August, when Madagascar "exports" moisture toward India. Mean rainfall reaches a maximum in January (Figure 3.5b), corresponding with rising sea surface temperatures and vegetation, and air "imported" from the northern Indian Ocean. Wet spells often occur at the end of December, end of January, and in early March (Wajsowicz and Schopf 2001).

Wind speeds at the northern and southern tips of the island are accelerated by the Bernoulli effect of the mountains and the shallow nature of trade winds, which blow from the western Indian Ocean. In the middle and lee of the island, winds are almost calm (Figure 3.5c). Together with the warm ocean, this makes outdoor recreational activities pleasant near Nosy Be and enables a productive prawn fishery near Mahajanga. At Tolagnaro the strong trade winds induce the upwelling of cooler waters along the south coast (see Figure 3.2d), favoring marine productivity and good fishing near Toliara, and semidesert conditions across the southwest (Figure 3.5c).

TROPICAL CYCLONES

Madagascar lies in the belt of tropical cyclones, which derive their energy from warm seas that give off high humidity. Tropical cyclones cross the island almost every year from December to March (Figure 3.6a). The impacts from these storms are significant and include flooding, landslides, coastal storm surges, and loss of life and property. In 1994, for example, three successive tropical cyclones hit the Toamasina harbor with 6 m storm surges that destroyed the country's main oil refinery (Naeraa and Jury 1998). Flooding caused by the passage of four tropical cyclones in early 2000 caused an estimated $1 billion in property and infrastructure losses, and over 1000 deaths. The structure and impacts of recent tropical cyclones are reviewed in Nassor and Jury (1998b). This provides a poignant illustration of humanity's vulnerability to extreme weather events.

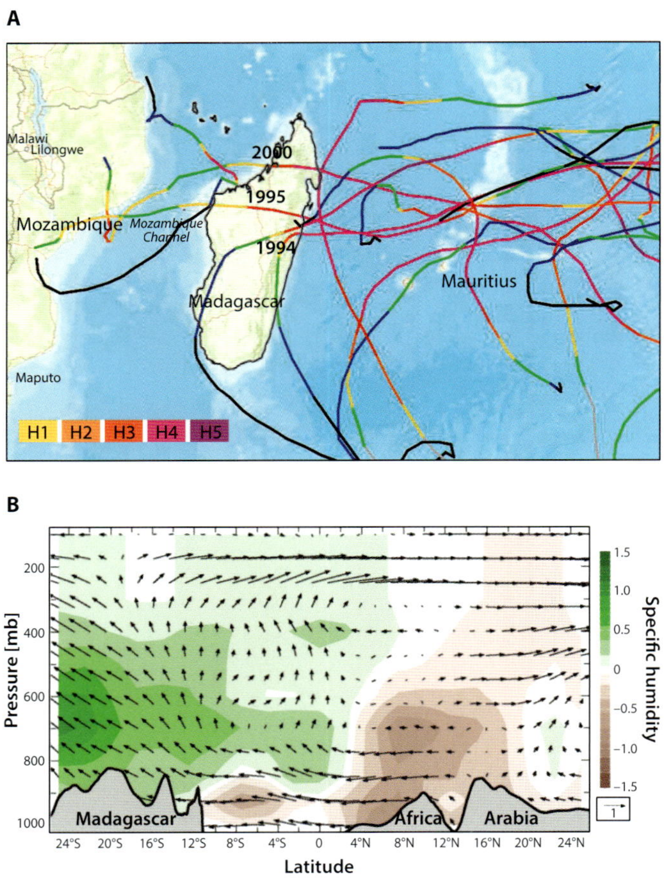

FIGURE 3.6 **A) Tracks of December–March tropical cyclones since 1990, with year labels for those striking Madagascar; intensity scale lower left. B) Meridional circulation and specific humidity anomalies for wet summers, south–north slice at 45–50°E with topography, revealing links with the Indian Ocean monsoon.** (SOURCE: modified from Jury 2016.)

CLIMATE VARIABILITY

In their analysis of Madagascar's rainfall, Dewar and Richard (2007) found an unusually high variability attributable to the present land/sea configuration and the Indian Ocean monsoon, which has prevailed over the past 5 million years. The unpredictable nature of rainfall comes from localized intraseasonal and interannual drought and flood events. Consequently, Madagascar's flora and fauna have evolved in distinctive ways to cope with sudden and random changes in climate.

The Indian Ocean monsoon's influence on summer rainfall is illustrated in Figure 3.6b as a north–south slice. The atmospheric circulation resembles a Hadley cell, with dry conditions over the Arabian Sea and moist rising air over Madagascar. Surface winds from the north and upper winds from the south complete the conveyor belt underpinning wet spells. In the east–west direction, we find a mechanism contributing to multiyear fluctuations of climate (Saji et al. 1999; Xie et al. 2001; Fauchereau et al. 2009).

The upper ocean to the northeast of Madagascar is sensitive to forcing by the Pacific Southern Oscillation (Hastenrath and Greischar 1989, 1991; McCreary et al. 1993). During the high phase of this index, which refers to cool La Niña conditions that recur every three to six years (Nicholson et al. 1988), sea surface temperatures and cloudiness decline to the northeast and increase to the southwest (Figures 3.7a and b). Simultaneously, the Pacific La Niña induces easterly upper-level winds over Madagascar (Figure 3.7c) that favor intense, westward-moving tropical cyclones (Jury et al. 1995).

Mechanisms for this oscillation have been related to the southern Indian Ocean Rossby wave (Huang and Kinter 2002; Jury 2018), which tilts the upper ocean warm layer to the east and west. This "seesaw" creates opposing cloud and rainfall regimes between southern Africa and northeastern Madagascar (Jury and Pathack 1991), as seen in Figure 3.7b.

ECONOMIC IMPACTS OF CLIMATE

Madagascar has abundant natural resources distributed over an area of 587,000 km^2, and a population of 25 million (2017 estimate), growing at 3% per annum (World Bank 2019). Life expectancy is 66 years, but several diseases (e.g., malaria, cholera) are significant climate-related threats. The gross domestic product (GDP) per capita stands at $400 per annum and has doubled in the past decade. An obstacle to growth is energy supply. There are few country-scale hydroelectric or solar power projects, although plans are advancing

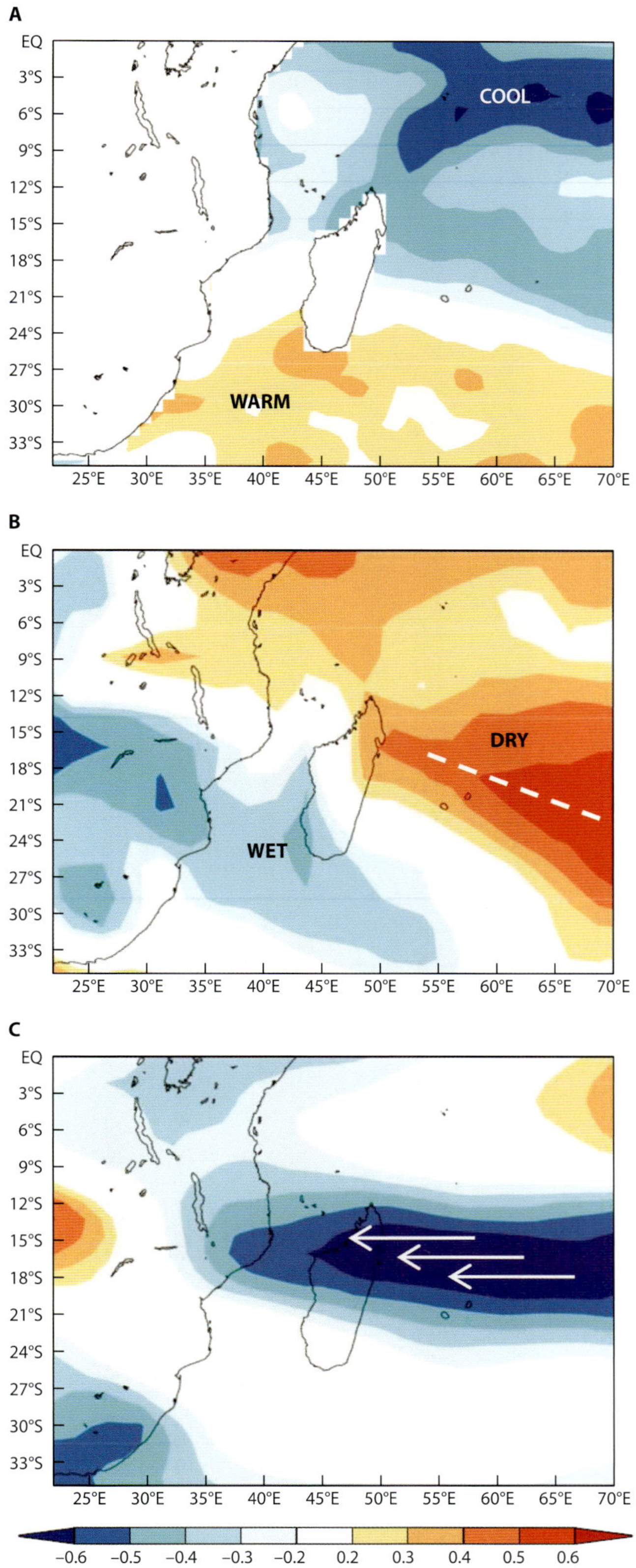

FIGURE 3.7 **Summer season correlation of the Pacific Southern Oscillation Index with A) sea surface temperatures, B) satellite net outgoing longwave radiation (cloudiness), and C) 500 hPa zonal winds, representing the local response to global La Niña conditions.**

for several such projects to be up and running in the 2020s. Rain-fed agriculture contributes about one-third of GDP, with exports of coffee, cotton, vanilla, and prawns, which are climate sensitive. France is the main trading partner, and tourism revenue is growing at about 20% per year. The GDP growth rate is directly suppressed by tropical cyclone damage.

CLIMATE CHANGE AND AIR CHEMISTRY

Long-term trends in island temperature and rainfall were analyzed for this chapter, using the latest data sets and projections from the European Community (EC) model of ECMWF. The observed surface air temperature shows a second-order trend that refers to an accelerating rate of warming (Figure 3.8a). The observed trend coincides with the model projection, which assumes a gradual doubling of CO_2. Air temperatures over Madagascar may rise from 24°C to 28°C by the year 2100. With higher temperatures holding more humidity, one might expect stormy weather (Tadross et al. 2008). However, both observed and projected trends for rainfall and vegetation-induced transpiration are downward (Figures 3.8b and c). Rainfall diminishes from an annual all-island average of 4.3 mm/day (in 1950) to 3.6 mm/day (in 2100), while transpiration is projected to decline ~15%. Any reduction of moisture input to the atmosphere translates into less daily rainfall. Regional assessments suggest that sinking motion across the Southern Hemisphere subtropics may lengthen the dry season (IPCC 2013), exacerbating Madagascar's soil erosion and deforestation. Southwestern areas of the island (see Figure 3.5c) could see hazardous water deficits.

The main driver of global warming is air chemistry. New satellite measurements are available to analyze the concentration of short-lived greenhouse gases: carbon monoxide (CO) and methane (CH_4), derived mainly from agricultural burning and livestock. The CO map (Figure 3.8d) shows a hotspot covering the western plains of Madagascar. Similarly, CH_4, a gas that traps five times more heat than CO_2 (IPCC 2013), shows that concentrations increase with elevation (Figure 3.8e), indicating that most livestock (especially cattle) are grazed in the highlands. Fires are set most years at the end of the dry season to clear brush associated with pastoral and crop farming activities. Vast areas of the Central Highlands and lowland plains are regularly burned (Figure 3.8f); only northeastern Madagascar near the Masoala Peninsula escapes this large-scale biomass burning.

CONCLUDING REMARKS

The island of Madagascar has a varied and interesting climate attributable to its position and complex topography. This review has sought to uncover many of its characteristics and local features. Its location in the subtropics and exposure to monsoons and tropical cyclones make for sudden swings in Madagascar's weather conditions, critical evolutionary forces in shaping its terrestrial biodiversity. With advanced satellite technology and high-resolution numerical data assimilation, earth scientists now have many tools to describe the local climate of this beautiful island.

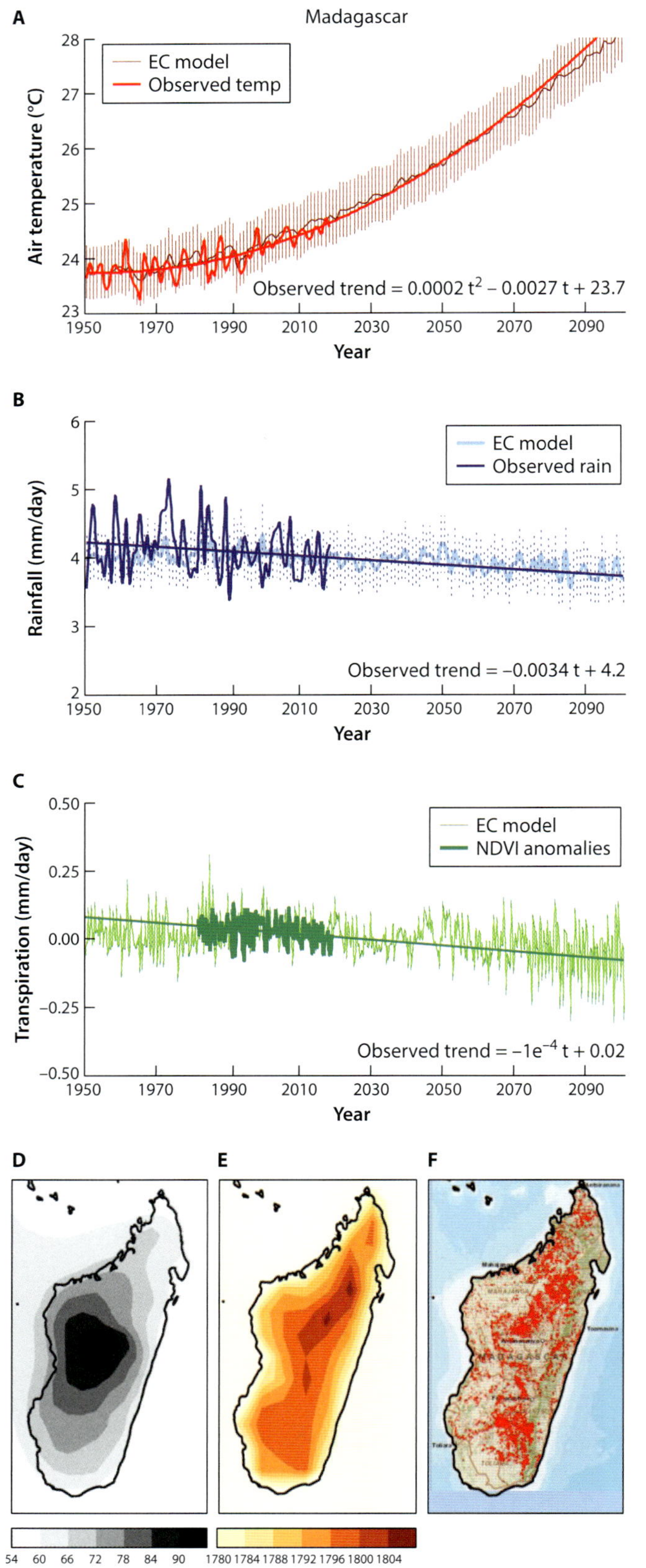

FIGURE 3.8 **Past observed and ECMWF (EC) model-projected trends of annual A) air temperature, B) rainfall, and C) transpiration over Madagascar. Long-term low-level mean air chemistry (ppb) measured by NASA satellite: D) CO, E) CH_4, and F) burned area at the end of a typical dry season based on satellite fire density (red dots).**

ACKNOWLEDGMENTS

Many of the maps and data for graphs were extracted from websites of the International Research Institute Climate Library, KNMI Climate Explorer, University of Hawaii APDRC, NOAA-Coast Hurricane, NASA Giovanni, and NASA FIRMS.

Subject editor: Steven M. Goodman

REFERENCES

Carton, J. A., and Giese, B. S. 2008. A reanalysis of ocean climate using simple ocean data assimilation (SODA). *Monthly Weather Review* 136: 2999–3017.

Dewar, R. E., and Richard, A. F. 2007. Evolution in the hypervariable environment of Madagascar. *Proceedings of the National Academy of Sciences of the USA* 104: 13723–13727.

Donque, G. 1972. The climatology of Madagascar. In *Biogeography and Ecology of Madagascar*, eds. R. Battistini and G. Richard-Vindard, pp. 87–144. The Hague: Junk.

Fauchereau, N., Pohl, B., Reason, C., Rouault, M., and Richard, Y. 2009. Recurrent daily OLR patterns in the southern Africa/southwest Indian Ocean region, implications for South African rainfall and teleconnections. *Climate Dynamics* 32: 575–591.

Funk, C. C., Peterson, P. J., Landsfeld, M. F., Pedreros, D. H., Verdin, J. P., Rowland, J. D., Romero, B. E., Husak, G. J., Michaelsen, J. C., and Verdin, A. P. 2014. A quasi-global precipitation time series for drought monitoring. US Geological Survey, Data Series 832. dx.doi.org/110.3133/ds832.

Griffiths, J. F., and Ranaivoson, R. 1972. Madagascar. In *Climates of Africa: World Survey of Climatology*, vol. 10, pp. 313–348. Amsterdam: Elsevier.

Halkides, D., and Lee, T. 2011. Mechanisms controlling seasonal mixed layer temperature and salinity in the southwestern tropical Indian Ocean. *Dynamics of Atmospheres and Oceans* 51: 77–93.

Hastenrath, S. 1985. *Climate and Circulation of the Tropics*. Dordrecht: D. Riedel.

Hastenrath, S., and Greischar, L. 1989. *Climate Atlas of the Indian Ocean*. Vol. 3, *Upper Ocean Structure*. Madison: University of Wisconsin Press.

———. 1991. The monsoonal current regimes of the tropical Indian Ocean: Observed surface flow fields and geostrophic wind-driven components. *Journal of Geophysical Research* 96: C7, 12619–12633.

Huang, B., and Kinter, J. L. 2002. Inter-annual variability in the tropical Indian Ocean. *Journal of Geophysical Research* 107. doi:10.1029/2001JC001278.

IPCC. 2013. *Climate Change 2013: The Physical Science Basis*. WG-1 5th Assessment Report, eds. T. F. Stocker, D. Qin, G.-K. Plattner, M. Tignor, S. K. Allen, J. Boschung, A. Nauels, Y. Xia, V. Bex, and P. M. Midgley. New York: Cambridge University Press.

Jury, M. R. 2016. Summer climate of Madagascar and monsoon pulsing of its vortex. *Meteorology and Atmospheric Physics* 128: 117–129.

———. 2018. South Indian Ocean Rossby waves. *Atmosphere Ocean* 56: 322–331.

Jury, M. R., and Pathack, B. 1991. A study of climate and weather variability over the tropical SW Indian Ocean. *Meteorology and Atmospheric Physics* 47: 37–48.

Jury, M. R., Parker, B. A., Raholijao, N., and Nassor, A. 1995. Variability of summer convection over Madagascar: Climatic determinants at inter-annual scales. *International Journal of Climatology* 15: 1323–1332.

McCreary, J. P., Kundu, P. K., and Molinari, R. L. 1993. A numerical investigation of dynamics, thermodynamics and mixed layer processes in the Indian Ocean. *Progress in Oceanography* 31: 181–244.

Naeraa, M., and Jury, M. R. 1998. Tropical cyclone composite structure and impacts over eastern Madagascar during January–March 1994. *Meteorology and Atmospheric Physics* 65: 43–53.

Nassor, A., and Jury, M. R. 1998a. Intra-seasonal climate variability of Madagascar, pt. 1: Mean summer conditions. *Meteorology and Atmospheric Physics* 65: 31–41.

———. 1998b. Intra-seasonal climate variability of Madagascar, pt. 2: Evolution of flood events. *Meteorology and Atmospheric Physics* 65: 243–254.

Nicholson, S. E., Kim, J., and Hoopingarner, J. 1988. *Atlas of African Rainfall and Its Interannual Variability*. Technical report. Tallahassee: Florida State University.

Riehl, H. 1979. *Climate and Weather in the Tropics*. New York: Academic Press.

Saji, N. H., Goswami, B. N., Vinayachandran, P. N., and Yamagata. T. 1999. A dipole mode in the tropical Indian Ocean. *Nature* 401: 360–363.

Sengupta, D., Senan, R., and Goswami, B. N. 2001. Origin of intra-seasonal variability of circulation in the tropical central Indian Ocean. *Geophysical Research Letters* 28: 1267–1270.

Tadross, M., Randriamarolaza, L., Rabefitia, Z., and Zheng, K. Y. 2008. *Climate Change in Madagascar: Recent Past and Future*. Washington, DC: World Bank Report.

Wajsowicz, R. C., and Schopf, P. S. 2001. Oceanic influences on the seasonal cycle of evaporation over the Indian Ocean. *Journal of Climate* 14: 1199–1226.

Williams, J. B. 1990. *Some Temporal and Regional Variations of Climate in Madagascar*. Technical report. Chatham Marine: Overseas Development Natural Resources Institute.

World Bank. 2019. https://data.worldbank.org/country/Madagascar.

Xie, S. P., Annamalai, H., Schott, F. A., and McCreary, J. P. 2001. Structure and mechanisms of south Indian Ocean climate variability. *Journal of Climate* 15: 864–878.

CHAPTER 4

FOREST AND GRASSLAND ECOLOGY

INTRODUCTION

A. H. Armstrong and S. M. Goodman

As one of the biologically richest areas on earth, Madagascar, an island with considerable abiotic complexity, has flora and fauna that occur in a highly varied mosaic of forest, thicket, and grassland ecosystems. The diversity of forest types is the combined result of Madagascar's geologic history and associated soil types, coupled with its broad range of environmental conditions that show considerable clinal variation (e.g., length of dry season). Madagascar's ecosystems, predominantly its natural forests, contain most of the island's floral diversity, which makes up 3.2% of that known across the planet (Myers et al. 2000). It is important to point out that Madagascar represents about 0.001% of the earth's surface area, which helps highlight the disproportionate role that this island nation plays in safeguarding our planet's natural patrimony.

In the following sections within this introduction, we briefly outline some of the abiotic parameters that help explain the vegetational and floral diversity on the island, which are important for better understanding of the different contributions that follow in this chapter. Thereafter, a short section is given on changes in ecosystem extent. Then in a separate section, we describe in some detail the major ecosystems discussed in this chapter.

MADAGASCAR'S TOPOGRAPHY AND CLIMATE

Temperature, rainfall, latitudinal, and topographic gradients underlie the range of climatic zones on Madagascar, which include the tropical eastern and western coastlines, temperate inland, and arid south. Considered to be a mini-continent, Madagascar extends from 12°30′S to 25°32′S and is about 1570 km from north to south, 560 km from east to west (at its widest), with a total area of 587,000 km^2. A spine of mountains runs north–south along the eastern portion of Madagascar, creating notable asymmetry to the island's east–west topographic configuration, with a series of peaks rising above 2000 m. To the west of this mountain chain is a vast zone making up nearly a third of the island's surface area, which we refer to herein as the Central Highlands (also often called the High Plateau or Central Plateau); it is generally defined as the land area above 800–900 m in elevation. The eastern-positioned mountain formation intercepts the prevalent southeasterly winds coming off the Indian Ocean, and as a result, its eastern region is notably wet, with rainfall averaging from 2400 to more than 6000 mm per year (see Jury, pp. 91–98, for further details on the island's climate). Annual rainfall averages decline sharply across the Central Highlands from east to west, following a gradient of 2400 mm down to 1600 mm per year. Farther west, from the western foothills of the Central Highlands to the coast, there is further reduction in annual rainfall, which becomes even more pronounced in the southwest (<600 mm per year).

Temperatures can also vary greatly with elevation and latitude across the island. At sea level, the mean temperatures of the coldest month range from more than 25°C at the northern tip to more than 20°C in the southeastern corner and 20°C in the dry south and southwest. Mean temperature ranges are between 25°C and 29°C along the eastern side from north to south during the hottest months, and between 27°C and 28°C in the south and southwest (see Jury, pp. 91–98). In the Central Highlands, the climate is considerably cooler, exhibiting a temperature gradient of 0.6°C for every 100 m in elevation change. For instance, mean temperatures at 1650 m near the town of Antsirabe are 20°C and 12.5°C during the warmest and coolest months, respectively (Raboin et al. 2010). However, it is common for cold-season low temperatures to fall below freezing, causing frost, especially at higher elevations.

GEOLOGIC HISTORY

Madagascar's geology also helps explain aspects of the evolutionary history of its unique biota, particularly its forest ecosystems. Once attached to Africa and other landmasses as part of the supercontinent of Gondwana, Madagascar, still attached to India and the granitic Seychelles (East Gondwana), broke away during the late Cretaceous period (dating from roughly 170 million years ago [Mya]; see Collins et al., pp. 45–51, for details on the island's geologic history); this separation commenced Madagascar's isolation in deep geologic time, making it the world's oldest island. A range of recent studies using molecular clock dating indicate that not very many members of the modern Malagasy biota have an origin dating to before the breakup of Gondwana. Instead, the vast majority of these organisms subsequently colonized Madagascar over water during different periods of geologic history, and a range of different factors and filters can explain their successful colonization (see Samonds et al., pp. 73–78). However, the timing of speciation of the island's forests and their greater floristic richness as compared to that of mainland Africa may be attributed to the fact that Madagascar underwent much less drying out during the Pleistocene, Pliocene, and probably late Miocene (Leroy 1978; Elton 2008; Hackel et al. 2018). It has also been hypothesized that the low stature of most Malagasy forests, lack of large-girth trees, and general small size and dearth of broadleaf herbs as compared to other tropical and subtropical forests worldwide are the result of Madagascar having old and nutrient-limited soils (Grubb 2003; Vågen et al. 2006; Styger et al. 2007).

EDAPHIC CONDITIONS

A good portion of the island's soils are red lateritic clay, a characteristic that has given rise to nicknames such as "the big red island." Soils in the wetter lowland areas in the east are derived from acidic rocks and have undergone long leaching; they are therefore low in pH and relatively poor in quality because of the lack of available nutrients (Vågen et al. 2006). Similarly, soils derived from sands on the narrow eastern plain containing littoral forests are especially nutrient poor. Forest nutrient cycling involves a set of direct and indirect edaphic feedback mechanisms (Brand and Pfund 1998; Castellanos et al. 2001). Biogeochemical cycles in forests essentially involve successive transfers of nutrients among compartments or pools (i.e., canopy, litter, humus, soil, etc.), the characteristics of which greatly depend on soil type (Schlesinger 1997; Vågen et al. 2006). It is generally understood that forests growing on nutrient-poor, acidic soils often exhibit especially closed nutrient cycling, as nutrients that become available from an event such as a tree fall are immediately incorporated into the tight system. Tight nutrient cycling has been shown in a number of studies of oxisols and ultisols on Madagascar, exemplified by low concentrations of nutrients in soil profiles (Brand and Pfund 1998; Vågen et al. 2006). These edaphic and climatic features have a direct relationship with the ranges of forest-dwelling species, their competitive strategies, and their adaptive resilience.

CHANGES IN ECOSYSTEM EXTENT

Changes in land cover and land use as a result of human activities have dramatically modified tropical forests, a process exacerbated by contemporary climate variability and change, with increased frequency and intensity of heat, drought, bushfires, and introduced plants. Madagascar has lost approximately 90% of its original forest cover (both closed- and open-canopy formations), and large areas of intact forest are projected to become disconnected patches with increasing human population. Though the full picture of deforestation and its causes prior to 1950 is incomplete, a study by Harper et al. (2007) determined that 27% of Madagascar was forested in 1950, a percentage that fell to around 16% in 2000. Recently, Vieilledent et al. (2018) combined studies from the last six decades, extending the analysis up to 2014 and identifying three main periods of forest change: 1) a high deforestation rate from 1950 to 2000, with an average exceeding 90,000 ha per year; 2) a slightly decreased rate from 1990 to 2005, with an average of about 50,000 ha per year; and 3) a continuous increase since 2005, with an average value of 90,000 ha per year. In fact, the deforestation rate more than doubled from 2010 to 2014, compared to the rate from 2000 to 2005. The ominous indicators were already clear some three decades ago when Green and Sussman (1990) showed that if deforestation rates continued along the trajectory at the time of their pre-1990 study, no remaining forest would exist outside protected areas by 2020. These dire predictions were partially eclipsed by an enlarged commitment to conservation enforcement during the early 2000s, including a large-scale increase in the designation of new protected areas to include more than 10% of the island's combined terrestrial and seascape areas (Goodman et al. 2018). The locations of the more than 120 protected areas correspond directly with the remaining forest cover.

Deforestation rates in protected areas have increased in recent years, at least in part because of political instability. Shifting cultivation over the past 50 years has been causally linked to deforestation, environmental degradation, and increasing population. In addition, population pressures combined with decreasing size of land holdings have caused a reduction in duration of fallow periods of cultivation in converted areas of once-moist evergreen forests (Brand and Pfund 1998; Böhning-Gaese et al. 1999; Holloway 2000; Dufils 2003). Because of this, land cleared by swidden agricultural techniques (*tavy*) is no longer allowed to return to its previous secondary forest state before it is cleared again and replanted; thus, the soil nutrient spike offered by biomass burning eventually dwindles (see Kull and Lehmann, pp. 197–203). In addition to *tavy*, mining for semiprecious stones and minerals, selective logging of very valuable hardwood species, charcoal production, livestock grazing, introduced species, and demand for firewood constitute threats to the health and future viability of Madagascar's remaining forests.

In order to appreciate how forest and grassland ecosystems are distributed across the landscape, it is important to understand the organizational structure of these ecosystems with respect to their environmental ranges, what pressures or threats they face, and how vulnerability and resilience to these threats affect their long-term viability. The following sections describe the structural characteristics, remaining extent, and other important physiognomic features of Madagascar's forested and grassland ecosystems, specifically moist evergreen forests, littoral forests, dry deciduous forests, tapia or sclerophyllous woodlands, dry spiny thickets (also often referred to as spiny bush), and native grasslands. An in-depth description of mangrove forests can be found in Cooke et al. (pp. 311–58). In general, we use the terms proposed by Gautier et al. (2018) for vegetation types.

FOREST AND GRASSLAND ECOSYSTEMS

Moist Evergreen Forests

Madagascar is widely considered to be among the most diverse and species-rich areas on earth, containing nearly 12,000 species of vascular plants, more than 82% of which are endemic, and at least 14,000 total floral species, with an overall endemism of about 87% (Callmander et al. 2011; Lowry et al. 2018; Madagascar Catalogue 2020), a large proportion of which occur in its moist evergreen forests. As clearly denoted in the taxonomic contributions in chapter 8, floral species richness on the island is extremely high, but we are still a long way from knowing with any certainty the exact number of plant species; botanical research through plant surveys and different types of taxonomic tools continue to yield a remarkable number of species new to science.

The moist evergreen forests are divided into two different types: 1) lowland moist evergreen forests from close to sea level to about 800–1000 m (depending on topography and edaphic conditions), and 2) medium-altitude moist evergreen forests from 800–1000 m to 2000 m (or lower, depending on tree line). These formations are located principally in the eastern zone of the island, transecting the eastern escarpment from the Central Highlands to the coast, and extending from Vohémar—where the forests transition to dry deciduous and the complex of more northerly massifs (Marojejy-Tsaratanàna-Manongarivo)—south to the Tolagnaro area. The structure of Malagasy lowland moist evergreen forests has been compared to that of the dipterocarp forests of Borneo and Papua New Guinea: Malagasy forests are smaller in stature than those of Amazonia or mainland Africa, with high stem densities and a multilevel canopy (Dufils 2003; Armstrong et al. 2011). The dominant canopy layer can reach 30 m in height in lowland moist evergreen forest, with canopy-emergent trees often exceeding 40 m. A sub-canopy layer is often dominated by palms, epiphytes, and lianas, the woody treelet layer is made up primarily of *Pandanus* and other small trees, and the forest floor is often sparsely vegetated. As with other rainforests of the world, multi-tiered structure provides a heterogeneous and vertically distributed habitat (see Mertz, pp. 134–41).

The lowland moist evergreen forests of Madagascar have been noted to be unique in their richness of palms, *Pandanus*, bamboo, and tree fern species, while also being of relatively low stature, lacking in large-girth trees, and having a poor diversity of large-leaved monocots (Grubb 2003; Barthlott et al. 2005; Gautier et al. 2018; Carvalho et al. 2020). The species of palms and *Pandanus* in these forests are both abundant and markedly diverse in size and form, a feature that has been commonly attributed to acclimation or adaptation to low water supply (Grubb 2003; see Rakotoarinivo et al., pp. 567–80, for palms; see Callmander et al., pp. 551–59, for *Pandanus*).

The medium-altitude moist evergreen forests form a clinal extension of the low-elevation formation, particularly on continuous slopes, but with decreasing stature of canopy trees (10–20 m in height), emergent up to 30 m, and increasing epiphytic loads as a function of increasing elevation (Gautier et al. 2018). This is the dominant forest type of the eastern escarpment, as well as some of the Central Highlands. The original extent included continuous forest between different sites, several of which are now integrated in the protected area system. Dominant tree species are in general different from those of lowland rainforest, with increased abundance of tree ferns (Cyatheaceae) and bamboo, which are also notably common elements in stands following natural or anthropogenic disturbance.

Of all the forest types on Madagascar, moist evergreen forests are as well known for their biotic diversity as they are for their highly threatened status. Swidden agriculture (*tavy*) has resulted in the large-scale clearance of vast areas of this forest type on the island. High annual rainfall, a warm tropical climate, and a nearly year-round growing season provide ideal conditions for agriculture; *tavy*-cleared lands are thus planted with subsistence (e.g., rice, manioc) and cash crops (e.g., cocoa, coffee, spices). In addition, illegal hardwood exploitation (e.g., rosewood, ebony) for foreign markets continues in some regions, further degrading these ecosystems. See Grinand and Nourtier (pp. 105–13) on changes in forest cover in this formation.

Littoral Forests

Madagascar's littoral forests are located for the most part along the east coast and at elevations from sea level up to 100 m (Gautier et al. 2018). This is one of the most fragmented forest types on the island. Its extent historically formed a continuous mosaic along the entirety of the east coast; today the largest remaining fragments are preserved in a few protected areas (Goodman et al. 2018). Littoral forests depend on sandy substrates; species composition, canopy height, and overall structure can differ locally from site to site depending on edaphic features, even under similar climatic conditions (Virah-Sawmy et al. 2009a). Floristic shifts, including the endemic species present, are also attributed to physiographic differences, including the north–south rainfall gradient, distance to the coast, and edaphic variation (Dumetz 1999).

As noted by Virah-Sawmy et al. (2009b), the littoral forests of Madagascar have been identified as a top conservation priority because of their quickly disappearing extent, even relative to Madagascar's 0.55% annual total deforestation rate. In addition to having gained the status of critically endangered hotspots, littoral forests are known for their important concentration of endemic species of plants, insects, and vertebrates (Ganzhorn et al. 2001). Mining, swidden agriculture, and firewood and charcoal production, along with anticipated sea-level rise, threaten to further diminish the surface area of this forest type.

Western Dry Deciduous Forests

Three types of forests are found in the western region of Madagascar, including moist semi-deciduous forests, dry deciduous forests, and sclerophyllous (*tapia*) woodlands; the latter formation, which also occurs in the Central Highlands, is discussed in detail by Kull and Birkinshaw (pp. 121–27). Moist semi-deciduous forests include sites with higher water availability because of topographic position, and fragments are found throughout the Western Domain, often at the base of limestone massifs (e.g., Beanka, Namoroka), in canyons cutting through such massifs, or in valley bottoms adjacent to riparian forests. The climate of areas where this forest formation occurs have moderate rainfall (600–1200 mm annually) and high temperatures that fluctuate little throughout the year. Characterized by a dense closed canopy 15–20 m in height and sparse undergrowth, these forests contain a mix of deciduous and evergreen species (Gautier et al. 2018). Because these relict forests occur naturally as fragments driven by topographic and geographic aspects, they are particularly vulnerable to climate change, as the western portion of the island is projected to warm by an average of 3°C by the end of the century (Rasmussen et al. 2016). In addition, these forests are often highly threatened by clearing for agriculture (Goodman et al. 2018).

Dry deciduous forests are the dominant forest type in both the north and west of Madagascar. Structurally, they are characterized by a multilayered closed canopy, typically composed of deciduous species between 10 and 20 m in height, and emergent trees about 30 m (Gautier et al. 2018). The epiphytes, mosses, and ferns prevalent in the moist evergreen forests are rare in dry deciduous forests; however, lianas (in particular Passifloraceae and Vitaceae) are more frequent. Further, the undergrowth in nondisturbed dry deciduous forests is generally sparse and without a continuous herbaceous layer.

Annual rainfall in western Madagascar ranges between 400 and 1400 mm, with a more pronounced dry season than in moist evergreen forests and with a duration of between four and nine months per year, depending on the latitude. Dry deciduous forests are found from sea level to 800 m and are represented in several protected areas. Dominant tree species vary among sites, distinguished by edaphic conditions ranging from sandy to lateritic and limestone soils (Gautier et al. 2018).

Dry deciduous forests have undergone the largest loss in extent over the past two decades. Swidden agriculture has increased with the rising demand for corn production. Rather than allowing an eventual return to a secondary forested state, the common cycle of planting and lying fallow results in diminishing soil health, and plots previously used to grow corn are replaced by secondary thickets, which are burned again for groundnut planting. The next anthropogenic grassland stage is then typically used to graze livestock. In addition, mining and oil exploration are threats to this forest type (e.g., in Menabe Antimena and Mikea; Goodman et al. 2018).

Dry Spiny Thickets

Dry spiny thickets, sometimes called spiny bush, refer to the dry deciduous southernmost formation that occurs from sea level to 300 m elevation, in the driest region of Madagascar. Occurring from the Mikea Forest (slightly north of Toliara) south to the southern limit of the island, and then east to the western slopes of the Anosyenne Mountains (east of Tolagnaro) and up to 100 km inland from the coast, dry spiny thickets are the dominant natural woody vegetation type of the south. Known for their unique appearance associated with a variety of adaptations to deal with the extended dry season, the thickets are composed of a closed, dense, often spiny shrub canopy 2–8 m in height (Gautier et al. 2018). As in other arid ecosystems, plants with smaller leaves are often present; however, deciduous species, meaning those that drop their leaves during a portion of the year, dominate. This ecosystem type is known for both its diversity and its exceedingly high levels of endemism. Resilient to hot and dry climatic conditions, dry spiny thickets typically receive less than 600 mm of rainfall per year, with a dry season of over 10 months, and temperatures among the highest on the island.

Though conservation efforts have been successful in many protected areas (Goodman et al. 2018), dry spiny thickets are most vulnerable to local and regional demands for charcoal and firewood. Swidden agriculture is less frequent in this formation, in part because agriculture is more difficult in such dry conditions than it is in more mesic areas of the island. However, grazing pressures from zebu and goats have increased over the past two decades, and charcoal production is another important threat.

Native Grasslands

Native grasslands are an understudied ecosystem on Madagascar, and in the precursor to this book (Goodman and Benstead 2003), this formation was not covered in any meaningful manner. This was certainly a direct result of research and associated conservation attention being focused on closed-canopy forest formations, and until recently native grasslands received little attention. However, based on advances over the past decade or so, including insightful molecular studies, it is now clear that Madagascar has a considerable diversity of native grasses with several endemic radiations (see Vorontsova et al., pp. 585–98). Further, current information and measures of species diversity indicate that Madagascar is second in endemic grass species only to south-central China (Vorontsova et al. 2020; also see Vorontsova et al., pp. 585–98).

Native grassland ecosystems are threatened on the island; introduced species encroachment and fire, liberally applied as soil amendment and weed control, are two major causes. Composed of both native and anthropogenic formations, grasslands make up more than 75% of the terrestrial land area of Madagascar. The long-held notion that they are derived exclusively as a consequence of human modifications to the environment has been recently challenged (Bond et al. 2008; Vorontsova et al. 2020). Further, in southeastern Madagascar, for instance, a multi-site paleoecological reconstruction demonstrated that the landscape is a natural mosaic of grasslands interspersed with a variety of forest types, and a formation that pre-dates human arrival (Virah-Sawmy et al. 2009b). While major advances have been made in understanding the origins and evolutionary history of the island's native grassland formations, numerous questions remain, some rather controversial, and these are discussed in an insightful contribution by Lehmann et al. (pp. 152–68).

THE MADAGASCAR LANDSCAPE MOSAIC

While the integrated nature of ecological, morphological, and geomorphological systems has given rise to the variety of forest ecosystem types, the landscape mosaic of Madagascar combined with anthropogenic pressures, changing climate, and introduced species has put many ecosystems at risk, associated with isolation from forested corridors and local extirpation events (see Vieilledent et al.

2018, for example). Until recently, available land-cover and land-use maps were not up to date and were unable to capture the subtle spatial and temporal changes in habitat quality at the scale needed to understand patterns of diversity and connectivity across the landscape mosaic through time. This is not simply a question of the presence or absence of forest formations, but also one of forest quality and change through time (see Brown et al., pp. 113–20). In addition, lack of fine-scale habitat data prevents greater understanding of the impacts of climate change on ecological processes and biodiversity, seriously limiting Madagascar's ability to develop and implement comprehensive conservation strategies, and hindering participation in programs like the United Nations Sustainable Development Goals (see Grinand and Nourtier, pp. 105–13). Further, long-term research, as exemplified by Kappeler et al. (pp. 127–32) on the Kirindy Forest CNFEREF (Centre National de Formation, d'Etudes et de Recherche en Environnement et Foresterie), and broad overviews such as patterns of frugivory and seed dispersal by vertebrates (see Razafindratsima et al., pp. 145–52) or the manner in which lemurs use vegetation substrates (see Mertz, pp. 134–41), provide important insight into ecosystem functioning and the critical information needed to advance conservation programs.

Though Madagascar has expanded its protected area system extensively from 3.2 to over 10 million ha in recent decades (see Jones et al., pp. 2130–40), its forests face increased threat directly related to the political landscape and other increasing anthropogenic pressures; the same problem exists for natural grasslands. Anthropogenic pressure on the moist evergreen forests of the island, for example, has intensified, and there is a critical need for further study and documentation before certain zones disappear and particular species become locally extirpated, or extinct in cases of endemics with limited geographic ranges.

Over the past two decades numerous studies have sought to understand forest dynamics and change at varying spatiotemporal scales and with varying methodologies (Green and Sussman 1990; Harper et al. 2007; Vieilledent et al. 2018; Carvalho et al. 2020; Schüßler et al. 2020; also see Brown et al., pp. 113–20 ; Grinand and Nourtier, pp. 105–13). An increase in studies addressing the drivers of change in the context of the vulnerability and resilience of Madagascar's forest ecosystems has initiated scientific discussion on the future state of forested ecosystems (Virah-Sawmy et al. 2009b; Fischer et al. 2014; Railsback et al. 2020; Wan et al. 2020). With the rise in the capability to study landcover, disturbance, land-use change and its drivers, and deforestation at increasingly higher resolution from space, on free and accessible platforms like Google Earth Engine (GEE), an expansion in studies that monitor the impacts of climate change in real time is expected. Concurrent with this rise in the ability to quantify and report the past and present states of forest cover change is the ability to analyze the risk of future degradation, as well as to quantify the subsequent impacts that Madagascar's fire habits, for instance, have and will have on global carbon emission budgets. The overarching goal of these scientific studies, other than to inform the conservation community, is to communicate threats and vulnerabilities to national and international decision-makers. The critical point is that the remaining natural forests of Madagascar provide ecosystem services to the Malagasy people, and without this vegetation cover, the future of the island nation is simply uncertain. Hence, the conservation of natural forests is synonymous with the protection of Madagascar's future.

Subject editors: Amanda H. Armstrong and Steven M. Goodman

FOREST DYNAMICS: CARBON, DRIVERS, AND TRENDS

C. Grinand and M. Nourtier

Over the past 15 years, a multitude of studies have recorded forest dynamics on Madagascar with varying scopes, spatiotemporal frameworks, and methodologies. This profusion of knowledge is undoubtedly explained by the country's invaluable natural resources and biodiversity, but also by its dramatic loss of forests over recent decades. These studies report historical forest cover change and the current intrinsic properties of forests (e.g., tree species, richness, biomass, soil organic matter), identify the drivers of change, combine knowledge to forecast deforestation, and, more broadly, analyze the risk of land degradation. The overarching goal of these studies is to alert and inform the conservation community, particularly decision-makers. Indeed, forest loss leads to important, often irreversible and underestimated impacts caused by shrinking habitat for habitat-dependent plants and animals, changes in water regulation in watersheds, and local to global climate perturbations (modifications of rainfall and water regimes and release of carbon to the atmosphere when trees are removed). Agriculture and land-use changes (AFOLU sector—Agriculture, Forestry and Other Land Use) are responsible for 23% of global anthropogenic emissions (IPCC 2019). Efficient environmental policies and the evaluation of their effectiveness rely on the ability to correctly estimate, map, and monitor forest changes, as well as on our full understanding of the causes of these changes. The objective of this contribution is to present insights into the forest dynamics of Madagascar based on forest cover and biomass change, drivers of change, and estimated future trends using Earth Observation and modeling technologies. Recent scientific studies on the island were fostered by international forest policy and the urgent need for better data and knowledge regarding changes to Malagasy forests.

UNDERSTANDING FOREST DYNAMICS

Forest dynamics are often assessed by the proxy of forest cover, thanks to the use of remote-sensing images and extensive image archives beginning in the 1970s. This enables researchers to have a biophysical, exhaustive, and frequently updated large-scale quantification of forest loss and gain. While essential to increasing our understanding of ongoing changes, remote-sensing methods still suffer from some limitations, especially in capturing ecosystem traits or subtle changes such as selective (legal or illegal) logging and forest regeneration (secondary forest or fallow). The uncertainty and gap between remote-sensing measurements and on-the-ground observations lead to endless debate and policy struggle over the definition of forest, deforestation, and forest degradation to establish reference emission levels (Dezécache et al. 2018), which are required in order to set up and define policy targets as well as measure progress.

Another property of the forest that drives international and Malagasy environmental policy is the carbon storage capacity of forest biomes, as the burning (emissions) of this carbon pool is a key variable for climate change mitigation. This information is estimated from the ground (forest inventory) and can be extrapolated using spatial explanatory variables of biomass stocks, such as elevation or climate. Indeed, location-based national forest inventories aiming to describe and document the ecological state of the forest can be used to estimate biomass at a large scale (Baccini et al. 2012; Vieilledent et al. 2013). These inventories are expensive, yet they are required for implementing environmental policy regarding climate change and conservation. Some authors suggest a link between forest carbon stock and biodiversity, observing more tree biomass in biodiversity-rich areas, but this should be assessed carefully since it is highly region dependent (Labrière et al. 2016).

In order to develop effective actions or policies to tackle forest loss on Madagascar, the causes and drivers of deforestation must first be finely understood. This requires socio-ecological surveys and statistical analyses to identify the most important variables and associated significant correlations. However, since correlation does not necessarily represent causality, expert knowledge is inevitably required to correctly interpret the role of the drivers. Indeed, analysis of forest change based on an international framework usually differentiates between proximate factors and underlying causes. However, the bias of such analyses can be high, as it relies on the survey itself: the types of questions, how the questions are asked, and the number of individuals or villages interviewed and their locations, as well as the statistical analyses carried out on the data collected.

Remote sensing can also help such analyses by identifying spatial factors (topographic or environmental, such as soil distance to forest, cities, etc.) that are correlated to forest cover losses and gains and can be used in prospective analyses. While still not broadly applied to Madagascar, some recent work presented below provides examples of future scenarios of change, highlighting the threats and opportunities of continuing with business as usual compared to scenarios of law enforcement and the development of efficient conservation programs.

FOREST COVER CHANGE

Protocols for measuring forest cover change, including tools to facilitate or reduce the cost of field inventories, satellite data pre- and post-processing methods, and classification algorithms are constantly evolving based on technological progress (GOFC-GOLD 2015). While such technology is operational in many countries (De Sy et al. 2012), challenges remain when it comes to choosing or developing methodologies adapted to country conditions. Madagascar is a large island marked by distinctly contrasting climates (from tropical humid, with rainfall >3000 mm per year, to arid, with rainfall <500 mm per year) and very steep relief in some regions with intact moist evergreen forests (also known as humid forests). Forest resources are highly solicited by rural populations to open up new areas for cultivation, provide building materials or firewood, or remove them via uncontrolled wildfire or illegal mining. Forest area monitoring techniques must consider the biophysical context (frequent cloud cover and steep relief) and the causes of deforestation that shape the landscape (small deforestation plots for cultivation, presence of tree fallows of various ages, and shrubby secondary areas), which are very different from other large-scale forms of deforestation encountered elsewhere in the tropics.

Several studies on forest cover change on Madagascar have been carried out on an island-wide scale: Harper et al. (2007) for the periods 1950-1975-1990-2000, MEFT et al. (2009) for the years 1990-2000-2005, and ONE et al. (2015) for the reference years 2005-2010-2013. Recently, Vieilledent et al. (2018) combined these previous studies for the last six decades and extended the analysis up to 2014 (Figure 4.1). These latter authors identified three main periods of forest change: 1) a high deforestation rate from 1950 to 2000, with more than 90,000 ha per year on average; 2) a slightly decreased rate of deforestation from 1990 to 2005, with around 50,000 ha per year; and 3) a continuous increase since 2005, with an average of 90,000 ha per year. In fact, the deforestation rate more than doubled from 2010 to 2014, compared to the rate from 2000 to 2005. Another island-wide study on the historical trend of deforestation (Hansen et al. 2013), annually updated through the Global Forest Watch portal, shows a similar pattern and reports a steady increase since 2014.

Despite some discrepancies between those studies, which can be explained by different forest definitions, classification algorithms, deforestation rate computation methods (F. Rakotomalala et al. 2015), and cloud removal techniques, there is broad agreement regarding national figures and historical trends. During the last two decades, when the same satellite imagery (Landsat) was mainly used, moist evergreen forests decreased from 4.8 to 4.3 million ha, dry deciduous forests from 3.0 to 2.6 million ha, dry spiny thickets from 1.8 to 1.5 million ha, and mangroves from 0.18 to 0.17 million ha (Vieilledent et al. 2018).

One should note that these studies analyze forest change mainly where forest clear-cutting occurs (e.g., shifting cultivation). The slow decrease in forest cover, and thus carbon stocks (referred to as "forest degradation" in the Intergovernmental Panel on Climate Change [IPCC] guidelines; IPCC 2006), is rarely measured; neither is tree regeneration (forest gain). Forest regeneration at a national scale has not yet been reported and would be more appropriately referred to as secondary regrowth, not recovery of relatively intact natural forest. The other main drawback is the lack

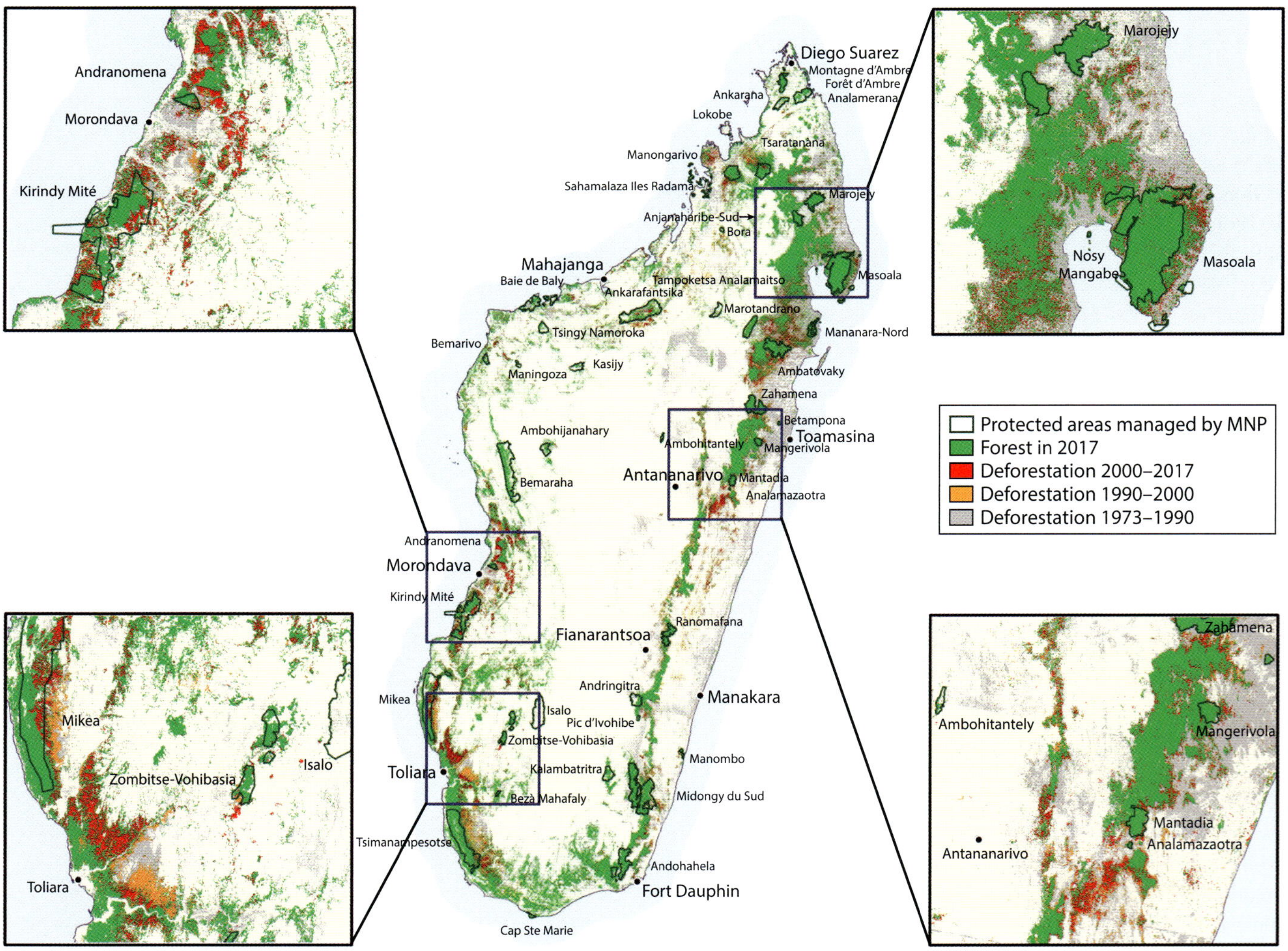

FIGURE 4.1 **Forest cover change from 1973 to 2017.** (SOURCE: modified from Vieilledent et al. 2018.)

of information on forest degradation. Few studies based on remote-sensing technologies have reported the importance of land degradation on Madagascar (Eckert et al. 2011; Allnutt et al. 2013). Eckert et al. (2011) differentiated various levels of degraded forest based on vegetation cover and high-resolution images, while Allnutt et al. (2013) used sub-pixel manipulation techniques to differentiate subtle changes in forest cover. Both of these studies reported that forest degradation is widespread on Madagascar. More recently, F. A. Rakotomalala et al. (unpublished data) found that forest degradation in the entire humid ecoregion from 2000 to 2015 represented a large portion of forest change—30,000 ha per year, more than half the rate of deforestation—confirming previous estimations on a local scale. Monitoring forest degradation on a large scale is still in its early development stage and requires combining information from various Earth Observation sensors (optical, radar, or lidar) that can reveal the vegetation understory or subtle changes in canopy structure (Mitchell et al. 2017).

Monitoring deforestation on a large scale is usually done with supervised classification techniques, as in several studies on Madagascar (Harper et al. 2007; MEFT et al. 2009; Grinand et al. 2013; F. Rakotomalala et al. 2015). This has the advantage of combining local knowledge (visual interpretation of the landcover) with the national forest definition based on tree height and canopy cover. However, these studies can be differentiated by their detection method: either using prior information on deforestation locations and processing the image time series in one step (pre-classification technique); or subtracting two forest maps (post-classification technique). The former requires correct identification of historical changes visually, while the second has the disadvantage of multiplying the errors embedded in both maps.

Global-scale studies are usually based on a rule-based method (decision trees), which can use local knowledge but might not be applicable over the entire island. In Hansen et al. (2013), the global and reference forest change map, as well as vegetation loss and gain information, is derived from analysis of vegetation reflectance change. Vegetation loss is defined as "a stand-replacement disturbance or complete removal or a change from a forest to non-forest state" from 2000 to 2014, omitting the selective removal of trees that does not lead to a nonforested state, this being called "forest degradation." Vegetation gain is defined as "the opposite of loss, or a non-forest to forest change entirely within the 2000–2012 period," omitting areas that might have been considered forest in 2000. While this approach is useful as a first and quick overview of forest change in a specific zone, such methodologies should be considered carefully before adopting them to report forest and deforestation values. As such studies do not include the national forest definition, results can be confounded and may be impacted by crop–fallow rotations, as well as nonforest vegetation in the growing season.

FOREST BIOMASS CHANGE

Estimating carbon stocks of trees necessarily relies on field inventory work. On Madagascar, the first ecological inventory at a national scale was the IEFN national forest inventory (Ministère de l'Environnement 1996). This inventory was conducted in 1993 and covered more than 700 plots representing the different forest types on the island. From 2007 to 2012 several inventories were conducted at regional scales to evaluate the carbon storage of standing trees. These surveys were carried out within different conservation and development projects. Recently, at the national scale, several inventories were conducted and led by the Malagasy government (Direction de la Valorisation des Ressources Forestières, and the Direction Générale de l'Ecologie) within the scope of the national program known as Reducing Emissions from Deforestation and Forest Degradation, sustainable forest management and enhancement of forest carbon stocks (REDD+). In 2014, the Programme Eco-Régional REDD+ des Forêts Humides (PERR-FH) inventoried 567 plots in the moist evergreen forest through a systematic grid for evaluation and monitoring purposes. In 2016, the PERR-FH survey was completed by an inventory of degraded patches of moist evergreen forest (northeastern region, 148 plots). Five classes were used to define the sampling plan for measuring degraded forest: 1) young forest regrowth, called "single layer"; 2) old forest regrowth after swidden agriculture (*tavy*), called "old *savoka*"; 3) agroforestry, zones composed of exotic fruit tree species associated (or not) with native forest trees and crops; 4) mixed *Ravenala* forests; and 5) *Ravenala* forests (MEEF 2017) (Table 4.1). Allometric equations were built for the formations with *R. madagascariensis* and for the young regrowth (Ramananantoandro et al. 2017). In 2017 another important survey inventoried the western dry deciduous forests using a random sampling plan (192 plots). The average values for each of the forest biomes were 262.2 t/ha (± 83.7) for moist evergreen forests and 63.1 t/ha (± 35.1) for dry deciduous forests (Table 4.1). Dry spiny thickets and mangrove forests have not yet been covered by a recent and well-distributed survey. Based on the IEFN (1996) survey, the figure for dry spiny thickets is 20.2 t/ha (± 14.5) (MEEF 2018). A regional study of mangroves shows average values of 168.3 t/ha for aboveground and belowground biomass (T. Jones et al. 2014).

One should note that these recent inventories are all based on ecoregion divisions of the island, defined based on the bioclimatic classification of Cornet (1974) and the vegetation classification from the IEFN national forest inventory (IEFN 1996). Initially, for inventory purposes, forests in the eastern region were stratified using a threshold of 800 m elevation (see PERR-FH inventory). However, an analysis with lidar technology at two sites in moist evergreen forest, one in the north and the other in the south, shows that delimitation based on elevation does not allow the proper separation of classes with significantly different carbon stocks (Asner et al. 2012).

Measuring the carbon contained in trees using field inventory techniques can be a long, expensive, and tedious process. It is possible, however, to optimize this inventory work and reduce the costs of measurement per hectare using techniques that combine satellite images and field inventories. On a pantropical scale, two studies on spatialized quantification of biomass carbon stocks (Saatchi et al. 2011; Baccini et al. 2012) were produced using similar satellite data (MODIS [Moderate Resolution Imaging Spectroradiometer] data and lidar data) combined with field data (forest inventories) and different spatial modeling techniques. Avitabile et al. (2016) combined the two previous studies with other inventory data for calibration and validation and found that these studies overestimated carbon stocks in aboveground biomass by 9–18%. Methods exist to

TABLE 4.1. **Measured carbon stocks in aboveground biomass from the different Madagascar forest inventories**

TREE COVER TYPE	CARBON STOCKS IN ABOVEGROUND BIOMASS (AVERAGE IN MgC ha^{-1})	STANDARD DEVIATION (MgC ha^{-1})	ALLOMETRIC EQUATION USED	SOURCE OF RESULTS	DATE OF INVENTORY
Moist evergreen forests	123.1	39.3	Vieilledent et al. (2012)	PERR-FH (2014)	2014
Dry deciduous forests	29.7	16.5	Vieilledent et al. (2012)	MEEF (2018)	2017
Dry spiny thickets	9.5	6.8	Chave et al. (2014)	MEEF (2018)	IEFN 1993
Mangroves (open to closed canopy)	16–90	Not available	Species specific (see T. Jones et al. 2014)	T. Jones et al. (2014)	2012
Young forest regrowth—"single layer"	74.9	45.4	Vieilledent et al. (2012)	MEEF (2017)	2016
Old forest regrowth	47.3	44.8	Vieilledent et al. (2012)	MEEF (2017)	2016
Agroforestry	21.2	12.7	Vieilledent et al. (2012)	MEEF (2017)	2016
Mixed *Ravenala* forests	74.1	57.2	Ramananantoandro et al. (2017)	MEEF (2017)	2016
Ravenala forests	63.2	50.9	Ramananantoandro et al. (2017)	MEEF (2017)	2016

reduce these uncertainties on a regional scale, using coupling between specific ground inventories (in the area to be characterized) and low-resolution optical satellite data (Le Maire et al. 2011), very high resolution data (Vågen and Winowiecki 2013), hyperspectral data (Gomez et al. 2008), or lidar airborne data (Asner et al. 2012).

On Madagascar, a national mapping of aboveground biomass was carried out in 2015 at a resolution of 250 m, based on a compilation of the historical forest inventories presented above (Vieilledent et al. 2016; 1771 plots). The authors produced a map using regression analysis. The model indicated a root-mean-square error of 44 tC/ha, or about 40% on average at the pixel level. These uncertainties are of the order of magnitude of those recorded with field inventories associated with different measurements and calculation errors inherent in the establishment of allometric equations, estimated to be around 30% (Chave et al. 2004). In addition, carbon maps can be averaged at the level of a given zone (e.g., a protected area), providing more robust and consistent values. Carbon mapping errors are associated with inventory measurements (e.g., field survey, inventory calculation method) and with spatial (e.g., geo-location of plots, under- and overrepresentation) and temporal variables (e.g., time difference between inventory dates, remote-sensing images). Carbon maps are needed to provide an overview of forest patterns, but more importantly, forest carbon change maps and detection are required to evaluate and understand the underlying dynamics.

A recent study on Madagascar for the entire humid ecoregion used field inventory and remote-sensing imagery from 2000 and 2015 to produce two different carbon maps at 30 m resolution (F. A. Rakotomalala et al., unpublished data). The research demonstrated the feasibility of detecting subtle biomass change such as forest degradation (selective logging and small-scale mining), forest regeneration (tree plantation and passive or active regeneration), nonforested regeneration (conversion of degraded soil or croplands into shrublands), and soil degradation (decrease in small vegetation biomass over 15 years). This type of analysis is still under development and requires multidisciplinary perspectives, including those of foresters, biologists, and remote-sensing experts.

DRIVERS OF DEFORESTATION AND FOREST DEGRADATION ON MADAGASCAR

On the island, there is a consensus that deforestation since the 1990s, for the most part, is due to swidden agriculture (Salvaterra and UCL 2017). It is often believed that deforestation is caused by smallholder farmers because of their poverty, subsistence agriculture including shifting cultivation practices, but the reality is much more complex (see Jones et al., pp. 2130–40). Indeed, the first study published on the causes and drivers of deforestation at the national level reveals some unexpected results. Gorenflo et al. (2011) indicated that there are no significant effects of rural population density or poverty level on deforestation, as shown at the global level (Busch and Ferretti-Gallon 2014). A recent regional study covering the period from 2000 to 2010 demonstrated that the correlation between population densities at the regional scale can be successfully used as a variable to project future changes in deforestation rate (Vieilledent et al. 2012). Common spatial analysis approaches to assess drivers of the location of deforestation at national or regional levels are based on a logistic model that involves linear relationships and can be biased when explanatory variables with different granularities are used (Gorenflo et al. 2011). These quantitative studies rely on socioeconomic data, which are usually limited, and when available the data are often aggregated at administrative levels and are rarely up to date. They are analyzed at the same level as other variables, which are available at much finer scales (e.g., biophysical variables or distance variables at a scale of 10 or 100 m). Despite these limitations, some studies agreed on several findings concerning the influence of biophysical and distance data (Gorenflo et al. 2011; Vieilledent et al. 2013; Grinand et al. 2020). Spatial factors such as topography and accessibility (elevation, slope, roads and paths, distance to population centers, etc.) emerge as strongly correlated with the rate of deforestation in the anticipated directions on national or regional scales. More precisely, deforestation decreases with elevation, and it logically increases with accessibility (proximity to roads, paths, and forest edges).

The influence of land tenure factors can have considerable bearing in explaining deforestation and forest degradation patterns. Protected areas appear to be effective in the long term in reducing deforestation and have about half the rates of deforestation of unprotected forest areas (Gorenflo et al. 2011; Eklund et al. 2016, 2019; Llopis et al. 2019). However, dynamics vary locally; for example, rates of forest cover loss are very high in the protected areas of the dry southwest, independent of the type of manager (Madagascar National Parks as compared to nongovernmental organizations [NGOs]). This can be related to the lack of financial means for management and to the difficulty of controlling migration and market-related agricultural expansion (Eklund et al. 2016, 2019; Waeber et al. 2019; Vieilledent et al. 2020). Transfert de Gestion des Ressources Naturelles (TGRN)—a system developed specifically on Madagascar to support communities in the management of natural resources—does not seem to have an effect on deforestation rates (Rasolofoson et al. 2015).

Rasolofoson et al. (2015) also demonstrated that the commercial use of forest products to instill a sense of value for this type of landcover is not an effective solution on Madagascar. Other causes of deforestation or forest degradation identified at the national level are mining and forest exploitation for precious wood, specifically illegal logging of hardwoods of the genera *Diospyros* (see Schatz and Lowry, pp. 739–44) and *Dalbergia* (see Phillipson et al., pp. 598–617) for the international market, construction materials, and to a lesser extent for charcoal or firewood (Salvaterra and UCL 2017). Cyclones and bushfires may also cause significant damage, particularly in the dry areas of the west (Salvaterra and UCL 2017; Vieilledent et al. 2020). Mangroves in Malagasy coastal waters are also subject to deforestation, mainly for fuelwood and timber (T. Jones et al. 2014; Scales and Friess 2019; Waeber et al. 2019).

Subsistence agriculture is the main cause of deforestation in some areas of the island, with swidden-style practices allowing maximization of labor productivity, as farmers benefit from soil fertility temporarily increased by the burning of the forest, and from less competition with weeds. Yet the development of cash crops, included in agroforestry systems, can be a source of increased pressure on forests even if it provides an augmentation of income for farmers practicing swidden agriculture and enables them to gain land and therefore improve their level of lifestyle. This explains why deforestation is not linked to poverty. In addition, swidden agriculture is a way for migrants to obtain land when they settle in a new area. Hence, deforestation cannot be summarized only as the continued search for fertile soils.

Behind this general national summary, there is considerable regional variation that depends on environmental conditions and the type of commercial exploitation. There is nonetheless a lack of fine-scale analysis of agrarian dynamics based on the regional socioeconomic and environmental contexts of the ecological complexity of the island and different cultural traditions. However, several studies show that in the dry areas of the southwest, specifically the regions of the Mikea and Menabe, deforestation is driven by 1) swidden agriculture for cash crops (maize and peanuts) intended mainly for the national market, maize being used mainly for livestock feed (Casse et al. 2004; Vieilledent et al. 2020); and 2) bushfires, which are used for opening or maintaining pastures and easily spread into forests (Vieilledent et al. 2020).

In the humid forest ecoregion of the northeast, while there are large protected areas, numerous cash crops have been developed for international markets, notably vanilla and cloves, sometimes at the expense of the forest. Those developments have enabled households to increase and diversify their income and to improve their well-being, making them less dependent on subsistence farming. However, this increase in income has also led to the reinvestment of part of the revenue in the expansion of cash crop farms by employing a labor force to deforest plots (Llopis et al. 2019, 2020). In the southeast, cash crops are much less developed, and swidden agriculture is practiced for subsistence. Deforestation in that case is the result of people seeking fertile land for agricultural expansion, through the employment of a labor force, and produce is sold in local markets; further, in this area migrants also obtain land for settlement. The question of migrants securing lands has nevertheless been common to all forested regions of the island since colonial times (Moizo 2000; Aubert et al. 2003; Mercandalli and Losch 2017).

Thus, swidden agriculture is practiced either for subsistence or to increase household income via cash crop production for local or international markets (Pollini 2014). This system allows farmers to benefit from the available fertile forest soil without having to spend time fighting weeds in open anthropogenic grasslands. Hence, in order to decrease deforestation, people need to obtain valuable new land (e.g., lowland rice paddies) outside extant forest ecosystems and optimize their labor efforts, for example through irrigation infrastructure, while protecting the remaining forestland with active control (optimization of labor productivity is often not considered when intensifying agriculture).

DRIVERS OF FOREST REGENERATION

Besides the fight against deforestation and forest degradation, another way to protect Malagasy biodiversity and contribute to the mitigation of climate change is to promote natural forest regeneration in the island's different ecoregions. Forest regeneration is often seen as letting trees grow without using the land, but to advance this process requires an in-depth knowledge of ecological processes and potential human interventions. Natural regeneration can be assisted by protecting some spaces from anthropogenic pressures such as fires or active cutting of vegetation. It is the most cost-effective way to restore forest, but it is possible only if there is local acceptance and a political will to enact appropriate policies to promote this technique and protect regenerating forests (Chazdon and Guariguata 2016). Examples of a significant increase in natural forest cover in several countries around the world show that natural regeneration can succeed when certain ecological and socioeconomic conditions are present. It can be effective to target areas with lower interest in agriculture. Hence, Grinand et al. (2020), from a spatial analysis in southeastern Madagascar, showed that areas on high slopes are more likely to be left largely undisturbed and are therefore potential candidates for natural regeneration.

Forest regeneration using monospecific (often introduced) plantations is often preferred by local organizations and government authorities for increasing tree cover because of the trees' rapid growth and easy management, but they do not provide the same ecological services and resilience as native trees (Chazdon and Guariguata 2016). Preference for this type of plantation is also the case on Madagascar, as described in the REDD+ National Strategy (BNC REDD 2018). Such plantations can serve as stepping-stones for wildlife dependent on arboreal structures, and these animals may enter into seed dispersal, as has been shown on a *Pinus* (Pinaceae) plantation in the Central Highlands of Madagascar (Randriambanona et al. 2019). These authors reported that a significant number of native tree species (zoochorous and anemochorous species) can regenerate below *Pinus* cover after selective logging operations. Pines can nevertheless have allelopathic effects on native vegetation (Kull et al. 2014).

Several studies show the importance of ecological conditions in facilitating native forest regeneration. Forest regeneration is assisted by the proximity of a natural forest, directly related to the presence of seed trees and frugivorous dispersers that do not move far from the forest edge (Cubiña and Aide 2001; McConkey et al. 2012). Indeed, on Madagascar a significant number of tree species depend on such dispersers (Ganzhorn et al. 1999; Razafindratsima 2014; see Razafindratsima et al., pp. 142–52). The importance of proximity to the forest edge has also been demonstrated using remote-sensing and spatial-modeling techniques (Vieilledent et al. 2013; Grinand et al. 2020). The presence of forest patches near the main block, or of isolated trees in the open system, can also contribute to the dispersal of seeds across deforested areas, particularly when animal dispersers are not under high local hunting pressure (Martin et al. 2012; McConkey et al. 2012; Razafindratsima 2014). In a meta-analysis, Gardner et al. (2019) asserted that the regeneration of trees with large seeds depends mostly on the presence of primates, which on Madagascar are lemurs, and, of further importance, that such trees are generally associated with high-carbon-stock forests. Loss of large-seed dispersers (primates or others such as fruit bats) can therefore be prejudicial to forest regeneration capacity, impacting biodiversity and carbon stocks.

Regeneration potential also depends on the local ecological conditions of the land and, notably, on competition with herbaceous or introduced species impacting seed germination and seedling survival. The negative impact of introduced species on seedling survival has been shown (Winchester et al. 2018), for example in a gallery forest along the Mandrare River in the extreme south of Madagascar, and such pressures from introduced species are often considered an important threat to Malagasy biodiversity (Irwin et al. 2010; Kull et al. 2014). These non-native plants can also influence soil properties and thus regeneration capacity, as in the case of the *Psidium cattleyanum* (Myrtaceae) invasion of eastern Madagascar (Rajaonarimamy et al. 2017). The previous level of human perturbation, as well as the period since deforestation, the number of past crop–fallow cycles, the frequency of fires, and the degree of cattle grazing will also influence competition with herbaceous or introduced species and the chances of seed survival (Chazdon and Guariguata 2016; Randriambanona et al. 2019). Landscape factor analysis (proximity to forest edge, slope, elevation, human density, vegetation type, etc.) with high-resolution environmental indicators, together with socio-ecological analysis, can be used to identify the most suitable areas in which to implement large-scale Forest Landscape Restoration (FLR) programs.

FUTURE CHANGES

The projection of future deforestation is an important challenge that can help determine forest and agricultural policies as well as potential funding for projects. There are currently no clear, commonly accepted methods or good practices for establishing scenarios for future change in land use. The subject is particularly complex because it requires understanding and quantifying the diverse interactions between the natural and human environments that cause changes, and in most cases these cannot be generalized for a country or even a region in a country. There are two main families of spatialized models for characterizing land-use change: process-based (or agent-based) and pattern-based (or data-driven) models (Castella and Verburg 2007). Process-based models involve the definition of agents, factors, and interactions using scientific expertise and local knowledge. They describe a general and comprehensive functioning, requiring little data but many parameters and hypotheses. The pattern-based model consists of developing statistical relationships between observed changes and factors, most of which are geo-localized. These models make it possible to quantify the importance of factors and spatialize the results, but they require a lot of data.

On Madagascar some pattern-based studies have attempted to draw spatialized scenarios of either forest biomass, or land-cover and land-use change on a landscape or species-distribution scale. Several studies show particular insights into probable forest change on Madagascar: Vieilledent et al. (2016) used climate change scenarios from the Intergovernmental Panel on Climate Change (IPCC) to estimate aboveground biomass change between 2050 and 2080; Grinand et al. (2020) developed scenarios of deforestation, degradation, and land regeneration in the southeast of the island. Recent new technologies and algorithms have combined years of biodiversity records at plot locations with high-resolution spatial data to map probable current and future species distributions (Knoploch 2019; Morelli et al. 2020).

Vieilledent et al. (2016) showed that for Madagascar, climate change is likely to induce a decrease in tropical forest carbon stocks.

This loss could be due to a decrease in average tree size and to shifts in tree species distribution. Indeed, given rapid climate change and the slow dispersal capacity of many tree species, certain species are likely to experience a distribution contraction. This is further exacerbated by climate change leading to widespread tree-mortality events. On a global scale, climate observations and model predictions suggest continued increases in temperature and decreases in precipitation over much of the humid tropics, thus suggesting a potential decrease in tropical tree growth and height in the future. The potential decrease of tropical forest carbon stocks with climate change, leading to a carbon-cycle feedback, might be of at least the same order of magnitude as emissions associated with anthropogenic deforestation.

Grinand et al. (2020) revealed that two national parks, Andohahela and Befotaka–Midongy du Sud, have very different threats and opportunities for land-use change in the future. Andohahela was shown to be potentially weakly affected by land-use change, with less than 3000 ha of cumulative land-use change estimated for the next two decades regardless of the scenario. On the other hand, land-use change in Befotaka–Midongy du Sud could be up to 18% (more than 34,321 ha of change for the next two decades) of its overall area for the business-as-usual "trend" scenario (with a linear increasing projection of the historical trend of deforestation rate) (Figure 4.2). The alternative scenario in this park shows high potential for reduced deforestation and degradation, and a clear pattern of potential regeneration (8253 ha compared to 2180 ha under the business-as-usual "average" scenario, which projects the historical average of the deforestation rate; i.e., a constant rate). The remaining unprotected area around Befotaka–Midongy du Sud shows considerable evidence of both deforestation and land degradation. Deforestation may affect more than 59,613 ha of forested areas in 20 years under the two ("trend" and "average") business-as-usual scenarios (Figure 4.2). The alternative scenario offers a relatively high potential for land regeneration (8485 ha), but this regeneration represents only a small share (0.6%) of the total unprotected area. The main reasons for these differences are the historical conservation activities and socioeconomic conditions in the neighboring communities. Indeed, Andohahela was created in 1939, in contrast to Befotaka–Midongy du Sud, which was created more recently, in 1997. This highlights the effectiveness of long-term conservation activities.

Several recent studies have developed new approaches and knowledge, especially within the scope of BioSceneMada, a five-year research project that simulated biodiversity change on Madagascar according to deforestation and climate change scenarios. Species distribution models (SDMs) based on field surveys and spatial co-variables showed that climate change is expected to decrease the habitat of certain lemur species by more than 60% on average (Knoploch 2019). This potential change is of the same extent as the threat of deforestation, which could be held responsible for a 50% reduction in lemur habitat when taken separately. These results stress that many lemur species are threatened by either climate change or deforestation, or both. Areas where lemurs may be located or displaced because of climate change are referred to as "climatic refuges." The results show that more than 55% of the climatic refuges are outside the current national protected area network. This underlines the need to further develop the current network and to target the most climate-stable sites for conservation priority. Moreover, 75% of

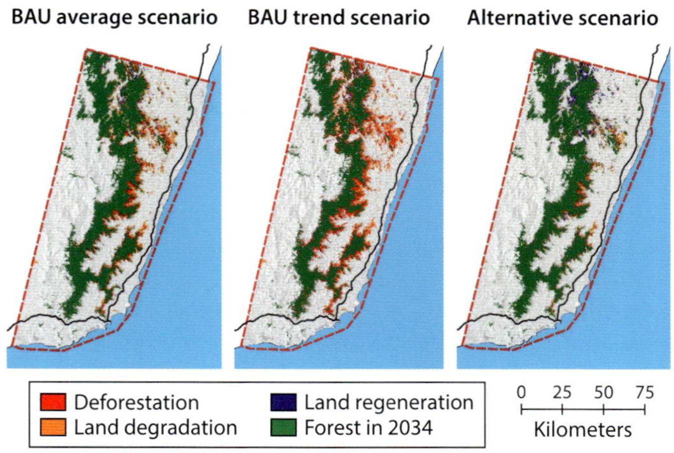

FIGURE 4.2 **Projected land-use change maps for southeastern Madagascar from 2014 to 2034 according to three scenarios.** (SOURCE: modified from Grinand et al. 2020.)

these climatic refuges are threatened by deforestation. These findings were corroborated by Morelli et al. (2020), who reported that suitable habitat for ruffed lemurs (*Varecia*, see Vasey et al., pp. 1957–63) could be reduced by 29–59% from deforestation, 14–75% from a climate change worst-case scenario, or 38–93% from both factors by 2070. These forecasts and spatial outputs of future species distributions will help guide managers, conservation organizations, and the Malagasy government in deciding where to invest their limited conservation resources (Kremen et al. 2008; Carrasco et al. 2020).

FOREST MANAGEMENT AND POLITICAL CONTEXT

Madagascar has a long history of programs for protected area management, which commenced in 1990 with the first Environmental Plan and included three subsequent phases up to 2014 (Langrand and Rene de Roland 2018). With the emergence of international discussion to avoid deforestation within the United Nations Framework Convention on Climate Change (UNFCCC), the REDD+ mechanism—Reducing Emissions from Deforestation and Forest Degradation (REDD), along with the sustainable management of forests, the increase of carbon stocks, and the conservation of forests—gained support from numerous countries, including Madagascar. These early environmental and conservation plans have shifted toward a so-called national REDD+ strategy, with a nationally elaborated preparation and implementation phase, from pilot projects to program and policy.

Madagascar has been committed to the REDD+ mechanism since 2008 and, with the help of the Forest Carbon Partnership Facility (FCPF), created the National REDD+ Coordination Office (BNC REDD+) in 2014 and had its national Readiness Preparation Proposal (RPP) for REDD+ validated in 2014. The REDD+ strategy was published in 2018 and relies on four pillars: 1) improving political and institutional framework, 2) promoting land-use planning, 3) promoting sustainable use of natural resources, and 4) improving living standards of local people associated with alternatives to nonsustainable agricultural practices.

The implementation of this strategy is based on three jurisdictional programs, one of which has started and two of which are still in the planning stage. The first is the Emission Reduction Program in the northeast portion of the island, which was approved by the FCPF in 2018 and for which the contract document known as Emission Reduction Purchase Agreements (ER-PA) was signed in 2019. The other programs still have to be identified; some will target the dry forest ecoregion where action is urgently needed. Unfortunately, the time needed to develop such programs does not reflect the urgency related to forest degradation and destruction in some areas. Hence, to be effective, those programs should start as soon as possible. In its strategy, the Malagasy administration is committed to reducing greenhouse gas (GHG) emissions by 14% in the forest sector before 2030, through increasing forest cover and reducing deforestation and forest degradation, and to increasing carbon absorption capacity (soils and forest biomass) to more than 32% (BNC REDD 2018). Achieving those targets will also contribute to the protection of biodiversity through the conservation of forest habitat. However, carbon sequestration targets include plantations of introduced trees that are not the most suitable species to provide habitat for native biota, although they provide services in terms of energy supply or construction wood as an alternative to natural forest exploitation.

In order to meet its commitments, BNC-REDD+ was merged in 2019 with the National Climate Change Office to form the National Office for Climate Change, Carbon, and Reduction of Emissions from Deforestation and Forest Degradation (BN-CCCREDD+), under the support of the Ministère de l'Environnement de l'Ecologie et des Forêts (MEEF). The mission of this organization is to coordinate the country's preparations to implement REDD+ at the national level by establishing monitoring methods for deforestation, degradation of forests, or plantations adapted to the country, while developing the institutional capacity to implement different mechanisms (benefit sharing systems, registry of emission reductions, mechanisms for payment and redistribution, monitoring, verification, etc.).

In the meantime, Madagascar has increased its area under protection since the declaration of former president Marc Ravalomanana at the Durban World Parks Congress in 2003. Many new protected areas were named under various International Union for Conservation of Nature (IUCN) statutes and manager types (international or national NGOs) (Gardner et al. 2018; Goodman et al. 2018; Waeber et al. 2019). This rapid increase has allowed the country to meet the objectives of what has been called the "Durban Vision" in terms of area under protection. However, these advances have also led to various complications in terms of management capacities, leaving some sites without any relevant conservation actions, sometimes referred to as "paper parks" (Gardner et al. 2018). Moreover, the country's protected area system shows different levels of effectiveness, also according to local socio-ecological conditions and management style (Eklund et al. 2016; Gardner et al. 2018). Most protected areas in the moist evergreen forests managed by Madagascar National Parks (MNP), the organization responsible for the majority of protected areas, show effectiveness (partly because they have been in place for many decades), but that is not the case for MNP sites in the dry western portion of the island (Eklund et al. 2016). As far as the sites managed by NGOs, some studies report that many of these have been launched too rapidly without clear management strategies or a good understanding of the specific socio-ecological conditions (Brimont and Leroy 2018; Gardner et al. 2018). Management is also complicated because neither MNP nor other protected area managers have authority to enforce laws associated with the exploitation of forest resources, leading to a range of complications with local police when bringing offenders to justice. Besides the evaluation of deforestation, knowledge and appropriate methods are lacking to perform relevant monitoring of the ecological effectiveness of Malagasy protected areas, and many managers do not use a landscape approach to document the evolution of biodiversity in the areas they are responsible for (Gardner et al. 2018).

A third mechanism aimed at protecting forest and natural resources on the island was developed in the late 1990s and referred to as Community Forest Management (CFM, or in French, Transfert de Gestion des Ressources Naturelles [TGRN]). The idea is to enable communities to take over the management of natural resources and to guarantee their preservation by making the communities responsible. Moreover, for some, commercial use of resources is possible, giving value to the forest. Thus, several mechanisms combining coercion and incentives, as well as several managers, from the public body to the communities through NGOs, are involved in forest conservation on Madagascar (see Jones et al., pp. 2130–40, for further discussion). Yet Brimont and Leroy (2018) found that the implementation of CFM often reflects the conservation vision of the organizations and not that of the communities. Moreover, they asserted that Madagascar's conservation philosophy is based on two contradictory systems, with protected areas excluding people and their extractive activities versus CFM putting communities at the heart of management. However, according to Rasolofoson et al. (2015), CFM can be effective at reducing deforestation on the island if the use of natural resources for commercial purposes is not allowed.

The REDD+ strategy and its implementation on Madagascar rely heavily on the development of protected areas and CFM. Since 2009, five REDD projects developed by NGOs have been validated by an international standard (Verra) and are implementing field actions in and around recently stabilized protected areas. To establish CO_2 emission reference scenarios, these projects use methodologies with major differences in terms of data, temporal and geographic scales, and techniques for modeling land-use change, making comparisons between sites difficult. Further, until now, forest degradation has not been considered in monitoring systems at national or local levels. This complicates the assessment of effectiveness. At the same time, the country has developed a reference level of emissions (RLE; MEEF 2018) and a monitoring, reporting, and verification system. Evaluation of REDD+ efficiency is in its early stage, since large-scale implementation of activities to incentivize forest protection while redistributing potential benefits is only starting and will require a consistent monitoring system.

CONCLUDING REMARKS

The last official estimations of forest dynamics for Madagascar were made in 2015 (BNC REDD 2018; Vieilledent et al. 2018). The fate of the forests suggests an urgent need to update these estimates and to monitor changes in a timely manner, increase efforts where required, identify notable changes in dynamics (new deforested areas or regeneration dynamics), and assess the impacts of policy. New remote-sensing technologies offer an unprecedented opportunity to overcome barriers to forest change evaluation and technological monitoring. Their resolution offers the possibility of decreasing the minimum detection unit, which may in turn increase certain areas detected as deforested. This would impact and complicate the evaluation and monitoring system of the country but would improve knowledge of forest dynamics (with more accurate and frequent measurements).

Many efforts are required to evaluate and monitor other forest-related properties, such as soil carbon change, biodiversity, and socioeconomic indicators, with the same requirements for precision. Such efforts also involve moving from the "static" mapping of the state and distribution of forest resources to a dynamic analysis of their removal and restoration. With its environmental issues taken into account, Madagascar must develop the tools and methods for monitoring the state of the forest and soils, with strong support from local and national governments, and at the same time respond to the needs of people, particularly those living in the countryside. Indeed, solutions to tackle forest resource depletion need to be adapted to the specific socioeconomic contexts of the Malagasy people, and their efficiency in improving smallholder livelihoods needs to be evaluated in depth.

Subject editors: Amanda H. Armstrong and Steven M. Goodman

ASSESSING THE QUALITY OF REMAINING FORESTS ON MADAGASCAR

K. A. Brown, G. Yesuf, and F. Carvalho

QUALITY OF REMAINING FORESTS: DROUGHT SUSCEPTIBILITY

Over the past 20 years, numerous studies have documented the rapid rate at which Madagascar's forests are disappearing (Ganzhorn et al. 2001; Harper et al. 2007; Vieilledent et al. 2018), and it is certain that such studies will continue to be published to evaluate the state of affairs. Although asking whether forests are "healthy" should be done in parallel with determining whether they are still extant, relatively few studies have documented the "state of health" of Madagascar's remaining forests (Irwin et al. 2010). Nonetheless, this question is also of great importance, since understanding ecosystem function and processes within remaining forests on Madagascar gives greater clarity regarding whether these forests can remain viable as habitat or can provide services to human communities now and in the future. Determining the general health of Madagascar's forests is challenging because of the wide geographic variation in its climate and the difficulty of identifying forest formations across different vegetation zones. It has been suggested that Madagascar has one of the most unpredictable climates on the planet (Dewar and Richard 2007). As a consequence, vegetation across the island exhibits different adaptations to extreme and erratic weather conditions, including floods (Brimont et al. 2015) and droughts (Harvey et al. 2014).

Another major unanswered question is whether the predicted rise in drought intensity will affect Madagascar's remaining forests, which would signal their increasing vulnerability to moisture stress. For example, rainfall is predicted to decline by approximately 20% up to the year 2100 across the island (IPCC 2014). Regionally, rainfall is projected to decrease in the southern region, an effect that is likely to spread along the east coast during June and July, with the southern half of the east coast projected to become increasingly drier by 2050 (Tadross et al. 2008; IPCC 2014). Median rainfall during the warm months (December–March) is predicted to increase across the country, though projections for the northwestern region are inconsistent, and it is unclear whether that region will become increasingly arid or wet in the future (Tadross et al. 2008). It is also expected that during El Niño events, the usual high mean annual rainfall on Madagascar will decrease by approximately 60% (Hannah et al. 2008; IPCC 2014). These expected shifts in precipitation are likely to have significant but unpredictable consequences for the quality of Madagascar's remaining natural forests. Therefore, there is an urgent need to better understand how the quality of the remaining vegetation on Madagascar will be affected by the unpredictable variability in future climate patterns.

With the exception of the Normalized Difference Vegetation Index (NDVI), other remotely sensed vegetation health (VH) indices have not featured prominently on Madagascar (Ingram and Dawson 2005b; Jacquin et al. 2010; Ramifehiarivo et al. 2017), even though they are all excellent tools for monitoring environmental impacts on vegetation. VH indices (including NDVI) have been used elsewhere in the world and allow for the determination of vegetation quality (Gidey et al. 2018). They are valuable for assessing regional and countrywide drought conditions associated with vegetation (Bento et al. 2018). For example, the Vegetation Condition Index (VCI) and the Temperature Condition Index (TCI) have been used extensively to monitor drought in areas outside Madagascar (Kogan 1995, 1997; Quiring and Ganesh 2010). Although NDVI can be a reliable indicator of fluctuations in precipitation (Dutta et al. 2015), VCI is an effective measure of prolonged moisture stress (rather than short-term precipitation deficiency). TCI reflects the relative greenness and temperature of plants (Kogan 1995, 1997) and is a good indicator of land surface temperature. Another important drought index is the Vegetation Health Index (VHI), a combination of TCI and VCI that can be used as an early warning tool for the onset of drought (Seiler et al. 1998). Alternatively, the Enhanced Vegetation Index (EVI) was developed to circumvent biases—such as saturation in high-biomass regions—associated with NDVI and NDVI-derived metrics (Anaya et al. 2009). EVI is an indicator of canopy photosynthetic capacity and can be used to detect leaf phenology (e.g., leaf turnover, leaf flush, leaf senescence) (Huete et al. 1997). EVI correlates positively with gross primary productivity (GPP) across multiple biome types, including temperate forests in North America (Rahman et al. 2005), seasonal dry forests and tropical rainforests in the Amazon (Samanta et al. 2010; Gonçalves et al. 2020), and tropical forests in the Caribbean (Schwartz et al. 2019). To our knowledge, TCI, VHI, and EVI have not been used to assess drought conditions and forest quality on Madagascar.

The aim of this contribution is to assess the state of health of Madagascar's remaining forests. We used two drought indicators to assess the vulnerability of Madagascar's forests to moisture stress, as well as a vegetation quality index to estimate forest sensitivity to continued forest degradation. The two drought indices—TCI and VHI—were implemented to determine whether the island's forests have been exposed to increasing drought intensity over the past two and a half decades. The forest quality index—EVI—was then used to evaluate forest response to environmental change over the past two decades. Our primary objective is to determine whether forests are increasingly susceptible to climate change, with particular focus on drought conditions exacerbated by changes in precipitation.

DROUGHT INDICES ON MADAGASCAR

Data Processing

We assessed spatial and temporal variations of drought conditions on Madagascar from 1995 to 2019 using VHI and TCI, which use satellite-derived imagery from the Advanced Very High Resolution Radiometer (AVHRR). The data sets were downloaded from the National Oceanic and Atmospheric Administration's Center for Satellite Application and Research portal (NOAA 2019) and have a spatial resolution of 4 km^2. The quality of the vegetation canopy was assessed using the EVI from the Moderate Resolution Imaging Spectroradiometer (MODIS) data set (USGS 2021), which has a spatial resolution of 1 km^2. Vegetation canopy assessment was conducted from 2000 to 2019, as MODIS archives commenced in the early 2000s. The VHI and TCI data sets were produced from weekly composites of the best pixels, while the EVI data set was produced from 16-day composites. In addition, VHI and TCI were derived from smoothed normalized vegetation and brightness temperature indices, which are themselves pre-calibrated for the detection and elimination of noise from atmospheric attenuation. As a result, there was no interference from cloud cover in the satellite imagery used in this assessment. TCI and VHI range from "extreme drought" (0 to 10) to "no drought" (50 to 100 for TCI and 40 to 100 for VHI; Table 4.2). EVI ranges from 0 to 1, where high values indicate high biomass and photosynthetic rates, while low values indicate the opposite (i.e., vegetation with low biomass) (Huete et al. 2006). We investigated island-wide annual and seasonal temporal trends, as well as regional variability in drought conditions and forest quality, by comparing annual means of TCI, VHI, and EVI against baseline values (calculated as the overall means for the study period: 1995 to 2019 for TCI and VHI, and 2000 to 2019 for EVI). We used three different periods within a single year to account for considerable seasonal variability in climatic conditions for different regions on Madagascar. We compared island-wide seasonal means of the dry season (26 August), the transition dry-wet season (26 November), and the wet season (26 February) against their respective means for the study periods.

TABLE 4.2. **Classification of remotely sensed drought indices: Temperature Condition Index (TCI) and Vegetation Health Index (VHI)**

CLASSIFICATION	TCI	VHI
Extreme drought	0–10	0–10
Severe drought	10–20	10–20
Moderate drought	20–30	20–30
Mild drought	30–40	30–40
Abnormally dry	40–50	NA[1]
No drought	50–100	40–100

Source: Based on Zou et al. (2020).
Note: Lower values for both TCI and VHI suggest greater drought intensity.
[1] VHI does not have an "abnormally dry" drought class; values ≥40 are considered "no drought." NA, not applicable.

A seasonal trend model (STM) was used to determine pixels with increasing and decreasing drought conditions (i.e., trends) on the island (Forkel et al. 2013). STM allowed for the decomposition of the TCI, VHI, and EVI time series data sets into elements that characterized structural changes during the 25-year and 20-year periods. The model allowed us to spatially categorize each pixel on the island into one of three categories: 1) significant positive trend (absence of drought conditions or increase in photosynthetic activity); 2) significant negative trend (increase in drought conditions or decrease in photosynthetic activity), or 3) no trend (null effect).

Spatial Variability in Drought Conditions

TCI and VHI (using STM) showed increased drought conditions between 1995 and 2019 in the southern and western dry forests (Figure 4.3). VHI (Figure 4.3b) showed a more intense drying trend in the western and southern regions than TCI (Figure 4.3a). Vegetation in the northwestern region was increasingly exposed to a drying trend when VHI was considered (Figure 4.3b), but no change was detected with TCI (Figure 4.3a). Positive trends were detected almost exclusively in the eastern forest corridor, though a

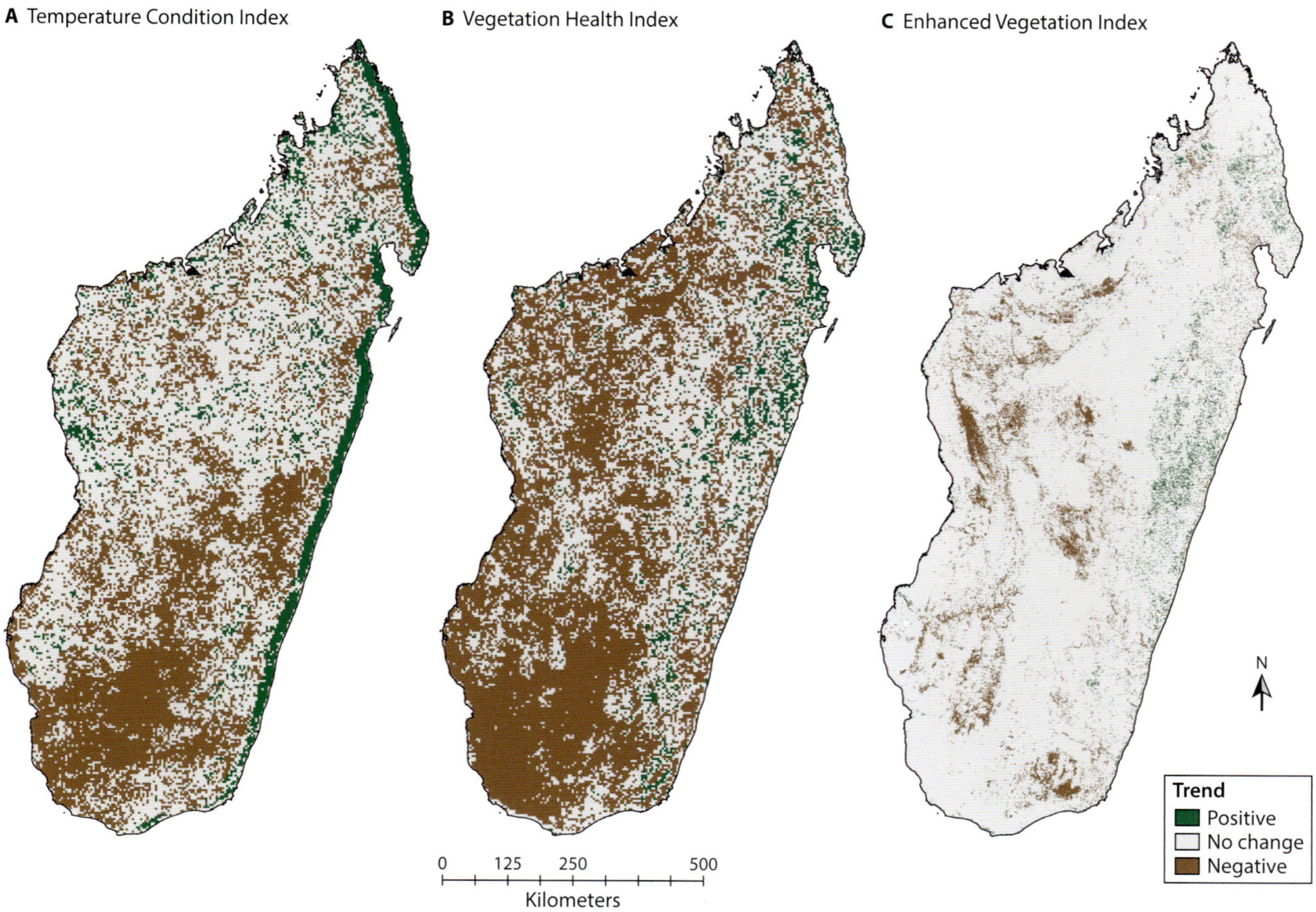

FIGURE 4.3 **Classification of pixels using a seasonal trend model (STM) for the A) Temperature Condition Index (TCI), B) Vegetation Health Index (VHI), and C) Enhanced Vegetation Index (EVI) as input. Areas with positive trends are associated with greening of vegetation (green), areas with negative trends are associated with drying up of vegetation (brown), and areas in gray are associated with null or no change over 1995–2019 for TCI and VHI and 2000–2019 for EVI.**

few areas in the west also showed a positive trend. TCI detected a long strip of positive trends running from north to south (Figure 4.3a), suggesting that vegetation in that portion of the island exhibited high chlorophyll and soil moisture content. This may be because of a combination of gallery forest and/or coastal soils with higher water content. The models also showed that approximately two-thirds of the island experienced no change (i.e., neutral trend) in either TCI or VHI in the past 25 years. This may be because of model sensitivity to natural vegetation or a reflection of large swaths of exposed surface (or rock outcrops) that have remained stable over time. Overall, both TCI and VHI suggest that Madagascar's vegetation was increasingly exposed to soil moisture stress over the study period.

EVI showed a similar pattern to the previous two indicators: there was mostly a positive greening trend along the eastern forest corridor and a negative browning trend in the western and southern regions of the country (Figure 4.3c). These negative trends in the western and southern regions suggest a decrease in photosynthetic rates and biomass over the study period, which may be an indication of forest degradation and forest conversions in those regions (e.g., shift in dominant vegetation from grassland mosaic to entirely grassland).

Temporal Variability in Drought Conditions

According to annual mean values of TCI, "no drought" conditions or "abnormally dry" years prevailed between 1995 and 2004, but years under moderate drought conditions became more common from 2008 to 2019 (Figure 4.4a). VHI values showed mostly "no drought" conditions between 1995 and 2007, but mild drought conditions were predominant from 2008 to 2019 (Figure 4.4b). Island-wide temporal trends showed consistently decreasing values of TCI from 2005 onward (Figure 4.4d) and of VHI from 2008 onward (Figure 4.4e) compared to baseline values, suggesting that the vegetation has been experiencing mild to moderate drought conditions more often in the last 12 to 15 years (2005–2019) than during the first 10 years of the study period (1995–2005). EVI showed relatively low variability between 2000 and 2013 (Figure 4.4c) but became more variable from 2014 to the present, with two exceptionally abnormal years in 2014 and 2017 compared to baseline values (Figure 4.4f).

Severe drought conditions during the dry season were recorded in 2008 and 2013 according to TCI seasonal mean values, with predominantly moderate drought conditions between 2010 and 2019 (Figure 4.5a). Moderate drought conditions also prevailed in the

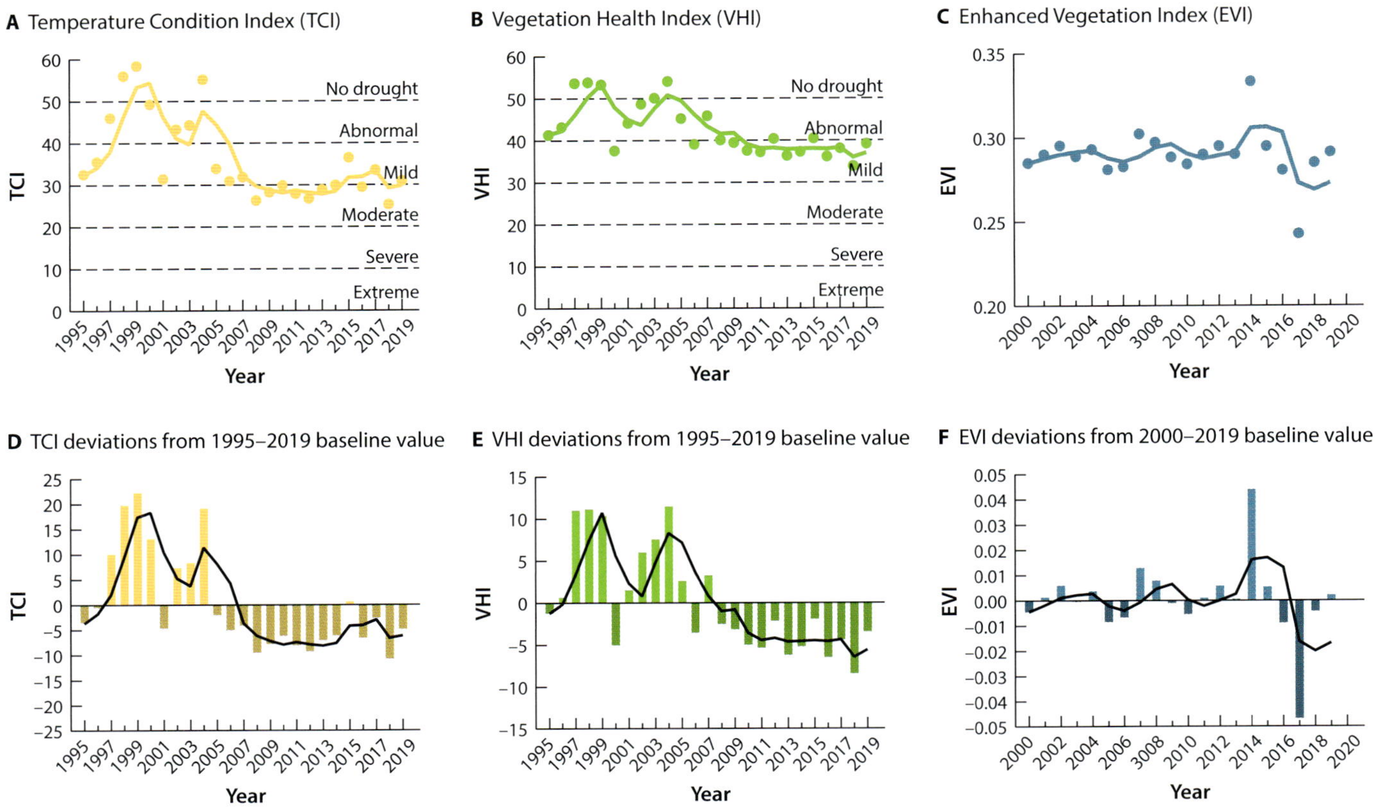

FIGURE 4.4 **Annual means (filled circles) and three-year moving averages (dashed lines) of the A) Temperature Condition Index (TCI), B) Vegetation Health Index (VHI), and C) Enhanced Vegetation Index (EVI) between 1995 and 2019 for TCI and VHI (classification follows that of Table 4.2) and between 2000 and 2019 for EVI. Annual deviations from 1995–2019 baseline values for TCI and VHI and from 2000–2019 for EVI are shown in D), E), and F), respectively, with three-year moving averages shown as black dashed lines. Baseline values are the overall means of TCI (35.89 ± 9.88, 1 SD) and VHI (42.41 ± 6.20, 1 SD) for 1995–2019 and of EVI (0.29 ± 0.02, 1 SD) for 2000–2019. Mean annual values higher than the long-term average are in light red, light green, and light blue, and those lower than the long-term average are in dark red, dark green, and dark blue for TCI D), VHI E), and EVI F), respectively. SD: one standard deviation of the mean.**

mid-season (transition) during the same period (Figure 4.5b), but the wet season experienced mostly mild drought conditions from 2010 onward (Figure 4.5c). The declining trend in seasonal TCI values was more consistent in the dry season (Figure 4.5d) than in the transition (Figure 4.5e) and wet seasons (Figure 4.5f), particularly between 2010 and 2019.

Seasonal VHI results showed mainly no drought conditions from 1995 to 2007 for the dry (Figure 4.6a) and transition (Figure 4.6b) seasons, but mild drought conditions were predominant afterward. The wet season seems to have been less affected, with "no drought" conditions prevailing throughout most of the last two and a half decades (Figure 4.6c). As with TCI, the declining trend in seasonal VHI values was more consistent in the dry (Figure 4.6d) than in the transition (Figure 4.6e) and wet (Figure 4.6f) seasons, particularly from 2008 onward. Generally, these results suggest that the vegetation on Madagascar has been increasingly exposed to moisture stress in the last 10 years (2010–2019). The trend is somewhat more accentuated for TCI than for VHI and for the dry season than for the transition and wet seasons.

Seasonal EVI values showed an expected "brown-down" in the dry season as a result of water stress (Figures 4.7a and d) and consequential declining photosynthetic capacity. There were both positive ("green-up") and negative anomalies during the transition months (Figures 4.7b and e), while the wet season exhibited mostly a positive anomaly, indicating "green-up" and increased photosynthetic activity during that period (Figures 4.7c and f). Exceptionally, there was a strong positive anomaly in EVI in 2014 during the dry season, suggesting a flush of new leaf growth during the typical dry season, and another very strong negative anomaly in 2017 during the wet season, indicating leaf senescence during a period when the opposite is expected to occur.

Implications and Summary

Our findings suggest that vegetation on Madagascar, particularly in the southern and northwestern regions, has been increasingly exposed to moisture stress in the past 10 years, which is likely driven by climate-induced changes in precipitation patterns. This coincides with future predictions suggesting decreased rainfall and drought for those regions (Hannah et al. 2008; IPCC 2014). The extent to which the vegetation's exposure to moderate and mild drought conditions will affect ecosystem function or community structure on Madagascar is unclear. Previous studies suggest that the prevalence of drought conditions may lead to notable changes

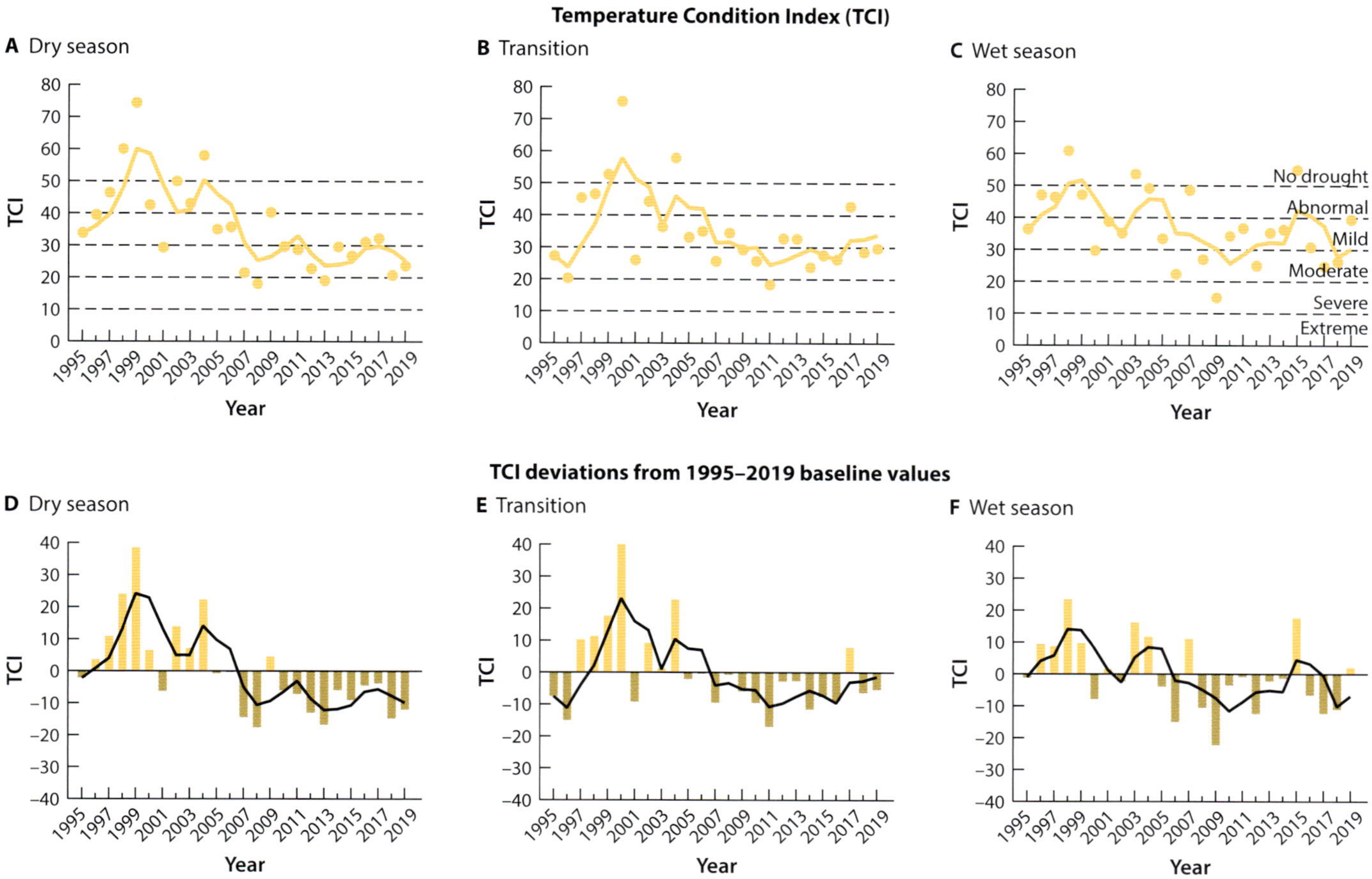

FIGURE 4.5 **Annual means (filled circles) and three-year moving averages (dashed lines) of the Temperature Condition Index (TCI) for the A) dry (August), B) transition (November), and C) wet (February) seasons (TCI classification follows that of Table 4.2). Seasonal deviations from 1995–2019 baseline values for the dry, transition, and wet seasons are shown in D), E), and F), respectively, with three-year moving averages shown as black dashed lines. Baseline values are the overall seasonal means of TCI for the dry (35.49 ± 13.94, 1 SD), transition (34.92 ± 13.03, 1 SD), and wet (37.25 ± 11.33, 1 SD) seasons for 1995–2019. Mean seasonal values higher than the long-term average are in light red, and those lower are in dark red. SD: one standard deviation of the mean.**

in the structure, composition, and function of Madagascar's vegetation communities (Ingram and Dawson 2005a; Virah-Sawmy et al. 2009a, 2009b), which is a general trend across Africa, where aridity has increased since the 1970s (Dai 2011). In Madagascar's southeastern moist evergreen forests, rainfall variability, exacerbated by drought conditions and intense dry periods, is known to drive shifts in tree phenology, with the peak of both fruiting richness and intensity shifting to later months (Dunham et al. 2018). Shifts in the periodicity of tree phenology are likely to have far-reaching impacts across trophic levels and to influence interactions between the vegetation and seed dispersers, seed predators, and frugivores (see Razafindratsima et al., pp. 142–52). Moreover, droughts have been linked to increasing rates of tree mortality in tropical forests (Phillips et al. 2009; Portillo-Quintero et al. 2015) and have been shown to amplify tree mortality in a number of forest types and climatic zones (Allen et al. 2010; Phillips et al. 2010), suggesting that mortality rates of trees in tropical forests can increase disproportionately with increasing levels of moisture stress.

Our findings contradict recent regional-scale NDVI estimates investigating the response of vegetation to increased temperatures in southern Africa that suggest future warming will likely lead to increased vegetation productivity on Madagascar (Lawal et al. 2019). Although all three metrics used here support this finding, EVI explicitly assesses vegetation productivity and biomass, and that metric does not show an increase in Madagascar's productivity over the study period. The contrasting findings are likely a consequence of the scale at which the two studies were conducted, with Lawal et al. (2019) unable to measure the nuances (e.g., seasonality) associated with the many different vegetation types on Madagascar, since that study was undertaken at a broad regional scale, as compared to focusing only on Madagascar. For instance, Jacquin et al. (2010) assessed grassland vegetation cover degradation on Madagascar using NDVI MODIS and found both positive and negative degradation trends, highlighting differences in results between single-country and multi-country analyses.

Although there has been no direct investigation of the current impact of drought on Madagascar's vegetation, paleoecological studies may help elucidate current patterns. Vegetation transitions as a consequence of moderate to severe drought have been documented on Madagascar during the Holocene (Virah-Sawmy et al. 2009b; 2010). For instance, southeastern Madagascar has experienced significant climatic aridity that may have triggered vegetation

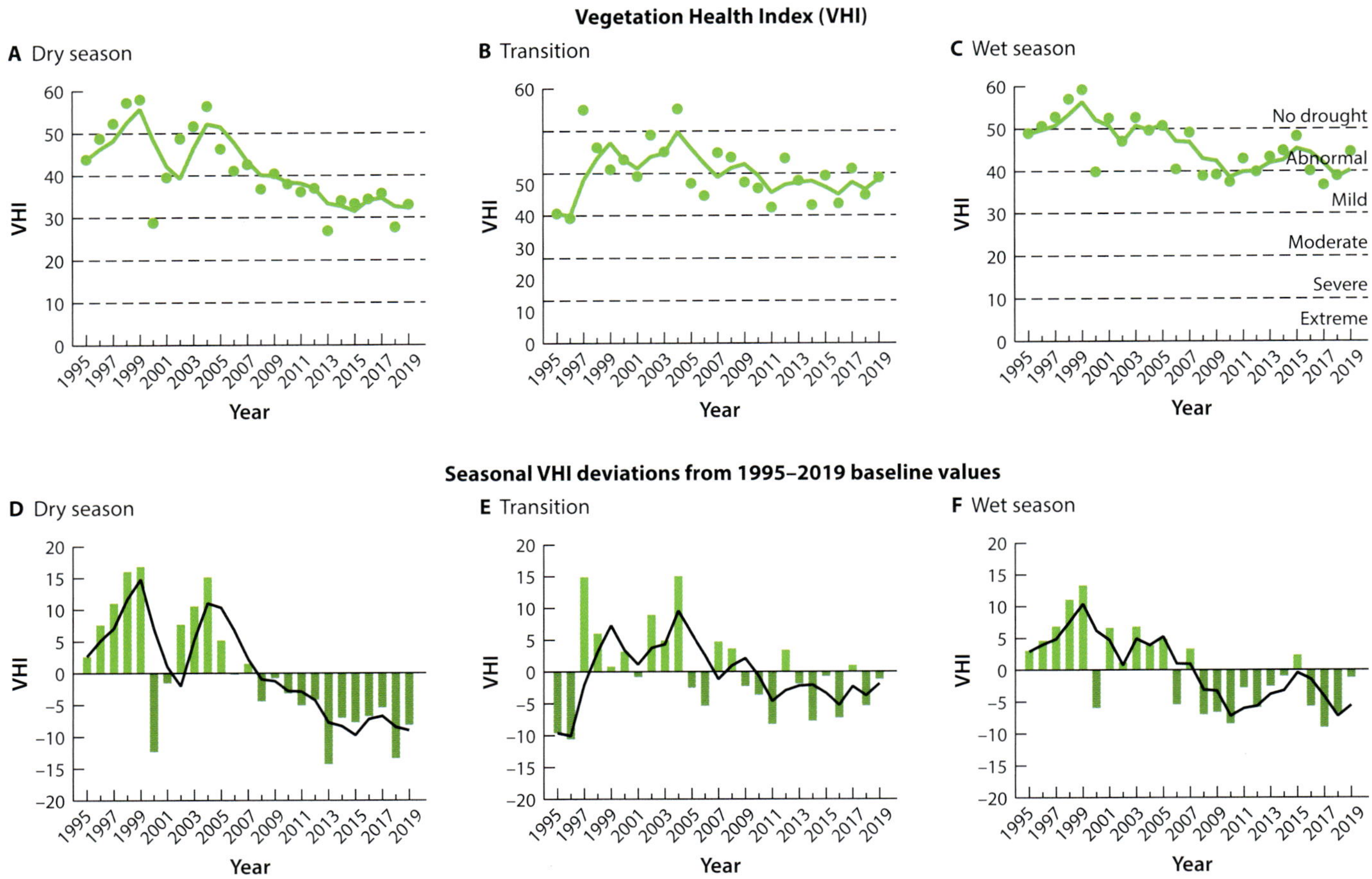

FIGURE 4.6 **Annual means (filled circles) and three-year moving averages (dashed lines) of the Vegetation Health Index (VHI) for the A) dry (August), B) transition (November), and C) wet (February) seasons (VHI classification follows that of Table 4.2). Seasonal deviations from 1995–2019 baseline values for the dry, transition, and wet seasons are shown in D), E), and F), respectively, with three-year moving averages shown as black dashed lines. Baseline values are the overall seasonal means of VHI for the dry (41.17 ± 9.17, 1 SD), transition (40.18 ± 6.83, 1 SD), and wet (45.88 ± 6.35, 1 SD) seasons for 1995–2019. Mean seasonal values higher than the long-term average are in light green and those lower are in dark green. SD: one standard deviation of the mean.**

transitions and species compositional changes from forests to ericoid and *Myrica* grasslands (Virah-Sawmy et al. 2010). Therefore, long-term aridification (over centuries) could have led to regional transformation of Madagascar's vegetation, from forested ecosystems to open grasslands in the southeast, northwest, and the Central Highlands (Virah-Sawmy et al. 2009b; Burney 1987a, 1993). However, there is disagreement as to whether Holocene aridification is driven by climate (natural) or deforestation. Crowley et al. (2017) suggested that these transitions may have been driven by anthropogenic factors (i.e., an increase in agro-pastoralist lifestyle) and were completely unrelated to drought. Additionally, an analysis of speleothems on Madagascar by Burns et al. (2016) showed a complete transformation from C_3 (woody) to C_4 (mostly grass) vegetation within one century, and this shift was unrelated to changes in precipitation. Regardless, current transformation of Madagascar's ecosystems is certainly driven by both climate and deforestation (Morelli et al. 2020) and, importantly, each of these is anthropogenic.

Simulation studies also offer a proxy for explaining how Madagascar's remaining vegetation may respond to drought conditions. Fischer et al. (2014) simulated the response of Madagascar's forests to forecasted declines in rainfall. The study predicted a shift in species composition from shade-tolerant trees to intermediate light-tolerant species better adapted to reduced rainfall. The authors also suggested a threshold response from vegetation: annual rainfall levels below 2100 mm (30% of current values) would significantly reduce biomass and productivity. If annual rainfall declined below 1500 mm (50% of current values), aboveground net primary productivity and carbon stocks would decrease by approximately 20%.

Droughts are also a direct threat to people's livelihoods, considering that a significant proportion of water on Madagascar is used by the agricultural sector for irrigation (96%), with a smaller proportion used for domestic consumption (2.9%) (Aquastat 2016). Even without drought, in terms of total rainfall, a delay in the onset of rains will reduce the growing season and affect agricultural productivity. Moreover, droughts can be a significant driver of forest degradation and deforestation on Madagascar, with important eco-regional distinctions (Desbureaux and Damania 2018). For example, between 2000 and 2013 drought-modulated

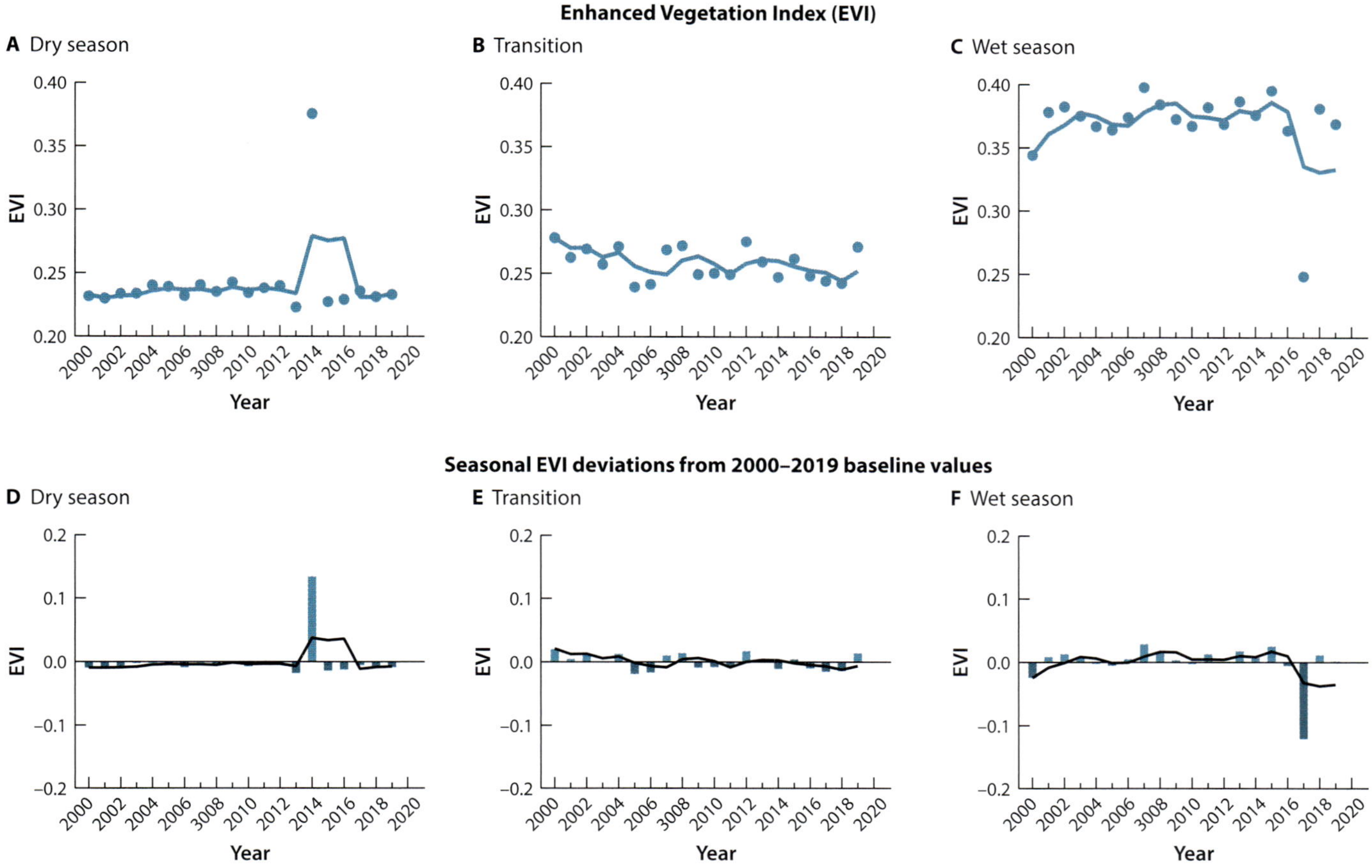

FIGURE 4.7 **Annual means (filled circles) and three-year moving averages (dashed lines) of the Enhanced Vegetation Index (EVI) for the A) dry (August), B) transition (November), and C) wet (February) seasons (EVI classification follows that of Table 4.2). Seasonal deviations from 2000–2019 baseline values for the dry, transition, and wet seasons are shown in D), E), and F), respectively, with three-year moving averages shown as black dashed lines. Baseline values are the overall seasonal means of EVI for the dry (0.24 ± 0.03, 1 SD), transition (0.26 ± 0.01, 1 SD), and wet (0.37 ± 0.03, 1 SD) seasons for 2000–2019. Mean seasonal values higher than the long-term average are in light blue, and those lower are in dark blue. SD: one standard deviation of the mean.**

deforestation and degradation were highest in the semiarid southern region, while in the humid eastern regions deforestation was unaffected by drought.

EVI is more likely to detect changes in biomass as a consequence of land-use change, for instance forest conversion to cropland, or forest degradation (Samanta et al. 2010). Therefore, the EVI trend analysis suggests that the western and southern regions of Madagascar have undergone relatively higher rates of forest conversion and degradation over the 20-year period covered by that metric compared to the eastern region. This effect is particularly severe in the southern region of the country, which harbors the vegetation zone (dry spiny thickets) estimated to have experienced the largest increase in forest degradation between 1994 and 2014 (Table 4.3; Yesuf et al. 2019). Moreover, anthropogenic disturbances, as evidenced by forest degradation measured by Allnutt et al. (2013) and Yesuf et al. (2019), undermine the conservation value of tropical forests. Barlow et al. (2016) found that forest degradation was partly responsible for declines in species of high conservation and functional value (e.g., plants with high wood density) in tropical forests in the Amazon basin. Disturbance has indeed recently been found to increase the proportion of trees with lower wood density and small-seeded species in tropical forest ecosystems (Hawes et al. 2020). This is most likely the case on Madagascar. Brown et al. (2013) showed that local communities in eastern Madagascar preferentially target trees with a particular suite of functional traits for certain provisioning ecosystem services, since plants with high wood density and thick bark are most often used for firewood. Therefore, local communities that rely on ecosystem services provisioned by Malagasy native forests seem to inadvertently modulate community assembly and functional trait expression through daily livelihood activities (Neugarten et al. 2016). This in turn acts as a negative feedback loop that leads to the ever-decreasing availability of preferred species vital for local people's livelihood and well-being. Consequently, forest degradation not only undermines the quality of remaining forests but also has long-lasting effects on ecosystem processes and services, since wood density is one of the most important predictors of carbon storage in forest ecosystems (Chave et al. 2006) and a key component in determining the drought sensitivity of tropical forests (Phillips et al. 2009).

TABLE 4.3. **Summary of forest degradation rates of the different vegetation zones on Madagascar**

VEGETATION TYPE	DEGRADATION (ha)		RoC (% yr^{-1})
	1994–2002	2002–2014	
Dry spiny thickets	13,217	15,039	0.14
Lowland moist evergreen forests	42,938	46,702	0.09
Littoral forests	135	143	0.06
Dry deciduous forests	22,775	17,602	–0.23
Medium-altitude moist evergreen forests	43,305	32,457	–0.25
Sclerophyllous woodlands	2142	834	–0.61

Source: Modified from Yesuf et al. (2019).
Note: Rates in each vegetation zone are listed in descending order of rate of change (RoC) percentage per year.

CONCLUSIONS

This study suggests that Madagascar's vegetation has been increasingly exposed to moderate to mild moisture stress, as evidenced by decreased chlorophyll and soil moisture content over the 25-year study period for TCI and VHI (1995–2019). These results are complemented by the forest quality index (EVI) suggestion that the state of health of Madagascar's forests is unsatisfactory, particularly in the western and southern regions, where the effects of forest degradation seem to modulate a trend promoting vegetation with relatively low biomass. Therefore, it is likely that the coupled effects of increased moisture stress and forest degradation for certain regions will erode the quality of the remaining vegetation on Madagascar. Moreover, our understanding of the current "state of health" of the island's remaining forests is poor. There are few recent studies investigating whether climate-induced droughts have affected forest health on Madagascar. Authors continue to assess the effects of anthropogenic disturbances on aboveground carbon stocks (Asner et al. 2012), soil carbon stocks (Grinand et al. 2017; Ramifehiarivo et al. 2017), and the deterioration of plant functional traits and ecosystem function (Razafindratsima et al. 2018c). However, unlike in other regions such as the Amazon basin, very few studies have investigated the impact of already observed and documented drought-like conditions and moisture stress on Madagascar's remaining forests. This knowledge gap should be addressed in the coming years. In this regard, future work should examine broad patterns suggested by remote-sensing techniques at the ground level and improve our understanding of the mechanisms of forest degradation and forest loss. Future research should leverage findings from remote-sensing and simulation studies that record current and future forest changes to improve ground-based methods that help us better understand the mechanisms of forest degradation, loss, or, more hopefully, recovery.

Subject editors: Amanda H. Armstrong and Steven M. Goodman

TAPIA WOODLANDS

C. A. Kull and C. R. Birkinshaw

Tapia woodlands (*bois de tapia*), named after the Tapia (*Uapaca bojeri*, Phyllanthaceae; see Ralimanana and Challen, pp. 649–54), the dominant tree species that is uniquely found in this vegetation type, are a type of vegetation, also referred to as sclerophyllous woodland (Gautier et al. 2018), found in the highlands of central and southwestern Madagascar (Figure 4.8a). These woodlands are a form of grassland, differentiated floristically from the scattered forest patches found in riparian areas and upland hollows in same region (C. Solofondranohatra et al. 2018). Humbert (1965) classified the tapia woodlands as part of the Western Slopes sector of the Central Domain vegetation region; Cornet and Guillaumet (1976) labeled the woodlands an anthropogenic formation within the "subhumid" vegetation stage (Lowry et al. 1997). This contribution surveys tapia woodlands, looking at their characteristics, origins, use by humans, and management, especially by fire.

FIGURE 4.8 **A) Typical hillside in the Col des Tapia zone between Antsirabe and Ambositra. Valley bottoms are cultivated with rice, lower hillslopes host tapia woodlands, and ridges include rare crop fields and open grassland used as pasture. B) Tapia woodland on the Ibity Massif showing open canopy and a grass-dominated ground layer.** (PHOTO A by C. Kull and B by C. Birkinshaw.)

TAPIA WOODLANDS

Tapia woodlands are found in several small clusters around the Central Highlands (Figure 4.9). The four major zones include Imamo, near Arivonimamo and Miarinarivo; the Col des Tapia between Ambositra and Antsirabe; Itremo, west of Ambatofinandrahana; and Isalo. They cover approximately 1319 km^2 (Moat and Smith 2007). Areas of tapia woodland are now included within three protected areas: Itremo, Ibity, and Isalo. These represent about 30% of the total remaining area of this vegetation type. Itremo and Ibity are both new protected areas (Goodman et al.

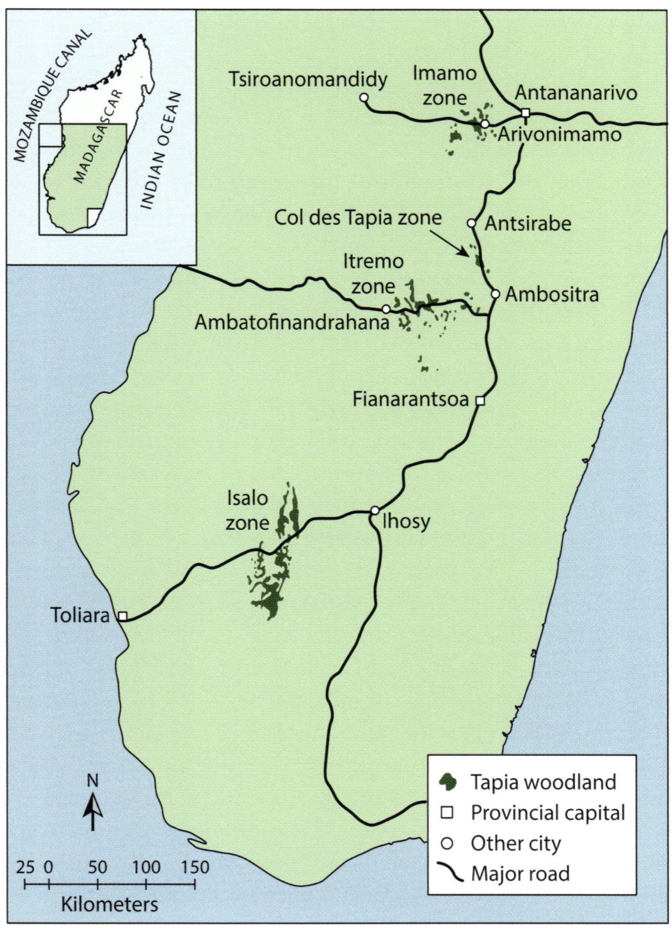

FIGURE 4.9 **Locations of tapia woodland zones on Madagascar.** (SOURCE: based on Foibe Tao-Tsaritan'i Madagasikara 1:500,000 series maps.)

FIGURE 4.10 **A) *Uapaca bojeri* tree; B) thick protective bark of *U. bojeri*; and C) stem of *U. bojeri* showing epicormic growth shooting up after cutting and burning.** (PHOTOS by C. Birkinshaw.)

2018), and much of the tapia woodland within these sites is included in zones of sustainable use (Zones d'Utilisation Durable) so that local people can continue to use the benefits traditionally derived from this vegetation.

Tapia woodlands are found at elevations ranging from 800 to 1800 m, in the bioclimate class "sH1e" of Cornet (1974), defined as subhumid with a distinct dry season of seven months from May to October, albeit attenuated by occasional winter clouds and drizzle. Precipitation ranges from 1000 to 1500 mm per year, and the mean annual temperature ranges from 17°C to 22°C. Worldwide, such climates are associated with fire-prone ecosystems (Hoffman et al. 2012) since there is sufficient rain to allow highly combustible C_4 grasses to grow abundantly but also a marked dry season that allows them to burn, and the tapia woodland is no exception. Edaphic factors also determine tapia woodland distribution; most are found on nutrient-poor rocky soils underlain by granites and gneisses.

Tapia woodlands are also known as mid-elevation sclerophyllous forests or western-slope sclerophyllous forests of the Sarcolaenaceae–*Uapaca bojeri* series (DEF 1996; Lowry et al. 1997). Most of the tree species in this habitat are similarly shaped, with tortuous trunks, low branches, and dull, dark green, fleshy or leathery leaves; maximum trunk diameters typically attain 40 cm, while the maximum height is between 8 and 12 m (Alvarado et al. 2014) (Figure 4.10a). The canopy of tapia woodland is more or less open (hence, following White 1983, the use of the term "woodland" rather than "forest" to describe this vegetation), with a shrub layer and a well-developed ground layer of grasses and forbs (Figure 4.8b).

As far as floristic composition, ecological surveys in the Col des Tapia, Ibity, and Itremo woodlands have found, respectively: 15, 12, and 11 tree species; 34, 21, and seven shrubs or nonherbaceous woody species; and *, 87, and 66 herbaceous species (*not recorded in Col des Tapia). The surveys were based on 30 (Ibity) and 21 (Itremo) plots of 1600 m^2 (Alvarado et al. 2014) and on a dozen plots of 500 m^2 at Col des Tapia (Kull et al. 2005). Tapia woodland is remarkable among the "natural" woody vegetation types of Madagascar in that the canopy is dominated by one tree species, *U. bojeri*. For example, in the tapia woodland at Col des Tapia, Ibity, and Itremo, this species represents 88%, 92.8%, and 78.7% of the canopy trees (Kull 2002; Alvarado et al. 2014). The shrub layer includes several species in the Sarcolaenaceae family (*Leptolaena*, *Schizolaena*, and *Xerochlamys*) and several *Erica* species, as well as *Vaccinium secundiflorum*, *Aphloia theiformis*, and *Asteropeia densiflora*. The ground layer includes numerous species from the Poaceae, Cyperaceae, Asteraceae, Lamiaceae, and Orchidaceae families—all species that are characteristic of grassland, rather than of degraded forest (C. Solofondranohatra et al. 2018). The species at these study sites, except for recently introduced *Pinus* spp. and *Eucalyptus* spp., are all native to Madagascar, and many are either regionally or locally endemic.

Sharing the landscape with tapia woodlands are vast areas of grassland and shrubland (sometimes dotted with more or less isolated *U. bojeri*) and small areas of moist evergreen forest. This forest formation is restricted to valley bottoms, which are better watered and sheltered from wildfires, and it is sometimes also found on steep south-facing, and therefore shady, slopes. The tapia woodland and neighboring evergreen forest share almost no plant species (C. Solofondranohatra et al. 2018). There is an abrupt transition between these relatively inflammable forests (where light-loving and highly combustible C_4 grasses are absent because of the dense canopy) and the surrounding flammable grassland, including tapia woodland.

ORIGIN OF TAPIA WOODLANDS

The extent to which tapia woodlands are natural or derived under anthropogenic pressures, especially fire, is uncertain. Analysis of lake sediment cores (Burney 1987b) originating from a landscape that now includes tapia woodland shows that immediately prior to the time of presumed human settlement within this landscape, estimated in this study to be between 1500 and 2000 BP, wildfires were present in the landscape and the vegetation included grassland, scrubland, and woodland and/or closed-canopy forest. These cores also show that around the time of human colonization here, there was an increase in fire frequency, a decrease in trees, and an increase in grasses and forbs. Pollen of *Uapaca* is present in the cores prior to human settlement but not abundantly so, and it is also uncertain whether this pollen originated from *U. bojeri* or a different forest-dwelling species in this genus.

The presence today of a species-diverse grassland flora constituting the ground layer in tapia woodland, overwhelmingly dominated by native plants and including many locally endemic species, supports the notion that this flora is not recently derived (Bond et al. 2008). However, as reported in woodlands elsewhere (e.g., Lawton 1978; Chidumayo 1989), it is probable that the increased fire frequency and especially the increased frequency of unseasonal fires led to a reduction in canopy cover and the loss of tree species that are less resilient and resistant to burning than the currently dominant *U. bojeri* (Gade 1985; Rakotondrasoa et al. 2012; Alvarado et al. 2014). Manzi (2019) reports that a similar process has led to the *Bismarckia nobilis*–dominated grassland in western Madagascar.

Certainly *U. bojeri* possesses the attributes of a fire-adapted grassland tree, as opposed to a forest tree, as described by Hoffman et al. (2012). These attributes include seeds whose germination and growth is favored in sparse grassland (such as after burning) and by direct sun exposure; young plants that accumulate protective bark (Figure 4.10b), enabling survival and rapid resprouting after top-kill from burning; leathery leaves that resist burning; and, should burning occur, the ability of new shoots to penetrate the bark to replace burnt stems (so-called epicormic spouting, Figure 4.10c) (Kuhnholtz-Lordat 1938; Koechlin et al. 1974; Rakotoarivelo 1993; Rasoafaranaivo 2005).

Apart from *U. bojeri*, other species occurring in tapia woodland have at least some tolerance to fire, and Rasoafaranaivo (2005) showed that burning in the wild did not increase mortality of mature plants compared to unburnt plants of any of a sample of 10 tapia woodland species. Rasoafaranaivo (2005) also showed that burnt individuals of most of these species were able to recover their pre-fire condition quite rapidly, although for some, flowering and fruiting were reduced in the season after burning compared to unburnt plants. However, Alvarado et al. (2015) found that high temperature, such as might be caused by fire, did not stimulate germination for any of six tapia woodland species, and that burning killed a large proportion of seedlings of four woody plants typical of tapia woodland, including *U. bojeri*, especially when the plants were small.

It is thus likely that today's tapia woodland is to some degree structurally and floristically different from its form prior to human settlement. Its fauna too is almost certainly different. The prehuman version of this vegetation provided habitat for a much wider diversity of large animals than today. For example, giant tortoises, now extinct, were certainly present and perhaps abundant in this landscape (Goodman and Jungers 2014; see Godfrey and Douglass, pp. 191–97). The cause of extinction of such animals is still hotly debated but is probably at least partly the result of hunting by human colonizers (Crowley 2010). Currently the fleshy palatable fruits of *U. bojeri* are undispersed except by humans, and presumably the past fauna would have included one or more seed dispersers for this plant. Furthermore, some of the lost fauna would have been herbivores, and their loss may have caused an accumulation of grassy biomass, leading to more frequent and more intense fires (Crowley 2010).

ECONOMY AND SUBSISTENCE

People living near tapia woodlands gain revenue and subsistence resources from tapia woodland products, including marketable fruit, wild silk, and firewood. Tapia leaves are the preferred fodder for *landibe*, an endemic silkworm (*Borocera madagascariensis*, Lepidoptera: Lasiocampidae). *Landibe* produces cocoons twice a year, in November–December and May–June. Production varies immensely from year to year in both quantity and location. Villagers painstakingly gather cocoons from tree branches, leaves, and grass tufts. The chrysalis is eaten, and the empty cocoons are cooked, spun, and woven into silk fabrics. Much *landibe* silk is used to produce ritual burial shrouds, *lambamena*, for funerals and reburial ceremonies (*famadihana*) throughout the Central Highlands (Gade 1985; Kull 2002), and for a variety of scarves and shawls that are sold locally and to tourists.

This silk-based economy has been important for several centuries, serving as a source of government revenue through royalties and concessions in both precolonial and colonial times. In the 1940s, the government began to establish silk cooperatives; collection and commercialization was limited to members, and guards watched for illegal harvesting. These cooperatives dissolved in the 1960s following independence. Currently, local governments exercise little, if any, control over silk harvesting and commerce.

The November–December silk harvest provides crucial cash income during the meager months before the rice harvest. In the Col des Tapia region, two-thirds of households collect *landibe*, one-third earn cash income from the harvest, and one in five women is involved in spinning and weaving. In 1998, 200 female *landibe* cocoons sold for 100–150 MGA or US\$0.10–0.15, and a finished 2 × 2 m *lambamena* for between 30,000 and 60,000 MGA (US\$30–60) in Antananarivo (Kull 2002; Kull et al. 2005). In the latter 20th century, the availability of cheap, long-lasting synthetic cloth dented the *lambamena* economy (Razafintsalama and Gautschi 1999); however, new products using this material, such as scarves, have been developed for sale to tourists. These items are dyed using locally collected plants, some also originating from the tapia woodland.

Uapaca bojeri produces large quantities of an edible fruit, *voan'tapia*; trade in this fruit has for many centuries provided income to communities living near the woodlands. The fruit is a small (2–3 cm diameter) round drupe, green to yellow on the tree and brown when ripe. As only fallen fruit is ripe, a strong taboo (*fady*) prohibits plucking fruit from the branches. In the Col des Tapia region, nine out of 10 households collect fruit; two-thirds earn cash income from the sale of fruit to urban consumers. In 1998, villagers earned 80 to 240 MGA per *katinina* basket, about 4 kg or 700 cm^3, which translates to about US\$0.02–0.06 per kg. During the harvest, the Col des Tapia woodlands daily produce

TABLE 4.4. **Tree species in Col des Tapia woodlands and their local uses**

SPECIES (FAMILY)	LOCAL NAME	DOMINANCE	USES
Uapaca bojeri (Phyllanthaceae)	*tapia*	88.3	Edible fruit, wood fuel, silkworm fodder, medicine (stomach, heart)
Sarcolaena eriophora (Sarcolaenaceae)	*voandrozana*	4.9	Wood fuel, charcoal, small edible fruit
Pinus patula/khasya (Pinaceae)[1]	*kesika*	3.7	Construction, wood fuel
Leptolaena spp. (Sarcolaenaceae)	*fotona*	1.4	Wood fuel, charcoal, small edible fruit
Trema spp. (Cannabaceae)	*andrarezina (tsivakimbaratra)*	0.34	Commercialized ashes
Xerochlamys bojeriana (Sarcolaenaceae)	*hatsikana (katsikana)*	0.34	Wood fuel, roots used to flavor rum, tannins, medicine (sick pigs)
Unidentified	*ndretsimora (andriatsimora)*	0.2	Antivenin for scorpions, medicine (diarrhea)
Unidentified	*fanazana*	0.2	Tea, medicine (stomach, paranoia)
Agauria salicifolia (Ericaceae)	*angavodiana*	0.18	Medicine (cuts/bleeding)
Neocussonia bojeri (Araliaceae)	*tsingila*	0.15	Medicine (stomach, last resort, cuts/bleeding)
Vaccinium emirnense (Ericaceae)	*voaramontsina*	0.15	Wood fuel, fruit edible, tasty
Aphloia theiformis (Aphloiaceae)	*voafotsy*	Very low value	Popular tea
Baronia taratana (Anacardiaceae)	*taratana*	Very low value	Medicine (stomach, last resort)
Tambourissa spp. (Monimiaceae)	*ambora*	Very low value	Medicine (teeth)

Source: Data based on Kull (2002).

Note: "Dominance" represents percentage of trees encountered in a dozen survey plots of 500 m^2 with dbh >5 cm.

[1] Non-native species.

approximately 4 kg of fruit per ha, an overall annual production of 600–1500 tons for the 50 km^2 zone. The fruit harvest, from mid-September to December, boosts family income at a critical time, allowing people to hire rice-transplanting labor and buy agricultural inputs such as seeds, manure, or fertilizer (Kull 2002; Kull et al. 2005).

Tapia woodlands provide other resources to the local subsistence economy. First, most villagers rely on the trees for wood fuel. Second, the woodlands host seven varieties of edible mushrooms. Most families collect mushrooms; some sell them locally and to regional markets. Third, many woodland species have medicinal value (Tables 4.4 and 4.5). Fourth, three mammals within the group of spiny tenrecs (subfamily Tenrecinae)—*Echinops telfairi* (only near the Isalo tapia area), *Setifer setosus*, and *Tenrec ecaudatus*—are occasionally hunted in and around these woodlands. Fifth, woodland insects, such as *saroa* caterpillars (*Antherina suraka*, Lepidoptera: Saturniidae) and *landibe* chrysalises, are collected, consumed, and sometimes sold, forming an important part of hungry-season protein intake (Gade 1985). Finally, the berries of several plants growing within the tapia woodland are edible and provide snacks. The tapia forest thus serves as a source of dietary supplements, especially during the hungry period before the rice harvest (Ramamonjisoa 1995).

The woodlands supply an average of 6.5% of the cash income of Col des Tapia households (Kull et al. 2005). However, dependence on woodlands for cash income varies from zero to 40%. Large poor families tend to be more dependent than others on the woodlands for cash and subsistence (Razafintsalama and Gautschi 1999; Kull 2002).

MANAGEMENT AND PROTECTION

The structure and flora of today's tapia woodlands are certainly, but to an unknown extent, the result of anthropogenic influences. These may be indirect and caused coincidentally but may also be caused by direct management interventions to favor revenue-generating forest products, as in imposing a fire regime that is beneficial to the useful and fire-adapted *Uapaca bojeri*; selective cutting; and protecting the woodlands (Kull 2002).

Most lightning strikes occur in the wet season, when the resultant fires will typically burn only small areas since the grassland vegetation is moist and the fires extinguished by rain; however, relatively rare strikes occurring during the transition between the dry and wet seasons may be intense and burn large areas (Ramos-Neto and Pivello 2000; W. Platt et al. 2015). Humans have drastically modified this natural regime; tapia woodlands now burn more frequently, normally during the dry season, but presumably less intensely since less fuel is available. In an 18 km^2 area of the Col des Tapia region, 37% of woodlands burned during 1998, a heavy fire year (Kull 2004), and on Ibity Massif between 2000 and 2017 some tapia woodlands burned every two years (Ramahefamanana et al. 2019).

TABLE 4.5. **Understory species in Col des Tapia woodlands**

SPECIES (FAMILY)	LOCAL NAME	USES
Aloe spp. (Asphodelaceae)	*vahona*	Medicine (stomach, cuts/bleeding)
?*Asteropeia densiflora* (Asteropeiaceae)	*fandambana*	Wood fuel
Brachylaena ramiflora (Asteraceae)	*hazotokana*	Medicine (broad usage)
Carissa edulis (Apocynaceae)	*voahangitanety*	Unknown
Cassia mimosoides (Caesalpiniaceae)	*kelimanendilanitra*	Medicine; ceremonial (ward off hail)
Caucalis melanantha (Apiaceae)	*kisetroka*	Medicine (headaches, cold, blurred vision)
Dombeya greveana (Malvaceae)	*ambiaty/ombiaty*	Burn to make commercial ashes
?*Dracaena reflexa* (Asparagaceae)	*ravoanjo/ranjo/ raivoanjo*	For toilet training dogs (by rubbing leaves on the ground to deter dog from using that location)
?*Embelia* spp. (Myrsinaceae)	*tateradela*	Medicine (for children, for cuts)
Erica spp. (Ericaceae)	*anjavidy*	Wood fuel, medicine (cough)
Helichrysum rusillonii (Asteraceae)	*ahibalala*	Medicine (stomach, cough, fever, last resort)
?*Helichrysum* spp.	*tsetsatsetsa*	Unknown
Maesa lanceolata (Myrsinaceae)	*rafy*	Small, sweet, edible fruit, medicine (teeth, chest pain)
Plectronia spp. (Rubiaceae)	*fatsikahidambo*	Medicine (paranoia)
Psiadia altissima (Asteraceae)	*dingadingana*	Unknown
Psorospermum spp. (Clusiaceae)	*tambitsy*	Medicine (general)
Pterocaulon decurrens (Asteraceae)	*ariandro*	Unknown
Radamaea montana (Scrophulariaceae)	*tambarasaha*	Wood fuel, cosmetic
Rubus apetalus (Rosaceae)	*rohifotsy*	Medicine (antivenin, heart, cuts)
Senecio faugasiodes (Asteraceae)	*hanidraisoa, koboi-boy*	Medicine (cracks in feet, *fery*)
Solanum spp. (Solanaceae)	*sevalahy*	Unknown
Tetradenia fruticosa (Labiaceae)	*bororohana*	Medicine (paranoia)
Vernonia glutinosa (Asteraceae)	*ramanjoko*	Medicine (fever)
Vernonia spp.	*kijejalahy*	Medicine (sexually transmitted diseases, fever, stomach, general)
Unidentified vine	*vahy famonololo*	Used to tie things, medicine (paranoia)
Unidentified	*arivoniraviny*	Wood for craft making
Unidentified	*fano*	Unknown
Unidentified	*hazomiarotena*	Unknown
Unidentified	*(keli) boloana*	Medicine (fever, last resort)
Unidentified	*kiripika*	Unknown
Unidentified	*reniomby*	Medicine (for cattle illness)
Unidentified	*voamasonomby*	Medicine (constipation)
Unidentified	*voatainosy*	Wood fuel, tiny edible fruit, flavors rum
Unidentified	*voatsitakazaza*	Tiny edible fruit

Source: Data based on Kull (2002).

Even under these fire regimes the edges of tapia woodland are remarkably stable, at least over the last century (Kull 2002; Ramahefamanana et al. 2019) (Figures 4.11a and b). However, there is also evidence that the anthropogenic fire regime, while having little impact on mature *U. bojeri* trees, may prevent their regeneration since small plants may be unable to escape the so-called fire trap in which they repeatedly burn to the ground and resprout, leaving intermediate size classes relatively impoverished (Alvarado 2012). For example, on the Ibity Massif, in three 0.16 ha plots established in tapia woodland that had burned at least six times between 2000 and 2017, there were on average just 21 stems of tree species (mainly *U. bojeri*) in the stem diameter class >1–5 cm; 13 in the class >5–10 cm; and 34 in the class >10 cm.

Tapia woodland is often associated with rocky terrain (Guillaumet et al. 1972–1973), perhaps because fire burns unevenly in such areas, allowing some young plants to escape the fire trap and grow sufficiently tall to avoid top-kill by future fires. Birkinshaw and Andriamihajarivo (2007) reported a positive correlation between species richness of woody plants in tapia woodland and the rockiness of the habitat; they explained this relationship as being the result of the rocks attenuating the impact of the fire and creating a patchy burn. Thus, while those wishing to nurture tapia woodland will want to maintain fire, they also need to consider the appropriate fire frequency and the appropriate timing of fires to enable regeneration—early dry-season fires, when grasses are still quite moist, are less intense and the burn is patchier. Protected-area managers of grassland ecosystems, including tapia woodland, wishing to encourage species diversity will likely seek to promote a mosaic of different fire regimes across the site that will favor regeneration of different species and not just *U. bojeri*.

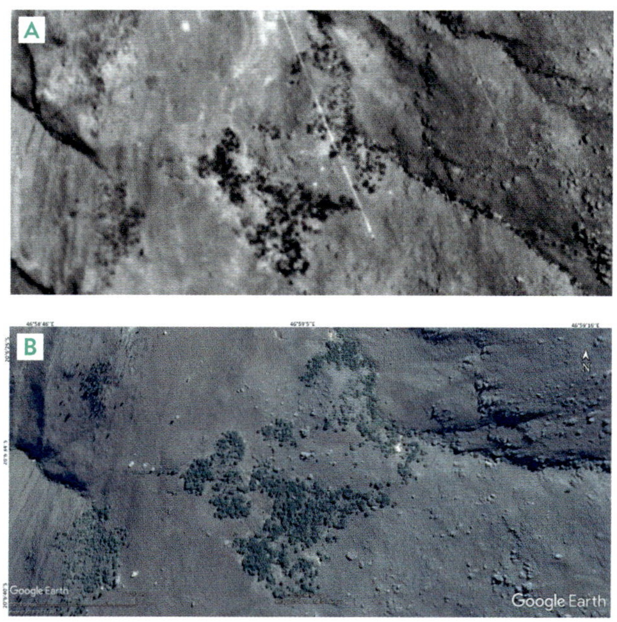

FIGURE 4.11 **A) An area of tapia woodland on the Ibity Massif in 1949; B) same area of woodland in 2016 showing little change in cover despite being in a zone that burns every two or three years.** (A: aerial photo from Foibe Tao-Tsaritan'i Madagasikara; B: image from Google Earth.)

Fire also plays a role in increasing silk production. Light understory fires during or after the rainy season (January–May) control predatory ant populations and stimulate resprouting of grass and young tapia leaves favored by *landibe*. In addition, burning plays a role in the production of firewood by creating dead and downed wood that villagers were by tradition allowed to collect, and also by providing rejuvenated pasture for grazing cattle. Collecting firewood and pasturing cattle are allowed in the Zone d'Utilisation Durable of some new protected areas.

The Malagasy people also significantly shape the woodland by selective cutting. Since nine out of 10 trees are *U. bojeri*, this tree contributes significantly to local wood fuel use. However, people gathering wood fuel are more aggressive in cutting trees other than *Uapaca*, like *Leptolaena* spp. and *Sarcolaena eriophora*, thus favoring the dominance of *U. bojeri*. In addition, long-established practices of wood fuel collection emphasize dead, downed, and sick branches and may have a pruning effect, removing inefficient lower branches, reducing the danger of crown fires, and perhaps increasing fruit and branch production (Kull 2002).

Overharvesting of firewood can degrade woodlands. However, a comparison of firewood use with forest growth in the Col des Tapia region tentatively suggests that firewood collection at its current level is sustainable (Kull 2002). Population growth may increase local demand for firewood yet may not degrade tapia woodlands because of protective rules (below) and increased reliance on alternatives such as introduced pine and eucalyptus (three-fifths of households in the Col des Tapia region grow these trees). Increased urban demand has been shown to cause massive private investment in fast-growing pine and eucalyptus woodlots in some areas, while increased localized demand is met from a mix of sources including native trees, introduced species (pine, eucalyptus, and mimosa), and trimmings from hedges and fruit trees.

Finally, tapia woodlands benefit from protection by local traditions and government rules. The woodlands have long been managed as community resources under formal state ownership. Since the French colonial period, successive laws have formally given adjacent communities traditional use rights. In all areas, the woodlands are guarded by local traditions that are more or less rigorously applied, including restrictions on cutting live trees, plucking fruit from trees, breaking large branches to access the spiny *landibe*, or outsiders commercially exploiting forest products. On top of local rules, the colonial and postcolonial Forest Service placed strict restrictions on forest cutting and burning. Enforcement during the colonial period was stricter than it is now, and there have been episodes when indiscriminate cutting led to tree loss. In the 1970s and 1980s, damage was done to Col des Tapia woodlands as people cut and burned tapia trees to make *laro*, ashes used in soap and tobacco factories. In several instances, entire stands were devastated for charcoal production. However, drastic violations can result in government prosecution or citizen protests, as was the case in a conflict over a mining concession near Arivonimamo in 2016. Around the Ibity Massif, prior to the designation of the site as a new protected area, some 50 families survived periods of hardship by converting woody trees found in tapia woodland, rarely including *U. bojeri*, into charcoal for sale. Fortunately, the ability of these cut tree species to respout, an adaptation against burning, means that the vegetation is quite resilient even to this treatment.

Legislation in 1996 and 1997 opened the way to officially decentralize the management of state-owned renewable natural resources, such as tapia woodlands, to adjacent communities. While under these rules there is no actual transfer of title from the state to the community, limited use rights are transferred to a local users' group. However, such contracts have proven highly legalistic and, without the support of NGOs and strong interest alignment (Horning 2018), have led to mediocre outcomes and only small livelihood benefits (Freudenberger 2010; Rasolofoson et al. 2017). Moreover, structural issues like legal prohibitions on burning mean that this legislation is not well adapted to traditional management of tapia woodlands (Razafintsalama and Gautschi 1999; Kull 2004).

Probably the most important immediate threat to tapia woodlands is neither cutting nor fire, but invasion by introduced species. Spontaneous colonization occurs from private and village woodlots, consisting particularly of pine (*Pinus khasya* and *P. patula*) in the Col des Tapia region (see Table 4.4) and *Eucalyptus* spp. in the Imamo area. According to villagers and local foresters, pines and eucalypts may damage tapia woodlands by shading out the heliophilic woodland species, modifying fire regimes, and changing soil characteristics; additional research is urgent.

Subject editors: Steven M. Goodman and Amanda H. Armstrong

FOREST ECOLOGY AND RESEARCH IN THE KIRINDY FOREST CNFEREF

P. M. Kappeler, R. M. Rasoloarison, L. Razafimanantsoa, M. Markolf, and C. Fichtel

The Kirindy Forest CNFEREF (Centre National de Formation, d'Etudes et de Recherche en Environnement et Foresterie; Alan'i Kirindy) is located in the central Menabe region, some 20 km east of the coast and 50 km northeast of Morondava. It has emerged as a prominent site for research and silviculture in western dry deciduous forests over the last decades. The former Centre de Formation Professionnelle Forestière (CFPF) de Morondava initiated these activities by setting up a 12,500 ha forestry concession and training site in 1978. The silvicultural activities carried out by the CFPF and the associated research projects conducted until about 1994 have been summarized by Ganzhorn and Sorg (1996) and Sorg et al. (2003). Faunal studies were intensified in 1993 with the establishment of a field station for the study of lemur behavior and ecology by Jörg Ganzhorn on behalf of the German Primate Center (DPZ; Figure 4.12a). The infrastructure and early history of this research station have been summarized by Kappeler and Fichtel (2012). The CFPF established infrastructure for local ecotourism after selective logging was abandoned in 1995. The ecotourism facilities are today operated by CNFEREF. In 2015, Kirindy Forest CNFEREF and most of the remaining forests in the region, notably Ambadira Forest, were officially safeguarded as part of the Menabe Antimena protected area. The intent of this contribution in light of this current chapter is to provide a broad overview of the importance of long-term research at a field station to understand the multifaceted aspects of forest ecology.

KIRINDY FOREST CNFEREF SITE DESCRIPTION

Kirindy Forest CNFEREF and the surrounding region harbor more than 300 plant species (Goodman et al. 2018), including about 200 woody species from 42 families and 142 genera (Rakotonirina 1996). It is characterized by sandy soils, except for some parts along the watercourses of the Kirindy River that represent a specific formation on vertisol. The forest shows a number of traits characteristic of dry deciduous forests: most trees of the canopy layer shed their leaves; an herbaceous layer is absent; flowering often precedes the first flush of leaves; and several adaptations exist to cope with prolonged water stress. In the most mesic portions of the forest, trees can grow up to 25 m tall, while at other sites they are rarely taller than 12–15 m. The dense undergrowth consists of 5000 to 19,000 stems per ha that are shorter than 5 m and smaller than 10 cm in diameter at breast height (dbh). Some of these species are evergreen; that is, they do not seasonally shed their leaves. The intermediate forest layer consists of 350–400 trees per ha that are 5–2 m tall and 12–25 cm in dbh, and its species composition depends strongly on the soil type. The upper layer consists of 10 to 50 trees per ha that are taller than 12 m and more than 25 cm in dbh.

The climate of the central Menabe region is classified as tropical dry with two distinct seasons: a hot wet season from November to March or April, and a dry season during the remaining months. The mean annual temperature at the Kirindy field station since 2000, when an automatic weather station was installed, is 24.9°C, means of monthly maxima and minima are 33.9°C and 17.6°C, respectively, and mean annual rainfall is 713 mm per year. The hottest and lowest recorded temperatures (since 2000) are 42.2°C and 2.9°C, respectively. Also during this period, the maximum annual rainfall was 1273 mm in 2000, and the lowest rainfall was 162 mm in 2010. Across the past two decades, a pronounced trend toward reduced annual rainfall with slightly increasing temperatures has been discernible (Figure 4.13a). The rainy season is variable and

FIGURE 4.12 **A) Aerial view of Kirindy Forest CNFEREF in the dry season with the research station and ecotourism lodge in the foreground. B) Students from the Université d'Antananarivo and University of Göttingen observing a group of lemurs during a field course. C) A group of individually marked *Eulemur rufifrons* (Red-fronted Brown Lemurs). D) Researcher radio-tracking lemurs.** (PHOTOS A and B by M. Markolf, C by C. Fichtel, and D by K. Rudolph.)

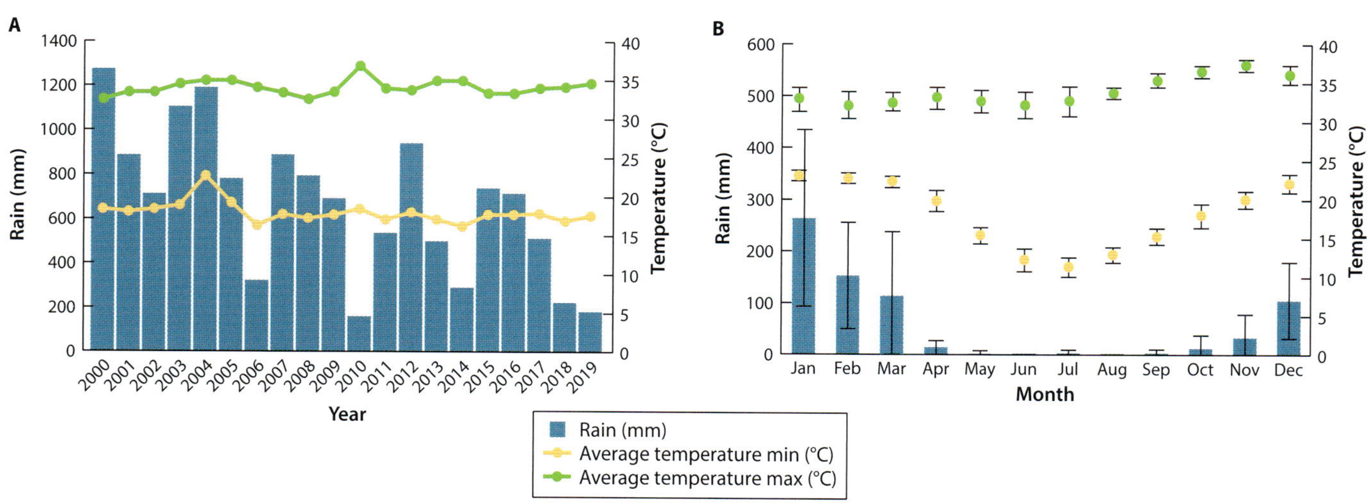

FIGURE 4.13 **Climate and forest phenology at Kirindy Forest CNFEREF. A) Total rainfall and mean annual maximum and minimum temperatures indicate a trend toward reduced rainfall over the last two decades. B) The standard deviation around the mean monthly rainfall and minimum and maximum temperatures reflects the unpredictability of seasonal patterns.**

characterized by sequences of very wet periods, with up to a third of the seasonal rainfall often concentrated in a 10-day period associated with the passage of a cyclone, so that the onset and magnitude of the rainy season are rather unpredictable (Figure 4.13b). As a result of the pronounced seasonality, the forest habitat changes dramatically between the wet and dry seasons.

Kirindy Forest CNFEREF and the greater Menabe Antimena protected area are also home to eight species of lemurs, two species of euplerid carnivorans, three endemic species of nesomyine rodents, eight species of tenrecs, 16 species of bats, 149 species of birds, 54 species of reptiles, and 15 species of amphibians (Goodman et al. 2018). The local invertebrate fauna remains poorly and incompletely studied. This site is the stronghold and last refugium for a number of vertebrate taxa in the western dry deciduous forests of Madagascar. Locally endemic species include the world's smallest primate (*Microcebus berthae*) and Madagascar's largest extant rodent (*Hypogeomys antimena*); other vertebrates with extremely restricted ranges found at Kirindy include the carnivoran *Mungotictis decemlineata*, the bird *Mesitornis variegatus*, and the tortoise *Pyxis planicauda*. Introduced *Mus musculus*, *Rattus rattus*, and *Potamochoerus larvatus* are also present.

FORESTRY RESEARCH

Between 1978 and 1992, research projects were focused on forest ecology, silviculture, and methods of forest exploitation and reforestation (Ganzhorn and Sorg 1996). One main aim was to better understand forest seasonality. To this end, the phenology of 55 different tree species, belonging to 42 genera and 26 families, was monitored over several years (Randrianasolo et al. 1996). These studies examined the relationships between climate, soil, and phenology (Sorg and Rohner 1996), as well as specific animal-plant interactions (Ganzhorn 1995; Ralisoamalala 1996; Scharfe and Schlund 1996; Böhning-Gaese et al. 1999). Data from the phenological transects indicate that leaf flush is triggered by very little rainfall. By the end of November, 76% of the trees have leaves; in January, all trees have leaves. There are substantial inter- and intraspecific differences that can be linked in part to edaphic characteristics. Among all species combined, trees on red and yellow soils are in full leaf for 122 ± 31 days, on brown soils for 152 ± 51 days, and on black soils for 195 ± 70 days.

Research at the community level has focused on possible effects of logging on various vertebrate taxa (Sorg et al. 2003). Selective logging at Kirindy focused on *Commiphora* spp. On average, 6.20 stems per ha were extracted, representing 4–15 m^3 wood volume. By international standards this level of exploitation would be considered very low impact logging. This low-intensity logging altered forest structure. On a larger scale, these changes were smaller than variation in vegetation structure from edaphic causes. On a small scale, low-level logging increased fruit production and improved leaf quality because of increased exposure of the remaining trees to sunlight. This resulted in shifts in population densities of lemurs and an ephemeral concentration of leaf- and fruit-eating lemurs in logged areas. In general, however, low-intensity logging had no discernible impact on the distribution or abundance of litter invertebrates, reptiles, birds, tenrecs, rodents, or lemurs (Ganzhorn et al. 1990, 1996; Ganzhorn 1995; Bloxam et al. 1996; Hawkins and Wilmé 1996; Olson and Andriamiadana 1996).

However, slight increases in the intensity of logging resulted in dramatic drops in lemur densities, probably because of the lack of shelter and the reduction of food or suitable substrates for arboreal locomotion. Using this type of habitat might result in negative energy budgets, especially for lemur species that have relatively high costs for locomotion in relation to their resting metabolic rate (Ganzhorn 1993; Drack et al. 1999). The effects of selective logging are still discernible decades later. In one continuous 25 ha study area, for example, *Microcebus murinus* (Gray Mouse Lemur) was found exclusively in the area that was selectively logged more than 20 years earlier, whereas *M. berthae* (Madame Berthe's Mouse Lemur) was restricted to the unlogged part of that study plot (Dammhahn and Kappeler 2008a). Similarly, we found that in selectively logged forest, colony density of the Malagasy wood ant *Aphaenogaster swammerdami* was lower and colony size larger than at undisturbed sites—20 years after the end of logging activities (Dittmann et al. 2014).

FAUNAL RESEARCH WITH AN EMPHASIS ON LEMURS

Faunal research in Kirindy Forest CNFEREF has traditionally concentrated on vertebrates, particularly lemurs. The results of basic faunal and floristic inventories and the first generation of studies of community ecology, food selection, habitat utilization, physiological ecology, and socioecology are summarized in Ganzhorn and Sorg (1996) and Sorg et al. (2003). In more recent years, the focus of research has shifted to topics in behavioral ecology, demography, health, and cognition of various lemur, carnivoran, and bird species, and the site has been regularly used for teaching field courses (Figure 4.12b).

In 1993, the DPZ project established two local study sites, in which a total of about 130 km of trails made approximately 230 ha of forest accessible for long-term research. The initial studies focused on individually marked populations of four lemur species (*Microcebus murinus*, *M. berthae*, *Eulemur rufifrons*, and *Propithecus verreauxi*). Over the years, thousands of individuals of these species have been individually marked with subdermal transponders so that detailed information about individual life histories can be collected via weekly censuses (diurnal species) or monthly recaptures (nocturnal species). Diurnal lemurs at these sites have also been equipped with unique individual collars, facilitating detailed behavioral observations (Figure 4.12c). These studies provide important basic data on population densities and dynamics, but also on species-specific life histories and social systems. Other studies, of shorter duration, have focused on a particular species or involved behavioral or cognitive experiments with mammals, with a particular focus on lemurs.

The large local study sites with their fine-grained trail systems (mostly every 25 m) permitted detailed study of the distribution of individuals in space and time—a core aspect of a species' behavioral ecology. Radio-tracking studies of nocturnal lemurs revealed previously unknown diversity in the social organization of sympatric lemur species (Figure 4.12d). Many examples could be presented on the results of these studies, and we give a few here.

In *Microcebus murinus*, male and female home ranges were found to overlap with those of several members of both sexes (Eberle and Kappeler 2002), whereas in *M. berthae*, male, but not female, ranges overlap (Dammhahn and Kappeler 2005). In contrast, in *Mirza coquereli*, female, but not male, ranges overlap (Kappeler 1997). Three other nocturnal lemur species previously believed to be solitary were found to be pair living: *Cheirogaleus medius* (Fietz et al. 2000), *Phaner pallescens* (Schülke and Kappeler 2003), and *Lepilemur ruficaudatus* (Zinner et al. 2003). Kirindy Forest CNFEREF is also the site where the only study of the social system of *Cryptoprocta ferox*, a euplerid carnivoran, has been conducted (see Gerber and Hawkins, pp. 1978–83). It revealed that females of this species are territorial, whereas males inhabit much larger, mutually overlapping home ranges, and some males form stable associations (Lührs et al. 2013). The social organization of the other euplerid, *Mungotictis decemlineata*, is remarkable because this species is characterized by gregarious sexual segregation: both sexes live in small same-sex associations that are more (females) or less (males) stable (Schneider and Kappeler 2016). In contrast, the ecologically very similar bird *Mesitornis variegatus*, which—like *M. decemlineata*—is also terrestrial and insectivorous, lives in small bisexual family groups (Gamero et al. 2014).

Because lemurs evolved diverse social systems independently of other primates, comparative studies of alarm call systems and other aspects of their communication and cognition are of interest to behavioral ecologists. Field experiments at Kirindy revealed that cathemeral *Eulemur rufifrons* and diurnal *Propithecus verreauxi* exhibited a mixed alarm call system, a then-novel system characterized by functionally referential alarm calls for aerial predators and general alarm calls for terrestrial predators, the latter of which are also given during agonistic encounters with conspecifics (Fichtel and Kappeler 2002). Nocturnal species, such as *Microcebus murinus* and *Lepilemur ruficaudatus*, do not rely on early warnings of conspecifics but produce general alarm calls that may have a recruiting and deterrence function (Fichtel 2007; Rahlfs and Fichtel 2010). In contrast to pair-living *L. ruficaudatus* and group-living *E. rufifrons* and *P. verreauxi*, solitary *M. murinus* does not associate a specific escape response with alarm calls (Rahlfs and Fichtel 2010; Fichtel et al. 2011), suggesting that with increasing social complexity, permanently associated group members appear to rely more on social information. Nocturnal lemurs, rather than evolving specific alarm calls for aerial predators, instead evolved general alarm calls for terrestrial predators that are also given during agonistic interactions with conspecifics; general alarm calls might thus represent the ancestral form of alarm calls in primates.

Core components of a species' ecology also depend on their cognitive abilities. In *E. rufifrons*, a potential behavioral tradition in the form of depletion of spider nests in the lean season has been observed (Schnoell and Fichtel 2013). Experimental investigations revealed that the lemurs use social information when learning a new foraging task (Schnoell and Fichtel 2012). However, experimentally seeded new traditions do not appear to result in long-term traditions (Schnoell et al. 2014). Individuals that were more efficient at solving new problems were those that exhibited higher persistence when learning the task (Huebner and Fichtel 2015). Persistence also facilitated problem solving in *M. berthae*, but not in *M. murinus* (Henke von der Malsburg and Fichtel 2018). Problem-solving abilities were also linked to a fitness indicator in *M. murinus*; individuals that learned a problem-solving task faster were more likely to maintain their body condition over the lean season (Huebner et al. 2018). Thus, variation in cognitive abilities within and between species can illuminate key aspects of the ecology of lemurs and other animals.

THREATS AND CONSERVATION

Research conducted in Kirindy Forest CNFEREF over the last decades has also contributed to the assessment of Madagascar's dry deciduous forests as one of the most threatened biomes in the world (Ganzhorn et al. 2001; Waeber et al. 2015). The establishment of a protected area in central Menabe in the context of the "Durban Vision" (see Jones et al., pp. 2130–40) was initiated and advanced by researchers and conservation organizations in the early 2000s. Under the leadership of the Malagasy NGO Fanamby, and with support of other local stakeholders such as CNFEREF, DPZ, and Durrell Wildlife, central Menabe obtained its first preliminary protective status in 2006. After a long administrative process interrupted by Madagascar's political crisis of 2009–2013, the Menabe Antimena Nouvelle Aire Protégée was finally officially created in 2015. The protected area encompasses a total surface area of 210,312 ha (Goodman et al. 2018) and includes two important freshwater lakes (Lake Bedo and Lake Kimanaomby), mangrove habitat, and dry deciduous forest. The site is categorized as a protected landscape (IUCN category V) aimed at conserving an important area where the interaction of people and nature over time has produced a zone of distinct character with significant ecological, biological, cultural, and scenic value. Accordingly, Menabe Antimena is divided into strict conservation zones, private and state-owned zones, and zones of sustainable resource use managed by local communities (*transfert de gestion*). One of the strict conservation zones is Kirindy Forest CNFEREF; the other strict conservation zone includes large parts of the remaining northern dry forests, called Ambadira (PAG Menabe 2014).

Despite official protection, the forest cover in the region continues to decline at an alarming rate (Figure 4.14) and could largely disappear within the next decades (Zinner et al. 2013). According to Hudson et al. (2019), annual forest loss within the protected area was relatively stable (below 1000 ha per year) from 2001 until 2009. Since 2009, annual deforestation rates have more than doubled, to estimates of about 4000 ha in 2014 and 2015. The authors forecasted that if deforestation continued at that rate ("worst-case scenario"), the dry deciduous forests would disappear within the next 10–20 years. According to Global Forest Watch, annual deforestation rates within Menabe Antimena have exceeded the "worst-case scenario" of Hudson et al. (2019), with approximately 8000 ha of annual forest loss in 2017 and 2018, respectively (Figure 4.14).

The main reason for deforestation is the practice of swidden agriculture for shifting cultivation, locally called *hatsake* (Figure 4.15). The understory of the forest is first cut and broadly distributed to allow effective propagation of fire. The forest is generally burned at the end of the dry season to make use of the burned area

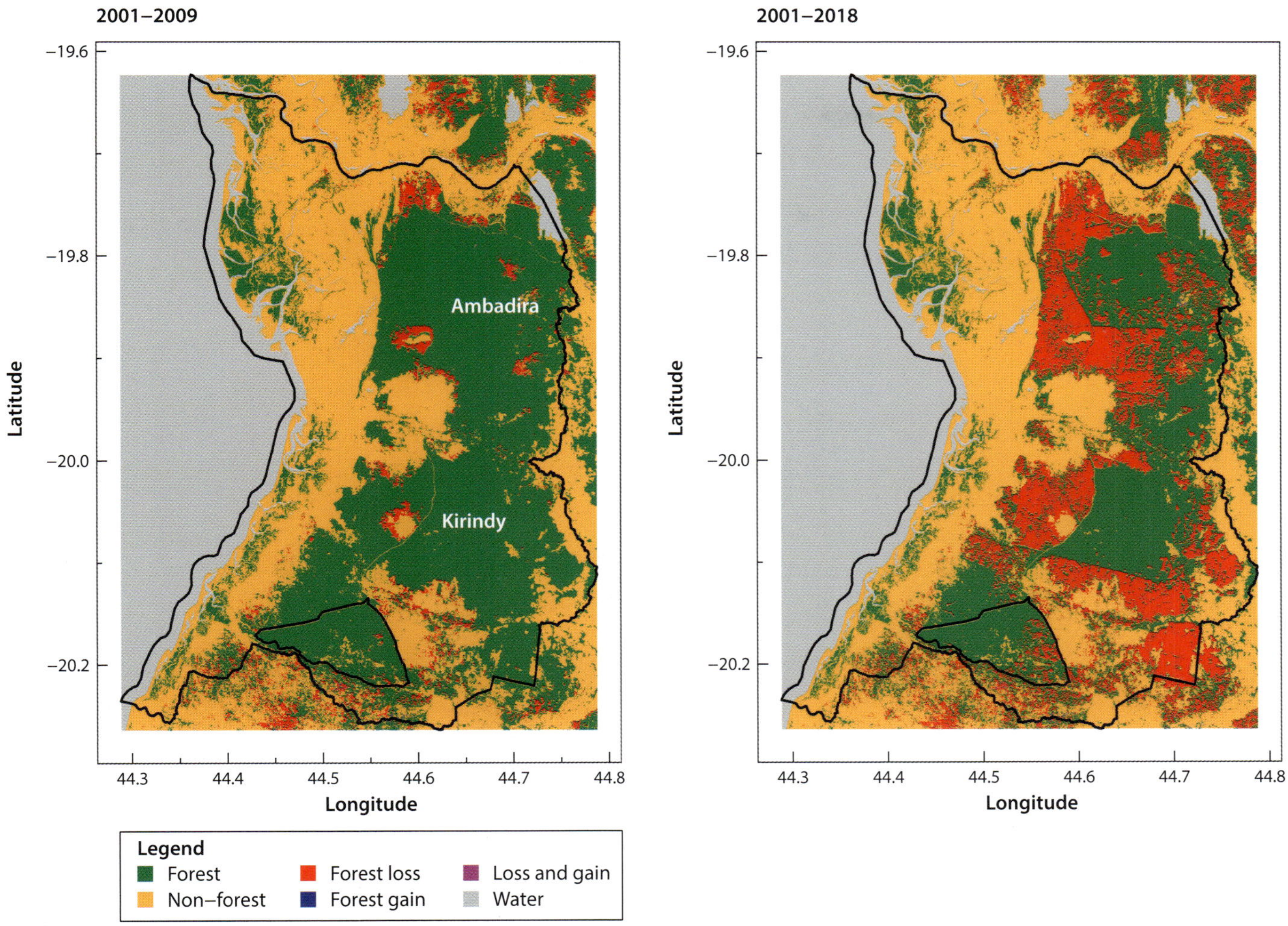

FIGURE 4.14 **Deforestation within the Menabe Antimena protected area (black solid line) and surrounding areas from 2001 to 2018.** (SOURCE: Hansen/UMD/Google/USGS/NASA; see Hansen et al. 2013.)

in the upcoming wet season. Maize is then usually planted for two years, followed by one or two more cycles of peanuts until the soil does not provide enough nutrients for another agricultural period. Consequently, a new area of forest is burned because the ash of freshly burned forest provides the necessary nutrients for the crops. At least some of the local population see this practice as sustainable and as the only appropriate method to receive sufficient harvest (Scales 2012). The poverty of the local population has usually been considered the primary driver of traditional swidden agriculture and deforestation on Madagascar (Waeber et al. 2015). However, in recent years this view has changed, and more complex and diverse drivers of deforestation in central Menabe have been identified. Historically, times of intense deforestation in the area have always been linked to export chains and global markets of crops (e.g., maize, which is also used to make beer), as well as waves of immigration (Klein et al. 2008; Scales 2011). Specifically, an influx of people from southern Madagascar to work for a local sisal plantation contributed to an erosion of local cultural taboos regarding traditional practices of forest use. Swidden agriculture in central Menabe today is therefore intended not only for subsistence but also for export production, and the use of forest resources, including hunting and collecting of animals, is diversified by various cultural ethnicities living in the area today.

Besides shifting cultivation, many other factors threaten the remaining forests in the region, such as illegal logging of precious wood (especially rosewood or palisander), production of charcoal, and use of firewood for cooking. In general, local populations make intensive use of natural forest products, such as tubers or bushmeat, which can cover most dietary needs of a local household in times of food scarcity. Although the amount of bushmeat consumption is difficult to quantify, it seems that wildlife hunting is still very prominent even though it is officially prohibited. An evaluation of the use of animal and forest products by schoolchildren participating in a regular environmental education camp conducted at CNFEREF in 2019 indicated that almost all boys regularly hunted wild animals, especially birds (M. Markolf and H. Rakotonirina, unpublished data). Whereas the consumption of lemurs still seems to be quite frequent in most households, most of the hunting is probably conducted by specialized hunters and the bushmeat sold to the population in illegal markets.

The decline of the natural forest cover, in combination with a fast-growing human population in central Menabe, exacerbates existing threats to local biodiversity. For example, decreasing habitat

FIGURE 4.15 **Aerial view of a recently cleared area within Kirindy Forrest CNFEREF and fires burning in the background.** (PHOTO by M. Markolf.)

and (natural) food scarcity in the dry season force the endemic carnivoran *Cryptoprocta* to attack poultry in villages close to the forest, creating conflicts with humans, which have resulted in retaliatory killings of a significant number of animals in recent years (Merson et al. 2019a; M. Markolf, unpublished data). Small and fragmented habitats additionally increase the accessibility of introduced species, such as domestic dogs and cats, which represent threats to the local endemic small mammal fauna (e.g., *Hypogeomys antimena*). In fact, the number of camera-trap records of dogs and cats in Andranomena Special Reserve, just south of the Menabe Antimena protected area, has already exceeded the number of *Cryptoprocta* photos (Merson et al. 2019b). Finally, deforestation has likely contributed to a trend toward reduced rainfall over the last two decades in the area (Figure 4.13a), indicating local climate change, which might complicate future sustainable development even further.

To effectively manage the Menabe Antimena protected area in the future, it will be essential to gain a complete understanding of the complexity of the socio-ecological, economic, and political drivers behind deforestation. Furthermore, there is a lack of specific judicial means to effectively enforce environmental laws and, more importantly, integrate the local population in sustainable land management and conservation initiatives. Although the CFPF, which became CNFEREF, initiated some research toward sustainable land management in the early 2000s (Sorg et al. 2003), detailed research on sustainable land management of dry forests remains one of the most significant knowledge gaps (Waeber et al. 2015; Frank and Schäffler 2019).

THE IMPORTANCE OF LONG-TERM RESEARCH

Given the ever-increasing anthropogenic pressures on the forests of the central Menabe region, the sheer long-term presence of the CNFEREF tourist facilities and the DPZ research station has been

instrumental in preserving Kirindy Forest CNFEREF and its animals. Two observations support this notion: Andranomena Special Reserve, which is surrounded by Sakalava villagers who traditionally use the forest for hunting, is essentially devoid of vertebrates, whereas Ambadira Forest, where swidden agriculture by immigrant Antandroy villagers went unchecked for the last 15 years, has largely disappeared. Even though many hectares of forest continue to be lost on its fringes and hunters are occasionally encountered, the permanent presence of researchers, tourists, and their supporting staff, along with their limited patrolling efforts, appeared to be sufficient to protect Kirindy Forest CNFEREF from a similar fate until now.

Furthermore, silvicultural research over the years has produced a body of knowledge that is now becoming increasingly important for reforestation plans. The precise timing and methods for seed collecting have been established for almost 60 species. Twenty of them can be grown in the nursery without problems and offer a basis for governmental and private initiatives to restore lost forest areas.

Finally, long-term monitoring of individual lemurs and other animals yields unique and valuable data on the life histories and species-specific adaptations to this seasonal environment (Kappeler et al. 2012). These data also provide an opportunity to constantly monitor population densities and to identify effects of climate change, providing a scientific basis for identifying conservation priorities.

Subject editors: Steven M. Goodman and Amanda H. Armstrong

THE EFFECTS OF HORIZONTAL AND VERTICAL ENVIRONMENTAL HETEROGENEITY ON LEMUR COMMUNITY STRUCTURE: A LANDSCAPE ECOLOGY APPROACH

E. Mertz

Understanding the effects of landscape-level ecological spatial patterns (composition and configuration) and heterogeneity on biodiversity survival is critical to successful land management. This is particularly relevant for landscape management on Madagascar, given the island's high species endemism and alarming rate of habitat loss and extinction risk (Goodman and Benstead 2005; Vieilledent et al. 2018; J. Jones et al. 2019). In particular, habitat loss and fragmentation caused by legal or illegal logging, charcoal production, and mining are negatively affecting lemur populations, leading to local extirpation. Based on the growing human population and Madagascar's need for economic growth, it is expected that areas of intact forest will continue to be transformed into a mosaic of forested and deforested areas, creating different landscape patterns, affecting forest structure, and subsequently altering lemur movement patterns, dispersal, and habitat use.

Fragmentation is an important variable to evaluate within the framework of landscape ecology (Fahrig 2003). The development of a landscape ecology framework that focuses on how land can be removed or replaced in order to minimize extinction risk can contribute to effective environmental policy and ecosystem sustainability. Quantifying variation in habitat use across the landscape and identifying forest structural variables and multi-scale patterns that may influence variation among lemurs are essential to understanding community assemblages in the remaining tracts of different forest types on Madagascar. This facet of landscape ecology research directly influences conservation policy by contributing much-needed data to advance informed decisions pertaining to land development based on lemur habitat preferences and movement patterns, where to try to restore habitat, where to protect habitat, and where to build or maintain connectivity.

Species persistence patterns and population viability in modified patchy forests depend on a detailed assessment of forest structure and the quantification of spatial heterogeneity (Turner 2005). The concept of patch quality is of central importance in that it influences survival, reproduction, dispersal, and successful locomotion for an organism. Operationally, however, patch quality is difficult to define and measure (Wiens 2002). Detailed assessments of forest patches are needed that go beyond broad categories such as primary versus degraded, logged or unlogged, continuous or fragmented, and that quantify rather than infer an organism's perspective relative to that of the researcher. This would include detailing not only patch composition, boundary length, and shape but also context. Patch context is the landscape mosaic in which the patches are embedded (Wiens 2002). Patch context may constrain certain organisms because of their habitat preferences and their ability or willingness to traverse gaps of unsuitable habitat (Lima and Zollner 1996; Wiens 2002). Documenting specific habitat structural variables, or keystone structures that support various organisms (e.g., sleeping trees or trees in a prime location to promote mobility from one area of the forest to another), may also be important in determining quality habitat from an organismal perspective (Tews et al. 2004).

This contribution presents a case study within Betampona Strict Nature Reserve that explores relevant methods for quantifying and defining vertical and horizontal structural habitat variation and composition, as well as identifying how attributes of patch and landscape scale can affect lemur communities in terms of species richness, composition, and relative abundance. Also discussed is how small-scale landscape attributes (microhabitat) in addition to patch configuration and composition (macrohabitat) affect habitat selection and lemur movement patterns. This case study sought to accomplish the following: 1) provide a detailed assessment of the vertical and horizontal structural heterogeneity of eight forest patches within Betampona; 2) investigate the effects of different levels of landscape spatial scale on the diurnal lemur community structure within the eight patches; and 3) consider how *Eulemur* perceives habitat quality, negotiates the dynamics of patch context, and is influenced by micro- and macrohabitat structural variables in selecting habitat and movement patterns.

STUDY SITE AND METHODS TO QUANTIFY FOREST STRUCTURE

Betampona Strict Nature Reserve is one of the last remaining tracts of central eastern lowland moist evergreen rainforest and is home to many endemic plant and animal species. Eleven lemur species are currently found at this site, including five diurnal species—*Propithecus diadema* (Diademed Sifaka), *Indri indri* (Indri), *Varecia variegata* (Black and White Ruffed Lemur), *Eulemur albifrons* (White-fronted Brown Lemur), and *Hapalemur griseus* (Gray Bamboo Lemur), and six nocturnal species—*Microcebus simmonsi* (Simmons' Mouse Lemur), *Cheirogaleus* cf. *major* (Greater Dwarf Lemur), *Phaner furcifer* (Fork-marked Lemur), *Lepilemur mustelinus* (Weasel Sportive Lemur), *Avahi laniger* (Eastern Woolly Lemur), and *Daubentonia madagascariensis* (Aye-aye) (Goodman et al. 2018). This study focuses on the diurnal species.

Except for sections of forest cleared prior to 1996 and the impact of landslides, the integrity of the Betampona forest is largely intact. Today, areas throughout the reserve are composed of nonprimary forest and different secondary habitats including ginger (*Aframomum angustifolium*, Zingiberaceae), Traveller's Palm (*Ravenala madagascariensis*, Strelitziaceae), and introduced species such as guava (*Psidium cattleyanum*, Myrtaceae). The undulating terrain in conjunction with introduced and invasive plant spread and regrowth has generated significant identifiable differences in habitat structure, configuration, and composition throughout the reserve. As such, the site's landscape is appropriate for investigating how environmental heterogeneity affects species diversity and community structure. The individual patches (i.e., the multiple elements of the landscape that create heterogeneity) within the protected area are separated by a certain degree of matrix, thus limiting connectivity and influencing ecological processes such as the movement and dispersal of organisms, resource use, and ultimately gene flow (Pearson et al. 1999), making a landscape ecology study relevant.

METHODOLOGY USEFUL IN CHARACTERIZING VERTICAL AND HORIZONTAL FOREST STRUCTURE

A detailed assessment of the vertical and horizontal structural heterogeneity within Betampona was completed in order to characterize the forest structure and develop a spatial framework within which to investigate the effects of landscape composition and configuration on the movement and patch use of the diurnal lemur community. First, eight plot locations were quantitatively defined throughout the forest (Table 4.6). Four 10 × 10 m plots were then placed within a 50 m radius at each of the eight plot locations. These plots collectively represented a patch, which is defined as a relatively homogeneous (e.g., similar in structure) area that differs from its surroundings. The first plot for each patch was placed at the GPS location of a previous plot established during preliminary research that assessed the significant identifiable differences in habitat structure, configuration, and composition throughout the reserve (Mertz 2006). The center of the next plot was located at a random compass direction and fixed distance of 30 m. The last two plots were positioned 120 degrees from the first (following Ralph et al. 1995). Table 4.6 presents the attributes quantified for each plot used to characterize the vertical and horizontal forest structure and define the patch.

TABLE 4.6. **Quantified attributes for each 10 × 10 m plot assessed in Betampona**

Number of new trees and herbaceous shrubs within a 1 m^2 block × 4
Tree composition and the number of each type of tree
Site position and elevation (Garmin GPS map 60CSx unit)
Each canopy level height (clinometer)
Canopy cover (spherical densiometer)
Canopy connectivity measured via the average distance between tree crowns in the canopy layer(s). The distance from one tree crown to the nearest tree in each canopy layer was recorded based on the average for the patch: A, connected (0 m); B, connected/small gap; C, small gap (1–3 m); D, small/medium gap; E, medium gap (4–6 m); F, large gap (7–9 m); G, very large gap (>10 m). The combination gaps are a mix of the two measurements indicated.
Average distance between tree trunks at a height of 5 m of varying diameter at breast height (dbh) (1–5 cm, 6–10 cm, 11–20 cm, and >21 cm)
Dbh of each tree (dbh tape)
Spatial distribution of tree trunks within each plot. Tree spacing was categorized as either equally spaced or clumped among different dbh categories: 1–5 cm, 6–10 cm, 11–20 cm, and >21 cm
Total number of lianas, tree hollows, emergent trees, dead standing trees, and fallen trees
Number and height(s) of *Ravenala*
Abundance of bamboo, *Aframomum*, and *Psidium* estimated based on a graded scale (0, none; 1, ¼ of the plot; 2, ½ of the plot; 3, ¾ of the plot; 4, dense)
Slope (clinometer)
Temperature and humidity (Kestrel pocket weather station)

Heterogeneity in Betampona

Quantifying habitat attributes and the landscape pattern of forest fragments is essential for understanding the response of a particular community, group, species, or individual to micro- and macrohabitat features that contribute to patch and landscape complexity. There were significant quantifiable differences among the eight patches (1600, 800–900, Sahakoho, Sahabefoza, Zubenubi, Betakonona, Fara, Guava) in every attribute measured in Betampona (Table 4.7), indicating a heterogeneous landscape. The following is a brief description of some of the general properties that define each patch (also see Figures 4.16b–k). The 1600 Patch was dominated by 1–5 cm dbh evenly spaced trees, whereas the Sahakoho Patch was characterized by a high abundance of 6–10, 11–20, and >21 cm dbh trees in close proximity and evenly spaced. The 800–900 Patch was a variable transitional area consisting of a high density of unequally distributed *Ravenala* and abundant low-lying vegetation, including viny bamboo. The Sahabefoza Patch was the only patch with a small stream, relatively abundant palms, and pockets of *Psidium*, with an adjacent patch of *Aframomum*. The Zubenubi Patch was characterized by dense lianas and vegetation and exhibited one of the highest total counts of fallen dead trees. The Betakonona Patch was often windy and blanketed in low cloud cover and consisted of undulant and steep terrain with increased vertical open space because of a higher canopy height with little or no *Ravenala*. Finally, the Fara Patch was primarily undisturbed forest with four canopy layers, including 30 m trees, whereas the Guava Patch consisted predominantly of thick tangles of *Psidium* and had a relatively short canopy height. The following paragraphs provide a more in-depth analysis of the main structural variables represented in three of the eight patches, the Guava, Sahabefoza, and Zubenubi Patches.

The Guava Patch (Figure 4.16k) was dominated by *Psidium*; it had low tree species diversity and was the only patch in this study with this vegetation structure. *Psidium* is a highly invasive plant that forms dense thickets that shade out and suffocate native vegetation. *Ravenala* was also prominent in the Guava Patch. This native tree, which can be invasive, initially establishes in forest light gaps and grows in clusters in secondary forest. *Ravenala* trees are important for lemurs. For example, *Eulemur* frequently used *Ravenala* seedpods and leaves both for negotiating the variable structure of the *Psidium* canopy and for resting and sleeping. *Eulemur* also consumed the nectar, flowers, and seeds of *Ravenala*.

TABLE 4.7. **Average counts of attributes from quantified patches per 100 m²**

PATCH NAME	CANOPY COVER (%)	ELEVATION (m)	1–5 cm dbh/100 m²	6–10 cm dbh/100 m²	11–20 cm dbh/100 m²	>21 cm dbh/100 m²
Guava	70.7	350	9.8	6.3	1.2	1.6
Zubenubi	77.1	453	12.8	13.8	5.3	1.8
Sahakoho	86.5	376	28.8	19.3	14.3	6.8
Sahabefoza	68.2	352	21.5	14.3	4.0	2.5
Fara	70.9	430	26.5	5.5	8.8	3.8
800–900	70.4	332	30.5	15.8	5.3	4.8
Betakonona	77.4	416	33.0	12.5	6.8	6.8
1600	94.5	394	42.8	8.0	7.5	3.0
PATCH NAME	**6–10 cm dbh TRUNK DISTANCE (TD) (m)**	**11–20 cm dbh TD (m)**	**21 cm dbh TD (m)**	**6–10 cm dbh TRUNK SPATIAL PATTERN (SP)**	**11–20 cm dbh SP**	**>21 cm dbh SP**
Guava	<1 to 2–3	3.8	1 to 3–4	Equal/clumped	Equal/clumped	Clumped
Zubenubi	1 to 3–4	1–2	4.0	Equal	Equal	Equal
Sahakoho	<1	<1	1–2	Equal	Equal	Equal
Sahabefoza	1.0	1–2	1–7	Equal	Equal	Clumped
Fara	1 to 3–4	1 to 4–5	1 to 4–5	Clumped	Equal	Clumped
800–900	1.0	2–3	1–6	Equal	Equal/clumped	Clumped
Betakonona	<1	1.0	1 to 3–4	Equal	Equal	Clumped
1600	1.0	1 to 2–3	2 to 4–5	Equal	Equal	Equal
PATCH NAME	**HEIGHT 1 TOTAL CANOPY DISTANCE (TCD)[1] (m)**	**HEIGHT 2 TCD (m)**	**HEIGHT 3 TCD (m)**	**CANOPY HEIGHT 1 (m)**	**CANOPY HEIGHT 2 (m)**	**CANOPY HEIGHT 3 (m)**
Guava	A	F	F	3.7	4.6	8.3
Zubenubi	A	C	E	6.3	9.1	12.3
Sahakoho	A	B	B	5.4	11.9	16.4
Sahabefoza	A	A	E	3.5	7.4	11.4
Fara	B	A	A	4.8	7.8	15.0
800–900	A	B	E	4.1	7.4	11.1
Betakonona	B	A	D	4.6	8.7	17.8
1600	A	B	E	5.2	9.4	14.0
PATCH NAME	**BAMBOO STALKS/100 m²**	**HERBS/100 m²**	**NEW GROWTH 0.3m/100 m²**	**NEW GROWTH 1.25 TO 1.9m/100 m²**	***RAVENALA*/100 m²**	***RAVENALA* HEIGHT (m)**
Guava	0.0	6.2	1.4	1.6	8.3	11.3
Zubenubi	0.0	2.5	1.3	1.0	0.3	11.9

PATCH NAME	BAMBOO STALKS/ 100 m²	HERBS/100 m²	NEW GROWTH 0.3M/100 m²	NEW GROWTH 1.25 TO 1.9m/ 100 m²	*RAVENALA*/ 100 m²	*RAVENALA* HEIGHT (m)
Sahakoho	0.0	4.4	1.2	0.8	3.0	11.3
Sahabefoza	0.0	6.8	0.5	0.7	2.3	7.3
Fara	2.3	13.6	1.3	1.0	0.0	0.0
800–900	0.0	5.1	0.8	2.0	4.8	6.5
Betakonona	0.0	6.1	0.8	2.0	0.0	0.0
1600	0.0	13.3	2.0	5.5	0.5	0.0
PATCH NAME	**GUAVA/ 100 m²**	**DEAD STANDING TREES/100 m²**	**DEAD FALLEN TREES/100 m²**	**SLOPE (DEGREES)**	**PALMS/100 m²**	**LIANAS/ 100 m²**
Guava	84.8	1.5	1.0	29.5	1.3	10.8
Zubenubi	0.0	0.8	4.5	24.3	0.8	110.0
Sahakoho	2.0	0.5	0.8	24.0	2.0	39.0
Sahabefoza	7.5	0.0	0.3	13.5	2.0	16.5
Fara	0.0	2.3	3.8	32.8	4.0	10.3
800–900	1.3	0.0	0.3	27.3	0.8	25.0
Betakonona	0.0	0.0	4.0	32.0	0.0	11.0
1600	0.0	0.0	1.0	20.0	0.0	42.0
PATCH NAME	**EMERGENT TREES/100 m²**	**EMERGENT TREE HEIGHT (m)**	**PRESENCE OF 4TH CANOPY LAYER**	**PRESENCE OF STREAM**	***AFRAMOMUM* IN PATCH**	***AFRAMOMUM* ADJACENT TO PATCH**
Guava	1.0	8.6	No	No	No	Yes
Zubenubi	1.0	20.3	No	No	No	No
Sahakoho	0.3	20.3	No	No	Yes	Yes
Sahabefoza	0.8	14.1	No	Yes	Yes	Yes
Fara	1.0	31.3	Yes	No	Yes	No
800–900	1.0	15.7	No	No	No	No
Betakonona	0.0	0.0	No	No	No	No
1600	1.3	15.6	No	No	No	No

[1] Canopy connectivity measured via the average distance between tree crowns in the canopy layer(s). The distance from one tree crown to the nearest tree in each canopy layer was recorded based on the average for the patch: A, connected (0 m); B, connected/small gap; C, small gap (1–3 m); D, small/medium gap; E, medium gap (4–6 m); F, large gap (7–9 m); G, very large gap (>10 m).

Beyond *Psidium* and *Ravenala*, *Streblus* sp. (Moraceae) trees were the most common in this patch. Canopy cover was variable and ranged from 95.3% to as little as 25.0%, using a spherical densiometer. With lower canopy heights, *Psidium* trunk and branch diameter at breast height (dbh) ranged from 5 to 7 cm, and stems grew several centimeters apart and often intertwined to create dense thickets. There were as many as 134 *Psidium* stems in a 100 m² plot. The Guava Patch had one of the highest temperature averages overall compared to the other patches, most likely because of its proximity to the reserve perimeter and open canopy. Microclimate at the forest edge has been found to differ from that of the forest interior in terms of altered light conditions, decreased humidity, and increased air temperature and wind speed, which in turn affect biological processes, including lemur distribution and occurrence (Burke and Lehman 2014).

FIGURE 4.16 **Examples of patch variation in Betampona. A) Photo looking out at Betampona; B) 1600 Patch; C) 800–900 Patch; D) Sahakoho Patch; E) Sahabefoza Patch; F) area adjacent to Sahabefoza Patch; G) and H) Zubenubi Patch; I) Betakonana Patch; J) Fara Patch; and K) Guava Patch.** (PHOTOS by E. Mertz.)

The Sahabefoza Patch (Figure 4.16f) exemplified Betampona's vegetational heterogeneity. The context of this patch was important in that the adjacent landscape consisted of a large expanse of *Aframomum* that was approximately 30 m wide and 700 m long. There were also two smaller 170 m^2 areas of *Aframomum* in this patch. This plant colonizes open gaps in the forest and can be found growing in patches of various sizes, down to just a few single plants growing randomly throughout the forest. *Aframomum* grows up to 2.5 m tall and there can be as many as 10 stalks in 1 m^2. The structure and composition of *Aframomum* may be a perceived barrier to certain lemur species based on their assessment of patch quality. For example, when *Eulemur* individuals moved through this patch, they often headed west using the smaller trees and low-lying liana tangles on the periphery of the *Aframomum* field. *Hapalemur*, in contrast, moved right through the field at about half a meter from the ground, vertically clinging and leaping from one support to the next.

The Sahabefoza Patch (Figure 4.16e) was the only patch in this study that contained a small stream. There were three main canopy levels, with canopy cover averaging between 55% and 70%. The occasional emergent tree (1/100 m^2) found here was shorter (15.6 m) than emergent trees in other patches. New *Psidium* plants were invading this patch with several thick stands (21/100 m^2). The number of palms was relatively high, and this patch had one of the highest counts of new plant (0–2 m) growth (n = 304). The most common tree species were *Eugenia* sp. (Myrtaceae), *Campylospermum* sp. (Anacardiaceae), and *Gaertnera* sp. (Rubiaceae).

The predominant feature in the Zubenubi Patch (Figure 4.16g) was the high density of lianas. The lianas in this patch formed tangles at all levels and angles, creating essentially one closed prominent canopy layer starting from the ground and extending up to 6.3–7.5 m, masking much of the vertical space. On average, 110 lianas were counted per 100 m^2, although in some areas the number of lianas was as high as 158 per 100 m^2. The height of the first canopy layer was the tallest of all the patches and was the only connected layer in this patch. The Zubenubi Patch had the lowest density of herbaceous new growth and moderate densities of taller new-growth trees. However, this patch exhibited one of the highest total counts of fallen and standing dead trees (n = 21). The most common trees here included *Diospyros haplostylis* (Ebenaceae), *Dombeya* sp. (Malvaceae), *Bronchoneura* sp. (Myristicaceae), and *Treculia* sp. (Moraceae). This detailed assessment of the structural variation within Betampona provides a framework within which to assess variation in lemur community structure, the focus of the next sections.

ASSESSING LEMUR COMMUNITY STRUCTURE AND PATCH USE

Point counts and radio-collared follows were used to investigate the effects of different levels of landscape spatial scale on lemur occurrence. The quantified vegetation patches were also point count stations. Lemurs utilizing these different patches were recorded using all-day fixed-radius (50 m) point counts. The purpose of the point count methodology was to assess the different lemur species that utilized a defined patch to determine how important each of these patches was to lemur community structure in terms of utilization and movement pathways. Three aspects of community structure were considered: the abundance, richness, and diversity of species. When a lemur group was detected in the patch, the following were recorded: species, group composition, group number, activity, positional behavior (e.g., locomotor, postural behaviors), the size, height, and orientation of the substrate used, and quadrant location. The vegetative substrates used by the lemurs were marked with flagging tape so that repeated use of trees and activity in those trees could be recorded. This provided data on the importance of local vegetation characteristics (microhabitat) within a patch to an individual lemur taxon and how this may affect the overall lemur community structure. Specific trees or structural types that were used repeatedly were considered keystone elements.

Radio-collared follows were also used to understand lemur behavior, movement patterns, and occupied areas across the landscape. Two groups of *Propithecus*, five groups of *Indri*, and one group of *Eulemur* were followed on a rotational basis in order to collect behavioral and movement data to complement the point count observations. The behavioral and ecological data described for the point counts were also collected for the radio-collared follows. Additionally, during all-day follows of the radio-collared lemurs, a quick habitat assessment was made for each area the lemurs used and/or moved through. Data were collected on the heights of the different canopy levels and the size of the canopy gap (e.g., connected, 0 m; small gap, 1–3 m; medium gap, 4–6 m; large gap, 7–9 m; extra large gap, >10 m), whether trees were clumped or equal at three different dbh divisions (6–10 cm, 11–20 cm, and 21+ cm), and the distance between the trees at each division. As in the point counts, the vegetative substrates used by the lemurs were marked with flagging tape indicating the date, lemur group, and behavior. Vegetation plots were later established in the primary areas the focus lemur groups utilized to provide a more detailed habitat assessment.

Simpson's Index

Different levels of spatial scale (macro- and microhabitat features) affect lemur community structure in Betampona. The variation observed among diurnal lemur species structure (richness, composition, and abundance) throughout the different quantified patches was detected using all-day fixed-radius (50 m) point counts within the eight quantified patches in Betampona. Simpson's Index (D) (Simpson 1949) was used to quantify the lemur diversity in each patch (Table 4.8). Simpson's Index is a measure that accounts for both richness and evenness. Table 4.8 lists the Simpson's Index along with the abundance, richness (S), and evenness (E) of lemur diversity in each quantified patch. For example, the only lemur observed to use the Guava Patch during the point counts was *Eulemur*, resulting in low species diversity (D = 1, E = 1) (Table 4.9). *Eulemur* groups were predominant in the 1600 Patch, with a couple of sightings of *Propithecus*. The total lemur abundance was high in the 1600 Patch, but this was largely because of one taxon, *Eulemur*. Hence, lemur species diversity was low (D = 0.87) in the 1600 Patch, being unevenly populated by two taxa (E = 0.43). The Fara Patch was one of the most diverse (D = 0.42), populated by four diurnal lemur taxa, and the total abundance of

TABLE 4.8. **Lemur taxa abundance, richness, and evenness in different patches in Betampona**

PATCH NAME	TOTAL ABUNDANCE	RICHNESS (S)	EVENNESS (E)	SIMPSON'S INDEX (D)
Guava	87	1	1	1
1600	56	2	0.43	0.87
Sahabefoza	41	2	0.41	0.82
Zubenubi	52	2	0.37	0.74
Sahakoho	22	3	0.17	0.52
800–900	50	3	0.16	0.47
Fara	55	4	0.11	0.42
Betakonona	28	3	0.13	0.39

TABLE 4.9. **Lemur taxa observed in each patch**

PATCH	GUAVA	800–900	1600	SAHABEFOZA	FARA	BETAKONONA	ZUBENUBI	SAHAKOHO
Lemur taxa	*Eulemur* (30)	*Eulemur* (30)	*Eulemur* (52)	*Eulemur* (37)	*Eulemur* (32)	*Eulemur* (13)	*Indri* (8)	*Indri* (3)
		Propithecus (4)	*Propithecus* (4)	*Hapalemur* (4)	*Hapalemur* (15)	*Indri* (11)	*Eulemur* (44)	*Eulemur* (15)
		Hapalemur (16)			*Propithecus* (3)	*Propithecus* (4)		*Propithecus* (4)
					Varecia (5)	*Avahi* (3)		

Note: (N) is total number of individuals observed.

lemurs was also high in comparison to the other patches. *Eulemur*, once again, was the most abundant in the Fara Patch, followed by *Hapalemur*, and then *Varecia* and *Propithecus* (E = 0.11). In sum, the most diversity was observed in the Fara Patch and the least diversity in the Guava Patch.

This study sought to understand the following questions: Why does this variation in lemur species richness, composition, and abundance exist, and how do local vegetation attributes within a patch and properties across the landscape affect this differing lemur community structure? Although a community ecology approach was used and is discussed in more depth elsewhere (Mertz 2012), *Eulemur* is the focus of the next section, which explores the aspects of perceived habitat quality, dynamics of patch context, and effects of micro- and macrohabitat structural variables on habitat selection and movement patterns.

Microhabitat

Microhabitat includes the small-scale attributes (e.g., vegetation structural characteristics such as tree dbh, canopy cover, height, connectivity; spatial distance and distribution of trees; temperature; keystone structures) defined in each patch. Microhabitat in each patch affected lemur community structure based on point counts, although the degree to which each lemur taxon was affected varied. Specifically, *Eulemur* utilized all eight of the quantified patches in Betampona. However, this species preferred certain patches over others and engaged in certain behaviors (e.g., resting, eating, sleeping, moving) at a higher frequency in some patches compared to others (χ^2 = 178.8, df = 14, p < 0.001). These more-frequented patches included 1600, 800–900, Guava, Zubenubi, and Sahabefoza. The least amount of time was spent in the Betakonona Patch.

This variation is perhaps attributable to microhabitat and forest structural attributes. For example, the 800–900 Patch had one of the highest average abundances of liana (25/100 m^2) and dead standing and fallen trees in the horizontal and vertical space. The 800–900 Patch also had a high density of 1–5 cm dbh trees, further contributing to the closed nature of this patch. Overall, the canopy height was also relatively low. A keystone feature that may have influenced the higher percentage of resting behaviors in this patch was several *Canarium madagascariense* (Burseraceae) trees covered with lianas, providing a protective refuge. Several different groups of *Eulemur* were observed using these structures for rest and different social interactions. They were also observed to preferentially occupy the Zubenubi Patch, another patch with a high abundance of lianas and fallen dead trees. This example highlights the importance of habitat quality classification criteria or standards from the point of view of the researcher versus the organism. Although these sites might be perceived as degraded by a researcher, they were nonetheless important areas for *Eulemur*.

In contrast, the Betakonona Patch, where *Eulemur* was less frequently observed, had low abundances of liana and dead trees/vegetation in comparison to the 800–900 Patch. Additionally, the Betakonona Patch had one of the tallest canopy heights, particularly for canopy layer three, and included a connected canopy layer one and two. The patch also had increased vertical open space because of the higher canopy and little or no *Ravenala*. *Eulemur* actively used *Ravenala* for feeding, resting, and moving, and a lack of these trees in an area possibly influenced their patch choice. The Betakonona Patch contained seven *Canarium* trees, but these were not used by *Eulemur* as observed in the 800–900 Patch. Notably, these trees were not taken over by dense understory and lianas like those trees in the 800–900 Patch.

Specific analysis of the vertical and horizontal substrate use by the radio-collared *Eulemur* group illustrated some patterns consistent with the use of patches containing certain quantified attributes observed in the point counts (e.g., the 800–900 Patch). This cohesive small group of three *Eulemur* spent 59.0% of the time in their total activity budget resting. *Eulemur* rested mainly on small oblique substrates at a height of 7–11 m in the periphery of the tree. These lemurs used other substrates outside the tree canopy for rest as well, including *Ravenala* seedpods and leaves, single lianas, and liana tangles. The connectivity between the canopy and vegetation also affected their resting behavior, where the group notably rested in connected canopy (49.5%). *Eulemur* frequently used space that was crowded with tree falls, dead fallen and standing trees, liana clusters, bamboo tangles, introduced species, and a low canopy.

In summary, *Eulemur* was found within patches that contained features often associated with "degraded" forest. *Eulemur* seems to prefer areas with abundant lianas that form dense thickets in the upper canopy or lower understory. The abundance and diversity of lianas has been observed to increase in areas of disturbed forest (Laurance et al. 2001), as well as in transitional areas between old-growth and secondary forests (DeWalt et al. 2000). Lianas can produce many rooting stems and therefore can colonize disturbed areas quite rapidly (Schnitzer and Bongers 2002). *Eulemur* used these dense liana thickets both as a food source, consuming the leaves and fruits, and as a safe refuge for resting behaviors. *Eulemur* also used individual lianas that bridged the gaps of sub-canopy openings.

Macrohabitat

Macrohabitat (e.g., landscape configuration and composition) influenced lemur community structure in Betampona. For example, the only lemurs observed transitioning out of the forest and into the Guava Patch were *Eulemur* and *Hapalemur*. *Propithecus* was observed in this transition area but not farther into the Guava Patch. This may have acted as a perceived boundary in the environment, thus limiting the connectivity of the forest for some of the lemur taxa. *Eulemur* was found to utilize a wide range of forest structures, including areas of undisturbed forest and the *Psidium*, *Aframomum*, and transition forest areas. As such, these lemurs were not limited in their dispersal or use of different patches throughout the entire reserve. This may indicate that macrohabitat and perceived landscape boundaries have less of an effect on brown lemurs in Betampona. This analysis provides further support for the behavioral and ecological flexibility observed within the genus *Eulemur*. This plasticity may also account for the consistently higher abundance of brown lemurs throughout the patches in Betampona in comparison to the other diurnal lemur taxa.

Social boundaries and habitat quality may be more limiting than landscape constraints in the small fragment of Betampona. For example, the focal *Eulemur* group had quite a small home range of 2.6 ha; this taxon is documented to have home ranges of 10–16 ha (Johnson et al., pp. 1941–46). This particular *Eulemur* group was often supplanted out of its space by other *Eulemur* groups and by other lemur species (e.g., *Varecia*). Results from *Indri* studies in Betampona suggest that habitat quality and degradation are most likely influential in determining the population density and range size of different groups of *Indri* (Britt et al. 2002; Glessner and Britt 2005). An increase in poor "quality" habitat may result in an increase in *Indri* density in suitable habitat, accompanied by a decrease in home range size because of the limited suitable habitat available. Based on the results of their density study of this species, Glessner and Britt (2005) suggest that unoccupied suitable habitat is limited in Betampona. Similar to *Indri*, *Eulemur* in Betampona may be affected by the paucity of suitable unoccupied habitat, with the response being smaller home ranges for some groups. Nonetheless, the heterogeneity within the small home range, in addition to a few keystone fruit trees, perhaps allowed *Eulemur* to persist in such a limited space.

Despite the limited forest surface area of Betampona, heterogeneity in the horizontal and vertical planes compensates for the relatively small area, supporting the coexistence of 11 lemur taxa. Spatial heterogeneity between the patches also supports abundant local biodiversity, with 639 species of flora and fauna identified in Betampona thus far (Goodman et al. 2018). Species-area relationships are often used to evaluate the loss of biodiversity (Ney-Nifle and Mangel 2000); however, area by itself cannot always completely explain the decline of some populations (Matias et al. 2011). The presence of more species in heterogeneous landscapes may be better explained by the presence or absence of particular types of sub-habitats, and not just by patch size alone. Heterogeneous environments maintain more species diversity than homogeneous ones, allowing for species coexistence, although negative heterogeneity-diversity relationships appear to be more common at smaller scales (e.g., Tamme et al. 2010). The structural variability that accompanies heterogeneity in the environment and the subsequent resource availability can affect the distribution of different species (Tews et al. 2004). Thus, a reduction in habitat heterogeneity is likely to also result in a reduction in species assemblages (McKinney 1998; Hanski 2005). Landscape patterns that continue to maintain a certain level of heterogeneity will produce the largest positive biodiversity response.

The results of this case study have critical implications for the direction of conservation management on Madagascar, as well as for understanding the complex processes that precede extinction. Understanding and predicting the impact of human behavior and modification on biodiversity is increasingly important to the survival and sustainability of ecosystems. Evaluating the prospects of the biodiversity that remains in small, isolated forests is central to conservation management on Madagascar.

Subject editors: Amanda H. Armstrong and Steven M. Goodman

FRUGIVORY AND SEED DISPERSAL

O. H. Razafindratsima, J. Tonos, V. Ramananjato, A. E. Dunham, and M. N. N. Andriamavosoloarisoa

The majority of flowering plants on Madagascar have traits adapted for primary seed dispersal (removal and movement of seeds away from the parent) by fruit-eating animals (frugivores), especially by vertebrates (Albert-Daviaud et al. 2018, 2020). Despite high plant diversity and endemism (Callmander et al. 2011), Madagascar's forest ecosystems have a low diversity of frugivorous species relative to the Neotropics or African forest systems (Fleming et al. 1987; Hawkins and Goodman 2003), and many of the Malagasy frugivores are highly threatened by pervasive anthropogenic pressures and climate change (Dunham et al. 2008; Dewar and Richard 2012; Schwitzer et al. 2014). This is alarming because Madagascar has already lost some of its seed dispersers, which has left many plant species "orphans," such that their continued existence is of great concern (Godfrey et al. 2008; Andriantsaralaza et al. 2010; Albert-Daviaud et al. 2020).

Seed dispersal is vital for plant fitness and plays a fundamental role in shaping the diversity, structure, composition, and spatial arrangement of plant communities, which can have important implications for ecosystem integrity (Howe and Smallwood 1982). Seed dispersal determines seedling establishment, maintains gene flow within and among plant populations, and allows the colonization of newly formed habitats (Howe and Smallwood 1982; Wang and Smith 2002; Beckman et al. 2019). Also, long-distance dispersal of seeds is crucial for population spread and the maintenance of genetic movement among populations (Nathan 2006). In addition, seed dispersal has the potential to influence the ability of a plant population to escape local environmental changes (Beckman et al. 2019), which is critical in the face of current global changes.

Animals can play an important role in primary seed dispersal by swallowing and defecating seeds (endozoochory), by carrying fruits and seeds that get stuck to feathers, fur, or skin (epizoochory), or by deliberately carrying seeds away (synzoochory) (Schupp et al. 2019) (Figure 4.17). The passage of seeds through the animal gut, including retention in the gizzard, can be critical for the germination of many plant species that are adapted for endozoochory. The removal of pulp and the mechanical and/or chemical scarification of the seed coat can improve a seed's capacity and speed of germination (Traveset and Verdú 2002; Traveset et al. 2007). Animal species with long gut-retention time and those that can travel long distances are particularly important in moving seeds far from their source. Some carnivores can also participate in seed dispersal through diploendozoochory (Figure 4.17), in which predators may inadvertently consume and deposit viable, intact seeds contained in the guts of their prey (Hämäläinen et al. 2017). Such a process could not only limit any potential damage that would otherwise occur within the prey's gut but could also allow seeds to be dispersed beyond the prey's home range (S. Platt et al. 2013; Hämäläinen et al. 2017). After reaching a surface, seeds can be secondarily dispersed by seed-caching animals through scatter-hoarding—the spatially scattered burial of single seeds in the soil or under piles of leaf litter (Forget 1990). Scatter-hoarding can enhance plant recruitment if the seeds are deposited in favorable locations with adequate conditions for germination (including protection against fires and desiccation) or are forgotten and not retrieved (Forget et al. 2001; Vander Wall and Longand 2004; Sommers and Chesson 2016).

The significant decline or loss of important seed dispersers on Madagascar could result in cascading negative impacts in an ecosystem, affecting not only the persistence of many plant species but also the ability of the ecosystem to provide vital goods and services to human society (Terborgh et al. 2008; Galetti and Dirzo 2013; Caughlin et al. 2014; Razafindratsima and Dunham 2015). For example, using empirical data from field observations and experiments, Razafindratsima and Dunham (2015) demonstrated that the absence of large-bodied lemur frugivores, which are responsible for nonrandom dispersal of seeds with respect to forest canopy cover, decreased per-seed sapling recruitment of the long-lived canopy tree *Cryptocarya crassifolia* fourfold in the moist evergreen forest of Ranomafana National Park. Additionally, in the same system, Razafindratsima et al. (2018a) reported that losing large lemur frugivores could result in a decrease in the forest's potential to store carbon, based on simulation models under different scenarios of plant community changes. If no other mechanism can fill the functional gap of seed dispersal loss, many plant species may become "living dead" (Janzen 2001), which may eventually lead to their extinction at local and even global scales (Vidal et al. 2014). Understanding which animal species function as seed dispersers and how they do so is important for assessing and mitigating the impacts of seed disperser loss on plants across Madagascar.

FIGURE 4.17 **Types of primary seed dispersal by animals.**

TABLE 4.10. **List of known extant vertebrate species on Madagascar consuming fruits and seeds, and their potential roles as primary or secondary seed dispersers**

SCIENTIFIC NAME	VERNACULAR NAME	SEED DISPERSAL ROLE	REFERENCES FOR FRUITS IN DIET AND/OR DISPERSAL ROLE
FISH			
Osteomugil robustus	Robust Mullet	Unknown	Thérézien 1963
Paratilapia polleni	Russian Desman	Unknown	Randrianjatovo 2010
Paretroplus kieneri	Kotsovato	Unknown	Thérézien 1963
P. petiti	Kotso	Unknown	Kiener 1963; Thérézien 1963
Scatophagus tetracanthus	Scatty	Unknown	Thérézien 1963
Tilapia rendalli	Blue Tilapia	Unknown	Thérézien 1963
REPTILES			
Astrochelys radiata	Radiated Tortoise	Unknown	Rasoma et al. 2013
Chalarodon madagascariensis	Malagasy Collared Lizard	Unknown	Blanc 1969
Erymnochelys madagascariensis	Madagascar Big-headed Turtle	Disperser	Garcia 2005
Furcifer oustaleti	Malagasy Giant Chameleon	Unknown	Takahashi 2008
Geckolepis maculata	Fish-scale Gecko	Unknown	Valido and Olesen 2019
Lygodactylus spp.	Dwarf geckos	Unknown	Valido and Olesen 2019
Oplurus cuvieri	Cuvier's Madagascar Iguana	Unknown	Ganzhorn et al. 1999; Randriamahazo and Mori 2012
Phelsuma spp.	Day geckos	Unknown	Valido and Olesen 2019
Pyxis planicauda	Flat-tailed Tortoise	Unknown	Ganzhorn et al. 1999
Zonosaurus laticaudatus	Western Girdled Lizard	Unknown	Ganzhorn et al. 1999
BIRDS			
Agapornis canus	Gray-headed Lovebird	Unknown	Razafindratsima et al. 2018b
Alectroenas madagascariensis	Madagascar Blue-pigeon	Disperser	Bollen et al. 2004a
Anas erythrorhyncha	Red-billed Duck	Unknown	Razafindratsima et al. 2018b
Artamella viridis	White-headed Vanga	Unknown	Razafindratsima et al. 2018b
Copsychus albospecularis	Madagascar Magpie-robin	Unknown	Razafindratsima et al. 2018b
Coracina cinerea	Madagascar Cuckooshrike	Unknown	Razafindratsima et al. 2018b
Coracopsis nigra	Lesser Vasa Parrot	Disperser / predator	Böhning-Gaese et al. 1995, 1999; Scharfe and Schlund 1996; Bleher and Böhning-Gaese 2001
C. vasa	Greater Vasa Parrot	Disperser / predator	Scharfe and Schlund 1996; Bollen et al. 2004a; Bollen and Van Elsacker 2004
Corvus albus	Pied Crow	Unknown	Razafindratsima et al. 2018b
Coua caerulea	Blue Coua	Unknown	Razafindratsima et al. 2018b
C. coquereli	Coquerel's Coua	Unknown	Razafindratsima et al. 2018b
C. cristata	Crested Coua	Unknown	Razafindratsima et al. 2018b
C. reynaudii	Red-fronted Coua	Unknown	Razafindratsima et al. 2018b

(continued overleaf)

TABLE 4.10. ***continued***

SCIENTIFIC NAME	VERNACULAR NAME	SEED DISPERSAL ROLE	REFERENCES FOR FRUITS IN DIET AND/OR DISPERSAL ROLE
C. ruficeps olivaceiceps	Olive-capped Coua	Unknown	Razafindratsima et al. 2018b
C. r. ruficeps	Red-capped Coua	Unknown	Razafindratsima et al. 2018b
C. serriana	Red-breasted Coua	Unknown	Razafindratsima et al. 2018b
C. verreauxi	Verreaux's Coua	Unknown	Razafindratsima et al. 2018b
Cyanolanius madagascarinus	Blue Vanga	Disperser	N. N. Raoelinjanakolona, unpublished data
Dendrocygna bicolor	Fulvous Whistling-duck	Unknown	Razafindratsima et al. 2018b
D. viduata	White-faced Whistling-duck	Unknown	Razafindratsima et al. 2018b
Dicrurus forficatus	Crested Drongo	Disperser / predator	Scharfe and Schlund 1996; Bleher and Böhning-Gaese 2001
Eurystomus glaucurus	Broad-billed Roller	Unknown	Razafindratsima et al. 2018b
Fulica cristata	Red-knobbed Coot	Unknown	Razafindratsima et al. 2018b
Gallinula chloropus	Eurasian Moorhen	Unknown	Razafindratsima et al. 2018b
Hartlaubius auratus	Madagascar Starling	Unknown	Goodman et al. 1997; Sewall 2008
Hypsipetes madagascariensis	Madagascar Bulbul	Disperser / predator	Scharfe and Schlund 1996; Bleher and Böhning-Gaese 2001; Bollen et al. 2004a; Bollen 2007
Leptopterus chabert	Chabert Vanga	Disperser	N. N. Raoelinjanakolona, unpublished data
Limosa lapponica	Bar-tailed Godwit	Unknown	Razafindratsima et al. 2018b
Margaroperdix madagarensis	Madagascar Partridge	Unknown	Razafindratsima et al. 2018b
Monias benschi	Subdesert Mesite	Unknown	Razafindratsima et al. 2018b
Monticola imerina	Littoral Rock-thrush	Unknown	Razafindratsima et al. 2018b
M. sharpei	Forest Rock-thrush	Unknown	Razafindratsima et al. 2018b
Nelicurvius nelicourvi	Nelicourvi Weaver	Unknown	Razafindratsima et al. 2018b
Neodrepanis coruscans	Common Sunbird-asity	Unknown	Razafindratsima et al. 2018b
Nesoenas picturata	Madagascar Turtle-dove	Predator	Bollen et al. 2004b; Bollen 2007
Numenius arquata	Eurasian Curlew	Unknown	Razafindratsima et al. 2018b
N. phaeopus	Whimbrel	Unknown	Razafindratsima et al. 2018b
Philepitta castanea	Velvet Asity	Disperser	Rakotomanana et al. 2003; Rakotomanana 2016
P. schlegeli	Schlegel's Asity	Unknown	Razafindratsima et al. 2018b
Saxicola torquatus	African Stonechat	Unknown	Razafindratsima et al. 2018b
Spatula hottentota	Hottentot Teal	Unknown	Razafindratsima et al. 2018b
Treron australis	Madagascar Green-Pigeon	Disperser	Bollen et al. 2004a
Zosterops maderaspatanus	Madagascar White-eye	Unknown	Goodman et al. 1997; Bollen et al. 2004b
PRIMATES			
Allocebus trichotis	Hairy-eared Dwarf Lemur	Unknown	Razafindratsima et al. 2018b
Avahi betsileo	Betsileo Woolly Lemur	Unknown	Razafindratsima et al. 2018b

SCIENTIFIC NAME	VERNACULAR NAME	SEED DISPERSAL ROLE	REFERENCES FOR FRUITS IN DIET AND/OR DISPERSAL ROLE
A. cleesei	Bemaraha Woolly Lemur	Unknown	Razafindratsima et al. 2018b
A. laniger	Eastern Woolly Lemur	Unknown	Razafindratsima et al. 2018b
A. meridionalis	Southern Woolly Lemur	Unknown	Razafindratsima et al. 2018b
A. peyrierasi	Peyriéras' Woolly Lemur	Unknown	Razafindratsima et al. 2018b
A. ramanantsoavani	Manombo Woolly Lemur	Unknown	Razafindratsima et al. 2018b
A. unicolor	Sambirano Woolly Lemur	Unknown	Razafindratsima et al. 2018b
Cheirogaleus crossleyi	Crossley's Dwarf Lemur	Disperser	Domoinaharivelo 2014
C. major	Greater Dwarf Lemur	Disperser	Bollen et al. 2004a, 2004b; Lahann 2007
C. medius	Fat-tailed Dwarf Lemur	Disperser	Bollen et al. 2004a, 2004b; Lahann 2007
C. sibreei	Sibree's Dwarf Lemur	Disperser	Domoinaharivelo 2014
Daubentonia madagascariensis	Aye-aye	Unknown	J. Solofondranohatra 2014
Eulemur albifrons	White-fronted Brown Lemur	Disperser	Randriatavy 2003; Razafindratsima 2009
E. cinereiceps	White-collared Brown Lemur	Unknown	Ralainasolo et al. 2008; Andriamaharoa et al. 2010; Rafenoarisoa 2016
E. collaris	Red-collared Brown Lemur	Disperser	Bollen et al. 2004b; E. Rakotonirina 2004; Bollen 2007
E. coronatus	Crowned Lemur	Disperser	Randriambololomamonjy 2006; Ravelomalala 2015
E. flavifrons	Blue-eyed Black Lemur	Unknown	Razafindratsima et al. 2018b
E. fulvus	Brown Lemur	Disperser	Rakotoson 2001; Sato 2012, 2018
E. macaco	Black Lemur	Disperser	Birkinshaw 1995, 1999, 2001
E. mongoz	Mongoose Lemur	Unknown	Razafindratsima et al. 2018b
E. rubriventer	Red-bellied Lemur	Disperser	Dew and Wright 1998; Overdorff and Strait 1998; Razafindratsima et al. 2014
E. rufifrons	Red-fronted Brown Lemur	Disperser	Scharfe and Schlund 1996; Dew and Wright 1998; Overdorff and Strait 1998; Spehn and Ganzhorn 2000; Razafindratsima et al. 2014
E. rufus	Rufous Brown Lemur	Unknown	Razafindratsima et al. 2018b
E. sanfordi	Sanford's Brown Lemur	Disperser	Chen et al. 2016
Hapalemur aureus	Golden Bamboo Lemur	Unknown	Tan 1999; Norosoarinaivo 2000; Rahalinarivo 2007
H. griseus	Gray Bamboo Lemur	Unknown	Ganzhorn 1987; Grassi 2006; Rahalinarivo 2007
H. meridionalis	Southern Bamboo Lemur	Unknown	Eppley et al. 2011
Indri indri	Indri	Disperser / predator	Powzyk and Mowry 2003; Randriamandratonirina 2003

(continued overleaf)

TABLE 4.10. ***continued***

SCIENTIFIC NAME	VERNACULAR NAME	SEED DISPERSAL ROLE	REFERENCES FOR FRUITS IN DIET AND/OR DISPERSAL ROLE
Lemur catta	Ring-tailed Lemur	Disperser	Bodin et al. 2006; Andriamalala 2007; Mertl-Millhollen et al. 2011
Lepilemur edwardsi	Milne-Edwards' Sportive Lemur	Unknown	Razanahoera 1981
L. leucopus	White-footed Sportive Lemur	Unknown	Petter et al. 1977; Ramalanjaona 2013
Microcebus berthae	Madame Berthe's Mouse Lemur	Unknown	Dammhahn and Kappeler 2008b; Mevanarivo 2008
M. bongolavensis	Bongolava Mouse Lemur	Unknown	Razafindratsima et al. 2018b
M. danfossi	Ambarijeby Mouse Lemur	Unknown	Razafindratsima et al. 2018b
M. griseorufus	Gray-brown Mouse Lemur	Disperser	Génin and Rambeloarivony 2018
M. jollyae	Jolly's Mouse Lemur	Disperser	Ramananjato et al. 2020
M. lehilahytsara	Goodman's Mouse Lemur	Unknown	Razafindratsima et al. 2018b
M. mamiratra	Nosy Be Mouse Lemur	Unknown	Razafindratsima et al. 2018b
M. mittermeieri	Mittermeier's Mouse Lemur	Unknown	Razafindratsima et al. 2018b
M. murinus	Gray Mouse Lemur	Disperser	Lahann 2007; Valenta et al. 2013
M. myoxinus	Peters' Mouse Lemur	Unknown	Razafindratsima et al. 2018b
M. ravelobensis	Golden-brown Mouse Lemur	Disperser	Valenta et al. 2013
M. rufus	Rufous Mouse Lemur	Disperser	Atsalis 1999
M. sambiranensis	Sambirano Mouse Lemur	Unknown	Razafindratsima et al. 2018b
M. simmonsi	Simmons' Mouse Lemur	Unknown	Razafindratsima et al. 2018b
M. tavaratra	Tavaratra Mouse Lemur	Unknown	Razafindratsima et al. 2018b
Mirza coquereli	Coquerel's Giant Mouse Lemur	Unknown	Razafindratsima et al. 2018b
M. zaza	Northern Giant Mouse Lemur	Unknown	Razafindratsima et al. 2018b
Prolemur simus	Greater Bamboo Lemur	Unknown	Tan 1999; Ravelojaona 2014
Propithecus candidus	Silky Sifaka	Unknown	Razafindratsima et al. 2018b
P. coquereli	Coquerel's Sifaka	Unknown	Razafindratsima et al. 2018b
P. coronatus	Crowned Sifaka	Disperser / predator	Razakanirina 2010
P. deckenii	Decken's Sifaka	Unknown	Razafindratsima et al. 2018b
P. diadema	Diademed Sifaka	Predator	Powzyk and Mowry 2003, 2007
P. edwardsi	Milne-Edwards' Sifaka	Disperser / predator	Dew and Wright 1998; Overdorff and Strait 1998; Wright et al. 2011
P. perrieri	Perrier's Sifaka	Unknown	Razafindratsima et al. 2018b
P. tattersalli	Tattersall's Sifaka	Unknown	Razafindratsima et al. 2018b
P. verreauxi	Verreaux's Sifaka	Disperser	Scharfe and Schlund 1996; Yamashita 1996; Simmen et al. 2003

SCIENTIFIC NAME	VERNACULAR NAME	SEED DISPERSAL ROLE	REFERENCES FOR FRUITS IN DIET AND/OR DISPERSAL ROLE
Varecia rubra	Red Ruffed Lemur	Disperser	Razafindratsima and Razafimahatratra 2010; Razafindratsima and Martinez 2012; Martinez and Razafindratsima 2014
V. variegata	Black and White Ruffed Lemur	Disperser	Dew and Wright 1998; Moses and Semple 2011; Razafindratsima et al. 2014
BATS			
Eidolon dupreanum	Malagasy Straw-colored Fruit Bat	Disperser	Picot et al. 2007; Racey et al. 2010
Pteropus rufus	Madagascar Flying Fox	Disperser	Bollen and Van Elsacker 2002; R. Jenkins et al. 2007; Long and Racey 2007; Racey et al. 2010; Oleksy et al. 2017
Rousettus madagascariensis	Madagascar Rousette	Disperser	Andrianaivoarivelo et al. 2011; Andrianaivoarivelo et al. 2012a; Vololona 2020
RODENTS			
Brachytarsomys albicauda	White-tailed Tree Rat	Unknown	Razafindratsima et al. 2018b
B. villosa	Hairy-tailed Tree Rat	Unknown	Razafindratsima et al. 2018b
Brachyuromys betsileoensis	Lesser Short-tailed Rat	Unknown	Razafindratsima et al. 2018b
B. ramirohitra	Greater Short-tailed Rat	Unknown	Razafindratsima et al. 2018b
Eliurus antsingy	Tsingy Tufted-tail Rat	Unknown	Razafindratsima et al. 2018b
E. ellermani	Ellerman's Tufted-tail Rat	Unknown	Razafindratsima et al. 2018b
E. grandidieri	Grandidier's Tufted-tail Rat	Unknown	Razafindratsima et al. 2018b
E. majori	Major's Tufted-tail Rat	Unknown	Razafindratsima et al. 2018b
E. minor	Lesser Tufted-tail Rat	Unknown	Razafindratsima et al. 2018b
E. myoxinus	Western Tufted-tail Rat	Unknown	Razafindratsima et al. 2018b
E. penicillatus	White-tipped Tufted-tail Rat	Unknown	Razafindratsima et al. 2018b
E. petteri	Petter's Tufted-tail Rat	Unknown	Razafindratsima et al. 2018b
E. tanala	Tanala Tufted-tail Rat	Unknown	Razafindratsima et al. 2018b
E. webbi	Webb's Tufted-tail Rat	Secondary disperser / predator	Goodman 1994; Goodman and Sterling 1996; Bollen et al. 2004a
Gymnuromys roberti	Robert's Forest Rat	Unknown	Razafindratsima et al. 2018b
Hypogeomys antimena	Malagasy Giant Jumping Rat	Unknown	Razafindratsima et al. 2018b
Macrotarsomys bastardi	Western Big-footed Mouse	Unknown	Razafindratsima et al. 2018b
M. ingens	Long-tailed Big-footed Mouse	Unknown	Razafindratsima et al. 2018b
Monticolomys koopmani	Koopman's Mountain-dwelling Mouse	Unknown	Razafindratsima et al. 2018b
Nesomys audeberti	Lowland Red Forest Rat	Unknown	Razafindratsima et al. 2018b
N. lambertoni	Tsingy Red Forest Rat	Unknown	Razafindratsima et al. 2018b
N. rufus	Eastern Red Forest Rat	Secondary disperser / predator	Razafindratsima 2017

(continued overleaf)

TABLE 4.10. ***continued***

SCIENTIFIC NAME	VERNACULAR NAME	SEED DISPERSAL ROLE	REFERENCES FOR FRUITS IN DIET AND/OR DISPERSAL ROLE
Rattus rattus	Black Rat	Secondary disperser / predator	Goodman and Sterling 1996; Bollen et al. 2004a
Voalavo gymnocaudus	Northern White-tailed Mountain Mouse	Unknown	Razafindratsima et al. 2018b
OTHER VERTEBRATES			
Eupleres goudotii	Falanouc	Unknown	Goodman 2012
Galidia elegans	Ring-tailed Vontsira	Unknown	Nowak 2005; Garbutt 2007
Potamochoerus larvatus	African Bush Pig	Disperser	Ganzhorn et al. 1999; Randriantavy et al. 2014
Salanoia concolor	Brown-tailed Vontsira	Unknown	Nowak 2005; Garbutt 2007

Note: "Unknown" seed dispersal role means that they have been observed to consume fruits and/or seeds but there is no known evidence of seed dispersal. A species is considered to have a "seed dispersal role" in this list if it has been observed to disperse seeds.

Here, we provide a comprehensive review of frugivory and seed dispersal by vertebrates across Madagascar's landscapes (Table 4.10). We include in this assessment any fruit or seed eaters that could provide seed-dispersal services. Although seed eaters may often destroy seeds, seed predation does not necessarily preclude the potential of a species to be an effective seed disperser because partially consumed seeds can still be viable (Vallejo-Marín et al. 2006; Loayza et al. 2014). In fact, if the cotyledon or the root apex of the predated seed is still intact, it can still germinate (Loayza et al. 2014). For each taxonomic group, we highlight what is known and present what is missing to direct future research. We identify their role in primary and secondary seed dispersal and discuss the consequences of the disruption of seed dispersal interactions in Malagasy ecosystems. Additionally, we briefly discuss seed dispersal by invertebrates on Madagascar.

CURRENT STATE OF KNOWLEDGE OF SEED DISPERSAL BY MALAGASY VERTEBRATES

Fish

Fish can play an important role in the dispersal of plant species along riparian zones and estuarine channels, in wetland ecosystems, and during high flooding following heavy rains (Tiffney 1984, 2004; Horn et al. 2011). They can help maintain upstream plant populations (Horn 1997) and ensure the long-distance dispersal of the plant species they consume (Anderson et al. 2011). While seed dispersal by fish (ichthyochory) has not yet been evaluated on Madagascar, at least six species of freshwater fish are reported to consume fruits and/or seeds on the island (Table 4.10), but whether they disperse seeds is unknown.

Reptiles

Seed dispersal by reptiles (saurochory) is an ancient seed dispersal mode thought to benefit the first gymnosperms and angiosperms (van der Pijl 1982; Tiffney 1984, 2004). Saurochory is still a common and important process for many island ecosystems (Olesen and Valido 2003), yet studies of saurochory are extremely rare on Madagascar. Three species of Malagasy lizards, *Chalarodon madagascariensis*, *Oplurus cuvieri*, and *Zonosaurus laticaudatus*, are known to consume fruits and/or seeds from shrubs and cactus-like plants, and herbaceous berries (Blanc 1969; Ganzhorn et al. 1999; Randriamahazo and Mori 2012). However, no research has been conducted yet to assess their seed-dispersal effectiveness (Valido and Olesen 2019). Among chameleons, only *Furcifer oustaleti* is reported to consume fruits, and the lingual prehension of fruits suggests that seeds are directly swallowed (Takahashi 2008); thus, the seeds could remain intact and are likely to germinate.

The seed-dispersal roles of Malagasy tortoises, such as *Astrochelys radiata* and *Pyxis planicauda* (see Pedrono et al., pp. 1463–68), have not yet been assessed either, despite reports of fruit consumption on both native and non-native plant species (Ganzhorn et al. 1999; Leuteritz 2003; Rasoma et al. 2013). However, *Erymnochelys madagascariensis* (Malagasy Big-headed Turtle) (Kuchling et al., pp. 1469–74) has been reported to disperse the seeds of various riparian plant species, which were defecated partially digested and viable (Garcia 2005).

Finally, crocodilians can act as either primary or secondary seed dispersers. On Madagascar, *Crocodylus niloticus* (Nile Crocodile) is a fearsome predator and is widespread across large lakes and rivers (Kuchling et al. 2003; Kuchling et al., pp. 1458–63). However, crocodilians may occasionally consume seeds as gastroliths (gizzard stones) to help digestion and may deliberately eat fruits when they are found on the shore (S. Platt et al. 2013). Up to 46 genera of plant species were reported to constitute crocodilian diets across the world (S. Platt et al. 2013), yet the germinability and survival of ingested seeds remain unexplored. Additionally, crocodilians may also participate in seed dispersal through diploendozoochory, but studies on such potential are currently lacking.

Birds

Approximately 18% of the 242 bird species on Madagascar are known to consume fruits (Razafindratsima et al. 2018b) (Table 4.10). The depauperate nature of the frugivorous bird community across the island is reflected in the fruit and seed traits of the island's fruiting plants, the majority of which are more closely associated with endozoochory by primates (Voigt et al. 2009; Albert-Daviaud et al. 2018). It has been proposed that the low richness of frugivorous birds might have resulted from the island's low diversity of keystone fruit species, such as figs, which are highly diverse in other tropical ecosystems (Goodman and Ganzhorn 1997; Wright et al. 2005). The lack of these keystone fruit resources, generally low fruit abundance, and periods of fruit scarcity may have prevented the evolution or establishment of a wider diversity of frugivorous birds on the island. Though their diversity is low, their high abundance, use of fragmented habitats, and consumption of smaller-seeded fruits may allow them to play a role complementary to that of the larger frugivorous lemurs; however, further work is still needed to quantify the contribution of Malagasy birds to seed dispersal services and to assess their complementary role.

Observations to date have indicated that various species may play an important role as seed dispersers, particularly in fragmented and degraded habitats (Table 4.10). Bollen et al. (2004a) showed that Madagascar's frugivorous pigeons (*Treron australis* and *Alectroenas madagascariensis*) and *Hypsipetes madagascariensis* (Malagasy Bulbul) dispersed seeds between forest fragments and deposited pioneer plant species into gaps. Such results highlight the important role that birds can play as dispersers across matrix habitats, which in general are avoided by lemur seed dispersers. These three species, as well as *Coracopsis vasa* (Greater Vasa Parrot) and *C. nigra* (Lesser Vasa Parrot), are also known to forage on *Ficus* fruits, though their role as dispersers is unresolved. The parrot species, in particular, may play dubious roles as dispersers, as they routinely peck at fruits, drop them near the parent tree, or simply destroy the seeds they consume by breaking or digesting them (Goodman and Ganzhorn 1997; Bollen et al. 2004a).

A study of the frugivorous *Philepitta castanea* (Velvet Asity) found it to be an effective disperser of various shrub species in forest understory with a dispersal distance of 33.3 m in one hour, which allows them to carry seeds beyond the parent plant (Rakotomanana et al. 2003; see Prum and Razafindratsita, pp. 1687–93). The results of germination after gut passage by *P. castanea* were, however, conflicting, with negative effects on some of the plant species they defecated or regurgitated (Rakotomanana et al. 2003; Razafindratsita and Zack 2009). *Philepitta castanea* is a forest-dependent understory species, and its role in dispersing the seeds of different understory plants at an ecosystem level remains largely unresolved.

Birds of prey could also contribute to seed dispersal through diploendozoochory (Figure 4.17), but studies are lacking. For instance, *Polyboroides radiata* (Madagascar Harrier-hawk) and *Accipiter henstii* (Henst's Goshawk) feed extensively on diurnal lemurs (Wright et al. 1997; Karpanty 2006; see Goodman and Ganzhorn, pp. 1829–38), most of which are highly frugivorous.

Primates

Madagascar's unique nonhuman primates, lemurs, have been recognized to play important roles in the dispersal of many flowering plant species (Razafindratsima 2014; Albert-Daviaud et al. 2018). Sixty-three extant lemur species are reported as having fruits and/or seeds in their diet, either exclusively or opportunistically (Table 4.10). They often disperse seeds through endozoochory, passing whole seeds intact through their digestive tracts.

The highly frugivorous, large-bodied lemur species in the genera *Eulemur* (see Johnson et al., pp. 1941–46) and *Varecia* (see Vasey et al., pp. 1957–63) appear to be the most important seed dispersers in many Malagasy forest ecosystems, particularly in dry deciduous and moist evergreen habitats. They eat a wide range of fruit species with a range of traits, often ingesting whole seeds without mastication, and therefore disperse seeds of diverse species and sizes (Dew and Wright 1998; Birkinshaw 2001; Sato 2012; Martinez and Razafindratsima 2014). Most studies of their impacts on seed fate have demonstrated enhanced seed germination and seedling growth as a result of the passage of intact seeds through their guts (Dew and Wright 1998; Razafindratsima and Razafimahatratra 2010; Moses and Semple 2011; Razafindratsima and Martinez 2012; Sato 2012), and increased recruitment probability as seeds are dispersed away from parent plants and into favorable microsites (Mertl-Millhollen et al. 2011; Razafindratsima and Dunham 2015). However, these impacts were often species specific, with different results across different lemur and plant species. For instance, the passage of seeds through the gut of certain lemurs, such as *E. rufifrons* (Red-fronted Brown Lemur) in the dry deciduous Kirindy Forest CNFEREF and *E. coronatus* (Crowned Lemur) at Montagne des Français, had no particular effect on the germination of some species and negative impacts on the survival of others (Scharfe and Schlund 1996; Spehn and Ganzhorn 2000; Ravelomalala 2015).

Furthermore, species in the genera *Eulemur* and *Varecia* were also found to influence plant community structure at multiple axes. For example, by using fruiting trees as seed-dispersal foci, frugivorous lemurs structured the spatial and phylogenetic patterns of early-stage plant-to-plant associations, setting the template for post-dispersal processes that would influence the ultimate patterns of plant recruitment (Razafindratsima and Dunham 2016). Additionally, *V. variegata* (Black and White Ruffed Lemur) has been shown to perform rare long-distance seed dispersal (Razafindratsima et al. 2014).

Lemur catta (Ring-tailed Lemur) has also been reported to have beneficial impacts on plants as a seed dispersal agent. It ensures genetic movement among populations between patches of forests (Bodin et al. 2006), improves the germination capacity of seeds (Andriamalala 2007), and increases the regeneration of some plant species (e.g., *Tamarindus indica*) away from the negative impacts of being near parent plants (Mertl-Millhollen et al. 2011).

Omnivorous lemur species (such as members of the genera *Cheirogaleus*, *Microcebus*, and *Mirza*) as well as folivores (such as *Hapalemur*, *Propithecus*, and *Indri indri*) also eat fruits and seeds; some of these species have been reported to have the ability to disperse the seeds of some plant species in Malagasy systems (Table 4.10). In particular, *Cheirogaleus medius* (Fat-tailed Dwarf Lemur) and *C. major* (Greater Dwarf Lemur) were observed to swallow and disperse seeds with a median length of 5.8 mm in the littoral forest of Mandena (Lahann 2007). Most species of mouse lemurs, *Microcebus* (see Kappeler et al., pp. 1927–32), have a high proportion of fruits in their diet (Atsalis 1999; Dammhahn and Kappeler 2008b) and defecate relatively intact seeds with size ranging up to 16 mm (Lahann 2007; Ramananjato et al. 2020). The limited studies investigating their effectiveness in seed dispersal services have shown positive impacts of *Microcebus* on plants (Génin and Rambeloarivony 2018; Ramananjato et al. 2020). For instance, germination experiments on defecated seeds from *M. rufus* (Rufous Mouse Lemur) at Ranomafana and *M. jollyae* (Jolly's Mouse Lemur) at Kianjavato have demonstrated that mouse lemurs facilitate seed germination and seedling growth (Ramananjato et al. 2020). Further, Génin and Rambeloarivonby (2018) showed that the nonrandom patterns of foraging and seed-dispersing activity of *M. griseorufus* (Gray-brown Mouse Lemur) in Berenty help structure plant neighborhood communities.

In some systems, *Microcebus* could be the only seed disperser for some plant species (Ramananjato et al. 2020). *Microcebus* species could further contribute to the spread of native plant species in degraded forest patches and favor their survival and regeneration since they have been found in open areas around forest edges and could survive and persist in degraded areas (Rendigs et al. 2003; Lehman et al. 2006; Knoop et al. 2018). In some areas, their density is higher in degraded formations than in more intact adjacent areas (S. M. Goodman, unpublished data). On the other hand, they could also act as a vector of biological invasion, as they also feed on and disperse the seeds of introduced and invasive species, such as *Clidemia hirta* and *Psidium cattleyanum* (Ramananjato et al. 2020).

For the case of different species of *Propithecus* (see Lawler and Richard, pp. 1971–74), despite spending a large proportion of their feeding time on fruits, most have been recognized as mainly seed predators because they masticate seeds and digest those that they ingest (Dew and Wright 1998; Overdorff and Strait 1998; Böhning-Gaese et al. 1999). The same is also observed in *Indri indri* (Powzyk and Mowry 2003; Powzyk and Mowry 2007; see Gamba et al., pp. 1967–71). Further study is needed to determine the impacts of partial consumption of seeds by these species on germination.

Bats

Madagascar hosts three species of frugivorous bats of the family Pteropodidae (Racey et al. 2009; see Andrianaivoarivelo et al., pp. 1911–16) that play important roles in seed dispersal, particularly over long distances in the island's predominantly fragmented landscapes. The limited studies on the diet and potential roles of Madagascar's fruit bats in seed dispersal present compelling evidence of their role, their importance in degraded and fragmented habitats, and the need to conserve these animals to prevent the loss of their unique ecological function. They have been found to forage and travel across multiple habitats, utilizing protected, degraded, and agricultural areas. Their long-distance travel and their use of, and sometimes preference for, non-native habitats may allow these species to serve a role that is ecologically distinct from that of frugivorous lemurs, many of which cannot utilize or easily navigate degraded-matrix habitats and have distinctly smaller home ranges, and thus a much shorter dispersal distance.

Pteropus rufus (Malagasy Flying Fox) has been found to consume whole seeds between 1.0 and 3.5 mm and to act as a disperser of at least 51 different plant species (Bollen et al. 2004a, 2004b; Long and Racey 2007). Raheriarisena (2005) also characterized the diet of *P. rufus* over seven months in a subarid region of southern Madagascar, identifying 15 fruit species consumed by these bats. The seeds of seven of these species were also found in *P. rufus* feces, indicating their potential role as dispersers. Though research on the effectiveness of this species as a disperser has been limited, it has been found to improve the germination and seedling establishment of multiple species (Bollen and Van Elsacker 2002; Oleksy et al. 2017). *Pteropus rufus* has also demonstrated a capacity for long-distance dispersal by traveling 3–5 km within 24–280 minutes of a foraging event and traveling up to 20 km from the roost to feeding trees (Oleksy et al. 2017).

Studies on seed dispersal and frugivory by *Eidolon dupreanum* (Malagasy Straw-colored Fruit Bat) are even more limited than those for the larger flying fox. Nonetheless, the available studies demonstrate that these fruit bats consume the fruits of at least 30 plant species, with seeds between 0.9 and 6.9 mm long (Picot et al. 2007; Ratrimomanarivo 2007). Gut passage of seeds by *E. dupreanum* was also found to have a positive effect on the germination of fig species while having variable effects on the germination of other species (Picot et al. 2007). Further work is necessary to assess the role of this widely distributed fruit bat as a seed disperser across Malagasy habitats.

Rousettus madagascariensis (Madagascar Rousette) is the smallest of the three Malagasy fruit bats and is the least threatened (Andriafidison et al. 2008). Its role as a seed disperser is yet to be examined, with seeds being rare in its feces, and seasonally common only from March to April (Andrianaivoarivelo et al. 2011; Vololona 2020). At least six seed species are dispersed by *R. madagascariensis*, with size ranging between 1.3 and 4.4 mm (Vololona 2020). A study on the effect of gut passage on the seeds of *Ficus rubra* found that it increased germination speed but resulted in germination rates similar to those of the controls (Andrianaivoarivelo et al. 2011). *Rousettus madagascariensis* was also shown to prefer native and introduced fruits with no commercial value over commercially valuable fruits (Andrianaivoarivelo et al. 2012b).

Rodents

Among the 27 species of endemic Malagasy rodents, 23 have fruits and/or seeds in their diet (Razafindratsima et al. 2018b) (Table 4.10), but most are considered seed predators (Goodman and Sterling 1996; Soarimalala and Goodman 2011). Their gnawing and mastication (Miltujin and Lehtonen 2008) can damage seed structures, preventing them from germinating (Vander Wall et al. 2005). However, partial seed predation might be nonlethal for the seeds, allowing them to still germinate. In addition, the small seeds with thick exocarp that they consume whole, such as the *Psidium cattleyanum* and *Gaertnera brevipedicellata* seeds consumed by *Nesomys rufus* (Eastern Red Forest Rat) and *Eliurus webbi* (Webb's Tufted-tail Rat) in Ranomafana (V. Ramananjato, unpublished data), may not be destroyed at all and could be defecated intact. If these rodents improve the germination of the non-native *P. cattleyanum* seeds that pass through their guts, they may facilitate the spread of this species in natural environments.

Another characteristic that may allow granivorous rodents to play an important role in seed dispersal is their tendency to store seeds in individual caches or in burrows for later consumption. On Madagascar, several rodent species—such as *N. rufus* and

E. webbi—have been observed to larder-hoard seeds in burrows (Goodman 1994; Goodman and Sterling 1996; Razafindratsima 2017). Larder-hoarders may unintentionally drop seeds on their way to hide them; this may allow the seeds to germinate. Scatter-hoarding has been observed only in *N. audeberti* (Lowland Red Forest Rat) at Kianjavato, where the animals took seeds away from an experimental seed station and chewed them partially before leaving them in a cache (Z. Rakotomalala, unpublished data). Secondary dispersal by rodents through scatter-hoarding needs special attention, as it may replace the dispersal service of extinct large-bodied animals, often referred to as megafauna, especially for large-seeded plant species, as observed in other tropical ecosystems (Jansen et al. 2012).

Other Vertebrates

Non-native African Bush Pigs, *Potamochoerus larvatus*, could also contribute to the seed dispersal of native and non-native plant species on Madagascar (Ganzhorn et al. 1999; Randriantavy et al. 2014). For instance, Randriantavy et al. (2014) reported that several clumps of the introduced *Psidium cattleyanum* grew from the feces of *P. larvatus* in the Betampona protected area. The bush pigs' tendency to plow soil can also regulate the seed bank by digging out buried seeds, which either triggers their germination as they are exposed to light or destroys them. Either outcome can regulate plant species abundance and structure plant communities. In addition, with their strong jaws (Herring 1985), bush pigs can also break hard-coated fruits, which can accelerate seed germination.

Carnivores such as *Cryptoprocta ferox* (Fosa) could participate in seed dispersal via diploendozoochory when they prey on frugivorous lemurs. Other carnivore species like *Eupleres goudotii* (Falanouc), *Galidia elegans* (Ring-tailed Vontsira), and *Salanoia concolor* (Brown-tailed Vontsira) have been observed to consume fruits (Nowak 2005; Garbutt 2007; Goodman 2012); however, their role in seed dispersal is unknown.

Invertebrates

Entomochory—seed dispersal by insects—has been recognized as an important process that often closes the seed-dispersal loop for many plant species (Li Vigni and Melati 1999; Culot et al. 2015, 2018). Among the diverse community of invertebrates occurring on Madagascar, ants are the most frequently reported to act as secondary seed dispersers (Böhning-Gaese et al. 1999; Spehn and Ganzhorn 2000; Voigt et al. 2002), especially for plants producing seeds with elaiosomes, fleshy structures rich in lipids and proteins attached to the seed. In the dry deciduous Kirindy Forest CNFEREF, for example, two omnivorous ant species—*Aphaenogaster swammerdami* and *Pheidole* sp.—were observed to collect, transport, and deposit the seeds of *Commiphora guillaumini* trees near or inside their nests (Böhning-Gaese et al. 1999; Voigt et al. 2002). Seeds dispersed by *Pheidole* were more likely to germinate, as the shelter the ants provide them protects them from predators, and the pile of detritus inside the colony could provide them enough nutrients to establish (Solano and DeJean 2004).

Various species of beetles (such as dung beetles) assist in the secondary dispersal of many plant species that either fall under the parent plant or are defecated by primary dispersers (Li Vigni and Melati 1999; Culot et al. 2018). On Madagascar, despite the occurrence of more than 60 species of dung beetles in the eastern moist evergreen forests (Hanski et al. 2008), their ecological role or relevance in seed-dispersal ecology remains poorly investigated. Recently, seed dispersal by wasps and hornets (vespicochory) has attracted scientific attention, as they can remove fruits or seeds from understory plants in China's rainforests (Chen et al. 2018), but investigations of such seed dispersal are currently lacking on Madagascar.

SEED DISPERSAL ANACHRONISM ON MADAGASCAR

Several thousand years ago, Madagascar had large-bodied herbivore species, including at least 17 species of giant lemurs spanning nine genera, three species of hippopotamuses, eight species of elephant birds, and two species of giant tortoises (Burney and Flannery 2005; Goodman and Jungers 2014). Some of these species were likely the main dispersers of large-seeded tree species (Crowley et al. 2011; Albert-Daviaud et al. 2020). However, by 1400–500 years BP, the entire endemic large mammal fauna assemblage was gone. The reasons for this loss are still debated, but hypotheses include habitat change from anthropogenic activity, changing climate, hunting, or a combination of these factors (Godfrey et al. 2019). With their extinction came a downsizing of the frugivores able to disperse seeds, leaving some large-seeded Malagasy plants without extant animal dispersers (Andriantsaralaza et al. 2010; Federman et al. 2016; Albert-Daviaud et al. 2018). Several large-seeded plant species on Madagascar, such as those in the genera *Adansonia*, *Borassus*, and *Dilobeia*, which are thought to have been dispersed mainly by ape-sized lemurs, are now orphaned (Federman et al. 2016). Large flightless elephant birds were probably important epizoochoric seed dispersers on the island (Midgley and Illing 2010), as suggested by the presence of large spiny trample bur fruits from an endemic Malagasy genus, *Uncarina*. The burs, with their large grapple hooks, drop as mature fruit to the ground and are thought to be an adaptation for latching on to the feet of elephant birds. An endemic baobab tree species, *Adansonia rubrostipa*, is also thought to have lost its dispersers as a result of the extinction of two species of Malagasy giant tortoises—*Aldabrachelys grandidieri* and *A. abrupta* (Andriantsaralaza et al. 2010, 2014; Pedrono et al. 2013). The consequences of such an anachronism could be dire for the survival of these plant species. Although some of these plant species with no known dispersers still survive on Madagascar (Federman et al. 2016), long-term persistence may be tenuous, and additional studies are needed to understand the impact of these past extinctions on Madagascar's flora, as well as in forested ecosystems in a greater sense. Future studies investigating seed fate and recruitment of these species with anachronistic fruits could provide important insights and help prioritize conservation action.

CONCLUSION

The current literature provides important insights regarding seed dispersal ecology on Madagascar, in both the primary and secondary stages—specifically, how zoochory can help maintain plant species diversity and support ecological restoration, and how its disruption in the face of increasing anthropogenic activities could negatively impact ecosystem functioning and resilience. However, as highlighted in this contribution, some important gaps remain and should be the focus of future research. Knowledge about seed dispersal ecology has important implications for prioritizing holistic approaches to biodiversity conservation of Madagascar's heterogeneous landscapes, instead of species-specific approaches, which sometimes neglect the ecological importance, roles, and consequences of a community or guild of animals and plants. We therefore recommend the integration of actions aimed at preserving and restoring seed-dispersal interactions into conservation and restoration efforts, given the important roles of such processes in influencing the continued existence of the interacting species and in affecting the composition and maintenance of diversity within Madagascar's biodiverse ecosystems.

Subject editors: Steven M. Goodman and Amanda H. Armstrong

THE GRASSY ECOSYSTEMS OF MADAGASCAR

C. E. R. Lehmann, C. L. Solofondranohatra, J. A. Morton, L. N. Phelps, H. Ralimanana, J. Razanatsoa, V. Rakotoarimanana, and M. S. Vorontsova

On the island of Madagascar, the narrative of grassy ecosystems as the product of deforestation over the last two thousand years has largely deterred researchers from examining their ecology, evolution, and ecosystem dynamics. While this is now changing, there remains a dearth of research into the grassy ecosystems that cover over half of the island. In this contribution, grassy ecosystems are defined as those where grasses dominate the ground layer with contiguous cover and where tree cover ranges from zero to 80%. Given that modern functional and structural definitions of ecosystems are unable to differentiate between ancient and derived (Veldman 2016), we seek to synthesize current understanding of all grassy ecosystems across the island to highlight available information, knowledge gaps, and present understanding of grassy ecosystems in a global context.

Across the tropics, grassy ecosystems from semidesert to montane environments, many with climates similar to those on Madagascar, are documented as covering around 20% of the global land surface (Lehmann et al. 2011). Paleontological research, using multiple proxies for vegetation reconstruction, has provided relatively little support for grassy ecosystems across Madagascar before human arrival (e.g., Burney 1987a, 1987c; Gasse and Van Campo 1998, 2001), although grassy ecosystems are not always easy to observe in the paleo record because of biases associated with the deposition and recovery of paleobotanical (sub)fossils (Strömberg 2004). However, disconnects between the Quaternary paleo record and biodiversity research see extant Malagasy grassy ecosystems as the subject of contention over their limits before human colonization of the island (see Wright and Rakotoarisoa, pp. 181–90, for further details).

Taxonomic and biodiversity studies have documented a diverse ancient grass flora (Vorontsova et al. 2016; Hackel et al. 2018; Vorontsova 2018), with numerous endemic plant and animal species, particularly in the Central Highlands (Bond et al. 2008; Alvarado et al. 2014). Ecological research has demonstrated functional and biogeographic differentiation among grassy ecosystems of the Central Highlands (C. Solofondranohatra et al. 2018, 2020). Indeed, ancient assemblages of grass species range from montane regions, such as Andringitra, to the vast open Central Highlands, with evidence of antiquity nested in phylogenetic and diversity patterns. Irrespective of the debate around ancient versus derived, modern Malagasy grassy ecosystems provide essential food, cultural, and financial resources to millions of people. Given the human dependency on grassy ecosystems, it is imperative to develop ecological understanding to support land management in the face of changing climate, especially where food security is precarious.

PALEOECOLOGICAL EVIDENCE FOR MALAGASY GRASSLANDS

In the historical literature concerning Madagascar, grassy ecosystems have been regarded as primarily of anthropogenic origin, derived from forest degradation after humans started to modify the landscapes of the island (e.g., Perrier de la Bâthie 1921; Humbert 1927; Koechlin et al. 1974; Lowry et al. 1997). Although human presence and anthropogenic environmental change—frequently linked to the expansion of grassy ecosystems—are indisputable over the past few millennia on the island (e.g., Burney 1993; Burney et al. 2004; Harper et al. 2007; Crowley 2010; Crowley and Samonds 2013; Burns et al. 2016; Crowley et al. 2017; Douglass et al. 2019), paleoecological evidence supports the existence of grasses long before the first evidence for human presence (c. 10,500 BP; Hansford et al. 2018) and anthropogenic landscape modification (c. 2300 BP; see Burney et al. 2004). Direct evidence for grassy ecosystems may be underrepresented in the paleo record because of differential production, transport, and preservation of botanical (sub)fossils, as well as sampling biases (e.g., Strömberg 2004).

TABLE 4.11. **Summary of paleoecological evidence for the persistence of open areas and grasses prior to the first evidence for human arrival (c. 10,500 BP) and anthropogenic landscape modification (c. 2300 BP)**

REGION	SITE	PROXY	HUMAN RELATION	TIME	INDICATION OF OPEN AND/ OR GRASSY AREA	SOURCE
North	Matsabory Ampozalana	Charcoal	**	c. 35,000–20,000 BP	• Elevated charcoal concentrations	Burney (1987c)
North	Loky Manambato, Daraina region	Population genetics	*	c. 10,000–2000 BP	• Most likely period for environmentally driven contraction of forest-dwelling lemur (*Propithecus tattersalli*) • Stable forest cover mosaic over past 60 years	Quéméré et al. (2012)
Northwest	Anjohibe	Pollen, charcoal	**	c. 40,000 BP	• High Poaceae values with traces of grassland and woodland tree pollen types	Burney et al. (1997)
		Fauna	*	c. 7150–2635 BP	• Faunal presence may indicate open/grassy areas: *Hippopotamus*, *Plesiorycteropus**** • High C_3 diets in seven hippos (*H. madagascariensis*: −21.0‰ to −24.3‰) suggest open areas are limited	Samonds et al. (2010); Crowley and Samonds (2013); Godfrey and Crowley (2016)
Northwest	Lake Mitsinjo	Pollen, charcoal	*	c. 3500–1200 BP	• Dry forest/grassland mosaic and occasional fires	Matsumoto and Burney (1994)
Northwest	Belobaka	Fauna	**	c. >20,500 BP	• Faunal presence could indicate open/grassy areas: hippo (*Hippopotamus laloumena*)	Faure et al. (2010); Samonds et al. (2019)
Northwest	Amparihingidro	Fauna	*	c. 7135 BP	• Faunal presence could indicate open/grassy areas: tortoise • High C_3 diet in one tortoise (*Aldabrachelys*: −23.2‰) suggests open areas are limited	Crowley (2010); Godfrey and Crowley (2016)
East	Mananjary	Fauna, isotopes	*	c. 2310 BP	• δ13C value for one hippo (*Hippopotamus laloumena*: −18.4‰) suggests minimal reliance on C_4/CAM plants	Burney et al. (2004); Godfrey and Crowley (2016)
Central	Tsaramody, Sambaina Basin	Pollen, fauna, isotopes	**	c. 17,000 BP	• Open landscapes with abundant grasses • Faunal presence could indicate open/grassy areas: hippo (*Hippopotamus guldbergi*), tortoise (*Aldabrachelys*), elephant birds (*Aepyornis hildebrandti*, *Mullerornis*) • δ13C value for one hippo (*H. guldbergi*: −15.9‰) suggests substantial reliance on C_4/CAM plants	Samonds et al. (2019)

(*continued overleaf*)

TABLE 4.11. ***continued***

REGION	SITE	PROXY	HUMAN RELATION	TIME	INDICATION OF OPEN AND/OR GRASSY AREA	SOURCE
Central	Tritrivakely	Pollen	**	c. 40,000 BP–recent	• Regional Poaceae signal from c. 40,000 BP to recent times • Late Pleistocene/early Holocene increase in grasses, woodland/grassland mosaic	Gasse and Van Campo (1998, 2001)
		Charcoal	*	c. 10,500–3500 BP	• Elevated charcoal concentrations	Burney (1987c)
Central	Ampasamba-zimba	Pollen, fauna	*	c. 8000–7000 BP	• Mosaic of woodlands, bushlands, and grasslands near the site • Faunal presence could indicate open/grassy areas: tortoises (*Aldabrachelys grandidieri*, *A. abrupta*), hippo (*Hippopotamus lemerlei*), elephant birds (*Aepyornis medius*, *A. agilis*, *A. hildebrandti*, *Mullerornis agilis*, *M. grandis*), *Plesiorycteropus madagascariensis****	MacPhee et al. (1985)
Central	Ampasamba-zimba	Fauna, isotopes	**	c. 33,000 BP	• δ13C values for one *Archaeolemur edwardsi* (−16.7‰ corr.) suggests substantial C_4/CAM dependence	Godfrey et al. (2016)
Central	Masinandraina	Fauna, isotopes	*	c. 5000 BP	• δ13C value for one elephant bird (*Aepyornis*: −15.2‰) suggests substantial reliance on C_4/CAM plants	Burney (1999); Crowley (2010); Godfrey et al. (2016)
South-central	Christmas River	Fauna	**	c. 11,000 BP	• Faunal presence could indicate open/grassy areas: hippo (*Hippopotamus lemerlei*), elephant birds (*Aepyornis* sp., *A. maximus*)***	Muldoon et al. (2012); Samonds et al. (2019)
Southwest	Ankilibehan-dry	Fauna, isotopes	*	c. 2340–2140 BP	• δ13C value for one hippo (*Hippopotamus lemerlei*: −21.1‰) suggests minimal reliance on C_4/CAM plants • Note: given the relatively late date, this finding could intersect with anthropogenic impacts	Crowley (2010); Godfrey and Crowley (2016)
Southwest	Ampoza-Ankazoabo	Fauna	*	c. 2670–2535 BP	• Faunal presence could indicate open/grassy areas: hippos (*Hippopotamus*, *H. lemerlei*) • High C_3 diet in two hippos (*Hippopotamus*, *H. lemerlei*: −22.8‰ to −23.6‰) suggests open areas are limited	Burney et al. (2004); Crowley (2010); Godfrey and Crowley (2016)
Southeast	Sainte Luce (SM-matrix)	Pollen, charcoal	*	c. 4800 BP	• Establishment of open ericoid-*Myrica* grassland • Dynamic, climatically sensitive vegetation mosaics including grassy ecosystems and fire	Virah-Sawmy et al. (2010)

REGION	SITE	PROXY	HUMAN RELATION	TIME	INDICATION OF OPEN AND/OR GRASSY AREA	SOURCE
Southeast	Andrahomana	Fauna, isotopes	*	c. 7000 BP	• δ13C value for one tortoise (*Aldabrachelys*: −16‰) suggests substantial reliance on C_4/CAM plants • δ13C values for two *Hadropithecus stenognathus* (−9.2 ± 0.6‰) suggest full reliance on CAM/C_4 plants	Crowley (2010); Crowley et al. (2011); Godfrey and Crowley (2016)
		Fauna, isotopes	*	c. 5000–2885 BP	• δ13C values for two *Hypogeomys australis* (−18.9 ± 2‰) suggest partial reliance on CAM/C_4 plants	Crowley (2010); Crowley et al. (2011)
South	Taolambiby	Fauna, isotopes	*	c. 2620–2470 BP	• δ13C values for six hippos (*Hippopotamus*: −18.3 to −21.2‰) suggest minimal reliance on C_4/CAM plants • δ13C value for one tortoise (*Aldabrachelys*: −21.2‰) suggests minimal reliance on C_4/CAM plants	Crowley (2010); Godfrey and Crowley (2016)
South	Anavoha	Fauna, isotopes	*	c. 2245–2200 BP	• δ13C values for two *Hadropithecus stenognathus* (−9.2 ± 0.6‰) suggest full reliance on C_4/CAM plants • Note: given the relatively late date, this finding could intersect with anthropogenic impacts	Burney et al. (2004); Crowley (2010); Crowley et al. (2011)
South	Faux Cap	Fauna	**	c. 50,000 BP	• Faunal presence could indicate open/grassy areas: elephant bird (*Aepyornis*)***	Clarke et al. (2006); Samonds et al. (2019)
		Fauna	*	c. 4625–3455	• Faunal presence could indicate open/grassy areas: elephant bird (*Aepyornis*)***	Crowley (2010)
South	Table Mountain	Fauna	*	c. 4000 BP	• Faunal presence could indicate open/grassy areas: elephant bird (*Aepyornis*) eggshell • Lowest δ13C eggshell value (*Aepyornis*: −21.4‰) suggests minimal reliance on C_4/CAM plants	Clarke et al. (2006)
South	Nasua	Fauna	**	Pleistocene	• Faunal presence could indicate open/grassy areas: elephant bird (*Aepyornis*) eggshell***	Clarke et al. (2006)
South	Songoritelo	Fauna	*	c. 4000 BP	• Faunal presence could indicate open/grassy areas: elephant bird (*Aepyornis*) eggshell***	Clarke et al. (2006)

Note: This table is not an exhaustive review of paleoecological evidence.
* Indicates grassy evidence dated prior to the first documented evidence of anthropogenic landscape modification, c. 2300 BP.
** Indicates grassy evidence dated prior to the first documented human presence on Madagascar, c. 10,500 BP.
*** Taxa presence may indicate open landscapes, but this is debated, as the habitat preference for the animal concerned is unclear: for example, elephant birds (Hansford and Turvey 2018; Torres and Clarke 2018), extinct large-bodied lemur species (e.g., Crowley et al. 2011; Godfrey et al. 2016), *Plesiorycteropus* (MacPhee 1994), and *Hypogeomys australis* (Crowley et al. 2011).

Here we summarize paleoecological support for the presence of grasses and grassy ecosystems prior to human influence (prehuman) using subfossil faunal, pollen, charcoal, and isotopic records (Table 4.11). Madagascar's subfossil record comprises a diverse assemblage of large-bodied animals, including herbivores such as the now-extinct hippos, giant tortoises, elephant birds, and lemur species (see Godfrey and Douglass, pp. 191–97). The extent to which Malagasy herbivores persisted in open spaces or consumed grasses is debated (e.g., Godfrey and Crowley 2016; Godfrey et al. 2016; Hansford and Turvey 2018; Torres and Clarke 2018).

Stable isotopes and radiocarbon dating of faunal remains have immensely advanced our understanding of diets of these extinct animals (Burney et al. 2004; Crowley 2010; Crowley et al. 2011), including the potential degree of reliance on plants using the C_3 photosynthetic pathway (low δ13C values) versus C_4 grasses (high δ13C values) or desert-associated CAM plants (intermediate δ13C values). However, interpretation of these data can be complex because plants using the C_3 photosynthetic pathway are all sedges, forbs, grasses, trees, and shrubs that reflect diverse plant life history strategies across both open and closed ecosystems. Hence, isotope data reflect the vegetation composition of ancient Malagasy landscapes, but partitioning the ratio or mix of vegetation types is more involved and requires calibration in modern landscapes. Isotopic studies have revealed that certain elements of the vanished large-bodied animals, often referred to as megafauna, at least partially consumed C_4 or CAM plants from prehistoric open habitats prior to the first evidence for anthropogenic landscape modification (Table 4.11). Nonetheless, most diets—including those of pygmy hippos and giant tortoises—were apparently heavily reliant on C_3 plants such as grasses, forbs, and shrubs, with limited but variable contributions of C_4 grasses and/or CAM plants (Crowley et al. 2011; Godfrey and Crowley 2016; Samonds et al. 2019). While African hippos and Aldabra giant tortoises are well known as grazers, they do have isotopically variable diets in those locations where they must incorporate both C_3 and C_4 plants (Boisserie et al. 2005; Cerling et al. 2008; van der Sluis et al. 2014). For example, one study found that giant tortoises preferred C_3 plants but varied their diets (C_4, CAM) to minimize interspecies competition (Burleigh and Arnold 1986). One extinct Malagasy giant tortoise species (*Aldabrachelys grandidieri*) consumed a uniquely high proportion of C_4 plants as a potential strategy to reduce competition with *A. abrupta*. Further, while African hippos are known to be instrumental in establishing lawns of C_4 grasses, these lawns can contain a variable component of C_3 forbs. Thus, faunal diets and isotopic signatures are indicative of environments, but variable feeding behaviors, seasonal environments requiring mixed diets, and the variable proportions of different plant life forms within grassy ecosystems may obfuscate the relationship. In this sense, reliance on C_4 plants is indicative of open grassy ecosystems, but C_3-dominated diets do not necessarily preclude open or grassy ecosystems. In addition, the ability to differentiate between CAM and C_4 plant contributions is limited, causing the distinction between desert- and grassland-associated vegetation to be ambiguous. Therefore, comparison with additional proxies, such as phytoliths, subfossil pollen, and stable N isotopes (Crowley and Godfrey 2013), is needed to help clarify the distribution of ancient grassy ecosystems on Madagascar.

Although pollen and charcoal records from the Quaternary are limited across Madagascar, existing data demonstrate that prehuman grasses were present in all ecoregions and that fire and open areas were varied but natural components of many ecosystems (e.g., Burney et al. 2004; Table 4.11). It has been argued that before human arrival, grazers were particularly dense in a woodland-grassland mosaic of the Central Highlands (Burney et al. 2003, 2004), although subfossil localities and stable isotope data are severely limited from this area (Godfrey and Crowley 2016). Recent work in the Sambaina Basin near Antsirabe in the Central Highlands supports open landscapes, abundant grasses, and mixed C_3 and C_4 in the diets of extinct large-bodied animals, but prehistoric vegetation change in the Central Highlands is highly complex (e.g., Samonds et al. 2019), and the potential impacts of early Holocene hunters as observed farther south (Hansford et al. 2018) are yet unknown. In addition, species that utilized open areas and were naive to predators were likely easy targets for human hunters, which potentially contributed to their rapid disappearance (e.g., Burney et al. 2004; Crowley 2010) and thus reduced associated open areas (e.g., Burney et al. 2003, 2004). To adequately understand the past distribution of Malagasy grassy ecosystems, further paleoecological investigation is required, particularly in the Central Highlands and dry deciduous forests of the north and west, where such work is relatively limited and where prehistoric wetlands may be less sampled because of farmland conversion (e.g., Samonds et al. 2019) or geomorphological constraints.

BIOGEOGRAPHY AND ORIGINS OF THE GRASSY BIOMES OF MADAGASCAR

A time-calibrated molecular phylogenetic analysis of 73% of Madagascar's grass flora found 69 independent endemic and Madagascar-originated lineages, including 44 C_4 grass lineages (Hackel et al. 2018). Among these 44 lineages are a number of ecologically important ones that shape the island's flora, specifically extant grassy ecosystems from montane habitats to the arid south, such as *Aristida* (Vorontsova 2013; Besnard et al. 2014), *Panicum* (Vorontsova 2018), and *Andropogon* (Vorontsova et al. 2013). All of these lineages contain species found as endemics across diverse grassy ecosystems shaped by processes of fire, grazing, shade, temperature, and aridity. The divergence and crown ages of these C_4 lineages generally coincide with the Miocene, suggesting that many of the existing C_4 grass lineages arrived on the island during the early Miocene or late Pliocene coincident with the global C_4 grassland expansion observed in the paleo record of Africa and Asia (Edwards et al. 2010).

In 1955, Humbert classified Malagasy vegetation domains into six ecoregions: Central, Eastern, High Mountain, Sambirano, Southern, and Western (Table 4.12). These same divisions were used by Koechlin (1993) to classify Malagasy grasslands based on their floristic composition, which was noted to vary from region to region broadly related to climate, topography, and soil properties. Koechlin (1993) distinguished five main divisions of herbaceous vegetation: gramineous formations of the Central Domain, gramineous formations of the Eastern Domain, grasslands of the High Mountains, gramineous formations of the Western Domain, and gramineous formations of the Southern Domain. Rakotoarimanana

(2008) classified grasslands based on the ecofloristic zone divisions established by Faramalala (1995). The divisions are based on climate, soil, and vegetation physiognomy. Both Koechlin (1968) and Rakotoarimanana (2008) reported that natural grassy formations must already have existed on the island before human arrival. However, Koechlin (1993) also posited numerous grasslands as the product of degradation.

We used a species checklist of 541 species (217 of these endemic; Vorontsova et al. 2016), with a Global Biodiversity Information Facility (GBIF) occurrence data set of 488 grass species (Rabarivola et al. 2019a, 2019b, 2019c, 2019d), to analyze correlations among endemic and nonendemic grasses by ecoregion (the most common ecoregion where species observations are found) and environment (annual mean temperature, annual mean precipitation, precipitation seasonality, temperature seasonality [from WorldClim v.2; Fick and Hijmans 2017], and mean elevation [from Shuttle Radar Topography Mission; Jarvis et al. 2008]). Malagasy grasses exhibit a remarkable diversity and level of endemism both within and across ecoregions (Figure 4.18, Table 4.12), consistent with long-term island evolution of an endemic flora (Vorontsova et al. 2016). Both endemic and nonendemic species show strong clustering by ecoregion (Figure 4.18). The results support biogeographic classification of grasses and highlight unique associations between climate and grass species distributions with both endemics and nonendemics; most important is that there are biogeographically distinct grass assemblages across the island. Climate is unlikely to be the sole determinant of the limits of grass species and the communities they form, especially at smaller scales where soils, tree cover, fire, and grazing are known to shape grassland ecosystems (C. Solofondranohatra et al. 2018, 2020). However, at an island-wide scale, climatic information is the only data that can be meaningfully integrated into such analyses.

Endemic Malagasy grass species are denoted hereafter as [e], as compared to those that are not endemic. Endemic grass species are often common and locally dominant, such as *Thuarea perrieri* [e], *Setaria madecassa* [e], and *Viguierella madagascariensis* [e] in the Western Domain; *Sclerodactylon macrostachyum* [e] in the Southern Domain (see Vorontsova et al., pp. 585–98, Figure 8.29); and *Panicum umbellatum* [e], *Aristida tenuissima* [e], *A. rufescens* [e], and *Brachiaria subrostrata* [e] in the Central Domain.

Across the island, endemic grasses often dominate the grassy ecosystems in which they are found. However, the aggregation of grasses into grassy ecosystems is not a given for the growth form. Functionally, tropical grassy ecosystems are shaped primarily by fire and grazing, processes that maintain open ecosystems (Bond 2019). Tropical montane grassy ecosystems are also often shaped by fire and grazing, but these occur in combination with lower mean temperatures and higher diurnal temperature variations, with grass assemblages distinct from those at lower elevations. Grassy ecosystems also form in tropical arid climates, often structured by both aridity and grazing. Across the tropics, edaphic grassy ecosystems are also formed by seasonal inundation, in heavy clay soils that prohibit tree recruitment, and in saline coastal environments. Ecosystems shaped by high tree cover and shade are clearly not grassy ecosystems, although they can have a grassy ground cover, especially at higher elevations. These ecosystems are typified by C_3 grass species, often creeping annuals. In these ecosystems, fire is rare and its passage is associated with drought or human modification. Pioneer grasses can be found in degraded ecosystems—both grassy ecosystems and forests—but we expect such grass species, which are invading and transforming ecosystems they were not originally a part of, to be generally functionally distinct from those forming stable grassy ecosystems shaped primarily by fire and grazing.

We believe we have sufficient field experience with 278 of Madagascar's 541 grass species to differentiate between species that form grassy ecosystems and those that are components of other ecosystems. We scored species against eight ecological filters; the species included shade and pioneer species, of which 86 (31%) do not contribute to grassy ecosystems. Species associated with fire, grazing, inundation, and cold, arid, and saline environments are capable of forming natural grassy ecosystems. We list 192 such species (see Vorontsova, pp. 585–98, Table 8.21). We have done this to attempt to quantify the endemism associated with Malagasy grasslands; the results are presented in Table 4.12. In this table, we extend the biogeographic descriptions by Koechlin (1993) and Rakotoarimanana (2008) of the five key ecoregions of Madagascar, all of which contain a unique grass flora and associated endemics; grassy ecosystem descriptions are given below. Some of these regions are poorly known and need to be a priority for research and botanical collections.

Central Highlands Areas: The Central Highlands ecoregion consists primarily of C_4-dominated grassy ecosystems interspersed with open woodlands dominated by tapia (*Uapaca bojeri* [e]; family Phyllanthaceae) in a series of disjunct populations (see Kull and Birkinshaw, pp. 121–27) on hillsides with closed gallery forest patches in valley bottoms along rivers, in the lee of hillsides, and in fire shadows (where these have not yet been converted for agriculture). While these grassy ecosystems have generally been considered degraded lands, surveys in protected areas such as Isalo (Box 1) and Itremo have revealed important species diversity within grassy ecosystems of endemic (61 potential species documented) and nonendemic (97) grass species (Nanjarisoa et al. 2017; N. Rakotomalala et al. 2021; Table 4.12; Boxes 1 and 2). Many endemic grasses are not fragile rarities but are dominant in dynamic ecosystems: dense tussocks of *Cenchrus* (*Pennisetum pseudotriticoides*) endemic to the southern Central Highlands withstand burning and resist grazing, increasing in abundance in disturbed roadsides and village pastures. Vast expanses of grassy ecosystems such as the frequently burned hills of the Ankazobe Plateau, including the area north of Ankafobe, are dominated by the morphologically plastic, fire-loving highland endemic *Aristida tenuissima* (Vorontsova 2013). Seasonally inundated, frequently burned grasslands in Itremo are dominated by the highland endemic *Setaria scottii* [e] (Nanjarisoa et al. 2017). Granite outcrops in the southern Central Highlands are carpeted with the endemic resurrection grass *Styppeiochloa hitchcockii*. At this stage, across the region, ecological and botanical data suggest three major grassy assemblages: 1) fire grassy ecosystems; 2) *Uapaca bojeri*–associated grassy ecosystems; and 3) grazing lawn ecosystems. Further assemblages will be associated with inundation, on which there has not been sufficient research. Undoubtedly, the Central Highlands is the best understood region, and later in this contribution we examine it in greater detail.

TABLE 4.12. **Madagascar's grassy ecosystems with corresponding grass species and subfamilies**

				THIS CONTRIBUTION		
HUMBERT'S ECOREGION (1955)	CLIMATE (AS DESCRIBED IN BURGESS ET AL. 2004)	KOECHLIN'S (1993) GRASSLAND TYPES AND THE DOMINANT GRASS SPECIES	RAKOTOARIMANANA'S (2008) GRASSLAND TYPES AND THE DOMINANT GRASS SPECIES	GRASSLAND TYPES AND THE DOMINANT GRASSES	NUMBER AND PROPORTION OF ENDEMIC (E) AND NONENDEMIC (N) SPECIES PER ECOREGION (TOTAL 541 SPECIES)	NUMBER AND PROPORTION OF ENDEMIC (E) AND NONENDEMIC (N) SPECIES FOUND WITHIN AN ECOREGION DETERMINED AS COMPONENTS OF GRASSY ECOSYSTEMS (TOTAL 278 SPECIES)
Central	Temperature: 15–25°C MAP Rainfall: Very variable, generally 1500–2500 mm Both temperature and precipitation seasonal	Gramineous formation of the Central Domain: – Community of low-growing grasses: *Aristida rufescens* [e], *Ctenium*, *Elionurus* [e], and *Sporobolus*. – Grass savanna, dominated by *Loudetia simplex*. – Western slope, dominated by *Loudetia* and *Aristida* [e].	Savannas of the east at mid-elevation: Characterized by an understory composed of *Hyparrhenia rufa*, *Heteropogon contortus*, and *Aristida* sp. [e]. Savannas of the west at mid-elevation: Composed of an herbaceous layer dominated by *Heteropogon contortus* and *Hyparrhenia rufa* on low-slope landscapes; *Aristida rufescens* [e] and *Loudetia simplex* on steep-slope landscapes; *Panicum maximum* and *Hyparrhenia variabilis* on colluvium; *Leersia hexandra*, *Cynodon dactylon*, and *Brachiaria arrecta* on bottomland.	Fire-maintained grassland: Dominated by *Loudetia simplex*, *Trachypogon spicatus*, and *Schizachyrium sanguineum*. Grazing-maintained grassland (grazing lawn): Dominated by *Panicum umbellatum* [e], *Digitaria longiflora*, and *Cynodon dactylon*.	E: 157 (45%) N: 193 (55%) Total: 350	E: 61 (39%) N: 97 (61%) Total: 158
Eastern	Temperature: 26°C AMT Rainfall: >2000 mm MAP, up to 6000 mm on Masoala Peninsula	Gramineous formation of the Eastern Domain: – Low-statured coastal grassland dominated by *Digitaria didactyla*, *Panicum umbellatum* [e], and *Stenotaphrum dimidiatum*. – Community of dense stand of *Andropogon eucomus*, *Hyparrhenia rufa*, and *Imperata cylindrica*.	Savannas of the east at low elevation: – Grassy savannas dominated primarily by two species: *Hyparrhenia rufa* and *Aristida rufescens* [e]. – Wooded savannas with the understory composed primarily of *Aristida similis* [e], *Imperata cylindrica*, and *Hyparrhenia rufa*.	Eastern grassland: Dominated by the subfamily Panicoideae, frequently *Panicum umbellatum* [e].	E: 63 (35%) N: 118 (65%) Total: 181	E: 18 (23%) N: 61 (77%) Total: 79

				This contribution		
HUMBERT'S ECOREGION (1955)	CLIMATE (AS DESCRIBED IN BURGESS ET AL. 2004)	KOECHLIN'S (1993) GRASSLAND TYPES AND THE DOMINANT GRASS SPECIES	RAKOTOARIMANANA'S (2008) GRASSLAND TYPES AND THE DOMINANT GRASS SPECIES	GRASSLAND TYPES AND THE DOMINANT GRASSES	NUMBER AND PROPORTION OF ENDEMIC (E) AND NONENDEMIC (N) SPECIES PER ECOREGION (TOTAL 541 SPECIES)	NUMBER AND PROPORTION OF ENDEMIC (E) AND NONENDEMIC (N) SPECIES FOUND WITHIN AN ECOREGION DETERMINED AS COMPONENTS OF GRASSY ECOSYSTEMS (TOTAL 278 SPECIES)
Western	Temperature: 8–21°C minimum 30–33°C maximum Rainfall: 1000–1500 mm MAP, pronounced dry season	Gramineous formation of Western Domain: – *Loudetia filifolia* community. – *Loudetia simplex* community. – *Heteropogon contortus* community.	Savannas of the west at low elevation: Composed of an herbaceous layer dominated by *Heteropogon contortus*.	Western grassland: Dominated by the subfamily Panicoideae.	E: 96 (33%) N: 199 (67%) Total: 295	E: 38 (27%) N: 101 (73%) Total: 139
Southern	Temperature: 21–33°C AMT Rainfall: <500 mm MAP, prolonged dry season	Gramineous formation of Southern Domain: Dominated by *Aristida adscensionis*, *A. congesta*, *Cenchrus ciliaris*, and *Panicum pseudovoeltzkowii* [e].	Savanna of the south at low elevation: Composed predominantly of *Heteropogon contortus*.	Southern grassland: Dominated by the subfamilies Aristidoideae, Chloridoideae, and Panicoideae.	E: 54 (34%) N: 104 (66%) Total: 158	E: 23 (29%) N: 56 (71%) Total: 79
Sambirano	Temperature: 15–30°C Rainfall: 2000 mm MAP		Savanna of the Sambirano: Dominated by *Imperata* sp. and *Hyparrhenia* sp.	Sambirano grassland: Dominated by the subfamily Panicoideae.	E: 31 (26%) N: 86 (74%) Total: 117	E: 12 (21%) N: 44 (79%) Total: 56
High mountains	Temperature: 10–20°C AMT, can be as low as -11°C Rainfall: 1500–2500 mm MAP	High mountain gramineous formation: Mountain ranges (Ankaratra, Andringitra) dominated by *Anthoxanthum*, *Alchemilla*, *Brachypodium*, *Epilobium*, *Poa*, and *Trifolium*.	Savanna of mountains: Composed predominantly of *Aristida multicaulis* [e] and *Heteropogon rufa*. Savanna of high mountains: Composed predominantly of *Panicum* sp.	High mountain grassland: Dominated by the subfamilies Panicoideae, Danthonioideae, and Pooideae. Ecologically significant endemic species differ between mountain ranges.	E: 87 (61%) N: 56 (39%) Total: 143	E: 31 (48%) N: 33 (52%) Total: 64

Source: As classified by Koechlin (1993), Rakotoarimanana (2008), and this contribution.

Note: From this contribution, dominant species are provided based on our field assessments over the last 10 years. We provide the number of endemic and nonendemic species recorded in each ecoregion based on the whole grass flora. To give an idea of region-specific endemicity, we also provide quantitative estimates of the number and proportion of endemic and nonendemic grass species that are unique to an ecoregion associated with fire, grazing, inundation, and cold, arid, and saline environments, and thus capable of forming natural grassy ecosystems. Species endemic to Madagascar and the Malagasy Region are marked with [e]. The general climate of each region (AMT is annual mean temperature; MAP is mean annual precipitation) as described in Burgess et al. (2004) is also given.

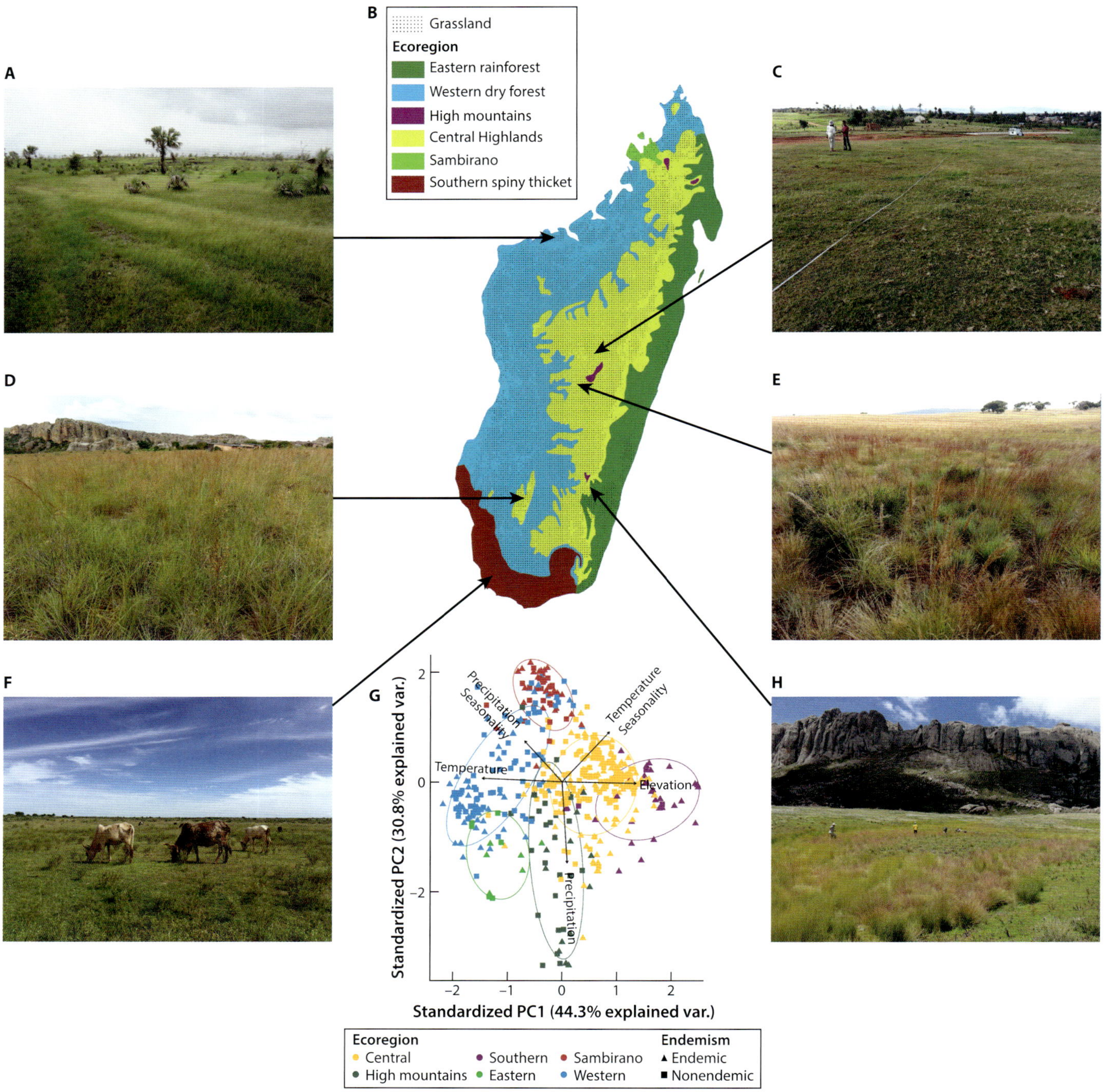

FIGURE 4.18 **Biogeography of the grasslands of Madagascar, including photos of Malagasy grasslands: A) palm (*Bismarckia nobilis* [e]) grassland, dominated by *Heteropogon contortus* and *Themeda quadrivalvis* near the coast at Mahajanga; B) map showing the six phytogeographic domains of Humbert (1955) along with the extent of grassy ecosystems ("plateau grassland-wooded grassland mosaic and wooded grassland-bushland") from Moat and Smith (2007); C) grazing lawn dominated by *Panicum umbellatum* [e] and *Digitaria longiflora* at Ibity; D) fire-maintained grassland dominated by *Loudetia filifolia* and *L. simplex* in Isalo National Park; E) fire-maintained grassland dominated by *L. simplex* and *Trachypogon spicatus* at Itremo (Central); F) grazing lawn dominated by *Aristida barbicollis* near Tsihombe; G) principal component analysis biplot of 488 grass species from Rabarivola et al. (2019a, 2019b, 2019c), with five environmental variables (annual mean temperature, annual mean precipitation, temperature seasonality, rainfall seasonality, and mean elevation) highlighting the ecoregions as originally defined by Humbert (1955); and H) grassland dominated by *Rhytachne rottboellioides* on the Andohariana Plateau, Andringitra. Species endemic to Madagascar or the Malagasy Region are denoted by [e].** (PHOTOS A, C, D, E, and H by M. S. Vorontsova; and F by C. L. Solofondranohatra.)

BOX 1 PALM GRASSLAND OF ISALO NATIONAL PARK

ISALO NATIONAL PARK is situated in a sparsely populated part of central western Madagascar on the boundary between the Central and Southern ecoregions, occupied by the seminomadic zebu-herding Bara people, who likely set fire to these grasslands annually until the establishment of Isalo National Park in 1962 (Rajaofera 2007; Zafisoalizy 2011). Isal National Park is home to 112 grasses, and the open grassy ecosystems here are the most species rich known on the island, with 45 species, and a species list closely matching that for *Uapaca bojeri*–dominated ecosystems (N. Rakotomalala et al. 2021). This particular grassy ecosystem is at 860 m elevation, approximately 10 km north of the main road, and is found on deep sandy soil with occasional mature pyrophytic endemic palms, *Bismarckia nobilis*, which are characteristic of western grasslands (Dransfield and Beentje 1995). At this site, there are seven perennial pyrophytic C_4 grasses within a 50 m^2 plot area. Five of these are illustrated in Figure 4.18 along with the percentage of 1 m diameter plot circles in which they were present. Fire-associated traits documented by C. Solofondranohatra et al. (2020) are evident in all five species: low leaf width to length ratio, low bulk density, high leaf thickness, and high leaf table height; black marks of recent burns are visible. None of the 10 endemic grasses found in the grassy ecosystems of Isalo National Park (N. Rakotomalala et al. 2021) are represented here; rather, all the species are common in African grassy ecosystems, but there is evidence that these species all are native to Madagascar. *Loudetia filifolia* and *L. simplex* are dominant; *L. simplex* is part of the hexaploid southern Madagascar cluster genetically distinct from both northern Madagascar and African populations of *L. simplex* (Hagl et al. 2020). *Heteropogon contortus* dispersed to Madagascar at least twice, likely prior to human arrival (Arthan et al. 2021). Nine species of forbs and a *Cyperus* species were also present at the site described here. Morat (1973) cited a lack of specialized fauna as evidence of their derived nature, although the fauna from this area has not been documented.

BOX 2 TAPIA WOODLAND IN THE IBITY PROTECTED AREA

THE IBITY MASSIF, located in the Central Highlands, is the highest quartzitic mountain on the island, reaching 2254 m. Large areas of Ibity are covered by grassy ecosystems with isolated stands of sclerophyllous woodland, a distinctive endemic formation dominated by *Uapaca bojeri* [e], a fire-tolerant tree (see Kull and Birkinshaw, pp. 121–27), in association with other woody species, many belonging to families endemic to Madagascar, especially Sarcolaenaceae and Asteropeiaceae. Alvarado et al. (2018) identified a fire-return interval of one to three years across the area, with limited influence of human intervention on the fire regime. Nine grass species were recorded in this 50 m^2 plot area, of which *Loudetia simplex*, *Trachypogon spicatus*, and *Schizachyrium sanguineum* are dominant. These are also the dominant species identified across the extensive grasslands of the region and are characterized by fire-associated traits (C. Solofondranohatra et al. 2020). Three endemic grass species are found here: *Panicum perrieri*, *P. ibityense*, and *Styppeiochloa hitchcockii*, all restricted to the Central Highlands (Rabarivola 2019d). *Panicum ibityense* is a bizarre species that drops its leaf blades at the end of the wet season and stores food in corm-like underground structures inaccessible to fire (Vorontsova 2018). In 1914, a single collection of *Sartidia perrieri* [e] was made by Perrier de la Bâthie around Antsirabe, at 1900 m elevation, likely in Ibity; the species is now assessed as extinct in the wild, as many searches for this plant have been conducted with no success (Vorontsova et al. 2015).

Montane Areas: Rising above the Central Highlands are isolated montane areas nested within the Central Highlands. These grassy ecosystems consist of a flora more dominated by C_3 grasses and have the highest levels of grass species endemism on the island (Figure 4.18, Box 3). The highest and most isolated montane areas, including Andringitra, Ankaratra, Marojejy, and Tsaratanàna, are each home to distinct endemic grass assemblages. Andringitra is best studied and to date the most remarkable. Most vegetation around its 2658 m Pic Imarivolanitra (Pic Boby) is narrow endemic grasses: creeping carpets of *Andropogon andringitrensis*, *Brachiaria dimorpha*, and *Panicum spergulifolium*; dense tussocks of *Merxmuellera ambalavaoensis* and *Pentameris andringitrensis*, with *Poa perrieri* by the watercourses; and fields of the *Erica*-mimicking flammable *Panicum cupressifolium*. There is no species overlap with the lower-elevation Andohariana Plateau assemblage (2000 m) described and illustrated in Box 3. Nearby is *Lecomtella madagascariensis* [e], a relict of one of the first grass radiations on Madagascar, 20–30 Mya (Besnard et al. 2013). These montane grassy ecosystems are hotspots for many other microendemic taxa. A survey of Andringitra's Andohariana Plateau by Rabetaliana et al. (1999) found more than 30 species of ground orchids, as well as grassy ecosystem forbs and larger plants such as *Aloe andringitrensis*, found only on the massif. These montane grassy ecosystems are fire maintained, where fire promotes orchid flowering and also acts to exclude encroachment by adjacent montane ericoid thicket dominated by *Erica* heathland (also a fire-maintained ecosystem with numerous

BOX 3 ANDRINGITRA NATIONAL PARK PLATEAU WITH *ERICA*

THE ANDRINGITRA MASSIF is home to more endemic grasses than anywhere else on Madagascar and likely in the world. The Central Highlands montane ericoid thicket and montane grasslands are the unique location of the relict grass lineage *Lecomtella madagascariensis* [e], which is thought to have arrived on the island 20–30 Mya (Besnard et al. 2013), and of the bizarre species *Panicum cupressifolium* [e]. *P. cupressifolium* is a mimic of woody *Erica* shrubs and acts in a functionally similar manner, accumulating biomass (Vorontsova 2018). The Andohariana Plateau at 2000 m is one of Madagascar's most popular tourist spots; a track leads to the country's second highest peak, Imarivolanitra (Pic Boby), reaching 2658 m. At this site (Figure 4.18h), seven grass species were recorded one year after a fire carried out by park management to reduce invasion by woody *Erica* and stimulate orchids for ecotourism interests. Five of the seven grass species within this 50 m^2 plot area are endemic: *Agrostis elliotii* [e], *Aristida tenuissima* [e], *Brachiaria epacridifolia* [e], *Elionurus tristis* [e], and *P. perrieri* [e]—all restricted to the Central Highlands (Rabarivola 2019d). The dominant grass is the endemic *A. tenuissima*, common and widespread across the Central Highlands, and the species is part of Madagascar's endemic radiation of *Aristida* dating to 8–11 Mya (Vorontsova 2013; Besnard et al. 2014; Hackel et al. 2018). *Brachiaria epacridifolia* [e] and *P. cupressifolium* [e] are members of the Madagascar shade clade, the largest Poaceae radiation on Madagascar, dating to 15–19 Mya (Hackel et al. 2018). *Ctenium concinnum* and *Sporobolus centrifugus* are also common in African savannas. Eight forb species were also recorded at this site.

endemic plant species). Because they are difficult to access, these montane grass floras remain some of Madagascar's least well documented. Many of Tsaratanàna's grasses are known only from the type specimen and have not been found for many years (Vorontsova et al. 2020).

Western Areas: The western grassy ecosystems are the country's largest by land area and are likely to have much in common with the Central Highlands. However, this region has had minimal study and attention, partly because of poor road access. A number of endemic species are restricted to the Western Domain that are dominant in the grassy ecosystems in which they are found: *Setaria madecassa* dominates some fire-driven systems, endemic monotypic genera *Yvesia* and *Viguierella* dominate edaphic and palm grassy ecosystems near Mahajanga, and the endemic mat-forming creepers *Neostapfiella perrieri* and *Thuarea perrieri* create grazing lawns near the coast.

Southern Areas: The southern region, characterized by an arid climate known for its dry spiny thickets, also has the most distinct ensemble of grass species of any region (Figure 4.18f). Aridity and drought have long characterized the region, where grasses are most abundant after irregular rains, in a boom-and-bust cycle like that observed across arid systems globally. Grasses common across the rest of the island are not found here, and there are numerous local endemic grasses (34% of the region's grass flora [Vorontsova et al. 2016], and 23% of the grassy biome species, Table 4.12). Many of these endemic species are the result of large species radiations (Vorontsova 2018), including the C_4 grass *Panicum voeltzkowii*, which is often dominant where found and is a key food source for cattle in the region. Other dominant species include *Brachiaria humbertiana* [e], a polymorphic grazing staple throughout the south, and locally unique grazing-adapted mat-forming species such as *Chloris humbertiana* [e] and *Neostapfiella humbertiana* [e]. Species in the endemic subfamily Didiereaceae (see Applequist, pp. 724–26), belonging to four genera (*Alluaudia*, *Alluaudiopsis*, *Decarya*, and *Didierea*), are limited to only this ecoregion, and Madagascar's strangest grass, *Decaryella madagascariensis* [e], grows underneath (Vorontsova and Rakotoarisoa 2014). Many of the endemic southern grasses are transient annuals, with species like *Decaryella* returning with irregular rains: *Eragrostis capuronii* [e] becomes seemingly omnipresent, while *E. chabouisii* [e] and *E. humbertii* [e] seem to be rarer. The windswept cliffs of Cap Sainte Marie are home to a tussock grassy ecosystem dominated by *Setaria humbertiana* [e] and *Chrysopogon humbertianus* [e] (Vorontsova et al. 2016). Paleo evidence from the region has mixed support for prehuman grassy ecosystems (Table 4.11). The numerous endemic grazing-adapted grass species that exist here suggest that large-bodied animals may have maintained grassy ecosystems and thickets as a mosaic through foraging and trampling. The extinction of these animals would have resulted in woody encroachment and would possibly have facilitated expansion of the thickets the region is known for. Megafauna-maintained mosaics of grassland and thicket vegetation are known from the arid east and west coasts of South Africa. Alongside research into the functional ecology of the region is a need to understand the dynamics of grassy-thicket mosaics and how these relate to modern patterns of species invasion, such as by *Opuntia* cactus.

Eastern and Sambirano Areas: While there are some open ecosystems in the eastern and Sambirano areas—comprising mostly taxa such as *Hyparrhenia rufa*, *Aristida similis/rufescens* [e], *Paspalum*, and *Stenotaphrum*—the warm, consistently wetter conditions are favorable to the development of moist evergreen and littoral forest. However, paleoecology has shown that mosaics of forest, grassland, and heathland have existed in parts of the southeast for thousands of years (Virah-Sawmy et al. 2009a, 2009b). Endemic-dominated grassy ecosystems seem largely restricted to those with *Panicum umbellatum* [e], a grazing-adapted endemic. Because of the common practice of swidden agriculture (*tavy*), it is in these regions that novel grasslands are most likely to be found, with reports of invasion of species such as *Imperata cylindrica*. However, the fire-associated

I. cylindrica, with its deep extensive rhizomes, while considered a pioneer species, is a globally common grass in higher-rainfall regions at forest-grassy margins stretching across Australia, Asia, and Africa. The presence of this species alone is not indicative of degradation given its ubiquity in grassy ecosystems worldwide. In the Amazon, grassy ecosystems do occur with high rainfall and are considered natural, although the first arrival of people may have expanded these systems (Rull et al. 2015). Edaphically derived grassy ecosystems associated with extremely nutrient-poor sands and/or soil drainage constraints are found across the tropics in areas of high rainfall (Daskin et al. 2019). Distinguishing ancient and derived grassy ecosystems in the high-rainfall eastern and Sambirano areas requires ecological surveys tied to mapping of land-use change.

The highly regionally distinct clusters of both endemic and non-endemic grass species point to the existence of ancient grassy ecosystems that formed across the island among diverse environments, in fact almost all environments across the island. The biogeographic patterns we report and the local endemism indicate that grassy ecosystems did not originate in one location and then spread across the island. If grassy ecosystems were formed primarily via anthropogenic means, we would expect homogeneity in the grass flora across the island.

THE CENTRAL HIGHLANDS: INSIGHT INTO GRASSY ECOSYSTEM DIVERSITY AND ECOLOGY

Central Highlands grassy ecosystems provide the best understanding of the modern ecology of Malagasy grassy ecosystems. All the diversity, phylogenetic, ecological, and phylogeographic studies of parts of the flora provide insight into grassy ecosystems and their assembly over time. The ages of C_4 endemic grass lineages common in these grassy ecosystems, including *Aristida rufescens, A. similis, A. tenuissima, Andropogon itremoensis, Panicum cinctum, P. luridum, P. umbellatum, Brachiaria subrostrata, Tristachya isaloensis,* and *T. humbertii,* are all consistent with a Pliocene or late Miocene origin of grassy ecosystems (Hackel et al. 2018).

Phylogenetic and population genetic analyses of grassy ecosystem trees and shrubs are far and few between. *Noronhia lowryi* (Oleaceae), an endemic grassy ecosystem shrub species, has a crown age of ~8.3 Mya, with clear divisions between populations only 100 km apart evident from ~6.2 Mya. Levels of genetic diversity suggest a wider distribution across the Central Highlands than is currently documented for what is considered an endangered species, suggestive of long-term open environments (Salmona et al. 2019). Phylogeographic data on sportive lemurs suggest the Central Highlands as a long-term barrier between the east and west coasts and a driver of speciation supportive of open environments (Lei et al. 2017). Equally, population genetic analyses of lemurs from northern Madagascar suggest open environments over the last 60,000 years, before human intervention (Quéméré et al. 2012). Phylogeographic analyses of mouse lemurs, including in the Central Highlands, suggest a mosaic of open and closed environments from at least 55,000 years ago (Yoder et al. 2016).

Population genetic analyses of *Loudetia simplex,* an ecologically important grass species that spans Africa and Madagascar within fire-maintained grassy ecosystems, found such substantial population differentiation in sampled populations from across Africa in South Africa, Burundi, and Burkina Faso as compared to Madagascar that African and Malagasy populations could be considered separate subspecies (Hagl et al. 2020). Phylogeographic analyses of African populations (from across South Africa, Tanzania, Uganda, Zimbabwe, and Zambia) and a Malagasy population suggest that *Themeda triandra,* a dominant grass species in the northwestern grasslands, likely arrived on Madagascar about 1.5 Mya, earlier than the species arrived in Africa (Dunning et al. 2017), where it is considered an integral ecological component of grassy ecosystems readily considered ancient. *Alloteropsis semialata,* a grass species with an almost cosmopolitan tropical distribution, arrived on Madagascar from Africa possibly via Asia or Australia more than 1 Mya, with clear phylogeographic distinction between Africa, Asia, and Madagascar (Lundgren et al. 2015). *Heteropogon contortus,* a common grass species worldwide that is adapted to both grazing and fire, is common in the southern parts of the Central Highlands and likely also arrived on Madagascar more than 1 Mya, spreading globally in the Pleistocene alongside *T. triandra* (Arthan et al. 2021). The presence of grass species with pantropical distributions is not a marker of either a recent arrival or a recent grassy ecosystem assembly. Rather, the dates of species arrivals and their differentiation from regionally proximate populations suggest long-term grassland presence, as these species are found only within grassy ecosystems shaped by fire and grazing worldwide. While these phylogeographic studies of grasses consistently suggest rapid dispersal of widely distributed grass species, that dispersal was a million or more years before humans were a blink in the eye of a lumbering giant tortoise.

Throughout these grassy ecosystems is an array of endemic plant species, such as fire-tolerant trees, shrubs, and palms, including *Uapaca bojeri; Pentachlaena latifolia, Xerochlamys bojeriana,* and *Sarcolaena oblongifolia* (Sarcolaenaceae); *Stereospermum euphorioides* (Bignoniaceae); *Noronhia lowryi; Dicoma incana* (Asteraceae); *Acridocarpus excelsus* (Malpighiaceae); and *Hyphaene shatan, Bismarckia nobilis, Dypsis decipiens,* and *Borassus madagascariensis* (Arecaceae) (S. Rakotoarisoa and L. Gardiner, unpublished data). However, none are likely to have ever formed the kind of continuous tree canopy suggested by Yoder et al. (2016). Nestled among the grassy ecosystems on hillsides and rocky outcrops are diverse endemic *Aloe* (Xanthorrhoeaceae) and *Pachypodium* (Apocynaceae) species specific to grassy ecosystems, many with narrow ranges (for example, four *Aloe* species are known from one grassy ecosystem locality—Ibity; see Box 2). Beyond the grasses, there has been little examination of the herbaceous flora, and this remains a key knowledge gap. Forb floras have been previously associated with the antiquity of grassy ecosystems (Veldman et al. 2015; Zaloumis and Bond 2016), although forb diversity and functional ecology vary relative to soil characters, such as clay content, depth, and drainage. A 2013 examination of the Cyperaceae flora found numerous C_4 endemics associated with wetlands of the Central Highlands, particularly in the genus *Bulbostylis* (Muasya et al. 2011; see Larridon et al., pp. 580–85).

Bond et al. (2008) combed the literature to list insects, birds, reptiles, and mammals endemic to grasslands. Endemic insects can be critical to sustainable regional livelihoods. For instance, the larvae of the silkworm *Borocera madagascariensis* (Lasiocampidae), obligately associated with *Uapaca bojeri*, are harvested for food, and the cocoons are collected for silk (Kull 2002). Madagascar's endemic giant earthworms (Kynotidae) include grassland species (Razafindrakoto et al. 2011). Unique communities of ants are associated with grasslands, tapia woodland, and forest (Fisher and Robertson 2002). A new species of an exclusively grassy-ecosystem ant in the genus *Camponotus* was found 2 m underground in Isalo National Park (A. Ravelomanana, unpublished data). Examples of endemic grassland birds are *Eremopterix hova* (Madagascar Lark), *Cisticola cherina* (Madagascar Cisticola), *Circus macrosceles* (Madagascar Harrier), *Turnix nigricollis* (Madagascar Buttonquail), *Pterocles personatus* (Madagascar Sandgrouse), and *Margaroperdix madagarensis* (Madagascar Partridge) (Bond et al. 2008). *Buteo brachypterus* (Madagascar Buzzard) prefers the forest-grassland interface. *Coarctotermes* is an endemic genus of specialist grass-feeding termites restricted to the Malagasy grasslands (Bond 2019; see Eggleton, pp. 963–68). Several butterfly species are characterized as being associated with transformed grasslands, such as *Strabena rakoto* and *Heteropsis ankaratra* (Nymphalidae), and *Fulda australis* and *F. lucida* (Hesperiidae). It is difficult to conceive of endemic butterfly species (or any other insect species) associated specifically with transformed lands, grassy ecosystems or otherwise. A wide-ranging review of existing species associations with what are currently considered transformed or secondary ecosystems through the lens of ecology might help rapidly upscale our understanding of diversity associated with grassy ecosystems.

The most common tree species, *Uapaca bojeri*, forms monodominant ecosystems in a series of disconnected populations stretching from Isalo at the southern limit of the Central Highlands to north of Antananarivo. The species is pyrophytic, with thick corky bark, and is a prolific resprouter (from both the stem and base), both functional traits characteristic of fire tolerance (see Kull and Birkinshaw, pp. 121–27). Anecdotal discussions with community members suggest that the species is fire tolerant when seedlings reach 1 m in height or four years of age, information suggestive of fire return periods that enable recruitment to adult size classes. Tree cover in these grassy woodland ecosystems ranges from 5% to 60%, much like the variable tree cover in African grassy ecosystems. While this species has previously been considered a relict of degraded forest, the species composition and functional traits of the associated grass assemblage are far more in line with adjacent grassy ecosystems than nearby gallery forests (C. Solofondranohatra et al. 2018). C. Solofondranohatra et al. (2018) combined functional and phylogenetic data for grass species assemblages with variation in bark thickness among *Uapaca* species (including *U. densifolia*) to show that *U. bojeri* ecosystems are grasslands rather than degraded forests, and that these ecosystems are also associated with a suite of endemic grass species shaped by fire (Box 2). Beyond the endemism of the grass assemblage, the high phylogenetic diversity of grasses relative to that of adjacent gallery forests suggests that this is a prehuman formation. The closest African analogue to these *U. bojeri* ecosystems is possibly that dominated by *Protea caffra* (Proteaceae), a tree species that occurs as a monodominant formation in fire-conditioned grasslands that stretch from South Africa to Mozambique at elevations similar to *U. bojeri*–dominated ecosystems (1400–1800 m). Indeed, key grass species are shared with these fire-conditioned ecosystems of Madagascar, such as *Loudetia simplex*, *Trachypogon spicatus*, and *Schizachyrium sanguineum* (Acocks 1988). There have been past comparisons with African grassy ecosystems dominated by *Brachystegia* sp. These high-tree-cover ecosystems are formed on deep granite-derived soils where the trees have deep clonal root systems. Such root systems would struggle to form over the skeletal soils of the Central Highlands.

At least two further grassy ecosystem assemblages are shaped by either fire or grazing; the functional ecology of constituent grass species highlights these as highly dichotomous assemblages with minimal species overlap (C. Solofondranohatra et al. 2020). First, it is surprising to find an obligate grazing grass assemblage, termed a grazing lawn, comprising short, laterally spreading, nutritious, high-bulk-density grasses. A grazing lawn assemblage can only be inferred to be maintained by herbivores, and in the case of modern Madagascar seems to be a relict of the recently extinct large animal fauna, with the assemblage sustained by the introduction of cattle in a landscape otherwise devoid of herbivores. In and of itself, this is evidence of prehuman grasslands. While the prehuman extent of these grassy ecosystems is unknown, we can speculate based on experience with grassy ecosystems worldwide. Given previously estimated densities of large-bodied fauna, grazing lawns are likely to have been widespread throughout the Central Highlands (and likely outside the region also, given that functional analogues can be identified in the Southern and Western Domains). The existence of a grazer-maintained grass assemblage is seemingly at variance with the isotope reconstructions of the diets of these large animals. However, it is worth remembering that the paleo record for the Central Highlands is very patchy, and much is yet to be understood about the paleo history of the region. Grazing lawns are home to the greatest concentration of endemic grasses, including those with broad distributions across Madagascar (*Aristida rufescens*, *Cyrtococcum deltoideum*, *Eragrostis lateritica*, *Panicum luridum*, *P. umbellatum*, and *Stenotaphrum oostachyum*) and those restricted to the Central Highlands (*Andropogon itremoensis*, *Brachiaria subrostrata*, and *S. unilaterale*). In the absence of extensive herbivory, short, laterally spreading grasses are rapidly overtopped and outcompeted by taller grasses (Hempson et al. 2019), where taller tropical grasses tend to be fire adapted (Linder et al. 2018). Extensive research from African ecosystems has demonstrated links between grass and grazer life history strategies (Hempson et al. 2019). Patterns from Africa are mirrored on Madagascar; diversity in Malagasy grazing lawns can be equal to or greater than that of equivalent African grass communities also shaped by intensive grazing (C. Solofondranohatra et al. 2020).

Alongside the grazing assemblage is a highly distinct fire-grass assemblage with 30–40% grass species endemism. Because site-specific diversity is often low (e.g., 6–12 species per 16.5 m^2), it might be natural to view fire-shaped grassy ecosystems as burning wastelands colonized by foreign adventitious weeds. The reality is that these grassy ecosystems and their analogues worldwide are dominated by a fire-adapted lineage of C_4 grasses, the Andropogoneae, which have transformed the earth's system since the Miocene (Linder et al. 2018). Within the fire-grass assemblage are numerous species with pan-African distributions shared with the *U. bojeri* woodland assemblage. We suggest that a large extent of these grassy ecosystems are natural to the region. While far better collaboration between paleo and ecological researchers, soil scientists, and geomorphologists is clearly required, so too is an understanding of biases in the paleo record with respect to documenting grassy environments, especially given the grazer-associated assemblage.

MALAGASY GRASSY BIOMES IN A GLOBAL CONTEXT

Grassy ecosystems across Madagascar are found predominantly within a range of 400–2000 mm mean annual precipitation (Figure 4.19), similar to the tropical grassy ecosystems of both Australia and South America, which occur with 300–2000 mm and 750–2500 mm mean annual precipitation, respectively (Lehmann et al. 2011). Just across the Mozambique Channel, the limits of grassy ecosystems range from 200 to 1750 mm mean annual precipitation across Africa, where the more arid limits of grassy ecosystems are likely tied to the extant African herbivore fauna that maintains open ecosystems in climates similar to the dry spiny thickets and dry deciduous forests in southern and northern Madagascar (Ringelberg et al. 2020). In both South America and Australia, the endemic megafauna of these regions was driven extinct with the arrival of people approximately 10,000 and 40,000 years ago, respectively. These regional differences in the arid limits of tropical grassy ecosystems are quite likely underpinned by regional variation in the extinct fauna, specifically large-bodied herbivores, that shaped these landscapes, along with the timing of their extinctions (Lehmann et al. 2011). In contrast, the mesic limits of the grassy ecosystems of South America, Australia, and Madagascar are quite consistent (Figure 4.19). While the overall likelihood of land area being grassy is higher on Madagascar than in South America (but virtually identical between Australia and Madagascar), it is also worth noting the differences in elevation between the Central Highlands grasslands (800–1800 m; Moat and Smith 2007) and the Cerrado of Brazil. On average the Cerrado is closer to sea level (100–1500 m; Oliveira-Filho and Ratter 2002), enabling a more seasonal and warmer environment. The length of the dry season on Madagascar is longer relative to that in the Brazilian Cerrado; the length of the dry season is a key correlate with the probability of occurrence of tropical grassy ecosystems worldwide. A dry season longer than four to five months equates to a more than 80% chance of grassy ecosystems being present (Lehmann et al. 2011).

Viewed from the air, the Central Highlands is a patchwork of closed and open ecosystems. The fragmented nature of forest in the region has been suggested as evidence that grassy ecosystems here are a product of people. Patchworks of abrupt ecosystem boundaries occur globally across the tropics (Bowman 2000). Stretching from tropical Australia, Asia, India, Africa, and South America, mosaics of forest and grassy ecosystems have previously been described as "islands of green in a land of fire" (White 1983; Sarmiento 1992; Bowman 2000). These abrupt boundaries of open and closed ecosystems represent alternative ecosystem states (Bond 2019). Over the last two decades, new research has enabled the formulation of a new theoretical and practical understanding of the distributions and dynamics of open and closed ecosystems. Multi-directional feedbacks among vegetation characteristics (i.e.,

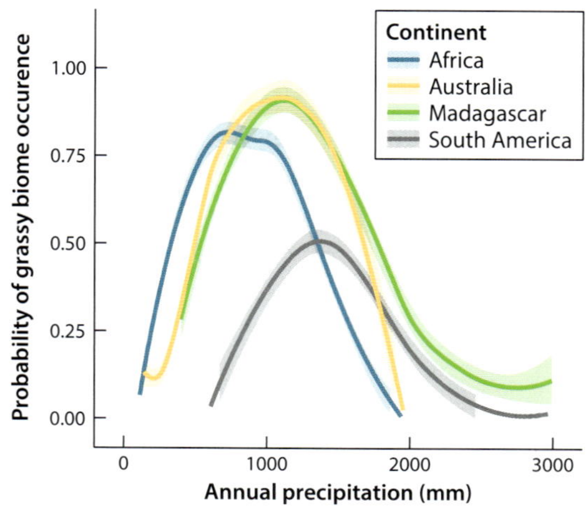

FIGURE 4.19 **The distribution of grassy ecosystems across the tropics relative to Madagascar. Probability (and current proportion) of grassy ecosystem occurrence in Africa, Australia, Madagascar, and South America along rainfall gradients.** (SOURCES: mean annual precipitation (mm) data for Madagascar are from the 0.5°-resolution WorldClim data [Bio_12; Fick and Hijmans 2017]; vegetation occurrence data are from Moat and Smith 2007; data for Australia, Africa, and South America are from Lehmann et al. 2011.)

plant growth and tolerance strategies among plant life forms), environment, and disturbance shape ecosystem boundaries that act like oil and water (e.g., Hoffmann et al. 2012). These adjacent biomes have opposing vegetation structure, species composition, and ecosystem function (Bond 2019), as well as notably distinct edge floras (distinct edge floras suggest the presence of vegetation boundaries over evolutionary timescales). Directly comparing species diversity and endemism in open and closed ecosystems is like comparing apples with oranges, where each set of systems is functionally shaped by different processes. Ecological surveys with population genetics studies from both open and closed ecosystems, alongside soil isotopic studies, might help explain the degree to which the open-closed mosaic has shifted over time and space, and how human action over the last 200 to 2000 years has altered the mosaic.

Regional comparisons of vegetation mosaics are informative for visual and botanical comparisons with the Central Highlands to help understand upland mosaic vegetation in equally topographically complex landscapes. In particular, four tropical regions have similar mosaics and environmental characteristics in terms of elevation, rainfall, and rainfall seasonality. These are the Drakensberg Mountains of South Africa; the Nyika Plateau of Malawi and Zambia; the Chimanimani Mountains of Zimbabwe and Mozambique, and the Shola of the Western Ghats in India (Figure 4.20). In all regions, patches of forest are confined to valley bottoms and the lee of hillsides in fire shadows, while grasslands stretch across plateaus, hillcrests, and ridges, as in Figure 4.20 (White 1983; Thomas and Palmer 2007). In each region, forests are better studied than the adjacent grasslands (White 1983; Thomas and Palmer 2007; Robin and Nandini 2012). In Africa, these vast productive grasslands that stretch across large upland areas even share key grass species with Madagascar, including *Loudetia simplex*, *Trachypogon spicatus*, and

FIGURE 4.20 **Tropical grassland-forest mosaics. Photos show visual comparisons between tropical Africa, India, and Madagascar: A) Itremo (Madagascar), B) Isalo (Madagascar), C) Ankafobe (Madagascar), D) Nyika Plateau (Malawi), E) Shola (India), and F) Drakensberg Mountains (South Africa).** (PHOTO A by C. L. Solofondranohatra; B, C, and F by M. S. Vorontsova; D by N. Owen-Smith; and E by A. Joshi.)

Schizachyrium sanguineum. These fire-conditioned grasslands support endemic plants and animals in each region, just as they do in Madagascar, a consequence of the persistence of such formations for a considerable time (Phipps and Goodier 1962; Lemon 1968; G. Jackson 1969; Meadows and Linder 1993).

WHAT DO WE NEED TO KNOW TEN YEARS FROM NOW?

The distinction between prehuman and modern grassy ecosystem extent remains persistently contentious and confusing. The patchy paleo record and the few population genetics studies lie in contrast to the evolving body of research demonstrating a multitude of ancient grass assemblages adapted to diverse environmental conditions in terms of temperature, aridity, shade, fire, and grazing. Ancient and derived grasslands have physiognomic similarity (Veldman 2016), and thus to an untrained eye, ancient and derived assemblages can be indistinguishable. We advocate the integration of new data collections involving soil isotopes (alongside bone and teeth isotopes of modern cattle and material of these animals in an archaeological context where diets are understood) along with biogeochemistry, modeling of fire spread across topographically complex landscapes, experimental work examining flammability of grass and litter fuels under varying tree cover, demographic modeling of rates and directions of human colonization across the island, niche modeling of extinct herbivores and associated isotope data from subfossils, and an understanding of plant and animal responses to fire at the grassland-forest edge. Both phylogenetic and population genetic examination of targeted genera with species in both open and closed ecosystems such as *Uapaca* and *Aloe*, for example, with many (or all) species on Madagascar endemic and with a number specific to grassy ecosystems, could help delineate prehuman grassland extents and any possible subsequent expansion of certain grassland types.

Undoubtedly, new paleo investigations are required to reconstruct the evolution of grasslands using proxies associated with grasslands such as phytoliths and *Sporormiella*, a fungus that occurs in the dung of herbivores. Phytoliths in geologic sediments are widely employed for reconstructing vegetation types in Pleistocene-Holocene paleoecology, and they have been successfully used to understand the evolution of grasslands in North America and elsewhere (Strömberg 2002). *Sporormiella* has been used in studies of the southwest, which is rich in subfossil sites (Burney et al. 2003). As agriculture developed in the Central Highlands, the region with the most expansive grasslands, areas of likely preservation would have been utilized early on for rice agriculture, requiring the plowing of sediments associated with bogs, lakes, and rivers. Therefore, areas that would have been ripe for sediment and fossil collection may also have been used for agriculture.

Endemic grasses are found across the island and are significant components of the grass flora in all ecoregions. However, grass sampling to date is heavily biased along the main road network and in the Central Highlands (Figure 4.21). In the Itremo and Isalo regions (Box 1), where grass species checklists were developed, Nanjarisoa et al. (2017) and N. Rakotomalala et al. (2021) both found 1) a diverse grass flora; 2) a high proportion of endemic grass species present across all local ecosystems; and 3) grass species new to science. At first glance, montane grassy ecosystems dominated by endemic grass species need to be more substantively sampled, not only for grasses but for the associated ground-layer floras such as the orchids of Andringitra. While our data show approximately 30% grass endemism in the Eastern, Western, and Southern Domains, these regions are vastly under-collected, and it will be

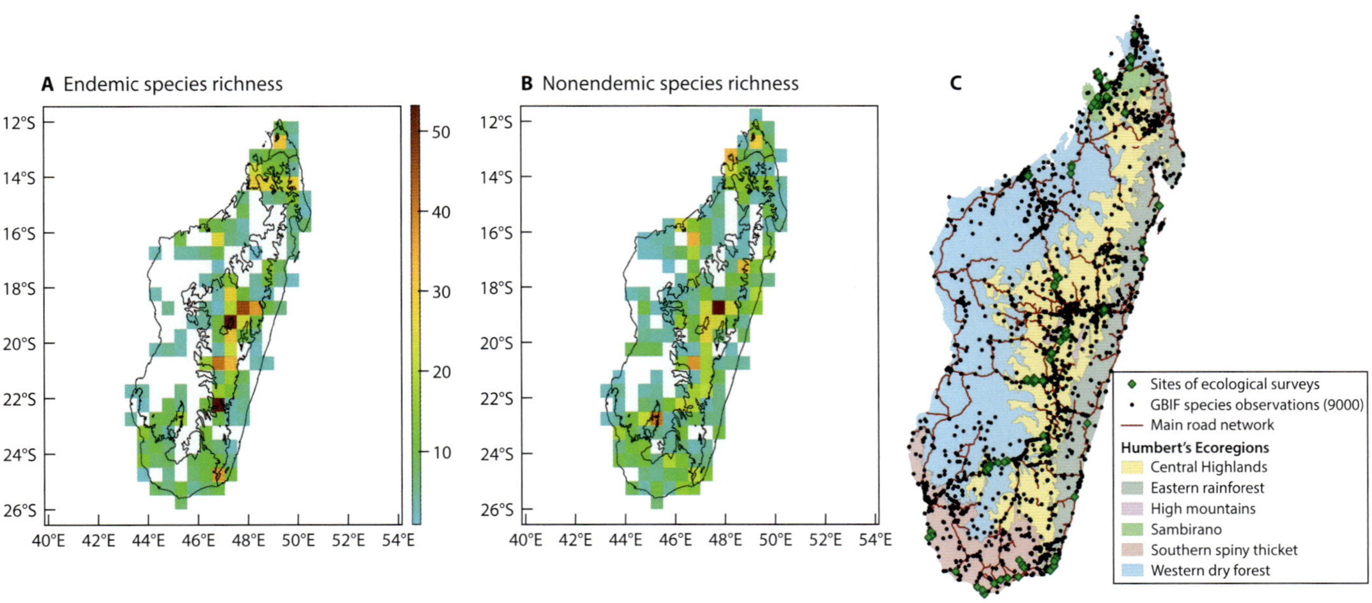

FIGURE 4.21 **Distribution of available grass species occurrence data for Madagascar based on herbarium records and field locations. A) Endemic species richness, and B) nonendemic species richness based on grass species records in the GBIF data set (Rabarivola et al. 2019a, 2019b, 2019c). C) Map highlighting our sites of vegetation surveys in 2013–2019 alongside GBIF species observations intersected with ecoregions. The color coding for A and B as defined in the vertical bar is a measure of species richness.**

equally important to extend ecological research to these regions, particularly in the west. New understanding of the relationship between environmental variation and grass functional ecology will enable identification of ancient versus novel assemblages of grass species.

Why is new knowledge important? Long-standing conservation efforts on Madagascar have been directed toward forests and spiny thickets. Consequently, land-use policies and interventions have gone unchecked in grassy ecosystems for over a century. There are intractable introduced plant problems across grassy ecosystems with *Acacia*, *Eucalyptus*, *Pinus*, *Agave*, and *Lantana*. While all were introduced for their utility in some form, these species are also known globally as invasive, transforming landscapes to create species-poor habitats (Richardson et al. 2011). These species are planted liberally without formalized planning and are spreading rapidly. They transform ecosystems, as has been documented the world over, leading to increased fire severity and associated risk to human life; changes in water tables and surface water flow that affect agriculture; reductions in biodiversity; and the further assembly of novel ecosystems. It is not a stretch to suggest that the long-standing disregard for grassy ecosystems has led to the severe degradation now ongoing through unchecked species introductions and an absence of land management and conservation of ecosystems historically considered wastelands.

THREATS TO MALAGASY GRASSY BIOMES

Amid the contention over grassy ecosystems, in 2019 and 2020 the Malagasy government, through the Ministère de l'Environnement et du Développement Durable, took a radical approach to forest conservation by legislating tree planting across the island. Tree planting was adopted as environmental policy for forest restoration, carbon sequestration, and fuelwood production; the government and nongovernmental sectors are projected to plant 40,000 ha across all ecoregions over the next five years. Tree planting is known as a process of degradation in grassy ecosystems (Bond et al. 2019). Fast-growing non-native species are often prioritized for planting generally, including *Eucalyptus*, *Acacia*, and *Pinus*.

Malagasy agriculture depends on sufficient water flow for rice production, and food security is highly precarious because of the increasing frequency of droughts (Ingram and Dawson 2005b). Planting exotic tree species at scale will not only damage biodiversity associated with grassy ecosystems but will likely lower water tables and reduce stream flow (R. Jackson et al. 2005). Numerous studies, for example, have found that extensive *Eucalyptus* plantations lower water tables (Bayle 2019), drawing groundwater away from surrounding grasslands (Engel et al. 2005). Moreover, tree planting has also been shown to increase fire risk (Jellinek et al. 2013), with greater flame heights and rates of spread (M. Jenkins et al. 2016), and this would be disastrous for Malagasy people, crops, and dwellings in communities with no capacity or resources to combat the intense fires produced by *Eucalyptus*.

All landscapes are mosaics of ecosystems that change in space and time in response to multitudes of interacting and reinforcing ecological and environmental factors. Natural, original, ancient, degraded, derived—these are all subjective and often misleading terms used against shifting baselines. The world over, and for over a century, there has been debate and contention around the limits of open and closed ecosystems, grassy and forest ecosystems, and what is "natural." Answers to these questions always depend on scale and baseline, and the same processes that shape Madagascar shape all ecosystems the world over. With that in mind, the diversity, ecology, and biogeography of grasses and the ecosystems they form suggest that grassy ecosystems have been a significant and widespread component of the island since the Miocene, shaped by aridity, temperature, fire, grazing, and their interactions.

ACKNOWLEDGMENTS

Caroline Lehmann acknowledges funding from the Royal Society (IC170015). Leanne Phelps acknowledges funding from the Swiss National Science Foundation (P2LAP2_187745). Thanks to Brian Fisher (California Academy of Sciences) for information on the new grassland ant species. Thanks to Solofo Rakotoarisoa and Lauren Gardiner for help listing endemic plant species. Many thanks to Kate Parr, Gareth Hempson, Nicola Steves, and Sally Archibald for useful discussions and to William Bond for reviewing the contribution.

Subject editors: Laurent Gautier and Steven M. Goodman

REFERENCES

Acocks, J.P.H. 1988. Veld types of South Africa. 3rd ed. *Memoirs of the Botanical Survey of South Africa* 57: 1–146.

Albert-Daviaud, A., Perillo, S., and Stuppy, W. 2018. Seed dispersal syndromes in the Madagascan flora: The unusual importance of primates. *Oryx* 52: 418–426.

Albert-Daviaud, A., Buerki, S., Onjalalaina, G., Perillo, S., Rabarijaona, R., Razafindratsima, O. H., Sato, H., Valenta, K., Wright, P. C., and Stuppy, W. 2020. The ghost fruits of Madagascar: Identifying dysfunctional seed dispersal in Madagascar's endemic flora. *Biological Conservation* 242: 108438.

Allen, C. D., Macalady, A. K., Chenchouni, H., Bachelet, D., McDowell, N., et al. 2010. A global overview of drought and heat-induced tree mortality reveals emerging climate change risks for forests. *Forest Ecology and Management* 259: 660–684.

Allnutt, T. F., Asner, G. P., Golden, C. D., and Powell, G.V.N. 2013. Mapping recent deforestation and forest disturbance in northeastern Madagascar. *Tropical Conservation Science* 6: 1–15.

Alvarado, S. T. 2012. Evaluation du rôle des feux de brousse sur la composition, la structure, la phénologie, et la résistance de la végétation des bois de tapia (*Uapaca bojeri*) du massif d'Ibity, Nouvelle Aire Protégée, en vue de sa gestion durable. PhD thesis, Sciences Agricoles, Université d'Avignon.

Alvarado, S. T., Buisson, E., Rabarison, H., Rajeriarison, C., Birkinshaw, C. R., and Lowry, P. P., II. 2014. Comparison of plant communities on the Ibity and Itremo Massifs, Madagascar, with contrasting conservation histories and current status. *Plant Ecology and Diversity* 7(4): 497–508.

———. 2015. Effects of heat on the germination of sclerophyllous forest species in the highlands of Madagascar. *Austral Ecology* 40(5): 601–610.

Alvarado, S. T., Silva, T.S.F., and Archibald, S. 2018. Management impacts on fire occurrence: A comparison of fire regimes of African and South American tropical savannas in different protected areas. *Journal of Environmental Management* 218: 79–87.

Anaya, J. A., Chuvieco, E., and Palacios-Orueta, A. 2009. Aboveground biomass assessment in Colombia: A remote sensing approach. *Forest Ecology and Management* 257: 1237–1246.

Anderson, J. T., Nuttle, T., Rojas, J.S.S., Pendergast, T. H., and Flecker, A. S. 2011. Extremely long-distance seed dispersal by an overfished Amazonian frugivore. *Proceedings of the Royal Society of London B: Biological Sciences* 278: 3329–3335.

Andriafidison, D., Cardiff, S. G., Goodman, S. M., Hutson, A. M., Jenkins, R.K.B., Kofoky, A. F., Racey P. A., Ranivo, J., Ratrimomanarivo, F. H., and Razafimanahaka, H. J. 2008. *Rousettus madagascariensis*. IUCN Red List of Threatened Species: e.T19750A9010077.

Andriamaharoa, H., Birkinshaw, C. R., and Reza, L. 2010. Day-time feeding ecology of *Eulemur cinereiceps* in the Agnalazaha Forest, Mahabo-Mananivo, Madagascar. *Madagascar Conservation and Development* 5: 55–63.

Andriamalala, S. 2007. Contribution à l'étude du rôle de *Lemur catta* dans la dissémination des graines forestières dans la Reserve Spéciale de Beza Mahafaly. Mémoire de DEA, Sciences Agronomiques, Université d'Antananarivo.

Andrianaivoarivelo, R. A., Ramilijaona, O. R., Racey, P. A., Razafindrakoto, N., and Jenkins, R.K.B. 2011. Feeding ecology, habitat use and reproduction of *Rousettus madagascariensis* Grandidier, 1928 (Chiroptera: Pteropodidae) in eastern Madagascar. *Mammalia* 75: 69–78.

Andrianaivoarivelo, [R.] A., Petit, E. J., Razafindrakoto, N., and Racey, P. A. 2012a. Alimentation et dispersion de graines chez *Rousettus madagascariensis* G. Grandidier 1928, dans le nord-ouest de Madagascar. *Revue d'Ecologie* 67: 179–191.

Andrianaivoarivelo, R. A., Jenkins, R. K., Petit, E. J., Ramilijaona, O., Razafindrakoto, N., and Racey, P. A. 2012b. *Rousettus madagascariensis* (Chiroptera: Pteropodidae) shows a preference for native and commercially unimportant fruits. *Endangered Species Research* 19: 19–27.

Andriantsaralaza, S., Pedrono, M., Tassin, J., Edmond, R., and Danthu, P. 2010. Baobabs de Madagascar: Un anachronisme de la dispersion? *Bois et Forêts des Tropiques* 306: 7–15.

Andriantsaralaza, S., Pedrono, M., Tassin, J., Roger, E., Rakouth, B., and Danthu, P. 2014. The role of extinct giant tortoises in the germination of extant baobab *Adansonia rubrostipa* seeds in Madagascar. *African Journal of Ecology* 52: 246–249.

Aquastat. 2016. Country profile and fact sheet for Madagascar. Accessed 15 Jan. 2020. http://www.fao.org/aquastat/en/countries-and-basins/country-profiles/country/MDG.

Armstrong, A. H., Shugart, H. H., and Fatoyinbo, T. E. 2011. Characterization of community composition and forest structure in a Madagascar lowland rainforest. *Tropical Conservation Science* 4(4): 428–444.

Arthan, W., Dunning, L. T., Besnard, G., Manzi, S., Kellogg, E. A., Hackel, J., Lehmann, C.E.R., Mitchley, J., and Vorontsova, M. S. 2021. Complex evolutionary history of two ecologically significant grass genera, *Themeda* and *Heteropogon* (Poaceae: Panicoideae: Andropogoneae). *Botanical Journal of the Linnean Society* 196: 437–455.

Asner, G. P., Clark, J. K., Mascaro, J., Vaudry, R., Chadwick, K. D., et al. 2012. Human and environmental controls over aboveground carbon storage in Madagascar. *Carbon Balance and Management* 7. https://doi.org/10.1186/1750-0680-7-2.

Atsalis, S. 1999. Diet of the brown mouse lemur (*Microcebus rufus*) in Ranomafana National Park, Madagascar. *International Journal of Primatology* 20: 193–229.

Aubert, S., Razafiarison, S., and Bertrand, A. 2003. Déforestation et systèmes agraires à Madagascar: Les dynamiques des *tavy* sur la côte orientale. Montpellier: CIRAD-CITE.

Avitabile, V., Herold, M., Heuvelink, G.B.M., Lewis, S. L., Phillips, O. L., et al. 2016. An integrated pan-tropical biomass map using multiple reference datasets. *Global Change Biology* 22: 1406–1420. doi:10.1111/gcb.13139.

Baccini, A., Goetz, S. J., Walker, W. S., Laporte, N. T., Sun, M., Sulla-Menashe, D., Hackler, J., Beck, P.S.A., Dubayah, R., and Friedl, M. A. 2012. Estimated carbon dioxide emissions from tropical deforestation improved by carbon-density maps. *Nature Climate Change* 2: 182–185.

Barlow, J., Lennox, G. D., Ferreira, J., Berenguer, E., Lees, A. C., et al. 2016. Anthropogenic disturbance in tropical forests can double biodiversity loss from deforestation. *Nature* 535: 144–147.

Barthlott, W., Mutke, J., Rafiqpoor, D., Kier, G., and Kreft, H. 2005. Global centers of vascular plant diversity. *Nova Acta Leopoldina*, neue folge, 92(342): 61–83.

Bayle, G. K. 2019. Ecological and social impacts of eucalyptus tree plantation on the environment. *Journal of Biodiversity Conservation and Bioresource Management* 5: 93–104.

Beckman, N. G., Aslan, C. E., Rogers, H. S., Kogan, O., Bronstein, J. L., et al. 2019. Advancing an interdisciplinary framework to study seed dispersal ecology. *AoB PLANTS* 11: plz048.

Bento, V. A., Trigo, I. F., Gouveia, C. M., and DaCamara, C. C. 2018. Contribution of land surface temperature (TCI) to vegetation health index: A comparative study using clear sky and all-weather climate data records. *Remote Sensing* 10: 1324.

Besnard, G., Christin, P.-A., Malé, P.-J.G., Coissac, E., Ralimanana, H., and Vorontsova, M. S. 2013. Phylogenomics and taxonomy of Lecomtelleae Poaceae, an isolated panicoid lineage from Madagascar. *Annals of Botany* 112: 1057–1066.

Besnard, G., Christin, P.-A., Malé, P.-J.G., Lhuillier, E., Lauzeral, C., Coissac, E., and Vorontsova, M. S. 2014. From museums to genomics: Old herbarium specimens shed light on a C_3 to C_4 transition. *Journal of Experimental Botany* 65: 6711–6721.

Birkinshaw, C. R. 1995. The importance of the black lemur, *Eulemur macaco* (Lemuridae, primates), for seed dispersal in Lokobe Forest, Madagascar. PhD thesis, University College London.

———. 1999. The importance of the black lemur (*Eulemur macaco*) for seed dispersal in Lokobe Forest, Nosy Be. In *New Directions in Lemur Studies*, eds. B. Rakotosamimanana, H. Rasamimanana, J. U. Ganzhorn, and S. M. Goodman, pp. 189–199. Boston: Springer.

———. 2001. Fruit characteristics of species dispersed by the black lemur (*Eulemur macaco*) in the Lokobe Forest, Madagascar. *Biotropica* 33: 478–486.

Birkinshaw, C. R., and Andriamihajarivo, T. H. 2007. Effect of human population density and "rockiness" of habitat on the species richness, frequency and biomass of woody plants on the quartzite massifs of central Madagascar. Poster presented to the AETFAT Congress in Yaoundé, Cameroon.

Blanc, C. P. 1969. Etudes sur les Iguanidae de Madagascar: Observations sur l'écologie de *Chalarodon madagascariensis* Peters, 1854. *Oecologia* 2: 292–318.

Bleher, B., and Böhning-Gaese, K. 2001. Consequences of frugivore diversity for seed dispersal, seedling establishment and the spatial pattern of seedlings and trees. *Oecologia* 129: 385–394.

Bloxam, Q.M.C., Behler, J. L., Rakotovao, E. R., Randriamahazo, H.J.A.R., Hayes, K. T., Tonge, S. J., and Ganzhorn, J. U. 1996. Effects of logging on the reptile fauna of the Kirindy Forest with special emphasis on the flat-tailed tortoise (*Pyxis planicauda*). In Ecology and economy of a tropical dry forest in Madagascar, eds. J. U. Ganzhorn and J.-P. Sorg. *Primate Report* 46–1: 189–201.

BNC REDD. 2018. *Stratégie Nationale REDD+, Madagascar*. Antananarivo: Bureau National de Coordination REDD+. https://www.forestcarbonpartnership.org/system/files/documents/Strate%CC%81gie%20Nationale%20REDD%2B%20Madagascar%20FINAL%2013-06-18%20accentue%CC%81_0.pdf.

Bodin, Ö., Tengö, M., Norman, A., Lundberg, J., and Elmqvist, T. 2006. The value of small size: Loss of forest patches and ecological thresholds in southern Madagascar. *Ecological Applications* 16: 440–451.

Böhning-Gaese, K., Gaese, B. H., and Rabemanantsoa, S. B. 1995. Seed dispersal by frugivorous tree visitors in the Malagasy tree species *Commiphora guillaumini. Ecotropica* 1: 41–50.

———. 1999. Importance of primary and secondary seed dispersal in the Malagasy tree *Commiphora guillaumini*. *Ecology* 80(3): 821–832.

Boisserie, J. R., Zazzo, A., Merceron, G., Blondel, C., Ignaud, P., Likius, A., Mackaye, H. T., and Brunet, M. 2005. Diets of modern and late Miocene hippopotamids: Evidence from carbon isotope composition and microwear of tooth enamel. *Palaeogeography, Palaeoclimatology, Palaeoecology* 221: 153–174.

Bollen, A. 2007. Fruit characteristics: Fruit selection, animal seed dispersal and conservation matters in the Sainte Luce forests. In *Biodiversity, Ecology, and Conservation of Littoral Ecosystems in the Region of Tolagnaro (Fort Dauphin), Southeastern Madagascar*, eds. J. U. Ganzhorn, S. M. Goodman, and M. Vincelette, pp. 127–145. Washington, DC: Smithsonian Institution.

Bollen, A., and Van Elsacker, L. 2002. Feeding ecology of *Pteropus rufus* (Pteropodidae) in the littoral forest of Sainte Luce, SE Madagascar. *Acta Chiropterologica* 4: 33–48.

———. 2004. The feeding ecology of the lesser vasa parrot, *Coracopsis nigra*, in south-eastern Madagascar. *Ostrich* 75: 141–146.

Bollen, A., Van Elsacker, L., and Ganzhorn, J. U. 2004a. Tree dispersal strategies in the littoral forest of Sainte Luce (SE-Madagascar). *Oecologia* 139: 604–616.

———. 2004b. Relations between fruits and disperser assemblages in a Malagasy littoral forest: A community-level approach. *Journal of Tropical Ecology* 20: 599–612.

Bond, W. J. 2019. *Open Ecosystems: Ecology and Evolution beyond the Forest Edge*. Oxford: Oxford University Press.

Bond, W. J., Silander, J. A., Jr., Ranaivonasy, J., and Ratsirarson, J. 2008. The antiquity of Madagascar's grasslands and the rise of C_4 grassy biomes. *Journal of Biogeography* 35(10): 1743–1758.

Bond, W. J., Stevens, N., Midgley, G. F., and Lehmann, C.E.R. 2019. The trouble with trees: Afforestation plans for Africa. *Trends in Ecology and Evolution* 34: 963–965.

Bowman, D.M.J.S. 2000. *Australian Rainforests: Islands of Green in a Land of Fire*. Cambridge: Cambridge University Press.

Brand, J., and Pfund, J. L. 1998. Site- and watershed-level assessment of nutrient dynamics under shifting cultivation in eastern Madagascar. *Agriculture, Ecosystems and Environment* 71(1–3): 169–183.

Brimont, L., and Leroy, M. 2018. Le mécanisme REDD+ et les projets pilotes à Madagascar : D'un idéal incitatif à la réalité des dispositifs de gestion. *Nature Science Sociétés* 26: 308–319. https://doi.org/10.1051/nss/2018043.

Brimont, L., Ezzine-de-Blas, D., Karsenty, A., and Toulon, A. 2015. Achieving conservation and equity amidst extreme poverty and climate risk: The Makira REDD+ project in Madagascar. *Forests* 6: 748–768.

Britt, A., Randriamandratonirina, N., Glasscock, K. D., and Iambana, B. R. 2002. Diet and feeding behaviour of *Indri indri* in a low-altitude rain forest. *Folia Primatologica* 73: 225–239.

Brown, K. A., Johnson, S. E., Parks, K. E., Holmes, S. M., Ivoandry, T., et al. 2013. Use of provisioning ecosystem services drives loss of functional traits across land use intensification gradients in tropical forests in Madagascar. *Biological Conservation* 161: 118–127.

Burgess, N., Hales, J., Underwood, E., Dinerstein, E., Olson, D., Itoua, I., Schipper, J., Ricketts, T., and Newman, K. 2004. *Terrestrial Eco-regions of Africa and Madagascar: A Conservation Assessment*. Washington, DC: Island Press.

Burke, R., and Lehman, S. 2014. Edge effects on morphometrics and body mass in two sympatric species of mouse lemurs in Madagascar. *Folia Primatologica* 85: 277–291.

Burleigh, R., and Arnold, E. N. 1986. Age and dietary differences of recently extinct Indian Ocean tortoises (*Geochelone s. lat.*) revealed by carbon isotope analysis. *Proceedings of the Royal Society of London B: Biological Sciences* 227: 137–144.

Burney, D. A. 1987a. Late Holocene vegetational change in central Madagascar. *Quaternary Research* 28: 130–143.

———. 1987b. Pre-settlement vegetation changes at Lake Tritrivakely, Madagascar. *Palaeoecology of Africa and Surrounding Islands* 18: 357–381.

———. 1987c. Late Quaternary stratigraphic charcoal records from Madagascar. *Quaternary Research* 28: 274–280.

———. 1993. Late Holocene environmental changes in arid southwestern Madagascar. *Quaternary Research* 40: 98–106.

———. 1999. Rates, patterns, and processes of landscape transformation and extinction in Madagascar. In *Extinctions in Near Time: Causes, Contexts, and Consequences*, ed. R.D.E. MacPhee, pp. 145–164. New York: Plenum.

Burney, D. A., and Flannery, T. F. 2005. Fifty millennia of catastrophic extinctions after human contact. *Trends in Ecology and Evolution* 20: 395–401.

Burney, D. A., James, H. F., Grady, F. V., Rafamantanantsoa, J.-G., Wright, H. T., and Cowart, J. B. 1997. Environmental change, extinction and human activity: Evidence from caves in NW Madagascar. *Journal of Biogeography* 24: 755–767.

Burney, D. A., Robinson, G. S., and Burney, L. P. 2003. *Sporormiella* and the late Holocene extinctions in Madagascar. *Proceedings of the National Academy of Sciences of the USA* 100: 10800–10805.

Burney, D. A., Burney, L. P., Godfrey, L. R., Jungers, W. L., Goodman, S. M., Wright, H. T., and Jull, A. T. 2004. A chronology for late prehistoric Madagascar. *Journal of Human Evolution* 47: 25–63.

Burns, S. J., Godfrey, L. R., Faina, P., McGee, D., Hardt, B., Ranivoharimanana, L., and Randrianasy, J. 2016. Rapid human-induced landscape transformation in Madagascar at the end of the first millennium of the Common Era. *Quaternary Science Reviews* 134: 92–99.

Busch, J., and Ferretti-Gallon, K. 2014. *What Drives Deforestation and What Stops It? A Meta-analysis of Spatially Explicit Econometric Studies*. Washington, DC: Center for Global Development.

Callmander, M., Phillipson, P. B., Schatz, G. E., Andriambololonera, S., Rabarimanarivo, M., Rakotonirina, N., Raharimampionona, J., Chatelain, C., Gautier, L., and Lowry, P. P., II. 2011. The endemic and non-endemic vascular flora of Madagascar updated. *Plant Ecology and Evolution* 144: 121–125.

Carrasco, J., Price, V., Tulloch, V., and Mill, M. S. 2020. Selecting priority areas for the conservation of endemic trees species and their ecosystems in Madagascar considering both conservation value and vulnerability to human pressure. *Biodiversity and Conservation* 29: 1841–1854. https://doi.org/10.1007/s10531-020-01947-1.

Carvalho, F., Brown, K. A., Gordon, A. D., Yesuf, G. U., Raherilalao, M. J., Raselimanana, A. P., Soarimalala, V., and Goodman, S. M. 2020. Methods for prioritizing protected areas using individual and aggregate rankings. *Environmental Conservation* 47(2): 113–122.

Casse, T., Milhøj, A., Ranaivoson, S., and Randriamanarivo, J. R. 2004. Causes of deforestation in southwestern Madagascar: What do we know? *Forest Policy and Economics* 6: 33–38.

Castella, J. C., and Verburg, P. H. 2007. Combination of process-oriented and pattern-oriented models of land-use change in a mountain area of Vietnam. *Ecological Modeling* 202: 410–420.

Castellanos, J., Jaramillo, V. J., Sanford, R. L., Jr., and Kauffman, J. B. 2001. Slash-and-burn effects on fine root biomass and productivity in a tropical dry forest ecosystem in Mexico. *Forest Ecology and Management* 148(1–3): 41–50.

Caughlin, T. T., Ferguson, J. M., Lichstein, J. W., Zuidema, P. A., Bunyavejchewin, S., and Levey, D. J. 2014. Loss of animal seed dispersal increases extinction risk in a tropical tree species due to pervasive negative density dependence across life stages. *Proceedings of the Royal Society of London B: Biological Sciences* 282: 20142095.

Cerling, T. E., Harris, J. M., Hart, J. A., Kaleme, P., Klingel, H., Leakey, M. G., Levin, N. E., Lewison, R. L., and Passey, B. H., 2008. Stable isotope ecology of the common hippopotamus. *Journal of Zoology* 276: 204–212.

Chave, J., Chust, G., Condit, R., Aguilar, S., Hernandez, A., Lao, S., and Perez, R. 2004. Error propagation and scaling for tropical forest biomass estimates. In *Tropical Forests and Global Atmospheric Change*, eds. Y. Malhi and O. Phillips, pp. 155–166. London: Oxford University Press.

Chave, J., Muller-Landau, H. C., Baker, T. R., Easdale, T. A., ter Steege, H., and Webb, C. O. 2006. Regional and phylogenetic variation of wood density across 2456 Neotropical tree species. *Ecological Applications* 16: 2356–2367.

Chave, J., Réjou-Méchain, M., Búrquez, A., Chidumayo, E., Colgan, M. S., et al. 2014. Improved allometric models to estimate the aboveground biomass of tropical trees. *Global Change Biology* 20: 3177–3190. https://doi.org/10.1111/gcb.12629.

Chazdon, R. L., and Guariguata, M. R. 2016. Natural regeneration as a tool for large-scale forest restoration in the tropics: Prospects and challenges. *Biotropica* 48: 716–730. https://doi.org/10.1111/btp.12381.

Chen, G., Wang, Z-W., Wen, P., Wei, W., Chen, Y., Ai, H., and Sun, W-B. 2018. Hydrocarbons mediate seed dispersal: a new mechanism of vespicochory. *New Physiologist* 220(3): 655–658.

———. 2016. Diet and effects of Sanford's brown lemur (*Eulemur sanfordi*, Archbold 1932) gut-passage on the germination of plant species in Amber forest, Madagascar. *Zoological Studies* 55: 1–13.

Chidumayo, E. N. 1989. Early post-felling response of Marquesia woodland to burning in the Zambian Copperbelt. *Journal of Ecology* 77: 430–438.

Clarke, S. J., Miller, G. H., Fogel, M. L., Chivas, A. R., and Murray-Wallace, C. V. 2006. The amino acid and stable isotope biogeochemistry of elephant bird (*Aepyornis*) eggshells from southern Madagascar. *Quaternary Science Reviews* 25: 2343–2356.

Cornet, A. 1974. *Essai de cartographie bioclimatique à Madagascar*. Notice Explicative No. 55. Paris: ORSTOM.

Cornet, A., and Guillaumet, J.-L. 1976. Divisions floristiques et étages de végétation à Madagascar. *Cahiers de l'ORSTOM*, série *Biologie* 9: 35–42.

Crowley, B. E. 2010. A refined chronology of prehistoric Madagascar and the demise of the megafauna. *Quaternary Science Reviews* 29: 2591–2603.

Crowley, B. E., and Godfrey, L. R. 2013. Why all those spines? Anachronistic defences in the Didiereoideae against now extinct lemurs. *South African Journal of Science* 109: 1–7.

Crowley, B. E., and Samonds, K. E. 2013. Stable carbon isotope values confirm a recent increase in grasslands in northwestern Madagascar. *Holocene* 23: 1066–1073.

Crowley, B. E., Godfrey, L. R., and Irwin, M. T. 2011. A glance to the past: Subfossils, stable isotopes, seed dispersal, and lemur species loss in southern Madagascar. *American Journal of Primatology* 73: 25–37.

Crowley, B. E., Godfrey, L. R., Bankoff, R. J., Perry, G. H., Culleton, B. J., Kennett, D. J., Sutherland, M. R., Samonds, K. E., and Burney, D. A. 2017. Island-wide aridity did not trigger recent megafaunal extinctions in Madagascar. *Ecography* 40: 901–912.

Cubiña, A., and Aide, T. M. 2001. The effect of distance from forest edge on seed rain and soil seed bank in a tropical pasture. *Biotropica* 33: 260–267. https://doi.org/10.1111/j.1744-7429.2001.tb00177.x.

Culot, L., Huynen, M.-C., and Heymann, E. W. 2015. Partitioning the relative contribution of one-phase and two-phase seed dispersal when evaluating seed dispersal effectiveness. *Methods in Ecology and Evolution* 6: 176–186.

———. 2018. Primates and dung beetles: Two dispersers are better than one in secondary forest. *International Journal of Primatology* 39: 397–414.

Dai, A. 2011. Drought under global warming: A review. *WIREs Climate Change* 2: 45–65.

Dammhahn, M., and Kappeler, P. M. 2005. Social system of *Microcebus berthae*, the world's smallest primate. *International Journal of Primatology* 26: 407–435.

———. 2008a. Small-scale coexistence of two mouse lemur species (*Microcebus berthae* and *M. murinus*) within a homogeneous competitive environment. *Oecologia* 157: 473–483.

———. 2008b. Comparative feeding ecology of sympatric *Microcebus berthae* and *M. murinus*. *International Journal of Primatology* 29: 1567–1589.

Daskin, J. H., Aires, F., and Staver, A. C. 2019. Determinants of tree cover in tropical floodplains. *Proceedings of the Royal Society of London B: Biological Sciences* 286(1914): 20191755.

DEF (Direction des Eaux et Forêts). 1996. Inventaire écologique forestier national. Report, November 1996.

Desbureaux, S., and Damania, R. 2018. Rain, forests and farmers: Evidence of drought induced deforestation in Madagascar and its consequences for biodiversity conservation. *Biological Conservation* 221: 357–364.

De Sy, V., Herold, M., Achard, F., Asner, G. P., Held, A., Kellndorfer, J., and Verbesselt, J. 2012. Synergies of multiple remote sensing data sources for REDD+ Monitoring. *Current Opinion in Environmental Sustainability* 4: 696–706. doi:10.1016/j.cosust.2012.09.013.

Dew, J. L., and Wright, P. 1998. Frugivory and seed dispersal by four species of primates in Madagascar's eastern rain forest. *Biotropica* 30: 425–437.

DeWalt, S. J., Schnitzer, S. A., and Denslow, J. S. 2000. Density and diversity of lianas along a chronosequence in central Panamanian lowland forest. *Journal of Tropical Ecology* 16: 1–9.

Dewar, R. E., and Richard, A. F. 2007. Evolution in the hypervariable environment of Madagascar. *Proceedings of the National Academy of Sciences of the USA* 104: 13723–13727.

———. 2012. Madagascar: A history of arrivals, what happened, and will happen next. *Annual Review of Anthropology* 41: 495–517.

Dezécache, C., Salles, J., and Hérault, B. 2018. Questioning emissions-based approaches for the definition of REDD+ deforestation baselines in high forest cover/low deforestation countries. *Carbon Balance Management* 13: 21. https://doi.org/10.1186/s13021-018-0109-1.

Dittmann, M. T., Dammhahn, M., and Kappeler P. M. 2014. The impact of selective logging on behavior and ecology of *Aphaenogaster swammerdami* (Formicidae): 20 years later—a happy ant? *Malagasy Nature* 8: 35–48.

Domoinaharivelo, N. 2014. Etude de l'écologie alimentaire de deux cheirogales, *Cheirogaleus sibreei* (Major 1986) et *Cheirogaleus crossleyi* (Grandidier, 1870) dans la forêt de Tsinjoarivo Ambatolampy: En période pré-hibernation et post-hibernation. Mémoire de DEA, Université d'Antananarivo.

Douglass, K., Hixon, S., Wright, H. T., Godfrey, L. R., Crowley, B. E., Manjakahery, B., Rasolondrainy, T., Crossland, Z., and Radimilahy, C. 2019. A critical review of radiocarbon dates clarifies the human settlement of Madagascar. *Quaternary Science Reviews* 221: 105878.

Drack, S., Ortmann, S., Bührmann, N., Schmid, J., Warren, R. D., Heldmaier, G., and Ganzhorn, J. U. 1999. Field metabolic rate and the cost of ranging of the red-tailed sportive lemur (*Lepilemur ruficaudatus*). In *New Directions in Lemur Studies*, eds. B. Rakotosamimanana, H. Rasamimanana, J. U. Ganzhorn, and S. M. Goodman, pp. 83–91. London: Kluwer Academic / Plenum.

Dransfield, J., and Beentje, H. 1995. *The Palms of Madagascar*. Richmond: Royal Botanic Gardens Kew.

Dufils, J.-M. 2003. Remaining forest cover. In *The Natural History of Madagascar*, eds. S. M. Goodman and J. P. Benstead, pp. 88–96. Chicago: University of Chicago Press.

Dumetz, N. 1999. High plant diversity of lowland rainforest vestiges in eastern Madagascar. *Biodiversity and Conservation* 8(2): 273–315.

Dunham, A. E., Erhart, E. M., Overdorff, D. J., and Wright, P. C. 2008. Evaluating effects of deforestation, hunting, and El Niño events on a threatened lemur. *Biological Conservation* 141: 287–297.

Dunham, A. E., Razafindratsima, O. H., Rakotonirina, P., and Wright P. C. 2018. Fruiting phenology is linked to rainfall variability in a tropical rain forest. *Biotropica* 50: 396–404.

Dunning, L. T., Liabot, A. L., Olofsson, J. K., Smith, E. K., Vorontsova, M. S., et al. 2017. The recent and rapid spread of *Themeda triandra*. *Botany Letters* 164: 327–337.

Dutta, D., Kundu, A., Patel, N. R., Saha, S. K., and Siddiqui, A. R. 2015. Assessment of agricultural drought in Rajasthan (India) using remote sensing derived Vegetation Condition Index (VCI) and Standardized Precipitation Index (SPI). *Egyptian Journal of Remote Sensing and Space Science* 18: 53–63.

Eberle, M., and Kappeler, P. M. 2002. Mouse lemurs in space and time: A test of the socioecological model. *Behavioral Ecology and Sociobiology* 51: 131–139.

Eckert, S., Ratsimba, H. R., Rakotondrasoa, L. O., Rajoelison, L. G., and Ehrensperger, A. 2011. Deforestation and forest degradation monitoring and assessment of biomass and carbon stock of lowland rainforest in the Analanjirofo region, Madagascar. *Forest Ecology and Management* 262: 1996–2007. https://doi.org/10.1016/j.foreco.2011.08.041.

Edwards, E. J., Osborne, C. P., Strömberg, C. A., Smith, S. A., and C_4 Grasses Consortium. 2010. The origins of C_4 grasslands: Integrating evolutionary and ecosystem science. *Science* 328: 587–591.

Eklund, J., Blanchet, F. G., Nyman, J., Rocha, R., Virtanen, T., and Cabeza, M. 2016. Contrasting spatial and temporal trends of protected area effectiveness in mitigating deforestation in Madagascar. *Biological Conservation* 203: 290–297. https://doi.org/10.1016/j.biocon.2016.09.033.

Eklund, J., Coad, L., Geldmann, J., and Cabeza, M. 2019. What constitutes a useful measure of protected area effectiveness? A case study of management inputs and protected area impacts in Madagascar. *Conservation Science and Practice* 1: e107. https://doi.org/10.1111/csp2.107.

Elton, S. 2008. The environmental context of human evolutionary history in Eurasia and Africa. *Journal of Anatomy* 212(4): 377–393.

Engel, V., Jobbágy, E. G., Stieglitz, M., Williams, M., and Jackson, R. B. 2005. Hydrological consequences of *Eucalyptus* afforestation in the Argentine Pampas. *Water Resources Research* 41. https://doi.org/10.1029/2004WR003761.

Eppley, T. M., Verjans, E., and Donati, G. 2011. Coping with low-quality diets: A first account of the feeding ecology of the southern gentle lemur, *Hapalemur meridionalis*, in the Mandena littoral forest, southeast Madagascar. *Primates* 52: 7–13.

Fahrig, L. 2003. Effects of habitat fragmentation on biodiversity. *Annual Review of Ecology and Evolutionary Systematics* 34: 487–515.

Faramalala, M. H. 1995. *Formations végétales et domaine forestier national de Madagascar*. Antananarivo: Conservation International.

Faure, M., Guérin, C., Genty, D., Gommery, D., and Ramanivosoa, B. 2010. The oldest fossil hippopotamus (*Hippopotamus laloumena*) of Madagascar (Belobaka, Mahajanga Province). *Comptes Rendus Palevol* 9: 155–162.

Federman, S., Dornburg, A., Daly, D. C., Downie, A., Perry, G. H., Yoder, A. D., Sargis, E. J., Richard, A. F., Donoghue, M. J., and Baden, A. L. 2016. Implications of lemuriform extinctions for the Malagasy flora. *Proceedings of the National Academy of Sciences of the USA* 113: 5041–5046.
Fichtel, C. 2007. Avoiding predators at night: Antipredator strategies in red-tailed sportive lemurs (*Lepilemur ruficaudatus*). *American Journal of Primatology* 69: 611–624.
Fichtel, C., and Kappeler, P. M. 2002. Anti-predator behavior of group-living Malagasy primates: Mixed evidence for a referential alarm call system. *Behavioral Ecology and Sociobiology* 51: 262–275.
Fichtel, C., Zucchini, W., and Hilgartner, R. 2011. Out of sight but not out of mind: Behavioral coordination in red-tailed sportive lemurs. *International Journal of Primatology* 32: 1383–1396.
Fick, S. E., and Hijmans, R. J. 2017. WorldClim 2: New 1-km spatial resolution climate surfaces for global land areas. *International Journal of Climatology* 37: 4302–4315.
Fietz, J., Zischler, H., Schwiegk, C., Tomiuk, J., Dausmann, K. H., and Ganzhorn, J. U. 2000. High rates of extra-pair young in the pair-living fat-tailed dwarf lemur, *Cheirogaleus medius*. *Behavioral Ecology and Sociobiology* 49: 8–17.
Fischer, R., Armstrong, A., Shugart, H. H., and Huth, A. 2014. Simulating the impacts of reduced rainfall on carbon stocks and net ecosystem exchange in a tropical forest. *Environmental Modelling and Software* 52: 200–206.
Fisher, B. L., and Robertson, H. G. 2002. Comparison and origin of forest and grassland ant assemblages in the High Plateau of Madagascar (Hymenoptera: Formicidae). *Biotropica* 34: 155–167.
Fleming, T. H., Breitwisch, R., and Whitesides, G. H. 1987. Patterns of tropical vertebrate frugivore diversity. *Annual Review of Ecology and Systematics* 18: 91–109.
Forget, P.-M. 1990. Seed-dispersal of *Vouacapoua americana* (Caesalpiniaceae) by caviomorph rodents in French Guiana. *Journal of Tropical Ecology* 6: 459–468.
Forget, P.-M., Hammond, D. S., Milleron, T., and Thomas, R. 2001. Seasonality of fruiting and food hoarding by rodents in Neotropical forests: Consequences for seed dispersal and seedling recruitment. In *Seed Dispersal and Frugivory: Ecology, Evolution, and Conservation*, eds. D. J. Levey, R. Silva, and M. Galetti, pp. 241–256. Wallingford: CABI.
Forkel, M., Carvalhais, N., Verbesselt, J., Mahecha, M. D., Neigh, C.S.R., and Reichstein, M. 2013. Trend change detection in NDVI time series: Effects of inter-annual variability and methodology. *Remote Sensing* 5: 2113–2144.
Frank, A.S.K., and Schäffler, L. 2019. Identifying key knowledge gaps to better protect biodiversity and simultaneously secure livelihoods in a priority conservation area. *Sustainability* 11: 5695.
Freudenberger, K. 2010. Paradise lost? Lessons from 25 years of USAID environment programs in Madagascar. Washington, DC: International Resources Group.
Gade, D. W. 1985. Savanna woodland, fire, protein and silk in highland Madagascar. *Journal of Ethnobiology* 5(2): 109–122.
Galetti, M., and Dirzo, R. 2013. Ecological and evolutionary consequences of living in a defaunated world. *Biological Conservation* 163: 1–6.
Gamero, A., Székely, T., and Kappeler, P. M. 2014. Delayed juvenile dispersal and monogamy, but no cooperative breeding in white-breasted mesites (*Mesitornis variegata*). *Behavioral Ecology and Sociobiology* 68: 73–83.
Ganzhorn, J. U. 1987. A possible role of plantations for primate conservation in Madagascar. *American Journal of Primatology* 12: 205–215.
———. 1993. Flexibility and constraints of *Lepilemur* ecology. In *Lemur Social Systems and Their Ecological Basis*, eds. P. M. Kappeler and J. U. Ganzhorn, pp. 153–165. New York: Plenum Press.
———. 1995. Low level forest disturbance effects on primary production, leaf chemistry, and lemur populations. *Ecology* 76: 2084–2096.
Ganzhorn, J. U., and Sorg, J.-P., eds. 1996. Ecology and economy of a tropical dry forest in Madagascar. *Primate Report* 46–1.
Ganzhorn, J. U., Ganzhorn, A. W., Abraham, J. P., Andriamanarivo, L., and Ramananjatovo, A. 1990. The impact of selective logging on forest structure and tenrec populations in western Madagascar. *Oecologia* 84: 126–133.
Ganzhorn, J. U., Sommer, S., Abraham, J.-P., Ade, M., Raharivololona, E. R., Rakotodrasoa, C., and Randriamarosoa, R. 1996. Mammals of the Kirindy Forest with special emphasis on *Hypogeomys antimena* and the effects of logging on the small mammal fauna. In Ecology and economy of a tropical dry forest in Madagascar, eds. J. U. Ganzhorn and J.-P. Sorg. *Primate Report* 46–1: 215–232.
Ganzhorn, J. U., Fietz, J., Rakotovao, E., Schwab, D., and Zinner, D. 1999. Lemurs and the regeneration of dry deciduous forest in Madagascar. *Conservation Biology* 13: 794–804.
Ganzhorn, J. U., Lowry, P. P., Schatz, G. E., and Sommer, S. 2001. The biodiversity of Madagascar: One of the world's hottest hotspots on its way out. *Oryx* 35(4): 346–348.
Garbutt, N. 2007. *Mammals of Madagascar: A Complete Guide*. New Haven: Yale University Press.
Garcia, G. 2005. Ecology, human impact and conservation for the Madagascan side-necked turtle (*Erymnochelys madagascariensis* Grandidier, 1876) at Ankarafantsika National Park, Madagascar. PhD thesis, University of Kent.
Gardner, C. J., Nicoll, M. E., Birkinshaw, C., Harris, A., Lewis, R. E., Rakotomalala, D., and Ratsifandrihamanana, A. N. 2018. The rapid expansion of Madagascar's protected area system. *Biological Conservation* 220: 29–36. https://doi.org/10.1016/j.biocon.2018.02.011.
Gardner, C. J., Bicknell, J. E., Baldwin-Cantello, W., Struebig, M. J., and Davies, Z. G. 2019. Quantifying the impacts of defaunation on natural forest regeneration in a global meta-analysis. *Nature Communications* 10: 4590. https://doi.org/10.1038/s41467-019-12539-1.
Gasse, F., and Van Campo, E. 1998. A 40,000-yr pollen and diatom record for Lake Tritrivakely, Madagascar, in the southern tropics. *Quaternary Research* 49: 299–311.
———. 2001. Late Quaternary environmental changes from a pollen and diatom record in the southern tropics (Lake Tritrivakely, Madagascar). *Palaeogeography, Palaeoclimatology, Palaeoecology* 167: 287–308.
Gautier, L., Tahinarivony, J. A., Ranirison, P., and Wohlhauser, S. 2018. Végétation / Vegetation. In *Les aires protégées terrestres de Madagascar: Leur histoire, description et biote / The Terrestrial Protected Areas of Madagascar: Their History, Description, and Biota*, eds. S. M. Goodman, M. J. Raherilalao, and S. Wohlhauser, pp. 207–242. Antananarivo: Association Vahatra.
Génin, F., and Rambeloarivony, H. 2018. Mouse lemurs (Primates: Cheirogaleidae) cultivate green fruit gardens. *Biological Journal of the Linnean Society* 124: 607–620.
Gidey, E., Dikinya, O., Sebego, R., Segosebe, E., and Zenebe, A. 2018. Using drought indices to model the statistical relationships between meteorological and agricultural drought in Raya and its environs, northern Ethiopia. *Earth Systems and Environment* 2: 265–279.
Glessner, K., and Britt, A. 2005. Population density and home range size of *Indri indri* in a protected low latitude rain forest. *International Journal of Primatology* 26: 855–872.
Global Forest Watch. Tree cover loss in Madagascar. Accessed 05 June 2020. www.globalforestwatch.org.
Godfrey, L. R., and Crowley, B. E. 2016. Madagascar's ephemeral palaeo-grazer guild: Who ate the ancient C_4 grasses? *Proceedings of the Royal Society of London B: Biological Sciences* 283: 20160360.
Godfrey, L. R., Jungers, W. L., Schwartz, G. T., and Irwin, M. T. 2008. Ghosts and orphans: Madagascar's vanishing ecosystems. In *Elwyn Simons: A Search for Origins*, eds. J. G. Fleagle and C. C. Gilbert, pp. 361–395. New York: Springer.
Godfrey, L. R., Crowley, B. E., Muldoon, K. M., Kelley, E. A., King, S. J., Best, A. W., and Berthaume, M. A. 2016. What did *Hadropithecus* eat, and why should paleoanthropologists care? *American Journal of Primatology* 78: 1098–1112.
Godfrey, L. R., Scroxton, N., Crowley, B. E., Burns, S. J., Sutherland, M. R., Pérez, V. R., Faina, P., McGee, D., and Ranivoharimanana, L. 2019. A new interpretation of Madagascar's megafaunal decline: The "Subsistence Shift Hypothesis." *Journal of Human Evolution* 130: 126–140.
GOFC-GOLD. 2015. *A Sourcebook of Methods and Procedures for Monitoring and Reporting Anthropogenic Greenhouse Gas Emissions and Removals Associated with Deforestation, Gains and Losses of Carbon Stocks in Forests Remaining Forests, and Forestation*. Report version COP21–1. Wageningen: GOFC-GOLD.
Gomez, C., Viscarra Rossel, R. A., and McBratney, A. 2008. Soil organic carbon prediction by hyperspectral remote sensing and field vis-NIR spectroscopy: An Australian case study. *Geoderma* 146: 403–411.
Gonçalves, N. B., Lopes, A. P., Dalagnol, R., Wu, J., Pinho, D. M., and Nelson, B. W. 2020. Both near-surface and satellite remote sensing confirm drought legacy effect on tropical forest leaf phenology after 2015/2016 ENSO drought. *Remote Sensing of Environment* 237: 111489.
Goodman, S. M. 1994. A description of the ground burrow of *Eliurus webbi* (Nesomyinae) and case of cohabitation with an endemic bird (Brachypteraciidae, *Brachypteracias*). *Mammalia* 58: 670–672.
———. 2012. *Les Carnivora de Madagascar*. Antananarivo: Association Vahatra.
Goodman, S. M., and Benstead, J. P. 2003. *The Natural History of Madagascar*. Chicago: University of Chicago Press.
———. 2005. Updated estimates of biotic diversity and endemism for Madagascar. *Oryx* 39: 73–77.

Goodman, S. M., and Ganzhorn, J. U. 1997. Rarity of figs (*Ficus*) on Madagascar and its relationship to a depauperate frugivore community. *Revue d'Ecologie* 52: 321–329.

Goodman, S. M., and Jungers W. L. 2014. *Extinct Madagascar: Picturing the Island's Past*. Chicago: University of Chicago Press.

Goodman, S. M., and Sterling, E. J. 1996. The utilisation of *Canarium* (Burseraceae) seeds by vertebrates in the Réserve Naturelle Intégrale d'Andringitra, Madagascar. In A floral and faunal survey of the eastern slopes of the Réserve Naturelle Intégrale d'Andringitra, Madagascar: With reference to elevational variation, ed. S. M. Goodman. *Fieldiana Zoology*, new series, 85: 83–89.

Goodman, S. M., Ganzhorn, J. U., and Wilmé, L. 1997. Observations at a *Ficus* tree in Malagasy humid forest. *Biotropica* 29: 480–488.

Goodman, S. M., Raherilalao, M. J., and Wohlhauser, S., eds. 2018. *Les aires protégées terrestres de Madagascar: Leur histoire, description et biote / The Terrestrial Protected Areas of Madagascar: Their History, Description, and Biota*. Antananarivo: Association Vahatra.

Gorenflo, L. J., Corson, C., Chomitz, K. M., Harper, G., Honzák, M., and Özler, B. 2011. Exploring the association between people and deforestation in Madagascar. In *Human Population: Its Influences on Biological Diversity*, eds. R. P. Cincotta and L. J. Gorenflo, pp. 197–221. Berlin: Springer.

Grassi, C. 2006. Variability in habitat, diet, and social structure of *Hapalemur griseus* in Ranomafana National Park, Madagascar. *American Journal of Physical Anthropology* 131: 50–63.

Green, G. M., and Sussman, R. W. 1990. Deforestation history of the eastern rain forests of Madagascar from satellite images. *Science* 248(4952): 212–215.

Grinand, C., Rakotomalala, F., Gond, V., Vaudry, R., Bernoux, M., and Vieilledent, G. 2013. Estimating deforestation in tropical humid and dry forests in Madagascar from 2000 to 2010 using multi-date Landsat satellite images and the random forests classifier. *Remote Sensing of Environment* 139: 68–80. https://doi.org/10.1016/j.rse.2013.07.008.

Grinand, C., Le Maire, G., Vieilledent, G., Razakamanarivo, H., Razafimbelo, T., and Bernoux, M. 2017. Estimating temporal changes in soil carbon stocks at ecoregional scale in Madagascar using remote-sensing. *International Journal of Applied Earth Observation and Geoinformation* 54: 1–14.

Grinand, C., Vieilledent, G., Razafimbelo, T., Rakotoarijaona, J. R., Nourtier, M., and Bernioux, M. 2020. Landscape-scale spatial modelling of deforestation, land degradation and regeneration using machine learning tools. *Land Degradation and Development*. doi:10.1002/ldr.3526.

Grubb, P. J. 2003. Interpreting some outstanding features of the flora and vegetation of Madagascar. *Perspectives in Plant Ecology, Evolution and Systematics* 6(1–2): 125–146.

Guillaumet, J.-L., Betsch, J.-M., Blanc, C., Morat, P., and Peyrieras, A. 1972–1973. Etude des écosystèmes montagnards dans la région malgache III. Le Marojejy IV. L'Itremo et l'Ibity. Géomorphologie, climatologie, faune et flore (campagne RCP 225). *Bulletin Muséum National d'Histoire Naturelle*, Paris, série 3, 309, *Ecologie Générale* 25: 29–67.

Hackel, J., Vorontsova, M. S., Nanjarisoa, O. P., Hall, R. C., Razanatsoa, J., Malakasi, P., and Besnard, G. 2018. Grass diversification in Madagascar: In situ radiation of two large C_3 shade clades and support for a Miocene to Pliocene origin of C_4 grassy biomes. *Journal of Biogeography* 45(4): 750–761.

Hagl, P. A., Gargiulo, R., Fay, M. F., Solofondranohatra, S. L., Salmona, J., et al. 2020. Geographical structure of genetic diversity in *Loudetia simplex* (Poaceae) in Madagascar and South Africa. *Botanical Journal of the Linnean Society*. doi.org/10.1093/botlinnean/boaa098.

Hämäläinen, A., Broadley, K., Droghini, A. Haines, J. A., Lamb, C. T., Boutin, S., and Gilbert, S. 2017. The ecological significance of secondary seed dispersal by carnivores. *Ecosphere* 8: e01685.

Hannah, L., Dave, R., Lowry, P. P., Andelman, S., Andrianarisata, M., et al. 2008. Climate change adaptation for conservation in Madagascar. *Biology Letters* 4: 590–594.

Hansen, M. C., Potapov, P. V., Moore, R., Hancher, M., Turubanova, S. A., et al. 2013. High-resolution global maps of 21st-century forest cover change. *Science* 342: 850–853.

Hansford, J. P., and Turvey, S. T. 2018. Unexpected diversity within the extinct elephant birds (Aves: Aepyornithidae) and a new identity for the world's largest bird. *Royal Society Open Science* 5: 181295.

Hansford, J. [P.], Wright, P. C., Rasoamiaramanana, A., Pérez, V. R., Godfrey, L. R., Errickson, D., Thompson, T., and Turvey, S. T. 2018. Early Holocene human presence in Madagascar evidenced by exploitation of avian megafauna. *Science Advances* 4: eaat6925.

Hanski, I. 2005. *The Shrinking World: Ecological Consequences of Habitat Loss*. Oldendorf / Luhe: International Ecology Institute.

Hanski, I., Wirta, H., Nyman, T., and Rahagalala, P. 2008. Resource shifts in Malagasy dung beetles: Contrasting processes revealed by dissimilar spatial genetic patterns. *Ecology Letters* 11: 1208–1215.

Harper, G. J., Steininger, M. K., Tucker, C. J., Juhn, D., and Hawkins, F. 2007. Fifty years of deforestation and forest fragmentation in Madagascar. *Environmental Conservation* 34: 325–333.

Harvey, C. A., Rakotobe, Z. L., Rao, N. S., Dave, R., Razafimahatratra, H., Rabarijohn, R. H., Rajaofara, H., and MacKinnon, J. L. 2014. Extreme vulnerability of smallholder farmers to agricultural risks and climate change in Madagascar. *Philosophical Transactions of the Royal Society of London B: Biological Sciences* 369: 20130089.

Hawes, J. E., Vieira, I.C.G., Magnago, L.F.S., Berenguer, E., Ferreira, J., et al. 2020. A large-scale assessment of plant dispersal mode and seed traits across human-modified Amazonian forests. *Journal of Ecology*. https://doi.org/10.1111/1365-2745.13358.

Hawkins, A.F.A., and Goodman, S. M. 2003. Introduction to the birds. In *The Natural History of Madagascar*, eds. S. M. Goodman and J. P. Benstead, pp. 1019–1044. Chicago: University of Chicago Press.

Hawkins, A.F.A., and Wilmé, L. 1996. Effects of logging on forest birds. In Ecology and economy of a tropical dry forest in Madagascar, eds. J. U. Ganzhorn and J.-P. Sorg. *Primate Report* 46–1: 203–213.

Hempson, G. P., Archibald, S., Donaldson, J. E., and Lehmann, C.E.R. 2019. Alternate grassy ecosystem states are determined by palatability–flammability trade-offs. *Trends in Ecology and Evolution* 34: 286–290.

Henke von der Malsburg, J., and Fichtel, C. 2018. Are generalists more innovative than specialists? A comparison of innovative abilities in two wild sympatric mouse lemur species. *Royal Society Open Science* 5: 180480.

Herring, S. W. 1985. Morphological correlates of masticatory patterns in peccaries and pigs. *Journal of Mammalogy* 66: 603–617.

Hoffmann, W. A., Geiger, E. L., Gotsch, S. G., Rossatto, D. R., Silva, L. C., Lau, O. L., Haridasan, M., and Franco, A. C. 2012. Ecological thresholds at the savanna-forest boundary: How plant traits, resources and fire govern the distribution of tropical biomes. *Ecology Letters* 15: 759–768.

Holloway, L. 2000. Catalysing rainforest restoration in Madagascar. In *Diversité et endémisme à Madagascar*, eds. W. R. Lourenço and S. M. Goodman, pp. 115–124. Paris: Société de Biogéographie.

Horn, M. H. 1997. Evidence for dispersal of fig seeds by the fruit-eating characid fish *Brycon guatemalensis* Regan in a Costa Rican tropical rain forest. *Oecologia* 109: 259–264.

Horn, M. H., Correa, S. B., Parolin, P., Pollux, B.J.A., Anderson, J. T., Lucas, C., Widmann, P., Tjiu, A., Galetti, M., and Goulding, M. 2011. Seed dispersal by fishes in tropical and temperate fresh waters: The growing evidence. *Acta Oecologica* 37: 561–577.

Horning, N. R. 2018. *The Politics of Deforestation in Africa: Madagascar, Tanzania, and Uganda*. Cham: Palgrave Macmillan.

Howe, H. F., and Smallwood, J. 1982. Ecology of seed dispersal. *Annual Review of Ecology and Systematics* 13: 201–228.

Hudson, M., Andrianandrasana, H., Lewis, R., Gerrie, R., and Concannon, L. 2019. Unprecedented rates of deforestation in Menabe Antimena: Can we halt this catastrophic damage? Durrell Wildlife Conservation Trust. https://www.documentcloud.org/documents/5744009-Durrell-2018-Unprecedented-rates-of.html.

Huebner, F., and Fichtel, C. 2015. Innovation and behavioral flexibility in wild redfronted lemurs (*Eulemur rufifrons*). *Animal Cognition* 18: 777–787.

Huebner, F., Fichtel, C., and Kappeler, P. M. 2018. Linking cognition with fitness in a wild primate: Fitness correlates of problem solving performance and spatial learning ability. *Philosophical Transactions of the Royal Society of London B: Biological Sciences* 373: 20170295.

Huete, A. R., Liu, H., and van Leeuwen, W.J.D. 1997. The use of vegetation indices in forested regions: Issues of linearity and saturation. In *IGARSS '97, IEEE International Geoscience and Remote Sensing Symposium Proceedings. Remote Sensing: A Scientific Vision for Sustainable Development*, pp. 1966–1968. Singapore: International Geoscience and Remote Sensing Symposium.

Huete, A. R., Didan, K., Shimabukuro, Y. E., Ratana, P., Saleska, S. R., Hutyra, L. R., Yang, W., Nemani, R. R., and Myneni, R. 2006. Amazon rainforests green-up with sunlight in dry season. *Geophysical Research Letters* 33: L06405.

Humbert, H. 1927. Destruction d'une flore insulaire par le feu: Principaux aspects de la végétation à Madagascar. *Mémoire de l'Académie Malgache* 5: 1–80.

———. 1955. Les territoires phytogéographiques de Madagascar. *Année Biologique* 31: 439–448.
———. 1965. Description des types de végétation. In *Notice de la carte de Madagascar*, eds. H. Humbert and G. Cours-Darne, pp. 46–78. *Travaux de la Section Scientifique et Technique de l'Institut Français de Pondichéry*, hors série, vol. 6.
IEFN. 1996. *Inventaire Ecologique Forestier National.* Antananarivo: Ministère de l'Environnement de Madagascar, Direction des Eaux et Forêts, DFS Deutsch Forest Service GmbH, Entreprise d'Etudes de Développement Rural "Mamokatra," FTM.
Ingram, J. C., and Dawson, T. P. 2005a. Inter-annual analysis of deforestation hotspots in Madagascar from high temporal resolution satellite observations. *International Journal of Remote Sensing* 26: 1447–1461.
———. 2005b. Climate change impacts and vegetation response on the island of Madagascar. *Philosophical Transactions of the Royal Society of London A: Mathematical, Physical and Engineering Sciences* 363: 55–59.
IPCC. 2006. IPCC guidelines for national greenhouse gas, Japan. https://www.ipcc-nggip.iges.or.jp/public/2006gl/index.html.
IPCC. 2014. Climate change 2014: Synthesis report. In *Contribution of Working Groups I, II and III to the Fifth Assessment Report of the Intergovernmental Panel on Climate Change*, eds. R. K. Pachauri and L. A. Meyer. Geneva: IPCC.
IPCC. 2019. Summary for policymakers. In *Climate Change and Land: An IPCC Special Report on Climate Change, Desertification, Land Degradation, Sustainable Land Management, Food Security, and Greenhouse Gas Fluxes in Terrestrial Ecosystems*, eds. P. R. Shukla, J. Skea, E. Calvo Buendia, V. Masson-Delmotte, H.-O. Pörtner, et al. Geneva: IPCC.
Irwin, M. T., Wright, P. C., Birkinshaw, C., Fisher, B. L., Gardner, C. J., et al. 2010. Patterns of species change in anthropogenically disturbed forests of Madagascar. *Biological Conservation* 143: 2351–2362. https://doi.org/10.1016/j.biocon.2010.01.023.
Jackson, G. 1969. The grasslands of Malawi, pt. 1. *Society of Malawi Journal* 22: 7–17.
Jackson, R. B., Jobbágy, E. G., Avissar, R., Roy, S. B., Barrett, D. J., Cook, C. W., Farley, K. A., Le Maitre, D. C., McCarl, B. A., and Murray, B. C. 2005. Trading water for carbon with biological carbon sequestration. *Science* 310: 1944–1947.
Jacquin, A., Sheeren, D., and Lacombe, J.-P. 2010. Vegetation cover degradation assessment in Madagascar savanna based on trend analysis of MODIS NDVI time series. *International Journal of Applied Earth Observation and Geoinformation* 12: S3–S10.
Jansen, P. A., Hirsch, B. T., Emsens, W. J., Zamora-Gutierrez, V., Wikelski, M., and Kays, R. 2012. Thieving rodents as substitute dispersers of megafaunal seeds. *Proceedings of the National Academy of Sciences of the USA* 109: 12610–12615.
Janzen, D. H. 2001. Latent extinction: The living dead. In *Encyclopedia of Biodiversity*, 2nd ed., ed. S. A. Levin, pp. 590–598. Waltham: Academic Press.
Jarvis, A., Reuter, H. I., Nelson, A., and Guevara, E. 2008. Hole-filled Shuttle Radar Topography Mission (SRTM) for the globe, version 4. Consultative Group on International Agricultural Research–Consortium for Spatial Information (CGIAR-CSI), Washington, DC. http://srtm.csi.cgiar.org.
Jellinek, S., Parris, K. M., Driscoll, D. A., and Dwyer, P. D. 2013. Are incentive programs working? Landowner attitudes to ecological restoration of agricultural landscapes. *Journal of Environmental Management* 127: 69–76.
Jenkins, M., Collins, L., Price, O., Penman, T., Zylstra, P., Horsey, B., and Bradstock, R. 2016. Environmental values and fire hazard of eucalypt plantings. *Ecosphere* 7: e01528.
Jenkins, R. K., Racey, P. A., Andriafidison, D., Razafindrakoto, N., Razafimahatratra, E., Rabearivelo, A., Ratsimandresy, Z., Andrianandrasana, R. H., and Razafimanahaka, H. J. 2007. Not rare, but threatened: The endemic Madagascar flying fox *Pteropus rufus* in a fragmented landscape. *Oryx* 41: 263–271.
Jones, J.P.G., Ratsimbazafy, J., Ratsifandrihamanana, A. N., Watson, J.E.M., Andrianandrasana, H. T., et al. 2019. Last chance for Madagascar's biodiversity. *Nature Sustainability* 2: 350–352.
Jones, T. G., Ratsimba, H. R., Ravaoarinorotsihoarana, L., Cripps, G., and Bey, A. 2014. Ecological variability and carbon stock estimates of mangrove ecosystems in northwestern Madagascar. *Forests* 5(1): 177–205. doi:10.3390/f5010177.
Kappeler, P. M. 1997. Intrasexual selection in *Mirza coquereli*: Evidence for scramble competition polygyny in a solitary primate. *Behavioral Ecology and Sociobiology* 41: 115–127.
Kappeler, P. M., and Fichtel, C. 2012. A 15-year perspective on the social organization and life history of sifaka in Kirindy Forest. In *Long-Term Field Studies of Primates*, eds. P. M. Kappeler and D. P. Watts, pp. 101–121. Heidelberg: Springer.
Kappeler, P. M., van Schaik, C. P., and Watts, D. P. 2012. The values and challenges of long-term field studies. In *Long-Term Field Studies of Primates*, eds. P. M. Kappeler and D. P. Watts, pp. 3–18. Heidelberg: Springer.
Karpanty, S. M. 2006. Direct and indirect impacts of raptor predation on lemurs in southeastern Madagascar. *International Journal of Primatology* 27(1): 239–261.
Kiener, A. 1963. Poissons, pêche et pisciculture à Madagascar. Nogent-sur-Marne: Centre Technique Forestier Tropical.
Klein, J., Réau, B., and Edwards, M. 2008. Zebu landscapes: Conservation and cattle in Madagascar. In *Greening the Great Red Island: Madagascar in Nature and Culture*, ed. J. C. Kaufman, pp. 157–178. Pretoria: African Institute of South Africa.
Knoop, S., Chikhi, L., and Salmona, J. 2018. Mouse lemurs' use of degraded habitat: A review of the literature. *Lemur News* 21: 20–31.
Knoploch, C. 2019. The importance of deforestation and climate change in shaping lemurs' distributions and identifying their areas of climatic refuges. Master 2 thesis, Université Aix Marseille.
Koechlin, J. 1968. Sur la signification des formations graminéennes à Madagascar et dans le monde tropical. *Annales de l'Université de Madagascar, Tananarive* 6: 213–234.
———. 1993. Grasslands of Madagascar. In *Natural Grasslands: Eastern Hemisphere and Resume, Ecosystems of the World*, ed. R. T. Coupland, pp. 291–301. Amsterdam: Elsevier.
Koechlin, J., Guillaumet, J. L., and Morat, P. 1974. *Flore et végétation de Madagascar*. Vaduz: J. Cramer.
Kogan, F. N. 1995. Application of vegetation index and brightness temperature for drought detection. *Advances in Space Research* 15: 91–100.
———. 1997. Global drought watch from space. *Bulletin of the American Meteorological Society* 78: 621–636.
Kremen, C., Cameron, A., Moilanen, A., Phillips, S. J., Thomas, C. D., et al. 2008. Aligning conservation priorities across taxa in Madagascar with high-resolution planning tools. *Science* 320: 222–226. https://doi.org/10.1126/science.1155193.
Kuchling, G., Lippai, C., and Behra, O. 2003. Crocodylidae, *Crocodylus niloticus*, Nile crocodile. In *The Natural History of Madagascar*, eds. S. M. Goodman and J. P. Benstead, pp. 1005–1007. Chicago: University of Chicago Press.
Kuhnholtz-Lordat, G. 1938. *La terre incendiée*. Nimes: Editions de la Maison Carrée.
Kull, C. A. 2002. The "degraded" tapia woodlands of highland Madagascar: Rural economy, fire ecology, and forest conservation. *Journal of Cultural Geography* 19(2): 95–128.
———. 2004. *Isle of Fire: The Political Ecology of Landscape Burning in Madagascar*. Chicago: University of Chicago Press.
Kull, C. A., Ratsirarson, J., and Randriamboavonjy, G. 2005. Les forêts de tapia des Hautes Terres malgaches. *Tany Malagasy / Terre Malgache* 24: 22–58.
Kull, C. A., Tassin, J., and Carrière, S. M. 2014. Approaching invasive species in Madagascar. *Madagascar Conservation and Development* 9: 60–70. https://doi.org/10.4314/mcd.v9i2.2.
Labrière, N., Locatelli, B., Vieilledent, G., Kharisma, S., Basuki, I., Gond, V., and Laumonier, Y. 2016. Spatial congruence between carbon and biodiversity across forest landscapes of northern Borneo. *Global Ecology and Conservation* 6: 105–120. http://dx.doi.org/10.1016/j.gecco.2016.01.005.
Lahann, P. 2007. Feeding ecology and seed dispersal of sympatric cheirogaleid lemurs (*Microcebus murinus, Cheirogaleus medius, Cheirogaleus major*) in the littoral rainforest of south-east Madagascar. *Journal of Zoology* 271: 88–98.
Langrand, O., and Rene de Roland, L. A. 2018. Histoire des aires protégées de Madagascar / History of Madagascar protected areas. In *Les aires protégées terrestres de Madagascar: Leur histoire, description et biote / The Terrestrial Protected Areas of Madagascar: Their History, Description, and Biota*, eds. S. M. Goodman, M. J. Raherilalao, and S. Wohlhauser, pp. 79–104. Antananarivo: Association Vahatra.
Laurance, W. F., Perez-Sallcrup, D., Delamonica, P., Fearnside, P. M., D'Angelo, S., Jerozolinki, A., Pohl, L., and Lovejoy, T. E. 2001. Rain forest fragmentation and the structure of Amazonian liana communities. *Ecology* 82: 105–116.
Lawal, S., Lennard, C., and Hewitson, B. 2019. Response of southern African vegetation to climate change at 1.5 and 2.0° global warming above the pre-industrial level. *Climate Services* 16: 100134.
Lawton, R. M. 1978. A study of the dynamic ecology of Zambian vegetation. *Journal of Ecology* 66: 175–198.
Lehman, S. M., Rajaonson, A., and Day, S. 2006. Edge effects and their influence on lemur density and distribution in southeast Madagascar. *American Journal of Physical Anthropology* 129: 232–241.
Lehmann, C.E.R., Archibald, S. A., Hoffmann, W. A., and Bond, W. J. 2011. Deciphering the distribution of the savanna biome. *New Phytologist* 191: 197–209.

Lei, R., Frasier, C. L., Hawkins, M.T.R., Engberg, S. E., Bailey, C. A., et al. 2017. Phylogenomic reconstruction of sportive lemurs (genus *Lepilemur*) recovered from mitogenomes with inferences for Madagascar biogeography. *Journal of Heredity* 108(2): 107–119.

Le Maire, G., Marsden, C., Nouvellon, Y., Grinand, C., Hakamada, J. S., and Laclau, J. P. 2011. MODIS NDVI time-series allow the monitoring of *Eucalyptus* plantation biomass. *Remote Sensing of Environment* 115: 2624–2625.

Lemon, P. C. 1968. Effects of fire on an African plateau grassland. *Ecology* 49: 316–322.

Leroy, J.-F. 1978. Une sous-famille monotypique de Winteraceae endémique à Madagascar: Les Takhtajanioideae. *Adansonia*, série 2, 17: 383–395.

Leuteritz, T. E. 2003. Observations on diet and drinking behaviour of radiated tortoises (*Geochelone radiata*) in southwest Madagascar. *African Journal of Herpetology* 52: 127–130.

Lima, S. L., and Zollner, P. A. 1996. Towards a behavioral ecology of ecological landscapes. *Trends in Ecology and Evolution* 11: 131–135.

Linder, H. P., Lehmann, C.E.R., Archibald, S., Osborne, C. P., and Richardson, D. M. 2018. Global grass (Poaceae) success underpinned by traits facilitating colonization, persistence and habitat transformation. *Biological Reviews* 93: 1125–1144.

Li Vigni, I., and Melati, M. R. 1999. Examples of seed dispersal by entomochory. *Acta Botanica Gallica* 146: 145–156.

Llopis, J. C., Harimalala, P. C., Bär, R., Heinimann, A., Rabemananjara, Z. H., and Zaehringer, J. G. 2019. Effects of protected area establishment and cash crop price dynamics on land use transitions 1990–2017 in north-eastern Madagascar. *Journal of Land Use Science* 14: 52–80. https://doi.org/10.1080/1747423X.2019.1625979.

Llopis, J. C., Diebold, C., Schneider, F., Harimalala, P. C., Patrick, L., Messerli, P., and Zaehringer, J. G. 2020. Capabilities under telecoupling: Human well-being between cash crops and protected areas in north-eastern Madagascar. *Frontiers in Sustainable Food Systems* 3: 126. doi:10.3389/fsufs.2019.00126.

Loayza, A. P., Carvajal, D. E., García-Guzmán, P., Gutierrez, J. R., and Squeo, F. A. 2014. Seed predation by rodents results in directed dispersal of viable seed fragments of an endangered desert shrub. *Ecosphere* 5: 1–9.

Long, E., and Racey, P. A. 2007. An exotic plantation crop as a keystone resource for an endemic megachiropteran, *Pteropus rufus*, in Madagascar. *Journal of Tropical Ecology* 23: 397–407.

Lowry, P. P, II, Schatz, G. E., and Phillipson, P. B. 1997. The classification of natural and anthropogenic vegetation in Madagascar. In *Natural Change and Human Impact in Madagascar*, eds. S. M. Goodman and B. D. Patterson, pp. 93–123. Washington, DC: Smithsonian Institution.

Lowry, P. P., II, Phillipson, P. B., Schatz, G. E., Rajaonary, F., and Andriambololonera, S. 2018. Flore / Flora. In *Les aires protégées terrestres de Madagascar: Leur histoire, description et biote / The Terrestrial Protected Areas of Madagascar: Their History, Description, and Biota*, eds. S. M. Goodman, M. J. Raherilalao, and S. Wohlhauser, pp. 243–255. Antananarivo: Association Vahatra.

Lührs, M.-L., Dammhahn, M., and Kappeler, P. M. 2013. Strength in numbers: Males in a carnivore grow bigger when they associate and hunt cooperatively. *Behavioral Ecology* 24: 21–28.

Lundgren, M. R., Besnard, G., Ripley, B. S., Lehmann, C.E.R., Chatelet, D. S., et al. 2015. Photosynthetic innovation broadens the niche within a single species. *Ecology Letters* 18: 1021–1029.

MacPhee, R.D.E. 1994. Morphology, adaptations, and relationships of *Plesiorycteropus*: And a diagnosis of a new order of eutherian mammals. *Bulletin of the American Museum of Natural History* 220: 1–214.

MacPhee, R.D.E., Burney, D. A., and Wells, N. A. 1985. Early Holocene chronology and environment of Ampasambazimba, a Malagasy subfossil lemur site. *International Journal of Primatology* 6: 461–487.

Madagascar Catalogue. 2020. Catalogue of the plants of Madagascar. Missouri Botanical Garden, St. Louis and Antananarivo. www.tropicos.org/project/mada.

Manzi, O.J.L. 2019. Impacts of human activities on the forest-savanna ecotone: Plant successions of Poaceae in Malagasy savannas and the dynamics of a palm "*Bismarckia nobilis* Hildebrandt & H. Wendl." MSc thesis, Erasmus Mundus Masters Course in Tropical Biodiversity and Ecosystems—TROPIMUNDO, Vrije Universiteit Brussel; Université de Guyane.

Martin, E. A., Viano, M., Ratsimisetra, L., Laloë, F., and Carrière, S. M. 2012. Maintenance of bird functional diversity in a traditional agroecosystem of Madagascar. *Agriculture, Ecosystems and Environment* 149: 1–9. https://doi.org/10.1016/j.agee.2011.12.005.

Martinez, B. T., and Razafindratsima, O. H. 2014. Frugivory and seed dispersal patterns of the red-ruffed lemur, *Varecia rubra*, at a forest restoration site in Masoala National Park, Madagascar. *Folia Primatologica* 85: 228–243.

Matias, M. G., Underwood, A. J., Hochuli, D., and Coleman, R. 2011. Habitat identity influences species-area relationships in heterogeneous habitats. *Marine Ecology Progress Series* 437: 135–145.

Matsumoto, K., and Burney, D. A. 1994. Late Holocene environments at Lake Mitsinjo, northwestern Madagascar. *Holocene* 4: 16–24.

McConkey, K. R., Prasad, S., Corlett, R. T., Campos-Arceiz, A., Brodie, J. F., Rogers, H., and Santamaria, L. 2012. Seed dispersal in changing landscapes. *Biological Conservation* 146: 1–13. https://doi.org/10.1016/j.biocon.2011.09.018.

McKinney, R. L. 1998. On predicting biotic homogenization: Species-area patterns in marine biota. *Global Ecological Biogeography* 7: 297–301.

Meadows, M. E., and Linder, H. P. 1993. A palaeoecological perspective on the origin of Afromontane grasslands. *Journal of Biogeography* 20: 345–355.

MEEF. 2017. *Inventaire forestier et évaluation de l'intégrité écologique dans le cadre de la REDD+: Rapport de synthèse*. Antananarivo: Ministère de l'Environnement, de l'Ecologie et des Forêts de Madagascar.

———. 2018. *Niveaux d'émissions de référence des forêts de Madagascar pour la réduction des émissions dues à la déforestation: Soumission à la Convention-Cadre des Nations Unies sur les Changements Climatiques*. Antananarivo: Bureau National de Coordination REDD+.

MEFT, USAID, and CI. 2009. *Evolution de la couverture de forêts naturelles à Madagascar, 1990-2000-2005*. Antananarivo: Ministère de l'Environnement, des Forêts et du Tourisme de Madagascar.

Mercandalli, S., and Losch, B., 2017. *Rural Africa in Motion: Dynamics and Drivers of Migration South of the Sahara*. Rome: FAO and CIRAD.

Merson, S. D., Dollar, L. J., Johnson, P. J., and Macdonald, D. W. 2019a. Retaliatory killing and human perceptions of Madagascar's largest carnivore and livestock predator, the fosa (*Cryptoprocta ferox*). *PLoS One* 14: e0213341.

Merson, S. D., Dollar, L. J., Tan, C.K.W., and Macdonald, D. W. 2019b. Activity patterns of sympatric living exotic and endemic carnivores (the fosa) in western Madagascar's deciduous forests. *Journal of Zoology* 307: 186–194.

Mertl-Millhollen, A. S., Blumenfeld-Jones, K., Raharison, S. M., Tsaramanana, D. R., and Rasamimanana, H. 2011. Tamarind tree seed dispersal by ring-tailed lemurs. *Primates* 52: 391–396.

Mertz, E. 2006. An organism-focused view of heterogeneity: The effect of landscape spatial pattern at multiple scales on the habitat use, behavior, and movement patterns of five diurnal lemurs in Betampona Natural Reserve, Madagascar. *American Journal of Physical Anthropology* 159: S62.

———. 2012. The effects of environmental heterogeneity at multiple scales on a community of five diurnal lemurs in Betampona Natural Reserve, Madagascar: A landscape ecology approach. PhD thesis, University of Colorado, Boulder.

Mevanarivo, Z. E. 2008. Caractéristiques de la forêt dense sèche de Kirindy et de ses environs comme habitat naturel de *Microcebus murinus* et *Microcebus berthae*. Mémoire de DEA, Université d'Antananarivo.

Midgley, J. J., and Illing, N. 2010. Were Malagasy *Uncarina* fruits dispersed by the extinct elephant bird? *South African Journal of Science* 105: 467–469.

Miltujin, A., and Lehtonen, J. T. 2008. Probability of competition between introduced and native rodents in Madagascar: An estimation based on morphological traits. *Estonian Journal of Ecology* 57: 133–152.

Ministère de l'Environnement. 1996. *IEFN: Inventaire Ecologique Forestier National*. Antananarivo: Ministère de l'Environnement de Madagascar, Direction des Eaux et Forêts, DFS Deutsch Forest Service GmbH, Entreprise d'Etudes de Développement Rural "Mamokatra," FTM.

Mitchell, A. L., Rosenqvist, A., and Mora, B. 2017. Current remote sensing approaches to monitoring forest degradation in support of countries measurement, reporting and verification (MRV) systems for REDD+. *Carbon Balance Management* 12: 9. https://doi.org/10.1186/s13021-017-0078-9.

Moat, J., and Smith, P. 2007. *Atlas of the Vegetation of Madagascar*. Kew: Royal Botanic Gardens.

Moizo, B. 2000. Déforestation et dynamiques migratoires (Madagascar). In *Du bon usage des ressources renouvelables*, eds. Y. Gillon, C. Chaboud, J. Boutrais, C. Mullon, and J. Weber, pp. 169–185. Paris: IRD.

Morat, P. 1973. Les savanes du sud-ouest de Madagascar. *Mémoires ORSTOM* 68: 1–235.

Morelli, T. L., Smith, A. B., Mancini, A. N., Balko, E. A., Borgerson, C., et al. 2020. The fate of Madagascar's rainforest habitat. *Nature Climate Change* 10: 89–96. https://doi.org/10.1038/s41558-019-0647-x.

Moses, K. L., and Semple, S. 2011. Primary seed dispersal by the black-and-white ruffed lemur (*Varecia variegata*) in the Manombo forest, south-east Madagascar. *Journal of Tropical Ecology* 27: 529–538.
Muasya, A. M., Larridon, I., Reynders, M., Huygh, W., Goetghebeur, P., Cable, S., Simpson, D. A., and Gehrke, B. 2011. The Cyperaceae in Madagascar show increased species richness in upland forest and wetland habitats. *Plant Ecology and Evolution* 144: 357–362.
Muldoon, K. M., Crowley, B. E., Godfrey, L. R., Rasoamiaramanana, A., Aronson, A., Jernvall, J., Wright, P. C., and Simons, E. L. 2012. Early Holocene fauna from a new subfossil site: A first assessment from Christmas River, south central Madagascar. *Madagascar Conservation and Development* 7: 23–29.
Myers, N., Mittermeier, R. A., Mittermeier, C. G., Da Fonseca, G. A., and Kent, J. 2000. Biodiversity hotspots for conservation priorities. *Nature* 403(6772): 853–858.
Nanjarisoa, O. P., Besnard, G., Ralimanana, H., Jeannoda, V., and Vorontsova, M. S. 2017. Grass survey of the Itremo Massif records endemic central highland grasses. *Madagascar Conservation and Development* 12: 1–7.
Nathan, R. 2006. Long-distance dispersal of plants. *Science* 313: 786–788.
Neugarten, R. A., Honzák, M., Carret, P., Koenig, K., Andriamaro, L., et al. 2016. Rapid assessment of ecosystem service co-benefits of biodiversity priority areas in Madagascar. *PLoS One* 11: e0168575.
Ney-Nifle, M., and Mangel, M. 2000. Habitat loss and changes in the species-area relationship. *Conservation Biology* 14: 893–898.
NOAA. 2019. STAR—Global Vegetation Health Products: Introduction. https://www.star.nesdis.noaa.gov/smcd/emb/vci/VH/index.php.
Norosoarinaivo, J. A. 2000. Etude du comportement chez *Hapalemur aureus* (B. Meier et coll.) du stade enfant jusqu'au stade juvénile dans le Parc National de Ranomafana. Mémoire de DEA, Université d`Antananarivo.
Nowak, R.M. 2005. *Walker's Carnivores of the World*. Baltimore: Johns Hopkins University Press.
Oleksy, R., Giuggioli, L., McKetterick, T. J., Racey, P. A., and Jones, G. 2017. Flying foxes create extensive seed shadows and enhance germination success of pioneer plant species in deforested Madagascan landscapes. *PLoS One* 12: e0184023.
Olesen, J. M., and Valido, A. 2003. Lizards as pollinators and seed dispersers: An island phenomenon. *Trends in Ecology and Evolution* 18: 177–181.
Oliveira-Filho, A. T., and Ratter, J. A. 2002. Vegetation physiognomies and woody flora of the Cerrado biome. In *The Cerrados of Brazil: Ecology and Natural History of a Neotropical Savanna*, eds. P. S. Oliveira and R. J. Marquis, pp. 91–120. New York: Columbia University Press.
Olson, D. M., and Andriamiadana, A. 1996. The effects of selective logging on the leaf litter invertebrate community of a tropical dry forest in western Madagascar. In Ecology and economy of a tropical dry forest in Madagascar, eds. J. U. Ganzhorn and J.-P. Sorg. *Primate Report* 46–1: 175–187.
ONE, DGF, MNP, WCS, and Etc Terra. 2015. *Changement de la couverture de forêts naturelles à Madagascar, 2005-2010-2013*. Antananarivo: Bureau National de Coordination REDD+. https://www.pnae.mg/couverture-de-forets-naturelles-2005-2010-2013.
Overdorff, D. J., and Strait, S. G. 1998. Seed handling by three prosimian primates in southeastern Madagascar: Implications for seed dispersal. *American Journal of Primatology* 45: 69–82.
PAG Menabe. 2014. Plan d'aménagement et de gestion de la nouvelle aire protégée Menabe Antimena. Morondava: Fanamby and Ministère des Eaux et Forêts.
Pearson, S. M., Turner, M. G., and Drake, J. B. 1999. Landscape change and habitat availability in the southern Appalachian highlands and the Olympic Peninsula. *Ecological Applications* 9: 1288–1304.
Pedrono, M., Griffiths, O. L., Clausen, A., Smith, L. L., Griffiths, C. J., Wilmé, L., and Burney, D. A. 2013. Using surviving lineage of Madagascar's vanished megafauna for ecological restoration. *Biological Conservation* 159: 501–506.
PERR-FH. 2014. *Définition des niveaux de référence et du système MRV de l'écorégion des forêts humides de l'est (PERR-FH). Composante 2: Scénario de Référence éco-régional 2015–2024. Livrable 2: Cartographie des stocks de carbone de la biomasse aérienne. Rapport de synthèse*. Antananarivo: Bureau National de Coordination REDD+.
Perrier de la Bâthie, H. 1921. La végétation malgache. *Annales du Musée Colonial de Marseille* 9: 1–266.
Petter, J.-J., Albignac, R., and Rumpler, Y. 1977. Mammifères lémuriens (Primates Prosimiens). *Faune de Madagascar* 44: 1–513.
Phillips, O. L., Aragão, L.E.O.C., Lewis, S. L., Fisher, J. B., Lloyd, J., et al. 2009. Drought sensitivity of the Amazon rainforest. *Science* 323: 1344–1347.
Phillips, O. L., van der Heijden, G., Lewis, S. L., López-González, G., Aragão, L.E.O.C., et al. 2010. Drought-mortality relationships for tropical forests. *New Phytologist* 187: 631–646.
Phipps, J. B., and Goodier, R. 1962. A preliminary account of the plant ecology of the Chimanimani Mountains. *Journal of Ecology* 50: 291–319.
Picot, M., Jenkins, R.K.B., Ramilijaona, O., Racey, P. A., and Carrière, S. M. 2007. The feeding ecology of *Eidolon dupreanum* (Pteropodidae) in eastern Madagascar. *African Journal of Ecology* 45: 645–650.
Platt, S. G., Elsey, R. M., Liu, H., Rainwater, T. R., Nifong, J. C., Rosenblatt, A. E., Heithaus, M. R., and Mazzotti, F. J. 2013. Frugivory and seed dispersal by crocodilians: An overlooked form of saurochory? *Journal of Zoology* 291: 87–99.
Platt, W. J., Orzell, S. L., and Slocum, M. G. 2015. Seasonality of fire weather strongly influences fire regimes in south Florida savanna-grassland landscapes. *PLoS One* 10(1): e0116952. https://doi.org/10.1371/journal.pone.0116952.
Pollini, J. 2014. Slash-and-burn agriculture. In *Encyclopedia of Food and Agricultural Ethics*, eds. P. B. Thompson and D. M. Kaplan. Wageningen: Springer.
Portillo-Quintero, C., Sanchez-Azofeifa, A., Calvo-Alvarado, J., Quesada, M., and do Espirito Santo, M. M. 2015. The role of tropical dry forests for biodiversity, carbon and water conservation in the Neotropics: Lessons learned and opportunities for its sustainable management. *Regional Environmental Change* 15: 1039–1049.
Powzyk, J. A., and Mowry, C. B. 2003. Dietary and feeding differences between sympatric *Propithecus diadema diadema* and *Indri indri*. *International Journal of Primatology* 24: 1143–1162.
———. 2007. The feeding ecology and related adaptations of *Indri indri*. In *Lemurs: Ecology and Adaptation*, eds. L. Gould and M. L. Sauther, pp. 353–368. Boston: Springer.
Quéméré, E., Amelot, X., Pierson, J., Crouau-Roy, B., and Chikhi, L. 2012. Genetic data suggest a natural prehuman origin of open habitats in northern Madagascar and question the deforestation narrative in this region. *Proceedings of the National Academy of Sciences of the USA* 109: 13028–13033.
Quiring, S. M., and Ganesh, S. 2010. Evaluating the utility of the Vegetation Condition Index (VCI) for monitoring meteorological drought in Texas. *Agricultural and Forest Meteorology* 150: 330–339.
Rabarivola, M. L., Vorontsova, M. S., Razanajatovo, H., Razafiniary, V., and Ralimanana, H. 2019a. All herbarium specimens of grasses from Madagascar and the surrounding islands: Family Poaceae, sector AFM. Version 1.24. Kew Madagascar Conservation Centre, Royal Botanic Gardens Kew. Accessed via GBIF.org 02 Nov. 2019. https://doi.org/10.15468/51pabx.
Rabarivola, M. L., Razafiniary, V., Razanajatovo, H., Rapanarivo S. H., Ralimanana, H., and Vorontsova, M. S. 2019b. All herbarium specimens of grasses held at TAN herbarium. Version 1.8. Kew Madagascar Conservation Centre, Royal Botanic Gardens Kew. Accessed via GBIF.org 02 Nov. 2019. https://doi.org/10.15468/v6mfx2.
Rabarivola, M. L., Razanajatovo, H., Razafiniary, V., Ralimanana, H., and Vorontsova, M. S. 2019c. Research database of Madagascar grasses compiled by Maria Vorontsova. Version 1.3. Kew Madagascar Conservation Centre, Royal Botanic Gardens Kew. Accessed via GBIF.org 02 Nov. 2019. https://doi.org/10.15468/umduhk.
Rabarivola, M. L., Razanajatovo, H., Razafiniary, V., Rasolohery, A., Ralimanana, H., and Vorontsova, M. S. 2019d. *Madagascar Grass Atlas*. Antananarivo: Kew Madagascar Conservation Centre.
Rabetaliana, H., Randriambolololona, M., and Schachenmann, P. 1999. The Andringitra National Park in Madagascar. *Unasylva* 50: 25–30.
Raboin, L. M., Ramanantsoanirina, A., Dzido, J. L., Andriantsimialona, D., Tharreau, D., Radanielina, T., and Ahmadi, N. 2010. Upland (aerobic) rice breeding for the harsh environment of the High Plateau of Madagascar. In *Innovation and Partnerships to Realize Africa's Rice Potential*, pp. 26–27. Bamako: Africa Rice Congress.
Racey, P. A., Goodman, S. M., and Jenkins, R. K. 2010. The ecology and conservation of Malagasy bats. In *Island Bats: Evolution, Ecology, and Conservation*, eds. T. H. Fleming and P. A. Racey, pp. 369–404. Chicago: University of Chicago Press.
Rafenoarisoa, F. 2016. Ecologie alimentaire de *Eulemur cinereiceps* (Grandidieri [*sic*] et Milne-Edwards, 1890) en vue de sa conservation dans la NAP Ankarabolava Angakatrika du District de Vangaindrano. Mémoire de Master II, Université d'Antananarivo.
Rahalinarivo, V. 2007. Etude comparative des activités (années 2003 et 2005) de *Hapalemur griseus* (Link, 1795), *Hapalemur aureus* (Meier et al, 1987) et *Prolemur simus* (Gray, 1871) dans le Parc National de Ranomafana Fianarantsoa—Madagascar. Mémoire de DEA, Université d'Antananarivo.

Raheriarisena, M. 2005. Régime alimentaire de *Pteropus rufus* (Chiroptera: Pteropodidae) dans la région sub-aride du sud de Madagascar. *Revue d'Ecologie* 60: 255–264.

Rahlfs, M., and Fichtel, C. 2010. Anti-predator behaviour in a nocturnal primate, the grey mouse lemur (*Microcebus murinus*). *Ethology* 116: 429–439.

Rahman, A. F., Sims, D. A., Cordova, V. D., and El-Masri, B. Z. 2005. Potential of MODIS EVI and surface temperature for directly estimating per-pixel ecosystem C fluxes. *Geophysical Research Letters* 32: L19404.

Railsback, L. B., Dupont, L. A., Liang, F., Brook, G. A., Burney, D. A., Cheng, H., and Edwards, R. L. 2020. Relationships between climate change, human environmental impact, and megafaunal extinction inferred from a 4000-year multi-proxy record from a stalagmite from northwestern Madagascar. *Quaternary Science Reviews* 234: 106244.

Rajaofera, C. 2007. Contribution à l'histoire des Zafimanely, l'exemple du royaume Barabe, de sa création au début de la période coloniale. Formation Doctorale Multidisciplinaire, Université de Toliara. http://biblio.univ-antananarivo.mg/pdfs/rajaoferaChristophe_FR_M2_07.pdf.

Rajaonarimamy, E., Rakotomalala, J., Rakotoarimanana, R., Rajaonarison, J., Rakotozafy, J.C.R., Randriambanona, H., Ramanankierana, H., Robin, D., and Andrianarisoa, B. 2017. Impact of *Psidium cattleianum* invasion on soil microbial functioning and on *Uapaca ferruginea* (Baill.) regeneration at forest edge in the eastern part of Madagascar. *International Journal of Ecosystem* 7: 17–20.

Rakotoarimanana, V. 2008. Feu, pâturage et dynamique des savanes à Madagascar. Mémoire de HDR, Biologie et Ecologie Végétales, Université d'Antananarivo.

Rakotoarivelo, L. A. 1993. Analyse sylvicole d'une forêt sclérophylle de moyenne altitude à *Uapaca bojeri* (tapia) de la région d'Arivonimamo. Mémoire de fin d'études, Département des Eaux et Forêts, Université d'Antananarivo.

Rakotomalala, F. A., Rabenandrasana, J. C., Andriambahiny, J. E., Rajaonson, R., Andriamalala, F., et al. 2015. Estimation de la déforestation des forêts humides à Madagascar entre 2005, 2010 et 2013. *Revue Française de Télédétection et Photogrammétrie* 211–212: 11–23.

Rakotomalala, N. H., Andriamanohera, M. A., Solofondranohatra, L. C., Ranaivojaona, A. E., Jeannoda, V., Ralimanana, H., and Vorontsova, M. S. 2021. Grasses of the Isalo Protected Area, Madagascar: Checklist, origins, and significance. *Madagascar Conservation and Development* 16(1): 14–24.

Rakotomanana, H. 2016. *La philépitte veloutée: Frugivorie et dispersion de graines*. Chişinău: Editions Universitaires Européennes.

Rakotomanana, H., Hino, T., Kanzaki, M., and Morioka, H. 2003. The role of the velvet asity *Philepitta castanea* in regeneration of understory shrubs in Madagascan rainforest. *Ornithological Science* 2: 49–58.

Rakotondrasoa, O. L., Malaisse, F., Rajoelison, G. L., Razafimanantsoa, T. M., Rabearisoa, M. R., et al. 2012. La forêt de tapia, écosystème endémique de Madagascar: Ecologie, fonctions, causes de dégradation et de transformation (synthèse bibliographique). *BASE: Biotechnology, Agronomy, Society and Environment* 16(4): 541–552.

Rakotonirina. 1996. Composition and structure of a dry forest on sandy soils near Morondava. In Ecology and economy of a tropical dry forest in Madagascar, eds. J. U. Ganzhorn and J.-P. Sorg. *Primate Report* 46–1: 81–88.

Rakotonirina, E. 2004. Contribution à l'étude comparative de l'alimentation intergroupe à taille différente d'*Eulemur collaris*. Mémoire de DEA, Université d'Antananarivo.

Rakotoson, S. R. 2001. Contribution à l'étude du rôle d'*Eulemur fulvus fulvus* dans la dissémination et la régénération des espèces forestières dans la réserve spéciale d'Ambohitantely (Ankazobe). Mémoire de DEA, Université d'Antananarivo.

Ralainasolo, F. B., Ratsimbazafy, J. H., and Stevens, N. J. 2008. Behavior and diet of the Critically Endangered *Eulemur cinereiceps* in Manombo forest, southeast Madagascar. *Madagascar Conservation and Development* 3: 38–43.

Ralisoamalala, R. C. 1996. Rôle d'*Eulemur fulvus rufus* (Audeberg, 1799) et de *Propithecus verreauxi verreauxi* (A. Grandidier 1867) dans la dissémination des graines. In Ecology and economy of a tropical dry forest in Madagascar, eds. J. U. Ganzhorn and J.-P. Sorg. *Primate Report* 46–1: 285–293.

Ralph, J. C., Sauer, J. R., and Droege, S. 1995. Monitoring bird populations by point counts. US Forest Service General Technical Report PSW-GTR-149. Albany, California.

Ramahefamanana, N., Rakotozafy, B.F.L., Birkinshaw, C. R., Tahirinirainy, D., and Raharimampionona, J. 2019. Evolution de la formation de bois de tapia aux différents régimes de feux. Poster for the Association of Tropical Biology and Conservation 2019 Annual Meeting, Antananarivo.

Ramalanjaona, M.H.N. 2013. Etude de la régénération et de la sénescence de *Tamarindus indica* et ses impacts et implications écologiques dans la réserve de Bezà Mahafaly. Mémoire de DEA, Université d'Antananarivo.

Ramamonjisoa, J. R. 1995. Le processus de développement dans le Vakinankaratra, Hautes Terres malgaches. Thèse de doctorat d'Etat, Université de Paris I—Panthéon/Sorbonne.

Ramananantoandro, T., Randrianasolo, Z. H., Randrianary, T. M., Razafimahatratra, A. R., and Razafinarivo, R.N.G. 2017. *Elaboration d'équations allométriques des formations forestières secondaires à dominance de* Ravenala madagascariensis *et détermination d'un facteur de biomasse des populations arbustives de savoka jeunes, en vue de l'évaluation des stocks de carbone de ces strates végétales dans l'écorégion des forêts humides de l'est de Madagascar.* Antananarivo: Bureau National de Coordination REDD+.

Ramananjato, V., Rakotomalala, Z., Park, D. S., DeSisto, C.M.M., Raoelinjanakolona, N. N., Guthrie, N., Fenosoa, Z.S.E., Johnson, S. E., and Razafindratsima, O. H. 2020. The role of nocturnal omnivores as seed dispersers in Malagasy rain forests. *Biotropica* 52: 758–765. https://doi.org/10.1111/btp.12789.

Ramifehiarivo, N., Brossard, M., Grinand, C., Andriamananjara, A., Razafimbelo, T., et al. 2017. Mapping soil organic carbon on a national scale: Towards an improved and updated map of Madagascar. *Geoderma Regional* 9: 29–38.

Ramos-Neto, M. B., and Pivello, V. R. 2000. Lightning fires in a Brazilian savanna national park: Rethinking management strategies. *Environmental Management* 26(6): 675–684.

Randriamahazo, H.J.A.R., and Mori, A. 2012. Examination of myrmecophagy and herbivory in the Madagascan spiny-tailed iguana, *Oplurus cuvieri* (Reptilia: Opluridae). *Current Herpetology* 31: 8–13.

Randriamandratonirina, N. J. 2003. Ecobiologie d'*Indri indri* (Gemlin, 1788), primate Indriidae dans la Réserve Naturelle Intégrale de Betampona (forêt humide orientale de basse altitude). Mémoire de DEA, Université d'Antananarivo.

Randriambanona, H., Randriamalala, J. R., and Carrière, S. M. 2019. Native forest regeneration and vegetation dynamics in non-native *Pinus patula* tree plantations in Madagascar. *Forest Ecology and Management* 446: 20–28. https://doi.org/10.1016/j.foreco.2019.05.019.

Randriambololomamonjy, O. C. 2006. Caractérisations des formations végétales et études écologiques de quelques espèces menacées de la Montagne des Français (Antsiranana II). Mémoire de DEA, Université d'Antananarivo.

Randrianasolo, J., Rakotovao, P., Deleporte, P., Rarivoson, C., Sorg, J.-P., and Rohner, U. 1996. Local tree species in the tree nursery. In Ecology and economy of a tropical dry forest in Madagascar, eds. J. U. Ganzhorn and J.-P. Sorg. *Primate Report* 46–1: 117–132.

Randrianjatovo, S. 2010. Etude bioécologique de poisson du lac Kinkony au sein de la Nouvelle Aire Protégée Complexe Mahavavy-Kinkony. Master II mémoire, Université d'Antananarivo.

Randriatavy, L. D. 2003. Etude de la régénération forestière et de quelques espèces végétales utilisées à la fois par *Varecia variegata variegata* et par l'homme dans la réserve naturelle intégrale n°1 de Betampona. Mémoire de DEA, Université d'Antananarivo.

Randriantavy, L. D., Rakotoarimanana, V., Roger, E., and Freeman, K. 2014. Essai de contrôle d'invasion de goyavier de Chine *Psidium catteleianum* Sabine dans la Réserve Naturelle Intégrale de Betampona. In *Colloque régional sur les espèces exotiques envahissantes dans les îles du sud-ouest de l'Océan Indien*, eds. B. Rakouth, J. Rasamy, and E. Roger, pp. 124–137. Antananarivo: Faculté des Sciences, Université d'Antananarivo.

Rasmussen, D. J., Meinshausen, M., and Kopp, R. E. 2016. Probability-weighted ensembles of US county-level climate projections for climate risk analysis. *Journal of Applied Meteorology and Climatology* 55(10): 2301–2322.

Rasoafaranaivo, M. H. 2005. Evaluation des impacts du feu sur la biologie de quelques espèces végétales du Massif d'Ibity (Antsirabe). Mémoire de DEA, Faculté des Sciences, Département de Biologie et Ecologie Végétales, Université d'Antananarivo.

Rasolofoson, R. A., Ferraro, P. J., Jenkins, C. N., and Jones, J.P.G. 2015. Effectiveness of community forest management at reducing deforestation in Madagascar. *Biological Conservation* 184: 271–277. https://doi.org/10.1016/j.biocon.2015.01.027.

Rasolofoson, R. A., Ferraro, P. J., Ruta, G., Rasamoelina, M. S., Randriankolona, P. L., Larsen, H. O., and Jones, J.P.G. 2017. Impacts of community forest management on human economic well-being across Madagascar. *Conservation Letters* 10(3): 346–353.

Rasoma, R.V.J., Raselimanana, A. P., Ratovonamana, Y. R., and Ganzhorn, J. U. 2013. Habitat use and diet of *Astrochelys radiata* in the subarid zone of southern Madagascar. *Chelonian Conservation and Biology* 12: 56–69.

Ratrimomanarivo, F. H. 2007. Etude du régime alimentaire d'*Eidolon dupreanum* (Chiroptera: Pteropodidae) dans la région anthropisée des hautes terres du centre de Madagascar. *Revue d'Ecologie* 62: 229–244.

Ravelojaona, R. 2014. Etude préliminaire de l'écologie du *Prolemur simus* dans la forêt de bambou de Vohitrarivo et Vohimarina Ifanadiana-Ranomafana. Mémoire de CAPEN, Université d'Antananarivo.

Ravelomalala, L. S. 2015. Biologie, écologie et multiplication de cinq espèces végétales consommées par *Eulemur coronatus* (Lemurideae) dans la Montagne des Français (Antsiranana II). Mémoire de DEA, Université d'Antananarivo.

Razafindrakoto, M., Csuzdi, C., and Blanchart, E. 2011. New and little known giant earthworms from Madagascar (Oligochaeta: Kynotidae). *African Invertebrates* 52: 285–294.

Razafindratsima, O. H. 2009. Etude du rôle écologique de *Varecia rubra* (Geoffroy, 1812) et d'*Eulemur albifrons* (Geoffroy, 1796) dans le corridor Ambatolaidama du Parc National Masoala. Mémoire de DEA, Université d'Antananarivo.

———. 2014. Seed dispersal by vertebrates in Madagascar's forests: Review and future directions. *Madagascar Conservation and Development* 9: 90–97. https://doi.org/10.4314/mcd.v9i2.5.

———. 2017. Post-dispersal seed removal by rodents in Ranomafana rain forest, Madagascar. *Journal of Tropical Ecology* 33: 232–236.

Razafindratsima, O. H., and Dunham, A. E. 2015. Assessing the impacts of nonrandom seed dispersal by multiple frugivore partners on plant recruitment. *Ecology* 96: 24–30.

———. 2016. Frugivores bias seed-adult tree associations through non-random seed dispersal: A phylogenetic approach. *Ecology* 97: 2094–2102.

Razafindratsima, O. H., and Martinez, B. T. 2012. Seed dispersal by red-ruffed lemurs: Seed size, viability, and beneficial effect on seedling growth. *Ecotropica* 18: 15–26.

Razafindratsima, O. H., and Razafimahatratra, E. 2010. Effect of red ruffed lemur gut passage on the germination of native rainforest plant species. *Lemur News* 15: 39–42.

Razafindratsima, O. H., Jones, T. A., and Dunham, A. E. 2014. Patterns of movement and seed dispersal by three lemur species. *American Journal of Primatology* 76: 84–96.

Razafindratsima, O. H., Gentles, A., Drager, A. P., Razafimahaimodison, J.-C., Razalazampirenena, C. J., and Dunham, A. E. 2018a. Consequences of lemur loss for above-ground carbon stocks in a Malagasy rainforest. *International Journal of Primatology* 39: 415–426.

Razafindratsima, O. H., Yacoby, Y., and Park, D. S. 2018b. MADA: Malagasy Animal trait Data Archive. *Ecology* 99(4): 990.

Razafindratsima, O. H., Brown, K. A., Carvalho, F., Johnson, S. E., Wright, P. C., and Dunham, A. E. 2018c. Edge effects on components of diversity and above-ground biomass in a tropical rainforest. *Journal of Applied Ecology* 55: 977–985.

Razafindratsita, V., and Zack, S. 2009. Frugivory and facilitation of seed germination by the velvet asity *Philepitta castanea* (Muller, 1776), in the rainforest understory of Ranomafana National Park, Madagascar. *Malagasy Nature* 2: 154–159.

Razafintsalama, A. S., and Gautschi, M. 1999. Etude des structures socio-organisationelles des villages pour l'identification et la formalisation d'un organe de gestion, dans le processus de transfert de gestion de la forêt de tapia (*Uapaca bojeri*) dans la région d'Arivonimamo. Rapport final de stage, Intercoopération, Projet FDP, ESSA-Forêts, et EPF Zürich.

Razakanirina, H. 2010. Suivi phénologique global et statut de conservation de 4 espèces végétales (*Strychnos decussata, Diospyros ferrea, Gardenia decaryi* et *Capurodendron gracilifolium*) consommées par *Propithecus coronatus* dans la forêt de Badrala. Mémoire de DEA, Université d'Antananarivo.

Razanahoera, M. R. 1981. Les adaptations alimentaires comparées de deux lémuriens folivores sympatriques *Avahi* et *Lepilemur*. Mémoire de DEA, Université d'Antananarivo.

Rendigs, A., Radespiel, U., Wrogemann, D., and Zimmermann, E. 2003. Relationship between microhabitat structure and distribution of mouse lemurs (*Microcebus* spp.) in northwestern Madagascar. *International Journal of Primatology* 24: 47–64.

Richardson, D. M., Carruthers, J., Hui, C., Impson, F. A., Miller, J. T., Robertson, M. P., Rouget, M., Le Roux, J. J., and Wilson, J. R. 2011. Human-mediated introductions of Australian acacias: A global experiment in biogeography. *Diversity and Distributions* 17: 771–787.

Ringelberg, J. J., Zimmermann, N. E., Weeks, A., Lavin, M., and Hughes, C. E. 2020. Biomes as evolutionary arenas: Convergence and conservatism in the trans-continental succulent biome. *Global Ecology and Biogeography* 29: 1100–1113.

Robin, V. V., and Nandini, R. 2012. Shola habitats on sky islands: Status of research on montane forests and grasslands in southern India. *Current Science* 103: 1427–1437.

Rull, V., Montoya, E., Vegas-Vilarrúbia, T., and Ballesteros, T. 2015. New insights on palaeofires and savannisation in northern South America. *Quaternary Science Reviews* 122: 158–165.

Saatchi, S. S., Harris, N. L., Brown, S., Lefsky, M., Mitchard, E.T.A., et al. 2011. Benchmark map of forest carbon stocks in tropical regions across three continents. *Proceedings of the National Academy of Sciences of the USA* 108: 9899–9904.

Salmona, J., Olofsson, J. K., Hong-Wa, C., Razanatsoa, J., Rakotonasolo, F., Ralimanana, H., Randiamboavonjy, T., Suescun, U., Vorontsova, M. S., and Besnard, G. 2019. Late Miocene origin and recent population collapse of the Malagasy savanna olive tree (*Noronhia lowryi*). *Biological Journal of the Linnean Society* 129: 227–243.

Salvaterra and UCL. 2017. *Analyse des moteurs de déforestation et de dégradation dans les écorégions des forêts humides de l'est et des forêts sèches de l'ouest de Madagascar: Rapport de synthèse*. Antananarivo: Bureau National de Coordination REDD+.

Samanta, A., Ganguly, S., Hashimoto, H., Devadiga, S., Vermote, E., Knyazikhin, Y., Nemani, R. R., and Myneni, R. B. 2010. Amazon forests did not green-up during the 2005 drought. *Geophysical Research Letters* 37: L05401.

Samonds, K. E., Parent, S. N., Muldoon, K. M., Crowley, E., and Godfrey, L. R. 2010. Rock matrix surrounding subfossil lemur skull yields diverse collection of mammalian subfossils: Implications for reconstructing Madagascar's paleoenvironments. *Malagasy Nature* 4: 1–16.

Samonds, K. E., Crowley, B. E., Rasolofomanana, T.R.N., Andriambelomanana, M. C., Andrianavalona, H. T., et al. 2019. A new late Pleistocene subfossil site (Tsaramody, Sambaina basin, central Madagascar) with implications for the chronology of habitat and megafaunal community change on Madagascar's Central Highlands. *Journal of Quaternary Science* 34: 379–392.

Sarmiento, G. 1992. A conceptual model relating environmental factors and vegetation formations in the lowlands of tropical South America. In *Nature and Dynamics of Forest-Savanna Boundaries*, eds. P. A. Furley, J. Proctor, and J. A. Ratter, pp. 583–601. London: Chapman and Hall.

Sato, H. 2012. Frugivory and seed dispersal by brown lemurs in a Malagasy tropical dry forest. *Biotropica* 44: 479–488.

———. 2018. Predictions of seed shadows generated by common brown lemurs (*Eulemur fulvus*) and their relationship to seasonal behavioral strategies. *International Journal of Primatology* 39: 377–396.

Scales, I. R. 2011. Farming at the forest frontier: Land use and landscape change in western Madagascar, 1896–2005. *Environment and History* 17: 499–524.

———. 2012. Lost in translation: Conflicting views of deforestation, land use and identity in western Madagascar. *Geographical Journal* 178: 67–79.

Scales, I. R., and Friess, D. A. 2019. Patterns of mangrove forest disturbance and biomass removal due to small-scale harvesting in southwestern Madagascar. *Wetlands Ecology and Management* 27: 609–625. https://doi.org/10.1007/s11273-019-09680-5.

Scharfe, F., and Schlund, W. 1996. Seed removal by lemurs in a dry deciduous forest of western Madagascar. In Ecology and economy of a tropical dry forest in Madagascar, eds. J. U. Ganzhorn and J.-P. Sorg. *Primate Report* 46–1: 295–304.

Schlesinger, W. H., ed. 1997. *Biogeochemistry*. Amsterdam: Elsevier.

Schneider, T. C., and Kappeler, P. M. 2016. Gregarious sexual segregation: The unusual social organization of the Malagasy narrow-striped mongoose (*Mungotictis decemlineata*). *Behavioral Ecology and Sociobiology* 70: 913–926.

Schnitzer, S. A., and Bongers, F. 2002. The ecology of lianas and their role in forests. *Trends in Ecology and Evolution* 17: 223–230.

Schnoell, A. V., and Fichtel, C. 2012. Wild redfronted lemurs (*Eulemur rufifrons*) use social information to learn new foraging techniques. *Animal Cognition* 15: 505–516.

———. 2013. A novel feeding behaviour in wild redfronted lemurs (*Eulemur rufifrons*): Depletion of spider nests. *Primates* 54: 371–375.

Schnoell, A. V., Dittmann, M. T., and Fichtel, C. 2014. Human-introduced long-term traditions in wild redfronted lemurs. *Animal Cognition* 17: 45–54.

Schülke, O., and Kappeler, P. M. 2003. So near and yet so far: Territorial pairs but low cohesion between pair-partners in a nocturnal lemur, *Phaner furcifer*. *Animal Behaviour* 65: 331–343.

Schupp, E. W., Zwolak, R., Jones, L. R., Snell, R. S., Beckman, N. G., et al. 2019. Intrinsic and extrinsic drivers of intraspecific variation in seed dispersal are diverse and pervasive. *AoB PLANTS* 11: plz067.

Schüßler, D., Mantilla-Contreras, J., Stadtmann, R., Ratsimbazafy, J. H., and Radespiel, U. 2020. Identification of crucial stepping stone habitats for biodiversity conservation in northeastern Madagascar using remote sensing and comparative predictive modeling. *Biodiversity and Conservation* 29: 2161–2184.

Schwartz, N. B., Budsock, A. M., and Uriarte, M. 2019. Fragmentation, forest structure, and topography modulate impacts of drought in a tropical forest landscape. *Ecology* 100: e02677.

Schwitzer, C., Mittermeier, R. A., Johnson, S. E., Donati, G., Irwin, M., et al. 2014. Averting lemur extinctions amid Madagascar's political crisis. *Science* 343: 842–843.

Seiler, R. A., Kogan, F., and Sullivan, J. 1998. AVHRR-based vegetation and temperature condition indices for drought detection in Argentina. *Advances in Space Research* 21: 481–484.

Sewall, B. J. 2008. Ecology and conservation of frugivores of Madagascar and the Comoro islands. PhD thesis, University of California, Davis.

Simmen, B., Hladik, A., and Ramasiarisoa, P. 2003. Food intake and dietary overlap in native *Lemur catta* and *Propithecus verreauxi* and introduced *Eulemur fulvus* at Berenty, southern Madagascar. *International Journal of Primatology* 24: 949–968.

Simpson, E. H. 1949. Measurement of diversity. *Nature* 163: 688.

Soarimalala, V., and Goodman, S. M. 2011. *Les petits mammifères de Madagascar: Guide de leur distribution, biologie et identification*. Antananarivo: Association Vahatra.

Solano, P. J., and DeJean, A. 2004. Ant-fed plants: Comparison between three geophytic myrmecophytes. *Biological Journal of the Linnean Society* 83: 433–439.

Solofondranohatra, C. L., Vorontsova, M. S., Hackel, J., Besnard, G., Cable, S., Williams, J., Jeannoda, V., and Lehmann, C.E.R. 2018. Grass functional traits differentiate forest and savanna in the Madagascar Central Highlands. *Frontiers in Ecology and Evolution* 6: 184.

Solofondranohatra, C. L., Vorontsova, M. S., Hempson, G. P., Hackel, J., Cable, S., Vololoniaina, J., and Lehmann, C.E.R. 2020. Fire and grazing determined grasslands of central Madagascar represent ancient assemblages. *Proceedings of the Royal Society of London B: Biological Sciences* 287(1927): 20200598.

Solofondranohatra, J. S. 2014. Ecoéthologie d'une femelle de *Daubentonia madagascariensis* dans la forêt classée de Kianjavato, sud-est de Madagascar. Mémoire de DEA, Universite d'Antananarivo.

Sommers, P., and Chesson, P. 2016. Caching rodents disproportionately disperse seed beneath invasive grass. *Ecosphere* 7: e01596.

Sorg, J.-P., and Rohner, U. 1996. Climate and phenology of the dry deciduous forest at Kirindy. In Ecology and economy of a tropical dry forest in Madagascar, eds. J. U. Ganzhorn and J.-P. Sorg. *Primate Report* 46–1: 57–80.

Sorg, J.-P., Ganzhorn, J. U., and Kappeler, P. M. 2003. Forestry and research in the Kirindy Forest / Centre de Formation Professionnelle Forestiére. In *The Natural History of Madagascar*, eds. S. M. Goodman and J. P. Benstead, pp. 1512–1519. Chicago: University of Chicago Press.

Spehn, S., and Ganzhorn, J. U. 2000. Influence of seed dispersal by brown lemurs on removal rates of three *Grewia* species (Tiliaceae) in the dry deciduous forest of Madagascar. *Ecotropica* 6: 13–21.

Strömberg, C.A.E. 2002. The origin and spread of grass-dominated ecosystems in the late Tertiary of North America: Preliminary results concerning the evolution of hypsodonty. *Palaeogeography, Palaeoclimatology, Palaeoecology* 177: 59–75.

———. 2004. Using phytolith assemblages to reconstruct the origin and spread of grass-dominated habitats in the Great Plains of North America during the late Eocene to early Miocene. *Palaeogeography, Palaeoclimatology, Palaeoecology* 207: 239–275.

Styger, E., Rakotondramasy, H. M., Pfeffer, M. J., Fernandes, E. C., and Bates, D. M. 2007. Influence of slash-and-burn farming practices on fallow succession and land degradation in the rainforest region of Madagascar. *Agriculture, Ecosystems and Environment* 119(3–4): 257–269.

Tadross, M., Randriamarolaza, L., Rabefitia, Z., and Zheng, K. Y. 2008. *Climate Change in Madagascar: Recent Past and Future*. Washington, DC: World Bank.

Takahashi, H. 2008. Fruit feeding behavior of a chameleon *Furcifer oustaleti*: Comparison with insect foraging tactics. *Journal of Herpetology* 42: 760–763.

Tamme, R., Hiiesalu, I., Laanisto, L., Szava-Kovats, R., and Partel, M. 2010. Environmental heterogeneity, species diversity and co-existence at different spatial scales. *Journal of Vegetation Science* 21: 796–801.

Tan, C. L. 1999. Group composition, home range size, and diet of three sympatric bamboo lemur species (genus *Hapalemur*) in Ranomafana National Park, Madagascar. *International Journal of Primatology* 20: 547–566.

Terborgh, J. W., Nuñez-Iturri, G., Pitman, N.C.A., Valverde, F.H.C., Alvarez, P., Swamy, V., Pringle, E. G., and Paine, C.E.T. 2008. Tree recruitment in an empty forest. *Ecology* 89: 1757–1768.

Tews, J., Brose, U., Grimm, V., Tielborger, K., Wichmann, M. C., Schwager, M., and Jeltsch, F. 2004. Animal species diversity driven by habitat heterogeneity/diversity: The importance of keystone structures. *Journal of Biogeography* 31: 79–92.

Thérézien, Y. 1963. Régime alimentaire de plusieurs espèces de poissons des lacs Kinkony, Sahapy et autres étangs de la région nord-ouest de Madagascar. *Bulletin Français de Pisciculture* 211: 37–48.

Thomas, S. M., and Palmer, M. W. 2007. The montane grasslands of the Western Ghats, India: Community ecology and conservation. *Community Ecology* 8(1): 67–73.

Tiffney, B. H. 1984. Seed size, dispersal syndromes, and the rise of the angiosperms: Evidence and hypothesis. *Annals of the Missouri Botanical Garden* 71: 551–576.

———. 2004. Vertebrate dispersal of seed plants through time. *Annual Review of Ecology, Evolution, and Systematics* 35: 1–29.

Torres, C. R., and Clarke, J. A. 2018. Nocturnal giants: Evolution of the sensory ecology in elephant birds and other palaeognaths inferred from digital brain reconstructions. *Proceedings of the Royal Society of London B: Biological Sciences* 285: 20181540.

Traveset, A., and Verdú, M. 2002. A meta-analysis of the effect of gut treatment on seed germination. In *Seed Dispersal and Frugivory: Ecology, Evolution, and Conservation*, eds. D. J. Levey, R. Silva, and M. Galetti, pp. 339–350. Wallingford: CABI.

Traveset, A., Robertson, W., and Rodriguez-Perez, J. 2007. A review of the role of endozoochory on seed germination. In *Seed Dispersal: Theory and Its Application in a Changing World*, eds. A. J. Dennis, R. J. Green, E. W. Schupp, and D. Westcott, pp. 78–113. Wallingford: CABI.

Turner, M. G. 2005. Landscape ecology: What is the state of the science? *Annual Review of Ecological Evolutionary Systematics* 36: 319–344.

USGS. 2021. Land Processes Distributed Active Archive Center (LP DAAC). https://lpdaac.usgs.gov/.

Vågen, T. G., and Winowiecki, L. A. 2013. Mapping of soil organic carbon stocks for spatially explicit assessments of climate change mitigation potential. *Environmental Research Letters* 8: 1–9. doi:10.1088/1748-9326/8/1/015011.

Vågen, T. G., Andrianorofanomezana, M. A., and Andrianorofanomezana, S. 2006. Deforestation and cultivation effects on characteristics of oxisols in the highlands of Madagascar. *Geoderma* 131(1–2): 190–200.

Valenta, K., Burke, R. J., Styler, S. A., Jackson, D. A., Melin, A. D., and Lehman, S. M. 2013. Colour and odour drive fruit selection and seed dispersal by mouse lemurs. *Scientific Reports* 3: 1–5.

Valido, A., and Olesen, J. M. 2019. Frugivory and seed dispersal by lizards: A global review. *Frontiers in Ecology and Evolution* 7: 49.

Vallejo-Marín, M., Domínguez, C. A., and Dirzo, R. 2006. Simulated seed predation reveals a variety of germination responses of Neotropical rain forest species. *American Journal of Botany* 93: 369–376.

van der Pijl, L. 1982. *Principles of Dispersal in Higher Plants*. New York: Springer-Verlag.

van der Sluis, L. G., Hollund, H. I., Buckley, M., De Louw, P. G., Rijsdijk, K. F., and Kars, H. 2014. Combining histology, stable isotope analysis and ZooMS collagen fingerprinting to investigate the taphonomic history and dietary behaviour of extinct giant tortoises from the Mare aux Songes deposit on Mauritius. *Palaeogeography, Palaeoclimatology, Palaeoecology* 416: 80–91.

Vander Wall, S. B., and Longand, W. S. 2004. Diplochory: Are two seed dispersers better than one? *Trends in Ecology and Evolution* 19(3): 155–161.

Vander Wall, S. B., Kuhn, K. M., and Beck, M. J. 2005. Seed removal, seed predation, and secondary dispersal. *Ecology* 86: 801–806.

Veldman, J. W. 2016. Clarifying the confusion: Old-growth savannahs and tropical ecosystem degradation. *Philosophical Transactions of the Royal Society of London B: Biological Sciences* 371: 20150306.

Veldman, J. W., Buisson, E., Durigan, G., Fernandes, G. W., Le Stradic, S., et al. 2015. Toward an old-growth concept for grasslands, savannas, and woodlands. *Frontiers in Ecology and the Environment* 13: 154–162.

Vidal, M. M., Hasui, E., Pizo, M. A., Tamashiro, J. Y., Silva, W. R., and Guimarães, P. R. 2014. Frugivores at higher risk of extinction are the key elements of a mutualistic network. *Ecology* 95: 3440–3447.

Vieilledent, G., Vaudry, R., Andriamanohisoa, S.F.D., Rakotonarivo, O. S., Randrianasolo, H. Z., Razafindrabe, H. N., Rakotoarivony, C. B., Ebeling, J., and Rasamoelina, M. 2012. A universal approach to estimate biomass and carbon stock in tropical forests using generic allometric models. *Ecological Applications* 22: 572–583. https://doi.org/10.1890/11-0039.1.

Vieilledent, G., Grinand, C., and Vaudry, R. 2013. Forecasting deforestation and carbon emissions in tropical developing countries facing demographic expansion: A case study in Madagascar. *Ecology and Evolution* 3(6): 1702–1716. doi:10.1002/ece3.550.

Vieilledent, G., Gardi, O., Grinand, C., Burren, C., Andriamanjato, M., et al. 2016. Bioclimatic envelope models predict a decrease in tropical forest carbon stocks with climate change in Madagascar. *Journal of Ecology* 104: 703–715. doi:10.1111/1365-2745.12548.

Vieilledent, G., Grinand, C., Rakotomalala, F. A., Ranaivosoa, R., Rakotoarijaona, J.-R., Allnutt, T. F., and Achard, F. 2018. Combining global tree cover loss data with historical national forest-cover maps to look at six decades of deforestation and forest fragmentation in Madagascar. *Biological Conservation* 222: 189–197. https://doi.org/10.1016/j.biocon.2018.04.008.

Vieilledent, G., Nourtier, M., Grinand, C., Pedrono, M., Clausen, A., et al. 2020. It's not only poverty: Uncontrolled global trade and bad governance are responsible for unceasing deforestation in western Madagascar. *BioRxiv*. doi:10.1101/2020.07.30.229104.

Virah-Sawmy, M. 2009. Ecosystem management in Madagascar during global change. *Conservation Letters* 2(4): 163–170.

Virah-Sawmy, M., Gillson, L., and Willis, K. J. 2009a. How does spatial heterogeneity influence resilience to climatic changes? Ecological dynamics in southeast Madagascar. *Ecological Monographs* 79: 557–574.

Virah-Sawmy, M., Willis, K. J., and Gillson, L. 2009b. Threshold response of Madagascar's littoral forest to sea-level rise. *Global Ecology and Biogeography* 18: 98–110.

———. 2010. Evidence for drought and forest declines during the recent megafaunal extinctions in Madagascar. *Journal of Biogeography* 37(3): 506–519.

Voigt, F. A., Burkhardt, J. F., Verhaagh, M., and Böhning-Gaese, K. 2002. Regional differences in ant community structure and consequences for secondary dispersal of *Commiphora* seeds. *Ecotropica* 8: 59–66.

Voigt, F. A., Arafeh, R., Farwig, N., Griebeler, E. M., and Böhning-Gaese, K. 2009. Linking seed dispersal and genetic structure of trees: A biogeographical approach. *Journal of Biogeography* 36: 242–254.

Vololona, J. 2020. Etude des interactions entre *Rousettus madagascariensis* G. Grandidier, 1928 (Chiroptera: Pteropodidae) et les plantes à fleurs de la Réserve Spéciale d'Ankarana, nord de Madagascar: Approche palynologique. PhD thesis, Université d'Antananarivo.

Vorontsova, M. S. 2013. Variable morphology of the Madagascar endemic *Aristida tenuissima* (Poaceae: Aristidoideae) and the absence of *Stipa* (Poaceae: Pooideae, Stipeae) from Madagascar. *Phytotaxa* 92: 55–58.

———. 2018. Revision of the group previously known as *Panicum* L. (Poaceae: Panicoideae) in Madagascar. *Candollea* 73: 143–186.

Vorontsova, M. S., and Rakotoarisoa, S. E. 2014. Endemic non-bambusoid genera of grasses (Poaceae) in Madagascar: Review of current knowledge. *Malagasy Nature* 8: 14–34.

Vorontsova, M. S., Ratovonirina, G., and Randriamboavonjy, T. 2013. Revision of *Andropogon* and *Diectomis* (Poaceae: Sacchareae) in Madagascar and the new *Andropogon itremoensis* from the Itremo Massif. *Kew Bulletin* 68(2): 193–207.

Vorontsova, M. S., Haevermans, T., Haevermans, A., Razanatsoa, J., Lundgren, M. R., and Besnard, G. 2015. The genus *Sartidia* (Poaceae: Aristidoideae) in Madagascar. *Systematic Botany* 40: 448–453.

Vorontsova, M. S., Besnard, G., Forest, F., Malakasi, P., Moat, J., et al. 2016. Madagascar's grasses and grasslands: Anthropogenic or natural? *Proceedings of the Royal Society of London B: Biological Sciences*, 283: 20152.

Vorontsova, M. S., Lowry, P. P., II, Andriambololonera, S. R., Wilmé, L., Rasolohery, A., Govaerts, R., Ficinski, S. Z., and Humphreys, A. M. 2020. Inequality in plant diversity knowledge and unrecorded plant extinctions: An example from the grasses of Madagascar. *Plants People Planet*. https://doi.org/10.1002/ppp3.10123.

Waeber, P. O., Wilmé, L., Ramamonjisoa, B., Garcia, C., Rakotomalala, D., Rabemananjara, Z. H., Kull, C. A., Ganzhorn, J. U., and Sorg, J.-P. 2015. Dry forests in Madagascar: Neglected and under pressure. *International Forestry Review* 17: 127–148.

Waeber, P. O., Rafanoharana, S., Rasamuel, H. A., and Wilmé, L. 2019. Parks and reserves in Madagascar: Managing biodiversity for a sustainable future. *Protected Areas, National Parks and Sustainable Future*. https://doi.org/10.5772/intechopen.85348.

Wan, J. N., Mbari, N. J., Wang, S. W., Liu, B., Mwangi, B. N., Rasoarahona, J. R., Xin, H. P., Zhou, Y. D. and Wang, Q. F. 2020. Modeling impacts of climate change on the potential distribution of six endemic baobab species in Madagascar. *Plant Diversity*. https://doi.org/10.1016/j.pld.2020.07.001.

Wang, B. C., and Smith, T. B. 2002. Closing the seed dispersal loop. *Trends in Ecology and Evolution* 17: 379–385.

White, F. 1983. *The Vegetation of Africa: A Descriptive Memoir to Accompany the UNESCO/AETFAT/UNSO Vegetation Map of Africa*. Paris: UNESCO.

Wiens, J. A. 2002. Central concepts and issues of landscape ecology. In *Applying Landscape Ecology in Biological Conservation*, ed. K. J. Gutzwiller, pp. 3–21. New York: Springer-Verlag.

Winchester, V., Hardwick, K., Rasamimanana, H., Raharison, S. M., Mertl-Millhollen, A., Gärtner, H., and McCrae, J. 2018. Berenty Reserve: A gallery forest in decline in dry southern Madagascar; Towards forest restoration. *Land* 7: 8. https://doi.org/10.3390/land7010008.

Wright, P. C., Heckscher, K., and Dunham, A. E. 1997. Predation on Milne-Edward's sifaka (*Propithecus diadema edwardsi*) by the fossa (*Cryptoprocta ferox*) in the rain forest of southeastern Madagascar. *Folia Primatologica* 68: 34–43.

Wright, P. C., Razafindratsita, V. R., Pochron, S. T., and Jernvall, J. 2005. The key to Madagascar frugivores. In *Tropical Fruits and Frugivores*, eds. J. L. Dew and J. P. Boubli, pp. 121–138. Dordrecht: Springer.

Wright, P. C., Tecot, S. R., Erhart, E. M., Baden, A. L., King, S. J., and Grassi, C. 2011. Frugivory in four sympatric lemurs: Implications for the future of Madagascar's forests. *American Journal of Primatology* 73: 585–602.

Yamashita, N. 1996. Seasonally and site specificity of mechanical dietary patterns in two Malagasy lemur families (Lemuridae and Indriidae). *International Journal of Primatology* 17: 355–387.

Yesuf, G., Brown, K. A., and Walford, N. 2019. Assessing regional-scale variability in deforestation and forest degradation rates in a tropical biodiversity hotspot. *Remote Sensing in Ecology and Conservation* 5: 346–359.

Yoder, A. D., Campbell, C. R., Blanco, M. B., Dos Reis, M., Ganzhorn, J. U., et al. 2016. Geogenetic patterns in mouse lemurs (genus *Microcebus*) reveal the ghosts of Madagascar's forests past. *Proceedings of the National Academy of Sciences of the USA* 113(29): 8049–8056.

Zafisoalizy, M. 2011. La société Bara et les feux de brousses (l'exemple du district de Sakaraha). Mémoire de DEA de Sciences Sociales, Université de Toliara.

Zaloumis, N. P., and Bond, W. J. 2016. Reforestation or conservation? The attributes of old growth grasslands in South Africa. *Philosophical Transactions of the Royal Society of London B: Biological Sciences* 371(1703): 20150310.

Zinner, D., Hilgartner, R. D., Kappeler, P. M., Pietsch, T., and Ganzhorn, J. U. 2003. Social organization of *Lepilemur ruficaudatus*. *International Journal of Primatology* 24: 869–888.

Zinner, D., Wygoda, C., Razafimanantsoa, L., Rasoloarison, R. M., Andrianandrasana, H., Ganzhorn, J. U., and Torkler, F. 2013. Analysis of deforestation patterns in the central Menabe, Madagascar, between 1973 and 2010. *Regional Environmental Change* 14: 157–166.

Zou, L., Cao, S., and Sanchez-Azofeifa, A. 2020. Evaluating the utility of various drought indices to monitor meteorological drought in tropical dry forests. *International Journal of Biometeorology* 64: 701–711.

CHAPTER 5

HUMAN ECOLOGY

THE RISE OF MALAGASY SOCIETIES: RECENT DEVELOPMENTS IN THE ARCHAEOLOGY OF MADAGASCAR

H. T. Wright and J.-A. Rakotoarisoa

The polymathic pioneers of the scientific study of Madagascar recognized that Malagasy cultural and material forms suggest a historical connection to Southeast Asia and Indonesia (summarized by Beaujard 2012). These include the Malagasy language (classified as an Austronesian language, with closest relatives in Indonesia; Adelaar and Himmelmann 2005), irrigated rice cultivation, outrigger canoes, and some musical instruments. African influence on the island is also considerable. The Malagasy language contains phonological features (Adelaar 2012) and words (Blench 2008) of Bantu origin. African cultural practices such as cattle earmarking (Hurvitz 1979) also occur. New studies of human genetics confirm the linguistic and cultural indications of contact. Malagasy populations show affinities with Indonesian (Kusuma et al. 2016) as well as African populations (Hewitt et al. 1996; Hurles et al. 2005; Pierron et al. 2017). However, linguistic, cultural, and genetic evidence, while demonstrating contacts, provides only approximate chronologies at best and furthermore provides little insight into developmental processes. We cannot evaluate propositions about past processes without the direct evidence of the past that is provided only (in the absence of written documents) by paleoecology and archaeology.

Fishing peoples were exploiting the offshore resources of the western Indian Ocean by early Holocene times, if not before (Costa and Tosi 1989). By the end of the Early Bronze Age, about 2200 BCE, southern Asian mariners were undertaking regular voyages from the Indus Valley to Mesopotamia and to Oman with its rich copper resources, a voyage across the open sea of about 400 km (Cleuziou and Tosi 1994; Ratnagar 2004). Similarly, large sailing craft of the Egyptian Old Kingdom were sailing on the Red Sea (Tallet and Marouard 2015) about 2550 BCE. Mariners with such ships could easily have explored along the coasts of Arabia and Africa. Indeed, there is one piece of archaeological evidence that such voyages took place. Chemical analysis of a pendant found in Iraq near modern Baghdad in a grave dated about 2000 BCE indicates that it was formed from a tree gum, or copal, probably derived from the genus *Hymenaea* (*Trachylobium*), which occurs today only in Zanzibar and Madagascar (Meyer et al. 1991). The distribution of this tree 4000 years ago is not yet known, however, and it could have occurred farther north along the coast of Africa. Also, there is a possibility that small amounts of gum were traded from hand to hand northward to the Horn of Africa and Arabia, without actual southward voyages. The gum merits more precise identification and dating. This occurrence, at the least, raises the possibility of maritime contacts between the Bronze Age civilizations of western and southern Asia and the southwestern Indian Ocean.

WHAT IS THE EVIDENCE OF AN EARLY HUMAN PRESENCE ON MADAGASCAR?

The first source of evidence to be widely cited is that of possibly butchered animals. The first such account was that of Alfred Grandidier, whose field agents recovered cut bones from Ambolisatra, now called Andolonomby (Figure 5.1a), near Toliara in the southwest (Grandidier and Filhol 1894). Almost a century later, these bones were directly dated to about 100 CE, and this find was placed in a context of changing environments (MacPhee and Burney 1991; Burney 1993). The paleoecology at this site has been confirmed by a recent restudy (Virah-Sawmy et al. 2016). A number of other finds of cut bone have been reinvestigated, particularly at Taolambiby (Godfrey et al. 2019), and worked eggshell of large extinct birds at has been reported from a rock shelter in the Velondriake area with associated dates of about 650 BCE (Douglass 2017; Douglass et al. 2019). A recent and very provocative find is the Christmas River locality, southeast of Isalo, which yielded the remains of crocodiles, tortoises, the elephant bird *Aepyornis maximus* (see Safford et al., pp. 1553–602), the large carnivoran

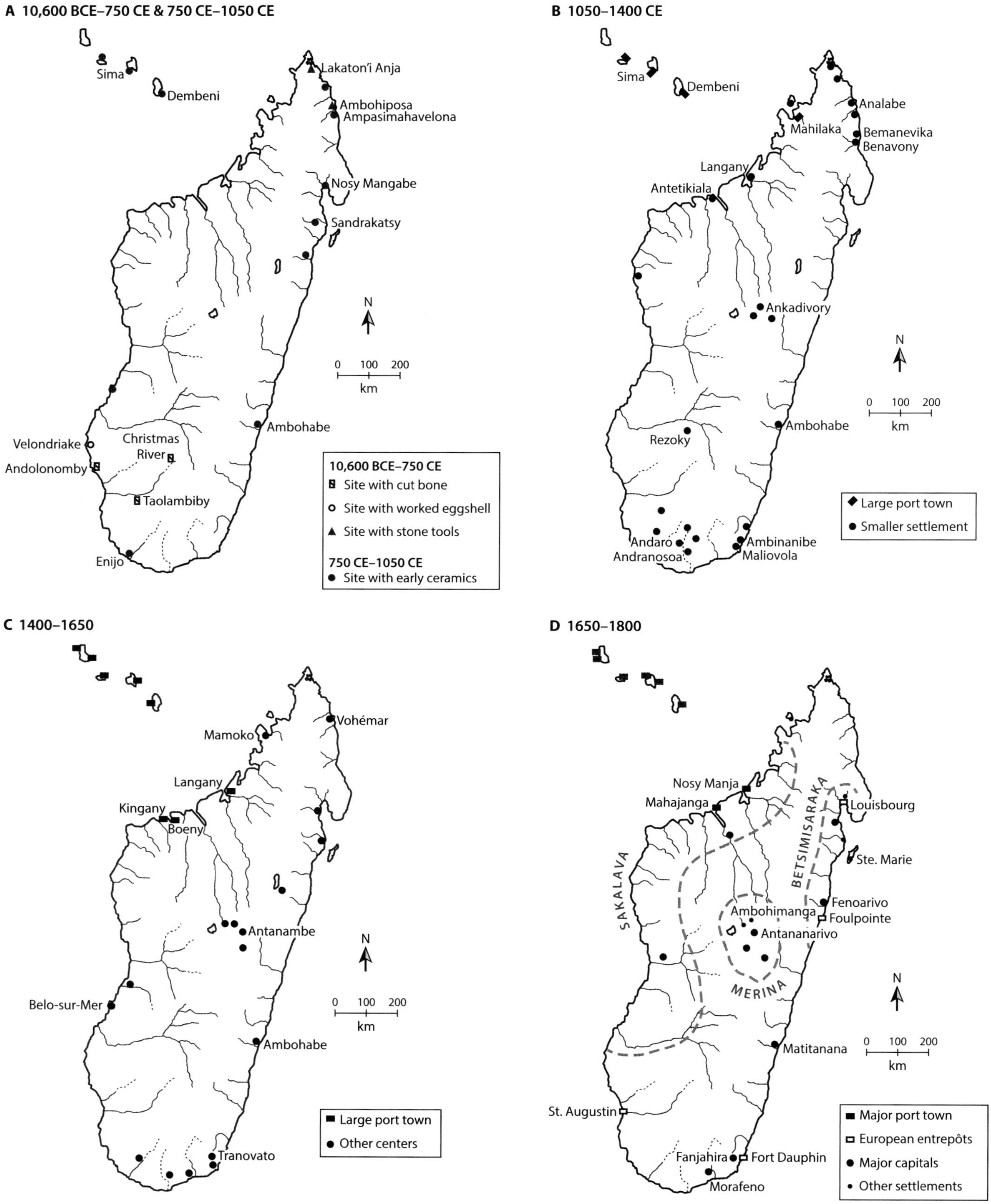

FIGURE 5.1 **Four phases of cultural development in Holocene Madagascar. Sites mentioned in the text are named; other sites are indicated.**

Cryptoprocta spelea, a number of large extinct lemurs (see Godfrey and Jungers, pp. 1824–28), including *Archaeolemur majori*, *Pachylemur insignis*, and *Megaladapis edwardsi*, and many dwarf hippos (*Hippopotamus lemerlei*), all dated to about 10,000 years ago (Muldoon et al. 2012; see Godfrey and Douglass, pp. 191–97). Restudy shows that some *Aepyornis* bones, reliably dated to 8650 BCE, exhibit multiple cut marks (Hansford et al. 2018). Further archaeological and geologic studies of this site are needed. While the causes of damage to, and the dating of, bones at some sites have been questioned (A. Anderson 2019), most researchers accept cut bones as evidence for early hunting.

Another source of evidence from Madagascar is that of imported exotic plants and animals. Evidence of casual visitors as early as 400 BCE, in the form of possible *Cannabis* pollen, has been found in the Central Highlands (Burney 1987a; Gasse and Van Campo 1998). The plant could have been introduced by sailors on the coast, then spread inland by birds. *Numida meleagris* (Helmeted Guineafowl) has been dated at Ankilitelo in southwestern Madagascar as early as 5350 BCE (Goodman et al. 2013; see Safford et al., pp. 1553–602). Other translocated plants and animals have so far yielded relatively recent dates (Douglass et al. 2019).

The most solid evidence would be that of ancient human settlements, with definite cultural remains and reliable dates. The oldest actual occupied site is a camp under the rock shelter of Lakaton'i Anja (Figure 5.1a) in the far north of Madagascar, first excavated by Dewar and Rakotovololona (1992); initial occupation has been dated with carbon 14 to about 450 CE. Reexcavation in 2011–2012 (Dewar et al. 2013), using optically stimulated luminescence (OSL), yielded deeper layers with evidence of periodic forager occupation, dated from older than 2300 BCE to 400 CE. The people who camped in Anja brought fish and shellfish several kilometers from the coast, hunted forest animals including extant small lemurs and the large extinct sloth lemur *Palaeopropithecus kelyus* (family Palaeopropithecidae; see Godfrey and Jungers, pp. 1824–28), and probably collected other forest resources. They used a flaked stone technology with crescentic and trapezoidal projectile points and various scraping and piercing tools. Critiques of the dating of the early occupations at Anja (A. Anderson 2019; Mitchell 2019) are founded on misunderstandings of the single-grain OSL dating method and failure to recognize that the occurrence of flakes does not diminish with depth (Dewar et al. 2013: Figure 5), as would occur if they were introduced into deeper layers by geologic processes. Nonetheless, Anja was a hunting camp occupied only sporadically, and the argument for early foraging sites would be more convincing if more-permanent residential camps could be found and studied.

In sum, the paleoecological and archaeological evidence indicates that Madagascar may have had human hunting as early as 8650 BCE and the campsites of foragers as early as 2300 BCE, when trading was becoming an important economic activity throughout the Indian Ocean (Dewar and Wright 1993; Dewar 1996). It is possible that, in addition to exploiting endemic flora and fauna, these foragers introduced *Potamochoerus larvatus* (African Bush Pig; see Goodman and Andrianjakarivelo, pp. 2003–6), guineafowl, and other nondomesticated taxa to hunt. Such "seeding" by foragers is documented on islands in inner Oceania (Flannery and White 1991) and the Mediterranean (Cherry 1990).

SETTLING THE COASTS: 750–1050 CE

Archaeological evidence points to increased settlement on the east coast beginning around 750 CE. Survey in the area of Vohémar under the direction of Robert Dewar and Chantal Radimilahy has revealed both village sites and small hamlets on the terraces of rivers entering the large Iharana Bay (Dewar et al. 2020). Their excavation at the village site of Ampasimahavelona (Figure 5.1a) yielded undisturbed features with very coarse, undecorated basins, bowls, and spherical jars; as well as charcoal dating to between 880 and 1020 CE. On the small island of Nosy Mangabe in Antongil Bay, 160 km south of Vohémar, soundings revealed that charcoal had been washed down the hill and sealed in layers with fragments of basins carved from chlorite schist, commonly termed soapstone; pottery fragments of very coarse, plain basins, bowls, and spherical jars; crystal quartz flakes; and slag from the forging or repair of iron implements. The earliest dated layer was emplaced between 680 and 970 CE (Vérin 1975: 879–891; Wright, forthcoming). The most reasonable interpretation of this site is as a camp below hill gardens burned for cultivation. Intriguingly, a few sherds of imported white-glazed bowls from the Persian Gulf were found on these small sites. Whether or not the iron, chlorite schist, and crystal were traded for ceramics and other exotic goods can be determined only when coastal ports of the 8th to 10th centuries CE are found (Horton et al. 2017).

On the mainland 70 km to the south, in the middle valley of the Mananara River, is the site of Sandrakatsy (Wright and Fanony 1992). This is a village site with pits, hearths, and iron-smelting areas on a high terrace surrounded by hills long used for dry rice cultivation, overlooking a marshy area today occupied by rice paddies. Charcoal from a pit filled with smelting debris dates to between 770 and 995 CE. There are a number of small hamlets of field campsites within a kilometer of Sandrakatsy. Isolated chlorite schist sherds, very coarse plain sherds, and concentrations of iron slag indicate widespread use of the landscape. At both Nosy Mangabe and Sandrakatsy, the use of water flotation to find carbonized seeds and the study of phytoliths revealed no definite evidence of early rice, but it is possible that crops such as yams or taro were grown. Similar village and hamlet sites have been found from the Antsiranana Bay in the far north to Fenoarivo Atsinanana, nearly 600 km to the south. Based on present evidence, these northeastern settlements seem to have been concentrated on the lower and middle reaches of the larger rivers. However, the scarcity of coastal sites could be a result of erosion as a consequence of a slightly higher sea level after the turn of the millennium and of frequent cyclones throughout history. To the south of Fenoarivo on the central-east and southeast coasts, very few sites of this period have been found; however, this may be because access is difficult and there has been little intensive survey or excavation on these coasts. The discovery of thick chlorite schist tempered sherds in deep layers at Ambohabe near Vohipeno (Griffin 2009, 2011) suggests early sites will be found far to the south. Also, there are a few finds of very coarse, plain pottery on the west coast (Wright et al., forthcoming). Excavation to date these finds precisely is needed.

In contrast to the coarse, plain ceramics of the north and east coasts, three small sites in the far south at Enijo (see Figure 5.1a) on the mouth of the Menarandra River, have yielded well-made sand-tempered jars with chevron-incised triangular motifs (Parker

Pearson 2010: Figures 4.14–16) similar to pottery from the east coast of Africa dated from 750 to 950 CE. Unfortunately, the best-preserved of these sites is covered by a cemetery and cannot be excavated. Exactly when and why these mariners would have crossed the Mozambique Channel to camp on this arid corner of Madagascar cannot be determined without excavation.

In sum, the earliest-known villagers settled on all of Madagascar's coasts after 700 CE. On the east, northeast, and far north coasts and probably on the northwest and west coasts, small villages and hamlets with coarse, plain ceramics are found on protected river estuaries. There is evidence of the use of marine and estuarine resources, and of potting and ironworking, but no sign of domesticates. The coincidence between the time of arrival of these people and language-based estimates of the time of departure of the Malagasy ancestors from Indonesia implies that these were Malagasy speakers, but there is no definitive evidence.

On the far south coast and perhaps on the southwest coast, the earliest-known village was settled at about the same time, but its inhabitants developed incised ceramics similar to those of the coast of eastern Africa, thought to have been made by speakers of a Bantu language. Until some of these sites are excavated, we can say little about these people's way of life. The evidence, however fragmentary, does imply that Africans and Southeast Asians arrived at about the same time on Madagascar. Though we now have the broad outlines of the earliest settlements by village peoples, we still lack a basic understanding of daily life. Researchers are only beginning to establish the dates when key domesticates such as rice, taro, yams, and cattle, and commensals such as cats, dogs, rats, and mice, became important (Burney et al. 2003; Crowther et al. 2016; Prendergast et al. 2017; Douglass et al. 2019). In no case do we have evidence of the social and economic organization of the 8th- to 10th-century communities, which archaeologists could recover from extensive excavation of areas with housing, workshops, and other such features.

SETTLING THE COASTS: 1050–1400 CE

Beginning in the 11th century, there is evidence of increased settlement along the northwest coast. The first major port, Mahilaka (Figure 5.1b), appeared on the northwest coast around 1050 CE and flourished until about 1400 (Radimilahy 1998). Adjacent to the coast, on the Ampasindava Bay, the town had masonry walls surrounding an area of 45 ha. Within these walls were mosques; elite residential structures; areas of ordinary pole-and-mat housing; and craft areas for smelting iron, producing iron tools, making glass vessels and beads, and carving vessels from chlorite schist, which was mined at least 100 km northwest of Mahilaka. The domestic ceramics had decoration with zigzag incising, punctations, and shell impressions, similar to those from other parts of northern Madagascar, as well as to those from ports such Dembeni and Sima on the nearby Comoro islands (Wright 1992, 1993). The food remains recovered from Mahilaka include carbonized rice grains, so far the earliest evidence of rice found on Madagascar (Crowther et al. 2016), and the bones of cows, sheep and/or goats, chickens, fish, turtles, and hunted wild animals (Rakotozafy 1996). People throughout the port town also had access to imported underglazed sgraffito ceramics from the Persian Gulf and glazed white and green wares from the Far East, as well as to imported glass beads, brass items, and doubtless perishable items of cloth, leather, and so on. Outside the town walls were suburbs, some with evidence of specialization in fishing and iron smelting, a port area now filled with sediment, and several reservoirs covering 1–2 ha created by building dams along a small valley on the southern edge of the town. In the vicinity are a few hamlet sites, probably devoted to fishing or paddy and swidden cultivation, but no larger villages. Presumably most land in the area around the town was farmed by the townspeople. Fifty kilometers to the north on the offshore island of Nosy Be, contemporary with Mahilaka, there were not only hamlets but small village sites and a few large village sites with local ceramics duplicating those of Mahilaka (Wright et al. 2005). These sites had evidence of the exploitation of fish, and the inhabitants were doubtless also involved in cultivation. There was no evidence of special crafts and only occasional fragments of exotic ceramics imported from the Persian Gulf. The evidence of pollen and charcoal from dated sediment cores raised from lakes and bogs throughout the Ampasindava region shows increased burning and a marked diminution in arboreal pollen beginning about 1100 CE. By about 1300, most pollen is from grassy and brushy vegetation (Burney 1999). Paleoecological studies farther south along the northwest coast show evidence of forest decline and increased grasslands, as indicated by a rapid increase in $\partial^{13}C$ between 890 and 1010 CE in accurately dated speleothems from Anjohibe Cave near the Mahajamba Bay (Burns et al. 2016; Godfrey et al. 2019). Studies of spores of *Sporormiella*, a fungus found in the dung of animals, show increases in such spores in a bog near Mahilaka dating to about 1000 CE (Burney et al. 2003). It seems likely that the deforestation and the increase in grassy vegetation were a consequence of increased human activity, including burning to facilitate both cultivation and cattle herding.

Two hundred kilometers to the east of Mahilaka, on the northeast coast, a reconnaissance by Vérin (1975: 845–872; 1986: 212, 260–264) revealed both large and small coastal villages, a pattern similar to that on Nosy Be, also using local ceramics similar to those of Mahilaka. Subsequent intensive studies in this area have demonstrated complex variation in time and space. Near Sambava are mining and smelting sites in the interior (Clist 1995; Serneels et al. 2017) and two large coastal settlements (Figure 5.1b): to the north is Bemanevika, an 11 ha site also with iron smelting and much evidence of schist working in the earlier layers (Vérin 1975: 854–860); to the south is Benavony (Serneels et al. 2017), a 21 ha site with evidence of iron smelting in its northern third and schist working throughout. Both sites have imported underglazed sgraffito bowls and other goods imported from the Near East. Near Vohémar, in the interior, are many quarries for mining chlorite schist, and in villages close to the coast, such as Analabe-Regis, covering 6 ha, chlorite-schist vessels were finished on lathes (Mouren and Rouaix 1913; Dewar et al. 2020), perhaps for export via Mahilaka to eastern Africa and beyond. Exotic ceramics imported from the Persian Gulf have been found at sites such as Vohémar. To date there is little evidence of 11th- to 14th-century settlement farther south around the Antongil Bay or on the northern part of the east coast.

At its height, Mahilaka was not only the center of a network of local communities in the Ampasindava area but connected with sites throughout the northwest coast, and even in the far south. Near and to the southwest of Mahajanga are a number of small hamlets on sandy beaches, doubtless concerned with fishing, characterized by local ceramics of the Antetikiala phase, similar to those of Mahilaka (Wright et al. 1996). Such sites are probably scattered all along the west coast, but this vast area has not yet been intensively surveyed.

However, in the far south of Madagascar, in the dry spiny thicket today occupied by Androy herders, an intensive survey has mapped a network of large centers bounded by embankments of earth or loose stone, locally termed *manda*, as well as smaller settlements (Parker Pearson 2010: 102–127). One of the largest of these settlements, Andranosoa (Figure 5.1b), dated to 1100–1300 CE, has been investigated in some detail (Radimilahy 1981). The site, on the left bank of the seasonal Manambovo River, had about 30 ha within its embankments. Occupational debris, primarily fragments of coarse, sandy ceramic basins and red-slipped bowls, is scattered along the south and west perimeter, around what may have been an open space. Ironworking debris and imported ceramics are concentrated at the southern end of the site, suggesting some economic and social differences within the community. The construction of the embankments suggests the presence of social authorities who could organize and support the labor required to build them. Though Andranosoa was investigated before the introduction of techniques useful in retrieving plant-food remains, an exemplary pioneering study of animal remains (Rasamuel 1985) shows that, in addition to the butchering of domesticated cows and sheep or goats, the hunting of an endemic mammal, *Tenrec ecaudatus* (Tail-less Tenrec, family Tenrecidae; see Goodman et al., pp. 1891–94), was an important activity. The imported ceramics are predominantly underglazed sgraffito from the Persian Gulf, along with some porcelain from China. This imported assemblage is similar to that from Mahilaka, indicating the southern peoples were in the same sphere of exchange. The site of Andaro, in the extreme southwest, had a stone embankment enclosing an area of 18 ha, replacing an earlier stockade, within which were the remains of small rectangular houses, smaller and earlier to the north and larger and slightly later to the south (Parker Pearson 2010: 127–171). The bones of domestic cows, sheep, goats, and chickens are reported. Both northern and southern parts of Andaro have similar types of local pottery as well as imported glass and Persian Gulf pottery. The smaller settlements lack imported goods, but none have been extensively excavated and we cannot be certain that they were occupied by people with lesser status and wealth.

This evidence of herding and hunting peoples in the far south with interregional connections raises several kinds of questions. To what extent did widespread herding change the vegetation of the west and south and contribute to the final disappearance of the large flightless birds and lemurs? Such questions will be answered by ongoing paleoecological research (Burns et al. 2016; Godfrey et al. 2019). Was the relation between Mahilaka in the northwest and settlements in the far south one of direct voyages from Mahilaka along the coast, or was there an overland exchange system that linked the interior valleys of the west to the northern ports? Maritime archaeology will help to answer this question. What did the far south produce that could be exchanged for such exotic items as the imported glass and pottery? All such questions require further archaeological survey and excavations in the south, on the west and east coasts, and in the interior valleys of the west.

Small communities with craft technologies similar to those of Andranosoa and other settlements of the dry spiny thickets occupied the estuaries and lowland moist evergreen forests of the southeast coast. In the Anosy region around Tolagnaro is the well-defined Maliovola cultural phase (Figure 5.1b), with pottery broadly similar to that of Andranosoa (Wright et al. 1993; Rakotoarisoa 1998: 45–58). It had a network of small village sites of a hectare or less, including coastal sites exploiting marine resources, sites on the estuaries with evidence of fishing and the exploitation of cattle, and sites in the river valleys without direct evidence of subsistence, but which are located close to marshes suitable for wet-ground cultivation of rice or tubers. Some of the pottery from these sites appears to have the impressions of rice leaves, and it is possible that Maliovola peoples were already cultivating rice, as do the Tanosy people today. Fortunately excellent paleoecological studies have been done in this area (Virah-Sawmy 2009; Virah-Sawmy et al. 2009a, 2009b, 2009c). In this area of small fishing, herding, and farming villages, there is evidence of increased forest burning and changing forest diversity around 1000 CE. The only evidence of distant relations of Maliovola communities is a few basin fragments of chlorite schist, the nearest known source of which is 250 km to the north (Griffin 2011). So far, no imports from the broader Indian Ocean have been reported. Future research, however, may well document more complex social and economic organization in the southeast.

In sum, during the 11th and 12th centuries CE, there was a rapid emergence of diverse and often complex settlement systems. Settlements spread widely around the coasts of Madagascar, with larger ones on bays or near river mouths. Present evidence indicates the humid northeast coast had networks of small and large villages; the arid far south had inland centers, within which were some social and economic differences; and the northwest coast had the major port town of Mahilaka, with considerable economic and perhaps political hierarchy, and with clear evidence of participation in the network of Islamized ports throughout the western Indian Ocean. Elsewhere, communities were few and far apart. In general, the population is known to have approached the densities of recent times only around the Ampasindava Bay near Mahilaka (Wright et al. 2005). Settlements on the north and west coasts of Madagascar were linked via the Indian Ocean maritime networks to the great centers of the Near East and China (Abu-Loghud 1989). Materials such as crystal quartz (Horton et al. 2017), chlorite schist and other stones, gold, iron, and turtle products were certainly exported, and rice, cattle products, and woods were perhaps exported. In return these communities received such imports as fine ceramics, glass items, finished metal items, and perhaps cloth and other perishable goods. This asymmetric exchange would have had an impact on Madagascar's environments. The elimination of forests—whether by burning of swaths for fields, burning of brush to encourage pasturage for cattle, or making of charcoal to smelt iron ores—is evident in the Mahilaka area and is likely to be documented elsewhere as more paleoecological studies are reported. The growth of secondary forest would have encouraged the spread of introduced species that would become invasive, such as *Rattus rattus* (Black Rat) and *Mus musculus* (House Mouse), which had an impact on forest-dwelling vertebrates and also on humans, through the association of these species with different zoonotic diseases (see Ramasindrazana et al., pp. 1872–80). They also consume large quantities of stored grain.

GROWTH OF THE POPULATION ALONG THE COASTS: CE 1400–1650

Around 1400 CE, the great port of Mahilaka diminished in size, and most of the villages in the region were abandoned. Only a few villages of the succeeding Mamoko cultural phase, characterized by a distinctive wavy-combed pottery, are found in the Ampasindava area (Wright et al. 2005). Burning decreased and arboreal pollen became frequent again at this time (Burney 1999). It seems clear that by 1400 CE the lowland forests had been virtually eliminated in some areas of the northwest, but that they at least partially regenerated when human pressure diminished. Paleoecological studies farther south in the lowland northwest show evidence of forest decline, indicated by a rapid increase in $\partial^{13}C$, between 890 and 1010 CE in accurately dated speleothems from Anjohibe Cave near Mahajamba Bay (Burns et al. 2016; Godfrey et al. 2019). The earliest-known site at Mahajamba is the large 14th- to 16th-century CE coastal site of Langany (discussed below), too late to be associated with the shift to grasslands. However, the area merits intensive survey. Still farther south near the Boeny Bay (Matsumoto and Burney 1994), an area of small-village occupation (Wright et al. 1996), there is evidence in a core from Lake Mitsinjo of forest decline and burning before 1200 CE, but it cannot be more precisely dated. Farther south on the southeast coast (Virah-Sawmy et al. 2016) there is no evidence of increased forest burning at this time. Whether the collapse in the Ampasindava area was a consequence of local ecological problems such as the burning of fields and pastures or exogenous factors such as a zoonotic disease epidemic or pirate raids, or some combination of factors, is a subject for future research.

Whatever the explanation for Mahilaka's sudden decline, growth continued elsewhere along the coasts. The villages of the far northeast persist, and the trading port of Vohémar—a town covering at least 13 ha, founded in about 1400 CE (Figure 5.1c)—has evidence of townspeople using a local variant of the wavy-combed pottery and exploiting the resources of the estuaries and reefs; there is also evidence of workshops for the finishing of chlorite-schist vessels (Dewar et al. 2020) and traditions of gold working (Flacourt 1658 [repr. 1995]). In turn, imports of Far Eastern porcelain and other goods are richly attested in Vohémar's cemeteries (Vernier and Millot 1971; Vérin 1975: 822–844, 1986: 201–260). Note, however, that the striking quantities of Chinese blue-and-white porcelain in the cemeteries are accumulated expressions of status and not an indication of the amounts traded. Excavations in the town site have not yielded the large proportions of porcelain we would expect if Chinese merchants were actually residing at Vohémar (*contra* Schreurs et al. 2011). Ceramics with wavy combing similar to the styles of the Ampasindava and Vohémar areas occur in coastal village sites scattered down the east coast (Wright et al. 1993; Dewar et al. 2011).

A number of new trading ports were flourishing on the northwest coast, among them Langany on Mahajamba Bay, north of Mahajanga (Vérin 1975: 520–522, 569–576), and Kingany, near Boeny Bay, south of Mahajanga (Vérin 1975: 295–337, 1986: 161–167; Wright et al. 1996) (Figure 5.1c). Kingany is the best known of these small ports of the 14th and 15th centuries. It faces the sea and has no good agricultural land in its vicinity, but there are several villages around the nearby Boeny Bay adjacent to land adequate for swidden farming and marsh cultivation. Its 3.5 ha extent is divided into several quarters, each with a few masonry houses and tombs and a small mosque, suggesting competing factions within the community. Cow and fish bones are frequently seen among the food remains. The local pottery is decorated with rows of triangular impressions. Common among the imported pottery are glazed water jars and fine, green-glazed bowls—celadon—from the Far East (Wright et al. 1996). No settlements have been found in the interior, but sediment samples from Lake Mitsinjo show increases in burning beginning in the 15th century, increased proportions of tree species that survive in frequently burned landscapes, and increased proportions of weeds associated with disturbed ground (Matsumoto and Burney 1994).

Farther down the west coast, archaeological survey is limited and only a few isolated sites are known. Around the well-studied small estuary of the Ampanareta River near Belo sur Mer, however, there is evidence of a different kind of settlement system dating from 1380 to 1600 CE (Wright et al., forthcoming), termed the Ampanareta phase. The scrub-covered dunes and mangroves, present then as they are today, could not sustain agriculture, and the estuary had a range of small village and hamlet sites, with evidence of shell gathering and fishing. The local ceramics are a simple version of Kingany ceramics, but there is no evidence of social hierarchy, broader exchange relations, or the adoption of Islam. These sites probably constitute the remains of communities very much like those of the present-day Vezo fishing people of the west and southwest coasts (B. Koechlin 1975; Astuti 1995). Whether they exchanged fish for grain, cattle, and craft goods such as iron tools with interior peoples, as the Vezo do today, is not yet known.

In the southeast, in the Anosy area, the earlier Maliovola cultural phase ceramics had been replaced by incised and appliqué-decorated ceramics of the Ambinanibe phase, but the low-density pattern of small villages, devoted either to marine resources or to estuary resources and cattle herding, continued to about 1400 CE (Wright et al. 1993; Rakotoarisoa 1998: 45–58). The villagers of the Anosy area obtained small quantities of Far Eastern green-glazed ware, perhaps through indirect exchange with west-coast peoples. It is only in the 15th century CE, during the Tranovato phase, that a pattern of differentiated large centers, small centers, and hamlets, all bounded by embankments and ditches and all probably dependent on wet-rice agriculture, developed. The inhabitants used both wavy-combed jars, similar to those of the northeast, and triangle-impressed vessels, similar to those of the west coast and the Central Highlands, and there is much evidence of ironworking. They obtained small quantities of Far Eastern green-glazed ware and blue-and-white porcelain. The latest of the large centers is Fanjahirambe, near modern Fanjahira, the seat of powerful paramounts who claimed to have come from the north and who subjugated the Anosy region. The Zafiraminy elite of Fanshere, as the site was then called, obtained 17th-century European stoneware, glazed ware, and glass bottles (Wright et al. 1993; Rakotoarisoa 1998). Fanjahirambe was destroyed by French forces from Fort Dauphin (Tolagnaro) on the nearby coast in 1651 CE. To the north of the Anosy region in the southern part of the east coast, only the Matitanana River valley has been thoroughly surveyed (Griffin 2009, 2011). Here, in about 1400 CE, the site of Ambohabe had grown to a large size, extending for about 700 m along the sea coast north of the estuary of the river, and there is much evidence of chlorite-schist carving and ironworking (Pannetier 1974, 1988). Smaller villages and hamlets lined the estuary in locations that would have been ideal for irrigated rice cultivation.

The only area of the southern interior for which there is widespread evidence of human communities prior to the 13th century CE is in the far south, as exemplified by Andranosoa and Andaro discussed above, in Settling the Coasts: 1050–1400 CE. By the 14th century CE, however, the settlements of nomadic herders and hunters had spread more widely in the southern interior. An example is the site of Rezoky (Figure 5.1b) (Vérin and Battistini 1972), on the plains to the west of the Isalo Massif, occupied from at least 1250 to 1500 CE. Rezoky is an extensive site, covering several hectares, near a large spring. Those who camped here used both the incised and appliqué-decorated pottery known from sites of the Ambinanibe phase in the southeast (Wright et al. 1993) and the triangle-impressed pottery known from sites on the west coast of the Kingany phase. The faunal remains had a majority of domestic cows, sheep or goats, a dog, plus possibly hunted lemurs and tenrecs and an elephant bird (Rakotozafy and Goodman 2005). There was iron slag, a number of iron tools, and sharpening stones, indicating local ironworking. There were also a few sherds of imported Persian Gulf glazed ceramics and Far Eastern green-glazed ware and some imported glass beads. Elsewhere in the southern plains and the far south, the large settlements with embankments, like Andranosoa and Andaro, were abandoned, and only small settlements with pottery similar to that of Rezoky survived (Parker Pearson 2010).

Paleoecological evidence from the Central Highlands indicates that early in the first millennium of our era, vegetation was being burned more frequently than we would expect from natural causes. At Kavitaha, near Lake Itasy, west of Antananarivo, beginning about 720 CE (Burney 1987b), there is an increase in the charred remains of grasses. Studies of fungal spores suggest an increase in cattle herding between 900 and 1200 CE (Burney et al. 2003). However, no archaeological sites of this early period have been found. If the burning was the work of transhumant foragers and herders, such sites would be ephemeral, and their discovery will require an intensive and inspired search.

However, about 1100 CE, at Kavitaha, there is a major increase in grass charcoal and grass pollen. Also, the pollen of *Ricinus communis* (Euphorbiaceae), the castor bean, an introduced commensal plant often found in disturbed areas near villages, indicates intensified gardening (Burney 1987b: Figures 3 and 4). Farther south at Lake Tritrivakely near Antsirabe, there is a major increase in the influx of grass pollen beginning about 1200 CE (Gasse and Van Campo 1998: Figures 1 and 2b). By 1200 CE, there is widespread evidence of village settlement throughout the Central Highlands, termed the Fiekena phase (Wright 2007: 77–79). In Imerina, villages of 1–2 ha are located in smaller marshy river valleys, occurring in isolation or in pairs, usually about 10 km apart. The site of Ankadivory (Figure 5.1b), a few kilometers north of Antananarivo, exemplifies the pioneering communities of the Central Highlands during the Fiekena phase (Rakotovololona 1994), reliably dated to 1150–1350 CE. A ditch and a riverbank define a semicircular area of 1.8 ha. In the center of this are areas with dense linear concentrations of larger postholes, suggesting either long houses or lines of adjacent rectangular houses. Other areas of smaller posts suggest storage racks. Features filled with fire-cracked stones and cattle bones indicate roasting. Areas of many small pits were also found, some with pottery-making materials. The local ceramics are decorated with arrays of impressed triangles, like those of Kingany and other west-coast sites but much finer. Some iron slag is distributed around the village, but major concentrations were found only at a small site 3 km from the nearest village. The evidence of subsistence is limited, with some cattle bone and seeds of marsh grasses, likely to have been cattle fodder or fuel (Wetterstom and Wright 1992). It is possible that root crops were important. Recently, however, rice phytoliths have been recovered from Ankadivory samples (D. Pearsall, unpublished data). That these villages are more or less of the same size and have similar kinds of wealth items sparsely scattered throughout indicate that there was very little social differentiation. Even such isolated, pioneering villages as these were tied into broader exchange networks, as indicated by pieces of chlorite schist from Madagascar's east coast, and glass beads and imported ceramics. Ankadivory had a majority of imported East Asian stoneware and a minority of Persian Gulf glazed wares, in contrast to sites in the west and south, suggesting more direct East Asian trading contacts via a port other than Mahilaka, perhaps on the largely unexplored east coast.

After 1350 CE, the Fiekena phase developed into the succeeding Antanambe and Ankatso phases (Wright 2007: 42–49, 79–83). The pollen evidence from Kavitaha indicates continued burning and cultivation (Burney 1987a). No major site excavations have been reported, but survey indicates the emergence of settlement clusters with hilltop centers, fortified with multiple polygonal ditches enclosing 2–6 ha, surrounded by smaller villages and hamlets with only a single ditch at best. The tradition of fine, triangle-impressed pottery continues. The centers had multitiered stone tombs inside the ditches, and they are the only sites with imported Far Eastern green-glazed ceramics, suggesting they were the homes of people of higher social status who had exclusive access to exotic goods. These settlement clusters, estimated to have each had a population of about 1000 people, are usually about 10 km apart (Kus and Wright 1986), with many hills and valleys being unoccupied. While competition may have been important in the transition from a network of villages to small, hierarchically organized clusters of sites, there is no evidence that this competition was due to scarcity of land, a common explanation for both the construction of ditches around settlements and the emergence of hierarchy.

Another highland area from which villages dating to 1350–1500 CE have been reported is the Manandona Valley, 135 km south of Antananarivo and to the south of Antsirabe. These tend to be substantial fortified villages on higher ridges and average 12 km apart (Raharijaona 1994). In contrast, in the Mangoro River valley, 60 km east of Antananarivo on the edge of the extant moist evergreen forests, small hamlets, many with ironworking installations, have been investigated (Ramilison 1984). North of the Mangoro River valley are large fortified sites and smaller villages of this period, on hills and high ridges overlooking Lake Alaotra (Fernandez 1970). All of our knowledge of the first stages of human activity in the interior comes from the Central Highlands. Little is known from the southern portion of the highlands around Fianarantsoa and Ambalavao, and nothing at all is known of the Northern Highlands around Mandritsara and Bealanana.

In sum, during the 14th and 15th centuries CE, Madagascar was divided into two cultural spheres. In the far north, Mahilaka's decline was followed by the spread of villages down the east coast. This sphere, marked by wavy-combed pottery and much local exchange of chlorite schist, has limited evidence of sociocultural differentiation or of broader exchange relations. Elsewhere on the northwest and west coasts, in the Central Highlands, and even in the southeast, the pattern is one of small centers with dependent hamlets. This sphere is marked by the use of triangle-impressed ceramics and Far Eastern green-glazed (celadon) bowls, the latter probably obtained from trading ports in the northwest, such as Kingany, or on the east coast. This widespread interaction and emergence of small socially differentiated polities would lay the foundations for the emergence of larger and more centralized polities. By this period, it is likely that the Malagasy language was established throughout the island, since it is widely attested in 16th-century sources. With this broader interaction there was more human impact on the environment. While some forests in the northwest appear to recover, there is evidence of damage to the vegetation elsewhere—for example, on the northwest coast near Boeny Bay (Matsumoto and Burney 1994) and in the Central Highlands (Burney 1987a). It is notable that the last large lemurs and flightless elephant birds disappear between 950 and 1500 CE. Often, the last known records of such animals are from localities in isolated, rugged areas that were forested until the 20th century. Extinction appears to be the result not so much of the activities of the early foragers but of the steady expansion of farmers and herders after 700 CE, which had, by 1500 CE, had an impact on most Malagasy landscapes (Godfrey et al. 2019).

DEVELOPING COMPLEX POLITICAL SYSTEMS: 1650–1800 CE

This was a time of accelerating trends toward higher populations and more centralized political systems in many parts of Madagascar. It was also a time of increasing contact with the emerging modern world system. We focus on three major areas for which we have some evidence of complex political development: the west coast, the east coast, and the Central Highlands.

On the west coast, early in this period, small Islamized trading ports for the most part controlled very limited areas. The best known of these is the site of Boeny (Figure 5.1c), or New Masalagem, on the Boeny Bay southwest of modern Mahajanga. After the destruction of Kingany, coastal settlement was focused on the more defensible island of Antsoheribory in the middle of the bay (Vérin 1975: 341–439, 1986: 284–307). The settlement had grown to cover the entire 26 ha extent of the island by the 16th century, and had town walls, residential quarters of both poorer and more prosperous people, and a quarter with much iron forging. The settlement had a small palace and at least one mosque, and the elaborate tombs of Boeny's sultans and their families. The population is estimated to have been about 5000 people. On the shores of the bay not far from Antsoheribory are at least seven village sites (Wright et al. 1996: Figure 11). In the interior of this region, a survey has recorded rectangular stone-slab tombs with offerings of Antsoheribory ceramics, but no village sites. Pollen evidence from Lake Mitsinjo, 20 km from the coast, however, shows that the area was frequently burned grassland but that agricultural weeds were common (Matsumoto and Burney 1994). The burning may have been the work of pastoralists, but the occurrence of weeds suggests that there were some interior farming villages, which may be found in future surveys. Nonetheless, the small size of the port site and the small number of nearby dependent villages indicate that this must have been a small polity. Documents indicate that it served primarily for the export of cattle, enslaved people, and a few goods transported from the interior (detailed in S. Ellis 1979; Armstrong 1984; Belrose-Huyghues 1984). Boeny was abandoned at the very beginning of the 18th century, when Sakalava rulers forced its merchants to move nearer to their capital, near the present site of Mahajanga, and at that time there may have been a brief recovery of the forest near Mitsinjo.

Boeny may have been typical of the small west-coast ports, but there were much larger and more complex polities. A number of documents refer to a powerful kingdom of the 16th century, somewhere north of modern Mahajanga, called Itongamaro (Grandidier et al. 1903), but Ankoala, the capital of this polity, has not yet been located. The extant Sakalava polities (Kent 1970; Lombard 1988; Feeley-Harnik 1991; Goedefroit 1998) trace their origin to a kingdom that arose to the south of Morondava on the central western coast during the mid-17th century. Sakalava rulers lived in elaborate courts, commanded powerful armies, and were remembered in elaborate mortuary cults. We know much about past environments, traditional agriculture, and herding during the 17th and 18th centuries. We have an understanding of the finely combed pottery made by communities in the Sakalava cultural sphere and used together with imported Chinese blue-and-white porcelain. Unfortunately, very little archaeological surveying has been attempted in the western coastal area, and not one of the known early Sakalava capitals has been studied in detail. Without a record of material remains, we are unable to assess the organizational complexity or effectiveness of these "kingdoms." The more evidence of burning in the past two centuries (Matsumoto and Burney 1994) may relate to the expansion of cattle production for export under the Sakalava rulers and subsequent Merina and French colonial rulers. Surprisingly, the more arid southwest and far south regions have better archaeological records of fishing (Douglass 2017), cattle herding (Rasolondrainy 2019), and demography and conflict (Parker Pearson 2010) than does the Sakalava heartland on the central western coast. In the far south, small settlements using triangle-impressed ceramics related to those of Tranovato in the southeast coalesced into several small polities. The capital of the polity of the Ampatres, which reportedly contained about 12,000 inhabitants, was on a hill from which reportedly one could view most of the c. 4000 km^2 of the Ampatres territory. This site, Morafeno (Figure 5.1d), visited and described by a lieutenant of Etienne Flacourt (for further details on Flacourt see Andriamialisoa and Langrand, pp. 1–38), covered less than a hectare and was defended by only a barrier of thorns. Pearson's excavations revealed a range of domestic features. In the center, it had a roughly rectangular building covering 18 m^2, thought to be the residence of the ruler. In addition to ceramics, the excavations revealed the bones of cows, sheep, goats, and chickens; iron scrap and slag; and two gunflints (Parker Pearson 2010). This "kingdom" was dwarfed by the contemporary Sakalava and the later Betsimisaraka and Merina polities.

On the southern part of the east coast, where the Matitanana River valley has been thoroughly surveyed (Griffin 2009, 2011), despite Ambohabe being abandoned, settlement continued to proliferate. Villages were closely spaced on the estuary and up the river, and European ships often visited the Matitanana (Figure 5.1d) in the 16th century CE, but an entrepôt has not yet been found. On the northern part of the east coast between the 15th and 17th centuries, the pattern of small coastal villages of the Seranambe phase developed, typically featuring a larger village with several smaller ones around it (Wright and Dewar 2000). In addition, there were interior settlements on the higher ridge crests. All settlements were relatively small, none larger than 2 ha having been recorded to date. These settlements funneled local products such as carved chlorite-schist vessels, gold, and doubtless wood and other forest products into coastal ports such as the large and prosperous port of Vohémar on the far northeast coast. Vohémar diminished in importance late in the 16th century, however, and the peoples of the northeast were drawn into close relations with European mariners, particularly with pirates, who maintained bases on the coasts and on the offshore Ile Sainte Marie, and also with French merchants and officials who had entrepôts at Louisbourg, Sainte Marie, Foulpointe, and Fort Dauphin (Figure 5.1d). The Europeans provided guns to the chiefs of the coastal polities in exchange for enslaved people (Berg 1985). Beginning about 1700 CE, the Ambitsika phase manifested a shift in basic domestic technology, with ceramic cooking pots disappearing in many areas, perhaps replaced by iron pots received in trade. Local serving bowls and plates with elaborate triangle impressions on the interior were used throughout the east coast, alongside imported Chinese blue-and-white porcelain. The coastal areas formerly preferred for settlement were largely abandoned, with only a few larger settlements close to anchorages—perhaps concerned with trade—flourishing. However, small settlements proliferated in the interior up to 20 km from the coast, most on hilltops and with surrounding ditches. Tombs in burial caves indicate only a modest degree of social differentiation (Wright and Fanony 1992: Figures 9 and 13). Documents of the mid-18th century refer to the conquest of the many small polities of the northeast and the creation of the Betsimisaraka polity by the ruler Ratsimilaho (Berg 1985; S. Ellis 2007). Archaeology, however, has yet to discover larger centers of this period, and there is little evidence of settlement hierarchy. Ratsimilaho's capital at Fenoarivo covered no more than 5 ha and had only a ditch and stockade (Wright et al. 2011). Based on present evidence, we are forced to conclude that Ratsimilaho's polity collapsed before the material infrastructure of state administration could be firmly put in place. Given this turmoil, and the reorienting of trade away from commodities and toward slave trafficking, we would predict that the regional moist evergreen forests would have recovered during the 18th century. However, there are few accurately dated paleoecological studies in this vast and important region that would allow us to evaluate such ideas.

In the Central Highlands, there was a very different development. The small, widely spaced hierarchical settlement clusters with centers and subsidiary villages and hamlets of the 15th century were replaced by a scatter of small villages of the Angavobe phase on higher ridges (Wright 2007: 84–85). Work on the fortified, mountain-top center of Fanongoavana (Rasamuel 2007) indicates that rice, probably irrigated in paddies and stored in silo pits, was very common (Wetterstrom and Wright 1992). Cattle bone occurs widely. The crafts were reorganized, with distinct workshop areas within villages for blacksmiths and potters. The impressed designs typical of earlier pottery almost completely disappear, and instead the display pottery used in feasts has highly burnished graphite coatings. Surprisingly, there is no imported pottery and little evidence of long-distance exchange in the archaeological record. During the succeeding Ambohidray phase of the late 16th and 17th centuries (Wright 2007: 86–88), while there was little change in technology and production, villages proliferated and grew, and by the Early Kaloy phase of the early 18th century, there is a dense packing of larger hierarchically organized settlement clusters, some controlling up to 4000 people, with major centers of up to 6 ha, subsidiary centers, and villages, but few hamlets. The earliest-known gunflint is from a Late Ambohidray archaeological context (Wright 2007: Figure 3.3p), and historical traditions indicate that this was a time of civil war (Callet 1974). However, Berg (1985) argues that guns were rare and served primarily as social valuables until after the emergence and initial expansion of the Merina state. The most recent sediments in Central Highland lake cores are not reliably dated, but travelers' accounts indicate that by the mid-18th century the area was completely deforested, with grassy hills and rice paddies dominating the landscape (Mayeur 1913a, 1913b), much as they do today. During the Late Kaloy phase of the middle and later 18th century, large capitals of 20 ha or more were massively fortified and dominated hierarchies of large centers, small centers, villages, and hamlets (Wright 2007: Figures 5.6 and 7). Linear frontiers of fortified settlements were constructed. The estimated mean settled population in eastern Avarandrano, the core of the emerging Merina state, increased from 4380 in the 17th century to 7930 in the early 18th century to 13,000 in the late 18th century (Dewar 2007). The rate of increase is so rapid that it exceeds ordinary rates of population growth and a politically motivated nucleating of population. Ambohimanga (Figure 5.1d), the capital of the Merina state founder, Andrianampoinimerina (Berg 1988), was so large that it exceeded the maximum estimated rice productivity of its local area, and rice must have been brought as tribute from distant villages (Schwartz 2007). This capital was reconstructed on a massive scale according to a newly elaborated cosmological layout (Kus 2007) with megalithic gates, echoed by smaller gates in other towns and villages of the polity (Gabler 2007). Historical traditions and visitors' accounts tell us that this is the period of formation of the Merina state under the ruler Andrianampoinimerina (Berg 1988; Kus 1989–90), a state that expanded to control most of the highlands by the early 19th century and most of Madagascar—including the territories of the former Betsimisaraka and Sakalava states—by the mid-19th century.

In sum, during the 16th to 18th centuries, the coastal people of Madagascar interacted with Indian Ocean merchants and pirates, receiving guns and display goods in return for cattle and enslaved people. The competition for slaves and cattle led to the formation of unstable militarized polities on the east and west coasts, which raided widely and rarely lasted beyond the lifetime of a single ruler. The continuing degradation of the dry deciduous forests of the west and the grasslands of the Central Highlands is evident in the pollen record. Both eastern and western polities attacked the peoples of the highlands. Called upon to defend themselves against both outside attack and attack from one another, highland rulers experimented with new political forms. Out of this developed the Merina state with its new royal ideology, military organization, administrative structures, and tribute-extracting systems, which enabled it to conquer the highlands and confront European powers, creating relations that would change Madagascar forever.

FUTURE PROSPECTS

Paleoecology and archaeology are still relatively new endeavors on Madagascar, and future work is likely to expand our understanding in surprising ways (see Godfrey and Douglass, pp. 191–97, for further details on this aspect). In the realm of paleoecological research, at present we have only one high-quality study of marshes in the lowland, forested southeast coast, near Mandena (Virah-Sawmy 2009; Virah-Sawmy et al. 2009a, 2009b, 2009c), and few records from the far north and northeast, the southern Central Highlands, the southern plains, and the far south. Even in those areas for which some knowledge is available, we can expect that more reliably dated paleoenvironmental records involving pollen, phytolith, and spore records taphonomically controlled with influx models, as well as stable-isotope records, will radically improve our knowledge of the contexts and consequences of human activity. We can expect other cases of early environmental devastation, such as that demonstrated in the Ampasindava area on the northwest coast in the 13th and 14th centuries, and it will also be interesting to see in which regions there are signs of habitat regeneration, such as that occurring in the same area in the 15th and 16th centuries.

In the realm of archaeological research, basic to any fieldwork focused on human ecology and organization are programs of intensive archaeological survey, in which all habitable land surfaces are examined in an effort to record all human occupational sites. The use of aerial photography in the Central Highlands to locate sites with visible ditches or architecture was developed by Mille (1970); more recently, full-color images from Google Earth have been used. We believe it is possible to locate almost all sedentary sites in this portion of the island occupied between 1100 CE and the present, and that fairly precise estimates of settlement numbers and size can be made, from which population estimates can be derived (Dewar 2007). In other parts of Madagascar that have more vegetation, archaeological sites are often not apparent on such images, and site discovery is dependent on survey teams working on foot. Though incomplete, survey data from forested areas provide information on land use and relative increases and decreases in population. While intensive surveys have been completed and published for the northern and southern coasts, many other areas have had no intensive surveys at all. Principal among these are the east and west coasts, the southern plains, the southern part of the Central Highlands, and the northern interior.

No less crucial than surveying in the realm of archaeological research is the excavation of archaeological sites. Small stratigraphic excavations—introduced by Vérin in the first years of the Musée d'Art et d'Archéologie—have often been integrated with survey projects. They are fundamental to both establishing the dates of artifacts, which allow us to ascribe surveyed sites to chronological periods, and recovery of plant remains and animal bones, which allow preliminary assessments of foraging, agriculture, and herding. Several projects have introduced innovations that will in the future—when widely practiced—answer key questions about social and economic organization and their ecological impacts. Systematic coring and chemical and geophysical sampling of large sites were introduced at Mahilaka during the 1990s in a project of the museum under Chantal Radimilahy (1998), in cooperation with the Urban Origins in Eastern Africa program coordinated by Paul Sinclair and based in Uppsala, Sweden. Large-area excavations that yield evidence of buildings and workshops were first used by David Rasamuel (2007) during the 1980s at the site of Fanongoavana in the Central Highlands. Mike Parker Pearson's excavations of key sites in the far south exemplify the power of this approach (Parker Pearson 2010). Maritime archaeology—the detailed recording of sunken ships and their cargoes—was introduced recently by Michael Tuttle in the Serapis Project (Tuttle et al. 2010) in the harbor of Ile Sainte Marie. Such methods, applied to sunken ships of Madagascar's first great period of maritime trade, from the 11th to 14th centuries CE, will be tremendously informative about trade and cultural contacts. Finally, new developments in archaeobiology promise to answer long-standing questions about human impact on Madagascar's endemic species and the introduction of animals and plants to the island. Since the beginning of the programs of the Musée d'Art et d'Archéologie, Université d'Antananarivo, in the 1960s, archaeological researchers have kept samples of animal bones and plant remains. Water flotation of sediments to recover carbonized seeds was introduced by Wetterstrom and Wright (1992) in 1986. With the Sealinks Project directed by Nicole Boivin, then of Oxford University, amplified flotation of very large samples by Alison Crowther and her team (2016) and ancient DNA studies by Mary Prendergast and colleagues (2017) have begun to answer questions about the introduction of rice, rats, chickens, and other organisms. The sequencing of bulk DNA from archaeological sites has been used to study fishing in lagoons and reefs of the southwest coasts (Douglass et al. 2018).

Such promising new approaches will, however, be very difficult to apply if key landscapes and sites are destroyed. The increasing pace of development around Madagascar's larger cities, especially Antananarivo, is accelerating the destruction of archaeological landscapes and sites. Intensive agriculture and, on the coasts, the development of beaches—often the very beaches that the early Malagasy found so attractive—for hotels and bungalows may take an even greater toll of archaeological sites. Nor are paleoecological sites immune. The exploitation of wetlands, the cutting out of ancient peats for fuel without adequate dating and study, or the use of clays to make bricks, is destroying localities with irreplaceable paleoenvironmental information. The histories of the adaption to many environmental changes by Madagascar's flora and fauna over millions of years and of the Malagasy peoples creating and adapting new cultural responses to crises and opportunities represent wisdoms that should be valued and conserved as guides to future action.

Subject editor: Steven M. Goodman

NEW INSIGHTS INTO THE RELATIONSHIP BETWEEN HUMAN ECOLOGICAL PRESSURE AND THE VERTEBRATE EXTINCTIONS

L. R. Godfrey and K. G. Douglass

Dewar (2003: 119) stated: "Madagascar's native vertebrate community has been substantially reduced over the past several thousand years by the extinction of dozens of species of birds, reptiles, and mammals. Much of the Malagasy countryside is now treeless grassland, often scarred by erosion, and these areas are seen by many observers as the product of a long history of human-driven deforestation" (see also Kull 2000; Pollini 2010). He continued, "In recent times, there is clear evidence of the rapid conversion of many Malagasy forests to fields and pasture" (e.g., Blanc-Pamard 2009; Brinkmann et al. 2014), and then he summarized the critical point: "Since the modern landscape is being transformed by people, it is tempting to suppose that more ancient transformations, such as the vertebrate extinctions, were equally so." However, evidence of drought at around the time of megafaunal collapse (Virah-Sawmy et al. 2010), coupled with a dearth of direct evidence of human interactions with megafauna (Douglass et al. 2018) and limited direct evidence of early large-animal hunting (Goodman and Jungers 2014), has prompted some researchers to warn against assuming a dominant role for humans in triggering Madagascar's faunal extinctions, including those of numerous large-bodied animals. In this contribution and building from Dewar (2003), we review the timing and pattern of human arrival and settlement on Madagascar, the timing of vertebrate extinctions, the island's late Holocene climate history, the nature of human activities that are documented archaeologically, and the likely links between ancient Malagasy communities and extinct animals. Also see Wright and Rakotoarisoa (pp. 181–90) for more details regarding Madagascar's archaeology, particularly evidence for the evolution of settlement, trading, and political systems, and their associated material culture.

THE ARRIVAL AND SETTLEMENT OF PEOPLE ON MADAGASCAR

When Dewar and Wright (1993) wrote their review of the prehistory of Madagascar, there was little evidence of human settlement prior to the end of the first millennium CE. An Indian Ocean trade network, stretching from eastern Africa to Indonesia, was known to have existed for over 2000 years, but Madagascar was not fully integrated into this extensive trading sphere until well into the second part of the first millennium CE (Radimilahy and Crossland 2015). There were traces of earlier human activity in a rock shelter called Lakaton'i Anja, near Antsiranana in the far north (Dewar and Wright 1993). These dated to the 5th century CE. However, there was no evidence of settlement pre-dating the arrival of iron-tool using agriculturalists on the island and no evidence of preagricultural hunting of large animals.

Archaeological exploration had yielded evidence of small hamlets and small agricultural villages in northern Madagascar beginning around 800 CE (roughly coeval with the earliest occupation of the Comoro islands at ~750 CE; Vérin and Chanudet 1996). These communities had iron tools (evidenced by iron slag) and carved chlorite-schist vessels (Wright and Fanony 1992). The middens of these early northern sites revealed communities supported by agropastoralism. By the end of the first millennium CE, the major Islamic trading post of Mahilaka had emerged in northern Madagascar, with artifacts imported from China and the Persian Gulf (Radimilahy 1998). Roughly simultaneously, small hamlets and villages appeared in the south; beginning in the 12th century CE, southern Madagascar had its own large settlement, Andranosoa near Tolagnaro (Dewar and Wright 1993; Parker Pearson 2010).

It was not long thereafter that archaeologists' understanding of early settlement of the island changed substantially. Both indirect and direct evidence challenged the hypothesis that humans first colonized Madagascar no earlier than a few centuries before the end of the first millennium CE (Douglass and Zinke 2015). Indirect evidence of earlier human arrival came from a variety of fields, including the study of lake sediment cores. Burney et al. (2003, 2004) attributed precipitous declines in the incidence of spores in lake sediment deposits of the dung fungus *Sporormiella* to the activities of humans. Because this fungus can complete its life cycle only on the dung of large herbivores, its spores can be used as proxies for large mammal biomass (Raper and Bush 2009). Burney et al. (2003) noted a pattern observed at multiple sites during the first half of the first millennium CE, well before any evidence for the introduction of domesticated herbivores like cattle: a sharp drop in *Sporormiella* spores preceded a spike in charcoal microparticles, the latter a proxy for fire. These authors interpreted this sequence as evidence of: 1) the decimation of endemic terrestrial large-bodied herbivore populations through hunting, followed by 2) an increase in the frequency and intensity of fire as a consequence of the near elimination of animals that would normally regulate the growth of grasses and terrestrial herbaceous vegetation, thereby limiting the intensity of natural fire. Burney et al. (2003, 2004) explicitly rejected the notion that the early settlers wiped out terrestrial large-bodied fauna via wholesale hunting, but they did see the fall of *Sporormiella* spores in sediment cores as indirect evidence of faunal exploitation resulting in local declines in the population density of terrestrial large-bodied herbivores.

Lake sediment cores also provided palynological evidence of early human settlement. The presence of pollen of introduced marijuana or hemp (*Cannabis sativa*, Cannabaceae) at Lake Tritrivakely in the Central Highlands at 2200 cal BP (calibrated years before present) seemed compelling (Gasse and Van Campo 1998). However, dates for most other plant introductions affirmed association with the expanded Indian Ocean trade network close to the end of the first millennium CE (e.g., Kull et al. 2011; Crowther et al. 2016; Beaujard 2017).

The presence of domesticated vertebrates or other introduced animals is also an important signal of human presence. Approaches for estimating the time of these introductions include genetic data (e.g., Sauther et al. 2020) and dated subfossil or archaeological records (Douglass et al. 2019; Hixon et al. 2021). With only a few exceptions, most vertebrates assumed to have been introduced by humans appear to have arrived late, starting in the second millennium CE, again with the expansion of the Indian Ocean trade network and the introduction of pastoralism (Godfrey et al. 2019). The most important exception is *Numida meleagris* (Helmeted Guineafowl); wild populations of this species are widely distributed and domestic forms are not uncommon in villages across the island. Radiocarbon dates of >13,000 cal BP at the subfossil site at Ankilitelo (northeast of Toliara) suggested to Goodman et al. (2013) that this species may not have been introduced by humans after all. Of course, if it was, then these dates signal very early human presence on the island (see Safford et al., pp. 1553–602, for further discussion of this point).

More direct evidence of early human arrival and large faunal exploitation by humans includes perimortem butchering traces on ancient animal bones. MacPhee and Burney (1991) described early first-millennium CE butchery of hippopotamuses (*Hippopotamus* sp.) at Lamboharana and Ambolisatra, two archaeological sites on the southwest coast. Perez et al. (2005) described slightly earlier butchery of the giant lemur *Palaeopropithecus* at Taolambiby in the southwest. Gommery et al. (2011) reported butchery traces on hippopotamus bones from Anjohibe in the northwest indirectly dating to ~4000 years ago, and Hansford et al. (2018, 2020) described even earlier butchering of elephant birds (*Aepyornis* sp.) at Lamboharana (>6000 years ago) and Christmas River, the latter in the south-central portion of the island (>10,000 years ago). The incidence of butchering marks (chops and cut marks) on large animal bones is very low prior to the first millennium CE and even during the first half of the first millennium CE. However, it increases dramatically after ~1200 cal BP (Godfrey et al. 2019; L. R. Godfrey et al., unpublished data) (Figure 5.2).

FIGURE 5.2 **Proximal end of femur of an extinct lemur, *Pachylemur insignis* (UA 3037), from a paleontological site (Tsirave) in south-central Madagascar. This specimen shows chop (black arrow) and cut (white arrow) marks on the femoral head, indicative of disarticulation of the hind limb at the hip joint, as is commonly seen when wild-caught primates are butchered today. Dated butchered specimens of *Pachylemur* from Tsirave are all younger than 1200 cal BP. Scale bar: 0.5 cm.** (PHOTO by V. Pérez.)

Stone tools are now known to have existed at human occupation sites. Rasolondrainy (2012) reported undated stone artifacts at Ampasimaiky Cave in the Isalo region of south-central Madagascar. Dewar et al. (2013) found stone blades and projectile tools at two rock shelters, Ambohiposa (near Vohémar in the northeast), and Lakaton'i Anja. The earliest cultural layers at both Ambohiposa and Lakaton'i Anja were dated to >4000 BP. These older layers did not yield evidence of large-animal exploitation, but several specimens of the giant extinct lemur *Palaeopropithecus maximus* (Palaeopropithecidae; see Godfrey and Jungers, pp. 1824–28), dating to between 1545 and 1305 cal BP, were found in cultural context at Lakaton'i Anja (Douglass et al. 2019).

Cave art at two sites, the first in the Isalo region in the central south and the second on the Beanka Massif in the central west, provided intriguing additional evidence of possible early human arrival (Rasolondrainy 2012; Burney et al. 2020a). At Ampasimaiky Cave (Isalo, where stone tools were also found), a vertical Libyco-Berber-like script occurs alongside seminaturalistic drawings of people and domesticated and perhaps wild animals, as well as amorphous and geometric shapes (Figure 5.3). Libyco-Berber scripts date to between 500 BCE and 800 CE in northern Africa (Rasolondrainy 2012). Hundreds of similar paintings adorn the walls of the canyons of the Makay, to the north of the Isalo Massif (Naturevolution 2020), although no vertical script has been reported there. Seminaturalistic paintings of humped cattle exist at both Ampasimaiky and Makay, suggesting that these bovids had been introduced into south-central Madagascar by the time these paintings were created. Radiocarbon dates for cattle in south-central and southwestern Madagascar prove that they were present in the region over the past millennium (Parker Pearson 2010; Douglass et al. 2018; Hixon et al. 2021).

Cave art found in Andriamamelo Cave at Beanka is stylistically distinct from that at Isalo and may be older (Burney et al. 2020a). There are no depictions here of humped cattle, but there are possible images of large-bodied animals, including those of extinct species such as an elephant bird (Aepyornithidae; see Safford et al., pp. 1553–602) and a slaughtered sloth lemur (family Palaeopropithecidae; see Godfrey and Jungers, pp. 1824–28), the latter in a frame

FIGURE 5.3 **Rock painting panel at Ampasimaiky rock shelter at Isalo, southwestern Madagascar, displaying schematic, geometric, or amorphous figures, depictions of cattle, and a possible inscription.** (PHOTO by T. Rasolondrainy.)

FIGURE 5.4 **Archaeological surface scatter comprising *toko* (cooking/hearth stones), marine shell, and coral fragments in the Velondriake Marine Protected Area, southwestern Madagascar.** (PHOTO by K. Douglass.)

interpreted as a hunting scene with dogs. Bones of extinct animals including sloth lemurs, some with butchery marks, occur at other caves at Beanka (Burney et al. 2020b). The time of arrival of dogs on Madagascar is unknown (Ardalan et al. 2015). Burney et al. (2020a) document possible ties for the paintings at Andriamamelo to rock art in ancient Egypt, Ethiopia, and Borneo around 2000 years ago.

Building on ground-based archaeological survey (Douglass 2016), Davis et al. (2020) used satellite-based remote sensing within the Velondriake Marine Protected Area in the southwest to further explore the extent of ancient human occupation in the region. They confirmed the presence of human occupation sites in high density, particularly in locations near important resources, like fresh water and coral reefs, and they concluded that some might be thousands of years old. Recent archaeological excavations in this region have verified the presence of coastal fishers and foragers during the early part of the first millennium CE, and potentially earlier (Douglass et al. 2018) (Figure 5.4). Modern human genetic data also support an initial arrival of at least 2000 BP; they also confirm arrival in separate waves by people from southern Africa and Southeast Asia (Pierron et al. 2017). The absence of genetic evidence of yet earlier populations originating elsewhere may mean that such earlier populations were small and disappeared prior to the arrival of the ancestors of modern Malagasy people from southern Africa and Southeast Asia. Finally, Douglass et al. (2019) employed statistical methods for estimating the timing of events such as human arrival to analyze all of Madagascar's known archaeological radiocarbon dates. They concluded with a high degree of confidence that human settlement on the island likely occurred by 2000 BP, and perhaps earlier.

Despite the above indicators of early human arrival, some scholars argue that people did not settle Madagascar until near the end of the first millennium CE (e.g., A. Anderson et al. 2018; Mitchell 2019, 2020). Indeed, debate on the timing of Madagascar's initial settlement is more intense today than ever before, and more field research is clearly warranted. At issue are the accuracy of the occupation dates at archaeological sites, the reliability of optically stimulated luminescence (OSL) versus carbon-14 dates, the effects of bioturbation on the stratigraphic integrity of dates, the accuracy of early butchery dates, whether apparent butchery traces on large animal bones are actually perimortem, and why there is scant evidence of faunal butchering of large-bodied animals in cultural context.

TIMING OF LARGE-ANIMAL EXTINCTIONS

Several tools have been used in recent years to reconstruct the trajectories of large-animal population collapse and to estimate species extinction dates. Crowley (2010) examined dates of last occurrence to estimate extinction dates for some of these animals in different ecoregions. Godfrey et al. (2019) and Faina et al. (2021) examined temporal changes in the ratios of extinct to extant species at subfossil sites. This statistical analysis is not designed to estimate species extinction dates but rather to describe changes in the pace of native large-animal decline and to reconstruct the timing of population crashes. Godfrey et al. (2019) found that megafauna began to decline rapidly at around 1250 BP (700 CE). Specimens dated as older than 1100 BP (850 CE) were more likely to be extinct than extant; after that point, the opposite was true. The collapse of large-bodied animal populations was virtually complete by ~1050 BP (900 CE), although some species survived in small pockets, sometimes for centuries, thereafter. Using an expanded carbon-14-dated subfossil database, Faina et al. (2021) found a similar interval of faunal collapse (between 1200 and 1000 cal BP) but with a peak around 100 years earlier in the southwest than in the northwest.

J. Hansford et al. (unpublished data) used radiometric date distributions to calculate confidence intervals for extinction of large-bodied species in particular regions; their conclusions are broadly similar to those of Godfrey et al. (2019) and Faina et al. (2021). Hixon et al. (2021) tackle the question of animal extinction by using dietary reconstruction of endemic and introduced domesticates (e.g., cattle, sheep, goats), in order to test whether endemic faunal population decline is linked to competition with introduced taxa. Of course, the success of any of these techniques in reconstructing extinction trajectories depends on sampling intensity. Some extinct species have been well sampled but most have not, and for the latter, extinction estimates are not very meaningful at the species and genus levels.

Nevertheless, we can be confident that most if not all Holocene faunal extinctions on Madagascar occurred after 1300 years ago—that is, after the expansion of the Indian Ocean trade network (Radimilahy and Crossland 2015). *All* genera represented by a minimum of five radiocarbon-dated specimens have at least one specimen dating to younger than 1300 cal BP (B. E. Crowley and L. R. Godfrey, unpublished data). This includes giant lemurs (*Archaeolemur, Megaladapis, Palaeopropithecus, Pachylemur, Babakotia*), elephant birds (*Aepyornis, Mullerornis*), and *Hippopotamus*. Even some taxa with fewer than five dated specimens have at least one sampled individual younger than 1300 cal BP. These include extinct giant lemurs *Daubentonia robusta* and *Mesopropithecus*, giant tortoises of the genus *Aldabrachelys*, and shelducks of the genus *Alopochen*.

A final intriguing piece of the fauna extinction puzzle is the many historical and contemporary stories and recorded sightings of species that may have gone extinct only within the past few centuries (Flacourt 1658 [repr. 1995]; Godfrey 1986; Burney and Ramilisonina 1998; Vasey and Godfrey, forthcoming). This suggests that there was a prolonged period of overlap between people and organisms that would subsequently go extinct, and that for some species at least, population decline preceded extinction by a half millennium or more.

LATE HOLOCENE CLIMATE HISTORY OF MADAGASCAR

Our understanding of Madagascar's paleoclimate has improved dramatically since about the start of the 21st century, particularly (but not exclusively) through the advances in the study of the stable isotopes preserved in cave calcium carbonate formations (stalagmites); stable oxygen and carbon isotope values can serve as proxies for rainfall and vegetation cover, respectively. It is through stalagmite research that we now know that the mean temperature in southwestern Madagascar during the Last Glacial Maximum

(LGM; ~21,000 years ago) was ~10°C colder than it is today and that, again during the LGM, rainfall amount was even more variable than it is today (Scroxton et al. 2019; Dawson et al. 2020). Stable nitrogen isotope values from fossils have also been used to reconstruct habitat moisture (Tovondrafale et al. 2014; Crowley et al. 2017; Hixon et al. 2018). Tovondrafale et al. (2014) sampled protein nitrogen isotopes in elephant bird eggshells taken from carbon-14-dated older and younger dunes at Faux Cap in the far south to assess long-term changes in habitat moisture. They showed that just over 1000 years ago, when the younger dunes accumulated, this region was significantly drier than it had been over 30,000 years ago, when the older dunes accumulated.

We now have high-resolution records, particularly for the northwest but also for the southwest, of late Holocene fluctuations in rainfall and how (and whether) they correlate with variation in vegetation cover (Burns et al. 2016; Scroxton et al. 2017; Voarintsoa et al. 2017; Wang et al. 2019; Railsback et al. 2020; Faina et al. 2021). Stable isotopes in stalagmites can help us to understand whether habitat transformations were likely triggered by changes in rainfall or by something else, such as human activities. Holocene climate data from central Madagascar (where there are no calcareous stalagmites) are less precise than those from northwestern and southwestern Madagascar, as they are taken from sediment cores with less chronological precision, but they are nevertheless important and, indeed, can potentially fill in information regarding periods that were too dry for stalagmites to grow.

For the northwest (at Anjohibe and neighboring caves, near Mahajanga), major habitat transformation at around the time of faunal collapse was entirely uncorrelated with change in rainfall amount. A centennial-scale pattern of hydroclimate fluctuation in the northwest was identified by Scroxton et al. (2017) and Voarintsoa et al. (2017). Over the past 2000 years, there have been alternating wet and dry intervals, each approximately 500 years long. Essentially, the first half of the first millennium CE was dry, the second wet, the first half of the second millennium dry, and the second half wet until a little over a century ago. There was a major vegetation transformation from a wooded landscape dominated by C_3 vegetation to an open landscape dominated by C_4 grasses (for further explanation see Lehmann et al., pp. 152–68). This transformation was rapid, at least at its start, which occurred ~1100 years ago. The transformation began during a wet interval and continued into a dry interval (Burns et al. 2016; Voarintsoa et al. 2017; Godfrey et al. 2019; Wang et al. 2019; Railsback et al. 2020). It was likely caused by a change in human activity, rather than a shift in climate, given the coincidence of this transformation with growing urbanism at sites linked to the expanding Swahili trade network (Radimilahy 1998). With it came wholesale changes in the mammal faunal community, with an influx of introduced animals consuming more C_4 foods, as was confirmed by stable carbon isotope values of subfossil bones buried in the Anjohibe Cave deposits before and after the habitat transformation (Crowley and Samonds 2013).

Changes in the hydroclimate of the Central Highlands have been documented mainly from the pollen and diatom records of a sediment core taken from Lake Tritrivakely (Gasse and Van Campo 1998). The core reveals a mid-Holocene dry period (~4000 years ago) followed by a warmer, wetter period with riparian forest. Through much of the Holocene, forests were supported at mid-elevation sites in areas that are now almost completely deforested (Samonds et al. 2019). A sharp increase in grasses occurred at ~700 cal BP (Gasse and Van Campo 1998). As in the northwest, this change was likely anthropogenic. Stable nitrogen isotope values for subfossils themselves show no evidence in central Madagascar that drought triggered the regional disappearance of endemic fauna (Crowley et al. 2017).

The coastal region of southwest Madagascar is the only place where there is strong evidence of drought having devastating effects on some animal populations. Stable nitrogen isotope values at the subfossil site of Ambolisatra (Andolonomby, north of Toliara) show progressive aridification of the coastal habitat occupied by large animals beginning less than ~3000 and extending to ~1000 years ago (Crowley et al. 2017). Stalagmite records at Asafora Cave (near the Fagnemotsy estuary) confirm gradual and relatively minor drying prior to the middle of the first millennium CE but also document the onset of severe drought at ~1560 cal BP (Faina et al. 2021). This drought lasted ~700 years, encompassing the period of most rapid faunal collapse in the southwest. It may have accelerated regional faunal crash, which occurred earlier here than in the northwest.

These aridification records are consistent with hydrological data from Lake Ihotry, 40 km northeast of Fagnemotsy (Vallet-Coulomb et al. 2006), and a pollen profile from a sediment core at Ambolisatra (Virah-Sawmy et al. 2016). These sources document simultaneous changes in vegetation (including the sudden loss of trees) at Ambolisatra and the transformation of Lake Ihotry from a large, freshwater lake into a smaller, hypersaline lake. Another lake that underwent salinization was Lake Tsimanampesotse, south of Toliara. The chronology of salinization at Lake Tsimanampesotse is unknown, but the loss of aquatic and semiaquatic vertebrates here is well known (Goodman and Jungers 2014). Some of these are known to have survived to the end of the first millennium CE in the general region (Goodman and Rakotozafy 1997; Faina et al. 2021; Rasolonjatovo et al. 2021).

Interestingly, even in the southwest, sites that are far from the coast such as Taolambiby and Tsirave show no evidence of aridification during the drought experienced on or closer to the coast (Crowley et al. 2017; Hixon et al. 2018). Sites like these, bordering rivers or streams, may have provided refuge for large fauna at that time. The most recent radiocarbon dates for any extinct fauna (~500 cal BP) are for several species of giant lemurs found at Ankilitelo, another inland southwestern site (Muldoon et al. 2009). The drought surely impacted the regional flora and fauna (perhaps over a long stretch of southwestern coastline), but human impacts, perhaps during and certainly after the drought, were likely equally important, as there is evidence of an expansion of pastoralist populations into the southwest after the drought ended (Yount et al. 2001; Hixon et al. 2021).

HUMAN ACTIVITIES OF ENVIRONMENTAL IMPORTANCE

The biological invasion hypothesis (Dewar 1984, 1997) proposed that the introduction of agropastoralism was paramount among human activities that negatively impacted large-bodied fauna and that transformed the environments of Madagascar (Figure 5.5). It was not just that introduced domesticated animals competed directly for resources with endemic terrestrial herbivores (e.g., possibly, pygmy hippopotamuses, giant tortoises, the more terrestrial giant lemurs, elephant birds) but that a suite of human activities associated with the introduction of agropastoralism negatively impacted large endemic herbivores. Dewar (2003: 122) noted, "The introduction of domestic stock has had great environmental impact in many areas of the world, often converting native forests to grasslands" (see also Atkinson 1987; Hofman and Rick 2017). Introduced ungulates can cause direct changes to plant communities adapted to fire-regime regulation by endemic herbivores and to a low incidence of natural fire. Madagascar's floral communities, adapted through millions of years of coevolution to consumption by Madagascar's endemic terrestrial herbivores, would not have been well equipped to handle the rapid introduction of domesticates, such as cattle, sheep, and goats, and the ensuing replacement of endemic herbivores.

Associated human activities of ecological importance would include setting deliberate fires to promote agriculture near settlements or animal husbandry further from settlements. Trees would have been cut for timber or the production of charcoal, the latter essential for smelting iron. Wherever there was strong archaeological evidence of iron smelting, there was also evidence of the progressive elimination of local forests (Burney 1999).

As succinctly summarized by Dewar (2003: 122):

> Grassland fires in Madagascar today can spread over hundreds of square kilometers, and they are frequently some distance from habitations. Once cattle herds became an important part of Malagasy economies, it is possible that some large areas of vegetation, relatively distant from villages, were subjected to intentional fires. In contrast, the clearance of forests for fields was unlikely to have occurred at great distance from settlements. ... Even today grassland wildfires are set by herders, either to stimulate regrowth during the dry season or to eliminate unpalatable herbaceous species. Even though fire had been a part of the Malagasy environment for thousands of years before human arrival (Burney 1997[a]), changes in the frequency or seasonality of fires may have dramatically altered the plant cover of regions being exploited by pastoralists.

CONCLUSIONS

Understanding Human Ecological Pressure on Faunal Communities

The first decades of the 21st century have seen a tremendous increase in our knowledge of early human settlements on Madagascar, of when the large-animal fauna declined, and of temporal and spatial changes in regional climate. There remain many open questions, but several conclusions can be drawn with confidence.

First, stone tools are indeed part of the archaeological record of Madagascar. There is evidence of cultures unrelated to modern Malagasy people. Whereas there continues to be no sign in the archaeological record of systematic, preagricultural large-animal hunting, there is evidence that early fishers, foragers, and hunters were present, likely in small numbers, prior to the introduction of agropastoralism. However, it was only with the expansion of the Indian Ocean trade network and the arrival of many cultivated plants and domesticated animals that pastoralism and associated human activities (including land modification and, most likely, an intensification of wild-animal hunting with growing human populations) combined to threaten the endemic fauna. A period of prolonged drought did occur in southwest Madagascar, resulting in local faunal and floral species declines, local extirpations, and possible extinctions, but the drought was not island-wide, and drought cannot be considered the main trigger for island-wide extinction. Drought may have accelerated the decline of certain organisms in the southwest, as the peak for large-animal faunal collapse appears to have occurred earlier in the drought-stricken southwest than the northwest.

FIGURE 5.5 **Zebu bull at the coastal archaeological site of Antsokobory, Velondriake Marine Protected Area, southwestern Madagascar, where remains of early foraging and fishing communities were recovered.** (PHOTO by K. Douglass.)

The debate regarding the duration of coexistence of humans and large native animals prior to the collapse of populations of the latter is relevant to the faunal extinction debate in only one way: the longer the period of overlap, the longer the period of coexistence with little or no impact on these animals. Whenever humans first arrived, it is becoming increasingly clear that the early fishers, foragers, and indeed hunters had little impact on them.

So much of what we understood to be true even two decades ago has been shown to be wrong or, at best, incomplete. Yet Dewar's (1984, 1997) fundamental insight that cattle and other domesticated animals may have been catalysts for biotic devastation may prove to be correct. Madagascar's archaeological record suggests that human activities varied temporally and regionally, and that impacts on endemic fauna were minimal before, and far greater after, the arrival of farming and pastoralism around 1000 years ago. Neither the marked changes in temperature nor the variation in rainfall that Madagascar experienced from the late Pleistocene through most of the Holocene resulted in faunal extinction. Surely there were climate fluctuations in the past that affected animal dispersal routes and caused populations to abandon particular locations in the course of tracking preferred habitats. Madagascar was always a large island, with a wide diversity of available environments. However, the arrival of pastoralism appears to have been far more lethal to larger-bodied species in all parts of Madagascar than were the earlier fluctuations in climate, or earlier human activities.

ACKNOWLEDGMENTS

In the previous version of this book, our late colleague Robert E. Dewar wrote the precursor text that was transformed into the current contribution. We are certain that our substantial revisions to the 2003 contribution would have delighted Bob, as they reflect the diligent work of many colleagues in recent years to address the fascinating, and often mystifying, questions regarding Madagascar's human past. We are honored to have had the opportunity to author this revised contribution and thank Bob for making it possible to "stand on his shoulders" as we forge ahead.

Subject editors: Steven M. Goodman and William L. Jungers

FIRE IN HIGHLAND GRASSLANDS: USES, ECOLOGY, AND HISTORY

C. A. Kull and C. E. R. Lehmann

Each year fires burn across around one-half of the grasslands that cover most of Madagascar's Central Highlands, particularly in open, less densely settled areas. Before humans arrived on the island (see Wright and Rakotoarisoa, pp. 181–90), lightning fires helped shape the temporal and spatial mosaic of highland vegetation. Since settlement, the Malagasy have harnessed fire for diverse resource-management goals while altering vegetation communities and biogeochemical processes (Figure 5.6). Due to the environmental consequences of fire, administrators sought to suppress fires throughout the 20th and 21st centuries. Government policies were contentious with rural communities and have seen little success in these inherently flammable landscapes (Kull 2004).

Here, we provide an overview of current understanding on fire in the Central Highlands, motivations for human use of fire, and the consequences of fire for the vegetation and broader ecological dynamics of the region, alongside how fire management has changed over time. The research presented is based on a synthesis of several sources: an ethnographic, archival, and socio-ecological research project conducted in the late 1990s (Kull 2004), updated via continued field visits and personal communication, combined with more recent ecological and remote-sensing research that brings expertise in African and Australian fire ecology to Madagascar (e.g., Lehmann et al. 2011, 2014; Lehmann and Parr 2016). We restrict our attention to fire in grass-dominated ecosystems, which include pure grasslands as well as "savanna woodlands" with their grassy ground layer, such as those dominated by *Uapaca bojeri* (Solofondranohatra et al. 2018). For the purposes of this contribution, the Central Highlands are defined as the zone west of the lowland moist evergreen forest escarpment consistently above 800 m. This zone forms a rough triangle from Andringitra in the south to the Bongolava chain in the northwest and across the Tampoketsa d'Ankazobe to the Anjafy Plateau northeast of the capital.

USES: TYPES AND PATTERNS OF FIRE

The vast majority of today's fires are lit by humans for specific resource-management goals, as in tropical grasslands worldwide (Laris 2002; Archibald 2016; Fowler and Welch 2018). However, not all fires are anthropogenic. Lightning, which is prevalent across the Central Highlands, doubtless caused fires before human arrival (Burney 1987b; Bovalo et al. 2012). Today, lightning fires represent a small fraction of burned areas and ignitions, largely because of preemptive anthropogenic burning (Bloesch 1999; Archibald et al. 2013).

Malagasy farmers and herders use fire for a wide variety of goals (Table 5.1). The dominant use of fire in highland Madagascar is in

FIGURE 5.6 **Different facets of fire in the Central Highlands. A) Peri-urban fire in a grazing pasture dense with invasive *Acacia dealbata*, *Lantana camara*, and other bushes in Central Highlands, near Ambositra, October 2018; B) fire-scar mosaic in grassland near riparian forest in western Central Highlands in Bongolava range, west of Tsiroanomandidy, July 1996; C) active grassland fire close to eucalyptus woodlots near Ambositra, June 1999; D) monitoring nighttime fire at village outskirts in western Central Highlands near Tsiroanomandidy, July 1994; E) fighting fire to protect homes and fields near Antsirabe, September 1998; and F) early season grass fire in tapia woodlands near Antsirabe, April 1998.** (PHOTOS by C. Kull.)

pasture management, to provide fresh, green, nutritious forage for cattle, as grasses rapidly regrow after fire, and to control tree and shrub encroachment in grasslands used for pasture (Andriamampionona 1992; Kull 2004; Klein et al. 2007). While near-village sites with concentrated heavy grazing and sufficient moisture support "grazing lawns" of high-quality forage that rarely burn, over the much wider grasslands fire produces green pick (early growth) for the cattle (Hempson et al. 2019; Solofondranohatra et al. 2020). Pasture and grassland fires make up 95–99% of all fires in terms of surface area burned in the Central Highlands (Kull 2004). These fires begin in western zones of the highlands in May, peak in August, and continue into November (Randriambelo et al. 1998; Alvarado et al. 2018). In extensive range management, with low stocking rates, large area, and low capital and labor inputs, fire is the most efficient way to sustainably manage pasture quality and availability, as is the case across the tropics.

Grassland fires serve two roles for pasture management (see Table 5.2 for a summary of main grass species; also see Lehmann et al., pp. 152–68 for a description of key grassland types across Madagascar). First, repeated fires maintain grass dominance, retarding woody-plant encroachment. Without periodic burning, highland pastures are rapidly invaded by shrub species such as *Sarcobotrya strigosa*, *Erica* spp., *Helichrysum* spp., or introduced *Acacia dealbata* (Cori and Trama 1979; J. Koechlin 1993; Bloesch et al. 2002) that do not provide forage to obligate grazers—namely, cattle. In eastern and southeastern Africa, woody-plant encroachment is recognized as a serious form of land degradation (Archer et al. 2017), reducing and altering ecosystem services (Lehmann and Parr 2016).

Second, fire renews grassland vegetation by removing the previous year's growth, thereby alleviating growth constraints due to self-shading (Linder et al. 2018). Flammable grasses senesce during the dry season, and with high carbon-to-nitrogen ratios in leaf

TABLE 5.1. **The purposeful uses of vegetation fire in Central Highlands of Madagascar (note that often one fire accomplishes several purposes)**

SECTOR	PURPOSE	SPECIFIC TASK OR USE
Cattle raising	Maintaining pasture	To fight bush encroachment For pasture renewal (green shoots)
	Pest control	To control tick populations
	Cattle control	To facilitate observation and mobility To collect free-ranging cattle
Agriculture	Field preparation	To clear brush for plowing/spade work To fertilize fields
	Downhill transfers	To encourage erosion to fertilize downstream fields To encourage runoff to speed up irrigation
	Cleaning	To clean out irrigation canals To remove pest habitat around fields (rats, birds)
Other	Wildfire prevention and control	Early burns for fuel management Burning firebreaks Back fires against wildfires
	Pest control	To ward off and/or collect locusts To control rats, ticks, mosquitoes
	Tapia woodland management	To maintain dominance of *Uapaca bojeri* To control silkworm parasites
	Woodlots and wood fuel	To encourage pine regeneration To create dead branches for wood fuel collection
	Travel	To clear trails and roadsides To light the way in the dark
	Ground clearance	To see mineral outcrops To see wild tuber crops
	Grass-species management	To encourage *Aristida rufescens*, used for brooms and roofing
	Celebration/spectacle	For natural firecrackers and entertainment
	Protest/revenge	Symbolic protest, arson

material they are poor in nutrition for cattle. At this time, the grasslands are inherently flammable landscapes with contiguous low-density fuel layers. Pasture renewal is critical to cattle health, for the protein-rich resprouts—even of poor-forage-quality native grass species such as *Aristida rufescens*—can carry the cattle through the end of the dry season when they no longer have access to crop stubble or rice straw as farmers prepare fields for planting and irrigation.

The Malagasy burn grasslands opportunistically in a spatial and temporal rotation (Kull 2004). Fires burn different areas in succession—filling in gaps as time goes on, covering 0.5 ha to over 100 ha per fire and much more in unpopulated areas—over the course of a year. The resulting patchy grassland includes unburned zones (also used for the collection of roofing thatch) and multiple zones with grasses in various stages of development. This patchiness serves to ensure resprouts over successive months and as a built-in protection against larger and uncontrolled running wildfires (Laris 2002; Kull 2004; Price et al. 2012). Essentially, people act to preempt the late-season fires that in a lightning-based fire regime would be associated with heavier fuels (more vegetation buildup), thus elongating the fire season forward in time. Increasing population densities in landscapes reduce the average fire size, although in these areas there may be more, if smaller and less intense, fires (Archibald et al. 2013).

As well as the larger grassland fires, farmers set numerous small-scale fires for crop-field preparation, burning the standing vegetation in the grassland or fallow plots they intend to cultivate, including encroached woody plants. Such burns can take place throughout the season and range from 0.01 to 0.2 ha in size. In some cases, farmers collect additional fuel to burn, such as rice stalks or cut grasses, particularly in fields destined to be flooded as rice nurseries. Other types of agricultural fires include burning of the catchment basin above rice paddies, to encourage the erosion of important nutrients or soil particles into the paddies, and burning to clean irrigation canals and field edges (Kull 2004).

TABLE 5.2. **Important Central Highlands grass species (Poaceae)**

GENUS AND SPECIES	LOCAL NAMES	COMMENTS
Aristida rufescens	*Horona* (SV, NV), *horombohitra* (T), *kofafa vavy* (A, N), *horombavy*, *pepeka*	Widespread, extremely fire tolerant, perennial; used to make grass roofs and brooms; little nutritious value when mature
A. similis	*Horombavy*, *kofafavavy*, *ahitsorohitra madinika* (SV)	Extremely fire tolerant, perennial, hygrophile; poor forage quality when mature but palatable as regrowth
*A. congesta**	*Kofafalahy* (N)	Smaller plant found in cooler, higher areas; not palatable
*Ctenium concinnum**	*Ahitsorohitra* (SV)	Perennial; mediocre forage; found in repeat-burned short-grass grasslands >900 m, associated with *Aristida* and *Loudetia*
*Cynodon dactylon**	*Kindresy* (N), *fandrotrarana* (SV), Bermuda grass	Good forage; found near villages and on cool, high pastures in grazing lawns; not tolerant to fire
*Heteropogon contortus**	*Danga* (SV, T), *ahidambo* (N), *lefondambo*, *ahimoso*	Perennial, moderately tolerant of both fire and grazing; common <1300 m in association with *Hyparrhenia rufa*; good forage when young
*Hyparrhenia rufa**	*Vero*, *verofotsy*, *veromena*, *fataka*	Perennial, less tolerant of fire; good forage (especially in association with *Heteropogon contortus*); commonly found along waterways
*H. cymbaria**	*Verobe*, *verotsanjy*, *vero*, *verovato*	Large perennial, intolerant of fire; found on good deep soils at forest edges
*Imperata cylindrica**	*Tenina* (SV), *manevika*, *fehena*, *antsoro* (NV)	Perennial, rhizomatous; found <2000 m in dry, well-drained spots, not on eroded soils, can be associated with tree cover at forest edges
Lasiorhachis viguieri	*Haravola* (SV, NV)	Used to make straw mats, baskets; cattle eat new shoots only; in higher locations remains green through winter
Loudetia simplex (var. *stipoides*)*	*Horona* (A), *horo* (N), *berambo*, *kilailay*, *kirodrotra*, *felika* (SV)	Perennial, quite fire resistant; widespread across Africa and Madagascar; poor pastoral value, found on leached, poorly drained soils
Panicum maximum (= *Urochloa maxima*)*	*Verotsanga* (T)	Large perennial bunch grass, decent forage; known as "Guinea grass"
Paspalum spp.*	*Gebona*, *gebo* (N)	High pastoral value, especially from March to May
Pennisetum pseudotriticoides	*Horompotsy* (NV), *tohiambazaha*	Endemic, 1000–2000 m, found on humid, cool, silty or sandy alluvions

Sources: Ratsimamanga (1968), Bosser (1969), Gade (1996), Bloesch (1997), and Kull (2004); see also Lehmann et al. (p. 152–68).
Note: Pantropical species are noted with an asterisk (*). Regional variations on local names are indicated as follows: SV, southern Vakinankaratra (Antsirabe); NV, northern Vakinankaratra (Ambatolampy); T, Tsiroanomandidy; A, Ambositra; N, Ambalavao–Andringitra.

Fires control a wide variety of pests harmful to crops, livestock, and humans. Small cleaning fires around crop fields and residences help reduce rat populations (see Ramasindrazana et al., pp. 1872–80) and destroy the brush in which rice-thieving birds such as *Foudia madagascariensis* (see Craig, pp. 1716–18) perch between raids. Fires help control cattle ticks, mosquitoes, and other insects. Vast areas are burned during locust invasions, when fires serve both to ward off locust swarms in flight and to facilitate the collection of resting locusts (Kull 2004). Of interest also, despite being outside the Central Highlands, is the fact that villagers burn wetland marshes of the Lake Alaotra region in the dry season in order to dig up the introduced fish *Channa maculata* (Copsey et al. 2009).

Another use of fire is to fight uncontrolled fire. Some fires are accidentally ignited, resulting from dropped cigarettes, campfires, or charcoal ovens, or were intentionally lit but burn more than expected. To avoid associated damage, low-intensity fires that are easily controlled can reduce fuel loads later in the season. Controlled fires around houses and private woodlots serve as firebreaks. The rotation of burns through the dry season establishes patchy, informal firebreaks that facilitate landscape-level control of more-dangerous late-dry-season fires. Finally, villagers ignite backfires to fight active wildfires (Kull 2004).

In highland tapia "savanna woodlands," villagers promote the dominance of pyrophytic *Uapaca bojeri* (see Kull and Birkinshaw, pp. 121–27), a fruit- and silkworm-bearing tree, through use of fire (Figure 5.6d). Although individual fires affect fruit production (Alvarado et al. 2014, 2015), regular fire may also reduce populations of silkworm parasites (Kull 2004).

In highland pine and eucalyptus plantations, some tree growers burn to provoke regeneration and in a precocious manner to clear out undergrowth that could lead to more serious wildfires. *Pinus patula* from Mexico and *P. khasya* from Southeast Asia both benefit from fire, which opens seeds and can facilitate regeneration (Schwilk and Ackerly 2001). Pines are invasive in many grassland areas, and frequent fires can be a tool to control such invasions as young pine trees are vulnerable to fire, which is not the case for larger trees.

Finally, due to its self-propagation and easily anonymous ignition, fire can also be used for destructive or criminal purposes, or for self-gratification. Criminal burning of houses, crop fields, or woodlots occurs for purposes of revenge, protest, jealousy, tenure conflict, or personal gain. Destructive fires in woodlots and forests may benefit nonowners if people may freely collect resulting deadwood for household fuel. Some fires are associated with cattle-thieving bandits, who purportedly use fire to hide traces of cattle rustling, to draw able-bodied men away from their homes, or to create green shoots to attract free-ranging cattle for theft (Kull 2004; Klein et al. 2007).

The size, extent, and intensity of fires vary in the highlands by region, by month, and from year to year. Kull (2004) estimated that roughly one-half of grassland zones burned annually at the turn of the century, equaling about one-third of the island. Advances in remote sensing allow for easier assessment of burnt area and active fire points, the latter notably with the MODIS (Moderate Resolution Imaging Spectroradiometer) satellite (Musinsky et al. 2018). Remote-sensing evidence shows that, viewed at regional scale, levels of burning in Madagascar's highland grasslands correspond to similar climate zones in upland southern Africa (Archibald et al. 2010). The limited investigation that has taken place has found fire return intervals in highlands are one to three years, similar to the previously mentioned parts of Africa (Alvarado et al. 2018). Alvarado et al. (2018) used remote sensing to document fires over a 27-year period at Ibity and Itremo, which have been named as protected areas since 2015, and showed that, following fire-suppression interventions at each site, the number of ignitions decreased but total burnt area was stable, with bigger and later fires.

ECOLOGY: THE EFFECTS OF VEGETATION BURNING

Despite their utility, fires can have negative impacts for human assets and air quality. Each year, fires incinerate some houses, crop fields, fruit trees, or pine and eucalyptus plantations (Figure 5.6e). However, the vast majority of grassland fires burn uneventfully (Figure 5.6c), stopping at the edge of crop fields because of sparse fuel or riparian forests owing to humidity and fuel moisture. Annually, smoke from fires envelopes many highland areas. Fires negatively affect air quality, contributing particulates, carbon monoxide, carbon dioxide, hydrocarbons, and tropospheric ozone (Randriambelo et al. 2000; Johnston et al. 2012).

The effects of fire in highland Madagascar on vegetation dynamics, nutrient cycling, erosion processes, atmospheric chemistry, and other processes are not well documented. In particular, research on fire, grasslands, and grazing in this portion of the island is limited, partly out of a long-standing bias that considers grassland ecosystems to be of lesser (or no) interest compared with forest ecosystems (Solofondranohatra et al. 2020). Here we summarize existing knowledge, drawing in part on parallels with grass-dominated-ecosystem research elsewhere.

Fire is an integral part of tropical grassland ecosystems (Bond et al. 2008; Parr et al. 2014). Increasing evidence suggests that several fire-adapted highland C_4 grassland communities, as well as associated fires linked to lightning or volcanism, long pre-date human arrival in this portion of the island (Bond et al. 2008; Vorontsova et al. 2016; Nanjarisoa et al. 2017; Hackel et al. 2018; Goel et al. 2020; Solofondranohatra et al. 2020). Different types of evidence suggest that the Central Highlands in the late Pleistocene were dry with widespread grassland vegetation, and that during the Holocene the highlands were a spatially and temporally varying mosaic of riparian and closed-canopy forest, "savanna woodlands," heath, and grassland shaped by fire and grazing large-animal fauna (Burney 1997a; Burney et al. 2003, 2004; Bond et al. 2008; Willis et al. 2008; Solofondranohatra et al. 2018).

Analysis of pollen and charcoal in sediment cores suggests that the period following human arrival was associated with an increase in fire frequency and an expansion of flammable grasslands at the expense of woody communities (Burney 1997b; Burney et al. 2004). The first influence of people on the regional fire ecology could have been indirect—for example, via the hunting of the herbivore megafauna. Herbivores "compete" with fire for vegetation; reducing herbivore populations would have rapidly transformed grassland ecosystems, enabling taller grass vegetation and therefore more fuel and hence more frequent fires (Hempson et al. 2019). That is, fire and herbivory support dichotomous communities of grasses (Solofondranohatra et al. 2020), and with human hunting and reduction of megafauna populations, herbivore-dominated grasslands may have been relatively rapidly replaced by fire-adapted grass communities. With the subsequent introduction of cattle by people, estimated to have been in the 9th to 12th centuries (Burney et al. 2004), cattle could have functionally replaced the herbivore megafauna in their ecological role (Solofondranohatra et al. 2020). Direct influence by people on fire would have come via fire ignitions. Compared with those started by natural lightning strikes, fires ignited by people notably occur much earlier in the season and are less concentrated on points of higher relief, like mountains.

Fires are frequently implicated in the degradation of the ecotone between grasslands and moist evergreen highland forests. However, elsewhere in the world tropical grassland-forest boundaries are typically structured by positive feedbacks (Hoffmann et al. 2012). Edges of intact Malagasy highland forests can remain stable in the face of fire in adjacent grasslands (Figure 5.6b), except where tree-cutting, cultivation, or charcoal-production activities provide entry points for more-flammable grassy vegetation that would carry fire. *Uapaca bojeri* (tapia) woodlands, a grassland formation, are in contrast fire adapted (Kull 2004; Solofondranohatra et al. 2018; see Kull and Birkinshaw, pp. 121–27).

The interactions of fire with highland grassland vegetation communities vary with frequency, season, species composition, plant maturity and density, flowering stage, air temperature and moisture, soil moisture, litter amount and quality, grazing intensity, wind, topography, time of day, direction of burn, nutrient legacy, and historical land use. These factors determine the spatial extent and intensity of fires and their effects on standing vegetation and soil microfauna. Influential mid-20th-century understandings of the effects of repeated fire saw vegetation communities follow a reverse successional model (retrogression), in which increasing fire frequency replaced forest, first with large, tall, albeit palatable grasses such as *Hyparrhenia rufa* and *Heteropogon contortus*, and later with a degraded system of low-value *Aristida* spp. characteristic of overgrazing (Perrier de la Bâthie 1921; Granier and Serres 1966; Bosser 1969). More recent research supports a different perspective in rangeland ecology in highland Madagascar, whereby actual transformations in grassland communities probably follow multiple transitions between different states, based on fire regime, grazing pressures, land use, climate, and initial plant community (Jacquin et al. 2010; Parr et al. 2014; Briske 2017).

Indications of fire-grazing-grassland interactions in the highlands can be gleaned from the limited research on the topic. Grass research at Itremo identified a "fire grass" group in grassland and tapia woodland areas that is tolerant of or dependent on frequent burning (Nanjarisoa et al. 2017). Such a finding is corroborated by a more recent analysis of grass functional traits and community composition across the Central Highlands, which shows the existence of an ancient fire-maintained assemblage grassland community (Solofondranohatra et al. 2020). Investigating the impacts of a 2003 fire at Ibity, Rasoafaranaivo (2005) found that fire had little negative impact on 10 endemic species characteristic of montane environments, while Randriatsivery (2005) found that grassland areas were comparatively more species rich and had higher vegetation cover after the passage of fire. A variety of species do co-occur with grasses, including herbs, tuberous geophytes, aloes, orchids, and *Pachypodium*, and exhibit fire adaptations (Lamont and Downes 2011; see Lehmann et al., pp. 152–68). Alvarado et al. (2018) demonstrated that fire exclusion is not attainable in highland grasslands, nor necessarily needed for conservation of this formation. Indeed, it is likely that fire exclusion in certain cases could decrease biodiversity, as found by Rakotoarimanana and Grouzis (2006) in the grasslands of the southwest, ecologically different from the Central Highlands, where the thesis of Rakotoarimanana (2002) remains one of the only detailed analyses of grazing, fire, and grassland interactions. Much future work is warranted, particularly in a context where policy makers not only seek to limit fires but also rush to plant trees in grassland areas, to meet carbon sequestration targets, without considering the alterations to fire regimes caused by such interventions (Veldman et al. 2015; Bond et al. 2019).

Knowledge of the relationship of grassland burning to soil erosion and pedogenesis in the Central Highlands is essentially limited to mid-20th-century studies at several sites, which demonstrated higher erosion rates in burnt areas, at least in the first post-burn rainy season, and which paid little attention to types of fire or vegetation (Kull 2004). Fires can cause soil compaction (Randriatsivery 2005) but also influence vegetation cover. In a general manner, impacts on erosion depend on timing with respect to rain or wind events, type of fire, and type of vegetation (Scott et al. 2014). The consequences of erosion can be locally severe, including siltation, flooding, and gullying, yet may be exaggerated owing to a failure to put erosion figures from test plots in context or by ignoring the positive inputs that erosion can provide downhill (Kull 2000).

HISTORY: FIRE MANAGEMENT AND THE ECONOMIC AND POLITICAL CONTEXT

Following the 1896 conquest, French colonial administrators sought to limit vegetation burning (Kull 2004; cf. Moura et al. 2019). While some district officers argued in favor of burning for pasture maintenance, colonial scientists argued that these practices resulted in the destruction of valuable forests and impoverished the soils (Perrier de la Bâthie 1921; Humbert 1949). Viewed from a European perspective that favored intensive cattle husbandry, the extensive fire-based system appeared wasteful and destructive. Confusion was (and continues to be) frequent between fires in different vegetation types, such as grassland versus forest, and between potentially useful fires and fires that threaten assets.

Legislation in 1907 banned all fires except for locust control and pasture renewal, with the idea that the development of "modern" intensive cattle husbandry would make pasture fires obsolete. New laws in 1930 tightened the screws but still allowed for pasture fires upon written authorization. At independence in 1960, Malagasy legislation echoed colonial laws, and the government organized periodic anti-fire awareness campaigns. In the 1970s, penalties for illegal wildfires were severely stiffened, yet enforcement fell far behind. Anti-fire propaganda and enforcement again intensified around 1990 as money associated with environmental conservation began to pour into the country; at this time the Forest Service also stopped issuing pasture-burning authorizations in many regions (Kull 2004).

Similar patterns continue into the 21st century (Rarivomanana 2017). During his 2002–2009 tenure as president of Madagascar, Marc Ravalomanana called bushfires a primary threat to development, and decreed an incentive system across the country to reward municipalities (*communes rurales*) who took action against bushfires. In 2003, the Ministère de l'Environnement, de l'Ecologie et des Forêts established a satellite-based fire-monitoring system in partnership with the United States Agency for International Development (USAID) and Conservation International, which was frequently used to identify hotspots and compare communal and regional performance (S. Ralaimihoatra 2008). Firefighting committees were widely established (Figure 5.6e), and moments of zealous enforcement sometimes led to heavy prison sentences. Despite political upheavals, there have been no important changes to bushfire policy and action in the most recent decade (2010–2020). Local authorities (mayors, gendarmes, and forest officers) have continued to seek to mobilize local communities to control burning, while in some protected areas they sought to protect forests using firebreaks and watchtowers. However, despite these different programs and efforts, fire policies and associated actions are frequently not implemented, and when applied they are characterized by inconsistencies and arbitrariness. Dramatic fires continue to periodically capture media attention, such as a 2019 blaze in the grasslands around and forests within Ankarafantsika National Park (C. Kull, unpublished data).

Despite 120 years of anti-fire policies and activities, fires continue to burn widely in the Central Highlands, which is characterized by flammable, fire-dependent grasses and a wet-dry climate. Alvarado et al. (2018) show that exclusion efforts lead to reduced ignitions but subsequently more prominent fires later in the season. As Kull (2004) argued, this is aided by the easy anonymity of fire ignition and fire's self-propagation, which allow people to start fires surreptitiously in order to accomplish their agropastoral tasks. Villagers protect one another from enforcement, and some lower-level officials are reluctant to enforce unpopular or lower-priority rules. Farmers light fires opportunistically (Figure 5.6f), following an unwritten management plan, in response to both bioclimatic factors (rainfall and vegetation growth) and political factors (moments of reduced enforcement of anti-fire laws, elections, or locust invasions).

Over the decades, some officials have sought alternative solutions to fire exclusion and bans (Kull 2004). All fire legislation reluctantly made some room for people to obtain authorization to burn pasture areas; this system worked in some historical locations and time periods, not in others. Specialists occasionally promoted burning outside the dry season, when fires would remain easier to control and burn less severely. However, such fires are less useful in providing the "green bite" for cattle. Despite policy failures and frequent claims that fires are increasing, fire use has decreased this century in highland areas where population density and/or intensive land use increased (Andela et al. 2017; cf. Archibald 2016 for the rest of Africa). In some areas, the expansion of crop fields due to population growth has squeezed out fire use; in other areas, the spread of important cash crops, such as eucalyptus woodlots or fruit orchards, has led to a limitation of burning (Kull 2004).

Community-based natural resource management policies in the 1990s allowed for the decentralization of the management of different habitats to local communities but were mainly applied to forest protection and usually took anti-fire approaches. These methods could have led to a new era of community fire management but did not (Kull 2004), though they may have contributed towards a lower fire frequency (Andrianandrasana 2016). In or around some protected areas, such as Ibity or Ankazobe (associated with Ambohitantely), efforts at involving communities in planned burning and the construction and maintenance of firebreaks have advanced, but these remain the exception.

CONCLUSION

In conclusion, what is clear is that in the wet-dry climate of the Central Highlands fires are an inevitable part of the landscape, were a feature of these landscapes with a different level of periodicity well before human settlement, and are likely to be around for a long time into the future. Research into fire in Madagascar, alongside research into grassland ecology, will be critical to dispelling myths about fire, as well as helping to develop approaches to burning that aid sustainable land management issues like invasive species (Figure 5.6a), such as *Pinus* and *Eucalyptus* at the forest edge. Fire can be used productively as a tool to manage landscapes just as it is across the wider wet-dry tropics. Policies of suppression serve only to create out-of-control fires, and with little available expertise in fire management they lead to disharmony between government administrators and local communities, who are aware of the value of fire for creating green pick for cattle in hungry months.

Subject editor: Steven M. Goodman

HUNTING AND THE CONSUMPTION OF WILDLIFE ON MADAGASCAR

C. D. Golden, C. DeSisto, C. Borgerson, and H. J. Randriamady

For decades, habitat loss through deforestation and swidden agriculture were considered the principal pressures on forest-dwelling animals, particularly mammals (Green and Sussman 1990), especially when considering the synergistic forces between deforestation and climate change (Morelli et al. 2020). Thus, the majority of conservation efforts since the early 21st century have focused on habitat loss as a primary issue in threatening the endemic mammals of Madagascar (e.g., Raik 2007; Irwin et al. 2010; Herrera 2017). More recently, hunting has been recognized as a significant threat to the persistence of animal populations, including in relatively intact forests, resonating with the concept of the "empty forest" (Redford 1992). The important impacts of hunting on wildlife persistence across a breadth of taxa have often been overlooked as an important pressure for conservation.

Although the dominant conservation paradigm has focused on the effect of deforestation on species' population declines, Madagascar has the highest number of endemic mammals (n = 46) threatened by hunting in the world (Ripple et al. 2016). Throughout the island, wildlife is sought for subsistence consumption and sale. The combined threat of habitat degradation and targeted hunting has led to dramatic reductions in wildlife populations throughout the country. The degree of hunting pressure on particular species is notably variable across the island, and important factors to explain this variation are related to sociocultural, economic, and ecological variables.

Here we present a systematic summary of what is known about the hunting techniques and varying levels of pressure on different taxonomic groups of animals. The following reports are focused on empirical data and are quantitative in nature, excluding some of the rich anecdotal and qualitative evidence of hunting across the island. In the following texts we cite Malagasy common names for the animals and trap types concerned, generally in the dialects of northeastern and eastern Madagascar.

BUSH PIGS, *LAMBO*, *LAMBODIA*, *LAMBOALA*

The hunting of *Potamochoerus larvatus* (African Bush Pig; Suidae; see Goodman and Andrianjakarivelo, pp. 2003–6), is common across Madagascar (Table 5.3). Bush pigs are captured by means of dogs in active pursuit, by spear, and by sophisticated trapping and snaring methods. *Potamochoerus larvatus* is unique among other animals hunted on Madagascar for several reasons: 1) it is an introduced species from Africa and therefore legal to hunt; 2) contact with this species is potentially dangerous for the hunter; and 3) it is large in size, weighing up to 55–70 kg, so that most hunters will gift, smoke, and sell portions of their catch (e.g., Andrianjakarivelo 2003; Golden 2005; Gardner and Davies 2014). According to local hunters, bush pigs tend to follow the same forest paths on a regular basis, even trailing their own footprints (Golden 2005). Hunters will place snares, called *fandrikandia*, directly over the footprints on the trails, where a noose made of rope, or sometimes metal cable, is attached to a strong, bent sapling (Figure 5.7a). The noose is covered by a thin layer of sticks and leaves. When these sticks are crushed by the pressure of a passing animal's foot, they bring down the trigger stick holding the snare trip (a small wooden bit attached to the rope or cable). Instantaneously after this treadle is detached, the noose will snap up and ensnare the leg of the bush pig.

In the protected areas of Makira and Masoala, nearly 30% of households hunt *P. larvatus*, accounting for 6% of the total wildlife biomass locally consumed (Golden et al. 2014a). Bush pigs in the forested area surrounding Makira are actively hunted with spears, but the majority of hunting is conducted with traps or snares. In Masoala, nearly 35% of households ate bush pigs during the course of a year, with their meat representing 65% of wildlife consumption by biomass (Golden et al. 2014a; Borgerson et al. 2019a). More than 20% of households in the communities surrounding the Betampona protected area consumed bush pigs, at an average rate of 250 g per year (Golden et al. 2014b).

In Kianjavato, 6.6% of the consumed wildlife was *P. larvatus* meat (Borgerson et al. 2018b), reflecting low levels of local abundance or local hunting. Although bush pigs were listed among the most preferred foods in the Alaotra-Mangoro Region (Jenkins et al. 2011), no surveyed household (n = 485) had consumed these animals in the immediate Lake Alaotra area, and local people reported their absence in the locality (Borgerson et al. 2018a).

On the western side of Madagascar, evidence that *P. larvatus* is hunted in Ankarafantsika was discovered in bone middens of a temporary raffia-harvesting camp (Garcia and Goodman 2003). More recently, Borgerson et al. (2019b) found during a survey conducted between 2014 and 2015 that more than one-third of households in the local communities surrounding Ankarafantsika National Park had eaten bush pigs during the previous year. Bush pigs are also one of the most commonly targeted animals in the Menabe Region of the central west (Randrianandrianina et al. 2011) and in the Ranobe area of the southwest (Gardner and Davies 2014).

In parts of the west, from north of Mahajanga to at least the Morondava area, there are different forms of commercial hunting of *P. larvatus*. This includes foreign and Malagasy sport hunters taking part in organized trips to shoot these animals, often at regularly visited sites that are baited by local people, to whom a portion of the meat is given. Further, at some large commercial installations in the countryside, such as shrimp farms (e.g., UNIMA site north of Besalampy), local and regional hunters are engaged to bring in bush pig carcasses to local markets, which are purchased and provide meat to feed workers (S. M. Goodman, unpublished data).

FIGURE 5.7 **Different styles of traps used to capture wild animals: A) a *fandrikandia* snare, used to capture *Potamochoerus larvatus* (African Bush Pig), photographed near Makira protected area; B) a *laly totoko* snare used to capture lemurs, near Makira Natural Park; C and D) two views of the *antombato* snare used to bait and capture carnivorans, particularly vontsira species and *Cryptoprocta ferox* (Fosa), near Makira protected area.** (PHOTOS A, C, and D by C. Golden; and B by J. Betz, National Geographic Society.)

SPINY TENRECS, *TRANDRAKA (TENREC), SOKINA (SETIFER), ANTSORA (HEMICENTETES)*

Of all mammal species on Madagascar, spiny tenrecs (Tenrecidae; Tenrecinae; see Goodman et al., pp. 1891–94) are the most commonly hunted and consumed in every region where research has documented quantitative rates of harvest (Table 5.3). Tenrecs are game species that can be hunted (without the use of dogs) during the legal hunting season from 1 April until 31 May (Decree 2006-400, Ordonnance MAP/FOR 60-126). In the eastern moist evergreen forests, spiny tenrecs (primarily *Tenrec ecaudatus*, *Setifer setosus*, *Hemicentetes semispinosus*) constitute the majority of wildlife consumption in any given study location.

In the Makira and Masoala protected areas, a 2011 survey of over 600 households in nearly 40 communities found that 91% of households had consumed spiny tenrecs over the previous 12 months, accounting for 75% of the total wildlife biomass consumed (Golden et al. 2014a; Figure 5.8a). In the Masoala, Borgerson et al. (2019a) showed lower pressure on tenrecs, with more than 50% of surveyed households eating them in 2014. These detailed surveys elucidated that the majority of spiny tenrec hunting occurred outside of the legal hunting season. Spiny tenrec hunting in this region is conducted primarily with dogs (Golden 2009) from November until May, a season characterized by low consumption of meat from domesticated animals and fish (Golden et al. 2019).

In the Alaotra-Mangoro Region of eastern Madagascar, more than 90% of interviewed individuals are estimated to have consumed *T. ecaudatus* and *H. semispinosus*, and more than 60% to have eaten *S. setosus*, in their lifetime (Jenkins et al. 2011). In the Lake Alaotra area specifically, more than 97% of the biomass of bushmeat that was consumed during a 2013 survey comprised various species of spiny tenrec (Borgerson et al. 2018a). Approximately one in 10 households had consumed spiny tenrec during the prior year, predominantly collecting these animals using trained dogs, a hunting method that is illegal across the island (Ordonnance MAP/FOR 60-126).

Farther south in the eastern moist evergreen forest belt, spiny tenrecs (*Tenrec*, *Setifer*, *Hemicentetes*) remain the most common form of wildlife consumed. In the immediate vicinity of the Betampona protected area, more than 50% of households eat spiny tenrecs within a given year, typically hunting these animals with dogs, and averaging four spiny tenrecs consumed per household per year (Golden et al. 2014b). In the Ambatovy mine area, 59% of survey respondents had consumed *H. semispinosus* and 66% *T. ecaudatus* (Randriamamonjy et al. 2015). In Kianjavato, nearly 50% of the biomass of wildlife consumed was spiny tenrecs, which were obtained through subsistence hunting (Borgerson et al. 2018b). Across the length of the eastern moist evergreen and littoral forest habitat, from Makira to Sainte Luce (Manafiafy), spiny tenrecs are hunted primarily with dogs at dusk or at night (e.g., Bollen and Donati 2006; Golden 2009; Borgerson et al. 2018a).

TABLE 5.3. **Quantitative estimates of average household-level wildlife consumption in 13 regions of Madagascar**

	ALAOTRA			KIANJAVATO			KIANJAVATO			MASOALA			MAKIRA			BETAMPONA		
	TOTAL NO. EATEN PER YEAR	NO. HOUSEHOLDS SURVEYED	MEAN NO. EATEN PER HOUSEHOLD PER YEAR	TOTAL NO. EATEN PER YEAR	NO. HOUSEHOLDS SURVEYED	MEAN NO. EATEN PER HOUSEHOLD PER YEAR	TOTAL NO. EATEN PER YEAR	NO. HOUSEHOLDS SURVEYED	MEAN NO. EATEN PER HOUSEHOLD PER YEAR	TOTAL NO. EATEN PER YEAR	NO. HOUSEHOLDS SURVEYED	MEAN NO. EATEN PER HOUSEHOLD PER YEAR	TOTAL NO. EATEN PER YEAR	NO. HOUSEHOLDS SURVEYED	MEAN NO. EATEN PER HOUSEHOLD PER YEAR	TOTAL NO. EATEN PER YEAR	NO. HOUSEHOLDS SURVEYED	MEAN NO. EATEN PER HOUSEHOLD PER YEAR
LEMURS	16	485	0.03	106	336	0.32	90	359	0.25	240	387	0.62	3722	1155	3.22	345	298	1.16
Eulemur albifrons	–	–	–	–	–	–	–	–	–	136	387	0.35	676	1155	0.59	1	298	0.00
E. rufifrons	–	–	–	1	336	0.00	–	–	–	–	–	–	–	–	–	–	–	–
E. fulvus	X	–	–	–	–	–	4	359	0.01	–	–	–	–	–	–	–	–	–
E. rubriventer	0	485	0.00	0	336	0.00	0	359	0.00	–	–	–	166	1155	0.14	–	–	–
E. mongoz	–	–	–	–	–	–	79	359	0.22	–	–	–	–	–	–	–	–	–
Varecia rubra	–	–	–	–	–	–	–	–	–	19	387	0.05	11	1155	0.01	–	–	–
V. variegata	X	–	–	2	336	0.01	2	359	0.01	–	–	–	86	1155	0.07	0	298	0.00
Microcebus berthae	–	–	–	–	–	–	–	–	–	–	–	–	–	–	–	–	–	–
M. jollyae	–	–	–	83	336	0.25	5	359	0.01	–	–	–	–	–	–	–	–	–
M. ravelobensis/M. murinus	–	–	–	–	–	–	–	–	–	–	–	–	–	–	–	–	–	–
M. rufus	–	–	–	–	–	–	–	–	–	–	–	–	–	–	–	–	–	–
M. simmonsi	–	–	–	–	–	–	–	–	–	–	–	–	–	–	–	323	298	1.08
Microcebus spp.	0	485	0.00	–	–	–	–	–	–	9	387	0.02	510	1155	0.44	–	–	–
Mirza coquereli	–	–	–	–	–	–	–	–	–	–	–	–	–	–	–	–	–	–
Allocebus trichotis	–	–	–	–	–	–	–	–	–	2	387	0.01	–	–	–	–	–	–
Cheirogaleus crossleyi	0	485	0.00	–	–	–	–	–	–	–	–	–	–	–	–	–	–	–
C. medius	–	–	–	–	–	–	–	–	–	–	–	–	–	–	–	–	–	–
C. major	–	–	–	3	336	0.01	–	–	–	19	387	0.05	734	1155	0.64	0	298	0.00
Phaner furcifer	–	–	–	–	–	–	–	–	–	1	387	0.00	–	–	–	–	–	–
Lepilemur seali	–	–	–	–	–	–	–	–	–	–	–	–	177	1155	0.15	–	–	–
L. scottorum	–	–	–	–	–	–	–	–	–	5	387	0.01	–	–	–	–	–	–
L. edwardsi	–	–	–	–	–	–	–	–	–	–	–	–	–	–	–	–	–	–
L. ruficaudatus	–	–	–	–	–	–	–	–	–	–	–	–	–	–	–	–	–	–
L. mustelinus	–	–	–	–	–	–	–	–	–	–	–	–	–	–	–	2	298	0.01
L. hollandorum	–	–	–	–	–	–	–	–	–	–	–	–	–	–	–	–	–	–
Hapalemur occidentalis	0	485	0.00	–	–	–	–	–	–	24	387	0.06	594	1155	0.51	–	–	–
H. griseus	–	–	–	9	336	0.03	0	359	0.00	–	–	–	–	–	–	7	298	0.02
H. alaotrensis	16	485	0.03	–	–	–	–	–	–	–	–	–	–	–	–	–	–	–
Prolemur simus	X	–	–	8	336	0.02	–	–	–	–	–	–	–	–	–	–	–	–
Avahi mooreorum	–	–	–	–	–	–	–	–	–	24	387	0.06	–	–	–	–	–	–
A. occidentalis	–	–	–	–	–	–	–	–	–	–	–	–	–	–	–	–	–	–

ANKARAFANTSIKA			MANANARA			MAHABO			AMBATOVY			ANDASIBE-MANTADIA			KIRINDY			LAMBOKELY			ANDRANOMENA		
TOTAL NO. EATEN PER YEAR	NO. HOUSEHOLDS SURVEYED	MEAN NO. EATEN PER HOUSEHOLD PER YEAR	TOTAL NO. EATEN PER YEAR	NO. HOUSEHOLDS SURVEYED	MEAN NO. EATEN PER HOUSEHOLD PER YEAR	TOTAL NO. EATEN PER YEAR	NO. HOUSEHOLDS SURVEYED	MEAN NO. EATEN PER HOUSEHOLD PER YEAR	TOTAL NO. EATEN PER YEAR	NO. HOUSEHOLDS SURVEYED	MEAN NO. EATEN PER HOUSEHOLD PER YEAR	TOTAL NO. EATEN PER YEAR	NO. HOUSEHOLDS SURVEYED	MEAN NO. EATEN PER HOUSEHOLD PER YEAR	TOTAL NO. EATEN PER YEAR	NO. HOUSEHOLDS SURVEYED	MEAN NO. EATEN PER HOUSEHOLD PER YEAR	TOTAL NO. EATEN PER YEAR	NO. HOUSEHOLDS SURVEYED	MEAN NO. EATEN PER HOUSEHOLD PER YEAR	TOTAL NO. EATEN PER YEAR	NO. HOUSEHOLDS SURVEYED	MEAN NO. EATEN PER HOUSEHOLD PER YEAR
78	**425**	**0.18**	**409**	**287**	**1.43**	**0**	**228**	**0.0**	**369**	**526**	**0.7**	**112**	**362**	**0.31**	**59**	**266**	**0.22**	**22**	**206**	**0.11**	**544**	**190**	**2.86**
–	–	–	–	–	–	–	–	–	–	–	–	–	–	–	–	–	–	–	–	–	–	–	–
–	–	–	–	–	–	–	–	–	X	–	–	–	–	–	20	266	0.08	–	–	–	31	190	0.16
48	425	0.11	–	–	–	–	–	–	158	526	0.3	23	362	0.06	–	–	–	–	–	–	–	–	–
–	–	–	–	–	–	–	–	–	–	–	–	–	–	–	–	–	–	–	–	–	–	–	–
X	–	–	–	–	–	–	–	–	–	–	–	–	–	–	–	–	–	–	–	–	200	190	1.05
–	–	–	–	–	–	–	–	–	–	–	–	–	–	–	–	–	–	–	–	–	–	–	–
–	–	–	55	287	0.19	–	–	–	–	–	–	2	362	0.01	–	–	–	–	–	–	–	–	–
–	–	–	–	–	–	–	–	–	–	–	–	–	–	–	5	266	0.02	–	–	–	2	190	0.01
–	–	–	–	–	–	–	–	–	–	–	–	–	–	–	–	–	–	–	–	–	–	–	–
0	425	0.00	–	–	–	–	–	–	–	–	–	–	–	–	–	–	–	–	–	–	–	–	–
–	–	–	–	–	–	–	–	–	–	–	–	–	–	–	–	–	–	–	–	–	200	190	1.05
–	–	–	–	–	–	–	–	–	–	–	–	–	–	–	–	–	–	–	–	–	–	–	–
1	425	0.00	76	287	0.26	–	–	–	–	–	–	0	362	0.00	–	–	–	–	–	–	–	–	–
–	–	–	–	–	–	–	–	–	–	–	–	–	–	–	–	–	–	–	–	–	3	190	0.02
–	–	–	–	–	–	–	–	–	–	–	–	2	362	0.01	–	–	–	–	–	–	–	–	–
–	–	–	–	–	–	–	–	–	–	–	–	0	362	0.00	–	–	–	–	–	–	–	–	–
15	425	0.04	–	–	–	–	–	–	–	–	–	–	–	–	–	–	–	20	206	0.10	1	190	0.01
–	–	–	49	287	0.17	–	–	–	–	–	–	–	–	–	–	–	–	–	–	–	–	–	–
–	–	–	–	–	–	–	–	–	–	–	–	–	–	–	–	–	–	–	–	–	–	–	–
–	–	–	–	–	–	–	–	–	–	–	–	–	–	–	–	–	–	–	–	–	–	–	–
–	–	–	–	–	–	–	–	–	–	–	–	–	–	–	–	–	–	–	–	–	–	–	–
12	425	0.03	–	–	–	–	–	–	–	–	–	–	–	–	–	–	–	–	–	–	–	–	–
–	–	–	–	–	–	–	–	–	–	–	–	–	–	–	–	–	–	–	–	–	3	190	0.02
–	–	–	–	–	–	–	–	–	–	–	–	6	362	0.02	–	–	–	–	–	–	2	190	0.01
–	–	–	64	287	0.22	–	–	–	–	–	–	–	–	–	–	–	–	–	–	–	–	–	–
–	–	–	43	287	0.15	–	–	–	–	–	–	–	–	–	–	–	–	–	–	–	–	–	–
–	–	–	–	–	–	–	–	–	–	–	–	12	362	0.03	–	–	–	–	–	–	–	–	–
–	–	–	–	–	–	–	–	–	–	–	–	–	–	–	–	–	–	–	–	–	–	–	–
–	–	–	–	–	–	–	–	–	–	–	–	2	362	0.01	–	–	–	–	–	–	–	–	–
–	–	–	–	–	–	–	–	–	–	–	–	–	–	–	–	–	–	–	–	–	56	190	0.30
2	425	0.00	–	–	–	–	–	–	–	–	–	–	–	–	–	–	–	–	–	–	–	–	–

(continued overleaf)

TABLE 5.3. ***continued***

	ALAOTRA			KIANJAVATO			KIANJAVATO			MASOALA			MAKIRA			BETAMPONA		
	TOTAL NO. EATEN PER YEAR	NO. HOUSEHOLDS SURVEYED	MEAN NO. EATEN PER HOUSEHOLD PER YEAR	TOTAL NO. EATEN PER YEAR	NO. HOUSEHOLDS SURVEYED	MEAN NO. EATEN PER HOUSEHOLD PER YEAR	TOTAL NO. EATEN PER YEAR	NO. HOUSEHOLDS SURVEYED	MEAN NO. EATEN PER HOUSEHOLD PER YEAR	TOTAL NO. EATEN PER YEAR	NO. HOUSEHOLDS SURVEYED	MEAN NO. EATEN PER HOUSEHOLD PER YEAR	TOTAL NO. EATEN PER YEAR	NO. HOUSEHOLDS SURVEYED	MEAN NO. EATEN PER HOUSEHOLD PER YEAR	TOTAL NO. EATEN PER YEAR	NO. HOUSEHOLDS SURVEYED	MEAN NO. EATEN PER HOUSEHOLD PER YEAR
A. peyrierasi	–	–	–	0	336	0.00	–	–	–	–	–	–	–	–	–	–	–	–
A. laniger	0	485	0.00	–	–	–	–	–	–	–	–	–	665	1155	0.58	7	298	0.02
Indri indri	X	–	–	–	–	–	–	–	–	–	–	–	85	1155	0.07	1	298	0.00
Propithecus diadema	–	–	–	–	–	–	–	–	–	–	–	–	–	–	–	0	298	0.00
P. coquereli	–	–	–	–	–	–	–	–	–	–	–	–	–	–	–	–	–	–
P. verreauxi	–	–	–	–	–	–	–	–	–	–	–	–	–	–	–	–	–	–
P. candidus	–	–	–	–	–	–	–	–	–	–	–	–	0	1155	0.00	–	–	–
Daubentonia madagascariensis	–	–	–	0	336	0.00	–	–	–	1	387	0.00	18	1155	0.02	4	298	0.01
CARNIVORANS	**0**	**485**	**0.00**	**12**	**336**	**0.04**	**22**	**359**	**0.06**	**85**	**387**	**0.22**	**24**	**1155**	**0.02**	**34**	**298**	**0.11**
Galidia elegans	0	485	0.00	0	359	0.00	17	359	0.05	25	387	0.06	14	1155	0.01	21	298	0.07
Galidictis fasciata	0	485	0.00	4	336	0.01	0	359	0.00	1	387	0.00	4	1155	0.00	3	298	0.01
Salanoia concolor	0	485	0.00	1	336	0.00	–	–	–	4	387	0.01	–	–	–	6	298	0.02
Cryptoprocta ferox	0	485	0.00	1	336	0.00	–	–	–	23	387	0.06	5	1155	0.00	4	298	0.01
Fossa fossana	–	–	–	6	336	0.02	5	359	0.01	13	387	0.03	0	1155	0.00	–	–	–
Mungotictis decemlineata	–	–	–	–	–	–	–	–	–	–	–	–	–	–	–	–	–	–
Eupleres major[1]	–	–	–	–	–	–	–	–	–	–	–	–	–	–	–	–	–	–
E. goudotii	0	485	0.00	–	–	–	–	–	–	19	387	0.05	1	1155	0.00	–	–	–
TENRECS	**947**	**485**	**1.95**	**347**	**336**	**1.03**	**2674**	**359**	**7.45**	**1755**	**387**	**4.53**	**2222**	**1155**	**1.92**	**1280**	**298**	**4.30**
Tenrec ecaudatus	947	485	1.95	282	336	0.84	695	359	1.94	1599	387	4.13	2209	1155	1.91	1030	298	3.46
Setifer setosus	0	485	0.00	61	336	0.18	–	–	–	71	387	0.18	13	1155	0.01	170	298	0.57
Echinops telfairi	–	–	–	–	–	–	59	359	0.16	–	–	–	–	–	–	–	–	–
Hemicentetes nigriceps	–	–	–	–	–	–	–	–	–	–	–	–	–	–	–	–	–	–
H. semispinosus	X	–	–	4	336	0.01	1920	359	5.35	85	387	0.22	–	–	–	80	298	0.27
BATS	**0**	**485**	**0.00**	**238**	**336**	**0.71**	**324**	**359**	**0.90**	**222**	**387**	**0.57**	**521**	**1155**	**0.45**	**82**	**298**	**0.28**
Pteropus rufus	0	485	0.00	22	336	0.07	324	359	0.90	201	387	0.52	4	1155	0.00	6	298	0.02
Rousettus madagascariensis/*Eidolon dupreanum*	X	–	–	216	336	0.64	–	–	–	9	387	0.02	506	1155	0.44	–	–	–
Insect-eating species	–	–	–	X	–	–	–	–	–	12	387	0.03	11	1155	0.01	76	298	0.26
INTRODUCED MAMMAL SPECIES	**13**	**485**	**0.03**	**52**	**336**	**0.15**	**239**	**359**	**0.67**	**407**	**387**	**1.05**	**138**	**1155**	**0.12**	**159**	**298**	**0.53**
Potamochoerus larvatus[2] (including pieces of meat)	0	485	0.00	50	336	0.15	227	359	0.63	347	387	0.90	98	1155	0.08	121	298	0.41
Viverricula indica	13	485	0.03	2	336	0.01	9	359	0.03	60	387	0.16	40	1155	0.03	38	298	0.13

ANKARAFANTSIKA			MANANARA			MAHABO			AMBATOVY			ANDASIBE-MANTADIA			KIRINDY			LAMBOKELY			ANDRANOMENA		
TOTAL NO. EATEN PER YEAR	NO. HOUSEHOLDS SURVEYED	MEAN NO. EATEN PER HOUSEHOLD PER YEAR	TOTAL NO. EATEN PER YEAR	NO. HOUSEHOLDS SURVEYED	MEAN NO. EATEN PER HOUSEHOLD PER YEAR	TOTAL NO. EATEN PER YEAR	NO. HOUSEHOLDS SURVEYED	MEAN NO. EATEN PER HOUSEHOLD PER YEAR	TOTAL NO. EATEN PER YEAR	NO. HOUSEHOLDS SURVEYED	MEAN NO. EATEN PER HOUSEHOLD PER YEAR	TOTAL NO. EATEN PER YEAR	NO. HOUSEHOLDS SURVEYED	MEAN NO. EATEN PER HOUSEHOLD PER YEAR	TOTAL NO. EATEN PER YEAR	NO. HOUSEHOLDS SURVEYED	MEAN NO. EATEN PER HOUSEHOLD PER YEAR	TOTAL NO. EATEN PER YEAR	NO. HOUSEHOLDS SURVEYED	MEAN NO. EATEN PER HOUSEHOLD PER YEAR	TOTAL NO. EATEN PER YEAR	NO. HOUSEHOLDS SURVEYED	MEAN NO. EATEN PER HOUSEHOLD PER YEAR
–	–	–	–	–	–	–	–	–	–	–	–	–	–	–	–	–	–	–	–	–	–	–	–
–	–	–	33	287	0.11	–	–	–	158	526	0.3	50	362	0.14	–	–	–	–	–	–	–	–	–
–	–	–	36	287	0.13	–	–	–	53	526	0.1	–	–	–	–	–	–	–	–	–	–	–	–
–	–	–	–	–	–	–	–	–	X	–	–	15	362	0.04	–	–	–	2	206	0.01	–	–	–
0	425	0.00	–	–	–	–	–	–	–	–	–	–	–	–	–	–	–	–	–	–	–	–	–
X	–	–	–	–	–	–	–	–	–	–	–	–	–	–	34	266	0.13	–	–	–	46	190	0.24
–	–	–	–	–	–	–	–	–	–	–	–	–	–	–	–	–	–	–	–	–	–	–	–
0	425	0.00	53	287	0.18	–	–	–	–	–	–	0	362	0.00	–	–	–	–	–	–	–	–	–
14	**425**	**0.03**	**290**	**287**	**1.01**	**0**	**228**	**0.0**	**105**	**526**	**0.2**	**17**	**362**	**0.05**	**0**	**266**	**0.0**	**160**	**206**	**0.78**	**4**	**190**	**0.02**
–	–	–	56	287	0.20	–	–	–	–	–	–	–	–	–	–	–	–	–	–	–	–	–	–
–	–	–	36	287	0.13	–	–	–	–	–	–	–	–	–	–	–	–	–	–	–	–	–	–
–	–	–	62	287	0.22	–	–	–	–	–	–	–	–	–	–	–	–	–	–	–	–	–	–
13	425	0.03	101	287	0.35	–	–	–	105	526	0.2	8	362	0.02	–	–	–	–	–	–	–	–	–
–	–	–	35	287	0.12	–	–	–	–	–	–	1	362	0.00	–	–	–	–	–	–	1	190	0.01
–	–	–	–	–	–	–	–	–	–	–	–	–	–	–	–	–	–	160	206	0.78	3	190	0.02
1	425	0.00	–	–	–	–	–	–	–	–	–	–	–	–	–	–	–	–	–	–	–	–	–
–	–	–	–	–	–	–	–	–	–	–	–	8	362	0.02	–	–	–	–	–	–	–	–	–
695	**425**	**1.64**	**248**	**287**	**0.86**	**3329**	**228**	**14.6**	**526**	**526**	**1.0**	**1487**	**362**	**4.11**	**709**	**266**	**2.67**	**343**	**206**	**1.67**	**571**	**190**	**3.01**
583	425	1.37	76	287	0.26	3329	228	14.6	263	526	0.5	601	362	1.66	545	266	2.05	326	206	1.58	126	190	0.66
112	425	0.26	121	287	0.42	–	–	–	–	–	–	–	–	–	–	–	–	–	–	–	–	–	–
–	–	–	–	–	–	–	–	–	–	–	–	144	362	0.40	164	266	0.62	17	206	0.08	445	190	2.34
–	–	–	–	–	–	–	–	–	X	–	–	–	–	–	–	–	–	–	–	–	–	–	–
–	–	–	51	287	0.18	–	–	–	263	526	0.5	742	362	2.05	–	–	–	–	–	–	–	–	–
66	**425**	**0.16**	**200**	**287**	**0.70**	**1095**	**228**	**4.80**	**–**	**–**	**–**	**10**	**362**	**0.03**	**119**	**266**	**0.45**	**71**	**206**	**0.34**	**44**	**190**	**0.23**
42	425	0.10	119	287	0.41	1095	228	4.80	–	–	–	10	362	0.03	65	266	0.24	41	206	0.20	40	190	0.21
–	–	–	–	–	–	–	–	–	–	–	–	–	–	–	54	266	0.20	30	206	0.15	4	190	0.02
24	425	0.06	81	287	0.28	–	–	–	–	–	–	–	–	–	–	–	–	–	–	–	–	–	–
544	**425**	**1.28**	**114**	**287**	**0.40**	**2555**	**228**	**11.21**	**–**	**–**	**–**	**246**	**362**	**0.68**	**289**	**266**	**1.09**	**176**	**206**	**0.85**	**144**	**190**	**0.76**
363	425	0.85	67	287	0.23	2555	228	11.21	–	–	–	242	362	0.67	273	266	1.03	158	206	0.77	143	190	0.75
126	425	0.30	47	287	0.16	–	–	–	–	–	–	3	362	0.01	10	266	0.04	18	206	0.09	0	190	0

(continued overleaf)

TABLE 5.3. ***continued***

	ALAOTRA			KIANJAVATO			KIANJAVATO			MASOALA			MAKIRA			BETAMPONA		
	TOTAL NO. EATEN PER YEAR	NO. HOUSEHOLDS SURVEYED	MEAN NO. EATEN PER HOUSEHOLD PER YEAR	TOTAL NO. EATEN PER YEAR	NO. HOUSEHOLDS SURVEYED	MEAN NO. EATEN PER HOUSEHOLD PER YEAR	TOTAL NO. EATEN PER YEAR	NO. HOUSEHOLDS SURVEYED	MEAN NO. EATEN PER HOUSEHOLD PER YEAR	TOTAL NO. EATEN PER YEAR	NO. HOUSEHOLDS SURVEYED	MEAN NO. EATEN PER HOUSEHOLD PER YEAR	TOTAL NO. EATEN PER YEAR	NO. HOUSEHOLDS SURVEYED	MEAN NO. EATEN PER HOUSEHOLD PER YEAR	TOTAL NO. EATEN PER YEAR	NO. HOUSEHOLDS SURVEYED	MEAN NO. EATEN PER HOUSEHOLD PER YEAR
Felis sp.	–	–	–	–	–	–	3	359	0.01	–	–	–	–	–	–	–	–	–
REPTILES	–	–	–	–	–	–	–	–	–	–	–	–	–	–	–	–	–	–
Acrantophis madagascariensis	–	–	–	–	–	–	–	–	–	–	–	–	–	–	–	–	–	–
Erymnochelys madagascariensis	–	–	–	–	–	–	–	–	–	–	–	–	–	–	–	–	–	–
Small freshwater turtles	–	–	–	–	–	–	–	–	–	–	–	–	–	–	–	–	–	–
Source	Borgerson et al. (2018a)			Borgerson et al. (2018b)			Merson et al. (2019a)			Borgerson et al. (2019a)			Brook et al. (2019a); Golden et al. (2014a)			Golden et al. (2016a)		

Notes: X, known to be eaten but quantity unknown; 0, no people reported eating. There are some differences in the reported level of precision of certain values between the different cited sources. In most cases these values have been rounded off to two decimal places.

[1] Now considered to be *E. goudotii*.

[2] These figures are based on the assumption that each individual is not divided between households and that all foods consumed in the previous 24 hours is representative of the daily diet.

On the western side of Madagascar, there is also evidence of pervasive hunting across geographic and sociocultural borders. In Ankarafantsika, there were observations of spiny tenrecs being hunted by raffia harvesters (Garcia and Goodman 2003). More recently, Borgerson et al. (2018b) found that nearly half of all households in Ankarafantsika consumed spiny tenrecs, and the majority actively hunted with dogs. Spiny tenrecs were also found to be the most commonly hunted animals, and one of the most preferred meats, in the Menabe Region of the central west (Merson et al. 2019a), and survey results showed that members of 95% of households had eaten *T. ecaudatus* (Razafimanahaka et al. 2012). In the Kirindy Forest CNFEREF (Centre National de Formation, d'Etudes et de Recherche en Environnement et Foresterie) area, north of Morondava, tenrecs were also hunted, though only occasionally (Ganzhorn et al. 1990). Farther south in the dry spiny thicket at Ranobe, spiny tenrecs (including *T. ecaudatus*, *Echinops telfairi*, *S. setosus*) are commonly hunted and favored for consumption (Gardner and Davies 2014).

BATS, *FANIHY*, *ANDREHY*, *MANAVY*

Throughout Madagascar, larger bat species, particularly fruit bats of the family Pteropodidae, including *Pteropus rufus* (Madagascar Flying Fox), *Eidolon dupreanum* (Madagascar Straw-colored Fruit Bat), and *Rousettus madagascariensis* (Madagascar Rousette) (all species endemic to the island; see Andrianaivoarivelo et al., pp. 1911–16, for a review of Malagasy Pteropodidae and Goodman et al., pp. 1894–911, for Malagasy bats in general), are preferred for human consumption (Jenkins and Racey 2008; Table 5.3). However, smaller, insectivorous bats of different families are also hunted and consumed (e.g., Jenkins and Racey 2008; Golden et al. 2014a). Fruit bats are generally hunted with nets, slingshots, and shotguns, typically in tree day roosts (*P. rufus*) or while feeding at night (all three species), and insectivorous bats are targeted in cave day-roost sites by throwing sticks and rocks while they are flying or often removed from perches (e.g, Decary 1939; Bollen and Van Elsacker, 2002; Golden 2005; Jenkins and Racey 2008; Andrianaivoarivelo et al. 2011). Bats are considered a game species on the island, with authorized hunting seasons. Insectivorous bats can be legally hunted from 1 February until 1 May, and pteropodids from 1 May until 1 September (Decree 2006-400, Ordonnance MAP/FOR 60-126).

In the Makira and Masoala protected areas, 16% of households hunt bats, which accounted for 1% of the total wildlife biomass consumed (Golden et al. 2014a). Insectivorous bats and fruit bats, specifically *P. rufus* and *R. madagascariensis*, are all hunted in the Makira (Golden 2009; Figure 5.8b). Fruit bat hunting in this area is seasonal, conducted in November and December (Golden et al. 2019). In Masoala, the same three types of bats are consumed by roughly 10% of households, constituting only 2% of total consumed wildlife biomass (Borgerson 2016; Borgerson et al. 2019a).

In the Alaotra-Mangoro Region of eastern Madagascar, *E. dupreanum* and *R. madagascariensis* are game species that are

ANKARAFANTSIKA			MANANARA			MAHABO			AMBATOVY			ANDASIBE-MANTADIA			KIRINDY			LAMBOKELY			ANDRANOMENA		
TOTAL NO. EATEN PER YEAR	NO. HOUSEHOLDS SURVEYED	MEAN NO. EATEN PER HOUSEHOLD PER YEAR	TOTAL NO. EATEN PER YEAR	NO. HOUSEHOLDS SURVEYED	MEAN NO. EATEN PER HOUSEHOLD PER YEAR	TOTAL NO. EATEN PER YEAR	NO. HOUSEHOLDS SURVEYED	MEAN NO. EATEN PER HOUSEHOLD PER YEAR	TOTAL NO. EATEN PER YEAR	NO. HOUSEHOLDS SURVEYED	MEAN NO. EATEN PER HOUSEHOLD PER YEAR	TOTAL NO. EATEN PER YEAR	NO. HOUSEHOLDS SURVEYED	MEAN NO. EATEN PER HOUSEHOLD PER YEAR	TOTAL NO. EATEN PER YEAR	NO. HOUSEHOLDS SURVEYED	MEAN NO. EATEN PER HOUSEHOLD PER YEAR	TOTAL NO. EATEN PER YEAR	NO. HOUSEHOLDS SURVEYED	MEAN NO. EATEN PER HOUSEHOLD PER YEAR	TOTAL NO. EATEN PER YEAR	NO. HOUSEHOLDS SURVEYED	MEAN NO. EATEN PER HOUSEHOLD PER YEAR
55	425	0.13	–	–	–	–	–	–	–	–	–	1	362	0.00	6	266	0.02	–	–	–	1	190	0.01
38	**425**	**0.09**	–	–	–	–	–	–	–	–	–	–	–	–	–	–	–	–	–	–	–	–	–
12	425	0.03	–	–	–	–	–	–	–	–	–	–	–	–	–	–	–	–	–	–	–	–	–
7	425	0.02	–	–	–	–	–	–	–	–	–	–	–	–	–	–	–	–	–	–	–	–	–
19	425	0.04	–	–	–	–	–	–	–	–	–	–	–	–	–	–	–	–	–	–	–	–	–
Borgerson et al. (2019b)			C. Golden, unpublished data			Randrianandrianina et al. (2010)			Randriamamonjy et al. (2015)			Merson et al. (2019b)			Merson et al. (2019a)			Merson et al. (2019a)			Merson et al. (2019a)		

consumed, albeit at low levels, while *P. rufus* is consumed at higher levels (Jenkins et al. 2011). In the immediate area of Lake Alaotra, bats were reportedly rarely seen, and no one reported eating bats in surveys (Borgerson et al. 2018a). Similarly, low levels of bat consumption were found in the immediate vicinity of the Betampona protected area, where only 2.5% of households in communities surrounding the reserve had consumed bats in the year prior to the 2013 survey (Golden et al. 2014b), and in Kianjavato, where 4.5% of households had consumed fruit bats in the year prior to the 2014 survey (Borgerson et al. 2018b). Although only a small proportion of households in Kianjavato hunted bats, they made up 31.5% of wildlife consumed by biomass, focusing primarily on *R. madagascariensis* and *P. rufus* (Borgerson et al. 2018b). In the southeastern towns of Vangaindrano and Farafangana, fruit bats are occasionally the targets of large-scale hunting, regularly being featured as the "plat du jour" in small roadside restaurants (*hotely*), showcasing the occasional large-scale commercial hunting that can take place on Madagascar (Racey et al. 2010).

Bats are also hunted across western Madagascar, using the same methods practiced in the east. Some evidence indicates that the consumption of fruit bats is much higher in the west, particularly the Menabe Region, than in eastern Madagascar, such as the area near Andasibe (Razafimanahaka et al. 2012). In the Menabe Region, *P. rufus* and *E. dupreanum* are often hunted at night, with nets placed in the upper portions of flowering or fruiting trees to capture foraging bats (Jenkins and Racey 2008). Bats are opportunistically hunted in Ankarafantsika National Park when local people are in the forest to collect tubers and encounter a bat roost in the foliage (Jenkins and Racey 2008). At this site, roughly 10% of surveyed households had consumed bats during the 12 months before the 2014 to 2015 survey, primarily targeting *P. rufus* (Borgerson et al. 2019b).

On the Mahafaly Plateau of the southwest, *Macronycteris commersoni* (Commerson's Leaf-nosed Bat; Hipposideridae) is targeted for hunting and consumption, whereas the capture of smaller insectivorous species is likely accidental (Goodman 2006). These nontargeted species include *Miniopterus gleni* (Miniopteridae) and *Triaenops menamena* (Rhinonycteridae). In and around Tsimanampesotse National Park, bats are hunted and consumed, with 30% of local survey respondents in 2016 reporting the presence of bat consumption in their communities (Fernández-Llamazares et al. 2018). *Eidolon dupreanum* and *Mormopterus jugularis* (Molossidae) hunting is conducted with nets, sticks, and stones in caves both within and around this protected area. In the far south, *P. rufus* is actively hunted using nets that target the bats when they feed on introduced *Agave sisalana* (Sisal) flowers at night (Jenkins and Racey 2008).

LEMURS

Although all lemur (order Primates) species are protected by law (Ordonnance MAP/FOR 1962-20, guaranteeing the protection of all lemurs), hunting is widespread across all forested areas of Madagascar (Table 5.3). Lemurs are endemic to Madagascar. Lemur

FIGURE 5.8 **Different images of preparation of wild animals. A) A local Betsimisaraka hunter near Makira protected area singeing the spines off a *Tenrec ecaudatus* (Tailless Tenrec) prior to cooking it for lunch; B) several *Rousettus madagascariensis* (Madagascar Rousette) being cooked near the Makira Forest; C) a local Betsimisaraka hunter has butchered a *Eulemur albifrons* (White-fronted Brown Lemur) prior to cooking it; and D) butchering and selling the meat of *Eretmochelys imbricata* (Hawksbill Turtle) for local consumption near Antongil Bay.** (PHOTOS by C. Golden.)

hunting practices have been present since the arrival of humans, though overall pressure has increased, owing to rapid human population increases of over 3% per annum (Stocker et al. 2019), lack of enforced conservation protection through a viable judicial system (Waeber et al. 2016), and political instability (Schwitzer et al. 2014).

In the Makira and Masoala protected areas, decreases in lemur species richness and population density are associated with forest habitat degradation and hunting pressure (Borgerson 2015; Farris et al. 2015). Roughly half of all surveyed households hunted at least one of 11 locally occurring lemur species, based on longitudinal surveys conducted between 2005 and 2013, and lemurs made up 11% of total harvested wildlife biomass (Golden et al. 2014a). Hunting in Makira tends to be more passive than active, focusing on traps and snares rather than pursuit hunting. While both men and women opportunistically hunt forest mammals, only men set snare traps (Golden 2009; Borgerson et al. 2016). While lemurs are occasionally actively hunted with slingshots, spears, and dogs, the majority of lemur hunting is passive, using snares called *laly* (Figure 5.7b). In this area, *laly totoko* are baited with bananas, *Canarium* fruits, *vongo* fruits, or others, whereas *laly lava* are not baited. These are similar to snaring techniques used in the extreme southeast of the island, where they are called *tandroho* (Randriamanalina et al. 2000). Hunters clear a small forest area and direct lemur movement across downed horizontal tree trunks resting off the ground, which act as bridges connecting the forest on either side of the cleared area. Snares are set along the bridge, sometimes using bananas or other fruits as bait. Snares are typically made on-site using forest products and consist of a noose attached to a strong, bent sapling. The noose is woven through a frame with a trigger mechanism that is placed vertically on the horizontal branch bridge directly above the food bait.

On the Masoala Peninsula, 89% of household members had eaten a lemur in their lifetime, with 19–36% having consumed lemur in the prior 12 months (Borgerson et al. 2016, 2019a). Nine out of the 10 lemur species in the Masoala area are hunted, even though hunting is legally prohibited for all species (Borgerson

2016). Lemurs, particularly *Eulemur albifrons* (White-fronted Brown Lemur) (Figure 5.8c) and *Varecia rubra* (Red Ruffed Lemur), constituted 13% of the bushmeat consumed in this area in terms of biomass.

In the communities surrounding the Betampona protected area, members of approximately one in five households had eaten a lemur in the prior 12 months, but at low quantities, with only 0.75 lemurs consumed per household per year (Golden et al. 2014b). In the Andasibe area in 2008, 29% of people ate *Propithecus diadema* (Diademed Sifaka), and 23% ate *E. fulvus* (Brown Lemur) (Razafimanahaka et al. 2012). In the nearby Ambatovy mine area, high%ages of local people ate lemur species, including *E. fulvus* (45%), *Avahi laniger* (Eastern Woolly Lemur) (42%), *P. diadema* (36%), and *Indri indri* (Indri) (17%) (Randriamamonjy et al. 2015). At Kianjavato, 5.7% of households ate lemurs in 2013, which made up 12.7% of the number of individual forest mammals consumed (Borgerson et al. 2018b).

In the area around Lake Alaotra, only 2.5% of households had eaten lemurs during the prior year, and 1.6% of the wildlife hunted was *Hapalemur alaotrensis* (Lake Alaotra Bamboo Lemur), classified as Critically Endangered on the Red List of Threatened Species (IUCN 2021) (Borgerson et al. 2018a). At least 10 lemur species, including the Critically Endangered *Varecia variegata* (Black and White Ruffed Lemur) and *Prolemur simus* (Greater Bamboo Lemur), are eaten in the Alaotra-Mangoro Region (Jenkins et al. 2011). *Eulemur fulvus* is the most preferred and the most commonly consumed.

There is also evidence of hunting in other parts of the eastern moist evergreen forests—for example, *P. edwardsi* (Milne-Edwards' Sifaka) in the Ranomafana area (Dunham et al. 2008). Near Moramanga, eating *P. diadema* and *E. fulvus* is common (Razafimanahaka et al. 2012). In the littoral forests of the extreme southeast, specifically near Sainte Luce (Manafiafy), *E. collaris* (Red-collared Brown Lemur) (Randriamanalina et al. 2000), *Cheirogaleus* spp. (dwarf lemurs), and *Microcebus* spp. (mouse lemurs) are eaten; the latter two genera are easily captured during the cooler season when they estivate/hibernate in the trunks of trees (Bollen and Donati 2006).

In the northwest, *E. macaco* (Black Lemur) is threatened by hunting pressure, such that its population was reduced to 30 individuals in 2005 (Bayart and Simmen 2005). Significant evidence of lemur hunting, especially of *E. fulvus* and *P. verreauxi* (Verreaux's Sifaka), was found in Ankarafantsika National Park, constituting the majority (68%) of wildlife hunted by raffia harvesters (Garcia and Goodman 2003). In a survey of households adjacent to the park, more than 10% of household members had eaten at least one of the five lemur species that were hunted in that area during the prior 12 months (Borgerson et al. 2019b). In the extreme southwest, seven lemur species are hunted near Ranobe, with *Microcebus* being the most common target (Gardner and Davies 2014).

Since about 2010, another form of lemur exploitation has been uncovered: the organized commercial or semicommercial capture of animals for an illicit bushmeat trade. For example, in the Daraina area, specifically in and around the Loky Manambato protected area, the carcasses of many tens of *E. coronatus* (Crowned Lemur) were confiscated (Goodman et al. 2018). The lemurs were apparently destined for the black market of Sambava. The animals were drugged with poison-laden fruits and captured, and in a drugged state were easy to handle. Some of these animals are immediately killed and then dried in the form of local biltong, *kitoza*. Others are given milk, the reputed antidote to the poison, and then kept in captivity to be fattened up and later sold as different forms of bushmeat. The estimated market value per individual was about US$5 (15,000 MGA). Unfortunately, this is not an isolated event, and similar capture for the black market is known from several sites in northern and northeastern portions of the island, although prices for a single lemur are much higher in the north and northeast. In Daraina there are also cases of *P. tattersalli* (Tattersall's Sifaka), a species considered Critically Endangered, being part of this illicit trade.

CARNIVORA

Members of the order Carnivora are hunted throughout continental Africa and Madagascar, primarily for food (Doughty et al. 2014; Farris et al. 2015; Table 5.3). In Madagascar, two different carnivoran groups occur, members of the endemic family Eupleridae (see Veron et al., pp. 1863–65) and three species of introduced animals (families Viverridae, Canidae, and Felidae). Large native euplerid carnivorans (*Cryptoprocta ferox*, *Fossa fossana*, *Eupleres goudotii*) are nationally protected, with hunting restricted, while all vontsira species (*Galidia elegans*, *Galidictis fasciata*, *Salanoia concolor*) are game species that can be hunted during the legal hunting season (1 April–30 June). Introduced non-native carnivorans are considered nuisance/pest species and can be hunted without restriction (e.g., *Viverricula indica*) (Decree 2006-400, Ordonnance MAP/FOR 60-126).

Carnivorans tend to be captured by dogs or snares. Frequently, snares are similar to those used to trap *Potamochoerus larvatus* (African Bush Pig) or lemurs and are positioned along forest trails or along a path leading to a permanent water source or to village chicken coops housing domesticated poultry. Hunters also construct a trap type targeting carnivorans called *antombato* (Figures 5.7c and d), which is located at the junction of branches and uses a chicken or other bird as bait. A noose is placed in the fork of the leaning branch and is surrounded by two branches with huge thorns, so that the carnivoran must go through the noose to reach the bait. The bird bait is attached to a vertical stick, which buttresses a horizontal stick. The horizontal stick acts as connector between the noose and a stone with a minimum weight of 2.5 kg. When the carnivoran reaches through the noose toward the bait, it jostles the vertical stick, which loosens the buttressed horizontal stick. This causes the noose to be dragged down by the weight of the stone, and the animal is typically strangled or immobilized.

Carnivoran hunting is common across the area within and surrounding the Makira and Masoala protected areas, including of six euplerid species (*Galidia elegans*, Ring-tailed Vontsira; *Galidictis fasciata*, Broad-striped Vontsira; *Salanoia concolor*, Brown-tailed Vontsira; *Cryptoprocta ferox*, Fosa; *Fossa fossana*, Spotted Fanaloka; *Eupleres goudotii*, Falanouc). The most heavily hunted carnivorans in these areas are the introduced *Viverricula indica* (Small Indian Civet), *Galidia elegans*, and *C. ferox* (Golden 2009; Farris et al. 2015; Borgerson 2016). In the Makira and Masoala protected areas, members of 40% of households hunted carnivoran species, which constituted 8% of the total local wildlife biomass consumed (Golden et al. 2014a). In a 2015 study of Masoala, more than 10% of surveyed household members consumed carnivorans in the 12 months prior to the study, and euplerids accounted for 7% of the wildlife biomass consumed (Borgerson et al. 2019a).

Similarly, 10% of households in the communities surrounding the Betampona protected area consumed carnivoran meat, eating on average 0.16 animals per household per year (Golden et al. 2014b). In the Ambatovy mine area, 12% of respondents reported that they had consumed *C. ferox* during the previous year (Randriamamonjy et al. 2015). At least five euplerids (*C. ferox*, *Galidia elegans*, *Galidictis fasciata*, *F. fossana*, *E. goudotii*) were reported to have been eaten during the prior year in the Alaotra-Mangoro Region (Jenkins et al. 2011), and the introduced carnivoran *Viverricula indica* constituted 1.2% of the wildlife hunted in the area surrounding Lake Alaotra (Borgerson et al. 2018a). Very low levels of carnivoran hunting occurred in Kianjavato, where carnivorans made up only 0.3% of total wildlife consumption (Borgerson et al. 2018b).

Carnivoran hunting has been observed in western Madagascar in the Menabe Region (Randrianandrianina et al. 2010) and in Ankarafantsika National Park (Garcia and Goodman 2003). *Cryptoprocta ferox*, *V. indica*, and *E. goudotii* were all hunted in Ankarafantsika National Park; members of one in four households ate *V. indica*, and less than 3% of household members hunted endemic euplerid carnivorans (Borgerson et al. 2019b).

BIRDS

Empirical data documenting rates of bird hunting are not well established in Madagascar, particularly with regard to forest-dwelling taxa. Birds are hunted across the island, with nearly every species from large to small a potential target for consumption. Bird hunting typically involves slingshots, though ground birds and seabirds are often snared. Although firearms are also occasionally used, that technique focuses on species that can be commercially sold for a high price. Harvesting of birds is typically driven by subsistence consumption, though some species (including Madagascar's three parrot species: *Coracopsis nigra*, Lesser Vasa Parrot; *C. vasa*, Greater Vasa Parrot; *Agapornis canus*, Gray-headed Lovebird) are captured for the pet trade (Reuter et al. 2017). There is regular hunting of birds along foot trails passing through forests, where people walking through such zones shoot birds with slingshots for food. Remnant piles of plucked feathers along a trail or by a temporary fire site are telltale signs of such exploitation, and often involve different species of couas (*Coua* spp.), doves and pigeons, and ground-rollers, all relatively large in body size. During the breeding season, there is also considerable exploitation of seabird eggs (Le Corre and Bemanaja 2009; see Le Corre et al., pp. 1637–50).

In the Alaotra-Mangoro Region, a variety of bird species are consumed. With the exception of *Numida meleagris* (Helmeted Guineafowl) and *Anas erythrorhyncha* (Red-billed Duck), most species are not frequently consumed (Jenkins et al. 2011). *Anas melleri* (Meller's Duck), as well as various other waterbirds, is hunted in and around the area of Lake Alaotra with snares and often with decoy ducks as bait (Randriamahefasoa 2001). There are also different hunting excursions arranged for national and international bird hunters, mostly associated with waterbirds, such as ducks, or game birds, such as *N. meleagris*, *Pterocles personatus* (Madagascar Sandgrouse), *Margaroperdix madagarensis* (Madagascar Partridge), and *Coturnix* spp. (quail).

In the Makira area, detailed analyses have shown that forest habitat degradation is associated with decreases in bird species richness and population densities (Farris et al. 2015). A variety of wild birds are commonly consumed in this region (Golden et al. 2019), though no calculations of rates or sustainability have yet been made. On the Masoala Peninsula, 72.9% of households surveyed in 2015 had consumed at least one forest bird in the previous 12 months, for a mean annual household consumption rate of 10.4 forest birds per year (Borgerson et al. 2019a). Additionally, forest birds accounted for 59.7% of the total number of forest animals caught. In Sainte Luce (Manafiafy), birds such as fruit pigeons (*Treron australis*, Madagascar Green-pigeon, and *Alectroenas madagascariensis*, Madagascar Blue-pigeon), *Coracopsis vasa* and *C. nigra* parrots, and *Hypsipetes madagascariensis* (Madagascar Bulbul) are hunted with snares, arrows, or slingshots (Bollen and Donati 2006).

Birds are hunted across the western parts of Madagascar as well. In the Menabe Region, although not a top taste preference, meat from five different wild bird species was consumed (Randrianandrianina et al. 2010). In the Mikea area, *Coua* spp. (couas), *Lophotibis cristata* (Madagascar Crested Ibis), *Numida meleagris*, *Athene superciliaris* (White-browed Owl), and *Upupa marginata* (Madagascar Hoopoe), as well as other passerines, were hunted and consumed (Goodman et al. 2004). In the Ranobe area of the southwest, birds are typically hunted by snaring or slingshots, primarily for subsistence consumption (Gardner and Davies 2014).

REPTILES AND AMPHIBIANS

Frogs, turtles, crocodiles, and tortoises are hunted for food and trade throughout Madagascar, while chameleons and snakes are most often avoided (Table 5.3). However, some snakes, particularly boas, are hunted for consumption (e.g., *Acrantophis madagascariensis*, Boidae, in Ankarafantsika National Park; Borgerson et al. 2019b). In the city of Andapa and the area of Makira, the Chinese-Malagasy population puts pressure on boa species, as evidenced by its availability in Chinese-owned restaurants. Large frogs tend to be harvested at night when they are active and their calls make them more noticeable, though they can be opportunistically harvested at all times of day. Turtles and tortoises are too slow to avoid targeted hunting.

In Makira and Masoala, the large frog *Mantidactylus grandidieri* (see Scherz et al., pp. 1365–68) is commonly hunted and eaten (C. Golden and C. Borgerson, unpublished data). At four different sites near Moramanga, frogs are commonly collected, and during the course of a year, an estimated >3200 frogs were delivered to a restaurant in eastern Madagascar (Jenkins et al. 2009). Only a few other frog species are known to be hunted for consumption throughout Madagascar (see Edmonds et al., pp. 1331–36). These include *Boehmantis microtympanum*, *Boophis goudotii*, *Hoplobatrachus* (introduced; see Vences et al., pp. 1402–3), and species in the genus *Mantidactylus* (Guarino et al. 2019).

In Ankarafantsika, turtles have been found in bone middens, having been hunted by raffia harvesters (Garcia and Goodman 2003). Several freshwater turtles, locally called *kapidolo*, *sokatra*, and *kapika andrano*, are hunted for food, though at relatively low rates (Borgerson et al. 2019b). *Erymnochelys madagascariensis* (see Kuchling et al., pp. 1469–74) is also hunted in this region, even though it is listed on the IUCN Red List as Critically Endangered and local conservation programming for this species is prominent and well established (Borgerson et al. 2019b).

In southwestern Madagascar, terrestrial reptiles in Ranobe are typically avoided for consumption, with the exception of the *Pyxis arachnoides* (Spider Tortoise) and *Astrochelys radiata* (Radiated Tortoise) (Gardner and Davies 2014; Pedrono et al., pp. 1463–68). Hunting of *A. radiata* is common in the extreme southwest of the island and occurs in both the dry and wet seasons, with between 270 and 2325 tortoises collected per year by one group of harvesters (O'Brien et al. 2003). In 2000, there were estimated to be about 13 harvester groups in this area, and thus the total annual regional tortoise harvest in this fashion was estimated to be from 2430 to 46,500 adult *A. radiata*. Monitoring of public trash dumps in the city of Toliara provided additional evidence of regional *A. radiata* consumption, with peaks in the presence of carapaces during May to June and October to December (Manjoazy et al. 2017). This species is also collected in and around the Andohahela National Park in the southeast for a larger regional market. Poachers target the largest tortoises in this park, leading to small sizes of individual tortoises and likely causing low recruitment rates (Paquette et al. 2009).

Declines in the number, average size, and nesting rate in Madagascar's sea turtles present a conservation challenge (Rakotonirina and Cooke 1994). Five species of marine turtle live along Madagascar's coastline, four of which—*Chelonia mydas* (Green Turtle), *Caretta caretta* (Loggerhead Turtle), *Eretmochelys imbricata* (Hawksbill Turtle), and *Lepidochelys olivacea* (Olive Ridley Turtle)—have previously been recognized to be hunted for their meat (Hughes 1973; Rakotonirina and Cooke 1994; Ratsimbazafy 2003). *Chelonia mydas* represents the vast majority (93.6%) of marine-turtle catches in southwestern Madagascar (Humber et al. 2010). *Eretmochelys imbricata* is typically hunted by employing traditional methods such as harpoons, nets, and grapnel (Hughes 1973). Though previously believed to be caught principally for their shells rather than meat (Rakotonirina and Cooke 1994), recent observations of their harvest for food show otherwise (Figure 5.8d). The remaining species, *Dermochelys coriacea* (Leatherback Turtle), is rarely caught. The total annual marine-turtle catch in southwestern Madagascar along the 1180 km of coastline of the former Toliara Province was estimated to be between 10,000 and 16,000 individuals (Humber et al. 2010).

Despite an internationally imposed moratorium on *Crocodylus niloticus* (Nile Crocodile) hunting and egg collecting in 2010, exploitation of this animal has persisted on Madagascar, with an estimated minimum of 2240 individuals hunted annually (CITES 2013). Crocodile hunters in Madagascar use nonselective traps and hunt from March to November, and the greatest number of individuals is harvested from the Melaky Region (CITES 2013). Although skins and eggs are the most common crocodile products in Madagascar, their meat, teeth, skulls, and oil are also utilized. The traditional Malagasy belief that *C. niloticus* individuals are human ancestors has led to various taboos (*fady*) that prevent the killing of this animal (Campbell 2013). These *fady* do not, however, appear to deter people from consuming crocodile meat or products; in Makira protected area only 4.9% of the population had consumption-based taboos for crocodiles (Golden and Comaroff 2015a).

INSECTS

Entomophagy is common on Madagascar, and the most frequently eaten insects in rural Madagascar include numerous forms from seven orders (Randrianandrasa and Berenbaum 2015; Dürr et al. 2020; see Fisher and Hugel, pp. 218–30). Additionally, arachnids are eaten, but the most commonly eaten insect group is Coleoptera, which is consistent with global trends (Randrianandrasa and Berenbaum 2015). Insects are typically grilled directly on fires, roasted on sticks, or toasted or fried in cooking pots.

The selection of insect species for consumption can be highly variable across regions of the island. In the Central Highlands, the most commonly consumed insect species are wild silkworms (as chrysalises), locusts, and beetles (Dürr et al. 2020). Similarly, in Ambatofinandrahana in the Central Highlands, silkworms are the most commonly consumed insect, followed by grasshoppers, saturniid larvae, dragonfly nymphs, and adult diving beetles (Randrianandrasa and Berenbaum 2015). In Anja, near Ambalavao, giant water bugs or water scorpions are the most commonly eaten, followed by cicadas, grasshoppers, adult Melolonthinae beetles, and adult diving beetles (Randrianandrasa and Berenbaum 2015).

In Mahabo, southwestern Madagascar, the most commonly consumed insects are fulgorid planthoppers, followed by adult diving beetles, cicadas, giant water bugs, water scorpions, and Coleoptera larvae (Randrianandrasa and Berenbaum 2015). In Vatomandry, the most commonly eaten insects are fulgorid planthoppers, vespid wasps, Coleoptera larvae, adult Melolonthinae beetles, and honeybee larvae (Randrianandrasa and Berenbaum 2015).

In the Maroantsetra area, the most frequently eaten insects are cicadas, fulgorid planthoppers, Coleoptera larvae, and giant water bugs (Randrianandrasa and Berenbaum 2015). In the Makira area, Coleoptera larvae, honeybee larvae, cicadas, rhinoceros beetles, and giant water bugs are frequently consumed (C. Golden, unpublished data). On the Masoala Peninsula, adult and late-instar fulgorid planthoppers (*Zanna tenebrosa*), adult and larval-stage coleopterans, nymphs of Odonata (specifically, dragonflies), and larval hymenopterans are the most commonly eaten insects, with households eating nearly three cups' worth of insect meat on average each year (C. Borgerson, unpublished data).

ECONOMICS OF WILDLIFE HUNTING AND TRADE

Wildlife trade is one of the major drivers of vertebrate extinction, and it affects 18% of all extant terrestrial vertebrate species on earth (5579 out of 31,745 vertebrate species; Scheffers et al. 2019). Wildlife enters the market system on Madagascar both as live animals for the pet trade (Reuter et al. 2016) and for human consumption in the form of bushmeat and a variety of different derivatives, such as oil, that have reported medicinal importance. It has been estimated that between 2010 and 2013, over 28,000 lemurs were likely impacted by illegal capture and sale for the pet trade (Reuter and Schaefer 2017). The reviewed evidence showed that local hunting was almost never induced by economic gain (e.g., Gardner and Davies 2014; Golden et al. 2014a; Borgerson et al. 2018a), but poverty was often the driver (Borgerson et al. 2016; Golden et al. 2016a). The pricing dynamics (typically household-to-household transactions) show that wildlife is almost always cheaper than the meat of domesticate alternatives (Randrianandrianina et al. 2010; Golden et al. 2014a).

Household wealth still plays an important role in determining the level of consumption of certain types of wildlife species, particularly fruit bats. Wealthier urban households are twice as likely (41%) to have consumed *Pteropus rufus* than rural houses (20%) in the Alaotra-Mangoro Region (Jenkins et al. 2011). *Potamochoerus larvatus* is likely the most commodified and marketed wildlife species, fetching a price of roughly US$1/kg in Makira in 2013 (2000 MGA to US$) (Golden et al. 2014a), in Masoala in 2015 (3000 MGA to US$) (Borgerson et al. 2019), and in Kianjavato in 2014 (3000 MGA to US$) (Borgerson et al. 2018b), or US$36 for an entire animal in the Menabe Region in 2007 and 2008 (Randrianandrianina et al. 2010).

There is also variation in the price of wildlife in various areas (Golden et al. 2014a), with spiny tenrec meat being the most expensive, and fruit bat meat the least expensive in Menabe (Randrianandrianina et al. 2010). In Makira, wildlife harvest and associated sales represented 57% of annual household cash income for local communities (Golden et al. 2014a). The price of wildlife had a negative relationship with consumption, and price increases led to reduced harvest for consumption. This type of evidence provides very optimistic signals for the potential for economic development to attenuate pressures on wildlife for food.

SUSTAINABILITY OF HUNTING

There is significant evidence of prehistoric foraging, hunting, and butchery of land vertebrates on Madagascar dating back thousands of years (e.g., Perez et al. 2005; Crowley 2010; Dewar et al. 2013; Hansford et al. 2018; see Wright and Rakotoarisoa, pp. 181–90; see Godfrey and Douglass, pp. 191–97). Although hunting may not have been the unilateral driver of past large-vertebrate extinctions on Madagascar, it was likely a strong contributing factor (Godfrey et al. 2019). More recently, it has become clear that hunting is a major driver of variation in localized species richness and population abundance. Yet, the empirical data required to power the sustainability modeling of extant species are often lacking. Below, we present the best available evidence of the impact of hunting on species persistence.

Spiny tenrec hunting is widespread across Madagascar, and in light of other confounding factors such as introduced zoonotic diseases, appears to be predominantly sustainable in the Makira area of Madagascar, given the high fecundity of the species concerned (*Tenrec* and *Setifer*) (Annapragada et al. 2021). However, the peak season for spiny tenrec hunting overlaps with the animals' pregnancy and lactation periods, which could have significantly negative impacts on the populations of these genera in the northeast (Borgerson 2016).

No formal sustainability assessments of bat hunting have been modeled. Yet, the hunting levels of insectivorous bats in the southwest surpass their breeding potential, leading to large-scale population declines and possible local extirpation of these animals over time (Goodman 2006). Because fruit bats produce only one offspring per year, they are especially susceptible to overhunting (Jenkins and Racey 2008). Rates of carnivoran hunting in the Masoala-Makira landscape were deemed unsustainable (Golden 2009; Farris et al. 2015), but have not been quantitatively evaluated elsewhere. Bird hunting practices have yet to be evaluated for sustainability. However, we know that the decline of *Aythya innotata* (Madagascar Pochard; see Rene de Roland and Young, pp. 1650–53) and extinction of *Tachybaptus rufolavatus* (Alaotra Grebe; see Young et al., pp. 1627–36) can be explained in part by hunting pressure (Randriamahefasoa 2001).

The current harvest rates for lemurs in Makira protected area are unsustainable (except for *Microcebus* spp. and *Cheirogaleus* spp.) (Golden 2009; Brook et al. 2019a). If the current rates of hunting persist, there will likely be regional extirpations of lemurs. Estimated local lemur densities are approximately inverse to body size, and hunting most severely threatens species with the largest body sizes. Additionally, simulations have shown that hunting is the most detrimental when it overlaps with the period lemurs give birth. In Ranomafana, hunting presents a major threat to *Propithecus edwardsi* populations (Dunham et al. 2008). Using a population viability analysis (PVA), these authors concluded that a combination of deforestation, hunting, and El Niño effects could likely lead to a 50% population decline within three generations. Another PVA was conducted for the Critically Endangered *Eulemur flavifrons* (Blue-eyed Black Lemur), where the simulations suggested that the first extinction of certain populations could take place within 13 years, with increased habitat destruction (Volampeno et al. 2015).

Throughout Madagascar, chelonians and crocodiles are directly threatened by high demand as bushmeat, and chameleons and a variety of other reptiles by the demands of the pet trade (Jenkins et al. 2014; see Carpenter et al., pp. 1452–55. In the extreme southwest there have been dramatic declines in the regional population of *Astrochelys radiata*, and its geographic range has contracted by 20% in recent decades (O'Brien et al. 2003).

INTERSECTIONS BETWEEN TASTE AND NUTRITION

Taste preferences seem to drive some of the variation in wildlife hunting patterns. Across Madagascar, people preferred the meat of domestic livestock and fish to that of wild animals (Merson et al. 2019a). In particular, chicken, beef, and pork were ranked as favorite domesticated meat dishes, while top preferences for wildlife were fish (26%), spiny tenrec (21%), *Numida meleagris* (20%), eel (16%), *Potamochoerus larvatus* (11%), lemur (2%), and bat (1%). Yet, this is not always the case, and lemurs can be top taste preferences at some locations (e.g., Golden 2005, 2009).

In the Alaotra-Mangoro Region, wildlife generally is not preferred, exceptions being *P. larvatus* and *Eulemur fulvus* as preferred meats (Jenkins et al. 2011). In the area around Lake Alaotra, non-bushmeat sources of animal protein (chicken, pork, beef, goose, and fish) were consistently ranked higher for taste preference compared with bushmeat (Borgerson et al. 2018a). Similarly, in the southwest, beef and chicken were preferred, and few bushmeat species were favored over domestic meat (Gardner and Davies 2014). Beef and chicken were the preferred meats, but some reported wild species to be equally preferable. In the communities surrounding the Betampona protected area, only 4% of households preferred wildlife to domesticated meats (Golden et al. 2014a). In the Menabe Region, wildlife is consistently ranked low among taste preferences, though spiny tenrec meat was ranked highest among wildlife (Randrianandrianina et al. 2010). The majority of urban insect consumers in the Central Highlands consider insects to be tasty (Dürr et al. 2020).

The vast majority of hunting on Madagascar is driven by subsistence consumption needs (Brashares et al. 2011; Golden et al. 2014b), even when there is little evidence that the hunting contributes significantly to nutritional status (Golden et al. 2014a; Borgerson et al. 2018a, 2018b). Although there is some evidence of wildlife consumption being used for traditional events (Bollen and Donati 2006) and national holidays (Gardner and Davies 2014), the principal reason for hunting is the critical role it plays in relieving food security problems in some locations on the island (Golden et al. 2011; Borgerson et al. 2019a). For example, poorer and more food-insecure households in the Makira protected area are more reliant on wildlife for food (Golden et al. 2016a).

Seasonality of wildlife hunting may play an important role in compensating for periods of food scarcity. In the Makira, lemur hunting is seasonal, with greatest pressure from February to May, the season that coincides with low consumption of domesticated meat and fish (Golden et al. 2019). Preadolescent children who consumed a greater quantity of wildlife had higher hemoglobin concentrations; losing access to wildlife in this area would induce an estimated 29% increase in the number of children suffering from anemia and a tripling in the number of anemia cases in children of the poorest households (Golden et al. 2011). Because people in the Masoala area consume more lemurs, *Potamochoerus larvatus*, and spiny tenrecs when they consume fewer domesticated animals and fish, these types of wildlife may have greater impacts on human health and nutrition than animals that are hunted primarily during seasons in which domestic animals are more frequently consumed (Borgerson 2016). Out of the total micro- and macronutrients derived from animals in this area, 44.5% of iron and 38.4% of protein was provided by the consumption of forest animals (Borgerson et al. 2019a).

Hunting of bats, such as *Eidolon dupreanum* and a variety of insectivorous species, in the area near and within the Tsimanampesotse National Park, and in a more general manner in the southwest, mainly occurred during periods of food shortage (Goodman 2006; Fernández-Llamazares et al. 2018). Additionally, edible insects in rural communities are most commonly found between October and March, which is a season that is associated with high food prices (Randrianandrasana and Berenbaum 2015). This highlights the importance of edible insects in alleviating food insecurity in rural areas of Madagascar. Insects can be important, free sources of food and nutrition, especially because their harvest coincides with the lean season, as most insects are consumed during November and December (Dürr et al. 2020).

CONCLUSION

In broad terms, we characterize hunting in Madagascar as largely subsistence, though not preferred; driven by poverty and food insecurity; and ecologically unsustainable. Although rare exceptions of taste preferences for certain wildlife species exist (e.g., Golden 2005; Jenkins et al. 2011), wildlife meat is almost categorically considered inferior in taste to domesticated meats (Merson et al. 2019a). Although not preferred, wild meats can serve a critical function in supporting human nutrition and health (e.g., Golden et al. 2011, 2019; Borgerson 2019a) and their consumption is nearly always associated with poverty (e.g., Borgerson et al. 2016; Golden et al. 2016a). Throughout Madagascar, it is evident that most species are unable to withstand current levels of hunting pressure (Randriamahefasoa 2001; O'Brien et al. 2003; Goodman 2006; Dunham et al. 2008; Jenkins and Racey 2008; Golden 2009; Farris et al. 2015; Brook et al. 2019b), with the possible exception of some spiny tenrec species (Annapragada et al. 2021). This is not surprising, given the life-history characteristics of these species and their evolutionary trajectories, which are largely disconnected from human impacts. Therefore, unsustainable hunting will lead, for local people living in the countryside of the island, to the self-depletion of their nutritional resources, disadvantaging their health and livelihoods, and at the same time to extinction at the population or species level of national biodiversity.

Subject editor: Steven M. Goodman

EDIBLE TERRESTRIAL ARTHROPOD TRADITIONS AND USES ON MADAGASCAR

B. L. Fisher and S. Hugel

In 1861, Emperor Napoleon III of France sent Dr. Auguste Vinson to Madagascar to attend the coronation of King Radama II. When the French envoy met the new ruler, the king's 10-year-old son was also present. Young Jon's pockets, Vinson reported, were filled with roasted pupae of the wild silkworm (*Borocera cajani*, Lasiocampidae), which he snacked on during the interview (1863c: 47; 1865: 310). Vinson was not the first visitor to observe the Malagasy custom of eating insects. Still, his story highlights two important aspects of edible-insect traditions on Madagascar. First, the culture of eating insects has long been widespread on the island—a tasty treat for hungry farmers and the highest members of the Merina Dynasty alike. Second, the most enthusiastic insect consumers on Madagascar, even today, are children.

Here we review the history of consumption of insects (entomophagy) and spiders on the island, and provide a list of commonly consumed species. We discuss past culinary practices, and suggest that edible insects offer a sorely needed solution to current social, nutritional, and biodiversity concerns on the island. The prevalence of insect consumption, species preferences, and preparations of the past provide a historical context for improving current efforts to use insects to address food insecurity and biodiversity preservation concerns on Madagascar.

EARLY ACCOUNTS

Early records of edible insects on Madagascar include discussion of three principal groups: fulgorids (Flatidae; see Świerczewski and Stroiński, pp. 987–91), moths (order Lepidoptera; see Lees and Minet, pp. 1141–72), and locusts (order Orthoptera; see Hugel, pp. 996–1014). Early records also include arachnids (order Araneae; see Wood and Griswold, pp. 878–93). These groups captured the interest of early travelers for different reasons. The fulgorids produced candy-like "manna"; the dual-purpose moths and spiders were both eaten and produced silk; and the dramatic swarms of locusts destroyed crops but were a cherished food staple across Madagascar. Our review focuses just on the literature that relates to insects and spiders as food or their potential as a food source. Honey and beeswax are another prevalent topic mentioned in very early reports (e.g., Cauche 1651: 35, 53, 78; Carpeau du Saussay 1722: 244), but here we limit the discussion of Hymenoptera to the consumption of larvae.

The principal publications documenting the practice and uses of edible insects on Madagascar include Flacourt (1658 [repr. 1995]; Hemiptera, Lepidoptera), Vinson (1863a, 1863b, 1863c; Araneae, Lepidoptera), Coquerel (1856, 1866; Lepidoptera), Sibree (1884; Orthoptera), Camboué (1886, 1888; Orthoptera), Grandidier and Grandidier (1908; insects in general), Perrier de la Bâthie (1905; insects eaten by the Sakalava), Decary (1925; Orthoptera), Zolotarevsky (1930; Orthoptera), Decary (1931, 1937, 1951; insects in general), and Gade (1985; tapia woodland insects) (see Kull and Birkinshaw, pp. 121–27). Other works that provide context for edible insects include Pollen (1868), Leguével de Lacombe and de Froberville (1840), W. Ellis (1858), Pfeiffer (1861), Lacaze (1881), and Osborn (1924). In most cases we are able to link discussions in the literature to current scientific names (Table 5.4).

The following works should not be viewed as primary sources. They summarize information from previous publications that include erroneous records from Madagascar: Hope (1842), Simmonds (1859, 1885), Sachot (1864), Macquarie (1884), Holt (1885), Bergier (1941), Théodoridès (1949), Bodenheimer (1951), Ramos-Elorduy et al. (2009), van Huis et al. (2013), Malaisse and Latham (2014), Dossey et al. (2016), and Mitsuhashi (2016). Since 2010, a growing number of studies have described modern insect-eating practices on Madagascar (Barsics et al. 2013a, 2013b; Randrianandrasana and Berenbaum 2015; Van Itterbeeck et al. 2019; Dürr et al. 2020); when appropriate, these are included in Table 5.4 and discussed below.

COLEOPTERA

Beetles are considered good sources of food in communities across the island. During their trip to Madagascar from May to September 1857, Joseph Lambert and Ida Pfeiffer were regularly invited to dine by Queen Ranavalona I. At these banquets, "the most exquisite treats (naturally for the palates of the natives) were served, among others ground and water beetles which, especially the last ones pass for delicious" (Pfeiffer 1861, our translation). Vinson (1863c: 45–46) found a number of beetle species being consumed and described how they were prepared. Along the irrigation channels of rice fields, scarab (Scarabaeidae) beetle larvae were dug up from the soil at about 20 cm depth. When boiled or fried, he noted, the larvae are considered quite tasty. Grandidier (1869: 154) observed that because excess digging for the larvae could damage irrigation channels for rice fields, these insects were collected far from villages, limiting their availability. In 1868–1869, Lacaze (1881: 67) noticed baskets containing beetle larvae in an Antananarivo market.

Large terrestrial beetles are consumed most often on Madagascar. These include species from the families Carabidae, Cerambycidae, Curculionidae, Lucanidae, Passalidae, and Scarabaeidae. Readily available near villages, they are eaten as larvae, pupae, and adults. The larvae are prized and often fried in their own fat or roasted with a little salt on hot coals. Charpentier de Cossigny (1799: 329), based on observations in 1773, noted the Malagasy ate palm weevil larvae raw. Today, adult beetles are often collected and eaten by children (Figures 5.9c–e). On B. Fisher's first visit to Madagascar in 1992, he saw children filling a *kapaoka* (a tin can) with adult Melolonthinae (Scarabaeidae) found on vegetation around a village at the edge of the Andohahela protected area.

TABLE 5.4. **Edible insects and arachnids consumed on Madagascar, which based on the literature includes records of one edible spider species and at least 101 edible insect species**

CLASSIFICATION	SPECIES	REFERENCES (OFTEN INCLUDING FIRST REFERENCE)
Araneae: Araneidae	*Nephila inaurata madagascariensis* (Vinson, 1863)	Vinson (1863d)
Coleoptera: Carabidae	*Scarites* sp.	Decary (1937); Barsics et al. (2013a); Randrianandrasana and Berenbaum (2015); Dürr et al. (2020)
Coleoptera: Cerambycidae	*Batocera rufomaculata* (De Geer, 1775)	Randrianandrasana and Berenbaum (2015)
Coleoptera: Curculionidae	*Eugnoristus monachus* Schoenherr, 1838	Bodenheimer (1951, stated without referencing); Barsics et al. (2013a)
	Rhina sp.	Bodenheimer (1951, stated without referencing); Barsics et al. (2013a)
	Rhynchophorus phoenicis Schoenherr, 1825	Probably what Vinson (1863c) refers to as "Conocephalas Guerini (Calandride)," B. Fisher (unpublished data)
	Rhynchophorus sp.	Bodenheimer (1951, stated without referencing); Barsics et al. (2013a); Dürr et al. (2020)
Coleoptera: Dytiscidae	*Cybister* spp.	Six species cited but with questionable identification: Decary (1937); Barsics et al. (2013a); Randrianandrasana and Berenbaum (2015)
	Rhantus latus (Fairmaire, 1869)	Ramos-Elorduy et al. (2009, stated without referencing)
Coleoptera: Gyrinidae	*Dineutus sinuosipennis* Laporte, 1840	Possibly the *Dineutus* sp. recorded by Randrianandrasana and Berenbaum (2015)
Coleoptera: Hydrophilidae	*Sternolophus* sp.	Randrianandrasana and Berenbaum (2015)
Coleoptera: Lucanidae	*Prosopocoilus serricornis* (Latreille, 1817)	Decary (1937); Barsics et al. (2013a); Randrianandrasana and Berenbaum (2015)
Coleoptera: Passalidae	Palmicolous passalid	Théodoridès (1949, citing a correspondence from R. Paulian); Barsics et al. (2013a)
Coleoptera: Scarabaeidae, Cetoniinae	*Bricoptis variolosa* (Gory & Percheron, 1833)	Dürr et al. (2020)
Coleoptera: Scarabaeidae, Dynastinae	*Hexodon unicolor* Olivier, 1789	Dürr et al. (2020)
	Oryctes boas (Fabricius, 1775)	Randrianandrasana and Berenbaum (2015)
	O. gigas Castelnau, 1840	Randrianandrasana and Berenbaum (2015)
	O. pyrrhus Burmeister, 1847	Randrianandrasana and Berenbaum (2015)
Coleoptera: Scarabaeidae, Melolonthinae	*Amphimallon solstitiale* (Linnaeus, 1758)	Dürr et al. (2020)
	Enaria limbalis Fairmaire, 1900	Randrianandrasana and Berenbaum (2015)
	Hoplochelus marginalis (Fairmaire, 1889)	Randrianandrasana and Berenbaum (2015)
	Hoplochelus spp.	Randrianandrasana and Berenbaum (2015)
	Phyllophaga sp.	Dürr et al. (2020)
	Proagosternus sp.	Decary (1937); Randrianandrasana and Berenbaum (2015)
	Proagosternus sp.	Barsics et al. (2013a)
	Serica sp.	Dürr et al. (2020)
	Tricholepis sp.	Decary (1937); Randrianandrasana and Berenbaum (2015); could be the Hannetons of Vinson (1863a)

(continued overleaf)

TABLE 5.4. ***continued***

CLASSIFICATION	SPECIES	REFERENCES (OFTEN INCLUDING FIRST REFERENCE)
Hemiptera: Belostomatidae	*Hydrocyrius punctatus* (Stål, 1865)	Probably the "aquatic cockroaches" of Lacaze (1881); Randrianandrasana and Berenbaum (2015)
Hemiptera: Cercopoidea	Indet.	Randrianandrasana and Berenbaum (2015); Dürr et al. (2020)
Hemiptera: Cicadidae	*Malagasia aperta* (Signoret, 1860)	Randrianandrasana and Berenbaum (2015)
	M. distanti (Karsch, 1890)	Randrianandrasana and Berenbaum (2015)
	Yanga andriana (Distant, 1899)	Randrianandrasana and Berenbaum (2015)
	Y. guttulata (Signoret, 1860)	Randrianandrasana and Berenbaum (2015)
Hemiptera: Flatidae	*Flatida coccinea* (Auber, 1955)	Randrianandrasana and Berenbaum (2015)
	F. rosea (Melichar, 1901)	Decary (1937); Randrianandrasana and Berenbaum (2015)
Hemiptera: Fulgoridae	*Zanna tenebrosa madagascariensis* (Signoret, 1860)	Gade (1985); Randrianandrasana and Berenbaum (2015)
	Z. tenebrosa (Fabricius, 1775)	Decary (1937); Randrianandrasana and Berenbaum (2015)
Hemiptera: Naucoridae	*Heleocoris naucoroides* Montandon, 1897	Randrianandrasana and Berenbaum (2015)
Hemiptera: Nepidae	*Laccotrephes* sp.	Probably the "nepa" of Decary (1937) and of Randrianandrasana and Berenbaum (2015)
Hemiptera: Notonectidae	Indet.	Randrianandrasana and Berenbaum (2015)
Hymenoptera: Apidae	*Apis mellifera unicolor* (Latreille, 1804)	Grandidier (1908); Perrier de la Bâthie (1905); Bodenheimer (1951), Randrianandrasana and Berenbaum (2015)
	Liotrigona madecassa (Saussure, 1890)	Grandidier (1908)
Hymenoptera: Vespidae	*Polistes olivaceus* (De Geer, 1773)	Mostly likely the *Polistes* referred to by Perrier de la Bâthie (1905) and Grandidier and Grandidier (1908); Decary (1937); Randrianandrasana and Berenbaum (2015)
	Ropalidia vitripennis (Saussure, 1899)	Randrianandrasana and Berenbaum (2015)
Lepidoptera: Bombycidae	*Bombyx mori* (Linnaeus, 1758)	Buet (1883: 28): "The Hovas naturalized in Antananarivo / mulberry and silkworm from China"; Conte (1910); after Fauchère (1914), introduced by Jean Laborde around 1844
Lepidoptera: Lasiocampidae	*Borocera cajani* Vinson, 1863	Vinson (1863d); Trimoulet (1865); Coquerel (1866); Decary (1937); Barsics et al. (2013); Randrianandrasana and Berenbaum (2015)
	B. madagascariensis Boisduval, 1833	Decary (1937); Gade (1985)
	B. marginepunctata Guérin-Méneville, 1844	T. Razafimanantsoa (unpublished data)
	Europtera punctillata Saalmüller, 1844	Randrianandrasana and Berenbaum (2015, as indet.); T. Razafimanantsoa (unpublished data)
Lepidoptera: Limacodidae	*Latoia albifrons* Guérin-Méneville, 1844	Vinson (1863a); Decary (1937); Barsics et al. (2013)
	L. singularis (Butler, 1878)	Barsics et al. (2013)
	Parasa ebenaui (Saalmüller, 1878)	Barsics et al. (2013)
Lepidoptera: Notodontidae	*Hypsoides antsianakana* (Oberthür, 1922)	Randrianandrasana and Berenbaum (2015)
	H. diego (Coquerel, 1855)	Decary (1937); Randrianandrasana and Berenbaum (2015)
	H. radama (Coquerel, 1855)	Decary (1937); Randrianandrasana and Berenbaum (2015)

CLASSIFICATION	SPECIES	REFERENCES (OFTEN INCLUDING FIRST REFERENCE)
	H. semifusca Kiriakoff, 1969	Randrianandrasana and Berenbaum (2015)
	H. singularis Kiriakoff, 1969	Randrianandrasana and Berenbaum (2015)
Lepidoptera: Psychidae	*Deborrea malgassa* (Heylaerts, 1884)	Decary (1931: 290); Decary (1937); Portier (1949, as *Psyche joannisii*); Bourgogne (1984); Grubenmann and Madle (2016)
Lepidoptera: Saturniidae	*Antherina suraka* (Boisduval, 1833) subsp. *suraka*	Decary (1937); Randrianandrasana and Berenbaum (2015); M. Ratsimbazafy (Sepali, unpublished data)
	Argema mittrei (Guérin-Méneville, 1847)	M. Ratsimbazafy (Sepali, unpublished data)
	Bunaea aslauga Kirby, 1877	Trimoulet (1865); Gade (1985); Barsics et al. (2013); Randrianandrasana and Berenbaum (2015)
	Ceranchia apollina Butler, 1878	M. Ratsimbazafy (Sepali, unpublished data)
	Maltagorea fusicolor (Mabille, 1879)	Gade (1985); Barsics et al. (2013)
	Hippotion gracilis (Butler, 1875)	Randrianandrasana and Berenbaum (2015) as indet. but this is the likely species
Lepidoptera: Sphingidae	Indet.	Decary (1931); DeFoliart (2002)
Odonata: Aeshnidae	Indet.	Randrianandrasana and Berenbaum (2015)
Odonata: Libellulidae	Indet.	Decary (1937); Randrianandrasana and Berenbaum (2015)
Orthoptera: Caelifera	*Acorypha decisa* (Walker, 1870)	Van Itterbeeck et al. (2019)
	Acrida madecassa (Brancsik, 1893)	Van Itterbeeck et al. (2019)
	Acrida sp.	Van Itterbeeck et al. (2019)
	A. subtilis Burr, 1902	Van Itterbeeck et al. (2019)
	Aiolopus thalassinus rodericensis (Butler, 1876)	May correspond to "*Epacromia*" cited in Camboué (1888: 796); Van Itterbeeck et al. (2019)
	Atractomorpha acutipennis (Guérin-Méneville, 1844)	Van Itterbeeck et al. (2019)
	Calephorus ornatus (Walker, 1870)	Van Itterbeeck et al. (2019)
	Catantopsis malagassus Karny, 1907	In Camboué (1888: 796) misidentified as *Catantops debilitatus*, but the Malagasy name given in the text corresponds to *C. malagassus* in Braud et al. (2014); Van Itterbeeck et al. (2019)
	C. sacalava (Brancsik, 1893)	Van Itterbeeck et al. (2019)
	Cyrtacanthacris tatarica (Linnaeus, 1758)	In Camboué (1888: 796) misidentified as *Anacridium aeruginosum*, but the Malagasy name given in the text corresponds to *C. tatarica* in Braud et al. (2014); Van Itterbeeck et al. (2019)
	Duronia chloronota (Stål, 1876)	Van Itterbeeck et al. (2019)
	Eyprepocnemis smaragdipes Bruner, 1910	Van Itterbeeck et al. (2019)
	Finotina radama (Brancsik, 1893)	Van Itterbeeck et al. (2019)
	Gastrimargus africanus madagascariensis Sjöstedt, 1928	Van Itterbeeck et al. (2019)
	Gelastorhinus edax Saussure, 1899	Van Itterbeeck et al. (2019)
	Gymnobothrus madacassus Bruner, 1910	Van Itterbeeck et al. (2019)

(continued overleaf)

TABLE 5.4. ***continued***

CLASSIFICATION	SPECIES	REFERENCES (OFTEN INCLUDING FIRST REFERENCE)
	G. variabilis Bruner, 1910	Van Itterbeeck et al. (2019)
	Heteracris nigricornis (Saussure, 1899)	Van Itterbeeck et al. (2019)
	Lemuracris longicornis Dirsh, 1966	Van Itterbeeck et al. (2019)
	Locusta migratoria migratorioides (Reiche & Fairmaire, 1849)	Sibree (1884: 412), as *Ædipoda migratoria* in his dictionary); Richardson (1885) indicated that *valala* correspond to *Æ. migratoria*; Camboué (1886: 172n, as *Locusta* sp.); Camboué (1888: 796, as *Pachytilus migratorioides*); Perrier de la Bâthie (1924, as *P. migratorioides*); Decary (1925, as *P. migratorioides*); Randrianandrasana (2014); Dürr et al. (2020); Van Itterbeeck et al. (2019)
	Nomadacris septemfasciata (Serville, 1838)	Gade (1985); Randrianandrasana (2014); Van Itterbeeck et al. (2019)
	Oedaleus virgula (Snellen van Vollenhoven, 1869)	In Camboué (1888: 796) as *Oedaeus* sp., and only *O. virgula* occurs on Madagascar (see Hugel, pp. 996–1014); Van Itterbeeck et al. (2019)
	Oxya hyla Serville, 1831	Camboué (1888: 796) as *Oxya* sp., and only *O. hyla* occurs on Madagascar (see Hugel, pp. 996–1014); Van Itterbeeck et al. (2019)
	Paracinema tricolor (Thunberg, 1815)	Camboué (1888: 796); Van Itterbeeck et al. (2019)
	Rhadinacris schistocercoides (Brancsik, 1893)	Van Itterbeeck et al. (2019)
	Rubellia nigrosignata Stål, 1875	Camboué (1888: 796); Van Itterbeeck et al. (2019)
	Trilophidia cinnabarina Brancsik, 1893	Van Itterbeeck et al. (2019)
Orthoptera: Ensifera	*Brachytrupes membranaceus colosseus* Saussure, 1899	Gade (1985: 121); Van Itterbeeck et al. (2019)
	Brachytrupes sp.	Grandidier and Grandidier (1908: 208, as *sahobaka*); Van Itterbeeck et al. (2019)
	Colossopus sp.	Van Itterbeeck et al. (2019)
	Conocephalus cf. *affinis*	*Conocephalus* sp. in Camboué (1888: 796); Van Itterbeeck et al. (2019)
	Fryerius sp.	Van Itterbeeck et al. (2019)
	Gryllus sp.	Van Itterbeeck et al. (2019); may correspond to the species identified as *Gryllus bimaculatus* in Dürr et al. (2020)
	Odontolakis sexpunctata (Serville, 1838)	Randrianandrasana (2014: 151)
	Modicogryllus sp.	Van Itterbeeck et al. (2019)
	Phaneroptera sparsa Stål, 1857	Van Itterbeeck et al. (2019)
	Phaneropterinae sp.	Van Itterbeeck et al. (2019)
	Pteronemobius malgachus (Saussure, 1877)	Van Itterbeeck et al. (2019)
	Ruspolia differens (Serville, 1838)	Van Itterbeeck et al. (2019)
	Ruspolia sp.	Van Itterbeeck et al. (2019)

Notes: "Indet." indicates unidentified species. The mention of consumption of the house cricket *Acheta domesticus* in Dürr et al. (2020) is most likely wrong, since this species does not occur on Madagascar (see Hugel, pp. 996–1014). The name "*Locusta cernensis*," sometimes cited in the literature on edible insects, was invented by Hope (1842: 137) to name the unidentified locusts mentioned in Ives (1773: 15). This does not correspond to a species name.

FIGURE 5.9 **Different uses of spiders and beetles on Madagascar. A) *Nephila inaurata madagascariensis* (Golden Orb Spider, Araneidae), known locally as *halabe*, is often eaten as a snack by boys herding cattle or given to children when they are sick. B) Madagascar was the site of a rare attempt to utilize spiders for commercial silk production. In the 19th century, a technical college was founded in Antananarivo where people were trained to farm spiders and spin their silk. The spider-silk-production tradition from this period has not survived. C–E) In Beroboka, a village near the Menabe Antimena Protected Area, children hunt for *Oryctes boas* (Rhinoceros Beetle), keep it as a pet, and consume it as a favorite snack. The wings are removed before cooking. F) Young girls collect small fish and edible insects from a pond near Ranobe in southwestern Madagascar.** (PHOTOS A and C–F by B. Fisher, and B courtesy of Fond Grandidier Library, Antananarivo.)

Aquatic beetles of families Dytiscidae (see Bergsten et al., pp. 1024–34), Gyrinidae (see Gustafson et al., pp. 1034–41), and Hydrophilidae are frequently collected by children while they net small fish in the rice fields (Figure 5.9f). Aquatic beetles are generally eaten as adults and cooked alongside the fish they are caught with.

HEMIPTERA

Etienne de Flacourt, who resided on Madagascar for several years, described planthopper honey, the sweet exudate produced by *Flatida* (Hemiptera: Flatidae) (see Świerczewski and Stroiński, pp. 987–91), in his history of the island (Flacourt 1658 [repr. 1995]: 225, our translation): "There is a kind of sugar which is formed by certain butterflies on Madagascar, on the leaves of a shrub, it is hard and soft like sugar, the inhabitants are fond of it." He goes on to describe the "butterfly" as "an admirable thing to see, that this creature spawns on the bark of the shrub in the form of a black fly whose wing ends are white, and this fly resembles a flower attached to the bark, which after a month detaches and turns into a small butterfly, some of which are red, others green and others yellow, which, for a time, will gnaw at the leaves of this shrub, then after, form this kind of sugar or honey which becomes hard like candy sugar, this sugar is very good for diseases of the lung or a chest cough."

Almost 100 years after these observations, M. Choron from the College de Saint-Denis, La Réunion, submitted a brief report independent of Flacourt's comments on "a new substance from Madagascar" (Choron 1847: 397, our translation): "The raw material resembles manna; it is found on certain trees; the natives eat it and say that it is deposited by a fly which they propose to send to us. I have just learned that the substance contained in the bottle is considered to be a hard gum in the country of Mahafaly, where it is called *tipinder*, and comes from a tree called *maroua* [*marohay*?]." Later, Tandrya and Payet (1898) noted that the Mahafaly eat a crystalized sugar deposited by ants on leaves of a tree called "*atembona*." By the 1930s, it had become clear that the "manna" was produced not by ants or butterflies but by a planthopper, *Flatida rosea* (Figure 5.10a) (Decary 1937; Scarone 1938).

FIGURE 5.10 The consumption of exudates and insect larvae on Madagascar. A) *Flatida rosea* (Flatidae) produces a sweet exudate, known locally as *tantely sakondry*, which is eaten by people and lemurs alike. B–D) Locally known throughout Madagascar as *sakondry*, *Zanna* spp. (Fulgoridae) are among the most-preferred edible insects because they are rich in nutrients and taste like fatty meat. These insects are prepared by washing and then cooking them in their own fat. E) After cocoons of *Borocera cajani* (Lasiocampidae) are removed for silk extraction, the pupae are sold at markets near Itremo. F) Though the domesticated silk moth (*Bombyx mori*, Bombycidae) industry has declined, the larvae are still sold today in markets of Antananarivo. (PHOTO A by C. Sharp, B and F by B. Fisher, C and D by S. Andrianantenaina, and E by Kew Madagascar Conservation Centre.)

Decary (1937) noted that the Sakalava, Bara, and Mahafaly people are particularly fond of planthopper honey, which they call *tantely sakondry*.

In the field, generally under forest cover, *Flatida* adults can be found clustered along thin branches. They look for all the world like bright red fruits until they shuffle in unison to the back of the twig when an observer draws too close or fly off in a flurry of crimson, emerald, or golden wings. Those who visit later in the year may be even more impressed to discover the larval form mimicking lichen, only with legs. The white, bushy-tailed larvae appear in September to November and prefer plants of the family Combretaceae. Like most hemipterans that feed on plant phloem, *Flatida* excretes excess water and carbohydrates in the form of honeydew: a white, slightly sweet substance, which oozes in droplets and eventually forms masses that may reach the size of a fist on branches or on the ground. Other primates such as *Microcebus* also enjoy this exudate (Joly-Radko and Zimmermann 2010). The insects can produce several times their body mass of honeydew per hour.

The French botanist Perrier de la Bâthie, sensing a business opportunity for a unique food, attempted to farm planthoppers in Combretaceae plantations. He found that the quantity collected was far too small to commercialize (Scarone 1938). Though eating *tantely sakondy* is not strictly entomophagy, it is interesting that some of earliest accounts of insect foods on Madagascar relate to this substance and that there have been attempts to expand production for human consumption on a large scale.

Other Hemiptera noted to be consumed on the island include species of Belostomatidae, Cercopoidea, Cicadidae, Fulgoridae, Naucoridae, Nepidae, and Notonectidae (Table 5.4). In an Antananarivo market, Lacaze (1881) noted baskets full of "aquatic cockroaches" that probably correspond to Belostomatidae; he pointed out that the Malagasy people are very fond of these insects. Decary (1937) noted that nepids are consumed but little appreciated and that he found their flavor unpleasant. During his trip in the Malagasy Region, François Pollen stopped on Mayotte in the Comoros. There, Madame Chaulier, the wife of his host, who was from Madagascar, prepared *Zanna tenebrosa* fried and salted. Madame Chaulier pointed out that she preferred the species from her native soil, which she called *sakondry* (Pollen 1868: 104). Indeed, in many coastal regions of Madagascar, especially in the east, the most preferred insect is *Zanna* (Fulgoridae), locally known as *sakondry* (Grandidier and Grandidier 1908: vol. 4, pt. 3, p. 210; Randrianandrasana and Berenbaum 2015). The genus *Zanna* is widespread on Madagascar (see Constant, pp. 991–93). The characters to differentiate species in this genus are poorly defined, as are their distribution ranges, but all *Zanna* spp. are thought to be consumed by humans.

Hemiptera are prepared by first washing the insects and then placing them in a preheated pan with fat or oil, or in just enough water to cover the bottom of the pot. *Sakondry* (*Zanna* spp.) is the one exception, for like bacon it can be cooked solely in its own fat (Figures 5.10b–d). *Sakondry* is often harvested before the winged adult stage. The wings of adults are sometimes removed before cooking. They are eaten plain with rice or prepared with greens (*ravina*). The taste is similar to fatty meat, which is why they are often referred to in English as bacon bugs.

HYMENOPTERA

The larvae of bees (*Apis* and *Liotrigona*) and wasps (Vespidae) are eaten in eastern Madagascar (Perrier de la Bâthie 1905; Grandidier and Grandidier 1908; Decary 1937; Randrianandrasana and Berenbaum 2015). Since about 2010, companies employing a network of collectors along the eastern coast have started exporting wasp larvae to La Réunion, including a company that managed to ship nine tons in 2014 from the port in Toamasina. One network leader south of Foulpointe who managed a team of collectors reported a decline in availability of larger nests in the secondary forests where they focus their wasp collecting. Collecting such large quantities of a predator may have unintended impacts on local forest communities. This critical question needs to be investigated. The larvae of Hymenoptera can be eaten raw but are most often cooked—after being removed from their cells, they are boiled in water and sautéed in a pan.

LEPIDOPTERA

Lepidopterans consumed on Madagascar include the larvae and pupae of what tend to be larger species reared or collected for the local silk industry. This food preference is especially common in the Central Highlands, where wild silk production is traditionally practiced in tapia woodlands (see Kull and Birkinshaw, pp. 121–27). Other lepidopterans consumed across Madagascar are those that are seasonally very abundant, such as *Latoia* (Limacodidae) and *Hypsoides* (Notodontidae).

Flacourt was the first to bring the attention of the Western world to the diversity of silk used on Madagascar. Of the four types he mentions, three can be associated with species consumed today:

> Silkworms, there are four kinds, namely: 1) those which produce a single shell as in France, except that it has small thorns which we call *landevé* and 2) those which produce small shells wrapped in a large one, in which there will sometimes be more than five hundred, which is called *landesaraha*; 3) those who make their silk in the *anacau* tree which is a tree on the seashore like the cypress. These hulls are the only ones hanging from a small web and filled all around with small fetuses of leaves of said tree. This silk is the finest and strongest of all, it is called *landeanacau*; and 4) those who make their silk in the *vontaquier*, which is in small shells alone, the silk is very fine, it is called *lande vaisaqua*. (Flacourt (1658 [repr. 1995]: 225; our translation)

The moth species responsible for the first three kinds of silks are 1) *Borocera madagascariensis* (*landevé*, Lasiocampidae), 2) *Hypsoides* spp. (*landesaraha*, Notodontidae), and 3) *Deborrea humberti* (Psychidae) with its host plant *Casuarina equisetifolia* (*landeanacau*, Casuarinaceae). However, the *lande vaisaqua* moth, which uses the host plant *Strychnos spinosa* (Loganiaceae), has yet to be identified.

Flacourt (1658 [repr. 1995]: 225) goes on to note that (our translation) "on the Isle of Sainte Marie, there is a quantity of silk, which the natives do not know how to spin; they throw it out and eat the pupae inside." He was likely referring to *Hypsoides radama*. Coquerel (1855b: 25) also noted this species was abundant, produced a beautiful strong silk, and that the locals on Ile Sainte Marie discarded the cocoons after eating the pupae inside. A similar practice continues today in the uplands of western Makira, where the young pupae of the silk moth *Ceranchia apollina* (Saturniidae) are collected by the Tsimihety solely for consumption (M. Ratsimbazafy, unpublished data). These two examples suggest that silkmoth pupae are sometimes valued solely as food.

After Flacourt, we next see a mention of silk by S. Dubois (1674: 147) during his travels to Madagascar between 1669 and 1672, where he marveled at the diversity and beauty of silk produced by local people. W. Ellis (1858) noted that the Betsileo collected a pupa enclosed in a very hard, ovoid cocoon the size of a small olive, strongly stuck to the branches of the tapia tree. He described the species as being very good to eat and sold in large quantities in markets. Ellis's description matches the silk moth *Latoia albifrons* (Limacodidae). Vinson describes the consumption of the same species in detail:

> There is a very curious little caterpillar, very plump and white with rows of spikelets of short, silky hairs; it gives birth to a chocolate-colored butterfly with a small cluster of white and green spots on the inner and upper part of the wings. But before reaching this perfect state, the caterpillar weaves an oval cocoon, hazel-colored and quite resistant, against a small branch: on the surface of the cocoon, there is a small groove for implantation against the branch that supports it. We open this little shell, in the middle of which the white, swollen, and fatty caterpillar shows itself like an almond in its envelope. (Vinson 1863c: 45; our translation; also see Vinson 1865: 309)

Vinson felt the flavor and texture of *L. albifrons* pupae to be quite adaptable to French cuisine (our translation): "Many of these white larvae are collected which have the appearance of curdled milk. They are fried in oil with a little grated cheese and a few egg yolks and rolled in a pan. It is a delicious dish, having the appearance of a dish of veal brains au gratin, only, it is more delicate, it is a dish of prince and nobleman in Antananarivo" (1863c: 45; 1865: 309).

Borocera cajani, or *landibe*, is the most important wild silk moth for the silk industry on Madagascar. The people of the Central Highlands have a long tradition of using this species to produce silk shrouds, as well eating the insects. They still use its silk to produce textiles today. The species is endemic to Madagascar and broadly distributed on the island, colonizing the host plant *Uapaca bojeri* (Tapia; Phyllanthaceae), of the Central Highlands. In the silk and edible-insect literature this species has been confused with *B. madagascariensis*, which is also consumed but is more abundant along the coastal portions of the island (Razafimanantsoa et al. 2012). Vinson (1863d) was impressed with the strong and beautiful silk from the wild silk moth. He admired the zero-waste model where cocoons are used for the silk industry while the pupae are consumed (Figure 5.10e). These pupae were served at the table of Radama I (Pfeiffer 1861) and were the treats eaten by the son of Radama II in the introduction.

Decary (1937) provides further details about *B. cajani* pupa preparation. After being killed in boiling water, they were fried or sometimes just cooked under ash. To further emphasize their gastronomic appreciation, in 1894, a dish of *Borocera* pupae prepared with béchamel sauce (white sauce made with cream and flour) was served at an official meal at the French governor's residence in Antananarivo.

Osborn also noted the favorable taste of silk moth pupae:

> The silkworm in the chrysalis stage is as much esteemed for food as the locust and these also are to be found in the markets and in well-provisioned homes. I saw more silkworms in the markets of the Betsileo country than else-where and especially in the region about Imamo. There was no dearth of them through Imerina, but in most places not so many as in Imamo, for here the tapia tree is autochthonous and plentiful. This is the food of the Madagascar silkworm and they are to be found in large numbers where it flourishes. Not at all second to the silkworm and the locust and grasshopper is a kind of big, fat, sweet spider. Once I had a delicious stew made from spiders, locusts, silkworms, grasshoppers, fish, manioc meal, rice and suet. When I ate it for the first time I did not know what it was made of, but fuller information did not prevent my enjoyment of the bug and worm stew several times afterwards. (Osborn 1924: 325)

The cocoons of *Borocera* are often collected by children, especially during the winter, when parents are occupied with agricultural work (Barsics et al. 2013a). The pupae accompany rice and are eaten soon after harvesting, unlike dried locusts, which can be stored for later use. The pupae are prepared for consumption by removal from the cocoon, after the plucking of the irritating hairs, which are more abundant in young pupae. The pupae are then washed, and a slit is made on the head to facilitate cooking. Though sometimes fried directly after washing, they are more often simmered in water for an hour, when salt and oil are added. Sometimes pupae are dipped in oil before cooking.

Decary (1931: 289; 1937: 171) wrote that he could find huge quantities of scalded pupae of *Deborrea malgassa* (Psychidae) with cocoons removed. Known locally as *fangalabola*, these pupae were sold in the markets of Antananarivo. This species can become locally abundant and can be a serious pest in forest plantations (Grubenmann and Madle 2016). Barsics et al. (2013b) noted that the tradition of feeding *D. malgassa* to children who wet their beds is still practiced today.

Members of the genus *Hypsoides* can also be abundant, a characteristic that people take advantage of to harvest these insects for food. In the north of the island, individuals of *H. diego* group together to pupate in a single large pouch. This species is highly sought after as food by the Antakarana. Special taxonomic attention was given to the *Hypsoides* of Madagascar because of their potential to replace *Bombyx mori* (Bombycidae) in the Malagasy Region. *Hypsoides diego* produces a finer silk than *B. mori* and is better adapted to the climate on Madagascar (Coquerel 1855a, 1855b).

There are also records of people consuming the larvae of moths in the families Saturniidae and Sphingidae. Younger pupae are preferred because older pupae can taste bitter. Barsics et al. (2013a) discussed two saturniid species in the Itasy area: *Bunaea aslauga* (*sarohy*) and *Maltagorea fusicolor* (*bokana*). As with *Borocera*, children collect the larvae while adults are busy working in the fields. The larvae are eaten with rice. While several different methods of preparation are known, all begin by emptying the larva's digestive tract. The body is first pressed lengthwise, from the head to the anus, to extract the excrement, then flattened in the other direction to evacuate any undigested plant material. Cooking methods include grilling for five minutes on hot coals or boiling in water after using a stick to turn the larvae inside out. After boiling for up to one hour, salt and oil are added. Alternatively, instead of boiling, the larvae can be fried or sautéed once turned inside out. *Maltagorea fusicolor* is prepared in the same way but is not necessary to turn inside out. Limacodid pupae are also eaten and prepared in a manner similar to that for other pupae, except that the incision in the head is not necessary. Harvesters are mostly children and the pupae are considered tastier than those of *Borocera*.

Even pupae of the introduced, domesticated silk moth *Bombyx mori* are eaten on Madagascar. Because Madagascar had already developed a silk tradition based on wild native lepidopterans, early Western visitors saw the island as a potential contributor to the global silk trade. The first attempts to improve the quality of silk produced on Madagascar involved selecting improved strains of *Borocera* and by employing spider silk (Fee 2013). There were even earlier calls to introduce *B. mori* to the island. For example, when Mayeur was in Madagascar (1758–1787) and did not observe *Bombyx* sericulture in Imerina, he strongly recommended introducing it (Mayeur 1913b: 41). Instead, the silk was initially imported as floss from Oman (Fee 2013).

The first introduction of *B. mori* appears to be around 1815, when the British governor of neighboring Mauritius, James Hastie, encouraged King Radama I to make *Bombyx* weaving an income generator for the Merina crown. James Hastie sent mulberry bushes (*Morus*, Moraceae), silkworms, and reeling machines, as well as Bengali convict-laborers to instruct the local people on technical aspects (C. Anderson 2000). After King Radama's death, *Bombyx* sericulture quickly collapsed as a state enterprise. However, the techniques spread to Merina villages and improved over time. Newer varieties of mulberries and silkworms were introduced by Jean Laborde in 1850 and by the sericulture service at the Nanisana agriculture station. These latterly introduced European breeds are still used in recent times (Prudhomme 1905). Along the way, *B. mori* was adopted as a food source across the Central Highlands; the larvae are still sold today in markets in Antananarivo (Figure 5.10f), such as at Mahamasina, where the pupae are sold next to shrimp at the same price as the crustaceans.

ODONATA

Dragonfly larvae are collected along with other aquatic insects and small fish year-round from rice paddies or streams (Decary 1937; Barsics et al. 2013a; for information on the order Odonata in Madagascar, see Dijkstra, pp. 953–63). Larger species such as those of the genus *Anax* (Aeshnidae) can be collected in marshes and rice fields. The legs are often removed before cooking on coals or frying.

ORTHOPTERA

Humans have long been awed by natural phenomena showcasing the abundance of life, from islands filled with penguins in the South Sea to migrating wildebeest in the Serengeti. The spectacular locust migrations that periodically invade Madagascar, however, are often met with shock from visitors, who see these clouds of insects as potential destroyers of crops in their path. Yet locusts also provide the Malagasy with a valuable food staple, as noted by some early observers. The arrival of locust swarms was even celebrated in the extreme south, which suffers from seasonal food insecurity. It is worth noting that even through literature accounts tend to focus on the periodic swarms, the same species of locust, along with many other orthopteran species such as *Brachytrupes membranaceus colosseus* (*sahobaka*; Figure 5.11a), are collected and consumed throughout the year (Van Itterbeeck et al. 2019). Here we review some of the principal accounts that show the historical magnitude of locust swarms, the use of locusts as a food source, and preparation methods for these insects over the past 400 years.

Locusts: Devourers and Great Providers

The first mention of locusts on the island comes from the Jesuit priest D'Azevedo, who on 23 May 1617 noted in a letter that people in the Menabe area of central western Madagascar eat dried insects and are extremely fond of eating locusts (Grandidier and Grandidier 1904: vol. 3, p. 243). Shortly afterward, in 1625, the skipper Willem Ysbrantsz Bontekoe, after arriving in the Manafiafy Bay north of Tolagnaro, described how locals captured locusts, removed their wings, and grilled them (Bontekoe 1663).

A more detailed account comes from François Martin in 1665 (Martineau 1931). He recounted the difficulty of finding rice during his travels on the east coast that year because locust swarms had destroyed the crop. He described witnessing locusts arriving to wreak incredible damage over the course of three days. He noted the swarm began to fly immediately after sunrise, stopped at sunset, and inflicted the greatest damage on fields where it spent the night. "The rice, which was very beautiful and whose harvest was near, was all lost. ... a damage one cannot imagine, unless one has witnessed it" (Martineau 1931: 129).

The devastation that locust swarms caused to crops, and the fact that locals consumed the locusts, was noted again in 1709 by Adrian van Broeck of Pirate Avery fame (van Broeck 1709). Avery's account was bolstered by Dr. Edouard Yves (Ives 1773: 15; Grandidier and Grandidier 1907: vol. 5, p. 267), who anchored in July 1754 at Saint Augustine Bay near Toliara. He proclaimed that the most extraordinary thing on the whole island was the sheer number of locusts he saw, which rose from the ground like thick clouds. He also noted that the locals preferred eating them to the best fish, frying them in oil after removing legs and wings. Charpentier de Cossigny in 1773 (1799: 358) described the locals' enjoyment of consuming locusts as on a par with seafood, and compared the taste to crayfish. He noted that when the insects were prepared by grilling on hot coals they turned reddish, a sign that they were ready to eat.

The accounts so far have noted the widespread consumption of locusts and the simple preparation methods. With Nicolas Mayeur in 1785, we begin to understand the importance of this food for the Malagasy people (Grandidier 1896a: 556, 1896b: 14–15; Mayeur 1913b: 32). Mayeur lived on Madagascar for about 30 years (1758–1787) and spoke Malagasy so fluently that he served as an interpreter at French government outposts on the northeastern coast. He described the arrival of a locust swarm during a fight between two tribes not far from Antananarivo along the banks of the Ikopa River near Alasora. The two tribes, with 12,000 soldiers, had been

FIGURE 5.11 **The consumption of different forms of the order Orthoptera is widespread on Madagascar. A) *Brachytrupes membranaceus colosseus*, locally known as *sahobaka*, for sale at a market near Ambanja. This is the largest cricket sold for consumption on Madagascar. B–D) *Locusta migratoria* (Acrididae), known locally as *valala*, is collected at Ranobe, north of Toliara, and prepared in a manner similar to that of other large orthopterans: the legs and wings are removed and the insects are fried in oil. They turn pink when ready to eat. E–F). Native cricket species of the genus *Gryllus* (Gryllidae) offer an opportunity to create small-scale and low-impact food production. The generic name, *Gryllus* ("grill us"), seems an invitation to cook them (Simmonds 1859).** (PHOTO A by F. Rajemison, and B–F by B. Fisher.)

fighting for 10 days. One side had received reinforcements of 3000 men and had just begun to march to secure victory when an immense cloud of locusts suddenly obscured the sky and settled upon the surrounding rice fields. The firing ceased immediately as soldiers from both sides rushed out to collect the insects. The women, children, and older men came out of hiding and joined the collecting, resulting in no fewer than 20,000 people crawling on all fours and busily engaged in catching this prized source of food. When questioned as to why the war was suspended with the arrival of the locusts, the king responded to Mayeur that while a war is most often of interest only to those who declared it, locusts are of interest to everyone.

This excitement at catching locusts probably reflects the importance of the insect to a household for its food security and also as a chance to earn income by selling the insects, in the form of dried or fried products. Locusts were not just consumed in the countryside but also sold in cities. Ellis visited Madagascar three times between 1853 and 1856. He described his horses being spooked by swarming locusts so numerous they resembled falling snow. "The women and children rush[ed] out with great clamor and endeavor to collect locusts using cloth (*lamba*) and baskets" (W. Ellis 1858: 211). They detached the legs and wings by shaking them from one end to the other of a long sack. The legs and wings were then winnowed away (an observation also reported earlier by Leguével de Lacombe and de Froberville [1840]), and the bodies were dried in the sun or fried in fat. Some were kept in sacks for food, and some sent to market in Betsileo and southward. Vinson (1865: 302) noted that on the steps of downtown Antananarivo, large baskets containing millions of dried locusts from three different species were for sale. He mentioned that locusts were common, highly sought-after foods. Similar observations of baskets containing locusts in Antananarivo markets were regularly reported by other authors (e.g., Lacaze 1881: 67; Perrier de la Bâthie 1924). Locusts were also observed in other markets: in 1863, James Sibree noticed great heaps of brown locusts for sale in the Betsimisaraka market in Toamasina.

Sibree (1884) described an encounter with a swarm on his way to preach in Analamahitsy, then on the outskirts of Antananarivo, on the afternoon of 21 September. He too compared the arrival of the locusts to a heavy snowfall, except the ground was not white. People were busy gathering the insects in baskets, and every child and adult he passed had a dozen or more locusts impaled on a straw for that night's dinner. Sibree (1915) mentioned that for a few days after each swarm, great brown heaps of locusts were seen at all the roadside shops. The locals describe the taste as akin to shrimp without any insides.

Camboué (1886) devoted an entire publication to the locusts of Madagascar. He noted that locusts are both a curse and a blessing on the country, both ravaging crops and serving as a resource for people to feed themselves and their domestic animals. He describes the preparation as follows: locusts were first boiled in large pots then laid out on large mats in the sun to completely dry, after which their legs, wings, and head were removed, and finally they were crushed into powder or stored whole for local consumption or to supply markets. He noted that once ground and dried, locusts could be kept for a very long time. For eating, they could be flavored with chili and salt or, even better, fried in fat. They were also boiled or cooked with chicken or beef to be eaten along with rice. Locusts could also be used to make broth, or *ro*, to accompany rice. Several authors noted that locusts were a food not only for the poor but for different strata of Malagasy society. Locusts were one of the delicacies served during the endless banquets given by Queen Ranavalona I (Pfeiffer 1861). Camboué noted that (our translation) "at the Tananarive palace, the royal table itself, which prides itself on progressive ideas, also serves them. The late queen of the Hovas, Ranavalona II, who had her hunters secure the best game from the forest, her fisherman to bring her the best fish from lakes and rivers, had women who scoured the countryside specifically to collect precious Orthoptera for her table" (Camboué 1886: 169–170). Camboué remembered that when Queen Ranavalona III was on an official visit to Ambohipo outside of Antananarivo with her husband, Ratrimo, she chased and gathered up locusts to take home to prepare for dinner. He also noted that many species of locusts were eaten, but not the large, colorful *valalanamboa* (*Phymateus saxosus*). Camboué pondered whether orthopterans could be developed as a food source for humans or at least for animals. He pointed out that grasshoppers have been eaten since antiquity and were recorded in Leviticus as a food source for the people of Israel. Preparations of locusts were relayed by Grandidier and Grandidier (1908: vol. 4, pt. 3, p. 208), who noted the enthusiasm of people across Madagascar for eating the insects.

Osborn's account includes one of the most colorful descriptions of both Malagasy locust-catching methods and how local people prepared them to sell or consume later (Osborn 1924). Importantly, he realized that the gathering of locusts was a means to secure a food supply for the lean months. He proclaimed that, thanks to locusts and other edible insects, there was no famine on Madagascar and that because of edible insects there was little worry over the question of food. Osborn summed up the central role of locusts in the local diet in this way: "All forward looking housekeepers in Madagascar have a goodly supply of dried locusts on hand" (Osborn 1924: 324). Collecting locusts, he found, was done mostly by women and children, who trapped the insects in flight by scooping them up in large baskets and on the ground by sweeping them into shallow depressions. He noted they could also be found in public markets, where they were sold in hundreds of huge, shallow baskets.

Decary (1925) noted that in the extreme south of Madagascar, a region prone to drought and famine, the Androy people celebrated the arrival of locusts as an essential source of food. In the Central Highlands, even though locusts can devastate rice fields, they were also collected to eat and sell, and as feed for pigs. The Androy, he wrote, ate dried locusts raw after removing the legs and wings. In 1925, while traveling in the southeast, he saw mats of drying locusts and described a chief giving a hat filled with locusts to his porters, who quickly finished off the treat. Decary also noted that locust commerce occurred across Madagascar. Locusts were given a high-speed transportation fee on the railway and were taxed at the same rate as game and fish. Decary (1925, 1937) also described how preparations differed among different species of locusts. Smaller species (*tsibody*) were cooked by placing them on hot ash until their abdomens burst. For larger locusts, two principal methods were employed. The first involved grinding the insects until they resembled powdered tobacco, then cooking them in water and eating them as a sauce (*laoka*) with rice. In the second method, the wings and legs were removed; the insects were then soaked for half an hour in salt water and finally fried in fat (Figures 5.11b–d). This second dish was most popular in the Central Highlands and appeared on princely tables, as described above. Drying locusts and grinding them into a powder eases both long-term storage and transport.

ARANEAE

The consumption of spiders might have been overlooked by early visitors to Madagascar if not for the popularity of their silk. These Europeans were keen to note any local resources that could be exploited commercially and considered the island's spiders a promising source of this valuable commodity.

While Vinson was on Madagascar for the coronation of Radama II in 1861, he also found time to study the island's spiders. He was the first to describe the consumption of *Nephila inaurata madagascariensis* (Golden Orb Spider), known locally as *halabe* (Figure 5.9a). Vinson noted, as Decary (1937) did later, that *Nephila* would be fried in oil or fat. Vinson was also the first to describe the impressively strong silk spun by this spider. He suggested that the silk might be of commercial use and value (Vinson 1863a: 193). Osborn (1924: 325) found spiders to taste sweet in a stew he was served. A number of large *Nephila* species are native to Madagascar and all are likely eaten by people. Barsics et al. (2013a) recently noted that young boys are the main consumers of *Nephila*, which they encounter while herding zebu. Further, some adults also consume spiders because they find this food boosts energy, and adults may also give grilled *Nephila* to their children when they are sick.

Though there are many ecological concerns with eating predators such as spiders or wasps, past efforts to farm spiders to produce a finer, glossier silk fiber provide insights into the feasibility of large-scale spider production. Building on Vinson's suggestion, Jacob Paul Camboué, a French Jesuit missionary and naturalist, began experimenting in the 1880s and 1890s with ways to extract the silk directly from the spider. This continued with French colonial administrator Nogué, who thought silk production could be a unique export for Madagascar. To support that effort, he created a hand-powered machine that could spin the silk from the live spiders while causing no harm to the arachnids. In the 19th century, a technical college was founded in Antananarivo where people were put to work to collect and spin silk from spiders raised in special gardens (Figure 5.9b). The spiders were periodically taken from their webs in the garden, then placed in special racks to enable silk to be drawn from their spinnerets and wound on a reel. The animals were later released back to the garden to recuperate (Petrunkevitch 1921), as excessive production of silk from a spider without recuperation would kill the animal. The silk produced by this spider was finer, lighter, and stronger than silk derived from the domesticated silkworm. Beautiful garments of high quality were even produced for the Paris Exposition in 1900. Unfortunately, the difficulties of procuring live insect food for these spiders made the use of their silk economically unviable, and attempts to farm them ended.

Though farmed spiders require a food source, it may be possible to sustainably harvest them for silk production. Textile maker Simon Peers, based in Antananarivo, demonstrated this when he captured and released over 1 million spiders in Antananarivo over a five-year period, using modifications of the technology developed by Nogué to harvest their silk. The resulting cloth is a testament to the beauty of this unusual silk (Morgan 2016).

FUTURE DIRECTIONS

Edible insects have a 400-year documented history on Madagascar. Most of the insects mentioned historically are still eaten today and prepared using similar methods. Their persistence in the Malagasy diet is a testament to their good flavor and value as food. There is growing interest in farming insects as an environmentally sustainable and nutritious alternative to traditional protein sources (van Huis et al. 2013). Insects reproduce quickly, have high growth rates, and are far more efficient at converting feed into body mass than mammalian livestock. The feed conversion of house crickets is estimated at twice that of chickens, four times that of pigs, and more than 12 times greater than that of cattle. This high conversion rate also means insects require much less water and cause far fewer environmental impacts per unit of protein produced. They are also valuable sources of minerals and vitamins essential for human development (Bednářová et al. 2014; Payne et al. 2015, 2016). In fact, the locusts that attack crops in southwestern Madagascar probably contain more iron than do the crops themselves (B. Fisher, unpublished data). Additionally, insects are ideal for small-scale community development projects because they are small, easy to breed, and require minimal investments in capital and land. Minimal investment and scalable farm modules make insect farming accessible to marginalized groups, enabling women and the rural poor to produce their own food and improving global food security (Figures 5.11e and f).

The farming of insects for food and animal feed has been increasing in continental Africa and Asia (van Huis 2020) and is both culturally and nutritionally relevant on Madagascar. Importantly, insect farming on the island should be restricted to species already present on the island, since introduction of new species could harm the native environment and/or human cultures. Though early attempts to farm *Flatida* planthoppers and *Nephila* spiders were not successful, other invertebrates present on Madagascar offer promise for large-scale farming. However, some of the most obvious candidate species may not be appropriate for large-scale propagation: locusts such as *Locusta migratoria* are highly allergenic and trigger occupational allergies among farmworkers in closed facilities (Burge et al. 1980; Lopata et al. 2005) and could represent a threat to culture in open-air farms.

Selecting species suitable for large-scale farming is therefore not a trivial task. The species presented in Table 5.4 should be evaluated to assess their suitability for commercial-scale farming. Such an analysis could include an evaluation of biological cycles, nutrient content, and other variables that affect environmental health and farming costs. It would also be important to survey local attitudes toward insect consumption to ensure the program is suitable for local markets. Insect farming offers great potential to help Madagascar to address development issues such as population growth, food security, climate change, diminishing water resources, child nutrition, and persistent poverty. By providing a protein source requiring little energy input yet offering high feed conversion rates, insect farming could help reduce bushmeat and beef-product consumption. With increased food security, forest conservation becomes more possible.

ACKNOWLEDGMENTS

We thank Balsama Rajemison, Andrianjaka Ravelomanana, and students and staff at the Madagascar Biodiversity Center, Tsimbazaza, Antananarivo. Special thanks go to Darren Goldin from Entomo Farms, Canada, for the discussion on the role of insects in fighting food insecurity. David Lees provided help sleuthing the moth species discussed by Flacourt. The work presented here was inspired by the Insects and People in the Southwest Indian Ocean (IPSIO) project supported by the Critical Ecosystem Partnership Fund (CEPF). The Critical Ecosystem Partnership Fund is a joint initiative of l'Agence Française de Développement, Conservation International, the European Union, the Global Environment Facility, the Government of Japan, the MacArthur Foundation, and the World Bank. A fundamental goal is to ensure civil society is engaged in biodiversity conservation.

Subject editor: Steven M. Goodman

ETHNOBOTANY OF MADAGASCAR

T. N. Randrianarivony, N. H. Rakotoarivelo, and F. Rakotoarivony

Madagascar is known not only for its biodiversity richness but also for the plurality of its ethnic groups. The people who settled the island and are represented in the modern population have diverse origins, including Austronesia, the Arabian Peninsula, Africa, and Europe. The estimated date of the first human presence on Madagascar has changed dramatically in past decades. People arrived on the island in several waves, coming from different parts of the Old World (for a review, see Wright and Rakotoarisoa, pp. 181–90). The complex history of the arrival of people on the island and their mixing with preexisting groups offers an interesting framework in which to consider the use of plants by Malagasy people, as an important aspect of ethnobotany is how people use plant resources and the evolution of that use over time and across cultures.

Although considerable efforts have been made to document how plants are used on Madagascar, ethnobotanical data and records are still partial. Interest in Malagasy ethnobotany is now increasing, based on the field's contributions to public health, economic development, natural-resource management, and understanding aspects of local community life. Despite this, a significant loss of traditional oral knowledge about the value of plants has been noted across the world (Reyes-García et al. 2013), and on Madagascar specifically, due to deforestation, immigration, and the invasion of other cultures (Randrianarivony et al. 2016). The aim of this contribution is to provide a broad overview of Malagasy ethnobotany over time, which in turn helps to identify gaps in the current literature.

HISTORY OF MALAGASY ETHNOBOTANY

Numerous works have been published on the use of plants on Madagascar. The first written documents from the island date from the late medieval period and are known as *sorabe*; these were transliterated from the Malagasy, which at that time was an oral language only, into a form of Arabic. This transliteration was undertaken by Arab immigrants who had integrated into the Antemoro Kingdom of that period, and the *sorabe* contain historical, cultural, medical, and divinatory passages. These texts cover the use of plant species such as *Ravenala madagascariensis* (Strelitziaceae; *ravinala*), *Cyperus latifolius* (Cyperaceae; *herana*), and *C. alternifolius* (*vinda*) for basketry; *Bremeria erectiloba* (Rubiaceae; *fatotra*) for making traditional musical instruments; *Cerbera manghas* (Apocynaceae; *tangena*) for judging offenders; and *Gnidia daphnifolia* (Thymelaeaceae; *havoha*) for production of Antemoro paper (Rombaka 1978). During the period of Austronesian trade in the 7th century, an inventory of new aromatic and medicinal plants of Madagascar was made (Domenichini 2016), which included *Piper borbonense* (Piperaceae; *tsiperifery*) and the cinnamon of Madagascar, *Cinnamosma fragrans* (Canellaceae).

The first written ethnobotanical inventory on Madagascar was initiated by Etienne de Flacourt in the 17th century, with a repertoire of certain medicinal plants, which are known in Malagasy as *raokandro* (Flacourt 1658 [repr. 1995]). Toward the end of the 19th century and the beginning of the 20th century, descriptions of preparations by traditional Malagasy diviners known as *ombiasy*, *mpisikidy*, *mpanandro*, or *mpahay* (in part depending on the region of the island) were recorded in several manuscripts, which listed many plant species used for supernatural purposes (Rabearimanana 1975).

During the colonial period, a catalog of the useful plants of Madagascar, in particular medicinal and toxic plants, was made by Heckel (1903). This collection contains Malagasy names and specific details on how some plants were used. A little later, an inventory was published of latex plants and precious Malagasy woods, with a view to their possible exportation (Geay 1911). Subsequent ethnobotanical research focused on medicinal plants and the determination of their pharmacological properties. This soon led to the discovery of therapeutic plants, and in some cases derived products, such as *Centella asiatica* (Apiaceae; *talapetraka*) and the creation of several centers for research on medicinal plants, such as the Institut Malgache de Recherches Appliquées (IMRA) and the Centre National d'Application des Recherches Pharmaceutiques (CNARP). Currently, several laboratories, such as Homeopharma and Masoala, are highlighting the benefits of natural products and plants of Madagascar.

Since the end of the 20th century, there have been several botanical research programs on the island that have provided fresh perspectives on traditional uses of plants in medicine, wild consumables, textiles, basketry, precious woods, cosmetics, and perfumery, as well as chemical derivatives. Thus, modern Malagasy ethnobotany is not limited to simple descriptions of plants and their uses, but examines in detail a range of relationships between humans and plants (Rakotoarivelo 2015; Randrianarivony 2015). Today, Malagasy ethnobotany is not concerned with just research into new pharmaceutical products but also has a clear focus on biodiversity conservation (Burney 2005).

ETHNOBOTANY IN GENERAL

A few definitions are in order to put certain aspects of ethnobotany into perspective. On Madagascar, ethnobotany is often confused with ethnopharmacology, which is the study of the knowledge and practices of different ethnic groups in the use of plants and their derivatives in health care, or ethnomedicine, which studies the practices and thought of all Western and non-Western medical and therapeutic traditions. Ethnobotany, however, is commonly associated with other, nonmedical, domains, such as taxonomy, biology, and anthropology.

Ethnobotanical studies on Madagascar are generally done by categories and subcategories of plant use (Table 5.5) or by region, ethnic

TABLE 5.5. **Categories and subcategories of plant use on Madagascar**

CATEGORY OF USE	SUBCATEGORY	DESCRIPTION
Food and animal feed	Beverages	Used in elaboration of fermented or unfermented beverages
	Foods	Edible foods, usually with little or no preparation
	Food additives	Ingredients used in food preparation and processing
	Edible oils	Edible fats
	Animal feed	Food for pets and farm animals
	Wildlife attraction	Plants that are eaten by animals and whose location constitutes preferential areas for hunting
Construction	Bridges	Materials for building bridges across streams and small rivers
	Houses	Materials for building houses, associated structures, and other types of construction such as temporary camps and domestic animal corrals
	Roofs	Materials for house roofing and other similar forms of construction
	Transport	Materials for carts, canoes, rafts, paddles or oars, and different forms of sealing materials
	Other	Materials used in canals or other forms of water channels
Cultural use	Clothing and accessories	Used to make articles of clothing and accessories such as hats
	Cosmetics	Used in beauty products, including perfumes, oils, shampoos, soaps, face masks, toothpaste, and different hair-care products
	Dyes	Used for dyeing of various materials (fibers) and painting of the body
	Personal decoration	Used to make necklaces, bracelets, earrings, armbands, pectoral bracelets, and ankle bracelets
	Recreation	Used to make musical instruments and toys; snuff
	Ritual	Uses related to mythical and religious aspects of culture, including festivals and celebrations, construction of coffins, sacred poles, etc.
	Magical	Uses related to supernatural aspects of culture: witchcraft, protection (anti-bullet and anti-lightning; against bad weather, bad spells, and different forms of attacks; protection of pregnancy, children, goods, rice fields and cattle), and charms to promote fertility, prosperity (goods, honor, power, production, zebu), and success
	Other	Uses not classified in the above subcategories
Utensils and tools	Domestic utensils and tools	Materials for baskets, fans, hammocks, bags, and household furniture
	Hunting and fishing tools	Used to make bows, arrows, harpoons, fishing nets, and traps
	Working tools	Materials for handles for agricultural and domestic tools, such as machetes, axes, and brooms
	Packaging	Packaging for materials and foodstuffs
	Rope and string	Used in manufacture of ropes and different forms of binding fibers
Environmental use	Agroforestry	Plants associated with agroforestry
	Fences	Materials for delimitation of properties and making barriers, including living fences
	Ornamental	Plants grown for ornamental purposes
	Soil improvement	Used as fertilizers, for soil protection, and soil-erosion-control agents

CATEGORY OF USE	SUBCATEGORY	DESCRIPTION
Fuel	Fuel wood	Wood for making fires (firewood, charcoal)
	Firelighter	Materials to start fires
	Lighting	Materials used in lamps, flashlights, and candles
Toxic and chemical	Chemical	Latex for the production of rubber
	Toxic	Plants that are toxic to mammals, fish, and humans
Medicinal	Digestive tract disease	Carminatives, emetics, purgatives, laxatives, and other agents for treating colic, flatulence, indigestion, gastric or intestinal ulcers, diarrhea, constipation, stomach pain, throat disease, liver disease, hepatitis, and bladder problems
	Sexual-organ related	To aid with menstruation, fertility, and menopause; to treat infectious diseases (gonorrhea and syphilis), prostate disease, and impotence; aphrodisiacs; contraceptives
	Traumatic injury, poisoning, and other consequences of external causes	To treat snake bites, scorpion stings, stingray stings, spider bites, and insect bites and stings
	Certain infectious and parasitic diseases	To treat malaria, measles, worms, lice, fleas, scabies, bilharzia, tetanus, and syphilitic wounds
	Respiratory-system diseases	To treat influenza, colds, loss of voice, bronchitis, pneumonia, coughs, and asthma; as an expectorant
	Nervous-system diseases	To treat migraines, mental disorders, epilepsy, and paralysis
	Skin and subcutaneous-cell tissue diseases	To treat acne, boils, eczema, burns; to aid extraction of thorns stuck in skin
	Pregnancy, childbirth, and postpartum	To aid with gestation, hemorrhage, childbirth, postnatal care and conditions, lactation, abortion, postpartum care and conditions, and certain conditions that originate in the perinatal period
	Diseases of the osteo-articular system, muscles, and connective tissue	To treat rheumatism, sprains and strains, fractures, sciatica, aches and pains, lumbago; to aid fontanel closure
	Endocrine, nutritional, and metabolic diseases	To treat diabetes and obesity; to aid weight loss
	Circulatory-system diseases	To treat cardiovascular problems and diseases, heart disease, varicose veins, and hypo- and hypertension
	Eye diseases	To treat eye infections, cataracts, and loss of vision
	Diseases of the blood and hematopoietic organs and certain disorders of the immune system	To treat anemia and hemorrhoids
	Diseases of the ear and the mastoid process	To treat loss of sense of smell, deafness, and ear infections
	General illness	To treat general illnesses such as body aches, malaise, weakness, headache, fever, and fatigue
	Tooth disease	To treat cavities and dental pain and aid with dental hygiene
	Other	Plants with medicinal uses or pharmacological properties but with insufficient information to assign to one of the described subcategories
Other		Use not classified in the cited categories above as indirect uses of the plant

Sources: Based in part on Cámara-Leret et al. (2012) and Rafidison et al. (2019).

group, or bioclimatic zone. In other cases they focus on a specific plant. Plants cited for the same usage category differ from one region to another based on what is locally available and on cultural aspects. Thus, depending on the research objective in the context of modern ethnobotanical research, different methods of data collection can be chosen and a variety of factors need to be considered. These factors at the outset relate to building of trust and gaining the agreement of informants to collaborate in the research. For this, the researcher must comply with social regulations, customs, and traditions of the local community, as well as international regulations, most notably the Nagoya Protocol (Convention sur la Diversité Biologique 2012). Following the application of this protocol, after explaining to the local community or representatives of the population—such as village chiefs, president of *fokontany* (village or group of villages), or commune mayor—the summary of the project, the expected results, and the benefits arising from the research, it is mandatory to obtain a signed agreement associated with the realization of the research.

Frequently used methods for ethnobotanical data collection include two types of interview (structured and semi-structured) with a range of informants (Alexiades 1996). The structured interview, based on unchanging questions that must be asked in a fixed order to informants, allows researchers to obtain quantitative and measurable information. For a semi-structured interview, a pre-established list of questions is employed only as a guide or checklist.

The types of information collected depend on the purposes of the study. The informants, however, in modern ethnobotanical study are chosen based on various parameters, including gender, marital status, and age, as well as the person's native village. Basic information to be collected for a given plant includes local names, uses, part(s) used, method of preparation, and different habitat types where it occurs. Collection of ethnobotanical data during surveys is always followed by the collection of a voucher specimen for the determination of a scientific name and archival deposition in a recognized herbarium.

To process ethnobotanical data, the information obtained during interviews is used as the basis for a database. In order to highlight the utilization of plants based on parameters such as category, type of use, and parts used, we have modified the system of Cámara-Leret et al. (2012) for the context of Madagascar (Table 5.5). Our categories of use include food (animal and human), construction, cultural, utensils and tools, fuel, environmental, toxic and chemical, medicinal and veterinary, and others. These categories are divided in turn into subcategories, and in the case of the medicinal category we have adopted the subcategories defined by Rafidison et al. (2019). The following sections present greater detail on the different categories in the context of Malagasy ethnobotany.

FOOD

Within this category, we have three subcategories, including human and animal food and beverages. A complete list of all the wild edible plant species of Madagascar has never been compiled. A list assembled by L. Ramamonjisoa and Rakotoarimanana (1996) included 150 species of forest fruit trees in 42 families and 82 genera of the moist evergreen forests of Madagascar. Some endemic forest fruit tree species were cited in that compilation, such as those in the families Malvaceae (*Adansonia* spp. except *A. digitata*) (see Karimi et al., pp. 706–10), Moraceae (*Ficus brachyclada, F. pachyclada, F. politoria*), Myrtaceae (*Syzygium bernieri, S. emirnense*), and some Sapotaceae (*Capurodendron ankaranense, Faucherea manongarivensis, Labramia boivinii, L. capuronii, L. costata, Mimusops capuronii, M. coriacea, M. perrieri, Sideroxylon gerrardianum*) (see Gautier, pp. 726–39). On Madagascar, species of the genus *Vaccinium* (Ericaceae) are all wild shrubs with edible fruits. Several studies have been carried out on the endemic edible-fruited species *Uapaca bojeri* (Phyllanthaceae) (Kull et al. 2005; Alvarado et al. 2014; see Kull and Birkinshaw, pp. 121–27). Finally, the endemic family Sarcolaenaceae includes three species of wild edible fruits: *Leptolaena pauciflora, Schizolaena cauliflora*, and *S. parviflora* (see Schatz and Lowry, pp. 726–39).

Around the beginning of the 21st century, there was an increased interest in research projects on the island focused on wild food plants related to crops. Since then, studies of Malagasy yams of the genus *Dioscorea* (Dioscoreaceae) have been examined in detail from a range of different ethnobotanical perspectives. About 40 species of the genus occur on the island, according to recent inventories (Jeannoda et al. 2003), with an endemicity rate of 82%, including many recently named taxa (see Wilkin et al., pp. 545–51). Of these, three species are cultivated and others are exploited from wild populations (Figure 5.12a). Apart from *Dioscorea*, other wild tuber species are highly appreciated in the diet of people living in the south, southeast, and southwest, including *Neoapaloxylon mandrarense* (Fabaceae), *Tacca ankaranensis*, and *T. soalala* (Dioscoreaceae).

Wild plants with edible leaves are mostly species in the families Amaranthaceae, such as *Alternanthera sessilis* and *Celosia argentea*; Asteraceae, such as *Bidens pilosa* and *Solanecio angulatus*; Cucurbitaceae, such as *Cucumis sativus*; an endemic species of Podostemaceae, *Thelethylax minutiflora*; and Solanaceae, with two endemic species, *Solanum erythracanthum* and *S. pyracanthos*. Some wild species of subsistence plants have also been inventoried, as well as two wild rice species: *Oryza longistaminata* and *O. punctata* (Poaceae). There is also a species of wild banana (*Ensete perrieri*, Musaceae), classified in the International Union for Conservation of Nature (IUCN) Red List as Critically Endangered.

Plants are used in beverages including herbal teas, coffees, and bitter drinks (*mangidy*), and plants form the components used to prepare fermented beverages. Herbal tea ingredients are mostly indigenous plants such as *Aphloia theiformis* (Aphloiaceae) and *Mystroxylon aethiopicum* (Celastraceae), but also forest species such as those in the family Rutaceae (*Ivodea reticulata, Vepris boiviniana*, and *Zanthoxylum asiaticum*). A total of 24 plants, including 10 endemic species, were identified during a recent survey of plants used for the manufacture of bitter beverages sold around Antananarivo (Rakotoarivelo et al. 2019). In the case of fermented beverages, 70 plant species were cited in the associated ingredients. Among them, endemic species such as *Bismarckia nobilis, Borassus madagascariensis*, and *Dypsis ampasindavae* (Arecaceae; see Rakotoarinivo et al., pp. 567–80) are used for the production of palm wines. A total of 55 different species in the family Rutaceae, which have a strong aroma, such as *Cedrelopsis grevei, Melicope bakeri, M. fatraina*, and *M. sambiranensis*, are used as additives to sugarcane for the production of traditional Malagasy alcoholic beverages (*toaka gasy* and *betsabetsa*) (Randrianarivony et al. 2017; see Rabarimanarivo et al., pp. 691–98).

FIGURE 5.12 **Different aspects of ethnobotany on Madagascar: A) collecting the edible plant *Dioscorea soso* (Dioscoreaceae; *sosa*); B) the medicinal plant *Maerua filiformis* (Capparaceae; *somangy*); C) sugarcane press made with *Dalbergia* sp. (Fabaceae; *manary*); D) house built with *Ravenala madagascariensis* (Strelitziaceae; *ravinala*); E) fishing trap made with *Raphia farinifera* (Arecaceae; *raffia*); F) sacred pillar, or *fisokina*, made with *Phylloxylon xylophylloides* (Fabaceae; *harahara*); and G) mat and hat made from *Lepironia articulata* (Cyperaceae; *penjy*).** (PHOTOS A, B, and E by T. N. Randrianarivony; and C, D, F, and G by N. H. Rakotoarivelo.)

Before the 21st century, studies of useful plants for animal fodder were not well represented in published ethnobotanical surveys. Since 2000, plants encountered in grassland or pastureland formations have become the focus of different research projects (see Lehmann et al., pp. 152–68). The well-known native forage species are in a range of families, including Poaceae (see Vorontsova et al., pp. 585–98), for example, *Aristida similis*, *Cynodon dactylon*, *Heteropogon contortus*, *Hyparrhenia cymbaria*, and *Urochloa maxima*; Asteraceae, such as *Helichrysum faradifani*; Fabaceae, including *Chamaecrista lateriticola*; and Rubiaceae, for example, *Oldenlandia herbacea*.

CONSTRUCTION

For centuries, wood from forest trees has been used to make tools and coffins, to build houses, in different forms of transportation, and in a range of artisanal products, often employing large trees such as *Faucherea* spp. (Sapotaceae; *nanto*), *Tambourissa* spp. (Monimiaceae; *ambora*), or *Intsia bijuga* (Fabaceae; *hintsy*). During the royal period, both in the Central Highlands and in lowland areas, houses were made entirely of wood or plant materials (E. Ralaimihoatra 1965). In Imerina in the 18th century, because of deforestation, hardwoods such as *Dalbergia* spp. (Fabaceae; *nanto*, *manary*), *Craspidospermum verticillatum* (Apocynaceae; *vandrika*), and *Diospyros* spp. (Ebenaceae; *hintsy* and ebony) were expensive and therefore used exclusively by the upper classes, and other, nonwoody, plant materials, such as grasses, large leaves, and reeds, were used to build houses for the general population (Sigaut 1975). In the 18th century, some Merina nobles took refuge in central eastern Madagascar to the south and east of Ambositra and became the Zafimaniry communities, who reside there to this day and who have a strong cultural tradition as woodworkers, producing artisanal products in particular. At least until a few decades ago, about 20 endemic tree species, including *Diospyros* and *Dalbergia* spp., were employed to build their houses (Rajemison 2013). Unfortunately, the large forest blocks in this portion of Madagascar have been destroyed, and the Zafimaniry now rely on introduced wood species like *Eucalyptus citriodora* and *Tectona grandis*, to make the artisanal goods, and they now build their houses out of bricks.

Toward the end of the 19th century, Malagasy rosewood was already being exported on a large scale. Perrier de la Bâthie (1928) published a monograph of the 13 most-used wood species on the west coast of Madagascar, and Guéneau (1975) wrote a booklet describing the wood of 82 species of Malagasy trees. At the beginning of the 21st century, after an explosion in the illegal exploitation of precious woods on the island, considerable work was devoted to the distribution, taxonomy, and conservation of Malagasy precious wood species (see Schatz and Lowry, pp. 739–44), and the *Atlas des bois de Madagascar* (Rakotovao et al. 2012) was produced, with descriptions of 187 forest-wood species. Subsequently, a scientific and technical assessment of Madagascar's precious woods was carried out, in light of the Convention on International Trade in Endangered Species of Wild Fauna and Flora (CITES) (World Resources Institute and World Bank 2016).

Some species of endemic plant families, such as Asteropeiaceae (*Asteropeia micraster*) and Sarcolaenaceae (*Leptolaena multiflora*, *L. pauciflora*, *Rhodolaena acutifolia*, *Xyloolaena speciosa*), are also severely exploited for their hardwood and these, as well as others, are classified as threatened species on the IUCN Red List. Endemic genera and species, such as *Abrahamia grandidieri* (Anacardiaceae), *Alluaudia procera* (Didiereaceae), *Capurodendron sakalavum*, *Cedrelopsis grevei*, and *Hazomalania voyronii* (Hernandiaceae), and various species in genera such as *Canarium* (Burseraceae), *Dalbergia*, *Faucherea*, and *Ocotea* (Lauraceae), are important for making house pillars in different parts of the island. In both dry and arid areas and more humid zones, plant materials from species in the family Poaceae, such as *Heteropogon contortus* (*danga* or *ahidambo*) and *Aristida rufescens* (*horona*), are frequently employed for house roofing, as well other aspects of house construction. *Ravenala madagascariensis* and some species of Arecaceae are among the important species for house construction in the lowland east (Figure 5.12d). Certain types of carts are made out of light woods such as *Broussonetia greveana* (Moraceae; *vory*) and *Tetrapterocarpon geayi* (Fabaceae; *voaovy*). Dugout canoes often employ *Albizia boivinii* (Fabaceae), *Canarium* spp. (*ramy*), *Delonix velutina* (Fabaceae; *hazondrangola*), and *Givotia madagascariensis* (Euphorbiaceae; *farafatsy*).

CULTURAL USES

This category includes plants used during ritual ceremonies and traditions, as well as the manufacture of traditional musical instruments, clothing and accessories, dyes, and traditional cosmetics. Many cultural practices, which often vary among ethnic groups on Madagascar, are generally based on a range of customs and various forms of ancestor veneration. In many cases these practices involve uses of plants in the realization of Malagasy customs and traditions, for both practical and supernatural purposes, that have been in place for many generations. The Malagasy to a large extent follow ancestor traditions that hold trees to have sacred powers, and these traditions are one of the main pillars of these practices, with the trees or woods often having a symbolic function. For example, during the 18th century, endemic plants were used during the circumcision ceremony of the kings' sons, including the dense hardwood of *Dalbergia* spp. (*nanto*), used in order that the kingdom would show the same level of endurance as the wood. Cord made out of the fibers of *Dombeya greveana* (Malvaceae; *somangana* tree) was used during a ceremony to bind and preserve the life of a child.

Throughout the eastern part of the island, the wood of *Phylloxylon xylophylloides* (Fabaceae; *harahara*), *Brachylaena merana* (Asteraceae; *merana*), and *Phyllarthron bojeranum* (Bignoniaceae; *zahana*) is employed to make the sacred pillars (*fisokina* or *jiro*) used during ancestor-veneration ceremonies (Figure 5.12f). In the south, traditional rites are performed around the *hazomanga*, a sort of pillar made from indigenous or endemic species like *Cordia monoica* (Cordiaceae) or *Vitex beraviensis* (Lamiaceae). Similarly, during the *bilo* ceremony (Elli 1993), an infusion is made of the powdered stems of endemic species including *Buddleja sphaerocalyx* (Scrophulariaceae), *Dracaena xiphophylla* (Asparagaceae), *Ocotea trichantha*, and *Suregada eucleoides* (Euphorbiaceae) and used to reinvigorate a sick person and to protect their whole family. In the Central Highlands, people use *Gambeya boiviniana* (Sapotaceae; *famelona*) for sacred sticks. Further, several species in the genus *Ficus* are grown in royal and sacred areas as good luck charms and are considered to aid mediation with supernatural forces (Rafidison 2013; see Rasplus et al., pp. 617–34). Species in the genus *Dracaena*, often referred to as *hasina*, are cultivated in villages in eastern Madagascar, as it is believed that the presence of these plants brings good luck and prosperity.

In the eastern part of the island, the resin of *Canarium madagascariense* is used as incense, or *emboka manitra*, during the ritual to call the spirits of deceased Betsimisaraka kings and other royalty (*mpanjaka*). Some species in the families Fabaceae (*Albizia tulearensis*, *Dalbergia* spp., *Phylloxylon xylophylloides*), Anacardiaceae (*Rhus perrieri*), Celastraceae (*Brexia humbertii*), Moringaceae (*Moringa drouhardii*), and Rutaceae (*Cedrelopsis grevei*) are used for coffin wood in different regions of Madagascar.

For the Malagasy divination called *sikidy* or *sikily* (*sikidy voampano* or *hazondrano*), an old practice brought to Madagascar by Arabs during the 10th and 11th centuries (Rabedimy 1976), the diviners always use seeds of native or introduced plants. In the arid south, seeds of *Entada chrysostachys* (Fabaceae; *fano*, *fany*, or *hazofany*) are used for this purpose, whereas in the humid east and Central Highlands, seeds of *Phaseolus vulgaris* (Fabaceae; *famelona*, or Common Bean), *Zea mays* (Poaceae; maize), and *Tamarindus indica* (Fabaceae; *kily*) are employed.

Many Malagasy people believe that plants are endowed with a magical force, and several species of trees are thus coveted for their beneficial or even evil powers. These are called magical plants (J. Ramamonjisoa 2009; Ravaosolo 2009) and are used for disenchantment; in charms for protection, love, or success; to become invisible; or to promote fertility. Scientists have studied the most important magical plants in the southeast (Beaujard 2009), southwest (Ravaosolo 2009; Randrianarivony 2015), and west (Jaovelo-Dzao 1947).

Also in the cultural category of use, 10 species have been cited as employed in the manufacture of traditional musical instruments, such as *jejolava*, *marovany*, and *lokanga*. Among these are six endemic species in the families Araliaceae (*Polyscias* sp.), Burseraceae (*Commiphora fraxinifolia*, *C. grandifolia*), Euphorbiaceae (*Macaranga alnifolia*), Monimiaceae (*Tambourissa purpurea*), and Rutaceae (*Zanthoxylum tsihanimposa*).

For fibers used in the production for traditional clothing, such as the *salaka* in the south and *akanjobe* in the east, six species, all introduced, have been identified. The well-known species are cotton (*Gossypium hirsutum*, Malvaceae), sisal (*Agave sisalana*, Agavaceae), and raffia (*Raphia farinifera*, Arecaceae). People of the Bara ethnic group from the central southwest use the bark of *Ficus reflexa* for their dress. Regarding plant dyes to color these fibers, Fee and Rasoarifetra (2009) have described products prepared by *ombiasy* (individuals who practice the use of traditional medicines) to obtain the different colors of the burial shroud, or *lambamena*, using 10 endemic species: *Anisophyllea fallax* (Anisophylleaceae; *amparimamy*), *Malleastrum gracile* (Meliaceae; *andriamanamona*), *Indigofera bosseri* (Fabaceae; *famamo*), *Bremeria erectiloba* (*fatotra*), *Indigofera blaiseae* (*hingitra*), *Weinmannia bojeriana* and *W. rutenbergii* (Cunoniaceae; *lalona*), *Rhopalocarpus similis* (Sphaerosepalaceae; *taolafoty*), *Danais cernua* (Rubiaceae; *vahatra*), *Aloe divaricata* (Asphodelaceae; *vahontsohy*), and *A. vaombe* (*vahombe*).

The Malagasy flora is also exploited for its wealth of cosmetic ingredients. At the beginning of the 21st century, plant inventories led to the discovery of wild species that have important potential in cosmetics and aromatics. Species in the genus *Aloe* and *Uncarina* (Pedaliaceae) are used in facial and scalp-care products. Malagasy people have for centuries used different wild endemic species to make sunscreen (*masonjoany*). *Ficus grevei* and *Coptosperma madagascariense* (Rubiaceae) are common for this use. Some people in rural areas use endemic species such as *Doratoxylon stipulatum* (Sapindaceae) and *Psiadia altissima* (Asteraceae) for soap (Randrianarivony 2015).

UTENSILS AND TOOLS

Since the beginning of agriculture and other technological developments on Madagascar, a range of tools, including basketry products, have been made by hand, especially in rural areas. Tool handles are fabricated from small-diameter tree trunks of hardwood species, including endemics like *Dalbergia* spp. (Figure 5.12c), *Memecylon delphinense* (Melastomataceae), *Rhopalocarpus lucidus*, *R. similis*, *Streblus dimepate* (Moraceae), and *Terminalia seyrigii* (Combretaceae). People in rural areas make mortars from a handful of endemic larger-diameter trees, such as *Abrahamia grandidieri*, *Albizia mainaea*, *Campylospermum deltoideum* (Ochnaceae), and *Faucherea laciniata*.

Madagascar is well known for its handicraft products, including baskets, wood products, bags, and hats, many of which have characteristic styles in different ethnic groups (e.g., Betsileo, Merina, Antandroy, Antemoro). In recent years, researchers have examined the economic importance of the plant species widely used in basketry, such as *Ravenala madagascariensis* (Rakotoarivelo et al. 2014), *Lepironia articulata* (Cyperaceae; Figure 5.12g) (Guillaud and Vermeulen 2014), *Lasiorhachis viguieri* (Poaceae; *haravola*) (Bussmann et al. 2018), and palm species (Byg and Balslev 2001; Bussmann et al. 2015). Wetland-inhabiting herbaceous species in the family Cyperaceae (see Larridon et al., pp. 580–85, for further details on this family), such as *Cyperus alternifolius*, *C. baronii*, *C. heterocladus*, *C. latifolius*, *Eleocharis dulcis*, and *Schoenoplectiella juncoides*, are common species in the manufacture of basketry products on the island. These plants are thought to be introduced (see Larridon et al., pp. 580–85) with the exception of *C. heterocladus*, which is an endemic species classified as Endangered on the IUCN Red List.

In some regions of Madagascar, traditional handicrafts like fishing traps (Figure 5.12e) are made from the leaves of tree species in the families Arecaceae (*Dypsis fibrosa*, *D. hildebrandtii*, *D. louvelii*, *Hyphaene coriacea*, *Raphia farinifera*, and *Ravenea lakatra*) (see Rakotoarinivo et al., pp. 567–80) and Pandanaceae (*Pandanus coronatus* [= *P. tectorius*] and *P. guillaumetii*) (see Callmander et al., pp. 551–59). The bark of *Bauhinia* spp. (Fabaceae), *Dombeya* spp., *Ficus* spp., and *Grewia* spp. (Malvaceae) is frequently collected for rope. Finally, for several decades, species of tree ferns of the family Cyatheaceae have been widely exploited by people living near forests for the production of ornamental flowerpots.

FUEL

Use of wood for a variety of fuel-related purposes is certainly one of the oldest practices on Madagascar, and this continues to date. During the colonial period, numerous fast-growing species were introduced and proposed as a source of firewood, and most are now considered to be invasive, including *Acacia* spp. (Fabaceae), *Eucalyptus* spp. (Myrtaceae), *Grevillea banksii* (Proteaceae), *Pinus* spp. (Pinaceae), and *Ziziphus* spp. (Rhamnaceae), were. Starting in the 19th century, charcoal production became increasingly important and is one of the main causes of deforestation on the island (Blanc-Pamard et al. 2005). Currently, wood for fuel is considered a basic necessity in the life of Malagasy people, both in rural and in urban areas. In the countryside, fuel is sometimes provided by the wood of endemic forest species such as *Abrahamia ditimena*, *Brachylaena merana*, *Cedrelopsis* spp., *Dicraeopetalum mahafaliense* (Fabaceae), *Phylloxylon xylophylloides*, *Rhigozum madagascariense* (Bignoniaceae), *Streblus dimepate*, and *Uapaca thouarsii*.

ENVIRONMENTAL USES

This category includes plants used for agroforestry practices, living enclosures such as cattle corrals, and plants for erosion management, ornamentation, and soil fertilization. To cite a few examples, species used as living fences or for soil fertilization are often introduced, such as *Agave sisalana*, *Cajanus cajan* (Fabaceae), *Jatropha curcas* (Euphorbiaceae), *Opuntia* spp. (Cactaceae), and *Tephrosia* spp. (Fabaceae), but some exceptions exist where native plants are employed, such as those of the genera *Commiphora*, as well as *Alluaudia* and *Didierea* (Didiereaceae). However, endemic forest species, many notably threatened, such as *Euphorbia ambovombensis*, *E. cap-saintemariensis*, *E. tulearensis* (Euphorbiaceae), and *Tahina spectabilis* (Arecaceae), are harvested and exported for the international ornamental market.

TOXIC AND CHEMICAL USES

Madagascar has a long cultural tradition of using toxic plants during judgment of criminal acts, to determine whether the accused is guilty, and concoctions from *Cerbera manghas* (*tangena*) and *Cryptostegia madagascariensis* (Apocynaceae; *lombiro*) have been administered for such purposes. Currently in certain rural areas, these plants are still employed for this purpose. Extracts from several forest species in the family Fabaceae, such as *Cadia ellisiana*, *Mundulea anceps*, *M. barclayi*, *M. sericea*, and *Sylvichadsia grandifolia*, are used to poison and catch fish. Similarly, forest species such as *Polyscias heineana* (Araliaceae) and *Dilobeia thouarsii* (Proteaceae) are cited as biological insecticides.

Latex plants used for the production of rubber are also classified in this chemical category. About 15 forest species belonging to the families Euphorbiaceae (*Euphorbia elastica*, *E. intisy*) and Apocynaceae (*Landolphia* spp., *Marsdenia verrucosa*, *Plectaneia thouarsii*, and *Secamone sparsiflora*) were inventoried for this purpose toward the end of the 19th century and overexploited during the colonial period (Perrier de la Bâthie 1949). These species are nowadays used mostly in the manufacture of glue.

MEDICINAL USES

This category has been the most-studied field of ethnobotany on Madagascar, since the first written documents from the medieval period concerning Malagasy traditions mentioned earlier in the context of *sorabe*. The first detailed inventory of medicinal plants was undertaken by Flacourt (1658 [repr. 1995]), and he had already mentioned the use of *Cedrelopsis grevei* (*katrafay*) in remedies. During the colonial period and thereafter, several works on medicinal plants from Madagascar, including native and introduced species, were published, for example Heckel (1903) and Debray et al. (1971).

Toward the end of the colonial period and subsequently, Professor Albert Rakoto Ratsimamanga was the first national to examine the scientific basis of Malagasy medicinal plants and traditional medicine. Since then, several researchers have published lists of medicinal plants of Madagascar with their botanical descriptions and therapeutic indications (e.g., Nicolas 2012; Gallé et al. 2014). Rafidison et al. (2019) recently published a synthesis on medicinal plants of Madagascar. Details on the utilization of medicinal plants from 20 books, 42 publications in scientific journals, 31 theses, and five reports, published from the colonial period to early 2019, have been entered into a database. This latest information reveals that 3245 species of medicinal plants belonging to 1050 genera and 203 families are documented on the island. Of these species, 60% are endemic. The most frequently cited endemic species are *Anthocleista madagascariensis* (Gentianaceae), *Baronia taratana* (Anacardiaceae), *Burasaia madagascariensis* (Menispermaceae), *Buddleja madagascariensis*, *Canarium madagascariense*, *Cassinopsis madagascariensis* (Icacinaceae), *Catharanthus roseus* (Apocynaceae), *Cinnamosma fragrans*, *C. macrocarpa*, *Helichrysum faradifani*, *Maerua filiformis* (Capparaceae) (Figure 5.12b), and *Psiadia altissima*.

CONCLUSION

A number of studies and compilations have been published on Malagasy ethnobotany, but many aspects remain to be explored. Gaps in ethnobotanical data are apparent from the northern and western parts of Madagascar, particularly from the ethnic groups Tsimihety, Sakalava, and Antakarana. Since ethnobotany is dependent largely on natural resources and cultural traditions, superimposed on the diverse ethnic groups of the island, the loss of knowledge on plant use is alarming, considering the decline of the island's biodiversity and the invasion of other styles of medicine, particularly from the West. Ethnobotany is a dynamic and multifaceted science, encompassing the fields of taxonomy, botany, pharmacology, anthropology, and sociology. Researchers are encouraged to explore further into the uses of plants by different ethnic groups and in other little-studied domains, such as the cultural, utensil and tool, and construction categories of use.

Subject editor: Steven M. Goodman

BIOCULTURAL LANDSCAPE DIVERSITY SHAPED BY AGRICULTURAL SYSTEMS

S. M. Carrière, H. Randriambanona, V. Labeyrie, D. Hervé, J. Mariel, S. Razanaka, and J. R. Randriamalala

If Madagascar's biodiversity, originality, and threats are recognized worldwide as associated with its forested ecosystems, this is not the case for a diversity of nonforested landscapes that human activities have produced over the course of centuries (Carrière-Buchsenschutz 2007; Amelot et al. 2011). These current Malagasy landscapes are the result of both old and more recent exploitation of ecosystems by humans and have generated some of the renowned agricultural systems that contribute to both Malagasy livelihoods and heritage. These diverse agricultural landscapes are not limited to the familiar images of treeless, homogeneous landscapes often distributed by the media and certain nongovernmental organizations (Figure 5.13a). As in many other regions of the world, on Madagascar, in addition to the important diversity of climate and soil conditions that shapes the different natural ecosystems, there are indigenous knowledge and practices associated with ecosystem usage. Further, there is a diversity of relationships that humans maintain with their environment, considered herein as cultural diversity, ultimately leading to a range of socio-spatial contexts, which we refer to here as *biocultural landscapes*.

As can be seen in the literature from the late 20th–early 21st century (e.g., Goodman and Benstead 2003), a large portion of research during that period in ecology, botany, and zoology concerned natural ecosystems with low human disturbance, and focused on inventory, description of biodiversity and biogeography, ecosystem dynamics, genetic diversity, and evolution and history. A large part of current research still focuses on these areas, but, more recently, Malagasy and international research programs have shed light on new aspects of and areas concerning biodiversity on Madagascar. This research focuses in part on spaces that can be referred to as "anthropized" and cultivated or open spaces (Carrière and Bidaud 2012). These human-modified areas, dominated by introduced species and depleted of native and endemic species, form new species assemblages called *novel ecosystems* (Hobbs et al. 2006), which are the starting point of tomorrow's ecosystems and ecological processes in open landscapes on the island. As is the case with protected areas (Janzen 1983), these novel ecosystems are not closed, in that the species they contain disperse and interact with other ecosystems, modifying native and endemic Malagasy species' distribution and dynamics. Thus, understanding how biocultural landscapes, as a result of human-nature interactions, have emerged and will evolve seems to us a fundamental prerequisite to better anticipate and understand the new ecological dynamics at work. Such understanding may help to better implement biodiversity conservation measures within and outside protected areas.

In this contribution, we present several biocultural landscapes on the island, providing examples in contrasting ecological situations. They include, for example, relatively old agricultural and agroforestry landscapes, which continue to evolve today, and which in turn make up relatively densely wooded landscapes without natural forest in an agroforestry landscape formed entirely by farmers. These cultivated landscapes, rich in cash crops, provide significant income to farmers, which makes such regions some of the most economically productive on the island. In contrast, the dry spiny thicket in the extreme south provides an example with rather different dynamics. Here, the different local cultural groups relying on agricultural activities (*hatsaky*, or swidden agriculture) or on hunting and gathering live in a rather ecologically extreme ecosystem. In the following sections, we present several biocultural landscapes and place each in its historical, biogeographical, human, and economic context. We also consider the consequences of human activities in terms of the non-native forest landscapes, including the effects of human practices on the ecological processes of forest regeneration and biodiversity dynamics, and sometimes both.

CLOVE AGROFORESTRY DYNAMICS IN VAVATENINA DISTRICT: TRANSITION FROM SWIDDEN CULTIVATION TO COMPLEX AGROFORESTRY SYSTEMS

On Madagascar, as compared with the tropics in general (Jose 2009; Tscharntke et al. 2012), agroforestry has not been the subject of much research. A wide range of agroforest types, adapted to a variety of biophysical environments and socioeconomic conditions, is observed across the island, with sometimes high levels of plant species richness (Arimalala et al. 2019), comprising both introduced and native plants. By comparing the current landscape to that described in the 1960s (Dandoy 1973), the area of Vavatenina, located along the central part of the eastern coast in the Analanjirofo Region, provides an illustrative case study of agroforestry diversification and complexification trajectories.

The Vavatenina area presents a tropical humid climate with two seasons, with average annual rainfall of about 2000 mm, mostly falling between November and April (Dandoy 1973). The landscape is topographically complex, with successions of hills (*tanety*) and valleys (*horaka*) oriented along a north–south axis, presenting elevations ranging from about 150 m in the Iazafo floodplain in the east to about 600 m in the mid-hills in the west. The commune of Vavatenina, which includes the main town of the district and the surrounding villages, has about 37,240 inhabitants, mostly of the Betsimisaraka cultural group.

There is evidence that this area has been deforested for some time. According to Dandoy (1973), the area was named *pays de Ghalemboule*—meaning "bamboo forest country"—by the first European explorers who crossed the region during the 17th century (e.g., Flacourt in 1661), which indicates that it was already largely covered by secondary vegetation at this time. In 1953, based on a

FIGURE 5.13 **Different biocultural landscapes on Madagascar. A) A biocultural landscape in the Central Highlands, north of Ambalavao; B) a complex, multispecific, and multilayered agroforest, called *tsabo*, in Vavatenina; C) long-distance view of the landscape at Ranomafana-Est, with relicts of forest on hilltops surrounded by *savoka* (post-agricultural secondary forest); D) land colonization along a valley for rice cultivation; E) ecological habitat diversity in the Ambositra–Vondrozo corridor; F) Sahabe biocultural landscape near Andringitra, dominated by land cover with herbaceous vegetation; G) agriculture established in dry spiny thicket in the Toliara region; and H) post-cultivation formation in dry spiny thicket of the southwest.** (PHOTOS A, B, and D–G by S. M. Carrière; C by H. Randriambanona; and H by J. Randriamalala.)

map derived from aerial images from Humbert (1965), the Vavatenina area appears almost fully deforested. Deforestation of the area was probably the result of earlier occupation and a high population density, which was estimated as one of the highest on the eastern coast in the 1950s at about 14 inhabitants/km^2, in comparison to the average in the Toamasina Province of 9.9 (Gourou 1967). This especially high population density in Vavatenina may be related to its location along the former Fenoarivo-Atsinanana–Imerimandroso road, which was an important commercial conduit connecting the coast to the Lake Alaotra region.

The in-depth study of Dandoy (1973), conducted in 1966 in the Vavatenina area, provides a valuable baseline to monitor local landscape evolution. He provided a detailed land-use map of a village located about 5 km north of the town of Vavatenina, showing that only small fragments of natural forest, including native biodiversity, remained, on the hilltops and along rivers. Most of the hills were covered by shrubby and herbaceous secondary fallow vegetation (with native, endemic, and introduced species), as local populations relied largely on swidden cultivation, or *tavy*, of rain-fed hill rice, which covered about 30% of the cultivated area and is the classical agricultural system of the Betsimisaraka (Aubert et al. 2003). Monospecific coffee (*Coffea arabica*) plantations during this period covered about the same surface area, as it was the main cash crop up to the 1980s and 1990s, when global prices decreased dramatically. Further, monospecific *Syzygium aromaticum* (Clove) plantations covered about 15% of the cultivated area (Dandoy 1973). Cloves were a secondary cash crop on the east coast at that time, for which the planted surface area increased considerably after the coffee crisis. In the 1990s, it became the first cash-crop income for Madagascar, along with vanilla (*Vanilla planifolia*) (Danthu et al. 2014). Clove trees were introduced in the Vavatenina area around 1930, and by the 1960s they covered about 8000 ha and accounted for about 20% of production at the country level (Dandoy 1973).

These days, landscapes in this area are different from those described around 50 years ago by Dandoy, reflecting major recent agricultural changes. The most striking change is the increase in tree cover—mostly introduced species—related to the development of agroforestry. Agroforests today cover about 20% of village territory, where in the 1970s they were limited to home gardens (Mariel 2016). These systems can be classified into two main types: parks, with scattered trees and annual crops or pasture beneath, and complex, multispecific, and multilayered agroforests, called *tsabo* (Arimalala et al. 2019; Figure 5.13b).

A wide range of *tsabo* occurs in the area in combination with different ligneous and nonligneous plants, either planted, encouraged, or tolerated, both native and introduced. *Tsabo* trees include cash crops collected by local economic operators and then exported, such as introduced cloves, vanilla, and litchi (*Litchi chinensis*), and also to a lesser extent other spices, such as cinnamon (*Cinnamomum verum*) and pepper (*Piper nigrum*). Various fruit trees are grown, the fruit being either for local consumption or to be sold in local markets; the most common are in the families Annonaceae (*Annona muricata*, *A. reticulata*, *A. squamosa*), Rutaceae (citrus), Moraceae (*Artocarpus heterophyllus*, Jackfruit), Musaceae (banana and plantain), and Bromeliaceae (*Ananas comosus*, Pineapple). Starchy-food plants (*bomafana*) include all crops nutritionally similar to rice, which may substitute for it in the diet, especially during periods of food shortage; this category comprises mainly plantain, banana, *Manihot esculenta* (Cassava), *Artocarpus altilis* (Breadfruit), and yams (Dioscoreaceae). Timber trees (*hazotrano*) and those used for firewood (*kitay*) are also frequent in agroforests. The need for the latter is especially important as clove-leaf distillation requires a lot of combustible energy; species used for these purposes are mainly eucalyptuses (*Eucalyptus robusta*, *E. camaldulensis*), *Grevillea banksii*, and bamboos (*Bambusa* spp.). Several introduced fruit trees, such as *Artocarpus heterophyllus* and *Mangifera indica* (Mango), are also used for firewood, as well as Fabaceae species such as *Albizia lebbeck* and *A. chinensis*, which were initially used as shade trees for coffee. These species of *Albizia* and other nitrogen-fixing plants, mainly *Gliricidia sepium* and *Pachira aquatica*, are used as stakes for vanilla or as living fences. Last, scattered coffee trees are also frequently found in *tsabo*, reflecting the progressive conversion of the former coffee plantations into agroforests. Production of coffee in this area of Madagascar is now mostly dedicated to self-consumption, as its sale price remains low.

In this region, the diversification of tree production is a widespread strategy developed by households to increase their resilience to the different ongoing economic and climatic changes, in a context of decreasing land availability and increasing monetarization of household economy (Dandoy 1973; Mariel 2016). Indeed, a certain portion of local households are not able to fulfill their food self-sufficiency and rely on the sale of agricultural products such as cloves, clove essential oil, or fruits, and on the production of supplementary food crops such as *Manihot esculenta* or *Artocarpus altilis*. Furthermore, the price of cash crops varies considerably over time, and cyclones frequently hit the area, which makes agricultural specialization a risk. Diversification also allows households to stabilize their income and food production over the year, as the different products become available during different seasons, as observed in Foulpointe (Mahavelona) (>30 km east of Vavatenina site) (Blanc-Pamard and Ruf 1992) in the late 1980s. Clove essential oil especially plays a key role in the economy of local households as it can be produced throughout the year, easily stored, and sold at any time.

The different diversification strategies implemented by farmers in Vavatenina have led to the emergence of different types of agroforests, the distribution of which in the landscape is not random. Fruit trees, coffee, breadfruit, bananas, and yams for household and animal consumption are planted in home gardens and fertilized by different forms of compost. These types of plant associations are also found in the humid valleys (*vavasaha*) and in old coffee plantations that have been progressively enriched with other plants. Litchi and banana are also frequently planted on the borders of irrigated rice plains, while clove trees are planted on hill slopes and often associated with pineapple, cassava, and some fruit and firewood trees. Woodlots are often located on hilltops and sometimes associated with various woody and nonwoody native and introduced tree species. All of this leads to complex and species-rich agroforests.

Most of the clove-complex agroforests occurring near Vavatenina are recent—that is to say, planted in the early portion of the 21st century—while the old clove and coffee plantations were mostly monocultures. Indeed, the cultivation of cloves by small farmers was supported by the French colonial administration, which provided advice and recommended growing this species in monospecific stands. Cloves progressively supplanted coffee, and their cultivation expanded in multispecific stands that associated introduced and native plant species. An important motivation for planting cloves on *savoka* (post-agricultural secondary forest) was also probably to secure individual property tenure (Aubert et al. 2003). According to village elders, the local hills were covered with clove plantations before Cyclone Honorinina hit the area in 1986, causing major damage to trees. They reported that people were discouraged of planting after Honorinina, and in the 1990s this problem, combined with low prices of export products and decreasing soil fertility, led many people to move elsewhere to find salaried work. Many of these individuals moved farther north to the Mananara-Nord area, where clove and vanilla production was less affected by the cyclone. This probably played a major role in the emergence of clove agroforests in Vavatenina, which probably began around 2000 when people returned to the area and started to plant again, encouraged by the increased market value of cloves and the absence of cyclones for about a decade, and inspired by the clove agroforests they had observed in Mananara-Nord. Vanilla cultivation also started during those years, but increased significantly around 2010 when prices increased.

Nowadays, farmers still refer with some nostalgia to the time when the Betsimisaraka planted their crops in the forest and where crops "grew by themselves," despite the forest having disappeared probably long before the 1950s. Indeed, the Betsimisaraka lived at the forest margin, practicing *tavy* (swidden cultivation) and gathering (Aubert et al. 2003). Even though the forest disappeared several generations ago in the Vavatenina area, people appear deeply imprinted by the forest, and this lasting memory may partly explain the return of a notable diversity and density of trees in the landscape. These agroforestry dynamics may open perspectives for enhancing agricultural production in a sustainable way and for contributing to the conservation of biodiversity outside of the protected-area system, as suggested by a recent study in the Andapa region (Hending et al. 2018). Research is now needed to investigate how the spread of trees in the agricultural landscapes of Vavatenina affects biodiversity, in particular of animal species. Indeed, studies conducted in different parts of the tropics over recent decades have provided ample evidence that agroforests enhance biodiversity, even though they are dominantly composed of introduced tree species (Tscharntke et al. 2015).

HUMID FOREST FRAGMENTS OF THE ATSINANANA REGION: THE VILLAGES OF BEFORONA AND RANOMAFANA-EST

The forest fragments in these areas represent relics of the moist evergreen forests of eastern Madagascar. The village of Beforona (Moramanga District) is located on the national road connecting Antananarivo to Toamasina, in a region where large forested areas coexist with a belt of open areas and forest fragments. The village of Ankorabe (commune of Ranomafana-Est, Brickaville District) is located along the same road. In the Ranomafana-Est area there are forest fragments, including the Vohilahy Forest (145 ha) near the village of Ankorabe.

Across these two study sites, the elevation varies from 20 to 340 m. The relief is dissected with V-shaped valleys, rice fields are rare in the low-lying areas, and most agricultural production is cultivated on slopes in the form of swidden agriculture (*tavy*), including at inclines of greater than 40%. This area is influenced by a tropical and perhumid climate, characterized by two alternating seasons: 1) a hot and rainy season from October to March, during which the temperature varies from 17°C to 30°C, and 2) a dry season from June to September, when the rains are less regular and average temperatures cooler. The wind is dominated by trade winds, which generally blow from the southeast toward the northwest. The average rainfall is 3000 mm per year. The soil is generally a yellow-red ferralitic type, resting on a crystalline base. Hydromorphic soils are found in the lowlands where rice growing is practiced.

The vegetation is made up of relict patches of lowland moist evergreen forest, a form of grassland, and post-agricultural regrowth in fallows (Figure 5.13c). There are five different types of vegetation found in the landscape:

1. Forests (*atiala*), which are multilayered, natural woody forests with 20–25 m high trees
2. Post-agricultural regrowth (*savoka*), where physiognomy and floristic composition vary according to the age of the fallow and the past cultivation intensity, crops, and practices (*tavy*, fallow period length, and tillage intensity) (e.g., one can find young shrubby regrowth with native species such as *Psiadia* spp. and *Harungana madagascariensis* and introduced species such as *Rubus moluccanus* and *Clidemia hirta*, but also shrubby regrowth dominated by the introduced *Lantana camara* and native *Psiadia altissima* with dense growths of the native fern *Pteridium aquilinum*)
3. Pseudo-steppe (*roranga alafamafa*), composed of a herbaceous carpet of mostly *Aristida similis* in discontinuous mats (the last stage of natural forest conversion)
4. *Tanety* crops, which consist essentially of rain-fed rice fields and cassava; the landscape is also formed of orchards (*Artocarpus heterophyllus*, *Coffea arabica*, banana trees, and *Pouteria hypoglauca*) around villages, where introduced species such as *Grevillea banksii* and eucalyptus form small plantations
5. Riparian forests or shrubby vegetation, which develops on the edges of rivers where frequent introduced species are *Eugenia* and the native *Pandanus* used for basketry

Archaeological excavations carried out in Antongombato near the Vohilahy Forest, within 5 km of Ankorabe, indicate the area has been occupied by humans since at least the 14th century (Randrianasolo 2014). Thus, these biocultural landscapes have probably been shaped by the exploitation of the forest over centuries. The intact forest, therefore, probably disappeared a long time ago, even if the "mature" or old secondary forest still persists today in some places. Similarly, the Beforona region was settled by Arab colonists in the 10th or 11th century (Pfund 2000). Currently, the population consists mainly of the local cultural group, Betsimisaraka, and migrant groups of Merina, Antesaka, and Antemoro. The dominant traditional farming system is *tavy*. According to Althabe (1982), this practice is part of the Betsimisaraka ethnic identity, as mentioned above for the Vavatenina region.

In this portion of central eastern Madagascar, swidden agriculture is one of the main causes of landscape degradation and deforestation (Styger et al. 2007). It is the dominant form of land use in this area, producing rain-fed rice and crops such as cassava and sweet potatoes on portions of cleared and then burned lowland moist evergreen forests at different stages (mature forest, secondary forest, or forest regrowth). A multidisciplinary research program on alternatives to swidden cultivation, linking social and biophysical issues, was launched in 1994 in the Beforona area (Pollini 2009), and agroforestry was proposed as a possible solution to reduce deforestation, but this was not achieved. In just 10 years, half of the land of Ambinanisahavolo (Beforona), in particular the hills, was cultivated and thus cleared, which is one of the important features of the landscape-degradation dynamics in this region (Styger et al. 2007).

In Ranomafana-Est Commune, natural, relatively intact forest cover in 2018 was about 3560 ha. Despite the creation of community-based management initiatives or associations known as CoBa established in 2001, annual natural forest loss of 3.28% was recorded between 1990 and 1998 and 2.82% from 1998 to 2018 (Rasoanaivo et al. 2019). To give a greater general context, in the eastern part of Madagascar between 2010 and 2015 annual deforestation rates fell within the range of 0.93–2.33% per year (Grinand et al. 2013). Currently, in the Beforona and Ranomafana-Est areas, forest relicts are found mainly on hill slopes, which corresponds to where Green and Sussman (1990) predicted remnant natural forests would be limited in the next 35 years if deforestation continued.

In this area with deforestation dating from several centuries ago and more recently, agricultural practices related to *tavy* and other types of resource exploitation have had direct and indirect effects on forest succession and dynamics. Different authors have tried to describe the ecosystem trajectories in this area following agricultural land use. Pfund (2000) proposed a multistep ecosystem change characterized by different types and stages of vegetation: from natural forest to fallows with forest components (peri-forest fallows and shrubby fallows), then to mixed fallows (densely populated with introduced invasive species such as *Lantana* and *Rubus*), and finally grassland vegetation. A decrease in plant biomass in secondary vegetation is recorded after the first two crop plantings and followed by radical changes in floristic composition. A study by Styger et al. (2007) in Vohidrazana (Beforona), on the edge of the Ankeniheny–Zahamena forest corridor, has shown that the period of time that plots lie fallow had been reduced from 8–15 years in the 1970s to 3–5 years between 1999 and 2001. This decrease has resulted in shorter and shorter crop cycles and fallow periods during which no vegetation regeneration occurs. This leads to a "vicious circle" that jeopardizes the sustainability of this form of swidden agriculture. According to some authors, this is caused by a lack of land, associated at least in part with population growth reinforced by immigration (Pfund 2000). Given this situation and these agricultural practices, it takes 15–20 years for trees to regenerate within herbaceous vegetation dominated by *Imperata* and by ferns (Styger et al. 2007). As lengthened fallow periods are not practiced, there is a need to intensify upland systems based on improved nutrient cycling, targeted inputs, less use of fire in land management, and diversification of land use (Styger et al. 2009) and agrobiodiversity.

HOW AGRICULTURAL PRACTICES HAVE SHAPED NATIVE BIODIVERSITY IN MID-ELEVATION LANDSCAPES AT THE MARGIN OF THE RANOMAFANA NATIONAL PARK

The biocultural landscapes located in the region of Haute-Matsiatra, in the west of the Corridor Forestier Fandriana-Ambositra-Vondrozo (COFAV; a protected forest corridor area that links Ambositra to Vondrozo and in some definitions also to Befotaka–Midongy du Sud), illustrate a very different socio-ecological situation to that of the other examples presented here. The COFAV, as one of the few remaining extensive tracts of forest in this part of Madagascar, has been under strict conservation regulations by law since a 2014 as a *nouvelle aire protégée* (NAP, new protected area) and includes preexisting protected areas such as Ranomafana, Andringitra, and Ivohibe. The protection of this biocultural landscape seeks to maintain both the forest's highly endemic biodiversity and its presumed ecological-corridor function between the two national parks (Goodman and Razafindratsita 2001; Carrière-Buchsenschutz 2007). Located in Betsileo, which is part of the Central Highlands, the village of Ambendrana, at the edge of the forest, in the commune of Androy, is part of the peripheral zone of the Ranomafana National Park. In the surroundings of this village, conservation measures that rely on the participation of the local population (in CoBa) (Blanc-Pamard and Ramiarantsoa 2007) were implemented when the COFAV was initiated.

Ambendrana is located around 1100 m above sea level and has a range of topographic factors and forest vegetation cover (Blanc-Pamard and Rakoto-Ramiarantsoa 2014). The climate is tropical, with 1300–1400 mm of rainfall per year, maximum precipitation from January to March, and a drier period from May to September. Temperatures are temperate and cool, especially during the southern winter, when the area can experience frost. The forested corridor is composed mainly of a dense medium-altitude moist evergreen forest dominated by *Weinmannia* spp. and *Tambourissa* spp. (J. Koechlin et al. 1974). This area is densely populated and mostly inhabited by the Betsileo ethnic group (Serpantié et al. 2007). Most local activities and forms of resource exploitation take place in the forest and at its margins (swidden agriculture, lowland rice farming, animal husbandry, hunting, fishing, and gathering) (Carrière et al. 2005). Paddy rice is the staple food and at the heart of social exchanges (Le Bourdiec 1978).

The village of Ambendrana dates back to about 1790, created by the Zafindrareoto people, a clan originating in the "eastern forest" (H. Dubois 1938). There are still remnants of old, abandoned villages in the forest, perhaps dating from this approximate period, but also more recent areas of refuge where one can still find planted trees from the period of the 1947 rebellion (Solondraibe 1991–1992; Carrière et al. 2007a). The forest is not intact in such areas; there are many traces of villages, different symbolic markers, long-lived pioneer tree species, and plantations of trees such as banana and avocado (Goodman and Rakotoarisoa 1998; Carrière et al. 2007a). It would appear that the previous strong link between the Betsileo and the forest has been gradually weakened, notably by the transition to agriculture and, more precisely, to rice growing (Kottak 1980; Moreau 2002). During this transitional period, land conquest for cultivation has been an important local demographic pressure and has extended into previously forested areas. This pressure on the remaining forest, particularly from young households, is still active, with the creation of small, secondary hamlets along the valleys moving away from the central valleys (Blanc-Pamard and Rakoto-Ramiarantsoa 2014; Figure 5.13d).

The current structure of the landscapes in this area follows these various historical processes of population establishment associated with the conversion of bottom lands into paddy fields (Figure 5.13e). In addition to a wide variety of natural forest types (medium-altitude moist evergreen forest, old and medium-aged secondary forests, wood-exploited forests, riparian forests; Carrière et al. 2007a), this agricultural landscape is now notably heterogeneous (Martin et al. 2009, 2012). It consists of a fine-grained mosaic of cultivated and noncultivated habitats, including medium-altitude moist evergreen forest fragments called *songon'ala* (Figure 5.13e), secondary medium-altitude forest at different succession ages (*kapoaka*), eucalyptus and other tree and crop plantations, swidden agricultural fields on slopes, and paddy fields on valley floors. In a sampled reference surface of 3320 ha (2004), habitat patches were composed of 23.7% dry crops, 10.7% herbaceous recruits, 14.2% irrigated rice fields, 7.4% reforestation areas, 2.1% medium-altitude natural forest, and 41.8% shrubby recruits. Open areas occupy 48.6% of these habitats (Martin et al. 2009) and are defined as areas either without dense vegetation cover or where the height of dense vegetation is less than 1 m. Various ecological studies have shown that in areas with relatively low-intensity agriculture and use of natural forest products forest-dependent animals (endemic bats and birds; Picot 2005; Picot et al. 2007; Martin et al. 2009, 2012) and forest plants (trees, lianas, shrubs, and herbaceous species; J. Randriamalala et al. 2012; Rakotoarimanana et al. 2008), native and endemic, are present. This is due to the diversity of ecological habitats (from secondary forests to shrubby and herbaceous vegetation types), with marked levels of habitat heterogeneity across the landscape, the high density of isolated trees of some value (*Ficus* spp., eucalyptus, fruit trees, *Harungana*, and *Anthocleista* spp.) (Martin et al. 2009; Rafidison et al. 2020) and plantations of introduced tree species, the plant diversity found in the various ecological habitats, and, in particular, the close proximity of the site to the forest corridor (J. Randriamalala et al. 2015a) (Figure 5.13e).

The dispersal of different plant and animal species in these landscapes, specifically at the edges of the natural forest patches and corridor, has also made possible the advancement of new ecological processes, including afforestation processes and native forest species' regeneration in cultivated spaces, which could contribute to the restoration of forests on Madagascar (Gérard et al. 2015). Studies have shown that artificial plantations of introduced species (such as *Pinus* and *Acacia*), which were originally planted in grassland areas, can act as a catalyst for the regeneration of native Malagasy and endemic plant species if in close proximity to natural forest parcels (Randriambanona et al. 2019). In this area, which has been affected by various disturbances (e.g., cyclones, logging, cultivation), *Pinus* plantations have become environments conducive to the regeneration of native species. A total of 125 species, 34 of which are endemic, from 46 families, were inventoried in disturbed *Pinus* plantations in approximately 200 plots of 100 m^2 at Ambendrana. These results also suggest that a low level of disturbance, such as that resulting from selective *Pinus* tree logging, can act as a catalyst for the establishment of native woodlands. However, excessive disturbance from sylvicultural and agricultural practices, such as frequent burning, heavy tillage, and a high number of crop-fallow cycles, may hinder, although it does not block, the establishment of native woodlands (Randriambanona et al. 2019).

These heterogeneous landscapes show successional stages through time (Carrière et al. 2007b; Martin et al. 2012): 1) increased landscape fragmentation and heterogeneity, which may be a consequence of the increase in human population density, in Ambendrana, and 2) in Sahabe, in the southwestern part of the corridor, the gradual replacement of a forested matrix by grasslands. First, in Ambendrana, based on 15 categories of ecological habitat listed for an area of 3300 ha, the landscape and its evolution were described in 1954, 1991, and 2004. The landscape structure in 1954 consisted of a mosaic of large, more or less homogeneous forest, agricultural, and grassland plots. In 1991, the mosaic was more complex. The plots of each category were smaller (on average 400 plots in 1954 and 750 in 1991) and the landscape was essentially open and made up of cultivated areas (rice fields and food crops). The landscape structure in 2004 was yet more complex than during the previous two periods, with a mosaic of small, heterogeneous plots (960 in total). By 2004, many habitat types—such as natural moist evergreen forest, grassland, woody fallows, and reforestation plots—were highly fragmented (Carrière et al. 2007b).

Over time, the increase in the heterogeneity of this biocultural landscape has been linked to landscape complexification, resulting from an increase in the variety of habitats, and to a fragmentation of each of the habitat types, which produces a larger number of habitat patches. Thus, a transition occurred from a landscape dominated by forest plantations, crops, and pseudo-steppe associated with cattle pastoralism in 1954 toward a fine landscape mosaic resulting from changes in agricultural use (reduction of pastoralism and increased rice cultivation), forest regeneration, and recolonization processes, which induced a diversity of forest regrowth stages. Many social, economic, and political factors were behind this dynamic shift since 1954. Indeed, the population density has more than tripled in 50 years in this region and the commune (Gourou 1967; Blanc-Pamard and Rakoto-Ramiarantsoa 2014), leading to an increase in the conversion of zones into lowland rice production. In addition, changes in household strategies, constraints linked to the development of new value chains (food, fruit, alcohol, wood, etc.), access to land, and fire and access bans in forests due to conservation measures, as well as insecurity, have led to a decrease in livestock grazing in the forest and therefore fire use (Serpantié et al. 2007). Finally, successive reforestation, disturbance, and afforestation lead to the establishment of native and introduced pioneer species in former herbaceous habitats (Randriambanona et al. 2019). In addition, on a finer scale, heterogeneity changes have been amplified by isolated tree plantations created for social, economic, and symbolic purposes (Martin et al. 2009; Rafidison et al. 2020).

Second, the pattern of forest regeneration after clearing for swidden agriculture seems to be similar throughout the forest corridor, but we observe that a provisional herbaceous state (observed at a low rate in Ambendrana and locally called *kilanjy*) has gradually become more common near Sahabe village, consisting of a mostly herbaceous matrix containing some forest fragments (J. Randriamalala et al. 2012). This situation is becoming widespread near the Andringitra National Park, specifically near Sahabe (Figure 5.13f).

The comparison of these different areas near the villages of Ambendrana and Sahabe between 1999 and 2009 illustrates some peculiarities of these landscapes. They have changed from a natural medium-altitude moist evergreen forest matrix, cleared in areas to cultivate hill rice and then for *tanety*, which once cultivated is first covered with shrubby and woody fallows and then gives rise to a herbaceous matrix. This matrix is dominated by plantations of introduced eucalyptus or by native medium-altitude moist evergreen forest, which has withstood fires when the zones included grasslands (Hervé et al. 2010). In Sahabe, the diversity of landscape patches is the same as in the Ambendrana area, but the proportions are different. This herbaceous matrix landscape, subject to an annual and therefore regular fire regime, dominates farther south in the area of Andringitra National Park.

HOW AGRICULTURAL PRACTICES MAY INFLUENCE DRY SPINY THICKET VEGETATION RECOVERY

This case study concerns human activities in a special type of dry ecosystem known as dry spiny thicket. It is a low-growing, open, dry ecosystem located in the most arid part of lowland southwestern Madagascar (J. Randriamalala et al. 2016). This vegetation covers approximately 5 million ha and is the oldest and most arid biome of Madagascar (Wells 2003). This area has the highest known proportion of endemic plants on the island (classified as "very high" level), reaching up to 90% of the documented 1100 plant species (Burgess et al. 2004). Most of the plant species of dry spiny thicket vegetation present adaptations for storing moisture efficiently and to minimize water loss (Gautier and Goodman 2003). Spiny thicket is also classified as an "endemic bird area" (Stattersfield et al. 1998), and is home to nine endemic threatened lemur species (IUCN 2003). The formation occurs on two main soil types, calcareous rocky soil and yellow sandy soil. The plant community on calcareous soil is more resistant to drought than that on yellow sandy soil, where water availability is higher (J. Koechlin et al. 1974).

The vegetation of dry spiny thicket provides several goods and ecosystem services, such as timber for building houses and pirogues, medicinal plants, food (tubers, honey, and meat from hunted animals), fuelwood and charcoal, and land for agricultural use or goat pasture (J. Randriamalala et al. 2016, 2017). Due to the multiple uses by human populations, conservation of its biodiversity remains difficult. Swidden agriculture, charcoal production, and, to a lesser extent, grazing of goats are the main human practices that impact this vegetation type, which is undergoing degradation and deforestation (Casse et al. 2004; J. Randriamalala et al. 2015b, 2016; Figure 5.13g). Furthermore, these thickets are considered to be less resilient to human disturbance compared with dry and moist evergreen forests because forest recovery is slow, as is regrowth of shrubs (Gaspard et al. 2018; J. Randriamalala et al. 2019).

On the Belomotse Plateau, although agriculture is not the main activity of people living in and around the dry spiny thicket, a form of swidden cultivation (*hatsaky*) is practiced to grow staple foods (J. Randriamalala et al. 2019) and is the main cause of deforestation (J. Randriamalala et al. 2015b). Swidden cultivation consists of cutting all trees and shrubs in a plot during the dry season (November–December), before the first rains, leaving them to dry for 2–10 days, and then burning the lot. Maize, peas, and cucurbitaceous plants are sown together after the first clearing, and then during the first two to three cropping periods. Plots on calcareous soils are abandoned after two to three years of cropping, while plots on yellow sandy soils may be exploited for a longer period, with cassava and/or sweet potato and sometimes with groundnuts, after manual soil plowing (J. Randriamalala et al. 2019). The overstory floristic composition of post-cultivation dry spiny thicket on both soil types does not vary based on secondary succession stages. However, structural parameters (height and basal area) increased significantly with age of abandonment, while diversity (species richness and evenness index) did not. Poor regeneration (J. Randriamalala et al. 2016, 2019) and the slow growth of shrub species (Gaspard et al. 2018) found after cultivation in this formation may explain the lack of change in diversity and floristic composition during secondary succession stages (Figure 5.13h).

The production of charcoal, derived from spiny thicket trees, and breeding of goats are the main income sources for local people (Raoliarivelo et al. 2010; Hänke and Barkmann 2017). The diet of the goats essentially consists of the leaves of shrubs and shoots of more than 100 shrubby and herbaceous species (H. Randriamalala 2014; Feldt et al. 2017). Charcoal production reduces shrub density and biomass and affects species composition (J. Randriamalala et al. 2016). It is an unsustainable activity that in certain circumstances results in the local loss of mature hardwood species. In contrast, goat grazing alone does not significantly affect the diversity, mean height, stem and leaf biomass, or species composition of dry spiny thicket growing on calcareous soil. Goat grazing at a moderate stocking rate (about one head per hectare) does not leave a significant footprint on the dry spiny thicket communities in terms of plant diversity, biomass, or regeneration rate (J. Randriamalala et al. 2016).

Dry spiny thicket vegetation is not resilient to cultivation and charcoal extraction, and these occurring together with goat production lead to notable habitat degradation of native habitats. Indeed, sustainable wood harvesting is difficult in this ecosystem. Consequently, sustainable management will necessarily require the reduction of pressures from cultivation and charcoal production by reducing the natural-resource dependence of local communities through alternative income-generating activities, such as goat breeding (J. Randriamalala et al. 2016, 2019). The regular sale of goats maintains low stocking densities and avoids overgrazing. Further, the income from breeding and selling goats is greater than can be achieved by charcoal production. However, in order to better understand the impact of goat foraging on dry spiny thicket vegetation additional research is needed and should examine the impact of interannual rainfall variability on plant regeneration and diversity. Further, the carrying capacity of dry spiny thicket for local goat populations needs to be properly measured in order to evaluate the optimal size of goat herds.

CONCLUSION

Madagascar is well known for its ecological specificities and unique biodiversity. As elsewhere in the world, the island has many biocultural landscapes in which people live, such as the Betsimisaraka vanilla and clove agroforestry systems and the famous Betsileo rice-terrace agricultural landscapes. Faced with the evolution of socioeconomic, political, and demographic contexts, many cultural groups on Madagascar are no longer able to provide well-being and sufficient food to their local populations by their traditional lifestyles. Because of these changes, associated with advancing problems of global warming, the ecological sustainability of agricultural systems is no longer guaranteed. Outside of biodiversity conservation—which tends to focus on species, habitats, and ecosystems—biocultural landscapes, which are present in many areas of the tropics, should be considered in greater detail to understand recent local and global changes and environmental issues of biodiversity loss (Hong 2014). In particular, it is important to gain an understanding of which practices, under which social and ecological conditions, best allow us to achieve the needed levels of social (in terms of equity and justice), economic (with acceptable ways of life and well-being), and ecological (maintaining the ecological functions essential to the functioning of ecosystems) sustainability.

The biocultural agricultural landscapes of Madagascar, which have a strong traditional component, are composed of different ecological habitats and ecosystems that comprise a mosaic of small-scale fields for crops; herbaceous, shrubby, and woody fallows; natural tropical forest patches at different levels of secondarization; and permanent agricultural cultivations, such as flooded paddy fields, orchards, and simple or complex agroforestry systems. As illustrated by the examples presented in this contribution, in these landscapes, one can find patches of natural ecological habitats and cultivated areas where native biodiversity and introduced agrobiodiversity coexist and interact.

These landscapes are poorer in endemic biodiversity than forests or natural ecosystems. They are spatially notably heterogeneous, with many different patches of vegetation types; they may serve as habitats or corridors for many native nonspecialist species and for some forest mammal and bird species. They also contain a diversity of plants, ranging from endemics to introduced and invasive species. In these landscapes, there is also an important level of agrobiodiversity, cultivated or uncultivated, which is essential to local communities and allows local people different means to enhance various aspects of their lives—providing foods, medicines, and materials for building and handicrafts. Combating deforestation and finding solutions so that these landscapes can retain a biodiversity beneficial to all of their constituent organisms will also ensure a good future for these human communities and proper buffer zones for protected areas. These biocultural landscapes represent the basis of future agroecological sustainable landscape pathways on Madagascar.

In the examples presented in this contribution, such as in the Vavatenina region and the Ranomafana–Andringitra forest corridor, spatial mosaics may form unique islands of species-rich communities in agricultural landscapes. The diversity of biocultural landscapes, which reflects a diversity of human-nature interactions on Madagascar, represents examples of different nature-based solutions to improve cultivation systems, inspired by both traditional and modern practices, which when combined may contribute to form more-sustainable agricultural systems. More incentives and innovative policies for sustainability, with consideration of the social, economic, and cultural agents in the biocultural landscape, should be combined to ensure proper traditional and modern approaches for food security without compromising biodiversity and sustainability in agricultural landscapes (Liu et al. 2014). With respect and recognition of these biocultural landscapes and their associated diversity, it will also be easier to work with communities for biodiversity conservation in protected areas, but also in cultivated landscapes. In order to find solutions, research and policy must adopt a new paradigm that recognizes the differences in the perceptions and priorities of the various actors (Scales 2014), such as where researchers work with communities to improve biocultural-landscape sustainability.

Subject editor: Steven M. Goodman

ONE HEALTH RESEARCH AND PRACTICE ON MADAGASCAR

C. L. Nunn, A. Solis, O. S. Rakotonarivo, C. D. Golden, and R. A. Kramer

A startling 77% of the earth's land surface has been transformed for human use (Watson et al. 2018), and this transformation is driving marked changes in species diversity worldwide, particularly where land use impacts intact forest ecosystems (Dornelas et al. 2014; Newbold et al. 2015; Betts et al. 2017). The effects of human activities on Madagascar's biodiversity are especially acute, given the high proportion of plants and animals that are found only on the island (see the different contributions in this book). As elsewhere in the world, anthropogenic land use influences the environment, with cascading effects on human populations. For example, loss of forests leads to erosion of land, with subsequent loss of soil necessary for agriculture (Benito et al. 2003; Zheng et al. 2005). These changes range from local or regional effects, such as disruption of the nitrogen or phosphorus cycles, to global effects, such as the impact of global climate change driven by burning of fossil fuels.

Emerging from the fields of veterinary and human medicine, the One Health approach examines the connections among human, animal, plant, and environmental health (Zinsstag et al. 2011, 2012). Research in One Health explicitly considers how human activities are influencing the environment and animals, including both domesticated and wild animals, and how these effects impact human health and well-being. Interdisciplinary collaboration is crucial to One Health research (Min et al. 2013), drawing on numerous fields, including veterinary medicine (Figure 5.14a),

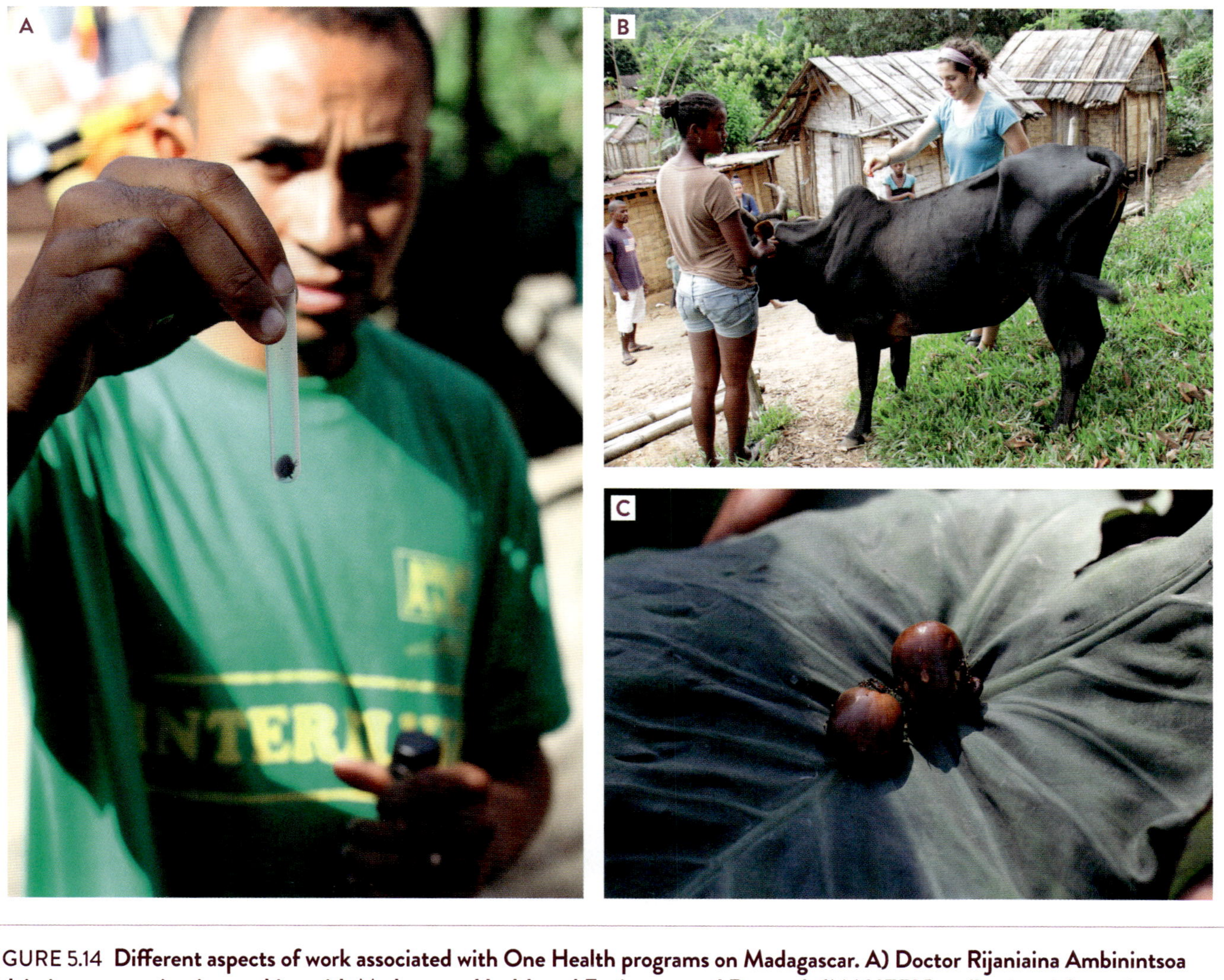

FIGURE 5.14 **Different aspects of work associated with One Health programs on Madagascar. A) Doctor Rijaniaina Ambinintsoa Ralaiarison, a veterinarian working with Madagascar Health and Environmental Research (MAHERY), collecting tick specimens from parasitized cattle; B) Melissa Manus swabs a zebu to collect samples of its skin microbiome outside Marojejy National Park; and C) engorged ticks (family Ixodidae) removed from zebu near Makira Natural Park.** (PHOTOS A and C by C. Golden, and B by C. Nunn.)

environmental sciences, public health, ecology, zoology, and social sciences. The perspectives associated with One Health have existed for centuries and were advocated prominently by Rudolf Virchow in the 1800s. The term itself, however, appears to have gained popularity only in the last 15 years and is increasingly recognized across the many disciplines that it aims to unite.

One Health has gained wide acceptance in the human and veterinary medicine communities. The One Health approach has also become embedded in the health programs of many governments, nongovernmental organizations (NGOs), and international agencies around the world, including the World Health Organization (WHO), the World Organization for Animal Health, the US Agency for International Development (USAID), and the Wellcome Trust. This acceptance is driven largely because of its utility for understanding and addressing the threats of antibiotic resistance, food security, and emerging zoonotic diseases, such as those caused by West Nile Virus, Ebola viruses, and the SARS-like coronaviruses. One Health has also advanced our understanding of food safety, nutrition, and the evolution of antimicrobial resistance. Despite these successes, the One Health approach has been criticized for insufficient consideration of environmental connections and limited incorporation of social-science perspectives (Buse et al. 2018; Rabinowitz et al. 2018).

This contribution will use the broadest definition of One Health and examine how One Health perspectives, findings, and approaches apply to several contexts on Madagascar. Much of what follows considers infectious disease. The health burden of infectious disease can disproportionately impact the subsistence of poor, rural households that rely on agriculture, including livestock, to support their economic and nutritional needs, and repeated infectious-disease events in humans can trigger cycles of economic disruption that can lead to poverty traps (Bonds et al. 2010, 2012; Rist et al. 2015a; Berthe et al. 2019). Livestock production can be negatively affected by infectious disease, which may increase poverty, malnutrition, and disease in similar ways to human diseases. The economic impacts can be direct, through loss of income, or indirect, through poor nutrition and health and reduced capital accumulation. Before considering examples of One Health research on Madagascar, we start by comparing One Health to two other fields that have emerged with similar themes and approaches: EcoHealth and Planetary Health.

THE ONE HEALTH APPROACH COMPARED WITH ECOHEALTH AND PLANETARY HEALTH

Two closely related frameworks, EcoHealth and Planetary Health, focus on integrated approaches to studying the health effects of environmental change. Like One Health, EcoHealth examines the connections between human and animal health and the surrounding ecosystems, with a particular emphasis on biodiversity. It draws on many disciplines, and has placed more attention on the social sciences and humanities than One Health has traditionally done (Lerner and Berg 2017). Planetary Health focuses on the impacts of human activity on the earth's natural systems and the resulting impacts on human health (Whitmee et al. 2015). As compared with One Health, Planetary Health has a more anthropogenic emphasis (Lerner and Berg 2017) and places greater attention on the limits of environmental destruction for survival and well-being of humans (Buse et al. 2018).

All of these fields represent a response to the challenge of rapidly changing environments. They aim to develop new approaches that transcend the mono-disciplinary focus of previous research, resulting in more integrative perspectives on human health. As such, they are more holistic approaches to understanding and protecting health that explicitly acknowledge complex interactions among ecosystems, humans, and other species. This has led Rabinowitz et al. (2018: 2) to call for "further development of the One Health framework to better incorporate Planetary and EcoHealth concepts and the sense of urgency regarding environmental support systems."

To expand their impact, these approaches will need to increase engagement with stakeholders, including individuals, households, and communities (Conrad et al. 2013), and deepen the integration of multiple technological and practical challenges associated with different industries, such as farming (Hinchliffe 2015). In addition, given One Health's focus on zoonotic disease, it is important to consider how biases toward wildlife species, which serve as infectious disease reservoirs, could impact the conservation of those species (Buttke et al. 2015). In the context of Madagascar, for example, this might result in conflicts between the goals of wildlife conservation and human health; examples include the potential for infectious diseases of fruit bats (Brook et al. 2019b) or lemurs (Andrianaivoarimanana et al. 2013) to transmit to humans.

PLAGUE: A ZOONOTIC DISEASE OF THE ECTOPARASITES OF SMALL MAMMALS

On Madagascar, mammal-borne diseases represent major health risks for humans, such as plague (Boisier et al. 2002; Migliani et al. 2006; Rahelinirina et al. 2010a; Andrianaivoarimanana et al. 2013; Vogler et al. 2017) and diseases caused by *Rickettsia* (Dietrich et al. 2014) and *Leptospira* (Rahelinirina et al. 2010b; Ratsitorahina et al. 2015). The importance of mammal-borne diseases for public health on Madagascar was highlighted by the 2017 plague outbreak, which resulted in 2417 confirmed cases and 209 deaths (Nguyen et al. 2018; Rabaan et al. 2019). Here, we consider how a One Health perspective applies to plague. Similar perspectives on leptospirosis—another zoonotic disease—can be found in Dietrich et al. (pp. 268–77).

Plague exhibits three human forms: bubonic plague, septicemic plague, and pneumonic plague. All three disease manifestations are caused by the gram-negative bacterium *Yersinia pestis*, which was first isolated and described in the late 1800s by Swiss French bacteriologist Alexandre Yersin (Hawgood 2008). Research has shown that *Y. pestis* diverged from the less virulent strain *Y. pseudotuberculosis* and that genetic changes in the *Y. pestis* lineage increased disease transmission (Chain et al. 2004; Sun et al. 2014). On Madagascar, the enzootic cycle of *Y. pestis* includes transmission from ectoparasites, predominantly fleas (see Duchemin et al., pp. 1074–80), to sylvatic reservoirs, primarily rodents (families Muridae and Nesomyidae; see Goodman and Soarimalala, pp. 1737–69) and other introduced small mammals, such as shrews (see Ramasindrazana et al., pp. 1872–80), and some evidence of the endemic family Tenrecidae (see Goodman et al., pp. 1891–94).

Globally, approximately 200 species of rodent reservoirs can sustain infections via multiple transmission mechanisms, which include flea bites, burrowing in contaminated soil, or consuming infected animals (Stoller 2015). Ground squirrels, chipmunks, prairie dogs, and *Rattus rattus* (Black Rat) are common rodent reservoirs, with the last serving as the global primary reservoir of plague. Additional hosts include cats, bobcats, dogs, camels, shrews, and rabbits. In humans, transmission varies among the three manifestations of plague. Transmission of bubonic plague and septicemic plague can occur via flea bites, while pneumonic plague, which is the most lethal, is transmitted via aerosolized infectious droplets, or can additionally develop from untreated bubonic and septicemic plagues.

Plague on Madagascar emerged and reemerged as a consequence of new *Y. pestis* variants, novel vectors, and novel reservoirs (Duplantier et al. 2005; Andrianaivoarimanana et al. 2013). The emergence of plague was due to the introduction of *Y. pestis* to port cities of Madagascar in the early 20th century (Duplantier et al. 2005). *Yersinia pestis* quickly evolved to use an endemic flea species, *Synopsyllus fonquerniei*, and the invasive host reservoir *R. rattus* (Duplantier et al. 2005; Andrianaivoarimanana et al. 2013, 2019). *Synopsyllus fonquerniei* commonly parasitizes *Rattus* in urban and rural environments, near homes, in rice fields, and in natural forests. This flea has also been found to parasitize tenrecs, endemic and introduced rodents, and lemurs, and it has a higher transmission efficacy in comparison with the classical plague vector, *Xenopsylla cheopis*.

In addition to infecting a novel flea vector, *Y. pestis* also began to infect on Madagascar another invasive and introduced rat species, *Rattus norvegicus* (Andrianaivoarimanana et al. 2013). This rodent is terrestrial and is distinctly more common on the island in urban environments, can be found in homes and sewage systems, and has been the reservoir responsible for urban plague outbreaks in Mahajanga and Antananarivo. *Rattus norvegicus* has low infection susceptibility to *Y. pestis*, and as a result promotes the maintenance of plague in urban environments. Plague transmission in rural environments is due to coexisting plague-resistant and susceptible rodent hosts, and also occurs via shrews and tenrecs. The introduced shrew *Suncus murinus* is also an important reservoir for the maintenance of *Y. pestis* (Rahelinirina et al. 2017). Due to the resistance of *S. murinus* to *Y. pestis* infection, it is hypothesized that it plays a vital role in transmission and maintenance of *Y. pestis*. Genetic analysis of *Y. pestis* isolated from *S. murinus* showed it to be genetically different from strains isolated from other reservoirs. Further genetic analysis also suggests that disease spillover occurs from *S. murinus* to humans and rats.

The Afro-Malagasy region accounts for over 90% of cases of plague worldwide (Andrianaivoarimanana et al. 2019). On Madagascar, plague undergoes regular outbreaks in humans, typically between September and April (Andrianaivoarimanana et al. 2019; Rabaan et al. 2019). Of the three forms of human plague, bubonic plague (93%) is the most common, followed by pneumonic plague (17%) (Andrianaivoarimanana et al. 2019). Madagascar has reported a total of 13,234 clinically suspected cases of plague between 1998 and 2016. Bubonic plague was more commonly reported in children and adolescents, while pneumonic plague—which is overall less common—was more commonly reported in adults older than 30 years of age, perhaps owing to activities that increase their exposure to fleas and/or rats, such as sleeping on floors or on flea-infested mats and bedding. Prevention of plague includes prophylactic antibiotics, including but not limited to streptomycin, gentamicin, and doxycycline. However, recent research has identified antibiotic-resistant strains of *Y. pestis* on Madagascar (Rabaan et al. 2019). Microscopy and F1 antigen rapid diagnostic tests are used for human surveillance to determine clinical cases of plague (Chanteau et al. 2003; Andrianaivoarimanana et al. 2019). To further understand, treat, and prevent plague outbreaks on Madagascar, additional and consistent human surveillance and government control strategies need to continue in urban and rural regions (Duplantier et al. 2005; Andrianaivoarimanana et al. 2019; Rabaan et al. 2019).

As noted by D'Ortenzio et al. (2018: 313), "Plague is the perfect example of a disease requiring a global response, drawing on animal, human and environmental health disciplines." In other words, a One Health interdisciplinary perspective is needed to understand and respond to plague. Here, we consider four specific ways that a One Health perspective is relevant to plague on Madagascar.

First, with *Rattus rattus* as an effective reservoir host, any factors that influence the population abundance and distribution of rats are expected to influence transmission dynamics of *Y. pestis* to humans. These rats are well known for their dispersal into human-dominated or human-modified habitats. Thus, land-use changes that stimulate population growth of rats or their fleas have the potential to increase transmission of *Y. pestis* (Duplantier et al. 2005). This is illustrated by an outbreak in the Ikongo area of southeastern Madagascar, which occurred following forest clearing and recolonization of a formerly abandoned village. Similar evidence has emerged from studies of land-use change and plague in East Africa; one study in Tanzania, for example, found substantially higher seroprevalence in agricultural than in conserved sites (McCauley et al. 2015).

Second, human plague outbreaks on Madagascar appear to be linked to host communities composed of multiple species, with outbreaks potentially triggered from infection in hosts that are especially susceptible to *Y. pestis* and experience high bacterial load when infected (D'Ortenzio et al. 2018). This would amplify the spread of the bacteria to fleas, and when the host populations crash, the fleas move to other hosts, including humans (Duplantier et al. 2005). Thus, an understanding of small-mammal communities, their fleas, and the factors that influence their population dynamics is essential for understanding plague.

Third, plague is a disease associated with poverty, high human population density, and other factors (Andrianaivoarimanana et al. 2013). Outbreaks tend to occur where humans are especially susceptible to infection with *Y. pestis* owing to poor nutrition, stress, or coinfection (Andrianaivoarimanana et al. 2018). In cities, poverty is associated with agricultural work, poor housing, and reduced access to clean water. In rural Madagascar, high-risk zones include areas on the periphery of villages (Duplantier et al. 2005), which may also reflect proximity to agricultural areas and mixed communities of reservoir hosts, including introduced rodents and spiny tenrecs (subfamily Tenrecinae). Some of these risk and exposure behaviors are well understood by local Malagasy populations. In fact, traditional ecological knowledge and traditional epidemiological knowledge have been credited with understanding potential transmission dynamics of bubonic plague by the Betsimisaraka and Tsimihety cultural groups (Golden and Comaroff 2015b). These factors highlight the need for social scientists to work with biologists, local human populations, and public-health experts to investigate the drivers of plague in humans and wildlife, thus engaging with the interdisciplinary approaches and stakeholder involvement that characterize One Health.

Finally, ecology and evolution are also important components of understanding plague on Madagascar. From a disease ecology perspective, for example, a recent theoretical model found that plague persistence can be attributed to a combination of human population structure (meta-populations) and resistance amongst rodent reservoir hosts, perhaps helping to maintain host and flea populations (Gascuel et al. 2013). In addition, molecular evidence suggests that persistent endemic cycles, in the epidemiological sense, are more important for the maintenance of plague on Madagascar than large-scale epidemics in the natural host populations (Vogler et al. 2017). Thus, a great need exists to understand the temporal and geographic dynamics of sylvatic reservoirs of plague, with an eye toward understanding and preventing the seasonal drivers of plague emergence.

ONE HEALTH AND DOMESTICATED ANIMALS: ZEBU CATTLE

The challenges of food supply in high-income countries are often considered in a One Health context, especially as applied to livestock (including mammals and fowl). One critical set of questions involves how animal housing and environments influence the risk of pathogen transmission to human populations (Leibler et al. 2016). Another set of questions involves the links between agricultural practices and exposure to antibiotic-resistent bacteria among farmworkers (Denis et al. 2009; Graveland et al. 2010). Yet other concerns involve whether access to healthy domesticated animals—and which animals—improves human nutrition on Madagascar, as found in other low-income settings (Randolph et al. 2007). We consider how similar questions may apply on Madagascar, with a focus on introduced cattle (commonly known as zebu).

Zoonotic disease from cattle and other livestock represents a major challenge worldwide (McDaniel et al. 2014), including in Africa (Kemunto et al. 2018). Relevant zoonotic disease organisms include *Brucella*, *Shigella*, *Salmonella*, and *Leptospira*. Given the agricultural lifestyles and close contact with zebu or their waste in many Malagasy rural settings, the infectious disease pathways between cattle and humans may be especially important. Several studies have examined the potential for disease transmission between zebu and humans. In one investigation, Manus et al. (2017) investigated shared microorganisms on the skin of humans and cattle (i.e., the skin microbiome, Figure 5.14b). Their research revealed that the skin microbiome varied considerably across the human body, with the microorganisms on the ankles showing greatest similarity to those of zebu, potentially owing to fecal contamination of the environment by cattle.

Other studies have investigated enteric pathogens of humans, cattle, and small mammals. For example, in one study conducted near Ranomafana National Park, Bublitz et al. (2014) found that 18% of livestock (cattle and pigs) showed infection with enteric pathogens of humans, including *Shigella*, *Salmonella*, and enteroinvasive *Escherichia coli*. Prevalence was higher in small mammals (*Rattus rattus* and *Mus musculus*) and humans than in livestock, and higher in pigs than in cattle. Prevalence varied geographically among different villages. In another study, also near Ranomafana, Bodager et al. (2015) found higher prevalence of *Cryptosporidium suis*—a zoonotic disease organism—in cattle than in pigs (27.4% versus 17.6%). Clearly, more research is needed across Madagascar to better understand the generality of these results, and the factors that explain them.

Zebu are often considered to be an important source of nutrition for the Malagasy, and are one of the most preferred foods (Merson et al. 2019a), although consumption of zebu likely varies greatly across the island and in relation to household wealth and season (e.g., Golden et al. 2019). Given their importance in Malagasy society and cultural history, maintaining healthy zebu is an important economic concern for many households and communities, and zebu contribute to food security in some regions. In high-income countries, the economic benefits of cattle are achieved through hormones, antibiotics, and diets that maximize the rate of growth and delivery to market, sometimes with negative effects on animal and human health, including environmental and human exposure to antibiotic-resistant organisms (Landers et al. 2012). Cattle farmers on Madagascar are less likely to use antibiotics; in one study, however, researchers found evidence for extended-spectrum-beta-lactamase-producing Enterobacteriaceae (ESBL-E) in 67% of cattle from Antsirabe (Gay et al. 2018). These authors also found evidence for antibiotic-resistant organisms (resistant to tetracycline) in 50% of the beef cattle that were sampled. This suggests that antibiotics are indeed being used, at least at the regional level, in Malagasy cattle production systems, with risks for human health. Similarly, another study found evidence of antibiotic drug residues in pork products (Rakotoharinome et al. 2014).

A final example of One Health approaches applied to Malagasy livestock involves infectious diseases of cattle. Here, we will focus on Rift Valley Fever Virus (RVFV) (see also Héraud et al., pp. 285–91). RVFV can infect a wide range of domesticated animals, including cattle, and also humans. It is typically spread through mosquitoes, but can also be transmitted through contact with blood or animal tissue, including when butchering, while caring for sick animals, or during obstetric assistance (Nanyingi et al. 2015; Tantely et al. 2015; Linthicum et al. 2016). In humans, symptoms are mild in approximately 90% of infections, but can include more serious expression as encephalitis, hemorrhagic fevers, and visual impairment; hemorrhagic fever is the most severe of these complications, with death occurring in 50% of cases. In livestock, RVFV more consistently causes severe disease, resulting in high rates of abortion, incapacitating illness, and death, all of which are likely to impact human livelihoods (Linthicum et al. 2016). RVFV outbreaks are known to be driven by climatic conditions, including increased rainfall (Nanyingi et al. 2015, Linthicum et al. 2016) and other climate anomalies associated with El Niño–Southern Oscillation (Anyamba et al. 2019).

RVFV has been documented on Madagascar over three separate time periods: 1979, 1990–1991, and 2008–2009. Epidemics may occur seasonally in southern Madagascar, but the virus is likely to also be spread through the imported animal trade (Tantely et al. 2015) and movement of animals around the island (Lancelot et al. 2017). At least 24 different mosquito species are involved in the spread of RVFV on Madagascar.

Given the connections among humans, animals (livestock and mosquitoes), and the environment, a One Health perspective has been recognized outside of Madagascar as important for understanding and controlling RVFV (Lancelot et al. 2017; Rostal et al. 2018; Fawzy and Helmy 2019). Environmentally, climatic factors and land cover influence the abundance of mosquito vectors and the potential for infected mosquito eggs and larvae to survive. In humans, medical surveillance should be augmented with social-sciences expertise to reduce the risks of Rift Valley fever in both humans and livestock. In livestock, veterinary approaches—combined with community engagement and monitoring of trade movements—are needed for better surveillance of RVFV in animals, which will contribute to understanding the ecological and environmental factors that predict patterns of infection in different geographic areas. Many of these factors also apply to wildlife, although given that larger ruminants are more typically reservoirs of RVFV in other parts of Africa (e.g., Britch et al. 2013) but are not found on Madagascar, this may be less important in the Malagasy context.

LEMUR HEALTH AND DISEASE IN RELATION TO ENVIRONMENTAL CHANGE

As an iconic example of Madagascar's endemic biodiversity, lemurs have also been a focus of One Health research. At a population and species level, human activities are reducing the abundance of lemurs and fragmenting and shrinking their geographic distributions (e.g., Brook et al. 2019a). Given that lemurs provide important economic benefits to Madagascar through tourism and research, declines in their populations are likely to have negative consequences for human livelihoods and health. At an individual level, human activities are impacting lemur exposure to toxins and infectious disease in ways that impair individuals' health and reproduction (see Rasambainarivo and Zohdy, pp. 298–302). Symmetrically, lemurs may also harbor some diseases relevant to human health, as discussed below, which provides several examples of One Health perspectives on wild lemurs and more generally of zoonoses understood as diseases shared by humans and animals.

Building on the results reviewed above (Bublitz et al. 2014) that sampled enteric pathogens in humans, livestock, and small mammals, Bublitz et al. (2015) sampled six species of wild lemurs from intact and degraded moist evergreen forest around Ranomafana National Park. They found that lemurs living in disturbed habitats harbored enteric pathogens, such as *Shigella*, *Escherichia coli*, and *Salmonella*, whereas those in less-disturbed settings did not harbor these organisms. For example, 61% (of 13) lemurs harbored enterotoxigenic *E. coli* in disturbed habitats, but none were found from lemur samples in largely intact forest. Moreover, the same organisms were found in cattle, rodents, and humans sampled outside the park. In addition to exposure to these pathogens in disturbed habitats, the authors noted that the stress of anthropogenic disturbance and reduced food quantity and quality may make the lemurs more susceptible to infection. Another study found a similar diversity of human viral pathogens in Ranomafana (Zohdy et al. 2015), and in Bezà Mahafaly Special Reserve, *Lemur catta* (Ring-tailed Lemur) individuals were observed to eat human, dog, and cattle feces (Fish et al. 2007). These and other findings suggest that as habitat is degraded through human activities, pathogenic bacteria can spread to wild lemurs, possibly through multiple mechanisms.

Climate change is a type of anthropogenic change that transcends the boundaries of any one country, and can impact animal health through changes in exposure to infectious diseases, including by changing the distribution of vectors. Climate change on its own—without the added effects of deforestation or hunting—is expected to reduce the geographic ranges of most primates (Brown and Yoder 2015). One study also modeled how climate change may influence the distribution of four helminth parasites and two ectoparasites that infect wild lemurs. Barrett et al. (2013) used species distribution models to forecast changes in parasite distribution based on projected climate data for 2080. They found a mixture of results, with some parasite ranges predicted to contract, while others were predicted to expand as the climate changes in the coming decades. However, one of the parasites with the most harmful effects on lemurs—the tapeworm *Hymenolepis*—showed the largest predicted range expansion, particularly in the west and northeast of Madagascar; this parasite can also infect humans. These findings suggest that climate change is, on average, likely to result in lemurs with smaller ranges and greater exposure to more virulent infectious organisms, some of which are also zoonotic.

As a final example of One Health research involving lemurs, we will consider vector-borne disease. Human-driven land-use change has been shown to increase human exposure to malaria (MacDonald and Mordecai 2019) and other vector-borne diseases (Norris 2004; Kilpatrick and Randolph 2012). The same may be true for other animals. A variety of researchers have investigated vector-borne diseases in lemurs, including ticks (Figure 5.14c). In one study, Qurollo et al. (2018) investigated tick-borne pathogens in 76 individuals of four lemur species in a region of disturbed moist evergreen forest that is associated with the Ambatovy cobalt and nickel mining project (see also Larsen et al. 2016). Using quantitative polymerase chain reaction (PCR), they found that nearly all animals were infected with *Babesia* (96%), with a substantial number also infected with *Neoehrlichia* (36%) and *Borrelia* (15%). All species were infected by at least one of the organisms. Future research will need to investigate the potential tick vectors that are transmitting these infectious organisms, and whether those vectors also feed on humans or domesticated animals.

CONCLUSIONS AND FUTURE ONE HEALTH DIRECTIONS ON MADAGASCAR

The examples considered in this contribution represent a small subset of One Health perspectives on Madagascar. Other examples to consider would include environmental change and malaria (as studied in the Americas by MacDonald and Mordecai [2019]) or the effects of human activities on infectious diseases and health of the many other remarkable endemic species of Madagascar, such as frogs (Daszak et al. 1999; Kolby 2014; see Bletz et al., pp. 1342–49) or fruit bats (Brook et al. 2019b). Several One Health–oriented topics are relatively unexplored on the island. For example, artisanal gold mining has marked environmental effects, especially when mercury is used to extract the gold, as reported in Peruvian communities (Diringer et al. 2015; Wyatt et al. 2017). These environmental impacts are expected to impact animal health, for both domesticated animals and wildlife, in addition to that of humans (Edwards et al 2014; Cabeza et al 2019).

Another area that is likely to become more important on Madagascar is effects on the food supply, especially in the longer term as the economy develops and agricultural practices from high-income countries are adopted more widely, such as use of growth hormones and antibiotics. This issue was touched upon above, but more work is clearly needed on Madagascar, including additional research that places these effects into the One Health lens. Access to marine foods may become increasingly threatened by sea temperature rise (Golden et al. 2016b) or increasing food-safety issues such as harmful algal blooms or toxins (Moore et al. 2008; Diogene et al. 2017). Similarly, for agricultural crops, a One Health perspective could add to improved food security through reductions in plant diseases.

Considering the future of One Health and livestock on Madagascar, an important area for future research involves poultry. Poultry populations on Madagascar are vulnerable to a variety of different diseases, and poultry farming provides an important source of protein in both urban and rural areas. Newcastle Disease Virus is a prominent challenge to chicken productivity, and has been shown to have significant impacts on both chickens and human nutrition (Rist et al. 2015b; Annapragada et al. 2019). A better understanding of this virus in a One Health context could make a major contribution to improving human health, nutrition, and livelihoods on Madagascar.

Coupled models of infectious disease and economics that incorporate feedback between livestock production, human capital, and human diseases can help estimate the livelihood costs of infectious diseases and inform their management. For example, Rist et al. (2015b) developed a coupled system of human health, livestock disease, and economic productivity for poultry production near Ifanadiana, in southeast Madagascar. Their model accounts for dynamic relationships between poultry disease and economic outcomes—infectious diseases impact human and animal health and, thus, negatively affect economic production by reducing poultry productivity and decreasing human capital (in the form of nutrition). By coupling susceptible-infectious-susceptible disease-type models with simple economic-growth models, they were able to measure the impacts of infectious disease on household income directly and on household capital accumulation. Their models suggested that households may lose 10–25% of their monthly income under current disease conditions. Similar coupled ecological-economic models are useful components of One Health approaches and represent important avenues for future research.

In conclusion, the impacts of anthropogenic change have far-reaching effects on human, animal, and global health. Rigorous and rich interdisciplinary approaches will be needed to reduce the harmful effects of human activities on wildlife, domesticated animals, and the environment, and their reciprocal negative effects on human health and livelihoods. Madagascar is a crucial test case of these One Health perspectives, and one in which they are increasingly applied. It is also a setting in which One Health can engage with conservation implications—particularly in the context of charismatic species that support economic activities such as tourism.

Subject editors: Pablo Tortosa and Steven M. Goodman

REFERENCES

Abu-Loghud, J. L. 1989. *Before European Hegemony: The World System A.D. 1250 to 1350*. New York: Oxford University Press.

Adelaar, A. 2012. Malagasy phonological history and Bantu influence. *Oceanic Linguistics* 51(1): 123–159.

Adelaar, A., and Himmelmann, N. P., eds. 2005. *The Austronesian Languages of Asia and Madagascar*. New York: Routledge.

Alexiades, M. N. 1996. Collecting ethno-botanical data: An introduction to basic concepts and techniques. In *Selected Guidelines for Ethnobotanical Research: A Field Manual*, ed. M. N. Alexiades, pp. 53–94. New York: New York Botanical Garden.

Althabe, G. 1982. *Oppression et libération dans l'imaginaire, les communautés villageoises de la côte orientale de Madagascar*. Paris: François Maspero.

Alvarado, S. T., Buisson, E., Rabarison, E., Rajeriarison, C., Birkinshaw, C., Lowry, P. P., and Morellato, L.P.C. 2014. Fire and the reproductive phenology of endangered Madagascar sclerophyllous tapia woodlands. *South African Journal of Botany* 94: 79–87.

Alvarado, S. T., Buisson, E., Carriere, S. M., Rabarison, H., Rajeriarison, C., Andrianjafy, M., and Birkinshaw, C. 2015. Achieving sustainable conservation in Madagascar: The case of the newly established Ibity Mountain Protected Area. *Tropical Conservation Science* 8: 367–395.

Alvarado, S. T., Silva, T.S.F., and Archibald, S. 2018. Management impacts on fire occurrence: A comparison of fire regimes of African and South American tropical savannas in different protected areas. *Journal of Environmental Management* 218: 79–87.

Amelot, X., Moreau, S., and Carrière, S. M. 2011. Des justiciers de la biodiversité aux injustices spatiales: L'exemple de l'extension du réseau d'aires protégées à Madagascar. In *Justice et injustices environnementales*, eds. D. Blanchon, J. Gardin, and S. Moreau, pp. 193–216. Nanterre: Presses Universitaires de Paris Ouest.

Andela, N., Morton, D. C., Giglio, L., Chen, Y., van der Werf, G. R., et al. 2017. A human-driven decline in global burned area. *Science* 356 (6345): 1356.

Anderson, A. 2019. Was there mid Holocene habitation in Madagascar? A reconsideration of the OSL dates from Lakaton'i Anja. *Antiquity* 93/368: 478–487.

Anderson, A., Clark, G., Haberle, S., Higham, T., Nowak-Kemp, M., et al. 2018. New evidence of megafaunal bone damage indicates late colonization of Madagascar. *PLoS One* 13 (10): e0204368. https://doi.org/10.1371/journal.pone.0204368.

Anderson, C. 2000. *Convicts in the Indian Ocean*. London: Palgrave Macmillan.

Andriamampionona, A. 1992. Les feux de brousse dans la région de l'Itasy. FAO/PNUD/MAG/88.032. Antananarivo: Food and Agriculture Organization of the United Nations.

Andrianaivoarimanana, V., Kreppel, K., Elissa, N., Duplantier, J.-M., Carniel, E., Rajerison, M., and Jambou, R. 2013. Understanding the persistence of plague foci in Madagascar. *PLoS Neglected Tropical Diseases* 7: e2382.

Andrianaivoarimanana, V., Bertherat, E., Rajaonarison, R., Rakotondramaro, T., Rogier, C., and Rajerison, M. 2018. Mixed pneumonic plague and nosocomial MDR-bacterial infection of lung: A rare case report. *BMC Pulmonary Medicine* 18: 92.

Andrianaivoarimanana, V., Piola, P., Wagner, D. M., Rakotomanana, F., Maheriniaina, V., Andrianalimanana, S., Chanteau, S., Rahalison, L., Ratsitorahina, M., and Rajerison, M. 2019. Trends of human plague, Madagascar, 1998–2016. *Emerging Infectious Diseases* 25: 220–228.

Andrianaivoarivelo, R. A., Andriafidison, D., Rahaingonirina, C., Raharimbola, S., Rakotoarivelo, A. A., Ramilijaona, O. R., Racey, P. A., and Jenkins, R.K.B. 2011. A conservation assessment of *Rousettus madagascariensis* (G. Grandidier, 1928, Pteropodidae) roosts in eastern Madagascar. *Madagascar Conservation and Development* 6(2): 78–82.

Andrianandrasana, H. 2016. Testing the effectiveness of community-based conservation in conserving biodiversity, protecting ecosystem services, and improving human well-being in Madagascar. PhD thesis, University of Oxford.

Andrianjakarivelo, V. 2003. *Potamochoerus larvatus*. In *The Natural History of Madagascar*, eds. S. M. Goodman and J. P. Benstead, pp. 1365–1367. Chicago: University of Chicago Press.

Annapragada, A., Borgerson, C., Iams, S., Ravelomanantsoa, M. A., Crawford, G. C., Helin, M., Anjaranirina, E.J.G., Randriamady, H. J., and Golden, C. D. 2019. Modeling the impact of Newcastle disease virus vaccinations on chicken production systems in northeastern Madagascar. *Frontiers in Veterinary Science* 6: 305.

Annapragada, A., Brook, C. E., Luskin, M. S., Rahariniaina, R. P., Helin, M., et al. 2021. Evaluation of tenrec population viability and potential sustainable management under hunting pressure in northeastern Madagascar. *Animal Conservation*. https://doi.org/10.1111/acv.12714.

Anyamba, A., Chretien, J. P., Britch, S. C., Soebiyanto, R. P., Small, J. L., et al. 2019. Global disease outbreaks associated with the 2015–2016 El Nino event. *Scientific Reports* 9: 1930.

Archer, S. R., Andersen, E. M., Predick, K. I., Schwinning, S., Steidl, R. J., and Woods, S. R. 2017. Woody plant encroachment: Causes and consequences. In *Rangeland Systems: Processes, Management and Challenges*, ed. D. D. Briske, pp. 25–84. Cham: Springer Open.

Archibald, S. 2016. Managing the human component of fire regimes: Lessons from Africa. *Philosophical Transactions of the Royal Society B: Biological Sciences* 371: 20150346.

Archibald, S., Scholes, R. J., Roy, D. P., Roberts, G., and Boschetti, L. 2010. Southern African fire regimes as revealed by remote sensing. *International Journal of Wildland Fire* 19: 861–878.

Archibald, S., Lehmann, C.E.R., Gómez-Dans, J. L., and Bradstock, R. A. 2013. Defining pyromes and global syndromes of fire regimes. *Proceedings of the National Academy of Sciences of the USA* 110(16): 6442–6447.

Ardalan, A., Oskarsson, M.C.R., van Asch, B., Rabakonandriania, E., and Savolainen, P. 2015. African origin for Madagascan dogs revealed by mtDNA analysis. *Royal Society Open Science* 2(5): 140552. https://doi.org/10.1098/rsos.140552.

Arimalala, N., Penot, E., Michels, T., Rakotoarimanana, V., Michel, I., Ravaomanalina, H., Roger, E., Jahiel, M., Leong Pock Tsy, J.-M., and Danthu, P. 2019. Clove based cropping systems on the east coast of Madagascar: How history leaves its mark on the landscape. *Agroforestry Systems* 93(4): 1577–1592.

Armstrong, J. C. 1984. Madagascar and the slave trade in the 17th century. *Omaly sy Anio* 17–20: 217–233.

Astuti, R. 1995. *People of the Sea*. Cambridge: Cambridge University Press.

Atkinson, I. 1987. Introduced animals and extinctions. In *Conservation for the Twenty-First Century*, eds. D. Western and M. Pearl, pp. 54–75. New York: Oxford University Press.

Aubert, S., Razafiarison, S., and Bertrand, A., eds. 2003. *Déforestation et systèmes agraires à Madagascar: Les dynamiques des tavy sur la côte orientale*. Paris and Antananarivo: CIRAD, CITE, and FOFIFA.

Barrett, M. A., Brown, J. L., Junge, R. E., and Yoder, A. D. 2013. Climate change, predictive modeling and lemur health: Assessing impacts of changing climate on health and conservation on Madagascar. *Biological Conservation* 157: 409–422.

Barsics, F., Malaisse, F., Razafimanantsoa, T. M., Haubruge, E., and Verheggen, F. 2013a. Les ressources sauvages comestibles des bois de tapias: Inventaire des produits connus et consommés par les villageois. In *Les vers à soie malgaches: Enjeux écologiques et socio-économiques*, eds. F. Verheggen, J. Bogaert, and E. Haubruge, pp. 189–204. Gembloux: Presses Agronomiques de Gembloux.

Barsics, F., Malaisse, F., Lognay, G., Wathelet, B., Haubruge, E., et al. 2013b. Les ressources sauvages comestibles des bois de tapias: Caractérisation alimentaire des produits consommés. In *Les vers à soie malgaches: Enjeux écologiques et socio-économiques*, eds. F. Verheggen, J. Bogaert, and E. Haubruge, pp. 205–218. Gembloux: Presses Agronomiques de Gembloux.

Bayart, F., and Simmen, B. 2005. Demography, range use, and behavior in black lemurs (*Eulemur macaco macaco*) at Ampasikely, northwest Madagascar. *American Journal of Primatology* 67(3): 299–312.

Beaujard, P. 2009. La place et les pratiques des devins-guérisseurs dans le sud-est de Madagascar. In *Madagascar revisitée: En voyage avec Françoise Raison-Jourde*, eds. D. Nativel and F. V. Rajaonah, pp. 259–285. Paris: Karthala.

———. 2012. *Les mondes de l'océan Indien*. Paris: Armand Colin.

———. 2017. *Histoire et voyages des plantes cultivées à Madagascar*. Paris: Karthala.

Bednářová, M., Borkovcová, M., and Komprda, T. 2014. Purine derivate content and amino acid profile in larval stages of three edible insects. *Journal of the Science of Food and Agriculture* 941: 71–76.

Belrose-Huyghues, V. 1984. La Baie de Boina entre 1580 et 1640. *Omaly sy Anio* 17–20: 165–194.

Benito, E., Santiago, J. L., de Blas, E., and Varela, M. E. 2003. Deforestation of water-repellent soils in Galicia (NW Spain): Effects on surface runoff and erosion under simulated rainfall. *Earth Surface Processes and Landforms* 28: 145–155.

Berg, G. M. 1985. The sacred musket: Tactics, technology, and power in eighteenth-century Madagascar. *Comparative Studies in Society and History* 27(2): 261–279.

———. 1988. Sacred acquisition: Andrianampoinimerina at Ambohimanga, 1777–1790. *Journal of African History* 29(2): 191–211.

Bergier, E. 1941. *Peuples entomophages et insectes comestibles: Etude sur les moeurs de l'homme et de l'insecte*. Avignon: Imprimerie Rullière Frères.

Berthe, S., Harvey, S. A., Lynch, M., Koenker, H., Jumbe, V., Kaunda-Khangamwa, B., and Mathanga, D. P. 2019. Poverty and food security: Drivers of insecticide-treated mosquito net misuse in Malawi. *Malaria Journal* 18: 320.

Betts, M. G., Wolf, C., Ripple, W. J., Phalan, B., Millers, K. A., Duarte, A., Butchart, S. H., and Levi, T. 2017. Global forest loss disproportionately erodes biodiversity in intact landscapes. *Nature* 547: 441.

Blanc-Pamard, C. 2009. The Mikea Forest under threat (southwest Madagascar): How public policy leads to conflicting territories. *Field Actions Science Reports* 3: 1–12.

Blanc-Pamard, C., and Rakoto-Ramiarantsoa, H. 2014. *Biodiversités en partage: Ruralités reconfigurées (corridor forestier Betsileo-Tanàla, Madagascar). Collection A travers champs*. Marseille: IRD Editions.

Blanc-Pamard, C., and Ramiarantsoa, H. R. 2007. Normes environnementales, transferts de gestion et recompositions territoriales en pays Betsileo (Madagascar). *Natures Sciences Sociétés* 15(3): 253–268.

Blanc-Pamard, C., and Ruf, F. 1992. *La transition caféière: Côte est de Madagascar.* Paris: Editions Quae.

Blanc-Pamard, C., Milleville, P., Grouzis, M., Lasry, F., and Razanaka, S. 2005. Une alliance de disciplines sur une question environnementale: La déforestation en forêt de Mikea (sud-ouest de Madagascar). *Nature Sciences Sociétés* 13(1): 7–20.

Blench, R. 2008. The Austronesians in Madagascar and their interaction with the Bantu of the east African Coast: Surveying the linguistic evidence for domestic and translocated animals. *Studies in Philippine Languages and Cultures* 18: 18–43.

Bloesch, U. 1997. *La problématique des feux sur le plateau de L'Andohariana (RNI 5) et sa zone périphérique*. Report. Antananarivo: WWF.

———. 1999. Fire as a tool in the management of a savanna/dry forest reserve in Madagascar. *Applied Vegetation Science* 2: 117–124.

Bloesch, U., Bosshard, A., Schachenmann, P., Rabetaliana, H. S., and Klötzli, F. 2002. Biodiversity of the subalpine forest-grassland ecotone of the Andringitra Massif, Madagascar. In *Mountain Biodiversity: A Global Assessment*, eds. C. Korner and E. M. Spehn, pp. 165–176. New York: Routledge.

Bodager, J. R., Parsons, M. B., Wright, P. C., Rasambainarivo, F., Roellig, D., Xiao, L., and Gillespie, T. R. 2015. Complex epidemiology and zoonotic potential for *Cryptosporidium suis* in rural Madagascar. *Veterinary Parasitology* 207: 140–143.

Bodenheimer, F. S. 1951. *Insects as Human Food: A Chapter of the Ecology of Man*. The Hague: W. Junk.

Boisier, P., Rahalison, L., Rasolomaharo, M., Ratsitorahina, M., Mahafaly, M., Razafimahefa, M., Duplantier, J.-M., Ratsifasoamanana, L., and Chanteau, S. 2002. Epidemiologic features of four successive annual outbreaks of bubonic plague in Mahajanga, Madagascar. *Emerging Infectious Diseases* 8: 311–316.

Bollen, A., and Donati, D. 2006. Conservation status of the littoral forest of south-eastern Madagascar: A review. *Oryx* 40(1): 57–66.

Bollen, A., and Van Elsacker, L. 2002. Feeding ecology of *Pteropus rufus* (Pteropodidae) in the littoral forest of Sainte Luce, SE Madagascar. *Acta Chiropterologica* 4(1): 33–47.

Bond, W. J., Silander, J. A., Jr., Ranaivonasy, J., and Ratsirarson, J. 2008. The antiquity of Madagascar's grasslands and the rise of C4 grassy biomes. *Journal of Biogeography* 35: 1743–1758.

Bond, W. J., Stevens, N., Midgley, G. F., and Lehmann, C.E.R. 2019. The trouble with trees: Afforestation plans for Africa. *Trends in Ecology and Evolution* 34: 963–965.
Bonds, M. H., Keenan, D. C., Rohani, P., and Sachs, J. D. 2010. Poverty trap formed by the ecology of infectious diseases. *Proceedings of the Royal Society B: Biological Sciences* 277: 1185–1192.
Bonds, M. H., Dobson, A. P., and Keenan, D. C. 2012. Disease ecology, biodiversity, and the latitudinal gradient in income. *PLoS Biology* 10: e1001456.
Bontekoe, W. Y. 1663. *Relation ou journal du voyage de Bontekoe aux Indes orientales*. Paris: T. Moette.
Borgerson, C. 2015. The effects of illegal hunting and habitat on two sympatric endangered primates. *International Journal of Primatology* 36(1): 74–93.
———. 2016. Optimizing conservation policy: The importance of seasonal variation in hunting and meat consumption on the Masoala peninsula of Madagascar. *Oryx* 50(3): 405–418.
Borgerson, C., McKean, M. A., Sutherland, M. R., and Godfrey, L. R. 2016. Who hunts lemurs and why they hunt them. *Biological Conservation* 197: 124–130.
Borgerson, C., Vonona, M. A., Vonona, T., Anjaranirina, E.J.G., Lewis, R., Ralainasolo, F., and Golden, C. D. 2018a. An evaluation of the interactions among household economics, human health, and wildlife hunting in the Lac Alaotra wetland complex of Madagascar. *Madagascar Conservation and Development* 13(1): 25–33.
Borgerson, C., Johnson, S. E., Louis, E. E., Homes, S. M., Anjaranirina, E.J.G., Randriamady, H. J., and Golden, C. D. 2018b. The use of natural resources to improve income, health, and nutrition within Kianjavato, Madagascar. *Madagascar Conservation and Development* 13(1): 45–52.
Borgerson, C., Razafindrapaoly, B., Rajaona, D., Rasolofoniaina, B.J.R., and Golden, C. D. 2019a. Food insecurity and the unsustainable hunting of wildlife in a UNESCO World Heritage Site. *Frontiers in Sustainable Food Systems* 3(99). doi.org/10.3389/fsufs.2019.00099.
Borgerson, C., Randrianasolo, J. F., Andraina, T. R., Anjaranirina, E.J.G., Randriamady, H. J., Merson, S., Dollar, L., and Golden, C. D. 2019b. Wildlife hunting in complex human-environmental systems: How understanding natural resource use and human welfare can improve conservation in the Ankarafantsika National Park, Madagascar. *Madagascar Conservation and Development* 14(1): 37–45.
Bosser, J. 1969. *Graminées des pâturages et des cultures à Madagascar*. Mémoire ORSTOM no. 35. Paris: ORSTOM.
Bourgogne, J. 1984. Insectes: Lépidoptères Psychidae Oiketicinae. *Faune de Madagascar* 63: 1–57.
Bovalo, C., Barthe, C., and Bègue, N. 2012. A lightning climatology of the south-west Indian Ocean. *Natural Hazards and Earth System Sciences* 12: 2659–2670.
Brashares, J. S., Golden, C. D., Weinbaum, K. Z., Barrett, C. B., and Okello, G. V. 2011. Economic and geographic drivers of wildlife consumption in rural Africa. *Proceedings of the National Academy of Sciences of the USA* 108(34): 13931–13936.
Braud, Y., Franc, A., and Gay, P. E. 2014. *Les acridiens des formations herbeuses de Madagascar*. Rome: Food and Agriculture Organization of the United Nations.
Brinkmann, K., Noromiarilanto, F., Ratovonamana, R. Y., and Buerkert, A. 2014. Deforestation processes in south-western Madagascar over the past 40 years: What can we learn from settlement characteristics? *Agriculture, Ecosystems and Environment* 195: 231–243. https://doi.org/10.1016/j.agee.2014.06.008.
Briske, D. D., ed. 2017. *Rangeland Systems: Processes, Management and Challenges*. Cham: Springer Open.
Britch, S. C., Binepal, Y. S., Ruder, M. G., Kariithi, H. M., Linthicum, K. J., Anyamba, A., Small, J. L., Tucker, C. J., Ateya, L. O., and Oriko, A. A. 2013. Rift Valley fever risk map model and seroprevalence in selected wild ungulates and camels from Kenya. *PLoS One* 8(6): e66626.
Brook, C. E., Herrera, J. P., Borgerson, C., Fuller, A. C., Andriamahazoarivosoa, P., et al. 2019a. Population viability and harvest sustainability for Madagascar lemurs. *Conservation Biology* 33(1): 99–111.
Brook, C. E., Ranaivoson, H. C., Broder, C. C., Cunningham, A. A., Heraud, J. M., Peel, A. J., Gibson, L., Wood, J.L.N., Metcalf, C. J., and Dobson, A. P. 2019b. Disentangling serology to elucidate henipa- and filovirus transmission on Madagascar fruit bats. *Journal of Animal Ecology* 88: 1001–1016.
Brown, J. L., and Yoder, Y. D. 2015. Shifting ranges and conservation challenges for lemurs in the face of climate change. *Ecology and Evolution* 5: 1131–1142.
Bublitz, D. C., Wright, P. C., Bodager, J. R., Rasambainarivo, F. T., Bliska, J. B., and Gillespie, T. R. 2014. Epidemiology of pathogenic enterobacteria in humans, livestock, and peridomestic rodents in rural Madagascar. *PLoS One* 9(7): e101456.
Bublitz, D. C., Wright, P. C., Rasambainarivo, F. T., Arrigo-Nelson, S. J., Bodager, J. R., and Gillespie, T. R. 2015. Pathogenic enterobacteria in lemurs associated with anthropogenic disturbance. *American Journal of Primatology* 77: 330–337.
Buet, C. 1883. *Madagascar, la reine des îles africaines: Histoire, mœurs, religion, flore, etc.* Paris: V. Palmé.
Burge, P. S., Edge, G., O'Brien, I. M., Harries, M. G., Hawkins, R., et al. 1980. Occupational asthma in a research centre breeding locusts. *Clinical Allergy* 104: 355–363.
Burgess, N., D'Amico, J., Hales, E., Underwood, E., Dinerstein, E., Olson, D., Itoua, I., Schipper, J., Ricketts, T., and Newman, K. 2004. *Terrestrial Ecoregions of Africa and Madagascar: A Continental Assessment*. Washington, DC: Island Press.
Burney, D. A. 1987a. Pre-settlement vegetation changes at Lake Tritrivakely, Madagascar. *Paleoecology of Africa* 18: 357–381.
———. 1987b. Late Quaternary stratigraphic charcoal records from Madagascar. *Quaternary Research* 28: 274–280.
———. 1993. Late Holocene environmental changes in arid southwestern Madagascar. *Quaternary Research* 40: 98–106.
———. 1997a. Theories and facts regarding Holocene environmental change before and after human colonization. In *Natural and Human-Induced Change in Madagascar*, eds. S. M. Goodman and B. P. Patterson, pp. 75–89. Washington, DC: Smithsonian Institution Press.
———. 1997b. Tropical islands as paleoecological laboratories: Gauging the consequences of human arrival. *Human Ecology* 25(3): 437–457.
———. 1999. Rates, patterns, and processes of landscape transformation and extinction in Madagascar. In *Extinctions in Near Time*, ed. R.D.E. MacPhee, pp. 145–164. New York: Kluwer Academic/Plenum.
———. 2005. Finding the connections between paleoecology, ethnobotany, and conservation in Madagascar. *Ethnobotany Research and Applications* 3: 385–389.
Burney, D. A., and Ramilisonina. 1998. The *kilopilopitsofy*, *kidoky*, and *bokyboky*: Accounts of strange animals from Belo-sur-Mer, Madagascar, and the megafaunal "extinction window." *American Anthropologist* 100(4): 957–966.
Burney, D. A., Robinson, G. S., and Burney, L. P. 2003. *Sporormiella* and the late Holocene extinctions in Madagascar. *Proceedings of the National Academy of Sciences of the USA* 100(19): 10800–10805.
Burney, D. A., Burney, L. P., Godfrey, L. R., Jungers, W. L., Goodman, S. M., Wright, H. T., and Jull, A.J.T. 2004. A chronology for late prehistoric Madagascar. *Journal of Human Evolution* 47(1–2): 25–63. https://doi.org/10.1016/j.jhevol.2004.05.005.
Burney, D. [A.], Hume, J. P., Randalana, R., Andrianarivoarivelo, R. A., Griffiths, O. L., Middleton, G., Rasolondrainy, T., Ramilisonina, and Radimilahy, C. 2020a. Rock art from Andriamamelo Cave in the Beanka Protected Area of western Madagascar. *Journal of Island and Coastal Archaeology*. https://doi.org/10.1080/15564894.2020.1749735.
Burney, D. [A.], Andriamialison, H., Andrianaivoarivelo, R. A., Bourne, S., Crowley, B. E., et al. 2020b. Subfossil lemur discoveries from Beanka Protected Area in western Madagascar. *Quaternary Research* 93: 187–203.
Burns, S. J., Godfrey, L. R., Faina, P., McGee, D., Hardt, B., Ranivoharimanana, L., and Randrianasy, J. 2016. Rapid human-induced landscape transformation in Madagascar at the end of the first millennium of the Common Era. *Quaternary Science Reviews* 134: 92–99. https://doi.org/10.1016/j.quascirev.2016.01.007.
Buse, C. G., Oestreicher, J. S., Ellis, N. R., Patrick, R., Brisbois, B., Jenkins, A. P., McKellar, K., Kingsley, J., Gislason, M., and Galway, L. 2018. Public health guide to field developments linking ecosystems, environments and health in the Anthropocene. *Journal of Epidemiology Community Health* 72: 420–425.
Bussmann, R. W., Kuhlman, A., Zambrana, N., Rakotoarivony, F., Razanatsima, A., Rakotoarivelo, N., Razafitsalama, J., and Randrianasolo, A. 2015. Palms and palm use in Ambalabe, a community in eastern Madagascar. *Ethnobotany Research and Applications* 14: 17–26.
Bussmann, R. W., Paniagua-Zambrana, N. Y., Randrianarivony, T. N., Andriamihajarivo, T. H., Rakotoarivony, F., Rakotoarivelo, N. H., and Randrianasolo, A. 2018. What really is "Harávola": Solving the mystery of the most common basket material in Madagascar. *Economic Botany* 72: 357–359.
Buttke, D. E., Decker, D. J., and Wild, M. A. 2015. The role of One Health in wildlife conservation: A challenge and opportunity. *Journal of Wildlife Diseases* 51: 1–8.
Byg, A., and Balslev, H. 2001. Diversity and use of palms in Zahamena, eastern Madagascar. *Biodiversity and Conservation* 10: 951–970.
Cabeza, M., Terraube, J., Burgas, D., Temba, E. M., and Rakoarijaoana, M. 2019. Gold is not green: Artisanal gold mining threatens Ranomafana National Park's biodiversity. *Animal Conservation* 22: 417–419.
Callet, F. 1974 [1908]. *Historie des rois, Tantara ny Andriana.* [Translation G.-S. Chapus and E. Ratsimba.] Antananarivo: Librarie de Madagascar.
Cámara-Leret, R., Paniagua-Zambrana, N. Y., and Macía, M. J. 2012. A standard protocol for gathering palm ethnobotanical data and socioeconomic variables across the tropics. In *Proceedings of the 52nd Annual Meeting of the Society for*

Economic Botany, St. Louis, Missouri, 9–13 July 2011, eds. B. E. Ponman and R. W. Bussmann, pp. 41–71. Trujillo: Graficart.

Camboué, R. P. 1886. Les sauterelles à Madagascar sur le riz malgache. *Bulletin Mensuel de la Société Nationale d'Acclimatation de France* 33: 168–172.

———. 1888. Les sauterelles à Madagascar. *Bulletin Mensuel de la Société Nationale d'Acclimatation de France* 35: 794–797.

Campbell, G. 2013. Eating the dead in Madagascar. *South African Medical Journal* 103(12): 1032–1034.

Carpeau du Saussay. 1722. Voyage de Madagascar connu aussi sous le nom de l'Isle de St Laurent, par M. de V ... commissaire provincial d'artillerie de France. Paris: Chez Jean-Luc Nyon.

Carrière, S. M., and Bidaud, C. 2012. En quête de naturalité: Représentations scientifiques de la nature et conservation de la biodiversité. In *Géopolitique et environnement: Les leçons de l'expérience malgache*, eds. H. Rakoto Ramiarantsoa, C. Blanc-Pamard, and F. Pinton, pp. 43–71. Marseille: IRD Editions.

Carrière, S. M., Andrianotahiananahary, H., Ranaivoarivelo, N., and Randriamalala, J. 2005. Savoirs et usages des recrus post-agricoles du pays Betsileo: Valorisation d'une biodiversité oubliée à Madagascar. *VertigO* 6(1): 10.

Carrière, S. M., Ratsimisetra, L., and Roger, E. 2007a. Le couloir forestier de Fianarantsoa: Forêt "primaire" ou forêt des hommes? In *Transitions agraires, dynamiques écologiques et conservation: Le "corridor" Ranomafana-Andringitra, Madagascar*, eds. G. Serpantié, B. M. Rasolofoharinoro, and S. Carrière, pp. 39–46. Paris and Antananarivo: IRD and CITE.

Carrière, S. [M.], Roche, P., Viano, M., Ifticène, E., Picot, M. M., and Tatoni, T. 2007b. Hétérogénéité des paysages, dispersion des graines et biodiversité: Le cas du terroir d'Ambendrana. In *Transitions agraires, dynamiques écologiques et conservation: Le "corridor" Ranomafana-Andringitra, Madagascar*, eds. G. Serpantié, B. M. Rasolofoharinoro, and S. Carrière, pp. 97–106. Antananarivo and Paris: CITE and IRD.

Carrière-Buchsenschutz, S. 2007. L'urgence d'une confirmation par la science du rôle écologique du corridor forestier de Fianarantsoa. In Quel développement à Madagascar?, eds. S. Goedefroit and J.-P. Revéret. *Etudes Rurales*, no. 178, 181–196.

Casse, T., Milhoj, A., Ranaivoson, S., and Randriamanarivo, J. R. 2004. Causes of deforestation in southwestern Madagascar: What do we know? *Forest Policy and Economics* 6: 33–48.

Cauche, F. 1651. *Relations véritables et curieuses de l'isle de Madagascar et du Brésil, avec l'histoire de la dernière guerre faite au Brésil entre les Portugais et les Hollandais, trois relations d'Egypte et une du royaume de Perse*. Paris: A. Courbé.

Chain, P. S., Carniel, E., Larimer, F. W., Lamerdin, J., Stoutland, P. O., et al. 2004. Insights into the evolution of *Yersinia pestis* through whole-genome comparison with *Yersinia pseudotuberculosis*. *Proceedings of the National Academy of Sciences of the USA* 101(38): 13826–13831.

Chanteau, S., Rahalison, L., Ralafiarisoa, L., Foulon, J., Ratsitorahina, M., Ratsifasoamanana, L., Carniel, E., and Nato, F. 2003. Development and testing of a rapid diagnostic test for bubonic and pneumonic plague. *Lancet* 361: 211–216.

Charpentier de Cossigny, J.-F. 1799. *Voyage à Canton, capitale de la province de ce nom, à la Chine, par Gorée, le cap de Bonne-Espérance et les îles de France et de la Réunion*. Paris: André.

Cherry, J. F. 1990. The first colonization of the Mediterranean islands. *Journal of Mediterranean Archaeology* 3(2): 145–222.

Choron, M. 1847. Communique les extraits suivant de lettres qui lui [M. Thenard] ont été adressées par M. Choron, professeur au collège de Saint-Denis (ile Bourbon). *Comptes Rendus Hebdomadaires des Séances de L'Académie des Sciences* (Paris) 25: 395–397.

Cleuziou, S., and Tosi, M. 1994. Black boats of Magan, some thoughts on Bronze Age water transport in Oman and beyond from the impressed bitumen slabs of Ra's al Junayz. In *South Asian Archaeology 1993*, eds. A. Parpola and P. Koskikallio-Soumalaisen, pp. 745–762. Helsinki: Tiedakatermian Toimituksia.

Clist, B.-O. 1995. New field data on the ancient iron metallurgy of Madagascar. *Nyame Akuma* 43: 23–27.

Conrad, P. A., Meek, L. A., and Dumit J. 2013. Operationalizing a One Health approach to global health challenges. *Comparative Immunology, Microbiology and Infectious Diseases* 36: 211–216.

Conte, M. A. 1910. Note sur les Borocera producteurs de soie à Madagascar. *Bulletin du Jardin Colonial* 87: 473–483.

Convention sur la Diversité Biologique. 2012. *Protocole de Nagoya sur l'accès aux ressources génétiques et le partage juste et équitable des avantages découlant de leur utilisation relative à la Convention sur la Diversité Biologique*. Montreal: Secrétariat de la CDB, Nations Unies.

Copsey, J. A., Jones, J.P.G., Herizo, A., Rajaonarison, L. H., and Fa, J. E. 2009. Burning to fish: Local explanations for wetland burning in Lac Alaotra, Madagascar. *Oryx* 43: 403–406.

Coquerel, C. 1855a. Bombyx de Madagascar qui fournissent de la soie. *Annales de la Société Entomologique de France* 2: 529–531.

———. 1855b. Sur les Bombyx qui produisent de la soie à Madagascar. *Bulletin de la Société Impériale Zoologique d'Acclimatation* 2: 25–32.

———. 1856. Observations entomologiques sur divers insectes recueillis a Madagascar. *Annales de la Société Entomologique de France* 43: 505–516.

———. 1866. Des différentes espèces de Bombyx qui donnent de la soie à Madagascar. *Annales de la Société Entomologique de France*, série 4, 6: 341–344, plates 345–346.

Cori, G., and Trama, P. 1979. *Types d'élevage et de vie rurale à Madagascar*. Travaux et Documents de Géographie Tropical no. 37. Bordeaux: Centre d'Etudes de Géographie Tropicale, Centre National de la Recherche Scientifique.

Costa, P., and Tosi, M. 1989. *Oman Studies: Papers on the Archaeology and History of Oman*. Serie Orientale Roma, no. 63. Rome: Istituo Italiano per il Medio ed Estremo Oriente.

Crowley, B. E. 2010. A refined chronology of prehistoric Madagascar and the demise of the megafauna. *Quaternary Science Reviews* 29(19–20): 2591–2603. https://doi.org/10.1016/j.quascirev.2010.06.030.

Crowley, B. E., and Samonds, K. E. 2013. Stable carbon isotope values confirm a recent increase in grasslands in northwestern Madagascar. *Holocene* 23(7): 1066–1073. https://doi.org/10.1177/0959683613484675.

Crowley, B. E., Godfrey, L. R., Bankoff, R. J., Perry, G. H., Culleton, B. J., Kennett, D. J., Sutherland, M. R., Samonds, K. E., and Burney, D. A. 2017. Island-wide aridity did not trigger recent megafaunal extinctions in Madagascar. *Ecography: Patterns and Process in Ecology* 40(8): 901–912. https://doi.org/10.1111/ecog.02376.

Crowther, A., Lucas, L., Helm, R., Horton, M., Shipton, C., et al. 2016. Ancient crops provide first archaeological signature of the westward Austronesian expansion. *Proceedings of the National Academy of Sciences of the USA* 113(24): 6635–6640.

Dandoy, G. 1973. Territoires et économie villageoise de Vavatenina. Paris: ORSTOM.

Danthu, P., Penot, E., Ranoarisoa, K. M., Rakotondravelo, J.-C., Michel, I., et al. 2014. The clove tree of Madagascar, a success story with an unpredictable future. *Bois et Forêts des Tropiques* 320: 83–96.

Daszak, P., Berger, L., Cunningham, A. A., Hyatt, A. D., Green, D. E., and Speare, R. 1999. Emerging infectious diseases and amphibian population declines. *Emerging Infectious Diseases* 5: 735–748.

Davis, D., Andriankaja, V., Carnat, T. L., Chrisostome, Z. M., Colombe, C., et al. 2020. Satellite-based remote sensing rapidly reveals extensive record of Holocene coastal settlement on Madagascar. *Journal of Archaeological Science* 115(105097): 1–13.

Dawson, R. R., Burns, S. J., McGee, D., Scroxton, N., Faina, P., Godfrey, L. R., and Swart, P. K. 2020. Using speleothem fluid inclusion isotopic composition to reconstruct the temperature and hydrologic record of the last 60,000 years in southwestern Madagascar. *Geological Society of America Abstracts with Programs* 52(6): 355941. https://gsa.confex.com/gsa/2020AM/meetingapp.cgi/Paper/355941.

Debray, M., Jacquemin, H., and Razafindrambao, R. 1971. *Contribution à l'inventaire des plantes médicinales de Madagascar*. Paris: ORSTOM.

Decary, R. 1925. Les invasions de criquets à Madagascar (*Pachytilus migratorioides* Reich.). *Bulletin de la Société Entomologique de France* 30(17): 290–292.

———. 1931. Chasses aux papillons à Madagascar. *L'Amateurs de Papillons* 5(17): 271–274; (18): 281–291; (19): 304–307.

———. 1937. L'entomophagie chez les indigènes de Madagascar. *Bulletin de la Société Entomologique de France* 42(11): 168–171.

———. 1939. La chasse et le piégeage chez les indigènes de Madagascar. *Journal de la Société des Africanistes* 9: 3–41.

———. 1951. *Moeurs et coutumes des Malgaches*. Paris: Payot.

DeFoliart, G. R. 2002. The human use of insects as a food resource: A bibliographic account in progress. https://insectsasfood.russell.wisc.edu/the-human-use-of-insects-as-a-food-resource/.

Denis, O., Suetens, C., Hallin, M., Catry, B., Ramboer, I., Dispas, M., Willems, G., Gordts, B., Butaye, P., and Struelens, M. J. 2009. Methicillin-resistant *Staphylococcus aureus* ST398 in swine farm personnel, Belgium. *Emerging Infectious Diseases* 15: 1098.

Dewar, R. E. 1984. Extinctions in Madagascar: The loss of the subfossil fauna. In *Quaternary Extinctions*, eds. P. S. Martin and R. G. Klein, pp. 574–593. Tucson: University of Arizona Press.

———. 1996. The archaeology of the early settlement of Madagascar. In *The Indian Ocean in Antiquity*, ed. J. Reade, pp. 471–487. London: Kegan Paul and the British Museum.

———. 1997. Were people responsible for the extinction of Madagascar's subfossils, and how will we ever know? In *Natural Change and Human Impact in Madagascar*, eds. S. M. Goodman and B. D. Patterson, pp. 364–377. Washington, DC: Smithsonian Institution Press.

———. E. 2003. Relationship between human ecological pressure and the vertebrate extinctions. In *The Natural History of Madagascar*, eds. S. M. Goodman and J. P. Benstead, pp. 119–122. Chicago: University of Chicago Press.

———. 2007. Processual assessment of population changes in western Avaradrano. In *Early State Formation in Central Madagascar*, Memoirs 43, ed. H. T. Wright, pp. 101–103. Ann Arbor: University of Michigan Museum of Anthropological Archaeology.

Dewar, R. E., and Rakotovololona, H. S. 1992. La chasse aux sub-fossiles, les preuves de du XIème aux XIIIème siècles. *Taloha* 11: 4–15.

Dewar, R. E., and Wright, H. T. 1993. The culture history of Madagascar. *Journal of World Prehistory* 7: 417–466.

Dewar, R. E., Radimilahy, C., Wright, H. T., and Darsot-Rasolofomampianina, L. 2011. Early settlement in the region of Fenoarivo Atsinanana. In *Civilisations des mondes insulaires*, eds. C. Radimilahy and N. Rajanarimanana, pp. 677–740. Paris: Karthala.

Dewar, R. E., Radimilahy, C., Wright, H. T., Jacobs, Z., Kelly, G. O., and Berna, F. 2013. Stone tools and foraging in northern Madagascar challenge Holocene extinction models. *Proceedings of the National Academy of Sciences of the USA* 110(31): 12583–12588. https://doi.org/10.1073/pnas.1306100110.

Dewar, R. E., Radimilahy, C., Wright, H. T., and Rakotozafy, L.M.A. 2020. *The Evolution of Settlement Systems in the Region of Vohemar, Northeast Madagascar*. Memoirs 62. Ann Arbor: University of Michigan Museum of Anthropological Archaeology.

Dietrich, M., Lebarbenchon, C., Jaeger, A., Le Rouzic, C., Bastien, M., et al. 2014. *Rickettsia* spp. in seabird ticks from western Indian Ocean islands, 2011–2012. *Emerging Infectious Diseases* 20: 838.

Diogene, J., Reverte, L., Rambla-Alegre, M., Del Rio, V., de la Iglesia, P., et al. 2017. Identification of ciguatoxins in a shark involved in a fatal food poisoning in the Indian Ocean. *Scientific Reports* 7: 8240.

Diringer, S. E., Feingold, B. J., Ortiz, E. J., Gallis, J. A., Araujo-Flores, J. M., Berky, A., Pan, W. K., and Hsu-Kim, H. 2015. River transport of mercury from artisanal and small-scale gold mining and risks for dietary mercury exposure in Madre de Dios, Peru. *Environmental Science: Processes and Impacts* 17: 478–487.

Domenichini, J. P. 2016. Histoire et culture malgaches. *Info Event* 2016: 20–25.

Dornelas, M., Gotelli, N. J., McGill, B., Shimadzu, H., Moyes, F., Sievers, C., and Magurran, A. E. 2014. Assemblage time series reveal biodiversity change but not systematic loss. *Science* 344: 296–299.

D'Ortenzio, E., Lemaitre, N., Brouat, C., Loubet, P., Sebbane, F., Rajerison, M., Baril, L., and Yazdanpanah, Y. 2018. Plague: Bridging gaps towards better disease control. *Médecine et Maladies Infectieuses* 48: 307–317.

Dossey, A. T., Morales-Ramos, J. A., and Guadelupe Rojas, M. 2016. *Insects as Sustainable Food Ingredients.* San Diego: Academic Press.

Doughty, H., Karpanty, S., Wilbur, H., and Doughty, H. 2014. Local hunting of carnivores in forested Africa: A meta-analysis. *Oryx* 49(1): 88–95.

Douglass, K. 2016. An archaeological investigation of settlement and resource exploitation patterns in the Velondriake Marine Protected Area, southwest Madagascar, ca. 900 BC to AD 1900. PhD thesis, Department of Anthropology, Yale University.

———. 2017. The diversity of late Holocene shellfish exploitation in Velondriake, southwest Madagascar. *Journal of Island and Coastal Archaeology* 12: 333–359.

Douglass, K., and Zinke, J. 2015. Forging ahead by land and by sea: Archaeology and paleoclimate reconstruction in Madagascar. *African Archaeological Review* 32(2): 267–299. https://doi.org/10.1007/s10437-015-9188-5.

Douglass, K., Antonites, A. R., Morales, E.M.Q., Grealy, A., Bunce, M., Bruwer, C., and Gough, C. 2018. Multi-analytical approach to zooarchaeological assemblages elucidates late Holocene coastal lifeways in southwest Madagascar. *Quaternary International* 471: 111–131. https://doi.org/10.1016/j.quaint.2017.09.019.

Douglass, K., Hixon, S., Wright, H. T., Godfrey, L. R., Crowley, B. E., Manjakahery, B., Rasolondrainy, T., Crossland, Z., and Radimilahy, C. 2019. A critical review of radiocarbon dates clarifies the human settlement of Madagascar. *Quaternary Science Reviews* 221: 105878. https://doi.org/10.1016/j.quascirev.2019.105878.

Dubois, H. 1938. *Monographie des Betsileo (Madagascar).* Travaux et mémoires de l'Institut d'Ethnologie no. 34. Paris: Université de Paris, Institut d'Ethnologie.

Dubois, S. 1674. *Les voyages faits par le sieur D. B. aux Isles Dauphine ou Madagascar, et Bourbon, ou Mascarenne, és années 1669, 70, 71 et 72: Dans laquelle il est curieusement traité du Cap Vert, de la ville de Surate, des isles de Sainte Helene, ou de l'Ascention.* Paris: Chez Claude Barbin.

Dunham, A. E., Erhart, E. M., Overdorff, D. J., and Wright, P. C. 2008. Evaluating effects of deforestation, hunting, and El Niño events on a threatened lemur. *Biological Conservation* 141(1): 287–297.

Duplantier, J.-M., Duchemin, J.-B., Chanteau, S., and Carniel, E. 2005. From the recent lessons of the Malagasy foci towards a global understanding of the factors involved in plague reemergence. *Veterinary Research* 36: 437–453.

Dürr, J., Andriamazaoro, H., Nischalke, S., Preteseille, N., Rabenjanahary, A., et al. 2020. "It is edible, so we eat it": Insect supply and consumption in the Central Highlands of Madagascar. *International Journal of Tropical Insect Science* 40: 167–179.

Edwards, D. P., Sloan, S., Weng, L., Dirks, P., Sayer, J., and Laurance, W. F. 2014. Mining and the African environment. *Conservation Letters* 7: 302–311.

Elli, L. 1993. Les Bara de Madagascar, une civilisation du bœuf, difficultés et perspectives d'une évangélisation. Mémoire de maîtrise, Université d'Ambozontany, Fianarantsoa.

Ellis, S. 1979. Un texte du XVIIème siècle sur Madagascar. *Omaly sy Anio* 9: 151–166.

———. 2007. Tom and Toakafo: The Betsimisaraka kingdom and state formation in Madagascar, 1715–1750. *Journal of African History* 48(3): 439–455.

Ellis, W. 1858. *Three Visits to Madagascar during the Years 1853–1854–1856: Including a Journey to the Capital; With Notices of the Natural History of the Country and of the Present Civilization of the People.* London: John Murray.

Faina, P., Burns, S. J., Godfrey, L. R., Crowley, B. E., Scroxton, N., McGee, D., Sutherland, M. R., and Ranivoharimanana, L. 2021. Comparing the paleoclimates of northwestern and southwestern Madagascar during the late Holocene: Implications for the role of climate in megafaunal extinction. *Malagasy Nature* 15: 108–127.

Farris, Z., Golden, C. D., Karpanty, S., Murphy, A., Stauffer, D., Ratelolahy, F., Andrianjakarivelo, V., Holmes, C. M., and Kelly, M. 2015. Hunting, exotic carnivores, and habitat loss: Anthropogenic effects on a native carnivore community, Madagascar. *PLoS One* 10(9): 1–20.

Fauchère, A. 1914. La sériciculture à Madagascar. *L'Agriculture Pratique des Pays Chauds* 153: 89–91.

Fawzy, M., and Helmy, Y. A. 2019. The One Health approach is necessary for the control of Rift Valley fever infections in Egypt: A comprehensive review. *Viruses* 11(2): 139. https://doi.org/10.3390/v11020139.

Fee, S. 2013. The shape of fashion: The historic silk brocades (*akotifahana*) of highland Madagascar. *African Arts* 463: 26–39.

Fee, S., and Rasoarifetra, B. 2009. Recipes from the past. *Etudes Océan Indien* 42–43. https://doi.org/10.4000/oceanindien.770.

Feeley-Harnik, G. 1991. *A Green Estate*. Washington, DC: Smithsonian Institution Press.

Feldt, T., Antsonantenainarivony, O., and Schlect, E. 2017. Feed selection on dry rangelands in southwestern Madagascar: Implication for ruminant nutrition in view of ecological and social challenge. *Journal of Arid Environments* 144: 81–90.

Fernandez, M. F. 1970. Contribution à l'étude de l'ancien peuplement de Lac Alaotra. *Taloha* 3: 3–54.

Fernández-Llamazares, A., López-Baucells, A., Rocha, R., Andriamitandrina, S.F.F., Andriatafika, Z. M., Burgas, D., Temba, E. M., Torrent, L., and Cabeza, M. 2018. Are sacred caves still safe havens for the endemic bats of Madagascar? *Oryx* 52(2): 271–275.

Fish, K. D., Sauther, M. L., Loudon, J. E., and Cuozzo, F. P. 2007. Coprophagy by wild ring-tailed lemurs (*Lemur catta*) in human-disturbed locations adjacent to the Beza Mahafaly Special Reserve, Madagascar. *American Journal of Primatology* 69: 713–718.

Flacourt, E. de. 1658 (repr. 1995). *Histoire de la grande isle Madagascar.* Edition présentée et annotée par Claude Allibert. Paris: INALCO-Karthala.

Flannery, T. F., and White, J. P. 1991. Animal translocation. *National Geographic Research and Exploration* 7(1): 96–113.

Fowler, C. T., and Welch, J. R., eds. 2018. *Fire Otherwise: Ethnobiology of Burning for a Changing World.* Salt Lake City: University of Utah Press.

Gabler, S. C. 2007. Entries, gates and discs in western Avaradrano. In *Early State Formation in Central Madagascar*, Memoirs 43, ed. H. T. Wright, pp. 62–66. Ann Arbor: University of Michigan Museum of Anthropological Archaeology.

Gade, D. W. 1985. Savanna woodland, fire, protein and silk in highland Madagascar. *Journal of Ethnobiology* 52: 109–122.

———. 1996. Deforestation and its effects in highland Madagascar. *Mountain Research and Development* 16: 101–116.

Gallé, J. B., Groeber, G., Ledoux, A., and Nicolas, J.-P. 2014. *Quelques plantes employées dans le sud-ouest de Madagascar*. Ethnobotanique/Monographies scientifiques. Brasparts: Jardins du Monde.

Ganzhorn, J., Ganzhorn, A. W., Abraham, J.-P., Andriamanarivo, L., and Ramananjatovo, A. 1990. The impact of selective logging on forest structure and tenrec populations in western Madagascar. *Oecologia* 84: 126–133.

Garcia, G., and Goodman, S. M. 2003. Hunting of protected animals in the Parc National d'Ankarafantsika, north-western Madagascar. *Oryx* 37(1): 115–118.

Gardner, C., and Davies, Z. 2014. Rural bushmeat consumption within multiple-use protected areas: Qualitative evidence from southwest Madagascar. *Human Ecology* 42(1): 21–34.

Gascuel, F., Choisy, M., Duplantier, J.-M., Debarre, F., and Brouat, C. 2013. Host resistance, population structure and the long-term persistence of bubonic plague: Contributions of a modelling approach in the Malagasy focus. *PLoS Computational Biology* 9: e1003039.

Gaspard, D., Venegas-González, A., Beeckman, H., Randriamalala, J. R., De Ridder, M., Tomazello-Filho, M., and Ramananantoandro, T. 2018. Tree ring responses to climate variability from xerophytic thicket of South Soalara, Madagascar. *Dendrochronologia* 49: 57–67.

Gasse, F., and Van Campo, E. 1998. A 40,000-yr pollen and diatom record from Lake Tritrivakely, Madagascar, in the southern tropics. *Quaternary Research* 49(3): 299–311. https://doi.org/10.1006/qres.1998.1967.

Gautier, L., and Goodman, S. M. 2003. Introduction to the flora of Madagascar. In *The Natural History of Madagascar*, eds. S. M. Goodman and J. P. Benstead, pp. 229–250. Chicago: University of Chicago Press.

Gay, N., Leclaire, A., Laval, M., Miltgen, G., Jego, M., Stephane, R., Jaubert, J., Belmonte, O., and Cardinale, E. 2018. Risk factors of extended-spectrum beta-lactamase producing Enterobacteriaceae occurrence in farms in Reunion, Madagascar and Mayotte islands, 2016–2017. *Veterinary Sciences* 5(1): 22.

Geay, F. 1911. 1904–1907 Rapport d'exploration aux régions N.E., S.S.W. et S.S.E. de Madagascar. Paris.

Gérard, A., Ganzhorn, J. U., Kull, C. A., and Carrière, S. M. 2015. Possible roles of introduced plants for native vertebrate conservation: The case of Madagascar. *Restoration Ecology* 23(6): 768–775.

Godfrey, L. R. 1986. The tale of the tsy-aomby-aomby: In which a legendary creature is revealed to be real. *Sciences* 26(1): 48–51. https://doi.org/10.1002/j.2326-1951.1986.tb02826.x.

Godfrey, L. R., Scroxton, N., Crowley, B. E., Burns, S. J., Sutherland, M. R., Perez, V. R., Faina, P., McGee, D., and Ranivoharimanana, L. 2019. A new interpretation of Madagascar's megafaunal decline: The "subsistence shift hypothesis." *Journal of Human Evolution* 130: 126–140.

Goedefroit, S. 1998. *A l'ouest de Madagascar: Les Sakalava de Menabe*. Paris: Karthala and ORSTOM.

Goel, N., Van Vleck, E., Aleman, J. C., and Staver, A. C. 2020. Dispersal limitation and fire feedbacks maintain mesic savannas in Madagascar. *bioRxiv*: 2020.01.14.905208.

Golden, C. D. 2005. Eaten to endangerment: Mammal hunting and the bushmeat trade in Madagascar's Makira Forest. Undergraduate thesis, Harvard University.

———. 2009. Bushmeat hunting and use in the Makira Forest, north-eastern Madagascar: A conservation and livelihoods issue. *Oryx* 43(3): 386–382.

Golden, C. D., and Comaroff, J. 2015a. Effects of social change on wildlife consumption taboos in northeastern Madagascar. *Ecology and Society* 20(2): 41.

———. 2015b. The human health and conservation relevance of food taboos in northeastern Madagascar. *Ecology and Society* 20(2): 42.

Golden, C. D., Fernald, L.C.H., Brashares, J. H., Rasolofoniaina, B.J.R., and Kremen, C. 2011. Benefits of wildlife consumption to child nutrition in a biodiversity hotspot. *Proceedings of the National Academy of Sciences of the USA* 108(49): 19653–19656.

Golden, C. D., Bonds, M. H., Brashares, J. H., Rasolofoniaina, B.J.R., and Kremen, C. 2014a. Economic valuation of subsistence harvest of wildlife in Madagascar. *Conservation Biology* 23(1): 234–243.

Golden, C. D., Rabehatonina, J.D.C., Raotosoa, A., and Moore, M. 2014b. Socio-ecological analysis of natural resource use in Betampona Strict Natural Reserve. *Madagascar Conservation and Development* 9(2): 83–89.

Golden, C. D., Gupta, A. C., Vaitla, B., and Myers, S. S. 2016a. Ecosystem services and food security: Assessing inequality at community, household and individual scales. *Environmental Conservation* 43(4): 381–388.

Golden, C. D., Allison, E. H., Cheung, W. W., Dey, M. M., Halpern, B. S., McCauley, D. J., Smith, M., Vaitla, B., Zeller, D., and Myers, S. S. 2016b. Nutrition: Fall in fish catch threatens human health. *Nature* 534: 317–320.

Golden, C. D., Vaitla, B., Ravaoliny, L., Vonona, M. A., Randriamady, H. J., Glahn, R. P., Guth, S. E., and Myers, S. S. 2019. Seasonal trends of nutrient intake in rainforest communities of north-eastern Madagascar. *Public Health Nutrition* 22(12): 2200–2209.

Gommery, D., Ramanivosoa, B., Faure, M., Guérin, C., Kerloc'h, P., Sénégas, F., and Randrianantenaina, H. 2011. Les plus anciennes traces d'activités anthropiques de Madagascar sur des ossements d'hippopotames subfossiles d'Anjohibe (Province de Mahajanga). *Comptes Rendus Palevol* 10(4): 271–278. https://doi.org/10.1016/j.crpv.2011.01.006.

Goodman, S. M. 2006. Hunting of Microchiroptera in south-western Madagascar. *Oryx* 40(2): 225–228.

Goodman, S. M., and Benstead, J. P., eds. 2003. *The Natural History of Madagascar*. Chicago: University of Chicago Press.

Goodman, S. M., and Jungers, W. L. 2014. *Extinct Madagascar: Picturing the Island's Past*. Chicago: University of Chicago Press.

Goodman, S. M., and Rakotoarisoa, J.-A. 1998. Un regard sur l'utilisation historique et sur la régénération des habitats naturels à Madagascar. *Akon'ny Ala* 24: 3–4.

Goodman, S. M., and Rakotozafy, L.M.A. 1997. Subfossils birds from coastal sites in western and southwestern Madagascar. In *Natural Change and Human Impact in Madagascar*, eds. S. M. Goodman and B. D. Patterson, pp. 257–279. Washington, DC: Smithsonian Institution Press.

Goodman, S. M., and Razafindratsita, V., eds. 2001. Inventaire biologique du Parc National de Ranomafana et du couloir forestier qui le relie au Parc National de l'Andringitra. *Recherches pour le Développement, Série Sciences Biologiques* 17: 1–243.

Goodman, S. M., Soarimalala, V.R.L., and Ganzhorn, J. U. 2004. La chasse aux animaux sauvages dans la forêt de Mikea. In Inventaire floristique et faunistique de la forêt de Mikea: Paysage écologique et diversité biologique d'une préoccupation majeure pour la conservation, eds. A. P. Raselimanana and S. M. Goodman. *Recherches pour le Développement, Série Sciences Biologiques* 21: 95–100.

Goodman, S. M., Raherilalao, M. J., and Muldoon, K. 2013. Bird fossils from Ankilitelo Cave: Inference about Holocene environmental changes in southwestern Madagascar. *Zootaxa* 3750: 534–548.

Goodman, S. M., Raherilalao, M. J., and Wohlhauser, S., eds. 2018. *Les aires protégées terrestres de Madagascar: Leur histoire, description et biote / The Protected areas of Madagascar: Their History, Description, and Biota*. Antananarivo: Association Vahatra.

Gourou, P. 1967. *Madagascar: Cartes de densité et de localisation de la population (Notice et 3 cartes)*. Paris: Cemubac and ORSTOM.

Grandidier, A. 1869. *Voyage a Madagascar: Notes et souvenirs*. N.p.

———. 1896a. *Congrès des sociétés savantes: Discours prononcés à la séance générale du Congrès, le samedi, 11 avril 1896*. Paris: Imprimerie nationale.

———. 1896b. Madagascar il y a cent ans: Les voyages de Mayeur. *Revue Scientifique* 518: 552–557.

Grandidier, A., and Filhol, H. 1894. Observations relatives aux ossements d'hippopotames retrouves dans les marais de Ambolisatra. *Annales des Sciences Naturelles*, série 7, 16: 151–190.

Grandidier, A., and Grandidier, G. 1904. *Collection des ouvrages anciens concernant Madagascar*. Vol. 2, *Ouvrages ou extraits d'ouvrages français (jusqu'à 1630), portugais, hollandais, anglais, allemands, italiens, espagnols et latins relatifs à Madagascar (1613 à 1640)*. Paris: Comité de Madagascar.

———. 1907. *Collection des ouvrages anciens concernant Madagascar*. Vol. 5, *Ouvrages ou extraits d'ouvrages anglais, hollandais, portugais, espagnols, suédois et russes (1718–1800)*. Paris: Comité de Madagascar.

———. 1908. *Ethnographie de Madagascar*. Vol. 4 pt. 3. Paris: Société d'Editions Géographiques Maritimes et Coloniales.

Grandidier, A., Charles-Roux, C., Delhorbe C., Froidevaux, H., and Grandidier, G., eds. 1903. *Collection des ouvrages anciens concernant Madagascar*. 5 vols. Paris: Comité de Madagascar.

Granier, P., and Serres, H. 1966. A propos de l'incidence des feux de brousse sur l'évolution des pâturages. *Bulletin de Madagascar* 16: 789–791.

Graveland, H., Wagenaar, J. A., Heesterbeek, H., Mevius, D., Van Duijkeren, E., and Heederik, D. 2010. Methicillin resistant *Staphylococcus aureus* ST398 in veal calf farming: Human MRSA carriage related with animal antimicrobial usage and farm hygiene. *PLoS One* 5(6): e10990.

Green, G. M., and Sussman, R. W. 1990. Deforestation history of the eastern rain forests of Madagascar from satellite images. *Science* 248(4952): 212–215.

Griffin, W. 2009. The Matitanana archaeological project: Culture history and social complexity in the seven rivers region of southeastern Madagascar. PhD thesis, University of Michigan.

———. 2011. Notes on the chlorite schist industry of Madagascar's southeast coast. *Etudes Océan Indien* 46–47: 222–273.

Grinand, C., Rakotomalala, F., Gond, V., Vaudry, R., Bernoux, M., and Vieilledent, G. 2013. Estimating deforestation in tropical humid and dry forests in Madagascar from 2000 to 2010 using multi-date Landsat satellite images and the random forests classifier. *Remote Sensing of Environment* 139: 68–80.

Grubenmann, M., and Madle, M. 2016. *Cyanodolius metallicus* Seyrig, 1952 (Hymenoptera: Ichneumonidae), a new parasitoid of *Deborrea malgassa* Heylaerts, 1884 (Lepidoptera: Psychidae). *Zeitschrift der Arbeitsgemeinschaft Österreichischer Entomologen* 68(November): 99–101.

Guarino, F., Crottini, A., Mazzasalma, M., Randrianirina, J., and Andreone, F. 2019. A skeletochronological estimate of age and growth in a large riparian frog from Madagascar (Anura, Mantellidae, *Mantidactylus*). *Herpetozoa* 32: 39–44.

Guéneau, P. 1975. *Bois et essences malgaches*. Vol. 1. Tananarive: Société Malgache d'Edition.

Guillaud, S., and Vermeulen, C. 2014. Enjeux et conséquences de la vannerie dans les aires protégées de Madagascar. *Bois et Forêts des Tropiques* 320(2): 43–57.

Hackel, J., Vorontsova, M. S., Nanjarisoa, O. P., Hall, R. C., Razanatsoa, J., Malakasi, P., and Besnard, G. 2018. Grass diversification in Madagascar: In situ radiation of two large C3 shade clades and support for a Miocene to Pliocene origin of C4 grassy biomes. *Journal of Biogeography* 45: 750–761.

Hänke, H., and Barkmann, J. 2017. Insurance function of livestock: Farmers coping capacity with crop failure in southwestern Madagascar. *World Development* 96: 264–275.

Hansford, J., Wright, P. C., Rasoamiaramanana, A., Pérez, V. R., Godfrey, L. R., Errickson, D., Thompson, T., and Turvey, S. T. 2018. Early Holocene human presence in Madagascar evidenced by exploitation of avian megafauna. *Science Advances* 4(9): eaat6925.

Hansford, J., Wright, P. C., Pérez, V., Muldoon, K. M., Turvey, S. T., and Godfrey, L. R. 2020. Evidence for early human arrival in Madagascar is robust: A response to Mitchell. *Journal of Island and Coastal Archaeology*. doi:10.1080/15564894.2020.1771482.

Hawgood, B. J. 2008. Alexandre Yersin (1863–1943): Discoverer of the plague bacillus, explorer and agronomist. *Journal of Medical Biography* 16: 167–172.

Heckel, E. M. 1903. *Les plantes médicinales et toxiques de Madagascar avec leurs noms et leurs emplois indigènes*. Marseille: Institut Colonial.

Hempson, G. P., Archibald, S., Donaldson, J. E., and Lehmann, C.E.R. 2019. Alternate grassy ecosystem states are determined by palatability-flammability trade-offs. *Trends in Ecology and Evolution* 34(4): 286–290.

Hending, D., Andrianiaina, A., Rakotomalala, Z., and Cotton, S. 2018. The use of vanilla plantations by lemurs: Encouraging findings for both lemur conservation and sustainable agroforestry in the Sava Region, northeast Madagascar. *International Journal of Primatology* 39(1): 141–153.

Herrera, J. P. 2017. Testing the adaptive radiation hypothesis for the lemurs of Madagascar. *Royal Society Open Science* 4: 161014.

Hervé, D., Andrianarivo, A., Randrianarison, A., Ratovonirina, G., Rakotoarimanana, V., and Razanaka, S. 2010. Dynamiques spatio-temporelles des savanes incluses en forêt (Madagascar). *Revue Télédétection* 9(3–4): 182–194.

Hewitt, R., Krause, A., Goldman, A., Campbell, G., and Jenkins, T. 1996. Beta-globin haplotype analysis suggests that a major source of Malagasy ancestry is derived from Bantu-speaking negroids. *American Journal of Human Genetics* 58: 1303–1308.

Hinchliffe, S. 2015. More than one world, more than one health: Re-configuring interspecies health. *Social Science and Medicine* 129: 28–35.

Hixon, S., Elliott Smith, E. A., Crowley, B. E., Perry, G. H., Randrianasy, J., Ranaivoarisoa, J. F., Kennett, D. J., and Newsome, S. D. 2018. Nitrogen isotope ($\delta^{15}N$) patterns for amino acids in lemur bones are inconsistent with aridity driving megafaunal extinction in south-western Madagascar. *Journal of Quaternary Science* 33: 958–968.

Hixon, S., Douglass, K. G., Crowley, B. E., Rakotozafy, L. M., Clark, G., et al. 2021. Late Holocene spread of pastoralism coincides with endemic megafaunal extinction on Madagascar. *Proceedings of the Royal Society B*. https://doi.org/10.1098/rspb.2021.1204.

Hobbs, R. J., Arico, S., Aronson, J., Baron, J. S., Bridgewater, P., et al. 2006. Novel ecosystems: Theoretical and management aspects of the new ecological world order. *Global Ecology and Biogeography* 15(1): 1–7.

Hoffmann, W. A., Geiger, E. L., Gotsch, S. G., Rossatto, D. R., Silva, L.C.R., Lau, O. L., Haridasan, M., and Franco, A. C. 2012. Ecological thresholds at the savanna-forest boundary: How plant traits, resources and fire govern the distribution of tropical biomes. *Ecology Letters* 15: 759–768.

Hofman, C. A., and Rick, T. C. 2017. Ancient biological invasions and island ecosystems: Tracking translocations of wild plants and animals. *Journal of Archaeological Research*. doi:10.1007/s10814-017-9105-3.

Holt, V. M. 1885. *Why Not Eat Insects?* London: Field and Tuer; Leadenhall; Simpkin; Marshall; and Hamilton, Adams.

Hong, S. K. 2014. Philosophy and background of biocultural landscapes. In *Biocultural Landscapes: Diversity, Functions and Values*, eds. S. K. Hong, J. Bogaert, and Q. Min, pp. 1–7. Dordrecht: Springer Netherlands.

Hope, F. W. 1842. XIX. Observations respecting various insects which at different times have afforded food to man. *Transactions of the Royal Entomological Society of London* 32: 129–150.

Horton, M. C., Boivin, N., Crowther, A., Gaskell, B., Radimilahy, C., and Wright, H. T. 2017. East Africa as a source for fatimid rock crystal: Workshops from Kenya to Madagascar. In *Gemstones in the First Millennium AD*, eds. A. Hilfner, S. Grief, and D. Quaft, pp. 103–118. Mainz: Verlag des Römisch-Germanisches Zentralmuseum.

Hughes, G. 1973. The survival situation of the hawksbill sea-turtle (*Eretmochelys imbricata*) in Madagascar. *Biological Conservation* 5(2): 114–118.

Humber, F., Godley, B. J., Ramahery, V., and Broderick, A. C. 2010. Using members to assess artisanal fisheries: The marine turtle fishery in Madagascar. *Animal Conservation* 14: 175–185.

Humbert, H. 1949. La dégradation des sols à Madagascar. *Mémoires de l'Institut de Recherche Scientifique de Madagascar* D1(1): 33–52.

———. 1965. Description des types de végétation. In Notice de la carte de Madagascar, eds. H. Humbert and G. Cours Darne, pp. 46–78. *Travaux de la Section des Sciences et Techniques de l'Institut Français de Pondichery*, hors série, 6.

Hurles, M. E., Sykes B. C., Jobling, M. W., and Forster P. 2005. The dual origin of the Malagasy in island Southeast Asia and East Africa: Evidence from maternal and paternal lineages. *American Journal of Human Genetics* 76: 894–901.

Hurvitz, D. J. 1979. Anjoaty cattle ear-marks. In *Madagascar in History: Essays from the 1970s*, ed. R. K. Kent, pp. 42–79. Albany: Foundation for Malagasy Studies.

Irwin, M. T., Wright, P. C., Birkinshaw, C., Fisher, B. L., Gardner, C. J., et al. 2010. Patterns of species change in anthropogenically disturbed forests of Madagascar. *Biological Conservation* 143(10): 2351–2362.

IUCN (International Union for Conservation of Nature). 2003. *Guidelines for Application of IUCN Red List Criteria at Regional Levels: Version 3.0*. IUCN Species Survival Commission. Gland: IUCN.

———. 2021. The IUCN Red List of threatened species. Accessed 23 Aug. 2021. www.iucnredlist.org.

Ives, E. 1773. *A Voyage from England to India*. London: E. and C. Dilly.

Jacquin, A., Chéret, V., Sheeren, D., and Goulard, M. 2010. Impact of fire on savanna vegetation trends in Madagascar assessed using a remote-sensing based statistical analysis. In Remote Sensing for Science, Education, and Natural and Cultural Heritage, ed. R. Reuter, pp. 409–422. Paris: EARSeL Conference Proceedings.

Janzen, D. H. 1983. No park is an island: Increase in interference from outside as park size decreases. *Oikos* 41: 402–410.

Jaovelo-Dzao, R. 1947. *Mythes, rites et transes à Madagascar: Angano, Joro et Tromba Sakalava*. Antananarivo: Ambozontany.

Jeannoda, V. H., Rakotozafy, H. M., Rajaonah, M. T., and Ramampiandra, N. 2003. Les ignames de Madagascar: Biodiversité, biologie, écologie et gestion de la ressource. Communication au Forum de la Recherche à Madagascar, Antananarivo.

Jenkins, R.K.B., and Racey, P. A. 2008. Bats as bushmeat in Madagascar. *Madagascar Conservation and Development* 3(1): 22–30.

Jenkins, R.K.B., Rabearivelo, A., Andre, C.T.C.W.M., Randrianavelona, R., and Randrianantoandro, J. C. 2009. The harvest of endemic amphibians for food in eastern Madagascar. *Tropical Conservation Science* 2(1): 25–33.

Jenkins, R.K.B., Keane, A., Rakotoarivelo, A. R., Rakotomboavonjy, V., Randrianandrianina, F. H., Razafimanahaka, J. H., Ralaiarimalala, S. R., and Jones, J.P.G. 2011. Analysis of patterns of bushmeat consumption reveals extensive exploitation of protected species in eastern Madagascar. *PLoS One* 6(12): e27570.

Jenkins, R.K.B., Tongelli, M. F., Bowles, P., Cox, N., Brown, J. L., et al. 2014. Extinction risks and conservation of Madagascar's reptiles. *PLoS One* 9(8): e100173.

Johnston, F. H., Henderson, S. B., Chen, Y., Randerson, J. T., Marlier, M., DeFries, R. S., Kinney, P., Bowman, D.M.J.S., and Brauer, M. 2012. Estimated global mortality attributable to smoke from landscape fires. *Environmental Health Perspectives* 120(5): 695–701.

Joly-Radko, M., and Zimmermann, E. 2010. Seasonality in gum and honeydew feeding in gray mouse lemurs. In *The Evolution of Exudativory in Primates*, eds. A. M. Burrows and L. T. Nash, pp. 141–153. New York: Springer.

Jose, S. 2009. Agroforestry for ecosystem services and environmental benefits: An overview. *Agroforestry Systems* 76(1): 1–10.

Kemunto, N., Mogoa, E., Osoro, E., Bitek, A., Kariuki Njenga, M., and Thumbi, S. M. 2018. Zoonotic disease research in East Africa. *BioMed Central Infectious Diseases* 18: 545.

Kent, R. K. 1970. *Early Kingdoms of Madagascar 1500–1700*. New York: Holt, Rinehart, Winston.
Kilpatrick, A. M., and Randolph, S. E. 2012. Drivers, dynamics, and control of emerging vector-borne zoonotic diseases. *Lancet* 380: 1946–1955.
Klein, J., Réau, B., Kalland, I., and Edwards, M. 2007. Conservation, development, and a heterogenous community: The case of Ambohitantely Special Reserve, Madagascar. *Society and Natural Resources* 20: 451–467.
Koechlin, B. 1975. *Les Vezo du sud-ouest de Madagascar*. Paris: Mouton.
Koechlin, J. 1993. Grasslands of Madagascar. In *Natural grasslands: Eastern Hemisphere and résumé*, ed. R. T. Coupland, pp. 291–301. Amsterdam: Elsevier.
Koechlin, J., Guillaumet, J.-L., and Morat, P. 1974. *Flore et végétation de Madagascar*. Vaduz: Editions J. Cramer.
Kolby, J. E. 2014. Presence of the amphibian chytrid fungus *Batrachochytrium dendrobatidis* in native amphibians exported from Madagascar. *PLoS One* 9(3): e89660.
Kottak, C. P. 1980. *The Past in the Present: History, Ecology and Cultural Variation in Highland Madagascar*. Ann Arbor: University of Michigan Press.
Kull, C. A. 2000. Deforestation, erosion, and fire: Degradation myths in the environmental history of Madagascar. *Environment and History* 6(4): 423–450. https://doi.org/10.3197/096734000129342361.
———. 2004. *Isle of Fire: The Political Ecology of Landscape Burning in Madagascar*. Chicago: University of Chicago Press.
Kull, C. A., Ratsirarson, J., and Randriamboavonjy, G. 2005. Les forêts de tapia des hautes terres malgaches. *Terre Malgache* 24(2): 22–58.
Kull, C. A., Tassin, J., Moreau, S., Ramiarantsoa, H. R., Blanc-Pamard, C., and Carrière, S. M. 2011. The introduced flora of Madagascar. *Biological Invasions* 14(4): 875–888. https://doi.org/10.1007/s10530-011-0124-6.
Kus, S. M. 1989–1990. Ambohimanga: State formation and the symbolic organization of space. *Omaly sy Anio* 29–32: 43–53.
———. 2007. Ambohimanga: Creating a capital in thought, deed, and dirt. In *Early State Formation in Central Madagascar*, Memoirs 43, ed. H. T. Wright, pp. 301–311. Ann Arbor: University of Michigan Museum of Anthropological Archaeology.
Kus, S. M., and Wright, H. T. 1986. Survey archéologique de la région de l'Aravandrano. *Taloha* 10: 49–72.
Kusuma, P., Brucato, N., Cox, M. P., Pierron, D., Razafindrazaka, H., Adelaar, A., Sudoyo, H., Letellier, T., and Ricaut, F.-X. 2016. Contrasting linguistic and genetic origins of the Asian source populations of the Malagasy. *Nature Scientific Reports* 6: 26066.
Lacaze, H. 1881. *Souvenirs de Madagascar*. Paris: Berger-Levraut et Cie.
Lamont, B. B., and Downes, K. S. 2011. Fire-stimulated flowering among resprouters and geophytes in Australia and South Africa. *Plant Ecology* 212: 2111–2125.
Lancelot, R., Béral, M., Rakotoharinome, V. M., Andriamandimby, S. F., Héraud, J.-M., et al. 2017. Drivers of Rift Valley fever epidemics in Madagascar. *Proceedings of the National Academy of Sciences of the USA* 114(5): 938–943.
Landers, T. F., Cohen, B., Wittum, T. E., and Larson, E. L. 2012. A review of antibiotic use in food animals: Perspective, policy, and potential. *Public Health Reports* 127: 4–22.
Laris, P. 2002. Burning the seasonal mosaic: Preventative burning strategies in the wooded savanna of southern Mali. *Human Ecology* 30: 155–186.
Larsen, P. A., Hayes, C. E., Williams, C. V., Junge, R. E., Razafindramanana, J., Mass V., Rakotondrainibe, H., and Yoder, A. D. 2016. Blood transcriptomes reveal novel parasitic zoonoses circulating in Madagascar's lemurs. *Biology Letters* 12: 20150829.
Le Bourdiec, F. 1978. *Hommes et paysages du riz à Madagascar*. Antananarivo: Imprimerie de Foiben-Taosarintanin'i Madagasikara.
Le Corre, M., and Bemanaja, E. 2009. Discovery of two major seabird colonies in Madagascar. *Marine Ornithology* 37: 153–158.
Leguével de Lacombe, B. F., and de Froberville, E. 1840. *Voyage à Madagascar et aux îles Comores (1823 à 1830)*. Paris: Desessart.
Lehmann, C.E.R., and Parr, C. L. 2016. Tropical grassy biomes: Linking ecology, human use and conservation. *Philosophical Transactions of the Royal Society B: Biological Sciences* 371: 20160329.
Lehmann, C.E.R., Archibald, S. A., Hoffmann, W. A., and Bond, W. J. 2011. Deciphering the distribution of the savanna biome. *New Phytologist* 191: 197–209.
Lehmann, C.E.R., Anderson, T. M., Sankaran, M., Higgins, S. I., Archibald, S., et al. 2014. Savanna vegetation-fire-climate relationships differ among continents. *Science* 343: 548–552.
Leibler, J. H., Zakhour, C. M., Gadhoke, P., and Gaeta, J. M. 2016. Zoonotic and vector-borne infections among urban homeless and marginalized people in the United States and Europe, 1990–2014. *Vector-Borne and Zoonotic Diseases* 16: 435–444.
Lerner, H., and Berg, C. 2017. A comparison of three holistic approaches to health: One Health, EcoHealth, and Planetary Health. *Frontiers in Veterinary Science* 4: 163.
Linder, H. P., Lehmann, C.E.R., Archibald, S., Osborne, C. P., and Richardson, D. M. 2018. Global grass (Poaceae) success underpinned by traits facilitating colonization, persistence and habitat transformation. *Biological Reviews* 93(2): 1125–1144.
Linthicum, K. J., Britch, S. C., and Anyamba, A. 2016. Rift Valley fever: An emerging mosquito-borne disease. *Annual Review of Entomology* 61: 395–415.
Liu, Y., Zhao, G., and Yu, Z. 2014. Developing integrated methods for biological conservation and sustainable production in agricultural landscapes. In *Biocultural Landscapes: Diversity, Functions and Values*, eds. S. K. Hong, J. Bogaert, and Q. Min, pp. 45–67. Dordrecht: Springer Netherlands.
Lombard, J. 1988. *Le royaume Sakalava du Menabe*. Paris: ORSTOM.
Lopata, A. L., Fenemore, B., Jeebhay, M. F., Gade, G., and Potter, P. C. 2005. Occupational allergy in laboratory workers caused by the African migratory grasshopper *Locusta migratoria*. *Allergy* 602: 200–205.
MacDonald, A. J., and Mordecai, E. A. 2019. Amazon deforestation drives malaria transmission, and malaria burden reduces forest clearing. *Proceedings of the National Academy of Sciences of the USA* 116(44): 22212–22218.
MacPhee, R.D.E., and Burney, D. A. 1991. Dating of modified femora of extinct dwarf *Hippopotamus* from southern Madagascar: Implications for constraining human colonization and vertebrate extinction events. *Journal of Archaeological Science* 18(6): 695–706.
Macquarie, J. L. 1884. *Voyage à Madagascar*. Paris: Dentu E.
Malaisse, F., and Latham, P. 2014. Human consumption of Lepidoptera in Africa: An updated chronological list of references (370 quoted!) with their ethnozoological analysis. *Geo-Eco-Trop* 382: 339–372.
Manjoazy, T., Razafimanahaka, J. H., Ronto, W., Randrianavelona, R., Ganzhorn, J., and Jenkins, R.K.B. 2017. The supply of illegal tortoise meat to Toliara City, south-western Madagascar. *Oryx* 51(3): 437–440.
Manus, M. B., Yu, J. J., Park, L. P., Mueller, O., Windsor, S. C., Horvath, J. E., and Nunn, C. L. 2017. Environmental influences on the skin microbiome of humans and cattle in rural Madagascar. *Evolution, Medicine, and Public Health* 2017: 144–153.
Mariel, J. 2016. Analyse des systèmes agroforestiers du territoire de Vavatenina à Madagascar: Stratégies de mise en valeur, perceptions paysannes et résilience. Mémoire de Master BEE, BioGET, Université de Montpellier.
Martin, E., Ratsimisetra, L., Laloë, F., and Carrière, S. 2009. Conservation value for birds of traditionally managed isolated trees in an agricultural landscape of Madagascar. *Biodiversity and Conservation* 18(10): 2719–2742.
Martin, E., Viano, M., Ratsimisetra, L., Laloë, F., and Carrière, S. 2012. Maintenance of bird functional diversity in a traditional agroecosystem of Madagascar. *Agriculture, Ecosystems and Environment* 142: 1–9.
Martineau, A. 1931. *Mémoires de François Martin, fondateur de Pondichéry (1665–1696)*. Vol. 1. Paris: Société de l'Histoire des Colonies Françaises.
Matsumoto, K., and Burney, D. A. 1994. Late Holocene environmental changes at Lake Mitsinjo, northwestern Madagascar. *Holocene* 4: 16–24.
Mayeur, N. 1913a. Voyage dans le sud et dans l'intérieur des terres et particulièrement au pays d'Hancove, Janvier 1777. *Bulletin Académie Malgache* 12(1): 139–176.
———. 1913b.Voyage au pays d'Ancove. *Bulletin Academie Malgache* 12(2): 13–49.
McCauley, D. J., Salkeld, D. J., Young, H. S., Makundi, R., Dirzo, R., Eckerlin, R. P., Lambin, E. F., Gaffikin, L., Barry, M., and Helgen, K. M. 2015. Effects of land use on plague (*Yersinia pestis*) activity in rodents in Tanzania. *American Journal Tropical Medicine and Hygiene* 92: 776–783.
McDaniel, C. J., Cardwell, D. M., Moeller, R. B., Jr., and Gray, G. C. 2014. Humans and cattle: A review of bovine zoonoses. *Vector-Borne and Zoonotic Diseases* 14: 1–19.
Merson, S. D., Dollar, L. J., Johnson, P. J., and Macdonald, D. W. 2019a. Poverty not taste drives the consumption of protected species in Madagascar. *Biodiversity and Conservation* 28(13): 3669–3689.
———. 2019b. Retaliatory killing and human perceptions of Madagascar's largest carnivore and livestock predator, the fosa (*Cryptoprocta ferox*). *PLoS One* 14(3): e0213341.
Meyer, C., Todd, J. M., and Beck, K. 1991. From Zanzibar to Zagros: A copal pendant from Eshnunna. *Journal of Ancient Near Eastern Studies* 50: 289–298.
Migliani, R., Chanteau, S., Rahalison, L., Ratsitorahina, M., Boutin, J. P., Ratsifasoamanana, L., and Roux, J. 2006. Epidemiological trends for human plague

on Madagascar during the second half of the 20th century: A survey of 20,900 notified cases. *Tropical Medicine and International Health* 11: 1228–1237.

Mille, A. 1970. *Contribution à l'étude des villages fortifiés de l'Imerina ancien*. Travaux et Documents 2. Antananarivo: Musée d'Art et d'Archéologie de l'Université d'Antananarivo.

Min, B., Allen-Scott, L. K., and Buntain, B. 2013. Transdisciplinary research for complex One Health issues: A scoping review of key concepts. *Preventive Veterinary Medicine* 112: 222–229.

Mitchell, P. 2019. Settling Madagascar: When did people first colonize the world's largest island? *Journal of Island and Coastal Archaeology*. doi:10.1080/15564894.2019.1582567.

———. 2020. Debating Madagascar: A reply to Hansford et al.'s response. *Journal of Island and Coastal Archaeology*. doi:10.1080/15564894.2020.1771483.

Mitsuhashi, J. 2016. *Edible Insects of the World*. Boca Raton: CRC Press.

Moore, S. K., Trainer, V. L., Mantua, N. J., Parker, M. S., Laws, E. A., Backer, L. C., and Fleming, L. E. 2008. Impacts of climate variability and future climate change on harmful algal blooms and human health. *Environmental Health* 7(suppl. 2): S4.

Moreau, S. 2002. Les gens de la lisière: La forêt, l'arbre et la construction paysanne Sud-Betsileo, Madagascar. Thèse de doctorat en Géographie, Ecole Doctorale. "Milieu, cultures et sociétés du passé et du présent," Université Paris X.

Morelli, T. L., Smith, A. B., Mancini, A. N., Balko, E. A., Borgerson, C., et al. 2020. The fate of Madagascar's rainforest habitat. *Nature Climate Change* 10(1): 89–96.

Morgan, E. 2016. Sticky layers and shimmering weaves: A study of two human uses of spider silk. *Journal of Design History* 291: 8–23.

Moura, L. C., Scariot, A. O., Schmidt, I. B., Beatty, R., and Russell-Smith, J. 2019. The legacy of colonial fire management policies on traditional livelihoods and ecological sustainability in savannas: Impacts, consequences, new directions. *Journal of Environmental Management* 232: 600–606.

Mouren and Rouaix. 1913. Industrie ancienne des objets de Vohémar. *Bulletin de l'Académie Malgache* 12(2): 3–12.

Muldoon, K. M., De Blieux, D. D., Simons, E. L., and Chartrath, P. S. 2009. The subfossil occurrence and paleoecological significance of small mammals at Ankilitelo Cave, southwestern Madagascar. *Journal of Mammalogy* 90(5): 1111–1131.

Muldoon, K. [M.], Crowley, B. E., Godfrey, L. R., Rasoamiaramanana, A., Aronson, A., Jernvall, J., Wright, P. C., Simons, E. L. 2012. Early Holocene fauna from a new subfossil site: A first assessment from Christmas River, south-central Madagascar. *Madagascar Conservation and Development* 7: 23–29.

Musinsky, J., Tabor, K., Cano, C. A., Ledezma, J. C., Mendoza, E., Rasolohery, A., and Sajudin, E. R. 2018. Conservation impacts of a near real-time forest monitoring and alert system for the tropics. *Remote Sensing in Ecology and Conservation* 4(3): 189–196.

Nanjarisoa, O. P., Besnard, G., Ralimanana, H., Jeannoda, V. H., and Vorontsova, M. S. 2017. Grass survey of the Itremo Massif records endemic central highland grasses. *Madagascar Conservation and Development* 12(1): 34–40.

Nanyingi, M. O., Munyua, P., Kiama, S. G., Muchemi, G. M., Thumbi, S. M., Bitek, A. O., Bett, B., Muriithi, R. M., and Njenga, M. K. 2015. A systematic review of Rift Valley fever epidemiology 1931–2014. *Infection Ecology and Epidemiology* 5: 28024.

Naturevolution. 2020. Exposition photographique: Les premières peintures rupestres de Madagascar. Accessed July 2020. https://www.naturevolution.org/que-faisons-nous/sensibilisation/grand-public/expositions/exposition-photographique-les-peintures-rupestres-du-makay/.

Newbold, T., Hudson, L. N., Hill, S. L., Contu, S., Lysenko, I., Senior, R. A., Börger, L., Bennett, D. J., Choimes, A., and Collen, B. 2015. Global effects of land use on local terrestrial biodiversity. *Nature* 520: 45–50.

Nguyen, V. K., Parra-Rojas, C., and Hernandez-Vargas, E. A. 2018. The 2017 plague outbreak on Madagascar: Data descriptions and epidemic modelling. *Epidemics* 25: 20–25.

Nicolas, J.-P. 2012. *Plantes médicinales du nord de Madagascar: Ethnobotanique Antakarana et informations scientifiques*. Brasparts: Jardins du Monde.

Norris, D. E. 2004. Mosquito-borne diseases as a consequence of land use change. *EcoHealth* 1: 19–24.

O'Brien, S., Emahalala, E. R., Beard, V., Rakotondriany, R. M., Reid, A., Raharisoa, V., and Coulson, T. 2003. Decline of the Madagascar radiated tortoise *Geochelone radiata* due to overexploitation. *Oryx* 37(3): 338–343.

Osborn, C. S. 1924. *Madagascar: Land of the Man-Eating Tree*. New York: Republic.

Pannetier, J. 1974. Archéologie des pays Antambahoaka et Antaimoro. *Taloha* 6: 53–71.

———. 1988. *Contribution à l'archéologie du sud-est de Madagascar*. Travaux et Documents 23. Antananarivo: Musée d'Art et d'Archéologie.

Paquette, S. R., Ferguson, B. H., Lapointe, F.-J., and Louis, E. E. 2009. Conservation genetics of the radiated tortoise (*Astrochelys radiata*) population from Andohahela National Park, southeast Madagascar, with a discussion on the conservation of this declining species. *Chelonian Conservation and Biology* 8(1): 84–93.

Parker Pearson, M. 2010. *Pastoralists, Warriors and Colonists: The Archaeology of Southern Madagascar*. With K. Godden, Ramilisonina, Retsihasetse, J.-L. Schweninnger, G. Huertebize, C. Radimilahy, and H. Smith. British Archaeological Reports International Series 2139. Oxford: British Archaeological Reports.

Parr, C. L., Lehmann, C.E.R., Bond, W. J., Hoffmann, W. A., and Andersen, A. N. 2014. Tropical grassy biomes: Misunderstood, neglected, and under threat. *Trends in Ecology and Evolution* 29(4): 205–213.

Payne, C.L.R., Umemura, M., Dube, S., Azuma, A., Takenaka, C., et al. 2015. The mineral composition of five insects as sold for human consumption in southern Africa. *African Journal of Biotechnology* 1431: 2443–2448.

Payne, C.L.R., Scarborough, P., Rayner, M., and Nonaka, K. 2016. Are edible insects more or less "healthy" than commonly consumed meats? A comparison using two nutrient profiling models developed to combat over- and undernutrition. *European Journal of Clinical Nutrition* 703: 285–291.

Perez, V. R., Godfrey, L. R., Nowak-Kemp, M., Burney, D. A., Ratsimbazafy, J., and Vasey, N. 2005. Evidence of early butchery of giant lemurs in Madagascar. *Journal of Human Evolution* 49(6): 722–742. https://doi.org/10.1016/j.jhevol.2005.08.004.

Perrier de la Bâthie, H. 1905. L'alimentation des Sakalaves. *Revue de Madagascar* 710: 308–314.

———. 1921. La végétation Malgache. *Annales du Musée Colonial de Marseille*, série 3, 9: 1–266.

———. 1924. Au sujet des Sauterelles. *Bulletin Economique (Tananarive)* 3–4: 219.

———. 1928. Les bois d'ébénisterie de la côte ouest de Madagascar. *Journal d'Agriculture Traditionnelle et de Botanique Appliquée* 83: 469–477.

———. 1949. Les plantes à caoutchouc de Madagascar: Valeur et possibilité de leur culture. *Journal d'Agriculture Traditionnelle et de Botanique Appliquée* 315–316: 17–20.

Petrunkevitch, A. 1921. Spider silk and its uses. *American Museum Journal* 21: 381.

Pfeiffer, I. 1861. *Reise nach Madagaskar: Nebst einer Biographie der Verfasserin, nach ihren eigenen Aufzeichnungen*. Vol. 1. Vienna: Gerold.

Pfund, J. L. 2000. Culture sur brûlis et gestion des ressources naturelle: Evolution et perspectives de trois terroirs ruraux du versant est de Madagascar. PhD in natural sciences, Département Sciences Forestières, Laboratoire de Gestion des Ecosystèmes, Ecole Polytechnique Fédérale de Zurich.

Picot, M. 2005. Etude de l'écologie du Mégachiroptère *Eidolon dupreanum* (Pollen, 1866) et de son rôle dans la dispersion des graines en lisière du corridor forestier reliant les parcs nationaux de Ranomafana et d'Andringitra. Mémoire de DEA en Biologie, Ecologie et Conservation Animales, Département de Biologie Animale, Université d'Antananarivo.

Picot, M., Jenkins, R.K.B., Ramilijaona, O., Racey, P. A., and Carrière, S. 2007. The feeding ecology of *Eidolon dupreanum* (Pteropodidae) in eastern Madagascar. *African Journal of Ecology* 45(4): 645–650.

Pierron, D., Heiske, M., Razafindrazaka, H., Rakoto, I., Rabetokotany, N., et al. 2017. Genomic landscape of human diversity across Madagascar. *Proceedings of the National Academy of Sciences of the USA* 114(32): E6498–E6506. https://doi.org/10.1073/pnas.1704906114.

Pollen, F. P. 1868. *Recherches sur la faune de Madagascar et de ses dépendances d'après les découvertes de François P. L. Pollen et D. C. Van Dam*. Pt. 1, *Relation de Voyage*. Leiden: J. K. Steenhof.

Pollini, J. 2009. Agroforestry and the search for alternatives to slash-and-burn cultivation: From technological optimism to political economy of deforestation. *Agriculture, Ecosystems and Environment* 133: 48–60.

———. 2010. Environmental degradation narratives in Madagascar: From colonial hegemonies to humanist revisionism. *Geoforum* 41(5): 711–722. https://doi.org/10.1016/j.geoforum.2010.04.001.

Portier, P. 1949. *La biologie des Lépidoptéres*. Paris: P. Lechevalier.

Prendergast, M. E., Buckley, M., Crowther, A., Eager, H., Frantz, L., et al. 2017. Reconstructing Asian faunal introductions to eastern Africa from multi-proxy biomolecule and archaeological datasets. *PLOS One* 12(8): e0182565. https://doi.org/10.1371/journal.pone.0182565.

Price, O. F., Russell-Smith, J., and Watt, F. 2012. The influence of prescribed fire on the extent of wildfire in savanna landscapes of western Arnhem Land, Australia. *International Journal of Wildland Fire* 21(3): 297–305.

Prudhomme, E. 1905. La sériciculture à Madagascar: Rapport de 1903. *L'Agriculture Pratique des Pays Chauds* 5(22): 11–21; (23): 101–111; (24): 204–222; (25):

311–325; (26): 389–402; (27): 481–490; (28): 50–65; (29): 109–127; (30): 212–229; (31): 327–340; (32): 395–403; (33): 475–491.

Qurollo, B. A., Larsen, P. A., Rakotondrainibe, H. H., Mahefarisoa, K., Rajaonarivelo, T., Razafindramanana, J., Breitschwerdt, E. B., Junge, R. E., and Williams, C. V. 2018. Molecular surveillance of novel tick-borne organisms on Madagascar's lemurs. *Ticks and Tick-Borne Diseases* 9: 672–677.

Rabaan, A. A., Al-Ahmed, S. H., Alsuliman, S. A., Aldrazi, F. A., Alfouzan, W. A., and Haque, S. 2019. The rise of pneumonic plague on Madagascar: Current plague outbreak breaks usual seasonal mould. *Journal of Medical Microbiology* 68: 292–302.

Rabearimanana, L. 1975. Mystique et sorcellerie dans le manuscrit de l'ombiasy (Manuscrit de Hova de la bibliothèque Grandidier). *Omaly sy Anio* 1–2: 295–323.

Rabedimy, J. F. 1976. *Pratiques de divination à Madagascar*. Travaux et documents de l'ORSTOM 51. Paris: ORSTOM.

Rabinowitz, P. M., Pappaioanou, M., Bardosh, K. L., and Conti, L. 2018. A planetary vision for One Health. *British Journal of Medicine Global Health* 3: e001137.

Racey, P. A., Goodman, S. M., and Jenkins, R. K. 2010. The ecology and conservation of Malagasy bats. In *Island Bats: Evolution, Ecology, and Conservation*, eds. T. H. Fleming and P. A. Racey, pp. 369–404. Chicago: University of Chicago Press.

Radimilahy, C. [M.] 1981. *Archéologie de l'Androy: Sud de Madagascar*. Recherche, Pédagogie et Culture 9(55). Paris: AUDECAM.

———. 1998. Mahilaka: An archaeological investigation of an early town in northwestern Madagascar. PhD thesis, Department of Archaeology and Ancient History, University of Uppsala.

Radimilahy, C. M., and Crossland, Z. 2015. Situating Madagascar: Indian Ocean dynamics and archaeological histories. *Azania* 50(4): 495–518. https://doi.org/10.1080/0067270X.2015.1102942.

Rafidison, V. M. 2013. Ethnobiologie et écologie des *Ficus* des terroirs Betsileo et du corridor Ranomafana–Andringitra. PhD thesis, Université d'Antananarivo.

Rafidison, V. M., Ratsimandresy, F., Rakotondrajaona, R., Rasamison, V., Rakotoarisoa, M., Rakotondrafara, A., and Rakotonandrasana, S. R. 2019. Synthèse et analyse de données sur les inventaires de plantes médicinales de Madagascar. *Ethnobotany Research and Applications* 18: 40.

Rafidison, V. M., Rakouth, B., Carrière, S. M., Kjellberg, F., and Aumeeruddy-Thomas, Y. 2020. Multiple values of isolated and clusters of *Ficus* tree species protected by Betsileo farmers in rural landscapes in Madagascar: Implications for biodiversity conservation. *Biodiversity and Conservation* 29(3): 1027–1058.

Raharijaona, V. 1994. Répartition des villages anciens dans une vallé des Hautes Terres Centrales: Archéologie de la Manandona. *Taloha* 12: 15–70.

Rahelinirina, S., Duplantier, J.-M., Ratovonjato, J., Ramilijaona, O., Ratsimba, M., and Rahalison, L. 2010a. Study on the movement of *Rattus rattus* and evaluation of the plague dispersion on Madagascar. *Vector-Borne and Zoonotic Diseases* 10: 77–84.

Rahelinirina, S., Leon, A., Harstskeerl, R. A., Sertour, N., Ahmed, A., et al. 2010b. First isolation and direct evidence for the existence of large small-mammal reservoirs of *Leptospira* sp. in Madagascar. *PLoS One* 5(11): e14111.

Rahelinirina, S., Rajerison, M., Telfer, S., Savin, C., Carniel, E., and Duplantier, J.-M. 2017. The Asian house shrew *Suncus murinus* as a reservoir and source of human outbreaks of plague in Madagascar. *PLoS Neglected Tropical Diseases* 11(11): e0006072.

Raik, D. 2007. Forest management in Madagascar: An historical overview. *Madagascar Conservation and Development* 2(1): 5–10.

Railsback, L. B., Dupont, L. A., Liang. F., Brook, G. A., Burney, D. A, Cheng, H., and Edwards, R. L. 2020. Relationships between climate change, human environmental impact, and megafaunal extinction inferred from a 4000-year multi-proxy record from a stalagmite from northwestern Madagascar. *Quaternary Sciences Reviews* 234: 106244.

Rajemison, A. A. 2013. Proposition d'essences de substitution aux bois précieux en épuisement par la connaissance des propriétés du matériau bois: Cas du Palissandre de Madagascar; Application en ameublement. PhD thesis, Université de Toulouse.

Rakotoarimanana, V. 2002. Feu, pâturage et dynamique des savanes à *Heteropogon contortus* (L) P. Beauv. Ex Roem and Shult. dans le sud ouest de Madagascar (région de Sakaraha). PhD thesis, Université d'Antananarivo.

Rakotoarimanana, V., and Grouzis, M. 2006. Influence du feu et du pâturage sur la richesse et la diversité floristiques d'une savane à *Heteropogon contortus* du sud-ouest de Madagascar (région de Sakaraha). *Candollea* 61(1): 167–188.

Rakotoarimanana, V., Gondard, H., Ranaivoarivelo, N., and Carrière, S. 2008. Influence du pâturage sur la diversité floristique, la production et la qualité fourragères d'une savane des Hautes Terres malgaches (région de Fianarantsoa). *Sécheresse* 19(1): 39–46.

Rakotoarisoa, J.-A. 1998. *Mille ans d'occupation humaine dans le sud-est de Madagascar: Anosy, une île au milieu des terres*. Paris: L'Harmattan.

Rakotoarivelo, N. H. 2015. Les plantes utiles de la Nouvelle Aire Protégée de Vohibe (commune rurale d'Ambalabe, district de Vatomandry): Inventaire, études ethnobotaniques et écologiques. PhD thesis, Université d'Antananarivo.

Rakotoarivelo, N. H., Razanatsima, A., Rakotoarivony, F., Rasoaviety, L., Ramarosandratana, A. V., Jeannoda, V., Kuhlman, A., Randrianasolo, A., and Bussmann, R. W. 2014. Ethnobotanical and economic value of *Ravenala madagascariensis* Sonn. in eastern Madagascar. *Journal of Ethnobiology and Ethnomedicine* 10: 57.

Rakotoarivelo, N. H., Randrianarivony, T. N., Rakotoarivony, F., and Randrianasolo, A. 2019. "Mangidy": Malagasy folk beverages sold in Madagascar's market places. *Ethnobotany Research and Applications* 18: 29.

Rakotoharinome, M., Pognon, D., Randriamparany, T., Ming, J. C., Idoumbin, J. P., Cardinale, E., and Porphyre, V. 2014. Prevalence of antimicrobial residues in pork meat on Madagascar. *Tropical Animal Health and Production* 46: 49–55.

Rakotonirina, B., and Cooke, A. 1994. Sea turtles of Madagascar: Their status, exploitation, and conservation. *Oryx* 28(1): 51–61.

Rakotovao, G., Rabevohitra, A. R., Chatelperron, P. C., Guibal, D., and Gérard, J. 2012. *Atlas de bois de Madagascar*. Versailles: Quae.

Rakotovololona, H. S. 1994. Ankadivory: Temoin d'une culture de l'Imerina ancient. *Taloha* 12: 7–24.

Rakotozafy, L.M.A. 1996. *Etudes de la constitution du régime alimentaire des habitants du site de Mahilaka de XIème au XIVème siècle à partir de produits des fouilles archéologiques*. PhD thesis, l'Université d'Antananarivo.

Rakotozafy, L.M.A., and Goodman, S. M. 2005. Contribution à l'étude zooarchéologique de la région du sud-ouest et extrême sud de Madagascar sur la base des collections de l'ICMAA de l'Université d'Antananarivo. *Taloha* 14–15. http://www.taloha.info/document.php?id=137.

Ralaimihoatra, E. 1965. *Histoire de Madagascar*. Tananarive: Société Malgache d'Edition.

Ralaimihoatra, S. N. 2008. Le système de suivi satellitaire des feux, un outil de gestion des Madagascar. In *Les XIèmes Journées Scientifiques du Réseau Ressources Naturelles à Télédétection de l'AUF, 03 au 07 novembre 2008*, eds. S. Randriamanga, S. Rakotoniaina, Y. Auda, S. Rakotondraompiana, and J.-P. Gastellu-Etchegorry, pp. 279–281. Antananarivo: Agence Universitaire de la Francophonie.

Ramamonjisoa, J.B.I. 2009. Sans la plante, point de devin guérisseur. *Etudes Océan Indien* 42–43: 321–338.

Ramamonjisoa, L., and Rakotoarimanana, J. 1996. Espèces forestières fruitières autochtones: Une nouvelle investigation réalisée à Madagascar. *Akon'ny Ala* 19: 5–13.

Ramilisonina. 1984. Quelques aspects de l'urbanisation en pays Bezanozano Mandialaza XIII–XIXth century. In *Urban Origins in Eastern Africa: Proceedings of the 1984 Workshop in Mombasa; A Regional Cooperation Programme in African Archaeology and Related Disciplines*, ed. P. J. Sinclair, pp. 95–131. Uppsala: Uppsala University, Department of Archaeology.

Ramos-Elorduy, J., Moreno, J.M.P., and Camacho, V.H.M. 2009. Edible aquatic Coleoptera of the world with an emphasis on Mexico. *Journal of Ethnobiology and Ethnomedicine* 51: 11.

Randolph, T. F., Schelling, E., Grace, D., Nicholson, C. F., Leroy, J. L., Cole, D. C., Demment, M. W., Omore, A., Zinsstag, J., and Ruel, M. 2007. Role of livestock in human nutrition and health for poverty reduction in developing countries. *Journal of Animal Science* 85: 2788–2800.

Randriamahefasoa, J. 2001. Impact of hunting on Meller's duck *Anas melleri* at Lac Alaotra, Madagascar. *Dodo* 37: 98.

Randriamalala, H. 2014. Etude des comportements alimentaires des caprins en zone semi-aride de Madagascar, cas de la commune rurale de Soalara Sud. Mémoire de DEA, ESSA-Forêts, Université d'Antananarivo.

Randriamalala, J. R., Hervé, D., Randriamboavonjy, J. C., and Carrière, S. M. 2012. Effects of tillage regime, cropping duration and fallow age on diversity and structure of secondary vegetation in Madagascar. *Agriculture, Ecosystems and Environment* 155: 182–193.

Randriamalala, J. R., Hervé, D., Letourmy, P., and Carrière, S. M. 2015a. Effects of slash-and-burn practices on soil seed banks in secondary forest successions in Madagascar. *Agriculture, Ecosystems and Environment* 199: 312–319.

Randriamalala, J. R., Hosnah, B. H., Ranaivoarimanana, S., and Ratovomalala, R. I. 2015b. Dynamiques spatiales des fourrés xérophiles de Betioky-Sud et Soalara-Sud (Madagascar). In *Transitions agraires au sud de Madagascar: Résilience et viabilité, deux facettes de la conservation; Actes du séminaire de synthèse du projet FPPSM*, eds. D. Hervé, S. Razanaka, S. Rakotondraompiana, F. Rafamantanantsoa, and S. M.

Carrière, pp. 113–121. Antananarivo: IRD-SCAC and Partenariat et Recherche dans le Secteur Rural.
Randriamalala, J. R., Radosy, H. O., Razanaka, S., Randriambanona, H., and Hervé, D. 2016. Effects of goat grazing and woody charcoal production on xerophytic thickets of southwestern Madagascar. *Journal of Arid Environments* 128: 65–72.
Randriamalala, J. R., Ramananantoandro, T., Radosy, H. O., Randriambanona, H., and Hervé, D. 2017. Annual biomass increment of xerophytic thickets and sustainability of woody charcoal production in southwestern Madagascar. *Forest Ecology and Management* 400: 139–149.
Randriamalala, J. R., Randriarimalala, J., Hervé D., and Carrière, S. M. 2019. Slow recovery of endangered xerophytic thickets vegetation after slash-and-burn cultivation in Madagascar. *Biological Conservation* 233: 260–267.
Randriamamonjy, V. C., Keane, A., Razafimanahaka, H. J., Jenkins, R.K.B., and Jones, J.P.G. 2015. Consumption of bushmeat around a major mine, and matched communities, in Madagascar. *Biological Conservation* 186: 35–43.
Randriamanalina, M. H., Rafararano, L., Babary, L., and Laha, R. 2000. Rapport des enquêtes sur les chasses dans les Fokontany d'Ivondro, d'Erara et d'Etsilesy. *Lemur News* 5: 11–14.
Randriambanona, H., Randriamalala, J. R., and Carrière, S. M. 2019. Native forest regeneration and vegetation dynamics in non-native *Pinus patula* tree plantations in Madagascar. *Forest Ecology and Management* 446: 20–28.
Randriambelo, T., Baldy, S., Bessafi, M., Petit, M., and Despinoy, M. 1998. An improved detection and characterization of active fires and smoke plumes in south-eastern Africa and Madagascar. *International Journal of Remote Sensing* 19(14): 2623–2638.
Randriambelo, T., Baray, J.-L., and Baldy, S. 2000. Effect of biomass burning, convective venting, and transport on tropospheric ozone over the Indian Ocean: Reunion Island field observations. *Journal of Geophysical Research* 105(D9): 11813–11832.
Randrianandrasana, M. 2014. *Antherina suraka* (Lepidoptera: Saturniidae): Ecology, systematics, and potential economic uses to promote conservation in Madagascar. PhD thesis, University of Illinois at Urbana-Champaign.
Randrianandrasana, M., and Berenbaum, M. R. 2015. Edible non-crustacean arthropods in rural communities of Madagascar. *Journal of Ethnobiology* 35(2): 354–383.
Randrianandrianina, F. H., Racey, P. A., and Jenkins, R.K.B. 2010. Hunting and consumption of mammals and birds by people in urban areas of western Madagascar. *Oryx* 44(3): 411–415.
Randrianarivony, T. N. 2015. Etudes ethnobotaniques et écologiques des plantes utiles de la Nouvelle Aire Protégée d'Analavelona (District de Sakaraha, Région du Sud-ouest de Madagascar). PhD thesis, Université d'Antananarivo.
Randrianarivony, T. N., Kuhlman, A. R., Rakotoarivony, F., Andriamihajarivo, T., Jeannoda, V., Ramarosandratana, A. V., Randrianasolo, A., and Bussmann, R. W. 2016. Value of services and goods of Analavelona sacred forest and the relationship with forest conservation. *Madagascar Conservation and Development* 11(2): 44–51.
Randrianarivony, T. N., Rakotoarivony, F., Randrianasolo, A., and Bussmann, R. W. 2017. Useful plants for traditional fermented beverages (TFB) in Madagascar. Paper presented at the 21ème Congrès de l'Association pour l'Etude Taxonomique de la Flore d'Afrique Tropicale (AETFAT), Nairobi.
Randrianasolo, E. 2014. Archéologie dans la forêt humide de l'est de Madagascar: Analyse archéométrique et pétrographique des poteries découvertes à Antongombato. Mémoire de DEA, Faculté des Lettres et des Sciences Humaines, Université d'Antananarivo.
Randriatsivery, F. M. 2005. Evaluation des impacts du feu sur la végétation des savanes du massif d'Ibity. Mémoire du DEA en Ecologie Végétale, Université d'Antananarivo.
Raoliarivelo, L.I.B., Masezamana, H. N., Andrianarisoa, J. H., and Randriamalala, J. R. 2010. *Impact de la fabrication de charbon de bois sur la production et la disponibilité fourragère de pâturage en zone subaride: Cas de la Commune de Soalara-Sud, Toliara II*. Ed. DERAD. Q909 project final report. Antananarivo: Eastern and Southern Africa Partnership Program.
Raper, D., and Bush, M. 2009. A test of *Sporormiella* representation as a predictor of megaherbivore presence and abundance. *Quaternary Research* 71(3): 490–496. https://doi.org/10.1016/j.yqres.2009.01.010.
Rarivomanana, H. T. 2017. Analyse de la mise en œuvre des stratégies de lutte contre les feux à Madagascar: Cas de la région Sofia. Mémoire de Master, Département des Sciences et Gestion de l'Environnement, Université de Liège.
Rasamuel, D. 1985. Alimentation et techniques anciennes dans le Sud-Malgache à travers une fosse à odure du XIème siècle. *Etudes Océan Indien* 4: 81–109.
———. 2007. *Fanongoavana: Une capitale princière malgache du XIVe siècle*. Paris: Quae.
Rasoafaranaivo, M. H. 2005. Evaluation des impacts du feu sur la biologie de quelques espèces végétales du massif d'Ibity (Antsirabe). Mémoire de DEA en Ecologie Végétale, Université d'Antananarivo.
Rasoanaivo, N., Randriambanona, H., Hervé, D., Carrière, S. M., Rakotoarimanana, V., Razanaka, S., and Randriamalala, J. R. 2019. The effectiveness of the community-based forest management system in reducing deforestation in eastern Madagascar. *56th Annual ATBC meeting*. Ivato ICC, Antananarivo, Madagascar. https://www.xcdsystem.com/atbc/program/MLpmKXQ/index.cfm?pgid=755&RunRemoveSessionFilter=1.
Rasolondrainy, T. 2012. Discovery of rock paintings and Libyco-Berber inscription from the Upper Onilahy, Isalo Region, southwestern Madagascar. *Studies in the African Past* 10: 173–195.
———. 2019. Decision-making in the face of unpredictable climate and intergroup conflicts in southwest Madagascar, Sixteenth to Nineteenth centuries C.E. PhD thesis, Yale University, New Haven.
Rasolonjatovo, H.A.M., Muldoon, K. M., Ranivoharimanana, L., Rakotoarijaona, M., and Goodman, S. M. 2021. Subfossil birds from a submerged cave in southwestern Madagascar. *Malagasy Nature* 15: 128–140.
Ratnagar, S. 2004. *Trading Encounters: From the Euphrates to the Indus in the Bronze Age*. New Delhi: Oxford University Press.
Ratsimamanga, A. R. 1968. *Dictionnaire des noms malgaches des végétaux*. Antananarivo: Institut Malgache de Recherches Appliquées.
Ratsimbazafy, R. 2003. Sea turtles. In *The Natural History of Madagascar*, eds. S. M. Goodman and J. P. Benstead, pp. 210–213. Chicago: University of Chicago Press.
Ratsitorahina, M., Rahelinirina, S., Michault, A., Rajerison, M., Rajatonirina, S., Richard, V., and 2011 Surveillance Workshop. 2015. Has Madagascar lost its exceptional leptospirosis free-like status? *PLoS One* 10(4): e0122683.
Ravaosolo, J. 2009. Les plantes dans la fabrication de talismans utilisés en phytothérapie dans le sud-ouest Malgache: Le cas de Toliara. *Etudes Océan Indien* 42–43: 339–348.
Razafimanahaka, J. H., Jenkins, R.K.B., Andriafidison, D., Randrianandrianina, F. H., Rakotomboavonjy, V., Keane, A., and Jones, J.P.G. 2012. Novel approach for quantifying illegal bushmeat consumption reveals high consumption of protected species in Madagascar. *Oryx* 46(4): 584–592.
Razafimanantsoa, T. M., Rajoelison, G., Ramamonjisoa, B., Raminosoa, N., Poncelet, M., et al. 2012. Silk moths in Madagascar: A review of the biology, uses, and challenges related to *Borocera cajani* (Vinson, 1863) (Lepidoptera: Lasiocampidae). *Biotechnology, Agronomy and Society and Environment* 162: 269–276.
Redford, K. H. 1992. The empty forest. *BioScience* 42(6): 412–422.
Reuter, K. E., and Schaefer, M. S. 2017. Illegal captive lemurs in Madagascar: Comparing the use of online and in-person data collection methods. *American Journal of Primatology* 79(11). doi:10.1002/ajp.22541.
Reuter, K. E., Gilles, H., Wills, A. R., and Sewall, B. J. 2016. Live capture and ownership of lemurs in Madagascar: Extent and conservation implications. *Oryx* 50(2): 344–354.
Reuter, K. E., Clarke, T. A., LaFleur, M., Rodriguez, L., Hanitriniaina, S., and Schaefer, M. S. 2017. Trade of parrots in urban areas of Madagascar. *Madagascar Conservation and Development* 12(1): 41–48.
Reyes-García, V., Guèzeb, M., Luz, A. C., Paneque-Gálvez, J., Macía, M. J., Orta-Martínez, M., Pino, J., and Rubio-Campillo, X. 2013. Evidence of traditional knowledge loss among a contemporary indigenous society. *Evolution and Human Behavior* 34(4): 249–257.
Richardson, J. 1885. *A New Malagasy-English Dictionary*. Antananarivo: London Missionary Society.
Ripple, W. J., Abernethy, K., Betts, M. G., Chapron, G., Dirzo, R., et al. 2016. Bushmeat hunting and extinction risk to the world's mammals. *Royal Society Open Science* 3(10). https://doi.org/10.1098/rsos.160498.
Rist, C. L., Garchitorena, A., Ngonghala, C. N., Gillespie, T. R., and Bonds, M. H. 2015a. The burden of livestock parasites on the poor. *Trends in Parasitology* 31: 527–530.
Rist, C. L., Ngonghala, C. N., Garchitorena, A., Brook, C. E., Ramananjato, R., et al. 2015b. Modeling the burden of poultry disease on the rural poor in Madagascar. *One Health* 1: 60–65.
Rombaka, J. P. 1978. Histoire des ancêtres Antemoro-Anteony, d'après la tradition donnée par Ramarosaona, Z. et Molet, L. In *Tradition et dynamique sociale à Madagascar*, eds. L. Poirier and A. Rabenoro, pp. 275–354. Nice: Institut d'Etudes et de Recherches Interethniques et Interculturelles.
Rostal, M. K., Ross, N., Machalaba, C., Cordel, C., Paweska, J. T., and Karesh, W. B. 2018. Benefits of a One Health approach: An example using Rift Valley fever. *One Health* 5: 34–36.

Sachot, O. 1864. *Madagascar et les Madécasses: Histoire, moeurs, productions, curiosités naturelles*. Paris: Victor Sarlit.

Samonds, K. E., Crowley, B. E., Rasolofomanana, T.R.N., Andriambelomanana, M. C., Andrianavalona, H. T., et al. 2019. A new late Pleistocene subfossil site (Tsaramody, Sambaina basin, central Madagascar) with implications for the chronology of habitat and megafaunal community change on Madagascar's Central Highlands. *Journal of Quaternary Science* 34(6): 379–392.

Sauther, M. L., Bertolini, F., Dollar, L. J., Pomerantz, J., Alves, P. C., et al. 2020. Taxonomic identification of Madagascar's free-ranging "forest cats." *Conservation Genetics* 21: 443–451.

Scales, I. R. 2014. The future of conservation and development in Madagascar: Time for a new paradigm? *Madagascar Conservation and Development* 9(1): 6–12.

Scarone, F. 1938. La manne de Madagascar. *L'Agronomie Coloniale* 242: 54–54.

Scheffers, B. R., Oliveira, B. F., Lamb, I., and Edwards, D. P. 2019. Global wildlife trade across the tree of life. *Science* 366(6461): 71–76.

Schreurs, G., Evers, S.J.T.M., Radimilahy, C., and Rakotoarisoa, J.-A. 2011. The Rasikajy civilization in northeast Madagascar: A pre-European Chinese community? *Etudes Océan Indien* 46–47: 107–132.

Schwilk, D. W., and Ackerly, D. D. 2001. Flammability and serotiny as strategies: Correlated evolution in pines. *Oikos* 94(2): 326–336.

Schwitzer, C., Mittermeier, R. A., Johnson, S. E., Donati, G., Irwin, M., et al. 2014. Averting lemur extinctions amid Madagascar's political crisis. *Science* 343(6173): 842–843.

Scott, A. C., Bowman, D.M.J.S., Bond, W. J., Pyne, S. J., and Alexander, M. E. 2014. *Fire on Earth: An Introduction*. Hoboken: Wiley Blackwell.

Scroxton, N., Burns, S. J., McGee, D., Hardt, B., Godfrey, L. R., Ranivoharimanana, L., and Faina, P. 2017. Hemispherically in-phase precipitation variability over the last 1700 years in a Madagascar speleothem record. *Quaternary Science Reviews* 164: 25–36.

———. 2019. Competing temperature and atmospheric circulation effects on southwest Madagascan rainfall during the last deglaciation. *Paleoceanography and Paleoclimatology* 34(2): 275–286. https://doi.org/10.1029/2018PA003466.

Secretariat of the Convention on International Trade in Endangered Species of Wild Fauna and Flora (CITES). 2013. Madagascar Crocodile Project final report. Report prepared by General Directorate for Forests, Ministry of Environment and Forests of Madagascar (CITES Management Authority), Geneva, Switzerland.

Serneels, V., Morel, M., Nitsche, C., Radimilahy, C., Rakotoarisoa, J.-A., Rasoarifetra, B., and Schreurs, G. 2017. Pierre et fer à Madagascar: Vestiges sidérurgiques de Benavony et la riviére Matavy. SLSA Jahresbericht, annual report. https://www.researchgate.net/publication/335911853_Pierre_et_Fer_a_Madagascar_1_-_Vestiges_siderurgiques_de_Benavony_et_de_la_riviere_Matavy?channel=doi&linkId=5d836f1a92851ceb79143584&showFulltext=true.

Serpantié, G., Rasolofoharinoro, B. M., and Carrière, S. M., eds. 2007. *Transitions agraires, dynamiques écologiques et conservation: Le "corridor" Ranomafana–Andringitra, Madagascar*. Antananarivo and Paris: CITE and IRD.

Sibree, J. 1884. The migratory locust. *Antananarivo Annual and Madagascar Magazine*, no. 8, 115–116.

———. 1915. *A Naturalist in Madagascar: A Record of Observation, Experiences, and Impressions Made during a Period of Over Fifty Years' Intimate Association with the Natives and Study of the Animal and Vegetable Life of the Island*. London: Seeley, Service.

Sigaut, F. 1975. Daniel Coulaud, les Zafimaniry, un groupe ethnique de Madagascar à la poursuite de la forêt (compte-rendu). *Etudes Rurales* 60: 119–120.

Simmonds, P. L. 1859. *The Curiosities of Food; or, The Dainties and Delicacies of Different Nations Obtained from the Animal Kingdom*. London: R. Bentley.

———. 1885. *The Animal Food Resources of Different Nations, with Mention of Some of the Special Dainties of Various People Derived from the Animal Kingdom*. London: E. and F. N. Spon.

Solofondranohatra, C. L., Vorontsova, M. S., Hackel, J., Besnard, G., Cable, S., Williams, J., Jeannoda, V., and Lehmann, C.E.R. 2018. Grass functional traits differentiate forest and savanna in the Madagascar Central Highlands. *Frontiers in Ecology and Evolution* 6: 184.

Solofondranohatra, C. L., Vorontsova, M. S., Hempson, G. P., Hackel, J., Cable, S., Vololoniainana, H. J., and Lehmann, C.E.R. 2020. Fire and grazing determined grasslands of central Madagascar represent ancient assemblages. *Proceedings of the Royal Society B: Biological Sciences*, 287: 20200598.

Solondraibe, T. 1991–1992. Communautés de base et pouvoirs politiques dans le Lalangina et le Vohibato (sud-Betsileo) du XVe au début du XXe siècle. *Omaly sy Anio* 33–36: 15–46.

Stattersfield, A. J., Crosby, M. J., Long, A. J., and Wege, D. C. 1998. *Endemic Bird Areas of the World: Priorities for Biodiversity Conservation*. Birdlife Conservation Series no. 7. Cambridge, UK: BirdLife International.

Stocker, M., Razafimanantsoa Harivelo, F. N., Desponts, C., and Lalaina, M. 2019. *Madagascar Economic Update: A New Start?* Washington, DC: World Bank.

Stoller, J. K. 2015. Murray and Nadel's textbook of respiratory medicine, 6th edition. *Annals of the American Thoracic Society* 12: 1257–1258.

Styger, E., Rakotondramasy, H. M., Pfeffer, M. J., Fernandes, E.C.M., and Bates, D. M. 2007. Influence of slash-and-burn farming practices on fallow succession and land degradation in the rainforest region of Madagascar. *Agriculture, Ecosystems and Environment* 119(3–4): 257–269.

Styger, E., Fernandes, E.C.M., Rakotondramasy, H. M., and Rajaobelinirina, E. 2009. Degrading uplands in the rainforest region of Madagascar: Fallow biomass, nutrient stocks, and soil nutrient availability. *Agroforestry Systems* 77(2): 107–122.

Sun, Y. C., Jarrett, C. O., Bosio, C. F., and Hinnebusch, B. J. 2014. Retracing the evolutionary path that led to flea-borne transmission of *Yersinia pestis*. *Cell Host and Microbe* 15: 578–586.

Tallet, P., and Marouard, G. 2015. The harbor of Khufu on the Red Sea at Wadi al-Jarf. *Near Eastern Archaeology* 77(1): 4–14.

Tandrya and Payet. 1898. Notes sur les Mahafalys. *Madagascar: Notes, Reconnaissances et Explorations* 4: 988–998.

Tantely, L. M., Boyer, S., and Fontenille, D. 2015. A review of mosquitoes associated with Rift Valley fever virus on Madagascar. *American Journal of Tropical Medicine and Hygiene* 92: 722–729.

Théodoridès, J. 1949. Les Coléoptéres comestibles. *Les Naturalistes Belges* 30: 126–137.

Tovondrafale, T., Razakamanana, T., Hiruko, K., and Rasoamiaramanana, A. 2014. Paleoecological analysis of elephant bird (Aepyornithidae) remains from the Late Pleistocene and Holocene formations of southern Madagascar. *Malagasy Nature* 8: 1–13.

Trimoulet, H. 1865. *Etat actuel de la sériciculture et description du nid d'un Bombyx exotique*. Bordeaux: Chez Coderc, Degretea et Poujol.

Tscharntke, T., Clough, Y., Wanger, T. C., Jackson, L., Motzke, I., Perfecto, I., Vandermeer, J., and Whitbread, A. 2012. Global food security, biodiversity conservation and the future of agricultural intensification. *Biological Conservation* 151(1): 53–59.

Tscharntke, T., Milder, J. C., Schroth, G., Clough, Y., DeClerck, F., Waldron, A., Rice, R., and Ghazoul, J. 2015. Conserving biodiversity through certification of tropical agroforestry crops at local and landscape scales. *Conservation Letters* 8: 14–23.

Tuttle, M., Carroll, N., Bumpass, R., Krivor, M., and Burns, J. 2010. *2008 Diver Investigations of the Suspected Serapis Site Ambodifototra, Isle Ste Marie, Madagascar*. [Plymouth, NH]: Serapis Project. https://mua.apps.uri.edu/project_journals/serapis08/report.pdf.

Vallet-Coulomb, C., Gasse, F., Robison, L., Ferry, L., Van Campo, E., and Chalié, F. 2006. Hydrological modeling of tropical closed Lake Ihotry (SW Madagascar): Sensitivity analysis and implications for paleohydrological reconstructions over the past 4000 years. *Journal of Hydrology* 331(1–2): 257–271. https://doi.org/10.1016/j.jhydrol.2006.05.026.

van Broeck, A. 1709. *The Life and Adventures of Capt. John Avery the Famous English Pirate, (Rais'd from a Cabbin-Boy, to a King) Now in Possession of Madagascar:* [...] *Written by a Person Who Made His Escape from Thence, and Faithfully Extracted from His Journal*. London: J. Baker.

van Huis, A. 2020. Importance of insects as food in Africa. In *African Edible Insects as Alternative Source of Food, Oil, Protein and Bioactive Components*, ed. A. A. Mariod, pp. 1–17. Cham: Springer International.

van Huis, A., Van Itterbeeck, J., Klunder, H., Mertens, E., Halloran, A., et al. 2013. *Edible Insects: Future Prospects for Food and Feed Security*. Rome: Food and Agriculture Organization of the United Nations.

Van Itterbeeck, J., Rakotomalala Andrianavalona, I. N., Rajemison, F. I., Rakotondrasoa, J. F., Ralantoarinaivo, V. R., et al. 2019. Diversity and use of edible grasshoppers, locusts, crickets, and katydids (Orthoptera) in Madagascar. *Foods* 8: 666. doi:10.3390/foods8120666.

Vasey, N., and Godfrey, L. R. Forthcoming. Lemur hunting in Madagascar's present and past: The case of *Pachylemur*. In *World Archeoprimatology: Interconnections of Humans and Nonhuman Primates in the Past*, eds. B. Urbani, D. Youlatos, and A. Antczak. Cambridge: Cambridge University Press.

Veldman, J. W., Overbeck, G. E., Negreiros, D., Mahy, G., Le Stradic, S., Fernandes, G. W., Durigan, G., Buisson, E., Putz, F. E., and Bond, W. J. 2015. Tyranny of trees in grassy biomes. *Science* 347(6621): 484–485.

Vérin, P. 1975. *Les échelles anciennes du commerce sur les côtes nord de Madagascar*. Lille: Service de Reproduction des Thèses.

———. 1986. *History of Civilization in North Madagascar.* The Hague: Balkema.
———., and Battistini, R. 1972. Les anciens habitats de Rezoky et d'Asambalahy. *Taloha* 4: 29–49.
Vérin, P., and Chanudet, C. 1996. The early pre-Islamic history of the Comores Islands: Links with Madagascar and Africa. In *The Indian Ocean in Antiquity*, ed. J. Reade, pp. 461–470. London: Kegan Paul.
Vernier, E., and Millot, J. 1971. *Archéologie malgache, comptoirs musulmans.* Paris: Musée de l'Homme.
Vinson, A. 1863a. *Aranéides des îles de la Réunion, Maurice et Madagascar.* Paris: Librairie Encyclopédique de Roret.
———. 1863b. Du ver a soie de Madagascar ou ver à soie de l'Ambrevade (*Borocera cajani*, Vinson). *Bulletin de la Société Impériale Zoologique d'Acclimatation* 10: 505–512.
———. 1863c. Entomologie utile à Madagascar. *Revue et Magasin de Zoologie Pure et Appliquée* 15: 45–47.
———. 1863d. Note sur le ver à soie de l'Ambrevate. *Revue et Magasin de Zoologie Pure et Appliquée* 15: 142–143.
———. 1865. *Voyage à Madagascar au couronnement de Radama II.* Paris: Librairie Encyclopédique de Roret.
Virah-Sawmy, M. 2009. Ecosystem management in Madagascar during global change. *Conservation Letters* 2(4): 163–170.
Virah-Sawmy, M., Bonsall, M. J., and Willis, K. J. 2009a. "Tales of *Symphonia*": Extinction dynamics in response to past climate change in Madagascan rainforests. *Biology Letters* 5(6): 821–825.
Virah-Sawmy, M., Gillson, L., and Willis, K. J. 2009b. How does spatial heterogeneity influence resilience to climatic changes? Ecological dynamics in southeast Madagascar. *Ecological Monographs* 79(4): 557–574.
Virah-Sawmy, M., Willis, K. J., and Gillson, L. 2009c. Threshold response of Madagascar's littoral forest to sea-level rise. *Global Ecology and Biogeography* 18: 98–110.
Virah-Sawmy, M., Willis, K. J., and Gillson, L. 2010. Evidence for drought and forest declines during the recent megafaunal extinctions in Madagascar. *Journal of Biogeography* 37(3): 506–519. https://doi.org/10.1111/j.1365-2699.2009.02203.x.
Virah-Sawmy, M., Gillson, L., Gardner, C. J., Anderson, A., Clark, G., and Haberle, S. 2016. A landscape vulnerability framework for identifying integrated conservation and adaptation pathways to climate change: The case of Madagascar's spiny forest. *Landscape Ecology* 31(3): 637–654. https://doi.org/10.1007/s10980-015-0269-2.
Voarintsoa, N.R.G., Railsback, L. B., Brook, G. A., Wang, L., Cheng, H., Li, X. L., Edwards, R. L., Rakotondrazafy, A.F.M., and Razanetseheno, M.O.M. 2017. Three distinct Holocene intervals of stalagmite deposition and nondeposition revealed in NW Madagascar, and their paleoclimate implications. *Climate of the Past* 13: 1771–1790.
Vogler, A. J., Andrianaivoarimanana, V., Telfer, S., Hall, C. M., Sahl, J. W., et al. 2017. Temporal phylogeography of *Yersinia pestis* on Madagascar: Insights into the long-term maintenance of plague. *PLoS Neglected Tropical Diseases* 11: e0005887.
Volampeno, M. S., Randriatahina, G. H., Kalle, R., Wilson, A. L., and Downs, C. T. 2015. A preliminary population viability analysis of the critically endangered blue-eyed black lemur (*Eulemur flavifrons*). *African Journal of Ecology* 53(4): 419–427.
Vorontsova, M. S., Besnard, G., Forest, F., Malakasi, P., Moat, J., et al. 2016. Madagascar's grasses and grasslands: Anthropogenic or natural? *Proceedings of the Royal Society B: Biological Sciences* 283: 20152262.
Waeber, P. O., Wilmé, L., Mercier, J. R., Camara, C., and Lowry, P. P. 2016. How effective have thirty years of internationally driven conservation and development efforts been in Madagascar? *PLoS One* 11(8): e0161115. https://doi.org/10.1371/journal.pone.0161115.
Wang, L., Brook, G. A., Burney, D. A., Voarintsoa, N.R.G., Liang, F., Cheng, H., and Edwards, R. L. 2019. The African Humid Period, rapid climate change events, the timing of human colonization, and megafaunal extinctions in Madagascar during the Holocene: Evidence from a 2m Anjohibe Cave stalagmite. *Quaternary Science Reviews* 210: 136–153. https://doi.org/10.1016/j.quascirev.2019.02.004.
Watson, J. E., Venter, O., Lee, J., Jones, K. R., Robinson, J. G., Possingham, H. P., and Allan, J. R. 2018. Protect the last of the wild. *Nature* 563: 27–30.
Wells, N. A. 2003. Some hypotheses on the Mesozoic and Cenozoic paleoenvironmental history of Madagascar. In *The Natural History of Madagascar*, eds. S. M. Goodman and J. P. Benstead, pp. 16–34. Chicago: University of Chicago Press.
Wetterstrom, W., and Wright, H. T. 1992. Une contribution à la paléoethnobotanique du plateau central de Madagascar. *Taloha* 11: 147–166.
Whitmee, S., Haines, A., Beyrer, C., Boltz, F., Capon, A. G., et al. 2015. Safeguarding human health in the Anthropocene epoch: Report of the Rockefeller Foundation–Lancet Commission on planetary health. *Lancet* 386: 1973–2028.
Willis, K. J., Gillson, L., and Virah-Sawmy, M. 2008. Nature or nurture: The ambiguity of C4 grasslands in Madagascar. *Journal of Biogeography* 35: 1741–1742.
World Resources Institute and World Bank. 2016. Le bois précieux de Madagascar: Evaluation scientifique et technique en vue de la réalisation des objectifs CITES. Final report. Washington, DC. https://www.profor.info/sites/profor.info/files/WRI-WB%20Malagasy%20Precious%20Woods%20Assessment_FR_1_0.pdf.
Wright, H. T. 1992. Early Islam, oceanic trade, and town development on Nzwani: The Comorian archipelago in the XIth–XVth. *Azania* 27: 81–128.
———. 1993. Trade and politics on the eastern littoral of Africa: A.D. 800–1300. In *The Archaeology of Africa: Food, Metals, and Towns*, eds. T. Shaw, P. Sinclair, B. Andah, and A. Okpoko, pp. 658–672. London: Routledge.
———, ed. 2007. *Early State Formation in Central Madagascar: An Archaeological Survey of Western Avaradrano.* Memoirs 43. Ann Arbor: University of Michigan Museum of Anthropological Archaeology.
———. Forthcoming. Early human impact on a forest in northeastern Madagascar: Note on an archaeological sounding on Nosy Mangabe. *Taloha.*
Wright, H. T., and Dewar, R. E. 2000. Northeast Madagascar in the XVth and XVIIth centuries. In *L'Extraordinaire et le quotidien: Variations anthropologiques*, eds. C. Allibert and N. Rajaonarimanana, pp. 287–311. Paris: Karthala.
Wright, H. T., and Fanony, F. 1992. L'évolution des systèmes d'occupation des sols dans la vallée de la rivière Mananara au nord-est de Madagascar. *Taloha* 11: 16–64.
Wright, H. T., Rakotoarisoa, J.-A., Heurtebize, G., and Vérin, P. 1993. The evolution of settlement systems in the Efaho River valley: A preliminary report on archaeological reconnaissances of 1983–86. *Indo-Pacific Prehistory Association Bulletin* 12: 2–20.
Wright, H. T., Vérin, P., Ramilisonina, Burney, D. A., Burney, L. P., and Matsumoto, K. 1996. The evolution of settlement systems in the Bay of Boeny and the Mahavavy River valley, north-western Madagascar. *Azania* 31: 37–73.
Wright, H. T., Radimilahy, C., and Allibert, C. 2005. L'évolution des systèmes d'installation dans la Baie d'Ampasindava et à Nosy-Be. *Taloha* 14–15.
Wright, H. T., Dewar, R. E., Radimilahy, C., and Darsot-Rasolofomampianina, L. 2011. Early settlement in the region of Fenoarivo Atsinanana. In *Civilisations des mondes insualires*, eds. C. Radimilahy and N. Rajanarimanana, pp. 677–740. Paris: Karthala.
Wright, H. T., Griffin, W., and Ramilisonina. Forthcoming. Early settlements near Belo-sur-Mer. *Taloha.*
Wyatt, L., Ortiz, E. J., Feingold, B., Berky, A., Diringer, S., Morales, A. M., Jurado, E. R., Hsu-Kim, H., and Pan, W. 2017. Spatial, temporal, and dietary variables associated with elevated mercury exposure in Peruvian riverine communities upstream and downstream of artisanal and small-scale gold mining. *International Journal of Environmental Research and Public Health* 14(12): 1582.
Yount, J. W., Tsiazonera, and Tucker, B. T. 2001. Constructing Mikea identity: Past or present links to forest and foraging. *Ethnohistory* 48(1–2): 257–291.
Zheng, F., He, X., Gao, X., Zhang, C. E., and Tang, K. 2005. Effects of erosion patterns on nutrient loss following deforestation on the Loess Plateau of China. *Agriculture, Ecosystems and Environment* 108: 85–97.
Zinsstag, J., Schelling, E., Waltner-Toews, D., and Tanner, M. 2011. From "One Medicine" to "One Health" and systemic approaches to health and well-being. *Preventive Veterinary Medicine Journal* 101: 148–156.
Zinsstag, J., Mackenzie, J. S., Jeggo, M., Heymann, D. L., Patz, J. A., and Daszak, P. 2012. Mainstreaming One Health. *Ecohealth* 9: 107–110.
Zohdy, S., Grossman, M. K., Fried, I. R., Rasambainarivo, F. T., Wright, P. C., and Gillespie, T. R. 2015. Diversity and prevalence of diarrhea-associated viruses in the lemur community and associated human population of Ranomafana National Park, Madagascar. *International Journal of Primatology* 36: 143–153.
Zolotarevsky, B. N. 1930. Le riz et les sauterelles à Madagascar. *Riz et Riziculture* 42: 87–94.

CHAPTER 6

ZOONOTIC PATHOGENS AND OTHER INFECTIOUS MICROBES: DIVERSITY, EVOLUTIONARY HISTORY, AND TRANSMISSION

INTRODUCING MICROBES IN THE CONTEXT OF THE MADAGASCAR BIODIVERSITY HOTSPOT

P. Tortosa

Biodiversity is acknowledged as a global heritage providing services to human populations at local or global scales and therefore deserving consideration and protective measures. Biodiversity and the effects of anthropogenic changes on species community composition is hence scrutinized by scientists in most ecoclimatic zones and ecospheres on earth. Although Madagascar is considered one of the five leading biodiversity hotspots worldwide (Myers et al. 2000), the investigation of microbial diversity has essentially, thus far, been left behind. The reasons for this are probably in part the result of technical challenges associated with the investigation of microbes, as compared to macroorganisms such as plants and animals. The exploration of microbial diversity and the identification of drivers shaping such diversity can hardly be achieved without robust skills in molecular microbiology and an access to sophisticated laboratory equipment. Besides, the popularization of microbes would require costly equipment to produce images of interest to the general public. Lastly and maybe most importantly, it has been claimed that there is no biogeography for organisms smaller than 1 mm and, hence, virtually no endemism in microbes. This claim relies mostly on Lourens Baas Becking's hypothesis that "everything is everywhere, but the environment selects" (Baas Becking 1934). This concept results from the acceptance that microbes 1) are extremely abundant, and 2) have infinite dispersal capacity. Microbial diversity is consequently expected to be evenly distributed worldwide, with only local differences resulting from the selective pressures that are at play in each specific environment.

This hypothesis, long considered as a paradigm, has been challenged in recent decades (Whitfield 2005), and the investigation of microbial biogeography, including island microbial biogeography (Bell et al. 2005), can be currently considered an emerging discipline (Fierer 2008). The development of next-generation sequencing (NGS) technologies has allowed for testing and establishing of biogeographic patterns for microbes and especially for soil microorganisms. Such patterns have been described at the scale of a country (Dequiedt et al. 2011; Ranjard et al. 2011), and the progress and gaps in soil microbial biogeography have been the subject of an increasing number of studies (Fierer 2008; E. K. Cameron et al. 2018). This research has now established that there are indeed biogeographic patterns for microbes, which are increasingly considered relevant biological models for studying ecological processes.

This current volume provides an interesting opportunity to introduce microbes into the picture with respect to Malagasy biodiversity. While several studies thus far have been inventorying the actual microbial diversity occurring on the island, ongoing research programs aim at disentangling the functional ecology of these microbes, some of which can be considered as endemic. Madagascar and surrounding islands—the archipelagoes of the Comoros (Mayotte, Grande Comore, Mohéli, and Anjouan), Seychelles, and

Mascarenes (Mauritius, La Réunion, and Rodrigues)—referred to herein as the Malagasy Region (Figure 6.1), are ideal natural laboratories facilitating the investigation of microbes. Indeed, examining the evolution, dispersal, and transmission of microorganisms is simplified by the limited number of species, including vectors or reservoirs, typical of insular ecosystems. In addition, islands are discrete, relatively closed environments interconnected through anthropogenic and non-anthropogenic routes that are more easily identifiable than in continental territories. Moreover, islands are exceptionally sensitive to species introduction, including that of microorganisms, which can lead to disease emergence, as best illustrated by the recent Chikungunya or Zika pandemics, flaring up in the Pacific and Indian Ocean islands a few months before spreading at a global scale (Dellagi et al. 2016; Kucharski et al. 2016). Lastly, the specific multi-insular system of the Malagasy Region comprises islands that are different in origin, geological age, surface area, and proximity to the African source continent (see Figure 6.1). Therefore, the different islands in this region host distinct species assemblages, including several endemics that allow for investigation of a variety of original transmission chains (Tortosa et al. 2012).

For reasons mostly to do with public health or funding opportunities, microbes that have been most intensively investigated on Madagascar are those of medical or veterinary importance—in particular, those that are associated with public health. These include microbes with zoonotic potential, meaning infectious pathogens that can be directly or indirectly transmitted between humans and nonhuman animals, as well as arthropod-borne parasites for which the biological cycle does not necessarily involve vertebrate reservoirs.

Among human infectious diseases, malaria was certainly among the first to be thoroughly documented on Madagascar, where all four *Plasmodium* species of global medical concern coexist. The sympatry of these plasmodial species within a limited land surface is unusual and likely mirrors the successive human-colonization events originating from Asia, Africa, and Europe that led to the current ethnic melting pot (Rousset and Andrianarivelo 2003). Interestingly, a recent genetic analysis suggested that human resistance to *P. vivax* on Madagascar is of African origin and has been positively selected for in the population over the past millennium (Pierron et al. 2018), hence, corroborating the long exposure of the Malagasy human population to plasmodial infection.

Besides the exploration of the epidemiology of malaria, understanding the mechanisms of establishment and maintenance of *Yersinia pestis*, responsible for plague, on Madagascar has been and still is a fascinating and important challenge. A significant knowledge of *Y. pestis* biology on the island has been gathered and has shown that plague bacillus, following its introduction in the early 20th century, has adapted to a flea species endemic to Madagascar, the current distribution of which mostly drives the distribution of human plague cases (Andrianaivoarimanana et al. 2013). Intensive screening of *Y. pestis* has additionally revealed an important genetic diversity, including some original lineages that are suspected to be linked to local transmission chains possibly involving endemic small mammals (Guiyoule et al. 1997). In any case, the investigation of

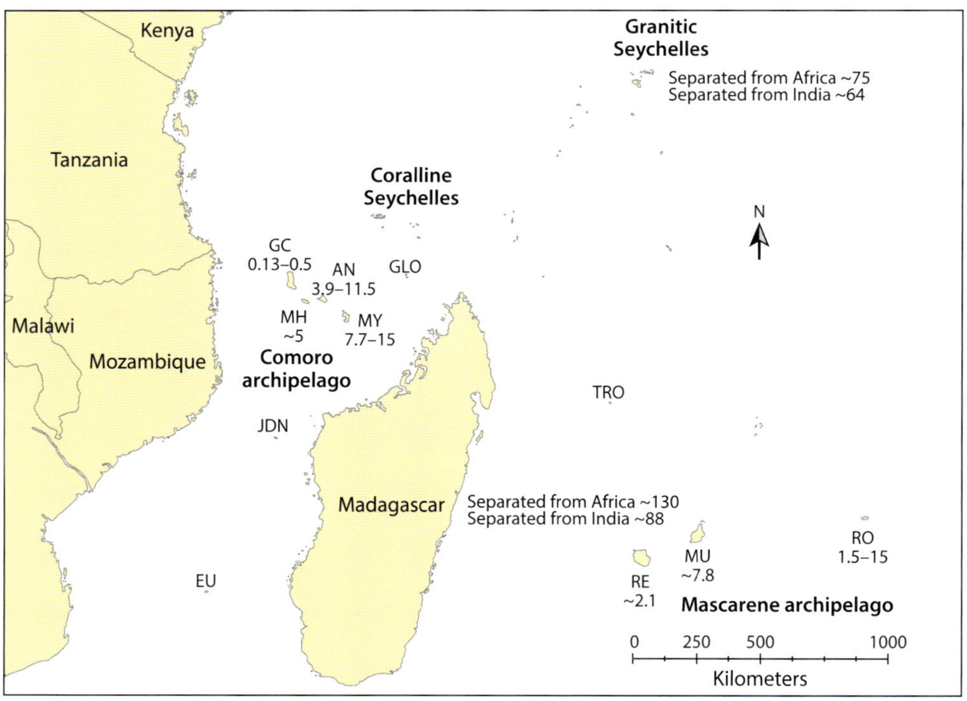

FIGURE 6.1 **Islands of the southwestern Indian Ocean. The map depicts the Seychelles archipelago, made of old granitic islands and younger coralline islands; the Comoro archipelago, composed of the Union of the Comoros (Grande Comore [GC], Anjouan [AN], and Mohéli [MH]) and the French-administered Mayotte Island (MY); and the Mascarene archipelago (La Réunion [RE], Mauritius [MU], and Rodrigues [RO]). The Iles Eparses (or Scattered Islands), a series of distantly placed islands (Europa [EU], Juan de Nova [JDN], Glorieuses [GLO], and Tromelin [TRO]), are also shown. The separation of landmasses and the period of in situ emergence for volcanic islands are indicated in Mya (million of years ago).** (SOURCE: modified from Tortosa et al. 2012.)

Y. pestis on Madagascar shows how the biogeography of a microbe is linked to that of its vertebrate or invertebrate host(s)/vector(s).

While the aforementioned malaria and plague agents are of introduced origin, the present chapter reviews several recent studies showing that the extant microbial diversity on Madagascar also comprises endemic organisms. This has been substantiated by recent screening of the wild fauna of Madagascar, largely carried out by biologists from regional scientific and medical institutions, which uncovered a remarkable diversity of infectious and potentially zoonotic agents in the Malagasy Region. A number of studies are bringing a sort of consensus to which viral and bacterial microorganisms, such as coronaviruses or pathogenic *Leptospira*, can undergo co-diversification processes with their hosts at evolutionary scales, as presented in the contribution herein by Dietrich et al. (pp. 268–77). Beside these mammal-borne infectious agents, viruses transmitted by arthropods (referred to as arthropod-borne viruses, or arboviruses) have been in the spotlight of the Malagasy and international scientific community because of several arboviruses recently emerging worldwide, including on islands in the Malagasy Region. Madagascar shelters an astonishing diversity of mostly endemic mosquito species (Tantely et al. 2016a; see Robert et al., pp. 1089–98); their role as vectors of West Nile, Dengue, and Rift Valley Fever viruses, all introduced to Madagascar, has been explored in the past decade and is presented herein (see Héraud et al., pp. 285–91). It is interesting to note that the investigation of the Chikungunya epidemic in the region has shed light on microevolution mechanisms involved in the adaptation of arboviruses to local mosquito populations (Schuffenecker et al. 2006); this is an interesting example of the contribution of the regional microbial diversity to a major scientific discovery. Finally, in keeping with the tight relationships linking invertebrates to their microbiota, the diversity of bacteria in arthropod vectors, regardless of their involvement in human diseases, has been explored on Madagascar through the advent of NGS technologies and especially metabarcoding. These studies, carried out on mosquitoes, ticks, and bat flies from Madagascar are presented herein by Wilkinson and Mavingui (see pp. 291–93), and feed the holobiont theory, which states that an animal and its associated microorganisms share biological functions and therefore should be considered together (Guégan et al. 2018).

The studies presented in this chapter have revealed an outstanding level of diversity of microbes and illuminated some important processes involved in the evolution, maintenance, transmission, and dispersal of infectious microorganisms. These studies have shown that Malagasy Region microbial diversity comprises both autochthonous and introduced lineages. The impact of pathogen introduction on wild fauna is extensively reviewed by Rasambainarivo and Zohdy (see pp. 298–302), who present several mechanisms through which introduced microbes can alter the transmission of autochthonous microbes and eventually have negative impacts on local endemic mammal communities. Symmetrically, the introduction of Malagasy tenrecs, specifically *Tenrec ecaudatus* (see Goodman et al., pp. 1891–94), on the neighboring island of Mayotte has been associated with the introduction of a pathogenic *Leptospira* that is involved in a number of human acute cases on that island (Lagadec et al. 2016). These examples show that microbes are a biological entity that is of interest not only to microbiologists. Indeed, the high diversity and prevalence of potentially zoonotic agents hosted by Malagasy wild fauna make these organisms relevant models to address research questions of major importance in the field of disease ecology, such as the mechanisms underlying dilution or amplification effects, or the importance of co-diversification as a driver of microbial endemism.

Considering the intensity of habitat disturbance on Madagascar, including forest fragmentation, the development of agriculture, uncertain impacts of climatic change, and a rapid human demographic increase, the island appears to be the perfect spot for disentangling complex ecological processes involved in pathogen evolution and maintenance, and gaining an understanding of how different ecological perturbations together with species introduction can lead to emergence episodes. The scientific contributions presented in this chapter hence pave the way for ambitious multidisciplinary investigations that are underway or in preparation. Such programs aim at answering key questions in the fields of disease ecology, conservation, and epidemiology. The knowledge generated by such programs will moreover allow researchers to determine the extent of the contact the Malagasy population, as well as people living on neighboring islands, have to microbial pathogens and advance understanding of the main drivers of human exposure, which may in turn have positive consequences concerning public health.

Subject editor: Steven M. Goodman

LEPTOSPIRA BACTERIA ON MADAGASCAR

M. Dietrich, Y. Gomard, C. Cordonin, and P. Tortosa

LEPTOSPIROSIS: THE DISEASE

Leptospirosis is a tropical disease associated with *Leptospira*, a genus of bacteria that are among the leading zoonotic causes of illness worldwide. According to a systematic review compiling most of the available morbidity and mortality data on human leptospirosis, the disease affects over 1 million individuals and causes nearly 60,000 deaths each year (Costa et al. 2015). However, this disease remains largely neglected from the perspective of diagnosis and treatment, as it affects tropical countries with reduced international monetary clout and because the symptoms associated with severe forms are nonspecific. Symptoms range from mild flu-like syndromes to severe forms, also known as Weil's disease, characterized by jaundice and multiorgan failure, leading to death in 10% of cases. In addition, the diagnosis of the disease is notoriously challenging, as it relies either on molecular detection using blood and/or urine samples or on time-consuming serological and bacteriological methods. In the absence of efficient molecular facilities, which is common in small, remote communities of tropical countries, and of reliable serological rapid tests, most cases are likely not detected. The lack of accessible diagnosis is critical, as reliable diagnostic tools could lead to an early antibiotic treatment and thus lower the morbidity and mortality rates of the disease in the developing countries that are most exposed to the disease.

Leptospirosis is a zoonosis maintained by reservoir animals, mostly mammals that contaminate the environment, where humans or domestic animals can be indirectly infected. Therefore, anthropogenic changes in habitats are expected to have major consequences on disease transmission, making leptospirosis a relevant disease model for investigating the impact of human disturbance on zoonotic spread. The disease is more prevalent in tropical countries (Pappas et al. 2008), and even more so on tropical islands, for unknown reasons, although it has been proposed that the limited diversity of reservoir species typical of insular ecosystems may increase disease transmission (Derne et al. 2011).

The epidemiology of the disease and the bacteria path in animal reservoirs and incident hosts have been clarified through experimental infection in lab mice. A bioluminescent *Leptospira* injected in mice enabled visualization of the systemic infection within a week, followed by a disappearance of the bacteria in the bloodstream and a subsequent colonization of the lumen of the renal tubules of the animals—this is where the bacteria are maintained and excreted until the death of the animal (Ratet et al. 2014). This experiment allowed for the description of the acute phase of the disease, which occurs within the first days or weeks postinfection, as well as the subsequent reservoir state, characterized by chronic infection of renal tubules and contamination of the environment by animal reservoirs through *Leptospira*-infected urine. Although the present contribution focuses on the reservoir-borne *Leptospira*, in which bacteria are likely maintained through the formation of stable biofilms (Ristow et al. 2008), it is critical to note that recent investigations carried out by the Institut Pasteur de Madagascar, and also briefly presented herein, suggest that the level of human infection of the disease may have been massively underreported on Madagascar, and hence, it obviously deserves further studies.

LEPTOSPIRA: THE BACTERIA

Leptospira are long, corkscrew-shaped, highly motile bacteria (Figure 6.2) belonging to the Spirochaetales, an ancient prokaryotic order that separated from other eubacteria during early evolutionary history and, hence, displays unique cell and genomic structures (Saier 2000). Although the double membrane of spirochetes is typical of gram-negative bacteria, gram staining is irrelevant for these bacteria, which can be visualized instead using a dark-field microscope. The peculiarities of the *Leptospira* cell wall include two periplasmic flagella together with a peptidoglycan layer in close proximity with the inner membrane (Raddi et al. 2012; C. E. Cameron 2015).

The slow growth of pathogenic *Leptospira* impedes the use of culture for early diagnosis. *Leptospira* detection and classification has been until recently based mainly on serological methods (e.g., microscopic-agglutination test, or MAT) using the lipopolysaccharides' antigenic properties, which facilitated the classification of *Leptospira* into nearly 30 serogroups and over 200 serovars. However, the development of molecular methods for detection and typing has accelerated the assembly of data that can be shared by the scientific community and allows the advancement of epidemiological investigations at local, regional, and global scales.

The genus *Leptospira* is notably diversified, comprising more than 20 species, of which 10 are considered pathogenic. The advent of deep-sequencing technologies is currently uncovering an astonishing diversity of thus far unknown *Leptospira* species or lineages and should in the near future replace targeted multiple-locus sequence typing by genomic single-nucleotide polymorphism analyses (Thibeaux et al. 2018; Guglielmini et al. 2019). However,

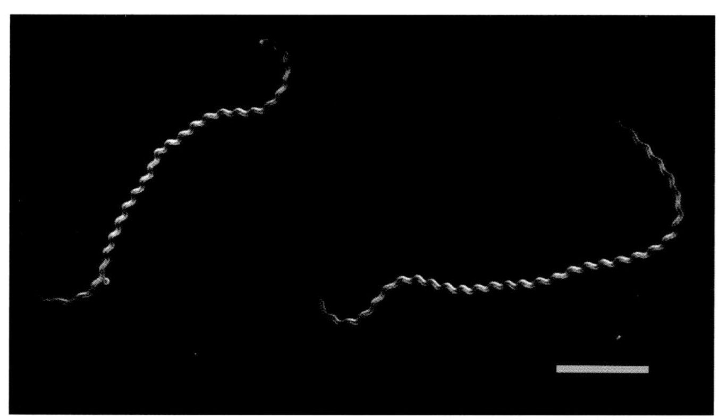

FIGURE 6.2 ***Leptospira interrogans* pyrogenes (×7500).** (PHOTO by R. Thibeaux, Institut Pasteur, CRESICA.)

multiple-locus sequence typing remains an efficient and low-cost genotyping method, as it allows for determining genotypes by following standardized protocols and, hence, mutualizing data at a global level. It uses the polymorphism of slowly evolving housekeeping genes to determine sequence types (STs) characterized by the identification of alleles at each locus. Several distinct typing schemes are available, and while it is out of the scope of the present contribution to discuss the pros and cons of each specific scheme, it is critical to use a scheme that has been previously used within an investigated island or region. Indeed, identified STs can then be compared to other STs previously reported in the same environmental setting, and transmission pathways can be inferred when identical STs are identified in human cases and reservoir animals.

HISTORICAL ASPECTS OF HUMAN LEPTOSPIROSIS RESEARCH ON MADAGASCAR

Confirmed diagnosis on Madagascar of human leptospirosis cases was until recently unknown, and it was not clear whether pathogenic *Leptospira* bacteria were actually present on the island. Although acute leptospirosis has never been formally reported on Madagascar, as compared to neighboring islands such as the Seychelles (Biscornet et al. 2017) and Mayotte (Bourhy et al. 2010), the documentation of rare confirmed human cases, mainly based on serological testing, shows that the human population actually is exposed to *Leptospira* (Table 6.1). However, the burden of the disease in humans is still unknown.

The earliest evidence of human leptospirosis on the island, reported in 1956, was revealed by the use the MAT method (Brygoo and Kolochine-Erber 1956). A single sample was positive, out of 40 tested subjects with symptoms suggestive of leptospirosis. A subsequent survey conducted in the Toliara District, on both clinically suspect patients and persons with professional activities at risk for leptospirosis, by contrast, showed very high seroprevalence levels, 51% (33/65) and 81% (43/53), respectively (Silverie et al. 1968). However, subsequent efforts to detect the infection failed to confirm this startling result. Indeed, in a survey conducted in Antananarivo and based on a large sample size (2646 serum samples) from subjects with no symptoms suggestive of leptospirosis, only five samples (<0.2%) were found to be seropositive (Lhuillier 1978). In an additional study, 105 workers from Antananarivo with possible occupational exposure to *Leptospira* underwent serological screening with both MAT and enzyme-linked immunosorbent assay (ELISA) techniques, and reactive antibodies were found in only one person (Ralaiarijaona et al. 2001). More recently, a cross-sectional study conducted in a community at Moramanga found a seroprevalence of 2.9% (n = 678) in healthy and febrile humans (Ratsitorahina et al. 2015), while a study published in 2018 reported no positive samples undergoing polymerase chain reaction (PCR) diagnosis among 1009 blood samples of patients from the Central Highlands with fever of unknown origin (Hagen et al. 2018).

In addition to studies carried out on Madagascar, two confirmed human cases were diagnosed with PCR on Mayotte and La Réunion and were suspected to have been imported from Madagascar. The human case detected on Mayotte was further genetically characterized as *L. kirschneri* (Bourhy et al. 2012). Sequencing of the infecting strain imported to La Réunion strongly suggested that it belonged to *L. interrogans* (Pagès et al. 2015). All together, there has been thus far little evidence on Madagascar of *Leptospira* infection in human acute cases. However, a recent survey carried out in the eastern portion of the island among febrile patients visiting the regional hospital at Ambatondrazaka suggested that nearly a fourth of acute cases were indeed associated with leptospirosis (Raharimanga et al. 2019), strengthening the need for a thorough evaluation of the exposure of the Malagasy human population to this neglected disease.

RECENT EVIDENCE OF PATHOGENIC *LEPTOSPIRA* IN THE MALAGASY FAUNA

Livestock and Domestic Animals

The rare investigations of animal reservoirs of *Leptospira* historically focused on livestock or domestic animals and were mainly based on serological testing (Table 6.1). Some of the surveys reported no positive evidence in several domestic animals, such as donkeys, sheep, pigs, and dogs (Brygoo and Kolochine-Erber 1956; Ralaiarijaona et al. 2001), while others revealed high seroprevalence in cattle and pigs (Silverie et al. 1968; Schafbauer et al. 2019), suggesting that these animals may act as *Leptospira* reservoirs or at least be heavily exposed to the infection. This was recently supported by a PCR-based study carried out in slaughterhouses in Antananarivo and Moramanga, which identified pathogenic species such as *L. borgpetersenii*, *L. kirschneri*, and *L. interrogans* in cattle and goats (Rahelinirina et al. 2019a). Only one recent study found positive cases in dogs and cats, and these samples were collected in villages near the Betampona protected area in the central eastern lowlands (Rasambainarivo et al. 2018). Despite a limited sample size (n = 57) and a screening focused on *L. interrogans*, this study shows that domesticated animals can carry potentially pathogenic *Leptospira*.

Introduced Rodents and Shrews

Until recently, the limited investigations of *Leptospira* in wild animals all reported negative results. Indeed, not one of the 55 introduced *Rattus rattus* (family Muridae) kidney samples collected at Marovitsika-Anjiro and tested using culture methods were found to be carrying *Leptospira* (Lhuillier 1978) (see Ramasindrazana et al., pp. 1872–80, for information on introduced small mammals on Madagascar). Moreover, the PCR screening of 115 rat kidneys from Ambositra (49 *R. rattus* and 66 *R. norvegicus*) did not yield positive samples (Ralaiarijaona et al. 2001). The first isolation of pathogenic *Leptospira* on the island was achieved in 2010 (Rahelinirina et al. 2010). This extensive study used a large sample (n = 269) of introduced rodents (*R. rattus*, *R. norvegicus*, and *Mus musculus*, all of the family Muridae) and introduced shrews (*Suncus murinus*, family Soricidae) from five localities, and combined MAT, real-time PCR, and culture methods on kidney and urine samples. Pathogenic *Leptospira* were detected in 33.9% of 268 small-mammal samples, and the prevalence was particularly high in and around the cities of Moramanga, Mahajanga, and Toliara, with no difference between rural and urban areas.

TABLE 6.1. **Overview of published studies conducted on Madagascar investigating the presence of *Leptospira* in humans and domestic and wild animals**

	ASSOCIATED STUDY	STUDY ORGANISM (NUMBER)	LOCATION	STUDY PERIOD	METHODS		
					MAT	CULTURE	PCR
HUMANS							
	Brygoo and Kolochine-Erber (1956)	**Suspected humans (40)**	Not specified	1955	yes	no	no
	Silverie et al. (1968)	**Suspected humans (65)**	Toliara	1968	yes	no	no
	Lhuillier (1978)	**Nonsuspected humans (2646)**	Antananarivo	1978	yes	no	no
	Ralaiarijaona et al. (2001)	**Nonsuspected humans (105)**	Antananarivo	2000	yes	no	no
	Ratsitorahina et al. (2015)	**Healthy and febrile humans (678)**	Moramanga	2011	yes	no	no
	Hagen et al. (2018)	Patients with fever of unknown origin (1009)	Antananarivo	2011–2013	no	no	yes
	Pagès et al. (2015)	**Confirmed human case**	La Réunion (imported)	2012	yes	no	yes
	Bourhy et al. (2012)	**Confirmed human case**	Mayotte (imported)	2007–2010	yes	yes	yes
LIVESTOCK AND DOMESTIC ANIMALS							
	Buck et al. (1956)	**Cattle (28)**	Many localities	1951–1953	yes	no	no
	Brygoo and Kolochine-Erber (1956)	**Cattle (65)** Dogs (24) Donkeys (10) **Horses (20)** Pigs (49) Sheep (18)	Not specified	1955	yes	no	no
	Silverie et al. (1968)	**Cattle (72)** **Pigs (25)**	Toliara	1968	yes	no	no
	Ralaiarijaona et al. (2001)	Cattle (50) Pigs (13)	Antananarivo, Ambositra	2000	no	no	yes
	Schafbauer et al. (2019)	**Cattle (201)**	Antananarivo-Atsimondrano	2012	yes	no	no
	Rahelinirina et al. (2019a)	**Cattle (55)** **Pigs (50)**	Antananarivo, Moramanga	2015	no	no	yes
	Rasambainarivo et al. (2018)	**Cats (9)** **Dogs (48)**	Betampona protected area	2014–2016	yes	no	no
INTRODUCED WILD MAMMALS							
	Lhuillier (1978)	*Rattus rattus* (55)	Marovitsika-Anjiro	1978	no	yes	no
	Ralaiarijaona et al. (2001)	*R. norvegicus* (66) *R. rattus* (49)	Antananarivo, Ambositra	2000	no	no	yes
	Rahelinirina et al. (2010)	***Mus musculus* (55)** ***R. norvegicus* (96)** ***R. rattus* (94)** ***Suncus murinus* (23)**	Moramanga, Antsiranana, Mahajanga, Toamasina, Toliara	2008–2009	yes	yes	yes

	ASSOCIATED STUDY	STUDY ORGANISM (NUMBER)	LOCATION	STUDY PERIOD	METHODS		
					MAT	CULTURE	PCR
	Rahelinirina et al. (2019b)	***M. musculus* (59)** ***R. norvegicus* (49)** *R. rattus* (2) *S. murinus* (4)	Antananarivo	2014	no	yes	yes
	Moseley et al. (2018)	***M. musculus* (119)** ***R. norvegicus* (36)** ***R. rattus* (347)** ***S. murinus* (60)**	Moramanga	2013–2015	no	no	yes
NATIVE WILD MAMMALS							
Terrestrial small mammals	Dietrich et al. (2014)	***Eliurus minor* (112)** *E. tanala* (4) *Gymnuromys roberti* (2) ***Hemicentetes semispinosus* (4)** ***H. nigriceps* (12)** ***Microgale cowani* (72)** *M. fotsifotsy* (1) *M. jobihely* (1) *M. gymnorhyncha* (4) ***M. longicaudata* (12)** ***M. majori* (10)** *M. parvula* (10) ***M. principula* (6)** *M. taiva* (6) ***Nesogale dobsoni* (54)** *N. talazaci* (2) *Nesomys rufus* (13) *Oryzorictes hova* (8) *Setifer setosus* (8) *Tenrec ecaudatus* (3)	Lakato, Ankazomivady	2010–2012	no	no	yes
	Moseley et al. (2018)	***Eliurus* spp. (108)** ***Hemicentetes semispinosus* (29)** ***Microgale* spp.** ***Nesomys rufus***	Moramanga	2013–2015	no	no	yes
Bats	Lhuillier (1978)	*Pteropus rufus* (50)	Marovitsika-Anjiro	1978	no	yes	no
	Lagadec et al. (2012)	*Hypsugo anchietae* (1) ***Miniopterus gleni* (7)** ***M. griffithsi* (2)** ***M. mahafaliensis* (10)** ***Mormopterus jugularis* (12)** ***Myotis goudoti* (1)** ***Otomops madagascariensis* (8)** ***Paratriaenops furculus* (1)** ***Triaenops menamena* (10)**	Many localities		no	no	yes

(*continued overleaf*)

TABLE 6.1. ***continued***

	ASSOCIATED STUDY	STUDY ORGANISM (NUMBER)	LOCATION	STUDY PERIOD	METHODS		
					MAT	CULTURE	PCR
	Gomard et al. (2016)	*Chaerephon atsinanana* (34) ***C. leucogaster* (94)** ***Coleura kibomalandy* (3)** *Eidolon dupreanum* (11) *Neoromicia bemainty* (2) ***Macronycteris commersoni* (27)** *Miniopterus aelleni* (7) *M. gleni* (22) ***M. griffithsi* (7)** ***M. griveaudi* (116)** ***M. mahafaliensis* (89)** ***M. majori* (7)** ***M. manavi sensu lato* (19)** ***M. sororculus* (22)** *Mops leucostigma* (68) *M. midas* (19) ***Mormopterus jugularis* (152)** ***Myotis goudoti* (48)** ***Laephotis malagasyensis* (2)** ***L. matroka* (4)** ***L. robertsi* (1)** ***Otomops madagascariensis* (39)** ***Paratriaenops furculus* (14)** *Paremballonura tiavato* (6) ***Pteropus rufus* (20)** *Pipistrellus/Laephotis* sp. (8) *P. hesperidus* (11) *P. raceyi* (3) ***Rousettus madagascariensis* (49)** ***Scotophilus marovaza* (1)** ***Triaenops menamena* (42)**	Many localities	2012–2013	no	no	yes
	Dietrich et al. (2018)	***Pteropus rufus* (20)**	Ambovondramanesy	2012	no	no	yes
Carnivora	Rasambainarivo et al. (2018)	***Cryptoprocta ferox* (7)** ***Galidia elegans* (26)** ***Galidictis fasciata* (28)** ***Salanoia concolor* (3)**	Betampona	2014–2016	yes	no	no

Note: Positive individuals are shown in bold.

The high prevalence (48.9%) observed in *R. norvegicus*, which is commonly encountered in rice fields, was associated with a likely enhanced survival of *Leptospira* bacteria in such humid environments. The amplification of 16S ribosomal RNA (rRNA) on 70 positive individuals within these samples showed a unique haplotype belonging to *L. interrogans*. Further characterization of strain isolates confirmed the presence of *L. interrogans* serogroup Canicola, serovar Kuwait. This study therefore showed that rodents and shrews are reservoirs of pathogenic *Leptospira* on Madagascar, which corroborates a worldwide pattern of infection in these animals.

These results were recently complemented by a study testing 114 kidney samples from rodents and shrews trapped in the urban area of Antananarivo. The authors found a high *Leptospira* prevalence in *R. norvegicus* (45%), excreting both *L. interrogans* and *L. borgpetersenii*, which suggests this rodent species should be considered a major public health risk for leptospirosis transmission in urban settings (Rahelinirina et al. 2019b).

Another recent study by Moseley et al. (2018) further expanded the diversity of *Leptospira* strains known in rats, identifying not only *L. interrogans* and *L. borgpetersenii* but also *L. mayottensis*, a species originally identified in human patients on Mayotte in the Comoro archipelago (Bourhy et al. 2014). The Moseley et al. study specifically designed quantitative PCRs targeting individual *Leptospira* species and revealed mixed infections in tested animals, especially in *R. rattus*. Moreover, the identification of an *lfb1* genotype in *Rattus* species identical to that of the human case identified on La Réunion (Pagès et al. 2015) indicates that rodent-borne transmission of *Leptospira* might be an underreported health problem on Madagascar (Moseley et al. 2018). Their study strongly suggests that commensal introduced rodents are a source of human infection for three of the four *Leptospira* species thus far reported on Madagascar.

Native Terrestrial Small Mammals

In addition to introduced rodent and shrew populations, several endemic small mammals have been shown to shed *Leptospira* (Table 6.1; see Goodman and Soarimalala, pp. 1737–69, for information on endemic terrestrial small mammals). The first evidence for the presence of pathogenic *Leptospira* across a range of endemic small mammal species came from a PCR-based study carried out

FIGURE 6.3 ***Hemicentetes semispinosus* (Lowland Streaked Tenrec) at Befotaka–Midongy du Sud in southeastern Madagascar. This species belongs to the highly diversified Tenrecidae family, endemic to Madagascar, members of which are reservoirs of pathogenic *Leptospira*, especially *L. mayottensis*.** (PHOTO by V. Soarimalala.)

in two medium-altitude moist evergreen forests of central-eastern Madagascar (Dietrich et al. 2014) that host a considerable diversity of small mammal species (Goodman et al. 1998; Soarimalala and Goodman 2011). In this region, endemic rodents were significantly more infected than endemic tenrecids (family Tenrecidae), and one rodent species, *Eliurus minor* (subfamily Nesomyinae), appeared to be highly infected (29%) and may thus represent an important maintenance host for *Leptospira*. In this study, three pathogenic *Leptospira* species were detected: *L. kirschneri* in two spiny tenrec species (*Hemicentetes nigriceps* and *H. semispinosus*; Figure 6.3), *L. borgpetersenii* in endemic rodents (*E. minor*) and shrew tenrecs (*Microgale* spp.), and *L. mayottensis* in shrew tenrecs (*Nesogale dobsoni* and *M. cowani*). Recent work revealed that endemic small mammals, specifically the rodents *Nesomys rufus* and *E. minor*, can be coinfected with different *Leptospira* species, including *L. interrogans* and either *L. borgpetersenii* or *L. mayottensis* (Moseley et al. 2018).

Bats

Bats have been identified as important hosts of *Leptospira* bacteria worldwide (Dietrich et al. 2015a). On Madagascar, an early study tested 50 *Pteropus rufus* (family Pteropodidae) kidney samples using culture methods but did not find any positive animals (Lhuillier 1978). More recently, other studies explored the presence of *Leptospira* in multiple bat species (Lagadec et al. 2012; Dietrich et al. 2015a, 2015b, 2018; see Goodman et al., pp. 1894–911, for information on Malagasy bats). Although Lagadec et al. (2012) used a limited sample size (n = 52), they revealed for the first time the presence of *Leptospira* in several insectivorous bat species. As some of the bat species found positive in this study often occupy synanthropic day roost sites, the authors suggested that there might be a risk of transmission of bat-borne *Leptospira* on Madagascar in such a context, although this has not been demonstrated elsewhere (Dietrich et al. 2015a). A more extensive study investigating 974 individual bats across different bioclimatic regions of Madagascar (see Figure 6.4, showing bat-sampling methods) reported a global prevalence of 21.4%, with 18 of the 31 tested bat taxa infected, thus highlighting that *Leptospira* infection is widespread among Malagasy bats (Gomard et al. 2016). Phylogenetic studies based on the sequencing of multiple genes showed that these bats predominantly carry diversified lineages of *L. borgpetersenii*, but they also carry *L. kirschneri* and probably undescribed *Leptospira* species (Dietrich et al. 2014; Gomard et al. 2016).

FIGURE 6.4 **Bat-sampling methods: A) a butterfly net is used in a cave in Isalo National Park to capture individuals resting on the walls or ceiling; B) a harp trap, in which it is relatively simple to capture actively foraging insectivorous species, is placed along a night flyway in dry spiny thicket in Tsimanampesotse National Park.** (PHOTOS by E. Lagadec.)

Native Carnivorans

Only one recent study investigated *Leptospira* infection in endemic Malagasy carnivorans (Rasambainarivo et al. 2018; see also Rasambainarivo and Zohdy, pp. 298–302; and Veron et al., pp. 1863–65, for further details). Patterns of exposure were assessed through serological testing in five species of the endemic family Eupleridae inhabiting lowland moist evergreen forest of eastern Madagascar (Betampona protected area). Forty-two serum samples were tested using five *L. interrogans* serovars usually associated with domestic animals or introduced species. The study reported positive individuals for all tested carnivoran species and a global seroprevalence of 40%, with *L. interrogans* serovar Icterohaemorrhagiae leading to highest seropositivity. The authors highlight that because endemic carnivorans prey upon both introduced and endemic rodents, as well as tenrecs, it would be important to determine whether these euplerids are exposed to a more diversified assemblage of *Leptospira* than just *L. interrogans* and whether they constitute a reservoir host for these bacteria as well.

EVOLUTIONARY HISTORY OF *LEPTOSPIRA* IN WILD MALAGASY MAMMALS

Molecular studies conducted on Malagasy terrestrial and volant small mammals have demonstrated that *Leptospira* display strong host specificity, with specific bacterial lineages associated to specific hosts (at the family, genus, or species level) (Dietrich et al. 2014, 2018; Gomard et al. 2016). As a result, the *Leptospira* community at a given site is shaped by the locally occurring mammal fauna (Dietrich et al. 2018). The presence of high *Leptospira* diversity within a wide host range of Malagasy species raises questions about the evolutionary history of *Leptospira* bacteria and their hosts. The uniqueness of the detected *Leptospira* lineages, genetically distinct from those classically recovered from humans and other animals worldwide, including African small mammals, supports the hypothesis of deep isolation and diversification of Malagasy *Leptospira* lineages.

The use of multi-locus sequence analysis has largely improved our view of the evolution of *Leptospira* diversity in the Malagasy wild fauna (Gomard et al. 2016; Dietrich et al. 2018). Co-phylogenetic analyses suggest that co-speciation processes took place during the diversification of tenrecs and rodents as well as different bat colonization events on Madagascar within 20–30 million years ago (Mya) (Poux et al. 2008; Samonds et al. 2013; see Goodman et al., pp. 1894–911) and led to host-parasite interactions driving strong host specificity (Gomard et al. 2016). Hence, the diversification on Madagascar of these unique lineages probably occurred millions of years ago (Dietrich et al. 2014)—notably, before humans arrived on the island with introduced mammals.

Multi-locus sequence analysis revealed a clear differentiation of *Leptospira* from different groups of endemic terrestrial small mammals. For example, current evidence shows that *L. kirschneri* is restricted to two spiny tenrec species of the genus *Hemicentetes* (subfamily Tenrecinae; Figure 6.3) (Dietrich et al. 2014). Host specificity is also clearly obvious within *L. borgpetersenii*, which is highly diversified among Malagasy endemic small mammals. Endemic rodents of the subfamily Nesomyinae and shrew tenrecs of the subfamily Oryzorictinae both harbor lineages closely related to *L. borgpetersenii* but genetically distinct from each other. This suggests very limited *Leptospira* exchange between these two subfamilies of mammals, although they often occur in strict sympatry. Finally, *L. mayottensis* was found to be mainly associated with tenrec species, including *Tenrec ecaudatus* (subfamily Tenrecinae) (Lagadec et al. 2016), and a handful of shrew tenrecs within the subfamily Oryzorictinae, such as *Microgale cowani*, *Nesogale dobsoni* (Dietrich et al. 2014, 2018), and *M. thomasi* (P. Tortosa et al., unpublished data). Recently, *L. mayottensis* was also identified in introduced rats on Madagascar, but essentially in coinfection with other *Leptospira* species (Moseley et al. 2018), and in introduced *R. rattus* on Mayotte (Desvars et al. 2012), suggesting the capacity of *L. mayottensis* to host shifts. These observations question the role of rats (especially *R. rattus*) in the transmission of endemic small-mammal-borne strains of *Leptospira* in humans and the ability of these strains, likely host-specific, to be sheltered by introduced reservoirs such as rats.

Malagasy bats provide a relevant biological framework in which to study the evolution of *Leptospira*, as the chiropteran fauna is composed of almost 50 species, nearly all endemic but representing multiple colonization events (see Goodman et al., pp. 1894–911), as compared to nesomyine rodents and tenrecs, with only two separate monophyletic radiations. In addition, bat day roosts can be either monospecific or have several distinct species of different families, providing the means to test possible host switches. The evolution of *Leptospira* in bats seems to be relatively ancient (16 Mya) compared to its evolution in terrestrial endemic small mammals (5 Mya) (Dietrich et al. 2014), which supports strong host specificity at different taxonomic levels (Gomard et al. 2016; Dietrich et al. 2018). In a broad manner, each bat species harbors its own *Leptospira* lineage(s). Therefore, a significant positive correlation exists between bat species richness at a given site and the associated genetic diversity of *Leptospira* (Gomard et al. 2016). Interestingly, molecular studies highlight that some African and Malagasy bats, such as *Miniopterus* spp. and *Triaenops menamena*, harbor closely related *Leptospira* lineages (Dietrich et al. 2018; C. Cordonin et al., unpublished data). These findings suggest that ancestral bat populations carrying their own *Leptospira* colonized Madagascar from continental Africa.

A similar pattern has been proposed to explain the presence of three related *L. borgpetersenii* lineages in three Molossidae bat species endemic to western Indian Ocean islands: *Mormopterus jugularis*, *M. francoismoutoui*, and *M. acetabulosus*, endemic to Madagascar, La Réunion, and Mauritius, respectively (Dietrich et al. 2018). Ecological features such as colony density, foraging behavior, and migration may also play a role in *Leptospira* evolution. For instance, individuals of *M. jugularis* harbor a unique *Leptospira* haplotype across a broad area of Madagascar, irrespective of the roost site type or bioclimatic zone, a pattern probably indicative of broad dispersal and this species being panmictic on the island (Ratrimomanarivo et al. 2009).

Despite the strong pattern of host specificity, coevolutionary analyses do not always give a clear signal of co-speciation between bats and their leptospires. The absence of such a signal may be linked to the poor resolution of the genetic marker used (such as *rrs2*) or, alternatively, to some level of lateral transfer (Lei and

Olival 2014; Gomard et al. 2016). Gomard et al. (2016) suggest that a combination of duplication, co-speciation, and host switching, as well as numerous sorting events, have shaped *Leptospira* genetic diversity in Malagasy bat communities. For instance, host switches might have occurred between *Miniopterus* species and *Myotis goudoti*, which often roost together and in physical contact (Figure 6.5) (Goodman 2011). The authors hypothesize that *M. goudoti* may further serve as a bridge species for *Leptospira* transmission between non-sympatric *Miniopterus* species. According to whole-genome (Bulach et al. 2006) and field-based studies (Cosson et al. 2014), which suggest that different *Leptospira* species have evolved toward different modes of transmission, bat species roosting in high-density colonies may be, for example, infected primarily by *Leptospira* dependent on host-to-host transmission, as hypothesized for *L. borgpetersenii*.

Experimental infections have been carried out to test the ability of *Leptospira* strains detected in wild mammals of Madagascar to infect *R. norvegicus*, a renowned *Leptospira* reservoir. These rats were challenged with bat-borne *L. borgpetersenii* (obtained from *Triaenops menamena*) and tenrec-borne *L. mayottensis* (obtained from *Tenrec ecaudatus* on Mayotte) isolates. None of the bat-borne or tenrec-borne isolates were able to colonize the kidneys or induce chronic infection in *R. norvegicus*, contrary to the rat-borne *L. interrogans* isolate (Cordonin et al. 2020). Our interpretation of these data suggests that host specificity may be linked to genetic incompatibility, which may hamper adhesion to host cells. However, these experimental infections did not explore coinfections, and it would be interesting to test whether rats chronically shedding *L. interrogans* may sustain subsequent renal colonization by *L. mayottensis*.

The virulence of endemic *Leptospira* lineages was recently addressed through experimental infection of hamsters (*Mesocricetus auritus*, family Cricetidae), used as models of acute infection. Neither of the two aforementioned bat-borne or tenrec-borne *Leptospira* resulted in visible clinical sign of disease, in contrast to the rat-borne *L. interrogans*, which led to the death of most experimentally infected hamsters (Cordonin et al. 2019). These data are in keeping with the severity of human leptospirosis, which is milder on Mayotte, where *L. mayottensis* is responsible for a number of cases, as opposed to Seychelles and La Réunion, where the disease is significantly more severe and overwhelmingly associated with *L. interrogans* (Tortosa et al. 2017; Cordonin et al. 2019).

CONCLUSIONS AND PERSPECTIVES FOR FUTURE RESEARCH

From a public heath standpoint, the burden of leptospirosis on Madagascar is still largely unknown, and there is an urgent need to evaluate the proportion of leptospirosis cases within the large number of human acute cases for which the etiologic agent is unknown. A first study conducted in the Central Highlands revealed no *Leptospira* DNA among blood samples from 1009 patients presenting acute fever (Hagen et al. 2018). This type of study should be repeated in other regions of Madagascar, especially in the warmer coastal lands where environmental conditions are more suitable to *Leptospira* survival. Moreover, these studies should broaden screening approaches by including PCR detection on blood and urine samples and, whenever possible, MAT, using a panel of strains comprising isolates from Madagascar such as *L. mayottensis*. The most recent reported survey, carried out in the more mesic portions of Madagascar with intense rice farming, suggests that leptospirosis may actually represent a fourth of the human acute-case consultations at the local hospital (Raharimanga et al. 2019). These figures suggest that leptospirosis is a disease of major concern in eastern areas of the island and indicate the need for a comprehensive assessment of the burden of the disease at a national scale.

Although a number of studies carried out over the last decade on Madagascar have identified several endemic and introduced mammal species acting as reservoirs of *Leptospira*, the transmission chains involved in human leptospirosis are still unidentified. Comprehensive epidemiological investigations conducted through a "One Health" perspective (see Nunn et al., pp. 247–52) and aimed at typing *Leptospira* in human and animal samples, such as those conducted on the neighboring islands of Mayotte (Bourhy et al.

FIGURE 6.5 **One single (red-haired) *Myotis goudoti* individual in physical contact with *Miniopterus* cf. *ambohitrensis* bats in a day cave roost at Montagne d'Ambre in far northern Madagascar. These contacts are common and thought to favor host switching of microparasites and ectoparasites (Gomard et al. 2016; Ramasindrazana et al. 2018).** (PHOTO by H. Schütz.)

2010; Lagadec et al. 2016), Seychelles (Biscornet et al. 2017), and La Réunion (Guernier et al. 2016), need to be set up in order to identify on Madagascar which animal reservoirs are mostly involved in human leptospirosis. Data produced by such programs will allow researchers to measure the burden of the disease on Madagascar, disentangling the transmission chains of medical importance, and to provide the needed information for designing effective control strategies.

Data obtained since about 2010 have significantly improved our knowledge of the evolutionary history of pathogenic *Leptospira* on Madagascar. Still, leptospirosis continues to be of potential medical concern on the island, and future research should be conducted in a multifaceted manner in order to generate data that will be useful from both medical and evolutionary perspectives.

Subject editors: Pablo Tortosa and Steven M. Goodman

VIRUS TRANSMISSION IN MAMMALIAN HOSTS

A. O. G. Hoarau, S. F. Andriamandimby, L. Joffrin, C. E. Brook, H. A. Rabemananjara, C. Filippone, D. Wilkinson, J.-M. Héraud, and C. Lebarbenchon

Worldwide emerging infectious diseases are responsible for morbidity and mortality in human populations but also cause significant economic losses in the agriculture and livestock industries (Binder 1999; Morens et al. 2004). Viruses are frequently involved in the emergence of new diseases (Jones et al. 2008), as highlighted by the recent pandemic of Severe Acute Respiratory Syndrome (SARS) Coronavirus 2 (responsible for coronavirus disease 2019, or Covid-19) (Huang et al. 2020), the recurrent emergence episodes of the Middle East Respiratory Syndrome (MERS) Coronavirus (Assiri et al. 2013), and Ebola viruses in western and central Africa (Leroy et al. 2004). These examples emphasize the many challenges associated with the prevention and control of emerging viruses, in particular those that arise from wildlife (Jones et al. 2008). Risk assessment of virus spillover from wild species is a priority for health agencies; however, understanding the mechanisms underlying virus spread across species barriers and adaptation to new hosts and/or environmental conditions remains challenging (Plowright et al. 2017).

Several studies have investigated the ecology, epidemiology, and evolutionary history of viruses associated with nonhuman mammalian hosts on Madagascar. These studies, focused mostly on viral families broadly identified as responsible for spillovers in human and livestock, have provided key information on virus genetic diversity, transmission dynamics, and coevolution with their associated hosts. The investigations have been based mainly on two complementary approaches: serology and molecular detection. Serology refers to the detection of antibodies in blood and is used to assess past history of exposure to a given pathogen in an individual animal or population. Molecular detection is based on the isolation of nucleic acids in order to identify individual animals carrying viruses at the time of sampling. These two approaches have been largely applied to disease ecology and provide a global picture of the diversity of host species and viruses in animal communities, as well as detailed information on the spatial and temporal variation of virus transmission. In this contribution, we update Rousset and Andrianarivelo (2003) and summarize current knowledge of viruses associated with wild mammals on Madagascar, in particular those of the following virus families: Astroviridae, Coronaviridae, Filoviridae, Hantaviridae, Hepeviridae, Paramyxoviridae, and Rhabdoviridae. Viruses transmitted by arthropod vectors (arboviruses) are presented in the contribution following this one.

ASTROVIRIDAE

Astroviruses (AstVs) are non-enveloped, positive-sense, single-strand RNA viruses belonging to the family Astroviridae. They are classified into two genera, based on their host type: *Avastrovirus* (bird hosts) and *Mamastrovirus* (mammal hosts) (Mendez and Arias 2007). AstVs are transmitted via the fecal-oral route. These viruses are mainly asymptomatic but can sometimes cause enteric diseases. In humans, eight serotypes have been described worldwide and are responsible for 2–9% of all acute nonbacterial gastroenteritis cases in children (Bosch et al. 2014). On Madagascar, simultaneous circulation of human-associated AstV genotypes has been reported among children under 24 months of age, although at low prevalence (2%, n = 237) (Papaventsis et al. 2008).

AstVs were first described in 1975, after a gastroenteritis outbreak in children in the United Kingdom (Appleton and Higgins 1975). Since then, AstVs have been reported in many hosts, especially domestic and farmed animals (>80 species), and the number of described AstVs increases each year. In wildlife, they have been detected in a large diversity of bat species from Asia, Europe, and Africa (e.g., Fischer et al. 2016; Hoarau et al. 2018). Recent phylogenetic studies suggest that AstVs are characterized by frequent cross-species transmission (Mendenhall et al. 2015), and AstVs with potential zoonotic transmission have been reported worldwide, highlighting the need for improved knowledge on their biology (Bosch et al. 2014).

One study reported AstVs in Malagasy bats (see Goodman et al., pp. 1894–911, for a review of these animals) captured at Ambohitantely in the Central Highlands and Anjohibe near Mahajanga (Lebarbenchon et al. 2017). Based on the detection of viral

RNA, endemic and native bats of six species tested positive for AstVs, which were found, notably, in 67% of *Triaenops menamena* (family Rhinonycteridae), 58% of *Miniopterus griveaudi* (family Miniopteridae), and 36% of *Paratriaenops furculus* (family Rhinonycteridae). AstVs were also detected at lower prevalence in *Myotis goudoti* (family Vespertilionidae), *Miniopterus gleni*, and *Rousettus madagascariensis* (family Pteropodidae). Significant variation in the infection prevalence was recorded among different species and sampling locations as was a high genetic diversity and a low degree of host-virus association. Overall, results suggested that Malagasy bats act as major reservoirs for AstVs, but few details are available on the ecology or evolution of these viruses on the island.

Future studies should investigate spatial and temporal variation in AstV transmission dynamics. Limited host restriction also suggests that viruses may be transmitted easily between bat species sharing the same roosting habitats (see Figure 6.5) and also to small terrestrial mammals. Madagascar is characterized by a remarkable diversity of rodents and tenrecs (see Goodman and Soarimalala, pp. 1737–69), which may also host a high diversity of AstVs. Finally, the high propensity of AstVs for host shifts highlights the need for an assessment of zoonotic transmission risk to human populations.

CORONAVIRIDAE

Coronaviruses (CoVs) are enveloped, positive-sense, single-strand RNA viruses belonging to the family Coronaviridae. The family is divided into two subfamilies: Letovirinae and Orthocoronavirinae, and the latter is subdivided into four genera: *Alphacoronavirus* (α-CoV), *Betacoronavirus* (β-CoV), *Deltacoronavirus* (δ-CoV), and *Gammacoronavirus* (γ-CoV) (Chan et al. 2013; Drexler et al. 2014). The α-CoV and β-CoV genera are specific to mammals, transmitted through droplets containing infectious particles or by the fecal-oral route, and responsible for moderate to severe respiratory or enteric infections in many hosts, including humans (Saif 2004; Chan et al. 2013). Four human-associated CoV genotypes circulate worldwide. However, during the past decades, zoonotic CoVs have been involved in the emergence of severe outbreaks of disease in humans, such as SARS CoV in 2003, MERS CoV in 2012 (Cui et al. 2019), and SARS CoV 2 in 2019, responsible for the global Covid-19 pandemic (Huang et al. 2020). On Madagascar, many human-associated CoVs, including SARS CoV 2, have been reported to circulate in hospitalized adults and children suffering from influenza-like illness or acute respiratory infections (Razanajatovo et al. 2011, 2015, 2018; Hoffmann et al. 2012).

Studies based on molecular detection of viral RNA have reported a large diversity of α-CoVs and β-CoVs in endemic and native bat species on Madagascar (Razanajatovo et al. 2015; Joffrin et al. 2020), which show no evidence of being transferred to humans. Alphacoronaviruses have been detected in insectivorous bats, notably in *Mormopterus jugularis* (family Molossidae) from the Ihorombe Region, but also in *Triaenops menamena* from the Atsimo-Andrefana Region and the Anjohibe Cave, and in *Mops midas* (family Molossidae) from the Atsimo-Andrefana Region (Joffrin et al. 2020). Betacoronaviruses have also been detected in all three of Madagascar's endemic fruit bat species (family Pteropodidae)—*Pteropus rufus*, *Eidolon dupreanum*, and *Rousettus madagascariensis*—in the Anjohibe Cave and Menabe Region (Razanajatovo et al. 2015; Joffrin et al. 2020). All detected CoVs were new genetic variants of CoVs, and a significant difference in the prevalence was found among species. All reported α-CoVs and β-CoVs were characterized by a strong signal of coevolution with their hosts, with associations between bat families and CoVs (Joffrin et al. 2020) (Figure 6.6). The β-CoV genotypes found in *P. rufus* and *E. dupreanum* may belong to a SARS-related subgroup of β-CoVs (Razanajatovo et al. 2015). However, these investigations were based on a limited sequence of virus genome and will require full genome analyses to precisely assess the level of relatedness between CoVs found in Malagasy bats and those responsible for outbreaks in humans known elsewhere in the world.

Madagascar is home to nearly 50 bat species with 80% endemism. The strong coevolution between CoVs and bat families suggests that a large diversity of CoVs circulate on the island. The investigation of CoVs in all Malagasy bat species should provide an estimation of this CoV diversity. The identification and isolation of these CoVs could also provide opportunities for the development of specific diagnostic tools, in order to assess human population exposure to these bat-borne viruses.

FILOVIRIDAE

Filoviruses are filamentous, enveloped, nonsegmented, negative-sense RNA viruses belonging to the family Filoviridae. The family is divided into five genera: *Cuevavirus*, *Ebolavirus*, *Marburgvirus*, *Striavirus*, and *Thamnovirus*. Among these, only *Cuevavirus*, *Ebolavirus*, and *Marburgvirus* are known to infect mammals (Taylor et al. 2010). The genotypes belonging to *Ebolavirus* and *Marburgvirus* rank among the most virulent zoonotic viruses known. They are responsible for severe hemorrhagic fever in human and nonhuman primates and cause case fatality rates ranging from 50% to 90% following emergence into human hosts (Guth et al. 2019). They are highly contagious and are mainly transmitted by direct contact with body fluids. To date, no filoviruses have been identified among humans on Madagascar, though a serological survey of human communities in several localities on the island highlighted seropositivity to Ebola-related filovirus in 5% of tested individuals (n = 381) (Mathiot et al. 1989).

The first filovirus, *Marburg marburgvirus*, was described in 1967 when laboratory workers in Germany contracted the virus after handling tissues from *Cercopithecus aethiops* (African Green Monkey, family Cercopithecidae) (Taylor et al. 2010). Subsequently, the virus has been repeatedly isolated from wild populations of *Rousettus aegyptiacus*, the recognized natural reservoir host for the virus on the African continent (Towner et al. 2009). Subsequent to the isolation of the Marburg Virus, two distinct strains of Ebola viruses (*Zaire ebolavirus* and *Sudan ebolavirus*) emerged in two simultaneous outbreaks in central Africa in 1976 (CDC 2018). To date, the natural reservoir host of the *Ebolavirus* genus has yet to be described, though repeated detection of *Ebolavirus* RNA, antibodies, and viral particles in bats support the prediction that these mammals are among the natural reservoir hosts for this viral genus (Taylor et al. 2010).

Madagascar has been classed within the "zoonotic niche" for both Ebola and Marburg virus diseases, based on ecological modeling of species distribution maps for bats related to posited filovirus

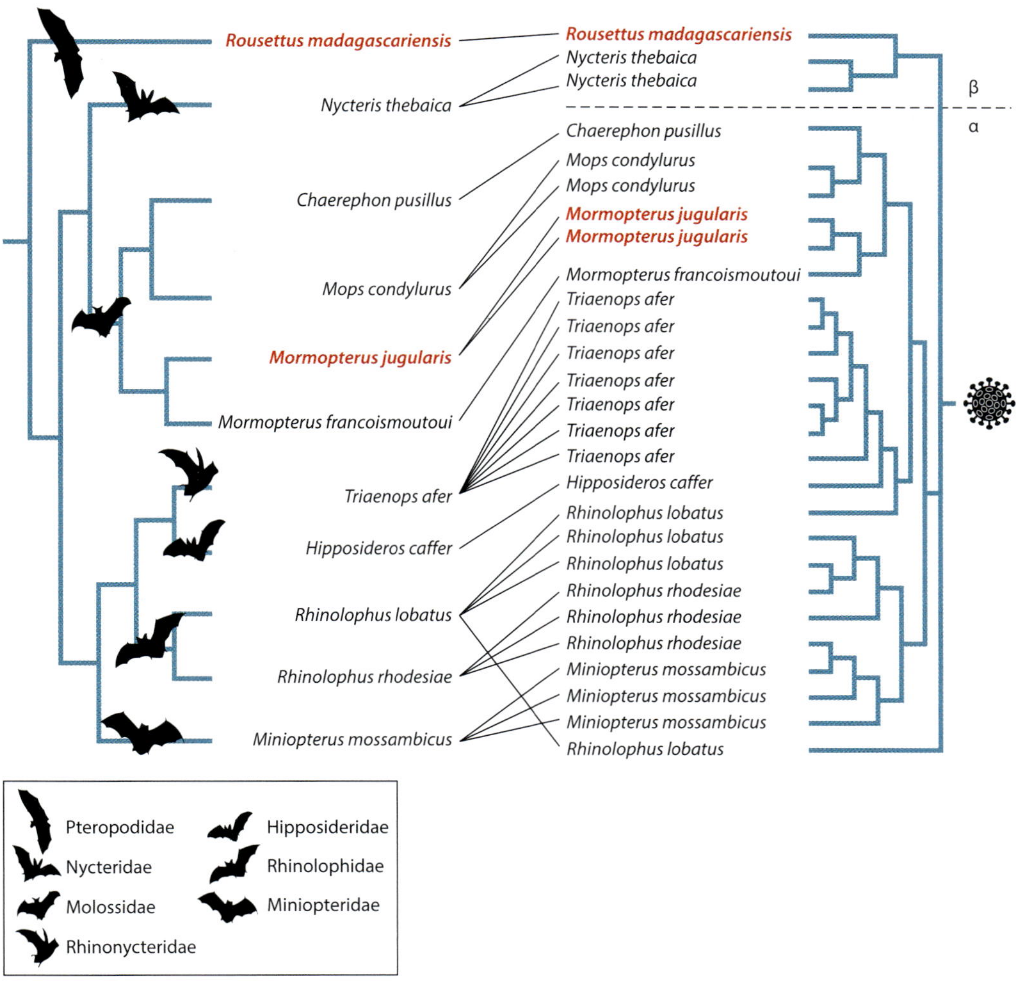

FIGURE 6.6 **Tanglegram representing host-virus coevolution between bats on islands in the western Indian Ocean and nearby portions of Africa and their associated coronaviruses (CoVs). Sequences of cytochrome b and CoVs from Malagasy species used to derive these relations are highlighted in red.** (SOURCE: modified from Joffrin et al. 2020.)

reservoirs (Pigott et al. 2014, 2015). The three endemic fruit bat species of the family Pteropodidae found on Madagascar belong to genera previously linked, via molecular or serological detection methods, to filovirus transmission elsewhere in the Old World (Towner et al. 2009; Olival et al. 2013; Olival and Hayman 2014). One study has reported antibodies against *Zaire ebolavirus* in serum from the Malagasy fruit bats *Pteropus rufus* and *Rousettus madagascariensis* but not from *Eidolon dupreanum* (Brook et al. 2019). The study also highlighted seasonal variation of seroprevalence at the individual and population levels, especially pronounced among female *P. rufus*, which increased during the gestation period and decreased postpartum and through the periods of lactation and weaning. An age-structured subset of data also suggested waning maternal immunity in neonates.

Despite serological evidence of circulation of filovirus-related strains, no Madagascar-derived filovirus genotypes have yet been reported from live virus or RNA sequencing. Moreover *Ebolavirus*-specific antibodies are notoriously cross-reactive against antigens within the genus (MacNeil et al. 2011); thus, serological data might indicate circulation of any number of known or previously undescribed forms of *Ebolavirus* in Madagascar's fruit bats. Estimates of divergence time for Madagascar fruit bats (Goodman et al. 2010; Almeida et al. 2014; Shi et al. 2014) pre-date the posited 10,000-year ancestry of Filoviridae, emphasizing the critical need for characterization of these viral genotypes to elucidate their evolutionary history as well as zoonotic potential.

HANTAVIRIDAE

Hantaviruses are enveloped, negative-sense, single-strand RNA viruses belonging to the family Hantaviridae. The family is divided into four subfamilies: Actantavirinae, Agantavirinae, Mammantavirinae, and Repantavirinae. The subfamily Mammantavirinae is specific to mammals and comprises four genera: *Loanvirus*, *Mobatvirus*, *Orthohantavirus*, and *Thottimvirus* (International Committee on Taxonomy of Viruses 2020). Hantaviruses are maintained and transmitted within host reservoirs (mainly rodents) by horizontal transmission, specifically through bites and scratches. Humans can be accidentally infected by these viruses through inhalation of contaminated fresh urine, droppings, or saliva, or more rarely through direct contact with infected small mammals. Depending on the virus species and genotype, as well as human host condition, infection can be asymptomatic, or it can cause hemorrhagic fever with renal syndrome (HFRS) or milder forms such as nephropathia epidemica (NE) or hantavirus cardiopulmonary syndrome (HCPS) (Jonsson et al. 2010; Watson et al. 2014). Every year, thousands of persons worldwide are infected by hantaviruses (Watson et al. 2014).

On Madagascar, one study, based on the detection of immunoglobulin G (IgG) antibodies, suggested that less than 3% of the general Malagasy population (n = 1680 individuals tested with random sampling) was exposed to hantaviruses associated with rodents of the introduced family Muridae (Papa et al. 2016; Institut Pasteur de Madagascar 2019; Rabemananjara et al. 2020). Interestingly, persons living near forests in the general Moramanga area were highly exposed (Rabemananjara et al. 2020; see also Institut Pasteur de Madagascar 2019), with 7% of them (n = 139) testing serologically positive to the Malagasy Anjozorobe Virus, a genetic variant of Thailand Orthohantavirus (Reynes et al. 2014), which is potentially associated with HFRS in Southeast Asia (Pattamadilok et al. 2006). However, no active cases of HFRS associated with viral infection in humans have been yet reported on Madagascar.

In mammals, both serological evidence and molecular detection have suggested that individuals of the introduced species *Rattus rattus* (family Muridae) are a major reservoir for hantaviruses on Madagascar. Indeed, in a study conducted at four different localities on the island, 24% of sampled rats tested positive for antibodies directed against Hantaan Virus, and 16% were positive for antibodies directed against Puumula Virus (Rollin et al. 1986). More recent studies focusing on *R. rattus* reported that 12% of animals captured in the Anjozorobe-Angavo forest, 30% of animals from rural sites close to natural forests areas in Moramanga, and 40% of animals sampled in 17 districts across the island are positive for hantavirus RNA and particularly Anjozorobe Virus; variation among sampling locations is probably related to climate and changing contact rates (Reynes et al. 2014; Raharinosy et al. 2018; Rabemananjara et al. 2020). Hantavirus antibodies have also been detected to a lesser extent in another introduced rodent, *R. norvegicus* (Rollin et al. 1986), with 20% of individuals testing positive in tests using antibodies directed against Hantaan Virus, and 8% in those using antibodies directed against Puumula Virus. In addition, Anjozorobe Virus RNA has been detected in one individual of the endemic rodent *Eliurus majori* (family Nesomyidae) (n = 15) and in two introduced *Mus musculus* (family Muridae) (n = 125) (Reynes et al. 2014; Raharinosy et al. 2018), indicating that hantaviruses may circulate in other rodents on Madagascar. Finally, antibodies directed against Hantaan Virus have been detected in one *Lemur catta* (Ring-tailed Lemur, family Lemuridae) from the area of Amboasary-Atsimo (among 218 sera collected in different areas) (Fontenille et al. 1988a).

Although these findings indicate that the main reservoir for hantaviruses in Madagascar may be introduced *R. rattus*, few data are available on the ecology and epidemiology of hantaviruses in this host. The limited presence of hantavirus RNA in other rodent species could indicate spillovers, highlighting the need for further investigations among rodent species. Finally, *R. rattus* is widespread across the island and often in contact with humans. Even though no severe or milder human cases of hantavirus infection have been reported so far, further studies need to provide more details on the genomic characterization of hantaviruses in *R. rattus*, as well as a risk assessment in human populations, such as investigations targeting the Malagasy hantavirus genetic variant.

HEPEVIRIDAE (HEPATITIS E VIRUS)

Hepatitis E Virus (HEV) is a non-enveloped, positive-sense single-strand RNA virus belonging to the family Hepeviridae. The family is divided into two genera: *Orthohepevirus*, infecting mammals and birds (Purdy and Khudyakov 2011), and *Piscihepevirus*, described in fish (Smith et al. 2014). The genus *Orthohepevirus* is divided into four species, *Orthohepevirus A* to *Orthohepevirus D* (Purdy and Khudyakov 2011), with distinct host specificity. *Orthohepevirus A*, or Hepatitis E Virus, which is known to be zoonotic (Primadharsini et al. 2019), comprises eight genotypes (HEV1 to HEV8), each one affecting particular species (Delarocque-Astagneau et al. 2012; Khuroo et al. 2016; Lee et al. 2016). Worldwide, HEV is the main etiologic agent of enterically transmitted viral hepatitis in humans (World Health Organization 2010). Generally, the infection is self-limiting, but in immunocompromised patients it can result in chronic hepatitis (Abravanel et al. 2014). HEV can also result in death, for example, in pregnant women, patients with underlying liver disease, and elderly people (Lhomme et al. 2016; Mancinelli et al. 2017).

HEV1 and HEV2 are restricted to humans, in particular in areas with poor sanitation, and transmitted via the fecal-oral route, usually through contaminated water, leading to the onset of large recurrent outbreaks (World Health Organization 2010). No outbreaks have been reported on Madagascar; however, antibodies against HEV have been reported in 14% of slaughterhouse workers in 12 of the 18 tested districts (Temmam et al. 2013). The seroprevalence ranged between 5% in the Bealanana District of the Sofia Region and 31% in the Fianarantsoa District of the Haute Matsiatra Region.

Swine have also been examined on Madagascar for previous HEV infection. Hundreds of swine sampled in slaughterhouses from 18 districts were tested for the presence of HEV antibodies (Temmam et al. 2013). Seropositive swine were detected in all 18 districts, and with overall high seroprevalence. Indeed, 71% of tested animals were positive for antibodies, but PCR screening yielded only three positive individuals (n = 250), two originating from Fianarantsoa and Miarinarivo, in the Central Highlands, and one from the Port-Bergé (Boriziny) District, in the northwest. The genotyping of the viruses revealed circulation of HEV3, previously identified in humans, swine, and other mammals; however, the origin of this virus, as well as its maintenance host in wild mammals on Madagascar, requires further investigation.

PARAMYXOVIRIDAE

Paramyxoviruses (PMVs) belong to the large family Paramyxoviridae (Amarasinghe et al. 2019), divided into four subfamilies: Avulavirinae, Metaparamyxovirinae, Orthoparamyxovirinae, and Rubulavirinae. Only Orthoparamyxovirinae and Rubulavirinae are known to infect mammals. PMVs are enveloped, negative-sense, single-strand RNA viruses. They are transmitted via several routes—fecal-oral, aerosol, or contact with urine—and are responsible for a diverse range of symptoms, including respiratory syndromes, neurological syndromes, and digestive symptoms. Among PMVs, zoonotic members of the Orthoparamyxovirinae are responsible for diseases of public health concern around the world. As an example, variants of *Henipavirus*, a genus of bat-borne viruses, are responsible for fatal encephalitis in humans, pigs, and horses (Kessler et al. 2018). The genus *Pararubulavirus*, of the Rubulavirinae, has been a significant public health burden, causing respiratory, reproductive, and central nervous system disorders in humans and other mammals.

PMVs have a global distribution and infect a broad range of hosts. Many members of the family are characterized by high virulence, particularly members of the Orthoparamyxovirinae, and are considered potential zoonotic pathogens that, in the future, may represent a threat to human health (Thibault et al. 2017). Responding largely to this concern, researchers have initiated a number of investigations of wild and domestic animals using molecular and serological approaches, improving our understanding of the distribution and host associations of PMVs across Madagascar and elsewhere.

Many common PMVs of medical importance are of significant public health concern on Madagascar. For example, over 175,000 cases on Madagascar of Measles Mobillivirus infection were reported during large measles outbreaks in 2003, 2004, and 2018 (Makoni 2019). Influenza-like illness is caused by Human Respirovirus 1 and Human Respirovirus 3, which are particularly common in children (Gideon Informatics 2019). Outside Madagascar, animal-associated PMVs are responsible for significant losses in domestic animals and meat production. For instance, Rinderpest Morbillivirus was responsible for high mortality of large ruminants until the 1990s, while Small Ruminant Morbillivirus still causes significant mortality in sheep and goat farms across large areas of continental Africa. However, Rinderpest Morbillivirus and Small Ruminant Morbillivirus have not been reported on Madagascar.

Canine Morbillivirus (previously known as Canine Distemper Virus), responsible for significant morbidity and mortality in many members of the Carnivora, has been reported on Madagascar (see Rasambainarivo and Zohdy, pp. 298–302). One study identified high prevalence of Canine Morbillivirus infections (45%, n = 60) in domestic dogs (*Canis lupus*, family Canidae) of Madagascar (Pomerantz et al. 2016). The study also examined the potential impact of the spread of Canine Morbillivirus between dogs and the endemic carnivoran *Cryptoprocta ferox* (Fosa, family Eupleridae; see Gerber and Hawkins, pp. 1978–83, for information on this animal). Very low antibody titers and minimal seroprevalence to Canine Morbillivirus in *Cryptoprocta* suggested either that these animals are not exposed to the virus or that the survival rate of exposed animals is low.

The reports of seropositivity against *Henipavirus* (subfamily Orthoparamyxovirinae) in Malagasy fruit bats (family Pteropodidae) are of notable concern given the zoonotic potential of the PMVs of this genus. Indeed, serological evidence of the circulation of several *Henipavirus* variants has been documented for all three endemic fruit bats across several areas of Madagascar (Iehlé et al. 2007; Brook et al. 2019). Antibodies against Hendra Virus were found in 15% of *Eidolon dupreanum*, 6% of *Pteropus rufus*, and 8% of *Rousettus madagascariensis* tested. Antibodies against Nipah Virus were also detected in 2% of *P. rufus* and in 19–24% of *E. dupreanum*, depending on the detection method used. Antibodies against Cedar Virus were reported in less than 1% of *E. dupreanum* and in 8% of *R. madagascariensis*. Finally, antibodies against Rubulavirus Tioman were identified in less than 1% of *P. rufus* and 20% of *R. madagascariensis*. Seasonal variation in seroprevalence has been described at individual and population levels, especially for Nipah Virus in female *P. rufus* and *E. dupreanum*, with an increase in seroprevalence across the gestation period. Notably, a biannual seroprevalence peak, at the height of the wet season and the end of gestation, has been observed for a subset of specimens of the same species (Brook et al. 2019).

Nonspecific molecular detection techniques have identified a large diversity of PMVs in endemic and introduced Malagasy mammals, including species of bats, tenrecs (family Tenrecidae), and rodents (families Nesomyidae and Muridae) (Figure 6.7). Globally, virus-host specificity was detected at the host order level (bats, tenrecs, and rodents). In bat samples collected across a broad coverage of Madagascar, overall prevalence in tested individualsranged from 11% to 29% depending on studies, with a significant variation among areas (Wilkinson et al. 2012, 2014a; Mélade et al. 2016a). Significant variation in prevalence was also observed among species, and circulation seemed to be more active in insectivorous bats at 11%, compared to 4% in frugivorous species (Mélade et al. 2016a). Four bat species were particularly infected by PMVs. Indeed, 20–63% of *Triaenops menamena*, 16–19% of *Mops*

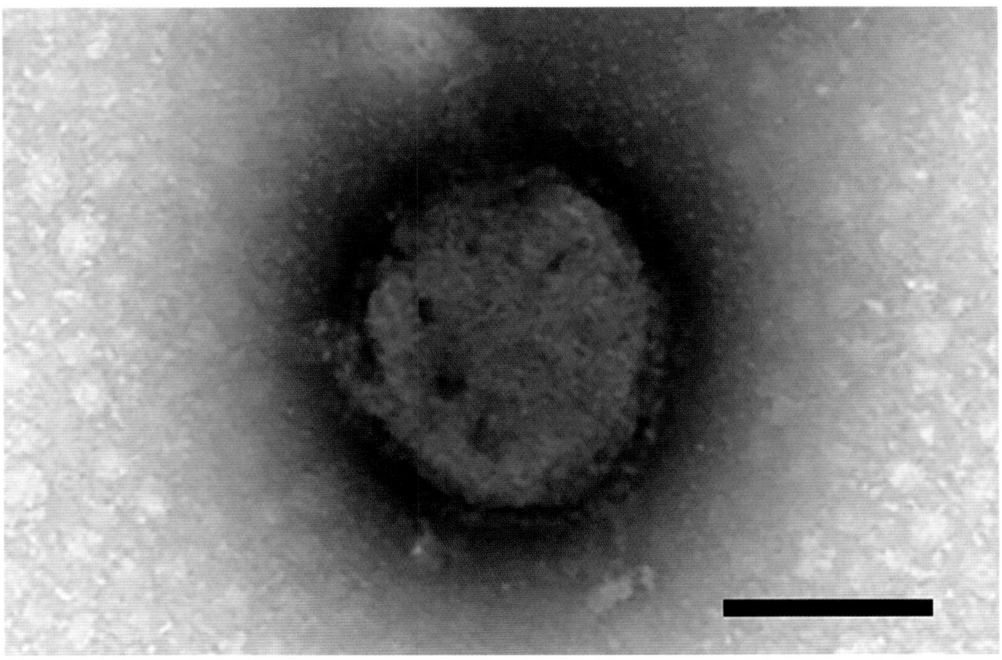

FIGURE 6.7 **Image of a paramyxovirus belonging to the same lineage as those found in mammals of Madagascar. (Electron microscopy; scale bar is 100 nm.)** (SOURCE: modified from Wilkinson et al. 2012.)

TABLE 6.2. **Viruses detected in Malagasy mammals (excluding arboviruses)**

VIRAL FAMILY	VIRUS	HOST SPECIES	METHODOLOGY	REFERENCES
Astroviridae	Astrovirus	*Miniopterus gleni*, *M. griveaudi*, *Myotis goudoti*, *Paratriaenops furculus*, *Rousettus madagascariensis*, *Triaenops menamena*	Molecular detection of pooled rectal and buccal swabs	Lebarbenchon et al. (2017)
Coronaviridae	Alphacoronavirus	*Mops midas*, *Mormopterus jugularis*, *Triaenops menamena*	Molecular detection of intestine and swabs	Joffrin et al. (2020)
	Betacoronavirus	*Eidolon dupreanum*, *Pteropus rufus*	Molecular detection of rectal swabs	Razanajatovo et al. (2015)
		Rousettus madagascariensis	Molecular detection of pooled rectal and buccal swabs	Joffrin et al. (2020)
Filoviridae	Zaire Ebola Virus	*Pteropus rufus*, *Rousettus madagascariensis*	Serology	Brook et al. (2019)
Hantaviridae	Anjozorobe Virus	*Eliurus majori*, *Mus musculus*, *Rattus rattus*	Molecular detection of liver and spleen	Reynes et al. (2014); Raharinosy et al. (2018); Rabemananjara et al. (2020)
	Hantaan Virus	*Lemur catta*, *Rattus norvegicus*, *R. rattus*	Serology	Rollin et al. (1986); Fontenille et al. (1988a)
	Puumula Virus	*Rattus norvegicus*, *R. rattus*		Rollin et al. (1986)
Hepeviridae	Hepatitis E Virus	*Sus scrofa domesticus*	Serology	Temmam et al. (2013)
			Molecular detection of liver	
Paramyxoviridae	Canine Morbillivirus	*Cryptoprocta ferox*	Serology	Pomerantz et al. (2016)
	Cedar Virus	*Eidolon dupreanum*, *Rousettus madagascariensis*		Iehlé et al. (2007); Brook et al. (2019)
	Hendra Virus	*Eidolon dupreanum*, *Pteropus rufus*, *Rousettus madagascariensis*		
	Nipah Virus	*Eidolon dupreanum*, *Pteropus rufus*		
	Rubulavirus Tioman	*Pteropus rufus*, *Rousettus madagascariensis*		
	Similarities with Beilong Virus and Tailam Virus	*Chaerephon leucogaster*, *Coleura kibomalandy*, *Miniopterus* cf. *ambohitrensis*, *M. gleni*, *M. griveaudi*, *M. mahafaliensis*, *M. sororculus*, *Mops leucostigma*, *M. midas*, *Mormopterus jugularis*, *Myotis goudoti*, *Otomops madagascariensis*, *Paratriaenops furculus*,	Molecular detection on pooled lung, kidney, and spleen	Wilkinson et al. (2012, 2014a); Mélade et al. (2016a)

VIRAL FAMILY	VIRUS	HOST SPECIES	METHODOLOGY	REFERENCES
		Pipistrellus hesperidus, Pteropus rufus, Triaenops menamena Microgale cowani, M. jobihely, M. gymnorhyncha, M. longicaudata, M. majori, M. principula, M. taiva, Nesogale dobsoni Eliurus minor, E. tanala, Rattus rattus		
Rhabdoviridae	Rabies Virus	*Canis lupus, Felis silvestris, Sus scrofa*	Molecular detection of brain, head, or corpse	Reynes et al. (2011); Andriamandimby et al. (2013)
	European Bat 1 Lyssavirus	*Macronycteris commersoni, Pteropus rufus*	Serology	Reynes et al. (2011)
	Duvenhage Lyssavirus	*Chaerephon leucogaster, Macronycteris commersoni, Miniopterus* cf. *ambohitrensis, M. griveaudi, Mormopterus jugularis, Otomops madagascariensis, Pteropus rufus, Rousettus madagascariensis*		Mélade et al. (2016b)
	Lagos Bat Virus	*Miniopterus griveaudi, Mops leucostigma, Mormopterus jugularis, Myotis goudoti, Otomops madagascariensis, Rousettus madagascariensis, Triaenops menamena*		Mélade et al. (2016b)

leucostigma, 15–24% of *Miniopterus griveaudi*, and 14–18% of *M. gleni*, tested positive. Twelve other bat species also tested positive for PMV RNA, but with lower prevalence (Table 6.2). Statistical modeling demonstrated that environments supporting multiple species were positively associated with viral transmission, with a marginal correlation to different natural habitats where the samples were collected (Mélade et al. 2016a).

In tests of terrestrial small mammals, the overall prevalence of PMVs was 25%. Eight species of the endemic genus *Microgale* (family Tenrecidae, subfamily Oryzorictinae), tested positive in the Lakato and Ankazomivady forests in or at the edge of the Central Highlands, with an overall prevalence of 40% (Wilkinson et al. 2014a; see Table 6.2). Finally, in rodents, PMVs have been reported in endemic and introduced species. Notably, viral RNA has been detected in 30% of introduced *Rattus rattus*, in 11% of the endemic *Eliurus minor*, and in a smaller percentage of *E. tanala*.

Phylogenetic analyses reported that PMVs detected in Malagasy mammals belonged to species of *Jeilongvirus* (subfamily Orthoparamyxovirinae) with strong genetic similarity to Beilong Virus and Tailam Virus, both of which were isolated and characterized in Asia along with other unclassified PMVs (Wilkinson et al. 2014a). Ancestral-state reconstructions of all PMVs detected in Malagasy mammals also revealed host-switching events (Figure 6.8), particularly among closely related species and among species of the same order. *Rattus rattus* is one of the species suspected to be most involved in viral transmission and dispersal, as phylogenetic reconstructions suggest host switches involving distinct animal orders—for example, from *R. rattus* (Rodentia) to *Microgale* (Afrosoricida), or between *R. rattus* and a range of different bat families (Chiroptera) (Wilkinson et al. 2014a)

Although serological and molecular screenings have highlighted a high diversity of PMVs circulating in mammals at the scale of the island, no information is thus far available regarding the risk posed to animal or human health. As *Henipavirus*-related antibodies have been detected in Malagasy fruit bats, and since PMVs belonging to *Jeilongvirus* seem to be subject to exchanges among species of different orders (Figure 6.8), it is crucial to reinforce research to broaden the identification of PMVs circulating on Madagascar and disentangle transmission processes.

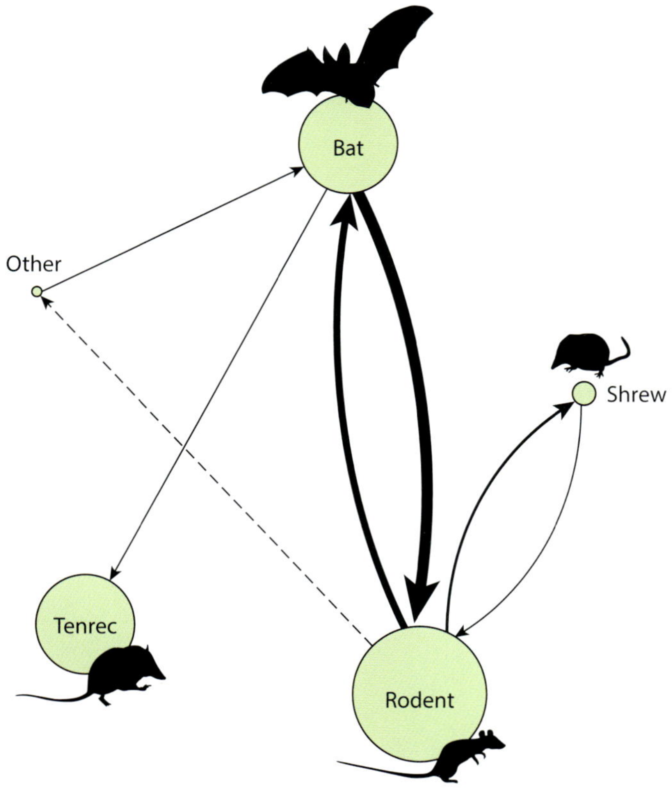

FIGURE 6.8 **Network diagram representing paramyxovirus host-switching events among different mammal categories. Alignment was performed on 495 paramyxovirus L gene sequences from different countries, and phylogenetic analysis was conducted in BEAST2 with an HKY substitution model and strict evolutionary clock over 10^8 iterations, and then 1000 trees were sampled from the posterior distribution. The number of estimated host-switching events was calculated using a parsimony model of reconstructed ancestral states averaged over all trees when specifying host as a categorical tip-associated variable using Mesquite (3.61). The resulting host-switching matrix was used to generate the above directed network graph representation using the igraph R package. Circle sizes denote node centrality, and arrow thickness denotes the relative number of host-switching events between mammal categories.**

RHABDOVIRIDAE

Lyssavirus represents one of 20 genera within the family Rhabdoviridae (Afonso et al. 2016). Lyssaviruses (including Rabies Lyssavirus, also known as Rabies Virus, or RABV) are enveloped, negative-sense, single-strand RNA viruses, responsible for rabies or rabies-like diseases, including fatal encephalitic diseases, in both humans and animals. Lyssaviruses and especially RABV are transmitted by saliva of infected animals via bites or scratches or through contact of infected saliva with damaged skin. Dogs are acknowledged to be the main reservoir of RABV and the source for more than 99% of human and other mammal rabies cases worldwide (Knobel et al. 2005). Other lyssaviruses can be transmitted by wild canids (e.g., foxes, coyotes, wolves), other Carnivora groups (e.g., raccoons, skunks, mongoose), and by bats, which are hosts for most lyssaviruses (Kuzmin et al. 2003; Kuzmin and Rupprecht 2007; Banyard et al. 2011; Rupprecht et al. 2017).

On Madagascar, RABV is endemic (i.e., the virus is maintained on the island); the first reported death occurred in 1896 (Brygoo and Sureau 1960; Morvan et al. 1993; Andriamandimby et al. 2013). RABV is prevalent in several areas of the island, and dogs are the main host reservoir (Reynes et al. 2011; Andriamandimby et al. 2013). To date, genetic sequences of RABV on Madagascar have been recovered from dogs, cats, swine, cattle, and humans. Phylogenetic analyses using these sequences suggest that RABV circulating on the island likely originated from an introduction during the 19th century, corresponding to a period of European colonization, as has been observed in other former French colonies in Africa (Talbi et al. 2009, 2010; Gauzère and Aubry 2013). Endemic circulation of RABV on Madagascar reflects patterns of human movement, as has been previously observed in North Africa, where genotypes track major roads (Talbi et al. 2010). Antananarivo plays a pivotal role in rabies transmission on the island, and geographic-sequence clusters have been identified in the north, in the southwest, and along the west coast (Andriamandimby et al. 2013).

All other lyssaviruses are associated with bats, and many such viruses circulate in virtually all portions of Madagascar. European Bat 1 Lyssavirus antibodies have been detected in 25% of *Macronycteris commersoni* (formerly *Hipposideros commersoni*, family Hipposideridae) (Mélade et al. 2016b) and in a small percentage of *Pteropus rufus* (Reynes et al. 2011). Duvenhage Lyssavirus antibodies have been reported in 17% of *M. commersoni*, 27% of *Miniopterus* cf. *ambohitrensis*, 35% of *M. griveaudi*, 32% of *Chaerephon leucogaster*, 29% of *Mormopterus jugularis*, 22% of *Otomops madagascariensis*, 45% of *P. rufus*, and 12% of *Rousettus madagascariensis* (Mélade et al. 2016b). Lagos Bat Virus antibodies have been detected in 15% of *O. madagascariensis*, 18% of *Triaenops menamena*, 20% of *R. madagascariensis*, 36% of *Myotis goudoti*, and to a smaller percentage in an additional three bat species (Mélade et al. 2016b; see Table 6.2). For these different viruses, seroprevalence was marked by significant differences related to bat species, roost sites, and bioclimatic regions.

RABV remains the most studied and documented lyssavirus on Madagascar. The detection of antibodies against bat lyssaviruses suggests a local maintenance in bats. Serological data nevertheless provide limited information on the genetic diversity of these viruses, and further work using complimentary approaches is needed to identify the evolutionary origin of these viruses as well as their natural biological cycle. Other hosts, including native Eupleridae carnivorans, have not been tested for the presence of RABV and lyssaviruses, but they may be present, especially after the occurrence of one human case involving possible transmission from a *Cryptoprocta ferox* (see Rasambainarivo and Zohdy, pp. 298–302).

CONCLUSION

In the 2003 book *The Natural History of Madagascar*, limited information was available regarding virus circulation among mammals on the island (Rousset and Andrianarivelo 2003). Nearly two decades later, our knowledge has improved considerably. The presence of major zoonotic viral families and the diversity of hosts and viruses have been assessed. However, most studies still remain descriptive and suffer from technical limitations. Serological tests can be affected by cross-reactivity—the reaction of one viral antigen with antibodies developed against another viral antigen—and this therefore limits the accuracy of viral identification and interpretations regarding transmission processes. Similarly, molecular detection is based on a limited portion of the whole genome, restricting conclusions on the relatedness and evolutionary history of the detected viruses. New approaches integrating whole-genome sequencing will facilitate more complete characterization of viruses and other pathogens, while longitudinal surveillance will be needed to elucidate the dynamics of their transmission. Resulting data will complement existing knowledge of microbe diversity but also inform understanding of microbial evolution and physiopathology.

The key role of intermediate hosts in regular contact with people—specifically, synanthropic species (some bats and introduced rodents and shrews), domestic animals, and livestock—should also be considered in future studies. Indeed, in some cases, intermediate hosts play a crucial role in viral emergence, acting as stepping-stones between wild reservoirs and human populations (as has occurred with SARS CoV, MERS CoV, Nipah Virus, Hendra Virus). For example, on Madagascar, introduced rodents could be involved in PMV exchanges and act as bridge species among mammals belonging to different orders. Further epidemiological surveillance carried out through a "One Health" approach (see Nunn et al., pp. 247–52) should investigate the links that may exist not only between different wild species but also between wild animals, livestock, and human populations.

During the past decades, Madagascar has faced major environmental changes related to human activities, from exploitation of natural resources to the introduction of alien species. Notably, between 1953 and 2014, Madagascar lost about 44% of its natural forest cover, and today the remaining forests are to a large extent fragmented (Vieilledent et al. 2018). Studies (albeit out of date) have shown that about 90% of Malagasy species rely on natural ecosystems and forests (Goodman and Benstead 2005; Allnutt et al. 2008). Infectious disease emergence is highly related to environmental changes, including forest fragmentation, that alter the ecology of both hosts and their associated infectious agents (Morse 1995). Several putative viruses of global health concern are maintained in Malagasy wild mammals (e.g., coronaviruses, filoviruses), some of which, in other portions of the world, have shown capacity to emerge in human populations after major environmental changes (e.g., *Henipavirus*). It is therefore critical to consider the effects of environmental changes on Madagascar not only in terms of biodiversity loss and impact on ecosystem function but also as a major and global health challenge for animal and human populations.

Subject editors: Pablo Tortosa and Steven M. Goodman

ARTHROPOD-BORNE VIRUSES OF MADAGASCAR

J.-M. Héraud, S. F. Andriamandimby, M.-M. Olive, H. Guis, V. Miatrana Rasamoelina, and L. Tantely

Arthropod-borne viruses (arboviruses) do not compose a formal virological taxonomic group but include those viruses that can be transmitted to vertebrates, including humans, by arthropod vectors such as mosquitoes and ticks. According the International Committee on Taxonomy of Viruses (ICTV), 492 viruses are currently acknowledged as recognized, probable, or possible arboviruses. They belong to nine viral families and 25 genera (Vasilakis and Gubler 2016). With the implementation of new molecular technology, allowing high-throughput metagenomic sequencing, the number of arboviruses is subject to regular updates and increases. To date, 135 arboviruses are known to infect humans worldwide, causing a significant burden in terms of morbidity and mortality. Arboviruses that represent an important threat for public health in general include Flaviviridae, Peribunyaviridae, and Togaviridae (Gubler 2002). Many arboviral infections are asymptomatic and/or benign, but in some cases, they can be severe and deadly, causing hemorrhagic fevers (e.g., dengue and Rift Valley) or invasive neurological diseases (e.g., Japanese encephalitis, West Nile, and Zika). As of early 2020, only three approved human vaccines were available, targeting Yellow Fever Virus, Japanese Encephalitis Virus, and Tick-borne Encephalitis Virus. The worldwide increasing incidence of arboviruses is stimulating the development of vaccines against other arboviruses of public health importance (e.g., Dengue Virus, Zika Virus, West Nile Virus, Chikungunya Virus, Rift Valley Fever Virus).

To be maintained in nature, most arboviruses display an enzootic cycle involving at least a vertebrate host and an arthropod vector. Spillover to humans or domestic animals can occur when these arboviruses enter the natural zoonotic cycle—that is, the typical arthropod vector obtains a blood meal from a nontypical host. For some arboviruses, such as Dengue Virus and Chikungunya Virus, vectors have adapted to a human environment, and transmission cycles involve only mosquito vectors and human hosts. Since arboviruses are strongly linked to their vectors, their global distribution somewhat mirrors the distribution of their vectors.

Environmental disturbances of anthropogenic origin (urbanization, travel, deforestation, agricultural practices, and global warming) will likely expand the distribution of vectors and arboviruses in the coming years, leading to the emergence and reemergence of arboviral diseases at a global level. Madagascar is an interesting setting in which to investigate the epidemiology and evolutionary histories of arboviral transmission cycles. Indeed, Madagascar is home to a considerable diversity of mosquito vectors (Tantely et al. 2016a),

TABLE 6.3. **Overview of published studies conducted on Madagascar investigating the presence of arboviruses in humans and domestic and wild animals**

FAMILY	GENUS	SPECIES	ABBREVIATION	HOST	VECTORS (WITH EVIDENCE OF VIRAL DETECTION)	TISSUE	METHODOLOGY	REFERENCES
Phenuiviridae	*Phlebovirus*	Rift Valley Fever Virus	RVFV	Humans, ruminants	Mosquitoes: *Anopheles* spp., *Mansonia* spp., *Coquillettidia* spp.	Mosquitoes	–	Clerc et al. (1981)
Nairoviridae	*Orthonairovirus*	Crimean-Congo Hemorrhagic Fever Virus	CCHFV	Zebu	Tick: *Boophilus* (now *Rhipicephalus*) *microplus*	Ticks	–	Mathiot et al. (1988)
Togaviridae	*Alphavirus*	Chikungunya Virus	CHIKV	Humans	Mosquito: *Aedes albopictus*	–	Molecular and serological	Schuffenecker et al. (2006); Ratsitorahina et al. (2008)
Flaviviridae	*Flavivirus*	Dengue Virus	DENV-1	Humans	Mosquitoes: *Aedes aegypti*, *A. albopictus*	Blood	–	Fontenille et al. (1988c)
		West Nile Virus	WNV	Parrots: *Coracopsis*	Unknown	–	–	Mathiot et al. (1984)
		Wesselsbron Virus	WSLV	Bats: *Chaerephon atsinanana*	Unknown	–	–	Cassel-Beraud et al. (1989)
		Dakar Bat Virus	DBV	Bats: *Chaerephon atsinanana*	Unknown	–	Isolation	Cassel-Beraud et al. (1989); Reynes et al. (2011)

both endemic species and species introduced to the island (see Robert et al., pp. 1089–98), which may allow the establishment of original transmission chains involving endemic mosquito species as primary or bridge vectors. Moreover, Madagascar's insularity facilitates the investigation of introduction and spread mechanisms, as exemplified by studies disentangling the epidemiology of Rift Valley fever outbreaks that occurred between the 1980s and 2020s.

We present in this contribution the current knowledge and most salient results reported in the past decades for four arboviral families documented on Madagascar: Phenuiviridae, Flaviviridae, Nairoviridae, and Togaviridae. Major publications along with relevant information regarding the identification or isolation of arboviruses on Madagascar are listed in Table 6.3.

PHENUIVIRIDAE

Introduction to Rift Valley Fever Virus (RVFV)

Rift Valley Fever Virus (RVFV) is an enveloped negative-sense, single-strand, segmented RNA virus. It belongs to order Buniavirales, family Phenuiviridae, genus *Phlebovirus*. RVFV is a mosquito-borne zoonotic virus affecting mainly domestic ruminants and humans in continental Africa and the Arabian Peninsula as well as islands of the southwestern Indian Ocean. During outbreaks, infections cause abortions in ruminants and high mortality among newborn animals. In humans, the infection can be asymptomatic or severe, in the latter case with hemorrhages that can lead to death. The virus is transmitted between ruminants mainly through vector-borne transmission, and humans are mostly infected directly via aerosols when handling infected animal tissues. The role of wildlife in the epidemiology of RVFV is still unknown.

The History of RVFV Circulation on Madagascar

This virus was initially identified on Madagascar in 1979 from several mosquito species, belonging to the genera *Anopheles*, *Mansonia*, and *Coquillettidia*, captured in the Périnet (Andasibe) Forest (Clerc et al. 1981). Despite the presence of this virus in these potential mosquito vectors, no associated epidemic was observed among livestock or humans in this district or elsewhere on the island. The RVFV strain isolated in 1979 was closely related to strains responsible for massive outbreaks in Egypt in 1977–1978 (Carroll et al. 2011).

Eleven years later, in 1990–1991, Madagascar experienced Rift Valley fever (RVF) outbreaks in the eastern lowlands and Central Highlands. First, an epizootic outbreak among bovine livestock occurred near Fenarivo-Atsinanana in March 1990 (Morvan et al. 1991). Then, a second epizootic occurred in the Central Highlands at the beginning of 1991 (Morvan et al. 1992a). These epizootics resulted in human deaths (Morvan et al. 1992b). After the 1990–1991 outbreaks, serological evidence of infection was found among staff in the principal slaughterhouse of Antananarivo. An extensive epidemiological investigation in sheep and goat populations from 1996 to 1998 supported the supposition that RVFV circulation was persisting at low levels on the island among livestock without causing outbreaks.

After a 17-year period of inter-epizootic transmission, a second major outbreak occurred in 2008–2009 in different areas of the island, particularly in the south, the north, and the Central Highlands (Andriamandimby et al. 2010). The outbreaks occurred in two epidemic waves during the two successive rainy seasons of 2007–2008 and 2008–2009. At the end of the epidemic, about 700 suspected human cases were recorded, of which 26 were fatal. At this time, RVFV had also been detected in three mosquito species—*Anopheles coustani*, *A. squamosus*, and *Culex antennatus* (Ratovonjato et al. 2011). The phylogenetic studies of the RVFV strains involved in the 2008–2009 outbreak showed that the viruses were closely related to those responsible for the Kenyan outbreaks in 2006–2007 (Carroll et al. 2011; Grobbelaar et al. 2011; Samy et al. 2017). After the 2008–2009 epidemic, RVFV circulation was detected between 2009 and 2012 among ruminants in the Central Highlands, specifically the Anjozorobe District (Chevalier et al. 2011; Nicolas et al. 2014); in the southwest, specifically the Morombe and Toliara Districts; in the east, specifically the Farafangana District; and between 2010 and 2014 in the Central Highlands, specifically the Tsiroanomandidy District (Olive et al. 2017). Lastly, interepidemic transmission was reported in humans in 2013 near Tsiroanomandidy in a healthy livestock herder (Gray et al. 2015) and in 2015 in a child clinically diagnosed with mumps living in the Mandritsara District (Guillebaud et al. 2018). Phylogenetic studies including all RVFV strains circulating on Madagascar were able to trace the origin of the successive outbreaks and indicated at least three independent RVFV introductions (Figure 6.9) (Carroll et al. 2011; Grobbelaar et al. 2011; Samy et al. 2017).

The Epidemiology of RVFV on Madagascar

After the 2008–2009 epidemics, several studies were undertaken to understand the epidemiology of RVFV on Madagascar. These studies included all components of the RVFV cycle, including hosts (livestock, humans, and wildlife) and vectors, as well as the environment.

A serological survey undertaken after the 2008 outbreak showed an overall seroprevalence of 25.8% and 24.7% in cattle and small ruminants, respectively, with seroprevalence being highly heterogeneous across the island (Jeanmaire et al. 2011). Later, in 2014, a serological survey highlighted an overall seropositivity rate in cattle and small ruminants averaging 7.9% (Olive et al. 2017). In humans, a national cross-sectional serologic survey among slaughterhouse workers showed that RVFV circulation during the 2008 outbreaks was also heterogeneous across the country (Andriamandimby et al. 2010). In 2011 and 2013, a national serological survey in asymptomatic adults estimated that seroprevalence was 9.5% and further highlighted contact with raw milk as a behavior putting people at risk for RVFV infection (Olive et al. 2016).

Wild ruminant species are reservoir hosts of RVFV on the African continent (Rostal et al. 2017), but these mammals are absent on Madagascar, with the exception of introduced species. Among the wild mammals (e.g., terrestrial small mammals, nonhuman primates, bats) present on the island, small mammals (rodents and tenrecs) and frugivorous bats were tested for the presence of antibodies directed against RVFV. Serologic results showed that these species were unlikely to be involved as reservoir hosts (Olive et al. 2012, 2013; M.-M. Olive, unpublished data).

Vectors play an important role in the maintenance and spread of RVFV. A recent review reported that 24 mosquito species present on Madagascar (including endemics) were associated with RVFV infection, and that some of these species are known or suggested to maintain the virus through vertical transmission in Africa or the Arabian Peninsula (Tantely et al. 2015). Among the species of importance, *Culex antennatus* is considered a major vector in Africa and probably on Madagascar (Ratovonjato et al. 2011; Tantely et al. 2015; Nepomichene et al. 2018). *Anopheles coustani* is also a good candidate vector, as competence studies showed that this species is susceptible to RVFV and can release RVFV in its saliva (Nepomichene et al. 2018). Moreover, *A. coustani* has been found in high abundance in areas where RVFV was known to circulate (Ratovonjato et al. 2011; Tantely et al. 2013; Nepomichene et al. 2015). Numerous other species such as *A. squamosus*, *Culex tritaeniorhynchus*, *C. pipiens*, and *Mansonia uniformis* are also relevant RVFV candidate vectors.

Phylogenetic and epidemiological analyses show that RVFV was introduced several times to Madagascar, probably through international ruminant trade, and spread within the country by movement of cattle through circulation routes (Figure 6.9) (Grobbelaar et al. 2011; Lancelot et al. 2017; Samy et al. 2017). These introductions and subsequent spread were responsible for RVFV epizootics and epidemics. In addition, the surveys mentioned above suggest that the Central Highlands and the southwest are at risk for RVFV outbreaks, whereas the northwest and lowland east are at risk for interepidemic and enzootic circulation (Olive et al. 2016, 2017).

FLAVIVIRIDAE

Flavivirus is a genus of viruses belonging to family Flaviviridae (Bente et al. 2013). To date, 53 species of flaviviruses have been described; the most prominent are Dengue Virus (DENV), Japanese Encephalitis Virus (JEV), West Nile Virus (WNV), Yellow Fever Virus (YFV), and Zika Virus (ZIKAV). Most flaviviruses are considered arboviruses and can be transmitted to humans via arthropod bites, mainly by mosquitoes and ticks (Pierson and Diamond 2007). Nevertheless, it has been suggested that some flaviviruses, especially ZIKAV, may use other transmission routes. Indeed, human transmission via sexual contact has been proposed as a secondary transmission route for ZIKAV, substantiated by the

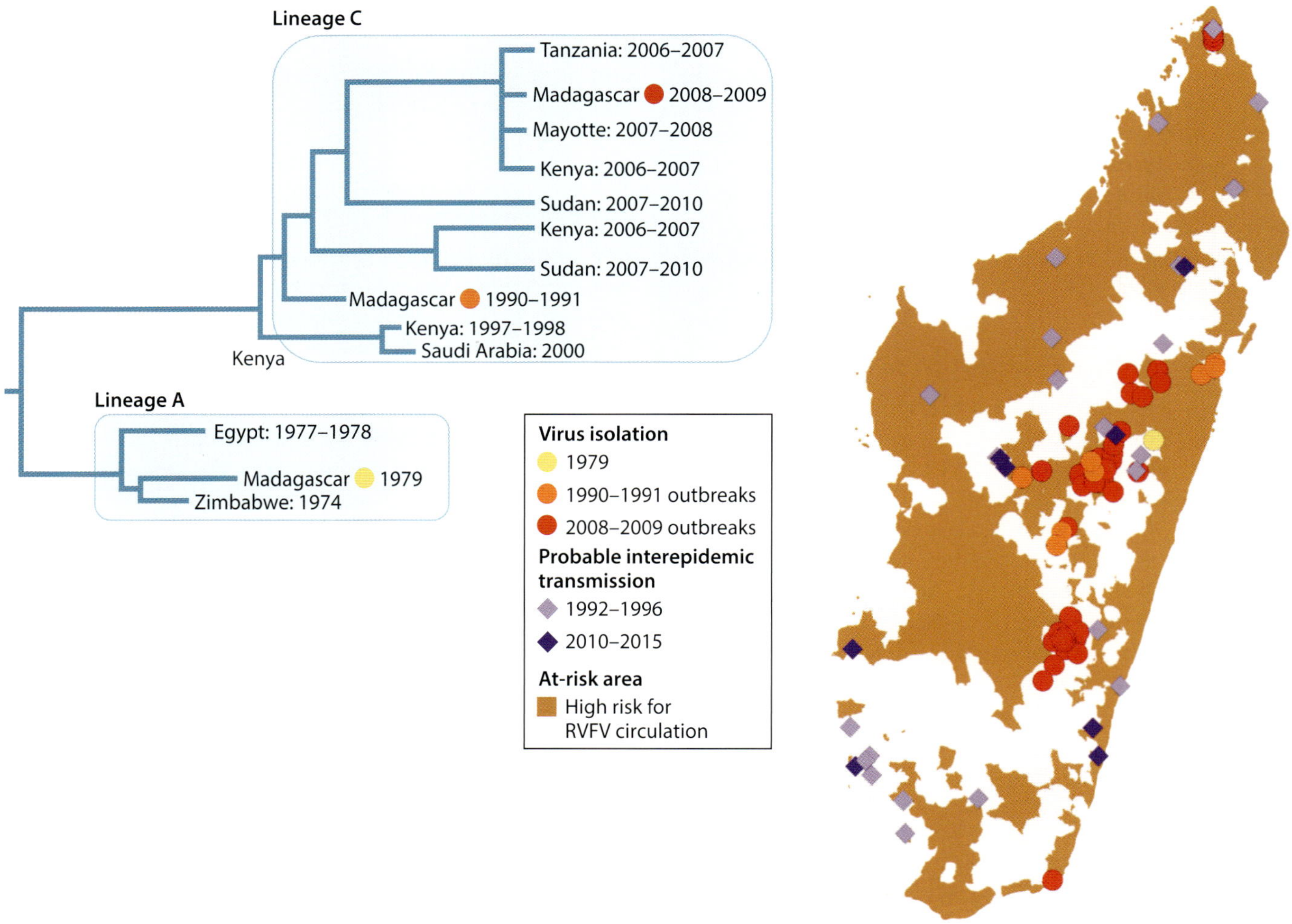

FIGURE 6.9 **Rift Valley Fever Virus (RVFV) circulation in Madagascar. On the left, schematic and simplified tree showing the phylogenetic relationships between RVFV Malagasy strains and other strains isolated in Africa, the Arabian Peninsula, and southwestern Indian Ocean islands. On the map, right, areas where RVFV was isolated are identified with circles, and areas where RVFV interepidemic transmission was detected are identified with diamonds.**

presence of infectious viral particles in semen from previously infected men (Counotte et al. 2018). Lastly, maternal-fetal transmission, in some cases, causes severe brain malformations in newborns (Rasmussen et al. 2016). Candidate vaccines are in development for DENV, WNV, and ZIKAV.

Flaviviruses can be found on all continents, and their distribution is often associated with global geographic distribution of both vectors and hosts. Like other arboviruses, flaviviruses have specific epidemiological cycles, and the complexity of these cycles (involving different reservoir hosts and vectors) challenges the development of control strategies aimed at reducing transmission to humans or domestic animals.

On Madagascar, based on viral isolation, molecular characterization, and serology, four species of flaviviruses have been detected: WNV, DENV, Wesselsbron Virus (WSLV), and Dakar Bat Virus (DBV). WNV and DENV can infect humans, while WSLV infects mainly sheep, goats, cattle, and pigs. DBV has been isolated from salivary glands of *Chaerephon atsinanana* (formerly known as *C. pumilus*), a bat belonging to the family Molossidae (Coulanges et al. 1974; Cassel-Beraud et al. 1989), but to date no vector has been identified for this virus, and no human infection has been reported.

Dengue Virus (DENV)

Dengue is an arbovirus widely distributed across the globe and probably the arbovirus with the highest burden in terms of human morbidity and mortality. Indeed, it is estimated that around 100 million symptomatic infections, resulting in 25,000 deaths, occur every year (World Health Organization 2021). Dengue is spread by the bite of the highly anthropophilic mosquito *Aedes aegypti* and, to a lesser extent, *A. albopictus*. Recent studies have provided evidence of widespread co-distribution and coinfection of Dengue and Chikungunya (CHIKV)—an alphavirus transmitted by *Aedes* spp. (Furuya-Kanamori et al. 2016). Although most DENV infections are asymptomatic or benign, infected humans, in rare cases, can develop severe symptoms, including hemorrhagic fever, which can lead to death. Four serotypes of DENV circulate worldwide and are responsible for major epidemics (DENV-1, DENV-2, DENV-3, and DENV-4). Recently, a fifth serotype was isolated in Thailand; little is known about this type, but it is suspected that it may be a new genotype of DENV-4.

On Madagascar, the first detection and isolation of DENV occurred in 2006 during a major outbreak that affected the city of Toamasina (Ratsitorahina et al. 2008). This outbreak was characterized by co-circulation of DENV-1 and CHIKV. Molecular characterization of these isolates showed that they were similar to DENV-1 strains circulating in 2004 on La Réunion. *Aedes albopictus* was the only urban vector of DENV or CHIKV detected during the Toamasina outbreak (Ratsitorahina et al. 2008). Before these molecular characterizations, serological studies had suggested a circulation of DENV-1 on Madagascar, more specifically on Nosy Be (Fontenille et al. 1988b). Since the last DENV epidemic in 2006, no other outbreak has been detected by the health surveillance system. Even if serological evidence of DENV (immunoglobulin M, or IgM) has been reported, no virus has been recently detected or isolated (Schwarz et al. 2012).

The data presented in this paragraph are based on unpublished information from the laboratory of J.-M. Héraud. A national serological survey conducted on Madagascar from 2011 to 2013 on 1680 adults showed that overall seroprevalence (IgG) for DENV was 6.5% (110/1680). Highest seroprevalence was observed on Nosy Be (48.3%) and in Toamasina (43.3%). Overall, locations in the lowland east and north exhibited the highest seroprevalence, suggesting that the humid bioclimate is a risk factor for the transmission of DENV on Madagascar. Since the study was conducted in adults born before 2006, it is not clear whether seroprevalence measured nationally is associated with the 2006 epidemic or if DENV is still circulating. A study conducted in 2009 among pregnant women living in the southeast showed the absence of IgM, supporting a hypothesis of no recent infections of DENV. Some questions remain open regarding the circulation of DENV on Madagascar. For instance, since *A. aegypti* is more competent than *A. albopictus* for DENV transmission, the local replacement of *A. aegypti* by *A. albopictus* (Raharimalala et al. 2012) may contribute to a decrease in DENV circulation.

West Nile Virus (WNV)

A zoonotic arbovirus widely distributed throughout the world, WNV is a positive-sense single-strand RNA virus and is part of the Japanese Encephalitis Virus serogroup, alongside nine other viruses (Simmonds et al. 2017). Although seven lineages (and two additional putative lineages) have been described to date (Fall et al. 2017), most human outbreaks have been attributed to lineages 1 and 2. Lineage 1 has a worldwide distribution (Africa, Asia, Europe, and the Americas), and lineage 2, originally distributed only in Africa, has emerged in Europe in the last 20 years. Both have caused important clinical outbreaks in humans, birds, and horses.

WNV is mainly a virus of birds and is maintained through enzootic transmission between birds and mosquitoes; however, several spillover events involving mammals, reptiles, and amphibians have been reported (Pierson and Diamond 2007). The main cycle of the virus involves birds as reservoirs and ornithophilic mosquitoes as vectors, while a fecal-oral route can also occur within carnivorous birds (Root et al. 2005). When viral amplification is sufficiently strong among bird communities, opportunistic vectors—so-called bridge-vectors—capable of taking blood meals from a variety of hosts, can transmit the virus to non-avian hosts such as humans and horses. Oral transmission may also occur when predators ingest infected animals (Klenk et al. 2004; Nemeth et al. 2009). Most non-avian secondary hosts are generally considered dead-end hosts, although some exceptions have been described.

On Madagascar, the first detections of human antibodies against *Flavivirus*, presumably WNV, dating from the 1950s and 1960s, were followed by viral isolation in 1978 from samples from an endemic parrot, *Coracopsis vasa* (family Psittacidae), in the Morondava area (Mathiot et al. 1984). Further viral isolations from samplings from birds, including *Egretta* (family Ardeidae) and *C. vasa*, then from mosquitoes and humans, together with high seroprevalence rates in humans (up to 41% in some areas), confirmed WNV as the most prevalent arbovirus on Madagascar (Fontenille et al. 1989). WNV antibodies have also been reported on the island in zebu, rats, lemurs, and bats (Coulanges et al. 1974; Fontenille et al. 1989). More recent studies have also confirmed high seroprevalence in horses (Cardinale et al. 2017; Guis et al. 2018) and in domestic and wild birds (Maquart et al. 2016; Rasamoelina et al. 2019). All strains thus far isolated on Madagascar belong to lineage 2. Despite an intense circulation, no clinical outbreak in humans or in animals has been described for Madagascar. Apart from presumed infections among patients hospitalized in Antananarivo, only one fatal case of human infection was reported, in 2011 (Larrieu et al. 2013).

A recent review listed 29 mosquito species that could be involved in WNV transmission on Madagascar, according to three criteria that define a vector species: natural infection in the field, vector competence addressed through experimental infection, and evidence of vector-host contact in the field (Tantely et al. 2016b). To the list of competent vectors should now be added *Aedemomyia madagascarica*, which was recently found WNV-positive in the endemic wetland area of western Madagascar (Maquart et al. 2016). Among these 30 taxa, four species (three belonging to *Culex* and one to *Mansonia*) fulfill all three criteria and can thus be considered major vectors, 10 are candidate vectors (fulfilling two criteria), while 16 are potential vectors (fulfilling only one criteria) (Tantely et al. 2016b, 2017). Overall, 17 vector species have been found naturally infected by WNV on Madagascar. Regarding human infections, a recent survey conducted from 2011 to 2013 in different areas of Madagascar showed that global seroprevalence remains high (IgG positivity rate of 12.7%), but WNV circulation is heterogeneous, with the humid environment of the north appearing to be an at-risk region for WNV transmission compared to cooler environments typical of the Central Highlands (J.-M. Héraud et al., unpublished data).

NAIROVIRIDAE

Crimean-Congo Hemorrhagic Fever Virus (CCHFV)

Crimean-Congo hemorrhagic fever (CCHF) is a tick-borne viral disease affecting humans, livestock, and wild vertebrates. Its widespread occurrence closely approximates the known world distribution of *Hyalomma*, a genus of ticks that is the principal vector (Whitehouse 2004). CCHF Virus (CCHFV) belongs to order Bunyavirales, family Nairoviridae, and the genus *Orthonairovirus* (Bente et al. 2013). The genome of CCHFV is a segmented, negative-sense RNA occurring in a loosely bound circular configuration within the nucleocapsids. Its genome is composed of small (S), medium (M), and large (L) segments, encoding, respectively, the nucleocapsid protein, the envelope glycoproteins, and the RNA polymerase. CCHFV circulates in many regions of Africa and Eurasia (including the Mediterranean region) and from the Middle East to India (Hoogstraal 1979; Bente et al. 2013; Gargili et al. 2017). Although outside of Madagascar ticks belonging to the genus *Hyalomma* are the principal vectors involved in transmission to humans, a number of alternative reservoirs and vectors exist in different ecological environments (Hoogstraal 1979). Humans can be infected via tick bites, but CCHFV infection can also occur through contact with patients during the acute phase of illness or through contact with blood or tissues of viremic animals (Whitehouse 2004).

CCHFV was first isolated on Madagascar in 1985, following the collection of introduced *Rhipicephalus microplus* ticks, formerly placed in the genus *Boophilus* (see Klompen and Apanaskevich, pp. 894–99, for information on Malagasy ticks) from cattle at the Antananarivo slaughterhouse (Mathiot et al. 1988). All CCHFV-positive ticks were collected from zebu originating from the Tsiroanomandidy area. A serological survey carried out on more than 2100 head of cattle revealed an average seroprevalence rate of 16.7%, with some zones, such as Mandoto in the Central Highlands, exhibiting a seroprevalence rate exceeding 50% (Fontenille et al. 1988a). Even if no human CCHF case has been reported on Madagascar, seroprevalence studies among slaughterhouse workers and among adult people showed serological evidence of recent and former infections (Mathiot et al. 1989; Andriamandimby et al. 2011).

TOGAVIRIDAE

Chikungunya Virus (CHIKV)

Chikungunya Virus (CHIKV) is an enveloped, positive-sense, single-strand RNA virus belonging to the family Togaviridae, genus *Alphavirus* (Bente et al. 2013). This virus was first isolated in 1952, following an epidemic in Tanzania. CHIKV is transmitted mainly via the bite of infected mosquitoes, but vertical transmission can exceptionally occur from mother to child during pregnancy or at birth (Lenglet et al. 2006). Two vectors are responsible for its transmission and spread: *Aedes aegypti* and *A. albopictus* (Weaver and Lecuit 2015). Historically, CHIKV originated from sub-Saharan Africa and involved a sylvatic transmission cycle connecting nonhuman primates as primary hosts and *Aedes* mosquitoes (mainly *A. aegypti*) as primary vectors. Recent outbreaks occurring in Central America, in Asia, and on Indian Ocean islands, including Madagascar, are characterized by an urban transmission cycle involving humans and both *A. albopictus* and *A. aegypti* vector species.

On Madagascar, the first detection and isolation of CHIKV was reported in 2006, after an epidemic that affected Nosy Be, Antsiranana, and Toamasina. In Toamasina during this outbreak, *A. albopictus* was the only identified vector. If the virus that emerged on Indian Ocean islands was from the eastern, central, and southern African enzootic lineage, a series of adaptive mutations of the virus resulted in a new lineage, known as the Indian Ocean Lineage (Schuffenecker et al. 2006). Recent studies conducted on Madagascar showed that IgG seroprevalence averaged 13.5% in the hot and humid eastern and northern lowland areas (J.-M. Héraud et al., unpublished data). The rate of IgG seropositivity in affected areas varies from 10% to 20%, though some areas, such as Sambava and Nosy Be, exhibit a seroprevalence exceeding 50% (Schwarz et al. 2012; J.-M. Héraud et al., unpublished data). A natural enzootic cycle on Madagascar is thus far unknown.

CONCLUSION

The arboviruses of current medical importance on Madagascar appear to have been introduced, as a result of movements of cattle or people from eastern Africa or India, with the Comoro archipelago as a stepping-stone. This has been substantiated by phylogenetic studies and by the temporal dynamics of the most recent RVF and Chikungunya epidemics. WNV may be one of the most ancient arboviruses of current concern, possibly as a result of non-anthropogenic introduction. However, the available data do not allow estimation of an introduction date through coalescent approaches.

The entomological situation of Madagascar and some other islands in the southwestern Indian Ocean provide interesting conditions that have illuminated some mechanisms of viral microevolution. Indeed, the co-occurrence of *Aedes albopictus* and *A. aegypti* may have facilitated the adaptation of CHIKV to *A. albopictus* (Schuffenecker et al. 2006; Tsetsarkin et al. 2007; Vazeille et al. 2007). Interestingly, such adaptation was later reported in continental Africa, India, and Sri Lanka, as an astonishing example of convergent adaptation in arboviruses (Vignuzzi and Higgs 2017). All together, gathered data exemplify how the peculiar properties of insular ecosystems facilitate the investigation of arboviral emergence (Tortosa et al. 2012) and, ultimately, the identification of transmission drivers (Lancelot et al. 2017).

Subject editors: Pablo Tortosa and Steven M. Goodman

ARTHROPOD-BORNE BACTERIA METABARCODING

D. Wilkinson and P. Mavingui

Metabarcoding is a technique of molecular biology that allows the composition of complex communities to be characterized by identifying specific DNA sequences from each organism in the community (Taberlet et al. 2012). Decades of genomic studies have resulted in the identification of specific gene loci that are suitable for such studies. Typically, these are short gene fragments (fewer than 500 base pairs) that vary between taxa but are flanked on either side by sequences that are conserved, allowing them to be targeted, amplified, and sequenced. The use of next-generation sequencing technologies, such as Illumina sequencing, allows large numbers of DNA sequences to be generated and analyzed, providing a semi-quantitative measure of relative organism abundance in complex samples (such as environmental DNA; Deiner et al. 2017) without the need to physically isolate any of the organisms present. Metabarcoding is, thus, a powerful and increasingly accessible tool for the description of the biodiversity contained within any sample.

There remain limits to what information can be extracted using metabarcoding techniques. Ideally, well-curated and exhaustive databases with sequence data from all species would exist for metabarcoding loci, allowing accurate species assignment; however, in practice, databases are often sparsely populated and contain misleading or erroneous data. Furthermore, limits to the length of DNA that can be sequenced typically mean that taxonomic classifications derived from metabarcoding data are limited to the level of family or genus.

The identification of bacterial taxa is one of the most common applications of metabarcoding and is frequently applied within the environmental and medical sciences where the composition of bacterial communities (also known as bacterial microbiomes or bacteriomes) provides some important insight, such as an indicator of health. Typically, bacterial metabarcoding exploits the 16S ribosomal RNA (rRNA). The 16S gene sequence has been well studied across all known orders, family, and genera of culturable bacteria. Well-curated 16S sequence data are available from large numbers of reference organisms in databases such as Greengenes (DeSantis et al. 2006), RDP (Cole et al. 2014), and SILVA (Quast et al. 2013). The 16S gene itself contains nine hypervariable regions with considerable genetic variability and areas of high conservation, making the locus ideally suited for metabarcoding analysis. The level of taxonomic classification that can be achieved differs between different bacterial taxa and the used hypervariable region(s) of the 16S gene.

There is a variety of motivations behind the study of bacteriome compositions. One common aim is the identification of specific taxa of known relevance; this could be, for example, markers of contamination in water samples (Li et al. 2018) or the detection of infecting, pathogenic bacteria in unwell animals or people. However, many studies are also interested in more indirect phenomena that are linked to bacteriome associations. For example, the composition of the gut or intestinal microbiome has been the subject of extensive study in people, domestic and wild animals, and other organisms such as arthropods. In such studies, it has been shown that the complex ensemble of microorganisms that inhabit the gut and the interactions they form with their host (the holobiont), can have a profound impact on the host's ability to carry out different functions. The scale of these functional changes is such that holobionts are thought to have developed over the evolutionary timescales of the host organisms, driven by the positive selection of host-microbe interactions that result in a survival benefit (Richardson 2017).

The study of arthropod microbiomes is largely motivated by the role that many of these organisms play as vectors of bacterial or viral disease, impacting human health, animal health, and crop production. The direct detection of vector-transmitted pathogenic agents can be achieved by bacterial metabarcoding. For instance, this method has been used for the identification of bacteria, such as *Coxiella* and *Rickettsia* spp., in ticks (Wilkinson et al. 2014b). However, many other arthropod-borne bacteria form mutualistic or symbiotic relationships with their hosts, providing nutritional benefits to hosts that have diets that are insufficient to provide a full ration of nutrition. These interactions have allowed arthropods to inhabit nutrient-low niches that are free from competition and become highly adapted specialists, and often their dietary regimes explain their association with the transmission of disease. This is the case, for example, in the tsetse fly *Glossina palpalis* (order Diptera), which transmits a variety of trypanosomal blood parasites while feeding (Aksoy et al. 2014), and whose diet relies exclusively on vertebrate blood for nutrition. This, and many other species of arthropod have evolved to nurture these bacterial interactions, possessing a dedicated organelle (named the bacteriome) housing mutualistic bacteria.

For similar reasons, mosquito midgut microbiomes are a subject of intensive study (Minard et al. 2013). It has been shown that the mosquito's holobiont can directly impact its capacity to transmit infectious agents such as Dengue Virus, or malaria parasites, and this is particularly true of interactions made with intracellular bacteria of the genus *Wolbachia* (Hegde et al. 2015). *Wolbachia* are known to inhabit many species of arthropods and nematodes, and often manipulate their host species by inducing reproductive biases through altered sex ratios, feminization, parthenogenesis, or breeding incompatibilities (Hurst et al. 2002). Metabarcoding approaches have been used to study *Wolbachia* associations, as well as many other mutualistic interactions, in different arthropod species (Minard et al. 2015) and are facilitating an increased understanding of global microbial diversity, as well as holobiont interactions, that are associated with disease transmission. To date, only a handful of studies have employed metabarcoding for the study of arthropod-associated bacterial diversity on Madagascar, and details are provided here.

TICKS OF LEMURS

Lado et al. (2018) used a metabarcoding approach to examine bacterial populations present within *Haemaphysalis lemuris* (Acari, family Ixodidae) collected from five lemur species (*Avahi laniger*, *Propithecus diadema*, *P. verreauxi*, *Prolemur simus*, and *Lepilemur mustelinus*) during veterinary health checks in different forest formations, including moist evergreen and dry deciduous forests. This study identified more than 500 bacterial taxa, with Actinobacteria, Firmicutes, and Proteobacteria accounting for more than 90% of the identified sequences from ticks. Sequences belonging to pathogen-associated bacteria *Rickettsia* spp. and *Francisella* spp. were also identified. These genera, as well as *Coxiella* spp., are known to form nondetrimental, mutualistic relationships with tick species (Bonnet et al. 2017), which then cause disease in exposed mammalian hosts. For example, *F. tulariensis* causes tularemia, and *Rickettsia* spp. cause several diseases in both animals and humans. *Bartonella* spp. were also identified in this study, suggesting *H. lemuris* may be a vector for pathogens of this genus, which are also responsible for several different diseases in both animals and humans. *Haemaphysalis lemuris* has been shown to be not host-specific with regard to the lemur species it parasitizes (see Klompen and Apanaskevich, pp. 894–99), indicating that it may play an important role in the maintenance and spread of disease between different lemur populations or species. Of note, there are reports of *H. lemuris* opportunistically biting humans.

APHID ENDOSYMBIONTS

De Clerck et al. (2014) used metabarcoding with a classical sequencing approach (preceded by the cloning of PCR products) to generate 16S gene sequence data for a small number of bacterial taxa associated with the Banana Aphid, *Pentalonia nigronervosa* (Hemiptera, family Aphididae), vector of Banana Bunchy Top Virus, which causes significant losses in banana production worldwide. Bacterial taxa in aphids from Arivonimamo and Ambodiafontsy in the Central Highlands of Madagascar were compared with those in similar species present in Burundi and Gabon. The study identified two predominant bacterial taxa in all studied aphids; *Buchnera aphidicola*, a known obligate symbiont of aphids that provides its host with a supplement of essential amino acids, thus allowing aphids to exploit the low-nutrient diet obtained from plant-phloem sap, and a *Wolbachia* sp. that showed genetic similarity to other *Wolbachia* spp. from both insects and nematodes.

BAT FLIES

Wilkinson et al. (2016) studied bacterial microbiomes of bat fly ectoparasites of the family Nycteribiidae (Diptera) (see Dick, pp. 1099–101); 16S gene metabarcoding data were generated from individual specimens, collected on different bat species, of six species of Malagasy nycteribiids: *Basilia* (*Paracyclopodia*) spp., *Cyclopodia dubia*, *Eucampsipoda madagascarensis*, *Nycteribia stylidiopsis*, *Penicillidia leptothrinax*, and *Penicillidia* sp. (cf. *fulvida*). *Eucampsipoda madagascarensis* and *C. dubia* are strict parasites of the fruit bat *Rousettus madagascariensis* (Figure 6.10) and *Eidolon dupreanum* (family Pteropodidae), respectively. In contrast, *P. leptothrinax*, *P. fulvida*, and *N. stylidiopsis* are promiscuous in their host associations and can be found parasitizing insectivorous *Miniopterus* spp. (family Miniopteridae) and *Myotis goudoti* (family Vespertilionidae).

A study found that *Gammaproteobacteria* and *Alphaproteobacteria*, together, constituted more than 90% of the bat fly bacteriome. *Gammaproteobacteria*, mainly known members of the functional group *Arsenophonous*-like-organisms (ALOs), made up approximately three-quarters of all identified 16S gene sequence data. ALOs are known obligate symbionts of nycteribiid bat flies (Duron et al. 2014), again providing a nutritional supplement to their host arthropod, which otherwise relies entirely on host bat blood for nutrition. Phylogenetic analyses suggested a host-specificity between ALOs and their arthropod hosts. Insectivorous bat-associated *Nycteribia* and *Penicillidia* possessed ALOs related to the *Aschnera* subgroup, whereas fruit-bat-associated *Eucampsipoda* and insectivorous-bat-associated *Basilia* (*Paracyclopodia*) spp. possessed ALOs belonging to the *Arsenophonus* subgroup. A previously undescribed taxon of ALO was also identified in *C. dubia* parasitizing *E. dupreanum*. The study also identified sequences from *Wolbachia* symbionts that showed genetic similarity to other *Wolbachia* spp. from both insects and nematodes, and *Bartonella* spp., many of which are known to be carried by bat species and for which bat flies are likely vectors.

As both De Clerck et al. (2014) and Wilkinson et al. (2016) extracted DNA from whole arthropod samples, it is possible that the identified *Wolbachia* spp. in these studies are associated with nematodes that were infecting the host arthropods (that were themselves parasites of a separate host). This form of hyperparasitism is a good example of the complex interactions that often go overlooked but that may have an importance in our understanding of disease transmission mechanisms.

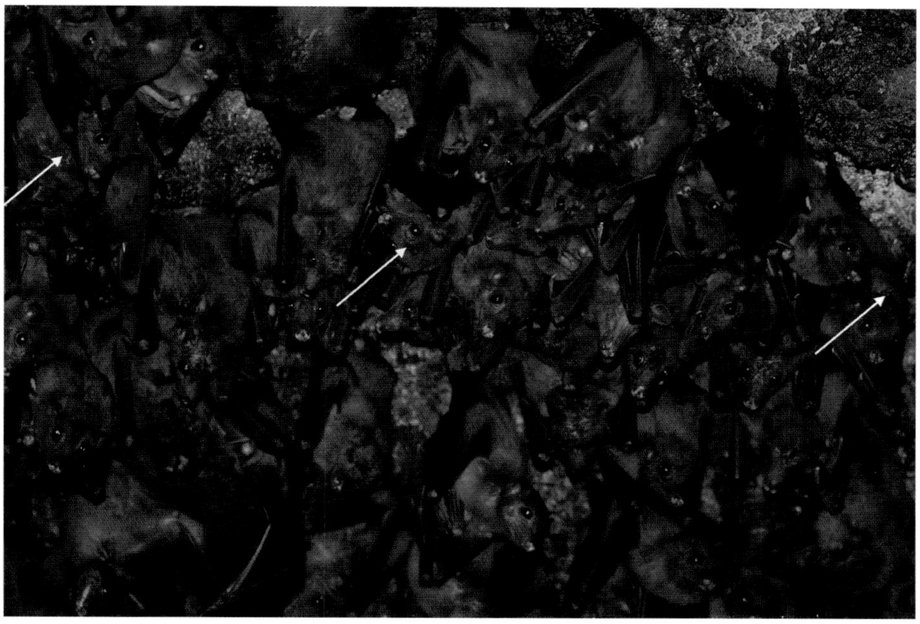

FIGURE 6.10 **A dense colony of *Rousettus madagascariensis* (Madagascar Rousette) with visible *Eucampsipoda madagascarensis* nycteribiid bat flies (white arrows).** (PHOTO by M. Ruedi.)

MOSQUITO MICROBIOME

Minard et al. (2014) used metabarcoding to study the bacterial microbiome of *Aedes albopictus* mosquitoes from the Antsiranana area of northern Madagascar. *Wolbachia* accounted for more than 95% of bacterial diversity in all tested samples. Unlike other *Aedes* spp., *A. albopictus* forms a strong obligate interaction with *Wolbachia*. When *Wolbachia* sequences were excluded, bacteria of the phylum Firmicutes were found to be the dominant group (67%), followed by Actinobacteria (4%), Bacteroidetes (3%), and Proteobacteria (2%). Using amplified ribosomal DNA restriction analysis (ARDRA) of the 16S gene, Valiente Moro et al. (2013) analyzed culturable bacteria in *A. albopictus* imagos from four different biotopes of Madagascar, including Tsimbazaza Park in Antananarivo, Ankazobe, Toamasina, and Ambohidratrimo. They found a total of 27 genera belonging to three major phyla, namely Actinobacteria, Proteobacteria, and Firmicutes, whose abundance varied depending on the sex of individual mosquitoes. *Pantoea* was the most common genus in both males and females; further study is needed to decipher its role in *A. albopictus* biology.

Zouache et al. (2011) used denaturing gradient gel electrophoresis (DGGE) of *rrs* amplicons for fingerprinting bacterial microbiomes in *A. albopictus* and *A. aegypti* from the regions of Analamanga, Boeny, and Atsinanana. Variation in fingerprint was observed between individuals of the same sex whether from the same site or not, and as expected, bacterial diversity varied also between females and males for both mosquito species. In addition, considering the possible influence of habitat on the microbiomes hosted by the mosquitoes, this study showed that bacterial taxa were linked to environmental characteristics, suggesting that some bacterial species may be acquired from the environment where mosquitoes breed. Overall, several bacterial phyla are similar to those already found in these mosquito species, such as Firmicutes and Proteobacteria. This study was the first to describe the genus *Asaia* in natural populations of both *Aedes albopictus* and *A. aegypti*. This is of considerable interest, as *Asaia* is a cultivable bacterium that can be maternally transmitted (through egg-smearing mechanism) in mosquito communities, suggesting that it may be used as a tool in vector control (Favia et al. 2008).

CONCLUSION

Historically, culturomics has made possible the discovery of many taxa and the study of bacterial diversity in different living organisms as well as in abiotic environments. The advent of culture-independent methods allows for the exploration of more complex environments and the discovery of unanticipated microbial diversity. This contribution focuses on the use of metabarcoding for the descriptive study of bacterial communities in different organisms on Madagascar. The future use of metabarcoding, in combination with high-throughput screening methods, will help decipher functional genes to better understand key functions associated with microbiomes in holobionts.

Subject editors: Pablo Tortosa and Steven M. Goodman

BLOOD PARASITES OF SMALL MAMMALS ON MADAGASCAR

B. Ramasindrazana, M. Rasoanoro, H. C. Ranaivoson, M. Randrianarivelojosia, P. Tortosa, and S. M. Goodman

The native community of small mammals on Madagascar includes terrestrial species (rodents and tenrecs) and flying species (bats). The native terrestrial small-mammal fauna comprises rodents of the subfamily Nesomyinae and tenrecs of the family Tenrecidae, all endemic to the island (see Goodman and Soarimalala, pp. 1737–69). The bat fauna is also highly original; nearly 80% of recognized species are endemic to the island (see Goodman et al., pp. 1894–911). In contrast with the endemic rodents and tenrecs, which each represent a single successful colonization event and a monophyletic lineage, the bats of Madagascar belong to nine different families and represent an estimated 28 or 29 different colonization events of the island.

While studies on the taxonomy of the different native terrestrial and flying small-mammal species have led to considerable progress over the period from about 1990 to 2020, there have been fewer advances in terms of the description and ecology of parasites hosted by these animals, including blood parasites and their invertebrate vectors. Protozoan blood parasites infect these mammals and most often display marked specificity toward their vertebrate hosts. Although different genera of blood parasites (*Polychromophilus*, *Babesia*, *Litomosa*, *Litomosoides*, and *Trypanosoma*) have been identified in bats from Madagascar, only *Achromaticus*, *Hepatozoon*, and *Trypanosoma* species, thus far, have been reported in terrestrial small mammals. Information from the literature, together with some of our ongoing work, is summarized herein. Parasite species, infected hosts, and corresponding literature are summarized in Table 6.4.

BLOOD PARASITES IN BATS

The first research reporting blood parasites from Malagasy bats was conducted by Raharimanga et al. (2003). In this study, based on microscopic screening of blood smears, the authors noted the presence of Haemoproteidae, microfilaria, and *Trypanosoma* in a range of bat species. Subsequently, different studies highlighted the taxonomy of blood parasites previously identified and the presence of other taxa infecting bats. These findings are detailed below.

Polychromophilus spp. (Haemosporida, Plasmodiidae) and Their Potential Invertebrate Vectors

Of the eight genera of haemosporidian parasites that are known to infect bats, namely *Biguetiella*, *Dionisia*, *Hepatocystis*, *Johnsprentia*, *Nycteria*, *Plasmodium*, *Polychromophilus*, and *Sprattiella* (Landau et al. 2012; Schaer et al. 2013, 2015), only *Polychromophilus* has been identified to date in Malagasy bats based on morphological and molecular tools. Within this genus, two species have been documented, although an ongoing study supports the existence of an additional taxa.

On Madagascar, *P. melanipherus* was initially reported in *Miniopterus manavi sensu lato* (Duval et al. 2012). In the last decade or so, there has been considerable taxonomic progress in the species delimitation of Malagasy members of this bat genus (Goodman et al. 2009; see Goodman et al., pp. 1894–911), resulting in the need for a reassessment of whether *P. melanipherus* does infect *Miniopterus* bats. Based on cytochrome b (cyt b) analysis, *P. melanipherus* was identified in 11 of the 12 currently described Malagasy Region species of *Miniopterus* (Duval et al. 2012; Ramasindrazana et al. 2018; M. Rasoanoro et al., unpublished data). All *P. melanipherus* sequences obtained from Malagasy Miniopteridae clustered with those reported in *M. schreibersii* from Switzerland, in *M. inflatus* from Gabon, and in *M. villiersi* from Guinea, suggesting a low genetic diversification of these parasites and a strong specificity of *P. melanipherus* toward this bat genus (Schaer et al. 2013; Witsenburg et al. 2015). One individual *Paratriaenops furculus* (family Rhinonycteridae) tested positive in the same analyses, suggesting some level of horizontal transfer or accidental infection.

On Madagascar, *Polychromophilus murinus* has been found thus far only in the endemic bat species *Myotis goudoti* (family Vespertilionidae) (Duval et al. 2012; Ramasindrazana et al. 2018). This bat genus has a wide distribution in the New and Old Worlds, and *M. goudoti* is part of the Afrotropical clade (Patterson et al. 2019). In contrast with the *P. melanipherus*–*Miniopterus* pattern, *P. murinus* sequences obtained from *Myotis goudoti* are not embedded within a *P. murinus* cluster composed of sequences obtained from European bat species, suggesting a different diversification history for these two *Polychromophilus* species.

In addition to *P. murinus* and *P. melanipherus*, recent investigations using blood smears and molecular analyses of bats from the eastern portion of Madagascar have identified a new *Polychromophilus* clade (M. Rasoanoro et al., unpublished data), and a comprehensive characterization of this taxon requires further molecular and morphological work.

Potential Vectors of Polychromophilus *spp.*

The transmission of *Polychromophilus* spp. involves Nycteribiidae flies (Figure 6.11) (Gardner and Molyneux 1988), which are wingless obligate blood-sucking Diptera parasites of bats (Tortosa et al. 2013; see also Dick, pp. 1099–101). Six out of 38 screened nycteribiid flies belonging to three species (*Penicillidia leptothrinax*, n = 17; *Penicillidia* sp., n = 2, and *Nycteribia stylidiopsis*, n = 19) were found positive for *Polychromophilus* by molecular screening. Flies testing positive for *P. melanipherus* included four *Penicillidia leptothrinax* sampled on *Miniopterus aelleni* (n = 2) and on *M.* cf. *manavi sensu lato* (n = 2), and a single *Nycteribia stylidiopsis* obtained from *M. gleni*. Further, a single *Penicillidia* sp. specimen collected on *M. griveaudi* tested positive for *Polychromophilus murinus*. Previously, *P. murinus* infection in Malagasy bats had been reported only in *Myotis goudoti* (Duval et al. 2012;

TABLE 6.4. **Blood parasites detected in flying and terrestrial small mammals of Madagascar**

FAMILY	PARASITE	POSITIVE HOST	METHOD: SMEAR SCREENINGS	METHOD: PCR	REFERENCE
BAT SPECIES					
Plasmodiidae	*Polychromophilus melanipherus*	*Paratriaenops furculus* *Miniopterus aelleni* *M. ambohitrensis* *M. brachytragos* *M. egeri* *M. gleni* *M. griffithsi* *M. griveaudi* *M. mahafaliensis* *M. majori* *M. manavi* *M. sororculus*	no no no no no no no no no yes yes no	yes yes yes yes yes yes yes yes yes yes yes yes	Raharimanga et al. (2003); Duval et al. (2012); Ramasindrazana et al. (2018)
	P. murinus	*Myotis goudoti*	yes	yes	Raharimanga et al. (2003); Duval et al. (2012); Ramasindrazana et al. (2018)
	Polychromophilus sp.	*Scotophilus robustus*	yes	yes	M. Rasoanoro et al. (unpublished data)
Babesiidae	*Babesia* sp.	*Pteropus rufus*	yes	yes	Ranaivoson et al. (2019)
Trypanosomatidae	*Trypanosoma*	*Miniopterus brachytragos* *M. mahafaliensis*	yes yes	no no	Raharimanga et al. (2003)
Onchocercidae	*Litomosa* clade 1	*Miniopterus manavi* *M. majori* *M. gleni* *M. sororculus* *M. griveaudi*	yes no no no no	yes yes yes yes yes	Ramasindrazana et al. (2016)
	Litomosa clade 2	*Miniopterus griffithsi* *M. sororculus* *M. mahafaliensis* *M. griveaudi*	no no yes no	yes yes yes yes	Ramasindrazana et al. (2016)
	Litomosa clade 3	*Miniopterus aelleni* *M. griveaudi*	no no	yes yes	Ramasindrazana et al. (2016)
	Litomosoides sp.	*Pipistrellus* cf. *hesperidus*	no	yes	Raharimanga et al. (2003)
TERRESTRIAL SMALL MAMMALS					
Babesiidae	*Achromaticus brygooi*	*Setifer setosus*	yes	no	Uilenberg (1967)
Hepatozoidae	*Hepatozoon hoogstraali*	*Hemicentetes semispinosus*	yes	no	Uilenberg (1970)
Trypanosomatidae	*Trypanosoma lewisi*	*Rattus rattus*	yes	yes	Laakkonen et al. (2003); M. Rasoanoro et al. (unpublished data)
	Trypanosoma sp.	*Nesomys rufus*	yes	no	Laakkonen et al. (2003)

Note: PCR refers to polymerase chain reaction diagnosis.

FIGURE 6.11 **Nycteribiid bat flies in a *Miniopterus gleni* colony; note the dense packing of the bats. Adult flies parasitizing bats are indicated with white arrows; pupae encased on the ceiling next to the colony are indicated with black arrows.** (PHOTO by M. Ruedi.)

Ramasindrazana et al. 2018). *Miniopterus griveaudi* and *Myotis goudoti* occur in the same, often dense, day cave roost sites and are in direct physical contact (see Figure 6.5), which may favor parasite host switching, as suggested for other types of infections (Gomard et al. 2016). Hence, it cannot be ruled out that this single nycteribiid fly testing positive for *P. murinus* infection had previously fed on *M. goudoti*.

Trypanosoma sp. (Kinetoplastida, Trypanosomatidae)

The only records of *Trypanosoma* in Malagasy bats are those of Raharimanga et al. (2003), with three individuals of the genus *Miniopterus* found positive, through the use of microscopic examination of blood smears. These three individuals were named in that publication as *M. manavi* but, based on subsequent taxonomic revisions, were reidentified as *M. brachytragos* and *M. mahafaliensis*. No molecular work was associated with this study, and we are unaware of any subsequent report of *Trypanosoma* in Malagasy bats.

Babesia (Piroplasmida, Babesiidae)

Until recently, the only known bat-infecting *Babesia* was *B. vesperuginis*, which was later shown to have a worldwide distribution, although restricted to insectivorous bats (Gardner et al. 1987; Corduneanu et al. 2017; Han et al. 2018). The Malagasy fruit bat *Pteropus rufus* was recently reported to harbor babesial infection (Ranaivoson et al. 2019), with nine out of 204 individuals testing positive through microscopy and molecular characterization. The babesial screening of the two other Malagasy pteropodid bats, namely *Eidolon dupreanum* and *Rousettus madagascariensis*, were all negative. Sequences of the 18S rRNA gene of the *Babesia* spp. detected in the nine *P. rufus* showed that this piroplasm is genetically distant from *B. vesperuginis* but more closely related to a *Babesia* sp. infecting Malagasy lemurs (Larsen et al. 2016; Ranaivoson et al. 2019). *Babesia* sp. recorded from *P. rufus* represents the first known *Babesia* to infect pteropodid fruit bats and may be associated with horizontal transfer from other local vertebrates rather than representing a *Babesia* species specifically infecting bats (Ranaivoson et al. 2019).

Filarial Infection in Bats

Malagasy bats are currently known to be infected by two genera of filaria, *Litomosa* and *Litomosoides* (Nematoda, Onchocercidae) (Martin et al. 2006; Ramasindrazana et al. 2016). Based on molecular analysis, the different-sequenced *Litomosa* represent a monophyletic cluster and the most diverse and prevalent filaria known to date in Malagasy bats. Three lineages, referred to as clades 1, 2, and 3, have been reported from eight *Miniopterus* species (Ramasindrazana et al. 2016). These different lineages are considered to be sister species of *L. chiropterorum*, previously reported from South African *M. natalensis* (Junker et al. 2009). *Litomosa* clade 3 is separated from clades 1 and 2, while the divergence between clades 1 and 2 is not fully supported. From a host perspective, *Litomosa* clade 1 was obtained from *M. gleni*, *M. griveaudi*, *M. majori*, *M. manavi sensu stricto*, and *M. sororculus*; *Litomosa* clade 2 from *M. griffithsi*, *M. mahafaliensis*, *M. sororculus*, and *M. griveaudi*; and *Litomosa* clade 3 from *M. aelleni* and *M. griveaudi*. While microfilaria within *Litomosa* clades 1 and 2 were observed on blood smears, no microfilaria associated with *Litomosa* clade 3 was found on blood smears (Ramasindrazana et al. 2016). Morphological studies of adult filaria from all three clades are ongoing, with the aim of elucidating the taxonomy of *Litomosa* spp. infecting Malagasy bats, specifically *Miniopterus*.

Based on morphological characterization, a new species of filaria, *Litomosa goodmani*, was described (Martin et al. 2006), with the holotype parasitizing *M. gleni* collected in a cave in the Ankarana National Park, northern Madagascar. These authors also reported from the same locality a female filarial specimen closely related to *L. goodmani*, recovered from a bat now referable to *M. aelleni*. While morphological differences were observed, the taxonomic identity of this adult female filaria was not addressed in a definitive manner, and the species was reported as *Litomosa* sp. These morphological differences need to be confirmed by molecular tools to address the actual diversity of *Litomosa* in Malagasy *Miniopterus*.

Molecular screening identified nematodes of the genus *Litomosoides* in two individuals of *Pipistrellus* cf. *hesperidus* (Ramasindrazana et al. 2016). Members of the genus *Litomosoides*, which is closely related to *Litomosa* (Guerrero et al. 2002; Bain et al. 2008), are known to parasitize different Neotropical mammal groups, including rodents, marsupials, and bats (Guerrero et al. 2006). Only one microfilaria was identified from one blood smear, while no adult filaria were recovered from the two positive *Pipistrellus* bats. Additional work on the morphology and molecular characterization of adult specimens of *Litomosoides* should be carried out to comprehensively identify these parasites.

BLOOD PARASITES IN TERRESTRIAL SMALL MAMMALS

The description of blood parasites in terrestrial small mammals was initiated by Uilenberg (1967, 1970), who reported the presence of *Babesia*-like organisms and *Hepatozoon* using morphological characters. Later, different studies highlighted the presence of *Trypanosoma* in rodents.

Uilenberg (1967) described *Achromaticus brygooi* (Piroplasmida, Babesiidae) in blood smears of *Setifer setosus* (family Tenrecidae; see Goodman and Soarimalala, pp. 1731–69, for information on these mammals). In his study, Uilenberg found that four out of the 15 screened specimens were positive for *A. brygooi*. He also reported previous experimental infections carried out by E. R. Brygoo, who challenged different captive mammal species (*Eulemur fulvus*, *Tenrec ecaudatus*, and laboratory mice) with blood from *S. setosus* infected with *A. brygooi*. All these attempts led to negative results. However, Uilenberg reports a possible infection of *Echinops telfairi* (family Tenrecidae) transmitted via blood from infected *S. setosus*.

The examination of blood smears from 69 *Hemicentetes semispinosus* (family Tenrecidae) revealed infection by *Hepatozoon* (Eucoccidiorida, Hepatozoidae) in 13 individuals; the identified form was named as a new species, *H. hoogstraali* (Uilenberg 1970). This is the only report of the presence of this genus of parasite in native Malagasy mammals, and the biology and life cycle were not defined, as only gametocytes were identified on the slides.

Trypanosoma infections have been reported in terrestrial small mammals from Madagascar. Two out of eight rodent species sampled in the Ranomafana National Park showed trypanosome infection. *Rattus rattus* (family Muridae), the only introduced rodent species in the sample, was found infected by *T. lewisi*, with infection rates ranging from 26% in 1998 to 47% in 2000. *Nesomys rufus* (subfamily Nesomyinae) was the only endemic rodent species found infected with a *Trypanosoma* sp., one that appeared morphologically different from *T. lewisi*, which led these authors to predict that *T. lewisi* was not a risk for the native rodent fauna (Laakkonen et al. 2003). An additional study on *Trypanosoma* infecting terrestrial native and introduced small mammals in the rural and forested regions of Fandriana and Ankazobe revealed that only *R. rattus* was infected by *T. lewisi* (M. Rasoanoro et al., unpublished data), supporting the previous hypothesis of an absence of effect of *T. lewisi* in native terrestrial small mammals.

CONCLUSION

In the years between 2010 and 2020, flying and terrestrial small mammals of Madagascar have been the subject of different studies focusing on micro- and macroparasites circulating in their blood. Until now, no information was available on the potential deleterious effect of these parasites on their hosts. Many aspects of the hematoparasites of Malagasy small mammals need to be elucidated, including their taxonomy and ecology. Future research will allow for better understanding of the drivers of blood parasite infection in these mammals and identification of potential interactions between microorganisms. Besides the importance of these parasites in terms of conservation (see Rasambainarivo and Zohdy, pp. 298–302, for information on pathogen pollution), such organisms could be useful biological models for addressing transmission networks within small-mammal communities and measuring the effects of environmental changes on disease transmission.

Subject editors: Pablo Tortosa and Steven M. Goodman

PATHOGEN POLLUTION: PATHOGEN TRANSMISSION BETWEEN INTRODUCED AND ENDEMIC SPECIES ON MADAGASCAR

F. Rasambainarivo and S. Zohdy

In different areas of our planet, human activities such as deforestation and hunting are threatening the survival of many wild animal species. Furthermore, accidental or intentional introductions of non-native organisms are exerting additional pressures on native wildlife (Boudjelas et al. 2000). In natural habitats, introduced animals have been shown to reduce or eliminate populations of endemic species through different mechanisms, such as direct predation or competition for available resources (Hughes and Macdonald 2013). Interactions between native and introduced organisms also present potential for "pathogen pollution," the introduction of a pathogen into a new geographic area or host species. Invaders may also act as additional competent hosts for native pathogens, thereby increasing infection rates of native species via spillback mechanisms (Lafferty and Gerber 2002; Kilpatrick et al. 2006). Lastly, invader-borne pathogens may have more subtle and persistent effects and alter the outcomes of trophic or competitive interactions through a process called apparent competition. This was illustrated by the success of the introduced *Sciurus carolinensis* (North American Gray Squirrel) and the decline of the native *S. vulgaris* (Eurasian Red Squirrel) in the United Kingdom, which was mediated through infection by a parapoxvirus (Rushton et al. 2000; Prenter et al. 2004). In general, species inhabiting island ecosystems tend to be more heavily affected by introduced species because they lack appropriate behavioral traits or immunological capacity, making them particularly vulnerable to the threat of introduced species and associated pathogens (Mooney and Cleland 2001; Medina et al. 2011). For example, high rates of bird extinction on Hawaii followed the introduction of arthropod vectors and the transmission of avian malaria and *Avipoxvirus* (van Riper et al. 1986, 2002).

Madagascar is a well-known biodiversity hotspot, and approximately 90% of plant and animal species are endemic, including all nonhuman primates (superfamily Lemuroidea), all native rodents (subfamily Nesomyinae), native carnivorans (family Eupleridae), and a radiation of insectivore-like animals (family Tenrecidae). The early separation of Madagascar from other landmasses also imposed different dispersal filters to many taxa that are otherwise present in nearby continental Africa (see Samonds et al., pp. 73–78). For instance, no member of the families Canidae, Felidae, and Bovidae is known to have naturally crossed the 400 km Mozambique Channel separating mainland Africa from Madagascar (see Goodman and Soarimalala, pp. 1737–69). This may have important implications for the sensitivity of Malagasy animals to diseases carried by introduced species.

The relatively recent human colonization of the island was associated with a series of introductions of domestic and peridomestic animals including zebu, dogs, cats, shrews (*Suncus* spp.), rats (*Rattus* spp.), and mice (*Mus musculus*). These introduced animals are negatively impacting endemic species and may even lead some native species to extinction (Goodman 1995; Farris et al. 2015, 2016; Dammhahn et al. 2017; Crowley et al. 2018). As elsewhere in the world, the reasons for the observed declines are likely a combination of factors including resource competition, predation, and disease (Vanak and Gompper 2010; J. Young et al. 2011; Ritchie et al. 2014). This contribution attempts to review the literature on pathogen establishment from non-native hosts and highlights the risk of pathogen introduction on the rich and unique fauna of Madagascar.

DISEASE RISKS TO AMPHIBIANS

The recent arrival of *Duttaphrynus melanostictus* (Asian Common Toad), introduced to the eastern part of Madagascar around 2010, is of concern for the endemic amphibian fauna for several reasons (see Freeman et al., pp. 1404–10). First, this invasive introduced amphibian may competitively exclude Malagasy amphibians, predate on smaller reptiles and amphibians, or affect Madagascar's native wildlife through its toxins (Döring et al. 2017; Reilly et al. 2017; Marshall et al. 2018). Additionally, this toad may spread pathogens to which Malagasy amphibians are not adapted. For instance, the chytrid fungus *Batrachochytrium dendrobatidis* (*Bd*) is a fungal pathogen that thickens amphibian skin, which in turn prevents osmoregulatory functions and is very often fatal (see Bletz et al., pp. 1342–49). This fungus is associated with major declines in amphibian populations worldwide. On Madagascar, *Bd* was recently detected on several anuran families across the island (Bletz et al. 2015a, 2015b). Although the detection of this specific pathogen in Malagasy anurans has not been empirically linked to the introduction of *Duttaphrynus*, further research is needed regarding any other pathogens the Asian Common Toad may carry.

Similarly, ranaviruses (genus *Ranavirus*) are viral amphibian pathogens responsible for mass mortalities of amphibians globally. On Madagascar, this virus type has been detected in several amphibians from two different sites but without noticeable population effects (Kolby et al. 2015; also see Bletz et al., pp. 1342–49). While some strains of chytrid fungus and ranaviruses may be endemic to Madagascar and may be benign to autochthonous species, the increase in economic trade, as well as human and animal movements into Madagascar, can lead to inadvertent introduction of amphibians and their pathogens. This situation warrants stringent precautionary measures, continuous monitoring, and pathogen surveillance of Madagascar's amphibian populations.

DISEASE RISKS TO BIRDS

Approximately 210 of the 304 bird species found on Madagascar are breeding residents, and only a few others undergo regular seasonal migration between sub-Saharan Africa and the Malagasy Region (see Safford et al., pp. 1553–602). In addition, several species were introduced either intentionally, for food production (e.g., poultry and other domestic fowl) or pest control (*Acridotheres tristis*, Common Myna), or accidentally (*Passer domesticus*, House Sparrow, and *Corvus splendens*, House Crow; see Safford et al., pp. 1553–602; Meier et al., pp. 1704–7). These non-native birds may facilitate the introduction of pathogens and pose different threats to the native Malagasy avifauna, as has been the case for bird populations elsewhere (van Riper et al. 1986, 2002; Parker et al. 2011).

Among the pathogens of concern to avian hosts, West Nile Virus (WNV), transmitted by mosquitoes, is a member of the Flaviviridae family, widely distributed in parts of the Old World (see Héraud et al., pp. 285–91). This virus was introduced to North America and caused morbidity and mortality of birds and mammals in the United States and Canada. On Madagascar, evidence of WNV exposure was found in several species of birds and mammals but to date has not been associated with population declines in the resident avifauna (McLean et al. 2002; Sondgeroth et al. 2007; Tantely et al. 2015, 2016b). In fact, the phylogenetics of the WNV strains isolated on Madagascar suggest a local WNV transmission cycle with no new recent viral introduction, despite the biannual migratory movements of birds, particularly waterbirds, between Eurasia and Africa, as well as the introduction of several bird and arthropod species on the island (Maquart et al. 2016). The introduction to Madagascar of a foreign strain of WNV may, however, have a dramatic effect on the local fauna.

Similarly, Newcastle Disease Virus (NDV) is a member of the family Paramyxoviridae (see Hoarau et al., pp. 277–85) that is distributed throughout the world and infects a range of birds. Virulent forms of this virus cause widespread and highly contagious disease in domestic and wild birds. On Madagascar, NDV is responsible for high mortality of chickens and also has been detected in wild bird species. Both domestic and wild birds appeared to be infected by the genotype XI of NDV (Maminiaina et al. 2007), suggesting viral transmission between wild and domestic birds, which may potentially affect either the native or introduced bird populations via spillover and spillback mechanisms (Servan de Almeida et al. 2013; Cappelle et al. 2015).

Mycoplasmosis, caused by *Mycoplasma gallisepticum* infection, is another disease of concern in avian hosts. Although *Mycoplasma* infections may remain clinically asymptomatic, they can make birds more prone to secondary infections such as NDV (Levisohn and Kleven 2000; Michiels et al. 2016). *Mycoplasma gallisepticum* primarily infects poultry but has also been described in many different bird species worldwide and is responsible for disease and population declines of passerines in North America (Hartup et al. 2001; Dhondt et al. 2005, 2017). This suggests that poultry can act as a reservoir of the pathogen for the endemic avifauna. In Madagascar, *M. gallisepticum* has been detected in backyard chickens neighboring protected areas as well as in live poultry markets, and such trade may facilitate its dissemination geographically and potentially to the endemic avifauna (F. Rasambainarivo, unpublished data).

DISEASE RISKS TO LEMURS

The future existence of the vast majority of lemur species on Madagascar is uncertain, as these mammals are facing multiple threats, mainly associated with human activities, including habitat destruction and fragmentation. Studies on the island have shown that lemurs living in habitats disturbed by human activities have compromised health conditions compared to those living in more pristine habitats (Irwin et al. 2010; Junge et al. 2011; Rasambainarivo et al. 2013; Bublitz et al., 2015; Zohdy et al. 2015; Ragazzo et al. 2018). This may affect lemur populations by reducing their fitness or facilitating the transmission of pathogens from introduced species. For example, the human-adapted protozoan *Cryptosporidium hominis* is now known in several lemur species living in Ranomafana National Park, such as *Microcebus rufus* and *Prolemur simus*, and in *Lemur catta* in southwestern Madagascar (Villers et al. 2008; Rasambainarivo et al. 2013). This fecally transmitted waterborne zoonotic protozoan has a high prevalence in people, domestic animals, and peridomestic rodents inhabiting villages in the vicinity of forested areas and was most likely transmitted to lemurs as a result of human encroachment (Bodager et al. 2015). In captive lemurs, *Cryptosporidium* sp. has caused high morbidity and mortality (Charles-Smith et al. 2010).

Similarly, lemurs inhabiting anthropogenically disturbed habitats are more likely to be infected with fecally transmitted, potentially pathogenic enterobacteria (family Enterobacteraceae) commonly found in humans, livestock, or peridomestic rodents, such as enterotoxigenic *Escherichia coli*, *Shigella* spp., *Salmonella* spp., *Yersinia* spp. or *Vibrio cholerae*, which are major causes of diarrhea and mortality in captive lemurs (Bublitz et al. 2014, 2015). For another example, the causative agent of amoebic dysentery, *Entamoeba histolytica*, which is typically thought of as a human pathogen, was recently detected in wild lemurs. Specifically, *Prolemur simus*, *Microcebus rufus*, and *Eulemur rufifrons* living in the Ranomafana National Park were found to be infected. Of critical importance with regard to human encroachment, those lemurs living in close proximity to settlements were more at risk of being infected with *Entamoeba histolytica* (Ragazzo et al. 2018).

Additionally, a diverse group of fecally transmitted enteric viruses known to cause diarrheal disease in humans, including adenoviruses, enteroviruses, rotaviruses, and noroviruses (genogroups GI and GII), was detected in wild lemur species in Ranomafana National Park (Zohdy et al. 2015). Specifically, seven species of lemur (*P. simus*, *M. rufus*, *Avahi laniger*, *E. rufifrons*, *E. rubriventer*, *Hapalemur aureus*, and *Propithecus edwardsi*) were found to be positive for one or more enteric virus, and neighboring human communities were positive for all four viral groups. Of the lemurs tested, *M. rufus* was found to have the highest infection prevalence for the enteric viruses. In the region of study, uninhibited defecation by humans at the edge of the village is a common practice (Wegner 2013), and it is possible that *M. rufus* living in degraded habitats encounter human pathogens more frequently than those occurring in relatively intact and secondary forest; these aspects may explain the high prevalence of these pathogens in the tested *Microcebus*. While the severity and symptoms of these pathogens associated with infection in lemur species remain to be explored, detection of human pathogens in wild primates living near human communities emphasizes the transmission and zoonotic potential of fecally transmitted enteric pathogens when lemurs and humans share an ecosystem.

Domestic dogs and cats, often associated with human settlements, may also spread pathogens that can potentially affect endemic primate populations. For example, the causative agent of canine heartworm disease, *Dirofilaria immitis*, is a mosquito-borne blood nematode that presents a significant health threat to dogs, and research in the last decade has revealed its zoonotic potential and global distribution. *Microcebus rufus* living in locations in southeastern Madagascar where there is high occupancy of free-roaming dogs have been found infected with *D. immitis* (Zohdy et al. 2019). The detection of this parasite in wild primates suggests that mosquitoes infected with *D. immitis* are blood feeding on lemurs, transmitting the parasite, and acting as bridge vectors between free-roaming introduced carnivorans and lemurs. Similarly, the spirurid parasite *Spirocerca lupi* is a nematode parasite that is prevalent in free-roaming rural dogs on the island. This parasite is presumably responsible for the death of several captive lemurs through the formation of aortic aneurysms and their subsequent rupture (Alexander et al. 2016). Whether *S. lupi* negatively affects endemic populations of lemurs and carnivorans is unknown and warrants further research.

DISEASE RISKS TO ENDEMIC CARNIVORANS

Madagascar's native carnivorans belong to an endemic family, the Eupleridae (see Veron et al., pp. 1863–65), and are among the least studied and arguably most endangered members of the order Carnivora in the world, as they face hunting pressures, habitat degradation, and competition and predation from introduced carnivorans (Brooke et al. 2014). In recorded history, three species of carnivorans, the domestic cat, domestic dog, and Indian civet (*Viverricula indica*), were introduced to Madagascar and are now widely distributed, even inside protected areas (Ardalan et al. 2015; Gaubert et al. 2017). In addition, several species of endemic carnivorans are often observed in or near villages neighboring forested areas, thus overlapping in space with dogs and cats within and outside natural habitats (Farris et al. 2015, 2016; Kotschwar Logan et al. 2015). These interactions may potentially facilitate the transmission of directly transmitted pathogens such as Rabies Virus and Canine Distemper Virus (also known as Canine Morbillivirus; see Hoarau et al., pp. 277–85). For example, Rabies Virus has circulated in Madagascar since the 19th century, and dogs constitute the main source of rabies for humans and other animals on the island (Reynes et al. 2011; see also Hoarau et al., pp. 277–85). Reports of rabies (RABV) in wild Malagasy animals are rare, but a strain of *Lyssavirus* has been isolated from the euplerid *Cryptoprocta ferox* (Figure 6.12) and was confirmed to be RABV and phylogenetically close to that circulating in dogs on Madagascar (Reynes et al. 2011). Since rabies is transmitted primarily through bites, this result indicates that dogs and *Cryptoprocta* are interacting directly and, in some cases, may share pathogens.

The absence of detection of Canine Distemper Virus antibodies in Malagasy carnivorans deserves a remark, as it may result from the absence of exposure to infective domestic dogs or from inadequate diagnostic methods. Another explanation is that infected euplerids succumb to the virus. A morbillivirus member of the Paramyxoviridae family, this virus is a lethal pathogen for a large number of terrestrial and marine mammal species (Beineke et al. 2015; Viana et al. 2015; Avendaño et al. 2016). It is considered one of the most important pathogens of Carnivora worldwide, responsible for mortalities in these animals around the globe (Deem et al. 2000). On Madagascar, the seroprevalence against canine distemper in domestic dogs inhabiting villages neighboring protected areas is high, highlighting the risk of transmission of this important pathogen between sympatric species and urging a surveillance of this virus in endemic carnivores (Pomerantz et al. 2016; Rasambainarivo et al. 2018). Serological analyses carried out on dogs and endemic carnivorans on Madagascar indicate an enzootic transmission of Canine Distemper Virus between dogs, with potential spillover to endemic euplerids (Pomerantz et al. 2016; Rasambainarivo et al. 2018). In fact, euplerids of two species, *Mungotictis decemlineata* and *Galidia elegans*, presented

FIGURE 6.12 **Young adult *Cryptoprocta ferox* (Fosa) from eastern lowland moist evergreen forest in the Betampona protected area. Members of the Eupleridae from this protected area were shown to interact and exchange pathogens with domestic animals from neighboring villages.** (PHOTO by F. Rasambainarivo.)

serological signatures of previous infections with this canine pathogen, but the effects of these infections on endemic carnivore populations remain unknown.

Introduced and endemic animals may also indirectly transmit infectious agents to one another through contaminated environments. The time interval between visits by a domestic or feral animal and a native animal may be sufficiently short to allow transmission of pathogens such as Canine Parvovirus (family Paroviridae) or any other environmentally resistant pathogens (Rasambainarivo et al. 2017). In different portions of the world, Canine Parvovirus may be transmitted between a wide variety of hosts, including species of Felidae, Canidae, Procyonidae, Mustelidae, Ursidae, and Viveridae, causing a wide range of symptoms including hemorrhagic gastroenteritis and myocarditis in some cases (Steinel et al. 2001). Similarly, a large proportion of the euplerids evaluated in different protected areas of Madagascar had antibodies against *Toxoplasma gondii* (Pomerantz et al. 2016; Rasambainarivo et al. 2018). The only known definitive hosts of this protozoan parasite are members of the family Felidae, represented in Madagascar by introduced cats. Evidence of exposure to this parasite in endemic species indicates a pathogen spillover from introduced to endemic carnivorans. This parasite has been associated with neurological disease and death in several captive Malagasy species (Spencer et al., 2004; Corpa et al., 2013), but its influence on the wild endemic euplerid and lemur populations is unknown.

On Madagascar, there is little recent information on ectoparasites and the transmission of vector-borne diseases between introduced animal species and endemic carnivorans. Ectoparasites, including ticks (see Klompen and Apanaskevich, pp. 894–99) and fleas (see Duchemin et al., pp. 1074–80), are major arthropod vectors of blood-borne pathogens such as plague, babesiosis, and ehrlichiosis, to name a few. Recent research has uncovered the presence of blood parasites in Malagasy carnivorans, which are likely transmitted by arthropods, but it appears that in some cases these parasites may be species-specific and endemic rather than the result of pathogen pollution from introduced species (F. Rasambainarivo, unpublished data). Further research is needed to elucidate this potential, especially because some arthropod ectoparasites infest both domestic animals and endemic wildlife, as recently reported in southwestern Madagascar, where *Galidictis fasciata grandidieri* was found infested with *Echidnophaga gallinacea*, an introduced flea species found on a wide range of birds and mammals worldwide (Ehlers et al. 2019).

DISEASE RISKS TO ENDEMIC RODENTS

On Christmas Island, in the eastern Indian Ocean, the trypanostomid parasite *Trypanosoma lewisii*, hosted by *Rattus rattus* (family Muridae), was associated with the infection and subsequent decline of a native rodent, *R. macleari*; the last verified record of Maclear's Rat was in 1903 (Wyatt et al. 2008). On Madagascar, such zoonotic disease transmission between introduced *R. rattus* and members of the endemic subfamily Nesomyinae is a concern. However, it seems that native rodents harbor different species of trypanostomid parasites than introduced murid counterparts (see Ramasindrazana et al., pp. 294–97). In the Ranomafana National Park, 30% of *R. rattus* individuals examined during a survey were infected by *T. lewisii*, while the native sympatric nesomyines belonging to the genus *Eliurus* were infected with a morphologically different trypanostomid (Laakkonen et al. 2003). The authors suggest that native rodents may not be infected by the parasite from introduced species or that the invasion of *Rattus* in the interior of the park has not resulted in the transmission of these parasites, highlighting the need for surveillance of this potentially devastating parasite in the endemic rodent fauna of Madagascar.

Recent research on Madagascar has revealed a virus of the genus *Morbillivirus*, currently placed with the Unclassified Morbilli-related paramyxoviruses (UMRVs) (Wilkinson et al. 2014a), that is thought to be widespread among endemic rodents, tenrecs, and bats, as well as introduced rodents, specifically *R. rattus*. Members of the Paramyxoviridae viral family have been associated with a number of emerging diseases that affect humans and natural animal populations, but only a few UMRVs have been reported to cause diseases in their natural animal hosts (Ghawar et al. 2017). Evidence indicates that *R. rattus* is an important spreader of UMRVs and that there is considerable lateral exchange of UMRVs between sympatrically occurring mammals, including rodents and bats (see Figure 6.8), which may thereby constitute a risk to the native fauna (Wilkinson et al. 2014a; Mélade et al. 2016a; Ghawar et al. 2017; see also Hoarau et al., pp. 277–85).

On Madagascar, endemic and introduced rodents are also known to exchange a number of ectoparasites, including the fleas *Synopsyllus estradei*, *S. fonquerniei*, and *Paractenopsyllus* spp., which have been observed on several species of Nesomyinae rodents and introduced *R. rattus* in forested protected areas (Goodman et al. 2015; Harimalala et al. 2018). Both *R. rattus* and *S. fonquerniei* are known reservoirs of *Yersinia pestis*, the causative agent of plague, especially in the rural areas of the Central Highlands (Andrianaivoarimanana et al. 2013). Similarly, blood parasites of the genus *Bartonella* were detected in *Rattus* hosts and associated arthropod ectoparasites in Madagascar (Brook et al. 2015). Despite the detection of *Y. pestis* and *Bartonella* in endemic rodents of Madagascar and their ectoparasites (Ehlers et al. 2020), it is unclear whether infection by these pathogens leads to disease and affects the health of endemic rodents, or if these rodent species may constitute reservoirs of pathogens and sources of outbreaks on the island.

EFFECTS OF INTRODUCED SPECIES ON THE ECOLOGY OF NATIVE PARASITES

While this contribution focuses on pathogen spillover from introduced and in some cases invasive species to native wildlife, there are also ways in which invasive species may influence the ecology of native parasites, by modifying risk of infection in native species. In a recent paper (Chalkowski et al. 2018), several new hypotheses were introduced presenting potential research questions and avenues for the exploration of mechanisms involved in pathogen spillover from invasive species to native wildlife. One hypothesis, termed *disease facilitation*, suggests that invasive species may increase risk of infection with native parasites in native wildlife by 1) amplifying parasites within the ecosystem (as reservoirs or vectors), 2) mechanically altering the exposure through habitat modifications that improve conditions for native parasites, or 3) dispersing pathogens from one place to another. *Suppressive spillover* is another hypothesis, in which parasites (native or invasive) may limit or suppress a species' ability to expand and become invasive. Such hypotheses need to be explored on Madagascar using introduced species and parasites as models. Few examples of this exist in the literature, but future research programs conducted on the island may help in understanding how parasites can alter the ability of introduced species to become invasive.

CONCLUSIONS

Introduced species are an increasingly dominant part of many natural and human-modified landscapes. It is estimated that introduced species, particularly invasive mammal predators such as dogs and cats, have caused the extinction of at least 87 bird species, 45 mammal species, and 10 reptile species worldwide, and they are currently threatening many more (Doherty et al. 2015, 2016). Some of these extinctions may have been mediated by the introduction of pathogens (H. S. Young et al. 2017). On Madagascar, several of the so-called worst invasive species have been introduced since human colonization. The impacts of pathogens associated with such invasive species on the fauna of Madagascar warrant further research. Through monitoring and surveillance activities, generated data will ultimately pave the way to successful strategies aimed at managing the risks of pathogen pollution and mitigating disease spillover to the native fauna of Madagascar.

Subject editors: Pablo Tortosa and Steven M. Goodman

REFERENCES

Abravanel, F., Lhomme, S., Chapuy-Regaud, S., Mansuy, J.-M., Muscari, F., Sallusto, F., Rostaing, L., Kamar, N., and Izopet, J. 2014. Hepatitis E virus reinfections in solid-organ-transplant recipients can evolve into chronic infections. *Journal of Infectious Diseases* 209: 1900–1906.

Afonso, C. L., Amarasinghe, G. K., Bányai, K., Bào, Y., Basler, C. F., et al. 2016. Taxonomy of the order Mononegavirales: Update 2016. *Archives of Virology* 161: 2351–2360.

Aksoy, S., Weiss, B. L., and Attardo, G. M. 2014. Trypanosome transmission dynamics in tsetse. *Current Opinion in Insect Science* 3: 43–49.

Alexander, A. B., Poirotte, C., Porton, I. J., Freeman, K.L.M., Rasambainarivo, F., Olson, K. G., Iambana, B., and Deem, S. L. 2016. Gastrointestinal parasites of captive and free-living lemurs and domestic carnivores in eastern Madagascar. *Journal of Zoo and Wildlife Medicine* 47: 141–149.

Allnutt, T. F., Ferrier, S., Manion, G., Powell, G.V.N., Ricketts, T. H., et al. 2008. A method for quantifying biodiversity loss and its application to a 50-year record of deforestation across Madagascar: Extinction estimates in Madagascar from deforestation. *Conservation Letters* 1: 173–181.

Almeida, F. C., Giannini, N. P., Simmons, N. B., and Helgen, K. M. 2014. Each flying fox on its own branch: A phylogenetic tree for *Pteropus* and related genera (Chiroptera: Pteropodidae). *Molecular Phylogenetics and Evolution* 77: 83–95.

Amarasinghe, G. K., Ayllón, M. A., Bào, Y., Basler, C. F., Bavari, S., et al. 2019. Taxonomy of the order Mononegavirales: Update 2019. *Archives of Virology* 164: 1967–1980.

Andriamandimby, S. F., Randrianarivo-Solofoniaina, A. E., Jeanmaire, E. M., Ravololomanana, L., Razafimanantsoa, L. T., et al. 2010. Rift Valley fever during rainy seasons, Madagascar, 2008 and 2009. *Emerging Infectious Diseases* 16: 963–970.

Andriamandimby, S. F., Marianneau, P., Rafisandratantsoa, J.-T., Rollin, P. E., Héraud, J.-M., Tordo, N., and Reynes, J.-M. 2011. Crimean-Congo hemorrhagic fever serosurvey in at-risk professionals, Madagascar, 2008 and 2009. *Journal of Clinical Virology* 52: 370–372.

Andriamandimby, S. [F.], Héraud, J.-M., Ramiandrasoa, R., Ratsitorahina, M., Rasambainarivo, J. H., Dacheux, L., Lepelletier, A., Goodman, S. M., Reynes, J.-M., and Bourhy, H. 2013. Surveillance and control of rabies in La Réunion, Mayotte, and Madagascar. *Veterinary Research* 44: 77.

Andrianaivoarimanana, V., Kreppel, K., Elissa, N., Duplantier, J.-M., Carniel, E., Rajerison, M., and Jambou, R. 2013. Understanding the persistence of plague foci in Madagascar. *PLoS Neglected Tropical Diseases* 7: e2382.

Appleton, H., and Higgins, P. G. 1975. Viruses and gastroenteritis in infants. *Lancet* 1(7919): 1297.

Ardalan, A., Oskarsson, M.C.R., van Asch, B., Rabakonandriania, E., and Savolainen, P. 2015. African origin for Madagascan dogs revealed by mtDNA analysis. *Royal Society Open Science* 2: 140552.

Assiri, A., McGeer, A., Perl, T. M., Price, C. S., Al Rabeeah, A. A., et al. 2013. Hospital outbreak of Middle East respiratory syndrome coronavirus. *New England Journal of Medicine* 369: 407–416.

Avendaño, R., Barrueta, F., Soto-Fournier, S., Chavarría, M., Monge, O., Gutiérrez-Espeleta, G. A., and Chaves, A. 2016. Canine distemper virus in wild felids of Costa Rica. *Journal of Wildlife Disease* 52: 373–377.

Baas Becking, L. G. M. 1934. *Geobiologie of inleiding tot de milieukunde*. The Hague: W. P. Van Stockum and Zoon.

Bain, O., Casiraghi, M., Martin, C., and Uni, S. 2008. The Nematoda Filarioidea: Critical analysis linking molecular and traditional approaches. *Parasite* 15: 342–348.

Banyard, A. C., Hayman, D., Johnson, N., McElhinney, L., and Fooks, A. R. 2011. Bats and lyssaviruses. *Advances in Virus Research* 79: 239–289.

Beineke, A., Baumgärtner, W., and Wohlsein, P. 2015. Cross-species transmission of canine distemper virus: An update. *One Health* 1: 49–59.

Bell, T., Ager, D., Song, J.-I., Newman, J. A., Thompson, I. P., Lilley, A. K., and van der Gast, C. J. 2005. Larger islands house more bacterial taxa. *Science* 308: 1884.

Bente, D. A., Forrester, N. L., Watts, D. M., McAuley, A. J., Whitehouse, C. A., and Bray, M. 2013. Crimean-Congo hemorrhagic fever: History, epidemiology, pathogenesis, clinical syndrome and genetic diversity. *Antiviral Research* 100: 159–189.

Binder, S. 1999. Emerging infectious diseases: Public health issues for the 21st century. *Science* 284: 1311–1313.

Biscornet, L., Dellagi, K., Pagès, F., Bibi, J., de Comarmond, J., et al. 2017. Human leptospirosis in Seychelles: A prospective study confirms the heavy burden of the disease but suggests that rats are not the main reservoir. *PLoS Neglected Tropical Diseases* 11: e0005831.

Bletz, M. C., Rosa, G. M., Andreone, F., Courtois, E. A., Schmeller, D. S., et al. 2015a. Consistency of published results on the pathogen *Batrachochytrium dendrobatidis* in Madagascar: Formal comment on Kolby et al. rapid response to evaluate the presence of amphibian *Chytrid fungus* (*Batrachochytrium dendrobatidis*) and Ranavirus in wild amphibian populations in Madagascar. *PLoS One* 10: e0135900.

———. 2015b. Widespread presence of the pathogenic fungus *Batrachochytrium dendrobatidis* in wild amphibian communities in Madagascar. *Scientific Reports* 5: 8633.

Bodager, J. R., Parsons, M. B., Wright, P. C., Rasambainarivo, F., Roellig, D., Xiao, L., and Gillespie, T. R. 2015. Complex epidemiology and zoonotic potential for *Cryptosporidium suis* in rural Madagascar. *Veterinary Parasitology* 207: 140–143.

Bonnet, S. I., Binetruy, F., Hernández-Jarguín, A. M., and Duron, O. 2017. The tick microbiome: Why non-pathogenic microorganisms matter in tick biology and pathogen transmission. *Frontiers in Cellular and Infection Microbiology* 7:236.

Bosch, A., Pintó, R. M., and Guix, S. 2014. Human astroviruses. *Clinical Microbiology Reviews* 27: 1048–1074.

Boudjelas, S., Browne, M., De Poorter, M., and Lowe, S. 2000. 100 of the world's worst invasive alien species: A selection from the Global Invasive Species Database. Auckland: IUCN Species Survival Commission.

Bourhy, P., Collet, L., Clément, S., Huerre, M., Ave, P., Giry, C., Pettinelli, F., and Picardeau, M. 2010. Isolation and characterization of new *Leptospira* genotypes from patients in Mayotte (Indian Ocean). *PLoS Neglected Tropical Diseases* 4: e724.

Bourhy, P., Collet, L., Lernout, T., Zinini, F., Hartskeerl, R. A., et al. 2012. Human *Leptospira* isolates circulating in Mayotte (Indian Ocean) have unique serological and molecular features. *Journal of Clinical Microbiology* 50: 307–311.

Bourhy, P., Collet, L., Brisse, S., and Picardeau, M. 2014. *Leptospira mayottensis* sp. nov., a pathogenic *Leptospira* species isolated from humans. *International Journal of Systematic and Evolutionary Microbiology* 64: 4061–4067.

Brook, C. E., Bai, Y., Dobson, A. P., Osikowicz, L. M., Ranaivoson, H. C., Zhu, Q., Kosoy, M. Y., and Dittmar, K. 2015. *Bartonella* spp. in fruit bats and blood-feeding ectoparasites in Madagascar. *PLoS Neglected Tropical Diseases* 9: e0003532.

Brook, C. E., Ranaivoson, H. C., Broder, C. C., Cunningham, A. A., Héraud, J., Peel, A. J., Gibson, L., Wood, J.L.N., Metcalf, C. J., and Dobson, A. P. 2019. Disentangling serology to elucidate henipa- and filovirus transmission in Madagascar fruit bats. *Journal of Animal Ecology* 88: 1001–1016.

Brooke, Z. M., Bielby, J., Nambiar, K., and Carbone, C. 2014. Correlates of research effort in carnivores: Body size, range size and diet matter. *PLoS One* 9: e93195.

Brygoo, E. R., and Kolochine-Erber, B. 1956. Research on leptospirosis in Madagascar. *Bulletin de la Société de Pathologie Exotique* 49: 686–698.

Brygoo, E. R., and Sureau, P. 1960. La rage à Madagascar de 1901 à 1958. *Archives Institut Pasteur Madagascar* 28: 61–96.

Bublitz, D. C., Wright, P. C., Bodager, J. R., Rasambainarivo, F. T., Bliska, J. B., and Gillespie, T. R. 2014. Epidemiology of pathogenic enterobacteria in humans, livestock, and peridomestic rodents in rural Madagascar. *PLoS One* 9: e101456.

Bublitz, D. C., Wright, P. C., Rasambainarivo, F. T., Arrigo-Nelson, S. J., Bodager, J. R., and Gillespie, T. R. 2015. Pathogenic enterobacteria in lemurs associated with anthropogenic disturbance. *American Journal of Primatology* 77: 330–337.

Buck, G., Kolochine-Erber, B., and Quesnel, J. 1956. Bovine leptospirosis should be suspected in Madagascar. *Bulletin de la Société de Pathologie Exotique* 49: 681–686.

Bulach, D. M., Zuerner, R. L., Wilson, P., Seemann, T., McGrath, A., et al. 2006. Genome reduction in *Leptospira borgpetersenii* reflects limited transmission potential. *Proceedings of the National Academy of Sciences of the USA* 103: 14560–14565.

Cameron, C. E. 2015. Leptospiral structure, physiology, and metabolism. *Current Topics in Microbiology and Immunology* 387: 21–41.

Cameron, E. K., Martins, I. S., Lavelle, P., Mathieu, J., Tedersoo, L., et al. 2018. Global gaps in soil biodiversity data. *Nature Ecology and Evolution* 2: 1042–1043.

Cappelle, J., Caron, A., Servan de Almeida, R., Gil, P., Pedrono, M., et al. 2015. Empirical analysis suggests continuous and homogeneous circulation of Newcastle disease virus in a wide range of wild bird species in Africa. *Epidemiology and Infection* 143: 1292–1303.

Cardinale, E., Bernard, C., Lecollinet, S., Rakotoharinome, V. M., Ravaomanana, J., et al. 2017. West Nile virus infection in horses, Indian Ocean. *Comparative Immunology, Microbiology and Infectious Diseases* 53: 45–49.

Carroll, S. A., Reynes, J.-M., Khristova, M. L., Andriamandimby, S. F., Rollin, P. E., and Nichol, S. T. 2011. Genetic evidence for Rift Valley fever outbreaks in Madagascar resulting from virus introductions from the East African mainland rather than enzootic maintenance. *Journal of Virology* 85: 6162–6167.

Cassel-Beraud, A. M., Fontenille, D., and Rabetafika, L. 1989. Etude bactérienne, virale et parasitaire d'une population de chauves-souris *Chaerephon pumila* à Anjiro, Madagascar. *Archives de l'Institut Pasteur de Madagascar* 56: 233–239.

CDC. 2018. Viral hemorrhagic fevers (VHFs): Filoviruses (Filoviridae). https://www.cdc.gov/vhf/virus-families/filoviridae.html.

Chalkowski, K., Lepczyk, C. A., and Zohdy, S. 2018. Parasite ecology of invasive species: Conceptual framework and new hypotheses. *Trends in Parasitology* 34: 655–663.

Chan, J.F.-W., To, K.K.-W., Tse, H., Jin, D.-Y., and Yuen, K.-Y. 2013. Interspecies transmission and emergence of novel viruses: Lessons from bats and birds. *Trends in Microbiology* 21: 544–555.

Charles-Smith, L. E., Cowen, P., and Schopler, R. 2010. Environmental and physiological factors contributing to outbreaks of *Cryptosporidium* in Coquerel's sifaka (*Propithecus coquereli*) at the Duke Lemur Center: 1999–2007. *Journal of Zoo and Wildlife Medicine* 41: 438–444.

Chevalier, V., Rakotondrafara, T., Jourdan, M., Héraud, J.-M., Andriamanivo, H. R., Durand, B., Ravaomanana, J., Rollin, P. E., and Rakotondravao, R. 2011. An unexpected recurrent transmission of Rift Valley fever virus in cattle in a temperate and mountainous area of Madagascar. *PLoS Neglected Tropical Diseases* 5: e1423.

Clerc, Y., Coulanges, P., Rodhain, F., Ricklin, B., Ranaivosata, J., and Albignac, R. 1981. Le programme arbovirus de l'Institut Pasteur de Madagascar: Bilan actuel. *Archives de l'Institut Pasteur de Madagascar* 48: 247–257.

Cole, J. R., Wang, Q., Fish, J. A., Chai, B., McGarrell, D. M., Sun, Y., Brown, C. T., Porras-Alfaro, A., Kuske, C. R., and Tiedje, J. M. 2014. Ribosomal Database Project: Data and tools for high throughput rRNA analysis. *Nucleic Acids Research* 42: 633–642.

Cordonin, C., Turpin, M., Bascands, J. L., Dellagi, K., Mavingui, P., Tortosa, P., and Roche, M. 2019. Three *Leptospira* strains from Western Indian Ocean wildlife show highly distinct virulence phenotypes through hamster experimental infection. *Frontiers in Microbiology* 10: 382.

Cordonin, C., Turpin, M., Bringart, M., Bascands, J. L., Flores, O., Dellagi, K., Mavingui, P., Roche, M., and Tortosa, P. 2020. Pathogenic *Leptospira* and their animal reservoirs: Testing host specificity through experimental infection. *Scientific Reports* 10: 7239.

Corduneanu, A., Hrazdilová, K., Sándor, A. D., Matei, I. A., Ionică, A. M., et al. 2017. *Babesia vesperuginis*, a neglected piroplasmid: New host and geographical records, and phylogenetic relations. *Parasites and Vectors* 10: 598.

Corpa, J. M., García-Quirós, A., Casares, M., Gerique, A. C., Carbonell, M. D., Gómez-Muñoz, M. T., Uzal, F. A., and Ortega, J. 2013. Encephalomyelitis by *Toxoplasma gondii* in a captive fossa (*Cryptoprocta ferox*). *Veterinary Parasitology* 193: 281–283.

Cosson, J.-F., Picardeau, M., Mielcarek, M., Tatard, C., Chaval, Y., Suputtamongkol, Y., Buchy, P., Jittapalapong, S., Herbreteau, V., and Morand, S. 2014. Epidemiology of *Leptospira* transmitted by rodents in Southeast Asia. *PLoS Neglected Tropical Diseases* 8: e2902.

Costa, F., Hagan, J. E., Calcagno, J., Kane, M., Torgerson, P., Martinez-Silveira, M. S., Stein, C., Abela-Ridder, B., and Ko, A. I. 2015. Global morbidity and mortality of leptospirosis: A systematic review. *PLoS Neglected Tropical Diseases* 9: e0003898.

Coulanges, P., Robin, Y., Le Gonidec, G., Mayoux, A., and Bordahandy, R. 1974. Chiroptères et arbovirus à Madagascar (isolement de souches de virus Dakar-bat—étude sérologique de chauves-souris frugivores). *Archives de l'Institut Pasteur de Madagascar* 43(1): 109–118.

Counotte, M. J., Kim, C. R., Wang, J., Bernstein, K., Deal, C. D., Broutet, N.J.N., and Low, N. 2018. Sexual transmission of Zika virus and other flaviviruses: A living systematic review. *PLoS Medicine* 15(7): e1002611.

Crowley, B. E., Castro, I., Soarimalala, V., and Goodman, S. M. 2018. Isotopic evidence for niche partitioning and the influence of anthropogenic disturbance on endemic and introduced rodents in central Madagascar. *Naturwissenschaften* 105: 44.

Cui, J., Li, F., and Shi, Z.-L. 2019. Origin and evolution of pathogenic coronaviruses. *Nature Reviews Microbiology* 17: 181–192.

Dammhahn, M., Randriamoria, T. M., and Goodman, S. M. 2017. Broad and flexible stable isotope niches in invasive non-native *Rattus* spp. in anthropogenic and natural habitats of central eastern Madagascar. *BMC Ecology* 17: 16.

De Clerck, C., Tsuchida, T., Massart, S., Lepoivre, P., Francis, F., and Jijakli, M. H. 2014. Combination of genomic and proteomic approaches to characterize the symbiotic population of the banana aphid (Hemiptera: Aphididae). *Environmental Entomology* 43: 29–36.

Deem, S. L., Spelman, L. H., Yates, R. A., and Montali, R. J. 2000. Canine distemper in terrestrial carnivores: A review. *Journal of Zoo and Wildlife Medicine* 31: 441–451.

Deiner, K., Bik, H. M., Mächler, E., Seymour, M., Lacoursière-Roussel, A., et al. 2017. *Molecular Ecology* 26: 5872–5895.

Delarocque-Astagneau, E., Abravanel, F., Moshen, A., Le Fouler, L., Gad, R. R., et al. 2012. Epidemiological and virological characteristics of symptomatic acute hepatitis E in Greater Cairo, Egypt. *Clinical Microbiology and Infection* 18: 982–988.

Dellagi, K., Salez, N., Maquart, M., Larrieu, S., Yssouf, A., Silaï, R., Leparc-Goffart, I., Tortosa, P., and de Lamballerie, X. 2016. Serological evidence of contrasted exposure to arboviral infections between islands of the Union of the Comoros (Indian Ocean). *PLoS Neglected Tropical Diseases* 10: e0004840.

Dequiedt, S., Saby, N.P.A., Lelievre, M., Jolivet, C., Thioulouse, J., Toutain, B., Arrouays, D., Bispo, A., Lemanceau, P., and Ranjard, L. 2011. Biogeographical patterns of soil molecular microbial biomass as influenced by soil characteristics and management. *Global Ecology and Biogeography* 20: 641–652.

Derne, B. T., Fearnley, E. J., Lau, C. L., Paynter, S., and Weinstein, P. 2011. Biodiversity and leptospirosis risk: A case of pathogen regulation? *Medical Hypotheses* 77: 339–344.

DeSantis, T. Z., Hugenholtz, P., Larsen, N., Rojas, M., Brodie, E. L., Keller, K., Huber, T., Dalevi, D., Hu, P., and Andersen, G. L. 2006. Greengenes, a chimera-checked 16S rRNA gene database and workbench compatible with ARB. *Applied and Environmental Microbiology* 72: 5069–5072.

Desvars, A., Naze, F., Vourc'h, G., Cardinale, E., Picardeau, M., Michault, A., and Bourhy, P. 2012. Similarities in *Leptospira* serogroup and species distribution in animals and humans in the Indian Ocean island of Mayotte. *American Journal of Tropical Medicine and Hygiene* 87: 134–140.

Dhondt, A. A., Altizer, S., Cooch, E. G., Davis, A. K., Dobson, A., et al. 2005. Dynamics of a novel pathogen in an avian host: Mycoplasmal conjunctivitis in house finches. *Acta Tropica* 94: 77–93.

Dhondt, A. A., Dhondt, K. V., and Nazeri, S. 2017. Apparent effect of chronic *Plasmodium* infections on disease severity caused by experimental infections with *Mycoplasma gallisepticum* in house finches. *International Journal of Parasitology: Parasites and Wildlife* 6: 49–53.

Dietrich, M., Wilkinson, D. A., Soarimalala, V., Goodman, S. M., Dellagi, K., and Tortosa, P. 2014. Diversification of an emerging pathogen in a biodiversity hotspot: *Leptospira* in endemic small mammals of Madagascar. *Molecular Ecology* 23: 2783–2796.

Dietrich, M., Mühldorfer, K., Tortosa, P., and Markotter, W. 2015a. *Leptospira* and bats: Story of an emerging friendship. *PLoS Pathogens* 11: e1005176.

Dietrich, M., Wilkinson, D. A., Benlali, A., Lagadec, E., Ramasindrazana, B., Dellagi, K., and Tortosa, P. 2015b. *Leptospira* and paramyxovirus infection dynamics in a bat maternity enlightens pathogen maintenance in wildlife. *Environmental Microbiology* 17: 4280–4289.

Dietrich, M., Gomard, Y., Lagadec, E., Ramasindrazana, B., Le Minter, G., et al. 2018. Biogeography of *Leptospira* in wild animal communities inhabiting the insular ecosystem of the western Indian Ocean islands and neighboring Africa. *Emerging Microbes and Infections* 7: 57.

Doherty, T. S., Dickman, C. R., Nimmo, D. G., and Ritchie, E. G. 2015. Multiple threats, or multiplying the threats? Interactions between invasive predators and other ecological disturbances. *Biological Conservation* 190: 60–68.

Doherty, T. S., Glen, A. S., Nimmo, D. G., Ritchie, E. G., and Dickman, C. R. 2016. Invasive predators and global biodiversity loss. *Proceedings of the National Academy of Sciences of the USA* 113: 11261–11265.

Döring, B., Mecke, S., Kieckbusch, M., O'Shea, M., and Kaiser, H. 2017. Food spectrum analysis of the Asian toad, *Duttaphrynus melanostictus* (Schneider, 1799) (Anura: Bufonidae), from Timor Island, Wallacea. *Journal of Natural History* 51: 607–623.

Drexler, J. F., Corman, V. M., and Drosten, C. 2014. Ecology, evolution and classification of bat coronaviruses in the aftermath of SARS. *Antiviral Research* 101: 45–56.

Duron, O., Schneppat, U. E., Berthomieu, A., Goodman, S. M., Droz, B., Paupy, C., Obame Nkoghe, J., Rahola, N., and Tortosa, P. 2014. Origin, acquisition and diversification of heritable bacterial endosymbionts in louse flies and bat flies. *Molecular Ecology* 23: 2105–2117.

Duval, L., Mejean, C., Maganga, G. D., Makanga, B. K., Mangama Koumba, L. B., Peirce, M. A., Ariey, F., and Bourgarel, M. 2012. The chiropteran haemosporidian *Polychromophilus melanipherus*: A worldwide species complex restricted to the family Miniopteridae. *Infection Genetics and Evolution* 12: 1558–1566.

Ehlers, J., Poppert, S., Ratovonamana, R. Y., Ganzhorn, J. U., Tappe, D., and Krüger, A. 2019. Ectoparasites of endemic and domestic animals in southwest Madagascar. *Acta Tropica* 196: 83–92.

Ehlers, J., Krüger, A., Rakotondranary, S. J., Ratovonamana, R. Y., Poppert, S., Ganzhorn, J. U., and Tappe, D. 2020. Molecular detection of *Rickettsia* spp., *Borrelia* spp., *Bartonella* spp. and *Yersinia pestis* in ectoparasites of endemic and domestic animals in southwest Madagascar. *Acta Tropica* 205: 105339.

Fall, G., Di Paola, N., Faye, M., Dia, M., Freire, C. C. de M., Loucoubar, C., Zanotto, P. M. de A., Faye, O., and Sall, A. A. 2017. Biological and phylogenetic characteristics of West African lineages of West Nile virus. *PLoS Neglected Tropical Diseases* 11: e0006078.

Farris, Z. J., Golden, C. D., Karpanty, S., Murphy, A., Stauffer, D., Ratelolahy, F., Andrianjakarivelo, V., Holmes, C. M., and Kelly, M. J. 2015. Hunting, exotic carnivores, and habitat loss: Anthropogenic effects on a native carnivore community, Madagascar. *PLoS One* 10: e0136456.

Farris, Z. J., Kelly, M. J., Karpanty, S., and Ratelolahy, F. 2016. Patterns of spatial co-occurrence among native and exotic carnivores in north-eastern Madagascar. *Animal Conservation* 19: 189–198.

Favia, G., Ricci, I., Marzorati, M., Negri, I., Alma, A., Sacchi, L., Bandi, C., and Daffonchio, D. 2008. Bacteria of the genus *Asaia*: A potential paratransgenic weapon against malaria. *Advances in Experimantal Medicine and Biology* 627: 49–59.

Fierer, N. 2008. Microbial biogeography: Patterns in microbial diversity across space and time. In *Accessing Uncultivated Microorganisms: From the Environment to Organisms and Genomes and Back*, ed. K. Zengler, pp. 95–115. Washington, DC: American Society for Microbiology.

Fischer, K., Zeus, V., Kwasnitschka, L., Kerth, G., Haase, M., Groschup, M. H., and Balkema-Buschmann, A. 2016. Insectivorous bats carry host specific astroviruses and coronaviruses across different regions in Germany. *Infection, Genetics and Evolution* 37: 108–116.

Fontenille, D., Mathiot, C., and Coulanges, P. 1988a. Les virus des fièvres hémorragiques à Madagascar. *Archives de l'Institut Pasteur de Madagascar* 54: 117–124.

Fontenille, D., Mathiot, C., Rodhain, F., and Coulanges, P. 1988b. Les arboviroses dans la région de Nosy-Bé, Madagascar: Données sérologiques et entomologiques. *Bulletin de la Société de Pathologie Exotique* 81: 58–70.

———. 1988c. Les arboviroses dans l'île de Nosy-Be données sérologioues et entomologiques. *Archives de l'Institut Pasteur de Madagascar* 54: 101–115.

Fontenille, D., Rodhain, F., Digoutte, J. P., Mathiot, C., Morvan, J., and Coulanges, P. 1989. Les cycles de transmission du virus West Nile à Madagascar, Océan Indien. *Annales de la Société Belge de Médecine Tropicale* 69: 233–243.

Furuya-Kanamori, L., Liang, S., Milinovich, G., Soares Magalhaes, R. J., Clements, A.C.A., Hu, W., Brasil, P., Frentiu, F. D., Dunning, R., and Yakob, L. 2016. Co-distribution and co-infection of chikungunya and dengue viruses. *BMC Infectious Diseases* 16: 84. doi.org/10.1186/s12879-016-1417-2.

Gardner, R. A., and Molyneux, D. H. 1988. *Polychromophilus murinus*: A malarial parasite of bats; Life-history and ultrastructural studies. *Parasitology* 96: 591–605.

Gardner, R. A., Molyneux, D. H., and Stebbings, R. E. 1987. Studies on the prevalence of haematozoa of British bats. *Mammal Review* 17: 75–80.

Gargili, A., Estrada-Peña, A., Spengler, J. R., Lukashev, A., Nuttall, P. A., and Bente, D. A. 2017. The role of ticks in the maintenance and transmission of Crimean-Congo hemorrhagic fever virus: A review of published field and laboratory studies. *Antiviral Research* 144: 93–119.

Gaubert, P., Patel, R. P., Veron, G., Goodman, S. M., Willsch, M., et al. 2017. Phylogeography of the small Indian civet and origin of introductions to Western Indian Ocean Islands. *Journal of Heredity* 108: 270–279.

Gauzère, B.-A., and Aubry, P. 2013. History of human epidemic and endemic diseases in the southwest Indian Ocean. *Médecine et Santé Tropicales* 23: 145–157.

Ghawar, W., Pascalis, H., Bettaieb, J., Mélade, J., Gharbi, A., Snoussi, M. A., Laouini, D., Goodman, S. M., Ben Salah, A., and Dellagi, K. 2017. Insight into the global evolution of Rodentia associated Morbilli-related paramyxoviruses. *Scientific Reports* 7: 1974.

Gideon Informatics. 2019. *Infectious Diseases of Madagascar*. Los Angeles: Gideon Informatics.

Gomard, Y., Dietrich, M., Wieseke, N., Ramasindrazana, B., Lagadec, E., Goodman, S. M., Dellagi, K., and Tortosa, P. 2016. Malagasy bats shelter a considerable genetic diversity of pathogenic *Leptospira* suggesting notable host-specificity patterns. *FEMS Microbiology Ecology* 92: fiw037.

Goodman, S. M. 1995. *Rattus* on Madagascar and the dilemma of protecting the endemic rodent fauna. *Conservation Biology* 9: 450–453.

———. 2011. *Les chauves-souris de Madagascar*. Antananarivo: Association Vahatra.

Goodman, S. M., and Benstead, J. P. 2005. Updated estimates of biotic diversity and endemism for Madagascar. *Oryx* 39: 73–77.

Goodman, S. M., Duplantier, J.-M., Rakotomalaza, P. J., Raselimanana, A. P., Rasoloarison, R., Ravokatra, M., Soarimalala, V., and Wilmé, L. 1998. Inventaire biologique de la forêt d'Ankazomivady, Ambositra. *Akon'ny Ala* 24: 19–32.

Goodman, S. M., Maminirina, C. P., Weyeneth, N., Bradman, H. M., Christidis, L., Ruedi, M., and Appleton, B. 2009. The use of molecular and morphological characters to resolve the taxonomic identity of cryptic species: The case of *Miniopterus manavi* (Chiroptera, Miniopteridae). *Zoologica Scripta* 38: 339–363.

Goodman, S. M., Chan, L. M., Nowak, M. D., and Yoder, A. D. 2010. Phylogeny and biogeography of western Indian Ocean *Rousettus* (Chiroptera: Pteropodidae). *Journal of Mammalogy* 91: 593–606.

Goodman, S. M., Andriniaina, H.R.R., Soarimalala, V., and Beaucournu, J.-C. 2015. The fleas of endemic and introduced small mammals in central highland forests of

Madagascar: Faunistics, species diversity, and absence of host specificity. *Journal of Medical Entomology* 52: 1135–1143.

Gray, G. C., Anderson, B. D., LaBeaud, A. D., Héraud, J.-M., Fèvre, E. M., et al. 2015. Seroepidemiological study of interepidemic Rift Valley fever virus infection among persons with intense ruminant exposure in Madagascar and Kenya. *American Journal of Tropical Medicine and Hygiene* 93: 1364–1370.

Grobbelaar, A. A., Weyer, J., Leman, P. A., Kemp, A., Paweska, J. T., and Swanepoel, R. 2011. Molecular epidemiology of Rift Valley fever virus. *Emerging Infectious Diseases* 17: 2270–2276.

Gubler, D. J. 2002. The global emergence/resurgence of arboviral diseases as public health problems. *Archives of Medical Research* 33: 330–342.

Guégan, M., Zouache, K., Démichel, C., Minard, G., Tran Van, V., Potier, P., Mavingui, P., and Valiente Moro, C. 2018. The mosquito holobiont: Fresh insight into mosquito-microbiota interactions. *Microbiome* 6: 49.

Guernier, V., Lagadec, E., Cordonin, C., Le Minter, G., Gomard, Y., Pagès, F., Jaffar-Bandjee, M.-C., Michault, A., Tortosa, P., and Dellagi, K. 2016. Human leptospirosis on Reunion Island, Indian Ocean: Are rodents the (only) ones to blame? *PLoS Neglected Tropical Diseases* 10: e0004733.

Guerrero, R., Martin, C., Gardner, S. L., and Bain, O. 2002. New and known species of *Litomosoides* (Nematoda: Filarioidea): Important adult and larval characters and taxonomic changes. *Copa* 69: 177–195.

Guerrero, R., Bain, O., Attout, T., and Martin, C. 2006. The infective larva of *Litomosoides yutajensis* Guerrero et al., 2003 (Nematoda: Onchocercidae), a *Wolbachia*-free filaria from bat. *Parasite* 13: 127–130.

Guglielmini, J., Bourhy, P., Schiettekatte, O., Zinini, F., Brisse, S., and Picardeau, M. 2019. Genus-wide *Leptospira* core genome multilocus sequence typing for strain taxonomy and global surveillance. *PLoS Neglected Tropical Diseases* 13: e0007374.

Guillebaud, J., Bernardson, B., Randriambolamanantsoa, T. H., Randrianasolo, L., Randriamampionona, J. L., et al. 2018. Study on causes of fever in primary healthcare center uncovers pathogens of public health concern in Madagascar. *PLoS Neglected Tropical Diseases* 12: e0006642.

Guis, H., Raveloarijaona, B. N., Rakotoharinome, V. M., Rabarisoa, R., Raveloson, B., et al. 2018. Prevalence and risk factors associated to horse and wild bird infection by West Nile virus in Madagascar. Poster. 15th International Symposium of Veterinary Epidemiology and Economics (ISVEE), Chiang Mai, Thailand.

Guiyoule, A., Rasoamanana, B., Buchrieser, C., Michel, P., Chanteau, S., and Carniel, E. 1997. Recent emergence of new variants of *Yersinia pestis* in Madagascar. *Journal of Clinical Microbiology* 35: 2826–2833.

Guth, S., Visher, E., Boots, M., and Brook, C. E. 2019. Host phylogenetic distance drives trends in virus virulence and transmissibility across the animal-human interface. *Philosophical Transactions of the Royal Society B: Biological Sciences* 374: 20190296.

Hagen, R. M., Frickmann, H., Ehlers, J., Krüger, A., Margos, G., et al. 2018. Presence of *Borrelia* spp. DNA in ticks, but absence of *Borrelia* spp. and of *Leptospira* spp. DNA in blood of fever patients in Madagascar. *Acta Tropica* 177: 127–134.

Han, H.-J., Liu, J.-W., Wen, H.-L., Qin, X.-R., Zhao, M., Wang, L.-J., Zhou, C.-M., Qi, R., Yu, H., and Yu, X.-J. 2018. *Babesia vesperuginis* in insectivorous bats from China. *Parasites and Vectors* 11: 317.

Harimalala, M., Miarinjara, A., Duchemin, J.-B., Ramihangihajason, T., and Boyer, S. 2018. Species diversity and phylogeny of fleas of small terrestrial mammals in the forests of the Central Highlands of Madagascar. *Zootaxa* 4399: 181.

Hartup, B. K., Dhondt, A. A., Sydenstricker, K. V., Hochachka, W. M., and Kollias, G. V. 2001. Host range and dynamics of mycoplasmal conjunctivitis among birds in North America. *Journal of Wildlife Diseases* 37: 72–81.

Hegde, S., Rasgon, J. L., and Hughes, G. L. 2015. The microbiome modulates arbovirus transmission in mosquitoes. *Current Opinion in Virology* 15: 97–102.

Hoarau, F., Le Minter, G., Joffrin, L., Schoeman, C. M., Lagadec, E., et al. 2018. Bat astrovirus in Mozambique. *Virology Journal* 15: 104.

Hoffmann, J., Rabezanahary, H., Randriamarotia, M., Ratsimbasoa, A., Najjar, J., Vernet, G., Contamin, B., and Paranhos-Baccalà, G. 2012. Viral and atypical bacterial etiology of acute respiratory infections in children under 5 years old living in a rural tropical area of Madagascar. *PLoS One* 7: e43666.

Hoogstraal, H. 1979. The epidemiology of tick-borne Crimean-Congo hemorrhagic fever in Asia, Europe, and Africa. *Journal of Medical Entomology* 15: 307–417.

Huang, C., Wang, Y., Li, X., Ren, L., Zhao, J., et al. 2020. Clinical features of patients infected with 2019 novel coronavirus in Wuhan, China. *Lancet* 395: 497–506.

Hughes, J., and Macdonald, D. W. 2013. A review of the interactions between free-roaming domestic dogs and wildlife. *Biological Conservation* 157: 341–351.

Hurst, G.D.D., Jiggins, F. M., and Pomiankowski, A. 2002. Which way to manipulate host reproduction? *Wolbachia* that cause cytoplasmic incompatibility are easily invaded by sex ratio-distorting mutants. *American Naturalist* 160: 360–373

Iehlé, C., Razafitrimo, G., Razainirina, J., Andriaholinirina, N., Goodman, S. M., Faure, C., Georges-Courbot, M.-C., Rousset, D., and Reynes, J.-M. 2007. Henipavirus and Tioman virus antibodies in pteropodid bats, Madagascar. *Emerging Infectious Diseases* 13: 159–161.

Institut Pasteur de Madagascar. 2019. Rapport d'activités 2018. http://www.pasteur.mg/publication/rapport-dactivites-2018.

International Committee on Taxonomy of Viruses. 2020. Virus taxonomy: 2020 release. https://talk.ictvonline.org/taxonomy/.

Irwin, M. T., Junge, R. E., Raharison, J.-L., and Samonds, K. E. 2010. Variation in physiological health of diademed sifakas across intact and fragmented forest at Tsinjoarivo, eastern Madagascar. *American Journal of Primatology* 72: 1013–1025.

Jeanmaire, E. M., Rabenarivahiny, R., Biarmann, M., Rabibisoa, L., Ravaomanana, F., et al. 2011. Prevalence of Rift Valley fever infection in ruminants in Madagascar after the 2008 outbreak. *Vector Borne and Zoonotic Diseases* 11: 395–402.

Joffrin, L., Goodman, S. M., Wilkinson, D. A., Ramasindrazana, B., Lagadec, E., et al. 2020. Bat coronavirus phylogeography in the western Indian Ocean. *Scientific Reports* 10: 6873.

Jones, K. E., Patel, N. G., Levy, M. A., Storeygard, A., Balk, D., Gittleman, J. L., and Daszak, P. 2008. Global trends in emerging infectious diseases. *Nature* 451: 990–993.

Jonsson, C. B., Figueiredo, L.T.M., and Vapalahti, O. 2010. A global perspective on hantavirus ecology, epidemiology, and disease. *Clinical Microbiology Reviews* 23: 412–441.

Junge, R. E., Barrett, M. A., and Yoder, A. D. 2011. Effects of anthropogenic disturbance on indri (*Indri indri*) health in Madagascar. *American Journal of Primatology* 73: 632–642.

Junker, K., Barbuto, M., Casiraghi, M., Martin, C., Uni, S., Boomker, J., and Bain, O. 2009. *Litomosa chiropterorum* Ortlepp, 1932 (Nematoda: Filarioidea) from a South African miniopterid: Redescription, *Wolbachia* screening and phylogenetic relationships with *Litomosoides*. *Parasite* 16: 43–50.

Kessler, M. K., Becker, D. J., Peel, A. J., Justice, N. V., Lunn, T., Crowley, D. E., Jones, D. N., Eby, P., Sánchez, C. A., and Plowright, R. K. 2018. Changing resource landscapes and spillover of henipaviruses: Resource landscapes and henipavirus spillover. *Annals of the New York Academy of Sciences* 1429: 78–99.

Khuroo, M. S., Khuroo, M. S., and Khuroo, N. S. 2016. Hepatitis E: Discovery, global impact, control and cure. *World Journal of Gastroenterology* 22: 7030.

Kilpatrick, A. M., Daszak, P., Goodman, S. J., Rogg, H., Kramer, L. D., Cedeño, V., and Cunningham, A. A. 2006. Predicting pathogen introduction: West Nile virus spread to Galápagos. *Conservation Biology* 20: 1224–1231.

Klenk, K., Snow, J., Morgan, K., Bowen, R., Stephens, M., et al. 2004. Alligators as West Nile virus amplifiers. *Emerging Infectious Diseases* 10: 2150–2155.

Knobel, D. L., Cleaveland, S., Coleman, P. G., Fèvre, E. M., Meltzer, M. I., Miranda, M.E.G., Shaw, A., Zinsstag, J., and Meslin, F.-X. 2005. Re-evaluating the burden of rabies in Africa and Asia. *Bulletin of the World Health Organization* 85: 360–368.

Kolby, J. E., Smith, K. M., Ramirez, S. D., Rabemananjara, F., Pessier, A. P., Brunner, J. L., Goldberg, C. S., Berger, L., and Skerratt, L. F. 2015. Rapid response to evaluate the presence of amphibian chytrid fungus (*Batrachochytrium dendrobatidis*) and ranavirus in wild amphibian populations in Madagascar. *PLoS One* 10: e0125330.

Kotschwar Logan, M., Gerber, B. D., Karpanty, S. M., Justin, S., and Rabenahy, F. N. 2015. Assessing carnivore distribution from local knowledge across a human-dominated landscape in central-southeastern Madagascar. *Animal Conservation* 18: 82–91.

Kucharski A. J., Funk S., Eggo R. M., Mallet H.-P., Edmunds W. J., and Nilles E. J. 2016. Transmission dynamics of Zika virus in island populations: A modelling analysis of the 2013–14 French Polynesia outbreak. *PLoS Neglected Tropical Diseases* 10: e0004726

Kuzmin, I., and Rupprecht, C. 2007. Bat rabies. In *Rabies*, eds. A. C. Jackson and W. H. Wunner, pp. 259–307. Amsterdam: Elsevier/Academic.

Kuzmin, I. V., Orciari, L. A., Arai, Y. T., Smith, J. S., Hanlon, C. A., Kameoka, Y., and Rupprecht, C. E. 2003. Bat lyssaviruses (Aravan and Khujand) from Central Asia: Phylogenetic relationships according to N, P and G gene sequences. *Virus Research* 97: 65–79.

Laakkonen, J., Goodman, S. M., Duchemin, J.-B., and Duplantier, J.-M. 2003. Trypomastigotes and potential flea vectors of the endemic rodents and the introduced *Rattus rattus* in the rainforests of Madagascar. *Biodiversity and Conservation* 12: 1775–1783.

Lado, P., Qurollo, B., Williams, C., Junge, R., and Klompen, H. 2018. The microbiome of *Haemaphysalis lemuris* (Acari: Ixodidae), a possible vector of pathogens of endangered lemur species in Madagascar. *Ticks and Tick-Borne Diseases* 9: 1252–1260.

Lafferty, K. D., and Gerber, L. 2002. Good medicine for conservation biology: The intersection of epidemiology and conservation theory. *Conservation Biology* 16: 593–604.

Lagadec, E., Gomard, Y., Guernier, V., Dietrich, M., Pascalis, H., Temmam, S., Ramasindrazana, B., Goodman, S. M., Tortosa, P., and Dellagi, K. 2012. Pathogenic *Leptospira* spp. in bats, Madagascar and Union of the Comoros. *Emerging Infectious Diseases* 18: 1696–1698.

Lagadec, E., Gomard, Y., Le Minter, G., Cordonin, C., Cardinale, E., Ramasindrazana, B., Dietrich, M., Goodman, S. M., Tortosa, P., and Dellagi, K. 2016. Identification of *Tenrec ecaudatus*, a wild mammal introduced to Mayotte Island, as a reservoir of the newly identified human pathogenic *Leptospira mayottensis*. *PLoS Neglected Tropical Diseases* 10: e0004933.

Lancelot, R., Béral, M., Rakotoharinome, V. M., Andriamandimby, S.-F., Héraud, J.-M., et al. 2017. Drivers of Rift Valley fever epidemics in Madagascar. *Proceedings of the National Academy of Sciences of the USA* 114: 938–943.

Landau, I., Chavatte, J. M., Karadjian, G., Chabaud, A., and Beveridge, I. 2012. The haemosporidian parasites of bats with description of *Sprattiella alecto* gen. nov., sp. nov. *Parasite* 19: 137–146.

Larrieu, S., Cardinale, E., Ocquidant, P., Roger, M., Lepec, R., et al. 2013. A fatal neuroinvasive West Nile virus infection in a traveler returning from Madagascar: Clinical, epidemiological and veterinary investigations. *American Journal of Tropical Medicine and Hygiene* 89: 211–213.

Larsen, P. A., Hayes, C. E., Williams, C. V., Junge, R. E., Razafindramanana, J., Mass, V., Rakotondrainibe, H., and Yoder, A. D. 2016. Blood transcriptomes reveal novel parasitic zoonoses circulating in Madagascar's lemurs. *Biology Letters* 12: 20150829.

Lebarbenchon, C., Ramasindrazana, B., Joffrin, L., Bos, S., Lagadec, E., et al. 2017. Astroviruses in bats, Madagascar. *Emerging Microbes and Infections* 6: e58.

Lee, G.-H., Tan, B.-H., Chi-Yuan Teo, E., Lim, S.-G., Dan, Y.-Y., et al. 2016. Chronic infection with camelid Hepatitis E virus in a liver transplant recipient who regularly consumes camel meat and milk. *Gastroenterology* 150: 355–357.e3.

Lei, B. R., and Olival, K. J. 2014. Contrasting patterns in mammal-bacteria coevolution: *Bartonella* and *Leptospira* in bats and rodents. *PLoS Neglected Tropical Diseases* 8: e2738.

Lenglet, Y., Barau, G., Robillard, P.-Y., Randrianaivo, H., Michault, A., et al. 2006. Chikungunya infection in pregnancy: Evidence for intrauterine infection in pregnant women and vertical transmission in the parturient; Survey of the Reunion Island outbreak. *Journal de Gynécologie Obstétrique et Biologie de la Reproduction* 35: 578–583.

Leroy, E. M., Rouquet, P., Formenty, P., Souquière, S., Kilbourne, A., et al. 2004. Multiple Ebola virus transmission events and rapid decline of Central African wildlife. *Science* 303: 387–390.

Levisohn, S., and Kleven, S. H. 2000. Avian mycoplasmosis (*Mycoplasma gallisepticum*). *Revue Scientifique et Technique–Office International des Epizooties* 19: 425–442.

Lhomme, S., Marion, O., Abravanel, F., Chapuy-Regaud, S., Kamar, N., and Izopet, J. 2016. Hepatitis E pathogenesis. *Viruses* 8: 212.

Lhuillier, M. 1978. Contribution à l'étude des leptospiroses à Madagascar (étude bactériologique et sérologique). *Archives de l'Institut Pasteur de Madagascar* 46: 429–439.

Li, F., Peng, Y., Fang, W., Altermatt, F., Xie, Y., Yang, J., and Zhang, X. 2018. Application of environmental DNA metabarcoding for predicting anthropogenic pollution in rivers. *Environmental Science and Technology* 52: 11708–11719.

MacNeil, A., Reed, Z., and Rollin, P. E. 2011. Serologic cross-reactivity of human IgM and IgG antibodies to five species of Ebola virus. *PLoS Neglected Tropical Diseases* 5: e1175.

Makoni, M. 2019. Madagascar's battle for health. *Lancet* 393: 1189–1190.

Maminiaina, O. F., Koko, M., Ravaomanana, J., and Rakotonindrina, S. J. 2007. Epidemiology of Newcastle disease in village poultry farming in Madagascar. *Revue Scientifique et Technique–Office International des Epizooties* 26: 691–700.

Mancinelli, S., Pirillo, M. F., Liotta, G., Andreotti, M., Jere, H., et al. 2017. Hepatitis E virus infection in HIV-infected pregnant women and their children in Malawi. *Infectious Diseases* 49: 708–711.

Maquart, M., Boyer, S., Rakotoharinome, V. M., Ravaomanana, J., Tantely, M. L., Héraud, J.-M., and Cardinale, E. 2016. High prevalence of West Nile virus in domestic birds and detection in 2 new mosquito species in Madagascar. *PLoS One* 11: e0147589.

Marshall, B. M., Casewell, N. R., Vences, M., Glaw, F., Andreone, F., Rakotoarison, A., Zancolli, G., Woog, F., and Wüster, W. 2018. Widespread vulnerability of Malagasy predators to the toxins of an introduced toad. *Current Biology* 28: 2194.

Martin, C., Bain, O., Jouvenet, N., Raharimanga, V., Robert, V., and Rousset, D. 2006. First report of *Litomosa* spp. (Nematoda: Filarioidea) from Malagasy bats: Review of the genus and relationships between species. *Parasite* 13: 3–10.

Mathiot, C., Clerc, Y., Rodhain, F., Digoutte, J. P., and Coulanges, P. 1984. Le virus West-Nile et Madagascar. *Archives de l'Institut Pasteur de Madagascar* 51: 113–123.

Mathiot, C. C., Fontenille, D., Digoutte, J. P., and Coulanges, P. 1988. First isolation of Congo-Crimean haemorrhagic fever virus in Madagascar. *Annales de l'Institut Pasteur/Virologie* 139: 239–241.

Mathiot, C. C., Fontenille, D., Georges, A. J., and Coulanges, P. 1989. Antibodies to haemorrhagic fever viruses in Madagascar populations. *Transactions of the Royal Society of Tropical Medicine and Hygiene* 83: 407–409.

McLean, R. G., Ubico, S. R., Bourne, D., and Komar, N. 2002. West Nile virus in livestock and wildlife. *Current Topics in Microbiology and Immunology* 267: 271–308.

Medina, F. M., Bonnaud, E., Vidal, E., Tershy, B. R., Zavaleta, E. S., Donlan, C. J., Keitt, B. S., Le Corre, M., Horwath, S. V., and Nogales, M. 2011. A global review of the impacts of invasive cats on island endangered vertebrates. *Global Change Biology* 17: 3503–3510.

Mélade, J., Wieseke, N., Ramasindrazana, B., Flores, O., Lagadec, E., Gomard, Y., Goodman, S. M., Dellagi, K., and Pascalis, H. 2016a. An eco-epidemiological study of Morbilli-related paramyxovirus infection in Madagascar bats reveals host-switching as the dominant macro-evolutionary mechanism. *Scientific Reports* 6: 23752.

Mélade, J., McCulloch, S., Ramasindrazana, B., Lagadec, E., Turpin, M., Pascalis, H., Goodman, S. M., Markotter, W., and Dellagi, K. 2016b. Serological evidence of lyssaviruses among bats on southwestern Indian Ocean islands. *PLoS One* 11: e0160553.

Mendenhall, I. H., Smith, G.J.D., and Vijaykrishna, D. 2015. Ecological drivers of virus evolution: Astrovirus as a case study. *Journal of Virology* 89: 6978–6981.

Mendez, E., and Arias, C. F. 2007. Astroviruses. In *Fields Virology*, 5th ed., eds. D. M., Knipe, P. M. Howley, D. E. Griffin, R. A. Lamb, M. A. Martin, B. Roizman, and S. E. Straus, pp. 981–1000. Philadelphia: Lippincott Williams and Wilkins.

Michiels, T., Welby, S., Vanrobaeys, M., Quinet, C., Rouffaer, L., Lens, L., Martel, A., and Butaye, P. 2016. Prevalence of *Mycoplasma gallisepticum* and *Mycoplasma synoviae* in commercial poultry, racing pigeons and wild birds in Belgium. *Avian Pathology* 45: 244–252.

Minard, G., Mavingui, P., and Valiente Moro, C. 2013. Diversity and function of bacterial microbiota in the mosquito holobiont. *Parasites and Vectors* 6: 146.

Minard, G., Tran, F.-H., Dubost, A., Tran-Van, V., Mavingui, P., and Valiente Moro, C. 2014. Pyrosequencing 16S rRNA genes of bacteria associated with wild tiger mosquito *Aedes albopictus*: A pilot study. *Frontiers in Cellular and Infection Microbiology* 4: 59.

Minard, G., Tran, F. H., Van, V. T., Goubert, C., Bellet, C., Lambert, G., Kim, K.L.H., Thuy, T.H.T., Mavingui, P., and Valiente Moro, C. 2015. French invasive Asian tiger mosquito populations harbor reduced bacterial microbiota and genetic diversity compared to Vietnamese autochthonous relatives. *Frontiers in Microbiology* 6: 970.

Mooney, H. A., and Cleland, E. E. 2001. The evolutionary impact of invasive species. *Proceedings of the National Academy of Sciences of the USA* 98: 5446–5451.

Morens, D. M., Folkers, G. K., and Fauci, A. S. 2004. The challenge of emerging and re-emerging infectious diseases. *Nature* 430: 242–249.

Morse, S. S. 1995. Factors in the emergence of infectious diseases. *Emerging Infectious Diseases* 1: 7–15.

Morvan, J., Saluzzo, J. F., Fontenille, D., Rollin, P. E., and Coulanges, P. 1991. Rift Valley fever on the east coast of Madagascar. *Research in Virology* 142: 475–482.

Morvan, J., Rollin, P. E., Laventure, S., Rakotoarivony, I., and Roux, J. 1992a. Rift Valley fever epizootic in the central highlands of Madagascar. *Research in Virology* 143: 407–415.

Morvan, J., Lesbordes, J. L., Rollin, P. E., Mouden, J. C., and Roux, J. 1992b. First fatal human case of Rift Valley fever in Madagascar. *Transactions of the Royal Society of Tropical Medicine and Hygiene* 86: 320.

Morvan, J. M., Rakoto-Andrianarivelo, M., Randriamihoatra, S., and Roux, J. 1993. Situation de l'endémie rabique à Madagascar. *Archives de l'Institut Pasteur de Madagascar* 5–8.

Moseley, M., Rahelinirina, S., Rajerison, M., Garin, B., Piertney, S., and Telfer, S. 2018. Mixed *Leptospira* infections in a diverse reservoir host community, Madagascar, 2013–2015. *Emerging Infectious Diseases* 24: 1138–1140.

Myers, N., Mittermeier, R. A., Mittermeier, C. G., da Fonseca, G.A.B., and Kent, J. 2000. Biodiversity hotspots for conservation priorities. *Nature* 403: 853–858.

Nemeth, N., Young, G., Ndaluka, C., Bielefeldt-Ohmann, H., Komar, N., and Bowen, R. 2009. Persistent West Nile virus infection in the house sparrow (*Passer domesticus*). *Archives of Virology* 154: 783–789.

Nepomichene, J.-M., Elissa, N., Cardinale, E., and Boyer, S. 2015. Species diversity, abundance, and host preferences of mosquitoes (Diptera: Culicidae) in two different ecotypes of Madagascar with recent RVFV transmission. *Journal of Medical Entomology* 52: 962–969.

Nepomichene, J. M., Raharimalala, F. N., Andriamandimby, S. F., Ravalohery, J.-P., Failloux, A.-B., Héraud, J.-M., and Boyer, S. 2018. Vector competence of *Culex antennatus* and *Anopheles coustani* mosquitoes for Rift Valley fever virus in Madagascar. *Medical and Veterinary Entomology* 32: 259–262.

Nicolas, G., Durand, B., Rakotoarimanana, T. T., Lacote, S., Chevalier, V., and Marianneau, P. 2014. A 3-year serological and virological cattle follow-up in Madagascar highlands suggests a non-classical transmission route of Rift Valley fever virus. *American Journal of Tropical Medicine and Hygiene* 90: 265–266.

Olival, K., and Hayman, D. 2014. Filoviruses in bats: Current knowledge and future directions. *Viruses* 6: 1759–1788.

Olival, K. J., Islam, A., Yu, M., Anthony, S. J., Epstein, J. H., et al. 2013. Ebola virus antibodies in fruit bats, Bangladesh. *Emerging Infectious Diseases* 19: 270–273.

Olive, M.-M., Goodman, S. M., and Reynes, J.-M. 2012. The role of wild mammals in the maintenance of Rift Valley fever virus. *Journal of Wildlife Diseases* 48: 241–266.

Olive, M.-M., Razafindralambo, N., Barivelo, T. A., Rafisandratantsoa, J.-T., Soarimalala, V., Goodman, S. M., Rollin, P. E., Héraud, J.-M., and Reynes, J.-M. 2013. Absence of Rift Valley fever virus in wild small mammals, Madagascar. *Emerging Infectious Diseases* 19: 1025–1027.

Olive, M.-M., Chevalier, V., Grosbois, V., Tran, A., Andriamandimby, S.-F., et al. 2016. Integrated analysis of environment, cattle and human serological data: Risks and mechanisms of transmission of Rift Valley fever in Madagascar. *PLoS Neglected Tropical Diseases* 10: e0004827.

Olive, M.-M., Grosbois, V., Tran, A., Nomenjanahary, L. A., Rakotoarinoro, M., Andriamandimby, S.-F., Rogier, C., Héraud, J.-M., and Chevalier, V. 2017. Reconstruction of Rift Valley fever transmission dynamics in Madagascar: Estimation of force of infection from seroprevalence surveys using Bayesian modelling. *Scientific Reports* 7: 39870.

Pagès, F., Kuli, B., Moiton, M.-P., Goarant, C., and Jaffar-Bandjee, M.-C. 2015. Leptospirosis after a stay in Madagascar. *Journal of Travel Medicine* 22: 136–139.

Papa, A., Vaheri, A., LeDuc, J. W., Krüger, D. H., Avšič-Županc, T., et al. 2016. Meeting report: Tenth International Conference on Hantaviruses. *Antiviral Research* 133: 234–241.

Papaventsis, D. C., Dove, W., Cunliffe, N. A., Nakagomi, O., Combe, P., Grosjean, P., and Hart, C. A. 2008. Human Astrovirus gastroenteritis in children, Madagascar, 2004–2005. *Emerging Infectious Diseases* 14: 844–846.

Pappas, G., Papadimitriou, P., Siozopoulou, V., Christou, L., and Akritidis, N. 2008. The globalization of leptospirosis: Worldwide incidence trends. *International Journal of Infectious Diseases* 12: 351–357.

Parker, P. G., Buckles, E. L., Farrington, H., Petren, K., Whiteman, N. K., Ricklefs, R. E., Bollmer, J. L., and Jiménez-Uzcátegui, G. 2011. 110 years of *Avipoxvirus* in the Galapagos Islands. *PLoS One* 6: e15989.

Pattamadilok, S., Lee, B.-H., Kumperasart, S., Yoshimatsu, K., Okumura, M., et al. 2006. Geographical distribution of hantaviruses in Thailand and potential human health significance of Thailand virus. *American Journal of Tropical Medicine and Hygiene* 75: 994–1002.

Patterson, B. D., Webala, P. W., Kerbis Peterhans, J. C., Goodman, S. M., Bartonjo, M., and Demos, T. C. 2019. Genetic variation and relationships among Afrotropical species of *Myotis* (Chiroptera: Vespertilionidae). *Journal of Mammalogy* 100: 1130–1143.

Pierron, D., Heiske, M., Razafindrazaka, H., Pereda-Loth, V., Sanchez, J., et al. 2018. Strong selection during the last millennium for African ancestry in the admixed population of Madagascar. *Nature Communications* 9: 1–9.

Pierson, T., and Diamond, M. 2007. Flavivirus. In *Fields Virology*, 5th ed., eds. D. M. Knipe, P. M. Howley, D. E. Griffin, R. A. Lamb, M. A. Martin, B. Roizman, and S. E. Straus, pp. 747–794. Philadelphia: Lippincott Williams and Wilkins.

Pigott, D. M., Golding, N., Mylne, A., Huang, Z., Henry, A. J., et al. 2014. Mapping the zoonotic niche of Ebola virus disease in Africa. *eLife* 3:e04395.

Pigott, D. M., Golding, N., Mylne, A., Huang, Z., Weiss, D. J., Brady, O. J., Kraemer, M.U.G., and Hay, S. I. 2015. Mapping the zoonotic niche of Marburg virus disease in Africa. *Transactions of the Royal Society of Tropical Medicine and Hygiene* 109: 366–378.

Plowright, R. K., Parrish, C. R., McCallum, H., Hudson, P. J., Ko, A. I., Graham, A. L., and Lloyd-Smith, J. O. 2017. Pathways to zoonotic spillover. *Nature Reviews Microbiology* 15: 502–510.

Pomerantz, J., Rasambainarivo, F. T., Dollar, L., Rahajanirina, L. P., Andrianaivoarivelo, R., Parker, P., and Dubovi, E. 2016. Prevalence of antibodies to selected viruses and parasites in introduced and endemic carnivores in western Madagascar. *Journal of Wildlife Diseases* 52: 544–552.

Poux, C., Madsen, O., Glos, J., de Jong, W. W., and Vences, M. 2008. Molecular phylogeny and divergence times of Malagasy tenrecs: Influence of data partitioning and taxon sampling on dating analyses. *BMC Evolutionary Biology* 8: 102.

Prenter, J., Macneil, C., Dick, J.T.A., and Dunn, A. M. 2004. Roles of parasites in animal invasions. *Trends in Ecology and Evolution* 19: 385–390.

Primadharsini, P. P., Nagashima, S., and Okamoto, H. 2019. Genetic variability and evolution of Hepatitis E virus. *Viruses* 11: 456.

Purdy, M. A., and Khudyakov, Y. E. 2011. The molecular epidemiology of hepatitis E virus infection. *Virus Research* 161: 31–39.

Quast, C., Pruesse, E., Yilmaz, P., Gerken, J., Schweer, T., Yarza, P., Peplies, J., and Glöckner, F. O. 2013. The SILVA ribosomal RNA gene database project: Improved data processing and web-based tools. *Nucleic Acids Research* 41: D590–D596.

Rabemananjara, H. A., Raharinosy, V., Razafimahefa, R. M., Ravalohery, J. P., Rafisandrantantsoa, J. T., et al. 2020. Human exposure to Hantaviruses associated with rodents of the *Murinae* subfamily, Madagascar. *Emerging Infectious Diseases* 26: 587–590.

Raddi, G., Morado, D. R., Yan, J., Haake, D. A., Yang, X. F., and Liu, J. 2012. Three-dimensional structures of pathogenic and saprophytic *Leptospira* species revealed by cryo-electron tomography. *Journal of Bacteriology* 194: 1299–1306.

Ragazzo, L. J., Zohdy, S., Velonabison, M., Herrera, J., Wright, P. C., and Gillespie, T. R. 2018. *Entamoeba histolytica* infection in wild lemurs associated with proximity to humans. *Veterinary Parasitology* 249: 98–101.

Raharimalala, F. N., Ravaomanarivo, L. H., Ravelonandro, P., Rafarasoa, L. S., Zouache, K., et al. 2012. Biogeography of the two major arbovirus mosquito vectors, *Aedes aegypti* and *Aedes albopictus* (Diptera, Culicidae), in Madagascar. *Parasites and Vectors* 5: 56.

Raharimanga, V., Ariey, F., Cardiff, S. G., Goodman, S. M., Tall, A., Rousset, D., and Robert, V. 2003. Hémoparasites des chauves-souris à Madagascar. *Archives de l'Institut Pasteur de Madagascar* 69: 70–76.

Raharimanga, V., Nadal, M., Rahanitraharinivo, A., Rabenindrina, N., Randriamantany, Z. A., et al. 2019. Etude des cas incidents et facteurs de risque de la leptospirose parmi les patients hospitalisés au Centre Hospitalier de Référence Régionale d'Ambatondrazaka. Poster. Deuxième Congrès de Santé Publique de l'Océan Indien, St. Leu, La Réunion, 11–14 Nov. 2019.

Raharinosy, V., Olive, M.-M., Andriamiarimanana, F. M., Andriamandimby, S. F., Ravalohery, J.-P., Andriamamonjy, S., Filippone, C., Rakoto, D.A.D., Telfer, S., and Héraud, J.-M. 2018. Geographical distribution and relative risk of Anjozorobe virus (Thailand orthohantavirus) infection in black rats (*Rattus rattus*) in Madagascar. *Virology Journal* 15: 83.

Rahelinirina, S., Léon, A., Harstskeerl, R. A., Sertour, N., Ahmed, A., et al. 2010. First isolation and direct evidence for the existence of large small-mammal reservoirs of *Leptospira* sp. in Madagascar. *PLoS One* 5: e14111.

Rahelinirina, S., Moseley, M. H., Allan, K. J., Ramanohizakandrainy, E., Ravaoarinoro, S., Rajerison, M., Rakotoharinome, V., and Telfer, S. 2019a. *Leptospira* in livestock in Madagascar: Uncultured strains, mixed infections and small mammal-livestock transmission highlight challenges in controlling and diagnosing leptospirosis in the developing world. *Parasitology* 146(14): 1707–1713.

Rahelinirina, S., Bourhy, P., Andriamiaramanana, F., Garin, B., and Rajerison, M. 2019b. High prevalence of *Leptospira* spp. in rodents in an urban setting in Madagascar. *American Journal of Tropical Medicine and Hygiene* 100: 1079–1081.

Ralaiarijaona, R. L., Bellenger, E., Chanteau, S., Roger, F., Pérolat, P., and Rasolofo Razanamparany, V. 2001. Recherche de réservoirs de la leptospirose à Madagascar par la technique d'amplification génique. *Archives de l'Institut Pasteur de Madagascar* 67: 34–36.

Ramasindrazana, B., Dellagi, K., Lagadec, E., Randrianarivelojosia, M., Goodman, S. M., and Tortosa, P. 2016. Diversity, host specialization, and geographic structure of filarial nematodes infecting Malagasy bats. *PLoS One* 11: e0145709.

Ramasindrazana, B., Goodman, S. M., Dsouli, N., Gomard, Y., Lagadec, E., Randrianarivelojosia, M., Dellagi, K., and Tortosa, P. 2018. *Polychromophilus* spp. (Haemosporida) in Malagasy bats: Host specificity and insights on invertebrate vectors. *Malaria Journal* 17: 318.

Ranaivoson, H. C., Héraud, J.-M., Goethert, H. K., Telford, S. R., Rabetafika, L., and Brook, C. E. 2019. Babesial infection in the Madagascan flying fox, *Pteropus rufus* E. Geoffroy, 1803. *Parasites and Vectors* 12: 51.

Ranjard, L., Dequiedt, S., Jolivet, C., Saby, N.P.A., Thioulouse, J., et al. 2011. Biogeography of soil microbial communities: A review and a description of the ongoing French national initiative. In *Sustainable Agriculture*, vol. 2, eds. E. Lichtfouse, M. Hamelin, M. Navarrete, and P. Debaeke, pp. 857–865. Netherlands: Springer.

Rasambainarivo, F. T., Gillespie, T. R., Wright, P. C., Arsenault, J., Villeneuve, A., and Lair, S. 2013. Survey of *Giardia* and *Cryptosporidium* in lemurs from the Ranomafana National Park, Madagascar. *Journal of Wildlife Disease* 49: 741–743.

Rasambainarivo, F. [T.], Farris, Z. J., Andrianalizah, H., and Parker, P. G. 2017. Interactions between carnivores in Madagascar and the risk of disease transmission. *Ecohealth* 14: 691–703.

Rasambainarivo, F. [T.], Andriamihajarivo, M. N., Dubovi, E., and Parker, P. G. 2018. Patterns of exposure of carnivores to selected pathogens in the Betampona natural reserve landscape, Madagascar. *Journal of Wildlife Disease* 54: 386–391.

Rasamoelina, M., Razafindratsima, O. H., Ravaomanana, F., Raveloson, B., Cêtre-Sossah, C., et al. 2019. West Nile virus seroprevalence and risk factors in wild birds in Madagascar. Poster. 56th Conference of the Association for Tropical Biology and Conservation (ATBC), Antananarivo, Madagascar.

Rasmussen, S. A., Jamieson, D. J., Honein, M. A., and Petersen, L. R. 2016. Zika virus and birth defects: Reviewing the evidence for causality. *New England Journal of Medicine* 374: 1981–1987.

Ratet, G., Veyrier, F. J., Fanton d'Andon, M., Kammerscheit, X., Nicola, M.-A., Picardeau, M., Boneca, I. G., and Werts, C. 2014. Live imaging of bioluminescent *Leptospira interrogans* in mice reveals renal colonization as a stealth escape from the blood defenses and antibiotics. *PLoS Neglected Tropical Diseases* 8: e3359.

Ratovonjato, J., Olive, M.-M., Tantely, L. M., Andrianaivolambo, L., Tata, E., Razainirina, J., Jeanmaire, E., Reynes, J.-M., and Elissa, N. 2011. Detection, isolation, and genetic characterization of Rift Valley fever virus from *Anopheles* (*Anopheles*) *coustani*, *Anopheles* (*Anopheles*) *squamosus*, and *Culex* (*Culex*) *antennatus* of the Haute Matsiatra region, Madagascar. *Vector Borne and Zoonotic Diseases* 11: 753–759.

Ratrimomanarivo, F. H., Goodman, S. M., Taylor, P. J., Melson, B., and Lamb, J. 2009. Morphological and genetic variation in *Mormopterus jugularis* (Chiroptera: Molossidae) in different bioclimatic regions of Madagascar with natural history notes. *Mammalia* 73: 110–129.

Ratsitorahina, M., Harisoa, J., Ratovonjato, J., Biacabe, S., Reynes, J.-M., Zeller, H., Raoelina, Y., Talarmin, A., Richard, V., and Soares, J. L. 2008. Outbreak of Dengue and Chikungunya fevers, Toamasina, Madagascar, 2006. *Emerging Infectious Diseases* 14: 1135–1137.

Ratsitorahina, M., Rahelinirina, S., Michault, A., Rajerison, M., Rajatonirina, S., and Richard, V., 2011 Surveillance Workshop Group. 2015. Has Madagascar lost its exceptional leptospirosis free-like status? *PLoS One* 10: e0122683.

Razanajatovo, N. H., Richard, V., Hoffmann, J., Reynes, J.-M., Razafitrimo, G. M., Randremanana, R. V., and Héraud, J.-M. 2011. Viral etiology of influenza-like illnesses in Antananarivo, Madagascar, July 2008 to June 2009. *PLoS One* 6: e17579.

Razanajatovo, N. H., Nomenjanahary, L. A., Wilkinson, D. A., Razafimanahaka, J. H., Goodman, S. M., Jenkins, R. K., Jones, J. P., and Héraud, J.-M. 2015. Detection of new genetic variants of Betacoronaviruses in endemic frugivorous bats of Madagascar. *Virology Journal* 12: 42. doi.org/10.1186/s12985-015-0271-y.

Razanajatovo, N. H., Guillebaud, J., Harimanana, A., Rajatonirina, S., Ratsima, E. H., et al. 2018. Epidemiology of severe acute respiratory infections from hospital-based surveillance in Madagascar, November 2010 to July 2013. *PLoS One* 13: e0205124.

Reilly, S. B., Wogan, G.O.U., Stubbs, A. L., Arida, E., Iskandar, D. T., and McGuire, J. A. 2017. Toxic toad invasion of Wallacea: A biodiversity hotspot characterized by extraordinary endemism. *Global Change Biology* 23: 5029–5031.

Reynes, J.-M., Andriamandimby, S. F., Razafitrimo, G. M., Razainirina, J., Jeanmaire, E. M., Bourhy, H., and Héraud, J.-M. 2011. Laboratory surveillance of rabies in humans, domestic animals, and bats in Madagascar from 2005 to 2010. *Advances in Preventive Medicine* 2011: 1–6.

Reynes, J.-M., Razafindralambo, N. K., Lacoste, V., Olive, M.-M., Barivelo, T. A., Soarimalala, V., Héraud, J.-M., and Lavergne, A. 2014. Anjozorobe Hantavirus, a new genetic variant of Thailand virus detected in rodents from Madagascar. *Vector Borne and Zoonotic Diseases* 14: 212–219.

Richardson, L. A. 2017. Evolving as a holobiont. *PLoS Biology* 15: e2002168.

Ristow, P., Bourhy, P., Kerneis, S., Schmitt, C., Prevost, M.-C., Lilenbaum, W., and Picardeau, M. 2008. Biofilm formation by saprophytic and pathogenic leptospires. *Microbiology* 154: 1309–1317.

Ritchie, E. G., Dickman, C. R., Letnic, M., and Vanak, A. T. 2014. Dogs as predators and trophic regulators. In *Free-Ranging Dogs and Wildlife Conservation*, ed. M. E. Gompper, pp. 55–68. Oxford: Oxford University Press.

Rollin, P. E., Mathiot, C., Nawrocka, E., Ravaoalimalala, V. E., Coulanges, P., Sureau, P., and McCormick, J. B. 1986. La fièvre hémorragique avec syndrome rénal à Madagascar. Première enquête séro-épidémiologique sur les populations de rats. *Archives de l'Institut Pasteur de Madagascar* 52: 181–186.

Root, J. J., Hall, J. S., McLean, R. G., Marlenee, N. L., Beaty, B. J., Gansowski, J., and Clark, L. 2005. Serologic evidence of exposure of wild mammals to flaviviruses in the central and eastern United States. *American Journal of Tropical Medicine and Hygiene* 72: 622–630.

Rostal, M. K., Liang, J. E., Zimmermann, D., Bengis, R., Paweska, J., and Karesh, W. B. 2017. Rift Valley fever: Does wildlife play a role? *ILAR Journal* 58: 359–370.

Rousset, D., and Andrianarivelo, M. R. 2003. Viruses. In *The Natural History of Madagascar*, eds. S. M. Goodman and J. P. Benstead, pp. 165–170. Chicago: University of Chicago Press.

Rupprecht, C., Kuzmin, I., and Meslin, F. 2017. Lyssaviruses and rabies: Current conundrums, concerns, contradictions and controversies. *F1000 Research* 6: 184.

Rushton, S. P., Lurz, P.W.W., Gurnell, J., and Fuller, R. 2000. Modelling the spatial dynamics of parapoxvirus disease in red and grey squirrels: A possible cause of the decline in the red squirrel in the UK? *Journal of Applied Ecology* 37: 997–1012.

Saier, M. H. 2000. Spirochetes: Evolution, genome analyses and physiology. *Journal of Molecular Microbiology and Biotechnology* 2: 339.

Saif, L. J. 2004. Animal coronaviruses: What can they teach us about the severe acute respiratory syndrome? *Revue Scientifique et Technique–Office International des Epizooties* 23: 643–660.

Samonds, K. E., Godfrey, L. R., Ali, J. R., Goodman, S. M., Vences, M., Sutherland, M. R., Irwin, M. T., and Krause, D. W. 2013. Imperfect isolation: Factors and filters shaping Madagascar's extant vertebrate fauna. *PLoS One* 8: e62086.

Samy, A. M., Peterson, A. T., and Hall, M. 2017. Phylogeography of Rift Valley fever virus in Africa and the Arabian Peninsula. *PLoS Neglected Tropical Diseases* 11: e0005226.

Schaer, J., Perkins, S. L., Decher, J., Leendertz, F. H., Fahr, J., Weber, N., and Matuschewski, K. 2013. High diversity of West African bat malaria parasites and a tight link with rodent *Plasmodium* taxa. *Proceedings of the National Academy of Sciences of the USA* 110: 17415–17419.

Schaer, J., Reeder, D. M., Vodzak, M. E., Olival, K. J., Weber, N., Mayer, F., Matuschewski, K., and Perkins, S. L. 2015. *Nycteria* parasites of Afrotropical insectivorous bats. *International Journal of Parasitology* 45: 375–384.

Schafbauer, T., Dreyfus, A., Hogan, B., Rakotozandrindrainy, R., Poppert, S., and Straubinger, R. K. 2019. Seroprevalence of *Leptospira* spp. infection in cattle from central and northern Madagascar. *International Journal of Environmental Research and Public Health* 16: 2014.

Schuffenecker, I., Iteman, I., Michault, A., Murri, S., Frangeul, L., et al. 2006. Genome microevolution of Chikungunya viruses causing the Indian Ocean outbreak. *PLoS Medicine* 3: e262.

Schwarz, N. G., Girmann, M., Randriamampionona, N., Bialonski, A., Maus, D., et al. 2012. Seroprevalence of antibodies against Chikungunya, Dengue, and Rift Valley fever viruses after febrile illness outbreak, Madagascar. *Emerging Infectious Diseases* 18: 1780–1786.

Servan de Almeida, R., Hammoumi, S., Gil, P., Briand, F.-X., Molia, S., et al. 2013. New avian paramyxoviruses type I strains identified in Africa provide new outcomes for phylogeny reconstruction and genotype classification. *PLoS One* 8: e76413.

Shi, J. J., Chan, L. M., Peel, A. J., Lai, R., Yoder, A. D., and Goodman, S. M. 2014. A deep divergence time between sister species of *Eidolon* (Pteropodidae) with evidence for widespread panmixia. *Acta Chiropterologica* 16: 279–292.

Silverie, R., Monnier, M., and Lataste-Dorolle, C. 1968. Recent survey of leptospirosis on Madagascar: Contribution to the study of human, bovine and porcine leptospirosis in the southern region. *Bulletin de la Société de Pathologie Exotique* 61: 346–359.

Simmonds, P., Adams, M. J., Benkő, M., Breitbart, M., Brister, J. R., et al. 2017. Consensus statement: Virus taxonomy in the age of metagenomics. *Nature Reviews Microbiology* 15: 161–168.

Smith, D. B., Simmonds, P., members of the International Committee on the Taxonomy of Viruses Hepeviridae Study Group, Jameel, S., Emerson, S. U., et al. 2014. Consensus proposals for classification of the family Hepeviridae. *Journal of General Virology* 95: 2223–2232.

Soarimalala, V., and Goodman, S. M. 2011. *Les petits mammifères de Madagascar*. Antananarivo: Association Vahatra.

Sondgeroth, K., Blitvich, B., Blair, C., Terwee, J., Junge, R., Sauther, M., and VandeWoude, S. 2007. Assessing flavivirus, lentivirus, and herpesvirus exposure in free-ranging ring-tailed lemurs in southwestern Madagascar. *Journal of Wildlife Diseases* 43: 40–47.

Spencer, J. A., Joiner, K. S., Hilton, C. D., Dubey, J. P., Toivio-Kinnucan, M., Minc, J. K., and Blagburn, B. L. 2004. Disseminated toxoplasmosis in a captive ring-tailed lemur (*Lemur catta*). *Journal of Parasitology* 90: 904–906.

Steinel, A., Parrish, C. R., Bloom, M. E., and Truyen, U. 2001. Parvovirus infections in wild carnivores. *Journal of Wildlife Diseases* 37: 594–607.

Taberlet, P., Coissac, E., Pompanon, F., Brochmann, C., and Willerslev, E. 2012. Towards next-generation biodiversity assessment using DNA metabarcoding. *Molecular Ecology* 8: 2045–2050.

Talbi, C., Holmes, E. C., de Benedictis, P., Faye, O., Nakoune, E., et al. 2009. Evolutionary history and dynamics of dog rabies virus in western and central Africa. *Journal of General Virology* 90: 783–791.

Talbi, C., Lemey, P., Suchard, M. A., Abdelatif, E., Elharrak, M., et al. 2010. Phylodynamics and human-mediated dispersal of a zoonotic virus. *PLoS Pathogens* 6: e1001166.

Tantely, L. M., Rakotoniaina, J.-C., Tata, E., Andrianaivolambo, L., Razafindrasata, F., Fontenille, D., and Elissa, N. 2013. Biology of mosquitoes that are potential vectors of Rift Valley fever virus in different biotopes of the central highlands of Madagascar. *Journal of Medical Entomology* 50: 603–610.

Tantely, L. M., Boyer, S., and Fontenille, D. 2015. A review of mosquitoes associated with Rift Valley fever virus in Madagascar. *American Journal of Tropical Medicine and Hygiene* 92: 722–729.

Tantely, L. M., Le Goff, G., Boyer, S., and Fontenille, D. 2016a. An updated checklist of mosquito species (Diptera: Culicidae) from Madagascar. *Parasite* 23: 20.

Tantely, L. M., Goodman, S. M., Rakotondranaivo, T., and Boyer, S. 2016b. Review of West Nile virus circulation and outbreak risk in Madagascar: Entomological and ornithological perspectives. *Parasite* 23: 49.

Tantely, L. M., Cêtre-Sossah, C., Rakotondranaivo, T., Cardinale, E., and Boyer, S. 2017. Population dynamics of mosquito species in a West Nile virus endemic area in Madagascar. *Parasite* 24: 3.

Taylor, D. J., Leach, R. W., and Bruenn, J. 2010. Filoviruses are ancient and integrated into mammalian genomes. *BMC Evolutionary Biology* 10: 193.

Temmam, S., Besnard, L., Andriamandimby, S. F., Foray, C., Rasamoelina-Andriamanivo, H., et al. 2013. High prevalence of Hepatitis E in humans and pigs and evidence of genotype-3 virus in swine, Madagascar. *American Journal of Tropical Medicine and Hygiene* 88: 329–338.

Thibault, P. A., Watkinson, R. E., Moreira-Soto, A., Drexler, J. F., and Lee, B. 2017. Zoonotic potential of emerging paramyxoviruses: Knowns and unknowns. *Advances in Virus Research* 98: 1–55.

Thibeaux, R., Iraola, G., Ferrés, I., Bierque, E., Girault, D., Soupé-Gilbert, M.-E., Picardeau, M., and Goarant, C. 2018. Deciphering the unexplored *Leptospira* diversity from soils uncovers genomic evolution to virulence. *Microbial Genomics* 4: 1.

Tortosa, P., Pascalis, H., Guernier, V., Cardinale, E., Le Corre, M., Goodman, S. M., and Dellagi, K. 2012. Deciphering arboviral emergence within insular ecosystems. *Infection, Genetics and Evolution* 12: 1333–1339.

Tortosa, P., Dsouli, N., Gomard, Y., Ramasindrazana, B., Dick, C. W., and Goodman, S. M. 2013. Evolutionary history of Indian Ocean nycteribiid bat flies mirroring the ecology of their hosts. *PLoS One* 8: e75215.

Tortosa, P., Dellagi, K., and Mavingui, P. 2017. Les leptospiroses dans les îles françaises de l'Océan Indien. *Bulletin Epidémiologique Hebdomadaire* 8–9: 157–161.

Towner, J. S., Amman, B. R., Sealy, T. K., Carroll, S.A.R., Comer, J. A., et al. 2009. Isolation of genetically diverse Marburg viruses from Egyptian fruit bats. *PLoS Pathogens* 5: e1000536.

Tsetsarkin, K. A., Vanlandingham, D. L., McGee, C. E., and Higgs, S. 2007. A single mutation in chikungunya virus affects vector specificity and epidemic potential. *PLoS Pathogens* 3: e201.

Uilenberg, G. 1967. Trois nouveaux parasites d'insectivores malgaches: *Achromaticus brygooi* sp. n. (Sporozoa, Babesiidae), *Eimeria setosi* sp. n., et *Eimeria madagascariensis* sp. n. (Sporozoa, Eimeriidae). *Annales de Parasitologie* 42: 387–398.

———. 1970. Quelques Protozoaires parasites de mammifères sauvages à Madagascar: Avec la description de trois nouveaux Sporozoaires. *Annales de Parasitologie* 45: 183–194.

Valiente Moro, C., Tran, F. H., Raharimalala, F. N., Ravelonandro, P., and Mavingui, P. 2013. Diversity of culturable bacteria including *Pantoea* in wild mosquito *Aedes albopictus*. *BMC Microbiology* 13: 70.

Vanak, A. T., and Gompper, M. E. 2010. Interference competition at the landscape level: The effect of free-ranging dogs on a native mesocarnivore. *Journal of Applied Ecology* 47: 1225–1232.

van Riper, C., van Riper, S. G., Goff, M. L., and Laird, M. 1986. The epizootiology and ecological significance of malaria in Hawaiian land birds. *Ecological Monographs* 56: 327–344.

van Riper, C., van Riper, S. G., and Hansen, W. R. 2002. Epizootiology and effect of avian pox on Hawaiian forest birds. *Auk* 119: 929–942.

Vasilakis, N., and Gubler, D. J. 2016. Arboviruses: Molecular biology, evolution and control. Norfolk: Caister Academic Press.

Vazeille, M., Moutailler, S., Coudrier, D., Rousseaux, C., Khun, H., et al. 2007. Two Chikungunya isolates from the outbreak of La Reunion (Indian Ocean) exhibit different patterns of infection in the mosquito, *Aedes albopictus*. *PLoS One* 2: e1168.

Viana, M., Cleaveland, S., Matthiopoulos, J., Halliday, J., Packer, C., et al. 2015. Dynamics of a morbillivirus at the domestic-wildlife interface: Canine distemper virus in domestic dogs and lions. *Proceedings of the National Academy of Sciences of the USA* 112: 1464–1469.

Vieilledent, G., Grinand, C., Rakotomalala, F. A., Ranaivosoa, R., Rakotoarijaona, J.-R., Allnutt, T. F., and Achard, F. 2018. Combining global tree cover loss data with historical national forest cover maps to look at six decades of deforestation and forest fragmentation in Madagascar. *Biological Conservation* 222: 189–197.

Vignuzzi, M., and Higgs, S. 2017. The bridges and blockades to evolutionary convergence on the road to predicting Chikungunya virus evolution. *Annual Review of Virology* 4: 181–200.

Villers, L. M., Jang, S. S., Lent, C. L., Lewin-Koh, S.-C., and Norosoarinaivo, J. A. 2008. Survey and comparison of major intestinal flora in captive and wild ring-tailed lemur (*Lemur catta*) populations. *American Journal of Primatology* 70: 175–184.

Watson, D. C., Sargianou, M., Papa, A., Chra, P., Starakis, I., and Panos, G. 2014. Epidemiology of hantavirus infections in humans: A comprehensive, global overview. *Critical Reviews in Microbiology* 40: 261–272.

Weaver, S. C., and Lecuit, M. 2015. Chikungunya virus infections. *New England Journal of Medicine* 373: 94–95.

Wegner, C. W. 2013. Human and animal behaviors as risk factors for diarrheal disease in rural Madagascar. PhD thesis, Emory University.

Whitehouse, C. A. 2004. Crimean-Congo hemorrhagic fever. *Antiviral Research* 64(3): 145–160.

Whitfield, J. 2005. Biogeography: Is everything everywhere? *Science* 310: 960–961.

Wilkinson, D. A., Temmam, S., Lebarbenchon, C., Lagadec, E., Chotte, J., et al. 2012. Identification of novel paramyxoviruses in insectivorous bats of the southwest Indian Ocean. *Virus Research* 170: 159–163.

Wilkinson, D. A., Mélade, J., Dietrich, M., Ramasindrazana, B., Soarimalala, V., et al. 2014a. Highly diverse morbillivirus-related paramyxoviruses in the wild fauna of southwestern Indian Ocean islands: Evidence of exchange between introduced and endemic small mammals. *Journal of Virology* 88(15): 8268–8277.

Wilkinson, D. A., Dietrich, M., Lebarbenchon, C., Jaeger, A., Le Rouzic, C., et al. 2014b. Massive infection of seabird ticks with bacterial species related to *Coxiella burnetii*. *Applied and Environmental Microbiology* 80(11): 3327–3333.

Wilkinson, D. A., Duron, O., Cordonin, C., Gomard, Y., Ramasindrazana, B., Mavingui, P., Goodman, S. M., and Tortosa, P. 2016. The bacteriome of bat flies (Nycteribiidae) from the Malagasy region: A community shaped by host ecology, bacterial transmission mode, and host-vector specificity. *Applied and Environmental Microbiology* 82(6): 1778–1788.

Witsenburg, F., Clément, L., López-Baucells, A., Palmeirim, J., Pavlinić, I., et al. 2015. How a haemosporidian parasite of bats gets around: The genetic structure of a parasite, vector and host compared. *Molecular Ecology* 24: 926–940.

World Health Organization. 2010. *The Global Prevalence of Hepatitis E Virus Infection and Susceptibility: A Systematic Review*. Geneva: World Health Organization.

———. 2021. Dengue and severe dengue. https://www.who.int/news-room/fact-sheets/detail/dengue-and-severe-dengue.

Wyatt, K. B., Campos, P. F., Gilbert, M.T.P., Kolokotronis, S.-O., Hynes, W. H., DeSalle, R., Ball, S. J., Daszak, P., MacPhee, R.D.E., and Greenwood, A. D. 2008. Historical mammal extinction on Christmas Island (Indian Ocean) correlates with introduced infectious disease. *PLoS One* 3: e3602.

Young, H. S., Parker, I. M., Gilbert, G. S., Sofia Guerra, A., and Nunn, C. L. 2017. Introduced species, disease ecology, and biodiversity-disease relationships. *Trends in Ecology and Evolution* 32: 41–54.

Young, J., Olson, K., Reading, R., Amgalanbaatar, S., and Berger, J. 2011. Is wildlife going to the dogs? Impacts of feral and free-roaming dogs on wildlife populations. *Bioscience* 6: 125–132.

Zohdy, S., Grossman, M. K., Fried, I. R., Rasambainarivo, F. T., Wright, P. C., and Gillespie, T. R. 2015. Diversity and prevalence of diarrhea-associated viruses in the lemur community and associated human population of Ranomafana National Park, Madagascar. *International Journal of Primatology* 36: 143–153.

Zohdy, S., Valenta, K., Farris, Z. J., Rabaoarivola, M., Chapman, C., Karanewsky, C., Pilotte, N., Zaky, W., and Williams, S. 2019. Causative agent of canine heartworm (*Dirofilaria immitis*) detected in wild lemurs. *International Journal of Parasitology: Parasites and Wildlife* 9: 119–121.

Zouache, K., Raharimalala, F. N., Raquin, V., Tran-Van, V., Raveloson, L.H.R., Ravelonandro, P., and Mavingui, P. 2011. Bacterial diversity of field-caught mosquitoes, *Aedes albopictus* and *Aedes aegypti*, from different geographic regions of Madagascar. *FEMS Microbiology Ecology* 75: 377–389.

CHAPTER 7

MARINE AND COASTAL ECOSYSTEMS

MARINE AND COASTAL BIODIVERSITY AND CONSERVATION

A. Cooke, S. Wells, J. Oates, P. Bouchet, H. Gilchrist, A. Leadbeater, C. L. A. Gough, R. Rasoloniriana, T. Randrianjafimanana, T. G. Jones, L. Aigrette, I. Ratefinjanahary, and J. Ravelonjatovo

This contribution provides an updated overview of scientific knowledge of the natural history of Madagascar's marine biodiversity (both ecosystems and species), excluding marine megafauna. It also summarizes the main ways in which marine biodiversity is being exploited and negatively impacted by anthropogenic factors, including climate change, and the current efforts underway to protect and manage it. The equivalent information relating to marine megafauna, including marine mammals, sea turtles, and large fishes (sharks, rays, sawfishes, *Latimeria chalumnae*, Western Indian Ocean Coelacanth), is covered in other contributions in this chapter. Seabirds are covered by Le Corre et al. (pp. 1637–50).

Since 2003, when a similar broad overview was provided in the precursor version of this book (A. Cooke et al. 2003a), scientific knowledge and understanding of Madagascar's marine biodiversity and ecosystems have expanded enormously. Until about 2000, information on marine species and ecosystems was based largely on descriptive work, species inventories, and taxonomic descriptions, and tended to be restricted to readily accessible coastal locations with a less extreme climate, such as Toliara and Nosy Be. Since then, research has expanded in geographic extent, adopted an ecosystem approach, and become more explicitly applied to sustainable use, management, and conservation.

The capacity of Malagasy researchers has grown over the same period across a range of disciplines and institutions, including the national marine research institutes, universities, ministries and government agencies, major conservation nongovernmental organizations (NGOs), and private sector environmental firms. There has been a proliferation of international cooperation, with researchers from many countries contributing both to the knowledge base and to building national capacity for marine research and conservation. The main national institutes and centers include the Institut Halieutique et des Sciences Marines (IHSM), Université de Toliara; Centre National de Recherches Océanographiques (CNRO), Nosy Be; Centre National de Recherches sur l'Environnement (CNRE), Antananarivo; the universities of Antananarivo, Toamasina, and Mahajanga; and the recently established Station de Recherches Océanographiques de Vangaindrano (SROV), an offshoot of CNRO. The ministry responsible for fisheries, Ministère de l'Agriculture, de l'Elevage et de la Pêche (MAEP), operates several units engaged in marine resources research: the Centre d'Etude et de Développement des Pêches (CEDP), the Centre de Surveillance des Pêches (CSP), Unité Statistique Thonière d'Antsiranana (USTA), and Unité de Recherche Langoustière (URL) of the Anosy Region.

This increase in interest in marine biodiversity and ecosystems has been facilitated by Madagascar's determination to meet its commitment to international targets under the Convention on Biological Diversity (CBD) in terms of establishing protected areas (see Conservation and Management, below). This triggered international assistance and led to a series of multilateral and bilateral donor-funded programs and investments in research and capacity building, in particular through the Indian Ocean Commission (IOC), the Nairobi Convention, and other regional and international institutions, including:

- IOC Regional Environment Project (PRE-IOC) (1993–2003);
- Marine Protected Area Network of the IOC Countries Project (MAPN-IOC) (2006);
- IOC ReCoMap project (2006–2011);
- Addressing Land-based Activities in the Western Indian Ocean (WIO-Lab) project (United Nations Environment Programme [UNEP], Global Environment Facility [GEF]) (2003–2010);
- Agulhas and Somali Current Large Marine Ecosystems (ASCLME) project (United Nations Development Programme [UNDP], GEF) (2005 onward);
- Toliara Fishing Communities Support Project (African Development Bank) (2006–2012);

- SMARTFISH (IOC, Food and Agriculture Organization of the United Nations [FAO], European Union [EU]) (2014–2017);
- SMARTFISH H2020 (2018–2021);
- Southwest Indian Ocean Fisheries Project (SWIOFP) (World Bank) (2006–2011);
- Second Southwest Indian Ocean Fisheries Project (SWIOFISH2) (World Bank) (2016 onward);
- Western Indian Ocean Marine Ecoregion (WIOMER) Regional Strategy initiative;
- Pêche Côtière Durable (Sustainable Coastal Fisheries; PCD) project, financed by the German development bank Kreditanstalt für Wiederaufbau (KfW) (2016–2021);
- The Census of Marine Life (2000–2010), which encouraged the *Atimo Vatae* and other research expeditions.

Several conservation NGOs, including the Wildlife Conservation Society (WCS), World Wide Fund for Nature (WWF), Conservation International (CI), Blue Ventures, Frontier, Reef Doctor, and Community Centered Conservation (C3), have permanently staffed marine conservation programs, and their work has contributed significantly to current knowledge of marine biodiversity. Of particular importance have been the three marine rapid assessment program (RAP) coral reef expeditions, led by CI, with teams of international and national researchers, which have generated information in support of marine protected area planning and selection. In parallel, international cooperation in scientific research and ocean resources management has resulted in oceanic and inshore expeditions and research programs that have increased knowledge of marine biodiversity.

Many of these more recent studies have revealed new and sometimes endemic marine species in Malagasy waters, improved understanding of the impact of human activities on marine biodiversity (e.g., climate change, sedimentation, overexploitation), and provided vital information for conservation and management. Furthermore, Madagascar's importance regionally and globally as a center of marine biodiversity and as a contributor to the maintenance of large marine ecosystem processes is now internationally demonstrated and understood. As the fourth-largest island in the world, Madagascar has one of the largest exclusive economic zones (EEZs) in the Indian Ocean, covering some 1.14 million km^2 (Barnes-Mauthe et al. 2013), and one of the longest coastlines (over 5000 km) and largest areas of shallow coastal and intertidal habitats, resulting in marine and coastal ecosystems considered the most biodiverse of the western Indian Ocean.

Global recognition of the significance of Madagascar's marine biodiversity has come alongside greater understanding of the enormous threat from overfishing, pollution (including sedimentation), climate change, and numerous other pressures. Marine biodiversity is essential for coastal livelihoods and food security, particularly for those communities in arid areas, where alternative livelihood options are scarce, that rely on fishing. Recognition of the economic importance of marine biodiversity and the immense pressure it is under has led to support from international and regional programs, extensive national efforts to protect and manage these resources, and, in particular, a growing movement of community-based marine management activities.

PHYSICAL CONTEXT AND ECOREGIONS

Foiben-Taosarintanin'i Madgasikara (FTM), also known as the Institut Géographique et Hydrographique de Madagascar, has set the length of Madagascar's coast, including the coastlines of the principal inhabited nearshore islands, at 5603 km (ASCLME 2012). The country spans almost 14 degrees of latitude (11°47′–25°35′S). While the majority of the coast lies within the southern tropics, the extreme south is distinctly subtropical and verges on temperate (P. Bouchet, unpublished data).

Bathymetry

The continental shelf covers about 117,000 km^2. Weathering and deposition over time have led to the erosion of Madagascar's Central Highlands and a consequent seaward extension of the coast and continental shelf on the west. On the west coast, the 100 m depth contour occurs up to ~90 km from shore, the larger protrusions corresponding to major river deltas. An exception is the Toliara coastline in the southwest, where the continental shelf is only a few kilometers wide owing to geological faulting and narrows to a few hundred meters opposite the Onilahy River mouth (Battistini et al. 1975). In contrast, on the east coast, wave action and sediment transport driven by the southeast trade winds have limited deposition, resulting in a narrow coastal plain and steep continental shelf.

Tides and Sea Temperature

The narrowness of the Mozambique Channel results in high tidal ranges along the west coast of Madagascar compared with the east coast, which faces a vast expanse of the Indian Ocean. Mean spring ranges are 3.8 m at Mahajanga and 2.6 m at Toliara. In the east, tidal range is about 1 m in the north and drops to about 0.5 m in the south (Hydrographer of the Navy 1990).

Sea temperatures around Madagascar are higher and less varied than would be expected for its partly subtropical position, owing to the surrounding warm waters of the South Equatorial Current. Mean annual open water sea surface temperatures (SST) range from 22°C in the south to 28°C in the north. The east coast has a marked and constant thermocline at 100 m, whereas the west coast has a poorly defined thermocline at about 150 m, which disappears completely between Maintirano (18°S) and Morondava (20°S) (Ranaivoson 1997).

Climate, Rainfall, and Wind

The eastern and northern coasts of Madagascar are humid and rainy, with high rainfall from October to March, while the western and southern coasts have a pronounced dry season, with associated seasonality in runoff and nutrient inputs into coastal marine ecosystems (see Jury, pp. 91–98, for further details). The balance between the southeastern trade winds and the monsoon, both of which affect Madagascar's inshore waters, is determined by shifts in position of the Mascarene anticyclone and a zone of low pressure that appears over the Mozambique Channel from May to July. The North Mozambique Channel experiences monsoon reversals, whereas in the South Mozambique Channel southeasterly winds dominate all year.

Throughout the cooler months (April–October), the Mascarene anticyclone dominates, reinforced by low pressure over the Mozambique Channel, bringing southeasterly trade winds to all of Madagascar's coasts. In the summer months (November–March), the northern monsoon system shifts southward, resulting in northerly winds in the northern part of the island, which become variable farther south (Hastenrath and Lamb 1979). In general, winds along the east coast are strong and southerly (Antsiranana in the extreme north and Tolagnaro in the southeast are the windiest coastal locations), and those along the west coast are variable and weaker. Nosy Be in the northwest is the least windy location, as it is protected by the Tsaratanàna Massif on the main island (Hydrographer of the Navy 1990).

From February to April, cyclones affect the country, traveling from the east of Madagascar between 5°S and 10°S and following a westward parabolic path with a turning point at about 20°S. Where the turning point lies close to the west coast of Madagascar, a single cyclone can cross Madagascar twice and strike the coast at several locations (Chaperon et al. 2005; see Jury, pp. 91–98). As a result, these events can have a major impact on marine and coastal ecosystems.

Currents and Oceanic Circulation

In the southern Indian Ocean, Madagascar causes an obstruction to the typical flow pattern found in major ocean basins, where surface circulations tend to be wind driven and anticyclonic, and intensify in the west to form strong boundary currents. The South Equatorial Current (the northern component of the southern Indian Ocean gyre) flows westward across the Indian Ocean, splitting when it reaches the east coast of Madagascar at about 18–20°S into the Southern East Madagascar Current (SEMC) and the Northern East Madagascar Current (NEMC) (Swallow et al. 1988; Halo et al. 2017) (Figure 7.1a).

The Seychelles Ridge, a granitic ridge to the east of Madagascar, which rises to depths of 100 m or less, has a major influence on oceanic circulation in this area by allowing the oligotrophic (deficient in dissolved salts needed for plant growth), warm surface flow of the South Equatorial Current to pass across to Madagascar, while diverting deeper, cooler, and less nutrient-depleted water southward to remain within the southern Indian Ocean gyre (Obura 2012). This accounts for the exceptionally low levels of nutrients and plankton in the waters off Madagascar's east coast.

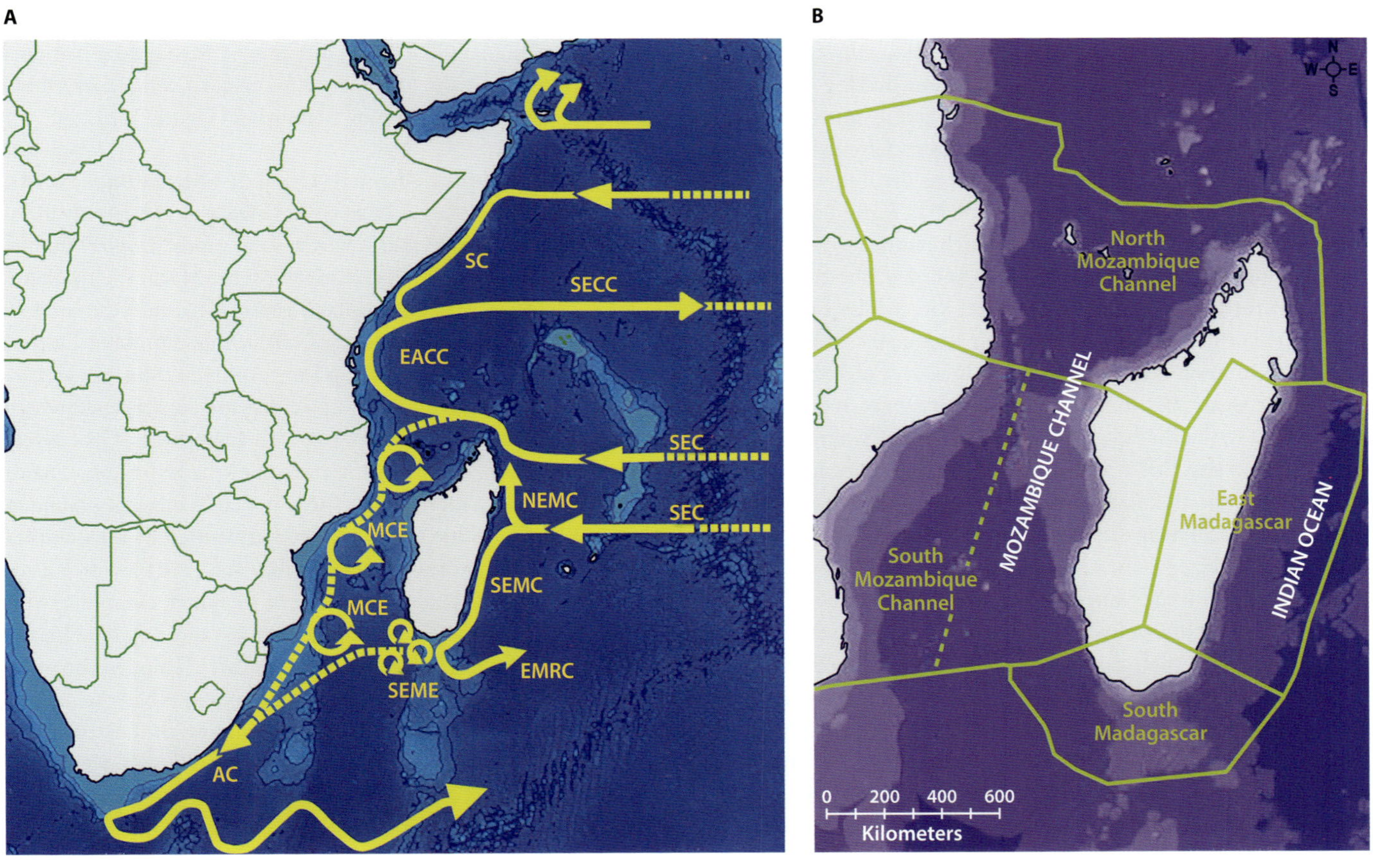

FIGURE 7.1 **A) Ocean surface circulation affecting Madagascar and surrounding region: SEC (South Equatorial Current), SECC (South Equatorial Counter Current), NEMC (Northern East Madagascar Current), SEMC (Southern East Madagascar Current), EMRC (East Madagascar Retroflection Current), EACC (East African Coastal Current), SC (Somalia Current), AC (Agulhas Current), MCE (Mozambique Channel Eddies), and SEME (Southeast Madagascar Dipole Eddies). Dotted lines indicate water transport, not current boundaries. B) Marine ecoregions of Madagascar.** (SOURCES: A) ASCLME 2012, reproduced in IUCN 2019; B) modified from MNP 2014.)

The SEMC is a strong boundary current of 150 cm/sec extending from the coast to 150 km offshore, peaking at 30–50 km offshore and extending deeper than the NEMC to 200 m (Halo et al. 2017). The SEMC flows southward along Madagascar's east coast to Tolagnaro and then in a south-southwesterly direction past Cap Sainte Marie, where it retroflects, with much of the flow turning southeastward before rejoining the main westward flow of the Agulhas Current. Another branch turns east to become the South Indian Current, corresponding to the return flow of the South Equatorial Current (Lutjeharms et al. 2000). Off Tolagnaro, where the SEMC moves from a narrow part of the continental shelf to a wider part, it causes an unusually intense, localized upwelling cell (Lutjeharms and Machu 2000; Ramanantsoa et al. 2018a). This results in considerable flow variability toward the south of Madagascar, increased by the presence of very intense anticyclonic deep-sea eddies, which appear to originate in the South Equatorial Current. Two upwelling cores, one at Tolagnaro and another seasonal cell to the west of Cap Sainte Marie, each create areas of elevated primary productivity in the deep south of Madagascar (Ramanantsoa et al. 2018a).

The NEMC is a weakly defined surface current (first 100 m) with northerly flow that is weak until it accelerates around the northern tip of Madagascar (Halo et al. 2017). It then flows westward into the Mozambique Channel, crossing to East Africa, turning south, and eventually joining the Agulhas Current off the coast of southeast Africa. The circulation along the northwest and west coasts is dominated by a series of southward-drifting eddies that bring warm water to western Madagascar and assimilate nutrient inputs from Madagascar's large western rivers. Circulation within the Mozambique Channel has long been recognized as extremely complex and variable (Lutjeharms et al. 1981; Ternon et al. 2014). Obura et al. (2019) summarize the research on the northern part of the Mozambique Channel since 2003 and describe the complex system of turbulent eddies—with about four eddies per year, approximately 100–300 km across—that dominates the flow, with the eddies' rotation extending down thousands of meters to the seabed (Swart et al. 2010). A cyclonic eddy has been repeatedly observed close to the Madagascar coast, at about 20°S, although there is no evidence that this is a permanent feature (Obura et al. 2019).

Both anticyclonic and cyclonic eddies occur, with the latter forcing deep water carrying dissolved nutrients upward into the depleted euphotic layer, where photosynthesis and new primary production may occur. When eddies move into productive coastal areas, they pull chlorophyll-rich waters toward the center of the Mozambique Channel, causing high biological productivity in this location. The cross-channel circulation patterns resulting from this eddy field may provide important connectivity throughout the channel (Hancke et al. 2014; Crochelet et al. 2016; Gamoyo et al. 2019). The eddies play a major role in water enrichment across the whole region (Schouten et al. 2003; Sabarros et al. 2009), resulting in rich pelagic productivity throughout the food web from zooplankton to pelagic fishes, seabirds, whales, and *Rhincodon typus* (Whale Shark) (Tew Kai et al. 2009; Sequeira et al. 2012).

Using data from research cruises, satellite remote-sensing observations, and modeling, an additional coastal surface poleward flow was identified off the west coast of Madagascar, which has been named the Southwest Madagascar Coastal Current (SMACC) (Ramanantsoa et al. 2018b). It is shallow (<300 m) and narrow (<100 km wide), warm and salty at the surface, and more intense in summer than winter. The SMACC appears to play a role in the seasonal variation of the upwelling cell identified west of Cap Sainte Marie (Ramanantsoa et al. 2018b).

Biogeography and Marine Ecoregions

Climate, currents, bathymetry, and other physical factors have a major influence on the distribution of marine biodiversity. The dominant habitats along the shallow, sloping west coast of Madagascar are coral reefs, mangroves, seagrass meadows, and mudflats; about 90% of all coral reefs and 98% of all mangroves of the island occur here. Tidal range combined with the drainage of Madagascar's largest rivers into the Mozambique Channel, bringing large quantities of fresh water and sediment, reducing salinity, increasing turbidity, and adding nutrients and suspended organic matter, account for the predominance of these habitats on the west coast. Steeply shelving beach and rocky shorelines predominate on the east coast.

To facilitate conservation planning and management, the concept of ecoregions is often used to ensure appropriate representation of different aspects of biodiversity in protected areas and other spatial planning measures. For the purposes of the Protected Area Network Management Plan (Plan stratégique de Gestion du Réseau des Aires Protégées, PlanGRAP) put together by Madagascar National Parks (MNP 2014), the four marine ecoregions defined by Obura (2012) are used for the planning framework (Figure 7.1b).

1. **North Mozambique Channel (Canal de Mozambique Nord):** The part of this ecoregion that covers Madagascar is heavily influenced by the NEMC and is Madagascar's most tropical marine area (the whole ecoregion extends across the Mozambique Channel to the East African mainland coast). On the west coast of Madagascar, the ecoregion extends from Cap d'Ambre (Tanjona Bobaomby) in the north to Cap Saint André in the south; at Cap Saint André there is a zone of upwelling and convergence, which marks the division between two sub-ecoregions (Groeneveld and Koranteng 2017). On the east coast, the ecoregion extends to just south of Antongil Bay. The very rich biodiversity found in this ecoregion is due to the connectivity caused by the complex currents and Comoros gyre (C. Collins et al. 2016), which leads to extensive circulation and mixing of the water, combined with the varied topography of the coastline and topographically abrupt submarine bathymetry. The result is rich biodiversity with mangroves, coral reefs of different types, seagrass beds, and islets. Coral, fish, and mollusk diversity are high, and the coast and waters are important for all five species of Indian Ocean marine turtles (see Walker et al., pp. 391–99); cetaceans (see Cerchio et al., pp. 411–24), including *Balaenoptera omurai* (Omura's Whale) (see Cerchio et al., pp. 424–29); *Dugong dugon* (Dugong) (see Davis et al., pp. 400–411); seabirds (see Le Corre et al., pp. 1637–50); and *Rhincodon typus* (Whale Shark) (see Diamant et al., pp. 381–85). Recent work has suggested that the North Mozambique Channel ecoregion as a whole might qualify as a "large marine ecosystem" on account of its biodiversity importance and unique oceanography (Obura et al. 2019), and that it may be the

second-most-important area of shallow marine biodiversity in the world (Tittensor et al. 2010; Obura 2012; Obura et al. 2019). It has been identified as a potential World Heritage site (Obura et al. 2012) and designated as an Ecologically or Biologically Significant Area (EBSA) (CBD 2012).

2. **South Mozambique Channel (Canal de Mozambique Sud):** The Malagasy component of this ecoregion runs from Cap Saint André, in the north, southward to 24°S, near Itampolo. It has extensive coral reefs (both barrier and fringing), the largest stands of mangroves in the western Indian Ocean, seagrass beds, and important populations of wetland birds, including endemics (see Young, pp. 1627–36). The coral reefs of Toliara are especially well known. Coral diversity is relatively high, with key areas for reefs including the Barren Islands and a string of islets along the southwest coast from Morombe to Anakao. This ecoregion is also important for threatened marine megafauna, including all five species of marine turtles and *Dugong dugon*.
3. **South Madagascar (Sud Madagascar):** This ecoregion, lying south of 24°S, also known as the Deep South, has only recently been surveyed (P. Bouchet, unpublished data). With rough seas, a subtropical to temperate climate, and an exposed coastline of rocky promontories interspersed with sandy beaches, this ecoregion has many unusual features. It is affected by permanent and seasonal upwelling cells around Tolagnaro and to the west of Cap Sainte Marie; the latter is influenced by the SMACC, which gives rise to a summer algal bloom and in turn forms the base of a food web attracting marine megafauna and oceanic seabirds. Reefs are primarily algal rather than coralline, although coral formations are found at Androka and Banc de l'Etoile in the southwest and at Lokaro (Sainte Luce) in the southeast (Figure 7.2a). This ecoregion has the highest algal diversity anywhere in Malagasy coastal waters. Marine faunal diversity is lower than elsewhere but with high levels of species endemism. This ecoregion has been identified as a potential World Heritage site (Obura 2012) and has been designated as an EBSA (CBD 2012).
4. **East Madagascar (Est Madagascar):** This ecoregion is the least well known. It extends from a line south of the Antongil Bay and north of Mananara southward along the rectilinear east coast to south of Vangaindrano, where waters begin to become subtropical. Coral reef development is limited by the lack of suitable substrate, high wave energy, and turbidity. The calmer, shallower waters in the northern part of the region between Toamasina and Ile Sainte Marie allow for the development of coral reefs, seagrass beds, and some mangroves. Ile Sainte Marie is an important breeding area for *Megaptera novaeangliae* (Humpback Whale) (see Rosenbaum and Chou, pp. 430–33) and the site of recent records of *Dugong dugon* (Davis et al., pp. 400–411).

Upwellings and Areas of High Productivity

The main drivers of productivity are upwelling, mesoscale eddy circulation, frontal systems, riverine outflow, and monsoon winds (which either mix or stratify surface waters). Surface water layers around Madagascar are mineral impoverished, and there is a peak of chlorophyll at 100 m (Groeneveld and Koranteng 2017). The seawater swept westward across the Indian Ocean by the South Equatorial Current is deficient in nutrients, resulting in generally low levels of biological productivity off the east coast. The rivers of the eastern escarpment contain low levels of nutrients, compounding the low natural productivity of eastern oceanic waters. An exception is Antongil Bay, a semi-enclosed bay fed by numerous rivers and with nutrient inputs associated with human settlements; the most productive fishery on the east coast is found here (Doukakis et al. 2007). A pair of upwelling cells of high productivity occur off Tolagnaro and to the west of Cap Sainte Marie (Ramanantsoa et al. 2018a). The research vessel *Dr Fridtjof Nansen* surveys found that nutrients from terrestrial sources appear to be of greater importance than upwelling sources for demersal organisms over soft sediments (Fennessy et al. 2017).

Nutrient levels are substantially higher off the west coast owing to complex mixing in the Mozambique Channel and to river inputs along the coasts of Madagascar and Mozambique. The highest levels of nutrients are found off the deltas, which support large shrimp fisheries. A zone of high productivity was previously identified

FIGURE 7.2 **Different underwater images from the Deep South. A) Shallow reef, showing its subtropical character; B) *Haliotis squamosa*, an endemic abalone from the Deep South.** (PHOTOS by P. Bouchet, *Atimo Vatae* expedition.)

around Toliara (Marsac 1998), although not explained and not confirmed by subsequent surveys. The highest levels of productivity are found in the Deep South (see Marine Species Diversity, below).

Following the *Dr Fridtjof Nansen* surveys of 2008 and 2009, four zones of upwelling are now confirmed for Madagascar (Halo et al. 2017):

1. At Cap d'Ambre, where the NEMC accelerates past the northern cape
2. Around Cap Saint André, at the junction between the North and South Mozambique Channel marine ecoregions
3. Off Tolagnaro, over the Madagascar Plateau, associated with the retroflection of the Agulhas Current and southeast trade winds (Ramanantsoa et al. 2018a)
4. A seasonally variable upwelling cell off the southwest of Faux Cap, whose seasonality is driven by the SMACC (Ramanantsoa et al. 2018b)

Offshore Waters, Abyssal Habitats, and Oceanic Banks

Pelagic waters over the continental shelf are more productive than oceanic waters, owing to higher temperature, the influence of river discharge, and vertical transfer of nutrients from bottom sediments. On the east coast, surface waters are oligotrophic, with moderate primary productivity (2–5 mg C m^{-2} d^{-1} in summer). On the west coast, productivity of offshore waters is moderate as far north as Maintirano, but higher in the northwest from Cap Saint André to Cap d'Ambre (5.1–10 mg C m^{-2} d^{-1} in summer) (Marsac 1998).

There is little information in the scientific literature about the abyssal habitats of Madagascar, but information may be available in studies of deep-sea fisheries or those conducted in connection with petroleum exploration. At Saint Augustin, the submarine canyon of the Onilahy River, which drops to 1500 m close to the coast (Battistini et al. 1975; Salomon 1986), supports a population of *Latimeria chalumnae* (Western Indian Ocean Coelacanth) (see Bruton et al., pp. 359–67).

A number of oceanic banks occur close to Madagascar's continental shelf in the northwest and south (within Madagascar's EEZ, except where otherwise indicated).

- Banc du Leven and the associated Banc de Castor constitute the largest, covering an area of about 2500 km^2 and lying ~40 km west-northwest of the Mitsio Island group; it effectively constitutes an extension to Madagascar's continental shelf.
- Banc du Geyser (outside Madagascar's EEZ) lies to the west of Banc du Leven and is part of the Comoro volcanic island chain. It is claimed by France, Comoros, and Madagascar and currently protected as part of the French marine protected area Iles Glorieuses.
- Ile Juan de Nova (outside Madagascar's EEZ) is an atoll with extensive coral reefs, lying about 150 km due west of Cap Saint André. Juan de Nova is one of the French Iles Eparses and is administered from La Réunion but also claimed by Madagascar; it is an Important Bird Area and a French protected area.
- Taunton Castle, Estaign, and Vines are three offshore banks to the south of Juan de Nova.
- Banc de Tabinta lies about 80 km south of Cap Sainte Marie, separated from the continental shelf by a small gap.
- Madagascar Ridge (partly outside Madagascar's EEZ) lies south of Banc de Tabinta and is an extension of Madagascar's continental mass, with depths of around 2000 m; it includes a number of mounts rising to within 500 m of the surface and several holes descending to over 3 km.
- Walters Shoals, an isolated seamount toward the southern end of the Madagascar Ridge (outside Madagascar's EEZ in the high seas), reaches to within 18 m of the surface. It is located about 400 nautical miles south of Madagascar and is identified as an EBSA (CBD 2012).

CORAL REEFS

Madagascar's coral reefs are the most extensive, structurally varied, and biologically diverse of the western Indian Ocean (Andréfouët et al. 2009; Obura 2012) and represent 2% of the world's coral reefs (Burke et al. 2011). Corals are found around most of the coastline apart from the Deep South, and reefs probably cover a linear distance of some 3540 km, including 1418 km of submerged coral banks along the northwest coast (A. Cooke et al. 2003a). Remote-sensing methods have reported coral reef area to be from 2230 km^2 (Spalding and Ravilious 2001) to 5076 km^2 (Obura et al. 2012), the differences being due to variations in the measurement techniques used. The figure of 3934 km^2 determined by Burke et al. (2011) is considered the most accurate.

Madagascar's coral reefs were first studied in the early 1960s (Thomassin 1971), the main focus being the Nosy Be and Toliara regions, particularly the Grand Récif barrier reef of Toliara (Clausade et al. 1971). The reefs of the Toliara region are among the best described in Malagasy waters and in the world (Andréfouët et al. 2009) (Figure 7.3), the research on the Grand Récif having helped establish a typology of reef geomorphology still in international use today. The work of the Institut Halieutique et des Sciences Marines in Toliara, which resulted in numerous publications during the 1960s and 1970s (including the classic work of Clausade et al. 1971), led to interest in monitoring reefs in the southwest, and subsequent publications in the 1970s and 1980s (e.g., Pichon 1978; Harmelin-Vivien et al. 1985; Vasseur et al. 1988). Since then, international conservation organizations, with the participation of coastal communities, have continued monitoring the reefs along this coastline, particularly at Itampolo (WWF), Andavadoaka (Blue Ventures), Ranobe (Reef Doctor), and Salary (WCS).

In this century, three rapid assessment program (RAP) surveys, using Conservation International's survey methodology, have provided a biogeographic understanding of the reefs of the northwest (McKenna and Allen 2003) and northeast (Maharavo et al. 2011; Obura et al. 2011). Baseline reef surveys have been undertaken in existing and proposed protected areas, including Velondriake (Harding et al. 2006), Nosy Hara (Obura 2009), the Barren Islands (Cripps 2010), and Ile Sainte Marie (Wickel and Nicet 2017). Other surveys have been carried out by the private sector; for example, in the course of environmental impact assessments, such as the extension of the Toamasina port (J.-P. Quod, unpublished data) and Ampasindava Peninsula (Ratsifandrihamanana 2014).

FIGURE 7.3 **Map showing the position of the coral reefs of Madagascar.** (SOURCE: modified from Andréfouët et al. 2009.)

Since 1998, annual monitoring of coral reefs in the western Indian Ocean, including those of Madagascar, has been coordinated by the organization Coastal Oceans Research and Development—Indian Ocean (CORDIO). Using a standardized methodology, reefs in Malagasy waters have been monitored annually at 12 principal sites along the east and west coasts (with multiple stations at some sites) and the results included in the most recent regional report (Obura et al. 2017). Reefs within some designated or potential marine protected areas are monitored using methodologies other than CORDIO's (e.g., Harris et al. 2010; Gilchrist et al. 2020). Several conservation organizations have established reef-monitoring citizen science projects, such as Blue Ventures and Reef Doctor in the southwest, Frontier around Nosy Be (Fairbrother 2020), and PRISM (Projet Récif Ile Sainte Marie) (Damien and Loncle 2019). Although efforts have increased markedly since 1998, reef monitoring is not fully coordinated or reported nationally and there is little standardization of methods or sampling strategies. This limits comparative analysis to the few isolated long-term monitoring efforts that have available and published data, and thus allows only identification of broad trends. There is nevertheless a growing understanding of the impacts of climate change on Malagasy coral reefs and of their resilience (e.g., Maina and Obura 2008; McClanahan et al. 2009). The Millennium Coral Reef Mapping Project developed a classification for the geomorphology of reefs, defining 966 different classes worldwide, 86 of which are found in Malagasy waters—the highest number in the western Indian Ocean (Andréfouët et al. 2006). The Grand Récif of Toliara alone exhibits 26 habitat classes (Andréfouët 2012).

Madagascar's coral reefs are structurally more complex than reefs anywhere else in the Indian Ocean (Andréfouët et al. 2009; Obura 2012). The zonation patterns of Madagascar's reefs were first described for the Grand Récif of Toliara and surrounding reefs in the southwest: Clausade et al. (1971) described the zones of the Grand Récif (from seaward slope to back reef), and this early categorization was used by Andréfouët et al. (2009), as it is still visible on the reef, despite years of degradation.

More recent studies in the southwest have shown that, while all reef zones tend to be dominated by *Acropora* species, those farther offshore have more abundant coral colonies of the genera *Porites*, *Favia*, and *Favites*, particularly in their massive growth forms, with inshore reefs having a greater proportion of *Pavona* and *Stylophora* (Blue Ventures, unpublished data). In areas of lower fishing pressure or that are less vulnerable to heat stress or cyclone impacts, fast-growing, branching acroporid and pocilloporid corals are more dominant, which is a common finding on reefs globally (Obura 2009; Harris et al. 2010). Contrastingly, in areas of greater climate-driven or anthropogenic stress, large massive or boulder growth forms are more successful, specifically those belonging to the families Poritidae and Faviidae (Harding et al. 2006; Harris et al. 2010).

Hard Coral Diversity

Madagascar's reef communities belong to the Indian Ocean faunal group, are very similar to those found from East Africa north to the Red Sea and east to the Pacific Ocean, and have long been recognized as including high coral species diversity. A. Cooke et al. (2003a) document early studies, and by 2003 over 380 hard coral species had been recorded in Madagascar's reefs (McKenna and Allen 2003), the highest number of any area in the western Indian Ocean at that time (Veron and Turak 2003). Veron et al. (2015) place Madagascar in a high diversity grouping (400–450 hard coral species), along with eastern Africa and the Mozambique Channel; this is similar to, but more diverse than, the Laccadives, Maldives, Rodrigues, Mauritius, La Réunion, or Seychelles (in the 350–400 species range).

The North Mozambique Channel has the highest diversity of corals recorded in the western Indian Ocean (Obura et al. 2019). The cyclonic eddy of warm surface water between the northwest coast of Madagascar and the Comoros (C. Collins et al. 2016) may function to retain species adapted to the warmer water, and encourage the development of coral-algal symbionts more resilient to raised temperatures and therefore to climate change (Obura et al. 2019). Eastern Madagascar, with its limited reef development, and the South Mozambique Channel have lower coral diversities than the North Mozambique Channel. The Deep South lacks true coral reefs and has relatively few hard coral species because of its high wave action and lower water temperatures.

About half the hard coral species found in Malagasy waters are widespread in the Indian Ocean. While no endemic genus is reported for Madagascar, the monospecific genus *Horastrea* (Siderastreidae) is considered restricted to East Africa, Madagascar, and the Mascarenes (Veron and Turak 2003). *Horastrea indica* was first described in Malagasy waters (Pichon 1971) and later found to occur more widely in the western Indian Ocean (Veron 2000). In part because of its rarity, *H. indica* is listed on the International Union for the Conservation of Nature (IUCN) Red List as Vulnerable (Sheppard et al. 2008). The North Mozambique Channel includes two potential Madagascar endemics: an undescribed *Turbinaria* species found in northeast and northwest Madagascar, and *Acropora variolosa*, a species difficult to distinguish from others in its group but which may be confined to Madagascar (Obura 2012). Two further species, *Craterastrea laevis* and *Anomastrea irregularis*, initially considered potentially endemic to the North Mozambique Channel, have been found to occur more widely.

Coral Reef Fish Diversity and Biomass

The diversity of coral reef fishes in Malagasy waters reflects the notable array of corals and range of reef types; a total count of 852 coral-reef-associated fish species was estimated by Maharavo et al. (2011), with the recent finding of *Apolemichthys kingi* around Ile Sainte Marie (Wickel et al. 2018) making a new total of 853 species.

About 38 species (or 4.8% of the total) are confined to the western Indian Ocean, with 10 near-endemic species confined to Madagascar and the Comoro islands, mainly small damselfishes (Pomacentridae) and Pseudochromidae. An additional seven species are confined to Madagascar and the Mascarenes, of which three extend to northern South Africa (G. Allen 2011). A commonly highlighted, attractive, and readily observed endemic or near endemic is *Pomacentrus caeruleopunctatus* (Blue Spotted Damselfish), first discovered in Malagasy waters (McKenna and Allen 2003; Maharavo et al. 2011). The most species-rich reef-associated families are gobies (Gobiidae), with 79 species; wrasses (Labridae), with 78 species; damselfishes (Pomacentridae), with 55 species; groupers (Serranidae), with 45 species; and seven other families with between 39 and 22 species—in total these make up about 56% of the total reef fauna (Maharavo et al. 2011).

Coral reef fish biomass varies substantially between sites and regions. This is an important measure, as fish biomass reflects the health of a coral reef and is also very sensitive to disturbance, particularly fishing. Estimates of fish biomass and fishes' spatial distribution can give a good indication of reef status in different places and are useful in prioritizing management activities. The lowest values for biomass are at sites in the East Madagascar ecoregion (Ile Sainte Marie, Toamasina), and the highest at west coast sites. In marine protected areas, levels of fish biomass are significantly higher (Samoilys et al. 2019; Gilchrist et al. 2020) than the western Indian Ocean average of 531 kg/ha (McClanahan et al. 2011). Overall, the average value for Madagascar (~709 kg/ha) is about 33% higher than the average value for fished coral reefs across the western Indian Ocean, suggesting that fishing pressures are less than the regional average, or that Madagascar's reefs are more productive, or both (Table 7.1).

TABLE 7.1. **Coral reef fish biomass at sites in Madagascar compared with the western Indian Ocean**

ECOREGION	ZONE	REFERENCE	LOCATION	BIOMASS MAX. (kg/ha)	BIOMASS MIN. (kg/ha)	AVERAGE (kg/ha)
NORTH (North Mozambique Channel)	NW	McKenna and Allen (2003)	Various	1720	3.1	182
	NNW	McKenna and Allen (2003)	Nosy Hara	1654	–	1654
	NNE	Maharavo et al. (2011)	Extreme NE	2965	51.2	900
	NNE	Samoilys et al. (2019)	Back lagoon, NE	1864	–	1864
	NE	Harding and Randriamanantsoa (2008)	Masoala National Park - Mananara	634	475	554
EAST (East Madagascar)	Mid E	Wickel and Nicet (2017)	Ile Sainte Marie (five sites)	246	95.7	171
	Mid E	Damien and Loncle (2019)	Ile Sainte Marie (five sites)	186	–	186
	Mid E	Biotope (2019)	Nosy Faho	173	–	173
WEST (South Mozambique Channel)	Mid W	C.L.A. Gough (unpublished data)	Belo sur Mer	711	183.1	372
	Mid W	Cripps (2010)	Barren Islands	2270	1329.0	1799
	SW	Gilchrist et al. (2020)	Velondriake fished reefs	247	–	247
	SW	Gilchrist et al. (2020)	Velondriake	786	–	786
	SW	Harding et al. (2006)	Andavadoaka	607	52.5	330
MADAGASCAR	All	References cited in this contribution	–	–	Average (Madagascar)	709
Western Indian Ocean (fished reefs)	–	McClanahan et al. (2011)	–	–	Average (western Indian Ocean)	531

Geographical Distribution of Reefs by Ecoregion

The marine ecological classification developed by Obura et al. (2012) defined four marine ecoregions as described above, largely on the basis of reef distribution and coral diversity. Reef descriptions are provided according to these ecoregions.

North Mozambique Channel Marine Ecoregion

The reefs in this ecoregion are the most diverse in Malagasy waters (Obura 2012) and are subject to the contrasting oceanographic and geological conditions of the east- and west-facing coasts. The northeast coast is mainly rocky with low tidal range, high wave action, high amounts of suspended sediments, and shallow reef profiles (typically 12–18 m) (e.g., Obura et al. 2011), but in sheltered bays, such as Ambodivahibe and Vohémar (Iharana), coral growth extends to depths of 30 m or more. The northwest coast is less exposed, subject to higher tidal range, and fringed with mangroves and coastal wetlands.

While fringing reefs are not well developed along the coast, they occur around the numerous offshore islands, with live coral cover extending to 50 m or more in depth around the Nosy Be area where waters are calm. Local high turbidity conditions occur owing to eddies created by the South Equatorial Current's interaction with the northern tip of the country, high rainfall, and a shallow, more extensive continental shelf allowing vertical sediment transport. An offshore ridge of fossil reefs along the continental shelf edge, extending to depths of as much as 70 m (Fourmanoir 1963a), shelters the larger bays such as Narindra and Mahajamba, limiting water circulation and retaining sediments and nutrients within the system. Since the early studies cited by A. Cooke et al. (2003a), two RAPs (McKenna and Allen 2003; Obura et al. 2011) and local coral reef monitoring and assessment have increased knowledge of the reefs in this ecoregion. The main reef areas are described below; those in the northeast are described first, followed by those in the northwest.

Northeast: Emergent coastal fringing and offshore reefs extend along much of the northeast coast from Toamasina to Cap d'Ambre (Pichon 1972; Battistini et al. 1975). Well-developed fringing reefs occur around the islands in the southern half of Antongil Bay and from Cap Masoala to Cap Est and Antalaha. Reefs then disappear until south of Vohémar, where there is a substantial barrier reef in association with Vohémar Bay. To the north of Vohémar, reefs are associated with the Nosy Ankao archipelago. In the far northeast, fringing and patch reefs occur in the sheltered waters of Antsiranana (Diégo Suarez) Bay and also in the Emerald Sea, which opens to the east (Maharavo et al. 2011). Coral formations in Antsiranana Bay include extensive beds of alcyonarians (soft corals and sea fans), which cover 1–16% of the seabed in the northwestern part of the bay. A total of 11 genera in four families of alcyonarians have been identified, with *Sinularia*, *Sarcophyton*, and *Rhytisma* (Alcyoniidae) the most abundant genera (Evans et al. 2011).

The key areas for reef development are as follows (many of these sites are now protected; see Conservation and Management, below):

Reefs around the islands of Mananara: These reefs, 15 km to the south of Masoala, lie within the Mananara-Nord Biosphere Reserve, and were surveyed and described by Randriamanantsoa and Brand (2000).

Antongil Bay: A series of islands in the middle of the bay are fringed with coral formations. Cap Masoala includes a well-developed fringing reef and protected lagoon. Reefs in the three marine protected areas that lie within Masoala National Park are relatively well known (Odendaal et al. 1995; McClanahan and Obura 1998; McClanahan et al. 2011).

Ambodivahibe Bay to Vohémar: Reefs varied in quality here in 2010, with some sites affected by sedimentation from rivers, and others in clear water (Obura et al. 2011). Overall coral cover was high, averaging 48%, with many large coral colonies present, high intactness overall, and high resilience to temperature stress compared with western reefs. In total, 281 species of hard corals were documented, but there may be over 310 species. There was relatively low reef fish diversity (271 species), but this may be an underestimate due to the methods used. Reefs of Ambodivahibe Bay are particularly important, having the highest coral diversity (281 species), high coral cover (48%), and the highest density of fish along the northeast coast, and were protected after their discovery in 2006. The 3 km long narrow bay covering 8.7 km^2 comprises a canyon, 40–200 m deep, with mangroves and seagrass beds along both sides. The bay is thought to be a climate refuge, buffered from spikes in sea surface temperature owing to the channeling of cooler, upwelling water from depth offshore. However, results from the surveys concluded that Ambodivahibe, similar to other parts of the northern coastline, shows significant impacts from human exploitation and high levels of sedimentation.

Nosy Ankao archipelago and Vohémar: Nosy Ankao is made up of islands and patch reefs exposed to ocean waves. Vohémar is a large, sheltered bay fed by a river, mostly made up of shallow and intertidal reef bank, with a well-developed, exposed fore-reef. The bay suffers from fishing pressure and eutrophication (Obura et al. 2011). At both sites there was lower coral diversity than elsewhere in the northeast (168 species at Nosy Ankao and 155 species at Vohémar), with relatively low habitat diversity. Nosy Ankao had the highest species richness for fish at 127 species, exceeding the average of 117 per site in northwest Madagascar given by McKenna and Allen (2003). In 2009, there was little fishing pressure around Nosy Ankao as these reefs were leased to a seaweed farming company that discouraged fishing activity (Obura et al. 2011). In 2010, Nosy Ankao and neighboring islands were included in the Loky Manambato protected area.

Northwest: This coastline has extensive offshore coral banks and shoals, nearshore fringing reefs, and patch reefs surrounding the complex island systems, which include striking eroded limestone pinnacles (*tsingy*), as well as volcanic cones. The best-known reefs are those of Nosy Hara, those around Nosy Mitsio, shallow (10–50 m) oceanic banks such as the Grand Banc de Castor, the coral banks of Nosy Be (Grand Banc de l'Entrée, Banc de Cinq Mètres, etc.), and reefs of Nosy Tanikely, Nosy Iranja, and those of the Radama Islands. Offshore there is an extensive submerged reef system that tracks most of the continental shelf edge as far south as Cap Saint André and beyond (Fourmanoir 1963a). Inshore reefs are scarcely developed between Katsepy and Cap Saint André because of the extensive inputs of fresh water and sediments from Madagascar's largest rivers. In the far northwest, reef development is limited owing to the effects of sediment and cyclones, but coral populations are nevertheless very diverse, particularly in the Nosy Mitsio area (McKenna and Allen 2003; Obura 2009). The importance of Madagascar's northwestern coral reefs as part of a regional center of coral reef diversity in the North Mozambique Channel has been firmly established (Obura 2012; Obura et al. 2019).

Important reef areas, many of which are protected (see Conservation and Management, below), include:

Nosy Hara and surrounding area: Nosy Hara was identified for protection in 1998 and designated in 2011 as a marine protected area. The zone is remarkable for its undersea landscape of volcanic cones and karstic stacks. The reefs were surveyed in 2002 (McKenna and Allen 2003): a total of 463 fish species were recorded and hard coral cover varied between 3% and 71%. Subsequent surveys in 2006 and 2007 found variable coral cover, with 18–53% in 2007 (Obura 2009). Coral mortality was attributed to historical mass bleaching events or cyclone damage.

Nosy Be and surrounding area: Waters around the numerous volcanic islands of Nosy Be are relatively calm, sheltered both by the Tsaratanàna Massif on the mainland and fossil reef banks offshore, which has resulted in extensive fringing reef development and habitat diversity. Monitoring in 1999 and 2002 of the single seaward reef (Dzamandzar) showed healthy live coral cover (50.9% and 48.2%, respectively) (Ahamada et al. 2002). Nosy Tanikely, a small island to the southwest of the main island of Nosy Be, protected since 1968, has higher hard coral diversity and fish density than other local sites (F. Webster and McMahon 2002; McKenna and Allen 2003). The Nosy Vorona Passage, lying to the south of Nosy Be, is characterized by patchy fringing reefs no deeper than 20 m, which are dominated by branching and massive growth forms as elsewhere around Nosy Be. In 2018 and 2019, hard coral cover was 21–38%, and at least one site had undergone a 50% decrease in coral cover, attributed to bleaching events in El Niño years (2014–2016 and 2018–2019) (Fairbrother 2020). There is a marked predominance of damselfishes (Pomacentridae), absence of larger fish species, and a high abundance of urchins, indicating high fishing pressure extending down the food chain, especially on the more accessible reefs (Frontier 2019a, 2019b).

Ampasindava Bay, south of Nosy Be: A baseline environmental survey in the seaward opening of the bay recorded 84 hard corals and six alcyonarians in 18 families and 25 genera (Ratsifandrihamanana 2014). Coral cover was high (40–60%) and most species were massive, typical of high sediment environments. A total of 112 fish species (28 families and 53 genera) were recorded, dominated by coral-reef-dependent species and species that are indicators of good reef health. Total fish biomass was measured at up to 5.5 tons (t)/ha, which is atypically high and was attributed to the presence of dense shoals of planktivorous fusiliers (Caesionidae) associated with the reef slope. A high incidence of coral disease was observed, potentially because of a lack of flushing or circulation and high sedimentation rates in the bay.

Seaward and offshore submerged reefs: The offshore submerged banks around Nosy Be are dominated by hard corals, with deep (30–50 m) slopes of platelike *Pachyseris speciosa* and *Montipora* spp., creating overhangs. Above 30 m, platelike corals give way to branching forms, accompanied by a diverse fauna of coral reef fishes (parrotfishes, wrasses, butterfly fishes, etc.). Farther offshore, along the continental shelf edge lie the remnants of an ancient barrier reef, in the form of a string of banks and shoals at 15–30 m depth (Fourmanoir 1963a). Coral cover here in the 1980s was low (about 10% on average), suggesting that this submerged reef is no longer growing (Jenkins 1987).

South Mozambique Channel Marine Ecoregion

Reef development is extensive along this part of the west coast, with barrier reefs, fringing reefs, and sand cays (Pichon 1972), which are part of an ancient submerged barrier system (Salomon 1980) running from the Mangoky River delta in the southwest to Mahajanga in the north, stretching over 1000 km. Today, this offshore reef is made up of scattered offshore banks at 15–30 m depth, broken up by deeper channels, and occasionally rising to <10 m depth, forming reefs and sand cays such as those found around Belo sur Mer and the Barren Islands. An extensive fringing and barrier reef system exists between Androka and Morombe, becoming fragmented north of Morombe. A submerged barrier system extends north from Morombe along the continental shelf, stretching over 1418 km to Cap d'Ambre (Salomon 1980; A. Cooke et al. 2000).

Extending north from Androka to Anakao, a narrow fringing reef lies close to the coast, enclosing a narrow lagoon, and expands seaward around Anakao. Nosy Vé has a well-developed fringing reef, and a true barrier reef (the Grand Récif) extends north from Sarodrano, past Toliara for 25 km, finishing at the mouth of the Fiherenana River. North of here, the broken barrier reef begins again just south of Ifaty (Ranobe Bay), with a large unbroken section of barrier reef extending from the mouth of the Manombo River all the way up to Baie des Assassins, followed by broken barrier reef and numerous islets extending north past Andavadoaka to Morombe and the Mangoky River delta. The entire reef system measures over 400 km in length, making it one of the most extensive in the western Indian Ocean. Key reef areas are (see Conservation and Management, below):

Barren Islands: This is an archipelago of nine islands lying about 40 km off the coast at Maintirano, and is vital for the livelihoods of the traditional fishers who migrate, in outrigger canoes, from communities up to 600 km away to catch sharks and other fishes, as well as harvesting sea cucumbers, once the cyclone season ends (Cripps and Gardner 2016). The area, spanning over 4300 km^2, is now protected. Reefs associated with the islands cover 869 km^2, with close to 90% being deep systems, with shallower reefs including fore-reefs (37 km^2), reef flats (38 km^2), and subtidal reef flats (26 km^2) making up the rest. Almost 40 hard coral genera from 16 families have been recorded, and average coral cover is 26%, rising to 59% on fringing reefs (Cripps 2010).

Belo sur Mer: This lies approximately 60 km south of Morondava at the northern end of a 55 km long coral reef system that extends from the Mangoky River delta. Due to the presence of large rivers to the north and south, the reef runs parallel to the shore approximately 15–20 km offshore, with a string of seven coral islands and shallow reef crests (Salomon 1980). These reefs were reported to be some of the richest coral reefs in Malagasy waters (A. Harris and J. Maharavo, unpublished data), with, prior to 2003, no signs of physical damage, overfishing, or sedimentation. Similar to other reefs in the region, the reefs of Belo sur Mer experienced high levels of bleaching in 1998 but had recovered to 57% live coral cover by 2002 (Ahamada et al. 2002). In 2009, Cyclone Fanele (category 4) passed within 15–20 km of the islands, and anecdotal evidence from fishers suggested extensive reef damage. Average coral cover of 19–24% was recorded on the reefs around the islands between 2009 and 2011 (C.L.A. Gough, unpublished data), and over 40 genera of corals were found, including the regional endemic *Horastrea indica*. Over 180 reef fish species have been documented, including the IUCN Red List Endangered *Cheilinus undulates* (Napoleon Wrasse) and the IUCN Red List Vulnerable *Epinephelus lanceolatus* (Giant Grouper). Average reef fish biomass across these reefs was 372.1 kg/ha, with high variation between islands (183.1–710.6 kg/ha) (Table 7.1).

Grand Récif of Toliara: This is a 17 km barrier reef off the coastal town of Toliara (Andréfouët 2012). In total, over 120 coral species and 552 fish species were originally recorded from the site (Pichon 1978; Harmelin-Vivien 1979). As Toliara, the regional capital, grew but continued to rely on resources from the Grand Récif, and deforestation of river catchments continued, the health and diversity of this reef system declined. Renewed interest in conservation of the Grand Récif in 1988 (Vasseur et al. 1988), including a proposal to make the Grand Récif a biosphere reserve, sparked further applied research (Laroche and Ramananarivo 1995; Vasseur 1997). Randriamanantsoa (1997) noted that transects across the reef flat could be completed much more quickly in the mid-1990s than was the case in the 1970s, because of the loss of habitat complexity. By the time of a survey by Harris et al. (2010), hard coral and coralline algae cover had halved and there was a complete absence of soft corals (which previously covered ~15% of the substrate), with large increases in macro and turf algae cover from ~5% to nearly 70%. The large expanses of *Acropora* recorded by Pichon (1978) had disappeared. Todinanahary et al. (2018) subsequently reported only about one-quarter of the coral genera recorded by Pichon (1978) and a 32.1% decline in the number of species recorded. Diversity has not declined for all species, on the Grand Récif however. In a recent study of black corals (Antipatharia) in shallow waters and mesophotic depths (10–25 m) at 15 sites along the southwest coast between Andavadoaka and Anakao, Terrana et al. (2019) reported the highest diversity of black corals in the northern pass of the Grand Récif, where they recorded 20 species, out of a diverse assemblage of 22 species of black corals, of six genera (*Antipathes*, *Arachnopathes*, *Cirrhipathes*, *Cupressopathes*, *Myriopathes*, *Stichopathes*) and two families (Antipathidae, Myriopathidae). A complementary study examined the functional diversity of antipatharians on the Grand Récif (Wiejeme 2019).

Ranobe Bay: Lying 25 km north of Toliara, less than 20 km north of the Fiherenana River, this bay is enclosed by a 32 km long barrier reef. The lagoon behind it is 8 km at its widest and contains patch reefs and seagrass beds. The lagoon and nearby reefs have been intensively fished for decades and are highly degraded. The small Massif des Roses protected reef was established here in 2007 (Belle et al. 2009). Reef monitoring is undertaken by the conservation organization Reef Doctor. Coral cover was extremely low in the lagoon, with means of 1.8% and 3.1% in 2005 and 2006, respectively, but was higher on the outer reef slopes (25.6% in 2006). A total of 181 fish species were recorded in these surveys.

Velondriake (including Andavadoaka): The area was first surveyed in 2003 (Lewis et al. 2004) and then more comprehensively in 2005 (Harding et al. 2006). In 2006, the area was protected as a locally managed marine area (LMMA) covering 640 km^2 and then designated as a marine protected area in 2015. A citizen science reef monitoring program has been underway since 2004, supported by Blue Ventures, to provide data to the LMMA's managing body—the Velondriake Association. Coral cover increased between 2005 (Nadon et al. 2005) and 2015 (Gilchrist et al. 2020), from 8% to 35.7% on fringing reefs and from 20% to 26% on the reefs near Andavadoaka. Cyclone Haruna in 2013 caused a dip in coral cover (which had reached 39.1% in 2012) and an increase in turf algae cover to about 45% in 2013, although this had dropped to 27.2% by 2015 (A. Carter et al., unpublished data). Fish biomass also increased in the community-managed no-take zones, rising to an average biomass of 786 kg/ha (excluding Caesionidae) by 2015, the end of the survey period (2009–2015), 189% higher than in the paired control sites (Gilchrist et al. 2020), and comparable to that of other protected areas in the western Indian Ocean (731 kg/ha) (McClanahan et al. 2011). However, reefs that are fished within the LMMA have a low biomass of 247 kg/ha, which is less than the average for fished reefs (531 kg/ha) in the western Indian Ocean (N. Graham and McClanahan 2013), and less even than the 300 kg/ha biomass typical of a degraded ecological state (McClanahan et al. 2011) (Table 7.1).

East Madagascar Marine Ecoregion

As noted above, conditions for reef development are mostly unfavorable in this ecoregion. The reefs that do occur are relatively low in diversity and productivity. Fish biomass levels are mostly below 300 kg/ha despite the generally low fishing pressures, perhaps related to the low primary productivity of the surface waters. The reefs of Ile Sainte Marie, Foulpointe, Toamasina, and the Toamasina cays form the principal series of fringing reefs along a 225 km stretch of coast (Maharavo et al. 2003), as described below:

Ile Sainte Marie: Reefs fringe the main island and the Ile aux Nattes to the south, spanning about 50 km. Several coral banks and an islet lie 5–10 km to seaward of the main island. Seaward reefs are well developed, with profiles to 20–25 m and less extensive reef development on the leeward side. On the outer reef slopes, mostly in the southern half of the island, live coral cover in 2017 was low to moderate (13–54%) and fish biomass was low (110–430 kg/ha) (Wickel and Nicet 2017). Monitoring at the same sites in 2018–2019 (Damien and Loncle 2019) showed no significant change, with coral cover in the range of 19–47% and fish biomass generally low with an average 96 kg/ha (range 5–186 kg/ha). A total of 119 fish species were recorded.

Foulpointe: Fringing reefs occur along a coastal rocky ridge trending south-southwest–north-northeast and a series of submerged coral banks (Banc de Foulpointe) extends about 15 km north-northeast of these. Between 1999 and 2002, coral cover on the seaward reef was about 35%, but over that period cover declined on the reef flats to 13%, attributed to overfishing and hyper-sedimentation (Ahamada et al. 2002). In 2003, there were extensive signs of sedimentation, probably due to a combination of inland deforestation and loss of vegetation on nearby coastal dune systems (Maharavo et al. 2003).

Toamasina: Farther south, from Ile aux Prunes, a system of coral cays extends south to Nosy Faho (Biotope 2019). The barrier and fringing reefs that create a protected harbor for Madagascar's main port, Toamasina, are similar to those farther north at Foulpointe and Ile Sainte Marie (J.-P. Quod, unpublished data). Well-developed reefs are also present around the Ile aux

Prunes to the north of Toamasina and around Nosy Faho to the south of Toamasina (J. Maharavo, unpublished data). Monitoring at Iles aux Prunes and Nosy Faho from 2008 to 2019, to determine the potential effects of the wastewater discharged by the Ambatovy nickel-processing plant, documented well-developed coral reef communities at both sites, with live coral cover ranging from 19% to 65%. Associated with the coral communities was an assemblage of 117 fish species, with a marked predominance of herbivores and very small carnivores (Serranidae), and low fish biomass (average 173 kg/ha). The annual monitoring found no significant change in live coral cover or fish biomass at either site from 2008 to 2015. In 2016, there was a marked dip in live coral cover, after the 2016 bleaching event, followed by recovery to lower levels than pre-2016, with an associated increase in calcareous algae cover (Biotope 2019).

South of Toamasina: Coral formations are sparse farther south, with a single observation, made by Professor Jean Maharavo while diving at Manakara in about 2000, of the existence of a series of three rocky reefs, possibly representing different sea-level episodes. On the most seaward reef, at about 10–15 m depth and about 1 km from the coast, the rocky surface was encrusted with sponges, small hard coral colonies, soft corals, hydroids, and ascidians, with an associated faunal assemblage of surgeonfishes (Acanthuridae), parrotfishes (Scaridae), small groupers (Epinephelidae), and lobsters. Highly coral-reef-dependent species such as butterfly fishes (Chaetodontidae) were absent (J. Maharavo, unpublished data).

South Madagascar Marine Ecoregion

The subtropical nature of this ecoregion precludes the development of true coral reefs. However, there are coral formations and colonies in the Tolagnaro area, notably at Lokaro Bay, where in 2001 coral was abundant below 5 m, with 75–100% live cover of *Montipora* and *Acropora* filling most of the sheltered center of the lagoon (EU-CARE 2001). Species recorded included 37 hard corals and 41 fishes. Coral growth ceased at 8 m depth on the seaward side of the bay. There was no evidence of recently bleached coral, and all dead coral was old and covered with fleshy algae or turf. Anecdotal reports by the conservation organization SEED-Madagascar (Sustainable Environment, Education and Development in Madagascar) (previously known as Azafady) suggested that bleaching had caused mass mortality in 1998; if this was the case, there had been substantial recovery by 2001.

Current Coral Reef Status

The 2016 regional assessment of reefs of the western Indian Ocean by the CORDIO program concluded that there has been an overall decline in the health of the coral reefs of Madagascar (Obura et al. 2017); based on previous information this is considered to be due primarily to climate change, sedimentation from watershed-based pollution, and fishing (Burke et al. 2011).

Since at least 1998, Madagascar has experienced regular coral-bleaching events (Ateweberhan and McClanahan 2010; Obura et al. 2017). Mortality from these events tends to be low compared with reefs in other countries in the western Indian Ocean, which may be because of the landmass of Madagascar sheltering the western reefs from the warm South Indian Ocean Current, and the cooling effect of the weather disturbances that are common during the summer months, associated with tropical storms (Ateweberhan and McClanahan 2010; Carrigan and Puotinen 2011). Northern reefs benefit from a weak upwelling system bringing cool water from depth (Riegl and Piller 2003; McClanahan et al. 2007; Ateweberhan and McClanahan 2010).

Between 1998 and 2016, across the western Indian Ocean, live coral cover declined from 50% to 30%, algal cover increased from 15% to 35%, and most reefs became algal dominated, with 80% of fish biomass made up of small herbivores. In 1998, 2005, and 2016, there were particularly strong bleaching events, which led to significant mortality and declines in coral cover in most countries in this region (Obura et al. 2017). The reefs of Madagascar reflected these trends, with coral cover declining from 50% in 1998 to 30% in 2016, and algal cover increasing from 15% to 30% over the same period. In 2010, the northeast suffered mild bleaching mortality (mean hard coral cover was 48% in 2010) (Obura et al. 2011). During the 2016 bleaching event, six Malagasy monitoring sites exhibited medium or high levels of bleaching at some point, with the southwest the worst affected. Overall, Madagascar was the worst affected country across the western Indian Ocean for bleaching in 2016 (although not mortality) after Seychelles and Tanzania (Obura et al. 2017). Coral cover in Malagasy waters has also been affected by cyclones, such as those in 2004–2005 and Cyclone Haruna in 2013 (A. Carter et al., unpublished data).

Over a period of almost 20 years (1998–2016), most reef-dependent carnivorous and corallivore reef fish species (Haemulidae, Scaridae, Chaetodontidae, Balistidae, Lethrinidae) have declined, while herbivores (Siganidae) and one family of carnivores (Serranidae) have increased, possibly owing to their adaptability to different conditions. Plankton and detritus feeders and some other herbivores (Caesionidae, Mullidae, Acanthuridae) have remained stable (Obura et al. 2017). In the northeast, by 2010 there was an absence of carnivorous sharks and corallivore *Bolbometopon muricatum* (Bumphead Parrotfish), and low densities of fishery-targeted species, such as lethrinids and lutjanids, due to high fishing pressure (Obura et al. 2011). Reefs have also been impacted by the loss of mangroves, which results in soil erosion and runoff, causing harmful siltation and pollution (Laroche and Ramananarivo 1995), and the loss of mangrove roots, which are refugia for many reef species when juveniles (Nagelkerken et al. 2008), may also have a negative effect.

SEAGRASS BEDS

Seagrasses are flowering plants (angiosperms) that have adapted to the sea via at least three separate lineages and are split into three families (Cymodoceaceae, Hydrocharitaceae, and Zosteraceae) (Waycott et al. 2004). A large part of each plant is the buried rhizome, which extends vertically and horizontally, with leaves originating from the vertical extensions. Seagrasses reproduce both sexually and vegetatively. They grow mainly in shallow tropical and temperate marine areas and thrive best in waters without strong currents or wave action and at shallow depths allowing photosynthesis, to a maximum of 90 m (Esteban et al. 2018). In Malagasy waters, seagrasses are found in a range of habitats, including estuarine and coastal areas, on reef flats, and in open water areas (Di Carlo and Tombolahy 2011). As with many other countries in the Indo-Pacific, the species diversity, distribution, abundance, and status of the seagrass around the island is poorly known (Short et al. 2011).

Seagrass Species Diversity and Community Structure

Chasse (1962) and Gravier (1970) described 10 species of seagrasses from the Toliara region. Compilation of the data from several surveys since 2000 indicates that the total number is potentially 11 species (Table 7.2). Further expert taxonomic study of collected material would be required to confirm the total number. Madagascar has one of several distinct genetic lineages of the species *Thalassia hemprichii* (Hydrocharitaceae) in the western Indian Ocean and is an important source of gene flow to populations on the East African coast owing to its upstream location in the South Equatorial Current (Jahnke et al. 2019).

Seagrasses often occur in mixed stands of two or three species, most commonly *Syringodium isoetifolium* and *T. hemprichii*. Only *Thalassodendron ciliatum* has been reported to form monospecific stands. *Cymodocea serrulata* tends to colonize coral rubble, while *Syringodium* and *Halophila* prefer silty substrate. Seagrass beds support an extensive resident fauna, notably burrowing mud lobsters (Callianissidae). Mud lobsters generate humps almost 1 m in diameter, which affects the structure and composition of the bed. The principal permanent residents of seagrass beds are the echinoderms—*Tripneustes gratilla* (Edible Urchin), *Echinothrix calamaris* (Black Urchin), two conspicuous starfishes (*Protoreaster lincki* and *Pentaceraster tuberculatus*), and various sea cucumbers, notably the

TABLE 7.2. **Seagrass species recorded at sites around Madagascar**

ECOREGION	SOUTH MOZAMBIQUE CHANNEL			NORTH MOZAMBIQUE CHANNEL				
SPECIES / SITE	BARREN ISLANDS	KIRINDY MITÉ	VELONDRIAKE	NORTHWEST	EXTREME NORTH	FAR NORTHEAST	NORTHEAST	ALL SITES
CYMODOCEACEAE								
Cymodocea rotundata	X	X	X	–	X	X	X	X
C. serrulata	X	X	X	X	X	X	X	X
Halodule uninervis	X	X	X	X	X	X	X	X
H. wrightii	X	X	–	X	X	X	X	X
Syringodium isoetifolium	X	X	X	X	X	X	X	X
Thalassodendron ciliatum	X	X	X	X	–	X	X	X
HYDROCHARITACEAE								
Halophila ovalis	–	–	X	X	X	X	X	X
H. stipulacea	–	–	X	X	–	X	X	X
H. decipiens	–	X	–	–	–	–	–	X
Halophila sp. (assumed to be *H. stipulacea* or *H. decipiens*)	X	–	–	–	–	–	–	n/a
Thalassia hemprichii	–	X	X	X	X	X	X	X
ZOSTERACEAE								
Zostera capensis	–	–	–	–	X	X	X	X
Total species	7	8	8	8	8	10	10	11

Sources: Data for Barren Islands from Cripps (2010), for Kirindy Mité from Gouvernement de la République de Madagascar (2014) and Ravaoarinorotsihoarana (2011), for Velondriake and northwest from R. Andriamanohisoa (unpublished data), for extreme north from C3 Madagascar and Indian Ocean Islands Programme (2010a), for far northeast from Obura et al. (2011) and Di Carlo and Tombolahy (2011), and for northeast from Andrianarivelo et al. (1998).
Note: MPA, marine protected area.

snakelike *Synapta maculata* (A. Cooke and Brand 2012). Other residents include *Dardanus megistos* (Red Hermit Crab) and carnivorous gastropods (*Murex* spp.). Rabbitfishes (*Siganus* spp.) are the dominant herbivorous fishes present (Laboute and Maharavo 1998).

The most frequently occurring marine turtle in Madagascar's coastal waters, *Chelonia mydas* (Green Turtle) (see Walker et al., pp. 391–99), grazes mainly on seagrass and in other parts of the world has been found to affect growth rate and primary production of seagrass beds (Kelkar et al. 2013). *Dugong dugon* (Dugong), which has become very rare around Madagascar (see Davis et al., pp. 400–411), grazes seagrass beds in lines, uprooting entire seagrass plants and leaving furrow trails. However, since Dugongs prefer the pioneering, fast-growing species such as *Halophila ovalis* and *Halodule uninervis*, they do not significantly impact permanent seagrass stands (Waycott et al. 2004).

Distribution of Seagrass Beds in Madagascar Waters

There has been no comprehensive mapping of seagrass beds around Madagascar, but surveys have been carried out at several sites, as described below; most information is available for the North Mozambique Channel and South Mozambique Channel marine ecoregions, and there is limited information for the east or south, where seagrass beds are infrequent.

North Mozambique Channel Marine Ecoregion

Andrianarivelo et al. (1998) recorded nine species of seagrasses at three sites around the Masoala Peninsula. Ten species were found at five sites in the extreme northeast (Ambodivahibe Bay, Loky Manambato, Vohémar, Andravina Bay, Nosy Ankao) (Di Carlo and Tombolahy 2011; Obura et al. 2011). In the northwest, eight species have been found at Ankazomborona, Analalava, and Ampasindava (R. J. Andriamanohisoa, unpublished data).

In the northeast, Di Carlo and Tombolahy (2011) found that larger species (e.g., *Thalassodendron ciliatum*, *Thalassia hemprichii*) were found on stable substrates, whereas smaller species (e.g., *Halodule uninervis*, *Halophila ovalis*) thrived on more mobile substrates, such as shallow sand banks and reef flats subject to wave action. The relative dominance of seagrass species at any location depended largely on depth and the type of sediment, and species diversity was positively associated with habitat diversity.

In the extreme north, sites around Antsiranana, on the west coast (Ampasindava, part of the Nosy Hara marine protected area), east coast (Andovokonko and Antaravy), and within Antsiranana Bay (Ramena) were assessed by remote sensing for potential *Dugong dugon* habitat in the form of seagrass beds, and the results subsequently ground-truthed using the Seagrass-Watch methodology (McKenzie et al. 2003). Eight seagrass species were identified (C3 Madagascar and Indian Ocean Island Programme 2010a) (Table 7.2). Mean seagrass cover was relatively low, varying from 7.5% to 38.6% with communities of *Halodule wrightii*, *H. uninervis*, and *Cymodocea serrulata* dominating at the seaward sites that are favored by *Dugong dugon* (Davis et al., pp. 400–411).

South Mozambique Channel Marine Ecoregion

In the Barren Islands, eight species of seagrasses have been recorded (Cripps 2010) (Table 7.2). A survey undertaken in 2018 by trained local community members, using Seagrass-Watch methods (McKenzie et al. 2003), showed that seagrass beds cover 5.9 km^2, with large beds occurring around the Marify Isles (289 ha) in the north and Maroantaly Isles (293 ha) farther south (Blue Ventures, unpublished data) (Figure 7.4). The beds were dominated by *Thalassodendron ciliatum* and *Cymodocea rotundata*. Less-abundant species included *Syringodium isoetifolium*, *Halodule uninervis*, *H. wrightii*, and *C. serrulata*. Farther south, smaller seagrass beds occur around the Andrano and Mangily Isles, where only *T. ciliatum* and *C. rotundata* were observed. *Cymodocea rotundata* was the only recorded species in the seagrass bed at the Abohazo Isles.

In the mid-west, surveys were conducted at nine sites in 2011 in the Kirindy Mité National Park and Biosphere Reserve, 60 km south of Morondava, which includes an estimated 2200 ha of seagrass beds (Ravaoarinorotsihoarana 2011; Gouvernement de la République de Madagascar 2014). Eight species were recorded, with no more than six taxa found at any one site. Each site is dominated by one or two species, particularly *S. isoetifolium*, *T. ciliatum*, *Thalassia hemprichii*, or *H. uninervis*. Seagrass coverage varied from 18% to 57%; sites with higher coverage tended to be dominated by *T. hemprichii*, which thrives in shallow water.

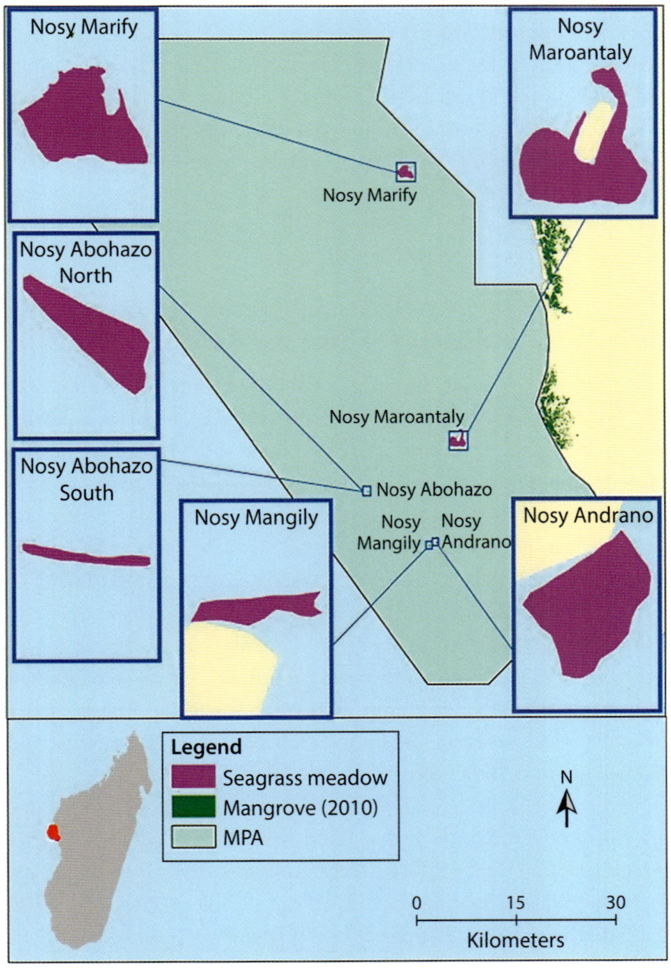

FIGURE 7.4 **Seagrass distribution in the Barren Islands, western Madagascar, MPA (marine protected area).** (SOURCE: Blue Ventures, unpublished data.)

In the southwest, monitoring and assessments have been undertaken at 11 sites in the northern, central, and southern zones of Velondriake LMMA (Hantanirina and Benbow 2013) using the Seagrass Net method (Short et al. 2006). Eight seagrass species were recorded (Table 7.2), the number of species decreasing significantly from north to south. Seagrass patches were dominated by *S. isoetifolium* in the northern zone and by *T. hemprichii* in the south. Seagrass coverage was estimated at 37%, with lower densities in the south than the north; in the central zone only two sites had high coverage (Hantanirina and Benbow 2013). The differences in coverage and diversity might be the consequence of high-intensity cyclones, since an assessment of the impact of Cyclone Haruna in the southwest showed a loss in seagrass cover (Hantanirina and Benbow 2013; Côté-Laurin et al. 2017).

South Madagascar Marine Ecoregion

Seagrass surveys have not been conducted in this marine ecoregion, and seagrass species were not mentioned in research reports on the Deep South (P. Bouchet, unpublished data). *Halodule uninervis* was recorded in brackish lakes of the Tolagnaro coastal lagoon complex (Réville et al. 2007), but seagrasses were not recorded during surveys in the Fausse Baie des Galions, an open marine bay near Tolagnaro (Jacques Whitford 2007).

East Madagascar Marine Ecoregion

Seagrass beds occur in coral reef areas at Mananara-Nord (Randriamanantsoa and Brand 2000), around Ile Sainte Marie (Wickel and Nicet 2017), Foulpointe (Maharavo et al. 2003), and Toamasina (Biotope 2019). Seagrass meadows can be presumed to occur in the Sainte Marie area given the number of *Dugong dugon* sightings there (see Davis et al., pp. 400–411). There are no other reports of seagrass beds on the rectilinear east coast.

Importance and Status of Seagrass Beds

Seagrass beds provide nursery, feeding, and shelter habitats for many marine fish species, notably emperors (Lethrinidae), parrotfishes (Scaridae), and wrasses (Labridae), and invertebrates. Seagrasses trap sediment and help to stabilize the seabed, thereby supporting other ecosystems, particularly coral reefs. Seagrasses also provide numerous environmental services, such as absorbing wave energy (which results in decreased coastal erosion inshore of the seagrass beds) and carbon sequestration. Seagrass ecosystems attract other marine living organisms, creating concentrations of biotic diversity, particularly of marine resources useful to local communities, such as the sea urchin *Tripneustes gratilla* (Edible Urchin). Seagrass meadows form an important bridge between estuarine and marine habitats (Di Carlo and Tombolahy 2011).

Seagrass beds, particularly because of their structural complexity, are important for both primary and secondary productivity (Saenger et al. 2013) and provide habitat for biotic diversity, fishes, crustaceans, and many other species. A significant proportion of fish species represented in fisheries globally spend a certain stage of their life cycle in these highly productive habitats (Unsworth et al. 2018). Moreover, fish species outside seagrass beds also benefit from this concentration of productivity through linkage to trophic food webs and the export of nutrients to the surrounding environment (Gillanders 2006; Saenger et al. 2013). Through these various ecological interactions, seagrass meadows provide ecosystem services that make a significant contribution to the livelihoods of coastal communities. Of particular importance is the direct contribution of resources to household incomes through gleaning of seagrass beds by women.

Seagrass meadows are very efficient carbon sequesters and can store 10 times more organic carbon per unit of area than terrestrial forests. Carbon is captured through the growth of the seagrasses, by the trapping of floating detritus, and through the accumulation of sediments stabilized by seagrass meadows. The rate of carbon accumulation increases with the density of shoots and rhizomes, and, hence, with the age of the meadows (Greiner et al. 2013). Conservation of seagrass beds can therefore help to mitigate climate change, while their degradation results in the release of carbon stored in the sediment, contributing to global warming.

No long-term data for seagrass beds in Malagasy waters are available, but the beds are subject to many of the pressures that are resulting in significant degradation in other parts of the world. Increased levels of human waste, coupled with a rise in the use of nonbiodegradable disposable products, and augmented levels of fishing may lead to declines in seagrass bed coverage and health. Coastal development, tourism, and the impact of events such as cyclones may further encourage this decline (Côté-Laurin et al. 2017). Heavy fishing of herbivorous fishes such as rabbitfishes (Siganidae), which live in seagrass meadows, can break the food web, resulting in blooms of epiphytic organisms that increase water turbidity and disable seagrass photosynthesis. Trampling associated with fishing or gleaning is expected to reduce seagrass biomass (Eckrich and Holmquist 2000).

It is known, however, that industrial shrimp trawling along the northwest coast has impacted large areas of seagrass bed, causing direct damage to the plants, and also removing fishes and other mobile fauna that contribute to the health of these and other benthic ecosystems (Hantanirina and Benbow 2013). The use of beach seine nets, which are dragged across the lagoon floor, directly uproots the seagrasses and releases sediment into the water column, limiting light penetration and seagrass regeneration. Additionally, outbreaks of herbivorous sea urchins such as *Tripneustes gratilla*, a result of the removal of their fish predators, decreases seagrass coverage; this is further exacerbated by local mangrove cutting, which increases siltation and water turbidity.

MANGROVES

The term *mangroves* is used for both the evergreen trees or shrubs and the communities they create, which grow in tropical intertidal mudflats. These plants are exposed at low tide and covered at high tide, and so characteristic features of mangroves include tolerance to salt and anoxic soils and resistance to wave action. Mangrove species regulate salt in their tissues in various ways, including excreting excess salt through the leaves, accumulating salt in their tissues, and active transport of salt across cell membranes in the roots (Kathiresan and Bingham 2001; Parida and Jha 2010). As an adaptation to anaerobic soils, mangrove tree species have aerial roots (pneumatophores), enabling the absorption of oxygen from the air or surrounding water for respiration (Tomlinson 1986). Mangrove root systems provide a tenacious grip on the substrate, making them highly resistant to wave action. Another distinguishing feature is that most mangrove species are viviparous, with the fruit germinating on the parent plant before release, allowing it to set down roots rapidly upon contact with suitable substrate (Kathiresan and Bingham 2001). Others produce heavy fruits that settle into the muddy substrate before germinating. With these and other adaptations, mangroves are able to benefit from the hot, wet, and nutrient-rich environment offered by tropical intertidal mudflats.

Mangrove Species Diversity

Mangroves are flowering plants (angiosperms), comprising about 70 species from 20 different plant families worldwide; the adaptations to living in intertidal marshes have arisen independently through multiple lineages. An analysis of the mangrove fossil record, modern and fossil distributions of mangroves and associated gastropods, and nestedness of mangrove plant and gastropod communities suggests that there were three independent regions of diversification of mangrove ecosystems: the Indian Ocean, Southeast Asia, and the Caribbean and eastern Pacific (Ellison et al. 2004).

In the western Indian Ocean, mangroves are represented by a relatively small number of genera and nine species. Eight of these occur in Malagasy waters, with most stands containing six species from four families (Table 7.3): 1) Rhizophoraceae (*Rhizophora mucronata*, *Bruguiera gymnorhiza*, *Ceriops tagal*), 2) Acanthaceae (*Avicennia marina*), 3) Lythraceae (*Sonneratia alba*), and 4) Combretaceae (*Lumnitzera racemosa*). The two less prominent species are *Xylocarpus granatum* (Meliaceae) (which is nonviviparous and produces large, heavy fruits) and *Heritiera littoralis* (Malvaceae), which is not always considered a true mangrove tree.

The primary colonizers located along the mangrove's seaward fringe are *S. alba* and *A. marina*. *Rhizophora mucronata* and *B. gymnorhiza* are found behind these species or along creeks. *Bruguiera gymnorhiza*, *C. tagal*, and *X. granatum* tend to occupy the areas flooded only at high tide, and *H. littoralis* occurs predominantly in the landward fringe. A few exceptional sites support all eight species, such as at Lavadanora, opposite Saint Augustin, in the Onilahy River estuary (Frontier-Madagascar 2003).

Distribution of Mangroves in Malagasy Waters

Malagasy mangroves are thought to make up about 2% of the global mangrove distribution, and have the fourth-largest area within Africa (FAO 2007; T. Jones et al. 2016a). The mangroves of the western Indian Ocean cover about 1 million ha, of which 90% is concentrated in four countries, with Madagascar having the second-largest area after Tanzania, and a greater area than Mozambique or Kenya (FAO 2007).

Total mangrove cover in Malagasy waters in the early 1970s was estimated at 327,000 ha, with about 98% occurring on the west coast, where the shallow slope of the western coastal plain, the many estuaries and deltas, large tidal range, and relatively protected sea conditions all combine to provide ideal conditions for mangrove development (Kiener 1972). The largest stands (>25,000 ha) are found in the deltas of major western rivers—Mahajamba, Betsiboka (including the Bombetoka Belobaka mangrove—see Bays, Estuaries, and Coastal Wetlands, pp. 331–38), Mahavavy, Besalampy, Tsiribihina, and Mangoky—and together account for over 75% of all of Madagascar's mangroves. Further studies in the 1980s added considerable additional information on structure, typology, ecology, and diversity (Lebigre 1990). The mangroves of the Tsiribihina River delta are particularly significant; some are protected as part of the Menabe Antimena protected area and have been the subject of a regional seascape program promoting the conservation and restoration of mangroves in the area.

Using United States Geological Survey (USGS) Landsat satellite imagery (Giri 2011), mangrove coverage in Malagasy waters circa 2010 was estimated to be about 213,000 ha, most of which was on the west coast (T. Jones et al. 2016a) (Figure 7.5). Only 4260 ha, or 2%, of Madagascar's mangroves are found on the east coast, of which nearly 90% (3831 ha) are found in the far north in the DIANA Region, including significant stands at Ambodivahibe, Rigny, and Irodo. Roughly 9% are scattered across the Analanjirofo Region, while the remaining 1% of eastern mangroves are found in the Atsinanana, Atsimo-Atsinanana, and Anosy Regions (Table 7.4).

TABLE 7.3. **Mangrove species on Madagascar, with international common and Malagasy vernacular names**

FAMILY	SCIENTIFIC NAME	INTERNATIONAL COMMON NAME	MALAGASY VERNACULAR NAME
Acanthaceae	*Avicennia marina*	Black Mangrove	*Mosotry, afiafy*
Combretaceae	*Lumnitzera racemosa*	White-flowered Black Mangrove	*Lovintso, rogno*
Meliaceae	*Xylocarpus granatum*	Cannonball Mangrove	*Antalaotra, fobo, sarigavy*
Rhizophoraceae	*Bruguiera gymnorhiza*	Large-leafed Mangrove	*Tsitolonina, tangampoly*
	Ceriops tagal	Spurred Mangrove	*Honkovavy, tangambavy*
	Rhizophora mucronata	Red Mangrove	*Honkolahy, tangandahy*
Lythraceae	*Sonneratia alba*	Mangrove Apple	*Farafaka, songery*
Malvaceae	*Heritiera littoralis*	Looking-glass Mangrove	*Moromony*

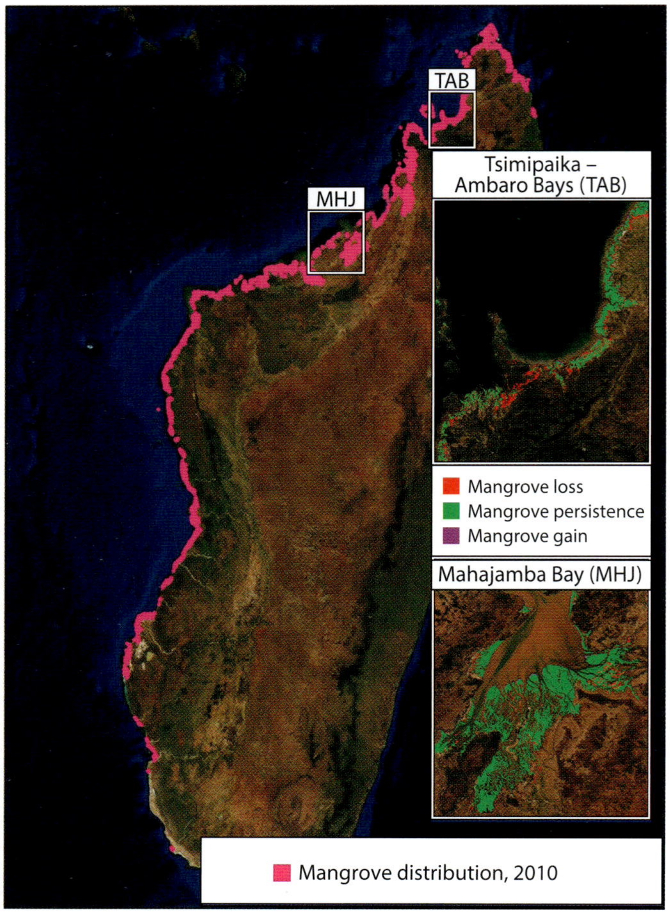

FIGURE 7.5 **The distribution of Madagascar's mangroves around 2010.** (SOURCE: based on data in Giri 2011 and analyzed by T. Jones et al. 2016a.)

Importance of Mangroves

Mangroves play an important role in the maintenance of other forms of biodiversity and are increasingly recognized for the important ecosystem services they provide to coastal communities, urban centers, and fisheries across the globe (Huxham et al. 2017; Himes-Cornell et al. 2018).

Malagasy mangroves are used by lemurs for foraging, sleeping, and traveling between terrestrial forest patches (Vavindraza 2003). At least 23 lemur species belonging to five families (Cheirogaleidae: seven species; Lepilemuridae: three species; Lemuridae: nine species; Indriidae: three species; Daubentoniidae: one species) have been observed in mangroves (Gardner 2016). Many birds also use and may even depend on mangroves. A study of Tsimipaika and Ambanja Bays recorded 73 bird species, while local respondents indicated the presence of 18 additional species (Gardner et al. 2016). About 55% were terrestrial species normally inhabiting forests, scrublands, or open areas; 37 species recorded in the study were endemic to Madagascar or the Malagasy Region; and four were globally threatened.

Mangroves on the west coast are important as breeding areas for several commercial fish species, such as mullets (Mugilidae), sicklefishes (Drepaneidae), and ponyfishes (Leiognathidae) (Andrianjohany 1992). Temporal patterns of fish assemblages documented in the Toliara mangroves confirm the key role that mangroves play in the life cycles of many coral reef fishes (Laroche et al. 1997).

The cyclical presence of fresh water in mangroves is vital to the breeding cycle of several species of shrimps, notably *Fenneropenaeus indicus* and *Penaeus monodon*. Juvenile penaeid shrimps are found in mangroves, where they undergo their fastest growth phase before returning to deeper water to breed as adults (Le Reste 1978). Large mangrove stands are associated with a high proportion of organic material in bottom sediments and high productivity of *F. indicus* (Razafindrainibe et al. 1996). Elevated catches by the Malagasy industrial shrimp fishery are associated with years of high rainfall and, in terms of distribution, tend to correlate with mangrove presence and periods of peak river flow, when the stocks are swept seaward (Lhomme 2000). A linear and significant correlation has been found between shrimp catch (all species) and coastal mangrove area (Voisin and Sandon 2008).

The edible mangrove mud crab *Scylla serrata* (Portunidae) occurs in this habitat from the plankton developmental stage of instar 1 to maturity, when it moves out into deep water to spawn (Walton et al. 2006; Mirera et al. 2014). Juvenile mud crabs are common in intertidal mangrove habitats, on mudflats, or in mangrove stands (Hill et al. 1982), while larger crabs are found in mangrove channels, near the shore, or in burrows. During low tides they are found in burrows in the mud within the mangrove roots or basal mangrove tree holes (Nandi and Dev Roy 1991). Mangroves also provide habitat for hermit crabs (*Coenobita*, Paguroidea, Coenobitidae), and large populations of the mangrove whelk *Terebralia* (= *Pyrazus*) *palustris*; the meat of the latter is eaten and the shells are fired to make lime (Scales et al. 2017).

Mangrove timber is a prized construction material for housing (pillars, frames, and fences), small-scale fishing boats, and aquaculture infrastructure and is also a valued fuel for domestic energy either as firewood or as charcoal (Rasolofo 1997). In some places mangroves provide a tourist attraction, with the introduction of boardwalks and pirogue safaris, such as at Kivalo and Menabe (USAID 2020).

Mangroves play a vital role in shoreline stabilization and storm protection (C. Andriamalala 2007) and can substantially reduce the vulnerability of adjacent coastal land from inundation and erosion (Chatenoux and Peduzzi 2007; Kerr and Baird 2007). The complex aerial root structures function as land builders by collecting sediment (Woodroffe 1992). By filtering out sediments, mangrove forests protect coral reefs and seagrass meadows. In a storm surge, mangroves can attenuate water levels by 5 cm to 50 cm per kilometer of mangrove width (from shore to seaward fringe) and potentially reduce surface wind wave action by over 75% over the same distance (McIvor et al. 2012).

Mangroves store and sequester significant quantities of carbon and play a potential key role in climate regulation (Nellemann and Corcoran 2009). In Malagasy waters, the potential for carbon sequestration and storage has been assessed at Tsimipaika and Ambanja Bays, Mahajamba Bay, and Baie des Assassins in the west, and at Rigny and Mananara-Nord in the north. Mean vegetation carbon content was in the range 22.5–100.9 megagrams (Mg)/ha, and soil carbon content within the mangroves was 294.4–337.8 Mg/ha (T. Jones et al. 2015,

TABLE 7.4. **Mangrove cover distribution on Madagascar**

ECOREGION	REGION	MAIN SITES	EXTENT (ha)	PERCENTAGE
North Mozambique Channel	DIANA	Tsimipaika and Ambaro Bays	25,664	13.0
		Irodo	1160	27.3
		Ambodivahibe	600	14.1
		Rigny	2071	48.6
	Sofia	Antsohihy	13,838	7.0
		Sahamalaza	10,956	5.6
		Narinda	2036	1.0
	Boeny	Mahavavy Sud	10,654	5.4
		Mahajanga	9574	4.9
		Mahajamba Bay	26,677	13.5
		Boeny	3867	2.0
		Baly and Soalala	3507	1.8
		Morovasa	1199	0.6
		Mariarano	2330	1.2
South Mozambique Channel	Melaky	Kamendriky and Tsilambana	5924	3.0
		Tambohorano	13,418	6.8
		Maintirano	5900	3.0
		Manampatra	1327	0.7
		Besalampy	3287	1.7
		Vilamatsa	1847	0.9
		Reharaka	1406	0.7
	Menabe	Kabatomena	1529	0.8
		Sohany	2025	1.0
		Mahabo and Andramy	5905	3.0
		Belo sur Mer	1917	1.0
		Tsiribihina and Manambolo deltas	20,242	10.3
		Ambondrombe	1109	0.6
		Morondava and Bosy	6123	3.1
	Menabe-Atsimo-Andrefana	Mangoky delta	9431	4.8
	Atsimo-Andrefana	Morombe	3035	1.5
		Baie des Assassins	1362	0.7
		Mangolovolo	1172	0.6
East Madagascar	Analanjirofo	Sainte Marie	173	4.1
		Manompana	98	2.3
		Mananara-Nord	100	2.4

Sources: T. Jones et al. (2016b); Rakotomavo (2018).

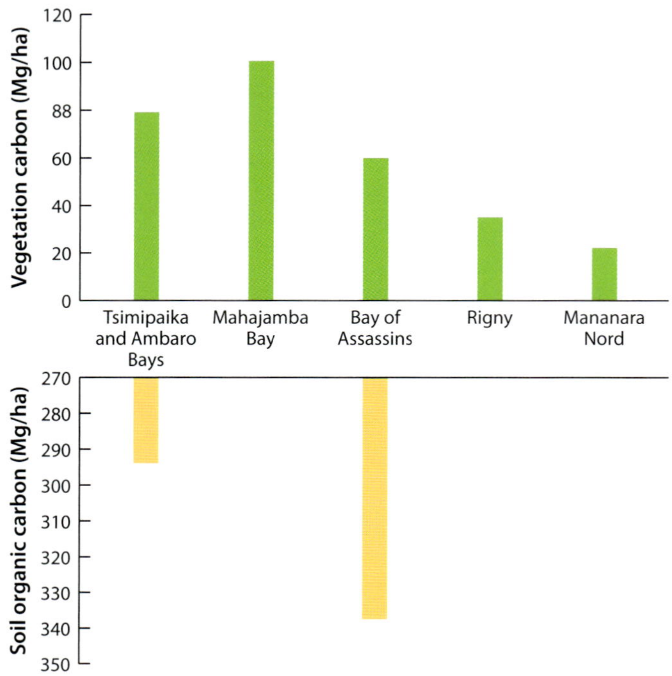

FIGURE 7.6 **Estimated carbon stocks (in megagrams/hectare) in both vegetation and soil in some representative Madagascar mangrove sites in the west (Tsimipaika and Ambanja Bays, Mahajamba Bay, Baie des Assassins) and east (Rigny, Mananara-Nord).** (SOURCES: T. Jones et al. 2016a, 2015, Benson et al. 2017, Rakotomavo 2018.)

2016a, 2016b; Benson et al. 2017; Rakotomavo 2018) (Figure 7.6). Total carbon stock (vegetation and soil) ranged from 184.5 Mg/ha in open-canopy mangrove to 454.9 Mg/ha in closed-canopy mangrove. In a mangrove forest, the bulk of the carbon stock is found in the soil, and can reach up to 381.0 Mg/ha in the top 100 cm of soil. Closed-canopy mangroves in Malagasy waters have, at times, higher above-ground and significantly higher below-ground carbon stocks than do boreal, temperate, and tropical forests.

The stabilization of land by the extensive mangrove root networks also helps to sequester and store considerable below-ground carbon (T. Jones et al. 2016b). This stored carbon is lost, however, if mangroves are cleared and the soil allowed to erode. An estimated 180 Mg/ha of the total carbon stock (vegetation and soil) were lost after 10 years of mangrove clearing, equivalent to 20% of total carbon (Arias-Ortiz et al. 2020). Annual carbon loss in soils in deforested mangrove was 4.5 times the carbon sequestration of soils in intact mangrove, highlighting that replanting mangroves alone cannot compensate for deforestation.

Mangrove Status

Tidal mudflats and the mangrove forests growing on them are dynamic ecosystems naturally subject to multiple processes of change. In areas of active sediment deposition and coastal extension, such as river deltas, such changes can be quite rapid (Lebigre 1988), but elsewhere mangroves in Malagasy waters can be relatively stable with little discernible change over decades (e.g., Be Totozafy 1994; Frontier-Madagascar 2003).

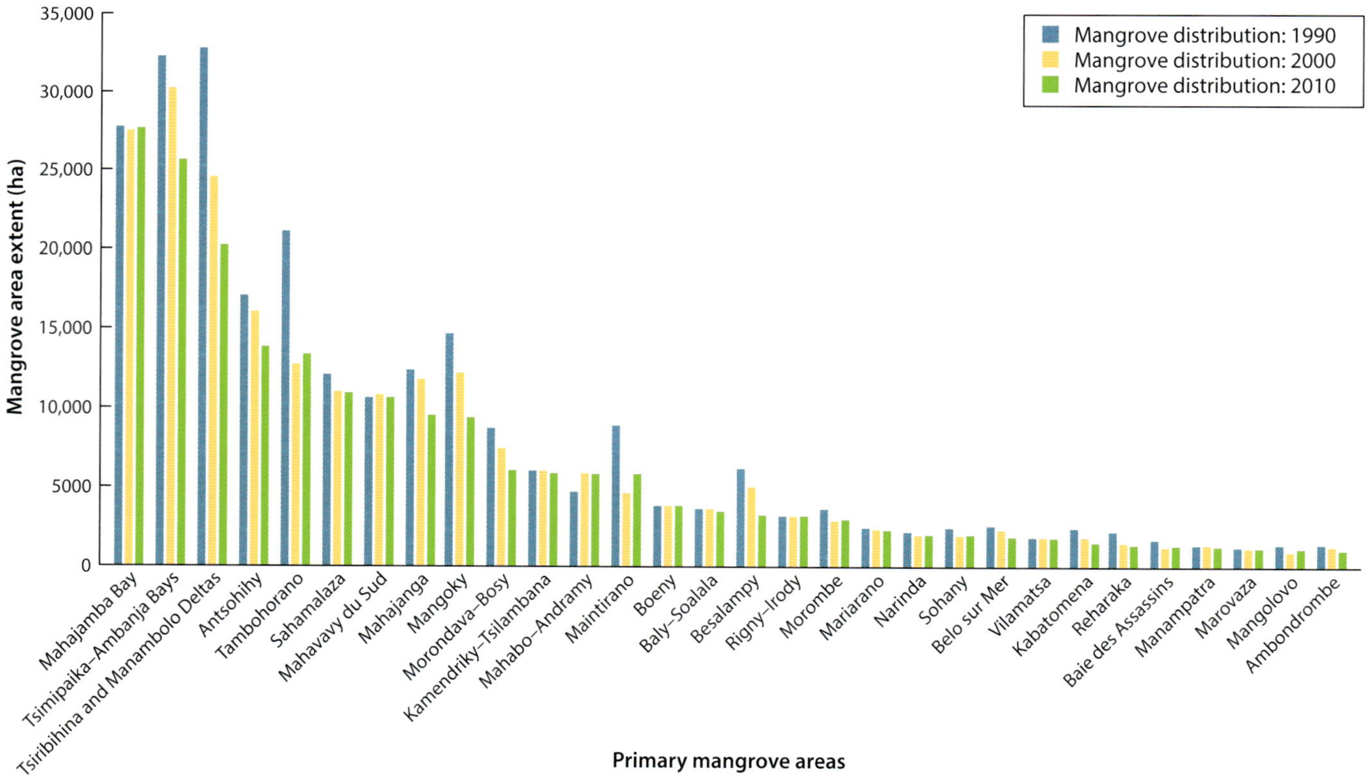

FIGURE 7.7 **Locations of areas of mangrove >1000 ha in 1990, 2000, and 2010.** (SOURCE: data modified from Giri 2011 and analyzed by T. Jones et al. 2016a.)

Anthropogenic activities are causing increased mangrove degradation and deforestation in many areas (T. Jones et al. 2016a). There was loss of an estimated 35% of the island's mangroves between the 1960s, when coverage was 327,000 ha (Kiener 1972), and 2010, when coverage was 213,000 ha (T. Jones et al. 2016a). USGS data (Giri 2011) provided a finer scale analysis (Figure 7.7). By 2010, Mahajamba Bay, the largest mangrove area, had lost 1251 ha, or 4.5%, since 1990, and the rate of loss was increasing, notably in the east. Tsimipaika and Ambaro Bays, also one of the largest mangrove areas in the country, had lost 7659 ha (23.7%) between 1990 and 2010 (T. Jones et al. 2016a).

Drivers for mangrove degradation and loss include the expansion of agriculture and increased demand for fuel and timber (T. Jones et al. 2014, 2016a). The effects of global climate change, such as sea-level rise and an increase in the frequency and intensity of tropical storms, are also predicted to lead to mangrove loss (Alongi 2008). The loss of mangroves is almost certainly contributing to significant reductions in the contribution of Madagascar's mangroves to the stabilization of climate, biodiversity maintenance, and to a range of valuable ecosystem goods and services that are important to the local livelihoods of coastal human populations and the country's overall economy.

BAYS, ESTUARIES, AND COASTAL WETLANDS

Madagascar has over 20 large bays, at least 30 substantial estuaries draining from many river basins (Chaperon et al. 2005), and more than 20 internationally important coastal wetlands. These features occupy over 20% of the total coastline and over 4 million ha (Table 7.5), mostly in the north and west, and are virtually absent from the Deep South and east coast. Bays, estuaries, and wetlands are closely related and often combine to create diverse and productive ecosystems. The interest of these sites and their constituent ecosystems is that they are the primary source of ecological connectivity between marine and terrestrial environments and are influenced by both.

Coastal embayments in Malagasy waters are exceptions to the usually low marine productivity in the region (Hugget and Kywalianga 2017). The numerous bays are important for fisheries, biodiversity, and the blue economy, and the ecosystems within them serve as critical habitat for many species. The larger bays are of tectonic or estuarine origin. The majority occur on the west coast, although the largest, Antongil, is a tectonic bay in the northeast, flanked by the Masoala Peninsula. South of Toamasina, the rectilinear east coast is virtually free of bays until the Tolagnaro area, which has several. In the remainder of the Deep South, bays are virtually absent.

Estuaries

An estuary is the tidal mouth of a river, where the freshwater outflow of the river meets the tidal waters of the marine environment. Madagascar has 18 major and 11 minor river basins covering the total surface area of Madagascar (595,000 km^2). Chaperon et al. (2005) identify three basin types (basins with high forest cover or floodplains, heavily degraded basins such as the Betsiboka and basins of the south, and basins intermediate between these extremes) and five different hydrological regimes:

1. North, including Montagne d'Ambre, Tsaratanàna (which corresponds to the Sambirano area), and the extreme northeast
2. East (from Masoala to Tolagnaro)
3. South (or Sahalien regime) (from west of Tolagnaro to Baie des Assassins on the southwest coast)
4. Southwest (from Morombe to Morondava)
5. West and northwest (from Morondava to Sahamalaza) (including the Maevarano, Tsiribihina, Morondava, and Mangoky river basins)

The principal river basins give rise to over 30 large rivers, each with a substantial estuary. The major rivers carry massive quantities of water and sediment to the estuaries and deltas, driving coastal extension and the transport of nutrients to marine and coastal ecosystems (Salomon 2009). Sedimentation due to deforestation of Madagascar's river basins is considered to outweigh the impacts of climate change on coral reefs and other coastal ecosystems (Maina et al. 2015).

The western rivers carry more sediment than the eastern rivers, but the latter experience the highest peak flood rates in the rainy season, attaining as much as 20 m^3/sec per km^2 of catchment. On the west coast, only the major rivers of the Sofia, Betsiboka, Tsiribihina, and Mangoky basins approach such high flood rates (Chaperon et al. 2005). The greatest volumes of sediment are transported by Madagascar's largest river, the Betsiboka, estimated at 35 km^3/year or an erosion rate of 250–400 t/ha/year for the entire river basin. The Betsiboka is estimated to have transported 45 billion t of sediment to the coast since 1891 (Salomon 2009). Salomon (2009) estimated sediment transport by western river basins including the Tsiribihina (142 megatons [Mt]/year), Mangoky (98 Mt/year), Morondava (11 Mt/year), Fiherenana (7 Mt/year), and Onilahy (17 Mt/year). Flood rates are higher for the southwestern rivers than the northwestern rivers, owing to the marked seasonality of rainfall in the southwestern catchments, resulting in extreme flooding rates.

There are marked differences in seasonal variation between east and north, and west and south, with much steadier flows from the eastern and Sambirano basins, in contrast to the "boom and bust" nature of the western and southern basins. Basins with the lowest ratio of dry to wet season discharge (6–11%) include the big southern rivers (Onilahy, Mangoky, Mananara Sud, and Mandrare), but also the far north (Tsaratanàna). For most rivers the ratio is >27%, corresponding to more sustained discharge in the dry season and less marked flooding in the rainy season. The lowest point of flow of most rivers around Madagascar is October to November, when the clarity of coastal waters is at its highest. The most irregular river flows are observed in the far south (Chaperon et al. 2005).

On the west coast, the rivers are long, wide, and often meandering, topography is mostly flat, tidal range is high, and wave action is moderate. As a result, all of Madagascar's major estuaries and deltas and well over 95% of estuarine and intertidal habitats are found in this zone. On the east coast, rivers tend to be narrow and not very long, and tidal range low, and so there is minimal estuarine habitat. The effects of wave action coming in from the vast Indian Ocean compound this effect by compressing the area of interface between marine and freshwater bodies (Salomon 2009).

TABLE 7.5. **Madagascar's important bays, estuaries, and coastal wetlands, with basic information**

R	SITE NAME(s)	BASIN	COORD.	AREA (ha)	STATUS	MAIN FEATURES	KEY REFERENCES
N	Antongil Bay	Rantabe	16.14°S 49.51°E	280,000	PA, WH, PAP	Largest semi-enclosed bay, tectonic; potential WH; major fishery; 2 MPAs and >20 LMMAs; shark sanctuary	Doukakis et al. (2007), Obura et al. (2012)
	Iharana Bay (Vohémar Bay)	Vohémar	13.21°S 50.00°E	32,000	None	Large estuarine bay with intertidal reef bank, well-developed fore-reef—large river draining into bay; mangroves; heavily sedimented	Obura et al. (2011)
	Lake Sahaka	Manambato	13.09°S 49.98°E	3000	PA, MG008	Largest lake of Antsiranana (1000 ha); floodplain of Manambato River; no longer connected to sea but lakes to north are brackish; part of Loky Manambato PA	Safford (2000), BirdLife (2020)
	East coast of Antsiranana wetlands	NE and Montagne d'Ambre	12.81°S 49.87°E	13,720	MG002	Temporary coastal lakes 60 km SE of Antsiranana; variable water level; dense mangroves, low canopy (3–5 m); shallow marine (0.7–2.5 m); nine islands; 29 bird species, three endemic; colony of *Onychoprion fuscatus* (Sooty Tern) on Nosy Manampao	Le Corre and Bemanaja (2009), Maharavo et al. (2011)
	Ambodivahibe Bay	NE and Montagne d'Ambre	12.22°S 49.27°E	39,794	PA	Estuarine bay and submarine canyon; considered a climate refuge for marine biodiversity; high marine biodiversity	Maharavo et al. (2011), Obura et al. (2011)
	Antsiranana Bay	NE and Montagne d'Ambre	12.23°S 49.29°E	163,100	PA, MG012	Extensive semi-enclosed lobate bay; side opening to east; six small islands, fringing coral reefs, extensive soft coral beds	Evans et al. (2011), Narozanski et al. (2011)
	Courrier Bay (Nosy Hara)	NE and Montagne d'Ambre	12.28°S 49.00°E	125,515	PA	Open marine bay, part of Nosy Hara archipelago national park; shores bordered by mangroves and Ambongoabo Massif	Randriamanantsoa and Brand (2000), Obura (2009)
	Ambavanankarana wetlands	Sambirano	13.07°S 48.46°E	61,220	MG009	Strip of mangrove along NW coast between Ambanja and north of Ambilobe; Ambaro Bay lies off its southern part; mangroves, mudflats, lakes, and salt marshes	BirdLife (2020)
	Ambaro Bay	Sambirano	13.34°S 48.67°E	870,000	PAP, Ramsar 2438	Large, open, mangrove-fringed bay fed by three rivers (Ifasy, Ambazoana, and Mahavavy in the north) from the Tsaratanàna catchment; estuarine and nonestuarine features; largest shrimp fishery (MSY 1600 t/year); fisheries management area 13,950 km^2	Piton and Magnier (1971), Razafindrainibe (2010), Rasolofo (2011)

R	SITE NAME(s)	BASIN	COORD.	AREA (ha)	STATUS	MAIN FEATURES	KEY REFERENCES
N	Ampasindava Bay and wetlands	Sambirano	13.24°S 48.18°E	163,100	MG012	Shallow, turbid, semi-enclosed bay; mangroves (10,000 ha); high productivity; important for water birds	Battistini (1960), Ratsifandrihamanana (2014)
	Sahamalaza Bay and wetlands	Sambirano	13.57°S 47.39°E	59,080	PA, Ramsar 2288,MG018, MAB	Semi-enclosed bay with multiple designations; peninsula, 30 km long bay, mangroves (8400 ha) and coral reefs (>10,000 ha); *Haliaeetus vociferoides* (Madagascar Fish-eagle) and flocks of *Thalasseus bengalensis* (Lesser Crested Tern)	WCS and DEC (2002)
	Loza Bay and wetlands	Sambirano	14.41°S 47.56°E	57,734	MG020	Estuarine bay; mudflats, mangrove (18,000 ha), surrounded by dry forest and grassland); low sedimentation rate; site of Melon-headed Whale (*Peponocephala electra*) stranding in 2008	Salomon (2009), Southall et al. (2013)
	Narindra Bay	Sofia	14.44°S 47.36°E	450,000	None	Semi-enclosed tectonic bay; 45 × 10 km, up to 60 m deep; fringed with mangroves; important shrimp fisheries—2nd after Ambaro Bay (MSY 720 t/year)	Razafindrainibe (2010)
	Mahajamba Bay and wetlands	Mahajamba	15.41°S 47.10°E	180,000	MG023	Estuarine bay fed by five rivers—Sofia, Tsiribihina (N), Mahajamba, Andranoboka, and Masokemja; 47,500 ha mangrove; 3rd shrimp fishery (MSY 300 t/year)	Razafindrainibe (2010), BirdLife (2020)
	Bombetoka Bay and wetlands	Betsiboka	15.81°S 46.27°E	148,200	PA, Ramsar 2048, MG024	Large estuarine bay with mangroves fed by Betsiboka, Madagascar's largest river—total floodplain 850 km^2; mangroves 7500 ha	BirdLife (2020), Ramsar
	Site Bioculturel d'Antrema	Betsiboka, Mahavavy	15.46°S 46.07°E	20,620	PA, Ramsar 2286	Coastal wetland with lakes, estuaries, and mangroves; 23 species of waterbirds and 21 species of fishes grouped in 16 families, of which 2 endemic	Ramsar Sites Information Service (2020)
	Mahavavy and Lake Kinkony wetlands	Mahavavy	16.08°S 45.51°E	258,900	PA, Ramsar 2048, MG025	Large delta—shallow lake—linked to satellite lakes (10,000 ha) in rainy season; delta 33,700 ha with 16,000 ha mangrove, 5200 ha mudflats, 12,500 ha marine	Ramsar Sites Information Service (2020)
	Baly Bay National Park	Mahavavy Sud	16.20°S 45.19°E	69,350	PA, MG026	Semi-enclosed bay; mangroves and coral reefs; *Dugong dugon* (Dugong) formerly present; 10,000 nesting *Sterna hirundo* (Common Tern) and *Thalasseus bengalensis*	BirdLife (2020)

(*continued overleaf*)

TABLE 7.5. ***continued***

R	SITE NAME(s)	BASIN	COORD.	AREA (ha)	STATUS	MAIN FEATURES	KEY REFERENCES
W	Cap Saint André forest and wetlands	Manambaho	16.17°S 44.37°E	90,110	MG028	Coastal wetland; at transition between North and South Mozambique Channel marine ecoregions; high marine productivity; mangrove, lakes, and forest	Obura et al. (2012), BirdLife (2020)
	Bemamba wetland complex	Manambaho	18.50°S 44.19°E	41,500	MG038	Wetland complex; shallow lakes (<2 m deep) and marshes; northern water bodies fresh and seasonal; southern water bodies increasingly saline to the south	BirdLife (2020)
	Manombolomaty wetland complex	Manombolo	18.56°S 44.23°E	15,145	Ramsar 963	Coastal wetland composed of four lakes—Ankerika, Antsamaka, Soamalipo, and Befotaka—surrounded by the Tsimembo dry forests; Lake Antsamaka is brackish	Ramsar Sites Information Service (2020)
	Tsiribihina delta wetlands and mangroves	Tsiribihina	19.44°S 44.27°E	264,100	PA, Ramsar 2302, MG059	Large dynamic delta; 2nd highest wet season discharge on Madagascar; coastal mudflats, mangroves (20,000 ha); salt flats, marsh; Ramsar site 47,218 ha; waters cover >700 km^2 in time of flood	Lebigre (1988), Chaperon et al. (2005), Salomon (2009)
	Complex of Lakes Ambondro and Sirave	Morondava	20.54°S 43.56°E	14,482	PA, Ramsar 2224, MAB	Coastal wetland lakes, part of Kirindy Mité National Park and Biosphere Reserve; dune lakes, mangrove forests, and tidal marshes; important for waterbirds, including four threatened and migratory waterbirds	BirdLife (2020), Ramsar Sites Information Service (2020)
	Lake Ihotry and Mangoky delta complex	Mangoky	21.55°S 43.40°E	176,105	PA, Ramsar, MG062	River delta and coastal lake (94 km^2) fed by Madagascar's largest river basin (54,000 km^2) with highest seasonal discharge, attaining 25,000 m^3/sec; one of the most sedimented deltas, with coastal accretion rate of 100–500 m/year	Chaperon et al. (2005), Salomon (2009), BirdLife (2020)
	Fagnemotsy Bay (Baie des Assassins)	Fiherenana	22.12°S 43.16°E	250,000	PA	Large, semi-enclosed tectonic bay subject to marine transgression; shallow bay fringed by 1507 ha of mangroves; seagrass beds and village called Lamboara (= Dugong); part of the Velondriake PA	Salomon (1986), Lebigre (1990), Benson et al. (2017)

R	SITE NAME(s)	BASIN	COORD.	AREA (ha)	STATUS	MAIN FEATURES	KEY REFERENCES
W	Saint Augustin Bay, Onilahy wetlands	Onilahy	23.30°S 43.42°E	42,950	PA, Ramsar 2304	Historic tectonic and estuarine bay with coastal cliffs and steep seafloor to >1000 m (Onilahy Canyon); connects to Onilahy River wetlands and Amoron'i Onilahy PA	Battistini et al. (1975), Salomon (1986)
	Lake Tsimanampesotse	Mahafaly Plateau	24.22°S 43.58°E	203,740	PA, Ramsar 962, MG069, MAB	Shallow alkaline lake with open water and mudflats; breeding colonies of *Tachybaptus pelzelnii* (Madagascar Grebe); large populations of migratory shorebirds including flamingos; part of the Littoral of South West Madagascar Biosphere Reserve	Gouvernement de la République de Madagascar (2016), BirdLife (2020), Ramsar Sites Information Service (2020)
S	Southwestern coastal wetlands	Menarandra	25.02°S 44.01°E	29,580	PA, MG074	Coastal wetlands (16–29 km^2), Linta delta, bays (Anataike, Androhakely, Fenambosy), Nosy Manitse; coral reefs; many *Thalasseus bengalensis* and *T. bergii*	BirdLife (2020)
	Lakes Anony and Erombo	Mandrare	25.14°S 46.49°E	4100	MG076	Coastal lagoons >45 km^2; Anony: brackish lake formerly connected to the sea, separated from Mandrare River mouth and ocean by dunes; flamingos' stopover	BirdLife (2020)
	Fausse Baie des Galions	Mandrare	25.02°S 46.60°E	12,000	None	12 km open bay; marine, no riverine input; high wave energy; part of monitoring area of QMM Mining project	Jacques Whitford (2007)
	Tolagnaro lagoon complex	Mandrare	25.02°S 47.00°E	45,000	None	Lagoon complex of six small lagoons; estuarine habitats behind Tolagnaro Bay; managed part of QMM mining concession	MacKay et al. (2017), Réville et al. (2007)
	Lokaro and Sainte Luce Bays	Mananara Sud	27.47°S 47.13°E	2500	None	Coastal bays—Lokaro semi-enclosed, Sainte Luce open—mangroves and small riverine inputs; Lokaro includes coral formations	EUCARE (2001)
E	North Pangalanes wetlands complex	Rianila, Mangoro	18.22°S 47.49°E	180,000	MG052	Series of >18 coastal lagoons interconnected by Pangalanes Canal; fed by nine rivers; minimal seawater incursion; total area 180 km^2	Birdlife (2020)
	TOTAL		4,366,645			Combined area of all bays, estuaries, and coastal wetlands (equivalent to about 7% of Madagascar's total land surface)	

Notes: Basin, river basin or watershed; Coord., geographical coordinates; E, East Madagascar; LMMA, locally managed marine area; MAB, Man and Biosphere Reserve; MG, Important Bird Area; MPA, marine protected area; MSY, maximum sustainable yield; N, North Mozambique Channel; NE, northeast; NW, northwest; PA, protected area; PAP, fisheries management area; QMM, QIT Madagascar Minerals; R, region; S, Deep South; SE, southeast; W, South Mozambique Channel; WH, World Heritage (potential).

Estuarine conditions are ecologically challenging for plants and animals, which must be able to tolerate variations in salinity, water depth, and sediment loads, and a lack of stable substrate. However, organisms able to successfully exploit these harsh estuarine conditions can achieve very high levels of abundance. Malagasy estuaries are critical habitat for numerous aquatic species that depend on fresh water for part of their life cycle, including migratory fishes (anguillid eels, sawfishes, sharks, and other euryhaline species) and invertebrates (notably penaeid shrimps). The mudflats of estuaries are also critical for a limited number of locally very abundant species, such as burrowing worms and gastropod and bivalve mollusks.

Coastal Wetlands

Coastal wetlands are areas of permanently or periodically flooded land along or adjacent to the coastal fringe, and include marshes, lakes, and lagoons of fresh, brackish, or salty water. Madagascar has about 2 million ha of coastal wetlands, over 95% of which are along the west coast; these include wetlands of the coastal plain, floodplains, and coastal lakes, some of which have only a relict connection to the sea. The combination of low coastal gradient with the weaker action of waves, winds, and currents, and the prolific growth of mangroves, allows the development of extensive tidal river deltas, floodplains, and lakes, creating very large areas of mixed brackish and freshwater coastal wetland.

The northwest coast, under the influence of the moist Sambirano climate combined with high tidal range, low wave action, and protection from the trade winds, is exceptionally favorable for the development of coastal wetlands, which extend from Cap Saint André all the way to Cap d'Ambre, including Baly Bay, Mahavavy Kinkony, Bombetoka–Marovoay, Mahajamba, Loza, Narindra, Sahamalaza, Ampasindava, Ambaro, and finally Ambavanankarana in the far northwest. These wetlands cover 1.1 million ha, making up almost 70% of all of Madagascar's coastal wetlands, and are the major coastal wetland component of the North Mozambique Channel ecoregion (Obura et al. 2019).

On the rectilinear east coast, the river mouths are dynamic, geomorphological features, while the lagoons behind the dunes may run for many kilometers, creating natural canals, lagoons, and lakes. Despite their proximity to the sea, as a result of high rainfall, these water bodies are primarily of acid, weakly mineralized fresh water typical of the related eastern rivers, supporting only very moderate biomass of aquatic organisms and birds, which interact minimally with the marine environment. Eastern wetlands of importance for birds represent less than 1% (9600 ha) of the Madagascar total (ZICOMA 2001). In the north, where the trade winds strike the coast at a shallow angle and dune formation is limited, there are only a few coastal wetlands, including an important relict coastal lake, Lake Sahaka, of about 1000 ha (Safford 2000), which is now part of the Loky Manambato protected area. In the far southeast, the lagoon complex of Tolagnaro and the Lakes Anony and Erombo are of importance for birds able to exploit both terrestrial and wetland habitats (e.g., Goodman et al. 1997), but are brackish and of mainly low productivity (Jacques Whitford 2007; Réville et al. 2007).

Significant Bays, Estuaries, and Coastal Wetlands According to Ecoregion

North Mozambique Channel Marine Ecoregion

Antongil Bay: This is the largest bay in Malagasy waters and one of the best studied, and, due to its many unique features and high biodiversity, it has been identified as having potential for World Heritage site status (Obura et al. 2012). It is a semi-enclosed bay covering 2800 km^2 with 270 km of coastline, and provides seasonal habitat for *Megaptera novaeangliae* (Humpback Whale) (see Rosenbaum and Chou, pp. 430–33) and other marine mammals (Y. Razafindrakoto et al. 2010). Situated in a high rainfall area (3800 mm/year), the bay is surrounded by lush tropical forests and fed by nine rivers, providing extensive wetland, estuarine, and marine habitats. Depths range from <2 m near shore to ~25–30 m in the northern and central reaches, gradually increasing southward to a maximum of ~65–70 m. The upper portion of the bay is a turbid, estuarine environment, characterized by fluctuations in salinity and turbidity dictated by tides, currents, and local rainfall patterns. Water circulation in the bay is clockwise, driven by the southeast trade winds. While the mouth of the bay is exposed to the oceanic swell, sea conditions to the north end of the bay are calmer. Coral communities are described above (see Coral Reefs). Small patches of mangrove can be found close to a few major rivers, but no significant mangrove stands exist. Reed beds can be found along many river systems entering the northern end of the bay. These habitats and their associated estuaries presumably are important habitat for juvenile fishes.

Antsiranana Bay (Diégo Suarez Bay): In the far north, this is one of Madagascar's largest semi-enclosed bays and one of the world's largest natural harbors. Opening to the east via the Emerald Sea, the bay comprises a central sound and four lobate extensions, and is fringed throughout by coral reefs, mangroves, and seagrass beds. It encompasses six small islands (Nosy Fano, Nosy Koba, Nosy Langoro, Nosy Laopasana, Nosy Volana, Nosy Longo), and is fed by several small rivers draining from the Montagne d'Ambre catchment, which locally create estuarine habitat. Coral communities are described above (see Coral Reefs).

Ampasindava Bay wetlands: On the northwest coast south of Nosy Be with an area of about 100,000 ha is Madagascar's second-largest semi-enclosed bay. The bay is fed on the east by the Sambirano River, and the seabed is shallow (maximum depth 12 m) and covered in fine sediments. The bay is fringed by mangroves, with well-developed and high-diversity coral reef formations in the mouth. Ampasindava Bay is listed as an Important Bird Area (IBA), most recently assessed in 2017, with 39 recorded species including 15 endemic species.

Bombetoka Bay, Betsiboka estuary, and Marovoay wetlands: Bombetoka Bay lies between Katsepy and the Marovoay floodplain and is fed by the Betsiboka estuary (and its large drainage basin of 11,800 km^2), creating Madagascar's largest coastal wetland complex. The bay consists of mangrove islets separated by channels and mudflats, with shallow subtidal waters in the estuary. The water is shallow (less than 5 m deep at low tide), except toward the mouth, and is very turbid. Northern mangroves are relatively degraded (3–4 m high), while those toward the south are in better condition; likewise, those on the coast are more intact than those in brackish, inland areas, where the canopy is 6–8 m high. The largest mudflats lie immediately seaward of the mangrove islets. A muddy bar crosses the mouth of the estuary, c. 10 m wide and covered with scattered mangroves. Major tributaries flowing into the complex are the Mahajamba, Isandrano, and Ikopa. The floodplain in the lower course of the Betsiboka has some 150 small lakes. A total of 60 bird species are known from the site, of which 10 are endemic to Madagascar.

South Mozambique Channel Marine Ecoregion

Wetlands of the Tsiribihina delta and upper Tsiribihina River: The Tsiribihina is one of the largest and most dynamic of the western river deltas (Lebigre 1988) with one of the largest areas of mangroves (about 20,000 ha). Located 35 km west of Belo sur Tsiribihina, toward the coast, is the river delta of sandbanks, lagoons, coastal mudflats, mangrove forests, salt flats, and areas of marsh and dry land. The salt flats are often flooded during the rainy season; the marshy areas are dominated by sedges and reeds and non-native water hyacinth (*Eichhornia*) grows in the less saline water. Some 82 bird species have been recorded from this site, of which 22 are endemic to Madagascar.

East and South Madagascar Marine Ecoregions

As indicated above, the bays, coastal wetlands, and estuaries of the eastern and southern coasts are of limited extent and productivity. A few sites have been studied in some detail, however, and are described here for illustrative purposes.

Pangalanes-east lagoon complex: This is the only eastern coastal wetland designated as an IBA, and includes a chain of over 18 essentially freshwater lagoons interconnected by the Pangalanes Canal. The largest lagoons are Nosive (35.7 km^2), Rasoabe (20 km^2), and Ampitambe-Irangy (11.5 km^2). Maximum water depths are generally 3–7 m, with the deepest (Rasoabe) reaching 12 m. Some 61 species of fishes are found in the lagoon, and many are euryhaline species (e.g., *Liza macrolepis*, *Mugil robustus*, *Arius africanus*, *Gerres* spp., *Leiognathus equulus*, *Paretroplus polyactis*, *Ptychochromis oligacanthus*). Abundances of both fishes and birds are low, however, owing to the characteristically low productivity of lagoons of the east coast.

Tolagnaro lagoon complex and Tolagnaro Bay: This lagoon complex consists of a series of small lagoons behind the dunes fringing Tolagnaro Bay and has been studied as it falls within the impact management zone of the Rio Tinto QMM ilmenite mineral extraction concession (Réville et al. 2007). The main lagoons are Anony (22.6 km^2) (not to be confused with Lake Anony) and Andriambe (7.0 km^2). Maximum depth is 5 m, but most are 1–3 m deep. Salinities range from freshwater (in the absence of a connection to the sea) to highly saline (where a permanent connection exists with the sea). In periods of flooding, the lake system connects to the sea and brackish water is flushed out with fresh water, causing reduced diversity and abundance (Réville et al. 2007). The lakes are of low productivity but of significant biodiversity; aquatic species richness and abundance are higher in the more saline and estuarine parts of these ecosystems (Mackay et al. 2017). Important macro-invertebrates are prawns, lobsters, and other crustaceans. The estuarine section of the complex is dominated by copepod and decapod crustaceans, including spiny lobsters and crabs (including the mud crab *Scylla serrata*). The most diverse and abundant benthos was found in the upstream section of the Anony River, which is the final and more saline section of the wetland before the sea. The lake flora includes one species of marine seagrass—*Halodule uninervis*. A total of 18 fish species have been recorded in fisheries, including the endemic *Paratilapia* and cichlids (*Ptychochromis* spp.). About 50 species of fishes in total are known from the lagoons, including euryhaline species, of which *Ambassis commersoni* is the most abundant; this fauna is dominated by highly resilient species typical for an estuarine system. Commercially important fish families include the Ambassidae, Gobiidae, Mugilidae, and Gerreidae, which migrate in and out of the lagoons. Birds visiting Andranasy and Andratoloharano lagoons include *Phoenicopterus roseus* (Greater Flamingo) and *Phoeniconaias minor* (Lesser Flamingo). Macroalgae in Tolagnaro Bay itself were surveyed in 2000: 43 species were recorded in the cool season and 57 in the warm season (Tombolahy 2000).

Fausse Baie des Galions: Near Tolagnaro (adjacent to the Baie des Galions), this is a 12 km wide, open marine bay, and the only such bay in the South Madagascar marine ecoregion to have been studied. A baseline environmental survey found that benthic habitats were dominated by macroalgae, notably *Gelidium madagascariense*. A total of 14 macroalgae were recorded, including 10 red (Rhodophyta) and four green (Chlorophyta) species, less than a quarter of the number found in Tolagnaro Bay. Coral reefs are absent but rocky bottoms support coral colonies as well as abundant sponges, soft corals, and encrusting coralline algae. Coral colonies are small, suggesting that larger ones are destroyed by wave surges. Only 28 hard coral species were recorded, consistent with the absence of coral reef development. No seagrasses or mangroves were reported (Jacques Whitford 2007).

Importance and Status of Bays, Estuaries, and Wetlands

Estuaries and coastal wetlands provide many important ecosystem services. They provide breeding and nursery sites for a range of other marine species, as is the case for Antongil Bay (Doukakis et al. 2007; Obura et al. 2012), which appears to be an important breeding habitat for *Sphyrna lewini* (Scalloped Hammerhead) and other species of sharks in the Carcharhinidae.

Estuaries and coastal wetlands also support important fisheries. Antongil Bay, with a high biomass of small pelagic fishes (estimated at 27,000 t), has a diverse nontarget fishery, which includes over 140 fish species from 69 families. Catches are dominated by Scombridae (47%) and Carangidae (16%) and also include sharks, shrimps, and marine mammals. Mean hourly catch rates are just under 1 kg/hour/fisher and mean daily catch rates are 4.4 kg/day/fisher, which are lower than those in other reef fisheries in Madagascar waters (e.g., Laroche and Ramananarivo 1995; Narozanski et al. 2011) but high for the east coast (Doukakis et al. 2007). It also supports industrial trawl fisheries, which catch an estimated 500 t of shrimp and a minimum of 2500 t of finfish annually. Antsiranana Bay supports significant small-scale fisheries using various gears to catch a broad range of pelagic and demersal fishes of different trophic specializations, and also carcharhinid sharks and dasyatid rays. Reported daily catch rates vary from 24 kg to 75 kg, which is very high for a small-scale fishery on the island. Most fishers reported a decline in captures, however (Narozanksi et al. 2011).

Coastal lagoons may also have significant fisheries. The Pangalanes-east lagoon complex is intensively fished; catches were 300–400 t/year in the period 1960–1975, but have declined in recent years to only 45 t/year, seemingly because of excessive fishing effort. The yield of 8 kg/ha/year is very low in comparison to lagoon fisheries elsewhere. *Paretroplus polyactis* and *Ptychochromis oligacanthus*, both endemic fish species, are important components of the catch. Fishing in lagoons near the town of Tolagnaro is also intense, and stocks are thought to be overexploited (Réville et al. 2007). Annual yield of fishes and crustaceans from lakes near Tolagnaro in 2007 was estimated at 33 t over an area of 5 km^2, or about 6.5 t/km^2/year—typical for lacustrine fisheries in Malagasy waters, which range between 1 and 13 t/km^2/year. The fishery at Fausse Baie des Galions is essentially marine and involves 59 species, with the most common species being mackerel (*Scomber* spp.), followed by *Selar crumenophthalmus* (Bigeye Scad), *Chirocentrus dorab* (Wolf Herring), and others. Seven of the 10 most common species were schooling pelagic fishes, consistent with high surface productivity and poorly developed benthos of the area. Threatened species included Carcharhinidae (requiem sharks); *Rhinobatos* spp. (guitarfish), which were caught mainly as juveniles; and *Sphyrna* spp. (hammerhead sharks) and the endemic and endangered *Argyrosomus hololepidotus* (Madagascar Meagre) (Jacques Whitford 2007).

MARINE SPECIES DIVERSITY

As mentioned in the introduction, the Malagasy marine fauna is one of the richest in the western Indian Ocean. Mollusk diversity is considered to be the best predictor of total coastal and marine diversity by some authors (Wafar et al. 2011). Using this taxonomic group and its estimated diversity of 1158 species (A. Cooke et al. 2003a), Madagascar's total coastal and marine species diversity (including both vertebrates and invertebrates) was estimated by Wafar et al. (2011) at 10,500 species, placing Madagascar in a medium-diversity grouping of islands, along with Maldives, La Réunion, Mauritius, and Sri Lanka. However, given that the number of known mollusk species has since increased through more recent surveys (e.g., Wells in McKenna and Allen 2003; the *Atimo Vatae* expedition), the above statistical extrapolation is likely to have underestimated total diversity. This section provides an update on marine fish species and invertebrates in Malagasy waters since A. Cooke et al. (2003a). Given the extensive new information from the *Atimo Vatae* expedition to the Deep South (P. Bouchet, unpublished data), the work of this team is described first, followed by sections focusing on marine fishes and invertebrates (including an update on diversity totals for the country, followed by more detail on species from the Deep South) and algae (a brief overview).

Marine Diversity of the Deep South

The Deep South is a region of high biological productivity, attributed to the complex upwelling and retroflection system of the Agulhas Current, including a permanent and large upwelling cell off the southeast coast and a smaller, seasonal upwelling cell west of the southern tip of Madagascar (Halo et al. 2017; Ramanantsoa et al. 2018b). These systems combine to bring up nutrients from deeper water, giving rise to the highest levels of primary productivity in any surface waters around Madagascar.

The Deep South is unique from a biodiversity standpoint. Early explorations of the Deep South included Crosnier (1973) and a 1983 *Dr. Fridtjof Nansen* fisheries survey (Anonymous 1983), which discovered vast areas of benthic communities dominated by large sponges, of evident biological interest but unsuitable for trawling. Commercial fishing using lobster traps in the 1980s and 1990s opened the region and started to generate rare and interesting seashells as a bycatch (Bouchet 1999; Korn et al. 2000; Bozzetti 2004; Lorenz 2004; numerous subsequent publications). Mollusk specialists thus recognized this area as a distinct biogeographic province (Lorenz 2004).

These initial findings triggered the 2010 *Atimo Vatae* research expedition (P. Bouchet, unpublished data), an initiative of the Muséum National d'Histoire Naturelle (MNHN), Paris, and the NGO Pro-Natura International, in collaboration with IHSM and WCS. The expedition was part of a wider initiative called Our Planet Reviewed, linked to the latter phases of the Census of Marine Life (2000–2010) and mobilized over 50 international and national scientists, who used the Institut de Recherche pour le Développement (IRD) research ship RV *Antea* as a dive platform and the converted shrimp trawler *Nosy Be 11* to undertake offshore benthic sampling by dredging and trawling. The expedition explored an area from Manantenina (north of Tolagnaro) around Cap Sainte Marie to Androka (south of Toliara), and out onto the continental shelf and slope to the 800 m isobath. To date, a total of 152 new marine species have been described as a result of the expedition, including fishes (four), urochordates (eight), echinoderms (five), brachiopods (four), mollusks (100), crustaceans (23), and algae (eight). Many more are still awaiting description (P. Bouchet, unpublished data).

The *Atimo Vatae* expedition significantly increased knowledge of marine biodiversity on Madagascar and in the Indian Ocean in general. It clearly demonstrated the unique character, high diversity, and high rates of endemism of the marine biota of the Deep South, while indicating that much still remains to be discovered. At the same time, the expedition has confirmed the connectivity of the Deep South with the rest of the Indian Ocean and far beyond into the Pacific. The work strongly justifies the classification of the Deep South as a separate marine ecoregion, now integrated into Madagascar's protected area network. It also has potential World Heritage site status, as proposed by Obura et al. (2012). A new marine protected area has been proposed for the Deep South and is being promoted by WCS.

Marine Fish Diversity

Madagascar has a rich and varied marine fish fauna, including *Latimeria chalumnae* (Western Indian Ocean Coelacanth) (see

Bruton et al., pp. 359–67), many elasmobranchs (sharks, rays, *Rhincodon typus* [Whale Shark], sawfishes) (see Séret, pp. 368–80; Leeney, pp. 386–90), and a high diversity of reef fishes (see Coral Reef Fish Diversity and Biomass, above). The diversity of demersal and pelagic fishes not associated with coral reefs is less well known.

Groeneveld and Koranteng (2017), in publishing the results of the *Dr Fridtjof Nansen* offshore cruises of 1983, 2008, and 2009, gave a total of 1497 teleost demersal and pelagic fishes for Madagascar and the southwest Indian Ocean, which is likely to include mostly non-reef-associated species given that the surveys were conducted offshore and outside coral reef systems. Fricke et al. (2018), in a comprehensive checklist for Malagasy fishes, which includes the results of the *Dr Fridtjof Nansen* and *Atimo Vatae* expeditions, gave a total of 1798 fish species in 257 families, of which 1708 species are marine, consisting of 13 worldwide temperate and tropical species (3.3%), 978 widespread tropical Indo-Pacific species (58.3%), 215 circumtropical or warm temperate species (12.8%), 453 Indian Ocean endemics (27%), 233 western Indian Ocean endemics (13.9%), 73 southwestern Indian Ocean endemics (4.4%), 16 species endemic to Madagascar and Mascarenes (1.0%), four species endemic to Madagascar and Comoros (0.2%), three species endemic to Madagascar and the Madagascar Ridge (0.2%), and 37 marine species endemic to Madagascar (2.2%). (For a list of the freshwater fishes, see Sparks and Stiassny, pp. 1245–60.)

Significantly, the three surveys by the *Dr Fridtjof Nansen* (of over 100 locations on the continental shelf) showed that the diversity, abundance, and distribution of offshore pelagic (six main families) and demersal fishes (over 40 families) around Madagascar had changed little in 2008 and 2009 compared with the baseline survey of 1983, suggesting that the offshore fish fauna and supporting ecosystem remain essentially intact (Groeneveld and Koranteng 2017).

Pelagic fishes: Madagascar's pelagic fish fauna is dominated by carangids and clupeids in shallow areas, with engraulids (anchovies) being common around high-productivity areas such as upwellings. Mackerels, important in small-scale fisheries, are generally coastal pelagic fishes, and include *Scomberomorus commersoni* (Kingfish), *Acanthocybium solandri* (Wahoo), and *Rastrelliger kanagurta* (Indian Mackerel).

Tuna are highly migratory carnivorous fishes with behavioral and physiological adaptations enabling them to exploit widely scattered pockets of productivity in the open ocean. As very versatile feeders, they hunt both on the surface for small pelagic fishes and crustaceans and at depth (100 m or more) for small fishes, crustaceans, and squids (Potier et al. 2004). The principal species of tuna found offshore around Madagascar are *Katsuwonus pelamis* (Skipjack), *Thunnus albacares* (Yellowfin), *T. obesus* (Bigeye Tuna), and *T. alalunga* (Albacore) (Doumenge 1998). *Gymnosarda unicolor* (Dogtooth Tuna) and the smaller *Euthynnus affinis* (Kawakawa, or Mackerel-tunny) are inshore species. *Thunnus maccoyii* (Southern Bluefin Tuna), considered on the IUCN Red List as Critically Endangered, occurs off southern Madagascar.

Tuna tend to aggregate above bottom features, such as seamounts, reefs, banks, or shipwrecks, or around floating objects (a tendency exploited by industrial fisheries). Feeding oceanic tuna in the western Indian Ocean migrate between seasonal areas of high primary productivity in areas of upwelling across the Seychelles Ridge and opposite the Somali coast and the nutrient-rich areas in the Mozambique Channel. *Katsuwonus pelamis* and *Thunnus albacares* migrate southward into Madagascar's waters during the warm season (October to April), and spawn primarily off the northwest. *Thunnus albacares* is found in Malagasy waters as far south as Toliara in the west and to about Toamasina in the east (Doumenge 1998); this species breeds April–June in the Mozambique Channel (Rajoharison 1994; Rajoharison and Conand 1995). *Thunnus alalunga* has a predominantly southerly distribution and occurs more often in the long-line fisheries in the southern half of Malagasy waters than in the northern purse-seine fishery; it predominates over *T. albacares* in southwestern waters (Doumenge 1998; ASCLME 2012).

Several large species of billfishes are also important in Malagasy waters and are associated with tuna and feed off them; these include *Makaira indica* (Black Marlin) and *M. mazara* (Blue Marlin), *Istiophorus platypterus* (Indo-Pacific Sailfish), *Tetrapturus angustirostris* (Short-billed Spearfish), and *Xiphias gladius* (Swordfish) (Bauchot and Bianchi 1984; ASCLME 2012). *Xiphias gladius* is abundant off the east, south, and southwest coasts of Madagascar (Doumenge 1998). *Istiophorus platypterus* is seasonally abundant around Nosy Be, where it is observed in large shoals around offshore banks during August–October (Laboute and Maharavo 1998). Various smaller pelagic and epipelagic fishes are associated with the tuna and form part of the purse-seine fisheries' bycatch, the most abundant being *Coryphaena hippurus* (Dolphinfish), *Elegatis bipinnulata* (Rainbow Runner), *Canthidermis maculata* (Rough Triggerfish), and *Acanthocybium solandri*, which make up 90% of the purse-seine bycatch (Ruiz et al. 2018). Total standing biomass of offshore pelagics around Madagascar was estimated by the *Dr Fridtjof Nansen* surveys at 107,000–129,500 t, but is probably closer to 150,000 t as there were recognized surveying problems. Nevertheless, biomass is low, which is consistent with Madagascar's status as a high-diversity, low-abundance country for offshore pelagic fish fauna (Krakstad et al. 2017).

Madagascar has a relatively diverse fauna of small coastal pelagic fishes (>30 species), especially on the west coast. The fauna comprises mainly clupeids (*Sardinella* spp., *Stolephorus* spp., *Dussumieria* spp.), carangids (*Alopes mate*, *Decapterus* spp., *Trachurus* spp., *Selar* spp.), scombrids (*Rastrelliger kanagurta* and *Scomber* spp.), and sphyraenids (small barracudas). Most concentrations of small pelagic fishes are found at shallow depths several kilometers offshore, especially in the west near Nosy Be, Maintirano, Mahajanga, and Morombe, the Deep South (Cap Sainte Marie), and in Antongil Bay (ASCLME 2012). Because of the higher productivity of coastal waters than offshore waters owing to river inputs, the biomass of small coastal pelagics is significant, but to date has been estimated only for Antongil Bay, where it was put at 27,000 t (Obura 2012). Further studies are needed to better quantify this resource.

Nonreef demersal fishes: Madagascar's demersal fish fauna is diverse, made up of about 40 principal families (Krakstad et al. 2017), and includes deepwater, continental slope, and shallow coastal assemblages. Many are of commercial importance, and this group requires careful conservation and management. Almost 20 deepwater species of sufficient abundance to be of commercial interest were identified at depths of 100–720 m through surveys by the research vessel *N. O. Vauban* in 1974 in the northwest (Crosnier and Jouannic 1974). The 1983 *Dr Fridtjof Nansen* expedition, trawling in the southwest, south, and east, found about 50 demersal species in commercial quantities, principally sciaenids (notably the endemic *Argyrosomus hololepidotus*, sparids, mullids, nemipterids, pomacentrids, serranids, lethrinids, and lutjanids, with higher diversity and abundance in the south than the east) (ASCLME 2012). Trawls by the RV *Algoa* in August 2003 at 355 m off Cap Tanjona in the northwest recorded 24 species of demersal and bathypelagic teleosts, with over 80% of catches made up of *Neoscopelus microchir*, *Polymixia berndti*, *Chlorophthalmus* cf. *punctatus*, *Rexia promenthoides*, *Diaphus* spp., and an undescribed *Pterotrigla* (ASCLME 2012).

Studies of the bycatch of the industrial shrimp fishery in 2004–2005 revealed a rich shallow demersal fish fauna of at least 47 species, dominated by leiognathids in the northwest and sciaenids in the west (Randriarilala et al. 2008). Bycatch studies using the vessel M/FV *Caroline* in 2011 revealed an additional 11 demersal species of commercial interest. These and other studies indicated a shallow coastal demersal fauna in 2012 of more than 50 species, including at least 27 species of commercial interest (defined as yielding more than 50 kg/hour in experimental trawls) (ASCLME 2012). Fish collections undertaken during the *Atimo Vatea* expedition, based on local catches from the market of Tolagnaro and on bottom trawls at about 200–800 m, added additional species, including a cryptic shallow-water sandperch (*Parapercis albiventer*) and a planktivorous fusilier (*Caesio xanthalytos*). Range extensions for 10 *Caesio* species were found, affirming the plankton-rich habitats of the Deep South (Holleman et al. 2013). Other finds included *Sillago caudicula* (Sandwhiting), previously known only from the coast of Oman in the Northern Hemisphere (Kaga and Heemstra 2013), and an Indo–West Pacific *Ebosia vespertina* (scorpionfish) (Matsunuma and Motomura 2015), which occurs off South Africa and Mozambique. Overall, this study demonstrated both the unique aspects of the fish fauna of the Deep South and its connectivity with the Indo-Pacific.

Marine Invertebrate Diversity

Using data from certain phyla (Porifera, Cnidaria, Mollusca, Echinodermata, Bryozoa, and Chordata) and other taxa (Crustacea), A. Cooke et al. (2003a) gave an estimate of 3272 marine invertebrate species for Malagasy waters, representing about 50% of the total known macro-invertebrate fauna for the same taxa (6820 species) in the western Indian Ocean (Richmond 2001). At the time, this was considered an underestimate for Madagascar and it was thought that much of the known invertebrate fauna of the southwest Indian Ocean would be found in Malagasy waters. A review of data published for the same key taxa since 2003, including reef-building corals (e.g., Veron and Turak 2003; Veron et al. 2015), shows that the total number of known macro-invertebrate species in Madagascar's waters is about 4140 species. The number of known marine invertebrate species for the western Indian Ocean has also increased, but there has been no consolidated synthesis to make a fresh comparison.

Research such as the *Atimo Vatae* expedition and other recent studies have highlighted significant rates of country endemism among marine macroinvertebrate taxa, up to 20% for some taxonomic groups, such as murex shells (Houart and Héros 2013, 2015). Madagascar's share of regional diversity will depend on the interplay between habitat diversity, with increased representation of regionally distributed species, and isolation (such as in the case of the Deep South), tending to raise the level of endemism and thus the uniqueness of Madagascar's marine invertebrate macrofauna.

Mollusks: Several spectacular species of coastal gastropods had been discovered in the 1990s–2000s in the Deep South, including the cowrie *Palmadusta androyensis*, the fasciolariid *Marmorofusus brianoi*, and the volute *Lyria patbaili* (P. Bouchet, unpublished data). The *Atimo Vatae* expedition sampled an estimated 1500 species of marine mollusks, notably greater than any previous survey, which have been only partly worked up by taxonomists but already revealed over 100 new species.

Two mollusk species, more than any other, encapsulate the originality of Madagascar's Deep South and its distinctiveness from the rest of Madagascar: an abalone and a giant clam. The former is *Haliotis squamosa*, a medium-size (90 mm) subtidal species endemic to the Deep South (Figure 7.2b). Abalones graze on algae and thrive in cold or cool waters; this species and the only other known Indian Ocean endemic (from Dhofar in the Arabian Sea) are both confined to seasonal upwellings. The clam *Tridacna elongatissima* is the only species of giant clam occurring in the Deep South and based on current information is endemic to the southwest Indian Ocean, also occurring on both sides of the Mozambique Channel and off La Réunion. Although it had been described as early as 1856 from Mozambique, *T. elongatissima* had been erroneously treated as a synonym of the widespread *T. maxima*, until it was recently recognized as a valid species (Fauvelot et al. 2020). Molecular phylogenies show that *T. elongatissima* forms a strongly supported clade with two other Indian Ocean endemic giant clams—namely, *T. rosewateri*, from Saya de Malha and Cargados Carajos, and *T. squamosina*, from the Red Sea and Gulf of Aden.

Because of their interest to collectors going back several centuries, the cone shells, or cone snails (Conidae), are among the best-surveyed mollusk families, making them models for biogeographic studies. The expedition sampled a total of 74 cone species (Monnier et al. 2018). Of these, 62 are also present in other areas of Madagascar, and most are widespread in the Indian Ocean or even the Pacific Ocean. Conversely, there are 29 species of cones inhabiting the warmer waters of Madagascar and unknown from the Deep South. Combining the numbers, the cone snail fauna of Madagascar is composed of at least 104 species (representing over 11% of the total known species in the world). Of these, 14 are Malagasy endemics, and among them 10 (or 13.3% of the local biota) are Deep South endemics, a high level of endemism for marine species.

In contrast to the Conidae, the Cerithiopsidae consists of minute (2–8 mm) sponge-eating gastropods, and the family has been poorly sampled and studied worldwide. The *Atimo Vatae* expedition documented 70 species, including 39 new to science (Cecalupo and Perugia 2014) plus 31 range extensions for species found across the Indo-Pacific, again highlighting the often wide distribution of marine mollusk species.

The expedition also achieved important advances in the knowledge of the Muricidae, a large and varied family of medium to large predatory sea snails, commonly known as murex snails or rock snails (with about 1850 living species worldwide). Like the Conidae, the Muricidae have long been the subject of much interest from amateurs and collectors, with relatively well documented distributions. The expedition documented over 90 species (Houart and Héros 2013, 2015; Houart 2015), including 12 new to science that are believed to be Deep South endemics. When the species discovered before the expedition are included, the level of endemism tops 20%, the highest so far reported in Malagasy waters for marine biota.

Among the many other discoveries, four species (two new) in the olive snail genus *Ancilla* (Ancillariidae) should be highlighted. There are 45 species of *Ancilla* worldwide, but the center of diversity is the Indian Ocean, and the south Madagascar species "flock" is a significant addition to the known diversity of this group. One of the new species, the most abundant in the Lavonono area where it was discovered, was named *A. atimovatae* after the expedition (Kantor et al. 2016).

Dredging produced several species in the Chilodontaidae, some new to science and several new records for Madagascar, including *Herpetopoma instrictum*, known also from the Kenyan coast and the Comoros, and *H. helix*, occurring along the South African coast and in southeast Madagascar (suggesting a mainly temperate distribution); the new species *Vaceuchelus jayorum* (which also occurs in the Mascarenes and Mozambique); *Perrinia konos* (also occurring in South Africa and Nosy Be); and *Granata cummingi* (a regional endemic) and *G. sulcifera* (widely distributed in the western Indian Ocean and Pacific) (Herbert 2012). Several range extensions were recorded among the Calliostomatidae, as well as nine new species, including four recorded only from the Deep South and presumably local endemics (Vilvens 2014).

Brachiopods: Brachiopods, or lantern shells, are an ancient, exclusively marine phylum, which superficially resemble bivalve mollusks but whose shells show bilateral symmetry. They are much less diverse than bivalves, with only 415 species worldwide. Bitner and Logan (2016) reported 23 species in Malagasy waters, with the highest diversity in the Deep South (17 species in 15 genera). The Malagasy brachiopod biota has strong similarities to that of southern Africa, sharing 12 out of 25 species.

Crustaceans: About 500 species of decapod crustaceans were sampled by the *Atimo Vatae* expedition. The resulting material contributed to a revision of the genus *Galathea* (squat lobsters), the description of 92 new species, and the recognition of new records for eight existing species. One entirely new species (*G. boucheti*) was described from the Deep South (Macpherson and Ainas-Barcia 2015), indicating the region as being important for this group. A new record in southern Madagascar was *Lauriae gardineri*, the most common galatheid species in Malagasy waters, but which is restricted to the western Indian Ocean (Macpherson and Ainas-Barcia 2013). Of 10 new western Indian Ocean squat lobster species belonging to the Munididae, Munidopsidae, and Eumunididae, four were recorded from the Deep South, including two (*Munida stomifera*, *Munidopsis columbae*) known only from there (Macpherson et al. 2017).

In contrast, the crab fauna was not distinctive. Of the 46 species of crabs sampled in eight families, 31 (67%) have a wide Indo-Pacific distribution, six (13%) are from the western Indian Ocean, six (13%) are so far known only from Madagascar, and one, *Goneplax clevai* (Goneplacidae), has a distribution between the eastern Atlantic, South Africa, and the south of Madagascar, illustrating the southern and temperate affinities of Madagascar's Deep South. A single species of *Ethusa* proved to be new to science (Castro 2013).

Algae

Based on a consolidation of available data, A. Cooke et al. (2003a) estimated that there were at least 200 species of macroalgae in Malagasy waters. This number will rise significantly once the results of the macroalgae studies of *Atimo Vatae* are fully written up, which could take macroalgal flora of Madagascar to well over 500 species (L. Le Gall, unpublished data). The southeast was already known as a rich area for this group, with 163 reported species (Tombolahy 2000). Red algae (Rhodophyta) dominate, with 93 species, followed by green algae (Chlorophyta) with 42 species, and brown algae (Phaeophyta) with 28 species. The presence of 14 species of calcareous red algae was a noteworthy feature of the southeast around Tolagnaro.

The *Atimo Vatae* expedition sampled about 500 species, mostly red algae. Algae take a dominant place, both in terms of density and diversity, in the seascapes of southern Madagascar, from the intertidal zone to about 20 m in depth. Intertidally, many species are decumbent or in cushion, including *Hypnea panosa*, remarkable for its iridescent blue color (despite belonging to the red algae!). Subtidally, algae occasionally form bushes up to 10–30 cm high. Soft species such as *Portieria*, *Plocamium*, *Gelidium*, *Halymenia*, and *Martensia* coexist alongside calcified species such as *Metamastophora flabellata*, *Actinotricha*, *Galaxaura*, and *Dichotomaria*. The cosmopolitan *Asparagopsis taxiformis* can be locally abundant. *Ptilophora spongiophila* is a new red alga discovered during the expedition, among five endemic species of this genus, for which the center of diversity appears to be Madagascar (Boo et al. 2018). The expedition reported two new endemic species, *Pterocladiella feldmannii* and *hamelii*, in a genus of red algae economically important and the source of agar and agarose used for food and biotechnology (Boo et al. 2016a). The collections confirmed the endemic status of the economically important *Gelidium madagascariense* (Andriamampandry 1988), which has been placed in a monophyletic group with two genera of the order Gelidales occurring in Western Australia and Thailand (Boo et al. 2016b).

PRESSURES ON MARINE BIODIVERSITY

Coastal communities throughout Madagascar are highly dependent on marine fisheries and other coastal resources for their livelihoods, and the country as a whole relies heavily on its blue economy—that is, the range of goods and services provided by the marine environment. Negative impacts on marine biodiversity will thus adversely affect both the national economy and the health and well-being of fishing communities, which are vulnerable to the impacts of climate change and of competition with foreign fishing vessels.

Several marine and coastal ecosystems are already under severe threat as indicated by Madagascar's 2019 Ecosystem Red List assessment (IUCN 2019), which included coral reefs, seagrass beds, estuaries, mangroves (submerged roots), and coastal brackish/saline lagoons, and marine lakes. The main threats identified were sedimentation, coastal development, physical destruction of littoral zones, overexploitation of marine and coastal resources, extractive activities, pollution, and climate change. Out of 13 ecosystems evaluated, three were considered Endangered (coral reefs of the east and west, mangroves of the west and southwest), three Vulnerable (reefs, seagrass beds, and mangroves of the northwest), and one Least Concern (reefs of the northeast). The remainder were assessed as Data Deficient (Table 7.6).

Fisheries

With close to 70% of the Malagasy population living below the US$1.90 international poverty line (UNDP 2018) and, in 2019, a population growth rate of 2.65% per year (World Bank 2019), Madagascar is especially reliant on its fisheries, and particularly small-scale fisheries, for food security and poverty alleviation (Barnes-Mauthe et al. 2013). Valued at over US$160 million annually in 2003 (World Bank 2003), Malagasy marine fisheries have declined and in 2015 were valued at as little as US$45 million annually, or about 1% of the country's gross domestic product (GDP) (MRHP 2015).

Offshore industrial fisheries are mostly conducted by foreign fleets of large long-liners and purse seiners (some of which are fishing illegally). Export-driven, often foreign-owned licensed tuna and shrimp fisheries account for much of the reported value of fisheries production. However, 70% of overall marine fisheries' production comes from small-scale fisheries (Breuil and Grima 2014). These provide an important national protein source, although the true economic value of small-scale fisheries has not been systematically assessed.

TABLE 7.6. **IUCN Red List assessments for Madagascar's marine and coastal ecosystems**

NO.	ECOSYSTEM OR BIOREGION	IUCN STATUS
1	Coral reefs of NE Madagascar	LC
2	Coral reefs of E Madagascar	EN
3	Coral reefs of S Madagascar	DD
4	Coral reefs of W and SW Madagascar	EN
5	Coral reefs of NW Madagascar	VU
6	Seagrass meadows of NE Madagascar	DD
7	Seagrass meadows of NW Madagascar	VU
8	Seagrass meadows of SW Madagascar	DD
9	Seagrass meadows of SE Madagascar	DD
10	Mangroves of NW Madagascar	VU
11	Mangroves of W Madagascar	EN
12	Estuaries and deltas of W Madagascar	DD
13	Coastal lagoon systems of Madagascar	DD

Source: IUCN 2019; see also Carré et al., pp. 2119–30.
Notes: DD, Data Deficient; EN, Endangered; LC, Least Concern; VU, Vulnerable.

About 75% of Madagascar's national fish production is marine and can be categorized as traditional methods, artisanal boats, and industrial vessels, which include the distant water fishing nation (DWFN) vessels that target tuna and tuna-like fishes. A vast range of species is targeted, with over 180 different catch items recognized in the national fisheries statistics. In 2014, annual national fishery production was estimated to be around 130,000 t, of which 90,000 t was marine (Breuil and Grima 2014). Small-scale marine fisheries and marine aquaculture enterprises contribute more than 60% of the total annual fish production, with the former producing about 80,000 t annually (MRHP 2015). There are significant interannual fluctuations in catches caused by changes in oceanographic conditions or the migration patterns of tuna and tuna-like species. Data submitted to the FAO are "official" figures and, as with many countries, tend to exclude substantial unreported landings or reflect coarse estimates of actual landings. Catch reconstructions have added more than 200% to official landing statistics (Le Manach et al. 2012)

Total marine fishery potential could be considerably more than current production if management were to sustainably exploit the full range of resources (Breuil and Grima 2014) and is estimated at about 200,000 t per year, including 52,000 t of tuna and tuna-like species, 45,000 t of demersal species, and up to 100,000 t of small and medium pelagics. Invertebrate fisheries include shrimps with an assumed potential of 10–12,000 t per year, lobsters (assumed potential 1000 t per year), crabs (assumed potential 7500 t per year), and cephalopods (assumed potential 2000 t per year), and unquantified potential for bivalves and holothurians.

Deepwater teleosts have not been legally exploited, with the exception of a pilot fishery for *Beryx splendens* (Alfonsino) by a foreign company undertaken over a seamount on the Madagascar Ridge located at 26°S, 46°E. The presence of *Hoplosthethus atlanticus* (Orange Roughy) and the cardinal *Epigonus telescopus* was reported in the catches (Centre de Surveillance des Pêches director, unpublished data). Larger species of scombrids (mackerels and tuna), together with *Coryphaena hippurus* (Dorado, or Dolphinfish; coryphaenid) and large billfishes (istiophorids), such as marlin, sailfish, swordfish, and spearfish, are important for offshore fisheries, whereas small pelagic species are a vital resource for small-scale coastal fisheries.

Rapid human population growth is increasing fishing effort (Long et al. 2017); the small-scale fishery landings may have already peaked (Le Manach et al. 2012), and fishers are being forced to move to less intensively fished areas (Cripps and Gardner 2016). As stated in Madagascar's blue economy policy of 2015 (MRHP 2015), most stocks are considered fully exploited and facing overexploitation, and shark (see Séret, pp. 368–80) and sea-cucumber stocks are near collapse (Rasolofonirina and Conand 1998; Le Manach et al. 2012; Purcell et al. 2013). According to FAO statistics from 2014 (Breuil and Grima 2014):

- all penaeid species were fully exploited;
- coastal demersal fishes were fully exploited, although some stocks were moderately exploited in remote areas;
- small pelagics were moderately to fully exploited;

- other coastal stocks were fully exploited, with the exception of crabs, which were moderately exploited; and
- tuna and tuna-like species were fully exploited.

Artisanal and Traditional Fisheries

The term *small-scale fisheries* (formerly referred to as "traditional" fisheries) generally refers to activities carried out principally from pirogues (78% of fishers), mainly with sails and a small number with motors of less than 15 horsepower (hp) (*lakana*), or on foot (22% of fishers) (MRHP 2012). West-coast pirogues (*lakana fiara*) usually possess an outrigger and a sail, and may have a fishing range of 10 km or more. East-coast pirogues are simple dugouts with a small fishing range. Fishing from pirogues involves hooks and line, spearguns, traps, gill nets, and trawl nets. In 1982, there were just 5000 pirogues nationwide (Beurrier 1982), but by 2012 there were over 48,000 (MRHP 2012). In 2012, the official national fisheries census reported 58,151 fishing households with 272,827 members, of which about 70% were in marine areas, as compared to freshwater.

Artisanal fisheries are those where larger motorized vessels are used. These were little developed in 2003, with only 150–200 vessels (A. Cooke et al. 2003a), but by 2012 there were 350 vessels, 65% of which were located in the north (DIANA Region) (MRHP 2012). Both artisanal and traditional fisheries target some 50, mainly demersal, fish species dependent on coral reefs, mangroves, seagrass beds, estuarine mudflats, steep beaches, and rocky shorelines (Fennessy et al. 2009). Some fisheries are even more diverse, such as in Antongil Bay where some 140 species are involved (Doukakis et al. 2007). Lethrinidae, Lutjanidae, Sparidae, Carangidae, and Mullidae are the most common families (Breuil and Grima 2014). Other groups targeted include scombrids (mackerels and small tuna), sharks, rays, and sawfishes. Small-scale and artisanal fisheries also target marine mammals (dolphins and *Dugong dugon*), sea turtles (especially *Chelonia mydas* [Green Turtle] and *Eretmochelys imbricata* [Hawksbill Turtle]), crustaceans (shrimps, lobsters, mangrove crabs), cephalopods (octopuses, squids, cuttlefish), gastropods (numerous species, including ornamental species), sea cucumbers and edible urchins, colloid-bearing seaweeds (*Eucheuma* spp. and *Gelidium* spp.), and seabirds (mainly the collection of tern eggs) (Laroche and Ramananarivo 1995; Le Manach et al. 2012; Cripps and Gardner 2016). Reef gleaning targets all exploitable resources of the reef flats, including fishes, echinoderms (edible urchins and ornamental sea stars), mollusks (octopuses, edible and ornamental gastropods, and bivalves), crustaceans (crabs and lobsters), and colloid-bearing seaweeds (Rabesandratana 1985; Westerman and Benbow 2013).

The total traditional catch of finfish was estimated at about 50,000 t annually in the 1990s, or an average of 2 t per pirogue per year, based on studies such as Rafalimanana (1991). Laroche and Ramananarivo (1995) reported an annual finfish yield of 12.13 t/km^2 for the Toliara barrier reef, indicating a total potential national annual yield from coral reefs of about 47,000 t, assuming 3934 km^2 of reefs (Burke et al. 2011). In practice, yields from reef fisheries are likely to be lower, considering the significant degradation of coral reefs and overfishing since 1995. However, the small-scale fisheries also target pelagic and nonreefal demersal resources, such that 50,000 t annually remains a credible estimate.

Expert opinion that most fishery resources are overexploited (Breuil and Grima 2014) is supported by numerous observations. Resource declines were first noted for the reefs of Toliara, where increasingly indiscriminate fishing methods were employed as resources became rarer (Vasseur et al. 1988). By 2000, carnivorous groupers (Serranidae) made up only 2.5% of the catch, with herbivorous and detritivorous species predominating (Gabrié et al. 2000). McClanahan and Obura (1998) reported standing fish biomass of about 350 kg/ha for the coral reefs of Masoala and considered that this indicated modest to intermediate fishing pressures compared with other areas in the western Indian Ocean. A few years later, fishers in the adjacent Antongil Bay reported fishery declines, blaming this on a combination of industrial shrimp trawling in the bay, which was taking a substantial bycatch of fishes as well as shrimps, and overexploitation by small-scale fishers themselves (Doukakis et al. 2007). Overfishing in small-scale multiple-species fisheries was similarly quantified in Menabe (Gough et al. 2020), with declines also driven by increases in effort within the small-scale fishery, through a diversification of fishing gears, in addition to direct competition with industrial shrimp trawls, which discard large volumes of finfish bycatch (Razafindrainibe 2010).

Sharp local declines or clear signs of overexploitation have been observed for some high-value stocks since the 1990s—notably, ornamental gastropods (WWF 1993), sea cucumbers (Remanevy et al. 1997), sharks (A. Cooke 1997), and lobsters (Rabarison 2000; Jacques Whitford 2007). More recent studies on shark fisheries (Cripps et al. 2015; Humber et al. 2015) confirm major declines in shark populations (see Séret, pp. 368–80). The decline of some small-scale fisheries can also be inferred from the success of a number of fishery no-take zones or temporary closure schemes, including the first such case in Malagasy waters at Mananara-Nord marine protected area (Grandcourt 1999), the octopus closures at Andavadoaka (Haridon 2006), and no-take zones in the same area (Gilchrist et al. 2020).

In addition to overexploitation of the target resources, small-scale fishing techniques (e.g., beach seines, poison fishing, and fine-mesh nets—like the mosquito nets distributed free to prevent malaria) are often destructive to the supporting ecosystem. Impacts of the traditional fishery in Toliara on ecosystems were first documented in the 1980s and 1990s, where the use of fine-mesh beach seines, reef-flat trampling, and poisoning were widespread and contributed to a pronounced degradation of shallow-water reef systems (Vasseur et al. 1988; Vasseur 1997; Gabrié et al. 2000). By 2010, degradation of the Toliara Grand Récif appeared complete (Harris et al. 2010). The practice of breaking and turning corals in order to expose octopus or other target species is particularly damaging (Andréfouët et al. 2013). On the Grand Récif the density of human reef gleaners may exceed 36 gleaners/km^2, and it has been estimated that they damage 22–36% of the reef flat annually (Randriamanantsoa 1997). Around the Masoala Peninsula, damage is caused by the removal of live coral to camouflage fish traps (McClanahan and Obura 1998). Poison, derived from the sap of *Euphorbia laro* (see Haevermans and Hetterscheid, pp. 645–49), is a traditional fishing method that is quite extensively used on reefs of the southwest, where it has been known to kill turtles (see Walker et al., pp. 391–99). Destructive fishing methods are stimulated by drought in the south, which attracts to fishing agriculturalists who lack the expertise to build or sail canoes. Dynamite fishing is virtually unknown in Malagasy waters.

Industrial Fisheries

The licensed industrial fisheries of Madagascar include 246 vessels comprising 168 offshore DWFN vessels targeting mainly tuna and tuna-like fishes and 78 national industrial vessels targeting pelagic and demersal finfishes, shrimps, and other resources, including four nonfishing support and collection vessels (MRHP et al. 2018). The national pelagic long-line fishery started in 2007 and has grown to seven licensed vessels of less than 25 m length operating out of Toamasina and Ile Sainte Marie in the range 14–22°S (in the zone of division between the north- and southbound branches of the East Madagascar Current). The fishery catches an average 338 t/year, made up of tuna (49%), billfishes (19%), sharks (12%), and other species (19%). The national industrial demersal fin fishery comprises just six vessels of less than 25 m, operating mainly in the southwest.

The DWFN fisheries are significantly larger. The main boats are from Europe and Asia and operate in Madagascar's exclusive economic zone (EEZ) and in the adjacent waters of other states or the high seas. They target *Thunnus albacares* (Yellowfin Tuna), *Katsuwonus pelamis* (Skipjack Tuna), and *T. obesus* (Bigeye Tuna), which, with other tuna-like species, migrate seasonally through Malagasy waters. The tuna catch from the Madagascar EEZ in 2014 was estimated at 15,000 t per year (Breuil and Grima 2014). The licensed offshore DWFN fishery has two components: the purse-seine fishery (46 vessels) and the long-line fishery (c. 100 vessels). The purse-seine fishery, mostly from the European Union with some Mauritian and Japanese vessels, targets mainly *K. pelamis* (70%) and *T. albacares* (25%); it operates principally in the northern or northwestern part of the Malagasy EEZ during January–June, with peak catches during March–May. The long-line fishery has two fleets, northern and southern. The northern fleet (50–60 vessels) operates mainly outside the Malagasy EEZ targeting *T. albacares* and *K. pelamis*. The southern fleet (40–50 vessels) operates mainly within the eastern part of Madagascar's EEZ and targets *Xiphias gladius* (Swordfish), tuna (mainly *T. alalunga*, *T. albacares*, and *T. obesus*), and other large teleosts—*Coryphaena hippurus* (Dorado, or Dolphinfish), *Istiophorus platypterus* (Indo-Pacific sailfish), *Makaira mazara* (Blue Marlin), *M. indica* (Black Marlin), and spearfishes (René et al. 1998; MRHP et al. 2018).

DWFN industrial fisheries are responsible for a substantial bycatch, which varies according to the fishing methods used. The bycatch of purse-seine fisheries, which set large nets underneath tuna shoals that are drawn to the surface before landing the catch, includes species trophically associated with the tuna (mainly billfishes, tuna-like fishes, and sharks) and species (such as triggerfish) attracted to the floating objects deployed to attract the target species, plus a smaller proportion of purely incidental captures (such as rays, marine turtles, and occasional cetaceans). Netting operations rarely cause direct injury and live release of nontarget species is generally possible even after landing (Ruiz et al. 2018). In a study of purse-seine bycatch in the EEZs of Madagascar and adjacent states (of which about 30% was in the northern and western Malagasy EEZ) (Ruiz et al. 2018), annual bycatch over the period 2008–2017 for the entire area averaged 9188 t. In the first years of the study, over 50% of the bycatch was discarded tuna, but this changed to over 50% nontarget teleosts by 2017, of which 15% were sharks (mostly *Carcharhinus falciformis*, Silky Shark [80%] and *C. longimanus,* Oceanic White-tip Shark) and 85% was billfishes, rays, and turtles; cetaceans were also recorded in the bycatch.

The long-line fishery operates mainly in the eastern and southern parts of Madagascar's EEZ. The long-line fishery also has an impact through bycatch, but this is less well documented. Madagascar does not enforce reporting by this fishery and has placed observers with its fishing vessels only twice (MRHP et al. 2018). Longlines are up to 180 km or more in length with regularly spaced droppers to up to 200 m, each gear consisting of thousands of hooks. Long-line bycatch in the Malagasy EEZ averaged about 7500 t annually for the period 2000–2017 and was primarily sharks (20–40%) (IOTC 2019). Shark bycatch rates are as much as 40–60% in swordfish fisheries, including those operating in the southern EEZ of Madagascar, where sharks are thought to be abundant. Over the period 2004–2006, for the Spanish Indian Ocean long-line fleet, whose operations included the western and eastern Madagascar EEZ (and can thus be regarded as representative), bycatch was 46.2% of the total weight landed and was composed mainly of *Xiphias gladius* (Swordfish), *Prionace glauca* (Blue Shark), and *Isurus oxyrhinchus* (Shortfin Mako Shark) (Ramos-Cartelle et al. 2008). Data from 2010–2017 indicate *Sphyrna lewini* (Scalloped Hammerhead) is the most common species in shark bycatch, followed by *I. oxyrhinchus*, *P. glauca*, thresher shark (*Alopias* spp.), and *Carcharhinus falciformis* (IOTC 2019).

Bycatch of sea turtles by DWFN long-line fleets operating in the eastern Malagasy EEZ is only partly known, but it can be assumed to be significant. The IOTC environmental risk assessment estimated ~3500 turtles annually caught by longlines for the entire Indian Ocean, and ~250 by purse seines, with a survival rate of 75% (IOTC 2019). Turtle bycatch is relatively well reported by the La Réunion fleet, which has shown that mortality of sea turtles for longlines is substantially higher (about 30% of turtles hooked) than for purse-seine fisheries (about 1% of turtles netted) (see Walker et al., pp. 391–99). Bycatch of seabirds is considered an issue only at latitudes above 25°S, which includes the southern part of Madagascar's EEZ, where Japanese and Taiwanese long-liners operate but for which Madagascar provides no reporting on effort or bycatch (IOTC 2019).

Shrimp Fisheries

Shrimp fisheries are important to the national economy and to the livelihoods of small-scale fishing communities in coastal areas. There are currently two types of shrimp fishery: industrial and small-scale (an intermediate artisanal fishery using small motorized vessels, mainly in the north, having disappeared in 2005) (UQAR-ISMER and Resolve 2019). The industrial fishery was established in 1967 on the west coast and is well documented and closely monitored (Breuil and Grima 2014). The small-scale fishery emerged in the late 1990s (Goedefroit 1999) and was first systematically surveyed in 2018, by which time it was widespread around most of Madagascar and very important to local livelihoods, especially in the Menabe and Melaky Regions of the west coast (UQAR-ISMER and Resolve 2019).

Industrial shrimp fishery and associated bycatch: Industrial shrimp vessels target mainly *Fenneropenaeus indicus* (Indian White

Shrimp, formerly *Penaeus indicus*) (70% of catch in most years), *Metapenaeus monoceros* (Speckled or Pink Shrimp), *P. semisulcatus* (Brown Shrimp), and *P. monodon* (Tiger Shrimp). Trawling is conducted close to the shore in depths of up to 10 m over soft bottoms, where shrimps are abundant at the start of the fishing season (usually November). Initially focused on the coastal waters near Mahajanga and Morondava, the fishery progressively expanded to cover about two-thirds of the west coast from Cap Saint Sébastien to Morombe, and the east coast from Antongil Bay to Manakara (Razafindrainibe 2010). On the west coast, trawling effort is primarily concentrated in Ambaro Bay, around Cap Saint André, and off the mangroves of the Tsiribihina River delta; on the east coast effort is focused mainly in Antongil Bay, south of Mananara, south of Ile Sainte Marie, and between the Mangoro and Mananjary Rivers (UQAR-ISMER and Resolve 2019).

Fishing effort grew steadily from 1967, reaching a peak in 2001 with 79 vessels. Catches were relatively constant (9000–12,000 t) for almost a decade (1995–2004) until 2005, when there was an abrupt decline, which affected both the industrial trawler fleet (reduced by almost 50%), and the artisanal fishery, which disappeared completely. A 55% decline in the industrial catch occurred from 7900 t in 2004 to 3700 t in 2012 (Breuil and Grima 2014). Vessel numbers dropped to just 32 in 2010, and had increased to 41 in 2018 (UQAR-ISMER and Resolve 2019). Stock assessments in 2013 (H. Razafindrakoto 2013) raised concerns that recruitment overfishing might be occurring by the small-scale fishery taking too many juveniles. The destruction of mangroves (important habitats for shrimps), climate change, and a lack of monitoring and compliance were also identified as contributing to the problem. A resource evaluation in 2018–2019 determined that essentially the entire decline in catch was due to *Fenneropenaeus indicus*, with no significant trend for the other species. The evidence for some recovery in catches since the reduction of effort indicated overfishing as the most likely cause. A precautionary management regime was recommended, along with research to better understand the small-scale fishery and the bycatch of both fisheries (UQAR-ISMER and Resolve 2019).

Finfish bycatch and discards are further issues associated with the industrial shrimp fishing industry, depriving small-scale fishers of the species involved, and negatively impacting the ecosystem through their removal (Le Manach et al. 2012). In the 1990s, the total annual finfish bycatch was estimated at 30,000 t, or five times that of the shrimp harvest, most of which was discarded (Jain 1995). In 2005, the average bycatch ratio was about 3:1, with fishes making up 93% of the bycatch, which involved at least 93 species of demersal and pelagic fish species (Randriarilala et al. 2008). The problem is further compounded by the tendency of shrimp trawlers to regear to target finfish to compensate for the declining shrimp catch. Bycatch of finfish had declined to 4000 t/year by 2010 as bycatch reduction devices (BRD) were being effectively used but increased again to 15,000 t in 2018 (UQAR-ISMER and Resolve 2019) as trawlers shifted to targeting fishes and used the fish bycatch as part of this catch. The industrial shrimp fishery has effectively transformed itself into a combined finfish and shrimp fishery with high potential impact if all 70 vessels reenter the fishery.

Small-scale shrimp fishery: Small-scale artisanal fishers exploit the seasonal migration of subadult shrimps from mangrove and estuarine areas into deeper water. Such harvesting was initially particularly intense in Ambaro Bay and Morondava but has since become more widespread across the country (UQAR-ISMER and Resolve 2019). This fishery targets the same shrimp species as the industrial fishery where they overlap geographically, but also operates elsewhere, most notably in the southwest and southeast. In 2018, 22,554 shrimp fishers were recorded in 131 villages, supporting an estimated 296,760 household members; however, this activity attracts significant seasonal migration of fishers, extending the footprint to a larger number of households. Monofilament nets are the main gear, and the fishery is highly targeted, with minimal bycatch (shrimp represent 80–100% of the catch). Fishers undertake about 70–110 fishing trips per season with an average catch of 16.6 kg per trip, suggesting a total yield countrywide well in excess of the industrial fishery.

Lobster Fisheries

Lobster fisheries are exclusively small-scale and target five species: *Panulirus homarus* (Red or Scalloped Spiny Lobster), which is the main species in the south and southeast and prefers rocky habitat; *P. versicolor* (Painted Lobster), which is the main species in the northwest and northeast and prefers coral reef habitat; *P. ornatus* (Ornate Lobster); *P. longipes* (Long-legged Lobster); and *P. penicillatus* (Pronghorn Lobster). Export in the 1990s was in the range 310–550 t/year, of which over 75% came from the Tolagnaro area, where the main fishery yielded about 250–300 t/year over the period 1988–1996 (Rabarison 2000). Lobster fisher numbers grew from 2000 onward, but the catch per unit of effort (CPUE) declined from 3.5 traps and 2.33 kg/day per fisher in 1989 to 10.5 traps and 0.68 kg/day per fisher in 2002, with a trend line to zero catch by 2015 (Jacques Whitford 2007). The small-scale lobster fishery in the southeast region of the Anosy Region is the main lobster fishery in the country (Sabatini et al. 2007), providing a livelihood for about 40 coastal communities (Long 2017). Traditional methods (hand-woven vine lobster pots deployed from wooden dugout canoes) are used. Once landed, lobsters are purchased on the beach, either by intermediaries or directly by the collectors themselves, or directly by the collectors themselves. The latter then transport the lobsters to the regional capital of Tolagnaro, where they are processed for local and national markets, as well as international export.

Recent decades have seen a dramatic decline in catch across the country (Sabatini et al. 2007; Skinner et al. 2016). National lobster landings fell from 550 t in 2006 to 240 t in 2012. Declines in the Anosy Region stock are attributed to increased fishing effort, driven by rapid population growth and export market demand (Sabatini et al. 2007; Holloway and Short 2014; Long 2017), but the high economic value of lobsters, coupled with a lack of viable alternative livelihoods, compels fishers, particularly in the poor southeast, to continue fishing (Long et al. 2019). Along with contravention of national lobster-fishing laws, current practices pose a significant threat to fishers' livelihoods, as well as the overall long-term sustainability of the fishery.

Other Invertebrate Fisheries

Sea cucumbers (holothurians): These animals have been intensively collected and exported since at least the 1920s, when exports were

50–140 t annually (Petit 1930). Export increased to a peak in the early 1990s, reaching 400–500 t, followed by a decline (A. Cooke et al. 2003a). By 2004, stocks of the main targeted species—including *Holothuria scabra*, *H. nobilisi*, *H. fuscogilva*, and *Thelenota ananas*—had become heavily depleted (Rasolofonirina et al. 2004), as indicated by the tendency of fishers to make camps at collection sites, collectors traveling farther to obtain product, sizes diminishing for all species, and all species being collected, regardless of value (Conand, in Gabrié et al. 2000). The fishery has not been recently assessed.

***Scylla serrata* (Mud Crab):** This species is harvested in most of the more than 800 villages in close proximity to mangroves, to meet the high Asian market demand, and provides a key livelihood. In the early 1990s, the sustainable yield from the Mahajanga mangroves was estimated at 1.7–1.8 t/km^2/year, extrapolated to about 5500 t/year for the country as a whole, assuming a mangrove area of 327,000 ha (Bautil et al. 1991). In 1992, a "conservative" maximum sustainable yield (MSY) for *Scylla serrata* was set by the fisheries ministry of 7500 t/year or 2.5 t/km^2 (Andrianaivojaona et al. 1992). This was considerably in excess of the MSY estimated by Bautil et al. (1991) but has been maintained since then (Breuil and Grima 2014). It can be assumed that the total potential yield has declined since the early 1990s, owing to the loss of about 30% of mangrove cover since 1990 (see Mangroves, above). There has also been a rapid increase in the number of Mud Crab permits issued since 2012: harvests increased from 4052 t in 2012 to 6018 t in 2017, driven by Asian demand for live crabs (including juveniles) (Zelasney et al. 2020). This considerably exceeds the original estimates for MSY, and Madagascar's Mud Crab resources are now considered overexploited (FAO 2020).

Cephalopods: Small-scale fisheries for octopus, squid, and cuttlefish exist in the majority of fishing areas of Madagascar. In most coral reef areas, three octopus species are fished: *Octopus cyanea* (Day Octopus), the main target and the only species in the southwest; *O. aegina* (Marbled Octopus); and the less common *O. macropus* (Long-armed Octopus) (FAO 1998). Fisheries for *O. cyanea* are of particular importance in the southwest. The pelagic squid (*Loligo* spp.) supports important fisheries in the Toliara area and around Nosy Be. Fisheries for cuttlefish are less developed, although the species *Sepia zanzibarica* is reported to be common in Nosy Be (Laboute and Maharavo 1998).

Gastropods: Gastropods are harvested for food in the Toliara region (Rabesandratana 1985). Mangroves are gleaned for the abundant mangrove whelk *Terebralia* (= *Pyrazus*) *palustris*, the shells of which are fired to make lime (Scales et al. 2017). In Toliara, up to 138 species of gastropods are exploited for the ornamental shell trade (Romaine 1997). Of these, several may be considered threatened with local extinction—notably, the helmet shells (*Cassis cornuta* and *Cypraecassis rufa*) and the cowries (Cypraeidae). In the 1990s, *Turbo maromorata* (Greensnail) and *Pinctada margaritifera* (Pearl Oyster) were exported for button making; a single exporter in Toliara exported an annual average of 8 t of ornamental shells and a further 50 t of industrial shells from 1989 to 1991 (WWF 1993). No more recent data are available.

Black corals (Antipatharia): Black coral, locally known as "rosewood of the sea," has been the target of low-level fishery for many decades, primarily in the Deep South, to supply the jewelry trade. About eight species are known from Faux Cap (IUCN 2019). A new fishery rapidly expanded from 2011, prompting official seizures in 2014 and 2015 amounting to 278 kg. The trade is highly lucrative, with export prices up to US$200/kg, and estimates suggest a total annual harvest in the south of 5200 kg (Todinanahary et al. 2016).

Mangrove Harvesting

Mangrove timber is a prized construction material for housing (pillars, frames, fences), fencing, small-scale fishing boats, and aquaculture infrastructure, as well as a valued source of domestic energy for firewood and charcoal and also tannin (Rasolofo 1997; Scales and Friess 2019). As inland forest resources decline, mangroves are increasingly exploited for wood, charcoal, and tannin. Several areas, including Ambaro and Ambanja Bay in particular, have been significantly exploited for charcoal (T. Jones et al. 2016b), but this is a nationwide issue. Other areas affected are mangroves near Mahajanga, Morondava, and Toliara.

Tourism

In recent years (up until the impact of Covid-19), Madagascar has become increasingly popular as a tourist destination, with about 300,000 visitors in 2016 (Jedrusik 2019), although numbers, compared with neighboring islands in the western Indian Ocean, such as the Seychelles and Mauritius, were still very small. Most tourism and recreational activity on coral reefs is in the north of Madagascar, on Nosy Be, and neighboring islands (Spalding et al. 2017). Reefs such as Nosy Tanikely undergo daily visitation by divers and snorkelers, which may have caused damage to reefs in 2002 (F. Webster and McMahon 2002). Reefs around Ile Sainte Marie have been popular with recreational divers and sports fishers for many years and became more widely known in the 1990s, when the first diving clubs were established on the island.

Whale-watching, particularly of *Megaptera novaeangliae* (Humpback Whale), became well established in Ile Sainte Marie in the early 1990s and spread to a lesser extent to Antongil Bay, resulting in an increased frequency of disturbance to these animals in their breeding habitat (see Rosenbaum and Chou, pp. 430–33). Dedicated watching tours for *Rhincodon typus* (Whale Shark) started in the Nosy Be area in 2011, and by 2017 unregulated mass Whale Shark–watching tours and associated activities were resulting in a range of different problems (see Diamant et al., pp. 381–85).

Climate Change

Climate stressors are inflicting increasing damage on Madagascar's marine and coastal habitats. Anomalously high sea temperatures occurred in 1998 and 2001, associated with El Niño–Southern Oscillation events in the eastern Pacific (when warm surface water extends farther westward than usual from Central America) when warm surface waters also persist in the western Indian Ocean. Sea surface temperatures in the western Indian Ocean increased by up to 0.018°C/year between 1950 and 2005 (McClanahan et al. 2009), and by 2008 climate models were projecting rises in mean sea surface temperatures throughout the country (Hannah et al. 2008).

Madagascar experiences regular coral-bleaching events, the most notable being those in 1998, 2005, and 2016 (Ateweberhan and McClanahan 2010; Obura et al. 2017), although coral mortality due to these is low in Malagasy waters compared with other western Indian Ocean countries. This may be because of the landmass of Madagascar sheltering its western reefs from the warm South Indian Ocean Current and the cooling effect of weather disturbances that are common during the summer months (Ateweberhan and McClanahan 2010; Carrigan and Puotinen 2011). Northern reefs benefit from a weak upwelling system bringing cool water from deeper areas (McClanahan et al. 2007; Ateweberhan and McClanahan 2010).

Severe weather disturbances and cyclones are likely to increase in frequency around Madagascar (Jury et al. 1999; P. Webster et al. 2005; Knutson et al. 2010). Strong storms can reduce reef structures to rubble, causing a decline in reef species diversity and abundance (Pratchett et al. 2014; Bozec et al. 2015), and damage seagrass beds (Côté-Laurin et al. 2017) and mangrove forests (Alongi 2008; Gilman et al. 2008).

Sedimentation

Hyper-sedimentation due to the erosion and transport of soil from Madagascar's 18 or more major river basins is a significant threat to marine and coastal biodiversity. It has been suggested that sedimentation is having a greater negative impact on coastal shallow-water ecosystems, including coral reefs, mangroves, and seagrass beds, than the effects of climate change (Maina et al. 2015). Following initial deforestation, repeated bush fires cause continuing soil erosion and sedimentation of rivers. Lying underneath forests and other vegetation is a vast supply of erodible laterite with the potential to generate sediments for millennia (Chaperon et al. 2005). Madagascar's major rivers deliver a minimum of 500 million tons of sediment annually into marine and coastal ecosystems (see Bays, Estuaries, and Coastal Wetlands, above).

Pollution

While Madagascar's marine and coastal ecosystems are potentially threatened by agricultural runoff (fertilizers and pesticides), factory and slaughterhouse discharges, oil spills, shipwrecks, and urban sewage as in other countries, the effects of these sources are minor compared with those of sedimentation. All major coastal towns lack sewage treatment systems, and only a small proportion of houses have adequate sanitation. Thus, town and city beaches serve as public latrines, and fecal pollution of urban shoreline areas can be an acute environmental health problem (CNRE et al. 1999). While this causes localized eutrophication, there has been no demonstrated link with biodiversity loss. In the 1990s, estimates of total land-based inputs into coastal ecosystems indicated low inputs of pollutants (with the exception of sediment from rivers), consistent with Madagascar's small population and low level of economic development at the time (Rakotoarinjanahary et al. 1994). This could potentially change rapidly. For example, supernatant wastewater discharge from the tailings facility of the Ambatovy nickel-processing plant at Toamasina contains elevated concentrations of nickel and other metals. These are discharged from an oceanic diffuser about 1 km offshore, near an estuary and a line of coral cays. Monitoring over 10 years has shown an increase in the concentration of nickel salts in bottom sediments, although to date no detrimental effect on coral reefs or fish populations has been observed (Biotope 2019).

As in most parts of the world, plastic debris is a major threat to marine biodiversity, and negative impacts of plastic pollutants been recorded in Malagasy waters in the case of marine turtles (see Walker et al., pp. 391–99) and *Rhincodon typus* (Whale Shark) (see Diamant et al., pp. 381–85). However, no systematic studies have yet been conducted in the country. To date, there has been no major oil spill or severe case of pollution from shipwrecks in Malagasy waters.

Offshore Oil and Gas Exploration

About 990,000 km^2 (54%) of Madagascar's combined land and EEZ area (1,803,782 km^2), has been identified as potentially containing exploitable petroleum reserves, mostly on the western half of the island and most of the EEZ.

There has been substantial offshore oil and gas exploration over the last 20 years along much of Madagascar's west coast, principally in the northwest, with at least 20 exploration projects using bathymetric sonar and seismic campaigns to evaluate seabed topography and petroleum prospects. Petroleum exploitation has been identified as a significant prospect for the North Mozambique Channel marine ecoregion, which is bordered by three geological provinces (including the Morondava province, corresponding to western Madagascar) and holds about 40% of the potential reserves for the Mozambique Channel, estimated at 27.6 billion barrels of oil, 441 billion cubic feet of gas, and 13.8 million barrels of liquid gas (Brownfield et al. 2012). Six maritime petroleum blocks in Madagascar's EEZ are currently attributed, mostly along the northwest coast and one offshore from Belo sur Mer (Figure 7.8).

CONSERVATION AND MANAGEMENT

Since 2003, the national and regional importance of Madagascar's marine biodiversity and the value of its multiple marine ecosystem services have come to be recognized, providing ample justification for the greatly expanded marine conservation efforts over the last 20 years. Madagascar now has considerable experience in the conservation and sustainable management of coastal resources, with the advent of community-based management of specific resources, establishment of a formal Marine Protected Area (MPA) network, as well an evolving network of locally managed marine areas (LMMAs), and the development of larger seascape approaches, as in Antongil Bay in the northeast (Figure 7.9). In many coastal and marine protected areas, conservation is being closely allied with community-based fisheries management, targeting the recovery of fast-growing species such as octopus, crab, and lobster to help

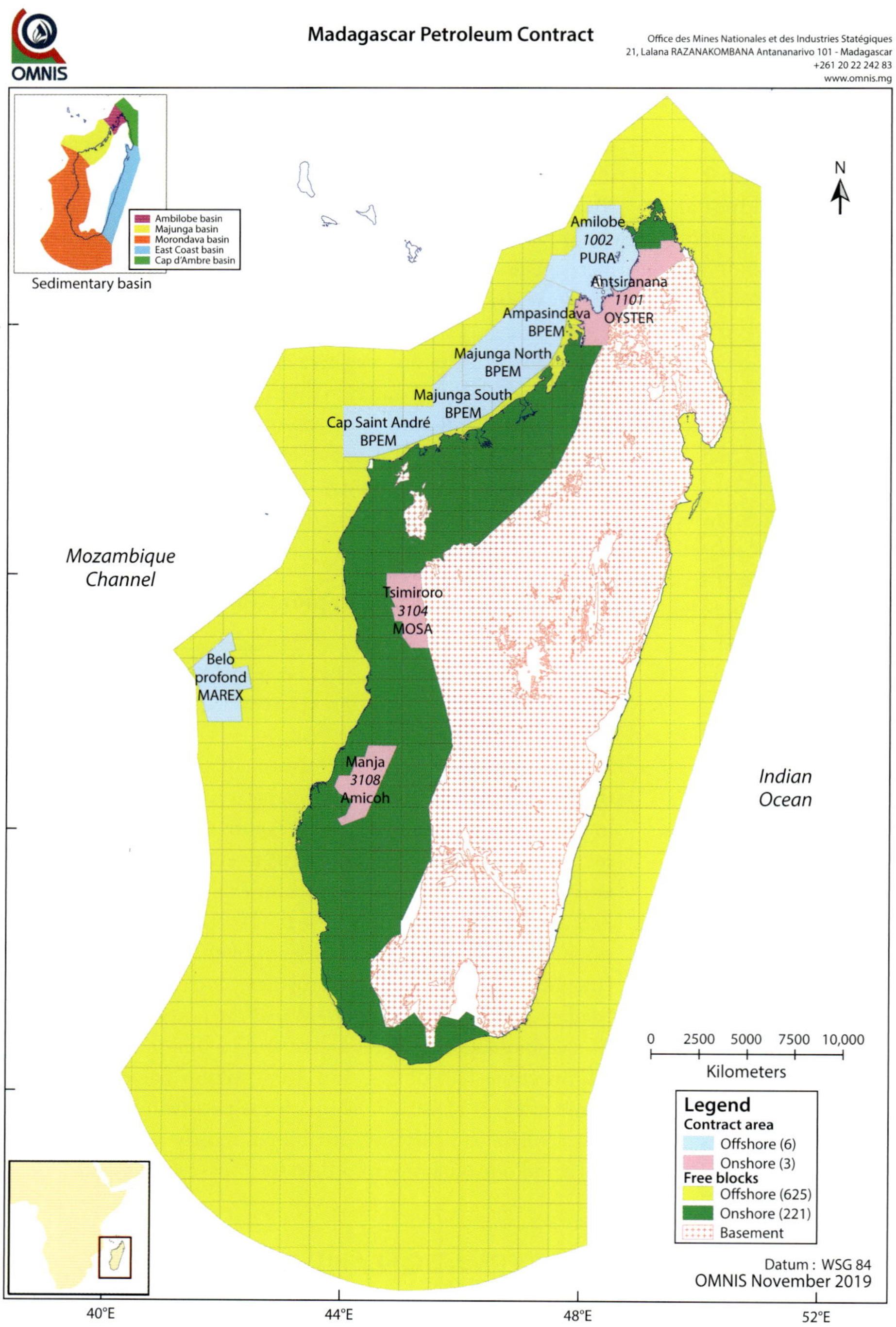

FIGURE 7.8 **Map showing the location of petroleum exploration blocks on Madagascar and in Malagasy waters that have been attributed or are available for attribution.** (SOURCE: OMNIS 2020.)

fishing-dependent communities derive meaningful livelihood benefits from resource management (Oliver et al. 2015; Long et al. 2017; Gardner et al. 2018).

Although there is national legislation to protect and sustainably manage much of the marine biodiversity of Madagascar, an ongoing issue is enforcement, compounded by lack of legal clarity in some instances, and lack of public awareness and understanding of regulations. Customary regulations that are created and enforced by local communities themselves—such as *dinas* (local legally binding conventions or bylaws) or *fady* (taboo)—can be used to manage a particular resource or to create temporary or permanent reserves. This approach tends to have greater success with compliance than enforcing national laws, but still faces challenges (Gardner et al. 2018). A *dina* is developed through a consensus-based process involving members of the community, including members of fishers' associations, who also determine the fines or sanctions to be imposed for infractions and the mechanisms for enforcement. *Dinas* can be recognized by regional courts, enabling them to have legal application (USAID 2016).

Marine Protected Areas

MPAs are the foundation of Madagascar's marine conservation efforts. The management of all protected areas in the national network, the Système des Aires Protégées de Madagascar (SAPM), is governed by the Protected Areas Management Code (COGAP,

FIGURE 7.9 **Map of Antongil Bay showing the combined presence of locally managed marine areas (LMMAs) and marine protected areas (MPAs) in a single managed seascape.** (SOURCE: WCS, unpublished data.)

Code de Gestion des Aires Protégées) (Law [Loi] 2015-005). Authority for the management of MPAs is exercised jointly by the Ministère de l'Environnement et du Développement Durable (MEDD) and the Ministère de l'Agriculture, de l'Elevage et de la Pêche (MAEP) (H. Ratsimbazafy et al. 2019); the authority for terrestrial protected areas is the MEDD alone.

In 2015, under Article 6 of the COGAP, formal recognition was given to four protected area governance types: 1) state governance, 2) shared governance (co-managed), 3) private governance, and 4) community-based governance. Two types of governance are most easily recognized in the case of MPAs (Gardner et al. 2018; H. Ratsimbazafy et al. 2019):

1. Protected areas whose management is delegated to Madagascar National Parks (MNP), formerly known as Association Nationale pour la Gestion des Aires Protégées (ANGAP). MNP is overseen by the Biodiversity Conservation/Protected Area System Directorate (DBC/SAP) within MEDD. In the case of MPAs, these may be stand-alone marine areas or a marine zone within a mixed marine and terrestrial protected area.
2. Protected areas that are governed by the COGAP but where management is delegated to other organizations, including international and national NGOs, often with the involvement of community associations (by sub-delegation).

Initially, protected area policy was oriented toward terrestrial ecosystems, given the global importance of Madagascar's unique terrestrial biodiversity and endemism. Madagascar's first marine reserve was created at Nosy Tanikely in 1968, and Nosy Antafana was created as part of the Mananara-Nord Biosphere Reserve in 1989. The National Environmental Action Plan (NEAP), which ran from 1990 to 2010, was implemented in three phases, and under the first phase the Masoala National Park was created and included three small MPAs. The second phase of NEAP included an initiative to establish APMCs (*aires protégées marines et côtières*), which resulted in a series of national network MPAs (Nosy Hara, Sahamalaza–Radama Islands, and Kirindy Mité) designed to align with an integrated coastal zone management (ICZM) approach.

The recognition of the need for greater attention to be paid to marine conservation came in 2003, at the World Parks Congress in Durban. A national pledge was made (although not formalized) at the congress, through a meeting facilitated by WWF Madagascar, to establish 1 million ha of new MPAs in Malagasy waters, and a fisheries and environment commission was subsequently set up under the Durban Initiative to identify potential sites. Under the third phase of the NEAP, a series of MPAs (Velondriake, Soariake [formerly Salary Bay], Ranobe Bay, and Nosy Androka) was established in the Toliara region with the support of WCS, WWF, African Development Bank, and Blue Ventures, designed more to address fishery concerns. During this phase of the NEAP, several coastal wetland protected areas were also established (Mahavavy Kinkony, Tsimembo–Manombolomaty, and Mangoky Ihotry).

Further impetus was provided in 2014 at the World Parks Congress in Sydney, when former president Hery Rajaonarimampianina committed to triple the area of Madagascar's MPAs by 2020 (IUCN 2014). In 2015, the COGAP was updated to include specific text for the management of MPAs, which further accelerated progress. Since then, an additional six sites have been established, bringing the total number of MPAs (i.e., sites containing at least some marine or intertidal habitat) to 24, covering 1.38 m ha of marine and intertidal habitats, or 12% of the continental shelf and 1.2% of the EEZ (Table 7.7). According to the Nairobi Convention "dashboard" (Nairobi Convention 2020), there are now 22 formal MPAs protecting 1.3% of Madagascar's EEZ (the slight difference is likely due to differences in measurement methods). In a global analysis of gaps in ocean protection, Gownaris et al. (2019) identified the Malagasy EEZ as a global priority area, where MPA coverage is still inadequate. Details of Madagascar's MPAs are provided in Table 7.7, and their locations are shown in Figure 7.10.

TABLE 7.7. **Marine and coastal protected areas by marine ecoregion (with terrestrial and marine habitat areas in hectares)**

ER	REGION	SITE NAME	TYPE (IUCN CATEGORY)	LABELS	MANAGER	YEAR	TOTAL AREA (ha)	MARINE AND INTERTIDAL (ha)	HABITATS	KEY MARINE SPECIES
N	DIANA	Nosy Hara island complex	National park (2)	IMMA	MNP	2011	125,471	122,827	Bay, islands (6), coral reefs, mangroves, seagrass, turtle nesting beach; terrestrial: karstic tsingy, dry bush	Cetaceans, *Dugong dugon*, sea eagles, sea turtles, fishes, sharks
	DIANA	Ankarea	Protected land/ seascape (5)	IMMA	WCS	2015	135,556	135,556	Coral reefs, islands, seagrass beds	Cetaceans, sea turtles, *Rhincodon typus* (Whale Shark)
	DIANA	Lokobe extension	National park (2)	IMMA	MNP	2011	862	120	Coral reefs, mangroves, seagrass beds	Cetaceans, sea turtles, *R. typus*
	DIANA	Ankivonjy	Protected land/ seascape (5)	IMMA	WCS	2015	139,410	139,410	Coral reefs, islands, mangroves, seagrass beds, coastal forest	Cetaceans, sea turtles
	DIANA	Nosy Tanikely (Nosy Be)	National park (2)	IMMA	MNP	2011	341	179	Coral reef, island, coastal forest	Cetaceans, sea turtles, *R. typus*
	SAVA	Sahamalaza–Radama Islands	National park (2)	MAB, IMMA Ramsar, IBA	MNP	2007	65,050	24,086	Coral reef, mangroves, seagrass beds, islands (4), turtle nesting beach, dry forests	Cetaceans, *D. dugon*, sea turtles
	Boeny	Mahavavy Kinkony wetlands	Protected land/ seascape (5)	IBA, IMMA	Asity	2015	302,000	18,200	Mangroves, wet and dry forests, rivers, lakes	Waterbirds
	Boeny	Baly Bay	National park (2)	IMMA IBA	MNP	1997	62,538	59,650	Bay, mangroves, dry forest	*Astrochelys yniphora* (Angonoka Tortoise), *D. dugon*, sea turtles
	DIANA	Ambodivahibe	Protected land/ seascape (5)	None	CI	2015	39,794	39,794	Coral reefs, mangroves, seagrass beds, deepwater marine (canyon)	*Bolbometopon muricatum* (Bumphead Parrotfish), *Cheilinus undulatus* (Napoleon Wrasse), sea turtles, *D. dugon*
	SAVA	Loky Manambato	Protected land/ seascape (5)	None	Fanamby	2015	250,000	15,000	Mangroves, islands, coral reefs, seagrass beds, turtle nesting	*D. dugon*, sea turtles
	SAVA	Parcs Marins de Masoala	National park (2)	IMMA	MNP	1997	230,000	13,183	Coral reefs, islands, seagrass beds and mangrove	Sea turtles
E	Analanjirofo	Mananara-Nord (Nosy Antafana)	National park (2)	Biosphere	MNP	1989	24,000	1000	Coral reefs, islands, mangrove, seagrass, forest	
S	Melaky	Cap Saint André coastal wetlands	Protected land/ seascape (5)	IBA IMMA	TPF	2015	90,110	9435	Mangroves, dry forests	Waterbirds

ER	REGION	SITE NAME	TYPE (IUCN CATEGORY)	LABELS	MANAGER	YEAR	TOTAL AREA (ha)	MARINE AND INTERTIDAL (ha)	HABITATS	KEY MARINE SPECIES
N	Melaky *continued*	Iles Barren	Protected land/ seascape (5)	Ramsar	Blue Ventures	2015	394,175	394,175	Islands (7), sea-turtle nesting, coral reefs, sandbanks, seabird nesting	Sea turtles, *D. dugon*, *Latimeria chalumnae* (Western Indian Ocean Coelacanth)
		NAP Tsimembo Manambolomaty	Protected land/ seascape (5)	Ramsar	TPF	2015	63,745	25,234	Forests, lakes, mangroves	Waterbirds
	Menabe	Menabe Antimena	Protected land/ seascape (5)	None	Fanamby	2015	210,312	16,890	Mangroves	Waterbirds
		Kirindy Mité	National park (2)	Biosphere	MNP	2015	156,350	27,910	Coral reefs, islands, mangroves, seagrass beds, coastal forest, turtle nesting	Sea turtles, *D. dugon*
	Menabe–Atsimo-Andrefana	Complexe Zones Humides Mangoky Ihotry	Protected land/ seascape (5)	IMMA	Asity	2015	426,146	9431	Mangroves	Waterbirds
	Atsimo-Andrefana	Velondriake	Protected land/ seascape (5)	IMMA	Blue Ventures	2015	173,623	109,638	Coral reefs, islands, mangroves, seagrass, coastal bush	*D. dugon*, sea turtles
		Soariake	Natural resources reserve (6)	IMMA	WCS	2015	113,070	74,777	Coral reefs, islands, mangroves, seagrass, dry coastal bush	*D. dugon*, sea turtles
		Ranobe Bay	Natural monument (3)	IMMA	WWF	2015	42,404	42,404	Coral reefs, mangroves, seagrass, dry coastal bush	Reef fishes
		Tsinjoriake	Protected landscape (5)	IMMA	GIZ	2015	5484	5484	Coral reefs, mangroves, seagrass beds	Reef fishes
		Amoron'i Onilahy	Protected landscape (5)	Ramsar	WWF	2015	100,482	4201	Estuary, mangroves	Waterbirds
		Nosy Vé Androka	National park (2)	Biosphere, IMMA, Ramsar	MNP	2015	91,445	91,445	Coral reefs, islands (2), mangroves, alkaline lake	Sea turtles, *Latimeria chalumnae*
	All regions	TOTAL PAs (ha)					3,242,368	1,380,029		
		EEZ (ha)					114,000,000	(1.21% of EEZ)		
		Continental shelf (ha)					11,700,000	(11.79% of continental shelf)		

Notes: CI, Conservation International; E, East Madagascar; EEZ, exclusive economic zones; ER, marine ecoregion; GIZ, Deutsche Gesellschaft für Internationale Zusammenarbeit; IBA, Important Bird Area; IMMA, Important Marine Mammal Area; MAB, Man and Biosphere Reserve; MNP, Madagascar National Parks; N, North Mozambique Channel; NAP, new protected area; Ramsar, Ramsar site; S, South Mozambique Channel; TPF, The Peregrine Fund; WCS, Wildlife Conservation Society; WWF, World Wide Fund for Nature.

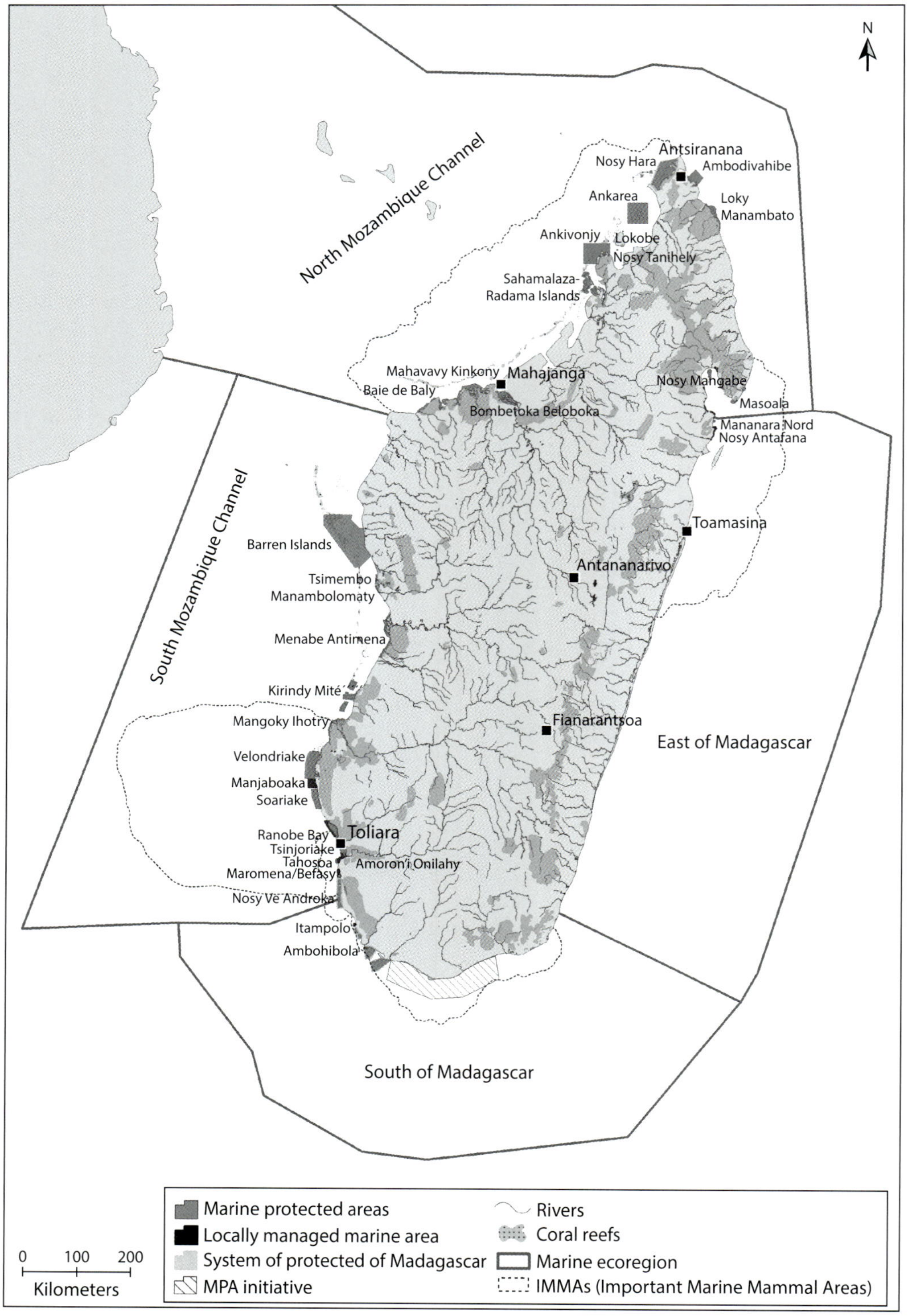

FIGURE 7.10 **Map of Madagascar's marine protected areas (MPAs) and locally managed marine areas (LMMAs).** (SOURCES: SAPM and WCS.)

Madagascar's national protected areas system is based on an ecoregional approach aimed at ensuring that all major habitat types are adequately represented. For marine and coastal environments, the four ecoregions defined by Obura (2012) are used (see Biogeography and Marine Ecoregions, above, and Figure 7.1b). Madagascar's protected area strategy for the period 2014–2024 (MNP 2014) lists the protected areas that were established or planned in each ecoregion at that time (2014), with recommendations for potential additions to the network.

North Mozambique Channel: MNP manages or co-manages five MPAs, including the three marine parks of Masoala, Nosy Hara, the Lokobe marine extension, Nosy Tanikely, Sahamalaza–Radama Islands, and Baly Bay. MPAs whose management has been delegated to other organizations (in brackets) are: Loky Manambato, including the Nosy Ankao archipelago (Fanamby), and Ambodivahibe (Conservation International) in the northeast; Ankarea, including Nosy Mitsio (WCS), Ankivonjy, including Nosy Iranja (WCS), and Mahavavy Kinkony (Asity) in the northwest. Additional MPAs may be proposed under the regional development plan for the DIANA Region.

South Mozambique Channel: MNP manages the marine extension of Kirindy Mité National Park, and the northern part of the Nosy Vé Androka Marine Park and Biosphere Reserve (the southern part lies in a different ecoregion). The MPAs managed by other organizations in this ecoregion are: Velondriake (Blue Ventures), Soariake (WCS), and Mangoky Ihotry (Asity) in the southwest; Cap Saint André coastal wetlands (Peregrine Fund), Menabe Antimena (Fanamby), and Tsimembo-Manambolomaty (Peregrine Fund) in the center; and the Barren Islands (Blue Ventures) in the northwest. A protected sanctuary for *Latimeria chalumnae* (Western Indian Ocean Coelacanth) has been recommended for the Onilahy submarine canyon at Saint Augustin near Anakao (see Bruton et al., pp. 359–67).

South Madagascar: MNP manages the southern part of Nosy Vé Androka Marine Park, within which there are community-managed octopus fishery closures. WCS is currently promoting the establishment of a new MPA for the Deep South between the Menarandra and Mandrare Rivers (WCS and Resolve 2018).

East Madagascar: MNP places Nosy Antafana Marine Park, which is part of the Mananara-Nord National Park and Biosphere Reserve, in this ecoregion (although it lies technically in the North Mozambique Channel marine ecoregion). The NGO Cetamada, via PRISM (Projet Récif Ile Sainte Marie), is currently undertaking baseline studies and monitoring in preparation for a future MPA around Ile Sainte Marie (Wickel and Nicet 2017; Damien and Loncle 2019).

At least eight of the 21 Ramsar sites in Malagasy waters contain mangrove forest. There are no marine World Heritage sites in the country, but Antongil Bay and the Deep South have both been identified as sites worthy of World Heritage status (Obura et al. 2012). Four of Madagascar's MPAs (Mananara-Nord, Sahamalaza–Radama Islands, Kirindy Mité, and Nosy Vé Androka) are designated as United Nations Educational, Scientific and Cultural Organization (UNESCO) biosphere reserves.

Community-Based Management

Decentralization of the management of renewable natural resources to local communities was a key component of the NEAP. Law 96-025 on community-based management (known as GELOSE, Gestion Locale des Ressources Naturelles Renouvelables, or Gestion Locale Sécurisée) laid the legal foundation for the transfer of management of natural resources to local communities. The legality of marine-resource management transfer was initially unclear, but the 2015 law on fisheries (see Fisheries Management, below) provides for the contractual transfer of management of aquatic resources (Transfert de Gestion des Ressources Halieutiques, or TGRH) to fishing associations or federations. For mangroves, the Gestion Contractualisée des Forêts (GCF, contractualized forest management), which is used for forests, is sometimes put in place.

A *dina* is at the heart of management transfer contracts of the GELOSE or GCF type and often serves as a first step toward a more fully formalized arrangement. Communities must be constituted by a *dina* and represented by an association appointed under the *dina* (typically called a *communauté de base*, or CoBa). The CoBa enters into a mediated contract with the state (and typically also the local commune) to manage natural resources in the area associated with the community in accordance with a management plan; the GCF is a simplified procedure that does not involve mediation by an independent chartered mediator or participation of the commune. The contract is initially for three years, can be renewed for a further 10 years based on a satisfactory performance evaluation, and is renewable thereafter.

LMMA is a term that evolved in Fiji and is now being applied in Malagasy waters to about 150 locally managed and co-managed marine areas that are supported by the MIHARI (Mitantana Harena Ranomasina avy eny Ifotony) network. LMMA is used to refer to any area that is effectively under community management, irrespective of its precise legal basis, which could include community management areas covering all or part of an MPA or of a fisheries management plan (*plan d'aménagement des pêches*, or PAP); a GELOSE, GCF, or TGRH contract; a stand-alone *dina*; or combinations of these.

NGOs and government entities have been involved in most effective LMMAs since as early as 1997 (when they were typically based on a simple *dina*), with different NGOs having established long-term commitments to particular geographic areas and communities where marine resources are in need of protection or management. Since the establishment of the first LMMAs as part of the Velondriake initiative in the southwest, there has been rapid expansion, establishment, and management supported by predominantly international NGOs and donor-funded projects (Rocliffe et al. 2014). Gardner et al. (2020) draw out some of the factors that have enabled effective conservation within Velondriake. These include the co-management approach, in which local communities receive sustained technical and financial support from a locally based NGO partner, and a diversified-funding model, where support is drawn from a range of donors, as well as local revenues from alternative livelihood activities. Velondriake's use of a combination of scientific monitoring and traditional ecological knowledge in coming to an agreement on zoning its various marine reserves has also been instrumental to building community support for management, with decision-making in the hands of the local management association. By 2017, the number of existing and initiated LMMAs, including those within existing MPAs and PAPs, had reached 149, and they covered as much as 17,500 km^2, or about 15% of the continental shelf (based on an area of 117,000 km^2; MIHARI 2017). Although the advantages of the LMMA approach are obvious and recognized on Madagascar, the lack of a clear legal definition of what constitutes an LMMA or distinguishes it from MPAs or other management areas has made it difficult to monitor them or to secure political backing. In the interim, the MIHARI network continues to lead a consultative process on the role of LMMAs and has developed a series of proposed criteria for LMMA status (Rakotondrazafy and Randriamihaja 2019).

Integrated Coastal Zone Management and the Seascape Approach

The Comité National de la Gestion Intégrée des Zones Côtières (CNGIZC), or National Committee for Integrated Coastal Zone

Management, was formally established in 2009, and modified in 2012 (Gouvernement de la République de Madagascar 2012) to promote ICZM for sustainable development. National legislation on ICZM (Decree [Décret] 2010-137) provides for the development and implementation of national and regional ICZM plans; the national blue economy policy (MRHP 2015) specifically calls for the integration of land and marine spatial planning in coastal areas, and the strategy for this is laid out in the national ICZM plan (CNGIZC 2019). Recognizing the need for regional ICZM planning, a broader ecosystem-based approach is increasingly being taken in the country, acknowledging that the effective management of individual MPAs and LMMAs requires an integrated spatial or seascape approach.

The Western Indian Ocean Marine Ecoregion (WIOMER) program of the Indian Ocean Commission (Olson 2015) has identified nine coastal seascapes in Malagasy waters of special significance with priority levels as indicated:

1. Antalaha to Mahavelona (known as the *triangle bleu* and including Masoala, Mananara-Nord, Ile Sainte Marie, and Foulpointe) (subregional)
2. Toliara - Cap Sainte Marie (part of the Deep South) (regional)
3. Morondava to Cap Saint Vincent (subregional)
4. The coast from Belo sur Tsiribihina to Cap Saint André (global)
5. The coast from Cap Saint André to the Bombetoka Bay (global)
6. The "three-bays complex" of the bays of Sakalava, Dunes, and Pigeon (subregional)
7. The coast from Cap d'Ambre to Narindra Bay (global)
8. The Mananjary eastern coast (subregional)
9. Northeast Madagascar (subregional)

These areas all have one or more MPAs or other designated sites, but few have coordinated or integrated seascape management programs. Two seascape programs are underway:

Antongil Bay: WCS has been supporting a seascape program here, and the area now includes some 16 LMMAs and three AMPs (Figure 7.9); the bay and the two terrestrial parks are now referred to as MaMaBay (Makira Natural Park–Masoala National Park–Antongil Bay). An ICZM process was first launched in Antongil Bay in 2003 (Doukakis et al. 2007). In 2014, the Antongil Bay Fisheries Co-Management Plan (ABFMP) was developed with support of WCS. In 2015, a marine sanctuary for sharks was created in the bay, and international fishing vessels were banned (USAID 2016).

Southwest Madagascar: Coordinated approaches are being facilitated with support from the MNP-led and KfW-funded project Pêche Côtière Durable, and help from several conservation organizations (including WCS, WWF, and Blue Ventures), to coordinate octopus fisheries management. Neighboring LMMA/MPA sites have been chosen in order to create a harmonized management area adjacent to MNP-protected areas (see South Madagascar in Marine Protected Areas, above) (Fishery Progress Organization 2020).

Marine ecosystems per se first received protection in 1997 when mangroves, coral reefs, and small islands were classified as "sensitive zones" under Order (Arrêté) 4355-97 (issued under the MECIE [Mise en Compatibilité des Investissements avec l'Environnement, or Environmental Compliance of Investments], Decree 92-926, and revised several times, now Decree 2004-167). This means that an environmental impact assessment (EIA) is automatically required for investment projects, including petroleum exploration, that potentially impact any of the aforementioned sensitive ecosystems. This has resulted in closer attention being paid to marine ecosystems in the environmental permitting process for investment projects (such as coastal aquaculture projects and hotels in coral-reef areas or on remote islands). In addition, legislation to revise the law on land tenure (Law 2008-013) extended the definition of natural public domain (*domaine public naturel*) to include the seabed up to the territorial limit of 12 nautical miles (22 km), including enclosed gulfs, bays, and straits, intertidal zones, and brackish waters connected to the sea, as well as estuaries and rivers. Under Decree 2008-1141, a permit is required for extraction from the *domaine public naturel* of water or materials, which could include coral, wood, sand, petroleum or seawater, thus providing some regulatory protection of coastal ecosystems from extractive activities. Given the high likelihood of discovering petroleum off northwestern Madagascar (see Offshore Oil and Gas Exploration, above), there is likely to be an urgent need for improved oil-spill contingency planning and coastal sensitivity mapping (Obura et al. 2019).

Given the global importance of Madagascar for its mangrove coverage, particular attention is being paid to this habitat. By virtue of being in the intertidal zone, mangroves are state owned, and their management falls under the mandate of multiple ministries. The Commission Nationale de Gestion Intégrée des Mangroves (CNGIM), or National Integrated Mangrove Management Commission, was created in 2015 (Gouvernement de la République de Madagascar 2015), led by MAEP and cochaired by the MEDD, to tackle barriers to mangrove conservation and governance. A key first step will be the development of a national mangrove strategy, which will be implemented through a collaborative agreement drawn up between MAEP and MEDD in 2019.

Under the Forests Law of 1995, communities have user rights to harvest timber and nontimber forest products, including mangroves. However, under the Fisheries Code of 2015 (see Fisheries Management, below), anyone who "cuts, collects, transports or sells mangrove wood without authorization" must pay between US$10,000 and 20,000 per hectare of mangrove area destroyed and/or face imprisonment of six to 12 months (Article 84). This conflict between the two pieces of legislation and the fisheries and forests jurisdictions has yet to be resolved. Customary rights of use are not affected under the Fisheries Code (Article 84.2). Anyone who violates the 10% share rule for mangrove destruction for aquaculture production, faces the same punishment (Article 139) (IUCN and Blue Ventures 2016).

Fisheries Management

The Law on Fisheries and Aquaculture (Law 2015-053) replaced Ordinance 93-022 and aims to provide a comprehensive framework for the sustainable management of the country's fisheries. The law affirms that customary use rights can be exercised in areas reserved for that purpose (Article 49), and under Article 20 special zones can be set up to preserve species; this could, for example, be used to exclude or regulate trawling in order to preserve such species. Madagascar fisheries management employs a number of classical technical management measures such as minimum mesh size, size restrictions on catch, prohibition of certain gears or fishing methods, and closed seasons, although compliance is not necessarily good. The government is establishing *plans d'aménagement des pêcheries* (PAPs) in priority areas, and has established a legal basis (Order 29211-2017) for transferring the management of fisheries resources and aquatic ecosystems to local communities, as described in Community-Based Management, above.

Regulatory and fishery improvement measures are in place and/or being planned for octopuses, shrimps, mud crabs, sea cucumbers, and lobsters, and also for fishes such as demersal fishes and tuna, although for these at present there is limited engagement and compliance. Fishery improvement plans (FIPs) are also being promoted to encourage responsible use of local marine resources, establish long-term economic benefits for communities and businesses, and facilitate access to global market spaces interested in responsibly sourced products (IUCN and Blue Ventures 2016). Fisheries management plans at the community level for species such as octopus have proved successful, and a Northwest Madagascar Shrimp FIP is being developed as a multi-partner initiative (see below). For octopuses, shrimps, and mud crabs, progress is being made.

Octopuses: In the southwest, the most important octopus fishery in the country, starting in 2004 temporary closures were established at locations determined by local communities. Results from 36 closures organized between 2004 and 2011 demonstrated octopus landings and catch per unit effort (CPUE) significantly increased in the 30 days following a closure's reopening, relative to the 30 days before closure (Oliver et al. 2015). Even after only two to three months' closure, both the size and number of octopuses harvested increased (Benbow and Harris 2011; Benbow et al. 2014). Success of the closures was enabled by the higher market price per kilogram for large octopuses (Humber et al. 2006), the comparatively rapid growth of octopuses (generating about 2 t/km^2/year, and their ability to thrive in degraded coral reef habitat (Haridon 2006).

Following this success, the same approach for enhancing octopus catches expanded to other communities across the region, and the need for coordination resulted in the creation of the Comité de Gestion de la Pêche aux Poulpes (CGP), or Octopus Fishing Management Committee, and a shared desire of this group and its stakeholders to improve the sustainability of the fishery. In 2019, an octopus FIP (Fishery Progress Organization 2020) was launched in this area, involving representatives of fishing communities, processors, and exporters (e.g., the firms Compagnie de Pêche Frigorifique de Toliara [Copefrito] and Murex) (Stop Illegal Fishing 2019). This is the first formal FIP for a small-scale octopus fishery in a low-income country. A pre-assessment against the standard for sustainable fisheries of the Marine Stewardship Council (MSC) has been undertaken and an action plan developed to align the fishery with the standard. The CGP is currently overseeing efforts to address gaps identified in the pre-assessment.

Shrimps: the Groupement des Aquaculteurs et Pêcheurs de Crevettes à Madagascar (GAPCM), or Association of Aquaculturists and Shrimp Fishers in Madagascar, has co-managed the industrial shrimp fishery with MAEP; the main issues have been regulating access to the fishery, preventing excessive bycatch, and limiting overall fishing effort. Historically, industrial trawling was banned within 2 nautical miles (3.2 km) of the shoreline. A legal exemption was established in 1971 to allow shrimp trawling, and apparently reversed in 1973 (Andrianaivojaona et al. 2020), but it is not clear whether the exemption covered trawling for fishes, which now accounts for most of the catch of shrimp trawling. As a result of an initiative by local communities and Blue Ventures, the shrimp industry agreed to a temporary no-trawl zone in 2017 in a 4300 km^2 area near the Barren Islands, but this has not been maintained. In 2020, the industrial fishery was suspended pending a new bidding process for fishing rights, which was launched in 2021, allowing trawling to resume in June 2021. The new fishing licenses provided for a 2-mile exclusion zone on the west coast, which was reduced to 0.7 mile on the east coast, although it remains unclear to what extent these were observed (GAPCM, unpublished data).

In 2003, bycatch reduction devices (BRDs) (and also turtle excluder devices, or TEDs—see Walker et al., pp. 391–99) were introduced through an initiative promoted by WWF, which had some effect in reducing bycatch and turtle mortality. All trawlers were fitted with TEDs in 2006 (Randriarilala et al. 2008) and are still used today according to GAPCM (GAPCM, unpublished data). However, compliance with the requirement to fit BRDs (see Pressures on Marine Biodiversity, above) has not been enforced. With declining shrimp stocks, fishes became an economically important part of the catch, and fishing companies became disinclined to use BRDs or use them correctly (Razafindrainibe 2010).

A Northwest Madagascar Shrimp FIP is being developed as a multi-partner initiative, including government agencies, local and international NGOs, and the fishing community, with the aim of certifying the shallow-water shrimp fishery under the MSC (FAO 2020). Following inconclusive pre-assessments in 2003 and 2009, the certification process for the shallow-water shrimp fishery was initiated again in 2017, through a partnership between the Ministère des Ressources Halieutiques et de la Pêche (MRHP), the fishing industry, and WWF. An evaluation of the industrial shrimp fishery and a systematic survey and description of the small-scale shrimp fishery were undertaken in 2019 as first steps in the process (UQAR-ISMER and Resolve 2019).

Mud crabs: In 2006, a management system for the mud crab fishery was established, with a ban on catching, collecting, transporting, processing, and sale/export of crabs with a shell width under 10 cm, as well as a ban on harvesting soft-shell (molting) crabs and gravid female crabs (Order 16365-2006). However, this was not fully implemented, and the order banning exploitation of soft and gravid crabs was revoked in 2014 by Order 32099-2014. In the same year, the minimum size was extended to 11 cm by Order 37206-2014, and limits for mud crab harvests and exports were set respectively at 5000 t and 4250 t, but with no regulatory measures or enforcement. National temporary closures were put in place in 2014 (Order 25830-2014) and 2016 (Order 14096-2016), but these were suspended in 2017 by the fisheries ministry. Following regional consultations in crab production areas, a national mud crab workshop in 2018 (MRHP and MIHARI 2018) recommended a two-month closure (September to October 2019), strict application of size limits, a fixed sustainable production limit, stock evaluation, mangrove restoration, and establishment of LMMAs. The minimum size limit was further revised to 12 cm after the results of the two-month closure research experiment were known. In the light of the uncontrolled expansion of the mud crab fishery, a much stronger management system needs to be put in place (MRHP and MIHARI 2018). Local management has focused on periodic site-based closures for crabs with varying levels of success (S. Rocliffe et al., unpublished data).

Mariculture

Mariculture in Malagasy waters did not become established until the 1990s. By 2011, other than penaeid shrimp farming, most mariculture was still at the pilot phase, despite suitable natural conditions and technically successful results (e.g., with oysters, milkfishes, or brine shrimps [*Artemia* spp.]), largely owing to economic isolation, insufficient training, and degraded road infrastructure (Iltis and Ranaivoson 2011). In 2012, the Polyaquaculture Research Unit (PRU) project was initiated (B. Pascal et al. 2013), aimed at improving sea-cucumber and seaweed farming, as well as investigating the feasibility of other aquaculture initiatives, such as coral aquaculture, and potential integration into communities (Todinanahary et al. 2017). Improvements in efficiency, competition, and the terms of contracts for aquaculture could increase profits both for communities and for the private sector (USAID 2016).

Industrial shrimp farming for *Penaeus monodon* started in the early 1990s and has received regular financial, technical, and infrastructure support from foreign investors. Annual production exceeded 8000 t between 2006 and 2008 but collapsed to 3000 t in 2009 as a result of a combination of increased international competition, declining shrimp prices, and rising costs of energy and fishmeal (Iltis and Ranaivoson 2011). Production has since recovered. Pond farming takes place behind mangrove areas along the northwest coast. While the use of open mudflats not colonized by mangroves helps to avoid direct deforestation, mangroves have come under threat through erosion, siltation, and related effects from ponds constructed on salt flats. More recently, small-scale shrimp farming has been promoted by NGOs (G. Robinson and Pascal 2011). An aquaculture plan, which includes protocols for identifying appropriate culture sites and biosecurity, guides the development of the sector and promotes small-scale commercial and family-based shrimp culture (Shipton and Hecht 2007). WWF and Blue Ventures have established partnerships with UNIMA, a private shrimp fishing and farming company whose facilities in northwest Madagascar recently became the first in Africa to receive Aquaculture Stewardship Council certification.

Seaweed (*Eucheuma* spp. and *Kappaphyccus alvarezii*) harvesting commenced in the late 1980s. Seaweed farming was introduced after 1998 and is today the second-largest contributor to mariculture production in terms of income after shrimp. Significant projects were established in the southwest (at Salary Bay) and in the northeast near Cap Est, Antalaha, and at Nosy Ankao, where it proved popular particularly with women. The northeastern operations have since closed down, and production persists only in the southwest. Copefrito, in partnership with Blue Ventures and IHSM, supported over 400 seaweed farmers along 200 km of coast, and now exports products to Europe (I. Eeckhaut, unpublished data). Culture of the blue-green "alga" *Spirulina* (a form of filamentous cyanobacteria) was trialed in saline coastal ponds in the southwest in the early 1990s. At least seven private operators were once involved in this activity, but now there are just two or three producers supplying a local and export market for dried spirulina powder.

Sea-cucumber culture, specifically of *Holothuria scabra*, started in 1999 in a partnership between the government and universities in Belgium (Eeckhaut et al. 2008). A hatchery, nursery site, and offshore cages were established south of Toliara to produce juveniles and grow them to commercial size (Iltis and Ranaivoson 2011). Subsequently, community-based sea-cucumber farming for export was initiated with the support of NGOs and the private sector, with the aim of reducing fishing pressure on wild populations (Rasolofonirina et al. 2004). Farms are mostly on the southwest coast, and have expanded since 2010, with production in weight (for export) and income rising steadily (Klückow 2020), although a temporary interruption was caused by Cyclone Haruna in 2013. Operators have identified the potential for combined seaweed and sea-cucumber farming by the communities and are promoting a polyaquaculture approach (B. Pascal et al. 2013; F. Pascal 2019).

A feasibility study of coral farming for the export trade has been undertaken with the species *Acropora nasuta* and *Seriatopora caliendrum* (Todinanahary et al. 2017), but commercial coral culture is not yet underway.

Marine Wildlife Protection

Some 55 marine vertebrates, 12 seabirds, and eight invertebrate species occurring in Malagasy waters are listed in one or more international wildlife conventions ratified by Madagascar or are listed by IUCN as threatened (A. Cooke and Brand 2012). However, only five marine species (all sea turtles) are explicitly protected under domestic wildlife legislation (under Decree 2006-400). In part, this is mitigated by the practice in Madagascar of applying certain international conventions (notably the Convention on International Trade in Endangered Species of Wild Fauna and Flora, or CITES) without implementing legislation, but there is an incomplete and uncertain degree of protection for many threatened marine species.

Old legislation, such as the fisheries decree of 1922, Decree 61-096, under Ordinance 60-126) on protected fauna and the 1966 Code Maritime and Decree 88-243 (an amendment to the protected fauna list), provided for regulation of exploitation of many marine species, including whales, *Dugong dugon*, turtles, lobsters, pearl oysters, ornamental shells, shells for button making, sponges, edible oysters, sea cucumbers, and algae. However, these laws have been superseded by more recent legislation (Humber et al. 2015). Decree 2006-400 on wildlife protection under Ordinance 60-126 revised the list of protected species, but neglected to list *D. dugon* or other marine mammals. The 2015 Fisheries Code (see Fisheries Management, above) applies protection to all marine species that are protected under other extant regulations. However, fishes are not included under any of the protected species legislation, and thus threatened fish species such as *Latimeria chalumnae* (Western Indian Ocean Coelacanth), *Rhincodon typus* (Whale Shark), and other sharks and rays are specifically not protected.

About 57 marine species or higher taxonomic groupings that occur in Malagasy waters are currently listed on CITES (A. Cooke and Brand 2012). Ordinance 75-014 of 1975 implements CITES, and subsequent decrees (Decrees 77-246 of 1977 and 83-108 of 1983) implement CITES Appendixes I, II, and III. As described elsewhere in this chapter, many CITES-listed marine species are still exported, such as sea turtles, teleost fishes, elasmobranchs (sharks and rays), and a range of invertebrates, including black corals (Antipatharia), hard corals (Sclearactinia), giant clams (Tridacnidae), conches (Megagastropoda), *Charonia tritonis* (Triton Trumpet Shell), commercial trochus shells (*Trochus niloticus*), pearl oysters (*Pinctada* spp.), and *Birgus latro* (Coconut Crab) (A. Cooke and Brand 2012; Todinanahary et al. 2016). This is due to the lack of enforcement but also to the fact that not all CITES-listed species have been included correctly in the national implementing legislation. *Dugong dugon*, cetaceans, and sea turtles have all been listed as Appendix I species in the national legislation, but *Latimeria chalumnae* is still listed as an Appendix II species (Decree 77-276 of 1977), and CITES-listed mollusks and hard corals are absent from domestic implementing texts.

Climate Change Adaptation and Mitigation

Madagascar's National Climate Change Policy of 2010 (Politique nationale de la lutte contre le changement climatique; MEEF 2010) highlights coastal zones as particularly vulnerable to climate change, and mentions the need to explore climate finance options at all levels, including voluntary carbon markets and REDD+ (Reducing Emissions from Deforestation and Forest Degradation). The importance of mangroves for flood and erosion control had already been recognized in the 2006 National Action Program for Adaptation to Climate Change (Programme d'Action National d'Adaptation au changement climatique, PANA). MPA programs, if appropriately undertaken, can help to integrate community climate change resilience into conservation planning, and potential for this has been studied in Malagasy waters (Obura 2009; Clausen et al. 2010).

The national ICZM action plan 2019–2023 identifies climate change impacts and the need for adaptation and mitigation measures and includes the integration of climate change adaptation and mitigation into national and regional ICZM planning. Restoration of mangroves and coral reefs and strengthening community resilience are identified as potential mitigation and adaptation actions (CNGIZC 2019). Madagascar's intended nationally determined contribution (INDC) for the United Nations Framework Convention on Climate Change (UNFCCC) makes specific reference to the dual roles of forest and biodiversity for ecosystem-based adaptation and mitigation and identifies mangroves as a key element for ecosystem-based adaptation. The restoration of 35,000 ha of primary forest and mangroves (see Mangrove and Coral Reef Restoration, below) was among the priority actions for 2020, with the aim of reaching 45,000–55,000 ha by 2030.

Blue carbon is the carbon stored or released by human activities from mangroves, salt marshes, and seagrasses. There is potential to transform these substantial carbon stocks into sustainable funding for coastal communities through the selling of carbon credits in international carbon markets, which in turn helps mitigate ongoing degradation and deforestation (see Grinand and Nourtier, pp. 105–13). Community initiatives are being set up to use carbon credits to finance mangrove conservation activities. With the support of Blue Ventures, the project Tahiry Honko (which means "preserving mangroves") has been established in the Velondriake seascape to develop a payment-for-ecosystem-services (PES) scheme to incentivize community-led mangrove conservation (Rakotomahazo et al. 2019). Activities include preventing mangrove conversion and restoring 1300 ha of mangrove forest surrounding Baie des Assassins. The carbon credits have been validated under the Plan Vivo Standard scheme. A similar initiative is being developed in Tsimipaika Bay, DIANA Region (Arias-Ortiz et al. 2020), using Verra's Verified Carbon Standard (VCS) and the Climate, Community and Biodiversity Alliance standard (CCBA). Carbon stock assessments were carried out, and management plans have been developed for an area of about 10,500 ha of mangroves.

Mangrove and Coral Reef Restoration

Active restoration is considered an important management intervention for mangroves, which are listed among the priorities in Madagascar's national landscape restoration strategy (MEEF 2017). Under the African Forest Landscape Restoration Initiative (AFR100), a country-led effort to restore 100 million ha of deforested and degraded landscapes across Africa by 2030, Madagascar has committed to restore 4 million ha of forest, including mangroves, although no specific target has been set for mangroves. Multiple stakeholders are contributing to mangrove replanting efforts, with local communities playing a key role through participatory mapping to identify degraded mangrove areas, organizing and leading the replanting work, and subsequent monitoring. Nursery culture is required for large replanting efforts of nonviviparous species (*Avicennia marina*, *Xylocarpus granatum*, *Sonneratia alba*). Although culture is possible for *Ceriops tagal*, *Rhizophora mucronata*, and *Bruguiera gymnorhiza*, it is not usually necessary as, for these species, the propagules can be collected immediately before planting. In most parts of Madagascar, the best time for planting mangroves is from October to April (the rainy season), when the propagules are abundant and mature. Planting takes place at low tide and at the beginning of the spring tide to ensure that the propagules are submerged twice daily for several days. Replanting seedlings from nurseries is feasible throughout the year, but it is better to do this during the rainy season to ensure a higher success rate.

Reef Doctor is trialing and implementing a coral reef restoration program in Ranobe Bay with volunteers, using the two-step restoration protocol known as coral gardening. Coral nurseries have been established in the Rose Garden Marine Reserve to grow coral fragments to sizes suitable for transplantation, which may take up to a year. Nursery-grown coral colonies are then transplanted onto degraded reef sites either directly or via simple artificial reef structures to stimulate natural regeneration and recovery, and to restore habitat complexity (Reef Doctor 2020).

Tourism Management

At present, there is comparatively little need for tourism management, and most efforts have been in the form of codes of conduct. In 2016, the Madagascar Whale Shark Project (MWSP) introduced a code of conduct, developed with the Mozambican-based

Marine Megafauna Foundation, aimed at regulating interactions between operators, tourists, and Whale Sharks (*Rhincodon typus*) in the waters off Nosy Be (see Diamant et al., pp. 381–85). In 2018, a request to add the code of conduct to a regulation restricting interactions with marine megafauna was submitted to the Ministère du Tourisme (Ministry of Tourism). Local empowerment of guides and operators through educational workshops so far has been successful, but further support is needed to reach more operators. Through collaboration with local NGO MADA Megafauna and the Marine Megafauna Foundation, the MWSP has initiated a school program for children on Nosy Be, and a popular movement called Les Gardiens des Océans was established, involving the youth of Nosy Be in a range of activities. The impact of divers on the reefs at Nosy Tanikely was addressed in the first management plan for the MPA (C. Webster 2008). Preparations are now afoot to develop one or more MPAs at Ile Sainte Marie to conserve the reefs and establish a baseline in order to better regulate such tourism activities (Wickel and Nicet 2017).

Blue Economy Policy Brief

Madagascar's blue economy policy brief for the fisheries and aquaculture sectors was adopted in 2015 (MRHP 2015) for a period of 10 years. The policy brief takes a coordinated, integrated, and ecosystem-oriented approach to sustainable wealth creation from the work of fishers and aquaculture producers, while taking account of the ecological well-being of marine living resources. It recognizes the Malagasy environmental code, protected areas code, land tenure reform, and food security policies, as well as the major productive marine and coastal ecosystems, including mangroves and coral reefs, the importance of small-scale marine fisheries, and the overexploitation of a number of stocks.

The policy brief underlines the primacy of the precautionary principle, the need for transparency, subsidiarity, and participation in management, including locally based management through transfer and concerted plans. The specific strategic measures of the blue economy brief include promoting aquaculture, evaluating overexploited stocks and priority value chains, elaborating management plans according to the ecosystem approach, promoting co-management, preserving sensitive aquatic ecosystems according to an integrated landscape/seascape approach, and promoting marine and freshwater protected areas.

CONCLUSION

The first two decades of the 21st century have seen a massive expansion of knowledge of the marine and coastal biodiversity of Madagascar, with development of a marine ecoregional classification that helps to structure conservation planning and seascape management. Madagascar is now widely recognized as a regional center for marine biodiversity and large-scale ecosystem processes. It has more extensive and diverse coral reefs than any other western Indian Ocean nation and one of the largest areas of mangroves. The characteristics of Madagascar's coral reefs will help to build an understanding of the regional effects of climate change on coral reefs and of the determinants of resilience. Knowledge of, and conservation efforts for, the marine megafauna, as described in other parts of this chapter, has also greatly increased, with the discovery of a new population of *Balaenoptera omurai* (Omura's Whale), confirmed sightings of *Dugong dugon* (Dugong), and regional cooperation in research and conservation of sea turtles, which has greatly improved knowledge of Malagasy turtle populations. Surveys and expeditions conducted since the precursor version of this book have shown that populations of some of the iconic large fish species—including *Bolbometopon muricatum* (Bumphead Parrotfish), considered Vulnerable by IUCN; *Cheilinus undulates* (Napoleon Wrasse), considered Endangered by IUCN; and many sharks and rays, including sawfishes—still occur in Malagasy waters, along with a resident population of *Latimeria chalumnae* (Western Indian Ocean Coelacanth).

The past 20 years have inevitably seen an increase in the pressures on Madagascar's marine biodiversity, particularly from sedimentation from rivers and industrial fishing. There has, nevertheless, been a major effort to understand, stabilize, and reverse these pressures in a coordinated manner, with collaboration emerging between government, communities, the private sector, the conservation movement, land-use planners, and other sectors. The area covered by formal MPAs and LMMAs has increased over 100-fold since 2003, and there is now recognition of the need for effective and equitable management of fisheries and coastal resources, and the ICZM approach. Community-based management, particularly through the establishment of LMMAs and village-based aquaculture, is fully endorsed and supported as the best way to provide sustainable benefits and food security for coastal populations and the national economy, while protecting marine biodiversity. The need for a national framework for fisheries management has also been recognized, with new fisheries legislation in place and initiatives underway to develop PAPs and fisheries improvement projects for several taxonomic groups. However, Madagascar's wildlife laws need revision to protect key threatened marine species, including *Dugong dugon*, sawfishes, *Latimeria chalumnae*, and *Rhincodon typus*. Building the resilience of marine and coastal biodiversity to climate change remains a major challenge, but encouraging work is underway through the blue carbon initiatives recently started.

There is still a critical need for better knowledge and understanding of marine and coastal ecosystem processes, and for better access to information and technical capacity to devise management solutions. With these and other measures, there is every reason to hope and strive for a sustainable future for Madagascar's marine and coastal ecosystems and the communities who generate livelihoods, food, and other benefits from these valuable and fragile ecosystems.

SYSTEMATIC ACCOUNTS

LATIMERIA CHALUMNAE, WESTERN INDIAN OCEAN COELACANTH, *FIANDOLO*

M. Bruton, A. Cooke, M. Ravoloharinjara, Toany, and C. Ravelo

When a living coelacanth was caught off the coast of South Africa near East London in December 1938 it caused an international sensation. Coelacanths were previously known only from the fossil record, and the group was thought to have gone extinct with the dinosaurs during the Cretaceous, some 65 million years ago. The Rhodes University scientist J.L.B. Smith named the new species *Latimeria chalumnae* (J. Smith 1939a, 1939b), after Marjorie Courtenay-Latimer, a museum scientist, and the Chalumna River, off which the specimen was caught. Smith predicted based on anatomy that the specimen was a stray from warmer rocky reefs in the western Indian Ocean. Over the next 14 years, Smith and his wife, Margaret, scoured the coasts of Mozambique, Tanzania, and Kenya looking for coelacanths, while also collecting other fishes (Bruton 2018). Their searches were confined to the African mainland coast and nearby islands (and later to the Seychelles); they did not explore Madagascar or the Comoros.

In December 1952, a second modern specimen was caught by a traditional fisherman off Anjouan (Nzwani) in the Comoros (J. Smith 1953). This catch appeared to confirm Smith's hunch, and, in one of the most remarkable episodes in ichthyology, he rushed to fetch the specimen from the Comoros in a South African military airplane (J. Smith 1956; Bruton 2018). The French government, which at that time exercised colonial authority over the Comoros (and Madagascar), was piqued at Smith's "fishjacking," and banned research on *Latimeria chalumnae* (and other fishes) by foreign scientists in the Comoros; this ban lasted until the Comoros (excluding Mayotte) declared independence from France in 1975. A third *L. chalumnae* was caught off Mutsamudu (Anjouan) in September 1953, and a further six individuals off Grande Comore or Anjouan in 1954 (Bruton and Coutouvidis 1991; Nulens et al. 2011). All these specimens, except one (which was lost), as well as the next 15, all obtained in the Comoros, were acquired by French scientists and initially lodged in French museums.

The third specimen was transported to the Tsimbazaza Museum in Antananarivo, where it was examined by Jacques Millot (see Andriamialisoa and Langrand, pp. 1–38, for details on Millot) and is currently on display at the Mention Zoologie et Biodiversité Animale, Université d'Antananarivo (which has adopted *L. chalumnae* as its emblem). Millot published a description of the specimen (Millot 1954), and subsequently was the first scientist to examine a living coelacanth, which he briefly observed in November 1954 off Mutsamudu (Millot 1955).

COELACANTH TAXONOMY AND PALEONTOLOGY

The word *coelacanth* means "hollow spine" and is derived from one of the diagnostic features of the genus *Coelacanthus*, which has hollow spines in the tail. Coelacanths are classified with the lungfishes (and four groups of extinct fishes) in the subclass Sarcopterygii, which gave rise to the tetrapods, and are therefore, with the lungfishes, more closely related to amphibians than to bony fishes from a cladistic perspective. They are classified in the superorder Crossopterygii together with numerous extinct lobe-finned fishes, in the order Coelacanthiformes, which includes four families, three of which are extinct (M. Smith and Heemstra 1986), and in the suborder Latimerioidea, which includes the families Latimeriidae, to which *Latimeria* belongs, and Mawsoniidae (now extinct).

Fossils of extinct coelacanths have been known from Madagascar for over 100 years. *Coelacanthus madagascariense* was described from the island in 1910, *Whiteia woodwardi* and *W. tuberculatae* in 1935, and *Piveteauia madagascariensis* in 1952, all from Lower Triassic deposits of the Sakamena basin in the southwest (Cloutier and Forey 1991), which are marine deposits of the Mediterranean type that are now located about 80–150 km inland (Radelli 1975).

The family Latimeriidae also includes the Indonesian Coelacanth, *L. menadoensis*, first discovered off North Sulawesi, Indonesia, in September 1997 (Erdmann 1999; Pouyaud et al. 1999). The most recent relatives of *Latimeria* are species in the extinct genus *Macropoma*, also members of the family Latimeriidae (Cloutier 1991; Forey 1991). The estimated time of divergence between *L. chalumnae* and *L. menadoensis* is 40–30 million years ago (Mya). This is consistent with the hypothesis that the collision between India and the Eurasian subcontinent about 50 Mya created a habitat disjunction, allowing coelacanth populations on either side to diverge (Inoue et al. 2005).

COELACANTH INVENTORY

Since 1972, an inventory of all coelacanth specimens known to science has been compiled in an internationally collaborative effort, culminating in the syntheses produced by Bruton and Coutouvidis (1991) and Nulens et al. (2011, with annual updates). Madagascar has already been a significant contributor to this inventory, which

TABLE 7.8. **Information on the *Latimeria chalumnae* specimens known to science captured in Malagasy waters between 1987 and 2019**

NUMBER	CCC NUMBER	DATE OF CAPTURE	SITE OF CAPTURE	DISTANCE FROM SHORE (km)	DEPTH OF CAPTURE (m)	WEIGHT (kg)	LENGTH (cm)	SEX	NUMBER OF EGGS	NUMBER OF PUPS	FISHING GEAR	CURRENT HOLDING
1	300	1987	Saint Augustin	Nd	Nd	30–35	121	M	–	–	Nd	MCSN
2	173	5 August 1995	Off mouth of Onilahy River	4–9	<190	34.98	134	M	–	–	*Jarifa*	IHSM
3	176	6 December 1997	Off mouth of Onilahy River	2–3	60	90	190	F	13	–	*Jarifa*	Tolagnaro town hall
4	177	3 March 2001	Fiherenamasay	3–4	100	75	160	F	9	–	Nd	IHSM
5	179	21 July 2001	Tsiandamba	5–6	>100	73	160	F	4	2	*Jarifa*	IHSM
6	205	18 May 2006	Nosy Lava	Nd	140	Nd	171	Nd	–	–	Nd	IHSM
7	231	18 February 2009	Fiherenamasay	Nd	200	Nd	Nd	Nd	–	–	*Jarifa*	IHSM
8	232	July 2002	Toliara	Nd	Nd	35	150	Nd	–	–	*Jarifa*	Not kept
9	244	20 September 2008	Cap Sainte Marie	80	Nd	40	150	Nd	–	–	*Jarifa*	Copefrito
10	245	April 2008	Maintirano	Nd	Nd	Nd	Nd	Nd	–	–	Nd	Not kept
11	251	22–29 March 2008	Fiherenamasay	Nd	120	80	180	F	2	–	*Jarifa*	IHSM
12	252	12 July 2005	Fiherenamasay	Nd	Nd	60.3	155	F	2	–	Nd	Not kept
13	284	22–23 September 2010	West of Nosy Vé	>2	>150	85	187	F	–	–	*Jarifa*	IHSM
14	285	22 November 2010	West of Nosy Vé	1–2	250	41	134	M	–	–	Nd	IHSM
15	310	April 2011	Onilahy canyon	Nd	>300	Nd	Nd	Nd	–	–	Nd	Not kept
16	288	May 2010	West of Nosy Vé	>1	150	Nd	Nd	F	–	–	*Jarifa*	Not kept
17	289	10 February 2011	West of Nosy Vé	20	200	80	175	F	–	–	*Jarifa*	IHSM
18	290	11 February 2011	West of Nosy Vé	2	200–300	60	149	F	–	–	*Jarifa*	IHSM
19	291	13 February 2011	Northwest of Sarodrano	7	200–300	75	170	F	–	–	*Jarifa*	Copefrito
20	292	12 March 2011	Northwest of Sarodrano	3	200–300	75.2	182	F	–	–	*Jarifa*	Copefrito
21	293	21 May 2011	West of Nosy Vé	2	150–200	29.45	130	M	–	–	*Jarifa*	Copefrito
22	294	2 July 2011	Andanora	7	150–200	84.64	170	F	–	–	*Jarifa*	Copefrito
23	295	3 August 2011	West of Nosy Vé	2	150–200	32	140	F	–	–	*Jarifa*	Murex
24	296	25 August 2011	West of Nosy Vé	2	150–200	62	170	F	–	–	*Jarifa*	Not kept
25	297	January 2012	Saint Augustin	Nd	Nd	Nd	Nd	Nd	–	–	*Jarifa*	MNHN

NUMBER	CCC NUMBER	DATE OF CAPTURE	SITE OF CAPTURE	DISTANCE FROM SHORE (km)	DEPTH OF CAPTURE (m)	WEIGHT (kg)	LENGTH (cm)	SEX	NUMBER OF EGGS	NUMBER OF PUPS	FISHING GEAR	CURRENT HOLDING
26	311	31 May 2012	Fiherenamasay	Nd	100–200	36	Nd	F	–	–	*Jarifa*	Not kept
27	298	July 2012	Toliara	Nd	Nd	Nd	"Very large"	F	–	–	*Jarifa*	Not kept
28	312	2012	Maintirano	Nd	100–200	36	Nd	Nd	–	–	Nd	IHSM
29	301	February 2013	Ambanilia	6	500	35	130	M	–	–	*Jarifa*	Eden
30	313	February 2013	Saint Augustin	Nd	Nd	35–50	150	Nd	–	–	Nd	Not kept
31	314	2015	Anakao	Nd	Nd	Nd	Nd	Nd	–	–	Nd	Jardin
32	315	11 June 2011	Toliara region	Nd	Nd	Nd	Nd	Nd	–	–	Nd	DRAEP
33	316	23 March 2019	Barnhill Point	0.8–1	200	79	150	F	–	–	*Jarifa*	DRAEP
34	317	13 May 2010	West of Nosy Vé	Nd	Nd	Nd	Nd	Nd	–	–	*Jarifa*	Not kept

Sources: Bruton and Coutouvidis (1991), Heemstra et al. (1996), Vincente (1997), Anonymous (2005), Niaina (2006), Nulens et al. (2011), Houssen (2012), Insacco et al. (2016), Ravololoharinjara (2019), and unpublished data as indicated in the text. Additional information on these specimens is given in the text.

Notes: CCC, Conseil pour la Conservation du Coelacanthe specimen number; Nd, no data; *jarifa*, large-mesh gillnet laid for sharks. Current holding: Copefrito, commercial fishing company, Toliara; DRAEP, Direction Régionale de l'Agriculture, de l'Elevage et de la Pêche, Toliara; Eden, Eden Ecolodge, Sarodrano; IHSM, Institut Halieutique et des Sciences Marines, Université de Toliara; Jardin, Jardin de Mer, Toliara; MCSN, Museo Civico di Storia Naturale, Comiso, Italy; MNHN, Muséum National d'Histoire Naturelle, Paris, France; Murex, commercial fishing company, Toliar.

has been updated during the preparation of A. Cooke et al. (2021) and this contribution. By May 2020, the inventory included 330 specimens from all known localities, including *L. menadoensis* in Indonesia. Specimens in the inventory are allocated a Coelacanth Conservation Council (Conseil pour la Conservation du Coelacanthe, CCC) number, and the inventory records other details when available.

COELACANTHS IN MALAGASY WATERS

Discovery

In his book *Old Fourlegs: The Story of the Coelacanth*, J. L. B. Smith predicted that coelacanths live off Madagascar, writing "there must be stretches of coast there that no enlightened scientific eye has ever seen," and even speculated that local people "feasting unsuspected on succulent coelacanth steaks on a Madagascan shore did not seem too fantastic" (J. Smith 1956: 66). When Hans Fricke first searched for the fish in 1969 in the western Indian Ocean, he chose to dive off Nosy Iranja, a small island off the northwest coast of Madagascar near Nosy Be (H. Fricke, unpublished data). Although he dived with scuba tanks to a depth of 85 m, he found no coelacanths and would later focus his research on coelacanths in the Comoros using submersibles.

Although *L. chalumnae* may have been caught earlier by traditional fishers off Madagascar, at least since the arrival of large-mesh gillnets for shark fishing in the 1980s, the first specimen caught off the island known to Western scientists until recently (CCC 173, see Table 7.8) was landed off Saint Augustin, south of Toliara, on 5 August 1995 (Heemstra et al. 1996). Our recent investigations uncovered an earlier specimen (CCC 300) caught in 1987 off Anakao and now on display in the Museo Civico di Storia Naturale in Comiso, Italy (Insacco et al. 2016; A. Cooke et al. 2021; Figure 7.11). Since then at least 32 additional specimens have been caught off Madagascar, although some have not been preserved (Ravololoharinjara 2019), and there is anecdotal evidence for at least a dozen more catches locally (F. Ratisfandrihamanana, unpublished data). The Western Indian Ocean Coelacanth has been caught frequently enough in Malagasy waters to have acquired a local name—*fiandolo*, or "ghost fish."

Heemstra et al. (1996) suggested that the 1995 specimen caught off Madagascar was most likely a stray from the Comoros, backing this up by a presumed lack of suitable habitat, Malagasy fishers' lack of local knowledge of the coelacanth, and the genetic similarity of the pups with the Comoros population. A. Cooke et al. (2003a) questioned this hypothesis because the steep slopes of the Onilahy submarine canyon would, in fact, provide ideal habitat, and because of the much greater geological age of Madagascar than the Comoros. Indeed, we propose that *L. chalumnae* populations off Madagascar are ancestral to those in the Comoros. Further, as mentioned above, there is fossil evidence of the coelacanth lineage in Triassic deposits of southwestern Madagascar.

Ramsay and Miller (2006) have suggested an alternate location for the founder population of Western Indian Ocean Coelacanths—the 222 km stretch of coast between Porto Amelie in the south northward to Olumbe in northern Mozambique, where

FIGURE 7.11 The first coelacanth from Madagascar known to science (CCC 300), caught in 1987 in Saint Augustin Bay and now on display in the Museo Civico di Storia Naturale in Coviso, Italy. (PHOTO by G. Insacco.)

satellite imagery has revealed a high density of submarine canyons, which have not been investigated by divers or submersibles. However, the evidence from Madagascar suggests that coelacanths are not restricted to canyons (A. Cooke et al. 2021) and we support Green et al. (2009) in predicting that *L. chalumnae* is likely to occur around the whole coast of Madagascar, and that, with its 5000+ km coastline, Madagascar is likely to harbor the largest populations of coelacanths in the western Indian Ocean.

Distribution

Our knowledge of coelacanth distribution, habitat preferences, and abundance in Malagasy waters has been derived from fishes caught by artisanal fishers, as no structured scientific survey has thus far been conducted. A total of 34 coelacanths have been caught off Madagascar and brought to the attention of scientists between 1987 and 2020 (Table 7.8), although many others have undoubtedly been caught by fishers and gone unrecorded.

One fisherman, Tine Hoe Julien, resident at Lovokampy, caught seven specimens in total off Nosy Vé, Sarodrano, and Andanora between May 2010 and July 2011. Another successful coelacanth fisher is Mr. Tinard from Lovokampy. In 2010, he and his team were reported to have caught "dozens of coelacanths in a single week, but they were all consumed." (Ravololoharinjara 2019). Furthermore, one of the authors (Toany) recalls a coelacanth captured at Fiherenamasay in 2008 or 2009 being brought to Toliara and acquired by a local artisan. None of these specimens was documented or preserved. In October 2008, a commercial fishing vessel, *El Amine*, which was arrested by the Centre de Surveillance des Pêches following a tip-off from the coast guard, was escorted to Toliara, where it was reported to have caught over 300 kg of coelacanths using *jarifa* (gillnets), and suggestions were made that the ship's owners were involved in the trafficking of coelacanths (Pêche illicite: Où sont les coelecanthes pris par *El-Amine?*, *Les Nouvelles* [Antananarivo], 21 October 2008).

Commercial Trade

While captures of *L. chalumnae* have been mostly incidental in the pursuit of sharks for the shark-fin trade, local fishers have shown expertise in targeting the coelacanth. The readiness of museums and collectors to pay US$40–110 per specimen makes the species a potentially lucrative bycatch (Baker-Médard and Faber 2020). One day in April 2012, fishers from Saint Augustin arrived at the Institut Halieutique et des Sciences Marines (ISHM) in Toliara with a cart carrying 10–12 coelacanths for sale, including four adults and at least six juveniles. The responsible staff at IHSM rejected the sale offer in fear of encouraging the practice (F. Ratsifandrihamanana, unpublished data). Such a large catch on a single day was likely due to the targeting of a single cave containing a group of coelacanths of various ages. There have been other anecdotal reports of mass captures of dozens of coelacanths (Ravololoharinjara 2019). From such incidents, we speculate that total captures of *L. chalumnae* in the Toliara region alone are likely to have exceeded 100 animals since 1990.

The details of all known coelacanth captures in Madagascar are given in Table 7.8, and capture locations, where known, are given in Figures 7.12a and b. The captures were made over a wide geographic range, extending from a site 80 km southwest of Cap Sainte Marie, the southernmost point of Madagascar, to as far north as at least two sites near Maintirano, including specimen CCC 205 (Figure 7.13)—a range of almost 1000 km. Of the 29 specimens for which the capture locality is known, 20 form a cluster in the southwest near the Onilahy submarine canyon (Anakao, Lovokampy, Soalara, Nosy Vé, Saint Augustin, Andanora, Sarodrano). The capture of coelacanths at Fiherenamasay and Tsiandamba, about 40 and 85 km north of Toliara respectively, where the shelf is narrow and no canyons are present, and off Maintirano, where the shelf is far offshore and canyons are also not present, suggests that their association with undersea canyons is not exclusive. In the case of specimen CCC 177, it was captured to the northwest of the Tsioapky false pass near Fiherenamasay, where the continental shelf descends steeply but there is no submarine canyon.

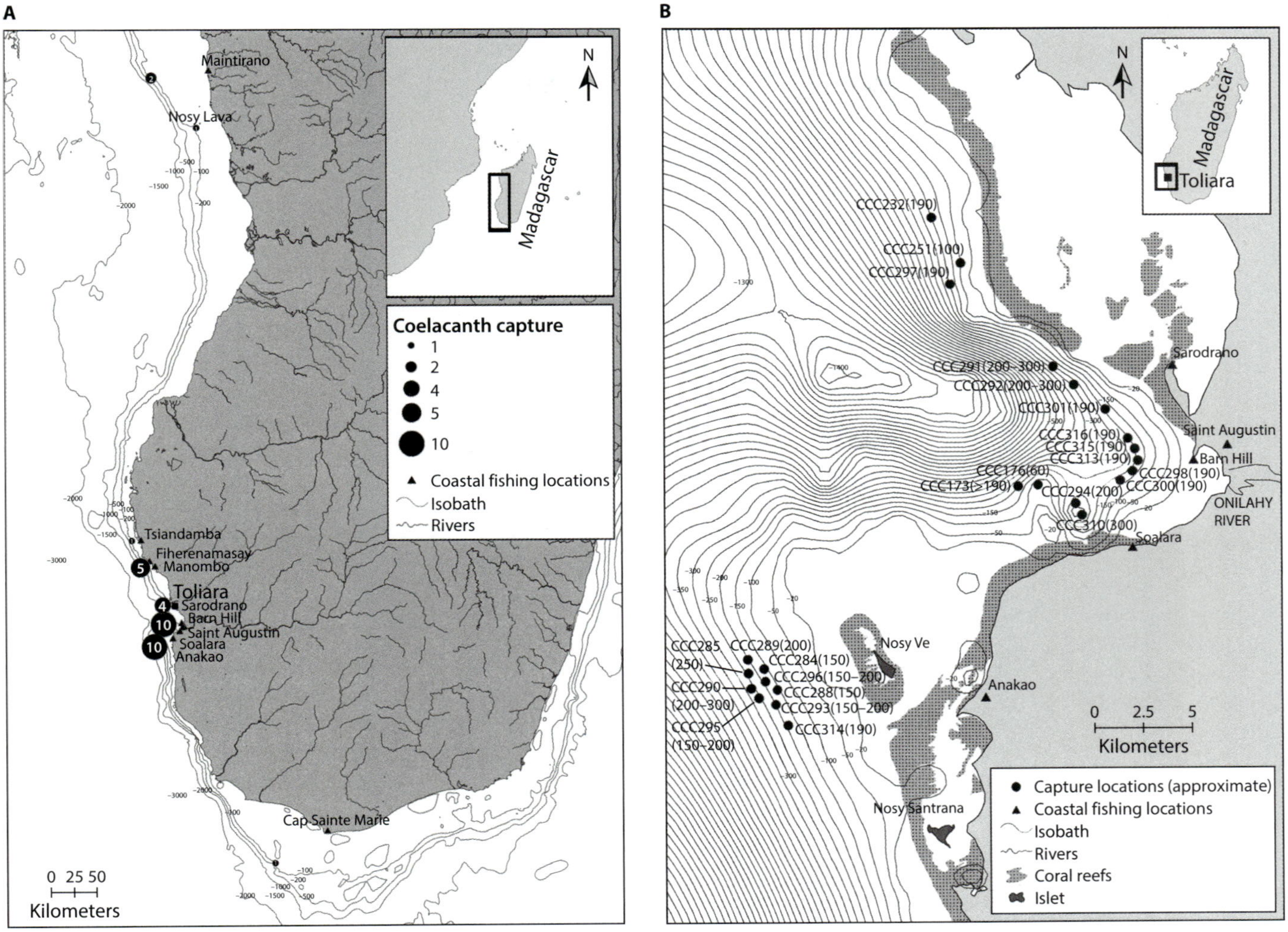

FIGURE 7.12 **Locations of documented coelacanth captures: A) across Madagascar and B) specifically in the Toliara region.**

FIGURE 7.13 **An individual (CCC 205) caught off Nosy Lava, Barren Islands, near Maintirano, in May 2006.** (PHOTO by WWF.)

Depth and slope may therefore be the primary determining factors of coelacanth presence, as also suggested by Green et al. (2009).

Despite the widespread and persistent practice of shark fishing using *jarifa* gillnets set at depths of 100 m or more throughout the island (A. Cooke 1997; du Feu 1998; Cripps et al. 2015), no coelacanth has yet been reported from the northwest around Nosy Be or at the northernmost point of the island near Antsiranana. There is no coelacanth record from the east coast of Madagascar, despite the presence of a steeply shelving continental slope and at least one submarine canyon (at Maningory, south of Ile Sainte Marie). The presence of coelacanths may also be influenced by thermoclines, which are well defined and constant at 100 m along the east coast, but along the west coast occur at about 150 m and disappear between Maintirano (18°S) and Morondava (20°S) (Ranaivoson 1997). Further research would be necessary to ascertain whether coelacanths do live in unexplored areas along the east coast.

Capture Sites

The distance from shore at which coelacanths were estimated by fishers to have been caught along the west coast of Madagascar ranged from 1 km to 20 km (average 9 km), which is farther offshore than in Grande Comore (85% less than 1.5 km from shore; Bruton and Stobbs 1991) and in Tanzania (average 6.9 km, range 0.5–8 km; Nulens et al. 2011). The estimated depth of capture in Malagasy waters ranged from 60 m to 500 m (average 192 m), shallower than in the steeply shelving seabed off Grande Comore (average 225 m; Stobbs and Bruton 1991; Nulens et al. 2011) but deeper than in Tanzania (average 141 m, range 50–250 m; Nulens et al. 2011). Eliminating one reported capture from Madagascar at a depth of 500 m (CCC 301), which may be an outlier, would render the average depth in Malagasy waters as 178 m. The distance from shore at which coelacanths are caught in Madagascar corresponds with the varying width of the continental shelf, which is as narrow as 1 km at Saint Augustin, where most captures have been recorded, extending to as much as 100 km off Cap Saint André on the west coast.

Seasonality

Coelacanth catches have been made in every month of the year except December in Malagasy waters, with most catches in February (six), May and July (five), and March (four), although the sample size (30 specimens for which the month of capture is known) is too small to show real trends. In the Comoros, coelacanth catches were also made throughout the year, with a peak from November to March (Stobbs and Bruton 1991), whereas in Tanzania catches peaked in September (21%) and August (17%) (Nulens et al. 2011).

Measurements

Latimeria chalumnae exhibits sexual dimorphism in size, with female adults being larger. The measured specimens caught off Madagascar ranged in weight from 29.5 kg to 90 kg (average 57.2 kg) and length from 121 cm to 190 cm (average 156.9 cm), equivalent to the range for female coelacanth catches in the Comoros (Bruton and Armstrong 1991; Nulens et al. 2011), reflecting the higher proportion of females caught off Madagascar. The 40 coelacanths caught off Tanzania (including Zanzibar) between 2003 and 2015 for which measurements are known averaged 41.3 kg (range 5.8–105 kg) and 133.7 cm (range 70–184 cm), substantially smaller than the coelacanths caught off Madagascar, although their weight range is wider (Nulens et al. 2011).

ECOLOGY AND BEHAVIOR

The ecology and behavior of *L. chalumnae* in Malagasy waters have not as yet been studied, so our knowledge of these topics is derived from research by mixed-gas divers, research submersible observers, and remote-operated vehicles in the Comoros, South Africa, and Tanzania. As all living coelacanths have a unique pattern of white spots on their bodies, which are effectively "fingerprints," individuals can be distinguished visually from one another.

Previous Research

Detailed studies have been carried out on the living coelacanth in the Comoros by Professor Hans Fricke and his team, from Germany. They have studied the distribution, depth preferences, abundance, feeding behavior, diel activity patterns, and other behaviors of 68 individually identified coelacanths over a 21-year period off Grande Comore (H. Fricke and Plante 1988; H. Fricke and Hissmann 1990, 1994, 2000; H. Fricke et al. 1991, 1995; Hissmann et al. 1998, 2000; H. Fricke 2007). In addition, between 2002 and 2004, Fricke and his research group, in collaboration with the African Coelacanth Ecosystem Programme (ACEP) team in South Africa, carried out detailed studies in the iSimangaliso Wetland Park in KwaZulu-Natal, South Africa, where they initially tracked 24 different coelacanths in three submarine canyons along a 48 km stretch of coast (Hissmann et al. 2006; Ribbink and Roberts 2006).

Coelacanths are large predatory fishes that may reach over 200 cm and 100 kg in size. Only the giant *Cheilinus undulatus* (Napoleon Wrasse), wreckfisheses (Polyprionidae), potato bass (*Epinephelus* spp.), and other groupers (Serranidae), among reef bony fishes, exceed their size. Despite their slow reproductive rate, coelacanths appear to grow quickly, averaging about 6.5 cm per year and reaching about 170 cm (in females only) in their 20th year (Bruton and Armstrong 1991). They may live to over 100 years.

Habitat Preferences

In general, the preferred habitat of *L. chalumnae* is steep, rocky slopes with little sediment, preferably with caves, overhangs, or other shelter where it can hide from predators and avoid strong currents during the day. It is also found on sandy continental shelves and on sandy slopes between canyons, most often at night. It typically lives at depths from 150 m to 400 m off Grande Comore, at the limit of or below the photic zone (0–200 m) and therefore primarily in darkness. It is a social animal that gathers in caves, with as many as 16 being observed in one cave off the Comoros. Over 21 years of observing the species from their submersible, Hans Fricke and his team never observed any aggressive behavior between individuals. In caves, it hovers in mid-water, never touching the substrate, sometimes resting upside down or head down.

Hunting Behavior

Latimeria chalumnae emerges at night to hunt, in darkness, drifting with the current, often following gullies into deeper water. It uses its paired, lobed fins to swim and stabilize, moving slowly just above the substrate, where it locates its food using mainly nonvisual cues, such as the detection of prey electrical fields. During its nocturnal hunting forays it often takes a head-down vertical position. These headstands may allow it to detect prey electrical fields in the dark or under sediment, using its rostral organ. In the early morning, the coelacanths return to their shallower, daytime caves, often to the same cave.

Its prey comprises both cartilaginous fishes, such as swell sharks (Scyliorhinidae), and bony fishes, including lanternfishes (Myctophidae), beardfishes (*Polymixia* spp.), *Beryx splendens* (Alfonsino), *Epigonus telescopus* (Deep-sea Cardinal Fish), snappers (Lutjanidae), witch eels (Nettastomatidae), eels (Anguilliformes, mostly deepwater species), and squids (Uyeno and Tsutsumi 1991). As coelacanths take a wide range of bait on hooks, including octopuses, snake mackerels (Gempylidae), tuna (Scombridae), and scads (Carangidae), they are clearly not prey specific in their hunting. In the Comoros, the traditional handline fishers mainly use the gempylid *Promethichthys prometheus* to catch their target species, the oilfish *Ruvettus pretiosus*, and land coelacanths as a bycatch (Stobbs and Bruton 1991).

Some individual coelacanths have fins missing, and sharks are considered to be likely predators (Bruton and Armstrong 1991). Coelacanths in Madagascar and the Comoros share their habitat with several species of large sharks, such as *Odontaspis ferox* (Small-toothed Sand Tiger), *Carcharias taurus* (Sand Tiger Shark), *Hexanchus griseus* (Six-gill Shark), and *Chlamydoselachus anguineus* (Frilled Shark), all of which are capable of preying on them.

Breeding Mode

Coelacanths have one of the most advanced breeding modes of any fish, shared by fewer than 5% of all fishes, as well as by some amphibians and reptiles and most mammals. They are internal bearers that produce a small number of very large eggs (the size of a grapefruit, the biggest eggs of any fish), which have a large amount of yolk (Wourms et al. 1991). Unlike Chondrichthyes (sharks, rays, and chimaeras), all of which have internal fertilization using specialized paired intromittent organs (Compagno 1990), coelacanths are the only live bearers among fishes in which the male does not have an intromittent organ—the female extrudes her oviduct to receive the sperm (Balon 1991a, 1991b; Balon et al. 1991).

The number of eggs produced by *L. chalumnae* normally ranges from two to 67, although a female caught off the Comoros in 1955 (CCC 10) contained an astonishing 197 eggs in three distinct size groups, which indicates that coelacanths can produce eggs and give birth in batches, like some sharks and rays. A female caught off Madagascar in July 2001 (CCC 179) contained four unhatched eggs and two unborn fetuses (Nulens et al. 2011; A. Cooke et al. 2021), although some young may have been lost during capture.

The eggs hatch inside the mother and the developing young feed on the yolk, as well as on oviductal fluids. They may also feed on unhatched eggs, like some live-bearing sharks, as more eggs are produced than juveniles. *Latimeria chalumnae* juveniles are large when they are born, usually 330 mm long and weighing about 500 g, with the maximum recorded being 410 mm and 530 g (Bruton et al. 1992; Nulens et al. 2011), and have fully developed jaws and teeth so that they can catch live prey immediately after birth.

The brood size of two to 26 is among the smallest of any fish. H. Fricke (2007) calculated that *L. chalumnae* females may produce only about 140 young during their life span, one of the lowest lifetime breeding rates of any fish. One of the most remarkable features of the coelacanth is its extraordinarily long gestation period of 36 months (Bruton 1989), by far the longest of any known animal and 1.7 times longer than that of the next candidate, the African elephant.

Habitat of Juveniles

During more than 200 dives over 21 years, Fricke and his team encountered only one juvenile coelacanth (length 50–60 cm) and never came upon juveniles with adults. In *L. menadoensis*, the Indonesian Coelacanth, juveniles have also not been seen with adults, although one sole juvenile has been photographed. The preferred habitat of juvenile *Latimeria* spp. is therefore not known and might be deeper or shallower than that of adults, as juveniles must live away from adults owing to the threat of cannibalism. Whether coelacanths exhibit some parental care soon after birth is also not known, although they do have the attributes of fishes that show parental care, such as a small number of large eggs and young, dense yolk, no larvae, large size at first external feeding, high parental developmental investment in each of a few young, high individual fitness of the young, and slow breeding rates.

INTERNATIONAL SIGNIFICANCE OF THE COELACANTH

The Western Indian Ocean Coelacanth, *L. chalumnae*, represents a highly significant species from several points of view. It belongs to an ancient group of fishes whose fossil record can be traced back 420 million years to an era when backboned animals were first evolving and that existed about 170 million years before the dinosaurs. Coelacanths were close to the epochal evolutionary transition of animals moving from water onto land about 320 Mya (million years ago) (Amemiya et al. 2013). When coelacanths first evolved there was a single supercontinent (Pangaea), which spilt into Gondwana and Laurasia from about 180 Mya. They have therefore survived monumental changes in their ocean habitat as continental drift has changed the shapes and locations of the continents and ocean basins, pushed up mountain ranges (in the sea and on land), and opened and closed channels between oceans.

Coelacanths have played a key role in promoting public understanding of evolution and, in doing so, have become important flagship species and the "panda of the seas," as they symbolize the conservation plight of many endangered marine animals. They also have a rich symbolic history, probably more than any other fish, as their iconic shape has been adopted by institutions, artists, and craftspeople, and their image has appeared on money and postage stamps (H. Fricke 1997; Bruton 2017). Coelacanths are thus highly symbolic fishes and it is imperative that we take advantage of every opportunity to study and conserve them.

THREATS

All *L. chalumnae* captures in Malagasy waters for which the method is known were made using deep-set *jarifa* gillnets (Nulens et al. 2011; A. Cooke et al. 2021), targeting sharks for the fin and oil trade. The mobility and skill of migratory Vezo fishers means that fishing pressure on coelacanths spreads along much of the west coast (Cripps and Gardner 2016). In 2019, an experienced Vezo fisherman (Mr. Tinard) reported to Ravololoharinjara (2019) that his family did not use *jarifa* gillnets in 2018 and caught no coelacanths in that year. In contrast, in the Comoros, all coelacanth catches were made using handlines until the arrival of gillnets and explosives in the 1990s (Bruton and Stobbs 1991; Stobbs and Bruton 1991). In Tanzania, 35 (87.5%) of the 40 coelacanths for which the capture method is known were caught between 2003 and 2015 using 15 cm mesh *jarifa* gillnets, except for two caught on handlines, two moribund specimens found floating on the water surface, and one caught in a ring net (Benno et al. 2006; Nulens et al. 2011).

Jarifa gillnets are therefore the main source of human-induced coelacanth mortality in Malagasy waters, but the effects of climate change and different forms of pollution (including sedimentation of their habitat) on these animals is unknown. Coelacanths are predators near the top of the food pyramid, one level below the large sharks that prey on them, and they are therefore susceptible to toxins that accumulate in the food chain. Two coelacanths from Grande Comore examined by scientists from the Virginia Institute of Marine Science were found to contain high concentrations of insecticides) in their tissues (Hale et al. 1991). No detailed studies have been done on the impact of plastic pollutants, but a 6 kg juvenile found floating on the water surface off Kitanga, Tanzania, had been suffocated by a plastic bag, and plastic has been found in the digestive tracts of adult coelacanths caught off Tanzania (Nulens et al. 2011; Bruton 2016). The dynamiting of reefs for harbor construction and gas mining in Tanzania and by fishers in the Comoros, which has killed coelacanths, does not take place in Madagascar.

The most likely aspect of global climate change that will affect coelacanths is ocean warming, which will force them away from shallow, warmer water into deeper, cooler water where oxygen saturations are higher but prey densities may be reduced (H. Fricke et al. 1995). Coelacanths have the lowest known hemoglobin count of any fish and a small gill surface area, which means that they have a restricted ability to absorb oxygen and must therefore live in well-oxygenated water.

The use of coelacanths as a food source is presumably the result of bycatch, as the animal's flesh is reported to be rancid and contains large amounts of urea, as well as oils, wax esters, and other compounds that are difficult for humans to digest. Madagascar is one of the few places where coelacanth flesh is regularly eaten, not only in times of food scarcity, such as specimen CCC 295 after Cyclone Haruna, but also under normal circumstances, as specimens CCC 298, 313, and 317 were all reported to have been confiscated from markets (Ravololoharinjara 2019).

CONSERVATION AND MANAGEMENT

Both the Western Indian Ocean Coelacanth, *L. chalumnae*, and the Indonesian Coelacanth, *L. menadoensis*, are listed on Appendix I of CITES (the Convention on International Trade in Endangered Species of Wild Fauna and Flora), which means that they may not be traded internationally without special permits. *Latimeria chalumnae* is rated as Critically Endangered by the International Union for Conservation of Nature (IUCN) and *L. menadoensis* as Vulnerable. Considering the international significance of *L. chalumnae*, and the fact that Madagascar is one of only four countries known to host breeding populations (with the Republic of the Comoros, South Africa, and Tanzania), although single specimens have been caught off Mozambique and Kenya, it is important for Madagascar to contribute to its conservation.

The conservation status of coelacanths in Malagasy waters cannot be determined until we have an estimate of the population size around the island. If coelacanths are found only at or near the currently known sites, or only at a small number of other sites, then there is reason for concern. If they occur around the whole coast of Madagascar, as we predict, then the total population could be regarded as stable as the catches made on the southwest and west coasts, even if several times greater than the currently documented rate (about one per year for 33 years) would probably be trivial in relation to the size of the whole population and mortalities caused by predation. However, we have anecdotal evidence that "dozens more" coelacanths have been caught off Madagascar in recent years than the number that has been officially recorded (Nulens et al. 2011; Ravololoharinjara 2019; A. Cooke et al. 2021).

Demographic studies on coelacanth populations off Grande Comore and Anjouan islands in the Comoros demonstrate that the known catch rates of 3.5 fish per year in the 1960s, 1970s, and 1980s were insignificant compared with natural mortality rates, which were calculated to be between 137 and 174 individuals per annum (Bruton and Armstrong 1991). Overfishing of coelacanth prey (demersal fishes and squids) by small-scale fishers in the Comoros and Madagascar is likely to have a greater impact on coelacanth populations. As the main source of natural mortality in coelacanths is predicted to be predation by large sharks, the capture of large sharks in or near coelacanth habitats in Madagascar may be of some benefit to them.

A trend of concern in coelacanth catches in Malagasy waters is the relatively high proportion of landed pregnant females. Of the 20 fishes caught off Madagascar whose sex is known, 15 were females. Eight of the females (53%) carried eggs and/or unborn pups, which suggests that pregnant females may be more vulnerable to *jarifa* gillnets than males. Given the breeding mode of coelacanths mentioned above, if pregnant females carrying eggs and unborn pups are killed, this represents a major setback for the population. There is evidence from other localities that pregnant coelacanths may be relatively vulnerable to net catches there as well. The only coelacanth caught so far off Mozambique (CCC 162) was a 98 kg, 179 cm female carrying 26 late-term pups and was landed using a trawl net (Bruton et al. 1992), and the only coelacanth known from Kenya (CCC 178) was a 77 kg, 170 cm female carrying 17 eggs caught in a trawl net in April 2001 (De Vos and Oyugi 2002). An 86.5 kg, 176 cm female caught in a net off

Zanzibar in July 2009 (CCC 253) was carrying 23 fully developed juveniles (Benno et al. 2006).

We offer the following recommendations to conserve populations of coelacanths in and around Malagasy waters.

1. **Conservation status:** Pass legislation adding *L. chalumnae* to the list of integrally protected species under Madagascar's wildlife laws, which forbid the capture, holding, transport, or sale of such species.
2. **Trade regulation and controls:** Reinforce the strict ban on the export of coelacanth specimens or body parts in accordance with CITES regulations. Review trade and customs regulations on coelacanths and implement relevant training for customs officers.
3. **Marine protected areas (MPAs):** Establish a protected coelacanth sanctuary within an MPA or regulated fisheries management area in the Onilahy submarine canyon at Saint Augustin, where the highest number of coelacanth captures occurs. Establish or extend other MPAs that have likely coelacanth habitats elsewhere in Madagascar, such as the Barren Islands, and add *L. chalumnae* as a conservation target species for those MPAs to improve the reporting of captures there.
4. **Fisheries management:** Ban the use of *jarifa* gillnets in MPAs established to conserve coelacanths, sawfishes, turtles, and *Dugong dugon* (Dugong), thereby setting an example to all countries in the western Indian Ocean region where *jarifa* gillnets pose a threat to the marine megafauna.
5. **Fisheries management areas:** Establish fisheries management areas (or *plans d'aménagement des pêches*), which cover valuable and threatened fish stocks, including coelacanths, and typically extend to the limit of the territorial waters. In these areas, the impact of *jarifa* gillnet fishing on target (shark) as well as nontarget species (coelacanths, sawfishes, turtles, and *Dugong dugon*) needs to be carefully evaluated. This assessment should take into account not only the commercial value but also the ecological role and value of target and nontarget species.
6. **Research management:** Provide incentives by paying registered fishers who catch coelacanths as a bycatch of the shark fishery to photograph, tag, and release caught coelacanths that are still alive. If a caught coelacanth has died, fishers should be incentivized to take the specimen to a scientific institution where its data can be recorded in a centralized Malagasy coelacanth database and on the international CCC Coelacanth Inventory. Also, implement an awareness-raising and information campaign that targets fishing communities in areas where coelacanths occur, discouraging the capture and landing of coelacanths, in support of the above initiative.
7. **Promotion of public awareness:** Continue to mount a nationwide public awareness campaign, including displays, media releases, television and radio interviews, public talks, talks at schools, and popular publications, on the importance of conserving the coelacanth in Madagascar. Encourage traditional leaders to support coelacanth conservation, given the venerated status that the species already enjoys in the migrant Vezo fishing culture.

CONCLUSION

Madagascar may have the largest population of *L. chalumnae* in the world, but few details are available on the species' distribution and natural history, and there are no laws, management plans, or monitoring systems in place for its protection. As *L. chalumnae* is an iconic flagship species, it is important that these shortcomings are rectified as soon as possible. Madagascar has a research infrastructure that is well placed to support research and conservation programs on *L. chalumnae* close to its largest known population, but a national conservation and management plan needs to be put in place and the laws need to be updated to protect the species. In addition to its national program, Madagascar should also play a leading role in research and conservation on a regional scale, not only of *L. chalumnae* but of the entire ecosystem that it shares with other marine organisms.

ACKNOWLEDGMENTS

We are grateful to Dr. Jamal Mahafina, director of the Institut Halieutique et des Sciences Marines (IHSM), for his support, and to Tantely Tianarisoa for the maps. We thank Gianni Insacco of the Museo Civico di Storia Naturale in Comiso, Italy, for permission to use his image of the first coelacanth specimen known to science from Madagascar (CCC 300), and to WWF Madagascar for permission to use the image of CCC 205. We also thank the staffs of the fisheries directorate of Toliara, fishing companies, and hotels who provided access to and information on coelacanth specimens in their possession. We are very grateful to Rik Nulens for bringing CCC 300 to our attention and for making available unpublished information on coelacanths in Malagasy waters.

Subject editor: Steven M. Goodman

CHONDRICHTHYAN FISHES (SHARKS, RAYS, AND CHIMAERAS)

B. Séret

Chondrichthyans are mainly defined as fishes with a cartilaginous skeleton. They include fishes that are commonly named sharks, rays, and chimaeras. This ancient, large, and diverse zoological class comprises 14 orders, 66 families, and 1296 species, including 554 sharks, 685 rays, and 57 chimaeras. Rays are "flattened" sharks, and chimaeras form a subclass of mainly deep-sea chondrichthyans with globular head, large eyes, and long tapering body, sometimes known as ghost fish.

Chondrichthyan fishes occur in all oceans, from coastal shallow waters to abyssal depths of 4000 m. A few species have adapted to live mostly in fresh water, and numerous species are euryhaline, able to tolerate extended periods in waters of low salinity. They are found across all latitudes, even in polar waters, but in common with most other marine fauna, exhibit their highest diversity in shallow tropical seas.

SPECIES DIVERSITY AND SCIENTIFIC RESEARCH ON THE MALAGASY FAUNA

Madagascar is an "island continent" occupying a tropical to subtropical location with 4820 km of coastline (not counting islands) and an exclusive economic zone (EEZ) of 1,225,259 km^2, offering a great variety of marine habitats, from coastal reefs and lagoons to offshore banks and shoals, extensive continental shelf and slope, and abyssal plains to 4500 m. These habitats are suitable for many different forms of sharks, rays, and chimaeras. To date, 117 species have been recorded from Malagasy waters, including 76 sharks, 40 rays, and one chimaera (Table 7.9).

Compared with the total numbers of chondrichthyan species globally, the Malagasy fauna has a relatively low diversity (representing c. 9% of the total number of known of chondrichthyans), despite Madagascar's varied marine geomorphological features and its biogeographic position at the "crossroads" of the southwest Indian Ocean, in the zone of influence of the Agulhas, Somali, and Benguela Currents, and waters of the Antarctic coming up from the south. Other countries of the same region exhibit considerably higher shark and ray diversities, suggesting that Madagascar's low measured species diversity is most likely due to a lack of research. For example, South Africa, which has a smaller EEZ (1,068,659 vs. 1,225,259 km^2) and a shorter coastline (2798 vs. 4828 km), has a higher chondrichthyan diversity. While South Africa's higher diversity can in part be explained by its coast spanning two oceans and a range of latitudes from tropical to temperate, the higher level of scientific research is likely to be a factor. South Africa has focused on shark research for decades, conducted through specific bodies such as the KwaZulu-Natal Sharks Board in Durban, which was originally established to protect swimmers and surfers on local beaches from shark attack.

The first scientific inventories of Malagasy chondrichthyans were published by the French ichthyologist Pierre Fourmanoir (1961, 1963b), who recorded 26 shark species and 15 ray species, respectively, including the earlier records in the scientific literature. The inventory of the island's chondrichthyans was subsequently advanced by various authors (e.g., Maugé 1967; Bauchot and Bianchi 1984; Compagno 1984a, 1984b; Séret 1986a, 1986b, 1987, 1989a, 1989b; McVean et al. 2006; Ebert 2013) and recently in a large-scale synthesis of Madagascar's fish diversity (R. Fricke et al. 2018). An updated list of chondrichthyan species recorded from Madagascar is provided in Table 7.10. Two species from the Madagascar Ridge (currently outside, but bordering, the EEZ of Madagascar), a skate and a longnose chimaera, are listed as potentially occurring in Malagasy waters.

TABLE 7.9. **Numbers and percentages of species of sharks, rays, and chimaeras recorded in Madagascar, compared to the total number of chondrichthyans known to date in the world, with the numbers in neighboring countries and the Agulhas Current Large Marine Ecosystem (ACLME)**

ENTITIES	NUMBER OF SHARK SPECIES	NUMBER OF RAY SPECIES	NUMBER OF ELASMOBRANCH SPECIES	NUMBER OF CHIMAERA SPECIES	NUMBER OF CHONDRICHTHYAN SPECIES
Worldwide	554 (43%)	685 (53%)	1239 (96%)	57 (4%)	1296
South Africa	108 (59%)	70 (38%)	178 (97%)	6 (3%)	184
Mozambique	67 (62%)	39 (36%)	106 (98%)	2 (2%)	108
Madagascar	77 (65%)	40 (34%)	116 (99%)	1 (1%)	118
Seychelles	38 (76%)	12 (24%)	50 (100%)	0 (0%)	50
Mayotte	26 (62%)	15 (36%)	41 (98%)	1 (2%)	42
Comoros	17 (85%)	3 (15%)	20 (100%)	0 (0%)	20
ACLME	67 (62%)	37 (35%)	103 (97%)	3 (3%)	107

TABLE 7.10. **Species of sharks, rays, and chimaeras recorded from Madagascar, with their English and Malagasy names, habitats, and CITES convention and IUCN Red List conservation status**

ORDER	FAMILY	SPECIES SCIENTIFIC NAME	AUTHORS	ENGLISH COMMON NAME	MALAGASY VERNACULAR NAMES	ENDEMISM	HABITAT 1	HABITAT 2	CITES	IUCN
Hexanchiformes	Hexanchidae	*Heptranchias perlo*	(Bonnaterre, 1788)	Sharpnose Sevengill Shark			Deep	Benthopelagic		NT
		Hexanchus griseus	(Bonnaterre, 1788)	Bluntnose Sixgill Shark	*Akiho*		Deep	Benthopelagic		NT
		H. nakamurai	(Teng, 1962)	Bigeye Sixgill Shark			Deep	Benthopelagic		DD
Orectolobiformes	Ginglymostomatidae	*Nebrius ferrugineus*	(Lesson, 1831)	Tyawny Nurse Shark	*Akiho, akio valovombose, ambontso*		Coastal	Benthopelagic		VU
		Pseudoginglymostoma brevicaudatum	(Günther in Playfair & Günther, 1867)	Short-tail Nurse Shark	*Akio voritse*		Coastal	Benthopelagic		VU
	Hemiscyllidae	*Chiloscyllium caeruleopunctatum*	Pellefrin, 1914	Blue-spotted Bamboo Shark	*Akiho, hiahia*	Endemic	Coastal	Benthic		NT
	Rhincodontidae	*Rhincodon typus*	Smith, 1828	Whale Shark	*Akiho*		Coastal and oceanic	Pelagic	Appendix II	EN
	Stegostomatidae	*Stegostoma fasciatum*	(Herman, 1783)	Zebra Shark	*Akiho, akio miroro, akio tsaka, jalinta*		Coastal	Benthopelagic		EN
Lamniformes	Alopiidae	*Alopias superciliosus*	Lowe, 1841	Bigeye Thresher Shark	*Akiho, akio santira*		Oceanic	Pelagic	Appendix II	VU
		A. vulpinus	(Bonnaterre, 1788)	Thresher Shark	*Akiho, akio santira*		Oceanic	Pelagic	Appendix II	VU
	Lamnidae	*Carcharodon carcharias*	(Linnaeus, 1758)	Great White Shark	*Farao, akio masiake*		Coastal and oceanic	Pelagic	Appendix II	VU
		Isurus oxyrinchus	Rafinesque, 1810	Shortfin Mako	*Akiho*		Oceanic	Pelagic	Appendix II	EN
		I. paucus	Guitart Manday, 1966	Longfin Mako	*Akiiho*		Oceanic	Pelagic	Appendix II	DD
	Odontaspididae	*Odontaspis ferox*	(Risso, 1810)	Smalltoothed Sand Tiger	*Akiho, akio foty*		Coastal and deep	Benthopelagic		VU
	Pseudocarchariidae	*Pseudocarcharias kamoharai*	(Matsubara, 1936)	Crocodile Shark			Deep	Benthopelagic		LC
Carcharhiniformes	Carcharhinidae	*Carcharhinus albimarginatus*	(Rüppel, 1837)	Silvertip Shark	*Akiho, akio fotyrambo, fotsy halalala*		Coastal	Benthopelagic		VU
		C. altimus	(Springer, 1950)	Bignose Shark	*Akiho*		Coastal	Benthopelagic		DD
		C. amblyrhynchos	(Bleker, 1856)	Gray Reef Shark	*Akiho, akio tomaninente, botra mavo*		Coastal	Benthopelagic		NT
		C. amboinensis	(Müller & Henle, 1839)	Pigeye Shark	*Akiho*		Coastal	Benthopelagic		DD
		C. brachyurus	(Müller & Henle, 1839)	Copper Shark	*Akio bato*		Coastal	Benthopelagic		NT

(continued overleaf)

TABLE 7.10. ***continued***

ORDER	FAMILY	SPECIES SCIENTIFIC NAME	AUTHORS	ENGLISH COMMON NAME	MALAGASY VERNACULAR NAMES	ENDEMISM	HABITAT 1	HABITAT 2	CITES	IUCN
Carcharhiniformes *continued*	Carcharhinidae *continued*	*C. brevipinna*	(Valenciennes in Müller & Henle, 1839)	Spinner Shark	*Akiho, akio maintepate*		Coastal	Benthopelagic		NT
		C. falciformis	(Bibron in Müller & Henle, 1839)	Silky Shark	*Akiho, akio gofo*		Coastal	Pelagic	Appendix II	VU
		C. galapagensis	(Snodgrass & Heller, 1905)	Galapagos Shark			Coastal	Benthopelagic		NT
		C. humani	White and Weigmann, 2014	Western Indian Ocean Blackspot Shark	*Akiho*		Coastal	Benthopelagic		NE
		C. leucas	(Valenciennes in Müller & Henle, 1839)	Bull Shark	*Akio boriloha, botra mavo*		Coastal	Benthopelagic		NT
		C. limbatus	(Valenciennes in Müller & Henle, 1839)	Blacktip Shark	*Akiho, akio maintepate, botra mavo*		Coastal	Benthopelagic		NT
		C. longimanus	(Poey, 1861)	Oceanic White-tip Shark	*Akiho, akio meso*		Coastal	Pelagic	Appendix II	VU
		C. melanopterus	(Quoy & Gaimard, 1824)	Blacktip Reef Shark	*Akiho, akio maintpate*		Coastal (reef)	Benthopelagic		NT
		C. obscurus	(LeSueur, 1818)	Dusky Shark	*Akiho, akio foty*		Coastal	Benthopelagic		VU
		C. plumbeus	(Nardo, 1827)	Sandbar Shark	*Akiho, akio bevombotse*		Coastal	Benthopelagic		VU
		C. sorrah	(Valenciennes in Müller & Henle, 1839)	Spot-tail Shark	*Akio maintpate, akio meso*		Coastal	Benthopelagic		NT
		C. wheeleri	Garrick, 1982	Shortnose Blacktail Shark	*Akiho*		Coastal (reef)	Benthopelagic		NE
		Galeocerdo cuvier	(Péron & LeSueur, 1822)	Tiger Shark	*Akiho, akio vorotse, akio bemaso, akio tsaka*		Coastal and oceanic	Benthopelagic		NT
		Loxodon macrorhinus	Müller & Henle, 1839	Sliteye Shark	*Akiho, lavahejaka*		Coastal	Benthopelagic		LC
		Negaprion acutidens	(Rüppel, 1837)	Sicklefin Lemon Shark	*Akiho, pampa maronto, pampa mi'tsanga*		Coastal	Benthopelagic		VU
		Prionace glauca	(Linnaeus, 1758)	Blue Shark	*Akiho*		Oceanic	Pelagic		NT
		Rhizoprionodon acutus	(Rüppel, 1837)	Milk Shark	*Akiho*		Coastal	Benthopelagic		LC
		Scoliodon laticaudus	Müller & Henle, 1838	Spadenose Shark			Coastal	Benthopelagic		NT
		Triaenodon obesus	(Rüppel, 1837)	Whitetip Reef Shark	*Akiho, maro alahala*		Coastal (reef)	Benthopelagic		NT

ORDER	FAMILY	SPECIES SCIENTIFIC NAME	AUTHORS	ENGLISH COMMON NAME	MALAGASY VERNACULAR NAMES	ENDEMISM	HABITAT 1	HABITAT 2	CITES	IUCN
	Hemigaleidae	*Hemipristis elongata*	(Klunzinger, 1871)	Snaggletooth Shark	*Akiho*		Deep	Benthopelagic		VU
		Paragaleus leucolomatus	Compagno & Smale, 1985	Whitetip Weasel Shark			Coastal	Benthopelagic		DD
	Pseudotriakidae	*Pseudotriakis microdon*	Brito Capello, 1868	False Catshark			Deep	Benthopelagic		LC
	Scyliorhinidae	*Apristurus* sp. n.?				Uncertain	Deep	Benthopelagic		NE
		Bythaelurus clevai	(Séret, 1987)	Broadhead Catshark		Endemic	Deep	Benthopelagic		DD
		Cephaloscyllium sufflans	(Regan, 1921)	Balloon Shark			Coastal	Benthopelagic		LC
		Holohalaelurus punctatus	(Gilchrist, 1914)	African Spotted Catshark			Coastal	Benthopelagic		EN
		Poroderma africanum	(Gmelin, 1789)	Striped Catshark	*Akiho, antsantsa, antsantsangory*		Coastal	Benthopelagic		NT
		P. pantherinum	(Gmelin, 1789)	Leopard Catshark			Coastal	Benthopelagic		DD
		Scyliorhinus comoroensis	Compagno, 1988	Comoro Catshark			Coastal	Benthopelagic		DD
	Sphyrnidae	*Sphyrna lewini*	(Griffith & Smith, 1834)	Scalloped Hammerhead Shark	*Akio viko, antenohomaso*		Coastal and oceanic	Benthopelagic	Appendix II	EN
		S. mokarran	(Rüppel, 1837)	Great Hammerhead Shark	*Akio viko, antenohomaso*		Coastal and oceanic	Benthopelagic	Appendix II	EN
		S. zygaena	(Linnaeus, 1758)	Smooth Hammerhead Shark	*Akio viko, antsantsongongo*		Coastal and oceanic	Benthopelagic	Appendix II	VU
	Triakidae	*Mustelus manazo*	Bleeker, 1855	Star-spotted Smoothhound			Coastal	Benthopelagic		DD
		Triakis megalopterus	(Smith, 1839)	Blackfin Houndshark			Coastal	Benthopelagic		NT
Squaliformes	Centrophoridae	*Centrophorus granulosus*	(Bloch & Schneider, 1801)	Gulper Shark			Deep	Benthopelagic		DD
		C. lesliei	White, Ebert, & Naylor, 2017	African Gulper Shark			Deep	Benthopelagic		NE
		C. moluccensis	Bleeker, 1860	Smallfin Gulper Shark			Deep	Benthopelagic		DD
		Deania calcea	(Lowe, 1839)	Birdbeak Dogfish			Deep	Benthopelagic		NE
	Dalatiidae	*Dalatias licha*	(Bonnaterre, 1788)	Kitefin Shark			Deep	Benthopelagic		LC
		Euprotomicrus bispinatus	(Quoy & Gaimard, 1824)	Pygmy Shark			Deep	Pelagic		VU
		Isistius brasiliensis	(Quoy & Gaimard, 1824)	Cookiecutter Shark			Deep	Pelagic		LC

(continued overleaf)

TABLE 7.10. ***continued***

ORDER	FAMILY	SPECIES SCIENTIFIC NAME	AUTHORS	ENGLISH COMMON NAME	MALAGASY VERNACULAR NAMES	ENDEMISM	HABITAT 1	HABITAT 2	CITES	IUCN
Squaliformes *continued*	Etmopteridae	*Etmopterus alphus?*	Ebert, Leslie, & Weigmann, 2016	Alphus Lanternshark			Deep	Benthopelagic		LC
		E. molleri	(Whitley, 1939)	Moller's Lanternshark			Deep	Benthopelagic		DD
		E. sentosus	Bass, D'Aubrey, & Kitsnasamy, 1976	Thorny Lanternshark			Deep	Benthopelagic		LC
	Oxynotidae	*Oxynotus centrina?*	(Linnaeus, 1758)	Angular Roughshark			Coastal and deep	Benthic		VU
	Somniosidae	*Centroscymnus coelolepis*	Barbosa du Bocage & Brito Capello, 1864	Portuguese Dogfish			Deep	Benthopelagic		NT
		C. owstonii	Garman, 1906	Roughskin Dogfish			Deep	Benthopelagic		VU
		Centroselachus crepidater	(Barbosa du Bocage & Brito Capello, 1864)	Longnose Velvet Dogfish			Deep	Benthopelagic		LC
		Somniosus antarcticus	Whitley, 1939	Southern Sleeper Shark			Deep	Benthopelagic		LC
	Squalidae	*Cirrhigaleus asper*	(Merrett, 1973)	Mandarin Dogfish			Deep	Benthopelagic		DD
		Squalus sp. cf. *blainvillei*	(Risso, 1810)	Longnose Spurdog			Coastal and deep	Benthopelagic		NE
		S. mahia	Viana, Lisher, & Carvalho, 2017	Malagasy Skinny Spurdog			Coastal and deep	Benthopelagic		NE
		S. misukurii	Jordan & Snyder, 1903	Shortspine Spurdog			Coastal and deep	Benthopelagic		DD
Pristiophoriformes	Pristiophoridae	*Pliotrema warreni*	(Regan, 1906)	Sixgill Sawshark			Deep	Benthopelagic		NT
		P. kajae	Weigmann, Gon, Leeney, Barrowclift, Berggren, Jiddawi, & Temple, 2020	Kaja's Sixgill Sawshark			Deep	Bentho pelagic		NE
		Pristiophorus nancyae	Ebert & Caillet, 2011	African Dwarf Sawshark			Deep	Benthopelagic		NE
Squatiniformes	Squatinidae	*Squatina africana*	Regan, 1908	African Angelshark			Coastal and deep	Benthic		NT
Torpediniformes	Narcinidae	*Narcine insolita*	Carvalho, Compagno, & Séret, 2002	Madagascar Numbfish			Coastal	Benthic		DD
	Narkidae	*Heteronarce garmani*	Regan, 1921	Natal Sleeper Ray			Coastal and deep	Benthic		VU
		Narke capensis	(Gmelin, 1789)	Cape Sleeper Ray			Coastal and deep	Benthic		DD

ORDER	FAMILY	SPECIES SCIENTIFIC NAME	AUTHORS	ENGLISH COMMON NAME	MALAGASY VERNACULAR NAMES	ENDEMISM	HABITAT 1	HABITAT 2	CITES	IUCN
	Torpedinidae	*Tetronarce nobiliana*	(Bonaparte, 1835)	Great Torpedo			Deep	Benthopelagic		DD
		Torpedo fuscomaculata	Peters, 1855	Blackspotted Electric Ray			Coastal	Benthic		DD
		T. sinuspersici	Olfers, 1831	Marbled Electric Ray			Coastal	Benthic		DD
Rhinopristiformes	Glaucostegidae	*Glaucostegus petiti?*	(Chabanaud, 1929)	Petit's Guitarfish		Endemic?	Coastal	Demersal		NE
	Pristidae	*Pristis pristis*	Linnaeus, 1758	Largetooth Sawfish	*Vavana*		Coastal	Demersal	Appendix I	CR
	Rhinidae	*Rhina ancylostoma*	Bloch & Schneider, 1801	Shark Ray	*Tandraly*		Coastal	Demersal	Appendix II	CR
		Rhynchobatus australiae	Whitley, 1939	Australian Wedgefish			Coastal	Demersal	Appendix II	CR
		R. djiddensis	(Forsskal, 1775)	Whitespotted Wedgefish	*Soroboa*		Coastal	Demersal	Appendix II	CR
	Rhinobatidae	*Acroteriobatus andysabini*	Weigmann, Ebert, & Séret, 2021	Grayspot Guitarfish			Coastal	Demersal		DD
		Rhinobatos austini	Ebert & Gon, 2017	Austin's Guitarfish			Coastal	Demersal		NE
		R. holcorhynchus	Norman, 1922	Slender Guitarfish			Coastal	Demersal		DD
Rajiformes	Anacanthobatidae	*Indobatis ori*	(Wallace, 1967)	Black Legskate			Deep	Demersal		DD
	Arhynchobatidae	*Notoraja hesperindica*	Weigmann, Séret, & Stehmann, 2021	Western Blue Skate			Deep	Benthic		NE
	Gurgesiellidae	*Fenestraja maceachrani*	(Séret, 1989)	Madagascar Pygmy Skate		Endemic	Deep	Benthic		DD
	Rajidae	*Dipturus crosnieri*	(Séret, 1989)	Madagascar Skate		Endemic	Deep	Benthic		VU
		D. springeri	(Wallace, 1967)	Springer's Skate			Deep	Benthic		DD
		Leucoraja sp. n.	B. Séret, unpublished data				Deep	Benthic		NE
		Raja clavata	Linnaeus, 1758	Thornback Skate			Coastal	Benthic		NT
		Rostroraja alba	(Lacepède, 1803)	White Skate			Coastal and deep	Benthic		EN
Myliobatiformes	Aetobatidae	*Aetobatus ocellatus*	(Kuhl, 1823)	Spotted Eagle Ray	*Fay tomily*		Coastal	Benthopelagic		VU
	Dasyatidae	*Dasyatis chrysonota*	(Smith, 1828)	Blue Stingray			Coastal	Benthic		LC
		Himantura uarnak	(Gmelin, 1789)	Coach Whipray			Coastal	Benthic		VU
		Neotrygon caeruleopunctata	Last, White, & Séret, 2016	Bluespotted Maskray			Deep	Benthic		NE
		Pastinachus ater	(Macleay, 1883)	Broad Cowtail Ray			Coastal	Benthic		LC

(continued overleaf)

TABLE 7.10. ***continued***

ORDER	FAMILY	SPECIES SCIENTIFIC NAME	AUTHORS	ENGLISH COMMON NAME	MALAGASY VERNACULAR NAMES	ENDEMISM	HABITAT 1	HABITAT 2	CITES	IUCN
Myliobatiformes *continued*	Dasyatidae *continued*	*Pateobatis jenkinsii*	(Annandale, 1909)	Jenkin's Whipray			Coastal	Benthic		VU
		Pteroplatytrygon violacea	(Bonaparte, 1832)	Pelagic Stingray			Oceanic	Pelagic		LC
		Taeniura lymma	(Forsskal, 1775)	Bluespotted Fantail Ray			Coastal (reef)	Benthic		NT
		Taeniurops meyeni	(Müller & Henle, 1841)	Blotched Stingray			Coastal	Benthic		VU
		Urogymnus asperrimus	(Bloch & Schneider, 1801)	Porcupine Whipray			Coastal	Benthic		VU
	Gymnuridae	*Gymnura poecilura*	(Shaw, 1804)	Longtail Butterfly Ray			Coastal	Demersal		NT
	Mobulidae	*Mobula alfredi*	(Krefft, 1868)	Reef Manta Ray			Coastal	Pelagic	Appendix II	VU
		M. birostris	(Walbaum, 1792)	Giant Manta Ray			Coastal and oceanic	Pelagic	Appendix II	VU
		M. kuhlii	(Valenciennes in Müller & Henle, 1841)	Kuhl's Devilray			Coastal and oceanic	Pelagic	Appendix II	DD
		M. mobular	(Bonnaterre, 1788)	Spinetail Devilray			Coastal and oceanic	Pelagic	Appendix II	EN
		M. thurstoni	(Lloyd, 1908)	Bentfin Devilray			Coastal and oceanic	Pelagic	Appendix II	NT
	Plesiobatidae	*Plesiobatis daviesi*	(Wallace, 1967)	Deepwater Stingray			Deep	Benthopelagic		LC
	Rhinopteridae	*Rhinoptera jayakari*	Boulenger, 1895	Shorttail Cownose Ray			Coastal	Benthopelagic		VU
Chimaeriformes	Chimaeridae	*Chimaera* sp. n.	Fricke et al. (2018)			Uncertain	Deep	Benthopelagic		NE
MADAGASCAR RIDGE										
Rajiformes	Arhynchobatidae	*Bathyraja tunae*	Stehmann, 2005	Cristina's Skate			Deep	Benthic		LC
Chimaeriformes	Rhinochimaeridae	*Rhinochimaera africana*	Compagno, Stehmann, & Eberte, 1990	African Longnose Chimaera			Deep	Benthopelagic		LC
	Chimaeridae	*Chimaera willwatchi*	Fricke et al. (2018)	Seafarer's Ghost Shark			Deep	Benthopelagic		DD

Notes: CR, Critically Endangered; DD, Data Deficient; EN, Endangered; LC, Least Concern; NE, Not evaluated; NT, Near Threatened; VU, Vulnerable.

The known Malagasy chondrichthyan fauna is composed of 65% sharks and 34% rays (Table 7.9). The ratio globally is 43% sharks to 53% rays (with 4% chimaeras), suggesting that Madagascar's ray fauna may be relatively under-researched. Sharks are mostly benthopelagic, living in the water column, but regularly descending to the seabed to feed or reproduce, a good example being the species-rich requiem sharks (*Carcharhinus* spp.). In contrast, rays are mostly benthic, living mainly on the seafloor, such as skates and ribbon tail rays. A few sharks and rays are exclusively pelagic, living permanently in the water column, such as oceanic sharks and the manta rays. The chimaeras are primarily mid- to deepwater benthopelagic species.

With regard their bathymetric distribution, the Malagasy chondrichthyans are mainly composed of coastal species, occurring on or over the continental shelf at depths of 0 to 200 m and around the offshore coral reefs and atolls. In this domain, the most common sharks include *Carcharhinus amblyrhynchos* (Gray Reef Shark), *C. galapagensis* (Galapagos Shark), *C. leucas* (Bull Shark), *C. melanopterus* (Blacktip Reef Shark), *C. plumbeus* (Sandbar Shark), *Galeocerdo cuvier* (Tiger Shark), *Negaprion acutidens* (Sicklefin Lemon Shark), *Triaenodon obesus* (Whitetip Reef Shark), and *Stegostoma fasciatum* (Zebra Shark).

Deepwater sharks and rays are relatively well represented in the Malagasy fauna, with 25 and 10 species, respectively. This information is at least in part the result of bycatch records from the former deepwater shrimp trawl fishery off northwest Madagascar, and recent cruises exploring deep-sea biodiversity in the southwestern Indian Ocean, such as the deep-sea exploration cruise of the *Miriki* around the north of Madagascar in 2009 and the series of cruises of the *Dr Fridtjof Nansen* to the west of Madagascar (Alvheim et al. 2009). Information on oceanic sharks and rays is derived mainly from tuna fishery research, as sharks are a common bycatch of pelagic tuna fisheries (Stretta et al. 1988; Cripps et al. 2015; Razafimandimby and Leslie 2017). Species commonly encountered include the *Carcharhinus falciformis* (Silky Shark), *C. longimanus* (Oceanic White-tip Shark), *Prionace glauca* (Blue Shark), *Isurus oxyrhinchus* and *I. paucus* (mako sharks), and various manta rays. The pelagic *Rhincodon typus*, or Whale Shark (Diamant et al. 2018), was formerly exploited by tuna purse seiners to encourage tuna shoals to aggregate, improving tuna catches but resulting in significant mortality of Whale Sharks. Thanks to conservation measures, Whale Sharks are now released alive from the purse seines (Resolution 2013/05 of the Indian Ocean Tuna Commission [IOTC]).

Carcharodon carcharias (Great White Shark) is a primarily coastal pelagic shark of temperate waters (Compagno 1984a); however, Great Whites are also ocean wanderers, and have been sporadically recorded from the tropical waters of Madagascar (Cliff et al. 2000). Zuffa et al. (2002) reported a total of 17 individuals caught off Tolagnaro (Fort Dauphin), Itampolo, Toliara, and Morombe. The tracking of individuals tagged in South Africa shows that some of them wander into the Malagasy EEZ on their migration routes across the Indian Ocean, including Maureen—an adult female of 4.4 m in total length (TL) (Figure 7.14).

The chondrichthyan fauna of Madagascar is mostly composed of Indo–West Pacific and cosmopolitan species, but there are a few endemic sharks and rays, which are of special interest. *Chiloscyllium caeruleopunctatum* (Blue-spotted Bamboo Shark) (Figure 7.15) is a small shark of about 67 cm in length found sporadically in Malagasy fish markets (Bauchot and Bianchi 1984; Compagno 1984a)

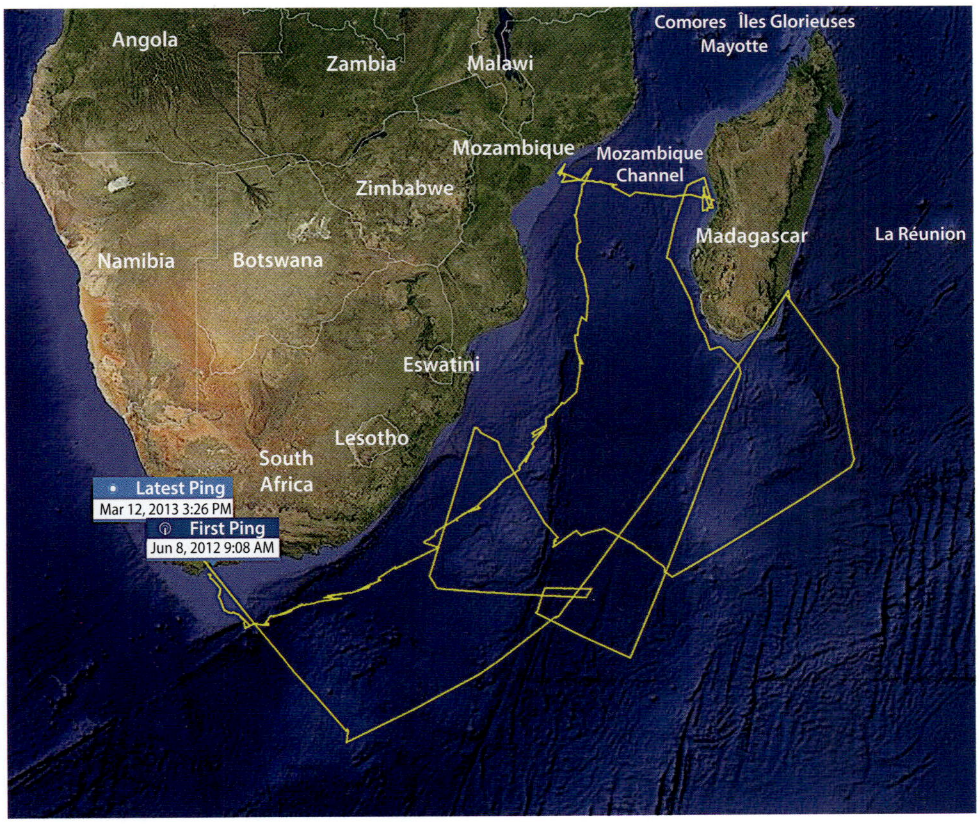

FIGURE 7.14 Trajectory of Maureen, a female *Carcharodon carcharias* (Great White Shark), wandering from South Africa to around Madagascar. (SOURCE: Ocearch Shark Tracker 2020).

FIGURE 7.15 **Specimen of *Chiloscyllium caeruleopunctatum* (Blue-spotted Bamboo Shark) caught off Toliara in 2006.** (PHOTO by B. Pascal.)

whose biology and ecology are unknown. Two deepwater skates, *Dipturus crosnieri* and *Fenestraja maceachrani*, and *Bythaelurus clevai* (Broadhead Catshark), are also known only from the continental slope of Madagascar. Collections of these three species were made during deep-trawling shrimp surveys on the western coast of Madagascar (Séret 1987, 1989a, 1989b). The status of the guitarfish *Glaucostegus petiti* needs to be confirmed; its type description is based on a juvenile male looking like a young *G. cemiculus* (Blackchin Guitarfish) (Séret and McEachran 1986), and the taxonomic status of this species needs further work.

CONSERVATION STATUS

Until the early 1990s, no sharks were listed as threatened on the International Union for Conservation of Nature (IUCN) Red List, but this changed rapidly with the boom in shark-fin trade associated with the rapid economic growth of China and some other Asian economies (Dockerty 1992). The shark-fin boom resulted in a massive increase in shark fishing in Madagascar (A. Cooke 1997; Cripps et al. 2015; Baker-Medard and Faber 2020). Shark fishing was even actively promoted by one development project of Deutsche Gesellschaft für Technische Zusammenarbeit (GTZ; German Technical Cooperation) (du Feu 1998). The result has been the rapid decline of shark populations at many locations around Madagascar (e.g., A. Cooke 1997; McVean et al. 2006; Cripps et al. 2015).

A first Red List assessment of sharks and rays in the western Indian Ocean was conducted in Durban in 2003. Madagascar participated and provided information on 31 sharks and 13 rays represented in the island's shark fisheries (A. Cooke et al. 2003b), which was subsequently consolidated into the IUCN SSC (Species Survival Commission) Shark Specialist Group global assessment of chondrichthyans (Fowler et al. 2005). To date, 104 (87%) of the 119 chondrichthyan species known to occur in Malagasy waters (including two species on the Madagascar Ridge) have been assessed (see IUCN Red List and Table 7.10), of which 39 (33%) are considered to be threatened globally. This latter group includes four species assessed as Critically Endangered (CR)—*Pristis pristis* (Largetooth Sawfish), *Rhina ancylostoma* (Shark Ray), *Rhynchobatus djiddensis* (Whitespotted Wedgefish), and *R. australiae* (Australian Wedgefish); eight species (six sharks and two rays) assessed as Endangered (EN)—*Rhincodon typus* (Whale Shark), *Stegostoma fasciatum* (Zebra Shark), *Isurus oxyrinchus* (Shortfin Mako), *Holohalaelurus punctatus* (African Spotted Catshark), *Sphyrna lewini* (Scalloped Hammerhead Shark), *S. mokarran* (Great Hammerhead), *Rostroraja alba* (White Skate), and *Mobula mobular* (Spinetail Devilray); and 27 species (17 sharks and 10 rays) as Vulnerable (VU). A further 24 species (20 sharks and 4 rays) were assessed as Near Threatened (NT), 25 as Data Deficient (DD), 14 Not Evaluated (NE), and 17 as Least Concern (LC) (Table 7.10).

Eleven shark species and nine ray species occurring in Malagasy waters are listed on the appendixes of the Convention on the International Trade in Endangered Species of Wild Fauna and Flora (CITES) and thereby the subject of a certain level of protection (Table 7.10). The sawfishes, being Critically Endangered, are listed on Appendix I, and their international trade is prohibited. Eleven other species of sharks (mostly large pelagic or benthopelagic species) and eight rays (including benthic and pelagic species) are listed on Appendix II, and their international trade may be authorized based on a valid export permit from the country of origin or re-export certificate. Madagascar's few endemic sharks and rays, however, do not benefit from any international listing or conservation protection because of the lack of data on their populations and biology.

For the protection and the conservation of sharks, Madagascar's authorities rely on the CITES listings and on the recommendations of the IOTC relating to the bycatch of pelagic tuna fisheries. In 2015, the local authorities created a pilot shark sanctuary at Antongil Bay, in which 19 species of sharks have been reported to occur (Doukakis et al. 2007).

Baker-Médard and Faber (2020) surveyed the fishing practices related to sharks and the shark-fin trade in Malagasy waters based on interviews. They pointed out that shark fisheries are not only a source of food for coastal populations but also contribute to improving the standard of living of the stakeholders in this sector. They suggest that management decisions should consider this reality, arguing that a complete ban of all shark fishing could have dramatic consequences for fishing communities, and that a large marine protected area in which shark fishing is forbidden could exacerbate the loss of food sovereignty of these communities. These authors concluded that interactions between nature and society being complex, fishing communities should be involved in the management of the shark fishery, as previously suggested by B. Pascal (2008).

SHARK ATTACKS AROUND MADAGASCAR

Very few shark attacks were recorded for Madagascar from 1844 to 2020 in international and global shark attack files (ISAF and GSAF), which include only eight cases, six of which were fatal. The shark species involved in these attacks are thought to be *Galeocerdo cuvier* (Tiger Shark), *Carcharhinus leucas* (Bull Shark), *C. longimanus* (Oceanic White-tip Shark), and *C. brachyurus* (Copper Shark). The recorded attacks took place in the northern part of the island (Nosy Hara, Nosy Mitsio, Nosy Be) and along the east coast near Toamasina.

These figures are presumed to be highly conservative and probably do not reflect the real number of shark attacks around the island. In the past, sharks proliferated in the coastal waters around the island and groups of sharks prowled around boats anchored in Toamasina harbor carrying cattle destined for the neighboring Mascarene islands. Slaughterhouses in this port were known to attract sharks, making it difficult to practice nautical activities! For many years, the Malagasy coastal communities have learned to live with shark risk, possibly considering that such fatalities were "ordinary" accidents of everyday life not worthy of reporting. A lack of communication is almost also certainly responsible for the small number of reported cases. More recent reports, on the other hand, have indicated very low rates of attack, possibly linked to the massive decline of shark populations since the early 1990s as a result of shark fishing to supply the shark-fin trade (e.g., Smale 1998).

CIGUATERA SHARK POISONING

Since the 1930s, numerous mass poisoning events are known from Madagascar (Champetier de Ribes et al. 1999). They are attributed to the consumption of particular fishes, sea turtles, and sharks. The phenomenon of intoxication by eating such food sources, known as ciguatera fish poisoning, is mostly caused by eating reef fishes whose flesh or organs (e.g., liver, skin) have accumulated toxins originating from small benthic microalgae (dinoflagellates of the genera *Gambierdiscus* and *Fukuyoa*). These toxins, known as ciguatoxins, are transferred along the food chain, finally reaching predators such as the carnivorous fishes. Sharks being top predators with high trophic position in the food chain accumulate these toxins by consuming fishes carrying them. The symptoms of ciguatera are gastrointestinal (e.g., diarrhea, vomiting) and neurological (numbness, itchiness, dizziness). Recovery from poisoning depends on the quantity of ingested toxins, but fatal cases are often reported and in some cases mass mortalities have occurred.

At least 160 episodes of ciguatera shark poisoning have been reported from Madagascar since 1930 (Table 7.11). Information on such events is often mixed and sometimes contradictory. The first significant event happened on 28 November 1993 in Manakara. According to Boisier et al. (1994, 1995), 188 persons were poisoned, with 65 fatalities, owing to the consumption of a single *Carcharhinus leucas*. The same event was reported by Habermehl et al. (1994), who stated that 500 persons consumed flesh and liver of a female *C. amboinensis* (Pigeye Shark), 400 of whom were poisoned and 98 died. These two shark species are difficult to distinguish, which may be part of the cause for the confusion, but the differences in numbers of victims and deaths are more difficult to explain. The old cases from 1930 to 1997 result from retrospective surveys made through interviews or compilation of public health data and most are not objectively documented (R. Robinson et al. 1998; Champetier de Ribes et al. 1999). The most recent scientifically documented cases date from 2013 or 2014 (ANSES 2015; Rabenjarison et al. 2016).

These events involved hundreds of people. In their retrospective study, Champetier de Ribes et al. (1999) tabulated 83 serious and 71 moderate incidents of ciguatera shark poisoning, affecting 1855 consumers, 78 of whom died, or a mortality rate of 4.2%. The number of deaths might be notably higher, as reported mortality rates varied from 20% to 30% depending on the data source. Ciguatera shark poisoning events occur irregularly, with a maximum number of cases in the period 1993–1997 (154 events) presumably associated with the increase in shark fishing during that period to supply the shark-fin trade (e.g., A. Cooke 1997). One consequence of the incidents was a marked reduction in shark-meat exports in 1994–1995. No further event was reported until November 2013, when 116 persons were poisoned after eating meat of a female *C. leucas*, and 11 of them died (Rabenjarison et al. 2016). Subsequently on 22 March 2020, four individuals of the same family were poisoned after eating shark meat in the village of Farahalana in the northeast, and one person died. Other inhabitants of the village were not ill although they had eaten meat of the same shark, but several pets died. The shark species was not identified (*Express de Madagascar*, 26 March 2020).

These poisoning events took place along the southeast coast (Manakara, Tolagnaro, and Vohipeno), northeast coast (Maroantsetra, Sambava, and Antsiranana), and the southwest coast (Befandela, Lanatsono, Lovokampy, and Toliara). The most common shark species involved in these events is *Carcharhinus leucas* (Bull Shark), a euryhaline coastal shark able to penetrate estuaries and rivers (Taniuchi et al. 2003). Other shark species identified, or presumed to be implicated, are *C. amboinensis* (Pigeye Shark), *C. sorrah* (Spot-tail Shark), *Sphyrna lewini* (Scalloped Hammerhead Shark), *Hemipristis elongata* (Snaggletooth Shark), *Galeocerdo cuvier* (Tiger Shark), and *Alopias superciliosus* (Bigeye Thresher Shark). Beside humans, domestic animals such as dogs and cats have also been victims of ciguatera shark poisoning.

The Malagasy population of *C. leucas*, involved in many poisoning cases, is connected to that of Seychelles, as shown by a tracking study (Lea et al. 2015) in which a 3 m pregnant female tagged in Seychelles traveled to Madagascar and followed the eastern coast to Tolagnaro, where it gave birth in shallow waters, then returned to Seychelles (where cases of shark poisoning are unknown!) (Table 7.11).

TABLE 7.11. **List of mass shark poisoning events on Madagascar from 1930**

YEAR	DATE	LOCALITY	GEOGRAPHIC SITUATION	NUMBER OF CONSUMERS	NUMBER OF POISONED PERSONS	NUMBER OF FATALITIES	MORTALITY RATE	SHARK SPECIES INVOLVED	REFERENCE
1993	28–29 November	Manakara	SE coast	188	188	50	26.6%	*Carcharhinus leucas* (~1.5–2 m TL)	Boisier et al. (1994, 1995)
1993	28 November	Manakara	SE coast	500	400	98	20%	*C. amboinensis* (female, 2 m TL)	Habermehl et al. (1994)
1995	October	Tolagnaro (Fort Dauphin)	SE coast	–	62	1 dog	–	Not identified	Champetier de Ribes et al. (1997)
1995	November	Vohipeno	SE coast	457	320	4+ dogs and cats	–	*C. amboinensis*	Champetier de Ribes et al. (1997)
1996	April	Maroantsetra	NE coast	59	59	3	–	*Sphyrna* sp.	Champetier de Ribes et al. (1997)
1996	May	Vohipeno	SE coast	500	250	–	–	*Galeocerdo cuvier*	Champetier de Ribes et al. (1997)
1996		Sambava	NE coast	–	–	–	–	Not identified	Champetier de Ribes et al. (1997)
1996		Mahanoro	E coast	–	–	–	–	Not identified	Champetier de Ribes et al. (1997)
1997		Toliara	SW coast	–	–	–	–	Not identified	Champetier de Ribes et al. (1997)
1993–1998	8 events	Vohipeno (2) Manakara (1) Sambava (1) Maroantsetra (1) Mahanoro (1) Tolagnaro (1) Toliara (1)	SE coast SE coast NE coast NE coast E coast SE coast SW coast		1269	68	5%	*C. leucas*, *C. amboinensis*, *G. cuvier*, *Sphyrna* spp.	Champetier de Ribes et al. (1998)
2013	14–19 November	Fenoarivo-Atsinanana	E coast	116	97 studied	9	11%	*C. leucas* (female, 1.5 m TL)	Rabenjarison et al. (2016)
2013	November			124		9	7%	*C. leucas* (female, 1.5 m TL)	ANSES (2015)
2014	February	?	?	?	?	?	?	Not identified	ANSES (2015)
2020	22 March	Farahalana	NE coast	several	4	1	–	Not identified	*L'Express de Madagascar*, 26 March 2020

DATA ON SHARK POISONING EVENTS IN MADAGASCAR COLLECTED FROM RETROSPECTIVE SURVEYS

PERIOD	NUMBER OF EVENTS	LOCALITIES	GEOGRAPHIC SITUATION	NUMBER OF POISONED PERSONS	NUMBER OF FATALITIES	MORTALITY RATE	SHARK SPECIES INVOLVED	REFERENCE
1945	–	Befandefa	SW coast	–	10	–	*Sphyrna lewini*	R. Robinson et al. (1998)
1992	–	Lanatsono	SW coast	–	3	–	*S. lewini*	R. Robinson et al. (1998)
1993	–	Lovokampy	SW coast	–	3	–	*S. lewini*	R. Robinson et al. (1998)
1993–1996	–	–	SW coast	21	–	–	*S. lewini*	R. Robinson et al. (1998)
1993–1996	–	–	SW coast	2	–	–	*Hemipristis elongata*	R. Robinson et al. (1998)
1993–1996	–	–	SW coast	1	–	–	*Carcharhinus sorrah*	R. Robinson et al. (1998)

PERIOD	NUMBER OF EVENTS	LOCALITIES	GEOGRAPHIC SITUATION	NUMBER OF POISONED PERSONS	NUMBER OF FATALITIES	MORTALITY RATE	SHARK SPECIES INVOLVED	REFERENCE
1993–1996	–	–	SW coast	1	–	–	*Alopias superciliosus*	R. Robinson et al. (1998)
1930–1997	83 serious cases	–	–	1855	78	4%	Sphyrnidae and Carcharhinidae	Champetier de Ribes et al. (1999)
1930–1997	66	Toamasina	E coast	–	–	–	–	Champetier de Ribes et al. (1999)
1930–1997	3	Toliara	SW coast	–	–	–	–	Champetier de Ribes et al. (1999)
1930–1997	8	Antsiranana	NE coast	–	–	–	–	Champetier de Ribes et al. (1999)
1930–1997	6	Fianarantsoa	E coast	–	–	–	–	Champetier de Ribes et al. (1999)
1930–1997	71 moderated cases	–	–					Champetier de Ribes et al. (1999)

Note: TL, total length.

SHARK ECOTOURISM IN MADAGASCAR

Ecotourism, or "green tourism," is defined as responsible travel by national or international visitors to natural areas, where the environment is preserved, for the benefit of the conservation of the fauna and flora of these natural environments and for the well-being of the local people. Shark ecotourism appeared on the international scene about two decades ago and is rapidly growing, with famous "shark spots" such as Dyer Island in South Africa, which offers "scary encounters" with Great White Sharks (*Carcharodon carcharias*). These activities generate important financial revenues, a portion of which can contribute to species conservation and research. In Madagascar, shark ecotourism began only recently (2011), and is focused on *Rhincodon typus* (Whale Shark) along the northwestern coast, mostly around Nosy Be, Nosy Mitsio, and the Radama Islands (Diamant et al. 2018). The development of these activities has been facilitated by the increasing recognition that Whale Sharks are present all year round in the area, with peaks of abundance during the southern summer plankton blooms, from September to December. *Rhincodon typus* is a totemic species, a peaceful giant that has been targeted by fishers for its fins and meat, which is soft and milky white like tofu, hence its name *tofu shark* in Asia.

Beside *R. typus*, certain species of sharks and rays are of considerable interest for local and regional ecotourism activities and attract a growing number of divers: *Stegostoma fasciatum* (Zebra Shark), *Pseudoginglymostoma brevicaudatum* (Short-tail Nurse Shark), the various requiem sharks (*Carcharhinus* spp.), the giant manta rays (*Mobula alfredi*, *M. birostris*, *M. mobular*), and the variegated stingrays (e.g., *Aetobatus ocellatus*, *Taeniura lymma*, *Taeniurops meyeni Urogymnus asperrimus*). Mechanisms need to be developed to help ensure that shark diving contributes to marine conservation.

SHARK FISHERIES AROUND MADAGASCAR

Sharks have been exploited in Malagasy waters for many decades, and associated fisheries have a long history (A. Cooke 1997; Le Manach et al. 2011; Cripps et al. 2015; Baker-Medard and Faber 2020). According to the Food and Agriculture Organization of the United Nations (FAO) database with associated statistics, known as FIGIS (FAO 2021), the exploitation of sharks and rays slowly increased from 550 t in 1950 to about 2000 t in 1978, followed by substantial and rapid growth to reach a peak of 6200 t in 1992 (Figure 7.16), also a peak year for shark-fin exports (A. Cooke 1997). This increase in production was driven by the strong demand for shark products, mainly shark fins, for international trade. Since 1997, levels of shark production in Madagascar's waters appear stable around 5700 t per year.

These official data—that is, the national data declared by Madagascar to the FAO—are not presented by species, so it is not possible to know which species are exploited and in what proportions. It is also likely that these data underestimate the true scale of catches. Le Manach et al. (2011) reconstructed marine fisheries data for Madagascar. For the period 1950–2008, these authors estimated that global captures were underreported by as much as 590% in the 1950s, dropping to about 40% in the 2000s. Their own estimates

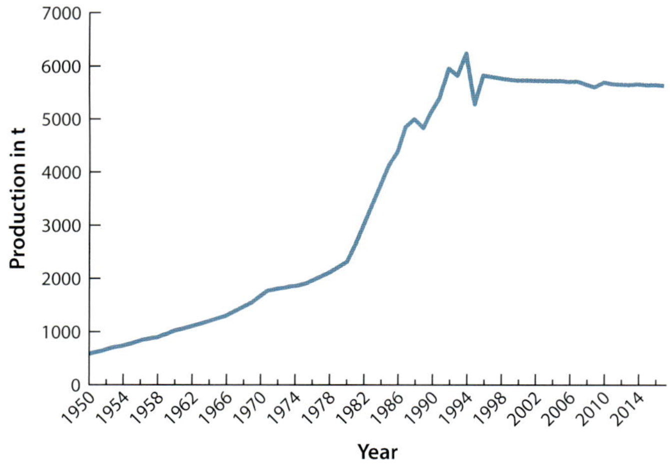

FIGURE 7.16 **Evolution of the production (in tons) of sharks and rays declared by Madagascar to the FAO since 1950.** (SOURCE: FAO 2021).

for shark catches were actually less than the official data reported to FAO, suggesting that the official data used for reporting to FAO were not available to them at the time of their study. Underreporting of shark-fin exports in particular was estimated at 40% for the peak year of 1992 (A. Cooke 1997). These discrepancies confirm that there is a real need to collect accurate data on shark catches around the island.

Commonly, three categories of fisheries are distinguished in Malagasy waters: 1) small-scale fisheries practiced with canoes (<15 horsepower [hp] if motorized) or on foot, 2) artisanal fisheries performed with motorized small boats (engines of 15–50 hp), and 3) industrial fisheries involving large vessels (engines >50 hp).

The small-scale fishery makes up the bulk of the national landed catch of sharks. Various studies carried out with the support of international nongovernmental organizations (NGOs) have surveyed these fisheries, but for short periods and for only a few selected fishing areas (A. Cooke 1997; McVean et al. 2006; Doukakis et al. 2007, 2011; Cripps et al. 2015; Humber 2015; Andriamanaitra et al. 2016; Humber et al. 2017a). Despite the limited geographic scope and duration of these studies, it is clear that shark populations have rapidly declined owing to overexploitation. About 25 shark species and five ray species are caught by these fisheries—the main ones being hammerhead sharks (mostly *Sphyrna lewini*), *Loxodon macrorhinus* (Sliteye Shark), and the guitar- and wedgefishes (mostly *Rhynchobatus djiddensis*)—and these species make up to 75% of the total catches. Other species include various requiem sharks: *Carcharhinus amblyrhynchos*, *C. melanopterus*, *C. sorrah*, *C. brevipinna*, and *Rhizoprionodon acutus* (Milk Shark).

Industrial fisheries are mostly conducted by foreign fleets of large long-liners and purse seiners. These fisheries are monitored by the IOTC, to which the countries fishing in the Indian Ocean are required to report annually the catches for each EEZ. Sharks are a significant bycatch of these pelagic fisheries. The national reports for Madagascar (Razafimandimby et al. 2015; Razafimandimby and Leslie 2017) indicate that sharks represented 10% to 16% of the total catch of tuna long-line fisheries in 2015–2017, with a decrease in production from 95 t in 2010 to 36 t in 2016, and the catch per unit effort (CPUE) also decreasing from 14 kg/100 hooks in 2012 to 3 kg/100 hooks in 2016. The main species captured as a result of these pelagic fisheries are *Prionace glauca* (Blue Shark; 61%), *Isurus oxyrhinchus* (Shortfin Mako; 32%), and *Carcharhinus falciformis* (Silky Shark; 10%). These figures appear inconsistent with the IOTC (2021) database, which reports a total of 5638 t of sharks declared for the Malagasy EEZ in 2017 for the western Indian Ocean. This figure corresponds closely to the 5700 t of the FAO database, suggesting that IOTC and FAO are using the same data sources, but that both are ignoring landed catches from small-scale coastal fisheries. Hammerhead and thresher sharks do not appear in the 2018 IOTC data, presumably because their catch is forbidden by IOTC resolutions. However, no information is available on accidental bycatch or subsequent release of these species.

LOOKING FORWARD

While sharks have been exploited for more than a century in Malagasy waters, they have received no legal protection (Humber et al. 2015) and little management attention. National legislation urgently needs to be updated in line with CITES and other treaties to protect the significant number of threatened species, including sawfishes, guitarfishes, and *Rhincodon typus* (Whale Shark). A recently announced national plan of action for sharks, which calls for a "shark trade surveillance program, a crackdown on illegal industrial fishing, establishment of more 'no-take' zones, and a concerted effort to collect better fisheries and trade data" (Carver 2019), needs to be formally adopted and implemented by the fisheries administration. Indeed, Madagascar needs to increase national capacity for monitoring and surveillance of all fisheries, including those involving sharks and rays, and to enforce the application of IOTC resolutions, including a ban on shark finning and on the capture of forbidden species (*R. typus*, hammerhead sharks, thresher sharks, oceanic sharks). To ensure a future for the shark and ray populations in Malagasy waters, conservation and protection measures should be urgently taken, and with the same urgency research programs should be developed to increase our scientific knowledge of these particular populations.

Subject editors: Andrew Cooke and Steven M. Goodman

RHINCODON TYPUS, WHALE SHARK, *MAROKINTANA*

S. Diamant, J. J. Kiszka, and S. J. Pierce

Rhincodon typus, or Whale Shark, is an iconic species: it is the world's largest fish, and indeed the largest of all living ectothermic (cold-blooded) animals. *Rhincodon typus* grows to a maximum length of around 20 m and over 30 t in weight (Chen et al. 1997) and is likely to live for more than a century (Perry et al. 2018; Ong et al. 2020). *Rhincodon typus* is the sole living member of the family Rhincodontidae. Coupled with the species' Endangered status on the International Union for Conservation of Nature (IUCN) Red List of Threatened Species (Pierce and Norman 2016), these factors have resulted in its listing as an EDGE (Evolutionarily Distinct and Globally Endangered) species, representing a high global priority for conservation owing to the significant level of unique evolutionary history it embodies (EDGE 2020). This species is also listed on Appendix I of the United Nations Convention on the Conservation of Migratory Species of Wild Animals (CMS) and Appendix II of the Convention on International Trade in Endangered Species of Wild Fauna and Flora (CITES).

Rhincodon typus displays a high level of morphological and ecological divergence from its distant relatives within the order Orectolobiformes, most of which are small to medium-size sharks that feed on crustaceans, mollusks, and small fishes. *Rhincodon typus*, in rather extreme contrast, is a highly mobile filter-feeding zooplanktivore that roams widely to exploit patchy prey resources in both coastal marine areas and the open ocean.

Rhincodon typus is a circumtropical species that seasonally penetrates temperate waters, preferring surface temperatures above 21°C (Duffy 2002; Afonso et al. 2014). Its presence is usually linked to food availability, and it can form aggregations of several hundred individuals in certain areas to exploit seasonal prey pulses, such as tuna spawning off the Quintana Roo coast of Mexico (de la Parra Venegas et al. 2011) and off Qatar (D. Robinson et al. 2013). Several significant feeding areas have also been noted in the western Indian Ocean, as detailed in the next section.

Outside such seasonal aggregations, *R. typus* individuals appear to live largely solitary lives. They are capable of long-distance movements—thousands of kilometers per year—and deep dives (recorded to 1928 m) in their search for food in the deep scattering layer of oceanic waters (R. Graham et al. 2006; Tyminski et al. 2015). In some regions, their presence is strongly linked with oceanographic fronts and upwelling zones (Ramírez-Macías et al. 2017; Ryan et al. 2017). *Rhincodon typus* is routinely viewed as an important ecological indicator of the presence of high-value commercial fishes such as tuna, with which it is strongly associated (Rowat and Brooks 2012; Fox et al. 2013).

Two genetically distinct populations of *R. typus* have been identified on a global level, in the Atlantic Ocean and Indo-Pacific region, respectively (Vignaud et al. 2014; Meekan et al. 2017; Yagishita et al. 2020). The latter, encompassing both the Indian and Pacific Oceans, is currently believed to hold approximately 63% of the global effective population of *R. typus*, based on mitochondrial DNA analysis. However, the absolute number of individuals in the Indo-Pacific has been significantly reduced, by an estimated 63%, since targeted fisheries began in the early 1980s (Pierce and Norman 2016). Incidental and directed captures in various fisheries are likely to be the main drivers of this decline. There are also strong indications that finer population structure is present across this vast region (Norman et al. 2017; Yagishita et al. 2020).

RHINCODON TYPUS IN THE WESTERN INDIAN OCEAN AND MADAGASCAR

Analysis of observations from tuna purse-seine fishing fleets indicates that the Mozambique Channel has some of the highest densities of *Rhincodon typus* observed in the Indian Ocean (Sequeira et al. 2012; Escalle et al. 2016). The seasonal movements of *R. typus* are currently unclear, however. Field data from satellite tracking (Diamant et al. 2018; Rohner et al. 2018), ocean-level photo identification (Andrzejaczek et al. 2016; Norman et al. 2017; Prebble et al. 2018), and biochemical tracer data (Prebble et al. 2018) all consistently indicate that short- to medium-term connectivity among individuals is limited between the known feeding aggregations in the western Indian Ocean. Such areas include the Inhambane coast of Mozambique, Mafia Island in Tanzania, Mahé in the Seychelles, the Gulf of Tadjoura in Djibouti, and other sites (Norman et al. 2017). However, all of these areas are dominated by juvenile male *R. typus*, generally 3–9 m in length, while the movements of adults are still poorly known in the region (Norman et al. 2017; Prebble et al. 2018).

In Malagasy waters, the distribution of *R. typus* extends from north to south along both coasts. In the west, it has been reported as seasonally present off Toliara from March to May (A. Cooke et al. 2003a) and is regularly sighted, and occasionally captured, by Vezo fishermen in the southwest of the country (Humber et al. 2015). In the east, this species has been observed in Antongil Bay and around Ile Sainte Marie in the northeast (A. Saloma, unpublished data); *R. typus* has also been documented from the Toamasina area and observed off Tolagnaro in April (A. Cooke et al. 2003a). One female *R. typus* satellite tagged in southern Mozambique traveled across the Mozambique Channel to southeast Madagascar, covering 1200 km in 87 days (Brunnschweiler et al. 2009). Most sightings of the species, though, come from the northwest. Its persistent presence in the northwest may be related to the spawning of *Thunnus albacares* (Yellowfin Tuna) and *Katsuwonus pelamis* (Skipjack Tuna), especially the latter, whose spawning area extends along the entire northwest coast, including Nosy Be (Stéquert and Marsac 1986).

According to local communities, *R. typus* has always been present in this region, particularly around Nosy Be. Rachel Graham from

MarAlliance, then with the Wildlife Conservation Society, conducted research on this species between 2005 and 2009 around Nosy Be, collecting photo-identification data and deploying both acoustic and satellite tags. She also initiated interviews with fishers to investigate the occurrence of *R. typus*, from which results were published by Jonahson and Harding (2007), confirming the regular presence of these animals in this area. In the course of this work, the Malagasy vernacular name for this species—*marokintana*, which means "[the shark with] many stars"—came to the attention of researchers.

Tourism associated with Whale Sharks started around Nosy Be in the late 2000s. Dedicated "swim with Whale Sharks" tourism providers started operations in 2011, generally working between September and December, the period when this species can be reliably found (Diamant et al. 2018). In 2015, S. Diamant began a long-term monitoring study, known as the Madagascar Whale Shark Project, in collaboration with Nosy Be tourism operator Les Baleines Rand'eau, the Marine Megafauna Foundation, and Florida International University. The project has demonstrated that northwest Madagascar is a hotspot for juvenile *R. typus*. Subsequent work, summarized below, has shown that the Nosy Be area is not only one of the larger Indian Ocean aggregation sites for this species, in terms of the number of individual sharks known to use the area, but also a significant site on a global level.

ECOLOGY

Rhincodon typus feeds on zooplankton and small fish species (Rowat and Brooks 2012). Primary productivity is relatively low and variable in tropical waters, and potential prey are patchily distributed. This species appears to use probabilistic foraging strategies, such as search behaviors (Sims et al. 2008), to find prey in the relatively homogeneous open-ocean environment. This behavior is characterized by a cluster of short steps, with seemingly haphazard changes in direction between them, followed by longer, straight-line movement steps. This "random" movement is thought to be the optimal search pattern while foraging for sparse prey that are beyond the sharks' sensory range.

Although its metabolism is relatively slow compared to similarly sized endotherms, such as baleen whales (Meekan et al. 2015), *R. typus* still requires a significant quantity of food. Captive Whale Sharks ingest ~1% of their body mass each day in the Okinawa Churaumi Aquarium (Matsumoto et al. 2017), and ~3–5% per week at Georgia Aquarium (Schreiber and Coco 2017). In the wild, the unpredictable nature of prey availability in the open ocean likely means that periods of enforced fasting are common (Wyatt et al. 2019). Unsurprisingly then, many individuals will regularly return to areas with predictable, seasonally high prey densities. For example, two animals have been observed to return to Ningaloo Reef off Western Australia almost every year for over 20 years (Norman and Morgan 2016), and a high degree of seasonal site fidelity is common at known feeding areas (Norman et al. 2017). While individuals will return to known feeding hotspots, population-level migratory behaviors (along regular corridors) are not known to occur in these animals.

The ecological roles of *R. typus* in the marine ecosystem are not well understood, but inferences can be made from other animals that share similar ecological traits, including baleen whales (Doughty et al. 2016; Estes et al. 2016). *Rhincodon typus* performs a variety of functions in ecosystems, as consumer, as prey, and as a source of detritus. The species consumes large quantities of biomass. For example, rough calculations from Mexico suggest that a medium-size juvenile individual (6.2 m in total length) would ingest 142.5 kg of tuna eggs during a day, equating to approximately 180,000 kilojoules (Tyminski et al. 2015). These consumption rates may have significant impact on prey dynamics (Estes et al. 2016) and on nutrient cycling. Owing to the nature of their movements (both horizontal and vertical), Whale Sharks have the potential to translocate nutrients between marine habitats through excretion and egestion (Roman et al. 2014; Estes et al. 2016). The importance of *R. typus* could be particularly significant in tropical oligotrophic waters. It dives extensively and likely plays a role in opposing the downward flux of carbon to the deep ocean, while transferring energy and materials, including key limiting nutrients such as nitrogen, from the mesopelagic (twilight zone) into the euphotic zone (0–200 m).

While even the larger *R. typus* may occasionally be prey to large marine predators, particularly *Orcinus orca* (Killer Whale), and possibly large sharks (Carcharhinidae and Lamnidae) (Rowat and Brooks 2012), it is while individuals are still relatively small (<2 m) that they are likely to be most vulnerable. Small individuals have been found in the stomachs of *Makaira mazara* (Indo-Pacific Blue Marlin) and *Prionace glauca* (Blue Shark) (Colman 1997). The uniquely large litter size of *R. typus* among live-bearing shark species, which can be ~300 pups (Joung et al. 1996), suggests an evolutionary strategy to counter a high pup mortality rate.

Natural and human-related mortality will have ecological consequences. After death, *R. typus* carcasses sink to the seafloor, where they provide food and habitat for deep-sea organisms (Higgs et al. 2014; Estes et al. 2016). While the carcasses of these fish have seldom been reported, carcasses, or "whale falls," have been subject to study. Their carcasses can go through progressive changes during decomposition over long, decadal time periods, during which time hundreds of different species are supported by this nutritionally rich, large-magnitude, and infrequent resource (Goffredi et al. 2004; Estes et al. 2016). Over 60 species of deep-sea macrofauna are known solely from whale falls, and numerous other species associated with cold seeps and hydrothermal vents have also been found within whale falls (Estes et al. 2016). Given the inherently short-lived nature of vent systems, whale—and Whale Shark—falls are likely to be important stepping-stones in the spatial ecology of the deep-sea environment.

THE MADAGASCAR WHALE SHARK PROJECT

The Madagascar Whale Shark Project has been monitoring the population of *Rhincodon typus* around Nosy Be since 2015, primarily through boat-based surveys from partner tourism operators, bolstered by tourism-independent small-boat surveys. From September to December, *R. typus* is typically seen around Nosy Be, associated with bait balls created by *Euthynnus affinis* (Mackerel Tunny or Kawakawa); *jodar* in Malagasy), feeding on juvenile Spanish mackerel (*Selar boops* and *S. crumenophthalmus*) and sardines (*Sardinella longiceps*) (Figure 7.17). These bait balls usually attract seabirds,

FIGURE 7.17 **A *Rhincodon typus* (Whale Shark) "vertical feeding" among tuna.** (PHOTO by S. Diamant.)

mostly terns (family Sternidae), and produce intense surface activity, easily visible from afar. One or more *R. typus* are routinely present. *Rhincodon typus* has the largest inner ear of any animal (Muller 1999) and is likely to be attuned to respond to long-wavelength and low-frequency sounds, such as the splashing sounds of baitfishes at the surface being attacked by predators (Fox et al. 2013). Similar behaviors have been reported in Djibouti (Boldrocchi and Bettinetti 2019), Honduras (Fox et al. 2013), and the Philippines (Araujo et al. 2019).

Associations between tuna and *R. typus* have been documented since decades (Silas 1986), but the drivers and dynamics of these interactions are not well understood. Around Nosy Be, the drivers of the association between *R. typus* and shoaling tunas have not yet been studied. There may be a mutual benefit for the tuna and sharks. Field observations suggest the panicked baitfishes will sometimes seek "refuge" around a shark, a phenomenon that is exploited by industrial purse-seine fishing (Fontes et al. 2020). The clustered fish will presumably prove an easier target for the tuna, and also enable the shark to employ suction feeding to ingest the small fish.

Surface associations between seabirds, tuna, and *R. typus* are easy to detect from small boats, which has helped us to conduct in-water observations and collect photo-identification data on individual animals. The sharks have varying spot patterns on their flanks, unique to each animal, which allows individuals to be easily distinguished through visual comparison (Norman et al. 2017; Pierce et al. 2018). In total, 408 *R. typus* individuals have been identified from over 1000 encounters off Nosy Be between 2015 and 2019, with 80 to 140 individual sharks identified each season. These sharks have all been added to the global online photo-identification database for the species, Wildbook for Whale Sharks (www.whaleshark.org), which holds records for over 11,000 identified *R. typus* from much of its worldwide range. To date, none of the sharks from Madagascar has been sighted in the waters of another country.

A combination of laser photogrammetry (Rohner et al. 2011, 2015) and visual estimation has been used to estimate the size of *R. typus* present off Nosy Be. To date, all the sharks seen since 2015 have ranged from 3 m to 8 m in total length (TL). Individuals of both sexes are thought to reach maturity at 9–10 m TL in the western Indian Ocean, based on the calcification of claspers in males (claspers are a pair of organs derived from the pelvic fins and used in mating) and on the examination of a small number of stranded female sharks. None of the male sharks sighted at Nosy Be had calcified claspers (an indication of sexual maturity). Pronounced sexual segregation is also present, with 81% of identified sharks around Nosy Be being juvenile males. Therefore, Nosy Be is important as a feeding area for juvenile *R. typus*, particularly males, rather than as a breeding site. This bias toward immature males is a common characteristic of coastal *R. typus* feeding aggregations throughout its range (Rohner et al. 2015; Norman et al. 2017).

Although interannual repeat-sighting rates are comparatively low, at about 25% to date, some individual sharks return to Nosy Be annually. One 5 m juvenile male, with the data code MD-151 and nicknamed Michel, has been sighted on more than 80 separate days across the 2015–2019 seasons. This highly philopatric individual holds the record as the most frequently seen shark every year since the project began (S. Diamant et al., unpublished data).

In October 2016, the project team deployed eight tethered SPOT5 satellite tags on juvenile *R. typus*, with successful tracking durations from 9 to 199 days, covering horizontal distances up to 4275 km (Diamant et al. 2018). Kernel density plots showed that the main activity hotspot for tagged sharks was around Nosy Be (Figure 7.18), confirming its importance as a feeding area. Interestingly, some of the sharks also spent a significant amount of time at a second area near Pointe Analalava, around 180 km south of Nosy Be. Further work in this geographic area will be carried out in upcoming years to investigate its importance for Whale Sharks as a feeding area. None of the eight tagged sharks returned to Nosy Be after the end of the tracking period "season" (December 2016), but six of them were sighted around Nosy Be in 2017, 2018, and 2019 (after the tags were shed), demonstrating again that individual sharks can show a high degree of site fidelity.

Alongside the research on population ecology, the project group is also working with operators to promote the use of international best practices in *R. typus* ecotourism (Figure 7.19), with educational workshops helping guides to build their knowledge base. Data have also been collected from tourists to calculate the economic value of these activities to the local economy.

The project, through collaboration with local nongovernmental organization MADA Megafauna, has initiated an educational program for schoolchildren on Nosy Be, building on materials developed by Marine Megafauna Foundation for Mozambique, and a popular movement called Les Gardiens des Océans, or Guardians of the Oceans. This initiative gathers youths living on Nosy Be for a range of projects, such as an annual marine biodiversity festival, street activities for the community, and weekly activities on the beach. The goal of the project is to empower and educate youths of Nosy Be about their marine environment. Together, these local projects aim to support the development of sustainable tourism and community-based conservation initiatives in Nosy Be and surrounding areas, using as *R. typus* as an excellent "ambassador species."

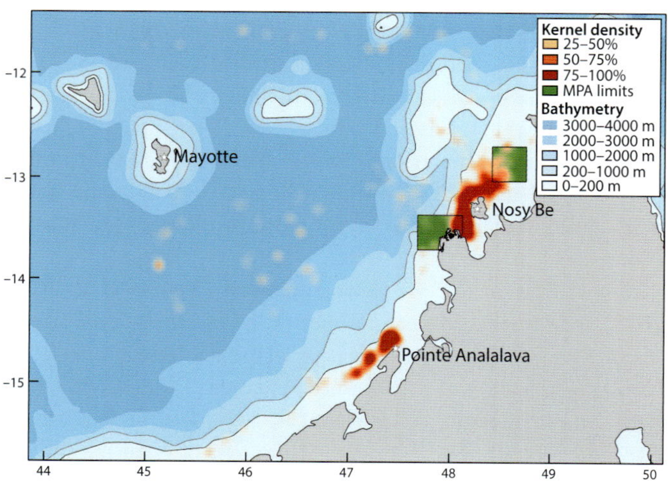

FIGURE 7.18 **Kernel density analysis of transmitted locations from Whale Sharks (*Rhincodon typus*) that were satellite tagged off Nosy Be.**

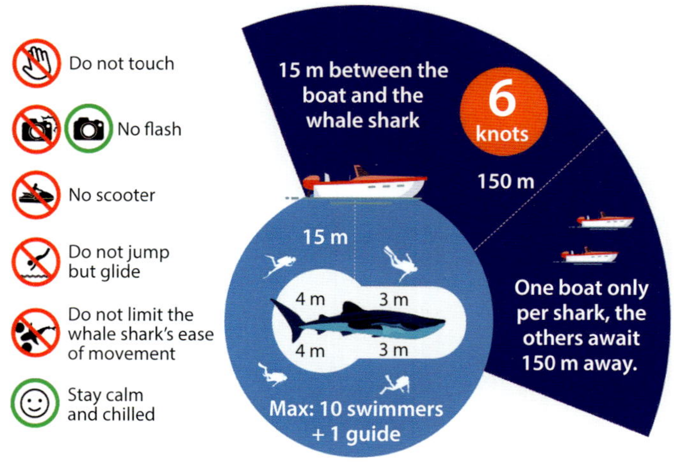

FIGURE 7.19 **Poster for the Madagascar Whale Shark Project's recommended code of conduct for Whale Shark interactions, specifically oriented for ecotourism.**

HUMAN THREATS AND CONSERVATION OPPORTUNITIES

As noted earlier, *Rhincodon typus* is considered globally Endangered by the IUCN. The species has suffered an estimated >50% population decline since the 1980s, when commercial target fisheries developed in the Indian and western Pacific oceans (Pierce and Norman 2016). Whale Sharks face ongoing threats from targeted fishing and bycatch (Li et al. 2012; Dulvy et al. 2017), ship strikes (Speed et al. 2008), and pollution (Germanov et al. 2018, 2019). In the western Indian Ocean specifically, they are caught as bycatch in gillnets (Kiszka and van der Elst 2015; Temple et al. 2019) and tuna purse-seine fisheries (Capietto et al. 2014), and are likely to be subjected to ship strikes (Speed et al. 2008).

Significant regional declines in *R. typus* sightings have been documented within the western Indian Ocean (Pierce and Norman 2016). A 79% decline in sightings of this species was observed from 2005 to 2011 off the Inhambane coast of Mozambique (Rohner et al. 2013), which has persisted since (Rohner et al. 2018). An ~50% decline in peak monthly sightings was also reported from the Mozambique Channel between 1991 and 2007 (Sequeira et al. 2013a, 2013b; Pierce and Norman 2016). Around Mahé in the Seychelles, where *R. typus* was seasonally common previously (Rowat et al. 2009, 2011), it has been sighted only rarely over the past few years (D. Rowat, unpublished data).

The primary cause of this decline in sightings remains unclear. While targeted commercial fisheries for *R. typus* have occurred in India and Southeast Asia in particular, these threats have not been directly linked to decreases in sightings of this species in the western Indian Ocean. To the best of our knowledge, *R. typus* has rarely been targeted in fisheries in the western Indian Ocean. While ongoing bycatch in the region remains a potential threat (Diamant et al. 2018; Rohner et al. 2018), the small catches documented to date are unlikely to be responsible for the rapid declines in sightings that have been noted from Mozambique and Seychelles. Changing environmental conditions, and subsequent shifts in *R. typus* foraging locations, may also be involved. More data are clearly required to evaluate the relative importance of direct and indirect influences on regional populations of this species.

Rhincodon typus represents a unique conservation opportunity for Madagascar. Discussions with communities around Nosy Be have led us to believe that these sharks are rarely, if ever, targeted by local fishers; rather, they are believed to be associated with good fortune and fish abundance (S. Diamant, unpublished data). Whale Sharks are also highly valuable to the growing marine tourism industry in this region. However, fishing pressure is increasing in northwest Madagascar, and *R. typus* is not legally protected from fishing in the country. While Madagascar is obliged to consider the conservation needs of *R. typus* following its listing in Appendix I of the CMS in 2017, and Madagascar originally proposed the listing of this species in Appendix II of the Convention on International Trade in Endangered Species of Wild Fauna and Flora (CITES) in 2002, no specific measures have been introduced to date, and it remains unprotected under national legislation other than that accorded in the context of marine protected areas (MPAs), where they occur.

At this stage, habitat degradation and disruption of shark foraging as a consequence of natural-resource extraction is likely to be a key threat to *R. typus* in this region. Multiple offshore seismic surveys have been undertaken over the last two decades by multinational oil and gas companies in the northwest. While the impact of seismic surveys on Whale Sharks remains unclear, such activities can affect zooplankton populations (McCauley et al. 2017) and potentially Whale Shark behavior (Ito et al. 2017). The planned development of a rare-earths mine on the Ampasindava Peninsula, south of Nosy Be, could also impact marine life in general, and *R. typus* populations specifically, if mitigation measures are not sufficient to prevent the release of sediments into the surrounding marine environment. Finally, given the close association between *R. typus* and small tuna species in this area, overfishing of tuna may also affect Whale Sharks.

Two community-managed MPAs, Ankivonjy (1394 km^2) and Ankarea (1356 km^2), have been created close to Nosy Be. These were established in 2010 by the Wildlife Conservation Society and given permanent protection status in April 2015. However, satellite-tracking results of *R. typus* have shown a limited overlap between these two MPAs and the preferred habitat of Whale Sharks (Diamant et al. 2018). The main foraging habitats are around Nosy Be and to the south near Pointe Analalava. These findings highlight the need to identify where habitat protection could be extended to benefit this species.

After initial discussions with stakeholders in 2016, a formalized (albeit voluntary) code of conduct for Whale Shark tourism based on standards used elsewhere in the Indian Ocean, such as in Mozambique, has been developed and is used by most local tourism operators. However, as some operators are informal, and private vessels are occasionally present, further licensing and management is required to maintain high Whale Shark tourism standards going forward. Over 40% of the identified *R. typus* population around Madagascar bear scars that are likely from lacerations by boat propellers. Boat collisions can result in serious injuries to the sharks. There are no regulations in place to mitigate this risk, other than the voluntary code of conduct, contrary to the case for Humpback Whale (*Megaptera novaeangliae*) watching, which has its own legislation (see Rosenbaum and Chou, pp. 430–33)

Unmanaged tourism could also disturb sharks as they engage in foraging or resting behavior (Haskell et al. 2015). In 2018, the Madagascar Whale Shark Project filed a request with the Ministère du Tourisme to add the above-mentioned code of conduct to an existing inter-ministerial order that regulates the commercial observation of *M. novaeangliae*. Upcoming survey data from tourist-expenditure studies are likely to reinforce the public benefit of applying best practices to tourism and providing further protection to the species.

In June 2019, the Madagascar government—through the leadership of both the Ministère de l'Agriculture, de l'Elevage et de la Pêche and the Ministère de l'Environnement et du Développement Durable and with support from Wildlife Conservation Society—released a national plan for the conservation and sustainable management of sharks and rays (see Séret, pp. 368–80). The plan calls for a shark-trade surveillance program, a crackdown on illegal industrial fishing, more no-take zones for key species, and a concerted effort to collect better data. The shark conservation plan could serve as a framework for the ongoing efforts to conserve one of Madagascar's most spectacular and valuable species of endangered marine megafauna.

Subject editors: Andrew Cooke and Steven M. Goodman

PRISTIDAE, SAWFISHES, *VAHAVAHA, VAVANA*

R. H. Leeney

Sawfishes are cartilaginous fishes belonging to the class Chondrichthyes (sharks, rays, and chimaeras). The sawfish family, the Pristidae, comprises five species of sawfishes worldwide, belonging to two genera. Of these, three species are known to have occurred historically in the western Indian Ocean: *Pristis pristis* (Largetooth Sawfish, also known in Australia as the Freshwater Sawfish), *P. zijsron* (Green Sawfish), and *Anoxypristis cuspidata* (Narrow Sawfish). Sawfishes are considered euryhaline (they can tolerate a wide range of salinities) and are found in rivers, lakes, estuaries, and marine waters. They are restricted to the nearshore waters of the continental shelves and regularly use shallow marine habitats. Young sawfishes prefer very shallow water, often being observed in depths of c. 0.25 m to help them avoid predators (Whitty et al. 2009; Simpfendorfer et al. 2010). The shallow depth distribution and the use of freshwater and estuarine habitats may reduce the risk of predation. As juvenile sawfishes grow in length and mass the risk of predation is likely to decrease, and they are found in more varied habitats and deeper waters (Simpfendorfer et al. 2014).

SAWFISH TAXONOMY

Following a thorough study of morphology, genetics, and distribution of living sawfishes and museum specimens, V. Faria et al. (2013) resolved the centuries-long confusion around sawfish taxonomy and determined that five species should be recognized. *Pristis pristis* has a circumtropical distribution with geographic structure represented by four genetic haplotype populations: eastern Pacific, western Atlantic, eastern Atlantic, and Indo–West Pacific. Some of these populations were previously considered to represent different species, including *P. microdon* and *P. perotteti*, which are now considered synonyms of *P. pristis*.

HISTORICAL DISTRIBUTION ON MADAGASCAR

The earliest known record for sawfishes in Malagasy waters is that of Pollen and Van Dam (1874), who noted that sawfishes were "not rare," especially in the Mozambique Channel, and that they had collected several rostra from fishers on Nosy Faly. Historical records indicate that sawfishes were present in a number of areas, including the Mananjary River (A. Grandidier 1899), Antongil Bay (Smale 1998), Nosy Be (Maillaud 1999), Bombetoka Bay and the mouth of the Betsiboka River (Taniuchi et al. 2003), Lake Kinkony (Kiener and Theresien 1965), and the Mangoky River (at Beroroha, c. 200 km from the river mouth; Kiener 1964).

At least two species of sawfishes were previously considered to exist in Madagascar's waters, based on historical reports, but there has until recently been some confusion around sawfish taxonomy. Kiener (1964) reported that *P. microdon* (now *P. pristis*) was relatively common, while "*P. cuspidatus*," now known as *Anoxypristis cuspidata*, had been caught occasionally in the northwest. There are no other reports of *A. cuspidata* from Madagascar, and all other historical records where species is specified refer either to *P. microdon* or *P. perotteti* (both now considered to be *P. pristis*). Records (including photographic evidence) of sawfishes encountered in the freshwater reaches of rivers and in Lake Kinkony (e.g., Kiener and Theresien 1965) indicate the presence of *P. pristis*, and this is the only sawfish species known to use freshwater habitats (Kyne et al. 2014). A baseline study between 2015 and 2017 to establish the historical distribution and current presence of sawfishes in Malagasy waters documented 30 rostra (R. H. Leeney and A. B. Adouhouri, unpublished data), and all were identified as *P. pristis* (Whitty et al. 2014), suggesting that this is the only species currently present in the country.

Sawfishes should not be confused with sawsharks (family Pristiophoriformes), which also occur in Malagasy waters and have been documented largely from the west coast. Specimens from southwest Madagascar have contributed to the description of a new species, *Pliotrema kajae* (Kaja's Sixgill Sawshark), which has been documented from southwestern Madagascar and the Mascarene Ridge (Weigmann et al. 2020; see Figure 7.20c). Sawsharks are physically distinct from sawfishes in a number of ways. All sawshark species have maximum lengths of less than 200 cm (*P. kajae* is thought to reach a maximum length of c. 143 cm), while *Pristis pristis* can reach over 7 m in length (Peverell 2009). Being true sharks, the gill slits of sawsharks are positioned laterally on the body, whereas in sawfishes they are found ventrally. Sawsharks have triangular rostra that taper to a point, whereas sawfishes and particularly *P. pristis* have a broad rostrum with roughly parallel edges and a rounded tip. In sawsharks, a barbel extends from both lateral edges of the rostrum. The rostral teeth are fine and needlelike in *Pliotrema kajae*, and one to four shorter teeth are found between longer teeth, of which there are between 22 and 31 per side (Weigmann et al. 2020). In *Pristis pristis*, there are between 14 and 24 rostral teeth per side (Whitty et al. 2014). These teeth are more uniform in length, and are thicker and larger, especially in adults.

LOCAL NAMES

Local Malagasy names for sawfishes include *pampa upanga* and *vavano* (Fourmanoir 1963b), *vava* or *vahavaha* (A. Cooke 1997; McVean et al. 2006), *varvana* or *vavana* (R. H. Leeney and A. B. Adouhouri, unpublished data), *vavàno* (Sibree 1915), and *vahy vahy* or *vaevae* (R. H. Leeney and A. B. Adouhouri, unpublished data). However, sawsharks are also called *vaevae* by fishers in Andavadoaka who catch sawsharks and who may not have encountered sawfishes, potentially causing some confusion.

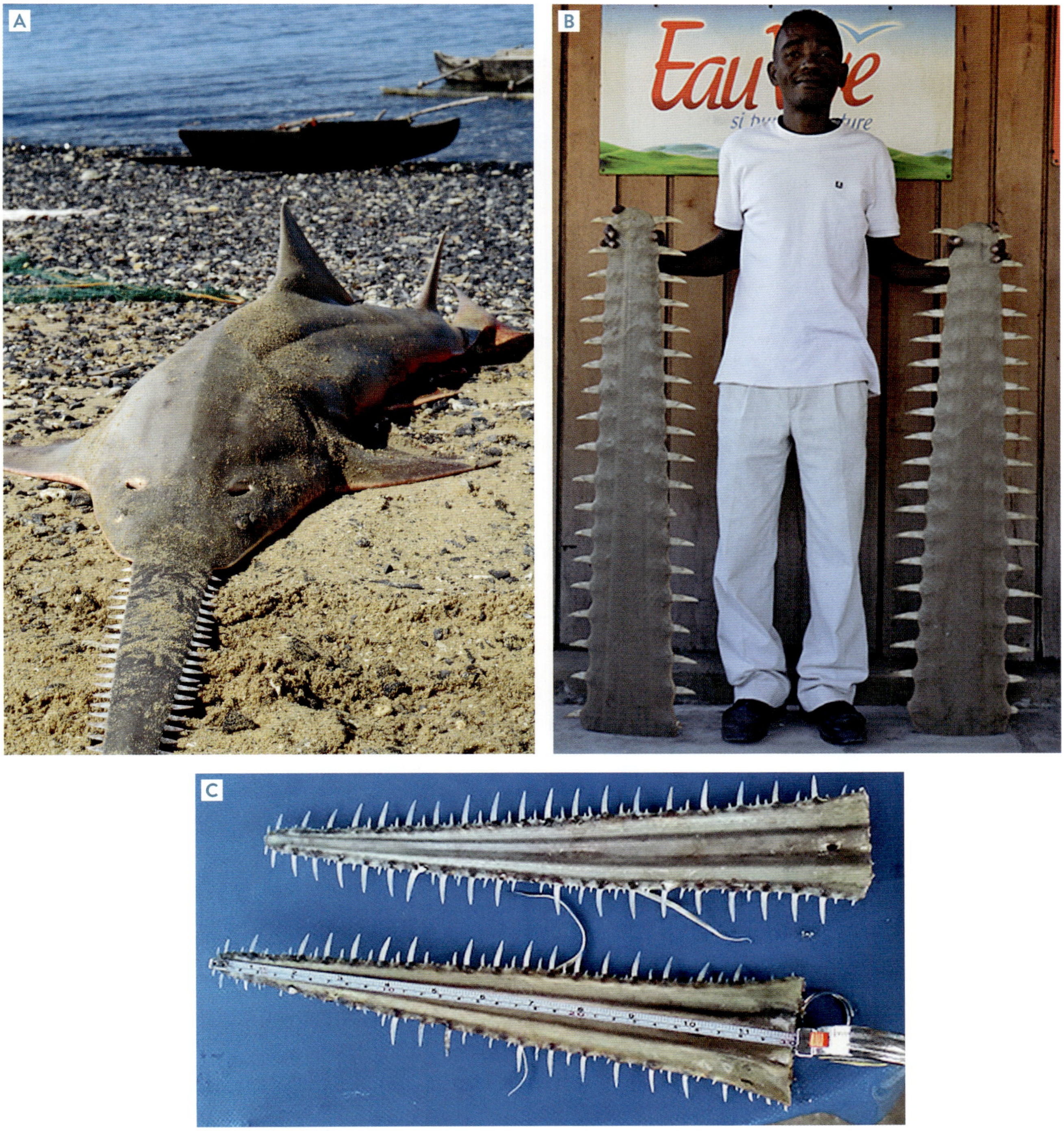

FIGURE 7.20 **A) *Pristis pristis* (Largetooth Sawfish) on a beach on Nosy Be in 2005; B) *P. pristis* rostra on display at a hotel in Morondava in 2015; and C) rostra from *Pliotrema kajae* (Kaja's Sixgill Sawshark), landed in Andavadoaka in 2016.** (PHOTO A by P. Laboute, IRD; B by R. H. Leeney; and C by M. Strogoff.)

PRISTIS PRISTIS

Biology and Ecology

At birth, *Pristis pristis* is between 73 cm and 91 cm in total length (from the tip of the rostrum to the upper tip of the tail; Thorson 1976; Peverell 2009). Adults can reach between 6 m and 7 m in length, making *P. pristis* the largest of all of the world's sawfish species (Figure 7.20a), and they are thought to live to a maximum age of 80 years (Peverell 2009). *Pristis pristis* has a forked tail and wider pectoral fins than other sawfish species, one of several diagnostic features that distinguish it from other sawfish species. The point where the front of the first dorsal fin meets the body is anterior to the point where the pelvic fins meet the body (V. Faria et al. 2014). The rostrum has between 14 and 24 teeth per side (Figure 7.20b), and is wider, relative to length, than rostra of all other sawfish species (Thorburn et al. 2007; Whitty et al. 2014). The rostral tooth gap at the tip of the rostrum is greater than the tooth gap that follows, on at least one side, in most *P. pristis*.

Reproduction in *P. pristis* is by means of aplacental viviparity (where embryos develop inside eggs that remain in the mother's body until they are ready to hatch), and litters can comprise between 1 and 15 pups (Thorson 1976; Leeney and Downing 2016). The pups are born with a soft sheath covering the rostral teeth, which degrades over several days after birth (Poulakis et al. 2011). The rostrum aids in prey detection and capture (Wueringer 2012). *Pristis pristis* is a euryhaline species and, within the sawfish family, has a unique ecology. Throughout the species' range, pups have been encountered in large rivers and in some places even lakes (e.g., Lake Nicaragua, Lake Sentani in West Papua, Lake Kinkony in northwestern Madagascar), and adult females have been encountered in several major river systems (e.g., Thorson 1976; Leeney and Downing 2016), suggesting that adult females swim into estuarine habitats and perhaps even into the freshwater reaches of large rivers to give birth. In Australia, juveniles have been documented moving from freshwater to marine habitats just before maturation, at about 2.8 m total length for females and 2.4 m for males (Thorburn et al. 2007). In Australia and Central America, pupping occurs during the rainy season; this may be to ensure that adult females can adequately access the shallow coastal habitats they use. It is thus likely that in Malagasy waters, pupping also occurs during the rainy season, between November and March.

The diet of Malagasy populations of *P. pristis* is unknown. In Australia, this species has been reported to consume various fishes, giant freshwater prawns (*Macrobrachium rossenbergii*), prawns (*Penaeus* spp.), and mollusks, depending on whether animals are encountered in marine, estuarine, or freshwater habitats (Thorburn et al. 2007; Peverell 2009).

Current Distribution

Interview data collected between 2015 and 2017 have provided insight into the current distribution and recent catches of sawfishes on Madagascar (R. H. Leeney and A. B. Adouhouri, unpublished data). Interviewees reported recent (within the last decade), but infrequent, observations of sawfishes around Nosy Be and in Ambaro Bay, in Mahajamba Bay, Bombetoka Bay and the Betsiboka River, the Mahavavy River (to the east of Lake Kinkony), the region around Besalampy, the Tsiribihina River, and the Mangoky River. Interviews on the east coast suggest that sawfishes were also encountered there, at least in the region between Andavakimena (southern Pangalanes Canal) and Antongil Bay, but the majority of interviewees who had encountered a sawfish had last seen them in the 1990s or before. The study did not have comprehensive coverage of Madagascar's extensive coastline, and no data collection was attempted on the south coast, as sawfishes were formerly thought to be unlikely to inhabit this region. Only one sawfish catch has been confirmed through photographic evidence, at least since this study was initiated. In April 2019, a sawfish (*Pristis pristis*) was caught in Bombetoka Bay and landed in a nearby village. The rostrum was 1.4 m in length, suggesting that the total length of the sawfish was around 6 m. The flesh was eaten locally and some was salted and dried for sale; the fins and rostrum were also dried and sold.

For the purposes of this contribution, data from the 2015–2017 interview surveys (including known landings and rostra from known locations), data from studies since the 1990s (A. Cooke 1997; Doukakis and Jonahson 2003), and earlier historical data on the locations of sawfish capture and fisheries on Madagascar were compiled and geographic coordinates generated and mapped to illustrate the historical distribution of sawfishes in the island's waters and in relation to major rivers and coastal protected areas (Figure 7.21).

Threats

Sawfishes are among the most threatened of all elasmobranch families (Dulvy et al. 2016), and *P. pristis* is listed as Critically Endangered on the International Union for Conservation of Nature (IUCN) Red List (Kyne et al. 2013). In the precursor version of this book, sawfishes were reported as increasingly rare in Madagascar's waters (A. Cooke et al. 2003a), but recent research indicates that they do still occur in several habitats, albeit in vastly reduced numbers (R. H. Leeney and A. B. Adouhouri, unpublished data). *Pristis pristis* has few natural predators, and individuals are vulnerable mainly as juveniles, before they reach a large size (Morgan et al. 2017). On Madagascar, they are most likely predated on by *Crocodylus niloticus* (Nile Crocodile; formerly widespread across portions of Madagascar but now distinctly rarer; see Kuchling et al., pp. 1458–63) and *Carcharhinus leucas* (Bull Shark), both of which can be found in freshwater environments inhabited by juvenile sawfishes. However, once they reach a certain size, the only threats to sawfishes on the island are anthropogenic.

Overfishing, both targeted and bycatch, and habitat loss have resulted in declines in sawfish populations worldwide (Simpfendorfer 2014; Kyne and Moore 2014). On Madagascar, the primary threats to sawfishes are likely to be fishing, at both industrial and artisanal scales, and habitat loss. Industrial trawl fisheries for prawns operated in the Ambaro Bay in the 1970s and 1980s, and regularly caught sawfishes as bycatch (R. H. Leeney and A. B. Adouhouri, unpublished data). Similarly, according to a trawler captain interviewed in 2000, up to three large sawfishes per month per vessel were reportedly caught by shrimp trawlers in the Morondava–Morombe zone (A. Cooke et al. 2003b). Small-scale fishers, using a wide array of gears, including nets and longlines, have also had an impact on sawfish populations in Madagascar's waters, and continue to do so, as many fishers are aware of the value sawfish fins have in the Asian shark-fin trade (R. H. Leeney and A. B. Adouhouri, unpublished data). Loss of shrimp prey, due to both industrial and small-scale shrimp fishing, may also have affected sawfish populations. Gillnets, sometimes referred to locally as *jarifa* or GTZ (after the German development program that first introduced these nets in northwest Madagascar; see du Feu 1998), and other types of net are the gears most commonly associated with incidental capture of sawfishes. Throughout their range, sawfishes are extremely vulnerable to capture in fishing nets of any type, as their rostra are easily entangled.

In the past, fishers may have released sawfishes from their nets, as adult sawfishes can be dangerous to handle and did not have a market value. However, with the growth of the shark-fin industry throughout Madagascar, a great many fishers are aware of the value of all shark fins, as well as those of sawfishes, guitarfishes (Rhinobatidae), and wedgefishes (Rhinidae) (Dent and Clarke 2015). In

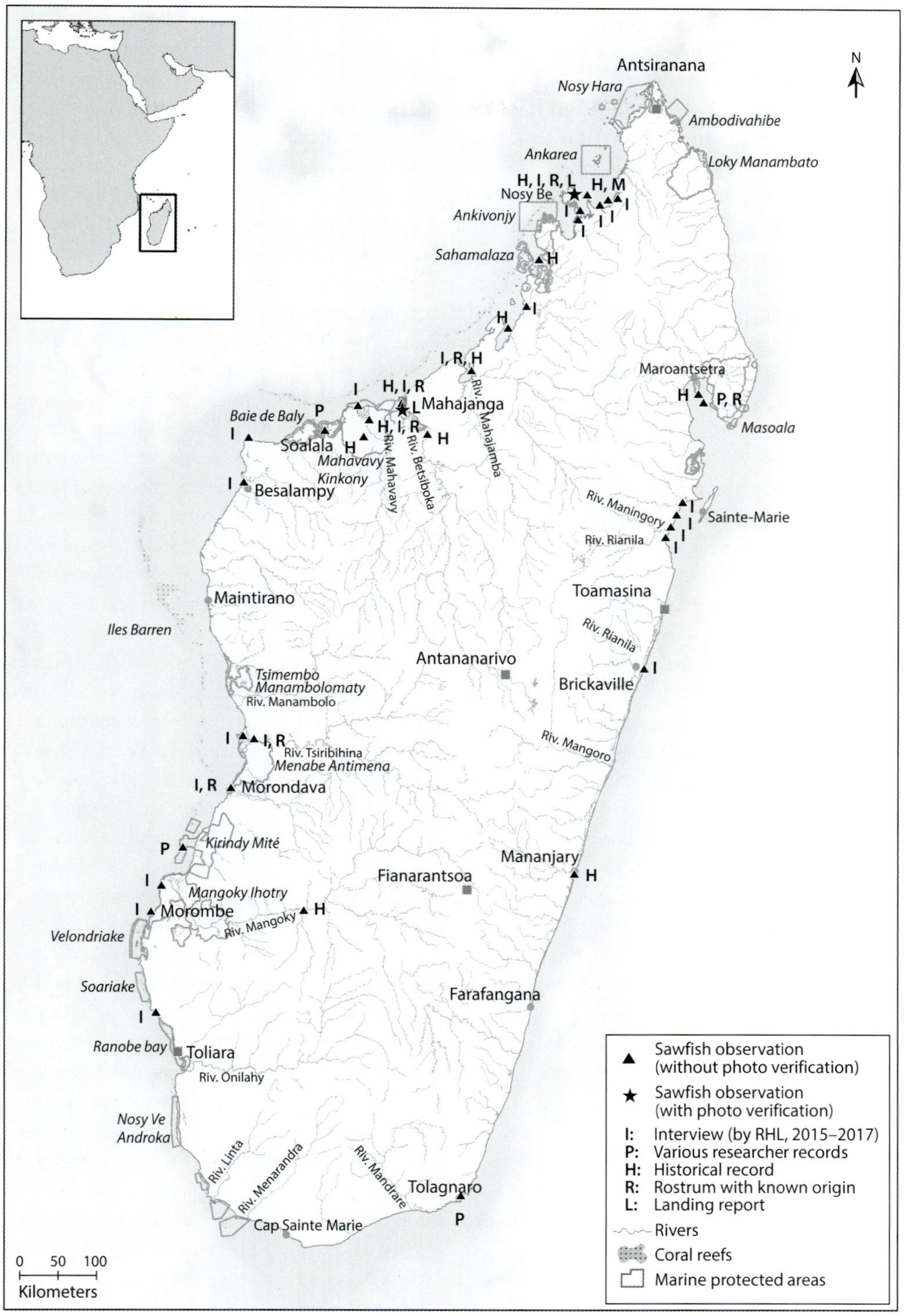

FIGURE 7.21 **Map of Madagascar showing the distribution of recent and historical records of sawfish captures and observations. "RHL" refers to R. H. Leeney.**

some parts of Madagascar, the rostra of sawfishes are also sold as curios or ornaments, especially in areas visited by tourists such as Nosy Be and Antananarivo (Figure 7.20b). These factors reduce the likelihood that a sawfish will be released alive. Directed shark fishing continues to be commonly practiced by artisanal and traditional fishers on Madagascar (Cripps et al. 2015; see Séret, pp. 368–80).

More than 20% of Madagascar's mangrove ecosystems have been heavily degraded or deforested since 1990, owing primarily to increased harvest for charcoal and timber and the expansion of agriculture and aquaculture (T. Jones et al. 2015, 2016a). This has been documented in several known historical habitats for sawfishes (e.g., T. Jones et al. 2016a). Sedimentation of important riverine habitats is also likely to have impacted Malagasy sawfish populations (R. H. Leeney and A. B. Adouhouri, unpublished data).

Sawfishes are also likely impacted indirectly by several other activities. Forest cover decreased by almost 40% between the 1950s and the end of the century (Harper et al. 2007). This deforestation, primarily for agriculture but also as a result of illegal logging activities, has caused soil erosion, leading to sedimentation in several major rivers and associated estuaries, including the Betsiboka River and associated Bombetoka Bay, as well as Mahajamba Bay (R. H. Leeney and A. B. Adouhouri, unpublished data). As river mouths become shallower, female sawfishes may be unable to enter those rivers they historically used to give birth. Research in Australia has revealed that female *P. pristis* return to the same river system in which they were born, to give birth (Feutry et al. 2015), and the consequences of not being able to access this habitat are unknown. If females are forced to give birth in deeper water or without mangrove habitat to provide some protection, the pups are likely to be more vulnerable to predators and may also not have access to the right size classes of food. Habitats subject to increased sediment loads may also become less suitable for juvenile sawfishes if they become too shallow or if the availability of prey species decreases.

Pristis pristis may be especially vulnerable to climate breakdown because of its complex life history, involving the use of multiple aquatic habitats, each of which may be impacted in different ways. Tropical sea surface temperatures have increased by up to 0.5–0.68°C since the mid-19th century (Meehl et al. 2007). As ectotherms, sawfishes are expected to exhibit elevated metabolic rates in response to warmer water and will become increasingly less able to tolerate the effects of even mild hypoxia associated with ocean deoxygenation. For some elasmobranch species, this phenomenon may lead to shifts in distribution (Sims 2019). Ocean acidification, caused by increased absorption of carbon dioxide by seawater, is expected to significantly decrease the pH of surface waters. The direct effect that decreasing pH may have on *P. pristis* is unknown, but it is likely to at least affect some of its prey species, such as crustaceans and mollusks. Extreme weather events, which research suggests are increasing as a result of climate breakdown (e.g., Knutson et al. 2010), are likely to cause additional erosion of coastal habitats and may thus add to the sedimentation of habitats already occurring because of deforestation. Although it is currently difficult to predict the effects of climate breakdown on Malagasy sawfish populations, impacts such as higher water and air temperatures, intensive rainfall leading to erosion, and changes in ecosystem function will compound those of fisheries and habitat loss, thereby accelerating current declines.

SAWFISH CONSERVATION

Historically, *Pristis pristis* had a wide distribution throughout tropical and subtropical waters, but populations have declined dramatically and the species is now considered to be locally extinct throughout much of its former range (Dulvy et al. 2016). The last record of *P. pristis* in South African waters was in 1999 (Everett et al. 2015), while the species is now considered rare in Mozambique (Leeney 2017) and Tanzania (Braulik et al. 2020). It is not clear whether the *P. pristis* population of Madagascar is large enough to be viable in the long term, but if it is, it would be the last such population in the western Indian Ocean.

Sawfishes are not currently protected under any national legislation of the Madagascar government. All sawfish species have been listed as Endangered or Critically Endangered on the IUCN Red List of Threatened Species, and are listed in Appendix I of the Convention on International Trade in Endangered Species of Wild Fauna and Flora (CITES), requiring ratifying states to prohibit trans-frontier trade in sawfishes and their products or parts. All five species are also listed on Appendixes I and II of the Convention on the Conservation of Migratory Species of Wild Animals (CMS) Memorandum of Understanding on the Conservation of Migratory Sharks. CMS parties are required to develop actions for the conservation of sawfish habitats and the prevention, reduction, or control of factors that are endangering or are likely to further endanger sawfishes. The Madagascar government has ratified both CITES and CMS, but, at least in so far as they relate to sawfishes (monitoring and shutting down trans-frontier trade in sawfish parts, protecting mangrove and riverine habitats, or reduction of shark bycatch and directed fisheries), Madagascar's obligations under these conventions are barely implemented.

Although the species is likely depleted, there are still opportunities to protect *P. pristis* on Madagascar. The protection of large embayments, mangrove ecosystems, and estuaries where sawfishes have been confirmed to be present—probably key habitats, especially for pupping and juveniles—would protect them in their vulnerable first few years of life. Such key habitats are represented in Madagascar's marine protected areas, especially those of the west coast, including sites where sawfishes have actually been reported in recent years (e.g., Sahamalaza–Radama Islands, Bombetoka Belobaka, Mahavavy Kinkony, and Mangoky Ihotry). Functional locally managed marine areas and regional fisheries management plans (*plans d'aménagement des pêches*) associated with zones of occurrence may also be able to provide regulation and monitoring. In such protected or regulated sites, sawfishes should be added as conservation target species and measures put in place to engage the communities in live release and documenting of all sawfish catches by fishers. In addition, providing sawfishes with legal protection and ensuring adherence to the law, through extensive checks on landings in small-scale fisheries and trade or exports of elasmobranch products, would be essential. Alternative livelihoods for fishers who fished with gillnets in those areas, or at least provision of alternative gears, would be necessary, as well as an education and local management program to ensure community buy-in and commitment to the measures implemented.

However, within the context of declining fish stocks and growing coastal populations resulting in increasing pressure on coastal ecosystems and populations of marine life (ASCLME 2012), protecting an iconic aquatic species is not a priority for impoverished Malagasy fishing communities. The protection of mangrove areas, which act as fish nurseries and blue-carbon sinks, provide resilience in the face of rising sea levels and extreme weather events, and provide significant ecosystem services to local communities, may provide some de facto protection for sawfishes. But the reality is that while forest clearing continues and the effects of climate breakdown worsen, the ecosystems upon which *P. pristis* relies will continue to be compromised. Further, while market demand for sawfish fins exists and fishers throughout Madagascar struggle to survive, the incentive to profit from a chance encounter with a sawfish is understandably strong. The fate of Madagascar's sawfish populations hangs in the balance.

Subject editors: Andrew Cooke and Steven M. Goodman

CHELONIIDAE AND DERMOCHELYIDAE, SEA TURTLES, *FANO*

R. C. J. Walker, S. Ciccione, N. S. Ranaivoson, and A. Cooke

The global marine environment supports seven species of sea turtles, including *Chelonia mydas* (Green Turtle), *Caretta caretta* (Loggerhead Turtle), *Lepidochelys kempii* (Kemp's Ridley), *L. olivacea* (Olive Ridley), *Eretmochelys imbricata* (Hawksbill Turtle), and *Natator depressus* (Flatback Turtle), all within the family Cheloniidae. The seventh species, *Dermochelys coriacea* (Leatherback Turtle), is the only extant member of the family Dermochelyidae.

Sea turtles are largely pelagic during the first three to five years of life. For example, juveniles of *Chelonia mydas* in the Caribbean are often found foraging and sheltering in mats of floating pelagic vegetation (Carr 1987; Dalleau et al. 2019). Sea turtles are highly migratory, and mature individuals of most species are known to migrate over thousands of kilometers between feeding grounds and nesting beaches. They also play varied roles within marine and coastal ecosystems, with *C. mydas* being primarily herbivorous and grazing mostly on reef algae and seagrass beds, helping to maintain the health and vigor of these ecosystems, and *E. imbricata* being primarily carnivorous and feeding on reef-associated species such as sponges and to a lesser extent soft coral, sea cucumbers, and mollusks.

Sea turtles have been exploited by humans for centuries, with some of the earliest records of turtles being captured for food, occurring within the Arabian Gulf, dating from 2100–1900 BCE (Olijdam 2001). Despite most coastal countries having some sort of legislative protection in place for these animals, they are still widely exploited for food and other uses, such as the use of shells as ornaments. Globally, sea-turtle populations have also suffered a multitude of threats, including bycatch in both industrial and artisanal fisheries, the ingestion of plastics and other marine pollutants, loss of nesting and foraging habitat, and disease and climate change (Wallace et al. 2011). *Eretmochelys imbricata* and *Lepidochelys kempii* are classified on the International Union for Conservation of Nature (IUCN) Red List as Critically Endangered, *Chelonia mydas* as Endangered, and *Caretta caretta*, *L. olivacea*, and *Dermochelys coriacea* as Vulnerable.

SEA TURTLES IN MALAGASY WATERS AND THE WESTERN INDIAN OCEAN

Five species of sea turtles—*Chelonia mydas*, *Eretmochelys imbricata*, *Caretta caretta*, *Lepidochelys olivacea*, and *Dermochelys coriacea*—are known to occur in the western Indian Ocean and in Madagascar's coastal waters (Rakotonirina and Cooke 1994). On Madagascar, all species are known to nest, with the exception of *D. coriacea*. The majority of marine turtle nesting sites on the island are on the western side, where beaches are wider and more shallowly sloping, owing to greater tidal range and more suitable foraging habitats (Table 7.12, Figure 7.22). Most known nesting sites in Malagasy waters support fewer than 50 nests per year, with the most recent estimates suggesting that Madagascar has approximately 1200 turtle nests per year (Bourjea et al. 2015; Humber et al. 2017b). The largest single nesting site, located on Nosy Hara, is thought to support around 500 nests of *Chelonia mydas* (Humber et al. 2017b) and around 100 *E. imbricata* nests per year (Metcalf et al. 2007). Other significant sites include Nosy Iranja (>100 nests of *C. mydas*) (Bourjea et al. 2006) and Nosy Ankazoberavina (supporting 50–100 nests of *E. imbricata*) (M. Felici and Nature Sauvage, unpublished data). In the following section we present, by species, different aspects of sea-turtle ecology, conservation status, and distribution within Madagascar and the western Indian Ocean.

Chelonia mydas, Green Turtle

Chelonia mydas is by far the most numerous species within Malagasy coastal waters, with the largest populations occurring along the northwest, western, and southern coasts. This species is sparsely distributed along the mid-eastern coast (Rakotonirina and Cooke 1994).

During the 1970s, the western Indian Ocean nesting population of *C. mydas* was thought to be in the region of 5500 individuals (Frazier 1975). However, this population has been subjected to high levels of exploitation within the last few decades, and as a result the population nesting on Mauritius was extirpated by the early 1970s (Hughes 1982). There are still small nesting populations on the outer Mauritian islands of Saint Brandon and Agalega (Griffiths and Tatayah 2007). The decline in Mauritius is mirrored throughout the region, particularly upon populated islands. The most significant breeding beaches for *C. mydas* are confined to remote, uninhabited islands such as Europa, supporting an estimated 8000–15,000 nesting females, and Tromelin, with an estimated 1500–2000 nesting females (Le Gall and Hughes 1987; Bourjea et al. 2013, 2015), with recent increased nesting activity recorded (Bourjea et al. 2015) and up to 27,000 nests per year within the western Indian Ocean region (van der Elst et al. 2012).

It is believed that Madagascar supports important foraging grounds for a proportion of the wider western Indian Ocean population of *C. mydas* (Dalleau et al. 2019). Recent satellite-tagging work by Bourjea et al. (2013) shows that 40% of tagged *C. mydas* from the nesting populations of Europa, Tromelin, Iles Glorieuses, Mayotte, and Mohéli use Madagascar's coastal waters as foraging grounds, with the Toliara barrier reefs having particular importance (Le Gall and Hughes 1987; Bourjea et al. 2013; Figure 7.23). Dispersal of this species across the southwest Indian Ocean is thought to result from a combination of passive drifting, using major currents, and active swimming to avoid colder water (Jensen et al. 2020). A review by Humber et al. (2017b) suggests that the islands off the northwest of Madagascar may be the nesting stronghold for *C. mydas* in Malagasy waters. Rakotonirina and Cooke (1994) and Metcalf et al. (2007) describe Nosy Sakatia, Nosy Iranja, and Nosy Hara as the most

TABLE 7.12. **Known active sea-turtle nesting localities in Madagascar, with location, species, and annual nesting numbers**

SITE	REGION	SPECIES	NUMBER OF NESTS (ANNUAL)	YEAR	DATA TYPE
1	Nosy Hara region	Cm	<1000	July–Dec. 2000	Body pit count
		Ei			
2	Ambolobozokely region	Un	<50	June 2011	Body pit count
3	Archipelago in far north referred to as “Barralums” (Rasolofo 2012)	Un	Not reported	Unknown	n/a
4	Analandrafia	Un	Not reported	2011	n/a
	Masoala			Unknown	
	Antongil Bay			Unknown	
	Ile Sainte Marie			Unknown	
	Manambato			Unknown	
5	96 km coastline north of Tolagnaro	Cc	<50	2011	Number of nests
		Un	<50		
6	Nosy Vé–Androka National Marine Park	Lo	Not reported	2011	n/a
		Dc			
7	Ambohibola–Nosy Manitse	Un	Not reported	Unknown	n/a
8	Beheloka–Besambay	Cm	Not reported	2002	n/a
		Ei			
		Cc			
9	Maromena	Cc	Not reported	2002	n/a
10	Salary Nord	Cm	Not reported	2011	n/a
11	Ankitambanga–Belavenoke	Cm	<50	2008	Number of nests
12	Lovobe–Antanimanimbo	Un	<50	2010–2015	Number of nests
13	Barren Islands	Cm	<50	2011–2014	Number of nests
		Ei	<50		
14	Radama Islands region	Cm	<50	2000–2019	Body pit count
		Ei	<150		
15	Nosy Iranja region	Cm	<100	2000–2008	Number of nests
		Ei	<50		
15a	Nosy Ankazoberavina	Ei	56–111	2009-2016	Number of nests annually
16	Nosy Be region	Cm	<50	2000–2001	Body pit count
17	Ankarana beach–Nosy Mitsio	Un	<50	2011	Body pit count

Sources: Data reproduced with kind permission of Fran Humber (Humber 2015), modified to include Nosy Ankazoberavina (added as site 15a) (M. Felici and Nature Sauvage, unpublished data) and with reference to the original source for site 3 (Rasolofo 2012).

Notes: Cm, *Chelonia mydas* (Green Turtle); Ei, *Eretmochelys imbricata* (Hawksbill Turtle); Cc, *Caretta caretta* (Loggerhead Turtle); Lo, *Lepidochelys olivacea* (Olive Ridley); Dc, *Dermochelys coriacea* (Leatherback Turtle); Un, unknown species. Site numbers refer to labels on Figure 7.22.

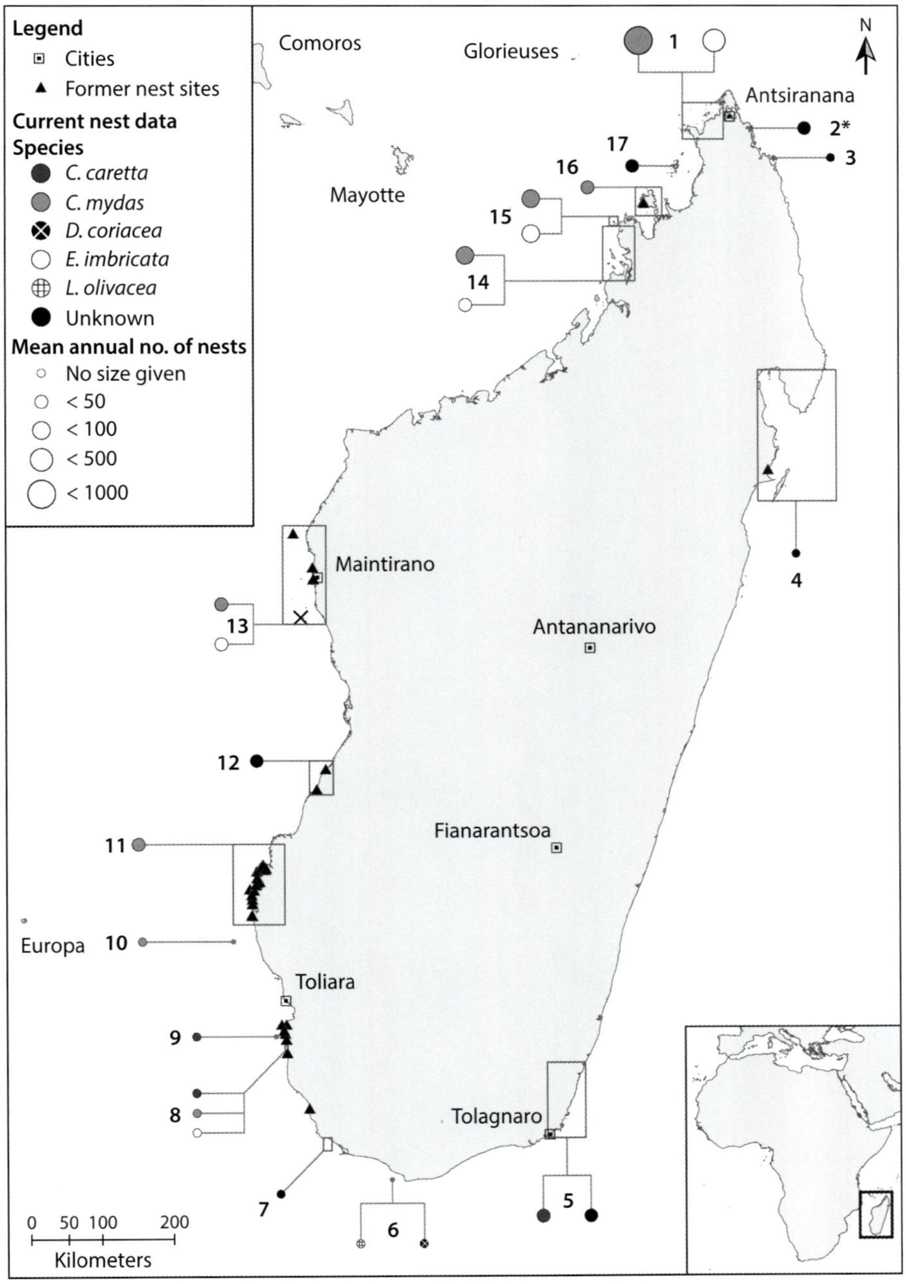

FIGURE 7.22 Locations of known current and former sea-turtle nesting sites in Malagasy waters. Details of nesting locations 1–17 are further described in Table 7.12. (SOURCES: map based on image produced by Humber 2015, and M. Felici and Nature Sauvage, unpublished data.)

significant nesting sites for *C. mydas* in Madagascar (approximately 500 nests). Humber et al. (2017b) report an average of 34 successful nests annually on the Barren Islands between 2011 and 2014. An estimated 74% ($n = 888$) of all the recorded sea-turtle nests on Madagascar were of *C. mydas*. Generally, this species appears to nest across beaches throughout the south and west, from near Tolagnaro, along the southern coast (Walker and Roberts 2005), and northward to islands around the Nosy Be region (Rakotonirina and Cooke 1994). More recently, a survey in the northeast reports more than 50 nests per year on Nosy Ankao and Nosy Manampao (S. Ciccione and N. S. Ranaivoson, unpublished data).

Eretmochelys imbricata, Hawksbill Turtle

The Indian Ocean has historically supported a significant *Eretmochelys imbricata* population; the major nesting beaches occur in the Seychelles, with around 1700 nesting females in the 1970s (Hughes 1973). This number declined throughout the 1980s and early 1990s, until significant conservation measures, controlling the trade in raw shells, were introduced in 1994 (Mortimer and Bresson 1999; Z. Allen et al. 2010). As of yet, it is unclear how the wider western Indian Ocean population is linked to the Malagasy population. In northwest Madagascar, the beaches of Nosy Iranja, Nosy Hara, the Radama Islands, and adjacent mainland are known to support the largest breeding colonies of *E. imbricata*, with collectively approximately 230 nesting sites (Metcalf et al. 2007; Humber et al. 2017b). There are recent reports of 50–100 nests per year of *E. imbricata* on Nosy Ankazoberavina, close to Nosy Iranja (M. Felici and Nature Sauvage, unpublished data). In the west, Humber et al. (2017b) recently confirmed that the Barren Islands supported an average of 11 successfully emerged *E. imbricata* nests per year between 2011 and 2014. Pedrono (2008)

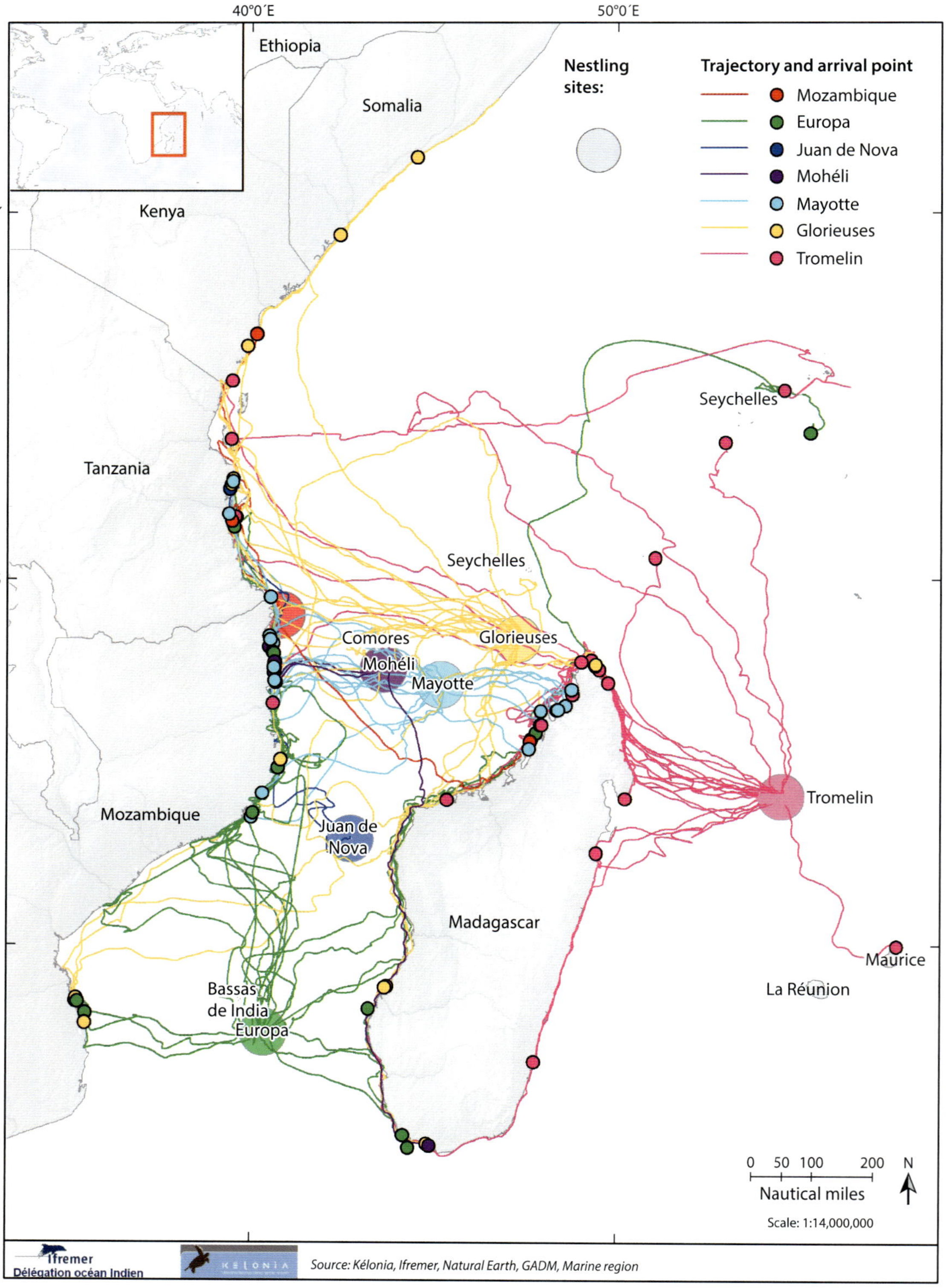

FIGURE 7.23 **Satellite-tracking data from tagged *Chelonia mydas*, tagged within nesting colonies of Europa, Tromelin, Iles Glorieuses, Mayotte, and Mohéli during 2015–2020. The track lines show the migration routes between these western Indian Ocean breeding grounds and the important foraging grounds for the species in northern and western Madagascar.** (SOURCE: Kelonia, unpublished data).

reports *E. imbricata* nesting in the southwest at Ifaty and Anakao, but this latter population is now extirpated (Walker and Roberts 2005). *Eretmochelys imbricata* is known to nest in the west (at Maintirano and Soalala) and in the northeast (Vohémar and Tanambao) (Rakotonirina and Cooke 1994). Walker and Roberts (2005) report small numbers of nesting individuals close to the village of Besambay, approximately 50 km south of Toliara. However, as with Anakao, it is likely that many of these remnant breeding colonies no longer exist. This species is reported to forage in all of the coastal regions of Madagascar, but primarily in the north and west (Rakotonirina and Cooke 1994). It is likely that Madagascar supports only a relict nesting population of this species, given the heavy, sustained exploitation over many centuries (Hughes 1973). *Eretmochelys imbricata* makes up only 18% of sea-turtle nesting within Madagascar (Humber et al. 2017b). More than 50 nests per year have been recently reported on Nosy Ankao and Nosy Manampao (S. Ciccione and N. S. Ranaivoson, unpublished data; Figure 7.24a).

FIGURE 7.24 **Sea turtles of Madagascar. A) *Eretmochelys imbricata* on a beach on Nosy Manampao, northeast Madagascar. B) Hatchling survey on Nosy Iranja, northwest Madagascar. C) *Chelonia mydas* carapace in an Anosy village, southeast Madagascar, collected by Bertin Rakotonirina of Institut Halieutique et des Sciences Marines (IHSM) (pictured). D) *Chelonia mydas* captured by an artisanal fisher on the west coast of Madagascar.** (PHOTOS by S. Ciccione.)

Caretta caretta, Loggerhead Turtle

Caretta caretta is one of the most migratory of all species of sea turtles and nests on a wide variety of beaches with varying morphology (Pedrono 2008). By far the largest nesting colony in the world occurs on Masirah Island, Oman, which supports between 20,000 and 40,000 individuals (P. Ross, unpublished data). This species has been recorded foraging around most coastal regions of Madagascar, with the most important nesting beaches in proximity to Madagascar found along the Tongaland coast of South Africa (Hughes 1974). This population is thought to be the second-largest breeding colony in the world, supporting over 400 nesting females, and is known through tag recoveries to be linked with the Malagasy population (Metcalf et al. 2007). There has been a significant decline in Madagascar's nesting population of this species over the last few decades (Rakotonirina and Cooke 1994) from the large numbers found nesting in the southeast during the 1970s (Hughes 1974). Only 23 nests were recorded in the same region during the 2000–2001 nesting season, of which half were harvested (Gladstone et al. 2003). In the 2016–2017 nesting season, five nests were recorded on a 7 km long beach in the north of Sainte Luce, approximately 30 km to the north of Tolagnaro (S. Ciccione and B. P. Rakotonirina, unpublished data). Humber et al. (2017b) note between 2011 and 2014 only two nests of *C. caretta* on the Barren Islands, and noted only 11 nests nationally (about 1% of all turtle nests). A report from 2007 for the QMM mining company noted nesting success of just two individuals of this species on the Ehoala Peninsula (near Tolagnaro) but higher numbers on the beaches near Manambato, 45 km north of Ehoala (Jacques Whitford 2007). Fishers within this southeast region also report encountering this species the most frequently. Most accounts appear to be in the southeast close to Tolagnaro, suggesting a regional concentration that could be very vulnerable given the frequent local reports of hunting (Jacques Whitford 2007).

Lepidochelys olivacea, Olive Ridley

The distribution of *Lepidochelys olivacea* in Malagasy coastal waters is largely confined to the west between Morombe and Mahajanga (Rakotonirina and Cooke 1994), with a patchy distribution elsewhere around the island. Subsistence fishing communities south of Toliara report catching *L. olivacea* (Walker and Roberts 2005), and carapaces of this species have been found on beaches near Tolagnaro in the southeast and Nosy Radama and Nosy Sakatia in the northwest (R. Ratsimbazafy 2003). Carapaces of this species have also been reported on the Masoala Peninsula (B. P. Rakotonirina, unpublished data). *Lepidochelys olivacea* was historically known to nest in large concentrations at Betania, south of Morondava (Rakotonirina and Cooke 1994), but this population has since been extirpated (Humber et al. 2017b). Significant feeding and nesting sites for *L. olivacea* close to Madagascar include the Mozambique coastline and the oceanic islands of the Mozambique Channel (Pedrono 2008). The most significant nesting ground for this species within the Indian Ocean occurs on the beaches of Odisha, India, which supports a population of approximately 600,000 nesting females (Chattopadhyay et al. 2018). However, this population is significantly threatened and declining, largely as a result of fisheries-related mortality (Shanker et al. 2004). Due to the species' low numbers in Madagascar's waters and susceptibility to fisheries mortality, Pedrono (2008) describes this species as one of the most threatened of the five locally occurring species, and says it may no longer nest in Malagasy waters.

Dermochelys coriacea, Leatherback Turtle

Dermochelys coriacea has been sparsely recorded in Malagasy waters in recent decades, with the low number of reports in coastal waters from the southeast, and extending from the west to the northwest of the island (Hughes 1974; Rakotonirina and Cooke 1994). R. Ratsimbazafy (2003) reports small numbers of *D. coriacea* captured by a fisher near Evatra (Tolagnaro), and Walker and Roberts (2005) report that fishers in Ambola, in the southwest, very occasionally catch this species. It is thought that a small *D. coriacea* nesting population once existed in parts of the east coast (Martel 2003). Breeding populations for this species within the western Indian Ocean appear sparse, with Botha (2010) reporting that around 60 per year nest within KwaZulu-Natal on the east coast of South Africa. Hughes (1996) reported that a female *D. coriacea* tagged in South Africa was recovered in Madagascar, suggesting a migration route between the two areas.

HISTORY OF RESEARCH AND CONSERVATION

Sea-turtle conservation in Madagascar began a century ago, following initial research and the introduction of the first regulations in 1923, based on evidence of population declines (Petit 1930). Remarkably little further attention was devoted to these aspects during the colonial period ending in 1960. The earliest turtle research following Madagascar's independence confirmed the local presence of *Chelonia mydas*, *Eretmochelys imbricata*, and *Caretta caretta*; at this time, hunting of *Chelonia mydas* for meat and *E. imbricata* for tortoiseshell was long established and both species appeared to be in decline (Hughes 1973). The 1970s work led to the establishment of a permanent research interest at the Station Marine de Toliara, now called the Institut Halieutique et des Sciences Marines (IHSM), resulting in the tagging of turtles, some of which were recovered in Durban, South Africa (Rakotonirina and Cooke 1994). In the 1970s, it became evident that sea turtles in the Indian Ocean were declining as a result of harvesting (Frazier 1975, 1980), but a further 10 years passed before sea-turtle research in Malagasy waters resumed with a national baseline survey (Rakotonirina 1987, 1989), which reported declining numbers and nesting frequency for *C. mydas*, *E. imbricata*, *Caretta caretta*, and *Lepidochelys olivacea*.

The first postcolonial publication on the subject was produced by Rakotonirina and Cooke (1994), giving a national overview of the status of all five species recorded in Madagascar's coastal waters. Research then expanded nationally with the support of international nongovernmental organizations (NGOs) and foundations, which became systematically interested in the subject. Additional surveys were conducted in the southeast (Gladstone et al. 2003) detailing nesting and harvest. Walker and Roberts (2005) revisited a number of the nesting areas in the southwest reported by Rakotonirina and Cooke (1994) and confirmed a continuing decline; they also conducted turtle market surveys in Toliara (Walker et al.

2004). The country's most significant nesting populations in the northwest and, in particular, Madagascar's largest *Chelonia mydas* nesting beaches on Nosy Iranja have been the focus of much of the recent work on Malagasy sea turtles (Bourjea et al. 2006; Metcalf et al. 2007; Allison 2008; Mealla 2011). The first monitoring system in Madagascar, using a permanent tagging system, was set up on Nosy Iranja by a team of researchers from Malagasy and British universities (Metcalf et al. 2007).

Of particular importance since the 1990s has been the advent of a regional turtle research program (Lauret-Stepler et al. 2007; Bourjea et al. 2013, 2015), using regional tagging projects and genetics studies, which has helped to place Madagascar's *C. mydas* populations in a regional context and to highlight the importance of Madagascar's coastal waters as foraging grounds (Dalleau et al. 2019; Jensen et al. 2020; Figure 7.23).

Humber et al. (2010) reviewed the literature on sea-turtle hunting, nesting, and egg collection in Malagasy waters, providing the most comprehensive review to date of the number and location of nesting sites by region (Table 7.12; Figure 7.22). Further, Humber et al. (2010, 2017b) report on the most comprehensive monitoring studies of turtle and egg collecting by artisanal fishing communities across approximately 60 km of coastline within the Velondriake and the Barren Islands marine protected areas (MPAs), respectively, in western and southwestern Madagascar.

CULTURAL IMPORTANCE, RESOURCE USE, AND THREATS

Sea turtles have a long history of cultural association and use as a food resource within a number of the coastal ethnic groups on the island, in particular the Vezo of the southwest (Astuti 1995) and Sakalava in the northwest (Campbell 2005).

Dependence upon sea turtles from a cultural perspective has diminished within recent decades among many coastal communities (Walker and Roberts 2005; Lilette 2006). Only the older members of a declining number of fishing communities in the southwest report adherence to cultural practices when hunting for turtles (Walker and Roberts 2005). A number of older fishers in Ambola, Maromena, and Beheloka reported using an *ombiasy* (spiritual leader and healer) to bring them luck when hunting. Research in the southwest during 2002 revealed persisting knowledge of cultural and spiritual traditions associated with turtle hunting, but little reliance upon them, with fishers claiming that the number of turtles caught depended on the methods used rather than on luck derived through spiritual means. Historically, Vezo fishers observed various practices such as sprinkling turtle blood on pirogues or painting hulls black according to tradition (Rakotonirina 1987, 1989). Other rituals included blessing of turtle spears, or *teza*, by *ombiasy* prior to the hunt. Rituals were also performed during the slaughter of sea turtles, whereby a *randra* or *ranjo* (altar) was built from mangrove branches. In the Anakao region, the butchering of the turtle was performed by cutting the aorta last, in an effort to retain the power of the fisher bestowed upon a person by the ancestors (Astuti 1995). Elders within the Anakao area state that a number of the traditional hunting practices ceased in the 1970s, around the time of increased availability of more modern fishing gears, such as nylon nets, which is likely to have modified the Vezo's relationship with sea turtles (Lilette 2006).

Some Malagasy ethnic groups, at least based on classical cultural dictates, do not consume turtle meat, such as the Antandroy in the south and Antakarana in the north, or in general people of Islamic faith (Rakotonirina and Cooke 1994). Taboos (*fady*) for the avoidance of certain species as food is commonplace throughout Madagascar, with these varying widely even within small geographic areas. On Nosy Radama and around Nosy Be the capture of turtles is considered *fady* (Metcalf et al. 2007). In addition, many coastal communities consider the meat of *Eretmochelys imbricata* to be poisonous (Pedrono 2008). Indeed, all species of turtles can be susceptible to bioaccumulation, with *E. imbricata* in particular being linked to a number of fatalities as a result of consumption of turtle meat (Pavlin et al. 2015).

As the Vezo of the southwest have transitioned from a largely nomadic, seafaring way of life to a more settled existence, the pressures upon local marine resources, including sea turtles, have intensified. Indeed, Walker and Roberts (2005) reported that targeted sea-turtle fisheries within the southwest have been replaced by multispecies fisheries using gillnets (*jarifa*), which catch sharks, large fishes, and turtles. Fishers within all eight communities surveyed by Walker and Roberts (2005) noted that turtle catch levels and general abundance had decreased progressively over the previous 10 years, with fishers in Anakao noting a 75% decrease in the number of turtles captured over that time period. Apart from *jarifa*, fishing gear employed to catch turtles includes spear guns, longline (as bycatch), and intertidal fish traps (*vitrana*) (Humber 2015). The use of *famata*, a fish poison extracted from plants of the family Euphorbiaceae, kills both fishes and sea turtles. While historically the consumption of turtle meat represented a gift to the community (Lilette 2006), and harvesting was largely a subsistence activity, the trade in turtles and their meat has become an economic feature in many coastal cities such as Toliara (Walker et al. 2004; Lilette 2006). Shipping routes used by collectors of octopuses and squids also sustain the turtle trade, via rapid transport of meat with other marine products (Lilette 2006).

It is clear from historical data and accounts that sea-turtle fisheries and their exploitation rates have fluctuated over recent centuries. *Eretmochelys imbricata* was historically commercially hunted in Madagascar for its shells, until overexploitation was thought to have caused the fishery to collapse (Pedrono 2008). Records of commerce for this species date back to the early 1600s, with more than 5400 individuals exported annually during the 19th century (Decary 1950). This was reduced to 1300 individuals during the 1950s, with the collapse of the wild population already reported by about 1930 (Petit 1930; Hughes 1973). *Caretta caretta* was exploited intensively over 150 years ago, with a focus of effort in the southwest and northwest (G. Grandidier 1910).

Despite these locally reported declines in abundance, the total captures of turtles by coastal subsistence fisheries in Madagascar have remained relatively constant over the last 40 years (Humber et al. 2010; Humber 2015). In 1980, estimates of turtle catches in Madagascar were over 13,000 individuals per year (Hughes 1973; Frazier 1980). By 1992, Rakotonirina and Cooke (1994) estimated the nationwide harvest as about 11,000 per year. The most up-to-date and comprehensive data set, established by Humber (2015), conservatively estimates the annual turtle catch in Madagascar to be between 10,000 and 16,000 individuals per year. The greatest intensity of harvest appears to be in the southwest and northwest, with several thousand individuals removed by coastal communities within both of these areas (Figures 7.24c and d).

Declines in nesting beaches, as a result of disturbance from egg harvesting, were apparent even 100 years ago (Petit 1930). This decline appears to have remained consistent; for example, during the 1980s there were nine *Chelonia mydas*, two *E. imbricata*, and two *Caretta caretta* nesting populations recorded along a 60 km coastal strip south of Toliara (Rakotonirina and Cooke 1994). These nesting beaches had declined by an estimated 70% when the area was resurveyed in 2002 (Walker and Roberts 2005). In their review of historical data for all species nesting within Madagascar's beaches, Humber et al. (2017b), report a total of 17 remaining nest sites around the country, compared with the 44 nesting sites around Madagascar reported within the historical literature. This decline has been attributed to egg-harvesting activity, but could also have resulted from sustained harvesting of adult females by fishers in inshore waters and other factors such as offshore bycatch by pelagic fisheries.

A multitude of global threats can impact Madagascar's turtles, given the ability of these animals to migrate across large distances. Bycatch by offshore pelagic long-line and seine fisheries has significant impacts on turtle populations (Peckham et al. 2008). Bourjea et al. (2008) suggest that bycatch from gillnet fisheries poses a significant threat to turtles within the western Indian Ocean region, particularly to *Chelonia mydas*, and that trawlers also pose a significant threat to this species and to *E. imbricata*. *Caretta caretta*, *E. imbricata*, and *Chelonia mydas* appear to be significantly impacted from the offshore long-line fishery to the east of Madagascar (La Réunion fishery) (Kelonia, unpublished data). The high level of erosion resulting from inland deforestation on Madagascar is also likely to have reduced the available area of suitable nesting sites through the covering of nesting beaches by coarse sediments. Hoarau et al. (2014) highlight the large quantity of plastic debris in the marine environment and its impact on *Caretta caretta* late juveniles in the southwest Indian Ocean.

Climate change may also constitute a threat to Madagascar's sea-turtle populations. Many aspects of sea-turtle life history are closely tied to climatic variables such as ambient temperature and storms (Hawkes et al. 2009). Climate may affect key habitats upon which turtles depend for foraging or nesting and could influence nest site selection. For example, nesting beaches could be reduced as a result of sea-level rise (Baker et al. 2006; A. Jones et al. 2007). The skewing of primary sex ratios toward a higher proportion of females as a result of raised incubation temperature is also considered a threat (Schmid et al. 2008). Climate change may also impact turtles while at sea—for example, by driving range shifts of prey species or affecting foraging habitats such as seagrass beds (Hawkes et al. 2009).

CONSERVATION

Efforts to conserve Malagasy sea turtles began in 1923, with the issue of two colonial orders: one (23 May 1923) prohibiting the capture of female sea turtles while they were nesting and individuals with a plastron length of less than 50 cm, and a second order (24 October 1923) designating a series of islands as nesting reserves—Nosy Anambo (Antsiranana), Nosy Iranja (Nosy Be), Nosy Chesterfield (Morondava), Nosy Trozona and Nosy Vé (Toliara), and Europa atoll. With the exception of Nosy Chesterfield, all of the above-mentioned sites within Malagasy territorial waters are within national protected areas, while Europa is strictly protected under French legislation.

Madagascar has ratified the main wildlife conventions providing protection of sea turtles, including the Algiers Convention of 1968 (listing sea turtles in Class A), the Convention on International Trade in Endangered Species of Wild Fauna and Flora (CITES) of 1973 (listing all sea turtles in Appendix I; law 75-014), the Nairobi convention of 1990 (listing turtles under Annexes 2 or 3), and the Bonn Convention on Migratory Species of 1979 (listing turtles under Annexes 1 and 2).

Under national wildlife legislation sea turtles have been fully protected since 1988. Decree (Décret) 88-243 under wildlife law (Loi) 60-122 of 1960 classed all sea turtles as fully protected, while specifically naming only *Dermochelys coriacea*. Decree 88-243 has since been replaced by Decree 400-2006, which specifically lists all five sea turtle species as integrally protected, clearing up the former ambiguity. Other national legislative procedures designed to improve the conservation of sea turtles include the legal requirement in 2003 for the industrial shrimp fishery to fit turtle exclusion devices (TEDs) to all trawl nets to reduce turtle bycatch (Razafindrainibe 2010).

The above laws have rarely been enforced in relation to sea-turtle exploitation in Malagasy waters. Such nonapplication is evident from the continuing and widespread hunting of sea turtles and open and sometimes officially recorded sale of turtle meat in markets of coastal towns such as Toliara (Walker et al. 2004) and Morombe (A. Cooke et al. 2003a). The decline of most nesting beaches is also an indication that the designated sea-turtle reserves have not been respected, one example being Nosy Vé, near Anakao, where the last nests to be reported were in 1986 (Rakotonirina 1989; Rakotonirina and Cooke 1994) and sometime in the 1990s (Walker and Roberts 2005). However, there have been exceptions. Nosy Iranja, which has been privately owned since colonial times, still supports a substantial nesting population of *Chelonia mydas* (Bourjea et al. 2006) and the substantial nesting numbers of *E. imbricata* on the privately managed Nosy Ankazoberavina (M. Felici and Nature Sauvage, unpublished data). Most important of all is the atoll of Europa, which was retained by France following Madagascar's independence and currently supports 15,000–20,000 nests, predominantly of *C. mydas*.

The limited enforcement of sea-turtle legislation in Malagasy waters has often been a source of concern and even consternation among conservationists. A lack of understanding of current national and international legislation concerning sea turtles was highlighted at a regional marine-turtle workshop in 2004 (Rakotonirina and Harding 2005) and a national workshop in 2011 (Humber and Hykle 2011). It was also thought that turtle conservation laws are not enforced owing to a lack of capacity for implementation, the immensity of the Malagasy coastline, and, above all, a reluctance to restrict a fishery with strong cultural links.

Traditional regulations that are followed at the local level, such as *fady* or *dina* (local legally binding conventions), have had greater success with compliance but still face challenges. In the Mahajanga area, *fady* dictated that collectors must leave between 1 and 20 eggs in exploited turtle nests (Durbin 1994). This strategy appears tokenistic, since the number of eggs left is so small and disturbance to the nest is likely to make the remaining eggs nonviable. The protection afforded to Nosy Vé's nesting sea turtles, as part of the 1923 decree, was incorporated into a local *dina* in the late 1990s but was apparently too late to be effective. However, such traditional regulations fail when outsiders from other communities pass through the area and ignore the local *fady*.

MPAs are also playing an important part, with Nosy Hara currently protecting the largest known sea-turtle nesting beach in Malagasy waters, with >500 nests annually, mostly of *Chelonia mydas*. Nosy Iranja and Nosy Ankazoberavina, now integrated into the Ankivonjy MPA, each support about 100 nests annually and are now effectively protected (Bourjea et al. 2006; M. Felici and Nature Sauvage, unpublished data), with nesting at these sites possibly increasing (Humber et al. 2017b; M. Felici and Nature Sauvage, unpublished data). Nosy Ankao and Nosy Manampao support about 50 nests annually that have become recently protected in the context of a private tourism project (S. Ciccione and N. S. Ranaivoson, unpublished data).

What is evident is that most, probably more than 90%, of Madagascar's sea-turtle populations are recruited from nesting grounds elsewhere in the western Indian Ocean (Bourjea et al. 2015; Humber et al. 2017b; Jensen et al. 2020). The total number of females nesting annually in the southwest Indian Ocean is likely to be in excess of 27,000 (van der Elst et al. 2012), which includes the estimated 1200 for Madagascar (Humber et al. 2017b). As a result, the creation of well-managed MPAs outside Madagascar's exclusive economic zone is a significant contributor to the maintenance of turtle populations within Malagasy coastal waters (Lauret-Stepler et al. 2007; Humber et al. 2017b). For example, MPAs such as the national parks of the Bazaruto and the Quirimbas archipelagoes in the Mozambique Channel support all five species of sea turtles (Costa et al. 2007) and are most likely sources of recruitment to Madagascar's waters. In the same manner, other significant nesting beaches for *C. mydas* within the region include the islands of Europa, Grande Glorieuse, and Tromelin (Bourjea et al. 2015). These are all well-managed protected areas, with *C. mydas* tracking studies showing that over the past 20 years (Figure 7.23) there has been an annual increase in nesting activity on Europa of 3% and on Grande Glorieuse of 6% (Lauret-Stepler et al. 2007). The effective protection of these source nesting beaches within the wider region is probably the key to maintaining sea-turtle populations in Madagascar's coastal waters but will not allow restoration of the relict nesting populations of Madagascar. For the latter, establishment and strict enforcement of national MPAs and nesting reserves will be required.

Humber et al. (2017b) also argue that higher levels of recruitment from these well-managed, protected nesting beaches elsewhere in the western Indian Ocean has helped to sustain the turtle fishery in Madagascar. Bourjea et al. (2007) suggest that the *C. mydas* population in the region is capable of supporting the current exploitation levels in Malagasy waters. However, Humber et al. (2017b) state that this hypothesis should be treated with caution, given sustained human population growth and increasing levels of marine and coastal environmental degradation and resource exploitation in Madagascar's coastal waters (Harris et al. 2010). Madagascar should therefore not rely upon the conservation actions of other neighboring nesting areas, but should make its own contribution and focus efforts on the effective protection and restoration of its relatively small but mostly unprotected nesting populations (Humber et al. 2017b). Sea turtles also offer the potential for local economic benefits from ecotourism and Madagascar's reputation as an international nature sanctuary.

Many of these smaller nesting sites around Madagascar, particularly in the northwest, are on islands that were once isolated. Today, a number of these islands have been developed for tourism, with some supporting small, sensitive ecotourism projects, involved in the monitoring or conservation of nesting beaches, such as on Nosy Iranja (Figure 7.24b), Nosy Ankazoberavina, and Nosy Ankao. This is done in collaboration with local research institutes, visiting biologists (Bourjea et al. 2006), conservation NGOs, and protected-area managers. Other smaller, local initiatives, such as the volunteer-based monitoring project on Nosy Komba and the monitoring and anti-poaching work on Nosy Ankao and Nosy Manampao, could become all the more important for the conservation of the smaller nesting populations of turtles around northern Madagascar. The Barren Islands monitoring initiative has a strong community engagement aspect, working with the migrant Vezo fishing community, which spends a significant part of the year within the region (Humber et al. 2017b). Monitoring in Nosy Iranja has shown an increase in nesting since 2000 (Bourjea et al. 2006), and monitoring in Ankazoberavina has also shown an increase over the past decade (M. Felici and Nature Sauvage, unpublished data).

Given the substantial numbers of turtles removed from the wild by fishing communities, Humber et al. (2010) observe that turtle conservation and fisheries-management measures focused on these communities would be beneficial. The western Indian Ocean Marine Turtle Task Force, formed in 2008, highlighted that Madagascar has a strong potential for turtle conservation developed within a system that embraces the community structure, respecting traditions, culture, and customs. Humber et al. (2017b) suggest that legal take quotas for artisanal turtle hunting in Malagasy waters could work, but would not be without challenges and should be considered as part of a broad-ranging conservation management plan, including the active conservation of nesting sites. The fact that hunters in Madagascar take numerous foraging turtles could undermine conservation efforts elsewhere in the western Indian Ocean (Mortimer et al. 2007). Nonetheless, these protected turtle populations could be the basis of a regional sustainable harvest.

To protect these nesting populations, illegal take and nest raiding must be reduced through strengthening existing legislation and empowering communities and NGOs to manage marine turtle populations and other marine resources using traditional conventions (*dina*), which have had known success at the local level (Evely et al. 2011; Harris 2011; Humber et al. 2017b). Gear restrictions could also be considered, given that *jarifa* nets are responsible for high levels of targeted catch and bycatch of marine megafauna, including sharks, turtles, and marine mammals (Y. Razafindrakoto et al. 2008). Malagasy legislation permits the transfer of natural resource management rights to communities, and as such, there has been an important growth of bottom-up conservation and management initiatives (Rakotoson and Tanner 2006; G. Andriamalala and Gardner 2010). Therefore, similar robust, community-led approaches to turtle conservation could be effective with the help and guidance of locally established NGOs.

Subject editor: Steven M. Goodman

DUGONG DUGON, DUGONG, *LAMBOHARA*

P. Z. R. Davis, S. Cerchio, A. Cooke, and N. Andrianarivelo

Dugong dugon (Dugong; Figure 7.25) is the only living representative of its family, Dugongidae, and one of four extant species within the order Sirenia, the other three being manatees within the family Trichechidae. *Dugong dugon* is strictly marine, feeds on seagrasses, and is found in the Indo-Pacific, between East Africa and Vanuatu. Sirenians emerged in the middle Eocene about 50 million years ago (Domning and Gingerich 1994) and share common ancestors with the elephants (Proboscidea), hyraxes (Hyracoidea), and the extinct and hippo-like Desmostylia. Molecular genetic studies have consistently shown that sirenians share a common ancestry with a clade of African mammals, the Afrotheria, which includes the elephants, hyraxes, aardvarks, elephant shrews, golden moles, and the tenrecs (Murata et al. 2003). A previously undescribed primitive dugong, named as *Eotheroides lambondrano* (Sirenia: Dugongidae), has recently been described from middle Eocene deposits at Ampazony in northwest Madagascar, confirming the presence of ancestral dugongs in Malagasy coastal waters prior to the emergence of modern dugongs (Samonds et al. 2009).

STATUS

Two decades ago it was already apparent that *D. dugon* was in critical need of conservation intervention (Marsh et al. 2002), particularly in the western Indian Ocean (WWF-EAME 2004). In the absence of anthropogenic impacts, this coastal marine mammal has a low maximum rate of population increase of only 5% per year (Boyd et al. 1999); hence, any additional mortality through hunting

FIGURE 7.25 **Dugong dugon feeding on seagrass.** (PHOTO by L. Dinraths.)

or accidental capture in nets can tip a small population into precipitous decline. Populations in the Indo-Pacific, particularly around islands, have suffered from overexploitation, primarily owing to direct and accidental capture (Marsh et al. 2002), and local extinctions in the western Indian Ocean region have been recorded from La Réunion, Mauritius, and Rodrigues (C3 Madagascar and Indian Ocean Islands Programme 2010b). The use of gillnets is considered a major cause of mortality in the southwest Indian Ocean, including Madagascar (Kizska et al. 2008).

The International Union for Conservation of Nature (IUCN) Red List considers the status of *D. dugon* as Vulnerable on a global scale (Marsh and Sobtzick 2019), with an estimated population decline of 20% in the last century (Marsh et al. 2002). However, this classification is based on a global average that includes significant populations in Australia (c. 85,000 individuals; CITES 2000) and the Arabian Gulf (5800 individuals; Preen 2004). In the western Indian Ocean, *D. dugon* would be more appropriately classified as Critically Endangered, based on the facts that: 1) the largest population in the region is considered to be in Mozambique (200–300 individuals; Findlay et al. 2011a), with only small, fragmented, and declining populations scattered across the coastlines of East Africa, Madagascar, Comoros, and Seychelles, and 2) recent mitochondrial DNA analyses reveal that the Malagasy and Comoran populations are genetically distinct from the East African population (Plon et al. 2019).

A century ago, along with other now-endangered marine megafauna such as the sawfish *Pristis pristis* (Moriceau 1902; see Leeney, pp. 386–90), *D. dugon* was common and present in herds and large groups around Madagascar's vast coastline (Petit 1927). However, over the past half century they have suffered a precipitous decline, with sightings now very rare and usually of lone individuals or mother-and-calf pairs. The absence of encounters with this elusive marine mammal is reflected in the associated loss of traditional ecological knowledge (stories, customs, and terminology) in the younger generation of fishers (Iyengar 2018).

DISTRIBUTION

The distribution of *D. dugon* is determined by the occurrence of its sole food source, seagrass meadows (Marsh et al. 2002), which it shares in common with *Chelonia mydas* (Green Turtle; see Walker et al., pp. 391–99). Prediction of its distribution in Malagasy waters has been hampered by the lack of systematic data on the distribution of seagrass beds (see Cooke et al., pp. 311–58). However, with the realization of several seagrass surveys over the past decade, a clearer picture is emerging of the distribution of this habitat, which is generally associated with coral reefs.

The extreme northern region of Madagascar is notably one of the last areas where *D. dugon* has continued to be observed in recent years by fishers, albeit infrequently, between the Sahamalaza Peninsula in the west and Vohémar in the east. As recently as 2010 *D. dugon* was also encountered and targeted by fishers in the southwest region around Andavadoaka and was sighted by aerial surveys in the northwest stretch of coast between Mahajanga and Sahamalaza.

Historical sightings, both anecdotal and verified, from the early 20th century to the present, have been noted throughout the shallow coastal zones of the island, from south of Anakao in the southwest, along the entire west coast and around Cap d'Ambre in the far north to Antongil Bay in the northeast, and farther down the east coast as far as Ile Sainte Marie and Foulpointe (Mahavelona). This is to be expected, since *D. dugon* can be wide-ranging and is dependent on relatively shallow, protected coastline where seagrass grows in abundance.

HISTORICAL AND CULTURAL CONTEXT

Local Vernacular Names

In different regions of Madagascar, *D. dugon* is known as *lambohara* or *lamboara* (*lambo* means "pig"; *hara*, "reef"), *lambodriake* (*riake*, "sea"), or *trozogno* or *trozo* (terms used for large marine megafauna, including whales). Outside of the northwest, *trozona* is used exclusively for "whale," so usage for *D. dugong* is considered regional to the northwest, where the Sakalava people have a *fady* (taboo) for eating pig, and therefore do not apply that term to an animal that they do eat. In some areas of the northwest, seagrass is referred to as *ahitrozona*, *ahotrozona*, or *ahitrozo*, meaning "grass of the dugong." Blench (2008) demonstrates a possible Bantu connection in the various Malagasy dialect words for *D. dugon* (*lembwara* means "large fish" or "whale" in Malay). Also, the Malagasy name for the wild pig, *lambo*, reflects Austronesian names for bovines. Near Andavadoaka in southwest Madagascar there is a Vezo fishing village named Lamboara, presumably after the Dugong. The variations in vernacular names are presented in Table 7.13.

Hunting and Exploitation in Madagascar

Dugong dugon in Madagascar was first described in French literature by early explorers (e.g., Leguat 1708) and later by Petit (1927), who describes in great detail the sanctity surrounding traditional hunting excursions and the slaughter and burial of the animal, in the southwest and northwest regions of Madagascar. Accounts of deliberate hunting excursions and encounters with herds of Dugongs persisted into the 1960s, which contrasts starkly with the situation only 30 years later, when most young fishers in the extreme northwest had never even heard of the animal and capture occurred only opportunistically or accidentally while out fishing (C3 Madagascar and Indian Ocean Islands Programme 2010a). Dedicated hunting trips were from this point likely to prove fruitless, given the scarcity of this species.

Rich folklore, beliefs, and taboos defined Malagasy peoples' traditional interactions with *D. dugon* (Petit 1927; Cunningham et al. 2011), a product of the danger and difficulty in the hunt, the recognition of physical similarities between humans and Dugongs, and the desire to appease both ancestors and the spirit of the deceased animal on slaughter and burial. In northern Madagascar, members or descendants of the Anjoaty tribe, known as mystics, or, alternatively, chief fishers from the village were the only people conferred the right to preside over ceremonial slaughter. Another clan traditionally associated with the hunting of Dugongs is the Kajemby of the Soalala region in the west, a subgroup of Sakalava people who specialize in fishing, hunting, and collecting marine resources, including Dugongs (Durbin 1994). From accounts gathered as part

TABLE 7.13. **Dialectal names with cultural affinity and interpretation of local names of *Dugong dugon* in Madagascar, by region**

LOCATION (DIALECT)	VERNACULAR NAME	COMMENT
Throughout Madagascar	*Lambohara*	*lambo* = "pig"; *hara* = "reef"
Masoala and Ile Sainte Marie (Betsimisaraka)	*Lambondrano, lamboaran'*	*lambo* = "pig"; *rano* = "water"; *ndrano*= "of the water"
Extreme northwest and northwest (Sakalava)	*Trozogno, trozo*	Lit. "whale"
West and southwest (Vezo)	*Lambondriake*	*lambo* = "pig"; *riake* = "sea"; *ndriake* = "of the sea"
Mayotte (Kiboshy)	*Lamboara*	Malay *lembwara*, "large fish," "whale"

of a cultural study in 2018 from southwestern, northeastern, and northwestern portions of the country, it was clear that in past times Dugong hunting existed, but was, on the whole, neither frequent nor indiscriminate (Iyengar 2018). Although it is worth noting that this is somewhat at odds with other interview survey work that reported fairly extensive hunting in the latter half of the 20th century, described in detail below.

The organization Community Centered Conservation (C3) conducted open-ended interviews with elder fishers in 2009 and 2017 in coastal settlements from Nosy Be in the northwest to Vohémar in the northeast, which provided insight into ancient capture methods. Traditionally, *D. dugon* was captured using the *valakira* method, whereby bamboo structures were set in the water to create a disturbance, which caused Dugongs to move out toward open water. The animals would then be pursued by boat until they became distressed and fatigued, which facilitated capture. A similar method was applied using a harpoon (*samandra*, *ranjo*, and *famono hosatra*), often equipped with a wooden float so that the speared Dugong could be pursued and asphyxiated once fatigued. These methods were generally reported by interviewees as outdated, although a harpoon may still be kept on board for this purpose according to two informants.

TABLE 7.14. **Accounts of *Dugong dugon* reported during socio-ecological interview surveys from 2008 to 2013 at 15 locations along the west coast from Nosy Mitsio to Ifaty and on the northeast coast at Masoala Peninsula**

LOCATION	INTERVIEWS/INDIVIDUALS	1950–1980	1980s	1990s	2000s
Nosy Mitsio	41/58	8/0/8	18/0/18	32/0/25	3/0/2
Ambaro Bay	60/250	483/479/4	233/230/3	31/26/5	25/4/19
Nosy Faly	22/141	1/1/0	22/21/1	23/20/3	0/0/0
Nosy Be	24/143	0/0/0	0/0/0	0/0/0	0/0/0
Ampasindava Peninsula	56/97	38/33/1	84/65/9	16/5/5	13/2/4
Mahajanga	13/27	4/0/0	1/0/0	1/0/1	6/0/6
Barren Islands	5/20	41/41/0	30/30/0	31/30/0	3/1/0
Ambozaka	4/13	2/0/0	0/0/0	0/0/0	0/0/0
Morondava	4/12	0/0/0	0/0/0	0/0/0	0/0/0
Belo sur Mer	30/107	6/5/0	6/1/4	4/3/1	1/0/0
Morombe	7/21	0/0/0	0/0/0	0/0/0	0/0/0
Bevato	9/15	89/80/1	59/52/3	21/12/5	33/22/2
Andavadoaka	28/57	30/0/0	26/6/0	26/14/1	28/15/7
Bevohitse	24/79	1/1/0	4/3/1	6/0/5	7/4/3
Ifaty	12/29	0/0/0	0/0/0	0/0/0	0/0/0
Masoala Peninsula	25/32	42/19/0	29/5/0	1/0/0	1/0/0
Totals	364/1101	744/659/14	512/413/39	192/110/51	120/48/43

Source: Cerchio et al. (2012).

Notes: Sample size is presented as "number of interviews"/"total number individuals interviewed," since in many cases there were focus groups.
Results are represented as number of individual Dugongs reported for each time period in three categories: "total reported"/"hunted"/"bycaught."

According to interviewees, contemporary methods for intentional capture are conducted from a 6–8 m motorized dugout canoe (pirogue) using gillnets (*ragaridy jarifa*, *zedazeda*), typically with a mesh size of 3–7 fingers, 3–7 m in height, and anywhere from 100 m to 900 m long, normally used to target large fishes. These nets, now widespread in Madagascar, are also thought to be the primary cause of incidental captures of *D. dugon*. Six men are required to capture a Dugong, four to manipulate the net and two to manage the boat. This is also to ensure compliance with *fady*, or local taboo, which requires six men from different families to confirm that sexual intercourse has not taken place with the animal (there is a similar requirement in Mohéli, Union of the Comoros). The Dugong is encircled with the net, and the fishers create noise to cause the animal to panic and become entangled in the net and asphyxiated. Similar techniques are reported for dolphin hunting in the southwest, both the shift from harpoons to monofilament net, and the driving of pods of dolphins into gillnets (Andrianarivelo 2001; Cerchio et al. 2015a).

The number of "dugong experts" estimated for each community (defined here as fishers who had knowledge on how to hunt *D. dugon* and had targeted it in the past) varied greatly between sites. Informants in the village of Ramena in Antsiranana Bay reported the highest number of dugong experts, with almost all fishers in the village believed to have captured Dugongs at some time (including incidental captures, not just deliberate hunting). At Ampasindava village, near Nosy Hara in the far northwest, estimates of between 10 and 50 dugong experts were recorded. In contrast, farther south at Nosy Faly near Nosy Be, only four such experts were identified. Certain older informants claimed to have killed between 10 and 200 Dugongs during their fishing careers, with five of them capturing Dugongs on normal fishing excursions and one (who claimed to have caught 200) targeting *D. dugon* exclusively. Dugong hunting specialists were also encountered during interviews in the southwest in Bevato and Andavadoaka, central west in the Barren Islands, and northwest in Ambaro Bay and on Ampasindava Peninsula, with individuals reporting that they had killed 25–150 individuals during periods ranging from 20 to 50 years (Cerchio et al. 2012) (Table 7.14).

The effort—in time, skill, and cost—involved in the capture of a Dugong (hunting excursion, killing, and ceremonial slaughter) was significant. The complex series of ritualistic activities that preceded and followed a Dugong capture indicate that there was deep respect both for the animal and the hunter. There is indication from key informants that this was an uncommon, not a regular, event.

After independence of Madagascar from French colonial rule in 1960, a range of factors facilitated intensive hunting and bycatch of the Dugong: lack of maritime law enforcement, advent of motorized craft, coastal population growth, erosion of traditional values and customs, and proliferation of monofilament gillnets. This period of technical change is correlated with a marked decline in *D. dugon* sightings based on interviews, from the 1980s onward, reported in independent and therefore corroborative interview surveys in both the northwest and southwest regions. A remark from a 103-year-old elder from Ambolobozokely, in the far north of Madagascar, was that the lack of respect of traditions had led to the disappearance of the Dugong (C3 2018).

RESEARCH STUDIES

Aerial Surveys

It is important to note that most recent information available on *D. dugon* in the coastal waters of Madagascar (apart from a couple of photographed kills) is based on fisher interviews and anecdotal communications; the exception was during a marine mammal aerial survey of northern and western Madagascar in 2009 (Figure 7.26), which resulted in rare direct observations (Van Canneyt et al. 2010). During these aerial surveys in December 2009, live Dugongs were sighted on seven occasions; one was in the Ampasindava region of the northwest and within Nosy Hara Marine Park, supporting earlier anecdotal evidence for an extant population in this region (A. Cooke et al. 2003a; Rosenbaum 2003a; C3 Madagascar and Indian Ocean Islands Programme 2010a). Six sightings occurred on an approximately 150 km stretch of coast in the northwest between Mahajanga and Sahamalaza, an area that is otherwise data poor, suggesting that this region may also support an extant population.

The Van Canneyt et al. (2010) aerial surveys also covered broad regions of the central-west coast, including the Barren Islands; the southwest coast, including the Andavadoaka region; and the northeast coast, including Antongil Bay and the Masoala Peninsula; but with no *D. dugon* sighting in these regions. However, it is important to note that the surveys were tailored for cetacean studies, and therefore the transect design was not at a fine-scale assessment of coastal or shallow-water Dugong habitat and is likely to have underestimated observations.

Interview Surveys

Locations where *D. dugon* has been observed, either dead or alive, across Madagascar and with data based on multiple sources, are displayed in Figure 7.27. Records of occurrence from 2000 to 2010 in the far north based on interview data (C3 2018), the region with the highest number of recent records, are presented in the inset of Figure 7.27. Below, in the section Dugong Occurrence and Its Relationship to Seagrass Habitat, we describe, by region, a number of interview surveys that revealed sighting locations across the lifetimes of fishers, with particular emphasis on those confirmed over the past 20 years.

Intensive interview surveys have been conducted with fishers since 2009 across northern Madagascar by various researchers, but it is not possible to compare data from these studies owing to methodological differences. In summary, the results confirm that *D. dugon* still occurs but is rarely encountered across the northwest and northeast coasts of Madagascar, based on observations of dead and live animals over the past 20 years. The main cause of death was accidental capture in gillnets, followed by opportunistic hunting.

C3's studies between 2009 and 2017, across the regions of Nosy Hara Marine Park, Ampobofofo, Bay of Rigny complex, and Ambodivahibe, confirm the far north of Madagascar is still an important habitat for *D. dugon*, with mother-and-calf pairs sighted most consistently in the bays and around the islets of Nosy Hara Marine Park (C3 Madagascar and Indian Ocean Islands Programme 2010a).

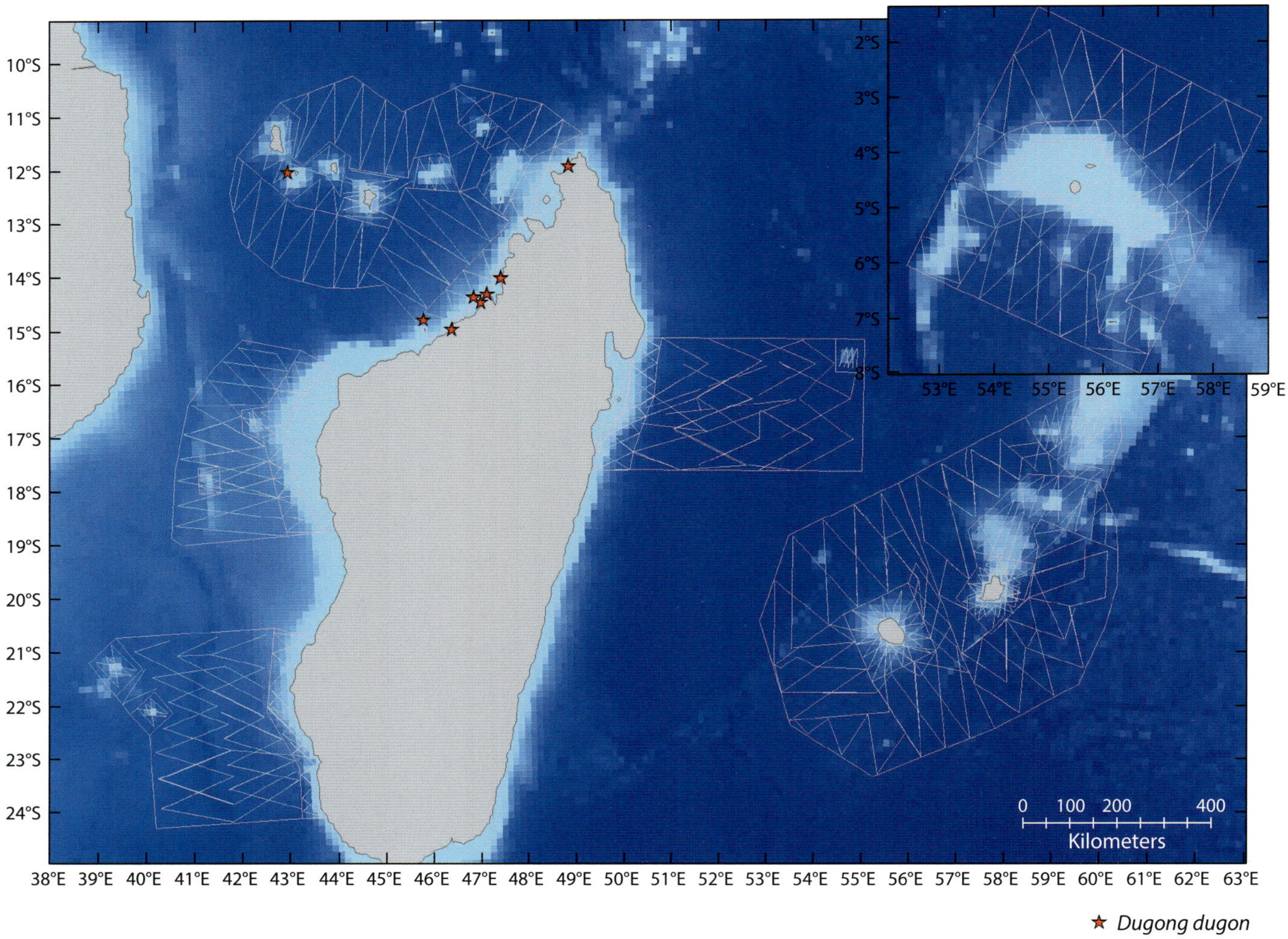

FIGURE 7.26 ***Dugong dugon* sightings during 2009 aerial survey conducted by REMMOA Indian Ocean.** (SOURCE: Observatoire Pelagis, CRMM, Université de La Rochelle.)

The most recent *D. dugon* mortality was recorded in 2018, when a fisher opportunistically encountered and killed a Dugong at Andovokonko near the village of Ivovona in the Ambodivahibe region. The meat was sold in the village at 10,000 MGA (US$2.80) per kilo. Samples of bone and tissue were collected and preserved for genetic analysis (C3 2018). There is virtually no awareness of the existence of *D. dugon* among fishers of less than 40 years old (Iyengar 2018).

DUGONG OCCURRENCE AND RELATIONSHIP TO SEAGRASS HABITAT

As a complement to the interviews in the extreme north, C3 conducted surveys and ground-truthing of shallow seagrass habitats where *D. dugon* had been reported to occur (C3 Madagascar and Indian Ocean Islands Programme 2010a). Spectral analysis of satellite imagery and examination of aerial photographs were employed to identify the potential location of seagrass habitats throughout the northern region of Madagascar, from Nosy Be to Vohémar. Ground-truthing at four sites where *D. dugon* had been observed (Ampasindava, Andovokonko, Antaravy, Ramena) confirmed the presence of seagrass beds with high diversity (eight species) and variable densities (7.5–38.6%) (see Cooke et al., pp. 311–58).

Seagrass studies at localities where *D. dugon* had been sighted in Nosy Hara Marine Park revealed the presence of *Thalassia hemprichii*, *Cymodocea serrulata*, *Halodule uninervis*, *H. wrightii*, and *Halophila ovalis*, all of which are commonly consumed by Dugongs. The seaward sites most preferred by *D. dugon* were characterized by seagrass communities dominated by *Halodule wrightii*, *H. uninervis*, and *C. serrulata* (C3 Madagascar and Indian Ocean Islands Programme 2010a).

The main threat to seagrass in this remote locality is potential wide-scale destruction during cyclonic events, which occur on a near-annual basis in the region. A study in 2013 in southwest Madagascar confirmed significant loss of seagrass after a cyclone (Côté-Laurin et al. 2017). Further, in eastern Australia, smothering by sediment and inundation from freshwater flooding associated with a cyclone led to large-scale die-off of seagrass, followed by starvation and mortality of significant numbers of Dugongs (Preen and Marsh 1995). However, food resource limitation is unlikely to impact the small remnant population of *D. dugon* in Malagasy waters.

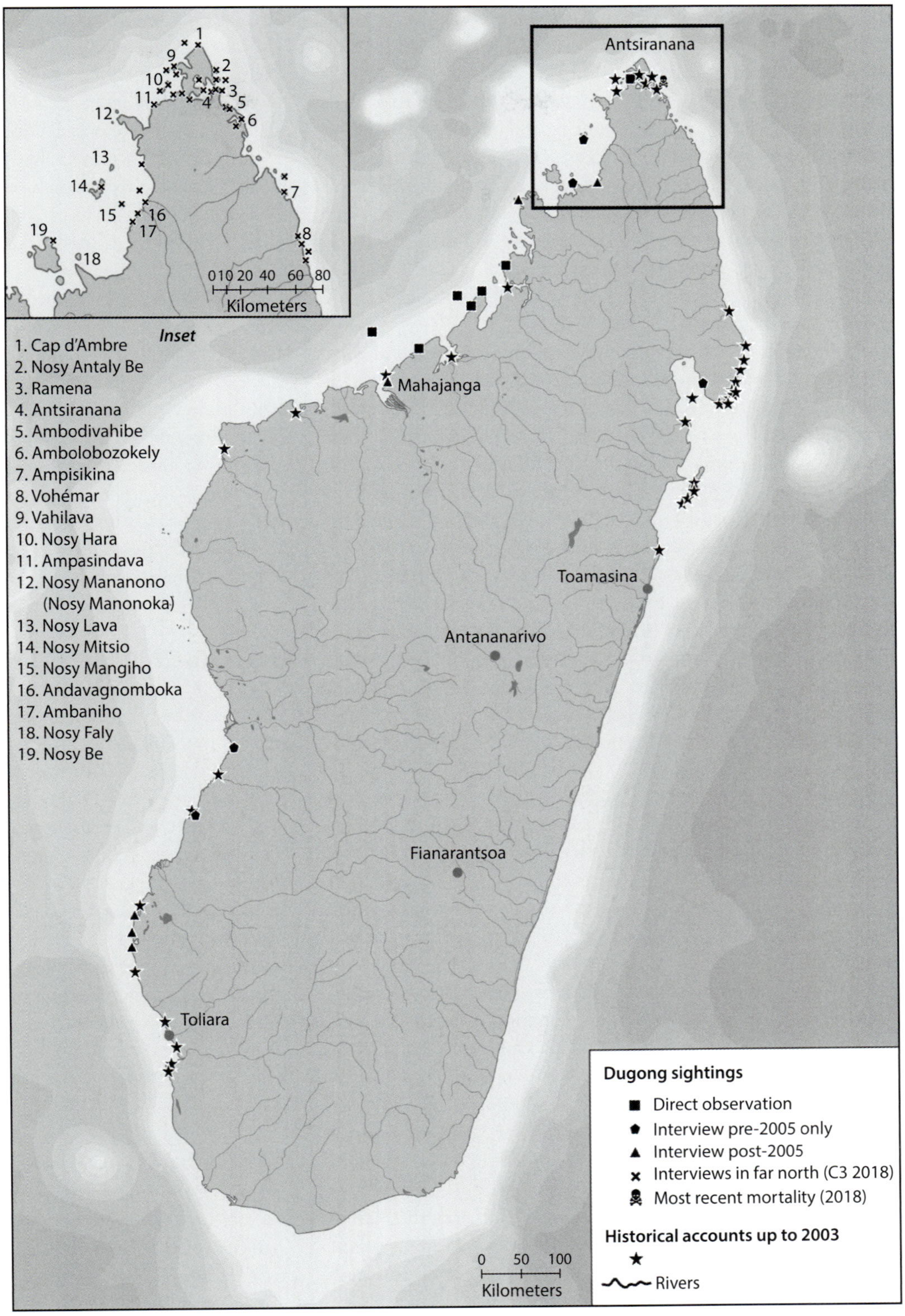

FIGURE 7.27 **Occurrence of *Dugong dugon* in Malagasy waters based on survey data and historical observations. Inset: Occurrence of Dugongs from 2000 to 2010 as reported from interview surveys in the far north of Madagascar.** (SOURCES: Survey data from C3 Madagascar and Indian Ocean Islands Programme 2010a, Van Canneyt et al. 2010, and Cerchio et al. 2012; historical observations as detailed in Table 7.15; inset survey data from C3 2018.)

Northwest

Interviews were conducted at 20 villages adjacent to Sahamalaza/Radama Islands Marine Park in 2015 (Y. Razafindrakoto 2018). Results revealed sightings as recent as 2015 of *D. dugon* in Ambatolava (east of Nosy Berafia), Ankasetra (west of Nosy Valiha), and Ambatobe (in Sahamalaza Bay), including mother-and-calf pairs. Seagrass beds were estimated to cover approximately 6465 ha and feeding trails were recorded. However, as in other localities, the majority of sightings were from the 1990s or earlier, and most young people were unaware of the existence of Dugongs.

West, Southwest, and Masoala Peninsula

Socio-ecological interview surveys were conducted in villages on the west coast of Madagascar during several expeditions between

2008 and 2013, focused on marine mammals including dolphins, whales, and *D. dugon* (Cerchio et al. 2012; S. Cerchio and N. Andrianarivelo, unpublished data). Individual and group interview surveys were held with fishers, aimed at gathering traditional knowledge and information on hunting and bycatch of all marine mammals, and conducted in 78 villages in 15 locations from Nosy Mitsio and Ambaro Bay in the northwest to Ifaty in the southwest. During the same period and effort, interviews were also conducted at five villages around the Masoala Peninsula in the northeast (B. Andrianantenaina, unpublished data). Overall, 1101 individuals were interviewed in 364 interview sessions (195 with individuals, and 169 with focus groups) (Table 7.14).

The interviews revealed accounts of hunting, bycatch, and sightings of live animals dating back to the 1950s and were grouped by decade to assess perceived trends in population status among the areas. Extensive hunting and bycatch were reported from Ambaro Bay and Ampasindava Peninsula (including Ankivonjy Marine Protected Area [MPA]) in the northwest, the Barren Islands in the central west, and Bevato in the southwest. Hunting was also reported to a somewhat lesser degree from Nosy Faly in the northwest; Belo sur Mer, Andavadoaka, and Bevohitse in the southwest; and Masoala in the northeast. Bycatch (but no directed hunting) was reported from Nosy Mitsio and Mahajanga (northwest), and only live sightings were reported from a few interviews in the Ambozaka region (central west). No accounts were reported during interviews at Morombe, Morondava, or Nosy Be, although there are previous reports from at least the two former areas, which had relatively little survey effort (Table 7.14).

Overall, reports pointed to decimation of *D. dugon* populations in recent decades, especially during and after the 1980s and 1990s. In most areas, the predominant reports were accounts prior to 2000, and some suggesting decline even between 2000 and 2010. In the northwest areas with the most accounts (Ampasindava Peninsula and Ambaro Bay), there was a precipitous decline in reports after 1990.

It should be noted that data from Ambaro Bay indicated a much higher occurrence of *D. dugon* accounts, particularly hunting, than any other region surveyed. It is possible that some of this is inflation due to a positive bias on the part of fishers to respond for some reason that is not understood; however, without any data on pre-exploitation abundance of *D. dugon* in northwest Madagascar during the first half of the 20th century, it is also feasible that a healthy population could be large enough to withstand this reported level of exploitation over a few decades. In such a scenario, these interview results could reflect the depletion of a relatively large population of *D. dugon* during the 1970s and 1980s, and population crash by the 1990s. Conversely, in the southwest hotspot (Andavadoaka and Bevato) the number of reports was relatively constant from the 1980s through the 2000s. As for the other regions surveyed, there was evidence for possible near extirpation (no reports since 2000 or 2005) around Nosy Mitsio, Nosy Faly, Belo sur Mer, the Barren Islands, and Masoala (Table 7.14).

After 2005 *D. dugon* was still being found and hunted in the northwest around the Ampasindava Peninsula and in Ambaro Bay, and in the southwest around Andavadoaka, but not much elsewhere in the surveyed area. In most villages where hunting was prevalent, key individuals were responsible for the majority of kills. In Ambaro Bay, two separate fishers each reported killing at least 150 Dugongs between 1960 and 1990, and 1965 and 1980, respectively, and a small focus group of two fishers reported hunting about three per year between 1950 and 1980, or approximately 120 Dugongs; this represented 57% of all hunted *D. dugon* in the surveyed Ambaro Bay villages. In the Barren Islands, two focus groups of eight and two fishers each reported hunting 50 Dugongs from 1960 to 2000 and 1950 to 2000, respectively. In Andavadoaka, a small focus group of two fishers reported hunting 25 Dugongs from 1990 to 2009. In Bevato (a village in the Andavadoaka area), a single fisher reported hunting at least 50 Dugongs between 1954 and 1995. Conversely, reports of bycatch were more evenly distributed across interviewed fishers. Cerchio et al. (2012) concluded that this was likely evidence for Dugong specialists, as identified in other studies in the northwest (C3 Madagascar and Indian Ocean Islands Programme 2010a). In summary, recent high hunting pressure was reported only in Ambaro Bay and Ampasindava Peninsula, including Ankivonjy MPA, in the northwest, and Andavadoaka (including Bevato) in the southwest. Previously important zones for *D. dugon* appeared to include Nosy Mitsio, the Barren Islands, and the Masoala Peninsula.

HISTORICAL ACCOUNTS

One of the authors of this contribution (AC) has maintained a record of miscellaneous accounts of *D. dugon* sightings in Madagascar (Table 7.15). These records document sightings of 63 Dugongs since the 1960s, save one very early, outlier observation from 1902 (Moriceau 1902). These mainly anecdotal records serve to illustrate the geographic range within which *D. dugon* has been observed over the past 50 or more years, while providing some additional contextual information and details. Such data complement the more targeted survey data summarized above and have been entered onto the distribution map (Figure 7.27) as points of historical occurrence. Perhaps of key importance is that the historical data highlight the northeast (Masoala and Ile Sainte Marie) for *D. dugon*, accounting for almost 50% of observations dating from 1973 to 2000, yet no reports since 2000.

EDGE STATUS AND GENETIC STUDIES

Due to its threatened status and evolutionary distinctiveness, *D. dugon* is classed as an EDGE (Evolutionarily Distinct and Globally Endangered) species with a very high evolutionary distinctiveness (ED) index of 59.29, placing it as the sixth-highest-rated mammal globally and well above the median rating of 7.56 for all EDGE mammals (EDGE 2020). The Dugong's extinction would therefore represent a disproportionally greater loss to global genetic biodiversity than the loss of most other mammal species.

Plon et al. (2019) investigated the phylogeography of *D. dugon* across its original range using museum material from 14 natural history museums. The mitochondrial DNA (mtDNA) control region was successfully amplified from samples of bone or tooth powder from 162 individuals collected between 1827 and 1996 and spanned the historical geographic range of the Dugong. The resulting mtDNA sequences match those from previous studies of Dugongs from Australia and Indonesia, but revealed several new and divergent mtDNA lineages in the Indian Ocean.

One mtDNA lineage includes most specimens from the western Indian Ocean, with another distinct lineage isolated to the waters of Madagascar and Comoros. There is little geographic structuring detectable among other populations in the western Indian Ocean, and all appear to have historically contained comparatively low levels of genetic diversity, suggesting a certain level of inter-locality dispersal. The genetic diversity of several Indian Ocean samples collected after 1950 was lower than that of the samples collected earlier from similar locations, a result coincident with the anecdotal reductions in population size. The Madagascar and Comoros lineage is of particular conservation importance and highlights the vulnerability of *D. dugon* populations in this portion of the western Indian Ocean.

LEGISLATION AND POLICY

Hunting of *D. dugon* was banned originally by the French administration in the 1920s (Baker-Medard 2020) based on observations of hunting and concerns about the perceived decline in the population, a concern maintained by Petit (1930). *Dugong dugon* was later integrally protected under Ordinance (Ordonnance) 60-126 of 1960 and its implementing decree (Decree [Décret] 61-096) of 1961. This species is listed in Appendix I of the Convention on International Trade in Endangered Species of Wild Fauna and Flora (CITES), Appendix I of the Convention on the Conservation of Migratory Species of Wild Animals (CMS), Annexes II and IV of the Nairobi Convention, and is listed as a Class A species under the African Convention on the Conservation of Nature and Natural Resources (Algiers, 1968), which Madagascar ratified in 1970 (Law [Loi] 70-004).

Dugong dugon enjoyed additional protection for a time under the fisheries law, Law 93-022, Article 9, which provided blanket protection for all marine mammals. However, since Decree 61-096 was substituted by Decree 2006-400, which does not list this species, and since Law 93-022 was replaced with the new fisheries law (Law 2015-053), which protects only species that are listed in existing regulations, Dugongs (and other marine mammals) have technically fallen out of national legal protection. A government report of 2018 confirms the lack of specific legal protection for *D. dugon* (MEEF 2018). This situation is a clear breach of international treaty obligations and needs to be rectified without delay; for example, by updating Decree 2006-400 to include Dugongs and other marine mammals.

Law enforcement will always be a considerable challenge across such a vast coastal region with poor infrastructure and limited government resources. In Malagasy waters, the future of the species depends very much on the behavior and decision-making of community members, particularly artisanal fishers, living in remote areas frequented by *D. dugon*. Combined with awareness of its status and national laws, Dugong protection can be incorporated into traditional resource management law, or *dina*. This has been successfully achieved by C3 in the communities of Nosy Hara Marine Park and Rigny Bay. Such approaches have also been successful in dolphin conservation in the Anakao region south of Toliara, where a combination of community engagement, development of *dina*, and alternative livelihood development has resulted in the cessation of organized dolphin hunting (Cerchio et al. 2015a).

Through the CMS of the United Nations Environmental Program (UNEP), an international memorandum of understanding (MoU) for the conservation of the Dugong and its habitat was established in 2007, to which Madagascar is a signatory. Although it is a nonbinding agreement with voluntary participation, this instrument encourages all signatory range states to develop national conservation management plans for the species' future protection. By becoming the first signatory state of this MoU, Madagascar has shown its political commitment to conservation action for this threatened species; however, a major weakness is the lack of legislation pertaining to *D. dugon* and its critical habitat. A policy gap analysis was conducted by the Malagasy government with regard to Dugongs and seagrasses in 2018, as part of the UNEP Global Environment Facility (GEF) Dugong and Seagrass Conservation Project (MEEF 2018). The report highlighted the gap in legal protection of the Dugong described above, but also the absence of any policy for the protection of its seagrass habitat.

Ultimately, the promulgation and enforcement of specific legislation for *D. dugon* will not alone be enough to prevent its extinction from Madagascar's waters. A national Dugong conservation management plan needs be developed and launched with a major focus on direct conservation and monitoring at community level. The plan must be appropriately geographically prioritized, based on the best available information on *D. dugon* distribution, in order to have the best chance for bringing the Madagascar Dugong back from the brink of extinction with the limited resources available and starting to rebuild Madagascar's once-important populations.

As part of the Dugong conservation management plan, based on proven successes, conservation programs with investment at the village level, led by key community members in conjunction with nongovernmental organizations (NGOs) and/or protected-area managers such as Madagascar National Parks involved in co-management, in the localities where the Dugong still persists, will be critical to its future survival in the decade to come.

CONSERVATION MEASURES

Results from all studies confirm that the *D. dugon* population in Malagasy waters—which, together with the Comoros population, represents a unique genetic lineage—has been greatly depleted and is near extinction, based on comparison with historical anecdotal records and local knowledge. Dugongs appeared in herds in some regions of the northwest up until the 1960s. They were intensively exploited by coastal communities for their meat and oil, and this increased with the introduction of motorized craft, and accidental bycatch escalated with the introduction and proliferation of monofilament gillnets in artisanal fisheries. The development and expansion of industrial shrimp trawling along sections of the western and eastern coasts from 1967 and the expanding use of gillnets for shark fishing from the early 1990s may have introduced additional sources of mortality. Loss of seabed habitat due to high amounts of

TABLE 7.15. **Historical Dugong observations up to 2003**

REGION	LOCATION	YEAR	NO.	EVENT	REMARKS	SOURCE
NORTH						
Extreme northeast	5 km SE of Antsiranana in Diégo Bay	1975	1	Seen from boat	February 1975	D. Halleux, unpublished data
	Northern part of Diégo Bay	1976	1	Seen from boat	December 1976	D. Halleux, unpublished data
	Andokovonko	2000	1	Accidental capture	Presence confirmed in Antsiranana region, but rare	Maharavo et al. (2011)
Northeast (Masoala Peninsula)	Ambohimahery	1973	1	Captured	–	Rakotonirina (1999)
	Cap Masoala	1980	1	Seen by fishers	Fishers hunting with harpoon	D. Halleaux (to M. Nicoll), unpublished data
	Ratsianarana	1980	2	Captured	–	Rakotonirina (1999)
		1997	3	Seen	2 adults; 1 juvenile	Rakotonirina (1999)
	Ambodilaitry	1988	6	Captured	Single hunt	Rakotonirina (1999)
		1964–1998	3	Captured	Additional to 1988 captures	Rakotonirina (1999)
	Ambohombato	1995	1	Seen by fishers	–	Rakotonirina (1999)
	Ratsianarana	1994	2	Seen by fishers	Adults	Odendaal et al. (1995)
	Cap Masoala	1994	1	Seen by fishers	Adult	G. van Schalkwyck, unpublished data
	Cap Est	1994	2	Seen by hotelier	Adults	
	Vinanivao	1997	1	Captured by fisher	Adult	Jaomanana and W. Rakotoarinivo, unpublished data
	Vinanivao	1997	1	Seen from air	January 1997	M. Hatchwell, unpublished data
	Antalaha	1998	3	Seen from air	October 1998	
	Antongil Bay	2000	2	Seen by fishers	Nandrasana/ Voloina	P. Doukakis and M. Jonahson, unpublished data
	Mananara-Nord	2000	1	Captured	–	
Extreme northwest	Ampasindava	2000	1	Captured	One skull retained	B. Rakotonirina and R. Ratsimbazafy, unpublished data
	Ampasindava	2000	3	Seen by fishers	August 2000	Metcalf and Gray (2001)
	Ramena	2003	1	Butchered	Photographed	WWF-EAME (2004)
	Nosy Hara	2003	1	Caught	August 2003; photographed by Lyn Robinson	WWF-EAME (2004); A. Cooke and Brand (2012)

REGION	LOCATION	YEAR	NO.	EVENT	REMARKS	SOURCE
Northwest	Anjeba, Mahajamba	1902	1	Caught	Photographed; male	Moriceau (1902)
	Soalala (Anky)	1990	1	Captured	Village of Anky—"have been rare for 20 years"	Durbin and Rakotoniaina (1991); Durbin (1994)
	Soalala (Antranolava)	1991	1	Captured with harpoons	Pregnant female; first for 10 years—"have been rare for 30 years"	Durbin and Rakotoniaina (1991); Durbin (1994)
	Mahajanga	1991	1	Captured	"In the Mahajanga region"	Cockcroft (1993)
	Analalava	1993	1	Captured	–	G. Gaultier, unpublished data
Central west	Morondava	1988	1	Captured	Last known for Morondava	Rakotonirina (1999)
	Belo sur Mer	1999	>1	Several seen by fishers	Occasional sightings	Rakotonirina (1999)
Southwest	Saint Augustin Bay	1990	1	Seen from yacht	–	Yacht skipper (pers. comm.)
	Morombe	1992	6	Captured	Caught by fishers; also reports no records between Toliara and Morombe	Cockcroft (1993)
	Morombe	1993	3	Captured	2 adults; 1 juvenile	Cooke and COUT (1994)
	Village south of Anakao	1996	1	Captured	Tail seen	G. Gaultier, unpublished data
	Salary, north of Toliara	2000	1	Captured	Remains seen	G. Gaultier, unpublished data
EAST						
Ile Sainte Marie	Dyke close to the main town	1982	1	Regularly seen	Injured, came regularly	D. Halleux, unpublished data
	Ile aux Nattes pass in the reef	1995	1	Seen from boat	1995	Fifou, CETAMADA, unpublished data
	Pointe de l'Ile aux Nattes	1997	1	Seen from boat	1997	Fifou, CETAMADA, unpublished data
	Vohilava, southwest coast of Ile Sainte Marie	1998	1	In a fisher's net	1998	H. Bellon, CETAMADA, unpublished data
	Foulpointe	1982	1	Harpooned by overseas development worker	Regularly seen, tame, near beach	D. Halleux, unpublished data
TOTAL		102 years	>63			

sedimentation may have further contributed to the decline of *D. dugon* populations.

The relative importance of different threats varies by region. In the extreme northwest, the greatest threat is from incidental bycatch in gillnets, since organized Dugong hunting is no longer viable following the decimation of the population (Temple et al. 2019; C3 Madagascar and Indian Ocean Islands Programme 2010a). Directed hunting may remain a serious threat in some areas of the northwest (Ambaro Bay and Ampasindava Peninsula) and southwest (Andavadoaka area), where there are more recent reports of *D. dugon* (Cerchio et al. 2012; S. Cerchio and N. Andrianarivelo, unpublished data). Opportunistic capture based on chance encounter and bycatch using gillnets are sources of threat in all regions. It is important to emphasize that robustness of these conclusions is limited by interview effort, as many regions have not been surveyed. There may be other areas (e.g., between Mahajanga and Sahamalaza, identified by REMMOA aerial surveys) where there are persisting populations that may still be under continued hunting pressure. The potential threat of industrial trawling for shrimps or other species in shallow coastal waters has never been assessed and no data are available.

Dedicated research and conservation efforts for *D. dugon* in Madagascar's waters began only in 2010. Prior to this, the focus of marine research and conservation campaigns has been on sustainable fisheries and cetaceans. Since 2010, C3 Madagascar has focused intense efforts on outreach to remote communities of Nosy Hara Marine Park, which includes incidental monitoring by members of the marine park committees (community representatives from 20 villages). Schools awareness campaigns and theatre and events are organized by the Junior Ecoguards youth network. The fact that mother-calf pairs are present in the park, especially around the small offshore islands, indicates the importance of the site for *D. dugon* conservation and the need to promote and maintain community involvement in monitoring and protection. Release from gillnets when entangled and absence of hunting are essential to the Dugong's survival in this region.

In Sahamalaza Marine Park, where mother-calf pairs have also been sighted, awareness campaigns, ranger capacity building, and monitoring were initiated in 2016 under the GEF Dugong and Seagrass Conservation Project. Outreach campaigns have been regularly conducted, with the production of communication materials on Dugongs (signboards, posters, brochures, children's storybooks, and touring theatre) by C3 via its Junior Ecoguard network, which is active in 100 schools from Nosy Be northward and east to Rigny Bay. In addition, training in seagrass and Dugong ecology, conservation, and monitoring has been offered to communities within national marine parks and locally managed marine areas (LMMAs) across the far north (Rakotoarimino and Davis 2017).

It is encouraging that areas of high priority for *D. dugon* with recent live sightings are located within or near to national MPAs (Nosy Hara, Ankarea, Ankivonjy, Sahamalaza, Ambodivahibe, Velondriake) and that LMMAs and regional fisheries management plans are also emerging in many areas important for Dugong (see Cooke et al., pp. 311–58). Furthermore, zones that were the focus of intense hunting in the recent past are also under protection (Andavadoaka LMMA, established in 2004; Barren Islands LMMA, established in 2004; Nosy Mitsio, within Ankarea MPA, established in 2011). However, it is critical that management plans include specific actions for the protection and monitoring of seagrasses and Dugongs, as well as explicitly engaging and incentivizing fishers in these efforts, otherwise the conventional focus of MPAs on artisanal fisheries and coral reefs will fail to assure the Dugong's future survival. This concern is illustrated by the continued hunting of dolphins, as well as Dugongs, in the Andavadoaka region (Cerchio et al. 2015a; see Cerchio et al., pp. 411–24) despite the existence of the LMMA and MPA (Velondriake). Many of the communities in these areas live in extreme poverty, often earning less than US$1/day, and are under pressure to exploit all available resources to survive. Economic incentives will be needed to secure community support for conserving *D. dugon* and its habitat in order to persuade fishers to end what is now primarily the opportunistic capture of Dugong.

According to studies by Baker-Médard (2020), a history of colonial fisheries-management policy based on European fisheries science, followed in most cases by similar top-down approaches to coastal resource conservation by international NGOs, has left an indelible mark on fishers' perceptions of marine conservation intervention in certain areas of the island. This is exemplified by the killing of *D. dugon* and sale of its meat in 2018 by a fisher within the Ambodivahibe LMMA, despite the existence of the "community-run" protected area since 2006 and associated conservation awareness building.

When fishers view conservation practices as another means of dispossessing them of their marine resources, exploitation of endangered species will continue to occur regardless of their awareness of laws and policies. The LMMA model is now due to be extended to encompass the entire Rigny Bay complex, another important remaining Dugong habitat; it is essential that aside from implementing MPAs, international NGOs and other actors should ensure meaningful engagement with communities in the design of specific conservation and development actions at the field level. If not, communities will continue to feel dispossessed of their rights of access, will resent the messaging pushed by conservation organizations, and could deliberately hunt endangered species in order to assert their control over local resources.

Across the Dugong's remaining range, awareness raising is still the most urgent and critical primary action that can be taken to help conserve the species, since most fishers, especially those under 40 years of age, are in fact unaware of the existence of *D. dugon*, its role in the ecosystem, or that it is highly endangered or protected by law. Without greater awareness, fishers are still likely to take Dugongs they come into contact with.

In most areas where initial interviews have been conducted in the far north and northwest, less than 10% of respondents were aware that *D. dugon* even exists, let alone of its endangered status or legal protection (C3 Madagascar and Indian Ocean Islands Programme 2010a). With a rapidly expanding young population, education about the species should target children from primary age and be integrated into marine biodiversity within the school syllabus as well as included in wider environmental awareness campaigns. Women (and women's associations) should be actively targeted in incentivized conservation schemes that concern Dugong protection; they have proven to be extremely motivated to learn about the status of their natural resources and take an active role in educating the wider community in sustainable use. Their main concern is the daily provision of food for the family, and they are often the most successful entrepreneurs, once given access to credit, in diversifying and/or increasing their household income.

Knowledge and respect for traditional customs and taboos should also be revived in conservation programs, with engagement of key elders in their design and delivery, since many elders attribute loss of respect and understanding of traditions as a contributing factor to the species' decline. The successful outreach and engagement of fishers, women, and youth in Dugong and seagrass monitoring and protection at Nosy Hara Marine Park and Sahamalaza Marine Park, integrated with an incentives scheme (e.g., provision of community services such as health care), proves that communities can be motivated to protect this rare species across its vast range. The Dugong's prior importance in Malagasy culture and tradition should be emphasized, particularly with the engagement of elders and youth together, in the wider context of sustainable fisheries management and habitat restoration and protection.

Subject editor: Steven M. Goodman

CETACEAN SPECIES DIVERSITY IN MALAGASY WATERS

S. Cerchio, S. Laran, N. Andrianarivelo, A. Saloma, B. Andrianantenaina, O. Van Canneyt, and T. Rasoloarijao

Cetacea is the group of marine mammals that encompasses all whales, dolphins, and porpoises. The group is nested within the mammalian order Cetartiodactyla (comprising all artiodactyls, or even-toed ungulates, and cetaceans), with the family Hippopotamidae being the most likely sister group (Geisler and Uhen 2005). The Committee on Taxonomy of the Society for Marine Mammalogy recognizes 91 species of cetaceans in the world, including 14 Mysticeti (baleen whales) and 77 Odontoceti (toothed whales, dolphins, and porpoises), of which one, *Lipotes vexillifer*, the Yangtze River Dolphin, is likely extinct (Committee on Taxonomy 2020).

Previous assessment of the species diversity of cetaceans in Malagasy waters (Rosenbaum 2003a) indicated only 12 species whose presence could be considered confirmed (three Mysticeti and nine Odontoceti) and an additional 13 species that were suspected or occurred elsewhere in the region (four Mysticeti and nine Odontoceti). Very little information existed prior to that review, and thus it was based primarily upon limited published studies focusing on single species, a few unpublished studies that targeted description of biodiversity, and anecdotal accounts. Since 2005, there have been several research groups targeting assessment of cetacean diversity in Malagasy waters that have substantially advanced our understanding, including small-boat-based work in the southwest region (Anakao) between 2005 and 2013, and the northwest region (Nosy Be) between 2008 and 2017 (Cerchio et al. 2009a, 2014a, 2015a, 2015b; S. Cerchio et al., unpublished data); ecotourism surveys off Ile Sainte Marie, Mahajanga, Ifaty, and Tolagnaro between 2009 and 2019 (A. Saloma and F.-X. Mayer, unpublished data); aerial surveys covering the northwest, midwest, southwest, and northeast coasts between mid-December 2009 and early January 2010 (REMMOA; Van Canneyt et al. 2010; Laran et al. 2017); and long-term passive acoustic monitoring along the west coast between 2015 and 2019 (Cerchio et al. 2018a; S. Cerchio and T. Rasoloarijao, unpublished data). We draw primarily upon these different surveys, with several additional studies and anecdotal accounts, to report the confirmed presence of 26 different species, including eight Mysticeti and 18 Odontoceti (Table 7.16). Based on accounts from adjacent areas and the availability of habitat, we infer the likely presence of at least an additional three species and the possible presence of two others. There is some overlap with the species reported in Rosenbaum (2003a) but also new inclusions, and exclusions of several species due to insufficient evidence.

We report the diversity of cetaceans geographically according to the four marine ecoregions that are proposed in the "Plan stratégique de gestion du réseau des Aires Protégées de Madagascar National Parks: 2014–2024" (see Cooke et al., pp. 311–58) and originally based upon Obura et al. (2012). These are the North Mozambique Channel ecoregion, the South Mozambique Channel ecoregion, the South Madagascar ecoregion, and the East Madagascar ecoregion. To the extent that available data allow, we describe in the subsequent sections the diversity of cetaceans for each of these marine ecoregions (Table 7.16). We define Malagasy waters as falling within Madagascar's exclusive economic zone (EEZ); however, when the Madagascar EEZ abuts the EEZ of another territory within 200 nautical miles of the Malagasy coast—for example, France (Mayotte, Iles Glorieuses) and the Union of the Comoros—we consider accounts from the adjoining EEZ to maintain geographic consistency (i.e., within a 200-nautical-mile swath around Madagascar). In some cases, we draw upon information outside of the 200-nautical-mile distance when informative as regards adjacent Malagasy waters for which data are lacking (e.g., observations on the Madagascar Ridge to the south of the Madagascar EEZ). Other contributions herein on Cetacea in Malagasy waters include one on *Megaptera novaeangliae* (Humpback Whale; see Rosenbaum and Chou, pp. 430–33 and *Balaenoptera omurai* (Omura's Whale; see Cerchio et al., pp. 424–29).

TABLE 7.16. **Cetacean species occurrence around Madagascar, subdivided by ecoregion, and categorized as confirmed to occur in Malagasy waters**

SCIENTIFIC NAME	COMMON NAME (ENGLISH)	ECOREGION				MADAGASCAR OVERALL
		NORTH MOZAMBIQUE CHANNEL	SOUTH MOZAMBIQUE CHANNEL	SOUTH MADAGASCAR	EAST MADAGASCAR	
MYSTICETI	**BALEEN WHALES**					
Balaenopteridae	**Rorquals**					
Balaenoptera musculus intermedia	Antarctic Blue Whale	X	X	*	*	X
B. m. brevicauda	Pygmy Blue Whale	X	X	X	*	X
B. physalus	Fin Whale	X	X	*	*	X
B. borealis	Sei Whale	?	?	*	?	*
B. edeni	Bryde's Whale		?	X	*	X
B. omurai	Omura's Whale	X	X	–	–	X
B. bonaerensis	Antarctic Minke Whale	X	X	*	*	X
B. acutorostrata ssp.	Dwarf Minke Whale	X	?	?	–	X
Megaptera novaeangliae	Humpback Whale	X	X	X	X	X
Balaenidae	**Right whales**					
Eubalaena australis	Southern Right Whale	?	X	X	X	X
ODONTOCETI	**TOOTHED WHALES AND DOLPHINS**					
Physeteridae	**Sperm whales**					
Physeter macrocephalus	Sperm Whale	X	X	X	X	X
Kogiidae	**Kogiid sperm whales**					
Kogia sima	Dwarf Sperm Whale	X	X	*	*	X
K. breviceps	Pygmy Sperm Whale	X	*	*	*	X
Ziphiidae	**Beaked whales**					
Ziphius cavirostris	Cuvier's Beaked Whale	X	X	X	X	X
Mesoplodon densirostris	Blainville's Beaked Whale	*	*	?	?	*
M. eueu	Ramari's Beaked Whale	–	?	*	?	*
M. ginkgodens	Ginkgo-toothed Beaked Whale	?	?		?	?
Indopacetus pacificus	Longman's Beaked Whale	X	*	*	X	X
Delphinidae	**Dolphins**					
Sousa plumbea	Indian Ocean Humpback Dolphin	X	X	X	–	X
Tursiops aduncus	Indo-Pacific Bottlenose Dolphin	X	X	*	X	X
T. truncatus	Common Bottlenose Dolphin	X	X	X	*	X
Steno bredanensis	Rough-toothed Dolphin	?	X	?	?	X
Stenella longirostris	Spinner Dolphin	X	X	*	X	X
S. attenuata	Pantropical Spotted Dolphin	X	X	*	X	X
S. coeruleoalba	Striped Dolphin	*	*	X	X	X
Lagenodelphis hosei	Fraser's Dolphin	X	X	*	X	X
Grampus griseus	Risso's Dolphin	X	X	*	X	X

SCIENTIFIC NAME	COMMON NAME (ENGLISH)	ECOREGION				MADAGASCAR OVERALL
		NORTH MOZAMBIQUE CHANNEL	SOUTH MOZAMBIQUE CHANNEL	SOUTH MADAGASCAR	EAST MADAGASCAR	
Peponocephala electra	Melon-headed Whale	X	X	X	X	X
Feresa attenuata	Pygmy Killer Whale	?	?	?	?	?
Pseudorca crassidens	False Killer Whale	X	X	*	X	X
Globicephala macrorhynchus	Short-finned Pilot Whale	X	X	X	X	X
Orcinus orca	Killer Whale	X	X	*	*	X

Notes: X, confirmed to occur in Malagasy waters; *, likely to occur in Malagasy waters, based upon different sources of information; *, unknown but possible to occur in Malagasy waters, based on occurrence in the region. Species are listed by taxonomic families within Mysticeti and Odontoceti. Rosenbaum (2003a) included four additional species as "suspected or probable occurrence" or "unknown but has been recorded in the region"; however, to the best of our knowledge, there is currently no substantiated evidence for them in Malagasy waters, and we have thus excluded *Caperea marginata* (Pygmy Right Whale), *Delphinus tropicalis* (Common Dolphin), *Mesoplodon hectori* (Hector's Beaked Whale), and *Globicephala melas* (Long-finned Pilot Whale).

THE NORTH MOZAMBIQUE CHANNEL MARINE ECOREGION (EXCLUDING THE NORTHEAST COAST OF MADAGASCAR)

The northwestern coast of Madagascar is a major component of the North Mozambique Channel ecoregion and includes the stretch of coast from Cap d'Ambre, the northern tip of Madagascar, to Cap Saint André—approximately 700 km, or one-third of Madagascar's west coast (Obura et al. 2019). It is characterized by a moderately wide continental shelf, ranging from 30 km to 60 km, fringed by multiple estuaries, embayments, and several archipelagoes, including over 150 small nearshore islands. Consequently, there is a large variety of habitats from coastal (including mangroves, coral reefs, and sandy and rocky shores) to neritic continental shelf and pelagic deep water. This is a highly diverse and important region for marine mammals encompassing important habitat for breeding, feeding, and migration, as well as small and resident populations for several cetacean species. The area includes the Nosy Be region from approximately 12.7°S to 13.7°S, including Nosy Be, Nosy Komba, Nosy Iranja, and the Nosy Mitsio archipelago, where several research programs focused on marine mammals have been conducted over the past 12 years. A minimum of 23 cetacean taxa (22 species, one represented by two different subspecies) have been recorded along this 600 km stretch of coast (Table 7.16), including six baleen whales, 16 toothed whales and dolphins, and an additional two species likely and five species possibly to occur (Van Canneyt et al. 2010; Cerchio et al. 2014a, 2018a). In addition, *Dugong dugon* (Dugong) has been documented in this region rather extensively, indicating important habitat for this vulnerable and locally endangered marine mammal (see Davis et al., pp. 400–411).

Cetaceans in the North Mozambique Channel Marine Ecoregion

Mysticetes, baleen whales: *Balaenoptera musculus* (Blue Whale) in the Southern Hemisphere is divided into at least two subspecies with overlapping distributions, and the different populations are distinguished by diagnostic song types (McDonald et al. 2006; Branch et al. 2007). The subspecies *B. m. intermedia* (Antarctic Blue Whale), which is Critically Endangered on the International Union for Conservation of Nature (IUCN) Red List (J. Cooke 2018a), has a circumpolar distribution and is estimated to comprise approximately 6500 individuals for the Southern Hemisphere, or less than 2% of its pre-whaling abundance. The subspecies spends austral summers at high latitudes along the Antarctic ice edge, from where the most extensive data are available. *Balaenoptera m. intermedia* migrates to winter habitat in low latitudes according to patterns that are still poorly understood at a global level. Winter habitat is presumably occupied during the breeding season and includes the tropical and subtropical Indian Ocean (or largely north of 30°S; Branch et al. 2007), but few data exist. The Antarctic subspecies is defined by a single song type, which has been documented in all Southern Hemisphere ocean basins. Passive acoustic monitoring from the shelf slope near Nosy Be indicated the presence of *B. m. intermedia* song off northwest Madagascar throughout the austral winter, from June to September, suggesting the existence of previously unrecognized breeding-season habitat (Cerchio et al. 2018a). Some loud acoustic detections indicated presence of *B. m. intermedia* within 10 km of the shelf edge, whereas most individuals were likely within 100 km of the coast, and it is likely that whales range farther offshore into the Mozambique Channel.

The subspecies *B. m. brevicauda* (Pygmy Blue Whale; Figure 7.28a), which is Endangered on the IUCN Red List, (J. Cooke 2018b), is divided into at least four populations in the Indian Ocean, each with diagnostic song type and regional distribution. Passive acoustic monitoring off Nosy Be led to extensive documentation of the southwest Indian Ocean (SWIO) population song type in the deep offshore waters, with similar offshore spatial distribution to *B. m. intermedia* (Cerchio et al. 2018a). The SWIO *B. m. brevicauda* song occurred in prominent bimodal peaks of singing activity during May–July and October–January, suggesting the existence of a previously unrecognized migratory corridor between summer feeding and winter breeding grounds south and north of Madagascar, respectively. This migratory corridor likely connects feeding habitat on the Madagascar Ridge (Best et al. 2003) with putative breeding habitat off Kenya and the Seychelles area (Branch

FIGURE 7.28 Examples of cetacean species found in Malagasy waters and discussed in this chapter: A) *Balaenoptera musculus brevicauda* photographed off Nosy Be near 2000 m depth contour; B) *B. omurai* mother and calf photographed by drone in neritic shelf waters north of Nosy Be; C) *Sousa plumbea* photographed in coastal waters of Nosy Be; D) *Tursiops aduncus* photographed in coastal waters off Nosy Be; E) *Stenella longirostris* photographed off Nosy Be; F) *Grampus griseus* photographed off Anakao; G) *Globicephala macrorhynchus* photographed off Anakao; and H) *Pseudorca crassidens* photographed in neritic waters off Nosy Be. (PHOTO A by N. Andrianarivelo, B–H by S. Cerchio.)

et al. 2007; Barber et al. 2016). The songs of two other *B. m. brevicauda* populations were also documented off Nosy Be, those of the central Indian Ocean population and northwestern Indian Ocean–Arabian Sea population, with far fewer detections, indicating either vagrant individuals or that Nosy Be lies at the geographic limits of these two populations (Cerchio et al. 2018a, 2020).

Balaenoptera physalus (Fin Whale) and *B. bonaerensis* (Antarctic Minke Whale) have circumpolar distribution in cold waters of high latitudes during the austral summer, and are thought to migrate to poorly understood winter ranges in tropical and warm temperate low latitudes during the austral winter breeding season, similarly to *B. m. intermedia*. Acoustic monitoring offshore of Nosy Be indicated the presence of *B. physalus* during the late austral winter, from early August to mid-September (Cerchio et al. 2018a), representing the first confirmed documentation of the species in Malagasy waters. The timing of *B. physalus* song implies a later arrival than *B. m. intermedia* and a lower rate of occurrence and occupancy, suggesting the northern extent of breeding habitat. *Balaenoptera bonaerensis* song was very commonly recorded off Nosy Be from early July to early December—the species therefore remaining seasonally later than *B. m. intermedia* or *B. physalus*—suggesting breeding-season habitat. *Balaenoptera acutorostrata* subsp. (Dwarf Minke Whale) is an as-yet unnamed Southern Hemisphere subspecies of *B. acutorostrata* (Common Minke Whale) with a distribution and migration pattern that is poorly studied, but which is found in shallow low latitude shelf habitat during austral winter in several regions around the globe, including eastern Africa. Song vocalizations of *B. acutorostrata* subsp. were detected on several days during nonsystematic review of acoustic data from continental shelf waters around Nosy Be; it is possible that future analyses will indicate regular presence during the austral winter, and thus breeding habitat (S. Cerchio and B. Andrianantenaina, unpublished data). For both *B. bonaerensis* and *B. acutorostrata* subsp., these data represent the first confirmation of species-level identification in Malagasy waters. In addition to this acoustic evidence, during REMMOA aerial surveys there was a single sighting of a minke whale of unidentified species off the northwest coast in deep water, and one close to Comoros (Van Canneyt et al. 2010).

Balaenoptera omurai (Omura's Whale) is the most recently named species of baleen whale in the world (Wada et al. 2003; Figure 7.28b), and work off Nosy Be documented the first detailed description of the species globally (Cerchio et al. 2015a, 2019; see Cerchio et al., pp. 424–29). These recent data indicate that this is a resident and nonmigratory population with a restricted range in the northwest and central-west coasts of Madagascar, and may be isolated within a fragmented oceanic/global range for the species.

Madagascar is a well-documented breeding area for the southwest Indian Ocean population of *Megaptera novaeangliae* (Humpback Whale), distributed throughout all coastal waters during the austral winter (Fossette et al. 2014; Cerchio et al. 2016; Dulau et al. 2017). Small-boat surveys indicate that it is common in coastal waters of the Nosy Be region during the mid to late breeding season, and year-long acoustic monitoring in the deep offshore waters of the Nosy Be region indicated near continuous presence of *M. novaeangliae* song from early July to mid-November (Cerchio et al. 2018a; S. Cerchio and T. Rasoloarijao, unpublished data). Satellite telemetry data indicate that this area of coast is a late season migratory corridor for *M. novaeangliae* during the southern migration to polar waters (Fossette et al. 2014; Dulau et al. 2017).

Odontocetes, toothed whales and dolphins: *Sousa plumbea* (Indian Ocean Humpback Dolphin; Figure 7.28c), which is Endangered on the IUCN Red List (Braulik et al. 2015, 2017), is widely distributed along the west coast of Madagascar (Y. Razafindrakoto et al. 2004; Cerchio et al. 2015a). There is confirmed documentation of *S. plumbea* in several northwest locales: in the far northwest off Nosy Be and Nosy Mitsio (Robineau and Rose 1984; Cockcroft and Young 1998; Cerchio et al. 2015a); on the lower-northwest coast in the Loza lagoon system, approximately 150 km north of Mahajanga (T. Collins et al. 2009), and off Mahajanga (Cockcroft and Young 1998; Y. Razafindrakoto et al. 2004); and during aerial surveys along extensive stretches of coast between Mahajanga and Nosy Be (Van Canneyt et al. 2010). All *Sousa* species are obligate shallow water species, and off Nosy Be and Nosy Iranja all encounters with *S. plumbea* occurred in depths of <25 m, with average depths of 8.2 m and 10.5 m, respectively (Cerchio et al. 2015a). *Tursiops aduncus* (Indo-Pacific Bottlenose Dolphin; Figure 7.28d) is also commonly encountered in the coastal waters of Nosy Be, Nosy Iranja, and Nosy Mitsio, and often in association with *S. plumbea*; however, its habitat is more diverse as it is found in coastal as well as neritic continental shelf habitat (Cerchio et al. 2014a, 2015a). It is also commonly encountered off Mahajanga (A. Saloma and F.-X. Mayer, unpublished data), and is likely distributed along the entire northwest coast.

Stenella longirostris (Spinner Dolphin; Figure 7.28e) was the most often sighted species of odontocete by number of individuals in the continental slope and offshore areas during small-boat surveys off Nosy Be (Cerchio et al. 2014a). *Stenella attenuata* (Pantropical Spotted Dolphin) was frequently sighted in the offshore areas during surveys around Nosy Be, at times in groups exceeding 500 individuals, and in combination with *S. longirostris*, as well as on the continental shelf in smaller-size groups (Cerchio et al. 2014a; S. Cerchio et al., unpublished data). *Stenella longirostris* was also commonly encountered off Mahajanga by an ecotourism and fishing operator, and more rarely *S. attenuata* (V. E. Bedier, unpublished data). *Stenella coeruleoalba* (Striped Dolphin) has been reported by an ecotourism group off Mahajanga (A. Saloma and F.-X. Mayer, unpublished data), and there is one documented stranding on Mayotte (Van Canneyt et al. 2011); however, the species appears to be rare around Madagascar given an absence of encounters in dedicated surveys, and some reports may represent confusion with other *Stenella* species, so for this region we consider it a likely but unconfirmed species.

Densities of odontocetes were estimated in a surveyed area within this ecoregion during the REMMOA aerial survey conducted in the southwest Indian Ocean region; in most cases similar-size species were lumped into species groups since it was not always possible to identify to the species level. Density of small Delphininae (likely *S. longirostris* and *S. attenuata*) was estimated at 18 individuals per 100 km^2 in the neritic, slope, and oceanic waters along the northwest coast (Laran et al. 2017; S. Laran et al., unpublished data). Large groups of *Lagenodelphis hosei* (Fraser's Dolphin), in excess of 100 individuals, were occasionally encountered in deep waters around Nosy Be, as were small groups of *Tursiops truncatus*

(Common Bottlenose Dolphin) offshore form (Cerchio et al. 2014a; S. Cerchio et al., unpublished data). For large Delphininae (potentially *T. truncatus*, *Sousa plumbea*, or *L. hosei*) density was estimated during REMMOA surveys at about seven individuals per 100 km^2 in the waters of the neritic slope area along the northwest coast of Madagascar (Laran et al. 2017).

Among the "blackfish" species (subfamily Globicephalinae), *Globicephala macrorhynchus* (Short-finned Pilot Whale; Figure 7.28g) in groups of up to more than 40 individuals has been sighted offshore of Nosy Be, along with similarly moderate-size groups of *Peponocephala electra* (Melon-headed Whale) and *Pseudorca crassidens* (False Killer Whale; Figure 7.28h) (Cerchio et al. 2014a; S. Cerchio et al., unpublished data). Off Mahajanga, large groups of *P. crassidens* and *Peponocephala electra* (in excess of 100 individuals) have been reported, along with a single very rare encounter with *Orcinus orca* (Killer Whale) (a group of three, including adult male, female, and juvenile) in deep offshore waters (V. E. Bedier, unpublished data with photographic documentation). Large groups of *P. electra* were encountered during REMMOA aerial surveys, resulting in a density of small Globicephalinae (likely *P. electra*, but potentially *Pseudorca crassidens*) of up to 50 individuals per 100 km^2 for oceanic waters off northwest Madagascar, similar to the value obtained for the Comoro archipelago (Laran et al. 2017). A mass stranding of c. 200 *Peponocephala electra* occurred in the Loza lagoon system in 2008, likely related to petroleum exploration activities (Collins et al. 2009; Southall et al. 2013). *Feresa attenuata* (Pygmy Killer Whale) has not been confirmed in Malagasy waters; however, four individuals were stranded in the nearby Glorieuses Islands in 2016 (Dars et al. 2018) and one small group was sighted off Mayotte (Kiszka et al. 2010a), suggesting it may be present in low numbers and requiring documentation. A single group of *Grampus griseus* (Risso's Dolphin) was encountered south of Radama Islands during REMMOA surveys, but its density was low compared with other species, around 0.6 individuals per 100 km^2. *Grampus griseus* has also been documented with relatively low encounter rate off Mayotte (Kiszka et al. 2007, 2010a), so although its presence has been documented in the North Mozambique Channel, its occurrence appears to be much less than in the South Mozambique Channel (see The South Mozambique Channel Ecoregion, below).

The families Ziphiidae (beaked whales) and Kogiidae (kogiid sperm whales) are offshore deepwater species that are rarely observed and notoriously difficult to document. Groups of *Ziphius cavirostris* (Cuvier's Beaked Whale) have been sighted on the slope off Nosy Be on two occasions (Cerchio et al. 2014a; S. Cerchio, unpublished data) and during the REMMOA aerial survey (Van Canneyt et al. 2010). An individual *Indopacetus pacificus* (Longman's Beaked Whale) was sighted off Nosy Be during the REMMOA aerial survey, and close to the Comoros coast, confirming previous sightings on the shelf waters of this island (Anderson et al. 2006, Kiszka et al. 2010b). *Mesoplodon densirostris* (Blainville's Beaked Whale) is a primarily warm water species that is widely distributed in the tropics around the world; there is documentation of the species off Mayotte and Comoros (Kiszka et al. 2007, 2010a, 2010b; Van Canneyt et al. 2010), and given the proximity and similar habitat it is likely found in the deep offshore waters of northwest Madagascar. Beaked whales as a group (including *Z. cavirostris*, *I. pacificus*, and unidentified ziphiids) were estimated at a density of 0.4 individuals per 100 km^2 during REMMOA surveys in the North Mozambique Channel, a relatively high density compared with other surveyed areas (Laran et al. 2017). Unidentified *Kogia* species were sighted during REMMOA surveys, with maximum abundance estimated for the North Mozambique Channel (0.08 individuals per 100 km^2; Laran et al. 2017). A *K. breviceps* (Pygmy Sperm Whale) live-stranded on Nosy Be in 2019 (MadaMegafauna, unpublished data with photographic documentation). An individual of *K. sima* (Dwarf Sperm Whale) was stranded in the nearby Glorieuses Islands (Dorémus et al. 2009), and two were sighted off Mayotte (Kiszka et al. 2010a), so it is clear that both *Kogia* species occur in these waters.

Physeter macrocephalus (Sperm Whale), which is Vulnerable on the IUCN Red List (Taylor et al. 2019), was historically hunted in the region (Townsend 1935); however, it has not been a focus of study in the waters of northwest Madagascar. The species uses the deep offshore waters of the region regularly and was encountered over the slope habitat during REMMOA aerial surveys in groups of up to four individuals (Van Canneyt et al. 2010). Boat surveys off Nosy Be resulted in several encounters near the 2000 m depth contour, including groups of up to nine individuals, and acoustic monitoring produced numerous, but as-yet unquantified, detections of *P. macrocephalus* clicks (Cerchio et al. 2014a; S. Cerchio and T. Rasoloarijao, unpublished data).

THE SOUTH MOZAMBIQUE CHANNEL MARINE ECOREGION

The South Mozambique Channel marine ecoregion includes the central-west and southwest coast of Madagascar from Cap Saint André to roughly Itampolo, approximately 1000 km of the west coast (Obura et al. 2019). The ecoregion encompasses diverse marine habitats, including coastal, continental shelf, continental slope, and around islands and seamount habitat around Juan de Nova Island and Europa and Bassas da India atolls. The continental shelf of Madagascar is at its broadest extent just south of Cap Saint André at about 100 km, and progressively narrows to the south to just a few kilometers from the coast, north of the city of Toliara. The region to the south of Toliara has several notable features that provide habitat for a diverse assemblage of cetaceans. The Grand Récif de Toliara is one of the largest barrier reef systems in the Indian Ocean, extending from north of Toliara to the village of Saint Augustin. The reef is made up of barrier and fringing reefs and extensive lagoons, including mangroves inside the main lagoon of the Grand Récif. At the southern end of the Grand Récif lies the Saint Augustin submarine canyon. The combination of the canyon cutting through the shelf and geological faulting brings deep water very close to the coast, providing suitable habitat for typically deepwater species. South of the canyon, the shelf is relatively narrow with a steep slope, from the village of Anakao as far south as Itampolo.

A high diversity of cetaceans is found in the Malagasy waters of the South Mozambique Channel, with at least 21 species documented (Table 7.16), including six mysticetes and 15 odontocetes, during small-boat surveys and acoustic monitoring in the Toliara area, and aerial surveys over a more extensive portion of the region (Cerchio et al. 2009a; Van Canneyt et al. 2010; S. Cerchio and N.

Andrianarivelo, unpublished data; A. Saloma and F.-X. Mayer, unpublished data). An additional four species are considered likely to occur and six species possibly to occur (Table 7.16). Therefore, the South Mozambique Channel clearly has high cetacean richness (Laran et al. 2017), with the Toliara–Saint Augustin submarine canyon area being a particular hotspot (S. Cerchio and N. Andrianarivelo, unpublished data).

Cetaceans in the South Mozambique Channel Marine Ecoregion

Mysticetes: Based upon the presence of *Balaenoptera musculus intermedia* song off the northwest coast of Madagascar during the austral winter (Cerchio et al. 2018a), it is certain that the species migrates through the Mozambique Channel and past this area. Preliminary findings from passive acoustic monitoring during austral summer and autumn off Toliara have confirmed the presence of *B. m. intermedia* song at least during late March and April, presumably during the northward migration from the Antarctic (S. Cerchio and T. Rasoloarijao, unpublished data). Similarly, the SWIO population of *B. m. brevicauda* migrates through this area, based upon the bimodal seasonal presence of its song off the northwest coast of Madagascar (Cerchio et al. 2018a). Recent passive acoustic monitoring from Toliara has confirmed the presence of its song during at least November to late January, presumably the end of the southward migration to the Madagascar Ridge, and during late March to April, presumably the beginning of the northward migration to breeding areas (S. Cerchio and T. Rasoloarijao, unpublished data). In addition to the two *B. musculus* subspecies, *B. physalus* and *B. bonaerensis* were also detected during the austral spring/summer (S. Cerchio and T. Rasoloarijao, unpublished data), likely on migration through this area as they have also been acoustically detected off northwest Madagascar during the austral winter (Cerchio et al. 2018a). *Balaenoptera physalus* was also encountered in the austral autumn (end of April) offshore in the South Mozambique Channel near Europa atoll during an oceanic ship survey (Dorémus et al. 2009).

Megaptera novaeangliae is commonly seen between July and September off the southwest coast of Madagascar, utilizing the area for breeding habitat. The Toliara–Saint Augustine submarine canyon–Anakao area is an active breeding area for this species, as evidenced by small-boat surveys (Cerchio et al. 2009a; S. Cerchio and N. Andrianarivelo, unpublished data) and satellite telemetry data (Cerchio et al. 2016; Trudelle et al. 2016). Breeding behavior was regularly observed during austral winter boat surveys, including singing, mothers with young calves, and competitive groups of males following a female. Satellite tracks of 11 whales tagged off Anakao indicated extensive movement through this region and along the southern coast of Madagascar to Tolagnaro. Satellite telemetry studies have documented migratory movements through the Mozambique Channel (Fossette et al. 2014; Cerchio et al. 2016; Trudelle et al. 2016); at least one *M. novaeangliae* tagged off Anakao transited nearly to Europa atoll, c. 270 km offshore, before the tag stopped transmitting (Cerchio et al. 2016).

Eubalaena australis (Southern Right Whale) has been rarely sighted in the waters of Madagascar, but there have been three documented sightings during boat surveys off Anakao and Ifaty, one of which was a mother-calf pair (Cerchio et al. 2009a; S. Cerchio and N. Andrianarivelo, unpublished data; A. Saloma and F.-X. Mayer, unpublished data). In general, *E. australis* is sighted infrequently but regularly around Madagascar, with anecdotal sightings on both the west and east coasts; it is unclear whether these individuals represent range expansion from the South African population, or potentially represent remnants of a historical and near-extirpated population from Mozambique–Madagascar (Rosenbaum et al. 2001; Banks et al. 2011) that was heavily hunted off the Crozet Islands (Townsend 1935).

Odontocetes: The region contains important habitat for small coastal populations of *Sousa plumbea* and *Tursiops aduncus*. Both species have been documented along the entire coast of this region, based on a combination of boat-based data (off Anakao, Andavadoaka, Belo sur Mer, and the Barren Islands) and aerial survey observations (off the central and southwestern coast), and reports from extensive socio-ecological interviews with local fishers at 10 locales spread throughout the region (Cerchio et al. 2015a). As reported for the northwest, *S. plumbea* prefers very nearshore shallow habitat, whereas *T. aduncus* is encountered more widely across neritic shelf waters.

Aside from *S. plumbea* and *T. aduncus*, *Grampus griseus* was the most frequently sighted odontocete during boat-based surveys off Anakao (Cerchio et al. 2009a; S. Cerchio and N. Andrianarivelo, unpublished data), as well as off Ifaty (A. Saloma and F.-X. Mayer, unpublished data). *Stenella longirostris* and *S. attenuata* were also frequently sighted off Anakao, at times in large (200–500 individuals) mixed-species groups (Cerchio et al. 2009a; S. Cerchio and N. Andrianarivelo, unpublished data). Vezo fishers practiced drive-hunts on pods of *S. longirostris* during periods when groups were resting near to reefs off Anakao, at times taking 100–200 individuals in a single hunt (Andrianarivelo 2001; Cerchio et al. 2009a, 2014a). *Globicephala macrorhynchus* was also relatively frequently sighted off Anakao; recent mitogenomic and nuclear single-nucleotide-polymorphism analyses indicated that Malagasy populations of this species are nested within the "Naisa" form, along with other Indian and West Pacific Ocean populations, which was recommended to be recognized as a distinct subspecies (Van Cise et al. 2019). Less frequently sighted species off Anakao included *Tursiops truncatus*, *Lagenodelphis hosei*, *Steno bredanensis* (Rough-toothed Dolphin), *Peponocephala electra*, and *Pseudorca crassidens*. *Orcinus orca*, along with *Grampus griseus*, *L. hosei*, and *Globicephala macrorhynchus*, has been sighted off Ifaty (A. Saloma and F.-X. Mayer, unpublished data). An *O. orca* was also reported stranded near Toliara (Andrianarivelo 2001).

During REMMOA aerial surveys, two surveyed blocks were included in this ecoregion: off the central-west coast from Maintirano, extending to Juan de Nova Island waters, and off the southwest coast from Toliara, extending to Europa and Bassas da India atolls. The most abundant species were large Delphininae (mostly *T. truncatus* and some *T. aduncus*, lumped as *Tursiops* spp.), with a relative density of 27 and 17 individuals per 100 km^2 in the central and south area, respectively, preferring oceanic waters, with smaller groups over the shelf and larger offshore (Laran et al. 2017). Dorémus et al. (2009) also noted large groups of *T. truncatus* during oceanic boat surveys offshore near to and south of Juan de

Nova. During REMMOA, small Delphininae (likely *Stenella* species) were encountered mostly in the central area, with 19 individuals per 100 km^2, compared with three individuals per 100 km^2 in the south area, with maximum density on the shelf. Small Globicephalinae (mostly *Peponocephala electra*) also preferred the central area on the slope habitat, with density estimates of 20 individuals per 100 km^2, compared with six individuals per 100 km^2 in the south area, and were encountered in both areas in large groups (Laran et al. 2017). Large Globicephalinae (mostly *Pseudorca crassidens* and some *Globicephala macrorhynchus*) had a relative density of 2–3 individuals per 100 km^2 in both surveyed areas, which were the second-highest densities encountered in the southwest Indian Ocean after the Seychelles. *Grampus griseus* density was similarly around 2.5 and 2.1 individuals per 100 km^2 in both surveyed areas, which were the highest densities for the species throughout the southwest Indian Ocean (Laran et al. 2017), as well as for all tropical areas surveyed by the REMMOA project (including the West Indies, French Guiana, French Polynesia, New Caledonia, Wallis and Futuna).

Numerous *Ziphius cavirostris*, unidentified *Mesoplodon* species, and other unidentified ziphiid groups were observed during REMMOA surveys in this region. Densities for the species group were about 0.5 individuals per 100 km^2 in the central and southern blocks; these were the highest densities observed for this species group throughout the southwest Indian Ocean (Laran et al. 2017). *Physeter macrocephalus* and *Kogia* species were also sighted during REMMOA, but each with an estimated density one order of magnitude lower than that of Ziphiidae (without correcting for the availability bias due to dive duration of these species). *Physeter macrocephalus* was historically hunted in the area (Townsend 1935), so might be expected to be more numerous than suggested by the aerial surveys. This species was acoustically detected during boat surveys off Anakao, and preliminary results of recent acoustic monitoring south of Toliara (on the north slope of the Saint Augustine submarine canyon) recorded frequent *P. macrocephalus* clicks between November and April (Cerchio et al. 2009a; S. Cerchio and T. Rasoloarijao, unpublished data); therefore, further work may reveal a more prominent presence. A single *Kogia sima* was identified during boat-based surveys off Anakao in the Saint Augustin submarine canyon, confirming the presence of the species (S. Cerchio and T. Andrianrivelo, unpublished data), but it is not clear if *K. breviceps* also occurs, and the REMMOA *Kogia* sightings were not identified to the species level (Van Canneyt et al. 2010).

THE SOUTH MADAGASCAR MARINE ECOREGION (INCLUDING THE DEEP SOUTH)

The South Madagascar ecoregion encompasses approximately 500 km of coastline from Itampolo on the southwest coast to just north of Tolagnaro on the southeast coast, and includes the area known as the *Deep South*. The neritic habitat of this ecoregion is characterized by a broad continental shelf that extends c. 80 km south of Cap Sainte Marie, the most southern point on Madagascar. Beyond this, the Madagascar Ridge extends farther south some 800 km to the Walters Shoals and beyond. This is a very poorly researched area for marine mammals, with a paucity of data for even the nearshore coastal region. We draw here upon a combination of anecdotal reports in the nearshore waters and a few surveys that occurred in the offshore deep water regions, primarily beyond the Madagascar shelf (Kasuya and Wada 1996; Best 2001, 2007; Best et al. 2003; Dorémus et al. 2009; Gadenne and Saloma 2017; Ternon et al. 2018). Despite the lack of research effort compared with other areas of Madagascar, 11 cetacean species were confirmed to occur in this ecoregion, including four mysticetes and seven odontocetes, with at least an additional 15 considered likely and four considered possibly to occur (Table 7.16).

Cetaceans in the South Madagascar Marine Ecoregion

Mysticetes: The SWIO population of *Balaenoptera musculus brevicauda* was well documented by Best et al. (2003) from the southwest tip of Madagascar along the Madagascar Ridge to approximately 800 km south of Madagascar, where population abundance was estimated to be 424–472 individuals in December 1996. This region is thought to be a summer feeding area for the population and is also where the first example of the diagnostic song for the population was recorded (McDonald et al. 2006). The population migrates northward through the Mozambique Channel, and likely up the east side of Madagascar as well, to suspected breeding areas from Kenya to Seychelles. It is likely that *B. m. intermedia* at least migrates through these waters as well, as it has been acoustically documented in the southwest and northwest of Madagascar as described previously, and has been recorded to the southeast of Madagascar between February and August (Dréo et al. 2019). Kasuya and Wada (1996) describe extensive Japanese survey data associated with factory-ship whaling fleets between 1965 and 1985, reporting sighting data on several species in 5° latitudinal × 5° longitudinal blocks to the south and east of Madagascar; they report *B. musculus* sightings just south of Madagascar (25–30°S, 40–50°E) on the northern Madagascar Ridge during December, corroborating the findings of Best et al. (2003).

During a large research-vessel survey down the Madagascar Ridge to Walters Shoals south of Madagascar in 2017 (Campagne scientifique Walters Shoals MNHN-IRD, N/O *Marion Dufresne*; see https://science4highseas.wixsite.com/waltersshoal), there were no sightings of cetaceans during transit, but several species were documented in the Walters Shoals area in April–May (Gadenne and Saloma 2017). These included three groups of *B. physalus*, and given documentation of *B. physalus* song off the west coast of Madagascar, it is likely that the species also occurs in the South Madagascar ecoregion, at least during migration periods. Kasuya and Wada (1996) report *B. physalus* sightings immediately south of Madagascar (25–30°S, 45–55°E) during December, likely on southern migration, but well south of 30°S from January to April in presumed feeding habitat.

The only reports of *B. borealis* (Sei Whale) near to Madagascar come from Kasuya and Wada (1996), who report some sightings just south of Madagascar (25–30°S, 40–45°E) during December, and much farther south of 35°S between January and April. However, several other studies report no accounts of the species in Malagasy waters: during an extensive survey south and east of Madagascar, Gambell et al. (1974) report *B. borealis* only in the extreme east of the surveyed region, beyond 65°E; other large-ship surveys in pelagic habitat report no *B. borealis* sightings (Dorémus et al. 2009; Gadenne and Saloma 2017; Ternon et al. 2018); and during long-term acoustic monitoring in the North Mozambique Channel, no diagnostic *B. borealis* vocalizations (e.g., paired down-sweeps) were recorded, despite an analysis protocol suitable for detecting them (Cerchio et al. 2018a). Best (2007) states that the summer distribution of *B. borealis* is between the Subtropical convergence and Antarctic convergence (30–40°S), and it migrates in winter to unknown temperate and tropical waters. Therefore, it appears that *B. borealis* may occur in the vicinity of southern Madagascar, possibly during winter, but is rare and may be generally distributed farther east and south.

Sightings of *B. edeni* (Bryde's Whale) were reported by Best (2001) over the Madagascar Ridge approximately 400 km south of Madagascar, and 105 were taken during Japanese whaling operations in the same area during 1977 (Ohsumi 1980). Best (2001) also surmises that 468 *B. edeni* taken by Soviet whalers in 1971 were likely taken off the southwest tip of Madagascar. Kasuya and Wada (1996) report *B. edeni* sightings just south of Madagascar (25–30°S, 45–50°E) from December through April. These are thought to be a distinct Malagasy population belonging to the subspecies *B. e. brydei* (Best 2007). Therefore, the range of this species includes the offshore waters of southern Madagascar; however, it is noted that there are no modern confirmed observations of it nearer to the Malagasy coast. Previous anecdotal reports of *B. edeni* on the west coast (Rosenbaum 2003a) are likely to have been of the similarly sized *B. omurai*, which was not described until 2003 or reported for Madagascar until 2015 (see Cerchio et al., pp. 424–29).

Minke whales (without species identification, but most likely *B. bonaerensis*) were reported in deep water roughly 100 km south of the Madagascar shelf during a large whale-marking cruise (Gambell et al. 1974). Kasuya and Wada (1996) also report minke whales south of Madagascar (25–30°S, 45–55°E) during December (likely *B. bonaerensis*) and southwest of Madagascar (20–30°S, 40–45°E) during February. The latter group may represent *B. acutorostrata* "dwarf" subspp., as the majority of minke whale sightings during this period are distributed south of 50°S, and Kasuya and Wada (1996) state that many low-latitude sightings may belong to the "diminutive form."

The southern Madagascar shelf is important breeding habitat for *Megaptera novaeangliae*, as satellite telemetry data indicate extensive use of this habitat during the height of the breeding season (Cerchio et al. 2016; Trudelle et al. 2016; Dulau et al. 2017). *Megaptera novaeangliae* individuals were satellite tagged during a dedicated project in the southwest off Anakao during mid-season (July 2013), deliberately timed to assess habitat utilization by breeding whales; several whales demonstrated extensive movements over the southern Madagascar shelf, some making the transit from the southwest to the southeast coasts and back repeatedly during the duration of the tag (Cerchio et al. 2016). In particular, the southeast coast, south of Tolagnaro, was an area where males and to a lesser extent females lingered and displayed movement patterns consistent with breeding behavior (i.e., mate searching), both for whales tagged off Anakao (Cerchio et al. 2016) and whales tagged off La Réunion (during August 2013) that made the transit to Madagascar (Dulau et al. 2017). There is a single *Eubalaena australis* record off Tolagnaro reported in Rosenbaum et al. (2001).

Odontocetes: *Sousa plumbea* has been reported in the Deep South near Cap Sainte Marie and on the southeast coast off Tolagnaro (M. Nicoll, as cited by Cerchio et al. 2015a). It is likely that this represents the extent of its range, which was proposed to be from the northwest along the entire western and southern coasts of Madagascar, but with no evidence along the east coast north of Tolagnaro. *Tursiops aduncus* has been sighted off Tolagnaro (A. Saloma and F.-X. Mayer, unpublished data), and is likely to occur throughout the southern coastal area. Dorémus et al. (2009), during a survey transiting over the continental slope south of Madagascar, sighted a large group of *Peponocephala electra* (approximately 200 individuals), *Stenella coeruleoalba* (with photographic documentation), and *Physeter macrocephalus* (including a group of seven individuals). Gambell et al. (1974) also report *S. coeruleoalba* within 100 km of the southern Madagascar shelf. Ternon et al. (2018) reported a group of approximately 30 *Globicephala macrorhynchus* off southern Madagascar during an expedition to the Madagascar Ridge. On a transit from the Madagascar shelf down the Madagascar Ridge, Gadenne and Saloma (2017) sighted five large groups of *T. truncatus* (estimated at up to 300 individuals).

Townsend (1935) reports historic catches of *P. macrocephalus* off Cap Sainte Marie and Tolagnaro, concentrated north of latitude 27°S; Kasuya and Wada (1996) note concentrations of *P. macrocephalus* south of Madagascar (25–30°S, 45–55°E) from December to April; and Gadenne and Saloma (2017) sighted several *P. macrocephalus* in the vicinity of Walters Shoals. *Ziphius cavirostris* has been sighted within 200 km off the southwest corner of Madagascar (Best 2007). MacLeod et al. (2006) report a sighting of *Mesoplodon mirus* (True's Beaked Whale; now considered *M. eueu*, Ramari's Beaked Whale, Carroll et al. 2021) in the vicinity of Walters Shoals at 33°S, 44°E; this is the only account of the species in the southwest Indian Ocean region aside from strandings on the coast of South Africa, and although Walters Shoals is over 800 km from Madagascar, it is postulated that *M. eueu* ranges farther north to southern Madagascar (Best 2007; Carroll et al. 2021). Several other Ziphiidae species, including *Berardius arnuxii* (Arnoux's Beaked Whale), *Tasmacetus shepherdi* (Shepherd's Beaked Whale), *Hyperoodon planifrons* (Southern Bottlenose Whale), *Mesoplodon hectori* (Hector's Beaked Whale), *M. grayi* (Gray's Beaked Whale), *M. bowdoini* (Andrew's Beaked Whale), and *M. layardii* (Strap-toothed Beaked Whale), have circumpolar or southern Indian Ocean distributions, and have either been sighted or are postulated to occur over the Madagascar Ridge, but are not here considered to occur around Madagascar, as they are generally thought to be cold or cold-temperate species with no evidence of ranging within Malagasy waters (Best 2007).

THE EAST MADAGASCAR MARINE ECOREGION (INCLUDING THE EAST COAST OF NORTHERN MADAGASCAR)

The East Madagascar marine ecoregion includes the entire east coast of Madagascar from just north of Tolagnaro to Cap d'Ambre, an approximately 1500 km length of coastline. (Of note is that the ecoregion as defined by Obura et al. 2012 and adopted in the Madagascar National Parks strategic plan places the most northeasterly coast of Madagascar, approximately 500 km from the Masoala Peninsula to Cap d'Ambre, into the North Mozambique Channel ecoregion. In the present contribution, we prefer to treat the northeast coast of Madagascar within the East Madagascar ecoregion for purposes of describing cetacean diversity.) The eastern coast of Madagascar is characterized by a relatively narrow continental shelf and a steep slope to abyssal plane depths and oceanic habitat. The shelf widens to a maximum of 60 km for an approximately 250 km stretch from the south end of the Masoala Peninsula to just north of Toamasina, but it is typically no more than 10 km wide aside from that region. The area of broader shelf includes Antongil Bay (approximately 60 km long × 30 km wide), Ile Sainte Marie, and the Sainte Marie Channel, two areas where extensive research has been conducted on the southwest Indian Ocean population of *Megaptera novaeangliae* (Rosenbaum et al. 1997; Cerchio et al. 2016; Trudelle et al. 2018) but where there is relatively low cetacean species diversity. Aside from work on *M. novaeangliae*, a section of the REMMOA surveys in 2009 were conducted from Ile Sainte Marie, extending offshore to Tromelin Island. The work to date has revealed a modest species diversity in this sub-region compared with the other regions of Madagascar, with a total of 14 confirmed species, including two mysticetes and 12 odontocetes, and an additional nine species likely to occur and six species possibly to occur in the area (Table 7.16).

Cetaceans in the East Madagascar Marine Ecoregion

Mysticetes: Branch et al. (2007) report scattered historic (prior to 1973) whaling catches of *Balaenoptera musculus* off the east coast of Madagascar, and a single modern anecdotal sighting in November. It is not clear whether these represent *B. m. intermedia* or *B. m. brevicauda*; however, given evidence off west Madagascar it seems likely that both subspecies are present. Best (2001) proposes that a Malagasy population of *B. edeni* migrates from the Madagascar Ridge in the south up the east coast of Madagascar to the Seychelles; however, aside from reports of sightings by Japanese whalers in pelagic waters between 50° and 70°E (Ohsumi 1980), there are no confirmed modern accounts of *B. edeni* off the eastern coast of Madagascar.

The southwest Indian Ocean breeding population of *Megaptera novaeangliae* has been studied extensively in the Antongil Bay and Ile Sainte Marie region. The area was first considered the primary breeding ground and destination within Madagascar (Rosenbaum et al. 1997; Ersts and Rosenbaum 2003), before aggregations were recognized off other parts of Madagascar. Photographic capture-recapture of individuals within Antongil Bay from 2000 to 2006 revealed very short residency periods, and it was postulated that there was a constant flow of individuals in and out of the bay (Cerchio et al. 2009b). Moreover, abundance was estimated at 5000–8000 individuals, and it was recognized that in Antongil Bay sampling was occurring of a very large population in only a fraction of its range. Despite a low capture probability, most individuals that were recaptured between years arrived each year within a few days on the Julian calendar, representing a highly consistent periodicity in migratory timing congruent with a population moving through the area with a defined movement pattern (Cerchio et al. 2009b).

Photographic recapture studies of *M. novaeangliae* between 1997 and 2006 indicated across-year recaptures of individuals between Antongil Bay and Mayotte or East Africa (Cerchio et al. 2008; Ersts et al. 2011a), and satellite telemetry studies in 2011 revealed that some animals tagged off Ile Sainte Marie were moving through the region migrating to the East African coast (Cerchio et al. 2016; Trudelle et al. 2016). Individuals tagged off Ile Sainte Marie and off La Réunion in 2011–2012 also revealed near constant movement around Madagascar, and preferred breeding habitat appeared to be in the south Sainte Marie Channel and on the shelf of central Madagascar in the vicinity of Toamasina, with no movement into Antongil Bay (Cerchio et al. 2016; Dulau et al. 2017). Females with calves tend to prefer shallower nearshore habitat (generally <30 m) in both Antongil Bay and the Sainte Marie Channel, despite the uniformly shallow and poorly contrasting bathymetry (generally <70 m) of both regions (Ersts and Rosenbaum 2003; Trudelle et al. 2018); however, satellite telemetry studies indicate that females with calves also make extensive movements in deep oceanic water, and active breeding habitat for females (with and without calves) extends into deeper shelf waters (to 200 m) (Cerchio et al. 2016; Trudelle et al. 2016).

Eubalaena australis has been sighted infrequently but regularly on the east coast of Madagascar, including initially two published sightings: an adult in Antongil Bay in July 1997 and a mother with a calf off Tolagnaro in November 1999 (Rosenbaum et al. 2001). Since then there have been sightings in the Sainte Marie Channel of an additional six groups during July–August in 2013, 2015, 2016, and 2018, including four different mother-calf pairs, one pair of adults, and one solitary adult (A. Saloma and F.-X. Mayer, unpublished data). These sightings, combined with three previously mentioned accounts in the southwest (Anakao and Ifaty, including an additional mother-calf pair in 2010), suggest that *E. australis* is a regular visitor to Madagascar, and the hypothesis that this may represent a remnant population that was heavily exploited in feeding grounds in the Crozet Islands should be revisited (Rosenbaum et al. 2001). The preponderance of mother-calf pairs in these sightings (five of nine documented groups) raises the possibility that females may be calving in these waters. The calves observed off Ile Sainte Marie were in all cases considered of small enough size to be neonates, likely born in Malagasy waters; in addition, in all but one case the mother-calf pairs lingered in the area, sighted on multiple successive occasions over periods ranging from two to 10 days (A. Saloma and F.-X. Mayer, unpublished data).

Odontocetes: *Tursiops aduncus* was frequently encountered in Antongil Bay and the Sainte Marie Channel (S. Cerchio and N. Andrianarivelo, unpublished data; A. Saloma and F.-X. Mayer, unpublished data), and appears to be the most commonly sighted coastal dolphin in the area. *Stenella longirostris* was sighted at least once in the mouth of Antongil Bay (S. Cerchio and N. Andrianarivelo, unpublished data), but was not possible to confirm around Ile Sainte Marie during extensive effort on ecotourism boats (A. Saloma and F.-X. Mayer, unpublished data). Therefore, it appears to be less common in at least this area compared with the northwest and southwest coasts, although there are several reports of the species farther north between Cap Est and Antalaha (A. Cooke, unpublished data). *Stenella coeruleoalba* was potentially encountered once off Ile Sainte Marie, and there was a confirmed stranding on the east coast of that island (A. Saloma and

F.-X. Mayer, unpublished data), so it appears to occur but, like *S. longirostris*, is infrequently sighted. In total, these three odontocete species represent a low diversity in the shallow waters of Antongil Bay and Sainte Marie Channel. *Stenella coeruleoalba* was also reported in deep water 100 km offshore the central-east coast (Gambell et al. 1974), suggesting that *Stenella* species are more common offshore.

The northeast coast of Madagascar (about 100 km north and south of Ile Sainte Marie) offshore to Tromelin Island was surveyed in January 2010 by REMMOA aerial survey (Van Canneyt et al. 2010). During this survey the presence of at least 10 species of odontocetes was confirmed. Relatively low density of small Delphininae (likely *Stenella* species) was encountered, with 0.4 individuals per 100 km^2 estimated for this survey block (Laran et al. 2017), the lowest value of the SWIO REMMOA survey, congruent with data from small-boat surveys mentioned above. *Stenella attenuata* was the only small Delphininae identified at the species level. Large Delphininae with *Tursiops truncatus* and one group of 200 *Lagenodelphis hosei* were encountered in addition to *Tursiops* species. Their global density was also the lowest estimated for the region, equivalent to that in Mauritian waters, with 2.4 individuals per 100 km^2. *Peponocephala electra* was the most abundant species in this surveyed area (recorded in large groups of up to 200 individuals), with a global density of small Globicephalinae estimated at 9.3 individuals per 100 km^2. This species has a strong preference for the slope habitat, with 80% of the sightings at less than 30 km from the 2000 m isobath contours. Several sightings of *Pseudorca crassidens* and one *Globicephala macrorhynchus* were identified offshore, between Tromelin and the Malagasy coast. Density of large Globicephalinae was estimated at 0.7 individuals per 100 km^2, an intermediate value for the region.

Grampus griseus was not identified in the area, although previously there was a single account reported 230 km off the east coast at 20.7°S (Gambell et al. 1974). Only one sighting of a *Kogia* species was reported between the Mascarene archipelago and the Malagasy coast, with species identification ambiguous. Among Ziphiidae, *Ziphius cavirostris* and *Indopacetus pacificus* were identified along the eastern slope (Van Canneyt et al. 2010), and there was a tentative sighting of *Mesoplodon ginkgodens* (Ginkgo-toothed Beaked Whale) far off eastern Madagascar, a species that is postulated to range throughout the region (Ballance and Pitman 1998; Best 2007). Density of Ziphiidae as a species group was estimated to an intermediate value of 0.2 individuals per 100 km^2 (Laran et al. 2017). Finally, *Physeter macrocephalus* was encountered along the Malagasy slope and offshore, in groups up to four individuals (although a likely underestimate of group size) and with a relative density of 0.09 individuals per 100 km^2; this is equivalent to the estimated density for Seychelles, the highest density for the species throughout the southwest Indian Ocean (Laran et al. 2017), and among the higher estimates for all tropical areas surveyed by the REMMOA project (including the West Indies, French Guiana, French Polynesia, New Caledonia, and Wallis and Futuna). In addition, there have been two stranded *P. macrocephalus* on Ile Sainte Marie, including a 10 m juvenile in 2012 and a nearly 20 m adult male in 2018 (A. Saloma and F.-X. Mayer, unpublished data). Therefore, this region is clearly important habitat for the species, including use by large bulls.

THREATS AND CONSERVATION

Several threats to cetaceans have been identified in Madagascar's waters. Much of the coastline of Madagascar is remote and undeveloped, although there are several developed and heavily populated centers, including the port cities of Mahajanga, Toliara, Tolagnaro, and Toamasina, and the tourism hubs around Nosy Be, Antsiranana, and Ile Sainte Marie. Hunting and bycatch of small cetaceans has been documented in coastal small-scale fisheries (Figures 7.29a and b), and although hunting is most prevalent in the southwest region, it not entirely absent on the northwest and east coasts (Cerchio et al. 2014a, 2015a). Coastal industrial fisheries (in the form of shrimp trawling) and offshore industrial fisheries (tuna purse-seine and long-line) may also impact cetaceans (IOTC 2019). Currently there is extensive offshore petroleum exploration (Figures 7.8 and 7.29c) planned at least in the northwest region, which presents a distinct threat to sensitive coastal populations of cetaceans (Cerchio et al. 2014a, 2019). Noise from large ships also impacts baleen whales by interfering with vocal communication (Cholewiak et al. 2018), and there are major shipping lanes through the South Madagascar ecoregion, as well as in the western Mozambique Channel (Figure 7.29d) (Vespe et al. 2015). The large volume of shipping traffic also presents the potential for lethal ship strikes of large whales, particularly around ports and when shipping lanes overlap with migration routes, as they do south of Madagascar.

There is also coastal industrial development in the form of proposed or active mining operations to the south of Nosy Be (proposed rare-earth mining on the Ampasindava Peninsula), at Tolagnaro (coastal mining of ilmenite sands), and at Toamasina (nickel-ore processing plant), which have the potential to pollute coastal waters. Marine pollution in the form of litter and debris was assessed during the REMMOA aerial surveys, with a maximum encounter rate of marine litter around the Comoro archipelago, as well as along the northwest and northeast coasts of Madagascar (Laran et al. 2017); included among marine debris are "ghost nets," discarded or lost drift nets, which continue to bycatch marine megafauna and pose a substantial threat to pelagic cetaceans (Anderson et al. 2020). Finally, climate change is an overarching threat for cetaceans on a global scale, through multiple direct and indirect impacts that are poorly understood but could have broad effects on abundance, distribution, migration, feeding ecology, reproductive ecology, and survival (Simmonds and Eliott 2009). Certain populations may be particularly vulnerable, such as resident populations with limited habitat or populations that are dependent on sea ice and polar productivity cycles. Potential indirect impacts on resident populations around Madagascar could occur through changes in rainfall, ocean circulation patterns, and primary productivity. Similarly, migratory species of baleen whales rely on Antarctic productivity cycles for seasonal feeding; as rapid changes in the Antarctic continue to progress these resources may come under increasing stress. For both these resident and migratory species, these changes could perturb the ecosystem and availability of food resources—thus, in turn, resulting in distribution shifts or potentially collapse of cetacean populations.

Focusing on a few of the most imminent threats to Malagasy cetaceans, possibly the most currently impactful is directed hunting and incidental bycatch of coastal dolphins in small-scale and

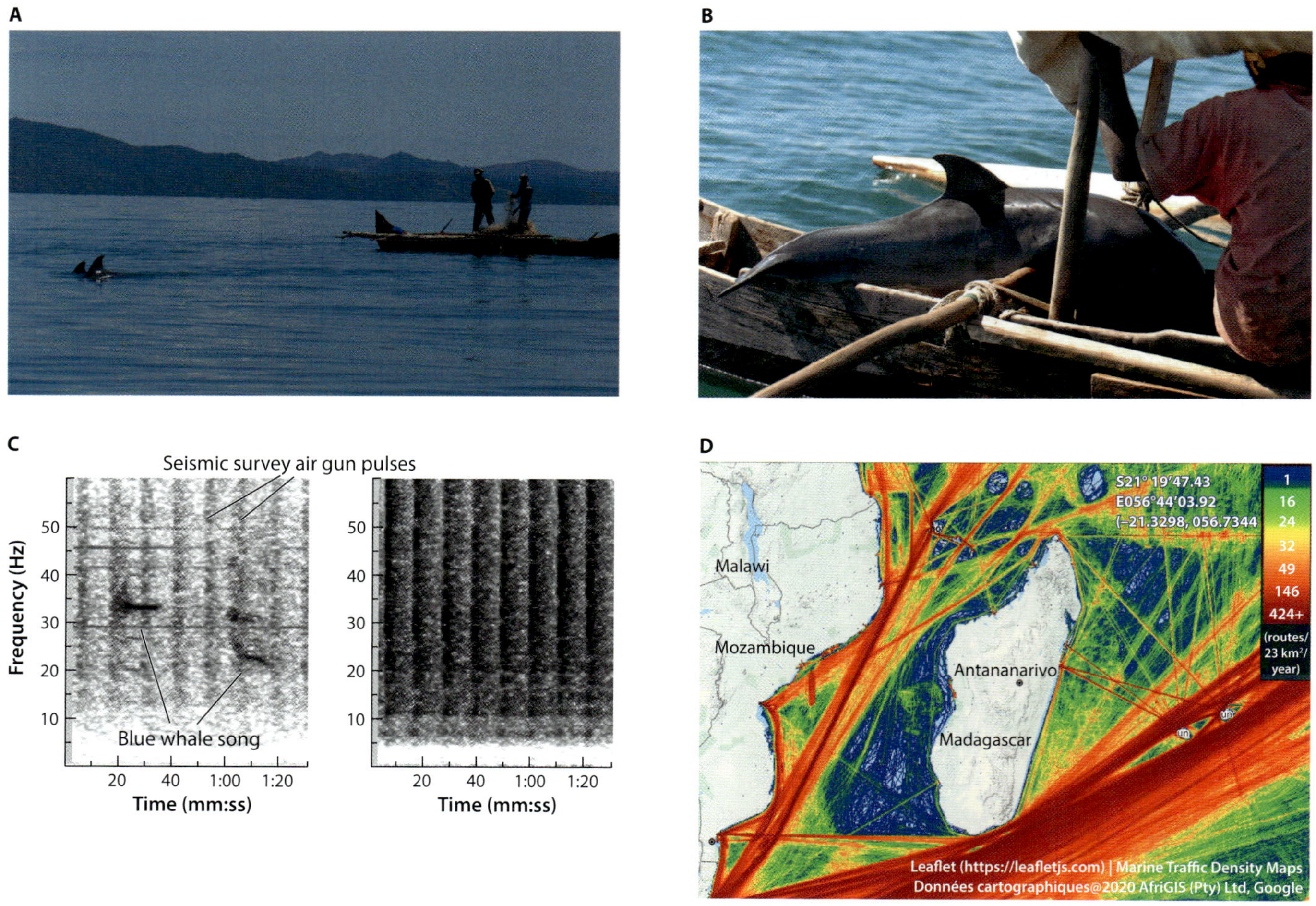

FIGURE 7.29 **Examples of threats to cetaceans in Malagasy waters. A) Small-scale fisheries and use of gillnets by Malagasy fishers from Nosy Faly, off the east side of Nosy Be. B) Bycatch of juvenile *Tursiops aduncus* by small-scale fishers in same event as illustrated in photo A. Observations over several weeks and discussions with these fishers suggested that they may have been setting their nets deliberately in areas where dolphins foraged, with the knowledge that dolphins may become entangled when attempting to depredate their nets. Thus, this behavior may be a form of "directed bycatch" and a step toward the directed hunting that is common in other regions (e.g., the southwest) but rare in Nosy Be. C) Acoustic interference of seismic-survey air-gun pulses as illustrated by sound spectrographs (graphic representation of sound with time on the *x* axis, and frequency or pitch on the *y* axis) of *Balaenoptera musculus brevicauda* song with a distant seismic survey in the background (*left*), and a much closer seismic survey (*right*) that would completely mask a *B. musculus* song. D) Density of shipping traffic around Madagascar as illustrated for 2017 in thousands of routes/23 km^2/year, showing the major shipping lane south of Madagascar and to a lesser extent to the west of Madagascar.** (PHOTO A by N. Andrianarivelo and B by S. Cerchio.) (SOURCES: C) from recordings off Nosy Be, Madagascar, S. Cerchio, unpublished data; D) from Marine Traffic, https://www.marinetraffic.com/.)

artisanal fisheries (Andrianarivelo 2001; Y. Razafindrakoto et al. 2004, 2008; Cerchio et al. 2009a, 2014a, 2015a). Active hunting by Vezo fishers of small coastal cetaceans, including primarily *Sousa plumbea*, *Tursiops aduncus*, and *Stenella longirostris*, was first documented in the Anakao region, where an estimated 7000 individuals were taken between 1985 and 2000, primarily in drive hunts where an entire pod of dolphins is killed in a single event (Andrianarivelo 2001). The hunting tradition was later found to be widespread in the southwest, based on affirmative reports in interviews from 10 of 11 surveyed localities encompassing 22 villages between the Barren Islands and Toliara (Cerchio et al. 2015a). This hunting tradition does not occur in the northwest of Madagascar, where the Sakalava people have a taboo (*fady*) on the hunting and eating of dolphins; however, incidental bycatch and some low-level hunting have been documented off Nosy Be (Figures 7.29a and b) (Cerchio et al. 2014a, 2015a). Based upon sighting data, interviews, and direct observation of mortality, *Sousa plumbea* in the Anakao area appears to be heavily impacted by this artisanal hunting and bycatch, with evidence of a decline in encounter rates and group size from 1999 to 2013. It is believed that this hunting pressure is unsustainable and may be leading to the extirpation of these southwest coastal populations. The northwest coast appears to be a haven for *S. plumbea* relative to much of the other parts of its range in Malagasy waters, as the species is frequently sighted around the Nosy Be region.

In the southwest, conservation efforts have involved engaging hunting communities to create community-based organizations for the conservation of cetaceans, implementation of traditional laws (*dina*) governing cetacean takes, education and awareness-raising campaigns, and development of alternative livelihoods (community-based ecotourism). These efforts have been successful in the Anakao region, with the creation of the locally managed Fikambanana Miaro ny Trozona sy Fesotra (FMTF, Association for the Protection of Whales and Dolphins) in 2007, followed by the ratification of a 24-article *dina* governing the protection of marine mammals and regulating community-based whale-watching. Yearly training in responsible whale-watching practices for local eco-guides and boat operators has been conducted since the creation of the FMTF by the Institut Halieutique et des Sciences Marines. These efforts have resulted in a reported cessation of the primary hunting effort since 2009 and rise of a local Malagasy whale-watching industry (Cerchio et al. 2014a; N. Andrianarivelo, unpublished data). The same conservation model was initiated in the Befandefa Commune (villages in the vicinity of Andavadoaka), where substantial hunting was reported, particularly from the village of Bevohitse; the initial response of the villages was promising, with the creation of locally managed associations and drafting of *dina* in four distinct locales (Cerchio et al. 2014a), but the program was abruptly ended before completion in 2015, when the nongovernmental organization (NGO) supporting the work shifted priorities. As a consequence the fishers resumed hunting, with documented drive hunts on approximately 100 *Stenella longirostris* off Bevohitse in 2016, and 30–40 *Grampus griseus* off Salary Bay (in the Soariake Marine Protected Area [MPA]) in June 2018 (T. Collins, unpublished data). These events emphasize the importance of following through with conservation actions for effective conservation to endure.

Aside from targeted small-scale fishery interactions, which have been documented, industrial fisheries involving both national and international fleets likely impact cetacean populations in the Malagasy EEZ but remain poorly documented. The main industrial fisheries in Malagasy waters include a national fleet of 78 trawlers and long-line vessels operating over the continental shelf and targeting shrimps, tuna, or other fishes, and a foreign fleet of 168 purse-seine and long-line vessels operating mainly beyond the continental shelf and targeting tuna and tuna-like fishes (see Cooke et al., pp. 311–58). However, there are virtually no data on the interactions of these fisheries with cetaceans in Madagascar's waters. There is some evidence for bycatch of cetaceans in industrial tuna purse-seine fisheries in the western Indian Ocean (Ruiz et al. 2018), but it remains unquantified for the Malagasy EEZ. Industrial tuna purse-seining operations elsewhere in the western Indian Ocean have been reported to be sometimes associated with baleen whales, but fatal or harmful interactions appear rare. In one study based on 494 sets, 45 were associated with baleen whales, primarily in the central equatorial Indian Ocean (outside of Malagasy waters), and notably with one fatality by entanglement of a baleen whale (Romanov 2002). Impacts of long-line fisheries on cetaceans in the Indian Ocean have not been well documented, but observer presence on board vessels is also very low (IOTC 2008), which could account for the lack of information. More recently, Indian Ocean Tuna Commission (IOTC) long-line fisheries have reported interactions with marine mammals in eastern and southern Malagasy waters, primarily involving *Grampus griseus* (IOTC 2019). Commercial gillnet (driftnet) tuna fisheries have been reported to have had a critical impact on cetaceans throughout the Indian Ocean through bycatch over the past half century or more, but there are no reports of such fishing in Madagascar's waters (Anderson et al. 2020). To conclude, more research is required to evaluate the impact on cetaceans of national and foreign commercial fisheries in Malagasy waters.

Oil and gas exploration utilizes intense sound sources for acoustically imaging the ocean floor and crust; these include high-intensity sonar at mid to high frequencies for detailed mapping of bathymetry, and geophysical seismic surveys that use low-frequency air guns for the acoustic imaging of substrata beneath the seabed (Figure 7.29c). These loud anthropogenic noises pose threats to cetaceans, including the potential for physical damage if in close proximity, disturbance of behavior, and interference with cetacean vocal communication (Nowacek et al. 2007; Clark et al. 2009; Cholewiak et al. 2018). Petroleum exploration has occurred off the coasts of Madagascar since at least 2005, and potential impacts on cetaceans have been documented on the northwest coast in particular. In May 2008, 100–200 *Peponocephala electra* entered the extensive Loza lagoon system, with numerous strandings recorded as far inland as the town of Antsohihy. Upon reviewing all available information related to the mass stranding, an independent scientific review panel concluded that the most likely cause was a behavioral startle response to multi-beam-echo-sounder bathymetric profiling that was being conducted on the continental slope prior to the commencement of geophysical seismic exploration for offshore petroleum reserves (Collins et al. 2009; Southall et al. 2013). Recent passive acoustic monitoring off Nosy Be documented the daily presence of seismic air guns for seven months from mid-October 2017 to late May 2018 (S. Cerchio and T. Rasoloarijao, unpublished data). These seismic surveys coincided with the southern migration of *Balaenoptera musculus brevicauda* through the eastern Mozambique Channel, and at times were intense enough to mask the songs of the migrating whales (Figure 7.29c). Continued seismic surveys are planned in the region starting as soon as 2021, overlapping with breeding habitat of Critically Endangered *B. m. intermedia*, among the other sensitive baleen whale populations that range in the Mozambique Channel.

The boundaries of several Madagascar MPAs overlap with the ranges of many of the cetaceans reported on here (see Cooke et al., pp. 311–58). Some of these were developed taking into consideration cetacean distribution patterns. In the northwest, the boundaries of the Ankarea protected seascape (135,556 ha; Decree [Décret] 2015-721) and Ankivonjy protected seascape (139,410 ha; Decree 2015-722) were created specifically in response to the cetacean diversity surveys in the Nosy Be region (S. Cerchio et al., unpublished data). During 2019, the IUCN Marine Mammal Protected Areas Task Force (MMPATF) convened a workshop of international marine mammal experts to identify Important Marine Mammal Areas (IMMAs) in the western Indian Ocean and Arabian Sea (IUCN-MMPATF 2019; Notarbartolo di Sciara and Hoyt 2020). In Madagascar's waters, eight distinct candidate IMMAs were identified as "discrete habitat areas, important for one or more marine mammal species, that have the potential to be delineated and managed for conservation" (IUCN-MMPATF 2019). Six of these candidates have already been designated as IMMA, largely aligning with the marine ecoregions (IUCN-MMPATF 2020; see

Cooke et al., pp. 311–58). These include: the Northwest Madagascar and Northeast Mozambique Channel IMMA (120,614 km^2); the Southwest of Madagascar and Mozambique Channel IMMA (139,494 km^2); the Toliara, Saint Augustin Canyon, and Anakao, Madagascar, IMMA (6069 km^2); the Southern Madagascar IMMA (18,575 km^2); and the Madagascar Central East Coast IMMA (55,524 km^2) (see Figure 7.10). Still pending final decisions are the Central Mozambique Channel candidate IMMA and the Madagascar Ridge candidate IMMA. Recognized by international experts as important habitat for marine mammals according to a rigorous and standardized set of criteria, these IMMAs do not carry any governance or protected status with respect to Malagasy legislation; rather they serve "to provide valuable inputs about marine mammals and their habitat which will contribute to existing national and international conservation initiatives" (IUCN-MMPATF 2019). As such, it is strongly recommended that the Malagasy authorities and conservation NGOs take into consideration the findings of the MMPATF IMMA committee in fisheries management and marine conservation planning in order to help protect Madagascar's rich cetacean fauna.

Subject editors: Andrew Cooke and Steven M. Goodman

BALAENOPTERA OMURAI, OMURA'S WHALE

S. Cerchio, T. Rasoloarijao, B. Andrianantenaina, and N. Andrianarivelo

Balaenoptera omurai (Omura's Whale) is the most recently described species of baleen whale in the world, established as a distinct species in 2003 (Wada et al. 2003). The species belongs to the Mysticeti family Balaenopteridae, or rorquals, which are characterized by their feeding mechanism and associated anatomical adaptations. Balaenopterids are "gulp" feeders, with a large gular pouch and many ventral pleats that allow the pouch to dramatically expand when the whale engulfs a large volume of water and prey. It then sieves the water through the relatively short baleen (compared with those of the Balaenidae, or right whales), retaining the prey in its mouth. Balaenopteridae feed primarily on zooplankton (such as euphausiids) and small schooling fishes (such as clupeids), and thus they represent secondary consumers that feed on low trophic levels where there is great available biomass. Species of the family range in size from *B. acutorostrata* (Common Minke Whale) at 7–9 m to *B. musculus* (Blue Whale) at 25–30 m, and most engage in long-range latitudinal migrations between seasonal winter and summer habitat. *Balaenoptera omurai* is considered a medium-size balaenopterid, with an exclusively tropical/warm temperate distribution and non-migratory life history, making it an unusual member of the family.

Previously, *B. omurai* was mistakenly identified as *B. edeni* (Bryde's Whale), and first recognized as a distinct form from nine specimens among 459 *B. edeni* taken in Japanese whaling operations in the late 1970s (Ohsumi 1980). These few specimens, from the Cocos (Keeling) Islands in the southeastern Indian Ocean and the Solomon Sea in the Indo-Pacific, were noted to be smaller than other typical *B. edeni* and phylogenetically distinct, earning the label "small form Bryde's whale" (Wada and Numachi 1991). At about the same time, skulls of *B. edeni* taken by artisanal hunters in the Bohol Sea, Philippines, were noted to be smaller than typical (Perrin et al. 1996), and phylogenetic analysis also indicated they were distinct (LeDuc and Dizon 2002), thus linking them to the "small form" described in the Japanese whaling operations. It was not until a whale was struck by a ship and stranded in the Sea of Japan in 1998 that a complete specimen was collected. This specimen, which would become the holotype of *B. omurai*, was linked to the Cocos and Solomon samples through genetic similarity and phylogenetic analysis, allowing the description of the species, which was named after the renowned Japanese cetologist Hideo Omura (Wada et al. 2003).

More extensive phylogenetic analysis indicated that *B. omurai* belonged to an ancient lineage with a divergence time estimated at 9–17 million years ago, basal to a clade formed by *B. edeni* (including both subspecies *B. e. edeni* and *B. e. brydei*, which some authors consider as separate species) and *B. borealis* (Sei Whale) (Sasaki et al. 2006). Thus, the confusion with *B. edeni* was based entirely on similarity in size and tropical habits, since the two species are neither sister taxa nor particularly closely related. For 10 years after its initial description, the species was known only from this handful of whaling specimens, and stranding specimens identified from skulls in museums from the western Pacific and eastern Indian Oceans (Yamada et al. 2006a, 2006b, 2008). The species' range was thought to be strictly eastern Indo-Pacific, and with no confirmed observations of live animals or ecological studies, there was a complete absence of natural history information, which feeds in to determining its conservation status.

Field surveys and acoustic monitoring conducted since 2011 have established the northwest waters of Madagascar, specifically off the island of Nosy Be, as a cetacean biodiversity hotspot, documenting at minimum 20 different cetacean species (IUCN-MMPATF 2020; see Cerchio et al., pp. 411–24). Among the species encountered during these surveys was the unexpected discovery in 2013 of a population of *B. omurai* (Cerchio et al. 2015b). Prior to this discovery, the nearest documentation of this species with respect to Madagascar was two captures in the aforementioned Japanese whaling operations over 5000 km away off the Cocos (Keeling) Islands (Wada et al. 2003). Thus, the Madagascar population was the first identified in the western Indian Ocean and represented a substantive expansion of the species' range. Work over the following years revealed the region to be an important habitat for *B. omurai*, and moreover provided the first in situ observations globally of this poorly known species. Extensive field observations from 2013 to 2014 in the Nosy Be region resulted in an initial study that included phylogenetic analysis of tissue samples from 18 animals, confirming that the Malagasy population was definitively *B. omurai*; the first accurate description of external appearance of the species; sighting data that included documentation of mothers with young calves and foraging behavior (including surface lunge feeding); and acoustic recordings in the presence of the whale documenting its diagnostic vocalizations for the first time (Cerchio et al. 2015b).

PHYSICAL APPEARANCE

Prior to the Madagascar discovery, details on the external characters of *B. omurai* were limited by what could be ascertained from dead stranded specimens and whaling logbook records (Wada et al. 2003). The body length at physical maturity was reported to be 10–12 m, smaller on average than *B. edeni* by 2–3 m. The head is slightly U-shaped when viewed from above and has a flat appearance, as in *B. musculus*. The ventral pleats extend past the umbilicus, separating it from *B. borealis*, and are finer and more numerous (80–90) than in *B. edeni* (42–54). The body was reported to be asymmetrically pigmented with similarity to *B. physalus* (Fin Whale); however, details were not available. The number of baleen plates (~200 on each side) is less than that known for any other *Balaenoptera* species. Several diagnostic skeletal features, particularly of the skull, were described and provided diagnostic identification of museum specimens obtained in Taiwan, Thailand, Philippines, and Australia (Yamada et al. 2006a, 2006b, 2008).

Extensive photographic and video documentation of live animals off Nosy Be provided the first detailed field description of the external appearance of *B. omurai* (Figure 7.30) (Cerchio et al. 2015b). Overall, *B. omurai* is smaller, more streamlined, and more strikingly marked than other balaenopterids. External proportions are similar to *B. edeni* and *B. borealis*, although more streamlined, giving live animals a distinctly serpentine appearance. The dorsal fin is relatively small, low, and strongly falcate. Absence of pronounced lateral ridges on the dorsal surface of the head distinguishes it from *B. edeni*, although slight ridges or grooves are detectable under some lighting conditions. *Balaenoptera omurai* are distinctly counter-shaded, slate gray above and off-white below, and have asymmetric body pigmentation that is in fact very similar to that of *B. physalus*; however, tending to be more complex and dramatic. The lower jaw is off-white on the right and dark gray on the left. The right side displays a lightly pigmented "blaze," which originates anterior to the eye, sweeps back over the right pectoral fin, and is bisected by 4 or 5 dark stripes. A lightly pigmented "chevron" sweeps forward on the flanks anterior to the dorsal fin and is asymmetric when viewed from above. On the right side, the forward portion of the chevron has the appearance of two interlocking curves or spirals originating dorsally and ventrally, diagnostic to the species. On the left side, there is no blaze, and the chevron is much reduced, composed of a thin irregular ribbon of light pigmentation. Variation in appearance or morphology across stocks has not been described; however, a review of photographs globally has indicated that the described characteristics are found in all populations where documentation exists (from the western Indian Ocean to the western Pacific Ocean and both Northern and Southern Hemispheres) (Cerchio et al. 2019). Off Nosy Be, subtle individual variations in pigmentation, along with nicks and scars, allow the positive photographic identification of different individuals, as is common among cetaceans.

GLOBAL RANGE AND REGIONAL PRESENCE

Since initial publication of the Malagasy observations, multiple accounts of *B. omurai* have been reported around the world. Thus, the availability of descriptions and vocalizations has spurred a surge of

FIGURE 7.30 **Illustration of *Balaenoptera omurai* (Omura's Whale), Madagascar population, showing asymmetric pigmentation between right and left sides, typical external characters, and markings on skin made by remora fish (Echeneidae).** (ILLUSTRATION by Frédérique Lucas, executed with photographic and video materials from Nosy Be, provided by S. Cerchio.)

interest in the species, and provided the information needed to distinguish it from congeners in the field. Cerchio et al. (2019) compiled accounts from all available sources in order to establish its currently known global range, verifying records based on genetic, morphological, photographic, acoustic, and/or detailed sighting data. It was found that *B. omurai* is widely distributed, and to date has been documented in tropical and/or warm temperate latitudes of all ocean basins, with the exception of the central and eastern Pacific Ocean. The majority of accounts were in the eastern Indo-Pacific: off southern Japan, Southeast Asia, the Malay Peninsula, Indonesia, Philippines, and the northern coasts of Australia. Outside of this core range, scattered accounts extend into the western Pacific and Oceania and throughout the Indian Ocean, and there are three accounts from the tropical Atlantic Ocean. There is a strong tendency toward a coastal and neritic distribution throughout the range, although there are also several pelagic records.

Within the southwest Indian Ocean, the only verified documentation of *B. omurai* is off the northwest coast of Madagascar, with the nearest confident account being acoustic evidence for a population off the Chagos archipelago at 7.6°S, 72.5°E (Cerchio et al. 2019). Between 2011 and 2017, the Madagascar Omura's Whale project documented 286 encounters with this species off Nosy Be, Nosy Mitsio, Nosy Iranja, and the Ampasindava Peninsula (Figure 7.31). During November 2016, satellite telemetry tags were deployed on four individual *B. omurai* and yielded over 1700 positions during transmission periods that ranged from 30 to 58 days, until the end of January 2017 (Cerchio et al. 2018b). Probably the most striking result of the satellite tracking was that all tagged individuals remained in a relatively restricted area along the northwest coast of Madagascar; all movement was in close proximity to the tagging site, covering a range of no more than 405 km of coastline (mean among individuals of 283 km). Moreover, all tagged individuals moved multiple times throughout the range of coast defined during the duration of the tag. This work defined the minimum extent of Madagascar's Omura's Whale population, with a northern extent to latitude 12.06°S near to Nosy Hao/Ambavanibé Bay, and a southern extent to latitude 14.83°S near to Moramba Bay, just to the north of Mahajamba Bay. Opportunistic photographs taken from boats (submitted to S. Cerchio for verification) in 2016 and 2020 extend the southerly extent of the range significantly to Cap Saint André

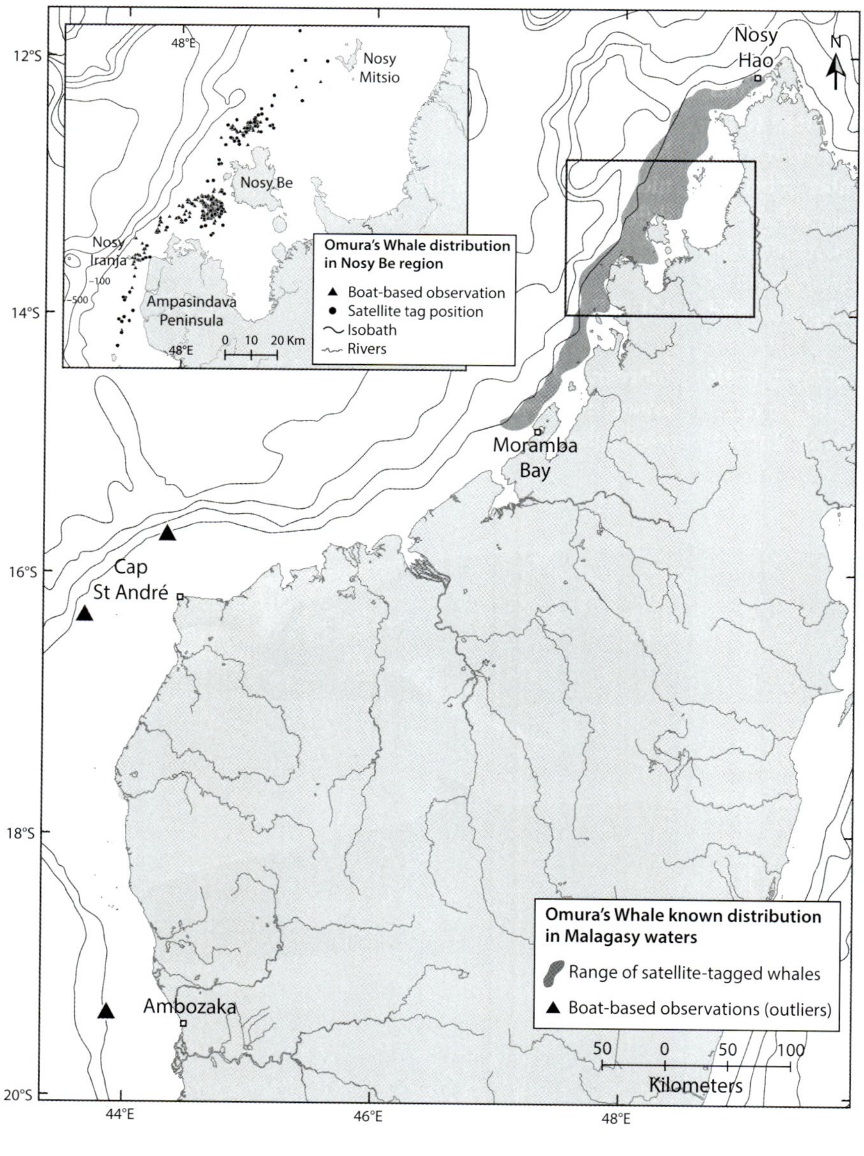

FIGURE 7.31 **Known distribution of *Balaenoptera omurai* around Madagascar, indicating all boat-based observations and extent of range for four individual whales equipped with satellite tags from November 2016 through January 2017. Inset: detail of Nosy Be region showing 273 positions of boat-based visual observations of Omura's Whales (between 2011 and 2017), and positions of satellite-tagged whales in 2016, for which low-error estimates (within <500 m) were obtained.**

(16.20°S) and offshore of Ambozaka (19.40°S) (Figure 7.31); however, the relationship of these animals to the Nosy Be population is not known (Cerchio et al. 2019). Extensive long-term surveys in the southwest Anakao and northeast Antongil Bay regions indicated no reports of *B. omurai* or *B. edeni*–like animals (S. Cerchio, unpublished data), so the distribution around Madagascar appears to be limited to the central-west and northwest coasts.

Boat surveys and encounters off Nosy Be indicate an exclusively shallow water and open shelf habitat preference, despite significant research effort in adjacent deep water and inshore near-coastal water. Depth at sighting locations averaged 52 m (range 36–63 m), sea surface temperature ranged from 28° to 30°C, and sightings were often along the edges of underwater banks that rose to a depth of 10 m or less (Cerchio and Yamada 2018). Satellite telemetry data corroborate these observations, with predominant movements along the shallow continental shelf and only short occasional forays into deep water on the continental slope by two individuals (Cerchio et al. 2018b). Habitat suitability modeling using a combination of the Madagascar boat-based sightings and satellite telemetry positions has indicated that shallow bathymetry provided the greatest predictive value, followed by the variable "Photosynthetically Active Radiation" (or the potential for photosynthesis). These results suggest both a preferred shallow water distribution and the influence of primary productivity processes, although the precise relationships are not clear. The predicted distribution map indicates favorable conditions for *B. omurai* along the west coast of Madagascar, particularly in the northwest, with little other predicted suitable habitat throughout the southwest Indian Ocean.

Seasonal presence of *B. omurai* was assessed using passive acoustic monitoring conducted during a complete year at four sites spread over an approximately 80 km stretch of documented Nosy Be habitat (Cerchio et al. 2018b). The species' song was recorded by all four monitoring devices, with spatial and temporal heterogeneity evident. At the most northerly recorder, 10 km north of Nosy Be, its song was detected in all but one week of the year, providing strong evidence for year-round residency in this region. Rate of occurrence of song varied across days and months, with peak concentrations in December–January, May, and October–November, but no clear seasonality. Choruses of three or more singers were heard throughout the year, and were common during peak periods. Presence of song at the other sites was much more variable and at the two most southerly sites (50 and 80 km south of the northern site) song was prevalent during only a few months of the year. This indicates that despite *B. omurai* being resident year-round in the Nosy Be region, there is distinct geographic variation at a local scale in its distribution and preferred habitat during the year. Combining this with the satellite telemetry data, it is apparent that the northwest Madagascar *B. omurai* population is nonmigratory and resident in these oligotrophic (generally low in primary productivity) waters, and likely has a small range. It is important to emphasize that this pattern is highly unusual in comparison to most other baleen whales.

ECOLOGY AND BEHAVIOR

Very little is known about the breeding ecology of *B. omurai*. Among five sexually mature females taken in whaling operations in the Solomon Sea and Cocos (Keeling) Islands during late October 1976 and mid-November 1978, respectively, a 10.1 m female of 18 years was not physically mature, but had indications of three previous ovulations (corpora albicantia); none was pregnant but two had indications of recent ovulation (corpora lutea) (Wada et al. 2003). A newborn was collected off southern Japan at the end of August (Cerchio and Yamada 2018). In Madagascar, young calves, as indicated by small size (c. 3–4 m) and other anatomical features, have been observed during the months of August and November (Cerchio et al. 2015b, 2018b). These limited reproductive data suggest a protracted breeding season or potentially aseasonal reproduction and parturition throughout the year. Off Nosy Be, at least one female was sighted in four of six years from 2012 to 2017, once with a calf; such a sighting history, particularly in this case of a reproductive female, suggests strong site fidelity and a potentially low reproductive rate (Cerchio et al. 2018b). Numbers of different mother-calf pairs sighted during field surveys off Nosy Be varied from a minimum of no calves to a maximum of five calves per year, also suggesting yearly variability in reproductive output of the population.

Acoustic recordings in the presence of several individual *B. omurai* and from archival recorders indicated a vocalization that is stereotyped, with a single recognizable phrase in the low-frequency spectrum (15–50 Hz). This phrase is uttered in a rhythmically repetitive manner, with a repetition rate of about 190 sec and long uninterrupted sequences ranging from 20 minutes to 12 hours. Frequently there are multiple overlapping sequences evident, indicating choruses of multiple individuals. These vocalization aspects in other balaenopterids are indicative of song and are therefore suggestive of a male breeding display (Cerchio et al. 2015b, 2018b). That the song is heard throughout the year without seasonality, unlike singing behavior in migratory baleen whales, is also suggestive that breeding may be aseasonal. Boat surveys indicate a social organization of loose aggregations of individuals spread across a few kilometers and separated by roughly 50–200 m. Up to 12 individuals have been photographically identified in these loose aggregations, which appear stable for at least several hours and may represent groups of displaying males, suggesting a lek-like mating system (Cerchio et al. 2015b, 2018b).

As for feeding ecology, prior to the Madagascar study the only information came from stomach contents of specimens, including a 7 m female stranded in the Sea of Japan that contained both crustacean and fish remains, whereas all specimens from the Solomon Sea and off the Cocos Islands fed only on the krill *Euphausia diomedeae* (Cerchio and Yamada 2018). From boat surveys off Nosy Be, feeding and defecating were observed on a near-daily basis during October to December, with whales making frequent lunges both subsurface and at the surface. Lunging sometimes involved a roll, particularly when feeding at the surface, typically with the right side facing down. Underwater observations indicated a proportionately large gular pouch in comparison to other balaenopterids, congruent with morphological observations of long and numerous pleats. Feeding on fish was not observed. Most commonly there was no densely aggregated prey obvious in the water column, but feeding on dense patches of krill was observed episodically. Sampled krill was identified based on morphology as *Pseudeuphasia latifrons*, a species known from shallow coastal waters throughout the Indo-Pacific, but previously unknown in the southwest Indian Ocean (Cerchio et al. 2018b).

During at least one season, a clear trophic progression or cascade was observed: early in November there were few observations of concentrated food resources, and feeding *B. omurai* was scarce; over the course of two weeks blooms of a cyanobacterium *Trichodesmium* sp. began to appear and progressed to form extensive mats over large stretches of coastal habitat; this was followed by dense patches of *P. latifrons*, which were fed upon by large multispecies aggregations of *B. omurai*, *Mobula mobular* (Spinetail Devilray), and *M. birostris* (Giant Manta Ray) for extended periods over the last two weeks of fieldwork in early December. During this time *Rhincodon typus* (Whale Shark; see Diamant et al., pp. 381–85) was also seen feeding on the same krill blooms, although more typically *R. typus* is not directly associated with *B. omurai*; *R. typus* instead is commonly associated with schools of mackerel tuna, and both appear to feed on small clupeid fishes (Diamant et al. 2018), the presence of which is likely the result of the same primary productivity processes. It is speculated that this trophic cycle may be a seasonal feature of this habitat, and the driver for the co-occurrence of these planktivorous megafauna (*B. omurai*, *M. mobular*, *M. birostris*, *R. typus*) during these months each year.

Synthesis of the Madagascar study data is beginning to provide a picture of the ecology of this newly described species. A key distinguishing feature of *B. omurai* relative to the majority of baleen whales is that it is adapted to a nonmigratory resident life-history pattern in an oligotrophic tropical habitat. The combination of direct observations on feeding ecology, satellite telemetry results, and application of habitat suitability modeling suggests that this species' distribution off northwest Madagascar may largely be determined by local ecological processes that are restricted to shallow water shelf environments. Its presence and spatiotemporal pattern of distribution within this habitat is likely strongly influenced by the distribution of patchy and ephemeral prey resources. Furthermore, our initial predictive modeling suggests that the appropriate habitat may not be common in the southwest Indian Ocean, and thus the northwest Madagascar population of *B. omurai* may be isolated within a fragmented oceanic/global range for the species and unique for the region.

ANTHROPOGENIC THREATS

With so little information available on *B. omurai* globally, the International Union for Conservation of Nature (IUCN) Red List of Threatened Species classifies the species as Data Deficient (J. Cooke and Brownell 2019). The near coastal distribution of this species places it at risk of impact from anthropogenic activities throughout its range, and its tropical distribution in poorly studied regions such as Madagascar makes documenting and assessing threats challenging. Cerchio et al. (2019) assessed documented threats across this species' global range, and found pressures from, at minimum, ship strikes, fisheries bycatch and entanglement, local directed hunting, petroleum exploration (seismic surveys), and coastal industrial development. Likely threats to the Malagasy population include entanglement in local fishery nets (although this has not to date been documented), impacts from oil and gas exploration, and terrestrial local mining operations in close proximity to the population's habitat.

Loud anthropogenic noises such as seismic survey air guns pose the potential for disturbance of cetacean breeding and resting behavior and even physical damage if in close proximity or with long exposure (Nowacek et al. 2007). Furthermore, noise from petroleum exploration and vessel traffic contributes significantly to ambient noise within the communication bandwidth of baleen whales, acting to mask communication and breeding displays (Clark et al. 2009; Cholewiak et al. 2018). Numerous studies on a variety of cetacean species globally have documented behavioral responses, such as changes in travel routes and distribution and shifts in vocal display behavior, to seismic air guns and echo sounders used in oil exploration (Nowacek et al. 2007; Cerchio et al. 2014b). Recent past seismic exploration activities in the lease blocks known as Majunga, Ampasindava, and Ambilobe overlap extensively with shallow water habitat of *B. omurai* (Cerchio et al. 2015b), although this activity was not monitored or assessed for potential impacts on the population. Since late 2020, the Chinese National Offshore Oil Corporation (CNOOC) has been negotiating exploration permits for three of four lease blocks covering 45,000 km^2 in the northwest of Madagascar previously held by ExxonMobil and BP (Africa Intelligence 2021). This large area of coastal and deep waters from Cap Saint André to the Ampasindava Peninsula overlaps entirely with this species' range based on satellite telemetry (Cerchio et al. 2018b). *Balaenoptera omurai* will be particularly vulnerable to such exposure within its habitat given restricted ranges and isolation within the region, resulting in a potential lack of alternative habitat into which to move. Furthermore, the shallow-water nature of its distribution could exacerbate the impact owing to the propagation characteristics of low-frequency noise from air guns, particularly if the source is in shallow water.

Additionally, a potentially imminent threat in the Nosy Be region comes from a mining operation for rare earth elements on the Ampasindava Peninsula, which poses the risk of coastal water contamination in the habitat of *B. omurai* and in a more general manner the waters of Madagascar's second-largest primarily marine protected area, Ankivonjy (139,410 ha). Rare earth elements extraction from ion-adsorptive clays, using surface mining and heap leaching or in situ leaching methods, is among the most environmentally damaging types of extraction because of its destruction of habitat, groundwater contamination, and mining effluent (Yang et al. 2013; Lei et al. 2017). The resultant pollutants have the potential to affect ecosystems at low trophic levels, possibly disrupting ecological processes that drive the occurrence and distribution of a diversity of marine megafauna. These effects are of particular concern in poorly regulated operations without adequate mitigation of environmental impacts (Yang et al. 2013; Vahidi et al. 2016). If not properly regulated, this industrial development poses serious concern for the entire ecology of an important and diverse ecosystem (Cerchio et al. 2019).

CONSERVATION AND RECOMMENDATIONS

Madagascar's *B. omurai* population is remarkable for its residency, well-defined distribution, and uniqueness within the region. The species' distinct habitat preference for the broad continental shelf on Madagascar's northwest coast is shared for at least some periods of the year with other planktivorous megafauna, notably *Rhincodon typus* (Diamant et al. 2018; see Diamant et al., pp. 381–85) and the rays *Mobula mobular* and *M. birostris*. This highlights the ecological importance of this region for a diverse community of marine megafauna that is likely supported by the same oceanographic processes.

The distributional range of *B. omurai* on Madagascar overlaps with the marine component of several large marine protected areas (MPAs) along Madagascar's northwest coast—from north to south: Nosy Hara National Park (122,827 ha), Ankarea protected seascape (135,556 ha), Ankivonjy protected seascape (139,410 ha), and Sahamalaza National Park and Biosphere Reserve (24,086 ha). The species' range may extend as far south as the Barren Islands, Madagascar's largest MPA (394,175 ha). The population's range also corresponds with the Malagasy segment of the "Northern Mozambique Channel," an area of about 700,000 km^2 that has been identified as a region of outstanding universal value qualifying for World Heritage status (Obura et al. 2012). More recently, the region has been identified as of prime importance for regional cooperation in coastal and oceans management (Obura et al. 2019). Moreover, an IUCN panel of marine mammal biology experts recently identified "Northwest Madagascar and Northeast Mozambique Channel" as an Important Marine Mammal Area (IMMA) (IUCN-MMPATF 2020), in part because of the presence of *B. omurai*. A minimum of 24 marine mammal taxa (23 cetaceans and *Dugong dugon*, see Cerchio et al., pp. 411–24) have been documented in the IMMA, which encompasses all identified habitat for *B. omurai*.

Despite the establishment of the aforementioned national protected areas, and recognition of the region by international conservation bodies, extractive industries continue to operate in this region within the boundaries of the MPAs and recognized sensitive habitat. The permanent presence of *B. omurai* adds forcefully to the conservation arguments for the North Mozambique Channel. In the light of this, we make the following specific recommendations:

- The MPAs of the region should each add *B. omurai* as a conservation target species and contribute as far as possible to the monitoring of the species in the zone.
- Collaborative research should be encouraged among the groups studying the marine megafauna in the Nosy Be region, to further understand the ecological processes that drive the distribution of the assemblage, and enhance coordinated monitoring of the marine megafauna.
- *Balaenoptera omurai* should be actively integrated into regional plans for conservation of the North Mozambique Channel ecoregion and designation of the region as marine world heritage.
- Fisheries management plans established within the region, notably for the "BATAN" area ("Baie d'Ampasindava, Tsimipaike, Ambaro et Nosy Be") and the Barren Islands, should include appropriate monitoring and conservation measures for *B. omurai*.
- Finally, developments in offshore petroleum exploration and exploitation and of the rare earths mine on the Ampasindava Peninsula should be reassessed for a realistic determination of the potential risks, including detailed baseline studies, before commencement of activities that could detrimentally impact *B. omurai* and other sensitive populations. If these activities are to continue, they need to be closely monitored to ensure that adequate mitigation measures are applied for the conservation of *B. omurai* and other important marine megafauna in the region.

Subject editors: Andrew Cooke and Steven M. Goodman

MEGAPTERA NOVAEANGLIAE, HUMPBACK WHALE, *TROZONA*

H. C. Rosenbaum and E. Chou

Megaptera novaeangliae (Humpback Whale; Cetacea) is a marine mammal belonging to the group of whales known as mysticetes (baleen whales). *M. novaeangliae* is found in all major oceanic basins in both the Northern and Southern Hemispheres, including the Southern Ocean around the Antarctic convergence. With the exception of *M. novaeangliae* in the Arabian Sea, all populations generally undertake long-distance seasonal migrations from winter breeding grounds in tropical waters (north of 23°30′S) to summer feeding grounds in polar waters and back (Dawbin 1966; Pomilla et al. 2014). In the Southern Hemisphere, *M. novaeangliae* feeding grounds are distributed across six primary areas in waters surrounding Antarctica (IWC 2011). This species migrates from these feeding grounds to seven distinct tropical wintering areas, where breeding and calving occur. Populations that occupy these distinct wintering areas are recognized by the International Whaling Commission (IWC) as separate breeding stocks, labeled A–G.

While in or on the way to wintering areas, *M. novaeangliae* generally does not feed, instead relying on fat stores from the blubber layer acquired during the austral summer feeding season. Migration by female *M. novaeangliae* to tropical breeding grounds may serve to improve growth rate of offspring in calmer and warmer waters (Clapham 1996; Corkeron and Connor 1999; Rasmussen et al. 2007) or reduce predation by, for example, *Orcinus orca* (Killer Whale) (Corkeron and Connor 1999). Site fidelity to these winter breeding areas is generally maternally driven.

Megaptera novaeangliae is well known and beloved by whale watchers for a range of surface active and acrobatic behaviors, such as breaching and lunges (Figure 7.32). It is distinguished from other large whales by its exceptionally long pectoral flippers, which can reach up to 5 m in length. Individuals can be identified by their unique tail fluke shape and ventral fluke pattern. In general, females reproduce about every two to three years and gestation lasts one year. Females can grow to a length of 19 m and weigh up to 36,000 kg; males are typically slightly smaller. Both females and males produce sounds known as *social calls*, thought to function in a social context (i.e., communication between individuals or groups),

FIGURE 7.32 **Megaptera novaeangliae (Humpback Whale) mother and calf breaching in Antongil Bay.** (PHOTO by Matthew S. Leslie, WCS Ocean Giants.)

which have been recorded during migration and on tropical breeding grounds (Rekdahl et al. 2016). Males produce complex vocalizations, defined as *song*, with a hierarchical organization composed of a series of sounds occurring in a regular sequence and patterned in time (Payne and McVay 1971). Song is thought to function particularly in a reproductive context as it is limited to males and primarily emitted on tropical breeding grounds and where groups of males, known as *competitive groups*, engage in physical male-male competition for females and "escort" mothers with calves (Tyack and Whitehead 1983; Clapham et al. 1999).

WHALING HISTORY

The first recorded large-scale catches of *M. novaeangliae* in the Southern Hemisphere date back to American pelagic whaling in the late 18th and 19th centuries, when an estimated 215,000 animals were hunted, severely depleting regional populations (Findlay 2001; Rocha et al. 2014). In the 20th century, these populations were again the subject of whaling, including illegal Soviet hunting, which further drastically reduced populations (IWC 2016). In the Indian Ocean, records from 19th-century American whalers confirm that whales have been hunted since the 1830s (Townsend 1935). Many of these ships focused their efforts in the coastal waters of eastern Africa and Madagascar. Other 19th- and some 20th-century documents show intensive hunting of *M. novaeangliae* in northeastern Madagascar around Antongil Bay (reviewed in Best et al. 1998). More modern, commercial whaling off the coast of Madagascar began in the early 1900s and catches were initially very low. Two further episodes of documented whaling occurred in Madagascar's waters, 1937–1939 and 1949–1950. These data correlate with observed peak abundance in winter season destinations such as Antongil Bay (Townsend 1935; Rosenbaum et al. 1997).

PHOTOGRAPHIC IDENTIFICATION OF INDIVIDUAL ANIMALS

The first large-scale monitoring and research of *M. novaeangliae* around Madagascar began in 1996 with daily boat-based field surveys between July and September in Antongil Bay (Rosenbaum et al. 1997; Ersts and Rosenbaum 2003). Antongil Bay covers nearly 2800 km^2, and provides a large area of shallow water, shown to be the preferred environment for calving females. When whales were encountered, information on location, group size, and group type was recorded. Photographic data of tail fluke shape and pattern of whales in and around Antongil Bay were collected and compared within and between years to identify individuals and determine the total number of animals, both of which allow for estimation of life history and demographic parameters.

Vély and Collin-Omnes (1997) documented seasonal presence in the Sainte Marie Channel between Ile Sainte Marie and mainland Madagascar based on photographic identifications. Photo-identification studies have identified the movement of individuals between Madagascar and other breeding stocks (e.g., Stevick et al. 2011), while other studies have provided evidence of isolation from other breeding stocks (e.g., Arabian Sea *M. novaeangliae*, ASHW, in Minton et al. 2010). M. Faria and Rakotoharimalala (2012) identified 29 occurrences of skin lesions and 26 occurrences of body anomalies on *M. novaeangliae* off Ile Sainte Marie, all of which are useful for identification of individual whales.

POPULATION ESTIMATES

The waters of the southwestern Indian Ocean surrounding Madagascar are termed Breeding Stock C (BSC) by the IWC. BSC is further divided into four sub-stocks (Figure 7.33). BSC1 occupies waters off southeastern Africa, although a majority of animals generally migrate past eastern South Africa to breeding areas off Mozambique (Findlay et al. 2011b, 2011c; Amir et al. 2012). BSC2 occurs in and around the Mozambique Channel, mainly around the Comoro archipelago, with fewer animals around the Seychelles archipelago (Kiszka et al. 2010b; Ersts et al. 2011b). BSC3 occupies southern and eastern Malagasy waters, although most available information concerns the well-studied populations in and around Antongil Bay and Ile Sainte Marie (e.g., Rosenbaum et al. 1997, 2000; Ersts and Rosenbaum 2003; Pomilla and Rosenbaum 2006; Cerchio et al. 2016; Trudelle et al. 2018). Finally, BSC4 occurs in the Mascarene archipelago (IWC 2007; Dulau-Drouot et al. 2012).

While population estimates for this species surrounding Madagascar prior to the late 20th century are deficient, Best et al. (1998) provided a first estimate of about 2532 whales based on line-transect surveys off southern Madagascar. However, the survey may have counted individuals congregating from multiple migratory corridors. Most recently, photographic identification data, as well as genetic data, have enabled population estimates of BSC1 and BSC3, which are 8439 (range 7072–14,630) and 8854 (range 6905–16,105), respectively (IWC 2010). Using these population estimates, projections to 2015 under a variety of assumptions indicate that BSC1 and BSC3 populations should have recovered to more than 90% of pre-20th-century whaling population levels (IWC 2016).

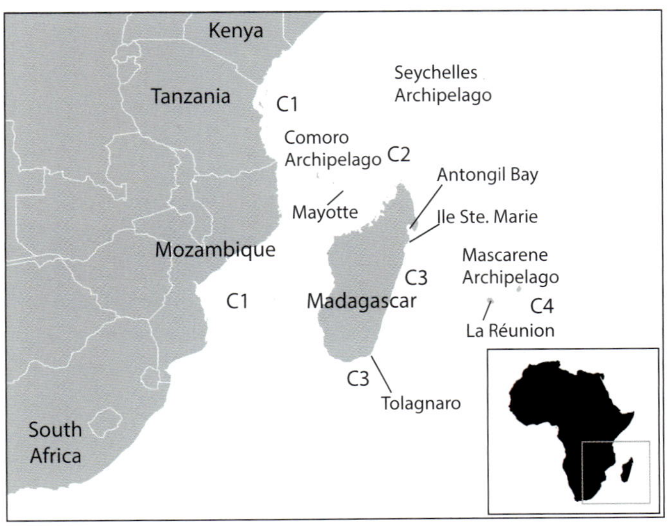

FIGURE 7.33 **Sub-stocks of Breeding Stock C (BSC) of *Megaptera novaeangliae* (Humpback Whale), as recognized by the International Whaling Commission.** (SOURCE: IWC 2016. Figure modified from Rosenbaum et al. 2017.)

POPULATION STRUCTURE, CONNECTIVITY, AND MIGRATORY MOVEMENTS

Within Malagasy breeding grounds, male and female *M. novaeangliae* generally utilize different habitats (Ersts and Rosenbaum 2003; Trudelle et al. 2016, 2018). In general, males tend to occupy waters farther offshore than females, as deeper waters are presumed to provide suitable conditions for male breeding displays and aggressive interactions within competitive groups. Females generally use nearshore and shallow waters. On the basis of current data, females in Antongil Bay with calves tend to stay closer to shore in shallower waters than those without calves (Ersts and Rosenbaum 2003). Whales with calves observed off Tolagnaro were also on average closer to shore (1.39 km) than solitary whales (2.45 km), with >90% of mother-calf pairs observed less than 2 km from the shore (Jacques Whitford 2007). One documented *M. novaeangliae* birth within 2 km of the southwestern coast of Ile Sainte Marie occurred in waters 20–50 m in depth (M. Faria et al. 2013).

Prior to modern-era research, the only direct evidence linking the migratory route of Madagascar's *M. novaeangliae* from wintering to feeding grounds came from two individuals tagged in the Antarctic and later killed south of Madagascar (Rayner 1940). The pathway of *M. novaeangliae* to Antongil Bay largely occurs along the southern and eastern Malagasy coasts, passing near Tolagnaro and Ile Sainte Marie (Cétamada 2021). Off Tolagnaro, whales move northeastward in May and June, returning in a southwesterly direction in July and August, with an apparent peak in numbers in August (Jacques Whitford 2007).

Though the IWC recognizes four distinct sub-stocks within BSC, recent evidence suggests differing levels of exchange between them. Movements of individuals from BSC2 to BSC3, BSC3 to BSC2, BSC3 to BSC1, and BSC4 to BSC3 suggest some level of connectivity between sub-stocks, and perhaps to a greater extent by males than females (Ersts et al. 2011b; Fossette et al. 2014; Cerchio et al. 2016; Dulau et al. 2017). Varying movements of individual *M. novaeangliae* within and between sub-stock regions (especially between BSC1 and BSC3) suggest the use of different sub-stock regions at different times throughout the breeding season (Cerchio et al. 2016). Even with all the recent tagging efforts and new knowledge about movements of whales from Madagascar, additional tracking studies with greater tag duration are needed to better understand connectivity from Madagascar to high-latitude feeding regions.

Genetic analyses indicate that BSC2 and BSC3 are less genetically distinct from each other than BSC3 and BSC1, and there is even evidence of some substructure within sub-stock BSC3 (Rosenbaum et al. 2009; Kershaw et al. 2017). The lack of genetic differentiation between BSC2 and BSC3 is further supported by photographic identification and satellite tagging data, which indicate BSC2 may consist of a migratory stream of animals from both mainland Africa and Madagascar (Ersts et al. 2011a; Fossette et al. 2014; Cerchio et al. 2016; Kershaw et al. 2017). Mixing between BSC sub-stocks, particularly between BSC2 and BSC3, is also supported though stable isotope analysis (comparing ratios of nitrogen and carbon), which allows for diet tracking through particular feeding areas (Montanari et al. 2020).

In addition to mixing between BSC sub-stocks, there is evidence of some mixing or exchange between BSC and breeding stocks off the west coast of Africa (BSB) and western Australia (BSD) (Rosenbaum et al. 2009, 2017; Amaral et al. 2016; Kershaw et al. 2017). Genetic capture-recapture studies (Pomilla and Rosenbaum 2005) documented possible interoceanic movement of a male first sampled in Antongil Bay and then two years later off Gabon in the southeastern Atlantic (BSB). One of the longest documented transoceanic movements of a female first identified off Albrolhos Bank, Brazil, and then off Ile Sainte Marie also indicates movement between breeding grounds (Stevick et al. 2011). While the extent of recent research surpasses what was known two decades ago (Rosenbaum 2003b), many details are still unclear about the mixing and fine-scale delineation of these sub-stocks. Further and extensive details about *M. novaeangliae* occurring in Malagasy waters can be found in different IWC documents (IWC 2007, 2010, 2011, 2016).

SONG AND THE ROLE OF BIOACOUSTICS

Y. Razafindrakoto et al. (2001) provided the first description of *M. novaeangliae* song structure in the western Indian Ocean. These songs were generally accordant with songs recorded in other wintering areas and along migratory corridors (Helweg et al. 1998) and other well-studied areas (Payne and McVay 1971; Winn et al. 1981).

Recent acoustic studies have identified some *M. novaeangliae* song to the level of subunits (compared with general units), providing detail of the complex acoustic display of males. These subunits were generally shorter in duration and more stable in frequency than general units (Pace et al. 2010). Off La Réunion (BSC4), both *M. novaeangliae* song and social calls were identified, with social calls observed throughout the breeding season and song peaking in mid-July and again in early August. *Megaptera novaeangliae* song analysis also provides insights into population connectivity and suggests limited interaction between BSC3 and populations off western Australia, as only one song phrase was shared between the two populations (Murray et al. 2011).

CURRENT THREATS AND CONCERNS

While *M. novaeangliae* is protected internationally by the IWC, the Convention on the Conservation of Migratory Species of Wild Animals (CMS), and the Convention on International Trade in Endangered Species of Wild Fauna and Flora (CITES), many populations still recovering from previous commercial whaling are subject to a host of modern threats in the oceanic environment. These threats include hydrocarbon (oil and gas) exploration and development, industrial fisheries, shipping, climate change, and underwater anthropogenic noise (associated with various industrial and military activities). The push for oil and gas exploration and production occurs in both nearshore and offshore areas, which represent important habitats for *M. novaeangliae*. Offshore oil- and gas-related surveys have been conducted in BSC regions, including Madagascar. Where petroleum production is established, there is the risk that oil spills in the marine environment result in hazardous crude oil components entering bottom sediments and the mesopelagic food chain and collecting at the water's surface where whales come to breathe. Throughout their lifetime, *M. novaeangliae* individuals may be impacted directly via ingestion or absorption of contaminants and indirectly through ingestion of contaminated prey (Bettridge et al. 2015).

Human presence in the oceans has facilitated rapid expansion of the global shipping industry and fisheries; the latter has resulted in increased amounts of active or discarded fishing gear in whale habitat (Pauly 2009). Fishing gear can become affixed to an animal, which can become more entangled in the gear as it tries to break free, leading to exhaustion, starvation, lacerations, infection, and ultimately, in some cases, death (e.g., Clapham et al. 1999; Moore and van der Hoop 2012). The expansion of shipping in the western Indian Ocean increases the risk of ship strikes, which can lead to massive blunt force trauma, bone fractures, hemorrhaging, amputations, and death (Fleming and Jackson 2011). Although information on the impact of fisheries is limited, stranding reports and bycatch data show entanglement of *M. novaeangliae* in gillnets off Tanzania, Mozambique, South Africa, and Mayotte (Y. Razafindrakoto et al. 2008; Kiszka et al. 2009).

Information is limited on other threats to *M. novaeangliae*, including from disease, pollutants (Das et al. 2017), tourism, and predation (see Bettridge et al. 2015 for a review). There is also a lack of information on the impacts of climate change, although changes to ocean temperature and acidity could lead to prey shifts or depletion or habitat shifts (as seen in some North Pacific cetacean populations). Finally, there is a lack of knowledge of populations, policy and regulation, and awareness among key stakeholders (Simmonds and Eliott 2009; Nowacek et al. 2011).

Anthropogenic underwater noise is of particular concern, as *M. novaeangliae* relies on sound for a variety of important life functions (including breeding, foraging, communication, and navigation), and disruption to the acoustic environment can lead to many adverse impacts including stress, disruption of important behaviors, communication masking, injury, and mortality (Southall et al. 2007; Cerchio et al. 2014b; Nowacek et al. 2015). Anthropogenic underwater noise is amplified by increasing fisheries and shipping operations, producing chronic noise, as well as hydrocarbon exploration, which involves seismic survey air guns producing repetitive underwater blasts.

TOWARD WIDER REGIONAL CONSERVATION AND COORDINATION

While the successful recovery of populations of *M. novaeangliae* has been due to dedicated conservation and management efforts, continued research plays a key role in demonstrating recovery and orientating conservation efforts. Research increases knowledge and awareness of the importance of Madagascar's coastal waters and is vital in making well-informed management decisions. In addition to the initial protection of *M. novaeangliae* in 1963, the IWC Indian Ocean Sanctuary, established in 1979, protects whale species throughout the Indian Ocean to 55°S and prohibits all whaling.

In Malagasy waters, research has contributed to a better understanding of the effects of disturbance to whales by the close approach of small boats, as occurs in whale-watching, which has become popular at several sites around the island. Recognizing the importance of this zone as critical wintering grounds and migratory corridors for *M. novaeangliae*, and commitments under the Washington, Bonn, and Nairobi conventions, the Malagasy government issued an interministerial order establishing regulations applicable to tour operators offering commercial whale-watching (Interministerial Order no. 2083-2000 for 2000). These regulations were adapted from a set of guidelines established for ecotourism in Antongil Bay and require keeping a minimum distance of 100 m between vessel and whale (or 200 m in the case of mother-calf pairs).

An important element of conservation and management is the designation of marine protected areas (MPAs) and Important Marine Mammal Areas (IMMAs). The Marine Mammal Protected Areas Task Force, created by the International Committee on Marine Mammal Protected Areas of the International Union for Conservation of Nature (IUCN) World Commission on Protected Areas (WCPA) and the IUCN Species Survival Commission, worked between 2016 and 2020 to identify important areas for cetacean conservation (IUCN-MMPATF 2019, 2020). In 2019, the task force held the first western Indian Ocean and Arabian Seas IMMA workshop, which designated 37 IMMAs, of which 16 address the conservation of *M. novaeangliae* and five of which exist around Madagascar (Figure 7.34).

Experience has shown that maintaining cetacean research efforts can be difficult, owing to the high cost, logistical challenges, and typically short duration of donor funding. The emergence of private tourism operations in various parts of Madagascar, combined with marine megafauna research, offers significant opportunities for collaboration within Madagascar and the surrounding region.

Other efforts, such as the Indian Ocean Cetacean Consortium (IndoCet 2021), offer great opportunities to collaborate on projects such as the photo identification of *M. novaeangliae* via an online regional platform. Such operations also provide opportunities for training conservationists and managers and developing citizen science initiatives, and ultimately are a source of advice and information for national and regional conservation programs. Aided by continued research and appropriate conservation recommendations, such partnerships have the potential to contribute to the continuing recovery of *M. novaeangliae* around Madagascar and in the wider western Indian Ocean region.

Subject editors: Andrew Cooke and Steven M. Goodman

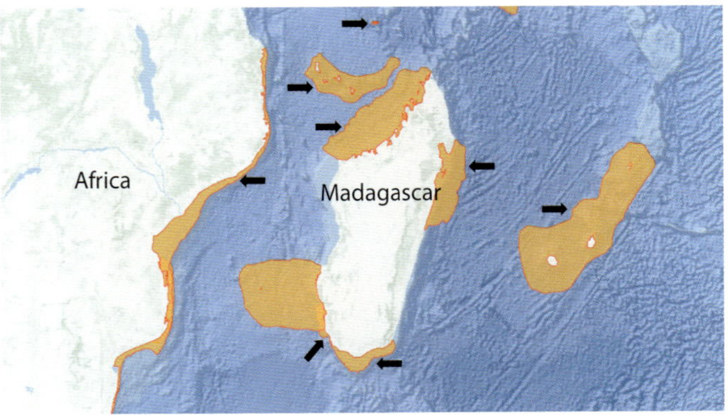

FIGURE 7.34 **Designated Important Marine Mammal Areas (IMMAs) around Madagascar, shown in orange. Black arrows indicate IMMAs that include *Megaptera novaeangliae* (Humpback Whale).** (SOURCE: adapted from IUCN-MMPATF 2020.)

REFERENCES

Afonso, P., McGinty, N., and Machete, M. 2014. Dynamics of whale shark occurrence at their fringe oceanic habitat. *PLoS One* 9: e102060.

Africa Intelligence. 2021. CNOOC hopes to bag former ExxonMobil and BP blocks. Africa Intelligence. Accessed 29 April 2021. https://www.africaintelligence.com/oil--gas_corporate-strategy/2021/04/29/cnooc-hopes-to-bag-former-exxonmobil-and-bp-blocks,109661794-gra

Ahamada, S., Bigot, L., Bijoux, J., Maharavo, J., Meunier, S., Moyne-Picard, M., and Paupiah, N. 2002. Status of coral reefs in the south west Indian Ocean island node: Comoros, Madagascar, Mauritius, Reunion and Seychelles. In *Status of the Coral Reefs of the World*, ed. C. Wilkinson, pp. 79–100. Townsville: Australian Institute of Marine Science.

Allen, G. R. 2011. Les poissons de récifs du nord-est de Madagascar. In *A Marine Biodiversity Assessment of the Extreme North East of Madagascar*, eds. J. Maharavo, T. Razafinjatovo, A. Oliver, and A. Rabearisoa, pp. 5–15. Antananarivo: Conservation International.

Allen, Z. C., Shah, N. J., Grant, A., Derand, G. D., and Bell, D. 2010. Hawksbill turtle monitoring in Cousin Island Special Reserve, Seychelles: An eight-fold increase in annual nesting numbers. *Endangered Species Research* 11: 195–200.

Allison, G. 2008. De la ponte à l'éclosion: Suivi de la reproduction de deux espèces menacées de tortues marines, la tortue verte et la tortue imbriquée, sur l'île de Nosy Iranja, Madagascar. Master 2, Biodiversité des Ecosystèmes Tropicaux, Université de La Réunion.

Alongi, D. 2008. Mangrove forests: Resilience, protection from tsunamis, and responses to global climate change. *Estuarine, Coastal and Shelf Science* 76: 1–13.

Alvheim, O., Torstensen, E., Fennessy, S., MacKay, F., Zaera, D. and Bemiasa, J. 2009. Cruise Reports "*Dr. Fridtjof Nansen*." West Madagascar: Pelagic Ecosystem Survey. SWIOFP/ASCLME/FAO 2009. Cruise 2, 25 Aug.–3 Oct. 2009. Preliminary report. Institute of Marine Research, Bergen, Norway; Oceanographic Research Institute, South Africa; Institut Halieutique et des Sciences Marines, Madagascar.

Amaral, A. R., Loo, J., Jaris, H., Olavarria, C., Thiele, D., Ensor, P., Aguayo, A., and Rosenbaum, H. C. 2016. Population genetic structure among feeding aggregations of humpback whales in the Southern Ocean. *Marine Biology* 163: 132.

Amemiya, C. T., Alföldi, J., Lee, A. P., Fan, S., Philippe, H., et al. 2013. The African coelacanth genome provides insights into tetrapod evolution. *Nature* 496: 311–316.

Amir, O. A., Berggren, P., and Jiddawi, N. S. 2012. Recent records of marine mammals in Tanzanian waters. *Journal of Cetacean Research and Management* 12: 249–253.

Anderson, R. C., Clark, R., Madsen, P. T., Johnson, C., Kiszka, J., and Breysse, O. 2006. Observations of Longman's beaked whale (*Indopacetus pacificus*) in the western Indian Ocean. *Aquatic Mammals* 32(2): 223–231.

Anderson, R. C., Herrera, M., Ilangakoon, A. D., Koya, K. M., Moazzam, M., Mustika, P. L., and Sutaria, D. N. 2020. Cetacean bycatch in Indian Ocean tuna gillnet fisheries. *Endangered Species Research* 41: 39–53.

Andréfouët, S. 2012. *Mozambique Channel Coral Reef Habitat Mapping*. Report to Collecte Localisation Satellites. Nouméa: IRD.

Andréfouët, S., Muller-Karger, F., Robinson, J., Kranenburg, C. J., Torres-Pulliza, D., Spraggins, S. A., and Murch, B. 2006. Global assessment of modern coral reef extent and diversity for regional science and management applications: A view from space. In *Proceedings of 10th International Coral Reef Symposium*, pp. 1732–1745. Townsville: ICRS.

Andréfouët, S., Chagnaud, N., and Kranenburg, C. J. 2009. *Atlas of Western Indian Ocean Coral Reefs*. Nouméa: IRD.

Andréfouët, S., Guillaume, M.M.M., Delval, A., Rasoamanendrika, F.M.A., Blanchot, J., and Bruggemann, J. H. 2013. Fifty years of changes in reef flat habitats of the Grand Récif of Toliara (SW Madagascar) and the impact of gleaning. *Coral Reefs* 32: 757–768.

Andriamalala, C.A.J. 2007. Etude écologique pour la gestion des mangroves à Madagascar, comparaison d'une mangrove littorale et d'estuaire à l'aide de la télédétection. PhD thesis, Universität Basel.

Andriamalala, G., and Gardner, C. J. 2010. L'utilisation du dina comme outil de gouvernance des ressources naturelles: Leçons tirés de Velondriake, sud-ouest de Madagascar. *Tropical Conservation Science* 3: 447–472.

Andriamampandry, A. V. 1988. *Beckerella pterocladioides* sp. nov. et *Gelidium madagascariense* sp. nov. deux espèces de Gelidiales-rhodophytes de Fort-Dauphin (Madagascar). *Cryptogamie, Algologie* 9: 243–259.

Andriamanaitra, S., Rafomanana, G., and Rakotozandriny, D.N.J. 2016. Dégradation de la pêche traditionnelle aux requins dans le nord-ouest de Madagascar: Cas des villages de Ramena, d'Ampasindava et de Port Saint Louis. *Akon'ny Ala* 33: 39–46.

Andrianaivojaona, C., Kasprzyk, Z. W., and Dasylva, G. 1992. *Pêches et aquaculture à Madagascar*. Antananarivo: Food and Agriculture Organization of the United Nations.

Andrianaivojaona, C.M.D., Levrel, A., and Provensal, M. 2020. *Evaluation de la gouvernance des droits d'usage de l'espace côtier et marin à Madagascar*. Antananarivo: United States Agency for International Development.

Andrianarivelo, N. 2001. Essai d'évaluation de l'importance de la pêche aux dauphins dans la région d'Anakao (sud-ouest de Madagascar). Mémoire de DEA, Institut Halieutique et des Sciences Marines, Université de Toliara.

Andrianarivelo, N., Lope, J. C., Rakotonirina, J. S., and Randriamanantsoa, B. J. 1998. *Suivi écologique des trois parcs marins et d'un Site Touristique dans la Presqu'île de Masoala. Rapport Définitif.* Report prepared for CARE International. Toliara: Cellule des Océanographes de l'Université de Toliara (COUT).

Andrianjohany, S. 1992. Inventaire de poissons des mangroves de Masoarivo. Mémoire de DEA, Université d'Antananarivo.

Andrzejaczek, S., Meeuwig, J., Rowat, D., Pierce, S., Davies, T., Fisher, R., and Meekan, M. 2016. The ecological connectivity of whale shark aggregations in the Indian Ocean: A photo-identification approach. *Royal Society Open Science* 3: 160455.

Anonymous. 1983. *Cruise Report R/V Dr. Fridtjof Nansen, Resources Survey, Madagascar, 16–28 June 1983*. Bergen: Institute of Marine Research.

Anonymous. 2005. Le cœlacanthe, icône de la Journeé mondiale du Tourisme. *Les Nouvelles*, 5 Oct. 2005.

ANSES (Agence Nationale de Sécurité Sanitaire de l'Alimentation, de l'Environnement et du Travail). 2015. Contamination des requins, notamment tigre et bouledogue, par des ciguatoxines: Occurrence, méthodes analytiques, cas humains rapportés et éléments d'éthologie. Avis de l'ANSES. Rapport d'expertise collective. Rev. ed. Jan. 2015.

Araujo, G., Agustines, A., Tracey, B., Snow, S., Labaja, J., and Ponzo, A. 2019. Photo-ID and telemetry highlight a global whale shark hotspot in Palawan, Philippines. *Scientific Reports* 9: 1–12.

Arias-Ortiz, A., Masqué, P., Glass, L., Benson, L., Kennedy, H., et al. 2020. Losses of soil organic carbon with deforestation in mangroves of Madagascar. *Ecosystems* 2020: 1–19.

ASCLME. 2012. *National Marine Ecosystem Diagnostic Analysis: Madagascar*. Contribution to the Agulhas and Somali Current Large Marine Ecosystems Project (supported by UNDP with GEF grant financing). Grahamstown: ASCLME Project.

Astuti, R. 1995. *People of the Sea: Identity and Descent among the Vezo of Madagascar*. Cambridge: Cambridge University Press.

Ateweberhan, M., and McClanahan, T. R. 2010. Relationship between historical sea-surface temperature variability and climate change-induced coral mortality in the western Indian Ocean. *Marine Pollution Bulletin* 608(7): 964–970.

Baker, J. D., Littnan, C. L., and Johnston, D. W. 2006. Potential effects of sea level rise on the terrestrial habitats of endangered and endemic megafauna in the north-western Hawaiian Islands. *Endangered Species Research* 2: 21–30.

Baker-Médard, M. 2020. Of whales and dugongs: Examining the rise of colonial conservation as development in Madagascar's marine history. *Environment and History*. doi:10.3197/096734019X15755402985622.

Baker-Médard, M., and Faber, J. 2020. Fins and (mis)fortunes: Managing shark populations for sustainability and food sovereignty. *Marine Policy* 113: 103805.

Ballance, L. T., and Pitman, R. L. 1998. Cetaceans of the western tropical Indian Ocean: Distribution, relative abundance, and comparisons with cetacean communities of two other tropical ecosystems. *Marine Mammal Science* 14: 429–459.

Balon, E. K. 1991a. Prelude: The mystery of a persistent life form. *Environmental Biology of Fishes* 32: 9–13.

———. 1991b. Possible evolution of the coelacanth's reproductive style: Lecithotrophy and orally feeding embryos in cichlid fishes and in *Latimeria chalumnae*. *Environmental Biology of Fishes* 32: 249–265.

Balon, E. K., Atz, J. W., and Stribling, M. D. 1991. Viviparity and the maternal-embryonic relationship in the coelacanth *Latimeria chalumnae*. *Environmental Biology of Fishes* 32: 225–248.

Banks, A., Best, P., Gullan, A., Guissamulo, A., Cockcroft, V., and Findlay, K. 2011. Recent sightings of southern right whales in Mozambique. Paper SC/S11/RW17 presented to the International Whaling Commission Scientific Committee. http://dolphincare.org/Research_files/Banks%20S11-RW17.pdf.

Barber, R., Sikora, I., and Nimak-Wood, M. 2016. Blue whales *Balaenoptera musculus* in offshore waters of Kenya. *African Journal of Marine Science* 38(2): 279–284.

Barnes-Mauthe, M., Oleson, K. L., and Zadindrasilivonona, B. 2013. The total economic value of small-scale fisheries with a characterization of post-landing trends: An application in Madagascar with global relevance. *Fisheries Research* 147: 175–185.

Battistini, R. 1960. Description géomorphologique de Nosy-Be, du delta du Sambirano et la Baie d'Ampasindava. *Mémoires de l'Institut Scientifique de Madagascar*, série F, 3: 121–243.

Battistini, R., Jouannjc, C., Maugé, L. A., Casellato, G., and Vernier, E. 1975. Morphologie et sédimentologie du canyon sous-marin de l'Onilahy (sud-ouest de Madagascar). *Cahiers de l'ORSTOM*, série *Géologie* 7(2): 95–100.

Bauchot, M.-L., and Bianchi, G. 1984. *Guide des poissons commerciaux de Madagascar*. Rome: Food and Agriculture Organization of the United Nations.

Bautil, B. R., Ramantoniaina, J., and Carrara, G. 1991. *Etude préliminaire de la ressource en crabe des mangroves (*Scylla serrata*) du nord-ouest de Madagascar*. Rome: Food and Agriculture Organization of the United Nations.

Belle, E.M.S., Stewart, G. W., De Ridder, B., Komeno, R.J.-L., Ramahatatra, F., Remy-Zephir, B., and Stein-Rostaign, R. D. 2009. Establishment of a community managed marine reserve in the Bay of Ranobe, southwest Madagascar. *Madagascar Conservation and Development* 4(1): 31–37.

Benbow, S., and Harris, A. 2011. Managing Madagascar's octopus fisheries. In *Proceedings of the Workshop on* Octopus cyanea *fisheries, 5–6 April 2011*. Toliara: Blue Ventures Conservation. 24 pages. https://blueventures.org/wp-content/uploads/2018/01/Benbow-Harris_2011_Proceedings-of-the-workshop-on-Octopus-cyanea-fisheries-5-6-April-2011-Toliara_Managing-Madagascar%E2%80%99s-octopus-fis.pdf.

Benbow, S., Humber, F., Oliver, T. A., Oleson, K.L.L., Raberinary, D., Nadon, M., Ratsimbazafy, H., and Harris, A. 2014. Lessons learnt from experimental temporary octopus fishing closures in south-west Madagascar: Benefits of concurrent closures. *African Journal of Marine Science* 36(1): 31–37.

Benno, B., Verheij, E., Stapley, J., Rumisha, C., Ngatunga, B., Abdallah, A., and Kalombo, H. 2006. Coelacanth (*Latimeria chalumnae* Smith 1939) discoveries and conservation in Tanzania. *South African Journal of Science* 102(9–10): 486–490.

Benson, L., Glass, L., Jones, T. G., Ravaoarinorotsihoarana, L., and Rakotomahazo, C. 2017. Mangrove carbon stocks and ecosystem cover dynamics in southwest Madagascar and the implications for local management. *Forests* 8(6): 190.

Best, P. B. 2001. Distribution and population separation of Bryde's whale *Balaenoptera edeni* off southern Africa. *Marine Ecology Progress Series* 220: 277–289.

———. 2007. *Whales and Dolphins of the Southern African Subregion*. Cambridge: Cambridge University Press.

Best, P. B., Findlay, K. P., Sekiguchi, K., Peddemors, V. M., Rakotonirina, B. P., Rossouw, A., and Gove, D. 1998. Winter distribution and possible migration routes of humpback whales *Megaptera novaeangliae* in the southwest Indian Ocean. *Marine Ecology Progress Series* 162: 287–299.

Best, P. B., Rademeyer, R. A., Burton, C., Ljungblad, D., Sekiguchi, K., Shimada, H., Thiele, D., Reeb, D., and Butterworth, D. S. 2003. The abundance of blue whales on the Madagascar Plateau, December 1996. *Journal of Cetacean Research and Management* 5: 253–260.

Be Totozafy, S. 1994. Contribution à l'étude de la régénération naturelle et de l'évolution spatio-temporelle de la mangrove de Masoarivo. Mémoire de DEA, Université d'Antananarivo.

Bettridge, S., Baker, C. S., Barlow, J., Clapham, P. J., Ford, M., et al. 2015. Status review of the humpback whale (*Megaptera novaeangliae*) under the Endangered Species Act. National Oceanic and Atmospheric Administration Technical Memorandum NMFS. NOAA-TM-NMFSSWFSC-540. www.nmfs.noaa.gov/pr/species/Status%20Reviews/humpback_whale_sr_2015.pdf.

Beurrier, J. P. 1982. *Les zones sous juridiction, la législation des pêcheries et l'organisation structurelle du secteur des pêches à Madagascar*. Rome: Food and Agriculture Organization of the United Nations.

Biotope. 2019. Avis d'expert dans le cadre d'une demande d'augmentation des rejets en mer: Mine de nickel/cobalt d'Ambatovy. Version 3. Report to Ambatovy Madagascar SA.

BirdLife. 2020. Important Bird Areas factsheets. Accessed 26 July 2020. http://datazone.birdlife.org/home.

Bitner, M. A., and Logan, A. 2016. Recent Brachiopoda from the Mozambique-Madagascar area, western Indian Ocean. *Zoosystema* 38(1): 5–41.

Blench, R. 2008. The Austronesians in Madagascar and their interaction with the Bantu of the east African coast: Surveying the linguistic evidence for domestic and translocated animals. *Studies in Philippine Languages and Cultures* 18: 18–43.

Boisier, P., Ranaivoson, G., Andriamahefazafy, B., Roux, J., Sataka, M., and Yasumoto, T. 1994. Fatal ichthyosarcotoxism after eating shark meat: Implications of two new marine toxins. *Archives de l'Institut Pasteur de Madagascar* 61(2): 81–83.

Boisier, P., Ranaivoson, G., Rasolofonirina, N., Andriamahefazafy, B., Roux, J., Chanteau, S., Sataka, M., and Yasumoto, T. 1995. Fatal mass poisoning in Madagascar following ingestion of a shark (*Carcharhinus leucas*): Clinical and epidemiologic aspects and isolation of toxins. *Toxicon* 33: 1359–1364.

Boldrocchi, G., and Bettinetti, R. 2019. Whale shark foraging on baitfish off Djibouti. *Marine Biodiversity* 49: 2013–2016.

Boo, G. H., Le Gall, L., Hwang, I. K., and Boo, S. M. 2016a. *Pterocladiella feldmannii* sp. nov. and *P. hamelii* sp. nov. (Gelidiales, Rhodophyta), two new species uncovered in Madagascar during the Atimo Vatae expedition. *Cryptogamie, Algologie* 37(3): 179–198.

Boo, G, H., Le Gall, L., Miller, K. A., Freshwater, D. W., Wernberg, T., Terada, R., Yoon, K. J., and Boo, S. M. 2016b. A novel phylogeny of the Gelidiales (Rhodophyta) based on five genes including the nuclear CesA, with descriptions of *Orthogonacladia* gen. nov. and Orthogonacladiaceae fam. nov. *Molecular Phylogenetics and Evolution* 101: 359–372.

Boo, G. H., Le Gall, L., Hwang I. K., Miller, K. A., and Boo, S. M. 2018. Phylogenetic relationships and biogeography of *Ptilophora* (Gelidiales, Rhodophyta) with descriptions of *P. aureolusa*, *P. malagasya*, and *P. spongiophila* from Madagascar. *Journal of Phycology* 54(2): 249–263.

Botha, M. 2010. Nest site fidelity and nest site selection of loggerhead, *Caretta caretta*, and leatherback, *Dermochelys coriacea*, turtles in KwaZulu-Natal, South Africa. MS thesis, Department of Zoology, Nelson Mandela Metropolitan University, Port Elizabeth.

Bouchet, P. 1999. A new *Lyria* (Gastropoda: Volutidae) from southeastern Madagascar. *Nautilus* 113: 1–3.

Bourjea, J., Ciccione, S., and Ratsimbazafy, R. 2006. Marine turtle surveys in Nosy Iranja Kely, north-western Madagascar. *Western Indian Ocean Journal of Marine Science* 5(2): 209–212.

Bourjea, J., Frappier, J., Quillard, M., Ciccione, S., Roos, D., Hughes, G., and Grizel, H. 2007. Mayotte Island: Another important green turtle nesting site in the southwest Indian Ocean. *Endangered Species Research* 3: 273–282.

Bourjea, J., Nel, R., Jiddawi, N., Koonjul, M., and Bianchi, G. 2008. Sea turtle bycatch in the west Indian Ocean: Review, recommendations and research priorities. *Western Indian Ocean Journal of Marine Science* 7: 137–150.

Bourjea, J., Ciccione, S., Behamou, S., and Dalleau, M. 2013. Post nesting migration of green turtle (*Chelonia mydas*) in the western Indian Ocean. Indian Ocean Tuna Commission Working Party on Ecosystems and Bycatch (WPEB) IOTC-2013-WPEB09-25. https://www.iotc.org/documents/post-nesting-migration-green-turtle-chelonia-mydas-western-indian-ocean.

Bourjea, J., Mortimer, J. A., Garnier, J., Okemwa, G., Godley, B. J., Hughes, G., Mayeul, D., Claire, J., Ciccione, S., and Delphine, M. 2015. Population structure enhances perspectives on regional management of the western Indian Ocean green turtle. *Conservation Genetics* 16: 1069–1083.

Boyd, I. L., Lockyer, C., and Marsh, H. 1999. Reproduction in marine mammals. In: *Biology of Marine Mammals*, eds. J. E. Reynolds III and S. A. Rommel, pp. 218–286. Washington, DC: Smithsonian Institution.

Bozec, Y. M., Alvarez-Filip, L., and Mumby, P. J. 2015. The dynamics of architectural complexity on coral reefs under climate change. *Global Change Biology* 21: 223–235.

Bozetti, L. 2004. *Conus solangeae* (Gastropoda: Prosobranchia, Conidae) dal Madagascar Meridionale. *Malacologia Mostra Mondiale* 43: 13–14.

Branch, T. A., Stafford, K. M., Palacios, D. M., Allison, C., Bannister, J. L., et al. 2007. Past and present distribution, densities and movements of blue whales *Balaenoptera musculus* in the Southern Hemisphere and northern Indian Ocean. *Mammal Review* 37: 116–175.

Braulik, G. T., Findlay, K., Cerchio, S., and Baldwin, R. 2015. Assessment of the conservation status of the Indian Ocean humpback dolphin (*Sousa plumbea*) using the IUCN Red List Criteria. In *Humpback Dolphins (*Sousa *spp.): Their Current Status and Conservation*, Advances in Marine Biology, vol. 72, eds. T. Jefferson and B. Curry, pp. 119–141. Oxford: Academic Press.

Braulik, G. T., Findlay, K., Cerchio, S., Baldwin, R., and Perrin, W. 2017. *Sousa plumbea*. IUCN Red List of Threatened Species 2017: e.T82031633A82031644. http://dx.doi.org/10.2305/IUCN.UK.2017-3.RLTS.T82031633A82031644.en.

Braulik, G., Kasuga, M., and Majubwa, G. 2020. Local ecological knowledge demonstrates shifting baselines and the large-scale decline of sawfishes (Pristidae) in Tanzania. *African Journal of Marine Science* 42(1): 67–79.

Breuil, C., and Grima, D. 2014. *Baseline Report Madagascar*. Ebène: SmartFish Programme of the Indian Ocean Commission, Fisheries Management FAO component.

Brownfield, M. E., Schenk, C. J., Charpentier, R. R., Klett, T. R., Cook, T. A., Pollastro, R. M., and Tennyson, M. E. 2012. Assessment of undiscovered oil and gas resources of four East Africa geologic provinces. US Geological Survey Fact Sheet 2012-3039. https://pubs.usgs.gov/dds/dds-069/dds-069-gg/REPORTS/69_GG_CH_11.pdf.

Brunnschweiler, J. M., Baensch, H., Pierce, S. J., and Sims, D. W. 2009. Deep-diving behaviour of a whale shark *Rhincodon typus* during long-distance movement in the western Indian Ocean. *Journal of Fish Biology* 74: 706–714.

Bruton, M. N., ed. 1989. *Alternative Life-History Styles of Animals*. London: Kluwer Academic.

———. 2016. *Traditional Fishing Methods of Africa*. Cape Town: Cambridge University Press.

———. 2017. *The Annotated Old Fourlegs: The Updated Story of the Coelacanth*. Cape Town: Struik Nature.

———. 2018. *The Fishy Smiths: A Biography of JLB and Margaret Smith*. Cape Town: Penguin.

Bruton, M. N., and Armstrong, M. J. 1991. The demography of the coelacanth *Latimeria chalumnae*. *Environmental Biology of Fishes* 32: 301–311.

Bruton, M. N., and Coutouvidis, S. 1991. An inventory of all known specimens of the coelacanth, *Latimeria chalumnae*, with comments on trends in the catches. *Environmental Biology of Fishes* 32: 371–390.

Bruton, M. N., and Stobbs, R. E. 1991. The ecology and conservation of the coelacanth *Latimeria chalumnae*. *Environmental Biology of Fishes* 32: 313–339.

Bruton, M. N., Cabral, A.J.P., and Fricke, H. 1992. First capture of a coelacanth, *Latimeria chalumnae* (Pisces, Latimeriidae) off Mozambique. *South African Journal of Science* 88: 225–227.

Burke, L., Reytar, K., Spalding, M., and Perry, A. 2011. *Reefs at Risk Revisited*. Washington, DC: World Resources Institute.

C3 Madagascar and Indian Ocean Islands Programme. 2010a. *Rapid Assessment of Dugongs and Their Seagrass Habitat in Northern Madagascar: A Report Submitted to the Convention on Migratory Species of Wild Animals (CMS) Secretariat, Abu Dhabi*. C3 Technical Report Series no. 6. London: Community Centred Conservation.

———. 2010b. Study to confirm the existence or extinction of Dugongs in the waters of Mauritius and Rodrigues. Report submitted to the Convention on Migratory Species of Wild Animals (CMS) Secretariat. Ed. P.Z.R. Davis. https://www.cms.int/dugong/en/project/study-confirm-existence-or-extinction-dugongs-waters-mauritius.

C3. 2018. *Final Report to UNEP GEF Dugong and Seagrass Conservation Project, Abu Dhabi*. London: Community Centered Conservation.

Campbell, G. 2005. *An Economic History of Imperial Madagascar, 1750–1895: The Rise and Fall of an Island Empire*. Cambridge: Cambridge University Press.

Capietto, A., Escalle, L., Chavance, P., Dubroca, L., Delgado de Molina, A., Murua, H., Floch, L., Damiano, A., Rowat, D., and Merigot, B. 2014. Mortality of marine megafauna induced by fisheries: Insights from the whale shark, the world's largest fish. *Biological Conservation* 174: 147–151.

Carr, A. 1987. New perspectives on the pelagic stage of sea turtle development. *Conservation Biology* 1(2): 103–121.

Carrigan, A. D., and Puotinen, M. L. 2011. Assessing the potential for tropical cyclone induced sea surface cooling to reduce thermal stress on the world's coral reefs. *Geophysical Research Letters* 38: L23604.

Carroll, E. L., McGowen, M. R., McCarthy, M. L., Marx, F. G., Aguilar, N., et al. 2021. Speciation in the deep: Genomics and morphology reveal a new species of beaked whale *Mesoplodon eueu*. *Proceedings of the Royal Society of London B: Biological Sciences* 288: 20211213.

Carver, E. 2019. Can a national management plan halt Madagascar's shark decline? *Mongabay*, 11 Nov. 2019. https://news.mongabay.com/2019/11/can-a-national-management-plan-halt-madagascars-shark-decline/.

Castro, P. 2013. Brachyuran crabs (Crustacea, Brachyura: Crossotonotidae, Ethusidae Euryplacidae, Goneplacidae Latreilliidae, Palicidae, Tetraliidae, Trapeziidae), of the MAINBAZA, MIRIKY and ATIMO VATAE expeditions to the Mozambique Channel and Madagascar. In *Tropical Deep-Sea Benthos*, vol. 27, eds. S. T. Ahyong, T.-Y. Chan, L. Corbari, and P. K. L. Ng. *Mémoires du Muséum National d'Histoire Naturelle* 204: 437–466.

CBD (Convention on Biological Diversity). 2012. *Report of the Southern Indian Ocean Regional Workshop to Facilitate the Description of Ecologically or Biologically Significant Marine Areas*. UNEP/CBD/RW/EBSA/SIO/1/4, 26 June 2013. Montreal: Secretariat of the CBD.

Cecalupo, A., and Perugia, I. 2014. The Cerithiopsidae (Caenogastropoda: Triphoroidea) of South Madagascar (Indian Ocean). *Bollettino Malacologico* 50: 63–65.

Cerchio, S., and Yamada, T. 2018. Omura's Whale: *Balaenopteridae omurai*. In *Encyclopedia of Marine Mammals*, 3rd ed., eds. B. Würsig, J.G.M. Thewissen, and K. Kovacs, pp. 656–659. San Diego: Academic Press.

Cerchio, S., Findlay, K., Ersts, P., Minton, G., Bennet, D., et al. 2008. Initial assessment of exchange between breeding stocks C1 and C3 of humpback whales in the western Indian Ocean using photographic mark–recapture data, 2000–2006. Paper SC/60/SH33 presented to the International Whaling Commission Scientific Committee. Available from archive@groups.iwc.int.

Cerchio, S., Andrianarivelo, N., Razafindrakoto, Y., Mendez, M., and Rosenbaum, H. 2009a. Coastal dolphin hunting in the southwest of Madagascar: Status of populations, human impacts and conservation actions. Paper SC/61/SM15 presented to the International Whaling Commission Scientific Committee. Available from archive@groups.iwc.int.

Cerchio, S., Ersts, P., Pomilla, C., Loo, J., Razafindrakoto, Y., et al. 2009b. Updated estimates of abundance for humpback whale breeding stock C3 off Madagascar, 2000–2006. Paper SC/61/SH7 presented to the International Whaling Commission Scientific Committee. Available from archive@groups.iwc.int.

Cerchio, S., Andrianarivelo, N., and Andrianantenaina, B. 2012. Sightings, incidental by-catch, and hunting of dugongs (*Dugong dugon*) on the west coast of Madagascar, as inferred from interviews with local fishers. Unpublished report to the Convention on Migratory Species.

Cerchio, S., Andrianarivelo, N., Andrianantenaina, B., and Cordi, V. 2014a. Ecology, status, fisheries interactions and conservation of coastal Indian Ocean humpback dolphins and Indo-Pacific bottlenose dolphins on the west coast of Madagascar. Paper SC/65B/SM21 presented to the International Whaling Commission Scientific Committee. https://archive.iwc.int/?r=4851&k=d4eb046ada.

Cerchio, S., Strindberg, S., Collins, T., Bennett, C., and Rosenbaum, H. 2014b. Seismic surveys negatively affect humpback whale singing activity off Northern Angola. *PLoS One* 9(3): e86464.

Cerchio, S., Andrianarivelo, N., and Andrianantenaina, B. 2015a. Ecology and conservation status of Indian Ocean humpback dolphins (*Sousa plumbea*) in Madagascar. In *Humpback Dolphins (*Sousa *spp.): Their Current Status and Conservation*, Advances in Marine Biology, vol. 72, eds. T. Jefferson and B. Curry, pp. 163–199. Oxford: Academic Press.

Cerchio, S., Andrianantenaina, B., Lindsay, A., Rekdahl, M., Andrianarivelo, N., and Raoloarijao, T. 2015b. Omura's whales (*Balaenoptera omurai*) in northwest Madagascar: Ecology, behavior and conservation needs. *Royal Society Open Science* 2: 150301. doi:10.1098/rsos.150301.

Cerchio, S., Trudelle, L., Zerbini, A. N., Charrassin, J.-B., Geyer, Y., Mayer, F.-X., Andrianarivelo, N., Jung, J. L., Adam, O., and Rosenbaum, H. C. 2016. Satellite telemetry of humpback whales off Madagascar reveals long range movements of individuals in the southwest Indian Ocean during the breeding season. *Marine Ecology Progress Series* 562: 193–209. doi:10.3354/meps11951.

Cerchio, S., Rasoloarijao, T., and Cholewiak, D. 2018a. Acoustic monitoring of blue whales (*Balaenoptera musculus*) and other baleen whales in the Mozambique Channel off the northwest coast of Madagascar. Paper SC/67B/SH/14 presented to the International Whaling Commission Scientific Committee. https://archive.iwc.int/?r=9333&k=ba10d84e2a.

Cerchio, S., Andrianantenaina, B., Zerbini, A., Pendleton, D., Rasoloarijao, T., and Cholewiak, D. 2018b. Residency, feeding ecology, local movements and potential isolation of the Madagascar Omura's whale (*Balaenoptera omurai*) population. Paper SC/67B/NH/09 presented to the International Whaling Commission Scientific Committee. https://archive.iwc.int /pages/view.php?search=%21collection29547+ &k=&modal=&display=list&order_by=title&offset=0&per_page=240&archive= &sort=DESC&restypes=&recentdaylimit=&foredit=&ref=9468.

Cerchio, S., Yamada, T. K., and Brownell, R. L., Jr. 2019. Global distribution of Omura's whales (*Balaenoptera omurai*) and assessment of range-wide threats. *Frontiers in Marine Science* 6: 67. doi:10.3389/fmars.2019.00067.

Cerchio, S., Willson, A., Leroy, E., Muirhead, C., Al Harthi, S., et al. 2020. A new blue whale song-type described for the Arabian Sea and western Indian Ocean. *Endangered Species Research* 43: 495–515.

Cétamada. 2021. Projets scientifiques. Accessed 3 Aug. 2021. https://www.cetamada.org/projet-scientifique.

Champetier de Ribes, G., Rasolofonirina, R., Ranaivson, G., Razafimahefa, N., Rakotoson, J., and Rabeson, D. 1997. Intoxications par animaux marins vénéneux à Madagascar (ichtyosarcotoxisme et chélonitoxisme): Données épidémiologiques récentes. Actes du Congrès SPE de l'Ile Maurice, Nov. 1996. Manuscript MR1996/022.

Champetier de Ribes, G., Ranaivoson, G., Ravanindrina, N., Rakotonjanabelo, A., Rasolofonirina, N., Roux, J., and Yasumoto, T. 1998. Un problème de santé réémergent à Madagascar: Les intoxications collectives par consommation d'animaux marins; Aspects épidémiologiques, cliniques et toxicologiques des épisodes de janvier 1993 à janvier 1998. *Archives de l'Institut Pasteur de Madagascar* 64(1–2): 71–76.

Champetier de Ribes, G., Ramarokoto, S., Rabearintsoa, S., Robinson, R., Ranaivoson, G., Rakotonjanabel, L. A., and Rabeson, D. 1999. Intoxications par consommation d'animaux marins à Madagascar. *Cahiers Santé* 9: 235–241.

Chaperon, P., Danloux, J., and Ferry, L. 2005. *Fleuves et rivières de Madagascar*. Paris: ORSTOM.

Chasse, C. 1962. Remarques sur la morphologie et la bionomie des herbiers de monocotylédones marines tropicales de la province de Tuléar (Madagascar). *Annales de l'Université de Madagascar*, série *Science de la Nature et Mathématiques* 1: 237–248.

Chatenoux, B., and Peduzzi, P. 2007. Impacts from the 2004 Indian tsunami: Analyzing the potential protecting role of environmental features. *Natural Hazards* 40: 289–304.

Chattopadhyay, N. R., Chetia, A., Machahary, K. Q., and Dupak, O. 2018. Assessment of conservation measures for olive ridley sea turtle (*Lepidochelys olivacea*) along Rushikulya Rookery, Ganjam Disrict, Odisha, India. *International Journal of Marine Biology and Research* 3(1): 1–9.

Chen, C.-T., Liu, K.-M., and Joung, S.-J. 1997. Preliminary report on Taiwan's whale shark fishery. *TRAFFIC Bulletin* 17: 53–57.

Cholewiak, D., Clark, C. W., Ponirakis, D., Frankel, A., Hatch, L. T., Risch, D., Stanistreet, J. E., Thompson, M., Vu, E., and Van Parijs, S. M. 2018. Communicating amidst the noise: Modeling the aggregate influence of ambient and vessel noise on baleen whale communication space in a national marine sanctuary. *Endangered Species Research* 36: 59–75.

CITES (Convention on International Trade in Endangered Species of Wild Fauna and Flora). 2000. Consideration of proposals for amendment of Appendices I and II. Proposal 11.26. https://www.cites.org/sites/default/files/eng/cop/11/prop/26.pdf.

Clapham, P. J. 1996. The social and reproductive biology of humpback whales: An ecological perspective. *Mammal Review* 26: 27–49.

Clapham, P. J., Young, S. B., and Brownell, R. L., Jr. 1999. Baleen whales: Conservation issues and the status of the most endangered populations. *Mammal Review* 29: 35–60.

Clark, C. W., Ellison, W. T., Southall, B. L., Hatch, L. T., Van Parijs, S. M., Frankel, A., and Ponirakis, D. 2009. Acoustic masking in marine ecosystems: Intuitions, analysis, and implications. *Marine Ecology Progress Series* 395: 201–222.

Clausade, M., Gravier, N., Picard, J., Pichon, M., Roman, M.-L., Thomassin, B., Vasseur, P., Vivien, M., and Weydert, P. 1971. Coral reef morphology in the vicinity of Tuléar (Madagascar): Contribution to a coral reef terminology. *Téthys*, suppl. 2: 1–76.

Clausen, A., Rakotondrazafy, H., Ralison, H. O., and Andrjamanalina, A. 2010. *Mangrove Ecosystems in Western Madagascar: An Analysis of Vulnerability to Climate Change*. Antananarivo: WWF.

Cliff, G., Compagno, L.J.V., Smale, M. J., van der Elst, R. P., and Wintner, S. P. 2000. First records of white sharks, *Carcharodon carcharias*, from Mauritius, Zanzibar, Madagascar and Kenya. *South African Journal of Science* 96: 365–367.

Cloutier, R. 1991. Patterns, trends, and rates of evolution within the Actinistia. *Environmental Biology of Fishes* 32: 23–58.

Cloutier, R., and Forey, P. L. 1991. Diversity of extinct and living actinistian fishes (Sarcopterygii). *Environmental Biology of Fishes* 32: 59–74.

CNGIZC (Comité National de la Gestion Intégrée des Zones Côtières). 2019. *Plan d'actions national pour la gestion intégrée des zones côtieres (PAN-GIZC): Période 2019–2023*. Antananarivo: Primature.

CNRE (Centre National de Recherches sur l'Environnement), CNRO (Centre National de Recherches Océanographiques), and CNRIT (Centre National de Recherches Industrielle et Technologique). 1999. Identification des caractéristiques des observatoires et établissement de plan local de prévention et réduction des pollutions et dégradations de la région de Nosy Be. Report prepared for the Office National pour l'Environnement.

Cockcroft, V. G. 1993. *A Preliminary Assessment of the Status of Madagascar Coastal Resources, with Special Reference to Marine Mammals and Reptiles*. Final report for United Nations Environment Programme, South African Department of Foreign Affairs, and African Wildlife. Nairobi: United Nations Environment Programme.

Cockroft, V., and Young, D. D. 1998. *An Investigation of the Status of Coastal Marine Resources along the West Coast of Madagascar*. Report prepared for WWF Madagascar. Homewood: Centre for Dolphin Studies.

Collins, C., Hermes, J. C., Roman, R. E., and Reason, C.J.C. 2016. First dedicated hydrographic survey of the Comoros Basin. *Oceans* 121(2): 1291–1305.

Collins, T., Moore, K., Cerchio, S., McAloose, D., Harry, C. T., Calle, P., Razafindrakoto, Y., Randriamanantsoa, B., McClave, C., and Rosenbaum, H. 2009. Madagascar melon-headed whale (*Peponocephala electra*) mass stranding event of May/June 2008: Final report—part I; Site description and mass stranding timeline. Wildlife Conservation Society and International Fund for Animal Welfare. https://iwc.int/private/downloads/PbLfG2TzkU6HfAk9--cmLw/WCS_IFAW_FINAL%20REPORT.pdf.

Colman, J. G. 1997. A review of the biology and ecology of the whale shark. *Journal of Fish Biology* 51: 1219–1234.

Committee on Taxonomy. 2020. List of marine mammal species and subspecies. Society for Marine Mammalogy, accessed 5 Aug. 2020. https://marinemammalscience.org/science-and-publications/list-marine-mammal-species-subspecies/.

Compagno, L.J.V. 1984a. *FAO Species Catalogue*. Vol. 4, *Sharks of the World: An Annotated and Illustrated Catalogue of Shark Species Known to Date*. Pt. 1, *Hexanchiformes to Lamniformes*. FAO Fisheries Synopsis, no. 125, vol. 4, pt. 1. Rome: Food and Agriculture Organization of the United Nations.

———. 1984b. *FAO Species Catalogue*. Vol. 4, *Sharks of the World: An Annotated and Illustrated Catalogue of Shark Species Known to Date*. Pt. 2, *Charcharhiniformes*. FAO Fisheries Synopsis, no. 125, vol. 4, pt. 2. Rome: Food and Agriculture Organization of the United Nations.

———. 1990. Alternative life-history styles of cartilaginous fishes in time and space. *Environmental Biology of Fishes* 28: 33–75.

Cooke, A. J. 1997. Survey of elasmobranch fisheries and trade in Madagascar. In *The Trade in Sharks and Shark Products in the Western Indian and Southeast Atlantic Oceans*, eds. N. T. Marshall and R. Barnett, pp. 101–130. Nairobi: TRAFFIC East/Southern Africa.

Cooke, A. J., and Brand, J. 2012. *Madagascar: A Guide to Marine Biodiversity*. Antananarivo: Wildlife Conservation Society.

Cooke, A. J., and COUT (Cellule des Océanographes de l'Université de Toliara). 1994. Toliara Coral Reef Expedition, Madagascar 1993: Final report. Dec. 1994.

Cooke, A. J., Ratomahenina, O., Ranaivoson, E., and Razafindrainibe, H. 2000. Madagascar. In *Seas at the Millennium: An Environmental Evaluation*, ed. C. Sheppard, pp. 113–131. Oxford: Pergamon.

Cooke, A. [J.], Lutjeharms, J.R.E., and Vasseur, P. 2003a. Marine and coastal ecosystems. In *The Natural History of Madagascar*, eds. S. M. Goodman and J. P. Benstead, pp. 179–209. Chicago: University of Chicago Press.

Cooke, A. [J.], Jonahson, M., Doukakis, P., Smale, M., and du Feu, T. 2003b. Sharks, shark fisheries and shark fin trade in Madagascar: Review and analysis, with suggestions for action. In *Proceedings of a Workshop on Shrimp and Other Fisheries in Madagascar, November 2002*. Antananarivo: CITE.

Cooke, A. J., Bruton, M. N., and Ravololoharinjara, M. 2021. Coelacanth discoveries in Madagascar, with recommendations on research and conservation. *South African Journal of Science* 117(3/4): article 8541. https://doi.org/10.17159/sajs.2021/8541.

Cooke, J. G. 2018a. *Balaenoptera musculus* ssp. *intermedia*. IUCN Red List of Threatened Species 2018: e.T41713A50226962. http://dx.doi.org/10.2305/IUCN.UK.2018-2.RLTS.T41713A50226962.en.

———. 2018b. *Balaenoptera musculus*. IUCN Red List of Threatened Species 2018: e.T2477A50226195. http://dx.doi.org/10.2305/IUCN.UK.2018–2.RLTS.T2477A50226195.en.

Cooke, J. G., and Brownell, R. L., Jr. 2019. *Balaenoptera omurai* (amended version of 2018 assessment). IUCN Red List of Threatened Species 2019: e.T136623A144790120. https://dx.doi.org/10.2305/IUCN.UK.2019–1.RLTS.T136623A144790120.en.

Corkeron, P. J., and Connor, R. C. 1999. Why do baleen whales migrate? *Marine Mammal Science* 15(4): 1228–1245.

Costa, A., Motta, H., Pereira, M.A.M., Videira, E.J.S., Louro, C.M.M., and João, J. 2007. Marine turtles in Mozambique: Towards an effective conservation and management program. *Marine Turtle Newsletter* 117: 1–3.

Côté-Laurin, M. C., Benbow, S.L.P., and Erzini, K. 2017. The short-term impacts of a cyclone on seagrass communities in southwest Madagascar. *Continental Shelf Research* 138: 132–141.

Cripps, G. 2010. *Feasibility Study on the Protection and Management of the Barren Isles Ecosystem, Madagascar*. Blue Ventures Conservation Report (2010), for WWF and the Réseau Interdisciplinaire pour une Gestion Durable de la Biodiversité Marine: Environnemental et social autour des tortues marines dans le sud-ouest de l'Océan Indien. London: Blue Ventures.

Cripps, G., and Gardner, C. J. 2016. Human migration and marine protected areas: Insights from Vezo fishers in Madagascar. *Geoforum* 74: 49–62.

Cripps, G., Harris, A., Humber, F., Harding, S., and Thomas, T. 2015. A preliminary value chain analysis of shark fisheries in Madagascar. Report to the Indian Ocean Commission SF/2015/34:1–82. https://blueventures.org/publication/a-preliminary-value-chain-analysis-of-shark-fisheries-in-madagascar/.

Crochelet, E., Roberts, J., Lagabrielle, E., Obura, D. O., and Petit, M. 2016. A model-based assessment of reef larvae dispersal in the western Indian Ocean reveals regional connectivity patterns: Potential implications for conservation policies. *Regional Studies in Marine Science* 7: 159–167.

Crosnier, A. 1973. *Résultats des chalutages effectués lors des sorties 5-73 et 6-73 du "Vauban" du 26 février au 4 mars au large de Tuléar et Fort-Dauphin et du 27 au 29 mars au large de Diégo-Suarez*. Nosy Be: ORSTOM.

Crosnier, A., and Jouannic, C. 1974. *Note d'information sur les prospections de la pente continentale malgache effectuées par le N.O. Vauban: Bathymétrie-sédimentologie-pêche au chalut*. Nosy Be: ORSTOM.

Cunningham, E., Davis, P., and Leandre, I. 2011. Can dugong taboos in northern Madagascar contribute to their effective conservation? *Sirenews* 55: 12–13.

Dalleau, M., Kramer Schadt, S., Gangat, Y., Bourjea, J., Lajoie, G., and Grimm, V. 2019. Modelling the emergence of migratory corridors and foraging hot spots of the green sea turtle. *Ecology and Evolution* 9: 10317–10342.

Damien, J., and Loncle, J. 2019. *Projet Récif Ile Ste Marie (PRISM): Rapport Annuel 2018–2019*. Antananarivo: Cetamada.

Dars, C., Dabin, W., Demaret, F., Dorémus, G., Meheust, E., Mendez-Fernandez, P., Peltier, H., Spitz, J., and Van Canneyt, O. 2018. Les échouages de mammifères marins sur le littoral français en 2017. Rapport scientifique de l'Observatoire Pelagis, La Rochelle Université, et Centre National de la Recherche Scientifique.

Das, K., Malarvannan, G., Dirtu, A., Dulau, V., Dumont, M., Lepoint, G., Mongin, P., and Covaci, A. 2017. Linking pollutant exposure of humpback whales breeding in the Indian Ocean to the feeding habitats and feeding areas off Antarctica. *Environmental Pollution* 220(B): 1090–1099.

Dawbin, W. H. 1966. The seasonal migratory cycle of humpback whales. In *Whales, Dolphins, and Porpoises*, ed. K. S. Norris, pp. 145–171. Berkeley: University of California Press.

de la Parra Venegas, R., Hueter, R., Cano, J. G., Tyminski, J., Remolina, J. G., Maslanka, M., Ormos, A., Weigt, L., Carlson, B., and Dove, A. 2011. An unprecedented aggregation of whale sharks, *Rhincodon typus*, in Mexican coastal waters of the Caribbean Sea. *PLoS One* 6: e18994.

Decary, R. 1950. *La faune malgache*. Paris: Payot.

Dent, F., and Clarke, S. 2015. State of the global market for shark products. FAO Fisheries and Aquaculture Technical Paper no. 590. Rome: Food and Agriculture Organization of the United Nations. http://www.fao.org/3/i4795e/i4795e.pdf.

De Vos, L., and Oyugi, D. 2002. First capture of a coelacanth, *Latimeria chalumnae* Smith, 1939 (Pisces: Latimeriidae) off Kenya. *South African Journal of Science* 98: 345–347.

Diamant, S., Rohner, C. A., Kiszka, J. J., D'Echon, A. G., D'Echon, T. G., Sourisseau, E., and Pierce, S. J. 2018. Movements and habitat use of satellite-tagged whale sharks off western Madagascar. *Endangered Species Research* 36: 49–58.

Di Carlo, G., and Tombolahy, M. 2011. Seagrasses and algae of north-eastern Madagascar. In A rapid marine biodiversity assessment of the coral reefs of northeast Madagascar, eds. D. Obura, G. Di Carlo, A. Rabearisoa, and T. Oliver. *RAP Bulletin of Biological Assessment* 61: 44–52.

Dockerty, T. 1992. *International Trade in Shark Fins*. Cambridge, UK: Wildlife Trade Monitoring Unit, World Conservation Monitoring Centre.

Domning, D. P., and Gingerich, P. D. 1994. *Protosiren smithae*, new species (Mammalia, Sirenia), from the late Middle Eocene of Wadi Hitan, Egypt. *Contributions of the Museum of Paleontology, University of Michigan* 29(3): 69–87.

Dorémus, G., Van Canneyt, O., Pusineri, C., Samaran, F., and Le Corre, M. 2009. Distribution et abondance des oiseaux et mammifères marins tropicaux (programme NAOMI), rapport de campagne de la mission "Eparse" 2009. Centre de Recherche sur ses Mammifères Marins, Université de la Rochelle.

Doughty, C. E., Roman, J., Faurby, S., Wolf, A., Haque, A., Bakker, E. S., Malhi, Y., Dunning, J. B., and Svenning, J. C. 2016. Global nutrient transport in a world of giants. *Proceedings of the National Academy of Sciences of the USA* 113: 868–873.

Doukakis, P., and Jonahson, M. 2003. Final report to the Wildlife Conservation Society: Fisheries of Antongil Bay, Madagascar (Madagascar Seascape Program). Unpublished report.

Doukakis, P., Jonahson, M., Ramahery, V., de Dieu Randriamanantsoa, B. J., and Harding, S. 2007. Traditional fisheries of Antongil Bay, Madagascar. *Western Indian Ocean Journal of Marine Science* 6(2): 175–181.

Doukakis, P., Hanner, R., Shivji, M., Bartholomew, C., Chapman, D., Wong, E., and Amato, G. 2011. Applying genetic techniques to study remote shark fisheries in northeastern Madagascar. *Mitochondrial DNA* 22(S1): 15–20.

Doumenge, F.A.J.-M. 1998. Tuna longliners fisheries and strategy of eastern fishing countries in the Indian Ocean. In *Tuna Prospects and Strategies for the Indian Ocean*, eds. P. Cayré and J.-Y. Le Gall, pp. 237–272. Paris: ORSTOM.

Dréo, R., Bouffaut, L., Leroy, E., Barruol, G., and Samaran, F. 2019. Baleen whale distribution and seasonal occurrence revealed by an ocean bottom seismometer network in the western Indian Ocean. *Deep Sea Research Part II: Topical Studies in Oceanography* 161: 132–144.

du Feu, T. A. 1998. Fisheries statistics for the large meshed gill net fishery: North west Madagascar. Report prepared for the Deutsche Gesellschaft für Technische Zusammenarbeit (GTZ) fisheries project, Nosy Be.

Duffy, C.A.J. 2002. Distribution, seasonality, lengths, and feeding behaviour of whale sharks (*Rhincodon typus*) observed in New Zealand waters. *New Zealand Journal of Marine and Freshwater Research* 36: 565–570.

Dulau, V., Pinet, P., Geyer, Y., Fayan, J., Mongin, P., Cottarel, G., Zerbini, A., and Cerchio, S. 2017. Continuous movement behavior of humpback whales during the breeding season in the southwest Indian Ocean: On the road again! *Movement Ecology* 5: 11. doi:10.1186/s40462-017-0101-5.

Dulau-Drouot, V., Boucaud, V., Fayan, J., and Mouysset, L. 2012. Occurrence and residency patterns of humpback whales off Réunion Island during 2004–2008. *Journal of Cetacean Research and Management* 12: 255–263.

Dulvy, N. K., Davidson, L.N.K., Kyne, P. M., Simpfendorfer, C. A., Harrison, L. R., Carlson, J. K., and Fordham, S. V. 2016. Ghosts of the coast: Global extinction risk and conservation of sawfishes. *Aquatic Conservation: Marine and Freshwater Ecosystems* 26: 134–153.

Dulvy, N. K., Robinson, D. P., Pierce, S. J., Norman, B., Fernando, D., Khan, M., Romanov, E., and Brown, J. 2017. Whale shark *Rhincodon typus* Smith, 1828. In *The Conservation Status of Sharks, Rays, and Chimaeras in the Arabian Sea and Adjacent Waters*, eds. R. W. Jabado, P. M. Kyne, R. A. Pollom, D. A. Ebert, C. A. Simpfendorfer, G. M. Ralph, and N. K. Dulvy, pp. 108–109. Abu Dhabi: Environment Agency.

Durbin, J. 1994. Integrating conservation and development: The role of local people in the maintenance of protected areas in Madagascar. PhD thesis, Durrell Institute of Conservation and Ecology, University of Kent.

Durbin, J., and Rakotoniaina, L.-J. 1991. *Project Anganoka: Local People and Conservation in the Soalala Region; Report of an Eight-Week Field Study from 24th June to 19th August 1991*. Antananarivo: Jersey Wildlife Conservation Trust.

Ebert, D. A. 2013. Deep-sea cartilaginous fishes of the Indian Ocean. *FAO Species Catalogue for Fishery Purposes*. Vol. 8. Pt. 1. Rome: Food and Agriculture Organization of the United Nations.

Eckrich, C. E., and Holmquist, J. G. 2000. Trampling in a seagrass assemblage: Direct effects, response of associated fauna, and the role of substrate characteristics. *Marine Ecology Progress Series* 201: 199–209.

EDGE. 2020. EDGE lists. 11 Sept. 2020. https://www.edgeofexistence.org/edge-lists/.

Eeckhaut, I., Lavitra, T., Rasoforirina, R., Rabenevanana, M.-W., Gildas, P., and Jangoux, M. 2008. "Madagascar Holothurie" (MH S.A.), the first trade company based on sea cucumber aquaculture in Madagascar. *SPC Bêche-de-Mer Information Bulletin* 28: 22–23.

Ellison, A. M., Farnsworth, E. J., and Merkt, R. E. 2004. Origins of mangrove ecosystems and the mangrove biodiversity anomaly. *Global Ecology and Biogeography*: 8: 95–115. https://doi.org/10.1046/j.1466-822X.1999.00126.x.

Erdmann, M. V. 1999. An account of the first living coelacanth known to scientists from Indonesian waters. *Environmental Biology of Fishes* 54: 439–443.

Ersts, P. J., and Rosenbaum, H. C. 2003. Habitat preference reflects social organization of humpback whales (*Megaptera novaeangliae*) on a wintering ground. *Journal of Zoology* 260: 337–345.

Ersts, P. J., Pomilla, C., Kiszka, J., Cerchio, S., Rosenbaum, H. C., Vely, M., Razafindrakoto, Y., Loo, J. A., Leslie, M. S., and Avolio, M. 2011a. Observations of individual humpback whales utilizing multiple migratory destinations in the southwestern Indian Ocean. *African Journal of Marine Science* 33(2): 333–338.

Ersts, P. J., Kiszka, J., Vély, M., and Rosenbaum, H. C. 2011b. Density, group composition, and encounter rates of humpback whales (*Megaptera novaeangliae*) in the eastern Comoro archipelago (C2). In Humpback whales: Status in the Southern Hemisphere, eds. N. Gales, J. L. Bannister, K. Findlay, A. Zerbini, and G. P. Donovan. *Journal of Cetacean Research and Management*, special issue 3: 175–182.

Escalle, L., Pennino, M. G., Gaertner, D., Chavance, P., Delgado de Molina, A., Demarcq, H., Romanov, E., and Merigot, B. 2016. Environmental factors and megafauna spatio-temporal co-occurrence with purse-seine fisheries. *Fisheries Oceanography* 25: 433–447.

Esteban, N., Unsworth, R.K.F., Gourlay, J.B.Q., and Hays, G. C. 2018. The discovery of deep-water seagrass meadows in a pristine Indian Ocean wilderness revealed by tracking green turtles. *Marine Pollution Bulletin* 134: 99–105.

Estes, J. A., Heithaus, M., McCauley, D. J., Rasher, D. B., and Worm, B. 2016. Megafaunal impacts on structure and function of ocean ecosystems. *Annual Review of Environment and Resources* 41: 83–116.

EUCARE. 2001. *Coral Awareness and Research Expedition, Madagascar: Final Report*. Edinburgh: University of Edinburgh.

Evans, A. J., Steer, M. D., and Belle, E.M.S. 2011. The Alcyonacea (soft corals and sea fans) of Antsiranana Bay, northern Madagascar. *Madagascar Conservation and Development* 6(1): 29–36.

Evely, A. C., Pinard, M., Reed, M. S., and Fazey, I. 2011. High levels of participation in conservation projects enhance learning. *Conservation Letters* 4(2): 116–126.

Everett, B. I., Cliff, G., Dudley, S.F.J., Wintner, S. P., and van der Elst, R. P. 2015. Do sawfish *Pristis* spp. represent South Africa's first local extirpation of marine elasmobranchs in the modern era? *African Journal of Marine Science* 37(2): 275–284.

Fairbrother, J. 2020. *Frontier-Madagascar: Madagascar Marine Conservation Research; The Extent that Hard Coral Cover Has Declined in Nosy Be, Madagascar, between 2011 and 2019*. Phase 201 Science Report. Jan.–Mar. 2020. London: Frontier.

FAO (Food and Agriculture Organization of the United Nations). 1998. Aperçu sur les zones de pêche traditionnelle maritime dans la Région de Toliara. Ministère de la Pêche et des Ressources Halieutiques, Programme Sectoriel Pêche. PNUD/ FAO/MAG/92/004-DT/10/98.

———. 2007. *The World's Mangroves 1980–2005*. FAO Forestry Paper 153. Rome: FAO.

———. 2020. *Report of the Ninth Session of the Scientific Committee of the Southwest Indian Ocean Fisheries Commission. Réunion, France, 16–19 July 2019/Rapport de la neuvième session du Comité Scientifique de la Commission des Pêches pour le sud-ouest de l'Océan Indien. La Réunion, France, 16–19 juillet 2019*. FAO Fisheries and Aquaculture Report FAO Fisheries and Aquaculture Report/FAO Rapport sur les pêches et l'aquaculture No. 1294. Maputo: FAO. https://doi.org/10.4060/ca7501b.

———. 2021. Global production statistics 1950–2019. Accessed 3 August 2021. http://www.fao.org/fishery/statistics/global-production/query/fr.

Faria, M. A., and Rakotoharimalala, S. 2012. A preliminary review of skin conditions and external anatomy anomalies from humpback whales, *Megaptera novaeangliae*, photographed in the Ste Marie Channel, Ste Marie Island, Madagascar. Technical Report. https://www.researchgate.net/publication/311584811.

Faria, M. A., DeWeerdt, J., Pace, F., and Mayer, F.-X. 2013. Observation of a humpback whale (*Megaptera novaeangliae*) birth in the coastal waters of Sainte Marie Island, Madagascar. *Aquatic Mammals* 39(3): 296–305.

Faria, V. V., McDavitt, M. T., Charvet, P., Wiley, T.R.R., Simpfendorfer, C. A., and Naylor, G.J.P. 2013. Species delineation and global population structure of Critically Endangered sawfishes (Pristidae). *Zoological Journal of the Linnean Society* 167: 136–164.

———. 2014. Taxonomy: How many sawfish species are there? In *Sawfish: A Global Strategy for Conservation*, eds. L. Harrison and N. K. Dulvy, pp. 22–25. Vancouver: IUCN Species Survival Commission's Shark Specialist Group.

Fauvelot, C., Zuccon, D., Borsa, P., Grulois, D., Magalon, H., Riquet, F., Andréfouët, S., and Berumen, M. J. 2020. Phylogeographical patterns and a cryptic species provide new insights into western Indian Ocean giant clams phylogenetic relationships and colonization history. *Journal of Biogeography* 47(5): 1086–1105.

Fennessy, S., Mohamed, A., Kaunda-Ara, B., Mkare, T., Ombuki, J., et al. 2009. *Regional Data Gap-Analysis for Component 3 (Demersal Fisheries) for SWIOFP*. Washington, DC: South West Indian Ocean Fisheries Project.

Fennessy, S., Krakstad, J. O., Groeneveld, J., Bianchi, G., and Everett, B. 2017. Demersal resources based on bottom trawl and other sampling methods. In *The RV* Dr Fridtjof Nansen *in the Western Indian Ocean: Voyages of Marine Research and Capacity Development; 1975–2016*, eds. J. C. Groeneveld and K. A. Koranteng, pp. 101–124. Rome: Food and Agriculture Organization of the United Nations.

Feutry, P., Kyne, P. M., Pillans, R. D., Chen, X., Marthick, J. R., Morgan, D. L., and Grewe, P. M. 2015. Whole mitogenome sequencing refines population structure of the Critically Endangered sawfish *Pristis pristis*. *Marine Ecology Progress Series* 533: 237–244.

Findlay, K. P. 2001. A review of humpback whale catches by modern whaling operations in the Southern Hemisphere. *Memoirs of the Queensland Museum* 47(2): 411–420.

Findlay, K. P, Cockcroft, V. G., and Guissamulo, A. T. 2011a. Dugong abundance and distribution in the Bazaruto archipelago, Mozambique. *African Journal of Marine Science* 33(3): 441–452.

Findlay, K. P., Best, P. B., and Meyer, M. 2011b. Migrations of humpback whales past Cape Vidal, South Africa, and an estimate of the population increase rate (1998–2002). *African Journal of Marine Science* 33(3): 375–392.

Findlay, K. P., Meyer, M., Elwen, S., Kotze, D., Johnson, R., et al. 2011c. Distribution and abundance of humpback whales, *Megaptera novaeangliae*, off the coast of Mozambique, 2003. In Humpback whales: Status in the Southern Hemisphere, eds. N. Gales, J. L. Bannister, K. Findlay, A. Zerbini, and G. P. Donovan. *Journal of Cetacean Research and Management*, special issue 3: 163–174.

Fishery Progress Organization. 2020. Southwest Madagascar octopus: Diving and gleaning. Fishery Improvement Project, Progress Tracking Database and Tools. Accessed 23 Aug. 2020. https://fisheryprogress.org/fip-profile/southwest-madagascar-octopus-diving-gleaning.

Fleming, A., and Jackson, J. 2011. Global review of humpback whales (*Megaptera novaeangliae*). National Oceanic and Atmospheric Administration Technical Memorandum NMFS. NOAA-TM-NMFS-SWFSC-474. https://swfsc-publications.fisheries.noaa.gov/publications/TM/SWFSC/NOAA-TM-NMFS-SWFSC-474.pdf.

Fontes, J., McGinty, N., Machete, M., and Afonso, P. 2020. Whale shark–tuna associations, insights from a small pole-and-line fishery from the mid-north Atlantic. *Fisheries Research* 229: 105598.

Forey, P. L. 1991. *Latimeria chalumnae* and its pedigree. *Environmental Biology of Fishes* 32: 75–97.

Fossette, S., Heide-Jørgensen, M. P., Jensen, M. V., Kiszka, J., Bérubé, M., Bertrand, N., and Vély, M. 2014. Humpback whale (*Megaptera novaeangliae*) post breeding dispersal and southward migration in the western Indian Ocean. *Journal of Experimental Marine Biology and Ecology* 450: 6–14.

Fourmanoir, P. 1961. Requins de la côte ouest de Madagascar. *Mémoires de l'Institut Scientifique de Madagascar*, série F, *Océanographie* 4: 1–81.

———. 1963a. Distribution écologique des poissons de récifs coralliens et d'herbiers de la côte ouest de Madagascar. *Revue d'Ecologie, la Terre et la Vie* 1: 81–100.

———. 1963b. Raies et requins-scie de la côte ouest de Madagascar (ordre des Batoidei). *Cahiers de l'ORSTOM*, série *Océanographie*, no. 6: 33–58.

Fowler, S. L., Cavanagh, R. D., Camhi, M., Burgess, G. H., Caillet, G. M., Fordham, S. V., Simpfendorfer, C. A., and Musick, J. A. 2005. *Sharks, Rays and Chimaeras: The Status of the Chondrichthyan Fishes*. Status Survey. IUCN/SSC Shark Specialist Group. Gland: IUCN.

Fox, S., Foisy, I., de la Parra Venegas, R., Galván Pastoriza, B. E., Graham, R. T., Hoffmayer, E. R., Holmberg, J., and Pierce, S. J. 2013. Population structure and residency of whale sharks *Rhincodon typus* at Utila, Bay Islands, Honduras. *Journal of Fish Biology* 83: 574–587.

Frazier, J. 1975. Marine turtles in the western Indian Ocean. *Oryx* 13(2): 164–175.

———. 1980. Exploitation of marine turtles in the Indian Ocean. *Human Ecology* 8(4): 329–370.

Fricke, H. 1997. Living coelacanths: Values, eco-ethics and human responsibility. *Marine Ecology Progress Series* 161: 1–15.

———. 2007. *Die jagt nach dem Quastenflosser, der Fisch, der aus der Urzeit kam*. Munich: Verlag C. H. Beck.

Fricke, H., and Hissmann, K. 1990. Natural habitat of coelacanths. *Nature* 346: 323–324.

———. 1994. Home-range and migrations of the living coelacanth *Latimeria chalumnae*. *Marine Biology* 120: 171–180.

———. 2000. Feeding ecology and evolutionary survival of the living coelacanth *Latimeria chalumnae*. *Marine Biology* 136: 379–386.
Fricke, H., and Plante, R. 1988. Habitat requirements of the living coelacanth *Latimeria chalumnae* at Grande Comore, Indian Ocean. *Die Naturwissenschaften* 75: 149–151.
Fricke, H., Hissmann, K., Schauer, J., Reinicke, O., Kasang, L., and Plante, R. 1991. Habitat and population size of the coelacanth *Latimeria chalumnae* at Grande Comore. *Environmental Biology of Fishes* 32: 287–300.
Fricke, H., Hissmann, K., Schauer, J., and Plante, R. 1995. Yet more danger for coelacanths. *Nature* 374: 314.
Fricke, R., Mahafina, J., Behivoke, F., Jaonalison, H., Léopold, M., and Ponton, D. 2018. Annotated checklist of the fishes of Madagascar, southwestern Indian Ocean, with 158 new records. *FishTaxa* 3(1): 1–432.
Frontier. 2019a. *Madagascar Marine Conservation Research Programme: Nosy Be, Madagascar*. MGM Phase 193 Science Report (June–Sept. 2019). London: Frontier.
———. 2019b. *Madagascar Marine Conservation Research Programme: Nosy Be, Madagascar*. MGM Phase 192 Science Report (Mar.–June 2019). London: Frontier.
Frontier-Madagascar. 2003. *Mangrove Biodiversity Survey South of the Onilahy River: Lavadanora, Lovokampy and Mangoro Systems*. Research Report 9. Toliara: Frontier Madagascar–University of Toliara, Institut Halieutique et des Sciences Marines.
Gabrié, C., Vasseur, P., Maharavo, J., Randriamiarana, H., and Mara, E. 2000. The coral reefs of Madagascar. In *Coral Reefs of the West Indian Ocean*, eds. T. R. McClanahan, D. O. Obura, and C.R.C. Sheppard, pp. 441–444. New York: Oxford University Press.
Gadenne, H., and Saloma, A. 2017. Observations des oiseaux et des mammifères marins: Campagne scientifique Walters Shoal. Unpublished report. Fonds Français pour l'Environnement Mondial.
Gambell, R., Best, P. B., and Rice, D. W. 1974. Report on the international Indian Ocean whale marking cruise. Paper SC/26/37 presented to the International Whaling Commission Scientific Committee. Available from archive@groups.iwc.int.
Gamoyo, M., Obura, D. O., and Reason, C. 2019. Estimating connectivity through larval dispersal in the western Indian Ocean. *JGR Biogeosciences* 124(8): 2446–2459.
Gardner, C. J. 2016. Use of mangroves by lemurs. *International Journal of Primatology* 37: 317–332.
Gardner, C. J., Andriamdahenina, Z., Carro, A., Jones, T. G., and Jasper, L. D. 2016. Rapid assessments and local knowledge reveal high bird diversity in mangroves of north-west Madagascar. *Wetlands Ecology and Management* 25: 45–58.
Gardner, C., Nicoll, M., Birkinshaw, C., Harris, A., Lewis, R., Rakotomalala, D., and Ratsifandrihamanana, A. 2018. The rapid expansion of Madagascar's protected area system. *Biological Conservation* 220: 29–36.
Gardner, C. J., Cripps, G., Day, L. P., Dewar, K., Gough, C., Peabody, S., Tahindraza, G., and Harris, A. 2020. A decade and a half of learning from Madagascar's first locally managed marine area. *Conservation Science and Practice*. https://doi.org/10.1111/csp2.298.
Geisler, J. H., and Uhen, M. D. 2005. Phylogenetic relationships of extinct cetartiodactyls: Results of simultaneous analyses of molecular, morphological, and stratigraphic data. *Journal of Mammalian Evolution* 12: 145–160.
Germanov, E. S., Marshall, A. D., Bejder, L., Fossi, M. C., and Loneragan, N. R. 2018. Microplastics: No small problem for filter-feeding megafauna. *Trends in Ecology and Evolution* 33: 227–232.
Germanov, E. S., Marshall, A. D., Hendrawan, I. G., Admiraal, R., Rohner, C. A., Argeswara, J., Wulandari, R., Himawan, M. R., and Loneragan, N. R. 2019. Microplastics on the menu: Plastics pollute Indonesian manta ray and whale shark feeding grounds. *Frontiers in Marine Science* 6: 679.
Gilchrist, H., Rocliffe, S., Anderson, L. G., and Gough, C.L.A. 2020. Reef fish biomass recovery within community-managed no take zones. *Ocean and Coastal Management* 192: 105201.
Gillanders, B. 2006. Seagrasses, fish, and fisheries. In *Seagrasses: Biology, Ecology and Conservation*, eds. A.W.D. Larkum, R. J. Orth, and C. Duarte. pp. 503–536. Berlin: Springer Verlag.
Gilman, E. L., Ellison, J., Duke, N. C., and Field, C. 2008. Threats to mangroves from climate change and adaptation options: A review. *Aquatic Botany* 89: 237–250.
Giri, C. 2011. *National-Level Mangrove Cover Data-Sets for 1990, 2000 and 2010*. Sioux Falls: United States Geological Survey.
Gladstone, N., Andriantahina, F., and Soafiavy, B. 2003. *Azafady Project Fanomena: Marine Turtle Conservation and Research in Southeast Madagascar; Report on Activities and Findings in the 2001–2002 Nesting Season*. London: Azafady.
Goedefroit, S. 1999. La ruée vers l'or rose: Stratégie d'accès et conflit d'usage de la ressource crevettière par les pêcheurs traditionnels de Madagascar. In *Les espaces de l'halieutique*, eds. D. Gascuel, P. Chavance, N. Bez, and A. Biseau, pp. 413–425. Paris: IRD.
Goffredi, S. K., Paull, C. K., Fulton-Bennett, K., Hurtado, L. A., and Vrijenhoek, R. C. 2004. Unusual benthic fauna associated with a whale fall in Monterey Canyon, California. *Deep-Sea Research I, Oceanographic Research Papers* 51: 1295–1306.
Goodman, S. M., Pidgeon, M., Hawkins, A.F.A., and Schulenberg, T. S. 1997. The birds of southeastern Madagascar. *Fieldiana: Zoology*, new series, 87: 1–132.
Gough, C.L.A., Dewar, K. M., Godley, B. J., Zafindranosy, E., and Broderick, A. C. 2020. Evidence of overfishing in small-scale fisheries in Madagascar. *Frontiers in Marine Science* 7: 317.
Gouvernement de la République de Madagascar. 2012. Arrête 22473/2012 abrogeant l'arrêté no. 2173/29 du 12 février 2009, et fixant l'organisation et fonctionnement du Comité National de Gestion Intégrée des Zones Côtières. Antananarivo: Gouvernement de Madagascar.
———. 2014. Proposition d'une réserve de biosphère marine à Madagascar: Formulaire de proposition pour le site de Belo sur Mer–Kirindy Mite. Antananarivo: Gouvernement de la République de Madagascar/Commission Nationale Malgache pour UNESCO.
———. 2015. Décret no. 2015-629 du 07 Avril 2015 portant création d'une Commission Nationale de Gestion Intégrée des Mangroves. Antananarivo: Gouvernement de Madagascar.
———. 2016. Formulaire de proposition pour le site de littoral du sud-ouest de Madagascar. Antananarivo: Gouvernement de la République de Madagascar/ Commission Nationale d'UNESCO.
Gownaris, N. J., Santora, C. M., Davis, J. B., and Pikitch, E. K. 2019. Gaps in protection of Important Ocean Areas: A spatial meta-analysis of ten global mapping initiatives. *Frontiers in Marine Science* 6: 650.
Graham, N., and McClanahan, T. R. 2013. The last call for marine wilderness? *Bioscience* 63: 397–402.
Graham, R. T., Roberts, C. M., and Smart, J.C.R. 2006. Diving behaviour of whale sharks in response to predictable food pulse. *Journal of the Royal Society Interface* 3: 109–116.
Grandcourt, E., ed. 1999. *Status and Management of the Marine Protected Areas of Madagascar*. International Coral Reef Action Network, Eastern African Component (ICRAN Project). MT/1100-99-70. Antananarivo: United Nations Environment Programme and Food and Agriculture Organization.
Grandidier, A. 1899. *Guide de l'immigrant à Madagascar: Rassemblés et mis en ordre par le capitaine Nèple*. Vol. 2. Paris: A. Colin.
Grandidier, G. 1910. Les tortues de mer à Madagascar. *La Revue de Madagascar* 1910: 1–11.
Gravier, N. 1970. Etude des hydraires épiphytes des Phanérogames marines de la région de Tuléar (sud-ouest de Madagascar). *Recueil des Travaux de la Station Marine d'Endoume*, fascicule hors-série, suppl. 10: 111–161.
Green, A., Uken, R., Ramsay, P., Leuci, R., and Perritt, S. 2009. Potential sites for suitable coelacanth habitat using bathymetric data from the western Indian Ocean. *South African Journal of Science* 105: 151–154.
Greiner, J. T., McGlathery, K. J., Gunnell, J., and McKee, B. A. 2013. Seagrass restoration enhances "blue carbon" sequestration in coastal waters. *PLoS One* 8(8): e72469.
Griffiths, O., and Tatayah, V. 2007. Rapid survey of marine turtles in Agalega, western Indian Ocean. *Marine Turtle Newsletter* 115: 14–16.
Groeneveld, J. C., and Koranteng, K. A., eds. 2017. *The RV* Dr Fridtjof Nansen *in the Western Indian Ocean: Voyages of Marine Research and Capacity Development; 1975–2016*. Rome: Food and Agriculture Organization of the United Nations.
Habermehl, G. G., Krebs, H. C., Rasoanaivo, P., and Ramialiharisoa, A. 1994. Severe ciguatera poisoning in Madagascar: A case report. *Toxicon* 32: 1539–1542.
Hale, R. C., Greaves, J., Gundersen, J. L., and Mothershead, R. F., II. 1991. Occurrence of organochlorine contaminants in tissues of the coelacanth *Latimeria chalumnae*. *Environmental Biology of Fishes* 32: 361–367.
Halo, I., Malauene, B., and Ostrowksi, M. 2017. Physical oceanography. In *The RV* Dr Fridtjof Nansen *in the Western Indian Ocean: Voyages of Marine Research and Capacity Development; 1975–2016*, eds. J. C. Groeneveld and K. A. Koranteng, pp. 37–54. Rome: Food and Agriculture Organization of the United Nations.

Hancke, L., Roberts, M. J., and Ternon, J. F. 2014. Surface drifter trajectories highlight flow pattern in the Mozambique Channel. *Deep-Sea Research II, Topical Studies in Oceanography* 100: 27–37.

Hannah, L., Dave, R., Lowry, P. P., Andelman, S., Andrianarisata, M., et al. 2008. Climate change adaptation for conservation in Madagascar. *Biology Letters* 4: 590–594.

Hantanirina, J., and Benbow, S. 2013. Diversity and coverage of seagrass ecosystems in south-west Madagascar. *African Journal of Marine Science* 35(2): 291–297.

Harding, S., Randriamanantsoa, B., Hardy, T., and Curd, A. 2006. *Coral Reef Monitoring and Biodiversity Assessment to Support the Planning of a Proposed MPA at Andavadoaka*. Blue Ventures Conservation Report. Toliara: Blue Ventures.

Harding, S., and Randriamanantsoa, B. 2008. Coral reef monitoring in reserves of northern Madagascar: Ten years after bleaching – Facing the consequences of climate change in the Indian Ocean. In *CORDIO Status Report 2008*, eds. D. O. Obura, J. Tamelander, and O. Linden, pp. 93–106. Mombasa: Coastal Oceans Research and Development in the Indian Ocean/Sida-SAREC.

Haridon, L. 2006. *Evolution de la collecte de poulpe sur la côte sud-ouest de Madagascar: Eléments de réflexion pour une meilleure gestion des ressources*. Toliara: Institut Halieutique et des Sciences Marines and Blue Ventures.

Harmelin-Vivien, M. L. 1979. Ichthyofaune de récifs coralliens de Tuléar, Madagascar: Ecologie et relations trophiques. Thèse Doctorat d'Etat-es-Sciences, Université d'Aix-Marseille 2.

Harmelin-Vivien, M., Harmelin, J. G., Chauvet, C., Duval, C., Galzin, R. et al. 1985. Evaluation visuelle des peuplements et populations de poissons: Méthodes et problèmes. *Revue d'Ecologie, la Terre et la Vie* 40: 467–539.

Harper, G., Steininger, M., Tucker, C., Juhn, D., and Hawkins F. 2007. Fifty years of deforestation and forest fragmentation in Madagascar. *Environmental Conservation* 34: 325–333.

Harris, A. R. 2011. Out of sight but no longer out of mind: A climate of change for marine conservation in Madagascar. *Madagascar Conservation and Development* 6(1): 7–14.

Harris, A., Manahira, G., Sheppard, A., Gouch, C., and Sheppard, C. 2010. Demise of Madagascar's once great barrier reef: Change in coral reef condition over 40 years. *Atoll Research Bulletin* 574: 1–16.

Haskell, P. J., McGowan, A., Westling, A., Méndez-Jiménez, A., Rohner, C. A., et al. 2015. Monitoring the effects of tourism on whale shark *Rhincodon typus* behaviour in Mozambique. *Oryx* 49: 492–499.

Hastenrath, A., and Lamb, P. J. 1979. *Climatic Atlas of the Indian Ocean*. 2 pts. Madison: University of Wisconsin Press.

Hawkes, L. A., Broderick, A. C., Godfrey, M. H., and Godley, B. J. 2009. Climate change and marine turtles. *Endangered Species Research* 7: 137–154.

Heemstra, P. H., Freeman, A.I.J., Yan Wong, H., Hensley, D. A., and Rabesandratana, H. D. 1996. First authentic capture of a coelacanth, *Latimeria chalumnae* (Pisces: Latimeriidae), off Madagascar. *South African Journal of Science* 92: 150–151.

Helweg, D. A., Cato, D. H., Jenkins, D. F., Garrigue, C., and McCauley, R. D. 1998. Geographic variation in South Pacific humpback whale songs. *Behaviour* 135(1): 1–17.

Herbert, D. G. 2012. A revision of the Chilodontidae (Gastropoda: Vetigastropoda: Seguenzioidea) of southern Africa and the south-western Indian Ocean. *African Invertebrates* 53(2): 381–502.

Higgs, N. D., Gates, A. R., and Jones, D.O.B. 2014. Fish food in the deep sea: Revisiting the role of large food-falls. *PLoS One* 9(5): e96016.

Hill, B. J., Williams, M. J., and Dutton, P. 1982. Distribution of juvenile, subadult and adult *Scylla serrata* (Crustacea: Portunidae) on tidal flats in Australia. *Marine Biology* 69(1): 117–120.

Himes-Cornell, A., Pendleton, L., and Atiyah, P. 2018. Valuing ecosystem services from blue forests: A systematic review of the valuation of salt marshes, seagrass beds and mangrove forests. *Ecosystem Services* 30: 36–48.

Hissman, K., Fricke, H., and Schauer, J. 1998. Population monitoring of the coelacanth (*Latimeria chalumnae*). *Conservation Biology* 12: 758–765.

———. 2000. Patterns of time and space allocation in coelacanths (*Latimeria chalumnae*), determined by ultrasonic telemetry. *Marine Biology* 136: 943–952.

Hissmann, K., Fricke, H., Schauer, J., Ribbink, A. J., Roberts, M. J., Sink, K., and Heemstra, P. C. 2006. The South African coelacanths: An account of what is known after three submersible expeditions. *South African Journal of Science* 102: 491–500.

Hoarau, L., Ainley, L., Jean, C., and Ciccione, S. 2014. Ingestion and defecation of marine debris by loggerhead sea turtles, *Caretta caretta*, from by-catch in the south-west Indian Ocean. *Marine Pollution Bulletin* 84(1–2): 90–96.

Holleman, W., Connell, A. D., and Carpenter, K. E. 2013. *Caesio xanthalytos*, a new species of fusilier (Perciformes: Caesionidae) from the western Indian Ocean, with records of range extensions for several species of Caesionidae. *Zootaxa* 3702(3): 262–272.

Holloway, G., and Short, S. 2014. Towards a more adaptive co-management of natural resources: Increasing social-ecological resilience in southeast Madagascar. *Madagascar Conservation and Development* 9(1): 36–48.

Houart, R. 2015. On some Indo West Pacific species of *Favartia* sensu stricto (Gastropoda: Muricidae: Muricospinae) with the description of three new species from the Indian Ocean and comments on related species. *Vita Malacologica* 15: 57.

Houart, R., and Héros, V. 2013. Description of new Muricidae (Mollusca: Gastropoda) collected during the Atimo Vatae expedition to Madagascar "Deep South." *Zoosystema* 35(4): 503–523.

———. 2015. New species of Muricidae Rafinesque 1815 (Mollusca: Gastropoda) from the western Indian Ocean. *Zoosystema* 37(3): 481–503.

Houssen, S. 2012. Le coelacanthe: Flaque et cours d'eau, janvier 2012. *Le Journal du Collège Etienne de Flacourt* 11(1): 1, 10.

Huggett, J., and Kywalianga, M. 2017. Ocean productivity. In *The RV* Dr Fridtjof Nansen *in the Western Indian Ocean: Voyages of Marine Research and Capacity Development; 1975–2016*, eds. J. C. Groeneveld and K. A. Koranteng, pp. 55–80. Rome: Food and Agriculture Organization of the United Nations.

Hughes, G. R. 1973. The survival situation of the hawksbill sea-turtle (*Eretmochelys imbricata*) in Madagascar. *Biological Conservation* 5(2): 114–118.

———. 1974. *The Status of Sea Turtles in South-East Africa*. Investigational Research Report 36. Durban: Oceanographic Research Institute.

———. 1982. Conservation of sea turtles in the southern Africa region. In *The biology and Conservation of Sea Turtles*, ed. K. Bjorndal, pp. 397–404. Washington, DC: Smithsonian Institution Press.

———. 1996. Nesting of the leatherback turtle (*Dermochelys coriacea*) in Tongaland, KwaZulu-Natal, South Africa, 1963–1995. *Chelonian Conservation and Biology* 2: 153–158.

Humber, F. 2015. Exploitation of marine turtles and elasmobranchs in Madagascar. PhD thesis, University of Exeter.

Humber, F., and Hykle, D. 2011. *Report on the Workshop for the Adoption of a Management and Conservation Plan for Marine Turtles in Madagascar*. London: Blue Ventures and IOSEA.

Humber, F., Harris, A., Raberinary, D., and Nadon, M. 2006. Seasonal closures of no-take zones to promote a sustainable fishery for *Octopus cyanea* (gray) in southwest Madagascar. Blue Ventures Conservation Report, London. http://blueventures.org/wp-content/uploads/2015/03/seasonal-closure-ntz-promote-sustainable-fishery.pdf.

Humber, F., Godley, B. J., Ramahery, V., and Broderick, A. C. 2010. Using community members to assess artisanal fisheries: The marine turtle fishery in Madagascar. *Animal Conservation* 14: 175–185.

Humber, F., Andriamahefazafy, M., Godley, B. J., and Broderick, A. C. 2015. Endangered, essential and exploited: How extant laws are not enough to protect marine megafauna in Madagascar. *Marine Policy* 60: 70–83.

Humber, F., Andriamahaino, E. T., Beriziny, T., Botosoamananto, R., Godley, B. J., Gough, C., Pedron, S., Ramahery, V., and Broderick, A. C. 2017a. Assessing the small-scale shark fishery of Madagascar through community-based monitoring and knowledge. *Fisheries Research* 186: 131–143.

Humber, F., Godley, B. J., Nicolas, T., Raynaud, O., Pichon, F., and Broderick, A. C. 2017b. Placing Madagascar's marine turtle populations in a regional context using community-based monitoring. *Oryx* 51: 542–553.

Huxham, M., Dencer-Brown, A., Diele, K., Kathiresan, K., Nagelkerken, I., and Wanjiru, C. 2017. Mangroves and people: Local ecosystem services in a changing climate. In *Mangrove Ecosystems: A Global Biogeographic Perspective*, eds. R. R. Twilley, V. H. Rivera-Monroy, E. Kristensen, and S. Y. Lee, pp. 245–274. Cham: Springer.

Hydrographer of the Navy. 1990. *South Indian Ocean Pilot*. 9th ed. Taunton: Hydrographer of the Navy.

Iltis, J., and Ranaivoson, E. 2011. A synopsis of marine aquaculture in Madagascar. In *Mariculture in the WIO Region: Challenges and Prospects*, eds. M. Troell, T. Hecht, M. Beveridge, S. Stead, I. Bryceson, N. Kautsky, F. Ollevier, and A. Mmochi, p. 17–18. Western Indian Ocean Marine Science Association Book Series no. 11.

Indocet. 2021. Research. Accessed 3 August 2021. https://indocet.org/research.

Inoue, J. G., Miya, M., Venkatesh, B., and Nishida, M. 2005. The mitochondrial genome of Indonesian coelacanth *Latimeria menadoensis* (Sarcopterygii: Coelacanthiformes) and divergence time estimation between the two coelacanths. *Gene* 349: 227–235.

Insacco, G., Nulens, R., and Zava, B. 2016. The coelacanth, *Latimeria chalumnae* Smith, 1939 at the Natural History Museum of Comiso, taxidermic preservation and notes on the other world specimens. *Natura Rerum* 4(1): 25–38.

IOTC. 2008. Report of the 4th session of the Indian Ocean Tuna Commission Working Party on Ecosystems and Bycatch. Bangkok, Thailand, 20–22 Oct. 2008. IOTC-2008-WPEB-R[E].

———. 2019. Report of the 15th session of the Indian Ocean Tuna Commission Working Party on Ecosystems and Bycatch. La Réunion, France, 3–7 Mar. 2019. IOTC-2019-WPEB15-R_Rev1.

———. 2021. Available datasets. Accessed 3 August 2021. https://iotc.org/data/datasets.

Ito, T., Onda, K., and Nishida, K. 2017. Effects of noise and vibration on the behavior and feeding activity of whale sharks, *Rhincodon typus* (Smith, 1828), in Osaka Aquarium Kaiyukan. In *The Elasmobranch Husbandry Manual II: Recent Advances in the Care of Sharks, Rays and Their Relatives*, eds. M. Smith, D. Warmolts, D. Thoney, R. Hueter, M. Murray, and J. Ezurra, 159–168. Special Publication of the Ohio Biological Survey. Columbus: Ohio Biological Survey.

IUCN (International Union for Conservation of Nature). 2014. Our commitment to action for the Promise of Sydney. IUCN World Parks Congress, Sydney 2014. Accessed 7 Feb. 2017. https://www.worldparkscongress.org/about/promise_of_sydney_commitments.

———. 2019. *Dynamiques spatiales des écosystèmes terrestres, côtiers et marins de Madagascar: Une première application des critères de la Liste rouge des écosystèmes de l'UICN*. Antananarivo: IUCN.

IUCN and Blue Ventures. 2016. *Mapping of Relevant Policies and Regulations for Coastal Carbon Ecosystem Management in 5 Countries: From Climate Change to Forestry and Coastal Marine Resource Management*. Antananarivo: IUCN and Blue Ventures.

IUCN-MMPATF (Marine Mammal Protected Areas Task Force). 2019. Final report of the fifth IMMA workshop: Regional Workshop for Western Indian Ocean and Arabian Seas, Salalah, Sultanate of Oman, 4–8 March 2019. https://www.marinemammalhabitat.org/download/final-imma-nw-indian-ocean-arabian-seas-workshop-report/.

———. 2020. Global Dataset of Important Marine Mammal Areas (IUCN-IMMA). June 2020. Made available under agreement on terms and conditions of use by the IUCN Joint SSC/WCPA Marine Mammal Protected Areas Task Force. Accessible via the IMMA e-Atlas, http://www.marinemammalhabitat.org/imma-eatlas/.

IWC (International Whaling Commission). 2007. Annex H: Report of the sub-committee on other Southern Hemisphere whale stocks. *Journal of Cetacean Research and Management* 9: 188–209.

———. 2010. Annex H: Report of the sub-committee on other Southern Hemisphere whale stocks. *Journal of Cetacean Research and Management* 11 (Suppl. 2): 218–251.

———. 2011. Annex H: Report of the sub-committee on other Southern Hemisphere whale stocks. *Journal of Cetacean Research and Management* 12: 203–226.

———. 2016. Annex H: Report of the sub-committee on other Southern Hemisphere whale stocks. *Journal of Cetacean Research and Management* 16: 196–221.

Iyengar, L. 2018. *Report of the Cultural Scoping Study for the Dugong Seagrass Conservation Project, December 2018*. Abu Dhabi: Community Centered Conservation.

Jacques Whitford. 2007. Marine environmental compliance monitoring in the new port at Ehoala in Fort Dauphin, Madagascar. Update baseline study. Final report prepared for QIT Madagascar Minerals SA.

Jahnke, M., Gullström, M., Larsson, J., Asplund, M. E., Mgeleka, S., Ogalo Silas, M., Hoamby, A., Mahafina, J., and Nordlund, L. M. 2019. Population genetic structure and connectivity of the seagrass *Thalassia hemprichii* in the western Indian Ocean is influenced by predominant ocean currents. *Ecology and Evolution* 9: 8953–8964.

Jain, M. 1995. *Inventory of Marine and Coastal Activities: A Strategy Proposal for Madagascar*. KEPEM Report no. 20. Antananarivo: United States Agency for International Development.

Jedrusik, M. H. 2019. Nosy Be (Madagascar) and the neighbouring islands versus tourism development. *Miscellanea Geographica* 23(1): 23–32.

Jenkins, M. D. 1987. *Madagascar: An Environmental Profile*. Cambridge, UK: IUCN.

Jensen, M. P., Dalleau, M., Gaspar, P., Lalire, M., Jean, C., et al. 2020. Seascape genetics and the spatial ecology of juvenile green turtles. *Genes* 11(3): 278.

Jonahson, M., and Harding, S. 2007. Occurrence of whale sharks (*Rhincodon typus*) in Madagascar. *Fisheries Research* 84: 132–135.

Jones, A. R., Gladstone, W., and Hacking, N. J. 2007. Australian sandy beach ecosystems and climate change: Ecology and management. *Australian Zoology* 34: 190–202.

Jones, T. G., Ratsimba, H. R., Ravaoarinorotsihoarana, L., Cripps, G., and Bey, A. 2014. Ecological variability and carbon stock estimates of mangrove ecosystems in northwestern Madagascar. *Forests* 5: 177–205.

Jones, T. G., Ratsimba, H. R., Ravaoarinorotsihoarana, L., Glass, L., Benson, L., et al. 2015. The dynamics, ecological variability and estimated carbon stocks of mangroves in Mahajamba Bay, Madagascar. *Journal of Marine Science and Engineering* 3: 793–820.

Jones, T. G., Glass, L., Gandhi, S., Ravaoarinorotsihoarana, L., Carro, A., et al. 2016a. Madagascar's mangroves: Quantifying nation-wide and ecosystem specific dynamics, and detailed contemporary mapping of distinct ecosystems. *Remote Sensing* 8: 106.

Jones, T. G., Ratsimba, H. R., Carro, A., Ravaoarinorotsihoarana, L., Glass, L., et al. 2016b. The mangroves of Ambanja and Ambaro Bays, northwest Madagascar: Historical dynamics, current status and deforestation mitigation strategy. In *Estuaries: A Lifeline of Ecosystem Services in the Western Indian Ocean*, eds. S. Diop, P. Scheren, and J. F. Machiwa, pp. 67–85. Cham: Springer International.

Joung, S. J., Chen, C. T., Clark, E., Uchida, S., and Huang, W.Y.P. 1996. The whale shark, *Rhincodon typus*, is a livebearer: 300 embryos found in one "megamamma" supreme. *Environmental Biology of Fishes* 46: 219–223.

Jury, M. R., Pathack, B., and Parker, B. 1999. Climatic determinants and statistical prediction of tropical cyclone days in the southwest Indian Ocean. *Journal of Climate* 12: 1738–1746.

Kaga, T., and Heemstra, E. 2013. First record of a rare sand whiting, *Sillago caudicula* (Perciformes: Sillaginidae), from Madagascar. *Marine Biology Research* 9: 316–320.

Kantor, Y. I., Fedosov A. E., Puillandre, N., and Bouchet, P. 2016. Integrative taxonomy approach to Indo-Pacific Olividae: New species revealed by molecular and morphological data. *Ruthenica* 26(2): 123–143.

Kasuya, T., and Wada, S. 1996. Distribution of large cetaceans in the Indian Ocean: Data from Japanese sighting records, November–March. In *Cetaceans and Cetacean Research in the Indian Ocean Sanctuary*, eds. S. Leatherwood and G. Donovan, pp. 139–170. United Nations Environment Programme Marine Mammal Technical Report no. 3. Nairobi: UNEP.

Kathiresan, K., and Bingham, B. L. 2001. Biology of mangroves and mangrove ecosystems. *Advances in Marine Biology* 40: 81–251.

Kelkar, N., Arthur, R., Marba, N., and Alcoverro, T. 2013. Green turtle herbivory dominates the fate of seagrass primary production in the Lakshadweep islands (Indian Ocean). *Marine Ecology Progress Series* 485: 235–243.

Kerr, A. M., and Baird, A. H. 2007. Natural barriers to natural disasters. *BioScience* 57: 102–103.

Kershaw, F., Carvalho, I., Loo, J., Pomilla, C., Best, P. B., et al. 2017. Multiple processes drive genetic structure of humpback whale (*Megaptera novaeangliae*) populations across spatial scales. *Molecular Ecology* 26(4): 977–994.

Kiener, A. 1964. Contribution à l'étude écologique et biologique des eaux saumâtres malgaches: Les poissons euryhalins et leur rôle dans le développement des pêches. PhD thesis, Université de Marseille.

Kiener, A. N. 1972. Ecologie, biologie et possibilités de mise en valeur des mangroves Malgaches. *Bulletin de Madagascar* 308: 49–84.

Kiener, A., and Theresien, Y. 1965. Principaux poissons du Lac Kinkony: Leur biologie et leur pêche. *Annales de l'Université de Madagascar* 204: 395–440.

Kiszka, J., and van der Elst, R. 2015. Elasmobranchs (sharks and rays): A review of status, distribution and interaction with fisheries in the southwest Indian Ocean. In *Offshore Fisheries of the Southwest Indian Ocean: Their Status and the Impact on Vulnerable Species*, eds. R. van der Elst and B. Everett, pp. 365–389. Oceanographic Research Institute Special Publication no. 10. Durban: Oceanographic Research Institute.

Kiszka, J., Ersts, P., and Ridoux, V. 2007. Cetacean diversity around the Mozambique Channel island of Mayotte (Comoro archipelago). *Journal of Cetacean Research and Management* 9: 105–109.

Kiszka, J., Muir, C., Poonian, C., Cox, T. M., Amir, O. A., Bourjea, J., Razafindrakoto, Y., Wambitji, N., and Bristol, N. 2009. Marine mammal bycatch in the southwest Indian Ocean: Review and need for a comprehensive status assessment. *Western Indian Ocean Journal of Marine Science* 7(2): 119–136.

Kiszka, J., Ersts, P., and Ridoux, V. 2010a. Structure of a toothed cetacean community around a tropical island (Mayotte, Mozambique Channel). *African Journal of Marine Science* 32(3): 543–551.

Kiszka, J., Vely, M., and Breysse, O. 2010b. Preliminary account of cetacean diversity and humpback whale (*Megaptera novaeangliae*) group characteristics around the Union of the Comoros (Mozambique Channel). *Mammalia* 74(1): 51–56.

Klückow, T. 2020. *Sandfish Farming Manual*. Antananarivo: Blue Ventures.

Knutson, T. R., McBride, J. L., Chan, J., Emanuel, K., Holland, G., Landsea, C., Held, I., Kossin, J. P., Srivastava, A. K., and Sugi, M. 2010. Tropical cyclones and climate change. *Nature Geoscience* 3: 157–163.

Korn, W., Niederhöfer, H.-J., and Blöcher, M. 2000. *Conus pennaceus* from Madagascar: A complex of geographical subspecies (Gastropoda: Conidae). *Stuttgarter Beiträge zur Naturkunde*, série A, *Biologie* 610: 1–25.

Krakstad, J. O., Munga, C. N., and Stromme, T. 2017. Pelagic resources based on acoustic recordings and trawl sampling. In *The RV* Dr Fridtjof Nansen *in the Western Indian Ocean: Voyages of Marine Research and Capacity Development; 1975–2016*, eds. J. C. Groeneveld and K. A. Koranteng, pp. 81–100. Rome: Food and Agriculture Organization of the United Nations.

Kyne, P. M., and Moore, A. 2014. Habitat degradation and loss. In *Sawfish: A Global Strategy for Conservation*, eds. L. Harrison and N. K. Dulvy, pp. 70–71. Vancouver: IUCN Species Survival Commission's Shark Specialist Group.

Kyne, P. M., Carlson, J., and Smith, K. 2013. *Pristis pristis*. IUCN Red List of Threatened Species 2013: e.T18584848A141788242. doi.org/10.2305/IUCN.UK.2013-1.RLTS.T18584848A141788242.en.

———. 2014. Largetooth sawfish (*Pristis pristis*) global. In *Sawfish: A Global Strategy for Conservation*, eds. L. Harrison and N. K. Dulvy, p. 37. Vancouver: IUCN Species Survival Commission's Shark Specialist Group.

Laboute, P., and Maharavo, J. 1998. Madagascar: Un monde sous la mer; Nosy Be et sa région. Unpublished manuscript. Centre National de Recherche Océanographique, Hell-Ville.

Laran, S., Authier, M., Van Canneyt, O., Dorémus, G., Watremez, P., and Ridoux, V. 2017. A comprehensive survey of pelagic megafauna: Their distribution, densities, and taxonomic richness in the tropical southwest Indian Ocean. *Frontiers in Marine Science* 4(139). doi:10.3389/fmars.2017.00139.

Laroche, J., and Ramananarivo, N. V. 1995. A preliminary survey of the artisanal fishery on coral reefs of the Tuléar region (southwest Madagascar). *Coral Reefs* 14(4): 193–200.

Laroche, J., Baran, E., and Rasoandrasana, N. B. 1997. Temporal patterns in a fish assemblage of a semiarid mangrove zone in Madagascar. *Journal of Fish Biology* 51: 3–20.

Lauret-Stepler, M., Bourjea, J., Roos, D., Pelletier, D., Ryan, P., Ciccione, S., and Grizel, H. 2007. Reproductive seasonality and trend of *Chelonia mydas* in the SW Indian Ocean: A 20 year study based on track counts. *Endangered Species Research* 3: 217–227.

Lea, J.S.E., Humphries, N. E., Clarke, C. R., and Sims, D. W. 2015. To Madagascar and back: Long-distance, return migration across open ocean by a pregnant female bull shark *Carcharhinus leucas*. *Journal of Fish Biology* 87: 1313–1321.

Lebigre, J.-M. 1988. Le marais maritime de la Tsiribihina à Madagascar: Paysage végétal et dynamique. *Revue Bois et Forêts des Tropiques* 215: 37–60.

———. 1990. Les marais maritimes du Gabon et de Madagascar. PhD thesis, Université de Bordeaux III.

Le Corre, M., and Bemanaja, E. 2009. Discovery of two major seabird colonies in Madagascar. *Marine Ornithology* 37: 153–158.

LeDuc, R., and Dizon, A. E. 2002. Reconstructing the rorqual phylogeny: With comments on the use of molecular and morphological data for systematic study. In *Molecular and Cell Biology of Marine Mammals*, eds. C. Pfeiffer and P. E. Nachtigall, pp. 100–110. Melbourne, FL: Krieger.

Leeney, R. H. 2017. Are sawfishes still present in Mozambique? A baseline ecological study. *PeerJ* 5: e2950. doi:10.7717/peerj.2950.

Leeney, R. H., and Downing, N. 2016. Sawfishes in the Gambia and Senegal: Shifting baselines over 40 years. *Aquatic Conservation: Marine and Freshwater Ecosystems* 26: 265–278.

Le Gall, J. Y., and Hughes, G. R. 1987. Migrations de la tortue verte *Chelonia mydas* dans l'Océan Indien sud-ouest observées à partir de marquages sur les sites de ponte Europa et Tromelin (1970–1985). *Amphibia-Reptilia* 8: 277–282.

Leguat, F. 1708. *Voyages et aventures de François Leguat et ses compagnons en deux iles desertes des Indes orientales*. London: David Mortier.

Lei, S., Na, W., Shuai, Z., and Li, G. 2017. Overview on China's rare earth industry restructuring and regulation reforms. *Journal of Resources and Ecology* 8: 213–222.

Le Manach, F., Gough, C., Humber, F., Harper, S., and Zeller, D. 2011. Reconstruction of total marine fisheries catches for Madagascar (1950–2008). In *Fisheries Catch Reconstructions: Islands, Part II*, eds. S. Harper and D. Zeller, pp. 21–37. Fisheries Centre Research Reports, vol. 19, no. 4. Vancouver: Fisheries Centre, University of British Columbia.

Le Manach, F., Gough, C., Harris, A., Humber, F., Harper, S., and Zeller, D. 2012. Unreported fishing, hungry people and political turmoil: The recipe for a food security crisis in Madagascar? *Marine Policy* 36: 218–225.

Le Reste, L. 1978. *Biologie d'une population de crevettes,* Penaeus indicus *H. Milne Edwards sur la côte nord-ouest de Madagascar*. Travaux et Documents de l'ORSTOM no. 99. Paris: ORSTOM.

Lewis, A., Prins, E., Andriamanantsoa, J., Dunstan, H., Jones, D., et al. 2004. *Collaborative Reef Research Expedition to Andavadoaka, South West Madagascar, 26 July to 8 August 2003*. Toliara: EUCARE and Institut Halieutique et des Sciences Marines.

Lhomme, F. 2000. Relation pêche-environnement chez les crevettes pénéides: Revue mondiale; Problème posé par l'application à Madagascar. In *Actes de l'atelier national sur l'aménagement de la pêche aux crevettes, Hotel Panorama, Antananarivo, Décembre 12–14, 2000*, eds. E. Ranaivoson and Z. Kaspezyk, pp. 113–129. Antananarivo: Groupement des Armateurs de la Pêche et de l'Aquaculture aux Crevettes à Madagascar.

Li, W., Wang, Y., and Norman, B. 2012. A preliminary survey of whale shark *Rhincodon typus* catch and trade in China: An emerging crisis. *Journal of Fish Biology* 80: 1608–1618.

Lilette, V. 2006. Mixed results: Conservation of the marine turtle and the red-tailed tropicbird by Vezo semi-nomadic fishers. *Conservation and Society* 4: 262–286.

Long, S. 2017. Short-term impacts and value of a periodic no take zone (NTZ) in a community managed small-scale lobster fishery, Madagascar. *PLoS One* 12(5): e0177858.

Long, S., Jones, P.J.S., Randriana, Z., and Hadj-Hammou, J. 2017. Governance analysis of a community managed small-scale crab fishery in Madagascar: Novel use of an empirical framework. *Marine Policy*. doi:10.1016/j.marpol.2017.11.022.

Long, S., Thurlow, G., Jones, P.J.S., Turner, A., Randrianantenaina, S. M., Gammage, T., and Ndriamanja, J. R. 2019. Critical analysis of the governance of the Sainte Luce locally managed marine area (LMMA), southeast Madagascar. *Marine Policy*. doi:10.1016/j.marpol.2019.103691.

Lorenz, F. 2004. Two new species of Conidae from southern Madagascar. *Visaya* 1(2): 19–23.

Lutjeharms, J.R.E., and Machu, E. 2000. An upwelling cell inshore of the East Madagascar Current. *Deep-Sea Research I, Oceanographic Research Papers* 47(12): 2405–2411.

Lutjeharms, J.R.E., Bang, N. D., and Duncan, C. P. 1981. Characteristics of the currents east and south of Madagascar. *Deep-Sea Research I, Oceanographic Research Papers* 28(9): 879–899.

Lutjeharms, J.R.E., Wedepohl, P. M., and Meeuwis, J. M. 2000. On the surface drift of the East Madagascar and the Mozambique Currents. *South African Journal of Science* 96(3): 141–147.

MacKay, F., Weerts, S., Gouws, G., and Maduna, S. 2017. Estuarine lakes: Linkages and lineages across longitudes in the western Indian Ocean. Presentation delivered at the 10th WIOMSA (Western Indian Ocean Marine Science Association) Symposium, Dar es Salaam, Oct. 2017.

MacLeod, C. D., Perrin, W. F., Pitman, R., Barlow, J., Ballance, L., et al. 2006. Known and inferred distributions of beaked whale species (Cetacea: Ziphiidae). *Journal of Cetacean Research and Management* 7: 271–286.

Macpherson, E., and Ainas-Barcia, A. 2013. A new genus and some new species of the genus *Lauriea* Baba 1971 (Crustacea: Decapoda: Galatheidae) from the Pacific and Indian Oceans, using molecular and morpohological characters. *Zootaxa* 3599(2): 136–160.

———. 2015. Species of the genus *Galathea* Fabricius 1793 (Crustacea, Decapoda, Galatheidae) from the Indian and Pacific Oceans, with descriptions of 92 new species. *Zootaxa* 3913(1): 1–355.

Macpherson, E., Rodríguez-Flores, P. C., and Machordom, A. 2017. New sibling species and new occurrences of squat lobsters (Crustacea, Decapoda) from the western Indian Ocean. *European Journal of Taxonomy* 343: 1–61.

Maharavo, J., Quod, J.-P., Troadec, R., and Ratomahenina, O.. 2003. *Cartographie et bilan diagnostique du complexe recifal de Foulpointe (côte est de Madagascar)*. Antananarivo: Centre National de Recherches sur l'Environnement and Agence pour la Recherche et la Valorisation Marine.

Maharavo, J., Razafinjatovo, P., Oliver, T. A., and Rabearisoa, A., eds. 2011. *A Marine Biodiversity Assessment of the Extreme Northeast of Madagascar*. Antananarivo: Conservation International.

Maillaud, C. 1999. Diving accidents related to sea-cucumber fishing at Nosy Be, Madagascar. *SPC Bêche-de Mer Information Bulletin* 11: 1–3.

Maina, J., and Obura, D. 2008. *Climate Change: Spatial Data for Coastal and Marine Ecosystem Vulnerability Assessments in Madagascar*. CORDIO (Coastal Oceans

Research and Development—Indian Ocean) East Africa. Antananarivo: WWF and Conservation International.

Maina, J., de Moel, H., Zinke, J., Madin, J., McClanahan, T., and Vermaat, J. E. 2015. Human deforestation outweighs future climate change impacts of sedimentation on coral reefs. *Nature Communications* 4: 1986.

Marsac, F. 1998. Oceanic environment and development of industrial fisheries: From local to global scales. In *Tuna Prospects and Strategies for the Indian Ocean*, eds. P. Cayré and Y.-L. Le Gall, pp. 139–176. Paris: ORSTOM.

Marsh, H., and Sobtzick, S. 2019. *Dugong dugon* (amended version of 2015 assessment). IUCN Red List of Threatened Species 2019: e.T6909A160756767. Accessed 13 Sept. 2020.

Marsh, H., Penrose, H., Eros, C., and Hugues, J. 2002. Dugong status report and action plans for countries and territories. Report Series. Early warning and assessment, United Nations Environment Program UNEP/DEWA/RS.02-1.

Martel, B. 2003. Les facteurs intervenant dans la sélection des sites de pont de la caouanne (*Caretta caretta*) sur les côtes de Madagascar. *Biogeographica* 79(4): 129–152.

Matsumoto, R., Toda, M., Matsumoto, Y., Ueda, K., Nakazato, M., Sato, K., and Uchida, S. 2017. Notes on husbandry of whale sharks, *Rhincodon typus*, in aquaria. In *The Elasmobranch Husbandry Manual II: Recent Advances in the Care of Sharks, Rays and Their Relatives*, eds. M. Smith, D. Warmolts, D. Thoney, R. Hueter, M. Murray, and J. Ezurra, pp. 15–22. Special Publication of the Ohio Biological Survey. Columbus: Ohio Biological Survey.

Matsunuma, M., and Motomura, H. 2015. A new species of scorpionfish, *Ebosia vespertina* (Scorpaenidae: Pteroinae), from the southwestern Indian Ocean. *Ichthyological Research* 63: 110–120.

Maugé, A. L. 1967. Contribution préliminaire à l'inventaire ichtyologique de la région de Tuléar. *Recueil des Travaux de la Station Marine d'Endoume*, suppl. 7: 101–132.

McCauley, R., Day, R. D., Swadling, K. M., Fitzgibbon, Q. P., Watson, R. A., and Semmens, J. M. 2017. Widely used marine seismic survey air gun operations negatively impact zooplankton. *Nature Ecology and Evolution* 1: 0195.

McClanahan, T., and Obura, D. 1998. Monitoring, training and assessment of the coral reefs of the Masoala peninsula. Report prepared for the Wildlife Conservation Society, Madagascar Programme.

McClanahan, T. R., Ateweberhan, M., Muhando, C. A., Maina, J., and Mohammed, M. S. 2007. Effects of climate and seawater temperature variation on coral bleaching and mortality. *Ecological Monographs* 77: 503–525.

McClanahan, T. R., Ateweberhan, M., Omukoto, J., and Pearson, L. 2009. Recent seawater temperature histories, status, and predictions for Madagascar's coral reefs. *Marine Ecology Progress Series* 380: 117–128.

McClanahan, T. R., Graham, N.A.J., MacNeil, M. A., Muthiga, N. A., Cinner, J. E., Bruggemann, J. H., and Wilson, S. K. 2011. Critical thresholds and tangible targets for ecosystem-based management of coral reef fisheries. *Proceedings of the National Academy of Sciences of the USA* 108: 17230–17233.

McDonald, M. A., Hildebrand, J. A., and Mesnick, S. L. 2006. Biogeographic characterization of blue whale song worldwide: Using song to identify populations. *Journal of Cetacean Research and Management* 8: 55–65.

McIvor, A., Spencer, T., Möller, I., and Spalding, M. 2012. Storm surge reduction by mangroves. Natural Coastal Protection Series, Report 2. Cambridge Coastal Research Unit Working Paper 41. Nature Conservancy and Wetlands International, Cambridge, UK. https://www.conservationgateway.org/ConservationPractices/Marine/crr/library/Pages/mangroves-storm-surge.aspx.

McKenna, S. A., and Allen, G. R., eds. 2003. A rapid marine biodiversity assessment of the coral reefs of northwest Madagascar. *Bulletin of the Rapid Assessment Program* 31: 1–124.

McKenzie, L. J., Campbell, S. J., and Roder, C. A. 2003. *Seagrass-Watch: Manual for Mapping and Monitoring Seagrass Resources by Community (Citizen) Volunteers*. 2nd ed. Cairns: Queensland Government, Department of Primary Industries, Marine Plant Ecology Group.

McVean, A. R., Walker, R.C.J., and Fanning, A. 2006. The traditional shark fisheries of southwest Madagascar: A study in the Toliara region. *Fisheries Research* 82: 280–289.

Mealla, R. A. 2011. Investigating marine turtle nesting sites, local perceptions and conservation strategies in northern Madagascar. MS thesis, Ecology, Evolution and Conservation, Imperial College London.

MEEF. 2010. *Politique nationale de la lutte contre le changement climatique*. Ministère de l'Environnement, Ecologie et Forêts. Antananarivo: MEEF.

———. 2017. *Stratégie nationale de restauration des paysages forestiers et des infrastructures vertes à Madagascar*. Ministère de l'Environnement, Ecologie et Forêts. February 2017. Antananarivo: MEEF.

———. 2018. *Analyse du cadre réglementaire afin d'instaurer la conservation des dugongs et d'herbiers marins a Madagascar*. Antananarivo: Ministère de l'Environnement, de l'Ecologie et des Forêts. https://www.dugongconservation.org/media/2018/06/Rapport-d-analyse_cadre-Dugongs.pdf.

Meehl, G. A., Stocker, T. F., Collins, W. D., Friedlingstein, P., Gaye, A. T., et al. 2007. Global climate projections. In *Climate Change 2007: The Physical Science Basis*, eds. S. Solomon, D. Qin, and M. Manning, pp. 686–688. Cambridge: Cambridge University Press.

Meekan, M. G., Fuiman, L. A., Davis, R., Berger, Y., and Thums, M. 2015. Swimming strategy and body plan of the world's largest fish: Implications for foraging efficiency and thermoregulation. *Frontiers in Marine Science* 2: 1–8.

Meekan, M., Austin, C. M., Tan, M. H., Wei, N.W.V., Miller, A., et al. 2017. iDNA at sea: Recovery of whale shark (*Rhincodon typus*) mitochondrial DNA sequences from the whale shark copepod (*Pandarus rhincodonicus*) confirms global population structure. *Frontiers in Marine Science* 4: 420.

Metcalf, J., and Gray, A. 2001. *Terrestrial Biodiversity of the Nosy Hara Region*. Oxford: Nosy Hara–Radama Islands Survey Initiative.

Metcalf, J., Hampson, K., Andriamizava, A., Andrianirina, R., Cairnes, T., Gray, A., Ramiarisoa, C., and Sondotra, H. 2007. The importance of north-west Madagascar for marine turtle conservation. *Oryx* 41: 232–238.

MIHARI. 2017. MIHARI (Mitantana Harena Ranomasina avy eny Ifotony) Database. Accessed 7 Feb. 2017. https://mihari-network.org/base-de-donnees/lmma-a-madagascar/.

Millot, J. 1954. Le troisième coelacanthe. *Le Naturaliste Malgache*, suppl. 1: 1–26.

———. 1955. First observations on a living coelacanth. *Nature* 175: 362–363.

Minton, G., Cerchio, S., Collins, T., Ersts, P., Findlay, K. P., et al. 2010. A note on the comparison of humpback whale tail fluke catalogues from the Sultanate of Oman with Madagascar and the East African mainland. *Journal of Cetacean Research and Management* 11(1): 65–68.

Mirera, D. O., Ochiewo, J., and Munyi, F. 2014. Social and economic implications of small-scale mud crab (*Scylla serrata*) aquaculture: The case of organised community groups. *Aquaculture International* 22(4): 1499–1514.

Marine Mammal Protected Area Task Force. 2016-2020. Accessed 3 August 2021. https://www.marinemammalhabitat.org/.

MNP. 2014. *Plan Stratégique de Gestion du Reseau d'Aires Protegees 2014–2024*. Antananarivo: Madagascar National Parks.

Monnier, E., Tenorio, M. J., Bouchet, P., and Puillandre, N. 2018. The cones (Gastropoda) from Madagascar "Deep South": Composition, endemism and new taxa. *Xenophora Taxonomy* 19: 25–75.

Montanari, S., Kershaw, F., and Rosenbaum, H. C. 2020. Feeding ecology and population delineation of south-eastern Atlantic and south-western Indian Ocean humpback whales using stable isotope analysis. *Aquatic Conservation: Marine and Freshwater Ecosystems* 30: 486–496.

Moore, M. J., and van der Hoop, J. M. 2012. The painful side of trap and fixed net fisheries: Chronic entanglement of large whales. *Journal of Marine Sciences* 2012: 230653.

Morgan, D. L., Somaweera, R., Gleiss, A. C., Beatty, S. J., and Whitty, J. M. 2017. An upstream migration fought with danger: Freshwater sawfish fending off sharks and crocodiles. *Ecology* 98(5): 1465–1467.

Moriceau, M. 1902. Le nord de la province de Majunga. *Revue de Madagascar* 4(12): 521–548.

Mortimer, J. A., and Bresson, R. 1999. Temporal distribution and periodicity in hawksbill turtles (*Eretmochelys imbricata*) nesting at Cousin Island, Republic of Seychelles, 1971–1997. *Chelonian Conservation and Biology* 3: 1971–1997.

Mortimer, J. A., Meylan, P. A., and Donnelly, M. 2007. Whose turtles are they, anyway? *Molecular Ecology* 16: 17–18.

MRHP. 2012. *Enquête cadre national 2011–2012*. Antananarivo: Ministère des Ressources Halieutiques et de la Pêche.

———. 2015. *Lettre de politique bleue, 2015*. Antananarivo: Ministère des Ressources Halieutiques et de la Pêche.

MRHP and MIHARI. 2018. *Meilleure valorisation de la production et gestion responsable du crabe de mangrove*. Workshop report. Antananarivo: Blue Ventures, WWF, WCS, and Conservation International.

MRHP, CSP (Centre de Surveillance des Pêches), and USTA. 2018. *Rapport national de Madagascar destiné au Comité scientifique de la Commission des thons de l'Océan Indien, 2018*. IOTC-2017-SC21-NR14. Antananarivo: Ministère des Ressources Halieutiques et de la Peche and Unité Statistique Thonière d'Antsiranana.

Muller, M. 1999. Size limitations in semicircular duct systems. *Journal of Theoretical Biology* 198: 405–437.

Murata, Y., Nikaido, M., Sasaki, T., Cao, Y., Fukumoto, Y., Hasegawa, M., and Okada, N. 2003. Afrotherian phylogeny as inferred from complete mitochondrial genomes. *Molecular Phylogenetics and Evolution* 28: 253–260.

Murray, A., Cerchio, S., McCauley, R., Jenner, C. S., Razafindrakoto, Y., and Coughran, D. 2011. Minimal similarity in songs suggests limited exchange between humpback whales (*Megaptera novaeangliae*) in the southern Indian Ocean. *Marine Mammal Science* 28(1): E41–E57.

Nadon, M.-O., Griffiths, D., and Doherty, E. 2005. *Les récifs coralliens d'Andavadoaka, sud ouest de Madagascar*. Toliara: Blue Ventures.

Nagelkerken, I., Blaber, S.J.M., Bouillon, S., Green, P., Haywood, M., et al. 2008. The habitat function of mangroves for terrestrial and marine fauna: A review. *Aquatic Botany* 89: 155–185.

Nairobi Convention. 2020. Madagascar marine and coastal resources governance. Accessed 15 Aug. 2020. https://www.nairobiconvention.org/madagascar-country-profile/madagascar-marine-and-coastal-resources-governance/.

Nandi, N. C., and Dev Roy, M. K. 1991. Burrowing activity and distribution of *Scylla serrata* (Forskal) from Hooghly and Matla estuaries, Sundarban, West Bengal. *Journal of the Bombay Natural History Society* 88(2): 167–171.

Narozanski, A. J., Belle, E.M.S, and Steer, M. D. 2011. Understanding local differences in small-scale fisheries: A comparison of two fishing settlements in Antsiranana Bay, northern Madagascar. *Madagascar Conservation and Development* 6(2): 68–77.

Nellemann, C., and Corcoran, E., eds. 2009. *Blue Carbon: The Role of Healthy Oceans in Binding Carbon*. N.p.: United Nations Environment Programme and Earthprint.

Niaina, N. 2006. A peine capturé un coelacanthe rejoint la marmite: Capture d'un spécimen de coelacanthe au large de Maintirano. *Les Nouvelles* 1 (July): 1–2.

Norman, B. M., and Morgan, D. L. 2016. The return of "Stumpy" the whale shark: Two decades and counting. *Frontiers in Ecology and the Environment* 14: 449–450.

Norman, B. M., Holmberg, J. A., Arzoumanian, Z., Reynolds, S. D., Wilson, R. P., et al. 2017. Undersea constellations: The global biology of an endangered marine megavertebrate further informed through citizen science. *BioScience* 67: 1029–1043.

Notarbartolo di Sciara, G., and Hoyt, E. 2020. Healing the wounds of marine mammals by protecting their habitat. *Ethics in Science and Environmental Politics* 20: 15–23.

Nowacek, D. P., Thorne, L. H., Johnston, D. W., and Tyack, P. L. 2007. Responses of cetaceans to anthropogenic noise. *Mammal Review* 37: 81–115.

Nowacek, D. P., Friedlaender, A. S., Halpin, P. N., Hazen, E. L., Johnston, D. W., Read, A. J., Espinasse, B., Zhou, M., and Zhu, Y. 2011. Super-aggregations to krill and humpback whales in Wilhelmina Bay, Antarctic Peninsula. *PLoS One* 6(4): e19173.

Nowacek, D. P., Clark, C. W., Mann, D., Miller, P.J.O., Rosenbaum, H. C., Golden, J. S., Jasny, M., Kraska, J., and Southall, B. L. 2015. Marine seismic surveys and ocean noise: Time for coordinated and prudent planning. *Frontiers in Ecology and the Environment* 13(7): 378–386.

Nulens, R., Scott, L., and Herbin, M. 2011. An updated inventory of all known specimens of the coelacanth, *Latimeria* spp. *Smithiana Special Publications* 3: 1–52.

Obura, D. O. 2009. Coral reef resilience assessment of the Nosy Hara Marine Protected Area, northwest Madagascar. Gland: IUCN.

———. 2012. The diversity and biogeography of western Indian Ocean reef-building corals. *PLoS One* 7(9): e45013.

Obura, D. O., Di Carlo, G., Rabearisoa, A., and Oliver, T. A., eds. 2011. A rapid marine biodiversity assessment of the coral reefs of northeast Madagascar. *RAP Bulletin of Biological Assessment* 61: 1–100.

Obura, D. O., Church, J. E., and Gabrié, C. 2012. *Assessing Marine World Heritage from an Ecosystem Perspective: The Western Indian Ocean*. Paris: World Heritage Centre, United Nations Education, Science and Cultural Organization (UNESCO). http://www.vliz.be/projects/marineworldheritage.

Obura, D. O., Gudka, M., Abdou Rabi, F., Gian, S. B., Bijoux, J., et al., eds. 2017. *Coral Reef Status Report for theWestern Indian Ocean (2017)*. N.p.: Global Coral Reef Monitoring Network (GCRMN) and International Coral Reef Initiative (ICRI).

Obura, D. O., Bandeira, S. O., Bodin, N., Burgener, V., Braulik, G., et al. 2019. The northern Mozambique Channel. In *World Seas: An Environmental Evaluation*, 2nd ed., vol. 2, *The Indian Ocean to the Pacific*, ed. C. Sheppard, pp. 75–99. London: Elsevier.

Ocearch Shark Tracker. 2020. Maureen, White Shark (*Carcharodon carcharias*). https://www.ocearch.org/tracker/detail/maureen.

Odendaal, F., Jaomanana, and Kroese, M. 1995. Delimitation of marine reserves on the Masoala peninsular, NE Madagascar. Report prepared for CARE International in Madagascar.

Ohsumi, S. 1980. Population study of the Bryde's whale in the Southern Hemisphere under scientific permit in the three seasons 1976/77–1978/79. *Reports of the International Whaling Commission* 30: 319–331.

Olijdam, E. 2001. Exploitation of sea turtles in the Early Dilmun period (c. 2100–1900 BC). In *Proceedings of the Seminar for Arabian Studies, The British Museum, London, 25–27 July 2014*, ed. O. Elmaz, pp. 195–202. Oxford: Archaeopress.

Oliver, T. A., Olesen, K.L.L., Ratsimbazafy, H., Raberinary, D., Benbow, S., and Harris, A. 2015. Positive catch and economic benefits of periodic octopus fishery closures: Do effective, narrowly targeted actions "catalyze" broader management? *PLoS One* 10: e0129075.

Olson, D. 2015. Western Indian Ocean islands marine ecoregion (WIOMER): A regional strategy and action plan for conserving marine ecosystems and fisheries; 2010–2015. Antananarivo: Indian Ocean Commission Project Management Unit.

OMNIS (Office des Mines Nationales et des Industries Stratégiques). 2020. Exploration blocks. Accessed 1 September 2020. https://www.omnis.mg/index.php?option=com_content&view=article&id=14&Itemid=138&lang=en.

Ong, J.J.L., Meekan, M. G., Hsu, H. H., Fanning, L. P., and Campana, S. E. 2020. Annual bands in vertebrae validated by bomb radiocarbon assays provide estimates of age and growth of whale sharks. *Frontiers in Marine Science* 7: 1–7.

Pace, F., Benard, F., Glotin, H., Adam, O., and White, P. 2010. Subunit definition and analysis for humpback whale call classification. *Applied Acoustics* 71(11): 1107–1112.

Parida, A. K., and Jha, B. 2010. Salt tolerance mechanisms in mangroves: A review. *Trees* 24(2): 199–217.

Pascal, B. 2008. De la "terre des ancêtres" aux territoires des vivants: Les enjeux locaux de la gouvernance sur le littoral sud-ouest de Madagascar. PhD thesis, Muséum National d'Histoire Naturelle, Paris.

Pascal, B., Lavitra, T., Dubois, P., Lepoint, G., Grosjean, P., Todinanahary, G.G.B., Tsiresy, G., and Eeckhaut, I. 2013. Presentation of the "Polyaquaculture in Madagascar": A research program to ensure sustainable coastal livelihoods in southwestern and northern regions of the Red Island. Poster. 21st International Seaweed Symposium, 21–23 Apr. 2013, Bali, Indonesia.

Pascal, F. 2019. Du bon usage de d'holothuriculture et de l'algoculture villageoises à Madagascar. Presentation. Atelier Crevette et Autres Ressources Halieutiques, June 2019, Antananarivo. Ministère de l'Agriculture, de l'Elevage et de la Pêche, Food and Agriculture Organization of the United Nations, Groupement des Aquaculteurs et Pêcheurs de Crevettes à Madagascar.

Pauly, D. 2009. Beyond duplicity and ignorance in global fisheries. *Scientia Marinia* 73: 215–224.

Pavlin, B. I., Musto, J., Pretrick, M., Sarofalpiy, J., Sappa, P., Shapucy, S., and Kool, J. 2015. Mass poisoning after consumption of a hawksbill turtle, Federated States of Micronesia, 2010. *Western Pacific Surveillance and Response Journal* 6(1): 25–32.

Payne, R. S., and McVay, S. 1971. Songs of humpback whales. *Science* 173: 585–597.

Peckham, S. H., Maldonado-Diaz, D., Koch, V., Mancini, A., Gaos, A., and Tinker, M. T. 2008. High mortality of loggerhead turtles due to bycatch, human consumption and strandings at Baja California Sur, Mexico, 2003 to 2007. *Endangered Species Research* 5: 171–183.

Pedrono, M. 2008. *The Tortoises and Turtles of Madagascar*. Kota Kinabalu: Natural History Publications.

Perrin, W. F., Dolar, M.L.L., and Ortega, E. 1996. Osteological comparison of Bryde's whales from the Philippines with specimens from other regions. Paper SC/47/NP2 presented to the International Whaling Commission Scientific Committee. https://www.omuraswhale.org/scientific-literature.

Perry, C. T., Figueiredo, J., Vaudo, J. J., Hancock, J., Rees, R., and Shivji, M. 2018. Comparing length-measurement methods and estimating growth parameters of free-swimming whale sharks (*Rhincodon typus*) near the South Ari Atoll, Maldives. *Marine and Freshwater Research* 69: 1487–1495.

Petit, G. 1927. Nouvelles observations sur la pêche rituelle du dugong à Madagascar. *Bulletins et Mémoires de la Société d'Anthropologie de Paris*, série 7, 8(4–6): 246–250.

———. 1930. *L'Industrie des pêches à Madagascar*. Paris: Société d'Editions Géographiques, Maritimes et Coloniales.

Peverell, S. C. 2009. Sawfish (Pristidae) of the Gulf of Carpentaria, Queensland Australia. MS thesis, James Cook University.

Pichon, M. 1971. *Horastrea indica* n.gen., n.sp., a new hermatypic scleractinian coral from the south west Indian Ocean (Cnidaria, Anthozoa, Madreporaria). *Revue de Zoologie et de Botanique Africaines* 83: 165–172.

———. 1972. The coral reefs of Madagascar. In *Biogeography and Ecology of Madagascar*, eds. G. Richard-Vindard and R. Battistini, pp. 367–410. The Hague: Junk.

———. 1978. Recherches sur les peuplements à base de Scléractiniaires dans les récifs de la Baie de Tuléar (sud-ouest de Madagascar). *Atoll Research Bulletin* 222: 1–447.

Pierce, S. J., and Norman, B. M. 2016. *Rhincodon typus*. IUCN Red List of Threatened Species 2016: e.T19488A2365291. http://dx.doi.org/10.2305/IUCN.UK.2016-1.RLTS.T19488A2365291.en.

Pierce, S., Holmberg, J., Kock, A., and Marshall, A. 2018. Photographic identification of sharks. In *Shark Research: Emerging Technologies and Applications for the Field and Laboratory*, eds. J. C. Carrier, M. R. Heithaus, and C. A. Simpfendorfer, pp. 220–234. Boca Raton: CRC Press.

Piton, B., and Magnier, Y. 1971. Les régimes hydrologiques de la baie d'Ambaro (nordouest de Madagascar). *Cahiers de l'ORSTOM*, série *Océanographie* 9(2): 149–166.

Plon, S., Thakur, V., Parr, L., and Lavery, S. D. 2019. Phylogeography of the dugong (*Dugong dugon*) based on historical samples identifies vulnerable Indian Ocean populations. *PLoS One* 14(9): e0219350.

Pollen, F.P.L., and Van Dam, D. C. 1874. *Recherches sur la faune de Madagascar et de ses dépendances, d'après les découvertes*. Pt. 4, *Poissons de Madagascar*. Leiden: E. J. Brill.

Pomilla, C., and Rosenbaum, H. C. 2005. Against the current: An inter-oceanic whale migration event. *Biology Letters* 1(4): 476–479.

———. 2006. Estimates of relatedness in groups of humpback whales (*Megaptera novaeangliae*) on two wintering grounds of the Southern Hemisphere. *Molecular Ecology* 15: 2541–2555.

Pomilla, C., Amaral, A. R., Collins, T., Minton, G., Findlay, K., Leslie, M. S., Ponnampalam, L., Baldwin, R., and Rosenbaum, H. 2014. The world's most isolated and distinct whale population? Humpback whales of the Arabian Sea. *PLoS One* 9: e114162.

Potier, M., Marsac, F., Lucas, V., Sabatie, R., Hallier, J.-P., and Ménard, F. 2004. Feeding partitioning among tuna taken in surface and mid-water layers: The case of yellowfin (*Thunnus albacares*) and bigeye (*T. obesus*) in the western tropical Indian Ocean. *Western Indian Ocean Journal of Marine Science* 3(1): 51–62.

Poulakis, G. R., Stevens, P. W., Timmers, A. A., Wiley, T. R., and Simpfendorfer, C. A. 2011. Abiotic affinities and spatiotemporal distribution of the endangered smalltooth sawfish, *Pristis pectinata*, in a south-western Florida nursery. *Marine and Freshwater Research* 62: 1165–1177.

Pouyaud, L., Wirjoatmodjo, S., Rachmatika, I., Tjakrawidjaja, A., Hadiaty, R. K., and Hadie, W. 1999. Une nouvelle espèce de coelacanthe: Preuves génétiques et morphologiques. *Comptes rendus de l'Acadèmie des Sciences*, série 3, *Sciences de la Vie* 322(3): 261–267.

Pratchett, M. S., Hoey, A. S., and Wilson, S. K. 2014. Reef degradation and the loss of critical ecosystem goods and services provided by coral reef fishes. *Current Opinion Environmental* 7: 37–43.

Prebble, C.E.M., Rohner, C. A., Pierce, S. J., Robinson, D. P., Jaidah, M. Y., Bach, S. S., and Trueman, C. N. 2018. Limited latitudinal ranging of juvenile whale sharks in the western Indian Ocean suggests the existence of regional management units. *Marine Ecology Progress Series* 601: 167–183.

Preen, A. 2004. Distribution, abundance and conservation status of dugongs and dolphins in the southern and western Arabian Gulf. *Biological Conservation* 118(2): 205–218.

Preen, A., and Marsh, H. 1995. Response of dugongs to large-scale loss of seagrass from Hervey Bay, Queensland Australia. *Wildlife Research* 22(4): 507–519.

Purcell, S. W., Mercier, A., Conand, C., Hamel, J.-F., Toral-Granda, M. V., Lovatelli, A., and Uthicke, S. 2013. Sea cucumber fisheries: Global analysis of stocks, management measures and drivers of overfishing. *Fish and Fisheries* 14: 34–59.

Rabarison, A. G. 2000. Rapport final du projet de recherche sur l'étude des stocks de langoustes neritiques. Ministère de la Recherche Scientifique, report prepared for the Office National de l'Environnement.

Rabenjarison, F., Ramarolahy, A.R.N., Velomora, A., Rahajaniana, M. P., and Raveloson, N. E. 2016. Ciguatera poisoning after consumption of shark in Fenerive-Est: Epidemiological and clinical aspects and laboratory results. *Revue d'Anesthésie-Réanimation, Médecine d'Urgence et Toxicologie* 8(1): 9–12.

Rabesandratana, H. D. 1985. Sur quelques utilisations récifales à Madagascar. In *Proceedings of the 6th International Coral Reef Congress, Townsville*, vol. 2, eds. J. H. Choat, D. Barnes, M. A. Borowitzka, J. C. Coll, P. J.Davies, et al., pp. 661–668.

Radelli, L. 1975. Geology and oil of Sakamena Basin, Malagasy Republic (Madagascar) 1. *AAPG Bulletin* 59(1): 97–114.

Rafalimanana, T. 1991. Estimation des captures de la pêche traditionnelle malgache en 1990. Ministère de la Production Animale, Eaux et Forêts, Direction de la Pêche et de l'Aquaculture, United Nations Development Programme project MAG/85/014, rapport de terrain.

Rajoharison, H. 1994. Note sur les indices gonadotrophiques et de la fécondité des albacores (*Thunnus albacares*) échantillonnés à Antsiranana en 1993: Résultats préliminaires. Documents Scienifiques AT/COI/PTR2. Commission de l'Océan Indien.

Rajoharison, H., and Conand, F. 1995. Etude de la reproduction de l'albacore dans le canal de Mozambique: Résultats de la campagne 1994. Documents Scientifiques AT/COI/PTR2. Commission de l'Océan Indien.

Rakotoarimino, L., and Davis, P.Z.R. 2017. Utilisation de mesures d'incitation centrés sur les communautés pour conserver les dugongs et les herbiers marins. In *Actes du forum de la recherche, 22–23 septembre 2017 a Nosy-Be: Biodiversité Marine*, pp. 128–130. Antananarivo: Ministère d'Education Supérieure et de la Recherche Scientifique (MESUPRES).

Rakotoarinjanahary, H., Razakafoniaina, T. N., Kaderbay, B., and Ranaivoson, R. L. 1994. Inventaire des sources de pollution et quantités de polluants à Madagascar. CNRO (Centre National de Recherches Océanographiques), OMS (World Health Organization, AFRO).

Rakotomahazo, C., Ravaoarinorotsihoarana, L. A., Randrianandrasaziky, D., Glass, L., Gough, C., Todinanahary, G.G.B., and Gardner, C. J. 2019. Participatory planning of a community-based payments for ecosystem services initiative in Madagascar's mangroves. *Ocean and Coastal Management* 175: 43–52.

Rakotomavo, A. 2018. The mangroves of the east of Madagascar: Ecological potentials and pressures. *Open Journal of Ecology* 8: 447–458.

Rakotondrazafy, V., and Randriamihaja, M. 2019. Developing a common definition for LMMAs in Madagascar. Poster. Coastal governance and policy theme. 11th WIOMSA (Western Indian Ocean Marine Science Association) Scientific Symposium, Mauritius, 1–6 July 2019.

Rakotonirina, B. P. 1987. Les tortues marines dans le sud de Madagascar: Étude bibliographique et enquêtes auprès des pécheurs; Recherche sur la biométrie et l'alimentation de la tortue verte, *Chelonia mydas* Linnaeus. Mémoire de DEA, Université de Toliara.

———. 1989. *Exploitation des tortues marines à Madagascar: Rapport des enquêtes, 1989*. Toliara: WWF Madagascar and Station Marine de Toliara.

———. 1999. Etude préliminaire des tortues marines dans la Presqu'île de Masoala: Rapport final, novembre–décembre, 1998. Report prepared for the Wildlife Conservation Society, Madagascar.

Rakotonirina, B. P., and Cooke, A. 1994. Sea turtles of Madagascar: Their status, exploitation and conservation. *Oryx* 28: 51–61.

Rakotonirina, B. P., and Harding, S. 2005. National status of sea turtle conservation and management: Madagascar. In *Proceedings of the Western Indian Ocean Region Marine Turtle Conservation Workshop, Mombasa, Kenya, 16–17 September 2004*, eds. G. Okemwa, N. Muthiga, and E. Mueni, pp. 4–5. Mombasa: Western Indian Ocean Marine Science Association.

Rakotoson, L., and Tanner, K. 2006. Community-based governance of coastal zone and marine resources in Madagascar. *Ocean and Coastal Management* 49: 855–872.

Ramanantsoa, J. D., Krug, M., Penvend, P., Rouault, M., and Gulad, J. 2018a. Coastal upwelling south of Madagascar: Temporal and spatial variability. *Journal of Marine Systems* 178: 29–37.

Ramanantsoa, J. D., Penven, P., Krug, M., Gula, J., and Rouault, M. 2018b. Uncovering a new current: The southwest Madagascar coastal current. *Geophysical Research Letters* 45(4): 1930–1938.

Ramírez-Macías, D., Queiroz, N., Pierce, S. J., Humphries, N. E., Sims, D. W., and Brunnschweiler, J. M. 2017. Oceanic adults, coastal juveniles: Tracking the habitat use of whale sharks off the Pacific coast of Mexico. *PeerJ* 2017: e3271.

Ramos-Cartelle, A., Garcia-Cortes, B., and Mejuto, J., 2008. Scientific estimates of bycatch landed by the Spanish longline fleet targeting swordfish (*Xiphias gladius*) in the Indian Ocean with special reference to the 2004–2006 period. IOTC-2008-WPEB-03. https://www.iotc.org/sites/default/files/documents/proceedings/2008/wpeb/IOTC-2008-WPEB-03.pdf.

Ramsar Sites Information Service. 2020. Ramsar sites information service. Accessed 26 July 2020. https://rsis.ramsar.org[/ris/Ramsar site number].

Ramsay, P. J., and Miller, W. R. 2006. Marine geophysical technology used to define coelacanth habitats on the KwaZulu-Natal shelf, South Africa. *South African Journal of Science* 102: 427–434.

Ranaivoson, E. 1997. Biodiversité côtière et marine. *Monographie Nationale sur la Biodiversité*, pp. 117–136. United Nations Environment Programme, Office National pour l'Environnement, and ANGAP (Association Nationale pour la Gestion des Aires Protégées).

Randriamanantsoa, B. J. 1997. Modifications de la morphologie et des sédiments du Grand Récif de Toliara (comparaisons 1969/70–1995/1996): Impacts sur la pêche et les ressources vivantes. Mémoire de DEA, Institut Halieutique et des Sciences Marines, Université de Toliara.

Randriamanantsoa, B. J., and Brand, J. 2000. *Eco-développement des populations de base pour la conservation de la Réserve de la Biosphère de Mananara-Nord (Phase II): Rapport succinct de Module 2; Etude de reconnaissance et zonage des écosystèmes marins*. Report prepared for Project UNESCO-MAB Mananara-Nord. Antananarivo: Development Environment Consultants.

Randriarilala, F., Rafalimanana, T., and Caveriviere, A. 2008. Les captures accessoires des crevettiers industriels et artisanaux de Madagascar. In *Les crevettes côtières de Madagascar: Biologie, exploitation, gestion*, eds. A. Caveriviere, C. Chaboud, and T. Rafalimanana, pp. 237–257. Marseille: IRD Editions.

Rasmussen, K., Palacios, D. M., Calambokidis, J., Saborío, M. T., Dalla Rosa, L., Secchi, E. R., Steiger, G. H., Allen, J. M., and Stone, M. 2007. Southern Hemisphere humpback whales wintering off Central America: Insights from water temperature into the longest mammalian migration. *Biology Letters* 3: 302–305.

Rasolofo, V. M. 1997. Use of mangroves by traditional fishermen in Madagascar. *Mangroves and Salt Marshes* 1(4): 243–253.

———. 2011. Etude écologique des ressources crevettières dans les mangroves de la Baie d'Ambaro (nord-ouest de Madagascar) en vue d'une gestion durable de leur exploitation. PhD thesis, Université d'Antananarivo.

Rasolofonirina, R., and Conand, C. 1998. Sea cucumber exploitation in the Toliara region of southwest Madagascar. *SPC Beche-de-mer Information Bulletin* 10: 10–13.

Rasolofonirina, R., Mara, E., and Jangou, M. 2004. Sea cucumber fishery and mariculture in Madagascar, a case study of Toliara, southwest Madagascar. In *Advances in Sea Cucumber Aquaculture and Management*, eds. A. Lovatelli, C. Conand, S. Purcell, S. Uthicke, J.-F. Hamel, and A. Mercier. Food and Agriculture Organization of the United Nations Fisheries Technical Paper 463. Rome: FAO.

Ratsifandrihamanana, F. 2014. Protocole de terrain pour l'étude de l'écosystème marin et côtier. Provisional report, Feb. 2014. Consortium Biotope and Resolve, Antananarivo.

Ratsimbazafy, H., Lavitra, T., Kochzius, M., and Huge, J. 2019. Emergence and diversity of marine protected areas in Madagascar. *Marine Policy* 105: 91–108.

Ratsimbazafy, R. 2003. Sea turtles. In *The Natural History of Madagascar*, eds. S. M. Goodman and J. P. Benstead, pp. 210–213. Chicago: University of Chicago Press.

Ravaoarinorotsihoarana, L. A. 2011. *Seagrass Meadows of Kirindy Mite: A Baseline Survey of the Seagrass Habitats of Kirindy Mite National Park, Menabe, Western Madagascar*. Antananarivo: Blue Ventures.

Ravololoharinjara, M. 2019. Rapport de mission a Toliara pour l'inventaire des captures et specimens de coelacanthes. Resolve sarl internal report, Nov. 2019. https://www.resolve.mg/publications/.

Rayner, G. W. 1940. Whale marking: Progress and results to December 1939. *Discovery Reports* 19: 245–284.

Razafimandimby, Y., and Joachim, L. D. 2017. Update on shark catch characteristics by national longline fleets in Madagascar (2010–2016). Indian Ocean Tuna Commission 13th Working Party on Ecosystems and Bycatch, Spain, 4–8 Sept. 2017. IOTC-2017-WPEB13-11. https://www.iotc.org/documents/update-shark-catch-characteristics-national-longliner-fleets-madagascar-2010-2016.

Razafimandimby, Y., Fanazava, R., and Joachim, D. L. 2015. Rapport national de Madagascar destiné pour la Comité Scientifique de la Commission des thons de l'Océan Indien, 2015. Indian Ocean Tuna Commission National Report IOTC-2015-SC18-NR15. https://www.iotc.org/documents/madagascar-%E2%80%93-national-report-2015.

Razafindrainibe, H. 2010. Baseline study of the shrimp trawl fishery in Madagascar and strategies for bycatch management. Food and Agriculture Organization of the United Nations. Final Report TCP/MAG/3201-REBYC2. http://www.fao.org/fishery/docs/DOCUMENT/rebyc/rebyc2/madagascar/report.pdf.

Razafindrainibe, H., Razakafoniaina, N. T., Rasolofo, V. M., Rakotoarinjanahary, H., Randriambololona, C., and Rasolonjatovo, H. 1996. *La pêche traditionnelle maritime dans le Menabe (côte ouest de Madagascar): Rapport des recherches*. Projet Etudes biologiques et socioéconomiques des pêches artisanales traditionnelles à Madagascar, phase II. Hell-Ville: Centre National de Recherches Océanographiques.

Razafindrakoto, H. L. 2013. *Les stocks de crevettes pénéides côtières exploitées à Madagascar: Situations*. Journée de réflexion pour le redressement de la pêche crevettière, Ministère de la Pêche et des Ressources Halieutiques, Mahajanga, 22 Feb. 2013. Mahajanga: Groupement des Aquaculteurs et des Pêcheurs de Crevette de Madagascar.

Razafindrakoto, Y. 2018. Integrated approaches to enhance the conservation of dugong and seagrass ecosystems in the Sahamalaza area. Report to United Nations Environment Programme Global Environment Facility Dugong and Seagrass Conservation Project. https://www.dugongconservation.org/impact/project-documents/?project_title=Integrated%2Bapproaches%2Bto%2Benhance%2Bthe%2Bconservation%2Bof%2Bdugong%2Band%2Bseagrass%2Becosystems%2Bin%2Bthe%2BSahamalaza%2Barea%2B%2528MG4%2529.&form-option=project-documents.

Razafindrakoto, Y., Rosenbaum, H. C., and Helweg, D. 2001. First description of humpback whale song from Antongil Bay, Madagascar. *Marine Mammal Science* 17(1): 180–186.

Razafindrakoto, Y., Andrianarivelo, N., and Rosenbaum, H. C. 2004. Sightings, catches, and other records of Indo-Pacific humpback dolphins in the coastal waters of Madagascar. *Aquatic Mammals* 30: 103–110.

Razafindrakoto, Y., Andrianarivelo, N., Cerchio, S., Rasomananto, I., and Rosenbaum, H. C. 2008. Preliminary assessment of cetacean incidental mortality in artisanal fisheries in Anakao, southwestern region of Madagascar. *Western Indian Ocean Journal of Marine Science* 7(2): 175–184.

Razafindrakoto, Y., Rosenbaum, H., Ersts, P., Pomilla, C., Rasoamampianina, V., Cerchio, S., Dushane, J., Murray, A., and Rakotosamimanana, T. 2010. Mammifères marins de la baie d'Antongil. Unpublished report. Wildlife Conservation Society.

Reef Doctor. 2020. Reef Restoration. Accessed 23 Aug. 2020. https://www.reefdoctor.org/projects/conservation/coral-reefs/reef-restoration/.

Rekdahl, M. L., Tisch, C., Cerchio, S., and Rosenbaum, H. 2016. Common non-song social calls of humpback whales (*Megaptera novaeangliae*) recorded off northern Angola, southern Africa. *Marine Mammal Science* 33(1): 365–375.

Remanevy, M. E., Rabesandratana, H. D., Conand, C., Rakotoarinivo, W., Rasolofonirina, R., Rasoandrasana, N. B., and Ravelo, I. 1997. *Etude de la pêcherie aux holothuries dans le sud-ouest de Madagascar et propositions de mesurés d'aménagement*. Report prepared for the Office National de l'Environnement, Dec. 1997. Toliara: Institut Halieutique et des Sciences Marines.

René, F., Poisson, F., and Tessler, E. 1998. Evolution of the swordfish longline fishery *Xiphias gladius* operating in the Indian Ocean from Reunion Island. In *Tuna Prospects and Strategies for the Indian Ocean*, eds. P. Cayré and J.-Y. Le Gall, pp. 287–312. Paris: ORSTOM.

Réville, J. P., Salley, S., Randrianasolnjanahary, J. P., Niget, J. M., Valentine, M., and Benjamina, A. 2007. Description of the Mandena aquatic ecosystem. In *Biodiversity, Ecology and Conservation of Littoral Ecosystems in Southeastern Madagascar, Tolagnaro (Fort Dauphin)*, eds. J. U. Ganzhorn, S. M. Goodman, and M. Vincelette, pp. 281–297. SI/MAB Series 11. Washington, DC: Smithsonian Institution.

Ribbink, A. J., and Roberts, M. 2006. African Coelacanth Ecosystem Programme: An overview of the conference contributions. *South African Journal of Science* 102: 409–415.

Richmond, M. D. 2001. The marine biodiversity of the western Indian Ocean and its biogeography: How much do we know? In *Marine Science Development in Eastern Africa: Proceedings of the 20th Anniversary Conference on Marine Science in Tanzania 28 June–1 July 2001*, eds. M. D. Richmond and J. Francis, pp. 241–262. Zanzibar: Institute of Marine Sciences and Western Indian Ocean Marine Science Association (WIOMSA).

Riegl, B., and Piller, W. E. 2003. Possible refugia for reefs in times of environmental stress. *International Journal of Earth Science* 92: 520–531.

Robineau, D., and Rose, J.-M. 1984. Les cétacés de Djibouti: Bilan de connaissances actuelles sur la faune cétologique de la Mer Rouge et du Golfe d'Aden. *Bulletin du Muséum d'Histoire Naturelle*, Paris 6: 219–249.

Robinson, D. P., Jaidah, M. Y., Jabado, R. W., Lee-Brooks, K., Nour El-Din, N. M., et al. 2013. Whale sharks, *Rhincodon typus*, aggregate around offshore platforms in Qatari waters of the Arabian Gulf to feed on fish spawn. *PLoS One* 8(3): e58255.

Robinson, G., and Pascal, B. 2011. Development of sea cucumber farming as an alternative livelihood in south-west Madagascar. In *Asia-Pacific Tropical Sea Cucumber Aquaculture: Proceedings of an International Symposium Held in Noumea, New Caledonia, 15–17 February 2011*, eds. C. A. Hair, T. D. Pickering, and D. J. Mills, pp. 142–155. Canberra: Australian Centre for International Agricultural Research (ACIAR).

Robinson, R., Champetier de Ribes, G., Ranaivoson, G., Rejely, M., and Rabeson, D. 1998. Etude CAP (connaissance–attitude–pratique) sur les intoxications par consommation d'animaux marins sur le littoral sud-ouest de Madagascar. Manuscript 1944, Santé publique. https://pathexo.societe-mtsi.fr.

Rocha, R. C., Clapham, P. J., and Ivashchenko, Y. V. 2014. Emptying the oceans: A summary of industrial whaling catches in the 20th century. *Marine Fisheries Review* 76(4): 37–48.

Rocliffe, S., Peabody, S., Samoliys, M., and Hawkins, J. P. 2014. Towards a network of locally managed marine areas (LMMAs) in the western Indian Ocean. *PLoS One* 9(7): e103000.

Rohner, C. A., Richardson, A. J., Marshall, A. D., Weeks, S. J., and Pierce, S. J. 2011. How large is the world's largest fish? Measuring whale sharks *Rhincodon typus* with laser photogrammetry. *Journal of Fish Biology* 78: 378–385.

Rohner, C. A., Pierce, S., Marshall, A., Weeks, S., Bennett, M., and Richardson, A. 2013. Trends in sightings and environmental influences on a coastal aggregation of manta rays and whale sharks. *Marine Ecology Progress Series* 482: 153–168.

Rohner, C. A., Richardson, A. J., Prebble, C.E.M., Marshall, A. D., Bennett, M. B., Weeks, S. J., Cliff, G., Wintner, S. P., and Pierce, S. J. 2015. Laser photogrammetry improves size and demographic estimates for whale sharks. *PeerJ* 3: e886.

Rohner, C. A., Richardson, A. J., Jaine, F.R.A., Bennett, M. B., Weeks, S. J., Cliff, G., Robinson, D. P., Reeve-Arnold, K. E., and Pierce, S. J. 2018. Satellite tagging highlights the importance of productive Mozambican coastal waters to the ecology and conservation of whale sharks. *PeerJ* 6: e4161.

Romaine, T. E. 1997. *Localized Marine Resource Exploitation in Toliara, Madagascar*. Project assignment report. Brattleboro: School for International Training.

Roman, J., Estes, J. A., Morissette, L., Smith, C., Costa, D., McCarthy, J., Nation, J. B., Nicol, S., Pershing, A., and Smetacek, V. 2014. Whales as marine ecosystem engineers. *Frontiers in Ecology and the Environment* 12: 377–385.

Romanov, E. V. 2002. Bycatch in the tuna purse-seine fisheries of the western Indian Ocean (statistical data included). *Fishery Bulletin* 100(1): 90–105.

Rosenbaum, H. C. 2003a. Marine mammals. In *The Natural History of Madagascar*, eds. S. M. Goodman and J. P. Benstead, pp. 213–216. Chicago: University of Chicago Press.

———. 2003b. *Megaptera novaeangliae*, humpback whale. In *The Natural History of Madagascar*, eds. S. M. Goodman and J. P. Benstead, pp. 217–221. Chicago: University of Chicago Press.

Rosenbaum, H. C., Walsh, P. D., Razafindrakoto, Y., Vély, M., and DeSalle, R. 1997. First description of a humpback whale breeding ground in Baie d'Antongil, Madagascar. *Conservation Biology* 11: 312–314.

Rosenbaum, H. C., Razafindrakoto, Y., Ersts, P., and Ventresca, G. 2000. A preliminary population estimate for humpback whales from the Antongil Bay, Madagascar wintering ground in the southwestern Indian Ocean. Report to the Scientific Committee of the International Whaling Commission SC/52/IA10

Rosenbaum, H. C., Razafindrakoto, Y., Vahoavy, J., and Pomilla, C. 2001. A note on recent sightings of southern right whales (*Eubalaena australis*) along the east coast of Madagascar. In *Right whales: Worldwide status*, eds. P. B. Best, J. L. Bannister, R. L. Brownell Jr., and G. P. Donovan. *Journal of Cetacean Research and Management*, special issue 2: 177–180.

Rosenbaum, H. C., Pomilla, C., Mendez, M., Leslie, M. S., Best, P. B., et al. 2009. Population structure of humpback whales from their breeding grounds in the South Atlantic and Indian Oceans. *PLoS One* 4(10): e7318.

Rosenbaum, H. C., Kershaw, F., Mendez, M., Pomilla, C., Leslie, M. S., et al. 2017. First circumglobal assessment of Southern Hemisphere humpback whale mitochondrial genetic variation and implications for management. *Endangered Species Research* 32: 551–567.

Rowat, D., and Brooks, K. S. 2012. A review of the biology, fisheries and conservation of the whale shark *Rhincodon typus*. *Journal of Fish Biology* 80: 1019–1056.

Rowat, D., Speed, C. W., Meekan, M. G., Gore, M. A., and Bradshaw, C.J.A. 2009. Population abundance and apparent survival of the Vulnerable whale shark *Rhincodon typus* in the Seychelles aggregation. *Oryx* 43: 591–598.

Rowat, D., Brooks, K., March, A., McCarten, C., Jouannet, D., Riley, L., Jeffreys, G., Perri, M., Vely, M., and Pardigon, B. 2011. Long-term membership of whale sharks (*Rhincodon typus*) in coastal aggregations in Seychelles and Djibouti. *Marine and Freshwater Research* 62: 621–627.

Ruiz, J., Abascal, F. J., Bach, P., Baez, J. C., Cauquil, P., et al. 2018. Bycatch of the European, and associated flag, purse seine tuna-fishery in the Indian Ocean for the period 2008–2017. 14th meeting of the Indian Ocean Tuna Commission Working Party on Ecosystems and Bycatch. IOTC-2018-WPEB14-15. https://www.iotc.org/documents/WPEB/14/15.

Ryan, J. P., Green, J. R., Espinoza, E., and Hearn, A. R. 2017. Association of whale sharks (*Rhincodon typus*) with thermo-biological frontal systems of the eastern tropical Pacific. *PLoS One* 12: 1–22.

Sabarros, P. S., Ménard, F., Lévénez, J. J., Tew Kai, E., and Ternon, J. F. 2009. Mesoscale eddies influence distribution and aggregation patterns of micronekton in the Mozambique Channel. *Marine Ecology Progress Series* 395: 101–107.

Sabatini, G., Salley, S., and Ramanamanjato, J.-B. 2007. A review of the spiny lobster fishery in the Tolagnaro (Fort-Dauphin) region. In *Biodiversity, Ecology and Conservation of Littoral Ecosystems in Southeastern Madagascar, Tolagnaro (Fort Dauphin)*, eds. J. U. Ganzhorn, S. M. Goodman, and M. Vincelette, pp. 299–307. SI/MAB Series 11. Washington, DC: Smithsonian Institution.

Saenger, P., Gartside, D., and Funge-Smith, S. 2013. *A Review of Mangrove and Seagrass Ecosystems and Their Linkage to Fisheries and Fisheries Management*. RP Publication 2013/09. Bangkok: Food and Agriculture Organization of the United Nations, Regional Office for Asia and the Pacific.

Safford, R. J., ed. 2000. *Etude environnementale et écologique du lac Sahaka, Madagascar*. London: Royal Holloway Institute for Environmental Research, University of London.

Salomon, J. N. 1980. Les récifs coralliens de Belo-sur-Mer: Etude géomorphologique (sud-ouest de Madagascar). *Madagascar: Revue de Géographie* 38: 87–109.

———. 1986. Le sud-ouest de Madagascar: Etude de géographie physique. Thèse de Doctorat d'Etat, Université d'Aix-Marseille.

———. 2009. L'accrétion littorale sur la côte ouest de Madagascar. *Physio-Géo* 3: 35–59.

Samoilys, M. A., Halford, A., and Osuka, K. 2019. Disentangling drivers of the abundance of coral reef fishes in the western Indian Ocean. *Ecology and Evolution* 9: 4149–4167.

Samonds, K. E., Zalmout, I. S., Irwin, M. T., Krause, D. W., Rogers, R. R., and Raharivony, L. 2009. *Eotheroides lambondrano*, new Middle Ecocene seacow (Mammalia, Sirenia) from the Mahajanga Basin, northwestern Madagascar. *Journal of Vertebrate Paleontology* 29(4): 1233–1243.

Sasaki, T., Nikaido, M., Wada, S., Yamada, T. K., Cao, Y., Hasegawa, M., and Okada, N. 2006. *Balaenoptera omurai* is a newly discovered baleen whale that represents an ancient evolutionary lineage. *Molecular Phylogenetics and Evolution* 41: 40–52. doi:10.1016/j.ympev.2006.03.032.

Scales, I. R., and Friess, D. A. 2019. Patterns of mangrove forest disturbance and biomass removal due to small-scale harvesting in southwestern Madagascar. *Wetlands Ecology and Management* 27: 609–625.

Scales, I., Friess, D., Glass, L., and Ravaoarinorotsihoarana, L. 2017. Rural livelihoods and mangrove degradation in south-west Madagascar: Lime production as an emerging threat. *Oryx* 52(4): 641–645.

Schmid, J. L., Addison, D. A., Donnelly, M. A., Shirley, M. A., and Wibbels, T. 2008. The effect of Australian pine (*Casuarina equisetifolia*) removal on loggerhead sea turtle (*Caretta caretta*) incubation temperatures on Keewaydin Island. *Florida Journal of Coastal Research* 55: 214–220.

Schouten, M. W., de Ruijter, W.P.M., van Leeuwen, P. J., and Ridderinkhof, H. 2003. Eddies and variability in the Mozambique Channel. *Deep-Sea Research II, Topical Studies in Oceanography* 50(12–13): 1987–2003.

Schreiber, C., and Coco, C. 2017. Husbandry of whale sharks. In *The Elasmobranch Husbandry Manual II: Recent Advances in the Care of Sharks, Rays and Their Relatives*, eds. M. Smith, D. Warmolts, D. Thoney, R. Hueter, M. Murray, and J. Ezurra, pp. 87–98. Special Publication of the Ohio Biological Survey. Columbus: Ohio Biological Survey.

Sequeira, A., Mellin, C., Rowat, D., Meekan, M. G., and Bradshaw, C.J.A. 2012. Ocean-scale prediction of whale shark distribution. *Diversity and Distributions* 18: 504–518.

Sequeira, A.M.M., Mellin, C., Delean, S., Meekan, M. G., and Bradshaw, C.J.A. 2013a. Spatial and temporal predictions of inter-decadal trends in Indian Ocean whale sharks. *Marine Ecology Progress Series* 478: 185–195.

Sequeira, A.M.M., Mellin, C., Meekan, M. G., Sims, D. W., and Bradshaw, C.J.A. 2013b. Inferred global connectivity of whale shark *Rhincodon typus* populations. *Journal of Fish Biology* 82: 367–389.

Séret, B. 1986a. Deep water skates from Madagascar (Chondrichthys, Rajoidei). In *Indo-Pacific Fish Biology: Proceedings of the Second International Conference on Indo-Pacific Fishes*, eds. T. Uyeno, R. Arai, T. Taniuchi, and K. Matsuura, pp. 256–260. Tokyo: Ichthyological Society of Japan.

———. 1986b. Deep water skates of Madagascar: Part 1, Anacanthobatidae (Pisces, Chondrichthys, Batoidea); Second record of the skate *Anacanthobatis ori* (Wallace, 1967) from off Madagascar. *Cybium* 10(4): 307–326.

———. 1987. *Halaelurus clevai*, sp. n., a new species of catshark (Scylliorhinidae) from off Madagascar, with remarks on the taxonomic status of the genera *Halaelurus* Gill and *Galeus* Rafinesque. *J.L.B. Smith Institute of Ichthyology Special Publication* 44: 1–27.
———. 1989a. Deep water skates of Madagascar: Part 2, Rajidae; *Gurgesiella (Fenestraja) maceachrani* sp. n. *Cybium* 13(1): 55–64.
———. 1989b. Deep water skates of Madagascar: Part 3, Rajidae (Pisces, Chondrichthyes, Batoidea); *Raja (Dipturus) crosnieri* sp. n. *Cybium* 13(2): 115–130.
Séret, B., and McEachran, J. D. 1986. Catalogue critique des types de poissons du Muséum national d'Histoire naturelle. *Bulletin du Muséum National d'Histoire Naturelle*, Paris, série 4, sect. A, *Zoologie, Biologie et Ecologie Animales*, 8(4): 3–50.
Shanker, K., Pandav, B., and Choudhury, B. C. 2004. An assessment of olive ridley (*Lepidochelys olivacea*) nesting population in Orissa on the east coast of India. *Biological Conservation* 115: 149–160.
Sheppard, C., Turak, E., and Wood, E. 2008. *Horastrea indica*. IUCN Red List of Threatened Species 2008: e.T133529A3788398. https://dx.doi.org/10.2305/IUCN.UK.2008.RLTS.T133529A3788398.en.
Shipton, T., and Hecht, T. 2007. Coastal mariculture assessment mission. Final Report. Regional Programme for the Sustainable Management of the Coastal Zones of the Indian Ocean Countries (ReCoMaP). https://iwlearn.net/resolveuid/fc44150e-31b8-41c4-9c0c-dd504f7b8e46.
Short, F. T., Koch, E. W., Creed, J. C., Magalhaes, K. M., Fernandez, E., and Gaeckle, J. L. 2006. SeagrassNet monitoring across the Americas: Case studies of seagrass decline. *Marine Ecology* 27(4): 277–289.
Short, F. T., Polidoro, B., Livingstone, S. R., Carpenter, K. E., Bandeira, S., et al. 2011. Extinction risk assessment of the world's seagrass species. *Biological Conservation* 144: 1961–1971.
Sibree, J. 1915. *A Naturalist in Madagascar*. Philadelphia: J. B. Lippincott.
Silas, E. G. 1986. The whale shark (*Rhiniodon typus* Smith) in Indian coastal waters: Is the species endangered or vulnerable? *Marine Fisheries Information Service, Technical and Extension Series* 66: 1–19.
Simmonds, M. P., and Eliott, W. J. 2009. Climate change and cetaceans: Concerns and recent developments. *Journal of the Marine Biological Association of the United Kingdom* 89(1): 203–210.
Simpfendorfer, C. A. 2014. Fisheries. In *Sawfish: A Global Strategy for Conservation*, eds. L. Harrison and N. K. Dulvy, p. 70. Vancouver: IUCN Species Survival Commission's Shark Specialist Group.
Simpfendorfer, C. A., Wiley, T.R.R., and Yeiser, B. G. 2010. Improving conservation planning for an endangered sawfish using data from acoustic telemetry. *Biological Conservation* 143: 1460–1469.
Simpfendorfer, C. A., Smith, K., and Carlson, J. K. 2014. The unusual biology of sawfishes. In *Sawfish: A Global Strategy for Conservation*, eds. L. Harrison and N. K. Dulvy, pp. 26–29. Vancouver: IUCN Species Survival Commission's Shark Specialist Group.
Sims, D. 2019. The significance of ocean deoxygenation for elasmobranchs. In *Ocean Deoxygenation: Everyone's Problem; Causes, Impacts, Consequences and Solutions*, eds. D. Laffoley and J. M. Baxter, pp. 431–448. Gland: IUCN.
Sims, D. W., Southall, E. J., Humphries, N. E., Hays, G. C., Bradshaw, C.J.A., et al. 2008. Scaling laws of marine predator search behaviour. *Nature* 451: 1098–1102.
Skinner, F., Burtenshaw-deVries, A., Long, S., Randrianantenaina, S., and Ellis, E. 2016. *Phase Two Project for Community Lobster Fishery Management in the Village of Sainte Luce (Project Oratsimba)*. Report SF-FAO/2016/xx. July 2016. Ebène: Food and Agriculture Organization of the United Nations, SmartFish Programme of the Indian Ocean Commission.
Smale, M. J. 1998. *Evaluation of Shark Populations around the Masoala Peninsular, North East Madagascar*. Final Report. Antananarivo: Wildlife Conservation Society, Madagascar Country Programme.
Smith, J.L.B. 1939a. A living fish of Mesozoic type. *Nature* 143: 455–456.
———. 1939b. A surviving fish of the order Actinistia. *Transactions of the Royal Society of South Africa* 27(1): 47–50.
———. 1953. The second coelacanth. *Nature* 171: 99–101.
———. 1956. *Old Fourlegs. The Story of the Coelacanth*. London: Longmans, Green.
Smith, M. M., and Heemstra, P. C., eds. 1986. *Smiths' Sea Fishes*. Johannesburg: Macmillan.
Southall, B. L., Bowles, A. E., Ellison, W. T., Finneran, J. J., Gentry, R. L., et al. 2007. Marine mammal noise exposure criteria: Initial scientific recommendations. *Aquatic Mammals* 33: 411–521.
Southall, B. L., Rowles, T., Gulland, F., Baird, R. W., and Jepson, P. D. 2013. Final report of the Independent Scientific Review Panel investigating potential contributing factors to a 2008 mass stranding of melon-headed whales (*Peponocephala electra*) in Antsohihy, Madagascar. https://iwc.int/2008-mass-stranding-in-madagascar.
Spalding, M., Burke, L., Wood, S. A., Ashpole, J., Hutchison, J., and Ermgassen, P. z. 2017. Mapping the global value and distribution of coral reef tourism. *Marine Policy* 82: 104–119.
Spalding, D., and Ravilious, C. 2001. *World Atlas of Coral Reefs*. Berkeley: University of California Press.
Speed, C. W., Meekan, M. G., Rowat, D., Pierce, S. J., Marshall, A. D., and Bradshaw, C.J.A. 2008. Scarring patterns and relative mortality rates of Indian Ocean whale sharks. *Journal of Fish Biology* 72: 1488–1503.
Stéquert, B., and Marsac, F. 1986. *La pêche de surface des thonidés tropicaux dans l'océan Indien*. FAO Fisheries Technical Paper 282. Rome: Food and Agriculture Organization of the United Nations.
Stevick, P. T., Neves, M. C., Johansen, F., Engel, M. H., Allen, J., Marcondes, M.C.C., and Carlson, C. 2011. A quarter of a world away: Female humpback whale moves 10 000 km between breeding areas. *Biology Letters* 7: 299–302.
Stobbs, R. E., and Bruton, M. N. 1991. The fishery of the Comoros, with comments on its possible impact on coelacanth survival. *Environmental Biology of Fishes* 32: 341–359.
Stop Illegal Fishing. 2019. Madagascar launches its first octopus fishery improvement project. 22 Feb. 2019. https://stopillegalfishing.com/press-links/madagascar-launches-its-first-octopus-fishery-improvement-project/.
Stretta, J.-M., de Molina, A. D., Ariz, J., Domalain, G., and Santana, J. C. 1998. Les espèces associées aux pêches thonières tropicales dans l'océan Indien. In *Le Thon—Enjeux et stratégies pour l'Océan Indien*, eds. P. Cayré and J.-Y. Le Gall, pp. 369–386. Paris: ORSTOM.
Swallow, J. C., Fieux, M., and Schott, F. 1988. The boundary currents east and north of Madagascar: Part I, geostrophic currents and transports. *Journal of Geophysical Research* 93(C5): 4951–4962.
Swart, N. C., Lutjeharms, J.R.E., Ridderinkhof, H., and de Ruijter, W.P.M. 2010. Observed characteristics of Mozambique Channel eddies. *Journal of Geophysical Research* 115: C09006.
Taniuchi, T., Ishihara, H., Tanaka, S., Hyodo, S., Murakami, M., and Séret, B. 2003. Occurrence of two species of elasmobranchs, *Carcharhinus leucas* and *Pristis microdon*, in Betsiboka River, west Madagascar. *Cybium* 27(3): 237–241.
Taylor, B. L., Baird, R., Barlow, J., Dawson, S. M., Ford, J., Mead, J. G., Notarbartolo di Sciara, G., Wade, P., and Pitman, R. L. 2019. *Physeter macrocephalus* (amended version of 2008 assessment). IUCN Red List of Threatened Species 2019: e.T41755A160983555. https://dx.doi.org/10.2305/IUCN.UK.2008.RLTS.T41755A160983555.en.
Temple, A. J., Wambiji, N., Poonian, C.N.S., Jiddawi, N., Stead, S. M., Kiszka, J. J., and Berggren, P. 2019. Marine megafauna catch in southwestern Indian Ocean small-scale fisheries from landings data. *Biological Conservation* 230: 113–121.
Ternon, J. F., Bach, P., Barlow, R., Huggett, J., Jaquemet, S., Marsac, F., Ménard, F., Penven, P., Potier, M., and Roberts, M. J. 2014. The Mozambique Channel: From physics to upper trophic levels. *Deep-Sea Research II, Topical Studies in Oceanography* 100: 1–9.
Ternon, J. F., Herbette, S., Roberts, M., Noyon, M., Ménard, F., Chérel, Y., and Jaquemet, S. 2018. Campagne "Mad-Ridge": Rapport de mission. Unpublished report, Institut de Recherche pour le Développement, France. http://stockage.univ-brest.fr/~herbette/L3_UEEXP_2019/Documents/Rapport%20de%20mission%20MAD-Ridge.pdf.
Terrana, L., Bo, M., Opresko, D. M., and Eeckhaut, I. 2019. Shallow-water black corals (Cnidaria: Anthozoa: Hexacorallia: Antipatharia) from SW Madagascar. *Zootaxa* 4286(1): 1–62.
Tew Kai, E., Rossi, V., Sudre, J., Weimerskirch, H., Lopez, C., Hernandez-Garcia, E., Marsac, F., and Garçon, V. 2009. Top marine predators track Lagrangian coherent structures. *Proceedings of the National Academy of Sciences of the USA* 106: 8245–8250.
Thomassin, B. 1971. Revue bibliographique des travaux de la Station Marine de Tuléar (Madagascar) 1961–1970. *Téthys*, suppl. 1: 3–49.
Thorburn, D. C., Morgan, D. L., Rowland, A. J., and Gill, H. S. 2007. Freshwater sawfish *Pristis microdon* Latham, 1794 (Chondrichthyes: Pristidae) in the Kimberley region of Western Australia. *Zootaxa* 1471: 27–41.
Thorson, T. B. 1976. Observations on the reproduction of the sawfish, *Pristis perotteti*, in Lake Nicaragua, with recommendations for its conservation. *Investigations of the Ichthyofauna of Nicaraguan Lakes* 53: 641–650.
Tittensor, D. P., Camilo Mora, I., Jetz, W., Lotze, H. K., Ricard, D., Vanden Berghe, E., and Worm, W. 2010. Global patterns and predictors of marine biodiversity across taxa. *Nature* 466: 1098–1101.

Todinanahary, G., Terrana, L., and Lavitra, T. 2016. First records of illegal harvesting and trading of black corals (Antipatharia) in Madagascar. *Madagascar Conservation and Development* 1(1): 6–11.
Todinanahary, G.G.B., Lavitra, T., Andrifanilo, H. H., Puccini, N., Grosjean, P., and Eeckhaut, I. 2017. Community-based coral aquaculture in Madagascar: A profitable economic system for a simple rearing technique? *Aquaculture* 467: 225–234.
Todinanahary, G. G., Refoty, M. E., Terrana, L., Lavitra, T., and Eeckhaut, I. 2018. Previously unlisted scleractinian species recorded from the Great Reef of Toliara, southwest Madagascar. *WIO Journal of Marine Science* 17(2): 67–77.
Tombolahy, M. 2000. Inventaire des algues macrobenthiques (Rhodophycées, Chlorophycées, Phéophycées) pour estimer l'impact de minerais de manganèse transporté par un navire échoué dans la baie de Tolagnaro, sud-est de Madagascar (l'exemple Wellborn-Monrovia). Mémoire de DEA, Institut Halieutique et des Sciences Marines, Université de Toliara.
Tomlinson, P. B. 1986. *The Botany of Mangroves*. Cambridge: Cambridge University Press.
Townsend, C. H. 1935. The distribution of certain whales as shown by logbook records of American whaleships. *Zoologica* 19: 1–50.
Trudelle, L., Cerchio, S., Zerbini, A. N., Geyer, Y., Mayer, F.-X., et al. 2016. Influence of environmental parameters on movements and habitat utilization of humpback whales (*Megaptera novaeangliae*) in the Madagascar breeding ground. *Royal Society Open Science* 3: 160616. doi:10.1098/rsos.160616.
Trudelle, L., Charrassin, J.-B., Saloma, A., Pous, S., Kretzschmar, A., and Adam, O. 2018. First insights on spatial and temporal distribution patterns of humpback whales in the breeding ground at Sainte Marie Channel, Madagascar. *African Journal of Marine Science* 40(1): 75–86.
Tyack, P., and Whitehead, H. 1983. Male competition in large groups of wintering humpback whales. *Behavior* 83(1): 132–154.
Tyminski, J. P., De La Parra-Venegas, R., Cano, J. G., and Hueter, R. E. 2015. Vertical movements and patterns in diving behavior of whale sharks as revealed by pop-up satellite tags in the eastern Gulf of Mexico. *PLoS One* 10(11): e0142156.
UNDP. 2018. *Human Development Indices and Indicators: 2018 Statistical Update*. New York: United Nations Development Program. http://hdr.undp.org/sites/default/files/2018_human_development_statistical_update.pdf.
Unsworth, R., Nordlund, L. M., and Cullen-Unsworth, L. 2018. Seagrass meadows support global fisheries production. *Conservation Letters*. doi:10.1111/conl.12566.
UQAR-ISMER (Université du Québec à Rimouski, Institut des Sciences de la Mer) and Resolve. 2019. Appui à la réalisation du projet d'amélioration de la pêcherie crevettière à Madagascar. DP no. 002/17-MRHP/SG/UGP-SWIOFish2. Credit no. Q979. Rapport Final d'exécution. May 2019. Evaluation des stocks de crevettes à Madagascar et développement d'indicateurs et de points de référence. Antananarivo: Resolve.
USAID (United States Agency for International Development). 2016. *Marine Biodiversity and Fisheries in Madagascar: A Biodiversity and Extractives Political Economy Assessment*. Antananarivo: USAID.
———. 2020. Guardians of the mangroves: Community-led protection in western Madagascar. 28 Jan. 2019. https://www.usaid.gov/madagascar/news/guardians-mangroves-community-led-protection-western-madagascar.
Uyeno, T., and Tsutsumi, T. 1991. Stomach contents of *Latimeria chalumnae* and further notes on its feeding habits. *Environmental Biology of Fishes* 32: 275–279.
Vahidi, E., Navarro, J., and Zhao, F. 2016. An initial life cycle assessment of rare earth oxides production from ion-adsorption clays. *Resources, Conservation and Recycling* 113: 1–11.
Van Canneyt, O., Dorémus, G., Laran, S., Ridoux, V., and Watremez, P. 2010. Distribution et abondance de la mégafaune marine dans le sud sud-ouest de l'Océan Indien tropical. REMMOA–Océan Indien. Rapport préliminaire. Université de La Rochelle.
Van Canneyt, O., Dabin, W., Demaret, F., Dorémus, G., and Gonzalez, L. 2011. Les échouages de mammifères marins sur le littoral français en 2010. CRMM (Centre de Recherche sur les Mammifères Marins) and Pelagis, report for the Ministère de l'Ecologie, de l'Energie et du Développement Durable et de la Mer. https://www.observatoire-pelagis.cnrs.fr/wp-content/uploads/2020/12/RapportEchouages2010.pdf.
Van Cise, A. M., Baird, R. W., Baker, C. S., Cerchio, S., Claridge, D., et al. 2019. Oceanographic barriers, divergence, and admixture: Phylogeography and taxonomy of two putative subspecies of short-finned pilot whale. *Molecular Ecology* 28: 2886–2902.
van der Elst, R., Fennessy, S., Everett, B., Mackay, F., Floros, C., Schleyer, M., Kiszka, J., Bourjea, J., and Wanless, R. 2012. *Mainstreaming Biodiversity in Fisheries Management: A Retrospective Analysis of Existing Data on Vulnerable Organisms in the South West Indian Ocean*. Durban: South West Indian Ocean Fisheries Project and Oceanographic Research Insitute.
Vasseur, P. 1997. Ecosystèmes côtiers en danger dans la région de Tuléar: Analyse des agressions humaines et problèmes de gestion. In *Milieux et sociétés dans le sud-ouest de Madagascar*, ed. J.-M. Lebigre, pp. 97–120. Bordeaux: Centre National de la Recherche Scientifique and Université de Bordeaux.
Vasseur, P., Gabrié, C., and Harmelin-Vivien, M. 1988. State of coral reefs and mangroves of the Tuléar region (SW Madagascar): Assessment of human activities and suggestions for management. In *Proceedings of the 6th International Coral Reef Symposium*, vol. 2, *Contributed Papers*, pp. 421–426. Townsville: ICRS.
Vavindraza. 2003. Caractérisation de quelques types de forêts fréquentées et étude phénologique des espèces végétales consommées par trois espèces de Lémuriens (*Propithecus verreauxi coronatus*, *Eulemur mongoz* et *Eulemur fulvus rufus*) dans la Station forestière à usage multiple d'Antrema. Mémoire de DEA, Université d'Antananarivo.
Vély, M., and Collin-Omnes, V. 1997. Contribution to the study of humpback whale (*Megaptera novaeangliae*) population wintering in the Sainte-Marie Island area, east coast of Madagascar. World Marine Mammal Science Conference, Monaco, 20–24 Jan. 1998.
Veron, J.E.N. 2000. *Corals of the World*. Townsville: Australian Institute of Marine Science.
Veron, J.E.N., and Turak, E. 2003. Zooxanthellate Scleractinia of Madagascar. In A rapid marine biodiversity assessment of northwest Madagascar, eds. S. A. McKenna and G. R. Allen. *Bulletin of the Rapid Assessment Program* 31: 23–31.
Veron, J., Stafford-Smith, M., DeVantier, L., and Turak, E. 2015. Overview of distribution patterns of zooxanthellate Scleractinia. *Frontiers in Marine Science* 1: 81. doi:10.3389/fmars.2014.00081.
Vespe, M., Greidanus, H., and Alvarez, M. A. 2015. The declining impact of piracy on maritime transport in the Indian Ocean: Statistical analysis of 5-year vessel tracking data. *Marine Policy* 59: 9–15.
Vignaud, T. M., Maynard, J. A., Leblois, R., Meekan, M. G., Vázquez-Juárez, R., et al. 2014. Genetic structure of populations of whale sharks among ocean basins and evidence for their historic rise and recent decline. *Molecular Ecology* 23: 2590–2601.
Vilvens, C. 2014. New species and new records of Calliostomatidae (Gastropoda: Trochoidea) from Madagascar. *Novapex*, hors série 9: 1–29.
Vincente, N. 1997. Un coelacanthe à Madagascar. *Océanorama* 27: 11–15.
Voisin, P., and Sandon, Y. 2008. Relations entre la pêche crevettière et les facteurs environnemtaux. In *Les crevettes côtières de Madagascar, Biologie, exploitation, gestion*, eds. A. Caverivière, C. Chaboud, and T. Rafalimanana, pp. 79–90. Marseille: IRD.
Wada, S., and Numachi, K. 1991. Allozyme analyses of genetic differentiation among the populations and species of the Balaenoptera. *Reports of the International Whaling Commission*, special issue 13: 125–154.
Wada, S., Oishi, M., and Yamada, T. K. 2003. A newly discovered species of living baleen whale. *Nature* 426: 278–281.
Wafar, M., Venkataraman, K., Ingole, B., Khan, S. A., and LokaBharathi, P. 2011. State of knowledge of coastal and marine biodiversity of Indian Ocean countries. *PLoS One* 6(1): e14613.
Walker, R.C.J., and Roberts, E. 2005. Notes on the status and incidental capture of marine turtles by the subsistence fishing communities of south west Madagascar. *Western Indian Ocean Journal of Marine Science* 4(2): 219–225.
Walker, R.C.J., Roberts, E., and Fanning, E. 2004. The trade in marine turtles in the Toliara region, southwest Madagascar. *Marine Turtle Newsletter* 106: 7–10.
Wallace, B. P., Di Matteo, A. D., Bolten, A. B., Chaloupka, M. Y., Hutchinson, B. J., et al. 2011. Global conservation priorities for marine turtles. *PLoS One* 6(9): e24510. https://doi.org/10.1371/journal.pone.0024510.
Walton, M. E., Le Vay, L., and Ut, V. N. 2006. Significance of mangrove-mudflat boundaries as nursery grounds for the mud crab, *Scylla paramamosain*. *Marine Biology* 149(5): 1199–1207.
Waycott, M., MacMahon, K., Mellors, J., Calladine, A., and Kleine, D. 2004. *A Guide to Tropical Seagrasses of the Indo-West Pacific*. Townsville: James Cook University.
WCS (Wildlife Conservation Society) and DEC (Development Environment Consult). 2002. *Etude de faisabilité de la création d'APMC et plan de développement pour le site de la RBM Sahamalaza–Nosy Radama*. Antananarivo: WCS and DEC.
WCS and Resolve. 2018. *Etude de faisabilité de la mise en protection dans la zone marine du Grand Sud de Madagascar à travers une aire marine protégée (AMP)*. Final report submitted to WCS. Antananarivo: WCS.

Webster, C. 2008. Dossier pour l'obtention du statut de protection temporaire du site Nosy Tanikely (Tany Hely). Feb. 2008. Report submitted to Project 'PIC' (Pôles Intégrées de Croissance).

Webster, F. J., and McMahon, K. 2002. An assessment of coral reefs in northwest Madagascar. In *Coral Degradation in the Indian Ocean: Status Report 2002*, eds. O. Linden, D. Souter, D. Wilhelmsson, and D. Obura, pp. 190–210. Kalmar: Coastal Oceans Research and Development—Indian Ocean.

Webster, P. J., Holland, G. J., Curry, J. A., and Chang, H. 2005. Changes in tropical cyclone number, duration, and intensity in a warming environment. *Science* 309: 1844–1846. doi:10.1126/science.1116448.

Weigmann, S., Gon, O., Leeney, R. H., Barrowclift, E., Berggren, P., Jiddawi, N., and Temple, A. J. 2020. Revision of the sixgill sawsharks, genus *Pliotrema* (Chondrichthyes, Pristiophoriformes), with descriptions of two new species and a redescription of *P. warreni* Regan. *PLoS One* 15(3): e0228791.

Westerman, K., and Benbow, S. 2013. The role of women in community-based small-scale fisheries management: The case of the southern Madagascar octopus fishery. *Western Indian Ocean Journal of Marine Science* 12(2): 119–132.

Whitty, J. M., Morgan, D., Peverell, S. C., Thorburn, D. C., and Beatty, S. J. 2009. Ontogenetic depth partitioning by juvenile freshwater sawfish (*Pristis microdon*: Pristidae) in a riverine environment. *Marine and Freshwater Research* 60: 306–316.

Whitty, J. M., Phillips, N. M., Thorburn, D. C., Simpfendorfer, C. A., Field, I., Peverell, S. C., and Morgan, D. L. 2014. Utility of rostra in the identification of Australian sawfishes (Chondrichthyes: Pristidae). *Aquatic Conservation: Marine and Freshwater Ecosystems* 24: 791–804.

Wickel, J., and Nicet, J. B. 2017. *Analyse des écosystèmes marins de l'île de Sainte-Marie, Madagascar*. Rapport MAREX pour le compte du Groupe de Recherche et d'Echanges Technologiques. Antananarivo: Cetamada.

Wickel, J., Landry, T. L., Pinault, M., Fricke, R., and Ponton, D. 2018. First record of the southwestern Indian Ocean endemic *Apolemichthys kingi* (Teloestei: Pomacanthidae) from Sainte Marie Island, Madagascar. *Cybium* 42(4): 383–385.

Wiejeme, N. 2019. Caractérisation fonctionnelle des coraux noirs (Hexacorallia Antipathearia) du sud-ouest de Madagascar. MS thesis, Oceanography, Liège Université.

Winn, H. E., Thompson, J. T., Cummings, W. C., Hans, J., Hudnall, J., Hays, J., and Steiner, W. W. 1981. Song of the humpback whale: Population comparison. *Behavioral Ecology and Sociobiology* 8: 41–46.

Woodroffe, C. 1992. Mangrove sediments and geomorphology. In *Tropical Mangrove Ecosystem*, eds. A. I. Robertson and D. M. Alongi, pp. 7–41. Washington, DC: American Geophysical Union.

World Bank. 2003. Madagascar rural and environment sector review. Report no. 26106-MG. http://documents1.worldbank.org/curated/en/305421468758692314/pdf/261060MG0vol2.pdf.

———. 2019. Population growth (annual %): Madagascar. Accessed 31 Aug. 2020. https://data.worldbank.org/indicator/SP.POP.GROW?locations=MG.

Wourms, J. P., Atz, J. W., and Stribling, M. D. 1991. Viviparity and the maternal-embryonic relationship in the coelacanth *Latimeria chalumnae*. *Environmental Biology of Fishes* 32: 225–248.

Wueringer, B. E. 2012. Electroreception in elasmobranchs: Sawfish as a case study. *Brain, Behaviour and Evolution* 80: 97–107.

WWF. 1993. *Coral Reefs and Coastal Zone of Toliara: Conservation and Development through Ecotourism; Pre-project*. Ed. A. J. Cooke. Antananarivo: WWF Madagascar.

WWF-EAME (Eastern African Marine Ecoregion). 2004. *Towards a Western Indian Ocean Dugong Conservation Strategy: The Status of Dugongs in the Western Indian Ocean Region and Priority Conservation*. Dar-es-Salaam: WWF.

Wyatt, A.S.J., Matsumoto, R., Chikaraishi, Y., Miyairi, Y., Yokoyama, Y., Sato, K., Ohkouchi, N., and Nagata, T. 2019. Enhancing insights into foraging specialization in the world's largest fish using a multi-tissue, multi-isotope approach. *Ecological Monographs* 89: 1–28.

Yagishita, N., Ikeguchi, S., and Matsumoto, R. 2020. Re-estimation of genetic population structure and demographic history of the whale shark (*Rhincodon typus*) with additional Japanese samples, inferred from mitochondrial DNA sequences. *Pacific Science* 74: 31.

Yamada, T. K., Chou, L. S., Chantrapornsyl, S., Adulyanukosol, K., Chakravarti, S. K., et al. 2006a. Middle-sized balaenopterid whale specimens (Cetacea: Balaenopteridae) preserved at several institutions in Taiwan, Thailand, and India. *Memoirs of the National Science Museum*, Tokyo 44: 1–10.

Yamada, T. K., Kemper, C., Tajima, Y., Umetani, A., Janetzki, H., and Pemberton, D. 2006b. Marine mammal collections in Australia. *National Science Museum Monographs* 34: 117–126.

Yamada, T. K., Kakuda, T., and Tajima, Y. 2008. Middle sized balaenopterid whale specimens in the Philippines and Indonesia. *Memoirs of the National Museum of Nature and Science*, Tokyo 45: 75–83.

Yang, X. J., Lin, A., Li, X., Wu, Y., Zhou, W., and Chen, Z. 2013. China's ion-adsorption rare earth resources, mining consequences and preservation. *Environmental Development* 8: 131–136.

Zelasney, J., Ford, A., Westlund, L., Ward, A., and Riego Peñarubia, O., eds. 2020. *Securing Sustainable Small-Scale Fisheries: Showcasing Applied Practices in Value Chains, Post-harvest Operations and Trade*. Food and Agriculture Organization of the United Nations Fisheries and Aquaculture Technical Paper no. 652. Rome: FAO.

ZICOMA (Zones d'Importance pour la Conservation des Oiseaux à Madagascar). 2001. Madagascar. In *Important Bird Areas in Africa and Associated Islands: Priority Sites for Conservation*, eds. L.D.C. Fishpool and M. I. Evans, pp. 489–537. Cambridge, UK: Pisces and BirdLife International.

Zuffa, M., Van Grevelynghe, G., De Maddalena, A., and Storai, T. 2002. Records of the white shark, *Carcharodon carcharias* (Linnaeus, 1758), from the western Indian Ocean. *South African Journal of Science* 98: 347–349.

CHAPTER 8

PLANTS

INTRODUCTION TO PLANTS

L. Gautier, P. P. Lowry II, and S. M. Goodman

One of the pronounced aspects of Madagascar's biota is the remarkable diversity of both its flora and ecological communities. The island, occupying an area of 587,000 km^2, slightly larger than France or the state of California, is about 600 km wide and extends nearly 1600 km from north to south, spanning a latitudinal gradient from 12.0°S to about 25.5°S, the southern portion of which reaches just outside the tropics. Madagascar has been separated from other landmasses since about 80 million years ago (Mya) (see Collins et al., pp. 45–51), and many plant groups reached the island by long-distance dispersal over significant distances of ocean. Madagascar has a wide variety of soil substrate types and significant topographic variation, particularly along a chain of inland mountains that traverses much of its length and includes several large massifs that reach over 2000 m, including the Tsaratanàna Massif, with its summit, Maromokotra, at 2870 m, the highest on the island. The Malagasy flora is rich, diverse, and highly endemic, with few parallels for a landmass of its size.

Little information is available regarding diversity and endemism among nonvascular plants, especially algae, which are still poorly known. Regarding lichens, which are only partly plants but nevertheless are treated in this chapter, a provisional species checklist contains a little over 500 entries (see Aptroot and Schumm, pp. 499–510), and endemism is reputed to be low. Bryophytes, which have received increased attention of late, are represented by 1045 species plus 170 infraspecific taxa, with a level of endemism of 33.8% in mosses and 18.3% in liverworts (see Marline et al., pp. 510–20).

Among vascular plants, a total of 253 families are represented on Madagascar, comprising 1747 genera (19% of which are endemic, Callmander et al. 2011a) and 11,866 native species, 9329 (79%) of which are endemic, based on data extracted in November 2020 from the Catalogue of the Plants of Madagascar (2020) (Madagascar Catalogue). These figures can be compared with two other species-rich tropical islands, each about one-third larger than Madagascar and both with more recent continental connections: New Guinea, which hosts 13,634 vascular plant species, and Borneo, which has 11,165 species (Cámara-Leret et al. 2020), both islands having significantly greater elevational amplitude than Madagascar, especially New Guinea, which has extensive areas above 3000 m. On Madagascar, an average of 58 new species were described per year between 2010 and 2020, and about 950 candidate species (known and well-circumscribed but undescribed species that remain to be formally named) are currently known across 162 of the 587 genera evaluated during that time. Factoring in the rate of discovery of new species from about 1990 to 2020, a recent estimate suggested that the total Malagasy flora will ultimately be shown to comprise at least 14,000 species, reaching a little over 85% endemism (Lowry et al. 2018), one of the highest levels in the world, along with Hawaii (89% endemic; Sakai et al. 2002), New Caledonia (75% endemic; Munzinger et al. 2020), and New Guinea (68% endemic; Cámara-Leret et al. 2020). With respect to Madagascar, this remarkable level of diversity and endemism has direct consequences for a variety of different evolutionary processes, including, for example, phytogeographic patterns, plant-animal interactions, and pollination ecology. Moreover, both ecological conditions (including weather patterns and soil type) and forest physiognomy vary considerably across the island's many botanical communities, with important implications for the diversity of organisms that inhabit these ecosystems.

This introductory contribution briefly presents a broad picture of recent advances in botanical science on Madagascar, with an emphasis on progress and major changes since the precursor volume (Goodman and Benstead 2003) was published. It covers the general working conditions of botanists and the rise of molecular systematics and its consequences, and it briefly outlines the main changes in taxonomy, significant advances, work in progress, and groups that are most urgently in need of revision. Biogeography and vegetation, as well as the dynamics of species conservation assessments, are briefly mentioned. A section covers the rise of new generations of Malagasy botanists, followed by an overview of the 50 contributions to this chapter, and it concludes with a broad overview of some other details concerning this chapter.

PROGRESS CONCERNING THE MALAGASY FLORA

General Overview

Major progress has been achieved in our knowledge of the Malagasy flora since Goodman and Benstead's precursor volume was published in 2003, in large part resulting from a significant effort to increase fieldwork and add to the number of available collections. After the first golden era of exploration—undertaken by Henri Perrier de la Bâthie (1873–1958) from 1896 to 1932, Henri Humbert (1887–1967), and others from the Muséum National d'Histoire Naturelle (MNHN) in Paris from the late 1920s through the early 1960s, as well as by the Service Forestier de Madagascar from the 1950s to the early 1970s under the direction of René Capuron (1921–1971)—the collection of new herbarium material was severely handicapped from the early 1970s. Starting in the late 1980s, a new wave of botanical exploration and collecting increasingly focused on poorly known or totally unexplored areas. This effort was led (official code of each herbarium in parentheses) initially by the Missouri Botanical Garden (MO), followed by the MNHN (P), the Royal Botanic Gardens, Kew (K), the Conservatoire et Jardin botaniques de la Ville de Genève (G), and the California Academy of Sciences (CAS) along with botanists from many other national and international institutions (see Collaboration with Overseas Herbaria and Institutions, pp. 462–63). It is estimated that the number of available collections has grown from about 110,000 in the early 1980s to more than 350,000 today, a more than threefold increase. The pace of advancement is brisk, and the figures presented in this contribution and elsewhere in this chapter date from November 2020.

Although the methods used by botanists to collect plants have changed very little over time, a few important improvements during the past few decades are worth mentioning, including the use of the global positioning system (GPS) and digital cameras, and the collection of leaf material dried in silica gel to preserve DNA. Initially, GPS units were seen merely as a simpler method to obtain geo-coordinates and to plot collections on maps, but with increasing signal accuracy and better performance, precise positions are now routinely recorded, enabling botanists to relocate a tree in the heart of a forest in order to gather additional material (e.g., fruits from a tree that had first been collected in flower). Digital cameras are now systematically used to take high-resolution photographs of living plants associated with pressed herbarium collections, representing a significant improvement that bridges the gap between living and preserved material, although this is more useful for families with showy flowers such as Orchidaceae than those with more cryptic reproductive structures such as Poaceae (the grass family). The regular use of silica gel to dry leaf material has contributed to the broad development of molecular phylogenetics (see Wojahn et al., pp. 464–70).

The availability of herbarium material for taxonomic study has also dramatically improved. Access to the largest collection from Madagascar, housed in the herbarium of the MNHN, has greatly improved thanks to extensive curation work conducted by the staff in Paris and numerous visiting botanists and to the comprehensive reorganization and scanning of the entire collection (MNHN 2021) recently undertaken as part of a complete renovation of the herbarium building, an effort that was largely spearheaded by the late Jean-Noël Labat (1959–2011). This was augmented by the Andrew W. Mellon Foundation's Global Plant Initiative, which funded a worldwide effort to scan hundreds of thousands of high-resolution images of type specimens and make them available online (JSTOR 2021), including nearly all of the types from Madagascar housed in P and the other herbaria with large holdings from the island such as G, K, and MO (see above for the definition of these codes). Access has also improved in Madagascar thanks to an expansion in 2004 of the herbarium at the Parc Botanique et Zoologique de Tsimbazaza (TAN), which houses the country's largest collection (>200,000 specimens), and the other principal herbarium at FOFIFA (in Malagasy, Foibem-pirenena momba ny Fikarohana ampiharina amin'ny Fampandrosoana ny eny Ambanivohitra) (TEF). In recent years, the herbarium in the Mention Biologie et Ecologie Végétale, Université d'Antananarivo (MBEV) has also undergone considerable expansion and infrastructure improvement.

Reliable, sustained annual funding of these reference collections is critical as they are the mandatory repository for botanical collections made on Madagascar and an essential resource for study by national botanists. A chronic lack of space, basic supplies (herbarium paper, glue, and insect repellent), equipment (storage cabinets and air conditioning), and personnel (curators and technicians) is impeding the routine operation of these facilities, and a considerable number of unmounted specimens stored in uncontrolled climatic conditions await processing and integration into the collections. A system of bench fees for the use of the collections by visiting botanists has been proposed to raise funds to support these herbaria, with different rates for resident and visiting botanists. Raising funds in this manner is, however, problematic as it discourages botanists from bringing their expertise to the collections and impedes the identification and curation of specimens housed in these herbaria. Well-established foreign institutions have regularly aided Madagascar's national herbaria by providing or securing supplies and infrastructure, but the problem of sustainability of the island's plant collections, which represent a part of the nation's natural heritage, remains to be solved.

A major effort has been achieved in compiling reliable information on the island's flora through the Madagascar Catalogue, an authoritative, publicly accessible, and continuously updated online resource delivered through the Missouri Botanical Garden's Tropicos database. The catalogue provides global, interactive access to specimens, names, maps, references, and many other valuable resources, and botanists studying the flora of Madagascar have never before been able to work so efficiently. As of the end of 2020, the catalogue included records for all 253 families and 1747 genera currently recognized on the island, as well as for 11,866 native species and an additional 467 non-native, naturalized species, with associated specimen records and a real-time-generated map for each species, often also accompanied by photos taken in the field. While the level and quality of data capture in the catalogue is very good for most plant groups, several families lag behind, including Poaceae and Cyperaceae. Incorporation of the nomenclature backbone from the Madagascar Catalogue into the African Plant Database (2020), a joint effort of Conservatoire et Jardin botaniques de la Ville de Genève and South African National Biodiversity Institute (SANBI), has stimulated standardization and corrections in both data sets, considerably enhancing their exactness and enabling accurate numerical comparisons between the floras of Madagascar and sub-Saharan Africa (Gautier et al. 2012a).

Opportunities to publish the results of botanical research and exploration have also improved since the early 2000s. The main institutional journals, *Adansonia* (Paris), *Novon*, and *Annals of the Missouri Botanical Garden* (Saint Louis), and others continue to publish the majority of taxonomic revisions and descriptions of new species associated with the Malagasy flora. Further, under the editorial direction of Martin Callmander, *Candollea* (Geneva) has significantly increased the publication of papers on the island's flora and established a dedicated series of short communications entitled Notes sur la Flore de Madagascar, in which 56 notes have been published since 2010. Furthermore, Geneva's monograph series *Boissiera* has published two volumes containing revisions of the important Malagasy genera *Noronhia* (Hong-Wa 2016) and *Abrahamia* (Randrianasolo et al. 2017). In addition, two new journals dedicated to Madagascar welcome botanical contributions: *Madagascar Conservation and Development* (14 volumes published since 2006) and *Malagasy Nature* (14 volumes since 2009). The *Flore de Madagascar et des Comores* series, published by the MNHN since 1936, went through a period of inactivity for several years but has recently been incorporated into the *Faune et Flore tropicales* series, and treatments of several families will soon appear.

Impact of Molecular Systematics

Progress in our understanding of the Malagasy flora has benefited significantly from the growing use of molecular phylogenetic research to clarify relationships (see Wojahn et al., pp. 464–70), including several that have been particularly challenging for plant taxonomists. One of the main consequences of molecular-based phylogenetic studies at higher taxonomic ranks has been change in family circumscriptions led by the Angiosperm Phylogeny Group (APG), which has published several successive new classification systems for flowering plants, probably the most significant being APG III (Angiosperm Phylogeny Group 2009). The main implications of these results for the flora of Madagascar are summarized here.

Some of the largest angiosperm plant families have experienced virtually no changes in their circumscription, including Orchidaceae, Asteraceae, and Rubiaceae, and the delimitation of others, such as Acanthaceae, remains essentially unchanged. The legumes are confirmed to be a single family, Leguminosae, although its infra-familial classification is still being refined (see Phillipson et al., pp. 598–617). The long-recognized families Bombacaceae (including the iconic genus *Adansonia*—the baobabs; see Karimi et al., pp. 706–10), Sterculiaceae, and Tiliaceae are now regarded as part of an expanded Malvaceae, currently the seventh-largest family on Madagascar (see Skema and Hanes, pp. 698–706). Apocynaceae has likewise been expanded to incorporate all genera previously placed in Asclepiadaceae and Periplocaceae, ranking it ninth in species richness for the island (see Liede-Schumann, pp. 774–83). Lamiaceae now includes many of the genera traditionally placed in Verbenaceae, some of which are quite speciose on Madagascar, such as *Clerodendrum* and *Vitex*. Conversely, Euphorbiaceae was shown to be polyphyletic, requiring the recognition of Phyllanthaceae and several smaller families (see Wurdack, pp. 634–39; Ralimanana and Challen, pp. 649–54). This is also the case with Clusiaceae, from which Calophyllaceae and Hypericaceae had to be resurrected.

Several once-recognized tropical families are presently included in a broadened circumscription of cosmopolitan entities, such as Myrsinaceae, now included in Primulaceae, and Flacourtiaceae, subsumed within Salicaceae. A few additional recent rearrangements are presented in this chapter in contributions dedicated to the orders Santalales (see Nickrent, pp. 717–23) and Boraginales (see Miller, pp. 808–11). Family circumscription among the petaloid monocots, previously placed in the order Liliales, has long been problematical, but molecular systematics has led to the recognition of two orders, Liliales (which includes Liliaceae and Smilacaceae) and Asparagales (including Amaryllidaceae, Asparagaceae, Asphodelaceae, Iridaceae, and others, along with Orchidaceae).

The people of Madagascar have long been proud of its endemic flowering plant families, and APG has had an impact on them as well. In the early 1990s, eight endemic families were recognized (Brummitt 1992), but two of the smaller ones have since been subsumed: the monotypic Diegodendraceae now included in Bixaceae; and Melanophyllaceae, from which *Melanophylla* was transferred to Torricelliaceae and *Kaliphora* to Montiniaceae. However, the most outstanding loss from the list of Malagasy endemic families is Didiereaceae, which still stands but has been expanded to include three African genera previously placed in Portulacaceae (see Applequist, pp. 724–26). Five families are nevertheless still regarded as endemic, and a series of taxonomic revisions led to the publication of a field guide treating them all (Ramananjanahary et al. 2010): Asteropeiaceae (one genus, eight described species), Barbeuiaceae (one, one), Physenaceae (one, two), Sarcolaenaceae (10, 72; see Schatz and Lowry, pp. 712–16), and Sphaerosepalaceae (two, 20; see Schatz and Lowry, pp. 711–12).

There have likewise been many changes at the generic level as a consequence of the application of the principle of monophyly based on results of molecular phylogenetic studies. Among the impacts on the Malagasy flora, several large genera have thus been split into smaller ones, including *Panicum* (Poaceae), *Schefflera* (Araliaceae; see Lowry and Plunkett, pp. 804–8), *Vernonia* (Asteraceae), and so forth, and others will be soon (e.g., *Bulbophyllum*, Orchidaceae). In other cases, small to medium-size endemic genera have been segregated from large nonendemic ones, such as *Abrahamia* (Anacardiaceae; see Randrianasolo, pp. 681–85) and *Ambilobea* (Burseraceae; see Raharimampionona et al., pp. 676–80). In parallel, molecular evidence has shown that many small endemic genera are nested within larger more widespread ones and as a consequence can no longer be considered valid, such as *Macrostelia* (Malvaceae), which has now been included within the pantropical genus *Hibiscus* (see Skema and Hanes, pp. 698–706).

Molecular studies were initially based on a limited number of loci, generally from the chloroplast (*trnH-psbA*, *matK*, and *rbcL*), and then from the nucleus (internal described spacer [ITS] and external described spacer [ETS]). It soon became clear, however, that these markers often provided inadequate resolution, especially among recently diverging lineages. While phenomena such as incomplete lineage sorting, paralogs, hybridization, and chloroplast capture have little impact on clarifying relationships among taxa at higher ranks (e.g., families, orders), they often confound studies at lower ranks (Naciri and Linder 2015). For poorly understood groups, where molecular phylogenetics is most needed, analyses based on just one or a few loci (plastid and/or nuclear) are often inadequate at the generic level and below. Thanks to the advent of next-generation sequencing (NGS) and gene capture, developed in the early 2010s, botanists are now able to sequence hundreds of loci quickly and cost-effectively, and to obtain much better success in sequencing leaf fragments from herbarium material, even from older collections. With the help of increasingly powerful bioinformatic tools, botanists are able to gain better insight into patterns of evolution among species and even down to the level of populations, provided that sufficient sampling is available. As a result, major advances have been made in species delimitation in many groups using these new techniques, and botanists have begun to explore questions at the population level. These improved molecular methods are currently being implemented to test the monophyly of species and to reveal cryptic species, and it should be possible to start tackling the Pandora's box of the recognition and delimitation of infraspecific taxa. The massive amount of information now available has also revealed the limits of the binomial system (genus and species) of naming living organisms, and has shown that a taxonomy based on a rigid binomial species concept may sometimes conflict with the evolutionary history of a group, with practical implications on matters such as binomial species-based conservation assessments. Nevertheless, molecular systematics has had a profound positive impact worldwide and has greatly contributed to progress on the Malagasy flora.

Groups Revised, Ongoing Work, and Major Gaps

Since around 2000, significant progress has been made on several large families that have not yet been treated in the *Flore de Madagascar et des Comores* series, or whose treatment is clearly outdated. Shortly before the precursor of this current book was published (Goodman and Benstead 2003), major updates were completed on three families in particular, Arecaceae (J. Dransfield and Beentje 1995; see Rakotoarinivo et al., pp. 567–80), Fabaceae (herein as Leguminosae) Du Puy et al. 2002; see Phillipson et al., pp. 598–617), and Orchidaceae (Hermans et al. 2007; see Hermans and Rajaovelona, pp. 559–67). Since then, work has progressed on many other families, some of which are treated in this chapter, including Cyperaceae (see Larridon et al., pp. 580–85), Euphorbiaceae (see Wurdack, pp. 634–39), Malvaceae (see Skema and Hanes, pp. 698–706), and Poaceae (see Vorontsova et al., pp. 585–98). We suggest that the most spectacular advances have been achieved through the joint effort of researchers from several institutions working on the diverse and notoriously difficult family Rubiaceae (see Razafimandimbison et al., pp. 744–53, introducing the family, and the subsequent contributions on various elements of Rubiaceae).

Major ongoing taxonomic work has also been conducted on several groups of economic importance as precious hardwoods. A comprehensive revision of Malagasy Ebenaceae, many species of which produce ebony wood, was initiated in 2009 and has increased the number of known species from 97 recognized in three genera in the *Flore de Madagascar et des Comores* (Perrier de la Bâthie 1952c) to a total of nearly 250 species in a single genus, *Diospyros* (see Schatz and Lowry, pp. 739–44), making this the largest genus of woody plants on the island. As part of an effort to control the illegal exploitation and international sale of valuable and highly sought-after rosewood (see Schuurman and Lowry 2009), obtained from several species of *Dalbergia* (Leguminosae), and to develop reliable identification tools for sustainable management and law enforcement (Mason et al. 2016), a careful review of the genus using both herbarium specimens and molecular phylogenetics has revealed that nearly 100 species occur on Madagascar, double the 48 species recognized in the most recent taxonomic revision (see Phillipson et al., pp. 598–617). A third source of precious wood, the family Sapotaceae, is becoming increasingly exploited and its members threatened. Ongoing and future work on this family includes generic circumscription and species delimitation, aiming at a full revision that will include some 130 species in 10 genera (see Gautier et al., pp. 726–39).

Several other groups are currently being studied, often by teams of two or more collaborators from different institutions. These include families such as Anacardiaceae (see Randrianasolo, pp. 681–85), Araliaceae (see Lowry and Plunkett, pp. 804–8), Bignoniaceae (see Callmander et al., pp. 800–804, Burseraceae (see Raharimampionona et al., pp. 676–80), Myrtaceae (see Snow and Byng, pp. 663–68), Pandanaceae (see Callmander et al., pp. 551–59), Sapindaceae (see Buerki et al., pp. 685–90), and Violaceae (see Wahlert, pp. 658–63), among others, as well as genera such as *Clerodendrum* (Lamiaceae), *Croton* (Euphorbiaceae) (see Berry and van Ee, pp. 640–44), *Dioscorea* (Dioscoreaceae) (see Wilkin et al., pp. 545–51), *Dombeya* (Malvaceae), *Euphorbia* (Euphorbiaceae) (see Haevermans and Hetterscheid, pp. 645–49), *Impatiens* (Balsaminaceae), *Ivodea* (Rutaceae) (see Rabarimanarivo et al., pp. 691–98), *Homalium* (Salicaceae) (see Applequist, pp. 654–58), *Noronhia* (Oleaceae) (see Hong-Wa et al., pp. 784–89), and *Peperomia* (Piperaceae) (see Mathieu, pp. 538–41), to name just a few.

Certain families and genera have been revised only in part but will require additional work. These include the large and complex genus *Grewia* (Malvaceae), a revision of which was initiated in the 1960s by Capuron (1963, 1964) prior to his premature death and partially completed by Mabberley (Capuron and Mabberley 1999; Mabberley and Capuron 1999, 2017) but remains incomplete. Several new species have been published more recently (Randrianasolo et al. 2013; Wahlert et al. 2014, 2015, 2016), but many others remain to be described. Another example is the family Meliaceae, for which a draft manuscript prepared by J.-F. Leroy (1915–1999) and M. Lescot (now retired) remains largely unpublished (but see Leroy and Lescot 1996) and will require significant updating to account for additional material collected during the past two decades, only a portion of which has been described (Callmander et al. 2009, 2012a; Randrianarivony et al. 2017a; Wahlert et al. 2019). The situation with the family Lauraceae is somewhat different: most of the species diversity has now been described (van der Werff 1991, 2003, 2006, 2008, 2013a, 2013b, 2017), but in the absence of a comprehensive revision of the group it is very difficult to identify material from these small-flowered trees, which are dominant in medium-altitude moist evergreen forests.

TABLE 8.1. **Classification of the main Malagasy vegetation types referred to in this chapter and throughout the book with their correspondence to previous classifications**

PRINCIPAL DETERMINING FACTORS			VEGETATION TYPES	BIOGEOGRAPHIC DOMAINS				
MAJOR	PRIMARY	SECONDARY	GAUTIER ET AL. (2018)	E	SB	C	W	S
Zonal vegetation: prevailing macroclimatic conditions	Dry season: <4 months	Temperature: warm, low daily, and seasonal amplitude (0–1000 m)	**Lowland moist evergreen forest**	+++	+++	–	–	–
		Temperature: medium, moderate daily amplitude (800–2000 m)	**Medium-altitude moist evergreen forest**	–	–	+++	–	–
		Temperature: low, high daily amplitude (>1600 m)	**Montane ericoid thicket**	–	–	++	–	–
			Montane grassland	–	–	+	–	–
	Dry season: 4–8 months	Temperature: warm, low daily, and seasonal amplitude (0–1000 m)	**Moist semi-deciduous forest**	–	+	–	++	–
		Temperature: medium, moderate daily amplitude (800–2000 m)	**Sclerophyllous woodland**	–	–	++	–	–
	Dry season: 6–10 months; annual rainfall: 400–1400 mm (0–800 m)		**Dry deciduous forest**	–	–	–	+++	+
	Dry season: >10 months; annual rainfall: <600 mm (0–800 m)		**Dry spiny thicket**	–	–	–	+	+++

CORRESPONDENCE WITH PREVIOUS CLASSIFICATIONS

PERRIER DE LA BÂTHIE (1921)	HUMBERT (1965)	CORNET AND GUILLAUMET (1976)	FARAMALALA ET AL. (1995)	DU PUY AND MOAT (1996)	MOAT AND SMITH (2007)	SAYRE ET AL. (2013)
Forêt orientale	Forêt dense ombrophile, série à Myristicaceae et *Anthostema*	Forêt dense humide sempervirente de basse altitude à Myristicaceae et *Anthostema*	Forêt dense humide sempervirente	**Evergreen humid forest: low altitude (0–800 m)**	Humid forest	Eastern Madagascar lowland rainforest, Western Madagascar subhumid forest (pp)
Forêt à sous-bois herbacé Silve des lichens	Forêt dense ombrophile, série à *Tambourissa* et *Weinmannia*, Sylve à lichens	Forêt dense humide sempervirente de moyenne altitude à *Tambourissa* et *Weinmannia*, Forêt dense humide de montagne, Forêt sclérophylle de montagne	Forêt dense humide sempervirente de moyenne altitude à *Tambourissa* et *Weinmannia*, Forêt dense humide de montagne, Forêt sclérophylle de montagne	**Evergreen humid forest: mid altitude (800–1800 m), Evergreen humid forest: lower montane (1800–2000 m)**		Eastern Madagascar montane forest, Eastern Madagascar subhumid forest (pp), Western Madagascar humid forest
Broussaille éricoïde des hautes altitudes	Végétation buissonnante éricoïde	Fourrés de montagne	Fourré à *Philippia*/ Fourré dense	**Montane (*Philippia*) scrubland (>1800 m)**		Malagasy montane scrub
	Savane d'altitude	Prairie altimontane	Savane d'altitude/ de montagne	–	–	
–	–	–	–	**Western sub-humid forest**	–	Eastern Madagascar subhumid forest (pp)
Bois des pentes occidentales	Forêt basse sclérophylle, série à *Uapaca bojeri* et Chlaenacées	Forêt sclérophylle de moyenne altitude à Chlaenacées et *Uapaca bojeri*	Forêt sclérophylle basse	**Evergreen sclerophyllous (*Uapaca*) woodland (800–1800 m)**	Tapia forest	Madagascar tapia forest
Bois des collines latéritiques, collines arénacées, plateaux calcaires	Série à *Dalbergia*, *Commiphora*, *Hildegardia*, Forêt dense sur argiles latéritiques, sols arénacés, plateaux calcaires	Forêt dense sèche à *Dalbergia*, *Commiphora* et *Hildegardia*, Faciès sur sols latéritiques, sols arénacés, calcaires	Forêt dense sèche; y-compris faciès karstique	**Deciduous, seasonally dry, western forest (0–800 m)**	Western dry forest	Madagascar western dry forest
Bush à *Didierea*, Bush à xérophytes	Série à Didiereaceae et *Euphorbia*	Fourré xérophile à Didiereacées et *Euphorbia*	Forêt dense sèche à *Didierea* et Euphorbiaceae, Fourré dense sec	**Deciduous, dry, southern forest and scrubland (0–300 m)**	South western dry spiny forest/ thicket, coastal bushland	Madagascar southwestern dry forest, thicket, coastal bushland

(continued overleaf)

TABLE 8.1. ***continued***

PRINCIPAL DETERMINING FACTORS			VEGETATION TYPES	BIOGEOGRAPHIC DOMAINS				
Azonal vegetation: prevailing site-specific conditions	Access to edaphic water	Running water	**Riparian forest**	+	++	+	++	++
		Stagnant water	**Swamp forest**	+	+	+	+	–
			Marsh and bog	+	+	+	+	–
		Salty or brackish water	**Mangrove**	+	++	–	++	+
	Sandy substrate	Exposed to sea spray	**Littoral thicket**	++	++	–	++	–
		Sheltered from sea spray	**Littoral forest**	++	–	–	–	–
	Rocky substrate		**Rupicolous vegetation**	+	+	++	–	–
Anthropic vegetation: prevailing human-induced and perpetuated by disturbance	Dry season: <4 months		**Secondary humid forest and thicket**	+++	+++	+	–	–
	Dry season: >4 months		**Secondary grassland and pasture**	+	+	+++	+++	+++

Source: Modified from Gautier et al. (2018).

Notes: Columns on the left indicate the factors driving vegetation types. The five columns under biogeographic domains indicate the relative importance of each vegetation type in the domain classification of Humbert (1955a), with the exception of the High Mountain Domain, which is included here in the Central Domain (C), following Cornet and Guillaumet (1976) and Guillaumet et al. (2008). Key to domain names: E, Eastern Domain; Sb, Sambirano Domain; C, Central Domain: W, Western Domain; S, Southern Domain. Key to symbols: *pp*, pro parte; +++, dominant vegetation; ++, frequent; +, occasional.

Our knowledge is badly out of date for several large genera that require extensive work. Each includes between 50 and 100-plus described species, but careful examination will surely result in significant increases, as has been the case for nearly every other group on Madagascar. These poorly known groups include, for example, three genera of Acanthaceae (*Anisostachya*, *Hypoestes*, and *Justicia*), while work on other genera in this family is ongoing (see Phillipson et al., pp. 789–99), and two genera of Melastomataceae (*Gravesia* and *Medinilla*, see Almeda et al., pp. 668–76), along with *Erythroxylum* (Erythroxylaceae) and *Oncostemum* (Primulaceae).

PHYTOGEOGRAPHY AND VEGETATION

Plant species assemble and form communities that together with other elements of the ecosystem (e.g., fungi, lichens, insects, vertebrates) are driven mostly by biotic and abiotic factors but also by disturbance, the most radical today on Madagascar being anthropogenic. The study of these plant assemblages is the topic of vegetation science. By contrast, plant species distributions can be studied per se, with no reference to environmental conditions except geographic ones, and handling this information, from the level of species to higher groups and from local to worldwide scales, is the topic of phytogeography. It is not the aim of this introduction to review these two fundamentally different approaches, which often converge to a certain extent and are thus often confused. The way they interact in the context of Madagascar has been covered in several successive publications, which also review the history of both types of classifications for the island (Cornet and Guillaumet 1976; Lowry et al. 1997; Gautier and Goodman 2003; Gautier et al. 2018).

Most of the contributions in this chapter refer to the revised vegetation classification published in a recent book dedicated to the

CORRESPONDENCE WITH PREVIOUS CLASSIFICATIONS

Forêt des alluvions et des bords des cours d'eau	Forêt des alluvions et des bords des cours d'eau	Forêt dense humide semi-décidue ripicole	Faciès ripicole	–	–	–
Marais à *Raphia*, Bois et bosquets littoraux (pp)	–	Forêt marécageuse	–	Marshland	Wetland	Malagasy tropical freshwater marsh
Marais et lagunes, Formation des marais	Marais	Marais, Marais herbeux et tourbières	–			
Mangrove	Mangrove	Mangrove	Mangrove	Mangrove	Mangrove	Indian Ocean mangrove
Bois et bosquets littoraux (pp)	–	Fourré littoral	–	–	–	–
	Forêt littorale	Forêt dense humide sempervirente littorale	Forêt littorale	Coastal forests (eastern)	Eastern littoral forest	Madagascar evergreen littoral forest
Pelouses à xérophytes	Pelouses à xérophytes	Rochers	–	–	–	Malagasy granite outcrop vegetation
Brousse des *tavy* ou *savoka*	*Savoka*	*Savoka* ou fourrés secondaires et forêts secondaires	Forêt secondaire mosaïque savane-culture-plantation	–	Degraded humid forest	"Savanna," Madagascar plateau woodland and grassland
Prairie	Savanes	Savanes herbeuses, Pseudo-steppe	Savane savane boisée	–	Wooded grassland/ bushland mosaic, Plateau grassland/wooded grassland mosaic	

protected areas of Madagascar (Gautier et al. 2018). The revised classification is summarized in Table 8.1, which includes the equivalent terms used in previous publications. Further important contributions on the vegetation of Madagascar can be found in chapter 4, dedicated to Forest and Grassland Ecology (see pp. 100–180), as well as in two contributions to the present chapter devoted to aquatic vegetation (see Manjato et al., pp. 470–92) and *tsingy* habitats (see Bardot-Vaucoulon and Gautier, pp. 492–99).

The phytogeography of the Malagasy flora as a whole can be considered at two different scales. The first involves a comparison of the island's flora with that of the rest of the world, examining themes such as endemism, vicariance, and long-distance dispersal. The relationships between the Malagasy flora and those of other tropical regions are unsurprisingly dominated by sub-Saharan Africa, given its proximity, although the influence of tropical Indo-Malayan components has long been recognized (Perrier de la Bâthie 1936a; Schatz 1996; Warren et al. 2010). Since the resurrection of the theory of plate tectonics some 50 years ago (see Collins et al., pp. 45–51), hypotheses regarding the constitution of Madagascar's flora and fauna have been divided between vicariance and long-distance dispersal, and in the precursor of this present book (Goodman and Benstead 2003), much hope was placed on the growing discipline of molecular phylogeny to bring objectivity to this debate. Although plant fossils from certain critical geologic periods are scarce on Madagascar, secondary calibrations dating the emergence and radiation of some groups have been possible. Following the seminal synthesis by Yoder and Nowak (2006), it has been increasingly demonstrated that vicariance has played a smaller role than anticipated in shaping the island's flora, and that in many cases several dispersal events have taken place within a given group, including back-and-forth dispersal between Madagascar and continental areas, mostly Africa. The growing body of dated phylogenies has enabled refined analyses, such as the recent study on the evolution and dispersal of Madagascar's endemic plant genera (Buerki et al. 2016a).

The second scale at which phytogeography can be considered concerns the way in which the elements of the Malagasy flora are distributed within the island, with the implicit aim of delimiting areas that contain a common pool of species. When the distribution of a taxon is indicated in a taxonomic treatment, a conservation assessment, or other study, without providing a map, it is often convenient to list the taxon's geographic range in terms of defined phytogeographic areas, and sometimes specimens are listed according to them. Political units, such as Madagascar's previous province system and the more recent region system, are generally inappropriate as their boundaries rarely coincide with biological limits. A long-used and widely accepted system for dividing Madagascar into distinct areas, most of which are relatively floristically homogeneous, is the *Domaines floristiques* of Humbert (1955), which was consistently followed for decades in the *Flore de Madagascar et des Comores* series and illustrated in the precursor of this book (Gautier and Goodman 2003: Figure 7.1). It has been re-used frequently with slight boundary modifications in several proposed classification systems (e.g., WWF Ecoregions). Humbert's system has, however, been criticized for not being rooted in an objective data-based approach (Lowry et al. 1997), and in the absence of other alternatives, a simplification of Cornet's (1974) bioclimate map has often been used (Schatz 2000). This latter classification, adopted in the Madagascar Catalogue (2020), is criticized, however, because it is based on environmental data and primarily emphasizes precipitation regimes while largely ignoring temperature (or its proxy: elevation). The retreat-dispersion watershed approach developed for vertebrates (Wilmé et al. 2006) has also been considered for plants but has not yet led to a significant improvement on the largely perception-based system for defining phytogeographic zones. Notwithstanding these considerations, it is clear that Humbert's (1955) classification is an empirical one, and that a system based on objective data is badly needed. With the vast corpus of georeferenced data for a wide range of floristic groups available through recent taxonomic revisions, and with the power of statistical spatial analyses now available, the time has come to address the need for a new phytogeographic framework for Madagascar.

SPECIES CONSERVATION ASSESSMENTS

The Madagascar Plant Specialist Group, established in 2000, is mandated to assess the risk of extinction of plant species according to the criteria of the International Union for Conservation of Nature Red List (IUCN 2012). This group, which comprises 50 members, 40 of whom are Malagasy botanists, has assessed more than 6000 species to date. In collaboration with the Global Tree Assessment project of Botanical Garden Conservation International, an assessment was conducted of 2904 species of endemic trees, 65% of which were determined to be threatened, that is, classified on the Red List as Vulnerable, Endangered, or Critically Endangered (Beech et al. 2021). Most of these assessments have been published on the IUCN Red List (IUCN 2020), and the group regularly holds workshops to verify and validate new assessments generated by members or proposed in published taxonomic revisions or descriptions of new species.

EVOLUTION OF MALAGASY ACADEMIC BOTANISTS OVER THE PAST DECADES

We suggest that one important sign of scientific advancement associated with the flora and vegetation of Madagascar, as well as an engagement of Malagasy nationals in conservation action, is the number of Malagasy botanists involved in scientific studies and with active research programs (Figure 8.1). Here we review the evolution of a few of these facets over the past decades, examining developments in publication patterns, which we consider to represent a critical aspect of being part of the international scientific community; the number of people obtaining university higher degrees, which reflects the level of interest in studies related to botany; and the mentoring by international scientific organizations of national graduate students in the Malagasy university system, indicating an engagement to advance future generations of national botanists and conservationists.

Publications

Since around 2000, and particularly since 2010, there has seen a considerable increase in the number of books, chapters in books, and papers in international journals published by Malagasy botanists, including established professors and researchers, as well as younger botanists close to finishing or having finished their higher university degrees. These publications span a diverse range of topics, and there has been a gradual shift during this period in which papers related to taxonomy, including the description of new taxa, have been augmented by publications in the fields of ecology, plant-animal interactions, ethnobotany, and molecular systematics. To simplify measures of this type of evolution through time, we make comparisons between the current volume and the precursor book (Goodman and Benstead 2003).

As can be appreciated from the figures presented in Table 8.2, the past two decades have seen a growth in the participation of Malagasy botanists contributing to these two books. Over the course of this period, contributions with Malagasy coauthors have increased from 13.3% to 31.4%, along with an increase from 15.5% to 21.6% in the number of Malagasy first-authored contributions, which we interpret as at least a portion of associated research programs being under the direction of national botanists. Further, there has been a notable increase in collaborative studies, with several contributions in the current book having multiple Malagasy coauthors, as measured by an increase from 15 in the 2003 book to 47 in the current book.

University Graduate Studies and Other National Institutions

Within the national university system, which has campuses in each of the six former provincial capitals, there are graduate students working in departments with research interests related to the field of botany. These different university departments, under the direction of the Ministère de l'Enseignement Supérieur et de la Recherche Scientifique, include (listed in alphabetical order by city): Mention Biologie et Ecologie Végétales (MBEV; formerly Département de Biologie et Ecologie Végétales or DBEV), Université d'Antananarivo; Faculté des Sciences, Université d'Antsiranana (UNA); Institut des Sciences et Techniques de l'Environnement (ISTE),

FIGURE 8.1 **A selection of Malagasy botanists associated with the California Academy of Sciences (CAS); Conservatoire et Jardin botaniques de la Ville de Genève (G); Mention de Biologie et Ecologie Végétale, Université d'Antananarivo (MBEV) and formerly Département de Biologie et Ecologie Végétale (DBEV); Missouri Botanical Garden (MBG); Madagascar Minerals (QMM QIT); and Parc Botanique et Zoologique de Tsimbazaza (PBZT). A) Jacquis Tahinarivony (Famelona) at Beampingaratra; B) Johny Rabentoandro (QMM) and Richard Razakamalala (MBG) at Bemangidy; C) The G-MBEV team at Ampasindava (left to right) Morgane Ammann, Cathy Madiomanana, and Jacquis Tahinarivony; D) Charles Rakotovao (MBG) at Galoko-Kalobinono Massif; E) Désiré Ravelonarivo (MBG) at Namoroka; F) Patrice Antilahimena (MBG; second from left) en route to Ankerana; G) the G-MBEV team at Montagne d'Ambre (left to right) Mialy Razanajatovo, Solotiana Ramandimbimanana, and Sonia Trigui; H) Jeannie Raharimampionona (MBG) identifying specimens; I) Rokiman Letsara (CAS) at Namoroka; J) Jacky Andriantiana (PBZT) in the field; K) Tefy Andriamihajarivo and Fidy Ratovoson (MBG) pressing plant specimens; L) Richard Randrianaivo (MBG) in the field; M) Aina Randriarisoa (G-MBEV) at Beampingaratra; N) Nadiah Manjato (MBG) collecting *Hydrostachys*; and O) Patrick Ranirison (Famelona) in Daraina.** (PHOTOS A, E, G, I, and M by L. Gautier; B, H, J, K, L, and N by MBG-Madagascar; C and O by L. Nusbaumer; D by M. Callmander; F by B. Ramandimbisoa.)

TABLE 8.2. **Comparisons of Malagasy authorship of contributions to the Plants chapter in *The Natural History of Madagascar* (Goodman and Benstead 2003) and the current book**

CATEGORY	GOODMAN AND BENSTEAD (2003)	CURRENT BOOK
Number of contributions to Plants chapter	45	50
Number of contributions with a Malagasy coauthor[1]	6 (13.3%)	20 (40%)
Number of contributions with a Malagasy first author or single author	7 (15.5%)	11 (22%)
Total number of Malagasy coauthors[2]	15	47

[1] The tally indicates that at least one Malagasy coauthor was involved in a given contribution but does not reflect the number of Malagasy nationals per contribution.

[2] The tally includes the total number of Malagasy authors involved in the Plants chapter, with certain contributions having more than one Malagasy coauthor.

Université de Fianarantsoa; Ecole Doctorale Ecosystèmes Naturels (EDEN), Université de Mahajanga; Institut Supérieur des Sciences Environnement Développement Durable (ISSEDD, formerly Gestion de Ressources Naturelles et Environnement or GRENE), Université de Toamasina; and Ecole Doctorale de Biodiversité et Environnements Tropicaux, Université de Toliara. There are other departments at these universities that have extensive programs in fields related to botany. To cite one of many examples, the Mention Foresterie et Environnement de l'Ecole Supérieure des Sciences Agronomiques (ESSA-Forêts), Université d'Antananarivo has an important research and pedagogic program associated with forestry and other related botanical studies.

Until a few years ago, before the Malagasy national university structure shifted toward the Anglophone Licence-master-doctorat (LMD) system, the higher degrees included Diplôme d'Etudes Approfondies (DEA), Thèse de Troisième Cycle, and Thèse d'Etat, and after this change these became to a large extent master's, PhD, and Habilitation à Diriger des Recherches (HDR), respectively. Over the past decades, there has been a considerable increase in the number of Malagasy students doing graduate studies in botany. Through the courtesy of colleagues in the MBEV, Université d'Antananarivo, we obtained a list of completed higher diplomas presented between 1971 and 2016 and represented in the department's library—the figures are shown in Figure 8.2a.

The surge over the past two decades in the number of botanical higher degrees presented at the Université d'Antananarivo is associated with several factors, including increased foreign collaboration (see Wojahn et al, pp. 464–70), as well as projects such as Sud Expert Plantes, financed via the Institut de Recherche pour le Développement (IRD), principally by the Fonds Français pour l'Environnement Mondial (FFEM), Agence Française de Développement (AFD), and Ministère et Affaires Etrangères et Européennes de France (MAEE). This multiple-phase program has funded research by numerous Malagasy students, professors, and researchers, as well as investing in infrastructure for the principal herbaria on the island.

A number of other Malagasy institutions have active programs associated with the fields of botany and agricultural development, and a short list includes (arranged alphabetically by organization name): Centre National de la Recherche Appliquée au Développement Rural or, in Malagasy, Foibem-pirenena momba ny Fikarohana ampiharina amin'ny Fampandrosoana ny eny Ambanivohitra (FOFIFA); Centre National de Recherches sur l'Environnement (CNRE); and Parc Botanique et Zoologique de Tsimbazaza (PBZT).

Collaboration with Overseas Herbaria and Research Institutions

One crucial aspect over the past decades in the advancement of botanical research on Madagascar, specifically by Malagasy students and researchers, has been collaborations with overseas institutions (herbarium-based research organizations and university departments) with active programs on the island. These projects have helped to finance various aspects of botany, including inventories of unknown or poorly known areas, with collection of plant specimens for which at least one duplicate is housed in a Malagasy herbarium, and the costs of student research and associated mentoring (the subject of this section); a range of research projects, including different types of laboratory analyses; resources to improve facilities in national herbaria; and baseline studies and associated infrastructure for the delimitation and creation of many new protected areas and their subsequent monitoring and advancement. It is important to point out that several foreign research organizations working at least in part in the field of botany are the managing authorities for recently established protected areas—Missouri Botanical Garden (12 sites), Muséum National d'Histoire Naturelle (one site), and Royal Botanic Gardens, Kew (one site) (Ranivo Rakotoson and Razafimahatratra 2018). This aspect clearly shows an additional important role of these institutions over and above mentoring Malagasy botanical students in the future of this island nation.

In Figure 8.2b we give numbers for higher degrees, separated as DEA/master's and PhD diplomas, presented between 1993 and 2018 by the Mention Biologie et Ecologie Végétale (MBEV), Université d'Antananarivo. Student mentoring was provided by three different foreign botanical institutions: the Missouri Botanical Garden (MBG), established on Madagascar in 1986 (62 DEAs/master's and seven PhDs); Royal Botanic Gardens, Kew, established on Madagascar in 1999 (10 DEAs/master's and six PhDs); and Conservatoire et Jardin botaniques de la Ville de Genève, active on Madagascar since 1993 (11 DEAs/master's and three PhDs).

Since around the start of the 21st century, there has been a notable increase in the number of Malagasy students mentored by these three organizations and associated with the MBEV, as well as many others not included in these tallies. In some respects, Figures 8.2a and b include largely the same data, but the manner in which they have been compiled presents different perspectives on advancements in botanical studies at MBEV. There is considerable variation in the number of higher degrees awarded each year; for example, 12 were presented in 2008, most associated with an MBG project dedicated to the advancement of Malagasy graduate

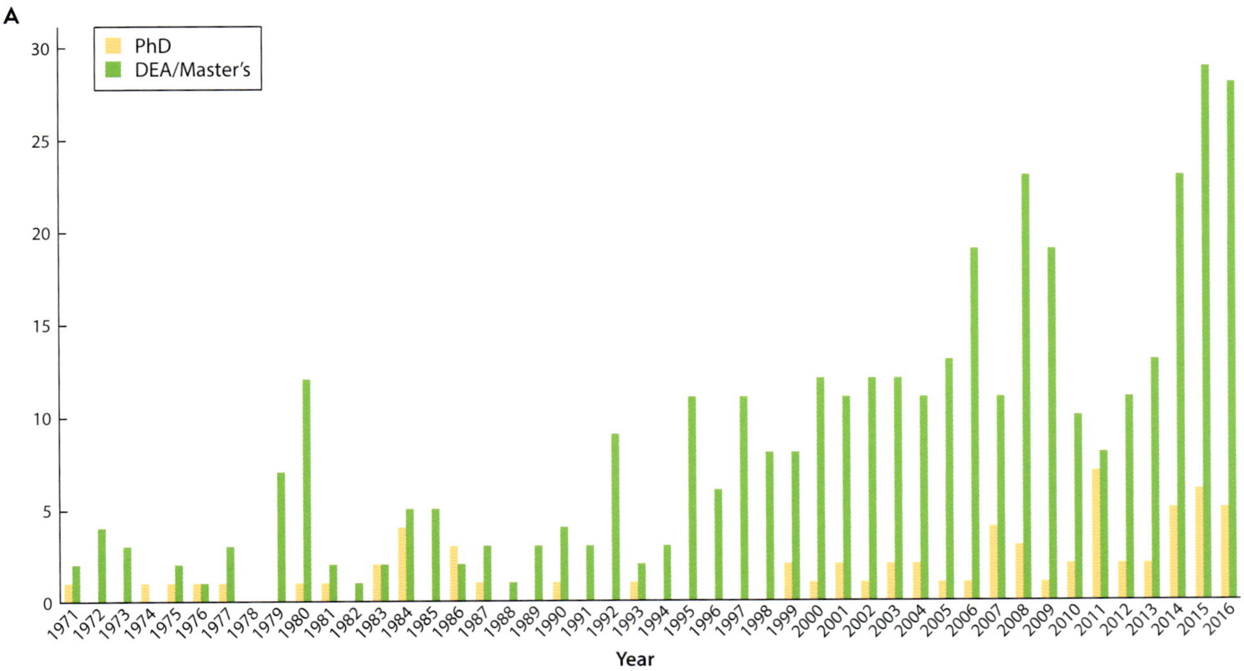

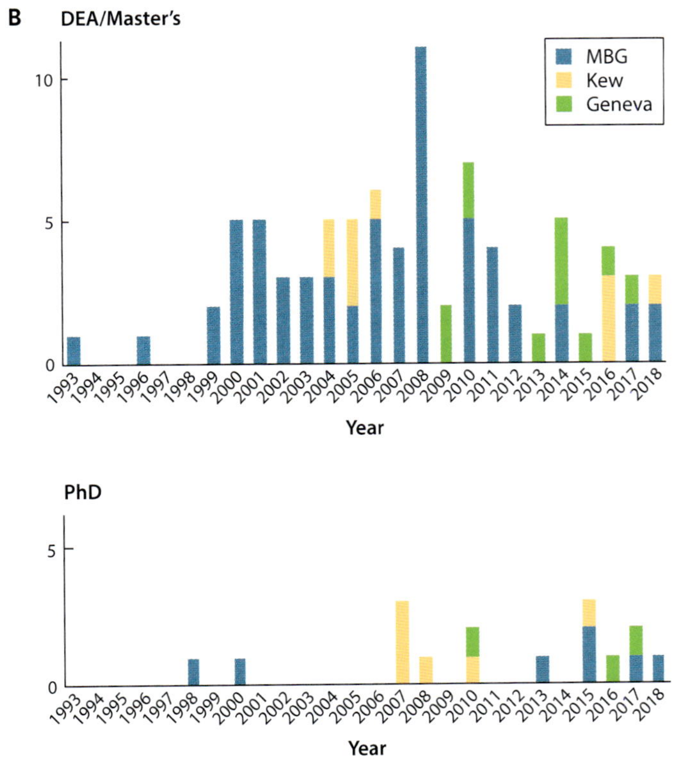

FIGURE 8.2 **Graphical representations of the expansion of botanical studies by Malagasy graduate students in the Mention Biologie et Ecologie Végétale, Université d'Antananarivo. A considerable amount of work has been conducted at other national universities, but given the large scope and availability of lists from the Université d'Antananarivo, we present data from that institution. A) Number of higher degrees presented and with associated documents (theses and memoirs) held in the department's library. The presented figures are not the total number presented between 1971 and 2016 but are certainly indicative of trends. B) Number of DEA/master's and PhDs presented between 1993 and 2018 under the support of three collaborating foreign institutions (Missouri Botanical Garden, St. Louis, Missouri, United States, and with offices in Madagascar; Royal Botanic Gardens, Kew, United Kingdom, and with offices in Madagascar; and Conservatoire et Jardin botaniques de la Ville de Genève, Switzerland).**

students and field workers in the domain of botany, while in the following year, 2009, only two were obtained as the university was largely closed during a nearly year-long Malagasy political crisis. In any case, foreign botanical institutions provide important support in the mentoring of Malagasy graduate students, and this effort has been of considerable importance, both promoting public universities and advancing generations of Malagasy students who have or will in future take important positions in governmental and non-governmental organizations. This is in direct parallel to the field of zoology at the same university.

INSIDE THE PLANTS CHAPTER

This chapter comprises 50 contributions by a total of 47 authors. The first contribution following this introduction presents the state of knowledge in the field of molecular systematics of the Malagasy flora. Then, two contributions on freshwater plants and the *tsingy* (Madagascar's karstic limestone areas) provide insights on several vegetation types worthy of a more in-depth treatment than that found in the vegetation chapter of the recent protected areas book (Gautier et al. 2018). This is followed by a series of taxonomic contributions that cover a significant portion of the groups currently being studied most actively. These contributions start with lichens, followed by bryophytes, and then angiosperms (no pteridophyte contribution is presented here). For angiosperms, the sequence of contributions follows the linear arrangement proposed by Haston et al. (2009). Most of the contributions deal with families, but some cover small orders or genera. They address a range of themes such as diversity, endemism, evolution, biogeography, and conservation, and some emphasize human uses or plant-animal interaction (e.g., *Ficus* spp. and their wasps; see Rasplus et al., pp. 617–34) or emerging native plant products with conservation issues (e.g., *tsiperifery*, see Razafimandimby et al., pp. 542–45).

For the vast majority of taxonomic contributions for vascular plant groups encompassing three or more genera, we present a standardized diagram illustrating diversity and endemicity in which the genera are listed vertically, usually grouped by higher units (tribe or subfamily). The length of the horizontal bar represents the number of species worldwide and comprises three additive categories: 1) species endemic to Madagascar in blue, 2) nonendemic native species in green (introduced species are not taken into account, even if naturalized), and 3) species not occurring naturally on Madagascar in yellow. When the third category is particularly large, the corresponding bar is broken to the right and an approximate figure is provided. The vertical spacing of genera and the horizontal scale of the bars are consistent across graphs so that they are comparable; that is, a species occupies the same area in each graph. Genera are arranged vertically one after another, except in graphs that deal with several families, in which they are clearly separated.

ACKNOWLEDGMENTS

We are grateful to Tabita Randrianarivony (MBG), Hélène Ralimanana (Kew), Tendro Radanielina and Patrick Ranirison (MBEV), and Jacquis Andonahary Tahinarivony (Famelona) for access to different files to document patterns of botanical advancement in Malagasy universities. Pete Phillipson kindly extracted figures from the Madagascar Catalogue, Sylvie Andriambololonera provided information on conservation assessments, and Yamama Naciri commented on the molecular systematics section.

Subject editors: Laurent Gautier and Steven M. Goodman

UPDATE ON THE PHYLOGENETIC FRAMEWORK OF MALAGASY ANGIOSPERMS

J. M. A. Wojahn, M. W. Callmander, P. P. Lowry II, P. B. Phillipson, and S. Buerki

The exceptional richness of Malagasy floristic diversity and its remarkable levels of endemism have been acknowledged since the first botanical collections were made on the island. The 20th-century scientist Henri Perrier de la Bâthie and several 21st-century researchers have confirmed Madagascar's botanical exceptionalism (Perrier de la Bâthie 1936a; Callmander et al. 2011a; Buerki et al. 2012; Lowry et al. 2018). For example, Madagascar is home to an estimated 14,000 species of vascular plants of which over 87% are endemic (Lowry et al. 2018). The angiosperm component represents 95% of the whole vascular plant flora, with 10,650 species (84% endemic) currently described, distributed among 1621 genera (19% endemic) (Callmander et al. 2011a). Madagascar has been designated one of the world's most important biodiversity hotspots, mainly because of the high level of diversity and endemism coupled with its unprecedented rate of deforestation, which threatens the survival of its biodiversity and the sustainability of its ecosystems (Myers et al. 2000). The island retains less than 10% of its natural surface habitats compared with their original extent before the arrival of the first humans, estimated to have been perhaps 10 millennia ago (see Wright and Rakotoarisoa, pp. 181–90). Some ecosystems have been reduced to less than 1% of their original area, and the entire eastern rainforest could be entirely eliminated by 2070 (Moat and Smith 2007; Morelli et al. 2020).

During the last two centuries, botanists have focused primarily on providing a taxonomic framework for the flora of Madagascar, but little is known about the evolutionary processes involved in shaping it (e.g., Buerki et al. 2012). One of the main barriers impeding a better understanding of these processes is the limited availability of well-supported molecular phylogenetic inferences that have been dated using robust calibrations from the fossil record. Buerki et al. (2012) reviewed current knowledge on this topic for endemic Malagasy genera of angiosperms and found phylogenetic information for only 184 of the 310 genera (59.3%), and divergence time estimates were available for only 67 of these genera (21.6%). The authors concluded that we were still in the infancy of our understanding of the phylogenetic relationships of the island's unique flora, and they called for more studies. In this contribution, we evaluate the current state of knowledge on the phylogenetic position of Malagasy angiosperms with the ultimate objective of inferring a unified phylogenetic framework for this unparalleled region of the world. Such a framework would provide a unique tool in support of our efforts to unravel the evolutionary mechanisms and biogeographic processes that have shaped the Malagasy flora, and it would also be an asset for the formulation of conservation strategies. Indeed, combining phylogenetic data with International Union for Conservation Nature (IUCN) Red List assessments (IUCN 2012) could inform an expansion of the process of prioritizing species conservation, going beyond one based simply on threats by factoring in evolutionary uniqueness. Known as the Evolutionarily Distinct and Globally Endangered (EDGE) approach (https://www.edgeofexistence.org), it was recently applied to gymnosperms worldwide (Forest et al. 2018). Such an ambitious endeavor would require synergy between conservationists and evolutionary biologists, but the result would be well worth the effort as it would provide a unique roadmap to support the conservation of Madagascar's exceptional flora.

OBJECTIVES

In this contribution, we provide an updated assessment of our knowledge of the available phylogenetic information for Malagasy angiosperms by using taxonomic data from the Catalogue of the Plants of Madagascar (Madagascar Catalogue 2020) via the Global Biodiversity Information Facility (GBIF 2019) and DNA sequences deposited in GenBank (as of 18 December 2019; NCBI 2021). We aim to answer the following questions:

1. What proportion of the Malagasy angiosperm flora has been sequenced?
2. What are the most commonly used DNA barcodes and regions?
3. Is there a geographic bias among the taxa sequenced?

In association with addressing each of these questions, we provide recommendations on how best to facilitate the completion of the phylogenetic framework of the Malagasy angiosperm flora.

WHAT PROPORTION OF THE MALAGASY ANGIOSPERM FLORA HAS BEEN SEQUENCED?

Knowledge provided by genomic data and DNA barcoding opens up a number of possible scientific analyses, such as inferring the phylogenetic position of a species or assessing its spatial and temporal origins (Hebert et al. 2003; Hollingsworth et al. 2011). Using DNA sequences that are associated with both peer-reviewed articles and voucher specimens is an important and unfortunately often-overlooked aspect of DNA barcode analyses. Without the centuries of accumulated knowledge generated by taxonomists—as provided through the study of herbarium specimens and associated published scientific articles and monographs—the correct identification of the source material of DNA sequences cannot be assured. Our analyses demonstrate that only 4335 species (representing 31% of the estimated 14,000 angiosperm species on Madagascar) have at least one DNA sequence available on GenBank (28,386 Malagasy sequences total), representing 1366 genera (84.3% of the island's angiosperm genera). Of these DNA sequences, only 9973 (35.1%) are underpinned by publications registered with PubMed (the literature database associated to GenBank accessions, see NCBI [2021]). For the 64.9% that are not documented by a publication, the validity of the taxonomic identification of the sample used to produce the sequences has not been verified through the necessary scientific processes. On average, 14 DNA sequences were produced per publication, with seven publications resulting in more than 200 DNA sequences each. A review of the publications containing the most DNA sequences showed that some studies produced data specifically for use in future DNA barcode libraries (e.g., Aubriot et al. 2013), which are underpinned by vouchers, while others generated environmental DNA results, which can never be taxonomically verified since there is no voucher (i.e., the authors have used a metabarcoding approach applied to feces or soil samples, e.g., see Kartzinel et al. 2015). In any case, the results summarized above show that, despite our best efforts to study this highly diverse and threatened flora, significant effort still needs to be allocated to complete its phylogenetic framework.

The percentages of species sequenced in the 50 most sequenced families of Malagasy plants are presented in Table 8.3. This and subsequently cited percentages represent just the currently described species sequenced, not the estimated total number of species in a given family. Over half of the species have been sequenced in 24 families (Table 8.3). The high proportion of these that are Leguminosae is most likely due to the efforts of the Legume Phylogeny Working Group (Azani et al. 2017). Rubiaceae also has a coordinated group of researchers, likely also resulting in a high level of sequencing (e.g., Razafimandimbison et al. 2002). Cyperaceae, although less species rich, is often used as an ecological indicator and thus might have received more attention than would be expected otherwise. Distressingly, despite being the most species-rich family on Madagascar, Orchidaceae (869 species) has DNA sequences representing only about a third of its species available in GenBank. This anomaly might be due to the protected status of orchids under the Convention on International Trade in Endangered Species (CITES) regulations, limiting collection and exportation of material. Moreover, for orchids, DNA must usually be extracted from flowers rather than leaves due to their mucilaginous and coriaceous nature. This latter feature makes obtaining tissue from orchid herbarium specimens extremely difficult since it implies destructive sampling of morphologically vital components of the specimen. Overall, since sequencing coverage differs from family to family, the amount of effort required to ensure that each family has some DNA sequences available for each of their species will vary between families. DNA sequences are totally lacking for 10 families, representing 28 species on Madagascar (Table 8.4).

Madagascar has five endemic families, each of which represents an evolutionary lineage unique to the island. The largest of these (Sarcolaenaceae, 78 species) (Table 8.5 and Aubriot et al. 2013, 2016) has been comparatively well sequenced, but more than 40% of its species still need to be sequenced. Only the two smallest families have been comprehensively sequenced: Physenaceae (two species) and Barbeuiaceae (one species).

Our analyses show that as you consider families of increasing diversity the number of species with at least one DNA sequence deposited in GenBank also increases (Figure 8.3). However, there remains a significant sequencing gap (shown by the distance

TABLE 8.3. **Malagasy plant families and species represented in GenBank**

FAMILY	NUMBER OF SPECIES IN GENBANK	PERCENTAGE OF FAMILY SEQUENCED	SPECIES RICHNESS RANK
Fabaceae	415	59.5	2
Poaceae	377	75.4	4
Rubiaceae	354	54.2	3
Orchidaceae	289	36.0	1
Euphorbiaceae	189	48.2	6
Compositae	155	31.4	5
Apocynaceae	153	47.7	8
Cyperaceae	139	54.3	10
Malvaceae	126	34.5	7
Acanthaceae	65	21.7	9
Melastomataceae	56	22.2	11
Convolvulaceae	55	62.5	22
Oleaceae	49	79.0	36
Solanaceae	48	75.0	31
Araliaceae	46	70.8	30
Annonaceae	45	62.5	26
Arecaceae	44	22.3	13
Sarcolaenaceae	44	65.7	28
Phyllanthaceae	42	42.9	19
Lamiaceae	40	17.1	12
Sapindaceae	39	38.2	18
Xanthorrhoeaceae	37	34.9	17
Sapotaceae	36	50.0	27
Cucurbitaceae	35	54.7	32
Crassulaceae	33	55.9	37
Anacardiaceae	32	48.5	29
Burseraceae	32	94.1	54
Ebenaceae	31	40.3	24
Gentianaceae	30	47.6	33
Bignoniaceae	28	45.2	35
Pandanaceae	27	30.3	21
Balsaminaceae	27	24.6	16
Passifloraceae	26	70.3	49
Asparagaceae	24	49.0	41
Moraceae	24	64.9	50
Primulaceae	23	20.7	15

TABLE 8.3. *continued*

FAMILY	NUMBER OF SPECIES IN GENBANK	PERCENTAGE OF FAMILY SEQUENCED	SPECIES RICHNESS RANK
Vitaceae	23	67.7	55
Meliaceae	22	26.5	23
Amaranthaceae	22	51.2	43
Gesneriaceae	22	51.2	44
Dioscoreaceae	21	51.2	46
Lauraceae	21	18.4	14
Celastraceae	21	58.3	53
Urticaceae	21	37.5	40
Hypericaceae	20	66.7	59
Boraginaceae	17	47.2	52
Violaceae	17	60.7	64
Piperaceae	17	37.8	42
Araceae	16	64.0	67
Myrtaceae	16	21.3	25

Source: Madagascar Catalogue (2020).
Note: Information is presented for the top 50 most sequenced families of the Malagasy flora.

TABLE 8.4. **Number of genera and species in each of the 10 plant families on Madagascar with no sequences in GenBank**

FAMILY	NUMBER OF GENERA	NUMBER OF SPECIES
Achariaceae	1	5
Cardiopteridaceae	1	2
Cytinaceae	1	2
Dichapetalaceae	1	8
Hydnoraceae	1	1
Ixonanthaceae	1	1
Kirkiaceae	1	1
Peraceae	1	1
Picrodendraceae	3	8
Trigoniaceae	1	1

Source: Madagascar Catalogue (2020).

between the total number of species in a family and the number of species sequenced, indicated by the optimum line) that will have to be overcome in order to complete the phylogenetic framework of Malagasy angiosperms. At this stage, very few families have some DNA sequences available for each of their species, and these are families with only one or two species on Madagascar.

WHAT ARE THE MOST USED DNA BARCODES/REGIONS?

Most of the DNA sequences available in GenBank were produced using the Sanger sequencing approach. This approach, invented in the mid-1970s (Sanger and Coulson 1975), involves sequencing DNA regions obtained from polymerase chain reactions (PCR). The first 30 DNA sequences were produced for Malagasy angiosperms 18 years after the invention of Sanger sequencing, all for the *rbcL* region (Figure 8.4). More than 28,000 DNA sequences are now available (see Figure 8.4 and Table 8.6). The rate of DNA sequencing was linear between 1993 and 2010 (during which time 5800 sequences were produced), after which point it began to increase exponentially, with more than 22,500 sequences generated in under a decade (Figure 8.4). This dramatic change could in part reflect the momentum provided by the DNA barcoding initiative (stimulated by the CBOL [Consortium for the Barcode of Life] Plant Working Group 2009, which relied on data produced by the Angiosperm Phylogeny Working Group) and the emergence of next-generation sequencing (NGS) techniques, which first became available in 2005.

The nuclear ribosomal internal described spacer (ITS) region and plastid coding *rbcL* and *matK* regions are those most frequently used for the study Malagasy angiosperms, with 9940, 6622, and 6338 DNA sequences, representing 2467, 1906, and 2200 species, respectively (see Figure 8.4 and Table 8.6). Thus, although a total of 4313 species have been sequenced, each of these three DNA regions provides a data set with limited species coverage. An increase

TABLE 8.5. **Number of species represented in GenBank for each of Madagascar's endemic plant families, the percentage of total species sequenced, and the species richness rank**

FAMILY	NUMBER OF SPECIES IN GENBANK	PERCENTAGE OF FAMILY SEQUENCED	NUMBER OF CURRENTLY RECOGNIZED SPECIES
Sarcolaenaceae	44	56	78
Sphaerosepalaceae	3	15	20
Physenaceae	2	100	2
Asteropeiceae	2	25	8
Barbeuiaceae	1	100	1

Source: Madagascar Catalogue (2020).

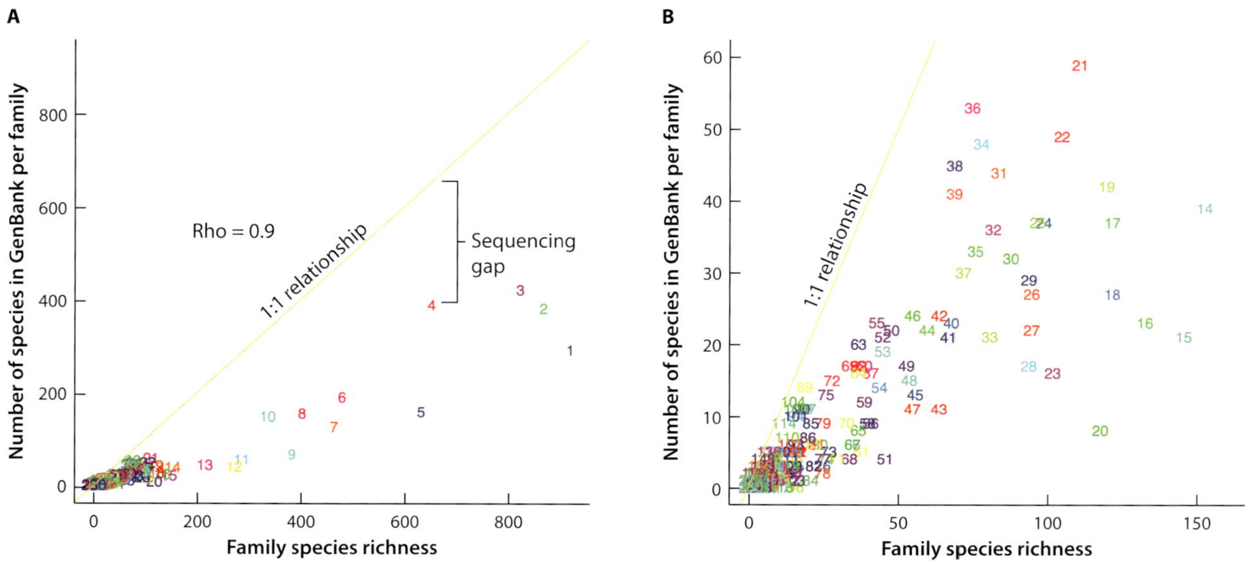

FIGURE 8.3 **A) Graph of the relationship between species richness per family and the number of species in GenBank per family for the Malagasy angiosperm flora (a positive correlation was inferred for this relationship, Rho = 0.9). Numbers represent the species richness rank as inferred from the Madagascar Catalogue (2020) and displayed in Table 8.3; the colors of the numbers are provided simply to facilitate their visual discrimination, especially where values are clumped. The gold line represents a 1:1 relationship, i.e., all the species within a family have been sequenced. B) Zoomed-in version of the bottom left section of the graph presented in part A.**

in the sampling of *rbcL* and *matK*—both of which are highly conserved regions in the chloroplast genome, useful in elucidating deep relationships—would make it possible to infer a stronger phylogenetic framework for the Malagasy angiosperms, whereas adding sequences of the nuclear ITS region—which is more variable and thus can be used to elucidate more recent divergences—would provide insight into species relationships. One could also imagine taking advantage of target-enriched library techniques (see Johnson et al. 2019) to develop a set of ribonucleic acid (RNA) probes allowing high-throughput sequencing of the top 12 DNA regions, shown in Table 8.6, for all Malagasy angiosperm taxa. Such libraries could then be pooled and sequenced on NGS machines. This approach would be very cost-effective and would make it possible to analyze a large set of taxa very rapidly using available bioinformatics pipelines.

Tissue and DNA banks housed in major institutions working on the Malagasy flora (e.g., the Missouri Botanical Garden and the Royal Botanic Gardens, Kew) could provide a second major impetus for the rapid production of DNA sequences for taxa that are currently unsampled. NGS techniques could also be used to tap into historical collections (as discussed in Buerki and Baker 2016). As the cost of producing genomic data continues to decrease, we argue in favor of producing a suite of barcodes for all taxa, which can be used to infer a unified phylogenetic framework of Madagascar's angiosperm flora. However, it will be important to make sure that high-quality genomic DNA extractions are stored for these taxa for subsequent analyses (such as efforts to improve our understanding of fine-scale evolutionary processes) and that all samples used are fully vouchered and reliably identified.

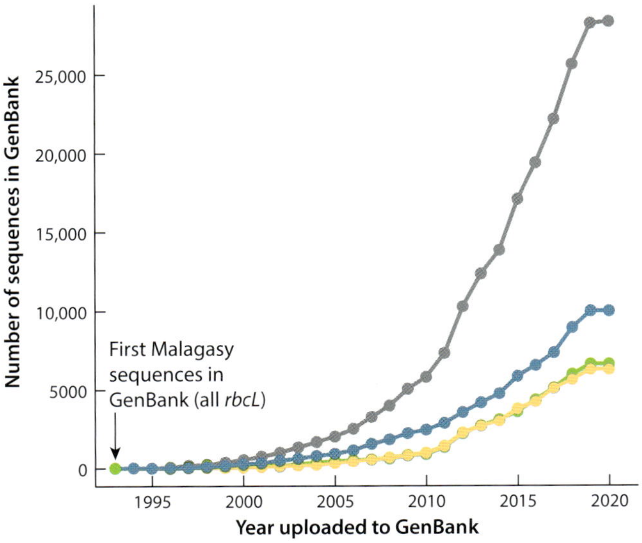

FIGURE 8.4 **Graph of the number of Malagasy plant barcode sequences uploaded to GenBank by year. The total number of sequences is represented by the gray line, *rbcL* by the green line, *matK* by the yellow line, and ITS by the blue line.**

IS THERE A GEOGRAPHIC BIAS AMONG THE TAXA SEQUENCED?

Here, we discuss progress made toward the completion of sequencing species in each of Madagascar's biomes, and we assess the percentage of species occurring exclusively outside of protected areas that remain to be sequenced. Our results demonstrate that the effort applied to sequencing species has not been even across the island (Figure 8.5). In general, sequenced species show the same pattern as species richness, with geographic clusters of DNA sequencing effort occurring at the boundaries between biomes. Although some geographic regions were sequenced more than others, there is still a vast majority of species requiring to be sequenced, therefore reinforcing the sequencing gap as defined above (Figure 8.3). This gap will have to be closed to obtain enough phylogenetic information to study plant communities. Sadly, it is unlikely that DNA can be extracted from some plant material, especially collections protected from rotting in the tropical climate by being preserved in ethanol, which significantly degrades plant DNA, and which were not accompanied by leaf samples dried in silica gel, a preferred medium for preserving DNA for extraction (Chase and Hills 1991). Targeted fieldwork will be required to build a comprehensive tissue bank of the Malagasy flora.

Our analyses showed that species present in protected areas were over-represented in the overall sampling used for DNA sequencing. The rate of sequencing of species recorded inside protected areas (42.1% of 7651 species) is 1.4 times higher than the rate of sequencing of all Malagasy angiosperm species (31.0%) (see Goodman et al. 2018 for a map and description of the terrestrial protected area system of Madagascar). Our analyses indicate that there are ~2960 species not known to occur within any protected area, and that 42.6% of them have at least one DNA sequence in GenBank. Although we have not critically evaluated the taxonomic identity of species in this latter list, we hypothesize that it would contain a large proportion of narrowly distributed species that are of high conservation value. Overall, this analysis suggests that botanists should focus more effort on securing DNA material of species occurring only outside of protected areas since they are, on average, in greater danger of extinction.

TABLE 8.6. **Number of sequences from Malagasy material for each of the 12 phylogenetically useful DNA regions and other details**

REGION	TYPE	NUMBER OF SEQUENCES	NUMBER OF SPECIES	PERCENTAGE OF SPECIES
ITS region	Nuclear	9940	2467	25.2%
matK	Plastid	6338	2200	22.5%
rbcL	Plastid	6622	1906	19.5%
trnL	Plastid	3038	1448	14.8%
trnF	Plastid	1314	767	7.8%
psbA	Plastid	1025	533	5.5%
trnH	Plastid	579	328	3.4%
atpH	Plastid	94	59	0.6%
psbK	Plastid	67	37	0.4%
psbI	Plastid	38	36	0.4%
rpoC1	Plastid	0	0	0.0%
rpoB	Plastid	0	0	0.0%

Note: Information on phylogenetically useful regions is after Hollingsworth et al. (2011).

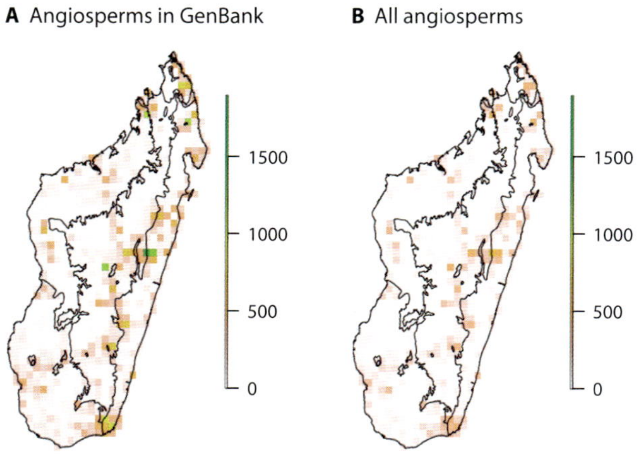

FIGURE 8.5 **Two species richness maps showing A) species richness for angiosperms on Madagascar and B) species richness of angiosperms with at least one DNA sequence in GenBank.**

PERSPECTIVES

Although botanists have been studying the Malagasy flora for centuries, sequencing technology has only been applied to the island's plants since 1993 (Figure 8.4). Given that more than 22,000 DNA sequences have been generated during just the decade up to 2020, we are very optimistic about the prospects for completing the phylogenetic framework for the angiosperms present on Madagascar. We advocate a coordinated international effort between in-country and international specialists, taxonomists, and phylogeneticists to bridge the remaining sampling gap, and to produce sequences for an adequately informative set of DNA barcodes for the remaining ~9500 species. These sequences could then be used to infer a complete phylogenetic framework for the angiosperms of Madagascar, providing an unparalleled opportunity to unravel the evolutionary and biogeographic mechanisms that shaped the origins of this remarkable flora.

Subject editors: Laurent Gautier and Steven M. Goodman

VASCULAR PLANTS OF MALAGASY FRESHWATER WETLANDS

N. V. Manjato, H. L. Ranarijaona, B. A. Randriamiarisoa, C. Maharombaka, P. P. Lowry II, and P. B. Phillipson

A contribution on aquatic and semiaquatic vascular plants was published (Andrianasetra Ranarijaona 2003) in the precursor to this book (Goodman and Benstead 2003). It provided information on the aquatic and semiaquatic vascular plants occurring in the freshwater and brackish lakes, marshes, and rivers of Madagascar, covering the taxonomy, species richness, ecology, and biogeographic affinities of these plants in lentic habitats, along with a floristic inventory of these habitats. This contribution also provided information on endemism and the importance of the aquatic ecosystems of the island. Since the early 2000s considerable new information has been gathered in terms of our knowledge of these plants and the conservation status of aquatic habitats, and in the present contribution we aim to build upon the foundation of the earlier contribution.

Reflecting a general trend in many parts of the world, freshwater wetlands on Madagascar have received less than adequate attention by researchers and conservationists. Madagascar is a global conservation priority due to its very diverse and highly endemic flora, which is widely threatened, but most conservation work has focused on protecting and managing forests. Of the 46 strict reserves, national parks, and special reserves established before 2011, all but one predominantly protect forest ecosystems. As of 2015, Madagascar had 122 protected areas (Goodman et al. 2018), many containing wetlands, and in most cases these habitats and the species within them were not generally considered as primary criteria for the selection or delimitation of these sites. As argued by Bamford et al. (2017), the profound degradation of the majority of wetlands on Madagascar has resulted in the widespread loss of native biodiversity, and many wetlands have been overtaken by a small number of pollution-tolerant native or introduced species. Madagascar is losing its natural wetland habitats even faster than its forests. For example, the highland regions are estimated to have lost 60% of their natural wetlands in the latter half of the 20th century (Kull 2012), although more research and ongoing monitoring is needed to assess the situation across the country more accurately. There are, however, some notable exceptions in which important wetland habitats have been incorporated into the protected area network and have benefited from other forms of protection. It is a positive sign that 18 of the 20 designated Ramsar sites on Madagascar are now included within the national protected area network, including important sites such as the Amoron'i Onilahy, Nosivolo River, Lake Alaotra, and Lake Rasoabe in Ankarafantsika National Park.

Freshwater wetlands are represented by two broad types of habitat system: 1) lentic habitats in which calm or even stagnant water conditions prevail, such as ponds, swamps, marshes, lakes, and wet grasslands; and 2) lotic habitats that consist of running water, such as rivers and streams. Plants that grow naturally in wetland habitats, including both freshwater and saltwater systems, and in temporary as well as permanent water bodies, are referred to as aquatic plants.

The term *microphyte* refers to tiny, short-lived, microscopic plants, including algae, which are hard to see with the naked eye, while the term *macrophyte* refers to larger, perennial species, most of which are vascular plants, and some trees (Chambers et al. 2008).

A distinction is also sometimes made between plants whose photosynthetically active parts are permanently submerged in water or floating on the water surface, known as *hydrophytes*, and those that are rooted underwater but have stems and leaves that develop predominantly above the water, or that inhabit boggy or other waterlogged habitats. The latter are sometimes termed *semiaquatic plants*; they are generally more tolerant of water stress and can sometimes survive longer periods of drought. However, in some plant groups, notably in families such as Asteraceae, Cyperaceae (see Larridon et al., pp. 580–85), and Poaceae (see Vorontsova et al., pp. 585–98), this definition is difficult to apply because it includes species that can also survive in temporarily dry areas but tend to be closely associated with wetland habitats. In these families and in other plant groups, species, referred to as *helophytes*, can be found that become totally dormant during drought periods, coming back to life when the ground floods. In this treatment we take a broad view of aquatic plants and include all vascular plants (but not algae) that have a clear association with a wetland habitat. We present a summary of information available on freshwater aquatic plants on the island, including published information and recent studies on the role of aquatic plants and the threats to them. This contribution serves as an update to that of Andrianasetra Ranarijaona (2003) on aquatic and semiaquatic vascular plants.

HISTORY OF RESEARCH ON MALAGASY AQUATIC PLANTS

Research on the Malagasy aquatic flora has mainly been conducted in the context of exploration and systematics. Each volume of the *Flore de Madagascar et des Comores* contains a treatment of the species of a particular plant family, including morphological descriptions along with illustrations, geographic information, and identification keys. Approximately 35 families containing aquatic and semiaquatic species have been treated to date in this series. As indicated by Morat and Lowry (1997), most of these taxonomic treatments were produced before 1960 and are therefore notably outdated given the number of new collections made and new localities explored in the past 60 years, and despite significant advances. As an example, in the treatment of Tardieu-Blot (1952), the aquatic fern family Marsileaceae comprised, for Madagascar, a single genus, *Marsilea*, with four species, whereas a taxonomic revision carried out almost 70 years later increased the number of species to seven (Bouchart-Dufay and Rakotondrainibe 2019).

In other areas of study, one of the first works to focus on aquatic plants and their habitats on Madagascar was that of Cabanis et al. (1969). This work contains descriptions and drawings of some floating, submerged, and emergent aquatic plants of Madagascar, whether endemic or not, along with an indication of their habitat, geographic distribution, and uses. In addition, swamps and mangrove species are also treated. From the 1960s, the use of aquatic plants for medicinal purposes also began to be studied in-depth. The work of Rakoto Ratsimamanga et al. (1969) mentions aquatic plants with medicinal value, such as *Ludwigia diffusa* (included here as a subspecies of *L. adscendens*) and *Crinum firmifolium* var. *hygrophylum*. We also note the work of Boiteau (1979, 1986) on the medicinal properties of aquatic, as well as terrestrial plants. More recently, Rakotoarivelo et al. (2020) studied medicinal and traditional uses of aquatic plants in and around Lake Alaotra. Other relatively recent studies on aquatic plants include research on the ecology of Lake Mandroseza (Alvarez 1982), the use of certain species in aquaculture (Andrianjohany 1988), and the ecology of *Lepironia mucronata* (Dama 1995).

RECENT INVENTORY OF AQUATIC HABITATS

Before 2010, fewer than 1000 specimens of aquatic macrophytes were present at the National Herbarium at Tsimbazaza (~0.5% of the collection). In 2010 the Missouri Botanical Garden (MBG) initiated a research program on the aquatic plants of Madagascar, which has generated more than 1200 new collections and significantly increased our knowledge of species distribution patterns while also leading to the rediscovery of some species that had not been documented for many decades. For example, the rediscovery of *Diospyros anosivolensis*, first collected in 1927 by Perrier de la Bâthie, then collected again by the Service Forestier in 1955, and only rediscovered in 2010 by the MBG team. Also, new discoveries such as *Dentella repens*, an introduced species, first recorded in 2016 from Madagascar (Razafimandimbison and Manjato 2019). Aquatic plant species previously unknown to science have also been identified, including new species of *Hydrotriche* (Plantaginaceae), a genus of aquatic macrophyte endemic to Madagascar. An important collection of aquatic macrophytes is also present at the Muséum National d'Histoire Naturelle herbarium in Paris, for which high-resolution images are available online, which includes a number of important historical collections and collections by Ranarijaona (1999) in the context of a project entitled Biodiversité et Biotypologie des Eaux Continentales Malgaches, which was under the direction of Jean-Marc Elouard. The zones explored for aquatic plants by the MBG team since 2010 and the areas explored by Ranarijaona are shown in Figure 8.6.

FLORISTIC DIVERSITY

We have compiled a list of 489 species of aquatic macrophytes from Madagascar from the taxonomic literature, inventories, herbarium collections, and unpublished fieldwork, including species from both lotic and lentic habitats (Table 8.7). Of the 253 families of vascular plants currently known to occur on Madagascar (Catalogue of the Plants of Madagascar [Madagascar Catalogue] 2020), 89 families include at least one aquatic or semiaquatic freshwater species, and 25 families are exclusively aquatic, four of which are pteridophytes including ferns and fern allies. There are also 21 spermatophyte families, including Aponogetonaceae (15 species), Hydrostachyaceae (14 species), Podostemaceae (six species), Potamogetonaceae (10 species), and Nymphaeaceae (two species).

A total of 233 genera contain aquatic or semiaquatic species, representing 13.3% of the 1747 genera of vascular plants of Madagascar (Madagascar Catalogue 2020). The most speciose genera are *Utricularia* (18 species), *Eriocaulon* (16 species), *Cyperus* (16 species), *Aponogeton* (15 species), *Hydrostachys* (14 species), *Helichrysum* (12 species), *Persicaria* (11 species), and *Potamogeton* (eight species). Exclusively aquatic genera include *Aponogeton*, *Hydrostachys*, *Najas*, *Nymphoides*, *Nymphaea*, *Potamogeton*, and *Thelethylax*, among others.

Of the 11,866 described species of vascular plants currently recognized from the island (Madagascar Catalogue 2020), 489 are

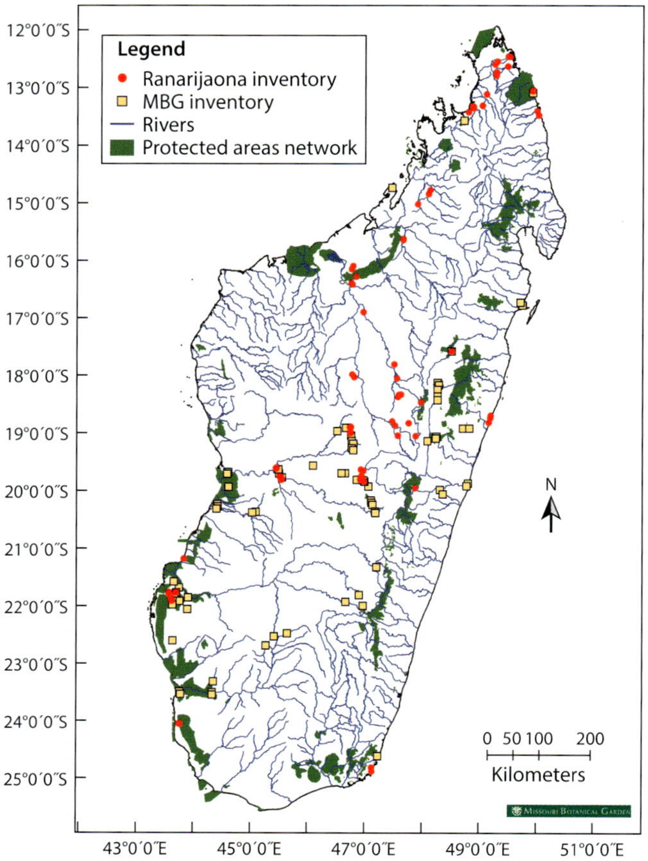

FIGURE 8.6 **Areas explored for aquatic plants since 1997. (Unpublished data from H. J. Ranarijaona and Madagascar Catalogue 2020.)**

aquatic vascular macrophytes, representing 4.1% of the total flora, the majority of which (347 species) can be characterized as semiaquatic, while 37 are helophytes (including *Ammannia quadriciliata*, *Hydrolea palustris*, *Leersia perrieri*), and 105 are hydrophytes. Among these hydrophytes, 13.3% have fixed roots with floating leaves (e.g., *Nymphaea nouchali*, *Nymphoides indica*), 19% are free floating (e.g., *Eichhornia natans*, *Lemna aequinoctialis*, *Azolla pinnata*), and 67.6% are fixed submerged (e.g., *Hydrostachys plumosa*, *Najas horrida*, *Tristicha trifaria*). Lentic habitats contain 93.7% of Madagascar's aquatic macrophyte species, whereas only 6.3% are found in lotic habitats, most of which are rheophytics (Table 8.7). These values are in line with figures for the approximately 2700 species of aquatic plants on earth as a whole (Chambers et al. 2008), of which hydrophytes and helophytes (i.e., excluding semiaquatic species) represent about 5.3% of the total.

NATURAL HISTORY ASPECTS OF AQUATIC PLANTS

Floristic Endemism

One of the most notable characteristics of the Malagasy flora is its high level of species endemism, estimated to be 87% (Lowry et al. 2018). Moreover, Madagascar has no fewer than 311 endemic genera and five endemic families (Madagascar Catalogue 2020), although none of the endemic families contain aquatic species. However, four of the endemic genera are aquatic, *Endocaulos* (one species), *Hydrotriche* (four species), *Paleodicraeia* (one species), and *Thelethylax* (two species), all of which occur in lotic habitats. Examples of species in lotic habitats are shown in Figure 8.7.

Among the aquatic macrophyte species, 49% are endemic to Madagascar, of which 81% are from lotic habitats, whereas the nonendemic native species comprise 43.6%, and the remaining 7.4% are naturalized introduced species. Many of the endemic species are known only from the type specimen (generally old collections made between 1800 and 1930) and/or from a single locality. Examples include: *Hydrostachys monoica* (known only from the Mangoro River), *Hydrotriche galiifolia* (Namoroka), *H. mayacoides* (Andringitra), and *Thelethylax isalensis* (Isalo), whereas other endemics are widely distributed, such as *Endocaulos mangorense* (Alaotra-Mangoro, Atsinanana, DIANA, Sofia, and Vatovavy-Fitovinany Regions); *T. minutiflora* (Alaotra-Mangoro, Amoron'i Mania, Analamanga, Anosy, Atsinanana, Betsiboka, DIANA, Haute Matsiatra, Itasy, Vakinankaratra, and Vatovavy-Fitovinany Regions); *H. hottoniiflora* (Alaotra-Mangoro, Boeny, DIANA, Melaky, Analamanga, and Vakinankaratra Regions); and *Lagarosiphon madagascariensis* (Alaotra-Mangoro, Analamanga, Anosy, Atsimo-Andrefana, Betsiboka, Boeny, DIANA, Haute Matsiatra, Itasy, Menabe, SAVA, Sofia, and Vakinankaratra Regions. Some of the naturalized introduced aquatic plants are harmful invasive species, including *Eichhornia crassipes* from South America, *Salvinia molesta* from southeastern Brazil, and *Azolla filiculoides* from temperate and tropical regions.

Specialized Adaptations

Aquatic plants have adapted to their distinctive environmental conditions by evolving a specialized set of forms and structures (Raynal-Roques 1980). These include the presence of air-filled tissues that are spongy or hollow, enabling the plant to float, or permitting submerged structures to be oriented upward. Various other types of structures are also found, such as spongy roots (*Ludwigia adscendens*) and swollen petioles (*Sagittaria guayanensis*, *Eichhornia crassipes*, and *Nymphaea* spp.). Some species have reduced leaves that act as floaters (*Lemna aequinoctialis* and *Azolla pinnata*), while others are completely submerged for their entire life cycle, whether free or fixed, with only their flowers emerging above the surface (*Lagarosiphon madagascariensis* and *Ottelia uvalifolia*). Some species have both submerged leaves and leaves that either float on the surface or are erect and held above the water (*Eichhornia natans* and *Potamogeton* spp.).

Carnivorous Plants

Four entirely aquatic genera occurring on Madagascar are carnivorous: *Drosera* (five species), *Nepenthes* (two species), *Genlisea* (one species), and *Utricularia* (18 species). Various types of traps are formed by modified leaves that serve to capture and digest prey and then assimilate the resulting nutrients (Barthlott et al. 2008). Species of *Drosera* have adhesive traps on the upper surface of their leaves, which are covered with glands that secrete a sticky mucilage.

TABLE 8.7. **Vascular aquatic species on Madagascar with information summary**

SCIENTIFIC NAME	ENDEMISM	LIFE-FORM	PLANT GROWTH TYPE	IUCN STATUS	BIOCLIMATIC ZONE
ACANTHACEAE					
Acanthopale breviceps (Benoist) Callm. & Phillipson	Endemic	Herb	Emergent	NE	HUM/SBH
Hygrophila anisocalyx Benoist	Endemic	Herb	Emergent	NE	DRY/SBA
H. baronii S. Moore	Endemic	Herb	Emergent	EN	DRY
H. velata Benoist	Endemic	Herb	Emergent	EN	DRY
AIZOACEAE					
Trianthema portulacastrum L.	Native	Herb	Emergent	NE	DRY/SBA/SBH
ALISMATACEAE					
Caldesia reniformis (D. Don) Makino	Native	Herb	Emergent	NE	HUM/SBH
Limnophyton obtusifolium (L.) Miq.	Native	Herb	Emergent	NE	DRY/SBA/SBH
Sagittaria guayanensis Kunth	Native	Herb	Emergent	NE	DRY/HUM/SBH
Wiesneria filifolia Hook. f.	Native	Herb	Emergent	NE	SBH
AMARANTHACEAE					
Achyranthes aspera L.	Naturalized	Herb	Emergent	NE	DRY/HUM/SBA/SBH
Alternanthera sessilis (L.) R. Br. ex DC.	Native	Herb	Emergent	NE	DRY/HUM/SBA
Arthrocnemum pachystachyum (Bunge ex Ung.-Sternb.) A. Chev.	Native	Herb	Emergent	NE	DRY/SBA
Celosia argentea L.	Naturalized	Herb	Emergent	NE	DRY/SBA
Centrostachys aquatica (R. Br.) Wall.	Naturalized	Herb	Emergent	NE	DRY
AMARYLLIDACEAE					
Crinum firmifolium Baker	Endemic	Herb	Emergent	NE	DRY/HUM/SBA/SBH
C. hardyi Lehmiller	Endemic	Herb	Emergent	NE	DRY
APIACEAE					
Centella asiatica (L.) Urb.	Naturalized	Herb	Emergent	NE	HUM/SBH
APOCYNACEAE					
Secamone ligustrifolia Decne.	Endemic	Shrub	Emergent	NT	SBH
Voacanga thouarsii Roem. & Schult.	Native	Tree	Emergent	NE	DRY/HUM/SBA/SBH
APONOGETONACEAE					
Aponogeton bernierianus (Decne.) Hook. f.	Endemic	Herb	Submerged	NT	HUM/SBH
A. boivinianus Baill. ex Jum.	Native	Herb	Submerged	NE	DRY/SBH
A. capuronii H. Bruggen	Endemic	Herb	Submerged	EN	HUM
A. cordatus Jum.	Endemic	Herb	Submerged	DD	HUM
A. decaryi Jum.	Endemic	Herb	Submerged	NT	DRY/SBA/SBH
A. dioecus Bosser	Endemic	Herb	Submerged	CR	SBH
A. eggersii Bogner & H. Bruggen	Endemic	Herb	Submerged	EN	HUM
A. gottlebei Kasselm. & Bogner	Endemic	Herb	Submerged	NE	Uncertain

(continued overleaf)

TABLE 8.7. ***continued***

SCIENTIFIC NAME	ENDEMISM	LIFE-FORM	PLANT GROWTH TYPE	IUCN STATUS	BIOCLIMATIC ZONE
A. longiplumulosus H. Bruggen	Endemic	Herb	Submerged	EN	DRY/HUM
A. madagascariensis (Mirb.) H. Bruggen	Endemic	Herb	Submerged	LC	DRY/HUM/SBH
A. masoalaensis Bogner	Endemic	Herb	Submerged	CR	HUM
A. schatzianus Bogner & H. Bruggen	Endemic	Herb	Submerged	EN	HUM
A. tenuispicatus H. Bruggen	Endemic	Herb	Submerged	EN	HUM
A. ulvaceus Baker	Endemic	Herb	Submerged	NT	DRY/SBA/SBH
A. viridis Jum.	Endemic	Herb	Submerged	EN	DRY
ARACEAE					
Colocasia esculenta (L.) Schott	Naturalized	Herb	Emergent	NE	HUM/SBH
Lemna aequinoctialis Welw.	Native	Herb	Free-floating	NE	DRY/HUM/SBH
Pistia stratiotes L.	Native	Herb	Free-floating	NE	DRY/HUM/SBA/SBH
Spirodela polyrhiza (L.) Schleid.	Native	Herb	Free-floating	NE	DRY/SBH
Typhonodorum lindleyanum Schott	Native	Herb	Emergent	NE	DRY/HUM/SBH
Wolffia arrhiza (L.) Horkel ex Wimm.	Native	Herb	Submerged	NE	DRY/HUM/SBH
ARALIACEAE					
Hydrocotyle bonariensis Lam.	Native	Herb	Emergent	NE	HUM/SBA/SBH
H. mannii Hook. f.	Native	Herb	Emergent	NE	HUM/SBH
H. ranunculoides L. f.	Native	Herb	Emergent	NE	SBH
H. sibthorpioides Lam.	Native	Herb	Emergent	NE	HUM/SBH
ARECACEAE					
Dypsis aquatilis Beentje	Endemic	Herb	Submerged	CR	HUM
D. crinita (Jum. & H. Perrier) Beentje & J. Dransf.	Endemic	Herb	Emergent	NT	DRY/HUM/SBH
Raphia farinifera (Gaertn.) Hyl.	Naturalized	Herb	Emergent	NE	HUM/SBH
Ravenea musicalis Beentje	Endemic	Herb	Emergent	CR	HUM
R. rivularis Jum. & H. Perrier	Endemic	Herb	Emergent	VU	SBA/SBH
ASTERACEAE					
Acmella caulirhiza Delile	Native	Herb	Emergent	NE	HUM/SBH
Amphidoxa demidium O. Hoffm.	Endemic	Herb	Emergent	VU	SBH
Blumea dregeanoides Sch. Bip. ex A. Rich.	Native	Herb	Emergent	NE	Uncertain
Catatia cordata Humbert	Endemic	Herb	Emergent	NE	SBH
Cineraria anampoza (Baker) Baker	Endemic	Herb/Shrub	Emergent	VU	HUM/SBH
Conyza andringitrana Humbert	Endemic	Herb	Emergent	NE	SBH
C. attenuata DC.	Native	Herb	Emergent	NE	HUM/SBH/SBA
C. longipedunculata Klatt	Endemic	Herb	Emergent	NE	SBH
C. mandrarensis Humbert	Endemic	Herb	Emergent	CR	SBH
C. neocandolleana Humbert	Endemic	Herb	Emergent	LC	DRY/HUM/SBH

SCIENTIFIC NAME	ENDEMISM	LIFE-FORM	PLANT GROWTH TYPE	IUCN STATUS	BIOCLIMATIC ZONE
C. perrieri Humbert	Endemic	Shrub	Emergent	VU	SBH
C. viguieri Humbert	Endemic	Herb	Emergent	NE	HUM/SBH
Cotula australis (Sieber ex Spreng.) Hook. f.	Naturalized	Herb	Emergent	NE	HUM/SBA/SBH
Crassocephalum crepidioides (Benth.) S. Moore	Native	Herb	Emergent	NE	DRY/HUM/SBA/SBH
C. lemuricum (Humbert) Humbert	Endemic	Herb	Emergent	NE	HUM/SBH
Dichrocephala integrifolia (L. f.) Kuntze	Native	Herb	Emergent	NE	SBH
Distephanus rochonioides (Humbert) H. Rob. & B. Kahn	Endemic	Shrub	Emergent	NE	DRY/SBA/SBH
Eclipta prostrata (L.) L.	Naturalized	Herb	Emergent	NE	DRY/HUM/SBA/SBH
Emilia adscendens DC.	Native	Herb	Emergent	NE	HUM/SBH
E. capillaris Humbert	Endemic	Herb	Emergent	NT	DRY/HUM/SBH
E. citrina DC.	Endemic	Herb	Emergent	LC	HUM/SBH
E. integrifolia Baker	Native	Herb	Emergent	NE	HUM/SBH
Ethulia conyzoides L. f.	Naturalized	Herb	Emergent	NE	DRY/HUM/SBH
Gamochaeta purpurea (L.) Cabrera	Native	Herb	Emergent	NE	HUM
Gerbera emirnensis Baker	Endemic	Herb	Emergent	NE	SBH
G. hypochaeridioides Baker	Endemic	Herb	Emergent	EN	SBH
Grangea gossypina (Baker) Fayed	Endemic	Herb	Emergent	NE	DRY
G. lyrata (DC.) Fayed	Native	Herb	Emergent	NE	DRY/HUM/SBH
G. madagascariensis Vatke	Endemic	Herb	Emergent	EN	DRY
G. maderaspatana (L.) Poir.	Native	Herb	Emergent	NE	DRY/SBA
Grangeopsis perrieri Humbert	Endemic	Herb	Emergent	EN	DRY/SBH
Helichrysum aphelexioides DC.	Endemic	Herb	Emergent	NT	SBH
H. coursii Humbert	Endemic	Herb	Emergent	CR	SBH
H. cryptomerioides Baker	Endemic	Herb/Shrub	Emergent	NE	SBH
H. dubardii R. Vig. & Humbert	Endemic	Herb	Emergent	EN	SBH
H. faradifani Scott-Elliot	Endemic	Herb/Shrub	Emergent	NE	DRY/HUM/SBH
H. filaginoides (DC.) Humbert	Endemic	Herb	Emergent	EN	SBH
H. flagellare Baker	Endemic	Herb	Emergent	VU	SBH
H. fulvescens DC.	Endemic	Herb/Shrub	Emergent	NE	HUM/SBH
H. luzulaefolium DC.	Endemic	Herb	Emergent	NT	SBH
H. mutisiaefolium Less.	Endemic	Herb/Liana	Emergent	NE	HUM
H. myriocephalum Humbert	Endemic	Shrub	Emergent	NE	SBH
H. tanacetiflorum Baker	Endemic	Herb	Emergent	EN	SBH
Hubertia myrtifolia (Klatt) C. Jeffrey	Endemic	Shrub	Emergent	VU	SBH
H. riparia (DC.) C. Jeffrey	Native	Shrub	Emergent	NE	SBH

(continued overleaf)

TABLE 8.7. ***continued***

SCIENTIFIC NAME	ENDEMISM	LIFE-FORM	PLANT GROWTH TYPE	IUCN STATUS	BIOCLIMATIC ZONE
Inula perrieri (Humbert) Mattf.	Endemic	Herb	Emergent	NT	HUM/SBH
I. speciosa (DC.) O. Hoffm.	Endemic	Herb	Emergent	LC	HUM/SBH
Launaea intybacea (Jacq.) Beauverd	Native	Herb	Emergent	NE	DRY/SBA
Melanthera scandens (Schumach. & Thonn.) Roberty	Native	Herb	Emergent	NE	HUM/SBH
Microglossa pyrifolia (Lam.) Kuntze	Native	Shrub	Emergent	NE	HUM/SBH
Pluchea bojeri (DC.) Humbert	Native	Shrub	Emergent	NE	DRY/HUM/SBA/SBH
P. grevei (Baill.) Humbert	Endemic	Shrub	Emergent	NT	SBA
P. ovalis (Pers.) DC.	Native	Shrub	Emergent	NE	DRY/SBA/SBH
P. rufescens (DC.) A. J. Scott	Endemic	Shrub	Emergent	VU	HUM
Pseudoconyza viscosa (Mill.) D'Arcy	Naturalized	Herb	Emergent	NE	DRY
Sphaeranthus africanus L.	Native	Herb	Submerged	NE	DRY
S. cotuloides DC.	Endemic	Herb	Submerged	NT	DRY/SBA
Struchium sparganophorum (L.) Kuntze	Naturalized	Herb	Emergent	NE	DRY/SBH
Vandellia humilis (Bonati) Eb. Fisch., Schäferh. & Kai Müll.	Native	Herb	Emergent	NE	SBA
Vernonia diversifolia Bojer ex DC.	Native	Herb/Shrub	Emergent	NE	DRY/HUM/SBH
V. platylepis Drake	Endemic	Shrub	Emergent	NT	DRY/SBH
Vernoniopsis caudata (Drake) Humbert	Endemic	Shrub/Tree	Emergent	NE	HUM
Youngia japonica (L.) DC.	Naturalized	Herb	Emergent	NE	HUM/SBH
ATHYRIACEAE					
Deparia marojejyensis (Tardieu) M. Kato	Endemic	Herb	Emergent	NE	SBH
BALSAMINACEAE					
Impatiens amphibia H. Perrier	Endemic	Herb	Emergent	NE	HUM
I. boinensis H. Perrier	Endemic	Herb	Emergent	CR	DRY
I. echinosperma H. Perrier	Endemic	Herb	Emergent	NE	DRY/HUM/SBH
I. rudicaulis H. Perrier	Endemic	Herb	Emergent	EN	HUM
I. sacculifera H. Perrier	Endemic	Herb	Emergent	NE	HUM
BEGONIACEAE					
Begonia erminea L'Hér.	Endemic	Herb	Emergent	EN	HUM
B. francoisii Guillaumin	Endemic	Herb	Emergent	NE	SBH
BORAGINACEAE					
Cynoglossum tsaratananense J. S. Mill.	Endemic	Herb	Emergent	CR	SBH
BRASSICACEAE					
Rorippa millefolia (Baker) Jonsell	Endemic	Herb	Emergent	EN	SBA/SBH
R. nasturtium-aquaticum (L.) Hayek	Naturalized	Herb	Emergent	NE	SBH

SCIENTIFIC NAME	ENDEMISM	LIFE-FORM	PLANT GROWTH TYPE	IUCN STATUS	BIOCLIMATIC ZONE
BUXACEAE					
Buxus itremoensis G. E. Schatz & Lowry	Endemic	Shrub	Emergent	EN	SBH
CAMPANULACEAE					
Gunillaea emirnensis (A. DC.) Thulin	Native	Herb	Emergent	NE	SBH
Lobelia agrestis E. Wimm.	Endemic	Herb	Emergent	NE	HUM/SBH
L. erinus L.	Native	Herb	Emergent	NE	SBH
L. fervens Thunb.	Native	Herb	Emergent	NE	HUM/SBH
L. lingulata E. Wimm.	Endemic	Herb	Emergent	EN	DRY
L. spathopetala Diels	Endemic	Herb	Emergent	NE	HUM/SBH
Wahlenbergia undulata (L. f.) A. DC.	Native	Herb	Emergent	NE	HUM/SBH
CANNACEAE					
Canna indica L.	Naturalized	Herb	Emergent	NE	HUM/SBH
CAPPARACEAE					
Crateva simplicifolia J. S. Mill.	Endemic	Shrub	Emergent	NE	HUM
CARYOPHYLLACEAE					
Cerastium indicum Wight & Arn.	Native	Herb	Emergent	NE	SBH
Corrigiola litoralis L.	Native	Herb	Emergent	NE	SBH
Drymaria cordata (L.) Willd. ex Schult.	Native	Herb	Emergent	NE	HUM/SBH
Polycarpon prostratum (Forssk.) Asch. & Schweinf. ex Asch.	Native	Herb	Emergent	NE	HUM/SBH
Stellaria mannii Hook. f.	Native	Herb	Emergent	NE	HUM/SBH
CERATOPHYLLACEAE					
Ceratophyllum demersum L.	Native	Herb	Submerged	NE	DRY/HUM/SBA/SBH
CLEOMACEAE					
Cleome augustinensis (Hochr.) Briq.	Endemic	Herb	Emergent	EN	DRY
C. hirta (Klotzsch) Oliv.	Naturalized	Herb	Emergent	NE	SBH
COMMELINACEAE					
Coleotrype lutea H. Perrier	Endemic	Herb	Emergent	NE	DRY/SBH
Commelina diffusa Burm. f.	Naturalized	Herb	Emergent	NE	DRY/HUM/SBA/SBH
C. humbloti H. Perrier	Endemic	Herb	Emergent	NE	HUM
C. mascarenica C. B. Clarke	Native	Herb	Emergent	NE	DRY/SBH
Floscopa glomerata (Willd. ex Schult. & Schult. f.) Hassk.	Naturalized	Herb	Emergent	NE	DRY/HUM/SBH
Murdannia nudiflora (L.) Brenan	Naturalized	Herb	Emergent	NE	DRY/HUM/SBH
M. simplex (Vahl) Brenan	Naturalized	Herb	Emergent	NE	DRY/HUM/SBA
CONVOLVULACEAE					
Ipomoea aquatica Forssk.	Native	Herb/Liana	Emergent	NE	DRY/HUM/SBA/SBH

(continued overleaf)

TABLE 8.7. ***continued***

SCIENTIFIC NAME	ENDEMISM	LIFE-FORM	PLANT GROWTH TYPE	IUCN STATUS	BIOCLIMATIC ZONE
CRASSULACEAE					
Kalanchoe daigremontiana Raym.-Hamet & H. Perrier	Endemic	Herb	Emergent	EN	SBA
CUCURBITACEAE					
Zehneria peneyana (Naudin) Schweinf. & Asch.	Naturalized	Herb/Liana	Emergent	NE	DRY
Z. thwaitesii (Schweinf.) C. Jeffrey	Naturalized	Herb/Liana	Emergent	NE	DRY/HUM/SBH
CYPERACEAE					
Bolboschoenus glaucus (Lam.) S. G. Sm.	?	Herb	Emergent	NE	DRY/SBA
Bulbostylis andringitrensis Cherm.	Endemic	Herb	Emergent	EN	SBH
B. perrieri Cherm.	Endemic	Herb	Emergent	EN	DRY/SBH
Carex hildebrandtiana Boeckeler	Endemic	Herb	Emergent	VU	SBH
Costularia melleri (Baker) C. B. Clarke ex Cherm.	Endemic	Herb	Emergent	EN	HUM/SBH
Cyperus alternifolius L.	Native	Herb	Emergent	NE	DRY/SBA/SBH
C. ankaratrensis Cherm.	Endemic	Herb	Emergent	EN	SBH
C. articulatus L.	Native	Herb	Emergent	NE	DRY/SBA/SBH
C. cancrorum Cherm.	Endemic	Herb	Emergent	VU	DRY/HUM/SBH
C. cylindrostachys Boeckeler	Native	Herb	Emergent	NE	SBA/SBH
C. heterocladus Baker	Endemic	Herb	Emergent	EN	SBH
C. imbricatus Retz.	Native	Herb	Emergent	NE	DRY/HUM/SBA/SBH
C. iria L.	Native	Herb	Emergent	NE	DRY/HUM/SBA/SBH
C. laevigatus L.	Native	Herb	Emergent	NE	SBA/SBH
C. michelianus (L.) Link	Native	Herb	Emergent	NE	DRY/SBH
C. procerus Rottb.	Native	Herb	Emergent	NE	DRY/SBH
C. prolifer Lam.	Native	Herb	Emergent	NE	DRY/HUM/SBA/SBH
C. rubicundus Vahl	Native	Herb	Emergent	NE	HUM/SBA/SBH
C. subaequalis Baker	Endemic	Herb	Emergent	VU	HUM/SBH
C. subbadius Kük.	Endemic	Herb	Emergent		HUM/SBH
C. tenuispiculatus Boeckeler	Native	Herb	Emergent	NE	SBH
Eleocharis acutangula (Roxb.) Schult.	Native	Herb	Emergent	NE	DRY/SBH
E. atropurpurea (Retz.) J. Presl & C. Presl	Native	Herb	Emergent	NE	DRY
E. caduca (Delile) Schult.	Native	Herb	Emergent	NE	SBA/SBH
E. dulcis (Burm. f.) Trin. ex Hensch.	Native	Herb	Emergent	NE	HUM/SBH
E. minuta Boeckeler	Native	Herb	Emergent	NE	DRY/HUM/SBH
E. nigrescens (Nees) Kunth	Native	Herb	Emergent	NE	DRY
E. spiralis (Rottb.) Roem. & Schult.	Native	Herb	Emergent	NE	HUM/SBA
Fimbristylis bisumbellata (Forssk.) Bubani	Native	Herb	Emergent	NE	DRY/SBA/SBH

SCIENTIFIC NAME	ENDEMISM	LIFE-FORM	PLANT GROWTH TYPE	IUCN STATUS	BIOCLIMATIC ZONE
F. dichotoma (L.) Vahl	Native	Herb	Emergent	NE	HUM/SBA/SBH
F. ferruginea (L.) Vahl	Native	Herb	Emergent	NE	DRY/HUM/SBA/SBH
Fuirena pubescens (Poir.) Kunth	Native	Herb	Emergent	NE	SBH
F. umbellata Rottb.	Native	Herb	Emergent	NE	DRY/HUM/SBA
Isolepis fluitans (L.) R. Br.	Native	Herb	Emergent	NE	SBH
I. humbertii (Cherm.) J. Raynal	Endemic	Herb	Emergent	VU	SBH
Kyllinga brevifolia Rottb.	Native	Herb	Emergent	NE	SBH
K. coriacea Cherm.	Native	Herb	Emergent	NE	DRY/SBH
K. melanosperma Nees	Native	Herb	Emergent	NE	HUM/SBH
K. nemoralis (J. R. Forst. & G. Forst.) Dandy ex Hutch. & Dalziel	Native	Herb	Emergent	NE	HUM/SBH
K. squamulata Thonn. ex Vahl	Naturalized	Herb	Emergent	NE	SBH
Lepironia articulata (Retz.) Domin	Native	Herb	Emergent	NE	HUM
Mapania mauritiana (Nees ex Kunth) Lye	Native	Herb	Emergent	NE	HUM/SBH
Oxycaryum cubense (Poepp. & Kunth) Palla	Native	Herb	Submerged	NE	DRY/HUM/SBH
Pycreus alleizettei Cherm.	Endemic	Herb	Emergent	EN	SBH
P. compressiformis Cherm.	Endemic	Herb	Emergent	EN	DRY
P. flavescens (L.) P. Beauv. ex Rchb.	Native	Herb	Submerged	NE	DRY/HUM/SBA/SBH
P. macrostachyos (Lam.) J. Raynal	Native	Herb	Submerged	NE	DRY/SBH
P. mundtii Nees	Native	Herb	Emergent	NE	DRY/SBA/SBH
P. polystachyos (Rottb.) P. Beauv.	Native	Herb	Submerged	NE	DRY/HUM/SBA/SBH
P. pumilus (L.) Nees	Native	Herb	Submerged	NE	Uncertain
Rhynchospora corymbosa (L.) Britton	Native	Herb	Emergent	NE	HUM/SBH
R. gracillima subsp. *subquadrata* (Cherm.) J. Raynal	Native	Herb	Emergent	NE	DRY/HUM/SBH
R. hildebrandtii Boeckeler	Endemic	Herb	Emergent	CR	SBH
Schoenoplectiella aberrans (Cherm.) Lye	Endemic	Herb	Emergent	CR	SBH
S. articulata (L.) Lye	Native	Herb	Emergent	NE	DRY
S. heterophylla (Schuyler) Lye	Endemic	Herb	Emergent	EN	DRY
S. perrieri (Cherm.) Lye	Endemic	Herb	Emergent	CR	DRY
Schoenoplectus corymbosus (Roth ex Roem. & Schult.) J. Raynal	Native	Herb	Submerged	NE	SBH
S. mucronatus (L.) Palla	Native	Herb	Submerged	NE	HUM/SBH
S. scirpoides (Schrad.) Browning	Native	Herb	Emergent	NE	SBA/SBH
S. subulatus (Vahl) Lye	Native	Herb	Emergent	NE	HUM
Scleria griegifolia (Ridl.) C. B. Clarke	Native	Herb	Emergent	NE	SBH
S. madagascariensis Boeckeler	Endemic	Herb	Emergent	NE	HUM/SBH

(continued overleaf)

TABLE 8.7. *continued*

SCIENTIFIC NAME	ENDEMISM	LIFE-FORM	PLANT GROWTH TYPE	IUCN STATUS	BIOCLIMATIC ZONE
Websteria confervoides (Poir.) S. S. Hooper	?	Herb	Submerged	NE	DRY/HUM/SBH
DROSERACEAE					
Drosera burkeana Planch.	Native	Herb	Emergent	NE	SBH
D. madagascariensis DC.	Native	Herb	Emergent	NE	HUM/SBH
D. natalensis Diels	Native	Herb	Emergent	NE	HUM/SBH
DRYOPTERIDACEAE					
Dryopteris manniana (Hook.) C. Chr.	Native	Herb	Emergent	NE	HUM/SBH
EBENACEAE					
Diospyros anosivolensis H. Perrier	Endemic	Shrub/Tree	Rheophyte	VU	HUM
D. cinnamomoides H. Perrier	Endemic	Shrub/Tree	Rheophyte	LC	DRY/HUM/SBH
D. decaryana H. Perrier	Endemic	Shrub/Tree	Rheophyte	VU	HUM
D. dicorypheoides H. Perrier	Endemic	Shrub	Rheophytic	EN	HUM
ELATINACEAE					
Elatine madagascariensis H. Perrier	Endemic	Herb	Fixed submerged	VU	SBH
E. triandra Schkuhr	Native	Herb	Emergent	NE	DRY
EQUISETACEAE					
Equisetum ramosissimum Desf.	Native	Herb	Emergent	NE	SBH
ERIOCAULACEAE					
Eriocaulon abyssinicum Hochst.	Native	Herb	Emergent	NE	SBH
E. alleizettei Moldenke	Endemic	Herb	Emergent	NE	SBH
E. apiculatum Lecomte	Endemic	Herb	Emergent	NE	HUM
E. fenestratum Bojer ex Körn.	Native	Herb	Emergent	NE	HUM/SBH
E. flumineum Moldenke	Endemic	Herb	Emergent	EN	HUM/SBH
E. heterochiton Körn.	Endemic	Herb	Emergent	NE	DRY/SBH
E. hildebrandtii Körn. ex Ruhland	Endemic	Herb	Emergent	CR	SBH
E. madagascariense Moldenke	Endemic	Herb	Submerged	NE	SBH
E. mokalense Moldenke	Endemic	Herb	Emergent	NE	HUM/SBH
E. mutatum N. E. Br.	Native	Herb	Emergent	NE	DRY/SBH
E. parvicapitulatum Moldenke	Endemic	Herb	Emergent	CR	SBH
E. piliflorum Ruhland	Endemic	Herb	Emergent	EN	HUM
E. setaceum L.	Native	Herb	Submerged	NE	SBH
E. sexangulare L.	Native	Herb	Emergent	NE	HUM/SBH
E. striatum Lam.	Native	Herb	Emergent	NE	HUM/SBH
E. trilobatum Ruhland	Endemic	Herb	Emergent	NE	HUM/SBH
Mesanthemum pubescens Körn.	Endemic	Herb	Emergent	NT	HUM/SBH
M. rutenbergianum Körn.	Endemic	Herb	Emergent	NT	HUM/SBH

SCIENTIFIC NAME	ENDEMISM	LIFE-FORM	PLANT GROWTH TYPE	IUCN STATUS	BIOCLIMATIC ZONE
Paepalanthus bosseri (Morat) Stützel	Endemic	Herb	Emergent	CR	SBH
P. itremensis (Morat) Stützel	Endemic	Herb	Emergent	VU	SBH
P. lamarckii Kunth	Native	Herb	Emergent	NE	DRY/HUM
Syngonanthus humbertii Moldenke	Endemic	Herb	Emergent	NE	HUM/SBH
EUPHORBIACEAE					
Euphorbia robivelonae Rauh	Endemic	Shrub	Rheophytic	EN	SBH
FABACEAE					
Aeschynomene elaphroxylon (Guill. & Perr.) Taub.	Naturalized	Herb	Emergent	NE	DRY/SBH
Cadia rubra R. Vig.	Endemic	Shrub	Emergent	NE	DRY
Dalbergia baronii Baker	Endemic	Shrub/Tree	Emergent	NE	HUM/SBH
Indigofera ankaratrensis R. Vig.	Endemic	Herb/Liana	Emergent	CR	SBH
I. pseudoparvula R. Vig.	Endemic	Shrub	Emergent	EN	SBA
Leptodesmia bojeriana (Baill.) Drake	Endemic	Herb	Emergent	EN	SBH
Neptunia oleracea Lour.	Native	Herb	Emergent	NE	DRY
Phylloxylon xiphoclada (Baker) Du Puy, Labat & Schrire	Endemic	Shrub	Emergent	EN	SBH
Pithecellobium dulce (Roxb.) Benth.	Naturalized	Shrub/Tree	Emergent	NE	DRY/SBA
Sesbania sesban (L.) Merr.	Naturalized	Shrub/Tree	Emergent	NE	Uncertain
GENTIANACEAE					
Exacum conglomeratum Klack.	Endemic	Herb	Emergent	CR	SBH
E. gracile Klack.	Endemic	Herb	Emergent	EN	DRY
E. nossibeense Klack.	Endemic	Herb	Emergent	CR	SBH
Klackenbergia stricta (Schinz) Kissling	Endemic	Herb	Emergent	EN	DRY
Sebaea brachyphylla Griseb.	Naturalized	Herb	Emergent	NE	SBH
Tachiadenus umbellatus Klack.	Endemic	Herb	Emergent	CR	SBH
GUNNERACEAE					
Gunnera perpensa L.	Native	Herb	Emergent	NE	SBH
HALORAGACEAE					
Laurembergia tetrandra (Schott) Kanitz	Native	Herb	Emergent	NE	HUM/SBH
Myriophyllum axilliflorum Baker	Endemic	Herb	Submerged	CR	SBH
M. mezianum Schindl.	?	Herb	Submerged	EN	DRY/HUM
HAMAMELIDACEAE					
Dicoryphe angustifolia Tul.	Endemic	Herb	Emergent	NE	HUM
HELIOTROPIACEAE					
Euploca perrieri (J. S. Mill.) J. S. Mill.	Endemic	Herb	Emergent	EN	DRY
HYDROCHARITACEAE					
Blyxa aubertii Rich.	Native	Herb	Submerged	NE	DRY/HUM/SBH

(continued overleaf)

TABLE 8.7. ***continued***

SCIENTIFIC NAME	ENDEMISM	LIFE-FORM	PLANT GROWTH TYPE	IUCN STATUS	BIOCLIMATIC ZONE
Lagarosiphon madagascariensis Casp.	Endemic	Herb	Submerged	LC	DRY/HUM/SBA/SBH
Najas australis Bory ex Rendle	Native	Herb	Submerged	NE	DRY/HUM/SBH
N. horrida A. Braun ex Magnus	Native	Herb	Submerged	NE	HUM
N. madagascariensis Rendle	Endemic	Herb	Submerged	NE	DRY/SBH
N. marina L.	Native	Herb	Submerged	NE	SBA
Ottelia ulvifolia (Planch.) Walp.	Native	Herb	Submerged	NE	HUM/SBH
HYDROLEACEAE					
Hydrolea palustris (Aubl.) Raeusch.	Native	Herb	Emergent	NE	HUM/SBH
HYDROSTACHYACEAE					
Hydrostachys decaryi H. Perrier	Endemic	Herb	Rheophytic	EN	HUM
H. distichophylla A. Juss.	Endemic	Herb	Rheophytic	NT	HUM/SBH
H. fimbriata C. Cusset	Endemic	Herb	Rheophytic	EN	HUM/SBH
H. imbricata A. Juss.	Endemic	Herb	Rheophytic	LC	HUM/SBH
H. laciniata Warm.	Endemic	Herb	Rheophytic	EN	HUM/SBH
H. longifida H. Perrier	Endemic	Herb	Rheophytic	NT	DRY/HUM/SBH
H. maxima H. Perrier	Endemic	Herb	Rheophytic	VU	SBA/SBH
H. monoica H. Perrier	Endemic	Herb	Rheophytic	CR	HUM
H. multifida A. Juss.	Endemic	Herb	Rheophytic	NT	DRY/HUM/SBA/SBH
H. perrieri C. Cusset	Endemic	Herb	Rheophytic	CR	HUM
H. plumosa A. Juss. ex Tul.	Endemic	Herb	Rheophytic	LC	DRY/HUM/SBH
H. stolonifera Baker	Endemic	Herb	Rheophytic	NT	HUM/SBH
H. trifaria H. Perrier	Endemic	Herb	Rheophytic	EN	HUM/SBH
H. verruculosa A. Juss.	Endemic	Herb	Rheophytic	VU	HUM/SBH
HYMENOPHYLLACEAE					
Didymoglossum pygmaeum (C. Chr.) Ebihara & Dubuisson	Endemic	Herb	Emergent	CR	HUM
HYPOXIDACEAE					
Hypoxis angustifolia Lam.	Native	Herb	Emergent	NE	DRY/HUM/SBH
ISOETACEAE					
Isoetes perrieriana Iversen	Endemic	Herb	Emergent	EN	SBH
I. schweinfurthii Baker	Native	Herb	Emergent	NE	DRY
I. welwitschii A. Braun ex Kuhn	Native	Herb	Emergent	NE	SBH
JUNCACEAE					
Juncus effusus L.	Native	Herb	Emergent	NE	HUM/SBH
J. maritimus Lam.	Native	Herb	Emergent	NE	HUM/SBA
JUNCAGINACEAE					
Triglochin striata Ruiz & Pav.	Native	Herb	Emergent	NE	SBA

SCIENTIFIC NAME	ENDEMISM	LIFE-FORM	PLANT GROWTH TYPE	IUCN STATUS	BIOCLIMATIC ZONE
LAMIACEAE					
Hyptis pectinata (L.) Poit.	Naturalized	Herb	Emergent	NE	DRY/SBH
Micromeria madagascariensis Baker	Endemic	Herb/Liana	Emergent	NE	SBH
Orthosiphon discolor A. J. Paton & Hedge	Endemic	Herb	Emergent	EN	SBH
Platostoma thymifolium (Benth.) A. J. Paton & Hedge	Endemic	Herb	Emergent	NE	SBH
Plectranthus papilionaceus Ranir. & Phillipson	Endemic	Herb	Emergent	NE	SBH
P. punctatus (L. f.) L'Hér.	Naturalized	Herb	Emergent	NE	SBH
LENTIBULARIACEAE					
Genlisea margaretae Hutch.	Native	Herb	Emergent	NE	SBH
Utricularia appendiculata E. A. Bruce	Native	Herb	Emergent	NE	SBH
U. arenaria A. DC.	Native	Herb	Emergent	NE	SBH
U. benjaminiana Oliv.	Native	Herb	Emergent	NE	HUM
U. bisquamata Schrank	Native	Herb	Emergent	NE	HUM/SBH
U. caerulea L.	Native	Herb	Emergent	NE	SBH
U. cymbantha Oliv.	Native	Herb	Emergent	NE	SBH
U. firmula Welw. ex Oliv.	Native	Herb	Emergent	NE	Uncertain
U. foliosa L.	Native	Herb	Submerged	NE	Uncertain
U. foveolata	Native	Herb	Emergent	NE	DRY
U. gibba L.	Native	Herb	Emergent	NE	SBH
U. inflexa Forssk.	Native	Herb	Emergent	NE	DRY/SBH
U. livida E. Mey.	Native	Herb	Emergent	NE	HUM/SBH
U. prehensilis E. Mey.	Native	Herb	Emergent	NE	SBH
U. reflexa Oliv.	Native	Herb	Emergent	NE	HUM
U. scandens Benj.	Native	Herb	Emergent	NE	DRY
U. stellaris L. f.	Native	Herb	Emergent	NE	SBH
U. subulata L.	Native	Herb	Free floating submerged	NE	HUM/SBH
U. welwitschii Oliv.	Native	Herb	Emergent	NE	SBH
LINDERNIACEAE					
Crepidorhopalon microcarpaeoides (Bonati) Eb. Fisch.	Endemic	Herb	Emergent	NE	DRY/SBH
Lindernia benthamii Eb. Fisch., Schäferh. & Kai Müll.	Native	Herb	Emergent	NE	SBH
L. bryoides Eb. Fisch.	Endemic	Herb	Emergent	NE	SBH
L. lemuriana Eb. Fisch., Schäferh. & Kai Müll.	Endemic	Herb	Emergent	NE	DRY/HUM/SBH

(continued overleaf)

TABLE 8.7. ***continued***

SCIENTIFIC NAME	ENDEMISM	LIFE-FORM	PLANT GROWTH TYPE	IUCN STATUS	BIOCLIMATIC ZONE
L. madagascariensis (Bonati) Eb. Fisch., Schäferh. & Kai Müll.	Native	Herb	Emergent	NE	DRY/SBH
L. natans Eb. Fisch.	Endemic	Herb	Submerged	CR	DRY
L. paludosa (Bonati) Eb. Fisch.	Endemic	Herb	Submerged	NE	DRY/HUM/SBA/SBH
L. rotundifolia (L.) Alston	Native	Herb	Emergent	NE	DRY/HUM/SBH
L. viguieri (Bonati) Eb. Fisch.	Endemic	Herb	Emergent	NE	HUM/SBH
Torenia crustacea (L.) Cham. & Schltdl.	Native	Herb	Emergent	NE	HUM
T. stolonifera Bojer ex Benth.	Endemic	Herb	Emergent	LC	DRY/HUM/SBA/SBH
T. thouarsii (Cham. & Schltdl.) Kuntze	Native	Herb	Emergent	NE	DRY/HUM/SBA/SBH
LINDSAEACEAE					
Osmolindsaea leptolepida Rouhan & Lehtonen	Endemic	Herb	Emergent	NE	HUM
LYTHRACEAE					
Ammannia alternifolia H. Perrier	Endemic	Herb	Emergent	CR	DRY
A. calcicola (H. Perrier) S. A. Graham & Gandhi	Endemic	Herb	Emergent	EN	DRY
A. capitellata (C. Presl) S. A. Graham & Gandhi	Native	Herb	Emergent	NE	HUM
A. cryptantha Baker	Endemic	Herb	Emergent	VU	SBH
A. heterophylla (H. Perrier) S. A. Graham & Gandhi	Endemic	Herb	Emergent	EN	DRY
A. pauciramosa S. A. Graham & Gandhi	Endemic	Herb	Emergent	EN	DRY
A. quadriciliata H. Perrier	Endemic	Herb	Emergent	EN	DRY/SBH
Marsilea aegyptica Willd.	Native	Herb	Fixed floating leaves	NE	HUM
MARSILEACEAE					
M. coromandelina Willd.	Native	Herb	Fixed floating leaves	NE	DRY/SBH
M. globulosa I. Bouchart	Endemic	Herb	Fixed floating leaves	NE	DRY
M. macrocarpa C. Presl	Native	Herb	Fixed floating leaves	NE	SBH
M. minuta L.	Native	Herb	Fixed floating leaves	NE	DRY/SBA/SBH
M. nubica A. Braun	Native	Herb	Fixed floating leaves	NE	DRY/SBH
M. pyriformis I. Bouchart	Endemic	Herb	Fixed floating leaves	NE	DRY
MENYANTHACEAE					
Nymphoides bosseri A. Raynal	Endemic	Herb	Submerged	EN	SBH
N. elegans A. Raynal	Endemic	Herb	Submerged	EN	DRY/SBA/SBH
N. indica (L.) Kuntze	Native	Herb	Fixed floating leaves	NE	DRY/HUM/SBA/SBH
MYRICACEAE					
Morella serrata (Lam.) Killick	Native	Herb	Emergent	NE	SBH

SCIENTIFIC NAME	ENDEMISM	LIFE-FORM	PLANT GROWTH TYPE	IUCN STATUS	BIOCLIMATIC ZONE
NEPENTHACEAE					
Nepenthes madagascariensis Poir.	Endemic	Herb	Fixed floating leaves	NE	HUM
N. masoalensis Schmid-Holl.	Endemic	Herb	Fixed floating leaves	NE	HUM
NYMPHAEACEAE					
Nymphaea lotus L.	Native	Herb	Emergent	NE	HUM/SBA
N. nouchali Burm. f.	Native	Herb	Submerged	NE	HUM
ONAGRACEAE					
Ludwigia abyssinica A. Rich.	Native	Herb	Emergent	NE	SBH
L. adscendens (L.) H. Hara	Native	Herb	Emergent	NE	HUM/SBA/SBH
L. erecta (L.) H. Hara	Native	Herb	Emergent	NE	HUM/SBA/SBH
L. leptocarpa (Nutt.) H. Hara	Native	Herb	Emergent	NE	DRY/HUM/SBH
L. nesaeoides H. Perrier	Native	Herb	Emergent	NE	DRY
L. octovalvis (Jacq.) P. H. Raven	Native	Herb	Emergent	NE	HUM/SBH
L. prostrata Roxb.	Native	Herb	Emergent	NE	SBA/SBH
ORCHIDACEAE					
Angraecum potamophilum Schltr.	Endemic	Herb	Emergent	NE	DRY
Benthamia africana (Lindl.) Hermans	Native	Herb	Emergent	NE	HUM/SBA/SBH
B. calceolata H. Perrier	Endemic	Herb	Emergent	EN	HUM
B. catatiana H. Perrier	Endemic	Herb	Emergent	CR	HUM
B. cuspidata H. Perrier	Endemic	Herb	Emergent	NE	HUM
B. dauphinensis (Rolfe) Schltr.	Endemic	Herb	Emergent	NE	HUM
Cynorkis marojejyensis Bosser	Endemic	Herb	Emergent	CR	HUM
C. souegesii Bosser & Veyret	Endemic	Herb	Emergent	NE	SBH
C. tenerrima (Ridl.) Kraenzl.	Endemic	Herb	Emergent	EN	HUM/SBH
Eulophia nervosa H. Perrier	Endemic	Herb	Emergent	CR	SBH
Liparis lutea Ridl.	Endemic	Herb	Emergent	NE	SBH
Tylostigma filiforme H. Perrier	Endemic	Herb	Emergent	CR	HUM/SBH
T. herminioides Schltr.	Endemic	Herb	Emergent	CR	SBH
T. hildebrandtii (Ridl.) Schltr.	Endemic	Herb	Emergent	EN	SBH
T. madagascariense Schltr.	Endemic	Herb	Emergent	CR	SBH
T. nigrescens Schltr.	Endemic	Herb	Emergent	EN	SBH
OROBANCHACEAE					
Buchnera hispida Buch.-Ham. ex D. Don	Native	Herb	Emergent	NE	DRY/HUM/SBH
B. leptostachya Benth.	Native	Herb	Emergent	NE	DRY/HUM/SBH
Rhamphicarpa fistulosa (Hochst.) Benth.	Native	Herb	Emergent	NE	DRY/HUM/SBA/SBH
Striga forbesii Benth.	Native	Herb	Emergent	NE	HUM

(continued overleaf)

TABLE 8.7. ***continued***

SCIENTIFIC NAME	ENDEMISM	LIFE-FORM	PLANT GROWTH TYPE	IUCN STATUS	BIOCLIMATIC ZONE
OSMUNDACEAE					
Osmunda regalis L.	Native	Herb/Shrub	Emergent	NE	HUM/SBH
PANDANACEAE					
Pandanus ambalavaoensis Huynh	Endemic	Tree	Emergent	CR	SBH
P. peyrierasii B. C. Stone & Guillaumet	Endemic	Shrub	Emergent	EN	HUM
P. platyphyllus Martelli	Endemic	Shrub/Tree	Emergent	NT	HUM
PHYLLANTHACEAE					
Phyllanthus venustulus Leandri	Endemic	Herb	Emergent	EN	SBH
PLANTAGINACEAE					
Bacopa crenata (P. Beauv.) Hepper	Native	Herb	Emergent	NE	HUM/SBA/SBH
B. monnieri (L.) Wettst.	Native	Herb	Emergent	NE	DRY/SBA
Callitriche peploides Nutt.	Naturalized	Herb	Emergent	NE	HUM/SBH
Hydrotriche bryoides A. Raynal	Endemic	Herb	Fixed submerged	EN	SBH
H. galiifolia A. Raynal	Endemic	Herb	Fixed submerged	EN	DRY
H. hottoniiflora Zucc.	Endemic	Herb	Fixed submerged	NT	DRY/HUM/SBH
H. mayacoides A. Raynal	Endemic	Herb	Fixed submerged	CR	SBH
Plantago tanalensis Baker	Endemic	Herb	Emergent	VU	HUM/SBH
POACEAE					
Echinochloa pyramidalis (Lam.) Hitchc. & Chase	Native	Herb	Emergent	NE	HUM
Eragrostis japonica (Thunb.) Trin.	Naturalized	Herb	Emergent	NE	SBA
E. stolonifera A. Camus	Endemic	Herb	Emergent	EN	SBH
Ischaemum heterotrichum Hack.	Native	Herb	Emergent	EN	HUM/SBH
Leersia hexandra Sw.	Native	Herb	Emergent	NE	HUM/SBH
L. perrieri (A. Camus) Launert	Native	Herb	Emergent	EN	DRY/SBH
Neostapfiella chloridiantha A. Camus	Endemic	Herb	Emergent	EN	DRY
Pennisetum pseudotriticoides A. Camus	Endemic	Herb	Emergent	EN	SBH
Phragmites australis (Cav.) Trin. ex Steud.	Naturalized	Herb	Emergent	NE	DRY/HUM
Sacciolepis delicatula Mez	Endemic	Herb	Emergent	EN	SBH
S. viguieri A. Camus	Endemic	Herb	Emergent	VU	SBH
Sporobolus elatior Bosser	Endemic	Herb	Emergent	EN	DRY
PODOSTEMACEAE					
Endocaulos mangorense (H. Perrier) C. Cusset	Endemic	Herb	Rheophytic	EN	DRY/HUM
Paleodicraeia imbricata (Tul.) C. Cusset	Endemic	Herb	Rheophytic	DD	Uncertain
Sphaerothylax abyssinica (Wedd.) Warm.	Native	Herb	Rheophytic	NE	SBH
Thelethylax isalensis (H. Perrier) C. Cusset	Endemic	Herb	Rheophytic	CR	SBH

SCIENTIFIC NAME	ENDEMISM	LIFE-FORM	PLANT GROWTH TYPE	IUCN STATUS	BIOCLIMATIC ZONE
T. minutiflora (Tul.) C. Cusset	Endemic	Herb	Rheophytic	LC	DRY/HUM/SBH
Tristicha trifaria (Bory ex Willd.) Spreng.	Native	Herb	Rheophytic	NE	HUM/SBH
POLYGONACEAE					
Persicaria acuminata (Kunth) M. Gómez	Native	Herb	Emergent	NE	DRY/HUM/SBH
P. barbata (L.) H. Hara	Native	Herb	Emergent	NE	DRY/HUM/SBH
P. decipiens (R. Br.) K. L. Wilson	Naturalized	Herb	Emergent	NE	HUM/SBA/SBH
P. dichotoma (Blume) Masam.	Naturalized	Herb	Emergent	NE	SBH
P. glabra (Willd.) M. Gómez	Naturalized	Herb	Emergent	NE	HUM/SBA/SBH
P. lapathifolia (L.) Gray	Naturalized	Herb	Emergent	NE	DRY/HUM/SBA/SBH
P. meisneriana (Cham. & Schltdl.) M. Gómez	Naturalized	Herb	Emergent	NE	HUM/SBA/SBH
P. minor (Huds.) Opiz	Naturalized	Herb	Emergent	NE	HUM/DRY/SBH
P. mitis (Schrank) Assenov	Naturalized	Herb	Emergent	NE	HUM
P. nepalensis (Meisn.) H. Gross	Native	Herb	Emergent	NE	SBH
P. senegalensis (Meisn.) Soják	Naturalized	Herb	Emergent	NE	DRY/HUM/SBH
Polygonum plebeium R. Br.	Naturalized	Herb	Emergent	NE	DRY/HUM/SBA/SBH
POLYPODIACEAE					
Loxogramme humblotii (C. Chr.) C. Chr.	Endemic	Herb	Emergent	LC	HUM/SBH
Zygophlebia subpinnata (Baker) L. E. Bishop ex Parris	Endemic	Herb	Emergent	LC	HUM
PONTEDERIACEAE					
Eichhornia crassipes (Mart.) Solms	Naturalized	Herb	Free-floating	NE	DRY/HUM/SBH
E. natans (P. Beauv.) Solms	Native	Herb	Emergent	NE	DRY
Scholleropsis lutea H. Perrier	Native	Herb	Fixed submerged	NE	DRY
POTAMOGETONACEAE					
Potamogeton × assidens Z. Kaplan, Zalewska-Gal. & Ronikier	Native	Herb	Fixed submerged	NE	SBH
P. nodosus Poir.	Native	Herb	Fixed submerged	NE	DRY/HUM/SBA/SBH
P. octandrus Poir.	Native	Herb	Fixed submerged	NE	HUM/SBH
P. parmatus Hagstr.	Endemic	Herb	Fixed submerged	EN	SBH
P. perfoliatus L.	Native	Herb	Fixed submerged	NE	DRY
P. richardii Solms	Native	Herb	Fixed submerged	NE	HUM/SBH
P. schweinfurthii A. Benn.	Native	Herb	Fixed submerged	NE	HUM/SBH
Stuckenia pectinata (L.) Börner	Native	Herb	Fixed submerged	NE	DRY/HUM/SBH
Zannichellia palustris L.	Native	Herb	Fixed submerged	NE	SBH
PRIMULACEAE					
Lysimachia nummularifolia (Baker) U. Manns & Anderb.	Endemic	Herb	Emergent	EN	SBH

(*continued overleaf*)

TABLE 8.7. ***continued***

SCIENTIFIC NAME	ENDEMISM	LIFE-FORM	PLANT GROWTH TYPE	IUCN STATUS	BIOCLIMATIC ZONE
L. ovalis (Ruiz & Pav.) U. Manns & Anderb.	Native	Herb	Emergent	NE	SBH
L. peploides (Baker) U. Manns & Anderb.	Endemic	Herb	Emergent	EN	SBH
L. rubricaulis (Duby) U. Manns & Anderb.	Endemic	Herb	Emergent	NT	SBH
Samolus valerandi L.	Native	Herb	Emergent	NE	SBA
PTERIDACEAE					
Acrostichum aureum L.	Native	Herb	Emergent	NE	DRY/HUM
Adiantum capillus-veneris L.	Native	Herb	Emergent	NE	DRY/SBA/SBH
Ceratopteris thalictroides (L.) Brongn.	Native	Herb	Emergent	NE	HUM
Pteris cretica L.	Native	Herb	Emergent	NE	HUM/SBH
P. vittata L.	Native	Herb	Emergent	NE	DRY/HUM/SBA
Trachypteris drakeana (Jeanp.) C. Chr.	Endemic	Herb	Emergent	VU	DRY/SBH
RANUNCULACEAE					
Ranunculus multifidus Forssk.	Native	Herb	Emergent	NE	HUM/SBH
RESTIONACEAE					
Platycaulos mahonii (N. E. Br.) H. P. Linder & C. R. Hardy	Native	Herb	Emergent	NE	SBH
RUBIACEAE					
Anthospermum palustre Homolle ex Puf	Endemic	Herb	Emergent	EN	SBH
Dentella repens (L.) J. R. Forst. & G. Forst.	Native	Herb	Emergent	NE	DRY
Ixora ripicola De Block	Endemic	Shrub/Tree	Emergent	NT	DRY/HUM/SBH
I. sambiranensis Homolle ex Guédès	Endemic	Shrub	Emergent	EN	SBH
Peponidium anoveanum (Cavaco) Razafim., Lantz & B. Bremer	Endemic	Shrub	Emergent	VU	HUM
SALVINIACEAE					
Azolla filiculoides Lam.	Naturalized	Herb	Free-floating	NE	SBA/SBH
A. pinnata R. Br.	Native	Herb	Free-floating	NE	DRY/SBA/SBH
Salvinia hastata Desv.	Native	Herb	Free-floating	NE	DRY/HUM/SBH
S. molesta D. S. Mitch.	Naturalized	Herb	Free-floating	NE	HUM
SAPOTACEAE					
Mimusops nossibeensis Capuron ex Aubrév.	Endemic	Shrub	Emergent	CR	HUM
SCHIZAEACEAE					
Schizaea pectinata (L.) Sw.	Native	Herb	Emergent	NE	SBH
SCROPHULARIACEAE					
Diclis ovata Benth.	Native	Herb	Emergent	NE	HUM/SBH
SPHENOCLEACEAE					
Sphenoclea zeylanica Gaertn.	Native	Herb	Emergent	NE	DRY/HUM/SBA/SBH

SCIENTIFIC NAME	ENDEMISM	LIFE-FORM	PLANT GROWTH TYPE	IUCN STATUS	BIOCLIMATIC ZONE
THELYPTERIDACEAE					
Cyclosorus interruptus (Willd.) H. Itô	Native	Herb	Emergent	NE	HUM/SBH
Pneumatopteris humbertii Holttum	Endemic	Herb	Emergent	VU	HUM/SBH
Pseudocyclosorus pulcher (Bory ex Willd.) Holttum	Native	Herb	Emergent	NE	HUM/SBH
Sphaerostephanos arbuscula (Willd.) Holttum	Native	Herb	Submerged	NE	HUM/SBH
Thelypteris confluens (Thunb.) C. V. Morton	Native	Herb	Emergent	NE	HUM/SBH
TYPHACEAE					
Typha domingensis Pers.	Native	Herb	Emergent	NE	DRY/HUM/SBA/SBH
URTICACEAE					
Elatostema madagascariense Wedd.	Native	Herb	Emergent	NE	HUM/SBH
E. subfavosum Leandri	Endemic	Herb	Emergent	EN	HUM/SBH
WOODSIACEAE					
Diplazium zanzibaricum (Baker) C. Chr.	Endemic	Herb	Emergent	NE	SBH
XYRIDACEAE					
Xyris anceps Lam.	Native	Herb	Emergent	NE	DRY/HUM/SBA/SBH
X. baronii Malme	Endemic	Herb	Emergent	VU	HUM
X. capensis Thunb.	Native	Herb	Emergent	NE	SBH
X. congensis Büttner	Native	Herb	Emergent	NE	HUM/SBH
X. humilis Kunth	Endemic	Herb	Emergent	NE	DRY/HUM/SBH
X. labatii Rakoton., Callm. & Phillipson	Endemic	Herb	Emergent	NE	SBH
X. marojejyensis Lock, Rakoton., Callm. & Phillipson	Endemic	Herb	Emergent	NE	HUM
X. straminea L. A. Nilsson	Native	Herb	Emergent	NE	DRY/SBH

Sources: Cornet (1974), as simplified by Schatz (2001) and IUCN (2020).
Notes: Endemism: Endemic, Native, Naturalized. Life-form: Tree, Shrub, Herb, Liana. Plant growth type: Emergent, Submerged, Free-floating, Fixed floating leaves, Fixed submerged, Rheophytic. IUCN status: CR, Critically Endangered; DD, Data Deficient; EN, Endangered; LC, Least Concern; NE, Not Evaluated; NR, Near Threatened; VU, Vulnerable. Bioclimatic zone: DRY, dry; HUM, humid; SBA, subarid; SBH, subhumid.

The leaves of *Nepenthes* spp. have evolved into a slip trap in the shape of an urn, horn, or cup, whose nectar and red, white, or yellow color attract invertebrate prey. Species of *Utricularia* and *Genlisea* have suction traps, located underground and derived from leaves, which have a small utricle with a flap bordered by lashes that close and trap an animal at the slightest touch (Barthlott et al. 2008). Figure 8.8 shows a few examples of carnivorous plants.

SPECIES DISTRIBUTION PATTERNS

The varied climate of Madagascar (see Jury, pp. 91–98) coupled with the island's diverse geomorphology, has led to the evolution of a variety of freshwater ecosystems, including rivers, streams, lakes, marshes, and swamps. Moreover, the geographic distribution of species across the island varies significantly among the bioclimatic zones.

With regard to the number of aquatic plant species known from a single bioclimatic zone (Cornet 1974, as simplified by Schatz 2001), the subhumid zone has the most (75 species), followed by the humid (61 species), dry (48 species), and subarid (seven species) zones. The fact that the highest number of species restricted to a single bioclimate zone is found in the subhumid zone could, at least in part, be because the headwaters of many large rivers are situated in these areas, which encompass the Central Highlands.

Among the species restricted to the subhumid bioclimatic zone, 58% are endemic to Madagascar, including *Lysimachia nummularifolia*, *Nymphoides bosseri*, *Paepalanthus bosseri*, and *Wiesneria filifolia*, whereas 38% are nonendemic native species such as *Drosera burkeana*, *Hydrocotyle ranunculoides*, and *Isoetes welwitschii*, while just 4% are naturalized non-natives.

Of the species found exclusively in the humid bioclimatic zone, 89% are endemic to Madagascar, such as *Aponogeton masoalaensis*,

FIGURE 8.7 **Species in lotic environments. A) *Hydrostachys imbricata* (Rakotonirina 536, Andohasira River); B) *H. laciniata* (Rakotovao 5367, Anosivolo River); C) *H. verruculosa* (Rakotovao 5380, Anosivolo River); D) *H. multifida*; and E) *H. distichophylla* (Razanatsoa 749, Menagisy Mahanoro).** (PHOTOS by N. V. Manjato.)

Ceratopteris thalictroides, *Hydrostachys monoica*, *Impatiens amphibia*, *Lepironia articulata*, and *Ravenea musicalis*, while 9% are nonendemic natives and 2% are naturalized non-natives.

Within the dry bioclimatic zone, 31 of the 48 species recorded (65%) are endemic to Madagascar, including *Ammannia calcicola*, *Hydrotriche galiifolia*, and *Lindernia natans*, whereas 32% are nonendemic natives such as *Marsilea coromandelina* and *Neptunia oleracea*. Finally, just two of the seven species restricted to the subarid bioclimatic zone are endemic to Madagascar (*Indigofera pseudoparvula* and *Pluchea grevei*), whereas four species are nonendemic natives, including *Triglochin striata*, *Samolus valerandi*, *Vandellia humilis*, and *Najas marina*, and one is a naturalized non-native, *Eragrostis japonica*.

More than 100 species occur in both the humid and subhumid bioclimatic zones, of which 41 are endemic to Madagascar, 53 are nonendemic natives, and 11 are naturalized non-natives. Some examples include *Inula perrieri*, *Eriocaulon alleizettei*, *Hydrostachys verruculosa*, and *Loxogramme humblotii*. A total of 48 widespread species are found in the four bioclimatic zones occupied by aquatic plants, 11 of which are endemic to Madagascar, such as *H. distichophylla*, *Lagarosiphon madagascariensis*, and *Nymphoides elegans*.

THE ROLE OF AQUATIC PLANTS

Aquatic plants play several very important functional roles in aquatic ecosystems, sometimes indirectly. They serve to buffer the impact of floods, help remove pollutants, and control erosion associated with rapid water flow. They are at the base of the food chain, providing nutrition for some fish species; generate oxygen; provide substrate for aquatic invertebrates; and provide habitat for certain animals, including *Hapalemur alaotrensis* (see Tan et al., pp. 1947–52), the world's only primate that lives exclusively in a wetland environment (Ralainasolo et al. 2013).

Many aquatic plants are intimately associated with the life of the local human population. On Madagascar, raw materials employed for the manufacture of handicraft products (mats, baskets, etc.) are derived from plants such as *Cyperus papyrus* subsp. *madagascariensis* (known locally as *zozoro*), *Lepironia articulata* (*penjy*, *mahampy*), and *Typhonodorum lindleyanum* (*viha*). The walls and roofs of traditional huts are built with *Typha domingensis* (*vondro*) and *Phragmites australis* (*bararata rano*). Other species are used for food, especially during periods of shortages, such as *Ottelia ulvifolia* (*voalefoka*), *Thelethylax minutiflora* (*anandriana*), and the tuberous roots of *Nymphaea* spp. (*voahirana*). Some species are incorporated

FIGURE 8.8 **Carnivorous aquatic plants on Madagascar. A) *Nepenthes madagascariensis* (Enato); B) *Utricularia livida* (Razanatsoa 519, Pointe à Larrée); C) *Genlisea margaretae* (Rabarimanarivo 620, Andranovelona); and D) *Drosera madagascariensis* (Rabarimanarivo 745, Ankazomivady).** (PHOTOS A and B by N. V. Manjato; C by S. Porembski; and D by S. Giebelmann.)

into the local pharmacopeia and used for the treatment of various diseases or disorders including *Ethulia conyzoides* (*revaka*) for colic or as a herbal tea, and *Parthenium hysterophorus* (*fotsivolo tanora*) for colic, or as cosmetics, such as *Centella asiatica* (*talapetraka*). Other aquatic plants are of cultural importance and are used to invoke ancestors (*joro*), such as *Azolla pinnata* (*ramilamina*), *Commelina madagascarica* (*ahibita*), *Hydrocotyle bonariensis* (*fieremana*), and *Nymphaea nouchali* (*tatamo*).

CONSERVATION STATUS OF SPECIES

The first assessments of the risk of extinction of the freshwater aquatic and semiaquatic species occurring on Madagascar were undertaken in 2017 in accordance with International Union for Conservation of Nature (IUCN) Red List criteria. These assessments, which were done for 169 of the 233 species that are endemic (Phillipson et al. 2018), 79% of which were found to be threatened, classified 34 species as Critically Endangered, 75 as Endangered, and 24 as Vulnerable. A total of 114 of these species occur in lentic habitats, whereas 19 are found in lotic habitats (Table 8.8). Two species (*Aponogeton cordatus* and *Paleodicraeia imbicata*) were determined to be Data Deficient.

When assessments were conducted for risks to habitats (see Carré et al., pp. 2119–30), 23 important rivers, lakes, and wetlands systems were validated as freshwater Key Biodiversity Areas (KBAs) (Maiz-Tomé et al. 2018). Two existing Ramsar sites (Nosivolo River and Lake Kinkony) and three protected areas (Isalo, Mikea, and Marojejy) contain species that have been assessed as threatened with extinction (following the IUCN Red List criteria), and therefore trigger Key Biodiversity Area status for these sites, for example, *Deparia marojejyensis*, *Dicoryphe angustifolia*, *Diospyros anosivolensis*, *D. dicoryphеoides*, *Hydrostachys laciniata*, *H. verruculosa*, *Indigofera pseudoparvula*, *Pneumatopteris humbertii*, and *Thelethylax isaloensis*.

TABLE 8.8. **Summary of IUCN status of threatened aquatic plants in lentic and lotic habitats**

IUCN STATUS	LENTIC HABITATS	LOTIC HABITATS
CR	29	5
EN	66	9
VU	19	5
Total	114	19

Source: IUCN (2020).
Note: IUCN status: CR, Critically Endangered; EN, Endangered; VU, Vulnerable.

THREATS TO SPECIES AND THEIR HABITATS

The most frequent threats to plant species are habitat degradation and unsustainable exploitation. The wetlands of Madagascar are subjected to many of the same pressures as elsewhere in the world. The Red List analyses of Phillipson et al. (2018) indicated 11 major types of threat listed by IUCN that impact aquatic species and their habitats. Rapid human population growth on the island leads to an ever-increasing need for agricultural land. Aquatic habitat loss through conversion to rice paddies and aquaculture is the most significant threat, while highly urbanized areas are subjected to impacts from land filling, dam construction, and sewage discharge.

Deforestation and bushfires in catchments surrounding aquatic environments have significant impacts on ecosystems and species by increasing erosion and subsequent silting of lowland areas. Invasive species, such as *Eichhornia crassipes* and *Salvinia molesta*, are considered to be the second most important cause of biodiversity loss after human-related habitat degradation, and are an important threat at the global level. Competition for light and nutrients from these rapidly proliferating invasives inhibit the growth of native species.

ADDITIONAL WORK NEEDED

Until the last years of the 20th century, aquatic habitats were under-emphasized in botanical research efforts on Madagascar. Most of the collections available were relatively old and lacked precise information on the location they were collected from; numerous species were known only from the type specimen and/or from a single locality. Despite the improved situation associated with renewed inventory effort and a growing recognition of the interest and importance of aquatic plants, there are still many gaps in our knowledge of these plants, and much work remains to be done. A striking example of this is *Paleodicraeia*, a genus in the family Podostemaceae and endemic to Madagascar, the single known species of which was collected once in the 18th century, probably somewhere along the east coast of the island but which has never been collected since.

While field surveys of aquatic plants are required across Madagascar, the need is especially acute in the western and northwestern parts of the island, for which there are particularly pronounced information gaps on aquatic and semiaquatic species, including distribution, use, and details of their habitat. Figure 8.6 shows that most of Madagascar's watercourses have not yet been the subject of recent inventory for aquatic plants. Information generated by additional targeted collecting will be particularly important for risk of extinction assessments using the IUCN Red List criteria and is needed to inform conservation decision-making. Given the importance of aquatic habitats and the remaining gap in knowledge, we suggest that a focus on these plants be regarded as a priority for future botanical field research.

Subject editors: Laurent Gautier and Steven M. Goodman

THE *TSINGY*: FLORA AND VEGETATION

M. Bardot-Vaucoulon and L. Gautier
Translated by F. Andriamialisoa and S. M. Goodman

The word *tsingy* (meaning "to tiptoe" in Malagasy) applies to a type of spectacular landscape found on Madagascar, but with equivalents in other parts of the world. It results from extreme erosion of limestone massifs that formed at the bottom of the oceans by the gradual accumulation of deposits of calcium carbonate from animal origin that were subsequently uplifted and exposed by the earth's tectonic movements. The main factors affecting erosion of these limestone outcrops (called karst when in an eroded state) are precipitation, temperature, and water acidity. The karst areas of the polar regions, for example in northern Norway or in Siberia, are subject to frost, as are those found at higher elevations in temperate regions. In arid regions, limestone outcrops are subject to little erosion because rainfall levels and humidity are normally very low. Karst erosion is most spectacular under heavy rainfall regimes where mean annual temperatures are close to 25°C (Salomon and Pulina 2005). In addition to Madagascar, *tsingy*-type landscapes are found in humid to subhumid tropical zones in Brazil, Kenya and Tanzania, China, New Guinea, Sarawak (Borneo), and in several regions of Australia (Veress et al. 2008). These habitats are home to a specialized floras and vegetation communities, resistant not only to the chemical stress generated by the limestone substratum, but also to the microclimatic and hydrographic conditions characteristic of these environments.

PRINCIPAL *TSINGY* AREAS AND THEIR DISTRIBUTION ON MADAGASCAR

On Madagascar, limestone bedrock is present as a wide band running parallel to the west coast along the island's nearly 1700 km length (Figure 8.9a), covering an area of about 30,000 km^2 (Rossi 1977). Some such areas are called *tsingy* because of their spectacular and distinctive aspect, the result of particularly intense erosion.

FIGURE 8.9 **Different aspects associated with limestone *tsingy* habitat on Madagascar. A) Limestone bedrock on Madagascar: light blue denotes deposits dating from the Mesozoic; dark blue those from the Tertiary (after Du Puy and Moat 1996, on Google Earth background). The main *tsingy* formations discussed in this contribution are circled in red, from north to south: Ankarana, Namoroka, Beanka, and Bemaraha. B) General aspect of a *tsingy* at Namoroka and C) at Ankarana. D) Canyon in Namoroka. E) Roots of *Mimusops occidentalis* in a cave in Namoroka. F) Fracture in Bemaraha.** (PHOTOS B, D, and E by L. Gautier, and C and F by M. Bardot-Vaucoulon.)

The most important limestone *tsingy* massifs, which date from the Mesozoic, are:

- The northwest–southeast-oriented Ankarana Massif (21,500 ha), located south of Montagne d'Ambre, in the DIANA Region, in the far north;
- Namoroka Massif (11,000 ha) in western Madagascar, near Soalala, in the Boeny Region;
- The north–south-oriented Bemaraha Massif (84,000 ha), located in the central west in the Melaky and Menabe Regions;
- Beanka Massif (24,000 ha) in the Melaky Region, which is the northern extension of the precedent.

Among the other limestone formations, which are not *tsingy* in the strict sense and not discussed here, the most extensive are the Causses d'Ankara and Causses de Kelifely (within the Kasijy protected area) in the Boeny region. Further south, the vast Mahafaly Plateau is also limestone but of more recent uplift (Tertiary). Located in the subarid zone, it presents a less advanced stage of karstification. These Tertiary limestones are associated with a series of geological formations on the northwestern coast, between Cap Saint André and Cap d'Ambre, including the Narindra (Sofia Region).

GEOLOGY AND GEOMORPHOLOGY

Tsingy are shallowly angled plateaus (between 5% and 15%) with a westerly (Bemaraha and Beanka) or southeasterly (Ankarana) orientation, determined by tectonic movements in the Tertiary and subsequently during the Quaternary. The flank on the highest side of these plateaus (east side for Bemaraha and Beanka, northwest side for Ankarana) presents exposed cliffs, ranging from a few meters to over 100 m high. Their surfaces are abundantly fractured and karstic. They are cut by gorges and deep canyons (Figures 8.9d and f), which follow the main fracture lines (Raunet 1997).

In the Late Jurassic (between 200 and 145 million years ago [Mya]), the opening of the Mozambique Channel coincided with a marine transgression west of Madagascar of dissolved carbonates precipitated by biological (e.g., corals) or chemical (oolites) action. During this nearly 60 million years of geological history, intercalations of pure, dolomitic, marly, or sandstone limestone accumulated in variable proportions. The crystalline limestones, mostly coral, formed locally thick and rigid deposits. Later, the expansion of the Central Highlands, caused by several phases of tectonic movements during the Cretaceous and Tertiary periods, contributed to the emergence (uplift) and inclination of these limestone blocks; once emerged they were shaped by differential erosion (Raunet 1997). The fine-grained, hard, very pure limestones (96% calcium carbonate) are exceptionally nonporous (Rossi 1973) but are sensitive to tectonic movements, and the resulting vertical fractures helped to form the *tsingy*.

The numerous vertical fractures distributed along a few preferential directions stimulated the flow of surface runoff water, shaping the towers, grooved walls, needles, stacks, jagged peaks, and pinnacles—with their slender edges as sharp as a knife blade—forming a landscape of lace-like rocks (Figures 8.9b and c). At the base of the layers, the water flow clears the stratification joints, cutting the *tsingy* into blocks. Those closest to the surface are unsteady and can topple, filling the underlying crevices. Dissolution of the surface layers can be locally important, leading to the formation of sinkholes, often cluttered at the bottom with fragments of eroded limestone. Under the surface, there are networks of caves and associated galleries cut by the flow of underground water. The caves near the surface are the oldest (epikarst) and became dry during the evolution of the karst and the deepening of the hydrographic network. The deepest network (endokarst) is active, with seasonally varying levels of water.

ENVIRONMENTAL CONDITIONS

Tsingy are associated with specific geological and structural conditions. On Madagascar, such formations are on the western side of the island, and the local tropical climatic conditions are characterized by a long dry season averaging six to eight months, generally from May to October (Gautier et al. 2018), alternating with a rainy season and annual rainfall that may exceed 1500 mm (Rossi 1977). Water from abundant rainfall runs down the rock walls, causing the calcium carbonate to dissolve. In the case of the purest limestone (mostly of coral origin) the process leaves practically no decalcification residues. The most spectacular needle-type erosion occurs in these pure limestones (Rossi 1980).

Temperatures remain high throughout the year, with an annual average of 25°C to 28°C. The seasonal temperature range is low. At the microclimatic scale, on facies lacking soil and vegetation cover, the daily thermal amplitude can be spectacular and temperatures exceeding 40°C locally are not uncommon, mirroring very low nightly values (L. Gautier, unpublished data).

On portions of the *tsingy* where the erosion processes are the most advanced, soil is largely absent and there exists a fine limestone powder associated with some organic debris accumulated in cavities and at crevice bottoms. Elsewhere, real soils can be found in between bare rock surfaces, composed of clay and organic matter in varying proportion, which include acrisols, ferralsols, and lixisols (all haplic) and leptosols (lithic) of variable thickness. The nature of these soils, especially their thickness, has a direct influence on the establishment of vegetation.

Tsingy formations have a very particular hydrographic regime. Due to the thinness or absence of soil, as well as the general porosity of the massif and all of its caves, faults, dykes, and cracks, rainfall rapidly disappears in the karstic network. Sheltered from evaporation, water flows slowly and eventually finds an outlet at the base of the massif in the form of outflowing streams and small rivers, which are often permanent and provide an annual source of fresh water for local plant and animal populations (Gautier et al. 2013a). Access to water is crucial for the plants that grow on the karst surface; most have a short life span, or a vegetation period limited to the rainy season, and they often present spectacular adaptations. Some species of trees living on the surface of the most barren facies have roots that are tens of meters long, weaving through the crevices to reach the water table of the endokarst, for example the roots of *Mimusops occidentalis* at a depth over 30 m in Namoroka (L. Gautier, unpublished data) (Figure 8.9e). These roots are often observed during cave exploration. In summary, the composition and structure of *tsingy* vegetation is strongly dependent on soil development and its capacity to retain water during the dry season, but also on its position relative to accessible water sources in the endokarst.

MORPHOLOGICAL AND BIOLOGICAL ADAPTATIONS

Undoubtedly, the most remarkable aspect of *tsingy* vegetation is the concentration of xerophytic species presenting morphological and biological adaptations (Koechlin et al. 1974) that enable them to survive in conditions of significant drought and with little or no soil. These types of plants comprise nearly one-third of the *tsingy* species, as well as species scattered in the nearby dry deciduous forest.

- **Pachycauly**: This applies to some trees that accumulate water reserves in their trunk tissues, such as *Adansonia* and *Pachypodium* (Apocynaceae), including some that are amphora-shaped like *Hildegardia erythrosiphon* (Malvaceae), *Delonix leucantha* (Leguminosae) at Namoroka, and *D. velutina* at Ankarana. In lianas, the perennial bases are swollen and produce long and flexible annual stems, such as those of *Cyphostemma macrocarpa* (Vitaceae) at Ankarana, and *C. sakalava* at Namoroka and Bemaraha, *Adenia* (Passerifloraceae), *Kedrostis* (Cucurbitaceae), and *Cissus* (Vitaceae).
- **Crassulescent leaves**: *Aloe* (Asphodelaceae), *Kalanchoe* (Crassulaceae), and some *Oeceoclades* (Orchidaceae): *O. maculata*, *O. spathulifera*, and *O. ambongensis* have crassulescent leaves with associated Crassulacean Acid Metabolism (CAM), adapted to minimal transpiration. *Oeceoclades* have pseudobulbs that wilt in the dry season.
- **Sclerophylly**: Some species of *Erythroxylum* (Erythroxylaceae), *Diospyros* (Ebenaceae), and *Coptosperma* (Rubiaceae) keep their leaves during the dry season; the leaves are hard and waxy, sometimes with involute margins.
- **Microphylly or aphylly**: Many species have reduced leaves, limiting water loss; others are completely aphyllous (leafless) and have stems that contain chlorophyll and are responsible for photosynthesis, including several Orchidaceae species (e.g., *Vanilla humbertii*, *V. bosserii*, *V. madagascariensis*), or the aerial roots in the case of the epiphytic genus *Microcoelia*.
- **Spinescence**: The presence of spines is very frequent, including on the trunks and branches of tree species such as *Zanthoxylum decaryi* (Rutaceae), *Erythina ankaranensis* (Leguminosae), and *Pachypodium* spp.; in some cactiform euphorbias, spines are associated with pachycaul stems (e.g., *Euphorbia viguieri*, *E. pachypodioides*, Euphorbiaceae; see Haevermans and Hetterscheid, pp. 645–49) and the leaves, if present, develop only at the end of the stems.
- **Geophytism**: These herbaceous plants only grow their aerial parts for a short period of time and accumulate reserves underground (bulb, corms, or tubers), which allows the plant to wait for favorable conditions. Geophytes are notably represented in the genera *Tacca* (Taccaceae), *Begonia* (Begoniaceae), *Talinella* (Talinaceae), *Disperis* (Orchidaceae), *Crinum* (Amaryllidaceae), and *Impatiens* (Balsaminaceae).
- **Revisvicence**: Particularly well known in ferns that dry out and then rehydrate at the first rainfall, including *Selaginella* spp. (Selaginellaceae), *Platycerium quadridichotomum* (Polypodiaceae), and *Adiantum papillio* (Pteridaceae) at Ankarana.

VEGETATION TYPES

As the *tsingy* are all located in the western part of Madagascar, their floras are phytogeographically part of the Western Domain (Humbert 1955). In these karst limestone environments, some families are dominant: Leguminosae, Euphorbiaceae, Rubiaceae, and Apocynaceae. The Leguminosae and Rubiaceae occupy mainly the tree and shrub strata, whereas the Euphorbiaceae and Apocynaceae are more often in the shrub and herbaceous strata, with lianaceous species, including the genera *Cephalocroton* and *Dalechampia* (Euphorbiaceae), *Cynanchum* and *Landolphia* (Apocynaceae), and numerous xerophytes of the genera *Euphorbia* (Euphorbiaceae) and *Pachypodium* (Apocynaceae). Some genera are very diverse, such as *Croton* (Euphorbiaceae), *Diospyros* (Ebenaceae), *Euphorbia* (16 species at Ankarana), *Ficus* (Moraceae), *Grewia* (Malvaceae), *Hibiscus* (Malvaceae), and *Noronhia* (Oleaceae) (Gautier et al. 2013b). Although the species differ from one *tsingy* to another, some genera are consistently present. Different analyses (Bardot-Vaucoulon 1991; Rabarison 2000; Rakotozafy et al. 2013) show that, depending on the massif, certain genera are more prominent: *Gyrocarpus* (Hernandiaceae), *Capurodendron* (Sapotaceae), and *Dupuya* (Leguminosae) at Bemaraha; *Breonia* (Rubiaceae), *Dalbergia* (Leguminosae), and *Diospyros* at Beanka; *Commiphora*, *Hildegardia* (Malvaceae), and *Neoharmsia*, *Delonix* (Leguminosae) at Namoroka; and *Dalbergia*, *Terminalia* (Combretaceae), and *Hildegardia* at Ankarana. This observation is confirmed for all strata; for example, the genus *Rinorea* (Violaceae), irregular in the shrub stratum of the dry forest at Ankarana, is abundant and well representated at Beanka.

The physiognomy of the vegetation is characterized by the caducity of the foliage for nearly 90% of species (Bardot-Vaucoulon 1991; Rabarison 2000). Thus, the forests are of the dry deciduous type with dominant elements being of the genera *Dalbergia*, *Commiphora*, and *Hildegardia* (Humbert 1965). Leaf loss occurs during the dry season, allowing the vegetation to withstand the lack of water. In a typical year—that is to say, one without the passage of a late cyclonic system—from the month of May the leaves turn yellow and fall. Recovery is gradual, depending on the species, from September onwards, with flowering preceding leafing in most cases. Plant phenology is dependent on both environmental conditions and internal factors. For most trees and shrubs, flowering and fructification coincide with the rainy season. The forest presents two contrasting stages: 1) the rainy season (closed canopy with multiple strata; access to light and evapotranspiration are limited for the lower strata) and, 2) the dry season (open canopy; light for the lower strata). An elusive "spring" flora is observed when plants, including therophytes and geophytes, take advantage of the first rains in the light under a still-open canopy.

These *tsingy* forests are in fact a set of tropophilous (adapted to a climate characterized by marked environmental changes) formations differentiated by their size and composition in accordance with the evolution of the substratum and soil development where they grow. A number of different formations occur in *tsingy* forests, which are presented in the following section.

Dry Deciduous Forest on Developed Soil

Growing on more or less karstified limestone slab outcrops, this form of high forest reaches 12 m to 15 m in height, with some emergent trees up to 20 m (Figure 8.10e). These trees belong to the genera *Delonix*, *Dalbergia*, and *Albizia* (Leguminosae), *Polyscias* (Araliaceae), *Hildegardia*, *Breonia* (Rubiaceae), *Terminalia*, *Givotia* (Euphorbiaceae), *Neobeguea* (Meliaceae), and *Commiphora*. The middle stratum is dense but discontinuous, irregularly distributed with species that have an arborescent or shrubby growth habit and an average height of 5 m to 8 m. In addition to the genera *Strychnos* (Loganiaceae), *Diospyros*, *Garcinia* (Clusiaceae), *Noronhia*, and *Rinorea*, the families well represented in this stratum are Rubiaceae, Euphorbiaceae, Vitaceae, and Acanthaceae. The herbaceous stratum is very irregular and occupies cavities and crevices with soil. It is particularly visible during the rainy season because, as well as some chamephytes (dwarf shrubs) belonging mainly to Acanthaceae and Leguminosae, it includes many seasonal species, especially geophytes such as *Crinum* (Amaryllidaceae), *Aulotandra* (Zingiberaceae), *Drimia*, and *Chlorophytum* (Asparagaceae); and pseudobulb orchids of the genus *Oeceoclades*. The bases of many lianas are also found here, both of large lianas that colonize and flourish in the upper strata, such as *Entada chrysostachys* (Leguminosae), and of understory lianas belonging to the families Cucurbitaceae, Passifloraceae, and Vitaceae, or to the genus *Combretum* (Combretaceae). This type of forest is poor in epiphytes—some orchids of the genera *Microcoelia*, *Angraecum*, and *Vanilla* (aphyllous liana) are well represented locally, and a reviviscent fern (*Platycerium quadridichotomum*) also occurs locally.

Dry Deciduous Forests on Slopes and Limestone Tables (Lapiez)

This forest type is present on steeper slopes or where more of the surface is covered with exposed rocks and the principal characteristics are decreased species richness, lower tree stature, and a shift in the proportions of the species represented (Figures 8.10c and d). Some species prosper in these ecological conditions, such as *Adansonia madagascariensis* (Malvaceae) and *Gyrocarpus americanus* (Hernandiaceae); others scattered in the forest include *Mimusops* sp. (Sapotaceae), *Poupartia gummifera* (Anacardiaceae), and *Givotia*. In areas of scree, where the soil is very discontinuous, the canopy does not exceed 12 m in height and stratification is less marked, other characteristic genera are found: *Abrahamia* or *Rhus* (Anacardiaceae), *Vitex* (Lamiaceae), *Neoharmsia*, *Dupuya*, and *Delonix* (Leguminosae), and *Strychnos* (Loganiaceae). The lower stratum is not very dense and includes shrubs of the genera *Hibiscus* (Malvaceae) and *Clerodendrum* (Lamiaceae); lianas such as *Cissus auricoma* (Vitaceae), *Sarcostemma* sp. (Apocynaceae), *Loeseneriella* sp. (Celastraceae), and *Monanthotaxis* (Annonaceae); herbaceous plants such as *Justicia*; geophytes such as *Carlephyton* (Araceae); and succulents such as *Euphorbia viguieri* or *Aloe* spp.

Rupicolous Vegetation of the *Tsingy*

The most pronounced karstic *tsingy* areas, located on terraces or the tops of limestone plateaus, are subject to severe climatic and edaphic conditions that only allow very discontinuous plant formation. Full exposure to sunshine and wind, as well as having no or little soil or water reserves, make these areas notably inhospitable environments. The number of species present is reduced and vegetation is mostly visible when leafed-out during the rainy season. A mosaic of shrub- and tree-covered islands in the crevices, isolated trees of reduced size (less than 6–8 m high), and scattered xerophytes with remarkable adaptations are observed in this environment, which predominantly consists of bare rock (Figures 8.10a and b). Species of deeper soil facies are nevertheless found here, such as *Hildegardia erythrosiphon* (Malvaceae), *Albizia* sp., and *Delonix boiviniana* (Leguminosae), but their size is reduced and their trunks are more tortuous, both signs of growth difficulties. In large crevices, where climatic conditions are more mesic and where humus has accumulated, trees of the genera *Terminalia*, *Grewia* (Malvaceae), *Commiphora*, *Hymenodictyon* (Rubiaceae), *Dracaena* (Asparagaceae), and *Ficus* (Moraceae) form small stands of which only the crowns emerge from the crevice. *Obetia radula* (Urticaceae); numerous dwarf shrubs of the genera *Euphorbia*, *Cyphostemma* (Vitaceae), and *Uncarina* (Pedaliaceae); lianas of the families Cucurbitaceae, Vitaceae, and Apocynaceae; and geophytes such as *Begonia* (Begoniaceae) or *Impatiens* (Balsaminaceae) are rooted in the stratification joints or crevices of the limestone. They all show remarkable adaptations to xeric conditions. The transition zones between the *tsingy* and the surrounding dense, dry forest are frequently occupied by species of the genera *Stereospermum* (Bignoniaceae) or *Pandanus* (Pandanaceae), both of which can form monospecific stands locally, or by *Bauhinia* (Leguminosae), *Pachypodium*, *Uncarina*, and *Euphorbia*.

Moist Semi-Deciduous Forest of Canyons

The rectilinear vertical fractures of the limestone (Figure 8.9f) can reach widths of tens of meters (Figure 8.9d). These canyons offer more favorable climatic and edaphic conditions than the upper surface of the *tsingy*. The litter accumulates and forms soils, often relatively thick, which in places reach close to the endokarst layer. Dense humid forests (Figure 8.10f) can form locally, in which only some trees shed their leaves, with a canopy exceeding 20 m (Chatelain et al. 2013). Larger individuals of dry deciduous forest species can be found on developed soil, including *Labramia ankaranensis* at Namoroka, which otherwise occurs on deep soil on a plateau at Ankarana, but also some widely distributed ombrophilous species. *Donella perrieri*, *Manilkara boivinii* (Sapotaceae), and *Erythroxylum sphaeranthum* (Erythroxylaceae), usually common in the Sambirano Region, and in the Central and Eastern Domains, are separated by distances of several hundred kilometers from their closest congeners.

CHARACTERISTICS OF THE DIFFERENT *TSINGY* MASSIFS

A comparative analysis of the floristic inventories of the principal *tsingy* massifs (Bolliger et al. 2015) revealed that 35–40% of the

FIGURE 8.10 **Different aspects of *tsingy* vegetation on Madagascar. A) Sparse rupicolous *tsingy* vegetation at Namoroka. B) Two species of pseudobulbous Orchidaceae (*Oeceoclades calcarata* and *O. beraviensis*) taking advantage of a small pocket of soil on the *tsingy* at Namoroka. C) The deeply fragmented rocks of the limestone table, a scree through which trees can root and form closed canopies, Ankarana. D) Dry deciduous forest on slopes and limestone tables, Beanka. E) Dry deciduous forest on developed soil, Beanka. F) Moist semi-deciduous forest of the canyons, Namoroka.** (PHOTOS A, D, E, and F by L. Gautier; and B and C by M. Bardot-Vaucoulon.)

species have a wide distribution throughout western Madagascar and are not restricted to limestone areas. The different karstic massifs, spread from north to central west, also harbor species strictly restricted to limestone, with a much stronger geographic structuring. A comparison of the flora of the limestone massifs discussed herein shows that the more distant they are, the fewer species they have in common. For example, Beanka shares 44 species with the neighboring Bemaraha, but only 12 with Ankarana, 550 km further north. The isolation of these massifs leads to marked local endemism, particularly with respect to strictly calcareous species (Bolliger et al. 2015).

Ankarana Massif

This is the northernmost *tsingy* massif and has a less rigorous climate than those further to the south, with an annual rainfall of up to 1650 mm and a dry season of only seven months (Goodman et al. 2018). Its peculiarity also lies in its proximity to the volcanic Montagne d'Ambre, whose recent Quaternary basaltic flows entered the northern portion of the Ankarana and penetrated some canyons and valleys (Bardot-Vaucoulon 1997). There, the deep soils, rich in organic matter, produce a moist semi-deciduous forest with large trees, sometimes exceeding 20 m, such as *Xanthocercis madagascariensis*, *Tetrapterocarpon septentrionalis*, *Xylia hoffmanii*, *Albizia* spp., *Dalbergia* ssp., and *Baudouinia* (Leguminosae); *Zanthoxylum tsihanimposa* (Rutaceae); *Canarium* (Burseraceae); *Givotia stipularis* (Euphorbiaceae); and *Ficus grevei* (Moraceae) forming the canopy. In the lower strata there is a rich layer of small trees and shrubs: *Sorindeia* (Anacardiaceae), *Rinorea* (Violaceae), *Psychotria* (Rubiaceae), and *Grewia* (Malvaceae). The middle and lower strata are well developed with large lianas such as *Gouania laxiflora* (Rhamnaceae), *Byttneria heterophylla* (Malvaceae), and *Dioscorea bemarivensis* (Dioscoreaceae). The herbaceous stratum includes members of the Acanthaceae and Poaceae families.

A total of 812 plant species are known from the massif, more than three-quarters of which are island endemics. They belong to 419 genera, 53 of which are endemic to Madagascar, distributed among 97 families, including nine pteridophytes. The endemic genus *Ambilobea* (Burseraceae), with a unique species, *A. madagascariensis*, only found on limestone substrates in the north, is of note. Remarkable local endemic species present on the *tsingy* include *Adenia lapiazicola* (Passifloraceae), *Cyphostemma rutilans* (Vitaceae), *Euphorbia pachypodioides*, *Humbertioturraea labatii* (Meliaceae), and *Impatiens barthlottii* (Balsaminaceae).

Namoroka Massif

This site is located in the west near Soalala. It receives about 1400 mm of annual rainfall and has a dry season of eight months. Unlike the other *tsingy* massifs, Namoroka has a gentle slope and water accumulated during the rainy season drains away more slowly than from other *tsingy* areas, so canyons are frequently flooded. The river that runs through the village of Namoroka has its source in the massif and flows permanently. It is bordered by a moist semi-deciduous forest, extending northwest of the massif, with trees that can exceed 20 m in height (Gautier 2018), including *Syzygium sakalavarum* (Myrtaceae), *Cryptocarya occidentalis* (Lauraceae), *Labramia* cf. *comorensis* (Sapotaceae), *Canarium madagascariense*, *Colea muricata* (Bignoniaceae), and *Breonadia salicina* (Rubiaceae), but also some palm trees, such as the rare *Ravenea rivularis* (Arecaceae), and numerous ferns.

One of the remarkable features of the Namoroka's dry, dense forest is the abundance of *Adansonia rubrostipa* (Malvaceae) stands in peripheral areas (Bardot-Vaucoulon 2015). The landscape is perforated by numerous sinkholes, whose lower sections are lined with impermeable sandy-clay alluvium causing them to be flooded during the rainy season; limestone boulders bear the mark of an algae line at the upper level of the water. The forest at the edge includes limestone-associated species such as *Terminalia mantaly* (Combretaceae), *Garcinia pervillei* (Clusiaceae), *Malleastrum gracile* (Meliaceae), *Rinorea greveana*, *Thilachium* sp. (Capparaceae), and *Hibiscus palmatifidus* (Malvaceae).

A total of 608 plant species have been recorded from the massif to date, of which more than two-thirds are Madagascar endemics; they represent 362 genera, of which 37 are endemic to the island. The local flora is represented by 96 families, including nine pteridophytes. Sixty species are local endemics found only in the central west of the island, or, more specifically, at Namoroka, such as *Delonix leucantha*, *Dombeya rosacea* (Malvaceae), *Dioscorea namorokaensis*, *Aloe namorokaensis* (Asphodelaceae), *Crinum filifolium* (Amaryllidaceae), *Colea muricata*, and *Eulophia perrieri* (Orchidaceae).

Beanka Massif

This massif, which is about 5 km wide and 40 km long, is a narrow formation. It is the northern extension of the Bemaraha Massif and subject to a dry seasonal climate, typical of the west, with ~1400 mm annual rainfall (Goodman et al. 2018) and a seven- to eight-month dry season (Cornet 1972). The main characteristic is the existence of a moist semi-deciduous forest, not only in the canyons, but on the lower slopes along the Kimanambolo River, which certainly benefits from the resurgence of limestone on the upper slopes (Chatelain et al. 2013). The dry deciduous forest on thicker soils is also well developed. Trees 17 m to 20 m high are abundant, the canopy is mostly closed, and the characteristic tree species are *Cynometra abrahamii* (Leguminosae), *Stadmania oppositifolia* (Sapindaceae), and *Tabernaemontana coffeoides* (Apocynaceae). The shrub stratum includes many representative evergreen species: *Rinorea arborea*, *Vepris boiviniana* (Rutaceae), *Erythroxylum corymbosum* (Erythroxylaceae), *Noronhia buxifolia* and *N. alleizettei* (Oleaceae), and *Coffea* ssp. (Rubiaceae) (Rakotozafy et al. 2013). Those limestone plateaus that have deep crevices protected from extreme drought harbor a unique community dominated by *Pandanus tsingycola* (Pandanaceae), which forms low thickets with some emergent plants.

At Beanka, 965 species have been identified, from 485 genera belonging to134 families, including 19 pteridophytes. The 29 species currently known only from this site and a few others, in particular Bemaraha, include *Socratina phillipsoniana* (Loranthaceae), *Psychotria biloba*, *Erythrophysa sakalava*, and *Tsingya bemarana* (Sapindaceae), and *Kirkia leandrii* (Kirkiaceae). Three species, *Aloe beankaensis*, *Pandanus tsingycola*, and *Pararistolochia enricoi* (Aristolochiaceae), are only known from Beanka.

Bemaraha Massif

This site is much more extensive than the other *tsingy* massifs, and is 80 km long and 20 km wide, culminating at Tsiandro Peak, at an elevation of 934 m. It was the first *tsingy* to be studied in some detail from a botanical perspective (Leandri 1936a, 1936b, 1951). Its large surface area causes local climatic variation, with the north of the massif receiving slightly more than 1500 mm of rainfall per year, and the dry season being slightly less pronounced (Bousquet and Rabetaliana 1992). The forest cover, as in Beanka, is denser than in Namoroka or Ankarana, with a greater proportion of evergreen species, such as *Homalium albiflorum* (Salicaceae; Figure 8.44c), *Plagioscyphus humbertii* (Sapindaceae), *Syzygium sakalavarum*, *Diospyros*, and *Rinorea arborea*.

It is the *tsingy* formation with the longest and deepest faults and canyons. They shelter moist semi-deciduous forests, which benefit from less severe climatic and edaphic conditions compared with the upper surface, specifically protection from the wind, reduced sunshine, and more consistent humidity. The bottom of these faults and canyons have more developed soils, and are favorable for species that are less heliophilic or that require more humidity. Trees such as *Givotia madagascariensis* and *Macaranga* (Euphorbiaceae), and *Diospyros*, or shrubs of the genera *Bauhinia* (Leguminosae), *Pandanus*, and *Croton* (Euphorbiaceae), occur on exposed rock portions of the massif and are fixed by roots extending several meters down into crevices. Others germinate at the bottom of these formations and develop slender vertical trunks hoisting their crowns up to the light above the crevice. In such niches, lianas, such as *Monanthotaxis boivinii* (Annonaceae), and epiphytes, such as *Platycerium dichotomum* (Polypodiaceae), are found.

To date, 833 species of plants have been recorded at Bemaraha, belonging to 469 genera (Gautier et al. 2013b) and distributed among 106 families; 35 genera are Madagascar endemics, and nearly 90 species are locally endemic or very rare on Madagascar, including *Begonia bekopakensis* (Begoniaceae), *Cyphostemma leandrii*, *Dombeya sely*, *Coffea labatii*, and *Paracorynanthe uropetala* (Rubiaceae), *Kirkia leandrii*, and *Tsingya bemarana*.

CONCLUSION

The *tsingy* formations of western Madagascar represent an important ecosystem, harboring important levels of biodiversity, including botanical diversity, with a remarkable number of xerophytic adaptations. A large number of plant species are common to these limestone areas, but each *tsingy* massif has certain peculiarities with regard to local endemics.

Associated with the harsh ecological conditions, these habitats are very fragile. The local geomorphology makes them naturally difficult to access, unattractive for agriculture, and resistant to fire, which affords some natural protection. They are nevertheless subject to many pressures, including timber extraction, charcoal-making, and the collection of rare plants of interest for commercial trade. Great vigilance is required for their preservation. The continued inventory of these areas is important to pursue. The geographic positions of these isolated *tsingy* massifs in western Madagascar render them particularly attractive for genetic studies examining patterns of isolation and speciation.

Subject editor: Steven M. Goodman

SYSTEMATIC ACCOUNTS: NONVASCULAR PLANTS

LICHENIZED ASCOMYCETES: LICHENS

A. Aptroot and F. Schumm

A lichen is a symbiotic system composed of a fungus living in partnership with an alga and/or cyanobacterium. The alga is a tiny green plant, usually consisting of loose, more or less round cells (at least in most of the types growing inside lichens). Cyanobacteria, also called blue-green algae, are primitive plant-like organisms that usually consist of cells in rows or in a gelatinous mass. Both fulfill the same role as photosynthesizers: they produce carbohydrates from water and carbon dioxide using the energy from sunlight. The fungal partner absorbs some of the manufactured nutrients and in return provides the plant partner or photobiont with shelter from ultraviolet radiation and immediate desiccation.

The relationship therefore has mutual advantages: in most cases, the fungi could not live without the carbon source, and the algae could not live in some of the places where lichens occur, and rarely in such masses, although they are frequently free-living as filmy growths of a few cells thick in suitable, damp places. The fungal partner constitutes the dominant part of the lichen and solely forms the outer layer and the fertile parts of the fruiting bodies. The algae or cyanobacteria are inside, often in a specific layer where they receive the optimum amount of sunlight. Fungi are composed of threadlike, microscopic filaments called hyphae. These form a continuous network rather than dividing into discrete units as in the cells of animal and plants, although partial walls called septa may intermittently divide them. The hyphae may become compacted to form tissues but remain very versatile in their branching; therefore, the growth form of the lichen colony is variable too, especially compared with higher plants and even to mosses. In lichens, this results in very few countable or measurable characters that are relatively constant. Lichens have no roots and no vessels inside to transport fluids. Thus, they must remain relatively small and thin in order for cells to obtain water and nutrition by diffusion.

Each lichen species has a unique fungal partner, but there are only several species of algae and cyanobacteria in the associations, which are not very specific to a species. Lichens do not form a single evolutionary group but an ecological group. In fact, various families of fungi have developed a lichenized habit. In several cases, lichen genera also comprise species without algae and without a visible macroscopic thallus. These are usually parasitic on other lichens from which they take carbohydrates and are known as lichenicolous species. In a strict sense, they are not lichens. Some are known from Madagascar, but they are not treated here.

Lichens are characterized by their drought resistance; they stop growing when completely dry but resume when moistened. They generally grow slowly and may survive to an impressive age, up to several centuries for a single specimen. There is not much seasonality, and they grow and produce fruiting bodies in summer and winter alike, whenever they are moist; a little fog suffices. They are often strongly glued to their substrate, which is most commonly rock or bark, both of which surfaces are rarely colonized by flowering plants. Their ecological function is that of primary colonizer, invading bare areas and thus creating conditions for other species such as mosses and liverworts to follow. Characteristic communities may form, governed by a wide range of factors including the physical hardness, moisture retention, chemistry, and nutrient status of the substrates, as well as their aspect, slope, and age. Lichens are affected by atmospheric conditions and different species display a range of sensitivities to pollution, which has enabled their wide use as bioindicators of air quality. Fortunately, the air is generally rather clean on Madagascar, and the flora is not noted for the characteristic pollution-tolerant species that have become abundant in industrialized parts of the world.

GROWTH FORMS

Lichens can be categorized by the five types of substrate on which they typically grow (Figure 8.11):

- **Corticolous**: on bark. Many lichen species are restricted to either smooth or rough bark and to exposed (sunny) or shaded trees.
- **Lignicolous**: on dead wood.
- **Foliicolous**: on living leaves.
- **Terricolous**: on soil. Lichen communities on the ground are widespread in a variety of conditions from upland screes to the crevices in coastal cliffs and dunes, wherever competing vegetation is kept in check by, for example, nutrient deficiency, drought, exposure to climatic extremes, or toxicity from heavy metals.
- **Saxicolous**: on rock. Rocky substrates contribute greatly to lichen diversity. In addition, there are artificial substrates, including cement and mortar, available for lichen colonization. However, when considering rock types one must always be aware that external factors, such as surface age and condition, aspect, and available nutrients, are important in determining the composition of the lichen community.

Some species are predominantly coastal. It must be noted here that many species characteristically grow only on one substrate, while others occur on more than one. Sometimes, characteristically saxicolous communities can be found on hardwood. Certain species may even occur on all five classes of substrate. In the latter case, this does not mean that they grow everywhere, but it shows that other ecological factors may have an overriding influence. There are examples of species that grow in sheltered places with high air humidity, whether rock, bark, or even living leaf. Others grow on dust-impregnated surfaces, whether rock, bark, or wood.

LICHENS OF MADAGASCAR

Madagascar is well known for its high numbers of endemic animal and plant species and genera. There are several factors that caused its unique biodiversity: it is geologically old and has a different origin from Africa; some original forest remains; and the island contains relatively high mountains. Different vegetation types can be distinguished on Madagascar (Gautier et al. 2018), each with a characteristic flora and fauna. As has occurred in many other areas of the tropics, including islands, humans have had a catastrophic impact on the natural environment since they arrived. Despite the problems, Madagascar still has a rich endemic flora of global conservation importance. As many of the lichens occupy the dry, unproductive coastal zone they have been less affected by agriculture and invasive plants. They are also unpalatable to local grazing animals. Thus, well-developed lichen communities still exist, and shrubby *Roccella* species still form the dominant vegetation cover in certain areas. All the lichens found on Madagascar arrived naturally or evolved there, mostly from African colonizers. Minute wind-blown spores can be dispersed for thousands of kilometers in atmospheric currents, and many lichens have very broad global ranges.

Lichens are not an obvious element of the vegetation on Madagascar. They are not conspicuous in dry coastal regions, especially in the southwest, and although diversity is relatively low there, there are some local endemics. More species occur in the tropical moist evergreen forests on the eastern slopes of the island and in areas of higher elevation, up to the montane ericoid thicket. Places around tombs, particularly those of royalty, are often associated with older secondary forest and full of upland lichens.

- The dry tropical area with open grasslands, dry deciduous forests, and dry spiny thickets covers most of the island in the west, south, and southwest, including coastal regions. These vegetation types occupy roughly one-third of the island. This zone also includes granitic inselbergs and some limestone karst.
- The wet tropical area extends from the coastal regions in the north and east (including small nearshore islands like Nosy Be, Nosy Komba, and Ile Sainte Marie) to the extreme southeast and inland up to the Central Highlands. This zone occupies roughly two-thirds of the island. The bedrock is mostly siliceous. There is no fundamental distinction in the lichen flora between the coastal and inland regions.

FIGURE 8.11 **Different aspects concerning Malagasy lichens. A) Exposed sedimentary outcrops in central Madagascar with saxicolous lichens. B) Tree at Berenty with *Pyxine* and other corticolous lichens. C) *Adansonia* (baobab) tree in the south with corticolous lichens. Some of the different growth forms of lichens include: D) *Brigantiaea tricolor*, corticolous; E) *Bullatina aspidota*, foliicolous; F) *Chiodecton papillosum*, corticolous; G) *Cladonia ceratophyllina*, terricolous; H) *C. hedbergii*, terricolous; I) *Graphis consimilis*, corticolous; J) *Haematomma africanum*, corticolous; and K) *Physma byrsaeum*, corticolous.**
(PHOTOS by F. Schumm.)

TABLE 8.9. **Checklist of lichens known from Madagascar**

Aderkomyces albostrigosa (R. Sant.) Lücking, Sérus. & Vězda—Aptroot (2016), leg. Aptroot & Hensen 1984 (BR)

Agonimia opuntiella (Buschardt & Poelt) Vězda—Aptroot (2016), leg. Aptroot & Hensen 1984 (BR)

Amandinea efflorescens (Müll. Arg.) Marbach—Aptroot (2016), leg. Aptroot & Hensen 1984 (BR)

Anisomeridium ambiguum (Zahlbr.) R. C. Harris—Aptroot (2016), leg. Aptroot & Hensen 1984 (ABL)

A. tamarindi (Fée) R. C. Harris—Harris (1995), Stizenberger (1890, as *Verrucaria vaga*)

Anthracothecium prasinum (Eschw.) R. C. Harris—Harris (1989), Stizenberger (1890, as *Verrucaria borbonica*)

Anzia parasitica (Fée) Zahlbr.—Abbayes (1956)

A. semiteres (Mont. & Bosch) Stizenb.—Abbayes (1956, as *Anzia madagascarensis* Abbayes)

Arthonia cyanea Müll. Arg.—Aptroot (2016), leg. Aptroot & Hensen 1984 (BR)

A. trilocularis Müll. Arg.—Santesson (1952: 84)

Arthopyrenia confluens R. C. Harris—Aptroot (2016), leg. Aptroot & Hensen 1984 (ABL)

Aspidothelium fugiens (Müll. Arg.) R. Sant.—Santesson (1952: 282)

Asterothyrium octomerum R. Sant.—Santesson (1952: 330)

Bacidina simplex var. *cyanophila* Lücking—Aptroot (2016), leg. Aptroot & Hensen 1984 (ABL)

Badimia dimidiata (Bab. ex Leight.) Vězda—Aptroot (2016), leg. Aptroot & Hensen 1984 (BR)

Baeomyces fungoides (Sw.) Ach.—Aptroot (1990: 402)

Bogoriella miculiformis (Nyl. ex Müll. Arg.) Aptroot & Lücking—Stizenberger (1890, as *Verrucaria micula* Flot.)

B. minutula (Müll. Arg.) Aptroot & Lücking—Stizenberger (1890, as *Verrucaria minutula* [Müll. Arg.] Stiz.)

Brigantiaea leucoxantha (Spreng.) R. Sant. & Hafellner—Aptroot (1990: 402)

B. tricolor (Mont.) Trevis.—Hafellner (1997: 70)

Bulbothrix goebelii—Vainio (1898, as *Parmelia scortella*), Abbayes (1961, as *Parmelia granatensis*)

B. isidiza (Nyl.) Hale—Hale (1976a: 16), Aptroot (1990: 402), Abbayes (1961, as *Parmelia isidiza*), Vainio (1898, as *Parmelia isidiza*)

B. meizospora (Nyl.) Hale—Aptroot (1990: 402)

B. sensibilis (J. Steiner & Zahlbr.) Hale—Aptroot (1990: 403)

B. suffixa (Stirton) Hale—Aptroot (1990: 403)

B. tabacina (Mont. & Bosch) Hale—Hale (1976a: 24), Aptroot (1990: 403)

Bunodophoron australe (Laurer) A. Massal.—Abbayes (1956, as *Sphaerophorus australis*)

B. diplotypum (Vain.) Wedin—Abbayes (1956), Vainio (1898, as *Sphaerophorus diplotypus*)

B. madagascareum (Nyl.) Wedin—Abbayes (1956, as *Sphaerophorus madagascareus*), Vainio (1898, as Pleurocybe madagascarea)

B. melanocarpum (Sw.) Wedin—Aptroot (2016), leg. Aptroot & Hensen 1984 (BR)

Byssolecania fumosonigricans (Müll. Arg.) R. Sant.—Aptroot (2016), leg. Aptroot & Hensen 1984 (BR)

Byssoloma discordans (Vain.) Zahlbr.—Santesson (1952: 488)

B. leucoblepharum (Nyl.) Vain.—Santesson (1952: 483), Vainio (1898, as *Pilocarpon leucoblepharum*)

B. subdiscordans (Nyl.) P. James—Santesson (1952: 490, as *Byssoloma rotuliforme*)

Calenia aspidota (Vain.) Vězda—Santesson (1952: 360, as *Gyalectidium aspidotum* [Vain.] R. Sant.)

Calicium chlorosporum F. Wilson—Aptroot (1990: 403)

C. hyperelloides Nyl.—Aptroot (1990: 403)

C. pluriseptatum Tibell & Frisch—Tibell and Frisch (2010)

Calopadia fusca (Müll. Arg.) Vězda—Santesson (1952: 532, as *Lopadium fuscum* Müll. Arg)

C. subfusca Kalb & Vězda—Aptroot (2016), leg. Aptroot & Hensen 1984 (BR)

Caloplaca crocea (Kremp.) Hafellner & Poelt—Hafellner and Poelt (1979: 23)

Candelaria concolor (Dickson) Steiner—Aptroot (1990: 403)

Candelariella reflexa (Nyl.) Lettau—Aptroot (2016), leg. Aptroot & Hensen 1984 (BR)

Canoparmelia amazonica (Nyl.) Elix & Hale—Aptroot (1991a: 150)

C. ecaperata (Müll. Arg.) Elix & Hale—Abbayes (1961, as *Parmelia ecaperata*)

C. epileuca (Hale) Elix & Hale—Aptroot (1991a: 150)

C. eruptens (Kurok.) Elix & Hale—Aptroot (1991a: 150)

C. pustulescens (Kurok.) Elix & J. Johnst.—Elix (2001: 210)

C. quintarigera Aptroot—Aptroot (1991a: 150)

C. rodriguesiana (Hue) Elix—Hale (1976b: 9, as *Pseudoparmelia rodriguesiana*), Swinscow and Krog (1988: 250 as *Pseudoparmelia rodriguesiana*)

C. somaliensis (Müll. Arg.) Elix & Hale—Hale (1976b, as *Pseudoparmelia somaliensis*), Swinscow and Krog (1988: 252, as *Pseudoparmelia somaliensis*)

C. texana—Aptroot (1990: 403), Abbayes (1961, as *Parmelia texana*), Hale (1976b, as *Pseudoparmelia texana*), Abbayes (1961, as *Parmelia confluescens*)

Carbacanthographis marcescens (Fée) Staiger & Kalb—Aptroot (2016), leg. Aptroot & Hensen 1984 (BR)

Catillaria ophthalmocarpa Vain.—Aptroot (2016), leg. Aptroot & Hensen 1984 (BR)

Chiodecton natalense Nyl.—Aptroot (2016), leg. Aptroot & Hensen 1984 (BR)

C. papillosum G. Thor—Henssen and Thor (1998)

C. pustuliferum Aptroot—Lumbsch et al. (2011: 39)

Chroodiscus mirificus (Kremp.) R. Sant.—Aptroot (2016), leg. Aptroot & Hensen 1984 (BR)

Cladia terebrata (Laurer) S. Parnmen & Lumbsch.—Lumbsch and Aptroot (1993: 239, as *C. aggregata* (Sw.) Nyl), Aptroot (1990: 403, as *C. aggregata*), Abbayes (1948: 59, as *Cladonia aggregata* (Sw.) Spreng. and *C. gorgonina* [Bory] Vain.), Vainio (1898: 34, as *C. aggregata*)

Cladonia abbatiana Stenroos—Stenroos (1991: 107)

C. boivinii Vain.—Ahti and Aptroot (1992: 119), Abbayes (1948)

C. borbonica Nyl.—Ahti and Aptroot (1992: 119)

C. candelabrum (Bory) Nyl.—Abbayes (1948)
C. centrophora Müll. Arg.—Abbayes (1948)
C. ceratophyllina (Nyl.) Vain. in Hue—Ahti and Aptroot (1992: 120)
C. chlorophaea (Sommerf.) Sprengel—Ahti and Aptroot (1992: 120)
C. chondroidea Abbayes—Abbayes (1948)
C. cinereorubens Abbayes—Abbayes (1948)
C. confusa R. Sant.—Abbayes (1948: 76, as *C. leptoclada* f. *cinerascens*), Ahti (1961: as *C. alpestroides*), Ahti and Aptroot (1992: 118)
C. crispatula (Nyl.) Ahti—Vainio (1898, as *C. rangiferina* f. *crispatula*)
C. didyma (Fée) Vain.—Ahti and Aptroot (1992: 120)
C. diplotypa Nyl.—Ahti and Aptroot (1992: 120)
C. fruticulosa Kremp.—Ahti and Aptroot (1992: 120)
C. gigantea (Bory) H. Olivier—Ahti and Aptroot (1992: 121), Czeczuga et al. (1998: 575)
C. glaucopallida Vain.—Ahti and Aptroot (1992: 121)
C. hedbergii Ahti—Ahti and Aptroot (1992: 121)
C. macilenta Hoffm.—Ahti and Aptroot (1992: 121)
C. medusina (Bory) Nyl.—Swinscow and Krog (1988: 50), Ahti and Aptroot (1992: 121), Czeczuga et al. (1998: 575)
C. pachyclados (Vain.) Ahti—Swinscow and Krog (1988: 52), Ahti and Aptroot (1992: 121)
C. peltasta Sprengel—Ahti and Aptroot (1992: 121)
C. perplexa Abbayes—Ahti and Aptroot (1992: 122)
C. perrieri Abbayes—Abbayes (1948: 60)
C. praetermissa A. W. Archer—Ahti and Aptroot (1992: 122)
C. rangiformis Hoffm.—Vainio (1898)
C. squamosa Hoffm.—Ahti and Aptroot (1992: 122), Czeczuga et al. (1998: 575)
C. subpityrea Sandst.—Swinscow and Krog (1988: 57)
C. subpungens Abbayes—Ahti and Aptroot (1992: 122)
C. subradiata (Vain.) Sandstede—Ahti and Aptroot (1992: 122)
C. subsquamosa Kremp.—Ahti and Aptroot (1992: 122)
C. valida (Abbayes) Stenroos—Stenroos (1991: 108)
C. varians Vain. ex Ahti—Vainio (1898: 40, as *C. pycnoclada* var. *granulosa*), Ahti and Aptroot (1992: 122)
C. verticillata (Hoffm.) Schaer.—Abbayes (1948)
C. vulcanica Zoll. & Moritzi—Abbayes (1948)
Clandestinotrema minutum Aptroot—Aptroot (2016)
Coccocarpia domingensis Vain.—Aptroot (1990: 403)
C. erythroxyli (Spreng.) Swinscow & Krog—Arvidsson (1982: 57), Aptroot (1990: 403), Czeczuga et al. (1998: 575)
C. filiformis Arvidsson—Aptroot (1990: 403)
C. flavicans Arvidsson—Aptroot (1990: 403)
C. palmicola (Sprengel) Swinscow & Krog—Arvidsson (1982: 72), Aptroot (1990: 403), Czeczuga et al. (1998: 575)
C. pellita (Ach.) Müll. Arg.—Aptroot (1990: 404)
C. smaragdina Pers.—Arvidsson (1982: 84), Aptroot (1990: 404), Vainio (1898, as *C. pellita* var. *Smaragdina*)
C. stellata Tuck.—Arvidsson (1982: 86), Aptroot (1990: 404)
Coccotrema porinopsis (Nyl.) Imshaug ex Yoshim.—Aptroot (2016), Aptroot and Hensen 13349, 1984 (BR)
Coenogonium epiphyllum Vain.—Aptroot (2016), leg. Aptroot & Hensen 1984 (BR)
C. interplexum Nyl.—Aptroot (2016), leg. Aptroot & Hensen 1984 (BR)
C. interpositum Nyl.—Aptroot (2016), leg. Aptroot & Hensen 1984 (BR)
C. madagascarense Vězda—Vězda (2004)
Collema leptaleum var. *biliosum* (Mont.) Degel.—Aptroot (1990: 404)
C. pulcellum var. *subnigrescens* (Müll. Arg) Degel.—Aptroot (1990: 404)
C. rugosum Kremp.—Aptroot (1990: 404)
Coniocarpon cinnabarinum DC.—Aptroot (2016), leg. Schumm 4029 (Hb. Schumm)
Constrictolumina leucostoma (Müll. Arg.) Lücking et al.— Aptroot (2016), leg. Aptroot & Hensen 12568, 1984 (ABL)
Cratiria lauricassiae (Fée) Marbach—Aptroot (2016), leg. Aptroot & Hensen 1984 (BR)
Crespoa crozalsiana (B. de Lesd. ex Harm.) Lendemer & B. P. Hodk.—Aptroot (1990: 403, as *Canoparmelia crozalsiana* [B. de Lesd. ex Harm.] Elix & Hale)
C. inhaminensis (C. W. Dodge) Lendemer & B. P. Hodk.—Aptroot (1990: 403, as *Canoparmelia inhaminensis* [C. W. Dodge] Elix & Hale)
Crocodia aurata (Ach.) Link—Galloway (1994: 119, as *Pseudocyphellaria aurata* [Ach.] Vain.), Abbayes (1956: 3, as *Sticta aurata* (Ach.), Vainio (1898: 32, as *P. aurata*)
C. clathrata (De Not.) Trevis.—Galloway (1994: 123, as *Pseudocyphellaria clathrata* [De Not.] Malme)
Crocynia gossypina (Sw.) A. Massal.—Aptroot (1990: 404)
Dermatiscum thunbergii (Ach.) Nyl.—Ertz et al. (2014a)
Dibaeis arcuata (Stirt.) Kalb & Gierl—Aptroot (2016), leg. Aptroot & Hensen 12364 & 13525, 1984 (BR)
D. sorediata Kalb & Gierl—Aptroot (2016), leg. Schumm (Hb. Schumm)
Dichosporidium brunnthaleri (Zahlbr.) G. Thor—Aptroot (2016), leg. Aptroot & Hensen 13365 & 13366, 1984 (B)
Dictyonema sericeum (Sw.) Berk.—Aptroot (1990: 404)
Diorygma confluens (Fée) Kalb, Staiger & Elix—Stizenberger (1890, as *Glyphis confluens*)
D. junghuhnii (Mont. & Bosch) Kalb, Staiger & Elix—Stizenberger (1890, as *Glyphis mendax*)
Diploschistes cinereocaesius (Sw.) Vain.—Doidge (1950: 248), Guderley and Lumbsch (1996: 275)
D. muscorum subsp. *bartlettii* Lumbsch—Lumbsch (1987)
D. scruposus (Schreb.) Norman—Aptroot (2016), leg. Aptroot & Hensen 1984 (BR)
D. thelenelloides Lumbsch & Aptroot—Lumbsch and Aptroot (1993)
Dirina madagascariensis Tehler et al.—Tehler et al. (2013: 456), Aptroot (1990: 404, as *D. ceratoniae* [Ach.] Fr.)
Dirinaria aegialita (Afz. in Ach.) Moore—Aptroot (1988: 143)
D. applanata (Fée) D. D. Awasthi—Aptroot (1988: 143)
D. complicata D. D. Awasthi—Swinscow and Krog (1988: 80), Aptroot (1988: 143)
D. confluens (Fr.) D. D. Awasthi—Aptroot (1988: 143)
D. consimilis (Stirt.) D. D. Awasthi—Awasthi (1975: 91)

(continued overleaf)

TABLE 8.9. ***continued***

D. picta (Sw.) Clem. & Shear—Aptroot (1988: 143), Czeczuga et al. (1998: 575)
Echinoplaca diffluens (Müll. Arg.) R. Sant.—Aptroot (2016), leg. Aptroot & Hensen 1984 (BR)
E. pachyparaphysata R. Sant.—Santesson (1952: 373)
E. pellicula (Müll. Arg.) R. Sant.—Santesson (1952: 367)
Endocarpon pusillum Hedw.—Schumm and Aptroot (2010: 373)
Ephebe solida Born.—Schultz and Aptroot (2008)
Erioderma leylandii (Taylor) Müll. Arg. subsp. *leylandii*—Jørgensen (2001: 528)
E. tomentosum Hue—Jørgensen (2001: 529), Vainio (1898: 33, as *E. groendalianum* [Ach.] Hue and as *E. polycarpum* Fée).
E. unguigerum (Bory) Nyl.—Vainio (1898)
Eschatogonia prolifera (Mont.) R. Sant.— Aptroot (2016), leg. Aptroot & Hensen 13338a, 1984 (BR)
Glyphis cicatricosa Ach.—Aptroot (1990: 404)
G. scyphulifera—Aptroot (1990: 404, as *Gyrostomum scyphuliferum*)
Graphis acharii Fée—Aptroot (2016), leg. Aptroot & Hensen 1984 (B)
G. anfractuosa (Eschw.) Eschw.—Aptroot (2016), leg. Aptroot & Hensen 1984 (B)
G. aperiens Müll. Arg.—Aptroot (2016), leg. Aptroot & Hensen 1984 (B)
G. argentia Makhija & Adaw.—Aptroot (2016), leg. Schumm (Hb. Schumm)
G. chlorotica A. Massal.—Aptroot (2016), leg. Aptroot & Hensen 1984 (B)
G. cincta (Pers.) Aptroot—Aptroot (2016), leg. Aptroot & Hensen 1984 (B)
G. consimilis Vain.—Aptroot (2016), leg. Aptroot & Hensen 1984 (B)
G. crebra Vain.—Aptroot (2016), leg. Aptroot & Hensen 1984 (B)
G. dracaenae Vain.—Aptroot (2016), leg. Aptroot & Hensen 1984 (B)
G. glaucescens Fée—Aptroot (2016), leg. Aptroot & Hensen 1984 (B)
G. renschiana (Müll. Arg.) Stizenb.—Lücking et al. (2009)
G. subserpentina Nyl.—Aptroot (2016), leg. Aptroot & Hensen 1984 (B)
Gyalolechia bassiae (Ach.) Søchting et al.—Aptroot (2016), Schumm 5788, p.p. (Hb. Schumm)
Gymnoderma coccocarpum Nyl.—Pino-Bodas et al. (2020), also as *Heterodea madagascarea* Nyl. and as *Baeoderma madagascareum* (Nyl.) Vain.
Haematomma africanum (J. Steiner) C. W. Dodge—Aptroot (2016), leg. Aptroot & Hensen 12815, 1984 (BR)
H. flexuosum Hillm.—Staiger and Kalb (1995: 108)
H. persoonii (Fée) A. Massal.—Aptroot (1990: 404, as *Haematomma puniceum*), Schumm and Aptroot (2010: 308)
Hafellia dissa (Stirt.) H. Mayrhofer & Sheard—Aptroot (1988: 146, as *Rinodina dissa*)
Hemithecium implicatum (Fée) Staiger—Aptroot (2016), leg. Aptroot & Hensen 1984 (BR)
Herpothallon roseocinctum (Fr.) Aptroot, Lücking & G. Thor—Aptroot et al. (2009: 60)
H. rubrocinctum (Ehrenb.) Aptroot, Lücking & G. Thor—Aptroot (1990: 403, as *Chiodecton rubrocinctum*)
Heterodermia albicans (Pers.) Swinscow & Krog—Aptroot (1988: 143)
H. barbifera (Nyl.) Kr. P. Singh—Stizenberger (1890, as *Physcia barbifera* var. *podocarpiza*)
H. comosa (Eschw.) Follm. & Redón—Aptroot (1988: 143), Czeczuga et al. (1998: 575)
H. dactyliza (Nyl.) Swinscow & Krog—Stizenberger (1890, as *Physcia speciosa* var. *dactyliza*)
H. dendritica (Pers.) Poelt—Abbayes (1956, as *Anaptychia dendritica*)
H. diademata (Taylor) D. D. Awasthi—Aptroot (1988: 143), Czeczuga et al. (1998: 575)
H. flabellata (Fée) D. D. Awasthi—Aptroot (1988: 143)
H. galactophylla (Tuck.) W. L. Culb.—Aptroot (1988: 143)
H. isidiophora (Vain.) D. D. Awasthi—Aptroot (1988: 144)
H. lutescens (Kurok.) Follm.—Aptroot (1988: 144)
H. obscurata (Nyl.) Trevis.—Aptroot (1988: 144), Czeczuga et al. (1998: 575)
H. podocarpa (Bél.) D. D. Awasthi—Aptroot (1988: 144), Abbayes (1956, as *Anaptychia podocarpa*), Vainio (1898, as *Anaptychia podocarpa*)
H. speciosa (Wulf.) Trevis.—Aptroot (1988: 144), Czeczuga et al. (1998: 575), Vainio (1898, as *Anaptychia speciosa*)
H. verrucifera (Kurok.) W. A. Weber—Aptroot (1988: 144)
Hyperphyscia granulata (Poelt) Moberg—Aptroot (1990: 404), Aptroot (1988: 145, as *H. adglutinata*)
H. syncolla (Nyl.) Kalb—Swinscow and Krog (1988: 105)
Hypotrachyna angolense (W. L. Culb. & C. F. Culb.) Divakar et al.—Aptroot (1991a: 152, as *Everniastrum angolense* [W. L. Culb. & C. F. Culb.] Sipman), Abbayes (1956: 9, as *Parmelia americana* [Meyen & Flot.] Mont.), Abbayes (1961: 88, as *P. americana*)
H. endochlora (Leighton) Hale—Swinscow and Krog (1988: 105), Vainio (1898, as *Parmelia madagascariensis*)
H. flavida (Zahlbr.) Hale—Abbayes (1961, as *Parmelia flava*)
H. gracilescens (Vain.) Hale—Abbayes (1961, as *Parmelia gracilescens*)
H. majoris (Vain.) Hale—Vainio (1898, as *Parmelia majoris*)
H. neodissecta (Hale) Hale—Aptroot (1990: 404)
H. osseoalba (Vain.) Park & Hale—Aptroot (1990: 404), Abbayes (1961, as *Parmelia formosana*)
H. revoluta (Flörke) Hale—Abbayes (1961, as *Parmelia revoluta*), Vainio (1898, as *Parmelia revoluta*)
H. rockii (Zahlbr.) Hale—Aptroot (1990: 404)
H. sinuosa (Sm.) Hale—Abbayes (1961, as *Parmelia sinuosa*)
H. sorocheila (Vain.) Divakar et al.—Abbayes (1961: 88, as *Parmelia sorocheila* Vain.)
H. sublaevigata (Nyl. ex Tuck.) Hale—Abbayes (1961, as *Parmelia sublaevigata*)
H. subsaxatilis (B. de Lesd.) Hale—Abbayes (1961, as *Parmelia subsaxatilis*)
Isalonactis madagascariensis Ertz. et al.—Ertz et al. (2014a)
Lacrymospora parasitica Aptroot—Aptroot (1991b: 95)
Lasioloma arachnoideum (Kremp.) R. Sant.—Santesson (1952: 547)
Lecanactis rubra Ertz & Sérus.—Ertz and Sérusiaux (2009)
L. spermatospora Egea & Torrente—Aptroot (2016), leg. Aptroot & Hensen 1984 (BR)

Lecanora epichlorina Vain.—Aptroot (2016), leg. Aptroot & Hensen 1984 (BR)
L. farinacea Fée—Aptroot (2016), leg. Aptroot & Hensen 12425, 1984 (BR)
L. flavidorufa Hue—Aptroot (2016), leg. Aptroot & Hensen 1984 (BR)
L. helva Stizenb.—Aptroot (2016), leg. Aptroot & Hensen 1984 (BR)
L. leprosa Fée—Aptroot (2016), leg. Aptroot & Hensen 1984 (BR)
L. pangerangoensis Zahlbr.—Aptroot (2016), leg. Aptroot & Hensen 1984 (BR)
L. pseudistera Nyl.—Aptroot (2016), leg. Aptroot & Hensen 1984 (BR)
L. subflava Tuck.—Aptroot (2016), leg. Aptroot & Hensen 1984 (BR)
L. tropica Zahlbr.—Aptroot (2016), leg. Aptroot & Hensen 1984 (BR)
Leioderma erythrocarpum (Delise ex Nyl.) D. J. Galloway & P. M. Jørg—Galloway and Jørgensen (1987)
Lempholemma polycarpum M. Schultz—Schultz and Aptroot (2008)
Lepraria finkii R. C. Harris—Aptroot (2016), leg. Aptroot & Hensen 1984 (BR)
L. pallida Sipman—Sipman (2004)
Leprocollema novacaledonianum A. L. Sm.—Aptroot (2016), leg. Aptroot & Hensen 13030, 1984 (BR)
Leptogium austroamericanum (Malme) C. W. Dodge—Aptroot (1990: 404)
L. azureum (Sw.) Mont.—Aptroot (2016), leg. Aptroot & Hensen 1984 (BR)
L. burgessii (L.) Mont.—Aptroot (2016), leg. Aptroot & Hensen 1984 (BR)
L. caesium (Ach.) Vain.—Vainio (1898)
L. cochleatum (Dicks.) P. M. Jørg. & P. James—Aptroot (2016), leg. Aptroot & Hensen 1984 (BR)
L. coralloideum (Meyen & Flot.) Vain.—Aptroot (2016), leg. Aptroot & Hensen 1984 (BR)
L. cyanescens (Rabenh.) Körb.—Aptroot (2016), leg. Aptroot & Hensen 1984 (BR)
L. denticulatum Tuck.—Aptroot (2016), leg. Aptroot & Hensen 1984 (BR)
L. diaphanum (Sw.) Mont.—Aptroot (2016), leg. Aptroot & Hensen 1984 (BR)
L. hibernicum M. E. Mitch.—Aptroot (2016), leg. Aptroot & Hensen 1984 (BR)
L. hypotrachynum Mull. Arg.—Aptroot (2016), leg. Aptroot & Hensen 1984 (BR)
L. inflexum Nyl.—Vainio (1898)
L. laceroides B. de Lesd.—Aptroot (2016), leg. Aptroot & Hensen 1984 (BR)
L. marginellum (Sw.) Gray—Aptroot (2016), leg. Aptroot & Hensen 1984 (BR)
L. phyllocarpum (Pers.) Mont.—Vainio (1898, including f. *caerulescens*)
L. tremelloides (L. f.) Gray—Abbayes (1956), Vainio (1898)
Letrouitia vulpina (Tuck.) Hafellner & Bellemère—Aptroot (1990: 405)
Leucodermia boryi (Fée) Kalb—Aptroot (1988: 144, as *Heterodermia leucomela* subsp. *boryi* [Fée] Swinscow & Krog), Stizenberger (1890, as *Physcia leucomela*), Czeczuga et al. (1998: 575), Vainio (1898: 32, as *Anaptychia leucomelaena* var. *multifida* [Meyen & Flot.] Vain.)
L. vulgaris (Vain.) Kalb—Aptroot (1988: 145, as *Heterodermia vulgaris* [Vain.] Follmann & Redón)
Lobaria isidiosa (Müll. Arg.) Vain.—Abbayes (1956), Vainio (1898, as *Lobaria retigera* var. *isidiosa*)
L. pulmonaria (L.) Hoffm.—Aptroot (2016), leg. Aptroot & Hensen 1984 (BR)
L. retigera (Bory) Trevis.—Vainio (1898, including var. *leptalea*)
Malmidea granifera (Ach.) Kalb, Rivas Plata & Lumbsch—Aptroot (2016), leg. Aptroot & Hensen 1984 (BR)
M. piperis (Spreng.) Kalb, Rivas Plata & Lumbsch—Aptroot (2016), leg. Aptroot & Hensen 1984 (BR)
Maronea constans (Nyl.) Hepp—Aptroot (2016), leg. Aptroot & Hensen 1984 (BR)
Mazosia dispersa (Hedrick) R. Sant.—Santesson (1952: 120)
M. melanophthalma (Müll. Arg.) R. Sant.—Santesson (1952: 117)
M. phyllosema (Nyl.) A. Zahlbr.—Santesson (1952: 123)
Megaloblastenia marginiflexa var. *dimota* (Malme) Sipman—Sipman (1986: 557)
Megalospora coccodes (Bél.) Sipman—Aptroot (2016), leg. Aptroot & Hensen 1984 (BR)
M. pruinata (Müll. Arg.) Sipman—Aptroot (2016), leg. Aptroot & Hensen 1984 (BR)
M. sulphurata var. *nigricans* (Müll. Arg.) Riddle—Sipman (1986: 561)
M. tuberculosa (Fée) Sipman—Sipman (1983)
Megalotremis pustulata Aptroot—Aptroot (2016), leg. Aptroot & Hensen 1984 (BR)
Menegazzia subsimilis (H. Magn.) R. Sant.—Abbayes (1961, as *Parmeliia terebrata*)
Micarea peliocarpa (Anzi) Coppins & R. Sant.—Aptroot (1990: 405)
Mycoporum californicum (Zahlbr.) R. C. Harris—Aptroot (2016), leg. Aptroot & Hensen 1984 (ABL)
M. eschweileri (Müll. Arg.) R. C. Harris—Aptroot (2016), leg. Schumm (Hb. Schumm)
Myelochroa aurulenta (Tuck.) Elix & Hale—Abbayes (1961, as *Parmelia aurulenta*)
Myeloconis erumpens P. M. McCarthy & Elix—Aptroot (2016), leg. Aptroot & Hensen 1984 (BR)
Nephroma helveticum Ach.—Aptroot (1990: 405)
Normandina pulchella (Borrer) Turner—Aptroot (1990: 405), Vainio (1898)
Ochrolechia africana Vain.—Aptroot (2016), leg. Aptroot & Hensen 1984 (BR)
Opegrapha simplicior (Nyl.) Nyl.—Ertz (2009: 107)
O. varians (Müll. Arg.) Vain.—Aptroot (2016), leg. Aptroot & Hensen 1984 (BR)
O. viridis (Ach.) Behlen & Desberger—Ertz (2009: 139)

(*continued overleaf*)

TABLE 8.9. ***continued***

Pannaria fulvescens (Pers.) Mont.—Aptroot (1990: 405)
P. lurida (Mont.) Nyl.—Aptroot (1990: 405), Vainio (1898)
Paraporpidia leptocarpa (Nyl.) Rambold & Hertel—Aptroot (2016), leg. Schumm (Hb. Schumm)
Parmeliella brisbanensis (C. Knight) P. M. Jørg. & D. J. Galloway—Aptroot (1990: 405, as *Parmeliella pannosa*)
P. endomilta (Vain.) Makhija & Adaw.—Jørgensen and Sipman (2006: 707)
P. mariana (Fr.) P. M. Jørg. & D. J. Galloway—Aptroot (1990: 405, as *Pannaria mariana*), Vainio (1898, as *Pannaria mariana* including f. *cinerascens*)
P. wallichiana (Taylor) Elix & Hale—Aptroot (1990: 405)
Parmelinopsis horrescens (Taylor) Elix & Hale—Aptroot (1990: 405)
P. megadactyla Aptroot—Aptroot (1991a: 152)
P. minarum (Vain.) Elix & Hale—Aptroot (1990: 405)
P. spumosa (Asahina) Elix & Hale—Aptroot (1991a: 152)
P. subfatiscens (Kurok.) Elix & Hale—Aptroot (1991a: 152)
Parmotrema abessinicum (Nyl. ex Kremp.) Hale—Aptroot (1991a: 153), Hale (1965: 320, as *Parmelia abessinica, also as P. glaucocarpa*)
P. aldabrense (C. W. Dodge) Hale—Swinscow and Krog (1988: 165), Hale (1965: 321, as *Parmelia aldabrensis*)
P. andinum (Müll. Arg.) Hale—Hale (1965: 237, as *Parmelia andina*)
P. appendiculatum (Fée) Hale—Abbayes (1956, as *Parmelia appendiculata*, including f. *disparilis*)
P. arnoldii (Du Rietz) Hale—Abbayes (1961, as *Parmelia arnoldii*)
P. austrosinense (Zahlbr.) Hale—Aptroot (1990: 405), Czeczuga et al. (1998: 575), Abbayes (1961, as *Parmelia austrosinensis*)
P. breviciliatum (Hale) Hale—Hale (1965: 282, as *Parmelia breviciliata*)
P. cetratum (Ach.) Hale—Abbayes (1961, as *Parmelia cetrata*), Aptroot (1991a: 154, as *Rimelia cetrata*)
P. clavuliferum (Räsänen) Streimann—Abbayes (1961, as *Parmelia reticulata* var. *corniculata*)
P. cooperi (J. Steiner & Zahlbr.) Sérus.—Swinscow and Krog (1988: 171), Aptroot (1991a: 153), Czeczuga et al. (1998: 575), Hale (1965: 323, as *Parmelia cooperi*), Abbayes (1961, as *Parmelia segreganda*)
P. crinitum (Ach.) M. Choisy—Abbayes (1961, as *Parmelia crinita*), Vainio (1898, as *Parmelia proboscidea*)
P. cristiferum (Taylor) Hale—Aptroot (1990: 405), Abbayes (1961, as *Parmelia cristifera*)
P. cryptoxanthum (Abbayes) Hale—Swinscow and Krog (1988: 172), Hale (1965: 286, as *Parmelia cryptoxantha*), Abbayes (1961, as *Parmelia cryptoxantha*)
P. defectum (Hale) Hale—Swinscow and Krog (1988: 172); Hale (1965: 245, as *Parmelia defecta*)
P. dilatatum (Vain.) Hale—Abbayes (1961, as *Parmelia dilatata*)
P. dolosum (Abbayes) Hale—Hale (1965: 334, as *Parmelia paulensis*), Abbayes (1961, as *Parmelia dolosa*)
P. endosulphureum (Hillmann) Hale—Hale (1965: 252, as *Parmelia endosulphurea*)
P. gardneri (C. W. Dodge) Sérusiaux—Aptroot (1990: 405)
P. hababianum (Gyeln.) Hale—Hale (1965: 327, as *Parmelia hababiana*)
P. hololobum (Hale) Hale—Aptroot (2016), leg. Aptroot & Hensen 1984 (BR)
P. lophogenum (Abbayes) Hale—Swinscow and Krog (1988: 182), Aptroot (1991a: 153)
P. maclayanum (Müll. Arg.) Hale—Swinscow and Krog (1988: 183), Aptroot (1991a: 153)
P. madagascariaceum (Hue) Hale—Hale (1965: 275 and 277, as *Parmelia xanthina* p.p.), Abbayes (1961, as *Parmelia madagascariacea* and as *Parmelia aberrans*)
P. melanothrix (Mont.) Hale—Abbayes (1956, 1961, as *Parmelia melanothrix*, including f. *regressa*), Vainio (1898, as *Parmelia melanothrix*)
P. mellissii (C. W. Dodge) Hale—Aptroot (1990: 405)
P. nilgherrense (Nyl.) Hale—Vainio (1898, as *Parmelia nilgherrensis*)
P. parahypotropum (W. L. Culb.) Hale—Aptroot (1990: 405)
P. perforatum (Jacq.) A. Massal.—Hale (1965: 337, as *Parmelia perforata*)
P. permutatum (Stirt.) Hale—Aptroot (1991a: 153)
P. poolii (C. W. Dodge) Krog & Swinscow—Swinscow and Krog (1988: 187), Aptroot (1991a: 153)
P. praesorediosum (Nyl.) Hale—Aptroot (1991a: 153), Abbayes (1961, as *Parmelia sanctae-crucis*)
P. rampoddense (Nyl.) Hale—Aptroot (1990: 406), Hale (1965: 305, as *Parmelia rampoddenseis*)
P. reticulatum (Taylor) M. Choisy—Aptroot (1990: 406), Abbayes (1961, as *Parmelia reticulata*), Vainio (1898, as *Parmelia cetrata* f. *sorediifera*)
P. sancti-angelii (Lynge) Hale—Aptroot (1990: 406), Hale (1965: 307, as *Parmelia sancti-angelii*), Abbayes (1961, as *Parmelia sancti-angelii*)
P. soyauxii (Müll. Arg.) Hale—Swinscow and Krog (1988: 190), Hale (1965: 264, as *Parmelia soyauxii*), Abbayes (1961, as *Parmelia nitens*)
P. subarnoldii (Abbayes) Hale—Swinscow and Krog (1988: 191), Aptroot (1991a: 153), Hale (1965: 309, as *Parmelia subarnoldii*) Abbayes (1961, as *Parmelia subarnoldii*)
P. subhanningtonianum Sérus.—Aptroot (1991a: 153)
P. subisidiosum (Müll. Arg.) Hale—Aptroot (1990: 406), Abbayes (1961, as *Parmelia subisidiosa*)
P. subrugatum (Kremp.) Hale—Abbayes (1956, 1961, as *Parmelia subrugata*)
P. subsumptum (Nyl.) Hale—Aptroot (1990: 406)
P. subtinctorium (Zahlbr.) Hale—Aptroot (1991a: 153)
P. tinctorum (Nyl.) Hale—Aptroot (1990: 406), Hale (1965: 266, as *Parmelia tinctorum*), Abbayes (1961, as *Parmelia tinctorum*)
P. umbrosum (Krog & Swinscow) Krog & Swinscow—Aptroot (1991a: 153)
P. wainii (A. L. Sm.) Hale—Abbayes (1961, as *Parmelia wainii*)
P. xanthinum (Müll. Arg.) Hale—Aptroot (1990: 406), Hale (1965: 276, as *Parmelia xanthina*)
Paulia perforata (Pers.) Asahina—Schultz and Aptroot (2008)
Peltigera dolichorrhiza (Nyl.) Nyl.—Abbayes (1956), Stizenberger (1890), Vainio (1898, as *Peltigera polydactylon* var. *dolichorrhiza*)

P. lambinonii Goffinet—Aptroot (2016), leg. Aptroot & Hensen 1984 (BR)
P. leptoderma Nyl.—Vainio (1898)
P. ulcerata Müll. Arg.—Aptroot (2016), leg. Aptroot & Hensen 1984 (BR)
Phaeographis intricans (Nyl.) Vain.—Aptroot (2016), leg. Aptroot & Hensen 1984 (BR)
Phaeophyscia hispidula (Ach.) Moberg—Aptroot (1988: 145), Stizenberger (1890, as *Physcia setosa*)
Phyllopsora buettneri (Müll. Arg.) Zahlbr. including var. *glauca* (Vain.) Zahlbr.—Brako (1991: 30)
P. confusa Swinscow & Krog—Brako (1991: 37)
P. furfuracea Zahlbr.—Brako (1991: 48)
P. kiiensis (Vain.) Gotth. Schneid.—Aptroot (2016), leg. Aptroot & Hensen 1984 (BR)
Physcia atrostriata Moberg—Aptroot (1988: 145)
P. erumpens Moberg—Aptroot (1988: 145)
P. integrata Nyl.—Stizenberger (1890)
P. krogiae Moberg—Aptroot (1988: 145)
P. poncinsii Hue—Aptroot (2016), leg. Schumm (Hb. Schumm)
P. sorediosa (Vain.) Lynge—Aptroot (1988: 145, as *P. fragilescens*)
P. stellaris (L.) Nyl.—Aptroot (1988: 145), Stizenberger (1890)
Physma byrsaeum (Ach.) Tuck.—Aptroot (1990: 406)
Placopsis parellina (Nyl.) I. M. Lamb—Aptroot (2016), leg. Aptroot & Hensen 1984 (BR)
Platythecium colliculosum (Mont.) Staiger—Aptroot (2016), leg. Aptroot & Hensen 1984 (BR)
Polyblastidium hypoleucum (Muhl.) Kalb—Vainio (1898: 32, as *Anaptychia hypoleuca* [Muhl.] Vain.)
P. japonicum (M. Satô) Kalb—Aptroot (1988: 144, as *Heterodermia japonica* [M. Satô] Swinscow & Krog)
Polychidium dendriscum (Nyl.) Henssen—Aptroot (2016), leg. Aptroot & Hensen 1984 (BR)
Porina africana Müll. Arg.—Aptroot (2016), leg. Aptroot & Hensen 1984 (ABL)
P. atrocoerulea Müll. Arg.—Aptroot (2016), leg. Aptroot & Hensen 1984 (BR)
P. epiphylla (Fée) Fée var. *epiphylla*—Santesson (1952: 234), Stizenberger (1890, as *Verrucaria epiphylla*)
P. internigrans (Nyl.) Müll. Arg.—Aptroot (2016), leg. Aptroot & Hensen 1984 (ABL)
P. lucida R. Sant. var. *lucida*—Lücking and Vězda (1998: 208)
P. mazosioides Lücking & Vězda—Lücking and Vězda (1998: 210)
P. nitidula Müll. Arg.—Santesson (1952: 225)
P. nuculastrum (Müll. Arg.) R. C. Harris—McCarthy (2003), Stizenberger (1890, as *Verrucaria nuculastrum*)
P. radiata Kalb, Lücking & Vězda—Lücking and Vězda (1998: 214)
P. rubentior (Stirt.) Müll. Arg.—Aptroot (2016), leg. Aptroot & Hensen 1984 (BR)
P. sphaerocephala Vain.—Santesson (1952: 264)
P. sphaerocephaloides Farkas—Aptroot (2016), leg. Aptroot & Hensen 1984 (BR)
P. tetramera (Malme) R. Sant.—Aptroot (2016), leg. Aptroot & Hensen 1984 (BR)
P. virescens (Kremp.) Müll. Arg.—Stizenberger (1890, as *Verrucaria virescens*)
Pseudocyphellaria argyracea (Delise) Vain.—Abbayes (1956), Vainio (1898, as *Sticta argyracea*)
P. beccarii (Kremp.) D. J. Galloway—Galloway (1994: 121)
P. billardierei (Delise) Räsänen—Abbayes (1956: 3, as *Sticta flotowiana* var. *subcyphellata* [Nyl.] Zahlbr.), Vainio (1898: 33, as *S. fossulata* var. *subcyphellata* [Nyl.]), J. Müller (1891: 374, as *S. damaecornis* var. *scrobiculata* Müll. Arg.)
P. crocata (L.) Vain.—Galloway (1994: 124), Vainio (1898: 32 and 33, also as *P. mougeotiana* var. *dissecta* Müll. Arg.)
P. desfontainii (Delise) D. J. Galloway—Vainio (1898, as *P. carpoloma* f. *desfontainii*)
P. dozyana (Mont. Bosch) D. J. Galloway—Aptroot (2016), leg. Aptroot & Hensen 1984 (BR)
P. gilva (Ach.) Malme—Aptroot (2016), leg. Aptroot & Hensen 1984 (BR)
P. intricata (Delise) Vain.—Vainio (1898)
P. sulphurea (Schaer.) D. J. Galloway—Galloway (1994: 155)
Pseudoparmelia sphaerospora (Nyl.) Hale—Hale (1976b: 49), Swinscow and Krog (1988: 252), Aptroot (1990: 406), Abbayes (1961, as *Parmelia sphaerospora*)
Pseudoramonia psoromica Aptroot—Aptroot (2016)
Punctelia borreri (Sm.) Krog—Aptroot (1990: 406)
P. rudecta (Ach.) Krog—Aptroot (1991a: 153), Abbayes (1961, as *Parmelia ruderata*)
P. subflava (Taylor) Elix & J. Johnst.—Aptroot (2016), leg. Aptroot & Hensen 12883, 1984 (BR)
P. subrudecta (Nyl.) Krog—Aptroot (1990: 406)
Pyrenula aggregata (Fée) Fée—Aptroot (2016), leg. Aptroot & Hensen 1984 (ABL)
P. anomala (Ach.) Vain.—Aptroot (2016), leg. Aptroot & Hensen 1984 (ABL)
P. aspistea (Ach.) Ach.—Aptroot (2016), leg. Aptroot & Hensen 1984 (ABL)
P. astroidea (Fée) R. C. Harris—Aptroot (2016), leg. Aptroot & Hensen 1984 (ABL)
P. breutelii (Müll. Arg.) Aptroot—Harris (1989, as *P. macularis*)
P. confinis (Nyl.) R. C. Harris—Aptroot (2016), leg. Aptroot & Hensen 1984 (ABL)
P. fetivica (Kremp.) Müll. Arg.—Aptroot (2016), leg. Aptroot & Hensen 1984 (BR)
P. hibernica (Nyl.) Aptroot—Aptroot (2016), leg. Aptroot & Hensen 1984 (ABL)
P. mamillana (Ach.) Trevis.—Stizenberger (1890, as *Verrucaria mamillana*)
P. microcarpa Müll. Arg.—Aptroot (2016), leg. Aptroot & Hensen 1984 (ABL)
P. nitidula (Bres.) R. C. Harris—Aptroot (2016), leg. Aptroot & Hensen 1984 (ABL)
P. parvinuclea (Meyen & Flot.) Aptroot—Stizenberger (1890, as *Verrucaria denudata*)

(continued overleaf)

TABLE 8.9. ***continued***

P. pyrenuloides (Mont.) R. C. Harris—Stizenberger (1890, as *Verrucaria pyrenuloides*)
P. quassiicola (Fée) Fée—Aptroot (2016), leg. Aptroot & Hensen 1984 (ABL)
P. rockii Zahlbr.—Aptroot (2016), leg. Aptroot & Hensen 1984 (ABL)
Pyrgillus javanicus (Mont. & Bosch) Nyl.—Aptroot (1990: 406, 1991b: 86)
Pyxine berteriana (Fée) Imshaug—Aptroot (1988: 145)
P. cocoes (Sw.) Nyl.—Aptroot (1988: 145)
P. copelandii Vain.—Aptroot (1988: 145)
P. coralligera Malme—Stizenberger (1890, as *P. cocoes* f. *isidiophora* Müll. Arg.)
P. glaucovirescens (Nyl.) Aptroot—Aptroot (1988: 146)
P. kibweziensis Swinscow & Krog.—Aptroot (1988: 146)
P. meissnerina Nyl.—Aptroot (1988: 146)
P. petricola Nyl.—Aptroot (1988: 146)
P. retirugella Nyl.—Aptroot (1988: 145, as *P. consocians* Vain.)
Ramalina arabum (Dill. ex Ach.) Meyen & Flot.—Krog (1994)
R. celastri (Sprengel) Krog & Swinscow—Aptroot (1990: 406)
R. consanguinea Müll. Arg.—Aptroot (1990: 406)
R. dendriscoides Nyl.—Aptroot (1990: 406)
R. fimbriata Krog & Swinscow—Aptroot (1990: 407)
R. praetermissa Abbayes—Abbayes (1956, including var. *amplior*)
Ramboldia russula (Ach.) Kalb et al.—Aptroot (2016), leg. Aptroot & Hensen 12972, 1984 (BR)
Relicina amphithrix Hale—Aptroot (1990: 407), Aptroot (1991a: 153, as *Relicina planiuscula*)
Rhabdodiscus auberianus (Mont.) Vain.—Aptroot (2016), leg. Aptroot & Hensen 13386 & 13721, 1984 (ABL)
R. subcavatus (Nyl.) Rivas Plata et al.—Aptroot (2016), leg. Aptroot & Hensen 13373, 1984 (ABL)
R. tanzanicus (Frisch) Rivas Plata et al.—Aptroot (2016), leg. Aptroot & Hensen 13376, 1984 (ABL)
Ricasolia comorensis Kremp.—Aptroot (2016), leg. Aptroot & Hensen, 1984 (BR)
R. discolor (Bory) Nyl.—Aptroot (2016), leg. Aptroot & Hensen, 1984 (BR)
R. marginata Müll. Arg.—Vainio (1898: 33, as *Lobaria marginata* [Müll. Arg.] Vain.)
Roccella africana Vain.—Aptroot and Schumm (2011: 17)
R. applanata M. Choisy—Aptroot and Schumm (2011: 17)
R. belangeriana D. D. Awasthi—Aptroot and Schumm (2011: 17)
R. boryi Delise ex Fée—Aptroot and Schumm (2011: 17)
R. linearis (Ach.) Vain.—Aptroot and Schumm (2011: 17)
R. montagnei Bél.—Aptroot (1990: 407), Aptroot and Schumm (2011: 17), Ertz et al. (2014a)
Sarcographa labyrinthica (Ach.) Müll. Arg.—Aptroot (1990: 407)
S. tricosa (Ach.) Müll. Arg.—Aptroot (2016), leg. Schumm (Hb. Schumm)
Savoronala madagascariensis Ertz et al.—Ertz et al. (2014b)
Sclerophyton madagascariense Sparrius—Sparrius (2004)
S. seriale (Ach.) Sparrius—Aptroot (2016), leg. Aptroot & Hensen 1984 (B)
Scoliciosporum arachnoideum Aptroot—Aptroot (2008: 120)
Siphula abbatiana A. Mathey—Mathey (1971: 853)
S. decumbens Nyl.—Aptroot (2016), leg. Aptroot & Hensen 13526, 1984 (BR)
S. mascarena A. Mathey—Aptroot (2016), leg. Aptroot & Hensen 13227, 1984 (BR)
Sporopodium leprieurii Mont.—Aptroot (2016), leg. Aptroot & Hensen 1984 (BR)
Stereocaulon anomalum I. M. Lamb—Sérusiaux (1979: 6), Swinscow and Krog (1988: 296), Aptroot (1990: 407)
S. meyeri B. Stein—Swinscow and Krog (1988: 299)
S. ramulosum Raeusch.—Abbayes (1956, including var. *macrocarpum*)
Sticta ambavillaria (Bory) Ach.—Vainio (1898)
S. brevipes (Müll. Arg.) Zahlbr—Aptroot (2016), leg. Aptroot & Hensen 1984 (BR)
S. damicornis (Sw.) Ach.—Abbayes (1956), Vainio (1898)
S. dichotoma Bory—Abbayes (1956)
S. fuliginosa (Dicks.) Ach.—Vainio (1898)
S. macrophylla Bory—Abbayes (1956)
S. orbicularis (A. Braun ex Meyen & Flot.) Hue—Vainio (1898)
S. papyracea Delise—Aptroot (2016), leg. Aptroot & Hensen 1984 (BR)
S. sinuosa Pers.—Vainio (1898)
S. variabilis Ach.—Vainio (1898), Abbayes (1956)
S. weigelii Isert—Vainio (1898)
Strigula complanata (Fée) Mont.—Santesson (1952: 190)
S. janeirensis (Müll. Arg.) Lücking—Santesson (1952: 196, as *Raciborskiella janeirensis*)
S. nemathora Mont. var. *nemathora*—Santesson (1952: 149)
S. nitidula Mont.—Santesson (1952: 179)
S. rostrata R. C. Harris & Aptroot—Harris (1995)
S. smaragdula Fr.—Stizenberger (1890, as *S. elegans*), Santesson (1952: 160, as *S. elegans*)
S. subtilissima (Fée) Müll. Arg.—Santesson (1952: 183)
Syncesia madagascariensis Ertz et al.—Ertz et al. (2010)
Teloschistes exilis (Michx.) Vain.—Almborn (1989: 527)
T. flavicans (Sw.) Norman—Almborn (1989: 529), Aptroot (1990: 407), Abbayes (1956), Stizenberger (1890, as *Physcia flavicans*)
T. perrugosus Müll. Arg.—Almborn (1989: 532)
Tephromela atra (Hudson) Hoffm.—Aptroot (1990: 407)
Thecaria quassiicola Fée—Staiger (2002: 446)
Thelotrema leucophthalmum Nyl.—Aptroot (2016), leg. Aptroot & Hensen 13753, 1984 (ABL)
Thyrea plectopsora A. Massal.—Schultz and Aptroot (2008)
Trapelia coarctata (Turner) M. Choisy—Aptroot (1990: 407)
T. pallidocervina (Kremp.) Hertel—Aptroot (2016), leg. Schumm (Hb. Schumm)
Trapeliopsis granulosa (Hoffm.) Lumbsch—Aptroot (1990: 407)
Traponora fusca Aptroot—Aptroot (2016), leg. Aptroot & Hensen 1984 (BR)
T. globosa Aptroot—Aptroot (2009)
Trichothelium alboatrum Vain.—Aptroot (2016), leg. Aptroot & Hensen 1984 (BR)
T. epiphyllum Müll. Arg.—Aptroot (2016), leg. Aptroot & Hensen 1984 (BR)

Triclinum cinchonarum f. *janeirense* (Müll. Arg.) Elix—Aptroot (2016), leg. Aptroot & Hensen 1984 (BR)
Trinathotrema stictideum (Nyl.) Lücking, R. Miranda & Kalb—Aptroot (2016), leg. Aptroot & Hensen 1984 (ABL)
Trypetheliopsis kalbii (Lücking & Sér.) Aptroot—Lücking and Sérusiaux (1996, as *Musaespora kalbii*)
Trypethelium eluteriae Spreng.—Aptroot (2016), leg. Schumm (Hb. Schumm)
Usnea ambigua Motyka—Motyka (1954)
U. baileyi (Stirton) Zahlbr.—Aptroot (1990: 407)
U. chrysoleuca Motyka—Motyka (1954)
U. complanata (Müll. Arg.) Motyka—Aptroot (2016), leg. Aptroot & Hensen 1984 (BR)
U. contorta Jatta—Abbayes (1956)
U. eburnea Motyka—Motyka (1954)
U. erinacea Vain.—Clerc (2004)
U. exasperata (Müll. Arg.) Motyka—Aptroot (1990: 407)
U. fragilescens var. *mollis* (Vain.) Clerc—Vainio (1898, as *U. barbata* var. *mollis*)
U. fuscorubens Motyka—Abbayes (1956)
U. gigas Motyka—Swinscow and Krog (1988: 335)
U. gracilis Ach.—Abbayes (1956)
U. horridula (Müll. Arg.) Motyka—Abbayes (1956)
U. humbertii Motyka—Motyka (1954)
U. implicata (Stirt.) Zahlbr.—Abbayes (1956)
U. indigena Motyka—Motyka (1954)
U. leprosa Motyka—Aptroot (2016), leg. Aptroot & Hensen 1984 (BR)
U. luteola Motyka—Motyka (1954)
U. maculata Stirt.—Swinscow and Krog (1988: 338)
U. nodulosa Swinscow & Krog—Aptroot (2016), leg. Aptroot & Hensen 1984 (BR)
U. perhispidella Steiner—Aptroot (1990: 407)
U. perplexans Stirt.—Vainio (1898, as *U. barbata* var. *perplexans*)
U. pulvinata Fr.—Motyka (1936: 319), Swinscow and Krog (1988: 341), Aptroot (1990: 407)
U. rubicunda Stirt.—Aptroot (1990: 407)
U. rubrotincta Stirt.—Abbayes (1956, as *U. rubescens* var. *rubrotincta*)
U.ērediosula (Müll. Arg.) Motyka—Aptroot (2016), leg. Aptroot & Hensen 1984 (BR)
U. sorosa Motyka—Motyka (1954)
U. subelegans (Vain.) Motyka—Vainio (1898, as *U. barbata* var. *subelegans*)
U. subfloridana (Zahlbr.) Motyka—Vainio (1898, as *U. barbata* var. *comosa*)
U. sulphurescens Motyka—Motyka (1954)
U. trichodeoides Vain.—Aptroot (1990: 407), Abbayes (1956)
U. undulata Stirt.—Aptroot (1990: 407)
Xanthoparmelia annexa (Kurok.) Elix—Aptroot (1991a: 152, as *Paraparmelia annexa*)
X. benyovskyana (Gyeln.) Hale—Hale (1990), Abbayes (1961, as *Parmelia benyovskyana*)
X. constrictans (Nyl.) Hale—Abbayes (1961, as *Parmelia constrictans*)
X. molybdiza (Nyl.) Blanco et al.—Elix (2001: 210, as *Paraparmelia molybdiza*), Aptroot (1991a: 152, as *Paraparmelia quartzitica* Aptroot)
X. phaeophana (Stirt.) Hale—Aptroot (1990: 408); Hale (1990)
X. suberadicata (Abbayes) Hale—Hale (1990), Abbayes (1961, as *Parmelia suberadicata*)
X. subflabellata (J. Steiner) Hale—Hale (1990), Ertz et al. (2014a, as *X. tananarivensis*), Abbayes (1961, as *Parmelia tananarivensis*)
X. subramigera (Gyeln.) Hale—Hale (1990), Abbayes (1961, as *Parmelia ambositrana*)

Source: Aptroot (2016), with recent additions. See that reference for explanation of abbreviations.
Note: Stizenberger (1890) sums up all early 19th-century information from papers that are not all named here.

- The Central Highlands tend to have a somewhat different set of species from the lowland areas, with relatively more macrolichens, but the original vegetation on the Central Highlands has vanished to such an extent that it is unknown what its original composition was.
- Disturbed areas in or near pristine lowland moist evergreen forests also have a higher proportion of macrolichens. Some of the (near) endemic *Cladonia* and Parmeliaceae species are currently known only from the Central Highlands, but others are also known from lowland localities, suggesting that there is a continuum.

The lichen flora of Madagascar is very poorly known. A few lichenologists have collected on the island, some long ago (Abbayes 1947, 1948, 1956, 1961); those who have been there more recently published only a few, selected, often new, species. In the 1980s, Aptroot collected plants from both accessible parts of Madagascar and remote, pristine areas of the Masoala Peninsula, subsequently publishing papers concerning *Cladonia* (Ahti and Aptroot 1992), Parmeliaceae (Aptroot 1991a), Physciaceae (Aptroot 1988), and miscellaneous species (Aptroot 1990). A checklist of the known lichen flora of the island is presented in Table 8.9. It is important to underline that this flora is too incomplete to allow definite conclusions about the lichenological affinities of Madagascar. It should be noted that the number of widespread pantropical species is higher than that of species restricted to Africa. Madagascar-endemic lichen species are a small proportion of the total diversity. Some, like the large and conspicuous *Sticta* species, are certainly endemic, but others may have been overlooked elsewhere, as was recently shown by the discovery of the lichen *Clandestinotrema minutum* in Brazil (A. Aptroot, unpublished data), formerly believed to be a Madagascar endemic.

Some comparisons can be made with the lichenologically better-known Seychelles islands (Seaward and Aptroot 2009; Schumm and Aptroot 2010) or to east Africa, from where the macrolichens are relatively well known (Swinscow and Krog 1988). It appears that Madagascar is especially rich in the genera *Cladonia* (Abbayes 1947, 1948; Ahti and Aptroot 1992), *Parmotrema*, *Pyrenula*, *Sticta*, and *Xanthoparmelia* (Abbayes 1961; Hale 1990; Aptroot 1991a). In the first and last of these genera, several species are known to be endemic to Madagascar or to the Mascarenes. In *Sticta* this is less certain; there is no recent treatment of the *Sticta* species from Madagascar, and, based on recent publications on this genus (A. Simon et al. 2018), where a much narrower species concept is used than in former days, it can be safely predicted that several of the *Sticta* species reported below (Table 8.9) actually refer to undescribed species.

The other Malagasy Region islands have different lichen floras. Mauritius (David and Hawksworth 1995) and Rodrigues (Crombie 1877) have lichen floras similar to the coastal parts of Madagascar, while La Réunion (van den Boom et al. 2011) has a lichen flora similar to that of the eastern slope of Madagscar.

Within Madagascar, there is a clear distinction between the lichen floras of the humid and dry biomes. From the dry tropical region, only relatively few (23) species are reported (including six *Roccella* species) (Aptroot 2016), mainly because the lichen flora is indeed poor due to the dry climate. All other species presented in Table 8.9 are known only from the wet tropical area.

Subject editors: Philippe Clerc and Steven M. Goodman

BRYOPHYTES: DIVERSITY, ENDEMISM, AND PHYTOGEOGRAPHY

L. Marline, C. Ah-Peng, and T. A. J. Hedderson

WHAT ARE BRYOPHYTES?

Bryophytes are (with a single exception) chlorophyllose land plants comprising three morphologically and phylogenetically distinct groups: liverworts (Marchantiophyta), mosses (Bryophyta), and hornworts (Anthocerotophyta). They diverged from each other early in land plant evolution and were probably differentiated from each other by 515–470 million years ago (Mya) (Morris et al. 2018). Bryophytes are generally small (a few millimeters to a few centimeters tall) but some aquatic and epiphytic species can reach 1 m or more in length. They lack lignified vascular tissue and do not possess roots but have threadlike rhizoids that anchor them to their substrate. Bryophyte leaves are mostly one (infrequently 2–3) cell thick. In terms of species numbers, range of habitats occupied, and distribution on all continents, they are the most successful group of plants other than angiosperms (Schofield and Crum 1972; Shaw 2001). They occur in almost all terrestrial habitats, from littoral to montane zones and from the polar regions to the tropics. There are more than 11,000 described species of bryophytes in the tropics (Norhazrina et al. 2017) and approximately 20,000 worldwide (Shaw 2001). Bryophytes inhabit a diversity of substrates such as tree trunks, rotten wood, rock, soil, fresh water, and humus, and occur in both wet and very arid habitats. They can also be found in unusual places such as on weevils in Papuan cloud forests (Gressitt et al. 1968) or on dung or whale bones.

THE LIFE CYCLE AND KEY FEATURES OF BRYOPHYTES

Although morphologically and evolutionarily divergent, the three main groups of bryophytes are united by a common life cycle (Figure 8.12). As with all land plants, the life cycle involves distinct haploid (gametophyte) and diploid (sporophyte) phases, but in contrast to most other land plants the dominant phase is the haploid one and produces a dependent (usually parasitic) diploid sporophytic phase. Multicellular haploid gametophytes develop from spores and produce antheridia and archegonia. Antheridia produce many biflagellate sperm by mitosis, and each archegonium produces a single egg. The sperm need a film of water to reach the archegonium. The zygote develops into the diploid sporophyte, which consists of a stalk and a single sporangium that emerges from the archegonium.

Bryophytes are poikilohydric, with the dominant gametophyte generally lacking cuticularization (Glime 2013). Their hydration status thus depends to a great extent on the water content of their surrounding environment, and their photosynthetic rates correspondingly depend on water availability, with limitations occurring under conditions of both water deficit and excess (Pardow et al. 2012). Bryophytes have a particularly high surface area; this feature, together with their high water-retention capacity, hygroscopic capacity as measured relative to dry weight, and capacity for capturing water from mist (Ah-Peng et al. 2017), contributes to bryophytes playing significant roles in many ecosystems, such as in the carbon cycle in cloud forests (Muchura et al. 2014). They contribute substantially to aboveground biomass (Gradstein and Pócs 1989), and provide habitats for microorganisms and other plants. They also host nitrogen-fixing bacteria, providing major soil nitrogen input, and play important roles in reducing soil erosion and maintaining soil fertility and moisture (Turetsky et al. 2010). Bryophytes play an important role in the process of ecological succession by developing suitable conditions for the emergence of subsequent groups, notably in primary succession or as pioneer species after disturbances such as fire. For instance, bryophytes are important first colonizers of lava fields, facilitating humus formation and nutrient accumulation (Ah-Peng 2007). Because of their short life cycles, very specific ecological requirements, high dispersal ability, and high dependence on atmospheric conditions for nutrients and water, they are often used as bioindicators.

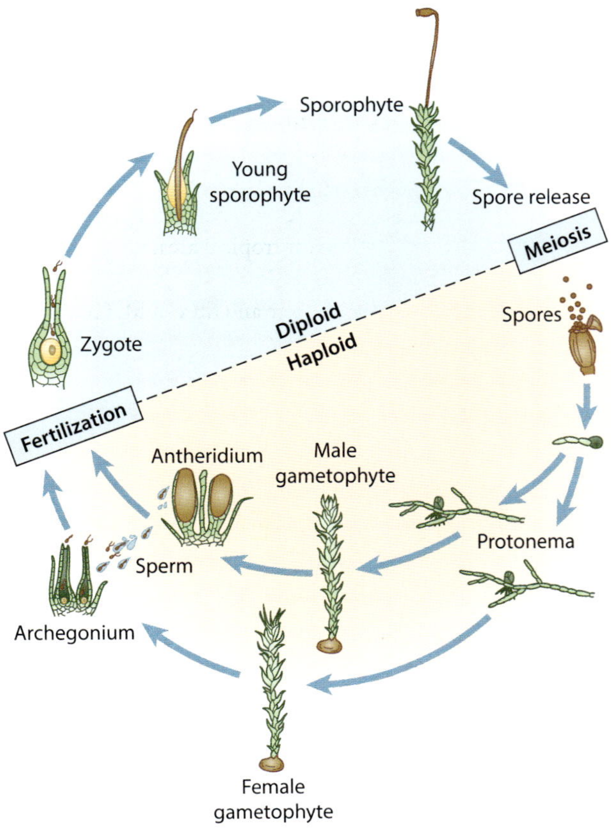

FIGURE 8.12 **Bryophyte life cycle.**

BRYOPHYTES, A POORLY KNOWN GROUP ON MADAGASCAR

Madagascar is one of the global biodiversity hotspots identified by Myers et al. (2000) and among the world's critical conservation priority areas. Its forests, some of most biologically rich and unique in the world, have been extensively inventoried including ecological surveys on many components of the fauna and flora (mostly vascular plants). Bryophytes, however, have received little attention and are among the least documented components of the rich biota of the island. Information is thus lacking on their diversity, distribution, and conservation requirements.

Based on examination of herbarium specimens, online databases, and literature, we provide 1) a review of bryological exploration on Madagascar, 2) updated information on bryophyte diversity and endemism, and 3) a preliminary analysis of their global phytogeographic patterns. Overall, we hope that this contribution will highlight what is known about Malagasy bryophytes and will stimulate enthusiasm among scientists and students to undertake studies on its bryophyte flora.

REVIEW OF BRYOLOGICAL EXPLORATION OF MADAGASCAR

The history of general botanical exploration, including bryophytes, on Madagascar is outlined in Dorr (1997). Bryophyte exploration started in the 18th century with soldiers, botanists, and missionaries, mainly from France, making early collections on the island. Later, French botanists such as Auguste Pervillé and Louis-Hyacinthe Boivin began to visit Madagascar. The latter, in particular, conducted extensive collecting and made observations that left a significant mark on the history of biological exploration of the island. During the French colonial period (1897–1960), intensive biological exploration of Madagascar occurred. Although floristic exploration was mostly focused on vascular plants, botanists, ethnobotanists, missionaries, and civil servants collected bryophytes during this period. This resulted in the discovery and description of more than half of the presently recognized species, including several putative endemics. After 1960, when Madagascar became independent, interest in the bryophytes of the island increased substantially, augmenting the number of recorded species as professional bryologists started to collect on the island. These bryophyte collections are housed in several major herbaria. In the 21st century, there has been a succession of expeditions including or dedicated specifically to bryophytes and, very recently, ecological studies have been conducted on the bryophytes of the island. In Table 8.10 we present a nonexhaustive list of collectors and bryological exploration that contributed significantly to knowledge of the island's bryophytes.

Literature on the bryophytes of Madagascar is sparse, mainly comprising species descriptions and inventories, and lacking the synthetic focus of a flora with, for example, geographic distribution maps. Hampe (1874) and C. H. Wright (1888) produced the first checklists for the Malagasy Region, while the first detailed and complete studies of the bryoflora were produced by Renauld (1897) and Renauld and Cardot (1915), based on herbarium collections. The former, in his *Prodrome de la Flore Bryologique de Madagascar, des Mascareignes et des Comores*, gives descriptions and geographic distributions for the 425 mosses reported for Madagascar at the time, along with an enumeration of some liverworts. Extending this work, Renauld and Cardot (1915) produced a volume on mosses for the Grandidier series *Histoire Physique, Naturelle et Politique de Madagascar* where they publish various new records and, for the first time, illustrations for all of the species. More recent enumerations have synthesized literature reports of the mosses and liverworts of Madagascar and its neighboring islands (Grolle and Onraedt 1974; Crosby et al. 1983). A perusal of the references listed in these publications shows that many bryologists of the 19th and early 20th centuries studied material from Madagascar. The synthetic works of O'Shea (2006) and Wigginton (2018), who published periodically updated checklists of bryophytes from sub-Saharan Africa, including Madagascar, are among the most recent enumerations. These report 1112 taxa for Madagascar, comprising 385 liverworts, 727 mosses, and two hornworts (O'Shea 2006; Wigginton 2018). A recent checklist by Marline et al. (2012) reports a total of 1144 species, comprising 390 liverworts, 751 mosses, and three hornworts.

Revisionary studies at family and genus level, including Malagasy representatives, are relatively few. *Leucoloma* (La Farge 2002a, 2002b, 2002c) is one of only a few comprehensively revised genera that include a significant number of Malagasy species. De Sloover conducted thorough taxonomic surveys of various African genera including *Breutelia*, *Leptodontium*, *Andreaea*, *Racomitrium*, *Gymnostomiella*, and *Thuidium* (De Sloover 1975a, 1977, 1987), all of which have some Malagasy representatives. To date, the most complete and

TABLE 8.10. **Bryophyte collectors and bryological expeditions on Madagascar**

BRYOPHYTE COLLECTORS	PERIOD	EXPEDITION/PROJECT DESCRIPTION	NUMBER OF COLLECTIONS	MAIN LOCALITY
Auguste Pervillé (Muséum National d'Histoire Naturelle, Paris)	1837–1841	Vascular plants and bryophytes	800 specimens of plants including 265 bryophytes	Nosy Be and Ampasindava
Louis-Hyacinthe Boivin, (Muséum National d'Histoire Naturelle, Paris)	1846–1852	Oise Expedition: Vascular plants and bryophytes	1000 specimens of bryophytes	Nosy Be, Antsiranana Bay, Rigny Bay, Vohémar, Ile Sainte Marie, and Lokobe
Pierre Louis Besson	1890–1897	Vascular plants and bryophytes	441 specimens of bryophytes	Mananjary, Fianarantsoa, Pays des Antanala, Sandravonona, and Ranomafana
Paul Camboué	1888–1907	Vascular plants and bryophytes	402 specimens of bryophytes including 191 species of mosses and 11 species of liverworts	Antananarivo, Analamazaotra, Arivonimamo, and Ambatovy
Raymond Decary	1916–1944	Vascular plants and bryophytes	254 specimens of bryophytes	Ankarafantsika and Ambatofinandrahana, Ambohimanga, Antananarivo, Tolagnaro
Perrier de la Bâthie (Muséum National d'Histoire Naturelle, Paris)	1904–1927	Vascular plant and bryophytes	684 specimens of bryophytes (mostly mosses)	All over Madagascar
Henri Humbert (Muséum National d'Histoire Naturelle, Paris)	1912–1934	Exploration of the flora of central mountains of Madagascar (including Marojejy and those in the southeast), the Imerina region, and southeast.	Unknown number of collections	All over Madagascar
Frère Maurice Onraedt	1969–1974	Vascular plant and bryophytes	586 known specimens of bryophytes	All over Madagascar
Támas Pócs (Department of Botany, Eszterházy College, Hungary)	1990–1994 and 2004	Bryologia Africana project: In 1990 and 1994, Pócs collected liverworts on Madagascar, aiming to provide up-to-date bryophyte flora of tropical Africa. Accompanied by colleagues, he conducted bryological exploration in 1998 and 2004 and made important contributions to new descriptions and taxonomical reviews on Malagasy bryophytes.	Unknown number of collections	Andringitra, Ankaratra, Antongil Bay, Andasibe-Analamazaotra, Tampolo, Toamasina, Isalo, Moramanga, Marojejy, and Ranomafana

BRYOPHYTE COLLECTORS	PERIOD	EXPEDITION/PROJECT DESCRIPTION	NUMBER OF COLLECTIONS	MAIN LOCALITY
Patricia Geissler (Conservatoire et Jardin Botaniques de Genève, Switzerland)	February–March 1999	Biological inventory of Manongarivo. This expedition organized by the Conservatoire et Jardin Botaniques de Genève and WWF–Madagascar was the first study that combined bryophytes with an inventory of fauna and vascular plants. Patricia Geissler was the only bryologist on this expedition.	800 bryophyte collections, 167 species (including mosses and liverworts), and 100 unidentified species recorded	Manongarivo
Catherine Reeb (Muséum National d'Histoire Naturelle, Paris) and Roger Lala Andriamiarisoa (Missouri Botanical Garden, Madagascar)	2006–2017	Taxonomy and survey of thalloid liverworts in Africa, including a thorough sampling of bryophytes at numerous sites on the island.	Unknown number of collections	Vohimana (2006–2012); Vohibola and Makirovana Ambanjavala complex (2010); Maromizaha (2012); Zahamena (2013); Namoroka (2016); Angavokely (2011); Makay Massif (2011–2017)
Claudine Ah-Peng (Université de La Réunion, France), Roger Lala Andriamiarisoa (Missouri Botanical Garden, Madagascar), Jacques Bardat (Muséum National d'Histoire Naturelle, Paris), Lova Marline (Université d'Antananarivo, Madagascar), Min Chuah Petiot (University of Sains Malaysia, Malaysia), and Nicholas Wilding and Terry Hedderson (University of Cape Town, South Africa)	2009	BRYOLAT project (Figure 8.13): survey of bryophyte diversity and distribution along an elevational gradient. The team included eight bryologists.	1739 samples comprising 848 floristic samples and 891 samples that were collected following a standardized ecological method. 265 species were identified.	Marojejy
Roger Lala Andriamiarisoa (Missouri Botanical Garden, Madagascar), Damien Ertz (Botanic Garden Meise, Belgium), Eberhard Fischer (University of Koblenz, Germany), Bernard Goffinet (University of Connecticut, USA), Emmanuel Sérusiaux (University of Liège, Belgium), and Vololotahina Razafindrahaja (Missouri Botanical Garden, Madagascar)	2015	Floristic expedition: collection of floristic samples of bryophytes and lichens.	Unknown number of collections/unpublished work	Marojejy, Ankarana, and Montagne d'Ambre

FIGURE 8.13 **BRYOLAT team in Marojejy National Park (November 2009). From left to right: Roger Lala Andriamiarisoa, Lova Marline, Terry Hedderson, Jacques Bardat, Claudine Ah-Peng, Nicholas Wilding, and Min Chuah Petiot.** (PHOTO by J. Kluge.)

thorough liverwort studies are Tixier's revisions of *Cololejeunea* and *Diplasiolejeunea* (Tixier 1985) and Vanden Berghen's revision of African representatives of genera including *Frullania*, *Plagiochila*, *Cheilolejeunea*, and *Ceratolejeunea* (Vanden Berghen 1950a, 1950b, 1951, 1981, 1984). Recent taxonomic revisions of Marchantiales (Reeb et al. 2018), *Enthostodon* (Wilding 2016), and Orthotrichaceae (Wilbraham 2016) from sub-Saharan Africa have also included Malagasy species.

BRYOPHYTE DIVERSITY AND ENDEMISM

Floristic Composition

Since the publication of the checklist of the bryophytes of Madagascar (Marline et al. 2012), reporting 1144 species, numerous changes in taxonomy have occurred, including synonymization of many taxa, and new records have been made for the island. As of December 2019, the known bryoflora of Madagascar comprised 1214 accepted names: 1138 species and 76 additional infraspecific taxa (Table 8.11). Based on the most up-to-date checklist of bryophytes, recent inventories, and literature, the moss flora consists of 60 families, 189 genera, and 766 species and infraspecific taxa. Liverworts comprise 31 families, 93 genera, and 447 species and infraspecific taxa. Hornworts are represented by only two families, four genera, and five species and, as in much of the world, are the most poorly documented group. Species richness is dominated by mosses, reflecting the global difference in diversity between the three groups. Bryophytes represent 9% of the land plant flora (i.e., bryophytes plus tracheophytes) of Madagascar. Synopses of families based on the classifications of Crandall-Stotler et al. (2009) for liverworts, Renzaglia et al. (2009) for hornworts, and Goffinet et al. (2009) for mosses are presented in Table 8.12. Representatives of each group were selected and are pictured in Figure 8.14.

For Malagasy mosses, the Dicranaceae is the largest family (85 species and infraspecific taxa of which 57 belong to *Leucoloma*), followed by the Orthotrichaceae (69 species and infraspecific taxa), and Bryaceae (44 species and infraspecific taxa). For liverworts, the Lejeuneaceae (225 species and infraspecific taxa), followed by Frullaniaceae (41 species and infraspecific taxa), and Plagiochilaceae (25 species and infraspecific taxa) are the richest families. Only 35% of moss families and 26% of liverwort families are represented by more than 10 species on the island. Twenty-five families (28%) are represented by only one species (Table 8.12).

The most species-rich moss genera are *Leucoloma* (Dicranaceae; 57 species), *Fissidens* (Fissidentaceae; 41 species), *Schlotheimia* (Orthotrichaceae; 34 species), *Bryum* (Bryaceae; 26 species), *Macromitrium* (Orthotrichaceae; 24 species), *Campylopus* and *Syrrhopodon* (Leucobryaceae and Calymperaceae, respectively; both 23 species). The most species-rich liverwort genera are *Cololejeunea* (Lejeuneaceae; 59 species), *Frullania* (Frullaniaceae; 41 species), *Diplasiolejeunea* and *Lejeunea* (both Lejeuneaceae; both 27 species), and *Plagiochila* (Plagiochilaceae; 25 species).

Endemism

The bryoflora of Madagascar displays a substantial level of endemism at the specific and infraspecific rank with 33.8% of mosses and 18.3% of liverworts restricted to the island (Table 8.11). For mosses, Dicranaceae has the largest number of endemic species (41/85), followed by Orthotrichaceae (39/69), and

TABLE 8.11. **Bryophyte species richness and endemism for Madagascar**

	RICHNESS					ENDEMISM	
	FAMILY	GENUS	SPECIES	INFRASPECIFIC TAXA	TOTAL	SPECIFIC LEVEL	INFRASPECIFIC LEVEL
Bryophyta (mosses)	62	189	715	51	766	225 (31.5%)	259 (33.8%)
Marchantiophyta (liverworts)	31	92	418	25	443	74 (17.7%)	81 (18.3%)
Anthocerotophyta (hornworts)	2	4	5	0	5	1 (20%)	1 (20%)
Total	95	285	1138	76	1214	300 (26.3%)	341 (28.1%)

Note: Figures shown as of December 2019.

TABLE 8.12. **Synopsis of the genera and families of liverworts, hornworts, and mosses**

MARCHANTIOPHYTA: LIVERWORTS
CLASS MARCHANTIOPSIDA
SUBCLASS MARCHANTIIDAE
Order Marchantiales
Family **Aytoniaceae**
- *Asterella* (4, 1)
- *Plagiochasma* (1)

Family **Cyathodiaceae**
- *Cyathodium* (1)

Family **Exormothecaceae**
- *Exormotheca* (1)

Family **Dumortieraceae**
- *Dumortiera* (1)

Family **Marchantiaceae**
- *Marchantia* (2)

Family **Ricciaceae**
- *Riccia* (8)

Family **Targioniaceae**
- *Targionia* (2)

CLASS JUNGERMANNIOPSIDA
SUBCLASS PELLIIDAE
Order Fossombroniales
Family **Calyculariaceae**
- *Calycularia* (1)

Family **Fossombroniaceae**
- *Fossombronia* (2)

Order Pallaviciniales
Family **Pallaviciniaceae**
- *Pallavicinia* (1)
- *Symphyogyna* (3)
- *Symphyogynopsis* (1)

SUBCLASS METZGERIIDAE
Order Pleuroziales
Family **Pleuroziaceae**
- *Pleurozia* (1)

Order Metzgeriales
Family **Aneuraceae**
- *Afroriccardia* (1)
- *Aneura* (3)
- *Riccardia* (7)

Family **Metzgeriaceae**
- *Metzgeria* (7)

SUBCLASS JUNGERMANNIIDAE
Order Porellales
Family **Frullaniaceae**
- *Frullania* (41, 4)

Family **Lejeuneaceae**
- *Acanthocoleus* (2)
- *Acrolejeunea* (3)
- *Allorgella* (2, 2)
- *Brachiolejeunea* (1)
- *Bryopteris* (1)
- *Capillolejeunea* (2, 1)
- *Caudalejeunea* (4, 1)

MARCHANTIOPHYTA: LIVERWORTS
- *Ceratolejeunea* (7, 2)
- *Cheilolejeunea* (14)
- *Cololejeunea* (59, 23)
- *Colura* (8, 2)
- *Dibrachiella* (3)
- *Diplasiolejeunea* (27, 13)
- *Drepanolejeunea* (9)
- *Frullanoides* (1)
- *Haplolejeunea* (1)
- *Lejeunea* (27, 5)
- *Lepidolejeunea* (5)
- *Leptolejeunea* (4)
- *Lopholejeunea* (16, 6)
- *Marchesinia* (2, 1)
- *Metalejeunea* (1)
- *Microlejeunea* (7, 2)
- *Myriocoleopsis* (1)
- *Odontolejeunea* (1)
- *Otolejeunea* (1, 1)
- *Prionolejeunea* (1)
- *Ptychanthus* (1)
- *Pycnolejeunea* (1)
- *Schiffneriolejeunea* (6, 1)
- *Symbiezidium* (2)
- *Taxilejeunea* (1)
- *Thysananthus* (3)
- *Xylolejeunea* (1)

Family **Porellaceae**
- *Porella* (5)

Family **Radulaceae**
- *Radula* (11, 1)

Order Jungermanniales
Family **Adelanthaceae**
- *Adelanthus* (1)
- *Cuspidatula* (1)
- *Denotarisia* (1)
- *Pseudomarsupidium* (1)
- *Syzygiella* (5)

Family **Anastrophyllaceae**
- *Anastrophyllum* (2)
- *Andrewsianthus* (1)
- *Plicanthus* (2)

Family **Arnelliaceae**
- *Gongylanthus* (1)

Family **Balantiopsidaceae**
- *Isotachis* (1)

Family **Calypogeiaceae**
- *Calypogeia* (7)
- *Mnioloma* (1)

Family **Cephaloziaceae**
- *Fuscocephaloziopsis* (1)
- *Odontoschisma* (1)

MARCHANTIOPHYTA: LIVERWORTS
Family **Cephaloziellaceae**
- *Amphicephalozia* (1, 1)
- *Cephaloziella* (4, 1)
- *Cylindrocolea* (3, 1)
- *Kymatocalyx* (3)

Family **Herbertaceae**
- *Herbertus* (2)

Family **Jungermanniaceae**
- *Gottschelia* (1)
- *Jensenia* (1)
- *Notoscyphus* (1)
- *Solenostoma* (4)

Family **Lepidoziaceae**
- *Amazoopsis* (1)
- *Bazzania* (17, 8)
- *Kurzia* (2)
- *Lepidozia* (3)
- *Telaranea* (3)

Family **Lophocoleaceae**
- *Clasmatocolea* (1)
- *Conoscyphus* (1)
- *Cryptolophocolea* (2)
- *Heteroscyphus* (4)
- *Leptoscyphus* (2)
- *Lophocolea* (7, 1)

Family **Mastigophoraceae**
- *Mastigophora* (1)

Family **Plagiochilaceae**
- *Plagiochila* (25, 2)

Family **Schistochilaceae**
- *Schistochila* (3, 1)

ANTHOCEROTOPHYTA: HORNWORTS
CLASS ANTHOCEROTOPSIDA
Order Anthocerotales
Family **Anthocerotaceae**
- *Anthoceros* (2)
- *Dendroceros* (1)
- *Folioceros* (1)

Order Notothyladales
Family **Notothyladaceae**
- *Phaeoceros* (1)

BRYOPHYTA: MOSSES
Superclass I
CLASS SPHAGNOPSIDA
Order Sphagnales
Family **Sphagnaceae**
- *Sphagnum* (16, 2)

Superclass II
CLASS ANDREAEOPSIDA
Order Andreaeales
Family **Andreaeaceae**

(continued overleaf)

TABLE 8.12. **continued**

BRYOPHYTA: MOSSES

Andreaea (2)

Superclass III

CLASS POLYTRICHOPSIDA

Order Polytrichales

Family **Polytrichaceae**

Atrichum (1)

Pogonatum (4)

Polytrichastrum (1)

Polytrichum (5, 2)

CLASS BRYOPSIDA

SUBCLASS FUNARIIDAE

Order Gigaspermales

Family **Gigaspermaceae**

Gigaspermum (1)

Oedipodiella (1)

Order Funariales

Family **Funariaceae**

Entosthodon (4, 2)

Funaria (6, 4)

Physcomitrium (2, 2)

SUBCLASS DICRANIDAE

Order Grimmiales

Family **Grimmiaceae**

Bucklandiella (1)

Grimmia (3)

Family **Ptychomitriaceae**

Ptychomitrium (2)

Order Archidiales

Family **Archidiaceae**

Archidium (2)

Order Dicranales

Family **Bruchiaceae**

Trematodon (7, 5)

Family **Calymperaceae**

Calymperes (10, 1)

Leucophanes (4)

Mitthyridium (2)

Octoblepharum (2)

Syrrhopodon (23, 2)

Family **Ditrichaceae**

Ceratodon (1)

Distichium (1)

Ditrichum (4, 2)

Garckea (1)

Pleuridium (1)

Family **Dicranaceae**

Anisothecium (1, 1)

Aongstroemia (2)

Dicranella (6, 1)

Dicranoloma (3)

Dicranum (1)

Holomitrium (11, 5)

Leptotrichella (2, 1)

Leucoloma (57, 33)

Microcampylopus (1)

BRYOPHYTA: MOSSES

Pseudephemerum (1)

Family **Eustichiaceae**

Eustichia (1)

Family **Erpodiaceae**

Erpodium (2, 1)

Family **Fissidentaceae**

Fissidens (41, 6)

Family **Leucobryaceae**

Atractylocarpus (1)

Campylopus (23)

Leucobryum (19, 9)

Ochrobryum (1, 1)

Family **Rhabdoweisiaceae**

Oreoweisia (1)

Family **Rhachitheciaceae**

Rhachithecium (1)

Order Pottiales

Family **Pottiaceae**

Anoectangium (3, 2)

Barbula (6, 2)

Bryoerythrophyllum (1)

Chionoloma (1)

Didymodon (1, 1)

Gymnostomiella (1)

Gymnostomum (1, 1)

Hymenostylium (1, 1)

Hyophila (8, 3)

Leptodontium (3)

Luisierella (1)

Pseudocrossidium (1)

Splachnobryum (2)

Streptopogon (2)

Tortella (1)

Tortula (4, 4)

Trichostomum (6, 4)

Weisiopsis (1)

Weissia (1)

Family **Serpotortellaceae**

Serpotortella (2)

SUBCLASS BRYIDAE

Superorder Bryanae

Order Splachnales

Family **Meesiaceae**

Leptobryum (1)

Family **Splachnaceae**

Brachymitrion (1)

Tayloria (4)

Order Bryales

Family **Bryaceae**

Anomobryum (2, 1)

Brachymenium (12, 1)

Bryum (26, 5)

Mniobryum (1, 1)

Rhodobryum (3)

BRYOPHYTA: MOSSES

Family **Mniaceae**

Epipterygium (1, 1)

Mielichhoferia (2, 2)

Plagiomnium (1)

Pohlia (4, 1)

Pseudopohlia (1)

Schizymenium (2, 2)

Order Bartramiales

Family **Bartramiaceae**

Bartramia (2)

Breutelia (8, 2)

Philonotis (7, 3)

Order Orthotrichales

Family **Orthotrichaceae**

Cardotiella (4, 2)

Groutiella (1)

Macrocoma (1)

Macromitrium (24, 15)

Schlotheimia (34, 19)

Ulota (1)

Zygodon (4, 3)

Order Hedwigiales

Family **Hedwigiaceae**

Braunia (1)

Bryowijkia (1)

Hedwigia (1)

Family **Rhacocarpaceae**

Rhacocarpus (1)

Order Rhizogoniales

Family **Rhizogoniaceae**

Pyrrhobryum (1)

Superorder Hypnanae

Order Hypnodendrales

Family **Racopilaceae**

Powellia (2, 1)

Racopilum (10, 4)

Order Hookeriales

Family **Hypopterygiaceae**

Hypopterygium (1)

Lopidium (1)

Family **Daltoniaceae**

Adelothecium (1)

Calyptrochaeta (1)

Daltonia (5, 1)

Distichophyllum (2, 1)

Family **Leucomiaceae**

Leucomium (1)

Family **Pilotrichaceae**

Callicostella (13)

Cyclodictyon (3)

Hookeriopsis (1)

Lepidopilidium (5, 4)

Lepidopilum (3, 1)

BRYOPHYTA: MOSSES

Order Hypnales

Family **Amblystegiaceae**
- *Amblystegium* (2, 1)
- *Hygrohypnum* (1, 1)

Family **Anomodontaceae**
- *Herpetineuron* (1)

Family **Brachytheciaceae**
- *Aerolindigia* (1)
- *Brachythecium* (2)
- *Eurhynchium* (2)
- *Helicodontium* (1, 1)
- *Palamocladium* (1)
- *Rhynchostegiella* (1)
- *Rhynchostegium* (5, 2)
- *Schimperella* (1, 1)
- *Squamidium* (1)

Family **Catagoniaceae**
- *Catagonium* (1)

Family **Cryphaeaceae**
- *Cryphaea* (2)
- *Schoenobryum* (1)

Family **Entodontaceae**
- *Campylodontium* (1, 1)
- *Entodon* (5, 5)
- *Erythrodontium* (1, 1)
- *Mesonodon* (1)

Family **Fabroniaceae**
- *Fabronia* (8, 7)
- *Rhizofabronia* (1)

Family **Hypnaceae**
- *Ectropothecium* (12, 3)
- *Gammiella* (1)
- *Glossadelphus* (3, 2)
- *Hypnum* (2)
- *Mittenothamnium* (7, 2)
- *Phyllodon* (2, 1)
- *Rhacopilopsis* (2)
- *Taxiphyllum* (1)
- *Vesicularia* (9, 5)

BRYOPHYTA: MOSSES

Family **Lembophyllaceae**
- *Orthostichella* (5)
- *Pilotrichella* (4)

Family **Leptodontaceae**
- *Leptodon* (1)

Family **Leskeaceae**
- *Pseudoleskea* (1, 1)

Family **Leucodontaceae**
- *Leucodon* (2)
- *Pterogoniadelphus* (1
- *Pterogonium* (2)

Family **Meteoriaceae**
- *Aerobryopsis* (1)
- *Barbella* (1)
- *Floribundaria* (4, 1)
- *Papillaria* (5, 3)
- *Trachypodopsis* (1)
- *Trachypus* (2)

Family **Neckeraceae**
- *Homaliodendron* (2)
- *Neckera* (2)
- *Neckeropsis* (5)
- *Pinnatella* (1)
- *Porotrichum* (5)
- *Thamnobryum* (1, 1)

Family **Phyllogoniaceae**
- *Phyllogonium* (1)

Family **Pterigynandraceae**
- *Trachyphyllum* (2, 1)

Family **Pterobryaceae**
- *Calyptothecium* (3, 1)
- *Hildebrandtiella* (3, 1)
- *Jaegerina* (2, 1)
- *Orthostichidium* (1)
- *Orthostichopsis* (5, 3)
- *Pterobryopsis* (1, 1)
- *Renauldia* (2, 2)

Family **Prionodontaceae**
- *Prionodon* (1)

BRYOPHYTA: MOSSES

Family **Pylaisiadelphaceae**
- *Isopterygium* (14, 9)
- *Taxithelium* (7, 4)
- *Wijkia* (4, 3)

Family **Regmatodontaceae**
- *Regmatodon* (1)

Family **Rigodiaceae**
- *Rigodium* (1)

Family **Rutenbergiaceae**
- *Rutenbergia* (5, 4)

Family **Sematophyllaceae**
- *Acanthorrhynchium* (1)
- *Acroporium* (5, 4)
- *Clastobryophilum* (1)
- *Macrohymenium* (4)
- *Meiothecium* (3, 2)
- *Radulina* (1)
- *Rhaphidorrhynchium* (3, 2)
- *Sematophyllum* (13, 8)
- *Trichosteleum* (10, 6)
- *Warburgiella* (1)

Family **Stereophyllaceae**
- *Entodontopsis* (2)
- *Stereophyllum* (1)

Family **Symphyodontaceae**
- *Symphyodon* (1)

Family **Thuidiaceae**
- *Pelekium* (7)
- *Rauiella* (1)
- *Thuidium* (3)

Sources: Synopses of genera and family are based on Crandall-Stotler et al. (2009) for liverworts, Renzaglia et al. (2009) for hornworts, and Goffinet et al. (2009) for mosses.

Notes: Taxa to family level are listed in phylogenetic order. Genera within families are listed alphabetically. The numbers in parentheses after the generic names indicate the number of taxa of specific or infraspecific rank (first figure) and the number of Malagasy endemic species within the genus (second figure if >0).

Sematophyllaceae (22/42) (Table 8.12). Sixty of the 81 endemic liverworts belong to the Lejeuneaceae, of which the most important is the epiphyllous genus *Cololejeunea* (23/59), which appears to have radiated throughout Madagascar and its neighboring islands (Tixier 1985), and *Diplasiolejeunea* (13/27) shows a similar pattern. The moss genera with the largest numbers of endemic species and infraspecifics are *Leucoloma* (33/57), *Schlotheimia* (19/34), and *Macromitrium* (15/24) (Table 8.12). There are a few genera that are represented by only endemic species: *Entodon* (five species), *Tortula* (four species), *Allorgella*, *Mielichhoferia*, *Physcomitrium*, *Renauldia*, and *Schizymenium* (two species), as well as 17 further genera with a single species: 15 moss genera (7.9% of all moss genera) and two liverwort genera. No endemic species is reported for hornworts.

Madagascar shows no endemism at the family or genus level for bryophytes. However, two moss families (Rutenbergiaceae and Serpotortellaceae) and a single liverwort family (Wiesnerellaceae) are endemic to the sub-Saharan region and all three are present on Madagascar. *Rutenbergia* (Rutenbergiaceae) comprises five species, of which four are endemic to the island. Serpotortellaceae is known only from Madagascar, La Réunion, and Seychelles and both of the species ascribed to this family occur on Madagascar. Of the 20 genera of mosses endemic to the sub-Saharan Africa region (O'Shea 1997, 2006), four (*Rutenbergia* [five species], *Rhizofabronia* [one], *Schimperella* [one], and *Serpotortella* [two]) are represented on Madagascar, while six of the 10 endemic liverwort genera are present on the island (*Otolejeunea* [three], *Symbiezidium* [two], *Amazoopsis* [one], *Bryopteris* [one], *Metalejeunea* [one] and *Xylolejeunea* [one]) (Wigginton 2018).

FIGURE 8.14 **Aspects of the bryophytes of Madagascar. A) The epiphytic hornwort *Dendroceros africanus*. B) The ground-dwelling Daltoniaceae moss. C) The humicolous leafy liverwort *Gottschelia schizopleura* and the thalloid liverwort *Riccardia* sp. D) The terricolous *Dumortiera hirsuta*, found in shaded environments. E) The epiphytic moss, *Ulota flava* with hairy calyptra. F) The ground-dwelling moss *Leucobryum* sp.** (PHOTOS B and F by R. L. Andriamiarisoa, and A, C, D, and E by J. Bardat.)

GLOBAL PHYTOGEOGRAPHIC PATTERNS OF THE BRYOPHYTES OF MADAGASCAR

One way of understanding the global context, importance, and uniqueness of Madagascar's bryophyte flora is to examine the worldwide distribution patterns of its component species. Thus, each taxon was assigned to one of eight global distribution types (Table 8.13; derived from Marline et al., pp. 521–37), using an adaptation of the phytogeographic groups recognized by Pócs and Geissler (2002).

1. **Endemic to Madagascar**. This group includes the 341 taxa of specific or infraspecific rank (28% of all Malagasy bryophytes: one hornwort, 81 liverworts, and 259 mosses) that are currently known only from Madagascar. Liverwort examples include *Bazzania decrescens* var. *ambahatrae*, *Ceratolejeunea saroltae*, *Cololejeunea diplasiolejeuneoides*, and *Plagiochila fracta*, while endemic mosses include *Breutelia madagassa*, *Leucobryum parvulum*, and *Leucoloma marojeziense*.
2. **Malagasy Region (subendemic)**. This group comprises the 156 (13%) taxa of specific or infraspecific rank (55 liverworts and 101 mosses) that occur on Madagascar and on one or more additional islands in the Malagasy Region (the archipelagoes of the Comoros, Mascarenes, and Seychelles). Examples include *Bryopteris gaudichaudii*, now known only from Mada-

gascar, as it was present (but now extinct) on La Réunion (Ah-Peng et al. 2012); *Leucoloma dichelymoides* known from the Comoros, Mauritius, Madagascar, and Seychelles; *Schlotheimia badiella* from Mauritius, Madagascar, and La Réunion; and *Leucobryum comorense*, which occurs on Madagascar, the Comoros, and Mauritius.

3. **African**. This group includes 408 (34%) species (160 liverworts and 248 mosses) that are otherwise restricted to the African continent, including its offshore islands. This is the largest group in the bryoflora of Madagascar. The most represented families, with more than 20 species, are the Lejeuneaceae (55 species), Leucobryaceae (25 species), Dicranaceae (21 species), Fissidentaceae (21 species), and Frullaniaceae (20 species). The African species may be subdivided into two subgroups:

3a. **Tropical African**. This subgroup includes 297 (24%) species (127 liverworts and 170 mosses) that are more or less continuously distributed over tropical Africa, including western African and Indian Ocean islands. Examples include the thalloid liverwort *Riccardia erosa* and the moss *Tayloria solitaria*, which are both tropical African montane forest species.

3b. **Malagasy–tropical African disjunction**. This subgroup includes 111 (10%) species (33 liverworts and 78 mosses) that occur on Madagascar and other islands in the Malagasy Region, with a disjunct distribution to certain regions of the African continent. The subgroup was further divided into four categories: Malagasy Region and central Africa (e.g., *Radula comorensis*); Malagasy Region and eastern Africa (e.g., *Leucobryum perrotii*); Malagasy Region and southern Africa (e.g., *Pogonatum capense*); Malagasy Region and western Africa (e.g., *Frullania gabonensis*).

4. **Paleotropical elements**. This group includes 67 (6%) species (37 liverworts and 30 mosses) that are found throughout the African, Asian, and Australasian tropics but not in the Neotropics. This element is dominated by the Lejeuneaceae (20 species). Examples of Paleotropical species include the liverworts *Mastigophora diclados* and *Pleurozia gigantea* and the mosses *Rhodobryum commersonii* and *Trachypodopsis serrulata*.

5. **Pantropical elements**. This group includes the 128 (11%) species (54 liverworts and 74 mosses) occurring throughout tropical regions, sometimes extending into the subtropics. Examples of pantropical species include *Herpetineuron toccoae*, *Dumortiera hirsuta*, *Eustichia longirostris*, and *Leucomium strumosum*.

6. **Tropical African–tropical American disjunction**. This group includes 55 (5%) species (28 liverworts and 27 mosses) that occur on the African mainland and its surrounding islands, and in the New World tropics. Examples of this element include *Pilotrichella flexilis*, *Leptodontium pungens*, *Fissidens submarginatus*, and *Isotachis aubertii*.

7. **Asian elements**. This group includes five (0.4%) species that are mainly distributed in tropical and eastern Asia from India to Japan, and on New Guinea, and reach Africa only in the Malagasy Region. These comprise a very small proportion of the Malagasy flora. Examples include *Gottschea neesii*, *Lepidolejeunea bidentula*, *Metzgeria quadrifaria*, *Odontoschisma jishibae*, and *Bryum neelgheriense* var. *wichurae*.

8. **Cosmopolitan and subcosmopolitan**. These two groups include 31 (3%) species that occur more or less globally, although possibly absent from the most extreme alpine and polar regions. The eight cosmopolitan species recorded on Madagascar are:

TABLE 8.13. **Bryophyte specific/infraspecific taxon distribution with respect to different phytogeographic patterns**

PHYTOGEOGRAPHIC PATTERN	TOTAL	LIVERWORTS AND HORNWORTS	MOSSES
1. Endemic to Madagascar (END)	341 (28%)	82 (18%)	259 (34%)
2. Malagasy Region (EMR)	157 (13%)	55 (12%)	102 (13%)
3. African (AFR), including:	408 (34%)	160 (36%)	248 (32%)
3a. Tropical African	297 (24%)	127 (16%)	170 (14%)
3b. Tropical African disjunction			
Malagasy Region–central Africa disjunction	12 (1%)	4 (1%)	8 (1%)
Malagasy Region–eastern Africa disjunction	80 (7%)	21 (5%)	59 (8%)
Malagasy Region–southern Africa disjunction	11 (1%)	5 (1%)	6 (1%)
Malagasy Region–western Africa disjunction	8 (1%)	3 (1%)	5 (1%)
4. Paleotropical (PAL)	67 (6%)	37 (8%)	30 (4%)
5. Pantropical (PAN)	130 (11%)	56 (13%)	74 (10%)
6. Tropical African–tropical American disjunction (Afr-Am)	55 (5%)	28 (6%)	27 (4%)
7. Asian elements (Afr-As)	5 (0.4%)	4 (1%)	1 (0%)
8. Cosmopolitan (COS) and subcosmopolitan (SCO)	31 (3%)	10 (2%)	21 (3%)
9. Pattern unknown (NA)	21 (2%)	16 (4%)	5 (1%)

Notes: Percentage of species present for each phytogeographic pattern is shown in parentheses. The phytogeographic regions/patterns referred to here are also used in Table 8.14, where they are indicated by the abbreviations in parentheses.

Bryum argenteum, *B. caespiticium*, *B. capillare*, *Funaria hygrometrica*, *Hedwigia ciliata*, *Leptobryum pyriforme*, *Luisierella barbula*, and *Polytrichum commune*. None of the liverwort species recorded from Madagascar has a cosmopolitan distribution.

Given the geographic proximity, it is not surprising that the African continent (particularly east Africa) and Madagascar share many species, and this African element comprises by far the largest proportion (34%) of the flora. Given that these are all species-level taxa it seems unlikely that the pattern pre-dates the separation of Madagascar from Africa ~160 Mya, but is more likely, for the majority of taxa, to be the result of recent dispersal between the two areas. It is not possible with current data to determine the extent and direction of such dispersal events; these, of course, could be species specific. Such questions could be addressed with appropriate molecular data. The apparent (based on morphology) lack of differentiation between the two areas suggests that gene flow is likely to be ongoing.

The second-largest element in the flora comprises the 328 (28%) endemic taxa. It is noteworthy that this high level of endemism is largely driven by mosses (34% endemic), while liverworts exhibit a considerably lower rate (18%). The island's long isolation, coupled with varied topography, vegetation, and precipitation regimes, are expected to promote diversification. This is clearly seen in *Leucoloma*, a recently thoroughly revised genus that has 33 well-demarcated endemics. For some other groups, however, the situation is less clear, and in some instances, revision is likely to result in extensive synonymization. Two groups where this is perhaps particularly true are Orthotrichaceae (J. Wilbraham, unpublished data) and Sematophyllaceae. On the other hand, many habitats on the island, perhaps especially vegetation types associated with arid zones, remain virtually unknown and may harbor substantial numbers of unique and unknown taxa. It is therefore difficult, at present, to evaluate the true level of bryophyte endemism present on Madagascar.

In addition to the strict endemics, a smaller but significant (13%) group is nearly endemic to Madagascar but shared with one or more of the nearby islands in the Malagasy Region. These islands are young (0.2–15 Mya) volcanic landmasses that have arisen in situ and have not been connected to each other or to Madagascar. In general, they share similar environments and the distances between them are relatively small. The limited available data show that the origin for most such taxa postdates the isolation of Madagascar. Studies are few, but in general it seems likely that these represent Malagasy groups that have subsequently dispersed to these new islands, although a number of alternative hypotheses are possible. This emphasizes the potentially significant role of "waif dispersal," the chance spread of a species across a barrier, in generating the present-day biodiversity on these islands (Strijk et al. 2012).

The remaining 25% of the bryophyte flora comprises species with essentially widespread distributions. These range from true cosmopolitan taxa to those exhibiting various degrees (sometimes rather extreme) of distributional disjunction. Bryophytes generally have broader geographic ranges than angiosperms, often extending over more than one continent. Explanations for these broad distributions have ranged from ancient vicariance via continental drift to long-distance dispersal (Federman et al. 2015). Further study is needed to determine the movement and the direction of dispersal of bryophytes in and out of Madagascar.

CONCLUSION

We provide an overview of current knowledge on the bryophyte flora of Madagascar in a floristic and biogeographic context. It is clear that the region hosts a rich and globally significant flora with a significant proportion of unique diversity in the form of endemic species. In addition, this flora constitutes the stronghold for the majority of the species endemic to the Malagasy Region, many of which have only a few known populations outside the island, thus conferring considerable conservation value on the Malagasy populations. Not surprisingly, the bryophyte flora shares a considerable number of species with Africa, and particularly the eastern part of the continent. In addition, there are substantial pantropical and Paleotropical elements. The history of these and how they relate to past and ongoing historical and dispersal processes is of great interest and of general relevance in understanding the processes of population differentiation and speciation. Such understanding will require the generation of extensive population-level DNA data that incorporate sufficient Malagasy representatives.

It is clear that much work remains to be done to improve knowledge of the regional bryophyte flora. It is evident from perusal of available herbarium material that previous collecting has been strongly biased toward moist evergreen forests. Knowledge of other habitats, such as the dry deciduous forests, for example, is either lacking or extremely fragmentary. Inventories of such habitats will undoubtedly reveal many new and biogeographically significant records for the island. A crucial task is to clarify the status of the large number of putatively endemic species, especially mosses. Many of these are in groups that have not been subject to recent taxonomic revision and need to be evaluated on a global, or at least a broad regional, basis. Such studies are likely to demonstrate extensive synonymy but are also likely to reveal previously unrecognized taxa. Revisions occurring within an explicitly molecular phylogenetic context would be especially useful as they would inform questions on the timing and origin of Madagascar's unique bryophytes.

Leveraging bryophytes as a basis for setting conservation priorities for particular sites or vegetation systems is in itself a fundamental objective. A better understanding of the overall bryophyte diversity as well as how it is packaged geographically is key for conservation. From this perspective, this contribution provides a basic preliminary knowledge of a poorly studied group in a globally important but highly threatened area. In future, we envisage using approaches such as, for example, stacking bryophyte species distribution models to generate maps of potential richness to provide criteria for conservation planning and the design of protected areas, or the identification of suitable areas for threatened or otherwise rare species. Similarly, better information on potential bryophyte responses to climate change and their roles in providing ecosystem services, both particularly lacking for tropical systems, would constitute a significant biodiversity resource that might be useful in setting conservation priorities for particular sites or vegetation types, and for predicting the influence of changing climate on the distribution of ecologically important species and ecosystems.

Subject editors: Michelle Price, Laurent Gautier, and Steven M. Goodman

CHECKLIST OF THE BRYOPHYTES OF MADAGASCAR

L. Marline, C. Ah-Peng, and T. A. J. Hedderson

Previously, enumerations used literature reviews to produce lists of the mosses and liverworts of Madagascar (Grolle and Onraedt 1974; Crosby et al. 1983). The synthetic works of O'Shea (2006) and Wigginton (2018), who published periodically updated checklists of the bryophytes from sub-Saharan Africa, including Madagascar and its neighboring islands (La Réunion, Mauritius, Rodrigues, Seychelles, and Comoros), are among the most relevant enumerations.

A recent checklist by Marline et al. (2012) reports a total of 1144 species, comprising 751 mosses, 390 liverworts, and three hornworts for Madagascar. Since then, considerable changes have been made in the nomenclature of different families and records of newly discovered species have been made. In 2017, a preliminary checklist of bryophyte species of Madagascar, based on Marline et al. (2012), was added to the online database, Catalogue of the Plants of Madagascar (Madagascar Catalogue 2021). This checklist provides a comprehensive list of bryophytes from Madagascar. It is largely based on literature records, herbarium specimens deposited in various herbaria (mainly at Muséum National d'Histoire Naturelle [P], Parc Botanique et Zoologique de Tsimbazaza [TAN], and Royal Botanic Garden Edinburgh [E]), and online databases (Catalogue of the Plants of Madagascar, Global Biodiversity Information Facility or GBIF [2021], and Index of Mosses database W^{3}MOST.

The enumeration in Table 8.14 contains 1214 species and infraspecific taxa including 766 mosses, 443 liverworts, and five hornworts. This checklist is not a taxonomic document and no new taxonomy is proposed herein.

Subject editors: Michelle Price, Laurent Gautier, and Steven M. Goodman

TABLE 8.14. **Checklist of the bryophytes known from Madagascar**

ANTHOCEROTOPHYTA: HORNWORTS

Anthoceros pseudocostus Steph. END (Stephani 1916)
A. punctatus L. NA (Grolle 1995; Villarreal et al. 2015)
Dendroceros cf. *africanus* Steph. EMR (Marline et al. 2012)
Folioceros fuciformis (Mont.) D. C. Bharadwaj NA (Grolle 1995; Villarreal et al. 2015)
Phaeoceros carolinianus (Michx.) Prosk. SCO (Grolle 1995)

MARCHANTIOPHYTA: LIVERWORTS

Acanthocoleus aberrans (Lindenb. & Gottsche) Kruijt PAN (Kruijt 1988; Grolle 1995)
A. madagascariensis (Steph.) Kruijt AFR (Grolle 1995; Pócs 1995; Pócs and Geissler 2002)
Acrolejeunea aulacophora (Mont.) Steph. AFR (Grolle 1995)
A. emergens (Mitt.) Steph. var. *emergens* PAN (Grolle 1995; Pócs and Geissler 2002)
A. pycnoclada (Taylor) Schiffn. PAL (Grolle 1995)
Adelanthus lindenbergianus (Lehm.) Mitt. Afr-Am (Grolle 1995)
Afroriccardia comosa (Steph.) Reeb & Gradst. AFR (Rabeau et al. 2017)
Allorgella rabenorii (Tixier) Bechteler, G. E. Lee, Schäfer-Verwimp & Heinrichs END (Grolle 1995)
A. subana (Pócs) Pócs END (Pócs 2004)
Amazoopsis diplopoda (Pócs) J. J. Engel & G. L. S. Merr. EMR (Grolle 1995; Pócs 1995)
Amphicephalozia geisslerae Pócs & Váňa END (Pócs and Váňa 2001; Pócs and Geissler 2002)
Anastrophyllum auritum (Lehm.) Steph. AFR (Marline 2018)
A. piligerum (Nees) Steph. PAN (Grolle 1995; Pócs 1995; Pócs and Geissler 2002)

MARCHANTIOPHYTA: LIVERWORTS

Andrewsianthus aberrans (Nees & Mont.) Grolle EMR (Pócs 1995)
Aneura "caespitans" Steph., nom. inval. AFR (Wigginton 2018)
A. latissima Spruce Afr-Am (Meenk and Pocs 1985)
A. "nudiflora" Steph., nom. dub. EMR (Wigginton 2018)
Asterella bachmannii (Steph.) S. W. Arnell AFR (Reeb et al. 2018)
A. coronata (Steph.) H. A. Mill. END (Stephani 1917; Grolle 1995)
A. marginata (Nees.) S. W. Arnell AFR (Reeb et al. 2018)
A. wilmsii (Steph.) S. W. Arnell AFR (Grolle 1995)
Bazzania comorensis Steph. EMR (Marline 2018)
B. curvidens Steph. END (Grolle 1995)
B. deciduifolia Onr. END (Grolle 1995)
B. decrescens var. *ambahatrae* Pócs END (Pócs and Geissler 2002)
B. decrescens (Lehm. & Lindenb.) var. *decrescens* AFR (Grolle 1995)
B. decrescens subsp. *molleri* (Steph.) E. W. Jones AFR (Marline et al. 2018)
B. decrescens subsp. *pumila* (Mitt.) Pócs AFR (Pócs 1995)
B. konratiana Sass-Gyarmati END (Sass-Gyarmati 2017)
B. lacouturei (Steph.) S. W. Arnell 1965, nom. inval. END (Wigginton 2018)
B. madagassa (Steph.) S. W. Arnell 1965, nom. inval. END (Wigginton 2018)
B. mascarena (Steph.) Herzog EMR (Grolle 1995)
B. nitida (F. Weber) Grolle PAN (Grolle 1995; Pócs 1995; Pócs and Geissler 2002)
B. orbanii Pócs END (Pócs 2010a)
B. perrotana (Steph.) E. W. Jones AFR (Jones 1975; Grolle 1995)

(continued overleaf)

TABLE 8.14. ***continued***

MARCHANTIOPHYTA: LIVERWORTS

B. praerupta (Reinw., Blume & Nees) Trevis. AFR (Grolle 1995; Pócs 1995)
B. reflexa (Gottsche) Steph. END (Grolle 1995)
B. roccatii Gola AFR (Marline et al. 2018)
Brachiolejeunea phyllorhiza (Nees) Kruijt & Gradst. AFR (Grolle 1995)
Bryopteris gaudichaudii Gottsche EMR (Grolle 1995; Pócs 1995)
Calycularia crispula Mitt. AFR (Ellis et al. 2017)
Calypogeia annabonensis Steph. AFR (Pócs and Geissler 2002)
C. arguta Nees & Mont. AFR (Grolle 1995)
C. bidentula (F. Weber) Nees AFR (Grolle 1995)
C. fissa (L.) Raddi. AFR (Marline et al. 2012)
C. longifolia Steph. AFR (Grolle 1995; Pócs 2005)
C. mascarenensis Bischl. EMR (Grolle 1995)
C. microstipula (Steph.) Steph. AFR (Grolle 1995)
Capillolejeunea geisslerae (Pócs) R. L. Zhu, Qiong He, Y. M. Wei & Pócs END (Pócs 2001; Pócs and Geissler 2002)
C. mascarena S. W. Arnell EMR (Zhu and Grolle 2003)
Caudalejeunea grolleana Gradst. END (Grolle 1995)
C. hanningtonii (Mitt.) Schiffn. PAN (Grolle 1995)
C. lewallei Vanden Berghen AFR (Grolle 1995)
C. reniloba (Gottsche) Steph. EMR (Grolle 1995)
Cephaloziella tenuissima (Lehm.) Steph. AFR (Pócs and Váňa 2015)
C. transvaalensis S. W. Arnell AFR (Pócs and Váňa 2015)
C. vaginans Steph. AFR (Marline 2018)
C. villaumei (Steph.) Váňa END (Grolle 1995)
Ceratolejeunea andringitrae Pócs END (Pócs 2011a)
C. belangeriana (Gottsche) Steph. PAL (Bonner 1953; Grolle 1995; Pócs and Geissler 2002; Pócs 2011a)
C. coarina (Gottsche) Schiffn. AFR (Pócs 2011a)
C. cornuta (Lindenb.) Schiffn. PAN (Grolle 1995; Pócs 2011a)
C. floribunda Stephani AFR (Marline 2018)
C. papuliflora Steph. AFR (Bonner 1953; Grolle 1995; Pócs 2011a)
C. saroltae Pócs END (Pócs 2011a)
Cheilolejeunea cordigera (Steph.) Grolle EMR (Grolle 1995; Pócs and Geissler 2002)
C. cordistipula (Steph.) Grolle ex E. W. Jones AFR (Grolle 1995)
C. decursiva (Sande Lac.) R. M. Schust. PAL (Grolle 1995; Pócs and Geissler 2002)
C. intertexta (Lindenb.) Steph. PAL (Grolle 1995; Pócs and Geissler 2002)
C. krakakammae (Lindenb.) R. M. Schust. PAL (Grolle 1995; Pócs and Geissler 2002)
C. montagnei (Gottsche) R. M. Schust. AFR (Grolle 1995; Pócs and Geissler 2002)
C. pluriplicata (Pearson) R. M. Schust. PAL (Grolle 1995)
C. pocsii E. W. Jones AFR (Grolle 1995)
C. rigidula (Nees ex Mont.) R. M. Schust. AFR (Grolle 1995; Pócs 1995; Pócs and Geissler 2002)
C. surrepens (Mitt.) E. W. Jones AFR (Grolle 1995; Pócs and Geissler 2002)
C. trapezia (Nees) Kachroo & R. M. Schust. PAL (Malombe 2007)

MARCHANTIOPHYTA: LIVERWORTS

C. trifaria (Reinw., Blume & Nees) Mizut. PAN (Grolle 1995; Pócs and Geissler 2002)
C. usambarana (Steph.) Grolle AFR (Malombe 2007)
C. xanthocarpa (Lehm. & Lindenb.) Malombe PAN (Pócs 1995; Malombe 2007)
Clasmatocolea vermicularis (Lehm.) Grolle Afr-Am (Engel 1980)
Cololejeunea adnata Tixier END (Tixier 1985; Grolle 1995)
C. andapania Tixier END (Tixier 1985; Grolle 1995)
C. ankaiana Tixier END (Tixier 1985; Grolle 1995)
C. appressa (A. Evans) Benedix PAN (Grolle 1995; Pócs and Geissler 2002)
C. auriculata (E. W. Jones) R. M. Schust. AFR (Tixier 1985; Grolle 1995; Pócs and Geissler 2002)
C. bidentula (Steph.) E. W. Jones AFR (Grolle 1995)
C. borbonica Tixier EMR (Grolle 1995)
C. camusii Tixier END (Tixier 1985; Grolle 1995)
C. capuronii Tixier END (Grolle 1995)
C. cardiocarpa (Mont.) A. Evans PAN (Tixier 1985; Grolle 1995)
C. cristata (Steph.) R. M. Schust. AFR (Tixier 1985; Grolle 1995)
C. cuneata (Lehm. & Lindenb.) Herzog PAL (Grolle 1995; Pócs 1995)
C. decemplicata (Steph.) Tixier EMR (Grolle 1995)
C. deroinii Tixier END (Tixier 1993; Grolle 1995)
C. diplasiolejeuneoides Tixier END (Tixier 1985; Grolle 1995)
C. disciflora Tixier END (Grolle 1995)
C. distalopapillata (E. W. Jones) R. M. Schust. AFR (Tixier 1985; Grolle 1995; Pócs and Geissler 2002)
C. dolichodonta Tixier END (Tixier 1985; Grolle 1995)
C. duvignaudii E. W. Jones var. *duvignaudii* AFR (Tixier 1985; Grolle 1995; Pócs and Geissler 2002)
C. duvignaudii var. *papillata* Tixier EMR (Grolle 1995)
C. elegans Steph. PAL (Tixier 1985; Grolle 1995; Pócs and Geissler 2002)
C. falcata var. *madecassa* Tixier END (Grolle 1995)
C. floccosa (Lehm. & Lindenb.) Schiffn. var. *floccosa* PAL (Grolle 1995)
C. floccosa var. *trivittata* Tixier PAL (Grolle 1995)
C. furcilobulata (Berrie & E. W. Jones) R. M. Schust. AFR (Grolle 1995)
C. haskarliana (Lehm. & Lindenb.) Schiffn. EMR (Marline et al. 2018)
C. hildebrandii (Austin) Steph. PAL (Tixier 1985; Grolle 1995)
C. inflectens (Mitt.) Benedix EMR (Pócs and Váňa 2015)
C. lanciloba (Steph.) PAL (Tixier 1985; Grolle 1995; Pócs and Geissler 2002)
C. leloutrei (E. W. Jones) R. M. Schust. var. *leloutrei* AFR (Grolle 1995; Pócs and Geissler 2002)
C. leloutrei var. *microlobulata* Tixier END (Tixier 1985; Grolle 1995)
C. leloutrei var. *ugulurica* Pócs ex Tixier AFR (Grolle 1995)
C. lemuriana Tixier AFR (Tixier 1985; Grolle 1995)
C. magillii Pócs EMR (Pócs et al. 2015)
C. marginata (Lehm. & Lindenb.) Schiffn. EMR (Grolle 1995; Pócs and Geissler 2002)

MARCHANTIOPHYTA: LIVERWORTS

C. microscopica var. *exigua* (A. Evans) Bernecker & Pocs Afr-Am (Grolle 1995; Pócs and Bernecker 2009)
C. mocambiquensis S. W. Arnell NA (Grolle 1995)
C. moramangae Tixier AFR (Grolle 1995; Pócs and Bernecker 2009)
C. nosykombae var. *laevis* A. Szabó & Pócs END (Szabó and Pócs 2015)
C. nosykombae A. Szabó & Pócs var. *nosykombae* END (Szabó and Pócs 2015)
C. obliqua (Nees & Mont.) Schiffn. PAN (Grolle 1995; Pócs and Geissler 2002)
C. obtusifolia (E. W. Jones) Tixier var. *obtusifolia* AFR (Grolle 1995; Pócs and Geissler 2002)
C. obtusifolia var. *madecassa* (Tixier) Pócs END (Grolle 1995)
C. peponiformis Mizut. EMR (Pócs et al. 2015; Zhu et al. 2015)
C. peraffinis var. *serrulata* Benedix END (Pócs and Geissler 2002)
C. plagiochiliana Tixier END (Grolle 1995)
C. platyneura (Spruce) A. Evans PAN (Grolle 1995; Pócs and Geissler 2002)
C. praeruptorum Tixier END (Tixier 1985; Grolle 1995)
C. pteroporum Tixier END (Tixier 1985; Grolle 1995)
C. raduliloba Steph. PAL (Tixier 1985; Grolle 1995)
C. saltuum Tixier END (Tixier 1985; Grolle 1995)
C. sambiroana Tixier END (Tixier 1985; Grolle 1995)
C. selangorensis Tixier PAL (Tixier 1985; Grolle 1995)
C. subinflata Tixier END (Tixier 1985; Grolle 1995)
C. succinea Tixier END (Tixier 1979a, 1985)
C. tamatavensis Tixier END (Tixier 1985; Grolle 1995)
C. tanzaniae Pócs AFR (Grolle 1995; Pócs and Geissler 2002)
C. vidaliana Tixier PAN (Grolle 1995)
C. zenkeri (Steph.) E. W. Jones AFR (Pócs and Geissler 2002)
Colura bicornis Jovet-Ast END (Grolle 1995; Pócs 1995)
C. digitalis (Mitt.) Steph. AFR (Pócs 1995; Pócs and Geissler 2002)
C. heimii Jovet-Ast EMR (Grolle 1995)
C. humbertii Jovet-Ast EMR (Grolle 1995)
C. inornata Jovet-Ast END (Grolle 1995; Pócs 1995)
C. obesa Jovet-Ast EMR (Grolle 1995)
C. obvoluta Jovet-Ast AFR (Jovet-Ast 1983; Grolle 1995)
C. tenuicornis (A. Evans) Steph. PAN (Grolle 1995)
Conoscyphus trapezioides (Sande Lac.) Schiffn. PAL (Grolle 1995; Pócs 1995; Pócs and Geissler 2002)
Cryptolophocolea martiana (Nees) L. Söderstr., Crand.-Stotl. & Stotler subsp. *martiana* AFR (Grolle 1995; Pócs 1995)
C. regularis (Steph.) L. Söderstr EMR (Grolle 1995)
Cuspidatula contracta (Reinw. et al.) Steph. PAL (Pócs 1995)
Cyathodium cavernarum Kunze AFR (Pócs and Geissler 2002)
Cylindrocolea abyssinica (Gola) Váňa AFR (Grolle 1995)
C. kiaeri (Austin) Váňa PAL (Grolle 1995; Pócs and Geissler 2002)
C. madagascariensis (Steph.) R. M. Schust. END (Grolle 1995)
Denotarisia linguifolia (De Not.) Grolle PAL (Pócs and Geissler 2002)

MARCHANTIOPHYTA: LIVERWORTS

Dibrachiella alata (Steph.) X. Q. Shi, R. L. Zhu & Gradst. PAN (Grolle 1995)
D. brevilobula (Steph.) X. Q. Shi, R. L. Zhu & Gradst. AFR (Grolle 1995)
D. elobulata (Steph.) X. Q. Shi, R. L. Zhu & Gradst. AFR (Marline et al. 2018)
Diplasiolejeunea andringitrae Pócs & Schafer-Verwimp END (Pócs and Schaefer-Verwimp 2006)
D. aulae E. W. Jones AFR (Grolle 1995)
D. auriculata Tixier END (Grolle 1995)
D. cavifolia Steph. PAN (Grolle 1995; Pócs and Geissler 2002)
D. cobrensis subsp. *antsirananae* Pócs END (Pócs 2001; Pócs and Geissler 2002)
D. cobrensis Gottsche ex Steph. subsp. *cobrensis* PAN (Grolle 1995; Pócs and Geissler 2002)
D. comorensis Tixier AFR (Grolle 1995)
D. cornuta Steph. AFR (Grolle 1995; Pócs 1995)
D. ensifera Tixier END (Grolle 1995)
D. hamata Tixier END (Grolle 1995)
D. insignis Tixier END (Grolle 1995)
D. jonesii Tixier END (Grolle 1995)
D. kraussiana (Lindenb.) Steph. AFR (Grolle 1995)
D. lemuriana Tixier END (Grolle 1995)
D. magnistipulata Tixier EMR (Tixier 1985; Grolle 1995)
D. ornata Pócs & Schäfer-Verwimp END (Pócs and Schaefer-Verwimp 2006)
D. palustrium Tixier END (Grolle 1995)
D. phyllarthonii Tixier END (Grolle 1995)
D. ramicola Tixier END (Grolle 1995)
D. ranomafanae Pócs & Schäfer-Verwimp END (Pócs and Schaefer-Verwimp 2006)
D. rudolphiana Steph. PAN (Pócs 2010b; Pócs and Váňa 2015)
D. russorensis Steph. PAN (Grolle 1995)
D. subcornuta Tixier PAN (Grolle 1995)
D. symoensii Vanden Berghen PAN (Grolle 1995)
D. utriculata Steph. PAN (Grolle 1995)
D. villaumei Steph. PAN (Grolle 1995)
D. zakiae Tixier PAN (Tixier 1977; Pócs and Geissler 2002)
Drepanolejeunea cultrella (Mitt.) Steph. AFR (Pócs and Geissler 2002)
D. dactylophora (Nees, Lindenb. & Gottsche) J. B. Jack & Steph. PAN (Pócs 2011b)
D. madagascariensis (Steph.) Grolle AFR (Grolle 2001; Pócs and Geissler 2002)
D. pentadactyla var. *dactylophoroides* (Herzog) Pócs NA (Pócs and Váňa 2015)
D. pentadactyla (Mont.) Steph. var. *pentadactyla* PAN (Mizutani 1975; Pócs 2011b)
D. physifolia (Gottsche) Steph. AFR (Grolle 1995; Pócs 1995; Pócs and Geissler 2002)
D. pocsii Grolle AFR (Pócs and Geissler 2002)

(continued overleaf)

TABLE 8.14. ***continued***

MARCHANTIOPHYTA: LIVERWORTS

D. trematodes (Nees) Bischl. AFR (Grolle 1995; Pócs and Geissler 2002)
D. vandenberghenii Buchbender & Eb. Fisch AFR (Marline 2018)
Dumortiera hirsuta (Sw.) Nees, PAN (Marline et al. 2012)
Exormotheca pustulosa Mitt. ANG (Reeb et al. 2018)
Fossombronia foveolata Lindb. AFR (Cargill 2001)
Fossombronia sp. NA (Pócs and Geissler 2002)
Frullania anderssonii Aongstr AFR (Grolle 1995)
F. angulata Mitt. var. *angulata* AFR (Grolle 1995; Pócs and Geissler 2002)
F. angulata var. *laciniata* Demaret & Vanden Berghen AFR (Grolle 1995)
F. apicalis Mitt. AFR (Grolle 1995; Pócs and Geissler 2002)
F. apiculata (Reinw. Blume & Nees) PAL (Grolle 1995; Pócs 1995; Pócs and Geissler 2002)
F. arecae (Spreng.) Gottsche var. *arecae* PAN (Grolle 1995)
F. borbonica Lindenb. EMR (Grolle 1995)
F. bullata Steph. AFR (Grolle 1995)
F. caffraria Steph. PAN (Grolle 1995)
F. capensis Gottsche AFR (Grolle 1995)
F. depressa Mitt. AFR (Grolle 1995)
F. diptera (Lehm.) Drège AFR (Grolle 1995)
F. ecklonii (Spreng.) Gottsche, Lindenb. & Nees AFR (Grolle 1995)
F. eplicata Stephani AFR (Marline 2018)
F. ericoides (Nees ex Mart.) Mont. PAN (Grolle 1995)
F. gabonensis Vanden Berghen AFR (Grolle 1995; Pócs 1995)
F. grossiclava Steph. AFR (Grolle 1995, 2001; Pócs 1995; Pócs and Geissler 2002)
F. humbertii Vanden Berghen EMR (Grolle 1995)
F. imerinensis Steph. AFR (Grolle 1995; Pócs and Geissler 2002)
F. letestui Vanden Berghen AFR (Marline 2018)
F. lindenbergii Lehm. AFR (Grolle 1995, 2001; Pócs 1995; Pócs and Geissler 2002)
F. longistipula Steph. END (Grolle 1995)
F. loricata var. *laxa* Pearson END (Grolle 1995)
F. loricata Pearson var. *loricata* AFR (Grolle 1995; Pócs and Geissler 2002)
F. nodulosa Reinw., Blume & Nees PAN (Grolle 1995; Pócs 1995)
F. obscura (Sw.) Mont. PAN (Grolle 1995)
F. obscurifolia Mitt. PAN (Grolle 1995; Pócs 1995)
F. purpurea Steph. AFR (Grolle 1995; Pócs 1995; Pócs and Geissler 2002)
F. repandistipula Sande Lac. PAL (Grolle 1995)
F. rigida Steph. END (Grolle 1995)
F. schimperi var. *laciniata* Vanden Berghen END (Grolle 1995)
F. schimperi Nees var. *schimperi* AFR (Grolle 1995; Pócs and Geissler 2002)
F. serrata var. *pertenuis* (Nees) Gottsche et al. PAL (Grolle 1995; Pócs 1995)
F. serrata Gottsche var. *serrata* PAL (Grolle 1995)
F. socotrana Mitt. AFR (Grolle 1995)
F. spongiosa Steph. AFR (Grolle 1995; Pócs 1995)
F. trinervis (Lehm.) Drège PAN (Grolle 1995)

MARCHANTIOPHYTA: LIVERWORTS

F. usambarana var. *reducta* Vanden Berghen EMR (Grolle 1995)
F. usambarana Schiffn. ex Steph. var. *usambarana* AFR (Grolle 1995; Pócs 1995)
F. vanden-berghenii Pócs NA (Grolle 1995; Pócs 1995)
F. variegata Steph. AFR (Grolle 1995; Pócs 1995; Pócs and Geissler 2002)
Frullanoides tristis (Steph.) Van Slageren PAN (Grolle 1995)
Fuscocephaloziopsis connivens subsp. *fissa* (Steph.) Váňa and L. Söderstr. PAN (Grolle 1995; Pócs 1995; Pócs and Geissler 2002)
Gongylanthus ericetorum (Raddi) Nees PAL (Grolle 1995)
Gottschelia schizopleura (Spruce) Grolle PAL (Grolle 1995; Pócs 1995; Pócs and Geissler 2002)
Haplolejeunea sticta Grolle EMR (Grolle 1995; Pócs and Geissler 2002)
Herbertus dicranus (Taylor ex Gottsche et al.) Trevis. PAN (Grolle 1995, 2001; Pócs 1995; Hodgetts 2008)
H. juniperoideus (Sw.) Grolle PAN (Grolle 1995, 2001; Pócs and Geissler 2002; Hodgetts 2008)
Heteroscyphus sp. nov. EMR (Marline 2018)
H. dubius (Gottsche) Schiffn. AFR (Grolle 1995)
H. spectabilis (Stephani) Schiffn. AFR (Marline 2018)
H. splendens (Lehm. & Lindenb.) Grolle PAL (Pócs 1995; Pócs and Geissler 2002)
Isotachis aubertii (Schwägr.) Mitt. Afr-Am (Grolle 1995; Pócs and Geissler 2002)
Jensenia spinosa (Lindenb. & Gottsche) Grolle PAN (Ellis et al. 2017)
Kurzia capillaris (Sw.) Grolle subsp. *capillaris* Afr-Am (Pócs 1995; Pócs and Geissler 2002)
K. capillaris subsp. *stephanii* (Renauld ex Steph.) Pócs AFR (Grolle 1995; Pócs 1995; Pócs and Geissler 2002)
Kymatocalyx dominicensis (Spruce) Váňa NEO (Gradstein and Váňa 1999)
K. madagascariensis (Steph.) Gradst. & Váňa EMR (Grolle 1995; Pócs 1995; Gradstein and Váňa, 1999; Pócs and Geissler 2002)
K. rhizomatica (Herzog) Gradst. & Váňa PAN (Pócs and Geissler 2002)
Lejeunea abyssinica (Gola) Cufod. AFR (Pócs and Geissler 2002)
L. alata Gottsche PAL var. *alata* (Grolle 1995; Pócs and Geissler 2002)
L. alata var. *patriciae* Pócs END (Pócs 2001; Pócs and Geissler 2002)
L. amaniensis E. W. Jones AFR (Grolle 1995)
L. anisophylla Mont SCO (Grolle 1985; Pócs and Geissler 2002; Pócs 2011b)
L. capensis Gottsche Afr-Am (Grolle 1995)
L. conformis Nees & Mont. AFR (Grolle 1995; Pócs and Geissler 2002)
L. ecarinata (Steph.) Steph. EMR (Grolle 1995)
L. eckloniana Lindenb. AFR (Grolle 1995; Pócs and Geissler 2002)
L. flava (Sw.) Nees subsp. *flava* PAN (Grolle 1995)

MARCHANTIOPHYTA: LIVERWORTS

L. flava subsp. *tabularis* (Spreng.) S. W. Arnell AFR (Grolle 1995; Pócs and Geissler 2002)
L. flavovirens Aongstr. AFR (Grolle 1995; Pócs and Geissler 2002)
L. helenae Pearson AFR (Marline 2018)
L. isophylla E. W. Jones AFR (Grolle 1995)
L. julacea Steph. END (Grolle 1995; Pócs 2011b)
L. leucosis Besch. & Spruce AFR (Grolle 1995; Pócs 2010b)
L. lomana E. W. Jones AFR (Marline 2018)
L. masoalae Pócs END (Pócs 2010b)
L. obtusata Gottsche AFR (Grolle 1995)
L. papilionacea Steph. AFR (Grolle 1995; Zhu and Grolle 2001)
L. phyllobola Nees & Mont. PAN (Pócs 1995)
L. ramosissima Steph. AFR (Marline 2018)
L. sikorae (Steph.) Steph. END (Grolle 1995)
L. tuberculosa Steph. PAN (Grolle 1995; Pócs and Geissler 2002)
L. villaumei (Steph.) Grolle AFR (Grolle 1995; Pócs and Geissler 2002)
L. vojtkoi Pócs END (Pócs 2010b)
L. vulgariformis Gottsche NA (Grolle 1995; Pócs 2010b)
Lepidolejeunea bidentula (Steph.) R. M. Schust. var. *bidentula* Afr-As (Piippo 1986; Grolle 1995; Zhu and So 2001)
L. epiphylla (Mitt.) Steph. PAL (Pócs and Geissler 2002)
L. maculata (Mitt.) Schiffn. PAN (Marline 2018)
L. subrotundifolia Herzog NA (Pócs and Váňa 2015)
L. vitrea (Nees) Schiffn. EMR (Marline et al. 2012)
Lepidozia cupressina subsp. *africana* (Steph.) Pócs PAN (Grolle 1995)
L. stuhlmannii Steph. AFR (Marline 2018)
L. succida Mitt. AFR (Grolle 1995; Pócs 1995)
Leptoscyphus expansus (Lehm.) Grolle Afr-Am (Grolle 1995)
L. infuscatus (Mitt.) E. W. Jones AFR (Pócs and Geissler 2002)
Leptolejeunea epiphylla (Mitt.) Steph. PAL (Pócs and Geissler 2002)
L. maculata (Mitt.) Schiffn. PAN (Marline 2018)
L. subrotundifolia Herzog NA (Pócs and Váňa 2015)
L. vitrea (Nees) Schiffn. EMR (Marline et al. 2012)
Lophocolea bidentata (L.) Dumort. NA (Grolle 1995; Pócs and Geissler 2002)
L. concreta Mont. Afr-Am (Grolle 1995; Pócs and Geissler 2002)
L. difformis Nees AFR (Pócs and Geissler 2002)
L. lucida (Spreng.) Mont. AFR (Grolle 1995; Pócs and Geissler 2002)
L. madagascariensis Gottsche END (Grolle 1995)
L. muhavurensis (S. W. Arnell) S. W. Arnell ex Pócs AFR (Pócs and Váňa 2015)
L. muricata (Lehm.) Nees PAN (Grolle 1995; Pócs and Geissler 2002)
Lopholejeunea borbonica Steph. EMR (Grolle 1995; Pócs and Geissler 2002)
L. erugata B. Thiers END (Grolle 1995)
L. eulopha (Taylor) Schiffn. PAN (Grolle 1995; Pócs and Geissler 2002; Zhu and Gradstein 2005)
L. grandicrista Steph. EMR (Grolle 1995; Pócs and Geissler 2002)

MARCHANTIOPHYTA: LIVERWORTS

L. leioptera Gyarmati END (Sass-Gyarmati 2001; Pócs and Geissler 2002)
L. lepidoscypha Kiaer & Pearson END (Grolle 1995)
L. minima Vanden Berghen EMR (Marline 2018)
L. multilacera Steph. EMR (Grolle 1995)
L. nigricans (Lindenb.) Schiffn. PAN (Grolle 2001; Zhu and Gradstein 2005)
L. onraedtii Vanden Berghen END (Grolle 2001)
L. paramultilacera Vanden Berghen EMR (Marline 2018)
L. quinquecarinata Vanden Berghen AFR (Grolle 2001)
L. sphaerophora (Lehm. & Lindenb.) Steph. EMR (Pócs and Váňa 2015)
L. subfusca (Nees) Schiffn. PAN (Grolle 1995; Pócs and Geissler 2002; Zhu and Gradstein 2005)
L. tixieriana Vanden Berghen END (Grolle 1995)
L. utriculata Steph. END (Grolle 1995)
Marchantia debilis Goebel AFR (Grolle 1995)
M. pappeana Lehm. subsp. *pappeana* AFR (Grolle 1995)
Marchesinia excavata (Mitt.) Schiffn. AFR (Pócs and Geissler 2002)
M. nobilis (Gottsche) X. Q. Shi, R. L. Zhu & Gradst. END (Grolle 1995)
Mastigophora diclados (Brid. ex F. Weber) Nees PAL (Grolle 1995; Pócs and Geissler 2002)
Metalejeunea cucullata (Reinw. et al.) Grolle Afr-Am (Grolle 1995)
Metzgeria consanguinea Schiffn. PAN (So 2004)
M. crassipilis (Lindb.) A. Evans AFR (Marline 2018)
M. furcata (L.) Dumort. SCO (So 2004)
M. leptoneura Spruce SCO (Grolle 1995; So 2004)
M. madagassa Steph. PAL (Grolle 1995; So 2004)
M. nudifrons Steph. EMR (So 2004)
M. quadrifaria Steph. Afr-As (So 2004)
Microlejeunea africana Steph. AFR (Grolle 1995)
M. ankasica E. W. Jones AFR (Marline 2018)
M. fissistipula Steph. END (Grolle 1995; Pócs and Geissler 2002)
M. inflata Steph. EMR (Grolle 1995; Pócs and Geissler 2002)
M. oblongistipula (Gottsche) Pearson EMR (Grolle 1995)
M. papulosa (Gottsche) Pearson END (Grolle 1995)
M. strasbergii Bardat & Ah-Peng EMR (Ellis et al. 2018)
Mnioloma fuscum (Lehm.) R. M. Schust. PAL (Grolle 1995; Pócs and Geissler 2002)
Myriocoleopsis minutissima (Sm.) R. L. Zhu, Y. Yu and Pócs SCO (Grolle 1995)
Notoscyphus lutescens (Lehm. & Lindenb.) Mitt. PAL (Grolle 1995; Pócs and Geissler 2002)
Odontolejeunea lunulata (F. Weber) Schiffn. Afr-Am (Grolle 1995; Pócs 1995; Pócs and Geissler 2002)
Odontoschisma jishibae (Steph.) L. Söderstr. Afr-As (Pócs 1995; Pócs and Geissler 2002)
Otolejeunea moniliata Grolle END (Grolle 1985, 1995)
Pallavicinia lyelii (Hook.) SCO (Marline et al. 2012)
Plagiochasma microcephalum (Steph.) Steph. var. *microcephalum* PAN (Grolle 1995)

(continued overleaf)

TABLE 8.14. ***continued***

MARCHANTIOPHYTA: LIVERWORTS

Plagiochila angusta Lindenb. EMR (Grolle 1995; Pócs and Geissler 2002)
P. barteri Mitt. var. *barteri* AFR (Grolle 1995; Pócs and Geissler 2002)
P. barteri var. *valida* (Steph.) Vanden Berghen AFR (Reeb et al. 2019)
P. boivinii Steph. EMR (Grolle 1995)
P. boryana Gottsche ex Steph. Afr-Am (Grolle 1995)
P. corrugata (Nees) Nees & Mont. AFR (Grolle 1995)
P. drepanophylla Sande Lac. AFR (Grolle 1995)
P. fracta Pócs END (Pócs and Geissler 2002)
P. fusifera Taylor NA (Marline 2018)
P. granditexta Steph. END (Grolle 1995)
P. incerta Gottsche EMR (Grolle 1995; Pócs and Geissler 2002)
P. integerrima Steph. AFR (Grolle 1995)
P. kiaeri Gottsche AFR (Grolle 1995; Pócs and Geissler 2002)
P. paucidentata Mont. & Gottsche EMR (Grolle 1995; Pócs and Geissler 2002)
P. pectinata Willd. ex Lindenb. AFR (Grolle 1995; Pócs and Geissler 2002)
P. pinniflora Steph. AFR (Marline et al. 2018)
P. punctata (Taylor) Taylor PAN (Grolle 1995; Pócs and Geissler 2002; Heinrichs et al. 2005)
P. renauldii Steph. EMR (Marline 2018)
P. repanda var. *perrotana* (Steph.) Vanden Berghen EMR (Grolle 1995)
P. repanda (Schwägr.) Lindenb. var. *repanda* AFR (Grolle 1995)
P. rodriguezii Steph. EMR (Grolle 1995)
P. squamulosa var. *crispulo-caudata* (Gottsche) Vanden Berghen AFR (Grolle 1995)
P. squamulosa var. *sinuosa* (Mitt.) Vanden Berghen AFR (Grolle 1995)
P. stricta Lindenb. PAN (Lindner et al. 2004)
P. terebrans Nees & Mont. ex Lindenb. AFR (Grolle 1995; Pócs and Geissler 2002)
Pleurozia gigantea (F. Weber) Lindb. PAL (Pócs and Geissler 2002)
Plicanthus birmensis (Steph.) R. M. Schust. NA (Grolle 1995)
P. hirtellus (F. Weber) R. M. Schust. SCO (Grolle 1995; Pócs and Geissler 2002)
Porella abyssinica var. *hoehnelii* (Steph.) Pócs AFR (Grolle 1995)
P. cucullistipula Steph. AFR (Grolle 1995)
P. madagascariensis (Nees & Mont.) Trevis. PAL (Grolle 1995)
P. montantii (Steph.) E. W. Jones AFR (Grolle 1995)
P. triquetra (Steph.) E. W. Jones AFR (Grolle 1995)
Prionolejeunea grata (Gottsche) Schiffn. AFR (Grolle 1995; Pócs and Geissler 2002)
Pseudomarsupidium decipiens (Hook.) Grolle Afr-Am (Pócs and Geissler 2002)
Ptychanthus africanus Steph. (Grolle 1995) AFR (Grolle 1995)
Pycnolejeunea contigua (Nees) Grolle Afr-Am (Grolle 1995; X. L. He 1999)
Radula ankefinensis Gottsche ex Steph. AFR (Grolle 1995, 2001; Pócs and Geissler 2002)

MARCHANTIOPHYTA: LIVERWORTS

R. appressa Mitt. AFR (Grolle 1995; Pócs 1995; Pócs and Geissler 2002)
R. boryana (F. Weber) Mont. Afr-Am (Grolle 1995, 2001; Pócs and Geissler 2002)
R. comorensis Steph. AFR (Pócs and Geissler 2002)
R. fulvifolia (Hook. f. & Taylor) Gottsche et al. AFR (Grolle 2001)
R. madagascariensis Gottsche AFR (Yamada 1975; Grolle 1995, 2001; Pócs 1995)
R. marojezica E. W. Jones END (Grolle 1995)
R. quadrata Gottsche Afr-Am (Grolle 1995)
R. silvestris Gottsche NA (Grolle 1995)
R. stenocalyx Mont. Afr-Am (Grolle 1995, 2001; Pócs 1995; Pócs and Geissler 2002)
R. voluta Taylor ex Gottsche et al. Afr-Am (Grolle 1995, 2001; Pócs 1995; Pócs and Geissler 2002)
Riccardia amazonica (Spruce) Schiffn. ex Gradst. Afr-Am (Pócs and Geissler 2002)
R. erosa (Steph.) E. W. Jones AFR (Pócs and Geissler 2002)
R. longispica (Steph.) Pearson AFR (Grolle 1995; Pócs and Geissler 2002)
R. multifida (L.) Gray PAL (Grolle 1995)
R. nudiflora (Steph.) Grolle EMR (Grolle 1995)
R. ramosissima (Steph.) Grolle AFR (Grolle 1995)
R. saccatiflora (Steph.) S. W. Arnell AFR (Grolle 1995)
Riccia atromarginata var. *jovet-astiae* Rauh & Buchloh AFR (Grolle 1995)
R. atropurpurea Sim. AFR (Reeb et al. 2018)
R. cavernosa Hoffm. SCO (Grolle 1995)
R. congoana Steph. AFR (Reeb et al. 2018)
R. crinita Taylor SCO (Grolle 1995)
R. perssonii Sultan Khan PAL (Perold 1995)
R. purpurascens Lehm. AFR (Marline et al. 2012)
R. stricta (Lindenb.) Perold. AFR (Reeb et al. 2018)
Schiffneriolejeunea madagascariensis (Steph.) Gradst. END (Grolle 1995)
S. pappeana (Nees) Gradst. var. *pappeana* AFR (Grolle 1995; Pócs and Geissler 2002)
S. pappeana var. *bidentata* Gradst. & Vanden Berghen AFR (Grolle 1995)
S. pappeana var. *integra* Gradst. & Vanden Berghen AFR (Grolle 1995)
S. parviloba (Steph.) Gradst. EMR (Pócs and Geissler 2002)
S. polycarpa (Nees) Gradst. Afr-Am (Grolle 1995; Pócs and Geissler 2002)
Schistochila alata (Lehm.) Schiffn. Afr-Am (Grolle 1995; Pócs 1995; Pócs and Geissler 2002)
S. neesii (Mont.) Limb. Afr-As (Grolle 1995; Pócs 1995; Pócs and Geissler 2002)
S. piligera Steph. END (Grolle 1995; Pócs 1995; Pócs and Geissler 2002)
Solenostoma borgenii (Gottsche) Steph. AFR (Grolle 1995)
S. onraedtii (Váňa) Váňa et al. NA (Grolle 1995)
S. renauldii (Váňa) Váňa et al. NA (Grolle 1995)

MARCHANTIOPHYTA: LIVERWORTS

S. sphaerocarpum (Hook.) Steph. NA (Grolle 1995)
Symbiezidium barbiflorum (Lindenb. & Gottsche) A. Evans Afr-Am (Sass-Gyarmati and Pócs 2002)
S. madagascariense Steph. EMR (Gradstein and van Beek 1985; Grolle 1995; Pócs 1995)
Symphyogyna brasiliensis Nees & Mont. Afr-Am (Grolle 1995)
S. podophylla (Thunb.) Mont. & Ness. Afr-Am (Marline et al. 2012)
S. aff. *podophylla* NA (Ellis et al. 2017)
Symphyogynopsis gottscheana (Mont. & Nees) Grolle AFR (Grolle 1995)
Syzygiella colorata (Lehm.) K. Feldberg et al. AFR (Pócs and Váňa 2015)
S. concreta (Gottsche) Spruce Afr-Am (Grolle 1995; Pócs and Geissler 2002)
S. manca (Mitt.) Steph. Afr-Am (Grolle 1995; Pócs 1995; Pócs and Geissler 2002)
S. purpurascens (Steph) Feldberg et al. AFR (Grolle 1995; Pócs 1995; Pócs and Geissler 2002)
S. sonderi (Gottsche) K. Feldberg et al. AFR (Grolle 1995)
Targionia dioica Schiffn. PAN (Grolle 1995)
T. hypophylla L. SCO (Grolle 1995)
Taxilejeunea furcicornuta Grolle EMR (Grolle 1995)
Telaranea bischleriana Pócs EMR (Pócs 2006)
T. coactilis (Spruce) J. J. Engel & G. L. S. Merr. AFR (Engel and Merrill 2004)
T. nematodes (Gottsche ex Austin) M. Howe Afr-Am (Grolle 1995)
Thysananthus auriculatus (Wilson) Sukkharak & Gradst. var. *auriculatus* Afr-Am (Grolle 1995)
T. auriculatus var. *rhodesicus* (Vanden Berghen) Sukkharak & Gradst. AFR (Grolle 1995)
T. spathulistipus (Reinw., Blume & Nees) Lindenb. PAL (Grolle 1995; Pócs and Geissler 2002)
Xylolejeunea grolleana (Pócs) X.-L. He & Grolle EMR (Pócs 1999; X.-L. He and Grolle 2001)

BRYOPHYTA: MOSSES

Acanthorrhynchium papillatum (Harv.) M. Fleisch. EMR (Crosby et al. 1983; Tixier 1995)
Acroporium depressum Thér. END (Crosby et al. 1983)
A. laevifolium (Renauld) Broth. END (Crosby et al. 1983)
A. megasporum var. *densum* (Renauld & Cardot) Wijk & Margad. END (Crosby et al. 1983)
A. megasporum (Duby) M. Fleisch. var. *megasporum* Afr-Am (Crosby et al. 1983)
A. stellatum (Renauld & Cardot) Broth. END (Crosby et al. 1983)
Adelothecium bogotense Hampe PAN (Crosby et al. 1983; Delgadillo et al. 1995)
Aerobryopsis capensis (Müll. Hal.) M. Fleisch. AFR (Crosby et al. 1983)
Aerolindigia capillacea (Hornsch.) M. Menzel PAN (Crosby et al. 1983)
Amblystegium chalaropelma Müll. Hal. ex Renauld END (Crosby et al. 1983)

BRYOPHYTA: MOSSES

A. riparium (Hedw.) Bruch, Schimp. & W. Guembel PAN (Crosby et al. 1983)
Andreaea subulata Harv. in Hook. PAN (Crosby et al. 1983)
A. tsaratananae Thér. EMR (Crosby et al. 1983)
Anisothecium madagassum Thér. END (Crosby et al. 1983)
Anoectangium impressum Hampe END (Crosby et al. 1983)
A. madagassum Renauld & Paris END (Crosby et al. 1983)
A. rufoviride Besch. AFR (Crosby et al. 1983)
Anomobryum filiforme var. *madagassum* Renauld & Cardot END (Crosby et al. 1983)
A. julaceum (P. Gaertn., B. Mey. & Scherb.) Schimp. var. *julaceum* AFR (Ochi 1972; Crosby et al. 1983)
Aongstroemia filiformis (P. Beauv.) Wijk & Margad. AFR (Crosby et al. 1983; Delgadillo et al. 1995)
A. julacea (Hook.) Mitt. PAN (Crosby et al. 1983)
Archidium ohioense Schimp. ex Müll. Hal. SCO (Marline et al. 2012)
A. subulatum Müll. Hal. AFR (Marline et al. 2012)
Atractylocarpus madagascariensis (Thér.) Padberg & J.-P. Frahm AFR (Crosby et al. 1983)
Atrichum androgynum (Müll. Hal.) A. Jaeger AFR (Crosby et al. 1983; De Sloover 1986)
Barbella capillicaulis (Renauld & Cardot) Cardot var. *capillicaulis* AFR (Crosby et al. 1983)
Barbula bolleana (Müll. Hal.) Broth. Afr-Am (Crosby et al. 1983)
B. eubryum Müll. Hal. AFR (O'Shea et al. 1997)
B. indica (Hook.) Spreng. in Steud. var. *indica* Afr-Am (Crosby et al. 1983)
B. jananicus O'Shea END (O'Shea 2008)
B. omissa Thér. AFR (Sim and Dixon 1922)
B. subobtusa Thér. END (Crosby et al. 1983)
Bartramia gigantea Bory AFR (Crosby et al. 1983)
B. longifolia Hook. Afr-Am (Crosby et al. 1983)
Brachymenium acuminatum Harv. in Hook. PAN (Ochi 1972; Crosby et al. 1983; Delgadillo et al. 1995)
B. apiculatum P. Beauv. EMR (Crosby et al. 1983)
B. capitulatum (Mitt.) Kindb. PAL (Crosby et al. 1983)
B. exile (Dozy & Molk.) Bosch & Sande Lac. PAN (Ochi 1972; Crosby et al. 1983; Delgadillo et al. 1995)
B. leptophyllum (Bruch & Schimp. ex Müll. Hal.) Bruch & Schimp. ex A. Jaeger PAL (Crosby et al. 1983)
B. madagassum Hampe END (Ochi 1972; Crosby et al. 1983)
B. nepalense Hook. in Schwägr. PAL (Ochi 1972; Crosby et al. 1983; Pócs and Geissler 2002)
B. nigrescens Besch. AFR (Ochi 1972; Crosby et al. 1983)
B. notarisii (Mitt.) A. J. Shaw AFR (Crosby et al. 1983)
B. philonotula Broth. AFR (Ochi 1972; Crosby et al. 1983)
B. pulchrum Hook. PAL (Ochi 1972; Crosby et al. 1983; Tixier 1995)
B. rigidum Broth. & Paris AFR (Crosby et al. 1983)
Brachymitrion moritzianum (Müll. Hal.) A. K. Kop. Afr-Am (Koponen and Weber 1972; Crosby et al. 1983)

(continued overleaf)

TABLE 8.14. *continued*

BRYOPHYTA: MOSSES
Brachythecium borgenii (Hampe) A. Jaeger AFR (Crosby et al. 1983)
B. decurrens Cardot EMR (Crosby et al. 1983)
Braunia secunda (Hook.) Bruch & Schimp. PAN (Marline et al. 2012)
Breutelia diffracta Mitt. AFR (Crosby et al. 1983)
B. gnaphalea P. Beauv. AFR (Crosby et al. 1983)
B. madagassa Thér. var. *madagassa* END (Crosby et al. 1983)
B. microdonta (Mitt.) Broth. Afr-Am (Crosby et al. 1983; Virtanen 1997)
B. perrieri Thér. AFR (Crosby et al. 1983)
B. sciuroides Thér. AFR (Crosby et al. 1983)
B. stuhlmannii Broth. AFR (De Sloover 1975a; Crosby et al. 1983)
B. viguieri Cardot END (Crosby et al. 1983)
Bryoerythrophyllum campylocarpum (Müll. Hal.) H. A. Crum AFR (Sollman 2009)
Bryowijkia madagassa Touw AFR (Touw 1993)
Bryum albo-marginatum Cardot in Thér. END (Ochi 1972; Crosby et al. 1983)
B. alpinulum var. *levieri* Renauld & Cardot END (Crosby et al. 1983)
B. alpinum Huds. ex With. var. *alpinum* PAN (Ochi 1972; Ochi 1973; Crosby et al. 1983)
B. apiculatum Schwägr. PAN (Ochi 1972; Crosby et al. 1983)
B. arachnoideum Müll. Hal. Afr-Am (Ochi 1972; Crosby et al. 1983)
B. argenteum Hedw. var. *argenteum* COS (Ochi 1972; Crosby et al. 1983; Pócs and Geissler 2002)
B. aubertii (Schwaegr.) Brid. AFR (Ochi 1972; Crosby et al. 1983)
B. billardierei Schwaegr. var. *billardierei* SCO (Ochi 1972; Mohamed 1979; Crosby et al. 1983)
B. caespiticium Hedw. var. *caespiticium* COS (Pócs and Geissler 2002)
B. capillare Hedw. var. *capillare* COS (Ochi 1972; Crosby et al. 1983)
B. coronatum Schwaegr. PAN (Ochi 1972; Crosby et al. 1983; Pócs and Geissler 2002)
B. dichotomum Hedw. SCO (Crosby et al. 1983)
B. erythrocaulon (Schwägr.) Brid. AFR (Mohamed 1979; Crosby et al. 1983)
B. huillense Welw. & Duby PAN (Ochi 1972; Crosby et al. 1983; Pócs and Geissler 2002)
B. imerinanus O'Shea AFR (O'Shea 2008)
B. leptospeiron Müll. Hal. EMR (Crosby et al. 1983)
B. megalacrion Schwaegr. EMR (Ochi 1972; Crosby et al. 1983)
B. neelgheriense var. *wichurae* (Broth.) Mohamed Afr-As (Pócs and Geissler 2002)
B. paradoxum Schwaegr. PAN (Ochi 1972; Crosby et al. 1983; Delgadillo et al. 1995)
B. perrieri Thér. END (Crosby et al. 1983)
B. pseudotriquetrum (Hedw.) P. Gaertn., B. Mey. & Scherb. var. *pseudotriquetrum* SCO (Crosby et al. 1983)
B. purpureonigrum Duby END (Crosby et al. 1983)

BRYOPHYTA: MOSSES
B. savondroninicus O'Shea END (Crosby et al. 1983; O'Shea 2008)
B. subargenteum Hampe AFR (Ochi 1972; Crosby et al. 1983)
B. viguieri Thér. AFR (Ochi 1972; Crosby et al. 1983)
B. voeltzkowii Broth. AFR (Ochi 1972; Mohamed 1979; Crosby et al. 1983)
Bucklandiella membranaceum (Mitt.) Paris NA (Crosby et al. 1983)
Callicostella africana Mitt. AFR (Crosby et al. 1983)
C. brevipes (Broth.) Broth. AFR (Crosby et al. 1983)
C. constricta (Müll. Hal.) Kindb. AFR (Crosby et al. 1983)
C. fissidentella (Besch.) Kindb. AFR (Crosby et al. 1983)
C. lacerans (Müll. Hal.) A. Jaeger AFR (Crosby et al. 1983)
C. leptocladula (Broth.) Broth. EMR (Crosby et al. 1983)
C. papillata var. *brevifolia* M. Fleisch. AFR (Crosby et al. 1983)
C. papillata (Mont.) Mitt. var. *papillata* PAN (Crosby et al. 1983; Pócs and Geissler 2002)
C. parvocellulata Mitt. NA (Crosby et al. 1983)
C. perrotii (Renauld & Cardot ex Paris) Broth. AFR (Crosby et al. 1983)
C. pusilla Demaret & P. de la Varde AFR (Crosby et al. 1983)
C. seychellensis (Besch.) Kindb. AFR (Crosby et al. 1983; Pócs and Geissler 2002)
C. tristis (Müll. Hal.) Broth. AFR (Pócs and Geissler 2002)
Calymperes afzelii Sw. PAN (Crosby et al. 1983; Pócs and Geissler 2002)
C. erosum Müll. Hal. PAN (Crosby et al. 1983)
C. hispidum Renauld & Cardot EMR (Crosby et al. 1983; Ellis 1988)
C. loucoubense Besch. END (Crosby et al. 1983)
C. palisotii Schwaegr. PAN (Crosby et al. 1983)
C. pallidum Mitt. PAN (Crosby et al. 1983; Delgadillo et al. 1995)
C. sanctae-mariae var. *mayottense* Besch. EMR (Marline et al. 2012)
C. taitense (Sull.) Mitt. PAN (Crosby et al. 1983; Orbán 1995)
C. tenerum Müll. Hal. PAN (Crosby et al. 1983)
C. venezuelanum (Mitt.) Broth. ex Pittier PAN (Orbán 2000)
Calyptothecium acutifolium (Brid.) Broth. in Paris NA (Reeb et al. 2019)
C. bescherellei (Renauld) Broth. END (Crosby et al. 1983)
C. planifrons (Renauld & Paris) Argent AFR (Argent 1973; Crosby et al. 1983; Delgadillo et al. 1995)
Calyptrochaeta asplenioides (Brid.) Crosby AFR (Crosby et al. 1983)
Campylodontium flavescens var. *viride* Cardot END (Crosby et al. 1983)
Campylopus arctocarpus subsp. *madecassus* (Besch.) J.-P. Frahm AFR (Crosby et al. 1983; Frahm 1985)
C. arcuatus (Brid.) A. Jaeger AFR (Crosby et al. 1983; Frahm 1985)
C. aureonitens (Müll. Hal.) A. Jaeger AFR (Crosby et al. 1983; Frahm 1985)
C. cambouei Renauld & Cardot AFR (Crosby et al. 1983; Frahm 1985)
C. catarractilis (Müll. Hal.) Paris PAL (Frahm 1985)

BRYOPHYTA: MOSSES

C. crateris Besch. AFR (Crosby et al. 1983; Frahm 1985)
C. decaryi Thér. AFR (Crosby et al. 1983; Frahm 1985)
C. filifolius (Hornsch.) Mitt. PAN (Crosby et al. 1983; Een 1993)
C. flaccidus Renauld & Cardot AFR (Crosby et al. 1983; Frahm 1985)
C. flexuosus (Hedw.) Brid. var. *flexuosus* AFR (Crosby et al. 1983; Frahm 1985)
C. hildebrandtii (Müll. Hal.) A. Jaeger AFR (Crosby et al. 1983)
C. jamesonii (Hook.) A. Jaeger PAN (Crosby et al. 1983; Frahm 1985)
C. julaceus subsp. *arbogastii* (Renauld & Cardot) J.-P. Frahm AFR (Crosby et al. 1983; Frahm 1985)
C. nanophyllus Müll. Hal. ex Broth. AFR (Crosby et al. 1983)
C. nivalis (Brid.) Brid. var. *nivalis* PAN (Frahm 1985)
C. perpusillus Mitt. AFR (Crosby et al. 1983; Frahm 1985)
C. pilifer Brid. subsp. *pilifer* PAN (Crosby et al. 1983; Frahm 1985)
C. pseudobicolor Müll. Hal. ex Renauld & Cardot AFR (Crosby et al. 1983; Frahm 1985)
C. robillardei Besch. AFR (Crosby et al. 1983; Frahm 1985; Pócs and Geissler 2002)
C. schmidii (Müll. Hal.) A. Jaeger PAN (Crosby et al. 1983; Frahm 1985)
C. smaragdinus (Brid.) A. Jaeger AFR (Crosby et al. 1983; Frahm 1985)
C. thwaitesii (Mitt.) A. Jaeger AFR (Crosby et al. 1983; Frahm 1985)
C. trachyblepharon subsp. *comatus* (Renauld & Cardot) J.-P. Frahm EMR (Crosby et al. 1983; Frahm, 1985)
Cardotiella appendiculata (Renauld & Cardot) Vitt EMR (Crosby et al. 1983; Goffinet 1996)
C. elimbata (Ther.) Goffinet END (Crosby et al. 1983; Goffinet 1996)
C. renauldii (Broth.) Vitt. END (Crosby et al. 1983; Goffinet 1996)
C. subappendiculata (Broth.) Vitt EMR (Crosby et al. 1983)
Catagonium nitens (Brid.) Cardot subsp. *nitens* AFR (Crosby et al. 1983)
Ceratodon purpureus subsp. *convolutus* (Reichardt) Burley EMR (Crosby et al. 1983; Burley and Pritchard 1990; Een 1993)
Chionoloma bombayense (Müll. Hal.) P. Sollm. PAN (Crosby et al. 1983)
Clastobryophilum bogoricum (Bosch & Sande Lac.) M. Fleisch. PAL (Crosby et al. 1983)
Cryphaea jamesonii Taylor PAN (Crosby et al. 1983; Rao 2001)
C. rutenbergii Müll. Hal. AFR (Crosby et al. 1983; Rao, 2001)
Cyclodictyon aubertii (P. Beauv.) Kuntze AFR (Crosby et al. 1983)
C. laetevirens (Hook. & Taylor) Mitt. AFR (Crosby et al. 1983)
C. vallis-gratiae (Müll. Hal.) Kuntze AFR (Crosby et al. 1983; Pócs and Geissler 2002)
Daltonia angustifolia Dozy and Molk. var. *angustifolia* AFR (Crosby et al. 1983)
D. cardotii Bizot & Onr. AFR (Crosby et al. 1983)
D. forsythii Cardot END (Crosby et al. 1983)

BRYOPHYTA: MOSSES

D. latimarginata Besch. var. *latimarginata* EMR (Crosby et al. 1983)
D. latimarginata var. *madagassa* Renauld AFR (Crosby et al. 1983)
Dicranella acroclada Cardot EMR (Crosby et al. 1983)
D. borbonica var. *madagascariensis* Thér. END (Crosby et al. 1983)
D. madagassa Renauld EMR (Crosby et al. 1983)
D. pervilleana Besch. EMR (Crosby et al. 1983)
D. polii Renauld & Cardot EMR (Crosby et al. 1983)
D. subsubulata (Hampe ex Müll. Hal.) A. Jaeger AFR (Crosby et al. 1983)
Dicranoloma billardierei (Brid. ex Anon.) Paris var. *billardierei* PAN (Crosby et al. 1983)
D. billardieri var. *patentifolium* (Renauld & Paris) Thér. AFR (Crosby et al. 1983)
D. billardieri var. *scopareolum* (Müll. Hal.) Thér. AFR (Crosby et al. 1983)
Dicranum johnstonii Mitt. AFR (Pócs and Geissler 2002)
Didymodon subrevolutus (Hampe) Broth. END (Crosby et al. 1983)
Distichium capillaceum (Hedw.) Bruch, Schimp. & W. Guembel var. *capillaceum* AFR (Crosby et al. 1983)
Distichophyllum mascarenicum Besch. EMR (Marline et al. 2012)
D. rakotomariae Crosby END (Crosby et al. 1983; Touw 1993)
Ditrichum difficile (Duby) M. Fleisch. PAN (Crosby et al. 1983)
D. luteum Dixon & Thér. END (Crosby et al. 1983)
D. madagassum (Renauld & Cardot) Paris END (Crosby et al. 1983)
D. pallidum (Hedw.) Hampe SCO (Crosby et al. 1983)
Ectropothecium chenagonii Renauld & Cardot AFR (Crosby et al. 1983)
E. chenagonii var. *hamatulum* Renauld & Cardot END (Crosby et al. 1983)
E. intertextum Renauld & Cardot EMR (Crosby et al. 1983)
E. mauritianum Renauld & Cardot EMR (Crosby et al. 1983)
E. occultum Renauld & Cardot EMR (Crosby et al. 1983)
E. ovalifolium (Besch.) W. R. Buck END (Crosby et al. 1983)
E. pailotii Renauld & Cardot AFR (Crosby et al. 1983)
E. perrieri Thér. END (Crosby et al. 1983)
E. perrotii Renauld & Cardot AFR (Crosby et al. 1983)
E. regulare (Brid.) A. Jaeger AFR (Crosby et al. 1983)
E. seychellarum Besch. EMR (Crosby et al. 1983)
E. tamatavense Broth. AFR (Crosby et al. 1983)
Entodon corbieri Renauld & Cardot END (Crosby et al. 1983; Tixier 1995)
E. felicis Renauld & Cardot var. *felicis* END (Crosby et al. 1983)
E. felicis var. *julaceus* Renauld & Cardot END (Crosby et al. 1983)
E. madagassus Geh. END (Crosby et al. 1983)
E. rutenbergii Geh. END (Crosby et al. 1983)
Entodontopsis nitens (Mitt.) W. R. Buck & Ireland Afr-Am (Crosby et al. 1983)
E. tenuinervis (Broth.) W. R. Buck & Ireland AFR (Crosby et al. 1983)
Entosthodon borbonicus Besch. AFR (Crosby et al. 1983)
E. marginatulus Müll. Hal. ex Geh. END (Crosby et al. 1983)

(continued overleaf)

TABLE 8.14. ***continued***

BRYOPHYTA: MOSSES

E. mauritianus Schimp. ex Besch. EMR (Marline et al. 2012)
E. renauldii Thér. in Renauld END (Crosby et al. 1983)
Epipterygium diversifolium Renauld & Cardot END (Tixier 1979b; Crosby et al. 1983)
Erpodium beccarii Müll. Hal. ex Venturi var. *beccarii* Afr-Am (Tixier 1979b; Crosby et al. 1983)
E. madagassum Paris & Renauld END (Crum 1972; Crosby et al. 1983)
Erythrodontium lacoutourei Renauld & Cardot END (Crosby et al. 1983)
Eurhynchium spinulinerve Kiaer ex Cardot EMR (Crosby et al. 1983)
E. striatum (Schreb. ex Hedw.) Schimp. AFR (Crosby et al. 1983)
Eustichia longirostris (Brid.) Brid. PAN (Crosby et al. 1983)
Fabronia campenonii Renauld & Cardot END (Crosby et al. 1983)
F. crassiretis Renauld & Cardot AFR (Crosby et al. 1983)
F. fastigiata var. *asperula* Renauld & Paris END (Crosby et al. 1983)
F. fastigiata Renauld & Cardot var. *fastigiata* END (Crosby et al. 1983)
F. garnieri (Paris & Renauld) Renauld & Paris END (Crosby et al. 1983)
F. lachenaudii Renauld END (Crosby et al. 1983)
F. motelayi Renauld & Cardot END (Crosby et al. 1983)
F. villaumii Renauld & Cardot END (Crosby et al. 1983)
Fissidens angustifolius Sull. PAN (Bruggeman-Nannenga 2009; Bruggeman-Nannenga and Arts 2010)
F. aristifer Brugg.-Nann. EMR (Bruggeman-Nannenga 2009)
F. asplenioides Hedw. PAN (Crosby et al. 1983; Bruggeman-Nannenga and Arts 2010)
F. bogosicus Müll. Hal. in Venturi AFR (Crosby et al. 1983; Bruggeman-Nannenga and Arts 2010)
F. borgenii Hampe AFR (Bruggeman-Nannenga 1993)
F. crispulus Brid. AFR (Crosby et al. 1983; Bruggeman-Nannenga and Arts 2010)
F. cryptarum Müll. Hal. AFR (Marline et al. 2012)
F. cryptoneuron P. de la Varde AFR (Crosby et al. 1983)
F. curvatus Hornsch. var. *curvatus* AFR (Crosby et al. 1983; Bruggeman-Nannenga and Arts 2010)
F. cyathaeicola Brugg. Nann. AFR (Marline et al. 2012)
F. darntyi Schimp. AFR (Crosby et al. 1983)
F. ellipticus Besch. AFR (Crosby et al. 1983)
F. flaccidus Mitt. PAL (Bruggeman-Nannenga 2009)
F. grainvillei Thér. END (Crosby et al. 1983)
F. hookerioides Bizot & Onr. END (Crosby et al. 1983)
F. hymenodon Besch. AFR (Crosby et al. 1983)
F. inclusus Bizot & Dury ex Pócs AFR (Bruggeman-Nannenga 2009)
F. intramarginatus (Hampe) A. Jaeger Afr-Am (Bizot 1974; Crosby et al. 1983; Bruggeman-Nannenga and Arts 2010)
F. leucocinctus Hampe AFR (Crosby et al. 1983; Bruggeman-Nannenga and Arts 2010)
F. madecassus Müll. Hal. EMR (Crosby et al. 1983; Bruggeman-Nannenga 2009; Bruggeman-Nannenga and Arts 2010)

BRYOPHYTA: MOSSES

F. mariei (Besch.) Broth. END (Crosby et al. 1983)
F. motelayi Renauld & Cardot END (Crosby et al. 1983)
F. ovatus Brid. AFR (Crosby et al. 1983; Bruggeman-Nannenga and Arts 2010)
F. pallidinervis Mitt. PAN (Reeb et al. 2019)
F. pellucidus Hornsch. var. *pellucidus* PAN (Crosby et al. 1983; Delgadillo et al. 1995; Bruggeman-Nannenga and Arts 2010)
F. planifrons Besch. PAL (Bruggeman-Nannenga and Arts 2010)
F. platyneuros Renauld & Cardot END (Crosby et al. 1983)
F. plumosus Hornsch. AFR (Bruggeman-Nannenga and Arts 2010)
F. pocsii Bizot & Dury ex Pócs AFR (Bruggeman-Nannenga 2009; Bruggeman-Nannenga and Arts 2010)
F. punctulatus Sande Lac PAL (Bruggeman-Nannenga and Arts 2010)
F. ramulosus Mitt. AFR (Crosby et al. 1983; Bruggeman-Nannenga and Arts 2010)
F. reflexus Hampe AFR (Crosby et al. 1983; Bruggeman-Nannenga 2009)
F. rosulatus P. de la Varde END (Crosby et al. 1983)
F. rufescens Hornsch. AFR (Bruggeman-Nannenga 2009)
F. sciophyllus Mitt. fo. *sciophyllus* AFR (Crosby et al. 1983; Bruggeman-Nannenga 1993; Bruggeman-Nannenga and Arts 2010)
F. scleromitrius (Besch.) Broth. AFR (Bescherelle 1891; Crosby et al. 1983)
F. serratus Müll. Hal. var. *serratus* PAN (Crosby et al. 1983; Delgadillo et al. 1995; Bruggeman-Nannenga 2010)
F. submarginatus Bruch ex C. Krauss Afr-Am (Crosby et al. 1983; Bruggeman-Nannenga and Arts 2010)
F. subplanifrons Bizot & Onraedt ex Brugg.-Nann NA (Bruggeman-Nannenga 2009)
F. subundatus Dury AFR (Crosby et al. 1983)
F. zollingeri Mont. PAN (Crosby et al. 1983; Bruggeman-Nannenga and Arts 2010)
Floribundaria floribunda (Dozy & Molk.) M. Fleisch. var. *floribunda* AFR (Crosby et al. 1983)
F. floribunda var. *madagassa* (Renauld & Cardot) Renauld & Cardot END (Crosby et al. 1983)
F. floribundula (Müll. Hal.) M. Fleisch. EMR (Crosby et al. 1983)
F. vaginans (Welw. & Duby) Broth. AFR (Crosby et al. 1983)
Funaria decaryi Thér. END (Crosby et al. 1983)
F. delicatula Thér. END (Crosby et al. 1983)
F. hygrometrica var. *calvescens* (Schwägr.) Kindb. PAN (Crosby et al. 1983; Pócs and Geissler 2002)
F. hygrometrica Hedw. var. *hygrometrica* COS (Crosby et al. 1983)
F. imerinensis Cardot in Grandid. END (Crosby et al. 1983)
F. subleptopoda Hampe END (Crosby et al. 1983)
Gammiella ceylonensis (Broth. in Herzog) B. C. Tan & W. R. Buck PAL (Crosby et al. 1983)
Garckea flexuosa (Griff.) Margad. & Nork. PAN (Tixier 1979b; Crosby et al. 1983)
Gigaspermum repens (Hook.) Lindb. AFR (Crosby et al. 1983)

BRYOPHYTA: MOSSES

Glossadelphus guineensis (Broth. & Paris) Crosby, B. H. Allen & Magill AFR (Crosby et al. 1983)
G. semiscabrus (Renauld & Cardot) Crosby, B. H. Allen & Magill END (Crosby et al. 1983)
G. viridis (Renauld & Cardot) Crosby, B. H. Allen & Magill END (Crosby et al. 1983)
Grimmia elatior Bruch ex Bals.-Criv. & De Not. SCO (Crosby et al. 1983)
G. elongata Kaulf. SCO (Crosby et al. 1983)
G. longirostris Hook. SCO (J. Muñoz 1998)
Groutiella laxotorquata (Besch.) Wijk & Margad. AFR (Crosby et al. 1983)
Gymnostomiella tuberculosa (Renauld & Paris) Arts & P. Sollm. AFR (O'Shea 2008)
Gymnostomum madagascariense O'Shea END (Crosby et al. 1983)
Hedwigia ciliata (Hedw.) Ehrh. ex P. Beauv. var. *ciliata* COS (Crosby et al. 1983)
Helicodontium fabroniopsis Müll. Hal. END (Crosby et al. 1983)
Herpetineuron toccoae (Sull. & Lesq.) Cardot PAN (Crosby et al. 1983)
Hildebrandtiella endotrichelloides Müll. Hal. EMR (Crosby et al. 1983)
H. longiseta Renauld & Cardot END (Crosby et al. 1983)
H. rotundifolia Renauld EMR (Crosby et al. 1983)
Holomitrium borbonicum Besch. var. *borbonicum* EMR (Crosby et al. 1983)
H. borbonicum var. *hamatum* (Müll. Hal.) Thér. AFR (Crosby et al. 1983)
H. camptocarpum P. de la Varde END (Crosby et al. 1983)
H. cylindraceum var. *cucullatum* (Besch.) Wijk & Margad. AFR (Crosby et al. 1983)
H. cylindraceum (P. Beauv.) Wijk & Margad. var. *cylindraceum* AFR (Crosby et al. 1983)
H. cylindraceum var. *obtusifolium* (Besch.) Wijk & Margad. AFR (Crosby et al. 1983)
H. gracilisetum Thér. END (Crosby et al. 1983)
H. hillieri Thér. END (Crosby et al. 1983)
H. lepervanchei Thér. EMR (Crosby et al. 1983)
H. rhyparodictyon P. de la Varde END (Crosby et al. 1983)
H. subglobosum Thér. END (Crosby et al. 1983)
Homaliodendron exiguum (Bosch & Sande Lac.) M. Fleisch. PAL (Crosby et al. 1983; Enroth 1993)
H. piniforme (Brid.) Enroth AFR (Crosby et al. 1983)
Hookeriopsis diversifolia (Renauld & Cardot) Broth. ex Cardot in Grandid. EMR (Crosby et al. 1983)
Hygrohypnum caussequei (Renauld & Cardot) Cardot in Grandid. END (Crosby et al. 1983)
Hymenostylium subcrispulum Thér. END (Crosby et al. 1983)
Hyophila acuminata Broth. & P. de la Varde AFR (Crosby et al. 1983)
H. angustifolia Paris & Renauld END (Crosby et al. 1983)
H. involuta (Hook.) A. Jaeger PAN (Crosby et al. 1983)
H. lanceolata Renauld & Cardot EMR (Crosby et al. 1983)

BRYOPHYTA: MOSSES

H. nymaniana (M. Fleisch.) M. Menzel PAN (Reeb et al. 2019)
H. parietalis Cardot in Grandid. END (Crosby et al. 1983)
H. potieri var. *atroviridis* Renauld & Cardot END (Crosby et al. 1983)
H. sakalavensis Paris & Renauld EMR (Crosby et al. 1983)
Hypnum jutlandicum Holmen & E. Warncke AFR (Crosby et al. 1983)
H. macrogynum Besch. AFR (Crosby et al. 1983)
Hypopterygium tamarisci (Sw. ex Sw.) Brid. ex Müll. Hal. PAN (Crosby et al. 1983; Kruijer 1997; Kruijer 2002)
Isopterygium ambreanum Renauld & Cardot END (Crosby et al. 1983)
I. antsihanakense Cardot END (Crosby et al. 1983)
I. argillicola (Renauld & Cardot) Broth. END (Crosby et al. 1983)
I. argyroleucum Besch. AFR (Crosby et al. 1983)
I. austrodenticulatum (Renauld & Cardot) Broth. END (Crosby et al. 1983)
I. combae Besch. END (Crosby et al. 1983)
I. gracile Renauld & Cardot EMR (Crosby et al. 1983)
I. intortum var. *chenagonii* Renauld & Cardot END (Crosby et al. 1983)
I. intortum (P. Beauv.) A. Jaeger var. *intortum* EMR (Crosby et al. 1983)
I. leptoblastum (Müll. Hal.) A. Jaeger EMR (Crosby et al. 1983)
I. luteonitens (Paris) Paris END (Crosby et al. 1983)
I. meylanii Cardot END (Crosby et al. 1983)
I. podorrhizum Renauld & Cardot END (Crosby et al. 1983)
I. subleptoblastum Müll. Hal. EMR (Crosby et al. 1983)
Jaegerina solitaria var. *nossi-beana* Besch. END (Crosby et al. 1983)
J. stolonifera (Müll. Hal.) Müll. Hal. subsp. *stolonifera* AFR (Argent 1973; Crosby et al. 1983)
Lepidopilidium attenuatum Thér. END (Crosby et al. 1983)
L. chenagonii (Renauld & Cardot) Cardot END (Crosby et al. 1983)
L. corbieri (Renauld & Cardot) Cardot END (Crosby et al. 1983)
L. parvulum Cardot END (Crosby et al. 1983)
L. subrevolutum (Renauld & Cardot) Cardot EMR (Crosby et al. 1983)
Lepidopilum hirsutum var. *tuberculatum* Thér. END (Crosby et al. 1983; Churchill 1988)
L. lastii Mitt. AFR (Crosby et al. 1983; Churchill 1988)
L. verrucipes Cardot AFR (Crosby et al. 1983)
Leptobryum pyriforme (Hedw.) Wilson COS (Crosby et al. 1983)
Leptodon fuciformis (Brid.) Enroth EMR (Crosby et al. 1983)
Leptodontium flexifolium (With.) Hampe in Lindb. PAN (Sollman 2006)
L. pungens (Mitt.) Kindb. Afr-Am (De Sloover 1987)
L. viticulosoides (P. Beauv.) Wijk & Margad. var. *viticulosoides* AFR (Zander 1972; Crosby et al. 1983; De Sloover 1987; Delgadillo et al. 1995)
Leptotrichella minuta (Hampe) Ochyra AFR (Crosby et al. 1983)

(continued overleaf)

TABLE 8.14. ***continued***

BRYOPHYTA: MOSSES

L. pallidiseta (Brid.) Ochyra END (Crosby et al. 1983)
Leucobryum acutifolium (Mitt.) Cardot AFR (Crosby et al. 1983)
L. boivinianum Besch. END (Crosby et al. 1983)
L. boryanum Besch. var. *boryanum* EMR (Crosby et al. 1983)
L. boryanum var. *minus* Cardot END (Crosby et al. 1983)
L. cambouei Cardot END (Crosby et al. 1983; Pócs and Geissler 2002)
L. comorense Müll. Hal. EMR (Crosby et al. 1983)
L. cucullatum Broth. var. *cucullatum* AFR (Crosby et al. 1983)
L. cucullatum var. *rutenbergii* (Geh.) Cardot AFR (Crosby et al. 1983)
L. galinonii Cardot & Paris END (Crosby et al. 1983)
L. heterodictyon Besch. var. *heterodictyon* END (Bescherelle 1891; Crosby et al. 1983)
L. heterodictyon var. *microphyllum* (Cardot) Wijk & Margad. END (Crosby et al. 1983)
L. isleanum var. *isleanum* Besch. AFR (Crosby et al. 1983)
L. isleanum var. *molle* (Müll. Hal.) Cardot AFR (Crosby et al. 1983)
L. madagassum Besch. AFR (Crosby et al. 1983)
L. mayottense Cardot AFR (Crosby et al. 1983)
L. parvulum Cardot END (Crosby et al. 1983; Pócs and Geissler 2002)
L. perrotii Renauld & Cardot AFR (Crosby et al. 1983; Pócs and Geissler 2002)
L. pseudomadagassum Cardot END (Crosby et al. 1983)
L. sanctae-mariae Cardot END (Crosby et al. 1983; Pócs and Geissler 2002)
Leucodon canariensis (Brid.) Schwägr. AFR (Crosby et al. 1983)
L. rutenbergii Müll. Hal. ex Geh. AFR (Crosby et al. 1983)
Leucoloma albocinctum Renauld & Cardot AFR (Crosby et al. 1983; La Farge 2002c)
L. allorgei Thér. END (Crosby et al. 1983; La Farge 2002c)
L. ambreanum Renauld & Cardot END (Crosby et al. 1983; La Farge 2002c)
L. bifidum (Brid.) Brid. EMR (Crosby et al. 1983)
L. boivinianum Besch. var. *boivinianum* EMR (Crosby et al. 1983)
L. boivinianum var. *brevifolium* Renauld END (Crosby et al. 1983; La Farge 2002c)
L. brevioperculatum Dixon END (Crosby et al. 1983; La Farge 2002c)
L. brotheri Renauld in Levier. AFR (Crosby et al. 1983; La Farge 2002c)
L. caespitulans (Müll. Hal.) A. Jaeger EMR (Marline et al. 2012)
L. candidum Broth. In Vœltzk. END (Crosby et al. 1983; La Farge 2002c)
L. capillifolium Renauld END (Crosby et al. 1983; La Farge 2002c)
L. chrysobasilare (Müll. Hal.) A. Jaeger var. *chrysobasilare* AFR (Crosby et al. 1983)
L. cinclidotioides Besch. EMR (Marline 2018)
L. cirrosulum Renauld END (Crosby et al. 1983; La Farge 2002c)
L. crosbyi La Farge-England END (La Farge-England 1992; La Farge 2002a, 2002c)

BRYOPHYTA: MOSSES

L. cuneifolium (Hampe ex Müll. Hal. & Geh.) C. H. Wright AFR (Crosby et al. 1983; La Farge 2002b, 2002c)
L. decaryi Thér. END (Crosby et al. 1983; La Farge 2002c)
L. delicatulum Renauld EMR (Crosby et al. 1983; La Farge 2002c)
L. dichelymoides (Müll. Hal.) A. Jaeger EMR (Crosby et al. 1983; La Farge 2002a)
L. fontinaloides Dixon END (Crosby et al. 1983; La Farge 2002a, 2002c)
L. fuscifolium var. *crispatulum* Renauld EMR (Crosby et al. 1983)
L. fuscifolium Besch. var. *fuscifolium* EMR (Crosby et al. 1983)
L. garnieri fo. *aquaticum* Thér. END (Crosby et al. 1983; La Farge 2002c)
L. garnieri Paris & Renauld fo. *garnieri* END (Crosby et al. 1983; La Farge 2002c)
L. gracilescens Broth. AFR (Marline et al. 2018)
L. grandidieri Renauld & Cardot END (Crosby et al. 1983; La Farge-England 1992; La Farge 2002a, 2002c)
L. grimmioides P. de la Varde AFR (Crosby et al. 1983; La Farge 2002b, 2002c)
L. holstii Broth. AFR (Marline 2018)
L. humbertii P. de la Varde END (Crosby et al. 1983; La Farge 2002b, 2002c)
L. incrassatum Thér. END (Crosby et al. 1983; La Farge 2002c)
L. lepervancheri Besch. AFR (La Farge 2002a; La Farge 2002c)
L. longifolium (Brid.) Wijk & Margad. EMR (Crosby et al. 1983; La Farge 2002c)
L. madagascariense La Farge END (La Farge 2002a, 2002c)
L. marojeziense La Farge END (La Farge 2002a, 2002b, 2002c)
L. membranaceum La Farge EMR (La Farge 2002a)
L. ochrobasilare subsp. *longifolium* (Ther.) La Farge END (Crosby et al. 1983; La Farge 2002a, 2002c)
L. ochrobasilare Renauld subsp. *ochrobasilare* EMR (Crosby et al. 1983; La Farge 2002a)
L. oncophorellum Müll. Hal. END (Crosby et al. 1983; La Farge 2002c)
L. perrieri Ther. END (Crosby et al. 1983; La Farge 2002c)
L. persecundum var. *perrotii* Renauld END (Crosby et al. 1983; La Farge 2002c)
L. persecundum Besch. var. *persecundum* EMR (Crosby et al. 1983)
L. pumilum C. H. Wright END (Crosby et al. 1983)
L. pusillum Cardot END (Crosby et al. 1983; La Farge 2002c)
L. rutenbergii var. *abbreviatum* Renauld END (Crosby et al. 1983)
L. rutenbergii var. *elatum* Renauld AFR (Crosby et al. 1983; La Farge 2002c)
L. rutenbergii var. *perrotii* Renauld END (Crosby et al. 1983; La Farge 2002c)
L. rutenbergii (Geh.) C. H. Wright var. *rutenbergii* END (Crosby et al. 1983; La Farge 2002c)
L. sanctae-mariae Besch. AFR (Crosby et al. 1983; La Farge 2002a, 2002c)
L. seychellense Besch. EMR (Crosby et al. 1983; La Farge 2002a, 2002c)
L. sinuosulum Müll. Hal. ex Besch. AFR (Crosby et al. 1983)

BRYOPHYTA: MOSSES

L. squarrosulum (Geh.) Wright END (Crosby et al. 1983)
L. subchrysobasilare Renauld END (Crosby et al. 1983; La Farge 2002a, 2002c)
L. talazaccii Renauld & Cardot END (Crosby et al. 1983; La Farge 2002a, 2002c)
L. thraustum Hampe ex Besch. END (Crosby et al. 1983; La Farge 2002a, 2002c)
L. thuretii Besch. END (Crosby et al. 1983; La Farge 2002a, 2002c)
L. tuberculosum Renauld END (Crosby et al. 1983; La Farge 2002a, 2002c)
L. villaumei Thér. END (Crosby et al. 1983; La Farge 2002c)
Leucomium strumosum (Hornsch.) Mitt. PAN (Crosby et al. 1983; B. Allen 1987; Pócs and Geissler 2002)
Leucophanes angustifolium Renauld & Cardot AFR (Marline 2018)
L. hildebrandtii Müll. Hal. AFR (Crosby et al. 1983; Salazar Allen 1993)
L. renauldii Cardot AFR (Crosby et al. 1983; Salazar Allen 1993; Pócs and Geissler 2002)
L. rodriguezii Müll. Hal. AFR (Salazar Allen 1993)
Lopidium struthiopteris (Brid.) M. Fleisch. PAL (Crosby et al. 1983; Kruijer 1997; Kruijer 2002)
Luisierella barbula (Schwägr.) COS (Reeb et al. 2019)
Macrocoma tenuis (Hook. & Grev.) Vitt subsp. *tenuis* PAN (Crosby et al. 1983)
Macrohymenium acidodon (Mont.) Dozy & Molk. AFR (Eakin 1976; Crosby et al. 1983; Een 1997)
M. muelleri Dozy & Molk. AFR (Eakin 1976)
M. rufum Müll. Hal. AFR (Eakin 1976)
M. strictum Bosch. & Sande Lac. PAL (Eakin 1976)
Macromitrium adelphinum Cardot END (Crosby et al. 1983)
M. ancistrophyllum Cardot END (Crosby et al. 1983)
M. anomodictyon Cardot END (Crosby et al. 1983)
M. calocalyx Geh. END (Crosby et al. 1983)
M. fasciculare var. *angustifolium* P. de la Varde END (Crosby et al. 1983)
M. fasciculare var. *fasciculare* Mitt. PAL (Crosby et al. 1983)
M. fimbriatum (P. Beauv.) Schwägr. EMR (Crosby et al. 1983)
M. mauritianum Schwägr. AFR (Crosby et al. 1983)
M. nanothecium Cardot var. *nanothecium* END (Crosby et al. 1983)
M. nanothecium var. *sublaeve* Thér. END (Crosby et al. 1983)
M. onraedtii Bizot END (Bizot, 1974; Crosby et al. 1983)
M. orthostichum Nees ex Schwägr. PAL (Crosby et al. 1983)
M. proximum Thér. END (Crosby et al. 1983)
M. rhizomatosum Müll. Hal. END (Crosby et al. 1983)
M. sanctae-mariae Renauld & Cardot END (Crosby et al. 1983)
M. sclerodictyon Cardot EMR (Crosby et al. 1983)
M. semipapillosum Thér. & P. de la Varde END (Crosby et al. 1983)
M. serpens (Bruch ex Hook. & Grev.) Brid. PAL (Crosby et al. 1983)
M. soulae Renauld & Cardot END (Crosby et al. 1983)
M. subpungens var. *madagassum* Cardot END (Crosby et al. 1983)

BRYOPHYTA: MOSSES

M. subpungens Hampe ex Müll. Hal. var. *subpungens* AFR (Crosby et al. 1983)
M. subtortum (Hook. & Grev.) Schwägr. END (Crosby et al. 1983)
M. sulcatum (Hook.) Brid. var. *sulcatum* AFR (Crosby et al. 1983; Ellis and Wilbraham 2008)
M. urceolatulum Müll. Hal. ex Geh. AFR (Crosby et al. 1983)
Meiothecium crassirete (Renauld & Cardot) Cardot END (Crosby et al. 1983)
M. madagascariense (Brid.) Broth. EMR (Crosby et al. 1983; Een 1997)
M. undulatum (Renauld & Cardot) O'Shea END (Crosby et al. 1983)
Mesonodon flavescens (Hook.) W. R. Buck AFR (Crosby et al. 1983)
Microcampylopus laevigatus (Thér.) Giese & J.-P. Frahm PAN (Crosby et al. 1983; Giese and Frahm 1985)
Mielichhoferia cardotii A. J. Shaw & H. A. Crum END (Crosby et al. 1983)
M. madagassa var. *gracilis* Thér. END (Crosby et al. 1983)
Mittenothamnium horridulum (Broth.) Cardot AFR (Crosby et al. 1983)
M. lacouturei (Renauld & Cardot) Cardot END (Crosby et al. 1983)
M. limosum (Besch.) Cardot EMR (Crosby et al. 1983)
M. madagassum (Besch.) Cardot EMR (Crosby et al. 1983; Een 1997)
M. microthamnioides var. *glauculum* (Cardot) Wijk & Margad. END (Crosby et al. 1983)
M. microthamnioides (Geh.) Wijk & Margad. var. *microthamnioides* AFR (Crosby et al. 1983; Een 1997)
M. reptans (Hedw.) Cardot PAN (Crosby et al. 1983)
Mitthyridium fasciculatum (Hook. & Grev.) H. Rob. var. *fasciculatum* EMR (Reese 1991)
M. subflavum (Renauld & Cardot) H. Rob. AFR (C. Müller 1897; Crosby et al. 1983)
Mniobryum perlaxum Thér. & P. de la Varde END (Crosby et al. 1983)
Neckera remota Bruch & Schimp. ex Müll. Hal. AFR (Crosby et al. 1983)
N. valentiniana Besch. AFR (Crosby et al. 1983)
Neckeropsis boiviniana (Besch.) Cardot EMR (Crosby et al. 1983)
N. disticha (Hedw.) Kindb. PAN (Marline et al. 2012)
N. foveolata (Mitt.) Broth. PAN (Reeb et al. 2019)
N. lepineana (Mont.) M. Fleisch. PAL (Crosby et al. 1983)
N. madecassa (Besch.) M. Fleisch. AFR (Crosby et al. 1983)
Ochrobryum sakalavum Cardot & Paris END (Crosby et al. 1983; B. Allen 1992; Pócs and Geissler 2002)
Octoblepharum africanum (Broth.) Cardot AFR (Crosby et al. 1983)
O. albidum Hedw. PAN (Crosby et al. 1983; Pócs and Geissler 2002)
Oedipodiella australis (Wager & Dixon) Dixon AFR (Marline et al. 2012)
Oreoweisia erosa (Müll. Hal.) Kindb. Afr-Am (Crosby et al. 1983)

(continued overleaf)

TABLE 8.14. ***continued***

BRYOPHYTA: MOSSES

Orthostichella longinervis (Renauld & Cardot) B. H. Allen & Magill. EMR (B. Allen and Magill 2007)
O. pentasticha (Brid.) W. R. Buck Afr-Am (Crosby et al. 1983)
O. rigida (Müll. Hal.) B. H. Allen & Magill PAN (B. Allen and Magill 2007)
O. versicolor (Müll. Hal.) B. H. Allen & Magill. PAN (Crosby et al. 1983; B. Allen and Magill 2003)
O. welwitschii (Duby) B. H. Allen & Magill. PAN (B. Allen and Magill 2007)
Orthostichidium involutifolium (Mitt.) Broth. subsp. *involutifolium* AFR (Crosby et al. 1983)
Orthostichopsis longinervis (Renauld & Cardot) Broth. EMR (Crosby et al. 1983)
O. madagassa Dixon END (Argent 1973; Crosby et al. 1983)
O. scaberula (Renauld & Cardot) M. Fleisch END (Crosby et al. 1983)
O. subimbricata var. *flageyi* (Renauld & Cardot) Cardot END (Crosby et al. 1983)
O. subimbricata (Hampe) Broth. var. *subimbricata* AFR (Argent 1973; Crosby et al. 1983)
Palamocladium leskeoides (Hook.) E. Britton PAN (Crosby et al. 1983; Hofmann 1997)
Papillaria africana (Müll. Hal.) A. Jaeger var. *africana* AFR (Crosby et al. 1983)
P. africana var. *gracilis* (Renauld & Cardot) Wijk & Margad. END (Crosby et al. 1983)
P. borchgrevinkii Kiaer AFR (Crosby et al. 1983)
P. flaccidula Cardot END (Crosby et al. 1983)
P. perichaetialis (Hampe) A. Jaeger END (Crosby et al. 1983)
Pelekium chenagonii (Müll. Hal. ex Renauld & Cardot) Touw AFR (Touw 1976; Crosby et al. 1983)
P. gratum (P. Beauv.) Touw AFR (Touw 1976, 2001; Crosby et al. 1983)
P. intricatum (A. Jaeger) Touw AFR (Pócs and Geissler 2002)
P. investe (Mitt.) Touw AFR (Touw 1976, 2001; Crosby et al. 1983; Pócs and Geissler 2002)
P. ramusculosum (Mitt.) Touw AFR (Touw 1976; Crosby et al. 1983)
P. varians (Welw. & Duby) Touw AFR (Touw 1976; Crosby et al. 1983)
P. versicolor (Müll. Hal.) Touw AFR (Touw 1976; Crosby et al. 1983; Touw 2001)
Philonotis byssiformis Müll. Hal. END (Crosby et al. 1983)
P. hastata (Duby) Wijk & Margad. SCO (Crosby et al. 1983)
P. mauritiana Aongstr. var. *mauritiana* AFR (Crosby et al. 1983)
P. mauritiana var. *stricta* Renauld & Cardot END (Crosby et al. 1983)
P. perpusilla Cardot END (Crosby et al. 1983)
P. perrieri Ther. AFR (Crosby et al. 1983)
P. sparsifolia (Hampe) A. Jaeger AFR (Crosby et al. 1983)
Phyllodon scutellifolius (Besch.) W. R. Buck END (Crosby et al. 1983; O'Shea and Buck 2001)

BRYOPHYTA: MOSSES

P. truncatulus (Welw. & Duby) W. R. Buck Afr-Am (Crosby et al. 1983)
Phyllogonium viscosum (P. Beauv.) Mitt. PAN (Crosby et al. 1983)
Physcomitrium coarctatum Cardot END (Crosby et al. 1983)
P. dilatatum Renauld & Cardot END (Crosby et al. 1983)
Pilotrichella flexilis (Hedw.) Aongstr. fo. *flexilis* Afr-Am (Crosby et al. 1983; B. Allen and Magill 2003)
P. flexilis fo. *nudiramulosa* (Müll. Hal.) B. H. Allen & Magill NA (B. Allen and Magill 2003)
P. mascarenica (Müll. Hal.) A. Jaeger AFR (Crosby et al. 1983; B. Allen and Magill 2003)
P. pseudo-imbricata (Müll. Hal.) A. Jaeger AFR (Crosby et al. 1983)
Pinnatella minuta (Mitt.) Broth. PAN (Crosby et al. 1983; Enroth 1994)
Plagiomnium rhynchophorum (Hook.) T. J. Kop. var. *rhynchophorum* AFR (Koponen 1981; Crosby et al. 1983)
Pleuridium nervosum (Hook.) Mitt. AFR (Tixier 1979b; Crosby et al. 1983)
Pogonatum belangeri (Müll. Hal.) A. Jaeger AFR (Hyvönen 1989; Pócs and Geissler 2002)
P. capense (Hampe) A. Jaeger AFR (Crosby et al. 1983; Hyvönen 1989; De Sloover 1986; Pócs and Geissler 2002)
P. convolutum (Hedw.) P. Beauv. EMR (Crosby et al. 1983; Hyvönen 1989; De Sloover 1986; Pócs and Geissler 2002)
P. gracilifolium Besch. AFR (Crosby et al. 1983)
Pohlia baronii Wijk & Margad. AFR (Crosby et al. 1983)
P. elongata Hedw. var. *elongata* AFR (Crosby et al. 1983; Delgadillo et al. 1995)
P. heribaudii var. *madagassa* (Renauld & Cardot) Wijk & Margad. AFR (Crosby et al. 1983)
P. lacouturei (Ther.) O'Shea END (Crosby et al. 1983)
Polytrichastrum formosum (Hedw.) G. L. Sm. PAL (Crosby et al. 1983)
Polytrichum commune Hedw. var. *commune* COS (Crosby et al. 1983; De Sloover 1986)
P. glabrum Schrad. EMR (Crosby et al. 1983)
P. juniperellum Geh. END (Crosby et al. 1983)
P. subformosum var. *parvisetum* (Müll. Hal.) Cardot END (Crosby et al. 1983)
P. subpilosum P. Beauv. AFR (Crosby et al. 1983; De Sloover 1986)
Porotrichum elongatum (Welw. & Duby) A. Gepp AFR (De Sloover 1983)
P. madagassum Kiaer ex Besch. AFR (De Sloover 1983)
P. stipitatum (Mitt.) W. R. Buck AFR (De Sloover 1983)
P. usagarum Mitt. AFR (De Sloover 1983)
P. variifolioides (De Sloover) Enroth AFR (De Sloover 1983)
Powellia elliptica (Renauld) Zanten END (Crosby et al. 1983; van Zanten 2003)
P. pocsii Zanten AFR (van Zanten 2003)
Prionodon ciliatus Besch. AFR (Crosby et al. 1983)
Pseudephemerum nitidum (Hedw.) Reimers SCO (Crosby et al. 1983)

BRYOPHYTA: MOSSES

Pseudocrossidium porphyreoneurum (Müll. Hal.) R. H. Zander AFR (Reeb et al. 2019)
Pseudoleskea obtusiuscula Renauld & Cardot END (Crosby et al. 1983)
Pseudopohlia microstoma (Harv.) Mizush. PAL (Crosby et al. 1983)
Pterobryopsis longissima Dixon END (Crosby et al. 1983)
Pterogoniadelphus assimilis (Müll. Hal.) Ochyra & Zijlstra AFR (Crosby et al. 1983)
Pterogonium gracile (Hedw.) Sm. PAN (Crosby et al. 1983)
P. gracile var. *madagassum* (Geh.) M. Fleisch. EMR (Crosby et al. 1983)
Ptychomitrium crispatum (Hedw.) A. Jaeger AFR (Crosby et al. 1983)
P. deltorii (Thér.) Broth. PAL (Crosby et al. 1983)
Pyrrhobryum spiniforme (Hedw.) Mitt. PAN (Crosby et al. 1983; Frahm et al. 2003; Delgadillo et al. 1995)
Racopilum africanum Mitt. AFR (Crosby et al. 1983)
R. cardotii Renauld END (Crosby et al. 1983)
R. ellipticum Renauld END (Crosby et al. 1983)
R. madagassum var. *grandistipulaceum* Thér. & Renauld END (Crosby et al. 1983)
R. madagassum Renauld var. *madagassum* AFR (Crosby et al. 1983)
R. marginatum Dixon AFR (Crosby et al. 1983)
R. mauritianum Müll. Hal. ex Besch. AFR (Crosby et al. 1983)
R. microdictyon Besch. EMR (Crosby et al. 1983)
R. perrieri Ther. END (Crosby et al. 1983)
R. plicatum Renauld & Cardot AFR (Crosby et al. 1983)
R. tomentosum (Hedw.) Brid. SCO (Crosby et al. 1983)
Radulina borbonica (Bel.) W. R. Buck PAL (Crosby et al. 1983)
Rauiella praelonga (Schimp. ex Besch.) Wijk & Margad. Afr-Am (Touw 1976; Crosby et al. 1983)
Regmatodon orthostegius Mont. PAL (Crosby et al. 1983; Eakin 1998)
Renauldia patentissima (Hampe) Broth. var. *patentissima* END (Argent 1973; Crosby et al. 1983)
R. patentissima var. *mutica* Thér. END (Crosby et al. 1983)
Rhachithecium perpusillum (Thwaites & Mitt.) Broth. Afr-Am (Crosby et al. 1983)
Rhacocarpus purpurascens (Brid.) Paris PAN (Crosby et al. 1983; Frahm 1996; Delgadillo et al. 1995)
Rhacopilopsis trinitensis (Müll. Hal.) E. Britton ex Dixon PAN (Crosby et al. 1983)
R. variegata (Welw. & Duby) M. C. Watling & O'Shea AFR (Buck 1993; Watling and O'Shea 2000)
Rhaphidorrhynchium angustissimum (Geh.) Broth. END (Crosby et al. 1983)
R. cambouei (Renauld & Cardot) Broth. END (Crosby et al. 1983)
R. rubricaule (Besch.) Broth. EMR (Crosby et al. 1983)
Rhizofabronia persoonii var. *sphaerocarpa* (Dusén) Bizot ex Ochyra AFR (Crosby et al. 1983; Touw 1993)
Rhodobryum commersonii (Schwägr.) Brid. PAN (Crosby et al. 1983; Pócs and Geissler 2002)

BRYOPHYTA: MOSSES

R. giganteum (Schwägr.) Paris AFR (Crosby et al. 1983; Ochi 1972)
R. ontariense (Kindb.) Paris Afr-Am (Crosby et al. 1983)
Rhynchostegiella microtheca (Renauld & Cardot) Broth. EMR (Crosby et al. 1983)
Rhynchostegium angustifolium Renauld & Cardot END (Crosby et al. 1983)
R. comorae (Müll. Hal.) A. Jaeger AFR (Crosby et al. 1983)
R. distans Besch. AFR (Crosby et al. 1983)
R. nervosum (Renauld) Cardot END (Crosby et al. 1983)
R. pseudodistans Cardot EMR (Crosby et al. 1983)
Rigodium toxarion (Schwägr.) A. Jaeger var. *toxarion* Afr-Am (Crosby et al. 1983; Zomlefer 1993)
Rutenbergia borbonica Besch. EMR (Crosby et al. 1983)
R. cirrata Renauld & Cardot END (Crosby et al. 1983)
R. limbata (Hampe) Besch. END (Crosby et al. 1983)
R. madagassa var. *flagelliformis* Renauld & Cardot END (Crosby et al. 1983)
R. madagassa Geh. & Hampe var. *madagassa* END (Crosby et al. 1983)
Schimperella rhynchostegioides Thér. END (Crosby et al. 1983)
Schizymenium commixtum (Ther.) A. J. Shaw END (Crosby et al. 1983)
S. madagassum (Renauld & Cardot ex Cardot) A. J. Shaw END (Crosby et al. 1983)
Schlotheimia acutifolia Renauld & Paris var. *acutifolia* END (Crosby et al. 1983)
S. acutifolia var. *angustifolia* Thér. END (Crosby et al. 1983)
S. angulosa P. Beauv. AFR (Marline 2018)
S. badiella Besch. var. *badiella* EMR (Crosby et al. 1983)
S. badiella var. *helicophylla* Besch. EMR (Crosby et al. 1983)
S. boiviniana Besch. EMR (Crosby et al. 1983)
S. conica Renauld & Cardot END (Crosby et al. 1983)
S. excorrugata Müll. Hal. ex Cardot AFR (Crosby et al. 1983)
S. ferruginea (Bruch ex Hook. & Grev.) Brid. AFR (Marline 2018)
S. fornicata var. *apiculata* P. de la Varde END (Crosby et al. 1983)
S. fornicata Duby var. *fornicata* EMR (Crosby et al. 1983)
S. fornicata var. *microtheca* P. de la Varde END (Crosby et al. 1983)
S. foveolata Renauld & Cardot var. *foveolata* END (Crosby et al. 1983)
S. foveolata var. *torquescens* Cardot END (Crosby et al. 1983)
S. gauthieri Thér. EMR (Crosby et al. 1983)
S. malacophylla Besch. AFR (Crosby et al. 1983)
S. microcarpa Geh. EMR (Crosby et al. 1983)
S. microphylla Besch. END (Crosby et al. 1983)
S. nossi-beana var. *linealis* (Geh.) Thér. END (Crosby et al. 1983)
S. nossi-beana Müll. Hal. var. *nossi-beana* END (Crosby et al. 1983)
S. pauli Renauld & Cardot END (Crosby et al. 1983)
S. percuspidata AFR (Marline 2018)
S. perrieri Thér. END (Crosby et al. 1983)

(continued overleaf)

TABLE 8.14. ***continued***

BRYOPHYTA: MOSSES

S. perrotii var. *breviseta* Thér. END (Crosby et al. 1983)
S. perrotii Renauld & Cardot var. *perrotii* END (Crosby et al. 1983)
S. robillardii Duby AFR (Crosby et al. 1983)
S. robusta Thér. AFR (Crosby et al. 1983)
S. semidiaphana (Renauld & Cardot) Cardot END (Crosby et al. 1983)
S. squarrosa Brid. EMR (Crosby et al. 1983; Delgadillo et al. 1995)
S. subfornicata Thér. EMR (Crosby et al. 1983)
S. tenuiseta Geh. END (Crosby et al. 1983)
S. trichophora var. *stenophylla* (Renauld & Cardot) Thér. END (Crosby et al. 1983)
S. trichophora Renauld & Cardot var. *trichophora* END (Crosby et al. 1983)
S. trypanoclada Geh. END (Crosby et al. 1983)
Schoenobryum concavifolium (Griff.) Manuel PAL (Crosby et al. 1983; O'Shea 2003)
Sematophyllum coppeyi (Cardot) Broth. END (Crosby et al. 1983)
S. crassiusculum (Brid.) Broth. EMR (Marline 2018)
S. dixonii (Thér.) O'Shea END (Crosby et al. 1983)
S. dubium (Renauld) Broth. END (Crosby et al. 1983)
S. nanopyxis (Geh.) O'Shea END (Crosby et al. 1983)
S. obtusifolium (Renauld & Cardot) Broth EMR (Crosby et al. 1983)
S. rigescens (Cardot) O'Shea END (Crosby et al. 1983)
S. schimperi (Besch.) Broth. AFR (Marline 2018)
S. sinuosulum var. *latifolium* (Cardot) Thér. END (Crosby et al. 1983)
S. sinuosulum (Besch.) Broth. var. *sinuosulum* AFR (Crosby et al. 1983)
S. subpinnatum (Brid.) E. Britton PAN (Crosby et al. 1983)
S. subrugifolium Dixon END (Crosby et al. 1983)
S. subscabrellum Renauld & Cardot END (Crosby et al. 1983)
Serpotortella chenagonii (Renauld & Cardot) W. D. Reese & R. H. Zander EMR (Crosby et al. 1983)
S. cyrtophylla (Besch.) W. D. Reese & R. H. Zander EMR (Reese and Zander 1987)
Sphagnum capense Hornsch. AFR (Eddy 1985)
S. ceylonicum Mitt. ex Warnst. AFR (Eddy 1985)
S. cuspidatulum Müll. Hal. PAL (Eddy 1985)
S. cuspidatum Hoffm. var. *cuspidatum* AFR (Eddy 1985)
S. davidii Warnst. AFR (Marline et al. 2012)
S. ericetorum Brid. EMR (Eddy 1985)
S. magellanicum subsp. *grandirete* (Warnst.) A. Eddy END (Eddy 1985)
S. perichaetiale Hampe Afr-Am (Eddy 1985)
S. perrieri Thér. END (Crosby et al. 1983)
S. planifolium var. *angustilimbatum* (Warnst.) A. Eddy AFR (Eddy 1985)
S. planifolium Müll. Hal. var. *planifolium* AFR (Eddy 1985)
S. rutenbergii Müll. Hal. EMR (Eddy 1985)
S. strictum subsp. *pappeanum* (Müll. Hal.) A. Eddy AFR (Eddy 1985)
S. truncatum var. *bordasii* (Besch.) A. Eddy AFR (Eddy 1985)
S. tumidulum Besch. var. *tumidulum* EMR (Eddy 1985)
S. violascens Müll. Hal. AFR (Eddy 1985)
Splachnobryum gracile Besch. AFR (Crosby et al. 1983)

BRYOPHYTA: MOSSES

S. obtusum (Brid.) Müll. Hal. PAN (Crosby et al. 1983; Arts 1996, 2001)
Squamidium brasiliense (Hornsch.) Broth. Afr-Am (Crosby et al. 1983; B. Allen and Crosby 1986; Delgadillo et al. 1995)
Stereophyllum radiculosum (Hook.) Mitt. Afr-Am (Crosby et al. 1983)
Streptopogon calymperes Müll. Hal. ex Geh. Afr-Am (Crosby et al. 1983)
S. erythrodontus (Taylor) Wilson PAL (Crosby et al. 1983; Delgadillo et al. 1995)
Symphyodon pygmaeus (Broth.) S. He & Snider PAN (Crosby et al. 1983; S. He and Snider 2000)
Syrrhopodon africanus (Mitt.) Paris var. *africanus* AFR (Crosby et al. 1983)
S. africanus var. *mandrakensis* (Tixier) W. D. Reese AFR (Tixier 1992; Pócs and Geissler 2002)
S. albidus subsp. *integrifolius* (E. B. Bartram) L. T. Ellis AFR (Pócs and Geissler 2002)
S. apertifolius Besch. EMR (Ellis 1995)
S. armatissimus W. D. Reese AFR (Reese 1991; Orbán 1995)
S. armatus subsp. *insularus* (Bizot & Onr.) Orbán & W. D. Reese AFR (Crosby et al. 1983; B. Allen and Crosby 1986; Delgadillo et al. 1995)
S. asper Mitt. AFR (Een 1993)
S. cuneifolius Thér. END (Orbán 1981; Crosby et al. 1983; Pócs and Geissler 2002)
S. dimorphophyllus L. T. Ellis AFR (Ellis 2005)
S. gardneri (Hook.) Schwägr. PAN (Orbán 1981; Crosby et al. 1983; Ellis 2002; Pócs and Geissler 2002)
S. gaudichaudii Mont. Afr-Am (Orbán 1981; Crosby et al. 1983; Ellis 2005)
S. graminifolius Renauld & Cardot EMR (Orbán 1981; Crosby et al. 1983)
S. hispidocostatus Renauld & Cardot in Renauld PAN (Orbán 1978, 1981; Crosby et al. 1983; Pócs and Geissler 2002; Ellis 2003, 2005)
S. involutus Schwägr. PAN (Orbán 1981; Crosby et al. 1983)
S. mauritianus Müll. Hal. ex Aongstr. AFR (Orbán 1981; Crosby et al. 1983)
S. parasiticus (Sw. ex Brid.) Besch. SCO (Crosby et al. 1983)
S. pottioides Orbán EMR (Orbán 1995)
S. prolifer var. *acanthoneuros* (Müll. Hal.) Müll. Hal. Afr-Am (Orbán 1981; Crosby et al. 1983; Ellis 2003)
S. prolifer Schwägr. var. *prolifer* PAN (Orbán 1981; Crosby et al. 1983; Delgadillo et al. 1995)
S. pulcher W. D. Reese PAL (Orbán 1995)
S. spiralis Renauld & Cardot AFR (Ellis 2005)
S. tixieri W. D. Reese END (Tixier 1992)
S. vardei L. T. Ellis AFR (Ellis 2005)
Taxiphyllum taxirameum (Mitt.) M. Fleisch. PAN (Crosby et al. 1983)
Taxithelium argyrophyllum Renauld & Cardot END (Crosby et al. 1983)
T. confusum Cardot END (Crosby et al. 1983)
T. glaucophyllum Besch. END (Crosby et al. 1983)

BRYOPHYTA: MOSSES

T. hirtellum Paris & Renauld END (Crosby et al. 1983)
T. nepalense (Schwägr.) Broth. PAL (Marline et al. 2012)
T. nossianum Besch. EMR (Crosby et al. 1983)
T. planulum Besch. EMR (Crosby et al. 1983)
Tayloria indica Mitt. PAL (Crosby et al. 1983)
T. isleana (Besch.) Broth. AFR (Crosby et al. 1983)
T. orthodonta (P. Beauv.) Wijk & Margad. AFR (Crosby et al. 1983; Pócs and Geissler 2002)
T. solitaria (Hedw.) T. J. Kop & W. Weber AFR (Crosby et al. 1983; Pócs and Geissler 2002)
Thamnobryum malgachum (Cardot) O'Shea END (Crosby et al. 1983)
Thuidium aculeoserratum Renauld & Cardot EMR (Touw 1976; Crosby et al. 1983)
T. assimile (Mitt.) A. Jaeger PAL (Touw 1976; Crosby et al. 1983)
T. pseudoinvolvens (Müll. Hal.) A. Jaeger AFR (Touw 1976; Crosby et al. 1983)
Tortella humilis (Hedw.) Jenn. SCO (Crosby et al. 1983)
Tortula madagassa Dixon END (Crosby et al. 1983)
T. muralis var. *madagascariensis* Thér. END (Crosby et al. 1983)
T. omissa Thér. END (Crosby et al. 1983)
T. subrufa Cardot END (Crosby et al. 1983)
Trachyphyllum borgenii (Renauld & Cardot) Broth. END (Buck 1979; Crosby et al. 1983; O'Shea 1999)
T. inflexum (Harv.) A. Gepp in Hiern PAL (Buck 1979; Crosby et al. 1983)
Trachypodopsis serrulata (P. Beauv.) M. Fleisch. var. *serrulata* PAN (van Zanten 1959; Crosby et al. 1983; Pócs and Geissler 2002)
Trachypus appendiculatus (Renauld & Cardot) Broth. AFR (van Zanten 1959; Crosby et al. 1983)
T. bicolor var. *viridulus* (Mitt.) Zanten PAN (van Zanten 1959; Crosby et al. 1983)
Trematodon curvicollis Cardot in Grandid. END (Crosby et al. 1983)
T. decaryi Thér. END (Crosby et al. 1983)
T. lacunosus Renauld & Cardot END (Crosby et al. 1983)
T. longicollis Michx. PAN (Crosby et al. 1983)
T. platybasis Müll. Hal. END (Crosby et al. 1983)
T. reticulatus Müll. Hal. ex Geh. END (Crosby et al. 1983)
T. viguieri Cardot EMR (Crosby et al. 1983)
Trichosteleum debettei var. *laevisetum* Cardot END (Crosby et al. 1983)
T. heterophyllum Bizot & Onr. END (Crosby et al. 1983)
T. leviusculum Renauld & Cardot AFR (Crosby et al. 1983)
T. microdontum var. *megapterum* Renauld & Cardot END (Crosby et al. 1983)
T. microdontum (Besch.) Renauld var. *microdontum* EMR (Crosby et al. 1983)
T. permixtum Cardot END (Crosby et al. 1983)
T. perrotii var. *eurydictyon* Renauld & Cardot END (Crosby et al. 1983)
T. perrotii (Renauld & Cardot) Renauld & Cardot var. *perrotii* EMR (Crosby et al. 1983)
T. pervilleanum (Müll. Hal. ex Geh.) W. R. Buck AFR (Crosby et al. 1983)

BRYOPHYTA: MOSSES

T. trachypyxis (Geh.) Renauld & Cardot END (Crosby et al. 1983)
Trichostomum brachydontium Bruch var. *brachydontium* PAN (Crosby et al. 1983)
T. pennequinii Renauld & Paris END (Crosby et al. 1983)
T. perrieri Thér. END (Crosby et al. 1983)
T. sporaphyllum (Renauld & Cardot) Cardot END (Crosby et al. 1983)
T. tenuirostre (Hook. & Taylor) Lindb. var. *tenuirostre* Afr-Am (Crosby et al. 1983)
T. villaumei Thér. END (Crosby et al. 1983)
Ulota fulva Brid. EMR (Crosby et al. 1983)
Vesicularia alboviridis var. *rufula* (Renauld & Cardot) Cardot END (Crosby et al. 1983)
V. ayresii (Besch.) Broth. EMR (Crosby et al. 1983)
V. combae (Renauld & Cardot) Broth. END (Crosby et al. 1983)
V. crassiramea (Renauld & Cardot) Broth. var. *crassiramea* EMR (Crosby et al. 1983)
V. crassiramea var. *laxifolia* (Renauld & Cardot) Cardot in Grandid END (Crosby et al. 1983)
V. galerulata (Duby) Broth. var. *galerulata* AFR (Crosby et al. 1983)
V. galerulata var. *subpiligera* (Renauld & Paris) Wijk & Margad. END (Crosby et al. 1983)
V. hygrobia (Besch.) Broth. EMR (Crosby et al. 1983)
V. immunda (Renauld) Cardot END (Crosby et al. 1983)
Warburgiella leptorrhyncha (A. Jaeger) Broth. AFR (Crosby et al. 1983)
Weisiopsis plicata (Mitt.) Broth. AFR (Crosby et al. 1983)
Weissia ayresii Schimp. in Besch. AFR (Crosby et al. 1983)
Wijkia bessonii (Renauld & Cardot) H. A. Crum END (Crosby et al. 1983)
W. madagassa (Thér.) H. A. Crum END (Crosby et al. 1983)
W. rutenbergii var. *eflagellaris* (Cardot) H. A. Crum AFR (Crosby et al. 1983)
W. rutenbergii (Müll. Hal.) H. A. Crum var. *rutenbergii* END (Crosby et al. 1983)
Zygodon laxifolius Thér. END (Crosby et al. 1983)
Z. leptocarpus Thér. END (Crosby et al. 1983)
Z. reinwardtii var. *madacassus* Cardot END (Crosby et al. 1983)
Z. reinwardtii (Hornsch.) A. Braun var. *reinwardtii* AFR (Crosby et al. 1983)

Sources: Species nomenclature follows Marline et al. (2012). Recent taxonomic modifications for liverworts based on the Söderström et al. (2016) world checklist of hornworts and liverworts. The phytogeographic groups are adapted from those used by Pócs and Geissler (2002).
Notes: Taxa are arranged alphabetically within Anthocerotophyta (hornworts), Marchantiophyta (liverworts), and Bryophyta (mosses). The abbreviations of the phytogeographic regions are: END, Endemic to Madagascar; EMR, Madagascar and its neighboring islands (subendemic); AFR, African; PAL, Paleotropical; PAN, Pantropical; Afr-Am, Tropical African–tropical American disjunction; Afr-As, Tropical African–Asian disjunction; SCO, Subcosmopolitan; COS, Cosmopolitan; NA, Pattern unknown.

SYSTEMATIC ACCOUNTS: VASCULAR PLANTS

PIPERACEAE: *PEPEROMIA*

G. Mathieu

Peperomia is a pantropical genus of terrestrial and epiphytic herbs that includes 1627 accepted taxa, comprising 1455 species and an additional 172 varieties and forms (Mathieu 2001–2020). Together with that other giant genus, *Piper*, and the small genera, *Manekia*, *Verhuellia*, and *Zippelia*, it belongs to the family Piperaceae, of which only *Peperomia* and *Piper* occur on Madagascar. Although *Peperomia* has its highest diversity in South and Central America, its diversity on Madagascar is notably high for the Paleotropics. Currently, 42 species are recognized from the island (Figure 8.15), about twice the number known from the entire African continent. For a long time, the richness of *Peperomia* on Madagascar remained underestimated. Fieldwork since 2001, and the collection of new material, combined with the study of herbarium specimens, has resulted in no fewer than 13 new species being described. A historical synopsis, including synonymy, and a key to all Malagasy *Peperomia* are presented here for the first time.

HISTORY

Seven *Peperomia* species were known from the Afrotropics before their occurrence on Madagascar became clear: *P. bangroana*, *P. elliptica*, *P. exigua*, *P. leptostachya*, *P. pellucida*, *P. retusa*, and *P. tetraphylla*. The first Malagasy specimens were apparently collected by Lyall, probably by the end of 1828. Based on these collections, C. de Candolle (1866, 1869) described *P. lyallii* and *P. madagascariensis* (= *P. villilimba*). Bernier made a collection in 1834 from the Tintingue Forest, along the east coast of Madagascar, facing Ile Sainte Marie. Miquel (1843) used this collection in his *Systema Piperacearum* and named *P. bernieriana*. For about 50 years no new *Peperomia* species were discovered on Madagascar until Hildebrandt made a number of collections in the 1880s. This material was used to describe *P. tanalensis* (= *P. leptostachya*), *P. baronii*, *P. trichophylla*, *P. brachytricha*, *P. dryadum*, *P. hildebrandtii*, *P. imerinae*, *P. silvicola*, and *P. truncicola* (J. G. Baker 1882, 1883, 1885,

FIGURE 8.15 **A range of Malagasy *Peperomia*: A) *P. pluvisilvatica* at Montagne d'Ambre; B) *P. trichophylla* at Ranomafana; C) *P. mantadiana* at Anjanaharibe-Sud; and D) *P. thomeana* at Montagne d'Ambre.** (PHOTOS by G. Mathieu.)

1889; C. de Candolle 1894). In the latter publication, a Baron collection served as the type for *P. rotundilimba*. Material obtained by Commerson was used to describe the still poorly known *P. commersonii* (Baillon 1885), and a specimen collected by Mocquerys was used as the type for *P. mocqerysii* (C. de Candolle 1898).

Using a variety of collections, C. de Candolle (1911) named a number of new taxa: *P. estaminea*, *P. forsythii* (= *P. trichophylla*), and *P. pubipetiola* based on material collected by Forsyth Major; *P. loucoubeana* and *P. nossibeana* from specimens obtained by Boivin; and *P. glabrilimba* and *P. villilimba* based on Baron collections. *Peperomia tenuispica* (= *P. retusa*) and *P. trichopoda* (= *P. trichophylla*) were the last new species from Madagascar to be described during the 20th century (C. de Candolle 1911).

During a 2001 expedition to Madagascar that focused on collecting *Peperomia*, several new endemic species were discovered in the east: *P. costata*, *P. humbertii*, *P. mantadiana*, *P. pluvisilvatica*, *P. ratticaudata*, and *P. terebinthina* (Mathieu 2003a). The Malagasy occurrence of the west African *P. thomeana* was also recognized, as well as two other continental African species, *P. fernandopoiana* and *P. molleri*. The study of a large number of herbarium specimens carried out under the auspices of this expedition revealed another novelty: *P. nicolliae* (Mathieu 2003b). From further study of comparative morphology, three other new species were described a few years later: *P. ankaranensis*, *P. erythrocaulis*, and *P. richardsonii* (Mathieu 2006). Finally, three new endemic species were presented recently: *P. irrasa*, *P. robusta*, and *P. variilimba* (Mathieu 2020a).

A collection in the British Museum annotated in pencil as "Madagascar Roxb[urgh] 1814" was cited as the syntype in the protologue of *P. mascarena* (= *P. bangroana*) (C. de Candolle 1866 [as *P. mascharena*, corrected by C. de Candolle 1869]) and it might be considered as the first Malagasy *Peperomia* collection, predating those by Lyall. However, the provenance is uncertain as it is questionable whether William Roxburgh (1751–1815) collected on Madagascar. The names of two exclusively Neotropical *Peperomia* have been erroneously applied to Malagasy species: *P. rotundifolia* for *P. bangroana* (Mathieu and Callejas-Posada 2006) and *P. blanda* for *P. leptostachya* (Mathieu 2020b).

PHYLOGENY

The genus *Peperomia* includes 14 subgenera (Frenzke et al. 2015), with three occurring on Madagascar. The vast majority, 38 species or 90% of the Malagasy *Peperomia* diversity, belongs to subgenus *Micropiper* whose fruits show a pericarp entirely covered with sticky papillae. Subgenus *Peperomia* is represented by three annual species: the pantropical *P. pellucida*, the Paleotropical *P. exigua*, and the endemic *P. ankaranensis*. The fruit pericarp of *Peperomia* is rugose (*P. exigua* and *P. pellucida*) or sticky papillate (*P. ankaranensis*). Subgenus *Pseudocupula* is represented by the pantropical *P. tetraphylla*; its fruits show a basal "pseudocupula," clearly demarcated from the apical part of the pericarp.

BIOGEOGRAPHY AND CONSERVATION

Occurrence of *Peperomia* in Africa and Asia appears to be the result of several waves of eastward dispersal from their South American cradle (Smith et al. 2008). Without doubt, extinction played an important role in the disappearance of members of this genus on the African continent. This is best illustrated by the current disjunct distribution of *P. thomeana*, which has a considerable west African occurrence and relict populations in Tanzania and Madagascar. A similar pattern is becoming evident for *P. fernandopoiana* and *P. molleri*. The distribution of *Peperomia* on Madagascar is predominantly in the eastern half due to wetter microclimates and the presence of suitable forest habitats. Two pantropical species occur on the island: *P. pellucida* and *P. tetraphylla*. Their International Union for Conservation of Nature (IUCN) Red List conservation status on Madagascar is Least Concern. This is also the case for the Paleotropical *P. exigua* and *P. leptostachya*. These four species are less demanding with regard to habitat and also occur in drier western Madagascar. Five species also occur on the African continent: *P. bangroana*, *P. fernandopoiana*, *P. molleri*, *P. retusa*, and *P. thomeana*, while three others, not occurring on the continent, are reported from neighboring islands: *P. baronii* (Comoros), *P. bernieriana* (Comoros, Mascarenes), and *P. elliptica* (Mascarenes). These eight species are also considered of Least Concern. The remaining 30 species, 71% of the Malagasy *Peperomia* diversity, are endemics. They are all threatened by the decline of suitable habitats and most of them are only found in protected areas. They are generally considered of Least Concern or Near Threatened apart from some that show a very limited Area of Occupancy or Extent of Occurrence, which were considered Vulnerable (IUCN 2019): *P. ankaranensis*, *P. erythrocaulis*, *P. loucoubeana*, *P. nossibeana*, *P. pluvisilvatica*, *P. ratticaudata*, and *P. richardsonii*.

Key to the species

1.	Annual herb	2
1a.	Perennial herb	4
2.	Leaves ovate, length/width ratio 1.3–1.9, margin ciliate	*P. ankaranensis*
2a.	Leaves deltoid or reniform, length/width ratio ≤1, margin eciliate	3
3.	Leaves reniform	*P. exigua*
3a.	Leaves deltoid	*P. pellucida*
4.	One leaf (exceptionally two) per node	5
4a.	More than one leaf per node	25

5.	Stem glabrous	6
5a.	Stem with indument	18
6.	Stem erect or decumbent at base	7
6a.	Stem creeping or scandent	17
7.	Leaf margin not ciliate or only at the very apex	8
7a.	Leaf margin ciliate entirely or for a large part	12
8.	Leaves both sides hyaline dotted	9
8a.	Leaves not hyaline dotted	10
9.	Leaves <5 × 2 cm	*P. hildebrandtii*
9a.	Leaves larger, 5–10 × 2 cm	*P. richardsonii*
10.	Leaf apex emarginate	*P. thomeana*
10a.	Leaf apex not emarginate	11
11.	Some pubescence on stem, petiole, lamina, peduncle	*P. terebinthina*
11a.	Glabrous (except ciliate leaf margin)	*P. pluvisilvatica*
12.	Leaves hyaline dotted	13
12a.	Leaves not hyaline dotted	16
13.	Leaves hyaline dotted abaxially only	*P. lyalii*
13a.	Leaves hyaline dotted on both sides	14
14.	Leaf glabrous	*P. molleri*
14a.	Leaf indument present on main nerves	15
15.	Leaves elliptic, ≤4 cm long	*P. imerinae*
15a.	Leaves ovate, ≤2.5 cm long	*P. erythrocaulis*
16.	Internodal ribs prominent	*P. costata*
16a.	Internodal ribs discrete	*P. fernandopoiana*
17.	(6a) Leaves large, <6.5 cm long, length/width ratio 2–3	*P. nossibeana*
17a.	Leaves smaller, <2(–3) cm long, length/width ratio 1.5–2	43
18. (5a)	Leaf apex obtuse or rounded	19
18a.	Leaf apex acuminate, acute, or subacute	23
19.	Stem erect or decumbent at base	20
19a.	Stem creeping or pendent	21
20.	Leaves 3.7–6.5 cm long, loosely pubescent	*P. trichophylla*
20a.	Leaves 0.8–1.3 cm long, densely pubescent	*P. brachytricha*
21.	Leaves 0.2–0.9 cm long, inflorescence <2 cm long	*P. bangroana*
21a.	Leaves 0.9–3.0 cm long, inflorescence >5 cm long	22
22.	Spadices erect, 4.5–10 cm long × 3 mm diameter	*P. variilimba*
22a.	Spadices decumbent, ≤27 cm long × 6 mm diameter	*P. ratticaudata*
23.	Leaves both sides dark hyaline dotted	*P. truncicola*
23a.	Leaves not hyaline dotted	24
24.	Indument pilose (trichomes curved)	*P. mocquerysii*
24a.	Indument hirtellous (trichomes short, erect)	*P. terebinthina*
25. (4)	Rarely more than two leaves per node	26
25a.	Usually more than two leaves per node	36
26.	Stem glabrous	27
26a.	Stem pubescent	30
27.	Leaf apex acuminate, acute, or subacute	*P. glabrilimba*
27a.	Leaf apex obtuse or rounded	28

28.	Leaves up to 5.5 × 2 cm, discrete 3(–5)-palmatinerved	*P. pubipetiola*
28a.	Leaves <2.5 × 1.5 cm, 1-nerved	29
29	Leaf length/width ratio 1.2–1.6, margin sparsely ciliate	*P. elliptica*
29a.	Leaf length/width ratio ~2, margin eciliate	*P. bernieriana*
30.	Leaf apex acuminate, acute, or subacute	*P. truncicola*
30a.	Leaf apex rounded	31
31	Stem erect or decumbent at base	32
31a.	Stem creeping or pendent	35
32.	Leaves 3–6 cm long	*P. leptostachya*
32a.	Leaves 1.5–3 cm long	33
33.	Leaves glabrous except around petiole insertion	*P. commersonii*
33a.	Leaves with indument on one or both sides	34
34.	Leaves both sides densely villous	*P. dryadum*
34a.	Leaves adaxially glabrous, abaxially pilose	*P. estaminea*
35.	Leaves hirsute abaxially	*P. rotundilimba*
35a.	Leaves villous both sides	*P. villilimba*
36. (25)	Leaves glabrous, or with trichomes at apical margin only	37
36a.	Leaves pubescent on one or both sides, or on the nerves	40
37.	Leaves <2 cm long	38
37a.	Leaves ≤5 cm long	39
38.	Stem erect, branched apically, leaves obovate-oblong	*P. baronii*
38a.	Cespitose, leaves orbicular-elliptic-rhombic	*P. tetraphylla*
39.	Leaf length/width ratio 5–7	*P. humbertii*
39a.	Leaf length/width ratio 2–2.5	*P. mantadiana*
40.	Leaves 3–7 cm long	*P. robusta*
40a.	Leaves <2 cm long	41
41.	Stem indument villous	*P. silvicola*
41a.	Stem indument not villous	42
42.	Stem indument short erect	*P. irrasa*
42a.	Stem indument curved in apical direction	*P. nicolliae*
43. (17)	Leaves 1-nerved	*P. retusa*
43a.	Leaves 3-palmatinerved	*P. loucoubeana*

Online access to protologues and photographs of the type specimens of the mentioned species is provided by Mathieu (2001–2020).

Subject editors: Laurent Gautier and Steven M. Goodman

PIPERACEAE: *PIPER*, PEPPER, *DIPOIVATRA*, *TSIPERIFERY*

H. Razafimandimby, N. V. Manjato, P. B. Phillipson, J.-M. Leong Pock Tsy, J. Queste, and L. Gautier
Translated from French by F. Andriamialisoa and S. M. Goodman

The order Piperales comprises three families. The small family Saururaceae (four genera and six species) is only found in southeast Asia and North America. The Aristolochiaceae (10 genera and 600 species) is represented on Madagascar by three species belonging to three different taxa: *Aristolochia albida*, a herbaceous climbing shrub, abundant in all regions (less so in the east) up to an elevation of 1500 m; *Pararistolochia enricoi*, recently described from the western limestone areas (Luino et al. 2016); and *Hydnora esculenta*, a parasitic herbaceous plant from the arid southwest. The family Piperaceae is a large one with five genera and 3600 species, the overwhelming majority of which belonging to two genera found on Madagascar: *Piper* and *Peperomia* (see Mathieu, pp. 538–41).

The genus *Piper* has a pantropical distribution. It was previously estimated that the genus contained 2000 species worldwide, of which only 545 had been described (Jaramillo and Manos 2001). These species mainly display a herbaceous or lianescent habit but can also be shrubby or even arborescent. Stems consist of very distinct sections of divaricated nodes and internodes. Inflorescences are cylindrical spikes forming at the nodes, opposite the leaves (alternate for *P. umbellatum*). The flowers are tiny, lacking calyx and corolla, and generally unisexual. Male and female inflorescences are commonly found on distinct plants (dioecy). The floral buds of the female inflorescence are sunk into the rachis and the flowers only emerge after fertilization. The fruit is a globular or ovoid drupe, sessile or with a supporting stipe. All plant parts have a characteristic smell and taste due to the presence of piperine (Vasavirama and Upender 2014), an alkaloid with many pharmacological properties. They are mostly forest species and mainly distributed between sea level and 2500 m but sometimes occur up to an elevation of 3000 m (Gentry and Dondson 1987).

PIPER ON MADAGASCAR

The family Piperaceae has not been covered to date in the *Flore de Madagascar et des Comores* series. The most recent treatment, dating back a century, was written by Casimir de Candolle (1923). The study examined the genus worldwide and for Madagascar was based on an extremely limited number of specimens. In other parts of the world, this old classification system was improved by, among others, Trelease and Yuncker (1950) for the northern part of South America and by Yuncker (1953) for the southern part of South America. In contrast to C. de Candolle's classification, with a large *Piper* genus with many subgenera Trelease opted for a generic taxonomy that was less extensive and structured, with distinct small segregated genera (Jaramillo et al. 2008). According to C. de Candolle (1923), the genus *Piper* is represented on Madagascar by nine species: five are introduced (*P. betle*, *P. nigrum*, *P. sarmentosum*, *P. sylvestre*, and *P. umbellatum*); four are indigenous, including one shared with the Mascarenes (*P. borbonense*) and another with Africa (*P. capense*); and two are endemic (*P. pachyphyllum* and *P. heimii*). In light of the material collected subsequently, this classification does not appear to accurately reflect the diversity of the genus on Madagascar, and there are three potential new species to be described (N. V. Manjato et al., unpublished data).

One of the introduced species, the black pepper *P. nigrum*, is a vine with sessile fruits; it is of Indian origin and cultivated broadly in the tropics. It is one of the main cash crops on Madagascar, along with vanilla, clove, and coffee. The country exports about 2000 metric tonnes of black pepper per year, at a price range of €8–10 per kilogram (Ministère du Commerce 2012). *Piper betle*, *P. sarmentosum*, and *P. umbellatum* (Figure 8.16) are from the tropical regions of America and Asia and also have sessile fruits. All three species are naturalized and common in the Sambirano Region in valleys, open habitats, and the forest understory, and also along small streams in the eastern part of the island. They are used in traditional medicine both in their countries of origin and on Madagascar (Schmelzer et al. 2008), which would explain their introduction. They are known under various vernacular names, the most common being *rambô* for *P. betle*, *dipoavatra dia* for *P. sarmentosum*, and *tongatra* for *P. umbellatum*. *Piper sylvestre* is a tall liana reaching 10 m in height which is native to tropical Asia (Sri Lanka and India). It is naturalized on all western Indian Ocean islands. There is little information available on its distribution on Madagascar as it is represented in herbaria by a very limited number of specimens.

Of the two nonendemic indigenous species, *P. capense* (Figure 8.16) can be easily identified. It is a sarmentuous shrub with a maximum height of 2 m. The stem is delicate, green, and with bulging nodes. The leaves are largely ovate to elliptic, palmatinerve, with an obtuse to rounded base, rarely cordate; they are discolorous, dark green on the upperside and light green or grayish on the underside. The inflorescence is opposite the leaf, terminal, or lateral, with a cream color. The fruit is a very fleshy, whitish, sessile, and globular drupe, with a brown seed. This species is found in the dense moist forests of Africa and the Indian Ocean islands. On Madagascar, it is present in valleys and along small streams, from the protected areas of Ranomafana in the south to Montagne d'Ambre in the north, at elevations between 800 and 2400 m, rarely below.

The main taxonomic issues in this genus on Madagascar pertain to the stipitate lianescent indigenous *Piper*, the "tailed wild pepper" most commonly known under the name *tsiperifery*. This name includes both endemic species noted by C. de Candolle (*P. heimii* and *P. pachyphyllum*), as well as *P. borbonense*. The *tsiperifery* fruit has been exploited by the Malagasy for a long time. It has only been included recently in the international spice trade where it is highly valued for its organoleptic characteristics, which are different from those of the common pepper. The rest of this contribution will focus on the tailed wild peppers of Madagascar, which will be

FIGURE 8.16 **Examples of *Piper* species introduced on Madagascar: A) *P. sarmentosum*, B) *P. betle*, and C) *P. capense*. Malagasy *tsiperifery*: D) adult plant climbing up a stake, E) adventitious roots, F) shoot with cordiform leaves, G) elliptic leaf with an asymmetrical base, H) elliptic leaf with a symmetrical base, I) male inflorescence with open flowers, J) female floral bud, K) female inflorescence with open flowers, L) juvenile infructescence, M) infructescence with ovoid fruits, N) infructescence with globose fruits, and O) dried fruits and their stipes.** (PHOTOS A–C, and E by N. V. Manjato; D, F–L, and N by H. Razafimandimby; M by A. Ramahefaharivelo; and O by P. B. Phillipson.)

treated under their vernacular name *tsiperifery* due to their unresolved taxonomy.

TSIPERIFERY: BIOLOGY AND TAXONOMY

Tsiperifery (Figure 8.16) are tall vines, climbing up to a height of 15 m with some form of support. The plant adheres to the support using adventitious roots that appear at the upper level of the thick internodes. Leaf dimorphism is often observed; on the same plant, orthotropic seedlings and stems produce cordiform leaves, while plagiotropic shoots have elliptic to oblong leaves, most often with an asymmetrical base (symmetrical for *P. pachyphyllum*). The plant is dioecious. The male inflorescence is longer and thinner than the female one. On the female inflorescence, floral buds are characterized by triangular bulges signaling the emergence of the stigma. The open flowers are evident when the stigma fully emerges; it is most often trifid and supported by ovaries still half sunken in the rachis. The flowers are sessile and apetalous. Fruits are reddish-orange berries at maturity, supported at the base of the ovary by a stipe that remains after the drying process, hence the common name *poivre sauvage à queue* (tailed wild pepper).

With regard to taxonomy, C. de Candolle distinguished three species: the two endemic species, *P. heimii* and *P. pachyphyllum*, and another species that he considered to be conspecific with *P. borbonense*, from the Mascarenes. However, Jaramillo et al. (2008) and Smith et al. (2008) only recognized one species for the islands of the western Indian Ocean: *P. borbonense*. For this same group of Malagasy indigenous stipitate peppers, N. V. Manjato et al. (unpublished data) suggested the existence of four new species endemic to Madagascar. This taxonomic uncertainty has led to confusion regarding the nomenclature, origin, and endemicity of *tsiperifery* for trade. The product is sold on the international market with the label "Madagascar endemic wild pepper," with the Latin name *P. borbonense*.

Recent morphological and genetic studies (Razafimandimby 2017; Razafimandimby et al. 2020), based on extensive fieldwork at five sites (Tsiazompaniry and Anjozorobe in the Analamanga Region; Beforona and Sandrangato in the Alaotra-Mangoro Region, and Kianjavato in the Vatovavy-Fitovinany Region), led to the classification of *tsiperifery* in four morphotypes (M1, M2, M3, and M4). Genetically, evidence showed that the four morphotypes are divided into two clades: M1 and M4 have large berries, while M2 and M3 have small berries. Both clades are genetically distinct from *P. borbonense* collected on La Réunion. The four morphotypes and *P. borbonense* form a monophyletic group that is close to *P. guineense*, the only stipitate wild species found in continental Africa, which is also exploited for its culinary and medicinal values (Nwinyi et al. 2009). *Piper guineense* presents some morphological similarities with *tsiperifery* and some specimens collected on Madagascar have been attributed to this species. Recently, using morphological, anatomical, and genetic criteria, Palchetti et al. (2018) described two new Malagasy endemic species (*P. malgassicum* and *P. tsarasaotrae*) based on samples collected around the region of Ambositra, but without properly considering variation in previously described taxa. A study is currently being completed of a taxonomic revision of the genus for islands in the Indian Ocean, with a genetic component that includes the two new species described by Palchetti et al. (2018); this has confirmed their validity and the taxonomic conclusions for the four morphotypes mentioned above, and of others in the Malagasy Region.

DISTRIBUTION AND ECOLOGY

On Madagascar, the *tsiperifery* are distributed in the dense moist evergreen forests of the eastern part of the country and in the Sambirano Region. They are found from Antsiranana to Tolagnaro and across the elevational band from the coast to over 1200 m. These forests are conditioned by an equatorial climate with no, or a low-intensity, dry season. Modeling of the ecological niche of the *tsiperifery* (Razafimandimby 2011) showed that precipitation and minimum temperature are the limiting factors to their distribution, as well as the presence of forest cover. They favor fertile forest soils with a thick humus layer (Andrianirinarimanana 2018). Around the Anjozorobe-Angavo protected area, their abundance is considered by the local communities as an indicator of soil fertility (Levesque 2012). Based on inventories by Razafimandimby (2017), *tsiperifery* appears to be more abundant in forest lowlands and talwegs than on slopes and virtually absent on ridges. Their preferred supporting species are trees with soft, coarse bark, such as *Cyathea* species.

USES AND TRADE

The *tsiperifery* are traditionally exploited and used by some local forest communities for their culinary, medicinal, and sociocultural values. Several vernacular names refer to such uses. Names related to their culinary use focus on the plant's value as a spice: *sakaiala* (forest hot pepper), *sakarivonala* (forest ginger), and *sakarivondambo* (ginger of the bushpig). Other traditional names pertain to morphology and other cultural aspects: *vahibe* (tall liana) and *tsimahalatsaka* (prevents the rain falling or the lightning striking). However, and oddly considering its main use, the most common vernacular name for this spice, and used as its trade name, refers to the wound-healing property of the leaves: *tsiperifery* literally means "what makes wounds not exist" (Razafimandimby et al. 2017). The plants are also used as a cure for respiratory issues, stomach pains, and for post-partum treatment (Touati 2012).

While initially the *tsiperifery* were primarily a traditional Malagasy spice, their use has been promoted in Europe since 2004 by renowned chefs (Couplan 2009). They are traded on the international market under the name of *tsiperifery* or *voatsiperifery* ("fruit of the *tsiperifery*"). The spice has attracted great interest and an increasing demand since 2010 (Scholtus 2017). Collectors and exporters of forest products soon saw the economic potential of the *tsiperifery* (Razafimandimby et al. 2017). Touati (2012) estimated the level of exportation at about 50 metric tonnes (dry weight) for the year 2011. In 2017, the price per kilogram at different preparation stages varied from €0.80 for fresh fruit sold in local markets near forests to €171 on average in the specialty food shops of France and Switzerland (Scholtus 2017). Even with a desiccation rate of about 20% (Weil et al. 2014), these figures highlight the highly uneven economic margins along the supply chain. The *tsiperifery* are currently not considered forest products by the Malagasy administration and are not subject to any regulation. They are classed with black pepper (Raharijaona 2015). Therefore, leverage to limit damaging aspects of trade is limited.

CONSERVATION AND DOMESTICATION

To address the increasing demand and the depletion of the resource due to overexploitation, collectors have gradually explored new supply areas. Harvesters are usually low-income farmers living close to the forest. The first large-scale harvests took place in the forested corridors of Angavo (exploited since 2006, including the Tsiazompaniry and Tsinjoarivo Forests) and Ankay (exploited since 2009). The harvesting areas have since extended to the corridors of Ranomafana-Fianarantsoa and Andohahela-Tolagnaro. Major illegal harvesting occurred in the Befotaka-Midongy du Sud National Park in 2016.

Initially harvested opportunistically, *tsiperifery* is now subject to systematic harvesting campaigns. The impact of this is exacerbated by destructive harvesting practices, such as uprooting the vine or even cutting the support and the vine to access the fruits on the plagiotropic shoots, which are often at 15 m above the ground. The practice leads to an imbalance in the demographic structure of the population. In unexploited forests, the female/male sex-ratio of individual adult plants varies from 1 to 0.8. This ratio declines to 0.1 to 0.0 in forests that have been harvested (Razafimandimby 2017), where only the male plants, which do not present an economic interest remain. These harvesting practices endanger the resource and the forest ecosystems. In addition, exploitation occurs even in protected areas. This leads to the depletion of the harvested areas in the short term and jeopardizes the sustainability of supply for this highly valued product.

In view of this situation, a consortium of researchers from FOFIFA (Foibem-pirenena momba ny Fikarohana ampiharina amin'ny Fampandrosoana ny eny Ambanivohitra), Université d'Antananarivo, and CIRAD (Centre de Coopération Internationale en Recherche Agronomique pour le Développement), with the support of private operators, carried out studies to promote the domestication and nondestructive harvesting of *tsiperifery*. Domestication is viewed as a solution that will reduce collection in forests, facilitate harvesting, and ensure the quality of the product, promoting both its economic development and its conservation. Research on domestication started in 2013, resulting in a protocol of harvesting cuttings from adult plants and forest enrichment (Queste et al. 2018). Since then, this method has been tested and adopted by farmers, leading to the reintroduction in forests of about 15,000 female seedlings. At the Mandraka site (Analamanga Region), plants produced their first fruits after four years. Vegetative propagation through sprouting is also currently being tested in laboratory conditions. Much remains to be done before reaching the level of production of other domesticated peppers such as *P. nigrum* and *P. longum*, but the research results obtained so far are promising for the future of this Malagasy resource, which is of social, economic, and ecological importance.

Subject editors: Guido Mathieu and Steven M. Goodman

DIOSCOREACEAE, YAMS, *OVY*, *OVIALA*, *ANGONA*

P. Wilkin, B. Bennett, S. Cameron, M.-J. Howes, V. Jeannoda, M. T. Rajaonah, F. Rakotoarison, L. Razanamparany, and J. Viruel

Dioscoreaceae, the most diverse family of the order Dioscoreales, contains over 700 species distributed across tropical regions worldwide, which are placed in four genera (Caddick et al. 2002 and subsequent publications). More than 85% of its species belong to *Dioscorea*, the yam genus. At least 60 forms of *Dioscorea*, with varying levels of domestication, provide an important human food source in the form of their starch-rich tubers. Certain taxa, principally those that are not eaten, are a key source of steroids and the origin of the contraceptive pill (Coursey 1967; Asiedu and Sartie 2010). Use of *Dioscorea* tubers for food is especially prevalent on Madagascar, and there are also medicinal uses, probably based on steroid content, so the island is rich in vernacular names (see Table 8.15) (e.g., Burkill and Perrier de la Bâthie 1950). Three of the four genera of Dioscoreaceae are found on Madagascar: *Tacca*, *Trichopus*, and *Dioscorea* (Burkill and Perrier de la Bâthie 1950; POWO 2020; Table 8.15). Its sister family, Burmanniaceae, is represented on the island by the largely mycoheterotrophic (nonphotosynthetic and deriving nutrition from fungi) genus *Burmannia* and the wholly mycoheterotrophic *Gymnosiphon* (Merckx et al. 2013).

Tacca is represented on Madagascar by non-twining herbs with basal leaves and pseudo-umbellate inflorescences. They include the widely distributed paleotropical species *T. leontopetaloiodes* (Table 8.15), the tuber of which provides an edible flour. This species name has been applied to most Malagasy material of this genus, which is highly diverse in vegetative form and ecological preference and has probably undergone human selection. A second species has been described from Ankarana (Bardot-Vaucoulon 1997), and other unnamed species may exist. Population genomic studies will probably be required to resolve taxon limits in the Malagasy members of this genus.

Trichopus has just two species of which one, *T. sempervirens*, is endemic and very distinctive (Caddick et al. 2002). As shown by

TABLE 8.15. **Checklist of the Dioscoreaceae on Madagascar**

SCIENTIFIC NAME	DISTRIBUTION	IUCN STATUS	VERNACULAR NAME(S)
Dioscorea	Pantropical	–	*Yam, ovy, oviala* (Madagascar-wide), *angona* (Antsiranana)
D. acuminate Baker	Central Highlands, four scattered sites	EN	*Ovy*
D. alata L.	Cultivated widely	NE	*Bemako, bodoa, bongela, majola, majola mena, makodradra, ovibe, ovy bleu, ovy bongan'omby, ovy gasy, ovy katso, ovy lalaina, ovy lava, ovy levilevy, ovy lohandambo, ovy masanivolo, ovy masoandrovolo, ovy poipoy, ovy randromiendaka, ovy revoroke, ovy rindrina, ovy rozia, ovy saonjo, ovy soroka, ovy tanty, ovy taretra, ovy tavoahangy, ovy tenany, ovy toko, ovy tranga, ovy vazaha, ovy voay*
D. alatipes L.	SW, around Toliara	VU	*Ovy*
D. analalavensis Jum. & H. Perrier	NW, around Analalava	NE	*Bemandry, berano, marahaly, milintognono*
D. antaly Jum. & H. Perrier	Widespread, especially western	LC	*Antady, antaly, antandena, babaina, lemenabaka, papa, tsihina, voaveo*
D. arcuatinervis Hochr.	E, to about 100 km inland	NT	*Makia, marika, mareky, ovifaitra, ovihazo, ovy vony*
D. bako Wilkin	W, Morondava to Beanka	EN	*Bako, kaokao*
D. bemandry Jum. & H. Perrier	W, Morondava to Mahajanga, patchy	NE	*Babo, babo menamionga, bemandry, marahaly*
D. bemarivensis Jum. & H. Perrier	W, Toliara to Antsiranana	NE	*Elakelaka, ovy laglasy, trengytrengy*
D. bosseri Haigh & Wilkin	W, Toliara to Antsiranana	LC	*Elakelaky*
D. buckleyana Wilkin	N, Antsiranana to Ankarana	EN	*Oviala, ovy, maragna, ovy malandy, taravy*
D. bulbifera L.	Widespread	NE	*Hofika, ovitra, pomme de l'air, hofika gasy, hofka mafaitra* (angular bulbils), *hofika mamy, hofim-bazaha* (rounded bulbils)
D. comorensis R. Knuth	Comoros (Grande Comore and Mohéli)	EN	*Chiyazi msiru, mtru*
D. decaryana H. Perrier	Ambatofinandrahana	CR	*Ovy*
D. esculenta (Lour.) Burkill	Infrequently cultivated especially in E; Tropical Asia to New Guinea	NE	*Mavondro*
D. fandra H. Perrier	SW and widespread	LC	*Andraha, anjiky, fandra*
D. heteropoda Baker	Central Highlands to Andringitra and Vohitrotsy	LC	*Oviala, ovimbato*
D. hexagona Baker	Central Highlands, widespread	NT	*Kitsaoso, kitaratara*
D. hombuka H. Perrier	SW	LC	*Hombuka, ataza, kato*
D. irodensis Wilkin, Rajaonah & Randriamb.	N, Antsiranana, Irodo to Ivovona	EN	*Bemandry, ovy lagilasy*
D. kimiae Wilkin	E, scattered	NT	*Oviala*
D. maciba Jum. & H. Perrier	W, Toliara to Antsiranana	LC	*Batatala, kasy, maromahay, masiba, malita ovy, ovy cable, ovy fotsy, ovy lasoie, ovy zaza, tsimanandreny*

SCIENTIFIC NAME	DISTRIBUTION	IUCN STATUS	VERNACULAR NAME(S)
D. madecassa H. Perrier	E, Manombo to Ifanadiana, scattered	EN	*Karatana, oviala, ovy taretra*
D. mamillata Jum. & H. Perrier	W, scattered	NE	Unknown
D. mayottensis Wilkin	Mayotte	VU	*Mitrou, oviala*
D. minutiflora Engl.	E, scattered, possibly formerly cultivated; continental Africa	LC	*Ovihazo*
D. nako H. Perrier	SW, Toliara to Tolagnaro	LC	*Bako, babona, mako, nako*
D. namorokensis Wilkin	Namoroka endemic	CR	Unknown
D. orangeana Wilkin	N, Antsiranana, Ivovona to Anjiabe	EN	*Angona, ovy, ovy fotsy, ovy jia*
D. ovinala Baker	W to Central Highlands, widespread	LC	*Angaraoko, angily behandaliny, mangararaoka, oviala, tsy matahodambo,*
D. proteiformis H. Perrier	E, Tolagnaro to N of Sambava	NT	*Manabandro*
D. pteropoda Boivin ex H. Perrier	N, Antsiranana to Ambilobe and Daraina	VU	*Ovy sofy, ovifotsy, ovindambo, ovy nylon, totongana*
D. quartiniana A. Rich.	Scattered, mainly W; continental Africa	LC	Unknown
D. sambiranensis R. Knuth	N, Antsiranana to Manongarivo and Daraina	NT	*Angona, angona mena, ovy jaune, marika, maherivahy, oviala*
D. sansibarensis Pax	Widespread, often near inhabited places	NE	*Angitriky, aranganarana, babanga, bekabiha, bemôra, haranarana, lepapa, fanganga, kaboma, makabiha, môra, rangitrika, sarimajola, veoveo*
D. seriflora Jum. & H. Perrier	E, Manombo to Nosy Be in N	LC	*Marana, ovifotsy, banabana, ovisofina, oviampasika, ovimanga, oviala, ovisotry, ovisera, ovy maintso, ovy sofy*
D. soso Jum. & H. Perrier	W, widespread	LC	*Bemandry, bontsaka, babo, babo gasy, baboke, babo menamionga, maromahay soso, sosan'ala, sosan-drano*
D. sterilis O. Weber & Wilkin	W, scattered	NT	*Bako, ovy, oviala*
D. trichantha Baker	Central Highlands, widespread	LC	*Oviala*
D. tsaratananensis H. Perrier	Tsaratanàna endemic	DD	*Ovihotra*
Trichopus	Madagascar; southern Indian subcontinent; peninsular Malaysia	–	NA
T. sempervirens (H. Perrier) Caddick & Wilkin	E	NE	*Avetra*
Tacca	Pantropical	–	NA
T. leontopetaloides L.	Pan-Palaeotropical	LC	*Tavolo, kabija, kabija bitra, kabija gasy*

Source: IUCN (2020).
Notes: In the distribution column, "widespread" (i.e., with broad geographic ranges) and N, S, E, W refer to distribution within Madagascar. IUCN status: CR, Critically Endangered; DD, Data Deficient; EN, Endangered; LC, Least Concern; NE, Not Evaluated; NT, Near Threatened; VU, Vulnerable.

Burkill and Perrier de la Bâthie (1950) and subsequent fieldwork and collections, it is endemic to the lowland moist evergreen and littoral forests of the east, occurring from Masoala to Tolagnaro and inland to about 100 km from the coast. This species is found at elevations from near sea level to about 250 m. It has a rhizomatous underground organ, sinistrorse (left-twining counterclockwise as viewed from above), twining stems to about 10 m in height, and cordate, alternate, entire leaves with campylodromous (all primary veins of similar size, originating at the blade base and most reaching the apex) venation, with the outermost pair of veins being marginal in the blade's basal sinus. Its white flowers are hermaphrodite (i.e., possessing both male and female organs), each with six long-acuminate, 15–30 mm long white tepals inserted on an inferior ovary. It is more usually encountered when in fruit, a three-winged dry but indehiscent capsule containing a single, wingless, trigonous-ovoid seed at its center, which is 12–15 mm long and has ruminate endosperm.

In contrast to *Trichopus*, *Dioscorea* has speciated extensively on Madagascar, as elsewhere in the seasonal tropics, and is distributed in all the biomes of the island (Burkill and Perrier de la Bâthie 1950). Underground organs are tuberous (Wilkin et al. 2007, 2009a; Figures 8.17b and f), with many possessing a rhizomatous crown that subtends two tubers, one in growth and one being absorbed, at least in the rainy season. These are the perennial edible parts of the plant that are eaten as yams (see Uses and Nutrition, pp. 550), as opposed to the usually annual, herbaceous stems (Figure 8.17e) that twine (with one exception, see Phylogeny, pp. 549) either dextrorse or sinistrorse (twining clockwise or counterclockwise, respectively, as viewed from above). Like *Trichopus*, leaf blade venation is campylodromous (Figures 8.17a, c, and d) although the outermost nerve pair are submarginal; blades vary from entire to compound. Some species possess axillary bulbils (aerial tubers) for vegetative reproduction, usually in addition to sexual organs. Flowers are dioecious (unisexual, male, and female flowers borne on separate plants) and solitary or in cymules (male only) on racemose or spicate, simple or compound (male only) inflorescences (Figures 8.17c and d); the six tepals are green or pigmented yellow, purple, or pink at anthesis; tepal length does not exceed 5 mm. In female plants (Figure 8.17d), flowers possess inferior ovaries and the fruit is a dehiscent, dry, three-winged capsule that contains six seeds (fewer by abortion), each of which is lens-shaped and has a marginal, papery wing for wind dispersal.

According to Plants of the World Online (POWO 2020) and the World Checklist of Dioscoreaceae (Govaerts et al. 2020a), there are currently 38 published species of *Dioscorea* on Madagascar (Table 8.15, in which the principal vernacular names for the different forms are presented). All except seven are endemic. The

FIGURE 8.17 **Form of reproductive and vegetative organs of *Dioscorea* on Madagascar, and yam cultivation and sale. A) Juvenile leaves of *D. orangeana* in the Forêt d'Orangea, showing campylodromous venation and variegation adjacent to the blade sinus (occasionally also observed in other species). B) A tuber of *D. bako* from Beroboka, Menabe Region. C) Leaf blade lower surface, petiole, and detached male inflorescences of *D. sambiranensis* ssp. *sambiranensis* from the Montagne d'Ambre. D) Leaf upper surface and detached immature infructescence of *D. sambiranensis* ssp. *sambiranensis* from Ambaharatra in the Sambirano Valley. The projections on the developing capsules are taxon-specific. E) A farmer in his plot of cultivated *D. alata* at Nosimbary in Mahavanona Commune, DIANA Region. F) Tubers of *D. maciba* on sale in the market of Port Bergé.** (PHOTOS A, C, D, and F by P. Wilkin; B by M. T. Rajaonah; and E by F. Rakotoarison.)

nonendemics are the two cultivated species of southeast Asian origin: *D. alata* (Figure 8.17e) and *D. esculenta*. The medicinal and edible *D. bulbifera* is the only pan-Paleotropical species. *Dioscorea minutiflora*, *D. quartinina*, and *D. sansibarensis* are of African origin. Finally, *D. bemarivensis* occurs in the Malagasy Region, and is also found in the Comoro archipelago, as well as on the islands of Aldabra and Assumption (Wilkin et al. 2007). Two further species, *D. comorensis* and *D. mayottensis*, with close systematic affinities to the Malagasy endemics, are endemic to Comoros and Mayotte, respectively (Wilkin et al. 2007).

The World Checklist of Flowering Plants records 629 species in *Dioscorea*. Thus, with 38 species, Madagascar holds about 6% of the world's diversity. Comparison with countries of similar size also suggests high diversity. Madagascar has an area of 587,000 km². Only Thailand (513,000 km²) with 47 species is at a similar level of species richness. Other countries across the tropics are much lower, such as Botswana (582,000 km², two species); Kenya (580,000 km², 10 species; Central African Republic (624,000 km², 19 species); Paraguay (407,000 km², 18 species). Thus, Madagascar is a global hotspot for diversity of this genus alongside Mexico, southern Brazil, Cuba, South Africa, and the pan-Himalaya.

There have been two principal eras of *Dioscorea* species discovery on Madagascar. The first was that of Perrier de la Bâthie, when botanists first began to gain an understanding of the scale and nature of Malagasy plant diversity, and the yam species of the island. At the same time, global knowledge of the genus was built by the the monograph of Knuth (1924). Between 1900 and 1950, Perrier de la Bâthie and colleagues described 19 species of *Dioscorea*, which were included in the *Flore de Madagascar et des Comores* treatment (Burkill and Perrier de la Bâthie 1950), which includes a key, illustrations, and information on ecology, distribution, vernacular names, and uses. The second wave of descriptions of new *Dioscorea* species involves the research group associated with this contribution who, in different combinations since 2000, have described nine new species (Wilkin et al. 2000, 2002, 2007, 2008a, 2008b, 2009a, 2009b, 2017; Haigh et al. 2005; Weber et al. 2005) and a new subspecies of *D. sambiranensis* (Wilkin et al. 2009a). These have been discovered in all parts of Madagascar except the extreme south and the Central Highlands, with three species being endemic to the former province of Antsiranana. Taxonomic resources and information can be found in IUCN (2020) and iNaturalist (2020).

Ethnobotanical research in a number of parts of Madagascar has provided important lists of locally distributed and utilized species, for example, Jeannoda et al. (2007), Cheban et al. (2009), and Andriamparany et al. (2014).

PHYLOGENY

Global Dioscoreaceae phylogenetics relevant to *Dioscorea*, *Tacca*, and *Trichopus* are not yet fully resolved (e.g., Caddick et al. 2002; Merckx et al. 2010). The only paper published to date to bear directly on the phylogenetics of *Dioscorea* on Madagascar was Wilkin et al. (2005). Based on sampling 12 endemic Malagasy species out of 50 from the genus as a whole, and using two plastid markers, the Malagasy endemic species were found to form a clade. The sole exception was *D. antaly*, which was nested with taxa including the pan-Paleotropical *D. bulbifera* (perhaps via historical cultivation). This placement was congruent with micromorphology and its rather bitter taste and unique tuber form. There has been significant work on the chemistry of this species (e.g., Rakotobe et al. 2010). Its phylogenetic placement was corroborated and shown to be related to a separate dispersal event by Viruel et al. (2016) and Couto et al. (2018). The other nonendemics listed above are nested with non-Malagasy species in other clades. Notably, *D. sansibarensis* may be sister to the Malagasy clade but the relationship has only weak support.

Wilkin et al. (2005) showed that there were two subclades within the Malagasy clade, which differ in some discrete characters. The first comprises a small number of species such as *D. arcuatinervis* and *D. bemarivensis*, which have seeds with a round wing around the margin. The underground parts of these species are long, terete tubers that spread horizontally through the soil and have swollen apices. In contrast, the majority of the endemic Malagasy species form a second, more species-rich subclade that has two vertically oriented tubers (one in growth and one being absorbed) of even thickness. Their seeds possess an elongate wing on only one side of the seed margin. Wilkin et al. (2005) showed that many of the species of the second subclade are found in areas of the island with seasonal climates and that stem twining has been lost once within this clade, in the grassland species *D. hexagona*, although some individuals show limited twining at stem tips. Reconstruction of twining direction on the phylogenetic trees showed that all endemic species of *Dioscorea* on Madagascar are sinistrorse. *Dioscorea minutiflora* may represent feral populations of formerly cultivated, introduced African guinea yams (*D. rotundata*/*D. cayenensis*). This species and *D. alata* are dextrorse.

A fully resolved phylogenomic tree for 35 Malagasy species of *Dioscorea* confirms monophyly in a relatively recent radiation within *Dioscorea* (J. Viruel et al., unpublished data), excluding *D. antaly* and the nonendemic taxa. A custom target capture kit designed for *Dioscorea* (Soto Gomez et al. 2019) permits sequencing of 260 low- to single-copy nuclear genes from herbarium specimens and estimation of ploidy levels (Viruel et al. 2019).

ENDEMISM

Thirty of Madagascar's 38 published *Dioscorea* species are endemic and one a Malagasy Region endemic. Thus, overall species endemism is about 79%. The numbers of species and endemics found in each of the six former provinces are summarized in Table 8.15. Numbers of species are highest in areas that possess multiple biomes (in particular both humid and seasonal biomes) and the largest elevational ranges (former provinces of Antsiranana and Fianarantsoa). The far north of the island is notably rich in species endemism, and the number of known endemics continues to expand via discovery of taxonomic novelties. Two of its endemics are known from just three populations (*D. orangeana*, Figure 8.17a, and *D. irodensis*). The other range-restricted endemics are *D. namorokensis*, *D. analalavensis*, *D. decaryana*, *D. madecassa*, *D. bako* (Figure 8.17b), *D. alatipes*, *D. buckleyana*, *D. pteropoda*, and *D. tsaratananensis* (Table 8.15).

USES AND NUTRITION

Yams are an important food source on Madagascar (e.g., Jeannoda et al. 2003, 2007; Wilkin et al. 2009a). Their tubers provide a starchy foodstuff that, in parts of the country, is only surpassed in importance by rice and are highly sought after, especially during "hungry gap" periods when stocks of other foods (especially rice) have been used up. For example, nearly 70% of people interviewed in the area of Ankarafantsika enter the protected area to illegally harvest wild yam species (Aymoz et al. 2013). While cultivated varieties are available, especially the white *ovibe* and purple *ovy lalaina* varieties of winged yam, *Dioscorea alata* (Table 8.15, which also presents vernacular names; Figure 8.17e), production can sometimes be limited which means much of Madagascar's rural community resort to eating wild yams. The endemic species are virtually all edible, either raw, cooked, or after more extensive preparation. Most extensively used are those that produce one tuber per rainy season. While some have historically been wild-harvested for food, at least in times of food shortages, the most favored and widely used edible wild species in the north that the authors encountered are *D. orangeana*, *D. buckleyana*, and *D. sambiranensis* (Figures 8.17a, c, and d, respectively); the latter appears to be the most preferred there. Elsewhere in Madagascar, *D. maciba* (Figure 8.17f) is prioritized by peoples from the length of the western dry deciduous forest area from Toliara to Antsiranana, *D. bako* (Figure 8.17b) in the Menabe area, and *D. seriflora* in the eastern moist evergreen forest area. These species tend to be relatively locally abundant, possess larger tubers, and are perceived to have better flavor. Note that two of the five are narrowly restricted endemics. Outside the areas where these five species are distributed it is principally winged yams that are encountered for sale. The Central Highlands has the lowest levels of yam use.

Wild yams are locally sourced from forest habitats and are available seasonally at markets ranging in location from rural communities to large cities such as Antsiranana where yams like *D. orangeana* can seasonally achieve prices significantly higher than rice does, depending on local supply and demand. Both cultivated winged and wild yams have been documented as being transported distances to market of up to 70 km using shoulder poles, zebu carts, or country buses. They can be bought whole and uncooked or cooked (usually boiled) for consumption in home settings. Alternatively, they may be bought by vendors and resold, or boiled into porridge and served with sugar in *hotelys* or by street sellers.

The scale of use means that Madagascar's yams are deeply embedded in daily life and culture. Winged yams are especially important due to their potential scale of production and storability; wild taxa are eaten soon after harvest. Beyond *D. alata* and *D. esculenta*, only one nonendemic is eaten, the domesticated form of *D. bulbifera*, which has larger and usually angular bulbils, albeit as a low-preference famine food. *Dioscorea antaly* is important in the areas around Port Bergé (Boriziny) and Morondava during the hungry gap period when it is second (or perhaps equal to) in preference after *D. maciba*. Its tubers are branching and yield up to 30 kg per plant (Burkill and Perrier de la Bâthie 1950) but require detoxification in running water and drying.

While the tubers of *Dioscorea* species are used as food on Madagascar, there are limited data available on their nutritional value (e.g., Jeannoda et al. 2007). Tubers of those species that have been evaluated have almost all been collected outside Madagascar, and may not reflect the nutritional profiles of those species grown on the island. Nevertheless, in general, considerable amounts of starch and lower levels of protein, with potassium as the most abundant detected mineral, have been recorded. For example, *D. esculenta* tubers contain similar high levels of starch (78% dry weight) to those of *D. alata* (Rinaldo 2020). Tubers from the latter species contain a high proportion of starch (65–84%) and approximately 7% protein (dry weight), although different cultivars may vary in their content of these macronutrients (Wanasundera and Ravindran 1994; Rinaldo 2020). These protein levels compare favorably with those of other tuber crops. *Dioscorea alata* also contains vitamin C (13–25 mg/100 g fresh weight, although some studies record lower values at 3–4 mg/100 g fresh weight) and minerals, with high levels of potassium compared with other detected minerals (Wanasundera and Ravindran 1994). *Dioscorea bulbifera* tubers also contain high levels of potassium (560 mg per 100 g) in addition to approximately 26 g per 100 g of total carbohydrate and provide 119 kcal per 100 g (fresh weight); essential amino acids also occur in this species, with the exception of tryptophan (Bhandari et al. 2003). Although nutritional data for *D. minutiflora* tubers are lacking, the related *D. cayenensis* provides approximately 108 kcal, 30 g carbohydrate, 3 g protein, and minerals, principally potassium (262 mg), as well as low quantities of fiber (0.2 g) and lipids (0.3 g) per 100 g in uncooked form (Adepoju et al. 2018). Thus, edible *Dioscorea* tubers on Madagascar are likely to provide nutritional value but studies on the composition of endemic species are needed.

In addition to their utilization as food, *Dioscorea* species have other uses on Madagascar. The toxic *D. sansibarensis* is said to be used in truth rituals (Burkill and Perrier de la Bâthie 1950), while other species have been recorded as medicinal plants. *Dioscorea alata* leaves have been documented as a traditional remedy for digestive disorders in the Tanala area in the central east (Riondato et al. 2019). In the Mahafaly region of the extreme south, the subterranean parts of *D. bemandry*, *D. fandra*, and *D. nako*, and the aerial parts of *D. ovinala*, are recorded as being used for medicinal purposes (Andriamparany et al. 2014), but specific information regarding usage was not provided.

CONSERVATION

International Union for Conservation of Nature (IUCN) Red List status has been published for 30 species of *Dioscorea* from Madagascar, and the two endemic species from the Comoro archipelago. Eight species have not been assessed although, as cultigens, *D. alata* and *D. esculenta* fall outside the scope of the Red List. Table 8.16 shows the numbers of species in each Red List category, which indicates that the overall percentage of threatened species is 34%. The addition of the threatened Comorian endemics pushes these figures in the Malagasy Region up to 12 threatened species. This relatively high level of threat is due to habitat loss and overexploitation.

It is noted that, as for most groups of plants studied (e.g., Rakotoarinivo et al. 2014) in the past two decades, new species of *Dioscorea* that are discovered are likely to be range restricted and threatened. Thus, the overall level of threat is likely to rise. Four of

TABLE 8.16. **Numbers of Malagasy Dioscoreaceae species assessed by the IUCN and classified by threat status**

IUCN STATUS	NUMBER OF SPECIES CLASSIFIED	%
CR	2	7
EN	6	20
VU	2	7
NT	6	20
LC	13	43
DD	1	3
Total	30	100

Source: IUCN (2020).
Note: IUCN status: CR, Critically Endangered; DD, Data Deficient; EN, Endangered; LC, Least Concern; NE, Not Evaluated; NT, Near Threatened; VU, Vulnerable.

the 10 threatened species are from northern Madagascar suggesting that it is both the center of diversity of Malagasy yams and the zone in which the greatest conservation effort should be made.

From 2015 to 2018 the authors of this contribution ran the project Conserving Madagascar's Yams through Cultivation for Livelihoods and Food Security. This project worked with rural communities in the former Antsiranana and Fianarantsoa Provinces, specifically the Fandriana-Ambositra-Vondrozo Corridor (COFAV) in the latter. Antsiranana has the highest diversity of threatened wild yams, while the COFAV is a center for cultivation of winged yams. Further work using the same approaches is taking place with communities in Morondava District and near Port Bergé and Analalava. Communities in those areas were supported to cultivate winged and wild yam species, especially those that are threatened, alongside conserving the latter in community and centralized living collections and seed banks. This conserved 25 species, an endemic subspecies, and five varieties of winged yam in germplasm collections and in cultivation; 23 were banked as seed. Using IUCN Red List criteria, 12 of the 25 have been demonstrated (some provisionally) to be threatened, including *D. acuminata*, *D. analalavensis*, *D. bako*, *D. irodensis*, *D. maciba*, *D. orangeana*, *D. sambiranensis*, and *D. seriflora*. At the same time, overall household annual calorific intake, annual protein intake, and annual income were increased for those communities. For example, mean annual income per household across the project as a whole increased from a baseline of 464,300 MGA (about US$135) to 537,600 MGA (about US$170).

WORK IN PROGRESS

Five new species of *Dioscorea* have been discovered, most from the extreme north of the island, and are yet to be described. At least three are likely to be classified as threatened. Two more novel species are expected to be resolved by a revision of a species complex that is in preparation (M. T. Rajaonah et al., unpublished data). We expect the estimate of the number of species on Madagascar to approach 50. An ongoing project is seeking to develop sustainable yam markets in both the north of the island and communities near the COFAV. This will support conservation of threatened wild yams and improve nutrition and livelihoods of local communities through developing business models, value chains, enhanced storage, and *Dioscorea* species nutritional profiles.

ACKNOWLEDGMENTS

Funding from the Darwin Initiative for the projects Conserving Madagascar's Yams through Cultivation for Livelihoods and Food Security (project 22005) and Sustainable Yam Markets for Conservation and Food Security in Madagascar (project EIDP0049) is gratefully acknowledged. We also thank the April Trust for their support for the project Yam Cultivation for Conservation and Livelihoods.

Subject editors: Laurent Gautier and Steven M. Goodman

PANDANACEAE, SCREW-PINES, *VAKOA*, *HOFA*, *FRANDRA*

M. W. Callmander, M. O. Laivao, and S. Buerki

PHYLOGENETIC INFERENCES AND NEW SYSTEMATIC INSIGHTS INTO MALAGASY PANDANACEAE

Our understanding of the paleotropical Pandanaceae family has significantly improved since a contribution (Callmander and Laivao 2003) to the precursor of this book (Goodman and Benstead 2003), in terms of both their evolutionary history and taxonomy. A first phylogenetic framework based on limited sampling (Callmander et al. 2003) provided the basis for the recognition of the new genus *Martellidendron*, endemic to Madagascar (five species) and the granitic islands of the Seychelles (one species). Later, a broader family-level phylogenetic framework was proposed to further investigate species relationships (Buerki et al. 2012). This latter work led to the description of a fifth Pandanaceae genus, *Benstonea* (61 species), distributed from India to Australia with its center of diversity shared between Borneo and peninsular Malaysia (Callmander et al. 2012b; Pandanaceae Project 2020). Finally, dated phylogenies provided our first insights into the origin and biogeography of the five genera of this family, *Benstonea*, *Freycinetia* (~250 species distributed from India to the south Pacific islands), *Martellidendron*, *Pandanus*, and *Sararanga* (two species in the Philippines and New Guinea) (Gallaher et al. 2015; Buerki et al. 2016b). Some details are presented here on the two genera occurring on Madagascar.

Martellidendron diverged from its most recent common ancestor in the late Eocene to early Miocene (15.1–38.1 million years ago [Mya]) (Gallaher et al. 2015; Buerki et al. 2016b; Figure 8.18). A long-distance ocean dispersal event was proposed to explain its current distribution (rather than vicariance as hypothesized by Callmander et al. 2003), which would have taken place from southeast Asia to Madagasacar and was most likely mediated by the westward oceanic current (Gallaher et al. 2015).

The genus *Pandanus* most likely originated during the Miocene (10–20 Mya) and is split into two clades (Buerki et al. 2012; Gallaher et al. 2015; Figure 8.18). All sampled Malagasy species are found in a grade at the base of clade II, with all African and Mauritian *Pandanus* species forming strongly supported subclades (Buerki et al. 2012). Finally, the rest of clade II is a strongly supported subclade containing species of the *P. tectorius* complex, which occurs from the eastern coast of Africa to the southern Pacific. Additional analyses support a single origin for Malagasy *Pandanus* species, mediated by a long-distance ocean dispersal event from the western Pacific region. This dispersal event was relatively recent (4.5–13.1 Mya ago [Gallaher et al. 2015]) and the origin of the considerable radiation of Malagasy *Pandanus* species, with 78 species currently recognized.

Morphological diversity in *Pandanus* is so important on Madagascar that B. C. Stone (1974) hypothesized close relationships between several Malagasy species and those occurring in the Indo-Malaysian region. For instance, he classified the Malagasy *P. platyphyllus* (growing along the Pangalanes Canal) in the Malaysian *Pandanus* subgenus *Rykia* based on its fruit morphology (drupe and stigma). The discovery of its staminate flowers (Huynh 1977), however, subsequently confirmed its placement with the Malagasy *Pandanus* subgenus *Vinsonia*. Even recently the subgenus *Vinsonia* was hypothesized to be polyphyletic due to the high level of morphological heterogeneity among species (Callmander and Laivao 2003), but phylogenetic analyses confirmed its monophyly (Buerki et al. 2012), pointing to a very fast morphological diversification (most likely tracking ecological niches of *Pandanus* species on the island).

Overall, Madagascar is the center of diversity of subgenus *Vinsonia* but this subgenus also occurs in continental Africa (around nine species [Beentje and Callmander 2014]), on western Indian Ocean Islands (Mayotte with two species [Huynh 1985], the Mascarenes archipelago with 25 species [Bosser and Guého 2003], the granitic islands of the Seychelles archipelago with two species [Callmander and Buerki 2004], and a single species on Aldabra Atoll, ~420 km northwest of Madagascar).

Finally, it is worth pointing out that the extraordinary morphological diversity of Malagasy *Pandanus* species is not reflected in the DNA regions classically used in phylogenetic studies, with all species having very high sequence homology (Buerki et al. 2012). Further studies using full chloroplast genomes and nuclear ribosomal RNA (rRNA) regions as DNA barcodes to infer species boundaries and phylogenetic relationships within *Pandanus* are ongoing. This approach is more promising and preliminary results confirm monophyly of Malagasy species and their close relationships with Mauritian and African species.

TAXONOMY, PHYTOGEOGRAPHY, AND ECOLOGY OF MALAGASY PANDANACEAE

In this section we will delve into the morphological characters supporting genera on Madagascar, as well as the infrageneric classification of *Pandanus*. Insights into species distributions and their ecology are also provided.

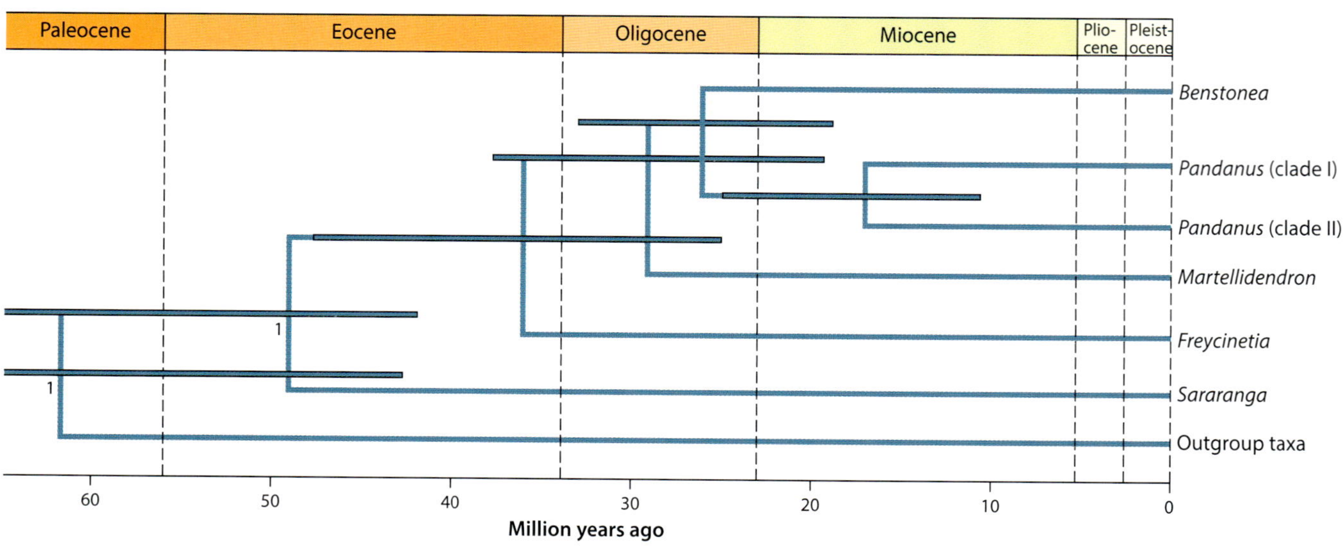

FIGURE 8.18 **Generic-level dated phylogenetic tree of Pandanaceae.** (SOURCE: modified from Buerki et al. 2016b.)

Martellidendron

Martellidendron, originally described at subgeneric level (Martelli and Pichi-Sermolli 1951; Callmander et al. 2003), is morphologically unique within the family based on the following characters: pollen grains (Hotton et al. 1994), anther structure (Huynh 1983), endocarp (Martelli and Pichi-Sermolli 1951), and its potentially bisexual flowers (presence of a pistillode and staminodes in the staminate and the pistillate flowers, respectively) (Callmander 2001). *Martellidendron* is also the only genus in the family in which the morphology of staminate flowers allows species-level determination (number of spikes in inflorescences, disposition of stamens, and the morphology of the anthers and the pistillode) (see Callmander 2000, 2001).

Five species are currently recognized on Madagascar, all occurring in the humid or subhumid areas in the eastern, central, and Sambirano phytogeographic regions (Humbert 1955). *Martellidendron cruciatum* has the broadest distribution, occurring across the humid to subhumid regions of the island and from sea level to 1200 m elevation. It is easily recognizable by its numerous aerial roots departing from the trunk at 5–10 m forming an entanglement of roots (Figure 8.19a) and glaucous adaxial leaf surface. Other species have more restricted ranges like *M. androcephalanthos*, endemic to the Sambirano, or *M. gallinarum*, known only from eastern lowland moist evergreen forests in the Mananara-Nord area.

Pandanus

The genus *Pandanus* is currently represented on Madagascar by 79 endemic species (Madagascar Catalogue 2020) (Table 8.17). Only one introduced species occurs, *P. utilis*, with its origins in the Mascarenes (Bosser and Guého 2003), which is occasionally cultivated. The Malagasy *Pandanus* species have been classified into 18 sections (for a key to those sections, see Laivao et al. 2006). This infrageneric classification follows a practical view initiated by B. C. Stone (1974), which originally aimed at underlining the considerable morphological diversity of the genus throughout its Old World distribution. Fifteen sections (out of the 18 present on Madagascar) are endemic to the island emphasizing the uniqueness of several Malagasy species (Table 8.17). The three nonendemic sections are shared with continental Africa and other western Indian Ocean Islands; these are: section *Dauphinensia* (four species on Madagascar and a single species in continental Africa), *Heterostigma* (six species on Madagascar and about 10 species in continental Africa), and *Mammillarisia* (nine species on Madagascar and one species endemic to Aldabra Atoll and another to Mayotte) (Laivao 2008).

Pandanus is known from all phytogeographic regions of Madagascar, but it is less diverse in the drier southwestern and western regions. The typical coniferoid (conifer-like) habit of section *Acanthostyla* is common in the swamps and marshes of the eastern and central regions (Figure 8.19b). The Pangalanes Canal is home to several endemic species (for example, *P. platyphyllus* and *P. rollotii*; Figure 8.19c). The dense moist evergreen forests, from sea level to the upper limit of forest on the highest mountains, contain species belonging to different sections. For example, on the Tsaratanàna Massif, *P. alpestris* (section *Acanthostyla*) occurs from lower elevations to the tree line at 2200 m, while species of sections *Foullioya* and *Souleyetia* are common along streams. The endemic species *P. biceps* (Figure 8.19d) can be found on the Ankarana Massif. Further, *P. pristis* and *P. grallatus* grow on limestone in the western dry deciduous forests. In this latter region, members of the section *Heterostigma* grow along rivers, including *P. barbellatus* (Figure 8.19e), while other species occur in the western limestone areas (*P. flagellibracteatus*, *P. oligocarpus*, and *P. tsingycola*).

The actual phytogeography of the genus on Madagascar is clearly a combination of dispersal strategies, with small fleshy fruits utilizing an animal-dispersal mechanism, while other species employ flotation (fruits contain aerenchym, tissue with thin walls separated by gas-filled spaces) (B. C. Stone 1974). Lemurs are seed predators (see Razafindratsima et al., pp. 142–52) and, for example, species of *Eulemur* are known to feed on fruits of various *Pandanus* species (Figure 8.19f) (Birkinshaw 2001; Andriamaharoa et al. 2010; Rafenoarisoa 2016). *Dipsochelys gigantea*, the giant tortoise of Aldabra Atoll, is known to feed on and disperse seeds of *P. aldabraensis*. Mauritian *Pandanus* species are likely to have been dispersed by extinct terrestrial turtles (M. Allet, unpublished data). On Madagascar, no studies have been conducted but it seems reasonable to hypothesize that extinct and extant terrestrial tortoises may be associated with the seed dispersal of *Pandanus* species.

Recent inventories in poorly known regions in northern and western Madagascar have led to the discovery of several restricted-range and morphologically isolated species in the Galoko-Kalobinono Massifs, western slopes of Montagne d'Ambre, and Beanka (see Callmander et al. 2008, 2009, 2013, 2020). Several new *Pandanus* species are still pending description, underlining the incredible radiation of this group of plants on the Great Island.

VERNACULAR NAMES AND LOCAL USES

Malagasy Pandanaceae species have several vernacular names such as *vakoa*, *hofa*, and *frandra*. Materials from these plants are used for building houses and weaving (mats, baskets, and other wickerwork) in the eastern and northeastern regions of the island. Several species are harvested by local people, such as *Martellidendron kariangensis* and *Pandanus madagascariensis* (Callmander and Laivao 2003), *P. guillaumetii* (Fedele et al. 2011) (Figure 8.19g), and *P. kimlangii* (Jones et al. 2008). In general, harvesting seems to follow traditional practices that do not seriously damage the central leaves (a method called *vololony* in the Fianarantsoa moist evergreen forest corridor) (Jones et al. 2008). However, this sustainable, long-standing tradition is not always respected, probably as a result of increasing resource scarcity (Fedele et al. 2011). Some people in the southeast eat the fruit of *P. platyphyllus* and its vernacular name is *fandramamy*, which means the sweet *Pandanus*. Two ethnobotanical studies have shown that *Pandanus* leaves are used medicinally to treat fatigue (Razafindraibe et al. 2013; Rabearivony et al. 2015).

FIGURE 8.19 **Malagasy Pandanaceae. A) Aerial roots of *Martellidendron cruciatum*; B) *P.* section *Acanthostyla* coniferoid habit near Andasibe; C) *P. rollotii* (front) and *P. platyphyllus*; D) *P. biceps* in the Ankarana Massif; E) *P. barbellatus*; F) *Eulemur cinereiceps* (White-collared Brown Lemur) feeding on a *Pandanus* fruit in Mahabo; G) *P. guillaumetii*; and H) *P. tsingycola*.** (PHOTOS A and D by M. W. Callmander, B by L. Allorge, C by S. Wohlhauser, E by F. Ratovoson, F by C. Birkinshaw, G by G. E. Schatz, and H by R. M. Hanitrarivo.)

TABLE 8.17. **The Pandanaceae flora of Madagascar with information on associated vegetation types and biogeography**

SCIENTIFIC NAMES	VERNACULAR NAMES	LOWLAND MOIST EVERGREEN FOREST	MEDIUM-ALTITUDE MOIST EVERGREEN FOREST	MOUNTAIN ERICOID THICKET	DRY DECIDUOUS FOREST	DRY SPINY THICKET	SWAMP FOREST	LITTORAL FOREST	RIPARIAN FOREST	BIOGEOGRAPHY
MARTELLIDENDRON										
M. androcephalanthos (Martelli) Callm. & Chassot		X	–	–	–	–	–	–	–	Sambirano Region
M. cruciatum (Pic. Serm.) Callm. & Chassot	*Tsiribe* (Mananara-Nord)	X	X	–	–	–	–	–	–	
M. gallinarum (Callm.) Callm.	*Tsirikeakoho* (Mananara-Nord)	X	–	–	–	–	–	–	–	East
M. kariangensis (Huynh) Callm.	*Akohomorika* (Manarana-Nord)	X	–	–	–	–	–	–	–	East
M. karaka (Martelli) Callm. & Chassot	*Karaka*	X	–	–	–	–	–	–	–	East
PANDANUS										
Section *Acanthostyla*	*Fandran*, *frandranolana* (Tolagnaro)									
P. andringitrensis Huynh		–	X	X	–	–	–	–	–	Central Highlands
P. alpestris Martelli		–	X	X	–	–	–	–	–	Northern mountains
P. alveolatus Huynh		X	X	–	–	–	–	–	–	North
P. ceratophorus Baker	*Maintsokely* (Manongarivo)	X	X	–	–	–	–	–	–	
P. comatus Martelli		–	–	–	–	–	X	X	–	East
P. kuepferi Callm., Laivao & Wohlh.		–	X	–	–	–	–	–	–	Northern mountains
P. longistylus Martelli & Pic. Serm.		X	–	–	–	–	–	X	–	Southeast
P. mangokensis Martelli		X	X	–	–	–	–	–	–	
P. marojejicus Callm. & Laivao		–	–	X	–	–	–	–	–	Marojejy
P. namakiensis Martelli		–	–	–	X	–	–	–	–	Central Highlands
P. pluriloculatus H. St John		X	–	–	–	–	–	X	–	East
P. pseudobathei Pic. Serm.		–	–	X	–	–	–	–	–	Northern mountains
P. sparganioides Baker	*Vakoaamboalavo* (northwest)	–	–	X	–	–	–	–	–	Northern mountains
P. spinifer Warb.		–	X	–	–	–	–	–	–	Central Highlands
P. tabellarius Huynh		–	X	–	–	–	–	–	–	Northern mountains
Section *Aquatiles*										
P. peyrierasii B. C. Stone & Guillaumet	*Fandradomano* (Tolagnaro)	–	–	–	–	–	X	–	–	Southeast

(continued overleaf)

TABLE 8.17. ***continued***

SCIENTIFIC NAMES	VERNACULAR NAMES	LOWLAND MOIST EVERGREEN FOREST	MEDIUM-ALTITUDE MOIST EVERGREEN FOREST	MOUNTAIN ERICOID THICKET	DRY DECIDUOUS FOREST	DRY SPINY THICKET	SWAMP FOREST	LITTORAL FOREST	RIPARIAN FOREST	BIOGEOGRAPHY
Section *Bicipites*										
P. biceps B. C. Stone & Guillaumet		–	–	–	X	–	–	–	–	Ankarana Massif
Section *Callmanderia*										
P. callmanderianus Laivao & Buerki		X	–	–	–	–	–	X	–	East
Section *Dauphinensia*	*Hofa*									
P. concretus Baker	*Vacoa* (Tolagnaro)	–	–	–	–	–	–	X	–	East
P. kimlangii Callm. & Laivao		–	X	–	–	–	–	–	–	East
P. linguiformis B. C. Stone		–	X	–	–	–	–	–	–	
P. spicatus H. St. John	*Vacoa madink*	–	X	–	–	–	–	–	–	Montagne d'Ambre
Section *Foullioya*	*Ritsika* (Tolagnaro)									
P. humbertii Laivao, Callm. & Buerki		X	–	–	–	–	–	–	–	Northeast
P. longecuspicatus Pic. Serm.		X	X	–	–	–	–	X	–	Northeast
P. malgassicus Pic. Serm.		X	–	–	–	–	–	X	–	East
P. pseudocollinus Pic. Serm.		X	–	–	–	–	–	X	–	East/Northeast
P. pygmaeus Thouars		X	X	–	–	–	–	–	–	
P. sylvicola Huynh		X	–	–	–	–	–	–	–	East
Section *Guillaumetia*										
P. guillaumetii B. C. Stone	*Tsiriky* (Mananara-Nord)	X	–	–	–	–	–	–	–	East
Section *Heterostigma*										
P. ambongensis Martelli		–	–	–	–	–	–	–	X	West/Central Highlands
P. bakeri Warb.		–	–	–	–	–	–	–	X	Central Highlands
P. barbellatus Huynh		X	–	–	–	–	–	–	–	Southeast
P. diffuses Martelli		X	–	–	–	–	–	–	–	East
P. myriocarpus Baker		–	–	–	–	–	–	–	X	West
P. variabilis Martelli		–	–	–	–	–	–	–	X	Central Highlands
Section *Imerinenses*										
P. imerinensis Martelli	*Bobaka* (center east)	X	–	–	–	–	–	X	–	East

SCIENTIFIC NAMES	VERNACULAR NAMES	LOWLAND MOIST EVERGREEN FOREST	MEDIUM-ALTITUDE MOIST EVERGREEN FOREST	MOUNTAIN ERICOID THICKET	DRY DECIDUOUS FOREST	DRY SPINY THICKET	SWAMP FOREST	LITTORAL FOREST	RIPARIAN FOREST	BIOGEOGRAPHY
Section *Insuetia*										
P. insuetus Huynh		X	–	–	–	–	–	–	–	Northeast (Masoala)
Section *Lonchostigma*										
P. rollotii Martelli	*Frandratoloha* (Tolagnaro), *fandranety* (center east)	–	–	–	–	–	X	–	–	East (Pangalanes)
Section *Mammillarisia*	*Fandrana*									
P. ankaranensis Callm. & Laivao		–	–	–	X	–	–	–	–	Ankarana Massif
P. aridus H. St. John	*Fandrana* (Tolagnaro)	–	–	–	X	X	–	–	–	Southeast
P. boivinii Solms		X	–	–	–	–	–	–	–	North
P. conatus H. St. John		X	X	–	–	–	–	–	–	North
P. grallatus B. C. Stone		–	–	–	X	–	–	–	–	North
P. manamboloensis Huynh		–	–	–	X	–	–	–	–	West
P. mammillaris Martelli & Pic. Serm.		X	X	–	–	–	–	–	–	Northern mountains
P. pervilleanus Solms		X	–	–	–	–	–	X	–	
P. saxatilis Martelli	*Maintsokely*, *hofa* (Manongarivo)	–	X	–	–	–	–	–	–	Northern mountains
Section *Phaenops*										
P. longissimepedunculatus Martelli		X	–	–	–	–	–	–	–	East coast
P. princeps B. C. Stone		X	–	–	–	–	–	–	–	East coast
Section *Platyphylla*										
P. platyphyllus Martelli	*Fandramamy* (Tolagnaro), *hofaradry* (center east)	–	–	–	–	–	X	–	–	East coast (Pangalanes)
Section *Rykiella*										
P. macrophyllus Martelli	*Vakoandrano* (center east)	X	–	–	–	–	–	–	–	East coast
Section *Souleyetia*										
P. ambalavaoensis Huynh		–	X	–	–	–	–	–	–	Central Highlands
P. analamerensis Huynh		–	–	–	X	–	–	–	–	North
P. arenicola Huynh		–	–	–	X	X	–	–	–	West
P. coriaceus Huynh		–	–	–	X	–	–	–	–	Northwest/North
P. dyckioides Baker		–	X	–	–	–	–	–	–	Central Highlands
P. flagellaris B. C. Stone		–	–	–	X	–	–	–	–	North

(continued overleaf)

TABLE 8.17. ***continued***

SCIENTIFIC NAMES	VERNACULAR NAMES	LOWLAND MOIST EVERGREEN FOREST	MEDIUM-ALTITUDE MOIST EVERGREEN FOREST	MOUNTAIN ERICOID THICKET	DRY DECIDUOUS FOREST	DRY SPINY THICKET	SWAMP FOREST	LITTORAL FOREST	RIPARIAN FOREST	BIOGEOGRAPHY
P. flagellibracteatus Huynh		–	–	–	X	–	–	–	–	West
P. freycinetioides (Gaudich.) Kurz		X	–	–	–	–	–	–	–	East
P. latistigmaticus Huynh		–	X	–	–	–	–	–	–	Montagne d'Ambre
P. leptopodus Martelli		X	X	–	–	–	–	–	–	East
P. longipes Perrier ex Martelli		–	X	–	–	–	–	–	–	Northern mountains
P. microcephalus Baker	*Tsirikaandjiantongatra* (Mananara)	X	–	–	–	–	–	–	–	East
P. neoleptopodus Pic. Serm.		X	–	–	–	–	–	–	–	East
P. oligocarpus Martelli	*Fandra* (Sakalava)	–	–	–	X	–	–	–	–	West
P. oligocephalus Baker		X	–	–	–	–	–	–	–	East
P. pristis B. C. Stone		–	–	–	X	–	–	–	–	Ankarana Massif
P. sambiranensis Huynh	*Maitsokely* (Manongarivo)	X	X	–	–	–	–	–	–	Northern mountains
P. tolanarensis Huynh		X	–	–	–	–	–	–	–	Southeast
P. tsaratananensis Martelli		–	X	–	–	–	–	–	–	Northern mountains
Section *Stephanostigma*										
P. analamazaoentrensis Martelli		–	X	–	–	–	–	–	–	East
P. bipyramidatus Martelli	*Hofavato* (Mananara-Nord), *kankona* (east)	X	X	–	–	–	–	–	–	East/Northeast
Section *Tridentistigma*										
P. maromokotrensis Callm. & Wohlh.		–	X	–	–	–	–	–	–	Northern mountains
P. tazoanii Callm. & Wohlh.		–	X	–	–	–	–	–	–	Northern mountains
Incertae sedis										
P. kalobinonensis Callm., Luino & Razakamal.		X	–	–	–	–	–	–	–	Kalobinono-Galoko
P. nusbaumeri Callm. & L. Gaut.		–	X	–	–	–	–	–	–	Montagne d'Ambre
P. perrieri Martelli		–	–	–	X	–	–	–	–	
P. sermollianus Callm. & Buerki		X	–	–	–	–	–	–	–	Kalobinono-Galoko
P. tsingycola Callm. & Nusb.		–	–	–	X	–	–	–	–	Beanka

Source: See Gautier et al. (pp. 452–64, Table 8.1) for definitions of vegetation types.

CONSERVATION STATUS

Callmander et al. (2007) showed that >90% of Malagasy Pandanaceae species are threatened with extinction and proposed 10 priority areas for Pandanaceae conservation. Most of those areas now have legal protection status, having been incorporated into the island's network of protected areas. The network comprises more than 120 protected areas and insures the protection of most of the richest habitat, of unparalleled diversity in Madagascar (Goodman et al. 2018), and includes some of the most endangered species, which have restricted ranges. *Pandanus peyrierasii* is known only from small populations in swamps between Manafiafy and Tolagnaro, that are now included in two protected areas, Mandena and Ambato Atsinanana (St. Luce), but still remains listed as Endangered on the International Union for Conservation of Nature Red List (IUCN 2020). *Pandanus tsingycola* (Figure 8.19h), only known from the dry deciduous forests of the karstic limestone areas (*tsingy*) of the central west (see Bardot-Vaucoulon and Gautier, pp. 492–99), is now known to occur in the Bemaraha protected area, but is still listed as Endangered on the IUCN Red List (IUCN 2020). Most Pandanaceae species on Madagascar remain threatened due to slash-and-burn agriculture and continuing decline of their habitat outside of the protected area network.

Subject editors: Laurent Gautier and Steven M. Goodman

ORCHIDACEAE

J. Hermans and L. Rajaovelona

The orchid family (Orchidaceae) is perhaps the largest family of flowering plants in the world with around 28,000 accepted species names (Govaerts et al. 2020b), placed in 736 genera (Chase et al. 2015), and over 175,000 registered artificial hybrids. New species and subspecies are still described regularly. Orchids share many features with related groups of monocots but the main distinguishing features of the family are: the stamens are all on one side of the flower, stamens and pistils are at least partly united, the seeds are tiny and numerous, the flowers have a lip (labellum) and are often resupinate, and the pollen is usually bound together in a few large masses (pollinia).

Orchids are found in virtually all terrestrial habitats from sea level to high-elevation alpine areas; they are present on all continents of the planet except Antarctica but are most numerous and diverse in the humid tropics and subtropics. They can be terrestrial, epiphytic, lithophytic, scrambling lianas, or sometimes saprophytic plants; all forms are represented on Madagascar.

HISTORY OF RESEARCH ON THE ORCHIDS OF MADAGASCAR

The earliest evidence of a Malagasy orchid in a herbarium can be found in the historical collections of the Muséum National d'Histoire Naturelle in Paris where there is a specimen collected by Etienne de Flacourt in southern Madagascar in the 1650s. The sheet has two sterile plants with somewhat compressed pseudobulbs, oblong leaves, and remnants of a thick peduncle base that are unmistakably *Bulbophyllum pentastichum*. The herbarium sheet is labeled "Ahatsendre" and was, like others of his collections, integrated into the herbarium of the botanist Sébastien Vaillant in 1715 and subsequently into the main Paris herbarium (Allorge and Ikor 2003: 121). Although of no taxonomic value, this specimen is interesting in that it is undoubtedly one of the first orchids brought to Europe from Madagascar.

Many other botanists and collectors have been involved in the discovery of the island's remarkable orchid flora, but only a few individuals are responsible for their formal description. Until the 1820s only a handful of orchid species were recognized from Madagascar. Aubert Aubert du Petit-Thouars (1822) described and illustrated 31 species from the island. Between 1824 and 1850, John Lindley added another 15 species. Heinrich Gustav Reichenbach described a further 51 between 1850 and 1885, mostly based on collections by Johann Hildebrandt and Léon Humblot. Between 1883 and 1886, Henry Ridley described 57 new species based on collections by various missionaries, mainly of the London Missionary Society, including William Deans Cowan, Richard Baron, and Joseph Tregelles Fox. Robert A. Rolfe added 23 species in the 1890s from a variety of sources but principally from commercial collectors. Rudolf Schlechter contributed no fewer than 282 new names to the list between 1911 and 1925 with most of them based on collections by the French explorer Henri Perrier de la Bâthie. Following Schlechter's death in 1925 Perrier de la Bâthie described many novelties and revised a number of genera. His work culminated in the orchid volumes of the *Flore de Madagascar et des Comores* (Perrier de la Bâthie 1939a, 1941). He described 195 novelties mainly based on his own collections but also those of Raymond Decary, Henri Humbert, and others working on the island during the French colonial era between 1929 and 1955. From the early 1960s until 2013, Jean Bosser, in collaboration with others, described 102 new taxa and published an illustrated orchid flora of the island with Marcel Lecoufle (Bosser and Lecoufle 2011). Recent work by Johan Hermans, Phillip Cribb, and collaborators has added 57 new orchids to the flora, most notably (Hermans et al. 2007, 2017, 2020a, 2020b, 2020c, 2021; Hermans and Cribb 2014) together with a new checklist, bibliography (Hermans et al. 2007), and field guide (Cribb and Hermans 2009). The most recent illustrated guide is by Hervouet (2018).

DISTRIBUTION AND ENDEMISM OF ORCHIDS ON MADAGASCAR

Orchids are found in almost every region and habitat on Madagascar, from the coast to the highest mountain summits and from the moist evergreen forests to the dry spiny bush. Their distribution is not even across these habitats but is dictated by soil, climate, elevation, and aspect. Generally, orchids are most abundant in the wetter habitats and least frequent in the drier areas, but even the driest locations can have their own peculiar orchid flora. They can form a major element of the vegetation in some places, whereas in others they are sparse and can be difficult to locate. Many orchids are relatively widespread and tolerant of a number of environments, whereas others are restricted to particular or specialized conditions. Roughly one-third of the species are terrestrial or semi-terrestrial, two-thirds are epiphytes or lithophytes, and a few are saprophytes.

The Orchidaceae is the largest plant family on Madagascar (Callmander et al. 2011a: 122). A new tabulation by the first author of all orchids currently recognized (November 2019) from Madagascar and surrounding western Indian Ocean islands shows that there are now a total of 1002 species, subspecies (1.7%), and varieties (5%) in 60 different genera known from Madagascar. Of these, about 85% are endemic to Madagascar (Figure 8.20) and this endemism increases to 97% when the surrounding archipelagoes of the Mascarenes, Comoros, and Seychelles are included.

Only about 3% have a wider distribution, principally on mainland Africa (including *Calanthe sylvatica*, *Habenaria cirrhata*, *Microcoelia aphylla*, *Oberonia disticha*, and *Satyrium trinerve*). Even fewer (0.6%) are not only known from mainland Africa but also have a more global distribution; these include: *Bulbophyllum longiflorum* (Malesia to the Pacific), *Eulophia pulchra* (west Pacific), *Liparis cespitosa* (south Pacific), *Oeceoclades maculata* (naturalized in South and Central America), and *Nervilia simplex* (tropical and subtropical Old World to southwest Pacific). *Cynorkis fastigiata* has been recorded from Fiji but it has been known to self-pollinate and seed propagate in cultivation all over the world.

Within the Orchidaceae of the Malagasy Region, defined here as Madagascar, the Mascarenes (La Réunion, Mauritius, and Rodrigues), and the other islands of the western Indian Ocean, there are several clear cases of recent morphological evolution between species on Madagascar and the Mascarenes. For example, *Angraecum arachnites* and *A. conchoglossum* from Madagascar have populations on La Réunion with not just peloric or partially peloric flowers in which the lip is more or less petal-like but also a spur that is greatly reduced or absent; on La Réunion they are known as *A. appendiculatum* and *A. corrugatum*, respectively (Hermans 2005a). The common and very variable *Cynorkis nutans* from Madagascar has an equivalent without a spur on Mauritius and La Réunion where it is known as *C. inermis* (Hermans et al. 2017). These mutations are probably due to evolution in pollinator interactions.

Research on the orchid flora of Madagascar has been somewhat island focused and was often undertaken by botanists who had limited knowledge of the flora of the surrounding archipelagoes and mainland Africa, let alone the more global flora. It is therefore likely that future research will augment the known distributional area of some of the species, as was found during the study of the Malaxidinae (Hermans et al. 2020a), when several species were identified as the same as those occurring on the Mascarenes.

There are very few introduced orchids or escapes from cultivation on Madagascar: *Epidendrum radicans* from South America has been reported from forest margins near inhabited areas, as have *Phaius tankervilleae* and *Arundina bambusifolia* from subtropical and tropical Asia. These records are still very rare and introduced species are certainly not as widespread as on the Mascarenes where they have become common weeds. *Vanilla planifolia* from South and Central America has been a major crop for the production of culinary vanilla since the 19th century on Madagascar. It is mainly cultivated in the northeast where it is a valuable export commodity.

OVERVIEW OF MALAGASY ORCHID GENERA AND THEIR CLASSIFICATION

In common with other plant families, the classification of the Orchidaceae has undergone major instability since the last years of the 20th century; the surge in molecular work, new techniques of analysis, and availability of data mean that there has been a great deal of progress in understanding the phylogenetics of this plant family. Here we followed a conservative approach, as advocated in *Genera Orchidacearum* (Pridgeon et al. 1999–2014) and by Chase et al. (2015). For the recognition of species, subspecies, and varieties we follow Govaerts et al. (2020b). Orchids on Madagascar (see Figure 8.21) are represented in three of the five subfamilies of the Orchidaceae.

Subfamily Vanilloideae

Tribe Vanilleae

The tribe Vanilleae has two genera on Madagascar: *Vanilla* (seven species on Madagascar), all scrambling or climbing vines, frequently with a warty stem and leaves reduced to scales, appearing leafless. Only *V. humblotii* has a wider distribution on the Comoro islands; the others are endemic. *Galeola* is another scrambling leafless saprophytic genus with one species, *G. humblotii*; until recently it was reported only from the Comoros but has now been found in several localities on Madagascar.

Subfamily Orchidoideae

Tribe Cranichideae

Subtribe Goodyerinae: This subtribe has 14 species. It has been not extensively studied on Madagascar and is often confused with other groups of orchids. Currently the following genera are represented: *Cheirostylis* (one species), *Goodyera* (six), *Hetaeria* (one), *Platylepis* (five), and *Zeuxine* (one). They are mainly terrestrial, often growing in deep shade on the forest floor. They have a creeping, fleshy rhizome and an erect leafy stem. The flowers are small and commonly glandular on the exterior. All 14 species are endemic to Madagascar and western Indian Ocean islands except for *Cheirostylis nuda*, which is also found in mainland Africa.

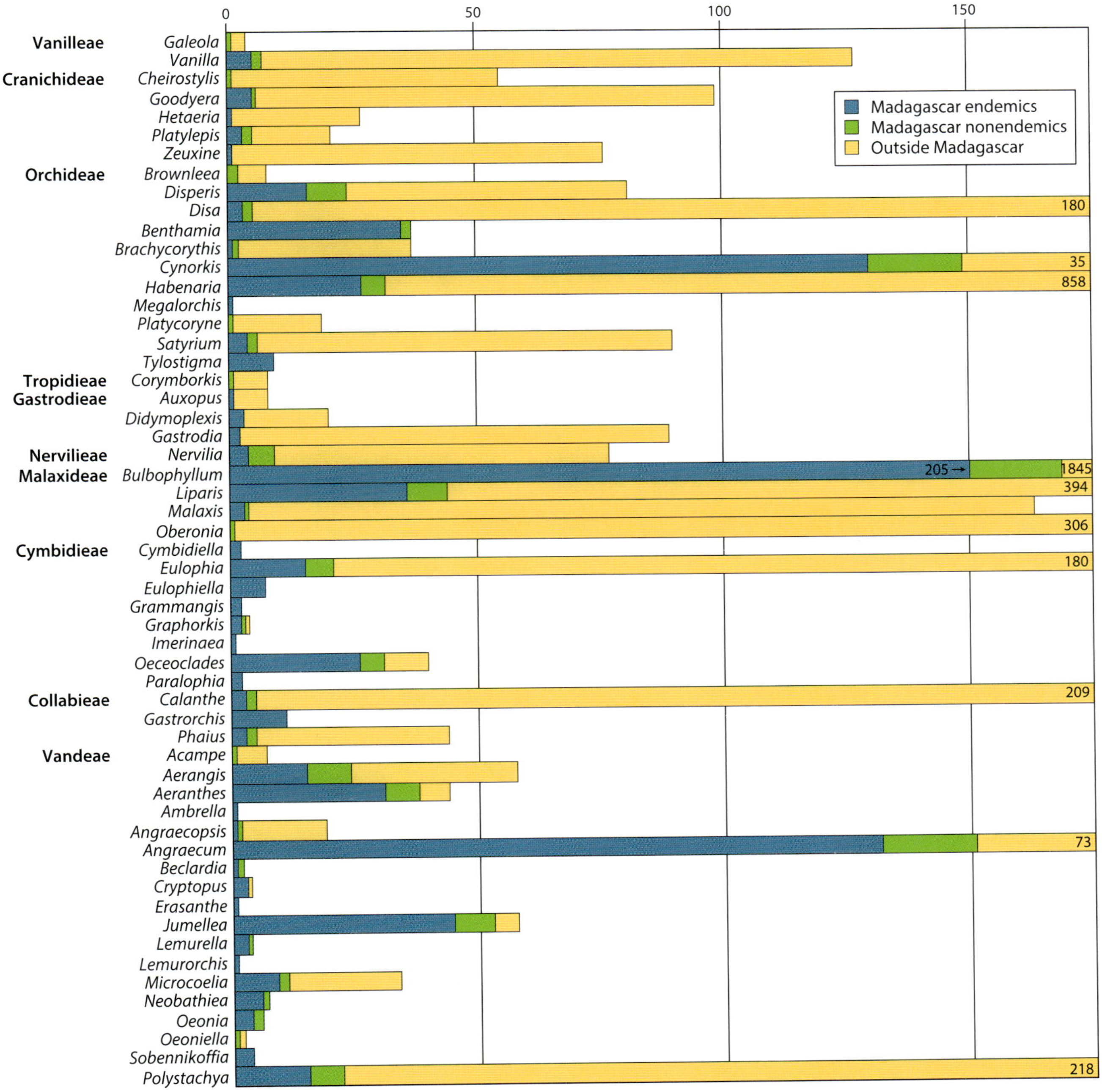

FIGURE 8.20 **Diversity and endemicity diagram of Malagasy Orchidaceae at the level of genera, showing three different species counts: 1) endemic to Madagascar, 2) nonendemic but native to Madagascar, and 3) those occurring elsewhere in the world (for further information see text). In cases when species diversity exceeds or does not conform to that presented on the horizontal graph scale, the figures are written along the respective horizontal line of a given genus.**

Tribe Orchideae

Subtribe Brownleeinae: There are two genera in this subtribe. *Brownleea* (two species), also found in southern Africa, are small terrestrial plants growing from tubers. *Brownleea coerulea* is found throughout central Madagascar; *B. parviflora* is much rarer and occurs in the same area. *Disperis* (23 species and one variety) is endemic to Madagascar and the western Indian Ocean islands. They are small terrestrial orchids growing from rounded tubers and have complex lip and column structure. The most recent revision was done by La Croix et al. (2002).

Subtribe Disinae: The genus *Disa* has five species on Madagascar including two shared with southern Africa, which is its main area of distribution. Its members are terrestrial with a leafy stem whose upper leaves are often similar to the lower bracts. The dorsal sepal is helmet-shaped and the lip is small.

Subtribe Orchidinae: This subtribe has the largest number of genera and species in the subfamily Orchidoideae on Madagascar and includes a great variety of mostly tuberous terrestrial orchids, many with a seasonal deciduous dormancy:

FIGURE 8.21 A range of Malagasy orchids from different areas of the island: A) *Angraecum lecomtei* is a fairly common species from the eastern forests near Analamazaotra; B) *Brachycorythis disoides* is a grassland species from the Central Highlands; C) *Bulbophyllum namoronae* is a rare plant growing near the Namorona River near Ranomafana; D) *Cryptopus dissectus* is now extremely rare in the central eastern forest; E) *Cynorkis uniflora*, one of the largest of the genus, often grows on inselbergs; F) *Eulophia rutenbergiana* is a common grassland species in the Central Highlands and often occurs in large groups; G) *Liparis sambiranoensis* is from northern Madagascar; H) *Platylepis polyadenia* grows in leaf litter in the shade of the eastern forest, and I) *Vanilla madagascariensis* is leafless and grows mainly in dry deciduous forest. (PHOTOS by Johan Hermans.)

1. *Benthamia* (30 species, one variety, and six subspecies on Madagascar) species are terrestrial or rarely epiphytic plants; the flowers are generally small and yellowish-green.
2. *Brachycorythis* (two species on Madagascar) is terrestrial and mainly distributed on mainland Africa. The leaves are arranged along the stem.
3. *Cynorkis* (129 species, 13 varieties, and one form on Madagascar) is by far the most diverse genus in the tribe. Its center of distribution is Madagascar, with a few species on the Mascarenes and mainland Africa. They are mainly tuberous terrestrials, semi-terrestrials, or, less commonly, epiphytes. The leaves are annual, and the flowers are often colorful, especially the lip. Several exciting new species have recently been described, including *C. christae*, the largest in the genus (Hermans et al. 2017). A number of natural hybrids have also been recorded (Hermans and Rajaovelona 2019).
4. *Habenaria* (33 species on Madagascar) is a large cosmopolitan genus of terrestrial plants with generally greenish flowers often with bifid petals and a deeply lobed lip. Much in need of revision, the species are mainly endemic to Madagascar, although four also occur in the Comoros and mainland Africa, and one on La Réunion.
5. *Megalorchis* has an elusive endemic species, *M. regalis*, known only from herbarium material collected in the 1940s; it is likely to belong in another genus.
6. *Platycoryne* contains a single eye-catching grassland species on Madagascar, *P. pervillei*, with bright orange flowers, which is also found in east Africa.
7. *Satyrium* (five species and one variety on Madagascar) is a large, globally widespread genus of terrestrial plants with the uppermost lip forming a hood; it is two-spurred at the back. The most widespread species on the island is *S. trinerve*, which is also widespread in tropical Africa. *Satyrium amoenum* is also found on La Réunion and the Comoros. The others are endemic.
8. *Tylostigma* (eight species and one subspecies) is endemic to Madagascar. All species are terrestrial, growing from a bundle of fusiform roots. The flowers are yellow, green, or white, and very small with an entire lip.

Subfamily Epidendroideae

Tribe Tropidieae

Corymborkis corymbis is the only species of Tropidieae on Madagascar and is widespread in eastern and southern Africa. It is a large terrestrial orchid that often grows in clumps; the stem is woody, and the inflorescences are lateral and terminal.

Tribe Gastrodieae

This tribe has its main distribution in Asia but there are three genera on Madagascar, all leafless saprophytes growing from fleshy underground tubers. Five out of seven species in this tribe have been described or recorded from Madagascar only during the last few decades, partly due to their leafless habit and sporadic flowering making them difficult to find. Their distribution and nomenclature are also still poorly known.

1. *Auxopus madagascariensis* is only known from the type collection and is a dubious species.
2. *Didymoplexis* (four species endemic to Madagascar) has sepals and petals that are partly fused, and the disc of the lip is usually papillate.
3. *Gastrodia* (two species endemic to Madagascar) has fused sepals and petals forming a tube, and the pedicel elongates after fertilization of the flower.

Tribe Nervilieae

Nervilia (eight species and one variety) is the single genus in this tribe on Madagascar. The plants have underground tubers and a solitary rounded leaf on a stalk; the inflorescence emerges before the leaf. Over half the species on Madagascar have a wide distribution. The most recent revision is by Pettersson (1991).

Tribe Malaxideae

Subtribe Dendrobiinae: Represented on the island by a single genus, *Bulbophyllum*, which is also the most varied. It is a very large cosmopolitan genus with Madagascar one of its main centers of distribution. There are currently a total of 224 species on Madagascar, five subspecies, and 15 varieties recognized; new species to science are regularly described (Hermans et al. 2020a). Around 10% of species also occur on surrounding archipelagoes and 1.5% have a global distribution. They are mainly epiphytes or lithophytes with lateral inflorescences and single-noded pseudobulbs.

Subtribe Malaxidinae: A major revision of the subtribe was recently published (Hermans et al. 2020a).

1. *Liparis* (44 species currently recognized on Madagascar and two more for the Malagasy Region) is a large cosmopolitan genus with a significant representation in Australasia, subtropical and tropical Americas, and Africa, with a few species in Europe and North America. Thirty-six species (~80%) are endemic. *Liparis cespitosa* is the only species with a much wider distribution in Africa and Australasia. *Liparis* species most often grow in moss and humus on the forest floor or quite low on fallen trees and shrubs. The pseudobulbs are ovoid to stem-like; the flowers have no spur or extension at the base of the flower and generally have an arching column and thin petals.
2. *Malaxis* (four species on Madagascar) consists of about 300 species found throughout the tropics and subtropics of the Old and New Worlds, with a few species in temperate regions of Europe, Asia, and the Americas. Three species are endemic to Madagascar. They are diminutive plants resembling some species of *Liparis*, with tiny flowers with a very short column.
3. *Oberonia* (one species on Madagascar) has around 150 species and its main distribution centered in tropical southern and southeastern Asia. *Oberonia disticha* is the only species on Madagascar and also occurs on the Mascarenes and in eastern and southern Africa. It is one of the most common orchids on Madagascar and is distinctive due to its distichous leaves and dense inflorescence of minute flowers.

Tribe Cymbidieae

Subtribe Eulophiinae:

1. *Cymbidiella* (three species) is entirely endemic to Madagascar and is rather remarkable. The species are scrambling terrestrials or epiphytes, generally with a long rhizome, distinct pseudobulbs with long strap-like leaves, and showy flowers.
2. *Eulophia* (21 species on Madagascar) is a large genus of about 250 species, which is most diverse in tropical and southern Africa and tropical Asia with a few species in the Americas. A quarter of the Madagascar species are also present in the Comoros and Mascarenes, and three have a more global distribution. They are pseudobulbous or rhizomatous terrestrials, or, less commonly, lithophytes; the inflorescence is basal and generally laxly flowered, and the lip is three-lobed.
3. *Eulophiella* (six recognized species and one supposed natural hybrid) is a showy and entirely endemic genus. With the exception of *E. galbana*, they are large pseudobulbous epiphytes on a long scrambling rhizome with flowers almost circular in outline. *Eulophiella roempleriana* is the largest and showiest of all orchids on Madagascar, but it is also one of the most endangered.
4. *Grammangis* (two species) is another showy, endemic genus. The plants have a dense mass of white erect roots, large angular pseudobulbs covered with silvery sheaths, strap-like leaves, and long racemes of large flowers. *Grammangis ellisii* has been extensively collected for the horticultural trade. *Grammangis spectabilis*, from dry deciduous forest in the southwest, has been classified as Critically Endangered under IUCN (International Union for Conservation of Nature) Red List criteria (IUCN 2020).
5. *Graphorkis* (three species) is a small genus of four species endemic to tropical Africa and two endemic to Madagascar. The large pseudobulbs are clustered and surrounded by erect roots.
6. *Imerinaea* is a monotypic genus endemic to Madagascar. *Imerinae madagascarica* is a peculiar epiphyte and resembles a small *Eulophia*, but the flowers are non-resupinate, they do not open widely, and the lip has a distinct callus.
7. *Oeceoclades* (31 species on Madagascar) comprises 45 species and has its main center of diversity on Madagascar where most of the species are endemic; the main overlap is five species shared with the Comoros. *Oeceoclades maculata* is weedy and has an actively expanding global distribution. The relationship between and within *Eulophia* and *Oeceoclades* remains unresolved and more research is needed. *Oeceoclades* species are generally terrestrials and most frequently somewhat succulent with leathery leaves that may be attractively marked with different colors and a branching inflorescence with many flowers.
8. *Paralophia* (two species) is an endemic genus recently segregated from *Eulophia*. Its species are epiphytes with long rhizomes and cylindrical stems and pseudobulbs; the flowers are showy and similar to those of *Eulophia*.

Tribe Collabieae

1. *Calanthe* (five species on Madagascar) is a large genus of over 200 species mostly from the Old World tropics and subtropics, extending to the Far East and the Pacific. Three species are endemic. There are dubious records of *C. millotae* from Mauritius and the Seychelles. *Calanthe sylvatica* is a highly variable species also found in the Mascarenes, the Comoros, and in tropical and southern Africa.
2. *Gastrorchis* (eight species and three varieties) is endemic to Madagascar and the Mascarenes. These plants are terrestrial or, less commonly, epiphytic with small pseudobulbs, large pleated leaves, and a racemose inflorescence with large attractive flowers. *Gastrorchis* is distinguished from *Phaius* by the short jointed pseudobulb, broad leaves, and the lip, which is basally free from the column and saccate at the base.
3. *Phaius* (two species and three varieties on Madagascar) is a genus of the Old World tropics and subtropics, with 41 recognized species and its main center of diversity in Indo-China and Indonesia. Several intermediate forms exist on Madagascar and have been considered by some as species in their own right. *Phaius pulchellus* is also found in the Mascarenes. Members of this genus are large terrestrial plants growing on the forest floor. A recent monograph reviewed both *Phaius* and *Gastrorchis* (J. Stone and Cribb 2017).

Tribe Vandeae

Recent research on this tribe and especially the subtribe Angraecinae includes work by Carlsward et al. (2006) and Micheneau et al. (2008); a comprehensive illustrated guide was published by Stewart et al. (2004).

Subtribe Polystachyinae: *Polystachya* (23 species and one variety are currently recognized from Madagascar), a large pantropical genus of more than 200 species, is Madagascar's representative of this subtribe. Most species are endemic but a few are also found on the Comoros and Mauritius, and *P. cultriformis* and *P. fusiformis* are quite common and also found in tropical and southern Africa. *Polystachya concreta*, under its current definition, has a global distribution. Members of this genus are generally small epiphytes, lithophytes, or rarely terrestrials. The pseudobulbs are clustered, the leaves lanceolate, the flowers non-resupinate, and the lip often has a callus and/or farinose hairs on the upper surface. A much-needed revision of the *Polystachya* from the Madagascar area is in progress.

Subtribe Aeridinae: There is just one Malagasy species, *Acampe pachyglossa*, in a genus that is predominantly Asian. This species is also found across the western Indian Ocean islands and mainland Africa. It is a stout epiphyte with leathery, distichous leaves and an axillar inflorescence with clustered colorful flowers.

Subtribe Angraecinae:

1. *Aerangis* (25 species on Madagascar, including one natural hybrid) is a genus of tropical Africa with about 50 species; seven Malagasy species are also found in the Comoros and one on La Réunion. They are epiphytes or rarely lithophytes with a fan of obovate or elliptic leaves that are often a little glossy. The flowers are almost invariably white with a distinct spur, and the column is elongate. The last revision of the genus was by La Croix (2014).
2. *Aeranthes* (39 species on Madagascar) is a genus centered in the Malagasy Region, with two species on mainland Africa. Four

Malagasy species are also found in the Comoros and three on La Réunion. They are epiphytes with fan-shaped, leathery leaves and usually wiry inflorescences, often bearing flowers in succession. The flowers are somewhat translucent green or white, the tepals often have slender tails, and the lip has a mentum and almost invariably a short spur.

3. *Ambrella* is a monotypic genus endemic to Madagascar. *Ambrella longituba* vegetatively resembles an *Aerangis* but the flowers have a tubular lip bearing hairs inside.
4. *Angraecopsis* (two species on Madagascar) is a small genus of 19 species, mostly found in tropical Africa. The plants are epiphytes with distichous leaves. The flowers are small and yellowish green, and the lip is entire or three-lobed.
5. *Angraecum* (148 species, two subspecies, and four varieties on Madagascar) is a large genus of over 200 species in Africa, and notably speciose on Madagascar. Just over 10% of Malagasy taxa also occur on the Mascarenes and the Comoros. They include the classical, star-shaped orchids with long spurs that are often associated with Madagascar, including the iconic *A. sesquipedale*, predicted by Charles Darwin to be associated with a pollinating moth with a huge proboscis that could reach the nectar in its long spur (Darwin 1904: 265). With notable exceptions, the plants are epiphytes, the flowers green or white, the lip entire, and the column short, fleshy, and lacking a foot.
6. *Beclardia* (two species) is a genus endemic to Madagascar and the Mascarenes. Its species are epiphytes with flattened distichous leaves, a three-lobed lip, and a spur that is funnel-shaped at the base.
7. *Cryptopus* is a genus of four species, three endemic to Madagascar, and one to the Mascarenes. They are all long scrambling epiphytes, the leaves are small and distichous, the petals often lobed, and the lip strongly three- to four-lobed.
8. *Erasanthe* is an endemic monotypic genus with one species. It used to be attached to *Aeranthes*, but the very large flowers and long spur make it distinct.
9. *Jumellea* (51 species, two subspecies, and one variety on Madagascar) has its greatest diversity on Madagascar; four species also occur on the Comoros and another four on the Mascarenes. Just two species are recorded from mainland tropical Africa. They are epiphytes or lithophytes with a great variety of plant habit and shape. The inflorescences are always single-flowered, the flowers are white, star-shaped, and have an entire lip broader than the other segments, often with a keel at the base, and the spur is generally longer than the lip and geniculate at the base.
10. *Lemurella* (four species) is an endemic genus; only *L. culicifera* is also found in the Comoros. They are small and generally twig epiphytes with yellow-green flowers; the lip is three-lobed, and the basal lobes flank the column.
11. *Lemurorchis* is a monotypic genus endemic to Madagascar. It is a robust epiphyte without a distinct stem but with distichous strap-like leaves. The flowers are held in a dense, many-flowered cylindrical rachis.
12. *Microcoelia* (11 species on Madagascar) is a genus of about 35 species in tropical Africa. The Malagasy species are endemic except for *M. cornuta*, which is also found in the Comoros and *M. aphylla*, which occurs on continental Africa. They are small twig epiphytes with clustered and photosynthetic roots. The leaves are scalelike and appear absent, and the flowers are small and generally white but orange in the fairly common *M. gilpinae*. The only revision of the genus was by Jonsson (1981).
13. *Neobathiea* (six species and one variety) is endemic to Madagascar with only *N. grandidieriana* also found on the Comoros. These plants are epiphytes, or rarely lithophytes, with the leaves often twisted at the base to lie in one plane. The inflorescences are single to few-flowered, and the flowers are relatively large with a large lip and the sepals more or less spatulate.
14. *Oeonia* (five species and one variety) is almost endemic to Madagascar with only *O. rosea* also found on La Réunion; records of *O. volucris* in the Mascarenes are dubious. They are scramblers or epiphytes with a long leafy stem, and the inflorescences are few-flowered. The flowers are showy, predominantly white, but sometimes marked with red or yellow on the lip.
15. *Oeoniella* has a single species plus one possible variant, endemic to all of the archipelagoes of the western Indian Ocean islands. *Oeoniella polystachys* is locally common on Madagascar. It is an epiphyte with long stems, the inflorescences are several-flowered, and the lip is trumpet-shaped and has a long apicule.
16. *Sobennikoffia* (four species) is endemic to Madagascar. The plants are robust with distichous, strap-like leaves The inflorescence has a few large flowers, each with a three-lobed lip and an up-curved spur.

ORCHID HABITATS ON MADAGASCAR

Historically, Madagascar has been divided into a number of fairly well-defined areas of vegetation and climate; but more recently detailed mapping techniques, such as satellite imaging, have been used to redefine some of these zones. Work by Moat and Smith (2007) and others is redefining the multitude of Malagasy habitats and their associated ecology. Meanwhile the most distinct formations of natural vegetation are summarized below together with some of their typical orchids. Here we largely follow the terminology of Gautier et al. (2018).

Central Highlands and Mountains

The Central Highlands cover nearly 40% of the island and include some significant mountain ranges. The climate is seasonal with an annual rainfall between 1200 and 2500 mm, and there are frequent mists in some areas. The remaining forests are fragmented and mainly composed of medium-altitude moist evergreen forest. At higher elevations or on exposed ridges there are formations of montane ericoid thickets with smaller trees and epiphytes, but the understory is quite open and the soil covered with moss and lichen. On the leeward western slopes, there are some remains of sclerophyllous woodland dominated by Tapia, *Uapaca bojeri* (see Kull and Birkinshaw, pp. 121–27). The trees have thick, fire-resistant bark allowing them to survive the fires that almost annually burn the coarse grassland around them and are good hosts for orchids.

There are different ecosystems toward mountain summits. Frosts and, in a few cases, snow have been reported during the early morning hours of the cold season, a period from the first portion of June to the end of August. These areas are recognized as containing many microendemic plants. The central area of the region is dotted with inselbergs, and these have similar characteristics. Most of the zone, however, consists of a complex blend of hills and valleys. Some of the montane grasslands containing endemic species are rich in terrestrial orchids, while other areas are covered by vast expanses of a few cosmopolitan fire-adapted grasses. The region generally rests on lateritic soils. Annual human-induced fires are used to produce new herbaceous growth for grazing. In localities protected from fire some forest survives, particularly in gullies. Orchids in these areas are becoming scarce, most relying on specific microhabitats to thrive. Terrestrial and lithophytic orchids are dominant in the grasslands, on rocky outcrops, and in gullies; they often thrive in the wetter areas but not exclusively so. Few orchids can survive the regular burning of grassland, and these areas are therefore species poor, but a few do thrive here, especially *Cynorkis* and *Eulophia* species with underground tubers.

Other common genera found in the Central Highlands and associated mountains are *Benthamia*, *Brownleea*, *Disperis*, *Habenaria*, and *Platycoryne*. *Cynorkis flexuosa* with its yellow flowers is one of the most common species; it also has a wide distribution. *Cynorkis gibbosa* can occasionally be seen on the roadside and is not uncommon in the foothills of some of the mountain ranges. Another locally abundant species found near cultivated land is *Eulophia plantaginea*, which grows along streams and has even been reported growing in drainage ditches around rice paddies. A few other orchids can be found on cultivated land too, including *C. speciosa* and *C. stolonifera*. Some of the most colorful terrestrials are: *Eulophia rutenbergiana* with bright yellow flowers and dark red markings in the corolla; *Brachycorythis disoides*, which is generally lilac and is also scented; the blue *Disa buchenaviana* is locally common in grassland; and *D. incarnata* grows in boggy ground, often with *Satyrium trinerve*. In more shaded or wetter areas, many other *Cynorkis* species can be found, including *C. ridleyi*, *C. baronii*, and *C. graminea*.

The granite and sandstone mountains, inselbergs, and rocky outcrops of the Central Highlands support a specialized and varied group of orchids: several species of *Angraecum*, *Bulbophyllum*, *Jumellea*, and *Polystachya* orchids can grow on almost bare rock or more commonly on the scattered trees and shrubs. Typical orchids from the region are *Aerangis ellisii*, *Angraecum longicalcar*, *A. magdalenae*, *A. protensum*, *Bulbophyllum baronii*, and *Jumellea rigida* growing in small groups on rocky outcrops, often sheltered by boulders or rock faces. *Angraecum sororium* is a species of mountainous ground and Tapia forest that can grow quite tall, up to 1 m. Smaller *Angraecum* species found in lichen forest or near the summit of some of the mountains are *A. popowii* and *A. rutenbergianum*, both with almost succulent leaves and bearing relatively large flowers. Several *Benthamia*, *Cynorkis*, *Eulophia*, and *Habenaria* inhabit the humus-filled cracks among the rocks.

Moist Evergreen Forest

This vegetation zone and has the greatest diversity of orchid species. This part of Madagascar is under the influence of the easterly trade winds, which promote cloud formation and heavy rainfall for much of the year. Average annual rainfall is over 2000 mm, topping 6000 mm in parts of the Masoala Peninsula, with little or no dry season along the eastern coast, grading to a more seasonal climate with two to six dry months in the Central Highlands and in the Sambirano Region. Primary vegetation is mostly lowland to medium-altitude moist evergreen forest with tall forest trees, but there are several distinct strata in the forest and a diffuse understory. Notwithstanding extensive deforestation it is arguably in better condition in the north and northeast than further south where only a patchwork remains.

The moist evergreen forests are home to numerous orchids, especially epiphytes growing in the high tree canopy and also lower down and on shrubs; most frequently seen are the genera *Aerangis*, *Aeranthes*, *Angraecopsis*, *Angraecum*, *Beclardia*, *Bulbophyllum*, *Imerinaea*, *Oberonia*, *Lemurorchis*, *Neobathiea*, *Polystachya* among others. Some are scrambling epiphytes or twig epiphytes, including several species of *Angraecum*, *Cryptopus*, *Lemurella*, *Microcoelia*, and *Oeonia*. In general, *Angraecum* and *Bulbophyllum* are the most numerous, both with over 200 different species. There are also several terrestrial or lithophyte species in similar genera to those found in the Central Highlands; *Cynorkis* species are particularly varied, including *C. lowiana* which is still plentiful on the roadside near Ranomafana National Park. On the forest floor and on moss and humus-covered lower branches or fallen branches there are various shade-loving orchids, including *Benthamia*, *Calanthe*, *Cynorkis*, *Disperis*, *Gastrorchis*, *Liparis*, *Nervilia*, *Phaius*, *Tylostigma*, and genera in the subtribe Goodyerinae. A few are leafless saprophytes, including *Gastrodia* and *Didymoplexis*, which grow in deep shade in deep leaf litter. At lower elevations, in eastern littoral forests and thickets, species numbers are lower though there is a similar diverity of genera as that found at higher elevations; however, several are endemc to this habitat, including *Corymborkis*, *Oeoniella*, and some *Vanilla* species.

A number of species are host-specific: *Eulophiella elisabethae* favors the palm *Dypsis fibrosa*, while *E. roempleriana* has only been recorded as growing on *Pandanus*, and is now very rare. *Cymbidiella falcigera* is more common and almost invariably found on *Raphia* in marshy areas. *Cymbidiella pardalina* often lives in association with the staghorn fern *Platycerium*.

Seasonal Areas of the West

This zone of the island gradually slopes westwards from the Central Highlands to the west coast with remaining forested areas occurring in patches. Rainfall averages 500 m to 1500 mm and there is an extended dry season of five to 10 months, which has a profound effect on the vegetation. On the western slopes intact vegetation is sclerophyllous woodlands, grading to dry deciduous forests at lower elevation. However, these formations form a mosaic with open to wooded secondary grasslands plus small patches of riparian forest and *Raphia* marshes. The limestone karst of the north and west has a relatively large orchid flora, partly because they are a natural refuge from fire and humans.

Dry Spiny Thicket

Annual precipitation drops dramatically toward the south of Madagascar and the dry deciduous forests change into dry spiny thickets in the region between Kirindy Mité and the Mikea Forest. The extreme south and southwest have an average rainfall of 700 mm with some areas receiving less than 400 mm of precipitation per year. The climate is arid and hot with an average annual maximum temperature of 30°C to 33°C and minimum of 15°C to 21°C. Many orchids here have adaptations to store what little moisture is available and to minimize water loss.

Orchids in these habitats are not plentiful, but they make up for this in their variety of form and interesting adaptations to extreme conditions. *Eulophia* and *Oeceoclades* have fleshy inflated pseudobulbs and leathery leaves. *Grammangis spectabilis* from the Zombitse-Vohibasia Forest is a smaller and modified form of *G. ellisii*, which is widespread in the moist evergreen forests to the east. *Paralophia* has long pseudobulbs and the roots go deeply into the moist and fibrous masses of organic material. Several of the epiphytic species of *Aerangis*, *Angraecum*, *Bulbophyllum*, *Erasanthe*, *Graphorkis*, *Jumellea*, and *Lemurella* have either inflated pseudobulbs or succulent foliage. The ultimate in succulence comes in leafless *Vanilla* growing in dry spiny thicket.

CONSERVATION

Notwithstanding the commitment by a multitude of non-governmental organizations (NGOs) and the Madagascar Government to its natural resources, there is little doubt that much of the island's unique orchid flora is under threat. The network of protected areas helps to safeguard the orchid flora to some extent and a few private reserves make notable efforts in conservation (Hervouet and Misandeau 2018), but encroachment on habitat is still considerable in the form of deforestation associated with human activities. Another threat to orchids and some other plants is the collecting of desirable species for local and international trade. International trade in all orchids is regulated by CITES (Convention on International Trade in Endangered Species of Wild Fauna and Flora) under Appendix II and therefore generally requires an export and/or import permit. One Malagasy species, *Aerangis ellisii*, is listed on Appendix I of CITES and therefore any trade or movement is strictly regulated. The online availability of distribution and herbarium data and Internet trade have added additional threats to orchid species. A few orchids are also harvested for medicinal purposes, including *Vanilla madagascariensis* and a few *Eulophia* and *Cynorkis* species.

A small number of projects have concentrated on the conservation and mapping of orchids on Madagascar, including those described in Cribb et al. (2005), From and Gouveia (2005), and Hermans and Cribb (2005). More recently the Kew Madagascar Conservation Centre in Antananarivo has started to assess the IUCN Red List conservation status of all orchid species using the IUCN Red List categories and criteria. The aim is to assess the current situation and conservation needs of orchids, which includes determining measures of risk of extinction for individual taxa, before developing adequate management strategies for their conservation. As of January 2020, only 186 species of Malagasy orchids (about 6%) were listed in the IUCN Red List of threatened species.

Preliminary results of these assessments of data for the currently recognized species suggest that for Madagascar's orchids:

- 76% of species are threatened and classified on the IUCN Red List as Vulnerable (VU), Endangered (EN), or Critically Endangered (CR);
- 48% of orchids classified as CR are found in the moist evergreen forests in the north of Madagascar, but more research is needed on the distribution of these threatened species;
- 7% are classed as Data Deficient (DD)—that is, there is incomplete information or doubts over identification, localities, or other data;
- 17% are Near Threatened (NT) or of Least Concern (LC). These are mainly species with a wide global distribution range or very widespread across Madagascar.

Subject editors: Laurent Gautier and Steven M. Goodman

ARECACEAE, PALMS

M. Rakotoarinivo, J. Dransfield, and H. Beentje

Palms are among the most conspicuous components of the flora of Madagascar. Early naturalists who visited the island between the late 16th century and mid-18th century noticed the peculiarity of the plants of Madagascar as well as the distinctiveness of its palm diversity (Rakotoarinivo and Dransfield 2013). From the early days of plant exploration on Madagascar, palms tended to receive little attention, despite their distinctive form. However, with increasing general field exploration in the 1920s and 1930s palm specimens accumulated in major herbaria, in particular the Muséum National d'Histoire Naturelle in Paris, where Jumelle and Perrier de la Bâthie (1945) synthesized what was known of the palms as the 30th volume of *Flore de Madagascar et des Comores*. This included 18 genera and 120 species.

After the 1940s, palm research was less intensive in comparison with some other groups of plants although a few palm species were described. Thorough renewed research in the 1980s and 1990s on Malagasy members of the family culminated in the publication of *The Palms of Madagascar* (J. Dransfield and Beentje 1995). Since 2000, research on Madagascar's palms has made significant progress with the development of new methodological tools, such as GIS (geographic information system) techniques for biogeography and ecological studies, and molecular approaches for taxonomic and phylogenetic studies. Many previously unexplored localities have been visited, as shown in Figure 8.22 by the number of collections made since 1995, yielding several unexpected novelties and new distribution records. Since 1995, 39 taxa new to science have been described (e.g., Rakotoarinivo and Dransfield 2010), which, combined with the 73 new species published by J. Dransfield and Beentje (1995), clearly underlines considerable progress in the availablity of information on the palms of the island. Further new taxa continue to be discovered.

The publication of the J. Dransfield and Beentje (1995) book increased awareness of the distinctiveness of the flora, especially among palm enthusiasts. Entering on tourist visas, enthusiasts have often collected seed without permits. At the same time, several Malagasy seed merchants have exported seeds under export license. Sometimes the seed has been correctly identified, but all too often it has been identified only using vernacular names. Some of the earlier introductions into cultivation have reached maturity overseas and attempts at their identification are often confounded by the fact that palms in intensive cultivation may look very different to the same species in the wild (J. Dransfield and Rakotoarinivo 2011). In some instances, new taxa based on cultivated specimens have been described as distinct species without knowledge of their natural distribution (e.g., J. Dransfield and Marcus 2002).

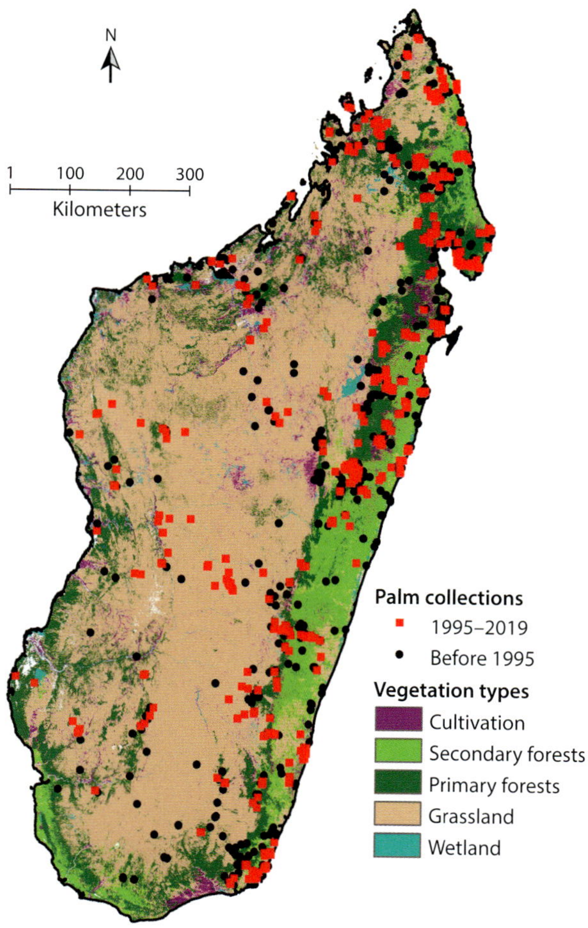

FIGURE 8.22 **Palm collections on Madagascar.** (SOURCE: Background vegetation map modified from Smith and Moat 2007.)

DIVERSITY, ENDEMISM, AND SYSTEMATICS

The palm flora of Madagascar is outstandingly rich in a global context (Kissling et al. 2012). Madagascar has a very diverse palm flora with over 208 indigenous species in 17 genera (Govaerts et al. 2020c), with representatives of four of the five recognized subfamilies in the family Arecaceae (Figure 8.23); only the monotypic Nypoideae is absent (native to Sri Lanka, and southeast Asia to the Pacific islands). This diversity rate represents a strong contrast to continental Africa where approximately 68 species in 18 genera are recorded (Stauffer et al. 2017). Of the 208 indigenous species on Madagascar, all but four are endemic (Figure 8.24; Table 8.18). The four native but nonendemic species are *Borassus aethiopum*, *Elaeis guineensis*, *Hyphaene coriacea*, and *Phoenix reclinata*. In addition, one cultivated species has become naturalized on Madagascar: *Cocos nucifera*, the coconut, widespread throughout the tropic coastline but native to the west Pacific. Finally, the status of the *Raphia* species found on Madagascar is still a matter of debate. It has been considered alternatively as *R. farinifera*, an important subsistence crop palm in east Africa, in which case it would have been introduced to Madagascar, or as a distinct endemic species.

At the generic level, eight of 17 genera on Madagascar are endemic. Among these, four are monotypic (*Satranala*, *Bismarckia*, *Tahina*, and *Voanioala*), three only have two species each (*Lemurophoenix*, *Masoala*, and *Marojejya*), and one has three species (*Beccariophoenix*). *Dypsis* and *Ravenea* are nearly endemic: *Ravenea* with a major radiation on Madagascar and two species in the Comoro archipelago, and *Dypsis* with a very large radiation in Madagascar and a few species in Comoros and one on Pemba Island, off the coast of Tanzania. The high level of endemism at both the generic and specific level is reflected by the fact that Madagascar has representatives of 12 different evolutionary lineages of palms, which may represent independent ancient colonization events or evolutionary events at the tribal or subtribal level on the island.

Subfamily Coryphoideae

This subfamily includes drought-tolerant species on Madagascar. Of the eight coryphoid tribes (J. Dransfield et al. 2008), three are present on the island: Phoeniceae, Borasseae, and Chuniophoeniceae.

Tribe Phoeniceae

Tribe Phoeniceae is represented by the nonendemic species *Phoenix reclinata*. With thin edible, fleshy fruits, its presence on Madagascar might be due to relatively recent dispersal from Africa by various animals (Lim 2011).

Tribe Borasseae

Tribe Borasseae is represented by four genera: *Borassus* from subtribe Lataniinae, and *Hyphaene*, *Bismarckia*, and *Satranala* from subtribe Hyphaeninae. The genus *Borassus* has two species on Madagascar: *B. aethiopum* and *B. madagascariensis*. A detailed systematic study (Bayton 2007) concluded that the species *B. sambiranensis*, formerly considered an endemic, does not differ from the African *B. aethiopum*, and is now regarded a synonym.

FIGURE 8.23 **Examples of habit and ecological diversities in palms of Madagascar. A) *Satranala decussilvae*, a tree palm from lowland evergreen moist forest of Mananara-Nord; B) *Tahina spectabilis*, a hapaxanthic tree palm from secondary grasslands and pastures of the Analalava area; C) *Ravenea musicalis* growing in a flowing river north of Tolagnaro; and D) *Dypsis prestoniana* in an open area of lowland evergreen moist forest of Vondrozo.** (PHOTOS A, B, and D by M. Rakotoarinivo; and C by J. Dransfield.)

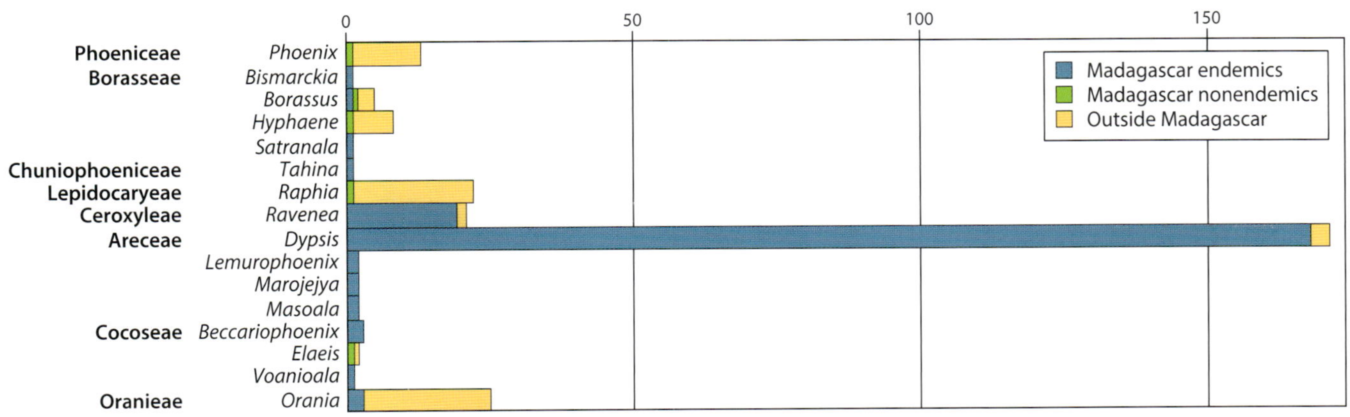

FIGURE 8.24 **Diversity and endemicity diagram of Malagasy Arecaceae at the level of genera, showing three different species counts: 1) endemic to Madagascar, 2) nonendemic but native to Madagascar, and 3) those occurring elsewhere in the world (for further information see text).**

TABLE 8.18. **Checklist of the 208 palms recognized on Madagascar and their distribution**

SCIENTIFIC NAME	YEAR OF PUBLICATION	IUCN STATUS	BIOGEOGRAPHY							
			E	C	HM	C(W)	SAMB.	W	S	ELEVATION (m)
SUBFAMILY CORYPHOIDEAE										
Tribe Phoeniceae										
Phoenix reclinata Jacq.	1801	LC	–	–	–	–	–	X	X	0–500
Tribe Borasseae										
Subtribe Hyphaeninae										
Bismarckia nobilis Hildebrandt & H. Wendl.	1881	LC	–	–	–	–	X	X	–	0–700
Hyphaene coriacea Gaertn.	1788	LC	–	–	–	X	–	X	X	0–900
Satranala decussilvae Beentje & J. Dransf.	1995	EN	X	–	–	–	–	–	–	0–600
Subtribe Lataniinae										
Borassus aethiopum Mart.	1838	LC	–	–	–	–	X	–	–	0–100
B. madagascariensis (Jum. & H. Perrier) Jum. & H. Perrier	1907 (1913)	EN	–	–	–	–	–	X	–	0–700
Tribe Chuniophoeniceae										
Tahina spectabilis J. Dransf. & Rakotoarin.	2008	CR	–	–	–	–	–	X	–	0–100
SUBFAMILY CALAMOIDEAE										
Tribe Lepidocaryeae										
Raphia sp. aff. *farinifera* (Gaertn.) Hylander		NE	X	–	–	–	–	X	–	0–800
SUBFAMILY CEROXYLOIDEAE										
Tribe Ceroxyleae										
Ravenea albicans (Jum.) Beentje	1933 (1994)	EN	X	–	–	–	–	–	–	0–800
R. beentjei Rakotoarin. & J. Dransf.	2010	CR	X	–	–	–	–	–	–	500–600
R. declivium J. Dransf. & Rakotoarin.	2012	NE	X	–	–	–	–	–	–	200–300
R. delicatula Rakotoarin.	2008	CR	–	X	–	–	–	–	–	800–900
R. dransfieldii Beentje	1994	EN	X	–	–	–	–	–	–	0–700
R. glauca Jum. & H. Perrier	1913	VU	–	–	X	X	–	–	–	600–1900
R. hypoleuca Rakotoarin. & J. Dransf.	2010	CR	X	–	–	–	–	–	–	200–600
R. julietiae Beentje	1994	EN	X	X	–	–	–	–	–	0–900
R. krociana Beentje	1994	EN	X	X	–	–	–	–	–	400–1000
R. lakatra (Jum.) Beentje	1927 (1994)	CR	X	X	–	–	–	–	–	0–900
R. latisecta Jum.	1927	CR	–	X	–	–	–	–	–	900–1100
R. louvelii Beentje	1994	CR	–	X	–	–	–	–	–	800–1200
R. madagascariensis Becc.	1906	LC	X	X	X	X	–	–	–	0–1600
R. musicalis Beentje	1993	CR	X	–	–	–	–	–	–	0–100

SCIENTIFIC NAME	YEAR OF PUBLICATION	IUCN STATUS	BIOGEOGRAPHY							
			E	C	HM	C(W)	SAMB.	W	S	ELEVATION (m)
R. nana Beentje	1994	EN	X	X	–	–	–	–	–	400–1600
R. rivularis Jum. & H. Perrier	1913	VU	–	–	–	–	–	X	–	400–900
R. robustior Jum. & H. Perrier	1913	NT	X	X	–	X	X	–	–	0–1700
R. sambiranensis Jum. & H. Perrier	1913	LC	X	X	–	–	X	–	–	0–1900
R. xerophila Jum.	1933	VU	–	–	–	–	–	–	X	100–700
SUBFAMILY ARECOIDEAE										
Tribe Oranieae										
Orania longisquama (Jum.) J. Dransf. & N. W. Uhl	1984 (1995)	LC	X	–	–	–	X	–	–	0–600
O. ravaka Beentje	1995	VU	X	–	–	–	–	–	–	0–600
O. trispatha (J. Dransf. & N. W. Uhl) Beentje & J. Dransf.	1984 (1995)	VU	X	–	–	–	–	–	–	0–400
Tribe Cocoseae										
Subtribe Attaleinae										
Beccariophoenix alfredii Rakotoarin., Ranariv. & J. Dransf.	2007	VU	–	–	–	X	–	–	–	1000–1200
B. fenestralis J. Dransf. & Rakotoarin.	2014	NE	X	–	–	–	–	–	–	50–100
B. madagascariensis Jum. & H. Perrier	1915	VU	X	X	–	–	–	–	–	0–1100
Voanioala gerardii J. Dransf.	1989	CR	X	–	–	–	–	–	–	400–600
Subtribe Elaeidinae										
Elaeis guineensis Jacq.	1763	LC	X	–	–	–	X	X	–	0–700
Tribe Areceae										
Subtribe Dypsidineae										
Dypsis acaulis J. Dransf.	1995	EN	X	–	–	–	–	–	–	0–100
D. acuminum (Jum.) Beentje & J. Dransf.	1922 (1995)	EN	X	X	–	–	–	–	–	700–1200
D. albofarinosa Hodel & Marcus	2004	EN	–	–	–	X	–	–	–	1300–1400
D. ambanjae Beentje	1995	CR	X	X	–	–	–	–	–	500–1100
D. ambilaensis J. Dransf.	1995	EN	X	X	–	–	–	–	–	0–900
D. ambositrae Beentje	1995	CR	–	–	–	X	–	–	–	1200–1700
D. ampasindavae Beentje	1995	EN	–	–	–	–	X	–	–	100–400
D. andapae Beentje	1995	EN	–	X	–	–	–	–	–	800–1300
D. andilamenensis Rakotoarin. & J. Dransf.	2010	CR	–	X	–	–	–	–	–	800–900
D. andrianatonga Beentje	1995	VU	X	X	X	–	–	–	–	300–1700
D. angusta Jum.	1918	EN	X	X	–	–	–	–	–	400–1300

(continued overleaf)

TABLE 8.18. ***continued***

SCIENTIFIC NAME	YEAR OF PUBLICATION	IUCN STATUS	BIOGEOGRAPHY							
			E	C	HM	C(W)	SAMB.	W	S	ELEVATION (m)
D. angustifolia (H. Perrier) Beentje & J. Dransf.	1939 (1995)	EN	X	X	–	–	–	–	–	0–1200
D. anjae Rakotoarin. & J. Dransf.	2010	CR	X	–	–	–	–	–	–	500–600
D. ankaizinensis (Jum.) Beentje & J. Dransf.	1922 (1995)	DD	–	–	X	–	–	–	–	1800–2000
D. ankirindro W. J. Baker	2009	NT	X	X	–	–	–	–	–	600–1200
D. antanambensis Beentje	1995	CR	X	–	–	–	–	–	–	200–400
D. aquatilis Beentje	1995	CR	X	–	–	–	–	–	–	0–50
D. arenarum (Jum.) Beentje & J. Dransf.	1922	CR	X	–	–	–	–	–	–	0–50
D. aurantiaca Eiserhardt & Rakotoarin.	2018	NE	X	–	–	–	–	–	–	200–300
D. baronii (Becc.) Beentje & J. Dransf.	1906 (1995)	LC	X	X	X	X	–	–	–	400–1800
D. basilonga (Jum. & H. Perrier) Beentje & J. Dransf.	1913 (1995)	CR	X	X	–	–	–	–	–	200–1400
D. beentjei J. Dransf.	1995	CR	X	–	–	–	–	–	–	200–400
D. bejofo Beentje	1995	VU	X	–	–	–	–	–	–	50–800
D. bernieriana (Baill.) Beentje & J. Dransf.	1894 (1995)	VU	X	–	–	–	–	–	–	100–800
D. betamponensis (Jum.) Beentje & J. Dransf.	1929 (1995)	VU	X	–	–	–	–	–	–	400–500
D. betsimisarakae Rakotoarin. & J. Dransf.	2010	VU	X	–	–	–	–	–	–	300–800
D. boiviniana Baill.	1894	EN	X	–	–	–	–	–	–	0–400
D. bonsai Beentje	1995	VU	X	X	X	–	–	–	–	700–1900
D. bosseri J. Dransf.	1995	EN	X	–	–	–	–	–	–	0–200
D. brevicaulis (Guillaumet) Beentje & J. Dransf.	1973 (1995)	CR	X	–	–	–	–	–	–	0–700
D. brittiana Rakotoarin.	2009	CR	–	X	–	–	–	–	–	900–100
D. canaliculata (Jum.) Beentje & J. Dransf.	1924 (1995)	CR	X	–	–	–	X	–	–	200–700
D. canescens (Jum. & H. Perrier) Beentje & J. Dransf.	1913 (1995)	DD	–	–	–	–	X	–	–	100–200
D. carlsmithii J. Dransf. & Marcus	2002	CR	X	–	–	–	–	–	–	0–100
D. catatiana (Baill.) Beentje & J. Dransf.	1893 (1995)	LC	X	X	X	–	–	–	–	300–1900
D. caudata Beentje	1995	CR	X	–	–	–	–	–	–	50–300
D. ceracea (Jum.) Beentje & J. Dransf.	1933 (1995)	EN	X	X	–	–	–	–	–	400–1100

SCIENTIFIC NAME	YEAR OF PUBLICATION	IUCN STATUS	BIOGEOGRAPHY							
			E	C	HM	C(W)	SAMB.	W	S	ELEVATION (m)
D. commersoniana (Baill.) Beentje & J. Dransf.	1894 (1995)	DD	X	–	–	–	–	–	–	0–200
D. concinna Baker	1887	NT	X	X	–	–	–	–	–	300–1600
D. confusa Beentje	1995	NT	X	X	–	–	–	–	–	0–1200
D. cookei J. Dransf.	1995	CR	–	X	–	–	–	–	–	1100–1600
D. coriacea Beentje	1995	NT	X	–	–	–	–	–	–	100–700
D. corniculata (Becc.) Beentje & J. Dransf.	1906 (1995)	EN	X	–	–	–	–	–	–	0–1000
D. coursii Beentje	1995	LC	X	X	–	–	–	–	–	400–1800
D. crinita (Jum. & H. Perrier) Beentje & J. Dransf.	1910 (1995)	NT	X	X	–	–	–	–	–	0–900
D. culminis Rakotoarin. & J. Dransf.	2010	EN	X	–	–	–	–	–	–	100–700
D. curtisii Baker	1887	EN	–	X	–	–	X	–	–	300–1700
D. decaryi (Jum.) Beentje & J. Dransf.	1933 (1995)	VU	–	–	–	–	–		X	0–500
D. decipiens (Becc.) Beentje & J. Dransf.	1906 (1995)	VU	–	X	–	X	–	–	–	800–1600
D. delicatula Britt & J. Dransf.	2005	VU	X	–	–	–	–	–	–	200–500
D. digitata (Becc.) Beentje & J. Dransf.	1914 (1995)	CR	X	–	–	–	–	–	–	0–100
D. dracaenoides Rakotoarin. & J. Dransf.	2010	EN	X	–	–	–	–	–	–	500–600
D. dransfieldii Beentje	1995	NT	X	–	–	–	–	–	–	0–300
D. elegans Beentje	1995	CR	X	–	–	–	–	–	–	0–700
D. eriostachys J. Dransf.	1995	EN	X	–	–	–	–	–	–	100–800
D. faneva Beentje	1995	EN	X	–	–	–	–	–	–	0–300
D. fanjana Beentje	1995	EN	X	X	–	–	–	–	–	0–900
D. fasciculata Jum.	1918	NT	X	X	–	–	–	–	–	0–1200
D. fibrosa (C. H. Wright) Beentje & J. Dransf.	1894 (1995)	LC	X	X	–	–	–	–	–	0–1100
D. forficifolia Noronha ex Mart.	1838	LC	X	–	–	–	–	–	–	0–1500
D. furcata J. Dransf.	1995	EN	X	–	–	–	–	–	–	0–300
D. gautieri Rakotoarin. & J. Dransf.	2010	VU	X	–	–	–	–	–	–	900–1100
D. glabrescens (Becc.) Becc.	1906 (1912)	EN	X	–	–	–	–	–	–	0–600
D. gronophyllum Rakotoarin. & J. Dransf.	2010	CR	X	–	–	–	–	–	–	500–600
D. henrici J. Dransf., Beentje & Govaerts	1933 (2006)	DD	X	–	–	–	–	–	–	200–400
D. heteromorpha (Jum.) Beentje & J. Dransf.	1924 (1995)	DD	–	–	X	–	–	–	–	1600–2500

(continued overleaf)

TABLE 8.18. ***continued***

SCIENTIFIC NAME	YEAR OF PUBLICATION	IUCN STATUS	BIOGEOGRAPHY							
			E	C	HM	C(W)	SAMB.	W	S	ELEVATION (m)
D. heterophylla Baker	1887	NT	X	X	–	–	–	–	–	300–1500
D. hiarakae Beentje	1995	VU	X	X	–	–	–	–	–	300–900
D. hildebrandtii (Baill.) Becc.	1894 (1912)	NT	X	X	–	–	–	–	–	0–1500
D. hovomantsina Beentje	1995	CR	X	–	–	–	–	–	–	0–500
D. humbertii H. Perrier	1939	VU	X	X	–	–	–	–	–	300–1300
D. humilis M. S. Trudgen	2009	CR	X	–	–	–	–	–	–	100–200
D. ifanadianae Beentje	1995	CR	X	–	–	–	–	–	–	200–600
D. integra (Jum.) Beentje & J. Dransf.	1929 (1995)	EN	X	–	–	–	–	–	–	0–800
D. intermedia Beentje	1995	CR	X	–	–	–	–	–	–	0–100
D. interrupta J. Dransf.	1995	CR	X	–	–	–	–	–	–	0–600
D. jeremiei Rakotoarin. & J. Dransf.	2010	CR	–	X	–	–	–	–	–	900–1000
D. jumelleana Beentje & J. Dransf.	1995	VU	X	X	–	–	–	–	–	500–1300
D. laevis J. Dransf.	1995	CR	X	–	–	–	–	–	–	0–100
D. lantzeana Baill.	1894	VU	X	–	–	–	–	–	–	0–900
D. lanuginosa J. Dransf.	1995	CR	X	–	–	–	–	–	–	300–500
D. lastelliana (Baill.) Beentje & J. Dransf.	1894 (1995)	LC	X	X	–	–	–	–	–	0–900
D. leptocheilos (Hodel) Beentje & J. Dransf.	1993 (1995)	CR	–	–	–	–	–	X	–	0–200
D. leucomalla J. Dransf. & Marcus	2013	NT	–	–	–	–	–	–	–	Unknown in the wild
D. ligulata (Jum.) Beentje & J. Dransf.	1924 (1995)	DD	–	–	–	–	–	X	–	0–100
D. lilacina J. Dransf. & Rakotoarin.	2012	NE	X	–	–	–	–	–	–	400–500
D. linearis Jum.	1918	EN	X	X	–	–	–	–	–	400–900
D. lokohoensis J. Dransf.	1995	VU	X	X	–	–	–	–	–	0–1200
D. louvelii Jum. & H. Perrier	1913	VU	–	X	–	–	–	–	–	100–1100
D. lucens (Jum.) Beentje & J. Dransf.	1995	DD	X	–	–	–	–	–	–	400–500
D. lutea (Jum.) Beentje & J. Dransf.	1995	EN	X	X	–	–	–	–	–	0–1100
D. lutescens (H. Wendl.) Beentje & J. Dransf.	1878 (1995)	NT	X	–	–	–	–	–	–	0–600
D. madagascariensis (Becc.) Beentje & J. Dransf.	1906 (1995)	LC	–	–	–	X	X	X	–	0–1000
D. mahia Beentje	1995	CR	X	–	–	–	–	–	–	0–100
D. makirae Rakotoarin. & Britt	2009	VU	X	X	–	–	–	–	–	600–1000
D. malcomberi Beentje	1995	EN	X	X	–	–	–	–	–	400–1200

SCIENTIFIC NAME	YEAR OF PUBLICATION	IUCN STATUS	BIOGEOGRAPHY							
			E	C	HM	C(W)	SAMB.	W	S	ELEVATION (m)
D. mananjarensis (Jum. & H. Perrier) Beentje & J. Dransf.	1913 (1995)	NT	X	–	–	–	–	–	–	0–800
D. mangorensis (Jum.) Beentje & J. Dransf.	1929 (1915)	CR	X	–	–	–	–	–	–	0–200
D. marojejyi Beentje	1995	VU	X	X	–	–	–	–	–	600–1200
D. mcdonaldiana Beentje	1995	EN	X	–	–	–	–	–	–	0–600
D. metallica Rakotoarin. & J. Dransf.	2010	CR	X	–	–	–	–	–	–	0–100
D. mijoroana Eiserhardt & W. J. Baker	2018	NE	X	–	–	–	–	–	–	100–200
D. minuta Beentje	1995	VU	X	–	–	–	–	–	–	200–300
D. mirabilis J. Dransf.	1995	EN	X	–	–	–	–	–	–	0–200
D. mocquerysiana (Becc.) Becc.	1906 (1912)	NT	X	X	–	–	–	–	–	0–1000
D. monostachya Jum.	1918	DD	X	X	–	–	–	–	–	500–900
D. montana (Jum.) Beentje & J. Dransf.	1928	VU	X	X	–	–	–	–	–	600–1200
D. moorei Beentje	1995	EN	X	–	–	–	–	–	–	0–500
D. nauseosa (Jum. & H. Perrier) Beentje & J. Dransf.	1913 (1995)	CR	X	–	–	–	–	–	–	0–600
D. nodifera Mart.	1849	LC	X	X	–	–	–	–	–	0–1700
D. nossibensis (Becc.) Beentje & J. Dransf.	1906 (1995)	CR	–	–	–	–	X	–	–	0–400
D. occidentalis (Jum.) Beentje & J. Dransf.	1929 (1995)	VU	–	X	–	X	X	–	–	400–1700
D. onilahensis (Jum. & H. Perrier) Beentje & J. Dransf.	1913 (1995)	VU	–	–	–	X	–	X	–	300–1400
D. oreophila Beentje	1995	VU	X	X	–	–	–	–	–	600–1700
D. oropedionis Beentje	1995	CR	–	–	–	X	–	–	–	1100–1500
D. ovobontsira Beentje	1995	CR	X	–	–	–	–	–	–	200–400
D. ovojavavy Eiserhardt & W. J. Baker	2018	NE	X	–	–	–	–	–	–	100–200
D. pachyramea J. Dransf.	1995	LC	X	–	–	–	–	–	–	0–400
D. paludosa J. Dransf.	1995	VU	X	–	–	–	–	–	–	0–600
D. perrieri (Jum.) Beentje & J. Dransf.	1928 (1995)	VU	X	X	–	–	–	–	–	0–900
D. pervillei (Baill.) Beentje & J. Dransf.	1894 (1995)	CR	X	–	–	–	–	–	–	300–400
D. pilulifera (Becc.) Beentje & J. Dransf.	1906 (1995)	VU	X	X	–	–	–	–	–	300–1000
D. pinnatifrons Mart.	1838	LC	X	X	–	–	–	–	–	0–1300

(continued overleaf)

TABLE 8.18. ***continued***

SCIENTIFIC NAME	YEAR OF PUBLICATION	IUCN STATUS	BIOGEOGRAPHY							
			E	C	HM	C(W)	SAMB.	W	S	ELEVATION (m)
D. plumosa Hodel	2009	DD	–	–	–	–	–	–	–	Unknown in the wild
D. plurisecta Jum.	1918	DD	X	–	–	–	–	–	–	0–100
D. poivreana (Baill.) Beentje & J. Dransf.	1995	EN	X	–	–	–	–	–	–	0–100
D. prestoniana Beentje	1995	VU	X	–	–	–	–	–	–	400–600
D. procera Jum.	1918	VU	X	–	–	–	–	–	–	0–600
D. procumbens (Jum. & H. Perrier) J. Dransf.	2006	NT	X	X	–	X	–	–	–	0–1800
D. psammophila Beentje	1995	EN	X	–	–	–	–	–	–	0–600
D. pulchella J. Dransf.	1995	CR	X	X	–	–	–	–	–	300–900
D. pumila Beentje	1995	CR	–	X	X	–	–	–	–	1000–2100
D. pusilla Beentje	1995	VU	X	–	–	–	–	–	–	0–400
D. pustulata J. Dransf. & Rakotoarin.	2012	NE	X	–	–	–	–	–	–	300–700
D. rabepierrei Eiserhardt & W. J. Baker	2018	NE	X	–	–	–	–	–	–	100–200
D. rakotonasoloi Rakotoarin.	2009	CR	–	X	–	–	–	–	–	900–1000
D. ramentacea J. Dransf.	1995	CR	X	–	–	–	–	–	–	0–100
D. reflexa Rakotoarin. & J. Dransf.	2010	CR	X	–	–	–	–	–	–	0–100
D. remotiflora J. Dransf.	1995	CR	X	X	–	–	–	–	–	0–900
D. rivularis (Jum. & H. Perrier) Beentje & J. Dransf.	1913 (1995)	EN	–	–	–	–	X	X	–	100–800
D. robusta Hodel	2005	CR	X	–	–	–	–	–	–	700–800
D. rosea J. Dransf.	2014	NE	–	–	–	–	–	–	–	Unknown in the wild
D. sahanofensis (Jum. & H. Perrier) Beentje & J. Dransf.	1922 (1995)	CR	X	X	–	–	–	–	–	200–1400
D. saintelucei Beentje	1995	EN	X	–	–	–	–	–	–	0–600
D. sancta Rakotoarin. & J. Dransf.	2010	CR	X	–	–	–	–	–	–	500–600
D. sanctaemariae J. Dransf.	1995	CR	X	–	–	–	–	–	–	0–100
D. scandens J. Dransf.	1995	CR	X	–	–	–	–	–	–	500–600
D. schatzii Beentje	1995	EN	X	–	–	–	–	–	–	300–700
D. scottiana (Becc.) Beentje & J. Dransf.	1906 (1995)	VU	X	–	–	–	–	–	–	0–800
D. serpentina Beentje	1995	VU	X	–	–	–	–	–	–	200–600
D. simianensis (Jum.) Beentje & J. Dransf.	1929 (1995)	EN	X	–	–	–	–	–	–	0–600
D. singularis Beentje	1995	CR	X	–	–	–	–	–	–	0–200
D. soanieranae Beentje	1995	DD	X	–	–	–	–	–	–	0–100

			BIOGEOGRAPHY							
SCIENTIFIC NAME	YEAR OF PUBLICATION	IUCN STATUS	E	C	HM	C(W)	SAMB.	W	S	ELEVATION (m)
D. spicata J. Dransf.	1995	LC	X	X	–	X	–	–	–	400–1200
D. subacaulis J. Dransf. & Rakotoarin.	2012	NE	X	–	–	–	–	–	–	100–200
D. tanalensis (Jum. & H. Perrier) Beentje & J. Dransf.	1913 (1995)	CR	X	–	–	–	–	–	–	100–700
D. tenuissima Beentje	1995	EN	X	–	–	–	–	–	–	500–700
D. thermarum J. Dransf.	1995	VU	X	X	–	–	–	–	–	400–1300
D. thiryana (Becc.) Beentje & J. Dransf.	1906 (1995)	VU	X	X	–	–	–	–	–	200–1300
D. thouarsiana Baill.	1894	DD	X	–	–	–	–	–	–	Unknown
D. tokoravina Beentje	1995	CR	X	–	–	–	–	–	–	400–800
D. trapezoidea J. Dransf.	1995	CR	X	–	–	–	–	–	–	200–500
D. tsaratananensis (Jum.) Beentje & J. Dransf.	1924 (1995)	DD	–	X	X	–	–	–	–	1100–2200
D. tsaravoasira Beentje	1995	VU	X	X	–	–	–	–	–	0–1200
D. turkii J. Dransf.	2003	EN	X	X	–	–	–	–	–	400–1000
D. utilis (Jum.) Beentje & J. Dransf.	1917 (1995)	EN	X	X	–	–	–	–	–	0–1000
D. viridis Jum.	1918	VU	X	–	–	–	–	–	–	100–700
D. vonitrandambo Rakotoarin. & J. Dransf.	2010	CR	X	–	–	–	–	–	–	0–100
Lemurophoenix halleuxii J. Dransf.	1991	EN	X	–	–	–	–	–	–	200–600
L. laevis J. Dransf. & Marcus	2018	NE	X	–	–	–	–	–	–	Unknown in the wild
Marojejya darianii J. Dransf. & N. W. Uhl	1984	EN	X	–	–	–	–	–	–	0–500
M. insignis Humbert	1955	LC	X	X	–	–	–	–	–	0–1200
Masoala kona Beentje	1995	EN	X	–	–	–	–	–	–	400–600
M. madagascariensis Jum.	1933	CR	X	–	–	–	–	–	–	0–500

Source: IUCN (2020).

Notes: Year of publication indicates year of first publication of the species name; year in parentheses indicates the date of the last taxonomic revision made for the name of the species. IUCN status: CR, Critically Endangered; DD, Data Deficient; EN, Endangered; LC, Least Concern; NE, Not Evaluated; NT, Near Threatened; VU, Vulnerable. Biogeography: the classification is based on phytogeographical classification of Humbert (1955): C, Central Domain (800–1700 m); C(W), Central Domain, western slopes (800–1700 m); E, Eastern Domain (0–800 m); HM, High Mountains Domain (over 1700 m), S, Southern Domain; Samb., Sambirano Domain (0–800 m); W, Western Domain (0–800 m). Elevations are the minimum and maximum elevation where the species is encountered.

The genus *Hyphaene* has about 10 species in Africa, Arabia, and western India but only *H. coriacea* has reached Madagascar. Previously recognized as an endemic species, *H. shatan* (with several synonyms), the Malagasy Palm, was more recently considered to fit within the morphological variation of the east African palm, *H. coriacea* (J. Dransfield and Beentje 1995). Current monographic studies in Geneva may throw new light on whether the Malagasy species is distinct. *Satranala* and *Bismarckia* may represent the remains of an early radiation of this lineage on Madagascar. *Bismarckia nobilis* is a majestic fan palm of grasslands and pastures in the west, often occurring in large stands. The species *S. decussilvae* is a rare palm of lowland moist evergreen forests in the northeast (Figure 8.23a) from scattered sites between Pointe à Larrée and the Masoala Peninsula. As the only fan palm of lowland moist evergreen forests on the island, it can be recognized instantly.

Tribe Chuniophoeniceae

Tribe Chuniophoeniceae is represented by the monotypic genus *Tahina* in the northwest. The species *T. spectabilis* is a massive hapaxanthic hermaphroditic palm (Figure 8.23b). The tribe, with four genera, displays a disjunct distribution including: notably, *Nannorrhops* in the Arabian Peninsula, Pakistan, and Iran; *Kerriodoxa* in southern Thailand; and *Chuniophoenix* in Vietnam and China.

Subfamily Calamoideae

The subfamily Calamoideae is represented on Madagascar by a single species of *Raphia*. Although it has been referred to by different species names (e.g., *R. pedunculata*, *R. ruffia*, etc.), it has been until recently regarded as conspecific with *R. farinifera* of mainland Africa. The occurrence of this palm, certainly in the east, is almost always associated with human presence, but it does occur in large stands in swampy areas in western Madagascar (Jumelle and Perrier de la Bâthie 1945; Gautier 2018). Whether it represents an early introduction for its extreme usefulness or occurred on the island before the advent of humans is still debated. Preliminary results of a study by Helmstetter et al. (2020) suggest that the Madagascar *Raphia* is molecularly distinct from mainland African *R. farinifera* and should thus be regarded as a distinct, endemic taxon. However, samples used in this study were limited, with only a single sample from eastern Madagascar. More extensive material from Malagasy populations, including those in the west, is needed to reach a more definitive conclusion.

Subfamily Ceroxyloideae

Of the three tribes in this subfamily, only the Ceroxyleae occurs on Madagascar, represented by the monophyletic genus *Ravenea*. With 21 species in total, *Ravenea* is represented by 19 endemic species on Madagascar and by two endemic species in the Comoros. This genus of dioecious palms varies from dwarf treelets or squat litter-trapping palms to immense canopy tree palms (J. Dransfield and Beentje 1995). The discovery of *R. delicatula*, with clustering and branching stems (Rakotoarinivo 2008), indicates unexpected morphological diversity for this genus. Its members colonize different habitats. *Ravenea xerophila* is the most xerophytic of all palms on Madagascar and occurs in dry spiny thickets in the southwest. One of the most remarkable species is the rheophytic *R. musicalis*, known only from a few rivers north of Tolagnaro (Figure 8.23c), where it grows in flowing water approximately 1 m deep; its seeds germinate while still attached to the parent tree (vivipary, a common strategy of mangrove trees), and when the fruit is dislodged the seedlings sink to the bottom of the river where their hooked scale leaves help them to attach to the river bed.

Subfamily Arecoideae

Three of the 13 currently recognized tribes of Arecoideae (J. Dransfield et al. 2008) occur on Madagascar: Oranieae, Areceae, and Cocoseae. Tribe Oranineae is monotypic, with the single genus *Orania*. It is widespread in southeastern Asia and Malesia and is particularly diverse on New Guinea. Altogether, there are 25 species in this genus, of which three are endemic to Madagascar.

Tribe Areceae is represented exclusively on Madagascar by subtribe Dypsidinae with four genera: *Dypsis*, *Lemurophoenix*, *Marojejya*, and *Masoala*. The subtribe is part of the Indo-Pacific pseudomonomerous clade, with the subtribe Oncospermatinae appearing to be the closest relative (W. J. Baker et al. 2011). Within the Dypsidinae, morphological synapomorphies have not been identified as there is considerable morphological variation among these taxa.

The genus *Dypsis* constitutes more than three-quarters of the species diversity of Madagascar palms with 168 endemic species (plus three extralimital species occurring in the Comoros and on Pemba). It is a complex and highly variable genus with species ranging from giant trees (e.g., *D. bejofo* or *D. prestoniana*, Figure 8.23d) to dwarf palms (e.g., *D. minuta* or *D. spicata*), climbing palms (e.g., *D. andilamenensis* or *D. scandens*), or even palms with forking branched stems (e.g., *D. crinita*, *D. fibrosa* or *D. serpentina*).

The complexity of the genus *Dypsis* suggests that the genus itself may not be monophyletic (W. J. Baker et al. 2011). It is hoped that current studies on the phylogeny of Malagasy palms will provide clear answers to this question. Species of *Dypsis* occur throughout the island, from the most humid to the driest bioclimatic regions, and have been recorded from near the tops of the highest mountains. Some species seem well adapted to the cloud-covered and relatively cold conditions of the forests of the Central Highlands, though several are now on the verge of extinction as the remaining forest disappears. An example is *D. oropedionis* at Ambohitantely, where forest fragments have been considerably reduced in size or have completely disappeared in the last few decades.

Lemurophoenix can be distinguished by its multistaminate male (with over 40 stamens rather than the three or six in other members of this subtribe). The embryo in the seed of *Lemurophoenix* is also apical rather than basal as in the rest of the subtribe (J. Dransfield et al. 2008). Two species are known: *L. halleuxii* is a spectacular palm of the lowland moist evergreen forest canopy and one of the most massive of all tree palms on Madagascar (up to 40 m tall); *L. laevis* is unknown from the wild and was described from cultivated material.

The two genera *Masoala* and *Marojejya* are relatively similar in general appearance. They are stocky, massive palms of the forest understory, with shuttlecock-like crowns of leaves that trap litter. The genera are distinguished by differences in the appearance of the inflorescences, which may be condensed and hidden among leaf bases within the crown (*Marojejya*) or showy, relatively robust, and diffusely branched (*Masoala*). The genus *Marojejya* has two species. The first, *M. insignis*, occurs throughout the lowland and medium-altitude moist evergreen forests from Marojejy to Andohahela. The second species, *M. darianii*, is much rarer as it is known only in the lowlands between Toamasina and Masoala. This latter species differs from all other palms on Madagascar in its massive leaves, up to 5 m long, which have an undivided blade when young. *Masoala* is represented by two species, both with restricted distributions and both with a shuttlecock crown that traps litter at its base. *Masoala madagascariensis* is known in the northeast, between Andapa and Mananara-Nord, while *M. kona* occurs in the southeast, between Ifanadiana and Vondrozo.

All other arecoid palms on Madagascar belong to tribe Cocoseae. Of these, *Cocos nucifera*, the coconut, native to the west Pacific, may well have been one of the first economically important plants introduced into Madagascar by seafaring people. It is now naturalized in coastal areas, particularly in the north and east of the island. *Elaeis guineensis*, the African oil palm, occurs along watercourses and is naturalized around villages through much of the northwest to east coast lowlands. Oil palms are cultivated in plantations in several places in the eastern lowlands but nowhere as intensively as occurs in tropical Asia, Malesia, and west Africa.

The two remaining genera of Cocoseae on Madagascar are *Beccariophoenix* and *Voanioala*. *Beccariophoenix* now comprises three described species. These are all magnificent tree palms, highly sought after in the horticulture trade, with a large shuttlecock of foliage and massive inflorescences resembling torpedoes. *Voanioala* may represent an ancient line of evolution that survives as a relict on Madagascar and is one of the rarest palms on the island. It is known only from areas bordering Antongil Bay, between the Masoala Peninsula and Rantabe. It is a tall tree palm reaching the sub-canopy of lowland moist evergreen forests.

BIOGEOGRAPHY

What makes the palm flora of Madagascar so peculiar is the very high rate of endemism and the taxonomically isolated nature of some of its components. This seems to argue for a long and isolated evolutionary history, which is confirmed and emphasized by the strong influence of paleoclimate to explain the current distribution patterns of species diversity and richness across the island (Rakotoarinivo et al. 2013).

Apart from the four nonendemic species, the palms of Madagascar are representatives of evolutionary lines that were perhaps present on the island before it became separated from Gondwana and then completely isolated from India in the Late Cretaceous (Armistead et al. 2018). Conforming to general patterns of palm occurrence throughout the world (e.g., J. Dransfield et al. 2008; Couvreur et al. 2011), more than 90% of indigenous species on Madagascar occur in lowland and medium-altitude moist evergreen forests.

Some species are widespread across a phytogeographic domain, but for many their distribution is governed by regional or even local climatic type. For instance, *Dypsis fibrosa*, *D. nodifera*, *D. pinnatifrons*, *Ravenea robustior*, and *R. sambiranensis* are present in all moist evergreen forests of the Sambirano in the northwest and from Daraina to Tolagnaro in the east. Similarly, *D. baronii* and *R. madagascariensis* are often present in the Central Highland flora. In the west, palms are represented mostly by *Bismarckia nobilis*, *D. madagascariensis* or *Hyphaene coriacea* across this large area.

At a smaller scale, the floristic composition is much more complex and more dependent on the influence of the major trade winds on the climate. The perhumid situation in the northeast (Masoala Peninsula and surrounding area) results in the regional endemism of species such as *D. lastelliana*, *D. tsaravoasira*, and *D. crinita*. The restriction of *D. mananjarensis* and *D. prestoniana* to the southeast seems to be correlated with the short dry season in this bioclimatic zone. In the Sambirano Region, the distribution range of several species, such as *D. ampasindavae*, *D. nossibensis* and *Borassus aethiopum*, seem to coincide with the area where the monsoon creates high humidity within a relatively seasonal climate.

CONSERVATION STATUS

Palms are among the most useful plant families for humans after grasses and legumes (Bennett 2011). They are vital in poor countries like Madagascar as they play an immense economic role at the rural village level or for people relying on forest products (J. Dransfield and Beentje 1995). In fact, palms provide multiple resources, such as materials for construction or weaving, food, medicine, and ornamental plants. Several ethnobotanical studies of palms attest to their importance in different regions and emphasize the relative importance of various species in the daily life of rural people. Unfortunately, these types of utilization are frequently non-sustainable, leading to the death of the individual palm and eventually to the local depletion of the species, some of which are already rare. Loss of reproductive individuals can have a big impact on population dynamics as palms are generally slow-growing plants (J. Dransfield et al. 2008) and particularly vulnerable to forest degradation. In most species, survival and recruitment are reduced when habitat quality declines or when habitats become fragmented.

The latest comprehensive species conservation status assessment using the IUCN (International Union for the Conservation of Nature) Red List criteria and categories, published in 2012, indicate that 83% of the endemic palm species of Madagascar are threatened. Of the 192 species that have been assessed, 149 were assigned the categories Critically Endangered (CR), Endangered (EN), and Vulnerable (VU); a further 13 species were classified as Data Deficient (DD) since there has been no sign of their occurrence in the wild during the past 30 years (Rakotoarinivo et al. 2014). The high proportion of threatened species is nearly four times the percentage estimated for plants globally (RBG Kew 2016). New species described since 1995 are usually known from a single location and have low population sizes, while their habitat is deteriorating and their population is exploited. For instance, *Tahina spectabilis* is known from fewer than 50 mature individuals across its distribution range.

Seed harvesting may become a potent tool in the conservation of palms and their associated habitats in Madagascar, as long as it is conducted legally and does not result in the cutting down of the parent tree. The controlled harvesting of seed of *T. spectabilis* and selling it overseas to palm growers resulted in substantial revenue that was put back into the local communities living in close proximity to the remaining populations of this species. This income supported school construction and maintenance and helped with agricultural microfinance, while at the same time funding simple conservation methods such as fencing and clearing of firebreaks (Gardiner et al. 2017).

The recent extension of Madagascar's protected area network is highly beneficial for palms, substantially increasing the number of populations of threatened species included within these sites. However, there are still about 28 species (out of 208) that are not recorded in any protected area, among them some very restricted-range species such as *Dypsis ifanadianae* and *D. scandens*. In terms of the general distribution pattern of Malagasy palms, the most important protected areas for their conservation are in the northeast and include Marojejy, Makira, Masoala, and Mananara-Nord; some newly created protected areas in other parts of the island, including Fandriana-Ambositra-Vondrozo Forested Corridor (COFAV) and Ankeniheny-Zahamena Forested Corridor (CAZ), also display a high degree of richness in palms, with a substantial number of local endemics. Nevertheless, protected areas do not in most cases reduce extinction risk as the majority of species that occur at such sites are often still assessed as threatened, indicating that important pressures persist in these areas.

Ex situ conservation is for the time being the mainstay of conservation efforts for some of the rarest species. For instance, the Parc Botanique et Zoologique de Tsimbazaza in Antananarivo and the Arboretum de Ranomafana, Ifanadiana, have some of the rarest species in their living collections; for example, the only known individual of *D. robusta* on Madagascar is at the Ranomafana site (J. Dransfield et al. 2012). Since its discovery in 1994, this single tree has continued providing seeds for horticulture. A conservation project is being undertaken in these two botanic gardens, which produces seedlings of rare and threatened species in nurseries for planting in public places across Madagascar in the near future in order to raise awareness of the importance of conserving palms.

At the moment, it is difficult to predict how many more palm taxa on Madagascar will be discovered and described. There remain significant areas of the island, such as the Tsaratanàna Massif, that are still underrepresented by palm specimens in herbaria. Fieldwork since 1995 shows clearly that small forest fragments in the east coast lowlands, or even unexpected dry habitat as where *Tahina* was found, are likely to yield further novelties. Species turnover seems to happen over very short distances. In some sites in the eastern region, such as Makira, Masoala, Andilamena, and Vondrozo, adjacent hills may possess quite different palm floras, and most of the new species recently described have been discovered from particular habitats. Most of the remaining humid evergreen lowland forests should be prioritized for further palms surveys, not only for completing the catalog of the flora of Madagascar, but also for documenting new population occurrences, which is important for defining the extinction risk for each species.

Unfortunately, threats to biodiversity continue to increase every year; many rare species might even become extinct before they are known to science. To prevent such biodiversity loss for Madagascar palms, a critical conservation strategy is required to focus attention on conservation priorities, to stimulate necessary action, and to raise public awareness. With the biodiversity crisis in Madagascar ongoing, the current phylogenetic studies of all Madagascar palms being conducted at Kew and Aarhus University will provide a framework for managing species information in the future.

Subject editors: Laurent Gautier and Steven M. Goodman

CYPERACEAE, SEDGES

I. Larridon, D. Spalink, P. Jiménez-Mejías, J. I. Márquez-Corro, S. Martín-Bravo, A. M. Muasya, and M. Escudero

DIVERSITY AND PHYLOGENY

Cyperaceae (sedges) is among the 10 largest families of angiosperms and is the third largest monocot family in the world. The main diagnostic characteristics of the Cyperaceae relate to their highly reduced flowers, often composed of three stamens and a single ovary placed on the axil of a glume or scale and arranged in the form of spikelets (Goetghebeur 1998). The perianth is missing or reduced to bristles or scales. The leaves are linear, with parallel nerves, much like in grasses (see Vorontsova et al., pp. 585–98). Sedges are often seen as a rather uniform group of plants from wetland environments, but like grasses they are phenotypically and ecologically very diverse (Naczi and Ford 2008). They are of great ecological importance in high-latitude and high-elevation ecosystems, as well as in wetland habitats where they may constitute the majority of the plant biomass. Although not to the level of the Poaceae, Cyperaceae also have an economic significance with about 10% of species used by humans (Simpson and Inglis 2001), several species being notorious weeds in agriculture, and a remarkable—and often overlooked—importance in human history (e.g., totora, papyrus) and evolution (Sponheimer et al. 2013; Dominy 2012). Despite their importance, many questions concerning their evolutionary history remain, and much work is needed to fully understand this interesting group of plants. For example, dozens of species continue to be described every year (e.g., Bauters et al. 2018; Larridon et al. 2019a), including from areas assumed to be well explored, such as Europe and North America (e.g., Derieg et al. 2013; Maguilla and Escudero 2016).

With 310 species, the Cyperaceae is among the top 10 most species-rich angiosperm families on Madagascar, and the island is among the four countries that are most species rich for sedges in the African-Malagasy region.

Madagascar is home to both subfamilies of Cyperaceae, the Mapanioideae and Cyperoideae (Figure 8.25). The latter is by far

TABLE 8.19. **The four most species-rich African-Malagasy countries for Cyperaceae**

COUNTRY	NUMBER OF SPECIES	AREA (km^2)
South Africa	452	1,221,037
Tanzania	450	947,303
Democratic Republic of Congo	318	2,345,409
Madagascar	310	587,041

Sources: Area figures from Wikipedia. Number of species follows Govaerts et al. (2020d).

FIGURE 8.25 **Summary phylogeny of the Cyperaceae family based on Semmouri et al. (2019), indicating the tribes and genera with species native to Madagascar (in blue). Tribal classification follows Semmouri et al. (2019) and Léveillé-Bourret and Starr (2019).**

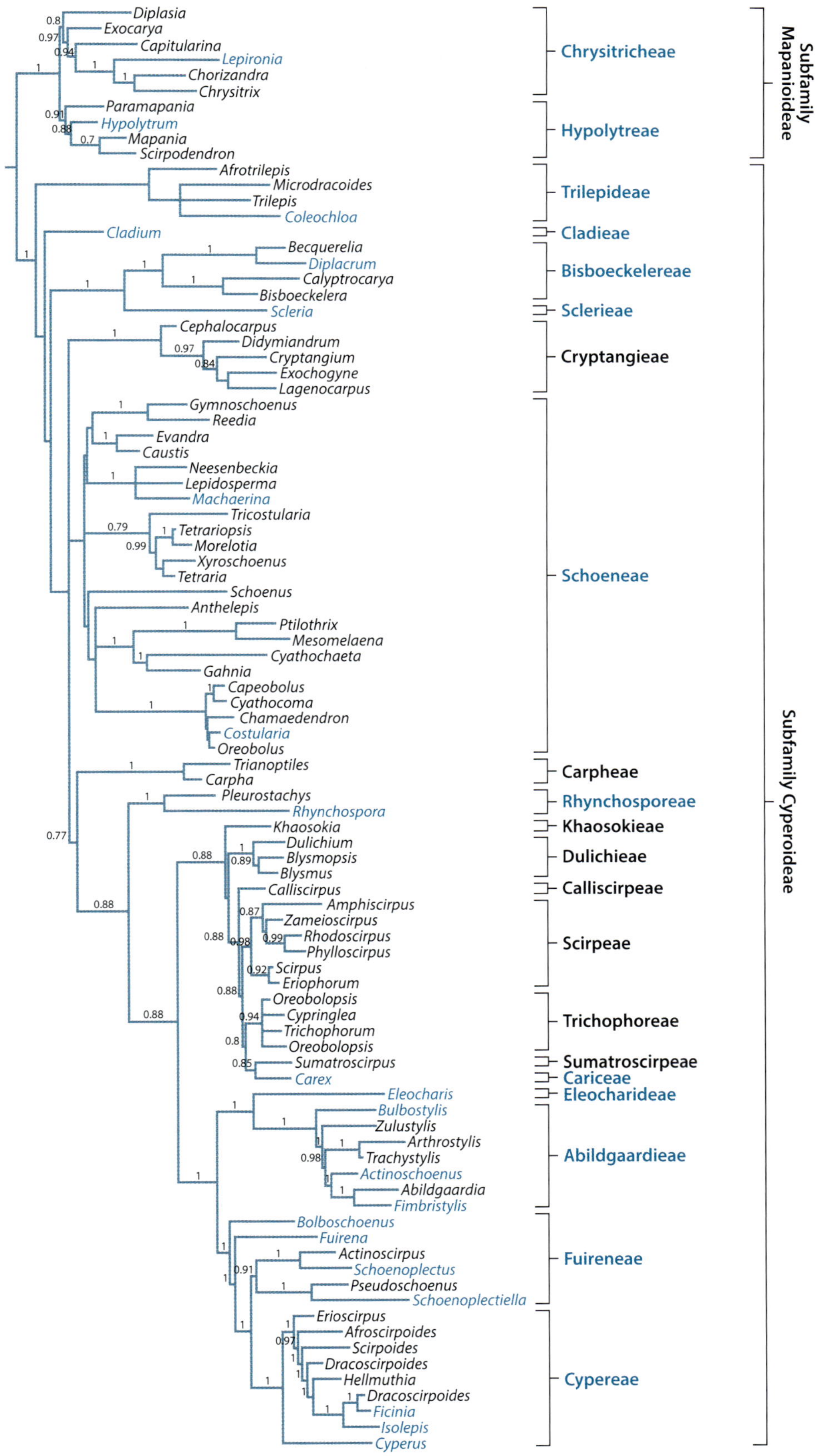

the more diverse, encompassing 99% of the species, and includes 12 tribes, 21 genera, and 308 species on the island (Govaerts et al. 2020d; Semmouri et al. 2019). The subfamily Mapanioideae, on the other hand, is limited to two species in two genera (*Lepironia* and *Hypolytrum*) (Govaerts et al. 2020d). This is not surprising as the subfamily encompasses ~3% of global Cyperaceae species diversity and is largely restricted to the tropics. Table 8.20 provides an overview of the Cyperaceae of Madagascar.

TABLE 8.20. **Overview of Cyperaceae diversity on Madagascar**

SUBFAMILY	TRIBE	GENUS	NUMBER OF SPECIES GLOBALLY	NUMBER OF SPECIES MADAGASCAR	NUMBER OF ENDEMIC SPECIES
Mapanioideae	Chrysitricheae	*Lepironia*	1	1	0
	Hypolytreae	*Hypolytrum*	61	1	1
Cyperoideae	Abildgaardieae	*Actinoschoenus*	8	1	0
		Bulbostylis	227	23	15
		Fimbristylis	322	17	2
	Bisboeckelereae	*Diplacrum*	10	1	0
	Cariceae	*Carex*	1996	30	26
	Cladieae	*Cladium*	3	1	0
	Carpheae	*Carpha*	15	1	1
	Cypereae	*Cyperus*	955	143	43
		Ficinia	80	1	1
		Isolepis	75	4	1
	Eleocharideae	*Eleocharis*	295	12	0
	Fuireneae	*Bolboschoenus*	15	1	0
		Fuirena	55	7	2
		Schoenoplectiella	53	12	5
		Schoenoplectus	26	2	0
	Rhynchosporeae	*Rhynchospora*	361	10	1
	Schoeneae	*Costularia*	15	11	11
		Machaerina	53	4	1
		Trichoschoenus	1	1	1
	Sclerieae	*Scleria*	258	25	8
	Trilepideae	*Coleochloa*	8	1	0

Sources: Classification based on Semmouri et al. (2019). Species numbers and distribution follow Govaerts et al. (2020d).

The largest tribes are Cypereae (48% of the sedge flora), Abildgaardieae (13%), and Cariceae (10%). Six tribes (Bisboeckelereae, Chrysitricheae, Carpheae, Cladieae, Hypolytreae, and Trilepideae) have only a single species on Madagascar. *Cyperus* is the most species-rich genus, encompassing about 46% of the flora, which makes sense given the Afrotropical center of diversity of this genus (Larridon et al. 2014a; Govaerts et al. 2020d). The second-richest genus is the mainly boreo-temperate *Carex* (10%). The genus with the highest proportion of endemic species is *Costularia* with 73% of the genus's global diversity endemic to the island. Ten genera have a single species (43% of all genera and representing ~3% of all species), one of which (*Trichoschoenus*) is a monotypic endemic genus only known from its type collection, made by Henri Humbert in 1955. Two species (*Bolboschoenus glaucus* and *Cladium mariscus*) that occur on Madagascar, but with cosmopolitan distribution, are wetland plants.

RECENT DEVELOPMENTS IN SYSTEMATICS

Since the review by Muasya et al. (2011) of the diversity and ecology of Malagasy Cyperaceae, which largely followed the classification of Goetghebeur (1998), the circumscriptions of several genera native to Madagascar have been altered. In the tribe Abildgaardieae, the circumscriptions of *Bulbostylis* and *Fimbristylis* have changed, although these changes do not concern species native to Madagascar. Recently, the small mainland African genus *Nemum* was synonymized with *Bulbostylis* (Roalson et al. 2019a; Larridon et al. 2019b). Also, the Australian monotypic genus *Crosslandia* was assimilated into *Fimbristylis* (Roalson et al. 2019b). More relevant to the knowledge of the systematics of Malagasy Cyperaceae are the taxonomic changes that occurred in the tribes Cariceae, Eleocharideae, and Cypereae.

Recently, the Global Carex Group (2015) recircumscribed the megadiverse genus *Carex* (~2000 species) as a monophyletic group. To do so, they synonymized the genera *Cymophyllus* (monotypic), *Kobresia* (~60 species), *Schoenoxiphium* (~15 species), and *Uncinia* (~70 species) with *Carex*. Two *Carex* species from Madagascar belong to the *Schoenoxiphium* group: *C. chermezonii*, previously known as *S. gracile*, and *C. multispiculata*, previously known as *S. madagascariense*. Most of the other *Carex* species on Madagascar belong to a single clade (the Asian-African-American clade of *Carex* section *Indicae*) (Martín-Bravo et al. 2019). An almost complete revision of the genus (excluding the species formerly placed in *Schoenoxiphium*) was recently carried out for the African-Malagasy region, including an exhaustive account of the Malagasy species and their subgeneric and section placement (Gehrke 2011). In the tribe Eleocharideae, the monotypic genus *Websteria* (with the aquatic species *W. confervoides*) was assimilated into the large and widely distributed wetland genus *Eleocharis* (Hinchcliff et al. 2010).

The biggest taxonomic changes have occurred in the tribe Cypereae. After the now monotypic tribe Cariceae, the second most species-rich tribe in Cyperaceae is Cypereae with well over 1000 species (Govaerts et al. 2020d). Before the molecular era, the tribe Cypereae was circumscribed based on embryo morphology; all species included in this tribe have either a *Cyperus*-type embryo or similar *Ficinia*-type embryo (Goetghebeur 1998; Semmouri et al. 2019). Studies have shown that embryos provide some of the best morphological characters to delimit Cyperaceae groups in accordance with molecular phylogenetic results (Semmouri et al. 2019). Two clades are distinguished in tribe Cypereae, the Ficinia clade and the Cyperus clade. Ficinia clade species are predominantly characterized by having spikelets with spirally arranged glumes. In Madagascar, this clade includes the genera *Ficinia* and *Isolepis*. In contrast, species of the Cyperus clade usually have spikelets with distichous or two-ranked glumes. Besides *Cyperus sensu stricto*, a range of segregate genera as circumscribed by the classification of Goetghebeur (1998) are included in the Cyperus clade. Nine of these genera (*Alinula*, *Ascolepis*, *Courtoisina*, *Kyllinga*, *Lipocarpha*, *Oxycaryum*, *Pycreus*, *Queenslandiella*, and *Remirea*) occur on Madagascar (Muasya et al. 2011), and most were originally described based on their derived spikelet morphologies (e.g., Larridon et al. 2013). Molecular phylogenetic studies revealed that these segregate genera of the Cyperus clade are all nested in *Cyperus sensu stricto* and that several of them do not form natural groups (Larridon et al. 2011a, 2013; Bauters et al. 2014). As a result, their species were recently transferred to *Cyperus* (Larridon et al. 2011b, 2014b; Bauters et al. 2014; Govaerts et al. 2020d). To summarize, while Muasya et al. (2011) recognized 33 genera on Madagascar, following the taxonomy presented herein, just 22 genera occur on the island; and the genus *Cyperus* went from encompassing 31% of the sedge flora to 46%.

ENDEMISM

In total, 5.5% of Cyperaceae species worldwide are native to Madagascar (or ~6% of the species richness of the native genera). Of the 310 species of Cyperaceae native to the island, 119 (38%) are endemic (Figure 8.26, Table 8.20). Although Madagascar has the second-highest level of endemism for Cyperaceae after the Cape Provinces (Muasya et al. 2011), compared with similar sized plant families such as Melastomataceae, its level of endemism is much lower (321 species, 99% endemic; Almeda 2003). Among large plant families, the level of endemism of the sedge family is only comparable to that in grasses, where ~40% of species are endemic to Madagascar (Vorontsova et al. 2016).

Nineteen lineages of endemic species were retrieved in a recent molecular phylogenetic reconstruction that included ~50% of

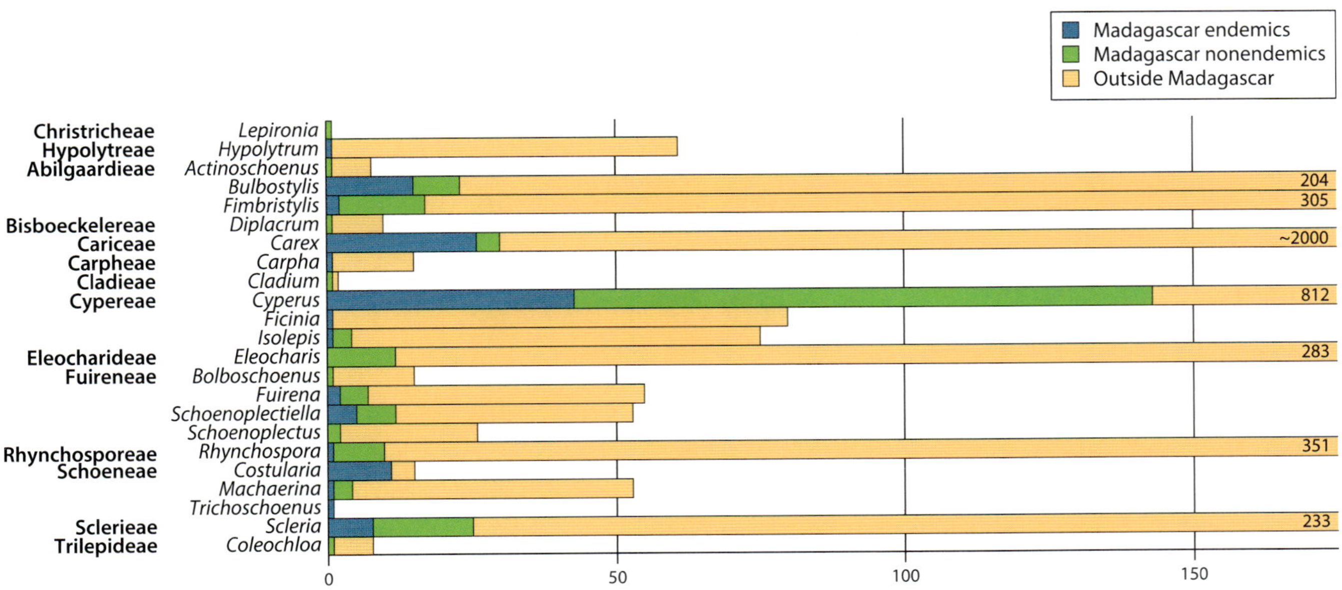

FIGURE 8.26 **Diversity and endemicity diagram of Malagasy Cyperaceae at the level of genera, showing three different species counts: 1) endemic to Madagascar, 2) nonendemic but native to Madagascar, and 3) those occurring elsewhere in the world (for further information see text). In cases when species diversity exceeds or does not conform to that presented on the horizontal graph scale, the figures are written along the respective horizontal line of a given genus.**

Cyperaceae species native to Madagascar (Larridon et al. 2019c). The taxonomic groups of Cyperaceae present on the island are more or less evenly distributed through the Cyperaceae phylogeny, with the exception of the Scirpo-Caricoid clade. This clade, dominated by the megadiverse, mostly temperate genus *Carex*, has limited presence on Madagascar in contrast to its high species diversity in temperate regions, especially in the Northern Hemisphere. The endemic lineages appear to have arrived on Madagascar in the last ~20 million years (Larridon et al. 2019c), and these are often species poor. Only a few lineages appear to have radiated within Madagascar.

Cyperaceae fruits are called nutlets and are often dispersed within persistent organs such as a hardened stylebase, a perianth, one to several glumes, or even the complete spikelet (Goetghebeur 1998). Although little data is available on dispersal of Cyperaceae, nutlets can be dispersed by water (sea or freshwater), wind, animals—particular ants and birds—and humans (Goetghebeur 1998). Although further research is necessary, the presence or absence of Cyperaceae lineages on Madagascar may reflect their long-distance dispersal capability.

The largest endemic radiation is represented by the Asian-African-American clade of *Carex* section *Indicae* (Martín-Bravo et al. 2019) with 23 out of 26 endemic *Carex* species belonging to this clade (Figure 8.27a). With about 90 species and a circumtropical distribution (Martín-Bravo et al. 2019), this section has apparently colonized the island at least once. Since *Carex* is mostly a cold-adapted genus, its presence in the tropics is limited to higher elevations. Species of section *Indicae* are the only group of *Carex* species that is almost entirely confined to tropical montane forests. The orography of eastern Madagascar seems to have enabled the establishment and diversification of this group in suitable habitats.

The genus *Costularia*, which was recently recircumscribed (Larridon et al. 2018), includes 15 species (Larridon et al. 2019a), 11 of

FIGURE 8.27 **Diversity of Malagasy endemic Cyperaceae species. A) *Carex haematosaccus*, B) *Costularia purpurea*, C) *Cyperus chamaecephalus*, and D) *C. sciaphilus*. All photographed in Mantadia National Park**
(PHOTOS A–C by I. Larridon, and D by M. Vorontsova.)

which are endemic to Madagascar. Most species of this genus grow in high-elevation ericoid vegetation (Figure 8.27b). *Cyperus* section *Incurvi* is a group of 32 *Cyperus* species distributed across Africa, Latin America, and Australasia (Larridon et al. 2011a). Nine species in this group are endemic to Madagascar; these are found mainly in the understory of moist evergreen forests and show clear adaptations to this habitat (e.g., broad and/or purplish leaves) (Figures 8.27c and d) (Gautier et al. 2010).

Scleria section *Abortivae* includes five species that are endemic to Madagascar and the western Indian Ocean islands (Galán Díaz et al. 2019). Two other genera include a significant number of endemic species: *Bulbostylis* and *Schoenoplectiella*. However, we lack sufficient sequence data and recent taxonomic treatments for these genera. Further study is required to assess whether these endemic species represent one or multiple arrivals to Madagascar.

CONSERVATION

The conservation status of 136 out of 310 species (~44%) have been assessed using the IUCN (International Union for the Conservation of Nature) Red List guidelines (IUCN 2019). Out of these 136 assessed species, five have been classified as Critically Endangered, 14 are Endangered, eight are Vulnerable, one Near Threatened, and two Data Deficient. The others, which are largely widely distributed species, were classified as of Least Concern. This means that ~20% of Cyperaceae species native to Madagascar are threatened, which is in line with the estimation that one in five plant species globally is threatened with extinction (RBG Kew 2016). When we look at the endemic Cyperaceae species, just 33 of the 119 species were assessed (~28%), with 75% of these species given a threatened category. This low percentage of species that have been assessed and high level of threat among those that have been highlights the need for more conservation studies to understand the future of the endemic Malagasy sedge flora.

WORK IN PROGRESS

Efforts are underway to study the Cyperaceae of Madagascar. This has already resulted in taxonomic revisions of the genera *Costularia* (Larridon et al. 2019a) and *Scleria* (Galán Díaz et al. 2019). Further research is ongoing to study the endemic species *Cyperus* section *Incurvi* (I. Larridon et al., unpublished data), and work is underway to generate a checklist of Cyperaceae for the Itremo Massif protected area (F. Rasaminirina et al., unpublished data). Furthermore, we aim to estimate the number, age, and origins of endemic sedge lineages in the Malagasy Region, and to compare the diversification of C_3 and C_4 taxa (see Lehmann et al., pp. 152–68, for further details). This may contribute to the growing literature on whether or not certain grassland ecosystems in Madagascar are natural or derive from human activities (Vorontsova et al. 2016). Revisionary work on *Carex* is also in preparation, and the vast majority of species will be reassigned to sections or informal groups. Other avenues for future research may include investigating key traits that have allowed some lineages to diversify successfully on Madagascar and the local and traditional uses of sedge species. In their revision of *Economic, Ethnobotanical and Horticultural Importance of Cyperaceae*, Simpson and Inglis (2001) only list uses for five species specifically on Madagascar. However, undoubtedly many more species are used, for example, as packing, matting, and basketwork material.

Subject editors: Laurent Gautier and Steven M. Goodman

POACEAE, GRASSES (INCLUDING BAMBOOS)

M. S. Vorontsova, S. Dransfield, J. A. Morton, R. A. Rakotonasolo, C. L. Solofondranohatra, N. H. Rakotomalala, H. Razanajatovo, D. Rabehevitra, S. Rakotoarisoa, J. Razanatsoa, and J. Hackel

The Poaceae (grasses), including bamboos, is one of the largest plant families both worldwide and on Madagascar, providing the majority of human food and driving ecosystem dynamics where they are abundant. They are found in all of the island's terrestrial habitats except the darkest moist evergreen forest understory. Most prominently, they dominate the vast open areas. Here we use the word "grassland" to denote both natural and secondary grass-dominated ecosystems, with or without trees. This contribution attempts to give an overview of Malagasy grass diversity as currently understood.

A full Poaceae species checklist of 541 species including 217 endemics (40% endemicity) was published by Vorontsova et al. (2016), building on Bosser (1969), who documented around half of the known species, as well as unpublished manuscripts by Emmet J. Judziewicz and Bryan K. Simon. As of March 2019, there were 14,670 Poaceae occurrence records from Madagascar available via the Global Biodiversity Information Facility or GBIF (Rabarivola et al. 2019a, 2019b, 2019c), including all herbaria holdings of the Muséum National d'Histoire Naturelle in Paris and Parc Botanique et Zoologique de Tsimbazaza in Antananarivo, the two herbaria together holding about 75% of these collections. The GBIF records include the 488 wild species listed in Table 8.21. Occurrence maps of every species are available in the *Madagascar Grass Atlas* (Rabarivola et al. 2019d). An identification guide (Vorontsova et al. 2018) presents a description and a color scan for each of the 144 genera in 10 subfamilies.

TABLE 8.21. **Checklist of the 488 species in the family Poaceae with wild occurrence on Madagascar**

Acrachne perrieri (A. Camus) S. M. Phillips EU [12]
Acroceras boivinii (Mez) A. Camus ES [20]
A. calcicola A. Camus EA [20]
A. debilis Judz. sp. nov. ined. EU [20]
A. hubbardii (A. Camus) Clayton NG [20]
A. ivohibense A. Camus ES [20]
A. tenuicaule A. Camus EU [20]
Adenochloa hymeniochila (Nees.) Zuloaga NI [19]
Agrostis elliotii Hook. ex Scott-Elliot EC [3]
A. emirnensis (Baker) Bosser EIC [3]
A. humbertii A. Camus EU [3]
A. marojejyensis A. Camus EU [3]
A. tsaratananensis A. Camus EU [3]
A. tsiafajavonensis A. Camus EU [3]
A. tsitondroinensis A. Camus EU [3]
Alloteropsis cimicina (L.) Stapf NP [20]
A. paniculata (Benth.) Stapf NIP [20]
A. semialata (R. Br.) Hitchc. NFG [20]
Andropogon andringitrensis (A. Camus) Voronts. EFC [17]
A. chinensis (Nees) Merr. NU [17]
A. eucomus Nees NF [17]
A. ibityensis A. Camus EF [17]
A. imerinensis Bosser EF [17]
A. itremoensis Voronts. EG [17]
A. ivohibensis A. Camus EF [17]
A. trichozygus Baker EF [17]
A. tsaratananensis A. Camus EU [17]
Anthoxanthum madagascariense Stapf EC [3]
Aristida adscensionis L. NFGAP [5]
A. ambongensis A. Camus EU [5]
A. barbicollis Trin. & Rupr. NAP [5]
A. congesta Roem. & Schult. NAP [5]
A. cumingiana Trin. & Rupr. NU [5]
A. decaryana A. Camus EU [5]
A. junciformis Trin. & Rupr. NU [5]
A. rufescens Steud. EFG [5]
A. similis Steud. EFG [5]
A. tenuissima A. Camus EFG [5]
Arthraxon antsirabensis A. Camus EI [17]
Arundinella nepalensis Trin. NFI [17]
Axonopus compressus (Sw.) P. Beauv. NG [16]
Bothriochloa bladhii (Retz.) S. T. Blake NU [17]
B. insculpta (Hochst. ex A. Rich.) A. Camus NU [17]
B. pertusa (L.) A. Camus NU [17]
Brachiaria antsirabensis A. Camus EFG [20]
B. bemarivensis A. Camus EAP [20]
B. comorensis (Mez) A. Camus NSA [20]
B. dimorpha A. Camus EFC [20]
B. epacridifolia (Stapf) A. Camus ES [20]
B. fragrans A. Camus EU [20]
B. fruticulosa A. Camus EU [20*]
B. humbertiana A. Camus EGA [23]
B. lactea (Mez) A. Camus EU [?]
B. lateritica A. Camus EU [?]
B. leandriana Bosser EGU [20]
B. mutica (Forssk.) Stapf NGAP [23]
B. nana Stapf EGAP [23]
B. perrieri A. Camus EU [?]
B. pseudodichotoma Bosser EG [23]
B. ramosa (L.) Stapf NU [23]
B. subquadripara (Trin.) Hitchc. NG [23]
B. subrostrata A. Camus EG [23]
B. tsiafajavonensis A. Camus ES [20]
B. umbellata (Trin.) Clayton NGP [23]
Brachypodium humbertianum A. Camus EU [3]
B. madagascariense A. Camus & H. Perrier EU [3]
B. perrieri A. Camus EU [3]
Bromus andringitrensis A. Camus EU [3]
B. pectinatus Thunb. NU [3]
B. trichodes (Schult & Schult. f.) Kunth. NU [3]
Cathariostachys capitata (Kunth.) S. Dransf. EP [4]
C. madagascariensis (A. Camus) S. Dransf. EP [4]
Cenchrus biflorus Roxb. NU [24]
C. ciliaris L. NGAP [24]
C. clandestinus Morrone AIG [24]
C. echinatus L. NU [24]
C. pedicellatus (Trin) Morrone NU [24]
C. polystachios (L) Morrone NFP [24]
C. purpureus (Schumach.) Morrone NI [24]
Centotheca lappacea (L.) Desv. NS [13]
Chasechloa egregia (Mez) A. Camus EU [20]
C. madagascariensis (Baker) A. Camus ES [20]
Chloris barbata Sw. NAP [12]
C. gayana Kunth. NP [12]
C. humbertiana A. Camus EGA [12]
C. pycnothrix Trin. NGP [12]
C. virgata Sw. NP [12]
Chrysopogon aciculatus (Retz.) Trin. NU [17]
C. humbertianus A. Camus EG [17]
C. serrulatus Trin. NF [17]
C. zizanioides (L.) Roberty AIU [17]
Coelachne africana Pilg. NI [7]
C. simpliciuscula Munro ex Benth. NI [7]
Coix lacryma-jobi L. NU [17]
Craspedorhachis africana Benth. NF [12]
Ctenium concinnum Nees NF [12]
Cymbopogon caesius (Hook. & Arn.) Stapf NF [17]
C. flexuosus (Nees ex Steud.) W. Watson NU [17]
C. giganteus Chiov. NU [17]
C. nardus (L.) Rendle NU [17]
C. schoenanthus (L.) Spreng. NU [17]
Cynodon dactylon (L.) Pers. NGA [12]
C. plectostachyus (K. Schum.) Pilg. NG [12]
C. radiatus Roth NG [12]
Cyphochlaena madagascariensis Hack. NS [20]
C. sclerioides (A. Camus) Bosser ES [20]
Cyrtococcum bosseri A. Camus ES [20]
C. deltoideum (Hack.) A. Camus EGS [20]

C. humbertianum A. Camus EU [20]
C. multinode (Lam.) Clayton NS [20]
C. patens (L.) A. Camus NU [20]
C. tamatavense A. Camus EU [20]
Dactyloctenium aegyptium (L.) Willd. NA [12]
D. australe Steud. NU [12]
D. capitatum A. Camus EU [12]
D. ctenoides (Steud.) Bosser NA [12]
D. geminatum Hack. NU [12]
D. giganteum B. S. Fisher & Schweick. NU [12]
Daknopholis boivinii (A. Camus) Clayton NGAP [12]
Decaryella madagascariensis A. Camus EA [12]
Decaryochloa diadelpha A. Camus ES [4]
Dichanthium annulatum (Forssk.) Stapf NU [17]
D. aristatum (Poir.) Hubbard NU [17]
Diectomis fastigiata Kunth. NF [17]
Digitaria abyssinica (Hochst. ex A. Rich.) Stapf NG [18]
D. andringitrensis A. Camus EU [18]
D. ankaratrensis A. Camus EG [18]
D. argyrotricha (Andersson) Chiov. NU [18]
D. atrofusca (Hack.) A. Camus NU [18]
D. bicornis (Lam.) Roem. & Schult. NAP [18]
D. bosseri Voronts. EU [24*]
D. ciliaris (Retz.) Koeler NGP [18]
D. debilis (Desf.) Willd. NP [18]
D. didactyla Willd. NU [18]
D. fulva Bosser EU [18]
D. glauca A. Camus EU [18]
D. horizontalis Willd. NU [18]
D. humbertii A. Camus EG [18]
D. longiflora (Retz.) Pers. NFG [18]
D. madagascariensis Bosser EU [18]
D. manongarivensis A. Camus EU [18]
D. nuda Schumach. NU [18]
D. perrieri A. Camus EU [18]
D. perrottetii (Kunth.) Stapf NU [18]
D. planiculmis Henrard EU [18]
D. psammophila Henrard EU [18]
D. pseudodiagonalis Chiov. NF [18]
D. radicosa (Presl.) Miq. NU [18]
D. sanguinalis (L.) Scop. NU [18]
D. setifolia Stapf NU [18]
D. thouarsiana (Flüggé) A. Camus NF [18]
D. velutina (Forssk.) P. Beauv. NU [18]
D. violascens Link NU [18]
Dimeria madagascariensis A. Camus EI [17]
D. manongarivensis A. Camus EI [17]
D. perrieri A. Camus EI [17]
Dinebra coerulescens (Steud) P. M. Peterson & N. Snow NU [12]
D. panicea (Retz.) P. M. Peterson & N. Snow NU [12]
D. perrieri (A. Camus) Bosser EU [12]
D. squarrosa (Pilg.) P. M. Peterson & N. Snow NU [12]
Diplachne fusca (L.) P. Beauv. ex Roem. & Schult. NU [12]
Echinochloa colona (L.) Link NGIP [20]
E. jubata Stapf NU [20]
E. pyramidalis (Lam.) Hitchc. & Chase NIP [20]
E. stagnina (Retz.) P. Beauv. NU [20]
Eleusine indica (L.) Gaertn. NGP [12]
Elionurus tristis Hack. NF [17]
Enneapogon cenchroides (Licht. ex Roem. & Schult.) C. E. Hubb. NAP [10]
Enteropogon prieurii (Kunth.) Clayton AIP [12]
E. sechellensis (Benth.) T. Durand & Schinz NU [12]
Eragrostis aethiopica Chiov. NU [10]
E. ambohibengensis A. Camus EU [10]
E. ambositrensis A. Camus EU [10]
E. ambrensis A. Camus EU [10]
E. aspera (Jacq.) Nees NP [10]
E. atrovirens (Desf.) Trin. ex Steud. NGP [10]
E. bemarivensis A. Camus NU [10]
E. betsileensis A. Camus EU [10]
E. boinensis A. Camus EA [10]
E. boivinii Steud. EU [10]
E. capensis (Thunb.) Trin. NU [10]
E. capuronii A. Camus EGAP [10]
E. chabouisii Bosser EU [10]
E. chapelieri (Knuth.) Nees EF [10]
E. cilianensis (All.) Janch. NP [10]
E. ciliaris (L.) R. Br. NU [10]
E. curvula (Schrad.) Nees NU [10]
E. cylindriflora Hochst. NAP [10]
E. gangetica (Roxb.) Steud. NU [10]
E. gummiflua Nees NU [10]
E. hildebrandtii Jedwabn. EGP [10]
E. humbertii A. Camus EU [10]
E. japonica (Thunb.) Trin. NU [10]
E. lateritica Bosser EG [10]
E. macilenta Steud. NU [10]
E. majungensis A. Camus EU [10]
E. mandrarensis A. Camus EU [10]
E. minor Host NU [10]
E. perrieri A. Camus EU [10]
E. pilosa (L.) P. Beauv. NU [10]
E. plana Nees NU [10]
E. racemosa (Thunb.) Steud. NGP [10]
E. sambiranensis A. Camus EU [10]
E. sarmentosa (Thunb.) Trin. NU [10]
E. stolonifera A. Camus EGP [10]
E. tenella (L.) Roem. & Schult. NGP [10]
E. tenuifolia L. NP [10]
E. unioloides (Retz.) Nees ex Steud. NU [10]
E. viguieri A. Camus EU [10]
Eriochloa barbatus (Trin) S. Yadav & M. R. Almeida NU [23]
E. meyeriana (Nees) Pilg. NU [23]
E. parvispiculata C. E. Hubb. NU [23]
E. procera (Retz.) C. E. Hubb. NU [23]
E. subulifera Stapf NU [23]

(continued overleaf)

TABLE 8.21. ***continued***

Euclasta condylotricha (Steud.) Stapf NGP [17]
Eulalia villosa (Spreng.) Nees NF [17]
Festuca camusiana Saint-Yves EG [3]
F. perrieri A. Camus EGC [3]
Hackelochloa granularis (L.) Kuntze NU [17]
Halopyrum mucronatum (L.) Stapf NSa [12]
Helictotrichon arrhenatheroides (Baker) A. Camus EU [3]
Hemarthria altissima (Poir.) Stapf NGP [17]
Heteropholis benoistii A. Camus EU [17]
Heteropogon contortus (L.) P. Beauv. ex Roem. & Schult. NFG [17]
H. melanocarpus (Elliott) Benth. NI [17]
Hickelia alaotrensis A. Camus EU [4]
H. madagascariensis A. Camus ES [4]
H. perrieri (A. Camus) S. Dransf. ES [4]
Hitchcockella baronii A. Camus ES [4]
Humbertochloa bambusiuscula A. Camus & Stapf EU [2]
Hyparrhenia cymbaria (L.) Stapf NU [17]
H. diplandra (Hack.) Stapf NU [17]
H. filipendula (Hochst.) Stapf NU [17]
H. hirta (L.) Stapf NU [17]
H. newtonii (Hack.) Stapf NF [17]
H. nyassae (Rendle) Stapf NF [17]
H. rudis Stapf NU [17]
H. rufa (Nees) Stapf NFGP [17]
H. schimperi (Hochst. ex A. Rich.) Andersson ex Stapf NF [17]
H. variabilis Stapf NU [17]
Hyperthelia dissoluta (Nees ex Steud.) Clayton NF [17]
Imperata cylindrica (L) P. Beauv. NFP [17]
Isachne ciliaris A. Camus NU [7]
I. humbertiana A. Camus EU [7]
I. humicola A. Camus ES [7]
I. mauritiana Knuth. NS [7]
I. muscicola A. Camus ES [7]
Ischaemum heterotrichum Hack. NU [17]
I. koleostachys Hack. NI [17]
I. polystachyum Presl. NI [17]
I. rugosum Salisb. NP [17]
Lasiorhachis hildebrandtii (Hack.) Stapf ES [17]
L. perrieri (A. Camus) Bosser EI [17]
L. viguieri (A. Camus) Bosser EF [17]
Lecomtella madagascariensis A. Camus EIC [15]
Leersia hexandra Sw. NI [2]
L. perrieri (A. Camus) Launert NI [2]
Leptaspis zeylanica Steud. NS [1]
Leptocarydion vulpiastrum (De Not.) Stapf NU [12]
Lepturus anadabolavensis A. Camus EA [12]
L. androyensis A. Camus EU [12]
L. boinensis A. Camus EU [12]
L. humbertianus A. Camus EGA [12]
L. perrieri A. Camus EU [12]
L. radicans (Steud.) A. Camus NG [12]
L. repens (G. Forst.) R. Br. NG [12]
Loudetia filifolia Schweick. NF [14]
L. simplex (Nees) C. E. Hubb. NF [14]
Maltebrunia leersioides Kunth. ES [2]
Megastachya mucronata (Poir.) P. Beauv. NS [13]
Melinis minutiflora P. Beauv. NFP [23]
M. nerviglumis (Franch.) Zizka NU [23]
M. repens (Willd.) Zizka NFGP [23]
Merxmuellera ambalavaoensis (A. Camus) Conert EC [8]
M. macowanii (Stapf) Conert EC [8]
M. tsaratananensis (A. Camus) Conert EU [8]
Microchloa kunthii Desv. NFG [12]
Microstegium nudum (Trin.) A. Camus NS [17]
Moorochloa eruciformis (Sm.) Veldkamp NU [23]
Nastus ambrensis A. Camus EU [4]
N. aristatus A. Camus ES [4]
N. borbonicus J. F. Gmel. EU [4]
N. decaryanus A. Camus EU [4]
N. elongatus A. Camus ES [4]
N. emirnensis (Baker) A. Camus ES [4]
N. humbertianus A. Camus EU [4]
N. lokohoensis A. Camus EU [4]
N. madagascariensis A. Camus EU [4]
N. manongarivensis A. Camus EU [4]
N. perrieri A. Camus ES [4]
N. tsaratananensis A. Camus EU [4]
Neostapfiella chloridiantha A. Camus EGAP [12]
N. humbertiana A. Camus EGAP [12]
N. perrieri A. Camus EGAP [12]
Neyraudia arundinacea (L.) Henrard NFP [9]
Oldeania humbertii (A. Camus) D. Z. Li, Y. X. Zhang & Haev. ES [4]
O. ibityensis (A. Camus) D. Z. Li, Y. X. Zhang & Haev. EC [4]
O. itremoensis D. Z. Li, Y. X. Zhang & Haev. EI [4]
O. madagascariensis (A. Camus) D. Z. Li, Y. X. Zhang & Haev. ES [4]
O. marojejyensis (A. Camus) D. Z. Li, Y. X. Zhang & Haev. ES [4]
O. perrieri (A. Camus) D. Z. Li, Y. X. Zhang & Haev. ES [4]
Olyra latifolia L. NS [4]
Oplismenus burmannii (Retz.) P. Beauv. NS [20]
O. compositus (L.) P. Beauv. NS [20]
O. flavicomus Mez ES [20]
O. hirtellus (L.) P. Beauv. NS [20]
Oryza longistaminata A. Chev. & Roehr. NI [2]
O. punctata Kotschy ex Steud. NI [2]
Oxyrhachis gracillima (Baker) C. E. Hubb. NU [17]
Panicum ambositrense A. Camus ES [21]
P. andringitrense A. Camus ESC [20]
P. ankarense A. Camus EU [23]
P. brevifolium L. NGS [21]
P. capuronii A. Camus EU [21]
P. cinctum Hack. EF [22]
P. crystallinum Judz. & Voronts. EU [?]
P. cupressifolium A. Camus EFC [20]
P. danguyi A. Camus EU [20]
P. dregeanum Nees EU [22]
P. flacourtii A. Camus EU [20]

P. humbertii A. Camus ES [20]
P. humile Steud. NU [22]
P. ibitense A. Camus EF [20]
P. inconspicuum Voronts. EU [?]
P. luridum Hack. ex Scott-Elliot EFG [22]
P. malacotrichum Steud. ESP [20]
P. manongarivense A. Camus ESI [20]
P. mitopus K. Schum. NS [20]
P. novemnerve Stapf NU [22]
P. oligoadenotrichum A. Camus EU [?]
P. palackyanum A. Camus EU [20]
P. perrieri A. Camus ES [21]
P. pleianthum Peter ES [21]
P. spergulifolium A. Camus EFC [20]
P. subalbidum Knuth. NIP [22]
P. subhystrix A. Camus EF [21]
P. trichocladum K. Schum. NP [23]
P. voeltzkowii Mez EFGP [22]
P. vohitrense A. Camus ES [20]
Paratheria prostrata Griseb. NU [24]
Paspalum conjugatum L. AIGP [16]
P. dilatatum Poir. AIU [16]
P. nutans Lam. NS [16]
P. paniculatum L. AISP [16]
P. scrobiculatum L. NFG [16]
P. vaginatum Sw. NGSa [16]
P. virgatum L. AIU [16]
Pennisetum pseudotriticoides (A. Camus.) ined. NFG [24]
Pentameris andringitrensis (A. Camus) Galley & H. P. Linder EC [8]
P. humbertii (A. Camus.) Galley & H. P. Linder EU [8]
Perotis arenacea (Judz.) P. M. Peterson EA [12]
P. humbertii A. Camus EU [12]
P. indica (L.) Kuntze NU [12]
P. patens Gand. NFP [12]
Perrierbambus madagascariensis A. Camus EU [4]
P. tsarasaotrensis A. Camus EU [4]
Phragmites mauritianus NI [6]
Poa ankaratrensis A. Camus & H. Perrier EU [3]
P. annua L. AICP [3]
P. madecassa A. Camus EU [3]
P. perrieri A. Camus EU [3]
Poecilostachys bakeri (Schinz) Hubbard ES [20]
P. baronis Stapf ES [20]
P. confertiflora A. Camus ES [20]
P. geminata (Baker) Hack. ES [20]
P. gougerotiana A. Camus EU [20]
P. hildebrandtii Hack. ES [20]
P. humbertii A. Camus EU [20]
P. mainborondroensis A. Camus EU [20]
P. marojejyensis A. Camus EU [20]
Pogonarthria squarrosa (Roem. & Schult.) Pilg NF [10]
Pseudechinolaena camusiana Bosser EU [20]
P. madagascariensis (A. Camus) Bosser EU [20]
P. moratii Bosser EU [20]
P. perrieri A. Camus ES [20]
P. polystachya (Kunth.) Stapf NS [20]
P. tenuis Bosser EU [20]
Pseudobromus ambilobensis A. Camus EU [3]
P. breviligulatus Stapf ex A. Camus ES [3]
P. humbertianus A. Camus EU [3]
P. tenuifolius A. Camus EU [3]
Pseudolasiacis bathiei (A. Camus) A. Camus ES [20]
P. leptolomoides A. Camus NS [20]
P. neoperrieri (A. Camus) A. Camus ES [20]
Rhytachne rottboellioides Desv. NF [17]
Rottboellia cochinchinensis (Lour.) Clayton NP [17]
Sacciolepis africana Hubbard & Snowden NI [21]
S. curvata (L.) Chase NI [21]
S. indica (L.) Chase NGIP [21]
S. micrococca Mez NU [21]
S. myosuroides (R. Br.) A. Camus NU [21]
S. viguieri A. Camus EU [21]
Sartidia isaloensis Voronts., Razanatsoa & Besnard EP [5]
S. perrieri (A. Camus) Bourreil EU [5]
Schizachyrium bemarivense A. Camus EU [17]
S. brevifolium (Sw) Buse NF [17]
S. exile (Hochst.) Pilg. NG [17]
S. platyphyllum (Franch.) Stapf NU [17]
S. sanguineum (Retz.) Alston NF [17]
Schoenefeldia gracilis Kunth. NU [12]
Sclerodactylon macrostachyum (Benth.) A. Camus NSaP [12]
Setaria ankarensis (A. Camus.) ined. EU [24]
S. barbata (Lam.) Kunth. NP [24]
S. bathiei A. Camus EU [24]
S. bosseri A. Camus EU [24]
S. fiherenensis Bosser EU [24]
S. geminata (Forssk.) Veldkamp NU [24]
S. humbertiana A. Camus EGA [24]
S. madecassa A. Camus EP [24]
S. megaphylla (Steud.) T. Durand & Schinz NS [24]
S. perrieri A. Camus EU [24]
S. pumila (Poir.) Roem. & Schult. NGP [24]
S. sagittifolia Walp. NU [24]
S. scottii (Hack.) A. Camus EFI [24]
S. sphacelata (Schumach.) Stapf & Hubbard ex Moss NGIP [24]
S. taolanensis A. Camus EU [24]
S. vatkeana K. Schum. ESP [24]
S. verticillata (L.) P. Beauv. NP [24]
Sirochloa parvifolia (Munro) S. Dransf. EP [4]
Sokinochloa australis S. Dransf. ES [4]
S. bosseri S. Dransf. ES [4]
S. brachyclada S. Dransf. EU [4]
S. chapelieri (A. Camus) S. Dransf. ES [4]
S. chiataniae S. Dransf. EU [4]
S. perrieri (A. Camus) S. Dransf. EU [4]
S. viguieri (A. Camus) S. Dransf. ES [4]

(continued overleaf)

TABLE 8.21. ***continued***

Sorghastrum incompletum (Presl.) Nash NF [17]
Sorghum arundinaceum (Desv.) Stapf NP [17]
Sporobolus africanus (Poir.) Robyns & Tournay NU [11]
S. bosseri A. Camus EU [11]
S. centrifugus (Trin.) Nees NFG [11]
S. coromandelianus (Retz.) Kunth. NSa [11]
S. elatior Bosser EU [11]
S. fimbriatus (Trin.) Nees NU [11]
S. halophilus Bosser ESaP [11]
S. indicus (L.) R. Br. NU [11]
S. ivakoanyensis A. Camus EU [11]
S. micranthus (Steud) T. Durand & Schinz NU [11]
S. molleri Hack. NP [11]
S. paniculatus (Trin.) T. Durand & Schinz NG [11]
S. perrieri A. Camus EU [11]
S. piliferus (Trin.) Knuth. NF [11]
S. pyramidalis P. Beauv. NGP [11]
S. rigidifolius (Trin.) Mez ex Veldkamp NU [11]
S. schoenoides (L.) P. M. Peterson NU [11]
S. stapfianus Gand. NU [11]
S. subtilis Kunth. NU [11]
S. subulatus Hack. NU [11]
S. tenuissimus (Schrank.) Kuntze NU [11]
S. tsiafajavonensis A. Camus EU [11]
S. virginicus (L.) Kunth. NGSa [11]
Stenotaphrum dimidiatum (L.) Brongn. NG [24]
S. oostachyum Baker EG [24]
S. unilaterale Baker EG [24]
Styppeiochloa hitchcockii (A. Camus) Cope EF [6]
Themeda quadrivalvis (L.) Kuntze NF [17]
Thuarea involuta (G. Forst.) R. Br. ex Sm. NGSaP [23]
T. perrieri A. Camus EGSa [23]
Trachypogon spicatus (L. f.) Kuntze NF [17]
Tragus berteronianus Schult. NGAP [12]
Trichanthecium brazzavillense (Franch.) Zuloaga & Morrone NF [21]
T. parvifolium (Lam.) Zuloaga & Morrone NP [21]
Tricholaena monachne (Trin.) Stapf & Hubbard NFP [23]
Trichopteryx dregeana Nees NI [14]
Tripogonella minima (A. Rich.) P. M. Peterson & Romasch. NU [12]
Trisetopsis elongata (Hoschst. A. Rich.) Röser & A. Wölk NC [3]
T. milanjiana (Rendle) Röser & A. Wölk NC [3]
Tristachya betsileensis A. Camus EF [14]
T. humbertii A. Camus EFG [14]
T. isalensis (A. Camus) ined. EFG [14]
Urelytrum agropyroides (Hack.) Hack. NF [17]
Urochloa arrecta (Hack. ex T. Durand & Schinz) Morrone & Zuloaga NG [23]
U. brizantha (A. Rich.) Webster NG [23]
U. deflexa (Schumach.) H. Scholz NGAP [23]
U. distachya (L.) Stapf NGAP [23]
U. eminii (Mez) Davidse NU [23]
U. glumaris (Trin.) Veldkamp NU [23]
U. maxima (Jacq.) R. D. Webster NFGP [23]
U. panicoides P. Beauv. NP [23]
U. plantaginea (Link) R. D. Webster NU [23]
U. ramosa (L.) T. Q. Nguyen NU [23]
U. reptans (L.) Stapf NGAP [23]
U. trichopus (Hochst.) Stapf NP [23]
Valiha diffusa S. Dransf. ESP [4]
V. perrieri (A. Camus.) S. Dransf. ES [4]
Viguierella madagascariensis A. Camus EGAP [10]
Yvesia madagascariensis A. Camus EFP [23]
Zoysia matrella (L.) Merr. NGSa [11]

Notes: E = endemic to Madagascar and nearby islands. N = either native or unknown origins. AI = introduced origins (please note this is very poorly known and not always evidence based; also see introduction to the Poaceae contribution). Data on ecological filters applies to Lehmann et al. (see pp. 152–68). U = species that have not been assigned to an ecological filter, often because the species has not been seen in the field by the authors. Species assigned to eight ecological filters: S = a species that grows under shade; P = a pioneer species; F = a species able to prosper in the face of repeated defoliation by fire; G = either 1) a species able to prosper in the face of repeated concentrated grazing, or 2) unpalatable hardy grasses remaining in place following overgrazing and degradation; I = grasses that cope with seasonal inundation or edaphic conditions in which root systems are functionally inundated, e.g., soils with high clay content forming edaphic water bodies. Both standing water and seasonal inundation are included in this water-associated group; C = cold climate, C_3 montane grasses; A = arid ecosystem grasses; and Sa = species predominantly occurring in saline and salty systems. Among these, F, G, I, C, A, and Sa contain potential species pool for grassy ecosystems, as well as Poaceae that do not form the bulk of grassy ecosystems. Clade numbers (see text and Figure 8.28) are given in square brackets. * = preliminary assignment based on unpublished molecular data. ? = species from unknown clades, which were not included in Figure 8.28. Please note the preliminary nature of this list, which was compiled from all herbarium specimens of Malagasy Poaceae in the Paris (P) and Tsimbazaza (TAN) herbaria (Rabarivola et al. 2019a, 2019b, 2019c). Extensive research is required to reconcile this list with the published checklists of Vorontsova et al. (2016).

A full treatment of all the species known from the island has not been attempted to date and most groups are in need of revision; research is required to reconcile the preliminary checklist published by Vorontsova et al. (2016) with the herbarium-derived species list in Table 8.21. At least 15 species are only known from a single collection. Despite dedicated searches, 18 species have not been found in the field (Vorontsova et al. 2020); *Sartidia perrieri* and *Chasechloa egregia* are likely extinct (Vorontsova et al. 2015; Silva et al. 2017). Malagasy grasses are poorly known compared with those in neighboring areas where complete treatments are available: *Flora Zambesiaca* (Launert 1971; Clayton 1989; Cope 1999, 2002), southern African grasses (Fish et al. 2015), and *Flora of the Mascarenes* (Renvoize 2019).

Separation between the study of wild and endemic species and introduced or cultivated grasses can be unhelpful for understanding Madagascar's living grass flora because many native species are pioneers and are frequently mistaken for introduced species, while cultivated and weedy grasses often appear similar to native and endemic species. This contribution tries to consider all Poaceae and associated human activities together, as they are found in modern-day Madagascar. Taxonomic work on Poaceae, related herbarium collections, and iNaturalist (2020) are unfortunately disconnected from more applied resources working to identify and control agricultural weeds (Husson et al. 2013) and the weed tracking citizen science system WIKTROP and WIKWIO (Le Bourgeois et al. 2019). Mid-20th century agricultural experimental stations left limited specimens that record their work in the Tsimbazaza herbarium, while modern commercial suppliers of decorative and forage plants introduce multiple cultivars without any records made by the government or scientific institutions. The real diversity of Poaceae on Madagascar is surely far greater than that recorded in this contribution.

THE MAJOR GROUPS OF GRASSES ON MADAGASCAR

Of the 12 Poaceae subfamilies (Kellogg 2015; Soreng et al. 2017), 10 are found on Madagascar. We present 24 major groups corresponding to these subfamilies or lower taxonomic ranks (Figure 8.28). Hackel et al. (2018) used 73% of the Malagasy grass species to build a phylogeny and estimated at least 69 dispersal events related to Madagascar that resulted in endemic lineages. Most of these dispersals originated in Africa and occurred during the last 20 million years. C_4 photosynthesis, with its high productivity in hot and dry climates, has evolved multiple times from the C_3 pathway in grasses, and species of most C_4 lineages are found on Madagascar. Of the C_4 species, around 28% are endemic, while in C_3 grasses, the proportion is higher (68%). The latter is due to two large endemic C_3 radiations, which are detailed below under Bambusoideae subtribe Hickeliinae and the panicoid "Madagascar shade clade" (Clade 20 below; Figure 8.28).

Clade 1 (Subfamily Pharoideae) Early Grasses

Of the three earliest-diverging Poaceae subfamilies, all C_3, only one species is found on the island, the paleotropical *Leptaspis zeylanica*, which has unusually inflated female lemmas and is found in the dark understory of northern moist evergreen forests.

Clade 2 (Subfamily Oryzoideae) Rice and Relatives

These are C_3 grasses occupying mostly wet and shady habitats. The Asian rice *Oryza sativa* arrived on Madagascar by the 1st century CE with Austronesian migrants and is the only cereal consistently recovered from Madagascar's archeological sites (Beaujard 2011; Boivin et al. 2013). Rice has been the mainstay of the modern human diet (e.g., Crowther et al. 2016) with riziculture occupying a prominent position in Madagascar's history and present-day society. Rice paddies provide habitat for numerous weedy grasses including native perennial African rice *O. longistaminata* and *O. punctata* (which can serve as occasional famine food, Bosser 1969). *Leersia hexandra* is a common weedy semiaquatic grass with spikelets resembling those of rice; the awned *L. perrieri*, an extant species on Mayotte and considered Endangered under International Union for the Conservation of Nature (IUCN) Red List criteria (Phillipson 2017), was recently found near Mahajanga. Endemic low-altitude moist evergreen forest genus *Maltebrunia* resembles palm seedlings; it has white rice spikelets and tolerates deeper shade than any other grass on the island. Sagittate-leaved *Humbertochloa bambusiuscula* looks and functions like a shrub rather than a grass and is abundant in many dry deciduous forest habitats. The first record of the weed *Ehrharta stipoides* was made by Vorontsova et al. (2014).

Clade 3 (Subfamily Pooideae) Temperate Grasses

These are C_3 grasses and comparatively uncommon on Madagascar since they are climatically restricted to higher elevation areas. They nevertheless include economically critical cereals: breadwheat *Triticum aestivum* and barley *Hordeum vulgare* from which beer is made. *Avena* is cultivated as forage. Perrier de la Bâthie (1933) judged all of these to be recent introductions since they lack Malagasy names. *Poa annua* is now common across disturbed parts of the Central Highlands and is thought to be an accidental introduction with European vegetable seeds (Perrier de la Bâthie 1933). Madagascar's mountains are home to the endemic *P. ankaratrensis* and *P. perrieri*. *Brachypodium* is common at forest margins in the Central Highlands and may include up to three endemic species pending taxonomic revision. The endemic *Calamagrostis emirnensis* is easy to find along Central Highland streams but the endemic *Agrostis* seems rarer. Broad-leaved *Pseudobromus* is common under forest understory but taxonomic work on it is challenging due to the florets falling off type specimens; members of this genus have now been shown to be a part of the broad-leaved *Festuca* clade (Minaya et al. 2017). The fine-leaved endemic *Festuca camusiana* is common in more open areas of the Central Highlands and is also in need of taxonomic revision. The African *Trisetopsis elongata* (previously *Helictotrichon elongata*) occurs in similar highland environments and can be difficult to distinguish from *Festuca* when fresh.

Clade 4 (Subfamily Bambusoideae) Bamboos

Bamboos flower rarely and can appear vegetatively homogenous, which is why species recognition in this group tends to be even more challenging than for other grasses. Bamboos introduced from Asia are tolerant of drier habitats than Malagasy natives and are usually the first seen by a visitor to Madagascar, especially the invasive running bamboo *Phyllostachys aurea*, planted as hedges in the Central Highlands and in the east. Pantropical clumping *Bambusa vulgaris* (with green and yellow culm varieties) is common in these same areas, mainly along river margins; the culms are used for construction and making boats. *Bambusa multiplex* is cultivated as a hedging plant, and the giant bamboo *Dendrocalamus giganteus* is planted on the eastern coast. Another large introduced bamboo, *Gigantochloa pseudoarundinacea/verticillata* (*volo surat*), is planted around Maroantsetra and is used for making the Malagasy musical instrument, the *valiha*. The most commonly collected Malagasy bamboo is the herbaceous scandent *Olyra latifolia*, which has asymmetric leaf bases.

Madagascar's almost endemic tropical bamboo subtribe Hickeliinae is one of the oldest endemic Poaceae lineages on the island and estimated to have arrived around 8.11 million years ago (Mya)

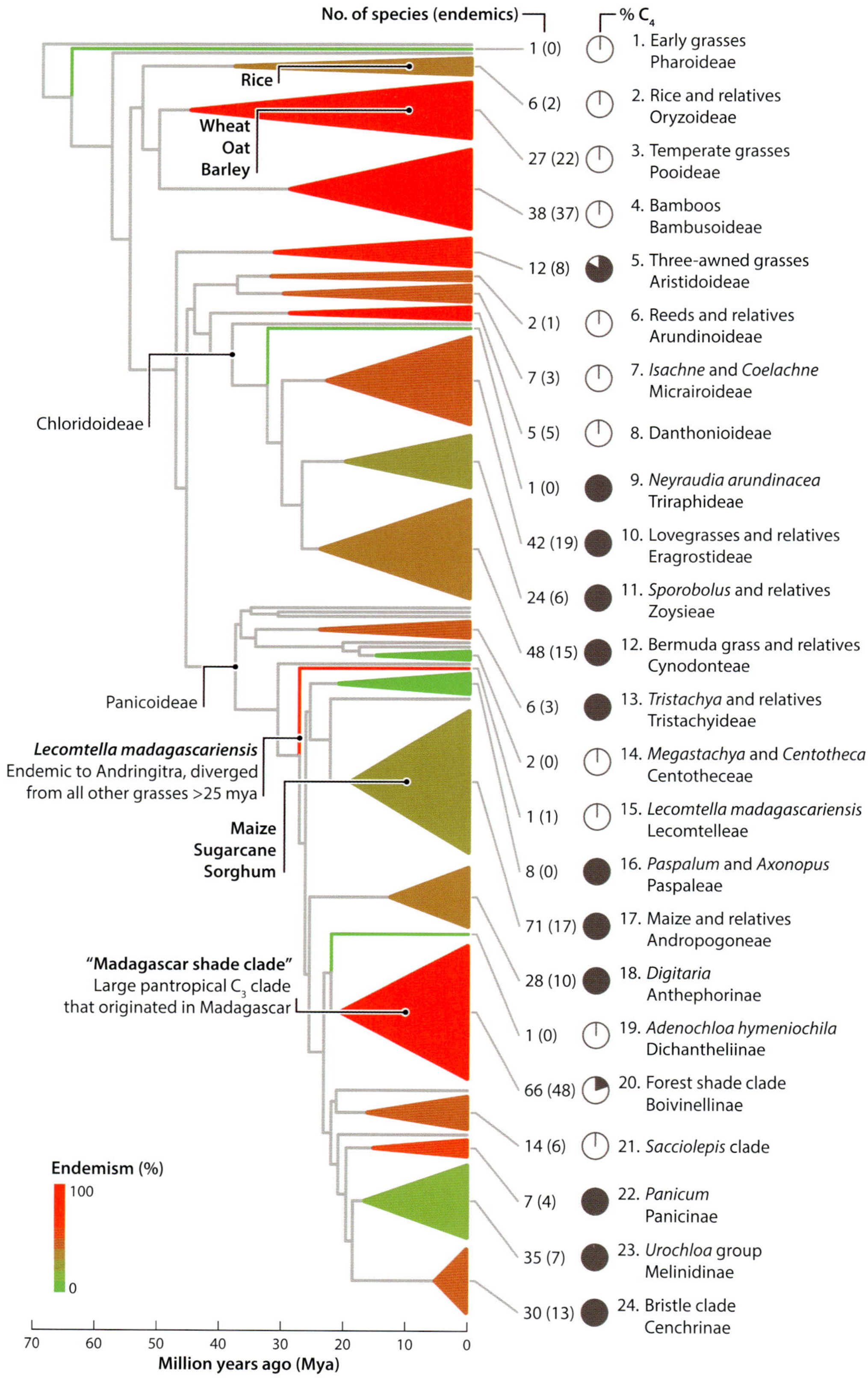

FIGURE 8.28 **Evolutionary history and present-day diversity of Madagascar's grasses. Timeline indicates the global origin of lineages, but only the wild species present on the island are included. The size of triangles is proportional to species number, and the color of the triangles indicates endemicity at the species level. Gray lines indicate ancestral lineages and modern-day lineages with no representatives on Madagascar. Numbers indicate how many wild and endemic species occur on Madagascar, circles show proportion of C_4 species, and small squares represent presence in different ecoregions of Madagascar. Clade numbers correspond to the text and to the species listed in Table 8.21. The most economically significant grasses, as well as notable examples of endemic lineages described in the text, are marked.** (SOURCES: Data from Vorontsova et al. 2016; Hackel et al. 2018; Rabarivola 2019a, 2019b, 2019c, 2019d; and J. Morton 2019; unpublished data from Jan Hackel was also used to assign a greater number of species to clades.)

(Hackel et al. 2018). This subtribe is characterized by having erect or climbing forms, determinate (terminating in a flower) inflorescences, zigzag culms, and nodes dipping downwards at the branch complement. Their taxonomy has been documented by Soejatmi Dransfield (1994, 1997, 1998, 2002, 2003, 2016), and their evolution is being studied by Rivontsoa Andrimalala Rakotonasolo. The most abundant endemic species is *Valiha diffusa* (*vologazy*), which has long-necked rhizomes and erect culms with arching tips; it is found in moist evergreen forests and on disturbed land on the eastern coast (S. Dransfield 1998). Culms of *vologazy* are utilized for making baskets and walls and roofs for houses; the leaf blades are eaten by bamboo lemurs (Tan 1999). The superficially similar *Perrierbambus* occurs in lowland western dry deciduous forests and needs further study.

The climbing genus *Nastus*, with about 10 species, occurs in medium-altitude moist evergreen forests and may be polyphyletic; it is currently being revised by Soejatmi Dransfield. *Sirochloa parvifolia* (S. Dransfield 2002) is an erect bamboo that becomes scrambling; it is found growing in white-sand forests on the east coast. The unique monotypic *Decaryochloa diadelpha*, which has the largest floret found in Poaceae (S. Dransfield 1997), is a medium-altitude moist evergreen forest climber. *Sokinochloa*, with about seven species, climbs under medium-altitude moist evergreen forest understory and produces globose inflorescences (S. Dransfield 2016). Similar capitate inflorescences are also found on the more robust and more erect *Cathariostachys*, which has long-necked rhizomes and consists of two or three species found growing in lowland to medium-altitude moist evergreen forests (S. Dransfield 1998). *Cathariostachys capitata* (*volozatsy*, *volosy*), *C. madagascariensis* (*voloto*, *volosangana*), and a species related to the latter and found in Ranomafana, are the main food sources for the bamboo lemurs (Tan 1999). *Hickelia* is a medium-altitude moist evergreen forest genus distinguishable by its glumes, which are often shiny after fertilization (S. Dransfield 1994).

The second group of Madagascar's endemic bamboos is the temperate *Oldeania*, previously placed in the genera *Arundinaria* or *Yushania*; these are erect species of montane understory, with one riverine highland endemic, *O. itremoensis*, and one rocky outcrop species known only from Ibity and Itremo, *O. ibityensis*, which has never been seen in flower (Y. X. Zhang et al. 2017). Many of Madagascar's mysterious bamboos still have not been identified or named; several taxa are awaiting description.

Clade 5 (Subfamily Aristidoideae) Three-awned Grasses

This is a small subfamily of grasses with distinctive triple awns and an ecological significance disproportionate to its species diversity, especially in dry pastures. The largely unpalatable fibrous *Aristida rufescens*, *A. similis*, and *A. tenuissima* are products of a single endemic radiation 8.11 Mya (Vorontsova 2013; Besnard et al. 2014), so abundant they are listed as markers of eastern and montane "savannas" by Koechlin (1993) and Rakotoarimanana (2008). Alongside the rest of this C_4 genus, *Aristida* species concepts remain difficult, and it is possible that *A. rufescens* (larger) and *A. similis* (smaller) are in fact the same species. *Aristida adscensionis* is abundant across the southeast. The identity and presence of many of Madagascar's *Aristida* species, such as "*A. junciformis*," remain doubtful and need further work. The morphologically similar but C_3 genus *Sartidia* is rare in comparison and likely more vulnerable to fire. *Sartidia perrieri* has been declared extinct while *S. isaloensis* has recently been seen on the sandstone cliffs of Isalo (Vorontsova et al. 2015; Rakotomalala et al. 2021).

Clade 6 (Subfamily Arundinoideae) Reeds and Relatives

Phragmites mauritianus (African Spiny-leaved Reed) dominates streambeds and lake shores across Madagascar. There are no confirmed records of the invasive giant reed *Arundo donax* on the island. The related resurrection grass *Styppeiochloa* probably represents several endemic species rather than one (J. Teisher, unpublished data).

Clade 7 (Subfamily Micrairoideae) *Isachne* and *Coelachne*

This group includes a radiation of C_3 shade grasses resembling *Panicum* but capable of producing two caryopses in each spikelet. *Isachne mauritiana* is a common moist evergreen forest understory climber with long culms and open panicles, related to several rare forest endemic species. *Coelachne* species are small aquatic grasses forming floating mats.

Clade 8 (Subfamily Danthonioideae) *Merxmuellera* and *Pentameris*

Montane austrotropical tufted perennials *Merxmuellera* and *Pentameris* constitute a significant biomass component of Madagascar's open montane grasslands above 1500 m, and most species are endemic. Montane grasslands remain poorly studied partly due to difficult access, and the exact number of locally occurring grass species has not been confirmed in spite of extensive recent work on this subfamily (e.g., Linder et al. 2010). The commonly cultivated pampas grass *Cortaderia selloana* has been introduced as a decorative plant near Antsirabe but does not seem to be naturalized or invasive to date.

Clade 9 (Tribe Triraphideae) *Neyraudia arundinacea*

This is an African shrub-like, fire-loving grass with woody culms and fluffy winter inflorescences that is common across Madagascar and often mistaken for *Phragmites* although it grows in drier places, often on rocks.

Clade 10 (Tribe Eragrostideae) Lovegrasses and Relatives

Eragrostis is one of the largest tropical grass genera and it occurs in all warm parts of Madagascar. It can be difficult to identify to species. It is in need of revision and the number of endemics remains unclear. The most commonly seen species are the paleotropical roadside weeds *E. tenuifolia* and *E. tenella*. *Eragrostis tef* (teff is a staple cereal crop in Ethiopia) has been cultivated in the Central

Highlands since the early 20th century and is said to have escaped from cultivation (Perrier de la Bâthie 1933), although there seem to be no herbarium records (Rabarivola et al. 2019a, 2019b). The southwestern *E. chabouisii* appears to be one of the oldest endemic C_4 grass lineages on Madagascar, diverging from other *Eragrostis* some 18 Mya. Other endemic *Eragrostis* species are prominant in Madagascar's ecosystems: tiny endemic annual *E. capuronii* is found in the southwest, and *E. lateritica* is typical of the Central Highlands. The *Eragrostis* clade includes morphologically dissimilar taxa: Madagascar's unusual monophyletic genus *Viguierella* (*V. madagascariensis*) of dry western areas, which has awns and every spikelet subtended by a bract (Figure 8.29e, Vorontsova and Rakotoarisoa 2014); the African *Pogonarthria squarrosa*, common in southern Madagascar, with its spikelets arranged on racemes; and the African *Enneapogon cenchroides*, which has fluffy inflorescences due to many plumose awns on each lemma, is common in southern Madagascar.

Clade 11 (Tribe Zoysieae) *Sporobolus* and Relatives

Sporobolus is an ecologically important C_4 genus much in need of study, which is difficult due to the blurry boundaries between its species. Malagasy *Sporobolus* species are diverse but seem to include only one endemic clade, which includes the salt-loving west coast species *S. halophilus* and a related undescribed species (Hackel et al. 2018); the disturbance-resilient *S. pyramidalis*, which is common across the island; and *S. virginicus*, which forms coastal ground cover similarly to the related but rarer *Zoysia matrella*.

Clade 12 (Tribe Cynodonteae) Bermuda Grass and Relatives

The creeping ground cover, forage plant, and weed *Cynodon* is abundant in all disturbed areas of Madagascar except the high mountains. The numerous introduced cultivars have interbred with native *Cynodon* so it is difficult to establish a species classification. *Cynodon dactylon* in the Central Highlands is particularly resilient to grazing and trampling due to its underground rhizomes, which can spread independently of its aboveground horizontal stolons; other species of *Cynodon* lack the rhizomes and seem to be more prevalent at lower elevations. Both *C. dactylon* and the similarly omnipresent and disturbance-resilient *Eleusine indica* are principal weeds according to Husson et al. (2013); the latter is listed as a foreign introduction by Perrier de la Bâthie (1933). African Finger Millet *E. coracana* has been cultivated as a food crop in the west (Perrier de la Bâthie 1933).

The widespread genus *Chloris* also contains a mixture of common, introduced forage species (*C. barbata* and *C. gayana*, Bosser 1969), and common, weedy, native, likely pioneer grasses, such as *C. pycnothrix*, which has rounded leaf apices, common in Antananarivo. Phylogenetic studies suggest that the characteristic spiny forest endemic *C. humbertiana*, which has winged lemmas, is nested in the endemic, creeping ground cover genus of arid places, *Neostapfiella*, and that the similar *Daknopholis boivinii* originated on Madagascar and then spread to surrounding islands and the African coast. The ancestor of *Neostapfiella*, *Daknopholis*, and *C. humbertiana* arrived on Madagascar about 8 Mya (Vorontsova and Rakotoarisoa 2014; Hackel et al. 2018).

The creeping coastal grass *Lepturus* has inflorescences like green tubes that are not prominent. Madagascar is home to the common Indian Ocean regional species *L. repens* and *L. radicans* but also an unconfirmed number of endemics including the distinctive southern endemic *L. anadabolavensis*.

Perhaps Madagascar's strangest grass is the spiny dry thicket endemic *Decaryella madagascariensis*, a small annual that drops its hairy awned spikelets together with a long pedicel; the dispersal mode is unknown (Vorontsova and Rakotoarisoa 2014). The stoloniferous sandy beach grass *Sclerodactylon macrostachyum* (Figure 8.29f), with bulky inflorescences, may be part of the same endemic radiation as the rare western endemic *Acrachne perrieri* (Hackel et al. 2018). *Ctenium concinnum*, which is common in highland grasslands, has racemes that dry into pretty, curved shapes. *Craspedorhachis africana* is also common in Central Highland grasslands and has a recognizable inflorescence shape, and its racemes are held horizontally. A pretty weed of disturbed areas, *Perotis patens* is commonly collected because of its ovate leaves, which are sometimes striped, and delicate fluffy white spikes; its rare dry spiny thicket endemic relative *P. arenacea* is less distinctive. *Dactyloctenium* has charismatic star-shaped inflorescences with pointed raceme apices and is abundant in warm low-elevation places—but distinguishing its species is tricky. *Tragus berteronianus* is a common southern weedy grass with hooked hairs on its glumes that attach the spikelet groups to passing animals.

Clade 13 (Tribe Tristachyideae) *Tristachya* and Relatives

These are largely perennial bunchgrasses, ecologically significant for central and montane grasslands. Madagascar's *Tristachya* form a single endemic radiation 5–7 million years old (Hackel et al. 2018): *T. betsileensis* is restricted to open grassland on quartz around Itremo (Nanjarisoa et al. 2017), while the spiny-leaved *T. humbertii* and *Danthoniopsis isalensis* (to be moved to genus *Tristachya*) are endemic to rocky outcrops around Isalo (Hackel et al. 2018; Rakotomalala et al. 2021). *Loudetia simplex* dominates extensive stretches of central Madagascar and has been shown to be genetically clearly distinct from the populations in continental Africa (Hagl et al. 2020).

Clade 14 (Tribe Centotheceae) *Megastachya* and *Centotheca*

Megastachya and *Centotheca* (Centotheceae) are both common broad-leaved C_3 forest grasses with spikelets resembling those of *Eragrostis*.

Clade 15 (Tribe Lecomtelleae) *Lecomtella madagascariensis*

The genus *Lecomtella* is thought to be a relict of the first Poaceae radiation among the extant lineages to reach Madagascar, possibly 20–30 Mya (Besnard et al. 2013). *Lecomtella madagascariensis* (Figure 8.29a) is restricted to the Andringitra Massif and produces only a few caryopses per inflorescence; it is apparently eaten by the bird *Foudia madagascariensis* (Madagascar Fody).

FIGURE 8.29 **Endemic grasses of Madagascar. A) *Lecomtella madagascariensis*, Lecomtelleae, at Andringitra; B) *Cyphochlaena madagascariensis*, Madagascar shade clade, at Ambilomagodro; C) *Thuarea perrieri*, Melinidinae, at Ankarana; D) *Setaria madecassa*, Cenchrinae, at Ambanja; E) *Viguierella madagascariensis*, Eragrostideae, at Manongarivo; and F) *Sclerodactylon macrostachyum*, Chloridoideae, at Cap Sainte Marie.** (PHOTOS by M. S. Vorontsova.)

Clade 16 (Tribe Paspaleae) *Paspalum* and *Axonopus*

Paspalum and *Axonopus* are Neotropical genera with common lawn, forage, and weedy presence in mesic and wet parts of Madagascar. Several of Madagascar's *Paspalum* species, with their round spikelets, are originally forage plants introduced from the New World; *P. dilatatum* was a forage introduction by the French colonial agricultural service (Perrier de la Bâthie 1933). The common *P. scrobiculatum* seems to be a native rangeland grass common in the Central Highlands. *Axonopus compressus* is a nutritious broad-leaved lawn grass and forage species originally from the Americas; it is commonly mistaken for *Digitaria* but has rounded leaf apices.

Clade 17 (Tribe Andropogoneae)

Sugarcane Clade (Subtribe Saccharinae)

The date of introduction of sugarcane (*Saccharum officinarum*) remains undocumented but it was grown in east Africa during the Swahili period between the 11th and 16th centuries (Boivin et al. 2013). The related genus *Sorghum* is notoriously complex. *Sorghum bicolor* is an African multipurpose dry land cereal thought to have been an early introduction by Bantu-speaking migrants around 1000 CE; African sorghums and millets seem to have been absent from Madagascar and the Comoros before this date (Beaujard 2011; Crowther et al. 2016). Its wild relative is *S. arundinaceum*. Multiple *Sorghum* forage cultivars were introduced to Madagascar by 20th-century experimental stations and earlier (Bosser 1969); modern forage cultivars are becoming available as high productivity fodder (W. Truter, unpublished data). No modern study of Madagascar's sorghums has been attempted. *Lasiorhachis* is an attractive endemic Central Highland genus related to sorghum, whose three species diversified into distinct habitats (Vorontsova et al. 2019). *Eulalia villosa* and *Trachypogon spicatus* are not endemic but likely associated with natural grasslands in the Central Highlands.

One of the IUCN's top 100 weeds in the world and a principal agricultural weed (Husson et al. 2013) is *Imperata cylindrica*, with its fluffy white inflorescences and bright red leaf apices commonly seen on roadsides after fire. It is a legendary plant in invasion science, driving up fire temperatures above 500°C and spreading vegetatively from pieces of its rhizomes, which form dense masses (e.g., Burrell et al. 2015). Commonly assumed to be an introduced plant, the origins of *I. cylindrica* on Madagascar have not actually been demonstrated.

Subtribe Andropogoninae

Most wild C_4 Andropogoninae tend to occupy mesic mid- and low-elevation ecosystems and have a pyrogenic, perennial, erect bunchgrass habit, often dominating wetter open grasslands of both Africa and Madagascar. *Hyparrhenia* and *Cymbopogon* are both common speciose genera with no endemic members, and their diversity needs further study. The aromatic lemongrass *C. citratus*, common across Madagascar and thought to be an ancient introduction (Perrier de la Bâthie 1933), has vegetative parts that are unusual in the otherwise homogenous *Cymbopogon* genus. *Schizachyrium* has ecological importance but is difficult taxonomically and requires further attention. At least three independent origins of endemic *Andropogon* are documented, including a recently described productive, creeping, pasture species, *A. itremoensis* (Vorontsova et al. 2013; Hackel et al. 2018).

Themeda is abundant to dominant in northwestern Madagascar in the wet season and presents an excellent example of how the origins of grasses can be misinterpreted. Perrier de la Bâthie (1933) described its rapid invasion into Ambongo and Boina in 1920–1921 after being unknown in the area prior to 1914, leading Morat (1973) to designate it as a recent introduction, and yet phylogenetic reconstruction suggests that *Themeda* arrived on Madagascar about 1.5 Mya, even earlier than its arrival in Africa (Dunning et al. 2017). According to Husson et al. (2013), *Heteropogon contortus* (*danga*, also known as spear grass) is a principal agricultural weed, dominating many heavily grazed pastures; it injures cattle with its propagules of multiple spikelets twisted together with their hairy awns and sharp outward-pointing calli, which penetrate skin. The closely related and similar *Bothriochloa* and *Dichanthium* are weedy, low-elevation species with finger-like inflorescences.

Maize and Relatives

The cultivation of corn or maize (*Zea mays*) requires less water than rice, and this crop is thought to have arrived on Madagascar comparatively late, in the 18th century (Perrier de la Bâthie 1933), becoming a cash crop in the 1930s (Scales 2011). Vetiver (*Chrysopogon zizanioides*, previously known as *Vetiveria zizanioides*) is planted extensively for soil stabilization as well as decoration, but according to Perrier de la Bâthie (1933) it was not brought to Madagascar until the French colonial era. The smell of vetiver roots and the derivative oil is important in Malagasy culture. The narrow endemic *C. humbertianus*, restricted to the area around Cap Sainte Marie, is a close relative of *C. serrulatus*, which is common in the Central Highlands but is not closely related to vetiver. *Coix lacryma-jobi*, with its distinctive shiny white-gray utricles, is used for making necklaces but does not seem to be eaten on Madagascar (Bosser 1969). *Rottboellia cochinchinensis*, a principal weed (Husson et al. 2013), is a tall annual of humid areas that is famous for stinging hairs on its leaf sheaths. *Urelytrum agropyroides* is another native of upland natural grasslands and is easily recognizable by its inflorescence that resembles a fish skeleton when mature. *Elionurus tristis* is an elegant endemic of Central Highland grasslands (Bosser 1969) but, oddly, was listed as an introduced species by Perrier de la Bâthie (1933).

Many of the following grasses are characteristic of wet areas: *Ischaemum rugosum* is a likely introduced, easily recognizable weed of rice fields; other members of the genus are native riverine grasses and share the characteristic racemes, which are flattened on one side. The attractive Central Highland endemic *Arthraxon antsirabensis* can be found along streams and roadside ditches. *Arundinella nepalensis* is a coarse perennial sometimes dominating swampy highland areas. *Dimeria* seems to be a group of endemic aquatic grasses, but they have never been taxonomically revised.

Clade 18 (Subtribe Anthephorinae) *Digitaria*

Digitaria is a common forage plant and weed of all climates on Madagascar and has small spikelets arranged on linear racemes resembling fingers. It is speciose and challenging to identify. The *Digitaria* species inventory remains incomplete: the rhizomatous endemic *D. humbertii* may actually be the same species as the problematic east African weed *D. abyssinica*.

Clade 19 (Subtribe Dichantheliinae) *Adenochloa hymeniochila*

Adenochloa hymeniochila is a common trailing aquatic grass growing in streams; it was previously placed in *Panicum* (Vorontsova 2018).

Clade 20 (Subtribe Boivinellinae) The Forest Shade Clade

The "Madagascar shade clade," within the forest shade clade, is thought be the largest Poaceae radiation on Madagascar (Hackel et al. 2018), and arrived an estimated 15–19 Mya. It diversified to give rise to C_3, then subsequently dispersed again to other continents and diversified further. Its species are predominantly broader-leaved inhabitants of forest edges and understory. Creeping, broad-leaved *Poecilostachys* (all but one of its species restricted to Madagascar) species form the common ground cover of medium-altitude moist evergreen forests, and the species delimitation of its numerous endemics remains unresolved. Its relative *Oplismenus* is vegetatively similar and has a much broader distribution range, both on Madagascar and elsewhere, occupying less shaded gaps and forest edges. *Oplismenus hirtellus* displays the rare phenomenon of gland secretion on its sticky awns, likely to aid grain dispersal; it is part of the same species complex as *O. undulatifolius* and *O. compositus*, which dispersed across the world. *Oplismenus burmannii* belongs to a northern Malagasy subclade that could represent distinct endemic taxa related to the western endemic dry forest genus *Cyphochlaena* (Figure 8.29b).

Pseudolasiacis is an endemic genus of three climbing and scrambling species of highland and western forests (Bosser and Florens 1999). *Chasechloa* is an endemic genus of deciduous forest grasses with inflorescences resembling toothbrushes and an oil-rich appendage on the upper floret, indicating ant-mediated seed dispersal; *C. egregia* has only been collected once, in Lokobe, and is likely extinct (Silva et al. 2017). All species of *Pseudechinolaena* are endemic except for one, and they have evolved a spectacular diversity of wings, bridles, and awns for dispersal (Bosser 1975). *Cyrtococcum* and *Acroceras* are common forest edge genera with numerous endemics including the common and attractive *C. deltoideum*, common in damp lawns in Antananarivo.

Many other unique and sometimes bizarre endemic grasses also belong to this clade but were previously described under polyphyletic genera and their names will be changed as taxonomic revisions advance. Only a few notable examples are listed here. *Panicum cupressifolium* (not a member of *Panicum sensu stricto* in the Panicineae) functions as a woody shrub resembling *Erica* species and is related to the other Andringitra (Madagascar's best place for odd grasses) endemic *P. spergulifolium*, which is the dominant ground cover of the Plateau d'Andohariana, at around 2000 m elevation (Vorontsova 2018). *Panicum ibitense* occurs under *Uapaca bojeri* trees, stores its food in bulbous underground storage organs, and drops its leaves in the dry season. The rare southern *Brachiaria fragrans* has scented inflorescences. *Brachiaria tsiafajavonensis* carpets forest understory and often has purple-brown stripes on its spikelets. *Panicum mitopus* and its endemic relatives hold their spikelets in clusters with distinctive dichotomous branching.

Outside this highly endemic C_3 group, the forest shade clade includes the common C_4 genus of wet habitats *Echinochloa*, which usually lacks ligules and has three species listed as significant rice paddy weeds by Husson et al. (2013): *E. colona* (annual, common in puddles across Madagascar), *E. pyramidalis* (rhizomatous in rice paddies), and *E. crus-galli*; species boundaries in this genus are difficult to define. The common coastal ground cover of Madagascar and nearshore islands is *Acroceras hubbardii*, which seems to belong in *Echinochloa* (Hackel et al. 2018). *Alloteropsis semialata*, whose Malagasy and other tropical populations are C_4 but which has C_3 populations in Southern Africa, most likely reached Madagascar once around 0.7 Mya (P.-A. Christin, unpublished data).

Clade 21 *Sacciolepis* Clade

Grasses with flattened spikelets with prominent veins are placed in *Sacciolepis*, which is usually associated with damp places; this genus is in need of revision to confirm the presence of endemics such as *Sacciolepis viguieri*. Related to *Sacciolepis* but taxonomically not well resolved is a group of *Panicum sensu lato* species, all C_3: the African *Trichanthecium brazzavillense*, and the endemic *P. capuronii*, *P. perrieri*, *P. ambositrense*, and *P. subhystrix* (Hackel et al. 2018; Vorontsova 2018; Zuloaga et al. 2018; also see next section on *Panicum*).

Clade 22 (Subtribe Panicinae) *Panicum*

The simplest panicoid grass morphology is an open panicle with panicoid spikelets. These grasses were traditionally placed in the large polyphyletic genus *Panicum*, but some species are now assigned to *Trichanthecium* and *Urochloa* although generic rearrangement is incomplete (Vorontsova 2018). Similar grasses with a small swelling under their spikelets are currently called *Eriochloa* but are also likely to be moved to *Urochloa*. *Panicum* in the strict sense is now understood to include only a small number of C_4 species (Zuloaga et al. 2018). The most ecologically significant endemic radiation of *Panicum sensu stricto* on Madagascar is that of *P. voeltzkowii* (dry, low elevations and surrounding islands), *P. luridum* (Central Highlands), and *P. cinctum* (wet Central Highlands; Vorontsova 2018).

Clade 23 (Subtribe Melinidinae) *Urochloa* Group

Urochloa maxima (previously called *Panicum maximum*) is a familiar and remarkably variable roadside weed with multiple Malagasy ecotypes, said to have been introduced from Africa (Bosser 1969) but also likely to contain native lineages, including species such as *P. mahafalense* (Vorontsova 2018). Two of Madagascar's most prominent weeds also belong to this group: *Melinis repens*, frequently collected thanks to its pretty pink spikelets; and *M. minutiflora*, which forms unpleasant-smelling sticky dense thickets. The unusual coastal genus *Thuarea*, which has a leaf folded over each raceme (Figure 8.29c), is related to the abundant, creeping, ground cover and significant forage species *Brachiaria umbellata* and the enigmatic endemics *B. subrostrata* and *Yvesia madagascariensis*; the latter is an annual restricted to shallow soils in the northwest (Vorontsova and Rakotoarisoa 2014).

Clade 24 (Subtribe Cenchrinae) Bristle Clade

This group is common and usually easily spotted by its members' multiple bristles or spines around their spikelets, which fall together with the spikelets in *Cenchrus* (genus now including *Pennisetum*) but stay on the plant in the other large genus *Setaria*. Pearl Millet *C. americanus* (previously called *P. glaucum*) is a common

African crop that is occasionally cultivated on Madagascar. Most visitors to Madagascar see the fluffy purple inflorescences of the widespread fire-loving *C. polystachios* by roadsides. *Cenchrus ciliaris* and *C. echinatus* are common southern grasses with sticky and spiny propagules that are listed as problematic weeds alongside *C. polystachios* by Husson et al. (2013). The Central Highland endemic *Pennisetum pseudotriticoides* is a tough deeply rooted bunchgrass resilient to both burning and grazing (Solofondranohatra et al. 2020). *Cenchrus clandestinus* (the species name is derived from the usually hidden flowers) was first introduced as drought-resilient forage in 1924 (François 1930) and its chunky stolons are now commonly sold to make drought-resistant lawns that do not need mowing.

The doubtfully distinct *Setaria pumila* and *S. sphacelata* are the most common members of their genus on Madagascar alongside the forest edge species *S. megaphylla*, which, with its broad, folded leaves, resembles a small palm. The open habitat–dominating perennial *S. madecassa* in the west (Figure 8.29d) and *S. scottii* in central areas are sister species of the same endemic radiation as the spectacular dry forest edge annual *S. vatkeana*; the other endemics, *S. humbertiana* in the south and *S. bathiei* in central areas, appear to have independent origins. The recently described unusual species of dry spiny thickets, *Digitaria bosseri* (Vorontsova 2017), seems to have bristles and may be a member of this clade rather than of *Digitaria*. The bristle-less, distinctive, creeping *Stenotaphrum*, with apically rounded leaves, is usually represented by the eastern rough lawn cover *S. dimidiatum*, but there are also two endemic Central Highland species: *S. unilaterale* and *S. oostachyum*.

FUTURE DIRECTIONS

The authors hope that this summary will encourage researchers and surveyors to collect and examine Poaceae during routine fieldwork across Madagascar in order to build up much-needed collections and knowledge of this large and fascinating but frequently neglected family. A dissecting microscope is strongly recommended for identification work at the species level, but in the absence of a microscope many genera can be recognized with the naked eye or using a hand lens.

ACKNOWLEDGMENTS

Thank you to Mark Nesbitt and Philippa Ryan (RBG-Kew) for assistance with the research on Madagascar crop arrival dates, and also to Sarah Ficinski (RBG-Kew) for composing the photo plate. Thank you also to Pascal-Antoine Christin (University of Sheffield) for information on the dates when *Alloteropsis semialata* reached Madagascar.

Subject editors: Laurent Gautier and Steven M. Goodman

LEGUMINOSAE (FABACEAE), LEGUMES

P. B. Phillipson, G. P. Lewis, S. Andriambololonera, N. Rakotonirina, M. Thulin, and N. Wilding

The Leguminosae, or Fabaceae as it is alternatively known, is the world's third largest flowering plant family: it includes close to 20,000 species spread across ~800 currently recognized genera (LPWG 2017; Angiosperm Phylogeny Website 2019; G. P. Lewis, unpublished data). The family is extremely diverse, ranging from small annual species to shrubs, lianas, and some of the largest trees on the planet, and its members occur in both humid and dry regions in both tropical and temperate parts of the world. The family is an important source of food plants, notably peas, beans, lentils, chickpeas, peanuts, and soya, as well as fodder for livestock. The ability of many species to fix atmospheric nitrogen through symbiotic relationships with bacteria in root nodules represents a key feature in the functioning of natural communities and makes the family especially valuable in rotational cropping in agricultural systems. This family is a source of innumerable medicinal products and garden ornamentals, and includes some of the world's most valuable hardwood timbers.

For Madagascar, the family was the subject of a detailed monograph that resulted in the publication of the *Leguminosae of Madagascar* (Du Puy et al. 2002). In that treatment exactly 100 genera and a total of 667 species were recognized and described, ranking the Leguminosae as the third-largest plant family on the island after the Orchidaceae and the Rubiaceae. Documentation was presented for 573 native species and 94 introduced species; most of the latter have become naturalized, and many have become widespread weeds and invasive trees and shrubs. A summary of the family (Labat and Moat 2003), based on this treatment, was published in the precursor to this book, which provided a useful synthesis of the taxonomy, ecology, biogeography, local uses, and conservation status of species in the family, much of which remains valid and useful today. The object of this contribution is not to repeat information available in Labat and Moat (2003), but to present the main changes to the taxonomy of Malagasy legumes, which has notable levels of local endemism (Figure 8.30), that have occurred in the past ~20 years and to emphasize the conservation problems surrounding this family.

The publication of a flora or monographic treatment for any group of organisms marks an important step in the understanding of the group concerned and it also provides a foundation for future research and a solid platform on which new information can build;

however, it also serves to highlight remaining taxonomic issues. This is very much the case for the Malagasy Leguminosae, and research on the island's Leguminosae flora continues. Ongoing botanical exploration of Madagascar since 2002 has resulted in more than 5000 new herbarium collections of Leguminosae species, and many of the specimens are associated with samples that can be used in molecular studies. During this period, efforts to resolve taxonomically problematic groups have advanced, and work currently in progress is starting to yield new insights, especially through the efforts of the active Legume Phylogeny Working Group (LPWG). The results of this collective effort that are relevant to Madagascar are presented in this account.

Revised generic circumscriptions have been published for many groups of Leguminosae, usually underpinned by molecular phylogenetic studies. These have resulted in 17 additional genera newly represented within the flora of Madagascar, three that have been lost to synonymy, the transfer of 53 species from one genus to another, corresponding name changes for these species (requiring 39 new names or combinations, and the resurrection of 14 existing older combinations). This work has provided an improved understanding of species already known to science and, coupled with the increased specimen base, it has facilitated the discovery of new taxa. Since the Leguminosae monograph was published, 10 species new to science have been discovered and published, one species has been placed in synonymy, and three introduced species have been documented from Madagascar for the first time. As of July 2020, the total number of native legume species recorded for Madagascar was 583, of which 469 are endemic (80.4%).

An outline of the classification and phylogeny of the Leguminosae as it pertains to Madagascar and details of the taxonomic changes since Du Puy et al. (2002) was published are presented below, as well as sections outlining other aspects of the natural history of the Leguminosae of Madagascar.

CLASSIFICATION AND PHYLOGENY OF THE LEGUMINOSAE

The family has traditionally been divided into three subfamilies, Caesalpinioideae, Mimosoideae, and Papilionoideae. However, it has long been known that the Caesalpinioideae is paraphyletic, and this was finally resolved with a new classification recognizing six subfamilies (LPWG 2017). These taxa correspond to the six primary lineages of legumes, all of which are robustly supported clades (Koenen et al. 2020). Under this new system, the former Mimosoideae is no longer recognized as a subfamily because it is nested within the recircumscribed Caesalpinioideae. It is now simply referred to as the mimosoid clade (LPWG 2017). Six legume subfamilies are now recognized of which only subfamily Duparquetioideae, which comprises a single species from west Africa, is not known from Madagascar. There are five subfamilies present on the island.

Caesalpinioideae

Caesalpinioideae includes the nested mimosoid clade (i.e., former subfamily Mimosoideae) plus four tribes of which the Cassieae, Caesalpinieae, and Dimorphandreae are represented on Madagascar. Within the mimosoid clade the traditionally recognized tribes Acacieae, Ingeae, and Mimoseae (now taken to include Parkieae) are all represented on the island, but all of these tribes are nonmonophyletic (LPWG 2013, 2017) and may be better grouped as a single tribe in the future. The tribal placement of certain genera in Caesalpinioideae *sensu* LPWG (2017) remains uncertain, including some that are important on Madagascar, such as *Delonix*, *Colvillea*, *Erythrophloeum*, and *Tetrapterocarpon*, which are provisionally retained in Caesalpinieae.

Cercidoideae

Cercidoideae includes *Bauhinia* and its relatives and is well represented on Madagascar (LPWG 2017); a recent study concluded that further subdivision of the subfamily into tribes is unnecessary (Sinou et al. 2020).

Detarioideae

Detarioideae is divided into six tribes (de la Estrella et al. 2018), of which the Afzelieae, Amherstieae, and Detarieae are present on Madagascar.

Dialioideae

Dialioideae is a small group comprising only 17 genera and ~85 species worldwide, but including three genera endemic to Madagascar: *Baudouinia*, *Eligmocarpus*, and *Mendoravia*, with a total of 11 species.

Papilionoideae

Papilionoideae (sometimes referred to as Faboideae when the family name Fabaceae is preferred)—circumscription of this group, the largest subfamily, remains unchanged under the new LPWG (2017) classification. Within Papilionoideae, tribal delimitations have been broadened in some cases; for example, the formerly recognized tribe Aeschynomeneae and two genera of Desmodieae (*Brya* and *Cranocarpus*, neither present on Madagascar) have been subsumed within a broadly circumscribed Dalbergieae (Klitgaard and Lavin 2005). In some other groups tribal delimitation has been narrowed and, in some cases, old tribal names have been resurrected, such as the Cadieae, which was reinstated to accommodate the Malagasy Region endemic genus *Cadia* (Boatwright et al. 2008). The tribal classification of the Papilionoideae remains in a state of flux and is likely to change as understanding of the phylogeny of the subfamily advances (e.g., Cardoso et al. 2013). Based on the existing tribal classification of Papilionoideae, 25 of the ~36 tribes that are currently recognized are represented on Madagascar (Angiosperm Phylogeny Website 2019.

TAXONOMIC CHANGES SINCE DU PUY ET AL. (2002)

Here we describe in detail the taxonomic changes since the publication of Du Puy et al. (2002). A summary of these changes is presented in Table 8.22. Here we report taxonomic and nomenclatural changes in three of the five subfamilies present on Madagascar; no new taxa or taxonomic changes for Madagascar have been made to the delimitation of genera and species in subfamilies Detarioideae (six genera, 17 species) and Dialioideae (four genera, 11 species) during this period. Taxonomic changes to Malagasy taxa within 11 different tribes of subfamilies Caesalpinioideae, Cercidoideae, and Papilionoideae are documented below.

Subfamily Caesalpinioideae, Tribe Caesalpinieae

Caesalpinia: This genus and its relatives have long been taxonomically problematic (Gagnon et al. 2016). Recent studies offer new insights into the group and have shown that the broad concept of the genus previously adopted, including Du Puy et al. (2002), failed to recognize the morphological, geographic, and molecular diversity of *Caesalpinia sensu lato* (Lewis 2005; Gagnon et al. 2016).

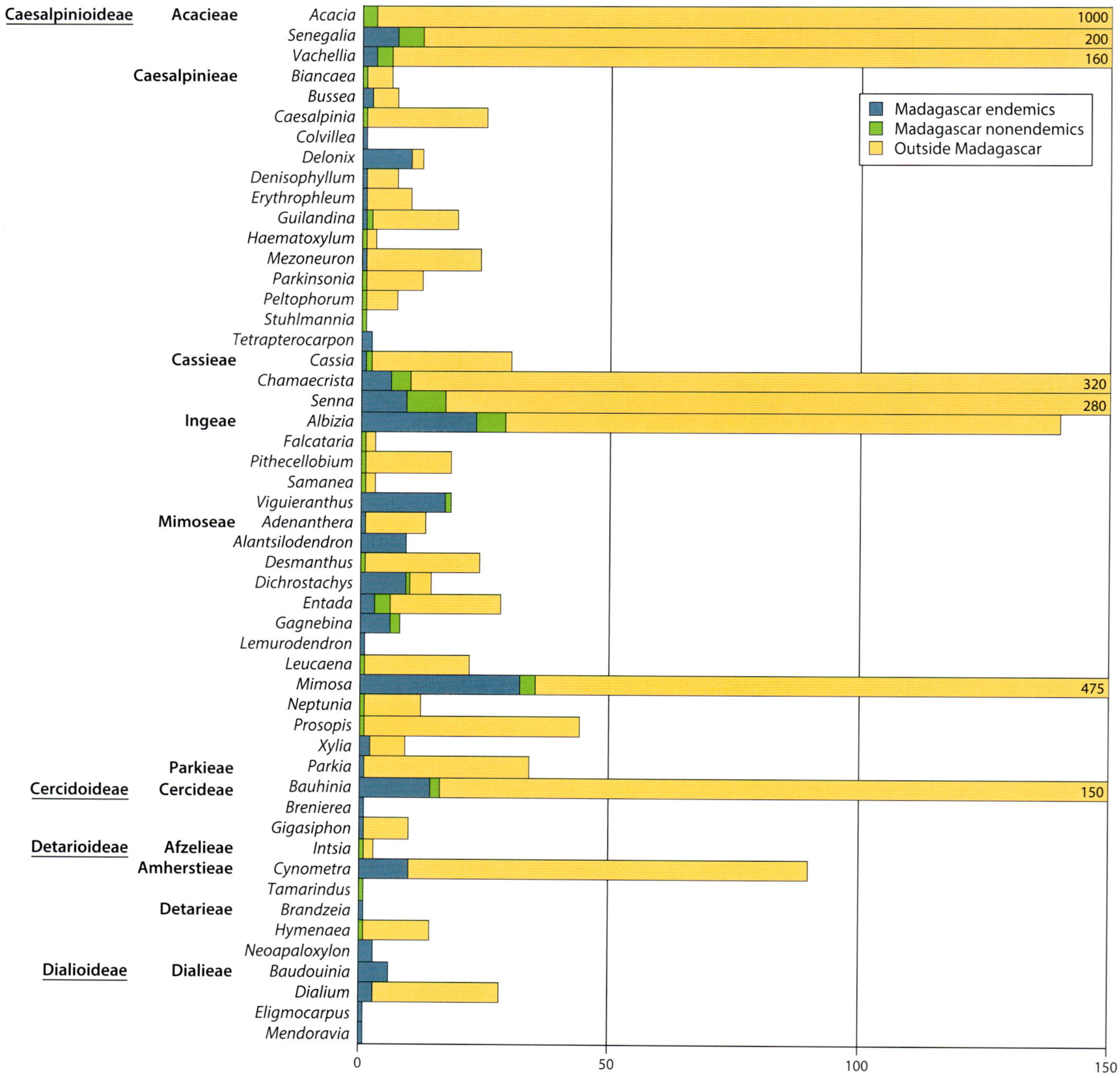

FIGURE 8.30 **Diversity and endemicity diagram of Malagasy Leguminosae at the level of genera, showing three different species counts: 1) endemic to Madagascar, 2) nonendemic but native to Madagascar, and 3) those occurring elsewhere in the world (for further information see text). In cases when species diversity exceeds or does not conform to that presented on the horizontal graph scale, the figures are written along the respective horizontal line of a given genus. Note that values do not take into account unpublished species mentioned in the text or species expected to be transferred in the future from one genus to another.**

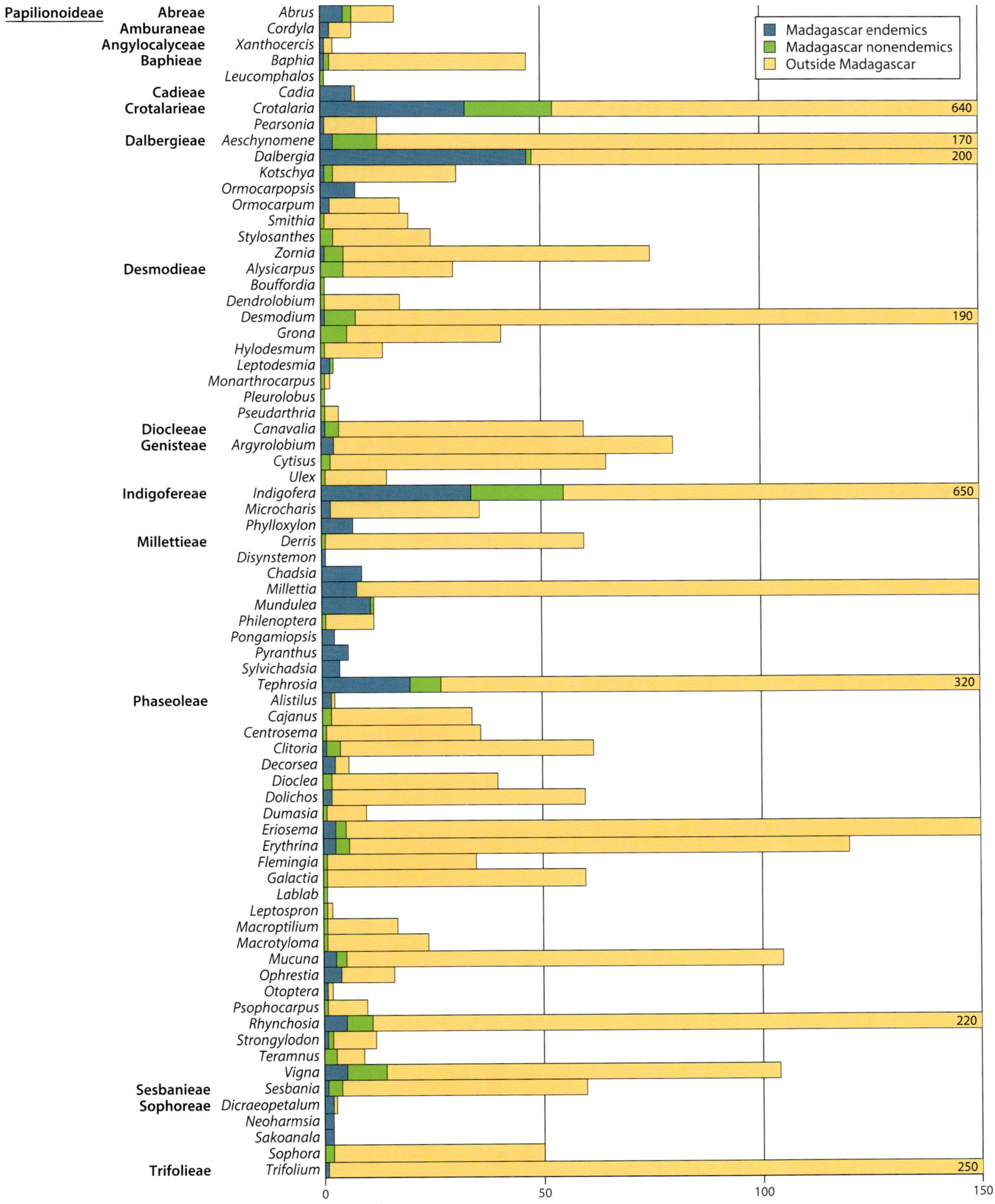

FIGURE 8.30 ***continued***

TABLE 8.22. **Summary of taxonomic changes in the Leguminosae since Du Puy et al. (2002)**

SUBFAMILY	TRIBE	GENUS	TAXONOMIC CHANGES
Caesalpinioideae	Caesalpinieae	*Caesalpinia*	Species transferred to *Denisophytum* (1), *Guilandina* (2), *Mezoneuron* (1), *Stuhlmannia* (1), and *Biancaea* (1); 1 species retained in *Caesalpinia*.
		Lemuropisum	Placed as a synonym of *Delonix*.
		Peltophorum	1 species recorded as naturalized.
	Acacieae	*Acacia*	Species transferred to *Senegalia* (12) and *Vachellia* (6). 3 species retained in *Acacia*.
	Ingeae	*Albizia*	Species transferred to *Samanea* (1).
	Ingeae	*Viguieranthus*	Now treated as a Malagasy Region endemic.
	Mimoseae	*Mimosa*	2 new species described.
Cercidoideae	–	*Bauhinia*	Species transferred to *Gigasiphon* (1); 15 species retained in *Bauhinia*; 1 new species described.
Papilionoideae	Cadieae	*Cadia*	1 new species described.
	Dalbergieae	*Dalbergia*	5 new species described.
		Peltiera	Reduced to a single species and transferred to *Ormocarpopsis*.
		Ormocarpopsis	1 new species described.
	Desmodieae	*Desmodium*	Species transferred to *Grona* (6), *Hylodesmum* (1), *Monarthrocarpus* (1), *Bouffordia* (1), and *Pleurolobus* (1); 8 species retained in *Desmodium*.
	Indigofereae	*Vaughania*	Species transferred to *Indigofera* (11).
	Millettieae	*Lonchocarpus*	Species transferred to *Philenoptera* (1); 1 species retained in *Lonchocarpus*.
	Phaseoleae	*Centrosema*	1 species recorded as naturalized.
		Vigna	Species transferred to *Leptospron* (1); 1 new name combination.
	Swartzieae	*Cordyla*	Generic placement in doubt.

For Madagascar, seven species were referred to *Caesalpinia* by Du Puy et al. (2002), but these are now spread across six different genera, one with a recently published new combination in *Guilandina* and five already with valid names in the recently reinstated genera (Lewis 2005, 2020; Gagnon et al. 2016). These include three endemic Malagasy species, each now referred to a separate genus.

1. *Denisophytum madagascariense*—endemic to northern Madagascar; the other six species of this genus occur in the Americas and in Africa (Gagnon et al. 2016).
2. *Guilandina delphinensis*—endemic to southeast Madagascar; the genus is pantropical and currently comprises 19 species (Lewis 2020).
3. *Mezoneuron hildebrandtii*—the only species of its genus present on Madagascar; the other 23 species are scattered from west Africa, through tropical Asia, Papua New Guinea, New Caledonia, and Australia, to a single species in Hawaii (Lewis 2005; Clark 2016).

Two native but nonendemic species recorded from Madagascar have been transferred to two separate genera: *Guilandina bonduc*, also widespread in Africa; and *Stuhlmannia moavi* from coastal east Africa and northern and northwestern Madagascar.

Two introduced and naturalized species of the group have been recorded from Madagascar; one has been transferred to *Biancaea*, *B. decapetala*, and the other is the sole species for Madagascar that remains in *Caesalpinia*, *C. pulcherrima*.

Lemuropisum: Comprising a single species, *L. edule*, *Lemuropisum* was described by Perrier de la Bâthie (1939b) on the basis of a single collection he made from the calcareous cliffs to the east of "Manampetsa" lake (certainly within what is now Tsimanampesotse National Park). The species was contrasted with those of the related genera *Colvillea* and what was then known as *Poinciana* in terms of its shrubby versus arborescent habit, highly reduced leaves, and morphologically different pods and seeds. This distinction was upheld by Du Puy et al. (2002), except that the Malagasy species formerly placed in *Poinciana* (and also in a fourth genus, *Aprevalia*) had been transferred to *Delonix*, some by Capuron (1968a) and the others by Du Puy et al. (1995). Two additional species of *Delonix* had also been described (*D. pumila* and *D. velutina*). Apart from the nine Malagasy species of *Delonix*

FIGURE 8.31 Subfamily Caesalpinioideae: A) *Delonix edule* (tribe Caesalpinieae) has a highly restricted distribution in the southwest. B) *Peltophorum dasyrhachis* (tribe Caesalpinieae), introduced and naturalized in Madagascar, visited here by a male Madagascar Green Sunbird (*Cinnyris notatus*). C) *Senegalia pervillei* (tribe Acacieae), an endemic lianescent shrub, is widespread in the west. D) *Mimosa manomboensis* (tribe Mimoseae) is known only from near Toliara. Subfamily Papilionoideae, tribe Swartzieae: E) *Cordyla haraka* is endemic to the humid northeast. F) *Cordyla madagascariensis* is widespread in the west, but subspecies *tamarindoides*, illustrated here, is known only from the Ankarana protected area. (PHOTOS A and F by F. Ratovoson, B by Z. Rogers, C and D by P. B. Phillipson, and E by P. Lowry.)

recognized, the genus was known from just two other species, the African-Asian *D. elata* and the African *D. baccal*. Supported by molecular, morphological, and ecological data, Babineau and Bruneau (2017) transferred *Lemuropisum edule* to *Delonix*, as *D. edule* (Figure 8.31a).

Peltophorum: A small genus of tropical trees, some *Peltophorum* species are widely cultivated as shade trees or ornamentals and sometimes become naturalized. Recently collected specimens identified as *P. dasyrhachis* var. *dasyrhachis* mark the first records for the genus on Madagascar. The specimens were found at two localities in the north (DIANA Region) where it had become naturalized: just outside the boundary of the Manongarivo Special Reserve and at the edge of degraded gallery forest in the Lokobe National Park (Figure 8.31b). This southeast Asian taxon is widely cultivated as an ornamental and has also become naturalized in some parts of Africa (Rogers and Thulin 2012).

Subfamily Caesalpinioideae, "Mimosoid clade," Tribe Acacieae

Acacia: *Acacia* was represented in Du Puy et al. (2002) by a total of 20 species, of which 10 were endemic to Madagascar, three were native to the African-Malagasy region, and seven were introduced and naturalized species. At that time, the genus was treated globally in a broad sense; it consisted of ~1450 species pantropically distributed but with nearly 1000 of them native to Australia. However, delimited in this way, *Acacia* had long been known to be polyphyletic and has now been segregated into seven genera, three of which occur on Madagascar (see J. T. Miller and Seigler 2012). Despite a long saga of nomenclatural wrangling, the taxonomically updated name combinations for all Malagasy species in the new generic system have now been published (Kyalangalilwa et al. 2013; Boatwright et al. 2015). None of Madagascar's native species belong in *Acacia sensu stricto* as it is now circumscribed, although three species have been introduced and become naturalized, and in some cases invasive (Kyalangalilwa et al. 2013; Boatwright et al. 2015). The Malagasy native species formerly included in *Acacia* are now divided between *Senegalia* and *Vachellia*. Species of these genera can be distinguished by the presence of thorns, spines, or prickles, which are absent from the introduced species of *Acacia sensu stricto* from Australia. *Senegalia* species have prickles along their stems and often on the leaf rhachis, and stipules that are not spinescent, while species of *Vachellia* lack prickles but have paired spinescent stipules.

Recently, specimens of a previously unrecorded species for Madagascar were identified: *S. senegal* (formerly *A. senegal*). This African-Asian species has apparently become naturalized near Toliara (Madagascar Catalogue 2020). Of the 12 species of *Senegalia* now known on Madagascar, 10 are native to the island, seven of which are endemic, while three also occur naturally in continental Africa, and two have been introduced and become naturalized. There are six species of *Vachellia* known from Madagascar, three endemic and the other three introduced and naturalized. The species formerly included in *Acacia* that are endemic to Madagascar are as follows: *Senegalia baronii*, *S. hildebrandtii*, *S. menabeensis*, *S. meridionalis*, *S. pervillei* (Figure 8.31c), *S. polhillii*, *S. sakalava*, *Vachellia bellula*, *V. myrmecophila*, and *V. viguieri*.

The species formerly included in *Acacia* that are native to Madagascar but not endemic are: *Senegalia kraussiana*, *S. pentagona*, and *S. rovumae*.

The species formerly included in *Acacia* that are naturalized on Madagascar, but not endemic are: *Senegalia rugata*, *S. senegal*, *Vachellia farnesiana*, *V. nilotica*, and *V. tortilis*.

Just three species on Madagascar are retained in *Acacia*; all three are introduced, naturalized species (two of which are native to Australia): *A. dealbata*, *A. heterophylla*, and *A. mearnsii*. Both the first and the third species are present primarily in disturbed areas in the Central Highlands; they are fire-resistant and are known to become highly invasive in many parts of the world and damage natural habitats (see Gwate et al. 2016), although the extent to which they are a threat on Madagascar is not known. The second species is endemic to La Réunion, but is cultivated and, apparently, locally naturalized on Madagascar. More information about this species, which has truly remarkable colonizing abilities and is a potential threat to native vegetation, is provided by Le Roux et al. (2014).

Subfamily Caesalpinioideae, "Mimosoid clade," Tribe Ingeae

Albizia: This genus included 30 species in Du Puy et al. (2002), three of which were introduced, naturalized species. One of these, *A. saman*, native to South America, is cultivated for shade and as an ornamental plant in lowland areas of Madagascar and has become locally naturalized. The species was transferred back into the reinstated genus *Samanea* by Barneby and Grimes (1996). Although not accepted by J.-F. Villiers in Du Puy et al. (2002), *S. saman* is the name currently in use.

Viguieranthus: Villiers (in Du Puy et al. 2002) described 18 species from Madagascar, and five species from Asia as *Viguieranthus*; however, studies by Lewis and Schrire (2003) and by de Souza et al. (2016) have shown that the Asian species are better placed in *Thailentadopsis* (three species) and *Sanjappa* (one species), with one species still to be transferred, and so *Viguieranthus* is now treated as a Malagasy Region endemic.

Subfamily Caesalpinioideae, "Mimosoid clade," Tribe Mimoseae

Dichrostachys: The treatment of *Dichrostachys* by Villiers (in Du Puy et al. 2002) includes 14 species, one of which, *D. cinerea*, is introduced and has become naturalized on Madagascar, while the remaining 13 species are endemic (one species mentioned in the treatment, "*Dichrostachys* sp. 1," lacks a valid name and formal description due to the lack of adequate material). Phylogenetic studies show that Malagasy *Dichrostachys* species do not form a monophyletic group, with some species more closely related to *Alantsilodendron* and *Gagnebina* (Hughes et al. 2003; Luckow 1995, 2002; M. Luckow, unpublished data). Four of the species that belong in *Gagnebina* are discussed in the next section. Two species, *D. richardiana* and *D. venosa*, belong in *Alantsilodendron* and will be transferred in an upcoming monograph (M. Luckow, unpublished data). The monograph will also recognize a new genus (for the remaining Malagasy species of *Dichrostachys*) in which two new species will be described and the necessary combinations will be made for the following seven taxa: *D. akataensis*, *D. arborescens*, *D. dumetaria*, *D. paucifoliolata*, *D. scottiana*, *D. tenuifolia*, and *D. unijuga*.

Gagnebina (Tribe Mimoseae): The treatment for *Gagnebina* by Villiers (in Du Puy et al. 2002) included just four species: two strictly endemic to Madagascar, one species that is also present in the Comoro and Mascarene Islands, and the fourth also recorded from the Seychelles (Aldabra, Astove, and Cosmoledo islands). Three additional endemic Malagasy species had previously been transferred to *Gagnebina* (*G. bernieriana*, *G. myriophylla*, *G. pervilleana*) (Lewis and Guinet 1986; Luckow 1995), but these transfers were not recognized by Villiers (in Du Puy et al. 2002) who included them in *Dichrostachys* (two were originally described in *Desmanthus*, a genus now limited to species from the Americas). However, evidence clearly supports their placement in *Gagnebina* (Luckow et al. 2003).

In addition, a new species, *G. bakoliae*, endemic to Madagascar, was described from Ankarana Special Reserve (Luckow and Du Puy 2000), bringing the total number of accepted described species in the genus to eight, and work is in progress to describe at least one more species of *Gagnebina* from Madagascar (M. Luckow, unpublished data).

Mimosa: *Mimosa* comprises more than 500 species worldwide (Lewis et al. 2005; M. F. Simon et al. 2011), mostly occurring in tropical and subtropical regions, with a few species that have become pantropical weeds. Diversity of the genus is centered in the Americas, with over 90% of the species, and with fewer than 10 native species occurring naturally across the whole of Asia and continental Africa, none native to Europe or Australia, but, remarkably, 32 species endemic to Madagascar—which is therefore a secondary center of endemism for the genus. The Old World clade of *Mimosa* is clearly deeply nested within the New World backbone in molecular phylogenies (M. F. Simon et al. 2011). Eleven of the known species on Madagascar were discovered and described during research by Du Puy et al. (2002), and two additional species, *M. dupuyana* and *M. manomboensis*, have been added subsequently; both occur near Toliara, in an area that is especially rich in members of the genus (Lefèvre and Labat 2006; Morales and Fortunato 2016) (Figure 8.31d).

Subfamily Cercidoideae

Bauhinia: Following a relatively conservative, all-inclusive approach to the delimitation of the genus, Du Puy et al. (2002) recognized 16 species of *Bauhinia* as native to Madagascar, of which 15 are strictly endemic and one, *B. hildebrandtii*, is also known from the Comoros (Anjouan). Recent global treatments of *Bauhinia* (Lewis and Forest 2005) have favored a narrower circumscription of the genus and the recognition of several generic segregates. Current evidence (Sinou et al. 2020) supports the reestablishment of the genus *Gigasiphon* for a single Malagasy species, *B. humblotiana*, together with three African species, while the other Malagasy species are retained in *Bauhinia sensu stricto*. In 2014 a new species of *Bauhinia*, *B. darainensis*, was published for Madagascar, occurring in what is now the Loky Manambato protected area; it is known only from two collections (Thulin et al. 2014).

Subfamily Papilionoideae, Tribe Cadieae

Cadia: After being described in 1775 for a single species from east and northeast Africa and Arabia, more than a hundred years later *Cadia* was found to occur on Madagascar. Six endemic species were accepted in Du Puy et al. (2002). In 2008 a seventh Malagasy species was published, *C. multifoliolata*, occurring in the Loky Manambato protected area and only known from the type collection (Nusbaumer and Labat 2008).

Subfamily Papilionoideae, Tribe Dalbergieae

Dalbergia: This is a pantropical genus of some 250 species of trees, shrubs, and lianas. The species diversity is centered in the Old World, with Africa and Madagascar being particularly rich: currently 48 species are accepted for Madagascar. *Dalbergia* is the third most species-rich genus of Leguminosae on Madagascar after *Indigofera* and *Crotalaria*. However, with all but one of the Malagasy species endemic to the country (*D. bracteolata* also occurs in east Africa), while *Indigofera* and *Crotalaria* include a large proportion of nonendemic and/or naturalized species, *Dalbergia* is by far the richest genus of Leguminosae in terms of endemic species.

The treatment by Du Puy et al. (2002) was based on revisionary work undertaken a few years earlier that resulted in the publication of no fewer than 22 new species (Bosser and Rabevohitra 1996), resulting in a total of 43 species for Madagascar. Subsequently, five additional species were published by Bosser and Rabevohitra (2005), all from northern Madagascar and mostly known only from recent collections: *D. gautieri*, *D. pseudoviguieri* (Figure 8.32a), *D. manongarivensis*, *D. masoalensis*, and *D. occulta*.

Dalbergia is the source of valuable hardwood timbers known as rosewood or palissander. These timbers have been traded around the world, and the Malagasy species are among the most sought after. Overexploitation of wild sources of rosewoods, as well as Malagasy ebony (species of *Diospyros*—Ebenaceae, see Schatz and Lowry, pp. 739–44), has reached critical levels in the past two decades. This is considered to be a major threat to the survival of targeted species (Barrett et al. 2010), which has led to the inclusion of both genera on CITES (Convention on International Trade in Endangered Species of Wild Fauna and Flora) Appendix II in 2013, thereby placing a total ban on international trade (Mason et al. 2016). Nevertheless, the desire to use these valuable resources sustainably has brought into focus the shortcomings of the existing taxonomic knowledge of these two genera and the need for better identification tools. Illegal exploitation has continued on Madagascar, even in protected areas (CITES 2019), and despite the considerable advances in the published information about Malagasy *Dalbergia*, as outlined here, not enough is known about the taxonomic relationships between the different species, the dynamics of their natural populations, or which species are targeted by the illegal loggers. A consortium of Malagasy and international institutions was established in 2017 to address these issues for both *Dalbergia* and *Diospyros*. The consortium is engaged in extensive fieldwork to develop a precious woods reference library in herbaria, comprising voucher specimens for long-term reference. In addition, wood, bark, leaves, and silica gel–dried wood and leaf material are being collected in support of taxonomic work to diagnose species and elucidate morphological traits, DNA barcodes, and anatomical and spectrometric characteristics of wood. These will form the basis for the development of practical, reliable field identification tools and forensic wood identification protocols. The program also provides for training of Malagasy students in these disciplines and the building of national capacity in tree, timber, and wood product identification.

The team charged with the taxonomic work on *Dalbergia*, led by Missouri Botanical Garden personnel, has already identified a number of new species and determined that some of the currently recognized species are in reality species complexes that require separation into more than one taxon. It is envisaged that this work might double the number of described species of *Dalbergia* on Madagascar (Madagascar Catalogue 2020; N. Wilding et al., unpublished data).

Ormocarpopsis: *Peltiera* was first described to accommodate two new Malagasy species (Labat and Du Puy 1997). The authors regarded the new genus as being allied to the genera *Ormocarpum* and *Ormocarpopsis* although differing from both by the morphology of its fruit. *Ormocarpum*, a genus of 18 species, has two species endemic to Madagascar with the others mostly occurring in Africa but one extending to Asia and another from Asia to northern Australia. *Ormocarpopsis* previously comprised six species endemic to Madagascar (Klitgaard and Lavin 2005). In Du Puy et al. (2002), these two genera were placed in the tribe Aeschynomeneae; however, recent work suggests that this tribe, and certain genera in other tribes, should be combined with the tribe Dalbergieae (Klitgaard and Lavin 2005).

The two species of *Peltiera* were both considered by Labat and Du Puy (1997) to be critically endangered and possibly extinct following a careful search at their recorded localities, which had become severely degraded: *P. alaotrensis*, known only from the type collection near Lake Alaotra (collected in 1944); and *P. nitida*, known from two

FIGURE 8.32 **Subfamily Papilionoideae, tribe Dalbergieae: A) *Dalbergia pseudoviguieri*, a lianescent shrub, is known only from Analamerana Special Reserve and Irodo Forest in the north. The flat, indehiscent, one- or two-seeded pods are characteristic of the genus. B) *Ormocarpopsis nitida* was originally described in the genus *Peltiera*; the unusual moniliform fruit is characteristic of the genus and is often reduced to a single segment. C) *Ormocarpopsis anosyana* is known only from a single locality just outside Andohahela National Park. D) Tribe Phaseoleae. *Strongylodon craveniae* is a moist evergreen forest liana of the east that has been observed being pollinated by *Cheirogaleus* spp. (dwarf lemurs including *C. medius*, Fat-tailed Dwarf Lemur). E) Tribe Indigofereae. The genus *Vaughania* is now reduced to synonymy under *Indigofera*. This photo shows *I. cloiselii*, a common shrubby species in the south, and one of the 11 species transferred from *Vaughania*.** (PHOTO A by C. R. Birkinshaw, B by P. Antilahimena, C and E by F. Ratovoson, and D by B. Pettersson and L. Anders Nilsson.)

collections, one from the Central Highlands, northwest of Antananarivo and the other from near Moramanga. The two species differed in the size and the number of leaflets of their pinnate leaves. Subsequently, renewed inventory effort in the Alaotra-Mangoro and Atsinanana Regions to the north of Moramanga, especially studies on and around the mine site at Ambatovy, as well as in several areas that are now included in the protected area network, generated more than 30 new collections that could be assigned to *Peltiera*. After examination of this new material, Thulin et al. (2013) concluded that the two species described by Labat and Du Puy were linked by intermediates and represented a single variable species. Furthermore, a molecular study based on chloroplast *trnK* and nuclear ribosomal internal transcribed spacer (ITS) sequences confirmed a close relationship between *Peltiera* and *Ormocarpopsis*, also supported by morphology. It was therefore proposed that *Peltiera* be synonymized under *Ormocarpopsis*, and the necessary new combination was made as *O. nitida* (Thulin et al. 2013) (Figure 8.32b).

A new species of *Ormocarpopsis* was also described recently, bringing the total number of species in this Malagasy endemic genus to eight. The new species, *O. anosyana*, is known from only two collections made in a single patch of dry spiny thicket adjacent to the Andohahela National Park (Thulin and Razafimandimbison 2016) (Figure 8.32c).

Subfamily Papilionoideae, Tribe Desmodieae

Desmodium: Du Puy et al. (2002) accepted a broad, pantropical circumscription of *Desmodium* comprising ~300 species of mostly herbs and small shrubs worldwide, with 17 species recorded for Madagascar. Of these, one is endemic to the island, nine are native but not endemic, and the rest are introduced and now naturalized. Phylogenetic study has shown the conventional broad concept of the genus to be paraphyletic and the delimitation of smaller more coherent taxa has advanced (see K. Ohashi et al. 2018 for a summary). Currently, the Malagasy species formerly included in *Desmodium* are assigned to five different genera. In addition, a recent collection from central Madagascar has been identified as *D. uncinatum*, the first record for this species in the country; it was reported to have become weedy along roadsides and in damp gullies. Further information on this species is provided below in the section on invasive introduced species.

Eight of the nine species recorded as native on Madagascar but not endemic have been transferred: six are now included in *Grona* (H. Ohashi and Ohashi 2018), one in the genus *Hylodesmum* (H. Ohashi and Mill 2000) and one in the genus *Monarthrocarpus* (H. Ohashi and Ohashi 2012). The species that have been transferred from *Desmodium* are: *G. adscendens*, *G. barbata*, *G. heterophylla*, *G. hirta*, *G. ramosissima*, *G. triflora*, *H. repandum*, and *M. dolabriformis*.

Two species, both native across much of tropical Asia and Africa, are recorded as introductions and are naturalized in the west; both are placed in monospecific genera: *Bouffordia*, *B. dichotoma* (H. Ohashi and Ohashi 2018) and *Pleurolobus*, *P. gangeticus* (K. Ohashi et al. 2018).

Eight species are currently retained in *Desmodium*, of which only two are regarded as native to Madagascar and only one is endemic; the six other species are naturalized: *D. incanum*—native to the Americas, *D. leiocarpum*—native to South America, *D. lobatum*—endemic to Madagascar, *D. ospriostreblum*—native to tropical Africa, *D. salicifolium*—native to Madagascar and Africa, *D. tortuosum*—native to Central America, *D. uncinatum*—native to Central and South America, and *D. velutinum*—native to Africa and southeast Asia.

Subfamily Papilionoideae, Tribe Indigofereae

Indigofera: *Vaughania* was originally established to accommodate a single highly distinctive species from Madagascar, *V. dionaeifolia* (Moore 1920). This was followed, nearly 90 years later, by a review of the tribe Indigofereae on Madagascar, in which six species previously described as species of *Indigofera* were transferred to *Vaughania*, and four new species were described (Du Puy et al. 1994), thus giving a total of 11 species of *Vaughania* (Du Puy et al. 2002). *Vaughania* was distinguished from *Indigofera* and other genera of the tribe Indigofereae by different overall morphology and was regarded as being endemic to Madagascar. Subsequent molecular studies have shown, unequivocally, that this group of species is nested within *Indigofera* (Barker et al. 2000; Schrire et al. 2003, 2009), despite their distinctive morphology. Recognizing *Vaughania* as a distinct genus would render *Indigofera* paraphyletic and the genus was returned to synonymy under *Indigofera* (Schrire 2008), and the necessary new combinations were proposed. The transfer of these species to *Indigofera* brings the total number of species of that genus on Madagascar to 55, of which 34 are endemic. Nineteen species are considered native on Madagascar but also occur elsewhere in the world, and two species were introduced and are naturalized. As such, *Indigofera* is the most species-rich genus of the Leguminosae on the island.

The 11 species formerly included in *Vaughania* are as follows: *I. cerighellii*, *I. cloiselii* (Figure 8.32e), *I. depauperata*, *I. dionaeifolia*, *I. humbertiana*, *I. interrupta*, *I. longidentata*, *I. mahafalensis*, *I. perrieri*, *I. pseudocompressa*, and *I. xerophila*.

One other name change is for the Malagasy species referred to as *I. nivea*. This species, known only from the Boeny Region, is now correctly named *I. viguieri*, since its original name is a later homonym of a species from South Africa: *I. nivea* (= *Indigastrum niveum*) (Callmander et al. 2010).

Subfamily Papilionoideae, Tribe Millettieae

Philenoptera: Two species of *Lonchocarpus* were treated in Du Puy et al. (2002): one, a native scrambling shrub or liana, known from the northeast of the island, but also occurring on Mayotte and possibly also native on Zanzibar; the second, an introduced tree from west Africa, thought to be "probably" naturalized. The native species *L. madagascariensis* had been transferred to *Philenoptera*, a small genus that had previously been synonymized under *Lonchocarpus* but was resurrected by Schrire (2000). The changed circumscription of *Lonchocarpus* and the reinstatement of *Philenoptera* were justified on morphological, chemical, and biogeographic grounds, but this work was evidently overlooked by Du Puy et al. (2002), although it has been generally accepted, for example, by Lewis et al. (2005).

Lonchocarpus sericeus, the introduced species native to South America and west Africa, in an otherwise entirely New World genus, is retained in *Lonchocarpus*. It was probably introduced to Madagascar for its timber and as an ornamental tree.

Subfamily Papilionoideae, Tribe Phaseoleae

Centrosema: This is a tropical American genus with several species that are widely cultivated as cover crops or green manure and frequently become naturalized. A species of this genus was first collected in central Madagascar in the 1960s and was identified as *C. pubescens*; however, there was no indication whether it was cultivated or naturalized and so it was omitted from the treatment of Du Puy et al. (2002). Subsequently, more material of the same species, which was clearly naturalized, has been collected from various localities at lower elevation near the east coast and in the north. A recent study has shown that this species, a vigorous, climbing or trailing herb that occurs widely across Africa and Asia as an introduction, has frequently been wrongly identified; it is correctly referred to *C. molle*, which is native to Central and South America (Duno de Stefano et al. 2008). We have re-examined the relevant material from Madagascar and we can confirm this identification.

Vigna: *Vigna* comprises over 100 species, many economically important crops including on Madagascar where 15 species have been recorded, four of which are endemic, others being probably native, and some that are naturalized introductions (Du Puy et al. 2002). The relationship between this genus and others in the Phaseoleae, a tribe that is well represented on the island, has been taxonomically challenging. A recent molecular study and phylogenetic analysis of the subtribe Phaseolinae has shown that *Vigna* is paraphyletic and a number of new genera need to be established to accommodate certain "American Clades" (Delgado-Salinas et al. 2011), although *Vigna sensu stricto* still does occur in the Americas. For Malagasy *Vigna* two changes are necessary. *Phaseolus diffusus*, a species based on specimens from the southeast, was placed in synonymy by Du Puy et al. (2002) under the South American species *V. longifolia*, on the assumption that it was an introduced species. This has subsequently been shown to be a mistake. A new combination has been provided for the Malagasy species, *V. diffusa*, and *V. longifolia* has been removed from the list of species present on Madagascar.

The second change is that the introduced species *V. adenantha*, a member of one of the "American Clades," has been referred to the newly established genus *Leptospron* as *L. adenanthum*, which was introduced to Madagascar, and is naturalized in the west and northwest (Delgado-Salinas et al. 2011).

Subfamily Papilionoideae, Tribe Swartzieae

Cordyla: *Dupuya* was described to accommodate two species from Madagascar that were formerly placed in *Cordyla* alongside five mainland African species. The two species differ from African species of *Cordyla* and other related genera based on different morphological characters (Kirkbride 2005); both are endemic to Madagascar.

However, subsequent analysis of foliar flavonoids in *Cordyla*, *Dupuya*, and *Mildbraediodendron* (a related monospecific African genus) by Veitch et al. (2008) has shown that 1) the two Malagasy species have significant chemical differences, 2) that *D. haraka* is chemically more similar to certain African species of *Cordyla*, and 3) that *D. madagascariensis* is set apart by certain distinctive chemical characteristics. The study also confirmed the close relationship of *M. excelsum* to *Cordyla sensu lato*. While the authors do not propose any taxonomic changes to reflect this, they suggest that further studies, including of certain related South America genera, and molecular work are necessary to fully understand the relationship within this group. They propose retaining the two Malagasy species, *C. haraka* and *C. madagascariensis*, in *Cordyla* until this work has been undertaken and relationships can be clarified, a point of view accepted by LPWG (2017) (Figures 8.31e and f).

ENDEMICITY IN THE MALAGASY LEGUMINOSAE

As of July 2020, the overall count of species in the Leguminosae of Madagascar stood at 668 species, including 595 native species of which 455 (76.5%) are endemic (Figure 8.30). This is a somewhat lower proportion of endemics than for the known vascular plant flora of the island generally, which in July 2020 was estimated at 11,362 native species with 9372 (82.5%) endemic (Madagascar Catalogue 2020). Figures for the legume family are slightly unreliable for some taxa because it is often very difficult to determine whether nonendemic species are truly native or whether they are introduced species that have become naturalized. Indeed, it could be argued that this distinction is somewhat arbitrary, although certain species are clearly the result of intentional introduction into the country and subsequent naturalization. The Malagasy endemic species represent 2.3% of the world's Leguminosae.

There are 19 genera, representing a broad range of legume tribes currently recognized as being endemic to Madagascar. These are listed below in decreasing order of number of species:

- *Alantsilodendron* (tribe Mimoseae)—nine species
- *Chadsia* (tribe Millettieae)—nine species
- *Ormocarpopsis* (tribe Dalbergieae)—eight species
- *Phylloxylon* (tribe Indigofereae)—seven species
- *Baudouinia* (tribe Dialieae)—six species
- *Pyranthus* (tribe Millettieae)—six species
- *Sylvichadsia* (tribe Millettieae)—four species
- *Neoapaloxylon* (tribe Detarieae)—three species
- *Pongamiopsis* (tribe Millettieae)—three species
- *Neoharmsia* (tribe Sophoreae)—two species
- *Sakoanala* (tribe Sophoreae)—two species
- *Tetrapterocarpon* (tribe Caesalpinieae)—two species
- *Brandzeia* (tribe Detarieae)—one species
- *Brenierea* (tribe Cercideae)—one species
- *Colvillea* (tribe Caesalpinieae)—one species
- *Disynstemon* (tribe Millettieae)—one species
- *Eligmocarpus* (tribe Dialieae)—one species
- *Lemurodendron* (tribe Mimoseae)—one species
- *Mendoravia* (tribe Dialieae)—one species

Other genera that are especially well represented on the island also belong to diverse tribes. The genera with a third or more of their species represented on Madagascar are listed below, together with the number of endemic species and the percentage this represents of the total number of species in the genus:

- *Viguieranthus* (tribe Ingeae)—17 (94.4%)
- *Mundulea* (tribe Millettieae)—11 (91.7%)
- *Delonix* (tribe Caesalpinieae)—10 (83.3%)
- *Gagnebina* (tribe Mimoseae)—six (75.0%)
- *Leptodesmia* (tribe Desmodieae)—two (66.7%)
- *Alistilus* (tribe Phaseoleae)—two (66.7%)
- *Dicraeopetalum* (tribe Sophoreae)—two (66.7%)
- *Dichrostachys* (tribe Mimoseae)—nine (64.3%)
- *Decorsea* (tribe Phaseoleae)—three (50.0%)
- *Otoptera* (tribe Phaseoleae)—one (50.0%)
- *Xanthocercis* (tribe Angylocalyceae)—one (33.3%)

Species endemism across the five subfamilies of Leguminosae present on Madagascar is high except in Papilionoideae. The list below shows percentage species endemism, number of genera containing native species, and number of native species:

- Caesalpinioideae—85.1% (26 genera, 175 species)
- Cercidoidesae—88.9% (three genera, 18 species)
- Detarioideae—82.4% (six genera, 17 species)
- Dialioideae—100% (four genera, 11 species)
- Papilionoideae—71.4% (64 genera, 371 species)

Patterns of species endemism across the 26 tribes of Leguminosae present on Madagascar generally show similar global trends to the subfamily to which they belong. Exceptions are indicated below (Cercidoideae and Dialioideae are not discussed since they both comprise a single tribe).

- Caesalpinioideae (six tribes on Madagascar)—Caesalpinieae has high species endemism (26 species, 90.5% endemic), while Cassieae is relatively low (29 species, 60.7% endemic).
- Detarioideae (tree tribes on Madagascar)—Afzelieae is low in endemism since it is represented by a single nonendemic native species on the island, while the other two tribes are high in ende-

mism: Amherstieae (11 species, 90% endemic) and Detarieae (five species, 80% endemic).

- Papilionoideae (16 tribes on Madagascar)—three small tribes show 100% species endemism on Madagascar: Amburaneae (*Cordyla* with two Malagasy species), Angylocalyceae (*Xanthocercis* with one Malagasy species), and Cadieae (*Cadia* with seven Malagasy species). The following tribes, which include numerous widespread species, have low levels of endemism (mostly less than 40%): Desmodieae, Diocleeae, Phaseoleae, and Sesbanieae. Surprisingly, the Dalbergieae (including *Dalbergia*, one of most speciose legume genera on Madagascar, with nearly all its species endemic, as well as the medium-size endemic genus *Ormocarpopsis*) has a level of endemicity only just above the average for the subfamily.

HUMAN UTILIZATION OF LEGUMINOSAE

On Madagascar, the ways in which different species of Leguminosae are itilized are numerous and diverse. Here we outline some of the principal uses. We include examples of native species that are used by local people, some of which have been exported and are used elsewhere. We also include species that have been introduced to Madagascar, either intentionally or by accident, and that have been cultivated or have become naturalized in natural or modified ecosystems. Certain species stand out as being of particular importance and often have cultural significance; for example, *Tamarindus indica*, which is the most important shade tree in the drier part of Madagascar, has multiple other uses as food, to make cordials, and as animal feed. This species is considered to be native but not endemic to Madagascar (Diallo et al. 2007).

Ornamental and Shade Trees

Different species of Leguminosae are important in most regions of Madagascar for shade and as ornamental trees of parks, gardens, and streets. They include native species, such as *Delonix regia*, which is endemic to Madagascar and widely cultivated on the island and throughout the tropics, and *Colvillea racemosa*, which is endemic to Madagascar and cultivated locally.

Introduced species are numerous and some are widespread, including naturalized drought-resistant species, such as *Albizia lebbeck*, *Parkinsonia aculeata*, and *Pithecellobium dulce*.

Other species are cultivated mainly in urban gardens and may be locally naturalized, including *Schizolobium parahyba*, *Peltophorum dasyrhachis*, and various species of *Bauhinia*.

Food Plants

Legumes are important food sources around the world, especially the pulses; peas, beans, lentils, and chickpeas, as well as peanuts and soya, are all rich in protein. On Madagascar they are a very important part of the diet, although primarily they are introduced species. These include:

- *Arachis hypogea*—peanuts are widely cultivated, especially in the west and south, but are not known to have become naturalized.
- *Decorsea meridionalis* (vernacular name: *fangitsa*, *sandrafé*) and *Dolichos fangitsa* (vernacular name: *fangitsa*, *fangitsy*)—the large fleshy tubers of these vines are eaten raw or sometimes cooked (*D. fangitsa*) in south Madagascar where they are both endemic.
- *Delonix* spp.—seeds of different species of this genus are eaten as a snack (vernacular name: *fengoky*).
- *Lablab purpureus*—the Hyacinth Bean or Bonavist-bean is regarded as native to Madagascar, Africa, and the Indian subcontinent, and is widely cultivated across its native range, as well as in other tropical regions. The beans are eaten cooked.
- *Lens culinaris* and *L. esculenta*—lentils are widely consumed and grown in some areas as a cash crop for export.
- *Phaseolus lunatus*—the Lima Bean (vernacular name: *kabaro*) is grown mainly in the south for its seeds and was intended originally for export, but one variety (vernacular name: *kalamaka*) is also used locally for its edible leaves.
- *P. vulgaris*—which constitutes a large proportion of the beans grown around the world for their edible pods and red, white, brown, black, and speckled seeds (on Madagascar mostly red or white varieties, vernacular name: *tsaramaso*). The species is not known to have become naturalized.
- *Vigna radiata*—the Mung Bean is grown in the west, mainly by Indian communities; it has become naturalized.
- *V. subterranea*—the Bambara Groundnut (vernacular name: *voanjobory*), originally from west Africa, is very popular in certain portions of Madagascar. It is an occasional garden escape.
- *V. umbellata*—the Rice Bean; its origin is uncertain.
- *V. unguiculata*—the Cow Pea is widely cultivated and naturalized; it probably originated in Africa.

Fodder for Livestock

Many plants are used as fodder on Madagascar; in additon to the native *Tamarindus indica* (mentioned above), favored Leguminosae fodder sources include the introduced species:

- *Leucaena leucocephala*—widely grown and naturalized on the east coast but known to be poisonous to some livestock.
- *Stylosanthes guianensis*—grown specifically for pasture improvement.
- *Vachellia farnesiana*—widely naturalized in the south and west.

Wood

Many native species provide strong and durable timber suitable for construction and are among the most valuable of all Madagascar's natural products. Predominant among these is the wood of various species of *Dalbergia*, including the so-called rosewoods, which are the most sought after of the Malagasy precious woods, followed by the wood of ebony (certain *Diospyros* spp., Ebenaceae, see Schatz and Lowry, pp. 739–44), and *nato* (various Sapotaceae, see Gautier et al., pp. 726–39). Lower quality *Dalbergia* wood is referred to as palissander and nevertheless yields very important timber. Export of precious woods has drastically reduced the native populations of most species; conserving these valuable species is discussed elsewhere.

Other native species that are widely used for construction and making furniture, tools, and cooking utensils, include *Intsia bijuga*,

Tamarindus indica, and members of the genera *Albizia*, *Baudouinia*, *Cordyla*, *Cynometra*, *Dialium*, *Millettia*, *Phylloxylon*, and *Pongamiopsis*.

Medicinal and Cultural Uses

The Leguminosae are very rich in medicinal properties and many have a role in traditional Malagasy cultural practices (see Lewis et al. 2005). Examples are numerous and there is a wealth of literature about traditional uses and modern pharmaceutical studies. Here we only mention three of the better-known examples. Traditional practices continue to be very important on Madagascar, even in the more developed areas (see Randriamiharisoa et al. 2015).

- *Abrus precatorius*—widely used as a medicine for coughs, throat infections, and bronchitis. However, the seeds contain the potent alkaloid abrin, a few crushed seeds of which are enough to kill a fully grown adult.
- *Erythrophleum couminga*—widely used in sorcery. It is highly toxic, due to the alkaloid erythrophlein, and it is reported that the odor of the flowers on these trees can cause headaches for anyone standing too near them. High doses can cause heart failure. Birds and animals are believed to have died from contact with the tree.
- *Baudouinia rouxevellei*—a source of valuable wood for ornaments and other carved objects; but it is also endowed by local belief with special powers to protect the household against theft, and there are certain taboos related to it that must be respected.

BIOLOGY OF THE LEGUMINOSAE

The importance of the legume family to humans globally as a source of food, timber, medicines, and ornament is covered by a broad literature (e.g., Maphosa and Jideani 2016; Martín-Cabrejas 2019). Furthermore, the unique association between many species of the family and nitrogen-fixing bacteria that populate their root nodules is of vital importance to natural ecosystems and to agriculture through the practice of crop rotation (O. N. Allen and Allen 1981). Here we add two further aspects of legume biology particular to Madagascar.

Pollination by Lemurs

The ecological importance of lemurs in the natural ecosystems of Madagascar has been the subject of extensive research, and they clearly provide many ecosystem services typically fulfilled by other animal groups elsewhere in the world. This includes various interactions with plants, including seed dispersal. Less apparent is the ability of lemurs to affect pollination of some plant species. Their climbing ability allows them to reach the flowers of tall canopy trees to pull open flower parts and gorge on the nectar. This has been well documented for the legume *Strongylodon* (subfamily Papilionoideae, tribe Phaseoleae), which is pollinated by members of the genus *Cheirogaleus* (dwarf lemurs) (L. A. Nilsson et al. 1993) (Figure 8.32d). Other species of lemurs visit the flowers of this species, but only *C. major* is completely nondestructive and can release the floral pollen-pump mechanism perfectly.

Invasive Introduced Species

Many genera of Leguminosae have species with an ability to rapidly colonize open habitats and become invasive. This is closely related to the widespread association of most legume species with nitrogen-fixing bacteria that assists them in colonizing nitrogen-poor and degraded soils (Parker et al. 2007). Inevitably, the intentional introductions of legume species for soil stabilization and as crops or ornamentals, as well as accidental introductions, result in the co-introduction of rhizobial bacteria. It has been shown that introduced legumes can benefit from the combination of their own bacteria and local native rhizobial bacteria in the soil (Rodríguez-Echeverría and Traveset 2015) but, on the other hand, the introduction of foreign bacteria can have a negative impact on the native plant species (Rodríguez-Echeverría et al. 2012).

In many parts of the world introduced species of plants reproduce spontaneously and escape from cultivation. Where these species become well established they can have a serious negative impact on local ecosystems and natural regeneration. Species of Leguminosae are among the primary culprits. For example, the introduction of Australian species of *Acacia* to South Africa for forestry, tannin production, dune stabilization, and ornament, and the subsequent invasive spread of these species, has been highly detrimental to the indigenous flora (Le Roux et al. 2011). On Madagascar the introduced legume flora has been estimated to total 224 species (Kull et al. 2012) with 76 species documented as naturalized (Madagascar Catalogue 2020), ranging from annual herbs to trees, and including potentially invasive species of *Acacia*. The Global Invasive Species Database (http://issg.org/database/welcome/) lists only two introduced legume species, *Acacia mearnsii* and *Leucaena leucocephala*, as well as the native *Abrus precatorius*, as invasive on Madagascar. However, as commented by Binggeli (2003), the state of our knowledge is fragmentary.

The legume *Desmodium uncinatum* is native to Central and South America and has been introduced in parts of Africa, Asia, and Australia as a fodder crop, where it frequently becomes naturalized. The species has been promoted for pest control in cropping systems by applying a push-pull technology (Z. Khan et al. 2016). For this technique, a crop is interplanted with two other plant species, one that is highly attractive to the prevalent crop pest (the pull) and a second species that is repellent to the pest (the push). *Desmodium uncinatum* produces volatile compounds that repel stem-boring Lepidoptera and, in addition, exude compounds into the soil that inhibit the growth of certain species of *Striga*, a semiparasitic plant that can drastically reduce crop yields or even cause crop failure. Although developed in sub-Saharan Africa against a species of *Striga* not recorded from Madagascar (*S. hermonthica*), the technique has been tested on the island with positive results against *S. asiatica* infestation (Randrianjafizanaka et al. 2018). A further attribute of *D. uncinatum* is that it serves as an insect trap, which may also be advantageous in agricultural systems (H. Ohashi 2005): the hooked (uncinate) hairs on the stems and foliage act like Velcro and insects are trapped and die. This phenomenon has been observed in parts of Madagascar (L. Featherstone, unpublished data) but, as well as insects, amphibians, small chameleons, and even bats also have been trapped, and the species potentially could decimate the endemic fauna.

TABLE 8.23. **Published IUCN status of Malagasy Leguminosae since 2002**

NAME	IUCN CRITERIA	YEAR
CRITICALLY ENDANGERED SPECIES		
Albizia verrucosa	CR B1ab(i,ii,iii,iv,v)+2ab(i,ii,iii,iv,v)	2019
Alistilus magnificus	CR B2ab(iii)	2016
Baudouinia capuronii	CR B1ab(i,ii,iii,iv,v)+2ab(i,ii,iii,iv,v)	2019
Cadia rubra	CR B2ab(iii,v)	2016
Crotalaria bosseri	CR B1ab(i,ii,iii,v)+2ab(i,ii,iii,v)	2017
C. peltieri	CR B1ab(i,ii,iii,iv)+2ab(i,ii,iii,iv)	2017
Dalbergia davidii	CR B1ab(i,ii,iii,iv,v)	2019
D. occulta	CR B1ab(i,ii,iii,v)+2ab(i,ii,iii,v)	2017
Delonix tomentosa	CR B1ab(iii)+2ab(iii)	2014
Desmodium lobatum	CR B1ab(i,ii,iii,iv)+2ab(i,ii,iii,iv)	2017
Eligmocarpus cynometroides	CR B1ab(iii,v); C2a(i,ii); D	2013
Gagnebina bakoliae	CR B2ab(i,ii,iii,iv,v)	2019
Indigofera ankaratrensis	CR B2ab(ii,iii,iv,v)	2017
I. suarezensis	CR B1ab(iii)+2ab(iii)	2012
Mimosa kitrokala	CR B1ab(iii)+2ab(iii)	2012
Senna suarezensis	CR B1ab(i,ii,iii,iv,v)+2ab(i,ii,iii,iv,v)	2019
Tephrosia pinifolia	CR B1ab(ii,iii)+2ab(ii,iii)	2018
NAME	**CRITERIA**	**YEAR**
ENDANGERED SPECIES		
Abrus sambiranensis	EN B1ab(iii,v)+2ab(iii,v)	2016
Acacia menabeensis[1]	EN B1ab(iii,iv)	2012
A. myrmecophila[2]	EN B1ab(i,ii,iii,iv)+2ab(i,ii,iii,iv)	2019
Aeschynomene laxiflora	EN B1ab(iii)+2ab(iii)	2016
Albizia balabaka	EN B2ab(i,ii,iii,iv,v)	2019
A. morombensis	EN B1ab(i,ii,iii,iv,v)+2ab(i,ii,iii,iv,v)	2019
NAME	**CRITERIA**	**YEAR**
A. numidarum	EN B1ab(i,ii,iii,iv,v)+2ab(i,ii,iii,iv,v)	2019
A. perrieri	EN B1ab(i,ii,v)+2ab(i,ii,v)	2019
A. sahafariensis	EN B1ab(i,ii,iv,v)+2ab(i,ii,iv,v)	2019
A. viridis	EN B1ab(i,ii,iii,iv,v)+2ab(i,ii,iii,iv,v)	2019
Baudouinia louvelii	EN B1ab(i,ii,iii,iv,v)+2ab(i,ii,iii,iv,v)	2019
B. orientalis	EN B2ab(i,ii,iii,iv,v)	2019
Bauhinia brevicalyx	EN B1ab(i,ii,iv,v)+2ab(i,ii,iv,v)	2019
B. decandra	EN B2ab(i,ii,iii,iv,v)	2019
B. pervilleana	EN B2ab(ii,iii,v)	2016
Bussea perrieri	EN B1ab(i,ii,iii,iv,v)+2ab(i,ii,iii,iv,v)	2019
Cadia commersoniana	EN B1ab(i,ii,iii,iv,v)+2ab(i,ii,iii,iv,v)	2018
C. pubescens	EN B1ab(iii)+2ab(iii)	2016
Chadsia longidentata	EN B2ab(iii,v)	2016
Chamaecrista brevifolia	EN B1ab(iii)	2017
Crotalaria calva	EN B1ab(i,ii,iii,v)+2ab(i,ii,iii,v)	2017
C. leandriana	EN B1ab(i,ii,iii,v)+2ab(i,ii,iii,v)	2017
C. poissonii	EN B1ab(i,ii,iii,v)+2ab(i,ii,iii,v)	2017
Cynometra ankaranensis	EN B1ab(iii,iv,v)+2ab(iii,iv,v)	2020
C. capuronii	EN B1ab(i,ii,iii,iv,v)+2ab(i,ii,iii,iv,v)	2017
C. madagascariensis	EN B2ab(i,ii,iii,iv,v)	2019
Dalbergia abrahamii	EN B1ab(i,ii,iii,v)+2ab(i,ii,iii,v)	2019
D. andapensis	EN B1ab(iii)+2ab(iii)	2012
D. suaresensis	EN B1ab(i,ii,iii,iv,v)+2ab(i,ii,iii,iv,v)	2019
D. tsiandalana	EN B2ab(i,ii,iii,iv,v)	2019
D. urschii	EN B1ab(i,ii,iii,iv,v)+2ab(i,ii,iii,iv,v)	2019

(continued overleaf)

TABLE 8.23. ***continued***

NAME	CRITERIA	YEAR
D. xerophila	EN B1ab(i,ii,iii,iv,v)+ 2ab(i,ii,iii,iv,v)	2019
Delonix pumila	EN B1ab(iii,iv,v)+ 2ab(iii,iv,v)	2014
D. velutina	EN B1ab(iii,v)+ 2ab(iii,v)	2014
Dichrostachys paucifoliolata	EN B1ab(i,ii,iii,iv,v)+ 2ab(i,ii,iii,iv,v)	2018
Dolichos minutiflorus	EN B2ab(i,ii,iii)	2017
Eriosema betsileense	EN B1ab(i,ii,iii,v)+ 2ab(i,ii,iii,v)	2017
Erythrina ankaranensis	EN B1ab(i,ii,iii,iv,v)+ 2ab(i,ii,iii,iv,v)	2019
E. hazomboay	EN B2ab(iii,iv,v)	2020
E. perrieri	EN B1ab(i,ii,iii,iv,v)+ 2ab(i,ii,iii,iv,v)	2019
Erythrophleum couminga	EN B2ab(i,ii,iii,v)	2019
Gigasiphon humblotianus	EN B2ab(i,ii,iii,v)	2020
Indigofera bemarahaensis	EN B1ab(iii,v)+ 2ab(iii,v)	2016
I. itremoensis	EN B1ab(iii)+ 2ab(iii)	2016
I. peltieri	EN B2ab(iii,v)	2016
I. pseudoparvula	EN B1ab(i,ii,iii,iv,v)+ 2ab(i,ii,iii,iv,v)	2017
Lemurodendron capuronii	EN B1ab(i,ii,iii,v)+ 2ab(i,ii,iii,v)	2020
Lemuropisum edule[3]	EN B1ab(ii,iii,iv,v)	2014
Leptodesmia bojeriana	EN B1ab(i,ii,iii,iv,v)+ 2ab(i,ii,iii,iv,v)	2017
L. perrieri	EN B2ab(ii,iii,v)	2017
Mendoravia dumaziana	EN B1ab(i,ii,iii,v)+ 2ab(i,ii,iii,v)	2020
Millettia hitsika	EN B1ab(i,ii,iii,iv,v)+ 2ab(i,ii,iii,iv,v)	2017
Mimosa dupuyana	EN B2ab(iii,v)	2020
M. haavoa	EN B2ab(i,ii,iii,iv,v)	2019
M. lingvatouana	EN B1ab(i,ii,iii,iv,v)+ 2ab(i,ii,iii,iv,v)	2019
Mucuna manongarivensis	EN B1ab(iii)+ 2ab(iii)	2016
Mundulea anceps	EN B2ab(iii)	2016
Neoharmsia baronii	EN B1ab(iii,iv,v)+ 2ab(iii,iv,v)	2020
N. madagascariensis	EN B2ab(i,ii,iii,iv,v)	2019
Ophrestia humbertii	EN B1ab(i,ii,iii,v)+ 2ab(i,ii,iii,v)	2017
Ormocarpopsis itremoensis	EN B1ab(i,ii,iii,iv,v)+ 2ab(i,ii,iii,iv,v)	2020
O. mandrarensis	EN B1ab(i,ii,iii,iv,v)+ 2ab(i,ii,iii,iv,v)	2019
Pearsonia madagascariensis	EN B1ab(i,ii,iii,v)+ 2ab(i,ii,iii,v)	2017
Phylloxylon arenicola	EN B1ab(i,ii,iii,iv,v)+ 2ab(i,ii,iii,iv,v)	2017
P. decipiens	EN B1ab(i,ii,iii,iv,v)+ 2ab(i,ii,iii,iv,v)	2019
P. phillipsonii	EN B1ab(i,ii,iii,iv,v)+ 2ab(i,ii,iii,iv,v)	2019
P. xiphoclada	EN B1ab(i,ii,iii,iv,v)+ 2ab(i,ii,iii,iv,v)	2017
Pyranthus ambatoanus	EN B1ab(iii)+ 2ab(iii)	2016
P. monanthus	EN B1ab(iii,v)+ 2ab(iii,v)	2016
Sakoanala madagascariensis	EN B2ab(i,ii,v)	2020
Senna ankaranensis	EN B1ab(i,ii,iii,iv,v)+ 2ab(i,ii,iii,iv,v)	2019
S. bosseri	EN B1ab(i,ii,iii,iv,v)+ 2ab(i,ii,iii,iv,v)	2019
S. perrieri	EN B1ab(i,ii,iii,iv,v)+ 2ab(i,ii,iii,iv,v)	2019
Sylvichadsia grandidieri	EN B1ab(i,ii,iii,iv,v)+ 2ab(i,ii,iii,iv,v)	2020
Tephrosia phylloxylon	EN B1ab(iii)+ 2ab(iii)	2016
T. retamoides	EN B1ab(iii,v)+ 2ab(iii,v)	2016
T. subaphylla	EN B1ab(iii)+ 2ab(iii)	2016
T. viguieri	EN B2ab(iii)	2016
Tetrapterocarpon septentrionalis	EN B1ab(i,ii,iii,iv,v)+ 2ab(i,ii,iii,iv,v)	2019

NAME	CRITERIA	YEAR
Vigna bosseri	EN B2ab(ii,iii,v)	2019
V. keraudrenii	EN B2ab(iii,v)	2016
Viguieranthus brevipennatus	EN B2ab(iii,iv)	2019
V. glandulosus	EN B2ab(ii,iii,iv)	2019
V. kony	EN B2ab(i,ii,iii,iv,v)	2019
V. longiracemosus	EN B1ab(i,ii,iii,iv)+ 2ab(i,ii,iii,iv)	2019
V. umbilicus	EN B1ab(i,ii,iii,iv,v)+ 2ab(i,ii,iii,iv,v)	2019
V. unifoliolatus	EN B1ab(i,ii,iii,iv,v)+ 2ab(i,ii,iii,iv,v)	2019

NAME	CRITERIA	YEAR
VULNERABLE SPECIES		
Acacia viguieri[4]	VU B1ab(i,ii,iii,iv)+ 2ab(i,ii,iii,iv)	2019
Aeschynomene schindleri	VU B1ab(iii)	2012
Baudouinia rouxevillei	VU B1ab(i,ii,iii,iv,v)+ 2ab(i,ii,iii,iv,v)	2019
B. sollyaeformis	VU B1ab(i,ii,iii,v)+ 2ab(i,ii,iii,v)	2018
Bauhinia aurantiaca	VU B2ab(i,ii,iii,iv,v)	2019
B. ombrophila	VU B1ab(i,ii,iii,iv,v)+ 2ab(i,ii,iii,iv,v)	2019
Cadia pedicellata	VU B1ab(iii,v)+ 2ab(iii,v)	2016
Caesalpinia madagascariensis[5]	VU B1ab(i,ii,iii,iv,v)+ 2ab(i,ii,iii,iv,v)	2019
Chadsia magnifica	VU B1ab(iii)	2012
Crotalaria androyensis	VU B1ab(i,ii,iii)+ 2ab(i,ii,iii)	2017
C. craspedocarpa	VU B1ab(i,ii,iii,v)+ 2ab(i,ii,iii,v)	2017
C. humbertiana	VU B2ab(ii,iii,v)	2017
C. manongarivensis	VU B1ab(i,ii,iii,iv)+ 2ab(i,ii,iii,iv)	2017
Cynometra dauphinensis	VU B1ab(i,ii,iii,iv,v)+ 2ab(i,ii,iii,iv,v)	2019
C. lyallii	VU B1ab(i,ii,iii,iv,v)+ 2ab(i,ii,iii,iv,v); D2	2019
C. pervilleana	VU B2ab(i,ii,iii,v)	2019

NAME	CRITERIA	YEAR
Dalbergia chlorocarpa	VU A4acd	2019
D. emirnensis	VU A4acd; B2ab(i,ii,iii,iv,v)	2019
D. glaberrima	VU A4acd; B2ab(i,ii,iii,iv,v)	2019
D. glaucocarpa	VU A4acd; B1ab(i,ii,iii,iv,v)+ 2ab(i,ii,iii,iv,v)	2019
D. greveana	VU A4acd	2019
D. hildebrandtii	VU A4acd; B2ab(i,ii,iii,iv,v)	2019
D. humbertii	VU A4acd; B2ab(i,ii,iii,iv,v)	2019
D. lemurica	VU A4acd; B2ab(i,ii,iii,iv,v)	2019
D. madagascariensis	VU A4acd	2019
D. mollis	VU A4acd	2019
D. neoperrieri	VU A4acd; B2ab(i,ii,iii,iv,v)	2019
D. peltieri	VU A4acd	2019
D. pervillei	VU A4cd	2019
D. pseudobaronii	VU A4acd; B2ab(i,ii,iii,iv,v)	2019
D. purpurascens	VU A4acd	2019
D. tricolor	VU A4acd	2019
D. viguieri	VU A4acd; B2ab(i,ii,iii,iv,v)	2019
Delonix decaryi	VU A3c	2014
Dialium madagascariense	VU B2ab(i,ii,iii,iv,v)	2019
Dichrostachys myriophylla[6]	VU B1ab(i,ii,iii,iv,v)+ 2ab(i,ii,iii,iv,v)	2019
Entada pervillei	VU B1ab(i,ii,iii,v)+ 2ab(i,ii,iii,v)	2019
Indigofera imerinensis	VU B1ab(iii)+ 2ab(iii)	2016
I. mahafalensis	VU B1ab(i,ii,iii,iv,v)+ 2ab(i,ii,iii,iv,v)	2019
I. mangokyensis	VU B1ab(i,ii,iii,iv,v)+ 2ab(i,ii,iii,iv,v)	2019
Millettia aurea	VU B2ab(i,ii,iii,iv,v)	2019
M. capuronii	VU B2ab(ii,iii,iv,v)	2020

(continued overleaf)

TABLE 8.23. ***continued***

NAME	CRITERIA	YEAR
M. nathaliae	VU B1ab(i,ii,iii,iv,v)+ 2ab(i,ii,iii,iv,v)	2019
M. taolanaroensis	VU B1ab(i,ii,iii,iv)+ 2ab(i,ii,iii,iv)	2018
Mimosa psoralea	VU B1ab(i,ii,iii,iv,v)+ 2ab(i,ii,iii,iv,v)	2018
Ormocarpopsis calcicola	VU B1ab(i,ii,iii,iv,v)+ 2ab(i,ii,iii,iv,v)	2019
O. tulearensis	VU B1ab(i,ii,iii,iv,v)+ 2ab(i,ii,iii,iv,v)	2019
Parkia madagascariensis	VU B1ab(i,ii,iii,iv,v)+ 2ab(i,ii,iii,iv,v)	2019
Phylloxylon spinosa	VU B1ab(i,ii,iii,iv,v)+ 2ab(i,ii,iii,iv,v)	2019
Pongamiopsis amygdalina	VU B1ab(i,ii,iii,iv,v)+ 2ab(i,ii,iii,iv,v)	2019
P. viguieri	VU B1ab(i,ii,iii,iv,v)+ 2ab(i,ii,iii,iv,v)	2019
Pyranthus alasoa	VU B2ab(iii,iv,v)	2020
P. tullearensis	VU B1ab(i,ii,iii,iv,v)+ 2ab(i,ii,iii,iv,v)	2020
Rhynchosia androyensis	VU B1ab(iii)+ 2ab(iii)	2016
R. baukea	VU B1ab(iii)+ 2ab(iii)	2016
Sakoanala villosa	VU B2ab(i,ii,iii,iv,v)	2019
Senna meridionalis	VU B1ab(i,ii,iii,iv,v)	2020
Sylvichadsia grandifolia	VU B1ab(v)+ 2ab(v)	2016
Tephrosia genistoides	VU B2ab(iii)	2016
T. parvifolia	VU B1ab(iii)+ 2ab(iii)	2016
Viguieranthus cylindricostachys	VU B2ab(i,ii,iii,iv,v)	2019
V. scottianus	VU B1ab(i,ii,iii,iv,v)+ 2ab(i,ii,iii,iv,v)	2018
Xylia fraterna	VU B1ab(i,ii,iii,iv,v)+ 2ab(i,ii,iii,iv,v)	2019
NAME	**CRITERIA**	**YEAR**
NEAR THREATENED SPECIES		
Abrus madagascariensis	NT B2ab(i,ii,iii,v)	2017
Cadia ellisiana	NT B2ab(iii,v)	2020
Crotalaria cornu-ammonis	NT B2b(iii)	2017
C. coursii	NT B2b(ii,iii)	2017
C. decaryana	NT B2b(iii)	2017
C. xanthoclada	NT B2b(i,ii,iii,v)	2017
Cynometra aurita	NT B1ab(i,ii,iii,iv,v)+ 2ab(i,ii,iii,iv,v)	2019
Dalbergia chapelieri	NT	2012
Delonix leucantha	NT	2014
Dialium unifoliolatum	NT	2017
Dicraeopetalum capuronianum	NT B1ab(i,ii,iii,iv,v)+ 2ab(i,ii,iii,iv,v)	2019
Entada louvelii	NT	2012
Millettia orientalis	NT B1ab(i,ii,iii,iv,v)+ 2ab(i,ii,iii,iv,v)	2019
Mundulea menabeensis	NT B2ab(iii,v)	2020
Ophrestia madagascariensis	NT	2012
Ormocarpopsis nitida	NT	2019
O. parvifolia	NT B1ab(iii)+ 2ab(iii)	2020
Phylloxylon xylophylloides	NT A4c	2019
Pterocarpus marsupium	NT C1	2017
Tephrosia pungens	NT B2ab(iii)	2020

NAME	YEAR
LEAST CONCERN SPECIES	
Albizia mahalao	2019
A. mainaea	2019
A. polyphylla	2019
A. tulearensis	2019
Alysicarpus bupleurifolius	2012
Argyrolobium pedunculare	2017
Baudouinia fluggeiformis	2018
Bauhinia grandidieri	2018
B. grevei	2019
B. madagascariensis	2018

NAME	YEAR
B. morondavensis	2019
B. podopetala	2019
B. purpurea	2012
Biancaea decapetala	2018
Brandzeia filicifolia	2019
Brenierea insignis	2019
Bussea sakalava	2019
Cajanus scarabaeoides	2012
Canavalia madagascariensis	2017
Cassia hippophallus	2019
Chadsia flammea	2017
C. salicina	2019
Chamaecrista absus	2012
C. pratensis	2012
Clitoria lasciva	2017
Colvillea racemosa	2014
Crotalaria capuronii	2012
C. cyanoxantha	2017
C. laevigata	2017
C. lanceolata	2019
C. mahafalensis	2012
C. micans	2012
C. uncinella	2012
Cynometra abrahamii	2017
C. commersoniana	2016
C. sakalava	2019
Dalbergia trichocarpa	2018
Decorsea grandidieri	2017
Delonix boiviniana	2014
D. brachycarpa	2014
D. floribunda	2014
D. regia	2014
Desmodium adscendens[7]	2012
D. barbatum[8]	2012
D. salicifolium	2012
Dialium occidentale	2019

NAME	YEAR
Dichrostachys arborescens	2012
D. cinerea	2012
D. unijuga	2019
Dicraeopetalum mahafaliense	2019
Disynstemon paullinioides	2012
Dolichos fangitsa	2017
Dumasia villosa	2012
Dupuya haraka[9]	2019
D. madagascariensis[10]	2019
Entada chrysostachys	2019
E. leptostachya	2019
Eriosema procumbens	2017
Erythrina variegata	2012
Gagnebina commersoniana	2012
Galactia tenuiflora	2012
Guilandina bonduc	2018
Haematoxylum campechianum	2018
Hymenaea courbaril	2012
Indigofera bojeri	2012
I. cloiselii	2019
I. compressa	2016
I. depauperata	2020
I. leucoclada	2016
I. lyallii	2019
I. oblongifolia	2012
I. perrieri	2020
I. trita	2012
Kotschya africana	2018
Mezoneuron hildebrandtii	2012
Microcharis phyllogramme	2017
Millettia lenneoides	2017
M. richardiana	2017

(continued overleaf)

TABLE 8.23. *continued*

NAME	YEAR
Mimosa savokaea	2012
Mucuna paniculata	2016
Mundulea antanossarum	2018
M. barclayi	2019
M. chapelieri	2019
M. laxiflora	2019
M. micrantha	2020
M. obovata	2015
M. stenophylla	2016
M. viridis	2016
Neoapaloxylon madagascariense	2019
N. tuberosum	2019
Neptunia oleracea	2018
Ophrestia lyallii	2017
Ormocarpopsis aspera	2019
Ormocarpum drakei	2017
Otoptera madagascariensis	2017
Phylloxylon perrieri	2019
Pongamiopsis pervilleana	2019
Rhynchosia minima	2012
Senna anthoxantha	2019
S. lactea	2019
S. leandrii	2019
S. obtusifolia	2018
S. petersiana	2019
S. viguierella	2019
Sesbania madagascariensis	2017
Strongylodon craveniae	2012
S. madagascariensis	2012

NAME	YEAR
Tephrosia tinctoria	2012
T. villosa	2012
Tetrapterocarpon geayi	2019
Ulex europaeus	2017
Vigna adenantha[11]	2019
V. angivensis	2019
V. gazensis	2019
V. luteola	2019
V. marina	2019
V. microsperma	2012
V. oblongifolia	2019
V. parkeri	2019
V. radiata	2019
V. reticulata	2019
Viguieranthus densinervus	2019
V. pervillei	2019
Xanthocercis madagascariensis	2019
Xylia hoffmannii	2019
Zornia puberula	2017

Source: IUCN (2020).
Note: See IUCN (2020) for an explanation of the criteria and assessments from 2012 and 2019 for further details of specific classifications.
[1] Now known as *Senegalia menabeensis*.
[2] Now known as *Vachellia myrmecophila*.
[3] Now known as *Delonix edule*.
[4] Now known as *Vachellia viguieri*.
[5] Now known as *Denisophytum madagascariense*.
[6] Now known as *Gagnebina myriophylla*.
[7] Now known as *Grona adscendens*.
[8] Now known as *Grona barbatum*.
[9] Currently retained as *Cordyla haraka*.
[10] Currently retained as *Cordyla madagascariensis*.
[11] Now known as *Leptospron adenanthum*.

CONSERVATION STATUS OF THE MALAGASY LEGUMINOSAE

Du Puy et al. (2002) included IUCN (International Union for the Conservation of Nature) Red List assessments for some 80 species (mostly trees and shrubs), and some of these were posted onto the IUCN Red List website (IUCN 2020). An analysis of the conservation status of Leguminosae species, based on their documented presence within the protected areas of Madagascar, was conducted by Labat and Moat (2003). Much of this information is now out of date as 1) land-use pressure has seriously impacted vast natural areas of Madagascar over the past 20 years, 2) the protected area network of Madagascar has been dramatically enlarged (Goodman et al. 2018), and 3) the categories and criteria for Red List assessment have changed since this data was published (IUCN 2012). Nevertheless, the efforts of many organizations and individuals to conduct Red List assessments in recent years have resulted in no fewer than 313 assessments (53%) for Malagasy species of Leguminosae having been published on the IUCN Red List website (IUCN 2020). A list of the species assessed with the criteria, category, and year of each assessment is presented in Table 8.23.

The genus with the most assessments is *Dalbergia*, with 27 species assessed (56% of its currently accepted species), doubtless reflecting the interest in this genus as an important and threatened source of hardwood. *Crotalaria* and *Indigofera* follow with 20 and 18 species assessed, respectively. Of the assessments, threatened status—Critically Endangered (CR), Endangered (EN), and Vulnerable (VU)—is recorded for 167 of the species, 53% of those assessed. Thirty-eight genera (31%) have had all their Malagasy species assessed; they are mostly genera with only five or fewer species on the island, but the following are larger:

- *Baudouinia*—endemic genus, six species (one CR, two EN, two VU, one LC [Least Concern])
- *Cynometra*—10 species, all endemic (three EN, three VU, one NT [Near Threatened], three LC)
- *Delonix*—near endemic genus, 10 species, all endemic (one CR, three EN, one VU, one NT, four LC)
- *Millettia*—eight species, all endemic (one EN, four VU, one NT, two LC)
- *Phylloxylon*—endemic genus, seven species (four EN, one VU, one NT, one LC)

Critically Endangered Species

Seventeen species (5.4% of the species assessed) across 14 genera have been classified as Critically Endangered, including two species in each of the largest genera of Leguminosae on Madagascar: *Crotalaria*, *Dalbergia*, and *Indigofera*. Among the endemic genera, this category also includes a single species of each of *Eligmocarpus* and *Baudouinia*, and also one in the near-endemic genus *Cadia*. Most are known from a single site and many of the species were recorded from sites near major cities on the island, in particular Antsiranana, Mahajanga, and Tolagnaro, where much of the natural vegetation has now been lost. Illegal harvesting of wood is a significant threat to *Dalbergia* species, *Baudouinia capuronii*, and *Eligmocarpus cynometroides*. Recent field searches for some species have been unsuccessful, so they may already be extinct (see for example Devey et al. 2013).

Endangered Species

Eighty-seven species (28% of the species assessed) across 42 genera have been assessed as Endangered; the genera with the highest number that have been assessed are *Albizia*, *Dalbergia*, and *Viguieranthus*, with six species each. While the first two of these are large, widespread pantropical genera, *Viguieranthus* is a Malagasy Region endemic genus comprising 18 species, of which one is also recorded from the Comoro islands. Nine genera have three or four species classified as Endangered, including the endemic genus *Phylloxylon*.

Vulnerable Species

Sixty-three (20.1% of the species assessed) species across 29 genera have been classified as Vulnerable, including 17 species of *Dalbergia*; no other genus in this category has had more than four species assessed.

ACKNOWLEDGMENTS

We wish to thank Melissa Luckow (Cornell University) and Colin Hughes (University of Zurich) for comments on an early draft of this contribution. We are grateful also to L. Anders Nilsson and the late Börge Pettersson of Uppsala University, and Patrice Antilahimena, Chris R. Birkinshaw, Fidy Ratovoson, Zachary Rogers, George E. Schatz, all of Missouri Botanical Garden, for permission to use their photographs.

Subject editors: Laurent Gautier and Steven M. Goodman

MORACEAE: *FICUS*, FIGS

J.-Y. Rasplus, Y. Aumeeruddy-Thomas, A. Cruaud, F. Kjellberg, V. M. Rafidison, D. McKey, and M. Hossaert-McKey

In this contribution, we discuss not only the natural history and biogeography of Malagasy fig trees (Moraceae, *Ficus*) but also that of some of their associated insects. We then address fig frugivory and its importance in different habitats on the island. We illustrate how chemical ecology is crucial to better understand interactions between fig and wasp, and fig and frugivore. Finally, we present the importance of figs to humans. The content of this chapter is based on a range of herbarium collections and Internet databases, as well as on a review of published and unpublished data concerning the evolutionary ecology of fig-wasp interactions, the phenology of figs and frugivory, and the ethnobiology of *Ficus*. We use the term Madagascar for the island of Madagascar in the strict sense, Malagasy Region for the group composed of Madagascar and surrounding archipelagoes (Comoros, Seychelles including Aldabra, and Mascarenes), continental Africa for the African subregion (thus excluding the Malagasy Region), and

Afrotropical (biogeographic) region for sub-Saharan continental Africa plus the Malagasy Region.

THE GENUS *FICUS* AND ITS POLLINATION BY MUTUALISTIC WASPS

Ficus is a pantropical genus of about 850 species (Berg and Corner 2005) characterized by the production of figs, which are urn-shaped receptacles each containing numerous unisexual flowers. Fig plants are well known for their obligate mutualism with agaonid wasps, which are their unique pollinators. Each *Ficus* species is associated with one to seven species of pollinating wasps (Chalcidoidea: Agaonidae), which mostly develop at the expense of seeds of a single *Ficus* species (Wiebes 1963). The genus *Ficus* is subdivided into six subgenera (namely *Ficus*, *Sycomorus*, *Sycidium*, *Synoecia*, *Pharmacosycea*, and *Urostigma*), all of them, except *Synoecia*, occurring in the Afrotropical region. Subgenera are subdivided into sections; for example, the subgenus *Urostigma* contains five sections, of which the sections *Urostigma* and *Galoglychia* occur in the Afrotropics. Very few agaonid wasp species are associated with two or more species of figs and this mostly happens in the Neotropics. The genus *Ficus* is morphologically diverse, comprising free-standing trees, hemi-epiphytes (stranglers), shrubs, and creepers (Rasplus et al. 2020). Size and morphology of figs and leaves are highly variable among species. Leaf morphology is also variable among conspecifics as well as within single individuals, which complicates identification.

In this pollination mutualism between *Ficus* and agaonids, female wasps enter the closed central cavity of the fig through the ostiole (an opening located at the distal part of the fig) by crawling through the ostiolar bracts. The architecture of the bracts limits entrance into the fig by nonadapted insects (Cook and Rasplus 2003). Once inside the fig, wasps lay eggs by inserting their ovipositor through the styles of some flowers and can pollinate either actively or passively (Kjellberg et al. 2001). Often, once they have laid eggs, female wasps cannot escape and die in the fig cavity. Flowers in which eggs have been laid are transformed into galls in which larvae of the new generation of wasps develop. Other female flowers that do not contain larvae develop seeds. By the time the wasp offspring emerge from the galls into the central cavity of the fig, male flowers (which produce pollen) have reached maturity. Male wasps emerge first and mate with females that are still enclosed in their galls. Then the females emerge and either actively collect pollen, which they load into thoracic structures called pollen pockets (active pollination: two-thirds of fig species worldwide), or are dusted with pollen by the natural dehiscence of the anthers (passive pollination: one-third of fig species). Finally, males dig tunnels through the fig wall and the short-lived female wasps fly away from their natal fig. They are attracted by chemical compounds emitted by receptive figs, which they enter and the cycle is repeated (Hossaert-McKey et al. 2010). In order to maintain this reproductive cycle, fig trees of the appropriate species should have receptive figs present all year around; this is the reason why fig species are mainly found (with some notable exceptions) in tropical or subtropical climates.

About half of the species worldwide, and most Afrotropical species, are monoecious. In these species, each fig contains both staminate (male) and pistillate (female) flowers and produces pollen, pollinators, and seeds (Cook and Rasplus 2003). Each fig contains both short-styled female flowers in which wasps preferentially lay their eggs and long-styled flowers in which wasps cannot oviposit. Thus, short-styled flowers mostly produce wasps and long-styled flowers mostly produce seeds. The other half of the world's fig species are gynodioecious. In these species, which are exclusively found in the Old World, mainly in the Oriental region, male function (pollen and pollinator production) and female function (seed production) are each performed by separate individual trees. About half of the individual trees contain only long-styled female flowers in which wasps are not able to lay eggs because of their very long styles, much longer than the wasps' ovipositors. In these individuals, wasps pollinate the flowers and often die within the fig. Consequently, these trees produce only seeds and neither pollinators nor pollen; such trees are morphologically and functionally female (Berg 1984). The other half of tree individuals produce figs with short-styled female flowers, frequently organized in two layers, as well as male flowers. The wasps are thus able to lay eggs in all ovaries, and their offspring will disseminate the pollen to other trees. These individual trees produce pollen and pollinating wasps but (almost) no seeds; although morphologically hermaphroditic, such trees are functionally male.

MALAGASY SPECIES OF *FICUS* AND FIG WASPS

Most *Ficus* species on Madagascar were first described by Perrier de la Bâthie (1928, 1952a) or by earlier botanists. Berg (1986) later revised their taxonomy and produced detailed descriptions of Malagasy species, but see also Berg and Wiebes (1992) and Rafidison et al. (2011). Malagasy *Ficus* belong to four subgenera (Table 8.24). Some allochthonous species were introduced to Madagascar in historic times, either for their edible fruits (e.g., *F. carica*) or as ornamentals (e.g., *F. elastica*, *F. pumila*) (Turk 1995) mostly without their pollinating wasps.

In comparison with southeast Asia (Corner 1965), Madagascar was formerly considered to be depauperate in *Ficus* species (Goodman and Ganzhorn 1997), but species richness on the island appears similar to that observed in drier parts of Africa, at least at regional or local scales (see Berg 1990; Rasplus et al. 2003), although this still needs to be formally tested. About two-thirds of Malagasy fig species are associated with relatively humid vegetation and the remainder with drier habitats; these proportions are comparable to those observed in continental Africa (Berg 1990).

Although Berg's (1986) revision clarified the taxonomic status of most species, a few changes are required. Indeed, Berg considered *F. sakalavarum* (subgenus *Sycomorus*) as a subspecies of *F. sycomorus*, but several lines of evidence suggest that it is a valid species (Kerdelhué et al. 1999; Rafidison et al. 2011), including morphological characters (figs and leaves) and them having their own distinct pollinating and non-pollinating wasps (Kerdelhué 1997). Ripe figs of *F. sakalavarum* are larger than those of *F. sycomorus*, the size difference being larger than that indicated by Berg (1986) and Berg and Wiebes (1992) (see Table 8.24). The report of *F. bojeri* from northern Madagascar by Berg (1986) is probably erroneous,

TABLE 8.24. **Ecological characteristics of Malagasy *Ficus* species**

INFRAGENERIC CLASSIFICATION	SPECIES	MATING SYSTEM[1]	LIFE-FORM	HEIGHT UP TO (m)[2]	MODE OF FIG INSERTION[3]	MAXIMUM SYCONIA DIAM. (cm)[4]	HABITAT	ELEVATION	DISTRIBUTION[5]
Subgenus *Sycidium*	*F. pachyclada* Baker	d	Tree	25 (–35)	R	1.5 D	Forest, often along rivers, marshes, sea coast	50–1090 (–1150)	M, Co
	F. brachyclada Baker	d	Shrub or treelet	8	C R	1 (2) F	Understory, often in riparian forest (syntopic with *F. brachyclada*)	(0–) 300–1600 (–2000)	M
	F. politoria Lamarck	d	Shrub or treelet	8	C R	1 F	Understory, abundant in patches, often in riparian forest	0–1700 (2500–2800)	M
Subgenus *Sycomorus*	*F. sycomorus* L.	m	Tree	15 (–30)	C	2.5 F	Woodlands, frequent near streams, in secondary growth. Possibly planted in some places[6]	(30–) 70–150 (–1250)	M, Co, CA
	F. sakalavarum Baker	m	Tree	–	–	8 (–10) F	Riparian forest, locally abundant	Low elevation (–1250)	M
	F. tiliifolia Baker	m	Tree	20 (–25)	–	1.5–5 F	Forest, sometimes planted	0–1700	M, Co
	F. torrentium H. Perrier	m	Tree	25	C R A	3 (–5) F	Medium-altitude moist evergreen forest, along streams	600–1200 (–1424)	M
	F. polyphlebia Baker	m	Shrub or treelet	10	C R A	3 (–6) F	Rupicolous near or in flowing water	(0–) 20–1200 (–1315)	M
	F. botryoides Baker	m	Tree	25	C[7]	2 (–3.8) F	Riparian forest	0–1600	M
	F. trichoclada Baker	m	Tree	15	C R A	3 (–4) F	Riparian forest	100–1500	M
Subgenus *Pharmacosycea* section *Oreosycea*	*F. assimilis* Baker	m	Tree	25		1.5 D	Forest	0–1000	M
	F. ampana Berg	m	Shrub, treelet (or tree?)	(25?)	–	8 D	Unknown	1000–1050	M
Subgenus *Urostigma*, section *Urostigma*	*F. madagascariensis* Berg	m	Shrub or tree	–	–	6 D	Dry deciduous forest and dry spiny thicket, as well as apparently near Toamasina	0–50	M
Subgenus *Urostigma*, section *Conosycea*	*F. menabeensis* H. Perrier	m	Shrub or tree	4 (–20)	A	8 D <10 F	Grasslands, dunes, riparian forest, often rupicolous	0–1200 (–1500)	M
	F. humbertii Berg	m	Shrub	2 (–5)	A	7 D	Unknown	0–80 (–100)	M

(*continued overleaf*)

TABLE 8.24. ***continued***

INFRAGENERIC CLASSIFICATION	SPECIES	MATING SYSTEM[1]	LIFE-FORM	HEIGHT UP TO (m)[2]	MODE OF FIG INSERTION[3]	MAXIMUM SYCONIA DIAM. (cm)[4]	HABITAT	ELEVATION	DISTRIBUTION[5]
Subgenus *Urostigma* section *Galoglychia*	*F. lutea* Vahl	m	Hemi-epiphytic tree	23	A	2.5 (−3.5) F	In forest, often riparian, marshes, littoral forest and thicket	0–1500	M, Co, Se, CA
	F. trichopoda Baker	m	Shrub or tree	10 (−20)	-	2 F	Wooded grasslands, marshy places. Sometimes planted near villages	500–1100	M, CA
	F. grevei Baillon	m	Hemi-epiphytic tree	20 (−35)	-	1.7 D	Dry deciduous forest, often riparian	30–200	M
	F. rubra Vahl	m	Hemi-epiphytic tree	8	-	0.6–1 D	Often rupicolous	(50–) 300–650 (−1000)	M, Me, Se, Al, Co
	F. marmorata Baker	m	Shrub or tree, possibly hemi-epiphytic	15	-	8 D	Forest, rupicolous	0–50 (−300)	M
	F. bivalvata H. Perrier	m	Tree	20 (−30)	-	2.5 × 1.2 D	Medium-altitude moist evergreen forest	1171–1700	M
	F. antandronarum (H. Perrier) Berg	m	Shrub or tree	20	-	1.3 D	Moist evergreen and riparian forests	0–1600	M, another subspecies in Co
	F. reflexa Thunberg (= *F. pyrifolia*)	m	Hemi-epiphytic shrub or tree	10 (−30)	A	1.2 D	In various types of forest	0–1700	M, Me. Two other subspecies in Se, Co, Al
	F. polita Vahl (= *F. megapoda*)	m	Hemi-epiphytic or secondarily terrestrial tree	15 (−40)	-	4 F	Moist evergreen and riparian forests	600–700	M, CA

Sources: Classification generally follows Berg (1986) and Berg and Wiebes (1992), as well as information from Perrier de la Bâthie (1952a), Compton (1992), Turk (1995), MBG (Tropicos database), Madagascar Catalogue (2020), Rafidison et al. (2011, 2020), C. Kerdelhué and J.-Y. Rasplus (unpublished data); many new observations by F. Kjellberg and V. Rafidison (unpublished data).

Note: "Planted" always means planted from cuttings.

[1] D, dioecious; m, monoecious.

[2] In the columns Height, Maximum syconia diam., and Elevation, extreme values are given in parentheses.

[3] C, cauliflorous; R, ramiflorous; A, axillary.

[4] D, when dry; F, when fresh.

[5] M, Madagascar (based on observations made only in central, eastern, and western provinces); Co, Comoros; Se, Seychelles; Me, Mascarenes; Al, Aldabra; CA, continental Africa.

[6] May apply both to *F. sycomorus* and *F. sakalavarum*.

[7] In *F. botryoides*, the mode of fig attachment includes large masses of fruits (up to 80 cm diam.) and decomposing organic matter, including rotted figs of previous crops.

and specimens previously identified under this name belong, in fact, to *F. brachyclada* (Rafidison et al. 2011).

As a consequence, we consider that the fig flora of Madagascar comprises 24 species (Table 8.24), including seven species from subgenus *Sycomorus*, most of them endemics. However, a thorough analysis of species in the subgenus *Sycidium* (*F. brachyclada* and *F. politoria*, Figures 8.33a and b) will most probably reveal that in their current configuration they constitute a species complex comprised of several more species.

Pollinators of 14 of the 24 Malagasy fig species have been described, which means that at least 40% of the agaonid species still await description. The pollinators of five rare or localized species still need to be discovered (*F. ampana*, *F. assimilis*, *F. bivalvata*, *F. marmorata*, and *F. torrentium*). With the exception of *F. sycomorus* and *F. politoria*, most of the Malagasy *Ficus* species host a single pollinator species (Table 8.25) (Berg and Wiebes 1992). Most pollinator species are endemic to the Malagasy Region, and most genera are also present in continental Africa, with the exception of the pollinator of *F. humberti*, which belongs to a new genus of Agaonidae, and *Maniella bergi* (previously included in *Platyscapa*), which belongs to an otherwise strictly Oriental and Australasian genus. The four *Ficus* species that occur on both Madagascar and continental Africa share the same agaonid species (though in two of the four cases different subspecies are described).

On Madagascar, *F. sycomorus* and *F. politoria* are each associated with multiple species of agaonids (J.-Y. Rasplus, unpublished data).

FIGURE 8.33 **Malagasy *Ficus*. A) *F. pachyclada*, B) *F. politoria*, C) *F. trichoclada*, D) *F. polyphlebia*, E) *F. menabeensis*, and F) *F. humberti*.** (PHOTOS A and C–E by F. Kjellberg, B by J.-Y. Rasplus, and F by Dr. Bing Liu of the Institute of Botany, Chinese Academy of Sciences.)

TABLE 8.25. **Pollinating fig wasps (Agaoninae) associated with *Ficus* on Madagascar**

FICUS	AGAONINAE (POLLINATORS)	DISTRIBUTION
F. ampana	Unknown	?
F. antandronarum	New species of *Elisabethiella*	M
F. assimilis	Unknown	?
F. bivalvata	Unknown	?
F. botryoides	*Courtella blommersi*	M
F. brachyclada	*Kradibia cowani*	M
F. grevei	New species of *Elisabethiella*	M
F. humbertii	New genus/species close to *Nigeriella*	M
F. lutea	*Allotriozoon heterandromorphum*[1]	M, Co, CA
F. madagascariensis	New species of *Platyscapa*	M
F. marmorata	Unknown	?
F. menabeensis	*Maniella bergi*[2]	M
F. pachyclada	New species of *Kradibia*	M
F. polita	*Courtella bekiliensis bekiliensis*	M, other subspecies in CA
F. politoria	*Kradibia saundersi* and new species	M
F. polyphlebia	*Courtella longimucro*	M
F. reflexa	*Elisabethiella reflexa*	M, Me
F. rubra	*Nigeriella avicola*	Me
F. sakalavarum	*Ceratosolen namorokensis*	M
F. sycomorus	*Ceratosolen arabicus* (pollinator) *Ceratosolen galili* (nonpollinating)	M, Co, CA M, Co, CA
F. tiliifolia	*Ceratosolen stupefactus*	M[3]
F. torrentium	Unknown	?
F. trichoclada	*Courtella blommersi*	M
F. trichopoda	*Elisabethiella bergi breviceps*	M, other subspecies in CA

Sources: Berg and Wiebes (1992), Compton (1992), Kerdelhué (1997), Kerdelhué et al. (1999), unpublished recent samplings of the authors of this contribution.
Note: Distribution: M, Madagascar; Co, Comoros; Se, Seychelles; Me, Mascarenes; CA, continental Africa.
[1] This species is a species complex.
[2] This species was previously classified within *Platyscapa* but belongs to another genus.
[3] Not known from *Ficus* cf. *tiliifolia* on Grande Comore (Compton 1992).

Ficus sycomorus is associated with two *Ceratosolen* species, namely *C. arabicus* and *C. galili*, which occur in sympatry throughout the whole geographic range of their host (Madagascar and continental Africa). More importantly, only *C. arabicus* pollinates its host. *Ceratosolen galili*, even though it has fully developed pollen pockets, does not exhibit pollinating behavior, and is therefore described as a cuckoo wasp (Compton et al. 1991), that is to say a parasite of the *F. sycomorus-C. arabicus* mutualism. *Ficus politoria* is associated with at least three different pollinator species (J.-Y. Rasplus, unpublished data). Finally, two Malagasy subgenus *Sycomorus* species (*F. botryoides* and *F. trichoclada*) appear to be pollinated by a same pollinator species, *C. blommersi*.

ASSOCIATED NONPOLLINATING INSECTS

In addition to its mutualistic partner, each fig species hosts a variety of nonpollinating fig wasps (NPFWs) that also develop in the flowers. Each of these wasps is mostly associated with one or a few species of figs, and each fig species hosts a community of NPFWs (Jousselin et al. 2008). These communities are relatively small in dioecious species (up to six species of NPFWs developing on a single fig species) but can be highly diversified in monoecious figs (up to 44 species of NPFWs on *F. microcarpa* in Asia) (Kerdelhué and Rasplus 1996a, 1996b). Most species of NPFWs are still undescribed and their biology poorly studied. Some are gall-makers and oviposit in the fig ovules, while others are parasitoids, hyperparasitoids, or inquilines (their larvae develop at the expense of the gall tissue induced by another wasp species). Inquilines lay eggs in gall-transformed ovaries that already contain a larva of a pollinator or a gall-maker. Some species are like the pollinator in that they enter into the fig through the ostiole (e.g., Sycophaginae and Sycoecinae on Madagascar) and oviposit in the ovaries. But most species of NPFWs oviposit from outside of the fig, through the fig wall, using long or coiled ovipositors (Sycoryctinae, Otitesellinae, Epichrysomallinae, Ormyridae, and Eurytomidae on Madagascar). Many open questions remain about numerous aspects of the ecology and evolution of NPFWs, as well as their phylogeny and biogeography, and their impact on the mutualism remains to be thoroughly studied.

Various other groups of insects also develop inside figs. One of these, the drosophilid fly genus *Lissocephala*, has undergone a highly specialized radiation on *Ficus* in the African region (Lachaise et al. 1996). These flies develop in the fig and take advantage of the fig–fig wasp mutualism without affecting any of the mutualistic partners. This genus is present in the Malagasy Region, and has strong affinities with continental Africa, but not with the Oriental-Australasian region (Lachaise et al. 1996). Tropical species of the weevil genera *Curculio* and *Omophorus* (Coleoptera: Curculionidae) are also specialized on figs (Rasplus et al. 2003). In this case, however, the development of the weevil larva in the fig cavity destroys seeds and wasp galls, and the impact on the mutualism is thus negative for both partners. On Madagascar, for instance, more than 50% of the crop (up to 100%) in a given tree of *F. botryoides* (Figure 8.34c), *F. polyphlebia* (Figure 8.33d), and *F. tiliifolia* (Figure 8.34d), can be parasitized by weevil larvae (A. Dalecky, unpublished data). Ants (Formicidae) patrol receptive figs and capture wasps as well as ripe figs to collect seeds (they were observed taking both on *F. tiliifolia*), and in *F. botryoides* ant nests can be found in the cauliflorous inflorescences (A. Dalecky, unpublished data; see also Cushman et al. 1998 for data including Malagasy *Ficus*).

BIOGEOGRAPHIC CONSIDERATIONS

Distribution maps (Figure 8.35) are tentative because data on the distribution of several rare *Ficus* species are scarce: some species have been described only recently and are still poorly known (see Berg 1986; Berg and Wiebes 1992); and the different regions of Madagascar have not been sampled with the same intensity. Some species are probably restricted to the moist evergreen forests of the Eastern, Central and/or Sambirano Domains (*sensu* Humbert 1955). These include *F. polyphlebia*, *F. botryoides*, *F. torrentium*, *F. antandronarum*, *F. politoria*, *F. brachyclada*, and *F. bivalvata*. Some species are probably restricted to the Southern and Western Domains (*sensu* Humbert 1955), including *F. marmorata* and *F. humberti* (Figure 8.33f). Other species are found across the island: *F. sakalavarum*, *F. tiliifolia*, *F. lutea*, *F. reflexa*, *F. polita*, and *F. pachyclada* (Figure 8.34a).

Seven of the 24 *Ficus* species of Madagascar are also present on surrounding islands (Table 8.24), and only 15 species are endemic to Madagascar. The nearby islands also host four other species (all endemic to the Malagasy Region) not present on Madagascar: *F. densifolia* (Seychelles and Mascarenes, with one doubtful citation of this species for Madagascar), *F. lateriflora* (Mascarenes), *F. mauritiana* (Mascarenes), and *F. karthalensis* (Comoros) (Berg and Van Heusden 1985; Berg and Wiebes 1992). Another species, *Ficus* cf. *tiliifolia*, may possibly occur in the Comoro islands (F. Kjellberg, unpublished data). In total, 86.2% (25 of 29) of the fig species are endemic to the Malagasy Region.

None of the Malagasy figs are found in any biogeographic region other than Africa. For most of the island's species that were included in a phylogenetic analysis (Cruaud et al. 2012; Harrison et al. 2012), their closest relative occurs in the Afrotropics (*Sycidium*, *Sycomorus*, and all *Galoglychia* species), with the following exceptions:

- *Ficus madagascariensis* appears to be sister to *F. densifolia* (Mascarenes) plus all other *Ficus* belonging to section *Urostigma*, which mostly occur in Asia (Chantarasuwan et al. 2016), but this requires confirmation, as another possible explanation is that this species originates from an early colonization event from Asia.
- *Ficus menabeensis* (Figure 8.33e) is the sole representative of the section *Conosycea* on Madagascar and is sister to *F. glaberrima*, a species occurring from India to Java. *Ficus humberti* is very probably a misclassified section *Galoglychia* species, thus originating from Africa (J.-Y. Rasplus, unpublished data).
- *Ficus assimilis* may also have colonized Madagascar from southeast Asia, as its closest relative, the rare *F. albipila*, occurs widely from Sumatra to Australia (Corner 1985).

Several subgenus *Sycomorus* species are endemic to Madagascar and may represent a local radiation. However, none of the phylogenetic studies has yet included a representative sampling of this Malagasy group of species. Harrison et al. (2012) analyzed several species of this group and found they did not form a unique radiation.

Reconstructing the history of colonization of Madagascar by the ancestors of the different fig clades is a difficult task. Indeed, the timing of the origin of the crown *Ficus* has been debated for the past 15 years, with some phylogenies supporting a Late Cretaceous origin (60–101.9 million years ago [Mya], Cruaud et al. 2012) and others an early Cenozoic origin (40.8–56 Mya, Q. Zhang et al. 2019). This huge uncertainty is probably due to differences in calibration scheme (stem versus crown, log-normal versus uniform, secondary calibration of the root, etc.). However, evidence from the agaonid wasps supports a Late Cretaceous origin of the crown *Ficus*. Two lines of evidence are consistent with this hypothesis: 1) agaonid divergence from their closest relatives has been estimated at 90 Mya using 37 fossils of Hymenoptera to calibrate the dates and ultraconserved genomic elements (UCE) markers (Branstetter et al. 2017); 2) a fossil discovered in the Insect Bed of Bembridge Marls (Isle of Wight, United Kingdom), and belonging to the wasp clade that pollinates *Galoglychia* fig trees, has been dated back to about 34 Mya (Compton et al. 2010). This age is 10 Mya older than the age estimates for stem *Galoglychia* in the early Cenozoic hypothesis and hence supports the Late Cretaceous origin hypothesis.

Fig trees and their pollinating wasps have independently colonized Madagascar at least eight times (Cruaud et al. 2012; Chantarasuwan et al. 2016). Using a Late Cretaceous hypothesis, the timing of these different colonization events ranges from ~36 Mya to 5 Mya. The

FIGURE 8.34 **Different cultural aspects of *Ficus* on Madagascar. A) *F. lutea* at the Rova Ambohimanga, Antananarivo, a tree of the 12 wives of King Andrianamipoimerina of the Merina; B) children collecting fruits of *F. botryoides*, *fompoha*, Fianarantsoa; C) *F. botryoides* in the Botanical Garden of Tsimbazaza, Antananarivo, with Martine Hossaert-McKey on left collecting samples; D) *F. tiliifolia*, local variety *voara bekobo*, literally "the *voara* with thick lips," referring to the unusual protuberant aspect of the ostiole; E) Finn Kjellberg collecting samples of *F. reflexa* from large cuttings planted around a *zebu* corral; F) *F. reflexa* growing on a stela, and local guide explaining the sacred nature of the stone and the plant; and G) isolated tree of *F. lutea* on agricultural land, Ambohimahamasina, near Ambalavao.** (PHOTOS by Y. Aumeeruddy-Thomas.)

most ancient colonization events appear to be those of *F. menabeensis* (36 Mya) and of the ancestor of the subgenus *Sycomorus* lineage (33 Mya). The colonization of Madagascar by the subgenus *Sycidium* may also be relatively ancient (~20 Mya), as may the colonization by subgenus *Urostigma* species. This last event is problematic as the position of *F. densifolia* differs between studies, being sister to all Oriental species of the section in Chantarasuwan et al. (2016), but nested with Oriental species and sister to *F. religiosa* in other studies.

In contrast, colonization of Madagascar by Afrotropical species of section *Galoglychia* by crossing the Mozambique Channel is recent (less than 10 Mya). Some *Galoglychia* species may have been introduced recently by humans. However, leaf prints of *F.* aff. *polita* found in clays along the Onilahy River at Benenitra, dating from at least the early Quaternary, suggest this species colonized Madagascar before humans (Perrier de la Bâthie 1928).

This tempo of colonization of Madagascar by figs is confirmed by the timing inferred from dated phylogenies of fig wasps. The oldest colonization of agaonids appears to be those of *Ceratosolen* species pollinating subgenus *Sycomorus* fig trees (~33 Mya, with a radiation around 25 Mya) and of *Maniella bergi*, the pollinator of

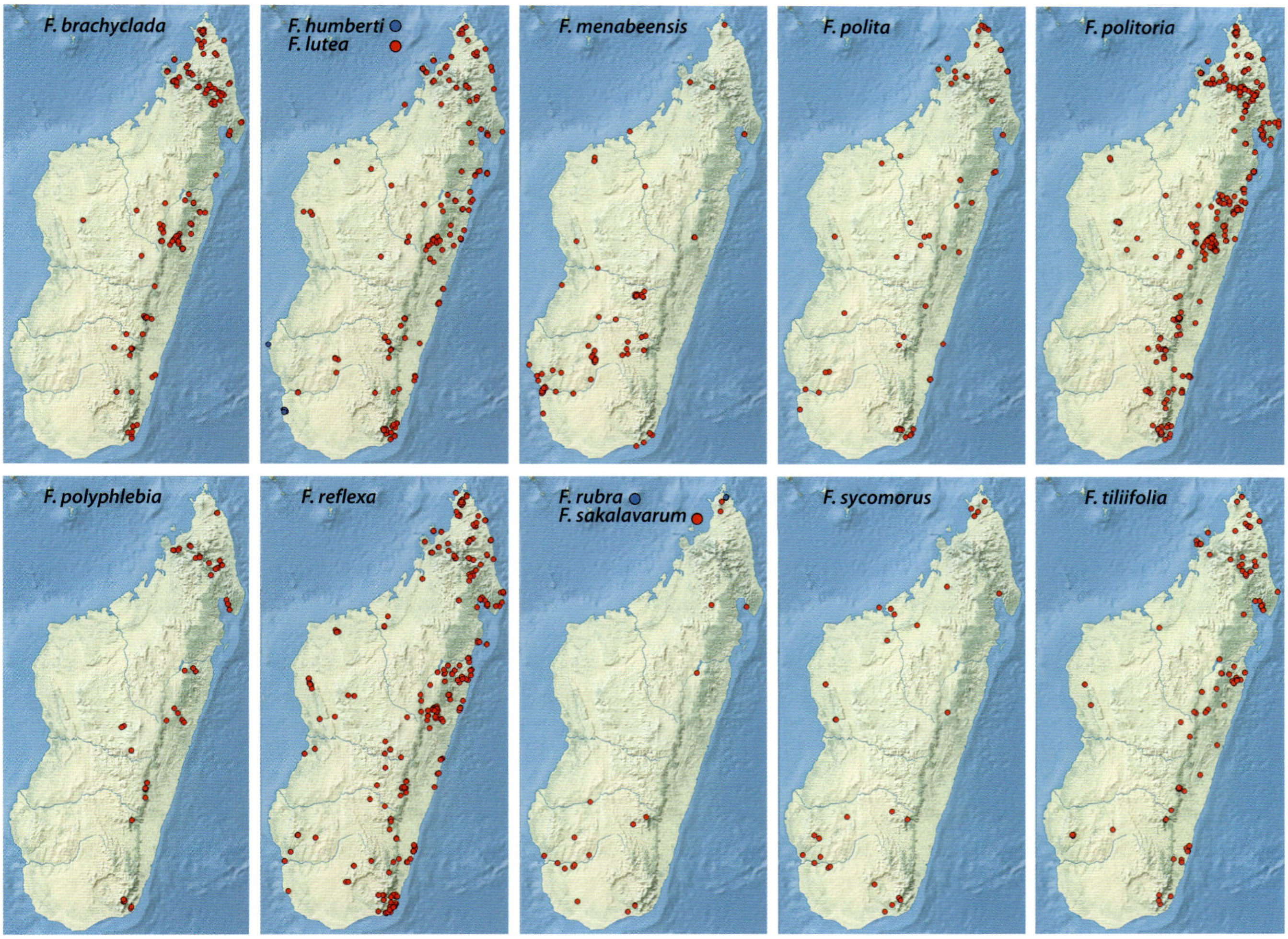

FIGURE 8.35 **Distribution of some *Ficus* species in Madagascar. Information regarding occurrences were retrieved from our samples, the literature, and the GBIF database (GBIF 2020). Original identifications were verified and sometimes corrected.**

F. menabeensis (between 29 and 12 Mya). Again, colonizations of Madagascar by pollinators of section *Galoglychia* species (from Africa) are more recent events (less than 12 Mya). Results for the few Malagasy nonpollinating fig wasps for which we have a time estimate of their colonization of Madagascar are consistent with those for figs and pollinating wasps.

Successful colonization of islands by fig trees is not easy as it necessitates colonization by compatible partners (*Ficus* and pollinating wasp). Pollination shifts between non-sister host species are relatively rare events in the Old World. Therefore, the colonizing fig tree requires pollination by its own pollinator or by a closely related species that must be 1) attracted by the odors of a nonhost fig, 2) capable of entering the fig (despite of co-adaptation of head and ostiole lengths), and 3) capable of using the female flowers (co-adaptation of ovipositor and style lengths). While fig seeds can be dispersed over rather long distances by frugivorous mammals (i.e., fruit bats) or birds (pigeons and parrots), the wasps only live for two or three days and are blown by the wind. Nevertheless, long-distance dispersal of fig wasps, up to tens of kilometers and sometimes over 100 km, has been observed (McKey 1989; Ahmed et al. 2009). The mutualistic interaction may constitute an important constraint to colonizing islands, compared with less specific pollination systems.

Colonization of Madagascar from the Oriental region (India) may have occurred through island hopping across the western Indian Ocean. Indeed, a series of islands emerged over the past 65 Mya (Chagos Plateau, Saya de Malha Bank, and Nazareth Bank), using which species belonging to subgenera *Sycidium*, *Sycomorus*, and *Conosycea* may have reached the Mascarenes, Madagascar, and subsequently Africa—such a scenario still requires validation.

FIG FRUGIVORY

In the obligate mutualism between figs and agaonid wasps, each partner provides an essential resource to the other. At any time of the year within a breeding population of fig trees, emerging wasps from a tree with ripening figs need to find a tree with receptive figs if the local population is to be maintained. Considering that pollinating wasps probably cannot survive for more than two to four days, and that flowering is relatively synchronous within a fig tree, between-tree flowering asynchrony in a population of fig trees is a key feature that maintains local populations of one or more pollinators (Janzen 1979; McKey 1989; Herre 1996). In turn, flowering asynchrony means that ripe figs of a given species are found year-round and may constitute a critical resource for frugivores, especially during lean periods of low fruit availability (Korine et al. 2000). Fruiting asynchrony among trees, the large crops of some fig trees, and the pulpy nature of the ripening inflorescences make figs a keystone resource for frugivore communities in Neotropical and Oriental tropical forests (Janzen 1979; Terborgh 1986). However, figs do not appear to have a key role in maintaining frugivore populations in some other tropical rainforests (Gautier-Hion and Michaloud 1989) and this could be the case in Madagascar (Goodman and Ganzhorn 1997).

Compared with other large islands in the Old World, Madagascar (587,000 km^2) is slightly smaller (75%) than Borneo (743,330 km^2) or New Guinea (775,210 km^2) but exhibits a much lower diversity of *Ficus* species (24 species versus about 150 and 157 species, respectively). At the local scale, the richness of Madagascar sites rarely exceeds more than 12 species of fig trees, while sites in Borneo and Papua can reach over 80 and 65 species, respectively. Africa is comparable to Madagascar: they share section *Galoglychia* and were colonized by most of the same fig lineages (section *Oreosycea* and subgenera *Sycidium* and *Sycomorus*) with the notable exception of section *Conosycea*, which only reached Madagascar. Some of the well-studied African sites also exhibit higher richness of figs, with about 30 species locally, compared with well-studied Malagasy sites (Harrison 2005). The low richness of fig species in Madagascar could easily be explained by the isolation of the island in deep geologic time and the low number of fig colonization events, as well as the low level of subsequent local diversification of fig lineages that reached Madagascar. Finally, Madagascar is globally drier than Borneo and New Guinea, which may also explain the lower richness of *Ficus*.

Compared with other tropical areas, Madagascar is also noteworthy for its relative paucity in frugivores (Table 8.26). Malagasy figs are eaten by several vertebrates, including lemurs, birds (pigeons, parrots, and bulbuls), bats, small rodents, and presumably introduced bushpigs (Perrier de la Bâthie 1928; Turk 1995; Goodman et al. 1997). The nonvolant mammalian frugivore fauna is dominated by lemurs and lacks ungulates, squirrels, and large rodents. Furthermore, among land birds only ~10% of the species occurring on Madagascar are at least partially frugivorous (Razafindratsima 2014).

Densities of fig trees have received little attention on Madagascar, but appear to be low, at least for hemi-epiphytic species, as observed in other tropical regions (Harrison 2005). Free-standing members of the subgenera *Sycomorus* and *Sycidium* species can be locally more abundant, especially along streams. Therefore, in Malagasy ecosystems, the contribution by figs to food resource availability, at least across seasons, appears relatively limited and globally low compared with fruit resources produced by other trees. It is possible that fig densities on the island are too low to allow their functioning as keystone species during the season of low availability of fruits, but better estimates of fig densities are required.

Reproductive phenology data for Malagasy fig species are also scarce. Dalecky et al. (2003) reported the phenologies of *F. brachyclada* and *F. politoria* over two years and of *F. botryoides*, *F. polyphlebia*, and *F. tiliifolia* over a single year in the moist evergreen forest of Ranomafana National Park (600–1100 m elevation). Stages of fig maturity were recorded following Galil and Eisikowitch (1968), and fig abundance was noted on a semiquantitative scale. All surveyed fig trees produced relatively small crops (<10 figs per tree); that may be sufficient to sustain fig wasp populations but is of limited importance for large frugivores. At Ranomafana, figs are available almost year-round (Dalecky et al. 2003), and the lack of fruiting individuals of some species (i.e., *F. politoria*) during some periods (July–November) may be artifactual due to insufficient sample size and local searches for figs. In dioecious figs, wasps may be locally extinct after period of strong drought (Harrison 2000) but can recolonize the area from nearby trees. In the moist evergreen forests of the island, ripe fig availability varied seasonally, with the summer months (December–February) most productive, and winter (June–August) the least (Hemingway and Overdorff 1999). Peak of fig production was in summer and did not correspond with maximum fig feeding in lemurs. At Ranomafana, during the winter season other fruits became scarcer and all lemur species fed on figs, but in the dry deciduous forests of the north there is concentrated fig fruiting during the winter months, and they are extensively fed upon by fruit bats (S. M. Goodman, unpublished data). Elsewhere on the island, few studies have been conducted to explore the importance of figs. In Madagascar, figs were found to be among the most important food sources for bats (Bollen and van Elsacker 2002) and for lemurs. However, most Malagasy frugivores exhibit a highly diverse diet, thereby dispersing a wide array of fruiting trees, among which fig trees represent only a small portion. This is different from what happens in Africa, where species richness patterns of figs and avian frugivores are linked via strong resource-consumer interactions (Kissling et al. 2007).

Few quantitative data on feeding by frugivorous vertebrates on figs are available for Madagascar (but see Goodman et al. 1997; Dalecky et al. 2003). In Ranomafana most lemur populations commonly exploited strangler fig species. Despite an overall similarity in species composition in the diets of these lemurs, there were notable differences in the quantity of figs consumed (Table 8.27), from 35.4% of overall feeding time in *Eulemur fulvus* (Brown Lemur) to 3.1% in the folivore *Hapalemur griseus* (Gray Bamboo Lemur). However, figs were clearly among the preferred fruit resources for *H. griseus*, comprising 23.1% of fruit feeding time. This species also feeds on *Ficus* leaves. There are a few cases of extreme specialization of frugivores on fig resource, but none are known from Madagascar (Shanahan et al. 2001). In Malagasy habitats, no frugivores have specialized on fig species, and most species appear to be generalists (Table 8.26).

Most species of Malagasy frugivores are not dependent on figs to survive during the lean season, as would be expected from classical descriptions of keystone resources. Most of these animals are generalists and can easily shift their diets, which might result from the seasonality of fruit availability. Frugivorous lemurs are also frequently folivorous and increase leaf consumption during periods of lower fruit availability (i.e., *Propithecus*). Only two lemur genera, *Varecia* and *Eulemur*, are considered to be mainly frugivorous and therefore may in some cases be dependent on fig trees that fruit during the period of fruit scarcity. *Eulemur* individuals at Andringitra were shown to depend heavily on *Ficus* (nearly exclusively *F. lutea*) during the winter months when fruits are scarce (including the studied *Ficus* species) (Dalecky et al. 2003). This site may represent the best candidate location identified to date for studying the role of *Ficus* as a keystone resource for frugivores. Further phenological surveys are necessary to evaluate the importance of *Ficus* to the

TABLE 8.26. **Main frugivorous vertebrates of Madagascar and *Ficus* (fig) species they consume, as reported in the literature**

		F. assimilis	*F. botryoides*	*F. brachyclada*	*F. grevei*	*F. humberti*	*F. lutea*	*F. marmorata*	*F. madagascariensis*	*F. menabeensis*	*F. pachyclada*	*F. polita*	*F. politoria*	*F. polyphlebia*	*F. reflexa*	*F. rubra*	*F. sakalavarum*	*F. sycomorus*	*F. tiliifolia*	*F. trichopoda*	*Ficus* sp.	No. *Ficus* species consumed by each frugivore species
Columbidae	*Alectroenas madagascariensis*	X	–	–	–	–	–	–	–	X	–	–	–	–	–	X	–	–	–	–	–	3
	Nesoenas picturata	–	–	–	–	–	–	–	–	–	–	–	–	–	–	–	–	–	X	–	–	1
	Treron australis	–	–	–	–	–	–	–	–	–	–	–	–	–	–	X	–	–	X	–	X	3
Philepittidae	*Philepitta castanea*	–	–	–	–	–	–	–	–	–	–	–	–	–	–	–	–	–	–	–	X	1
Psittaculidae	*Coracopsis nigra*	–	–	–	–	–	–	–	–	–	–	–	–	–	–	X	–	–	X	–	–	2
Pycnonotidae	*Hypsipetes madagascariensis*	X	–	–	–	–	–	–	–	–	–	–	–	–	–	–	–	–	X	–	X	3
Sturnidae	*Hartlaubius auratus*	–	–	–	–	–	–	–	–	–	–	–	–	–	–	–	–	–	X	–	X	2
Zosteropidae	*Zosterops maderaspatanus*	–	–	–	–	–	–	–	–	–	–	–	–	–	–	–	–	–	X	–	X	2
Cheirogaleidae	*Cheirogaleus major*	–	–	–	–	–	–	–	–	–	–	–	X	–	–	–	–	–	–	–	–	1
	C. medius	–	–	–	–	–	–	–	–	X	–	–	–	–	–	–	–	–	–	–	–	1
	C. sp.	X	–	–	–	–	X	–	–	X	–	–	–	–	–	X	–	–	–	–	–	4
	Microcebus rufus	–	–	–	–	–	–	–	–	–	–	–	–	–	–	X	–	–	–	–	X	2
Indriidae	*Propithecus coronatus*	–	–	–	–	–	–	–	–	–	–	–	–	–	–	X	–	–	–	–	–	1
	P. diadema	–	–	–	–	–	–	–	–	–	–	–	–	–	–	–	–	–	X	–	–	1
	P. edwardsi	–	–	–	–	–	–	–	–	–	–	–	–	–	–	–	–	–	–	–	X	1
	P. verreauxi	–	–	–	–	–	–	–	X	–	–	–	–	–	–	–	–	X	–	–	X	3
Lemuridae	*Eulemur cinereiceps*	–	–	–	–	–	X	–	–	–	–	–	X	–	–	X	–	–	X	–	X	5
	E. collaris	X	–	–	–	–	X	–	–	–	–	–	–	–	–	X	–	–	–	–	X	4
	E. flavifrons	–	–	–	–	–	–	–	–	–	–	–	–	–	–	–	–	–	X	–	X	2
	E. fulvus	–	–	–	–	–	–	–	–	–	X		X	–	–	X	–	X	X	–	–	5
	E. macaco	X	–	–	–	–	X	–	–	–	–	X	X	–	–	X	X	X	–	–	–	7
	E. mongoz	–	–	–	–	–	–	–	–	–	–	–	X	–	–	–	–	X	–	–	–	2
	E. rubriventer	–	X	X	–	–	–	–	–	–	X	–	X	–	X	X	–	–	X	–	X	8
	E. rufifrons	–	X	–	–	–	X	–	–	–	–	–	X	–	X	–	–	–	X	–	–	5
	E. rufus	–	X	X	–	–	–	–	–	–	X	–	X	–	–	X	–	–	X	–	–	6
	E. sanfordi	–	X	–	–	–	X	–	–	X	–	–	–	X	–	–	–	–	–	–	–	–
	Hapalemur griseus	–	–	X	–	–	X	–	–	–	X	X	–	–	X	–	–	–	–	–	–	5
	Lemur catta	–	–	–	X	–	X	X	–	–	X	X	X	–	–	–	–	X	–	–	–	7
	Varecia rubra	–	–	–	–	–		–	–	–	–	–	–	–	–	–	–	–	–	–	X	1
	V. variegata	X	X	–	–	–	X	–	–	–	–	–	X	–	X	X	–	–	X	–	X	8

TABLE 8.26. **continued**

		F. ASSIMILIS	*F. BOTRYOIDES*	*F. BRACHYCLADA*	*F. GREVEI*	*F. HUMBERTI*	*F. LUTEA*	*F. MARMORATA*	*F. MADAGASCARIENSIS*	*F. MENABEENSIS*	*F. PACHYCLADA*	*F. POLITA*	*F. POLITORIA*	*F. POLYPHLEBIA*	*F. REFLEXA*	*F. RUBRA*	*F. SAKALAVARUM*	*F. SYCOMORUS*	*F. TILIIFOLIA*	*F. TRICHOPODA*	*FICUS SP.*	NO. *FICUS* SPECIES CONSUMED BY EACH FRUGIVORE SPECIES
Lepilemuridae	*Lepilemur sahamalazensis*	–	–	–	–	–	–	–	–	–	–	–	–	–	–	–	–	–	X	–	–	1
Muridae	*Rattus rattus*[1]	X	–	–	–	–	–	–	–	X	–	–	–	–	–	–	–	–	–	–	–	2
Nesomyidae	*Eliurus webbi/ ellermani*	X	–	–	–	–	–	–	–	X	–	–	–	–	–	X	–	–	–	–	–	3
Pteropodidae	*Eidolon dupreanum*	–	X	–	X	–	X	–	–	–	–	X	X	–	X	X	X	–	–	X	–	9
	Pteropus rufus	X	–	X	X	X	X	–	X	X	X	X	–	–	X	–	–	–	–	–	–	10
	Rousettus madagascariensis	–	X	–	–	–	X	–	–	–	–	–	X	–	–	X	X	–	–	–	–	5
No. documented frugivore species that consume each fig species		9	7	4	3	1	12	1	2	7	6	5	12	1	6	16	3	5	15	1	14	

[1]Species introduced to Madagascar.

TABLE 8.27. **Feeding on *Ficus* as a proportion of time spent feeding for five lemur populations**

SITE	LEMUR SPECIES	% FEEDING[1]	% FRUIT[2]	MOST COMMONLY USED SPECIES
Vevembe	*Eulemur cinereiceps*	7.7%	11.6%	*F. rubra*
Andringitra	"*E. albocollaris* [= *cinereiceps*] × *E. rufus* hybrid"	35.3%	39%	*F. lutea*
Ranomafana	*E. rufus*	10.8%	13.7%	*F. rubra*
Ranomafana	*E. rubriventer*	12.5%	13.7%	*F. rubra*
Ranomafana	*Hapalemur griseus*	3.1%	23.1%	*F. reflexa*

Notes: Consumption of all *Ficus* species is combined. Data from each study for time spent feeding has been combined.

[1] Time spent feeding on figs compared to overall feeding time for each lemur population.

[2] Time spent feeding on figs compared to total time feeding on fruits for each lemur population.

frugivore community on the island, and for comparing patterns in the moist evergreen, semi-deciduous, and dry deciduous forests. Among the community of Malagasy vertebrate frugivore species, a few species can be considered as seed predators (e.g., introduced Muridae rodents, endemic nesomyine rodents, *Coracopsis* parrots), whereas most other species are seed dispersers (Bollen et al. 2004a).

Studies on Malagasy frugivores have mostly focused on the feeding ecology and the role of mammals (lemurs and bats) in dispersal (Dew and Wright 1998; Ganzhorn et al. 1999; Bollen and van Elsacker 2002; Bollen et al. 2004b). On the island, sizes of ripe figs range from ~4 mm (*F. antandronarum*) to over 50 mm in *F. sakalavarum*, one of the two *Ficus* species with the largest ripe figs in the Afrotropical region. Within forest fragments, large and medium-size figs are mostly dispersed by frugivorous lemurs with large home ranges (>100 ha) and long daily distances traveled. Frugivorous bats, *Alectroenas* and *Treron* fruit pigeons, and *Hypsipetes madagascariensis* (Madagascar Bulbul) are probably the most important dispersers of seeds across forest fragments (Bollen and van Elsacker 2002).

Seeds of *Ficus* are small (1 to 2 mm long in Malagasy species) (Volona and Goodman 2019) and appear to germinate faster after they have passed through the digestive tract of their dispersers

(Oleksy et al. 2017). Deposition of seeds in feces may have complex effects on post-dispersal predation as well as on the probability of germination in favorable sites. On Madagascar, this has been demonstrated for seeds of *F. assimilis*, *F. polita*, *F. grevei*, and *F. lutea* after ingestion by *Pteropus rufus* (Bollen and van Elsacker 2002; Oleksy et al. 2017) and for seeds of *F. brachyclada* and *F. menabeensis* after ingestion by *Eidolon dupreanum* (Picot et al. 2007). Germination success is also increased, as shown for seeds of *F. rubra* ingested by *Rousettus madagascariensis* (Andrianaivoarivelo et al. 2011). Other Malagasy frugivorous mammals (Dew and Wright 1998) and birds (Razafindratsita and Zack 2009) also have positive effects on seed germination.

Hence, despite the lack of fig specialists, certain frugivores depend on *Ficus* in some seasons, as proposed for other tropical forests (McKey 1989). *Ficus* may not play a role of staple year-round food in Malagasy forest habitats. However, the role of *Ficus* during lean periods needs further documentation and may be of importance for different endemic species on the island.

CHEMICAL ECOLOGY OF FIG POLLINATION AND SEED DISPERSAL

Chemical signaling is crucial at two stages of the fig's life cycle: when receptive figs must attract their specific pollinators, and when mature figs must attract frugivores that will disperse their seeds. Many studies show that pollinating fig wasps are attracted by volatile organic compounds emitted by figs at receptivity (Grison-Pigé et al. 2002; Hossaert-McKey et al. 2010). Maximum distances from which wasps can detect receptive figs are not known, but scent plumes produced by flowers emitting volatile organic compounds or VOCs (including VOCs present in fig emissions) are typically detectable by insects over distances of a few hundreds of meters (Fuentes et al. 2016). Moreover, each fig wasp species is usually only attracted by the odor of its own host fig (Proffit et al. 2009; Souto-Vilarós et al. 2018). Specificity is often ensured by qualitative differences in the compounds present (mainly monoterpenes, sesquiterpenes, shikimic compounds, and some fatty acid derivatives) and by quantitative differences in the relative proportions of major and minor common compounds. In a very few species the odor is composed of rare compounds as a private sensory channel (Chen et al. 2009) between the fig and its pollinating wasp. In a few examples it has also been shown that nonpollinating fig wasps locate their host species by using the volatile compounds that are emitted by figs during the stage of development at which each species can oviposit within the fig (Proffit et al. 2007). Further research is required to investigate the function of fig scents in the attraction of nonpollinating fig wasps. Scents as cues for host location are also important to explain why wasps still continue to visit female figs in which they cannot reproduce. In some dioecious species (Hossaert-McKey et al. 2016) it has been shown that male and female figs at receptivity produce the same volatile organic compounds and in similar proportions, and that fig wasps are not able to discriminate between figs of the two sexes, supporting the hypothesis of chemical mimicry (Ashman 2009).

Finally, scents are important cues in fig-frugivore interactions, mainly for mammalian frugivores (Borges et al. 2008; Hodgkison et al. 2013; Soler et al. 2018). The volatile compounds emitted by figs differ between the receptive phase and dispersal phase of figs of the same species, although both are composed mainly of fatty acid derivatives and terpenes.

On Madagascar, chemical mediation of fig interactions with their mutualistic partners remains to be studied. Odors of receptive figs have been investigated in only two species, the monoecious species *F. botryoides* and one of the three dioecious species present on the island, *F. pachyclada*. This last species is characterized by a high proportion of 2-heptanone (an odorant ketone), which is associated with some minor compounds such as 6-methyl-3-hepten-2, benzaldehyde, and α-cedrene. The olfactory signal emitted by figs of *F. botryoides* is mainly composed of monoterpenes such as (E)-ocimene, ρ-cymene and sabinene (C. Soler, unpublished data). Finally, only one species has been studied at the dispersal phase, *F. lutea*. In this species, the volatile organic compounds are emitted by ripe figs, both on the island and in South Africa, and in both cases odors of ripe fruits comprised about 50% fatty acid derivatives (such as undecane, (Z)-3-hexenol, (E)-2-hexenol). The main difference between the two sites was the significantly higher proportion of sesquiterpenes (α-bergamotene, β-caryophyllene, and α-copaene) emitted by this fig on Madagascar. Detailed studies of such intraspecific variation in fruit scent should help determine if, among possible causes such as isolation by distance and insular isolation, the very peculiar fauna of Madagascar frugivores could be a driving force.

FIGS AND HUMANS

In this section, we present knowledge and practices of Malagasy people related to fig species, their symbolic meanings, roles in Malagasy history, as well as practical uses and linkages to vernacular taxonomy and naturalist knowledge of *Ficus* species. We use case studies conducted by ethnoecologists, especially among the Betsileo and the Merina, and data from other regions, both from literature and from our field observations.

To set the scene, those who travel to Madagascar and have a strong interest in figs will come across children on the road or in small villages in the Central Highlands who systematically recall a short poem used in schools to learn how to count, which goes as follows: "*Isa ny amontana* [one, *F. lutea*], *roa ny aviavy* [two, *F. polita*], *telo fangady* [three, *angady*, the Malagasy typical spade]". This poem probably diffused across portions of the island during the period when the Merina attempted to extend their control over more than two-thirds of the land and a large part of the population of Madagascar in the early 19th century (Kottak 1977). This poem was a means of associating these two *Ficus* species to the Merina culture and the symbolic importance of these plants to the royal family (Razafiarivony 2006; Aumeeruddy-Thomas et al. 2018). Andrianapoinimerina (c. 1745–1810), one of the best known of the kings from this period, used to deliver his public speeches to the people under a *F. lutea*, which is still present at his ancient residence, Rova Ambohimanga, near Antananarivo. In addition, the Merina planted *F. lutea* well beyond its natural area of distribution, as one of their symbols to mark new territories over which they gained control (Aumeeruddy-Thomas et al. 2018; Rafidison et al. 2020).

TABLE 8.28. **Vernacular names of Malagasy *Ficus* species**

FICUS	VERNACULAR NAMES	LOCATIONS AND ETHNIC GROUPS (IN PARENTHESES)	REFERENCES
F. ampana	*Ampana*	Toamasina: Sandrangato	4, 5
F. antandronarum	*Nonoka vaventiravina [mandressi angabou* on Mayotte]	Fianarantsoa: Ranomafana NP	1, 4
F. assimilis	*Karay*	?	1
	Kivozy	Toliara: Manamby	1
	Ampany, arostro, fihamy, tsitindrika	?	10
F. botryoides	*Afompo*	Antsiranana: Montagne d'Ambre NP	1
	Voara rano	Fianarantsoa: Ranomafana NP	1, 2, 9
	Voara ranoambohitra	Fianarantsoa: Ranomafana NP	2, 3
	Voara fopohondahy	Fianarantsoa: Ranomafana NP	2
	Fompoha	Fianarantsoa: Ambohimahamasina, Ambendrana (Betsileo)	12
F. brachyclada	*Ampaly*	Antananarivo: Mandraka FS	1
	Ambaly?	Antsiranana: Manongarivo SR	1
	Ampalifotsy	Antsiranana: Marojejy NP	1
	Mamoakely	Antsiranana: Ambalavoaniho	1
	Fotsiditiala	Toamasina: Soanierana Ivongo	1
	Famakilela [vaventiravina]	Fianarantsoa: Ranomafana NP	1, 3, 9
F. grevei	*Mandresy*	Antsiranana: Analamerana SR	1
	Fihamy, amota	(Sakalava)	10
	Fiambena	Toliara: Miary	1
F. lutea	*Nonobe*	Toliara: Andohahela NP	1
	Aviavi?	Toliara: Andranolahy	1
	Aviavi(n)dahy	(Betsileo)	6, 10
	Aviavindrano	(Sakalava)	10
	Nohondahy	(Masikoro)	10
	Nonoka vaventiravina	Fianarantsoa: Ranomafana NP	2
	Amontana (or *amotana*)	Antsiranana: Montagne d'Ambre NP	1, 2, 6, 7, 9, 10, 12
		Toamasina?: Manakana	
		Fianarantsoa: Ranomafana NP	
		Toamasina: Masoala NP	
		Antanala	
	Amonta	(Antaisaka)	6, 10
		Fianarantsoa: Ambendrana, Ambohimahamasina (Betsileo)	12

TABLE 8.28. ***continued***

FICUS	VERNACULAR NAMES	LOCATIONS AND ETHNIC GROUPS (IN PARENTHESES)	REFERENCES
	Amontana	Antananarivo, royal palaces (*rova*) surrounding Antananarivo (Merina)	13
		(Merina)	
	Amontambavy	(Merina)	6
	Amontandahy	French	6
	"grand figuier des rovas"		6
F. madagascariensis	*Hampana*	Toamasina: Soanierana Ivongo	4
F. marmorata	*Lazo*	(Androy)	10
F. menabeensis	*Hazotsikirova*	Toliara: Ankoratsaka	1
F. pachyclada	*Ampana*	Toamasina: Antanandava, Androna	1, 10
	Apana	Fianarantsoa: Ranomafana NP	1, 9, 3
	Ampaly	Fianarantsoa:	
	Voara	Ambendrana, Ambohimahamasina (Betsileo)	10
	Voaramongy	(Sakalava)	10
	Ampalibe	(Sihanaka)	10
	Kivozy	Ambendrana, Sahabe (Betsimisaraka, Betsileo)	10, 12
	Kivozo	Fianarantsoa: Andrambovato FS	1
F. polita	*Aviavy*	(Sakalava)	7, 10
	Aviavindrano	(Sakalava)	10
	Mandresy	(Antanala, Antaimoro, Masikoro?, Merina?)	8, 10, 13
	Tsaramady	Fianarantsoa: Ambendrana, Ambohimahamasina	12
F. politoria	*Ambora*	Antsiranana: Montagne d'Ambre NP	1
	Ampalifotsy	Antsiranana: Marojejy NP; Toamasina: Tampolo FS	1
	Marandravy	Toliara: Andohahela NP	1
	Ampaly	Toliara: Andohahela NP, Fianarantsoa, Ambendrana, Ambohimahamasina (Betsileo) Toamasina: Analamay	1, 6, 12
	Ampaliala	(Merina)	6
	Ramy rindritra	Toamasina: Analamazaotra SR	1
	Ramiraningitra	(Tsimihety)	6
	Andriambololonkazo	?	6
	Kivozy	Fianarantsoa: Ambendrana, Ambohimahamasina (Merina, Betsileo)	6, 12

(continued overleaf)

TABLE 8.28. ***continued***

FICUS	VERNACULAR NAMES	LOCATIONS AND ETHNIC GROUPS (IN PARENTHESES)	REFERENCES
	Kivozo	Fianarantsoa: Ranomafana NP	3
	Horondry	Toamasina: Betampona INR	1
	Famakilela (or *madinidravina*)	Fianarantsoa: Ranomafana NP, Ampamaherana FS	1, 3, 9
F. politoria and/or *F. brachyclada* (under "*F. soroceoides*")	*Ampaly*	Fianarantsoa: Ambendrana, Ambohimahamasina (Betsileo)	12
	Avozo	?	10
	Kivozy	Fianarantsoa: Ambendrana, Ambohimahamasina (Betsileo)	11 12
F. polyphlebia	*Voara*	Toamasina: Antalavia	1
	Voara rano	Antsiranana: Marojejy NP	1
		Fianarantsoa: Ranomafana NP	3
	Fopohonona	Fianarantsoa: Ranomafana NP	1
	Adabo	Antsiranana: Mandrizavona	1
	Sandrohy	Toliara: Andohahela NP	1
F. reflexa	*Nonoka*	Antsiranana: Ambato Fianarantsoa: Betsileo, Ambendrana, Ambohimahamasina, Antananarivo (Merina)	1, 7, 3 12 13
	Nonoka madinidravina	Fianarantsoa: Ranomafana NP	1
F. rubra	*Nonoka*	?	6
	Nonoka siay	Fianarantsoa: Ranomafana NP	2
	Nonoka madinidravina	Fianarantsoa: Ranomafana NP	2
F. sycomorus and/or *F. sakalavarum*	*Aviary*	Fianarantsoa: Andringitra NP	1
	Hara	Toliara: Andohahela NP	1
	Voara	Fianarantsoa: Ranomafana NP	9
	Adabo [*Adabou* on Mayotte]	Toliara: Analafaly, Miary	1, 7, 10 4
F. tiliifolia	*Voara* (Or *voara bekoube, voara malefaka*)	Antsiranana: Marojejy NP, Lokobe NP Fianarantsoa: Ranomafana NP, Ranomena, Andranobetokana Fianarantsoa: Ambendrana Toamasina: Nosy Mangabe SR, Masoala NP	1, 7, 9 12
	Voara tenany	Fianarantsoa: Ranomafana NP	1, 2, 3
	Voarabe	Toamasina: Antalavia	1
	Voara mamoahahezana (or *mamoatahezana*?)	Fianarantsoa: Ranomafana NP	1, 2
	Ara	Fianarantsoa: Ambohimahamasina	1

FICUS	VERNACULAR NAMES	LOCATIONS AND ETHNIC GROUPS (IN PARENTHESES)	REFERENCES
	Aravola	Fianarantsoa: location?	1
	Voarandambo	Fianarantsoa: Ranomafana NP	1
	Apana?	Fianarantsoa: Ranomafana NP	3
F. torrentium	*Voara*	Antsiranana: Marojejy NP, Manongarivo SR	1
	Ramiringitra	Toamasina (Bezanozano)	10
	Adabo	Antsiranana: Anjanaharibe-Sud SR	1
F. trichoclada	*Fopohana?*	Fianarantsoa: Ambatofinandrahana	1
	Fopohona?	Fianarantsoa: Ambatofinandrahana	4
	Fompohana?	Fianarantsoa: Ampamaherana FS	1
	Fompoha *Fopoha?*	Fianarantsoa: Ambendrana, Ambohimahamasina (Betsileo) Toliara: Andohahela NP	1 12
	Sandrohy	Toliara: Andohahela NP	1
F. trichopoda	*Zavy*	(Betsimisaraka, Sakalava)	10
	Aviavindrano	(Merina, Betsileo)	10
	Aviavy	Fianarantsoa: Ambendrana, Ambohimahamasina (Betsileo)	9
	Nonoka	Fianarantsoa: Ranomafana NP	9

Notes: Vernacular terms used on other Indian Ocean islands that are roughly similar to that in Malagasy are given in square brackets. Locations and, when possible, the province for each site is given before the colon. NP, National Park or Parc National; INR, Integrated Nature Reserve or Réserve Naturelle Intégrale; SP, Special Reserve or Réserve Spéciale; FS, Forestry Station or Station Forestière. References: 1, MBG (Tropicos database); 2, Turk (1995); 3, Unpublished observations of authors; 4, Madagascar Catalogue (2020); 5, Berg (1986); 6, Boiteau and Allorge (1998), Samyn (1999); 7, Decary (1946); 8, Beaujard (1988); 9, Goodman et al. (1997); 10, Perrier de la Bâthie (1952a); 11, Berg and van Heusden (1985); 12, Rafidison et al. (2016, 2020); and 13, Aumeeruddy-Thomas et al. (2018).

Betsileo inhabitants still plant *F. lutea* in front of their houses, and many are among the ancient members of the Betsileo noble class who had close relationships with the Merina kings (e.g., Harper 2003). Investigations of the 12 sacred hills surrounding Antananarivo, directly linked to the former royal families, found planted *F. lutea* and *F. polita*, which today still represent symbols of power and sacredness, or *hasina*, a concept used by many Malagasy cultural groups that relates simultaneously to the power of nature and its sacred dimension (Aumeeruddy-Thomas et al. 2018) (see Figure 8.34a). However, in some parts of Madagascar, other trees are of greater symbolic importance. Nevertheless, Sakalava people living in the western lowlands do plant or protect some *Ficus* species on their lands, such as *F. sycomorus*, for medicinal use of the bark, and for its edible fruits.

Turk (1995) assembled a list of names in Malagasy for fig species, to which we add new data (Table 8.28), but such vernacular names are lacking from certain areas of the island. Variations in naming of the same *Ficus* species are apparent, a situation common in vernacular taxonomy in most traditional and modern societies throughout the world as names vary from one ethnic group to another (and even within ethnic groups), indicating linguistic and cultural identity. In Madagascar, linguistic diversity is high due to ancient influences of Austronesian and African languages, and local dialects therefore introduce variations in naming (e.g., Beaujard 2011). Most vernacular *Ficus* names on the island are linked to uses, origin, or biological aspects. All names collected to date refer to figs at the species level and in some cases are associated with regional variations. For example, *F. lutea* in Antananarivo is called *amontana*, while the same species is *amonta* for the Betsileo (Rafidison et al. 2020). Naming intraspecific variation is rare but is known for *F. tiliifolia*, known as *voara* or *ara*. This tree is highly appreciated for its fruits by the Betsileo, who recognize two varieties, *voara bekobo* and *voara malefaka*, in villages near Fianarantsoa. The names refer to the shape and taste of fruits of the two varieties (Figure 8.34d).

The following physical characteristics of different *Ficus* are used jointly or separately to distinguish the species and are most often linked to uses, ecology, or beliefs:

- The white latex flowing abundantly from cut bark—*Ficus* latex is used in different portions of the island for hunting birds or for medicinal purposes, and is believed to improve water retention in soils and to improve breast feeding by women (Rafidison 2013; Rafidison et al. 2016; Aumeeruddy-Thomas et al. 2018). *Ficus reflexa*, named *nonoko* or *laza*, meaning literally "feeding breast," is named after this particular characteristic, although other species used by groups other than the Betsileo or Merina may be called *nonoka*, an analogy to *F. reflexa*.

- Use of the fibrous bark of *Ficus* to make ropes or barkcloth (called *fato*)—The bark of both *F. tiliifolia* (*voara*) and *F. botryoides* (*fompoha*) are used to make *fato* (MBG Tropicos database; Turk 1995; Rafidison 2013; Rafidison et al. 2016, 2020).
- The shape and quality of the fruits, including the presence or not of internal insects—Some people talk of parasites that affect the fruit (e.g., of *F. lutea* in Antananarivo) but not of the role of these insects in the pollinating process (Aumeeruddy-Thomas et al. 2018; Rafidison et al. 2020). Two species, *F. botryoides* (Figure 8.34c) and *F. trichoclada* (Figure 8.33c), are both named *fompoha*. *Fompoha* literally means "to blow" and refers to the gesture of blowing on the opened ostiole to produce a small cloud of tiny insects. Children are very good observers of the presence of insects and know how to clear away the insect debris before consuming fruits (Figure 8.34b). The fruits of many species are locally eaten by people as snacks (Rafidison et al. 2020). The cauliflorous habit is also recognized as a characteristic of some *Ficus* species, and, more generally, where on the tree the fruit is located is a trait that is used locally to distinguish between species (Figure 8.34c).
- The leaves are also a feature used to identify certain species groups—*F. politoria* and *F. brachyclada* bear the same name due to a particular leaf characteristic; they have rough leaves and are both called either *kivozy* or *ampaly*, literally meaning "scabrous." These leaves are often used to polish wood.
- Their ease of propagation from woody cuttings—This technique is frequently used to make hedges. The Betsileo use *F. reflexa* and *F. lutea* in hedges for cattle (*zebu*) corrals. Such structures serve multiple functions: they protect against soil erosion and have supernatural power to protect cattle as well as people from evil spirits, while bringing happiness and well-being (Figure 8.34e).
- The hemi-epiphytic or hemi-epilithic (growing on rocks) habit of some *Ficus* species is linked to beliefs regarding the sacred nature of these plants. They are believed to have been planted by intangible creatures and symbolize the sacred power of nature (*hasina*) due to their capacity to grow on natural rocks, steles (megaliths), tombs, or cliffs (Figure 8.34f) without requiring any visible soil substratum.

As a result of their multiple values, several *Ficus* species are planted and these, as well as those growing naturally near villages, are protected (Table 8.24, Figure 8.34g) (Rafidison et al. 2020). These trees constitute an attractive resource for frugivores and may increase seed dispersal of fig species, facilitating and accelerating succession, which means they serve an important conservation role.

Subject editors: Laurent Gautier and Steven M. Goodman

EUPHORBIACEAE AND ITS SEGREGATES PERACEAE, PICRODENDRACEAE, AND PUTRANJIVACEAE

K. J. Wurdack

INTRODUCTION AND CLASSIFICATION

The circumscription of Euphorbiaceae has changed dramatically in modern classifications and since this family was treated in the precursor to this book (Hoffmann and McPherson 2003a). The present widely accepted circumscription recognized by Angiosperm Working Group IV (Chase et al. 2016) is derived from molecular phylogenetic studies that resolved the traditional pre–Angiosperm Working Group family (i.e., Euphorbiaceae *sensu lato*) into six lineages. These lineages, now recognized as Euphorbiaceae, Pandaceae, Peraceae, Phyllanthaceae, Picrodendraceae, and Puntrinjivaceae, are all more or less closely related in the order Malpighiales, and in part follow divisions evident in older subfamily classifications, which emphasized ovule number and pollen type. Five of these six family-level lineages (except Pandaceae) are represented on Madagascar. While the phylogenetic resolution within Malpighiales is still poor at many deeper nodes, it is clear that Euphorbiaceae and Peraceae are closely related, as are Phyllanthaceae and Picrodendraceae (Wurdack and Davis 2009; Xi et al. 2012; Cai et al. 2019). The Angiosperm Working Group had previously classified Peraceae with Euphorbiaceae, but it was split off to accommodate Rafflesiaceae, which is presently resolved as the sister group to Euphorbiaceae. The relationships of parasitic Rafflesiaceae remain difficult to reconstruct due to the divergent nature of their morphology and unusual molecular evolution.

In its Angiosperm Working Group IV (2016) narrow circumscription, the family Euphorbiaceae contains over 6000 species in about 230 genera. They are grouped into four subfamilies (Acalyphoideae, Cheilosoideae, Crotonoideae, and Euphorbioideae) that may need further taxonomic adjustments, as do many existing tribes (Radcliffe-Smith 2001; Webster 2014) and some genera (especially in tribe Hippomaneae), which differ significantly in circumscription from molecular phylogenetic results. The family can be recognized by usually alternate, simple leaves, simple unisexual flowers with petals often small or absent, floral glands (a disc) usually present, superior tri-locular ovaries containing one pendulous ovule per locule, fruits as explosively dehiscing capsules (sometimes indehiscent), and seeds frequently arillate (usually a caruncle). Pseudanthia—inflorescences that group many small flowers together to resemble a single functional blossom—have evolved twice in Euphorbiaceae (*Dalechampia* and tribe Euphorbieae, which contains four genera), as well as once each in Peraceae and Phyllanthaceae. Breeding systems are diverse, with varied grouping of the male and female flowers in monoecious species, or more rarely complete separation of the sexes in dioecy. Foliar glands (extrafloral nectaries) of diverse forms are usually present, which attract insects, especially ants. Latex (usually white but exudates can be clear or colored) is present in some groups and can contain toxic secondary compounds and a poorly known flora of commensal microbes living within the fluid (see Gunawardana et al. 2015). Euphorbiaceae species are distributed worldwide, but their greatest diversity is in the wet tropics with relatively few lineages extending into temperate regions. Many taxa are adapted to dry environments, especially as succulents of diverse forms, and thus are prominent in the floras of Africa and Madagascar.

THE EUPHORBIACEAE OF MADAGASCAR

Madagascar possesses a diverse and phylogenetically interesting Euphorbiaceae flora with over 450 indigenous species in 40 genera. Two additional taxa, *Aleurites* and *Ricinus*, both with a long history of cultivation and widespread distribution in the Paleotropics, are naturalized. Species of additional genera are cultivated for food or medicine (see Uses by Humans). Three of four subfamilies of Euphorbiaceae (except Cheilosoideae) are represented on Madagascar. Madagascar is rich in undescribed species of Euphorbiaceae including those in the genera *Acalypha*, *Alchornea*, *Croton*, *Euphorbia*, *Excoecaria*, and *Omphalea*.

Euphorbiaceae species are present in all ecological formations of Madagascar, from moist evergreen to dry deciduous forests, dry spiny thickets, rock outcrops in the limestone *tsingy*, and granitic inselbergs. However, the phylogenetic diversity is uneven across habitats, being greatest in wetter formations, while the driest (i.e., spiny thicket) are limited to xerophytic *Euphorbia* species. The most species-rich genera on Madagascar are *Euphorbia* (~150 species), *Croton* (~140 species), and *Acalypha* (32 species), which mirrors their status as the three largest genera in the family. The correlates and causes of species richness in those genera are generally not well understood, but they all display remarkable ecological breadth elsewhere in the world. It is clear from the high degree of endemism (Figure 8.36) that the large genera have successfully diversified since arriving on Madagascar (see Berry and van Ee, pp. 640–44 on *Croton* and see Haevermans and Hetterscheid, pp. 645–49 on *Euphorbia*). In the case of *Euphorbia*, repeated shifts in photosynthetic systems, especially from C_3 to Crassulacean Acid Metabolism (CAM), may have caused bursts in diversification during past geological periods of aridification (Horn et al. 2014). Late Miocene diversification on the island has been indicated in divergence-dating analyses of several genera of Euphorbiaceae. While phylogenetic studies of *Croton*, *Euphorbia*, *Hancea* and related *Mallotus* (Kulju et. al. 2007; van Welzen et al. 2014), and tribe Plukenetieae (Armbruster et al. 2013; Cardinal-McTeague and Gillespie 2016; Cardinal-McTeague et al. 2019) are well developed for Malagasy species (with unpublished work for *Acalypha*, G. Levin et al., unpublished manuscript; and for *Omphalea* and tribe Hippomaneae, K. Wurdack et al., unpublished manuscript), relationships are otherwise coarsely known for most of the other native genera (e.g., Wurdack et al. 2005; Cervantes et al. 2016; Van Welzen et al. 2020).

Five monotypic genera (*Anomostachys*, *Bossera*, *Cladogelonium*, *Conosapium*, and *Radcliffea*) are endemic to Madagascar, and monotypic *Droceloncia* is a Malagasy Region endemic (shared with the Comoro islands). The generic status of some of these taxa may not survive phylogenetic scrutiny (e.g., *Conosapium* groups with *Excoecaria* in phylogenetic analyses of tribe Hippomaneae, [K. Wurdack, unpublished data], and should be transferred to the latter, [V. Malécot, unpublished data]). A further six small genera each with two to 11 species are endemic (*Benoistia*, *Claoxylopsis*, *Lobanilia*, and *Sphaerostylis*) or nearly endemic (*Amyrea* and *Orfilea*) to Madagascar. Despite the modest (nine of 40) generic endemism, an estimated 94% of Malagasy Euphorbiaceae species are endemic to the island. The majority of the nonendemic genera are common to the Malagasy Region (Madagascar and the archipelagoes of the Comoros, Mascarenes, and Seychelles) and/or continental Africa. *Claoxylon*, *Cephalocroton*, *Givotia*, *Excoecaria*, *Macaranga*, *Mallotus*, *Pantadenia*, and *Suregada* are more broadly distributed in Africa and Asia, and some of them extend to Australia. *Cephalocroton* and *Givotia* are noteworthy for being African-Malagasy genera with one species each on the Indian subcontinent.

TAXONOMY

Euphorbiaceae systematics and identifications are often considered to be challenging due to their small, unisexual flowers. Although no treatment of the Euphorbiaceae was completed by J. D. Leandri (1903–1982), a specialist for this family in a past era of Malagasy botany, for the *Flore de Madagascar et des Comores*, numerous generic revisions have been subsequently published, and the identification of the woody genera aided by Schatz (2001). For further information at the generic level see: *Acalypha* (I. M. Muñoz et al. 2018a, 2018b, 2020), *Amyrea* (Radcliffe-Smith 1998a), *Argomuellera* (McPherson 2017), *Benoistia* and *Claoxylopsis* (Radcliffe-Smith 1988), *Cephalocroton* (Radcliffe-Smith 1973), *Cleidion* (Leandri 1972), *Croton* (see Berry and van Ee, pp. 640–44), *Dalechampia* (Pereira-Silva et al. 2020), *Euphorbia* (see Haevermans and Hetterscheid, pp. 645–49), *Givotia* (Radcliffe-Smith 1968), *Grossera* (Barberá et al. 2014), *Hancea* (McPherson 2012), *Jatropha* (Radcliffe-Smith 1997), *Lobanilia* (Radcliffe-Smith 1989), *Macaranga* (McPherson 1996), *Mallotus* (McPherson 1995), *Necepsia* (Bouchat and Léonard 1986), *Omphalea* (Gillespie 1997), *Pantadenia* (Rabevohitra and McPherson 2012), *Plukenetia* (Gillespie 2007), *Pycnocoma* (Léonard 1959), *Radcliffea* (Hoffmann and Wurdack 2006), *Sclerocroton* (Kruijt 1996), *Suregada* (Radcliffe-Smith 1991), and *Tannodia* (Radcliffe-Smith 1998b).

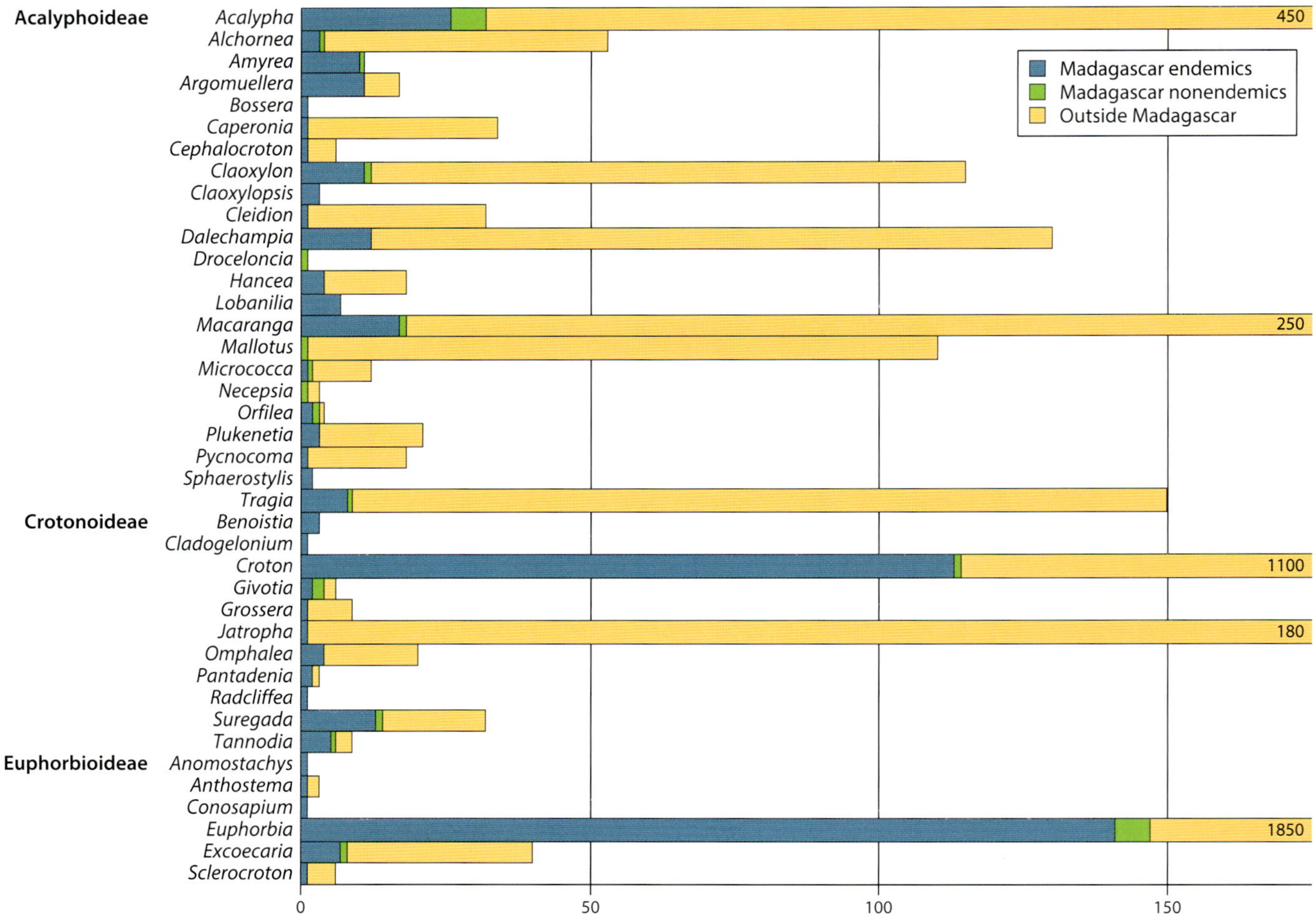

FIGURE 8.36 **Diversity and endemicity diagram of Malagasy Euphorbiaceae at the level of genera, showing three different species counts: 1) endemic to Madagascar, 2) nonendemic but native to Madagascar, and 3) those occurring elsewhere in the world (for further information see text). In cases when species diversity exceeds or does not conform to that presented on the horizontal graph scale, the figures are written along the respective horizontal line of a given genus.**

Subfamily Acalyphoideae

The Acalyphoideae family includes 24 Malagasy genera (of 104-plus worldwide) that are distinguished by the absence of latex, but otherwise extremely diverse in floral and pollen morphology. *Acalypha*, the third most species-rich genus of Malagasy Euphorbiaceae, comprises shrubs to small trees of somewhat untidy appearance, with tiny apetalous staminate flowers and pistillate flowers with feathery red styles subtended by conspicuous protective bracts (Figure 8.37b; I. M. Muñoz et al. 2018a, 2018b, 2020). *Argomuellera*, *Droceloncia*, and *Pycnocoma* form a closely related African-Malagasy group (Wurdack et al. 2005; McPherson 2017). *Cephalocroton* is appropriately named for superficially resembling a *Croton* (and often so misidentified) but with a dense head of staminate flowers and finely divided styles (Figures 8.37e and h). The six species are mostly African with one species each in Sri Lanka and Madagascar. Those outliers had formed the segregate genus *Adenochlaena*, but current taxonomy resurrects a broadly circumscribed *Cephalocroton* (Radcliffe-Smith 1973, 2001; Webster 2014).

Dalechampia, *Plukenetia*, *Sphaerostylis*, and *Tragia*, all closely related in tribe Plukenetieae, are characterized by a usually climbing habit (vines or lianas) and stinging trichomes (lacking in *Plukenetia*), which are otherwise rare in the family. Each had a single colonization event into Madagascar during the late Miocene from African (*Dalechampia*, *Plukenetia*, and *Tragia*) or Australasian (*Sphaerostylis*) ancestors, followed by modest diversification (Cardinal-McTeague et al. 2019; W. M. Cardinal-McTeague et al., unpublished data). *Dalechampia* is primarily a New World group that bears bisexual pseudanthia of five to more than 50 flowers subtended by colorful (purple, yellow, or white) bracts (Figure 8.37c). They are well studied in the New World for their unusual pollination biology, which provides rewards of resin (for nest construction by bees), fragrance, or pollen. A generalized pollination syndrome evolved on Madagascar due to the absence of resin-collecting bees resulting in the loss of the resin-secreting pseudanthial gland, which is present in African ancestors. However, among a subset of the 12 Malagasy species there is a subsequent shift back to specialized pollination (termed paedomorphic specialization) via staminate flowers that barely open and contain the pollen until vibrated, a form of the "buzz pollination" syndrome (Armbruster and Baldwin 1998; Armbruster et al. 2013; Pereira-Silva et al. 2020).

FIGURE 8.37 **Diversity of endemic Malagasy Euphorbiaceae, Picrodendraceae, and Putranjivaceae. A)** ***Cladogelonium madagascariense*****, flattened green stems and leaves at nodes; B)** ***Acalypha andringitrensis*****, female flowers with leafy bracts; C)** ***Dalechampia clematidifolia*****, pseudanthia with yellow bracts surrounding clusters of unisexual flowers; D)** ***Cladogelonium madagascariense*****, staminate flowers; E)** ***Cephalocroton leucocephalus*****, white styles of pistillate flowers and central staminate head in bud; F)** ***Jatropha mahafalensis*****, staminate flower; G)** ***Anthostema madagascariense*****, large three-locular fruit; H)** ***Cephalocroton leucocephalus*****, head of staminate flowers; I)** ***Omphalea ankaranensis*****, staminate flowers on leafing-out shoot tips; J)** ***Stachyandra viticifolia*****, compound leaves and sheathing stipules at swollen branch tips; and K)** ***Drypetes madagascariensis*****, staminate flowers.** (PHOTOS A, D, E, and J by K. Wurdack; B by G. Levin; C and I by L. Gillespie; F by P. B. Phillipson; G and H by B. van Ee; and K by A. Razanatsima.)

Subfamily Crotonoideae

Crotonoideae include 11 Malagasy genera (of 78-plus worldwide) with latex present (often reddish), indument of diverse forms, nonglandular bracts, staminate perianth usually covering the anthers in bud, petals present, and an unusual pollen type (a *Croton*-pattern wall, and often inaperturate). All but *Benoistia* have been sampled for molecular phylogenetic analyses but intergeneric resolution is poor (Wurdack et al. 2005; van Welzen et al. 2020). Except for *Suregada* and species-rich *Croton* (see Berry and van Ee, pp. 640–44), most genera have little species diversification in Madagascar. *Suregada* species are small to medium-size trees with bright green, pellucid-punctate leaves, and leaf-opposed inflorescences. The genus is distributed from Africa to tropical Asia, and includes 14 Malagasy species. Monotypic *Cladogelonium* is closely related to *Suregada* but is highly specialized as a 1–5 m tall, finely branched shrub with unusual, flattened green stems (phylloclades) and small, drought-deciduous leaves (Figures 8.37a and d). It has a disjunct distribution between northeastern and central western Madagascar in humid habitats within dry deciduous forests. Monotypic *Radcliffea* was a surprising discovery from dry deciduous forests of Bemaraha (Hoffmann and Wurdack 2006), and is unusual for its unilocular ovary. *Jatropha* is well diversified in the Neotropics and Africa (with a few species in southwestern Asia), but with *J. mahafalensis* the sole Malagasy representative (Figure 8.37f). This small tree, which reaches 8 m tall, occurs in the southwest and has been considered distinctive enough to warrant classification in its own subgenus (Radcliffe-Smith 1997). Given its species propensity for arid environments, enabled by xerophytic adaptations such as (sub) succulent stems and caudices, it is surprising that *Jatropha* has only a single native species on Madagascar and is not more diverse.

Omphalea contains about 20 species with a pantropical distribution in the Neotropics, northeastern Australia, Malesia, Africa (one species in Tanzania), and a radiation of four or more species on Madagascar (Gillespie 1997). The genus displays an unusual diversity of growth form (canopy lianas, shrubs, and large trees), striking differences in juvenile and adult leaf form, unusual mushroom-shaped fused stamens (Figure 8.37i), and large fruits containing some of the largest seeds in the family. Evergreen *O. oppositifolia* is vegetatively especially variable and widespread in the moist evergreen low- to medium-altitude forests of the east, while the other three rarer deciduous Malagasy species occur in western dry deciduous forests. Most collections of *Omphalea* are made in fruit and thus challenging to identify.

Subfamily Euphorbioideae

Euphorbioideae include six Malagasy genera (of 46-plus worldwide) that are distinguished by the character combination of the presence of white latex, which can have starch grains, inflorescences that often have glandular bracts, flowers lacking petals or discs, tiny to absent staminate perianths such that the anthers are often not fully covered in bud, and relatively homogeneous tricolporate (three compound apertures) pollen. Natural divisions in the subfamily follow striking differences in inflorescence structure, and among the six Malagasy genera there is a pseudanthial clade, containing *Anthostema* and *Euphorbia*, whereas the others are racemose (or spicate). Much of the morphological diversity and species richness in the subfamily is contained in *Euphorbia* (see Haevermans and Hetterscheid, pp. 645–49); closely related *Anthostema* includes three African species and one Madagascar endemic (*A. madagascariense*), a large tree of moist evergreen forests along the east coast (Figure 8.37g). The inflorescences (pseudanthia) in *Anthostema* are morphologically intermediate in a series of floral modifications in subtribe Euphorbieae; the greatest reduction is in the cyathia (a specialized type of pseudanthium) of *Euphorbia* (Prenner and Rudall 2007). The remaining four genera (*Anomostachys*, *Conosapium*, *Excoecaria*, and *Sclerocroton*), all of tribe Hippomaneae, have elongate, racemose inflorescences and are taxonomically challenging, especially *Excoecaria*, which contains many undescribed species. This genus contains several widespread Australasian mangrove species that have not dispersed to Madagascar.

USES BY HUMANS

Few native species of Euphorbiaceae have economic importance on Madagascar, except incidental local use for construction and firewood. Some easily propagated taxa with dense branching are used to create living fences (*Jatropha mahafalensis* and *Euphorbia* spp.). Given the diverse phytochemistry of members of Euphorbiaceae, it is not surprising that native and introduced Euphorbiaceae species are locally used as medicinal plants, especially as teas (e.g., Novy 1997; Razafindraibe et al. 2013; Randrianarivony et al. 2017b). Nonindigenous species are cultivated as crops, notably *Manihot esculenta* (cassava) with its starchy tubers that are cooked with meat or converted to flour for baking, and the pounded leaves are widely eaten as a vegetable and often mixed with meat or fish (Rajaonarivony 1995). *Vernicia fordii* (tung-oil tree) and *Ricinus communis* (castor bean) are grown for seed oil, and *Aleurites moluccana* (candlenut) has edible oily seeds. *Jatropha mahafalensis* has potential as an indigenous biofuel (oil content 35–55% of seed weight) that could be developed in the manner of well-known *J. curcas* (Sonnleitner et al. 2013).

CONSUMPTION BY ANIMALS

Native and introduced members of this family are widely consumed by different lemur species in the various vegetation types on the island (see Eppley et al., pp. 1839–59). Furthermore, other groups of land vertebrates have been reported to feed on fruits of this family (and likely disperse their seeds), including fruit-consuming parrots and understory birds (Bollen and van Elsacker 2004; Bollen et al. 2004a). Euphorbiaceae species worldwide have numerous specialist insect herbivores and seed parasites but this subject remains poorly studied in Madagascar. However, *Omphalea* spp. are food plants for Uraniidae moths, and the Malagasy species are consumed by larvae of the spectacular diurnal Madagascan Sunset Moth (*Chrysiridia rhipheus*), which sequester toxic polyhydroxy alkaloids from the plants (Lees and Smith 1991; Gillespie 1997). These alkaloids are also present in distantly related *Suregada*, which is consumed by larvae of the uraniid genus *Urapteritra* (Kite et al. 2005).

CONSERVATION OF MALAGASY EUPHORBIACEAE

Given the high degree of endemism and the number of species with highly localized distributions (or that are poorly collected), the Malagasy members of Euphorbiaceae are greatly threatened by habitat destruction and fragmentation. Some genera (e.g., species of *Croton* and *Macaranga*) are common elements of secondary vegetation and may be more successful at persisting despite disturbance. The succulent species of *Euphorbia* are notably of concern and listed by CITES (Convention on International Trade in Endangered Species of Wild Fauna and Flora) due to threats from collectors and illegal export for the horticultural trade (see Haevermans and Hetterscheid, pp. 645–49 on *Euphorbia*). Timber exploitation appears minimal. International Union for the Conservation of Nature (IUCN) Red List assessments of Euphorbiaceae are very incomplete and best developed for *Euphorbia*. Among the 23 taxa currently classified as Critically Endangered, 20 are *Euphorbia* species, and the remainder are *Claoxylon flavum*, *Cleidion capuronii*, and *Radcliffea smithii*.

SEGREGATE FAMILIES

Peraceae

The Peraceae family contains four genera and about 125 species, which are pantropical but especially diverse in southern Africa and northern South America. The genera were previously usually classified as the first tribes of Euphorbiaceae before being segregated as a separate family. The sole Malagasy representative is *Chaetocarpus rabaraba*, a large dioecious tree (to 30–35 m high and 1 m diameter at breast height) endemic to lowland moist evergreen forests in the vicinity of Mahavelona (Foulpointe). The spiny (muricate) surface of the thick, woody fruit walls and the shiny black seeds are characteristic of the genus. Capuron (1972) named the species after its Malagasy vernacular name. *Chaetocarpus* contains 16 species with an unusual distribution of two in west Africa, one in Madagascar, and the rest scattered across the Neotropics, India, and Malesia. *Chaetocarpus rabaraba* is sought after as a local timber tree with durable wood suitable for construction; it is categorized by the IUCN Red List as Endangered. The few remaining reproductive individuals are mostly male and attempts at ex situ conservation have had poor success (Skema 2004; Birkinshaw et al. 2015).

Picrodendraceae

Picrodendraceae contains 25 genera and about 100 species, which are two-thirds Australasian with the rest scattered across Africa and the New World. Within the former Euphorbiaceae *sensu lato*, they formed a distinct group (as subfamily Oldfieldioideae) due to the unusual spiny (echinate) pollen, two ovules per locule, and often opposite leaves (Webster 2014). Molecular phylogenetic evidence indicates the family is most closely related to Phyllanthaceae. In Madagascar four genera (*Androstachys*, *Aristogeitonia*, *Stachyandra*, and *Voatamalo*) and 10 species are present. Those genera are all closely related in a mostly palmately compound-leaved (also unifoliolate or simple), African clade. Divergence dating with limited taxon sampling has indicated that this clade originated in the early Eocene (Grímsson et al. 2019). Of the native species, only the evergreen tree *Androstachys johnsonii* is not endemic, occurring in southern Madagascar and also southeastern Africa where it locally dominates patches of dry forest. *Stachyandra* spp. (four species) were segregated from *Androstachys* (they are sister groups and could be merged again) and are restricted to northeastern Madagascar (Radcliffe-Smith 1990). They are conspicuous because of their large sheathing stipules and 3–7-foliolate compound leaves with pilose indument (Figure 8.37j), but poorly known reproductively as they are rarely collected in flower (usually sterile or fruiting). *Stachyandra* and *Androstachys* have unusual, almost catkin-like staminate flowers with numerous stamens arranged on elongate axes. *Voatamalo*, with an etymology based on a Malagasy vernacular name, contains two species of poorly known trees from eastern coastal forests (Bosser 1976). IUCN Red List assessments indicate that nearly all endemic species of Picrodendraceae are Endangered or Critically Endangered (two poorly collected species are not yet assessed).

Putranjivaceae

Putranjivaceae contains two genera and about 225 species (221 *Drypetes* and four *Putranjiva*), which are mostly found in the Paleotropics, with few in the Neotropics (Levin 2014). Although traditionally included with the part of former Euphorbiaceae *sensu lato* that is now classified as Phyllanthaceae (see Ralimanana and Challen, pp. 649–54), their closest relative is monotypic Lophopyxidaceae, an odd liana from Malesia and the western Pacific (Wurdack and Davis 2009). Most of the 10 *Drypetes* species (nine endemic) on Madagascar occur in moist evergreen forests along the eastern and northern coasts; an additional two species are restricted to the Comoro islands (McPherson 2000, 2014). *Drypetes* species are dioecious trees or shrubs with (sub)coriaceous leaves, apetalous flowers in axillary clusters, two ovules per locule (only one develops in fruit), and notable for producing mustard-oils (glucosinolates), a biochemical convergence with Brassicales (Figure 8.37k). Their drupaceous fruits can be fleshy and colored at maturity, and are likely bird-dispersed (Levin 2014). The species can be challenging to identify without diagnostic reproductive features, and the two most widespread Malagasy taxa (*D. madagascariensis* and *D. perrieri*) are especially variable vegetatively. Spiny-dentate leaves irregularly occur in some *Drypetes* species and also in seedlings of entire-margin taxa, suggesting that such spines may be a juvenile trait. Most of the endemic representatives of *Drypetes* are known from a few collections and are likely vulnerable as moist forest species, but several are widespread.

Subject editors: Laurent Gautier and Steven M. Goodman

EUPHORBIACEAE: *CROTON*

P. E. Berry and B. W. van Ee

Croton is a mainly tropical genus that is distributed worldwide with about 1300 species. Some of the tree species from South America are called "dragon's blood," due to their reddish sap, and they are used medicinally by local inhabitants. Croton oil is obtained from *C. tiglium*, which is cultivated in Asia and used as a purgative. Many species have different terpenoid compounds that give them a distinctive aromatic odor, and which are used medicinally as well. The genus can be recognized by a suite of characteristics, such as the indumentum on the leaves—with hairs that are either stellate (branched like a many-armed star) or lepidote (scales that are often silvery) (see Figure 8.38f). There is usually a pair of glands at the junction of the leaf blade and the petiole (Figure 8.38c), and when the leaves grow old, they often turn a characteristic orange color before they fall off (Figure 8.38e). Species of *Croton* generally have small, whitish male flowers and slightly larger whitish to greenish female flowers. These are grouped together in structures called thyrses, with male flowers toward the tips and female flowers at the base (Figure 8.38h). As with other Euphorbiaceae species, the flowers are unisexual and the plants are monoecious. The anthers of the male flowers are characteristically bent inwards in bud (still partly visible in the open male flower of Figure 8.38g). The male flowers of *Croton* species are generally quite similar, with five sepals and five whitish petals and no vestiges of an aborted ovary, and they differ mainly in their size and in the number of stamens (from roughly five to 50). The female flowers vary more widely than the males, in size, the degree of division of the stigmas, the size of the fruits, and their pubescence; they generally lack petals altogether, although there are notable exceptions as in *C. mongue*, *C. goudotii*, and others. *Croton* species are insect pollinated, generally by a variety of bees and flies, and fruits open explosively and spread the seeds out around the mother plants. The seeds are sometimes secondarily dispersed by ants, which feed on a lipid-rich appendage (the caruncle) that most of them possess. Most species have trilocular capsules with a single ovule per locule, but rarely there are species that have only one or two locules.

As is the case with the other large Euphorbiaceae genus, *Euphorbia* (see Haevermans and Hetterscheid, pp. 645–49), Madagascar harbors a very high degree of diversity in *Croton*, with an estimated 140 species, more than 10% of the total worldwide number of species in the genus, and over 1% of the native Malagasy plant species. These species occur in nearly all of the vegetation types on the island, from dry spiny thicket at sea level in the southwest to 2400 m elevation in upper portions of the medium-altitude moist evergreen forests below the summit of Tsaratanàna in the north. All species are woody and most are shrubs, but quite a few are trees that can reach 25 m tall, and these have been used as construction material in local communities. The main contributions to the taxonomic understanding of Malagasy *Croton* were made by Jacques Leandri, who named approximately a third of the currently recognized species in a series of 14 different publications between 1931 and 1976. His most comprehensive publication was Leandri (1939a), which was essentially a monograph of the genus for Madagascar and the Malagasy Region. More recently, the genus has been the subject of study by the authors at a worldwide level as well as with a special focus on Madagascar, with a revised nomenclator of Malagasy species published by Berry et al. (2017) and a monograph in preparation. Our estimate of 140 species on Madagascar is based on the 114 species included in the recent nomenclator and another 25 or so undescribed species that should likely be published soon.

PHYLOGENY AND BIOGEOGRAPHY OF MALAGASY *CROTON*

In his worldwide sectional synopsis of *Croton*, Webster (1993) recognized 40 sections in the genus, of which he considered 29 to be entirely New World, seven strictly Old World, and four to consist of both New World and Old World members. All of the molecular phylogenetic studies conducted to date, however, have failed to recover any species groups with both New World and Old World members. Instead, all of the included Old World taxa emerged as a monophyletic group, nested within major clades of New World taxa (Berry et al. 2005; van Ee et al. 2011, 2015; Haber et al. 2017; Meléndez González 2019; Ngumbau et al. 2020). Van Ee et al. (2015) identified two African clades of *Croton*, one consisting of African and Arabian Peninsula species with both stellate and lepidote indument and sister to the rest of the Old World species (equivalent to the combined Africa and Malagasy Region clades in Figure 8.39), and the other of exclusively stellate species embedded within a broader clade of Asian and Australian species (equivalent to the Africa, Asia, and Australia clade in Figure 8.39). All Malagasy species were recovered as a monophyletic group within the African and Arabian clade. The ancestral state biogeographic reconstructions performed by Haber et al. (2017) point to mainland Africa as the most likely origin of the Malagasy Region species of *Croton*, although the possibility remains that Madagascar was first colonized from Asia, and that the African and Arabian clade was subsequently founded from there.

The results of the taxonomically broadly sampled phylogeny of Haber et al. (2017) support the Malagasy Region species of *Croton* as a monophyletic group, and within that group those species now found in the Mascarene and Comoro archipelagoes are embedded within different clades of Malagasy species, as are two small groups in mainland Africa (*C. pseudopulchellus* and the *C. menyharthii*-*C. dichogamus*-*C. kilwae* clade shown in Figure 8.39). Haber et al. (2017) also largely rejected the Malagasy species groups delineated by Leandri (1939a), although a few groups, such as the Adenophorus, Mongue, and Argyrodaphne groups, were supported as being monophyletic based on the species sampled. Recently, Ngumbau et al. (2020) documented a likely third dispersal event from

FIGURE 8.38 **Examples of Malagasy *Croton* species. *Croton aleuritoides* A) trunk, B) canopy, C) leaf base and petiole showing acropetiolar pair of glands, and D) seeds and fruit—the capsule does not dehisce until well after falling to the ground, unlike most other crotons, which open explosively on the plant; E) *C. macrobuxus*, showing the nearly glabrous leaves and orange senescent leaves, the green calyx of the pistillate flowers, and young fruits with widely spaced, brown lepidote scales; F) *C. crossolepis*, showing the indumentum of lepidote scales. Glands can also be seen at the base of the blade; G) *C. manampetsae*, showing the stellate trichomes and a young staminate flower with filaments still inflexed; H) *C. chrysodaphne*, showing an abbreviated thyrse with a staminate flower and two pistillate flowers together with several male (?) flower buds; and I) *C. nobilis*, showing a pistillate flower with thick, recurved sepals and very short stigmas.** (PHOTOS by P. E. Berry.)

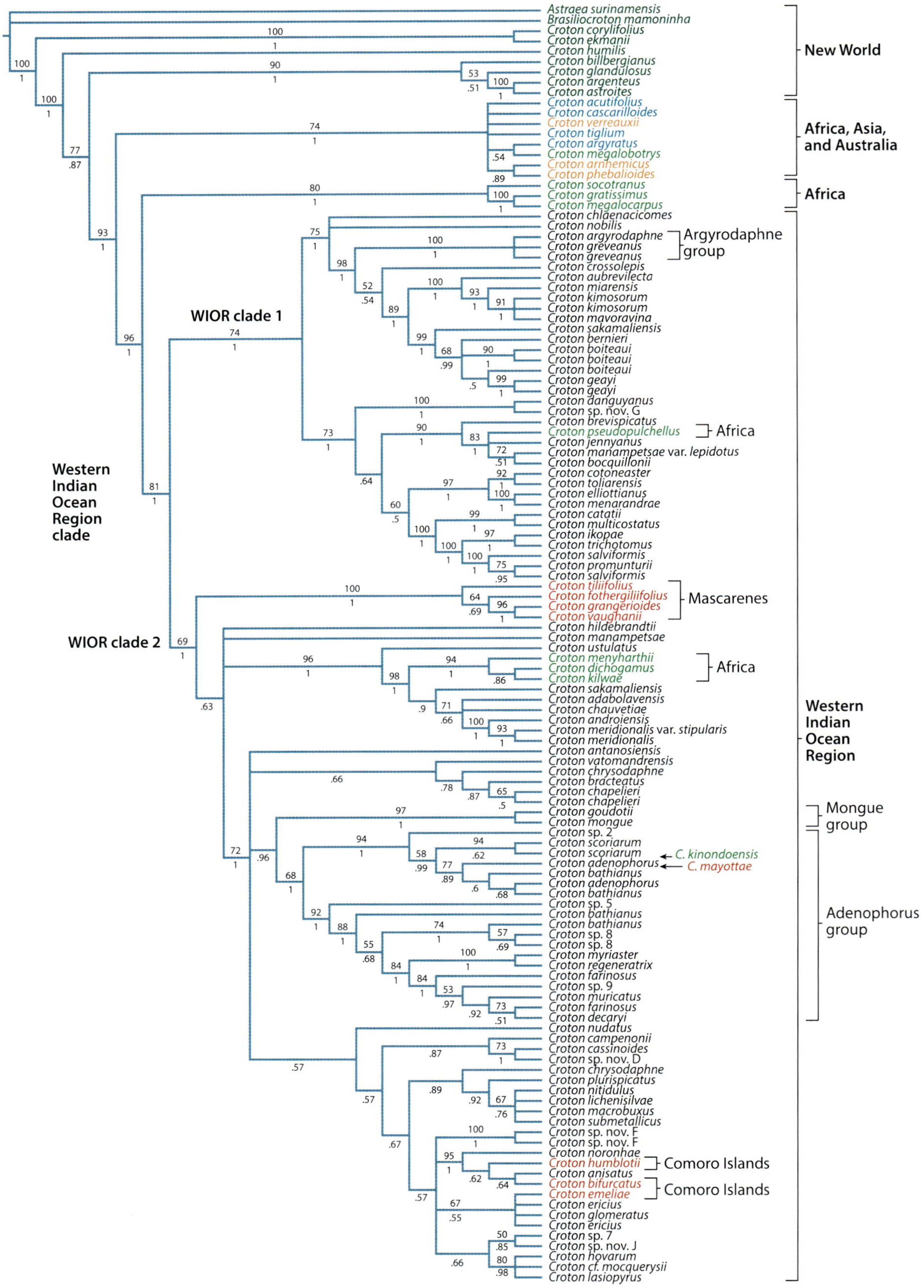

FIGURE 8.39 **Phylogenetic hypothesis for the Malagasy Region species of *Croton* obtained from a combined Bayesian analysis of nuclear (ITS) and plastid (*matK*, *trnL-F*, and *trnH-psbA*) data. Bootstrap support values from a Maximum Likelihood analysis are indicated above the branches, and Bayesian posterior probability support values are given below the branches. The geographic distribution of clades is indicated by the vertical bars to the right, as are some species groups (dark green, New World; light blue, Asia; orange, Australia; mid-green, Africa; black, Madagascar; red, Mascarene and Comoro islands). WIOR, Western Indian Ocean Region. This is a modified version of Figure 1 in Haber et al. (2017), with the same topology, except that about one-third of the species determinations have been updated, and the positions of *C. mayottae* and *C. kinondoensis* are indicated given the findings of Ngumbau et al. (2020).**

Madagascar to coastal east Africa, represented by *C. kinondoensis*, as well as a separate dispersal to the Comoro archipelago, represented by *C. mayottae*.

Given the apparently recent and rapid speciation of *Croton* on Madagascar, the molecular divergence of species there appears to lag behind their morphological divergence, with some readily distinguished species having nearly identical DNA sequences. Some instances of this, such as *C. bocquillonii* from the former province of Mahajanga and the similar but distinct *C. manampetsae* var. *lepidotus* from the southeast of Toliara (which will soon be treated as a distinct species), appear to be the result of allopatric speciation. Other cases, such as the small-leaved *C. kimosorum* and the sympatric, larger-leaved *C. mavoravina*, may be the result of a polyploidization event in the larger-leaved species.

Recent DNA sequence–based studies have been invaluable for understanding relationships between species, as well as in the interpretation of characters used to delimit species. Haber et al. (2017) rejected the hypothesis that the large tree species of Malagasy *Croton* (Table 8.29) form a single clade, and they found several species that were previously thought to be closely related were well apart from each other in the phylogeny. Similarly, the phylogeny of Meléndez González (2019) rejected the hypothesis that the small-leaved species of southern Madagascar form a clade, and instead found that there have been multiple evolutionarily convergent shifts to a small-leaved, water-conserving morphology in the arid south.

TABLE 8.29. **Medium to large tree species of *Croton* on Madagascar, and their distribution presented by former provinces**

C. aleuritoides P. E. Berry (ANTS)
C. argyrodaphne Baill. (ANTS, MAHA, TOAM, TOLI)
C. campenonii Baill. (ANTA, ANTS, FIAN, MAHA)
C. catatii Baill. (ANTA, ANTS, FIAN, MAHA, TOAM, TOLI)
C. chrysodaphne Baill. (ANTS, FIAN, MAHA, TOAM, TOLI)
C. cupreolepis P. E. Berry, B. W. van Ee & Kainul. (ANTS, FIAN, TOAM, TOLI)
C. goudotii Baill. (ANTA, ANTS, FIAN, MAHA, TOAM, TOLI)
C. isomonensis Leandri (TOLI)
C. maevaranensis Leandri (ANTS, MAHA)
C. mongue Baill. (ANTA, ANTS, FIAN, MAHA, TOAM, TOLI)
C. multicostatus Müll. Arg. (FIAN, TOLI)
C. myriaster Baker (ANTA, ANTS, FIAN, MAHA, TOAM, TOLI)
C. nobilis Baill. (TOLI)
C. plurispicatus P. E. Berry, Kainul. & B. W. van Ee (TOAM)
C. regeneratrix Leandri (ANTA, FIAN)
C. stanneus Baill. (ANTA, ANTS, FIAN, MAHA, TOAM, TOLI)
C. submetallicus Baill. (FIAN, TOAM)

Note: ANTA, Antananarivo; ANTS, Antsiranana; FIAN, Fianarantsoa; MAHA, Mahajanga; TOAM, Toamasina; and TOLI, Toliara.

TAXONOMY AND SPECIES DELIMITATION IN MALAGASY *CROTON*

After four extended field trips to Madagascar and repeated visits to the main herbaria where Malagasy *Croton* specimens are housed, we have made major advances in our understanding of the species of *Croton* that occur in Madagascar (Berry and van Ee 2011; Berry et al. 2011, 2016a, 2016b, 2017; Kainulainen et al. 2016, 2017a, 2017b; Berry and Kainulainen 2017; Meléndez González 2019). The most significant of these papers for the review presented herein is entitled "A nomenclator of *Croton* (Euphorbiaceae) in Madagascar, the Comoros Archipelago, and the Mascarene Islands" (Berry et al. 2017), because it lists all of the species that we recognized in the Malagasy Region at that time, including full synonymy distributions on Madagascar by the former province system. To do this, we had to contend with a rather unfortunate posthumous publication (Radcliffe-Smith 2016), which was a hasty effort by Martin Cheek at Kew to validate the names of new taxa of Malagasy *Croton* proposed by the late Alan Radcliffe-Smith in a manuscript that he left to be published in 2003, at the time of his retirement. This manuscript added 150 new names of *Croton* from Madagascar and the Comoros, consisting of 26 new species, three new subspecies, and 121 new varieties. However, after careful review, all but four of these taxa were relegated to synonymy or else considered as *incertae sedis* (22 varieties), often because they were based on single and/or incomplete specimens (see Berry et al. 2017).

Berry et al. (2017) recognized 114 species of *Croton* as occurring natively on Madagascar. All of them are endemic there, with the possible exception of *C. adenophorus*, which has a historical record from Mayotte. The authors did not address the backlog of unidentified specimens in that article, and we estimate there are another 25 or so species that still need to be described. Many of them come from recently explored areas in the eastern part of the island, but others come from relatively well-explored areas in the north and south and belong to difficult species complexes, such as the coppery, lepidote-leaved species. These new taxa should be published soon, and are also scheduled to appear in an upcoming monograph of the genus for Madagascar.

Some of the species included in Berry et al. (2017) involve extensive synonymy, such as *C. chapelieri* and *C. stanneus*, with eight and six synonyms, respectively. This suggests that they have been poorly understood in the past, mostly due to poor type material and inadequate descriptions. In the case of *C. chapelieri*, three previous authors (Baillon 1861; Leandri 1939a; Radcliffe-Smith 2016) treated it as an accepted species, but only known from the late 18th-century type specimen, which had no specific locality information. After field-, herbarium-, and literature-based studies, Kainulainen et al. (2017a) and Berry et al. (2017) determined that this is in fact a widespread species along the eastern coastal zone of Madagascar, and that it had been described eight other times under different names, all of which are now considered to be synonyms. A rather extreme case of a species described from poor material is the deciduous *C. nudatus*, which was named from a completely leafless specimen (just stems and seeds). *Croton chrysodaphne* was another particularly tricky species to unravel (Berry et al. 2011). It is a tree species that Baillon (1861) described based on three specimens (syntypes), which each turned out to correspond to different species. Consequently, we had to confine its use to the species occurring in the eastern lowland moist evergreen forests, whereas the other two syntypes represent the very different *C. argyrodaphne* and the recently described *C. cupreolepis*.

An indication of the recent progress in species delimitation is that since our initial phylogenetic analysis of Malagasy Region *Croton* species in Haber et al. (2017), we have updated the determinations of over a third of the 71 species of Malagasy *Croton* included in that study. This has been enabled by continued taxonomic studies, such as that of Meléndez González (2019), which focused on the small-leaved species from the south of Madagascar, and our work on our upcoming monograph. Ultimately, we believe that accurate species delimitations in Malagasy *Croton* will be fully resolved only with a solid understanding of their variation and habitats through careful study in the field by local and visiting botanists.

TREE SPECIES OF *CROTON* ON MADAGASCAR

All species of *Croton* on Madagascar are woody, but most species are shrubs or else transitional between shrubs and small trees. In Table 8.29 we list those species considered to be true trees (medium to large in size). That said, some can still appear shrub-like in certain circumstances, such as *C. catatii*, *C. isomonensis*, *C. multicostatus*, *C. plurispicatus*, *C. stanneus*, and *C. submetallicus*. The remaining species are all consistently large trees.

Croton mongue is the most prominent *Croton* tree on the island. It occurs in all six former provinces and occurs in medium-altitude moist evergreen forests, although it can occur closer to sea level in extreme southeastern Madagascar. A somewhat smaller tree that shares similar habitats and is equally widespread is the lobed-leafed *C. goudotii*, and indeed the two appear to hybridize in areas where they co-occur. *Croton myriaster* is similarly widespread and occurs in the same kind of cloud forest edge habitat as *C. mongue* and *C. goudotii*. *Croton argyrodaphne* is the most common tree species in the genus in more lowland, moderately dry areas across the northern and western part of the island. Another widely distributed and morphologically variable species is *C. catatii*, which has strongly bicolored leaves and occurs over a broad elevational range. In somewhat drier habitats and generally of smaller stature, *C. stanneus* occurs in all six former provinces of Madagascar. Finally, *C. cupreolepis* is a coppery-leaved species that was only recently described (Berry et al. 2016b), yet it occurs in medium-altitude moist evergreen forests all along the eastern side of the island.

Among the much rarer tree species, *C. nobilis* is an unusually large-fruited species that is found only in medium-altitude moist evergreen forests in the extreme southeast; it has been confused in the past with *C. chrysodaphne*, which occurs sporadically in the lowland moist evergreen forests of the island (Figures 8.38h and i). *Croton isomonensis* is a kind of smaller cousin of *C. nobilis* and inhabits somewhat drier forests in the southeastern portion of the former Toliara Province. *Croton multicostatus* is a small tree with narrow leaves that is restricted to remnant patches of forest in the southeast around Tolagnaro and has a convoluted taxonomic history (Berry and van Ee 2011). Perhaps the most enigmatic *Croton* tree species of all in Madagascar is *C. aleuritoides* (Figures 8.38a–d), which was recently described from a very limited area of Montagne des Français east of Antsiranana in the north (Berry et al. 2016a). We had seen just two herbaria collections of this species before we visited Montagne des Français in 2016, the original one from 1958 without specific coordinates, and the second from 2005 with accurate locality data. *Croton aleuritoides* are very large trees that grow in a very restricted area of dry deciduous forest at the base of limestone cliffs, and they are unusual in the genus in having large ashy-colored capsules that do not open up until well after they have fallen to the ground (Figure 8.38d). This species is perhaps the epitome of the many rare species on the island that appear to be on the verge of extinction.

CONSERVATION STATUS OF *CROTON* SPECIES ON MADAGASCAR

Although many species of *Croton* are elements of secondary vegetation and forest edges, they are vulnerable to the profound environmental changes that have occurred in many parts of Madagascar. Recently, there has been a concerted effort by Malagasy botanists to provide International Union for the Conservation of Nature (IUCN) Red List of Threatened Species assessments for all of the tree species on the island (*Croton* mostly submitted by N. Ravololomanana). A few other *Croton* tree species were treated separately and have already been published, such as *C. argyrodaphne* and *C. cupreolepis* (Faranirina 2019a, 2019b). The concept of tree species used there includes many shrubby species, so there are more taxa included than what we consider to be unambiguous trees in Table 8.29. Of the 36 "tree" species evaluated, one was categorized as Critically Endangered, 14 as Endangered, eight as Vulnerable, two as Near Threatened, and 11 as Least Concern.

The bulk of the smaller, shrubby species still need to be evaluated for their Red List status, but there were eight shrubby species listed as of July 2020 (*C. cassinoides*, *C. chapelieri*, *C. crossolepis*, *C. droguetioides*, *C. enigmaticus*, *C. ferricretus*, *C. humbertii*, and *C. lichenisilvae*), with five of them categorized as Endangered and three as Vulnerable (IUCN 2020). Among the remaining species, we anticipate a similar proportions of Endangered and Least Concern species as for the tree species, given that many of the shrubby species are habitat specific.

Subject editors: Laurent Gautier and Steven M. Goodman

EUPHORBIACEAE: *EUPHORBIA*

T. Haevermans and W. L. A. Hetterscheid

On Madagascar the genus *Euphorbia* is morphologically varied, displaying a tremendous array of growth forms (Figure 8.40) and is especially known for its succulent species, which are of considerable interest to collectors of xerophytic plants. The Malagasy members of the genus range from small prostrate herbs to trees dominating the forest canopies. The genus is defined by a synflorescence known as cyathium (a cup-shaped structure containing either the male flowers reduced to a stamen, or the female flowers reduced to a gynoecium). The cyathium is subtended by two bracts called cyathophylls, which are more or less developed and colored.

This genus is particularly diverse on Madagascar where approximately 200 native taxa are recognized (with 98% endemism, not taking into account four pantropical weeds [*E. cyathophora*, *E. hirta*, *E. hypericifolia*, and *E. prostrata*]), representing approximately 10% of the total number of *Euphorbia* species in the world. In order to store water essential for survival in arid habitats, several forms of *Euphorbia* have developed various succulent adaptations that are associated with the roots, stems, and leaves. Several species of the forest understory occurring in relatively moist zones also show adaptations to xerophytism, although the habitats in which they occur probably do not experience extreme dry seasons. This is the case for *E. boissieri*, occurring on the Masoala Peninsula, which possesses a succulent main stem. Also notable is *E. robivelonae*, which can grow with its "feet in the water," and is found along small streams in the Iharana (Vohémar) region. This phenomenon of succulence within plants that are not subject to prolonged water stress is not exclusive to *Euphorbia*.

We are unaware of any study conducted on the island concerning the pollination ecology of *Euphorbia*, but all members of this genus and all parts of the plant, without any exception, are toxic to vertebrates, which suggests entomophilous pollination. The fruits are mostly explosively dehiscent capsules that generally release the seeds by throwing them some distance from the mother plant, but there are Malagasy species with large fleshy fruits such as *E. intisy* from the arid south (Haevermans 2003a) or large seeds such as those of *E. tetraptera*, which are eaten by rodents (Bollen et al. 2004a). Herein, we provide an update related to aspects of the Malagasy members of the genus following our previous treatment (Haevermans 2003b), which appeared in the precursor of this book. In particular we present aspects of the phylogenetic and evolutionary history and how these aspects can be used in a coherent taxonomic classification.

DIVERSITY AND TAXONOMY OF MALAGASY *EUPHORBIA*

The different species of *Euphorbia* present on Madagascar appear to belong to several morphological groups, which has led several authors to propose noncongruent classifications that do not reflect the phylogenetic history of this genus. Following progress based on molecular studies during the last two decades, the phylogeny-based grouping of Malagasy *Euphorbia* is now much better understood. The diversification on Madagascar is clearly the result of several independent colonization events, with some groups extremely speciose and others with a reduced number of extant taxa (Haevermans 2003a; Aubriot 2012; Yang et al. 2012; Dorsey et al. 2013). Several pantropical weeds from subgenus *Chamaesyce* are present in Madagascar, such as *E. cyathophora* in section *Poinsettia* subsection *Stormieae*, and three species in section *Anisophyllum* subsection *Hypericifoliae*.

CURRENT CLASSIFICATION OF MALAGASY *EUPHORBIA*

As presently understood, the genus *Euphorbia* on Madagascar is best divided into four separate subgenera and each of these often into several different sections (* denotes a Malagasy endemic; details on the species occurring on Madagascar are given in brackets).

1. *Euphorbia* subgenus *Athymalus* Neck. ex Rchb. (Peirson et al. 2013)
    - Section ***Antso*** P. E. Berry*.

Section *Antso*, with only one species *E. antso* restricted to Madagascar is the sole Malagasy member of subgenus *Athymalus* [*E. antso* Denis*].

2. *Euphorbia* subgenus *Esula* (Riina et al. 2013)
    - Section ***Aphyllis*** Webb & Berthel. subsection ***Africanae*** Molero & Barres [*E. orthoclada* Baker*].
    - Section ***Esula*** (Pers.) Dumort. [*E. emirnensis* Baker*].
    - Section ***Exiguae*** (Geltman) Riina & Molero [*E. dracunculoides* Lam.].

There are few Malagasy members of this subgenus, with each section being represented on the island by one species. Two of them are herbaceous plants, and the third (*E. orthoclada*) is a stem succulent from the arid south.

3. *Euphorbia* subgenus *Chamaesyce* (Yang et al. 2012)
    - Section ***Denisiae*** Haev. & X. Aubriot*.

Newly recognized, this small group of Malagasy endemics is characterized by their lenticellate bark and especially their subpeltate leaves, which allow morphological separation from some unrelated members of section *Pervilleanae* in subgenus *Euphorbia* [two species: *E. denisii* Oudejans* and *E. subpeltatophylla* Rauh*].

- Section ***Bosseriae*** Haev. & X. Aubriot*.

FIGURE 8.40 **Examples of Malagasy *Euphorbia* species. A) *Euphorbia xylophylloides* (section *Tirucalli*); B) *E. viguieri* (section *Goniostema*); C) *E. antso* (section Antso); D) *E. primulifolia* var. *begardii* (section *Goniostema*); E) *E. boissieri* (section *Goniostema*); F) *E. orthoclada* (section *Aphyllis*); G) *E. cedrorum* (section *Deuterocalli*); and H) *E. subapoda* (= *E. quartziticola*; section *Goniostema*).** (PHOTOS by T. Haevermans.)

This small group of species, previously classified among the coral-like *Euphorbia* (Cremers 1984), deserves separate status based on morphology (Rauh 1998, 1999) and molecular evidence (Haevermans 2003b; Yang et al. 2012). These plants are characterized by their shrubby habit, more or less prostrate and creeping growth form, and sympodial branching [three species: *E. bosseri* Leandri*, *E. platyclada* Rauh*, and *E. bemarahaensis* Rauh & Mangelsdorff*].

- Section ***Plagianthae*** Haev. & X. Aubriot*.

This group of species was previously included in the informal coral-like euphorbias in subgenus *Euphorbia*, but molecular evidence demonstrates that they are best placed in a separate section in another subgenus. This group is characterized by its unique morphology, defined by the very peculiar lenticellate bark, which has peeling rolls [two species: *E. plagiantha* Drake*, *E. salota* Leandri*].

- Section ***Anisophyllum*** Roep. subsection ***Hypericifoliae*** Boiss.

Malagasy endemic members of this subsection are rare and understudied prostrate or small herbaceous plants, and no recent material exists for most species. The herbarium collections contain numerous specimens of the common *E. hypericifolia* and other weedy pantropicals, such as *E. hirta* and *E. prostrata* [six other species on Madagascar: *E. grandidieri* Baill.*, *E. humbertii* Denis*, *E. mertonii* Fosberg, *E. pellegrinii* Leandri*, *E. trichophylla* Baker*, *E. vezorum* Leandri*].

4. *Euphorbia* subgenus *Euphorbia* (Dorsey et al. 2013)
   - Section ***Pachysanthae*** X. Aubriot & Haev.*.

Members of section *Pachysanthae* occur in forests, and are either shrubby or huge bottle trees reminiscent of a slender baobab. This group is characterized by having the largest fruits and seeds of the Malagasy euphorbias [six species: *E. elastica* Jum.*, *E. haevermansii* X. Aubriot & Lowry*, *E. nusbaumeri* X. Aubriot & Lowry*, *E. mananarensis* Leandri*, *E. mandravioky* Baill.*, *E. pachysantha* Baill.*].

- Section ***Pervilleanae*** Haev. & X. Aubriot*.

This group of plants is the only one of the Malagasy *Euphorbia* species (apart from *E. antso* and some members of section *Pachysanthae*) to possess a capsule diversely ornamented with soft fleshy spines and comparatively large seeds. On the basis of molecular studies (Haevermans 2003a; Dorsey et al. 2013) this group appears to be sister to the section *Tirucalli* Boiss. [eight species: *E. adenopoda* Baill.*, *E. analamerae* Leandri*, *E. erythroxyloides* Baker*, *E. intisy* Drake*, *E. pervilleana* Baill.*, *E. randrianjohanyi* Haev. & Labat*, *E. rauhii* Haev. & Labat*, and *E. tetraptera* Baker*].

- Section ***Tirucalli*** Boiss.

The species belonging to this section are commonly referred to as coral-like euphorbias and are well represented in the vegetation of southwestern Madagascar where they, along with Didiereaceae, are important structural elements of the regional flora. Members of this group are usually known by their vernacular name *famata*. The mature plants generally show a main stem that is unbranched at the base, covered with scars of fallen twigs, and topped with a crown of branches. The coral-like euphorbias are succulent trees adapted to the extreme climate of the dry spiny thicket, where they are the most diverse; however, they can also be found growing in the Central Highlands and throughout the west coast up to Antsiranana in the far north. They are all characterized by their cylindrical photosynthetic twigs, which are more or less flattened depending on the species, and small caducous or early deciduous leaves. They are generally dioecious (male flowers and female flowers on separate individuals), but a poorly known hermaphrodite species exists (*E. ramofraga*) and deserves detailed study. The root system is poorly documented but bears swellings that are used by the plant to store water. The section is not restricted to Madagascar with members occurring in mainland Africa and its surrounding islands (Dorsey et al. 2013). The only nonendemic Malagasy species is *E. tirucalli*, which has a wide range in the Old World [12 species: *E. alcicornis* Baker*, *E. analalavensis* Leandri*, *E. arahaka* Poiss.*, *E. boinensis* Denis ex Humbert & Leandri*, *E. decorsei* Drake*, *E. fiherenensis* Poiss.*, *E. kamponii* Rauh & Petignat*, *E. mainty* (Poiss.) Denis ex Leandri*, *E. ramofraga* Denis & Humbert ex Leandri*, *E. stenoclada* Baill.*, *E. tirucalli* L., *E. xylophylloides* Brongn. ex Lem.*].

- Section ***Goniostema*** Baill. ex Boiss.*

The representatives of this section are all restricted to Madagascar and contain the most sought-after ornamental plants. They all possess hermaphrodite cyathia usually subtended by two developed and showy cyathophylls. The leaves are well developed and clustered toward twig extremities. They are shrubs, often branched from the base, with succulent twigs, and spines in clusters of two or more around each leaf scar. The best-known species from this group is *E. milii* (and its varieties), called "crown-of-thorns," and known in Malagasy by the collective name *songosongo*. Ursch and Leandri (1954) described this section in detail, and its nomenclature and typification has been more recently addressed (Haevermans et al. 2009). Various types of succulence and architecture are found throughout Madagascar and the species can be informally grouped by the plants being root-succulents, stem-succulents or leaf-succulents, branching shrubs, or geophytes (Evans et al. 2014) [around 130 species allied to *E. milii* Des Moul.*].

- Section ***Deuterocalli*** Croizat*.

Plants of this group are all restricted to Madagascar and other islands of the Malagasy Region. They form shrubs or small trees and can be found in rocky and dry places in most areas of the island. Their leaves are notably reduced and usually early deciduous; the photosynthetic stems are covered in a layer of wax in some species that grow in dry spiny thickets [four species: *E. alluaudii* Drake*, *E. cedrorum* Rauh & Hebding*, *E. famatamboay* F. Friedmann & Cremers*, *E. oncoclada* Drake*].

- Section ***Denisophorbia*** (Leandri) Croizat, Malagasy Region.

These plants are all characterized by a very peculiar plagiotropic architecture (i.e., slanting from the vertical line). All the species appear dioecious in the wild, but certain individuals in cultivation seem to

TABLE 8.30. **Novelties for *Euphorbia* published since 2003**

Euphorbia* section *Antso P. E. Berry, *Taxon* 62(6): 1189, 2013
Euphorbia* section *Bosseriae Haev. & X. Aubriot, *Taxon* 61(4): 778, 2012
Euphorbia* section *Denisiae Haev. & X. Aubriot, *Taxon* 61(4): 778, 2012
Euphorbia* section *Pachysanthae X. Aubriot & Haev., *Taxon* 62(2): 309, 2013
Euphorbia* section *Pervilleanae Haev. & X. Aubriot, *Taxon* 62(2): 309, 2013
Euphorbia* section *Plagianthae Haev. & X. Aubriot, *Taxon* 61(4): 779, 2012
Euphorbia* subsection *Deuterocalli (Croizat) Bruyns, *Taxon* 55(2): 415, 2006
E. ambatomenahensis Rebmann, *Cactus and Succulent Journal U. S.* 5(1): 4, 2013
E. ambonaivoensis Rebmann, *Cactus and Succulent Journal U. S.* 8(2): 34, 2016
E. ambovombensis var. *ambatomenaensis* Rebmann, *Succulentes* 2003(3): 20, 2003, nom. inval., contrary to Art. 37.6 ICBN (2000)
E. ambovombensis var. *ambatomenahensis* Rebmann, *Cactus and Succulent Journal U. S.* 2(1): 30, 2010, nom. inval., without Latin description
E. berevoensis Lawant & Buddens., *Euphorbia World* 4(1): 6, 2008
E. beuginii Rebmann, *Cactus and Succulent Journal U. S.* 4(2): 45, 2012
E. boiteaui* var. *ampanihyensis (Cremers) J.-P. Castillon & J.-B. Castillon, *Candollea* 71(1): 156, 2016
E. boiteaui* var. *spirosticha (Rauh & Buchloh) J.-P. Castillon & J.-B. Castillon, *Candollea* 71(1): 156, 2016
E. castillonii Lavranos, *Succulentes* 2002(3): 5 (2002), synonym of *E. rangovalensis* Leandri (Haevermans 2006)
E. decaryi* var. *crassicaulis (Rauh) J.-P. Castillon & J.-B. Castillon, *Candollea* 71(1): 153, 2016
E. denisiana* var. *ankarensis (Boiteau) Houyelle, *Euphorbia World* 14(1): 12, 2018
E. denisiana* var. *maromokotrensis (Rebmann) Houyelle, *Euphorbia World* 14(1): 13, 2018
E. emilienneae Rebmann, *Cactus and Succulent Journal U. S.* 9(1): 28, 2017, nom. inval., no page number given, contrary to Art. 41.5 ICN (2012)
E. erythrocucullata Mangelsdorff, *Haseltonia* 11: 3, 2005
E. gigantea J.-P. Castillon, *Adansonia* 40(2): 164, 2018
E. haevermansii X. Aubriot & Lowry, *Phytotaxa* 159(3): 225, 2014
E. helenae Rebmann, *Cactus and Succulent Journal U. S.* 8(2): 35. 2016, nom. illeg., later homonym
E. longitubicinicyathium J.-P. Castillon & J.-B. Castillon, *Candollea* 73(2): 188, 2018
E. mahafalensis* var. *itampolensis (Rauh) J.-P. Castillon & J.-B. Castillon, *Candollea* 74(2): 160, 2019
E. maromokotrensis Rebmann, *Cactus and Succulent Journal U. S.* 1(2): 44, 2009
E. marotsipoyana Rebmann, *Cactus and Succulent Journal U. S.* 11(2): 43, 2019
E. milii subsp. *breonii* Rebmann, *Cactus and Succulent Journal U. S.* 8(1): 21, 2016, nom. inval., no holotype cited, only neotype
E. milii* var. *roseana Marn.-Lap. ex Demoly, *Journal de Botanique de la Société Botanique de France* 18–19: 189, 2002
E. neoelliotii J.-P. Castillon & J.-B. Castillon, *Candollea* 73(1): 23, 2018
E. nicaisei Rebmann, *Cactus and Succulent Journal U. S.* 5(1): 11, 2013
E. nusbaumeri X. Aubriot & Lowry, *Phytotaxa* 159(3): 231, 2014
E. pseudodidieroides J.-P. Castillon & Rajaov. *Malagasy Nature*, 13: 60–64, 2019
E. ramena Buddens. & Razaf., *Euphorbia World* 11(3): 13, 2015
E. randrianjohanyi Haev. & Labat, *Systematic Botany* 29(1): 119, 2004
E. rauhii Haev. & Labat, *Systematic Botany* 29(1): 122, 2004
E. razafindratsirae Lavranos, *Succulentes* 2002(3): 7, 2002
E. valeryae J.-P. Castillon, *Adansonia* 40(2): 166, 2018
E. xylophylloides* subsp. *crassa (Cremers) S. Carter, *Euphorbia World* 10(2): 19, 2014

Source: Haevermans (2003b).
Note: Validly published names in **bold**.

exhibit flowers of both sexes. Several forms obviously new to science and awaiting description have been found in the wild during our fieldwork and among specimens housed in the herbarium of the Muséum National d'Histoire Naturelle, Paris [13 species: *E. ankaranae* Leandri*, *E. aprica* Baill.*, *E. boivinii* Boiss.*, *E. bongolavensis* Rauh*, *E. elliotii* Leandri*, *E. hedyotoides* N. E. Br.*, *E. mahabobokensis* Rauh*, *E. mangorensis* Leandri*, *E. martinae* Rauh*, *E. neoelliotii* J.-P. Castillon & J.-B. Castillon*, *E. physoclada* Boiss. (*E. pyrifolia* Lam.?), *E. rangovalensis* Leandri*, and *E. zakamenae* Leandri*].

EVOLUTION OF SUCCULENCE

The genus *Euphorbia* is mostly represented on Madagascar by clades of endemic, very succulent plants (through roots, leaves, or stem-succulence). Most of those clades contain nonsucculent taxa which makes this case ideal for studying the evolution of this trait within endemic radiations as succulence is ancestral in almost all Malagasy clades (Haevermans 2003a). Evans et al. (2014) investigated the evolution of succulence in Malagasy *Euphorbia* and the correlation of environmental parameters with the various developed adaptations. One of the results was the discovery that two types of succulence (leaf succulence and geophytism) are associated with the driest areas of the island, while cactiform euphorbias favor less arid areas.

USE IN HORTICULTURE AND EX SITU COLLECTIONS

Wild succulent *Euphorbia* species are of considerable interest to plant collectors from all over the world. *Euphorbia milii* and relatives have produced a wide range of diversified hybrids thanks to the possibility of species of the same section hybridizing. The most common are hybrids between *E. milii* × *E. lophogona* (= *E.* × *lomi* Rauh 1979), *E. milii* × *E. moratii*, *E. milii* × *E. decaryi* var. *spirosticha*, and *E. milii* × *E. pedilanthoides*.

In Thailand, a group of *Euphorbia* resulting from the selection of *E.* × *lomi*, called "poysean," has inflorescences reminiscent of hydrangeas (see Jankalski 2000 for a detailed review of these hybrids). The cultivated form predominantly found throughout Antananarivo and the Central Highlands seems to be a robust cultivar of *E. milii* var. *hislopii*. It should be noted that, in spite of about 170-plus indigenous species of succulent *Euphorbia* with ornamental appeal, this plant is virtually the only form commonly found in Malagasy gardens, the remaining species being not usually cultivated. However, several extensive private or institutional collections exist in the world and preserve several of those rare and threatened taxa, emphasizing the importance of living ex situ collections for conservation (Delmas et al. 2011).

CONSERVATION

Almost all the succulent species of *Euphorbia* on Madagascar are endemics with restricted geographic ranges, and 80% of the taxa belong to one of the extinction risk categories on the International Union for the Conservation of Nature (IUCN) Red List (Haevermans 2004). Further, the majority of these species are listed in Appendix I or Appendix II of the Convention on International Trade in Endangered Species of Wild Fauna and Flora (CITES). Many of these listed species have extremely limited ranges and are highly threatened by habitat destruction and plundering for commercial purposes. There is a substantial world market for collectors of these succulent plants, increasing the threat to wild populations. This form of exploitation is ongoing as demonstrated by yearly customs seizures of illegal wild-collected plants, most of the time wrongly labeled in order to escape trade regulations. A recent paper demonstrates that the identification of these plants, generally seized in sterile condition, is only possible based on DNA barcode sequences, which could ideally be conducted without the assistance of plant specialists (Aubriot et al. 2013).

FUTURE WORK

Within the sections of the genus *Euphorbia* outlined above, several species are often rather difficult to distinguish from one another, and the lack of a revision of Malagasy *Euphorbia* or a worldwide review impedes progress in defining species limits. The last revision of Malagasy *Euphorbia* was that of Boissier (1862), and at that time more than half of the species recognized today were yet undescribed. Several novelties have been published since Haevermans (2003a) (Table 8.30), both in peer-reviewed and amateur journals. Many of these forms have yet to be properly assessed, and to date only a few groups or sections have been formally revised (Haevermans and Labat 2004; Aubriot et al. 2014). After a first attempt at revisiting the nomenclature of the most speciose group (Haevermans et al. 2009), the two authors of this contribution are now working toward completing the treatment of the genus *Euphorbia* for the *Flore de Madagascar et des Comores*.

Subject editors: Laurent Gautier and Steven M. Goodman

PHYLLANTHACEAE

H. Ralimanana and G. Challen

Euphorbiaceae *sensu lato*, as traditionally recognized, is one of the largest families of angiosperms, ranked sixth after Asteraceae, Poaceae, Leguminosae, Orchidaceae, and Rubiaceae. It is distributed in temperate as well as tropical areas. Euphorbiaceae in this broad sense is a complex family with considerable variation in vegetative and floral morphology. Molecular work by Chase et al. (1993) was the first to show that this huge family was polyphyletic and, since then, many molecular studies have supported this conclusion. The Angiosperm Phylogeny Group IV (2016) classification recognizes five lineages of Euphorbiaceae *sensu lato*: Euphorbiaceae *sensu stricto*, Pandaceae, Phyllanthaceae, Picrodendraceae, and Putranjivaceae (see Wurdack, pp. 634–39).

Phyllanthaceae is the largest family segregated from Euphorbiaceae *sensu lato* and comprises about 2000 species and 59 accepted genera. It is distributed in the New and Old World tropics. The family is more or less the equivalent of subfamily Phyllanthoideae *sensu* Webster (1994), but includes the genera *Croizatia*, *Dicoelia*, and *Tarcarcuna*, and excludes *Drypetes*, *Phyllanoa*, *Putranjiva*, and *Sibangea*. It is also equivalent to subfamily Phyllanthoideae *sensu* Radcliffe-Smith (2001), but excludes *Centroplacus*. Subsequently, molecular studies were expanded by Wurdack et al. (2004), Kathriarachchi et al. (2006), and Samuel et al. (2005) to review the circumscription of the Phyllanthaceae. Within this family, Hoffmann et al. (2006) recognized two subfamilies (Phyllanthoideae and Antidesmatoideae) and 10 tribes (Antidesmateae, Bischofieae, Bridelieae, Jablonskieae, Phyllantheae, Poranthereae, Scepeae, Spondiantheae, Uapaceae, and Wielandieae).

PHYLLANTHACEAE OF MADAGASCAR

Phyllanthaceae is among the medium to large families of plants on Madagascar with 118 species, 89% of which are endemic (Figure 8.41). *Phyllanthus* is its largest genus with 53 species (Table 8.31). Several researchers have devoted their investigations to the composition of the family, as well as to the taxonomic revision of its genera. The most important series of contributions were made by Jacques Leandri who published on the Malagasy members of this group (Leandri 1933, 1934, 1938, 1939b, 1957). He studied critically the composition of two of the subfamilies of Euphorbiaceae *sensu lato*, Phyllanthoideae and Oldfieldioideae, and compiled his findings in the *Flore de Madagascar et des Comores* (Leandri 1958). The subfamily Phyllanthoideae was treated in this volume and included the Phyllanthaceae as considered herein, but also the genus *Drypetes*, now included in Putranjivaceae. The rest of the family Euphorbiaceae *sensu lato* was to be treated in the second volume, which has yet to be published.

Brunel, and collaborators (Brunel 1987; Brunel and Roux 1981, 1982) also contributed to knowledge of the Phyllanthaceae, and a portion of his work focused on the genus *Phyllanthus* together with some genera close to the tribe Phyllantheae of tropical Africa and Madagascar. In his treatment, which was based on morphological and palynological analysis, he formulated broad criteria to define, classify, and record African-Malagasy Phyllantheae taxa. He proposed an infrageneric classification of some Malagasy *Phyllanthus* and also published new taxa of Phyllanthaceae from Madagascar, such as *Meineckia websteri*, *P. nummulariifolius* subsp. *vinanibeae*, and *P. andranovatensis*. He also anticipated the need for a critical review for some genera in the Phyllanthaceae, such as *Glochidion*.

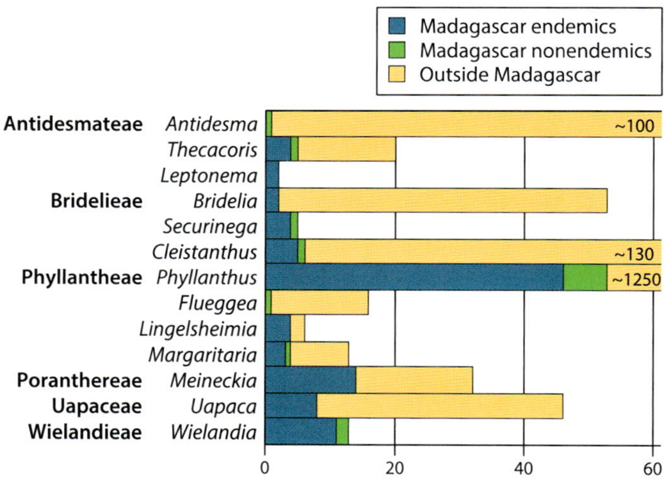

FIGURE 8.41 **Diversity and endemicity diagram of Malagasy Phyllanthaceae at the level of genera, showing three different species counts: 1) endemic to Madagascar, 2) nonendemic but native to Madagascar, and 3) those occurring elsewhere in the world (for further information see text). In cases when species diversity exceeds or does not conform to that presented on the horizontal graph scale, the figures are written along the respective horizontal line of a given genus.**

Since Leandri's treatment and the increase in phylogenetic studies in the 1990s, the classification has been updated and several new species have been named. From 2000, Petra Hoffmann and her colleagues have intensively studied the Malphigiales, including those on Madagascar. Taxonomic revision of some Malagasy genera has been undertaken. Hoffmann (2000) described two new species of *Andrachne*, *A. cerebroides* and *A. gracilipes*. Both of these species were recently moved to *Meineckia* when Vorontsova et al. (2007) and Vorontsova and Hoffmann (2008) studied the classification and circumscription of the tribe Porantherae. After studying herbarium specimens from Madagascar, Hoffmann and McPherson (2003b) moved *Glochidion sensu* Leandri to *Phyllanthus*, which resulted in a series of new combinations.

The molecular analysis conducted by Kathriarachchi et al. (2006) generated new information on the systematic placement of some *Phyllanthus* from Madagascar. Since then, a broad review of the taxonomy, conservation, and distribution of Malagasy and Comorian members of this genus has been undertaken (Ralimanana 2007; Ralimanana and Hoffmann 2011, 2014; Ralimanana et al. 2013; Ralimanana and Cable 2020). On the basis of this work, the genus *Phyllanthus* is composed of 53 species, including nine new species recently recognized for Madagascar. The work of Ralimanana continues, and includes the recent description of four new species, *M. nusbaumeri* and *M. ranirisonii* from the Loky Manambato (Daraina) area (Ralimanana 2017), *P. ankirindrensis*, and *P. razakamalalae* (Ralimanana and Cable 2020).

MORPHOLOGY

On Madagascar, members of the Phyllanthaceae are monoecious or dioecious trees, shrubs, or herbs. They are recognized by the alternate or spiral, but very rarely opposite, simple or rarely compound leaves; and stipules are always present. The inflorescences are axillary, rarely cauline or terminal, racemose or spicate, rarely paniculate or glomerulate. The flowers are generally whitish and relatively small, unisexual (the flower has either stamens or pistil), or very rarely bisexual. The calyx has three to eight free or fused sepals, and the corolla has four to six petals, rarely two, or the petals are absent. The disc may be present or absent, with separate or annular glands. There are three to 10 stamens in the male flower, and these are free or completely fused, three-lobed or entire, and the pistillode may be present or absent. The ovary of the female flower is superior with two to five (exceptionally, 1–15) locules, the styles are free or fused, and staminodes absent. The fruit is generally a dehiscent capsule or an indehiscent drupe or berry. Seeds are ecarunculate or minutely carunculate, colored or not, and endosperm is present or absent. In practice, when you find herbs, shrubs, or trees with simple and alternate leaves with stipules, no latex, and capsular fruits, put them first in Phyllanthaceae then check the characters above for verification (Figure 8.42).

DISTRIBUTION AND HABITAT

Phyllanthaceae species are found in all phytogeographic domains of Madagascar, but most of them have narrow distributions ranges

TABLE 8.31. **Phyllanthaceae on Madagascar and their distribution**

SCIENTIFIC NAME	GEOGRAPHIC DISTRIBUTION
***ANTIDESMA* (1)**	PaleoT
A. madagascariense Lam.	MR (Comoros, Madagascar, and Mascarenes)
***BRIDELIA* (2)**	PaleoT
B. pervilleana Baill.	M
B. tulasneana Baill.	M
***CLEISTANTHUS* (6)**	PaleoT
C. boivinianus (Baill.) Müll. Arg.	M
C. capuronii Leandri	M
C. occidendalis (Leandri) Leandri	M
C. perrieri Leandri	M
C. stenonia (Baill.) Jabl.	MR (Comoros and Madagascar)
C. suarezensis Leandri	M
***FLUEGGEA* (1)**	PanT
F. virosa (Roxb. ex Willd.) Voigt	PaleoT
***LEPTONEMA* (2)**	M
L. glabrum (Leandri) Leandri	M
L. venosum (Poir.) A. Juss.	M
***LINGELSHEIMIA* (4)**	AfrM
L. abbayesii (Leandri) Radcl.-Sm.	M
L. ambigua (Leandri) Radcl.-Sm.	M
L. fiherenensis (Leandri) Radcl.-Sm.	M
L. manongarivensis (Leandri) G. L. Webster	M
***MARGARITARIA* (4)**	PanT
M. anomala (Baill.) Fosberg	MR (Aldabra, Comoros, Madagascar, and Mascarenes)
M. decaryana (Leandri) G. L. Webster	M
M. hispidula G. L. Webster	M
M. rhomboidalis (Baill.) G. L. Webster	M
***MEINECKIA* (14)**	PanT
M. baronii (Hutch.) G. L. Webster	M
M. cerebroides (Petra Hoffm.) Voronts. & Petra Hoffm.	M
M. decaryi (Leandri) Brunel ex Radcl.-Sm.	M
M. gracilipes (Petra Hoffm.) Voronts. & Petra Hoffm.	M
M. humbertii G. L. Webster	M
M. leandrii G. L. Webster	M
M. madagascariensis (Leandri ex Humbert) G. L. Webster	M
M. nusbaumeri Ralim.	M
M. orientalis (Leandri) G. L. Webster	M
M. peltata (Hutch.) G. L. Webster	M
M. pubiflora G. L. Webster	M
M. ranirisonii Ralim.	M
M. trichogynis (Baill.) G. L. Webster	M
M. websteri Jean F. Brunel & Jacq. Roux	M
***PHYLLANTHUS* (53)**	PanT
P. amarus Schumach. & Thonn.	PanT
P. ambatovolana Leandri	M
P. ampandrandavae Leandri	M
P. analamerae Leandri	M
P. andranovatensis Jean F. Brunel & Jacq. Roux	M
P. ankarana Leandri	M
P. ankaratrae (Leandri) Petra Hoffm. & McPherson	M
P. ankazobensis Ralim. & Petra Hoffm.	M
P. ankirindrensis Ralim. & Cable	M
P. bathianus Leandri	M
P. bemangidiensis Ralim.	M
P. bernieranus Baill. ex Müll. Arg.	M
P. betsileanus Leandri	M
P. bojerianus (Baill.) Müll. Arg.	M
P. casticum P. Willemet	MR (Madagascar and Mascarenes)
P. coluteoides Müll. Arg	M
P. coodei Ralim. & Petra Hoffm.	M
P. coursii Leandri	M
P. cryptophilus (A. Juss.) Müll. Arg.	M
P. fuscoluridus Müll. Arg.	M
P. gordonii Ralim. & Petra Hoffm.	M
P. goudotianus (Baill.) Müll. Arg.	M
P. humbertianus Leandri	M
P. humbertii (Leandri) Petra Hoffm. & McPherson	M
P. iratsiensis Leandri	M
P. isomonensis Leandri	M

(continued overleaf)

TABLE 8.31. ***continued***

SCIENTIFIC NAME	GEOGRAPHIC DISTRIBUTION
P. ivohibeus Leandri	M
P. lichenisilvae (Leandri) Petra Hoffm. & McPherson	M
P. lokohensis Leandri	M
P. madagascariensis Müll. Arg.	M
P. maderaspatensis L.	PaleoT
P. mananarensis Leandri	M
P. mantadiensis Ralim. & Petra Hoffm.	M
P. marojejiensis (Leandri) Petra Hoffm. & McPherson	M
P. matitanensis Leandri	M
P. melleri Müll. Arg.	M
P. moramangicus (Leandri) Leandri	M
P. multiflorus Poir.	M
P. nummulariifolius Poir.	Afr, MR
P. nummulariifolius Poir. subsp. *vinanibeae* Jean F. Brunel & J. P. Roux	M
P. obdeltophyllus Leandri	M
P. oreichtitus Leandri	M
P. perrieri (Leandri) Petra Hoffm. & McPherson	M
P. pervilleanus (Baill.) Müll. Arg.	MR (Comoros)
P. philippioides Leandri	M
P. rangoloakensis Leandri	M
P. razakamalalae Ralim. & Cable	M
P. sambiranensis Leandri	M
P. tenellus Roxb.	Afr (Mozambique, Tanzania, and Yemen), MR
P. urinaria L.	PanT
P. vakinankaratrae Leandri	M
P. vatovaviensis Leandri ex Ralim. & Petra Hoffm.	M
P. venustulus Leandri	M
P. vergens Baill.	M
***SECURINEGA* (5)**	MR
S. antsingyensis Leandri	M
S. capuronii Leandri	M
S. durissima J. F. Gmel.	MR (Madagascar and Mascarenes)
S. perrieri Leandri	M
S. seyrigii Leandri	M
***THECACORIS* (5)**	Afr, M
T. cometia Leandri	M
T. humbertii Leandri	M
T. madagascariensis A. Juss.	M
T. perrieri Leandri	M
T. spathulifolia (Pax) Leandri	Afr (Kenya, Mozambique, and Somalia)
***UAPACA* (8)**	Afr, M
U. ambanjensis Leandri	M
U. amplifolia Denis	M
U. bojeri Baill.	M
U. densifolia Baker	M
U. ferruginea Baill.	M
U. littoralis Denis	M
U. louvelii Denis	M
U. thouarsii Baill.	M
***WIELANDIA* (13)**	Afr, MR
W. bemarensis (Leandri) Petra Hoffm. & McPherson	M
W. bojeriana (Baill.) Petra Hoffm. & McPherson	M
W. danguyana (Leandri) Petra Hoffm. & McPherson	M
W. elegans Baill.	MR (Comoros)
W. laureola (Baill.) Petra Hoffm. & McPherson	M
W. fadenii (Radcl.-Sm.) Petra Hoffm. & McPherson	Afr (Kenya), MR (Comoros)
W. leandriana (Petra Hoffm. & McPherson) Petra Hoffm. & McPherson	M
W. mimosoides (Baill.) Petra Hoffm. & McPherson	M
W. oblongifolia (Baill.) Petra Hoffm. & McPherson	M
W. platyrachis (Baill.) Petra Hoffm. & McPherson	M
W. ranavalonae (Leandri) Petra Hoffm. & McPherson	M
W. tanalorum (Leandri) Petra Hoffm. & McPherson	M
W. unifex Petra Hoffm. & McPherson	M

Notes: Number of species in Madagascar in parentheses after genus name. Afr, Continental Africa; M, Madagascar; MR, Malagasy Region; PaleoT, Paleotropical; PanT, Pantropical.

FIGURE 8.42 **Examples of Phyllanthaceae species on Madagascar: A) *Uapaca bojeri*, male flowers; B) *Antidesma madagascariense* with fruits; C) *Wielandia platyrachis* with fruit; and D) *Phyllanthus philippioides*, fruits and flowers.** (PHOTOS by H. Ralimanana.)

and are known from only a few collection sites. Some species are microendemics and confined to a small geographic area, such as *Margaritaria hispidula* near Befandriana Sud, *Meineckia nusbaumeri* and *M. ranirisonii*, which are endemic to the Loky Manambato (Daraina) area, *Phyllanthus coodei*, found only on a single hill near Tolagnaro, and *P. philippioides* restricted to a hill near Tsinjoarivo.

Data from herbarium studies and surveys undertaken in different areas of Madagascar indicate that members of Phyllanthaceae show a range of variation in their habitats. It is well represented in different vegetation types from grasslands (Ralimanana and Hoffmann 2011, 2014) to dry deciduous and moist evergreen forests (Petignat et al. 1997; Birkinshaw et al. 2000; Ranarivelo and Kotozafy 2001; Gautier et al. 2003). With some exceptions, such as the genera *Antidesma*, *Cleistanthus*, *Uapaca*, *Bridelia*, and some *Phyllanthus* species, Malagasy Phyllanthaceae species are often of shade-tolerant inhabitants of the moist evergreen forest understory, supporting C. C. Davis et al. (2005) who inferred that tropical rainforest is the ancestral habitat of the Malpighiales.

POLLINATION AND SEED DISPERSAL

Little is known about the pollination of Malagasy Phyllanthaceae. Some genera (*Phyllanthus* and *Uapaca*) in this family are visited by bees (*Apis mellifera* var. *unicolor*) for their nectar and pollen (Ralalaharisoa-Ramamonjisoa 1992; Ralimanana 1994), and these bees are considered important for pollination. Kawakita and Kato's studies (2004, 2009) also showed an obligatory mutualism with moths for some Malagasy species (*P. marojejiensis* and *P. humbertii*). *Epicephala* moths, whose larvae feed on the seed, collect and transport pollen between flowers.

Dispersal is sometimes insured by the plant itself in a phenomenon called autochory, where capsular fruits explode, projecting the seeds. It can also be carried out by birds, lemurs, or humans for species with fleshy fruits (see Razafindratsima et al., pp. 142–52), such as *Antidesma madagascariensis*, *Phyllanthus*, and *Uapaca*. Some research projects undertaken on Madagascar revealed that some species of Phyllanthaceae are among the preferred food plants of *Lemur catta* (Ring-tailed Lemur). This species plays an important role in Phyllanthaceae seed dispersal. As shown by LaFleur and Sauther (2015), *A. madagascariense* (mature leaves, flowers, fruits), *Flueggea virosa* (mature leaves), and *P. casticum* (young and mature leaves, leaf buds, flowers and fruits) are among the species eaten by this lemur. Seeds of plants growing in riverbeds and in nearby rocky areas seem to be dispersed by high water and these include, for example, *P. bernieranus* and *P. rangoloakensis*.

USES AND CONSERVATION

Phyllanthaceae species have multiple uses in Madagascar, and the wood is often used for fuel. People in some areas eat ripe fruits of *Phyllanthus casticum*. Wild and captive silkworms feed on the leaves of *Uapaca bojeri*; their fruits are also edible.

It is hard to ensure conservation of species without a comprehensive knowledge of their threats, and this is the case for many members of this family. Therefore, species assessments are important for identifying priority actions for threatened species. Little progress has been made for assessing the extinction risk of Phyllanthaceae to date (April 2020), and only 37 species (31%) of the Malagasy members have been published in the International Union for the Conservation of Nature (IUCN) Red List. Among these, 21 species are considered threatened, including five Critically Endangered, nine Endangered, and seven Vulnerable. It is probably the case that most threatened Phyllanthaceae species become so due to habitat degradation and their occurrence outside of protected areas.

Phyllanthaceae members on Madagascar require much further study of their ecology and systematics, and few taxa have been included in molecular studies. Field observations and collections are essential for better understanding the poorly known Malagasy members of this family. However, the great diversity of flower and fruit morphology in the family causes difficulties in identification and tends to discourage collection and study. Given the current rate of loss of natural forest on Madagascar, IUCN assessment of the family should be completed to improve understanding of the extinction risk of certain taxa and to identify priority action for their conservation.

Subject editors: Laurent Gautier and Steven M. Goodman

SALICACEAE

W. L. Applequist

The family Salicaceae now includes, in addition to the familiar temperate genera *Salix* and *Populus*, dozens of tropical to subtropical woody genera that were formerly classified within Flacourtiaceae, an ill-defined group that proved to be polyphyletic (e.g., Chase et al. 2002) and is no longer recognized. On Madagascar, Salicaceae is one of the more important woody families in terms of taxonomic diversity, and several genera are endemic to the island or have a primary center of diversity there.

DIVERSITY

Table 8.32 summarizes major distinguishing features of the genera of Salicaceae in Madagascar. Numbers of species recognized in each genus are reported from the *Flore de Madagascar et des Comores* treatment (Perrier de la Bâthie 1946a), which is known to be quite obsolete: from later generic revisions by Hermann O. Sleumer, who substantially increased the number of species known but sometimes took an unduly conservative approach to species circumscription; and from recent revisions or preliminary evaluations from the Missouri Botanical Garden's Catalogue of the Plants of Madagascar project (Madagascar Catalogue 2020). A total of 10 genera are present on Madagascar, with the currently estimated 138 species showing notable levels of species endemism (Figure 8.43). Several genera have not yet been carefully assessed in the modern era, so this estimate of species numbers is certainly an underestimate.

The tropical genera of Salicaceae have small flowers that, unlike those of *Salix* and *Populus*, have one or two perianth whorls and frequently have well-developed nectar-producing glands. Flowers are white to greenish or, less commonly, pink or red. Few observations of pollination have been made, but the unspecialized floral morphology suggests likely insect pollination; *Homalium* species have been recorded or reported as being visited by bees (e.g., Applequist 2018b; Rasoloarijao et al. 2019). The fruits are small capsules or thin-fleshed berries, drupes, or bacciform semi-fleshy capsules. In taxa with capsular fruits the entire flower often appears to be the unit of dispersal, with the perianth persistent and sometimes accrescent (e.g., some species of *Homalium*), presumably facilitating wind dispersal.

Fleshy fruits of *Ludia*, *Scolopia* (Figure 8.44e), and *Flacourtia* species are reported to be eaten by, and the seeds dispersed by, multiple species of lemurs native to diverse forest types (e.g., Bollen et al. 2004a; Thorén et al. 2011; P. C. Wright et al. 2011; Sato 2012), while *Flacourtia* fruit is eaten by bats (Raheriarisena 2005; Racey et

TABLE 8.32. **Genera of Salicaceae occurring on Madagascar, their distribution, and species richness on the island**

GENUS	DISTRIBUTION	NOTABLE FEATURES	NUMBER OF MALAGASY SPECIES RECOGNIZED		
			PERRIER DE LA BÂTHIE	SLEUMER (DATE)	CURRENT (SOURCE)
Bembicia	Madagascar	Flowers hermaphroditic; sepals 5, unequal; glands small, in groups of 2–4; petals present; stamens numerous; ovary half-inferior; fruit dry, single-seeded, concealed by bracts	1		2 species accepted, both endemic, 1 unpublished (Madagascar Catalogue 2019)
Bivinia	Madagascar to east Africa	Flowers hermaphroditic; sepals 5–6; petals absent; glands large, 1 per sepal; stamens numerous; ovary superior; fruit a capsule	1		1 species, also in east Africa (Madagascar Catalogue 2019)
Calantica	Madagascar	Flowers hermaphroditic; sepals 4–8; glands large, 1 per sepal; petals present; stamens 1 or 3–6 per petal; ovary superior; fruit a capsule	5	7 (1972a)	10 species, all endemic (Applequist et al. 2014)
Casearia	Pantropical	Flowers hermaphroditic; sepals 4–6; sepal glands absent or greatly reduced; petals absent; stamens 2 per sepal, with staminodes present; ovary superior; fruit a somewhat fleshy, but dehiscent capsule	5	1 (1971)	2 species accepted, both endemic; not yet evaluated (Madagascar Catalogue 2019)
Flacourtia	Africa to Pacific	Dioecious in Madagascar; sepals 4–5; glandular disc annular, entire, or lobed; petals absent; stamens numerous; ovary superior; fruit a drupe	2		1 species occurring in the wild, Native; not yet evaluated (Madagascar Catalogue 2019)
Homalium	Pantropical	Flowers hermaphroditic, with unusually variable morphology; sepals 4–10(–11); glands large, 1 per sepal; petals present; stamens 1 or 3(–5) per sepal; ovary half-inferior; fruit a capsule	34	36 (1973)	62 species, all endemic (Applequist 2016a, 2018a, 2018b, 2020; Wassel and Applequist 2020)
Ludia	Madagascar (to Mascarenes, east Africa)	Flowers hermaphroditic; sepals 5–8(–10), often pink to red; lobed glandular disk or small glands sometimes present; petals absent; stamens numerous; ovary superior; fruit a berry or bacciform, dehiscent	5	21 (1972b)	23 published species accepted, 22 endemic; not yet evaluated (Madagascar Catalogue 2019)
Salix	Temperate, mostly circumboreal	Flowers unisexual, in bracteate catkins; sepals and petals absent; glandular cupule present; ovary superior; fruit a capsule	2		2 published species accepted, both endemic; not yet evaluated (Madagascar Catalogue 2019).
Scolopia	Old World tropics	Flowers hermaphroditic; sepals 4–8(–10); glands small, numerous or 2 per sepal, or an irregular disc; petals present, not much differentiated from sepals; stamens numerous; ovary superior; fruit a berry	9	13 (1972c)	14 species, all endemic (Applequist and Schatz 2016)
Tisonia	Madagascar	Flowers hermaphroditic; sepals 3, unequal, accrescent and surrounding fruit, frequently reddish; petals present or absent; hypogynous disc present, sometimes divided; stamens numerous; ovary superior; fruit a capsule	10	15 (1970)	21 species accepted, all endemic, 8 of them unpublished (Madagascar Catalogue 2019)

Notes: Numbers of Malagasy species recognized by Perrier de la Bâthie (1946a), in generic revisions by Sleumer, and recent estimates in most cases from revisions or preliminary evaluations associated with the Madagascar Catalogue project (2019).

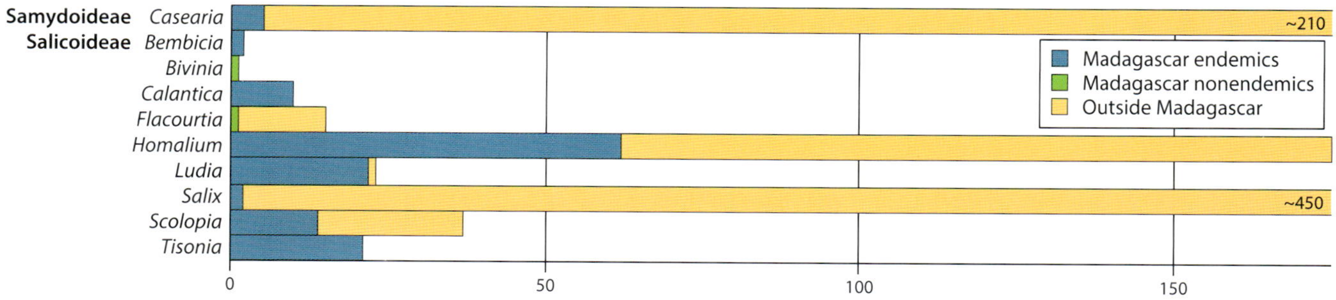

FIGURE 8.43 **Diversity and endemicity diagram of Malagasy Salicaceae at the level of genera, showing three different species counts: 1) endemic to Madagascar, 2) nonendemic but native to Madagascar, and 3) those occurring elsewhere in the world (for further information see text). In cases when species diversity exceeds or does not conform to that presented on the horizontal graph scale, the figures are written along the respective horizontal line of a given genus.**

FIGURE 8.44 **Examples of Malagasy Salicaceae. A) *Bivinia jalbertii*, B) *Calantica lucida* flowers, C) *Homalium albiflorum* flowers, D) *H. axillare* flowers, E) *Scolopia* sp. fruits, and F) *Tisonia* sp. fruits covered by persistent calyx.** (PHOTOS A and D by P. B. Phillipson; B by P. Lowry; C and E by G. Schatz; and F by C. Birkinshaw.)

al. 2009). Rodents and birds may act as seed predators (Bollen et al. 2004a), including *Coracopsis vasa* (Lesser Vasa Parrot), which is also a seed predator of the small dry fruits of *Homalium* and *Bembicia* (Bollen and van Elsacker 2004). In addition, leaves of *Ludia*, *Scolopia*, *Homalium*, and *Flacourtia* species are eaten by folivorous lemurs (e.g., Simmen et al. 2006; Andriamaharoa et al. 2010; Norscia et al. 2012). This family therefore provides important food resources for some of Madagascar's most iconic animals.

Ecologically, the Salicaceae of Madagascar clearly favor moist evergreen and littoral forests. The large majority of species of the largest genus, *Homalium*, are found in these forests, ranging from the extreme north to the extreme southeast, although several species are native to dry deciduous or dry spiny thicket regions. *Homalium* has been reported to be among the most diverse or most abundant genera in littoral forest fragments (Cadotte et al. 2002; Vary et al. 2011). Most species of *Tisonia*, *Calantica*, and *Scolopia* are also native to moist evergreen forest regions, although each genus includes a few western to southwestern species. In *Scolopia*, the species from dry regions form a morphologically well-differentiated group, often shrubby and usually spiny, with one-flowered inflorescences. *Ludia* is unique among the moderately sized genera in having a large fraction of known species native to western Madagascar. *Casearia* and *Bembicia* are primarily eastern but extend somewhat into the dry northwest; both genera are in need of taxonomic revisionary studies, and the northwestern populations may represent unrecognized species. *Flacourtia ramontchi*, a widespread Old World species often cultivated for its edible fruits, and *Bivinia jalbertii* (Figure 8.44a), which extends to east Africa, range from dry deciduous to moist evergreen forests and appear to be unusually unselective in habitat requirements. Probably as a result, they are important in transitional habitats such as forest margins prone to fire and as early successional species after the abandonment of farmed land. Finally, the two very rare *Salix* species are from the Central Highlands and specifically associated with wetland habitats.

ENDEMISM

The genera of Salicaceae on Madagascar can be roughly divided into three categories: the endemic genera; those genera that are not endemic, but for which much or most of the taxonomic diversity is native to Madagascar; and widespread genera that have small representation on the island. In the first category, *Bembicia*, *Calantica*, and *Tisonia* are endemic genera. In the second category, all but one species of *Ludia* are endemic to Madagascar, while *Bivinia* contains a single species that occurs mostly in Madagascar but is not endemic. All Malagasy species of the pantropical genus *Homalium* are endemic. These represent about a third of the species in that genus worldwide; however, six of the 10 sections recognized in the current infrageneric classification (Applequist 2016b) are present in Madagascar, and five are endemic, making Madagascar a major center of diversity for *Homalium*.

Among the widespread genera with lesser representation on Madagascar, *Scolopia* is best represented with 14 species, all endemic. *Casearia* has had one to five species recognized in Madagascar, all endemic. The five species recognized by Perrier de la Bâthie (1946a) should be accepted, and additional undescribed species exist; the treatment of Sleumer (1971), lumping all Malagasy populations into a single species due to their similar floral anatomy, was evidently incorrect. One species of *Flacourtia*, *F. ramontchi*, is native but not endemic; a second species has reportedly been introduced but is not found in the wild (Madagascar Catalogue 2020). Two species of *Salix* (*S. madagascariensis* and *S. perrieri*), known from at most a handful of collections in central Madagascar, are believed to be endemic. As Madagascar is an unusual location for *Salix*, further investigation of these species would be desirable.

Only three of the currently estimated 138 known species (published or unpublished) of Salicaceae that occur in the wild in Madagascar are not endemic to the country (Figure 8.43), and it has a total endemism rate of 97.8% (a conservative estimate, as additional endemic species are expected to be described in future studies). Many species are endemic to regions subject to severe habitat degradation and as such may be threatened or endangered. Formal International Union for the Conservation of Nature (IUCN) Red List assessments to date (IUCN 2020) list three species of *Homalium*, and one each of *Calantica*, *Casearia*, *Ludia*, and *Scolopia* as Vulnerable, while one species of *Scolopia*, two of *Homalium*, three of *Calantica*, and six of *Ludia* are classed as Endangered. Most seriously, six species—*C. pseudobiseriata*, *H. brachyrhachis*, *H. intercedens*, *L. imontiensis*, *L. myrtoides*, and *S. septentrionalis*—are listed as Critically Endangered and may be at immediate risk of extinction. The threat has been understated, however, because certain species that are categorized as Least Concern due to their apparently wide distribution, especially *H. albiflorum* and *Casearia nigrescens*, have been much too broadly circumscribed and will be divided into multiple, more geographically cohesive species in future revisionary treatments.

SYSTEMATICS AND PHYLOGENY

Alford's (2005) dissertation presented a chloroplast DNA–based phylogenetic study of Salicaceae that included representatives of several Malagasy genera. The family as most broadly circumscribed was divided into two main clades, which he proposed to recognize at family level as Salicaceae in a narrower sense and Samydaceae. *Scyphostegia* was sister to Salicaceae *sensu stricto* and would be recognized as the sole genus in Scyphostegiaceae. These segregate families do display morphological differences, such as the presence of salicoid leaf teeth (where teeth are present) in Salicaceae *sensu stricto* compared with theoid leaf teeth in Samydaceae. The only genus occurring on Madagascar that would be placed in Samydaceae is *Casearia*.

A subsequent student thesis (Diffey 2017) used sequences of the nuclear granule-bound starch synthase (GBSSI) gene to examine relationships within Salicaceae. In those studies, *Ludia* appeared to be closely related to *Scolopia* and possibly to have evolved within that genus; this is plausible as, except for its derived lack of petals, it is very similar to *Scolopia* in morphology. The analysis found that sequences from *Homalium*, *Calantica* (if included), and *Bembicia* were grouped together. As *Calantica* closely resembles certain sections of *Homalium*, except in having a fully superior ovary, it might be suspected that *Homalium* is paraphyletic. These five genera that have centers of diversity in Madagascar were closely related but did not form a monophyletic group as genera not found in Madagascar were interspersed among them. Neither phylogenetic study included enough species or sequence data to provide strong support for rearrangements of infra-familial classification. Future work examining this group in more depth would be highly desirable.

WORK IN PROGRESS

Existing revisionary treatments for most genera that have not been subject to recent study, including *Ludia*, *Tisonia*, *Casearia*, and *Bembicia*, are considered to be outdated. The current Madagascar Catalogue gives two species each for *Bembicia* and *Casearia*, which are clearly underestimates; preliminary studies now in progress suggest that several undescribed species are present in each. *Ludia* and *Tisonia* are moderate-size genera in which, if past experience is any guide, additional new species are likely to be found when full revisionary studies are done.

Subject editors: Laurent Gautier and Steven M. Goodman

VIOLACEAE

G. A. Wahlert

Violaceae is a medium-size cosmopolitan family with 28 genera and about 1100 species of herbs, lianas, shrubs, and trees (Ballard et al. 2014). On Madagascar, the family is represented by 29 recognized species with notable levels of endemism (Figure 8.45) and in three genera: *Viola*, *Afrohybanthus*, and *Rinorea*. The taxonomy of *Viola* and *Afrohybanthus* is well worked-out, but over the course of revising *Rinorea*, it became clear that the most recent taxonomic treatment, from nearly 70 years ago, by Perrier de la Bâthie (1949a), is of limited utility. Perrier de la Bâthie's revision recognized 24 species of *Rinorea* on the island, with two additional species described in recent years based on newly collected specimens (Wahlert et al. 2013; Wahlert 2016). Following a brief outline of *Viola* and *Afrohybanthus*, a synopsis of Malagasy *Rinorea* is presented below. The summary is based on a forthcoming revision by the author and reflects the current understanding of the taxonomic diversity of *Rinorea* on Madagascar.

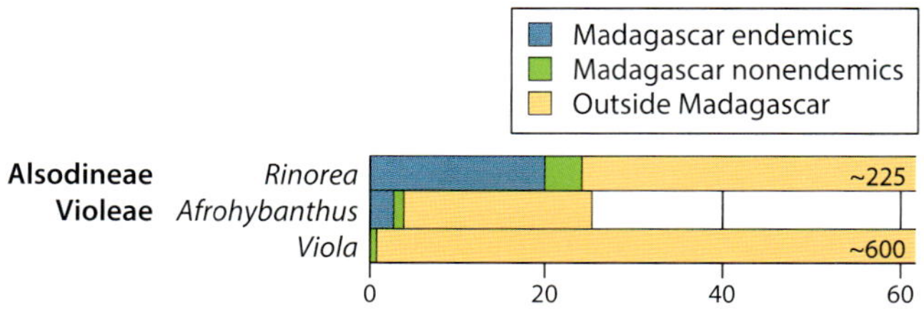

FIGURE 8.45 **Diversity and endemicity diagram of Malagasy Violaceae at the level of genera, showing three different species counts: 1) endemic to Madagascar, 2) nonendemic but native to Madagascar, and 3) those occurring elsewhere in the world (for further information see text). In cases when species diversity exceeds or does not conform to that presented on the horizontal graph scale, the figures are written along the respective horizontal line of a given genus.**

VIOLA AND *AFROHYBANTHUS*

The genus *Viola* is represented by a single species on Madagascar: *V. abyssinica*, a taxon which also occurs in east Africa and has a disjunct population in Cameroon. Typical of other species of *Viola* that occur in the tropics, *V. abyssinica* occurs in montane regions across its range. On Madagascar, the species is restricted to humid, subhumid, and montane areas from 900 to 2500 m and occurs on many of the island's tallest mountains, including Tsaratanàna, Ankaratra, and Andringitra (Figure 8.46a). This herbaceous perennial has a trailing habit, roots at the nodes, and presents solitary flowers borne on long pedicels. It grows on rocky areas, grasslands, and inselbergs, as well as disturbed sites, such as roadsides and secondary forests.

Afrohybanthus (Figures 8.46b–e and 8.47a) is one of several genera recently segregated from the polyphyletic *Hybanthus*, a move supported by molecular phylogenetic and morphological evidence (Flicker and Ballard 2015). Of the four Malagasy species, three are endemic, while the fourth, *A. enneaspermus*, is widely distributed across tropical and subtropical Africa and Asia. The three endemic species *A. buxifolius*, *A. danguyanus*, and *A. decaryanus* are all clearly delineated from one another. On Madagascar, the habit of *Afrohybanthus* varies from annual (*A. danguyanus*) and herbaceous perennial (*A. enneaspermus*) to suffrutescent plants (*A. buxifolius* and *A. decaryanus*).

DIVERSITY OF *RINOREA*

The pantropical *Rinorea* is the second-most species-rich genus in the Violaceae worldwide after *Viola* and contains about 250 species of trees and shrubs (Wahlert 2016). On Madagascar, the genus is represented by 24 species and an additional approximately 14 undescribed taxa (Table 8.33). Since Perrier de la Bâthie's treatment of the genus (1949a), an abundance of new herbarium material has become available, allowing a thorough reevaluation of the species

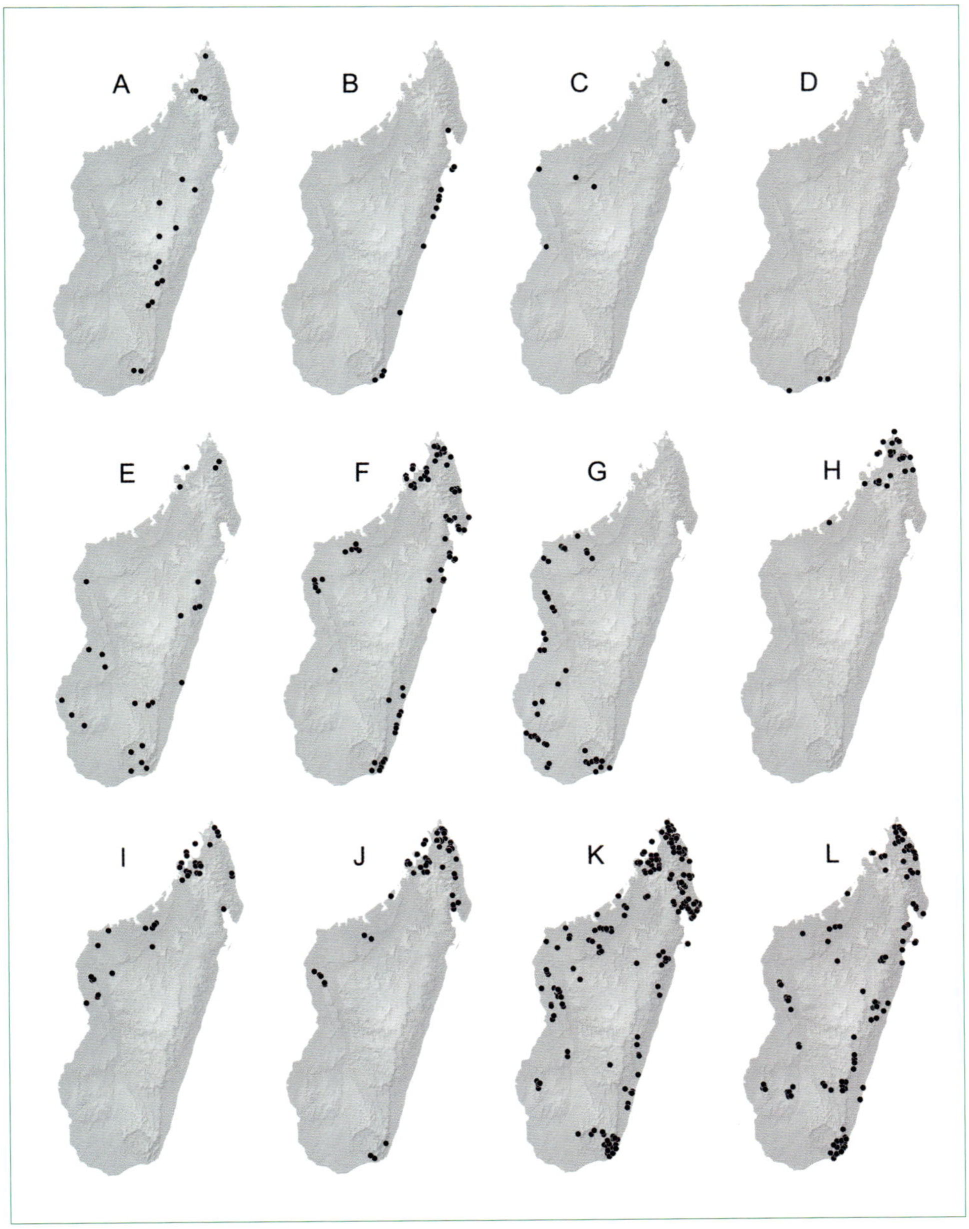

FIGURE 8.46 **Distribution maps of Malagasy Violaceae species and species groups, based in part on Wahlert (2010). A) *Viola abyssinica*; B) *Afrohybanthus buxifolius*; C) *A. danguyanus*; D) *A. decaryanus*; E) *A. enneaspermus*; F) *Rinorea angustifolia*; G) *R. greveana*; H) *R. pugionifera*; I) *R. ilicifolia* subsp. *spinosa*; J) *R. squamosa*; K) *Rinorea Arboreae* group (two species and around eight undescribed); and L) *Rinorea Verticillatae* group (17 species and around six undescribed).**

recognized in his revision and the eventual description of several new species. After years of study by the author, the most recent estimate for the number of *Rinorea* taxa on Madagascar—including undescribed species—is 38 taxa. Of these, 35 are endemic to the island, resulting in a 92% rate of endemism for *Rinorea* in Madagascar—a figure that exceeds the estimated 84.4% rate for Malagasy angiosperms in general (Madagascar Catalogue 2020).

A provisional infrageneric classification of the 175 or so species of African and Malagasy *Rinorea* suggests that they can be classified into 11 infrageneric groups equivalent to the rank of section, each of which are supported by morphological and molecular phylogenetic evidence (Wahlert and Ballard 2012; van Velzen et al. 2015). Of these 11 groups, six are represented on Madagascar, five have species or close relatives that occur both in Africa and on Madagascar (*Ilicifoliae*, *Squamosae*, *Choriandra*, *Arboreae*, and *Ardisianthus*), while the sixth group—*Verticillatae*—is endemic to Madagascar and the Comoro islands (Table 8.33; informal group names follow Wahlert and Ballard 2012). The *Arboreae* and *Verticillatae* groups each contain several species and undescribed entities in Madagascar that have presented challenges to taxonomic revision.

The *Rinorea Ilicifoliae* group contains a single taxon on Madagascar: *R. ilicifolia* subspecies *spinosa*. This small shrub is commonly found in dry deciduous forests in western and northern Madagascar, but there are also a few disjunct populations in moist evergreen forests around Iharana (Vohémar) and the Masoala Peninsula (Figure 8.46i). The subspecies also occurs on several islands in the Mozambique Channel, including Nosy Be, Nosy Mitsio, and Nosy Ankarea (Madagascar), and Mohéli and Mayotte (Comoro archipelago). Subspecies *spinosa* varies subtly in vegetative morphology from subspecies *ilicifolia*, which is widely distributed in tropical Africa (Wahlert et al. 2020). On Madagascar, this form is differentiated from other *Rinorea* by its spinose leaf margin, a narrowly cylindrical terminal inflorescence, a subzygomorphic calyx with sepals ribbed fanwise, and fruit with six tan-colored tetrahedral seeds (Figure 8.47f).

FIGURE 8.47 **Representative Violaceae species on Madagascar. Taxon name followed by the specimen (in parentheses). A) *Afrohybanthus enneaspermus* (R. Razakamalala et al. 7831); B) *Rinorea angustifolia* (C. Rakotovao et al. 4466); C) *R. pugionifera* (R. Randrianaivo et al. 1494); D) *R. arborea* (T. Randrianarivony et al. 215); E) *R. analavelensis* (T. Randrianarivony et al. 730); F) *R. ilicifolia* subsp. *spinosa* (C. Rakotovao 4248); and G) *R. greveana* (C. Rakotovao et al. 5965).** (PHOTO A by N. V. Manjato; B, F, and G by C. Rakotovao; C by C. Claude; and D and E by F. Rakotoarivony.)

TABLE 8.33. **Distribution of Violaceae occurring on Madagascar**

SPECIES	DISTRIBUTION
***VIOLA* (1 SPECIES)**	**COSMOPOLITAN**
V. abyssinica Steud. ex Oliv.	Africa; M (C, E, M, Sb)
***AFROHYBANTHUS* (4 SPECIES)**	**PALEOTROPICAL**
A. buxifolius (Vent.) Flicker*	M (E)
A. danguyanus (H. Perrier) Flicker*	M (W, S)
A. decaryanus (H. Perrier) Flicker*	M (S): Androy
A. enneaspermus (L.) Flicker	Africa; M (C, E, M, Sb, S); Southern Arabian Peninsula; Yemen (Socotra); India; Sri Lanka; N. Australia; Indonesia (Java); Timor; China (Hainan)
***RINOREA* (~38 SPECIES, INCLUDING UNDESCRIBED TAXA)**	**PANTROPICAL**
R. analavelensis H. Perrier*	M (W): Atsimo-Andrefana: Analavelona
R. angustifolia (Thouars) Baill.	East Africa; M (E, Sb, W)
R. arborea (Thouars) Baill.	East Africa; Comoros islands; M (C, E, Sb, S, W)
R. auriculata (Tul.) Baill.	Comoros islands; M (W)
R. boinensis H. Perrier*	M (W)
R. bullata H. Perrier*	M (C): Alaotra-Mangoro: Analamazoatra area
R. callmanderi Wahlert*	M (Sb): DIANA: Galoko Mountains
R. cornigera H. Perrier*	M (C)
R. diversifolia H. Perrier*	M (W)
R. greveana Baill.*	M (S, W)
R. humblotiana H. Perrier*	M (C): Alaotra-Mangoro: Lake Alaotra area
R. ilicifolia subsp. *spinosa* (Boivin ex Tul.) Grey-Wilson	Comoro islands; M (E, Sb, W)
R. longipes (Tul.) Baill.*	M (Sb, W): DIANA, SAVA
R. mandrarensis H. Perrier*	M (S, W)
R. microphylla H. Perrier*	M (E): Atsinanana
R. mutica (Tul.) Baill.*	M (Sb): DIANA: Nosy Be
R. pauciflora (Thouars) Baill.*	M (E): Alaotra-Mangoro, Analanjirofo
R. pugionifera (Oudem.) H. Perrier*	M (C, E, Sb, W)
R. ranirisonii Nusb. & Wahlert*	M (C): SAVA: Loky Manambato area
R. rubra (Tul.) Baill.*	M (E); Analanjirofo: Ile Sainte Marie
R. squamosa (Boivin ex Tul.) Baill.	Comoro islands; M (C, E, Sb, W)
R. ternifolia H. Perrier*	M (E)
R. urschii H. Perrier*	M (E, C)
R. verticillata (Tul.) Baill.*	M (W): DIANA: Nosy Mitsio islands

Notes: Only accepted species included. Further species of *Rinorea* are yet to be described. An asterisk (*) indicates the species is endemic to Madagascar. M, Madagascar, with abbreviations of phytogeographic regions (based on Humbert 1955, revised by Du Puy and Moat in Du Puy et al. 1999) in parentheses: C, Central; E, Eastern; Sb, Sambirano; S, Southern; and W, Western. The political subdivision of region is listed only for narrowly distributed species.

Rinorea squamosa is the only Malagasy representative of the *Rinorea Squamosae* group. The habitat preference and geographic distribution of this shrub closely mirrors that of *R. ilicifolia* subspecies *spinosa*, except that *R. squamosa* has a disjunct population in southern Madagascar (Figure 8.46j). The species also occurs on several islands, including Nosy Be, Nosy Ankarea, and Tsarabanjina (Madagascar), and Mayotte (Comoro archipelago). It is distinguished from other Malagasy *Rinorea* by a combination of characters: a racemose inflorescence, which is often subtended by several persistent tan-colored bracts, and ovaries with six ovules.

Rinorea angustifolia, in the *Rinorea Ardisianthus* group, is a common shrub distributed widely across Madagascar (Figure 8.46f) and east Africa, but unknown from the Comoros. The species is variable in the color of petals and androecium, suggesting a degree of morphological diversification among populations in Madagascar. However, floral color is not preserved in herbarium specimens, thus making any new species segregation unwarranted until additional evidence becomes available. The species is easily recognized by the petals, which are strongly reflexed at anthesis (Figure 8.47b).

The *Rinorea Choriandra* group is represented on Madagascar by two species of small trees: *R. greveana* and *R. pugionifera*. *Rinorea greveana* occurs in southern and western Madagascar (Figure 8.46g), while *R. pugionifera* grows in the north, including on Nosy Be and Nosy Mitsio (Figure 8.46h). These two related species have narrowly lanceolate stipules up to 1 cm long, which appear as bud scales but are quickly caducous, and racemose inflorescences that are sometimes fascicled. The fruits of *R. greveana* and *R. pugionifera* are divergent in the genus, appearing at maturity as a one-seeded, bright red fleshy drupe (Figure 8.47c). The only other species in the genus with this type of fruit appears to be the closely related *R. elliptica* from Africa and the Comoros. Simmen et al. (1999) have documented that *Lemur catta* (Ring-tailed Lemur) feeds on the fruit of *R. greveana* in the Berenty Reserve.

The *Rinorea Arboreae* group contains two recognized Malagasy species: *R. arborea* and *R. longipes* (G. A. Wahlert, unpublished data), with the latter restricted to Antsiranana Province. In contrast, *R. arborea* is widely distributed on Madagascar, east Africa, and the Comoros and presents patterns of morphological variability that have made taxonomic circumscription difficult. On Madagascar, the two species and the undescribed taxa belonging to the *Arboreae* group are collectively distributed in a variety of vegetation communities (Figure 8.46k). After several years of study, the author aims to recognize about eight new species that will be segregated from *R. arborea sensu lato*. Species boundaries will be based mainly on the morphology and size of the leaf, petiole, inflorescence, and fruit, and patterns of indumentum. Most new segregates will result in narrowly distributed endemic species. For example, three undescribed entities have their respective limited ranges in the Antsahabe Forest in the Loky Manambato protected area, and the massifs of Marojejy and Andohahela. Members of the *Arboreae* group are distinguished from other Malagasy *Rinorea* by panicle-like, or sometimes racemose, inflorescences; a well-developed glabrous staminal tube; and hard capsules that are brown-green at maturity and contain three shiny brown-black seeds (Figure 8.47d).

The sixth infrageneric group of *Rinorea* on Madagascar is the *Verticillatae* group, which is instantly recognized by its opposite-leaf arrangement (Figure 8.47e). The only other groups of opposite-leaved species in the Violaceae are the unrelated *Rinorea* section *Pubiflora* and some species of *Pombalia*, both from the Neotropics (Wahlert et al. 2017). The *Verticillatae* group is endemic to Madagascar (Figure 8.46l) and the Comoro islands and is represented by 17 species, two of which also occur in the Comoros. Taxonomic revision of the group will result in a further six or so new species (G. A. Wahlert, unpublished data). Based on the opposite-leaved phyllotaxy, it is not clear to which group of *Rinorea* the *Verticillatae* are most closely related. Species in the group are delimited primarily by inflorescence architecture, and floral and vegetative morphology.

HISTORICAL BIOGEOGRAPHY

Analyses of the historical biogeography of *Viola* and *Afrohybanthus* have not been carried out. However, given the wide distributions of *V. abyssinica* in the mountains of Africa and Madagascar, and *A. enneaspermus* across tropical and subarid Africa and Asia, interesting scenarios of long-distance dispersal are likely to be inferred to explain their present distributions.

For many of the Malagasy *Rinorea* species, phylogenetic and morphological evidence support an African mainland origin (Wahlert and Ballard 2012). Four taxa, each representing four different infrageneric groups of *Rinorea*, are shared between Africa and Madagascar: *R. angustifolia*, *R. arborea*, *R. squamosa*, and *R. ilicifolia*. Wahlert and Ballard (2012) hypothesized that these taxa arrived on Madagascar via long-distance dispersal from east Africa, where they are common in dry tropical forests similar to those in western and northern Madagascar. While they did not test the directionality of dispersal, they reasoned that the source of the ancestral species likely originated in continental Africa and later dispersed to Madagascar. Similarly, *R. greveana* and *R. pugionifera* on Madagascar have been shown to be close relatives of *R. elliptica*, which occurs in east Africa and the Comoro islands. The modern distribution of these three species, along with molecular phylogenetic evidence, suggests a fifth example of long-distance dispersal to Madagascar where the ancestral species, perhaps using the Comoro islands as a stepping-stone, gave rise to *R. greveana* and *R. pugionifera*.

Further inferences of historical biogeography of *Rinorea* in Africa and Madagascar are now being conducted by R. van Velzen et al. (unpublished data). Initial findings confirm five independent dispersals of *Rinorea* from Africa to Madagascar, perhaps as late as the Pleistocene. It is hoped that their final results will shed light on the dispersal and origins of *Rinorea* on Madagascar, especially the unresolved source of the following *Verticillatae* group.

More enigmatic is the origin of the opposite-leaved *Rinorea Verticillatae* group. Phylogenetic analyses recovered the *Verticillatae* group and several Asian *Rinorea* as sister clades in a larger clade nestled among African and Malagasy species (Wahlert and Ballard 2012). This pattern of relationships suggests, among other scenarios, a long-distance dispersal of an ancestral Asian species to Madagascar, which established and later diversified into the most species-rich group of *Rinorea* on the island. However, there are no obvious morphological traits linking species in the *Verticillatae* with any Asian species of *Rinorea*, which presents a fascinating and unsolved biogeographic mystery.

CONSERVATION

The greatest species diversity of Violaceae on Madagascar is in the DIANA and SAVA Regions, formerly part of the Antsiranana Province. Other areas that are particularly rich in *Rinorea* species include the Andohahela Massif, the littoral forests near Tolagnaro, and the dry deciduous forests of western Madagascar. Across the island, species of Violaceae are vulnerable to the same types of threats as other plant species, including grazing, *tavy* agriculture, logging, fire, and invasive exotic species. These threats are partially mitigated by the fact that about 38 described and undescribed species (~90%) of Violaceae presently occur in areas with some form of protected status (Madagascar Catalogue 2020).

Based on herbarium specimen label data, some species seem to be able to persist in secondary or lightly degraded forests (e.g., *R. ilicifolia* subsp. *spinosa*, *R. squamosa*, *R. longipes*), but many other species, particularly in the *Verticillatae* group, cannot tolerate disturbance and are quickly extirpated locally. Preliminary conservation assessments using International Union for the Conservation of Nature (IUCN) criteria (IUCN 2012) range from Least Concern (e.g., *Viola abyssinica*, *Afrohybanthus buxifolius*, *A. enneaspermus*, *R. angustifolia*, *R. squamosa*, *R. ilicifolia* subsp. *spinosa*, *R. arborea*, *R. greveana*, and *R. pugionifera*) to Critically Endangered (*R. analavelensis*, *R. microphylla*, *R. pauciflora*, *R. rubra*, *R. verticillata*) (Wahlert 2010). Some species assessed as Critically Endangered have not been collected in over 100 years and may be extinct.

Subject editors: Laurent Gautier and Steven M. Goodman

MYRTACEAE, *GAVO*, *ROTRA*

N. Snow and J. W. Byng

Myrtaceae is the eighth-most diverse family of flowering plants worldwide (Snow et al. 2011; Christenhusz and Byng 2016). Recent estimates of this exclusively woody, evergreen family include approximately 134–142 genera and some 5500–5828 species (Wilson 2011; WCSP 2020). As currently known, all native species of Myrtaceae on Madagascar are endemic to the island and number around 90 species in two genera, *Syzygium* and *Eugenia* (Madagascar Catalogue 2020; WCSP 2020). Reports of the west African species *S. guineense* on Madagascar were erroneous. That taxon is grossly polyphyletic, and its modified circumscription will restrict it to west central Africa; the Malagasy specimens are an undescribed species endemic to Madagascar (J. Byng, unpublished data). *Syzygium* and *Eugenia* are the first- and second-largest genera in the family, respectively (Wilson 2011; WCSP 2020). With ~1200–1500 species, the exclusively Paleotropical genus *Syzygium* is believed to be the largest exclusively woody genus of flowering plants (SWG 2016). *Eugenia*, which is unique among Myrtaceae members in having a nearly pantropical distribution, comprises over 1000 species and likewise is among the largest exclusively woody genera (Christenhusz et al. 2018). Their high diversity levels have attracted recent attention phylogenetically (e.g., Biffin et al. 2010; Vasconcelos 2017; Mazine et al. 2018 and references therein) and ecologically (Staggemeier et al. 2010; Bünger et al. 2016).

DISTRIBUTION

Myrtaceae species occur predominantly in the Southern Hemisphere, ranging from areas around the Pacific and Australia west through Malesia, southern Asia, Africa, and the New World from the northern portion of the Cono del Sur in South America to the Caribbean and southern Florida. All terrestrial hotspot areas of the Southern Hemisphere identified by Myers et al. (2000) harbor high levels of species diversity in Myrtaceae. Although the family is widespread in Africa south of the Sahara, its generic and specific diversity there is relatively low.

Madagascar and Africa present an interesting contrast with much of the rest of the world in that relatively few native genera of Myrtaceae occur across this wide expanse. In Africa, the type genus of the family, *Myrtus*, is mostly restricted to the Atlas Mountains. The phylogenetically basal genera of the family, *Heteropyxis* and *Psiloxylon* (Wilson et al. 2005), are restricted respectively to southern Africa and the Mascarenes. *Eugenia* and *Syzygium* range across much of continental Africa but are considerably more diverse on Madagascar. Thus, whereas most areas of the Southern Hemisphere have moderate to abundant generic diversity of Myrtaceae, Madagascar hosts only *Eugenia* and *Syzygium*, but has abundant specific diversity in both genera. *Eugenia* and *Syzygium* also are native to, and have a high degree of endemism in, the Comoros, Mascarenes, and Seychelles (Byng et al. 2016).

On Madagascar, *Eugenia* species most commonly occur from the far northeast to the far southeast, with a few collections from the Central Highland forests and drier western and southern regions (Figure 8.48h). *Syzygium* is common across the eastern forests from the far north to the far south, with a reasonable number of records also scattered in the western and southern regions (Figure 8.48d).

Regarding vegetation types, few species of *Eugenia* or *Syzygium* occupy drier parts of Madagascar, mirroring their habitat preferences elsewhere and general preference for moist to wet climates.

FIGURE 8.48 **Upper panel associated with *Syzygium*: A) *S. emirnense* branch and B) typical terminal inflorescence; C) individual flower of *Syzygium* sp. nov.; and D) distribution map of known *Syzygium* records on Madagascar. Lower panel associated with *Eugenia*: E) *E. alaotrensis* branch showing ramiflorous inflorescence and F) an individual flower; G) fruit of *E. zygophylla* showing persistent sepals; and H) distribution map of known *Eugenia* records on Madagascar.** (PHOTOS A, E, and F by P. Antilahimena; B and C by M. W. Callmander; and G by A. Razanatsima.)

Although vegetation types are noted only infrequently on collection labels, and then typically only in broad terms, few species occur in sclerophyllous woodlands, dry deciduous forests, or dry spiny thickets. Other vegetation types unlikely to harbor many representatives of Myrtaceae include mangrove zones, rupicolous vegetation, swamp forests, and marshes and bogs.

FAMILY CHARACTERS

Malagasy Myrtaceae species are generally identifiable by their combination of opposite, exstipulate leaves with entire (nondivided) margins, (usually) visible venation, intramarginal veins, and the blades typically being moderately to densely glandular on one or both surfaces. Atypically for the family, some species of *Syzygium* have reddish glands. The punctate glands produce the characteristic fragrance common to well-known genera such as *Eucalypytus*, *Melaleuca*, *Psidium*, and most other genera. Species in the family vary from small (occasionally) prostrate shrubs to erect shrubs or tall trees. Prior to their harvest in the 1800s, the world's tallest plant species was likely *E. regnans*, in Tasmania, which was estimated to reach possibly 125 m in height. Species of *Syzygium* on Madagascar are typically 5–25 m in height and are usually distinctive in the field by the red to salmon flush to the young leaves, a condition also shared by many *Eugenia*.

The most obvious characters of the flowers are their inferior ovaries (evident in flower and fruit) and display of numerous, well-exserted stamens. The stamens likely signal pollinators as much as the petals, if not more. In Malagasy species, the petals of *Eugenia* are white, cream, pinkish, or magenta (Snow et al. 2015) and are usually conspicuous and persistent. In contrast, petals of *Syzygium* are nearly always calyptrate, falling early as a united cap, and white to cream.

Eugenia and *Syzygium* are frequently confused in sterile condition with *Memecylon* (Melastomataceae), given the latter's inferior ovaries and exstipulate, opposite leaves (R. D. Stone 2012). However, members of *Memecylon*, which is also species rich on Madagascar, have uninervate leaves and lack the punctate oil glands and characteristic myrtaceous odor of the leaves (R. D. Stone 2012). Some *Memecylon* species resemble Asian members of *Syzygium*, including *M. capuronii* with its long leaves and strongly four-angled stems, but its inflorescences are axillary, and the tertiary leaf venation is less prominent.

CHARACTER DIFFERENCES BETWEEN *EUGENIA* AND *SYZYGIUM*

Although many authors combined these two genera for many decades, molecular data unequivocally corroborated their distinction and placement in separate tribes (Wilson et al. 2005), and demonstrated that baccate fruits (indehiscent berries) evolved more than once from the ancestral condition of capsular (dry, dehiscent) fruits. The genera resemble one another morphologically only in their possession of baccate fruit and a globular embryo with barely (if at all) differentiated cotyledons.

Both genera can have solitary flowers, but *Syzygium* usually has many-flowered panicles that are terminal (Figure 8.48a) or in the upper axils of the leaves, and often with several orders of branching (Figure 8.48b). In contrast, inflorescences of Malagasy *Eugenia* may be terminal, axillary, on short shoots (e.g., *E. quadriphylla*), or be ramiflorous (Figure 8.48e) or cauliflorous. The inflorescence of *Eugenia* varies from solitary flowers to simple or more complex cymes or panicles (termed botryoid and metabotryoid by some authors). Species with more highly branched inflorescences include specimens presently identified as *E. hazompasika* var. *extensa*, *E. ombrophila*, *E. pluricymosa*, and *E. thouvenotiana*. Variations of inflorescence architecture in *Eugenia* is much more pronounced in South America, as discussed by Mazine et al. (2018, and references therein).

With few exceptions on Madagascar, members of *Eugenia* have four well-defined, apically rounded calyx lobes and a well-defined (typically squarish) staminal ring (Figure 8.48g), a rounded to conical hypanthium, and distinct petals (Figure 8.48f). In comparison, many species of Malagasy *Syzygium* have poorly defined calyx lobes, a calyptrate calyx, stamens borne along the apex of a narrow hypanthial rim, a sunken (relative to the staminal rim) ovary apex, a conical hypanthium (Figure 8.48c), and nearly always calyptrate petals. Species of *Eugenia* sometimes have short, forked (dibrachiate) hairs on the branchlets, foliage, or inflorescences and flowers. *Syzygium* is universally glabrous on Madagascar, although approximately 10 species in Asia are pubescent. Most species of *Eugenia* are shrubs or trees of relatively low (up to 10 m) stature, whereas species of *Syzygium* are trees up to 25 m in height (Snow et al. 2015).

NON-NATIVE TAXA

Many non-native taxa of Myrtaceae on Madagascar are grown as hedgerows, sources of fruit, spices, or timber. These include (with one common English name for each): *Eugenia uniflora* (Suriname cherry), *E. brasiliensis* (Brazil cherry), *Pimenta dioica* (allspice), *P. racemosa* (bay rum), *Syzygium aromaticum* (cloves), *S. cumini* (Java plum), *S. jambos* (rose apple), *Psidium guajva* (guava), *P. cattleyanum* (strawberry guava), and at least several dozen species of *Eucalyptus*. The exotic members of *Eugenia* and *Syzygium* are usually easily differentiated from native species with the exception of *S. cumini*, which is morphologically diverse.

IDENTIFICATION OF SPECIES

The authors of this contribution have examined the majority of herbarium specimens from Madagascar. Given that the identity of a few hundred specimens in each genus remain indetermined, known distributions remain tentative (Table 8.34). Likewise, the taxonomic identities of some species complexes and the correct application of nomenclature is uncertain, which makes our overview of the family tentative. Many Malagasy *Eugenia* species are locally restricted and known from few collections. In contrast and as currently known (Madagascar Catalogue 2020), some *Syzygium* species (e.g., *S. emirnense*, *S. bernieri*) are known from scores of specimens from across the island and an elevational range from sea level to 2000 m, and the genus includes a number of widespread morphologically heterogeneous taxonomic complexes. A complete revision of *Syzygium* is approaching completion and includes 30–40 new species to science (J. Byng, unpublished data). Given the unpublished condition of some aspects of *Syzygium*, we focus somewhat more in the following section on the genus *Eugenia*.

DIVERSITY

As indicated above, recent estimates of the global species diversity suggest approximately 1200–1500 species of *Syzygium* and in excess of 1000 species for *Eugenia* (WCSP 2020). Few angiosperm genera have tallied as many newly proposed species in the past few decades as these two genera. For example, each had 35 species described in a single paper (Barrie 2004; Ashton 2006), and new species are described annually for both genera, most frequently from India, New Caledonia, Malesia, and South America.

Focusing on Madagascar, 34 species of *Eugenia* have been published after several decades of inactivity (J. S. Miller 2000; Snow 2008, 2011; Snow and Callmander 2016; Snow et al. 2012, 2015, 2020), for a current total of approximately 71 species, of which 67 have been described (Table 8.34). The circumscription, nomenclature, and application of type specimens as described by Perrier de la Bâthie (1953a, 1953b) remain uncertain for some species (e.g., *E. tropophylla*, *E. viguieriana*, *E. zygophylla*), and alpha taxonomic work is far from complete. Although only two new species of *Syzygium* have been described recently (Snow 2010), several more are nearing completion (J. Byng, unpublished data).

ECOLOGY AND DISTRIBUTION

Most species of *Eugenia* occur from the sandy littoral zone in the southeast near Tolagnaro, north along the eastern coast up to the central escarpment, and in the north to elevations of 2350 m on the Tsaratanàna Massif. Particularly high species diversity occurs in the region near Tolagnaro (Snow et al. 2015), the Masoala Peninsula, and regions north and west of Antongil Bay (Snow et al. 2020). Species from drier regions include the only known collection of *E. ankarensis* from the former province of Mahajanga in the Boeny Region (about 315 m) on an inselberg rock face, *E. madagascariensis* from a few collections in the Central Highlands and near the northwest coast, and *E. philippioides* from the center of the Central Highlands. Species occurring on nearshore islands include *E. nosibensis* (Nosy Be) and *E. gandhii* (Nosy Mangabe). Nearly all members of *Syzygium* are from humid forests, although *S. sakalavarum* and *S. tapiaka* are from the drier, western forests.

No species of *Eugenia* on Madagascar is ecologically dominant. Species grow as low shrubs to trees of nearly 20 m in height (e.g., *E. cloiselii*, *E. thouvenotiana*). Based on herbarium specimens, species that can be relatively common locally include *E. alaotrensis* in the Moramanga region, *E. gandhii* on Nosy Mangabe, and *E. zygophylla* (= *E. oligantha*) in eastern and northern forests.

Lemurs feed on some species (Snow et al. 2012, 2015). Black Lemurs (*Eulemur macaco*) consume *Eugenia nosibensis* on Nosy Be, where the plant species is said to be common in the Lokobe protected area (Snow 2011). The fruits of an indeterminate but common species of *Syzygium* is an important food source for a species of flying fox (*Pteropus rufus*) in the littoral forests at Sainte Luce (Bollen and van Elsacker 2002). *Coracopsis vasa* (Greater Vasa Parrot) has been observed eating fruits of an undetermined species each of *Eugenia* and *Syzygium* near Sainte Luce (Bollen and van Elsacker 2004).

Myrtle Rust, *Austropuccinia psidii*, is native to South America and increasingly, and often aggressively, globally infecting species of Myrtaceae (Winzer et al. 2018). It causes moderate to severe foliage damage and ultimately plant death (CABI 2019). At the time of writing it is unknown on Madagascar (CABI 2019), but it almost assuredly will arrive and spread.

An unidentified genus of white flies (Aleyrodidae) has been found on *E. manonae*, and leaf-cutter bees (Megachilidae) have been suggested as foraging on leaves of *Eugenia* (Snow et al. 2012).

TABLE 8.34. **Native species of *Eugenia* from Madagascar, with IUCN status and geographic distribution of known occurrence**

SPECIES	IUCN STATUS	DISTRIBUTION	VERNACULAR NAME(S)
E. alaotrensis H. Perrier	NE	E forests	–
E. ambanizanensis N. Snow	NE	Masoala (S1)	–
E. analamerensis H. Perrier	NE	NC	–
E. andapae N. Snow	VU (S4)	Andapa Basin, Masoala	–
E. ankarensis (H. Perrier) A. J. Scott	NE	Boeny	–
E. antilahimenae N. Snow, Callm. & Byng	LC (S5)	Antongil Bay	–
E. antongilensis H. Perrier	NE	Antongil Bay	–
E. ardyceae N. Snow	EN (S2)	Petriky	*Ropasilahy* (RR)
E. arenicola H. Perrier	EN	SE littoral	*Ropasy* (S3), *ropoaka*
E. arthroopoda H. Perrier	NE	E forests	*Gavoala*
E. barriei N. Snow	CR (S4)	NW dryland	–
E. bemangidiensis N. Snow	CR (S4)	SE littoral	–
E. calciscopulorum N. Snow	CR (S4)	NE coastal limestone	–
E. cassinoides Lam.	NE	E forests	–
E. cloiselii H. Perrier	EN	SE (Tolagnaro region)	*Ropasina, gavoala* (RR), *ompa*
E. coursiana H. Perrier	NE	NE mountains	–
E. delicatissima N. Snow, Callm. & Philippson	VU (S4)	N mountains	–
E. diospyroides H. Perrier	NE	E forests	–
E. echinulata N. Snow	VU (S2)	E escarpment	*Rotra*
E. gandhii N. Snow	LC (S4)	Masoala and Marojejy regions	*Gavoala, gavoalabe* (S4)
E. goviala H. Perrier	NE	EC and littoral forests	*Ompa*
E. guajavoides N. Snow & F. Randriat.	EN (S3)	SE littoral	*Sarigoavy* (S3)
E. guillotii Hochr.	NE	Littoral	*Hompa, voabe*
E. hazompasika H. Perrier	NE	E forests	*Goviala*
E. hazonjia N. Snow	EN (S4)	NE	–
E. hovarum H. Perrier	NE	Central Highlands	–
E. iantarensis N. Snow	LC (S4)	E forests	*Rotramena vaventiravina, rotra*
E. lacerosepala N. Snow	EN (S2)	NE littoral	–
E. lokohensis H. Perrier	NE	Littoral forests	*Gavoala*
E. louiseae N. Snow	EN (S2)	SE near coast	*Malamasafoina, tsihanihamposa* (S1; RR)
E. louvelii H. Perrier	NE	NE coast, Masoala	*Hompa*
E. madagascariensis H. Perrier	NE	Central Highlands, W coast	–
E. malcomberi N. Snow	VU (S4)	S humid forests	–
E. manomboensis N. Snow	CR (S4)	SE littoral	–
E. manonae N. Snow & Rabenant.	VU (S3)	SE littoral	–
E. musicola H. Perrier	NE	N mountains	–

SPECIES	IUCN STATUS	DISTRIBUTION	VERNACULAR NAME(S)
E. nompa H. Perrier	NE	EC forests	*Ompa*
E. nosibensis N. Snow	VU (S2)	NW coastal island	*Voararano* (S2)
E. obovatifolia N. Snow	EN (S4)	EC to SE littoral	–
E. petrikensis N. Snow & Randriat.	EN (S3)	SE littoral	*Ropasy lahiny* (S3)
E. philippioides H. Perrier	NE	Central Highlands	–
E. pluricymosa H. Perrier	NE	E forests	*Gavoala*
E. quadriflora H. Perrier	NE	SE forests	–
E. quadriphylla N. Snow & Callm.	EN (SC)	NE forests	–
E. radiciflora H. Perrier	NE	Central Highlands, NE, Masoala	*Gavoala*
E. randrianasoloi J. S. Mill.	NE	NE mountains	*Hompa*
E. ranomafana N. Snow & D. Turk	VU (S4)	SEC	–
E. ravelonarivoi N. Snow	VU (S4)	N mountains	*Gavoalehely* (S4); *gavoala* (S4)
E. razakamalalae N. Snow & Callm.	EN (S4)	NE near coast	–
E. richardii (Blume) N. Snow, Callm. & Phillipson	EN (S4)	NE coastal	–
E. rosiopetiolata N. Snow & S. Cable	EN (S3)	SE littoral	–
E. schatzii J. S. Mill.	NE	NE forest	–
E. scottii H. Perrier	NE	?	*Ropasina* (RR)
E. sihanakensis H. Perrier	NE	Masoala	–
E. stibephylla N. Snow & Rabeh.	VU (S3)	SE littoral	–
E. stictophylla N. Snow & Razafim.	EN (S3)	SE littoral	–
E. thouvenotiana H. Perrier	NE	EC coastal	*Gavoala*
E. tiampoka N. Snow & Callm.	EN (S4)	N Highlands	–
E. tropophylla H. Perrier	NE	?	–
E. urschiana H. Perrier	NE	EC forests	–
E. vanwykiana N. Snow	EN (S4)	NE littoral	–
E. vatomandrensis H. Perrier	NE	EC littoral	–
E. viguieriana H. Perrier	NE	E forests	–
E. vilersii H. Perrier	NE	EC	–
E. williamsiana N. Snow	NE	Masoala	*Ompangavo* (S1)
E. wilsoniana N. Snow	CR (S4)	EC forests	–
E. zygophylla Govaerts	NE	E and N forests	*Ompa, tsimahamasantsokina, menahihy*

Sources: Information for IUCN status and vernacular names derived from Randriatifika and Rabenantoandro 2008 (abbreviated as RR); Snow and Callmander 2016 (SC); Snow 2008 (S1); Snow 2011 (S2); Snow et al. 2012 (S3); Snow et al. 2015 (S4); and Snow et al. 2020 (S%).

Notes: IUCN status abbreviations: CR, Critically Endangered; DD, Data Deficient; EN, Endangered; LC, Least Concern; NE, Not evaluated; NT, Near Threatened; VU, Vulnerable. Vernacular names without a cited reference were taken from one or more herbarium specimens, some of whose determinations have not been confirmed; a question mark indicates missing information or taxonomic uncertainty. For distributions, geographic abbreviations follow standard usage (e.g., NC, north central; SEC, southeast central); a question mark indicates too much taxonomic uncertainty to assign distribution confidently. Updates will periodically appear at http://legacy.tropicos.org/Name/40006825?projectid=17. A similar summary of *Syzygium* can be found at: http://legacy.tropicos.org/Name/40009310?projectid=17.

Since knowledge of the reproductive ecology of the Myrtaceae remains limited (Nic Lughadha and Proença 1995), similar studies on Madagascar would be valuable.

MORPHOLOGICAL DIVERSITY

Eugenia in general is characterized by a tetramerous perianth in which the calyx lobes are usually unfused in the bud and often dimorphic with larger outer lobes; they have numerous stamens, a bicarpellate (or infrequently tricarpellate) inferior ovary with axile placentation, and few to many ovules; baccate fruits with a membranous, leathery, or sometimes hard and furrowed testa; and relatively few globular seeds with fused (often indistinguishable) cotyledons, with globular and typically smooth fruits. Exceptions to this modal floral morphology of *Eugenia* are numerous (e.g., Snow 2008; Snow and Callmander 2016; Giaretta et al. 2019). Species may have slightly (*E. nosibensis*) to coarsely verrucose fruits (e.g., *E. lacerosepala*, *E. antilahimenae*) and some have whorled leaves (*E. quadriphylla*). The most atypical floral morphology on Madagascar occurs in *E. ambanizanensis*, which possesses numerous and succulent, broad, closely imbricate bracts subtending the hypanthium (Snow 2008), a condition unknown elsewhere in the genus. In addition, *E. ambanizanensis*, *E. andapae*, *E. iantarensis*, *E. lacerosepala*, and *E. quadriphylla* have splitting sepal lobes, a feature also found occasionally in other members of the genus (e.g., Giaretta et al. 2019). Ribbed fruits, a recurring homoplastic character in *Eugenia* and some other genera of Myrtaceae, also characterize *E. ankarensis*, *E. madagascariensis* (Perrier de la Bâthie 1953b), and *E. quadriphylla* (Snow and Callmander 2016).

FUTURE DIRECTIONS AND PRIORITIES

A high taxonomic priority for the Malagasy Myrtaceae is to clarify boundaries of some taxa described by Perrier de la Bâthie (1953a, 1953b) and complete the alpha taxonomy. In particular, several species of *Eugenia* were described initially as having numerous subspecies, often with many syntypes cited, but also typically with limited descriptions and often with uncertainties about correct nomenclatural applications. In addition, relatively few Malagasy species of *Eugenia* have been sampled in molecular works. A number of Malagasy *Syzygium* have been sequenced with a range of markers (J. Byng, unpublished data), but the resolution is extremely weak and results in a polytomy. This suggests species of this genus have rapidly evolved on Madagascar as in other geographic regions, given that the same markers provide reasonably supported phylogenetic structure elsewhere. Detailed species delimitation based on herbarium specimens is the first priority, ideally in conjunction with more comprehensive molecular studies. This is particularly important considering that large areas of forest are being deforested rapidly and the urgent need to determine which species are rare or threatened with extinction in order to conserve them.

Subject editors: Laurent Gautier and Steven M. Goodman

MELASTOMATACEAE, PRINCESS FLOWER FAMILY

F. Almeda, H. Ranarivelo, and R. D. Stone

Melastomataceae (about 177 genera and 5750 species; Michelangeli et al. 2020) belongs to the order Myrtales and is among the 10 largest families of flowering plants. The distribution of its members is pantropical, though relatively few members are found in temperate zones (e.g., *Rhexia* with 13 species in eastern North America). The group has its greatest diversity in the New World tropics where ~70% of the known species occur (Veranso-Libalah et al. 2018). Members of this family, known as princess flowers, are readily recognized by their opposite, decussate leaves and distinctive acrodromous venation pattern (in which two or more main veins arise at, or close to, a common point at the base of the blade and converge in arcuate fashion toward the apex; see Figures 8.49i and 8.50a–c). Additional diagnostic features of the Melastomataceae include the complex trichomes, anther connectives often appendaged at the base (Figure 8.50e), poricidally dehiscent anthers, and fruits that are capsular or baccate with numerous small seeds (Dahlgren and Thorne 1984). Within the family, there is, however, one morphologically anomalous group, which comprises the Paleotropical *Memecylon*, the Neotropical *Mouriri* and *Votomita*, and three other allied Paleotropical genera, *Lijndenia*, *Spathandra*, and *Warneckea*. This memecyloid group (Figure 8.49) has been alternatively treated as the subfamily Olisbeoideae (R. D. Stone 2006a) (and as Memecyleae or Memecyloideae by previous authors) or as a separate but closely related family, Memecylaceae (Renner 1993; Clausing and Renner 2001). It consists of mainly forest understory shrubs and trees with very hard wood, usually one-nerved leaves (multinervate in *Spathandra*, *Lijndenia*, and *Warneckea*), general lack of indumentum, presence of a dorsal oil-gland on the anther connectives (gland reduced or absent in some descendant taxa), and baccate fruits (Figure 8.49j) with one to few large seeds (Figure 8.49f) (Dahlgren and Thorne 1984; R. D. Stone 2004). In one molecular study (Clausing and Renner 2001), a memecyloid clade was recovered as the sister group of Melastomataceae, but statistical support for this hypothesis was weak, and the *rbcL* and *ndhF* sequence data

FIGURE 8.49 **Malagasy Melastomataceae, subfamily Olisbeoideae: A) *Lijndenia darainensis*, B) *L. roborea*, C) *Memecylon galeatum*, D) *M. hazonjia*, sp. nov. ined., E) *M. mocquerysii*, F) *M. strumosum*, G) *M. xiphophyllum*, H) *Warneckea masoalae*, and I and J) *W. sansibarica sensu lato*.** (PHOTOS A and F by L. Gautier; B by G. E. Schatz; C by F. Rakotoarivony; D, I, and J by C. Christian; E by F. Almeda; G by P. Lowry; and H by R. D. Stone.)

FIGURE 8.50 **Malagasy Melastomataceae, subfamily Melastomatoideae: A) *Amphorocalyx multiflorus*, B) *A. rupestris*, C) *Antherotoma naudinii*, D) *Dichaetanthera cordifolia*, and E) *D. hirsuta*.** (PHOTOS by F. Almeda.)

sets contain significantly conflicting phylogenetic information. In subsequent analyses (R. D. Stone 2004; Veranso-Libalah et al. 2018; Bacci et al. 2019; Zhou et al. 2019), the memecyloid clade was placed as the sister group of *Pternandra* (tribe Kibessieae), suggesting that the Melastomataceae family is paraphyletic if the circumscription does not include the Olisbeoideae. Until further analyses indicate otherwise, a broad definition is adopted here that includes the Olisbeoideae within Melastomataceae *sensu lato*.

In the nearly 20 years since the previous version of this review was published (Almeda 2003), additional fieldwork and collections have led to advances in our understanding of the phylogeny and historical biogeography of Malagasy Melastomataceae, especially of the subfamily Olisbeoideae (*Memecylon* and relatives) and the tribe Melastomateae (including the endemic genera *Amphorocalyx*, *Dionycha*, and *Rousseauxia*). Through collections-based research, several new Malagasy species have been recently described in *Memecylon* (17), *Lijndenia* (three), *Gravesia* (two), *Dichaetanthera* (one), and *Warneckea* (one), and the description of several more species is currently in progress. Further discoveries have been made regarding the ecology of Malagasy Melastomataceae, for example, the use of certain species as food plants by lemurs and Giraffe-necked Weevils, as well as the presence of domatia (structures to shelter symbiotic ants) in two species of *Gravesia*.

DIVERSITY AND ENDEMISM

On Madagascar, the 346 indigenous species of Melastomataceae are grouped into two subfamilies, three tribes, and 12 genera (Table 8.35). In addition, one species in each of three other genera (*Heterotis rotundifolia* species complex, *Melastoma malabathricum* subsp. *malabathricum*, and *Miconia crenata*, which was previously known as *Clidemia hirta*) are now naturalized adventives in wet lowland sites along the island's east coast. Composition of the

TABLE 8.35. **Diversity of indigenous Melastomataceae on Madagascar and their worldwide distribution**

SCIENTIFIC NAME	SPECIES NUMBERS	GEOGRAPHIC DISTRIBUTION
SUBFAMILY MELASTOMATOIDEAE		
Melastomateae		
Amphorocalyx	5/5/5	Endemic to Madagascar
Antherotoma	10/1/0	Tropical Africa, Madagascar, Comoros
Dichaetanthera	36/28/28	Tropical Africa, Madagascar
Dionycha	3/3/3	Endemic to Madagascar
Nerophila	8/1/1	Tropical Africa, Madagascar
Rousseauxia	13/13/13	Endemic to Madagascar
Tristemma	15/1/0	Tropical Africa, Madagascar, Comoros, Mascarenes
Sonerileae		
Gravesia	115/110/110	Tropical Africa, Madagascar
Medinilla	400/70/70	Tropical Africa, Madagascar, India, SE Asia, Malesia, Australia
SUBFAMILY OLISBEOIDEAE		
Memecyleae		
Memecylon	388/96/96	Africa, Madagascar, Comoros, Mascarenes, Seychelles, S and SE Asia, Malesia, Oceania
Lijndenia	16/9/9	Tropical Africa, Madagascar, Sri Lanka, Malesia, Philippines
Warneckea	49/9/9	Africa, Madagascar, Mauritius
Total species on Madagascar	346	
Endemic species on Madagascar	344	

Sources: Based, in part, on Perrier de la Bâthie (1951), Humbert (1955), Jacques-Félix (1973, 1976, 1984, 1985, 1994), B. C. Stone (2006b, 2017, 2018, 2020), R. D. Stone and Callmander (2011), Almeda and Ranarivelo (2018, 2019), Ranarivelo and Almeda (2019), Veranso-Libalah et al. (2020).
Note: The central column shows for each genus the number of currently recognized species worldwide (figure on left), species numbers in Madagascar (figure in middle), and number of species endemic to Madagascar (figure on right).

Malagasy melastome flora is notable for several reasons. Seven of the 12 indigenous genera belong to a single tribe, the Melastomateae, which is also well represented in Africa (Veranso-Libalah et al. 2017, 2020), with two other genera centered in Asia (*Osbeckia sensu stricto* and *Melastoma*). All three of the Malagasy endemic genera (*Amphorocalyx*, *Dionycha*, and *Rousseauxia*) belong to the Melastomateae, but none is particularly rich in species. *Dichaetanthera*, with 28 Malagasy species, is the only African-Malagasy genus of the tribe Melastomateae with a center of diversity on the island. Considering the family as a whole, approximately 80% of Malagasy species belong to just three genera—*Gravesia*, *Medinilla*, and *Memecylon* (Table 8.35; Figures 8.49, 8.50, and 8.51)—in tribes Sonerileae and Memecyleae, respectively. Madagascar is the center of speciation for *Gravesia*, a genus that has few equals in terms of growth habit diversity on landmasses of comparable size anywhere else in the tropics. The island is also a significant center of radiation for *Medinilla*, a genus that is otherwise species poor in Africa but well represented in tropical Asia, Malesia, and the Philippines. As for the Paleotropical genus *Memecylon*, it ranks among the 10 largest woody genera on Madagascar (cf. Schatz 2001), and the island contains by far the highest concentration of species proportionate to land area (R. D. Stone 2012). The tribes Astronieae, Melastomateae, and Sonerileae, and subfamily Olisbeoideae occur in both the New World and Old World tropics, but no genera of Melastomataceae are shared between these regions (Michelangeli et al. 2020).

One-quarter of Madagascar's melastome genera are endemic to the island. For a sizable flowering plant family, this figure is significant because 19% of the vascular plant genera on Madagascar is believed to be endemic (Callmander et al. 2011a). At the species level, 99% of the Malagasy melastome species are endemic (Figure 8.52). This is notably higher than the figure of 82% for the vascular flora of the island as a whole (Callmander et al. 2011a) but is close to the figure of ~96% endemism for species of trees and large shrubs (Schatz 2000). In the case of the species-rich genus *Memecylon*, all of the Malagasy species are endemic to the island, with the majority being known from just one or two sites (R. D. Stone 2012). For the Melastomataceae, as for most flowering plant families, Madagascar

FIGURE 8.51 **Malagasy Melastomataceae, subfamily Melastomatoideae: A) *Dionycha bojeri*, B) *Gravesia erecta*, C) *G. pusilla*, D) *G. vestita*, E) *G. thymoides*, F) *Rousseauxia marojejensis* subsp. *lepidota* var. *hirsuta*, and G) *R. marojejensis* subsp. *marojejensis*.** (PHOTOS A–D by F. Almeda; E by A. Sieder; and F and G by H. Ranarivelo.)

harbors a higher incidence of species-level endemism than any area of comparable size anywhere in the world. Endemism, therefore, in addition to species and morphological diversity, is an outstanding feature of Madagascar's melastome flora.

RECENT DEVELOPMENTS IN SYSTEMATICS AND BIOGEOGRAPHY

Within the tribe Melastomateae, molecular investigations (Michelangeli et al. 2013; Veranso-Libalah et al. 2017) have revealed the African members to be a monophyletic group with two phylogenetically nested subclades, the first consisting of Asian Melastomateae (*Melastoma* and *Osbeckia sensu stricto*) and the second of the Malagasy endemic genera (*Amphorocalyx*, *Dionycha*, and *Rousseauxia*; see Figures 8.50a and b; 8.51a, f, and g). According to these results, *Osbeckia* does not occur on the African continent, and the Malagasy species placed in that genus by Perrier de la Bâthie (1932, 1951) are referable to *Rousseauxia* (Jacques-Félix 1973; Ranarivelo 2010; but see below under Work in Progress). A subsequent biogeographic study (Veranso-Libalah et al. 2018) found that the endemic Malagasy Melastomateae lineage arrived from Africa during the Miocene (stem age ~13 million years ago [Mya]; 95% highest probability density [HPD] 9.7–15.9 Mya), in

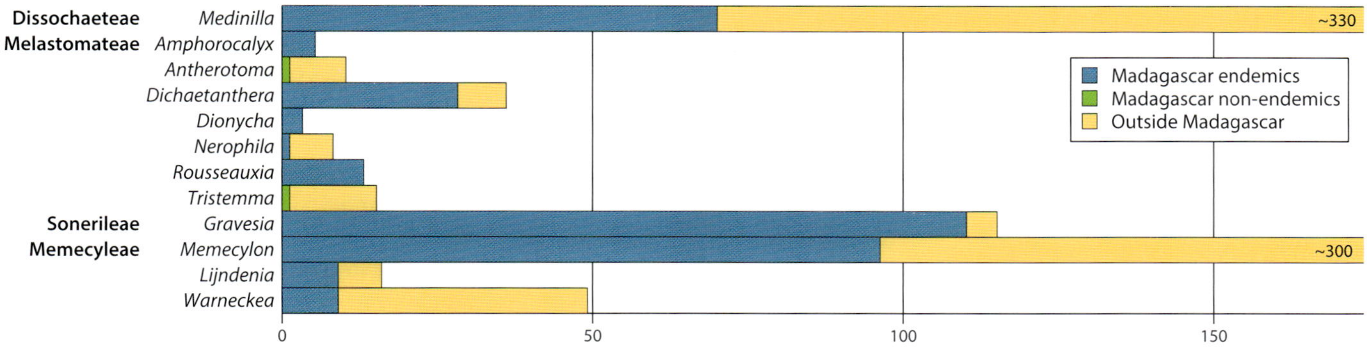

FIGURE 8.52 **Diversity and endemicity diagram of Malagasy Melastomataceae at the level of genera, showing three different species counts: 1) endemic to Madagascar, 2) nonendemic but native to Madagascar, and 3) those occurring elsewhere in the world (for further information see text). In cases when species diversity exceeds or does not conform to that presented on the horizontal graph scale, the figures are written along the respective horizontal line of a given genus.**

agreement with the previous age estimate of Renner (2004); but see Morley and Dick (2003) for a much older, Late Cretaceous age based on a "missing fossils" hypothesis. In addition to dispersal of the endemic Malagasy Melastomateae lineage, Veranso-Libalah et al. (2018) inferred at least three other independent dispersal events from Africa to Madagascar involving the *Dichaetanthera* lineage, as well as *Tristemma mauritianum* and *Antherotoma naudinii* (the latter two likely representing relatively recent introductions; cf. Jacques-Félix 1994: 279). Taken together, these inferred dispersals of African Melastomateae are consistent with the conclusion that "most of the present-day biota of Madagascar is comprised of the descendants of Cenozoic dispersers, predominantly with African origins" (Yoder and Nowak 2006; but see Warren et al. 2010).

Within the Olisbeoideae, molecular analyses (R. D. Stone 2006a) have confirmed that *Memecylon sensu stricto*, *Lijndenia*, and *Warneckea* are reciprocally monophyletic groups and should be treated as separate genera, in accordance with earlier morphological and anatomical evidence (Jacques-Félix 1978, 1984, 1985; K. Bremer 1982). A subsequent molecular phylogenetic study of *Warneckea* (R. D. Stone and Andreasen 2010) found that nine of the 10 currently recognized Malagasy species belong to *Warneckea* section *Warneckea*, together with *W. trinervis* of Mauritius and nine other species from eastern and southern Africa. Also occurring in western and extreme northern Madagascar is the predominantly east African *Warneckia* subgenus *Carnosae*, including plants previously treated as *W. sansibarica sensu lato* (but see below under Work in Progress).

Within *Memecylon*, further molecular results (R. D. Stone 2014) have shown that the Malagasy species are resolved in two clades that are not each other's closest relatives. The first of these groups is rich in species and centered on the island's eastern moist evergreen forests, yet phylogenetically nested within this clade are some endemic lineages of the neighboring Comoro and Mascarene archipelagoes (indicating that these originated by dispersal from Madagascar). The second Malagasy species group is phylogenetically nested within the predominantly eastern and southern African *Buxifolia* clade, and consists of at least three species (*M. buxifolium*, *M. multinode*, and *M. amplifolium*) inhabiting the dry deciduous forests in the west and extreme northern parts of the island. A recent biogeographic study of *Memecylon* (Amarasinghe 2020) identified two independent colonizations of Madagascar from the African continent, the first of these originating in the Oligocene (stem age 29.3 Mya; 95% HPD 24.9–33.9 Mya) and leading to rampant diversification of the species-rich eastern rainforest clade. The second colonization involved the east African *Buxifolia* lineage and evidently took place during the Miocene (stem age 9.8 Mya; 95% HPD 7.1–12.7 Mya). These findings clearly contradict the previous speculation of Perrier de la Bâthie (1932) that the Malagasy *Memecylon* species are most closely related to those of Indo-Malesia. Also to be rejected is the hypothesis of Jacques-Félix (1984, 1995) that Gondwanan vicariance can explain the disjunction of *Memecylon* between Africa and Madagascar, because the molecular age estimates for these events are far too young to have been caused by tectonic separation of the former supercontinent.

Among the closely related tribes Sonerileae and Dissochaeteae, the berry-fruited and presumably bird-dispersed *Medinilla* lineage was estimated to have arrived in Madagascar during the Miocene, perhaps by long-distance dispersal from tropical Asia (Renner 2004; see also see Zhou et al. 2019), although this conclusion was based on limited taxonomic sampling (and only a few samples from Africa or Madagascar). As for the species-rich genus *Gravesia*, the recent study by Zhou et al. (2019) suggests that it is not monophyletic. This hypothesis was weakly supported and based on limited taxonomic sampling of Malagasy and African species. These authors also proposed that the Sonerileae and Dissochaeteae originated in South America and reached Africa/Madagascar and Asia by long-distance dispersal in the Eocene and mid-Oligocene. This scenario, which is not strongly supported by their analysis, contradicts Renner's (2004) hypothesis that the Sonerileae dispersed from Asia to Africa and then to Madagascar during the Miocene. These preliminary conflicting hypotheses about the evolutionary history of Sonerileae, Dissochaeteae and *Gravesia* require additional study (also see Work in Progress).

GROWTH HABITS, HABITATS, AND ADAPTATIONS

On Madagascar, melastomes grow in a variety of habitats from littoral forests (near sea level) to exposed rocky sites at high elevations

(2200 m). They reach their greatest diversity in moist evergreen forest environments up to about 1400 m. This corresponds to the elevational range of lowland moist evergreen forests (0–800 m) and medium-altitude moist evergreen forests (800–1300 m) in the eastern portion of the island. *Antherotoma naudinii* (Figure 8.50c) and *Tristemma mauritianum* are native sun-loving, locally abundant colonizers of disturbed habitats, as is the invasive adventive *Miconia crenata*. *Nerophila pauciflora* is a suffrutescent (woody only at the base) perennial of rocky grasslands; it has tuber-like roots that allow it to persist in areas subjected to periodic brush fires. According to Perrier de la Bâthie (1932), populations of this species have contracted significantly because its capsules and seeds are often burned before they mature.

Some species of *Dichaetanthera* and the two endemic genera *Amphorocalyx* and *Dionycha* are also plants of rocky sites or seasonally dry wooded areas. These species have evolved adaptations like early leaf fall and tuberous roots (especially young plants) as drought-evasion strategies; these are comparable to some species of *Pleroma* that grow in similar seasonally stressed Cerrado environments in Brazil. In general, few Malagasy melastomes exhibit true xerophytic adaptations. The several species of *Memecylon* that grow in drier areas of the Central Highlands and the west are for the most part plants that grow near streams or in locally humid areas. Virtually all other Malagasy species are plants of humid or very wet forest habitats. The family is completely absent from the dry spiny thicket of the Southern Domain (Perrier de la Bâthie 1951).

The Malagasy melastomes are largely a family of the moist evergreen and semi-deciduous forests of the Eastern and Sambirano Domains. The forest species generally fall into one of three ecological groups dictated by microhabitat. Most are herbs, shrubs, or small trees that require filtered light, moisture, and the availability of humus on the forest floor for seedling establishment and survival. The genus *Dichaetanthera* consists of pioneering tree species of successional habitats, forest edges, riverbanks, and treefall gaps. Seeds of its species germinate only in or close to a forested environment and may also require the presence of mycorrhizae (Perrier de la Bâthie 1932). The third group consists of obligate or facultative epiphytic species. In *Gravesia* the epiphytic habit is largely restricted to the 17 species of *Gravesia* section *Scandentes* (Perrier de la Bâthie 1951), all of which are climbing epiphytes with copious adventitious roots that cling to tree trunks (Figure 8.51e). A majority of *Medinilla* species are woody epiphytes with thick fleshy or leathery leaves, tuberous roots for water storage, flowers borne at the nodes of defoliated branches, and fleshy bird-dispersed fruits. Some have sessile, more or less clasping leaves that may facilitate detritus accumulation as a possible source of mineral nutrition.

FLORAL STRUCTURE, POLLINATION, AND DISPERSAL

The flowers of most princess flowers are radially symmetrical, generally bisexual, typically tetramerous or pentamerous, and epigynous with a hypanthium that bears calyx lobes, petals, and stamens on a well-defined vascular rim (Figures 8.50 and 8.51). There are usually twice as many stamens as petals (diplostemonous). Half of the stamens in a flower are inserted on the rim opposite the petals (antipetalous), and half are inserted opposite the calyx lobes (antisepalous). The stamens are typically tubular and release their pollen through one or two terminal pores or slits. In many (but not all) genera the androecium is dimorphic; the two whorls of stamens differ in size, color, and shape, and their declinate posture together with that of the style lends a pseudozygomorphic effect when seen in lateral view (Figures 8.50 and 8.51). The anther connective can also be prolonged and elaborated into dorsal or ventral appendages of varying size and shape (Figures 8.50d and e). These features may serve to enhance the visual attractiveness of the flowers and facilitate handling and strategic contact by pollinating insects. There are no publications addressing floral biology, genetic compatibility relations, or pollinator spectra for any Malagasy species. Renner (1989) has surveyed the field for Neotropical members of the family. Much of what is known for these species should provide a useful model for future studies of the Malagasy species.

The vast majority of melastone flowers, about 98% of species studied to date, rely on pollen as the pollinator reward (Renner 1989). In the case of the Olisbeoideae, an additional reward consists of fatty oils produced by the gland on the anther connectives (Buchmann and Buchmann 1981; Buchmann 1987; Oliveira 2016). The type of reward, in turn, determines the pollinator spectrum of a species and is correlated with morphological features that facilitate pollen extraction and deposition on a receptive stigma. Pollen flowers among Neotropical melastomes are visited by a broad assemblage of the bee fauna, but not all visitors are effective pollinators. Because most species do not shed pollen passively, insect-mediated extraction (buzz pollination) and stigmatic contact are essential for fertilization and optimal seed set. Large bees, presumably carpenter bees in the genus *Xylocopa*, were observed (F. Almeda, unpublished data) visiting the flowers of *Dichaetanthera cordifolia* (Figure 8.50d) and *D. oblongifolia* at Ranomafana in November of 1998.

While nectar-producing flowers among melastomes are much less common, nectar production has evolved in a diverse group of Neotropical melastome lineages. The spectrum of floral nectar collectors includes birds, bats, rodents, and bees, but most nectar flowers in the family appear to be pollinated by hummingbirds. None of the Malagasy melastomes, however, stand out as possible candidates for bird or mammal pollination.

Malagasy birds and perhaps some mammals are believed to be important dispersal agents for the 164 species with fleshy fruits (Perrier de la Bâthie 1932). Goodman et al. (1996) reported that *Hypsipetes madagascariensis* and *Philepitta castanea* (see Prum and Razafindratsita, pp. 1687–93) feed on the fruits of *Medinilla ericarum*, and that the latter species also consumes the fruits of *Gravesia calliantha*. These same authors noted *Cinnyris sovimanga* visiting *M. torrentum* and apparently piercing the base of unopened flowers with its bill.

Turk (1995) remarked that lemurs eat the fruits of *Memecylon corymbiforme* at Ranomafana. One of the present authors (R. D. Stone, unpublished data) has observed *Eulemur sanfordi* (Sanford's Brown Lemur) eating fruits of *Warneckea sansibarica* at the Campement des Princes at Ankarana. Different lemur species have been documented to consume the fruits of native and introduced melastomes. For native species Eppley et al. (pp. 1839–59) reported that 27 lemur species consumed different vegetative parts of melastomes.

Aside from the above observations, seed-dispersal and seed-recovery studies documented by field observations are otherwise lacking for all capsular-fruited and a majority of the berry-fruited melastome species of Madagascar. The Neotropical melastome flora is rich and diverse at higher elevations (1500–3400 m) where the vertebrate-pollinated species occur. On Madagascar, however, melastome diversity appears to exhibit a distinct decline above 1400 m, whereas rodent diversity and abundance reach a peak at 1200–1600 m (Goodman et al. 2000). Vertebrates appear not to have played a role in the pollination systems of Malagasy Melastomataceae. This is corroborated by the paucity of nectar-feeding birds (Langrand 1990) and the numerous dietary studies showing that the three endemic Malagasy fruit bat species are unknown to feed on the nectar or fruits of melastomes (see Andrianaivoarivelo et al., pp. 1911–16).

OTHER PLANT-ANIMAL INTERACTIONS

One of the most intriguing and fascinating interactions between Malagasy melastomes and insects is the strict relationship between two species of *Dichaetanthera*, *D. cordifolia* (Figure 8.50d) and *D. arborea*, and the Giraffe-necked Weevil (*Trachelophurus giraffa*; family Attelabidae; tribe Trachelophorini). The life cycle of this charismatic beetle depends on *Dichaetanthera*, as the females lay their eggs on their leaves; either of the two *Dichaetanthera* species may be used. The female of *T. giraffa* rolls the *Dichaetanthera* leaf into a perfect cone in which it lays a single egg. The rolled *Dichaetanthera* leaf sheltering the egg is then severed from the plant and drops on the ground. The larvae were observed (H. Ranarivelo, unpublished data) eating their rolled-leaf shelters in Mantadia National Park. Adult males and females of *T. giraffa* also consume *Dichaetanthera* leaves. The weevil-plant relationship as we currently understand it appears to be commensalistic since the weevils are using the leaves of *Dichaetanthera* as egg nurseries, and adult weevils and larvae consume the leaves. Additional fieldwork is needed to determine whether the Giraffe-necked Weevils keep other phytophagous insects away from their two host species of *Dichaetanthera*.

A number of Neotropical melastome species in about 10 genera can also be counted among those vascular plants that have evolved complex morphological structures designed to shelter ants. These structures, or domatia as they are called, consist of hollow internodal chambers or paired inflated pouch-like outgrowths borne along the stems just below the nodes, along the petioles, or between the primary and secondary veins at the base of abaxial surfaces of leaf blades. Students of plant-ant interactions agree that ants benefit plants in one of two ways. First, ants can defend their plant hosts from herbivore attack. Second, through nest construction, ants may also accumulate nutrient-rich organic debris from which plants can obtain both macronutrients and, in some cases, a suitable rooting substrate (Benson 1985; Huxley 1991). *Gravesia ecalcarata* and *G. hirtopetala* appear to be the only Malagasy melastomes involved in ant-plant mutualism (F. Almeda and H. Ranarivelo, unpublished data; also see Fisher, pp. 1173–88 for further details). Both of these species have well-defined perforations near the nodes of uppermost branches that lead to hollow internodal chambers that harbor unidentified species of ants. If a mutualistic relationship has evolved among other Malagasy species, then the approximately 48 epiphytic species of *Medinilla* are likely candidates because plants that obtain nutrients from ants are prevailingly epiphytes (Huxley 1991).

Other distinctive but not particularly conspicuous features of several Neotropical species of *Axinaea*, *Bellucia*, *Blakea*, *Chalybea*, *Graffenrieda*, *Meriania*, *Miconia*, and *Monochaetum* are the specialized pit, pocket, or hair-tuft chambers housing mites (acarodomatia) in the vein axils of abaxial leaf surfaces (Almeda 1989, 1990; Alvear and Almeda 2019). Relatively recent work has shown that the plant-mite relationship is a mutualistic interaction (Pemberton and Turner 1989; Turner and Pemberton 1989). The domatia appear to serve as egg nurseries and help to shelter the mites from predators. The mites, in turn, benefit the plants by feeding on fungal spores and the eggs of predaceous insects.

The occurrence and significance of acarodomatia has been overlooked by most melastome specialists. A detailed survey of museum specimens and field study are needed to determine whether acarodomatia are found in Malagasy species. The abaxial leaf surfaces of *Rousseauxia chrysophylla* and *R. minimifolia*, for example, have structures at the point of primary vein divergence that are a good match for the pocket domatia found in species of *Clidemia* that are now included in the genus *Miconia* (Almeda 1989). If acarodomatia are ultimately discovered among other Malagasy melastomes, it would not be surprising because plant-mite associations are found in several Neotropical species of the family, they are widespread geographically, and they involve a broad assemblage of flowering plants (O'Dowd and Willson 1989).

WORK IN PROGRESS

Molecular systematic research on the Melastomataceae is ongoing and in recent years has led to the recognition of several new groups at tribal level in the subfamily Melastomatoideae (Penneys et al. 2010; Michelangeli et al. 2011; Rocha et al. 2018; Bacci et al. 2019; Bochorny et al. 2019). While previous studies have relied on a relatively small number of plastid or nuclear loci, we are now well embarked into the "genomics era," with the tantalizing prospect of being able to carry forward analyses involving literally hundreds if not thousands of informative genetic loci. In the context of recent investigations of the African Melastomateae (Veranso-Libalah et al. 2017, 2018), two of the present authors (H. Ranarivelo and F. Almeda) are currently conducting focused projects on the systematics of *Dichaetanthera* and the endemic Malagasy clade (*Amphorocalyx*, *Dionycha*, and *Rousseauxia*) with increased taxonomic sampling. Preliminary molecular and morphological analyses to date indicate that both *Dichaetanthera* and *Rousseauxia* are monophyletic, but the other two genera as currently delimited are not. Additional work on the phylogenetics of *Gravesia* and other members of African-Malagasy Sonerileae is being carried out in Gudrun Kadereit's lab at Johannes Gutenberg University, Mainz. Tribal limits of Sonerileae and the closely related Dissochaeteae are further being tested in the course of that project.

Taxonomy of Malagasy *Memecylon* was substantially revised 35 years ago (Jacques-Félix 1984, 1985). Since that time many new collections have become available for study, and much of this additional material appears to represent species new to science (R. D. Stone 2012). Work toward another comprehensive revision is ongoing, with more than 60 novelties currently being described, in addition to the 17 already published by R. D. Stone (2006b, 2020). When these are formally published they will increase the number of known

Malagasy *Memecylon* species to about 150 (an increase of 88% from our state of knowledge in 1985). The infrageneric classification of Malagasy *Memecylon* is also in need of revision in view of molecular analyses (R. D. Stone 2014; R. D. Stone, unpublished data) indicating that at least some of the seven sections previously recognized by Jacques-Félix (1984, 1985) are not monophyletic. Another memecyloid group in need of revision is *Warneckea* subgenus *Carnosae* (i.e., *W. sansibarica sensu lato*), and a recent morphometric study of this species complex (Tenza 2015) found several characters of taxonomic importance. Molecular analyses with increased sampling further indicate that treating this group as a single polymorphic species would underrepresent its genetic diversity (R. D. Stone, unpublished data).

CONSERVATION CONCERNS

Because the lion's share of melastome diversity is centered in Madagascar's moist evergreen forests, the long-term survival of this family, like that of the forest flora generally, will depend on critical habitat protection. A large portion of Madagascar's moist evergreen forest has disappeared during the past century. Of the 261 species of indigenous melastomes known to Perrier de la Bâthie (1932), 170 were recorded from a single locality, 82 species had been collected from several sites (two to six localities), and only seven species were known to have broader ranges. If these figures are representative of the original ranges of most Malagasy melastomes, one can only surmise that many species have gone extinct as the native forests have been cleared.

In areas where the forest has been destroyed or severely degraded, one now encounters only the weedy *Antherotoma naudinii* and *Tristemma mauritianum* or the introduced *Miconia crenata*. Unlike the Neotropics, where there are many weedy species that can survive in marginal habitats with high insolation and nutrient-poor soils, a much larger number of the Malagasy melastomes seem to require the microenvironments that only an intact tropical forest can provide. On the other hand, recent collecting efforts have led to the rediscovery of some species, for example, *Memecylon crassinerve* and *Lijndenia melastomoides*, which are seemingly very rare and had not been seen for several to many decades (R. D. Stone 2012, 2017). Positive discoveries like these offer hope that, with additional field work, more of these "forest phantoms" may be found.

Subject editors: Laurent Gautier and Steven M. Goodman

BURSERACEAE

J. Raharimampionona, M. Gostel, and D. C. Daly

Burseraceae is known as the family of frankincense and myrrh. This pantropical family comprises 17 genera and an estimated 800 species. Members of the family are distributed throughout low-elevation humid forest, seasonally dry forest, and desert. The growth habit ranges from small, sometimes succulent, shrubs to very tall trees, which are occasionally saxicolous or epiphytic.

The members of this family are characterized by fragrant resins that are translucent or milky and nonallergenic, and these are present in all vascularized parts of the plant (Figure 8.54d–f). In the volatile fraction of the resins, monocyclic and bicyclic monoterpenes are equally important constituents of oleoresins. The volatile sequiterpenes are of more restricted occurrence but are strongly diversified in *Canarium* and *Commiphora*, while triterpenes are frequent and highly diversified in the family (review in Daly et al. 2011). The best-known aromatic resins are myrrh, from species of the genus *Commiphora*, and frankincense, from species of *Boswellia*. However, the family also includes important timber trees, notably *Aucoumea klaineana* from the Congo Basin (Thulin et al. 2008).

SYSTEMATICS AND PHYLOGENY

The Burseraceae and Anacardiaceae have long been accepted as being closely related (e.g., Cronquist 1981), and during the 19th century a number of genera were placed in one or the other family or as part of a broadly defined and changeable Terebinthaceae (Weeks et al. 2014). The two families show considerable morphological convergence, especially in dry tropical habitats where species of both families can display a densely branched, tortuous habit; succulent branchlets; deciduous, imparipinnate leaves congested toward the branchlet apices; and usually drupaceous fruits, although these are eventually dehiscent in many Burseraceae (Mitchell and Daly 1991). Changes in ordinal placement have been made over time: for example, in the early 1800s, the family was placed in the order of Burserales with the families Anacardiaceae and Podoaceae. In the mid-1800s and early 1900s, the family was placed in the order of Geraniales based on strict embryological definitions (e.g., Engler 1896a). In the mid-1900s the family was placed in the Rutales. Finally, in the late 1900s, the family joined the Sapindales, together with Aceraceae, Anacardiaceae, Meliaceae, Rutaceae, Sapindaceae, and several other small families.

Lam (1932) divided the Burseraceae into three tribes, Bursereae, Canarieae, and Protieae. As treated in the context of pollen morphological studies by Harley et al. (2005), tribe Bursereae was predominantly African and Mesoamerican and included the genera *Aucoumea*, *Beiselia*, *Boswellia*, *Bursera*, *Commiphora*, and *Triomma*. Tribe Canarieae was largely Malesian and comprised the genera *Canarium*, *Dacryodes*, *Haplolobus*, *Pseudodacryodes*, *Rosselia*, *Santiria*, *Scutinanthe*, and *Trattinnickia*. Tribe Protieae was predominantly

Neotropical and integrated *Crepidospermum*, *Garuga*, *Protium*, and *Tetragastris*. The taxonomic history of the family is discussed in detail by Harley and Daly (1995).

Phylogenetic studies by several researchers (Becerra 2003; Fine et al. 2005; Weeks et al. 2005; Weeks and Simpson 2007; Thulin et al. 2008), and the recent work of Weeks et al. (2014), have shown that some infra-familial relationships in the Burseraceae are in fact unresolved. Daly et al. (2011) proposed a classification of this family based on five alliances (*Beiselia*, *Protium*, *Boswellia*, *Bursera*, and *Canarium*) using a combination of molecular phylogenetic and morphological data. A recent, thorough reexamination of Protieae confirmed that it is strongly supported as a monophyletic, monogeneric group consisting of *Protium*, with nine well-supported sections including *Crepidospermum* and *Tetragastris*, formerly recognized as genera (Daly and Fine 2018).

MALAGASY GENERA

Four genera are recognized from Madagascar, including *Ambilobea*, *Canarium*, *Commiphora*, and *Protium*, and based on recent taxonomic revisions there are about 80 species (D. C. Daly, unpublished data). The Burseraceae occurring on Madagascar show high levels of endemism (Figure 8.53)

The genus *Ambilobea* was proposed for the species *Boswellia madagascariensis* (Thulin et al. 2008). *Ambilobea* differs from *Boswellia* by being dioecious and by having valvate petals; furthermore, it is unique in the family due to its winged tips to the petioles, pyrenes that remain attached to the detached valves of the fruit at dehiscence, and spherical pollen with long spines.

Canarium is a Paleotropical genus. In the *Flore de Madagascar et des Comores*, only three species were recognized by Perrier de la Bâthie (1946b): *C. madagascariense* (including *C. multiflorum*, *C. harami*, and *C. greveanum*); *C. boivinii* (including *C. obtusifolium*, Figure 8.54a); and *C. pulchrebracteatum*. The taxonomic treatment of Leenhouts (1959), recognized only one species on Madagascar, *C. madagascariense*, with three subspecies corresponding to the species of Perrier de la Bâthie. Recent taxonomic work revealed the presence of 33 species, 27 of which were new to science (Daly et al. 2015). This establishes Madagascar as a major center of diversity for the genus. Investigations in a number of herbaria and fieldwork on Madagascar and other countries (D. C. Daly, unpublished data) suggest that the total number of species in the genus is about 150, of which about one-third are undescribed. Investigation of the historical biogeography of *Canarium* on Madagascar has confirmed that the genus is monophyletic with respect to the island and suggests a late Miocene origin via long-distance dispersal from southeast Asia followed by a considerable in situ radiation on the island (Federman et al. 2015).

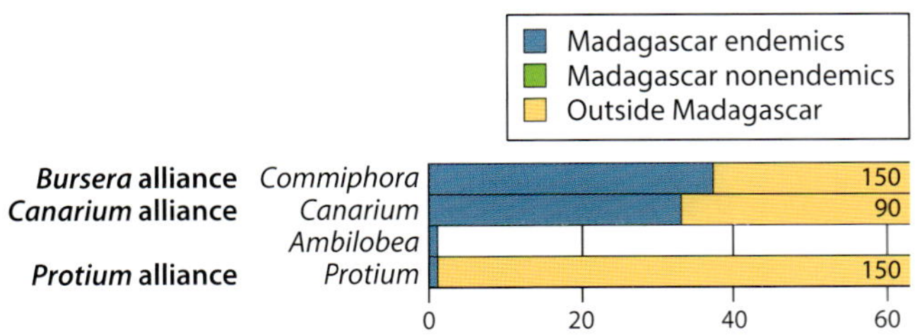

FIGURE 8.53 Diversity and endemicity diagram of Malagasy Burseraceae at the level of genera, showing three different species counts: 1) endemic to Madagascar, 2) nonendemic but native to Madagascar, and 3) those occurring elsewhere in the world (for further information see text). In cases when species diversity exceeds or does not conform to that presented on the horizontal graph scale, the figures are written along the respective horizontal line of a given genus.

Commiphora was first described in 1797 by Jacquin. The type species, *C. madagascariensis*, is based upon an illustration from the volume in which it was originally described; however, as noted by Gillett (1991), the species has never been collected on Madagascar and is known only from Tanzania. Worldwide, this genus includes approximately 190 species with a center of diversity in tropical east Africa, but its range extends into northern, southern, and western Africa; southern and southeast Asia; and South America. On Madagascar, *Commiphora* is currently represented by 32 species, but a number of additional novelties are known by specialists and are awaiting description (Gostel et al. 2016a; P. Phillipson and J. Raharimampionona, unpublished data). Perrier de la Bâthie's (1946b) treatment of *Commiphora* included 20 species. Capuron (1962) described another four species, one additional species was subsequently transferred from a genus of Meliaceae by Cheek and Rakotozafy (1991), and one species was described by Bardot-Vaucoulon (2002). More recently, Gostel et al. (2016b) described another four new species and identified an additional 13 new species from Madagascar that are awaiting description. Due in large part to three characteristics of this genus (they are androdioecious, deciduous, and precocious), species description is challenging because collections are rarely complete. Most collections are represented by only staminate or carpellate flowers with young leaves, mature leaves with immature fruit, or fruit with no leaves. Gillett (1973) cited these characteristics as particularly challenging for a revision of the genus in tropical east Africa. All 37 published species, plus the 13 as yet undescribed taxa, are endemic to Madagascar, and recent molecular phylogenetic studies suggest that the genus is represented on the island by four distinct and well-supported clades (Weeks and Simpson 2007; Gostel et al. 2015, 2016a). It is interesting to note that one Malagasy species, *C. lasiodisca*, is sister to all other species in the genus and that Madagascar holds approximately 25% of the described species in the genus.

The genus *Protium* is represented on Madagascar by one endemic species, *P. madagascariense* (synonym *P. beandou*). Like *Commiphora*, *P. madagascariense* has a four- or five-parted perianth, but *Protium* is distinguished by its equal stamens (on Madagascar), four- or five-locular ovary (versus two or three locules in *Commiphora*), and the fruits dehiscing to reveal two to five pyrenes covered with a sweet pulp (versus one or two pyrenes and a fleshy pseudaril in *Commiphora*, Figure 8.54b). *Canarium* has trimerous flowers and indehiscent fruits with a single, normally three-locular pyrene, of which one or two locules are always aborted. *Protium madagascariense* differs from *Ambilobea* by the former's petiole apex being terete (versus winged); four- or five-locular (versus three-locular) ovary; pyrenes tenuously attached to the columella apex (not to the valve) and enveloped in a sweet reddish pulp (not dry); and the

FIGURE 8.54 **Examples of fruits and resins of Malagasy Burseraceae. A) Fruits of *Canarium obtusifolium* (Daly et al. 12952) in Masoala; B) mature fruits of *Commiphora* sp., showing dehiscence of the fleshy mesocarp, the pyrene, and fleshy, red pseudaril (Gostel 139); C) fruits of *Protium madagascariense* (Daly et al. 12960) in Tampolo; D) dry white crystallized resin on a buttress of *Canarium* in Lokobe; E) reddish translucent resin of *Commiphora humbertii* (Gostel 232) dried on a trunk that has been tapped, with exfoliating outer bark; and F) milky resin from a freshly cut branch of *C. pervilleana* (Gostel 102).** (PHOTOS A, C, and D by D. C. Daly, and B, E, and F by M. R. Gostel.)

rounded seeds (versus flattened). Perrier de la Bâthie (1946b) recognized two species of *Protium*, but more recent sampling, morphological examination, and molecular studies (P. V. A. Fine, unpublished data) suggest that there is only one variable species, originally published as the genus *Marignia*, now *Protium* section *Marignia*. Worldwide, the genus comprises about 151 species, with one of each for Madagascar, the Philippines, Mauritius, New Guinea, Australia, continental southeast Asia, and Indonesia, with the remainder in the Neotropics.

SPECIES DISTRIBUTION AND HABITAT

Ambilobea

The name *Ambilobea* is derived from Ambilobe, a city in northwestern Madagascar with several nearby collecting localities for the plant, including the type locality (Massif d'Andavakoera). *Ambilobea madagascariensis*, its only species, is limited to the extreme northern portion of the island where it grows in dry deciduous forests on limestone or on unconsolidated sand. It is known up to 500 m above sea level (Thulin et al. 2008).

Canarium

This genus on Madagascar is found in all bioclimatic zones of the island, with the exception of the arid south. Fourteen species occur in at least two to four bioclimatic zones, following Schatz (2000), while three appear to be restricted to a single type of bioclimate. In general, *Canarium* species are present below 1200 m; 14 species have not been found below 500 m and 19 species are more abundant at 0–800 m, while four species (*C. findens*, *C. scholasticum*, *C. lamianum*, and *C. subsidarium*) are abundant at higher elevations (600–1200 m) and exceptionally found at 1400 m). In general,

Canarium can colonize diverse types of substrate including basement rock, limestone, and sandstone (Daly et al. 2015). The fruits of this genus are eaten by at least eight species of lemurs (Vasey 2000) and is a preferred food of *Daubentonia madagascariensis* (Aye-aye) (see Sterling et al., pp. 1975–78). In particular, the seed can provide an important source of lipids and protein, but the endocarp is very hard, and most animals eat the fleshy mesocarp and reject the endocarp immediately or excrete it later (Vasey 2000). It is also known to be eaten by some endemic and introduced rodents (Goodman and Sterling 1996).

Commiphora

All Malagasy species of *Commiphora* are endemic to the island, and they grow throughout much of the west from the extreme north to the far south in dry deciduous forests and dry spiny thickets. Most taxa are microendemics with narrow geographic distributions, but a few taxa are widespread, including *C. aprevalii*, *C. guillauminii*, *C. humbertii*, *C. marchandii*, *C. orbicularis*, *C. pervilleana*, and *C. simplicifolia*. Perhaps most common is *C. grandifolia*, which grows across the range of this genus on the island. In his description of the vegetation types of Madagascar, Humbert (1965) regarded the presence of *Commiphora* (together with *Dalbergia*, Leguminosae, and *Hildegardia*, Malvaceae) as an indicator for western dry deciduous forests. Indeed, *Commiphora* is abundant in these dry and seasonally dry regions, as well as in the dry spiny thickets of the southwest. Malagasy *Commiphora* species include both edaphic generalists and specialists and occur on different substrates, particularly limestone where high species diversity is found on the karstic massifs of Ankarana, Bemaraha, and Namoroka. Numerous species are also common on rocky or sandy and other siliceous soils; more rarely, *Commiphora* can be found on lateritic or igneous substrates. Members of this genus are most commonly found at 0–50 m elevation, particularly in the south and southwest, but a few species extend up to 800 m (rarely to 1000 m), such as *C. marchandii* and *C. pervilleana*.

The fruits of *C. arafy* and other unspecified taxa of *Commiphora* are eaten by sifaka lemurs (e.g., *Propithecus verreauxi*, *P. coronatus*, *P. tattersalli*) according to a survey by Pichon et al. (2010) and information recorded on herbarium labels. Few ecological studies exist for species of *Commiphora* on Madagascar, but Böhning-Gaese et al. (1999) undertook an extensive study of mechanisms of seed dispersal in *C. guillauminii* and found that the pyrenes are dispersed by both *Coracopsis nigra* (Lesser Vasa Parrot) and *Aphaenogaster swammerdami* (ant). A study of flower-visiting fauna to *Commiphora guillauminii* by Farwig et al. (2004) revealed diverse potential pollinators that included mostly Hymenoptera but also Lepidoptera, Diptera, Heteroptera, and occasionally birds.

Protium

Generally, *P. madagascariense* grows in different moist evergreen forests in the regions of DIANA, SAVA, Analanjirofo, Atsinanana, Vatovavy-Fitovinany, Atsimo-Atsinanana, and Anosy. The species prefers humid and subhumid bioclimates, including the Sambirano area. This species occurs from sea level to about 1000 m.

LOCAL ETHNOBOTANICAL USES

There is a fascinating convergence of human use of members of this family throughout its distribution. For example, in portions of Central America, species of *Bursera* are planted as living fences, like *Commiphora* is on Madagascar. The use of *Canarium* resins (Figure 8.54d) in spirit possession ceremonies (*tromba*) on Madagascar is similar to the manner of the ritual use of other Burseraceae resins in a range of cultures from Bahia, Brazil to Martinique, Central America, Arabia, and North Africa. The use of these resins in caulking canoes is also widely practiced from Madagascar to Gabon to Amazonia. The resins figure prominently in traditional medicine throughout the family's range as well.

Canarium

On Madagascar, *Canarium* has multiple uses and is well known by local populations. Despite the diversity of species and uses of the genus on the island, almost all species are popularly known as *ramy*. The pulp and seeds of the fruit can be edible (Styger et al. 1999). Different parts of the plant are used medicinally, mainly the resins but also the leaves, seeds, and bark for various ailments such as urinary tract infections (Perrier de la Bâthie 1946b), dental cavities, rheumatism, and injuries. For headaches and other pains, the resin is heated and its vapor inhaled (Brink 2008). Although the wood is not the subject of regular exportation, it is used for many purposes on Madagascar, including general construction and making canoes, boxes, crates, tool handles, matches, household furniture, veneers, plywood, hardboard, and chipboard. The wood is also considered suitable for carpentry and sometimes for floors and posts. The wood of Malagasy *Canarium* is not particularly durable, being susceptible to attack by fungi and insects (including termites and borers), although it is resistant to salt water (Daly et al. 2015). As noted above, *Canarium* also has important cultural value on Madagascar because the resin is used during the *tromba* spirit possession ceremony during which it acts as an olfactory guide for the spirit so that it can find the host or sometimes even chase away bad spirits (Daly et al. 2015). Further, the resin is very volatile and widely used in the countryside to start outdoor cooking fires when it is raining or the firewood is damp.

Commiphora

As noted above, *Commiphora* is often propagated locally and cultivated as a living fence in villages. This use can have a negative impact on wild populations, but it can also conserve the local genetic heritage as natural habitats disappear (Gostel et al. 2016b). *Commiphora aprevalii* is frequently used as a living fence in villages throughout the southwest, and this may be associated with its artificially expanded distribution. There are few if any recorded instances of commercial trade in *Commiphora* for this purpose. The ethnobotanical uses of other species in this genus are poorly known and documented on Madagascar, but certain species have been observed that are tapped for resin (M. Gostel, unpublished data). In many tropical regions, a single vernacular name is used for several different species, as is the case for *C. arafy* and *C. morondavensis*, both of which are called *arafy*. Other common Malagasy vernacular names for *Commiphora* include *daro*, *daro fotsy*, *daro mangory*, and *matambelo*.

CONSERVATION

Ambilobea

Ambilobea madagascariensis is endemic in the northern part of Madagascar, mainly in disturbed habitats. It has been categorized as Vulnerable on the International Union for the Conservation of Nature (IUCN) Red List. It is known to occur in the following protected areas: Loky Manambato, Andrafiamena-Andavakoera, Montagne d'Ambre (western slopes), Montagne des Français, and Ankarana.

Canarium

In light of its many uses and the often large size of the trees, *Canarium* wood is frequently among the first trees to be selectively exploited at certain sites. In the eastern moist evergreen forests, for example, in the Ifanadiana region, where Ranomafana National Park is located, *Canarium* is one of the eight genera for which logging concessions have been granted (Arrigo-Nelson 2006). Due to its cultural importance, as described in the Local Ethnobotantical Uses section, individuals of *Canarium* are often the last trees still standing on some exploited sites.

All Malagasy species of this genus are endemic to the island and many are probably Endangered, based on IUCN Red List criteria (J. Raharimampionona, unpublished data); depending on the species and site, trees of this genus can be abundant to very rare. There are 12 species that are not represented in protected areas; some species are known from only one or two collection localities outside the protected area network. On the basis of recent collection data, five species are only known from a single protected area: *C. ampasindavae* in Ampasindava and *C. arcuatum* on Nosy Mangabe, *C. betamponae* and *C. obovatum* in Betampona, *C. fugax* in Masoala, and *C. galokense* in Galoko-Kalobinono. In contrast, three species are very common and widespread and can be found in more than 10 protected areas: C. *lamianum*, *C. globosum*, and *C. scholasticum*.

In our experience, at sites where *Canarium* occurs there can be up to six sympatric species, and there appears to be some niche separation related to variables such as elevation and exposure; various taxa have different flowering and fruiting phenologies as well as fruit size. This suggests the possibility that at a given locality, frugivorous lemurs may depend on more than one species of *Canarium*. Based on information from the IUCN Red List, the conservation statutes for 27 species have been assessed: four are Critically Endangered, 12 Endangered, five Vulnerable, one Near Threatened, and five of Least Concern.

Commiphora

Among the many species of *Commiphora* on Madagascar, some are narrowly endemic (e.g., *C. andranovoryensis*, *C. tsimanampetsae*), in some cases known only from a single collection. Other species are common and occupy very broad ranges that extend across the entire range of suitable habitat for the genus on Madagascar (e.g., *C. grandifolia*). Until recent field collection efforts, several species had been known only from type material (e.g., *C. stellulata*). Focused collecting efforts during the past 10 years have greatly improved documentation of the genus on Madagascar, in some cases resulting in the rediscovery of species thought possibly to be extinct.

Outside of conservation zones, deforestation associated with logging and burning has dramatically impacted the survival of populations of *Commiphora*. Within the protected area network on Madagascar, trees of this genus can be found in many different sites, as well as in smaller protected areas and private reserves. Many species of *Commiphora* are known only from protected areas (e.g., *C. andranovoryensis*), while several species are known only outside of protected areas (e.g., *C. stellulata* and several unnamed species). Seven species are categorized as threatened based on recent IUCN Red List assessment (Gostel et al. 2016b): one Critically Endangered (*C. stellulata*), two Endangered (*C. andranovoryensis* and *C. razakamalalae*), two Vulnerable (*C. falcata* and *C. morondavensis*), one Near Threatened (*C. elliptica*), and one Least Concern (*C. aprevalii*).

Protium

Protium madagascariense is endemic to the island and present in various protected areas including Loky Manambato, Lokobe, Galoko-Kalobinono, Tsaratanàna, Marojejy, Anjanaharibe-Sud, Masoala, Nosy Mangabe, Tampolo, and Betampona. The species has yet to be assessed under IUCN Red List criteria.

WORK IN PROGRESS

While it is not anticipated that additional species of *Ambilobea* or *Protium* will be discovered, the taxonomy of Malagasy *Canarium* and *Commiphora* is still poorly resolved, mostly due to inadequate sampling and incomplete collections, and quite a number of new species remain to be resolved and published. Recent field expeditions have resulted in the collection of six additional new species of *Commiphora* that have been added to a molecular phylogeny, and their description is in progress. More thorough botanical exploration will have significant impacts on the true diversity and conservation status of Malagasy Burseraceae.

Subject editors: Laurent Gautier and Steven M. Goodman

ANACARDIACEAE

A. Randrianasolo

Anacardiaceae is primarily a tropical and subtropical plant family, with a few representatives extending into the warm temperate zones of both hemispheres (Cronquist 1981; Pell et al. 2011). Its members are mainly trees and shrubs, and rarely lianas. Anacardiaceae members are characterized by having resin canals in the bark, leaves, flowers, and fruits and exudate substances of different colors (transparent, milky white, reddish) from these canals; the exudate of some species causes dermatitis (Mitchell 1990; Pell et al. 2011). Most Anacardiaceae taxa have drupaceous or samaroid fruits with usually one to five locules, each locule containing only one seed.

Anacardiaceae is an economically important family and its members have been used by humans for a variety of purposes for centuries. For example, the early Greeks used *Rhus coriaria* as a valued medicine and as a source of tannin and spice. Similarly, Native Americans in the southwestern United States used different species of *Schmaltzia* as a source of food, medicine, and basketry materials. *Mangifera indica* (mango) and some *Spondias* species, such as *S. dulcis* and *S. mombin*, are edible and delicious tropical fruits. *Anacardium occidentale* (cashews) and *Pistacia vera* (pistachios) are valuable commercial nuts. In South Africa, fruits of *Sclerocarya birrea* is the source of an economically valuable oil used in cosmetics, and in Madagascar, ripe fruits of *Sorindeia madagascariensis* are edible and sold in markets. These are just a few examples of useful species out of the many Anacardiaceae members that are valuable for humans.

Anacardiaceae comprises about 81 genera and 800 species (Pell et al. 2011), but like many other primarily tropical families, detailed studies across all genera are still incomplete. Surveys of embryology and fruit development (Von Teichman 1992), fruit structure (Von Teichman and Van Wyk 1996), and wood anatomy (Terrazas 1994) have been based on small numbers of available species and have seldom included an even representation of the taxonomic diversity in the family. Furthermore, the problem is compounded by the majority of available descriptions having resulted from regional floristic studies rather than efforts to compile parallel data across genera.

TAXONOMY

The family Anacardiaceae was originally described by R. Brown (1818) and has traditionally been placed in Sapindales or Rutales (Cronquist 1981). An early molecular study confirmed that Anacardiaceae is indeed one of the families forming the core of the Sapindales (Gadek et al. 1996). A year later Takhtajan (1997), in his plant classification system, placed this family in the Bursales. However, in a more recent publication, Pell et al. (2011) recognized the Anacardiaceae as a member of the order Sapindales, based on molecular data.

Since the family's original description, there have been a number of infra-familial classifications proposed, based primarily on leaf morphology and floral characters (e.g., number of carpels or locules, number of stamens, style morphology) (Wannan and Quinn 1991). Bentham and Hooker (1862) recognized two tribes, Anacardieae and Spondieae, with 46 genera in the family, while Barkley (1957) recognized five tribes, Mangifereae, Spondieae, Semecarpeae, Rhoideae, and Dobineae, including 77 genera. Takhtajan (1987) distinguished five subfamilies, Anacardioideae, Dobineoideae, Spondioideae, Julianoideae, and Pistacioideae. Subsequently, in 1997, he recognized only four of these five subfamilies and elevated Dobineoideae to a family rank under the name Podoaceae, which, together with Anacardiaceae and Burseraceae, formed the order Burserales. This segregation of these families, however, is not in agreement with more recent findings. According to Pell et al. (2011), based on molecular data, the inclusion of families previously segregated from Anacardiaceae, such as Podoaceae, is justified. This controversy indicates that infra-familial classification of Anacardiaceae is not quite settled, but with ongoing studies this matter should be resolved in the future. Herein, for the Malagasy taxa, we follow Pell et al. (2011) in dividing Anacardiaceae into two subfamilies: Anacardioideae and Spondioideae.

Members of Anacardiaceae are trees, shrubs or lianas with simple or compound, alternate or subopposite, persistent or caducuous leaves. The inflorescences are axillary or terminal panicles or thyrses, occasionally racemes or spikes, or the flowers may be cauliflorous. The perianth is two-whorled, rarely one-whorled, and present in most species although it is occasionally reduced in some genera (e.g., *Haplorhus*, *Pistacia*), or lacking in female flowers (*Dobinea*), or completely absent (*Orthopterygium* and *Amphipterygium*). The calyx is usually tetramerous or pentamerous, sometimes more, sometimes reduced to trimerous, with imbricate or valvate lobes, and is caducuous or persistent, rarely accrescent. The petals are tetramerous or pentamerous, imbricate or sometimes valvate, and absent in some genera such as *Haplorhus*. The number of stamens varies greatly in this family, ranging from two (e.g., *Fegimanra*) to over 100 (e.g., *Gluta*). The anthers are introrse, dorsifixed or basifixed, or versatile with longitudinal slits. An intrastaminal or extrastaminal nectary is often present. The ovary is superior or inferior, with the number of carpels varying greatly, from one up to 13 (Wannan and Quinn 1991). Locules in Anacardiaceae have only one ovule, with the funicle apically, basally, or laterally attached to the internal wall of the carpel; they are described as anatropous or apotropous by Mitchell and Daly (1993). There may be one or three to five styles, occasionally more, which are either connate at the base or separate. The stigmas are capitate, papillose, or sometimes lobed (Pell et al. 2011). Fruits of Anacardiaceae are generally drupaceous (Wannan and Quinn 1990) but sometimes samaroid; they usually have a single seed per fruit but some genera have more (e.g., *Spondias* with four or five seeds and *Pleiogynium* with up to 13 seeds).

MALAGASY ANACARDIACEAE TAXONOMY

On Madagascar, the Anacardiaceae family provides another example of the great speciation events that typify the Malagasy flora, and according to Pell et al. (2011) the island is one of the centers of Anacardiaceae biodiversity. The only comprehensive treatment to date of the island's Anacardiaceae (Perrier de la Bâthie 1946c) recognized 13 genera and 38 species, but publications from recent revisionary studies almost triple the number of accepted species. In the precursor of this book it was mentioned (Randrianasolo 2003) that, associated with the revision of *Operculicarya* (Eggli 1995), *Campnosperma* (Randrianasolo and Miller 1998), *Poupartia* (Randrianasolo and Miller 1999a), and *Micronychia* (Randrianasolo 2000), the number of recognized species on the island had increased to 44. In this contribution, 75 species are recognized, of which three are introduced, another three occur in the African mainland and one on the Mascarenes, and the remaining 68 (~91%) are endemic to Madagascar. At the generic level, the number of recognized genera has also increased since Randrianasolo (2003) to include the description of two new genera, *Abrahamia* (Randrianasolo et al. 2017) and *Poupartiopsis* (Mitchell et al. 2006), and the resurrection of the genus *Baronia* (Pell et al. 2008, 2011). This brings the number of Anacardiaceae genera on Madagascar to 16, of which two are introduced, eight have representatives outside Madagascar, and, excluding the Malagasy *Rhus*, five are endemic to the island (Figure 8.55). According to Pell et al. (2011), Madagascar is among the places considered as a center of biodiversity for Anacardiaceae.

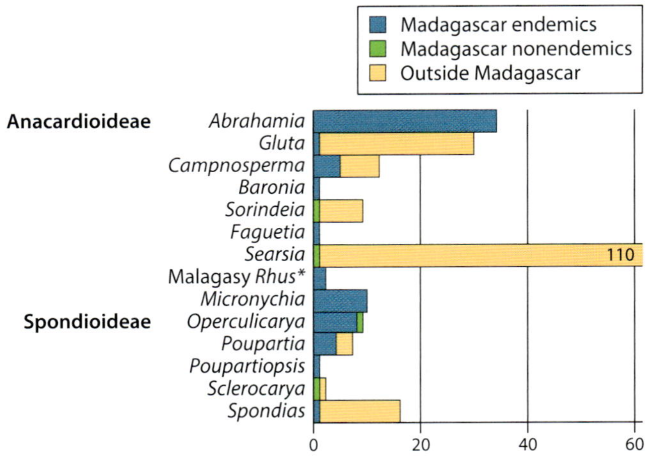

FIGURE 8.55 **Diversity and endemicity diagram of Malagasy Anacardiaceae at the level of genera, showing three different species counts: 1) endemic to Madagascar, 2) nonendemic but native to Madagascar, and 3) those occurring elsewhere in the world (for further information see text). In cases when species diversity exceeds or does not conform to that presented on the horizontal graph scale, the figures are written along the respective horizontal line of a given genus. *Malagasy species included in the polyphyletic *Rhus* but representing separate endemic lineages.**

Taxonomic Revisions

Associated with recent revisions, the taxonomy of several genera of Anacardiaceae on Madagascar has changed. Besides *Anacardium* and *Mangifera*, which are each represented by one introduced species, most of the remaining genera have undergone some changes in their species circumscription since Randrianasolo (2003). The most noticeable taxonomic changes are those concerning the following genera.

Abrahamia

Randrianasolo (1998) proposed that the Malagasy species included in the genus *Protorhus* should be separated from the African species based on cladistic and morphological analyses. *Protorhus* was treated by Perrier de la Bâthie (1946c) and found to comprise 16 species, 15 endemic to Madagascar and *P. longifolia*, type species of the genus, the only one restricted to southern Africa. Randrianasolo suggested a new generic name be given to the Malagasy species and *Abrahamia* was chosen to commemorate Jean Prosper Abraham (1936–1996), a well-known Malagasy forester with a remarkable knowledge of Malagasy woody plants. This new genus has been validly published (Randrianasolo et al. 2017) and 34 species recognized, 19 of which were newly described. *Abrahamia* is endemic to Madagascar (Figures 8.56d–f).

Micronychia

The revision of the genus *Micronychia* was also undertaken by Randrianasolo (1998, 2000). He recognized at that time four previously described species and one variety, described *M. acuminata*, and placed *M. humberti* as a synonym of *Rhus taratana*. Around a decade later, Randrianasolo and Lowry (2009) described four additional new species in this genus (*M. bemangidiensis*, *M. benono*, *M. kotozafyii*, and *M. striata*) and elevated *M. tsiramiramy* var. *minutiflora* to specific rank (*M. minutiflora*), increasing the number of species of *Micronychia* to 10. This genus is endemic to Madagascar (Figure 8.56g).

Operculicarya

When first described by Perrier de la Bâthie (1944), the genus comprised three species: *Operculicarya decaryi*, *O. hyphanoides*, and *O. monstruosa*. Eggli (1995) revised it and made some taxonomic changes, which included retaining the first two species, and accepting Capuron's (1962) decision of placing *O. monstruosa* in the genus *Commiphora* (Burseraceae). He also described three additional species in this genus: *O. borealis*, *O. hirsutissima*, and *O. pachypus*. Randrianasolo and Lowry (2006) reevaluated the taxonomy of this genus and described two more new species (*O. capuronii* and *O. multijuga*), and subsequently Randrianasolo and Lowry (2015) named an additional new species (*O. calcicola*), bringing the total number in the genus to nine. All species of *Operculicarya* are endemic to Madagascar except *O. gummifera*, which is also found on the Mascarene islands.

Spondias

The genus *Spondias* comprises 16 or more species distributed in the Americas and Asia (Pell et al. 2011). Many of these species were introduced to the African continent for their edible fruits. On Madagascar, it has been thought for a considerable period that this

FIGURE 8.56 **Different forms of Malagasy Anacardiaceae. *Spondias tefyi*: A) inflorescences, B) young fruits, and C) mature fruits; D) inflorescences of *Abrahamia elongata*; E) mature fruits of *A. ditimena*; F) mature fruits of *A. grandidieri*; G) *Micronychia macrophylla*; H) infructescences of *Faguetia falcata*; and I) fruits of *Poupartia orientalis*.** (PHOTOS by A. Randrianasolo.)

genus is only represented by the introduced species *S. dulcis*, a very well-known plant species due to its very delicious fruits; it known by a range of vernacular names such as ambarella or golden or June apple in English, and *zevi* or *sakoa* in Malagasy. However, recent exploration of the Analavelona Forest (Alandraza Analavelo) resulted in the discovery of a new and first native species, *S. tefyi* (Mitchell et al. 2012) (Figures 8.56a–c).

Campnosperma

This is a nonendemic genus also represented in South America and Asia, recognized by Perrier de la Bâthie (1946c) to have only one Malagasy species (*C. micranteium*). Randrianasolo and Miller (1998) revised this taxon and added an additional three species (*C. lepidotum*, *C. parvifolium*, and *C. schatzii*). Subsequently, Randrianasolo and Lowry (2004) described another new species (*C. zacharyi*), bringing the total species of this genus on Madagascar to five.

Further Taxonomic Notes

The actual total number of Anacardiaceae species on Madagascar will undoubtedly change in the future as several other genera besides those mentioned above are under study.

Faguetia (Figure 8.56h), *Poupartiopsis*, and *Baronia* are monotypic and endemic to Madagascar. *Sclerocarya* and *Gluta* are not endemic: *Sclerocarya* has two species in Africa, one of them shared with Madagascar; *Gluta* has about 30 species in Asia and one endemic Malagasy species. The ongoing revision of *Sorindeia*, *Poupartia*, and the remaining taxa included in the genus *Rhus* by Perrier de la Bâthie (1946c) will result in new taxa. The following are important taxonomic notes around the study of these three genera.

Sorindeia

This is an African genus described by Du Petit Thouars (1806), but it was A. P. de Candolle (1825) who described the first two species, *S. madagascariensis* and *S. africana*. Subsequently, more species were described, and continental sub-Saharan Africa is clearly the center of diversity for this genus. Estimates of the size of this genus vary from 15 to 40 species (Perrier de la Bâthie 1946c; Van der Veken 1960; Kokwaro 1986). However, Breteler's revision of the entire genus (2003) recognized eight species, and many previously described taxa were placed in synonymy. The eight species he distinguished are mostly restricted to the Africa mainland; the exception is *S. madagascariensis*, which occurs on Madagascar and the Comoro islands. In his treatment of Malagasy Anacardiaceae, Perrier de la Bâthie (1946c) recognized two species of *Sorindeia*: *S. madagascariensis* and *S. goudotii*. However, Breteler (1997) examined the type specimen of *S. goudotii* and found it to be identical to *S. madagascariensis*, and the latter became a synonym of the former. More recently, in the context of ongoing research Randrianasolo and Lowry examined herbarium specimens from Madagascar, and the preliminary results indicate that multiple species of *Sorindeia* should be recognized on Madagascar.

Poupartia

This is a genus endemic to Madagascar and the Mascarene islands. Perrier de la Bâthie (1946c) recognized five species on Madagascar, including *P. gummifera* and *P. caffra*. These two species, however, were transferred to *Operculicarya* and *Sclerocarya* by Capuron (1975) and Kokwaro (1986), respectively. Friedmann (1994), in the *Flore de Seychelles*, challenged Capuron's argument and maintained the genus *Poupartia* for *gummifera*, which was also the conclusion of Eggli (1995). Contrary to Friedman and Eggli's views, Randrianasolo and Lowry (2006) confirmed the placement of this species in *Operculicarya* rather than in *Poupartia*. In the case of *P. caffra*, on the basis of floral and fruit morphology, as well as its inflorescence structure, I suggest that this species belongs to the genus *Sclerocarya*. Currently, the genus *Poupartia* includes three of Perrier's species along with *P. orientalis* (Figure 8.56i), a more recently described species (Randrianasolo and Miller 1999a).

Rhus

Perrier de la Bâthie (1946) recognized four species for Madagascar. Along with *R. natalensis*, he established the *Rhus* section *Baronia*, in which he included *Baronia taratana*, *Protorhus thouarsii*, and *P. perrieri*. Recent phylogenetic studies based on molecular data (A. J. Miller et al. 2001; Pell et al. 2008) indicated that the *Rhus* complex (*sensu lato*) is polyphyletic; thus, some of its subgenera are segregated from the *Rhus sensu stricto*. To that effect, all African species previously within the genus *Rhus* are now included in *Searsia*, a segregated genus established by Barkley (1942) to include the Old World *Rhus* species. Thus, currently *R. natalensis* is now known as *S. natalensis* (Moffet 2007). As for the three species included in the *Rhus* section *Baronia*, according to Pell et al. (2008), they are morphologically distinct from the species of *Searsia* and *Rhus sensu stricto*. Furthermore, Pell et al. (2008) also indicated that the *Rhus* section *Baronia* is polyphyletic and formed two distinct lineages with *R. taratana* being a sister taxa to *Abrahamia* and the two other species sister to each other. This indicates that *Rhus* section *Baronia* should be dissolved, and both groups should be placed in separate genera. Pell et al. (2008) resurrected the genus *Baronia* to include the type species of the section, *R. taratana*; however, the two other species still remain assigned to *Rhus* until the establishment of a new genus.

ECOLOGY AND DISTRIBUTION

Members of the Anacardiaceae family are found across a great diversity of habitats on Madagascar, and the vegetative parts of both endemic and introduced members are consumed by a variety of lemur species (see Eppley et al., pp. 1839–59). Members of Anacardiaceae occur throughout the lowland moist evergreen forests, dry deciduous forests, dry spiny thickets, and sclerophyllous woodlands, as well as in some medium-altitude moist evergreen forests of the Central Highlands. However, despite this wide range of habitats, there are genera that have more specific habitat requirements. The most extreme are *Faguetia* and *Poupartiopsis*, two monotypic endemic genera that only occur in a narrow band of littoral forests resting on sand along the east coast. Another example is *Operculicarya*, which only occurs in dry deciduous forests, dry spiny thickets, and sclerophyllous woodlands (Eggli 1995). Four of the five species of *Operculicarya* (*O. decaryi*, *O. hirsutissima*, *O. hyphanoides*, and *O. pachypus*) are restricted to the southern portion of the island and grow on limestone outcrops or gneissic soils. One disjunct species, *O. borealis*, is limited to the dry deciduous forests on sand near Antsiranana. The genus *Gluta*, represented by one endemic species, *G. tourtour*, is only found in forests of the Sambirano Region. Similarly, the genus *Spondias* is represented on Madagascar by one native species, *S. tefyi*, found only in an isolated patch of subhumid forest on the Analavelona Massif in the southwest. Two other genera, *Campnosperma* and *Micronychia*, are restricted to the moist evergreen forests, from sea level up to 1500 m. Except *C. schatzii*, which reaches the moist evergreen forests of the northwest, all species of this genus occur mainly along the eastern slopes of the island. Contrarily, the genus *Sclerocarya*, represented on Madagascar by *S. birrea* subsp. *caffra*, occurs in a variety of habitats on the western slopes, from sandy to lateritic soils, and from sea level to 1000 m. This taxon is also found on the African mainland and it is very common to find it growing near villages on Madagascar because of its edible fruits (*sakoambanditse*). Finally, the remaining genera (*Abrahamia*, *Poupartia*, *Sorindeia*, and *Baronia*) are widely distributed and represented in almost all of Madagascar's major vegetation types.

CONSERVATION

With regard to the conservation of Malagasy Anacardiaceae, many of its species are threatened because their preferred natural habitats are increasingly degraded and reduced in size. The International

Union for the Conservation of Nature (IUCN) Red List (2020) published 18 threatened species of Malagasy Anacardiaceae; among these, two are Critically Endangered (*Operculicarya capuronii* and *Micronychia benono*), nine Endangered (*Abrahamia louvelii*, *A. oblongifolia*, *M. bemangindiensis*, *M. danguyana*, *O. borealis*, *O. multijuga*, *O. calcicola*, *O. hyphanoides*, and *O. pachypus*), and seven Vulnerable (*A. deflexa*, *A. humbertii*, *A. latifolia*, *A. lecomtei*, *Faguetia falcata*, *O. hirsutissima*, and *Spondias tefyi*). The number of threatened species of Malagasy Anacardiaceae will likely continue to increase in the future as long as deforestation does not cease to occur on the island. For example, as previously indicated, many species of Anacardiaceae are restricted to the moist evergreen forests, which are still subject to swidden agriculture. The situation of the monotypic genus *Poupartiopsis*, which is restricted to the eastern littoral forest, is alarming, and many sites *P. spondiocarpus* was known from have been deforested bringing this species to the brink of extinction. It may soon become so if its habitat continues to be destroyed. Similarly, populations of *Abrahamia ibityensis* and *A. buxifolia*, species locally endemic to the Central Highlands, have declined due to the continuation of burning for cattle grazing or other agricultural purposes. We believe these two taxa are in peril along with many other endemic plant species restricted to this region of Madagascar.

Subject editors: Laurent Gautier and Steven M. Goodman

SAPINDACEAE

S. Buerki, P. B. Phillipson, P. P. Lowry II, J. M. A. Wojahn, S. Andriambololonera, and M. W. Callmander

Phylogenetic analyses of the plant family Sapindaceae inferred from nuclear and plastid sequence data have revealed a high level of para- and polyphyly at the subfamilial, tribal, and generic levels (Harrington et al. 2005; Buerki et al. 2009). Family delimitation within the sapindaceous clade has been the subject of debate over the last decade (reviewed in Buerki et al. 2009) leading to the recent adoption of a narrowed circumscription of Sapindaceae based on molecular, biogeographic, temporal, and morphological evidence, and the reinstatement of the long-recognized families Aceraceae and Hippocastanaceae, as well as the description of a new family, Xanthoceraceae, to accommodate the Chinese and Korean species *Xanthoceras sorbifolium*, found to be sister to the remainder of Sapindaceae *sensu lato* (Buerki et al. 2010a). This reinstated circumscription of Sapindaceae, whose members are restricted to subtropical and tropical regions and include about 1900 species in 136 genera placed in two subfamilies (Dodonaeoideae and Sapindoideae), very closely resembles that proposed nearly eight decades ago by Radlkofer (1933) in his first treatment of the family. Within Sapindaceae, a new infra-familial classification was proposed, mainly based on molecular data, to accommodate the high level of para- and polyphyly of tribes, and to provide a framework for developing improved generic circumscriptions that meet the criterion of monophyly (Buerki et al. 2009, 2021) (Figure 8.57).

On Madagascar, Sapindaceae includes about 130 native species (119 of which are endemic, representing ~91.5%) in 24 genera (eight endemic; see Figure 8.58). Sapindaceae is the 18th-most species-rich family on Madagascar, and 38.2% of its species have been sequenced for at least one shared DNA region (see Wojahn et al., pp. 464–70). Malagasy members of the family are mostly shrubs or trees, with the exception of the single species of *Cardiospermum*, which is a vine, as is the naturalized *Paullinia pinnata*.

Capuron's treatment of the family (1969) contributed greatly to our taxonomic knowledge of Malagasy Sapindaceae, including the description of four new genera (*Beguea*, *Chouxia*, *Neotina*, and *Tsingya*) and 40 new species. Recent phylogenetic data have demonstrated, however, that the fruit morphology, used initially by Radlkofer and subsequently adopted by Capuron (1969) to assign genera into tribes, did not provide shared ancestral characters to support clades and that many of the groups previously recognized are not monophyletic. In this contribution, we review the current taxonomy of Malagasy Sapindaceae in light of phylogenetic evidence (mostly based on Buerki et al. 2009, 2010a, 2010b, 2011a, 2011b, 2014), which includes sampling from all but two genera, *Camptolepis* and *Zanha*. We also provide key diagnostic morphological characters for each genus (mainly based on Capuron 1969; Schatz 2001) and devote a section to the biogeography and conservation of the family on Madagascar.

OVERVIEW OF GENERA OCCURRING ON MADAGASCAR PRESENTED IN A PHYLOGENETIC FRAMEWORK

In Figure 8.57 we provide a summary of the phylogenetic positions within Sapindaceae. The genera found on the island belong to two subfamilies and nine tribes, as defined by Buerki et al. (2009, 2021). Below, we discuss each genus based on its subfamilial assignment and tribal placement. Finally, a list of morphological characters diagnostic of each genus belonging to phylogenetic groups is also provided.

Subfamily Dodonaeoideae

This subfamily is subdivided into two tribes (Doratoxyleae and Dodonaeae), both of which are represented on Madagascar (Figure 8.57). Members of Doratoxyleae are characterized by

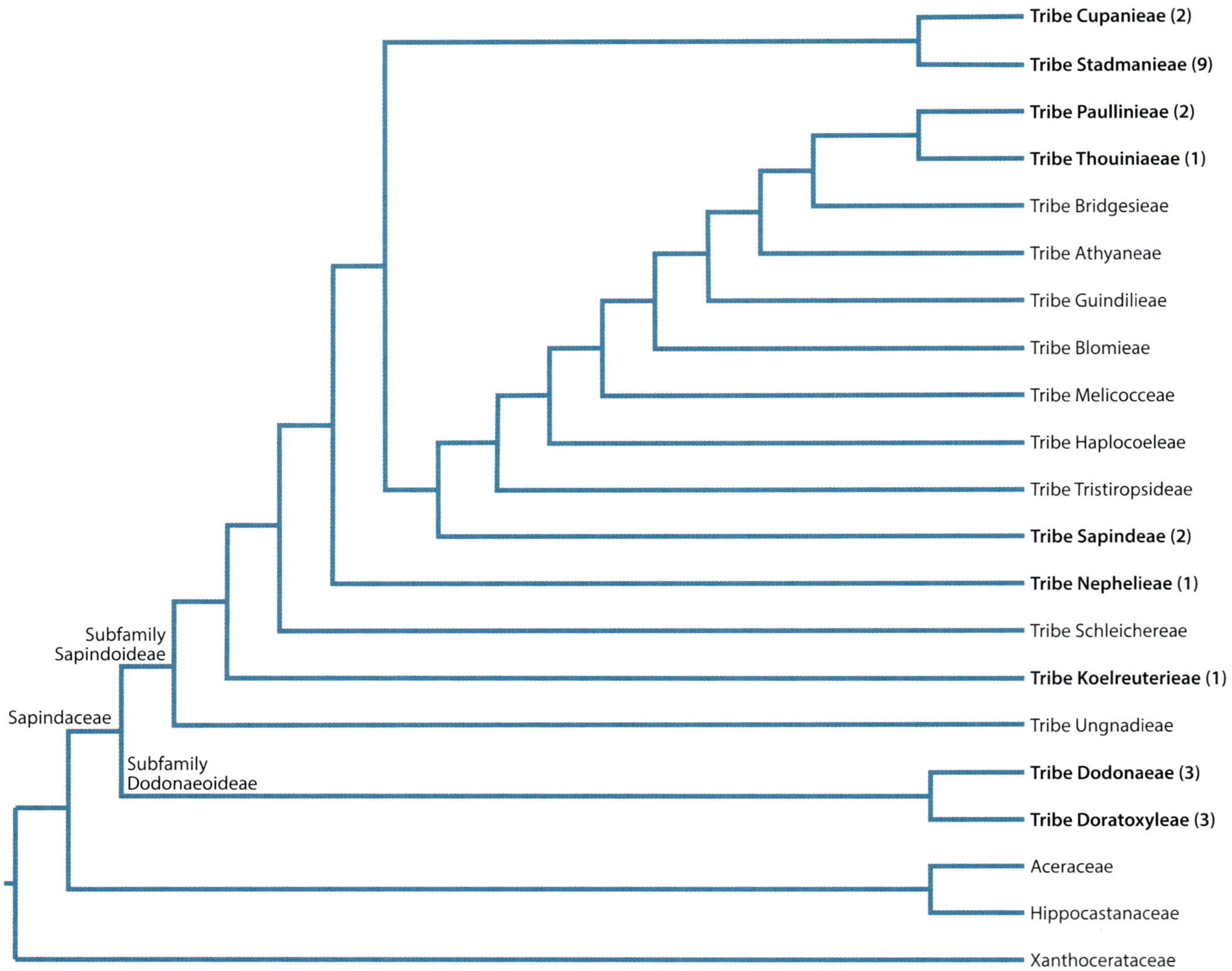

FIGURE 8.57 **Simplified infra-familial relationships within Sapindaceae and allied families based on nuclear Angiosperms353 target gene sequences (modified from Buerki et al. 2021). Tribes occurring on Madagascar are displayed in bold and numbers in the parentheses correspond to the number of genera occurring on the island.**

indehiscent berrylike fruits and occur from Africa and Madagascar to Australasia, whereas Dodonaeae, which are characterized by dry, dehiscent, winged fruits, occur primarily in South America, Madagascar, Australasia, and the Pacific islands (see below for more details on distributions). The only exception to this is a single species, *Dodonaea viscosa*, which has a worldwide distribution that includes Madagascar.

Tribe Doratoxyleae

Doratoxylon (with five species on Madagascar) and *Filicium* (three species on Madagascar) are sister lineages and they in turn are sister to a lineage comprising representatives of *Ganophyllum* (Buerki et al. 2009), a small genus of two species ranging from western and central Africa, to the Andaman and Nicobar Islands, northeastern Australia, the Solomon Islands, and Malesia.

Doratoxylon species range from dioecious shrubs to large trees. Species of this genus can be recognized by their paripinnately compound leaves with entire leaflets, small flowers borne on densely rusty-brown pedicels, pubescent sepals, and lack of petals. Moreover, they have large, fleshy, and indehiscent fruits and their seeds lack arillodes. *Filicium* are monoecious small to large trees. Species of this genus exhibit different types of leaf morphologies (e.g., simple in *F. longifolium* or paripinnately compound in *F. longifolium*); however, their inflorescences are always axillary panicles, and their flowers are small and regular, with five sepals, five petals, and five stamens. Their fruits are usually large, fleshy, indehiscent, and one-seeded.

The tropical African and Malagasy genus *Zanha* was recently retrieved as part of this tribe (Buerki et al. 2021). The only species occurring on Madagascar, *Z. suaveolens*, is endemic and occurs in dry deciduous forests and spiny thickets (Capuron 1969) from Morondava south to Toliara. Its indehiscent fruit morphology (despite the presence of a fleshy arillode covering the seed) is characteristic of Doratoxyleae. *Z. suaveolens* can be easily recognized by its trunk, which is distinctly constricted at the apex and has reddish to orange bark that exfoliates in plates. The bark contains saponins that are utilized as soap.

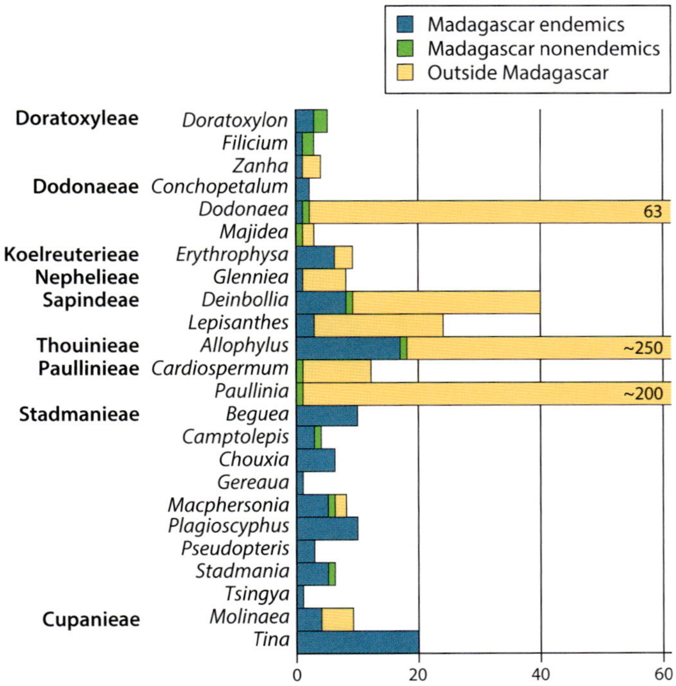

FIGURE 8.58 **Diversity and endemicity diagram of Malagasy Sapindaceae at the level of genera, showing three different species counts: 1) endemic to Madagascar, 2) nonendemic but native to Madagascar, and 3) those occurring elsewhere in the world (for further information see text). In cases when species diversity exceeds or does not conform to that presented on the horizontal graph scale, the figures are written along the respective horizontal line of a given genus.**

Tribe Dodonaeae

The genera *Conchopetalum*, *Dodonaea*, and *Majidea* are the members of this tribe that occur on Madagascar; 13 other genera occur elsewhere (see Buerki et al. 2021). *Majidea*, *Conchopetalum*, and the monotypic southeast Asian genus *Arfeuillea* form a lineage sister to the rest of the clade (Buerki et al. 2021). *Majidea* is represented by one species on Madagascar, *M. zanguebarica*, which also occurs in Africa. Additional taxonomic work is, however, required to assess the systematics of this species on Madagascar. *Dodonaea* is sister to the endemic Australian genus *Diplopeltis* (Buerki et al. 2009). On Madagascar, *Dodonaea* has two species, the endemic *D. madagascariensis* and the widespread *D. viscosa*. The former is found in medium-altitude moist evergreen forests above 1500 m, whereas the latter occurs in the same forest type, but has a considerably wider range, extending from sea level to higher elevations, as well as in dry deciduous forests in the north and the west. *Dodonaea* species are dioecious shrubs to small trees, with all parts bearing circular, sessile glands rendering them sticky and viscous. Species of this genus exhibit different types of leaf morphology (e.g., simple in *D. viscosa* or paripinnately compound in *D. madagascariensis*); however, their inflorescences are always terminal pyramidal panicles, and their flowers are small, regular, with four to seven (occasionally three) sepals, no petals, and five to 14 stamens. Finally, fruits of these species are usually large, dry, winged capsules. *Majidea zanguebarica* is a dioecious tree that can easily be recognized by its fasciculate-stellate pubescence; terminal, distinctly bracteate, paniculate inflorescences bearing small irregular flowers with four petals shorter than the sepals; and trivalved capsular fruits with finely pubescent seeds. Members of *Conchopetalum* are monoecious large shrubs to small trees. Species of this genus can be recognized by their condensed cauliflorous or axillary inflorescences with relatively large, bright flowers and large, slightly inflated capsular fruits.

Subfamily Sapindoideae

This subfamily is by far the most diverse lineage within the Sapindaceae in terms of genera and species. Recent phylogenetic studies have led to the recognition of 16 tribes within the Sapindoideae (Figure 8.57). The members of this subfamily that occur on Madagascar belong to seven of these tribes, although most are placed in the Stadmanieae tribe.

Tribe Koelreuterieae

Erythrophysa (six endemic species) is the only genus in this tribe (comprising three genera) that has members on Madagascar. It is worth noting that this group has a disjunct distribution between Africa and the Malagasy Region (*Erythrophysa*), southern China and Japan (*Koelreuteria)*, and eastern Iran and Afghanistan (*Stocksia*).

Erythrophysa species are monoecious small to medium trees. Species of this genus can be recognized by their imparipinnately or impari-bipinnately compound leaves with opposite leaflets, terminal, pyramidal panicles, and relatively large, irregular flowers with clawed petals. *Stadmania* species are dioecious or rarely monoecious medium to large trees. They can be recognized by their paripinnately compound leaves with often dentate leaflets, densely pubescent fruits, and seeds that are each surrounded by a fleshy, translucid arillode.

Tribe Nephelieae

Glenniea (one endemic species) is the only genus in this tribe (comprising a total of 16 genera) that occurs on Madagascar. *Glenniea pervillei* was originally described in the genus *Crossonephelis*, and this was accepted by Capuron (1969), but Leenhouts (1975) transferred it to *Glenniea*, a predominantly Malesian genus. Unpublished molecular data that we have recently generated, including sequences from other Malesia members of *Glenniea*, indicate that the Malagasy taxon, *G. pervillei*, belongs to this latter genus, thus confirming Leenhouts's interpretation.

Glenniea are dioecious trees. The only Malagasy species, *G. pervillei*, can be recognized by its paripinnately compound leaves with two to three pairs of subopposite leaflets, terminal inflorescences with small tetramerous flowers lacking petals, and large, fleshy, indehiscent, bilobed, and laterally compressed fruits.

Tribe Sapindeae

Only two genera belonging to this tribe (out of 13 genera) occur on Madagascar: *Deinbollia* (nine species, eight endemic) and *Lepisanthes* (three endemic species). *Deinbollia* is restricted to Africa and Madagascar, whereas *Lepisanthes* is largely distributed across Africa, Madagascar, Malesia, and Australia.

Deinbollia comprises dioecious shrubs that are usually slender and monopodial (unbranched) with a palmiform habit, or sometimes lianas (but not on Madagascar). Species of this genus can be easily recognized by their large, fleshy, globose, and nearly separate mericarps in clusters of up to five. Species of *Lepisanthes* are monoecious small to medium trees. Species of this genus can be recognized by their paripinnately compound leaves with one to three pairs of subopposite leaflets, terminal paniculate inflorescences with small flowers (with petals), and fruit that generally only develop one carpel.

Tribe Stadmanieae

Nine out of 10 genera of this tribe occur on Madagascar (the exception is the African monospecific genus *Pappea*). Stadmanieae members are restricted to the island, the Mascarenes, and Africa, including seven of Madagascar's eight endemic genera in this tribe. This tribe corresponds to the Macphersonia group of Buerki et al. (2009, 2010a, 2014), and excludes *Conchopetalum*, which had been unexpectedly retrieved within the Macphersonia group but is now proved to be part of the Dodonaeae, but includes the African-Malagasy genera *Camptolepis* (four species, three endemic) and *Stadmania* (six species, five endemic) (Buerki et al. 2021). Buerki et al. (2014) showed that the Macphersonia group comprises two clades (A and B). The expanded sampling of Buerki et al. (2014) included material from the newly rediscovered monotypic genus *Tsingya* and of a species of *Chouxia*, which had not been available for previous analyses. *Tsingya* was only known by its type collection from the Bemaraha Massif (Capuron 1969) until it was rediscovered by R. Mitia Hanitrarivo more than 60 years later in the dry deciduous forest of Beanka, just to the north of Bemaraha (Buerki et al. 2014). Molecular analyses placed *T. bemarana* in clade A, closely related to the South African *Pappea capensis* (Buerki et al. 2014) and also related to the endemic Malagasy genus *Plagioscyphus*, to which *Stadmania*, occurring on Madagascar and the Mascarenes, and in Africa (Buerki et al. 2021), was also added. Capuron (1969) hypothesized that *Tsingya* was closely related to *Beguea* based on the absence of a corolla, but our results showed that *Beguea* belongs to clade B. Moreover, the seed morphology of *Tsingya* is very similar to that of *Plagioscyphus*, which further supports the maintenance of *Tsingya* as a distinct genus, differing from *Plagioscyphus* based on fruit indumentum (stellate trichomes in *Tsingya* versus simple in *Plagioscyphus*) and the absence of a corolla (versus present in *Plagioscyphus*). *Stadmania* species are dioecious or rarely monoecious medium to large trees. They can be recognized by their paripinnately compound leaves with often dentate leaflets, densely pubescent fruits, and seeds that are each surrounded by a fleshy, translucid arillode.

Clade B of the Macphersonia group includes members of the endemic genera *Pseudopteris* (three species), *Gereaua* (one species), *Chouxia* (six species; see Schatz et al. 1999a for a taxonomic revision), and *Beguea* (10 species; see Schatz et al. 2017 for a taxonomic revision), as well as the African-Malagasy genus *Macphersonia* (six species on Madagascar, five endemic). *Gereaua* was recently described to accommodate part of the polyphyletic genus *Haplocoelum* (Buerki et al. 2010b). The latter genus is now part of the tribe Haplocoeleae (Figure 8.57). *Gereaua* is easily morphologically distinguished from *Haplocoelum* by the following characters: 1) sexually dimorphic inflorescences in racemules (versus monomorphic inflorescences in fascicules of cymes); 2) a bilocular (versus trilocular) ovary; 3) rudimentary pistillode in staminate flowers (versus no pistillode); 4) corolla with four or five petals (versus apetalous); and 5) pubescent (versus glabrous) fruit (Buerki et al. 2010b). A full list of morphological characters distinguishing the genera in clade B can be found in Buerki et al. (2010b). It is worth mentioning that the genera *Macphersonia* and *Plagioscyphus* are in need of a careful taxonomic revision.

Beguea species are large dioecious trees. Species of this genus can be recognized by their long, slender, tight, racemose inflorescences, with small flowers lacking petals. *Chouxia* species are dioecious treelets. They can be identified by their slender, sparsely branched habit, leaves nearly always with pseudostipules, and cauliflorous inflorescences. The only species of *Gereaua*, *G. perrieri*, is a dioecious tree. It can be recognized by its paripinnately compound leaves; distal leaflets that are bract-like or form pseudostipules; axillary, racemose inflorescences bearing small flowers (with petals); and large fruits with seeds each surrounded by a translucid arillode.

Macphersonia species are dioecious or rarely monecious small to medium trees. Species of the genus can be recognized by their biparipinnately compound leaves (with the exception of *M. chapelieri*, which has paripinnnate leaves), and small, pentamerous, pink to purple flowers. Fruits in the genus are usually large, fleshy, and indehiscent, with a fleshy, translucid arillode surrounding each seed. Species of *Plagioscyphus* are dioecious or monoecious treelets to large trees. They can be identified by their leaflets, which often have serrate-dentate to serrate-spinose margins and densely reticulate tertiary venation. Fruits in the genus are large, fleshy, and one- to three-seeded indehiscent berries; each seed is surrounded by a translucid arillode, which is edible and sought after by lemurs (Schatz 2001). The single *Tsingya* species, *T. bemarana*, is a monoecious large tree with platanoid bark (i.e., exfoliating in plates). It can be recognized by the dense fascicled-stellate pubescence its young branches are covered with; paripinnately compound leaves with two to five pairs of opposite to alternate leaflets; axillary, racemose inflorescences bearing small flowers lacking petals; and large, fleshy fruits with each seed surrounded by a translucid arillode.

Camptolepis has now been sequenced (Buerki et al. 2021) and its phylogenetic position was confirmed within the tribe Stadmanieae. Capuron (1969) had already hypothesized that this genus was related to *Haplocoelum perrieri* (now *Gereaua perrieri*), and this recent study confirmed the relationship (Buerki et al. 2021). *Camptolepis* are dioecious trees with paripinnately compound leaves characterized by a rudimentary distal leaflet. Species have racemose inflorescences in short thyrses with actinomorphic flowers (five sepals and five petals). The fruits are indehiscent and seeds are completely covered by a translucent arrillode.

Tribe Cupanieae

This tribe (comprising a total of 36 genera with two occurring on Madagascar) has a wide distribution, with taxa also occurring in Africa, Australasia, Asia, and South America (Buerki et al. 2021). Phylogenetic analyses have revealed that the Malagasy members of the Cupania group are sister to the South American genera *Cupania*, *Matayba*, *Pentascyphus*, and *Vouarana* (Buerki et al. 2009). Generic circumscriptions within Malagasy members of this tribe (which includes species previously assigned to *Molinaea*, *Neotina*, *Tina*, and *Tinopsis*) have been problematic. Phylogenetic analyses supported the monophyly of the group and its subdivision into three clades (Buerki et al. 2011b). All species of *Molinaea* belong to a clade that is sister to a second clade comprising *Neotina*, *Tina*, and *Tinopsis*, within which one subclade encompasses *Tinopsis* and *Neotina* (the latter nested within the former), and another comprises all taxa of *Tina*. Members of the second clade can be easily distinguished from *Molinaea* by having two rather than three carpels, which represents an unambiguous shared ancestral character. Given the paraphyly of *Tinopsis* with regard to *Neotina*, and the strong support for the monophyly of *Tina*, two potentially viable options were available for the generic delimitation of the taxa in this clade: 1) to recognize two genera (*Tina* and *Tinopsis*), or 2) to place all of the species in a single genus, in which case the name *Tina* would have priority. Based on morphological evidence, the second option was favored and consequently a broad generic concept was applied in which species of *Neotina* and *Tinopsis* were transferred to *Tina* (Callmander et al. 2011b). Although we have resolved generic delimitations within this group, a taxonomic revision of species of *Tina* is still needed.

Molinaea species are monoecious shrubs to medium-size trees. They are distinguished from other members of the Cupanieae on Madagascar by their ovaries, which have three carpels (versus two in *Tina*). The fruit in this genus is a dehiscent, winged capsule, and each seed is surrounded at the base by a solid, waxy, yellow to red arillode. *Tina* comprises dioecious or monoecious trees. Species of this genus are characterized by fruits that can be dehiscent or indehiscent (but they usually split into two erect valves at maturity), and the seeds are surrounded by an arillode, which can be solid, as in *Molinaea*, or fleshy and usually translucid, as in *Macphersonia*.

Tribe Thouinieae

A single genus of this tribe (comprising a total of three genera) occurs on Madagascar: *Allophylus* (with about 18 currently recognized species, all but one being endemic to the island; Figure 8.58) (Buerki et al. 2021). This circumtropical genus is one of the most species-rich genera of Sapindaceae, with ~270 species (Buerki et al. 2009). A genus-wide phylogenetic study should include Malagasy material of this very challenging genus, which includes many problems of species delimitation.

Allophylus species are monoecious shrubs to medium-size trees. They can be easily recognized by their trifoliate or less often unifoliate leaves; simple, axillary racemes (sometimes cymes); small, zygomorphic, tetramerous flowers; and small, fleshy fruits.

Tribe Paullinieae

The center of diversity of this tribe (comprising a total of six genera) is in South America. Paullinieae is represented on the island by a single native species of vine, *Cardiospermum halicacabum* (which also occurs in Africa and the Americas), in addition to the widely naturalized introduced vine *Paullinia pinnata*.

Cardiospermum are monoecious, herbaceous vines. The only species of this genus on Madagascar can be recognized by its ternately compound leaves with minute stipules and axillary inflorescences forming thyrses that bear tendrils at base of the rachis. Flowers of this genus are zygomorphic, tetramerous, and small; the fruits are inflated capsules with black seeds with a small, heart-shaped, whitish hilum surrounding the micropyle. *Paullinia* species are woody vines, usually producing milky sap. Leaves of the only species on the island are alternate, pinnate with five leaflets, and with minute to large stipules. Inflorescences in the genus are axillary thyrses with a pair of tendrils at the base of rachis. The flowers are small, zygomorphic, and tetramerous or pentamerous (with a basally adnate hood-shaped appendage on each petal), and the fruits are capsules with globose seeds, each covered by a partial to nearly complete sarcotesta.

BIOGEOGRAPHY AND CONSERVATION OF MALAGASY SAPINDACEAE

The distribution of Malagasy Sapindaceae is largely skewed toward humid ecosystems (Figure 8.59), mostly at low elevation, as shown by an analysis of 2479 Sapindaceae collections (underpinned by vouchers) (GBIF 2020), which indicated that species occur most often in the humid and subhumid bioclimatic zones, whereas the dry and subarid bioclimatic zones have lower species diversity (Figure 8.59, Table 8.36). Species richness is highest in

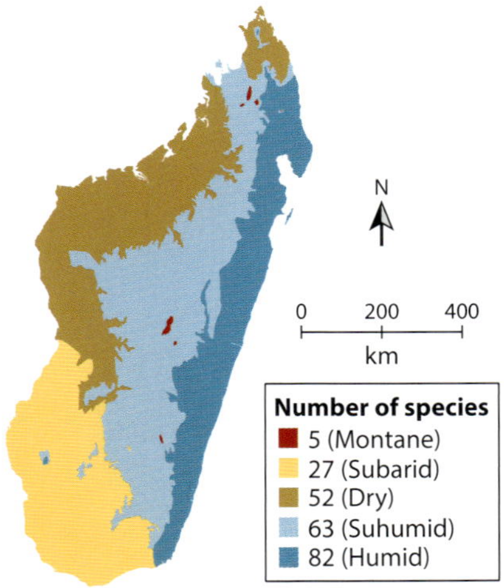

FIGURE 8.59 **Map of the five simplified bioclimatic zones proposed by Schatz (2000): Southwest, subarid; west and extreme north, dry; centre, subhumid; east, humid. Sapindaceae species richness is colored according to the bioclimatic zones.**

TABLE 8.36. **Number of Sapindaceae species known to occur in each of the five Malagasy bioclimatic zones as defined by Schatz (2000)**

BIOCLIMATIC ZONE	NUMBER OF SPECIES
HUM	82
SBH	63
DRY	52
SBA	27
MON	5

Note: Bioclimatic zone: DRY, dry; HUM, humid; MON, Montane; SBA, subarid; SBH, subhumid.

TABLE 8.37. **The distribution of Sapindaceae genera on Madagascar in relation to bioclimatic zones**

GENUS	BIOCLIMATIC ZONE(S)	SPANNING MULTIPLE BIOCLIMATIC ZONES?	TYPE OF BIOME(S)
Allophylus	HUM, SBH, MON, DRY, SBA	Yes	Mixed
Beguea	HUM, SBH	Yes	Wet
Camptolepis	HUM, SBH, DRY, SBA	Yes	Mixed
Cardiospermum	HUM, SBH, DRY, SBA	Yes	Mixed
Chouxia	HUM, SBH, DRY	Yes	Mixed
Conchopetalum	HUM, SBH	Yes	Wet
Deinbollia	HUM, SBH, DRY, SBA	Yes	Mixed
Dodonaea	HUM, SBH, MON, DRY, SBA	Yes	Mixed
Doratoxylon	HUM, SBH, DRY, SBA	Yes	Mixed
Erythrophysa	HUM, DRY, SBA	Yes	Mixed
Filicium	HUM, SBH, DRY, SBA	Yes	Mixed
Gereaua	HUM, SBH, DRY	Yes	Mixed
Glenniea	HUM, SBH, DRY	Yes	Mixed
Lepisanthes	SBH, DRY	Yes	Mixed
Macphersonia	HUM, SBH, DRY, SBA	Yes	Mixed
Majidea	HUM, SBH, DRY, SBA	Yes	Mixed
Molinaea	HUM, SBH, DRY	Yes	Mixed
Paullinia	HUM, SBH, DRY	Yes	Mixed
Plagioscyphus	HUM, SBH, DRY	Yes	Mixed
Pseudopteris	HUM, SBH, DRY	Yes	Mixed
Stadmania	HUM, SBH, DRY, SBA	Yes	Mixed
Tina	HUM, SBH, MON, DRY, SBA	Yes	Mixed
Tsingya	DRY	No	Dry
Zanha	DRY	No	Dry

Note: Bioclimatic zone: DRY, dry; HUM, humid; MON, Montane; SBA, subarid; SBH, subhumid.

the lowland moist evergreen forests on the Masoala Peninsula and at the junction of the humid, subhumid, and subarid bioclimatic zones in the Tolagnaro area, which is a sort of phytogeographic crossroads. Although the center of diversity of Sapindaceae is concentrated in the humid bioclimatic zone, most genera span across two or more bioclimatic zones (91.3%, Table 8.37). Of those that straddle two or more bioclimatic zones, the vast majority (90.5%) occur in bioclimatic zones that are both wet and dry (including subarid), with the rest restricted only to the wet bioclimatic zone. Only two genera, *Tsingya* and *Zanha*, are restricted to a single (dry) bioclimatic zone.

When species presence in the network of protected areas is taken into consideration, it becomes clear that not all Malagasy Sapindaceae members are fully protected. An inspection of published International Union for the Conservation of Nature (IUCN) Red List assessments for Sapindaceae species on Madagascar shows that only 28 (representing 12 genera) have been assessed, all but seven (25%) of which are threatened (IUCN 2020). Risk of extinction assessments are needed for the remaining 102 species, starting with those belonging to the eight endemic genera.

Subject editors: Laurent Gautier and Steven M. Goodman

RUTACEAE

M. Rabarimanarivo, P. P. Lowry II, P. B. Phillipson, and N. Rakotonirina

Worldwide, the family Rutaceae has an estimated 2085 species in 161 genera (Angiosperm Phylogeny Website 2019). Members of the family are mainly shrubs or trees, rarely herbs or lianas, and are sometimes prickly. They are characterized by the presence of secretory cavities, particularly in the leaves and reproductive structures, sieve tubes with S-type plastids, estipulate leaves, and a superior ovary (Chase et al. 1999; Groppo et al. 2008). They are distributed mainly in tropical and subtropical regions of both the New World and the Old World, with a few genera in temperate zones (Appelhans et al. 2012). Most Rutaceae members are aromatic and the family is of considerable interest to phytochemists for the wide range of chemical compounds found among its members, including alkaloids, flavonoids, limonoids, coumarins, and volatile oils (Mziray 1992; Groppo et al. 2008). Economically, the family is important, with different species of the genus *Citrus* being widely grown for their fruit, including oranges (*C.* × *sinensis*) and lemons (*C.* × *limon*) among others. Some Rutaceae species are also important as commonly grown ornamentals (e.g., *Skimmia* sp., *Choisya* sp.).

Classification of the Malagasy Rutaceae was revised by Perrier de la Bâthie (1948), who subsequently treated the family for the *Flore de Madagascar et des Comores* (Perrier de la Bâthie 1950). In these works, a total of 43 species were recognized, all but one endemic to Madagascar, within six genera: *Diphasia*, *Euodia* (as *Evodia*), *Teclea*, *Toddalia*, *Vepris*, and *Zanthoxylum*. A decade later, Capuron (1961) described two endemic species of *Fagaropsis*, one endemic species of *Chloroxylon*, and the endemic genus *Ivodea*, with six species and one variety. In 1967, Capuron described an additional new endemic species of *Chloroxylon*, one new species of *Euodia*, and four new species and one more variety of *Ivodea*. The latter genus was regarded as endemic to Madagascar until the discovery of a new species, *I. choungiensis*, from the Comoro islands (Labat et al. 2005). Hartley (2001) transferred all species of *Euodia*, including the Malagasy ones, to *Melicope*. The genus *Cedrelopsis*, which was included in Ptaeroxylaceae by Leroy and Lescot (1991), was later transferred to Rutaceae by Razafimandimbison et al. (2010a) based on a phylogenetic study. *Cedrelopsis* comprises eight species, all of which are endemic to Madagascar. A revision of *Ivodea* was published recently (Rabarimanarivo et al. 2015), which added 15 new species for Madagascar and two more for the Comoro islands. More recently, a study by Appelhans et al. (2018a) has shown that *Toddalia*, with a single species on Madagascar, is nested within *Zanthoxylum*, and has accordingly been placed in synonymy.

DISTRIBUTION, DIVERSITY, AND ENDEMISM

On Madagascar, Rutaceae is currently represented by seven native genera, with *Cedrelopsis* being the only one that is strictly endemic, while *Ivodea* is shared between Madagascar and the Comoro islands. The other genera present on Madagascar, *Chloroxylon*, *Fagaropsis*, *Melicope*, *Vepris*, and *Zanthoxylum*, are more widely distributed but are concentrated mainly in the Old World tropics. Two other genera occurring in Madagascar, *Citrus* and *Clausena*, are introduced and represented by naturalized as well as cultivated species.

Malagasy Rutaceae comprise a total of 84 published, accepted native species. Nearly all of them (93%) are endemic to the island (Figure 8.60), except for six species, five of which occur in both Madagascar and the Comoro islands, *V. boiviniana*, *V. parvicalyx*, *V. spathulata*, *V. unifoliolata*, and *I. choungiensis*, and one species that is also widespread in Africa and Asia, *Z. asiaticum* (formerly treated as *Toddalia asiatica*) (Madagascar Catalogue 2020).

RECENT DEVELOPMENTS IN THE SYSTEMATICS OF RUTACEAE

A recent comprehensive taxonomic reassessment of all native members of Rutaceae was undertaken for the Catalogue of the Plants of Madagascar project (Phillipson et al. 2006). A review based on morphological features, some of which can be viewed in Figure 8.61) showed the need for significant taxonomic changes regarding the number and delimitation of species in at least the larger genera on the island (Madagascar Catalogue 2020). This process led directly to the revision of *Ivodea* (Rabarimanarivo et al. 2015) and to ongoing work being undertaken on the genera *Melicope*, *Vepris*, and *Zanthoxylum*. The need for taxonomic revision of these genera is mainly a consequence of the significant enrichment of botanical

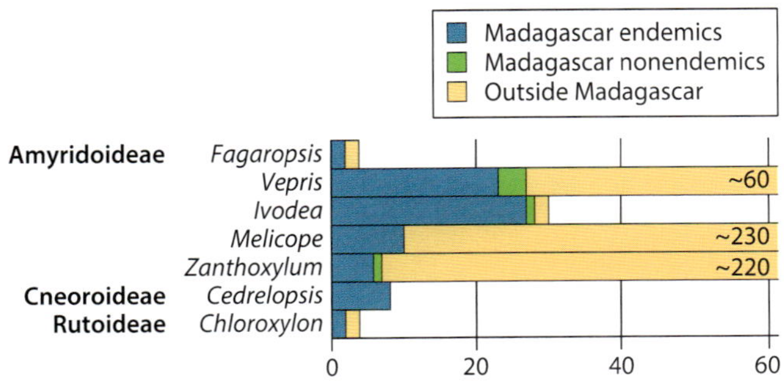

FIGURE 8.60 **Diversity and endemicity diagram of Malagasy Rutaceae at the level of genera, showing three different species counts: 1) endemic to Madagascar, 2) nonendemic but native to Madagascar, and 3) those occurring elsewhere in the world (for further information see text. In cases when species diversity exceeds or does not conform to that presented on the horizontal graph scale, the figures are written along the respective horizontal line of a given genus.**

FIGURE 8.61 **Examples of Rutaceae on Madagascar. A) *Cedrelopsis microfoliolata* at Imonty, Tolagnaro (Ratovoson 1531); B) *Ivodea razakamalalae* at Tsitongambarika (Rakotovao 4922); C) *Melicope* sp. nov. at Ankarongameloka, Andapa (Rakotovao et al. 2956); D) *M. madagascariensis* at Antongona, Imerintsiatosika (Rabarimanarivo and Porembski 969); E) *Vepris macrophylla* at Corridor Forestier Analamay-Mantadia (Rakotovao 5833); F) *Zanthoxylum asiaticum* at Analavelona (Rakotoarivelo et al. 410); G) *Z. madagascariense* at Vohimena (Rakotoarivelo et al. 766); and H) *Z. decaryi* at Ranobe PK32 (Ranaivojaona and Phillipson 1396).** (PHOTO A by F. Ratovoson; B by P. Lowry; C and E by C. Rakotovao; D by S. Porembski; F by R. L. Andriamiarisoa; G by A. Razanatsima; and H by P. B. Phillipson.)

collections available since Perrier de la Bâthie's publication of the family treatment in 1950, as well as changes in the species concept used for plants. Based on this work, approximately 120 native species of Rutaceae are currently recognized for Madagascar across the seven native genera, including 36 new to science and as yet undescribed (Table 8.38), 114 of which are endemic to Madagascar. This represents a net increase of over 170% in the number of recognized species since Perrier de la Bâthie's Rutaceae treatment was published. In Table 8.38 we provide a summary of each genus recognized today, including the number of currently accepted published species, the estimated number of undescribed species, and estimated totals.

THE NATIVE GENERA OF RUTACEAE ON MADAGASCAR

Cedrelopsis

Previously included in Ptaeroxylaceae in the *Flore de Madagascar et des Comores* (Leroy and Lescot 1991), this genus is the only one in Rutaceae that is strictly endemic to Madagascar; it comprises eight species distributed mainly in the dry to subarid and subhumid bioclimatic zones at low and mid-elevations (0–499 m, 500–999 m), rarely at high elevations or in areas with a humid bioclimate. It is absent from the Central Highlands (Schatz 2001). This genus of

TABLE 8.38. **Distribution, diversity, and endemism of Malagasy native genera of Rutaceae**

SUBFAMILY (*SENSU* C. M. MORTON AND TELMER 2014)	TRIBE (*SENSU* ENGLER 1931)	GENUS	GENUS DISTRIBUTION	SPECIES DISTRIBUTION BY BIOCLIMATIC ZONES	SPECIES GLOBALLY	SPECIES MADAGASCAR	MADAGASCAR ENDEMICS	MADAGASCAR ENDEMICS UNPUBLISHED	MADAGASCAR NONENDEMICS	OUTSIDE MADAGASCAR
Amyridoideae	Toddalieae	*Fagaropsis*	Africa, Madagascar	DRY, SBA	4	2	2	1	0	2
		Vepris	Tropical Africa, Madagascar, southwest India	SBH, HUM, SBA, DRY, MON	86	27	23	8	4	59
	Zanthoxyleae	*Ivodea*	Malagasy Region endemic (including the Comoros)	HUM, DRY, SBA, SBH	30	28	27	0	1	2
		Melicope	Madagascar, Comoros, Mascarenes, Tropical Asia-Pacific	HUM, SBH, MON	240	10	10	17	0	230
		Zanthoxylum	Pantropical	SBH, HUM, SBA, DRY, MON	225	7	6	10	1	218
Cneoroideae	Spathelieae	*Cedrelopsis*	Endemic	DRY, SBH, SBA, HUM	8	8	8	0	0	0
Rutoideae	Flindersieae	*Chloroxylon*	Madagascar, south India, Sri Lanka	DRY, HUM, SBA	4	2	2	0	0	2
Totals					**597**	**84**	**78**	**36**	**6**	**513**

Note: Simplified bioclimatic zones (Schatz 2000; after Cornet 1974) from the highest to the lowest number of species occurrence: Humid, HUM; Subhumid, SBH; Montane, MON; Dry, DRY; and Subarid, SBA.

unarmed shrubs and trees can be recognized by its paripinnately compound leaves that are usually alternate, axillary inflorescences, and dehiscent fruits (capsules).

Chloroxylon

This genus comprises just four species, two from India and two endemic to Madagascar. The latter have restricted distributions at low elevations (0–500 m), one in the west (dry and subhumid bioclimatic zones) and the other in the northeast (humid bioclimate). Species in this genus are unarmed trees distinguished by their alternate, paripinnately compound leaves, terminal inflorescences, and dehiscent fruits (capsules). This is the only monoecious genus among the native Malagasy Rutaceae (all others are dioecious or polygamo-dioecious).

Fagaropsis

There are two endemic species of *Fagaropsis* on Madagascar and one additional unpublished new species, as well as two other species in Africa. Members of this genus occur only at low elevations (0–499 m) and are restricted to the dry and subarid bioclimatic zones. They are deciduous, unarmed shrubs or trees distinguished by opposite, imparipinnately compound leaves, terminal inflorescences, and indehiscent fruits (drupes).

Ivodea

This is a regionally endemic genus (present also on the Comoros), which is represented on Madagascar by 28 species, all but one of which are endemic, the only exception, *I. choungiensis*, being shared with the Comoros (where two other species are endemic). Members of the genus are present in all of Madagascar's bioclimates and elevational ranges except the montane bioclimatic zone at high elevation (over 2000 m). Nearly all species have restricted distributions (Rabarimanarivo et al. 2015). They are shrubs, easily recognized by their unifoliolate or simple, alternate to subopposite leaves and the fruits are dehiscent follicles that are usually striated longitudinally.

Melicope

This is a large, widely distributed genus that occurs across the tropical and southern zones of the Pacific basin, including southeast Asia, the Hawaiian islands, Australia, and New Zealand (Harbaugh et al. 2009), as well as on Madagascar. Malagasy species belonging to the genus were treated under the name *Euodia* by Perrier de la Bâthie (1950). It comprises 10 published endemic species with an estimated 17 additional unpublished species. *Melicope* appears to be absent from Madagascar's dry and subarid bioclimates. Members of the genus occur in all elevational ranges, from sea level to over 2000 m. They are unarmed shrubs or trees with usually flattened branches and swollen nodes. *Melicope* is easily recognized by its opposite, decussate, usually uni- to trifoliolate or rarely simple leaves, and dehiscent fruits (follicles).

Vepris

Mainly present in tropical Africa, this is the largest genus of Rutaceae on Madagascar, where it comprises 27 accepted published native species, 23 of which are endemic. The remaining four also occur on the Comoro islands. In addition, there are eight potential undescribed new species on the island. Members of the genus are unarmed shrubs or trees and occur in a wide range of habitats and in humid and subarid bioclimates, but rarely in the montane bioclimatic zone at elevations over 2000 m (*V. dicarpella* only). *Vepris* is particularly speciose in humid and subhumid bioclimates and at elevations below 1000 m. Members of the genus are easily recognized by their usually alternate leaves and indehiscent fruits (drupes).

Zanthoxylum

This largely pantropical genus is represented on Madagascar by seven published species, of which six are endemic, along with 10 additional, potentially new, undescribed species. The genus is represented in all bioclimatic zones and elevation ranges, although it is rare at montane sites over 2000 m elevation (where it is represented by *Z. asiaticum* and *Z. madagascariense*). Most species have a conspicuous armament of sharp prickles on the stems and leaves, whereas no other genus of Rutaceae on Madagascar includes species that are armed. The stout prickles of the main stem and branches persist and become enlarged and suberized and can be a conspicuous feature of the trunk of large trees. The genus includes mainly trees and shrubs, rarely scrambling shrubs or lianas (*Z. asiaticum*), that are usually dioecious. Species of this genus are distinguished by their alternate, imparipinnately compound leaves, rarely uni- to trifoliolate (*Z. asiaticum*), that are mostly grouped at the apex of the branches, and their axillary or upper axillary inflorescences. The dehiscent, but somewhat fleshy or woody, single-seeded capsules are also quite distinctive.

DIVERSITY, ENDEMISM, AND DISTRIBUTION OF MALAGASY RUTACEAE

In Table 8.38 we indicate the distribution, diversity, and endemism of Malagasy native genera of Rutaceae, while in Table 8.39 we summarize their distinctive characteristics and provide some vernacular names. *Vepris* is the largest genus, with an estimated 35 species, followed by *Ivodea* (28 species), *Melicope* (27 species), and *Zanthoxylum* (17 species). These genera are represented in all five of Madagascar's bioclimatic simplified zones (Schatz 2000, based on Cornet 1974) and in elevational ranges from sea level to over 2000 m. Among the 84 published species, most (45) occur in the humid bioclimatic zone and 61 (73%) are found between sea level and 500 m elevation. Members of Rutaceae are rare in the montane bioclimatic zone, where four species are known, *M. tsaratananenis*, *V. dicarpella*, *Z. madagascariense*, and the widespread *Z. asiaticum*. *Fagaropsis* is restricted to dry and subarid bioclimates, and many species of *Cedrelopsis* are found there as well, though *Melicope* is not. *Chloroxylon* is restricted to low-elevation sites, from sea level to 500 m, and occurs in areas with dry and subarid bioclimates, although one species, *C. faho*, is also found in the humid northeast.

TABLE 8.39. Distinctive characteristics of the native Rutaceae genera with Malagasy vernacular names

GENUS	LIFE-FORM	PRICKLES	LEAVES	INFLORESCENCE	FLOWER	FRUIT	VERNACULAR NAMES
Cedrelopsis	Shrub/tree	Absent	Alternate, paripinnately compound	Axillary	Dioecious	Dehiscent (capsule)	*Hazondranta, katrafay, maninjo, valotra*
Chloroxylon	Tree	Absent	Alternate, paripinnately compound	Terminal	Monoecious (hermaphroditic)	Dehiscent (capsule)	*Faho, hazondinta, vaovy*
Fagaropsis	Deciduous shrub/tree	Absent	Opposite, imparipinnately compound	Terminal	Dioecious	Indehiscent (drupe)	*Mandakola, mandakolahy*
Ivodea	Shrub	Absent	Alternate (rarely subopposite), unifoliolate, or simple	Axillary/upper axillary/terminal	Dioecious	Dehiscent (follicle)	*Ambiotry, ampody, ampoly, tsivoangivoangy*
Melicope	Shrub/tree	Absent	Opposite, 1–3 foliolates (rarely simple)	Axillary/upper axillary	Dioecious (rarely polygamo-dioecious)	Dehiscent (follicle)	*Ampody, balankazo, bilahy, fatraina, rebosa*
Vepris	Shrub/tree	Absent	Alternate (rarely subopposite), 1–3 foliolates/palmately compound	Axillary/terminal/cauliflorous	Dioecious (rarely polygamo-dioecious)	Indehiscent (drupe)	*Ampody, ampoly, fitoravy, voangiala*
Zanthoxylum	Shrub/tree (rarely liana)	Present	Alternate, 1–3 foliolates to imparipinnately compound	Axillary/upper axillary	Dioecious or polygamo-dioecious	Dehiscent (capsule), rarely indehiscent[1] (drupe)	*Fahavalonkazo, manongo, tsihanimposa*

[1] Characteristics just for *Zanthoxylum asiaticum*.

PHYLOGENY

The classification and phylogenetic history of Rutaceae are both complex. The family has at various times been placed in several different orders, including Geraniales, Rutales, Sapindales, and Terebinthales (see Scott et al. 2000). Its modern position within Sapindales is, however, strongly supported by molecular data (Angiosperm Phylogeny Group III 2009). As a member of Sapindales, Rutaceae is closely related to the following families that are also present on Madagascar: Anacardiaceae, Burseraceae, Kirkiaceae, Meliaceae, Sapindaceae, and Simaroubaceae (Angiosperm Phylogeny Group IV 2016).

Rutaceae have traditionally been divided into the subfamilies, tribes, and subtribes defined by Engler (1874, 1896b, 1931). He provided the first comprehensive monograph of the family, using gynoecial and fruit characters to recognize seven subfamilies, 11 tribes, and 23 subtribes. In the context of the modern classification of Rutaceae, based on molecular phylogenetic analyses, this traditional classification is controversial and has been shown to be in need of revision (Chase et al. 1999; Poon et al. 2007; Groppo et al. 2008; C. M. Morton and Telmer 2014). Various changes have been suggested. Among the seven subfamilies defined by Engler, one, Rhabdodendroideae, is now recognized as a distinct family, Rhabdodendraceae. While no Malagasy species were included in the study of C. M. Morton and Telmer (2014), which was based on representative sampling from all Rutaceae subfamilies and tribes, the study did include genera present on Madagascar. Their results supported the recognition of four subfamilies: Amyridoideae, Aurantioideae, Cneoroideae, and Rutoideae.

Generic circumscriptions are also problematic in Rutaceae, as shown by recent studies focusing on several large genera, including *Melicope* (Appelhans et al. 2014a, 2014b, 2018b), *Vepris* (C. M. Morton 2017), and *Zanthoxylum* (Appelhans et al. 2014a, 2018a), all of which are polyphyletic and in need of taxonomic revision. Appelhans and Wen (2020) reviewed the phylogenetic relationships of Malagasy Rutaceae and were the first to include material of *Ivodea* and Malagasy species of *Vepris*. Their results showed that *Ivodea* is monophyletic and has a sister-taxon relationship with *Vepris*, whereas each of the other genera represented on Madagascar were found to belong to a different lineage with either African or Asian affinities, although sampling was insufficient to infer the timing and direction of dispersal. Two native genera, *Fagaropsis* and *Zanthoxylum*, are members of the proto-Rutaceae group, and characterized by the presence of special alkaloids (Appelhans et al. 2018a, 2020; Ling et al. 2009).

Recent studies have also confirmed that the traditional classification of Engler, based mainly on fruit characters, is not appropriate to delimit subfamilies and tribes within Rutaceae. For example, *Ivodea* was placed in Rutoideae because of its dehiscent follicular fruits, whereas *Vepris* was assigned to Toddalioideae given its indehiscent, drupaceous fruits; yet molecular data have clearly shown that they are close relatives (Appelhans and Wen 2020). Similarly, the dehiscent capsular fruits of *Zanthoxylum* led Engler to place it in Rutoideae, while he assigned *Toddalia*, with its indehiscent, drupaceous fruits, to Toddalioideae; yet we now know that *Toddalia* is nested within *Zanthoxylum* (Appelhans et al. 2018a).

TABLE 8.40. **Conservation status of Malagasy species of Rutaceae**

SCIENTIFIC NAME	IUCN STATUS	RED LIST CRITERIA	YEAR PUBLISHED (IUCN)
Cedrelopsis ambanjensis J.-F. Leroy	EN	B1ab(i,ii,iii,iv,v)+2ab(i,ii,iii,iv,v)	2018
C. gracilis J.-F. Leroy	CR	B1ab(iii,v)+2ab(iii,v)	2018
C. grevei Baill.	LC	–	2018
C. longibracteata J.-F. Leroy	EN	B2ab(i,ii,iii,iv,v)	2018
C. microfoliolata J.-F. Leroy	LC	–	2020
C. rakotozafyi Cheek & Lescot	EN	B1ab(i,ii,iii,iv,v)+2ab(i,ii,iii,iv,v)	2018
C. trivalvis J.-F. Leroy	LC	–	2018
Chloroxylon faho Capuron	VU	B1ab(i,ii,iii,iv)+2ab(i,ii,iii,iv)	2019
C. falcatum Capuron	EN	B1ab(i,ii,iii,iv,v)+2ab(i,ii,iii,iv,v)	2019
Fagaropsis glabra Capuron	EN	B1ab(i,ii,iii,iv)+2ab(i,ii,iii,iv)	2019
Ivodea analalavensis Rabariman., Rakoton., Phillipson & Lowry	EN	B1ab(i,ii,iii,iv,v)+2ab(i,ii,iii,iv,v)	2019
I. antilahimenae Rabariman., Rakoton., Phillipson & Lowry	EN	B1ab(i,ii,iii,iv)+2ab(i,ii,iii,iv)	2019
I. delphinensis Rabariman., Rakoton., Phillipson & Lowry	EN	B1ab(i,ii,iii,iv,v)+2ab(i,ii,iii,iv,v)	2019
I. macrocarpa Rabariman., Rakoton., Phillipson & Lowry	CR	B1ab(i,ii,iii,iv,v)+2ab(i,ii,iii,iv,v)	2019
I. mahaboensis Rabariman., Rakoton., Phillipson & Lowry	EN	B1ab(i,ii,iii,iv,v)+2ab(i,ii,iii,iv,v)	2019
I. mananarensis Rabariman., Rakoton., Phillipson & Lowry	EN	B1ab(i,ii,iii,iv,v)+2ab(i,ii,iii,iv,v)	2019
I. razakamalalae Rabariman., Rakoton., Phillipson & Lowry	EN	B1ab(i,ii,iii,iv,v)+2ab(i,ii,iii,iv,v)	2019
Melicope bakeri T. G. Hartley	VU	B1ab(i,ii,iv,v)+2ab(i,ii,iv,v)	2019
M. balankazo (H. Perrier) T. G. Hartley	EN	B1ab(i,ii,iii,iv,v)+2ab(i,ii,iii,iv,v)	2019
M. discolor (Baker) T. G. Hartley	EN	B1ab(i,ii,iii,iv)+2ab(i,ii,iii,iv)	2019
M. fatraina (H. Perrier) T. G. Hartley	CR	B1ab(ii,iii,iv,v)+2ab(ii,iii,iv,v)	2019
M. floribunda (Baker) T. G. Hartley	EN	B1ab(i,ii,iii,iv,v)+2ab(i,ii,iii,iv,v)	2019
M. sambiranensis (H. Perrier) T. G. Hartley	EN	B1ab(i,ii,iii,iv,v)+2ab(i,ii,iii,iv,v)	2019
M. tsaratananensis (Capuron) T. G. Hartley	EN	B1ab(i,ii,iii,iv,v)+2ab(i,ii,iii,iv,v)	2019
Vepris ampody H. Perrier	LC	–	2020
V. aralioides H. Perrier	LC	–	2020
V. arenicola H. Perrier	VU	B2ab(i,ii,iii,iv,v)	2020
V. cauliflora H. Perrier	VU	B2ab(i,ii,iii,iv,v)	2020
V. decaryana H. Perrier	EN	B1ab(i,ii,iii,iv,v)+2ab(i,ii,iii,iv,v)	2020
V. densiflora (Baker) I. Verd.	EN	B1ab(i,ii,iii,iv,v)	2020
V. dicarpella H. Perrier	VU	B1ab(i,ii,iii,iv,v)+2ab(i,ii,iii,iv,v)	2020
V. elliotii (Radlk.) I. Verd.	LC	–	2020
V. fitoravina H. Perrier	LC	–	2020
V. humbertii H. Perrier	EN	B2ab(i,ii,iii,iv,v)	2020
V. leandriana H. Perrier	VU	B2ab(i,ii,iii,iv,v)	2020

SCIENTIFIC NAME	IUCN STATUS	RED LIST CRITERIA	YEAR PUBLISHED (IUCN)
V. lepidota Capuron	EN	B2ab(i,ii,iii,iv)	2020
V. louvelii H. Perrier	DD	–	2020
V. macrophylla (Baker) I. Verd.	LC	–	2020
V. madagascarica (Baill.) H. Perrier	VU	B1ab(i,ii,iii,iv,v)+2ab(i,ii,iii,iv,v)	2019
V. nitida (Baker) I. Verd.	LC	–	2020
V. peraperta H. Perrier	VU	B1ab(i,ii,iii,iv)+2ab(i,ii,iii,iv)	2020
V. polymorpha (Danguy ex Lecomte) H. Perrier	LC	–	2020
V. sclerophylla H. Perrier	EN	B1ab(i,ii,iii,iv,v)+2ab(i,ii,iii,iv,v)	2020
Zanthoxylum decaryi H. Perrier	LC	–	2019
Z. madagascariense Baker	LC	–	2019
Z. subspicatum H. Perrier	CR	B1ab(i,ii,iii,v)+2ab(i,ii,iii,v)	2020
Z. thouvenotii H. Perrier	VU	B1ab(i,ii,iii,iv,v)+2ab(i,ii,iii,iv,v)	2020
Z. tsihanimposa H. Perrier	NT	–	2019

Source: IUCN (2020).
Note: IUCN status abbreviations: CR, Critically Endangered; DD, Data Deficient; EN, Endangered; LC, Least Concern; NT, Near Threatened; VU, Vulnerable.

CONSERVATION AND LOCAL USES

The majority of Malagasy Rutaceae species occur in humid and subhumid bioclimates at low elevations. Most also have restricted distributions or are locally endemic. Habitat degradation and destruction are the greatest threats, caused mainly by forest exploitation and clearing for swidden agriculture (*tavy*) and logging (Desbureaux et al. 2016). Moreover, some species are widely used and often overexploited by the local population for medicinal purposes (*Cedrelopsis* spp. and *Zanthoxylum* spp.), carpentry and construction (*Chloroxylon* spp. and *Cedrelopsis* spp.), fuelwood, charcoal making, and other uses. Species of *Melicope* have become rare and threatened due to unsustainable traditional use of the bark to flavor a local alcoholic beverage (*betsabetsa*). Almost all species of *Melicope*, including several new ones (25 of the estimated total of 27), are reported to be used for the manufacture of this local rum and have become very rare in their natural habitat, with the exception of the *M. madagascariensis* complex.

The same is true for *Cedrelopsis*, known as *katrafay*, whose species are all used for multiple purposes and have been assessed as threatened under the International Union for the Conservation of Nature (IUCN) Red List criteria (Rabarison et al. 2013). They are valuable, both locally and nationally, mainly for traditional medicine and the production of essential oils, and have become rare in the wild. The wood of *C. grevei*, known locally as white palisander, is of high quality, equal to that of some *Dalbergia* species (rosewood and palisander), and some half-finished products are exported from Madagascar to La Réunion (Dongock Nguemo 2008) for different forms of wood products. An essential oil from *katrafay* is commonly traded for both foreign and local pharmaceutical use, and among the key aromatic and medicinal plant products for export, its low cost makes it comparatively attractive economically. The price of essential oils from endemic species is generally higher on national and international markets than that of nonendemic species. Overexploitation is known to impact some endemic members of Rutaceae (notably species of *Cedrelopsis* and *Melicope*), which have become rare and threatened in the wild, prompting their cultivation in private plots.

Among the 84 accepted described species of Malagasy Rutaceae, published risk of extinction assessments are available on the IUCN Red List website for 48 species (IUCN 2020), including four determined to be Critically Endangered (CR), 21 Endangered (EN), nine Vulnerable (VU), one Near Threatened (NT), one Data Deficient (DD), and 12 Least Concern (LC) (Table 8.40). According to Rabarimanarivo et al. (2015), all 28 native species of *Ivodea* are threatened (10 CR, 10 EN, and eight VU), based on currently unpublished assessments of their conservation status.

The Rutaceae family is known mainly for the numerous edible fruits of members of the exotic genus *Citrus*, which are economically important and widely consumed. This genus was introduced to Madagascar long ago (Perrier de la Bâthie 1950; Madagascar Catalogue 2020) and is represented by several cultivated species namely: *C. aurantiifolia* (limes, *tsoha*, *voasary makirana*), *C. limon* (lemon, *tsoha*, *voasary makirana*), *C. maxima* (pomelo, shaddock, *voasary angy be*), *C. reticulata* (mandarin and tangerine), and *C. sinensis* (sweet orange, *voasary*, *voahangy*). Four of these are known to be naturalized (*C. aurantium*, *C. limon*, *C. medica*, and *C. reticulata*). The Asian species *Clausena excavata* has been introduced for its many valuable medicinal properties. It has become naturalized in northeast Madagascar, where it can become invasive and locally very abundant.

Many species of Rutaceae are among the Malagasy woody plants exploited by lemurs and bats as food. Eppley et al. (pp. 1839–59) list Rutaceae, including both native and alien species, among those eaten by lemurs. Twenty-nine species of lemurs are reported to consume native Rutaceae species, and three species of lemurs eat alien species. They exploit the leaves, inflorescences, fruits, and exudates. *Phaner* species (fork-marked lemurs) eat the exudates of *Zanthoxylum tsihanimposa*, which is restricted to the dry areas on Madagascar. *Cedrelopsis grevei*, typically found in dry spiny thickets, is listed as one of plants consumed by *Lemur catta* (Ring-tailed Lemur) in the south (Simmen et al. 2006). In the littoral forests of southeastern Madagascar, fruits of three native species of Rutaceae (*Vepris elliotii*, *V.* aff. *elliotii*, and *V. fitoravina*) are reported to be eaten by four species of lemurs and one fruit bat (*Pteropus rufus*), promoting seed dispersal (Bollen 2003).

Subject editors: Laurent Gautier and Steven M. Goodman

MALVACEAE

C. Skema and M. Hanes

DIVERSITY AND ENDEMISM

Madagascar has representatives from seven of the 10 families in the order Malvales (Angiosperm Phylogeny Group IV 2016): Bixaceae, Cytinaceae, Dipterocarpaceae, Malvaceae, Thymelaeaceae, Sarcolaenaceae, and Sphaerosepalaceae, the latter two of which are endemic to the island. As such, it represents a region of extraordinary diversity for the order. The most species-rich family on the island in the order is Malvaceae *sensu lato*, whose delimitation now includes the previously recognized families Bombacaceae, Sterculiaceae, and Tiliaceae. Within Malvaceae, seven of the nine subfamilies recognized are represented on the island (Figure 8.62), those missing being Tilioideae and Helicteroideae. On a global scale, roughly 18% of approximately 243 total genera, and 10% of around 4622 species, occur on Madagascar; 4% of the genera and nearly 9% of the species are endemic to the island (numbers for taxa outside of Madagascar are based on Bayer and Kubitzki 2003). On Madagascar, genera in this family range in species diversity from one of the larger plant genera on the island (*Dombeya* with 158 recognized species) to four monospecific genera (*Cheirolaena*, *Helicteropsis*, *Jumelleanthus*, and *Paramelhania*). There are 43 genera and 486 species of Malvaceae on Madagascar, of which nine genera and 409 species are endemic (Table 8.41, Figure 8.62). Thus, 84% of the species of Malagasy Malvaceae are endemic, a percentage on a par with endemicity estimates for all angiosperm species indigenous to Madagascar (Callmander et al. 2011a). Using total plant species estimates from Callmander et al. (2011a), Malvaceae makes up 4.3% of the Malagasy vascular flora.

MORPHOLOGY AND BIOTIC INTERACTIONS

The extraordinary morphological diversity in Malvaceae is well represented on Madagascar, with plant forms including herbs, lianas, shrubs, and trees. Leaves vary dramatically in shape, thickness, pubescence, venation, and in the forms of and presence/absence of leaf domatia. Leaves are usually simple, though palmately compound leaves occur (e.g., *Adansonia*, *Sterculia*) as does heterophylly (e.g., *Byttneria* and rarely in *Dombeya*; Arènes 1959). There is a wide diversity of floral and inflorescence forms (Figures 8.62 and 8.63), with variability in merosity (tetramerous or pentamerous), the degree of fusion in each floral whorl (including the epicalyx), flower color, petal shape (particularly complex in Byttnerioideae), the persistence of perianth parts, number of stamens (four to >1500), anther thecae (one or two), carpel number (one to 20), and in the presence/absence of an epicalyx, petals, staminodia, and an androgynophore. Fruit form (Figure 8.62) varies from the typical (± woody) capsule, such as in the schizocarps of tribe Malveae (e.g., many flattened mericarps in *Abutilon*) or some Byttnerioideae (e.g., armed mericarps in *Byttneria*), to the drupaceous fruit of *Grewia*, the large indehiscent spongy fruits of *Adansonia*, and the apocarpous follicles of Sterculioideae (e.g., indehiscent, woody follicles in *Heritiera littoralis* that are adept ocean floaters, P. T. Green 1999). Seed dispersal is diverse and is presumably aided by, for example, winged follicles (e.g., *Hildegardia*), winged seeds (e.g., *Helmiopsis*, *Helmiopsiella*, *Nesogordonia*, *Pterygota*), or accrescent (epi)calyxes (e.g., *Humbertiella*, *Megistostegium*, *Seringia*) (Figure 8.62).

As elsewhere in its distribution, on Madagascar Malvaceae is dominated by hermaphroditic flowers, though dioecy and polygamy occur in the Sterculioideae and dioecy in Brownlowioideae (Schatz 2001) and possibly in *Grewia* (Mabberley and Capuron 2017). Strict monoecy in Malagasy Malvaceae may occur in *Dombeya* (Arènes 1959). However, there have been no studies of functional sexual expression in Malagasy Malvaceae, and thus cryptic deviations from cosexuality are possible.

Biotic interactions of Malvaceae with pollinators, fruit/seed dispersers, pests, and symbionts, and the coevolution of all these taxa, is a promising but largely unstudied subject. Floral variation is, of course, likely closely tied to pollinator diversity, though few formal pollinator studies have been carried out in the family on Madagascar. All species in the endemic genus *Megistostegium* produce copious

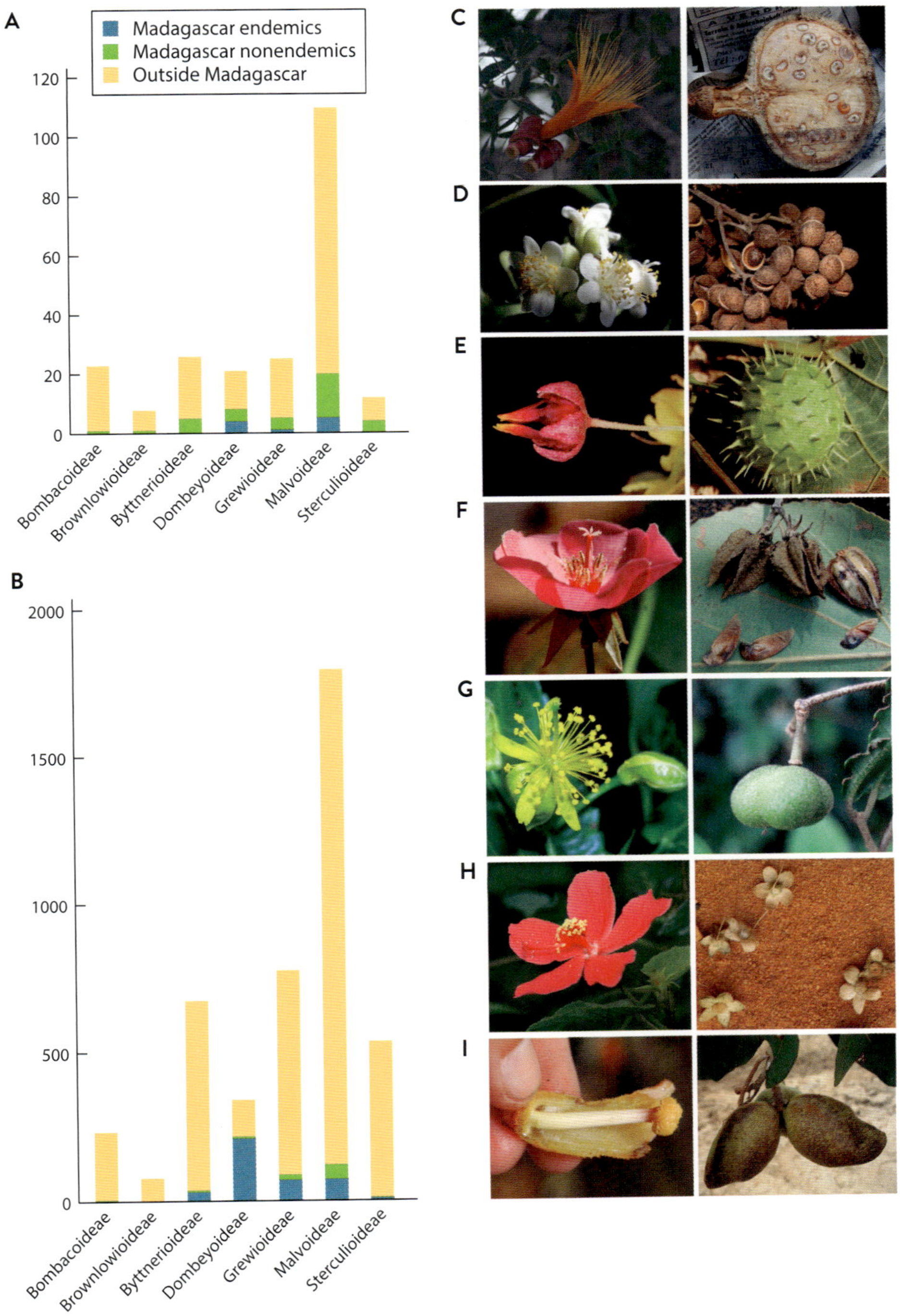

FIGURE 8.62 **Diversity and endemicity diagram for A) genera and B) species of Malvaceae by subfamily, with one representative flower (left) and fruit (right) image per subfamily, as follows: C) Bombacoideae, *Adansonia za* and *Adansonia*** (PHOTO left by N. Karimi and right by C. Skema)**; D) Brownlowioideae, *Christiana africana*** (PHOTO left by C. Rakotovao and right by D. Harris)**; E) Byttnerioideae, *Byttneria heterophylla*** (PHOTO left by E. Bidault and right by C. Skema)**; F) Dombeyoideae, *Dombeya rottleroides* and *Helmiopsis pseudopopulus*** (both PHOTOS by C. Skema)**; G) Grewioideae, *Grewia*** (PHOTO left by F. Rakotoarivony and right by A. Razanatsima 260)**; H) Malvoideae, *Hibiscus ferrugineus* and *Humbertiella*** (Both PHOTOS by M. Hanes)**; and I) Sterculioideae, *Hildegardia perrieri* and *Heritiera littoralis*** (PHOTO left by C. Skema and right by C. Rakotovao 6489)**.**

amounts of sweet nectar in a large trichome-filled cavity in basal petal tissue, and at least one species (*M. microphyllum*) is pollinated by a sunbird (*Cinnyris sovimanga*) (Koopman 2005). Antandroy children also enjoy the nectar as a sugar source (M. Hanes, unpublished observation). The six insect-pollinated species of *Humbertiella* have elaborate staminal glands called coronules (Dorr 1990). The ~17 insect-pollinated species of *Perrierophytum sensu lato* (including some Malagasy members of *Kosteletskya*; Koopman and Baum 2008) have diverse floral morphologies and colors (white, pink, or green flowers). Within *Dombeya*, significant variation in inflorescence type (e.g., umbellate, corymbose, or scorpioidal cymes) and presentation (e.g., upright, pendulous), size and number of flowers, petal color (white, pink, red, lavender), and distance between nectar and pollen presentation (Figure 8.63) indicate pollinator diversity. Further morphological variation suggests additional intriguing interactions with other organisms, for example, the ant-attracting secretions of *D. mandenensis* (C. Skema, unpublished data).

TAXONOMIC AND PHYLOGENETIC UNDERSTANDING

No taxonomic treatment for Malvaceae as currently circumscribed has been completed for Madagascar, though it has been

TABLE 8.41. **The genera in Malvaceae on Madagascar and other associated details**

SUBFAMILY	TRIBE	GENUS	NUMBER OF SPECIES (ENDEMIC)	GENUS ENDEMIC?	DISTRIBUTION AND VEGETATION TYPES
Bombacoideae		*Adansonia*	7(6)	No	Widespread; dry spiny thicket to moist semi-deciduous forest
Brownlowioideae		*Christiana*	1(0)	No	N, W; moist semi-deciduous to dry deciduous forest, often disturbed areas
Byttnerioideae	Byttnerieae	*Byttneria*	27(26)	No	Widespread
	Hermannieae	*Melochia*	4–5(0–3)	No	N, E, W; usually disturbed areas
		Waltheria	2(1)	No	Widespread; warm areas, typically disturbed, often on sand
	Lasiopetaleae	*Commersonia*	1(1)	No	Central Highlands, E, S; grassland, *savoka*, sclerophyllous woodland, montane ericoid thicket, moist evergreen forest
		Seringia	1(1)	No	E (known only from Ambatovy); moist evergreen forest
Dombeyoideae		*Andringitra*	6(6)	Yes	Central Highlands, S; montane ericoid thicket, moist evergreen, moist semi-deciduous and riparian forests, often on granite massifs
		Cheirolaena	1(0)	No	N, E, W; on sand
		Dombeya	158(155)	No	Widespread
		Helmiopsiella	4(4)	Yes	N, SW, W; dry spiny thicket and dry deciduous forest
		Helmiopsis	11(11)	Yes	N, SW, W; dry spiny thicket and dry deciduous forest, often on sand
		Melhania	19(18)	No	S, SW; dry spiny thicket and dry deciduous forest
		Nesogordonia	17(17)	No	N, E, W; dry deciduous to moist evergreen forest
		Paramelhania	1(1)	Yes	S; dry spiny thicket, often on sand
Grewioideae	Apeibeae	*Corchorus*	6(0)	No	Widespread
		Pseudocorchorus	6(6)	Yes	Widespread
		Sparrmannia	3(2)	No	Widespread
		Triumfetta	5(0)	No	Central Highlands
	Grewieae	*Grewia*	69(63)	No	Widespread

SUBFAMILY	TRIBE	GENUS	NUMBER OF SPECIES (ENDEMIC)	GENUS ENDEMIC?	DISTRIBUTION AND VEGETATION TYPES
Malvoideae	Gossypieae	*Gossypioides*	1(1)	No	NW, W
		Gossypium	3(2)	No	W, extreme N
		Thespesia	2(1)	No	Coastal, widespread
	Hibisceae	*Abelmoschus*	3(0)	No	Widespread
		Helicteropsis	1(1)	Yes	N, dry deciduous forests on karstic limestone
		Hibiscus	65(44)	No	Widespread
		Humbertiella	6(6)	Yes	SW; dry spiny thicket
		Jumelleanthus	1(1)	Yes	N, moist evergreen forests
		Kosteletskya	9(8)	No	SW, Central Highlands; dry spiny thicket
		Malachra	1(0)	No	S (single specimen from Tolagnaro)
		Megistostegium	3(3)	Yes	SW, dry spiny thicket
		Pavonia	3(1)	No	Central Highlands
		Perrierophytum	9(8)	No	W, dry spiny thicket and dry deciduous forest
		Urena	1(0)	No	Widespread
	Malveae	*Abutilon*	5(1)	No	Widespread
		Malva	1(0)	No	Central Highlands
		Malvastrum	1(0)	No	Central Highlands
		Sida	7(0)	No	Widespread
		Wissadula	1(0)	No	Unknown (single specimen without locality)
Sterculioideae		*Heritiera*	1(0)	No	Coastal; mangrove or littoral forest
		Hildegardia	4(4)	No	All but Central Highlands; dry deciduous to moist evergreen forest
		Pterygota	2(2)	No	E, W; dry deciduous to moist evergreen forest
		Sterculia	2–6(2–5)	No	N, E, W; moist evergreen and littoral forests
	Totals	43 genera	486(409)	9 endemic genera	

Note: Vegetation types follow Gautier et al. (2018).

done in part (in families as previously recognized, Hochreutiner 1955; Perrier de la Bâthie and Hochreutiner 1955; Arènes 1959; Capuron 1963, 1964). Here we aim to highlight key taxonomic developments and summarize what is known about phylogenetic relationships among members of Malvaceae on Madagascar. Since the last major treatments for the Malagasy Malvaceae, one new genus (*Andringitra*, Skema 2012) (see section on Hibisceae for discussion of *Talipariti*) and 44 new species have been described from Madagascar (Table 8.42). Like most groups on the island, many more species await description. The four largest genera in

FIGURE 8.63 **Examples of inflorescence and floral diversity within the genus *Dombeya*. Top row, left to right: *D. dolichophylla*, *D. befotakensis*, *D. lucida*, and *D. baronii*; middle row, left to right: *D. palmatisecta*, *D. mollis*, *D. cacuminum*, and *D. australis*; bottom row, left to right: *D. erythroclada*, *D. mandenensis*, *D. magnifolia*, and *D. acutangula*.** (PHOTOS by C. Skema.)

the family on the island (*Dombeya* 158 species; *Grewia* >69 species; *Hibiscus* 65 species; *Byttneria* 27 species) together represent 66% of the species diversity within the Malagasy Malvaceae. Malagasy members of three of these four genera have been examined recently in a phylogenetic context. For the taxa that remain understudied we briefly summarize what is known about the group on Madagascar.

Bombacoideae

The Bombacoideae, a predominantly Neotropical subfamily, is represented on Madagascar by the vast majority of the species of the iconic genus *Adansonia*, the baobabs (see Karimi et al., pp. 706–10).

Brownlowioideae

Brownlowioideae is represented by a sole species, *Christiana africana*, in western and northern Madagascar. This species is also widely distributed from tropical Central and South America to tropical continental Africa (Capuron 1963). We are unaware of any phylogenetic studies focused on Brownlowioideae or *Christiana*.

Byttnerioideae

Byttnerieae

Byttnerieae is the most species-rich tribe in this subfamily on Madagascar, with 27 species of unarmed lianas in the genus *Byttneria*, of which 26 are endemic (*B. melleri* occurs also in the Comoros) (Arènes 1959; Whitlock and Hale 2011). In a molecular study, all Malagasy accessions sampled (representing four species) formed a well-supported monophyletic group (Whitlock and Hale 2011).

Lasiopetaleae

Recent molecular and taxonomic work in Lasiopetaleae affected both of the two species known on Madagascar. The Malagasy endemic *Keraudrenia macrantha* became *Seringia macrantha* when *Keraudrenia* was subsumed into *Seringia*, because neither genus was monophyletic based on morphology and molecular data (Wilkins and Whitlock 2015). A second molecular study found members of *Rulingia* and *Commersonia* interdigitated (Whitlock et al. 2011), and resulting revisionary (Wilkins and Whitlock 2011) and molecular (B. Whitlock, unpublished data) work formed the new combination *C. madagascariensis* for the Malagasy endemic previously known as *Rulingia madagascariensis*.

TABLE 8.42. **Summary of new species described, with relevant citations, since the last major treatments for the Malagasy Malvaceae**

GENUS	NUMBER OF NEW SPECIES	REFERENCES
Adansonia	1	Capuron (1960a)
Dombeya	10	Barnett and Dorr (1986); Applequist (2009b); Skema and Dorr (2010); Applequist (2014)
Grewia	16	Capuron and Mabberley (1999); Mabberley and Capuron (1999); Randrianasolo et al. (2013); Wahlert et al. (2014, 2015, 2016)
Helmiopsis	2	Barnett (1987a); Applequist (2009a)
Hibiscus	6	Callmander et al. (2009); Pignal and Phillipson (2010); Hanes et al. (2020)
Hildegardia	1	Zaborsky (2009)
Humbertiella	1	Dorr (1990)
Nesogordonia	5	Barnett (1987b); Callmander et al. (2009); Skema and Dorr (2011); Rakotoarivelo et al. (2014)
Sterculia	1	Dorr (2004)
Thespesia	1	Capuron (1968b)
Total	44	

Notes: Only spp. nov. are included here (not comb. nov., nom. nov., or stat. nov). Last major treatments are considered to be: Hochreutiner (1955), Perrier de la Bâthie and Hochreutiner (1955), and Arènes (1959) for those taxa previously included in Malvaceae *sensu stricto*, Bombacaceae, and Sterculiaceae, respectively, in the *Flore de Madagascar et Comores* series, and Capuron (1963, 1964) for those taxa previously included in Tiliaceae.

Hermannieae

Two genera are known from tribe Hermannieae on Madagascar. *Waltheria* comprises two species on the island, the widespread weed *W. indica* and the under-collected *W. madagascariensis*. The taxonomy of the Malagasy members of *Melochia* seems to be complicated by the weediness of the genus and opinions vary on the number of Malagasy species and their endemic status (Arènes 1959; Goldberg 1967; Madagascar Catalogue 2019). Little is known about the phylogenetics of *Melochia* or *Waltheria* in general, beyond confirming their tribal membership (Whitlock et al. 2001).

Dombeyoideae

The Dombeyoideae family is a key component of the Malvaceae of Madagascar, with nearly half (45%) of the Malagasy Malvaceae species occurring in this subfamily. Nearly 62% of dombeyoid species worldwide are endemic to Madagascar and the subfamily includes four of the nine Malvaceae genera endemic to Madagascar (Table 8.41), as well as the regional endemic *Cheirolaena*, which also occurs on the island of Juan de Nova (in a single population, E. Bidault, unpublished data). The genus *Dombeya* alone makes up nearly 33% of the species diversity of all Malagasy Malvaceae and 1.3% of the entire Malagasy vascular flora, representing a truly spectacular example of plant evolution on Madagascar.

A phylogeny of the subfamily Dombeyoideae worldwide has been reconstructed (C. Skema et al., unpublished data). Regarding the Malagasy genera, *Nesogordonia* is the earliest-diverging lineage within the dombeyoids, and *Melhania*, *Paramelhania*, and *Cheirolaena* sit together in a well-supported clade sister to *Dombeya sensu lato* (Le Péchon et al. 2010; Skema 2012; C. Skema, unpublished data). Five genera (*Eriolaena*, *Helmiopsiella*, *Helmiopsis*, *Ruizia*, and *Trochetia*) are embedded in *Dombeya sensu lato* (Le Péchon et al. 2010; Skema 2012). Segregation of *Dombeya* subsection *Macranthae* + *D. moratii* into the new genus *Andringitra*, based on molecular and morphological data, was a start at the recircumscription of *Dombeya* from Madagascar (Skema 2012). Species with winged seeds have been pulled out of *Dombeya* and moved to *Helmiopsis* or *Helmiopsiella* based on morphology and sometimes molecular data (Barnett 1988a; Dorr 2001; Skema 2012). In this winged seed clade of the dombeyoids, a reevaluation of generic boundaries between *Helmiopsiella*, *Helmiopsis*, and *Eriolaena*, with further sampling and molecular work, is needed (Skema 2012; Dorr and Wurdack 2018).

Revisions of *Nesogordonia* (Barnett 1988b) and *Helmiopsis* (Applequist 2009a) have been completed. The two major revisions of Malagasy *Dombeya* undertaken since *Flore de Madagascar et des Comores* (Arènes 1959) show a marked decrease from the number of species recognized by Arènes (*Dombeya* section *Decastemon* lost 15 species to synonymy in Applequist 2014; *Dombeya* section *Hilsenbergia* lost nine species to synonymy in Skema 2014). Certainly, one issue was the problem of working with insufficient material for *Flore de Madagascar et des Comores*; nearly half of the 187 species of *Dombeya* treated by Arènes were known only from the type specimen in 1959. There is considerable revisionary work left to do in this subfamily.

Grewioideae

Grewieae

The only member of Grewieae on the island, *Grewia* comprises approximately 300 Paleotropical species of trees, shrubs, and lianas worldwide. Treatments in three subgenera have been published (Capuron 1964; Capuron and Mabberley 1999; Mabberley and Capuron 1999) for Madagascar. *Grewia* on Madagascar is currently represented by 69 species, which occur throughout a wide variety of habitats and bioclimes, and about 20 additional species await description (Mabberley and Capuron 2017; Madagascar Catalogue 2019). Most described species from Madagascar are trees or shrubs, though five species are known to grow as lianas (Randrianasolo et al. 2013). With upwards of half the world's diversity of *Grewia* occurring on Madagascar, the island is an important center of diversity for the genus (Mabberley and Capuron 2017). Molecular phylogenies are necessary to investigate species relationships and test current taxonomic hypotheses for *Grewia* on Madagascar.

Apeibeae

On Madagascar, Apeibeae includes more genera (four) than Grewieae but far fewer species (19 or 20). *Corchorus* is found throughout the tropics and subtropics (Bayer and Kubitzki 2003) with most species living in continental Africa and Australia. Madagascar is home to six species in the genus, and none are restricted to the island (Capuron 1963). The morphologically similar genus *Pseudocorchorus* is endemic to Madagascar and comprises six species. Recent molecular work demonstrated that *Pseudocorchorus* is monophyletic but nested within *Corchorus* (Benor 2018), suggesting that species of *Pseudocorchorus* would be better placed in *Corchorus*.

There are three described species of *Sparrmannia* on the island; two are endemic to Madagascar and the third is also found in continental Africa. However, several undescribed species exist and the genus is under revision (Madagascar Catalogue 2019). The work of Alverson et al. (1999) suggests that *Sparrmannia* is sister to the New Zealand monotypic *Entelea*.

Malvoideae

Gossypieae

The genus *Gossypioides* comprises two species, the Malagasy endemic *G. brevilanatum* and its east African congener *G. kirkii* (Hutchinson 1943). *Gossypioides* is sister to the Hawaiian genus *Kokia* (Seelanan et al. 1997). These genera together are sister to the genus *Gossypium* (cotton). In spite of an extraordinary body of evolutionary work on some species of *Gossypium*, *Gossypioides* and species of *Gossypium* endemic to Madagascar have received little phylogenetic attention thus far.

Hibiscus humbertianus is a Malagasy species that was transferred to *Cienfuegosia* (a genus in the tribe Gossypieae) by Fryxell (1974) because it appeared to possess gossypol glands. Tests for terpenoid gossypol, however, did not match those of other *Cienfuegosia*, and phylogenetic analyses indicate that this taxon is closely related to other Malagasy members of *Hibiscus* suggesting that this taxon is best placed in *Hibiscus* (Koopman and Baum 2008).

Hibisceae

This tribe has 102 species known from Madagascar, including four endemic genera (Table 8.41). Currently the island is home to 65 described species of *Hibiscus*; however, the genus is not monophyletic (Pfeil et al. 2002). In a study focused on Malagasy Hibisceae, Koopman and Baum (2008) demonstrated that several Malagasy genera (*Macrostelia*, *Helicteropsis*, and *Jumelleanthus*) are embedded in *Hibiscus*. Likewise, *Talipariti tiliaceum* is nested in *Hibiscus* and is here treated as *H. tiliaceus*. All members of *Macrostelia* Hochr. have recently been transferred to *Hibiscus* to reflect this phylogenetic understanding (Hanes et al. 2020).

Koopman and Baum (2008) also showed that the diversity of Hibisceae on Madagascar falls into two clades, resulting from at least two independent migration events to the island. The first is a formally recognized clade called Euhibiscus (Koopman and Baum 2008) that houses the majority of the Hibisceae on Madagascar. A second clade, Megistohibiscus (39 species), includes Malagasy members of *Hibiscus* section *Azanza* and *Kosteletskya* as well as three monophyletic genera, two endemic (*Humbertiella*, *Megistostegium*), and one regional endemic (*Perrierophytum*, one species occurs on Grande Glorieuse and Juan de Nova; Boullet et al. 2018). The Megistohibiscus clade is sister to the remainder of tribe Hibisceae and is united by several molecular synapomorphies. It is also clear that Malagasy endemic species currently placed in the genus *Kosteletskya* should be moved out of the genus (Koopman and Baum 2008; Blanchard 2012) and would be better incorporated into the genus *Perrierophytum*.

Malveae

This tribe is represented on Madagascar by 15 species in five genera. Only one species is endemic (*Abutilon greveanum*). Little phylogenetic work has been done to investigate taxa on Madagascar.

Sterculioideae

Four genera but only a dozen or so species of Sterculioideae occur on Madagascar. *Heritiera littoralis*, a widespread mangrove/littoral species, occurs on the shores of islands in the Indian and Pacific oceans and has been collected throughout the coastal regions of Madagascar and eastern Africa. All Malagasy species of both *Hildegardia* (four species) and *Pterygota* (two species) are endemic (Arènes 1959; Zaborsky 2009). The taxonomy of the Malagasy members of the large pantropical genus *Sterculia* remains in flux (Schatz 2001; Dorr 2004; Madagascar Catalogue 2019). Phylogenetic relationships within Sterculioideae are known only in the broadest of brush strokes, with poor sampling from Madagascar (Wilkie et al. 2006). Of interest, two species of *Hildegardia* (neither Malagasy) were interdigitated with two species of *Firmiana* (a genus from southeastern Asia), and morphology of these species indicated support for Dorr and Barnett's (1990) observation that African and Malagasy species in *Hildegardia* form a distinct, cohesive group based on floral characters (Wilkie et al. 2006).

SPATIAL AND TEMPORAL PATTERNS

Within Madagascar

Locality data from 7794 unique herbarium specimen records (GBIF 2019) demonstrate that Malvaceae taxa occur across Madagascar, with a high density of collections in nearly all regions (Figure 8.64a), though these data are very likely influenced by collecting behavior. Manipulation of these data suggest that some genera remain under-collected (e.g., *Dombeya*, *Melhania*) while others are over-collected (e.g., *Adansonia*, *Nesogordonia*), if we expect the percentage of species diversity of Malagasy Malvaceae within a genus to be roughly equal to the percentage of collections of Malagasy Malvaceae for that genus. Species distribution patterns and abundance in Malvaceae are poorly understood in general on Madagascar.

Connections between Madagascar and the Rest of the World

Biogeographic connections between Malagasy Malvaceae and the rest of the world based on molecular phylogenetic data are summarized in Figure 8.64b. The resulting patterns imply both short-distance (e.g., continental Africa, the Mascarenes) and long-distance (e.g., Australasia, Neotropics) dispersal in and out of Madagascar, including some repeated dispersal events to and from a region within a taxon (e.g., *Dombeya*). Our summary confirms strong floristic affinities within Malvaceae between Madagascar and continental Africa and also indicates that these regions have many sister species relationships. Current understanding of biogeographic connections in the family, between Madagascar and Asia, instead suggest the two regions are more linked by generic sister relationships. Figure 8.64b further highlights an important connection with Australasia. At present, the dombeyoids appear to dominate colonization of the Mascarenes (Le Péchon et al. 2010) though new data in *Hibiscus* also indicate several interesting patterns (M. Hanes and B. Mashburn, unpublished data). For Malvaceae, relationships to other islands off Madagascar (e.g., Comoros, Ile Europa, Iles Glorieuses, Juan de Nova) are much less studied, though we know from distributional data that some genera on Madagascar include species endemic to these islands (e.g., *Dombeya*, *Nesogordonia*, *Perrierophytum*) as well as species that occur both on these islands and on Madagascar (e.g., *Byttneria*, *Cheirolaena*, *Dombeya*) (Arènes 1959; Boullet et al. 2018). More phylogenetic work with thorough sampling is needed to better understand biogeographic patterns of Malagasy Malvaceae, particularly for cosmopolitan species, widespread genera, and movement around the Indian Ocean flora region.

About two-thirds of the endemic plant genera on Madagascar originated in the Miocene or more recently (Buerki et al. 2013). While admitting the need for better paleobotanical data to evaluate endemicity through time, this suggests that many endemic genera have undergone speciation on Madagascar recently and rapidly. Though the period of origin for most clades in Malvaceae on Madagascar has yet to be estimated, the evidence we do have supports these broader patterns. The endemic Malagasy clade Megistohibiscus was derived from a single introduction in the mid-Miocene (11.5–14.5 million years ago [Mya]) (Koopman and Baum 2008). A second independent migration to Madagascar of Hibisceae, whose members are embedded in the Euhibiscus clade, has been estimated to have occurred more recently (3.7–5 Mya) (Koopman and Baum 2008). Divergence estimates between *Gossypioides* and its sister genus *Kokia* range from 3 to 4.8 Mya (Seelanan et al. 1997; Koopman and Baum 2008); however, no estimates yet exist for the split between the two

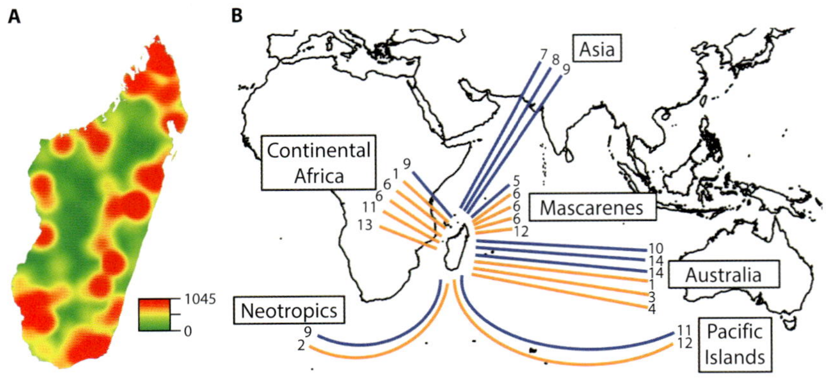

FIGURE 8.64 **A) Map of Madagascar showing density of unique collections of Malvaceae, from GBIF (2019). Records are of preserved specimens with location coordinates, collector name, and collector number (7794 records), including records from Missouri Botanical Garden (MO), Muséum National d'Histoire Naturelle (P), and US herbaria. Collector names were standardized then combined with collector number to form a unique identifier to remove duplicate records. Density was mapped via kernel density tool with a cell size of 0.01 and color ramp values stretched through the histogram equalize function in ArcGIS (Version 10.6, Environmental Systems Research Institute, Inc.). B) Summary of biogeographic connections of Malagasy Malvaceae throughout the world that are supported with molecular phylogenetic data. Orange lines indicate that sister species to Malagasy taxa within the named genus occur between regions. Blue lines indicate that a sister taxon to an entire named genus occurs between regions. Numbers correspond to genera as follows: Bombacoideae: 1, *Adansonia*. Byttnerioideae: 2, *Byttneria*; 3, *Commersonia*; 4, *Seringia*. Dombeyoideae: 5, *Andringitra*; 6, *Dombeya*; 7, *Helmiopsiella*; 8, *Nesogordonia*. Grewioideae: 9, *Pseudocorchorus*; 10, *Sparrmannia*. Malvoideae: 11, *Gossypioides*; 12, *Hibiscus*; 13, *Thespesia*. 14, Tribe Hibisceae.** SOURCES: Seelanan et al. (1997), Alverson et al. (1999), Koopman and Baum (2008), Le Péchon et al. (2010), Whitlock and Hale (2011), Skema (2012), Areces-Berazain and Ackerman (2016), Benor (2018), Karimi et al. (2020); M. Hanes and B. Mashburn, unpublished data; B. Whitlock, unpublished data.

species of *Gossypioides*. See Karimi et al. (pp. 706–10) for *Adansonia* estimates. Clade ages have been estimated for some Dombeyoideae in a study focused on the Mascarenes (Le Péchon et al. 2015), and dating with more thorough taxon sampling across the subfamily is in progress (T. Le Péchon et al., unpublished data).

SPECIES DELIMITATION IN RECENTLY DIVERGED TAXA: PROBLEMS AND PROGRESS

Inference of species relationships between recently diverged species in Malvaceae on Madagascar has proven difficult using traditional molecular markers in plant systematics due to incongruence; a lack of resolution and/or a lack of monophyly for species, some of which has been shown to be due to hybridization; incomplete lineage sorting; polyploidy; and ongoing gene flow between nascent species (Koopman and Baum 2010; Koopman 2011; Skema 2012; Skema 2014; see Karimi et al., pp. 706–10). Here we summarize work on two of the largest groups in the family on Madagascar, which C. Skema and M. Hanes are working with to explicitly test speciation hypotheses in *Dombeya* and in tribe Hibisceae, respectively.

The genus *Dombeya* provides an ideal opportunity to study plant speciation on Madagascar given that all geological formations and all but one habitat type (mangroves) on the island overlap with the combined geographic distribution of its 158 species. The morphologically cohesive group of five species within *Dombeya* section *Hilsenbergia* provides a good start for looking at speciation within the genus. A plastid phylogeny of this section shows a geographic signal, while a nuclear marker groups species into relationships corroborated by morphological similarities (Skema 2014). A hybridization zone between three co-occurring species has been hypothesized at Vohiparara (upper portion of Ranomafana National Park) based on multiple individual plants showing morphologically intermediate characters between these species. An examination of niche space in *Dombeya* section *Hilsenbergia* is in progress to elucidate how these species are biologically isolated from one another given incomplete geographic and/or genetic separation due to the broad sympatry of three of the five species and putative hybridization in the section. Morphological observations also hint at some intriguing differences in biotic interactions that might maintain species boundaries in section *Hilsenbergia*. Unlike the other species in the section, one species, *D. cannabina*, typically has pocket domatia on the underside of its leaves, suggesting it could be housing predators (e.g., predatory mites) of its herbivorous pests. This potential difference in tri-trophic interactions for this species may enable its occupation of different niche space in terms of pest pressures and thus new habitat. Another species, *D. wallichii*, has distinct floral characters (red flowers in an umbellate inflorescence and shorter staminal tubes) that differ dramatically from *D. cannabina*, a close relative in the section (off-white to salmon-colored flowers, flat-topped inflorescences, a sweetly yeasty smell, and longer staminal tubes). These floral differences likely represent differences in pollinators. Further fieldwork on *Dombeya* section *Hilsenbergia* is required to gather data about characteristics on the microniche level (e.g., soils) and the potential role of biotic interactions in species isolation.

The roles of biome, soil, topographic complexity, rivers, and recent climatic shifts in the diversification of the Megistohibiscus clade (Hibisceae; Malvoideae) are being explored to understand the processes that have been most important in the evolution of the highly endemic and understudied flora of the dry spiny thicket of southwestern Madagascar. The phylogeographic relationships in two species each of the three endemic genera in the Megistohibiscus clade have been reconstructed through the collection, analysis, and comparison of RADseq data. Working with genomic data at the population level has helped to resolve species relationships in previously difficult to resolve lineages (e.g., *Megistostegium*, M. Hanes, unpublished data). Genomic data are being combined with spatial and temporal hypothesis testing to evaluate whether similar landscape features structure populations of co-occurring genera across southern Madagascar and if they diversified at similar times. Tests for environmental similarity between sister species provide evidence for different patterns in each genus. For example, the niches of sister species are, in most cases, more different than is expected by chance in *Humbertiella* suggesting niche divergence as at least one factor driving speciation in the genus. A pattern of niche conservatism is, instead, recovered in comparisons between the nearly entirely sympatric species in the genus *Megistostegium* (M. Hanes, unpublished data).

Subject editors: Laurent Gautier and Steven M. Goodman

MALVACEAE: *ADANSONIA*, BAOBAB, *BOZY*, *FONY*, *RENALA*, *RINGY*, *ZA*

N. Karimi, D. A. Baum, O. H. Razanamaro, J.-M. Leong Pock Tsy, and P. Danthu

The baobabs are members of the genus *Adansonia* (Malvaceae). All species are deciduous trees with trunks that are thick relative to their crowns and fat, often gnarly, branches. As a result, they have a very distinctive form, especially in a leafless state (Figure 8.65). Baobabs occur in continental Africa (one species), northwest Australia (one species), and Madagascar (six species). However, the continental African species, *A. digitata*, has been widely dispersed by humans and by water (Wickens 1983; Leong Pock Tsy et al. 2009), and has become naturalized in several places, including some sites in northwestern Madagascar.

FIGURE 8.65 **Examples of the different growth forms of the endemic Malagasy *Adansonia*. A) *A. grandidieri* near Morondava; B) *A. madagascariensis* at Ankarana; C) *A. za* in dry deciduous forests near Morondava; D) *A. rubrostipa* near Tsimanampesotse; E) *A. rubrostipa* in dry deciduous forest near Morondava; F) *A. grandidieri* trees standing in the remnants of burned forests near Lake Ihotry; and G) *A. za* in dry spiny thicket near Beloha.** (PHOTOS A, B, C, E, and G by D. A. Baum; and D and F by N. Karimi.)

DISTRIBUTION ON MADAGASCAR

The seven species of baobab that occur on Madagascar are largely restricted to dry deciduous forest on the western side of the island (Baum 1995a, 1996). In the north, however, some species may occur in moist semi-deciduous forests. There is extensive overlap in the distributions of the six endemic Malagasy species (Figure 8.66) and two (or rarely three) species may occur in the same locality. For

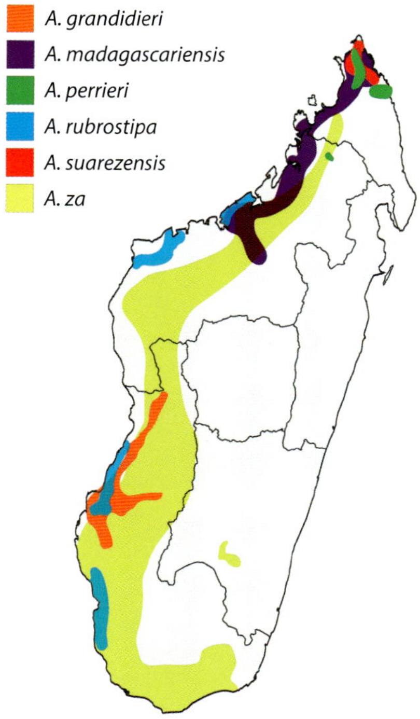

FIGURE 8.66 **Distribution map of the six species of baobab endemic to Madagascar.**

example, near Toliara, *A. rubrostipa* (formerly called *A. fony*) may be found growing within a few hundred meters of *A. za* (the latter being a larger tree on richer soils). These same two species are also intermingled in extensive forests near Morondava, along with a third species, *A. grandidieri*, which primarily occurs close to rivers and waterholes. In the northwest, *A. madagascariensis* occurs in sympatry with *A. za* (e.g., near Maromandia), with *A. perrieri* (e.g., in Ankarana), with *A. suarezensis* (around the Antsiranana Bay), or with *A. rubrostipa* in the Boeny Region. Co-occurring species are generally easy to tell apart (Baum 1995a) and have flowering periods that are largely, though not completely, non-overlapping (Leong Pock Tsy et al. 2013).

VEGETATIVE MORPHOLOGY

Baobabs are characterized by deciduous palmately compound leaves with five to nine sessile (except southern populations of *A. za*), entire (serrate in some *A. rubrostipa*) leaflets. Seedlings and saplings may have simple or trifoliate leaves and are more likely to have leaflets with serrate margins. Leaves are borne on the trees throughout the wet season from October/November until approximately May. Leafing out can precede the onset of the rains—enabled by water stored in the large trunks of low-density wood (Chapotin et al. 2006). The bark is fibrous, and, based on work on the African species (*A. digitata*), can remain photosynthetically active even when trees are leafless (Kotina et al. 2017). The wood and bark of baobabs show an unusual capacity to regenerate following damage (Fisher 1981).

In general, baobabs are canopy or emergent trees, having a stature to match the forest in which they grow. When growing in dry, sandy soils in southern dry spiny thickets or on limestone (*tsingy*) outcrops they form stunted trees that may reach maturity when as little as 3 m in height. In contrast, in the rich, dry deciduous forests of the west (e.g., the baobab-dominated forests near Morondava) or the moist semi-deciduous forests of the northwest (e.g., the Sambirano Region) they may attain 20–25 m. In the moist semi-deciduous forests of the northern base of Montagne d'Ambre, one species, *A. perrieri*, may attain 30 m in height.

The unique architecture of baobabs, with their massive trunks, suggests notable longevity. Radiocarbon dating of some of the largest baobabs on Madagascar has confirmed that their life span can be well over 1000 years. A large *A. rubrostipa* located in Tsimanampesotse in the southwest has an estimated age of 1600 years (Patrut et al. 2015a), and a large *A. grandidieri* has been dated at 1200 years old (Patrut et al. 2015b). Considering that Patrut and colleagues interpret each baobab tree as a fusion of several independent trunks, their estimated ages may be significant underestimates if these baobab individuals are actually single-trunked trees.

FLOWER BIOLOGY

All species of baobab have large, actinomorphic (radially symmetrical) flowers that open around dusk. Anthesis takes as long as 15 minutes (e.g., *A. digitata*, *A. grandidieri*) or as little as one minute (e.g., *A. rubrostipa*, *A. za*). While corolla and stamens may remain attached to trees for as long as four days, it appears that the flowers of all species are receptive for only a single night.

The arrangement of flower parts is the same in all species. The calyx is nectar-secreting and comprises a calyx tube and five valvate lobes. The corolla has contorted aestivation (spirally overlapping petals) and is composed of five free petals attached to the base of the staminal tube. The androecium (the stamen derived parts) is composed of a staminal tube surmounted by many free filaments with anthers composed of two pollen chambers. The gynoecium (the carpel-derived parts) comprises a superior, pentalocular or octalocular ovary and an unbranched style with a terminal, somewhat lobed, stigma. Nonetheless, there is extensive variation in flower form and pollination system (Baum 1995b).

Adansonia grandidieri and *A. suarezensis* have white flowers near the tips of leafless branches that are produced in the dry season, generally May to July. They are borne erect and have a cup-like, open calyx tube that can accumulate as much as 2 ml of nectar. The petals are reflexed, narrow, and strap-like. The staminal tube is short and surmounted by numerous (600–1100) elongated filaments, each with a large, rigidly attached anther.

Adansonia za, *A. rubrostipa*, *A. madagascariensis*, and *A. perrieri* flower during the wet season, with the greatest rainfall generally between December and April. In all four species the elongated flowers (up to 29 cm) show red and yellow coloration. The inner surfaces of the long, strap-like calyx lobes are dark red (sometimes pale pink or almost white in *A. perrieri*), the corolla is bright yellow (sometimes red in *A. madagascariensis* or pale yellow in *A. perrieri*), the androecium is pale yellow, and the style and stigma are usually dark pinkish red (sometimes pale pink in *A. perrieri*). The calyx tube fits tightly around the petal bases, and nectar is accessible to flower visitors via narrow openings between the petal bases, inside the corolla whorl. The nectar accumulates in modest amounts (rarely over 300 μL) in a nectar chamber below the petal bases. The androecium comprises either a very long, thin staminal tube with short free filaments (*A. perrieri*) or a shorter, stouter staminal tube with longer free filaments (the other three species). In either case the anthers are relatively few in number (90–250), small, and show versatile anther-insertion. *Adansonia rubrostipa* is unique in having a central bundle of 10–20 filaments that are fused into a bundle beyond the top of the staminal tube. These species have fragrant flowers that are dominated by aromatic (e.g., 2-phenylacetonitrile and 2-phenylethanol) compounds (Razanamaro et al. 2015).

The African baobab (*A. digitata*) has white flowers that hang down on dangling peduncles. Nectar is secreted by a flattened calyx, which is held in place by broad, rounded petals. The staminal tube is elongated and surmounted by numerous filaments that are quite short. The style is often bent over at a right angle above the top of the androecium. Floral odor is musky, which is attributable (at least in west Africa) to the presence of numerous sulfurous compounds (Knudsen and Tollsten 1995).

POLLINATION

Adansonia grandidieri and *A. suarezensis* are mammal pollinated, with fruit bats (*Eidolon dupreanum* and *Rousettus madagascariensis*) predominating in *A. suarezensis* and *Phaner* sp. (fork-marked lemurs) in *A. grandidieri* (Baum 1995b). *Pteropus rufus* also occurs across the range of *A. suarezensis* and *A. grandidieri*, likely pollinating both species. In both cases the animals extract nectar nondestructively and move between trees. Other flower visitors include hawkmoths (e.g., *Nephele comma*, *Hippotion celerio*) and sunbirds (*Cinnyris notatus* and *C. sovimanga*), but neither group contributes significantly to pollination since they approach flowers from below or laterally and tend not to make contact with the stigma. Furthermore, sunbird activity is restricted to daytime whereas baobabs are nocturnally receptive.

Adansonia za, *A. rubrostipa*, *A. madagascariensis*, and *A. perrieri* are primarily pollinated by the hawkmoths *Coelonia solanii* and *Agrius convolvuli*, with additional other hawkmoth species contributing in some species (e.g., *Xanthopan morganii* in *Adansonia perrieri*; *C. brevis* in *A. za*) (Baum 1995b; Ryckewaert et al. 2011). The pollinating hawkmoths extract nectar by briefly hovering in front of a flower and inserting their long proboscis (commonly attaining 25 cm) into the nectar chamber. Other floral visitors include lemurs (*Cheirogaleus medius* and *Phaner* sp.), bees, small moths, and, rarely, butterflies or sunbirds. None of these are likely to be significant visitors, but occasional pollination by lemurs cannot be ruled out (Baum 1995b).

The pollination of the African species *A. digitata* has not been studied on Madagascar where it usually occurs in villages or cities (e.g., in Antsiranana and Mahajanga). However, elsewhere it is known to be pollinated by bats (Jaeger 1945; Start 1972), bushbabies (Coe and Isaac 1965; Wickens 1983), and hawkmoths (N. Karimi et al., unpublished data).

FRUITS AND DISPERSAL

Regardless of whether flowering occurs in the early wet season (*A. za*, *A. perrieri*, and *A. digitata*), the late wet season (*A. rubrostipa* and *A. madagascariensis*), or in the dry season (*A. suarezensis* and *A. grandidieri*) fruit matures in the late dry season or early wet season. Fruits are many-seeded, dry berries with a woody and sometimes fibrous pericarp. The edible pulp is whitish and spongy or chalky with a pleasant, acidic taste. The seeds are the size of a large bean and kidney-shaped with a very durable seed coat. Water dispersal is important in some species (e.g., *A. za*, *A. madagascariensis*, *A. perrieri*), whereas others appear adapted to animal dispersal (especially *A. grandidieri* and *A. suarezensis*). It has been hypothesized that dispersal was carried out by animals that went extinct during the Quaternary, for example the baboon-like *Archaeolemur* (Baum 1995a) and giant tortoises *Aldabrachelys grandidieri* and *A. abrupta* (Andriantsaralaza et al. 2010). Some species of baobab require scarification for germination (Razanameharizaka et al. 2006) and have been shown during experiments to remain viable following extended gut passage (15–23 days) in the extant Aldabra Giant Tortoise (*A. gigantea*) (Andriantsaralaza et al. 2014). In the absence of Malagasy megafauna, the larger extant lemurs might contribute to recruitment and dispersion in some areas, although more data are needed. Seed germination can be either cryptocotylar (the cotyledons remain at least partly within the seed coat at ground level) as in *A. suarezensis* and *A. grandidieri* or phanerocotylar (the cotyledons break out of the seed coat and are raised above the ground) as in the other species.

The chromosomes of baobabs are small and difficult to count, which probably explains the range of chromosome numbers reported in the literature. Newer counts (Baum and Oginuma 1994; Cron et al. 2016) suggest that all the Malagasy baobabs (like the Australian species) have a diploid number of 2n = 88, whereas *A. digitata* appears to be a tetraploid with 2n = 160–166.

PHYLOGENETICS AND SYSTEMATICS

Phylogenetic analysis of *Adansonia* (Baum et al. 1998; Leong Pock Tsy et al. 2013; Karimi et al. 2020) suggests that the six Malagasy species form a monophyletic group whose relationship to the African and Australian species remains uncertain (Figure 8.67). The closest extant relatives of *Adansonia* occur in South America (Carvalho-Sobrinho et al. 2016), and the origin of the genus is most likely continental Africa followed by near-simultaneous dispersals to Madagascar and Australia. Based on molecular clock inferences and fossil pollen records for Neotropical taxa, dispersal from the New to the Old World occurred between about 8 and 45 million years ago (Mya), with dispersal events among Africa, Madagascar, and Australia dated much more recently at approximately 5 to 10 Mya (Zizka et al. 2020). Dispersal to Australia could have involved direct long-distance oceanic transport or dispersal of seeds via now extinct populations of baobabs along the northern rim of the Indian Ocean. Reconstruction of the group's floral evolution implies that the ancestral pollination system was that of hawkmoths, with two parallel switches to mammal pollination, one in Africa and one on Madagascar, possibly aided on the island by the transfer of traits though introgressive hybridization (Karimi et al. 2020; Figure 8.67).

Within the Malagasy clade, the two white-flowered, mammal-pollinated species (*A. suarezensis* and *A. grandidieri*) are well-supported sister species. *Adansonia rubrostipa* is a distinct

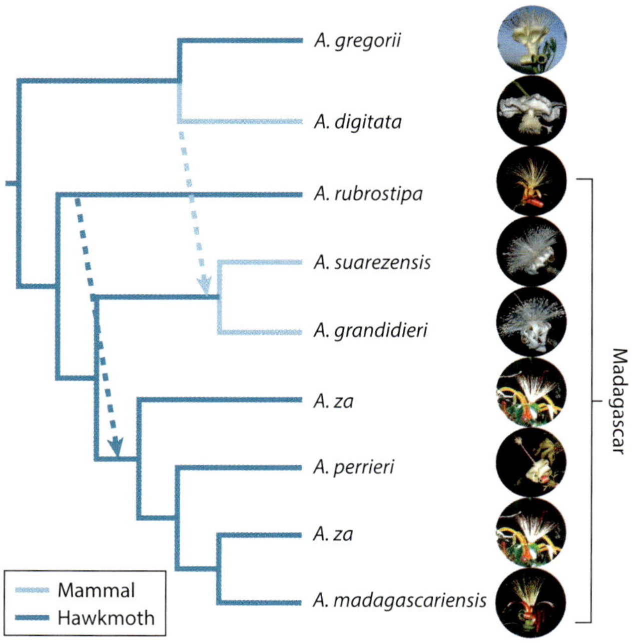

FIGURE 8.67 Current estimate of the phylogeny of *Adansonia* based on DNA sequence data with inference of introgressive hybridization (dashed arrows) and current and ancestral pollination states mapped onto the tree (Karimi et al. 2020). The pollinator type for each baobab species is color coded following the key.

lineage from the three other pigmented, hawkmoth-pollinated species, which form a clade for most of the genome. Phylogenomic data suggest that *A. rubrostipa* has a history of hybridization with ancestral lineages and perhaps extant populations of *A. za* and *A. madagascariensis* (Leong Pock Tsy et al. 2013; Karimi et al. 2020; N. Karimi et al., unpublished data).

Recent and ongoing phylogeographic studies suggest that populations representing *A. za* north of the Sambirano River are genetically distinct from southern populations (Figure 8.67) and share genetic similarities with *A. perrieri* (Leong Pock Tsy et al. 2013; Karimi et al. 2020; N. Karimi et al., unpublished data). The distinctiveness of northern *A. za* is consistent with previous classifications, which recognized northern *A. za* as *A. bozy* (Jumelle and Perrier de la Bâthie 1910) or *A. za* var. *bozy* (Perrier de la Bâthie 1952b). Further work is needed to determine whether *A. bozy* should be recognized as a distinct species and, likewise, whether northern *A. rubrostipa*, which seems to have acquired significant genetic input from *A. madagascariensis* (N. Karimi et al., unpublished data), should be recognized as a distinct species from more southern populations.

CULTURAL AND SOCIAL VALUE

The Malagasy baobabs provide a number of valuable resources for humans (Baum 1996). In particular, fruits and seeds are eaten, cooking oil is extracted from seeds (*A. suarezensis* and *A. grandidieri*), leaves are used as fodder for cattle, bark is used to make ropes, and wood strips are used for thatching. Baobab seed oil contains a high content of linoleic and oleic acids in the African species, and a high content of palmitic acid in *A. suarezensis* and *A. grandidieri* (Razafimamonjison et al. 2017). The high fatty acid composition has generated international demand for seed oil of the African species (Kumar 2018) and a growth in local commercial production on Madagascar of the endemic species. Edible mushrooms (*Volvaria esculenta*) can also be found growing on decaying baobabs and are reported to be exported internationally (Wickens and Lowe 2008). Additionally, probably on account of their striking appearance, baobabs are much revered and are often identified as sites of magical, religious, or spiritual significance (Wickens and Lowe 2008; Marie et al. 2009; P. Danthu, unpublished data). *Adansonia grandidieri* is called "mother of the forest" (*reniala* or *renala*) or "true mother of the forest" (*reniala tenany*). They are considered as never having been planted by humans, like the rest of the forest, but by *Zanahary* (God). Thus, the baobab is associated with wild nature. The status of mother (*reny*) that the people attribute to the baobab refers to its wood, rich in water, and to the symbolism of the pregnant woman designated by "she who carries water" (*mitondra rano*).

SPECIES CONSERVATION STATUS

Baobabs play an important ecological role in many Malagasy ecosystems (Baum 1996), especially the aptly named baobab forests. These were historically most abundant in the region from just north of Morondava to just south of Toliara, but also occur further north, such as in Ankarana, Montagne des Français, and Analamerana. Sadly, however, many populations of all the Malagasy species are threatened due to human activities, especially excessive forest burning and forest clearance for agriculture. In particular, *A. suarezensis* and *A. perrieri* may be headed toward extinction in the wild given their restricted distribution, projected sensitivity to climate change, lack of in situ recruitment, and declining number of mature individuals (Vieilledent al. 2013). According to the International Union for the Conservation of Nature (IUCN) Red List criteria (IUCN 2017), *A. perrieri* is classified as Critically Endangered (Letsara et al. 2019a) and *A. suarezensis* as Endangered. *Adansonia grandidieri* is also listed as Endangered (Ravaomanalina and Razafimanahaka 2016) due in part to the high economic demand for the seeds, intense deforestation, and limited in situ protection (Vieilledent et al. 2013). *Adansonia madagascariensis* was classified as Near Threatened in IUCN's last assessment of this species (World Conservation Monitoring Centre 1998). *Adansonia rubrostipa* and *A. za* are currently classified as Least Concern (Letsara et al. 2019b, 2019c) given their more widespread distributions, but this may be optimistic given active deforestation and browsing in most sites where baobabs are or were abundant. Local development and conservation objectives need to be combined and embraced by residents in order to achieve long-term sustainability of these majestic trees (Marie et al. 2009). As charismatic megaflora the iconic baobabs may help to inspire awareness and spur action to advance plant conservation on Madagascar, and perhaps throughout the entire world.

Subject editors: Laurent Gautier and Steven M. Goodman

SPHAERÓSEPALACEAE

G. E. Schatz and P. P. Lowry II

Sphaerosepalaceae is the second largest of Madagascar's five endemic vascular plant families, the others being Sarcolaenaceae (72 species), Asteropeiaceae (eight species), Physenaceae (two species), and Barbeuiaceae (one species) (Ramananjanahary et al. 2010; Madagascar Catalogue 2020). In total, Sphaerosepalaceae comprises two genera and 20 species (Schatz et al. 1999b; Schatz and Lowry 2006). Members of Sphaerosepalaceae are small to large trees with copious mucilage, particularly evident in cut fruits. Sphaerosepalaceae species can be recognized by their alternate, entire leaves with intrapetiolar stipules and large tetramerous flowers that have four sepals arranged in two pairs oriented perpendicularly to each other, delicate, white petals that fall off early in the flowering period, and many stamens. Fruits or individual mericarps are fleshy to woody, indehiscent, and presumably dispersed by vertebrates, but virtually no details are documented on this aspect.

Sphaerosepalaceae belong to the order Malvales *sensu* Angiosperm Working Group IV (2016), where they are closely related to the families Bixaceae (including the endemic Malagasy genus *Diegodendron*) and Thymelaeaceae, and somewhat more distantly related to Madagascar's largest endemic family, Sarcolaenaceae. The

FIGURE 8.68 **Examples of Malagasy Sphaerosepalaceae. A) *Dialyceras coriaceum*, flowers (Schatz 3848, Fampanambo); B) *D. parvifolium*, fruiting branches at Ambanizana, Masoala (Schatz 3082); C) *Rhopalocarpus coriaceus*, flower at Sainte Luce (Ratovoson 1847); D) *R. coriaceus*, fruit at Petriky (Swenson 1721); E) *R. lucidus*, fruit at Andohahela, parcel 3 (Randrianaivo 1756); F) *R. macrorhamnifolius* at Ambalabe (A. Randrianasolo 1376); and G) *R. thouarsianus* at Tampolo (Schatz 3634).** (PHOTO A by P. Lowry; B and G by G. Schatz; C by F. Ratovoson; D by U. Swenson; E by R. Randrianaivo; and F by F. Rakotoarivony.)

majority of Sphaerosepalaceae species occur in humid littoral and low-elevation moist evergreen forests, but one species occurs in dry spiny thickets (*Rhopalocarous lucidus*), and several species occur in dry deciduous forests in the west (*R. similis*) and far north (*R. suarezensis*, *R. triplinervius*, and *R. undulatus*).

THE GENERA OF SPHAEROSEPALACEAE

Dialyceras

This genus comprises three species of large trees in low-altitude moist evergreen forests from Betampona to slightly north of Sambava. It is characterized by leaves with penninerved venation, and a gynoecium of four separate carpels; the resulting fruit a cluster of separate, sessile, one-seeded mericarps (Figures 8.68a and b).

Rhopalocarpus

This genus comprises 17 species with highly variable leaf venation ranging from penninerved to often palmatinerved, or distinctly bi- or triplinerved, and a gynoecium of two to four fused carpels to form a compound ovary, resulting in one- to four-seeded fruit (Figures 8.68c–g).

CONSERVATION STATUS OF SPECIES

Risk of extinction assessments for all 20 species of Sphaerosepalaceae are published on the International Union for the Conservation of Nature (IUCN) Red List, including five species that are Endangered, nine Vulnerable, and six Least Concern.

Subject editors: Laurent Gautier and Steven M. Goodman

SARCOLAENACEAE

G. E. Schatz and P. P. Lowry II

Sarcolaenaceae is the largest of Madagascar's five endemic families, the others being Asteropeiaceae (eight species), Barbeuiaceae (one species), Physenaceae (two species), and Sphaerosepalaceae (20 species) (Madagascar Catalogue 2020). In all, Sarcolaenaceae comprises 10 genera and 72 described species (see Table 8.43), as well as one undescribed species of *Eremolaena* and six of *Sarcolaena* (Madagascar Catalogue 2020; A. Randrianasolo et al., unpublished data). A broad taxonomic review of the family was initiated in the late 1990s resulting in a series of generic revisions (Lowry et al. 1999, 2000, 2002; Randrianasolo and Miller 1999b; Schatz et al. 2000, 2001; Hong-Wa 2009) and descriptions of new species (Randrianasolo and Miller 1994; Lowry and Rabehevitra 2006; Rabehevitra and Lowry 2009; Lowry et al. 2014; Andriamihajarivo et al. 2016), which together more than doubled the 33 species recognized by Cavaco (1952a) in his treatment for the *Flore de Madagascar et des Comores*, under its earlier name Chlaenacées.

Members of Sarcolaenaceae are shrubs and trees, and the family is represented in nearly all of Madagascar's bioclimatic zones and vegetation types. Sarcolaenaceae members can be recognized by their alternate, simple, entire leaves with stipules, and often large and showy flowers with a pentamerous corolla and superior ovary. They are also characterized by the presence of a distinctive extrafloral involucre that expands in many taxa after anthesis to form a fleshy or woody structure, which sometimes completely encloses the fruit, a condition referred to as angiocarpy. The vegetative portions of members of this family are widely consumed by a variety of lemurs (see Eppley et al., pp. 1839–59). In the genera accounts presented here we summarize some details on vertebrate consumption of Sarcolaenaceae fruits.

Sarcolaenaceae belongs to the order Malvales *sensu* Angiosperm Working Group IV (2016), where they are closely related to the families Cistaceae and Dipterocarpaceae, and somewhat more distantly related to Madagascar's second-largest endemic family, Sphaerosepalaceae. Until recently, however, Sarcolaenaceae was represented by only a few exemplar taxa in phylogenetic studies, which made it impossible to assess whether the family is monophyletic or to elucidate relationships among its genera. The study of Aubriot et al. (2016), based on broad sampling that included 46 of the 72 recognized species at that time and full generic representation, confirmed the monophyly of the family, as well as eight of the 10 currently recognized genera. Species of *Rhodolaena* were, however, placed in two well-supported clades, although the lack of resolution among these and the other lineages comprising a large basal polytomy in the phylogenetic tree precludes a decision on whether they represent different genera. The monophyly of *Eremolaena* could not be tested because only a single sample was included. With *Sarcolaena* embedded in *Leptolaena sensu lato*, the phylogenetic study supported the recognition of the genera *Mediusella* and *Xerochlamys* as distinct from *Leptolaena*, an interpretation adopted by Capuron (1970a) based on morphology and by Hong-Wa (2008, 2009) based on morphometric analyses, rather than treating them as subgenera within a broadly defined *Leptolaena*, as had been done by earlier authors such as Cavaco (1951, 1952a, 1952b).

TABLE 8.43. **Species of Sarcolaenaceae on Madagascar and their IUCN status**

SPECIES	IUCN STATUS
Eremolaena darainensis Nusb. & Lowry	EN
E. humblotiana Baill.	VU
E. rotundifolia (F. Gérard) Danguy	LC
Leptolaena abrahamii G. E. Schatz & Lowry	NT
L. cuspidata Baker	LC
L. delphinensis G. E. Schatz & Lowry	VU
L. gautieri G. E. Schatz & Lowry	LC
L. masoalensis G. E. Schatz & Lowry	CR
L. multiflora Thouars	LC
L. pauciflora Baker	LC
L. raymondii G. E. Schatz & Lowry	EN
Mediusella arenaria (F. Gérard) Hong-Wa	NT
M. bernieri (Baill.) Hutch.	EN
Pentachlaena betamponensis Lowry, Haev., Labat & G. E. Schatz	CR
P. latifolia H. Perrier	EN
P. orientalis Capuron	EN
P. vestita Andriamih., Lowry & G. E. Schatz	EN
Perrierodendron boinense (H. Perrier) Cavaco	VU
P. capuronii J.-F. Leroy, Lowry, Haev., Labat & G. E. Schatz	EN
P. occidentale J.-F. Leroy, Lowry, Haev., Labat & G. E. Schatz	VU
P. quartzitorum J.-F. Leroy, Lowry, Haev., Labat & G. E. Schatz	CR
P. rodoense J.-F. Leroy, Lowry, Haev., Labat & G. E. Schatz	CR
Rhodolaena acutifolia Baker	VU
R. altivola Thouars	VU
R. bakeriana Baill.	LC
R. coriacea G. E. Schatz, Lowry & A.-E. Wolf	LC
R. humblotii Baill.	LC
R. leroyana G. E. Schatz, Lowry & A.-E. Wolf	VU
R. macrocarpa G. E. Schatz, Lowry & A.-E. Wolf	EN
Sarcolaena codonochlamys Baker	NT
S. delphinensis Cavaco	EN
S. eriophora Thouars	NT
S. grandiflora Thouars	VU
S. humbertiana Cavaco	CR
S. isaloensis Randrian. & J. S. Mill.	CR
S. multiflora Thouars	LC
S. oblongifolia F. Gérard	LC
Schizolaena capuronii Lowry, G. E. Schatz, J.-F. Leroy & A.-E. Wolf	EN
S. cauliflora Thouars	LC
S. cavacoana Lowry, G. E. Schatz, J.-F. Leroy & A.-E. Wolf	EN
S. charlotteae Lowry & G. E. Schatz	EN
S. elongata Thouars	LC
S. exinvolucrata Baker	LC
S. gereaui Lowry, G. E. Schatz, J.-F. Leroy & A.-E. Wolf	LC
S. hystrix Capuron	LC
S. isaloensis Rabehevitra & Lowry	EN
S. manomboensis Lowry, G. E. Schatz, J.-F. Leroy & A.-E. Wolf	EN
S. masoalensis Lowry, G. E. Schatz, J.-F. Leroy & A.-E. Wolf	EN
S. microphylla H. Perrier	VU
S. milleri Lowry, G. E. Schatz, J.-F. Leroy & A.-E. Wolf	EN
S. noronhae (Tul.) G. E. Schatz & Lowry	EN
S. parviflora (F. Gérard) H. Perrier	VU
S. parvipetala Randrian. & Hong-Wa	EN
S. pectinata Capuron	VU
S. raymondii Lowry & Rabehevitra	CR
S. rosea Thouars	VU
S. tampoketsana Lowry, G. E. Schatz, J.-F. Leroy & A.-E. Wolf	CR
S. turkii Lowry, G. E. Schatz, J.-F. Leroy & A.-E. Wolf	EN
S. viscosa F. Gérard	VU
Xerochlamys bojeriana (Baill.) F. Gérard	NE
X. coriacea Hong-Wa	VU
X. diospyroidea (Baill.) F. Gérard	EN
X. elliptica F. Gérard	EN
X. itremoensis Hong-Wa, G. E. Schatz & Lowry	EN
X. tampoketsensis F. Gérard	VU
X. undulata Hong-Wa	EN
X. villosa F. Gérard	EN
Xyloolaena humbertii Cavaco	EN
X. perrieri F. Gérard	VU
X. richardii (Baill.) Baill.	LC
X. sambiranensis Lowry & G. E. Schatz	VU
X. speciosa Lowry & G. E. Schatz	VU

Notes: All species listed are endemic. IUCN status abbreviations: CR, Critically Endangered; DD, Data Deficient; EN, Endangered; LC, Least Concern; NE, Not Evaluated; NT, Near Threatened; VU, Vulnerable.

SPECIES DIVERSITY, DISTRIBUTION, AND ENDEMISM

The 10 genera of Sarcolaenaceae vary in size from two species in *Mediusella* to 22 species in *Schizolaena*. Ramananjanahary et al. (2010) provide a key to the genera as well as keys to the members of each genus and descriptions of all species. All 72 described species of the family are endemic to Madagascar (Figure 8.69). The majority of them have very restricted geographic distributions and are rarely or infrequently encountered in the field, including many known from just one or a few localities, such as *Leptolaena masoalensis, L. raymondii, Pentachlaena latifolia, P. vestita, Rhodolaena macrocarpa, Sarcolaena isaloensis, S. humbertiana, Schizolaena capuronii, S. charlotteae, S. masoalensis, S. parvipetala, S. raymondii, and S. tampoketsana*. A few species, such as *L. pauciflora* and *Sarcolaena multiflora*, are widespread and often common in the areas where they occur, reflecting the fact that they are tolerant of fire and other forms of disturbance (Ramananjanahary et al. 2010; Madagascar Catalogue 2020).

Species belonging to several different genera of Sarcolaenaceae frequently co-occur, a phenomenon believed to be related to the fact that they have evolved a characteristic symbiotic relationship with ectomycorrhizal fungi, a feature also found in the closely related family Dipterocarpaceae (Ducousso et al. 2004). Sarcolaenaceae species frequently occur in formations that also include species of *Uapaca* (Phyllanthaceae; see Kull and Birkinshaw, pp. 121–27) and members of two other families endemic to Madagascar, Asteropeiaceae and Sphaerosepalaceae, which are also associated with ectomycorrhizal fungi (Ducousso et al. 2008). Several areas are particularly rich in Sarcolaenaceae, such as around Antongil Bay, where 11 species have been recorded; Betampona Reserve, with 11 species; and the tiny Analalava Reserve (229 ha), where nine species have been documented (Madagascar Catalogue 2020).

Sarcolaenaceae members occur in littoral forests and low-altitude moist evergreen forests (e.g., *Eremolaena rotundifolia, Leptolaena delphinensis, Rhodolaena altivola, Schizolaena elongata, S. noronhae*) but are most diverse in medium-altitude moist evergreen forests, with only a single species reaching 1700 m above sea level (*R. coriacea*). The family is also well represented in sclerophyllous woodlands (e.g., *Pentachlaena latifolia, Perrierodendron quartzitorum, Sarcolaena oblongifolia, Schizolaena microphylla, S. tampoketsana, Xerochlamys bojeriana*), in a few cases extending above 1800 m (*X. diospyroidea* and *X. itremoensis*). Sarcolaenaceae species are also found in dry deciduous forests (e.g., *Leptolaena cuspidata, Mediusella arenaria, M. bernieri, Perrierodendron boinense, S. parviflora, S. viscosa, Xyloolaena perrieri*) but are not known to occur in montane ericoid thicket or dry spiny thicket vegetation.

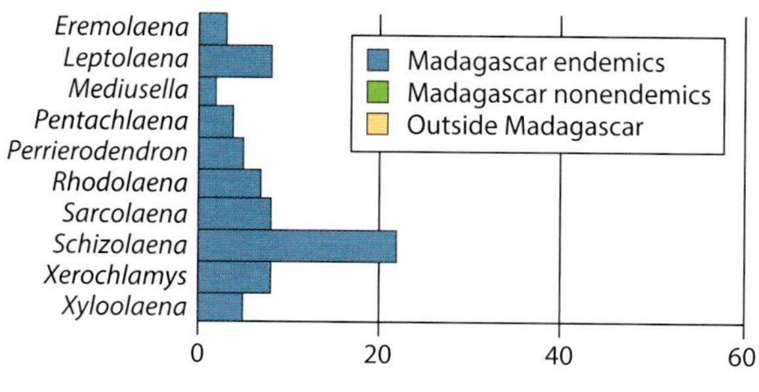

FIGURE 8.69 **Diversity and endemicity diagram of Malagasy Sarcolaenaceae at the level of genera, showing three different species counts: 1) endemic to Madagascar, 2) nonendemic but native to Madagascar, and 3) those occurring elsewhere in the world (for further information see text).**

THE GENERA OF SARCOLAENACEAE ON MADAGASCAR

Eremolaena

This genus comprises three described species and one that remains to be named. Species of *Eremolaena* are characterized by the presence of stellate and lepidote indumentum on most of their parts, large flowers with unequally sized sepals, a white corolla, and a tricarpellate ovary, and dehiscent fruits subtended by an involucre that is non-accrescent (Ramananjanahary et al. 2010). One of the described species occurs in littoral forests (*E. rotundifolia*), one in moist evergreen forests (*E. humblotiana*) (Figures 8.70a and b), and one in moist semi-deciduous forests (*E. darainensis*) (Madagascar Catalogue 2020).

Leptolaena

All eight species of *Leptolaena* have free stipules, small flowers with a white corolla and six to 12 stamens, and fruits that are completely enveloped by a woody involucre (Ramananjanahary et al. 2010). The genus is mostly found in littoral forests and low- to medium-altitude moist evergreen forests, evergreen forests extending into subhumid areas, and one species occurs in moist semi-deciduous and dry deciduous forests in the far northwest (*L. cuspidata*) (Madagascar Catalogue 2020).

Mediusella

This is the smallest genus of Sarcolaenaceae, with just two species. They have free stipules, large flowers with a white corolla and more than 20 stamens, and fruits that are completely enveloped by the woody involucre (Ramananjanahary et al. 2010). Both are found in dry deciduous forests, one in the northwest and far north (*M. arenaria*) and the other only in the far north (*M. bernieri*) (Figure 8.70e) (Madagascar Catalogue 2020).

Pentachlaena

This genus has four species characterized by stellate and lepidote indumentum on most of their parts, large flowers with equally sized sepals, a white corolla, and a pentacarpellate ovary, and fruits that are dehiscent (Ramananjanahary et al. 2010). Two species of *Pentachlaena* are found in low- to medium-altitude moist evergreen forests (*P. betamponensis* and *P. orientalis*) and the other two occur in sclerophyllous woodlands (*P. latifolia* [Figures 8.70f and g] and *P. vestita* [Figure 8.70h]) (Madagascar Catalogue 2020).

FIGURE 8.70 **Examples of Malagasy Sarcolaenaceae. A) *Eremolaena humblotiana* at Forêt d'Ampasimpotsy (Syde 163); B) *E. humblotiana* at Analalava Reserve (Birkinshaw 2079); C) *Leptolaena raymondii* at Analalava Reserve (Birkinshaw 2063); D) *L. pauciflora* at Antaniditra Forest (Antilahimena 7042); E) *Mediusella bernieri* at Sahafary (Schatz 4266); F) *Pentachlaena latifolia* at Ibity (Schatz 4135); G) *P. latifolia* at Ibity (Lowry 7286); H) *P. vestita* at Ambohipiandrianana-Ambohibary (Andriamihajarivo 1907); I) *Perrierodendron quartzitorum* at Itremo (Schatz 3973); J) *Rhodolaena altivola* at Analalava (Birkinshaw 1736); K) *R. humblotiana* at Betampona (Schatz 4469); L) *R. leroyana* at Forêt d'Alahambana (Syde 302); M) *Sarcolaena multiflora* at Sainte Luce (Ratovoson 1630); N and O) *Sarcolaena* sp. at Ambatovy (Rakotovao 3986); P) *Sarcolaena* sp. at Forêt d'Ampanola (Razakamalala 5575); Q) *Schizolaena microphylla* at Forêt Classée de Faliarivo (Lowry 5817); R) *S. cauliflora* at Forêt d'Ampasimadinika (Syde 296); S) *S. manomboensis* at Analalava (Birkinshaw 1739); T) *S. elongata* at Pointe à Larrée (Razanatsoa 524); U) *S. viscosa* at Forêt de Galoko (Randriatsivery 460); V) *Xerochlamys bojeriana* at Col des Tapia (Lowry 7066A); W) *X. diospyroides* at Itremo (Schatz 3960); X) *Xyloolaena richardii* at Cap Est, Masoala Peninsula (Schatz 3812); Y) *X. perrieri* at Antsotso (Razakamalala 7737); and Z) *X. humbertii* at Andohahela (Lowry 6968).** (PHOTOS A and L by A. Syde; B, C, J, and S by C. Birkinshaw; D and R by P. Antilahimena; E, G, I, K, Q, W, and X by G. Schatz; F, V, and Z by P. Lowry; H by T. Andriamihajarivo; M by F. Ratovoson; N–P by C. Rakotovao; T by N. V. Manjato; U by M. Randriatsivery; and Y by R. Randrianaivo.)

Perrierodendron

The five species of this genus have stellate indumentum, large flowers with a white corolla and a bicarpellate ovary, and indehiscent fruits (Ramananjanahary et al. 2010). Three species of *Perrierodendron* occur in dry deciduous forests in the west and far north, one is found in sclerophyllous woodlands (*P. quartzitorum*) (Figure 8.70i), and one in medium-altitude moist evergreen forests (*P. capuronii*) (Madagascar Catalogue 2020).

Rhodolaena

In the study of Aubriot et al. (2016), the first *Rhodolaena* clade includes five species characterized by large flowers with five sepals, a magenta corolla, and an involucre that does not expand to surround the dehiscent fruits (Ramananjanahary et al. 2010). The members of this clade occur in low- to medium-altitude moist evergreen forests (Madagascar Catalogue 2020). The second clade, which may represent a new genus, comprises two species of low-altitude moist evergreen forests; they are characterized by large flowers with a cream to yellow corolla and an involucre that expands to become fleshy and completely surrounds the dehiscent fruit.

Sarcolaena

This genus includes eight described species and potentially six undescribed species. Its members have fused stipules, leaves that are superficially triplinerved or palmatinerved due to the presence of vernation traces on either side of the midvein as a result of folding in bud (except in *S. isaloensis*), medium-size to large flowers with a white or yellow corolla, and fruits that are completely enclosed by the fleshy involucre (Ramananjanahary et al. 2010). They occur in littoral forests, low- to medium-altitude moist evergreen forests, and sclerophyllous woodlands (Madagascar Catalogue 2020). *Eulemur collaris* (Red-collared Brown Lemur) and *Pteropus rufus* (Madagascar Flying Fox) have been observed feeding on fruits of *S. multiflora* and are considered to be likely seed dispersers (Bollen 2003; Donati et al. 2011), whereas *Coracopsis nigra* (Lesser Vasa Parrot), acts as a seed predator (Bollen and van Elsacker 2004).

Schizolaena

The largest genus in the family, *Schizolaena* has 22 species characterized by small to large, paired flowers with three sepals, a white to pink corolla, and an involucre that is strongly accrescent and fleshy, completely surrounding the dehiscent fruit (Ramananjanahary et al. 2010). Members of the genus occur in littoral forest, low- to medium-altitude moist evergreen forests, moist semi-deciduous forest, and sclerophyllous woodlands (Madagascar Catalogue 2020).

Xerochlamys

The eight species in this genus are characterized by fused stipules, large flowers with a white to pink corolla and more than 20 stamens, and an involucre that completely encloses the flowers and fruits, becoming fleshy (Ramananjanahary et al. 2010). Species of *Xerochlamys* occur in moist semi-deciduous forests and dry deciduous forests, as well as sclerophyllous woodlands (Madagascar Catalogue 2020).

Xyloolaena

This genus comprises five species whose large flowers have a corolla that is cream-colored to yellow, salmon (*X. speciosa*), or red (*X. perrieri*) (Figure 8.70y), and the fruits are indehiscent and completely enclosed within the accrescent woody involucre (Ramananjanahary et al. 2010). They are found in littoral forests and low-altitude moist evergreen forests (*X. richardii*) (Figure 8.70x), medium-altitude moist evergreen forests in the far southeast (*X. humbertii*) (Figure 8.70z), dry deciduous forests in the west (*X. perrieri*), and low-altitude moist evergreen forests in the far northwest (*X. sambiranensis* and *X. speciosa*). The upright, red flowers of *X. perrieri* suggest that sunbirds may be pollinators.

CONSERVATION STATUS OF SPECIES

Published risk of extinction assessments using the International Union for the Conservation of Nature (IUCN) Red List criteria (IUCN 2012) are available for 54 species of Sarcolaenaceae, including eight species that are Critically Endangered (CR), 13 Endangered (EN), 14 Vulnerable (VU), three Near Threatened (NT), and 16 Least Concern (LC) (IUCN 2020). Four species have, however, recently been reassessed and the Red List will soon be updated; assessments for an additional 18 species will likewise be published shortly, bringing the totals to eight CR, 25 EN, 17 VU, four NT, and 16 LC.

Subject editors: Laurent Gautier and Steven M. Goodman

SANTALALES, ORDER OF THE SANDALWOOD FAMILY

D. L. Nickrent

BACKGROUND INFORMATION, DIVERSITY, AND ENDEMISM

Parasitic flowering plants possess a haustorium, an organ that forms a morphological and physiological link between parasite and host plant. Another group of angiosperms, the mycoheterotrophs feed on plant roots via mycorrhizal fungi or directly on saprophytic fungi (Leake 1994). Both groups can be described as heterotrophic; that is to say, they derive at least part of their nutrition from sources other than photosynthesis. Haustorial parasites can attach to any part of the host plant, but generally these plants are referred to as stem or root parasites. Hemiparasites are green (have chlorophyll), retain at least some photosynthesis, and obtain water by attaching to host xylem via a haustorium. A more advanced nutritional mode is seen in holoparasites, which are not green, lack photosynthesis, and derive carbohydrates as well as water from the host. The only holoparasitic Santalales family on Madagascar is Balanophoraceae.

Based on extant groups, haustorial parasitism has arisen in angiosperms 12 times (Nickrent 2020), and six of these clades have representatives in the flora of Madagascar. The other clades are as follows: *Cassytha* in Lauraceae (Laurales), *Hydnora* in Hydnoraceae (Piperales), *Cytinus* in Cytinaceae (Malvales), *Cuscuta* in Convolvulaceae (Solanales), and Orobanchaceae (Lamiales). Overall, the angiosperm parasite flora on Madagascar consists of 120 species in 36 genera, 1.1% and 2.2%, respectively, of all Malagasy angiosperm species and genera. The denominator values for these calculations were taken from Callmander et al. (2011a) and are comparable to the worldwide percentages for parasitic angiosperm genera and species (2.2% and 1.6%, respectively). Among the 36 genera on Madagascar, 27 have at least one species that is endemic to the island, and 12 of the genera are entirely endemic. This chapter discusses one of these clades, the sandalwood order (Santalales), which is represented on Madagascar by 16 genera and 82 species, most of which are stem parasites (53 mistletoe species). Over 90% of these species are endemics, and six of the genera are endemic: *Phanerodiscus*, *Pilgerina*, *Staufferia*, *Bakerella*, *Socratina*, and *Ditepalanthus* (Figure 8.71). Two genera, *Bakerella* (Loranthaceae) and *Viscum* (Viscaceae) have the highest number of species of all parasitic angiosperms on the island. Explanations for why these two genera underwent major radiations are not immediately clear, although host tree diversity and biotic interactions with pollinators and seed dispersers could be postulated. The root-parasitic genus *Thesium*, which has over 300 species elsewhere in the world, is present but has not expanded on Madagascar. A similar situation exists for *Buchnera* (Orobanchaceae) and *Cuscuta* (Convolvulaceae).

The classification of parasitic angiosperms has been greatly influenced by molecular phylogenetic studies at all taxonomic ranks (Nickrent 2020). The system adopted here is similar to the Angiosperm Phylogeny Group IV (2016) treatment, with the following exceptions that were discussed more fully in Nickrent (2020). The family circumscriptions of Santalales, first proposed by Nickrent et al. (2010), later extended by Su et al. (2015), augmented in Nickrent et al. (2019), and thoroughly reviewed in Nickrent (2020) are based upon solid molecular phylogenetic evidence. The current Angiosperm Working Group IV (2016) system apparently ignored these data, choosing instead to recognize nonmonophyletic groups (e.g., Balanophoraceae *sensu lato*, Olacaceae *sensu lato*) and to lump (with no justification) seven families into Santalaceae *sensu lato*. The classification of Santalales presented here (Figure 8.72) is based entirely on monophyletic groups (clades) whose integrity is supported by molecular, as well as morphological, synapomorphies. Of the 19 families in the order, nine occur on Madagascar. Additional information on these parasitic plants can be found on the Parasitic Plant Connection website (Nickrent 1997 onward). For synonyms of names accepted here, see the extensive lists provided in the Madagascar Catalogue (2020).

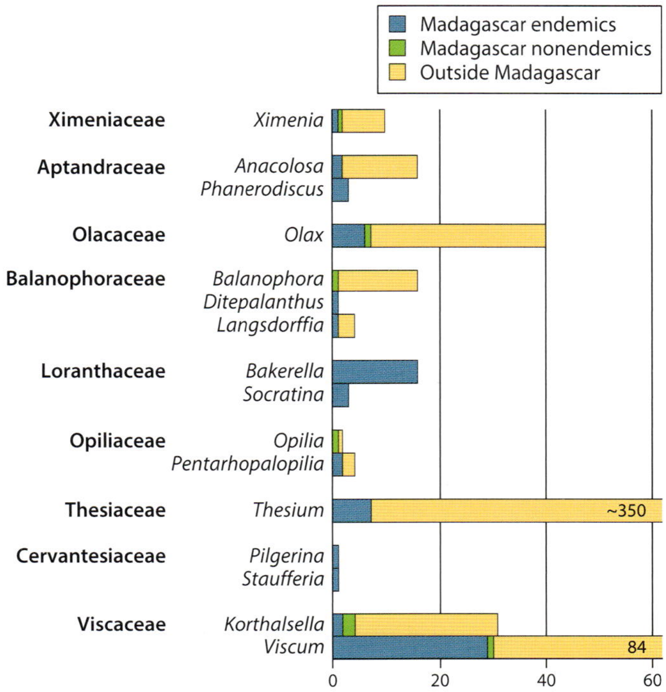

FIGURE 8.71 **Diversity and endemicity diagram of Malagasy Santalales at the level of genera, showing three different species counts: 1) endemic to Madagascar, 2) nonendemic but native to Madagascar, and 3) those occurring elsewhere in the world (for further information see text). In cases when species diversity exceeds or does not conform to that presented on the horizontal graph scale, the figures are written along the respective horizontal line of a given genus.**

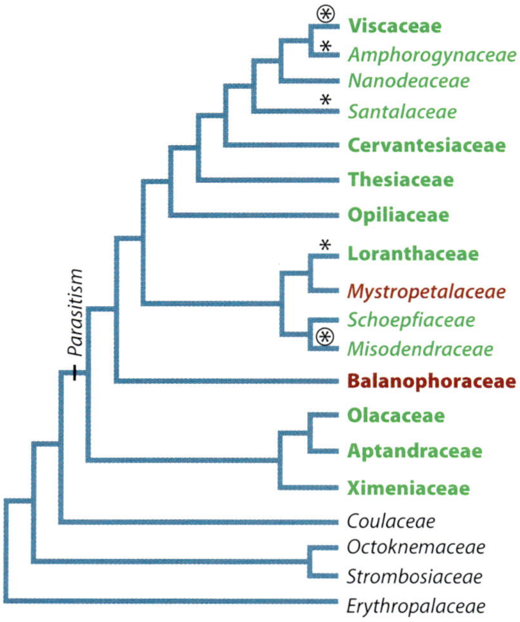

FIGURE 8.72 **Current concept of relationships among the families of Santalales. These data derive from Nickrent et al. (2019) and Nickrent (2020). Names in green are hemiparasites, those in red are holoparasites, and those in black represent outgroups with respect to the apparition of parasites within the Santalales. Names in large bold text represent those families present on Madagascar. The stars indicate the presence of aerial parasites (including mistletoes); circled stars represent families in which all members are mistletoes.**

SANTALALES OCCURRING ON MADAGASCAR

Ximeniaceae

The small family of Ximeniaceae is strongly supported as monophyletic in all molecular phylogenetic investigations conducted to date. In addition to *Ximenia*, the family includes the Neotropical genera *Curupria* and *Douradoa*, as well as *Malania* from China. The latter three genera are monotypic, whereas *Ximenia* comprises 10 species, all but three of which are Neotropical. The typical variety of *X. caffra* is known from west and southern Africa, whereas *X. caffra* var. *natalensis* is found in eastern Africa and Madagascar. *Ximenia perrieri* (Figure 8.73a) is endemic to Madagascar. Finally, *X. americana* is a pantropical species that surprisingly is not known from Madagascar. Among the four genera, positive evidence for parasitism exists only for *Ximenia* (DeFilipps 1969).

Ximenia are small trees or shrubs with simple, alternate leaves often arranged in a whorl on short shoots and with or without spines. The flowers are axillary and solitary (*X. perrieri*) or in umbellate fascicles (*X. caffra* var. *natalensis*). Flowers can be bisexual (e.g., *X. americana*) or unisexual, the latter condition first reported by Cavaco and Keraudren (1955) for *X. perrieri* and *X. caffra* var. *natalensis* (as *X. madagascariensis*). These two species are likely dioecious (Schatz 2001). The flowers of the genus are readily recognized by the densely pilose interior surface of the petals. The fruit is a large drupe that is not surrounded by an accrescent calyx. The overripe fruit of the *X. caffra*, known as sour plum (and many other vernacular names), can be eaten raw and the leaves and roots are used medicinally (Maroyi 2016). *Ximenia caffra* var. *natalensis* is present in the northern half of Madagascar in humid to dry bioclimatic zones. In constrast, *X. perrieri* appears to be restricted to the subarid zones in the southwest.

Aptandraceae

Although the genera in Aptandraceae have traditionally been considered a part of Olacaceae *sensu lato* (a polyphyletic taxon), phylogenetic analyses yield a monophyletic family with fully resolved intergeneric relationships (Ulloa et al. 2010; Nickrent et al. 2019). It is characterized by simple, distichous leaves, stamens in one whorl opposite the petals, and fruits with accrescent structures. Interestingly, positive evidence for parasitism is still lacking for any member of the family. Its phylogenetic position (Figure 8.72) suggests these plants are hemiparasites but this requires confirmation. *Anacolosa*, along with *Phanerodiscus* (Madagascar) and *Cathedra* (Brazil) occur in the proposed *Anacolosa* clade which is sister to the *Aptandra* clade (five genera). Most of the 16 species occur in southeast Asia and India, and one species (*Anacolosa uncifera*) is from eastern Africa.

The two Malagasy endemics *Anacolosa casearioides* and *A. pervilleana* are shrubs or small trees. They can be recognized by their axillary fasciculate inflorescences of mostly sessile flowers and fruit that are nearly completely surrounded by an accrescent disc (Schatz 2001). *Anacolosa casearioides* is nearly restricted to the humid zone, with a few collections from the Sambirano Region. In contrast, *A. pervilleana* is found mainly in the dry and subhumid zones of the west.

In Aptandraceae, various floral structures are accrescent in fruit. In the *Aptandra* clade this structure is the calyx. As mentioned, in *Anacolosa* (and the Neotropical *Cathedra*), the intrastaminal disc expands upon fruiting. The situation in the Malagasy endemic genus *Phanerodiscus* is quite different, as in contrast to what its name would suggest, neither the disc nor the calyx is accrescent. In fact, the disc (and attached stamens and petals) is caducous in fruit. A structure called the induvium, not visible in the flower, develops in the fruit between the disc and the calyx. This forms an induvial cupule (Malécot et al. 2003) (*cupule extradiscale* in Capuron 1968c), which surrounds the base of the fruit. From this structure develops a massive ballooning expansion called the induvial membrane (*coupe induviale* in Capuron 1968c), which apparently has no counterpart among other angiosperms (Figure 8.73b). Hidden inside the induvial membrane is the fruit itself, a drupe that contains a seed with oily endosperm.

The three species of *Phanerodiscus* are small trees with exfoliating bark and all parts smelling of bitter almond. The flowers occur in axillary fascicles on leafless branches. These species can be distinguished based on fruit differences. The induvial membrane of *P. perrieri* lacks festoons (present in the other two species), and this species occurs in the dry bioclimatic zone in the central west and northwest. Most collections of *P. diospyroidea* are from the extreme north, whereas the rarest species, *P. capuronii* (Malécot et al. 2003), is only known from littoral forests south of Toamasina.

Olacaceae

With ~40 species, the genus *Olax* is classified here in Olacaceae *sensu stricto*, a family that also includes *Dulacia* (13 species of

FIGURE 8.73 **Representatives of the nine Santalales families present on Madagascar. A) *Ximenia perrieri* (Ximeniaceae), thorny branch with fruit; B) *Phanerodiscus diospyroidea* (Aptandraceae), fruit (drupe) surrounded by the induvial membrane; C) *Olax dissitiflora* (Olacaceae), shoot with fruit (drupe) surrounded by accrescent calyx; D) *Balanophora abbreviata* (Balanophoraceae), cluster of monoecious inflorescences; E) *Bakerella clavata* (Loranthaceae), inflorescence; F) *Socratina keraudreniana* (Loranthaceae), shoot with inflorescences; G) *Pentarhopalopilia madagascariensis* (Opiliaceae), flowering shoots and fruit (inset); H) *Thesium* sp. (Thesiaceae), inflorescences, possibly a new species; I) *Pilgerina madagascariensis* (Cervantesiaceae), shoot with inflorescence; J) *Staufferia capuronii* (Cervantesiaceae), fruiting shoot; K) *Korthalsella taenioides* (Viscaceae), habit of mistletoe on host branch; and L) *Viscum cuneifolium* (Viscaceae), shoots with atypically showy female flowers.** (PHOTOS A, E, and H by C. Davidson; B by C. Rakotovao; C and I by Z. Rogers; D by T. Sando (Thailand); F by F. Rakotoarivony; G by G. Schatz; J by M. W. Callmander; and K and L by P. Antilahimena.)

South America) and *Ptychopetalum* (two species in South America and two to three species in Africa). Christenhusz et al. (2018) transferred all 10 species of *Dulacia* to *Olax* based on the molecular phylogenetic study of Su et al. (2015), who sampled four species of *Olax* and one species of *Dulacia*. The family is strongly supported as monophyletic and may be sister to Aptandraceae (Nickrent et al. 2019). *Olax* is clearly parasitic as demonstrated by the presence of haustoria in *O. phyllanthi* (Pate et al. 1990). Six of the seven species of *Olax* on Madagascar are endemic (*O. dissitiflora* also occurs in Africa).

Understanding of relationships among the *Olax* taxa collected on Madagascar was greatly clarified by Rogers et al. (2006). Members of the genus can be recognized by their simple, alternate, distichous leaves on branches that often zigzag. The inflorescences are axillary and racemose (sometimes reduced and seemingly solitary). The flowers are variable in merousity, with three to six (occasionally seven) white, valvate petals. The stamens are in one or two whorls, and numbers of stamens and staminodes vary; the latter have bifid apices (antherodes). The ovary is mostly superior and surrounded by a calyx that is accrescent, eventually tightly enveloping the drupe. The two most widespread *Olax* species on Madagascar are *O. dissitiflora* (Figure 8.73c) and *O. madagascariensis*, which occur in a variety of bioclimatic zones. *Olax emirnensis* and *O. thouarsii* are found in humid and subhumid zones along the length of the island. *Olax antsiranensis* and *O. capuronii* are almost entirely restricted to sandy or calcareous forest fragments in the far north. Finally, *O. lanceolata* is known from dry and subarid zones from Morondava south to Toliara.

Balanophoraceae

Balanophoraceae is one of two holoparasitic families in Santalales (Figure 8.72). The other is Mystropetalaceae, which includes *Dactylanthus* (New Zealand), *Hachettea* (New Caledonia), and *Mystropetalon* (South Africa). These two families are distinct as shown by floral morphology and molecular phylogenetics (Su et al. 2015) and therefore should not be combined as was done by Angiosperm Working Group IV (2016). Balanophoraceae comprises 12–14 genera, which together are pantropical in distribution.

The genus *Balanophora* has at least 16 species, which range from Pacific islands, through Australia, Malesia, India, Madagascar, and Africa. Indeed, the only species present on Madagascar, *B. abbreviata* (Figure 8.73d), has a disjunct distribution, occurring also in Africa (Republic of the Congo), southeast Asia, Malesia, and Papua New Guinea (Hansen 1972). It is also present on Mayotte, Anjouan, and Grande Comore of the Comoro archipelago. This species is creamy white in color and very much resembles a fungus. The aerial inflorescence arises endogenously from a subterranean structure called the tuber. It is subtended by large bracts and forms a club-like terminal portion containing thousands of minute female flowers. The plant is monoecious, so just below the female flowers are a few whorls of much larger male flowers. This species has a wide distribution on Madagascar, occurring in humid, subhumid, and dry bioclimatic zones.

Ditepalanthus malagasicus was first described by Jumelle and Perrier de la Bâthie (1912) as a species of *Rhopalocnemis*, a genus now known to be restricted to southeast Asia and Malesia. Fagerlind (1938) transferred it to *Ditepalanthus*, which was supported by Hansen (1974). This monoecious holoparasite forms tubers on host roots and its stems (inflorescences) form endogenously and emerge from the tuber to form a volva. The club-shaped inflorescence is covered with dense hairs among which are embedded the male and female flowers. The entire cone-like structure is then enveloped by peltate bracts, which dehisce when the flowers mature. This morphology clearly places *Ditepalanthus* in the Balanophoraceae subfamily Helosidoideae (Harms 1935) along with the Neotropical genera *Corynaea* and *Helosis*, as well as *Rhopalocnemis* and *Exorhopala*. A study of the morphology of these four genera (Eberwein and Weber 2004) concluded that it was not only *Exorhopala* that should be combined into *Helosis* but also possibly *Corynaea* and *Ditepalanthus*. No molecular data are currently available to address these issues. Most Malagasy collections of *Ditepalanthus* are from moist evergreen forests of the far north, although it is also known from the central east.

The genus *Langsdorffia* has four species with widely disjunct distributions in tropical America, New Guinea, and Madagascar. *Langsdorffia malagasica* was first named as a species of the African genus *Thonningia* (Fawcett 1886), but based on the structure of the male flower, Hansen (1974) made the transfer. The relationship of these two genera has long been recognized; for example, they were classified in subfamily Balanophoroideae, tribe Langsdorffieae by Harms (1935), a classification supported by molecular phylogenetic data (D. L. Nickrent, unpublished data). Unlike the spherical tubers seen in other Malagasy Balanophoraceae, *Langsdorffia* forms rhizome-like tubers that branch and spread horizontally. Moreover, the plants are dioecious, forming separate male and female inflorescences that arise from the apex of stems that bear numerous, spirally arranged scalelike leaves. The male flowers have anthers joined into a synangium, and the angular female flowers lack a perianth entirely. *Langsdorffia malagasica* has been collected from the northern to the southeastern part of the island, in the east and the Sambirano lowland, in medium-altitude moist evergreen forests. *Langsdorffia* (as well as *Cytinus*, Cytinaceae) are valued food sources for *Propithecus diadema* (Diademed Sifaka) who use olfaction to find these holoparasites buried in the leaf litter (Irwin et al. 2007).

Loranthaceae

With 76 genera and over 1000 species, Loranthaceae is the largest family in Santalales. This family has been studied from a number of perspectives including cytology, anatomy, morphology, taxonomy, ecology (e.g., pollination and fruit dispersal), and more recently phylogenetics and biogeography. The first major molecular phylogenetic study was by Vidal-Russell and Nickrent (2008a), and this was used to propose a classification for the family (Nickrent et al. 2010). Barlow (1983, 1990) hypothesized that the main lineages of Loranthaceae were separated by vicariance, specifically, the breakup of the supercontinent Gondwana. This hypothesis was challenged by Vidal-Russell and Nickrent (2008b) who provided a time-calibrated molecular tree that showed the family originated 75–85 million years ago (Mya), long after Gondwana fragmentation, which commenced in the Early Jurassic (see Collins et al., pp. 45–51). This conclusion was supported by the biogeographic study of Liu et al. (2018) who showed that the crown group for the family arose ~60 Mya. In the Early Cretaceous, Madagascar was still attached to India and became progressively more isolated through the Late Cretaceous. Thus, the island did not harbor Loranthaceae until later when the ancestral loranth was dispersed from continental Africa. Loranthaceae is represented by 20 genera and over 200 species on continental Africa. These occur in two clades (subtribes Emelianthinae and Tapinanthinae), which diversified most recently owing to co-adaptation with birds (Liu et al. 2018).

On Madagascar and surrounding islands, *Bakerella* is represented by 16 species and is common in native forests. The only other member of Loranthaceae on these islands is *Socratina* with three species. These mistletoes (as well as members of Viscaceae) have been extensively studied by Simone Balle whose classifications (Balle 1964a, 1964b) are widely followed. *Bakerella* can be recognized by the axillary inflorescences, which are either umbels, few-flowered fascicles, or rarely sessile at the end of short shoots (*B. microcuspis*). The corolla is clavate when in bud and composed of five petals, which develop a unilateral split when opening. In full flower the corolla lobes usually do not reflex and each bears an erect stamen with linear anthers. Corolla colors vary widely and include pink, red, yellow, orange, purple, and green.

Although *Bakerella* is sometimes considered closely related to *Taxillus*, it differs by having five petals (not four), is glabrous, and has sclereids in its vegetative and floral organs. Molecular phylogenetics (Vidal-Russell and Nickrent 2008a; Nickrent et al. 2019) suggested the closest generic relative to *Bakerella* is not *Taxillus* but *Plicosepalus* of eastern Africa.

Species such as *B. ambongoenensis*, *B. clavata* (Figure 8.73e), *B. grisea*, and *B. hoyifolia* are widely distributed on Madagascar. Others are more restricted to particular bioclimatic zones; for example, *B. belohensis* is known only from the subarid zone of the south, *B. mangindranensis* from the high-elevation belt of the northern mountains, and *B. tricostata* from the dry zone of the central west.

In terms of ecological importance, the *Propithecus diadema* (Diademed Sifaka) utilizes *B. clavata* as a primary food source during the dry season (Irwin 2007). During the rainy season, groups living in intact forest continue to eat leaves and flowers of this mistletoe species when other foods are not available, whereas groups occurring in forest fragments eat the leaves, flowers, and fruits all year. In the moist evergreen forests at least, *Bakerella* flowers throughout the year (Atsalis 1999). The flowers of this genus are widely visited by a number of Madagascar's nectivorous birds, particularly the family Nectariniidae (sunbirds) and subfamily Philepittinae (sunbird-asities; see Prum and Razafindratsita, pp. 1687–93), and this plant is presumed to be a critical food source for these birds during periods when few forest plants are flowering (S. M. Goodman, unpublished data). Further, *Philepitta castanea* (Velvet Asity) and lemurs of the genus *Cheirogaleus* are known to consume the fruits of *Bakerella* (Razafindratsita and Zack 2009; see Blanco, pp. 1922–26) as do mouse lemurs of the genus *Microcebus* (Radespiel 2006; Atsalis 2008).

Like *Bakerella*, *Socratina* was segregated at the generic level from *Taxillus*. The presence of multicellular hairs on the middle part of the style prompted Balle (1964b) to propose a relationship with *Vanwykia remota* from southeastern Africa. This association was borne out by molecular phylogenetic analyses (Vidal-Russell and Nickrent 2008a; Nickrent et al. 2019), which showed strong support for this sister relationship. This tree topology, separate from *Bakerella*, also shows that these two genera have different evolutionary origins and, thus, that they arrived on Madagascar via different dispersal events. Three species of *Socratina* exist on Madagascar, *S. bemarivensis*, *S. keraudreniana* (Figure 8.73f), and *S. phillipsoniana* (Callmander et al. 2014). All can be distinguished from the glabrous *Bakerella* by the pubescence type. *Socratina* also has the unusual character of stiff, simple hairs on the inside of the corolla lobes (Balle 1964b). *Socratina bemarivensis* and *S. phillipsoniana* flowers open by unilateral slits as opposed to the "Chinese lantern" style as in *S. keraudreniana* (Bernhardt and Calder 1980); in other words, the lobes remain coherent at the tip and open laterally by five vents. Pollination in *S. bemarivensis* involves coiling of the filaments, thereby dehiscing pollen onto the small bees that seek nectar at the bottom of the corolla tube (from quotation by Perrier de la Bâthie in Balle 1964b). The three *Socratina* species have allopatric distributions: *S. bemarivensis* in the dry zone of DIANA and Sofia Regions, *S. keraudreniana* in the subarid zone of Atsimo-Andrefana Region, and *S. phillipsoniana* in the dry *tsingy* zones of Bemahara and Beanka.

Opiliaceae

Molecular data strongly support the monophyly of Opiliaceae, a family of 11 genera and 36 species distributed across the Neotropics and Paleotropics. On Madagascar the family is represented by two genera, *Opilia* and *Pentarhopalopilia*. These genera, along with *Rhopalopilia*, are closely related, as shown by a recent phylogenetic analysis (Nickrent et al. 2019). All members of Opiliaceae (except *Anthobolus*) have simple, alternate leaves with cystoliths in the leaf mesophyll that are visible as tubercles on dry specimens. Flowers are bisexual (unisexual outside Madagascar), have valvate petals, and have a prominent intrastaminal disc. The ovary is superior and produces a fruit without accrescent structures. Parasitism has been documented in all genera except *Gjellerupia* (Kubat 1987).

Opilia amentacea is a widespread species known from Africa, India, southeast Asia, Malesia, and Australia. Because of this wide range, considerable morphological variability exists and informal groups (a–d) were designated by Hiepko (1982). The single collection (Geay 3320) of this species from Madagascar is from the southwest along the Fiherenana River. This specimen belongs to group c "*tomentella*" (also present in Mozambique), which is characterized by tomentellous young branches. This species is a woody shrub or small tree, which climbs or scrambles on adjacent vegetation. The inflorescence is a bracteate raceme, but composed of dyads and triads (thus a thyrse). The fruit is an orange to yellow drupe with no accrescent structures.

Pentarhopalopilia has two species in Africa and two on Madagascar (Hiepko 1987). The genus can generally be recognized by its umbellate inflorescence placed at the top of a well-developed peduncle. *Pentarhopalopilia madagascariensis* (Figure 8.73g) is a climbing shrub whose branches have upwardly curving hairs and mostly glabrous leaves and fruits. This differs from *P. perrieri*, which is an erect shrub 3–4 m in height that has short and long shoots. Its young branches, petioles, and inflorescence peduncles are densely covered with olive-yellow pubescence that disappears on adult organs (Capuron 1968c). *Pentarhopalopilia madagascariensis* is widespread in dry deciduous forests across the island, whereas *P. perrieri* is restricted to dry spiny thickets in the extreme south.

Thesiaceae

Thesiaceae was segregated from Santalaceae *sensu lato* by Nickrent et al. (2010). With the recognition of the South African genus *Lacomucinaea* (Nickrent and García 2015), the family now contains four genera (García et al. 2018) with the root hemiparasite *Thesium* (Figure 8.73h) being by far the largest (over 350 species). This genus is particularly abundant in the Cape region of South Africa, with lesser numbers of species in tropical Africa, Europe, Asia, Australia, and South America. In contrast to continental Africa, Madagascar has only seven species. A molecular phylogeny of *Thesium* (M. A. García and D. L. Nickrent, unpublished data) shows that the three species sampled (*T. humbertii*, *T. madagascariense*, and *T. pseudocystoseiroides*) occur in different clades suggesting separate dispersal events from tropical Africa.

Cervantesiaceae

In 1968, René Capuron published a technical report that described two arborescent taxa he designated "Santalaceae A" and "Santalaceae B". At that time he only had fruiting material, but later more complete collections allowed these taxa to be described as two new endemic genera, *Pilgerina* (Figure 8.73i) and *Staufferia* (Figure 8.73j) (Rogers et al. 2008). The molecular phylogenetic analyses showed that both were components of Cervantesiaceae (Nickrent et al. 2010). Specifically, the genera were part of a clade that included *Pyrularia* (Asia and North America), *Scleropyrum* (Asia and New Guinea), and *Okoubaka* (Africa), and that clade was sister to a New World clade containing *Acanthosyris*, *Cervantesia*, and *Jodina*. This family is characterized by the presence of large drupaeous fruits with bony mesocarps (i.e., with pyrenes). All members of the *Pyrularia* clade except *Pilgerina* have unisexual flowers, whereas all *Cervantesia* clade members have bisexual flowers. The drupes of *Staufferia* are obovoid and the pyrene is enveloped by a fleshy exocarp with five segments, each separated longitudinally by densely pubescent furrows (Figure 8.73j). *Staufferia capuronii* is distributed widely in the moist evergreen forests from the north to the eastern side of the island, and in littoral forests in the southeast.

Because pistillate flowers were not seen in *Staufferia*, Kuijt (2015) suggested that the flowers may be bisexual, and therefore proposed that *Pilgerina* could be conspecific with it. Although clearly related to *Staufferia*, *Pilgerina* differs from it in several features such as its bisexual flowers, racemose (versus thyrsoid) inflorescences, and a drupaceous fruit that lacks the longitudinal furrows. Further arguments for maintaining these as separate genera are given in Rogers et al. (2008). *Pilgerina madagascariensis* is distributed in a variety of forest types, from the extreme north to the extreme southeast, and from sea level to 1200 m.

Viscaceae

Although the mistletoe family Viscaceae was previously considered a subfamily (Viscoideae) of Loranthaceae, evidence for their separate origins comes from many sources (Calder 1983) including molecular phylogenetics (Nickrent et al. 2010, 2019). The Angiosperm Working Group IV (2016) recognized a broadly defined Santalaceae, whereas here three families are accepted: Cervantesiaceae, Thesiaceae, and Viscaceae as justified in Nickrent (2020). Although Balle (1964a, 1964b) treated Loranthaceae in the broad sense, her keys and descriptions provided ample evidence that the subfamilies represented separate evolutionary lines. Resolving phylogenetic relationships among the seven genera of Viscaceae remains elusive as different studies gave different results (e.g., Maul et al. 2019; Nickrent et al. 2019).

Korthalsella is a remarkable genus for many reasons, one of which is its distribution. There are about 30 species of these monoecious, flabellate (stems with scale leaves only) mistletoes distributed from Africa to Asia, Australia, and widely across the Indo-Pacific region, including Hawaii. The tiny male and female flowers are arranged in highly condensed inflorescences that occur on hairy floral cushions in the stem axils. Much of the taxonomy of the genus has been based on vegetative characters such as the degree of flattening of the phylloclades. The first taxonomic revisions of *Korthalsella* were by Danser (1937, 1940) and these species concepts were followed by Balle (1964a, 1964b) who listed three species for Madagascar: *K. commersonii*, *K. madagascarica*, and *K. opuntia*, the latter comprising two varieties, var. *richardii*, and var. *gaudichaudii*. The molecular phylogeny by Sultan et al. (2019) marked a major advancement in clarifying relationships among species that have widespread morphological parallelism. Two of the four Malagasy taxa, *K. madagascarica* and *K. taenioides* (Figure 8.73k; synonym *K. commersonii*), emerged in the same clade despite having markedly different growth forms; the former has terete stems and the latter has broad phylloclades. The endemic *K. madagascarica* has been collected at several locations spanning north to south on Madagascar, from humid to dry bioclimatic zones. The other endemic, *K. taenioides*, is known from mountainous areas in the medium-altitude moist evergreen areas.

The taxonomy of the other two *Korthalsella* species on Madagascar and surrounding islands is more complex. The phylogenetic tree in Sultan et al. (2019) included one taxon labeled as *K. opuntia* var. *gaudichaudii*, which was present in a clade with the other two varieties of this species (var. *richardii* and *bojeri*). Those authors realized that *K. opuntia* is an illegitimate name, but used it to avoid confusion. The Catalogue of Life (Hassler 2019) uses *K. gaudichaudii*, which will be followed here for the Malagasy taxon. It is documented from just a few localities, such as Tsiafajovona (Ankaratra Massif) and the forests near Tolagnaro, as well as on La Réunion.

With 29 species, *Viscum* is the most diverse mistletoe genus on Madagascar. Of approximately 115 species of *Viscum* worldwide, three or fewer species occur in Europe, Australia, and New Guinea, and the majority occur in Africa (43) and Asia (37). *Viscum* can be easily recognized and distinguished from Loranthaceae by the presence of small, unisexual flowers (Figure 8.73l). The plants can be mono- or dioecious and the stems flabellate or leafy. Prophyllar leaves often occur, sometimes fused in pairs, edge to edge, thus forming a perule that covers the young bud. The inflorescences are axillary or terminal cymules that may or may not be enclosed in a bibracteal cup. The cup may contain flowers of one sex or mixtures of male and female flowers. Flowers are generally trimerous or tetramerous, small, and composed of petals (often called tepals) that top the inferior ovary in female flowers and contain stamens in male flowers. The sessile male flowers have anthers that open by pores (locules). Because *Viscum* has no true ovules, the berries are referred to as false fruits with "seeds". The pericarp of the fruit can be white, translucent, orange, or red and may be smooth or warty. The mesocarp is mucilaginous and contains viscin, the sticky strands that attach the "seed" to the host branch following bird dispersal.

The fruits of various *Viscum* species are utilized as food by endemic Malagasy mammals. Animals of the *Microcebus rufus* group (mouse lemurs) consume fruits from *Bakerella* (Loranthaceae) as well as those from *Viscum* (Atsalis 1999). The nocturnal *M. griseorufus* (Gray-brown Mouse Lemur) primarily feeds on small, green fruits among which are those produced by *V. trachycarpum*. Génin and Rambeloarivony (2018) report that *Viscum* plants are more spatially aggregated in matriarchal core areas of *M. griseorufus* that are used as crèches for weaned infants, thereby implying inadvertent mistletoe gardening.

A molecular phylogeny of *Viscum* (53 species) was recently published (Maul et al. 2019), which examined the evolution of leaf morphology, sexual mode, and host preference, as well as biogeography. In that study, 11 of the 12 sampled Malagasy *Viscum* species are endemics; *V. triflorum* also occurs in eastern Africa and the Comoro islands. All of these species were found to be monophyletic, but that clade also included two Australian species (*V. bancroftii* and *V. whitei*) as well as *V. decurrens* from tropical Africa. The former suggests long-distance dispersal out of Madagascar, the latter dispersal to the island.

Although the presence of scale leaves is used in nearly all *Viscum* taxonomic keys (Balle 1964a; Polhill and Wiens 1998), this phenomenon has evolved independently at least 10 times, and, thus, these flabellate mistletoes are not necessarily closely related. Reconstruction of sexual modes suggests that the common ancestor of *Viscum* was dioecious. All but five of the species on Madagascar are dioecious, the monoecious ones being *V. ambongoense*, *V. hexapterum*, *V. tsaratananense*, *V. tsiafajavonense*, and *V. triflorum*. The latter species is also present in east Africa, again suggesting a dispersal event out of Madagascar. Monoecy may facilitate establishment following dispersal because of the possibility of self-fertilization.

Chromosome numbers in African and Malagasy Loranthaceae and Viscaceae have been surveyed (Wiens 1975). The base number for Loranthaceae is x = 12, but all African and Malagasy genera show x = 9 via aneuploid reduction. In contrast, the base number for Viscaceae is x = 14, and within *Viscum* a series of aneuploid reduced numbers exists (x = 13, 12, 11, 10). Of the seven Malagasy *Viscum* surveyed (Wiens 1975), all have x = 13 except *V. echinocarpum* (x = 11) and *V. rhipsaloides* (x = 14). For the latter, the base number could reflect retention of an ancestral condition, but this conflicts with the phylogenetic tree topology (Maul et al. 2019) in which it is not sister to other Malagasy taxa. Alternately, the base number could have evolved via increasing aneuploidy (Wiens 1975). Some populations of *V. multiflorum* are x = 13 whereas others are polyploid x = 24, 26—a rare condition in mistletoes. Translocation heterozygosity occurs in many dioecious *Viscum* species (Wiens and Barlow 1979), but this has yet to be documented for *Viscum* on Madagascar.

FUTURE DIRECTIONS

Parasitic organisms are frequently scorned because of their negative impact on human activities, but among parasitic angiosperms, only about 25 of the 285 genera have pathogenic species (Nickrent and Musselman 2016). Indeed, many parasitic plants are rare and deserve protection and others, such as most mistletoes, are considered keystone species: ones that have a disproportionate and positive impact on ecosystem functions despite relatively low biomass (Watson 2001; Watson and Herring 2012). This relationship is demonstrated on Madagascar by *Bakerella* and *Viscum*, which provide crucial food reserves for organisms that pollinate their flowers and disperse their seeds. As natural forest areas decrease, potential host trees available for colonization also decrease, thus resulting in declines in mistletoe diversity (Devkota et al. 2010). Several *Bakerella* species (e.g., *B. collapsa*, *B. tandrokensis*) are rare, as are at least seven species of *Viscum*. Surveys should be conducted to determine whether such species are extant and, if so, whether they occur in protected areas.

This treatment of the sandalwood order (Santalales) on Madagascar may give the impression that little remains for study, but this is not the case. The following is a list of subjects for future research projects that would expand scientific knowledge about these plants. For most groups, very little is known about pollination and fruit/seed dispersal; such studies would fill important gaps in understanding ecological functional relationships. Similarly, host ranges have not been exhaustively documented for most groups. For Aptandraceae, positive evidence of parasitism has not been obtained for any member of the family, and this information could be obtained by excavating the roots of *Anacolosa* or *Phanerodiscus*. Although exemplars of Malagasy Santalales have been included in various phylogenetic studies, much work remains. Future molecular phylogenetic work on Malagasy Santalales could include: 1) species relationships in the genus *Olax* (Olacaceae) using broad sampling within and outside of Madagascar; 2) intergeneric relationships between *Ditepalanthus* and other members of Helosoideae (Balanophoraceae); 3) species-level phylogeny of *Bakerella* (Loranthaceae) including its closest generic relative as an outgroup; and 4) expansion of the study of Maul et al. (2019), which sampled only 12 of the 29 Malagasy *Viscum* species. A *Viscum* study could also address other aspects such as karyology, the presence of translocation heterozygosity, morphological evolution, ecological niche partitioning, and biogeography.

Subject editors: Laurent Gautier and Steven M. Goodman

DIDIEREACEAE

W. L. Applequist

The Didiereaceae family forms an iconic component of the dry spiny thicket vegetation (Gautier et al. 2018) of subarid southern Madagascar (Domaine du Sud *sensu* Humbert 1955). In this very harsh environment, spiny, thorny and/or succulent plants dominate. The Didiereaceae taxa native to Madagascar comprise four genera and 11 woody, usually dioecious species that have a distinctive morphology, often with thick stems, and leaves and spines generally borne together in small clusters. The largest species have columnar stems and, at up to 10–15 m high, are often the most conspicuous plants in their environment. Because they are appealing to collectors of succulents and other exotic plants, they are all listed on Appendix II of the Convention on International Trade in Endangered Species of Wild Fauna and Flora (CITES), and some are of conservation concern.

DIVERSITY

Didiereaceae as traditionally circumscribed included four genera, all endemic to Madagascar. Molecular evidence indicated that the family had evolved within Portulacaceae, as then circumscribed, and was related in particular to three small, more or less xerophytic, woody African genera that were atypical within Portulacaceae: *Calyptrotheca*, *Ceraria*, and *Portulacaria*. The transfer of those genera to Didiereaceae, segregated into subfamilies Calyptrothecoideae and Portulacarioideae, was therefore proposed (Applequist and Wallace 2003) and is accepted in the most recent classification of Portulacineae (Nyffeler and Eggli 2010), resulting in the family no longer being endemic to Madagascar.

The four Malagasy genera that now constitute the subfamily Didiereoideae are dioecious, woody plants that bear spines and small, thick green photosynthesizing leaves together in small clusters that represent usually reduced, but in one genus conspicuous, short shoots (brachyblasts). In most species the spines are longer than the leaves and fairly dense on the stem, creating an obvious deterrent to herbivory. Some species have thin twigs, but in others all stems are markedly thick. Species with thick stems often have chambered hollow spaces in the center of the stem (Rauh 1961). Each genus has distinctive vegetative features that allow easy recognition in the field (Figure 8.74).

Didiereoideae species have an extended period of immaturity after which they flower, though seldom. Flowering of *Didierea madagascariensis* is observed in the field to occur in the early part of the rainy season. Their short-lived flowers open in the morning and and are visited by bees for their nectar (Rauh 1961). The perianth in most species is whitish or cream and of modest size, but the inflorescences are often numerous or large, making flowering conspicuous. Flowers have two involucral bracts (which, as in other members of this group of families, are often termed sepals) and four tepals (often termed petals) that are borne in two alternating whorls (Erbar and Leins 2006). Male flowers have six to 10 (rarely to 12) stamens, usually with red filaments. The single-seeded fruit is a small wind-dispersed nut surrounded by the persistent bracts, which aid dispersal.

Alluaudia

The six species of *Alluaudia* are dioecious and more or less arborescent. Brachyblasts usually consist of clusters of one spine and two leaves. They have been divided into two separate taxonomic sections. Section *Alluaudia* includes three species with seldom-branching, thick, erect to ascending stems, which are all decaploid (having 10 copies of each chromosome, with a base number of $x = 24$ chromosomes, $2n = 240$; all chromosome counts are from Schill et al. 1974). *Alluaudia ascendens* is confined to a small region of the southeast that includes the drier portion of the Andohahela National Park (parcel 2), while the vegetatively very similar *A. montagnacii* occurs in a small portion of the southwestern coastal region. *Alluaudia procera* is widely distributed in the subarid south, in the west extending as far north as the southern edge of the Menabe Region, and is probably the species most cultivated.

Alluaudia section *Androyella* includes three species of small trees with slender often-branching twigs. Among these, *A. dumosa* is distinctive for its plump, greenish, nearly smooth stems; its leaves are rapidly deciduous and spines are few and short. *Alluaudia comosa* is notable for having a broad, flattened crown at maturity and usually only one leaf per spine. All three species have or have had a relatively broad distribution in the south, especially *A. humbertii*, which is known at elevations to 900 m, though it has not recently been documented from the northern part of its range and may have been extirpated there. *Alluaudia dumosa* is octoploid (having eight copies of each chromosome, $2n = 192$); the other two are diploid ($2n = 48$).

Alluaudiopsis

The two species of *Alluaudiopsis* are relatively small, shrubby dioecious plants with slender twigs, both diploid ($2n = 48$). *Alluaudiopsis marnieriana* bears clusters of two spines and one leaf and is distinguished from all other species by its large, bright red flowers. It is confined to a very small part of the southwestern coastal region near Toliara. *Alluaudiopsis fiherenensis* bears clusters of one spine and two leaves, like most *Alluaudia* species, but the leaves are long, narrow, and subcylindrical. It has a broader distribution in the low-elevation southwest, relatively near the coast, from Bevoalava to Miary.

Decarya

Decarya includes one species, *D. madagascariensis*, which is found in the extreme south from arid parts of the southeast (Andohahela)

FIGURE 8.74 **Different members of the Didiereaceae: A) *Didierea madagascariensis* habit; B) *Alluaudia comosa* habit; C) *D. trollii* stem; D) *A. dumosa* young and mature stems; E) *A. comosa* twigs; F) *D. madagascariensis* stem; and G) *Decarya madagascariensis* stem.** (PHOTOS by W. L. Applequist.)

to the southwest. It is arborescent at maturity. Young twigs are slender with a strongly zigzag appearance, paired spines, and a single deciduous leaf at each node. It is octoploid (2n = 192). *Decarya madagascariensis* appears to be gynodioecious, unlike any other species, having both female and bisexual flowers, but it is not clear whether any fruit set by bisexual flowers is viable.

Didierea

Didierea includes two arborescent, dioecious, decaploid (2n = 240) species that have brachyblasts bearing clusters of usually four spines and four or five leaves. The stems are thick and the brachyblasts are well developed, forming visible short shoots. In *D. madagascariensis* these can be over 2 cm long and the leaves are narrow and elongated, creating a very distinctive appearance. This species is almost entirely confined to a narrow strip along the southwestern coast but extends much farther north than most Didiereaceae, as far as Menabe (approximately 20°30'S). The second species, *D. trollii*, has a more typical southern distribution.

ENDEMISM

All species of Didiereaceae subfamily Didiereoideae are endemic to Madagascar, and to a limited portion of the island. Most are restricted to the dry spiny thicket vegetation of southwestern to extreme southern Madagascar, and some of those are endemic to very small areas, while a few species extend into the southern part of the Western Domain (Humbert 1955), where dry deciduous forests dominate. *Alluaudia montagnacii* and *Alluaudiopsis marnieriana* have been classed as Endangered under International Union for the Conservation of Nature (IUCN) Red List criteria and *Alluaudia ascendens*, *A. comosa*, *Alluaudiopsis fiherenensis*, and *Didierea trollii* have been classed as Vulnerable (IUCN 2019).

SYSTEMATICS AND PHYLOGENY

The unusual morphology and anatomy of the Malagasy species of Didiereaceae (now Didiereoideae) complicated early efforts to determine their relationships, though multiple lines of evidence supported their placement within Caryophyllales. Molecular systematic studies (e.g., Bruyns et al. 2014) reported that they are related to the genera *Ceraria*, *Portulacaria*, and *Calyptrotheca*, previously placed within Portulacaceae *sensu lato* but now transferred to Didiereaceae. It is noteworthy that Rauh and Schölch (1965) had identified morphological similarities between Didiereaceae and *Ceraria*, including the shared presence of brachyblasts in some species, while Landrum (2002) noted similarities in vegetative anatomical characters.

The most complete phylogeny of Didiereaceae (Bruyns et al. 2014) found all genera of Didiereoideae to be monophyletic (i.e., natural groups), although species of *Ceraria* and *Portulacaria* were commingled into a single clade, justifying the transfer of all *Ceraria* species into *Portulacaria*. *Alluaudiopsis* appeared as the basal lineage in the subfamily, while *Decarya* was sister to *Didierea*. The two sections of *Alluaudia* were not found to be monophyletic, with *A. ascendens* appearing among the species of section *Androyella*. However, branch lengths are very short in chloroplast DNA studies, due to slow rates of change in this group, so results that are unexpected given the species' morphological features and ploidy levels may not be presumed to be definitive.

Most recently, Wang et al.'s (2018) phylogeny of Portulacineae based on transcriptomic data, which included seven representatives of Didiereoideae, reported *Alluaudiopsis fiherenensis* to be included in a clade with *Alluaudia* species. However, for each hypothesized branch within Didiereoideae numerous conflicting genes (whose sequences suggested different relationships) existed. In contrast, the branch supporting all Didiereoideae was consistently supported. Wang et al. identified over 4000 gene duplications on that branch, indicating a whole-genome duplication (WGD) shared by Didiereoideae. Some duplicated genes associated with stress tolerance were shown to be under positive selection, leading to their conclusion that the WGD in the ancestor of Didiereoideae facilitated adaptation to extreme environments. In addition, chromosome counts (Schill et al. 1974) show that repeated episodes of polyploidization (increase in the number of copies of each chromosome, which is sometimes caused by hybridization between distantly related species) occurred later in the group's evolution. It would be of interest for future work to explore the nature and adaptive significance of those events.

The species of Didiereoideae are conspicuous and botanically interesting so have been thoroughly studied, and the revisionary treatment of Rauh (1961, 1963; also followed by Rowley 1992) may be taken as definitive. Substantial information is available on vegetative, inflorescence and floral anatomy and development, pollen, and microanatomical characters and phytochemistry (e.g., Rauh and Reznick 1961; Rauh and Schölch 1965; Rauh and Dittmar 1970; Nowicke 1975; Straka 1975; Rabesa 1982; Cremers and Sell 1986; Landrum 2002; Erbar and Leins 2006).

Subject editors: Laurent Gautier and Steven M. Goodman

SAPOTACEAE, *NANTO*, *FAMELONA*

L. Gautier, C. G. Boluda, A. Randriarisoa, R. Randrianaivo, and Y. Naciri

Sapotaceae is a medium-size plant family of ~1300 species in 65–70 genera (Swenson et al. 2020) distributed essentially in the intertropical zone, with a few exceptions in the genus *Sideroxylon*, the distribution of which extends to several subtropical regions (southern Morocco, Canary Islands, southern Africa, southeastern United States). They are generally slow-growing hard-timber trees (Figure 8.75a), sometimes shrubs, and are often prominent components of mature forests. The bark is often much fissured (Figures 8.75b and 8.76e) but can also be smooth and exfoliate as plates (Figure 8.75c). A white sticky sap (latex) is generally present in all parts of the plant (Figure 8.75d). Pubescence consists of unicellular malpighian (T-shaped) trichomes. The growth pattern is typically bayonet-shaped, with foliage often grouped at the end of twigs (Figure 8.75f). Leaves of Sapotaceae are alternate and spirally arranged, simple and entire, with or without stipules (Figure 8.76l). Inflorescences are borne on twigs, generally among or more frequently below the leaves, but sometimes also on branches or trunks. They consist of solitary (Figure 8.76g) or fasciculate (Figure 8.75p) flowers, and are never branched but can be very profuse (Figure 8.75e). Flowers (Figures 8.75 and 8.76) are actinomorphic with fused petals and a superior ovary with one ovule per carpel, but are variable in all other aspects such as base number of parts, and the presence of staminodes and appendices on corolla lobes. Fruits (Figures 8.75 and 8.76) are fleshy, one- to several-seeded berries,

FIGURE 8.75 **Examples of Malagasy Sapotaceae. A) Trunk of *Labourdonnaisia* sp. in the Beampingaratra Forest being examined by Aina Randriarisoa; B) bark of *Capurodendron* sp. aff. *mandrarense* at Bezà-Mahafaly (Gautier 6349); C) bark of *Labramia sambiranenis* at Andrafiamena (Gautier 5466); D) slash of *Labourdonnaisia* sp. tree trunk at Pointe à Larrée showing latex (Randriarisoa 102); E) massive inflorescence of *Sideroxylon beguei* at Ankarabolava Forest (Gautier 5769); F) Aubréville's growth pattern in *L. bojeri* at Manankatafana (Randriarisoa 81); G) flowers of *Bemangidia lowryi* at Bemangidy Forest, Tsitongambarika (Lowry 6657); H) brachyblast in *Capurodendron aubrevillei* at Tanandava Forest (Randriarisoa 125); I) seeds of *S. betsimisarakum* at Masoala (Gautier 5502); J) seeds of *Tsebona macrantha* (Service Forestier 27675in Paris herbarium); K) seed of *B. lowryi* at Bemangidy Forest, Tsitongambarika (Gautier 5789); L) seed of *C. apollonioides* (FOFIFA herbarium); M) seed of *L. costata* at Masoala (Randrianaivo 105); N) seed of *Mimusops voalela* at Analalava (Randrianaivo 3113); O) flower of *S. saxorum* at Lake Mandrozo (Gautier 6192); P) flowers of *S. gerrardianum* at Masoala (Gautier 5499); Q) leaf, fruits, and seeds of *T. macrantha* at Mananara-Nord (Randrianaivo 3019); R) areolate tertiary venation of *S. beguei* at Mahatalaky (Ratovoson 1760); and S) flowers of *T. macrantha* at Analalava (Randrianaivo 3132).**
(PHOTOS A–C, E, I–M, O, and P by L. Gautier; D, F, H, N, Q, and S by C. Boluda; G by P. Lowry; and R by F. Ratovoson.)

FIGURE 8.76 **Examples of Malagasy Sapotaceae. A) Leaves of *Bemangidia lowryi* at Bemangidy Forest, Tsitongambarika (Gautier 5784); B) flowering shoot of *Capurodendron schatzii* at Masoala (Schatz 3786); C) flowers of *C. delphinense* at Petriky (Gautier 5801); D) fruit of *C. perrieri* at Andranomena (Randrianaivo 2979); E) bark of *Mimusops* sp. at Tanandava Forest (Randriarisoa 126); F) *Mimusops coriacea* at Cap Est (Gautier 6006); G) calyx and gynoecium of *M. antongilensis* at Tanandava Forest (Randriarisoa 122); H) fruits of *M. lecomtei* at Tampolo (Randrianaivo 3096); I) fruit of *M. raymondii* at Lake Sahaka, Loky Manambato (Gautier 6035); J) flowering shoot of *Manilkara boivinii* at Beanka (Hanitrarivo 258); K) flower of *M. boivinii* at Beanka (Hanitrarivo 258); L) flowering shoot of *Labramia costata* at Sahafina; M) leaf of *Labramia* sp. at Beampingaratra Forest showing impressed venation; N) flower of *L. bojeri* at Maroantsetra (Gautier 5494); O) fruit of *L. costata* at Farafangana-Vohipeno (Gautier 5752); P) parallel venation with indistinct secondaries and tertiaries of *Labourdonnaisia madagascariensis* at Soanierana Ivongo (Randriarisoa 85); Q) flower of *L. manongarivensis* at Masoala (Gautier 6015); R) fruit of *Labourdonnaisia* cf. *madagascariensis* at Beampingaratra (Randriarisoa 198); S) *Donella ranirisonii* at Andrafiamena (Gautier 5387); T) *Gambeya boiviniana* at Betampona (Randrianaivo 3135); U) *G. boiviniana* at Manombo (Gautier 5764); V) stump of *Mimusops* sp. at Sahafary Forest; and W) unidentified Sapotaceae tree felled and prepared as "Bois carré" at Masoala with Richard Randrianaivo.** (PHOTO A by U. Swenson; B by G. Schatz; C, F, I, N, O, Q, S, U, and W by L. Gautier; D by R. Randrianaivo; E, G, H, L, M, P, R, and T by C. Boluda; J and K by M. Hanitrarivo; and V by A. Randriarisoa.)

with rare exceptions of dehiscent, seed-expelling fruits (ballistic dispersal) in a few African rainforest genera. Seeds of Sapotaceae always have a smooth, shiny surface and a rugose scar (Figures 8.75i–n). The position of the seed scar as well as its shape and area relative to the shiny part of the seed surface is very variable and taxonomically informative.

Members of the family produce valuable timber sold on the international market, including the iconic Moabi (*Baillonella toxisperma*) from central Africa. The latex of a few species has been actively exploited, particularly the Indonesian Gutta-percha (extracted from *Palaquium* spp., notably *P. gutta*), whose trade had a considerable economic importance in the second part of the 19th century for the insulation of telegraphic wires. Gutta-percha has since been almost completely replaced by plastics for most of its numerous uses, except for medical ones, particularly dentistry. The latex of the Central American Chicle (*Manilkara zapota*) was used in the past for the production of chewing gum but has been replaced by synthetic products. Sapotaceae members are also known for the oil content of their seeds, especially the Moroccan Argane oil (*Sideroxylon spinosum*) and the Sudano-Sahelian Shea Tree (*Vitellaria paradoxa*). Many Sapotaceae fruits are edible, although only a few species are commercialized and only in tropical areas (e.g., *Chrysophyllum cainito*, *M. zapota*, *Pouteria* spp.).

Sapotaceae belongs to the order Ericales, sister to Ebenaceae and Primulaceae. The family appeared some 100–110 million years ago (Mya) (Armstrong et al. 2014; Rose et al. 2018), probably in the Indo-Malaysian region, where the basal genera *Sarcosperma* and *Eberhardtia* occur today. These genera diverged in the Late Cretaceous (Armstrong et al. 2014; Stride et al. 2014). Then, the history of the family seems to involve an initial dispersal to the Afrotropics, from where most major extant lineages originated, followed by numerous dispersal events to other continents.

Generic circumscription within Sapotaceae, as well as suprageneric classification, has always been problematic, and 20th-century monographers accepted between 122 (Aubréville 1964) and 53 (Pennington 1991) genera. The contribution of molecular phylogenetics has been essential to disentangle the systematics of the family, revealing that these taxonomic problems stemmed from the difficulty of identifying clear ancestral characters. Due credit needs to be given to Aubréville for his narrow generic concept, which has in many instances been validated by molecular phylogenetic studies over the past few decades. Many of his smaller genera are now being resurrected.

Three subfamilies are currently recognized (Swenson and Anderberg 2005): Sarcospermatoideae (a small basal lineage), Chrysophylloideae, and Sapotoideae (the latter two forming the major part of the family). Chrysophylloideae comprises a single tribe, Chrysophylleae, within which many clades are nested within others, precluding the delimitation of finer monophyletic suprageneric taxa, whereas five monophyletic tribes have been circumscribed in Sapotoideae (Swenson and Anderberg 2005; Gautier et al. 2013c; L. Gautier et al., unpublished data), with a few genera still unplaced.

SAPOTACEAE ON MADAGASCAR

Being mostly huge, slow-growing trees that flower late and infrequently in their lifetime, the taxonomy of Madagascar Sapotaceae has clearly been delayed by a lack of fertile herbarium collections. The most common species were known by the end of the 19th century, but it is only since the tremendous efforts of the Service Forestier de Madagascar from the 1950s that herbarium specimens systematically collected in the remote forests have become available to botanists. The key step was the collaboration of René Capuron (1921–1971), head of the Service Forestier (and a Sapotaceae enthusiast), with André Aubréville (1897–1982), professor of botany in Paris and a leading worldwide expert on the family. Their collaboration culminated with the publication of a monograph on the family in the *Flore de Madagascar et des Comores* series (Aubréville 1974). In this milestone publication, 85 species are recognized in 11 genera.

For a family in which fertile material is difficult to find, Aubréville endeavored to be practical, basing his species keys essentially on vegetative characters. Because many of the new species he described were known from one or two collections, species delimitation was, of course, rudimentary. As a consequence, identification of Malagasy Sapotaceae has remained problematic. Most of the specimens that have subsequently been accumulated need attention in order to better delimit the species and revise the whole family for Madagascar, an initiative that the team responsible for this contribution has embarked on.

In the course of the almost 50 years since the publication of Aubréville's Sapotaceae treatment, a 200% increase in Sapotaceae herbarium collections has accumulated as part of routine flora and vegetation surveys. Furthermore, five dedicated expeditions (so-called Nanto Trips) were conducted by the authors of this contribution, along with colleagues, to various parts of the island (initials refer to authors of this contribution): Maroantsetra and eastern Masoala (2010: L. G., R. R., and U. Swenson); southern part of the eastern coast (2011: same team as 2010); eastern part of Masoala to Vohémar (2013: same team as 2010 plus Y. N.); Toliara to Tolagnaro (2017: L. G., R. R., Y. N., and L. Garnier), Morondava (R. R. alone), and the Antsiranana area (A. R. alone); and to the central part of the eastern coast (2018: R. R., A. R., and C. B.). All collections included associated silica gel–dried leaves for molecular studies, a practice that was implemented some years earlier by L. G. and his colleagues for all Sapotaceae collected during general surveys. As a consequence, molecular analyses are now systematically integrated into taxonomic revisions.

Since 1974, one new genus has been published and two synonymized, while 19 new species have been described and only two synonymized (Friedman 1980; Schatz and Gautier 1996; Gautier et al. 2013c; Randrianaivo 2013; Mackinder et al. 2016; Gautier and Naciri 2018; Randriarisoa et al. 2020; C. G. Boluda et al., unpublished data; L. Gautier and R. Randrianaivo, unpublished data). It is estimated that probably 20–30 more species will be described in the course of the ongoing revisions. This will ultimately bring the size of the family on Madagascar to 10 genera (including three strict endemics and two endemics to the Malagasy Region) and about 125 species, all but three endemic to the island (97.6%; Figure 8.77).

ECOLOGY

Sapotaceae species are mainly found in moist evergreen forests in the Eastern, Central, and Sambirano phytogeographic domains (*sensu*

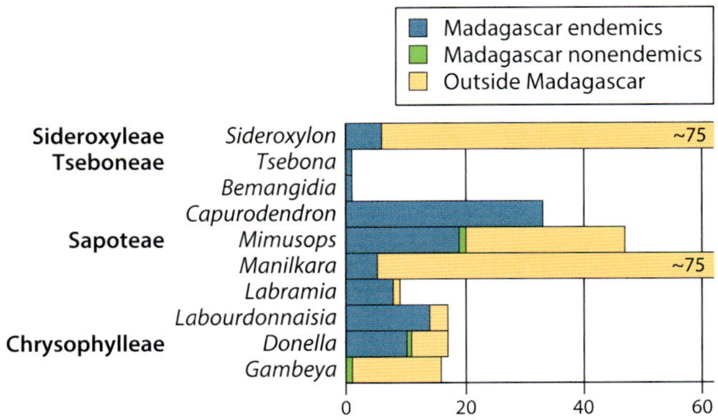

FIGURE 8.77 Diversity and endemicity diagram of Malagasy Sapotaceae at the level of genera, showing three different species counts: 1) endemic to Madagascar, 2) nonendemic but native to Madagascar, and 3) those occurring elsewhere in the world (for further information see text). In cases when species diversity exceeds or does not conform to that presented on the horizontal graph scale, the figures are written along the respective horizontal line of a given genus.

Humbert 1955). There, they often rank among the 10 most prevailing families in forest inventories, as elsewhere in the tropics. In elevational transects, their importance index is high from sea-level littoral forests to medium-altitude moist evergreen forests at about 1200 m, and drops off thereafter at higher elevations (Gautier 2003 and references therein). Above 1500 m, only a few species of *Labourdonnaisia*, one *Donella*, and the ubiquitous *Gambeya boiviniana* can be found. In the seasonal Western Domain, the family is less diverse and abundant, although genera such as *Capurodendron* or *Sideroxylon* are nevertheless well represented in the dry deciduous forests, with many species adapted and/or restricted to limestone substrates (Gautier et al. 2013b). Both genera are also represented in the dry spiny thickets of the Southern Domain by a few species: *C. androyense*, *C. mandrarense* (*sensu lato*), *C. nanophyllum*, and *S.* cf. *saxorum*. Areas with outstanding species richness include the most humid part of the eastern coast (from Mananara-Nord to Masoala and inland), as well as transition zones in the extreme north (from Vohémar to Antsiranana) and the southwest (Tolagnaro and surroundings).

In evergreen and deciduous forests, Sapotaceae species often rank among the tallest trees, producing straight trunks with the lowest branches at 15 m or more. The tallest individuals of many species produce buttresses (Figure 8.75a), increasing tree stability against strong wind. As a rule, they require shade for germination and during the first years of growth, and they are poorly adapted to secondary environments, with the exception of *Gambeya boiviniana* and *Donella perrieri*, which thrive in forest gaps (L. Gautier, unpublished data). Early growth is essentially vertical, producing long and thin but sturdy trunks. During that stage, juvenile leaves can be very different in shape from the adult leaves, making confident morphological identification difficult. When a tree reaches the canopy, the lower branches are lost, resulting in a single, straight bole. Upper horizontal branches elongate and generally display a growth pattern referred to as Aubréville's model by Hallé et al. (1978): the apical bud curves vertically to produce a flush of leaves and its growth is slowed, while a lateral bud develops horizontally to form the next elongation shoot, which will repeat this pattern (Figure 8.75f). In dry deciduous forests, this growth pattern is highly seasonal. Brachyblasts (club-like short thickened shoots that bear leaves or flowers, with numerous crowded scars of organs of recent years) occur in some species, as a consequence of extreme reduction in stem growth (Figure 8.75h).

Sapotaceae leaves, despite their coriaceous texture, frequently show signs of insect damage, although massive attacks are rare. Latex is often interpreted as being a defense against insects either through its chemical toxicity (Sapotaceae latex is not, however, reported as poisonous, at least for mammals) or mechanically by sticking to the mouthparts of insects (Agrawal and Konno 2009). Sapotaceae species are susceptible to gall formation, but gall-associated insects have apparently not been studied in Malagasy members of the family, although they are usually Hemiptera or Hymenoptera (C. G. Boluda, unpublished data). Gall shape is variable depending on the species, from simple inflated structures to sea urchin–like morphs, and can be produced by the total transformation of a young leaf or by the formation of cavities or wart-like structures in the leaf blade. In some cases, galls are massive formations across the whole tree, as has been observed on *Sideroxylon gerrardianum* in littoral forests. Some *Labourdonnaisia* species develop galls on flowers; these can develop on pedicelled fruit-like structures more than 5 cm in diameter, with a hard, woody cover containing an internal cavity with a single hemipteran larva persisting for at least several months. Sapotaceae leaves are frequently colonized by various groups of Ascomycota fungi, which include conspicuous black networks with protruding fruiting bodies, small membrane-like films, or more frequently epiphyllous micrometric fruiting bodies on both the upper and lower surfaces. Many of these fungi seem specific to Sapotaceae, being absent from leaves of neighboring plant species. Their diversity is, however, not documented.

Annual onset of flowering at the end of the dry season seems to be the prevalent pattern in Malagasy Sapotaceae of western dry deciduous forests, but little is known about the phenology of species in moist evergreen forest. Massive flowering is often observed in some species but this is not always the rule. Pollination remains to be studied, but flowers are frequently whitish-cream and have a sweet fragrance produced by a poorly differentiated nectary ring at the base of the ovary (Pennington 2004). Some species seem clearly to be adapted to generalist pollination, with nectar access not controlled by any dedicated flower structure. For example, in *Labramia costata*, the numerous flower clusters are visited by various species of Diptera, Hymenoptera, and even birds (C. G. Boluda, unpublished data). Other Sapotaceae members produce more specialized structures, for example, stamens in bundles of three in *Tsebona macrantha*, or valvate staminodes that enclose a chamber over the ovary, concealing the nectar in *Capurodendron* (Figure 8.76c). Although fruit bats (family Pteropodidae; see Andrianaivoarivelo et al., pp. 1911–16) have been sporadically observed on *Capurodendron* flowers (Vololona et al. 2020), it is doubtful that they are their principal pollinators, as staminodes prevent them from accessing nectar. Fruit bats are most probably attracted by the massive flowering and the smell and/or the pollen rather than by any nectar reward (Racey et al. 2009).

Mature fruits of members of the family are fleshy, mostly yellowish or reddish, and 1–5 cm long. Bats, lemurs, and birds act as the main seed dispersers (Bollen and van Elsacker 2002; Bollen et al. 2004b; see Razafindratsima et al., pp. 142–52). However, not all frugivores are efficient dispersers (Andrianaivoarivelo et al. 2012), as some destroy the seed while feeding on fruits. Although lemurs like *Eulemur coronatus* (Crowned Lemur) or *E. macaco* (Black Lemur) have been observed eating the fruit pulp, they do not swallow the medium-size or large seeds, which are dropped under the parent tree (C. G. Boluda, unpublished data). *Mimusops coriacea* is a littoral forest species that produces fruits appreciated by many frugivores, but which are also found floating at sea or on the beach with viable seeds inside, an indication of hydrochory. *Tsebona macrantha* produces the largest fruits of Malagasy Sapotaceae, reaching 10 cm diameter (Figure 8.75q), which are likely not eaten and dispersed by birds. Its large, recalcitrant seeds, 6 cm in length, cannot be swallowed by any extant mammal. Secondary dispersal in historic times by extinct large lemurs or giant tortoises, following fruit fall, cannot be ruled out, as hypothesized, for example, for *Canarium* (see Federman et al. 2016). If that hypothesis is correct, *T. macrantha* may be suffering from the lack of extant dispersers.

TAXONOMIC OVERVIEW OF MALAGASY SAPOTACEAE

The two main subfamilies, Sapotoideae and Chrysophylloideae, are unequally represented on Madagascar: with the current taxonomic effort the first will reach more than 100 species in eight genera and three tribes (Sideroxyleae, Tseboneae, and Sapoteae), whereas the second has only 11 described species in the two genera of its only tribe (Table 8.44).

Tribe Sideroxyleae

Sideroxylon: This is a pantropical genus of about 80 species worldwide, mainly occurring in seasonal dry or subarid regions, especially with deciduous vegetation. It has six described endemic species and three additional varieties on Madagascar. Flowers of *Sideroxylon* have five imbricate sepals and a corolla without appendages but with developed staminodes (Figure 8.75o), which are crimson in several species (Figure 8.75p). It can be distinguished from all other Malagasy Sapotaceae by its areolate tertiary venation (Figure 8.75r) and seeds with a basal scar (Figure 8.75i).

The biogeographic relationships of the genus worldwide indicate that the Malagasy and Mascarene species form a clade that diverged from the larger African/Arabian clade during the Oligocene and colonized Madagascar by over-sea dispersal, with the three Mascarene species analyzed so far forming a clade with a crown age of 2–6 Mya (late Miocene to Pliocene; Stride et al. 2014). On Madagascar, the genus has one variable widespread dry forest species, *S. saxorum*, which extends south to dry spiny thicket, and five moist evergreen forest species, including the widespread *S. gerrardianum*. Varieties have been described within *S. saxorum* and *S. beguei*, but the taxonomic importance of these will need to be assessed. The genus as a whole requires further attention, and may contain as many as 12 undescribed species.

Tribe Tseboneae

This recently described tribe is endemic to Madagascar and comprises three genera (Gautier et al. 2013c): *Tsebona* and *Bemangidia*, as currently recognized (both are monotypic and occurring in lowland moist evergreen forests); and *Capurodendron*, with multiple species that have radiated across the island in most vegetation types. The origin of the tribe is still under investigation. It is part of a Paleotropical group with mainly African but also Indo-Pacific lineages and is presumably the result of a colonization event estimated to have occurred during the Eocene (C. G. Boluda et al., unpublished data). Tseboneae flowers have five imbricate sepals, a corolla without appendages, developed staminodes, and seeds with a basiventral to ventral scar, lacking endosperm.

Tsebona: *T. macrantha* (*tsebona*) is the only described species in the genus. This huge tree exceeds 30 m in height and 1 m in diameter, and is found in the northern half of the eastern lowland moist evergreen forest. It is recognizable by its very thick terminal twigs 2–3 cm in diameter, its large leaves with very evident parallel secondary venation contrasting with tertiary venation (Figure 8.75q), flowers with five bundles of three stamens (Figure 8.75s), and fruits containing one to several seeds, each with a scar covering about three-quarters of the surface (Figures 8.75j and q). The seeds of *Tsebona* are sensitive to desiccation and germination is hypogeal (C. G. Boluda, unpublished data). A surprising variation in the number of secondary veins (from 10 to 40 pairs) does not seem to be correlated with geography, elevation, or genetics. In turn, a recent specimen collected much further south in Ankarabolava, has distinctive seeds and is also genetically different.

Bemangidia: The recently described genus *Bemangidia* (Gautier et al. 2013c) is endemic to lowland moist evergreen forests of the southeast. The only described species, *B. lowryi*, is a medium-size tree with large leaves (Figure 8.76a) and large flowers (Figure 8.75g) that are similar to those of *Tsebona*, except that each has five solitary stamens. Its fruit contains a single seed with a scar covering only one-quarter of the seed surface (Figure 8.75k). This species is known from a handful of collections made between 250 and 400 m in the Bemangidy Forest of the Tsitongambarika protected area. A population documented by three collections with immature flowers made in the same forest but on ridges and summits around ~600 m has significantly smaller leaves and seems to be genetically different. Mature flowers and fruits would be needed in order to assess its taxonomic status. Attempts to locate the genus in the nearby Beampingaratsy Forest, west of Manantenina, have been so far unsuccessful.

Capurodendron: With 33 accepted species, including 10 recently described, and 15 additional new species under study, *Capurodendron* qualifies as the most species-rich endemic flowering plant genus on Madagascar (based on the figures of Callmander et al. 2011a). It is distributed in all main forest types across all phytogeographic domains (*sensu* Humbert 1955) except the High Mountains. It thrives from sea level to about 1200 m and in humid to subarid climates. Except for the basal *C. madagascariense*, which diverged in the Eocene, the diversification leading to all extant *Capurodendron* took place more recently. This rapid radiation may be related to back-and-forth dispersal between dry and humid forest ecosystems, together with geographic isolation and

TABLE 8.44. **Accepted described genera and species of Malagasy Sapotaceae, with taxonomic status, worldwide distribution, Madagascar distribution, and IUCN status**

SCIENTIFIC NAME	TAXONOMIC STATUS	WORLDWIDE DISTRIBUTION	DISTRIBUTION ON MADAGASCAR	IUCN STATUS
***BEMANGIDIA* L. GAUT.**	Another undescribed species suspected	M	E	–
B. lowryi L. Gaut.	–	M	E [Anosy]	CR
***CAPURODENDRON* AUBRÉV.**	Two species complexes awaiting resolution	M	E, Sb, C, W, S	–
C. andrafiamenae L. Gaut. & Boluda	–	M	W [DIANA]	NE
C. androyense Aubrév.	Introgression with *C. mandrarense*	M	S	LC
C. ankaranense Aubrév.	–	M	W [DIANA to Boeny]	VU
C. antongiliense Aubrév.	–	M	E [Analanjirofo]	NE
C. apollonioides Aubrév.	–	M	E [Analanjirofo]	NE
C. aubrevillei L. Gaut. & Boluda	–	M	E [SAVA to Atsinanana]	NE
C. bakeri (Scott-Elliot) Aubrév.	–	M	S-E Transition [Anosy]	NE
C. bakeri var. *antalahense* Aubrév.	Unclear	M	E [SAVA]	NE
C. birkinshawii L. Gaut. & Boluda	–	M	S [Anosy]	NE
C. costatum Aubrév.	–	M	W [Melaky]	CR
C. darainense L. Gaut. & Boluda	–	M	W [SAVA]	
C. delphinense Aubrév.	–	M	E [Anosy]	EN
C. gracilifolium Aubrév.	–	M	C, W, S [Melaky to Atsimo-Andrefana, Anosy and Ihorombe]	NT
C. greveanum Aubrév.	–	M	W [DIANA and SAVA, disjunct with Melaky to Atsimo-Andrefana]	LC
C. ludiifolium Aubrév.	–	M	E [Atsinanana, Analanjirofo]	VU
C. madagascariense (Lecomte) Aubrév.	–	M	W [SAVA to Melaky]	EN
C. mandrarense Aubrév.	Introgression with *C. androyense*	M	C, W, S [Atsimo-Andrefana, Androy, Anosy and Ihorombe]	NE
C. microphyllum (Scott-Elliot) Aubrév.	–	M	S-E Transition [Anosy]	NE
C. naciriae L. Gaut. & Boluda	–	M	W [SAVA]	NE
C. nanophyllum L. Gaut. & Naciri	–	M	S [Androy]	CR
C. nodosum Aubrév.	–	M	W [DIANA and SAVA]	VU
C. oblongifolium L. Gaut. & Boluda	–	M	W [Sofia]	NE
C. perrieri (Lecomte) Aubrév.	–	M	W [Boeny to Atsimo-Andrefana]	NT
C. pervillei (Engl.) Aubrév.	–	M	W [Sofia to Melaky]	NT

SCIENTIFIC NAME	TAXONOMIC STATUS	WORLDWIDE DISTRIBUTION	DISTRIBUTION ON MADAGASCAR	IUCN STATUS
C. pseudoterminalia Aubrév.	–	M	E [Atsinanana]	NE
C. randrianaivoi L. Gaut. & Boluda	–	M	W [DIANA]	NE
C. rubrocostatum (Jum. & H. Perrier) Aubrév.	–	M	C, W [Boeny to Atsimo-Andrefana, Betsiboka]	LC
C. rufescens Aubrév.	–	M	E [Atsinanana, Analanjirofo]	NE
C. sahafariense L. Gaut. & Naciri	–	M	W [DIANA]	CR
C. sakalavum Aubrév.	–	M	W [DIANA, Boeny and Melaky]	VU
C. schatzii L. Gaut. & Naciri	–	M	E [SAVA]	CR
C. suarezense Aubrév.	–	M	W [DIANA]	EN
C. tampinense (Lecomte) Aubrév.	Unclear	M	E	NE
C. tampinense var. *analamazaotrense* Aubrév.	Unclear	M	E, C [Alaotra-Mangoro, Analanjirofo]	NE
C. terminalioides Aubrév.	–	M	C, W [Ihorombe, Atsimo-Andrefana and Anosy]	NE
***DONELLA* PIERRE EX BAILL.**	–	PaleoT	E, Sb, C, W	–
D. ambrensis Aubrév.	–	M	C [DIANA]	NE
D. analalavensis Aubrév.	–	M	W [SAVA to Boeny]	EN
D. capuronii (G. E. Schatz & L. Gaut.) Mackinder & L. Gaut.	–	M	E [SAVA and Analanjirofo]	NE
D. delphinensis Aubrév.	–	M	E [SAVA to Anosy]	VU
D. fenerivensis Aubrév.	–	M	E [Analanjirofo, Atsinanana]	NE
D. guereliana (Aubrév.) Mackinder	–	M	W [SAVA and DIANA, disjunct with Melaky]	EN
D. humbertii Capuron ex Mackinder & L. Gaut.	–	M	W [Boeny, Melaky]	NE
D. lanceolata (Blume) Aubrév.	–	M-As	E, C [DIANA to Anosy]	LC
D. masoalensis Aubrév.	–	M	C [SAVA]	NE
D. perrieri Lecomte	–	M	E, Sb, C [DIANA to Anosy], W [Melaky]	NE
D. ranirisonii L. Gaut. & Mackinder	–	M	W [DIANA]	NE
***GAMBEYA* PIERRE**	–	–	E, Sb, C	–
G. boiviniana Pierre	–	MR	E, Sb, C [DIANA to Anosy]	LC
***LABOURDONNAISIA* BOJER**	Revision needed	MR	E, Sb, C	–
L. ambrensis comb. nov. ined.	Unclear	M	E, C	NE
L. ambrensis var. *marojejyensis* comb. nov. ined.	Unclear	M	C	NE

(continued overleaf)

TABLE 8.44. ***continued***

SCIENTIFIC NAME	TAXONOMIC STATUS	WORLDWIDE DISTRIBUTION	DISTRIBUTION ON MADAGASCAR	IUCN STATUS
L. glutinosa comb. nov. ined.	Unclear	M	E	NE
L. hexandra Lecomte	Unclear	M	E	NE
L. laciniata comb. nov. ined.	Unclear	M	E, C	NE
L. lecomtei Aubrév.	Unclear	M	E	NE
L. longepedicellata comb. nov. ined.	–	M	E [Analanjirofo]	CR
L. madagascariensis Pierre ex Baill.	Unclear	M	E	NE
L. manongarivensis comb. nov. ined.	Unclear	M	E, Sb	NE
L. parvifolia comb. nov. ined.	Unclear	M	E, C	NE
L. richardiana Pierre ex Aubrév.	Unclear	M	E	NE
L. sambiranensis comb. nov. ined.	Unclear	M	E, Sb	NE
L. tampoloensis comb. nov. ined.	Unclear	M	E	NE
L. thouvenotii comb. nov. ined.	Unclear	M	E, C	NE
L. urschii comb. nov. ined.	Unclear	M	E	NE
***LABRAMIA* A. DC.**	Revision needed	MR	E, Sb, C, W	–
L. ambondrobeensis L. Gaut. & Randriarisoa	–	M	E-W Transition [SAVA]	CR
L. ankaranaensis Aubrév. var. *ankaranaensis*	–	M	Sb, W [DIANA to Melaky]	LC
L. ankaranaensis var. *antsyngiensis* Aubrév.	Unclear			NE
L. boivinii (Pierre) Aubrév. var. *boivinii*	Unclear	M	E	NE
L. boivinii var. *mananarensis* Aubrév.	Unclear	M	E	NE
L. bojeri A. DC.		M	E [SAVA to Anosy]	NE
L. capuronii Aubrév.	Unclear	M	E	NE
L. costata (M. Hartog ex Baill.) Aubrév.	–	M	E [SAVA to Vatovavy-Fitovinany]	LC
L. louvelii Aubrév.	Unclear	M	E, C	NE
L. platanoides Capuron ex Aubrév.	–	M	W [DIANA, SAVA]	NT
L. sambiranensis Capuron ex Aubrév.	–	M	Sb [DIANA]	NE
***MANILKARA* ADANS.**	–	PanT	E, Sb, C, W	NE
M. boivinii Aubrév.	Unclear	M	E, Sb, W	NE
M. capuronii Aubrév.	–	M	W [Sofia]	NE
M. perrieri Aubrév.	–	M	E, C [Analanjirofo to Anosy]	EN
M. sahafarensis Aubrév.	–	M	W [DIANA]	CR
M. suarezensis Capuron ex Aubrév.	–	M	W [DIANA]	CR
***MIMUSOPS* L.**	Revision needed	PaleoT	E, Sb, C, W	–
M. ankaibeensis Capuron ex Aubrév.	–	M	E, C [SAVA]	NE
M. antongilensis Aubrév.	Unclear	M	E	NE

SCIENTIFIC NAME	TAXONOMIC STATUS	WORLDWIDE DISTRIBUTION	DISTRIBUTION ON MADAGASCAR	IUCN STATUS
M. antorakensis Aubrév.	Unclear	M	E	NE
M. antsiranensis F. Friedmann	–	M	W [DIANA]	EN
M. boeniensis Randrianaivo	–	M	W [DIANA to Melaky]	VU
M. capuronii Aubrév. var. *capuronii*	–	M	E	NE
M. capuronii var. *retusa* Aubrév.	Specifically distinct	M	W [DIANA, SAVA]	NE
M. capuronii var. *salicifolia* Aubrév.	Doubtful	M	Sb	NE
M. coriacea (A. DC.) Miq.	–	MR	E, Sb [DIANA to Anosy]	NE
M. lecomtei H. J. Lam	Hybrids suspected	M	E [Analanjirofo, Atsinanana]	NE
M. lohindri Aubrév.	–	M	E [SAVA, Analanjirofo]	NE
M. longepedicellata Aubrév.	Doubtful	M	E	NE
M. masoalensis Randrianaivo	–	M	E [SAVA, Analanjirofo]	NE
M. membranacea Aubrév.	–	M	E [SAVA, Analanjirofo]	NE
M. nossibeensis Capuron ex Aubrév.	Unclear	M	Sb	CR
M. occidentalis Aubrév.	–	M	W [Sofia to Melaky]	VU
M. perrieri Capuron ex Aubrév.	–	M	E [SAVA to Atsinanana]	NE
M. sambiranensis Aubrév.	–	M	Sb, W [DIANA]	EN
M. voalela Aubrév.	Unclear	M	E	NE
***SIDEROXYLON* L.**	Revision needed	PanT	E, C, W, S	–
S. beguei Capuron ex Aubrév. var. *beguei*	Confused	M	E	NE
S. beguei var. *saboureaui* Aubrév.	Confused	M	E	NE
S. beguei var. *longepedicellata* Aubrév.	Confused	M	E	NE
S. betsimisarakum Lecomte	–	M	E, C [SAVA to Vatovavy-Fitovinany]	NE
S. capuronii Aubrév.	–	M	E, C [Analanjirofo]	NE
S. gerrardianum (Hook. f.) Lecomte	–	M	E, C [DIANA to Anosy]	VU
S. saxorum Lecomte var. *saxorum*	–	M	W [DIANA to Atsimo-Andrefana], S?	VU
S. saxorum var. *collinum* Lecomte	Doubtful			NE
S. tambolokoko Aubrév.	–	M	S-E Transition [Anosy]	NE
***TSEBONA* CAPURON**	A second species to be described	M	E	–
T. macrantha Capuron	–	M	E [SAVA to Atsinanana]	Draft available

Notes: Worldwide distribution: M, Madagascar endemic; MR, Malagasy Region (western Indian Ocean islands) endemic; MR-Afr, Malagasy Region and continental Africa; M-As, Madagascar and Asia; PaleoT, Paleotropical; PanT, Pantropical. Madagascar distribution: phytogeographical domains following Humbert (1955): E, Eastern; Sb, Sambirano; C, Central; W, Western; S, Southern. [Administrative regions in square brackets.] IUCN status abbreviations: CR, Critically Endangered; DD, Data Deficient; EN, Endangered; LC, Least Concern; NE, Not Evaluated; NT, Near Threatened; VU, Vulnerable.

adaptation to different substrates, producing six main extant lineages. As a result, *Capurodendron* is vegetatively the most variable genus of all Malagasy Sapotaceae. It includes shrubs (*C. androyense* and *C. nanophyllum*) or small trees (*C. mandrarense*) in arid regions, and large trees in lowland moist evergreen (*C. antongiliense* and *C. apollonioides*) or dry deciduous (*C. madagascariense*, *C. sakalavum*, and *C. suarezense*) forests. Leaves are highly variable in the genus, from less than 1 cm in length and caducous to more than 30 cm long and perennial, and from glabrous and flat to tomentose and bullate. By contrast, the flowers of *Capurodendron* (Figures 8.76b and c) are remarkably homogeneous, with five hirsute, valvate staminodes covering the ovary and forming a chamber, with the only exception being the basal *C. madagascariense*, which lacks such a chamber. Fruits (Figure 8.76d) have a solitary seed that can be rounded, or elongated in a few forest species (Figure 8.75l). Morphological convergence is common in *Capurodendron*, and phylogenetically distant species sometimes have similar morphologies, while closely related taxa often display very different leaf shapes and venation patterns. In such cases, seed shape, size, and scar characteristics are taxonomically more informative. Many *Capurodendron* species are Critically Endangered under the International Union for the Conservation of Nature (IUCN) Red List criteria, and some are only known from a single old collection made in an area that is now deforested (e.g., *C. antongiliense*, *C. birkinshawii*, *C. nanophyllum*) and consequently might be extinct.

Tribe Sapoteae

This tribe is most probably of African origin and stemmed from the Paleocene–Eocene transition, with a first divergence of a basal clade now represented by three African genera (*Baillonella*, *Vitellaria*, and *Vitellariopsis*, all with two whorls of four sepals), and then a major Oligocene divergence between the *Mimusops* plus allies lineage (subtribe Mimusopineae, also with two whorls of four sepals) and the *Manilkara* lineage (subtribe Manilkarineae, calyx reduced to two whorls of three sepals, including the western Indian Ocean island endemics *Labourdonnaisia* and *Labramia*). Several colonization events from Africa to Madagascar have been inferred to explain the presence of the four genera that occur on the island (Armstrong et al. 2014).

Mimusops: This is essentially an African-Malagasy genus, with three species in Asia (including the widespread and variable *M. elengi*), which extends from west Africa to northern Australia, with one species in the Comoros, three in the Mascarenes, and one in the Seychelles. Closely related genera are the African *Tieghemella* and *Autranella*, also with two whorls of four sepals. The phylogenetic relationships of members of the genus remain to be explored, but preliminary results by Armstrong et al. (2014) based on 20% of the species show a dichotomy of two similarly sized sister clades, one from continental Africa that also includes *M. comorensis* and *M. elengi*, and another with all the sampled Madagascar species. The numbers of described and accepted species on continental Africa and Madagascar are comparable (23 and 20, respectively), but morphological variability across species appears to be higher on Madagascar, with leaf size ranging from about 1 cm^2 to the size of a table tennis paddle. On Madagascar, species of *Mimusops* are understory to canopy trees that generally display a dark and deeply fissured bark. The genus is easily recognized for flowering or fruiting individuals by its persistent calyx with two whorls of four sepals (Figure 8.76f). The corolla is highly complex, with eight petals, each with two multifid appendages (Figure 8.76g). Fruits of *Mimusops* (Figures 8.76h and i) are mostly single-seeded, except in the common *M. coriacea*. The seed scar is basiventral (Figure 8.75n). In addition to the 15 species accepted in the *Flore de Madagascar* (Aubréville 1974), three have been described subsequently (Friedman 1980; Randrianaivo 2013) and an additional one is in preparation (L. Gautier and R. Randrianaivo, unpublished data).

Mimusops is well represented in lowland to medium-altitude moist evergreen forests in the East and Sambirano Domains (*sensu* Humbert 1955). There are also several species in the littoral forests, including *M. coriacea*, which is widely distributed along the eastern and northwestern coasts and extends to Anjouan in the Comoros. In the dry deciduous forests of Madagascar, several species occur in the north and west, sometimes on limestone, including *M. boeniensis* and *M. occidentalis*, which extend south to Lake Mandrozo and Bemaraha, respectively. The genus is not recorded further south in the drier climates of the Menabe and the Southern Domain. The entire genus is under study, and two species complexes may contain as many as 10 additional species.

Manilkara: The pantropical genus *Manilkara* has been demonstrated to be polyphyletic, with three of the Indo-Pacific species being sister to *Labourdonnaisia*, thus requiring recognition as a separate genus (Armstrong 2010, 2013; Armstrong et al. 2014; A. Randriarisoa et al., unpublished data). The common ancestor of these two genera diverged from the lineage comprising *Labramia* and *Manilkara sensu stricto* in the early Oligocene and the two diverging in the middle Oligocene. *Manilkara sensu stricto* comprises about 80 extant species in two major clades: one has a few African species as well as a group that dispersed to and speciated in the Neotropics; the other contains the bulk of African species along with a clade of Asian species. The Malagasy members of the group originated from at least two dispersal events out of this main African clade (Armstrong et al. 2014). The genus is recognized by a characteristic shiny silvery or golden appearance on the underside of the leaves and rather faint venation (Figure 8.76j). The flowers (Figure 8.76k) are typical for the subtribe, with two whorls of three sepals, a six-lobed corolla with a pair of appendages on each lobe, and six stamens. The fruits are generally single-seeded, with a basiventral seed scar. Malagasy *Manilkara* were recently revised (Plana and Gautier 2008), and five species were accepted. *Manilkara perrieri* is a medium-altitude moist evergreen forest species, while *M. boivinii* is found in lowland moist evergreen forests in the Eastern and Sambirano Domains, as well as in isolated edaphic humid situations in the western karsts of Bemaraha and Beanka protected areas. *Manilkara suarezensis* is a rare species found in dry deciduous forests on limestone in the north, whereas *M. capuronii*, known only from the type collected in transitional areas southwest of the Manongarivo Massif, is possibly extinct. As for the remaining species on the island, *M. sahafarensis*, it is not closely related to the others, and represents a lineage that reached the island by a separate dispersal event. It is known only from the dry deciduous forest on sands at

Sahafary, 30 km south-southeast of Antsiranana. *Manilkara boivinii*, as presently circumscribed, might include several taxa and should receive further attention.

Labramia: This genus is endemic to the Malagasy Region, and probably reached Madagascar in the late Miocene with subsequent dispersal resulting in one species (*L. mayottensis*) on Mayotte (R. Randriarisoa et al., unpublished data). *Labramia* is a clearly defined genus with a classical Manilkarineae flower (Figure 8.76n) distinct from other members of the subtribe by its glabrous ovary and elongated ventral seed scar (Aubréville 1964; Pennington 1991; Figure 8.75m). The style is often persistent on the fruit (Figure 8.76o). The trunk of *Labramia* is generally smooth, light colored, and exfoliating (Figure 8.75c). The secondary and tertiary venation is impressed or sunken on herbarium specimens of many species, a feature that can be checked in the field by examining dry leaves that have fallen at the base of the tree; it can also sometimes be observed on fresh leaves (Figure 8.76m). The monophyly of the genus is highly supported by molecular evidence (R. Randriarisoa et al., unpublished data). With the addition of a recently described species, there are currently nine accepted species of *Labramia*, eight of which are endemic to Madagascar.

The geographic distributions of members of the genus extend mainly along the moist evergreen forests of the East (*L. boivinii*, *L. capuronii*, *L. costata*, and *L. louvelii*) and the Sambirano Domains (*L. sambiranensis*). Eastern littoral forests host the most common species, *L. bojeri*. However, one species occurs in the karstic limestone massifs in the west and the north (*L. ankaranensis*), where it is associated with edaphic humidity, and another species is found in dense humid semi-deciduous or dry deciduous forests in the north (*L. platanoides*). The newly described species *L. ambondrombeensis* grows in littoral forest in a climate transition area in the northeast (Randriarisoa et al. 2020). Species delimitation in this genus requires further attention and an in-depth molecular study is underway.

Labourdonnaisia (including ***Faucherea***): This genus is endemic to the Malagasy Region, with three species in the Mascarenes and probably 15–25 species on Madagascar. The only distinction between *Labourdonnaisia* and *Faucherea* was the merosity of corolla lobes and stamens, often a weak character in Sapotaceae (Kümpers et al. 2016). A recent molecular phylogeny based on 638 genes supports the preliminary results of Armstrong (2010), showing no phylogenetic differentiation between the two genera and indicating clearly that they should be united (A. Randriarisoa et al., unpublished data). The genus, as broadly circumscribed here, is characterized by a highly variable number of corolla lobes and stamens (six to 18), the absence of corolla appendages, and the presence of rudimentary staminodes (Figure 8.76q). The leaves have many parallel veins, often making it impossible to distinguish secondaries from the tertiary network (Figure 8.76p). Fruit (Figure 8.76r) is generally single-seeded, with a few exceptions.

Labourdonnaisia and the three atypical Asian *Manilkara* diverged in the early Miocene, and *Labourdonnaisia* started to diversify on Madagascar and the Mascarenes in the late Miocene (A. Randriarisoa et al., unpublished data). Malagasy *Labourdonnaisia* species are distributed in lowland and medium-altitude moist evergreen and littoral forests, in the Eastern and Sambirano Domains, but are totally absent from the west and the south, even in edaphically humid situations. The taxonomy of *Labourdonnaisia* on Madagascar, with 14 described species, is in considerable need of revision. Species delimitation is poorly understood and most names have been widely misapplied, making it impossible to analyze species distributions and conduct conservation assessments. Multi-gene molecular analyses will soon be extended to include much broader sampling to address species delimitation issues, revise the genus, and validate several new species that have been suspected based on morphology.

Tribe Chrysophylleae

Three genera belonging to this tribe that occur on Madagascar were recognized in the *Flore de Madagascar et des Comores* (Aubréville 1974), which were later included in an expanded, pantropical interpretation of *Chrysophyllum* (Pennington 1991; Schatz and Gautier 1996). Molecular studies (Swenson et al. 2008) have since revealed that this broad circumscription was untenable, and the Malagasy species have now been placed back in two of the three original genera, *Donella* and *Gambeya*. They share tiny pentamerous flowers (Figure 8.76u) with short corolla lobes that lack appendages, have no staminodes, and have typically five-seeded fruits (Figure 8.76s). The two genera differ markedly in leaf venation.

Donella: This mainly African-Malagasy genus was recently revised to include *Austrogambeya* (Mackinder et al. 2016); it has 17 species, six in continental Africa, and 11 on Madagascar, one of which is also present in the Indo-Pacific. *Donella* is believed to have an African origin and could have diverged from its closest extant relative (*Breviea*) as early as the Paleocene (Bartish et al. 2011). On Madagascar, members of the genus are mostly small to medium-size trees, rarely large. The commonest species is the widespread and variable *D. perrieri*, which is found in all types of moist evergreen forest from sea level to about 1000 m, including in isolated, edaphically humid situations in the west. Other species are found in littoral forests (*D. delphinensis*), lowland moist evergreen forests (*D. capuronii*, *D. fenerivensis*, and *D. lanceolata*), medium-altitude moist evergreen forests up to 1800 m elevation (*D. masoalensis*), including on volcanic substrate (*D. ambrensis*), and dry deciduous forests in the north and the west (*D. analalavensis*, *D. humbertiana*, and *D. ranirisonii*), including on limestone (*D. guereliana*). Leaves of *Donella* species have numerous secondary nerves that are hardly distinguishable from the parallel network of tertiary venation. The occurrence on Madagascar of the widespread Asian species *D. lanceolata* (the only Malagasy Sapotaceae shared with territories outside the western Indian Ocean islands) is surprising and deserves further investigation.

Gambeya: This is essentially an African genus, with 15 species in the humid forests of the continent. The single homogenous species on Madagascar, *G. boiviniana* (*famelona*), is believed to be related to the *G. africana* group and to have originated from a relatively recent dispersal event. It is easily recognized by its discolorous leaves, which are green above and shiny copper below (Figure 8.76t), with conspicuous and regular secondaries contrasting sharply with the faint perpendicular tertiary venation. It is found throughout moist evergreen forest, from about 50 m to 1700 m, but it is absent from littoral forests. *Gambeya boiviniana* is ecologically distinctive in comparison with most other Malagasy species: although a large tree, it displays secondary life traits, such as rapid growth and a high output of widely dispersed fruits. As a consequence, it is frequently found in clearings and other disturbed areas in moist evergreen forests. This species is also present in the Comoros (Anjouan), where it was once considered as a distinct variety.

USES

As elsewhere in the tropics, Sapotaceae members furnish high-quality timber for construction. The wood is generally very strong and resists degradation by insects or fungi. It is widely appreciated (Figures 8.76v and w) for heavy duty domestic uses such as for pillars, boats, furniture, railroad ties, and cart wheels (Boiteau 1999). The Malagasy vernacular names for members of the family are also used for geographic names, such as Nosy Ankao (*ankao*), an islet between Vohémar and Antsiranana, named after the Malagasy name for *Capurodendron greveanum*, which is locally a dominant tree in the remaining forests (S. M. Goodman, unpublished data), or Nosy Nato (*nato*), an islet south of Ile Sainte Marie, named after a local abundance of trees belonging to the Sapotaceae family. Nowadays, not a single tree remains, reflecting intensive timber exploitation during the early growth of the city of Toamasina.

The bark of trees of the Sapotaceae is used in rituals (*joro*); the red sap is extracted from the bark to represent blood (Boiteau 1985) but is more generally used as a red dye for silk and cotton (Aubréville 1974; Boiteau 1979), including shrouds (Dubard 1914; Randrianaivo 2013). Several Malagasy sayings refer to its dyeing properties:

1) "*Lambamena asoka hodi-nanto, izay mamerina indroa manana ny antitra.*" [A shroud dyed twice with *nanto* has a deeper color] (Randrianaivo 2013), which signifies that you should think twice before undertaking an action.
2) "*Aza mitondra hodi-nato miantsinanana.*" [Do not bring nanto bark to the east (i.e.,where it comes from)] (Cousins and Parrett 1871), meaning that it is unwise to bring something where it can be found profusely (or to bring assistance where it is not needed).
3) "*Hodi-nato voazehy, ketsa voasoritra, vomanga voaisa.*" [This is measured *nanto* bark, marked paddy, counted potatoes] (Veyrières and Meritens 1967), meaning that the matters have been definitively settled.

The latex is used as birdlime (Boiteau 1999). The fruits of many species are reported to be edible, such as those of *Labramia costata* (Figure 8.76o), *Labourdonnaisia manongarivensis*, and *Mimusops coriacea* (Aubréville 1974; Boiteau 1999), the latter being often sold at markets and its tree preserved in anthropogenic landscapes (Gautier et al. 2012b). The seeds have been used in the past to produce oil, but only those of *Labramia bojeri* have been analyzed to date (Margaillan 1929). In comparison with other families occurring on Madagascar, there is relatively little information on medicinal uses of Sapotaceae species. The bark of *Mimusops coriacea* is reported to be antipyretic (Heckel 1910), and *Chrysophyllum boivinianum* leaves are often sold in markets for medicinal purposes. According to Aubréville (1974), crushed leaves of this tree are used to make a plaster to heal scorpion stings. Boiteau (1979) reports the same use involving a direct application of fresh leaves. This species is also reported to be used in the Lake Alaotra region against cold and fever (Rabesa 1986).

VERNACULAR NAMES

Most Malagasy members of Sapotaceae subfamily Sapotoideae are generically referred to as *nato* or *nanto*, with the addition of locally specific epithets to distinguish between genera and species (e.g., *ankao*, *lohindry*, *makaka*, *sohihy*, *tambolokoko*, *tsebona*, *vasihy*, *voalela*). These names vary from one place to another, according to the local flora and dialect; for a comprehensive account, see Boiteau (1999). However, widely used specific names are used for some important, widespread species, such as *voranto* for the edible *Mimusops coriacea*, *famelona* for *Gambeya boiviniana*, and *mahogo* or *hazo mahogo* for *Donella perrieri*, the latter two belonging to subfamily Chrysophylloideae.

Names have clearly been exchanged between Malagasy and Mascarene creole, e.g.: *tambalacoque* on Mauritius and *tambolokoko* on Madagascar, both of which designate species of *Sideroxylon*, which, by the way, is a Greek translation of the La Réunion name Bois de Fer). Botanists such as R. Capuron and A. Aubréville often used Malagasy vernacular names when naming new species of Sapotaceae, as for the genus *Tsebona* and several specific epithets, such as *Mimusops voalela* and *M. lohindri*.

CONSERVATION

Because most members of Sapotaceae grow slowly, begin reproducing late, and produce moderate amounts of fruit, they are generally adapted to the relatively stable environment of intact forests. As a consequence, the family is poorly represented in secondary environments, where they are essentially found as stump resprouts, with little or no recruitment. Logging places significant pressure on the populations of many species, which can easily become unsustainable. Consequently, many Sapotaceae species are particularly dependent on the network of protected areas. Recent illegal and unsustainable exploitation (e.g., the plunder of the Tampolo Forest Reserve observed in 2018) highlight the interest of the illegal international market for Sapotaceae and ebonies (*Diospyros*, Ebenaceae; see Schatz and Lowry, pp. 739–44), once exploitable rosewoods have become rare, which demonstrates the fragility of this protection. Ongoing Malagasy conservation initiatives aim to collect seeds and develop Sapotaceae trees in nurseries so that they can be systematically included in the second stages of ecological reforestation programs in protected areas.

Two-thirds of the recognized species of Malagasy Sapotaceae have been assessed using the IUCN Red List categories, the reminder being considered as Data Deficient (DD) because of uncertainty in species circumscription. Of the 67 species assessed to date, nine are considered to be Least Concern and seven Near Threatened, whereas 51 (76%) are threatened, including 11 classed as Vulnerable (VU), 24 as Endangered (EN), and 16 as Critically Endangered (CR). Assessments of the 20–30 expected new species should increase the proportion of species classed as CR and EN, as exemplified by the four most recently published ones, all assessed as CR. Another example is the case of *Capurodendron ludiifolium*, considered "only" as VU due to its large range, but which has been recently demonstrated to comprise four different, restricted-range species, probably all CR, or at least EN. This exemplifies the necessity of a sound taxonomic background for threat assessments. Until further taxonomic work is carried out, many species in the genera *Labourdonnaisia*, *Labramia*, and *Mimusops*, as currently delimited, will have to be classed as Data Deficient.

Subject editors: Peter P. Lowry II and Steven M. Goodman

EBENACEAE, EBONIES

G. E. Schatz and P. P. Lowry II

Worldwide, the family Ebenaceae comprises ~760 described species (Govaerts 2020), along with an additional ~155 as yet undescribed taxa, bringing the total to about 925 species. Most members of the family are tropical shrubs and trees, although several species occur in temperate regions, including a few that are the source of edible fruit such as the kaki (*Diospyros kaki*, native to Asia) and persimmon (*D. virginiana*, from North America). The Ebenaceae family is also the source of ebony hardwood, prized for different types of woodworking, including the fret boards of stringed musical instruments.

Diospyros is the largest genus in the family, with nearly 97% of the currently recognized species (Govaerts 2020), and is the only genus occurring on Madagascar (Madagascar Catalogue 2020). It comprises species that are dioecious (male and female flowers borne on separate plants). Their flowers are rather uniform in size and shape and are usually white or occasionally flesh-colored and often fragrant (Figure 8.78); they are probably visited by generalist insects, including beetles, bees, and thrips. The fruits of *Diospyros* constitute a keystone resource for vertebrate frugivores.

Generic delimitations in Ebenaceae have fluctuated over the last 200 years, but recent molecular phylogenetic studies by Duangjai et al. (2006, 2009) have led to the generally accepted recognition of four genera: *Diospyros* (including *Maba* and *Tetraclis*), *Euclea*, *Lissocarpa*, and *Royena*. *Lissocarpa* is sister to all other members of the family; *Euclea* and *Royena* form a clade that is in turn sister to *Diospyros*. Some authors, however, place African *Royena* in synonymy under *Diospyros* (e.g., White 1980; Govaerts 2020), and another alternative interpretation would be to expand *Diospyros* to incorporate both *Euclea* and *Royena*.

EBENACEAE OF MADAGASCAR

One of the main centers of diversity of Ebenaceae occurs on Madagascar where the family is found in nearly all parts of the island and is often represented by numerous co-occurring species, especially in forested environments. For example, 12 sympatric species of *Diospyros* were collected in fruit on the same day in 1989 on the island of Nosy Mangabe (Figure 8.78a; see also Schatz and Lowry 2018). In his treatment for the *Flore de Madagascar et de Comores*, Perrier de la Bâthie (1952c) enumerated 112 taxa (including 97 species and 15 infraspecific taxa), recognizing *Maba* (21 species) and *Tetraclis* (three species) as distinct from *Diospyros* (74 species). While Perrier de la Bâthie's work drew extensively on his personal knowledge of the group built over decades of fieldwork on Madagascar, and of research on its flora, he nevertheless had access to only 313 collections when he wrote his treatment. As a consequence, many of the species he recognized were known from just one or a few specimens. During the decades that followed, several waves of intensive exploration, notably by the Service Forestier of Madagascar and more recently a multi-institutional effort involving Malagasy and international botanists, greatly increased the specimen base such that more than 4000 collections are deposited in the world's main herbaria with holdings from the island. However, efforts to identify newly collected material often ended in frustration because the keys provided by Perrier de la Bâthie (1952c) were difficult to use, and his revision clearly included only a portion of the overall species diversity.

By the turn of the 21st century, most of the collections of Ebenaceae from Madagascar were identified only to genus. This situation prompted the authors of the present contribution to undertake a comprehensive revision of the group starting in 2009. We began with a thorough review of the accepted species leading to the publication of a paper (Schatz and Lowry 2011) containing nomenclatural notes, including the transfer of species from *Maba* and *Tetraclis* to *Diospyros* and the placement in synonymy of 10 species and eight infraspecific taxa that had been recognized by Perrier de la Bâthie (1952c). Since that paper was published, detailed study of herbarium material, primarily at the Muséum National d'Histoire Naturelle in Paris and the Missouri Botanical Garden in St. Louis, as well as at the two main herbaria on Madagascar, also revealed an amazing (but not totally unexpected) number of new species. The first seven of these novelties were recently published (Schatz and Lowry 2018), bringing the total number of currently recognized species to

FIGURE 8.78 **Examples of Malagasy *Diospyros* (Ebenaceae). A) 12 sympatric species of *Diospyros* collected in fruit on the same day in 1989 on Nosy Mangabe; B) *D. torquata*, Bernieriana group, at Kirindy Mité, fruit with accrescent calyx (Phillipson 6146); C) *D.* "*bemangidiensis*" ined., Calophylla group, at Tsitongambarika, female flowers (Lowry 6690); D) *D. cupulifera*, Forbesia group, at Andohahela, fruit (Lowry 6906); E) *D.* "*labatiana*" ined., Gracilipes group, at Ambatovy, male flowers (Rakotovao 3956); F) *D. anosivolensis*, Gracilipes group, at Anosivolo River, Ambodiriana, fruits (Rakotovao 5164); G) *D.* "*ratovosonii*" ined., Pruinosa group, at Ambalabe, female flowers (Randrianasolo 1360); H) *D. pruinosa*, Pruinosa group, at Andavakoera, fruits (Ratovoson 1424,); I) *Diospyros* sp. nov., Sclerophylla group, at Antsolatra Massif, at Mahatsara, fruits with reflexed calyx lobes (Birkinshaw 1972); J) *D. squamosa*, Squamosa group, fruit on pedicel with bract scars (Lowry 7534); K) *D. mangabensis*, Subsessilifolia group, at Ambodivohitra Forest, female flowers (Ravelonarivo 3510); L) *D. clusiifolia*, Tetraclis group, at Amparafaravay Forest, fruit (Syde 316); M) *D. ferrea*, unplaced, at Antetezana, female flowers (Lowry 7511); N) *D. humbertiana*, unplaced, at Ambatoabo, young fruit (Lowry 6916); and O) *D. humbertiana*, at Ambatoabo, male flowers (Ratovoson 1507).** (PHOTOS A by G. Schatz; B by P. B. Phillipson; C, D, J, M, and N by P. Lowry; E and F by C. Rakotovao; G by F. Rakotoarivony; H and O by F. Ratovoson; I by C. Birkinshaw; K by D. Ravelonarivo; and L by P. Antilahimena.)

91, only three of which are not endemic (two that also occur on the Comoro islands and one that is also found from coastal east Africa to Sri Lanka and perhaps farther east). We have also identified and delimited some 155 additional new species that are now being described (Schatz and Lowry 2020; Schatz et al. 2020; Linan et al. 2021; Mas et al. in press; G. Schatz and P. Lowry, unpublished data). All of the new species are endemic to the island, and the total level of endemism will thus unquestionably exceed 98%. In all, there are nearly 250 species of *Diospyros* on Madagascar, making it the largest genus in the flora.

RELATIONSHIPS WITHIN MALAGASY *DIOSPYROS*

In the course of examining the large number of herbarium specimens from Madagascar and clarifying species limits, it quickly became evident that several morphologically coherent groups could be recognized within Malagasy *Diospyros*, each with its own set of distinctive features. Together they encompass most of the species diversity, and, given the massive size of the genus, these informal groups offered a convenient framework for beginning the task of describing a significant portion of the new species. A complementary approach is also being used to describe novelties from particular geographic areas, such as the island of Nosy Mangabe (Schatz and Lowry 2018), or from ecosystems such as eastern littoral forests (G. Schatz and P. Lowry, unpublished data).

One of these informal groups, referred to as the Gracilipes group, is easily recognized by the powdery, waxy, white coating on the flowers and especially the fruits (Figures 8.78e and f). A taxonomic revision has been completed (Mas et al. in press) in which 22 species are recognized, all endemic to Madagascar, 13 of which are newly described. Revisions of three other informal groups of Malagasy *Diospyros* are in press or nearing completion: the Squamosa group, with nine species (all but one endemic), including six new to science, characterized by flowers enclosed within multiple, overlapping bracts in bud (Figure 8.78j; note bract scars at the base of the fruit) (Schatz and Lowry 2020); the Bernieriana group, comprising seven species (all but one endemic), including four new species, whose members have a long, accrescent calyx mostly obscuring the fruit (Figure 8.78b), which tears and breaks off irregularly during fruit maturation (Schatz et al. 2020); and the Forbesia group, with 17 species on Madagascar, 13 of which are new (another new member of the group occurs on Mayotte in the Comoro archipelago), distinguished by shiny fruits with a depressed apex surrounded by a scarious calyx (Figure 8.78d) (Linan et al. 2021). Species limits have largely been clarified in five other groups for which revisions are now being prepared: the Calophylla group (~17 species), characterized by pseudostipular leaves subtending the whorls of new lateral branches and congested fruits subtended by an appressed calyx with an irregularly lobed margin (Figure 8.78c); the Pruinosa group (~15 species), whose members have a shallowly abaxially cupular calyx that resembles a flaring skirt and is often glaucous, and globose fruits that are likewise glaucous (Figures 8.78g and h); the Sclerophylla group (~28 species), whose members have strongly reflexed calyx lobes in fruit (Figure 8.78i); the Subsessilifolia group (~13 species; Figure 8.78k), characterized by flattened twigs and subsessile leaves; and the Tetraclis group (~15 species), characterized by lamina with a mucronate apex and pseudovalvate corolla aestivation (Figure 8.78l). While the monophyly of these and other groups has not yet been formally tested, they constitute useful working hypotheses of relationships. A recent molecular study by Linan et al. (2019) focusing primarily on Mascarene *Diospyros* did, however, provide support for several of the groups recognized on Madagascar based on morphology, albeit with limited sampling. This study also revealed that all but one of the 13 species in the Mascarenes (Richardson 1980) belong to a clade that includes two species from Africa and the members of the Forbesia group on Madagascar and the Comoros, which together correspond to *Diospyros* section *Forbesia*, recognized by White (1980).

ECOGEOGRAPHY OF MALAGASY *DIOSPYROS*

Diospyros is represented in all of Madagascar's bioclimatic zones and vegetation types, but the genus is most diverse in moist evergreen forests. For example, 46 species of *Diospyros* have been documented in the lowland moist evergreen forests surrounding the Bay of Antongil, including both published and unpublished taxa, and 26 species have been recorded from the Vohimena Mountains in the southeastern part of the island (Madagascar Catalogue 2020; G. Schatz and P. Lowry, unpublished data). Madagascar's eastern littoral forests, now reduced to scattered remnant patches (Consiglio et al. 2006), have 40 species of *Diospyros* (Madagascar Catalogue 2020; G. Schatz and P. Lowry, unpublished data), and the dry deciduous forests of the far north are also very rich, with 34 species, including 11 of the 17 Malagasy species belonging to *Diospyros* section *Forbesia* (Linan et al. 2021). Four species, *D. humbertiana* (Figures 8.78n and o), *D. latispathulata*, *D. manampetsae*, and *D. nidiformis*, are endemic to the dry spiny thickets in the southwest (Madagascar Catalogue 2020).

ECOLOGICAL AND ECONOMIC IMPORTANCE OF *DIOSPYROS*

Fruits of *Diospyros* are keystone food resources for frugivorous vertebrates on Madagascar, especially lemurs. A review summarizing the literature on lemur food plants includes references that cite 20 different species of lemurs as feeding on *Diospyros* fruits (see Eppley et al., pp. 1839–59). Lemurs undoubtedly play an important role in *Diospyros* seed dispersal, having been implicated as dispersers in several studies (e.g., Birkinshaw 1999; Lahann 2007). Species of *Diospyros* with smaller fruits are probably eaten and dispersed by Madagascar's larger frugivorous birds, such as *Alectroenas madagascariensis* (Madagascar Blue-pigeon) and *Treron australis* (Madagascar Green-pigeon), but there are no published records of *Diospyros* being consumed by large fruit bats (*Pteropus rufus* and *Eidolon dupreanum*) or by *Coracopsis* parrots.

It is not yet clear which Malagasy species of *Diospyros* produce black heartwood and thus provide ebony for commerce and trade. Species reported to provide ebony wood include *D. perrieri* in western dry deciduous forests, as well as *D. ferrea* (Figure 8.78m)

TABLE 8.45. **Species of *Diospyros* (Ebenaceae) on Madagascar, their level of endemism, and Red List status**

SPECIES	ENDEMISM	IUCN STATUS
D. aculeata H. Perrier	Endemic	LC
D. analamerensis H. Perrier	Endemic	VU
D. anosivolensis H. Perrier	Endemic	EN
D. antongilensis G. E. Schatz & Lowry	Endemic	NT
D. baroniana H. Perrier	Endemic	LC
D. bemarivensis H. Perrier	Endemic	VU
D. bernieriana (Baill.) H. Perrier	Native	LC
D. bezofensis H. Perrier	Endemic	EN
D. boinensis (H. Perrier) G. E. Schatz & Lowry	Endemic	NT
D. boivinii Hiern	Endemic	LC
D. calophylla Hiern	Endemic	LC
D. cinnamomoides H. Perrier	Endemic	LC
D. clusiifolia (Hiern) G. E. Schatz & Lowry	Endemic	NT
D. comorensis Hiern	Native	NT
D. coursiana H. Perrier	Endemic	DD
D. cupulifera H. Perrier	Endemic	LC
D. danguyana H. Perrier	Endemic	LC
D. decaryana H. Perrier	Endemic	VU
D. decaryoides G. E. Schatz & Lowry	Endemic	EN
D. dicorypheoides H. Perrier	Endemic	EN
D. ebenifera (H. Perrier) G. E. Schatz & Lowry	Endemic	EN
D. erinacea (H. Perrier) G. E. Schatz & Lowry	Endemic	EN
D. erythrosperma H. Perrier	Endemic	LC
D. ferrea (Willd.) Bakh.	Native	LC
D. filipes H. Perrier	Endemic	VU
D. fuscovelutina Baker	Endemic	NT
D. geayana (H. Perrier) G. E. Schatz & Lowry	Endemic	EN
D. gracilipes Hiern	Endemic	LC
D. greveana H. Perrier	Endemic	VU
D. haplostylis Boivin ex Hiern	Endemic	LC
D. hazomainty H. Perrier	Endemic	DD
D. heterosepala H. Perrier	Endemic	NE
D. humbertiana H. Perrier	Endemic	LC
D. implexicalyx H. Perrier	Endemic	VU
D. kely G. E. Schatz & Lowry	Endemic	VU
D. ketsensis H. Perrier	Endemic	CR
D. laevis Bojer ex A. DC.	Endemic	NE
D. lanceolata Poir.	Endemic	NT
D. latispatulata H. Perrier	Endemic	LC
D. leucocalyx Hiern	Endemic	LC
D. lokohensis (H. Perrier) G. E. Schatz & Lowry	Endemic	LC
D. louvelii H. Perrier	Endemic	EN
D. maculata G. E. Schatz & Lowry	Endemic	NT
D. madecassa H. Perrier	Endemic	VU
D. manampetsae H. Perrier	Endemic	LC
D. mangabensis H. Perrier	Endemic	LC
D. mangorensis H. Perrier	Endemic	DD
D. mapingo H. Perrier	Endemic	LC
D. masoalensis H. Perrier	Endemic	NT
D. mcphersonii G. E. Schatz & Lowry	Endemic	EN
D. meeusiana (H. Perrier) G. E. Schatz & Lowry	Endemic	EN
D. microrhombus Hiern	Endemic	NT
D. myriophylla (H. Perrier) G. E. Schatz & Lowry	Endemic	LC
D. myrtifolia H. Perrier	Endemic	LC
D. nidiformis G. E. Schatz & Lowry	Endemic	EN
D. obducta (H. Perrier) G. E. Schatz & Lowry	Endemic	EN
D. occlusa H. Perrier	Endemic	LC
D. olacinoides(H. Perrier) G. E. Schatz & Lowry	Endemic	LC
D. parifolia H. Perrier	Endemic	NT
D. parvifolia Hiern	Endemic	LC
D. perglauca H. Perrier	Endemic	EN
D. perreticulata H. Perrier	Endemic	LC

SPECIES	ENDEMISM	IUCN STATUS
D. perrieri Jum.	Endemic	NT
D. pervilleana (Baill.) G. E. Schatz & Lowry	Endemic	LC
D. pervillei Hiern	Endemic	EN
D. platycalyx Hiern	Endemic	NT
D. pruinosa Hiern	Endemic	LC
D. quercina (Baill.) G. E. Schatz & Lowry	Endemic	VU
D. rubripetiolata G. E. Schatz & Lowry	Endemic	LC
D. sakalavarum H. Perrier	Endemic	LC
D. sclerophylla H. Perrier	Endemic	VU
D. sphaerosepala Baker	Endemic	NT
D. squamosa Bojer ex A. DC.	Endemic	LC
D. stenocarpa (H. Perrier) G. E. Schatz & Lowry	Endemic	VU
D. subacuta Hiern	Endemic	VU
D. subbullata G. E. Schatz & Lowry	Endemic	EN
D. subenervis (H. Perrier) G. E. Schatz & Lowry	Endemic	VU
D. subfalciformis H. Perrier	Endemic	EN
D. subsessilifolia H. Perrier	Endemic	LC
D. subtrinervis H. Perrier	Endemic	CR
D. tampinensis H. Perrier	Endemic	VU
D. tetraceros H. Perrier	Endemic	EN
D. tetrapoda H. Perrier	Endemic	CR
D. thouarsii Hiern	Endemic	EN
D. torquata H. Perrier	Endemic	NT
D. toxicaria Hiern	Endemic	LC
D. tropophylla (H. Perrier) G. E. Schatz & Lowry	Endemic	LC
D. ultima G. E. Schatz & Lowry	Endemic	EN
D. urschii H. Perrier	Endemic	NT
D. velutipes (H. Perrier) G. E. Schatz & Lowry	Endemic	LC
D. vescoi Hiern	Endemic	LC

Note: IUCN Red List status: CR, Critically Endangered; DD, Data Deficient; EN, Endangered; LC, Least Concern; NE, Not Evaluated; NT, Near Threatened; VU, Vulnerable.

and *D. toxicaria* in eastern lowland moist evergreen and littoral forests. Of the estimated 250 species of Malagasy *Diospyros*, 73 are recorded to reach 20 m in height, and are thus large enough trees to be potential sources of commercially valuable hardwood. These include 39 described species and 34 new species that are in the process of being described.

Illegal and unsustainable exploitation of Malagasy precious woods, in particular *Diospyros*, along with *Dalbergia* (the source of rosewood), led to both genera being listed on Appendix II of the Convention on International Trade in Endangered Species of Wild Fauna and Flora (CITES) in 2013, thereby placing a total legal embargo on international trade (Mason et al. 2016). Because these precious woods are so valuable and sought after, and thus represent a significant potential source of badly needed foreign income for Madagascar and for its poor rural population (Randriamalala and Liu 2010), pressure has been mounting to end the embargo by enabling the sustainable exploitation of this important resource. In order to do so, however, careful control and regulation would have to be established and maintained by Madagascar's forest administration along the entire process from harvest to export, with strict limits on the level of harvest of each exploitable species and a total exclusion of those that require conservation. Implementing such a system would require, among other things, the ability to identify standing trees, logs, sawn wood, and finished products with a high degree of accuracy, something that is currently not possible on the island. A consortium of Malagasy and international institutions was established in 2017 to address this need by 1) conducting extensive fieldwork to develop a precious woods reference library comprising voucher herbarium specimens, wood, bark, leaves, and silica gel–dried wood and leaf material, in support of both 2) taxonomic work to clarify species limits and describe all large tree species, and 3) establishing an integrated research program to elucidate morphological and DNA barcode characters, as well as anatomical and spectrometric features of the wood that can be used for 4) developing practical, reliable field identification tools and forensic wood identification protocols. The consortium members are also training Malagasy students in each of these disciplines and building national expertise to identify trees in forestry concessions as well as timber and wood products destined for the domestic and international markets.

CONSERVATION STATUS OF SPECIES

Risk of extinction assessments for 70 species of *Diospyros* have been published on the International Union for the Conservation of Nature (IUCN) Red List (IUCN 2020), including three species that were classified as Critically Endangered (CR), 15 as Endangered

(EN), and 12 as Vulnerable (VU), along with 11 found to be Near Threatened (NT), and 29 as of Least Concern (LC); three were regarded as Data Deficient (DD) (Table 8.45). Assessments of a further 15 species have been completed and will soon appear on the Red List, including four that are EN, two VU, six LC, and three NT. In addition, assessments will soon be published for 48 new species (one CR, 18 EN, 17 VU, four NT, and nine LC). In all, risk of extinction assessments have thus been completed for a total of 133 Malagasy *Diospyros* species, including, in summary, four that are CR, 37 EN, 31 VU, 18 NT, and 44 LC.

Subject editors: Laurent Gautier and Steven M. Goodman

RUBIACEAE: PROGRESS SINCE 2003

S. G. Razafimandimbison, K. Kainulainen, and P. De Block

BACKGROUND

The coffee family (Rubiaceae) is the fourth-largest flowering plant family with about 13,000 species and 610 genera of mostly understory shrubs and small trees (A. P. Davis et al. 2009). This group of plants is sister to the rest of the order Gentianales (e.g., B. Bremer 1996) and is distributed pantropically, with only few species in the temperate regions (Robbrecht 1988). Members of Rubiaceae are important components of various terrestrial ecosystems, including moist evergreen forests, dry deciduous forests, dry spiny thickets, grasslands and mangroves. They can easily be recognized by their opposite leaves, interpetiolar stipules and sympetalous flowers with inferior ovaries. The family encompasses some economically important plants, including *Coffea*, source of coffee, *Cinchona*, source of the antimalarial alkaloid quinine, the nutriceutical *Morinda citrifolia*, and some *Gardenia*, *Ixora*, and *Mussaenda* species with high horticultural value.

A. P. Davis and Bridson's (2003) last estimates of the total number of the Malagasy taxa of the family Rubiaceae were about 660 species in 89 genera, making it the largest woody plant family on Madagascar and the second-largest flowering plant family after the orchid family (Orchidaceae). The Rubiaceae constitutes 7–9% of the land plant diversity of Madagascar, with the level of specific endemism being almost 100% (29% at generic level) (A. P. Davis and Bridson 2003). None of the tribes occurring on Madagascar is endemic to the island; however, the tribes Alberteae and Danaideae are centered on Madagascar. Most of the Malagasy Rubiaceae members are shrubs or small trees, with the herbaceous plants belonging to the tribes Knoxieae, Rubieae, and Spermacoceae in the subfamily Rubioideae. The lianescent plants belong to three genera: *Danais* (Danaideae), *Paederia* (Paederieae), and *Sabicea* (Sabiceeae) (Table 8.46).

A flora treatment for the Malagasy Rubiaceae is still lacking. Since the publication of its first overview (A. P. Davis and Bridson 2003), our understanding of the systematics of the island's Rubiaceae (and the family as a whole) has progressed greatly as a result of several taxonomic revisions and molecular phylogenetic studies at all taxonomic levels. Extensive field collecting trips on Madagascar during the past couple of decades have resulted in the discovery of numerous new taxa and generated many new specimens of previously poorly known species. Here, we present an overview of the taxonomic and phylogenetic progress on the Malagasy Rubiaceae since 2003. This overview is subsequently followed by the presentation of six separate Malagasy Rubiaceae contributions, which are successively arranged according to the latest phylogeny-based subfamilial and tribal classifications of the family: tribe Guettardeae and the Hymenodictyeae-Naucleeae clade (subfamily Cinchonoideae *sensu* Manns and Bremer 2010); the Mussaendeae-Sabiceeae clade and the Coffeeae and Vanguerieae alliances (subfamily Ixoroideae *sensu* Kainulainen et al. 2013); and the Psychotrieae and Spermacoceae alliances (subfamily Rubioideae *sensu* Rydin et al. 2009). Within the alliances the tribes are presented in alphabetical order.

UPDATES ON SPECIES AND GENUS COUNTS AND GENERIC AND TRIBAL CLASSIFICATIONS

Three genera, *Meyna*, *Parapentas*, and *Scyphiphora*, are not included in this overview because their occurrence on Madagascar remains unconfirmed. The Mascarene genus *Fernelia* is no longer part of the Malagasy Rubiaceae flora (cf. Kainulainen et al. 2017c). The endemicity graph (Figure 8.79) is based primarily on numbers of described species of the endemic and indigenous genera (including recent colonizers and those unintentionally introduced, see Table 8.46). The newly described genus (*Tarenella*, De Block et al. 2021) and new species of some of the recently or currently revised genera, including *Coptosperma*, *Melanoxerus*, *Paracephaelis*, *Payera*, *Phialiphora*, *Razafimandimbisonia*, and *Schismatoclada*, are also taken into account. On the other hand, all species or genera deliberately introduced by humans for medicinal (e.g., *Cinchona calysaya*) and horticultural (e.g., *Ixora coccinea*, *Pentas lanceolata*, *Serissa japonica*) purposes are not considered in the endemicity graph. The genus *Bullockia* is excluded as it is represented by two undescribed species that are known from single fruiting specimens (Razafimandimbison et al. 2009a).

TABLE 8.46. **Rubiaceae genera of Madagascar, their current subfamily and tribe, life-forms, and number of described and expected species**

GENUS	LIFE-FORM	ENDEMISM	NUMBER OF DESCRIBED SPECIES	NUMBER OF EXPECTED SPECIES
SUBFAMILY CINCHONOIDEAE				
Tribe Cinchoneae				
Cinchona L.	Tree/shrub	Introduced	2	2
Tribe Guettardeae				
Antirhea Comm. ex A. Juss.	Tree/shrub	Native	2	2
Guettarda L.	Tree	Native	1	1
Tribe Hymenodictyeae				
Hymenodictyon Wall.	Tree/shrub	Native	13	14
Paracorynanthe Capuron	Tree/shrub	Endemic	2	2
Tribe Naucleeae				
Breonadia Ridsdale	Tree	Native	1	1
Breonia A. Rich. in DC.	Tree	Endemic	20	20
Gyrostipula J. Leroy	Tree	Native	2	2
Janotia J. Leroy	Tree	Endemic	1	1
Uncaria Schreb.	Liana	Native	1	1
SUBFAMILY IXOROIDEAE				
Tribe Mussaendeae				
Bremeria Razafim. & Alejandro	Tree/shrub/scandent	Native	17	31
Landiopsis Capuron ex Bosser	Shrub	Endemic	1	1
Mussaenda L.	Scandent shrub	Native	1	1
Tribe Sabiceeae				
Sabicea A. Rich. ex DC.	Liana/shrub	Native	5	5
Tribe Bertiereae				
Bertiera Aubl.	Shrub	Native	3	3
Tribe Alberteae				
Nematostylis Hook. f.	Shrub	Endemic	1	2
Razafimandimbisonia Kainul. & B. Bremer	Shrub	Endemic	5	6
Tribe Coffeeae				
Coffea L.	Tree	Native	60	60
Empogona Hook. f.	Shrub	Native	1	1
Tricalysia A. Rich. ex DC.	Tree/shrub	Native	12	12
Tribe Gardenieae				
Catunaregam Wolf	Tree/shrub	Native	1	2

(continued overleaf)

TABLE 8.46. *continued*

GENUS	LIFE-FORM	ENDEMISM	NUMBER OF DESCRIBED SPECIES	NUMBER OF EXPECTED SPECIES
Gardenia Ellis	Tree/shrub	Native	4	4
Hyperacanthus E. Mey. ex Bridson	Tree/shrub	Native	9	41
Melanoxerus Kainul. & B. Bremer	Tree	Endemic	1	4
Tribe Octotropideae				
Canephora Juss.	Tree/shrub	Endemic	7	10
Chapelieria A. Rich. ex DC.	Tree/shrub	Endemic	4	4
Cremaspora Benth.	Tree/shrub	Native	1	1
Flagenium Baill.	Tree/shrub	Endemic	6	8
Gallienia Dubard & Dop	Tree/shrub	Endemic	1	1
Jovetia Guédès	Shrub	Endemic	1	1
Lemyrea (A. Chev.) A. Chev. & Beille	Tree/shrub	Endemic	4	4
Mantalania Capuron ex J. Leroy	Tree/shrub	Endemic	3	3
Polysphaeria Hook. f.	Tree/shrub	Native	9	10
Pseudomantalania J. Leroy	Tree/shrub	Endemic	1	1
Tribe Pavetteae				
Coptosperma Hook. f.	Tree/shrub	Native	8	40
Exallosperma De Block	Tree/shrub	Endemic	1	1
Helictosperma De Block	Tree/shrub	Endemic	2	2
Homollea Arènes	Tree/shrub	Endemic	5	5
Paracephaelis Hook. f.	Tree/shrub	Native	5	17
Pseudocoptosperma De Block	Tree/shrub	Endemic	1	1
Robbrechtia De Block	Tree/shrub	Endemic	2	2
Schizenterospermum Homolle ex Arènes	Tree/shrub	Endemic	4	4
Tarenella De Block	Shrub	Endemic	5	5
Tarenna Gaertn.	Tree/shrub	Native	7	10
Tulearia De Block	Tree/shrub	Endemic	2	2
Tribe Ixoreae				
Ixora L.	Tree/shrub	Native	31	40
Tribe Vanguerieae				
Bullockia (Bridson) Razafim., Lantz & B. Bremer	Tree/shrub	Native	0	2
Peponidium (Baill.) Arènes	Tree/shrub	Native	45	55
Psydrax Gaertn.	Tree/shrub	Native	7	7

GENUS	LIFE-FORM	ENDEMISM	NUMBER OF DESCRIBED SPECIES	NUMBER OF EXPECTED SPECIES
Pyrostria Comm. ex A. Rich.	Tree/shrub	Native	33	70
Rytigynia Blume	Tree/shrub	Native	6	6
Vangueria Juss.	Tree/shrub	Native	1	1
SUBFAMILY RUBIOIDEAE				
Tribe Lasiantheae				
Saldinia A. Rich. ex DC.	Tree/shrub	Native	21	25
Tribe Urophylleae				
Pauridiantha Hook. f.	Tree/shrub	Native	1	1
Tribe Craterispermeae				
Craterispermum Benth.	Tree/shrub	Native	3	10
Tribe Gaertnereae				
Gaertnera Lam.	Tree/shrub	Native	43	43
Tribe Morindeae				
Gynochthodes Blume	Liana	Native	1	5
Morinda L.	Tree/shrub	Native/ introduced	1	1
Tribe Palicoureeae				
Chassalia Comm. ex Poir.	Shrub	Native	38	40
Geophila D. Don	Herb	Native	2	2
Puffia Razafim. & B. Bremer	Herb	Endemic	1	1
Tribe Psychotrieae				
Psychotria L.	Tree/shrub	Native	147	147
Tribe Anthospermeae				
Anthospermum L.	Subshrub/herb	Native	8	8
Tribe Danaideae				
Danais Comm. ex Vent.	Liana	Native	34	34
Payera Baill.	Tree/shrub	Endemic	10	15
Schismatoclada Baker	Tree/shrub	Endemic	20	30
Tribe Knoxieae				
Carphalea Juss.	Shrub	Endemic	3	3
Otiophora Zucc.	Herb	Native	2	2
Paracarphalea Razafim., Ferm, Kårehed & B. Bremer	Tree/shrub	Endemic	3	3
Pentanisia Harv.	Herb	Native	1	1
Pentas Benth.	Herb	Native	1	1

(continued overleaf)

TABLE 8.46. ***continued***

GENUS	LIFE-FORM	ENDEMISM	NUMBER OF DESCRIBED SPECIES	NUMBER OF EXPECTED SPECIES
Phyllopentas (Verdc.) Kårehed & B. Bremer	Herb	Native	6	6
Triainolepis Hook. f.	Tree/shrub	Native	12	12
Tribe Paederieae				
Paederia L.	Liana	Native	11	11
Serissa Comm. ex A. Juss.	Liana	Introduced	1	1
Tribe Rubieae				
Galium L.	Herb	Native	5	5
Tribe Spermacoceae				
Agathisanthemum Klotzsch	Herb	Native	1	1
Amphistemon Groeninckx	Herb	Endemic	2	2
Astiella Jovet	Herb	Endemic	12	12
Cordylostigma Groeninckx & Dessein	Herb	Native	2	2
Dentella L.	Herb	Recent colonizer	1	1
Edrastima Raf.	Herb	Native	1	1
Gomphocalyx Baker	Herb	Endemic	1	1
Hedyotis L.	Subshrub	Native	1	1
Hexasepalum Bartl. ex DC.	Herb	Native	1	3–5
Lathraeocarpa Bremek.	Shrub	Endemic	2	2
Mitracarpus Zucc. ex Schult. & Schult. f.	Herb	Recent colonizer	1	1
Mitrasacmopsis Jovet	Herb	Native	1	1
Oldenlandia L.	Herb	Native/ naturalized	7	20
Pentodon Benth.	Herb	Native	1	1
Phialiphora Groeninckx	Herb	Endemic	2	4
Phylohydrax Puff	Herb	Native	1	1
Richardia L.	Herb	Recent colonizer	1	1
Spermacoce L.	Herb	Native/ naturalized	8	15
Thamnoldenlandia Groeninckx	Herb	Endemic	1	1
Total number of species:			790	1010–1012

Table 8.46 encompasses all Rubiaceae species and genera occurring on Madagascar (including the introduced ones and recent colonizers). Since 2003 the total number of accepted described Malagasy Rubiaceae has increased from 660 to 790 species and from 89 to 95 genera, all classified in 27 tribes and three subfamilies. There are at least 220 undescribed species, bringing the total number of species to at least 1010. Subfamily Cinchonoideae is represented by three tribes, Guettardeae, Hymenodictyeae, and Naucleeae. Subfamily Ixoroideae contains 10 tribes, which are grouped in three major lineages: the Mussaendeae-Sabiceeae clade, the Coffeeae alliance (Alberteae, Bertiereae, Coffeeae, Gardenieae, Octotropideae, and Pavetteae), and the Vanguerieae alliance (Ixoreae and Vanguerieae). Finally, subfamily Rubioideae is represented by 13 tribes, which are grouped in four major lineages: tribe Lasiantheae, tribe Urophylleae, the Psychotrieae alliance (Craterispermeae, Gaertnereae, Morindeae, Palicoureeae, and Psychotrieae), and the

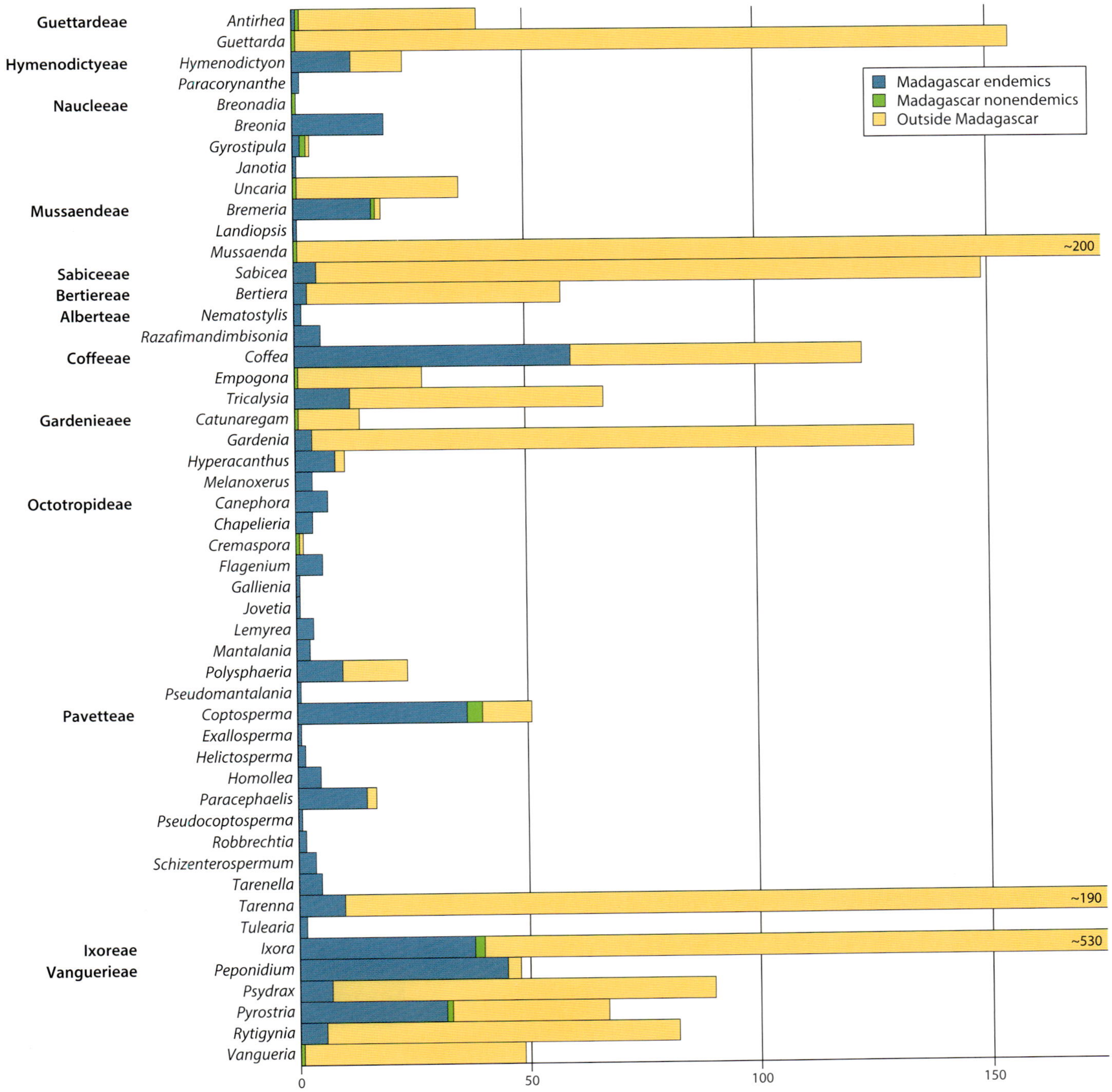

FIGURE 8.79 **Diversity and endemicity diagram (this page and overleaf) of Malagasy Rubiaceae at the level of genera, showing three different species counts: 1) endemic to Madagascar, 2) nonendemic but native to Madagascar, and 3) those occurring elsewhere in the world. In cases when species diversity exceeds or does not conform to that presented on the horizontal graph scale, the figures are written along the respective horizontal line of a given genus.**

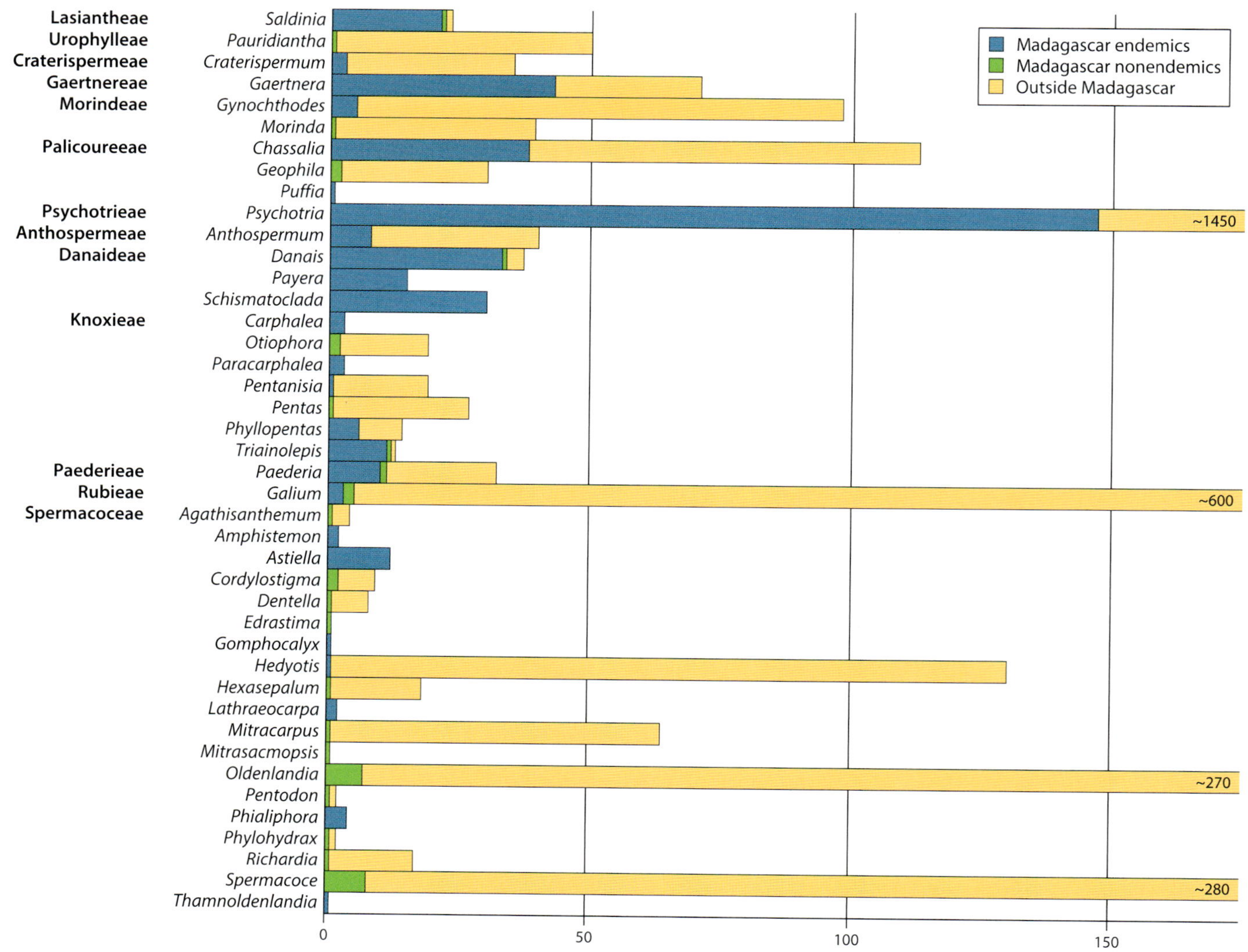

FIGURE 8.79 *continued*

Spermacoceae alliance (Anthospermeae, Danaideae, Knoxieae, Paederieae, Rubieae, and Spermacoceae) (Table 8.46). Further, Cinchonoideae, Ixoroideae, and Rubioideae encompass about 45, 323, and 422 described species, respectively. Their respective total numbers of species become 46, 486, and 478 if the undescribed species are taken into account.

ASSESSMENTS OF THE TAXONOMIC PROGRESS OF THE MALAGASY RUBIACEAE FLORA

Taxonomic Changes at Tribal Level

Five new tribes, Bertiereae, Hymenodictyeae, Knoxieae, and Palicoureeae, are now recognized in the Malagasy Rubiaceae flora. Within Ixoroideae, Bridson and Verdcourt (2003) raised the subtribe Bertierinae (previously in tribe Gardenieae) to become the tribe Bertiereae, reflecting that it is more closely related to the tribe Coffeeae (e.g., Kainulainen et al. 2013) than it is to Gardenieae. The circumscription of the tribe Octotropideae has been broadened to include the Malagasy genus *Mantalania*, formerly placed in Gardenieae (Mouly et al. 2014). The close relationship between the Malagasy genera *Pseudomantalania* and *Mantalania* on morphological grounds implies that the former should also be transferred to the broadly circumscribed Octotropideae.

Within Rubioideae a narrow circumscription of the tribe Psychotrieae was adopted by Robbrecht and Manen (2006) to include only the pantropical genus *Psychotria* and its allied genera. The tribe Palicoureeae, sister to Psychotrieae *sensu stricto*, was described to accommodate the Neotropical genus *Palicourea* and its allied genera from the Neotropics and Paleotropics. These sister tribes differ generally in their stipules (deciduous in Psychotrieae versus persistent or marcescent in Palicoureeae), their pyrenes (entire versus with preformed germination slits), their seed coats (with an ethanol-soluble red pigment versus without), the color of their dry leaves (brown to gray versus green) (Robbrecht and Manen 2006), and the presence/absence of cyclotide peptides (absent in Psychotrieae, present in Palicoureeae) (Koehbach et al. 2013). Further, three tribal names in Rubioideae have been reduced to synonymy:

"Hedyotideae," "Lathraeocarpeae," and "Triainolepideae." The Malagasy, monogeneric tribe "Lathraeocarpeae" was subsumed into the tribe Spermacoceae as the genus *Lathraeocarpa* is sister to a clade formed by *Gomphocalyx* and *Phylohydrax* within the *Pentanopsis* clade (Groeninckx et al. 2009a). Kårehed and Bremer (2007) found *Triainolepis* was nested in Knoxieae, and consequently synonymized "Triainolepideae" under that name. The former "Hedyotideae" genera *Carphalea*, *Otiophora*, *Pentanisia*, and *Pentas* were also shown by Kårehed and Bremer (2007) to belong to Knoxieae, while the single Malagasy species of the genus *Hedyotis* is now placed in the tribe Spermacoceae.

Taxonomic Changes at Generic Level

Here, we present the taxonomic changes at the generic level that concern only the Malagasy Rubiaceae flora. Within the subfamily Ixoroideae, the Paleotropical genus *Mussaenda* (tribe Mussaendeae) has been shown to be polyphyletic as the Malagasy and the Mascarene species form a clade that is sister to the monospecific Malagasy genus *Landiopsis*. As a result, the genus *Bremeria* was described to accommodate the Malagasy and Mascarene species of *Mussaenda* (Alejandro et al. 2005).

The generic limits of four tribes within the Coffeeae alliance have been greatly modified. The genus *Alberta* of the tribe Alberteae was shown to be paraphyletic with respect to the Malagasy genus *Nematostylis*, which is sister to the clade formed by the Malagasy *Alberta*. Consequently, the genus *Razafimandimbisonia* was described to accommodate the Malagasy species of *Alberta* (Kainulainen and Bremer 2009). The genus *Empogona* of the tribe Coffeeae was resurrected to accommodate the members of the *Tricalysia* subgenus *Empogona* that are not closely related to *Tricalysia* subgenus *Tricalysia* (= *Tricalysia sensu stricto*) (Tosh et al. 2009). The Malagasy genus *Melanoxerus* of the tribe Gardenieae was described to accommodate the Malagasy *Euclinia suavissima*, which was shown to be only distantly related to the African *Euclinia* (Kainulainen and Bremer 2014). Furthermore, six Malagasy genera of the tribe Pavetteae, namely *Exallosperma*, *Helictosperma*, *Pseudocoptosperma*, *Robbrechtia*, *Tarenella*, and *Tulearia*, were described to accommodate 13 morphologically distinct species (De Block 2003; De Block et al. 2018, 2020). The Malagasy monospecific genus *Homolliella* was subsumed into the Madagascar-centered genus *Paracephaelis* to render this latter genus monophyletic (De Block et al. 2015).

Within the Vanguerieae alliance the generic limits within the tribe Vanguerieae have been changed as the result of the paraphyly of the Paleotropical genus *Pyrostria* (Razafimandimbison et al. 2009a) and the polyphyly of the genus *Canthium* (Lantz and Bremer 2004). The present circumscription of *Pyrostria* encompasses all its Malagasy satellite genera, *Leroya*, *Neoleroya*, and *Pseudopeponidium*, and the Rodrigues monotypic genus *Scyphochlamys* (Razafimandimbison et al. 2009a). The western Indian Ocean species previously placed in the genus *Canthium* have all been transferred to other genera, the majority of them to the genera *Peponidium* and *Pyrostria* (see Razafimandimbison et al. 2007; Kainulainen and Razafimandimbison 2016). *Canthium* subgenus *Bullockia* was raised to generic level (genus *Bullockia*) with at least two undescribed Malagasy species (Razafimandimbison et al. 2009a). *Canthium sensu stricto* is now restricted to tropical Asia and Africa (Lantz and Bremer 2004).

The generic limits of the Rubioideae have also been greatly modified. Within the Psychotrieae alliance, the Malagasy monospecific genus *Hymenocnemis* was subsumed into the Paleotropical genus *Gaertnera* of the tribe Gaertnereae to render this latter genus monophyletic (Malcomber and Davis 2005). Within the tribe Morindeae the genus *Morinda* was shown to be highly paraphyletic as the lianescent *Morinda* species form a monophyletic group with the genus *Gynochthodes*; they have therefore been transferred to this latter genus. Accordingly, the pantropical genus *Morinda* was recircumscribed to include only the arborescent *Morinda* species (Razafimandimbison et al. 2009b). Within the tribe Palicoureeae, the pantropical genus *Geophila* was shown to be nonmonophyletic as the Malagasy *Geophila gerrardii* is sister to the African genus *Hymenocoleus*. As a result, the monospecific Malagasy genus *Puffia* was described to accommodate the Malagasy species (Razafimandimbison et al. 2014). Finally, a new circumscription of the pantropical genus *Psychotria* of the tribe Psychotrieae was proposed by Razafimandimbison et al. (2014) as all its satellite genera, namely *Mapouria*, the mostly Malagasy genera *Apomuria* and *Cremocarpon*, the western Indian Ocean genus *Psathura*, the Malagasy genus *Trigonopyren*, the myrmecophytic genus *Hydnophytum* and its allied genera, the genus *Amaracarpus*, and the Pacific genus *Calycosia* and its allied genera, were shown to be nested within a broadly delimited *Psychotria*.

Within the Spermacoceae alliance, the Malagasy genus *Carphalea* of the tribe Knoxieae was shown to be paraphyletic with respect to the Madagascar-centered genus *Triainolepis*. Accordingly, the Malagasy genus *Paracarphalea* was described to accommodate three of the six species of *Carphalea* (Ferm et al. 2016). The genus *Phyllopentas* was recognized by Kårehed and Bremer (2007) to render *Pentas* monophyletic and to accommodate the members of *Pentas* subgenera *Phyllopentas* and *Vignaldiopsis* (Kårehed and Bremer 2007). Within the tribe Spermacoceae, the genus *Kohautia* was shown to be biphyletic and the genus *Cordylostigma* was thus recognized to accommodate the members of *Kohautia* subgenus *Pachystigma* (Groeninckx et al. 2010a). Three Spermacoceae genera, namely *Amphistemon*, *Phialiphora*, and *Thamnoldenlandia*, were described by Groeninckx et al. (2010b, 2010c) to accommodate morphologically distinct species. Finally, a new record of the genus *Dentella*, represented by *D. repens* (Spermacoceae), was recently reported from northwestern Madagascar (Razafimandimbison and Manjato 2019).

Recent Taxonomic Revisions

Nineteen genera have been the subject of modern taxonomic revisions: *Amphistemon* and *Thamnoldenlandia* (Groeninckx et al. 2010b), *Astiella* (Groeninckx et al. 2017), *Bertiera* (Wittle and Davis 2010), *Exallosperma*, *Helictosperma*, *Pseudocoptosperma*, and *Tulearia* (De Block et al. 2018), *Flagenium* (Ruhsam and Davis 2007), *Gaertnera* (Malcomber and Taylor 2009; Taylor et al. 2014), *Gardenia* (Rakotonirina et al. 2012), *Homollea* (De Block 2018), *Hymenodictyon* and *Paracorynanthe* (Razafimandimbison and Bremer 2006), *Phialiphora* (Groeninckx et al. 2010c; De Block et al. 2020), *Puffia* (Razafimandimbison et al. 2014), *Robbrechtia* (De Block 2003), *Tarenella* (De Block et al. 2021), and *Tricalysia*

(Ranarivelo-Randriamboavonjy et al. 2007), as well as the *Baracoffea* alliance of the genus *Coffea* (A. P. Davis and Rakotonasolo 2008). These revisions encompassed a total of 130 species, of which 80 (62%) were newly described. Forty-four additional new species have been described in 14 genera: *Chapelieria* (Davies and Davis 2014; Kainulainen and Razafimandimbison 2015), *Coffea* (A. P. Davis et al. 2005; A. P. Davis and Rakotonasolo 2008), *Craterispermum* (De Block and Randriamboavonjy 2015), *Danais* (Taylor and Rogers 2013), *Gyrostipula* (Emanuelsson and Razafimandimbison 2007), *Ixora* (De Block 2007, 2008, 2014), *Lemyrea* (J. R. Stone and Davis 2004), *Mantalania* (De Block et al. 2006), *Peponidium* and *Pyrostria* (Lantz et al. 2007), *Phyllopentas* (Andriamihajarivo et al. 2011), *Schismatoclada* (Strid et al. 2019), and *Tarenna* (De Block 2005). In total, 124 new species have been described between 2003 and 2020, about seven new species per year.

New Combinations and Names

A total of 137 new combinations in 14 genera of the Malagasy Rubiaceae flora have been made between 2003 and 2020: 21 for *Bremeria* (Mussaendeae); five in *Razafimandimbisonia* (Alberteae), one in *Melanoxerus* (Gardenieae), five in *Coptosperma*, three in *Paracephaelis*, and one in *Tarenna* (Pavetteae)—all in the Coffeeae alliance; 20 in *Peponidium*, 25 in *Pyrostria*, and two in *Rytigynia* (Vanguerieae)—all in the Vanguerieae alliance; two in *Gynochthodes* (Morindeae), one in *Puffia* (Palicoureeae), and 44 in *Psychotria* (Psychotrieae)—all in the Psychotrieae alliance); three in *Paracarphalea* and five in *Phyllopentas*—all in the Spermacoceae alliance. Finally, 52 new names have been published within the same period: one in *Peponidium*, two in *Pyrostria*, 48 in *Psychotria*, and one in *Phyllopentas*.

Species Diversity and Endemism

Vanguerieae and Psychotrieae are the most species-rich tribes with about 92 and 147 known species on Madagascar, respectively. The pantropical *Psychotria* is by far the most species-rich genus with 147 described species on Madagascar, all endemic (about 19% of the species richness of the Malagasy Rubiaceae), followed by *Coffea*, *Peponidium*, and *Gaertnera* with 60, 45, and 43 species, respectively (Figure 8.79; Table 8.46). Seven genera, *Chassalia*, *Coffea*, *Danais*, *Gaertnera*, *Ixora*, *Peponidium*, and *Pyrostria* have between 30 and 60 known species each, which together currently comprise about 36% (about 284 species) of the species richness of Rubiaceae on Madagascar (excluding undescribed species). Fifty-nine of the 95 genera (about 62%), including recent colonizers, are indigenous but not endemic to Madagascar, and contribute 82.3% (about 650 species) of the species richness of the family. Other than three introduced genera, the 34 remaining genera are endemic to Madagascar and contribute about 17.5% of the species richness of the family. Finally, 11 of the 34 endemic genera are monospecific and 10 of them have only two to three species.

BIOGEOGRAPHY

The information about the biogeographic history of the Malagasy Rubiaceae presented here is based on the molecular dating analyses of 16 tribes (Alberteae, Bertiereae, Coffeeae, Gaertnereae, Gardenieae, Hymenodictyeae, Knoxieae, Morindeae, Naucleeae, Octotropideae, Paederieae, Palicoureeae, Pavetteae, Psychotrieae, Spermacoceae, and Vanguerieae) (Tosh et al. 2009; Wikström et al. 2010; Manns et al. 2012; Nie et al. 2013; Smedmark et al. 2014; Janssens et al. 2016; Kainulainen et al. 2017c; Razafimandimbison et al. 2017). The arrival of all studied Malagasy lineages significantly postdate the sequential breakup of the major components of Gondwana in the Jurassic and Early Cretaceous. These lineages are the results of multiple Cenozoic long-dispersal events mostly from Africa (e.g., Wikström et al. 2010; Kainulainen et al. 2017c; Razafimandimbison et al. 2017). Despite the proximity of Madagascar to Africa, some Rubiaceae show close affinities with Asia (e.g., *Paederia*, Wikström et al. 2010; Nie et al. 2013; *Catunaregam*, Kainulainen et al. 2017c), the Pacific region (e.g., *Gynochthodes*, Razafimandimbison et al. 2009b), or the Neotropics (e.g., *Saldinia*, Lasiantheae, Smedmark et al. 2014; Spermacoceae, Janssens et al. 2016).

The ancestors of the Malagasy Rubiaceae that had fleshy, drupaceous fruits are postulated to have colonized Madagascar via avian or fruit bat dispersals. The Malagasy *Psychotria* with dry schizocarpous fruits were inferred to have evolved from a common ancestor with schizocarpous fruits, which in turn evolved from an ancestor with drupaceous fruits (Razafimandimbison et al. 2014). This suggests that this ancestor with drupaceous fruits reached Madagascar via bird or fruit bat dispersal. On the other hand, the placement of the Comorian *P. boiviniana* with schizocarpous fruits within one of the two Malagasy *Psychotria* clades bearing the same fruit type indicates that the Malagasy ancestor of the Comorian species had schizocarps. Thus, it was argued that strong winds (e.g., tropical cyclones) could effectively disperse the mericarps of this *Psychotria* species over a long distance (Razafimandimbison et al. 2017). Further, other Rubiaceae taxa, such as *Morinda citrifolia*, with multiple fruits and buoyant seeds, and the Paleotropical, seashore species *Guettarda speciosa*, which has air-filled fruits, may have arrived on Madagascar via ocean drifting (Razafimandimbison et al. 2010a. Finally, the ancestors of the Malagasy Spermacoceae and *Anthospermum*, all with capsular fruits, may have reached Madagascar via exo-ornithochory or wind dispersal (Janssens et al. 2016; Thureborn et al. 2019).

Most of the colonization events on Madagascar were followed by subsequent diversifications, giving rise to numerous endemic species on the island. Africa is the main source of dispersal to Madagascar, which in turn serves as a stepping-stone for subsequent events to neighboring archipelagoes, but also for back-colonization to Africa (e.g., in *Coptosperma*, *Psychotria*; Kainulainen et al. 2017c; Razafimandimbison et al. 2017).

CONSERVATION

Population fragmentation due to habitat destruction and fires is the main threat for Malagasy plants and animals. Using IUCN Red List criteria, several species of Rubiaceae occurring on the island, in particular those with narrow geographic distributions, are classified as Critically Endangered. Some species are on the verge of extinction, such as *Carphalea linearifolia* (Ferm et al. 2016) and

Landiopsis capuronii (Andriambololonera 2013). Other species that are only known from single collections are thought to have gone extinct, including *Gyrostipula obtusa* (Emanuelsson and Razafimandimbison 2007). Therefore, ex situ conservation programs are urgently needed, because not one of the Malagasy endemic Rubiaceae species is currently in cultivation on Madagascar.

FUTURE PERSPECTIVES

Taxonomic revisions of 13 genera, *Bremeria*, *Coptosperma*, *Chapelieria*, *Craterispermum*, *Gynochthodes*, *Ixora*, *Melanoxerus*, *Paracephaelis*, *Payera*, *Pyrostria*, *Razafimandimbisonia*, *Schismatoclada*, and *Tarenna* are underway and are expected to be completed within the next five years. A revision of the Malagasy *Peponidium* is urgently needed as no identification key is available for the broadly delimited *Peponidium sensu* Razafimandimbison et al. (2009a), which now includes about half of the Malagasy *Canthium* species. An estimated 212 species of Malagasy Rubiaceae remain to be described. At the rate of description between 2003 and 2020 (on average seven species per year), it may take Rubiaceae specialists another 30 years to finish describing them.

Subject editors: Laurent Gautier and Steven M. Goodman

RUBIACEAE, TRIBE GUETTARDEAE AND HYMENODICTYEAE-NAUCLEEAE CLADE, SUBFAMILY CINCHONOIDEAE

S. D. Löfstrand and S. G. Razafimandimbison

The primarily Neotropical subfamily Cinchonoideae *sensu* B. Bremer and Eriksson (2009) is represented on Madagascar by three tribes, namely Guettardeae, Hymenodictyeae, and Naucleeae. Hymenodictyeae and Naucleeae are sisters (Razafimandimbison and Bremer 2001) and this clade is in turn sister to the Guettardeae-Rondeletieae clade (Rydin et al. 2017). The biogeographic origin of this lineage containing the Guettardeae-Rondeletieae and Hymenodictyeae-Naucleeae clades is to date unsettled, but it has been estimated to have emerged in the early Eocene (Manns and Bremer 2010; Manns et al. 2012; Rydin et al. 2017).

GUETTARDEAE

Guettardeae is a pantropical group that is sister to the Neotropical tribe Rondeletieae. The tribe is represented on Madagascar by the two species of the Paleotropical genus *Antirhea* (*A. borbonica* and *A. madagascariensis*; Figure 8.80a) and one species of the pantropical genus *Guettarda*, *G. speciosa* (Figure 8.80b). *Antirhea* includes dioecious shrubs to medium-size trees with verticillate leaves, axillary inflorescences with scorpioid axes, small sessile flowers, and small, drupaceous fruits (Figure 8.80a). The Malagasy *A. madagascariensis* and the Mauritian-Reunionese-Malagasy *A. borbonica* (type of the genus) are sisters, and belong to the *Antirhea* subgenus *Antirhea* (Chaw and Darwin 1992). We suspect these sister species form a monophyletic group with the Rodrigues species *A. bifurcata*, which is thought to have gone extinct (Verdcourt 1983). The *A. borbonica*-*A. madagascariensis* clade has been shown to be sister to a southeast Asian clade of the genus *Timonius* (Manns and Bremer 2010), indicating that the lineage possibly has an Asian origin. The present circumscriptions of *Antirhea* and *Guettarda* are highly polyphyletic (Achille et al. 2006; Manns and Bremer 2010).

Guettarda speciosa is a perennial, seashore shrub with relatively large oval-shaped leaves and fragrant flowers with white corollas. This plant is commonly found throughout the Paleotropics and its Paleotropical distribution is mainly attributed to its large fruits (Figure 8.80b) with air-filled cavities, which enhance their natural dispersal by oceanic floating. Interestingly, *G. speciosa* has been shown to belong in a Neotropical *Guettarda* clade (Achille et al. 2006; Manns and Bremer 2010), suggesting its Neotropical origin.

THE HYMENODICTYEAE-NAUCLEEAE CLADE

The Hymenodictyeae-Naucleeae clade emerged in the early to middle Eocene (Wikström et al. 2015), presumably in Africa (Manns et al. 2012). Both tribes are predominately native to the Old World, with only a few species of Naucleeae native to the New World (Löfstrand et al. 2014). Hymenodictyeae, as well as subtribe Breoniinae of Naucleeae, have a clear center of diversity on Madagascar (Razafimandimbison and Bremer 2002, 2006). *Breonadia* (Figure 8.80f) and *Hymenodictyon* (Figures 8.80c and d) are present in tropical Africa, the latter also in Asia. *Gyrostipula* (Figure 8.80i) is represented on Madagascar and the Comoros. *Breonia* (Figures 8.80g and h) and *Janotia* are exclusively Malagasy. Outside the subtribe Breoniinae, only one Naucleeae species, *Uncaria africana*, is native to Madagascar, but also widespread in tropical Africa. Apart from general characteristics for Rubiaceae and Cinchonoideae, the tribes share a few morphological similarities, but they are easily distinguished from each other by, for example, elongated inflorescences (Figure 8.80c), conspicious nectary discs, and lenticellate individual fruits in Hymenodictyeae (Figure 8.80d) as opposed to globose inflorescences (Figure 8.80f and g), inconspicous, deeply embedded nectary discs,

FIGURE 8.80
Malagasy members of the subfamily Cinchonoideae. A) *Antirhea borbonica*; B) *Guettarda speciosa*; C) *Hymenodictyon tsingyi*; D) *H. perrieri*; E) *Paracorynanthe antankarensis*; F) *Breonadia salicina*; G) *Breonia taolagnaroensis*; H) *B. decaryana*; and I) *Gyrostipula foveolata*. (PHOTO A by K. Kainulainen; B by T. Randrianarivony; C and D by S. G. Razafimandimbison; E by L. Gautier; F by F. Rakotoarivony; G by T. Randrianarivony; H by A. Razanatsima; and I by C. Rakotovao.)

and nonlenticellate individual fruits in Naucleeae (Figure 8.80h; Razafimandimbison and Bremer 2006).

Hymenodictyeae

The Paleotropical Hymenodictyeae comprise two genera, *Paracorynanthe* (two species; Figure 8.80e) and *Hymenodictyon* (24 formally described species and one undescribed Malagasy species; Figures 8.80c and d), with their highest species diversity found on Madagascar: *Paracorynanthe* is endemic as are 15 of the 24 recognized *Hymenodictyon* species (Razafimandimbison and Bremer 2006). The genera are distinguished from each other by, for example, thin, plated bark, corolla lobes bearing conspicuous appendages, and oblanceolate, angular placentae in *Paracorynanthe*, as opposed to thick, nonplated bark, unappendaged corolla lobes, and fusiform, bilaterally flattened placentae in *Hymenodictyon* (Razafimandimbison and Bremer 2006).

The monophyly of the tribe was first demonstrated by Razafimandimbison and Bremer (2001), whereas the monophyly of, and sister relationship between, the genera was first demonstrated by Löfstrand et al. (2014). The latter study also found that the Malagasy *Hymenodictyon* species form a well-supported clade in the genus, but its exact position within *Hymenodictyon* remains unsettled. The sister relationship between the east African *H. parvifolium* subsp. *scabrum* and the Malagasy clade is, however, supported, as is the position of an undescribed Malagasy species as sister to the crown group (Löfstrand et al. 2014). The biogeographic origin of Hymenodictyeae is unknown (but potentially mainland Africa; see Manns et al. 2012); however, the Malagasy *Hymenodictyon* clade is likely the result of species radiation after a single long-distance dispersal from mainland Africa (Löfstrand et al. 2014).

The following morphological descriptions are derived from Razafimandimbison and Bremer (2006). Most species are medium-size to large trees (obligate and facultative epiphytes are represented in *Hymenodictyon*, but none on Madagascar), typically growing on rocky substrates. Most Malagasy species are restricted to exposed areas of dry deciduous forests in northern, western, or southern Madagascar (but *H. occidentale* grows in the semi-deciduous forests of the Sambirano area). Leaves are typically petiolate, small to medium in size, simple, opposite, decussate, and bearing deciduous black colleters along the leaf margins; tuft-type domatia are known to occur in the axils of secondary leaf veins in *Hymenodictyon* but are absent in *Paracorynanthe*. Stipules are interpetiolar, triangular (to broadly oblong, rarely foliaceous in *Hymenodictyon*), and deciduous. Inflorescences (Figure 8.80c) are terminal in most *Hymenodictyon*, terminal and axillary in *Paracorynanthe* (Figure 8.80e) and some *Hymenodictyon*, and vary from spicate or racemose to compound spicate, racemose, thyrsoid, or umbelliform. Each flowering unit is composed of a long and slender, puberulous to pubescent peduncle, generally bearing long-petiolate, foliaceous bracts, pubescent rhachis subtended by sessile bracts, and single, few, or many-flowered cymules with individual flowers subtended by a sessile bracteole. Flowers (Figures 8.80c and e) are pedicellate (rarely sessile), hermaphroditic, protandrous, homostylous, and typically pentamerous in perianth and androecium, with bicarpellate, inferior gynoecia. Calyx tubes are absent and calyx lobes are well developed and variable among species. Corollas are typically narrowly tubular for half their length, at which point they abrubtly form an open cup in *Hymenodictyon*, as opposed to being wineglass shaped in *Paracorynanthe*. Corolla lobes are valvate in bud and adorned by filiform and densely bristled appendages, which end in a club in *Paracorynanthe*. Stamens have basifix, introrse, longitudinally dehiscing anthers borne on the widened part of the corolla; styles are exserted and bear clavate to globose stigmas (Figure 8.80c). Ovaries are topped by conspicuous nectary discs; the placentae are axile and bilaterally flattened fusiform (*Hymenodictyon*) or oblanceolate, angular, and pendant (*Paracorynanthe*), bearing one or two (*Paracorynanthe*) or two to 14 (*Hymenodictyon*; 20–40 in some African species) ovules. Fruits (Figures 8.80d and e) in both genera are narrowly to broadly elliptic, loculicidal capsules, typically adorned by elongate to spherical, typically nonelevated lenticels containing winged seeds.

No traditional uses are known for Malagasy species in the tribe, but both mainland African and Asian species of *Hymenodictyon* are utilized for their high-quality wood, as well as in folk medicine (Razafimandimbison and Bremer 2006). The dry capsular fruits of *Hymenodictyon* and *Paracorynanthe* are not known to be eaten by any land vertebrates. Several Malagasy species are listed as Vulnerable or Endangered on the International Union for Conservation of Nature's (IUCN) Red List due to declining populations of mature trees and habitat loss (IUCN 2019).

Naucleeae

The pantropical tribe Naucleeae comprises 17 genera with the highest species diversity in the Paleotropics (Razafimandimbison and Bremer 2002; Löfstrand et al. 2014). Five genera are found on Madagascar: *Breonadia* (monotypic, indigenous; Figure 8.80f), *Breonia* (20 species, endemic; Figures 8.80g and h), *Gyrostipula* (two of the three species, endemic; Figure 8.80i), *Janotia* (monotypic, endemic), and *Uncaria* (one of the three African species is indigenous). The first four of these genera form a monophyletic group, subtribe Breoniinae, whose phylogenetic position in Naucleeae remains unsettled (Löfstrand et al. 2014). The biogeographic origins of Naucleeae and their subtribes and genera are to date somewhat unclear but the tribe might have originated in Africa (Manns et al. 2012). The colonization of Madagascar is likely the result of at least two long-distance dispersal events from Africa (at least once for *U. africana* and at least once for Breoniinae; see Löfstrand et al. 2014).

Within Breoniinae, *Breonadia* is sister to the remainder of the subtribe. *Breonia* is resolved in two supported clades, one thereof (unsupportedly) resolved as sister to a clade formed by *Janotia* and monophyletic *Gyrostipula* (likely the result of conflicting positions of *Janotia* in the nuclear ribosomal data set and the chloroplast data set; Löfstrand et al. 2014). Consequently, *Breonia* may turn out to be nonmonophyletic, in which case a new genus endemic to Madagascar may warrant description. No clear morphological or biogeographic differences between the two clades are known, but Löfstrand et al.'s (2014) "*Breonia* clade A" appears to have a northern and western distribution (one species, *B. fragifera*, has a northern and eastern distribution), whereas members of "*Breonia* clade B" have a northern and/or eastern distribution. Razafimandimbison (2002) subdivided *Breonia* into two informal, morphological groups, but the characters utilized are apparently homoplasious without distinct phylogenetic patterns (Löfstrand et al. 2014). To date, no molecular study has included the type of *Breonia*, *B. madagascariensis*, further complicating a potential segregation of the clades. Within the subtribe, there are some morphological differences at the generic level (Razafimandimbison 2002). *Breonadia* is clearly distinct from the other genera by its verticillate leaves (Figure 8.80f), intrapetiolar stipules, interfloral bracteoles, and wingless seeds. *Breonia* (Figure 8.80g and h) has flowers with fused hypanthia and fleshy multiple fruits, as opposed to unfused hypanthia and distinct capsular fruits in the other three genera. *Gyrostipula* (Figure 8.80i) is distinguished from the other genera by its long, red, and convolute stipules and long, filiform calyx lobes; and *Janotia* is easily identified by its large leaves and persistent, foliaceous stipules.

Uncaria forms the monogeneric, primarily Asian-Australasian, subtribe Uncariinae, sister to the Paleotropical Naucleinae. The phylogenetic position of the Naucleinae-Uncariinae clade within Naucleeae, like that of Breoniinae, remains unsettled (Löfstrand et al. 2014). Within *Uncaria*, the African-Malagasy *U. africana* is resolved in a clade together with two Neotropical species. *Uncaria africana* is easily distinguished from the other Malagasy members of Naucleeae by its lianescent habit and adapted claw-shaped stipules (Razafimandimbison and Bremer 2001).

The following morphological descriptions are derived from Ridsdale (1978a, 1978b), Razafimandimbison (2002), and

Razafimandimbison and Bremer (2001, 2002). The Malagasy members of Naucleeae are trees, rarely shrubs or lianas (*Uncaria* only), growing in a variety of habitats, including moist evergreen forests, swampy or riverine forests, and dry deciduous forests, but absent from the dry spiny thickets of the south. As is common in Rubiaceae, leaves are simple, opposite (Figure 8.80h and i; verticillate in *Breonadia* (Figure 8.80f), typically glabrous, and petiolate; most species have small to medium-size leaves (but the leaves of *Janotia* and some *Breonia* species are conspicuously large). Domatia are present in vein axils in most species. Stipules are interpetiolar (intrapetiolar in *Breonadia*) and highly variable in shape and size among species and mostly deciduous (conspicously large and persistent in *Janotia*; modified to claws and persistent in *Uncaria*).

Inflorescences (Figures 8.80f and g) are axillary (and terminal in *Uncaria*), many-flowered, and globose, and surrounded by calyptra-like bracts when young (reduced in *Uncaria*). Individual flowers are distinct (*Breonadia*, *Gyrostipula*, *Janotia*, and *Uncaria*) or hypanthia are at least basally fused among flowers (*Breonia*). Bracteoles are absent in *Breonia*, *Gyrostipula*, and *Janotia* but present in *Breonadia* and *Uncaria*. Flowers (Figures 8.80f and g) are (sub)sessile, hermaphroditic, protandrous, homostylous, and tetramerous or pentamerous in perianth and androecium with bicarpellate, inferior gynoecia. Calyx tubes vary from reduced to conspicuous and are fused variously among flowers in *Breonia* spp.; calyx limbs are mostly triangular or oblong (long and linear in *Breonadia* and *Janotia*). Corollas are salverform to hypercrateriform, abaxially pubescent, puberulous, or villous, with imbricate (Breoniinae) or valvate (*Uncaria*) lobes in bud. Stamens are interpetiolar with basifix, introrse, longitudinally dehiscing, included anthers. Styles are exserted and bear clavate to globose stigmas. Ovaries are topped by inconspicuous nectary discs (these continue growing throughout fruit development in *Breonia*). Placentation is basal (*Uncaria*, some *Breonia*) or axillary, bearing one to 15 (Breoniinae) or many ovules (*Uncaria*) on variously shaped placentae (useful for species delimitation). Fruits are free loculicidal capsules (*Uncaria*) or loculicidal and septicidal capsules (*Breonadia*, *Gyrostipula* [Figure 8.80i], and *Janotia*), or fleshy, multiple fruits (*Breonia*; Figure 8.80h), each fruit containing one to 15 (Breoniinae) or many (*Uncaria*) seeds (winged in *Gyrostipula*, *Janotia*, and *Uncaria*; unwinged in *Breonadia* and *Breonia*).

All Malagasy species of Naucleeae are locally known as *valotra*, *valotro*, or *valompangady*, and were used for posts placed around villages to protect against enemies from the 19th century through the mid-20th century. All *Breonia* species have various local uses (e.g., for building boats, bridges, furniture), and are frequently used for general construction purposes due to their high-quality hardwood (Razafimandimbison 2002). *Breonadia salicina* (locally known as *sohihy*) is a major and ubiquitous component of riverine forests throughout Madagascar (except in the southwest); its wood is highly prized for structural parts in marine carpentery (N. Quehen, unpublished data). Several Naucleeae species are also used medicinally; for instance, the bark of *B. salicina* is used to induce human abortions in western and northern Madagascar (S. Razafimandimbison, unpublished data). The fleshy infructescences of *Breonia* are eaten by both forest vertebrates (e.g., lemurs) and humans (Razafimandimbison 2002).

Most *Breonia* species are IUCN Red Listed as Vulnerable to Critically Endangered due to declining populations of mature trees and habitat loss, whereas *Breonadia* is listed as of Least Concern (accounting for the entire range), and no information is available for *Gyrostipula*, *Janotia*, or *Uncaria* (IUCN 2019). *Gyrostipula obtusa* is only known from its type specimen, and has been classified as Data Deficient by Emanuelsson and Razafimandimbison (2007); the species is possibly extinct from its natural habitat.

Subject editors: Laurent Gautier and Steven M. Goodman

RUBIACEAE, MUSSAENDEAE-SABICEEAE CLADE, SUBFAMILY IXOROIDEAE

S. Andriambololonera and S. G. Razafimandimbison

The tribes Sabiceeae and Mussaendeae are sister groups (Alejandro et al. 2005) and belong in the subfamily Ixoroideae (*sensu* Kainulainen et al. 2013). The Mussaendeae-Sabiceeae clade encompasses 11 genera and about 400 species, which are distributed in tropical Africa and Asia, the Neotropics, and the Pacific islands. This group of plants is represented on Madagascar by four genera, namely *Bremeria*, *Mussaenda*, *Landiopsis*, and *Sabicea* (Figures 8.81a–i), and about 40 species, which grow on various habitats ranging from lowland to medium-altitude evergreen forests, montane ericoid thickets, secondary grasslands, and sclerophyllous woodlands.

MUSSAENDEAE

Mussaendeae *sensu* Alejandro et al. (2005) is a Paleotropical group of about 200 species in six genera (*Bremeria*, *Heinsia*, *Mussaenda*, *Neomussaenda*, *Pseudomussaenda*, and *Schizomussaenda*), whose distribution ranges from tropical Africa, Indian Ocean islands (including Madagascar), and southeast Asia, to the Pacific. *Mussaenda* is the most species rich with 132 species (66% of the total species richness of the tribe) and tropical Africa and Asia are the centers of species diversity of the tribe and of *Mussaenda*. There is considerable

FIGURE 8.81 **Malagasy members of the Mussaendeae-Sabiceeae clade. A)** ***Bremeria erectiloba*****; B)** ***B. fuscopilosa*****; C)** ***B. vestita*****; D and E)** ***Mussaenda arcuata*****; F and G)** ***Landiopsis capuronii*****; H)** ***Sabicea seua*****; and I)** ***Sabicea*** **sp.** (PHOTO A by U. Swenson; B by P. Antilahimena; C, D, F, and G by S. Andriambololonera; and E, H, and I by C. Rakotovao.)

variation in growth habit, including erect shrubs and trees, scandent or scrambling shrubs, true lianas, and small suffrutices. This group of plants is characterized by its bifid stipules, shaggy trichomes, terminal inflorescences, heterostylous flowers, corolla lobes with tail-like projections, and discoid placentae. Its fruits have tanniniferous idioblasts and numerous small seeds (less than 1 mm long), which are cubic or more or less irregular in shape, and have brown or golden-brown, thick, hail-like seed coats (Alejandro et al. 2005).

Alejandro et al. (2005) revealed that *Mussaenda* is polyphyletic as the Malagasy and Mascarene endemic species form a clade that is sister to the Malagasy monospecific genus *Landiopsis*. The African-Asian *Mussaenda* clade is sister to the African genus *Pseudomussaenda*. Hence, the genus *Bremeria* was described to accommodate all Malagasy and Mascarene endemic *Mussaenda* species. The *Bremeria-Landiopsis* clade is distinct by its distylous flowers with very large corollas and pubescent styles. *Bremeria* is distinguished from *Landiopsis* by its reduplicate- and induplicate-valvate aestivation and indehiscent, nonlenticellate dry fruits (Figures 8.81a–c) as opposed to imbricate corolla aestivation and capsular, lenticellate fruits in the latter (Figures 8.81f and g). *Bremeria* differs from *Mussaenda sensu stricto* in its reduplicate- and induplicate-valvate aestivation and densely pubescent styles versus reduplicate-valvate aestivation and glabrous styles in the latter genus. On Madagascar, the tribe Mussaendeae is represented by the Malagasy-Mascarene *Bremeria*, the Malagasy endemic *Landiopsis*, and the African-western Indian Ocean *M. arcuata* (Figures 8.81d and e).

Bremeria encompasses trees and shrubs that sometimes have lianescent branches (Figures 8.81a–c). Very little is known about their pollination but visitors are observed to be Lepidoptera (moths, family Sphyngidae) and Hymenoptera (bees, family Apidae, and ants, family Formicidae), and birds (sunbirds, family Nectariniidae) (Andriambololonera 2013). An ongoing taxonomic revision of the genus recognizes 31 species, 27 of which are endemic to Madagascar (S. R. Andriambololonera et al., unpublished data). The genus is mainly found in moist evergreen forests, and more than 75% of its species richness is in lowland and medium-altitude moist evergreen forests. Two species seem to be restricted to the semi-deciduous forests of the Sambirano Region, a few species are found in high montane forests, and some are common in secondary vegetation and grasslands. Locally known as *fatora*, *nofotrakoho*, and *trotroka*, *Bremeria* trees that are over 20 m tall and have a diameter of over 30 cm are exploited for lumber, charcoal production, carving of small art objects, and firewood. Some species are locally used for medicinal purposes (treating wounds and stomachaches or used as purgative), and most species have a high horticultural value because of their large and sturdy flowers (Figure 8.81b and c). Mascarene *Bremeria* trees have been selected for forest restoration programs on Mauritius. The fast-growing *Bremeria* species such as *B. pervillei* and *B. erectiloba* could be potential candidates for the restoration programs of Malagasy rainforests. Surprisingly, we found no report of *Bremeria* fruits being consumed by any forest-dwelling mammals; however, based on a note associated with a herbarium specimen, *Propithecus edwardsi* (Milne-Edwards' Sifaka) was noted to consume young leaves of *B. erectiloba* in the Ranomafana National Park in October 1987.

Bosser and Lobreau-Callen (1998) published the monospecific *Landiopsis*, typified by *L. capuronii*; *Landiopsis* is one of the 14 endemic Malagasy monotypic genera of the family Rubiaceae. Like most representatives of the Mussaendeae tribe, *L. capuronii* is a shrubby, heliophilous species up to 5 m tall, and has sizeable flowers with enlarged, white, petaloid sepals (semaphylls) that attract pollinators. The nocturnal flowers have the attributes of entomogamic flowers: fragrant, white vexillary apparatus visible from a distance, and a white corolla (Figure 8.81f). *Landiopsis* is one of the three genera of Mussaendeae with dry capsular fruits (Figure 8.81g).

For some time *L. capuronii* was known only from the type locality in northern Madagascar—the Ankotekona Massif south of the Ambararata Bay, Antsiranana Province—from two collections made in 1966. Surveys carried out in the same locality by the Missouri Botanical Garden failed to relocate the species. In 2004, more than 40 years after its description, *L. capuronii* was rediscovered by the botanists from the Conservatoire et Jardin botaniques de la Ville de Genève and the Université d'Antananarivo in the Loky Manambato Forest, specifically in a secondary dry deciduous forest on the Soanilampina Massif. This species appears to be restricted to northern Madagascar, loses its leaves during the dry season, and grows new leaves before the flowering period of January and February. The seeds of *L. capuronii* seem to germinate easily, and from field observations the plant appears to be resistant to the passage of fire. Our assessment of the conservation status of this species using International Union for Conservation of Nature Red List (IUCN) criteria (2019) classifies it as Critically Endangered (Andriambololonera 2013).

Mussaenda arcuata is the only member of *Mussaenda* known in the western Indian Ocean islands, and it is widely distributed between the extreme north and Befotaka-Midongy du Sud. It is a scandent shrub up to 5–8 m long, which has faintly scented flowers with yellow corollas (Figure 8.81d) and bacciform fruits (Figure 8.81e). This heliophilous species is frequently recorded in secondary vegetation, in open areas, or at forest edges. Known under the Malagasy names *anandaingo*, *lengo an-tsavoka*, and *tsikirity*, ripe fruits are reported to be edible and leaves are cooked as a green. In Ranomafana National Park, it is reported that the fruits of this scandent shrub are occasionally consumed by *Philepitta castanea* (Razafindratsita and Zack 2009; see Prum and Razafindratsita, pp. 1687–93). The species has an IUCN Red List status of Least Concern. It belongs in one of the African *Mussaenda* clades identified by Alejandro et al. (2005) and represents a long-distance dispersal from Africa.

SABICEEAE

The current and broad circumscription of the tribe Sabiceeae was adopted by S. A. Khan et al. (2008) to include the members of the tribe Virectarieae. This group of plants comprises four genera: *Hekistocarpa*, *Sabicea sensu lato* (including *Pseudosabicea*, *Schizostigma*, and *Stipularia*), *Tamridaea*, and *Virectaria* and in total represents 180 species. The tribe is distributed in the Neotropics, tropical Africa, Madagascar, Sao Tomé Island, Socotra Island, and Sri Lanka. *Sabicea* is found in tropical Africa, Madagascar, Sri Lanka, and the Neotropics, and is the most species-rich genus of the tribe with 146 species. Zemagho et al. (2016) proposed the first subgeneric classification of *Sabicea*, in which the majority of the Old World species (including Madagascar) belong to *Sabicea* subgenus *Sabicea*. Members of *Sabicea* include twining vines or sometimes erect shrubs and are characterized by their generally ovate, well-developed entire stipules; opposite to verticillate anisophyllous leaves; axillary (in both axils) or pseudoaxillary (i.e., developed in only one axil at a node), rather short inflorescences (Figures 8.81h and i); bisexual, homostylous, or distylous flowers; five-lobed calyx limb; salveriform to funneliform, white to pink corollas with five valvate lobes; five-locular ovaries; and five-locular, baccate, generally red to purple or black, fleshy berries with numerous small seeds (S. A. Khan et al. 2008).

On Madagascar, *Sabicea* is represented by six endemic species: *S. acuminata*, *S. angustifolia*, *S. diversifolia*, *S. marojejyensis*, *S. seua*, and *S. verticillata*. *Sabicea diversifolia* is a widespread species. However, the current classification of *S. verticillata* in *Sabicea* remains controversial. They are locally known as *seva*, *sevandolo*, *sevantrandraka*, *tsimiramira*, and *tsevamanitsy*. Members of the genus are characterized by simple but multifid stipules and a corolla throat with long multicellular trichomes inside (Zemagho et al. 2016). They are found in lowland and medium-altitude moist evergreen forests, including secondary formations; the center of species diversity is in the north. *Sabicea diversifolia* is the most common species, and, based on a herbarium specimen label, seems to be used for treating coughs. S. A. Khan et al. (2008) indicated an African origin of the Malagasy *Sabicea* species resulting from one long-distance dispersal from continental Africa.

Subject editors: Laurent Gautier and Steven M. Goodman

RUBIACEAE, COFFEEAE ALLIANCE, SUBFAMILY IXOROIDEAE

K. Kainulainen, S. G. Razafimandimbison, and P. De Block

The Coffeeae alliance is sister to the Vanguerieae alliance; these two lineages constitute the core groups in the subfamily Ixoroideae (Kainulainen et al. 2013). The Coffeeae alliance is a clade that on Madagascar is represented by the tribes Alberteae, Bertiereae, Coffeeae, Gardenieae, Octotropideae, and Pavetteae. Morphologically, this clade is characterized by contorted corolla-lobe aestivation, secondary pollen presentation (pollen being deposited on a specialized area on the style), and fleshy indehiscent fruits (with a few exceptions that are mentioned below). All species are shrubs or trees.

ALBERTEAE

On Madagascar, Alberteae comprises the endemic genera *Nematostylis* and *Razafimandimbisonia*. The latter was segregated from *Alberta* in a phylogenetic study by Kainulainen et al. (2009), and *Alberta* is now considered to be restricted to eastern South Africa. *Nematostylis* consists of semi-succulent (sub)shrubs, whereas *Razafimandimbisonia* members are shrubs or trees. Both genera have flowers with expanded and colorful calyx lobes (calycophylls) and more or less curved corollas (Figure 8.82a). Very little is known about their pollination. *Nematostylis* has narrowly tubular flowers in umbel-like inflorescences, and is presumably pollinated by Lepidoptera, whereas species of *Razafimandimbisonia* have infundibular and usually downward facing flowers and pollination by both butterflies and sunbirds has been observed (Kainulainen et al. 2009). Unlike other genera of the Coffeeae alliance, the fruits of Alberteae are not fleshy but schizocarps or dry indehiscent fruits. The calycophylls are persistent in the fruit stage and aid dispersal by wind. Both genera are widely distributed on Madagascar, but they do not occur in the western dry deciduous forests. *Nematostylis* is usually only found in exposed, rocky habitats. Alberteae was thoroughly revised by Puff et al. (1984); however, the molecular phylogenetic results presented by Kainulainen et al. (2009) indicate that hybridization may have occurred within *Razafimandimbisonia* and that the species delimitations need further study. In addition, at least one species has yet to be described. A biogeographic analysis by Kainulainen et al. (2017c) indicates that the *Nematostylis-Razafimandimbisonia* clade likely dispersed to Madagascar from Africa.

BERTIEREAE

Bertiera is the only genus in tribe Bertiereae. Wittle and Davis (2010) revised the Malagasy members and recognized three species on Madagascar. All are shrubs or small trees that are conspicuously puberulent to pubescent with strigose trichomes in all parts. The inflorescences are terminal thyrses, usually with many largely white flowers. The fruits, which are berries with numerous small seeds, change color as they mature—first turning white and eventually dark blue (Figure 8.82b; Wittle and Davis 2010). They are presumably dispersed by birds. *Bertiera* is found in moist evergreen and semi-deciduous forests in eastern and northwestern Madagascar. The Malagasy species are endemic, but the genus has a wide distribution, occurring in tropical Africa, other western Indian Ocean islands, and in the Neotropics. The center of diversity is western Africa (Robbrecht et al. 1994). A biogeographic analysis by Kainulainen et al. (2017c) showed that the species on western Indian Ocean islands form a monophyletic clade, that the Mascarene species is sister to those from Madagascar, and that this clade in turn is sister to a clade of west African species. Surprisingly, the east African species do not appear to be closely related to the Malagasy species.

COFFEEAE

Malagasy Coffeeae comprises the genera *Coffea*, *Empogona*, and *Tricalysia*—all shrubs or trees with axillary inflorescences in which

FIGURE 8.82 **Examples of the Malagasy members of the Coffeeae alliance. A) *Razafimandimbisonia minor*; B) *Bertiera crinita*; C) *Coffea richardii*; D) *Tricalysia dauphinensis*; E) *Gardenia brevicalyx*; F) *Hyperacanthus* sp.; G) *Melanoxerus* sp.; H) *Flagenium petrikense*; and I) *Coptosperma* sp.** (PHOTOS by K. Kainulainen.)

the bracts and bracteoles are fused to form cup-like calyculi (Figures 8.82c and d). The fruits are drupe-like with two grooved seeds (beans) in *Coffea*, whereas the fruits of *Empogona* and *Tricalysia* usually have more seeds, and these are not grooved. *Coffea* is unusual in the Coffeeae alliance in that the flowers lack secondary pollen presentation (A. P. Davis et al. 2007), and the Malagasy *Tricalysia* are unusual in that most species are dioecious or gynodioecious (Ranarivelo-Randriamboavonjy et al. 2007). A. P. Davis et al. (2006) have provided a taxonomic conspectus of Malagasy *Coffea*, and the genus has also been partly reviewed (A. P. Davis and Rakotonasolo 2008). Ranarivelo-Randriamboavonjy et al. (2007) have revised the Malagasy *Tricalysia* and, subsequently, the only nonendemic species, *T. ovalifolia*, was transferred to the resurrected African genus *Empogona* (Tosh et al. 2009).

Madagascar is the center of diversity for *Coffea* with 60 out of 124 currently recognized species worldwide (A. P. Davis et al. 2011). *Coffea* is also cultivated commercially on Madagascar, in particular *C. arabica* and *C. canephora*. Native species and those from overseas are cultivated for research and conservation purposes at Kianjavato Coffee Research Station. All Malagasy *Coffea* are endemic to the island, as are the 12 species of *Tricalysia*. *Empogona ovalifolia* is the sole representative of this genus on Madagascar but also occurs in east Africa, Aldabra Atoll, and the Comoros. Unlike *Empogona*, most Malagasy Coffeeae species have narrow distributions. They occur in many different vegetation types, but the moist evergreen forests of the east are the most species rich (A. P. Davis et al. 2006). A few dry-adapted *Coffea* species are restricted to the lowland dry deciduous forests of the west. They have been formally recognized as *Coffea* subgenus *Baracoffea* but have more recently been referred to as the Baracoffea group by Hamon et al. (2017) who, in a molecular phylogenetic study, found that they are nested within a clade of Malagasy species from *Coffea* subgenus *Coffea*. This result indicates that the adaptation to a dry climate of the Malagasy *Coffea* species evolved on the island. Hamon et al. (2017) further found that the *Coffea* species from Madagascar and the Comoros form a monophyletic clade and are sister to the species from the Mascarenes. A single introduction from west/central Africa to Madagascar, followed by species diversification and out-of-Madagascar dispersals to the Mascarenes and the Comoros, was found to be the most likely biogeographic scenario in that study. In contrast, the Malagasy *Tricalysia* are not monophyletic (Kainulainen et al. 2017c), suggesting that more than one dispersal event from Africa to Madagascar is likely in this genus. The widespread *Empogona ovalifolia* appears to be a recent arrival to Madagascar.

GARDENIEAE

Gardenieae is represented on Madagascar by the genera *Catunaregam*, *Gardenia*, *Hyperacanthus*, and *Melanoxerus*. They are trees or shrubs, many of which have showy and very fragrant flowers (Figures 8.82e and f). Little is known about their pollination, but moth-pollination is probably most common. Except for the widespread *Hyperacanthus*, the Malagasy Gardenieae species are mainly restricted to drier habitats (although *Gardenia* and *Melanoxerus* can also be found in the subhumid Sambirano Region). *Hyperacanthus* occurs in most of the island's vegetation types, and with its many and morphologically diverse species appears to be a good example of an adaptive radiation. Madagascar is its center of diversity and home to about 50 endemic species (Rakotonasolo and Davis 2006). Two species also occur in South Africa. *Catunaregam* and *Gardenia* are widespread genera in tropical and subtropical Africa and Asia, but, unlike *Hyperacanthus*, they are not species rich on Madagascar. Rakotonirina et al. (2012) revised the Malagasy *Gardenia* and recognized four species, all endemic and restricted to the western part of the island. The Malagasy *Catunaregam* is poorly known but appears to comprise a single species in southwestern Madagascar. The genus *Melanoxerus* (Figure 8.82g) is endemic to Madagascar and was recently described by Kainulainen and Bremer (2014) based on a species previously misplaced in *Euclinia*—a genus now considered restricted to western and central tropical Africa. *Melanoxerus* occurs in northernmost Madagascar and in the southern and western regions but is absent from the Central Highlands and the east coast. So far *Gardenia* is the only genus to have been revised for Madagascar, and one species in *Catunaregam*, three in *Melanoxerus*, and many in *Hyperacanthus* still await description. The biogeographic analysis by Kainulainen et al. (2017c) indicates that *Gardenia*, *Hyperacanthus*, and *Melanoxerus* have all dispersed to Madagascar from Africa. *Catunaregam* may have dispersed out of Asia, although this result based on chloroplast DNA (cpDNA) data was poorly supported and in conflict with nuclear DNA (nDNA) data which instead indicated a closer relation to the sampled African species.

OCTOTROPIDEAE

Octotropideae has a center of diversity on western Indian Ocean islands and several genera are endemic to Madagascar: *Canephora*, *Chapelieria*, *Flagenium*, *Gallienia*, *Jovetia*, and *Lemyrea*. *Polysphaeria*, which is widespread in tropical Africa, is also present and is the most species rich of the Malagasy Octotropideae. The genus has historically been confused with *Cremaspora*, but the latter is probably not present on Madagascar, although it has been cited as such (Madagascar Catalogue 2020). *Galiniera myrtoides* is a poorly known species from the Boeny Region that is probably better placed in the genus *Lamprothamnus* (see Kainulainen et al. 2017c). Following the molecular phylogenetic results of Mouly et al. (2014), the genera *Mantalania* and *Pseudomantalania*—previously considered part of Gardenieae—are now tentatively part of the tribe (as Octotropideae *sensu lato*). However, based on morphology it is not apparent that they belong in this tribe. The habit of *Mantalania* and *Pseudomantalania* is very distinct within Rubiaceae—they form sparsely branched shrubs or trees with three to nine or more large verticillate leaves aggregated at the shoot apices. The flowers are pentamerous to decamerous, in subsessile or long-pedunculate and pendulous axillary cymes. The fruits are large and fleshy-woody indehiscent. Octotropideae *sensu stricto* species are characterized by articulate petioles, (supra-)axillary inflorescences, ovaries with axile placentation, and pendulous ovules (Figure 8.82h; J. R. Stone and Davis 2004).

Notable genera include *Canephora*, whose members have winged peduncles, and the xerophytic, sometimes prostrate shrub *Jovetia*, which has tiny leaves clustered on brachyblasts. Very little is known about pollination and seed dispersal in Octotropideae. Members of the Malagasy Octotropideae are found in many different habitats, from littoral thickets (e.g., *Canephora*, *Chapelieria*, *Flagenium*) to medium-altitude evergreen forests (e.g., *Canephora*, *Lemyrea*). The monospecific *Jovetia* is perhaps the most specialized in its habitat as it is only found on calcareous rocks. It is rarely collected and unusual in the tribe in being restricted to the dry southwestern part of Madagascar. Most Malagasy Octotropideae species are instead found in northern Madagascar and in the eastern moist evergreen forests, although the distributions of *Chapelieria* and *Gallienia* also extend into the Central Highlands. *Polysphaeria* is probably the most widespread genus, but it does not occur in the Central Highlands or in the dry southwest. Ruhsam and Davis (2007) revised *Flagenium*, which is so far the only genus with a comprehensive recent revision. New species have been described in *Canephora* (Dawson 2016), *Chapelieria* (Davies and Davis 2014; Kainulainen and Razafimandimbison 2015), and *Lemyrea* (J. R. Stone and Davis 2004), but undescribed species are known in all these genera. There are also taxa awaiting formal description in both *Mantalania* and *Pseudomantalania*, although De Block and Davis (2006) have provided a species identification key for *Mantalania*. A biogeographic analysis by Kainulainen et al. (2017c) indicates that the Malagasy Octotropideae *sensu lato* represents at least four independent dispersal events from Africa to Madagascar.

PAVETTEAE

The tribe Pavetteae is represented on Madagascar by 11 genera and about 90 species expected, many of which remain to be described. The largest genus is the African-Malagasy *Coptosperma*, which comprises approximately 40 species on the island, most of which are endemic, and another 11 in continental eastern and central Africa and the Comoros. *Coptosperma* has been shown to be polyphyletic and will need to be redelimited (De Block et al. 2015). *Paracephaelis* (including *Homolliella*; De Block et al. 2015), is centered on islands in the western Indian Ocean with 17 endemic species on Madagascar, one species in east Africa and the Seychelles, and another species endemic to the Comoro islands. All other Pavetteae genera present on Madagascar are endemic to the island: *Exallosperma*, *Helictosperma*, *Homollea*, *Pseudocoptosperma*, *Robbrechtia*, *Schizenterospermum*, *Tarenella*, *Tulearia*, and the Malagasy *Tarenna* species, which De Block et al. (2015) showed not to be part of the paleotropical genus *Tarenna* but deserving separate generic status. The tribe Pavetteae is mostly distributed in the dry vegetation areas of western, southern, and northern Madagascar, but there are some exceptions. This is the case for *Robbrechtia*, *Tarenella*, some *Tarenna*, and some large-leaved, as yet undescribed *Coptosperma* (Figure 8.82i), which occurs in littoral forests and lowland to medium-altitude moist evergreen forests.

According to Buerki et al. (2013), the Malagasy flora is characterized by a relatively high number of endemic genera with low species diversity. Pavetteae also shows this pattern: *Exallosperma* and *Pseudocoptosperma* are monospecific; *Helictosperma*, *Robbrechtia*, and *Tulearia* each consist of two species; *Schizenterospermum* has four species; and *Homollea* and *Tarenella* each have five species. Comprehensive recent revisions exist for *Exallosperma*, *Helictosperma*, *Homollea*, *Pseudocoptosperma*, *Robbrechtia*, and *Tulearia* (De Block 2003, 2018; De Block et al. 2018). Revisions for *Tarenella*, *Paracephaelis*, *Coptosperma*, *Schizenterospermum*, and the Malagasy species of *Tarenna* are in preparation by P. De Block. Most Malagasy Pavetteae species are endemic to the island and have a restricted distribution. However, some species are shared with east Africa and other western Indian Ocean islands and have an almost island-wide distribution on Madagascar. This is the case, for example, with *Coptosperma supra-axillare*, *C. nigrescens*, and *Paracephaelis cinerea*.

The best-known member of Pavetteae is undoubtedly the endemic species *C. madagascariensis*, which is used by women in the northwest and west as a facial cosmetic under the vernaular name *masonjoany*. The wood of this species, especially the roots, contains an aromatic essential oil. The wood is ground and mixed with water to produce a paste, which is applied to the face to protect the skin against the sun and as a beauty mask (Ramiandrasoa 2019). The aromatic wood of *C. madagascariensis* is also exported to India, where it is used as incense in funeral ceremonies (Humbert 1937).

Pavetteae species are characterized by pauci- to many-flowered terminal inflorescences (with the exception of *C. supra-axillare*), pentamerous (occasionally tetramerous) flowers with a hypocrateriform corolla tube, corolla lobes contorted to the left in bud and spreading at anthesis, secondary pollen presentation, bilocular ovaries with a single to many ovules per locule, drupaceous fruits, seeds with an adaxial excavation, which is usually deep, and exotestal cells, which are either parenchymatic or have thickenings along the outer tangential wall. Pavetteae taxa show great diversity in seed number and structure, ranging from a single, deeply ruminate seed with superficial hilum to several seeds per fruit, either angular with a deep ovate hilum or laterally flattened with an elongated superficial hilum, both with entire endosperm. The great diversity of Pavetteae on islands in the western Indian Ocean appears to be derived from a single dispersal from Africa to Madagascar followed by several dispersal events to the surrounding islands, as well as back to Africa (Kainulainen et al. 2017c).

Subject editors: Laurent Gautier and Steven M. Goodman

RUBIACEAE, VANGUERIEAE ALLIANCE, SUBFAMILY IXOROIDEAE

P. De Block and S. G. Razafimandimbison

The Vanguerieae alliance is sister to the Coffeeae alliance and these two sister lineages constitute the core Ixoroideae in the subfamily Ixoroideae (Kainulainen et al. 2013). The alliance comprises two tribes, Ixoreae and Vanguerieae, both of which are present on Madagascar (Figures 8.83a–i). Members of the Vanguerieae alliance have a single apically attached, pendulous ovule per locule and two- to seven-locular drupaceous fruits, as well as secondary pollen presentation, a biological strategy that occurs in the whole subfamily Ixoroideae. This phenomenon promotes outbreeding since there is a temporal separation between pollen reception for self-pollination and the reception of outcross pollen. Prior to anthesis, pollen is released from the anthers and deposited onto the unripe stigma and the upper portion of the style (pollen presenter). After anthesis, the pollen is presented to and removed by pollinators, after which the receptive surfaces of the stigma become functional. Dispersal of Ixoreae and Vanguerieae is endozoochorous; the small fleshy drupes are eaten and their seeds dispersed by frugivorous birds and various groups of mammals.

Except for a few shared characters, the two tribes differ markedly from each other, such as in their terminal inflorescences, contorted corolla aestivation, lobed stigma, and colporate pollen in Ixoreae versus axillary inflorescences, valvate aestivation, cylindrical or

FIGURE 8.83
Examples of Malagasy members of the Vanguerieae alliance. A) *Ixora foliicalyx*; B) *I. densithyrsa*; C) *I. rakotonasoloi*; D) *I. hookeri*; E) *I. homolleae*; F) *Peponidium velutinum*; G) *Pyrostria* sp.; H) *Psydrax* sp.; and I) *Rytigynia* sp.
(PHOTOS A and E by F. Van Caekenberghe, Meise Botanic Garden; B by F. Rakotonasolo; C and D by P. De Block, Meise Botanic Garden; and F–I by K. Kainulainen.)

knob-like stigma, and porate pollen in Vanguerieae. The pantropical, monogeneric Ixoreae has an estimated 40 Malagasy species belonging to *Ixora*. The Paleotropical Vanguerieae tribe is represented by six genera and a total that is expected to reach 140 Malagasy species (Govaerts et al. 2020e). Members of both tribes are easily recognized at tribal level (e.g., by the articulate petioles in *Ixora* or the cylindrical or knob-like stigmas in Vanguerieae), but identification at species level is more difficult. Taxonomic revisions are needed for both tribes and new species remain to be described.

IXOREAE

Ixora has about 40 species in continental Africa and about 40 species on Madagascar. Africa and Madagascar have no species in common, although the Malagasy species *I. cremixora* and *I. platythyrsa* are also present in the Comoros. Many *Ixora* are handsome plants with striking inflorescences, often consisting of more than 100 flowers (Figures 8.83a and b). They would make beautiful ornamentals, but hitherto only Asiatic species, such as *I. chinensis* and *I. coccinea*, with orange and red flowers, respectively, have been used in horticulture.

The Malagasy *Ixora* are shrubs, small to medium-size trees or, more rarely, small subshrubs less than 0.5 m tall. They have the following characters: vegetative parts that are generally glabrous; leaves without domatia (minute structures in the axils of secondary veins on the lower leaf surface that house mites and other small arthropods); articulate petioles (i.e., the transition between petiole and stem is not continuous, but a distinct articulation is visible with the naked eye); stipules topped by a needle-like awn; one- to many-flowered terminal inflorescences (Figures 8.83a–c), with trichotomous, articulate, and opposite branching; bracts and bracteoles; flowers that are white or white with a pink tinge, tetramerous (with parts arranged in sets of four); narrow corolla tubes, 1–23 cm long; secondary pollen presentation; two-locular ovaries, more rarely three- or four-locular, with a single, apically attached, pendulous ovule per locule; two-lobed stigma, more rarely three- or four-lobed; and drupaceous, red or black fruits (Figures 8.83d and e) containing two hemi-ovoid seeds (or three to four seeds in the shape of a spherical wedge) with a large adaxial excavation.

The Malagasy *Ixora* are moth pollinated, either phalaenophilous (pollination by small moths; L. A. Nilsson et al. 1990) or sphingophilous (pollination by hawkmoths and other nocturnal

Lepidoptera). Local uses of *Ixora* seem to be mainly restricted to firewood or wood for construction. However, the fruits of at least one species, *I. homolleae* (Figure 8.83e; De Block 2014) are described as edible.

Ixora species occur most frequently in littoral forests and lowland and medium-altitude moist evergreen forests, but are also found in dry deciduous forests. On Madagascar they occur along the entire eastern portion in the north, and in the west as far south as about Morondava; they do not occur in the dry spiny thickets of the southwest. Currently, 31 species have been named but about 10 still await description, and endemism is close to 100%. No species is shared with continental Africa and only two species are also found in the Comoros (*I. cremixora* and *I. platythyrsa*).

Recent molecular phylogenetic studies of *Ixora* (Mouly et al. 2009a, 2009b; Tosh et al. 2013) showed that two major clades occur in the genus, an Asian-Pacific clade and a Neotropical-Africa-Madagascar-Mascarene clade. In this second clade the Mascarene taxa form a lineage that is sister to the rest of that clade and the Neotropical taxa form a lineage that is sister to the African-Malagasy taxa. A similar close relationship between the Malagasy and Neotropical taxa is found in the tribe Spermacoceae (subfamily Rubioideae; Janssens et al. 2016).

Tosh et al. (2013) showed that the radiation of *Ixora* in continental Africa started in the late Miocene (~8 million years ago [Mya]). The Malagasy *Ixora* belong to two separate lineages. One clade, consisting exclusively of the Malagasy species, began to diversify in the Miocene–Pliocene (~5 Mya). A second clade, nested within the continental African species, reached Madagascar as a result of one long-distance dispersal event from eastern Africa in the late Pliocene (~3 Mya), and subsequently underwent a rapid diversification continuing into the Pleistocene. Both lineages show the same morphological innovations, which are otherwise rare within the genus, notably tending toward uni- or pauciflorous inflorescences (Figure 8.83c) and extreme lengthening of the corolla tube (Figure 8.83b), from which it can be concluded that the selective pressures acting upon both lineages are the same (Tosh et al. 2013). The recent radiation of *Ixora* on Madagascar seems to have been driven by increased ecological opportunities following periods of habitat contraction and expansion during the Pliocene/Pleistocene, coupled with increased pollinator specificity resulting in corolla tube length diversification (Tosh et al. 2013).

VANGUERIEAE

The Paleotropical tribe Vanguerieae has about 650 named species in 28 genera. It is centered in Africa and Madagascar with about 400 named species in continental Africa and almost 100 named Malagasy species (Govaerts et al. 2020e). At least another 50 or so species remain to be described for Madagascar (Razafimandimbison et al. 2009a). More than 95% of the Malagasy species are endemic.

Malagasy Vanguerieae members are shrubs or small to medium-size trees. They can be recognized by the following characters: opposite, axillary inflorescences consisting of one to many flowers; campanulate corolla and usually <1(–2.5) cm long; valvate corolla-lobe aestivation; secondary pollen presentation; flowers often pentamerous, often functionally dioecious; cylindrical or knob-like stigma; ovary bi- to plurilocular with a single apically attached, pendulous ovule per locule; drupaceous fruits; pyrenes often strongly woody with apical preformed germination slits; and seeds with large embryos with superior radicles (Bridson 1998). Since Vanguerieae show secondary pollen presentation, they are most probably insect pollinated; the length of the flowers suggests pollination by bees or butterflies. Vanguerieae species are common across Madagascar in seasonal vegetation types (dry deciduous forests, dry spiny thickets, sclerophyllous woodlands, and secondary grassands) but also occur in moist evergreen forests.

Within the tribe, generic delimitations have long been problematic, with most species relegated to the large and variable genus, *Canthium*. Over the years, *Canthium* has continuously been reduced in scope and many species, both African and Malagasy, have been transferred to other genera (e.g., Lantz and Bremer 2004). In a molecular study, Razafimandimbison et al. (2009a) showed that the last Malagasy remnants of *Canthium* are better placed in the genera *Bullockia* or *Peponidium*, thereby dismantling *Canthium* on Madagascar. Razafimandimbison et al. (2009a) also resolved the delimitation problems for the genera with functionally dioecious flowers: *Bullockia*, *Peponidium*, and *Pyrostria*. They form a monophyletic group with ~125 described and undescribed species on Madagascar. *Bullockia* has six species in continental Africa and two, as yet undescribed, in western Madagascar, which probably reached the island as the result of a single long-distance dispersal event from Africa. For *Peponidium* (Figure 8.83f), 45 described Malagasy endemic species are currently known and a few other species have colonized the archipelagoes of the Comoros and Seychelles via dispersal from Madagascar. *Pyrostria* (Figure 8.83g) occurs in Asia (seven species), continental Africa (14 species), in the Comoro, Seychelles, Mascarenes, and Socotra archipelagoes (11 species), and on Madagascar (33 endemic species currently named and close to 40 new species to be described). Only *P. bibracteata* is shared between Madagascar, the Seychelles, and continental Africa. The origin of *Pyrostria* clearly lies on Madagascar with multiple dispersals from the island toward continental Africa and other islands in the western Indian Ocean. *Pyrostria* and *Peponidium* can be distinguished by the nature of the bracts at the base of the inflorescence. *Peponidium* has small cupular, deciduous bracts that never enclose the young inflorescence, whereas *Pyrostria* has persistent, basally connate, and long-acuminate, paired bracts, completely enclosing the young inflorescence.

In the dioecious Vanguerieae, flowers are morphologically hermaphroditic but functionally dioecious, meaning that male flowers have nonfunctional ovaries and stigmas but fertile anthers, and female flowers have sterile anthers but functional ovaries and fertile stigmas; male and female flowers occur on separate individuals as is typical in dioecious plants. In many species, there is also a difference in flower number per inflorescence: functionally male flowers occur in many-flowered infloresences and functionally female flowers in one- to few-flowered inflorescences. The functional dioecy of Vanguerieae originated from hermaphroditism, as evidenced by the presence of nonfunctional sexual organs of the opposite sex, and may be a transitional stage toward true dioecy (absence of sexual organs of the opposite sex). However, Razafimandimbison et al. (2009a) showed that reversals toward hermaphroditism also occur.

The Malagasy Vanguerieae with hermaphroditic flowers belong to three genera. The Paleotropical *Psydrax* (Figure 8.83h) has seven species on Madagascar and can be recognized by the bilocular ovaries and the style, which is at least twice as long as the corolla tube. The African-Malagasy *Rytigynia* is represented by six endemic species on Madagascar (Figure 8.83i), which are characterized by long and often conspicuous corolla-lobe appendages. The mostly African *Vangueria* is represented by one species, *V. madagascariensis*. These three genera form separate lineages within the tribe, and therefore are likely to have reached Madagascar through independent long-distance dispersal events from Africa. With the exception of *V. madagascariensis*, which is naturalized in the Comoros, the Mascarenes, and the Seychelles, none of these genera reached neighboring western Indian Ocean archipelagoes. *Vangueria madagascariensis* is the best-known species of the Vanguerieae. It can easily be recognized by large inflorescences consisting of divaricate branches up to 4.5 cm long and large spherical fruits, 2.5–5 cm in diameter, which turn orange when ripe and are edible.

Subject editors: Laurent Gautier and Steven M. Goodman

RUBIACEAE, PSYCHOTRIEAE ALLIANCE, AND SOME RELATED GROUPS, SUBFAMILY RUBIOIDEAE

C. M. Taylor and S. G. Razafimandimbison

Herein we treat members of the Psychotrieae alliance and the tribes Lasiantheae and Urophylleae (subfamily Rubioideae, Rubiaceae) of Madagascar. The Psychotrieae and Spermacoceae alliances are sister to one another, and form the core Rubioideae. The phylogenetic positions of Lasiantheae and Urophylleae within the subfamily are currently unknown, but the two tribes together with the sister tribes Colletoecemeae and Seychelleeae and the tribes Coussareeae and Ophiorrhizeae are likely to form a basal grade in Rubioideae (Razafimandimbison et al. 2020). The closely related group of nine tribes called the Psychotrieae alliance (Razafimandimbison et al. 2008) is one of the largest lineages of Rubiaceae worldwide, and is represented on Madagascar by the tribes Craterispermeae, Gaertnereae, Morindeae, Palicoureeae, and Psychotrieae. Members of the Psychotrieae alliance plus these other two tribes are predominantly woody, and include 10 genera on Madagascar (Figure 8.84). One of these genera, *Psychotria*, is one of the most speciose plant genera in the world with an estimated 1600 species (Razafimandimbison et al. 2014). Only two of these genera are centered on islands in the western Indian Ocean: *Puffia* (Palicoureeae) is endemic to Madagascar and *Saldinia* (Lasiantheae) has all but one species occurring on the island. Most of the other genera of this group are also found in Africa, but several also range to Asia, and a few are pantropical (*Geophila*, *Morinda*, and *Psychotria*).

DIVERSITY AND ENDEMISM

The Psychotrieae alliance, together with Lasiantheae and Urophylleae, encompasses about 260 species on Madagascar, about 97% of which are endemic; most belong to the Psychotrieae alliance. Several of the genera in this group are morphologically unusual for Rubiaceae (and sometimes not even recognized as belonging to this family [Figure 8.84i]). Some of the genera have notably large species radiations and morphological diversification on the island (Figure 8.84). Below, some notable ecological aspects of this group are provided and more details can be found in Table 8.46.

ECOLOGY

The Malagasy species of this group are generally shrubs and small trees that are common components of the forest understory and secondary vegetation. Most species are found in moist evergreen forests, but they are also represented in the dry deciduous forests of the west and dry spiny thickets of the south.

These plants grow on various substrates, including limestone and different types of sands; some species seem to be substrate specialists but most are generalists. Some species and perhaps entire genera of this group are aluminum hyper-accumulators; they grow on various substrates and have much higher concentrations of that element in their tissues than their substrates have (Jansen et al. 2000). The function of this physiology for the plant is unknown, but it may be a defense against herbivory. Dried specimens of these accumulator species often have a distinctive bluish-black or yellowed color, so this biology can be noted without chemical analysis. Plants of this group all contain tiny inclusions in the form of raphides throughout, inside their tissues. Raphides are hard, needle-shaped crystals of calcium oxalate that are grouped in pressurized vacuoles inside the cells, and they shoot out like little knives when an insect eats through the cell wall. These crystals are assumed to be a defense against herbivory. Raphides are found in only some genera of Rubiaceae and are visible with a hand lens and can aid identification. Raphides are the only intracellular structures noted here; the bacterial nodules noted below are located in spaces between the leaf cells, and the acarodomatia are located on the surface of the leaf.

The inflorescences of most of these species produce a dozen to hundreds of flowers, with only one or a few flowers open each day

FIGURE 8.84 **Examples of Malagasy members of the Psychotrieae alliance. A) *Pauridiantha paucinervis*; B) *Saldinia* sp.; C and D) *Craterispermum* sp.; E) *Gaertnera bambusifolia*; F) *Gaertnera* sp.; G) *Gynochthodes retusa*; H) *Chassalia* sp.; I) *Puffia gerrardii*; J) *Psychotria armandii*; K) *Psychotria* sp.; and L) *Psychotria* sp.** (PHOTOS A–F and H–J by K. Kainulainen; G by S. Razafimandimbison; K by T. Eriksson; and L by P. Antilahimena.)

so flowering continues over a period of days or weeks. The inflorescences are basically all similar in development, but their form varies widely from short to long and few to many branches, reduced to large bracts, and solitary flowers to tightly grouped heads (Figures 8.84a–l). The presentation of the flowers varies between the genera and also among the species of many genera, which suggests that diversification of pollination mode has been a factor in the associated large radiation of species. *Morinda* and *Gynochthodes* are unusual in their globose inflorescences, which have the ovaries of all the individual flowers fused together so the inflorescence produces one multiple fruit (Figure 8.84g). Similar inflorescences are found in the Malagasy *Breonia* (Rubiaceae), pineapples, and some Moraceae fruits. In general, the plants of this group cannot self-pollinate, so the packaging of several separate fruits together for dispersal may help ensure the establishment of a new population. Bollen (2004) listed the Malagasy *Gynochthodes* species, namely *G. retusa* (as *Morinda retusa*) and one undescribed new species (as *M. umbellata*), among the Rubiaceae species whose fruits were eaten by lemurs, including *Eulemur collaris* (Red-collared Brown Lemur) and *Cheirogaleus major* (Greater Dwarf Lemur). Her findings are consistent with Birkinshaw's (1995) study on *E. macaco* (Black Lemur) in the Lokobe National Park, which found that they spent up to 25% of their feeding time on the fruits of *B. boivinii* and *B. sambiranensis* during January and February.

The flowers in the Psychotrieae alliance are generally up to 1 cm long, white to yellow (Figures 8.84a-c, i, and k), and presumably pollinated by insects. Essentially, nothing is actually known about pollination in this group beyond notes on the herbarium labels of bees collected while visiting an inflorescence. A few species have flowers that are larger than this and/or brightly colored, and could be bird pollinated. Rubiaceae flowers are characterized as radially symmetric (actinomorphic) (Figures 8.84c, i, and k), but a number of species in this group have weakly asymmetric (zygomorphic) flowers. The asymmetric flowers sometimes have a corolla tube that is curved along its length and/or asymmetrically swollen at the base, or may have exserted anthers and stigmas that are all positioned on one side of the flower. This asymmetry can be striking in living plants but not evident on dried specimens, so it has hardly been documented.

Most species of the Psychotrieae alliance have bisexual flowers with distylous reproductive biology (also referred to as heterostylous with two forms, or heterodistylous). This biology is quite uncommon among the world's vascular plants but is found in more than half of the species of Rubiaceae, and this family includes most of the world's distylous plants. Distylous plants have two different flower forms, which have reciprocal placement of the stigmas and anthers. Here, each individual plant has only one flower form: some plants produce long-styled (pin) flowers, with the stigmas exserted and held above the anthers, and other plants have short-styled (thrum) flowers, with the anthers exserted and held above the stigmas (Figure 8.84f). Distylous flowers can only pollinate flowers of the opposite form, and local populations generally have a 50:50 ratio of long-styled to short-styled plants. Because of the physical arrangement of the flowers, pollen is transferred quite directly from the anthers of one flower form to the stigmas of the other form; however, the two flower forms are incompatible at the cellular level. The fruits of all of the distylous species in this group contain more than one seed, so they have a 50% chance of having seeds of both forms. A number of studies have found that distyly is sometimes lost in some populations that are isolated on the periphery of the plant's range or on islands. The presence of distyly in so many genera of Rubiaceae on Madagascar suggests that the original colonizers arrived as more than one seed. Whether distyly also promotes some of the notable species radiations in the Psychotrieae alliance remains to be studied. Distyly is thought to sometimes be an intermediate stage between isostylous (i.e., only one form) bisexual flowers and dioecy, and some such cases are found in Rubiaceae. *Gaertnera* is distylous in Africa, Sri Lanka, and Madagascar (so far as is known), while its more evolutionarily derived species of eastern Asia are dioecious (Malcomber 2002, Figure 8.84f). In an otherwise (apparently) distylous tribe, *Saldinia* is cryptically dioecious (Figure 8.84b) and *Gynochthodes* is polygamous to dioecious (Figure 8.84g).

Fruits in the seven tribes discussed here are generally fleshy and range from black, purple, red, white, or yellow to bright blue. These are apparently eaten and dispersed by birds and lemurs, and some fruits of *Morinda* may also be effectively dispersed by ocean currents. Generally, a plant ripens only one or a few of its fruits each day, so it produces new fruits for some time and is an important source of food for animal communities. The fruits of *Pauridiantha* (Urophylleae) are berries with numerous small seeds embedded in the pulp (Figure 8.84a), but the genera of the Psychotrieae alliance and Lasiantheae have fruits (Figures 8.84b, d, h, j, and l) with one to several hard pyrenes (i.e., stones) that each contain one seed. These pyrenes need scarification by the disperser's digestive acids to open and release the seed to germinate, so they are dependent on their dispersers and not usually found growing from seeds that fall directly off the mother plants. These fruits with pyrenes are referred to in Rubiaceae as drupaceous, and the hard wall of the pyrene is formed from the inner tissue of the fruit wall, not the seed coat. A few species of this group appear to have accessory structures on their fruits, in the form of swollen, colored peduncles that may also be eaten by the disperser (*Chassalia* and *Psychotria*). Razafindratsita and Zack (2009) reported that half of the fruits consumed by *Philepitta castanea* (Velvet Asity) (see Prum and Razafindratsita, pp. 1687–93), in the Ranomafana National Park were from the families Myrsinaceae and Rubiaceae, in particular *Psychotria* with red and orange fruits.

A number of species of the Psychotrieae alliance are widely distributed on Madagascar, especially across its eastern section. There is also some regional endemism in this group, especially in northern Madagascar and the southernmost area. Some of the genera that are not endemic to Madagascar are also found in continental Africa (*Craterispermum* and *Pauridiantha*), widely across the Paleotropics (*Chassalia*, *Gaertnera*, and *Gynochthodes*), or pantropically (*Geophila*, *Morinda*, and *Psychotria*). Several genera have an unusually wide morphological diversification on the island (Taylor 2020), and appear to have diversified into niches that perhaps are not available to them in continental areas.

UROPHYLLEAE

The tribe Urophylleae is pantropical with slightly more than 10 genera that each have somewhere between 12 and 24 species (Ntore 2008). *Pauridiantha* is one of its largest genera, and is found widely across tropical Africa. One of its African species, *P. paucinervis*

(Figure 8.84a), is also found on Madagascar (but apparently not in the Comoros). Its presence on Madagascar is most likely the result of recent long-distance dispersal from Africa. This species is a slender, much-branched shrub that is common and widespread in moist evergreen secondary vegetation and appears to flower and fruit continually throughout the year. The capacity of this plant to occupy secondary habitat may have aided its establishment on Madagascar. This species is quite variable in leaf shape and size of leaf, stipule, and inflorescence, but the Malagasy population is overall less variable than the African plants.

LASIANTHEAE

The tribe Lasiantheae is pantropical with six genera. The largest genus in the tribe is *Lasianthus*, which is found in the Neotropics, Africa, and Asia but, perhaps surprisingly, not on Madagascar and other western Indian Ocean islands. The only locally occurring Lasiantheae genus is *Saldinia* (Figure 8.84b), endemic to Madagascar and the Comoros. This genus is widely distributed in moist evergreen forests on Madagascar, but its center of species richness is the eastern littoral forests (Bremekamp 1957). The biogeographic origin of *Saldinia* remains unknown, specifically due to the phylogenetic relationships within the *Trichostachys-Ronabea-Saldinia* clade being unresolved (Smedmark et al. 2014).

Saldinia species are slender, usually low shrubs with quite small flowers and fruits, and they are often difficult to distinguish from each other. As noted above, the plants appear to be distylous but are actually dioecious. The small fruits are drupaceous and shiny blue-black or bright blue, and are presumably dispersed by birds. There appear to be undescribed species of this genus, but most of the known species are separated by vegetative rather than reproductive characters, so the biological dynamics of the species recognized in this group are not well understood.

CRATERISPERMEAE

The tribe Craterispermeae includes one genus with about 24 species, most of them in tropical Africa, plus a few in the Seychelles and on Madagascar. The Malagasy *Craterispermum* form a monophyletic group, which is the result of a single long-distance dispersal from Africa (Razafimandimbison et al. 2017). The Malagasy members of this genus are shrubs and small trees with small flowers and fruits (Figures 8.84c and d), found in the littoral and lowland moist evergreen forests of the east and the medium-altitude moist evergreen forests of the Central Highlands. The leaves are often dry with a stiff texture and a distinctive yellowish-green to golden yellow color, and the plants are known aluminum hyper-accumulators. The small succulent fruits are purple-black at maturity, but often pass through a bright red immature stage (Figure 8.84d) that is mistaken for maturity by people. The fruits contain a single, rounded seed of unusual form, with a deep indentation on one side that gives it a shape like a bowl; the function of this distinctive seed form is unknown. *Craterispermum* is not well studied in any region, and is particularly poorly known on Madagascar (De Block and Randriamboavonjy 2015). The three Malagasy species are separated mainly by vegetative characters and inflorescence size, rather than an understanding of reproductive differences, and certainly there are additional species. The Malagasy species have been confused with African species of the genus until recently, which has confused the biogeography of both regions.

GAERTNEREAE

The tribe Gaertnereae is pantropical with two genera: *Pagamea* in the Neotropics and the Paleotropical *Gaertnera*, which is found from Africa to southeastern Asia. The Malagasy *Gaertnera* species form a single clade, and the presence of this genus on the island results from a range expansion from Asia to Madagascar in the Miocene–Pliocene (Razafimandimbison et al. 2017). Gaertnereae is unusual for a Rubiaceae in its superior ovaries and fruits (Figure 8.84e and f), and its species are often mistaken for members of the family Loganiaceae. The ovary here forms initially in an inferior position, and then grows from the upper surface to become secondarily superior. The Malagasy *Gaertnera* species are shrubs and small trees found widely in moist evergreen forests. This genus has distinctive stipules that are tubular and fringed at the top, and it can usually be easily identified without flowers or fruits. *Gaertnera* varies quite widely on Madagascar in leaves, inflorescences, flowers, plant size, and habitat, and its species radiation here represents about half the genus (Malcomber and Taylor 2009; Taylor et al. 2014), not including additional undescribed Malagasy species (C. M. Taylor, unpublished data).

MORINDEAE

The tribe Morindeae is pantropical and has five genera (Razafimandimbison et al. 2009b), two of them on Madagascar: *Gynochthodes* ranges across the western Pacific region and Indian Ocean islands to its easternmost point on Madagascar, and *Morinda* is pantropical overall, with *M. citrifolia* its most widespread species on the island. *Gynochthodes* is found widely on Madagascar in moist evergreen forests.

Gynochthodes species are sprawling or lianescent low shrubs with fruits (Figure 8.84g) that turn orange or bluish-black when ripe and flowers that are polygamous or dioecious. The breeding biology of this genus was characterized based on Pacific and Asian species, though, and postulated to be the same for the Malagasy species, which have not been directly studied. *Gynochthodes* has not been studied taxonomically in general or on Madagascar. Its Malagasy species appear to be endemic but this is not yet confirmed, and there appear to be several undescribed taxa. The Malagasy *Gynochthodes* species are the result of two independent long-distance dispersal events from the Pacific to Madagascar, and form two groups (Razafimandimbison et al. 2017). Malagasy *Gynochthodes* with orange fruits form a monophyletic group that is endemic to Madagascar and sister to the Sri Lankan *G. umbellata*; this lineage dispersed to Madagascar during the Miocene–Pleistocene (Razafimandimbison et al. 2017). The other *Gynochthodes* group occurring on the island has bluish-black fruits and is sister to the orange-fruited group; this comprises the Malagasy *G. retusa* (Figure 8.84g) plus several Asian, Australian, and Pacific species, and it colonized Madagascar in the last 11.6 million years.

Morinda citrifolia is a tree or shrub, and, as in general in this genus, it has bisexual, distylous, and self-pollinated flowers and fruits that are dull white to yellowish-brown when ripe. Razafimandimbison et al. (2010b) showed that *M. citrifolia* originated in the region of Micronesia in the Pacific, and subsequently dispersed to the world's tropical seacoasts. This wide distribution is mainly attributed to the transoceanic dispersal of its buoyant seeds. On Madagascar, *M. citrifolia* is known from natural populations along the eastern coast (Razafimandimbison et al. 2010b). Despite their dull appearance, its fruits are succulent and edible and are eaten locally; it is more widely used as a nutriceutical and is cultivated worldwide as noni or Indian mulberry for its fruits. This species was also recently brought into wide cultivation on Madagascar as a medicinal plant.

PALICOUREEAE

The tribe Palicoureeae is pantropical and has nine genera. Several of these are relatively large, with more than a hundred species. The Malagasy genera of the tribe were studied by Bremekamp (1962, 1963), who described most of the currently recognized species. Palicoureeae is represented by three genera on Madagascar: *Chassalia* (Figure 8.84h) is woody, while *Puffia* (Figure 8.84i) and *Geophila* are creeping herbs that are sometimes not recognized as Rubiaceae. *Puffia* diverged from its sister genus, the African *Hymenocoleus*, in the Miocene and subsequently dispersed to Madagascar. *Chassalia* has about 100 species, which are found in humid vegetation from Africa to southeastern Asia. The Malagasy species appear to be derived from two distantly related lineages, which are the result of two independent dispersal events. The two Malagasy *Chassalia* clades are ecologically and geographically distinct, with one restricted to the dry deciduous forests of Madagascar and the other formed by species from the moist evergreen forests of the Comoros, the Mascarenes, and central and eastern Madagascar. These lineages are the result of two independent long-distance dispersal events from Africa between the Miocene and Pliocene (Razafimandimbison et al. 2017). *Geophila* is pantropical with centers of diversity in central Africa and western South America. It is represented on the island by two species (*G. obvallata* and *G. uniflora*), both found on Madagascar and Africa. The Malagasy and Comorian *G. uniflora* form a monophyletic group, suggesting that they had one common ancestor whose origin is currently unknown. The Malagasy-Comorian *G. uniflora* clade is sister to a clade formed by the African, Asian, and Pacific *G. uniflora* (Razafimandimbison et al. 2017). The Malagasy *G. obvallata* is most likely the result of long-distance dispersal from Africa.

All the Malagasy *Chassalia* species are endemic, and all but two were described by Bremekamp (1962). The oddly shaped pyrenes of this genus are similar to those of *Craterispermum*, with the form of a shallow bowl. The inflorescence and infructescences' axes are red, pink (Figure 8.84h), or white. The flowers of some *Chassalia* species are unusual in Rubiaceae, having a curved flower tube and winged buds. Bremekamp (1962) characterized *Chassalia* species as distylous or isostylous (i.e., homostylous, with only one flower form) based on herbarium specimens, but this has not been confirmed with field observations. Bremekamp (1962) used this flower biology, isostylous versus distylous, as the main distinction in his key to *Chassalia*, so fruiting plants are sometimes difficult to identify. Beyond this, Bremekamp distinguished *Chassalia* species to a very large extent based on vegetative characters. There appear to be additional undescribed species in this genus, which are under study by Kew botanists (A. Davis, unpublished data). The fruits are fleshy, drupaceous, and turn black when fully mature (Figure 8.84h).

Geophila and *Puffia* are slender creeping herbs with stems that root at the nodes, small heart-shaped leaves (Figure 8.84i), and small red, yellow, or purple-black fruits. *Geophila* is variable in its reproductive biology, with some species distylous and others isostylous (Verdcourt 1976); both of the Malagasy species are nonendemic and distylous in their African populations, but have not been been studied on Madagascar. *Puffia* was reported to be isostylous (Razafimandimbison et al. 2014), but recent collections now show it is distylous. *Geophila* is notable for its varied fruit colors, which are generally consistent within a species and differ from *Puffia*'s fruits. These herbs are known from scattered localities in moist evergreen forest understory, and they may be rare but possibly they are overlooked because of their small size and infrequent flowering. One of the *Geophila* species, *G. obvallata*, was discovered quite recently, and the related genus *Hymenocoleus* may perhaps also be expected to occur on Madagascar.

PSYCHOTRIEAE

The tribe Psychotrieae includes one genus, *Psychotria*, which is pantropical and one of the largest genera of all flowering plants. As with any large, diverse plant group, *Psychotria* includes a very wide range of morphological variation and is not always quickly recognizable, especially on Madagascar where some of its forms are unique in the genus (Taylor 2020; Figures 8.84j–l). All of the Malagasy *Psychotria* species are endemic and they are found across nearly the whole of the island, from sea level to mountain tops, and from wet to quite dry habitats. This species diversity results from at least three long-distance dispersal events, which gave rise to three major lineages (Razafimandimbison et al. 2017): the western Indian Ocean *Psychotria* clade; the African-western Indian Ocean *Psychotria* clade (bacterial leaf-nodulated clade); and the African-Asian-western Indian Ocean *Psychotria* clade. The first clade is centered on Madagascar and its common ancestor dispersed to Madagascar from the Pacific or Asia in the Oligocene–Miocene; winds blowing across the Indian Ocean from Australia and southeast Asia toward Madagascar may well have facilitated such a dispersal route. The Malagasy and Comorian species with schizocarpous fruits form a basal grade within the western Indian Ocean clade. The Malagasy *Psychotria* clade within the bacterial-leaf-nodulated lineage originated from Africa, and expanded to Madagascar sometime in the Miocene–Pliocene. Within the African-Asian-western Indian Ocean *Psychotria* clade, the biogeographic origin of the Malagasy clade that includes most of the species with yellow flowers is unknown (Razafimandimbison et al. 2017).

Psychotria has an unusually large number of species on Madagascar for the island's land area, and is one of the largest plant genera on the island. *Psychotria* is also one of the two or three largest genera in some other tropical island groups; the intrinsic characteristics of these plants and tropical islands that facilitate this radiation are not known, but Madagascar may be a good laboratory to study this phenomenon. The Malagasy species of *Psychotria* vary in habit, habitat, leaf form, inflorescence, flower size and color, and fruit size and color (Taylor 2020). Bremekamp (1963) separated several Malagasy genera with unusual characteristics, but these are now all included in *Psychotria*. The flowers are distylous in most if not all the species. The fruits are mostly small, juicy, and variously red, orange, blue, or purple-black. A few Malagasy *Psychotria* species, however, have larger, firmly fleshy, dull purple or brown fruits that appear to be adapted for lemur dispersal (Taylor 2020). Some other species on the island are apparently unique in this genus due to their dry fruits that are schizocarpous (i.e., splitting into two smaller parts, mericarps, which do not open further).

Many species of *Psychotria* have acarodomatia on the leaves, small pockets of tissue or dense tufts of pubescence in the axils of the secondary veins on the underside of the leaf blade, which are visible with a hand lens. These structures protect mites that live on the leaf's surface and help the plant by eating fungi and herbivorous insects. This mutualism is found in many *Psychotria* species, but not all; the presence and form of the acarodomatia often help identify particular species.

A few *Psychotria* species on Madagascar also have bacterial domatia, another unusual feature in Rubiaceae. These domatia are nodules or pockets in spaces inside the leaf tissue, between the cells, that contain symbiotic, nitrogen-fixing bacteria. The bacteria belong to the genus *Burkholderia*, a complex and poorly known group that is found worldwide and includes free-living organisms and pathogens as well as symbionts (Eberl and Vandamme 2016). The bacteria in Rubiaceae leaf nodules are obligate symbionts and fix nitrogen from the air, which is then taken up by the plant (Pinto-Carbo et al. 2016). The bacterial nodules are usually clearly visible as spots or branched structures in the leaf blade, but some leaves have only a few nodules, which can be overlooked. No correlation between habitat and the presence of bacterial nodules has yet been found.

The extensive botanical exploration of recent decades has found some but not all of the *Psychotria* species Bremekamp studied, and has resulted in the discovery of more than 20 new species (Taylor 2020). This suggests that many Malagasy *Psychotria* species have rather localized distributions, and perhaps that the fine-scale phytogeographic landscape is complex here. This is difficult to confirm because much wide-scale degradation of the island's natural vegetation happened before the genus was extensively documented. Hence, the ranges known today for many *Psychotria* species may be relictual rather than representative of their original distribution.

Subject editors: Laurent Gautier and Steven M. Goodman

RUBIACEAE, SPERMACOCEAE ALLIANCE, SUBFAMILY RUBIOIDEAE

P. De Block and S. G. Razafimandimbison

The Spermacoceae alliance is sister to the Psychotrieae alliance and these two sister lineages constitute the core group of the subfamily Rubioideae (B. Bremer and Eriksson 2009). On Madagascar, the alliance comprises six tribes, Anthospermeae, Danaideae, Knoxieae, Paederieae, Rubieae, and Spermacoceae, which encompass 33 genera and about 164 named species (Figures 8.85a–i). Species of this alliance are characterized by the presence of raphides (calcium oxalate crystals) in their tissues and typically have fimbriate stipules and a valvate corolla aestivation (in flower bud the corolla lobes meet at their edges but do not overlap). Other characters occurring in a majority of taxa but not in all are a herbaceous habit, heterostylous flowers, and dry fruits.

ANTHOSPERMEAE

Anthospermeae members, of which there are 12 genera and approximately 210 species, are distributed in the Southern Hemisphere (Australia, Australasia, South America, Africa, and more rarely in Asia) with only a few species occurring north of the equator. *Anthospermum*, with eight endemic species, is the only genus present on Madagascar. The Malagasy *Anthospermum* (Figure 8.85a) species are perennial herbs with woody rootstock, dwarf shrubs, or shrubs to 2 m tall. They have small, narrow, subsessile leaves, 5–25(–35) × 0.3–5 mm in size, with strongly revolute margins. Small flowers (corolla tube <2 mm long) occur in few- to several-flowered inflorescences. Ovaries are bilocular with a single, basally attached ovule per locule. The small fruits are dry and split into two mericarps (part of fruit consisting of a single carpel), which act as the dispersal unit. Dispersal is probably by wind, birds, and various groups of small mammals or water (Puff 1986). *Anthospermum* species are wind pollinated, and the flowers are well adapted to this rather than pollination by insects and vertebrates: the perianth is small and not optically attractive; flowers are odorless and do not produce nectar; the bilobed stigmas are long (Figure 8.85a) with the receptive surfaces increased by hairs; anthers are exserted on long filaments and produce masses of small-size pollen grains; and species either have dioecious flowers or show a trend toward dioecy (Puff 1986).

The Malagasy *Anthospermum* species often grow at higher elevations of (400–)800–2600 m in rocky areas, often as undergrowth in

FIGURE 8.85
Examples of the Malagasy members of the Spermacoceae alliance. A) *Anthospermum* sp.; B) *Payera* sp.; C) *Triainolepis* sp.; D) *Phyllopentas* sp.; E) *Paederia farinosa*; F) *Gomphocalyx herniarioides*; G) *Lathraeocarpa acicularis*; H) *Phialiphora bevazahensis*; and I) *Cordylostigma virgatum*. (PHOTO A by S. Razafimandimbison; B, C, E, F, and H by P. De Block, Meise Botanic Garden; D by P. Antilahimena; and G and I by S. Dessein, Meise Botanic Garden.)

sclerophyllous woodlands or montane ericoid thickets. They are also found in disturbed sites along roads or in *savoka*. One species, *A. palustre*, seems restricted to peat bogs. *Anthospermum* is absent from western Madagascar and mostly occurs in the mountain areas in the north, center, and south.

DANAIDEAE

This tribe, comprising three genera and 68 named species, is centered on Madagascar. *Payera* (10 species; Figure 8.84b; Buchner and Puff 1993; Govaerts et al. 2020e) and *Schismatoclada* (20 species, Strid et al. 2019; Govaerts et al. 2020e) are endemic to the island, whereas *Danais* has 38 species, 33 of which are endemic to Madagascar (Puff and Buchner 1994; Krüger et al. 2012; Taylor and Rogers 2013; Govaerts et al. 2020e). There are three *Danais* species in the Mascarenes: one on Rodrigues and two on Mauritius, of which *D. sulcata* is endemic and *D. fragrans* is shared with La Réunion. *Danais humblotii* is shared between the Comoros and Madagascar.

Members of Danaideae have hermaphrodite, heterostylous, pentamerous (occasionally tetramerous or hexamerous) flowers, bilocular ovaries with a large, peltate placenta with numerous ovules per locule, capsular fruits, and winged seeds. The genus *Danais* consists of woody lianas or climbing shrubs, and is well supported as a monophyletic group that is sister to the *Payera*-*Schismatoclada* clade (Krüger et al. 2012). Several characters were used by Buchner and Puff (1993) to differentiate between *Payera* and *Schismatoclada*, notably the presence/absence of large bracts subtending the inflorescence (absent in *Schismatoclada* versus present in *Payera*), corolla aestivation (valvate-reduplicate versus valvate), dehiscence of capsule (septicidal versus loculicidal), and seed shape (length-width ratio at least 4:1 versus 2–3:1). However, Krüger et al. (2012) showed that the delimitation of the two genera is not so clear-cut.

Danaideae species occur in moist evergreen forests and montane ericoid thickets of eastern, central, and northwestern Madagascar. Some species, for example, *S. marojejyensis*, are restricted to high mountains. The three genera are insect pollinated. Depending on the length of the flowers, pollination is executed by bees, long-tongued flies, butterflies, moths, and even hawkmoths (Buchner and Puff 1993). The capsular fruits of Danaideae open while still on the plant. The winged seeds are wind dispersed.

Regarding the taxonomy of the Danaideae, it should be noted that recent treatments of *Danais* exist (Puff and Buchner 1994; Krüger et al. 2012; Taylor and Rogers 2013), whereas revisions for *Payera* and *Schismatoclada* are underway by S. Razafimandimbison. Several new species remain to be described in these last two genera.

The tribe Danaideae is the largest Rubiaceae tribe centered on Madagascar. With *Payera* and *Schismatoclada* as well as the earliest divergent representatives of *Danais* endemic to the island, a Malagasy origin of the tribe is suggested. Krüger et al. (2012) further showed that the *Danais* species occurring in east Africa and on other western Indian Ocean islands are the result of several independent out-of-Madagascar dispersals.

KNOXIEAE

The generic delimitation in the tribe Knoxieae was reassessed by Kårehed and Bremer (2007). The tribe is centered in Africa and comprises about 130 species in 16 genera. On Madagascar, seven genera occur, with approximately 28 species; two of the genera are endemic. The tribe occurs across the island. Four genera are herbaceous, either annual or perennial with a woody base: *Otiophora*, *Pentanisia*, *Pentas*, and *Phyllopentas*. The other genera are shrubs or trees. Knoxieae species are variable in their characters; for example, inflorescences are usually terminal but may also be axillary, the number of ovules per locule varies from one to many, and calyxes have unequal/enlarged lobes or not. The fruits are dry, bilocular capsules, dehiscent or not, except in *Triainolepis* (Figure 8.85c), which has bilocular to decalocular fleshy fruits.

Enlarged, colored, petaloid calyx lobes (calycophylls) are especially remarkable in the two genera endemic to Madagascar: *Carphalea* and *Paracarphalea*. In *Paracarphalea* the calyx lobes are dark pink to red, and in *Carphalea* white or white-tinged pink (Puff 1988; Ferm et al. 2016). In both genera, either all calyx lobes or a single one may be enlarged. *Carphalea cloiselii* is the only species of these two genera in which the calyx lobes expand only during fruit stage, which is an indication that the enlarged calyx lobes aid in the dissemination of the fruit, functioning as dispersal unit. In the other species, the enlarged calyx lobes also function to enhance the optical attractiveness of inflorescences and flowers to pollinators. Other genera showing enlarged foliaceous calyx lobes are *Phyllopentas* (one or two; Figure 8.85d) and *Otiophora* (one or two, green). *Carphalea*, *Paracarphalea*, and *Triainolepis* occur in the western, northern, and southern portions of the island in secondary grasslands, dry deciduous forests, and dry spiny thickets. *Phyllopentas*, *Pentas*, and *Otiophora* occur mostly in the east and north, whereas *Pentanisia* is restricted to the Central Highlands.

In a biogeographic analysis, Wikström et al. (2010) inferred five independent long-distance dispersal events out of eastern and southern Africa toward Madagascar. They also reconstructed three out-of-Madagascar dispersals, one to eastern tropical Africa and one to Africa and the Comoros for *Triainolepis*, and a third dispersal to Africa for *Otiophora*.

PAEDERIEAE

The tribe Paederieae comprises five genera and about 85 species and occurs mostly in Asia. Only the genus *Paederia* has a wider distribution, with 10 species endemic to Madagascar and one shared between the island, east Africa, and the Comoros. Only two further African species exist, and these are endemic to east Africa and the Comoros, respectively (Puff 1991a). Members of this genus are lianas or climbing shrubs, characterized by a fetid odor when leaves or stems are damaged. Flowers are pentamerous, hermaphroditic, homostylous, and have bilocular ovaries with a single basally attached ovule per locule. Fruits are dry, laterally compressed, and contain two winged diaspores (dispersal units). Leaflike bracts are present in the proximal part of the inflorescences; often these are similar to the vegetative leaves, though smaller in size. Some Malagasy species are unique in the genus in that the leaflike bracts are colored (silvery, white, pink, reddish, or lilac). These colored bracts enhance the attractiveness of the inflorescences. Depending on the length and the width of the corolla tube, *Paederia* species are pollinated by bees, butterflies, moths, hawkmoths, and long-proboscis flies (Puff 1991b). Several species with shorter corolla tubes have a conspicuous reddish to maroon throat, the darker color serving as a nectar guide for bees.

Paederia is wind dispersed. The diaspores consist of a laterally flattened seed and a thin endocarp that has grown into a wing-like structure. After the exocarp of the fruit has fallen off, the two diaspores remain suspended from threadlike carpophores (structures bearing the dispersal units; in the case of *Paederia*, the carpophores are thickened vascular bundles from the fruit wall), which hold them in a vertical position so that they are effectively exposed to wind. The wings of the diaspores and the carpophores clearly are adaptations to wind dispersal (Igersheim and Puff 1991).

On Madagascar, *Paederia* (Figure 8.85e) is almost exclusively restricted to the seasonal climates of the south, west, and north, with *P. thoursiana* being the only species occurring in moist evergreen forests of the east. The other species prefer seasonal habitats such as littoral, riparian, moist semi-deciduous, or dry deciduous forests; sclerophyllous woodland; dry spiny thickets, as well as secondary grasslands, mainly in lowland; and medium-altitude moist evergreen forest areas. Biogeographic analyses (Wikström et al. 2010; Nie et al. 2013) showed that the Malagasy *Paederia* species form a monophyletic group and result from a single dispersal event out of east Africa. However, before this took place, another dispersal event happened from Asia to Africa/Madagascar. Therefore, the Malagasy *Paederia* species originated in Asia.

A second genus of the Paederieae represented on Madagascar, the monospecific *Serissa*, is native in southeast Asia, and *S. japonica* was probably introduced to Madagascar as an ornamental and has naturalized there. The species is a dense shrub up to 60 cm tall with small leaves, a profusion of small white flowers, and, in contrast to the dry fruits in *Paederia*, reddish fleshy fruits that are tardily dehiscent.

RUBIEAE

Rubieae has a cosmopolitan distribution and is the only Rubiaceae tribe that has reached the Mediterranean and temperate regions. The tribe comprises about 1000 species in approximately 11 genera, the largest one being *Galium* with about 630 species worldwide. *Galium* is the only Rubieae genus present on Madagascar, with five species occurring in montane vegetation types at elevations above 2000 m, as well as at somewhat lower elevations in sheltered moist locations containing pockets of montane vegetation (Puff and Mantell 1982). Since they are rarely found below 1500 m elevation, their distributions are typically disjunct. The Malagasy members of *Galium* are perennial herbs with a woody base or well-developed root system. They have flowers with a rudimentary calyx, a bilocular ovary with a single ovule per locule, pluricolpate pollen, and small black, fleshy, and didymous fruits. They are recognized most easily by their herbaceous habit and by their verticillate leaves, which are in fact whorls of opposite leaves and leaflike stipules or stipule segments.

Endemism is low in the Malagasy *Galium* species, since two of the five species are shared with the African mainland. Two other species seem closely allied to mainland Afromontane species. These four species probably reached Madagascar through independent, relatively recent long-distance dispersal events. The fifth Malagasy species, *G. polyacanthum*, differs from the four others by the relatively long corolla tube, a character considered "primitive" within the genus. Puff and Mantell (1982) speculated that this species may be an older Malagasy endemic without close allies. It would be interesting to resolve the affinity and biogeography of the Malagasy *Galium* species through a molecular study.

SPERMACOCEAE

The pantropical Spermacoceae comprises about 62 genera and more than 1200 species (Groeninckx et al. 2009a). On Madagascar, they are represented by approximately 47 named species in 19 genera. The Neotropical *Mitracarpus* and *Richardia* and the Asian/Pacific *Dentella*, are each represented on Madagascar by a single species—all recent colonizers. The genus *Hexasepalum* occurs in North and South America as well as in Africa. Currently, it is unknown whether the three to five species present on Madagascar are all naturalized or whether some of them are indigenous. Six genera are endemic to the island: *Amphistemon*, *Astiella*, *Gomphocalyx* (Figure 8.85f), *Lathraeocarpa* (Figure 8.85g), *Phialiphora* (Figure 8.85h), and *Thamnoldenlandia*. Three genera are pantropical (*Oldenlandia*, *Spermacoce*, and *Edrastima*), while *Agathisanthemum*, *Cordylostigma* (Figure 8.85i), *Mitrasacmopsis*, *Pentodon*, and *Phylohydrax* have wider African/Indian Ocean island distributions. For *Oldenlandia* and *Spermacoce*, both indigenous and naturalized species are present on Madagascar. *Hedyotis* is exclusively Asian, with the exception of the Malagasy endemic species *H. trichoglossa*, whose taxonomic position remains unclear. Because of the relatively high number of naturalized species and recent colonizers in the Malagasy Spermacoceae, the level of endemism at species level is less than 90% in this tribe, which is unusually low for the family Rubiaceae. While the Spermacoceae has the highest diversity at the generic level in the Spermacoceae alliance, this is not the case at species level. Eleven genera have only a single species on Madagascar. Four others have two Malagasy representatives. The largest genera are *Phialiphora* (four species), *Oldenlandia* (close to 20 species), *Spermacoce* (close to 15 species), and *Astiella* (12 species).

Recent studies by Groeninckx et al. (2009b, 2010a, 2010b, 2010c, 2017) helped clarify the taxonomic framework of the Malagasy Spermacoceae. However, the tribe is still in need of study. Most urgent are the revisions of the genera *Hexasepalum*, *Oldenlandia*, and *Spermacoce*, for which the exact number of species is currently unknown. The taxonomy of these genera is complicated by the presence of naturalized species from other continents, the great intraspecific variability of the species, and the fact that plant collecting on Madagascar has heavily focused on woody species.

Members of Spermacoceae are predominantly herbaceous, although perennial species often have a woody base. Only two of the 19 Malagasy Spermacoceae genera are woody, both being endemic: *Thamnoldenlandia ambovombensis* is a densely branched shrub to 1.5 m tall and the two *Lathraeocarpa* species (Figure 8.85g) are subshrubs up to about 25 cm tall with well-developed woody taproots (Groeninckx et al. 2009b, 2010c). In addition to the predominant herbaceous habit, Spermacoceae members are characterized by fimbriate stipules (exception: *Lathraeocarpa*), tetramerous flowers (exceptions: *Pentodon* and *Richardia*), bilocular ovaries (exceptions: *Lathraeocarpa* and *Richardia*), and dry fruits (exception: *Lathraeocarpa*). The tribe is less uniform in other characters and representatives can be iso- or heterostylous, or uni- or multi-ovulate. Other variable features include terminal, pseudoaxillary, or axillary inflorescences; tri- to multicolporate pollen; seeds with or without a ventral groove; and indehiscent or dehiscent fruits, the dehiscent ones opening loculicidally or septicidally. A useful table giving the main characters of each genus is presented by Groeninckx et al. (2010b).

Most Spermacoceae species occur in dry vegetation types in western, southern, and northern Madagascar, although some are also found in the eastern moist evergreen forests, such as some *Astiella* species and *Hedyotis trichoglossa*. Other species are weeds, sometimes invasive, and are found along roadsides, in cultivated fields, or in other disturbed landscapes. Several genera show very specific adaptations to drought, such as the rosette habit of *Phialiphora* (with a basal leaf rosette; Figure 8.85h) or the well-developed woody taproots of *Lathraeocarpa* and *Gomphocalyx*.

Janssens et al. (2016) estimated a late Eocene origin for the Spermacoceae and diversification of the tribe during the Oligocene and the Miocene. They inferred two colonization events for the Malagasy endemic Spermacoceae: the first long-distance dispersal from Africa gave rise to *Lathraeocarpa*, *Phylohydrax*, and *Gomphocalyx*, and the second long-distance dispersal took place from tropical America and gave rise to the endemic genera *Astiella*, *Phialiphora*, *Thamnoldenlandia*, and *Amphistemon*. For all studied nonendemic Malagasy Spermacoceae, an African origin was inferred. An out-of-Madagascar dispersal toward east Africa was assumed for *Phylohydrax carnosa*.

Subject editors: Laurent Gautier and Steven M. Goodman

APOCYNACEAE

S. Liede-Schumann

The Apocynaceae is one of the few families not yet completely treated for the *Flore de Madagascar et des Comores* series. In 1976, Markgraf published the volume in the series on Apocynaceae *sensu stricto* (thus including apocynoids and rauvolfioids only), and this contribution included 23 genera and 146 species. Nobody imagined that 40 years later the treatment of what was then considered the sister family, Asclepiadaceae, would still be unpublished; this is probably because of the much higher number of species, the small complex flowers, and the often difficult species delimitation (e.g., *Ceropegia, Cynanchum*). The Catalogue of the Plants of Madagascar provides a summary overview of the complete family, including revisionary work conducted in the meantime, mainly by the Wageningen Agricultural University team of A. Leeuwenberg (e.g., Leeuwenberg 1997), resulting in different species numbers for most genera compared with those of Markgraf (1976).

During this interim period, there was a general change in systematic botany, away from the morphological assessment of relationships and toward a DNA-based molecular phylogenetic classification. Livshultz et al. (2007) were the first to demonstrate that the two subfamilies Rauvolfioideae and Apocynoideae, once considered to constitute Apocynaceae, formed grades in which Periplocoideae, Secamonoideae, and Asclepiadoideae are nested (Figure 8.86). These results were supported by all subsequent studies, such as Straub et al. (2014) and Fishbein et al. (2018). Therefore, the informal names rauvolfioids and apocynoids should be used, indicating that these groups do not constitute monophyletic entities. Periplocoideae, Secamonoideae, and Asclepiadoideae are each monophyletic, but only the latter two are in a sister-group position, while the position of Periplocoideae as sister to Secamonoideae + Asclepiadoideae is still controversial (cf. Livshultz et al. 2007; Fishbein et al. 2018); Periplocoideae obviously constitute an independent lineage. The current circumscription of the family Apocynaceae (according to M. E. Endress et al. 2018) is therefore as follows:

- **Rauvolfioids** (treated in Markgraf 1976): anthers free from style-head; corolla-lobe aestivation in bud typically sinistrorse (overlapping to the left), rarely dextrorse; fruit dehiscent or indehiscent, syncarpous or apocarpous, a berry, drupe, follicle, or capsule; seeds naked, with wings, or arils, but almost never with a coma (an easily detached tuft of hairs) at one end. Includes 79 genera in 11 tribes worldwide; 14 genera with 59 species in eight tribes native to Madagascar, four genera cultivated (cultivated genera are indicated by **; number of species in each genus is given in parentheses/brackets, with the number of species currently accepted in the Madagascar Catalogue [2020] and the number of species accepted in the earlier treatment of Apocynaceae by Markgraf [1976] on the right): *Allamanda***, *Ancylobothrys* (one/one), *Carissa* (three/nine), *Catharanthus* (eight/eight), *Cerbera* (one/one), *Craspidospermum* (one/one), *Gonioma* (one/one), *Landolphia* (nine/13), *Petchia* (six/zero, species treated under *Cabucala* [18]), *Plectaneia* (three/12), *Plumeria***, *Rauvolfia* (three/three), *Saba* (one/one), *Stephanostegia* (two/five), *Tabernaemontana* (15/zero, treated under *Capuronetta* [one], *Hazunta* [one], *Muntafara* [one], *Pandaca* [26], *Pandacastrum* [one]), *Thevetia***, *Vinca***, and *Voacanga* (one/one).
- **Apocynoids** (treated in Markgraf 1976): corolla-lobe aestivation in bud typically dextrorse (overlapping to the right) or valvate, rarely sinistrorse; anthers adnate to the style-head, four-locular; pollen almost always shed as monads; nectaries, if present, encircling the base of the ovary as five distinct lobes, or fused to varying degrees into a lobed or crenulate annulus, rarely two distinct lobes alternating with the carpels; fruit dehiscent, almost always apocarpous, with a pair of follicles, sometimes reduced to one by abortion or postgenitally fused; seeds small, almost always with a coma at one end. Includes 77 genera in nine tribes worldwide; five genera with 38 species in three tribes native to Madagascar, three cultivated (cultivated genera are indicated by **) and the double number system follows that presented above under rauvolfioids: *Alafia* (eight/10), *Beaumontia***, *Mascarenhasia* (eight/12), *Nerium***, *Oncinotis* (one/two), *Pachypodium* (20/12), *Strophanthus* (one/zero, treated under *Roupellina* [one]), and *Trachelospermum***.
- **Subfamily Periplocoideae**: corolla-lobe aestivation in bud typically dextrorse or valvate, rarely sinistrorse; anthers four-locular, adnate to the style-head; pollen shed as tetrads, loose on spoon-shaped receptacle or translator, the sticky end of which adheres to pollinator or gathered into pollinia; nectaries located in alternistaminal pockets on staminal feet or staminal tube; fruit dehiscent, usually consisting of a pair of follicles; seeds small, almost always with a coma at one end. Includes 33 genera in the Paleotropics; five genera with 42 species native to Madagascar: *Baroniella* (10), *Camptocarpus* (eight), *Cryptostegia* (two), *Ischnolepis* (one), and *Pentopetia* (24).
- **Subfamily Secamonoideae**: anthers four-locular, with pollen in pollinia. Includes eight genera in the Paleotropics; four genera and 97 species native to Madagascar: *Calyptranthera* (13), *Pervillaea* (six), *Secamone* (76), and *Secamonopsis* (two).
- **Subfamily Asclepiadoideae**: anthers two-locular, with pollen in pollinia. Includes 182 genera in five tribes worldwide; 10 genera in three tribes native to Madagascar (three naturalized genera are denoted by *): *Asclepias**, *Calotropis**, *Ceropegia* (22), *Cynanchum* (80; including *Decanema, Folotsia, Karimbolea, Mahafalia, Nematostemma, Platykeleba, Pycnoneurum, Sarcostemma, Vohemaria*), *Gomphocarpus**, *Gymnema* (one), *Leptadenia* (one), *Marsdenia* (seven), *Microloma* (one, probably not native), *Pentatropis* (one), *Stapelianthus* (seven), *Stephanotis* (four), *Telosma* (two), *Vincetoxicum* (five; including *Pleurostelma* [one], and *Tylophora* [four]).

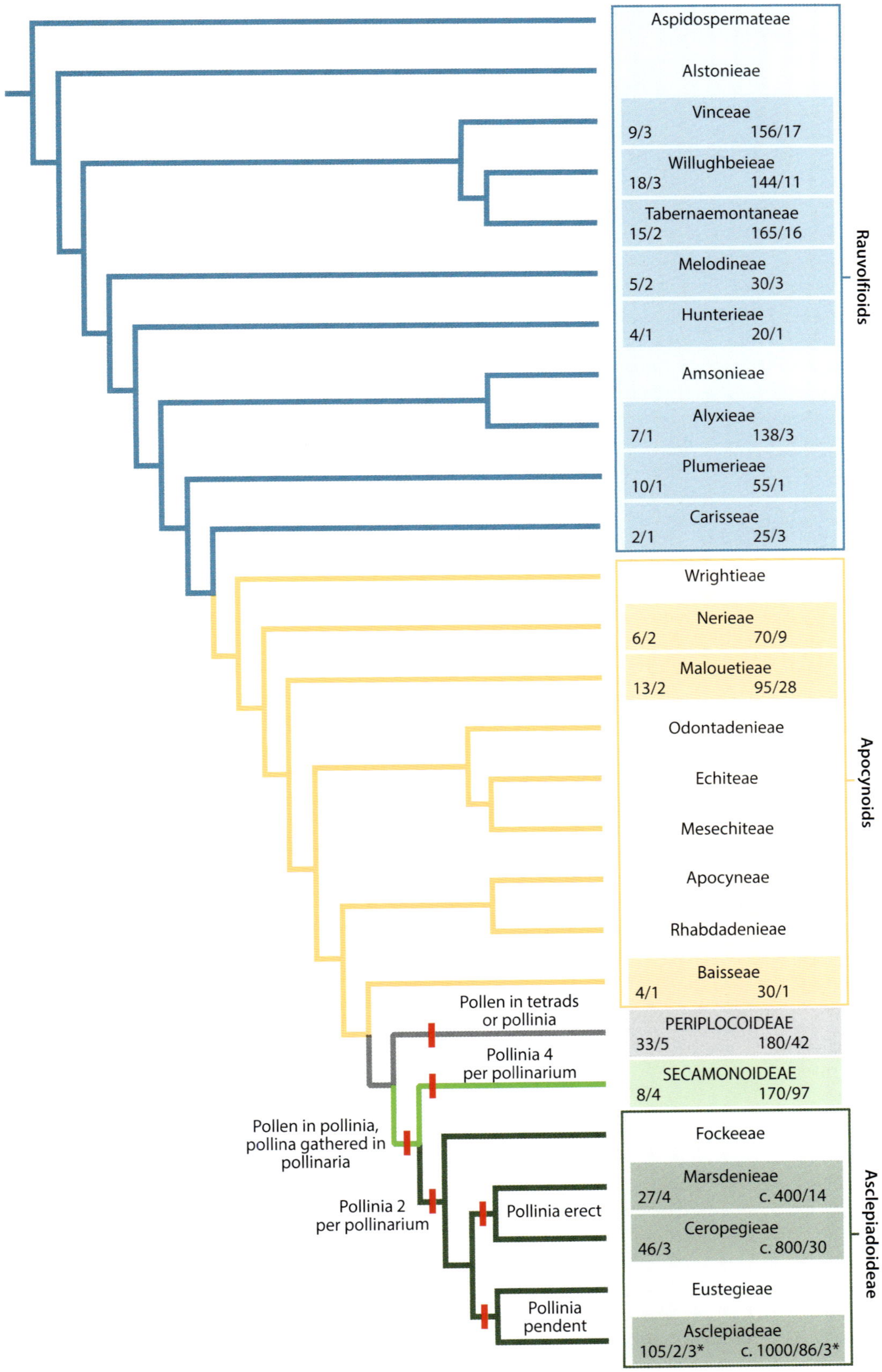

FIGURE 8.86 **Family structure of Apocynaceae, according to Cole (2019). Numbers on the left indicate the total number of genera/number of genera native to Madagascar, and those to the right indicate the total number of species/species native to Madagascar. Naturalized genera/species are indicated by *. Tribes without members on Madagascar are indicated by name only.**

BIOGEOGRAPHIC RELATIONSHIPS OF MALAGASY APOCYNACEAE

Of the 40 genera of Apocynaceae native to Madagascar, 12 (*Baroniella*, *Calyptranthera*, *Craspidospermum*, *Cryptostegia*, *Ischnolepis*, *Pentopetia*, *Pervillaea*, *Plectaneia*, *Secamonopsis*, *Stapelianthus*, *Stephanostegia*, and *Stephanotis*) are endemic to Madagascar, the Comoros, and the Mascarenes—which are defined herein as the Malagasy Region. Of these, *Pentopetia* is the largest with 24 species, followed by *Calyptranthera* (13 species), and *Baroniella* (10 species). In general, the majority of genera in this family occurring on Madagascar show high rates of endemism at the species level (Figure 8.87). However, due to the absence of dated phylogenies, the evolutionary history of these genera in relation to the known paleogeographic history of the island has not yet been assessed (Buerki et al. 2013). The largest radiation in nonendemic genera is found in *Cynanchum* (~80 species), followed by *Secamone* (76 species), *Ceropegia* (22 species), and *Pachypodium* (20 species).

Nevertheless, the available phylogenetic studies allow the description of some patterns in all five major Apocynaceae subdivisions. Among rauvolfioids, some of the Malagasy genera show close ties to the Indian subcontinent (*Catharanthus* and *Petchia*, Simões et al. 2016). The endemic, monotypic *Craspidospermum* is sister to the Asian-Pacific genus *Melodinus* (Fishbein et al. 2018) and the likewise endemic *Plectaneia* is sister to *Pteroalyxia* and *Alyxia*, also distributed throughout tropical Asia and the Pacific (M. E. Endress et al. 2007; Fishbein et al. 2018). *Cerbera* is represented on Madagascar only by the coastal tree *C. manghas*, widespread from the east African coast to Pitcairn Island (Pacific Ocean), and the only member of the genus extending beyond the Asian-Pacific region. Other genera, however, have their closest relatives in Africa (*Rauvolfia*, Simões et al. 2016; *Ancylobothrys*, *Landolphia*, and *Saba*, Morokawa 2014; *Voacanga*, Meve and Liede 2002a; Fishbein et al. 2018). The bitypic *Gonioma* has a single endemic species on Madagascar, and one in southeastern Africa, and is sister to an entirely African clade. For some genera, the closest relatives show an ambiguous pattern—Asia and Africa—(*Tabernaemontana*, Fishbein et al. 2018) or have not yet been included in molecular phylogenies (*Carissa* and *Stephanostegia*).

Among the apocynoids, African relationships are predominant (e.g., *Alafia*, *Oncinotis*, Livshultz et al. 2007). *Pachypodium* has five species in southern Africa and 20 endemic species on Madagascar. However, despite a thorough species-level analysis, it has not yet been clarified whether the genus originated on Madagascar (and spread from there to mainland Africa) or arrived on Madagascar from Africa and underwent an adaptive radiation on the island (Burge et al. 2013). On the other hand, the relationships of *Mascarenhasia*, which has seven species on Madagascar and is almost endemic to the island but reaches east Africa with one species, are clearly tropical Asian (Livshultz et al. 2007). *Strophanthus boivinii*

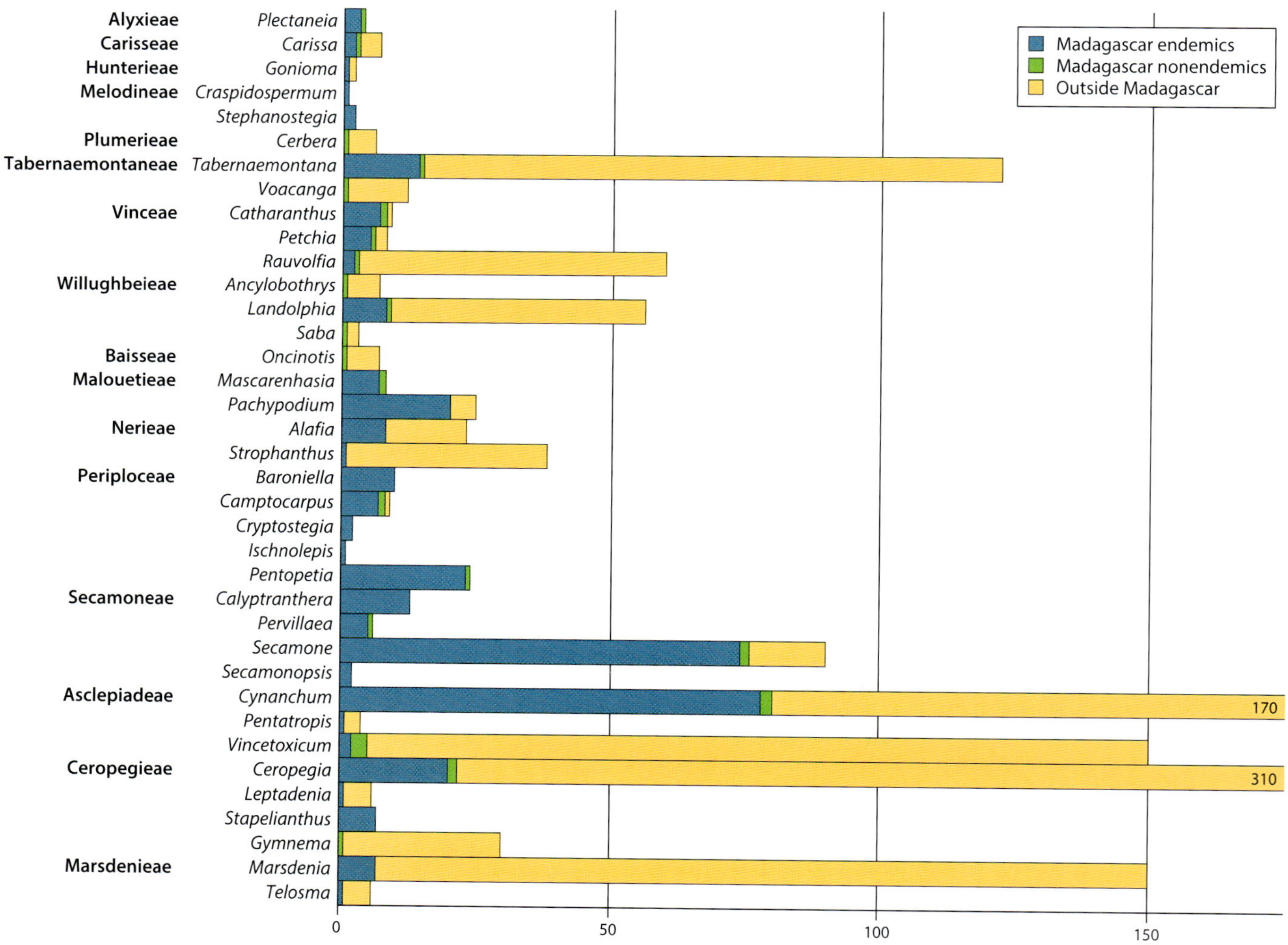

FIGURE 8.87 **Diversity and endemicity diagram of Malagasy Apocynaceae at the level of genera, showing three different species counts: 1) endemic to Madagascar, 2) nonendemic but native to Madagascar, and 3) those occurring elsewhere in the world (for further information see text). In cases when species diversity exceeds or does not conform to that presented on the horizontal graph scale, the figures are written along the respective horizontal line of a given genus.**

is the only Malagasy species in the genus of 38 species (M. E. Endress et al. 2018), and its relationships to African or Asian species are still ambiguous (Livshultz et al. 2007; Fishbein et al. 2018).

A recent molecular study (Joubert et al. 2016) has shown that the five Malagasy Periplocoideae genera are monophyletic inside the clade referred to as the "grooved translator clade". Of the 45 published species, 43 are endemic to Madagascar, and the remaining two extend to other parts of the Malagasy Region but not to mainland Africa. This Malagasy clade branches off second after *Petopentia natalensis*, a monotypic caudiciform genus from eastern South Africa, and is sister to the two top clades of the "grooved translator clade," of which one is Asian, the other one African.

Our knowledge of Secamonoideae is far less detailed, even though this subfamily harbors many Malagasy species and is the second-largest Apocynaceae genus on Madagascar (*Secamone*, Klackenberg 1992). Lahaye et al. (2005) present a phylogenetic tree in which the Malagasy Region endemics *Calyptranthera* (Klackenberg 1996a) and *Pervillaea* (Klackenberg 1996b) form a basal grade in sister-group positon to *Secamonopsis*, *Secamone*, and *Toxocarpus*, suggesting a Malagasy origin for the subfamily. In this phylogenetic tree, Malagasy *Secamone* is not monophyletic, but interspersed with African, Asian, and Australian species, suggesting that the diversity of Malagasy *Secamone* is derived from several lineages; this result is supported by Fishbein et al. (2018) but in need of confirmation from a worldwide phylogenetic study of the subfamily.

Asclepiadoideae is represented on Madagascar by members of the three large tribes, Marsdenieae (four genera), Ceropegieae (three genera), and Asclepiadeae (four or five genera), while the two small tribes Eustegieae and Fockeeae are restricted to mainland Africa (Figure 8.87). For Marsdenieae no published phylogeny is presently available and nothing is known about the relationships of the Malagasy species.

For the Ceropegieae, the position of the single Malagasy species in the small genus *Leptadenia*, distributed from northern Africa to the Indian subcontinent, is still unknown. The seven species of the endemic *Stapelianthus* are monophyletic (Bruyns and Klak 2004) and imbedded in the "soft-stemmed southern clade" of stem-succulent Stapeliads, comprising species of the southern half of Africa (Meve and Liede 2002b). All 22 published Malagasy *Ceropegia* species bear well-developed pitfall-flowers; species with open flowers (*Brachystelma*-type) are absent. Of these, 20 species are endemic to the area (Meve and Liede 2002a). Ten Malagasy species have been included in recent molecular phylogenies (Meve and Liede-Schumann 2007; Bruyns et al. 2015, 2017) and of these, eight form a well-supported monophylum sister to a small east African clade. The two nonendemic species, *C. ampliata* and *C. racemosa*, belong to two different, independent lineages (Bruyns et al. 2015), but both have colonized Madagascar from the African mainland, undergoing tetraploidization on the way (Meve and Liede 2002a).

Of Asclepiadeae, the occurence of *Microloma* (subtribe Astephaninae) is still unsettled, because two old Madagascar herbarium specimens of the southwest African *M. incanum* are extant without any indication that they were prepared from cultivated plants. Beyond this, only two of the 11 subtribes naturally occur on Madagascar. Tylophorinae, lately reduced to only two genera, *Pentatropis* and *Vincetoxicum* (Liede-Schumann et al. 2012, 2016; Liede-Schumann and Meve 2018), is comparatively species poor on the island. All species studied show African affinities, with two species, *P. madagascariensis* (Figure 8.88i) and *V. cernuum*, mainly distributed along the coast. *Vincetoxicum sylvaticum* represents one of the few widespread tropical African species that extended its area of distribution to Madagascar by a long-distance dispersal event (according to Meve and Liede 2002a). The existence of two additional endemic *Vincetoxicum* species is suggested but not yet published (Catalogue of the Plants of Madagascar).

The other subtribe, Cynanchinae, has also been reduced to two genera following molecular analysis (Khanum et al. 2016), the ditypic southeast African *Schizostephanus* and the pantropical *Cynanchum* with ~250 species. *Cynanchum* is the most species-rich Apocynaceae genus on Madagascar, and all 80 Malagasy species are members of a single radiation, which is sister to all other species of the genus. In this radiation, the stem-succulent leafless species form a well-supported clade nested in the leafy species. Here, two instances of a rare dispersal starting from Madagascar can be identified. First, stem-succulent *C. gerrardii*, widespread on Madagascar, has settled along the African east coast (Meve and Liede 2002a) and is starting to diversify there (Meve et al. 2016). Second, in the well-supported group characterized by a double corona of an outer ring and inner staminal lobes (formerly separated as genus *Sarcostemma*), several species and subspecific entities are known all over Africa, tropical Asia, and Australia as far as New Caledonia. However, the evolutionary pathway leading to this radiation, including the question of whether this successful lineage was exported once or several times from Madagascar, is still unclear.

DISTRIBUTION OF APOCYNACEAE ON MADAGASCAR

Members of Apocynaceae are generally found all over the island, with hotspots in the DIANA and SAVA Regions of the north, Alaotra-Mangoro and Atsinanana Regions in the east, and Atsimo-Andrefana and Anosy Regions in the south (Figure 8.89). Closer analysis (details not shown) reveals, though, that the northern and eastern hotspots are settled mainly by rauvolfioids which, except for *Catharanthus*, found mainly in the Central Highlands and toward the south, often prefer forests, woodlands, and thickets of the lowlands or are associated with dunes and strands (*Ancylobothrys*, *Cerbera*, and *Saba*). The southern hotspots, in contrast, are mainly created by the diversity in *Cynanchum*. Combining the high diversity of the rauvolfioids and *Cynanchum*, the Anosy Region is the top hotspot for Apocynaceae.

NEOPHYTES IN AND FROM MADAGASCAR

Several species of Apocynaceae from other parts of the world have become naturalized on Madagascar. *Allamanda cathartica*, a large climbing shrub from tropical America, has been naturalized mainly in northern Madagascar, and the same area has also been invaded by the tropical milkweed, *Asclepias curassavica*, also from tropical America, and the African *Calotropis procera*. *Gomphocarpus fruticosus*, in contrast, is found over the whole island, while *Vincetoxicum indicum*, an Indian species, is only known from Nosy Be.

FIGURE 8.88 **Examples of Malagasy Apocynaceae. A)** ***Pachypodium rutenbergianum*** **bearing a big clump of entangled** ***Cynanchum floriferum*** **(=** ***Folotsia floribunda*****) and a leafy, unidentified** ***Cynanchum*** **on the left side-branch, at Montagne des Français; B)** ***Craspidospermum verticillatum*** **near Brickaville (P. Antilahimena 8002); C)** ***Rauvolfia obtusiflora*** **at Andrafiamena (Z. Burivalova 151); D)** ***Secamone varia*** **at Montagne d'Ambre (S. M. Trigui 024); E)** ***Pentopetia grevii*** **near Toliara (Liede and Conrad 2804); F)** ***Marsdenia brevisquama*** **near Amboasary-Atsimo (D. Ravelonarivo 4582); G)** ***Stapelianthus pilosus*****, without original locality and in horticulture setting; H)** ***Cynanchum implicatum*** **at Ankarana (U. Meve 1176); and I)** ***Pentatropis madagascariense*** **near Toliara (Liede and Conrad 2794).** (PHOTOS A, E, and G–I by U. Meve; B by P. Antilahimena; C by Z. Burivalova; D by S. M. Trigui; and F by D. Ravelonarivo).

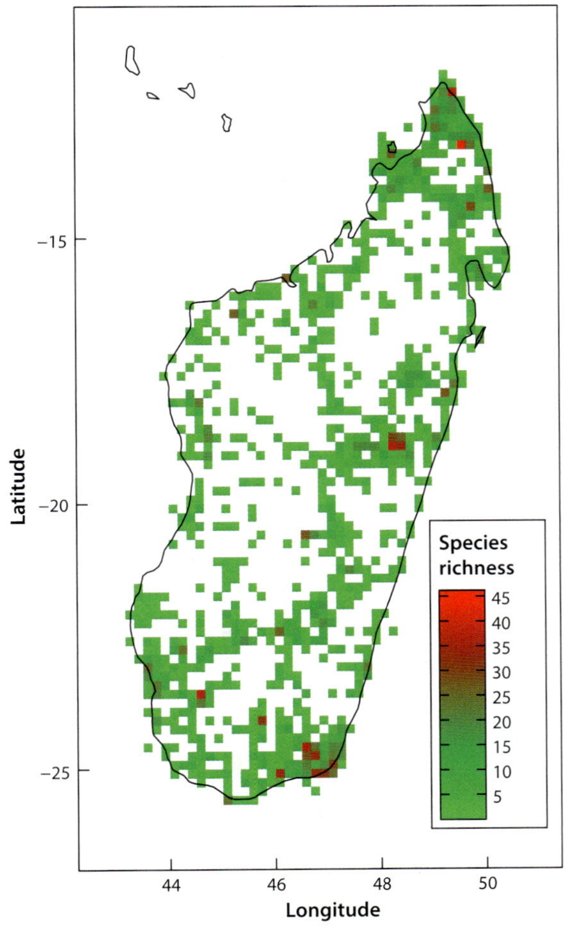

FIGURE 8.89 **Distribution of Apocynaceae on Madagascar. Data derived from the Catalogue of the Plants of Madagascar (rauvolfioids, 2966 data points; apocynoids, 1069 data points; Periplocoideae 705 data points; Secamonoideae 913 data points; and Asclepiadoideae, 1973 data points). Only records identified to species have been included.**

Conversely, few Malagasy Apocynaceae have invaded other parts of the world: foremost is *Cryptostegia grandiflora*, which is a weed in the southern United States and Australia (Camarero 2019 and references therein); to a lesser extent *C. madagascariensis* is fairly common outside Madagascar (USDA Plant Database, https://plants.usda.gov/core/profile?symbol=CRMA10). A few Malagasy plants (e.g., *Catharanthus roseus*, *Stephanotis floribunda*) have conquered the tropics as much-grown ornamentals and occasionally naturalize (e.g., Fosberg 1948) but have hitherto not become invasive.

LIFE FORMS OF MALAGASY APOCYNACEAE

In general, Apocynaceae comprises trees, shrubs, shrublets, lianas, herbaceous twiners with or without a woody base, and erect or decumbent, nontwining herbs with or without leaves. All parts of the plants contain latex in nonarticulated lactifers. The latex is usually white, more rarely yellow or translucent.

Most rauvolfioids constitute trees or large shrubs, but the Willughbeieae (*Ancylobothrys*, *Landolphia*, and *Saba*) comprises woody lianas with curled tendrils and *Catharanthus* is herbaceous, but often basally woody. There is no correlation between the number of endemic species and growth form.

Apocynoids are most often stem-succulents in the genus *Pachypodium*, always with spines at nodes, often with a xylopod, and usually shedding leaves in the dry season. With this often bizarre, drought-adapted growth form, *Pachypodium* includes 20 endemic species. Other less successful forms are large, woody lianas (*Alafia* with eight endemic species) or nontwining shrubs and small trees (*Mascarenhasia* with seven endemic species).

Members of Periplocoideae are most frequently suffrutescent, rarely herbaceous twiners or nontwining shrubs; only *Ischnolepis graminifolia* is a weak shrub with long, grass-like leaves that is very characteristic of grasslands and inselbergs. All Secamonoideae species are lianas, vines, or shrubs.

Asclepiadoideae have a diverse range of growth forms. Most genera adhere to the most frequent growth form in the family, being twiners, which are frequently herbaceous or only very basally suffrutescent.The entirely stem-succulent, low-growing *Stapelianthus* (Figure 8.88g) has diversified to seven endemic species, while *Ceropegia* comprises ~22 endemic species. The largest endemic species group is *Ceropegia* section *Dimorpha*, which includes eight stem-succulents, with or without a small root tuber, while the remainder are twiners with fibrous or tuberous root systems and membraneous or (sub)succulent leaves. In *Cynanchum*, about half of the species show variations of the leafy twining growth form, of which the tuberous, resprouting species of inselbergs are unique in the genus, while the other half are stem-succulents (Figure 8.88h). Two species, *C. pachycladon* and *C. pycnoneuroides*, combine stem-succulence with the possession of leaves, but the majority of stem-succulent species possesses only leaf scales, and the stems take on the function of photosynthesis (Liede 1992). Pachycauls, mainly *Pachypodium*, and stem-succulent *Cynanchum* species (Figure 8.88a), together with succulent members of other plant families, are characteristic of the vegetation of the semiarid south of Madagascar and the inselbergs (Rauh 1995, 1998).

FLOWERS

Most Apocynaceae bear their flowers in many- to few-flowered inflorescences; strictly single-flowered species are rare. Terminal thyrsoidal inflorescences are regarded as the plesiomorphic condition throughout the family; the diversity of inflorescences found in the family results from different degrees of reduction (Liede and Weberling 1995) in combination with different length relationships between peduncle, rhachis, and pedicels. In rauvolfioids and apocynoids inflorescences are usually terminal (e.g., *Ancylobothrys*, *Cerbera*, *Gonioma*, *Rauvolfia*, Figure 8.88c), but often additionally (e.g., *Carissa*, *Landolphia*) or exclusively (e.g., *Pachypodium*) axillary. In *Tabernaemontana* and *Voacanga*, inflorescences usually stand paired in branch forks, and in *Catharanthus* they usually alternate on subsequent nodes. Many-flowered thyrses (e.g., *Craspidospermum*, Figure 8.88b), several-flowered (e.g., *Mascarenhasia*) to few-flowered, fasciculate, or umbelloid cymes (e.g., *Catharanthus*, *Petchia*) are the most common forms encountered. In Periplocoideae, inflorescences are rarely terminal (*Cryptostegia*), usually paired (*Baroniella*), or solitary, but always axillary. In Asclepiadoideae and most Secamonoideae (except for *Secamone*, which produces axillary thyrsoidal inflorescences), the extra-axillary inflorescence position of most species is interpreted as a terminal inflorescence with cymosely branched partial inflorescences displaced into a lateral position by the development of the stronger of the two vegetative buds (Liede and Weberling 1995). In both subfamilies, simple inflorescences are most frequent. In some species of *Vincetoxicum* (e.g., *V. sylvaticum*), one branch of the sympodial system supports the continuation of the inflorescence, while the other one produces a more or less dense bostryx, resulting in a loose, somewhat zigzagging inflorescence. The frequent and characteristic geminiflorous helices found in *Cynanchum* can also be attributed to the same construction process, with the bostryx reduced to a single flower. Frequently, a shortening of the internodes results in a sciadioidal inflorescence (Weberling 1989: Figure 146VI), often incorrectly termed as a pseudo-umbelliferous or umbelliferous inflorescence.

Flowers of Apocynaceae species show the highest degree of synorganization in dicotyledonous angiosperms and have therefore been termed "orchids of the dicotyledons" (P. K. Endress 2016). A uniform and highly determined phyllotaxis, resulting in an almost constant number and arrangement of floral parts throughout the family, is a predisposition for both tangential, circumferential synorganization among the organs of a whorl (synsepaly, sympetaly, synstemony, and syncarpy) and sectorial synorganization (in Apocynaceae, as in Orchidaceae, between stamens and carpels). Apocynaceae flowers are almost always pentamerous, with each type of organ arranged in a whorl except for the gynoecium, which is composed of two carpels. Calyx and a corolla are always present, though either may be minute. Corolla lobes are normally contorted and the direction of contortion is a systematically important character (M. E. Endress et al. 1990). Dextrorse aestivation is found in all groups except for rauvolfioids, which are sinistrorse. The degree of fusion between the corolla lobes is decisive for both appearance and functionality of the flower, and flowers with long-tubular corollas have evolved in various subfamilies and tribes (e.g, *Mascarenhasia*, *Cryptostegia*, *Ceropegia*).

The corona is an important feature of the flower, and can be simple to very elaborate outgrowths. Depending on their location, they may be grouped into two main types, corolline (in most rauvolfioids, apocynoids, and Periplocoideae, Kunze 1990; Figure 8.88e) and gynostegial (Asclepiadoideae and most Secamonoideae; Figure 8.88d). Gynostegial coronas, which have their origin as outgrowths (emergences) from the back of the stamens, are interstaminal elements (usually combined with the staminal elements) and are apomorphic in Asclepiadoideae (Kunze 1990). A system of classification of the multitude of sometimes extravagant corona forms has been developed by Liede and Kunze (1993). Basic corona composition (e.g., whether it is just in the staminal sector, or in both staminal and interstaminal sectors) has been used widely for recognizing larger taxonomic categories, but has been found to be misleading in several examples (e.g., *Cynanchum* [former *Sarcostemma*], Liede and Täuber 2000) because of frequent parallelisms.

Stamens are morphologically clearly differentiated into anther and filament in rauvolfioids, apocynoids, and Periplocoideae, but anthers are (almost) sessile on a tube in Secamonoideae and Asclepiadoideae. Anthers are introrse and each anther contains two thecae with two pollen sacs, except for Asclepiadoideae, in which the dorsal pollen sac in each theca has been lost, so that in each anther only the two ventral pollen sacs develop. In rauvolfioids and apocynoids, pollen is usually shed as monads and tetrads in all Malagasy Periplocoideae (S. Nilsson et al. 1993). In Secamonoideae and Asclepiadoideae, pollen is combined in pollinia; in Secamonoideae, four pollinia are produced in each anther, whereas in Asclepiadoideae, only two pollinia are produced (Civeyrel et al. 1998).

Lignified anther margins (anther wings) are present in apocynoids, Secamonoideae, and Asclepiadoideae. The anther wings of adjacent anthers are separated only by a narrow slit and are synorganized to function as guide rails, steering the pollinator's proboscis or leg into the pollination unit. The anthers are postgenitally united with the style-head forming a gynostegium (except in rauvolfioids). This results in a pentamerous revolver flower (i.e., a radial flower with more than one access to nectar, that has to be probed to exploit the entire nectar content) with five separate nectar/pollination chambers.

The majority of genera produce nectar. Distinct nectary lobes are found in rauvolfioids and some apocynoids. In most genera, nectar is secreted by specialized patches of epithelium, which are found in five pockets (chambers) on the staminal tube beneath the guide rail bases (Kunze 1997). In most Periplocoideae, nectar is secreted on the sides of the thickened corona lobes (or the region between them) below the filament. In Asclepiadoideae, nectar is frequently collected and presented in cups formed by the gynostegial corona.

The gynoecium is composed of two carpels and is apocarpous, except in Willughbeieae (*Ancylobothrys*, *Landolphia*, and *Saba*) and Carisseae (*Carissa*), for which congenital syncarpy is characteristic. Usually, the gynoecium is differentiated into ovaries, style and style-head, but the style is lacking in most Asclepiadoideae. In genera with apocarpous gynoecia, the carpel apices undergo a temporary postgenital fusion where the flanks of the two carpels come together. The upper part of the postgenitally fused region develops into an enlarged style-head, the sometimes elaborate apices of which contribute to flower attraction and pollinator control (e.g., *Vincetoxicum cernuum*, *Cynanchum eurychiton*). Generally, the stigmatic region is located beneath or on the lower half of the style-head, and in Asclepiadoideae it is restricted to five stigmatic chambers on the underside of the style-head, alternating with the stamens and behind the guide rails. In almost all genera of Apocynaceae, the style-head is differentiated into zones, and the five regions between the adnate anthers secrete the adhesive used in pollen transport. In Periplocoideae, Secamonoideae, and Asclepiadoideae these secretions harden into acellular bodies called translators, which aid in the transport of pollen.

In Periplocoideae, differentiation of the two adhesive components is both temporal and spatial. The firmer adhesive component forms a firm spoonlike translator, which is differentiated into three regions: a broad pollen-presenting scoop, which is an inwardly rolled stalk; a broadened, flattened base; and a foamy component that helps pollen tetrads adhere to the scoop on the one end and the translator adhere to the pollinator on the other. In Secamonoideae and Asclepiadoideae, the translators are formed from the firmer secretory components (Schick 1982; Kunze et al. 1994) and differentiate into a hard clip-like corpuscle to which the pollinia are attached. In Asclepiadoideae, additionally, two slender, more flexible arms (caudicles) are secreted by which the pollinia are attached to the corpuscle (Kunze et al. 1994). In *Secamonopsis*, slender threadlike caudicles are present (Civeyrel 1995). Thus, in Secamonoideae and Asclepiadoideae, pollinia of neighboring anthers are joined in a pollinarium. Details of pollinaria morphology are the basis of tribal delimitation in Asclepiadoideae. Marsdenieae and Ceropegieae have erect pollinia, and in Ceropegieae sterile insertion crests are always present on the inner pollinium side. Asclepiadeae almost always have pendent pollinia (with the exception of *Cynanchum verrucosum*, which was formerly placed in the genus *Karimbolea* for this reason).

REPRODUCTIVE BIOLOGY AND POLLINATION

Flowers of Apocynaceae are bisexual throughout, although rare cases of functional dioecy have been reported. The flowers are protandrous. The complex flower construction suggests that the family is predominantly out-crossing (P. Albers and Van der Maesen 1994). Almost all Apocynaceae species are entomophilous, but very rare cases of ornithophily have been reported (Pauw 1998). A wide variety of pollinator guilds is employed, with flies (myiophily) and wasps (sphecophily) being the most commonly found pollinators in Asclepiadoideae; but butterflies (psychophily), hawk moths and nocturnal Lepidoptera (sphingophily and phalaenophily) also can act as pollinators. A survey of pollination patterns in Apocynaceae is reported on by Ollerton et al. (2019).

The floral reward is consistently nectar (Galetto 1997), but in some Ceropegieae (*Stapelianthus*) no floral reward is produced and pollination is by deceit as the visual and olfactory clues promise a reward but provide none (Meve and Liede 1994). In rauvolfioids and apocynoids night-flowering occurs sporadically in many tribes, whereas in Asclepiadoideae night-flowering seems to be restricted to Marsdenieae (*Stephanotis* and *Telosma*) and Asclepiadeae (*Vincetoxicum*), though it may occur more frequently.

The pollination mechanism of the Apocynaceae is complex and centers around the specialized secretions produced by the style-head. In rauvolfioids and apocynoids, in which the secretions usually remain undifferentiated, the most common flower shape is a salverform corolla with a constricted orifice (e.g., Figure 8.88c), although large infundibuliform corollas, which serve to protect the delicate pollen from desiccation, can be found in genera that have anthers with hardened guide rails. The inner surface of the corolla tube often has various sorts of emergences (e.g., corona lobes, protruding ridges below the stamens, rings or ridges, etc.), which guide the proboscis of the pollinating insect into one of the five nectar channels of the revolver flower construction.

In Periplocoideae (Figure 8.88e), the floral structure is usually more open, and the secretions harden into distinctly shaped translators. Here the nectar is generally openly presented in shallow pockets into which the insect can crawl or easily reach with its proboscis. Dangling directly above the nectar pocket is the sticky base of the translator, which becomes stuck to the pollinator. When the pollinator flies away, it pulls the translator (and its load of pollen tetrads) free from the style-head. When it visits the next flower, some pollen will hopefully be rubbed off in the vicinity of the nectar pocket, which is also the stigmatic region (S. Nilsson et al. 1993). In Secamonoideae and Asclepiadoideae the construction is reminiscent of that in apocynoids (Safwat 1962), with the proboscis or leg of the pollinator being caught between the guide rails of adjacent anthers (Kunze 1991). In order to free itself it must proceed upwards. In these two subfamilies the corpuscle constitutes a hard, narrow clamp into which the proboscis or leg is threaded and becomes wedged. In order to escape, the insect must pull the corpuscle (with its attached pollinia) free from the style-head. When it visits the next flower, pollination is achieved when a pollinium becomes wedged in one of the five pollination chambers, which lie just behind the narrow slit between the guide rails. Occasionally the entire pollinium is inserted into the pollination chamber, but usually just a basal or apical part of the pollinium; in species with an insertion crest, only the crest is inserted.

Despite the wide variety of floral sizes, shapes, colors, and constructions indicating that pollination is a major driver of evolution, very little is known about pollination in Malagasy Apocynaceae. In Periplocoideae, *Cryptostegia madagascariensis* has been observed to be pollinated by sphingids (Walther 1994) and by carpenter bees of the genus *Xylocopa* by S. Vogel (Ollerton et al. 2019). In four species of *Secamone* (*S. buxifolia*, *S. geayi*, *S. mintifolia*, and *S. sparsiflora*), L. Civeyrel (Ollerton et al. 2019) has observed bees, wasps, butterflies, and hawkmoths at the flowers. Diptera are known to constitute the main pollinators of the trap-flowers of *Ceropegia*, and Malagasy *Ceropegia* is no exception. *Desmometopa interfronatalis* has been observed with pollinia at *C. ambovombensis* (Ollerton et al. 2009), and other Milichiidae and a Cecidomyiidae have been observed at *C. albisepta*, Sciaridae at *C. madagascariensis* and *C. petignatii*, and Chloropidae at *C. scabra* and an unidentified *Ceropegia* species (Ollerton et al. 2009, 2017). In addition, a Nematocera has been observed at *C. madagascariensis*, and a Mymaridae at *C. scabra* (Ollerton et al. 2009).

Even more scarce are data on *Cynanchum*. W. Rauh (1995) observed a danaid butterfly on *C. floriferum* (*Folotsia floribunda*), and R. Mangelsdorff (Ollerton et al. 2019) saw a species of Diptera on *C. phillipsonianum*. P. Phillipson (Ollerton et al. 2019) observed a sphecid wasp on *C. itremense*, and U. Meve (unpublished data) photographed a scoliid wasp working the flowers of *C. obovatum*, one of the most widespread species of *Cynanchum* on Madagascar (see also Ollerton 2019). S. Liede-Schumann (unpublished data) observed a tiger moth (subfamily Arctiinae) on *C. analamazaotrense*.

FRUITS, SEEDS, AND DISPERSAL

Except for rauvolfioids, wind dispersal is the rule for the majority of Apocynaceae, with the dispersal unit being the comose seed. Malagasy rauvolfioids possess a wide variety of fruits. *Tabernaemontana* and *Voacanga* produce leathery, often paired, follicles with thick spongy mesocarp (follicarium) containing numerous seeds with pulpy, white, gray, yellow, or red arils, which are sometimes edible (e.g., *T. retusa*, Styger et al. 1999). The follicarium of *T. stellata* is distributed by birds (Albert-Daviaud et al. 2020). Drupaceous fruits are found in *Carissa*, *Cerbera*, *Petchia*, *Plectaneia*, and *Rauvolfia*, while *Ancylobothrys*, *Landolphia*, and *Saba* produce colorful berries. The highly poisonous drupes of *Cerbera* are adapted to water dispersal, possessing a thick, spongy mesocarp. In contrast, the drupes of *Carissa boiviniana* (identified as *C. sessiliflora* in Styger et al. 1999) are highly appreciated as fruit (*voatsikopika*) by local people, and those of *C. spinosa* (identified as *C. edulis* in Styger et al. 1999) and *Petchia cryptophlebia* are also consumed (Styger et al. 1999). Berries of several *Landolphia* species are consumed by people (Styger et al. 1999) and are also consumed and dispersed by lemurs (Birkinshaw 2001), as are the drupes of some *Petchia* (Razafindratsima and Dunham 2016) and *Plectaneia* species (Razafindratsima et al. 2014). In *Gonioma* and *Stephanostegia* the paired follicles are dry, and the likewise dry seeds are surrounded by a papery wing or flattened, fringed emergences around the margin in *Craspidospermum*, and thus adapted to wind disperal. The wingless seeds produced by the dry follicles of the low-growing *Catharanthus* simply fall down next to the mother plant, or are occasionally transported by ants (Plaizier 1981).

In all other groups, the bicarpellate, apocarpous gynoecium results in a fruit that is apocarpous and consists of a pair of follicles (mericarps), each one of which dehisces at maturity along the ventral suture, releasing the seeds. In some of the pollinium-forming genera, a compitum (a common base of the stylar channels [Kunze 1991]) allows fertilization of both ovaries by a single pollinium (e.g., *Secamone,* most *Vincetoxicum*), resulting in the regular formation of two mericarps, while in others (e.g., *Cynanchum*) the two stylar channels are strictly separated so that insertion of a single pollinium results in a single mericarp.

In the majority of genera the follicles are slenderly fusiform or linear and nonfleshy, and occasionally woody at maturity. In some genera of Asclepiadoideae (e.g., *Marsdenia*) the follicles can be rather stout and are often winged. The pericarp (fruit wall) is most commonly smooth, but can be covered by a dense indument (e.g., *Pervillaea tomentosa*); roughened with dense, short, conical projections (e.g., *M. verrucosa*); tuberculate (e.g., *M. brevisquama*); or possess two to three undulate wings (e.g., *Cynanchum danguyanum* and relatives).

The number of seeds per follicle is highly variable, ranging from one to a few hundred. Except in rauvolfioids, seeds in Apocynaceae are generally small, lightweight, and almost always have a coma at one end. In Periplocoideae the coma is often yellowish, while it is silky and white in Secamonoideae and almost all Asclepiadoideae. Fruits and seeds of Asclepiadoideae are often parasitized by Tephritidae (Landolt 1994; Meve 1995; Solbreck 2000). The testa of the cylindrical to flat seeds of Periplocoideae, Secamonoideae, and Asclepiadoideae can be smooth, papillate, distinctly tuberculate or hairy; further, in many species the seeds are distinctly winged.

KARYOLOGY

Karyological information, on a worldwide scale, is available for about half of genera in Apocynaceae. The basic chromosome number of x = 11 is predominant, and is found in 60% of the genera of rauvolfioids and apocynoids (Van der Laan and Arends 1985), all counted Periplocoideae and Secamonoideae, and 96% of the genera of Asclepiadoideae (F. Albers and Meve 1991, 2001). In rauvolfioids and apocynoids polyploidy has been reported in nine genera (~13%), and in Asclepiadoideae with ~6% of the taxa, with tetraploidy being by far the most common condition (cf. F. Albers and Meve 2001; M. E. Endress et al. 2018).

Of Malagasy Rauvolfioideae, chromosome numbers are known, with 2n = 16 (32) for *Catharanthus*, and 2n = 22 for *Carissa* species (see compilation in Van der Laan and Arends 1985). For Malagasy Apocynoideae, counts are only available for *Pachypodium* (with 2n = 18 throughout [e.g., Schill and Leuenberger 1972]).

The homogeneity of the karyotypes of Periplocoideae and Secamonoideae with 2n = 22 throughout is confirmed by the few counts available for Malagasy species: *Camptocarpus mauritianus* (F. Albers and Meve 2001, under *C. crassifolius*), *Cryptostegia madagascariensis* (F. Albers and Meve 2001), and *C. grandiflora* (Navaneetham 1981), and *Ischnolepis graminifolium*, *Pentopetia albicans*, and *P. grevii* (U. Meve, unpublished data), as well as the only count for Malagasy Secamonoideae, *Pervillaea venenata* (U. Meve, unpublished data).

The same holds true for most Asclepiadoideae, for which many Malagasy endemics of *Ceropegia*, *Cynanchum*, and *Stapelianthus*, as well as *Marsdenia verrucosa* and *Pentatropis madagascariense* have been confirmed as diploids with 2n = 22 (cf. F. Albers and Meve 2001). However, in *Ceropegia*, the Malagasy subspecies of *C. ampliata* and *C. racemosa* are tetraploids with 2n = 44, whereas the autonymous African subspecies are diploids in both cases (cf. Meve and Liede 2002a; Meve 2010).

PHYTOCHEMISTRY AND USES

Apocynaceae is well known as a family whose members contain poisonous and bioactive compounds; these evolved as a response to attacks by microorganisms or herbivores experienced by the plants (e.g., Wink 2020). In rauvolfioids, taxa in seven of the 11 tribes produce a vast array of monoterpenoid indole alkaloids (M. E. Endress et al. 2018). On Madagascar, *Catharanthus* (Vinceae), in particular, is known for its pharmacological potency, and *C. roseus* is now grown in many tropical areas as an ornamental and medicinal plant. It contains more than 400 different alkaloids, of which vinblastine and vincristine show considerable anticancer properties, and vindoline, vindolidine, vindolicine, and vindolinine are used as antidiabetics (Das and Sharangi 2017).

However, in three rauvolfioid tribes (Carisseae, Plumerieae, and Alyxieae) indole alkaloids have been lost, and the role of protection against predators has been taken over by other secondary metabolites (M. E. Endress et al. 2018). The leaves and fruits of *Cerbera manghas* (Plumerieae) contain the potent cardiac glycoside cerberin and other glycosidic steroids, which are extremely poisonous if ingested. On Madagascar, the seeds were used in ordeals called *tangena*, the native name of the tree, with often deadly results (Carlier et al. 2014).

In Periplocoideae, Secamonoideae, and Asclepiadoideae steroidal glycosides are the most important components, but cardenolides are also widespread (M. E. Endress et al. 2018). The two *Cryptostegia* species, which are invasive in many tropical areas, are used more intensively in their introduced areas (e.g., El-Ghani 2016; Singh and Shahi 2017) than on Madagascar, where they are sometimes utilized for criminal purposes because of their toxicity (Boiteau and Allorge-Boiteau 1997; Neuwinger 1994).

Among secamonoids, *Pervillaea venenata* is rich in cardiotonic heteroside, namely digitoxigenine. Nevertheless, it was used as purgative and emetic, and the grated root is employed to treat several ailments. The main use, however, is for trial by ordeal, and criminal and suicide poisoning (Gurib-Fakim and Brendler 2004, as *Menabea venenata*).

In Asclepiadoideae, glycosides and esters with pregnane skeletons are widely distributed (M. E. Endress et al. 2018), but only a few local uses have been reported from Madagascar (e.g., *Leptadenia madagascariensis*, Gurib-Fakim and Brendler 2004). Heavily used is the naturalized *Gomphocarpus fruticosus*, known for its cardenolides (Boiteau and Allorge-Boiteau 1997).

In addition to pharmacological use, many species (e.g., species of *Landolphia*, *Mascarenhasia*, and *Cryptostegia*, and *Plectaneia thouarsii*, *Pentopetia grevei*, and *Secamonopsis madagascariensis*) are sources of rubber (Canaby 1932) and used as tying material (e.g., *Alafia nigrescens*, *Cryptostegia* species), and many tree species are esteemed for their timber (e.g., *Craspidospermum verticillatum*) (Fern and Fern 2014 onward). Finally, the ornamental value of several species (e.g., *Catharanthus roseus*, *Ceropegia* sp., *Strophanthus boivinii*, *Pachypodium* sp., *Cryptostegia* sp., *Stephanotis* sp.) needs to be mentioned.

CONSERVATION

Of the 359 taxa of Apocynaceae (335 species, 16 subspecies, and eight varieties) listed in the Catalogue of the Plants of Madagascar, 27% (96 taxa) are known only from a single locality, and another 25% (91 taxa) from less than four localities. Many of the species known from a single locality may possibly be extinct, as in several cases the only record dates back more than 50 years. About a third (116 taxa) are known from five to 20 localities, and only 15% (56 taxa) are known from more than 20 localities, including 11 common taxa with more than 50 localities (Figure 8.90). Most genera harbor both reasonably common and rare taxa, but an exception is *Calyptranthera*, for which all species seem rare.

International Union for Conservation of Nature (IUCN) Red List assessments (IUCN 2020) are available for 80 species. Of these, 35 are listed as of Least Concern; 14 as Vulnerable (*Baroniella* [one], *Camptocarpus* [one], *Gonioma* [one], *Mascarenhasia* [one] *Pachypodium* [three], *Pentopetia* [three], *Stephanotis* [one], *Tabernaemontana* [three]); two as Near Threatened (*Baroniella* [one], *Secamone* [one]); 24 as Endangered (*Baroniella* [one], *Calyptranthera* [one], *Camptocarpus* [one], *Cynanchum* [three], *Mascarenhasia* [two], *Pachypodium* [two], *Pentopetia* [seven], *Petchia* [one], *Rauvolfia* [one] *Secamone* [four], *Tabernaemontana* [one]); four as Critically Endangered (*Camptocarpus* [one], *Pachypodium* [two], *Tabernaemontana* [one]); and one species as Possibly Extinct (*Camptocarpus cornutus*). The long-term future for species with these conservation statuses is uncertain. The remaining species have not yet been assessed, but similar percentages of threatened species are likely. While in most cases habitat destruction for various reasons (logging, fire, agriculture, settlements, and mining) is the primary cause for the decline of species, for *Pachypodium* illegal collecting and horticultural trade play important roles, even though three species are protected by Appendix I of the Convention on International Trade in Endangered Species of Wild Fauna and Flora (CITES 2020), and all remaining species by CITES (2020) Appendix 2.

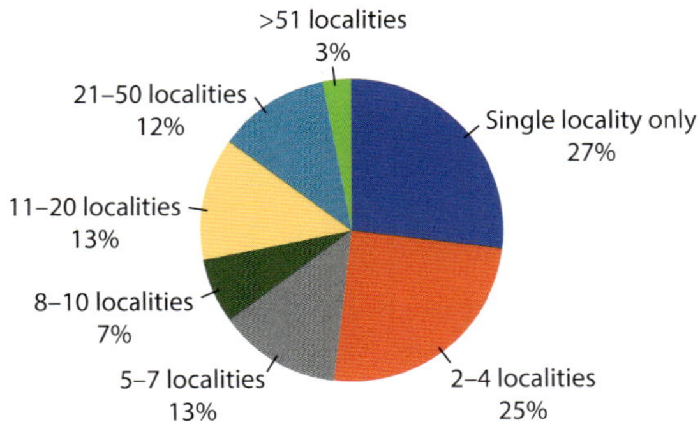

FIGURE 8.90 Frequency of Apocynaceae species on Madagascar (N_{taxa} = 359: 335 species, 16 subspecies, and eight varieties). Data derived from the Catalogue of the Plants of Madagascar.

ACKNOWLEDGMENTS

For the data used to produce the distribution maps, I owe gratitude to Peter B. Phillipson, Missouri Botanical Garden. For production of the map, thanks are due to Samuel Hoffman of the Biogeography Department of University of Bayreuth. For stimulating discussions, unpublished data, photographs, and help with the layout of a figure, I owe gratitude to Ulrich Meve, Department of Plant Systematics, University of Bayreuth.

Subject editors: Laurent Gautier and Steven M. Goodman

OLEACEAE, OLIVES

C. Hong-Wa, G. Besnard, J. Salmona, C. Frasier, P. B. Phillipson, and G. E. Schatz

A medium-size family of 27 genera worldwide, of which one is extinct, and nearly 700 species, Oleaceae's representatives are found in temperate and tropical areas throughout the world. Members of the family can be easily recognized by their estipulate, opposite, simple or compound leaves; actinomorphic flowers that are typically tetramerous and often bearing two stamens, fused sepals and petals, two-lobed superior ovary; and bacciform, capsular, drupaceous, or samara fruits. Despite its moderate size, the family is remarkable for the economic significance of several of its members as a source of food and oil (*Olea*); craft materials and timber (*Fraxinus*, *Olea*, and *Syringa*); fragrance (*Jasminum* and *Osmanthus*); herbal medicines (*Chionanthus*, *Ligustrum*, and *Osmanthus*); and ornamentals (*Forsythia*, *Jasminum*, *Ligustrum*, *Syringa*, etc.).

Taxonomic information for the Malagasy Oleaceae dates as far back as the late 18th century, with the earliest descriptions of three native species by Lamarck (1791). However, for more than 150 years, it advanced only by sporadic work (e.g., Du Petit-Thouars 1806; J. G. Baker 1881) that did not crystallize into a comprehensive synthesis until Perrier de la Bâthie first published a treatment for the entire family on Madagascar (1949a). Today, five genera are recognized on the island: *Comoranthus*, *Jasminum*, *Noronhia*, *Olea*, and *Schrebera*. Published accounts on their uses are scarce and the family rather lacks a tangible economic importance on the island despite common usage in traditional medicine and beliefs as well as in construction. Perrier de la Bâthie (1949b) mentioned some potential large-scale uses for various taxa and noted, in particular, the oleiferous property of two northern species, but cautioned also against the exploitation of already rare and threatened taxa.

More recently, the ecological importance of Malagasy Oleaceae in supporting the native fauna has advanced through dietary and feeding behavior studies of different species of birds (e.g., *Coracopsis*, *Hypsipetes*, *Nesoenas*), diurnal and nocturnal lemurs (e.g., *Eulemur*, *Lemur*, *Microcebus*, *Varecia*), and rodents (e.g., endemic *Eliurus*, introduced *Rattus*) (Birkinshaw 2001; Bollen and van Elsacker 2004; Radespiel 2007; Moses and Semple 2011). The berries and drupes of *Jasminum*, *Noronhia*, and *Olea* are consumed mostly ripe but sometimes also unripe, and, in general, the seeds are swallowed although some of the consumers behave more as predators than as dispersers (e.g., *Coracopsis*; Bollen and van Elsacker 2004). The capsular fruits of *Comoranthus* and *Schrebera* are also possibly eaten when fresh, but the presence of winged seeds suggests that dispersal in these two genera is anemochorous. Unlike dispersal, knowledge of pollination biology in Malagasy Oleaceae is hampered by a lack of systematic study, but it certainly involves insects. The typically short-tubed flowers of *Noronhia* and *Olea* are likely pollinated by bees and other short-tongued insects, while the long-tubed and fragrant flowers of *Jasminum* and *Schrebera* are probably moth pollinated and could possibly attract small bats although the scarcity of nectar on these flowers may preclude bat pollination.

DIVERSITY

Currently, 99 native species of Oleaceae are recognized from Madagascar, which represent approximately 15% of the family's species diversity worldwide and twice that of the entire African continent. The bulk of the diversity on Madagascar can be attributed to a single genus, *Noronhia*, with 83 known species, and which is more diverse on the island than anywhere else, while the other genera only have two to nine representatives (Table 8.47). The contrast in diversity between *Noronhia* and the other Malagasy Oleaceae genera is quite remarkable given that each seemingly colonized the island during approximately the same period (Hong-Wa and Besnard 2013; Olofsson et al. 2019), and thus all lineages have had an equal amount of time to diversify, although the date of arrival of *Jasminum* is still unknown. These genera also co-occur within the same bioclimatic zones (Table 8.47; see also Madagascar Catalogue

TABLE 8.47. **Diversity and endemism of Oleaceae in Madagascar**

GENUS	TOTAL DESCRIBED NATIVE SPECIES	ENDEMIC SPECIES (% PER GENUS)	BIOCLIMATIC ZONES OCCUPIED
Comoranthus	3	2 (67%)	DRY, SBA, SBH
Jasminum	8	7 (88%)	DRY, HUM, SBA, SBH
Noronhia	83	82 (99%)	DRY, HUM, MON, SBA, SBH
Olea	2	0 (0%)	DRY, HUM, MON, SBH
Schrebera	3	2 (67%)	DRY, HUM, MON, SBA, SBH
Total	99	93	

Note: Bioclimatic zone: DRY, dry; HUM, humid; MON, Montane; SBA, subarid; SBH, subhumid.

2020), which comprise the dry, humid, montane, subarid, and subhumid zones as defined by Schatz (2000, after Cornet 1974). This suggests that time and macroclimate alone cannot explain the stark difference in diversity between *Noronhia* and its Malagasy confamilials and that other factors, such as key innovations (e.g., floral pigmentation and corolla shape variation in *Noronhia*, suiting a broad range of pollinators), have likely influenced variation in diversification rates among these lineages.

Far from being among the larger plant families on the island, the Oleaceae is nonetheless a common element of the native vegetation, frequently occupying the understory of moist evergreen and dry deciduous forests, but sometimes reaching into the canopy, or being prominent dwellers in grasslands and thickets, where they can form dense populations. Species richness varies greatly among the five bioclimatic zones, with the dry and humid zones both harboring the highest number of species of Oleaceae, whereas the montane bioclimatic zone only has a few of them. Similarly, there is considerable variation in species composition, with many species unique to a given bioclimatic zone. However, some widespread species occur in two or more adjacent zones; these are usually the ones that reach into montane areas, such as *N. similis*.

The non-native oleaceous species of Madagascar that are cultivated for timber, hedging, or for ornament, belong primarily to the genera *Fraxinus* and *Ligustrum*; they are few and have been introduced recently. They are also mostly localized in the Central Highlands, centered on Antananarivo. Although there is less likelihood of the species that are cultivated sparingly, such as *F. chinensis* and *F. pennsylvanica*, becoming invasive, the risk is higher for the more widely cultivated *L. lucidum* and *L. vulgare*. These species are established in disturbed habitats (García-Robledo and Murcia 2005; Dreyer et al. 2019) and can probably colonize areas around the capital city and beyond, given ongoing environmental changes and enough time. As such, they could become more problematic in the future. By contrast, *Jasminum sambac*, an introduced tropical Asian species, which arrived around the late 1800s or early 1900s, has only been collected from gardens. Thus, it may not have naturalized yet, although the paucity of preserved specimens does not necessarily help to ascertain its presence or absence from natural habitats.

ENDEMISM

Endemism in Malagasy Oleaceae is high, with 93 of the 99 currently recognized species being unique to Madagascar (Figure 8.91, Table 8.47), highlighting the family's unique evolutionary history on the island and its significance as a lineage of conservation interest. Within each genus, endemism ranges from 0 to 99%, with *Noronhia* having the highest rate, while *Olea* lacks any species endemic to Madagascar, at least under current circumscriptions. Other than *Olea*, all genera show a level of endemism above 60%, and while most genera are represented in different parts of the world, *Comoranthus* is strictly endemic to Madagascar and the adjacent Comoro islands.

Of the five genera of Oleaceae on Madagascar, both *Jasminum* and *Noronhia* are geographically widespread on the island, whereas the other three taxa exhibit a somewhat longitudinal distribution pattern, occurring mostly in either the more humid eastern (*Olea* and *Schrebera*) or drier western (*Comoranthus*) parts. Moreover, there is an obvious pattern of ecological adaptation, with 50 species considered to be specialists occurring only in a single bioclimatic zone. Most of these specialists are found in the humid bioclimatic zone, and in decreasing numbers in the dry, subhumid, and subarid zones, while none occur in the montane bioclimatic zone. In general, species of the Central Highlands are localized in pockets of remnant forests toward the northern part of this region or present in shrublands toward its southern portion.

Some species are known to have a very restricted range. Indeed, Oleaceae occupy a diversity of habitats from sea level to above 2000 m and some species are specialists on specific substrates. For instance, *N. lowryi* is found only on marble or quartzite from Ibity to Itremo in the Central Highlands, while *N. planifolia* grows only on limestone and old lava flows at Ankarana. Within *Jasminum*, *J. pteropodum* has only been recorded from basaltic or calcareous rocks around the Plateau d'Ankara and Antsalova in the west. Thus, the pattern of microendemism observed in Malagasy Oleaceae, which reflects also a more general pattern within the Malagasy flora, may have resulted from rapid and/or recent, adaptive evolution (Hong-Wa and Besnard 2014). It seems that an interplay among topography, climate, and substrate may have favored such localized diversification. However, hybridization and polyploidization, which appear to have been rather common within some genera (e.g., *Noronhia*, *Olea*), may have also played a major role in the geographic modes of speciation and subsequent patterns of distribution of the Malagasy Oleaceae (Hong-Wa and Besnard 2014). Additionally, the types of dispersal agents on which the Oleaceae species depend, and different aspects of their natural history, may also limit their range expansion, at least in part associated with short-distance dispersal of fruits and seeds (Salmona et al. 2020).

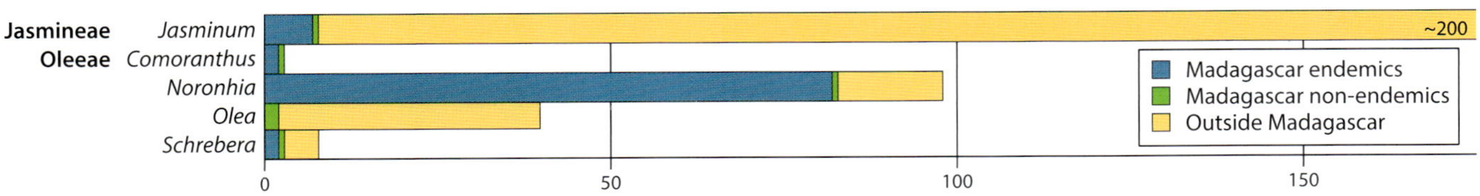

FIGURE 8.91 **Diversity and endemicity diagram of Malagasy Oleaceae at the level of genera, showing three different species counts: 1) endemic to Madagascar, 2) nonendemic but native to Madagascar, and 3) those occurring elsewhere in the world (for further information see text). In cases when species diversity exceeds or does not conform to that presented on the horizontal graph scale, the figures are written along the respective horizontal line of a given genus.**

RECENT DEVELOPMENT IN SYSTEMATICS

The last comprehensive taxonomic treatment of the Malagasy Oleaceae was completed by Perrier de la Bâthie (1952d) for the *Flore de Madagascar et des Comores*. It included five genera, of which two were considered endemic to Madagascar and the Comoro islands. These were *Comoranthus* and *Noronhia*, with three and 41 species, respectively. The other three genera (*Jasminum*, *Linociera*, and *Olea*) were not only more speciose but also widely distributed in different parts of the world, although most of their species found on Madagascar were considered endemic.

In the decades that followed Perrier's treatment, several changes occurred: the description of four new species of *Noronhia* on Madagascar and the Comoros (Bosser 1973; Labat et al. 1999; Callmander et al. 2009), the inclusion of *Linociera* within the genus *Chionanthus* (Stearn 1976, 1980), the discovery of the genus *Schrebera* on Madagascar (Bosser and Rabevohitra 1985), and the recircumscription of the Malagasy species of *Olea*, with two endemic species being subsumed under *O. capensis* subsp. *macrocarpa* (P. S. Green 2002). Then came the molecular revolution of the 2000s, which brought new light into the systematics of the Oleaceae as a whole (Wallander and Albert 2000) and to the genera found on Madagascar (Besnard et al. 2009; Hong-Wa and Besnard 2013, 2014). Interestingly, there was also a sort of renaissance in botanical exploration on the island starting in the 1980s, which resulted in exploration of poorly known areas and a large volume of new herbarium material.

While there are still five genera of Oleaceae currently recognized on Madagascar, their composition is notably different from that proposed by Perrier de la Bâthie over 60 years ago. The Malagasy members of the family belong to two tribes, namely Jasmineae and Oleeae, and in the latter tribe, the subtribes Oleinae and Schreberinae. These Malagasy Oleaceae represent distinct evolutionary lineages that postdate the breakup of Gondwana. A brief discussion of each of these five genera with respect to Madagascar is presented below.

Comoranthus

Known only by three species, of which two are endemic to Madagascar and mostly found in dry deciduous forests and dry spiny thickets in the west and southwest (Perrier de la Bâthie 1952d), *Comoranthus* can be recognized by its simple leaves, externally and internally pubescent flowers (Figure 8.92b), and woody loculicidal capsules (Figure 8.92a). Described in 1934 by Knoblauch and accepted by Perrier de la Bâthie in his treatments (1949c, 1952d), its status as a distinct genus has been questioned (Schatz 2001) due to the distinctive capsular fruit with winged seeds that it shares with *Schrebera*. The affinity of these two genera has repeatedly been confirmed by molecular data, which placed them in their own clade, forming the subtribe Schreberinae.

Jasminum

A large genus of woody climbers with ~200 species worldwide, *Jasminum* is the only member of the tribe Jasmineae on Madagascar, where it is represented by eight native species, of which seven are endemic to the island, and one is shared with the Comoros (Perrier de la Bâthie 1949c, 1952d). *Jasminum* is found in both moist evergreen and dry deciduous forests on Madagascar. It can be recognized by its lianescent habit, simple or compound leaves, fragrant flowers with a long and slender corolla tube (Figure 8.92d), and one- or two-lobed, berry-like fruits (Figure 8.92c).

Noronhia

With 83 species on Madagascar, *Noronhia* is by far the largest genus of Oleaceae on the island. Based on phylogenetic analyses, it currently includes species formerly placed in the genera *Chionanthus*, *Linociera*, and *Olea* (Hong-Wa and Besnard 2013, 2014; Hong-Wa 2016). It has also been expanded to accommodate the African lineage that gave rise to the spectacular radiation of the genus on Madagascar (Hong-Wa and Besnard 2013), making it the third-largest genus of Oleaceae in the world. *Noronhia* exhibits considerable morphological variation and ecological adaptation. Its species can be recognized by their thinly to thickly coriaceous leaves, axillary inflorescences, flowers with a thick and fleshy corolla (Figure 8.92f), drupaceous fruits (Figure 8.92e), woody petiole, and the frequent presence of a corona inside the flower. They occur across the island and are a ubiquitous component of the native vegetation.

Noronhia emarginata, an attractive species of the eastern littoral forests, with thick, coriaceous leaves and large, fleshy fruits, was introduced as early as the 18th century to the Mascarenes as an ornamental, where it has naturalized. It was also introduced at a later time to other neighboring islands in the Indian Ocean (e.g., Seychelles) and to other areas as far as Bermuda, Florida, and Hawaii, where it escaped from cultivation and is largely considered an invasive species.

Olea

Despite being widely distributed in nearby Africa, *Olea* is currently known on Madagascar by two species, *O. capensis* and *O. lancea*, of which the latter is endemic to the islands of the western Indian Ocean (i.e., Madagascar, the Mascarenes, and Rodrigues). While four species were initially recognized by Perrier de la Bâthie on Madagascar (1949c, 1952d), *O. ambrensis* has been subsumed under *Noronhia*, based on molecular data (Hong-Wa and Besnard 2014; Hong-Wa 2016), and both *O. madagascariensis* and *O. perrieri* are currently considered to be synonyms of *O. capensis* subsp. *macrocarpa* (P. S. Green 2002). However, there seems to be more complexity among the Malagasy taxa than currently acknowledged, which may require further taxonomic investigation. Moreover, *Olea* is a polyphyletic group (Besnard et al. 2009; Olofsson et al. 2019) requiring nomenclatural adjustments to accommodate phylogenetic frameworks. Conveniently though, the Malagasy taxa belong to the core *Olea* group (*O.* subgen. *Olea* section *Ligustroides*; P. S. Green 2002). On Madagascar, *Olea* (Figures 8.93g and h) are medium to large trees found mainly in moist evergreen forests. They can be distinguished from *Noronhia* by their pointed leaves; terminal inflorescences; flowers with a very short-tubed corolla, parts being fused only at their base; longer filaments; and the absence of both a corona and a woody petiole. The

FIGURE 8.92 **Different forms of Oleaceae: A) *Comoranthus obconicus* (Rakotovao 6293); B) *C. minor* (Ratovoson 1457); C) *Jasminum octocuspe* (Nusbaumer 1739); D) *J. kitchingii* (Swenson 1665); E) *Noronhia aminae* (Razafitsalama 1224); F) *N. seyrigii* (Andriamihajarivo 1100); G) *Olea capensis* subsp. *macrocarpa* (Ravelonarivo 4128); H) *O. capensis* subsp. *macrocarpa* (Ranirison 507); I) *Schrebera* sp.; and J) *Schrebera* sp.** (PHOTO A by C. Rakotovao; B, E, I, and J by F. Ratovoson; C by L. Nusbaumer; D by U. Swenson; F by F. Rakotoarivony; G by D. Ravelonarivo; and H by P. Ranirison.)

flowers are commonly white, whereas in *Noronhia* they vary extensively in color, including shades of yellow, green, brown, and red, as well as white.

Schrebera

A small genus of eight species worldwide, of which one is found in Peru and two others in India and southeast Asia, *Schrebera* (Figure 8.92i and j) is predominantly African and Malagasy, each region harboring two endemic species and sharing another. The two endemic Malagasy species have compound leaves (Bosser and Rabevohitra 1985), a feature that is shared with just one of the African species, *S. alata*. Medium to large trees, the genus occurs in moist evergreen and dry deciduous forests on the island, and can be recognized easily by its relatively large flowers with a dark-tinted hairy throat and its capsular fruits (Figure 8.92j). There is a paucity of herbarium specimens for all three species on Madagascar, and this may be due to the large size of the trees making the collection of specimens particularly difficult.

PHYLOGENY

Apart from the molecular study of *Noronhia* (Hong-Wa and Besnard 2013, 2014), which focused primarily on Madagascar, a few other phylogenetic studies on the family have included representatives of the Malagasy Oleaceae (Wallander and Albert 2000; Besnard et al. 2009; Olofsson et al. 2019). Together these studies provide a broader understanding of the relationships among Malagasy genera, none of which are closely related except *Comoranthus* and *Schrebera*, as well as of their placement within the family as a whole as part of different tribes and subtribes.

The most compelling results of these phylogenetic studies are perhaps related to the characterization of the polyphyletic or paraphyletic nature of several genera. *Olea*, for instance, is largely polyphyletic (Besnard et al. 2009; Olofsson et al. 2019), and it was discovered that one former Malagasy member was embedded within *Noronhia* (Hong-Wa and Besnard 2014). Similarly, *Chionanthus* is broadly polyphyletic, with several members from the western Indian Ocean region also nested within *Noronhia* (Hong-Wa and Besnard 2013, 2014). These complex phylogenetic relationships necessitated a new delimitation of the polyphyletic genera *Olea* and *Chionanthus*, and for the latter genus the Malagasy members were transferred to *Noronhia* (Hong-Wa 2016), thereby removing the genus *Chionanthus* from the island altogether. Within Schreberinae, Malagasy species of *Comoranthus* and *Schrebera* are sisters and form a clade diverging from the African species *S. alata* (Olofsson et al. 2019), rendering the genus *Schrebera* paraphyletic and thus requiring a nomenclatural adjustment.

While phylogenetic studies of *Jasminum* are still scarce, it has nonetheless been shown that this genus is also paraphyletic with regard to *Menodora* (Lee et al. 2007; Jeyarani et al. 2018). However, to date, none of its Malagasy species have been phylogenetically analyzed, and it is not known whether they form a clade. So far, none of them have been formally assigned to any of the five sections traditionally recognized within *Jasminum* (A. de Candolle 1844; P. S. Green 2001), of which one was recently elevated to generic rank (Banfi 2014). At the very least, Malagasy members can be categorized into two groups: those with simple or unifoliolate leaves and those with either trifoliate or pinnately compound leaves (Perrier de la Bâthie 1952d).

Except for *Jasminum*, all Malagasy Oleaceae taxa seem affiliated with African counterparts (Besnard et al. 2009; Hong-Wa and Besnard 2013, 2014; Olofsson et al. 2019), suggesting an African origin followed by a dispersal to Madagascar, which likely happened contemporaneously in the early to mid-Miocene (Hong-Wa and Besnard 2013; Olofsson et al. 2019). Thus, it would not be surprising if Malagasy *Jasminum* also originated in Africa and had similar migration patterns and timings as the other genera. For each genus, diversification on Madagascar, however, seems to have been staggered, and, in the case of *Noronhia*, was followed by dispersal to the Comoros and the Mascarenes (Hong-Wa and Besnard 2013). This is probably true for *Comoranthus* and *Olea* as well, which are also present in at least one of these archipelagoes.

WORK IN PROGRESS

Taxonomically, the Malagasy members of the Oleaceae are far from being fully resolved. In light of recent phylogenetic studies, generic limits between *Comoranthus* and *Schrebera* need to be reconciled so that any named groups in a classification are monophyletic. Work is underway to recircumscribe the limits of *Comoranthus*, subsuming it under *Schrebera*, and to simultaneously revise the taxonomy of the genus, with recognition of new species endemic to Madagascar (C. Hong-Wa et al., unpublished data). Similarly, revisionary work is underway for *Jasminum* and suggests that new species need to be described, putting the total number of species on the island at 11, of which 10 are endemic (C. Frasier et al., unpublished data). In addition, an ongoing and extensive phylogenomic study of Oleaceae worldwide (J. Dupin et al., unpublished data) includes at least five Malagasy species of *Jasminum*, and the results will provide, for the first time, insights into their relationships, origin, and time of arrival on the island.

Although no work is currently being conducted on Malagasy *Olea*, the recognition of only two species and, more specifically, the inclusion of all Malagasy species within a single subspecies, *O. capensis* subsp. *macrocarpa* (P. S. Green 2002), overlooks morphological variation among these taxa on Madagascar (C. Hong-Wa and G. Besnard, unpublished data). Besides, the only comprehensive phylogenetic assessment of *Olea*, which included several accessions of *O. capensis* subsp. *macrocarpa* from Africa and Madagascar, did not resolve the monophyly of this subspecies, nor did it reveal a distinct cluster of Malagasy representatives (Besnard et al. 2009). Therefore, further taxonomic and phylogenetic studies need to be conducted on *Olea* to improve current understanding of the Malagasy species.

Revisionary work has been recently completed for *Noronhia*, expanding its circumscription and raising the number of species described from Madagascar from 42 to 83 (Hong-Wa 2016), as well as expanding its range to include the Mascarenes and much of sub-Saharan Africa (Hong-Wa and Besnard 2013; Hong-Wa et al. 2014). However, further study of both newly collected and previously unidentified specimens suggests that more Malagasy entities await description. In addition, population-level studies are needed to help delimit a few species for which ambiguity in their boundaries remains, such as the morphologically variable and geographically widespread *N. linocerioides*. Such population-level studies will also help understanding of the extent and frequency of hybridization, which may have been rampant within *Noronhia* (C. Hong-Wa and G. Besnard, unpublished data).

Moreover, the extensive field, herbarium, and laboratory studies of *Noronhia* not only resulted in a revised taxonomy of the genus but also provided the foundation for more in-depth analyses of large- and small-scale biological processes that have shaped the remarkable diversity in the genus, which could also offer insights into the diversification of the Malagasy flora. Recent advances in phylogenomics have overcome the limitation of the marker-based approach, and the island-wide sampling efforts, particularly since the start of the 21st century, offer opportunities to obtain genomic data from several hundred specimens of *Noronhia*. This may fine-tune the systematics of this speciose genus and unravel the micro- and macro-evolutionary mechanisms that led to its explosive diversification on Madagascar. Additionally, determining effective pollen and seed dispersers through direct observation and/or evidence gathered from camera traps and fecal analyses would aid understanding of the ecological processes involved in this diversification.

A recent genetic study of the population of the only species of the genus occurring in grasslands, *N. lowryi*, shed light on both its effective dispersal and population demography, and contrasting dispersal patterns of pollen and fruits, the former flowing efficiently within the landscape, while the latter is seemingly more spatially constrained. In addition, the results testify to the antiquity of woody elements in the grasslands of the Central Highlands (Salmona et al. 2020; see Lehmann et al., pp. 152–68). Meanwhile, another recent local-scale study that sampled exhaustively at sites in northern Madagascar confirmed the high level of endemism and richness of *Noronhia* in this area (cf. Hong-Wa 2016). Notably, over 25 lineages of *Noronhia* were found in the fragmented forests of Loky Manambato. Ongoing landscape genetics and population demography analyses that target this region will infer effective dispersal across the landscape for a few species of *Noronhia* (J. Salmona et al., unpublished data). This research holds the potential to reveal factors involved in gene dispersal, to inform understanding of the timing of habitat fragmentation in the region, and to provide baseline information for priority conservation activities for forest trees and their dispersers.

Subject editors: Laurent Gautier and Steven M. Goodman

ACANTHACEAE

P. B. Phillipson, L. Andriamahefarivo, M. W. Callmander, T. F. Daniel, I. Darbyshire, C. A. Kiel, R. Letsara, L. McDade, and E. Tripp

The Acanthaceae is among the world's 12 largest flowering plant families, with at least 4750 currently accepted species spread among about 190 accepted genera (Daniel and McDade 2014), which occur in warm temperate and tropical regions of the world, from arid to humid bioclimatic zones. Species of Acanthaceae have relatively few important economic uses, although some are grown as ornamentals, and many are used in traditional medicine. Research has shown that biologically active compounds occur that have potential use for a variety of medical purposes (Awan and Aslam 2014). Certain species have been reported as effective in soil and dune stabilization in dry habitats (e.g., Mndela et al. 2020), and thus may play important ecological roles. With their attractive flowers of diverse sizes, shapes, and colors (see Figures 8.93 and 8.94), essentially all Acanthaceae taxa are animal pollinated, making them important partners in plant-animal interactions (Tripp and Manos 2008).

The Acanthaceae of Madagascar were the subject of detailed studies by French botanist Raymond Benoist (1881–1970), who worked on the island between 1949 and 1952 (Dorr 1997). He first described taxonomic novelties from Madagascar in 1910, and he continued until 1967, clocking up a total of 337 new species of Malagasy Acanthaceae. His work was intended to result in a complete flora treatment of the family in *Flore de Madagascar et des Comores*, but this was never finished. In 1967, a first volume was published in the flora series, which treated in their entirety two of the three subfamilies recognized at the time (Benoist 1967a): Thunbergioideae and Nelsonioideae, and part of the third subfamily: Acanthoideae. A total of 174 species were treated, of which 161 were endemic to Madagascar. The second volume was intended to treat the single remaining tribe of the Acanthoideae, the Justicieae, by far the most diversified on the island, including the three currently most species-rich genera: *Anisostachya* (61 species), *Hypoestes* (93 species), and *Justicia* (86 species), together with the remaining smaller genera. Clearly, at the time of his death, Benoist's work on the Acanthaceae was still "work in progress," and there are signs that in the later years some errors were made; for example, a number of taxa lacking valid names were published. Nevertheless, his overall contribution to our knowledge of Malagasy Acanthaceae is highly impressive.

During the past 50 years a vast quantity of new plant material has been collected on Madagascar. Various botanists have undertaken taxonomic work on Malagasy Acanthaceae, mostly focused on individual genera and often part of a study with a broader geographic scope.

FIGURE 8.93 **Floral diversity in Acanthaceae I. Tribe Acantheae: A) *Crossandra stenandrium* in the Farafara Forest, Anosy Region (Razakamalala 4236). Tribe Barlerieae: B) *Barleria alluaudii* in the spiny thicket at Sarikady, Ranopiso, Anosy Region (Rakotovao 5449); C) *Podorungia lantzei* in forest on the Masoala Peninsula near Ambanizana, Analanjirofo Region (Phillipson 6629). Tribe Ruellieae: D) *Ruellia albopurpurea* in thicket on La Table, Toliara, Atsimo-Andrefana Region (Ramon 761); E) *Brillantaisia madagascariensis* in Andramanalana Forest near Andapa, SAVA Region (Rakotovao 3110); F) *Acanthopale madagascariensis* in the Analamay-Mantadia forest corridor, near Morarano Gara, Moramanga, Alaotra Mangoro Region (Rakotovao 5752). Tribe Whitfieldieae: G) *Camarotea souiensis* in Ranobe Forest, north of Toliara, Atsimo-Andrefana Region (Phillipson 5947).** (PHOTOS A, B, E, and F by C. Rakotovao; C and G by P. B. Phillipson; and D by L. Ramon.)

FIGURE 8.94 **Floral diversity in Acanthaceae II: Tribe Justicieae: A) *Anisostachya betsimisaraka* in the Analamay-Mantadia forest corridor, near Morarano Gara, Moramanga, Alaotra-Mangoro Region (Antilahimena 7973); B) *Anisotes madagascariensis* on white sand dune near Toliara, Atsimo-Andrefana Region (Ramon 371); C) *Hypoestes* cf. *pulchra* in moist evergreen forest at Ankerana near Brickaville, Atsinanana Region (Antilahimena 7635); D) *H. decaryana* in Ranobe Forest, north of Toliara, Atsimo-Andrefana Region (Manjakahery 119); E) *H. diclipteroides* in the Analamay-Mantadia forest corridor, near Morarano Gara, Moramanga, Alaotra-Mangoro Region (Rakotovao 5928); F) *Brachystephanus lyallii*, in moist evergreen forest at Ankerana near Brickaville, Atsinanana Region (Antilahimena 8191); G) *Ecbolium madagascariense* at Anadabolava in the Complexe Vohidava-Betsamalaho, Anosy Region (Randrianarivony 499); and H) *Oplonia* cf. *minor* at Ambatoabo, 2 km east of Imonty Forest, Mandrare Basin, Anosy Region (Ratovoson 1495).** (PHOTOS A, C, and F by P. Antilahimena; B by L. Ramon; D by P. B. Phillipson; E by C. Rakotovao; G by T. Randrianarivony; and H by F. Ratovoson.)

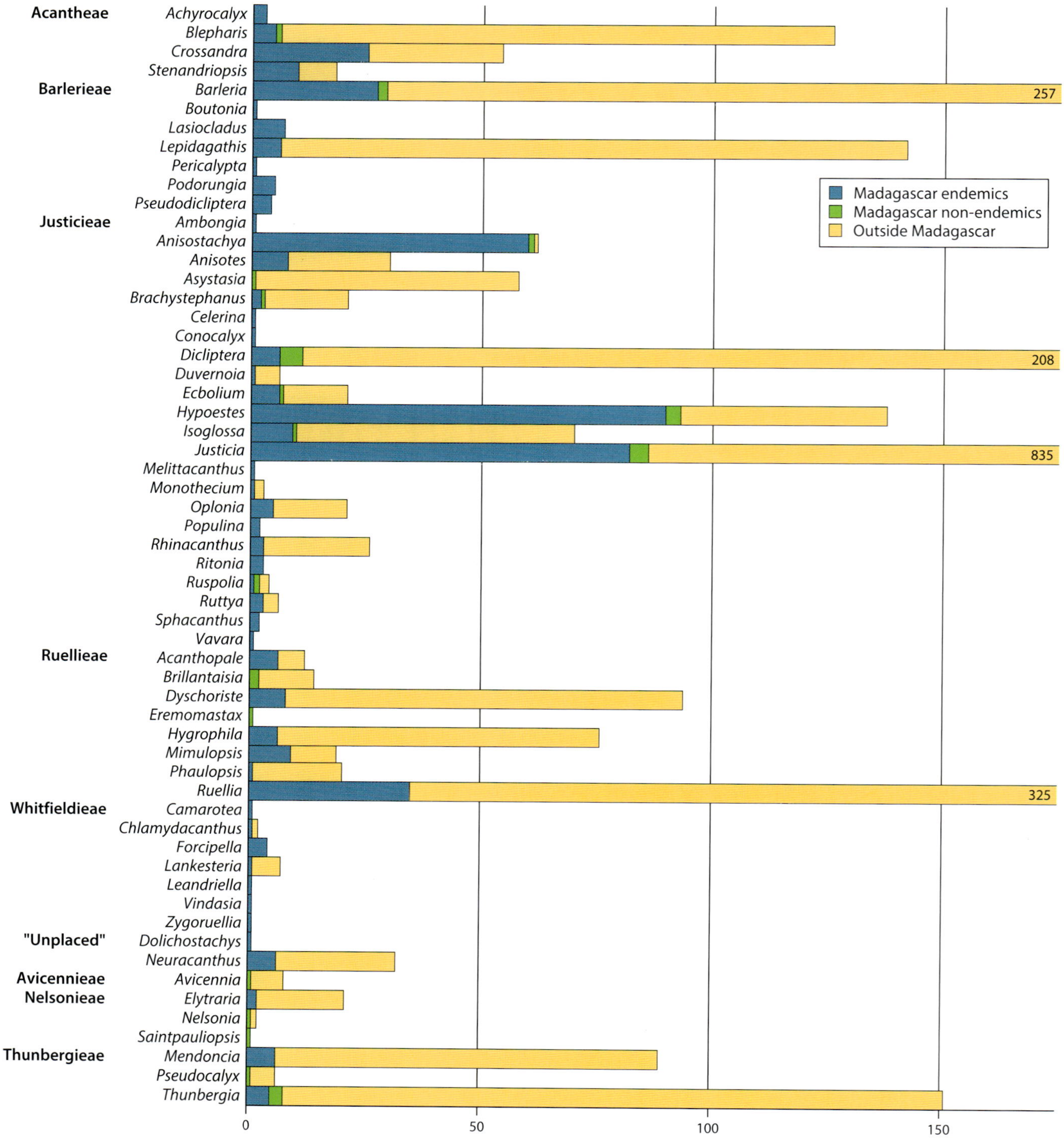

FIGURE 8.95 **Diversity and endemicity diagram of Malagasy Acanthaceae at the level of genera, showing three different species counts: 1) endemic to Madagascar, 2) nonendemic but native to Madagascar, and 3) those occurring elsewhere in the world. In cases when species diversity exceeds or does not conform to that presented on the horizontal graph scale, the figures are written along the respective horizontal line of a given genus. Note that values do not take into account unpublished species mentioned in the text or species expected to be transferred in the future from one genus to another.**

Furthermore, phylogenetic studies on the Acanthaceae based on morphological and molecular data have provided new insights for understanding the evolution and diversification of the family, and from this a revised taxonomic framework is being built (e.g., McDade et al. 2005, 2008). This has implications at all taxonomic levels, and even the circumscription of the family itself has changed to accommodate new insights. Specifically, the formerly recognized family Avicenniaceae, including a single genus of mangrove trees, *Avicennia*, has now been found irrefutably to be embedded within the Acanthaceae (Schwarzbach and McDade

2002; Tripp and McDade 2014) and is now treated as the subfamily Avicennioideae.

Currently 59 genera are recognized as native to Madagascar, of which 19 are endemic, although many of these are doubtfully distinct from other more widespread taxa (Onjalalaina and Darbyshire 2016). Apart from the three largest genera mentioned above, which account for 240 of the 510 species of Acanthaceae on Madagascar, the remaining 270 species are spread across 55 other genera, and 12 of these currently comprise a single species endemic to Madagascar (see Figure 8.95).

CLASSIFICATION AND PHYLOGENY

Four subfamilies are currently recognized, each of which has been treated as a distinct family in the past by certain authors, and all occur on Madagascar. By far the largest of these is Acanthoideae, which includes over 200 genera and at least 75% of all species of Acanthaceae, and which has been variously subdivided into tribes and subtribes in the past (Scotland and Vollesen 2000). Recently, molecular studies have provided a robust phylogenetic model for the diversity of this large subfamily, and the results are generally serving to confirm an overall taxonomic plan—with the subfamily Acanthoideae now generally divided into distinct tribes (McDade et al. 2008). However, tribal and generic delimitation within the subfamily has been in a state of flux, especially in the case of the tribe Justicieae (Kiel et al. 2017), which includes about 50% of the species worldwide. The other tribes currently recognized in the subfamily include: Acantheae, Andrographideae, Barlerieae, Ruellieae, and Whitfieldieae, all of which are present on Madagascar except Andrographideae. The subfamily consists predominantly of herbs, but some genera include subshrubs, shrubs, or even small trees.

The tribe Acantheae includes four genera present on Madagascar, of which just one, *Achyrocalyx*, is endemic. The other three have important centers of diversity on the island, especially *Crossandra*, with nearly half of its 54 known species endemic to Madagascar (Figure 8.93a). The tribe comprises a total of 44 species on Madagascar, all but one endemic.

The tribe Barlerieae includes seven genera known from Madagascar, five of which are endemic, and a total of 18 species. These genera, *Boutonia*, *Lasiocladus*, *Pericalypta*, *Podorungia* (Figure 8.93c), and *Pseudodicliptera*, are characterized by flowers that have four stamens and bithecous anthers; this and molecular evidence points to a close relationship with the African genus *Crabbea* (McDade et al. 2008). The species are, however, mostly poorly known and generic limits are still uncertain in the group. The two nonendemic genera, *Barleria* (Figure 8.93b) and *Lepidagathis*, are pantropical in distribution and account for 35 species on the island, all but two endemic.

The tribe Justicieae comprises 23 genera on Madagascar with 307 known species, over 93% of which are endemic. Nine of the genera are endemic to the island, but some of these are doubtfully distinct from other more widespread genera. The tribe includes the three most species-rich Acanthaceae genera on Madagascar, each with more than 60 currently accepted species: *Anisostachya* (Figure 8.94a), *Hypoestes* (Figures 8.94c–e), and *Justicia*; the latter is pantropical and comprises an estimated 921 species (POWO 2020). Madagascar is the primary center of diversity for both *Anisostachya* and *Hypoestes*. The tribe accounts for about 60% of the Malagasy Acanthaceae flora and was not treated by Benoist (1967a).

The tribe Ruellieae comprises eight genera on Madagascar, including three highly diversified, pantropical genera: *Dyschoriste*, *Hygrophila*, and *Ruellia* (Figure 8.93d). Ruellieae also has five less species-rich genera, which are largely confined to Africa and Madagascar: *Acanthopale* (Figure 8.93f), *Brillantaisia* (Figure 8.93e), *Eremomastax*, *Mimulopsis*, and *Phaulopsis* (referred to as *Micranthus* by Benoist 1967a). Three genera treated under the tribe by Benoist (1967a) are now placed in other tribes, these are: *Forsythiopsis* (referred to as *Oplonia* by Stearn 1971) now in Justicieae, and *Lankesteria* and *Zygoruellia* now in Whitfieldieae.

The need to recognize a new tribe in the Acanthoideae to accommodate certain problematic genera of Acanthaceae became evident through the work of Manktelow and McDade (2001), and eventually the tribe Whitfieldieae was formally established (Reveal 2012). As currently circumscribed, the tribe comprises eight genera, five of which are endemic to Madagascar: *Camarotea* (Figure 8.93g), *Forcipella*, *Leandriella*, and *Vindasia* and *Zygoruellia*, together containing a total of eight species. Two further genera, *Chlamydacanthus* and *Lankesteria*, each have a single species that is endemic to Madagascar but have other species in Africa; *Whitfieldia* is not present on Madagascar. Some genera within subfamily Acanthoideae remain unplaced at tribal level; for Madagascar these include *Dolichostachys* and *Neuracanthus*.

Among the smaller subfamilies, the Nelsonioideae is superficially similar morphologically to the Acanthoideae, although some of its species were originally placed in other families of the Lamiales. It consists of five genera (three on Madagascar), comprising about 175 species in total, all herbaceous (McDade et al. 2012; Angiosperm Phylogeny Website 2019). The Thunbergioideae include five genera (three on Madagascar) of erect woody or herbaceous twining vines and about 190 species (Angiosperm Phylogeny Website 2019). Finally, the Avicennioideae comprises a single genus, *Avicennia*.

THE GENERA OF MALAGASY ACANTHACEAE

Subfamily Acanthoideae, Tribe Acantheae

Achyrocalyx: The Malagasy endemic genus *Achyrocalyx* comprises three poorly known species, all limited to the subarid southwest. Benoist (1967a) recognized the genus as distinct on the basis of its zygomorphic corolla that contrasted with the corolla of five subequal lobes in the Malagasy species of the related *Stenandriopsis*, a genus that has subsequently been placed in synonymy under *Stenandrium* (but see *Stenandriopsis*, below). However, as currently circumscribed, *Stenandriopsis* includes species with both zygomorphic and subequal lobed corollas, so this character no longer serves to distinguish the genera. Furthermore, a molecular phylogeny shows that *Achyrocalyx* is part of a monophyletic clade with *Stenandriopsis*, and it seems best that it is treated as a synonym of this latter genus (McDade et al. 2005).

Blepharis: This distinctive genus of 126 species of mostly bristly and prickly herbs and subshrubs, with highly zygomorphic corollas, is widespread across Africa and southern Asia, and has six species in the drier parts of Madagascar. Seven species of *Blepharis* were recognized by Benoist (1967a) for Madagascar, all endemic except one, *B. maderaspatensis* (formerly known as *B. boerhaviifolia*), a widespread species that also occurs in Africa, Asia, and the Comoro islands. Subsequently, Vollesen (2000) reduced the total number of species recognized for Madagascar by one, with *B. madagascariensis* placed as a synonym of *B. glomerans*.

Crossandra: *Crossandra* (Figure 8.93a), with its 54 species, has a similar distribution to *Blepharis*, but with 25 known species on Madagascar, all endemic. Only 16 species were known to Benoist (1967a), but in a revision of the genus for Madagascar, Vollesen (1997) recognized nine additional species, and more species remain to be described (P. B. Phillipson, unpublished data). The genus is well known as a garden ornamental, especially the Indian species *C. infundibuliformis* with its large, bright yellow or orange flowers and its robust subshrubby habit; the Malagasy species are also highly decorative and merit horticultural consideration.

Stenandriopsis: This genus consists of 18 species, with 10 endemics occurring on Madagascar, and the other species spread across central parts of Africa. The genus has been treated as a synonym of the New World genus *Stenandrium*, and the African-Malagasy species were revised in this context by Vollesen (1992). However, recent molecular studies (McDade et al. 2005) have shown that the New and Old World groups of species belong to separate clades; as such, resurrection of *Stenandriopsis* for Old World species is warranted. It is likely that the three currently recognized species of *Achyrocalyx*, all endemic, will need to be transferred to *Stenandriopsis* (see *Achyrocalyx*, above).

Subfamily Acanthoideae, Tribe Barlerieae

Barleria: *Barleria* (Figure 8.93b) is a large pantropical genus of about 300 species, with its highest concentration of species in east Africa (Darbyshire et al. 2019). It includes 29 species on Madagascar, extending from the south to the north of the country but mostly in the dry and subarid regions; all but two of the species are endemic. Since Benoist's treatment in the flora, three new species have been described (Darbyshire et al. 2014), all from the north. During the evaluation of the genus for the Madagascar Catalogue (2020), we concluded that a number of taxonomic rearrangements are needed and that three additional new species require description, based largely on newly collected specimens.

Boutonia: This genus comprises a single species endemic to Madagascar, *B. cuspidata*, which is widespread in moist evergreen forests above 900 m in the Central Highlands, on the Analavelona Massif in the southwest, and in the northern mountains (e.g., Tsaratanàna). The identity and nomenclature of this plant have been a source of confusion but were eventually resolved (see Bosser 1987; Vollesen 1990).

Lasiocladus: Benoist (1967a) accepted four species in the Malagasy endemic genus *Lasiocladus*, one of which, *L. anthospermifolius*, included four varieties that had originally been described as distinct species. Based on the material now available, we prefer to resurrect some of these species (Madagascar Catalogue 2020), bringing the number of currently recognized species to seven. Most of the species occur in the subarid southwest of Madagascar, but *L. rufopilus* is known only from Nosy Be. It is likely that the species of *Lasiocladus* will need to be transferred to *Crabbea*, but further study is needed (McDade et al. 2008).

Lepidagathis: *Lepidagathis*, consisting of 142 species globally, occurs across the tropics of America, Africa, and Asia. Six endemic species were described by Benoist (1967a) for Madagascar, scattered across the different bioclimatic zones, with the exception of the high mountains. One additional species remains undescribed (P. B. Phillipson, unpublished data).

Pericalypta: This genus comprises a single species, *P. biflora*, endemic to Madagascar and known from just a handful of specimens from four eastern moist evergreen forest sites: Betampona, Marojejy, Makira, and Masoala.

Podorungia: *Podorungia* (Figure 8.93c) is another Malagasy endemic genus. It comprises five species, one of which, *P. gesneroides*, was discovered and described recently (Onjalalaina and Darbyshire 2016). Five species were recognized by Benoist (1967a), but one, *P. decaryi*, is now considered to be a synonym of *P. humblotii* (Madagascar Catalogue 2020). The species usually occur in the most humid parts of Madagascar, but one species, *P. serotina*, is found only in the dry west.

Pseudodicliptera: *Pseudodicliptera* is another rather paradoxical genus endemic to Madagascar. It was described by Benoist (1939) and now comprises four species, each currently known only from its type collection: *P. coursii* was collected near Lake Alaotra, *P. humilis* at Analavelona, and *P. longifolia* and *P. sulfureolilacina* in the southeast. *Pseudodicliptera longifolia* was originally described by Benoist (1948) who put it in a separate monospecific genus, *Delphinacanthus*, but it was subsequently transferred to *Pseudodicliptera*.

Subfamily Acanthoideae, Tribe Justicieae

Ambongia: This poorly known genus with a single species, *A. perrieri*, is endemic to Madagascar and known only from four sites on *tsingy* limestone massifs in the northwest.

Anisostachya: The genus *Anisostachya* (Figure 8.94a) has been reduced to the level of a subsection of the genus *Justicia* by some authors (e.g., Graham 1988); however, a recent study (Kiel et al. 2017) has shown that it represents a distinct lineage that is almost entirely confined to Madagascar. Benoist published no fewer than 54 of the 62 currently recognized species of *Anisostachya* (Madagascar Catalogue 2020) in a series of articles, two of which are particularly important (Benoist 1965, 1967b). *Anisostachya tenella* is the only species known to occur on Madagascar that is also found across tropical Africa, and another species, *A. paucinervis*, is probably endemic to the Comoros (P. B. Phillipson and L. Andriamahefarivo, unpublished data). Furthermore, Kiel et al. (2017) pointed out that at least one additional Malagasy species described from *Justicia* belongs to the *Anisostachya*, and work is currently in progress to revise these genera (P. B. Phillipson and L. Andriamahefarivo, unpublished data). The genus is most diverse in the humid and subhumid bioclimatic regions of Madagascar and is a common constituent of the forest floor flora.

Anisotes: *Anisotes* (Figure 8.94b) occurs across tropical Africa, the Arabian Peninsula, the Comoro islands, and Madagascar. It comprises a total of 30 species of which eight are endemic to Madagascar. *Anisotes madagascariensis* was described over 90 years ago and occurs in the semiarid southwest. Six newly described species from Madagascar have recently been published, two more from the southwest and the other four from the northwest (Daniel et al. 2007, 2013; Daniel 2015); an additional species from the Central Highlands, originally described in the monospecific genus *Danguya*, has now been transferred to *Anisotes* (Daniel et al. 2019). However, recent molecular studies suggest that *Anisotes* is polyphyletic as currently circumscribed (McDade et al. 2021).

Asystasia: The genus *Asystasia* comprises 58 species centered in tropical Africa but extending across the Arabian Peninsula to India and southeastern Asia and the Pacific islands. A single widespread species, *A. gangetica*, occurs on Madagascar and is represented by *A. g. micrantha*, which often occurs in disturbed habitats.

Brachystephanus: This genus (Figure 8.94f) comprises 21 species confined to Africa and Madagascar. It was treated by Figueiredo and Jury (1996) who recognized three species on Madagascar: *B. densiflorus* is known only from Anjanaharibe-Sud, Marojejy, and Tsaratanàna; *B. lyallii* is widespread in high-elevation forests; and *B. africanus*, which also occurs in east and central Africa, is known from scattered localities in northern Madagascar, the Malagasy population being separated as *B. a.* var. *madagascariensis*. These taxa were retained in a subsequent revision of the genus (Champluvier and Darbyshire 2009), but the authors expressed doubt about the distinction of the two endemic species.

Celerina: *Celerina* is a poorly known monospecific genus endemic to Madagascar. It is assumed to be part of the *Tetramerium* lineage (Daniel et al. 2008), related to *Ecbolium* and *Populina*, but the single species, *C. seyrigii*, is only known to have been collected three times in the Mandrare River basin, most recently in 1943.

Conocalyx: This monospecific genus is endemic to Madagascar but poorly known, and the name is not validly published. It is close to *Isoglossa* and should possibly be synonymized under that genus (Kiel et al. 2006). However, in contrast to *Celerina*, the single species, *Conocalyx laxus*, is known from numerous collections from the west.

Dicliptera: The genus *Dicliptera* comprises about 220 species spread across the tropics and warm temperate regions of the world. On Madagascar it is represented by 11 species, six endemic to the island, and five also occurring on the Comoros, in Africa, and/or in Asia. A number of species originally described in *Peristrophe* have been transferred to *Dicliptera* (Darbyshire and Vollesen 2007). On Madagascar the genus remains poorly understood and is in need of thorough revision.

Duvernoia: Treated in many works in synonymy under *Justicia*, the position of this genus remains somewhat ambiguous (Kiel et al. 2017). However, the genus has been retained in certain flora treatments until additional studies bring resolution. Currently, six apparently closely related species are recognized, including *D. curviflora*, known only from the southwest (Zombitse-Vohibasia), and five species on continental Africa. A second endemic species from Madagascar has been identified but has not yet been described (P. B. Phillipson, unpublished data).

Ecbolium: This genus (Figure 8.94g) comprises 21 species distributed in south and east Africa, the Arabian Peninsula, and south Asia, as well as on Madagascar, which holds a third of the species. Vollesen (1989) revised the genus globally, recognizing a total of seven species on Madagascar, all endemic except *E. syringifolium*, which also occurs on the Comoros. On Madagascar the species are mostly concentrated in the south and southwest, but there are scattered occurrences of certain species in the west, while *E. palmatum* is known only from Montagne des Français.

Hypoestes: This genus has 93 species known from Madagascar, all but three endemic to the island, and is currently the most species-rich genus of Acanthaceae on the island. The genus is broadly distributed across tropical and southern Africa, the Arabian Peninsula, south and southeast Asia, and other Indian Ocean islands. However, the diversity across this large part of the globe includes only 45 species and is dwarfed by the extraordinary diversity on Madagascar. *Hypoestes* is present across Madagascar in a wide range of habitats, and encompasses rather diverse growth forms, ranging from tiny herbs to shrubs and small trees, which also display a remarkable diversity of floral morphology (see Figure 8.94c–e). On the basis of the wealth of new herbarium material available, work now underway suggests that many more species await description (P. B. Phillipson, unpublished data).

Isoglossa: The genus *Isoglossa* has a broad distribution in tropical and southern Africa, a somewhat scattered presence in southeast Asia, and occurs in southeast Australia as well as on Madagascar. It includes about 70 species of which 10 have been recorded from Madagascar. In addition to nine endemic species, the southern African *I. hypoestiflora* has been recorded on the island, but it is doubtful whether this is a correct identification. Most of the material available comes from the humid or subhumid parts of the island, mostly from mountainous areas. This is a genus in need of revision.

Justicia: Delimitation of the genus *Justicia* has been highly problematic, with highly divergent approaches and measures of species diversity: POWO (2020) lists 920 species and WFO (2020) 652 species. As mentioned earlier, phylogenetic studies are starting to clarify generic limits in the Justicieae as a whole and the genus *Justicia* in particular (Kiel et al. 2017, 2018). It seems clear that certain genera that have been synonymized under *Justicia* in some flora treatments will need to be resurrected. Even following a broad circumscription of the genus, its diversity is especially high in the tropical and warm temperate parts of the Americas and Africa. There are currently 86 species of *Justicia* recognized for Madagascar, spread across the different bioclimatic regions, with all but four of them endemic to the island. No fewer than 65 Malagasy species of *Justicia* were described by Benoist in a series of publications between 1939 and 1963, but not one since. Species from Madagascar currently included in *Justicia* are morphologically very diverse, and it is certain that many will be better included in segregate genera as these delimitations become clearer. We anticipate that many species of *Justicia* from Madagascar will be better placed in *Anisostachya* (P. B. Phillipson and L. Andriamahefarivo, unpublished data).

Melittacanthus: This genus is monospecific and represented by *M. divaricatus*, endemic to Madagascar and close to *Isoglossa* (C. Kiel and I. Darbyshire, unpublished data). It is known from only a few scattered collections from the Central Highlands, and only one specimen has been collected in the last 85 years.

Monothecium: *Monothecium* comprises three species of which two are widespread, one across central Africa, India, and Sri Lanka and the second from central to northeast Africa; the third species, *M. leucopterum*, is endemic to Madagascar and only known from Ankarana. McDade et al. (2021) show that the Malagasy species is only distantly related phylogenetically to its two congeners and is part of the clade that includes the genus *Anisostachya*.

Oplonia: This genus (Figure 8.94h) includes 21 accepted species, of which five are endemic to Madagascar. The other species occur in South America and in the Caribbean region. The Malagasy species were treated by Benoist (1967a; in Ruellieae) as constituting a Malagasy endemic genus, *Forsythiopsis*, with just two species. Stearn (1971) concluded that *Forsythiopsis* was congeneric with *Oplonia*, and, in addition to transferring the species recognized by Benoist to *Oplonia*, Stearn described two new Malagasy species and raised one of Benoist's varieties, *F. vincoides* var. *minor*, to species level. McDade et al. (2021) show that Malagasy *Oplonia* (albeit with only a single species sampled) are phylogenetically distinct from New World plants. Resurrection of *Forsythiopsis*, but within Justicieae, seems warranted.

Populina: This genus is endemic to Madagascar and consists of two species: *P. perrieri*, known from the northwest (Boeny Region), and *P. richardii* from the extreme north. Molecular evidence (Daniel et al. 2008; McDade et al. 2018) suggests that these species should be included within *Ecbolium*.

Rhinacanthus: This genus comprises 26 species spread across tropical and southern Africa, India, southeast Asia, and Madagascar, where three endemic species occur. Work in progress has shown that, in addition, at least three undescribed endemic species are present on the island, mostly in the west (P. B. Phillipson and M. W. Callmander, unpublished data). Among the published species, *R. humilis* and *R. perrieri* are both known mainly from the Sambirano Region, while *R. osmospermus* is widespread across the Central Highlands and also extends to the west coast.

Ritonia: This genus is endemic to Madagascar and comprises three species, all poorly known, from the west or southwest. Its placement is still uncertain, and the material available shows a possible morphological relationship with *Oplonia* (P. B. Phillipson and M. W. Callmander, unpublished data). Further study is needed to clarify the status of these plants.

Rungia: This genus comprises 81 known species distributed across the African and Asian tropics (POWO 2020); although two species from Madagascar have been referred to *Rungia*, both are now placed in the genus *Justicia*. These include *R. grandiflora*, an invalid name for *J. madagascariensis*, and *R. rosacea* is a synonym of *J. trifolioides*. However, Kiel et al. (2017) show that *Rungia* is part of a clade that is morphologically well marked, and our ongoing review of the Malagasy species of Acanthaceae has shown that at least three endemic species of *Rungia* occur on the island, two currently undescribed and one that requires transfer from *Justicia*, following current generic circumscription (P. B. Phillipson, unpublished data). Although much work remains to be done on the nomenclature of the justicioid lineage (*sensu* Kiel et al. 2017, 2018; McDade et al. 2021), we recommend retaining these Malagasy species in *Rungia* at present.

Ruspolia: A genus of five recognized species, two of which have been recorded on Madagascar: *R. humbertii*, which is endemic but has never been validly published, and *R. decurrens*, which also occurs in tropical Africa and is sometimes confused with *R. seticalyx*, also from Africa and sometimes cultivated as an ornamental. The identity of a third species, *R. paniculata*, is in doubt, and this name is not validly published.

Ruttya: This genus comprises six accepted species, of which three are endemic to Madagascar. All three are very poorly known, occurring in rather scattered localities and documented only from old collections. *Ruttya bernieri* is known from the north, including from Loky Manambato; *R. fragrans* is known just from the Fiherenana and Manombo River valleys near Toliara, and from near Mahajanga; and the third species, *R. tricolor*, is from the Menavava River valley in the Boina Region.

Sphacanthus: This genus comprises just two species, both endemic to southwest Madagascar.

Vavara: This genus comprises a single, very poorly known species endemic to Madagascar, described from the southeastern mountains (Benoist 1962). The name is apparently not validly published.

Subfamily Acanthoideae, Tribe Ruellieae

Acanthopale: This genus (Figure 8.93f) was treated under *Strobilanthes* by Benoist (1967a) who recognized eight species on Madagascar, all endemic. However, more recent evidence suggests that the latter genus should be limited to Asian species, and that the African and Malagasy species are better referred to other genera (Tripp et al. 2013). This arrangement has been followed in subsequent treatments on the African continent, although some Asian species of *Strobilanthes* have been introduced and naturalized in

Africa. Callmander and Phillipson (2015) examined the Malagasy species and concluded that these were all best accommodated in *Acanthopale*, and the necessary new combinations were provided. These authors reduced the number of accepted species to six. Five of the species occur in the mountainous humid and subhumid bioclimatic regions of Madagascar, and *A. perrieri* is found in the dry western region. One additional species is known that is as yet undescribed.

Brillantaisia: All 14 known species of *Brillantaisia* occur in tropical Africa, and two of them also occur on Madagascar: *B. madagascariensis* (Figure 8.93e) and *B. pubescens*. The former species is widespread in the subhumid upland forests of Madagascar and across a large area of sub-Saharan Africa, while the latter species occurs in the dry west of Madagascar and in the south of tropical Africa.

Dyschoriste: This genus of 94 accepted species occurs across most of the tropical and warm temperate regions of the globe (POWO 2020). On Madagascar eight species are recognized (Benoist 1967a), all endemic and mostly restricted to the Central Highlands or the dry west and north of the island. Most of the recognized taxa are known from few collections, with the exception of *D. siphonantha*. Benoist (1967a) divided that species into four varieties, but it is rather doubtful whether these represent meaningful taxa.

Eremomastax: This genus is monospecific, with *E. speciosa* being native to tropical Africa, where it is widely distributed. Benoist (1967a) treated material from Madagascar as an endemic species under the invalid name "*Paulo-wilhelmia decaryi*". It is now regarded as conspecific with the African species (Madagascar Catalogue 2020), but is still only known from two early 20th-century collections from the northern mountains.

Hygrophila: This is a pantropical genus of 76 known species (POWO 2020). It is unusual in the Acanthaceae for comprising mainly small plants that occur in wet habitats, some being fully aquatic species growing immersed in streams and lakes. Some become weedy in irrigation and drainage ditches. Six endemic species are recognized for Madagascar, known mainly from the west but all from few collections.

Mimulopsis: This genus comprises 19 accepted species, nine of which occur on Madagascar where they are endemic, occurring mostly in the Central Highlands; the others occur in Africa. Based on a phylogenetic study (Tripp and Darbyshire 2020), the only Malagasy species in the genus *Mellera*, originally described in the monotypic genus *Ionacanthus* (Benoist 1940), is now placed in *Mimulopsis* (E. Tripp et al., unpublished data). A recent review of *Mimulopsis* on Madagascar indicates that there may be five undescribed species (P. B. Phillipson et al., unpublished data).

Phaulopsis: This genus comprises 21 species, two of which occur on Madagascar (Manktelow 1996). One, *P. rupestris*, is endemic and known from only a few specimens from subhumid forests at mid- to high elevations. The second, *P. imbricata*, is divided into two subspecies, one occurring only in Africa, and the other, *P. i.* subsp. *madagascariensis*, in subhumid forests of Madagascar and also on the Comoros. The other species of the genus are spread across tropical and southern Africa, the Arabian Peninsula, and southern and southeastern Asia.

Ruellia: *Ruellia* (Figure 8.93d) is the fourth-most species-rich genus of Acanthaceae on Madagascar with 35 accepted species. These species are distributed across a large part of the island, with more than half occurring in the subarid bioclimatic region. Many of the species are highly localized, and while some are highly distinctive, others are difficult to identify, and in some cases have been divided into varieties of dubious value. The genus is rich globally and has a pantropical distribution, which extends into many warm temperate regions, and, according to some estimates, there are 350 accepted species (Tripp 2007; Tripp and Darbyshire 2017).

Subfamily Acanthoideae, Tribe Whitfieldieae

Camarotea: This genus is currently known from a single species, *C. souiensis* (Figure 8.93g), which is endemic to Madagascar. It is a shrub that occurs in the subarid southwest where it is quite frequent in dry spiny thickets. *Forcipella bosseri* and *F. longistaminea* are both regarded as synonyms of *C. souiensis*, but a second undescribed species is known from the north (P. B. Phillipson, unpublished data).

Chlamydacanthus: This genus is represented on Madagascar by a single endemic species, *C. euphorbioides*, which has only been recorded from the limestone areas of Ankarana and Montagne des Français. The genus is also represented in Kenya and Tanzania by a single species, *C. lindavianus*.

Forcipella: Four species of this endemic genus are currently recognized (Madagascar Catalogue 2020). None is well known, and the genus is in need of further study. Two species formerly included in the genus, *F. bosseri* and *F. longistaminea*, are now regarded as synonyms of *Camarotea souiensis*.

Lankesteria: The single species of this genus that occurs on Madagascar, *L. glandulosa*, is known from several sites in the west and north. It appears to be largely confined to karstic limestone areas, including Namoroka and Ankarana. It is quite similar to the west African species *L. brevior* but, nevertheless, appears to be distinct. Five other species occur in central and east Africa.

Leandriella: This genus was described by Benoist (1939) to accommodate a single species, *L. valvata*, an endemic to the Ankara Plateau to the north of Maevatenana. Later, Benoist (1966) described a second species, *L. oblonga*, from Firingalava, a site a little further south, but a number of additional collections of *Leandriella* are now available, and the two taxa described by Benoist are now considered conspecific (M. W. Callmander and P. B. Phillipson, unpublished data).

Vindasia: This genus comprises a single species, *V. virgata*, which is endemic to the southwest and is poorly known.

Zygoruellia: *Zygoruellia* is a monospecific genus endemic to Madagascar. Its single species, *Z. richardii*, is known from scattered

TABLE 8.48. **Malagasy Acanthaceae: IUCN Red List assessment criteria since 2002**

SPECIES	IUCN CRITERIA	YEAR
CRITICALLY ENDANGERED		
Crossandra acutiloba	CR B2ab(iii)	2015
C. cinnabarina	CR B2ab(iii)	2015
ENDANGERED		
Barleria brevituba	EN B2ab(iii,v)	2015
B. decaisniana	EN B2ab(ii,iii,v)	2015
B. dulcis	EN B1ab(iii,v)+ 2ab(iii,v)	2015
B. glandulostamina	EN B1ab(i,ii,iii,iv,v)+ 2ab(i,ii,iii,iv,v)	2019
B. insolita	EN B2ab(iii,v)	2015
B. laeta	EN B2ab(iii,v)	2015
B. leandrii	EN B1ab(i,ii,iii,v)+ 2ab(i,ii,iii,v)	2015
B. longipes	EN B1ab(iii,v)+ 2ab(iii,v)	2015
B. paucidentata	EN B1ab(i,ii,iii,iv,v)+ 2ab(i,ii,iii,iv,v)	2019
B. perrieri	EN B2ab(iii,v)	2015
B. pulchella	EN B1ab(i,ii,iii,iv,v)+ 2ab(i,ii,iii,iv,v)	2019
Blepharis crinita	EN B2ab(iii,v)	2015
B. maculata	EN B2ab(iii,v)	2015
Chlamydacanthus euphorbioides	EN B1ab(i,ii,iii,iv,v)+ 2ab(i,ii,iii,iv,v)	2019
Crossandra cloiselii	EN B1ab(i,ii,iii,iv,v)+ 2ab(i,ii,iii,iv,v)	2018
C. humbertii	EN B2ab(iii,v)	2015
C. isaloensis	EN B1ab(iii,v)+ 2ab(iii,v)	2015
C. nobilis	EN B1ab(iii,v)+ 2ab(iii,v)	2015
C. pilosa	EN B2ab(iii,v)	2015
C. poissonii	EN B2ab(iii,v)	2015
C. quadridentata	EN B1ab(iii,v)+ 2ab(iii,v)	2015
Ecbolium benoistii	EN B2ab(ii,iii,v)	2015
Hygrophila baronii	EN B1ab(i,ii,iii,iv,v)+ 2ab(i,ii,iii,iv,v)	2017
H. velata	EN B1ab(i,ii,iii,iv,v)+ 2ab(i,ii,iii,iv,v)	2017
Hypoestes acuminata	EN B2ab(i,ii,iii)	2019
H. taeniata	EN B1ab(i,ii,iii,iv,v)+ 2ab(i,ii,iii,iv,v)	2019
Justicia rigens	EN B2ab(i,ii,iii,iv,v)	2019
Lepidagathis madagascariensis	EN B2ab(iii,v)	2015
L. mucida	EN B2ab(iii,v)	2015
Melittacanthus divaricatus	EN B2ab(i,ii,iii,iv,v)	2019
Oplonia vincoides	EN B1ab(i,ii,iii,iv)+ 2ab(i,ii,iii,iv)	2018
Podorungia lantzei	EN B2ab(iii,v)	2015
P. serotina	EN B1ab(iii,v)+ 2ab(iii,v)	2015
Stenandriopsis amoenum (as *Stenandrium*)	EN B1ab(i,ii,iii,iv,v)+ 2ab(i,ii,iii,iv,v)	2019
VULNERABLE		
Crossandra albolineata	VU B1ab(i,ii,iii,v)+ 2ab(i,ii,iii,v)	2018
C. multidentata	VU B1ab(i,ii,iii,iv,v)+ 2ab(i,ii,iii,iv,v)	2019
Hypoestes isalensis	VU B1ab(i,ii,iii,iv,v)+ 2ab(i,ii,iii,iv,v)	2019
H. maculosa	VU B1ab(i,ii,iii,iv,v)+ 2ab(i,ii,iii,iv,v)	2019
Lepidagathis perrieri	VU B1ab(iii,v)+ 2ab(iii,v)	2015
Podorungia clandestina	VU B1ab(iii,v)+ 2ab(iii,v)	2015
P. humblotii	VU B1ab(iii,v)+ 2ab(iii,v)	2015
Zygoruellia richardii	VU B2ab(i,ii,iii,iv,v)	2019
LEAST CONCERN		
Barleria kitchingii		2015
Crossandra stenandrium		2015
Ecbolium madagascariense		2015
Mendoncia cowanii		2015
M. flagellaris		2015
M. vinciflora		2015

Source: Red List assessments derived from IUCN (2020).
Note: For the definitions of the different criteria see IUCN (2019).

localities in the west and north where it is confined to areas of karstic limestone, such as Bemaraha, Namoroka, and the Montagne des Français. It is a small shrub of valleys.

Subfamily Acanthoideae, Unplaced Genera

Dolichostachys: Affinities of this endemic genus are unclear (McDade et al. 2008), and its single described species, *D. elongata*, is known from two collections made at eastern coastal sites in the Analanjirofo Region over a hundred years ago.

Neuracanthus: *Neuracanthus* comprises 32 species spread across the Old World tropics with its highest diversity in east and northeast Africa. Six species are recognized on Madagascar, all endemic and concentrated in the subarid southwest and dry west (Bidgood and Brummitt 1998).

Subfamily Avicennioideae, Tribe Avicenniea

Avicennia: The widespread mangrove tree, *A. marina*, is a common constituent of mangrove habitat on Madagascar. It also occurs along the east coast of Africa, and in portions of tropical Asia and Australasia.

Subfamily Nelsonioideae, Tribe Nelsonieae

Elytraria: This genus comprises 21 species worldwide, and ranges from the New World tropics to most of tropical Africa, India, and Sri Lanka, and certain species have become naturalized in other regions of the world. Two endemic species of *Elytraria* occur on Madagascar: *E. madagascariensis* from the north and northwest, with only a single collection over the past 60 years, and *E. nodosa*, known from just a single 19th century collection. These species were treated by Benoist (1967a) under the genus *Tubiflora*, now considered a synonym of *Elytraria*.

Nelsonia: A single species of this genus on Madagascar was recognized by Benoist (1967a) as *N. campestris*; however, this species is now correctly referred to as *N. canescens* (Vollesen 1994). It is widespread in tropical Africa and is also native to India, southeast Asia, Australasia, and the New World (Daniel and McDade 2014). It is widely distributed on Madagascar, occurring mostly in damp places and in humid regions. The reported occurrence of *N. smithii* on the island likely refers to *N. canescens*; *N. smithii* was treated as a synonym of the latter by Daniel and McDade (2014). One other species is currently recognized in the genus, *N. gracilis*, which is known only from central Africa.

Saintpauliopsis: The single species of this genus, *S. lebrunii*, is native to central and east Africa, as well as Madagascar. It is known from only a few scattered localities on the island, including the Manongarivo Massif and forests along the eastern escarpment.

Subfamily Thunbergioideae, Tribe Thunbergieae

Mendoncia: *Mendoncia* is a genus of 89 species of scandent shrubs that occur in the American and African tropics. Six species of *Mendoncia* are currently recorded from Madagascar, all endemic and found primarily in moist evergreen forests of the east; one additional undescribed species is known. Benoist (1967a) accepted three species, but recent revisionary work (Magnaghi and Daniel 2014) has resulted in the description of two additional species, *M. delphina* and *M. kely*, and the elevation of a variety of *M. cowanii* to species rank, *M. decaryi*.

Pseudocalyx: This genus comprises six species worldwide, and, like *Mendoncia*, they are all scandent shrubs. *Pseudocalyx* is restricted to Africa, with a single species, *P. saccatus*, found also on Madagascar.

Thunbergia: This genus is native to Africa, Asia, and Madagascar, and comprises 151 species of herbs and shrubs (POWO 2020), the majority of which are scandent. The genus is represented by eight species on Madagascar, five of which are endemic. Among the other three, only one, *T. alata*, was considered native (Benoist 1967a), and it also occurs in Africa. The other two species, *T. erecta* and *T. grandiflora*, were introduced as ornamentals and have become naturalized. The endemic Malagasy species mostly occur on the Central Highlands, but they are poorly known and are in need of further study.

CONSERVATION STATUS

Relatively little effort has been made to publish International Union for Conservation of Nature (IUCN) Red List assessments for Malagasy Acanthaceae, no doubt related to the need to clarify species limits in many genera, and because many species are under-collected. In total, 50 species assessments of Malagasy members of this family, representing 15 genera, have been published on the Red List since 2002 (Table 8.48), although many preliminary assessments have been published in the taxonomic literature. Notably, only six species were classified as being of Least Concern, whereas 44 are classified as threatened. The genera with most assessments are *Barleria* and *Crossandra*, both with 11 of their 12 assessed species considered as threatened (one species in each genera was classified as Least Concern): for *Barleria* all 11 were classified as Endangered; for *Crossandra* two species were considered Critically Endangered, seven Endangered, and two Vulnerable.

Subject editors: Laurent Gautier and Steven M. Goodman

BIGNONIACEAE

M. W. Callmander, P. B. Phillipson, and S. Buerki

The Bignoniaceae family on Madagascar is remarkable: it is second in the world in terms of species richness after the Bignoniaceae of South America, and there are more native species known from Madagascar than from continental Africa and tropical and subtropical Asia combined (Gentry 1988). Currently, on Madagascar the family comprises 83 accepted native species, all endemic to the island. They are distributed across eight genera, two of which are strict endemics and three Malagasy Region (Madagascar and the Comoros, Mascarenes, and Seychelles archipelagoes) endemics (Figure 8.96). We estimate that no fewer than 35 new species on Madagascar await formal description, which would bring the total number of species to ~120 (Callmander et al. 2016; Madagascar Catalogue 2020). The eight Bignoniaceae genera present on the island have historically been divided in two tribes, based primarily on fruit dehiscence: the Coleeae (four genera with indehiscent fruits, endemic to the Malagasy Region) and the Tecomeae (four genera with dehiscent fruits, three widely distributed and one endemic to Madagascar) (Gentry 1976).

More recently, molecular phylogenetic studies have provided support for a Coleeae clade, sister to a grade of Old World genera previously assigned to the broadly circumscribed tribe Tecomeae, the entire lineage being referred to as the "Paleotropical clade." These studies suggest that the Tecomeae should be more narrowly circumscribed and thus restricted to the Neotropics (Zjhra et al. 2004; Olmstead et al. 2009; Callmander et al. 2016). On Madagascar, the Coleeae is more speciose in the humid regions than in the dry and subarid regions, while in the Paleotropical clade diversification is greater in the dry and subarid regions.

Perrier de la Bâthie (1938a, 1938b) published the first and only comprehensive taxonomic treatment for Madagascar Bignoniaceae, in which 54 species and numerous varieties and forms were recognized. Subsequently, 29 additional species have been described: five by Capuron (1960b, 1970b), one by Gentry (1977), 11 by Zjhra (2006), and 13 by the authors of this contribution and their collaborators (Callmander and Phillipson 2011, 2012; Callmander et al. 2011c, 2012c, 2016), who in addition have reduced certain species to synonymy and raised other taxa from infraspecific to species rank.

Eighty years after Perrier de la Bâthie's treatment, the species diversity of Malagasy Bignoniaceae, and the Coleeae in particular, remains to be adequately documented, and a fully revised account of the family is urgently needed to guide conservation priorities in places where most of the species are narrowly distributed and threatened by habitat loss (Good et al. 2006). Out of the 12 endemic Malagasy species described after 2010, 11 were classified as threatened based on International Union for Conservation of Nature (IUCN) Red List categories and criteria (IUCN 2012).

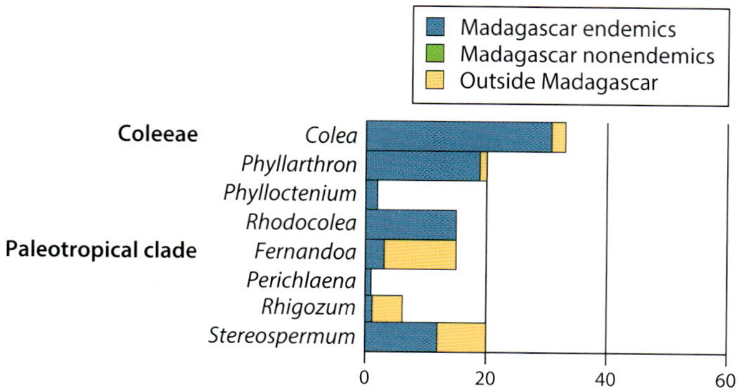

FIGURE 8.96 **Diversity and endemicity diagram of Malagasy Bignoniaceae at the level of genera, showing three different species counts: 1) endemic to Madagascar, 2) nonendemic but native to Madagascar, and 3) those occurring elsewhere in the world (for further information see text).**

SUMMARY OF CURRENT KNOWLEDGE OF THE MALAGASY GENERA

Tribe Coleeae

Colea: *Colea* is the most species-rich genus of Bignoniaceae on the island, currently with 31 accepted species. The genus is a Malagasy regional endemic with just a single species on Mauritius (*C. colei*) and another in the Seychelles (*C. seychellarum*). Species of *Colea* are mostly small monocaulous trees or treelets growing in humid or subhumid forests. The leaves are imparipinate (reduced to a single terminal leaflet in *C. unifoliolata*), borne in whorls, or occasionally opposite, with conspicuous leafy or spicate prophylls. Inflorescences are usually cauliflorous, most often compact but sometimes elongated and pendulous, or even sprawling along the ground, and they persist for multiple seasons. The flowers mostly possess conspicuous trumpet-shaped corollas of various colors, but some have more strongly zygomorphic corollas, apparently adapted to bird-pollination, and unilocular anthers. The fruits are indehiscent, sometimes with a sticky surface or visibly glandular. They are very variable in form (from ovoid to fusiform) and frequently have elaborate surface sculpturing including conspicuous, highly developed ridges, papillae, or surface protrusions of various kinds (Figure 8.97a), but are sometimes quite smooth.

Colea is a taxonomically difficult genus on Madagascar. For example, *C. floribunda* is highly variable in morphological aspects and forms a species complex throughout much of the humid and subhumid regions of the island. Further study of its different forms is required to determine whether discrete taxa can be recognized.

Perrier de la Bâthie (1938a) described *Ophiocolea* based on its bilocular ovaries and the long, narrow, and smooth fusiform fruit, whereas *Colea* has unilocular ovaries and ovoid to conical, ridged

FIGURE 8.97 **Morphology of the Malagasy Bignoniaceae. A) *Colea fusca*, B) *Phyllarthron longipedunculatum*, C) *Phylloctenium* sp. nov., D) *Rhodocolea involucrata*, E) *Fernandoa* sp. nov., F) *Perichlaena richardii*, and G) *Phyllarthron* sp. nov.** (PHOTOS A and F by P. Antilahimena; B by N. V. Manjato; C by L. Nusbaumer; D by D. Rabehevitra; E by Z. Burivalova; and G by X. Aubriot.)

fruits. However, *O. delphinensis* was seen as an exception to these latter features, with its longitudinally ridged fruits. Moreover, a recent molecular study has shown that recognition of *Ophiocolea* would render *Colea* paraphyletic, and that other recently discovered species also defy Perrier de la Bâthie's concepts of *Colea* and *Ophiocolea* (Callmander et al. 2016). The inclusion of *Ophiocolea* within *Colea*, regardless of differences in reproductive and fruit structures, is a practical solution to this problem.

Phyllarthron: This genus is a regional endemic, and currently comprises 19 species from Madagascar and one from the Comoro archipelago (*P. comorense*) (Callmander and Phillipson 2016). It resembles *Rhodocolea* in its flower and fruit structure (Perrier de la Bâthie 1938a), but its leaves, which are reduced to phyllodes comprising an enlarged articulate rachis (sometimes reduced to a single article, as in *P. ilicifolium* and *P. longipedunculatum*; Figure 8.97b), make it unique within the Coleeae. The flowers of this genus are all zygomorphic to some degree, but two species, *P. antongiliense* and *P. cauliflorum*, have strongly zygomorphic flowers, which prompted Leroy (1972) to assign them to a separate genus, *Paraphyllarthron*. Morphological features and molecular evidence do not support this segregation and a single genus, *Phyllarthron*, characterized by its unique morphological phyllodes, should be recognized (Callmander et al. 2016). The variation in flower symmetry might have evolved as a response to available pollinator communities, a phenomenon documented by Zjhra (2008).

Phyllarthron is the only genus of the tribe Coleeae that is well diversified in both the dry and humid regions (the other genera occur predominantly in either dry or humid habitats; see Gentry 1988). Callmander et al. (2016) hypothesized that *Phyllarthron* originated in dry regions and subsequently colonized humid regions by taking advantage of drier periods during the climatic oscillations of the last Quaternary. This hypothesis is supported by the general occurrence of phyllodes in this genus, which are seen as an adaptation to drought by reduction of a pinnate compound leaf to its axis.

The taxonomic framework of the genus *Phyllarthron* is currently unreliable, and accurate identification of specimens is difficult or impossible using the available taxonomic circumscriptions based on the existing treatment. Several species are characterized by resistant wood, known as *zahana*, which has traditionally been used to make weapon handles, especially for spears (Perrier de la Bâthie 1936b).

Phylloctenium: This is a small genus restricted to Madagascar, occurring predominantly in northern, western, and southern dry and subarid regions. The genus exhibits unique morphological characters representing adaptation to dry environments and browsing, notably the small simple leaves borne on persistent petioles (Figure 8.97c) that thicken and harden after leaf-drop to form straight or curved spines. Although some species may become small trees, most are shrubby, with one, *P. bernieri*, tending to scramble among other woody plants using its curved spines to obtain support. On the basis of a recent molecular study, *Phylloctenium* is the first extant lineage in the tribe Coleeae in the Malagasy Region to have diverged (Callmander et al. 2016).

Perrier de la Bâthie (1938a, 1938b) recognized two species in the genus, *P. bernieri* and *P. decaryanum*, based on 15 collections, eight of which he collected himself. In the course of reviewing *Phylloctenium*, which is now much better represented in herbaria, we have concluded that Perrier de la Bâthie's treatment does not deal adequately with the diversity in the genus, and we are currently engaged in a taxonomic revision from which we expect to recognize six species.

Rhodocolea: This genus is endemic to Madagascar and currently comprises 15 species of trees and shrubs that occur mainly in the more humid parts of the country. The genus can be recognized by the combination of its imparipinnate, opposite leaves (as opposed to verticillate in *Colea*), often showy flowers with trumpet- to bell-shaped corollas and bilocular anthers, but at first glance can be easily confused with *Colea*. Three morphological groups can be distinguished within the genus: the first one includes species characterized by a substantial terminal panicle of large pink or white flowers (e.g., *R. telfairiae*); the second one includes species characterized by numerous lateral (sometimes cauliflorous) racemose or spicate inflorescences of variously colored flowers (e.g., *R. racemosa*); and the third one has mostly terminal or sometimes cauliflorous short fasciculate or capitate inflorescences with predominantly red flowers (e.g., *R. involucrata*; Figure 8.97d). Phylogenetic evidence confirmed the monophyly of *Rhodocolea* as whole but not of these three morphological groups, and further studies are therefore required to better understand the infrageneric relationships (Callmander et al. 2016).

Perrier de la Bâthie (1938a, 1938b) recognized only six species in the genus, one of which, *R. racemosa*, he divided into numerous varieties and taxonomic forms. Reevaluation of the species complex has resulted in the recognition of four well-circumscribed species thanks to the wealth of herbarium material now available for the group (Phillipson and Callmander 2015). The genus also contains several undescribed species.

Some species of *Rhodocolea* are highly decorative, and while *R. telfairiae* is often planted as an ornamental in the Central Highlands and called *kifatra* or *hitsikitsika* (Perrier de la Bâthie 1938a), other species also merit cultivation. Some species of *Rhodocolea* are characterized by a hard wood called *ébène vert* (Perrier de la Bâthie 1936b).

Paleotropical Clade

Fernandoa: This genus comprises 15 species spread across Asia and Africa, with three species currently recognized on Madagascar. However, we have identified six additional species, and work to describe them is currently in progress. *Fernandoa* comprises mainly medium to large trees with imparipinnate leaves, and in their upper branches they bear robust flowers with large, mostly bright red, trumpet- to funnel-shaped corollas, and bilocular anthers. While these are apparently adapted to bird pollination there is evidence that some of the undescribed Malagasy species are pollinated by nocturnal mammals; these species bear cauliflorous flowers, often borne near the ground, and predominantly have pale yellow, somewhat bell-shaped corollas (Figure 8.97e).

Perichlaena: This genus is monospecific and a Malagasy endemic. Its lianescent habit is unique among the island's Bignoniaceae (one species of *Phylloctenium* can be somewhat scrambling in habit), although lianas are plentiful within the family in the New World and in Asia. This habit and the zygomorphic and bilabiate corolla (usually with brown or black petals) together provide key characters allowing recognition of this genus in Madagascar (Figure 8.97f). *Perichlaena richardii* is confined to the dry and subhumid forests of northern Madagascar. *Perichlaena* is the only endemic Malagasy genus in the family that is not placed in the tribe Coleeae (Gentry 1988; Callmander et al. 2016).

Rhigozum: This is a genus of six species of shrubs or small trees occurring in dry regions of Africa and Madagascar. Only one species occurs on the island, *R. madagascariense*, which is endemic and essentially confined to the southern subarid zone where it is a common constituent of the dry spiny thicket vegetation. It is the only Malagasy Bignoniaceae with alternate leaves, regular (actinomorphic) flowers with five fertile stamens, and small dehiscent capsules (Perrier de la Bâthie 1938a), but it is nevertheless morphologically rather variable with respect to stem and leaf indument, as well as corolla size and color.

Stereospermum: This genus is distributed from Africa (four species) and Madagascar (12 species) to southern and southeastern Asia (four species) (Callmander et al. 2012c). It can be recognized easily by its flowers, which have a narrowly cylindric corolla tube and spreading lobes, and by its cylindric, dehiscent, pod-like fruit (Figure 8.97g) that have a bony seed chamber possessing alternating deep cavities in which the seeds are lodged. Certain Malagasy species are quite widespread, notably *S. euphorioides*, which occurs throughout much of the west and central regions, while others are locally endemic, such as *S. longiflorum* in the dry deciduous forests of the extreme north and *S. gentryi*, endemic to the moist evergreen forests in the southeast. The main species diversity is in the dry deciduous forests of the west and north, and in the subarid forests and dry spiny thickets of the southwest. Most of the species are tall trees with hard, resistant wood of a dark ebony color. These species are known in Malagasy as *mangarahara*, *fangalitra*, and *mahafangalitra* (Perrier de la Bâthie 1938a).

On Madagascar, the geographic ranges of several species overlap, and intermediate individuals at several localities have been observed by botanists that are thought to be the result of hybridization. Consequently, species delimitation in the genus is difficult and introgressive hybridization is likely to be the source of the variability in some species. Two clear-cut new species of *Stereospermum* have nevertheless been described recently (Callmander et al. 2012c), and three possible undescribed species may occur, but further collections are needed to confirm their identity (Madagascar Catalogue 2020).

BIOGEOGRAPHY AND EVOLUTIONARY HISTORY OF BIGNONIACEAE ON MADAGASCAR

The most recent and complete molecular phylogenetic evidence brought new insights into the evolutionary history of Bignoniaceae on Madagascar (Callmander et al. 2016). Within Coleeae, the genus *Phylloctenium* is the basal lineage with *Phyllarthron* the next lineage to branch out, followed by the separation of *Rhodocolea* from its sister clade, which comprises *Colea* (Figure 8.98). As previously hypothesized by Gentry (1976) and Zjhra et al. (2004), Callmander et al. (2016) suggested a shift in the mode of seed dispersal from wind (e.g., in the genus *Stereospermum*) to lemur dispersal in the early evolution of the tribe Coleeae. The adaptation to lemur dispersal might have been the trigger for the remarkable diversification of the species-rich, mammal-dispersed genera of the tribe Coleeae in comparison with the wind-dispersed genera, which are generally less diversified on Madagascar, notably *Perichlaena* and *Rhigozum*.

A review of the literature on the diets of lemurs feeding on Coleeae showed that fruits of *Phylloctenium decaryanum* are commonly eaten by *Cheirogaleus medius* (Fat-tailed Dwarf Lemur) (Ganzhorn and Kappeler 1996). Fruits of species in the genera *Colea* and *Phyllarthron* are also eaten by *Cheirogaleus* (*C. major* and *C. medius*) and by species of *Eulemur* (*E. collaris*, *E. macaco*, and *E. fulvus*) (Fietz and Ganzhorn 1999; Birkinshaw 2001; Bollen et al. 2004a, 2004b). *Colea delphinensis* is known to be consumed by the flying fox *Pteropus rufus* (Bollen and van Elsacker 2002).

Although phylogenetic data alone do not provide a full interpretation of the bioclimatic origin of the Coleeae of Madagascar, when coupled with our knowledge of the ecology and morphology of its species, such information can serve as a basis for interpreting aspects of its evolutionary history. With the exception of species of *Phylloctenium* and *Phyllarthron* that have evolved some key morphological adaptations to cope with arid conditions (reduced leaves and spines in *Phylloctenium* and phyllodes in *Phyllarthron*), all species

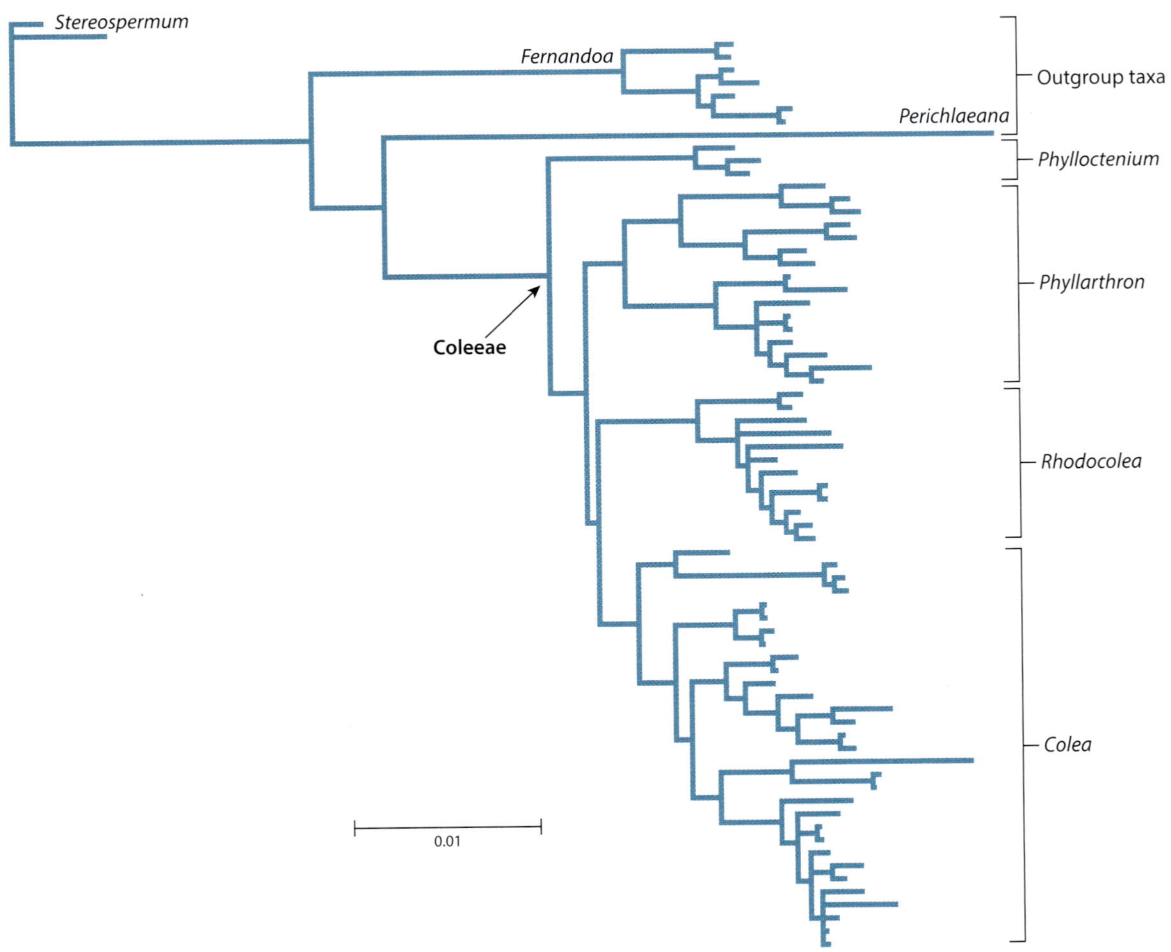

FIGURE 8.98 **Simplified Bayesian phylogenetic tree of Coleeae (Bignoniaceae) (modified from Callmander et al. 2016). Outgroup taxa belong to the Paleotropical clade. See text for more details.**

of the other taxa have large pinnate leaves and occur in humid (or subhumid) habitats. When this evidence is combined with the phylogenetic framework, it leads to the hypothesis that if the tribe originated in dry and subarid regions of Madagascar (where *Phylloctenium* is restricted and several species of *Phyllarthron* occur), two dispersal events toward the moist evergreen forest biome would have to have taken place: one by the most recent common ancestor of the *Rhodocolea* and *Colea* clade (presumably a leafy species) and another within the *Phyllarthron* clade (Figure 8.98). On the other hand, if we hypothesize an origin of the tribe in the humid or subhumid regions, that would also require two dispersal events into the drier areas: one for the ancestor of *Phylloctenium* and one within the *Phyllarthron* clade. However, independent of the bioclimatic origin of the tribe, both fruit morphology and ecological observations support the hypothesis that mammals mediated the movement of Coleeae species between these two different climatic zones.

Phylogenetic data also suggest several dispersal events to neighboring islands, including one to the Seychelles (*C. seychellarum*), one to Mauritius (*C. colei*), and at least two to the Comoros (*C. comorensis* and *Phyllarthron comorense*). Malagasy endemic genera have shown strong biogeographic affinities with the smaller islands of western Indian Ocean (Buerki et al. 2013). In the case of Coleeae, the colonization patterns are of interest due to their apparent specific dispersal syndrome. We are not aware of any evidence for the natural occurrence of lemur species on islands in the Malagasy Region (the archipelagoes of the Comoros, Mascarenes, and Seychelles), other than Madagascar. There is good evidence that *Eulemur fulvus* (Brown Lemur) and *E. mongoz* (Mongoose Lemur) were introduced by people to the Comoros (see Johnson et al., pp. 1941–46). Very little is known about the relationships between individual Bignoniaceae plant species and their lemur dispersers and this requires further investigation, which may shed light on the evolutionary history and the ecology of Coleeae. Overall, a better knowledge of seed-dispersal mechanisms in Coleeae is crucial to establish long-term conservation strategies for these iconic species of the Malagasy flora and their dispersers.

Subject editors: Laurent Gautier and Steven M. Goodman

ARALIACEAE

P. P. Lowry II and G. M. Plunkett

The largely tropical family Araliaceae comprises about 1900 species belonging to 44 genera, including several widely used plants such as *Panax* spp. (the ginsengs), *Hedera* spp. (ivy), and *Tetrapanax papyrifer* (the source of rice paper) (Plunkett et al. 2018; Lowry et al. 2019). While some mostly herbaceous species occur in temperate regions, this primarily woody group is much more diverse in the tropics, especially on the islands of the Pacific, in southeastern Asia and tropical South America, and on Madagascar. Long regarded as forming a family pair with the largely herbaceous Apiaceae, the systematics of Araliaceae have been profoundly transformed over the past 25 years based on results from molecular phylogenetic studies coupled with extensive fieldwork and collections-based morphological research. This has clarified relationships within the order Apiales (Plunkett and Lowry 2001; Plunkett et al. 2004a) and led to changes in the delimitation of its constituent families, including a recircumscription of Araliaceae (Plunkett et al. 2004a), a reordering of its genera (Lowry et al. 2004; Plunkett et al. 2004b, 2018), and the discovery of significant poly- and paraphyly in several genera (Plunkett et al. 2001, 2005; Plunkett and Lowry 2010).

ARALIACEAE OF MADAGASCAR

On Madagascar, Araliaceae were, until recently, thought to be represented by the genera *Cuphocarpus*, *Gastonia*, *Polyscias*, and *Schefflera* (Bernardi 1969, 1971, 1980). Molecular phylogenetic work has demonstrated, however, that *Cuphocarpus* and *Gastonia* (along with four other genera not found on Madagascar) are nested within a well-defined *Polyscias* clade (Plunkett et al. 2001, 2004c; Plunkett and Lowry 2010), which led to the adoption of a significantly broadened concept of this Paleotropical genus that includes the entire clade (Lowry and Plunkett 2010). By contrast, phylogenetic studies showed that the pantropical genus *Schefflera* comprises five separate, non-sister clades (Plunkett et al. 2005), each occurring in a different geographic region. This necessitated a breakup of *Schefflera*, and because the type of the generic name belongs to the smallest of the five clades, comprising eight species restricted to islands of the southwest Pacific Ocean, the members of each of the four other clades had to be transferred elsewhere (Lowry et al. 2019; Plunkett et al. 2020). Regarding the African-Malagasy clade, a recent study showed that it comprises two distinct, well-delimited groups (Gostel et al. 2017), which have now been recognized as separate genera, *Astropanax* and *Neocussonia* (Lowry et al. 2017), both of which are also present in Africa, while *Astropanax* also occurs in the Comoro islands and *Neocussonia* in the Seychelles. Finally, as part of the phylogenetic realignment of Apiales, the genus *Hydrocotyle*, traditionally placed in Apiaceae, was shown to belong to Araliaceae despite its herbaceous habit (Plunkett et al. 2004a, 2018; Nicolas and Plunkett 2009), bringing the total number of genera on Madagascar to four (Madagascar Catalogue 2020).

TABLE 8.49. **Species of Araliaceae on Madagascar, their origin status, and IUCN status**

SPECIES	ENDEMISM	IUCN STATUS
Astropanax humblotianus (Drake) Lowry, G. M. Plunkett, Gostel & Frodin	Endemic	EN
A. monophyllus (Baker) Lowry, G. M. Plunkett, Gostel & Frodin	Endemic	LC
A. myrianthus (Baker) Lowry, G. M. Plunkett, Gostel & Frodin	Endemic	NT
Hydrocotyle bonariensis Lam.	Naturalized	LC
H. mannii Hook. f.	Native	LC
H. ranunculoides L. f.	Naturalized	LC
H. sibthorpioides Lam.	Naturalized	LC
H. verticillata Thunb.	Naturalized	NE
Neocussonia bojeri (Seem.) Hutch.	Endemic	LC
N. bracteolifera (Frodin) Lowry, G. M. Plunkett, Gostel & Frodin	Endemic	VU
N. capuroniana (Bernardi) Lowry, G. M. Plunkett, Gostel & Frodin	Endemic	EN
N. favargeri (Bernardi) Lowry, G. M. Plunkett, Gostel & Frodin	Endemic	NT
N. fosbergiana (Bernardi) Lowry, G. M. Plunkett, Gostel & Frodin	Endemic	EN
N. frodiniana (Bernardi) Lowry, G. M. Plunkett, Gostel & Frodin	Endemic	LC
N. halleana (Bernardi) Lowry, G. M. Plunkett, Gostel & Frodin	Endemic	LC
N. litoralis (Bernardi) Lowry, G. M. Plunkett, Gostel & Frodin	Endemic	VU
N. longipedicellata (R. Vig. & Danguy ex Lecomte) Lowry, G. M. Plunkett, Gostel & Frodin	Endemic	LC
N. moratii (Bernardi) Lowry, G. M. Plunkett, Gostel & Frodin	Endemic	VU
N. rainaliana (Bernardi) Lowry, G. M. Plunkett, Gostel & Frodin	Endemic	EN
N. staufferiana (Bernardi) Lowry, G. M. Plunkett, Gostel & Frodin	Endemic	LC
N. vantsilana (Baker) Lowry, G. M. Plunkett, Gostel & Frodin	Endemic	LC
N. weibeliana (Bernardi) Lowry, G. M. Plunkett, Gostel & Frodin	Endemic	LC
Polyscias aculeata (Decne. & Planch.) Harms	Endemic	LC
P. amplifolia (Baker) Harms	Endemic	LC
P. anacardium Bernardi	Endemic	VU
P. andrearum Bernardi	Endemic	NT
P. ariadnes Bernardi	Endemic	LC
P. aubrevillei (Bernardi) Bernardi	Endemic	VU
P. baehniana (Bernardi) Bernardi	Endemic	VU
P. baretiana Bernardi	Endemic	VU
P. boivinii (Seem.) Bernardi	Endemic	LC
P. briquetiana (Bernardi) Lowry & G. M. Plunkett	Endemic	LC
P. carolorum Bernardi	Endemic	LC
P. chapelieri (Drake) Harms ex R. Vig.	Endemic	LC
P. cissiflora (Baker) Harms	Endemic	VU
P. compacta Lowry & G. M. Plunkett	Endemic	VU
P. confertifolia (Baker) Harms	Endemic	VU
P. cussonioides (Drake) Bernardi	Endemic	EN
P. duplicata (Thouars ex Baill.) Lowry & G. M. Plunkett	Native	NE
P. floccosa (Drake) Bernardi	Endemic	NT
P. fraxinifolia (Baker) R. Vig.	Endemic	LC
P. gruschvitzkii Bernardi	Endemic	CR
P. heineana Bernardi	Endemic	VU
P. humbertiana (Bernardi) Lowry & G. M. Plunkett	Endemic	LC
P. kalabenonensis Lowry & Callm.	Endemic	CR
P. lancifolia (Drake) R. Vig.	Endemic	EN
P. lantzii (Drake) Harms ex R. Vig.	Endemic	VU
P. leandriana (Bernardi) Lowry & G. M. Plunkett	Endemic	LC
P. madagascariensis (Seem.) Harms	Endemic	LC
P. maralia (Roem. & Schult.) Bernardi	Endemic	LC
P. multibracteata (Baker) Harms	Endemic	LC

(continued overleaf)

TABLE 8.49. *continued*

SPECIES	ENDEMISM	IUCN STATUS
P. muraltiana Bernardi	Endemic	VU
P. myrsine Bernardi	Endemic	LC
P. nossibensis (Drake) Harms	Endemic	NT
P. ornifolia (Baker) Harms	Endemic	LC
P. pachypedicellata Lowry & Callm.	Endemic	EN
P. pentamera (Baker) Harms	Endemic	VU
P. rainaliorum Bernardi	Endemic	EN
P. tafondroensis (Drake) Harms ex R. Vig.	Endemic	VU
P. terminalia Bernardi	Endemic	VU
P. tripinnata Harms	Endemic	LC
P. wohlhauseri Lowry & Callm.	Endemic	CR
P. zanthoxyloides (Baker) Harms	Endemic	LC

Source: Red List assessments derived from IUCN (2020).
Note: IUCN status abbreviations: CR, Critically Endangered; DD, Data Deficient; EN, Endangered; LC, Least Concern; NE, Not Evaluated; NT, Near Threatened; VU, Vulnerable.

The vast majority of Malagasy members of Araliaceae occur in lowland and medium-altitude moist evergreen forests, although some species can be found in other types of vegetation (Madagascar Catalogue 2020). For example, several members of the family, such as *Neocussonia litoralis* and *N. rainaliana*, are restricted to littoral forests, which form a narrow, nowadays highly fragmented band along the east coast. Other species, including *N. bracteolifera*, *Polyscias aubrevillei*, and *P. terminalia*, occur only at high-elevation sites in montane grasslands and montane ericoid thickets, while *P. baehniana*, *P. boivinii*, and *P. floccosa* are found in moist semi-deciduous forests in the north and west. *Neocussonia bojeri*, one of the few Araliaceae of sclerophyllous woodlands, is a common and widespread fire-resistant species. The family is likewise rare in dry deciduous forests and dry spiny thickets, where only a few species occur, including *Polyscias confertifolia*.

SPECIES DIVERSITY AND ENDEMISM

Bernardi's work on Malagasy Araliaceae led him to recognize a total of 55 species (Bernardi 1980), nearly half of which he described. These included five species of *Cuphocarpus*, one of *Gastonia*, and 33 of *Polyscias* (Bernardi 1971, 1980). All are now included in *Polyscias* (Lowry and Plunkett 2010), which together with newly described species has brought the total number of currently recognized species of *Polyscias* in Madagascar to 41 (Table 8.49; Madagascar Catalogue 2020). Bernardi also recognized 16 species of *Schefflera* (Bernardi 1969, 1980), three that are now placed in *Astropanax* and 11 in *Neocussonia*, plus two more now regarded as synonyms (Madagascar Catalogue 2020). Extensive work in both herbaria and the field conducted since the mid-1980s has led to the publication of three new species of *Polyscias* (Callmander et al. 2009) and the identification of three additional species of *Astropanax*, 25 of *Neocussonia*, and more than 90 of *Polyscias* (P. Lowry and G. M. Plunkett, unpublished data; Madagascar Catalogue 2020), all now in the process of being published. Along with the five (including four introduced weeds) currently recognized species of *Hydrocotyle* (Madagascar Catalogue 2020), this brings the projected total number of Araliaceae on the island to at least 175 species.

Araliaceae have a higher level of endemism than the estimated 87% for the native Malagasy vascular flora as a whole (Lowry et al. 2018). All currently recognized members of *Astropanax* and *Neocussonia* are restricted to the island, as are all but one species of *Polyscias*, whereas the single native species of *Hydrocotyle* occurs elsewhere (Figure 8.99, Table 8.49). In all, 96.6% of Madagascar's native Araliaceae taxa are thus endemic. Furthermore, nearly half of the 56 published native species have restricted geographic distributions, often occurring on a single mountain or protected area (Madagascar Catalogue 2020). All of the species that remain to be described are endemic, and nearly all of them have highly restricted distributions.

THE GENERA OF ARALIACEAE ON MADAGASCAR

Astropanax

The six Malagasy species belonging to this genus (three of which are now being described) were, until recently, included in the large, polyphyletic genus *Schefflera* and therefore exhibit its general features: palmately compound leaves, flowers borne on an unarticulated pedicel, and a lack of spines or prickles (Plunkett et al. 2005). *Astropanax* can be distinguished from *Neocussonia*, and also segregated from *Schefflera*, by its five- to nine-carpellate ovary with five to nine styles, and its generally acute to acuminate or caudate leaflets (Figure 8.100a) (see below for the diagnostic features of *Neocussonia*) (Lowry et al. 2017). Some species are terrestrial, while

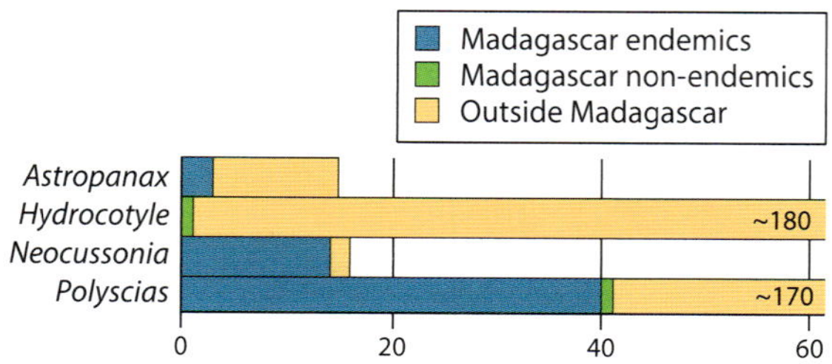

FIGURE 8.99 **Diversity and endemicity diagram of Malagasy Araliaceae at the level of genera, showing three different species counts: 1) endemic to Madagascar, 2) nonendemic but native to Madagascar, and 3) those occurring elsewhere in the world (for further information see text). In cases when species diversity exceeds or does not conform to that presented on the horizontal graph scale, the figures are written along the respective horizontal line of a given genus.**

FIGURE 8.100 **Examples of Malagasy Araliaceae. A) *Astropanax monophyllus* at Marojejy (Ravelonarivo 3348); B) *Hydrocotyle bonariensis* at Omboué, Gabon (Bidault 2691); C and D) *Neocussonia* sp. nov. at Bemangidy, Tsitongambarika (Lowry 7157); E) *N. capuroniana* at Ambohitantely (Plunkett 2328); F) *Polyscias chapelieri* at Bevoay, Tsitongambarika (Lowry 7161); and G and H) *Polyscias* sp. nov. at Bemangidy, Tsitongambarika (Lowry 6708).** (PHOTO A by D. Ravelonarivo; B by E. Bidault; and C–H by P. Lowry).

others are hemi-epiphytic trees or lianas. *Astropanax* is richest in continental Africa, where 11 species occur, while the Comoros and the Seychelles each have a single endemic species. The Malagasy species occur in humid, subhumid, and montane forest. Two of them are relatively widespread (*A. monophyllus* and *A. myrianthus*), whereas the others have restricted ranges in the northeastern and central eastern part of the island (P. Lowry and G. M. Plunkett, unpublished data; Madagascar Catalogue 2020).

Hydrocotyle

This genus, traditionally treated in Apiaceae, was transferred to Araliaceae on the basis of phylogenetic studies. Its species are annual or perennial herbs, often prostrate and rooting at the nodes, with membranaceous leaves that are typically simple and orbicular (sometimes peltate), and/or palmately lobed to compound (Figure 8.100b). Its flowers are bicarpellate but otherwise pentamerous, usually arranged in few- to many-flowered umbels (simple or compound), but sometimes forming more complex inflorescences. The fruits are flattened laterally and usually five-ribbed, and unlike most other Araliaceae, dry and schizocarpic. With approximately 180 species, *Hydrocotyle* is a cosmopolitan genus, most diverse in the Neotropics and Australia, and the great majority of its species are restricted to humid sites such as stream banks and seepage areas. In Madagascar, it is represented by five species, four of which are widespread introduced weeds (*H. bonariensis*, *H. ranunculoides*,

H. sibthorpioides, and *H. verticillata*), while *H. mannii* is native to Madagascar and tropical Africa (Madagascar Catalogue 2020).

Neocussonia

This genus, also previously included in *Schefflera*, has nearly 40 species in Madagascar (14 currently recognized and the remainder now being described), as well as two representatives in Africa (Lowry et al. 2017). In addition to having palmately compound or unifoliolate leaves and unarticulated pedicels, and lacking spines or prickles, it can be distinguished from *Astropanax* by its two- to five-carpellate ovary with two to five styles, and leaflets with a generally truncate apex (rounded in *N. halleana*) with an evident notch and a small bump formed by an extension of the midvein (Figures 8.100c–e). They are all terrestrial trees, and most species have more or less restricted distributions in humid, subhumid, and montane forest, some at low-elevation sites and others as high as 2600 m, although the fire-resistant species *N. bojeri* is found in dry and subhumid areas, and three species, *N. longipedicellata*, *N. staufferiana*, and *N. vantsilana*, are more widespread in humid and subhumid environments (Madagascar Catalogue 2020).

Polyscias

This genus, now circumscribed to include species previously placed in *Cuphocarpus* and *Gastonia*, has about 130 species on Madagascar (41 currently recognized and the remainder now being described). They are characterized by pinnately compound leaves (a few species are unifoliolate) and flowers borne on articulated pedicels (Figures 8.100f–h). Species of *Polyscias* are terrestrial trees or shrubs, and they occur in a wide range of habitats. All but four species belong to *Polyscias* subgenus *Maralia* (Lowry and Plunkett 2010), a group centered on Madagascar but also with two species in Africa and one on the Comoro islands. Members of this subgenus are distinguished by having ovaries with four to numerous carpels and persistent leaves. The Malagasy species are found in humid, subhumid, or montane forests. *Polyscias* subgenus *Sciadopanax*, characterized by ovaries with two carpels and deciduous leaves, has three species on Madagascar (the most widespread being *P. boivinii*), as well as nine in Africa and one on the Comoros. The Malagasy members are restricted primarily to dry and subhumid areas in the western and northern parts of the island. *Polyscias* subgenus *Cuphocarpus* has a single species, *P. aculeata*, which is widespread in lowland moist evergreen forests and is characterized by an ovary composed of a single carpel. This feature is shared, however, with four species in subgenus *Maralia* that occur in mid- to high-elevation humid, subhumid, and montane forest, the most widespread of which is *P. briquetiana* (Madagascar Catalogue 2020).

CONSERVATION STATUS OF SPECIES

Risk of extinction assessments using the International Union for Conservation of Nature (IUCN) Red List criteria (IUCN 2012) were recently conducted for three species of *Astropanax*, four of *Hydrocotyle*, 14 of *Neocussonia*, and 40 of *Polyscias* (Table 8.49), and are available on the published Red List (IUCN 2020). A total of 27 species were found to be threatened, including three that were classified as Critically Endangered (*Polyscias gruschvitzkii*, *P. kalabenonensis*, and *P. wohlhauseri*), eight as Endangered, and 16 as Vulnerable, whereas five were found to be Near Threatened, and 29 were of Least Concern. As most of the threatened species occur in forest environments, in particular low- and mid-elevation rainforests as well as subhumid forests, by far the main threat they face is degradation and loss of their habitat, primarily due to shifting agriculture and, to a lesser extent, to fire, mining, and the indirect consequences of selective forest exploitation. A few restricted-range species known only from protected areas, such as *Neocussonia frodiniana*, *N. halleana*, *Polyscias humbertiana* and *P. leandriana*, do not appear to be threatened.

Subject editors: Laurent Gautier and Steven M. Goodman

BORAGINALES

J. S. Miller

Boraginales is a natural order containing about 125 genera and 2700 species distributed nearly worldwide. The order, as presently defined, is the consequence of generic delimitation and assignment that results from two decades of molecular evidence (summarized in Luebert et al. 2016a), but the classification of the constituent groups has been the subject of much debate over the decades. On Madagascar the Boraginales comprises five families with a total of 52 species, half of which are endemic (Figure 8.101). The order is of little economic importance except for some members of the Boraginaceae and Heliotropiaceae that are grown as ornamentals.

SYSTEMATICS OF THE BORAGINALES

While molecular evidence has recently led to major changes in circumscription of the order, the core—the family Boraginaceae in its conventional sense—has long been recognized as a natural

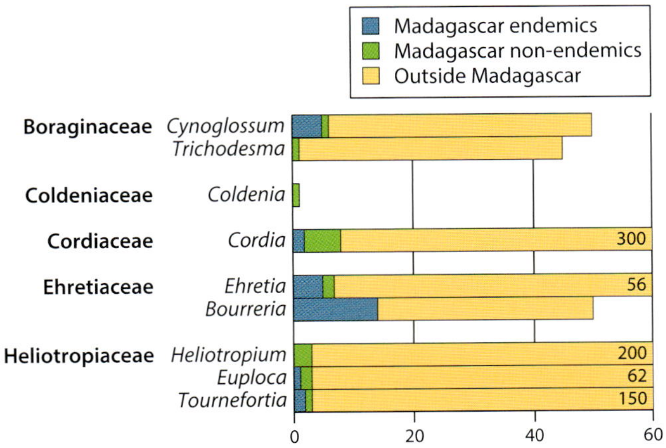

FIGURE 8.101 Diversity and endemicity diagram of Malagasy Boraginales at the level of genera, showing three different species counts: 1) endemic to Madagascar, 2) nonendemic but native to Madagascar, and 3) those occurring elsewhere in the world (for further information see text). In cases when species diversity exceeds or does not conform to that presented on the horizontal graph scale, the figures are written along the respective horizontal line of a given genus.

assemblage. The family has traditionally been composed of plants with radially symmetric pentamerous and sympetalous flowers, a bicarpellate gynoecium that is falsely four-locular by intrusion of placenta, and generally scorpioid inflorescences (Buys and Hilger 2003). Early molecular evidence suggested that Hydrophyllaceae is embedded in the traditional Boraginaceae (Ferguson 1999), but more recent studies have shown that among them one clade was best placed in another order (Refulio-Rodriguez and Olmstead 2014; Weigend et al. 2014). To date, accumulated molecular evidence has provided guidance as to which groups are best included and excluded from a more broadly defined Boraginales. The most recent evidence (Luebert et al. 2016a, 2016b) recognizes Boraginales as having 11 constituent families, all of which are both monophyletic and recognizable.

Boraginaceae has traditionally been divided into four to five distinct subfamilies (A. de Candolle 1845, 1846; Johnston 1930), Cordioideae, Ehretioideae, Heliotropioideae, and Boraginoideae, plus the genus *Wellstedia*, which has been considered allied and recognized as either a monogeneric subfamily (Mabberley 2008) or a family (Merxmuller 1960; Dahlgren 1980; Takhtajan 1980). All five of these subfamilies are elevated to familial status in a revised Boraginales (Luebert et al. 2016a), with the addition of three distinct clades of Hydrophyllaceae, plus Coldeniaceae (allied with Cordiaceae and not Ehretiaceae [Weigend et al. 2014; Luebert et al. 2016a]), Hoplestigmataceae, and Lennoaceae (Weigend et al. 2014).

Recent data have shown that Hydrophyllaceae consist of four distinct clades, most of which are only distantly related (Gottschling et al. 2001; Nazaire and Hufford 2012; Refulio-Rodriguez and Olmstead 2014). *Hydrolea* has been erroneously placed in Hydrophyllaceae, but recent evidence supports its recognition as a distinct, monogeneric family within Solanales (Bittrich and Amaral 2016). *Codon*, a genus of two South African herbaceous species, is allied with Boraginaceae *sensu stricto* and Wellstediaceae, the three taxa forming a predominantly herbaceous clade in the order. Traditionally, Hydrophyllaceae are divided into two clades, Hydrophyllaceae *sensu stricto*, with a majority of herbaceous genera, and Namaceae, with the four woody genera *Eriodictyon*, *Nama*, *Turricula*, and *Wigandia*.

The two additional families that are included in the order are Hoplestigmataceae, with the sole genus *Hoplestigma* consisting of two central African species of trees, and Lennoaceae, with two genera in southwestern United States, Mexico, and northwestern South America.

Plant groups that have been shown by molecular evidence to best be placed in other orders include the genera *Hydrolea* and *Pteleocarpa*, and the families Tetrachondraceae and Vahliaceae. *Hydrolea*, traditionally included in the Hydrophyllaceae, is more closely related to Solanales (Cosner et al. 1994; Soltis et al. 2000). The genus *Pteleocarpa*, with a single species from Malaysia and Borneo, has been placed in the Ehretioideae (now Ehretiaceae), but molecular evidence indicates it is best considered to belong to the Gelsiminaceae in the Gentialales (Refulio-Rodriguez and Olmstead 2014). Thorne (1992) and Takhtajan (1997) considered Tetrachondraceae allied with Boraginaceae, but Savolainen et al. (2000) demonstrated that it is best placed in Lamiales. Vahliaceae has also been considered allied with Boraginaceae (e.g., B. Bremer et al. 2002), but it is better placed in Lamiales (Weigend et al. 2014) or Solanales (Refulio-Rodriguez and Olmstead 2014).

Collectively, a wealth of molecular data now support a broadly defined Boraginales with 11 constituent families (Luebert et al. 2016a). Each of these families is monophyletic and has a distinguishing series of morphological characters.

SYSTEMATICS OF MALAGASY BORAGINALES

Boraginaceae in its traditional sense has not been previously treated for the *Flore de Madagascar et des Comores*, but a monograph has recently been published in the series (J. S. Miller et al. 2021). A few species were described by early authors based on accumulated specimens. In the 1960s, René Capuron conducted a review of material from the family in the herbarium of the Muséum National d'Histoire Naturelle in Paris and made annotations on some specimens, including a few cases for unpublished names, and he left notes in the archives of the same institution. Unfortunately, no comprehensive work on the family was completed by Capuron before his premature death. The present author began work on Malagasy Boraginaceae in 1988, including fieldwork in southern Madagascar, and reviewed specimens in Paris, the two herbaria in Antananarivo, and other important European and North American herbaria. Studies progressed through 2005 with the completion of description of 26 new species in six genera (J. S. Miller 2001a, 2001b, 2002, 2003a, 2003b, 2005a, 2005b). Five of the families that comprise a newly constituted Boraginales occur on Madagascar and in the Comoro archipelago: Boraginaceae, Coldeniaceae, Cordiaceae, Ehretiaceae, and Heliotropiaceae and include a total of 52 species in 10 genera (J. S. Miller et al. 2021).

Since completion of studies of individual genera, molecular data have shown that some of the species of *Heliotropium* are best accommodated in the genus *Euploca* and that all of the species of *Hilsenbergia* are nested within the genus *Bourreria* (Luebert et al. 2016a). Nomenclatural changes to accommodate these recircumscriptions have now been published (J. S. Miller and Gottschling 2017). In addition, the species originally treated as conspecific with a known species from east Africa, *H. teitensis* (J. S. Miller 2005b), has now been recognized as distinct and described as a new species, *B. scabra* (Thulin and Razafimandimbison 2017).

Out of the 52 species of Boraginales that occur on Madagascar and the Comoros, 46 are native and 29 are endemic. Almost all of those on Madagascar occur in dry spiny thickets of the south and southwest, with fewer species in the western dry deciduous forests and just a handful in the north; members of this group are seldom significant constituents of forests. Most of these species are uncommon or rare, and essentially none occur in large numbers at any given place. *Cynoglossum lowryanum* is known only from the type, and that was also the case for *B. angustifolia*, but it has recently been rediscovered growing at the type locality (J. S. Miller, unpublished data). Nearly half of the 29 endemic species are known from 10 or fewer collections, and several of the nonendemic species are known from only a single or very limited number of collections. The only species seen in abundance is *Cordia myxa*, which is widespread in the Old World and frequently cultivated near villages because, when severely pruned, it produces long unbranched stems that are used as lateral pieces in the construction of mud houses.

TABLE 8.50. **Threatened Boraginales from Madagascar and the Comoros**

SPECIES	IUCN STATUS	REGION
Bourreria angustifolia (J. S. Mill.) J. S. Mill. & Gottschling	CR	Southwest
B. apetala (J. S. Mill.) J. S. Mill. & Gottschling	EN	West
B. capuronii (J. S. Mill.) J. S. Mill. & Gottschling	VU	Southwest
B. comorensis (J. S. Mill.) J. S. Mill. & Gottschling	CR	Comoros
B. croatii (J. S. Mill.) J. S. Mill. & Gottschlingen	EN	Southwest
B. darcyana (J. S. Mill.) J. S. Mill. & Gottschling	VU	West
B. labatii (J. S. Mill.) J. S. Mill. & Gottschling	VU	North
B. leslieae (J. S. Mill.) J. S. Mill. & Gottschling	VU	Southwest
B. lowryana (J. S. Mill.) J. S. Mill. & Gottschling	EN	Southwest
B. moratiana (J. S. Mill.) J. S. Mill. & Gottschling	EN	North
B. randrianasoloana (J. S. Mill.) J. S. Mill. & Gottschling	EN	Southwest
B. schatziana (J. S. Mill.) J. S. Mill. & Gottschling	EN	Northeast
Cordia lowryana J. S. Mill.	VU	Northeast
C. schatziana J. S. Mill.	EN	West
Cynoglossum birkinshawii J. S. Mill.	CR	North
C. cernuum Baker	VU	Central
C. lowryanum J. S. Mill.	CR	East
C. monophlebium Baker	VU	Central
C. tsaratananense J. S. Mill.	CR	North
Ehretia australis J. S. Mill.	EN	South
E. decaryi J. S. Mill.	EN	South
E. meyersii J. S. Mill.	EN	Northeast
E. phillipsonii J. S. Mill.	EN	Southwest
E. seyrigii J. S. Mill.	VU	West
Euploca perrieri (J. S. Mill.) J. S. Mill. & Gottschling	CR	West
Tournefortia kirkii (I. M. Johnston) J. S. Mill.	VU	North

Note: IUCN status abbreviations: CR, Critically Endangered; DD, Data Deficient; EN, Endangered; LC, Least Concern; NE, Not Evaluated; NT, Near Threatened; VU, Vulnerable.

THE FIVE FAMILIES OF MALAGASY BORAGINALES

Key to the Families of Boraginales on Madagascar

1.	Style divided once or twice, two or four stigmas	2
1a.	Style undivided; one stigma	4
2.	Style divided once; two stigmas	3
2a.	Style divided twice; four stigmas	CORDIACEAE
3.	Plants annual; prostrate herbs	COLDENIACEAE
3a.	Plants perennial; shrubs or small trees	EHRETIACEAE
4.	Style terminal; stigmas mostly conical	HELIOTROPIACEAE
4a.	Style gynobasic; stigmas mostly clavate to filiform	BORAGINACEAE

Boraginaceae

Boraginaceae is a family of about 80 genera and 1600 species known from temperate and high-elevation tropical regions. All species are herbaceous (*Echium* in the Canary Islands is exceptional in being shrubby), and they generally have scorpioid cymose inflorescences and gynobasic styles. Two genera are known from Madagascar. *Cynoglossum*, with about 50 species worldwide, has six species on Madagascar, scattered across the Central Highlands, mostly in open high-elevation areas. *Trichodesma*, with about 45 species worldwide, is a herb with anthers united in a cone surrounding the style and known on Madagascar from a single weedy species, *T. zeylanicum*, which occurs in disturbed areas and cornfields in the west.

Coldeniaceae

Coldeniaceae is a monotypic family with its single species, *Coldenia procumbens*, widespread in the Old World throughout tropical Africa, tropical Asia, Australia, and western and northwestern Madagascar. It is a procumbent annual herb that has two separate styles and distinctive leaves in which the secondary veins end in the sinuses of the marginal serrations.

Cordiaceae

Cordiaceae is a family of two genera and about 450 species. *Cordia* contains about 300 species worldwide and is widespread in the tropics. A greater number of species occur in the New World, and *Varronia*, representing more than 135 species, is restricted to the Neotropics, with the exception of a single species that has become naturalized in some areas of the Old World tropics. There are 10 species of *Cordia* in western, southern, and northern Madagascar, at low elevations, and all are small trees or shrubs. Eight of these are native, including two endemics. *Varronia curassavica* is naturalized on Madagascar and can be found along railroad tracks on Nosy Be; with its bird-dispersed fruit the plant will probably become invasive as it has in other locations in the Old World (Nowicke and Miller 1991).

Ehretiaceae

This family is pantropical and composed mostly of trees and shrubs (*Tiquilia* being low and suffrutescent), including six genera and about 150 species. Two genera are found on Madagascar—*Ehretia* with seven species (five endemics) of trees and shrubs and *Bourreria* with 14 endemic species of trees and shrubs—both in western, southern, and northern areas of the island.

Heliotropiaceae

Heliotropiaceae is a family widespread in tropical and subtropical regions and composed of two to four (or more) genera and about 350 species. The historical distinction between *Heliotropium* (herbs with dry fruits) and *Tournefortia* (woody trees, shrubs, and lianas) is clearly demonstrated as artificial by molecular evidence, but sampling remains inadequate for comprehensively redefining these genera. Three genera occur on Madagascar. *Heliotropium* (~200 species worldwide) is known from six nonendemic species on Madagascar and the Comoros; three are introduced weeds, two of them being known from a single collection and clearly non-native. All six species are herbs distributed mostly in western Madagascar. *Euploca* (perhaps several dozen species worldwide) is known on Madagascar from three herbaceous species, all found in the west, one of them being endemic. *Tournefortia* comprises about 150 species, mostly in the Neotropics, but with a few species in Africa, Madagascar, Asia, and the Pacific, with three native species known from eastern Madagascar, two of them endemic.

CONSERVATION

Twenty-six of the 52 species of Boraginales that occur on Madagascar have been assigned to one of the three International Union for the Conservation of Nature (IUCN) Red List threatened categories (IUCN 2001; J. S. Miller and Porter-Morgan 2011). Forty-six species on the island are native and 29 are endemic. Of the 46 native species, six are classed as Critically Endangered, 11 are Endangered, nine are Vulnerable (Table 8.50), and 20 are of Least Concern. The six non-native naturalized species are all uncommon, known from a single or few collections. The current protected areas system includes some portion of the range of 36 of the 46 native species of Boraginales (J. S. Miller and Porter-Morgan 2011). These numbers indicate that Boraginales are unusual as a plant group in being low in endemism.

Subject editors: Laurent Gautier and Steven M. Goodman

REFERENCES

Abbayes, H. des. 1947. *Cladonia* (lichens) nouveaux de la région malgache. *Revue Bryologique et Lichénologique* 16: 47–94.

———. 1948. Caractères et affinités de la flore des *Cladonia* (lichens) de la région malgache. *Mémoires de l'Institut Scientifique de Madagascar*, série B, 1(2): 57–63.

———. 1956. Lichens de la région malgache. I. Especes foliacées et fruticuleuses récoltées á Madagascar, principalement par H. Humbert, et á Mohéli (Comores), par l'Institut de Recherches scientifiques de Madagascar. *Mémoires de l'Institut Scientifique de Madagascar*, série B, 6(1): 1–25.

———. 1961. Lichens récoltes á Madagascar et á La Réunion (Mission H. des Abbayes, 1956). I. Introduction. II. Parmeliaceaes. *Mémoires de l'Institut Scientifique de Madagascar*, série B, 19(2): 81–121.

Achille, F., Motley, T. J., Lowry, P. P., and Jéremie, J. 2006. Polyphyly in *Guettarda* L. (Rubiaceae, Guettardeae) based on nrDNA ITS sequence data. *Annals of the Missouri Botanical Garden* 93: 103–121.

Adepoju, O. T., Boyejo, O., and Adeniji, P. O. 2018. Effects of processing methods on nutrient and antinutrient composition of yellow yam (*Dioscorea cayenensis*) products. *Food Chemistry* 238: 160–165.

African Plant Database. 2020. Conservatoire et Jardin botaniques de la Ville de Genève and South African National Biodiversity Institute, Pretoria. http://africanplantdatabase.ch.

Agrawal, A. A., and Konno, K. 2009. Latex: A model for understanding mechanisms, ecology, and evolution of plant defense against herbivory. *Annual Review of Ecology, Evolution and Systematics* 40: 311–331.

Ahmed, S., Compton, S. G., Butlin, R. K., and Gilmartin, P. M. 2009. Wind-borne insects mediate directional pollen transfer between desert fig trees 160 kilometers apart. *Proceedings of the National Academy of Sciences of the USA* 106(48): 20342–20347.

Ah-Peng, C. 2007. Diversité, distribution, et biogéographie des coulées de lave du Piton de La Fournaise. PhD thesis, Université de La Réunion.

Ah-Peng, C., Bardat, J., Pócs, T., Söderström, L., Staménoff, P., and Strasberg, D. 2012. Red List of liverworts and hornworts for Réunion (Mascarene archipelago). *Phytotaxa* 68: 1–23.

Ah-Peng, C., Cardoso, A., Flores, O., West, A., Wilding, N., Strasberg, D., and Hedderson, T.A.J. 2017. The role of epiphytic bryophytes in interception, storage, and the regulated release of atmospheric moisture in a tropical montane cloud forest. *Journal of Hydrology* 548: 665–673.

Ahti, T. 1961. Taxonomic studies on reindeer lichens (*Cladonia*, subgenus *Cladina*). *Annales Botanici Societatis Zoologicae Botanicae Fennicae "Vanamo"* 32(1): 1–160.

Ahti, T., and Aptroot, A. 1992. Lichens of Madagascar: Cladoniaceae. *Cryptogamie, Bryologie et Lichénologie* 13: 117–124.

Albers, F., and Meve, U. 1991. Mixoploidy and cytotypes: A study of possible vegetative species differentiation in stapeliads (Asclepiadaceae). *Bothalia* 21: 67–72.

———. 2001. A karyological survey of Asclepiadoideae, Periplocoideae and Secamonoideae, and evolutionary considerations in Apocynaceae *s.l. Proceedings of the International Botanical Congress 1999*, eds. M. E. Endress and W. D. Stevens, pp. 624–656, St. Louis: International Botanical Congress.

Albers, P., and van der Maesen, L.J.G. 1994. Pollination of Apocynaceae. *Wageningen Agricultural University Papers* 94: 61–81.

Albert-Daviaud, A., Buerki, S., Onjalalaina, G. E., Perillo, S., Rabarijaona, R., Razafindratsima, O. H., Sato, H., Valenta, K., Wright, P. C., and Stuppy, W. 2020. The ghost fruits of Madagascar: Identifying dysfunctional seed dispersal in Madagascar's endemic flora. *Biological Conservation* 242: 108438.

Alejandro, G. D., Razafimandimbison, S. G., and Liede-Schumann, S. 2005. Polyphyly of *Mussaenda* inferred from ITS and *trn*T-F data and its implication for generic limits in Mussaendeae (Rubiaceae). *American Journal of Botany* 92: 544–557.

Alford, M. H. 2005. Systematic Studies in Flacourtiaceae. PhD thesis. Ithaca: Cornell University.

Allen, B. 1987. A revision of the genus *Leucomium* (Leucomiaceae). *Memoirs of the New York Botanical Garden* 45: 661–677.

———. 1992. A revision of *Ochrobryum* (Leucobryaceae). *Contributions of the University of Michigan Herbarium* 18: 113–130.

Allen, B., and Crosby, M. R. 1986. Revision of the genus *Squamidium* (Musci: Meteoriaceae). *Journal of the Hattori Botanical Laboratory* 61: 423–476.

Allen, B., and Magill, R. E. 2003. A revision of *Pilotrichella* (Lembophyllaceae: Musci). *Acta Academiae Paedagogicae Agriensis, Sectio Biologiae* 24: 43–83.

———. 2007. A revision of *Orthostichella* (Neckeraceae). *The Bryologist* 110 (1): 1–45.

Allen, O. N., and Allen, E. K. 1981. *The Leguminosae: A Source Book of Characteristics, Uses and Nodulation*. Madison: University of Wisconsin Press.

Allorge, L., and Ikor, O. 2003. *La fabuleuse odyssée des plantes*. Paris: JC Lattès.

Almborn, O. 1989. Revision of the lichen genus *Teloschistes* in central and southern Africa. *Nordic Journal of Botany* 8: 521–537.

Almeda, F. 1989. Five new berry-fruited species of tropical American Melastomataceae. *Proceedings of the California Academy of Sciences* 46(5): 137–150.

———. 1990. New species and new combinations in *Blakea* and *Topobea* (Melastomataceae), with an historical perspective on generic limits in the tribe Blakeeae. *Proceedings of the California Academy of Sciences* 46(14): 299–326.

———. 2003. Melastomataceae, Princes Flowers. In *The Natural History of Madagascar*, eds. S. M. Goodman and J. P. Benstead, pp. 375–379. Chicago: University of Chicago Press.

Almeda, F., and Ranarivelo, H. 2018. A new *Gravesia* (Melastomataceae, Sonerileae) from the Bemangidy-Ivohibe rainforest of southeastern Madagascar. *Candollea* 73: 1–5.

———. 2019. *Gravesia serratifolia* (Melastomataceae: Sonerileae), a new species from Marojejy National Park, Madagascar. *Phytotaxa* 391: 115–121.

Alvarez, M. F. 1982. Contribution à l'étude écologique du lac de Mandroseza (étude de la flore). Mémoire de DEA, Université d'Antananarivo.

Alvear, M., and Almeda, F. 2019. Revision of *Monochaetum* (Melastomataceae: Melastomateae) in Colombia. *Systematic Botany Monographs* 109: 1–153.

Alverson, W. S., Whitlock, B. A., Nyffeler, R., Bayer, C., and Baum, D. A. 1999. Phylogeny of the core Malvales: Evidence from *ndh*F sequence data. *American Journal of Botany* 86(10): 1474–1486. https://doi.org/10.2307/2656928.

Amarasinghe, P. R. 2020. Evolution of *Memecylon* (Melastomataceae) in the Old World tropics at multiple phylogenetic and spatial scales. PhD thesis, University of Florida, Gainesville.

Andriamaharoa, H., Birkinshaw, C., and Reza, L. 2010. Day-time feeding ecology of *Eulemur cinereiceps* in the Agnalazaha Forest, Mahabo-Mananivo, Madagascar. *Madagascar Conservation and Development* 5: 55–63.

Andriambololonera, S. R. 2013. Etude systématique et conservation du clade *Landiopsis-Bremeria* (Mussaendeae, Ixoroideae, Rubiaceae). PhD thesis, Université d'Antananarivo.

Andriamihajarivo, T. H., Razafimandimbison, S. G., and Kårehed, J. 2011. *Phyllopentas flava* (Rubiaceae), a new morphologically heterodistylous and functionally dioecious species from Madagascar. *Systematic Botany* 36: 1024–1027.

Andriamihajarivo, T. H., Lowry II, P. P., and Schatz, G. E. 2016. Endemic families of Madagascar. XIV. A new restricted range species of *Pentachlaena* H. Perrier (Sarcolaenaceae) from central Madagascar. *Candollea* 71: 167–172.

Andriamparany, J. N., Brinkmann, K., Jeannoda, V., and Buerkert, A. 2014. Effects of socio-economic household characteristics on traditional knowledge and usage of wild yams and medicinal plants in the Mahafaly region of south-western Madagascar. *Journal of Ethnobiology and Ethnomedicine* 10: 82.

Andrianaivoarivelo, R. A., Ramilijaona, O. R., Racey, P. A., Razafindrakoto, N., and Jenkins, R.K.B. 2011. Feeding ecology, habitat use and reproduction of *Rousettus madagascariensis* Grandidier, 1928 (Chiroptera: Pteropodidae) in eastern Madagascar. *Mammalia* 75: 69–78.

Andrianaivoarivelo, R. A., Petit, E. J., Razafindrakoto, N., and Racey, P. A. 2012. Alimentation et dispersion de graines chez *Rousettus madagascariensis* G. Grandidier 1928, dans le nord-ouest de Madagascar. *Revue d'Ecologie (La terre et la Vie)* 67: 179–191.

Andrianasetra Ranarijaona, H.L.T. 2003. Aquatic and semiaquatic vascular plants. In *The Natural History of Madagascar*, eds. S. M. Goodman and J. P. Benstead, pp. 250–256. Chicago: University of Chicago Press.

Andrianirinarimanana, M. 2018. Facteurs prépondérants pour l'évaluation de la productivité des *Tsiperifery* (*Piper* spp.) en milieu naturel, Cas de la commune rurale Ambongamarina-District Anjozorobe. Mémoire de Masters, Ecole Supérieure des Sciences Agronomiques, Université d'Antananarivo.

Andrianjohany, B. S. 1988. Analyse sur l'influence des plantes aquatiques sur la production piscicole du lac Itasy. Rapport PNUD.

Andriantsaralaza, S., Pedrono, M., Tassin, J., Roger, E., and Danthu, P. 2010. Baobabs de Madagascar: Un anachronisme de la dispersion? *Bois et Forêts des Tropiques* 306: 7–15.

Andriantsaralaza, S., Pedrono, M., Tassin, J., Roger, E., Rakouth, B., and Danthu, P. 2014. The role of extinct giant tortoises in the germination of extant baobab *Adansonia rubrostipa* seeds in Madagascar. *African Journal of Ecology* 52: 246–249.

Angiosperm Phylogeny Group III (APG III). 2009. An update of the Angiosperm Phylogeny Group classification for the orders and families of flowering plants: APG III. *Botanical Journal of the Linnean Society* 161(2): 105–121. https://doi.org/10.1111/j.1095-8339.2009.00996.x.

Angiosperm Phylogeny Group IV (APG IV). 2016. An update of the Angiosperm Phylogeny Group classification for the orders and families of flowering plants: APG IV. *Botanical Journal of the Linnean Society* 181(1): 1–20. https://doi.org/10.1111/boj.12385.

Angiosperm Phylogeny Website. 2019 (by P. F. Stevens from 2001). Version 14 July 2017. Accessed 31 July 2020. http://www.mobot.org/MOBOT/research/APweb/.

Appelhans, M. S., and Wen, J. 2020. Phylogenetic placement of *Ivodea* and biogeographic affinities of Malagasy Rutaceae. *Plant Systematics and Evolution* 306: 7. https://doi.org/10.1007/s00606-020-01633-3.

Appelhans, M. S., Keßler, P.J.A., Smets, E., Razafimandimbison, S. G., and Janssens, S. B. 2012. Age and historical biogeography of the pantropically distributed Spathelioideae (Rutaceae, Sapindales). *Journal of Biogeography* 39: 1235–1250. https://doi.org/10.1111/j.1365-2699.2012.02686.x.

Appelhans, M. S., Wen, J., and Wagner, W. L. 2014a. A molecular phylogeny of *Acronychia*, *Euodia*, *Melicope* and relatives (Rutaceae) reveals polyphyletic genera and key innovations for species richness. *Molecular Phylogenetics and Evolution* 79: 54–68. https://doi.org/10.1016/j.ympev.2014.06.014.

Appelhans, M. S., Wen, J., Wood, K. R., Allan, G. J., Zimmer, E. A., and Wagner, W. L. 2014b. Molecular phylogenetic analysis of Hawaiian Rutaceae (*Melicope*, *Platydesma* and *Zanthoxylum*) and their different colonization patterns. *Botanical Journal of the Linnean Society* 174(3): 425–448. https://doi.org/10.1111/boj.12123.

Appelhans, M. S., Reichelt, N., Groppo, M., Paetzold, C., and Wen, J. 2018a. Phylogeny and biogeography of the pantropical genus *Zanthoxylum* and its closest relatives in the proto-Rutaceae group (Rutaceae). *Molecular Phylogenetics and Evolution* 126: 31–44. https://doi.org/10.1016/j.ympev.2018.04.013.

Appelhans, M. S., Wen, J., Duretto, M., Crayn, D., and Wagner, W. L. 2018b. Historical biogeography of *Melicope* (Rutaceae) and its close relatives with a special emphasis on Pacific dispersals. *Journal of Systematics and Evolution* 56: 576–599.

Applequist, W. L. 2009a. A revision of the Malagasy endemic *Helmiopsis* (Malvaceae *s.l.*). *Annals of the Missouri Botanical Garden* 96(4): 521–540. https://doi.org/10.3417/2007184.

———. 2009b. Two new species of *Dombeya* (Malvaceae) from Madagascar. *Novon* 19(3): 289–294. https://doi.org/10.3417/2007183.

———. 2014. A taxonomic revision of *Dombeya* sect. *Decastemon* (Malvaceae). *Annals of the Missouri Botanical Garden* 99(4): 553–619. https://dx.doi.org/10.3417/2011113.

———. 2016a. A revision of the Malagasy species of *Homalium* sect. *Eumyriantheia* Warb. (*Salicaceae*). *Candollea* 71: 33–60.

———. 2016b. A reconsideration of the infrageneric classification of *Homalium* Jacq. (*Salicaceae*). *Candollea* 71: 231–256.

———. 2018a. A revision of *Homalium* sect. *Odontolobus* (*Salicaceae*) endemic to Madagascar. *Candollea* 73: 27–48.

———. 2018b. A revision of the Malagasy species of *Homalium* sect. *Blackwellia* (*Salicaceae*). *Candollea* 73: 221–244.

———. 2020. A revision of *Homalium* sect. *Rhodonisa* (*Salicaceae*) endemic to Madagascar. *Candollea* 75: 245–268.

Applequist, W. L., and Schatz, G. E. 2016. A synoptic revision of the Malagasy species of *Scolopia* Schreb. (Salicaceae, Scolopieae). *Adansonia*, série 3, 38: 99–115.

Applequist, W. L., and Wallace, R. S. 2003. Expanded circumscription of Didiereaceae and its division into three subfamilies. *Adansonia*, série 3, 25: 13–16.

Applequist, W. L., Phillipson, P. B., and Schatz, G. E. 2014. A synoptic revision of the Malagasy endemic genus *Calantica* (Salicaceae). *Adansonia*, série 3, 36: 83–102.

Aptroot, A. 1988. Lichens of Madagascar: The Pyxinaceae (syn. Physciaceae). *Cryptogamie, Bryologie et Lichénologie* 9: 141–147.

———. 1990. Lichens of Madagascar: New and interesting records and species. *Cryptogamie, Bryologie et Lichénologie* 11: 401–408.

———. 1991a. Lichens of Madagascar: New records and species of Parmeliaceae. *Cryptogamie, Bryologie et Lichénologie* 12: 149–154.

———. 1991b. A monograph of the Pyrenulaceae (excluding *Anthracothecium* and *Pyrenula*) and the Requienellaceae, with notes on the Pleomassariaceae, the Trypetheliaceae and *Mycomicrothelia*. *Bibliotheca Lichenologica* 44: 1–178.

———. 2008. A new *Scoliciosporum* from Madagascar. *Lichenologist* 40: 119–122.

———. 2009. The lichen genus *Traponora*. *Bibliotheca Lichenologica* 100: 21–30.

———. 2016. Preliminary checklist of the lichens of Madagascar, with two new thelotremoid Graphidaceae and 132 new records. *Willdenowia* 46: 349–365.

Aptroot, A., and Schumm, F. 2011. *Fruticose Roccellaceae, an Anatomical-Microscopical Atlas and Guide with a Worldwide Key and Further Notes on some Crustose Roccellaceae or Similar Lichens*. Norderstedt: Books on Demand.

Aptroot, A., Thor, G., Lücking, R., Elix, J. A., and Chaves, J. L. 2009. The lichen genus *Herpothallon* reinstated. *Bibliotheca Lichenologica* 99: 19–66.

Areces-Berazain, F., and Ackerman, J. D. 2016. Phylogenetics, delimitation and historical biogeography of the pantropical tree genus *Thespesia* (Malvaceae, Gossypieae). *Botanical Journal of the Linnean Society* 181: 171–198. https://doi.org/10.1111/boj.12414.

Arènes, J. 1959. Sterculiacées. *Flore de Madagascar et des Comores* 131: 1–537.

Argent, G.C.G. 1973. A taxonomic study of African *Pterobryaceae* and *Meteoriaceae* II. *Pterobryaceae*. *Journal of Bryology* 7: 563–602.

Armbruster, W. S., and Baldwin, B. G. 1998. Switch from specialized to generalized pollination. *Nature* 394(6694): 632.

Armbruster, W. S., Lee, J., Edwards, M. E., and Baldwin, B. G. 2013. Floral paedomorphy leads to secondary specialization in pollination of Madagascar *Dalechampia* (Euphorbiaceae). *Evolution* 67: 1196–1203.

Armistead, S. E., Collins, A. S., Payne, J. L., Foden, J. D., De Waele, B., Shaji, E., and Santosh, M. 2018. A re-evaluation of the Kumta Suture in western peninsular India and its extension into Madagascar. *Journal of Asian Earth Sciences* 157: 317–328.

Armstrong, K. 2010. Systematics and biogeography of the pantropical genus *Manilkara* Adans. (Sapotaceae). PhD thesis, University of Edinburgh.

———. 2013. A revision of the Asian-Pacific species of *Manilkara* (Sapotaceae). *Edinburgh Journal of Botany* 70: 7–56.

Armstrong, K., Stone, G., Nicholls, J., Valderrama-Escallon, E., Anderberg, A., Smedmark, J., Gautier, L., Naciri, Y., Milne, R., and Richardson, J. E. 2014. Patterns of diversification amongst tropical regions compared: A case study in Sapotaceae. *Frontiers in Genetics* 5: 362.

Arrigo-Nelson, S. A. 2006. The impact of habitat disturbance on the feeding ecology of the Milne-Edwards' Sifaka (*Propithecus edwardsi*) in Ranomafana National Park. PhD thesis, Stony Brook University, Stony Brook.

Arts, T. 1996. The genus *Sphlachnobryum* in Africa, with new combinations in *Bryum* and *Gymnostomiella*. *Journal of Bryology* 19: 65–78.

———. 2001. A revision of the Splachnobryaceae (Musci). *Lindbergia* 26: 77–96.

Arvidsson, L. 1982. A monograph of the lichen genus *Coccocarpia*. *Opera Botanica* 67: 1–96.

Ashman, T. L. 2009. Sniffing out patterns of sexual dimorphism in floral scent. *Functional Ecology* 23: 852–862.

Ashton, P. S. 2006. New *Syzygium* (*Myrtaceae*) from northern Borneo. *Kew Bulletin* 61: 107–144.

Asiedu, R., and Sartie, A. 2010. Crops that feed the World 1. Yams: Yams for income and food security. *Food Security* 2: 305–315.

Atsalis, S. 1999. Diet of the brown mouse lemur (*Microcebus rufus*) in Ranomafana National Park, Madagascar. *International Journal of Primatology* 20: 193–229.

———. 2008. *A Natural History of the Brown Mouse Lemur*. London and New York: Routledge, Taylor and Francis.

Aubréville, A. 1964. Les Sapotacées: Taxonomie et phytogéographie. *Adansonia, Mémoires* 1: 1–157.

———. 1974. Sapotacées. *Flore de Madagascar et des Comores* 164: 1–128.

Aubriot, X. 2012. Radiations évolutives, "innovations clés" et notions d'espèces dans le genre *Euphorbia* L. à Madagascar. PhD thesis, Muséum National d'Histoire Naturelle, Paris.

Aubriot, X., Lowry II, P. P., Cruaud, C., Couloux, A., and Haevermans, T. 2013. DNA barcoding in a biodiversity hot spot: Potential value for the identification of Malagasy *Euphorbia* L. listed in CITES Appendices I and II. *Molecular Ecology Resources* 13: 57–65. https://doi.org/10.1111/1755-0998.12028.

Aubriot, X., Lowry II, P. P., and Haevermans, T. 2014. Taxonomic revision of the Malagasy endemic and enigmatic *Euphorbia* section *Pachysanthae* (Euphorbiaceae). *Phytotaxa* 159: 221–235. https://doi.org/10.11646/phytotaxa.159.3.5.

Aubriot, X., Soulebeau, A., Haevermans, T., Schatz, G. E., Cruaud, C., et al. 2016. Molecular phylogenetics of Sarcolaenaceae (Malvales), Madagascar's largest endemic plant family. *Botanical Journal of the Linnean Society* 182: 729–743.

Aumeeruddy-Thomas, Y., Rafidison, M. V., Kjellberg, F., and Hossaert-McKey, M. 2018. Sacred hills of Imerina and the voyage of *Ficus lutea* Vahl (Amontana) in Madagascar. *Acta Oecologica* 90: 18–27.

Awan, A. J., and Aslam, M. S. 2014. Family Acanthaceae and genus *Aphelandra*: Ethnopharmacological and phytochemical review. *International Journal of Pharmacy and Pharmaceutical Sciences* 6(10): 44–55.

Awasthi, D. D. 1975. A monograph of the lichen genus *Dirinaria*. *Bibliotheca Lichenologica* 2: 1–108.

Aymoz, B.G.P., Randrianjafy, V. R., Randrianjafy, Z.J.N., and Khasa, D. P. 2013. Community management of natural resources: A case study from Ankarafantsika National Park, Madagascar. *Ambio* 42: 767–775.

Azani, N., Babineau, M., Bailey, C.D., Banks, H., Barbosa, A.R., et al. 2017. A new subfamily classification of the Leguminosae based on a taxonomically comprehensive phylogeny: Legume Phylogeny Working Group (LPWG). *Taxon* 66: 44–77.

Babineau, M., and Bruneau, A. 2017. Phylogenetic and biogeographical history of the Afro-Madagascan genera *Delonix*, *Colvillea*, and *Lemuropisum* (Fabaceae: Caesalpinioideae). *Botanical Journal of the Linnean Society* 184(1): 59–78.

Bacci, L. F., Michelangeli, F. A., and Goldenberg, R. 2019. Revisiting the classification of Melastomataceae: Implications for habit and fruit evolution. *Botanical Journal of the Linnean Society* 190: 1–24.

Baillon, H. 1861. Euphorbiacées africaines. pt. 2, Afrique Orientale (Bourbon, Maurice, Madagascar, Zanguebar, etc.). *Adansonia* 1: 139–173.

———. 1885. *Bulletin Mensuel de la Société Linnéenne de Paris* 1: 479.

Baker, J. G. 1881. Notes on a collection of flowering plants made by L. Kitching, Esq., in Madagascar in 1879. *Journal of the Linnean Society*. *Botany* 18: 272–273.

———. 1882. Contributions to the flora of central Madagascar. *Journal of Botany, British and Foreign*, new series, 20: 244.

———. 1883. Contributions to the flora of Madagascar. *Journal of the Linnean Society*. *Botany* 20: 239.

———. 1885. Further contributions to the flora of Madagascar. *Journal of the Linnean Society*. *Botany* 21: 436.

———. 1889. Further contributions to the flora of Madagascar. *Journal of the Linnean Society*. *Botany* 25: 342.

Baker, W. J., Norup, M. V., Clarkson, J. J., Couvreur, T. L., Dowe, J. L., Lewis, C. E., and Chase, M. W. 2011. Phylogenetic relationships among arecoid palms (Arecaceae: Arecoideae). *Annals of Botany* 108(8): 1417–1432.

Ballard, H. E., Jr., de Paula-Souza, J., and Wahlert, G. A. 2014. Violaceae. In *The Families and Genera of Vascular Plants. Vol. 6, Flowering plants. Dicotyledons: Malpighiales*, ed. K. Kubitzki, pp. 303–322. Berlin: Springer.

Balle, S. 1964a. Loranthacées. *Flore de Madagascar* 60: 1–124.

———. 1964b. Les Loranthacées de Madagascar et des archipels voisins. *Adansonia*, nouvelle série, 4: 105–141.

Bamford, A. J., Razafindrajao, F., Young, R. P., and Hilton, G. M. 2017. Profound and pervasive degradation of Madagascar's freshwater wetlands and links with biodiversity. *PLoS One* 12(8): e0182673.

Banfi, E. 2014. *Chrysojasminum*, a new genus for *Jasminum* sect. *Alternifolia* (Oleaceae, Jasmineae). *Natural History Sciences* 1: 3–6.

Barberá, P., Velayos, M., and Aedo, C. 2014. Taxonomic revision of *Grossera* (Crotonoideae, Euphorbiaceae): A central African genus. *Systematic Botany* 39(2): 490–509.

Bardot-Vaucoulon, M. 1991. Analyse floristique et mise en évidence des groupes écologiques sur faciès karstique dans le massif de l'Ankarana (zone du Lac Vert). Mémoire de DEA, Université d'Antananarivo.

———. 1997. Observations sur le milieu et la végétation du Massif de l'Ankarana (Nord de Madagascar) et description de trois nouvelles espèces de *Chlorophytum* (Liliaceae), *Tacca* (Taccaceae) et *Adenia* (Passifloraceae). *Adansonia*, série 3, 19: 139–163.

———. 2002. Une nouvelle espèce de *Commiphora* (Burseraceae) du nord de Madagascar. *Adansonia*, série 3, 24(1): 43–47.

———. 2015. Une formidable réserve de biodiversité. In *Namoroka: Mission à Madagascar*, eds. L. Allorge and T. Haevermans, pp. 76–84. Paris: Muséum National d'Histoire Naturelle et Editions Privat.

Barker, N. P., Schrire, B. D., and Kim, J.-H. 2000. Generic relationships in the tribe Indigofereae (Leguminosae: Papilionoideae) based on sequence data and morphology. In *Advances in Legume Systematics 9*, eds. P. S. Herendeen and A. Bruneau, pp. 311–337. Kew: Royal Botanic Gardens.

Barkley, F. A. 1942. A key to the genera of the Anacardiaceae. *American Midland Naturalist* 28: 465–474.

———. 1957. Generic key to the sumac family (Anacardiaceae). *Lloydia* 20: 255–265.

Barlow, B. A. 1983. Biogeography of Loranthaceae and Viscaceae. In *The Biology of Mistletoes*, eds. D. M. Calder and P. Bernhardt, pp. 19–46. New York: Academic Press.

———. 1990. Biogeographical relationships of Australia and Malesia: Loranthaceae as a model. In *The Plant Diversity of Malesia*, eds. P. Baas, K. Kalkman, and R. Geesink, pp. 273–292. Netherlands: Kluwer Academic.

Barneby, R. C., and Grimes, J. W. 1996. Silk tree, guanacaste, monkey's earring: A generic system for the synandrous Mimosaceae of the Americas. Part 1. *Abarema*, *Albizia*, and allies. *Memoirs of the New York Botanical Garden* 74(1): 1–292.

Barnett, L. C. 1987a. An unusual new species of *Helmiopsis* H. Perrier (Sterculiaceae) from Madagascar. *Annals of the Missouri Botanical Garden* 74(2): 450–452.

———. 1987b. Two new species of *Nesogordonia* (Sterculiaceae) from Madagascar. *Bulletin du Muséum National d'Histoire Naturelle*, Section B, *Adansonia* 1: 95–100.

———. 1988a. New combinations in the genus *Helmiopsiella* (Sterculiaceae). *Bulletin du Muséum National d'Histoire Naturelle*, Section B, *Adansonia* 1: 69–76.

Barnett, L. C. 1988b. Systematics of *Nesogordonia* Baillon (Sterculiaceae). PhD thesis, University of Texas, Austin.

Barnett, L. C., and Dorr, L. J. 1986. A new species and variety of *Dombeya* (Sterculiaceae) from Madagascar. *Bulletin du Muséum National d'Histoire Naturelle*, Section B, *Adansonia* 8: 365–371.

Barrett, M. A., Brown, J. L., Morikawa, M. K., Labat, J.-N., and Yoder, A. D. 2010. CITES designation for endangered rosewood in Madagascar. *Science* 328(5982): 1109–1110. https://doi.org/10.1126/science.1187740.

Barrie, F. R. 2004. Thirty-five new species of *Eugenia* (Myrtaceae) from Mesoamerica. *Novon* 15: 4–49.

Barthlott, W., Porembski, S., Seine, R., and Theisen, I. 2008. *Plantes carnivores. Biologie et culture*. Paris: Editions Belin.

Bartish, I. V., Antonelli, A., Richardson, J. E., and Swenson, U. 2011. Vicariance or long-distance dispersal: Historical biogeography of the pantropical subfamily Chrysophylloideae (Sapotaceae). *Journal of Biogeography* 38: 177–190.

Baum, D. A. 1995a. A systematic revision of *Adansonia* (Bombacaceae). *Annals of the Missouri Botanical Garden* 82: 440–470.

———. 1995b. The comparative pollination and floral biology of baobabs (*Adansonia*—Bombacaceae). *Annals of the Missouri Botanical Garden* 82: 322–348.

———. 1996. The ecology and conservation of the baobabs of Madagascar. *Primate Report* 46: 311–327.

Baum, D. A., and Oginuma, K. 1994. A review of chromosome numbers in Bombacaceae with new counts for *Adansonia*. *Taxon* 43: 11–20.

Baum, D. A., Small, R. L., and Wendel, J. F. 1998. Biogeography and floral evolution of baobabs (*Adansonia*, Bombacaceae) as inferred from multiple data sets. *Systematic Biology* 47: 181–207.

Bauters, K., Larridon, I., Reynders, M., Huygh, W., Asselman, P., Vrijdaghs, A., Muasya, A. M., and Goetghebeur, P. 2014. A new classification for *Lipocarpha* and *Volkiella* as infrageneric taxa of *Cyperus s.l.* (Cypereae, Cyperoideae, Cyperaceae): Insights from species tree reconstruction supplemented with morphological and floral developmental data. *Phytotaxa* 166: 1–32.

Bauters, K., Goetghebeur, P., Asselman, P., Meganck, K., and Larridon, I. 2018. Molecular phylogenetic study of *Scleria* subgenus *Hypoporum* (Sclerieae, Cyperoideae, Cyperaceae) reveals several new species to science. *PLoS One* 13: e0203478.

Bayer, C., and Kubitzki, K. 2003. Malvaceae. In *The Families and Genera of Vascular Plants*, vol. 5, *Flowering plants: Dicotyledons*, eds. K. Kubitzki and C. Bayer, pp. 225–311. Berlin, Heidelberg: Springer.

Bayton, R. 2007. A revision of *Borassus* L. (Arecaceae). *Kew Bulletin* 62: 561–586.

Beaujard, P. 1988. Plantes et médecine traditionnelle dans le sud-est de Madagascar. *Journal of Ethnopharmacology* 23: 165–265.

———. 2011. The first migrants to Madagascar and their introduction of plants: Linguistic and ethnological evidence. *Azania* 46: 169–189.

Becerra, J. X. 2003. Evolution of Mexican *Bursera* (Burseraceae) inferred from ITS, ETS, and 5S nuclear ribosomal DNA sequences. *Molecular Phylogenetics and Evolution* 26(2): 300–309.

Beech, E., Rivers, M., Rabarimanarivo, M., Ravololomanana, N., Manjato, N., et al. 2021. Red List of Trees of Madagascar. Richmond, UK: BGCI. https://www.bgci.org/resources/bgci-tools-and-resources/the-red-list-of-trees-of-madagascar.

Beentje, H. J., and Callmander, M. W. 2014. Pandanaceae. In *Tropical African Flowering Plants—Ecology and Distribution*, vol. 8, eds. J. P. Lebrun and A. L. Stork, pp. 316–323. Geneva: Conservatoire et Jardin Botaniques de la Ville de Genève.

Bennett, B. C. 2011. Twenty-five economically important plant families. *Encyclopedia of Life Support Systems*. http://www.eolss.net/Sample-Chapters/C09/E6-118-03.pdf.

Benoist, R. 1939. Nouvelles Acanthacées malgaches. *Notulae Systematicae* 8: 135–161.

———. 1940. Descriptions de nouvelles Acanthacées malgaches. *Notulae Systematicae* 9: 65–66.

———. 1948. Contribution à la connaissance des Acanthacées malgaches. *Notulae Systematicae.* 13: 196.

———. 1962. Nouvelles Acanthacées de Madagascar. *Bulletin de la Société Botanique de France* 109: 129–135.

———. 1965. Nouvelles espèces malgaches du genre *Anisostachya* (Acanthacees). *Bulletin de la Société Botanique de France* 112: 533–540.

———. 1966. Contribution à la connaissance des Acanthacées malgaches. *Bulletin de la Société Botanique de France* 113: 531–536.

———. 1967a. Acanthacées. *Flore de Madagascar et des Comores* 182: 1–219.

———. 1967b. Contributions à la connaissance des *Anisostachya* malgaches. *Bulletin de la Société Botanique de France* 114: 441–443.

Benor, S. 2018. Molecular phylogeny of the genus *Corchorus* (Grewioideae, Malvaceae *s.l.*) based on nuclear rDNA ITS sequences. *The Crop Journal* 6: 552–563. https://doi.org/10.1016/j.cj.2018.03.007.

Benson, W. W. 1985. Amazon ant-plants. In *Amazonia*, eds. G. T. Prance and T. E. Lovejoy, pp. 239–266. Oxford: Pergamon Press.

Bentham, G., and Hooker, J. D. 1862. Anacardiaceae. In *Genera Plantarum* 1, pp. 415–428. London: Reeves.

Berg, C. C. 1984. Floral differentiation and dioecism in *Ficus* (Moraceae). In *Minisymposium on Figs and Fig Insects*, eds. F. Kjellberg, F. and G. Valdeyron, pp 15–25. Montpellier: CNRS.

———. 1986. The *Ficus* species (Moraceae) of Madagascar and the Comoro Islands. *Bulletin du Muséum National d'Histoire Naturelle, Paris*, série 4, 8, Section B, *Adansonia* 1: 17–55.

———. 1990. Distribution of African taxa of *Ficus* (Moraceae). *Mitteilungen aus dem Institut für allgemeine Botanik in Hamburg* 23: 401–405.

Berg, C. C., and Corner, E.J.H. 2005. Moraceae—*Ficeae*. *Flora Malesiana*, series I, 17(2): 1–70.

Berg, C. C., and van Heusden, E.C.H. 1985. Moracées. *Flore des Mascareignes* 164: 1–21.

Berg, C. C., and Wiebes, J. T. 1992. *African Fig Trees and Fig Wasps*. Amsterdam: Verhandelingen der Koninklijke Nederlandse Akademie van Wetenschappen.

Bernardi, L. 1969. Araliacearum Madagascariae et Comores exordium. 1. Revisio et taxa nova Scheffllerarum. *Candollea* 24: 89–122.

———. 1971. Araliacearum Madagascariae et Comores propositum. 2. Revisio et taxa nova Polysciadim. *Candollea* 26: 13–89.

———. 1980. Synopsis Araliacearum Madagascariae et Comorarum Insularum (auxilio methodi “Ferulago”). *Candollea* 35: 117–132.

Bernhardt, P., and Calder, D. M. 1980. Comparative breeding systems and adaptive floral morphologies of *Amyema linophyllum* and *Amyema preisii* (Loranthaceae). *Phytomorphology* 30: 271–289.

Berry, P. E., and Kainulainen, K. 2017. *Croton crossolepis* (Euphorbiaceae), a new species with an unusual trichome type from southwestern Madagascar. *Phytotaxa* 307: 95–100.

Berry, P. E., and van Ee, B. W. 2011. Recognition of *Croton multicostatus* Müll.Arg. (Euphorbiaceae) as native to Madagascar. *Candollea* 66: 109–112.

Berry, P. E., Hipp, A. L., Wurdack, K. J., van Ee, B. W., and Riina, R. 2005. Molecular phylogenetics of the giant genus *Croton* and tribe Crotoneae (Euphorbiaceae *sensu stricto*) using ITS and *trn*L-*trn*F DNA sequence data. *American Journal of Botany* 92: 1520–1534.

Berry, P. E., van Ee, B. W., and Haber, E. A. 2011. Resolving the tangled identity of *Croton chrysodaphne* Baill. (Euphorbiaceae) in Madagascar. *Candollea* 66: 113–118.

Berry, P. E., van Ee, B. W., Kainulainen, K., and Razafindraibe, H. 2016a. *Croton aleuritoides* P. E. Berry (Euphorbiaceae), a distinctive new tree species from Montagne des Français in northern Madagascar. *Candollea* 71: 181–188.

———. 2016b. *Croton cupreolepis* (Euphorbiaceae), a new coppery-lepidote tree species from eastern Madagascar. *Systematic Botany* 41: 977–982.

Berry, P. E., Kainulainen, K., and van Ee, B. W. 2017. A nomenclator of *Croton* (Euphorbiaceae) in Madagascar, the Comoros archipelago, and the Mascarene Islands. *PhytoKeys* 90: 1–87.

Bescherelle, E. 1891. Selectio novorum muscorum. *Journal of Botany (Morot)* 5(9): 142–148.

Besnard, G., Rubio de Casas, R., Christin, P.-A., and Vargas, P. 2009. Phylogenetics of *Olea* (Oleaceae) based on plastid and nuclear ribosomal DNA sequences: Tertiary climatic shifts and lineage differentiation times. *Annals of Botany* 104: 143–160.

Besnard, G., Christin, P. A., Malé, P.J.G., Coissac, E., Ralimanana, H., and Vorontsova, M. S. 2013. Phylogenomics and taxonomy of Lecomtelleae (Poaceae), an isolated panicoid lineage from Madagascar. *Annals of Botany* 112: 1057–1066.

Besnard, G., Christin, P. A., Malé, P.J.G., Lhuillier, E., Lauzeral, C., Coissac, E., and Vorontsova, M. S. 2014. From museums to genomics: Old herbarium specimens shed light on a C_3 to C_4 transition. *Journal of Experimental Botany* 65: 6711–6721.

Bhandari, M. R., Kasai, T., and Kawabata, J. 2003. Nutritional evaluation of wild yam (*Dioscorea* spp.) tubers of Nepal. *Food Chemistry* 82(4): 619–623.

Bidgood, S., and Brummitt, R. K. 1998. A revision of the genus *Neuracanthus* (Acanthaceae). *Kew Bulletin* 53(1): 1–76.

Biffin, E., Lucas, E. J., Craven, L. A., da Costa, I. R., Harrington, M.G., and Crisp, M. D. 2010. Evolution of exceptional species richness among lineages of fleshy-fruited Myrtaceae. *Annals of Botany* 106: 79–93.

Binggeli, P. 2003. Introduced and invasive plants. In *The Natural History of Madagascar*, eds. S. M. Goodman and J. P. Benstead, pp. 257–268. Chicago: University of Chicago Press.

Birkinshaw, C. R. 1995. The importance of the black lemur (*Eulemur macaco*, Lemuridae—Primates), for seed dispersal in the Lokobe forest, Madagascar. PhD thesis, University College, London.

———. 1999. The importance of the black lemur (*Eulemur macaco*) for seed dispersal in Lokobe forest, Nosy Be. In *New Directions in Lemur Studies*, eds. B. Rakotosamimanana, H. Rasamimanana, J. U. Ganzhorn, and S. M. Goodman, pp. 189–199. New York: Springer.

———. 2001. Fruit characteristics of species dispersed by the black lemur (*Eulemur macaco*) in the Lokobe forest, Madagascar. *Biotropica* 33: 478–486.

Birkinshaw, C. [R.], Ralimanana, H., Ranaivojaona, R., Randrianaivo, R., and Ravololonanahary, H. 2000. Flore et structure de la forêt de la Réserve spéciale d'Ambohitantely. In Monographie de la forêt d'Ambohitantely, eds. J. Ratsirarson and S. M. Goodman. *Recherches pour le Développement, série Sciences Biologiques*, 16: 11–27.

Birkinshaw, C. [R.], Freeman, K., and Schatz, G. 2015. Ex situ conservation of endangered Malagasy trees at Parc Ivoloina. *BGjournal* 12(2): 26–29.

Bittrich, V., and Amaral, M.C.E. 2016. Hydroleaceae. In *The Families and Genera of Vascular Plants*, vol. 14: *Flowering Plants: Eudicots—Aquifoliales, Boraginales, Bruniales, Dipsacales, Escalloniales, Garryales, Paracryphiales, Solanales (except Convolvulaceae), Icacinaceae, Metteniusaceae, Vahliaceae*, eds. J. W. Kadereit and V. Bittrich, pp. 217–220. Springer Nature.

Bizot, M. 1974. Enumeratio muscorum novarum. *Revue Bryologique et Lichénologique* 40: 101–139.

Blanchard, O. J., Jr. 2012. Chromosome numbers, phytogeography, and evolution in *Kosteletzkya* (Malvaceae). *Rhodora* 114(957): 37–49. https://doi.org/10.3119/0035-4902-114.957.37.

Boatwright, J. S., Savolainen, V., van Wyk, B.-E., Schutte-Vlok, A. L., Forest, F., and van der Bank, M. 2008. Systematic position of the anomalous genus *Cadia* and the phylogeny of the tribe Podalyrieae (Fabaceae). *Systematic Botany* 33: 133–147.

Boatwright, J. S., Maurin, O., and van der Bank, M. 2015. Phylogenetic position of Madagascan species of *Acacia s.l.* and new combinations in *Senegalia* and *Vachellia* (Fabaceae, Mimosoideae, Acacieae). *Botanical Journal of the Linnean Society* 179(2): 288–294.

Bochorny, T., Michelangeli, F. A., Almeda, F., and Goldenberg, R. 2019. Phylogenetics, morphology and circumscription of Cambessedesieae: A new Neotropical tribe of Melastomataceae. *Botanical Journal of the Linnean Society* 190: 281–302.

Böhning-Gaese, K., Gaese, B. H., and Rabemanantsoa, S. B. 1999. Importance of primary and secondary seed dispersal in the Malagasy tree *Commiphora guillauminii*. *Ecology* 80: 821–832.

Boissier, E. 1862. Euphorbiaceae subordo I. Euphorbieae. *DC Prodromus* 15: 3–188.

Boiteau, P. 1979. *Précis de matière médicale malgache.* Antananarivo: Librairie de Madagascar.

———. 1985. *Dictionnaire des noms malgaches de végétaux.* Microédition N. 850410. Archives et Documents. Paris: Muséum National d'Histoire Naturelle.

———. 1986. *Médecine traditionnelle et pharmacopée. Précis de matière médicale malgache.* Paris: Agence de Coopération Culturelle et Technique.

———. 1999. *Dictionnaire des noms malgaches des végétaux.* Grenoble: Claude Alzieu.

Boiteau, P., and Allorge, L. 1998. *Plantes médicinales de Madagascar.* CD-ROM. Saint-Rémy: Lune Rouge.

Boiteau, P., and Allorge-Boiteau, L. 1997. *Plantes médicinales de Madagascar.* Paris: Karthala.

Boivin, N., Crowther, A., Helm, R., and Fuller, D. Q. 2013. East Africa and Madagascar in the Indian Ocean world. *Journal of World Prehistory* 26: 213–281.

Bollen, A. 2003. Fruit-frugivore interactions in a Malagasy littoral forest: A community-wide approach of seed dispersal. PhD thesis, Department of Biology, University of Antwerp.

Bollen, A., and van Elsacker, L. 2002. Feeding ecology of *Pteropus rufus* (Pteropodidae) in the littoral forest of Sainte Luce, SE Madagascar. *Acta Chiropterologica* 4: 33–47.

———. 2004. The feeding ecology of the Lesser Vasa Parrot, *Coracopsis nigra*, in south-eastern Madagascar. *Ostrich* 75(3): 141–146.

Bollen, A., van Elsacker, L., and Ganzhorn, J. U. 2004a. Relations between fruits and disperser assemblages in a Malagasy littoral forest: A community-level approach. *Journal of Tropical Ecology* 20(6): 599–612.

———. 2004b. Tree dispersal strategies in the littoral forest of Ste. Luce (SE-Madagascar). *Oecologia* 139: 604–616.

Bolliger, R., Callmander, M. W., Bardot-Vaucoulon, M., and Gautier, L. 2015. Le caractère singulier des tsingy malgaches. In *Namoroka: Mission à Madagascar*, eds. L. Allorge and T. Haevermans, pp. 73–75. Paris: Muséum National d'Histoire Naturelle et Editions Privat.

Bonner, C.E.B. 1953. De Hepaticis III. *Candollea* 14: 163–252.

Borges, R., Bessière, J.-M., and Hossaert-McKey, M. 2008. The chemical ecology of seed dispersal in monoecious and dioecious figs. *Functional Ecology* 22: 484–493.

Bosser, J. 1969. *Graminées des pâturages et des cultures à Madagascar.* Paris: Orstom.

———. 1973. Deux nouvelles espèces de *Noronhia* Stadm. ex Thouars (Oleaceae) de Madagascar. *Adansonia* 13: 461–466.

———. 1975. Note sur les Graminées de Madagascar. IX. Identité du genre *Perulifera* A. Camus et révision du genre *Pseudechinolaena* (Hook. f.) Stapf. *Adansonia* 2: 121–137.

———. 1976. *Voatomalo*, nouveau genre d'Euphorbiaceae de Madagascar. *Adansonia*, série 2, 15: 333–340.

———. 1987. Description de deux nouvelles espèces de *Clerodendrum* L. (Verbenaceae) et identité de *C. brunsvigioides* Baker, *C. insolitum* Mold. et *C. villosicalyx* Mold. *Bulletin Muséum National d'Histoire Naturelle*, Section B, *Adansonia*, série 4, 9: 341–347.

Bosser, J., and Florens, D. 1999. *Pseudolasiacis* (A. Camus) A. Camus (Poaceae) à Madagascar, aux Comores et aux Mascareignes. *Adansonia* 21: 231–237.

Bosser, J., and Guého, J. 2003. Pandanaceae. In *Flore des Mascareignes* 190, eds. J. Bosser, I. K. Ferguson, and C. Soopramanien. Paris, Réduit, and Kew: IRD Editions, MSIRI, and Royal Botanic Gardens.

Bosser, J., and Lecoufle, M. 2011. *Les Orchidées de Madagascar*. Mèze: Biotope.
Bosser, J., and Lobreau-Callen, G. 1998. *Landiopsis* Capuron ex Bosser, genre nouveau de Rubiaceae de Madagascar. *Adansonia* 20: 131–137.
Bosser, J., and Rabevohitra, R. 1985. Présence du genre *Schrebera* Roxb. (Oleaceae) à Madagascar. *Bulletin du Muséum National d'Histoire Naturelle* 7: 59–66.
———. 1996. Taxa et noms nouveaux dans le genre *Dalbergia* (Papilionaceae) à Madagascar et aux Comores. *Bulletin de la Muséum National d'Histoire Naturelle, Paris*, série 4, Section B, *Adansonia* 18: 171–212.
———. 2005. Espèces nouvelles dans le genre *Dalbergia* (Fabaceae, Papilionoideae) à Madagascar. *Adansonia*, série 3, 27(2): 209–216.
Bouchart-Dufay, I., and Rakotondrainibe, F. 2019. Révision du genre *Marsilea* L. (Marsileaceae) à Madagascar. *Adansonia*, série 3, 41(1): 1–16.
Bouchat, A., and Léonard, J. 1986. Révision du genre *Necepsia* Prain (Euphorbiacée africano-malgache). *Bulletin du Jardin Botanique National de Belgique* 56: 179–194.
Boullet, V., Hivert, J., and Gigord, L.D.B. 2018. An updated account of the vascular flora of the Iles Eparses (southwest Indian Ocean). *Atoll Research Bulletin* 614: 1–64.
Bousquet, B., and Rabetaliana, H. 1992. *Site du patrimoine mondial des Tsingy de Bemaraha et autres sites d'intérêt biologique et écologique du fivondronana d'Antsalova: Evaluation et plan d'aménagement*. Paris: UNESCO.
Brako, L. 1991. *Phyllopsora* (Bacidiaceae). *Flora Neotropica* 55: 1–66.
Branstetter, M. G., Danforth, B. N., Pitts, J. P., Faircloth, B. C., Ward, P. S., Buffington, M. L., Gates, M. W., Kula, R. R., and Brady, S. G. 2017. Phylogenomic insights into the evolution of stinging wasps and the origins of ants and bees. *Current Biology* 27: 1019–1025.
Bremekamp, C.E.B. 1957. Monographie du genre *Saldinia* A. Rich. (Rubiaceae). *Candollea* 16: 995–1001.
———. 1962. Révision des *Chassalia* de Madagascar. *Candollea* 18: 195–238.
———. 1963. Sur quelques genres de Psychotriées (Rubiacées) et sur leurs représentants Malgaches et Comoriens. *Verhandelingen der Koninklijke Akademie van Wetenschappen, Afdeeling Natuurkunde*, Section 2: 1–181.
Bremer, B. 1996. Phylogenetic studies within Rubiaceae and relationships to other families based on molecular data. *Opera Botanica Belgica* 7: 33–50.
Bremer, B., and Eriksson, T. 2009. Time tree of Rubiaceae: Phylogeny and dating the family, subfamily, and tribes. *International Journal of Plant Sciences* 170: 766–793.
Bremer, B., Bremer, K., Heidari, N., Erixon, P., Olmstead, R. G., Anderberg, A. A., Kallersjo, M., and Barkhordarian, E. 2002. Phylogenetics of asterids based on 3 coding and 3 non-coding chloroplast DNA markers and the utility of non-coding DNA at higher taxonomic levels. *Molecular Phylogenetics and Evolution* 24: 274–301.
Bremer, K. 1982. *Lijndenia*, a re-established paleotropical genus of the Melastomataceae—Memecyleae. *Nordic Journal of Botany* 2: 121–124.
Breteler, F. J. 1997. Identité de *Sorindeia goudotii* (Anacardiaceae) de Madagascar. *Adansonia*, série 3, 19(2): 329–330.
———. 2003. The African genus *Sorindeia* (Anacardiaceae): A synoptic revision. *Adansonia*, série 3, 25(1): 93–107.
Bridson, D. M. 1998. Rubiaceae (tribe Vanguerieae). In *Flora Zambesiaca*, ed. G. V. Pope, pp. 211–377. Kew: Royal Botanic Gardens.
Bridson, D. M., and Verdcourt, B. 2003. Rubiaceae, pt. 3. In *Flora Zambesiaca* 5(3), ed. G. V. Pope, pp. 379–720. Kew: Royal Botanic Gardens.
Brink, M. 2008. *Canarium madagascariense* Engl. In PROTA (Plant Resources of Tropical Africa / Ressources végétales de l'Afrique tropicale), ed. D. Louppe, A. A. Oteng-Amoako, and M. Brink. Wageningen: PROTA Network Office Europe.
Brown, R. 1818. Anacardiaceae (nom. cons.). In *Narratives of an Expedition to Explore the River Zaire*, eds. J. H. Tuckey and J. M. Toner, p. 431. New York: Kirk and Mercein.
Bruggeman-Nannenga, M. A. 1993. Taxonomic Results of the BRYOTROP expedition to Zaire and Rwanda. 15. Fissidentaceae. *Tropical Bryology* 8: 141–148.
———. 2009. Notes on *Fissidens* VII–IX. *Journal of Bryology* 31: 106–116.
Bruggeman-Nannenga, M. A., and Arts T. 2010. A revision of the Fissidentaceae (Musci) of La Réunion (including all species known from Mauritius and Rodriguez). *Journal of Bryology* 32: 170–207.
Brummitt, R. K. 1992. *Vascular Plant Families and Genera*. Kew: Royal Botanic Gardens.
Brunel, J. F. 1987. Sur le genre *Phyllanthus* L. et quelques genres voisins de la Tribu des Phyllantheae Dumort. (Euphorbiaceae, Phyllantheae) en Afrique intertropicale et à Madagascar. PhD thesis, Université Louis Pasteur, Strasbourg.
Brunel, J. F., and Roux, J. 1981. Phyllantheae de Madagascar I: A propos de deux de la sous–section Swartziani Webster. *Adansonia* 2: 393–403.
———. 1982. Phyllantheae de Madagascar III: Une nouvelle espèce du genre *Meineckia*. *Bulletin du Muséum National d'Histoire Naturelle*, Paris, série 4, Section B, *Adansonia* 1–2: 79–84.
Bruyns, P. V., and Klak, C. 2004. Revision of the Madagascan endemic *Stapelianthus* (Apocynaceae) based on molecular and morphological characters. *Annals of the Missouri Botanical Garden* 91: 410–437.
Bruyns, P. V., Oliveira-Neto, M., Melo-de-Pinna, G. F., and Klak, C. 2014. Phylogenetic relationships in the Didiereaceae with special reference of subfamily Portulacarioideae. *Taxon* 63: 1053–1064.
Bruyns, P. V., Klak, C., and Hanáček, P. 2015. Recent radiation of *Brachystelma* and *Ceropegia* (Apocynaceae) across the Old World against a background of climatic change. *Molecular Phylogenetics and Evoution* 90: 49–66.
———. 2017. A revised, phylogenetically-based concept of *Ceropegia* (Apocynaceae). *South African Journal of Botany* 112: 399–436.
Buchmann, S. L. 1987. The ecology of oil flowers and their bees. *Annual Review of Ecology and Systematics* 18: 343–369.
Buchmann, S. L., and Buchmann, M. D. 1981. Anthecology of *Mouriri myrtilloides* (Melastomataceae: Memecyleae), an oil flower in Panama. *Biotropica* 13(2, suppl.): 7–24.
Buchner, R., and Puff, C. 1993. The genus complex *Danais-Schismatoclada-Payera* (Rubiaceae). Character states, generic delimitation and taxonomic position. *Adansonia* 15: 23–74.
Buck, W. R. 1979. A revision of the moss genus *Trachyphyllum* Gepp (Thuidiaceae). *Brittonia* 31(3): 379–394.
———. 1993. Taxonomic Results of the BRYOTROP expedition to Zaire and Rwanda. 24. Leskeaceae, Plagiotheciaceae, Entodontaceae, Sematophyllaceae, Hypnaceae (except *Hypnum*). *Tropical Bryology* 8: 199–218.
Buerki, S., and Baker, W. J. 2016. Collections-based research in the genomic era. *Biological Journal of the Linnean Society* 117: 5–10.
Buerki, S., Forest, F., Acevedo-Rodríguez, P., Callmander, M. W., Nylander, J.A.A., Harrington, M., Sanmartin, I., Küpfer, P., and Alvarez, N. 2009. Plastid and nuclear DNA markers reveal intricate relationships at subfamilial and tribal levels in the soapberry family (Sapindaceae). *Molecular Phylogenetics and Evolution* 51: 238–258.
Buerki, S., Lowry II, P. P., Alvarez, N., Razafimandimbison, S. G., Küpfer, P., and Callmander, M. W. 2010a. Phylogeny and circumscription of Sapindaceae revisited: Molecular sequence data, morphology and biogeography support recognition of a new family, Xanthoceraceae. *Plant Ecology and Evolution* 143: 148–161.
Buerki, S., Phillipson, P. B., Lowry II, P. P., and Callmander, M. W. 2010b. Molecular phylogenetics and morphological evidence support recognition of *Gereaua*, a new endemic genus of Sapindaceae from Madagascar. *Systematic Botany* 35: 172–180.
Buerki, S., Forest, F., Salamin, N., and Alvarez, N. 2011a. Comparative performance of supertree algorithms in large data sets using the soapberry family (Sapindaceae) as a case study. *Systematic Biology* 60: 32–44.
Buerki, S., Lowry II, P. P., Andriambololonera, S., Phillipson, P. B., Vary, L., and Callmander, M. W. 2011b. How to kill two genera with one tree: Clarifying generic circumscriptions within an endemic Malagasy clade of Sapindaceae. *Botanical Journal of the Linnean Society* 165: 223–234.
Buerki, S., Callmander, M.W., Devey, D. S., Chappell, L., Gallaher, T., Munzinger, J., Haevermans T., and Forest, F. 2012. Straightening out the screw-pines: A first step in understanding phylogenetic relationships within Pandanaceae. *Taxon* 61: 1010–1020.
Buerki, S., Devey, D. S., Callmander, M. W., Phillipson, P. B., and Forest, F. 2013. Spatio-temporal history of the endemic genera of Madagascar. *Botanical Journal of the Linnean Society* 171(2): 304–329. https://doi.org/10.1111/boj.12008.
Buerki, S., Doherty, R., Gautier, L., and Callmander, M. W. 2014. Rediscovery of the genus *Tsingya* Capuron (Sapindaceae) and its phylogenetic position. *Candollea* 69: 195–200.
Buerki, S., Devey, D. S., Callmander, M. W., Phillipson, P. B., and Forest, F. 2016a. Spatio-temporal history of the endemic genera of Madagascar. *Botanical Journal of the Linnean Society* 171: 304–329.
Buerki, S., Gallaher, T., Booth, T., Brewer, G., Forest, F., Perreira, J. T., and Callmander, M. W. 2016b. Biogeography and evolution of the screw-pine genus *Benstonea* Callm. and Buerki (Pandanaceae). *Candollea* 71: 217–229.
Buerki, S., Callmander, M. W., Acevedo-Rodriguez, P., Lowry II, P. P., Munzinger, J., et al. 2021. An updated infra-familial classification of Sapindaceae based on targeted enrichment data. *American Journal of Botany* 108(7): 1234–1251.
Bünger, M. O., Mazine, F. F., Forest, F., Bueno, M. L., Stehmann, R., and Lucas, E. J. 2016. The evolutionary history of *Eugenia* sect. *Phyllocalyx* (Myrtaceae)

corroborates historically stable areas in the southern Atlantic forests. *Annals of Botany* 118: 1209–1223.

Burge, D. O., Mugford, K., Hastings, A. P., and Agrawal, A. A. 2013. Phylogeny of the plant genus *Pachypodium* (Apocynaceae). *PeerJ* 1: e70.

Burkill, I. H., and Perrier de la Bâthie, H. 1950. Dioscoréacées. *Flore de Madagascar et des Comores* 44: 1–78.

Burley, J. S., and Pritchard N. M. 1990. A revision of the genus *Ceratodon* (Bryophyta). *Havard Papers in Botany* 2: 17–76.

Burrell, A. M., Pepper, A. E., Hodnett, G., Goolsby, J. A., Overholt, W. A., Racelis, A. E., Diaz, R., and Klein, P. E. 2015. Exploring origins, invasion history and genetic diversity of *Imperata cylindrica* (L.) P. Beauv. (Cogongrass) in the United States using genotyping by sequencing. *Molecular Ecology* 24: 2177–2193.

Buys, M. H., and Hilger, H. H. 2003. Boraginaceae cymes are exclusively scorpioid and not helicoid. *Taxon* 52: 719–724.

Byng, J. W., Barthelat, F., Snow, N., and Bernardini, B. 2016. Revision of *Eugenia* and *Syzygium* (Myrtaceae) from the Comoros Archipelago. *Phytotaxa* 252: 163–184.

Cabanis, Y., Chabouis, L., and Chabouis, F. 1969. *Végétaux et groupements végétaux de Madagascar et Mascareignes*, vol. 4. Tananarive: Bureau pour le Développement de la Production Agricole.

CABI. 2019. Invasive species compendium. *Austropuccinia psidii* (myrtle rust). Accessed 22 Nov. 2019. https://www.cabi.org/isc/datasheet/45846#todistributionTable.

Caddick, L. R., Rudall, P. J., Wilkin, P., Hedderson, T.A.J., and Chase, M. W. 2002. Phylogenetics of Dioscoreales based on combined analyses of morphological and molecular data. *Botanical Journal of the Linnean Society* 138: 123–144.

Cadotte, M. W., Rakotonasolo, F., Ludovic, R., and Jovett-Doust, J. 2002. Tree and shrub diversity and abundance in fragmented littoral forest of southeastern Madagascar. *Biodiversity and Conservation* 11: 1417–1436.

Cai, L., Xi, Z., Amorim, A. M., Sugumaran, M., Rest, J. S., Liu, L., and Davis, C. C. 2019. Widespread ancient whole-genome duplications in Malpighiales coincide with Eocene global climatic upheaval. *New Phytologist* 221(1): 565–576.

Calder, D. M. 1983. Mistletoes in focus: An introduction. In *The Biology of Mistletoes*, eds. D. M. Calder and P. Bernhardt, pp. 1–17. New York: Academic Press.

Callmander, M. W. 2000. *Pandanus* subg. *Martellidendron* (Pandanaceae) pt. 1: New findings on *Pandanus hornei* Balf. f. (sect. Seychellea) from the Seychelles. *Webbia* 55: 317–329.

———. 2001. *Pandanus* subg. *Martellidendron* (Pandanaceae) pt. 2: Revision of sect. *Martellidendron* Pic. Serm. in Madagascar. *Botanical Journal of the Linnean Society* 137: 353–374.

Callmander, M. W., and Buerki, S. 2004. Biogeography, conservation and diversity of Pandanaceae in the granitic Seychelles Islands. *Kapisen* 17: 8–9.

Callmander, M. W., and Laivao, M. O. 2003. Biogeography and systematics of the Madagascan *Pandanus* (Pandanacaeae). In *The Natural History of Madagascar*, eds. S. M. Goodman and J. P. Benstead, pp. 460–467. Chicago: University of Chicago Press.

Callmander, M. W., and Phillipson, P. B. 2011. Four new species of the endemic genus *Rhodocolea* Baill. (Bignoniaceae). *Adansonia*, série 3, 33: 311–321.

———. 2012. Two new species in the genus *Colea* Bojer ex Meisn. (Bignoniaceae) endemic to Madagascar. *Adansonia*, série 3, 34: 115–122.

———. 2015. The transfer of the Malagasy species of *Strobilanthes* Blume to *Acanthopale* C. B. Clarke (Acanthaceae). *Candollea* 70(2): 253–256.

———. 2016. *Phyllarthron longipedunculatum* Callm. & Phillipson, sp. nov. (Bignoniaceae): A new species from northern Madagascar. *Adansonia*, série 3, 38(2): 275–280.

Callmander, M. W., Chassot P., Küpfer, P., and Lowry II, P. P. 2003. Recognition of *Martellidendron*, a new genus of Pandanaceae, and its biogeographic implications. *Taxon* 52: 747–762.

Callmander, M. W., Schatz, G. E. Lowry II, P. P., Laivao, M. O., Raharimampionona, J., Andriambololonera, S., Raminosoa, T., and Consiglio, T. 2007. Application of IUCN Red List criteria and assessment of Priority Areas for Plant Conservation in Madagascar: Rare and threatened Pandanaceae indicate new sites in need of protection. *Oryx* 41: 168–176.

Callmander, M. W., Buerki, S., and Wohlhauser, S. 2008. A new threatened species of Pandanaceae from northwestern Madagascar, *Pandanus sermolliana*. *Novon* 18: 421–424.

Callmander, M. W., Rakotovao, C., Razafitsalama, J., Phillipson, P. B., Buerki, S., et al. 2009. New species from the Galoka and Kalabenono Massifs: Two unknown and severely threatened mountainous areas in NW Madagascar. *Candollea* 64: 179–202.

Callmander, M. W., Labat, J.-N., and Schrire, B. D. 2010. Dealing with *Indigofera nivea* (Leguminosae)—a new name for Madagascar and a new combination for Africa. *Candollea* 65(2): 363–364.

Callmander, M. W., Phillipson P. B., Schatz G. E., Andriambololonera, S., Rabarimanarivo, M., Rakotonirina, N., Raharimampionona, J., Chatelain, C., Gautier, L., and Lowry II, P. P. 2011a. The endemic and non-endemic vascular flora of Madagascar updated. *Plant Ecology and Evolution* 144: 121–125. https://doi.org/10.5091/plecevo.2011.513.

Callmander, M. W., Buerki S., and Phillipson, P. B. 2011b. Nomenclatural changes in the endemic genus *Tina* (Sapindaceae) in Madagascar. *Candollea* 66: 124–126.

Callmander, M. W., Phillipson, P. B., Razanajatovo, M., and Nusbaumer, L. 2011c. The genus *Ophiocolea* (Bignoniaceae) in northern Madagascar with description of four new species and two lectotypifications. *Candollea* 66: 133–142.

Callmander, M. W., Phillipson, P. B., and Lowry II, P. P. 2012a. Novelties from the Northern Mountains Complex of Madagascar. III. Two new species of *Turraea* L. (Meliaceae). *Adansonia*, série 3, 34(1): 93–102.

Callmander, M. W., Lowry II, P. P., Forest, F., Devey, D. S., Beentje, H., and Buerki, S. 2012b. *Benstonea* Callm. and Buerki (Pandanaceae): Characterization, circumscription, and distribution of a new genus of screw-pines, with a synopsis of accepted species. *Candollea* 67: 323–345.

Callmander, M. W., Phillipson, P. B., and Schatz, G. E. 2012c. Two new species of the genus *Stereospermum* (Bignoniaceae) from Madagascar. *Novon* 22: 141–147.

Callmander, M. W., Bolliger, R., Hanitrarivo R. M., and Nusbaumer, L. 2013. *Pandanus tsingycola* Callm. and Nusb. (Pandanaceae), a new species endemic to western Madagascar. *Candollea* 68: 229–235.

Callmander, M. W., Luino, I., Da-Giau, S., Rakotovao, C., and Gautier, L. 2014. A synoptic revision of the Malagasy endemic genus *Socratina* Balle (Loranthaceae). *Candollea* 69: 65–73.

Callmander, M. W., Phillipson, P. B., Plunkett, G. M., Edwards, M. B., and Buerki, S. 2016. Generic delimitations, biogeography and evolution in the tribe Coleeae (Bignoniaceae), endemic to Madagascar and the smaller islands of the western Indian Ocean. *Molecular Phylogenetics and Evolution* 96: 178–186.

Callmander, M. W., Razakamalala, R., Luino, I., Andriamarisoa, R. L., and Buerki, S. 2020. Novelties from the Northern Mountains Complex of Madagascar V: A new threatened *Pandanus* (Pandanaceae) from the Kalobinono Massif. *Candollea* 75: 99–105.

Cámara-Leret, R., Frodin, D. G., Adema, F., Anderson, C., Appelhans, M., et al. 2020. New Guinea has the world's richest island flora. *Nature* 584: 579–583.

Camarero, P. 2019. Exotic vine invasions following cyclone disturbance in Australian Wet Tropics rainforests: A review. *Australian Ecology* 44: 1359–1372. https://doi.org/10.1111/aec.12810.

Canaby, M. 1932. Le Caoutchouc de cueillette à Madagascar. *Journal d'Agriculture Traditionnelle et de Botanique Appliquée* 12: 609–621.

Capuron, R. 1960a. Contribution à l'étude de la flore forestière de Madagascar. *Notulae Systematicae* 16: 60–80.

———. 1960b. Contributions à l'étude la flore forestière de Madagascar. 5. Trois Bignoniacées nouvelles. *Notulae Systematicae* 16: 71–80.

———. 1961. Contributions à l'étude de la flore forestière de Madagascar, III. Sur quelques plantes ayant contribué au peuplement de Madagascar. *Adansonia*, nouvelle série, 1: 65–92.

———. 1962. Contributions à l'étude de la flore forestière de Madagascar. VI. Note sur les Burséracées. *Adansonia*, nouvelles séries, 2: 268–283.

———. 1963. Révision des Tiliacées de Madagascar et des Comores (pt. 1). *Adansonia*, nouvelle série, 3(1): 91–129.

———. 1964. Révision des Tiliacées de Madagascar et des Comores (suite). Les *Grewia* de la section Axillares Burret. *Adansonia*, nouvelle série, 4: 269–300.

———. 1967. Nouvelles observations sur les Rutacées de Madagascar. *Adansonia*, nouvelle série, 7(4): 479–500.

———. 1968a. Contributions à l'étude de la flore forestière de Madagascar. *Adansonia*, nouvelle série, 8(1): 11–16

———. 1968b. Contributions à l'étude de la flore forestière de Madagascar: Un *Thespesia* nouveau de Madagascar (Malvacées). *Adansonia*, série 2, 8(1): 5–9.

———. 1968c. *Les Olacacées, Opiliacées et Santalacées arbustives ou arborescentes de Madagascar.* Tananarive: Centre Technique Forestier Tropical.

———. 1969. Révision des Sapindacées de Madagascar et des Comores. *Mémoires du Muséum National d'Histoire Naturelle*, série B, Botanique, 19: 1–189.

———. 1970a. Observations sur les Sarcolaenacées. *Adansonia*, nouvelle série, 2: 247–265.

———. 1970b. Deux nouvelles Bignoniacées. *Adansonia*, série 2, 10: 501–506.

———. 1972. Contribution à l'étude de la flore forestière de Madagascar. *Adansonia*, série 2, 12: 205–211.

———. 1975. Contribution à l'étude de la flore forestière de Madagascar. *Adansonia*, série 2, 14(4): 571–572.

Capuron, R., and Mabberley, D. J. 1999. Révision des Malvaceae-Grewioideae ("Tiliacées", p.p.) de Madagascar et des Comores. III. Les *Grewia* du sous-genre *Vincentia* (Benth.) Capuron. *Adansonia*, série 3, 21(1): 7–23.
Cardinal-McTeague, W. M., and Gillespie, L. J. 2016. Molecular phylogeny and pollen evolution of Euphorbiaceae tribe Plukenetieae. *Systematic Botany* 41: 329–347.
Cardinal-McTeague, W. M., Wurdack, K. J., Sigel, E. M., and Gillespie, L. J. 2019. Seed size evolution and biogeography of *Plukenetia* (Euphorbiaceae), a pantropical genus with traditionally cultivated oilseed species. *BMC Evolutionary Biology* 19(1): 29.
Cardoso, D.B.O.S., Pennington, R. T., de Queiroz, L. P., Boatwright, J. S., Van Wyk, B.-E., Wojciechowski, M. F., and Lavin, M. 2013. Reconstructing the deep-branching relationships of the papilionoid legumes. *South African Journal of Botany* 89: 58–75.
Cargill, D. C. 2001. A taxonomic revision of Fossombronia and Sewardiella, suborder Fossombroniineae (Marchantiophyta, Metzgeriidae), within the continent of Africa, southwest Asia and the sub-continent of India. PhD thesis, Southern Illinois University, Carbondale.
Carlier, J., Guitton, J., Bévalot, F., Fanton, L., and Gaillard, Y. 2014. The principal toxic glycosidic steroids in *Cerbera manghas* L. seeds: Identification of cerberin, neriifolin, tanghinin and deacetyltanghinin by UHPLC–HRMS/MS, quantification by UHPLC–PDA-MS. *Journal of Chromatography B* 962: 1–8.
Carlsward, B., Whitten, M., Williams, N., and Bytebier, B. 2006. Molecular phylogenetics of Vandeae (Orchidaceae) and the evolution of leaflessness. *American Journal of Botany* 93: 770–786.
Carvalho-Sobrinho, J. G., Alverson, W. S., Alcantara, S., Queiroz, L. P., Mota, A. C., and Baum, D. A. 2016. Revisiting the phylogeny of Bombacoideae (Malvaceae): Novel relationships, morphologically cohesive clades, and a new tribal classification based on multilocus phylogenetic analyses. *Molecular Phylogenetics and Evolution* 101: 56–74.
Cavaco, A. 1951. Remarques sur les genres *Leptolaena* et *Xerochlamys* (Chlaenacées). Un nouveau genre de Chlaenaceae. *Bulletin du Muséum National d'Histoire Naturelle* 2: 133–139.
———. 1952a. Chlaenaceae. *Flore de Madagascar et des Comores* 126: 1–37.
———. 1952b. Recherches sur les Chlaenacées. Famille endémique de Madagascar. *Mémoire de l'Institut Scientifique de Madagascar*, série B, 4: 59–92.
Cavaco, A., and Keraudren, M. 1955. Sur le *Ximenia* (Olacacées) de Madagascar, une nouvelle espèce d'*Olax*. *Bulletin de la Société Botanique de France* 102: 117–119.
CBOL Plant Working Group 2009. A DNA barcode for land plants. *Proceedings of the National Academy of Science of the USA* 106: 12794–12797.
Cervantes, A., Fuentes, S., Gutiérrez, J., Magallón, S., and Borsch, T. 2016. Successive arrivals since the Miocene shaped the diversity of the Caribbean Acalyphoideae (Euphorbiaceae). *Journal of Biogeography* 43: 1773–1785.
Chambers, P. A., Lacoul, P., Murphy, K. J., and Thomaz, S. M. 2008. Global diversity of aquatic macrophytes in freshwater. *Hydrobiologia* 595: 9–26.
Champluvier, D., and Darbyshire, I. 2009. A revision of the genera *Brachystephanus* and *Oreacanthus* (Acanthaceae) in tropical Africa. *Systematics and Geography of Plants* 79(2): 115–192.
Chantarasuwan, B., Ronsted, N., Kjellberg, F., Sungkaew, S., and van Welzen, P. C. 2016. Palaeotropical intercontinental disjunctions revisited using a dated phylogenetic hypothesis with nearly complete species level sampling of *Ficus* subsect. *Urostigma* (Moraceae). *Journal of Biogeography* 43: 384–397.
Chapotin, S. M., Razanameharizaka, J. H., and Holbrook, N. M. 2006. Baobab trees (*Adansonia*) in Madagascar use stored water to flush new leaves but not to support stomatal opening before the rainy season. *New Phytologist* 169: 549–559.
Chase, M. W., and Hills, H. H. 1991. Silica gel: An ideal material for field preservation of leaf samples for DNA studies. *Taxon* 40: 215–220.
Chase, M. W., Soltis, D. E., Olmstead, R. G., Morgan, D., Les, D. H., et al. 1993. Phylogenetics of seed plants: An analysis of nucleotide sequences from the plastid gene *rbcL*. *Annals of the Missouri Botanical Garden* 80: 528–580.
Chase, M. W., Morton, C. M., and Kallunki, J. A. 1999. Phylogenetic relationships of Rutaceae: A cladistic analysis of the subfamilies using evidence from *rbcL* and *atpB* sequence variation. *American Journal of Botany* 86(8): 1191–1199. https://doi.org/10.2307/2656983.
Chase, M. W., Zmarzty, S., Lledó, M. D., Wurdack, K. J., Swensen, S. M., and Fay, M. F. 2002. When in doubt, put it in Flacourtiaceae: A molecular phylogenetic analysis based on plastid *rbcL* DNA sequences. *Kew Bulletin* 57: 141–181.
Chase, M. W., Cameron, K., Freudenstein, J., Pridgeon, A., Salazar, G., and van den Berg, C. 2015. An updated classification of Orchidaceae. *Botanical Journal of the Linnean Society* 177: 151–174.
Chase, M. W., Christenhusz, M.J.M., Fay, M. F., Byng, J. W., Judd, W. S., Soltis, D. E., Mabberley, D. J., Sennikov, A. N., Soltis, P. S., and Stevens, P. F. 2016. An update of the Angiosperm Phylogeny Group classification for the orders and families of flowering plants: APG IV. *Botanical Journal of the Linnean Society* 181(1): 1–20.
Chatelain, C., Hanitrarivo, M. R., Rakotozafy, B.F.L., Bolliger, R., Luino, I., Ranirison, P., and Gautier, L. 2013. Cartographie de la couverture forestière du massif de Beanka, Région Melaky, Ouest de Madagascar. In La forêt de Beanka, Région Melaky, Ouest de Madagascar, eds. S. M. Goodman, L. Gautier, and M. J. Raherilalao. *Malagasy Nature* 7: 85–103.
Chaw, S. M., and Darwin, S. P. 1992. A systematic study of the Old World species of *Antirhea* (Rubiaceae: Guettardeae). *Tulane Studies in Zoology and Botany* 28: 25–118.
Cheban, S. A., Rejo-Fienena, F., and Tostain, S. 2009. Etude ethnobotanique des ignames (*Dioscorea* spp.) dans la forêt Mikea et le couloir d'Antseva (sud-ouest de Madagascar). *Malagasy Nature* 2: 111–126.
Cheek, M., and Rakotozafy, A. 1991. The identity of Leroy's fifth sub-family of the Meliaceae, and a new combination in *Commiphora* (Burseraceae). *Taxon* 40: 231–237.
Chen, C., Song, Q. S., Proffit, M., Bessière, J.-M., Li, Z. B., and Hossaert-McKey, M. 2009. Private channel: A single unusual compound assures specific pollinator attraction in *Ficus semicordata*. *Functional Ecology* 23: 941–950.
Christenhusz, M.J.M., and Byng, J. W. 2016. The number of known plant species in the world and its annual increase. *Phytotaxa* 261: 201–217.
Christenhusz, M.J.M., Fay, M. F., and Byng, J. W. 2018. Special edn., GLOVAP Nomenclature pt. 1, vol. 4. Bradford, UK: Plant Gateway.
Churchill, S. P. 1988. A revision of the moss genus *Lepidopilum* (Callicostaceae). PhD thesis, City University of New York.
CITES (Convention on International Trade in Endangered Species on Wild Fauna and Flora). 2019. Draft decisions on Malagasy palisanders and rosewoods (*Dalbergia* spp.) and ebonies (*Diospyros* spp.). CoP18 Com. 2.8. Convention on International Trade in Endangered Species of Wild Fauna and Flora. Eighteenth meeting of the Conference of the Parties, Geneva (Switzerland), 17–28 August 2019. https://cites.org/sites/default/files/eng/cop/18/Com_II/E-CoP18-Com-II-08.pdf.
———. 2020. Appendices 1, 2, and 3. Accessed 10 June 2020. https://cites.org/sites/default/files/eng/app/2019/E-Appendices-2019-11-26.pdf.
Civeyrel, L. 1995. Pollen morphology and ultrastructure of the genus *Secamone* in Africa. *2nd Symposium on African Palynology, Tervuren (Belgium)*, eds. A. Le Thomas and E. Roche, pp. 207–215. Orléans: CIFEG.
Civeyrel, L., Le Thomas, A., Ferguson, K., and Chase, M. W. 1998. Critical reexamination of palynological characters used to delimit Asclepiadaceae in comparison to molecular phylogeny obtained from plastid *mat*K sequences. *Molecular Phylogenetics and Evolution* 9: 517–527.
Clark, R. 2016. A taxonomic revision of *Mezoneuron* (Leguminosae: Caesalpinioideae: Caesalpinieae). *Phytotaxa* 274(1): 1–72.
Clausing, G., and Renner, S. S. 2001. Molecular phylogenetics of Melastomataceae and Memecylaceae: Implications for character evolution. *American Journal of Botany* 88: 486–498.
Clayton, W. D. 1989. Gramineae. In *Flora Zambesiaca* 10 (3), eds. E. Launert and G. V. Pope. Kew: Royal Botanic Gardens.
Clerc, P. 2004. Notes on the genus *Usnea* Adanson. II. *Bibliotheca Lichenologica* 88: 79–90.
Coe, M. J., and Isaac, F. M. 1965. Pollination of the baobab, *Adansonia digitata* L., by the lesser bushbaby, *Galago crassicaudatus* E. Geoffroy. *East African Wildlife Journal* 3: 123–124.
Cole, T.C.H. 2019. Apocynaceae phylogeny poster. https://www.researchgate.net/publication/332934701_Apocynaceae_Phylogeny_Poster_ApocynPP.
Compton, S. G. 1992. New records of *Ficus* species and their pollinators on Grand Comore. *Bothalia* 22(1): 46–47.
Compton, S. G., Holton, K. C., Rashbrook, V. K., van Noort, S., Vincent, S. L., and Ware, A. B. 1991. Studies of *Ceratosolen galili*, a non-pollinating Agaonid fig wasp. *Biotropica* 23(2): 188–194.
Compton, S. G., Ball, A. D., Collinson, M. E., Hayes, P., Rasnitsyn, A. P., and Ross, A. J. 2010. Ancient fig wasps indicate at least 34 Myr of stasis in their mutualism with fig trees. *Biology Letters* 6: 838–842.
Consiglio, T., Schatz, G. E., McPherson, G., Lowry II, P. P., Rabenantoandro, J., and Rogers, Z. S. 2006. Deforestation and plant diversity of Madagascar's littoral forests. *Conservation Biology* 20: 1799–1803.
Cook, J. M., and Rasplus, J.-Y. 2003. Mutualists with attitude: Coevolving fig wasps and figs. *Trends in Ecology and Evolution* 18: 241–248.

Cope, T. A. 1999. Gramineae. In *Flora Zambesiaca* 10(2), eds. T. A. Cope and G. V. Pope. Kew: Royal Botanic Gardens.

———. 2002. Gramineae. In *Flora Zambesiaca* 10(4), eds. G. V. Pope and E. S. Martins. Kew: Royal Botanic Gardens.

Corner, E.J.H. 1965. Check-list of *Ficus* in Asia and Australasia, with keys to identification. *Gardens' Bulletin of Singapore* 21: 1–186.

———. 1985. Essays on *Ficus*. *Allertonia* 2: 125–168.

Cornet, A. 1972. *Carte bioclimatique de Madagascar*. Tananarive: Office de la Recherche Scientifique et Technique.

———. 1974. *Essai de cartographie bioclimatique à Madagascar*. Carte à 1/200.000 et notice no. 55. Paris: ORSTOM.

———., and Guillaumet, J.-L. 1976. Divisions floristiques et étages de végétation à Madagascar. *Cahier de l'ORSTOM*, série Biologie 9: 35–42.

Cosner, M. E., Jansen, R. K., and Lammers, T. G. 1994. Phylogenetic relationships in the Campanulales based on *rbcl* sequences. *Plant Systematics and Evolution* 190: 79–95.

Couplan, F. 2009. *Le régal végétal: plantes sauvages comestibles*, vol. 1. Paris: Editions Sang de la Terre.

Coursey, D. G. 1967. *Yams: An Account of the Nature, Origins, Cultivation and Utilisation of the Useful Members of the Dioscoreaceae*. London: Longmans.

Cousins, W. E., and Parrett, J. 1871. *Malagasy Proverbs*. Antananarivo: L.M.S. Press.

Couto, R. S., Martins, A. C., Bolson, M., Lopes, R. C., Smidt, E. C., and Braga, J. M. A. 2018. Time calibrated tree of *Dioscorea* (Dioscoreaceae) indicates four origins of yams in the Neotropics since the Eocene. *Botanical Journal of the Linnean Society* 188: 144–160.

Couvreur, T.L.P., Forest, F., and Baker, W. J. 2011. Origin and global diversification patterns of tropical rain forests: Inferences from a complete genus-level phylogeny of palms. *BMC Biology* 9: 44.

Crandall-Stotler, B., Stotler, R. E., and Long, D. G. 2009. Phylogeny and classification of the Marchantiophyta. *Edinburgh Journal of Botany* 66: 155.

Cremers, G. 1984. Les euphorbes coralliformes de Madagascar. *Bulletin du Jardin Botanique National de Belgique, Brussels* 54: 23–64.

Cremers, G., and Sell, Y. 1986. Architecture végétative et structures inflorescentielles chez les Didiereaceae de Madagascar. *Beitrage zur Biologie der Pflanzen* 61: 381–400.

Cribb, P., and Hermans, J. 2009. *Field Guide to the Orchids of Madagascar*. Kew: Royal Botanic Gardens.

Cribb, P., Roberts, D., and Hermans, J. 2005. Distribution, ecology and threat to selected Madagascan orchids. *Selbyana* 26: 125–133.

Crombie, J. M. 1877. Lichenes Insulae Rodriguesii. An enumeration of the lichens collected by Dr. J. B. Balfour during the Venus-Transit Expedition 1874. *Journal of the Linnean Society* 15: 431–445.

Cron, G. V., Karimi, N., Glennon, K. L., Udeh, C. A., Witkowski, E. T., Venter, S. M., Assogbadjo, A. E., and Baum, D. A. 2016. One African baobab species or two? Synonymy of *Adansonia kilima* and *A. digitata*. *Taxon* 65: 1037–1049.

Cronquist, A. 1981. *An Integrated System of Classification of Flowering Plants*. New York: Columbia University Press.

Crosby, M. R., Schultze-Motel, U., and Schultze-Motel, W. 1983. Katalog der Laubmoose von Madagascar und den Umliegenden Inseln. *Willdenowia* 13: 187–255.

Crowther, A., Lucas, L., Helm, R., Horton, M., Shipton, C., et al. 2016. Ancient crops provide first archaeological signature of the westward Austronesian expansion. *Proceedings of the National Academy of Sciences of the USA* 113: 6635–6640.

Cruaud, A., Rønsted, R., Chantarasuwan, B., Siang Chou, L., Clement, W., et al. 2012. An extreme case of plant–insect codiversification: Figs and fig-pollinating wasps. *Systematic Biology* 61: 1029–1047.

Crum, H. 1972. A taxonomic account of the Erpodiaceae. *Nova Hedwigia* 23: 201–224.

Cushman, J. H., Compton, S. G., Zachariades, C., Ware, A. B., Nefdt, R.J.C., and Rashbrook, V. K. 1998. Geographic and taxonomic distribution of a positive interaction: Ant-tended homopterans indirectly benefit figs across southern Africa. *Oecologia* 116: 373–380.

Czeczuga, B., Bhat, R. B., Aptroot, A, Mies, B., and Czeczuga-Semeniuk, E. 1998. Carotenoids in some lichen species from South Africa, Madagascar and Cape Verde Islands. *Feddes Repertorium* 109: 573–580.

Dahlgren, R.M.T. 1980. Revised system of classification of the angiosperms. *Botanical Journal of the Linnean Society* 80: 91–124.

Dahlgren, R.[M.T.], and Thorne, R. F. 1984. The order Myrtales: Circumscription, variation, and relationships. *Annals of the Missouri Botanical Garden* 71: 633–699.

Dalecky, A., Kerdelhué, C., Johnson, S., Razafindratsita, V. R., Grassi, C., Razafiarimalala, A. C., Overdorff, D. J., and Rasplus, J.-Y. 2003. Moraceae, *Ficus* and associated fauna. In *The Natural History of Madagascar*, eds. S. M. Goodman and J. P. Benstead, pp. 322–334. Chicago: University of Chicago Press.

Daly, D. C., and Fine, P.V.A. 2018. Generic limits re-visited and an updated sectional classification for *Protium* (tribe Protieae). Studies in Neotropical Burseraceae XXV. *Brittonia* 70: 418–426.

Daly, D. C., Harley, M. M., Martínez-Habibe, M. C., and Weeks, A. 2011. Burseraceae. In *The Families and Genera of Vascular Plants*, vol. 10, ed. K. Kubitzki, pp. 76–104. New York: Springer.

Daly, D. C., Raharimampionona, J., and Federman, S. 2015. A revision of *Canarium* (Burseraceae) in Madagascar. *Adansonia*, série 3, 37: 277–345.

Dama. 1995. Contribution à l'étude de *Lepironia mucronata* L. C. Rich (Cyperaceae) dans le Sud-Est de Madagascar, biologie, écologie, essai de régénération et aspect socio-économique. Mémoire de DEA., Université d'Antananarivo.

Daniel, T. F. 2015. *Anisotes tablensis* (Acanthaceae), a new species from southwestern Madagascar. *Proceedings of the California Academy of Sciences*, series 4, 62: 451–455.

Daniel, T. F., and McDade, L. A. 2014. Nelsonioideae (Lamiales: Acanthaceae): Revision of genera and catalog of species. *Aliso* 32(1): 1–45.

Daniel, T. F., Mbola, B.A.V., and Almeda, F. 2007. *Anisotes* (Acanthaceae) in Madagascar. *Proceedings of the California Academy of Sciences* 58: 121–131.

Daniel, T. F., McDade, L. A., Manktelow, M. E., and Kiel, C. 2008. The "*Tetramerium* Lineage" (Acanthaceae: Acanthoideae: Justicieae): Delimitation and intra-lineage relationships based on cp and nrITS sequence data. *Systematic Botany* 33(2): 416–436.

Daniel, T. F., Letsara, R., and Martín-Bravo, S. 2013. Four new species of *Anisotes* (Acanthaceae) from Madagascar. *Novon* 22(4): 396–408.

Daniel, T. F., Letsara, R., and Rakotonasolo, F. 2019. Incorporation of *Danguya* into *Anisotes* (Acanthaceae: Justicieae), a new combination, and lectotypification of *D. pulchella*. *Proceedings of the California Academy of Sciences* 66: 51–59.

Danser, B. H. 1937. A revision of the genus *Korthalsella*. *Bulletin du Jardin Botanique Buitenzorg* 14: 115–159.

———. 1940. A supplement to the revision of the genus *Korthalsella*. *Bulletin du Jardin Botanique Buitenzorg* 16: 329–342.

Darbyshire, I., and Vollesen, K. 2007. The transfer of the genus *Peristrophe* to *Dicliptera* (Acanthaceae), with a new species described from eastern Africa. *Kew Bulletin* 62(1): 119–128.

Darbyshire, I., Phillipson, P. B., and Rakotonasolo, F. 2014. Additions to the genus *Barleria* in Madagascar. *Kew Bulletin* 69: 1–11.

Darbyshire, I., Fisher, A. E., Kiel, C. A., and McDade, L. A. 2019. Phylogenetic relationships among species of *Barleria* (Acanthaceae, Lamiales): Molecular data reveal complex patterns of morphological evolution and support a revised classification. *Taxon* 68: 92–111.

Darwin, C. 1904. *The Various Contrivances by Which Orchids are Fertilised by Insects*. London: John Murray.

Das, S., and Sharangi, A. B. 2017. Madagascar periwinkle (*Catharanthus roseus* L.): Diverse medicinal and therapeutic benefits to humankind. *Journal of Pharmacognosy and Phytochemistry* 6: 1695–1701.

David, J. C., and Hawksworth, D. L. 1995. Lichens of Mauritius I: Some new species and records. *Bibliotheca Lichenologica* 57: 93–111.

Davies, N.M.J., and Davis, A. P. 2014. *Chapelieria septentrionalis* and *C. multiflora* spp. nov. (Rubiaceae, Octotropideae) and an emended description for *C. madagascariensis*. *Nordic Journal of Botany* 32: 691–700.

Davis, A. P., and Bridson, D. 2003. Introduction to the Rubiaceae. In *The Natural History of Madagascar*, eds. S. M. Goodman and J. P. Benstead, pp. 431–434. Chicago: University of Chicago Press.

Davis, A. P., and Rakotonasolo, F. 2008. A taxonomic revision of the baracoffea alliance: Nine remarkable *Coffea* species from western Madagascar. *Botanical Journal of the Linnean Society* 158: 355–390.

Davis, A. P., Bridson, D. M., and Rakotonasolo, F. 2005. A reexamination of *Coffea* subgenus *Baracoffea* and comments on the morphology and classification of *Coffea* and *Psilanthus* (Rubiaceae–Coffeeae). *Monographs in Systematic Botany* 104: 398–420.

Davis, A. P., Govaerts, R., Bridson, D. M., and Stoffelen, P. 2006. An annotated taxonomic conspectus of the genus *Coffea* (Rubiaceae). *Botanical Journal of the Linnean Society* 152: 465–512.

Davis, A. P., Chester, M., Maurin, O., and Fay, M. F. 2007. Searching for the relatives of *Coffea* (Rubiaceae, Ixoroideae): The circumscription and phylogeny of Coffeeae based on plastid sequence data and morphology. *American Journal of Botany* 94: 313–329.

Davis, A. P., Govaerts, R., Bridson, D., Rusham, M., Moat, J., and Brummitt, A. A. 2009. A global assessment of distribution, diversity, endemism, and taxonomic efforts in Rubiaceae. *Annals of the Missouri Botanical Garden* 96: 68–78.

Davis, A. P., Tosh, J., Ruch, N., and Fay, M. F. 2011. Growing coffee: *Psilanthus* (Rubiaceae) subsumed on the basis of molecular and morphological data; implications for the size, morphology, distribution and evolutionary history of *Coffea*. *Botanical Journal of the Linnean Society* 167: 357–377.

Davis, C. C., Webb, C. O., Wurdack K. J., Jaramillo, C. A., and Donoghue, M. J. 2005. Explosive radiation of Malpighiales supports a mid-Cretaceous origin of modern tropical rain forests. *The American Naturalist* 4(3): 36–65.

Dawson, S. E. 2016. Characteristics of the Madagascan genus *Canephora* (Rubiaceae: Octotropideae), and the description of two new species. *Kew Bulletin* 71: 45.

De Block, P. 2003. *Robbrechtia*, a new Rubiaceae genus from Madagascar. *Systematic Botany* 28: 145–156.

———. 2005. Notes on *Tarenna* (Pavetteae) as a precursor to a checklist of the Rubiaceae of Madagascar and the Comores. *Systematics and Geography of Plants* 75: 107–116.

———. 2007. Three new Madagascan *Ixora* species (Rubiaceae) with flowers up to 25 cm long. *Nordic Journal of Botany* 25: 75–84.

———. 2008. Synopsis of the uniflorous Madagascan *Ixora* (Rubiaceae) species belonging to section *Microthamnus*. *Belgian Journal of Botany* 141: 141–156.

———. 2014. A synopsis of the multilocular species of *Ixora* (Rubiaceae) from Madagascar. *Phytotaxa* 162: 121–133.

———. 2018. Revision of the Madagascan endemic *Homollea* (Rubiaceae-Pavetteae), with description of two new species. *European Journal of Taxonomy* 423: 1–24.

De Block, P., and Davis, A. P. 2006. A new *Mantalania* species (Rubiaceae) from Madagascar. *Botanical Journal of the Linnean Society* 151: 421–424.

De Block, P., and Randriamboavonjy, T. 2015. Three new species of *Craterispermum* (Rubiaceae) from Madagascar. *Phytotaxa* 206(1): 79–89.

De Block, P., Rakotonasolo, F., and Tosh, J. 2006. *Mantalania longipedunculata* revisited. *Systematics and Geography of Plants* 76: 236–240.

De Block, P., Razafimandimbison, S. G., Janssens, S., Ochoterena, H., Robbrecht, E., and Bremer, B. 2015. Molecular phylogenetics and generic assessment in the tribe Pavetteae (Rubiaceae). *Taxon* 64: 79–95.

De Block, P., Rakotonasolo, F., Ntore, S., Razafimandimbison, S. G., and Janssens, S. 2018. Four new endemic genera of Rubiaceae (Pavetteae) from Madagascar represent multiple radiations into drylands. *Phytokeys* 99: 1–66.

De Block, P., Rakotonasolo, F., Vrijdaghs, A., and Dessein, S. 2020. Two new species of *Phialiphora* (Spermacoceae, Rubiaceae) exemplify drought adaptations in western Madagascar. *Plant Ecology and Evolution* 153(2): 267–282.

De Block, P., Rakotonasolo, F., Razafimandimbison, S. G., Davis, A. P., and Janssens, S. B. 2021. *Tarennella*, a new Pavetteae (Rubiaceae) genus from eastern Madagascar. *Plant Ecology and Evolution* 154(1): 87–110.

de Candolle, A. 1844. Corolliflorae. In *Prodromus systematis naturalis regni vegetabilis*, vol. 8, pt. 8–13. Paris: Sumptibus Sociorum Treuttel and Würtz.

———. 1845. *Prodromus systematis naturalis regni vegetabilis*, vol. 9. Paris: Sumptibus Sociorum Treuttel et Würtz.

———. 1846. *Prodromus systematis naturalis regni vegetabilis*, vol. 10. Paris: Sumptibus Sociorum Treuttel et Würtz.

de Candolle, A. P. 1825. Terebinthaceae. In *Prodromus systematis naturalis regni vegetabilis*, vol. 2, ed. A. P. de Candolle, pp. 61–92. Paris: Sumptibus Sociorum Treutel et Würtz.

de Candolle, C. 1866. Piperaceae novae. *Journal of Botany, British and Foreign* 4: 132–147, 161–166, 210–219, 300.

———. 1869. Piperaceae. *Prodromus systematis naturalis regni vegetabilis*, vol. 16(1): 235–471. Paris: Masson.

———. 1894. Piperaceae Africanae et Madagascariensis. *Botanische Jahrbücher für Systematik, Pflanzengeschichte und Pflanzengeographie* 19: 224–230.

———. 1898. Piperaceae novae—III Peperomieae. *Annuaire du Conservatoire et Jardin Botaniques de Genève* 2: 276–288.

———. 1911. Pipéracées de Madagascar, espèces et localités nouvelles. *Notulae Systematicae* 2: 46–50.

———. 1923. Piperacearum Clavis analytica. *Candollea* 1: 65–415.

Decary, R. 1946. Plantes et animaux utiles de Madagascar. *Annales du Musée Colonial de Marseille*, 54ème année, série 6, 4: 1–234.

DeFilipps, R. A. 1969. Parasitism in *Ximenia* (Olacaceae). *Rhodora* 71: 439–443.

de la Estrella, M., Forest, F., Klitgård, B., Lewis, G. P., Mackinder, B. A., de Queiroz, L. P., Wieringa, J. J., and Bruneau, A. 2018. A new phylogeny-based tribal classification of subfamily Detarioideae, an early branching clade of florally diverse tropical arborescent legumes. *Scientific Reports* 8(1): 6884. https://doi.org/10.1038/s41598-018-24687-3.

Delgadillo M. C., Bello. B., and Cirdenas, A. 1995. LATMOSS, a catalogue of Neotropical mosses. *Monographs in Systematic Botany from the Missouri Botanical Garden* 56: 1–191.

Delgado-Salinas, A., Thulin, M., Pasquet, R., Weeden, N., and Lavin, M. 2011. *Vigna* (Leguminosae) *sensu lato*: The names and identities of the American segregate genera. *American Journal of Botany* 98(10): 1694–1715.

Delmas, M., Larpin, D., and Haevermans, T. 2011. Rethinking the links between systematic studies and ex situ living collections as a contribution to the Global Strategy for Plant Conservation. *Biodiversity and Conservation* 20: 287–294. https://doi.org/10.1007/s10531-010-9985-8.

Derieg, N. J., Weil, S. J., Reznicek, A. A., and Bruederle, L. P. 2013. *Carex viridistellata* sp. nov. (Cyperaceae), a new cryptic species from prairie fens of the eastern United States. *Systematic Botany* 38: 82–91.

Desbureaux, S., Aubert, S., Brimont, L., Karsenty, A., Lohanivo, A. C., Rakotondrabe, M., Razafindraibe, A. H., and Razafiarijoana, J. 2016. The impact of protected areas on deforestation: An exploration of the economic and political channels for Madagascar's rainforests (2001–12). https://halshs.archives-ouvertes.fr/halshs-01278872.

De Sloover, J. L. 1975a. Note de bryologie Africaine IV—*Breutelia*. *Bulletin du Jardin Botanique National de Belgique* 45: 237–271.

———. 1975b. Note de bryologie africaine. III. *Physcomitriella magdalenae* sp. nov. *Bulletin du Jardin Botanique National de Belgique* 45: 131–135.

———. 1977. Note de bryologie africaine. IX. *Andreaea, Racomitrium, Gymnostomiella, Thuidium*. *Bulletin du Jardin Botanique National de Belgique* 47: 155–181.

———. 1983. Note de bryologie africaine XII. *Porotrichum* et *Porothamnium*. *Bulletin du Jardin Botanique National de Belgique* 53: 97–152.

———. 1986. Note de bryologie africaine XIII. Polytrichaceae. *Bulletin du Jardin Botanique National de Belgique* 56: 241–300.

———. 1987. Note de bryologie africaine XIV. *Leptodontium*. *Bulletin du Jardin Botanique National de Belgique* 57: 425–451.

Devey, D. S., Forest, F., Rakotonasolo, F., Ma, P., Dentinger, B.T.M., and Buerki, S. 2013. A snapshot of extinction in action: The decline and imminent demise of the endemic *Eligmocarpus* Capuron (Caesalpinioideae, Leguminosae) serves as an example of the fragility of Madagascan ecosystems. *South African Journal of Botany* 89: 273–280.

Devkota, M. P., Joshi, G. P., and Parajuli, P. 2010. Diversity, distribution and host range of mistletoe in protected and unprotected areas of Central Nepal Himalayas. *Banko Janakari* 20: 14–20.

Dew, J. L., and Wright, P. 1998. Frugivory and seed dispersal by four species of primates in Madagascar's eastern rain forest. *Biotropica* 30: 425–437.

Diallo, B. O., Joly, H. I., McKey, D., Hossaert-McKey, M., and Chevallier, M. H. 2007. Genetic diversity of *Tamarindus indica* populations: Any clues on the origin from its current distribution? *African Journal of Biotechnology* 6: 853–860.

Diffey, J. M. 2017. Phylogenetic relationships of Salicaceae based on analyses of nuclear DNA data. Honors Thesis. Hattiesburg: University of Southern Mississippi.

Doidge, E. M. 1950. The South African fungi and lichens to the end of 1945. *Bothalia* 5: 1–94.

Dominy, N. J. 2012. Hominins living on the sedge. *Proceedings of the National Academy of Sciences of the USA* 109: 20171–20172.

Donati, G., Kesch, K., Ndremifidy, K., Schmidt, S., Ramanamanjato, J.-P., Borgognini-Tarli, S., and Ganzhorn, J. U. 2011. Better few than hungry: Flexible feeding ecology of collared lemurs *Eulemur collaris* in littoral forest fragments. *PLoS One* 6(5): e19807. https://doi.org/10.1371/journal.pone.0019807.

Dongock Nguemo, D. 2008. *Cedrelopsis grevei* Baill. In *Plant resources of tropical Africa* 7(1), *Timbers* 1, eds. A. A. Oteng-Amoako and M. Brink, pp. 142–145. Netherlands: PROTA Foundation / Backhuys / CTA.

Dorr, L. J. 1990. An expansion and revision of the Malagasy genus *Humbertiella* (Malvaceae). *Bulletin du Muséum National d'Histoire Naturelle*, Section B, *Adansonia*, 12(1): 7–27.

———. 1997. *Plant collectors in Madagascar and the Comoro Islands*. Kew: Royal Botanic Gardens.

———. 2001. A new combination in the endemic Malagasy genus *Helmiopsis* (Malvaceae-Dombeyoideae). *Adansonia*, série 3, 23(1): 151–153.

———. 2004. A remarkable new species of *Sterculia* (Sterculioideae, Malvaceae) from Madagascar. *Adansonia*, série 3, 26(2): 161–165.

Dorr, L. J., and Barnett, L. C. 1990. A new species of *Hildegardia* (Sterculiaceae) from Somalia. *Kew Bulletin* 45(3): 577–580.

Dorr, L. J., and Wurdack, K. J. 2018. A new disjunct species of *Eriolaena* (Malvaceae, Dombeyoideae) from continental Africa. *PhytoKeys* 111: 11–16. https://doi.org/10.3897/phytokeys.111.29303.

Dorsey, B. L., Haevermans, T., Aubriot, X., Morawetz, J. J., Riina, R., Steinmann, V. W., and Berry, P. E. 2013. Phylogenetics, morphological evolution, and classification of *Euphorbia* subgenus *Euphorbia*. *Taxon* 62: 291–315. https://doi.org/10.12705/622.1.

Dransfield, J., and Beentje, H. J. 1995. *The Palms of Madagascar*. Kew: International Palms Society and Royal Botanic Gardens.

Dransfield, J., and Marcus, J. 2002. *Dypsis* "stumpy". *Palms* 46(1): 47–51.

Dransfield, J., and Rakotoarinivo, M. 2011. The biogeography of Madagascar palms. In *The Biology of Island Floras*, eds. D. Bramwell and J. Caujapé-Castells, pp. 179–196. Cambridge: Cambridge University Press.

Dransfield, J., Uhl, N. W., Asmussen, C. B., Baker, W. J., Harley, M. M., and Lewis, C. E. 2008. *Genera Palmarum, the Evolution and Classification of Palms*. Kew: Royal Botanic Gardens, International Palm Society, and Bailey Hortorium.

Dransfield, J., Marcus, J., and Turk, D. 2012. *Dypsis robusta* found in the wild. *Palms* 56(1): 28–30.

Dransfield, S. 1994. The genus *Hickelia* (Gramineae: Bambusoideae). *Kew Bulletin* 49: 429–443.

———. 1997. Notes on the genus *Decaryochloa* (Gramineae-Bambusoideae) from Madagascar. *Kew Bulletin* 52: 593–600.

———. 1998. *Valiha* and *Cathariostachys*, two new bamboo genera (Gramineae-Bambusoideae) from Madagascar. *Kew Bulletin* 53: 375–397.

———. 2002. *Sirochloa*, a new bamboo genus from Madagascar (Poaceae-Bambusoideae). *Kew Bulletin* 57: 963–970.

———. 2003. Poaceae, Bambuseae, bamboos. In *The Natural History of Madagascar*, eds. S. M. Goodman and J. P. Benstead, pp. 467–471. Chicago: University of Chicago Press.

———. 2016. *Sokinochloa*, a new bamboo genus (Poaceae-Bambusoideae) from Madagascar. *Kew Bulletin* 71: 40.

Dreyer, J.B.B., Higuchi, P., and Silva, A. C. 2019. *Ligustrum lucidum* W. T. Aiton (broad-leaf privet) demonstrates climatic niche shifts during global-scale invasion. *Scientific Reports* 9: 3813.

Duangjai, S., Wallnöfer, B., Samuel, R., Munzinger, J., and Chase, M. W. 2006. Generic delimitation and relationships in Ebenaceae *sensu lato*: Evidence from six plastid DNA regions. *American Journal of Botany* 93: 1808–1827.

Duangjai, S., Samuel, R., Munzinger, J., Forest, F., Wallnöfer, B., Barfuss, M.H. J., Fischer, G., and Chase, M. W. 2009. A multi-locus plastid phylogenetic analysis of the pantropical genus *Diospyros* (Ebenaceae), with an emphasis on the radiation and biogeographic origins of the New Caledonian endemic species. *Molecular Phylogenetics and Evolution* 52: 602–620.

Dubard, M. 1914. Description de quelques *Manilkara*. *Notulae Systematicae* 3: 45–47.

Ducousso, M., Bena, G., Bourgeois, C., Buyck, B., Eyssartier, G., Vincelette, M., Rabevohitra, R., Randrihasipara, L., Dreyfus, B., and Prin, Y. 2004. The last common ancestor of Sarcolaenaceae and Asian dipterocarp trees was ectomycorrhizal before the India-Madagascar separation, about 88 million years ago. *Molecular Ecology* 13: 231–236.

Ducousso, M., Ramanankierana, H., Duponnois, R., Rabevohitra, R., Randrihasipara, L., Vincelette, M., Dreyfus, B., and Prin, Y. 2008. Mycorrhizal status of native trees and shrubs from eastern Madagascar littoral forests with special emphasis on one new ectomycorrhizal endemic family, the Asteropeiaceae. *New Phytologist* 178: 233–238.

Dunning, L. T., Liabot, A. L., Olofsson, J. K., Smith, E. K., Vorontsova, M. S., et al. 2017. The recent and rapid spread of *Themeda triandra*. *Botany Letters* 164: 327–337.

Duno de Stefano, R., Fantz, P. R., Fernández-Concha, G. C., and Itza, L.L.C. 2008. *Centrosema* and *Clitoria* (Leguminosae: Papilionidae: Phaseoleae: Clitoriinae) in the Mexican Yucatán Peninsula, including three lectotypifications. *Vulpia* 7: 1–15.

Du Petit-Thouars, L.-M.A.A. 1806. *Genera nova Madagascariensia secundum methodum Jussiaeanam disposita*. Paris.

———. 1822. *Histoire particulière des Plantes Orchidées recueillies sur les trois Îles Australes d'Afrique*. Paris: Bertrand, Treuttel and Wurtz.

Du Puy, D. J, and Moat, J. 1996. A refined classification of the primary vegetation of Madagascar based on the underlying geology: Using GIS to map its distribution and to assess its conservation status. In *Biogéographie de Madagascar*, ed. W. R. Lourenço, pp. 205–218. Paris: Editions ORSTOM.

Du Puy, D. J., Labat, J.-N., and Schrire, B. D. 1994. Revision du genre *Vaughania* S. Moore (Leguminosae-Papilionoideae-Indigofereae). *Bulletin de la Muséum National d'Histoire Naturelle, Paris*, série 4, Section B, *Adansonia* 16(1): 75–102.

Du Puy, D. J., Phillipson, P. B., and Rabevohitra, R. 1995. The genus *Delonix* (Leguminosae: Caesalpinioideae: Caesalpinieae) in Madagascar. *Kew Bulletin* 50(3): 445–475.

Du Puy, D. J., Cribb, P., Bosser, J., Hermans J., and Hermans, C. 1999. *The Orchids of Madagascar*. Kew: Royal Botanic Gardens.

Du Puy, D. J., Labat, J.-N., Rabevohitra, R., Villiers, J. F., Bosser J., and Moat J. 2002. *The Leguminosae of Madagascar*. Kew: Royal Botanic Gardens.

Eakin, D. A. 1976. A taxonomic revision of the moss genera *Rhegmatodon* and *Macrohymenium*. PhD thesis, University of Florida.

———. 1998. A taxonomic revision of the moss genus *Rhegmatodon*. *Nova Hedwigia* 67: 139–152.

Eberl, L., and Vandamme, P. 2016. Members of the genus *Burkholderia*: Good or bad guys *F1000Research* 5, (Faculty Rev.): 1007. https://doi.org/10.12688/f1000research.8221.1.

Eberwein, R. K., and Weber A. 2004. *Exorhopala ruficeps* (Balanophoraceae): Morphology and transfer to *Helosis*. *Botanical Journal of the Linnean Society* 146: 513–517.

Eddy, A. 1985. A revision of African Sphagnales. *Bulletin of the British Museum (Natural History) Botany* 12(3): 77–162.

Een, G. 1993. Mosses from Africa 3 *sensu* Index Muscorum. (Manuscript on disc, dated 22/07/1993).

———. 1997. Mosses from the Mascarenes—6. *Tropical Bryology* 13: 21–34.

Eggli, U. 1995. A synoptical revision of *Operculicarya* (Anacardiaceae). *Bulletin du Muséum National d'Histoire Naturelle*, série 4, 17(3–4): 149–158.

El-Ghani, M.M.A. 2016. Traditional medicinal plants of Nigeria: An overview. *Agriculture and Biology Journal of North America* 7: 220–247.

Elix, J. A. 2001. A revision of the lichen genus *Paraparmelia* Elix and J. Johnst. *Bibliotheca Lichenologica* 80: 1–224.

Ellis, L. T. 1988. Taxonomic notes on *Calymperes* 2. *Journal of Bryology* 15: 127–140.

———. 1995. Taxonomic notes on some species of *Calymperes* occurring in the islands of the western Indian Ocean. *Journal of Bryology* 18: 824–827.

———. 2002. Taxonomic notes on some African species in the family *Calymperaceae* (Musci). *Bulletin of the Natural History Museum* [London], *Botany series* 32: 1–5.

———. 2003. A revised synonymy for *Syrrhopodon trachyphyllus* (*Calymperaceae*, Musci) and some related Old World taxa. *Systematics and Biodiversity* 1: 159–172.

———. 2005. A revision of some Old World moss taxa in the *Syrrhopodon prolifer* complex (Musci: Calymperaceae), and a new species from Malawi. *Systematics and Biodiversity* 3: 159–178.

Ellis, L. T., and Wilbraham, J. 2008. New synonymy in *Macromitrium* (Musci, Orthotrichaceae) and *Syrrhopodon* (Musci, Calymperaceae) in the bryoflora of Réunion Island. *Cryptogamie, Bryologie* 29(1): 23–31.

Ellis, L. T., Afonina, O. M., Andriamiarisoa, R. L., Bednarek-Ochyra, H., Cykowska-Marzencka, B., et al. 2017. New national and regional bryophyte records, 53. *Journal of Bryology* 39(4): 368–387.

Ellis, L. T., Afonina, O. M., Aleffi, M., Andriamiarisoa, R. L., Bačkor, M., et al. 2018. New national and regional bryophyte records, 55. *Journal of Bryology* 40(2): 173–187.

Emanuelsson, E., and Razafimandimbison, S. G. 2007. A new species of *Gyrostipula* (Rubiaceae, Naucleeae) from Madagascar. *Novon* 17: 421–423.

Endress, M. E., Hesse, M., Nilsson, S., Guggisberg, A., and Zhu, J.-P. 1990. The systematic position of the Holarrheninae (Apocynaceae). *Plant Systematics and Evolution* 171: 157–185.

Endress, M. E., van der Ham, R.W. J.M., Nilsson, L. A., Civeyrel, L., Chase, M. W., et al. 2007. A phylogenetic analysis of Alyxieae (Apocynaceae) based on *rbc*L, *mat*K, *trn*L intron, *trn*L-F spacer sequences and morphological characters. *Annals of the Missouri Botanical Garden* 94: 1–35.

Endress, M. E., Meve, U., Middleton, D. J., and Liede-Schumann, S. 2018. Apocynaceae. In *The Families and Genera of Vascular Plants*, vol. 15, *Flowering Plants: Eudicots*, eds. J. Kadereit and V. Bittrich, pp. 207–411. Springer.

Endress, P. K. 2016. Development and evolution of extreme synorganization in angiosperm flowers and diversity: A comparison of Apocynaceae and Orchidaceae. *Annals of Botany* 117: 749–767.

Engel, J. J. 1980. A monograph of *Clasmatocolea*. *Fieldiana: Botany*, new series, 3: 1–229.

Engel, J. J., and Merrill, G.L.S. 2004. Austral Hepaticae. 35. A taxonomic and phylogenetic study of *Telaranea* (Lepidoziaceae), with a monograph of the genus in

temperate Australasia and commentary on extra-Australasian taxa. *Fieldiana: Botany*, new series, 44: 1–265.
Engler, A. 1874. Rutaceae. In *Flora Brasiliensis*, eds. C.F.P. Martius and A. G. Eichler, vol. 12, pt. 2, pp. 75–196. Munich: Typographia Regia.
———. 1896a. Burseraceae. In *Die natürliche Pflanzenfamilien*, 1st ed., vol. 4, eds. A. Engler and K. Prantl, pp. 231–257. Leipzig: Engelmann.
———. 1896b. Rutaceae. In *Die natürlichen Pflanzenfamilien*, 1st ed., vol. 4, eds. A. Engler and K. Prantl, pp. 95–201. Leipzig: Engelmann.
———. 1931. Rutaceae. In *Die natürlichen Pflanzenfamilien*, 2nd ed., vol. 19a, eds. A. Engler and K. Prantl, pp. 187–359. Leipzig: Engelmann.
Enroth, J. 1993. Taxonomic results of the BRYOTROP expedition to Zaire and Rwanda. 23. *Neckeraceae, Pterobryaceae, Hypopteryagiaceae. Tropical Bryology* 8: 193–198.
———. 1994. A taxonomic monograph of the genus *Pinnatella* (Neckeraceae, Bryopsida). *Acta Botanica Fennica* 151: 1–90.
Erbar, C., and Leins, P. 2006. Floral ontogeny and systematic position of the Didiereaceae. *Plant Systematics and Evolution* 261: 165–185.
Ertz, D. 2009. Revision of the corticolous *Opegrapha* species from the Palaeotropics. *Bibliotheca Lichenologica* 102: 1–176.
Ertz, D., and Sérusiaux, E. 2009. A new species of *Lecanactis* (Arthoniales, Roccellaceae) from Madagascar. *Lichenologist* 41: 147–150.
Ertz, D., Killmann, D., Razafindrahaja, T., Sérusiaux, E., and Fischer, E. 2010. Two new species of *Syncesia* (Arthoniales, *Roccellaceae*) from Africa. *Lichenologist* 42: 43–49.
Ertz, D., Fischer, E., Killmann, D., Razafindrahaja, T., and Sérusiaux, E. 2014a. *Isalonactis*, a new genus of *Roccellaceae* (Arthoniales), from southern Madagascar. *Lichenologist* 46: 159–167.
Ertz, D., Tehler, A., Fischer, E., Killmann, D., Razafindrahaja, T., and Sérusiaux, E. 2014b. *Savoronala*, a new genus of Malmideaceae (Lecanorales) from Madagascar with stipes producing sporodochia. *Mycological Progress* 12: 645–656.
Evans, M.E.K., Aubriot, X., Hearn, D., Lanciaux, M., Lavergne, S., Cruaud, C., Lowry II, P. P., and Haevermans, T. 2014. Insights on the evolution of plant succulence from a remarkable radiation in Madagascar (*Euphorbia*). *Systematic Biology* 63: 698–711. https://doi.org/10.1093/sysbio/syu035.
Fagerlind, F. 1938. *Ditepalanthus*, eine neue Balanophoraceen-Gattung aus Madagaskar. *Arkiv för Botanik Stockholm* 29A: 1–15.
Faramalala, M. H., Vincelette, M., and Razafindramboa, G. 1995. *Formations végétales et domaine forestier national de Madagascar*. Antananarivo: CI, DEF, CNRE, FTM.
Faranirina, L. 2019a. *Croton argyrodaphne*. The IUCN Red List of Threatened Species 2019: e.T128096815A128098634. Accessed 2 July 2020. https://dx.doi.org/10.2305/IUCN.UK.2019-2.RLTS.T128096815A128098634.en.
———. 2019b. *Croton cupreolepis*. The IUCN Red List of Threatened Species 2019: e.T128096967A128098642 Accessed 2 July 2020. https://dx.doi.org/10.2305/IUCN.UK.2019-2.RLTS.T128096967A128098642.en.
Farwig, N., Randrianirina, E. F., Voigt, F. A., Kraemer, M., and Böhning-Gaese, K. 2004. Pollination ecology of the dioecious tree *Commiphora guillauminii* in Madagascar. *Journal of Tropical Ecology* 20: 307–316.
Fawcett, W. 1886. On new species of *Balanophora* and *Thonningia*, with a note on *Brugmansia Lowi*, Becc. *Transactions of the Linnean Society*, 2nd series, 2: 233–247.
Fedele, G., Urech, Z. L., Rehnus, M., and Sorg, J.-P., 2011. Impact of women's harvest practices on *Pandanus guillaumetii* in Madagascar's lowland rainforests. *Economic Botany* 65: 158–168.
Federman, S., Dornburg, A., Downie, A., Richard, A. F., Daly, D. C., and Donoghue, M. J. 2015. The biogeographic origin of a radiation of trees in Madagascar: Implications for the assembly of a tropical forest biome. *BMC Evolutionary Biology* 15: 216.
Federman, S., Dornburg, A., Daly, D. C., Downie, A., Perry, G. H., Yoder A. D., Sargis, E. J., Richard, A. F., Donoghue, M. J., and Badenh, A. L. 2016. Implications of lemuriform extinctions for the Malagasy flora. *Proceedings of the National Academy of Sciences of the USA* 113: 5041–5046.
Ferguson, D. M. 1999. Phylogenetic analysis and relationships in Hydrophyllaceae based on *ndhf* sequence data. *Systematic Botany* 23: 253–268.
Ferm, J., Kårehed, J., Bremer, B., and Razafimandimbison, S. G. 2016. *Paracarphalea*, a new genus of the coffee family segregated from the Malagasy endemic genus *Carphalea* (Rubiaceae, Rubioideae, Knoxieae). *Phytotaxa* 263: 98–112.
Fern, K., and Fern, A. 2014 onward. Useful Tropical Plants. Accessed 21 Feb. 2020. http://tropical.theferns.info/.
Fietz, J., and Ganzhorn, J. U. 1999. Feeding ecology of the hibernating primate *Cheirogaleus medius*: How does it get so fat? *Oecologia* 121: 157–164.
Figueiredo, E., and Jury, S. L. 1996. Notes on *Brachystephanus* (Acanthaceae). *Kew Bulletin* 51(4): 753–763.
Fine, P. V., Daly, D. C., Villa, G., Mesones, I., and Cameron, K. M. 2005. The contribution of edaphic heterogeneity to the evolution and diversity of Burseraceae trees in the western Amazon. *Evolution* 59: 1464–1478.
Fish, L., Mashau, A. C., Moeaha, M. J., and Nembudani, M. T. 2015. *Identification Guide to Southern African Grasses: An identification Manual with Keys, Descriptions and Distributions*. Pretoria: South African National Biodiversity Institute.
Fishbein, M., Livshultz, T., Straub, S.C.K., Simões, A. O., Boutte, J., McDonnell, A., and Foote, A. 2018. Evolution on the backbone: Apocynaceae phylogenomics and new perspectives on growth forms, flowers, and fruits. *American Journal of Botany* 105: 495–513.
Fisher, J. B. 1981. Wound healing by exposed secondary xylem in *Adansonia* (Bombacaceae). *IAWA Journal* 2: 193–199.
Flicker, B. and Ballard, H. E., Jr. 2015. *Afrohybanthus* (Violaceae), a new genus for a distinctive and widely distributed Old World hybanthoid lineage. *Phytotaxa* 230: 39–53.
Forest, F., Moat, J., Baloch, E., Brummitt, N. A., Bachman, S. P., et al. 2018. Gymnosperms on the EDGE. *Scientific Reports* 8: 6053
Fosberg, R. 1948. Immigrant plants in the Hawaiian Islands. II. *University of Hawaii Occasional Papers* 46: 1–17.
Frahm, J. P. 1985. Afrikanische *Campylopus*-Arten (Dicranaceae, Musci). *Bryophyterum Bibliotheca* 31: 1–216.
———. 1996. Revision der Gattung *Rhacocarpus* Lindb. (Musci). *Cryptogamie, Bryologie, Lichénologie* 17(1): 39–65.
Frahm, J. P., Rembold, K., Roever, T., and Schamell, T. 2003. Synopsis der Gattung *Pyrrhobryum* (Musci, Rhizogoniaceae). *Tropical Bryology* 24: 115–127.
François, E. 1930. De l'emploi de l'herbe Kikuyu à Madagascar. *Revue de Botanique Appliquée et d'Agriculture Coloniale* 10(105): 287–292.
Frenzke, L., Scheiris, E., Pino, G., Symmank, L., Goetghebeur, P., Neinhuis, C., Wanke, S., and Samain, M.-S. 2015. A revised infrageneric classification of the genus *Peperomia* (Piperaceae). *Taxon* 64: 424–444.
Friedman, F. 1980. Une espèce nouvelle du genre *Mimusops* (Sapotaceae) à Madagascar. *Adansonia*, série 2, 20: 229–233.
Friedmann, F. 1994. Anacardiacées. In *Flore des Seychelles. Dicotylédones*, , pp. 417–422. Paris and Marseille: Muséum National d'Histoire Naturelle and Institut de Recerche pour le Développement.
From, M., and Gouveia, T. 2005. Conserving orchids in the eastern rain forest of Madagascar: An integrated approach to linking local residents and biotechnology. *Selbyana* 26: 89–91.
Fryxell, P. A. 1974. *Cienfuegosia* Cav. extended to Madagascar. *Annals of the Missouri Botanical Gardens* 61: 491–493.
Fuentes, J. D., Chamecki, M., Roulston, T., Chen, B., Kenneth, R., and Pratt, K. R. 2016. Air pollutants degrade floral scents and increase insect foraging times. *Atmospheric Environment* 141: 361–374.
Gadek, P. A., Fernando, E. S., Quinn, C. J., Hoot, S. B., Terrazas, T., Sheahan, M. C., and Chase, M. W. 1996. Sapindales: Molecular delimitation and infraordinal groups. *American Journal of Botany* 83(6): 802–811.
Gagnon, E., Bruneau, A., Hughes, C. E., de Queiroz, L. P., and Lewis, G. P. 2016. A new generic system for the pantropical Caesalpinia group (Leguminosae). *PhytoKeys* 71: 1–160.
Galán Díaz, J., Bauters, K., Rabarivola, L., Xanthos, M., Goetghebeur, P., and Larridon, I. 2019. A revision of *Scleria* (Cyperaceae) in Madagascar. *Blumea* 64: 195–213.
Galetto, L. 1997. Flower structure and nectar chemical composition in three Argentine Apocynaceae. *Flora* 192: 197–207.
Galil, J., and Eisikowitch, D. 1968. Pollination ecology of *Ficus sycomorus* in east Africa. *Ecology* 49: 260–269.
Gallaher, T., Callmander, M. W., Buerki, S., and Keeley, S. 2015. A long distance dispersal hypothesis for the Pandanaceae and the origins of the *Pandanus tectorius* complex. *Molecular Phylogenetic and Evolution* 83: 20–32.
Galloway, D. J. 1994. Studies in Pseudocyphellaria (lichens) IV. Palaeotropical species (excluding Australia). *Bulletin of the Natural History Museum* [London], *Botany series*, 24: 115–159.
Galloway, D. J., and Jørgensen, P. M. 1987. Studies in the lichen family Pannariaceae II. The genus *Leioderma* Nyl. *Lichenologist* 19: 345–400.
Ganzhorn, J. U., and Kappeler, P. M. 1996. Lemurs of the Kirindy forest. *Primate Report* 46(1): 257–274.
Ganzhorn, J. U., Fietz, J., Rakotovao, E., Schwab, D., and Zinner, D. 1999. Lemurs and the regeneration of dry deciduous forest in Madagascar. *Conservation Biology* 13: 794–804.

García, M. A., Nickrent, D., and Mucina, L. 2018. *Thesium nautimontanum*, a new species of Thesiaceae (Santalales) from South Africa. *Phytokeys* 109: 41–51.
García-Robledo, C., and Murcia, C. 2005. Comparative habitat susceptibility to invasion by Chinese ash (*Fraxinus chinensis*: Oleaceae) in a tropical Andean landscape. *Biological Invasions* 7: 405–415.
Gardiner, L., Rabehevitra, D., Letsara, R., and Shapcott, A. 2017. *Tahina spectabilis*: An exciting new discovery in Madagascar ten years on. *Palms* 61(2): 69–82.
Gautier, L. 2003. Sapotaceae. In *The Natural History of Madagascar*, eds. S. M. Goodman and J. P. Benstead, pp. 342–346. Chicago: University of Chicago Press.
———. 2018. Site 8: L'Ankarana, Site 69: Namoroka, Site 82: Bemaraha, Végétation. In *Les aires protégées terrestres de Madagascar: Leur histoire, description et biote / The Terrestrial Protected Areas of Madagascar: Their History, Description, and Biota*, eds. S. M. Goodman, M. J. Raherilalao, and S. Wohlhauser, pp. 561–566, pp. 1309–1313, pp. 1459–1464. Antananarivo: Association Vahatra.
Gautier, L., and Goodman, S. M. 2003. Introduction to the flora of Madagascar. In *The Natural History of Madagascar*, eds. S. M. Goodman and J. P. Benstead, pp. 229–250. Chicago: University of Chicago Press.
Gautier, L., and Naciri, Y. 2018. Three Critically Endangered new species of *Capurodendron* (Sapotaceae) from Madagascar. *Candollea* 73: 121–129.
Gautier, L., Messmer, N., and Rakotomalaza, P. J. 2003. Les listes commentées d'échantillons de phanérogames récoltés dans les massifs montagneux de Marojejy et d'Anjanaharibe-Sud, Madagascar. In Nouveaux résultats d'inventaires biologiques faisant référence à l'altitude dans la région des massifs montagneux de Marojejy et d'Anjanaharibe-Sud, eds. S. M. Goodman and L. Wilmé. *Recherches pour le Développement, série sciences biologiques*, 19: 69–98.
Gautier, L., Nusbaumer, L., Larridon, I., and Callmander, M. W. 2010. Distribution of *Cyperus chamaecephalus* Cherm., a forest undergrowth species with inconspicuous inflorescences. *Candollea* 65: 364–367.
Gautier, L., Chatelain, C., Callmander, M. W., and Phillipson, P. B. 2012a. Richness, similarity and specificity of Madagascar flora compared with Sub-Saharan Africa. *Scripta Botanica Belgica* 50: 322–331.
Gautier, L., Nusbaumer, L., Garratt, R., Randrianaivo, R., and Phillipson, P. B. 2012b. *Mimusops coriacea* (A. DC.) Miq. (Sapotaceae): Nomenclature, distribution and ecology. *Candollea* 67: 148–151.
Gautier, L., Goodman, S. M., and Raherilalao, M. J. 2013a. Introduction et présentation du milieu. In La forêt de Beanka, Région Melaky, Ouest de Madagascar, eds. S. M. Goodman, L. Gautier, and M. J. Raherilalao. *Malagasy Nature* 7: 3–13.
Gautier, L., Bolliger, R., Callmander, M., Hanitrarivo, M. R., Luino, I., et al. 2013b. Inventaire des plantes vasculaires de la région de Beanka, Région Melaky, Ouest de Madagascar. In La forêt de Beanka, Région Melaky, Ouest de Madagascar, eds. S. M. Goodman, L. Gautier, and M. J. Raherilalao. *Malagasy Nature* 7: 127–160.
Gautier, L., Naciri, Y., Anderberg, A. A., Smedmark, J.E.E., Randrianaivo, R., and Swenson, U. 2013c. A new species, genus and tribe of Sapotaceae, endemic to Madagascar. *Taxon* 62: 972–983.
Gautier, L., Tahinarivony, J. A., Ranirison, P., and Wohlhauser, S. 2018. Végétation / Vegetation. In *Les aires protégées terrestres de Madagascar: Leur histoire, description et biote / The Terrestrial Protected Areas of Madagascar: Their History, Description, and Biota*, eds. S. M. Goodman, M. J. Raherilalao, and S. Wohlhauser, pp. 207–242. Antananarivo: Association Vahatra.
Gautier-Hion, A., and Michaloud, G. 1989. Are figs always keystone resources for tropical frugivorous vertebrates? A test in Gabon. *Ecology* 70(6): 1826–1833.
GBIF. 2019–2020. Global Biodiversity Information Facility (GBIF). https://www.gbif.org.
———. 2021. GBIF Backbone Taxonomy. Plantae. https://www.gbif.org/species/6.
Gehrke, B. 2011. Synopsis of *Carex* (Cyperaceae) from sub-Saharan Africa and Madagascar. *Botanical Journal of the Linnean Society* 166: 51–99.
Génin, F., and Rambeloarivony, H. 2018. Mouse lemurs (Primates: Cheirogaleidae) cultivate green fruit gardens. *Biological Journal of the Linnean Society* 124: 607–620.
Gentry, A. H. 1976. Relationships of the Malagasy Bignoniaceae: A striking case of convergent evolution. *Plant Systematics and Evolution* 126: 255–256.
———. 1977. *Phyllarthron bilabiatum*: A new species of Bignoniaceae from Madagascar. *Annals of the Missouri Botanical Garden* 64: 139–141.
———. 1988. Distribution and evolution of the Madagascar Bignoniaceae. *Monographs in Systematic Botany from the Missouri Botanical Garden* 25: 175–185.
Gentry, A. H., and Dondson, C. 1987. Diversity and biogeography of Neotropical vascular epiphytes. *Annals of the Missouri Botanical Garden* 78: 273–295.
Giaretta, A., Vasconcelos, T.N.C., Mazine, F. F., Faria, J.E.Q., Flores, R., Holst, B., Sano, P. T., and Lucas, E. 2019. Calyx (con)fusion in a hyper-diverse genus: Parallel evolution of unusual flower patterns in *Eugenia* (Myrtaceae). *Molecular Phylogenetics and Evolution* 139: 1–15.
Giese, M., and Frahm, J. P. 1985. A revision of *Microcampylopus* (C. Müll.) Fleisch. *Lindbergia* 11: 114–124.
Gillespie, L. J. 1997. *Omphalea* (Euphorbiaceae) in Madagascar: A new species and a new combination. *Novon* 7: 127–136.
———. 2007. A revision of paleotropical *Plukenetia* (Euphorbiaceae) including two new species from Madagascar. *Systematic Botany* 32(4): 780–802.
Gillett, J. B. 1973. *Commiphora* Jacq. (Burseraceae)—Englerian species which "disappear". *Kew Bulletin* 28: 25–28.
———. 1991. Burseraceae. In *Flora of Tropical East Africa*, ed. R. M. Polhill, pp. 1–95. Rotterdam: A. A. Balkema.
Glime, J. M. 2013. Adaptive strategies: Growth and life forms. *Bryophyte Ecology* 1: 4–5.
Global Carex Group. 2015. Making *Carex* monophyletic (Cyperaceae, tribe Cariceae): A new broader circumscription. *Botanical Journal of the Linnean Society* 179: 1–42.
Goetghebeur, P. 1998. Cyperaceae. In *The Families and Genera of Vascular Plants*, vol. 4, Flowering Plants, Monocotyledons, ed. K. Kubitzki, pp. 141–190. Berlin: Springer.
Goffinet, B. 1996. *Cardotiella elimbata* (Thér) Goffinet, comb. nov., and *C. apendiculata* new to Mauritius (Musci, Orthotricaceae). *The Bryologist* 99: 390–396.
Goffinet, B., Buck, W. R., and Shaw, A. J. 2009. Morphology and classification of the Bryophyta. In *Bryophytes Biology*, eds. B. Goffinet and A. J. Shaw, pp. 55–138, Cambridge: Cambridge University Press.
Goldberg, A. 1967. The genus *Melochia* L. (Sterculiaceae). *Contributions from the United States National Herbarium* 34: 191–363.
Good, T. C., Zjhra, M. L., and Kremen, C. 2006. Radiation and risk. Dealing with data deficiency in classifying extinction risk: A case study of a radiation of Bignoniaceae from Madagascar. *Conservation Biology* 20: 1099–1110.
Goodman, S. M., and Benstead, J. P. eds. 2003. *The Natural History of Madagascar*. Chicago: University of Chicago Press.
Goodman, S. M., and Ganzhorn J. U. 1997. Rarity of figs (*Ficus*) on Madagascar and its relationship to a depauperate frugivore community. *Revue d'Ecologie (Terre et Vie)* 52: 321–329.
Goodman, S. M., and Sterling, E. J. 1996. The utilization of *Canarium* (Burseraceae) seeds by vertebrates in the Réserve Naturelle Intégrale d'Andringitra, Madagascar. In a floral and faunal inventory of the eastern slopes of the Réserve Naturelle Intégrale d'Andringitra, Madagascar: With reference to elevational variation, ed. S. M. Goodman. *Fieldiana: Zoology*, new series, 85: 83–89.
Goodman, S. M., Lewis, B. A., Phillipson, P. B., and Raherilala, J. 1996. Vertebrate food plants on the eastern slopes of the Réserve Naturelle Intégrale d'Andringitra. In A floral and faunal inventory of the eastern slopes of the Réserve Naturelle Intégrale d'Andringitra, Madagascar: With reference to elevational variation, ed. S. M. Goodman. *Fieldiana: Zoology*, new series, 85: 72–75.
Goodman, S. M., Ganzhorn, J. U., and Wilmé, L. 1997. Observation at a *Ficus* tree in Malagasy humid forest. *Biotropica* 29: 480–488.
Goodman, S. M., Jenkins, P. D., and Rakotondravony, D. 2000. The biogeography of rodents (Rodentia: Muridae: Nesomyinae) and tenrecids (Lipotyphla: Tenrecidae) in the eastern forests of Madagascar: An assessment of altitudinal zonation along a latitudinal gradient. In *Diversité et Endémisme à Madagascar*, eds. W. R. Lourenço and S. M. Goodman, pp. 127–138. Paris: Mémoires de la Société de Biogéographie.
Goodman, S. M., Raherilalao, M. J., and Wohlhauser, S., eds. 2018. *Les aires protégées terrestres de Madagascar: Leur histoire, description et biote / The Terrestrial Protected Areas of Madagascar: Their History, Description, and Biota*. Antananarivo: Association Vahatra.
Gostel, M. R., Coy, K. A., and Weeks, A. 2015. Microfluidic PCR-based target enrichment: A case study in two rapid radiations of *Commiphora* (Burseraceae) from Madagascar. *Journal of Systematics and Evolution* 53: 411–431.
Gostel, M. R., Phillipson, P. B., and Weeks, A. 2016a. Phylogenetic reconstruction of the myrrh genus, *Commiphora* (Burseraceae), reveals multiple radiations in Madagascar and clarifies infrageneric relationships. *Systematic Botany* 41: 67–81.
Gostel, M. R., Weeks, A., Raharimampionona, J., and Phillipson, P. B. 2016b. A partial taxonomic revision of the Rhynchocarpa clade of *Commiphora* (Burseraceae) endemic to Madagascar. *Systematic Botany* 41: 1004–1019.
Gostel, M. R., Plunkett. G. M., and Lowry II, P. P. 2017. Straddling the Mozambique Channel: Molecular evidence for two major clades of Afro-Malagasy *Schefflera*

(Araliaceae) co-occurring in Africa and Madagascar. *Plant Ecology and Evolution* 150: 87–108.
Gottschling, M., Hilger, H. H., Wolf, M., and Diane, N. 2001. Secondary structure of the ITS1 transcript and its application in a reconstruction of the phylogeny of Boraginales. *Plant Biology* 3: 629–636.
Govaerts, R. 2020. World Checklist of Ebenaceae. Facilitated by the Royal Botanic Gardens, Kew. http://wcsp.science.kew.org/.
Govaerts, R., Wilkin, P., Raz, L., and Téllez-Valdés, O. 2020a. World Checklist of Dioscoreaceae. Facilitated by the Royal Botanic Gardens, Kew. http://wcsp.science.kew.org/.
Govaerts, R., Bernet, P., Kratovchil, K., Gerlach, G., Carr, G., et al. 2020b. World Checklist of Orchidaceae. Facilitated by the Royal Botanic Gardens, Kew. http://wcsp.science.kew.org/.
Govaerts, R., Dransfield, J., Zona, S., Hodel, D. R., and Henderson, A. 2020c. World Checklist of Arecaceae. Facilitated by the Royal Botanic Gardens, Kew. http://wcsp.science.kew.org/.
Govaerts, R., Jiménez-Mejías, P., Koopman, J., Simpson, D. A., Goetghebeur, P., Wilson, K. L., Egorova, T., and Bruhl, J. J. 2020d. World Checklist of Cyperaceae. Facilitated by the Royal Botanic Gardens, Kew. http://wcsp.science.kew.org/.
Govaerts, R., Ruhsam, M., Andersson, L., Robbrecht, E., Bridson, D. M., Davis, A. P., Schanzer, I., and Sonké, B. 2020e. World Checklist of Rubiaceae. Facilitated by the Royal Botanic Gardens, Kew. http://wcsp.science.kew.org/.
Gradstein, S. R., and Pócs, T. 1989. Bryophytes. In *Tropical Rainforest Ecosystems*, eds. H. Lieth and M.J.A. Werger, pp. 311–325. Amsterdam: Elsevier.
Gradstein, S. R., and Váňa J. 1999. On the taxonomy of *Kymatocalyx* and *Stenorrhipis* (Cephaloziellaceae). *Haussknechtia* 9: 155–170.
Gradstein, S. R., and van Beek, J. A. 1985. A revision of the genus *Symbiezidium* Trevis. *Beiheft Nova Hedwigia* 80: 221–248.
Graham, V.A.W. 1988. Delimitation and infra-generic classification of *Justicia* (Acanthaceae). *Kew Bulletin* 43: 551–624.
Green, P. S. 2001. Studies in the genus *Jasminum*, XVII: Sections *Trifoliolata* and *Primulina*. *Kew Bulletin* 56: 903–915.
———. 2002. A revision of *Olea* L. (Oleaceae). *Kew Bulletin* 57: 91–140.
Green, P. T. 1999. Greta's Garbo: Stranded seeds and fruits from Great Beach, Christmas Island, Indian Ocean. *Journal of Biogeography* 26: 937–946.
Gressitt, J. L., Samuelson, G. A., and Vitt, D. H. 1968. Moss growing on living Papuan Moss-forest weevils. *Nature* 217: 765–767.
Grímsson, F., Graham, S. A., Coiro, M., Jacobs, B. F., Xafis, A., Neumann, F. H., Scott, L., Sakala, J., Currano, E. D., and Zetter, R. 2019. Origin and divergence of Afro-Indian Picrodendraceae: Linking pollen morphology, dispersal modes, fossil records, molecular dating and paleogeography. *Grana* 58(4): 227–275.
Grison-Pigé, L., Bessière, J.-M., and Hossaert-McKey, M., 2002. Specific attraction of fig-pollinating wasps: Role of volatile compounds released by tropical figs. *Journal of Chemical Ecology* 28: 283–295.
Groeninckx, I., Dessein, S., Ochoterena, H., Persson, C., Motley, T. J., Kårehed, J., Bremer, B., Huysmans, S., and Smets, E. 2009a. Phylogeny of the herbaceous tribe Spermacoceae (Rubiaceae) based on plastid DNA data. *Annals of the Missouri Botanical Garden* 96: 109–132.
Groeninckx, I., De Block, P., Rakotonasolo, F., Smets, E., and Dessein, S. 2009b. Rediscovery of Madagascan *Lathraeocarpa* reveals its taxonomic position within Rubiaceae. *Taxon* 58: 209–226.
Groeninckx, I., Ochoterena, H., Smets, E., and Dessein S. 2010a. Molecular phylogenetic and morphological study of *Kohautia* (Spermacoceae, Rubiaceae), with the recognition of the new genus *Cordylostigma*. *Taxon* 59: 1457–1471.
Groeninckx, I., De Block, P., Robbrecht, E., and Dessein, S. 2010b. *Amphistemon* and *Thamnoldenlandia*, two genera of Rubiaceae (Spermacoceae) endemic to Madagascar. *Botanical Journal of the Linnean Society* 163: 447–472.
Groeninckx, I., Briggs, M., Davis, A. P., De Block, P., Robbrecht, E., Smets, E., and Dessein, S. 2010c. A new herbaceous genus endemic to Madagascar: *Phialiphora* (Spermacoceae, Rubiaceae). *Taxon* 59: 1815–1829.
Groeninckx, I., Janssens, S., Smets, E., and Verstraete, B. 2017. Description of 11 new *Astiella* (Spermacoceae, Rubiaceae) species endemic to Madagascar. *European Journal of Taxonomy* 312: 1–40.
Grolle, R. 1985. Zur Kenntnis der Lebermoosgattung *Otolejeunea*. *Haussknechtia* 2: 45–56.
———. 1995. The Hepaticae and Anthocerotae of the East African islands. An annotated catalogue. *Bryophytorum Bibliotheca* 48: 1–178.
———. 2001. Miscellanea hepaticologica 291–300. *Haussknechtia* 8: 59–69.
Grolle, R., and Onraedt, M. 1974. Lebermoose aus Madagaskar und den Maskarenen (1). *Lindenbergia* 2: 230–233.
Groppo, M., Pirani, J. R., Salatino, M.L.F., Blanco, S. R., and Kallunki, J. A. 2008. Phylogeny of Rutaceae based on two non-coding regions from cpDNA. *American Journal Botany* 95: 985–1005. https://doi.org/10.3732/ajb.2007313.
Guderley, R., and Lumbsch, H. T. 1996. The lichen genus *Diploschistes* in South Africa *Mycotaxon* 58: 269–292.
Guillaumet J.-L., Betsch J.-M., and Callmander M. W. 2008. Renaud Paulian et le programme du CNRS sur les hautes montagnes à Madagascar: Etage vs domaine. *Zoosystema* 30(3): 723–748.
Gunawardana, M., Hyde, E. R., Lahmeyer, S., Dorsey, B. L., La Val, T. P., Mullen, M., Yoo, J., Knight, R., and Baum, M. M. 2015. *Euphorbia* plant latex is inhabited by diverse microbial communities. *American Journal of Botany* 102(12): 1966–1977.
Gurib-Fakim, A., and Brendler, T. 2004. Medicinal and aromatic plants of Indian Ocean Islands: Madagascar, Comoros, Seychelles and Mascarenes. Stuttgart: Medpharm GmbH Scientific.
Gwate, O., Mantel, S. K., Finca, A., Gibson, L., Munch, A. Z., and Palmer, A. R. 2016. Exploring the invasion of rangelands by *Acacia mearnsii* (black wattle): Biophysical characteristics and management implications. *African Journal of Range and Forage Science* 33(4): 265–273.
Haber, E. A., Kainulainen, K., van Ee, B. W., Oyserman, B. O., and Berry, P. E. 2017. Phylogenetic relationships of a major diversification of *Croton* (Euphorbiaceae) in the western Indian Ocean region. *Botanical Journal of the Linnean Society* 183: 532–544.
Hackel, J., Vorontsova, M. S., Nanjarisoa, O. P., Hall, R. C., Razanatsoa, J., Malakasi, P., and Besnard, G. 2018. Grass diversification in Madagascar: In situ radiation of two large C_3 shade clades and support for a Miocene to Pliocene origin of C_4 grassy biomes. *Journal of Biogeography* 45: 750–761.
Haevermans, T. 2003a. Le genre *Euphorbia* L. à Madagascar : phylogénie moléculaire et systématique. PhD thesis, Muséum National d'Histoire Naturelle, Paris.
———. 2003b. *Euphorbia*. In *The Natural History of Madagascar*, eds. S. M. Goodman and J. P. Benstead, pp. 384–391. Chicago: University of Chicago Press.
———. 2004. Euphorbia. The IUCN Red List of Threatened Species. https://www.iucnredlist.org.
———. 2006. Taxonomy of the *Euphorbia pyrifolia* clade. *Euphorbia World* 2: 21–24.
Haevermans, T., and Labat, J.-N. 2004. A synoptic revision of the Malagasy endemic *Euphorbia pervilleana* group. *Systematic Botany* 29: 118–124. https://doi.org/10.1600/036364404772974266.
Haevermans, T., Rouhan, G., Hetterscheid, W., Teissier, M., Belarbi, K., Aubriot, X., and Labat, J.-N. 2009. Chaos revisited: nomenclature and typification of the Malagasy endemic *Euphorbia* subgenus *Lacanthis* (Raf.) M. G. Gilbert. *Adansonia* 31: 279–299. https://doi.org/10.5252/a2009n2a5.
Hafellner, J. 1997. A world monograph of *Brigantiaea* (lichenized Ascomycotina, Lecanorales). *Symbolae Botanicae Upsalienses* 32(1): 35–74.
Hafellner, J., and Poelt, J. 1979. Die arten der gattung *Caloplaca* mit pluriloculären sporen (*Meroplacis*, *Triophthalmidium*, *Xanthocarpia*). *Journal of the Hattori Botanical Laboratory* 46: 1–41.
Hagl, P. A., Gargiulo, R., Fay, M. F., Solofondranohatra, S. L., Salmona, J., et al. 2020. Geographical structure of genetic diversity in *Loudetia simplex* (Poaceae) in Madagascar and South Africa. *Botanical Journal of the Linnean Society*. https://doi.org/10.1093/botlinnean/boaa098
Haigh, A., Wilkin, P., and Rakotonasolo, F. 2005. A new species of *Dioscorea* L. (Dioscoreaceae) from western Madagascar and its distribution and conservation status. *Kew Bulletin* 60(2): 273–281.
Hale, M. E. 1965. A monograph of *Parmelia* subgenus *Amphygymnia*. *Contributions from the United States National Herbarium* 36: 193–358.
———. 1976a. A monograph of the lichen genus *Bulbothrix* Hale (Parmeliaceae). *Smithsonian Contributions to Botany* 32: 1–29.
———. 1976b. A monograph of the lichen genus *Pseudoparmelia* Lynge (Parmeliaceae). *Smithsonian Contributions to Botany* 31: 1–62.
———. 1990. A synopsis of the lichen genus *Xanthoparmelia* (Vainio) Hale (Ascomycotina: Parmeliaceae). *Smithsonian Contributions to Botany* 74: 1–250.
Hallé, F., Oldeman, R.A.A., and Tomlinson, P. B. 1978. *Tropical Trees and Forests—An Architectural Analysis*. Berlin: Springer.
Hamon, P., Grover, C. E., Davis, A. P., Rakotomalala, J. J., Raharimalala, N. E., et al. 2017. Genotyping-by-sequencing provides the first well-resolved phylogeny for coffee (*Coffea*) and insights into the evolution of caffeine content in its species: GBS coffee phylogeny and the evolution of caffeine content. *Molecular Phylogenetics and Evolution* 109: 351–361.
Hampe, E. 1874. Musci novi insula Madagascar. *Linnaea* 38: 207–222.
Hanes, M., Schatz, G. E., and Callmander, M. W. 2020. Transfer of the Malagasy genera *Humbertianthus* and *Macrostelia* to *Hibiscus* (Malvaceae): With description of four new species. *Candollea* 75: 193–202.

Hansen, B. 1972. The genus *Balanophora*: A taxonomic monograph. *Dansk Botanisk Arkiv* 28: 1–188.
———. 1974. Notes on some Balanophoraceae from Madagascar. *Botanisk Tidsskrift* 69: 58–59.
Harbaugh, D. T., Wagner, W. L., Allan, G. J., and Zimmer, E. A. 2009. The Hawaiian archipelago is a stepping stone for dispersal in the Pacific: An example from the plant genus *Melicope* (Rutaceae). *Journal of Biogeography* 36(2): 230–241.
Harley, M. M., and Daly, D. C. 1995. Burseraceae Kunth, Protieae March. em. Engl. *World Pollen Spore* 20: 1–44.
Harley, M. M., Song, U., and Banks, H. I. 2005. Pollen morphology and systematics of Burseraceae. *Grana* 44(4): 282–299.
Harms, H. 1935. Balanophoraceae. In *Die Natürlichen Planzenfamilien*, eds. A. Engler and K. Prantl, pp. 296–339. Leipzig: Wilhelm Engelman.
Harper, J. 2003. Memories of ancestry in the forests of Madagascar. In *A Landscape Memory and History*, eds. P. J. Stewart and A. Strathern, pp. 89–107. London: Pluto Press.
Harrington, M. G., Edwards, K. J., Johnson, S. A., Chase, M. W., and Gadek, P. A. 2005. Phylogenetic inference in Sapindaceae *sensu lato* using plastid *matK* and *rbcL* DNA sequences. *Systematic Botany* 30: 366–382.
Harris, R. C. 1989. A sketch of the family Pyrenulaceae (Melanommatales) in eastern North America. *Memoirs of the New York Botanical Garden* 49: 74–107.
———. 1995. *More Florida Lichens.* Bronx: Self-published.
Harrison, R. D. 2000. Repercussions of El Niño: Drought causes extinction and the breakdown of mutualism in Borneo. *Proceedings of the Royal Society of London B: Biological Sciences* 267: 911–915.
———. 2005. Figs and the diversity of tropical rainforests. *Bioscience* 55: 1053–1064.
Harrison, R. D., Ronsted, N., Xu, L., Rasplus, J.-Y., and Cruaud, A. 2012. Evolution of fruit traits in *Ficus* subgenus *Sycomorus* (Moraceae): To what extent do frugivores determine seed dispersal mode? *PLoS One* 7: e38432.
Hartley, T. G. 2001. On the taxonomy and biogeography of *Euodia* and *Melicope* (Rutaceae). *Allertonia* 8: 1–319.
Hassler, M. 2019. World plants: Synonymic checklists of the vascular plants of the world (version Nov. 2019). In *Species 2000 and ITIS Catalogue of Life*, eds. Y. Roskov et al. Leiden: Naturalis.
Haston, E., Richardson, J.-E., Stevens, P., Chase, M. W., and Harris, D. J. 2009. The linear angiosperm phylogeny group (LAPG) III: A linear sequence of the families in APG III. *Botanical Journal of the Linnean Society* 161: 128–131.
He, S., and Snider, J. 2000. A taxonomic revision of *Symphyodon* (Musci: Symphyodontaceae). *The Bryologist* 103: 52–81.
He, X. L. 1999. A taxonomic monograph of the genus *Pycnolejeunea* (Lejeuneaceae: Hepaticae). *Acta Botanica Fennica* 163: 1–77.
He, X. L., and Grolle, R. 2001. *Xylolejeunea*, a new genus of the Lejeuneaceae (Hepaticae) from the Neotropics, Madagascar and the Seychelles. *Annales Botanici Fennici* 38: 25–44.
Hebert, P. D., Cywinska, A., Ball, S. L., and deWaard, J. R. 2003. Biological identifications through DNA barcodes. *Proceedings of the Royal Society of London B: Biological Sciences* 270: 313–321.
Heckel, E. 1910. Les plantes utiles de Madagascar. *Annales du Musée Colonial de Marseille*, série 2, 8: 1–372.
Heinrichs, J., Lindler, M., Groth, H., and Renker, C. 2005. Distribution and synonymy of *Plagiochila punctata* (Taylor) Taylor, with hypotheses on the evolutionary history of *Plagiochila* sect. *Arrectae* (Plagiochilaceae, Hepaticae). *Plant Systematics and Evolution* 250: 105–117.
Helmstetter, A. J., Kamga, S. M., Bethune, K., Lautenschläger, T., Zizka, A., et al. 2020. Unraveling the phylogenomic relationships of the most diverse African palm genus *Raphia* (Calamoideae, Arecaceae). *Plants* 9(4): 549.
Hemingway, C. A., and Overdorff, D. J. 1999. Sampling effects on food availability estimates: Phenological method, sample size, and species composition. *Biotropica* 31(2): 354–364.
Henssen, A., and Thor, G. 1998. Studies in taxonomy and developmental morphology in *Chiodecton*, *Dichosporidium*, *Erythrodecton* and the new genus *Pulvinodecton* (Arthoniales, lichenized Ascomycetes). *Nordic Journal of Botany* 18: 95–120.
Hermans, J., and Cribb, P. 2005. Orchids of Madagascar, a conservation challenge. *Orchids (AOS)* 74: 836–847.
———. 2014. New species and new names in Malagasy orchids (Orchidaceae). *Kew Bulletin* 69(9517): 1–16.
Hermans, J., and Rajaovelona, L. 2019. A new natural hybrid in *Cynorkis* from Madagascar. *Orchids (AOS)* 88: 547–550.
Hermans, J., Hermans, C., Du Puy, D., Cribb, P., and Bosser, J. 2007. *Orchids of Madagascar*, 2nd ed. Kew: Royal Botanic Gardens.
Hermans, J., Andriantiana, J. L., Sieder, A., Kiehn, M., Cribb, P., Rajavelona, L., and Gardiner, L. 2017. New species and nomenclatural changes in *Cynorkis* (Orchidaceae: Orchidoideae) from Madagascar and the Mascarenes. *Kew Bulletin* 72(38): 1–31.
Hermans, J., Verlynde, S., Cribb, P., Ramandimbisoa, B., Hervouet, J.-M., and Bernet, P. 2020a. Malaxideae (Orchidaceae) in Madagascar, the Mascarenes, Seychelles and Comoro Islands. *Kew Bulletin* 75(1): 1–184.
Hermans, J., Rajaovelona L., Cribb, P., Hervouet, J.-M., Sieder, A., and Andriantiana, J. 2020b. New species and nomenclatural changes in *Cynorkis* (Orchidaceae) from Madagascar, the Comoros and the Mascarenes. *Kew Bulletin* 75: 50. https://doi.org/10.1007/s12225-020-09904-5.
Hermans, J., Verlynde, S., Rajaovelona, L., Cribb, P., and Hervouet, J.-M. 2020c. New species and nomenclatural changes in *Angraecum* (Orchidaceae) from Madagascar. *Kew Bulletin* 75: 49. https://doi.org/10.1007/s12225-020-09902-7.
Hermans, J., Gamisch, A., Rajaovelona L., Fischer, G. A., Cribb, P., Sieder, A., and Andriantiana, J. 2021. New species and nomenclatural changes in *Bulbophyllum* (Orchidaceae) from Madagascar. *Kew Bulletin* 76, 1–38.
Herre, E. A. 1996. An overview of studies on a community of Panamanian figs. *Journal of Biogeography* 23(4): 593–607.
Hervouet, J.-M. 2018. *A la recherche des Orchidées de Madagascar*. Mèze: Biotope.
Hervouet, J.-M., and Misandeau, C. 2018. La défense de la forêt d'Ambodiriana. *Orchidophile (Asnières)* 49: 5–10.
Hiepko, P. 1982. A revision of Opiliaceae II. *Opilia* Roxb. *Willdenowia* 12: 161–182.
———. 1987. A revision of Opiliaceae IV. *Rhopalopilia* Pierre and *Pentarhopalopilia* (Engler) Hiepko gen. nov. *Botanische Jahrbücher für Systematik, Pflanzengeschichte und Pflanzengeographie* 108: 271–291.
Hinchcliff, C. E., Lliully A., A. E., Carey, T., and Roalson, E. H. 2010. The origins of *Eleocharis* (Cyperaceae) and the status of *Websteria*, *Egleria* and *Chillania*. *Taxon* 59: 709–719.
Hochreutiner, B.P.G. 1955. Malvacées. *Flore de Madagascar et des Comores* 129: 1–170.
Hodgetts, N. G. 2008. Bryological monograph. A morphological revision of the genus *Herbertus* S. Gray (Herbertaceae, Marchantiophyta) in Africa, including the East African islands. *Journal of Bryology* 30: 239–263.
Hodgkison, R., Ayasse, M., Häberlein, C., Schulz, S., Zubaid, A., Mustapha, W.A.W., Kunz, T. H., and Kalko, E.K.V. 2013. Fruit bats and bat fruits: The evolution of fruit scent in relation to the foraging behaviour of bats in the New and Old World tropics. *Functional Ecology* 27: 1075–1084.
Hoffmann, P. 2000. Revision of *Andrachne* section *Pseudophyllanthus* (Euphorbiaceae), with the description of two new species from Madagascar. *Adansonia*, série 3, 22(1): 123–133.
Hoffmann, P., and McPherson, G. 2003a. Euphorbiaceae—overview. In *The Natural History of Madagascar*, eds. S. M. Goodman and J. P. Benstead, pp. 379–383. Chicago: University of Chicago Press.
———. 2003b. Transfer of Madagascan *Glochidion* to *Phyllanthus*. *Novon* 13: 307–310.
Hoffmann, P., and Wurdack, K. J. 2006. *Radcliffea*, a new genus of Euphorbiaceae *sensu stricto* from Madagascar. *Kew Bulletin* 61: 193–197.
Hoffmann, P., Kathriarachchi, H., and Wurdack, K. J. 2006. A phylogenetic classification of Phyllanthaceae (Malpighiales; Euphorbiaceae *sensu lato*). *Kew Bulletin* 61: 37–53.
Hofmann, H. 1997. A monograph of the genus *Palamocladium* (*Brachytheciaceae*, Musci). *Lindbergia* 22: 3–20.
Hollingsworth, P. M., Graham, S. W., and Little, D. P. 2011. Choosing and using a plant DNA region. *PLoS One* 6: 19254.
Hong-Wa, C. 2008. Multivariate analyses of morphological characters of *Leptolaena* Thouars *s.l.* subgenera *Mediusella* and *Xerochlamys* (Sarcolaenaceae). *Botanical Journal of the Linnean Society* 157: 559–574.
———. 2009. Endemic families of Madagascar. XII. Resurrection and taxonomic revision of the genera *Mediusella* (Cavaco) Hutchinson and *Xerochlamys* Baker (Sarcolaenaceae). *Adansonia*, série 3, 31: 311–339.
———. 2016. A taxonomic revision of the genus *Noronhia* (Oleaceae) in Madagascar and the Comoro Islands. *Boissiera* 70: 1–291.
Hong-Wa, C., and Besnard, G. 2013. Intricate patterns of phylogenetic relationships in the olive family as inferred from multi-locus plastid and nuclear DNA sequence analyses: A close-up on *Chionanthus* and *Noronhia* (Oleaceae). *Molecular Phylogenetics and Evolution* 67: 367–378.
———. 2014. Species limits and diversification in the Madagascar olive (*Noronhia*, Oleaceae). *Botanical Journal of the Linnean Society* 174: 141–161.
Hong-Wa, C., Callmander, M. W., and Baider, C. 2014. Taxonomy and conservation of the genus *Noronhia* Thouars (Oleaceae) in Mauritius. *Candollea* 69: 157–163.

Horn, J. W., Xi, Z., Riina, R., Peirson, J. A., Yang, Y., Dorsey, B. L., Berry, P. E., Davis, C. C., and Wurdack, K. J. 2014. Evolutionary bursts in *Euphorbia* (Euphorbiaceae) are linked with photosynthetic pathway. *Evolution* 68(12): 3485–3504.

Hossaert-McKey, M., Soler, C., Schatz, B., and Proffit, M. 2010. Floral scents: Their roles in nursery pollination mutualisms. *Chemoecology* 20: 75–88.

Hossaert-McKey, M., Proffit, M., Soler, C., Chen, C., Bessière, J.-M., Schatz, B., and Borges, R. M. 2016. How to be a dioecious fig: Chemical mimicry between sexes matters only when both sexes flower synchronously. *Scientific Reports* 6: 21236.

Hotton, C. L., Leffingwell, H. A., and Skvarla, J. J. 1994. Pollen ultrastructure of Pandanaceae and the fossil genus Pandaniidites. In *Ultrastructure of fossil spores and pollen*, eds. M. H. Kurmann and J. A. Doyle, pp. 173–191. Kew: Royal Botanic Gardens.

Hughes, C. E., Bailey, C. D., Krosnick, S., and Luckow, M. A. 2003. Relationships among genera of the informal *Dichrostachys* and *Leucaena* groups (Mimosoideae) inferred from nuclear ribosomal ITS sequences. In *Advances in Legume Systematics 10, Higher Level Systematics*, eds. B. B. Klitgaard, and A. Bruneau, pp. 221–238. Kew: Royal Botanic Gardens.

Humbert, H. 1937. Sur un *Brachylaena* nouveau exploite comme santal de Madagascar. *Bulletin de la Société Botanique de France* (Paris) 84: 203–209.

———. 1955. Les territoires phytogéographiques de Madagascar. Leur cartographie. *Année Biologique*, série 3, 31: 439–448.

———. 1965. Description des types de végétation. In *Notice de la carte de Madagascar*, eds. H. Humbert and G. Cours-Darne, pp. 46–78. *Travaux de la Section Scientifique et Technique de l'Institut Français de Pondichéry*, hors-série, 6.

Husson, O., Séguy, L., Charpentier, H., Rakotondramanana, Michellon, P., et al. 2013. *Manuel pratique du semis direct sur couverture végétale permanente (SCV). Application à Madagascar.* Antananarivo: GSDM/CIRAD.

Hutchinson, J. 1943. A note on *Gossypium brevilanatum* Hochr. *Tropical Agriculture* 20: 123–141.

Huxley, C. R. 1991. Ants and plants: A diversity of interactions. In *Ant-plant interactions*, eds. C. R. Huxley and D. F. Cutler, pp. 1–11. Oxford: Oxford University Press.

Huynh, K.-L. 1977. L'appareil mâle de quelques *Pandanus* du sous-genre *Vinsonia* (Pandanaceae) et sa signification taxonomique, phylogénique et évolutive. *Beiträge Biologie Pflanzen* 53: 447–471.

———. 1983. The taxonomic significance of the anther structure in the genus *Pandanus* (Pandanaceae) with reference to *Pandanus* sect. *Martellidendron*. *Webbia* 37: 141–148.

———. 1985. *Pandanus associatus* (Pandanaceae) de l'archipel des Comores. *Candollea* 40: 583–593.

Hyvönen, J., 1989. A synopsis of the genus *Pogonatum* (Polytrichaceae, Musci). *Acta Botanica Fennica* 138: 1–87.

Igersheim, A., and Puff, C. 1991. The fruits, diaspores and seeds of *Paederia* L. (Rubiaceae-Paederieae). *Opera Botanica Belgica* 3: 89–102.

iNaturalist. 2020. Zavamaniry Gasy. Plants of Madagascar. https://www.inaturalist.org/projects/zavamaniry-gasy-plants-of-madagascar.

Irwin, M. T. 2007. Living in forest fragments reduces group cohesion in Diademed Sifakas (*Propithecus diadema*) in eastern Madagascar by reducing food patch size. *American Journal of Primatology* 69: 434–447.

Irwin, M. T, Raharison, F. J., Rakotoarimanana, H., Razanadrakoto, E., Ranaivoson, E., Rakotofanala J., and Randrianarimanana, C. 2007. Diademed sifakas (*Propithecus diadema*) use olfaction to forage for the inflorescences of subterranean parasitic plants (Balanophoraceae: *Langsdorffia* sp., and Cytinaceae: *Cytinus* sp.). *American Journal of Primatology* 69: 471–476.

IUCN. 2001. IUCN Red List Categories and Criteria, v. 3.1. IUCN Species Survival Commission. Gland, Switzerland and Cambridge, UK: IUCN. https://portals.iucn.org/library/sites/library/files/documents/RL-2001-001.pdf.

———. 2012. IUCN Red List Categories and Criteria, v. 3.1. 2nd ed. IUCN Species Survival Commission, pp. 32. Gland, Switzerland and Cambridge, UK: IUCN. https://www.iucn.org/content/iucn-red-list-categories-and-criteria-version-31-second-edition.

———. 2019. Guidelines for using the IUCN Red List categories and criteria, v. 14, prepared by the Standards and Petitions Subcommittee. http://cmsdocs.s3.amazonaws.com/RedListGuidelines.pdf.

———. 2020. The IUCN Red List of Threatened Species, v. 2020–1. Accessed 10 June 2020. https://www.iucnredlist.org.

IUCN SSC Madagascar Plant Specialist Group and Missouri Botanical Garden. 2017. *Adansonia suarezensis* (errata version published in 2019). IUCN Red List of Threatened Species 2017. Accessed 13 Nov. 2021. https://dx.doi.org/10.2305/IUCN.UK.2017-3.RLTS.T30389A145519699.en.

Jacques-Félix, H. 1973. Contribution à l'étude du genre *Rousseauxia* (Melast.). *Adansonia*, série 2, 13: 177–193.

———. 1976. Le genre *Tristemma* Jussieu (Melastomataceae). *Bulletin du Muséum National d'Histoire Naturelle*, série 3, *Botanique* 28: 137–206.

———. 1978. Les genres de Memecyleae (Melastomataceae) en Afrique, Madagascar et Mascareignes. *Adansonia*, série 2, 18: 221–235.

———. 1984 [1985]. Les Memecyleae (Melastomataceae) de Madagascar (pt. 1). *Bulletin du Muséum National d'Histoire Naturelle*, série 4, Section B, *Adansonia* 6: 383–451.

———. 1985. Les Memecyleae (Melastomataceae) de Madagascar (pt. 2). *Bulletin du Muséum National d'Histoire Naturelle*, série 4, Section B, *Adansonia* 7: 3–58.

———. 1994 [1995]. Histoire des Melastomataceae d'Afrique. *Bulletin du Muséum National d'Histoire Naturelle*, série 4, Section B, *Adansonia* 16: 235–311.

Jaeger, M. P. 1945. Epanouissement et pollinisation de la fleur du Baobab. *Comptes Rendus Hebdomadaires des Séances de L'Académie des Sciences, Paris*, 220: 369–371.

Jankalski, S. 2000. "Crown of Thorns" hybrids—past and present. *Cactus and Succulent Journal* 72: 202–204.

Jansen, S., Dessein, S., Piesschaert, F., Robbrecht, E., and Smets, E. F. 2000. Aluminium accumulation in leaves of Rubiaceae: Systematic and phylogenetic implications. *Annals of Botany* 85: 91–101.

Janssens, S. B., Groeninckx, I., De Block, P., Verstraete, B., Smets, E. F., and Dessein, S. 2016. Dispersing towards Madagascar: Biogeography and evolution of the Madagascan endemics of the Spermacoceae tribe (Rubiaceae). *Molecular Phylogenetic Evolution* 95: 58–66.

Janzen, D. H. 1979. How to be a fig. *Annual Review of Ecology and Systematics* 10: 13–51.

Jaramillo, M. A., and Manos, P. S. 2001. Phylogeny and patterns of floral diversity in the genus *Piper* (Piperaceae). *American Journal of Botany* 88(4): 706–716.

Jaramillo, M. A., Callejas, R., Davidson, C., Smith, J. F., Stevens, A. C., and Tepe, E. J. 2008. A phylogeny of the tropical genus *Piper* using ITS and the chloroplast intron *psbJ–petA*. *Systematic Botany* 33(4): 647–660.

Jeannoda, V. H., Jeannoda, V., Hladik, A., and Hladik, C. M. 2003. Les ignames de Madagascar : diversité, utilisations et perceptions. *Hommes et Plantes* 47: 10–23.

Jeannoda, V. H., Razanamparany, J., Rajaonah, M. T., Monneuse, M. O., Hladik, A., and Hladik, C. M. 2007. Les ignames (*Dioscorea* spp.) endémiques et cultivées de Madagascar: Diversité, perception, valeur nutritionnelle et systèmes de gestion. *Revue d'Ecologie (La Terre et la Vie)* 62: 191–207.

Jeyarani, J. N., Yohannan, R., Vijayavalli, D., Dwivedi, M. D., and Pandey, A. K. 2018. Phylogenetic analysis and evolution of morphological characters in the genus *Jasminum* L. (Oleaceae) in India. *Journal of Genetics* 97: 1225–1239.

Johnson, M. G., Pokorny, L., Dodsworth, S., Botigué, L. R., Cowan, R. S., et al. 2019. A universal probe set for targeted sequencing of 353 nuclear genes from any flowering plant designed using k-medoids clustering. *Systematic Biology* 68: 594–606.

Johnston, I. M. 1930. Studies in the Boraginaceae VIII. 1. Observations on the species of *Cordia* and *Tournefortia* known from Brazil. *Contributions from the Gray Herbarium* 92: 3–89.

Jones, E. W. 1975. African Hepatics XXVII. *Bazzania*. *Journal of Bryology* 8: 71–75.

Jones, J.P.G., Andriamarovololona, M. M., and Hockley, N. 2008. The importance of taboos and social norms to conservation in Madagascar. *Conservation Biology* 22: 976–986.

Jonsson, L. 1981. A monograph of the genus *Microcoelia*. *Acta Universitatis Upsaliensis, Symbolae Botanicae Upsalensis* 23: 1–151.

Jørgensen, P. M. 2001. The present status of the names applicable to species and infraspecific taxa of *Erioderma* (lichenised ascomycetes) included in Zahlbruckner's Catalogus. *Taxon* 50: 525–541.

Jørgensen, P. M., and Sipman, H. J. M. 2006. The lichen family Pannariaceae in the montane regions of New Guinea. *Journal of the Hattori Botanical Laboratory* 100: 695–720.

Joubert, L., Klak, C., Venter, A. M., Venter, H. J. T., and Bruyns, P. V. 2016. A widespread radiation in the Periplocoideae (Apocynaceae): The case of *Cryptolepis*. *Taxon* 65: 487–501.

Jousselin, E., van Noort, S., Rasplus, J.-Y., Rønsted, N., Erasmus, C., and Greeff, J. 2008. One tree to bind them all: Host conservatism in a fig wasp community unraveled by cospeciation analyses among pollinating and non-pollinating fig wasps. *Evolution* 62: 1777–1797.

Jovet-Ast, S. 1983. *Colura* nouveaux d'origines diverses (Hepatiques, Lejeuneacees). *Cryptogamie Bryologie Lichenologie* 4: 205–216.

JSTOR. 2021. Global Plants. https://plants.jstor.org.

Jumelle, H., and Perrier de la Bâthie, H. 1910. Fragments biologique de la flore de Madagascar. *Annales de l'Institut Botanico-Géologique Colonial de Marseille*, série 2, 8: 373–468.

———. 1912. Quelques phanérogames parasites de Madagascar. *Revue Générale de Botanique* 24: 321–328.

———. 1945. Famille—Palmiers. *Flore de Madagascar et des Comores* 30: 1–186.

Kainulainen, K., and Bremer, B. 2009. Molecular phylogenetic analysis of the tribe Alberteae (Rubiaceae) with description of a new genus, *Razafimandimbisonia*. *Taxon* 58: 757–768.

———. 2014. Phylogeny of *Euclinia* and allied genera of Gardenieae (Rubiaceae), and description of *Melanoxerus*, an endemic genus of Madagascar. *Taxon* 63: 819–830.

Kainulainen, K., and Razafimandimbison, S. G. 2015. *Chapelieria magna*, a new species of Rubiaceae from eastern Madagascar. *PhytoKeys* 44: 89–95.

———. 2016. New combinations in West Indian Ocean Vanguerieae (Rubiaceae). *Phytotaxa* 282(4): 267–272.

Kainulainen, K., Mouly, A., Khodabandeh, A., and Bremer, B. 2009. Molecular phylogenetic analysis of the tribe Alberteae (Rubiaceae), with description of a new genus, *Razafimandimbisonia*. *Taxon* 58: 757–768.

Kainulainen, K., Razafimandimbison, S. G., and Bremer, B. 2013. Phylogenetic relationships and new tribal delimitations in subfamily Ixoroideae (Rubiaceae). *Botanical Journal of the Linnean Society* 173: 387–406.

Kainulainen, K., van Ee, B. W., Antilahimena, P., Razafindraibe, H., and Berry, P. E. 2016. New species and species reports of *Croton* (Euphorbiaceae) from the eastern forest corridor of Madagascar. *Candollea* 71: 327–356.

Kainulainen, K., Berry, P. E., and van Ee, B. W. 2017a. Rediscovery of two species of *Croton* L. (Euphorbiaceae) from littoral habitats of eastern Madagascar. *Candollea* 72: 35–44.

Kainulainen, K., van Ee, B. W., Razafindraibe, H., and Berry, P. E. 2017b. A revision of the Adenophorus Group and other glandular-leaved species of *Croton* (Euphorbiaceae) from northern Madagascar and Mayotte, including three new species. *Candollea* 72: 371–402.

Kainulainen, K., Razafimandimbison, S. G., Wikström, N., and Bremer, B. 2017c. Island hopping, long-distance dispersal and species radiation in the western Indian Ocean: Historical biogeography of the Coffeeae alliance (Rubiaceae). *Journal of Biogeography* 44: 1966–1979.

Kårehed, J., and Bremer, B. 2007. The systematics of Knoxieae (Rubiaceae): Molecular data and their taxonomic consequences. *Taxon* 56: 1051–1076.

Karimi, N., Grover, C. E., Gallagher, J. P., Wendel, J. F., Ané, C., and Baum, D. A. 2020. Reticulate evolution helps explain apparent homoplasy in floral biology and pollination in baobabs (*Adansonia*; Bombacoideae; Malvaceae). *Systematic Biology* 69(3): 462–478. https://doi.org/10.1093/sysbio/syz073.

Kartzinel, T. R., Chen, P. A., Coverdale, T. C., Erickson, D. L., Kress, W. J., Kuzmina, M. L., Rubenstein, D. I., Wang, W., and Pringle, R. M. 2015. DNA metabarcoding illuminates dietary niche partitioning by African large herbivores. *Proceedings of the National Academy of Science of the USA* 112: 8019–8024.

Kathriarachchi, H., Samuel, R., Hoffmann, P., Mlinarec, J., Wurdack, K. J., Ralimanana, H., Stuessy, T. F., and Chase, M. W. 2006. Phylogenetics of tribe Phyllantheae (Phyllanthaceae; Euphorbiaceae *sensu lato*) based on *nrITS and* plastid *matK* DNA sequence data. *American Journal of Botany* 93(4): 637–655.

Kawakita, A., and Kato, M. 2004. Evolution of obligate pollination mutualism in New Caledonian *Phyllanthus* (Euphorbiaceae). *American Journal of Botany* 91: 410–415.

———. 2009. Repeated independent evolution of obligate pollination mutualism in the *Phyllantheae-Epicephala* association. *Proceedings of the Royal Society of London B: Biological Sciences* 276: 417–426.

Kellogg, E. A. 2015. Flowering plants. Monocots: Poaceae. In *The Families and Genera of Vascular Plants*, vol. 13, ed. K. Kubitzki. Heidelberg: Springer.

Kerdelhué, C. 1997. Les communautés de Chalcidiens sycophiles associées aux figuiers du sous-genre *Sycomorus*: écologie et évolution. PhD thesis, Institut National Agronomique Paris-Grignon.

Kerdelhué, C., and Rasplus, J.-Y. 1996a. Non-pollinating Afrotropical fig wasps affect the fig-pollinator mutualism in *Ficus* within the subgenus *Sycomorus*. *Oikos* 75: 3–14.

———. 1996b. The evolution of dioecy among *Ficus* (Moraceae): An alternative hypothesis involving non-pollinating fig wasp pressure on the fig-pollinator mutualism. *Oikos* 77(1): 163–166.

Kerdelhué, C., Le Clainche, I., and Rasplus, J.-Y. 1999. Molecular phylogeny of the *Ceratosolen* species pollinating *Ficus* of the subgenus *Sycomorus sensu stricto*: Biogeographical history and origins of the species-specificity breakdown cases. *Molecular Phylogenetics and Evolution* 11(3): 401–414.

Khan, S. A., Razafimandimbison, S. G., Bremer, B., and Liede-Schumann, S. 2008. Sabiceeae and Virectarieae (Rubiaceae, Ixoroideae): One or two tribes? New tribal and generic circumscriptions of Sabiceeae and biogeography of *Sabicea s. l. Taxon* 57: 7–23.

Khan, Z., Midega, C.A.O., Hooper, A., and Pickett, J. 2016. Push-pull: Chemical ecology–based integrated pest management technology. *Journal of Chemical Ecology* 42(7): 689–97. https://doi.org/10.1007/s10886-016-0730-y.

Khanum, R., Surveswaran, S., Meve, U., and Liede-Schumann, S. 2016. *Cynanchum* (Apocynaceae: Asclepiadoideae): A pantropical asclepiadoid genus revisited. *Taxon* 65: 467–486.

Kiel, C., McDade, L. A., Daniel, T. F., and Champluvier, D. 2006. Phylogenetic delimitation of Isoglossinae (Acanthaceae: Justicieae) and relationships among constituent genera. *Taxon* 55(3): 683–694.

Kiel, C., Daniel, T. F., Darbyshire, I., and McDade, L. A. 2017. Unraveling relationships in the morphologically diverse and taxonomically challenging "justicioid" lineage (Acanthaceae: Justicieae). *Taxon* 66(3): 645–674.

Kiel, C., Daniel, T. F., and McDade, L. A. 2018. Phylogenetics of New World "justicioids" (Justicieae: Acanthaceae): Major lineages, morphological patterns, and widespread incongruence with classification. *Systematic Botany* 43(2): 459–484.

Kirkbride, J. H. 2005. *Dupuya*, a new genus of Malagasy legumes (Fabaceae). *Novon* 15: 305–314.

Kissling, W. D., Rahbek, C., and Böhning-Gaese, K. 2007. Food plant diversity as broad-scale determinant of avian frugivore richness. *Proceedings of the Royal Society of London B: Biological Sciences* 274: 799–808.

Kissling, W. D., Eiserhardt, W. L., Baker, W. J., Borchsenius, F., Couvreur, T.L.P., Balslev, H., and Svenning, J.-C. 2012. Cenozoic imprints on the phylogenetic structure of palm species assemblages worldwide. *Proceedings of the National Academy of Sciences of the USA* 109: 7379–7384.

Kite, G. C., Hoffmann, P., Lees, D. C., Wurdack, K. J., and Gillespie, L. J. 2005. α-Homonojirimycin and other polyhydroxyalkaloids in *Suregada* Roxb. ex Rottl. (Euphorbiaceae). *Biochemical Systematics and Ecology* 11(33): 1183–1186

Kjellberg, F., Jousselin, E., Bronstein, J. L., Patel, A., Yokoyama, J., and Rasplus, J.-Y. 2001. Pollination mode in fig wasps: The predictive power of correlated traits. *Proceedings of the Royal Society of London B: Biological Sciences* 268: 1113–1121.

Klackenberg, J. 1992. Taxonomy of *Secamone s. lat.* (Asclepiadaceae) in the Madagascar region. *Opera Botanica a Societate Botanica Lundensis* 112: 1–126.

———. 1996a. The new genus *Calyptranthera* (Asclepiadaceae) from Madagascar. *Novon* 6: 25–27.

———. 1996b. Revision of the Malagasy genus *Pervillea* (Asclepiadaceae) and its phylogenetic relationship to *Calyptranthera*. *Nordic Journal of Botany* 16: 165–184.

Klitgaard, B. B., and Lavin, M. 2005. Dalbergieae. In *Legumes of the World*, eds. G. Lewis, B. Schrire, B. Mackinder, and M. Lock, pp. 307–335. Kew: Royal Botanic Gardens.

Knoblauch, E. F. 1934. Eine neue Oleaceen-Gattung der Comoren. *Notizblatt des Botanischen Gartens und Museums zu Berlin-Dahlem* 101–110: 1032–1033.

Knudsen, J. T., and Tollsten L. 1995. Floral scent in bat-pollinated plants: A case of convergent evolution. *Botanical Journal of the Linnean Society* 119: 45–57.

Knuth, R. 1924. Dioscoreaceae. In *Das Pflanzenreich*, vol. 87, ed. H.G.A. Engler, pp. 1–387. Leipzig: Verlag von Wilhelm Engelmann.

Koechlin, J. 1993. Grasslands of Madagascar. In *Natural Grasslands: Eastern Hemisphere and Résumé, Ecosystems of the World*, ed. R. T. Coupland, pp. 291–301. Amsterdam: Elsevier.

Koechlin, J., Guillaumet, J.-L., and Morat, P. 1974. *Flore et végétation de Madagascar*. Vaduz: J. Cramer.

Koehbach, J., Attah, A. F., Berger, A., Hellinger, R., Kutchan, T. M., and Carpenter, E. J. 2013. Cyclotide discovery in Gentianales revisited: Identification and characterization of cyclic cystine-knot peptides and their phylogenetic distribution in Rubiaceae plants. *Biopolymers* 100: 438–452.

Koenen, E. J., Ojeda, D. I., Steeves, R., Migliore, J., Bakker, F. T., et al. 2020. Large-scale genomic sequence data resolve the deepest divergences in the legume phylogeny and support a near-simultaneous evolutionary origin of all six subfamilies. *New Phytologist* 225(3): 1355–1369.

Kokwaro, J. O. 1986. Anacardiaceae. In *Flora Tropical East Africa*, ed. R. M. Polhill, pp. 1–59. Kew: Royal Botanic Gardens.

Koopman, M. 2005. Ny Zavamaniry sy ny mpamindra vovobony (Pollination observations of *Nectarinia* on *Megistostegium*). *Ravintsara* 3(1): 10.

———. 2011. A synopsis of the Malagasy endemic genus *Megistostegium* Hochr. (Hibisceae, Malvaceae). *Adansonia* 33(1): 101–114. https://doi.org/10.5252/a2011n1a7.

Koopman, M., and Baum, D. A. 2008. Phylogeny and biogeography of Hibisceae (Malvaceae) on Madagascar. *Systematic Botany* 33: 364–374. https://doi.org/10.1600/036364408784571653.

———. 2010. Isolating nuclear genes and identifying lineages without monophyly: An example of closely related species from southern Madagascar. *International Journal of Plant Sciences* 171: 761–771. https://doi.org/10.1086/654847.

Koponen, T. 1981. A synopsis of *Mniaceae* (Bryophyta) V. Taxa in Africa south of the Sahara. *Annales Botanici Fennici* 18: 105–111.

Koponen, T., and Weber, W. A. 1972. A revision of African Tayloriae (Splachnaceae), including *Bryomnium*. *Annales Botanici Fennici* 9: 126–134.

Korine, C., Kalko, E.K.V., and Herre, E. A. 2000. Fruit characteristics and factors affecting fruit removal in a Panamanian community of strangler figs. *Oecologia* 123: 560–568.

Kotina, E. L., Oskolski, A. A., Tilney, P. M., and Van Wyk, B. E. 2017. Bark anatomy of *Adansonia digitata* L. (Malvaceae). *Adansonia* 39: 31–40.

Kottak, P. C. 1977. The process of stable formation in Madagascar. *Human Ecology* 4(1): 136–155.

Krog, H. 1994. Typification and interpretation of *Ramalina arabum*. *Acta Botanica Fennica* 150: 99–104.

Krüger, Å., Razafimandimbison, S. G., and Bremer, B. 2012. Molecular phylogeny of the tribe Danaideae (Rubiaceae, Rubioideae)—another example of out-of-Madagascar dispersals. *Taxon* 61: 629–636.

Kruijer, J. D. 1997. British Bryological Society Expedition to Mulanje Mountain, Malawi. 6. *Hypopterigiaceae* (Musci). *Journal of Bryology* 19: 515–520.

———. 2002. Hypopterygiaceae of the World. *Blumea Supplement* 13: 1–388.

Kruijt, R. C. 1988. A monograph of the genera *Dicranolejeunea* and *Acanthocoleus*. *Bryophyterum Bibliotheca* 36: 1–136.

———. 1996. A taxonomic monograph of *Sapium* Jacq., *Anomostachys* (Baill.) Hurus., *Duvigneaudia* J. Léonard and *Sclerocroton* Hochst. (Euphorbiaceae Tribe Hippomaneae). *Bibliotheca Botanica* 146: 1–109.

Kubat, R. 1987. Report of the first investigations of parasitism in Opiliaceae (Santalales). In *Proceedings of the 4th International Symposium Parasitic Flowering Plants*, eds. H. C. Weber and W. Forstreuter, pp. 489–492. Marburg: Philipps-Universität.

Kuijt, J. 2015. Santalales. In *The families and genera of vascular plants. XII Flowering plants: Eudicots Santalales, Balanophorales,* vol. 12, ed. K. Kubitzki, pp. 1–189. Cham: Springer International.

Kulju, K. K., Sierra, S. E., Draisma, S. G., Samuel, R., and van Welzen, P. C. 2007. Molecular phylogeny of *Macaranga*, *Mallotus*, and related genera (Euphorbiaceae *s.s.*): Insights from plastid and nuclear DNA sequence data. *American Journal of Botany* 94(10): 1726–1743.

Kull, C. A. 2012. Air photo evidence of land cover change in the highlands: Wetlands and grasslands give way to crops and woodlots. *Madagascar Conservation and Development* 7: 144–152.

Kull, C. A., Tassin, J., Moreau, S., Rakoto Ramiarantsoa, H., Blanc-Pamard, C., and Carrière, S. M. 2012. The introduced flora of Madagascar. *Biological Invasions* 14: 875–888.

Kumar, D. S. 2018. The baobab tree. *Hygeia: Journal for Drugs and Medicines* 10: 1–2.

Kümpers, B.M.A., Richardson, J. E., Anderberg, A. A., Wilkie, P., and Ronse de Craene, L. P. 2016. The significance of meristic changes in the flowers of Sapotaceae. *Botanical Journal of the Linnean Society* 180: 161–192.

Kunze, H. 1990. Morphology and evolution of the corona in Asclepiadaceae and related families. *Tropische und Subtropische Pflanzenwelt* 76: 1–51.

———. 1991. Structure and function in asclepiad pollination. *Plant Systematics and Evolution* 176: 227–253.

———. 1997. Corona and nectar system in Asclepiadinae (Asclepiadaceae). *Flora* 192: 175–183.

Kunze, H., Meve, U., and Liede, S. 1994. *Cibirhiza albersiana*, a new species of Asclepiadaceae, and establishment of the tribe Fockeeae. *Taxon* 43: 367–376.

Kyalangalilwa, B., Boatwright, J. S., Daru, B. H., Maurin, O., and van der Bank, M. 2013. Phylogenetic position and revised classification of *Acacia s.l.* (Fabaceae: Mimosoideae) in Africa, including new combinations in *Vachellia* and *Senegalia*. *Botanical Journal of the Linnean Society* 172(4): 500–523.

Labat, J.-N., and Du Puy, D. J. 1997. A revision of *Peltiera*, a new, poorly known and probably extinct genus of Leguminosae (Papilionoideae-Aeschynomeneae) from Madagascar. *Adansonia*, série 3, 19(1): 85–91.

Labat, J.-N., and Moat, J. 2003. Leguminosae (Fabaceae). In *The Natural History of Madagascar*, eds. S. M. Goodman and J. P. Benstead, pp. 346–373. Chicago: University of Chicago Press.

Labat, J.-N., Pignal, M., and Pascal, O. 1999. Trois espèces nouvelles d'Oleaceae et note sur la présence d'*Olea capensis* dans l'Archipel des Comores. *Novon* 9: 66–72.

———. 2005. Deux espèces nouvelles et une combinaison nouvelle chez les Rutaceae de l'Archipel des Comores. *Monograph in Systematic Botany from the Missouri Botanical Garden* 104: 362–365.

Lachaise, D., Harry, M., and Solignac, M. 1996. Affinités biogéographiques des Drosophilidae de Madagascar et des îles de l'Océan Indien. In *Biogéographie de Madagascar*, ed. W. R. Lourenço, pp. 467–478. Paris: Editions ORSTOM.

La Croix, I. 2014. *Aerangis*. Portland and London: Timber Press.

La Croix, I., Bosser, J., and Cribb, P. 2002. The genus *Disperis* (Orchidaceae) in Madagascar, the Comores, the Mascarenes and the Seychelles. *Adansonia* 24: 55–87.

La Farge, C. 2002a. *Leucoloma* I: A revision of subgenus *Leucoloma* (Dicranaceae, Bryopsida) in Africa and Madagascar. *The Bryologist* 105: 509–590.

———. 2002b. *Leucoloma* II: A revision of *Leucoloma* series *Holomitrioidea* (Dicranaceae). *The Bryologist* 105: 591–605.

———. 2002c. *Leucoloma* III: A species synopsis: Typification, synonymy and excluded names. *The Bryologist* 105: 606–624.

La Farge-England, C. 1992. *Leucoloma crosbyi* (Dicranaceae), a new species endemic to northern Madagascar. *Novon* 2: 119–122.

LaFleur, M., and Sauther, M. L. 2015. Seasonal feeding ecology of ring-tailed lemurs: A comparison of spiny and gallery forest habitats. *Folia Primatologica* 86: 25–34.

Lahann, P. 2007. Feeding ecology and seed dispersal of sympatric cheirogaleid lemurs (*Microcebus murinus*, *Cheirogaleus medius*, *Cheirogaleus major*) in the littoral rainforest of south-east Madagascar. *Journal of Zoology* 271: 88–98.

Lahaye, R., Klackenberg, J., Källersjö, M., and Civeyrel, L. 2005. Phylogeny and biogeography of the Secamonoideae (Apocynaceae *s.l.*). In XVII International Botanical Congress. 100 years after the II IBC in Vienna 1905. Abstracts, eds. M. Popp, M. Hesse, T. Stuessy, J. Greimler, and H. Bohar-Nodenkampf, p. 398. Vienna: Koeltz Scientific Books.

Laivao, M. O. 2008. Contribution à la systématique du genre *Pandanus* (Pandanaceae) à Madagascar. PhD thesis, Université de Neuchâtel.

Laivao, M. O., Callmander, M. W., and Buerki, S. 2006. Sur les *Pandanus* (Pandanaceae) à stigmates saillants de la Côte Est de Madagascar. *Adansonia*, série 3, 28: 267–285.

Lam, H. J. 1932. Beiträge zur morphologie der Burseraceae. Insbesondere der Canarieae. *Annales du Jardin Botanique de Buitenzorg* 42: 202.

Lamarck, J.-B.A.P.M. 1791. *Tableau encyclopédique et méthodique des trois règnes de la nature. Botanique*. Tome 1. Paris: Panckoucke.

Landolt, P. J. 1994. Fruit of *Morrenia odorata* (Asclepiadaceae) as a host for the papaya fruit fly, *Toxotrypana curvicauda* (Diptera: Tephritidae). *The Florida Entomologist* 77: 287–288.

Landrum, J. V. 2002. Four succulent families and 40 million years of evolution and adaptation to xeric environments: What can stem and leaf anatomical characters tell us about their phylogeny? *Taxon* 51: 463–473.

Langrand, O. 1990. *A Guide to the Birds of Madagascar*. New Haven: Yale University Press.

Lantz, H., and Bremer, B. 2004. Phylogeny inferred from morphology and DNA data: Characterizing well-supported groups in Vanguerieae (Rubiaceae). *Botanical Journal of the Linnean Society* 146: 257–283.

Lantz, H., Klackenberg, J., Razafimandimbison, S. G., and Mouly, A. 2007. Three new species of Vanguerieae from Madagascar. *Adansonia* 29: 129–136.

Larridon, I., Reynders, M., Huygh, W., Bauters, K., Van de Putte, K., Muasya, A. M., Boeckx, P., Simpson, D. A., Vrijdaghs, A., and Goetghebeur, P. 2011a. Affinities in C_3 *Cyperus* lineages (Cyperaceae) revealed using molecular phylogenetic data and carbon isotope analysis. *Botanical Journal of the Linnean Society* 167: 19–46.

Larridon, I., Reynders, M., Huygh, W., Bauters, K., Vrijdaghs, A., Leroux, O., Muasya, A. M., Simpson, D. A., and Goetghebeur, P. 2011b. Taxonomic changes in C_3 *Cyperus* (Cyperaceae) supported by molecular phylogenetic data, morphology, embryology, ontogeny and anatomy. *Plant Ecology and Evolution* 144: 327–356.

Larridon, I., Bauters, K., Reynders, M., Huygh, W., Muasya, A. M., Simpson, D. A., and Goetghebeur, P. 2013. Towards a new classification of the giant paraphyletic genus *Cyperus* (Cyperaceae): Phylogenetic relationships and generic delimitation in C_4 *Cyperus*. *Botanical Journal of the Linnean Society* 172: 106–126.

Larridon, I., Bauters, K., Muasya, A. M., Vrijdaghs, A., Simpson, D. A., and Goetghebeur, P. 2014a. A new understanding of the giant genus *Cyperus*: Impacts on African plant taxonomy. In *Biodiversity of African Plants. Challenges in a*

Changing World. Abstracts of the 20th AETFAT Congress—South Africa, 12–18 Jan. 2014. *Scripta Botanica Belgica* 52: 235.

Larridon, I., Bauters, K., Huygh, W., Reynders, M., and Goetghebeur, P. 2014b. Taxonomic changes in C_4 *Cyperus* (Cypereae, Cyperoideae, Cyperaceae): Combining the sedge genera *Ascolepis*, *Kyllinga* and *Pycreus* into *Cyperus s.l. Phytotaxa* 166: 33–48.

Larridon, I., Semmouri, I., Bauters, K., Viljoen, J.-A., Prychid, C. J., Muasya, A. M., Bruhl, J. J., Wilson, K. A., and Goetghebeur, P. 2018. Molecular phylogenetics of the genus *Costularia* (Schoeneae, Cyperaceae) reveals multiple distinct evolutionary lineages. *Molecular Phylogenetics and Evolution* 126: 196–209.

Larridon, I., Rabarivola, L., Xanthos, M., and Muasya, A. M. 2019a. Revision of the Afro-Madagascan genus *Costularia* (Cyperaceae): Infrageneric relationships and species delimitation. *PeerJ* 7: e6528.

Larridon, I., Goetghebeur, P., and Roalson, E. H. 2019b. New combinations and a new name for including *Nemum* species in *Bulbostylis* (Abildgaardieae: Cyperaceae). *Phytotaxa* 418: 112–114.

Larridon, I., Spalink, D., Jiménez-Mejías, P., Márquez-Corro, J. I., Martín-Bravo, S., and Escudero, M. 2019c. Origins and diversification of Cyperaceae in Madagascar. *Abstract Book 56th Annual Association for Tropical Biology and Conservation (ATBC) meeting in Antananarivo, Madagascar from 30 July to 3 August 2019*, p. 90. Antananarivo: Association for Tropical Biology and Conservation.

Launert, E. 1971. Gramineae. In *Flora Zambesiaca* 10 (1), eds. A. Fernandes, E. Launert, and H. Wild. Kew: Royal Botanic Gardens.

Leake, J. 1994. The biology of myco-heterotrophic ("saprophytic") plants. *New Phytologist* 127: 171–216.

Leandri, J. 1933. Nouveaux *Phyllanthus* de Madagascar. *Bulletin de la Société Botanique de France* 80: 371–373.

———. 1934. Espèces et localité nouvelles d'Euphorbiaceae d'Afrique et Madagascar. *Bulletin de la Société Botanique de France* 81: 449–454.

———. 1936a. Le milieu et la végétation de la Réserve Naturelle de l'Antsingy (Madagascar). *Bulletin du Muséum de Paris*, série 2, 8: 557–572.

———. 1936b. Reconnaissance botanique de la partie médiane de l'Ouest Malgache (la région de l'Antsingy). *Bulletin de l'Académie Malgache*, nouvelle série, 19: 1–35.

———. 1938. Contribution à l'étude des Euphorbiacées de Madagascar (suite). *Notulae Systematicae* 6(4): 185–199.

———. 1939a. Les Crotons de Madagascar et de îles voisines. *Annales du Musée Colonial de Marseille*, série 5, 7 (1): 1–100.

———. 1939b. Contribution à l'étude des Euphorbiacées de Madagascar. *Notulae Systematicae* 7: 168–187.

———. 1951. Sur quelques traits de la végétation des plateaux calcaires dans l'ouest de Madagascar. *Webbia* 8: 155–176.

———. 1957. Notes systématiques sur les Euphorbiacées, *Phyllanthus* de Madagascar. *Mémoire de l'Institut Scientifique de Madagascar* 8: 205–234.

———. 1958. Euphorbiaceae. *Flore de Madagascar et des Comores* 111(1): 1–199.

———. 1972. Le genre *Cleidion* (Euphorbiacées) à Madagascar. *Adansonia*, nouvelle série, 12: 193–196.

Le Bourgeois, T., Grard, P., Andrianaivo, A. P., Gaungoo, A., Ibrahim, Y., et al. 2019. WIKTROP—Weed Identification and Knowledge in the Tropics and Mediterranean area—Web 2.0 participatory portal. European Union programme ACP SandT II, Cirad, IFP, MCIA/MSIRI, FOFIFA, CNDRS. http://portal.wiktrop.org.

Lee, H.-L., Jansen, R. K., Chumley, T. W., and Kim, K.-J. 2007. Gene relocations within chloroplast genomes of *Jasminum* and *Menodora* (Oleaceae) are due to multiple, overlapping inversions. *Molecular Biology and Evolution* 24: 1161–1180.

Leenhouts, P. W. 1959. Revision of the Burseraceae of the Malaysia area in a wider sense. *Blumea* 9: 275–475.

———. 1975. Taxonomic notes on *Glenniea* (Sapindaceae). *Blumea* 22: 411–414.

Lees, D. C., and Smith, N. G. 1991. Foodplant associations of the Uraniinae and their systematic, evolutionary and ecological significance. *Journal of the Lepidopterist's Society* 45: 296–347.

Leeuwenberg, A.J.M. 1997. Series of revisions of Apocynaceae XLIV. *Craspidospermum* Boj. ex A. DC., *Gonioma* E. Mey., *Mascarenhasia* A. DC., *Petchia* Livera, *Plectaneia* Thou., and *Stephanostegia* Baill. *Wageningen Agricultural University Papers* 97–2: 1–124.

Lefèvre, G., and Labat, J.-N. 2006. A new species of *Mimosa* (Fabaceae, Mimosoideae) from Madagascar. *Novon* 16(1): 74–77.

Léonard, J. 1959. Observations sur les genres *Pycnocoma* et *Argomuellera*. *Bulletin de la Société Royale de Botanique de Belgique* 91: 267–281.

Leong Pock Tsy, J.-M., Lumaret, R., Mayne, D., Vall, A.O.M., Abutaba, Y. I., Sagna, M., Raoseta, S.N.O.R., and Danthu, P. 2009. Chloroplast DNA phylogeography suggests a West African centre of origin for the baobab, *Adansonia digitata* L. (Bombacoideae, Malvaceae). *Molecular Ecology* 18: 1707–1715.

Leong Pock Tsy, J.-M., Lumaret, R., Flaven-Noguier, E., Sauve, M., Dubois, M. P., and Danthu, P. 2013. Nuclear microsatellite variation in Malagasy baobabs (*Adansonia*, Bombacoideae, Malvaceae) reveals past hybridization and introgression. *Annals of Botany* 112: 1759–1773.

Le Péchon, T., Dubuisson, J., Haevermans, T., Cruaud, C., Couloux, A., and Gigord, L.D.B. 2010. Multiple colonizations from Madagascar and converged acquisition of dioecy in the Mascarene Dombeyoideae (Malvaceae) as inferred from chloroplast and nuclear DNA sequence analyses. *Annals of Botany* 106: 343–357. https://doi.org/10.1093/aob/mcq116.

Le Péchon, T., Dai, Q., Zhang, L. B., Gao, X. F., and Sauquet, H. 2015. Diversification of Dombeyoideae (Malvaceae) in the Mascarenes: Old taxa on young islands? *International Journal of Plant Sciences* 176(3): 211–221. https://doi.org/10.1086/679350.

Le Roux, J. J., Brown, G. K., Byrne, M., Ndlovu, J., Richardson, D. M., Thompson, G. D., and Wilson, J.R.U. 2011. Phylogeographic consequences of different introduction histories of invasive Australian *Acacia* species and *Paraserianthes lophantha* (Fabaceae) in South Africa. *Diversity and Distributions* 17(5). https://doi.org/10.1111/j.1472-4642.2011.00784.x.

Le Roux, J. J., Strasberg, D., Rouget, M., Morden, C. W., Koordom, M., and Richardson, D. M. 2014. Relatedness defies biogeography: The tale of two island endemics (*Acacia heterophylla* and *A. koa*). *New Phytologist* 204: 230–242.

Leroy, J.-F. 1972. La genèse d'un genre chez les Bignoniacées-Crescentiées de Madagascar. *Compte rendu hebdomadaire des séances de l'Académie des Sciences*, série D, 275: 2675–2678.

Leroy, J.-F., and Lescot, M. 1991. Ptaeroxylacées. *Flore de Madagascar et des Comores* 107 bis: 87–117.

———. 1996. Taxons nouveaux de Trichilieae (Meliaceae-Melioideae) de Madagascar. *Bulletin du Muséum National d'Histoire Naturelle*, série 4, Section B, *Adansonia*, 18: 3–34.

Letsara, R., Faramalala, M., Razafindrahaja, V., and Faranirina, L. 2019a. *Adansonia perrieri*. IUCN Red List of Threatened Species 2019: e. T33612A64366847.

Letsara, R., Faranirina, L., Razafindrahaja, V., and Faramalala, M. 2019b. *Adansonia rubrostipa*. IUCN Red List of Threatened Species 2019: e.T37679A64366919.

Letsara, R., Faramalala, M., Razafindrahaja, V., and Faranirina, L. 2019c. *Adansonia za*. IUCN Red List of Threatened Species 2019: e.T37680A64367122.

Léveillé-Bourret, E., and Starr, J. R. 2019. Molecular and morphological data reveal three new tribes within the Scirpo-Caricoid Clade (Cyperoideae, Cyperaceae). *Taxon* 68: 218–245.

Levesque, A. 2012. Etude de différents schémas de vie mis en œuvre sur le *Tsiperifery*—poivre sauvage malgache. Mémoire de fin d'études, Ecole Nationale Supérieure Agronomique, Montpellier.

Levin, G. 2014. Putranjivaceae. In *The Families and Genera of Vascular Plants.* Volume XI. *Flowering Plants. Eudicots. Malpighiales*, ed. K. Kubitzki, pp. 273–276. Berlin: Springer.

Lewis, G. P. 2005. Tribe Caesalpinieae. In *Legumes of the World*, eds. G. Lewis, B. Schrire, B. Mackinder, and M. Lock, pp. 126–161. Kew: Royal Botanic Gardens.

———. 2020. New combinations in *Guilandina* (Leguminosae: Caesalpinioideae). *Kew Bulletin* 75: 1–3.

Lewis, G. P., and Forest, F. 2005. Tribe Cercideae. In *Legumes of the World*, eds. G. Lewis, B. Schrire, B. Mackinder, and M. Lock, pp. 56–67. Kew: Royal Botanic Gardens.

Lewis, G. P., and Guinet, P. 1986. Notes on *Gagnebina* (Leguminosae-Mimosoideae) in Madagascar and neighboring islands. *Kew Bulletin* 41: 463–470.

Lewis, G. P., and Schrire, B. D. 2003. *Thailentadopsis* Kostermans (Leguminosae: Mimosoideae: Ingeae) resurrected. *Kew Bulletin* 58: 491–494.

Lewis, G. P., Schrire, B., Mackinder, B., and Lock, M., eds. 2005. *Legumes of the World*. Kew: Royal Botanic Gardens.

Liede, S. 1992. Milkweed life forms. *National Geographic Research and Exploration* 8: 108–115.

Liede, S., and Kunze, H. 1993. A descriptive system for corona analysis in Asclepiadaceae and Periplocaceae. *Plant Systematics and Evolution* 185: 275–284.

Liede, S., and Täuber, A. 2000. *Sarcostemma* R. Br. (Apocynaceae:Asclepiadoideae)—a controversial generic circumscription reconsidered: Evidence from *trn*L-F Spacers. *Plant Systematics and Evolution* 225: 133–140.

Liede, S., and Weberling, F. 1995. Inflorescence structure in Asclepiadaceae. *Plant Systematics and Evolution* 197: 99–109.

Liede-Schumann, S., and Meve, U. 2018. *Vincetoxicum* (Apocynaceae: Asclepiadoideae) expanded to include *Tylophora* and allies. *Phytotaxa* 369: 129–184.

Liede-Schumann, S., Kong, H.-H., Meve, U., and Thiv, M. 2012. *Vincetoxicum* and *Tylophora* (Apocynaceae: Asclepiadoideae: Asclepiadeae)—two sides of the same medal: Independent shifts from tropical to temperate habitats. *Taxon* 61: 803–825.

Liede-Schumann, S., Khanum, R., Mumtaz, A. S., Gherghel, I., and Pahlevani, A. 2016. Going west—A subtropical lineage (*Vincetoxicum*, Apocynaceae: Asclepiadoideae) expanding into Europe. *Molecular Phylogenetics and Evolution* 94: 436–446.

Lim, T. K. 2011. *Phoenix reclinata*. In *Edible Medicinal and Non-medicinal Plants*, ed. T. K. Lim, pp. 419–422. New York: Springer.

Linan, A. G., Schatz, G. E., Lowry II, P. P., Miller, A., and Edwards, C. E. 2019. Ebony and the Mascarenes: The evolutionary relationships and biogeography of *Diospyros* L. (Ebenaceae) in the western Indian Ocean. *Botanical Journal of the Linnaean Society* 190: 359–373.

Linan, A. G., Schatz, G. E., and Lowry II, P. P. 2021. Taxonomic studies of *Diospyros* L. (Ebenaceae) from the Malagasy region. VII. Revision of *Diospyros* L. section *Forbesia* (Ebenaceae) in Madagascar and the Comoro islands. *Annals of the Missouri Botanical Garden* 106: 72–110.

Linder, H. P., Baeza, M., Barker, N. P., Galley, C., Humphreys, A. M., et al. 2010. A generic classification of the Danthonioideae (Poaceae). *Annals of the Missouri Botanical Garden* 97: 306–364.

Lindner, M., Pócs, T., and Heinrichs, J. 2004. On the occurrence of *Plagiochila stricta* on Madagascar, new to Africa. *Journal of the Hattori Botanicla Laboratory* 96: 261–271.

Ling, K. H., Wang, Y., Poon, W. S., Shaw, P. C., and But, P.P.H. 2009. The relationships of *Fagaropsis* and *Luvunga* in Rutaceae. *Taiwania* 54(4): 338–342.

Liu, B., Le, C. T., Barrette, R. L., Nickrent, D. L., Chen, Z., Lu, L., and Vidal-Russell, R. 2018. Historical biogeography of Loranthaceae (Santalales): Diversification agrees with emergence of tropical forests and radiation of songbirds. *Molecular Phylogenetics and Evolution* 124: 199–212.

Livshultz, T., Middleton, D. J., Endress, M. E., and Williams, C. 2007. Phylogeny of Apocynoideae and the APSA clade (Apocynaceae *s.l.*). *Annals of the Missouri Botanical Garden* 94: 324–359.

Löfstrand, S. D., Krüger, Å., Razafimandimbison, S. G., and Bremer, B. 2014. Phylogeny and generic delimitation in the sister tribes Hymenodictyeae and Naucleeae (Rubiaceae). *Systematic Botany* 89: 1027–1041.

Lowry II, P. P., and Plunkett, G. M. 2010. Recircumscription of *Polyscias* (Araliaceae) to include six related genera, with a new infrageneric classification and a synopsis of species. *Plant Diversity and Evolution* 128: 55–84.

Lowry II, P. P., and Rabehevitra, D. 2006. Endemic families of Madagascar. IX. A new littoral forest species of *Schizolaena* (Sarcolaenaceae). *Adansonia*, série 3, 28: 149–153.

Lowry II, P. P., Schatz, G. E., and Phillipson, P. B. 1997. The classification of natural and anthropogenic vegetation in Madagascar. In *Natural Change and Human Impact in Madagascar*, eds. S. M. Goodman and B. D. Patterson, pp. 93–123. Washington, DC: Smithsonian Institution Press.

Lowry II, P. P., Schatz, G. E., and Wolf, A.-E. 1999. Endemic families of Madagascar. III. A synoptic revision of *Schizolaena* (Sarcolaenaceae). *Adansonia*, série 3, 21: 183–212.

Lowry II, P. P., Haevermans, T., Labat, J.-N., Schatz, G. E., Leroy, J.-F., and Wolf, A.-E. 2000. Endemic families of Madagascar. V. A synoptic revision of *Eremolaena*, *Pentachlaena* and *Perrierodendron* (Sarcolaenaceae). *Adansonia*, série 3, 22: 11–31.

Lowry II, P. P., Schatz, G. E., and Wolf, A.-E. 2002. Endemic families of Madagascar. VIII. A synoptic revision of *Xyloolaena* Baill. (Sarcolaenaceae). *Adansonia*, série 3, 24: 7–19.

Lowry II, P. P., Plunkett, G. M., and Wen, J. 2004. Generic relationships in Araliaceae: Looking into the crystal ball. *South African Journal of Botany* 70: 382–392.

Lowry II, P. P., Nusbaumer, L., Randrianasolo, A., Schatz, G. E., and Hong-Wa, C. 2014. Endemic families of Madagascar. XIII. New, restricted range species of *Eremolaena* Baill. and *Schizolaena* Thouars (Sarcolaenaceae). *Candollea* 69: 183–193.

Lowry II, P. P., Plunkett, G. M., Gostel, M. R., and Frodin, D. G. 2017. A synopsis of the Afro-Malagasy species previously included in *Schefflera* J. R. Forst. and G. Forst. (Araliaceae): Resurrection of the genera *Astropanax* Seem. and *Neocussonia* (Harms) Hutch. *Candollea* 72: 265–282.

Lowry II, P. P., Phillipson, P. B., Andriamahefarivo, L., Schatz, G. E., Rajaonary, F., and Andriambololonera, S. 2018. Flore / Flora. In *Les aires protégées terrestres de Madagascar: Leur histoire, description et biote / The Terrestrial Protected Areas of Madagascar: Their History, Description, and Biota*, eds. S. M. Goodman, M. J. Raherilalao, and S. Wohlhauser, pp. 243–255. Antananarivo: Association Vahatra.

Lowry II, P. P., Plunkett, G. M., Mora, M. M., Cano, A., Fiaschi, P., et al. 2019. Studies in Neotropical Araliaceae. I. Resurrection of the genus *Sciodaphyllum* P. Browne to accommodate most New World species previously included in *Schefflera* J. R. Forst. and G. Forst. *Brittonia* 72: 1–15. https://doi.org/10.1007/s12228-019-09593-w.

LPWG (Legume Phylogeny Working Group). 2013. Legume phylogeny and classification in the 21st century: Progress, prospects and lessons for other species-rich clades. *Taxon* 62(2): 217–248.

———. 2017. A new subfamily classification of the Leguminosae based on a taxonomically comprehensive phylogeny. *Taxon* 66(1): 44–77.

Lücking, R., and Sérusiaux, E. 1996. *Musaespora kalbii* (lichenized Ascomycetes: Melanommatales), a new foliicolous lichen with a pantropical distribution. *Nordic Journal of Botany* 16: 661–667.

Lücking, R., and Vězda, A. 1998. Taxonomic studies in foliicolous species of the genus *Porina* (lichenized Ascomycotina: Trichotheliaceae)—II. The *Porina epiphylla* group. *Willdenowia* 28: 181–225.

Lücking, R., Archer, A. W., and Aptroot, A. 2009. A world-wide key to the genus *Graphis* (Ostropales: Graphidaceae). *Lichenologist* 41: 363–452.

Luckow, M. 1995. A phylogenetic analysis of the *Dichrostachys* group (Mimosoideae: Mimoseae). In *Advances in Legume Systematics*, pt. 7, *Phylogeny*, eds. M. D. Crisp and J. J. Doyle, pp. 63–75. Kew: Royal Botanic Gardens.

———. 2002. Anatomical features of the leaves in the Dichrostachys group (Leguminosae: Mimosoideae) and their utility for phylogenetic studies. *Systematic Botany* 27: 29–40.

Luckow, M., and Du Puy, D. J. 2000. A new species of *Gagnebina* (Leguminosae: Mimosoideae) from Madagascar. *Novon* 10: 220–223.

Luckow, M., Miller, J. T., Murphy, D. J., and Livschulz, T. 2003. A phylogenetic analysis of the Mimosoideae (Leguminosae) based on chloroplast DNA sequence data. In *Advances in Legume Systematics*, pt. 10, *Higher Level Systematics*, eds. B. B. Klitgaard, and A. Bruneau, pp. 197–220. Kew: Royal Botanic Gardens.

Luebert, F., Cecchi, L., Frohlich, M. W., Gottschling, M., Guilliams, M., et al. 2016a. Familial classification of the Boraginales. *Taxon* 65: 502–522.

Luebert, F., Couvreur, T.L.P., Gottschling, M., Hilger, H. H., Miller, J. S., and Weigend, M. 2016b. Historical biogeography of Boraginales: West Gondwanan vicariance followed by long-distance dispersal? *Journal of Biogeography* 44: 158–169.

Luino, I., Callmander, M. W., Poncy, O., Da-Giau, S., and Gautier, L. 2016. A new *Pararistolochia* Hutch. and Dalziel (Aristolochiaceae) from the Beanka tsingy (western Madagascar). *Candollea* 71: 135–141.

Lumbsch, H. T. 1987. Eine neue subspecies in der Flechtengattung *Diploschistes* aus der Sudhemisphare. *Herzogia* 7: 601–608.

Lumbsch, H. T., and Aptroot, A. 1993. Studien über die Flechtengattung *Diploschistes* II. *Nova Hedwigia* 56: 237–239.

Lumbsch, H. T., Ahti, T., Altermann, S., Amo De Paz, G., Aptroot, A., et al. 2011. One hundred new species of lichenized fungi: A signature of undiscovered global diversity. *Phytotaxa* 18: 1–127.

Mabberley, D. J. 2008. *Mabberley's Plant-book: A Portable Dictionary of Plants, Their Classification, and Uses*, 3rd ed. Cambridge: Cambridge University Press.

Mabberley, D. J., and Capuron, R. 1999. Révision de Malvaceae-Grewioideae ("Tiliacées", p.p.) de Madagascar et des Comores. IV. Les *Grewia* du sous-genre *Burretia* (Hochr.) Capuron. *Adansonia*, série 3, 21(2): 283–300.

———. 2017. Two *nomina nova* in Malagasy *Grewia* L. (Malvaceae-Grewioideae). *Telopea* 20: 85–88.

Mackinder, B., Harris, D. J., and Gautier, L. 2016. A reinstatement, circumscription and revision of the genus *Donella* (Sapotaceae). *Edinburgh Journal of Botany* 73: 297–339.

Madagascar Catalogue 2017–2021. Catalogue of the Plants of Madagascar. Saint Louis and Antananarivo: Missouri Botanical Garden. http://www.tropicos.org/Project/Madagascar.

Magnaghi, E. B., and Daniel, T. F. 2014. Three new species of *Mendoncia* (Acanthaceae) from Madagascar. *Novon* 23(2): 187–196.

Maguilla, E., and Escudero, M. 2016. Cryptic species due to hybridization: A combined approach to describe a new species (*Carex*: Cyperaceae). *PLoS One* 11: e0166949.

Maiz-Tomé, L., Sayer, C., and Darwall W. 2018. *The Status and Distribution of Freshwater Biodiversity in Madagascar and the Indian Ocean Islands Hotspot*. Gland, Switzerland and Cambridge, UK: IUCN.

Malombe, I. 2007. Systematics of *Cheilolejeunea* (Spruce) Schiffn. (Lejeuneaceae) in continental Africa and its ecological significance in conservation of Kakamega and Budongo rainforests. PhD thesis, University of Koblenz-Landau.

Malcomber, S. T. 2002. Phylogeny of *Gaertnera* Lam. (Rubiaceae) based on multiple DNA markers: Evidence of a rapid radiation in a widespread, morphologically diverse genus. *Evolution* 56: 42–57.

Malcomber, S. T., and Davis, A. P. 2005. Six new species of *Gaertnera* (Rubiaceae) from Madagascar and phylogenetic analyses that support *Hymenocnemis* as a synonym of *Gaertnera*. *Monographs in Systematic Botany* 104: 371–397.

Malcomber, S. T., and Taylor, C. M. 2009. A systematic revision of *Gaertnera* (Rubiaceae, Gaertnereae). *Annals of the Missouri Botanical Garden* 96: 575–671.

Malécot, V., Schatz, G. E., and Bosser, J. 2003. Révision synoptique du genre *Phanerodiscus* Cavaco (Olacaceae) à Madagascar. *Adansonia* 25: 119–128.

Manktelow, M. 1996. *Phaulopsis* (Acanthaceae)—a monograph. *Symbolae Botanicae Upsalienses* 31(2): 1–184.

Manktelow, M., and McDade, L. A. 2001. The enigmatic tribe Whitfieldieae (Acanthaceae): Delimitation and phylogenetic relationships based on molecular and morphological data. *Systematic Botany* 26(1): 104–111.

Manns, U. and Bremer, B. 2010. Towards a better understanding of intertribal relationships and stable tribal delimitations within Cinchonoideae *s.s.* (Rubioideae). *Molecular Phylogenetics and Evolution* 56: 21–39.

Manns, U., Wikström, N., Taylor, C. M., and Bremer, B. 2012. Historical biogeography of the predominately Neotropical subfamily Cinchonoideae (Rubiaceae): Into or out of Africa? *International Journal of Plant Sciences* 173: 261–286.

Maphosa, Y., and Jideani, V. A. 2016. *The Role of Legumes in Human Nutrition*. IntechOpen. https://doi.org/10.5772/intechopen.69127.

Margaillan, M. L. 1929. Nouvelles recherches sur quelques graines oléagineuses des pays chauds. *Annales du Musée Colonial de Marseille*, série 4, 7(3): 5–32.

Marie, C. N., Sibelet, N., Dulcire, M., Rafalimaro, M., Danthu, P., and Carrière, S. M. 2009. Taking into account local practices and indigenous knowledge in an emergency conservation context in Madagascar. *Biodiversity and Conservation* 18: 2759–2777.

Markgraf, F. 1976. Apocynacées. *Flore de Madagascar et des Comores* 169: 1–318.

Marline, L. 2018. Diversity and biogeography of Madagascan bryophytes with an analysis of taxic and functional diversity along an elevational gradient in Marojejy National Park. PhD thesis, University of Cape Town.

Marline, L., Andriamiarisoa, R. L., Bardat, J., Chuah-Petiot, M., Reeb, C., Strasberg, D., Wilding, N., and Ah-Peng, C. 2012. Checklist of the bryophytes of Madagascar. *Cryptogamie, Bryologie* 33(3): 199–255.

Maroyi, A. 2016. *Ximenia caffra* Sond. (Ximeniaceae) in sub-Saharan Africa: A synthesis and review of its medicinal potential. *Journal of Ethnopharmacology* 184: 81–100.

Martelli, U., and Pichi-Sermolli, R. 1951. Les Pandanacées récoltées par H. Perrier de la Bâthie à Madagascar. *Mémoires de l'Institut Scientifique de Madagascar*, série B, *Biologie Végétale*, 3: 1–174.

Martín-Bravo, S., Jiménez-Mejías, P., Villaverde, T., Escudero, M., Hahn, M., et al. 2019. A tale of worldwide success: Behind the scenes of *Carex* (Cyperaceae) biogeography and diversification. *Journal of Systematics and Evolution* 57: 695–718.

Martín-Cabrejas, Á. M., ed. 2019. *Legumes: Nutritional Quality, Processing and Potential Health Benefits*. London: Royal Society of Chemistry.

Mas, C., Lowry II, P. P., and Schatz, G. E. In press. Révision taxonomique des *Diospyros* L. (Ebenaceae) de la région Malgache. VI. Le groupe Gracilipes. *Boissiera*.

Mason, J., Parker, M., Vary, L., Lowry II, P. P., Hassold, S., and Ruta, G. 2016. Malagasy precious hardwoods: Scientific and technical assessment to meet CITES objectives. Report submitted by the World Resources Institute and the World Bank. 54 pp. https://www.scribd.com/document/318123493/WRI-WB-Malagasy-Precious-Woods-Assessment-1-pdf.

Mathey, A. 1971. Contribution à l'étude du genre *Siphula* (lichens) en Afrique. *Nova Hedwigia* 22: 795–878.

Mathieu, G. 2001–2020. Taxonomic Repertory of the genus *Peperomia* (TRGP), https://www.peperomia.net.

———. 2003a. New endemic *Peperomia* species (Piperaceae) from Madagascar. *Systematics and Geography of Plants* 73: 71–81.

———. 2003b. Notes on tropical African plants—*Peperomia nicolliae*, a new endemic species (Piperaceae) from Madagascar. *Systematics and Geography of Plants* 73: 288–290.

———. 2006. More new *Peperomia* species (Piperaceae) from Madagascar. *Systematics and Geography of Plants* 76: 221–228.

———. 2020a. Endemic *Peperomia* (Piperaceae) novelties from eastern Madagascar. *Candollea* 75(1): 75–82.

———. 2020b. *Peperomia leptostachya* Hook. Arn. (Piperaceae) revived. *Candollea* 75(1): 45–49.

Mathieu, G., and Callejas-Posada, R. 2006. New synonymies in the genus *Peperomia* Ruiz and Pav. (Piperaceae)—an annotated checklist. *Candollea* 61: 331–363.

Maul, K., Krug, M., Nickrent, D. L., Müller, K. F., Quandt, D., and Wicke, S. 2019. Morphology, geographic distribution and host preference are poor predictors of phylogenetic relatedness in the mistletoe genus *Viscum* L. *Molecular Phylogenetics and Evolution* 131: 106–115.

Mazine, F. F., Faria, J.E.Q., Giaretta, A., Vasconcelos, T.N.C., Forest, F., and Lucas, E. J. 2018. Phylogeny and biogeography of the hyperdiverse genus *Eugenia* (Myrtaceae: Myrteae), with emphasis on *E.* sect. *Umbellatae*, the most unmanageable clade. *Taxon* 67: 752–769.

McCarthy, P. M. 2003. Catalogue of the lichen family Porinaceae. *Bibliotheca Lichenologica* 87: 1–164.

McDade, L. A., Daniel, T. F., Kiel, C., and Vollesen, K. B. 2005. Phylogenetic relationships among Acantheae (Acanthaceae): Major lineages present contrasting patterns of molecular evolution and morphological differentiation. *Systematic Botany* 30(4): 834–862.

McDade, L. A., Daniel, T. F., and Kiel, C. A. 2008. Toward a comprehensive understanding of phylogenetic relationships among lineages of Acanthaceae *s.l.* (Lamiales). *American Journal of Botany* 95: 1136–1152.

McDade, L. A., Daniel, T. F., Kiel, C. A., and Borg, A. J. 2012. Phylogenetic placement, delimitation, and relationships among genera of the enigmatic Nelsonioideae (Lamiales: Acanthaceae). *Taxon* 61: 637–651.

McDade, L. A., Daniel, T. F., and Kiel, C. A. 2018. The *Tetramerium* Lineage (Acanthaceae, Justicieae) revisited: Phylogenetic relationships reveal polyphyly of many New World genera accompanied by rampant evolution of floral morphology. *Systematic Botany* 43(1): 97–116.

McDade, L. A., Daniel, T. F., Darbyshire, I., and Kiel, C. A. 2021. Justicieae II: Resolved placement of many genera and recognition of a new lineage sister to Isoglossinae. *Aliso* 38(1). doi:10.5642/aliso.20213801.02.

McKey, D. B. 1989. Population biology of figs: Applications for conservation. *Experientia* 45: 661–673.

McPherson, G. 1995. On *Mallotus* and *Deuteromallotus* (Euphorbiaceae) in Madagascar. *Adansonia*, série 4, 17: 169–173.

———. 1996. A new species of *Macaranga* (Euphorbiaceae) from Madagascar. *Adansonia*, série 4, 18: 275–278.

———. 2000. *Drypetes* (Euphorbiaceae) in Madagascar and the Comoro Islands. *Adansonia* 22(2): 205–209.

———. 2012. A new Madagascan species of *Hancea* Seem. (Euphorbiaceae). *Adansonia* 34(1): 71–75.

———. 2014. A new species of *Drypetes* (Putranjivaceae or Euphorbiaceae *s.l.*) from Madagascar. *Novon* 23(1): 62–64.

———. 2017. Six new species of *Argomuellera* (Euphorbiaceae) from Madagascar. *Novon* 25(3): 286–297.

Meenks, J., and Pócs, T. 1985. East African bryophytes IX. Aneuraceae. *Abstracta Botanica* 9: 79–98.

Meléndez González, M. 2019. Taxonomic treatment and molecular analyses of the small-leaved species of *Croton* (Euphorbiaceae) from Toliara, Madagascar. MS thesis, University of Puerto Rico-Mayagüez. https://scholar.uprm.edu/handle/20.500.11801/2538.

Merckx, V.[S.F.T.], Huysmans, S., and Smets, E. F. 2010. Cretaceous origins of myco-heterotrophic lineages in Dioscoreales. In *Diversity, Phylogeny, and Evolution in the Monocotyledons*, eds. O. Seberg, G. Petersen, A. S. Barfod, and J. I. Davis, pp. 39–53. Aarhus: Aarhus University Press.

Merckx, V.S.F.T., Bidartondo, M. I., and Rudall, P. J. 2013. *Mycoheterotrophy: The Biology of Plants Living on Fungi*. New York: Springer.

Merxmuller, H. 1960. Wellstediaceae. *Mitteilungen der Botanischen Staatssammlung München* 3: 619–622.

Meve, U. 1995. A review of phytophagous insects on stapeliads (Asclepiadaceae). *Cimbebasia* 14: 103–106.

———. 2010. Apocynaceae (Asclepiadoideae-Ceropegieae). In IAPT/IOPB chromosome data 10, ed. K. Marhold. *Taxon* 59: 1934–1935, E4-E5.

Meve, U., and Liede, S. 1994. Floral biology and pollination in stapeliads—new results and a literature review. *Plant Systematics and Evolution* 192: 99–116.

———. 2002a. Floristic exchange between mainland Africa and Madagascar: A case study of Apocynaceae-Asclepiadoideae. *Journal of Biogeography* 29: 865–873.

———. 2002b. A molecular phylogeny and generic rearrangement of the stapelioid Ceropegieae (Apocynaceae-Asclepiadoideae). *Plant Systematics and Evolution* 234: 171–209.

Meve, U., and Liede-Schumann, S. 2007. *Ceropegia* (Apocynaceae, Ceropegieae, Stapeliinae): Paraphyletic, but still taxonomically sound. *Annals of the Missouri Botanical Garden* 94: 392–406.

Meve, U., Newton, L. E., and Liede-Schumann, S. 2016. Diversity in the *Cynanchum gerrardii* complex (Apocynaceae-Asclepiadoideae). *Symbolae Botanicae Upsalienses* 38: 13–18.

Michelangeli, F. A., Nicolas, A., Morales-Puentes, M. E., and David, H. 2011. Phylogenetic relationships of *Allomaieta*, *Alloneuron*, *Cyphostyla*, and *Wurdastom* (Melastomataceae) and the resurrection of the tribe Cyphostyleae. *International Journal of Plant Sciences* 172: 1165–1178.

Michelangeli, F. A., Guimarães, P.J.F., Penneys, D. S., Almeda, F., and Kriebel, R. 2013. Phylogenetic relationships and distribution of New World Melastomeae (Melastomataceae). *Botanical Journal of the Linnean Society* 171: 38–60.

Michelangeli, F.[A.], Almeda, F., Goldenberg, R., and Penneys, D. 2020. A guide to curating New World Melastomataceae collections with a linear generic sequence to world-wide Melastomataceae. *Preprints* 2020: 2020100203. https://doi.org/10.20944/preprints202010.0203.v1.

Micheneau, C., Carlsward, B. S., Fay, M. F., Bytebier, B., Pailler, T., and Chase, M. 2008. Phylogenetics and biogeography of Mascarene angraecoid orchids (Vandeae, Orchidaceae). *Molecular Phylogenetics and Evolution* 46: 908–922.

Miller, A. J., Young, D. A., and Wen, J. 2001. Phylogeny and biogeography of *Rhus* (Anacardiaceae) based on ITS sequence data. *International Journal of Plant Sciences* 162: 1401–1407.

Miller, J. S. 2000. New taxa and nomenclatural notes on the flora of the Marojejy Massif, Madagascar. IV. Myrtaceae: New species of *Eugenia* L. *Adansonia*, série 3, 22: 111–116.

———. 2001a. Two new species of *Cordia* L. (Boraginaceae) from Madagascar. *Adansonia*, série 3, 23: 289–295.

———. 2001b. *Tournefortia kirkii* (I. M. Johnston) J.S. Mill. (Boraginaceae): A new combination for a species from Madagascar. *Adansonia*, série 3, 23: 297–301.

———. 2002. A revision of *Ehretia* (Boraginaceae) for Madagascar and the Comoro Islands. *Adansonia*, série 3, 24: 137–157.

———. 2003a. A new species of *Heliotropium* L. (Boraginaceae) from Madagascar. *Adansonia*, série 3, 25: 115–118.

———. 2003b. Classification of Boraginaceae subfam. Ehretioideae: Resurrection of the genus *Hilsenbergia* Tausch ex Meisen. *Adansonia*, série 3, 25: 151–189.

———. 2005a. A synopsis of the genus *Cynoglossum* L. (Boraginaceae) in Madagascar and the Comoro Islands. *Adansonia*, série 3, 27: 113–127.

———. 2005b. Validation of *Hilsenbergia teitensis* (Gurke) J. S. Mill. (Boraginaceae). *Adansonia*, série 3, 27: 129.

Miller, J. S., and Gottschling, M. 2017. Generic transfers in Malagasy Boraginales. *Candollea* 72: 329–332.

Miller, J. S., and Porter-Morgan, H. 2011. Assessing the effectiveness of Madagascar's changing protected areas system: A case study of threatened Boraginales. *Oryx* 45: 201–209.

Miller, J. S., Rogers, Z. S., Malécot, V., Sales, F., and Hedge, I. C. 2021. Boraginales, Olacaceae and allies, Apiaceae. *Flore de Madagascar et des Comores* 50: 1–448.

Miller, J. T., and Seigler, D. S. 2012. Evolutionary and taxonomic relationships of *Acacia s. l.* (Leguminosae: Mimosoideae). *Australian Systematic Botany* 25: 217–224.

Minaya, M., Hackel, J., Namaganda, M., Brochmann, C., Vorontsova, M. S., Besnard, G., and Catalán, P. 2017. Contrasting dispersal histories of broad- and fine-leaved temperate Loliinae grasses: Range expansion, founder events, and the roles of distance and barriers. *Journal of Biogeography* 44: 1980–1993.

Ministère du Commerce. 2012. *Secteur du poivre: une quantité minimale à l'exportation*. Antananarivo: République Démocratique de Madagascar.

Miquel, F.A.W. 1843. *Systema Piperacearum*. Rotterdam: H. A. Kramers.

Mitchell, J. D. 1990. The poisonous Anacardiaceae genera of the world. *Advances in Economic Botany* 8: 103–129.

Mitchell, J. D., and Daly, D. C. 1991. *Cyrtocarpa* (Anacardiaceae) in South America. *Annals of the Missouri Botanical Garden* 78(1): 184–189.

———. 1993. A revision of *Thyrsodium* (Anacardiaceae). *Brittonia* 45(2): 115–129.

Mitchell, J. D., Daly, D. C., Pell, S. K., and Randrianasolo, A. 2006. *Poupartiopsis* gen. nov. and its context in Anacardiaceae classification. *Systematic Botany* 31(2): 337–348.

Mitchell, J. D., Daly, D. C., and Randrianasolo, A. 2012. The first report of *Spondias* native to Madagascar: *Spondias tefyi* sp. nov. (Anacardiaceae). *Brittonia* 64(3): 263–267.

Mizutani, M. 1975. Epiphyllous species of Lejeuneaceae from the Philippines. *Journal of the Hattori Botanical Laboratory* 45: 375–387.

Mndela, M., Madakadze, C. I., Nherera-Chokuda, F., and Dube, S. 2020. Is the soil seed bank a reliable source for passive restoration of bush-cleared semi-arid rangelands of South Africa? *Ecological Processes* 9(1): 1–16.

MNHN. 2021. Plantes vasculaire: Base de données de la collection. https://science.mnhn.fr/institution/mnhn/collection/p/item/search/form.

Moat, J., and Smith, P. 2007. *Atlas of the Vegetation of Madagascar*. Kew: Royal Botanic Gardens.

Moffett, R. O. 2007. Name changes in Old World *Rhus* and recognition of *Searsia* (Anacardiaceae). *Bothalia* 37(2): 165–175.

Mohamed, M.A.H. 1979. A taxonomic study of *Bryum billardieri* Schwägr. and related species. *Journal of Bryology* 10: 401–465.

Moore, S. 1920. Alabastua Diversa, Part XXXIII. *Journal of Botany* 58: 188.

Morales, M. and Fortunato, R. H. 2016. A new xerophytic species of *Mimosa* (Mimosoideae, Leguminosae) from Madagascar. *Phytotaxa* 270(4): 277–285.

Morat, P. 1973. Les savanes du sud-ouest de Madagascar. *Mémoires ORSTOM* 68: 1–235.

Morat, P., and Lowry II, P. P. 1997. Floristic richness in the Africa-Madagascar region: A brief history and prospective. *Adansonia*, série 3, 19: 101–115.

Morelli, T. N., Smith, A. B. Mancini, A. N., Balko, E. A., Borgerson, C. et al. 2020. The fate of Madagascar's rainforest habitat. *Nature Climate Change* 10: 89–96.

Morley, R. J., and Dick, C. W. 2003. Missing fossils, molecular clocks and the origin of the Melastomataceae. *American Journal of Botany* 90: 1638–1645.

Morokawa, R. 2014. Biogeography of ViWiTa clade and phylogeny of Willughbeieae (Apocynaceae, Rauvolfioideae). PhD thesis, Universidade Estadual de Campinas, Instituto de Biologia, Brazil.

Morris, J. L., Puttick, M. N., Clark, J. W., Edwards, D., Kenrick, P., Pressel, S., Wellman, C. H., Yang, Z., Schneider, H., and Donoghue, P.C.J. 2018. The timescale of early land plant evolution. *Proceedings of the National Academy of Sciences of the USA* 115: e2274-e2283.

Morton, C. M. 2017. Phylogenetic relationships of *Vepris* (Rutaceae) inferred from chloroplast, nuclear, and morphological data. *PLoS One* 12(3): e0172708. https://doi.org/10.1371/journal.pone.0172708.

Morton, C. M., and Telmer, C. 2014. New subfamily classification for the Rutaceae. *Annals of the Missouri Botanical Garden* 99(4): 620–641. https://doi.org/10.3417/2010034.

Morton, J. 2019. Does climate influence genome size diversity? A study of genome size–environment associations across the Madagascar grass flora. MSc thesis, Queen Mary's University of London/Royal Botanic Gardens, Kew.

Moses, K. L., and Semple, S. 2011. Primary seed dispersal by the black-and-white ruffed lemur (*Varecia variegata*) in the Manombo forest, south-east Madagascar. *Journal of Tropical Ecology* 27: 529–538.

Motyka, J. 1936. *Lichenum generis Usnea studium monographicum. Pars systematica*, vol.1. Leopoli: Nakladem Universytetu Marie Curie-Sklodowskiej.

———. 1954. O kilku nowych i mniej znanych gatunkach rodzaju *Usnea* (L.). Species nonnullae novae vel minus cognitae generis *Usnea* L. *Fragmenta Floristica and Geobotanica* (Krakow) 1(2): 25–37.

Mouly, A., Razafimandimbison, S. G., Florence, J., Jérémie, J., and Bremer, B. 2009a. Paraphyly of *Ixora* and new tribal delimitation of Ixoreae (Rubiaceae): Inference from combined chloroplast (*rps16*, *rbcL*, and *trn*T-F) sequence data. *Annals of the Missouri Botanical Garden* 96:146–160.

Mouly, A., Razafimandimbison, S. G., Khodabandeh, A., and Bremer, B. 2009b. Phylogeny and classification of the species-rich Pantropical showy genus *Ixora* (Rubiaceae-Ixoeae) with indications of geographical monophyletic units and hybrids. *American Journal of Botany* 96: 686–706.

Mouly, A., Kainulainen, K., Persson, C., Davis, A. P., Wong, K. M., Razafimandimbison, S. G., and Bremer, B. 2014. Phylogenetic structure and clade circumscriptions in the Gardenieae complex (Rubiaceae). *Taxon* 63: 801–818.

Muasya, A. M., Larridon, I., Reynders, M., Huygh, W., Goetghebeur, P., Cable, S., Simpson, D. A., and Gehrke, B. 2011. The Cyperaceae in Madagascar show high diversification in high altitude forest and wetland habitats. *Plant Ecology and Evolution* 144: 357–362.

Muchura, H. M., Chua-Petiot, M. S., Mworia, J. K., and Gichuki, N. N. 2014. Role of bryophytes and tree canopy in mist trapping in Mt. Marsabit forest. *Journal of Environment and Earth Science* 4: 128–138.

Müller, C. 1897. Synopsis generis Harrisonia. *Oesterreichische Botanische Zeitschrift* 47: 417–420.

Müller, J. 1891. Lichenologische Beiträge 35. *Flora* 74: 371–382.

Muñoz, I. M., Cardiel, J. M., and Levin, G. A. 2018a. Nomenclatural review of *Acalypha* (Euphorbiaceae) of the Western Indian Ocean Region (Madagascar, the Comoros Archipelago, the Mascarene Islands and the Seychelles Archipelago). *PhytoKeys* 108: 85–116.
———. 2018b. A new species of *Acalypha* subgenus *Linostachys* (Euphorbiaceae, Acalyphoideae) from Madagascar. *South African Journal of Botany* 119: 420–423.
———. 2020. Discovery of three new species of *Acalypha* L. (Euphorbiaceae, Acalyphoideae) from Madagascar and their conservation status. *Systematic Botany* 45(1): 122–130.
Muñoz, J. 1998. Material towards a revision of *Grimmia* (Musci, Grimmiaceae): Nomenclature and taxonomy of *Grimmia longirostris*. *Annals of the Missouri Botanical Garden* 85: 352–363.
Munzinger, J., Morat, P., Jaffré, T., Gâteblé, G., Pillon, Y., Rouhan, G., Bruy, D., Veillon, J.-M., and Chalopin, M. 2020 onwards. FLORICAL: Checklist of the Vascular Indigenous Flora of New Caledonia. http://publish.plantnet-project.org/project/florical.
Myers, N., Mittermeier, R. A., Mittermeier, C. G., da Fonseca, G.A.B., and Kent, J. 2000. Biodiversity hotspots for conservation priorities. *Nature* 403: 853–858.
Mziray, W. 1992. Taxonomic studies in Toddalieae Hook. f. (Rutaceae) in Africa. *Acta Universitatis Upsaliensis, Symbolae Botanicae Upsaliensis* 30(1): 1–95.
Naciri, Y., and Linder, P. 2015. Species delimitation and relationships: The dance of the seven veils. *Taxon* 64(1): 3–16.
Naczi, R.F.C., and Ford, B. A. 2008. *Sedges: Uses, Diversity, and Systematics of Cyperaceae*. St. Louis: Missouri Botanical Garden Press.
Nanjarisoa, O. P., Besnard, G., Ralimanana, H., Jeannoda, V., and Vorontsova, M. S. 2017. Grass survey of the Itremo Massif records endemic central highland grasses. *Madagascar Conservation and Development* 12: 1–7.
Navaneetham, N. 1981. Chromosome number reports LXXII. *Taxon* 30: 696.
Nazaire, M., and Hufford, L. 2012. A broad phylogenetic analysis of Boraginaceae: Implications for the relationships of *Mertensia*. *Systematic Botany* 37: 758–783.
NCBI. 2021. GenBank Database. Accessed 18 Dec. 2019. https://www.ncbi.nlm.nih.gov/genbank.
Neuwinger, H. D. 1994. *Afrikanische Arzneipflanzen und Jagdgifte*. Stuttgart: Wissenschaftliche Verlagsgesellschaft.
Ngumbau, V. M., Nyange, M., Wei, N., van Ee, B. W., Berry, P. E., Malombe, I., Hu, G.-W., and Wang, Q.-F. 2020. A new species of *Croton* (Euphorbiaceae) from a Madagascan lineage discovered in coastal Kenya. *Systematic Botany* 45: 242–248.
Nickrent, D. L. 1997 onwards. The Parasitic Plant Connection. http://www.parasiticplants.siu.edu.
———. 2020. Parasitic angiosperms: How often and how many? *Taxon* 69: 5–27. https://doi.org/10.1002/tax.12195.
Nickrent, D. L., and García, M. 2015. *Lacomucinaea*, a new monotypic genus in Thesiaceae (Santalales). *Phytotaxa* 224: 173–184.
Nickrent, D. L., and Musselman, L. J. 2016. Introduction to parasitic flowering plants. *Plant Health Instructor*. American Phytopathological Society APSnet Education Center, Plant Health Instructor web publication. https://www.apsnet.org/edcenter/disandpath/parasiticplants/intro/Pages/ParasiticPlants.aspx.
Nickrent, D. L., Malécot, V., Vidal-Russell, R., and Der, J. P. 2010. A revised classification of Santalales. *Taxon* 59: 538–558.
Nickrent, D. L., Anderson, F., and Kuijt, J. 2019. Inflorescence evolution in Santalales: Integrating morphological characters and molecular phylogenetics. *American Journal of Botany* 106: 402–414.
Nic Lughadha, E. M., and Proença, C.E.B. 1995. A survey of the reproductive ecology of the Myrtoideae (Myrtaceae). *Annals of the Missouri Botanical Garden* 83: 480–503.
Nicolas, A. N., and Plunkett, G. M. 2009. The demise of subfamily Hydrocotyloideae (Apiaceae) and the re-alignment of its genera across the entire order Apiales. *Molecular Phylogenetics and Evolution* 53: 134–151.
Nie, Z.-L., Deng, T., Meng, Y., Sun, H., and Wen, J. 2013. Post-boreotropical dispersals explain the pantropical disjunction in *Paederia* (Rubiaceae). *Annals of Botany* 111: 873–886.
Nilsson, L. A., Rabakonandrianina, E., Pettersson, B., and Ranaivo, J. 1990. "Ixoroid" secondary pollen presentation and pollination by small moths in the Malagasy treelet *Ixora platythyrsa* (*Rubiaceae*). *Plant Systematics and Evolution* 170: 161–175.
Nilsson, L. A., Rabakonandrianina, E., Pettersson, B., and Grünmeier, R. 1993. Lemur pollination in the Malagasy rainforest liana *Strongylodon craveniae* (Leguminosae). *Evolutionary Trends in Plants* 7: 49–56.
Nilsson, S., Endress, M. E., and Grafström, E. 1993. On the relationship of the Apocynaceae and Periplocaceae. *Grana* 21(supplement 2): 3–20.
Norhazrina, N., Wang, J., Hagborg, A., Geffert, J. L., Mutke, J., Gradstein, S. R., Baselga, A., Vanderpoorten, A., and Patiño, J. 2017. Tropical bryophyte floras: A homogeneous assemblage of highly mobile species? Insights from their spatial patterns of beta diversity. *Botanical Journal of the Linnean Society* 183: 16–24.
Norscia, I., Ramanamanjato, J.-B., and Ganzhorn, J. U. 2012. Feeding patterns and dietary profile of nocturnal southern woolly lemurs (*Avahi meridionalis*) in southeast Madagascar. *International Journal of Primatology* 33: 150–167.
Novy, J. W. 1997. Medicinal plants of the eastern region of Madagascar. *Journal of Ethnopharmacology* 55(2): 119–126.
Nowicke, J. W. 1975. Pollen morphology in the order Centrospermae. *Grana* 15: 51–77.
Nowicke, J. W., and Miller, J. S. 1991. Boraginaceae. *Flora of Ceylon* 7: 3–33.
Ntore, S. 2008. Révision du genre afrotropical *Pauridiantha* (Rubiaceae). *Opera Botanica Belgica* 15: 1–227.
Nusbaumer, L., and Labat, J.-N. 2008. *Cadia multifoliolata* Nusb. and Labat (Fabaceae, Papilionoideae), a new species from Madagascar. *Candollea* 63(2): 189–195.
Nwinyi, O. C., Chinedu, N. S., Ajani, O. O., Ikpo Chinwe, O., and Ogunniran, K. O. 2009. Antibacterial effects of extracts of *Ocimum gratissimum* and *Piper guineense* on *Escherichia coli* and *Staphylococcus aureus*. *African Journal of Food Science* 3(3): 77–81.
Nyffeler, R., and Eggli, U. 2010. Disintegrating Portulacaceae: A new familial classification of the suborder Portulacineae (Caryophyllales) based on molecular and morphological data. *Taxon* 59: 227–240.
Ochi, H. 1972. A revision of the African *Bryoideae*, Musci (pt. 1). *Journal of the Faculty of Education, Tottori University* 23: 1–126.
———. 1973. A revision of the African *Bryoideae*, Musci, pt. 2. *Journal of the Faculty of Education, Tottori University* 24: 23–50.
———. 2005. Tribe Desmodieae. In *Legumes of the World*, eds. G. Lewis, B. Schrire, B. Mackinder, and M. Lock, pp. 432–445. Kew: Royal Botanic Gardens.
O'Dowd, D. J., and Willson, M. F. 1989. Leaf domatia and mites on Australasian plants: Ecological and evolutionary implications. *Biological Journal of the Linnaean Society* 37: 191–236.
Ohashi, H. 2005. Tribe Desmodieae. In *Legumes of the World*, eds. G. Lewis, B. Schrire, B. Mackinder, and M. Lock, pp. 432–445. Kew: Royal Botanic Gardens.
Ohashi, H., and Mill, R. R. 2000. *Hylodesmum*, a new name for *Podocarpium* (Leguminosae). *Edinburgh Journal of Botany* 57(2): 171–188.
Ohashi, H., and Ohashi, K. 2012. A new combination in *Monarthrocarpus* (Leguminosae: tribe Desmodieae). *Journal of Japanese Botany* 87: 392–394.
———. 2018. *Grona*, a genus separated from *Desmodium* (Leguminosae tribe Desmodieae). *Journal of Japanese Botany* 93: 104–120.
Ohashi, K., Ohashi, H., Nemoto, T., Ikeda, T., Izumi, H., Kobayashia, H., Muragakia, H., Nata, K., Satoa, N., and Suzukia, M. 2018. Phylogenetic analyses for a new classification of the *Desmodium* group of Leguminosae tribe Desmodieae. *Journal of Japanese Botany* 93: 165–189.
Oleksy, R., Giuggioli, L., McKetterick, T. J., Racey, P. A., and Jones, G. 2017. Flying foxes create extensive seed shadows and enhance germination success of pioneer plant species in deforested Madagascan landscapes. *PLoS One* 12(9): e0184023.
Oliveira, F. dos Santos. 2016. Ecologia da polinização e análise da composição química do óleo floral de duas espécies de *Mouriri* (Melastomataceae) e sua importância na atração dos visitantes. PhD thesis, Universidade Federal do Maranhão, São Luís, Brazil.
Ollerton, J. 2019. Tantalising evidence for a new type of pollination system in Madagascan Apocynaceae. https://jeffollerton.wordpress.com/2019/01/25/tantalising-evidence-for-a-new-type-of-pollination-system-in-madagascan-apocynaceae.
Ollerton, J., Masinde, S., Meve, U., Picker, M., and Whittington, A. E. 2009. Fly pollination in *Ceropegia* (Apocynaceae: Asclepiadoideae): Biogeographic and phylogenetic perspectives. *Annals of Botany* 103: 1501–1514.
Ollerton, J., Dötterl, S., Ghorpadé, K., Heiduk, A., Liede-Schumann, S., Masinde, S., Meve, U., Peter, C. I., Prieto-Benítez, S., and Punekar, S. A. 2017. Diversity of Diptera families that pollinate *Ceropegia* (Apocynaceae) trap flowers: An update in light of new data and phylogenetic analyses. *Flora* 234: 233–244.
Ollerton, J., Liede-Schumann, S., Endress, M. E., Meve, U., Rech, A. R., et al. 2019. The diversity and evolution of pollination systems in large plant clades: Apocynaceae as a case study. *Annals of Botany* 123: 311–325.
Olmstead, R. G., Zjhra, M. L., Lohmann, L. G., Grose, S. O., and Eckert, A. J. 2009. A molecular phylogeny and classification of Bignoniaceae. *American Journal of Botany* 96(9): 1731–1743.

Olofsson, J. K., Cantera, I., Van de Paer, C., Hong-Wa, C., Zedane, L., Dunning, L. T., Alberti, A., Christin, P.-A., and Besnard, G. 2019. Phylogenomics using low-depth whole genome sequencing: A case study with the olive tribe. *Molecular Ecology Resources* 19: 877–892.

Onjalalaina, G. E., and Darbyshire, I. 2016. An endangered new species of *Podorungia* (Acanthaceae), with notes on the tribe Barlerieae in Madagascar. *Kew Bulletin* 71(44): 1–2.

Orbán, S. 1978. Studies on African *Calymperaceae* II. *Acta Botanica Academicae Scientiarum Hungaricae* 24: 113–120.

———. 1981. Studies in African *Calymperaceae* III. Conspectus of the African species of *Syrrhopodon* Schwägr. *Acta Botanica Academicae Scientarum Hungaricae* 27: 169–177.

———. 1995. East African Bryophytes, XV. *Calymperaceae* species collected in Seychelles Island in 1993. *Fragmenta Floristica et Geobotanica* 40: 279–287.

———. 2000. *Calymperes venezualanum*, a newly discovered American-African disjunct element in the flora of Madagascar. *The Bryologist* 103(1): 145–146.

O'Shea, B. J. 1997. The mosses of sub-Saharan Africa 2. Endemism and biodiversity. *Tropical Bryology* 13: 75–85.

———. 1999. British Bryological Society Expedition to Mulanje Mountain, Malawi. 11. Pterigynandraceae M. Fleisch. and Rigodiaceae H.A. Crum (Bryopsida) in Africa. *Journal of Bryology* 21: 323–327.

———. 2003. A revision of *Schoenobryum* (Cryphaeaceae, Bryopsida) in Africa. British Bryological Society Expedition to Mulanje Mountain, Malawi, 16. *Tropical Bryology* 24: 147–159.

———. 2006. Checklist of the mosses of sub-Saharan Africa (version 5, 12/06). *Tropical Bryology Research Reports* 6: 1–252.

———. 2008. Name change for 13 African mosses with invalid names. *Tropical Bryology* 29: 4–5.

O'Shea, B. J., and Buck, W. R. 2001. Bryophytes of Uganda. 5. *Bryocrumia* L. E. Anderson (Hypnaceae), a monotypic moss genus new to Africa. *Tropical Bryology* 20: 103–107.

O'Shea, B. J., Eggers, J., Pursell, R. A., Sollman, P., and Stevenson, C. R. 1997. New bryophyte taxon records for tropical countries. 1. *Tropical Bryology* 13: 175–183.

Palchetti, E., Biricolti, S., Gori, M., Rota Nodari, G., Gandolfi, N., and Papini. 2018. Two new species of genus *Piper* L. (Piperaceae), *Piper malgassicum* and *Piper tsarasaotrae*, and their phylogenetic position. *Turkish Journal of Botany* 42: 1–13.

Pandanaceae Project. 2020. Conservatoire et Jardin Botaniques de la Ville de Genève and Missouri Botanical Garden (coordination). https://www.tropicos.org/Project/Pandanaceae.

Pardow, A., Gehrig-Downie, C., Gradstein, R., Lakatos, M., Pardow, A., Lakatos, A. M., and Gradstein, R. 2012. Functional diversity of epiphytes in two tropical lowland rainforests, French Guiana: Using bryophyte life-forms to detect areas of high biodiversity. *Biodiversity and Conservation* 21: 3637–3655.

Parker, M. A., Wurtz, A. K., and Paynter, Q. 2007. Nodule symbiosis of invasive *Mimosa pigra* in Australia and in ancestral habitats: A comparative analysis. *Biological Invasions* 9: 127–138.

Pate, J. S., Davidson, N. J., Kuo, J., and Milburn, J. A. 1990. Water relations of the root hemiparasite *Olax phyllanthi* (Labill) R. Br. (Olacaceae) and its multiple hosts. *Oecologia* 84: 186–193.

Patrut, A., Karl, F., Danthu, P., Léong Pock-Tsy, J.-M., Patrut, R. T., and Lowy, D. A. 2015a. Searching for the oldest baobab of Madagascar: Radiocarbon investigation of large *Adansonia rubrostipa* trees. *PLoS One* 10: 3.

Patrut, A., von Reden, K. F., Danthu, P., Léong Pock-Tsy, J.-M., Rakosy, L., Patrut, R. T., Lowy, D. A, and Margineanu, D. 2015b. AMS radiocarbon dating of very large Grandidier's baobabs (*Adansonia grandidieri*). *Nuclear Instruments and Methods in Physics Research* 361: 591–598.

Pauw, A. 1998. Pollen transfer on birds' tongues. *Nature* 394(6695): 731–732.

Peirson, J. A., Bruyns, P. V, Riina, R., Morawetz, J. J., and Berry, P. E. 2013. A molecular phylogeny and classification of the largely succulent and mainly African *Euphorbia* subg. *Athymalus* (Euphorbiaceae). *Taxon* 62: 1178–1199.

Pell, S. K., Mitchell, J. D., Lowry II, P. P., Randrianasolo, A., and Urbasch, L. E. 2008. Phylogenetic split of Malagasy and African taxa of *Protorhus* and *Rhus* (Anacardiaceae) based on CpDNA *trn*L-*trn*F and nrDNA ETS and ITS data. *Systematic Botany* 33: 375–383.

Pell, S. K., Mitchell, J. D., Miller, A. J., and Lobova, T. A. 2011. Anacardiaceae. In *The Families and Genera of Vascular plants*, vol. 10, ed. K. Kubitzki, pp. 7–50. Berlin: Springer.

Pemberton, R. W., and Turner, C. E. 1989. Occurrence of predatory and fungivorous mites in leaf domatia. *American Journal of Botany* 76: 105–112.

Penneys, D. S., Michelangeli, F. A., Judd, W. S., and Almeda, F. 2010. Henrietteeae (Melastomataceae): A new Neotropical berry-fruited tribe. *Systematic Botany* 35: 783–800.

Pennington, T. D. 1991. *The Genera of Sapotaceae*. Kew: Royal Botanic Gardens.

———. 2004. Sapotaceae. In *The Families and Genera of Vascular Plants*, vol. 6, ed. K. Kubitzki, pp. 390–421. Berlin: Springer.

Pereira-Silva, R. A., Athiê-Souza, S. M., Fabriani, F., Laurênio de Melo, A., Ferreira de Sales, M., and Armbruster, W. S. 2020. Taxonomic revision of *Dalechampia* (Euphorbiaceae) in Madagascar. *Systematic Botany* 45(2): 254–267.

Perold, S. M. 1995. A survey of the Ricciaceae of tropical Africa. *Fragmenta Floristica et Geobotanica* 40: 53–91.

Perrier de la Bâthie, H. 1921. La végétation malgache. *Annales du Musée Colonial de Marseille*, série 3, 9: 1–268.

———. 1928. Les *Ficus* de Madagascar. *Archives de Botaniques*, II, *Bulletin Mensuel* 8–9: 137–180.

———. 1932. Les Mélastomacées de Madagascar. *Mémoires de l'Académie Malgache* 12: 1–292.

———. 1933. Les plantes introduites à Madagascar: listes des plantes cultivées rudérales, messicoles ou naturalisées croissant dans l'Ile; suivie d'un aperçu sur les plantes autochtones devenues anthropophiles. Extracts from *Revue International de Botanique Appliquée et d'Agriculture Tropicale* 11–12.

———. 1936a. *Biogéographie des plantes de Madagascar*. Paris: Société d'Editions Géographiques, Maritimes et Coloniales.

———. 1936b. Les Bois et les Fruits des Bignoniacées de Madagascar. *Revue de Botanique Appliquée et d'Agriculture Coloniale* 183: 907–910.

———. 1938a. Les Bignoniacées de la région malgache (Madagascar, Mascareignes, Seychelles et Comores). *Annales du Musée Colonial de Marseille* série 5, 6: 1–101.

———. 1938b. Bignoniacées. *Flore de Madagascar et des Comores* 178: 1–91.

———. 1939a. *Famille–Orchidées*. Tome I. *Flore de Madagascar* 49e: 1–477.

———. 1939b. Un nouveau genre malgache de Caesalpiniacées. *Bulletin de la Société Botanique de France* 85: 494.

———. 1941. *Famille–Orchidées*. Tome II. *Flore de Madagascar* 49e: 1–387.

———. 1944. Anacardiacées de Madagascar et des Comores. *Mémoire du Muséum Histoire naturelle Paris* 18: 252–269.

———. 1946a. Flacourtiacées. *Flore de Madagascar et des Comores* 140: 1–131.

———. 1946b. Burséracées. *Flore de Madagascar et des Comores* 106: 1–50.

———. 1946c. Anacardiacées. *Flore de Madagascar et des Comores* 114: 1–85.

———. 1948 [publ. 1949]. Révision des Rutacées de Madagascar et des Comores. *Mémoires de l'Académie des sciences de l'Institut de France* 67: 1–39.

———. 1949a. Révision des Violacées de Madagascar et des Comores. *Mémoires de l'Institut Scientifique de Madagascar*, série B, *Biologie Végétale*, 2: 311–331.

———. 1949b. Oléacées utiles ou utilisables de la région malgache. *Revue Internationale de Botanique Appliquée et d'Agriculture Tropicale* 321–322: 412–413.

———. 1949c. Révision des Oléacées de Madagascar et des Comores. *Mémoire de l'Institut Scientifique de Madagascar* 2: 275–310.

———. 1950. Rutacées. *Flore de Madagascar et des Comores* 104: 1–89.

———. 1951. Mélastomatacées. *Flore de Madagascar et des Comores* 153: 1–325.

———. 1952a. *Ficus* Tourn. ex L. *Flore de Madagascar et des Comores* 55: 40–71.

———. 1952b. *Adansonia* de Madagascar. Clef et diagnoses. *Notulae Systematicae* 14: 300–304.

———. 1952c. Ebenacées. *Flore de Madagascar et des Comores* 165: 1–129.

———. 1952d. Oléacées. *Flore de Madagascar et des Comores* 166: 1–89.

———. 1953a. Les Myrtaceés de Madagascar et des Comores, révision, diagnoses et biologie. *Mémoires de l'Institut Scientifique de Madagascar*, série B, 4(2): 161–202.

———. 1953b. Myrtaceae. *Flore de Madagascar et des Comores* 152: 1–80.

Perrier de la Bâthie, H., and Hochreutiner, B.P.G. 1955. Bombacacées. *Flore de Madagascar et des Comores* 130: 1–21.

Petignat, H., Rakotomalaza P. J., and Petignat, S. 1997. Composition botanique et diversité spécifique des forêts de Vohibasia, d'Anjoho et d'Isoky-Vohimena. In Inventaire biologique forêt de Vohibasia et d'Isoky-Vohimena, eds. O. Langrand and S. M Goodman. *Recherches pour le Développement, série Sciences Biologiques*, 12: 53–103.

Pettersson, B. 1991. The genus *Nervilia* (Orchidaceae) in Africa and the Arabian Peninsula. *Orchid Monographs* 5: 1–69.

Pfeil, B. E., Brubaker, C. L., Craven, L. A., and Crisp. M. D. 2002. Phylogeny of *Hibiscus* and the tribe Hibisceae (Malvaceae) using chloroplast DNA sequences of *ndhF* and the *rpl16* intron. *Systematic Botany* 27: 333–350.

Phillipson, P. [B.]. 2017. *Leersia perrieri*. The IUCN Red List of Threatened Species 2017: e.T69727203A69727205.

Phillipson, P. B., and Callmander, M. W. 2015. Notes on the *Rhodocolea racemosa* (Lam.) H. Perrier (Bignoniaceae) species complex. *Candollea* 70: 257–265.

Phillipson, P. B., Schatz, G. E., Lowry II, P. P., and Labat, J.-N. 2006. A catalogue of the vascular plants of Madagascar. In *Taxonomy and Ecology of African Plants, Their Conservation and Sustainable Use–Proceedings of the 17th AETFAT Congress*, Addis Ababa, Ethiopia, 2003, eds. S. A. Ghazanfar and H. J. Beentje, pp. 613–627. Kew: Royal Botanic Gardens.

Phillipson, P. B., Andriambololonera, S., Letsara, R., Maharombaka, C., Ramiandrisoa, B., Manjato, N., and Ranarijaona, H. L. 2018. Status and distribution of Madagascar aquatic plants. In *The Status and Distribution of Freshwater Biodiversity in Madagascar and the Indian Ocean Islands Hotspot*, eds. L. Maiz-Tomé, C. Sayer, and W. Darwall, pp. 59–74. Gland, Switzerland and Cambridge, UK: IUCN.

Pichon, C., Ramanamisata, R., Tarnaud, L., Bayart, F., Hladik, A., Hladik, C. M., and Simmen, B. 2010. Feeding ecology of the crowned sifaka (*Propithecus coronatus*) in a coastal dry forest in northwest Madagascar (SFUM, Antrema). *Lemur News* 15: 42–46.

Picot, M., Jenkins, R.K.B., Ramilijaona, O., Racey, P. A., and Carrière, S. M. 2007. The feeding ecology of *Eidolon dupreanum* (Pteropodidae) in eastern Madagascar. *African Journal of Ecology* 45(4): 645–650. https://doi.org/10.1111/j.1365-2028.2007.00788.x.

Pignal, M., and Phillipson, P. B. 2010. A new species of *Hibiscus* (Malvaceae) from Madagascar. *Phytotaxa* 14(1): 43–48. https://dx.doi.org/10.11646/phytotaxa.14.1.3.

Piippo, S. 1986. A monograph of the genera *Lepidolejeunea* and *Luteolejeuna* (Lejeuneaceae, Hepaticae). *Acta Botanica* 132: 1–69.

Pino-Bodas, R., Ahti, T., and Stenroos, S. 2020. Taxonomic notes on *Pycnothelia* Dufour and *Gymnoderma* Nyl. (Cladoniaceae) in Madagascan Region. *Cryptogamie, Mycologie* 41: 109–118.

Pinto-Carbo, M., Sieber, S., Dessein, S., Wicker, T., Verstraete, B., Gademann, K., Eberl, L., and Carlier, A. 2016. Evidence of horizontal gene transfer between obligate leaf nodule symbiots. *The ISME Journal* 10: 2092–2105.

Plaizier, A. C. 1981. A revision of *Catharanthus roseus* (L.) G. Don (Apocynaceae). *Mededelingen landbouwhogeschool Wageningen, Nederland* 81–9: 1–12.

Plana, V., and Gautier, L. 2008. Taxonomic revision of the genus *Manilkara* (Sapotaceae) in Madagascar. *Edinburgh Journal of Botany* 65: 433–446.

Plunkett, G. M., and Lowry II, P. P. 2001. Relationships among "ancient araliads" and their significance for the systematics of Apiales. *Molecular Phylogenetics and Evolution* 19: 259–276.

———. 2010. Paraphyly and polyphyly in *Polyscias sensu lato*: Molecular evidence and the case for recircumscribing the "pinnate genera" of Araliaceae. *Plant Diversity and Evolution* 128: 23–54.

Plunkett, G. M., Lowry II, P. P., and Burke, M. K. 2001. The phylogenetic status of *Polyscias* (Araliaceae) based on nuclear ITS sequence data. *Annals of the Missouri Botanical Garden* 88: 213–230.

Plunkett, G. M., Chandler, G. T., Lowry II, P. P., Pinney, S. M., and Sprenkle, T. S. 2004a. Recent advances in understanding Apiales and a revised classification. *South African Journal of Botany* 70: 371–381.

Plunkett, G. M., Wen, J., and Lowry II, P. P. 2004b. Infrafamilial relationships in Araliaceae: insights from plastid (*trn*L-*trn*F) and nuclear (ITS) sequence data. *Plant Systematics and Evolution* 245: 1–39.

Plunkett, G. M., Lowry II, P. P., and Vu, N. V. 2004c. Phylogenetic relationships among *Polyscias* (Araliaceae) and close relatives from the western Indian Ocean Basin. *International Journal of Plant Science* 165: 861–873.

Plunkett, G. M., Lowry II, P. P., Frodin, D. G., and Wen, J. 2005. Phylogeny and geography of *Schefflera*: Pervasive polyphyly in the largest genus of Araliaceae. *Annals of the Missouri Botanical Garden* 92: 202–224.

Plunkett, G. M., Wen, J., Lowry II, P. P., Henwood, M. J., Fiaschi, P., and Mitchell, A. D. 2018. Araliaceae. In *The Families and Genera of Vascular Plants*, vol. 15, eds. J. W. Kadereit and V. Bittrich, pp. 413–446. Berlin: Springer.

Plunkett, G. M., Lowry II, P. P., Fiaschi, P., Frodin, D. G., and Nicolas, A. N. 2020. Phylogeny, biogeography, and morphological evolution among and within the Neotropical and Asian clades of *Schefflera* (Araliaceae). *Taxon* 68: 1278–1313.

Pócs, T. 1995. East African Bryophytes, XIV. Hepaticae from the Indian Ocean Islands. *Fragmenta Floristica et Geobotanica* 40(1): 251–277.

———. 1999. *Trachylejeunea grolleana*, a new representative of the Neotropical subgenus *Hygrolejeuneopsis* in Madagascar. *Haussknechtia Beiheft* 9: 283–290.

———. 2001. East African Bryophytes, XVI. New taxa of Lejeuneoideae (Lejeuneaceae) collected in Manongarivo Special Reserve N.W. Madagascar. *Candollea* 56: 69–78.

———. 2004. New or little known epiphyllous liverworts, XI. *Otolejeunea subana* sp. nov. from Madagascar. *Acta Acadaemiae Paedagogicae Agriensis, Sectio Biologiae* 25: 49–57.

———. 2005. East African Bryophytes, XX. Observations on some Calypogeiaceae. *Acta Academiae Paedagogicae Agriensis, Sectio Biologiae* 32: 29–35.

———. 2006. East African Bryophytes, XXI. Two new species of *Telaranea*, sect. *Tenuifoliae* and records on *Amazoopsis* (Lepidoziaceae) from the Indian Ocean Islands. *Acta Botanica Hungarica* 48(1–2): 119–137.

———. 2010a. *B. orbanii* (Lepidoziaceae), a new species from Madagascar. East African Bryophytes, XXVIII. *Acta Biologica Plantarum Agriensis* 1: 15–22.

———. 2010b. On some new or less known *Lejeunea* (Lejeuneaceae, Jungermaniopsida) species in Tropical Africa. East African Bryophytes, XXVII. *Nova Hedwigia, Beiheft* 138: 99–116.

———. 2011a. The Ceratolejeunea (Lejeuneaceae) species of the Indian Ocean islands. East African bryophytes, XXIX. *Polish Botanical Journal* 56(2): 131–153

———. 2011b. Type studies of some African Lejeuneaceae. *Acta Botanica Hungarica* 52(3–4): 195–206.

Pócs, T., and Bernecker, A. 2009. Overview of *Aphanolejeunea* (Jengermaniopsida) after 25 years. *Polish Botanical Journal* 54(1): 1–11.

Pócs, T., and Geissler, P. 2002. The bryophytes collected in the Réserve Spéciale de Manongarivo, Madagascar. In Inventaire floristique et faunistique de la Réserve Spéciale de Manongarivo, (NW Madagascar), eds. L. Gautier and S. M. Goodman. *Boissiera* 59: 41–76.

Pócs, T., and Schaefer-Verwimp, A. 2006. East African Bryophytes, XXIII. Three new species of *Diplasiolejeunea* (Lejeuneaceae, Jungermanniopsida) from Madagascar. *Cryptogamie, Bryologie* 27: 439–452.

Pócs, T., and Váňa, J. 2001. A new species of *Amphicephalozia* (Hepaticae) from Madagascar. *Polish Botanical Journal* 47: 11–20.

———. 2015. East African Bryophytes XXX. *Acta Biologica Plantarum Agriensis* 46: 145–150.

Pócs, T., Zhu, R. L., Söderström, L., Hagborg, A., and Von Konrat, M. J. 2015. Notes on early land plants today. 67. Notes on Lejeuneaceae subtribus Cololejeuneinae. *Phytotaxa* 202: 63–68.

Polhill, R., and Wiens, D. 1998. *Mistletoes of Africa*. Kew: Royal Botanic Gardens.

Poon, W. S., Shaw, P. C., Simmons, M. P., and But, P. P. H. 2007. Congruence of molecular, morphological, and biochemical profiles in Rutaceae: A cladistic analysis of the subfamilies Rutoideae and Toddalioideae. *Systematical Botany* 32: 837–846.

POWO. 2020. Plants of the World Online. Kew Science. Board of Trustees of the Royal Botanic Gardens, Kew. Accessed on 16 Aug. 2020. http://powo.science.kew.org/.

Prenner, G., and Rudall, P. J. 2007. Comparative ontogeny of the cyathium in *Euphorbia* (Euphorbiaceae) and its allies: Exploring the organ–flower–inflorescence boundary. *American Journal of Botany* 94(10): 1612–1629.

Pridgeon, A. M., Cribb, P. J., Chase, M. W., and Rasmussen F. N. (1999–2014). *Genera Orchidacearum.* Oxford: Oxford University Press.

Proffit, M., Schatz, B., Borges, R. M., and Hossaert-McKey, M. 2007. Chemical mediation and niche partitioning in non-pollinating fig-wasp communities. *Journal of Animal Ecology* 76: 296–303.

Proffit, M., Chen, C., Soler, C., Bessière, J.-M., Schatz, B., and Hossaert-McKey, M. 2009. Can chemical signals responsible for mutualistic partner encounter promote the specific exploitation of nursery pollination mutualisms?—The case of figs and fig wasps. *Entomologia Experimentalis et Applicata* 131: 46–57.

Puff, C. 1986. *A Biosystematic Study of the African and Madagascan Rubiaceae-Anthospermeae*. Vienna: Springer.

———. 1988. Observations on *Carphalea* Juss. (Rubiaceae, Hedyotideae), with particular reference to the Madagascan taxa and its taxonomic position. *Bulletin du Jardin Botanique National de Belgique* 58: 271–323.

———. 1991a. Revision of the genus *Paederia* L. (Rubiaceae-Paederieae) in Africa and Madagascar. *Opera Botanica Belgica* 3: 293–322.

———. 1991b. Selected aspects of the reproductive biology of *Paederia* L. (Rubiaceae-Paederieae). *Opera Botanica Belgica* 3: 167–178.

Puff, C., and Buchner, R. 1994. Revision of *Danais* Vent. (Rubiaceae) in Madagascar and the Comores. *Bulletin du Muséum National d'Histoire Naturelle*, section B, *Adansonia*, 16: 11–64.

Puff, C., and Mantell, D. E. 1982. Revision and affinities of *Galium* (Rubiaceae) in Madagascar. *Plant Systematics and Evolution* 140: 57–73.

Puff, C., Robbrecht, E., and Randrianasolo, V. 1984. Observations on the South East African Madagascan genus *Alberta* and its ally *Nematostylis* (Rubiaceae, Alberteae), with a survey of the species and a discussion of the taxonomic position. *Bulletin van de Nationale Plantentuin van Belgiee* 54: 367–391.

Queste, J., Razafimandimby, H., Leong Pock Tsy, J.-M., Ramahavalisoa, F., and Sedera, N. 2018. *Guide de bonnes pratiques pour la culture durable des poivres à queue de l'Océan Indien. Le cas de Tsiperifery*. Saint Pierre, La Réunion: CIRAD.

Rabarimanarivo, M., Rakotonirina, N., Phillipson, P. B., Lowry II, P. P., and Labat, J.-N. 2015. Révision du genre *Ivodea* Capuron (Rutaceae), endémique de Madagascar et de l'archipel des Comores. *Adansonia*, série 3, 37(1): 63–102.

Rabarison, H. 2000. Etude phytoécologique des principaux types de formations végétales dans le Tsingy de Bemaraha (méthodes classiques et analyse multidimensionnelle): Utilisation des ressources forestières. PhD thesis, Université d'Antananarivo.

Rabarison, H., Rakotondrafara, A., Razafimandimbison, S. G., Michel Ratsimbason, M., Rakotonandrasana, S. R., Rajeriarison, C., and Randrianarivelojosia, M. 2013. Evaluation du risque d'extinction des *Cedrelopsis* (Rutaceae) de Madagascar. *Scripta Botanica Belgica* 50: 41–49.

Rabarivola, M. L., Vorontsova, M. S., Razanajatovo, H., Razafiniary, V., and Ralimanana, H. 2019a. All herbarium specimens of grasses from Madagascar and the surrounding islands: Family Poaceae, sector AFM. Version 1.24. Kew Madagascar Conservation Centre, Royal Botanic Gardens Kew. Occurrence data set. https://doi.org/10.15468/51pabx. Accessed via GBIF.org on 11 Feb. 2019.

Rabarivola, M. L., Razafiniary, V., Razanajatovo, H., Rapanarivo S. H., Ralimanana, H., and Vorontsova, M. S. 2019b. All herbarium specimens of grasses held at TAN herbarium. Version 1.8. Kew Madagascar Conservation Centre, Royal Botanic Gardens Kew. Occurrence data set. https://doi.org/10.15468/v6mfx2. Accessed via GBIF.org on 11 Feb. 2019.

Rabarivola, M. L., Razanajatovo, H., Razafiniary, V., Ralimanana, H., and Vorontsova M. S. 2019c. Research database of Madagascar grasses compiled by Maria Vorontsova. Version 1.3. Kew Madagascar Conservation Centre, Royal Botanic Gardens Kew. Occurrence data set. https://doi.org/10.15468/umduhk. Accessed via GBIF.org on 11 Feb. 2019.

Rabarivola, M. L., Razanajatovo, H., Razafiniary, V., Andriambolantsoa, R., Ralimanana, H., and Vorontsova, M. S. 2019d. *Madagascar Grass Atlas*. Antananarivo: Kew Madagascar Conservation Centre.

Rabearivony, A. D., Kuhlman, A. R., Razafiariso, Z. L., Raharimalala, F., Rakotoarivony, F., Randrianarivony, T., Rakotoarivelo, N., Randrianasolo, A., and Bussmann, R.W. 2015. Ethnobotanical study of the medicinal plants known by men in Ambalabe, Madagascar. *Ethnobotany Research and Applications* 14: 123–138.

Rabeau, L., Gradstein, S. R., Dubuisson, J.-Y., Nebel, M., Quandt, D., and Reeb, C. 2017. New insights into the phylogeny and relationships within the worldwide genus *Riccardia* (Aneuraceae, Marchantiophytina). *European Journal of Taxonomy* 273: 1–26.

Rabehevitra, D., and Lowry II, P. P. 2009. Endemic families of Madagascar. XI. A new critically endangered species of *Schizolaena* (Sarcolaenaceae) from Tapia woodland in south-central Madagascar. *Adansonia*, série 3, 31: 149–155.

Rabesa, Z. A. 1982. Recherches chimiosystématiques sur les flavonoides des Didiéréacées. *Tropische und Subtropische Pflanzenwelt* 37: 339–358.

———. 1986. *Pharmacopée de l'Alaotra*. Antananarivo: Edition Fanantonana.

Rabevohitra, R., and McPherson, G. 2012. A new species of *Pantadenia* Gagnep. (Euphorbiaceae) from Madagascar. *Adansonia* 34(1): 77–81.

Racey, P. A., Goodman, S. M., and Jenkins, R.K.B. 2009. The ecology and conservation of Malagasy bats. In *Island Bats: Evolution, Ecology, and Conservation*, eds. T. H. Fleming and P. A. Racey, pp. 369–404. Chicago: University of Chicago Press.

Radcliffe-Smith, A. 1968. An account of the genus *Givotia* Griff. (Euphorbiaceae). *Kew Bulletin* 22: 493–505.

———. 1973. An account of the genus *Cephalocroton* Hochst. (Euphorbiaceae). *Kew Bulletin* 28: 123–132.

———. 1988. Notes on Madagascan Euphorbiaceae I. On the identity of *Paragelonium* and on the affinities of *Benoistia* and *Claoxylopsis* (Euphorbiaceae). *Kew Bulletin* 43: 625–647.

———. 1989. Notes on Madagascan Euphorbiaceae II. *Claoxylon* sect. *Luteobrunnea*. *Kew Bulletin* 44: 333–340.

———. 1990. Notes on Madagascan Euphorbiaceae III. *Stachyandra*. *Kew Bulletin* 45: 561–568.

———. 1991. Notes on Madagascan Euphorbiaceae IV. The genus *Suregada* in Madagascar and the Comoro Islands. *Kew Bulletin* 46: 711–726.

———. 1997. Notes on Madagascan Euphorbiaceae V. *Jatropha*. *Kew Bulletin* 52: 177–181.

———. 1998a. A synopsis of the genus *Amyrea* Leandri (Euphorbiaceae-Acalyphoideae). *Kew Bulletin* 53: 437–451.

———. 1998b. A synopsis of *Tannodia* Baill. (Crotonoideae-Aleuritideae-Grosserinae) with special reference to Madagascar, and the subsumption of *Domohinea* Leandri. *Kew Bulletin* 53: 173–186.

———. 2001. *Genera Euphorbiacearum*. Kew: Royal Botanic Gardens.

———. 2016. The genus *Croton* in Madagascar and the Comoro Is. Pre-print submitted on 23 Dec. 2016: 1–213.

Radespiel, U. 2006. Ecological diversity and seasonal adaptations of mouse lemurs (*Microcebus* spp.). In *Lemur Ecology and Adaptation*, eds. L. Gould and M. L. Sauther, pp. 211–233. New York: Springer.

Radlkofer, L. 1933. Sapindaceae. In *Das Pflanzenreich* IV, 165 (Heft 98a-h), ed. A. Engler. Leipzig: Von Wilhelm Engelmann.

Rafenoarisoa, F. 2016. Ecologie alimentaire de *Eulemur cinereiceps* (Grandidieri [*sic*] et Milne-Edwards, 1890) en vue de sa conservation dans la NAP Ankarabolava Angakatrika du district de Vangaindrano. Mémoire de Master, Université d'Antananarivo.

Rafidison, V. M. 2013. Ethnobiologie et écologie des *Ficus* des terroirs Betsileo et du corridor Ranomafana—Andringitra. PhD thesis, Faculté des Sciences, Université d'Antananarivo.

Rafidison, V. M., Rabevohitra, R., Aumeeruddy-Thomas, Y., Hossaert-McKey, M., Rasplus, J.-Y., and Kjellberg, F. 2011. Notes taxonomiques et identification des *Ficus* malgaches. *Acta Botanica Gallica* 158(4): 453–472.

Rafidison, V. M., Rakotoanadahy, B., Rakototomaro, J. F., Rafanomezantsoa, E., Rasabo, E., Rakotozafy, R., and Aumeeruddy-Thomas, Y. 2016. Pratiques et connaissances naturalistes des communautés Betsileo: lisière du corridor forestier Andringitra-Ranomafana, Madagascar. In *Indigenous and Local Knowledge of Biodiversity and Ecosystem Services in Africa*, eds. M. Roué, N. Césard, Y. C. Adou Yao, and A. Oteng-Yeboah, pp. 96–107. Paris: UNESCO.

Rafidison, V. M., Rakouth, B., Carrière, S. M., Kjellberg, F., and Aumeeruddy-Thomas, Y. 2020. Local knowledge, practices and uses relating to isolated *Ficus* trees in Betsileo rural landscapes in Madagascar. Implications for biodiversity conservation. *Biodiversity Conservation* 29: 1027–1058.

Raharijaona, A. S. 2015. L'importance de l'identification juridique des participants à la gestion durable du *Tsiperifery*: Cas d'Anjozorobe. Mémoire de Masters, Faculté de Droit, Economie, Gestion et Sociologie, Université d'Antananarivo.

Raheriarisena, M. 2005. Régime alimentaire de *Pteropus rufus* (Chiroptera: Pteropodidae) dans la région sub-aride du sud de Madagascar. *Revue d'Ecologie* 60: 255–264.

Rajaonarivony, M. 1995. Consommation et préparations culinaires du manioc à Madagascar. In *Transformation alimentaire du Manioc*, eds. T. Agbor-Egbe, A. Brauman, D. Griffon, and S. Treche, pp. 101–105. Paris: ORSTOM.

Rakotoarimanana, V. 2008. Feu, pâturage et dynamique des savanes à Madagascar. Mémoires de HDR, Biologie et Ecologie Végétales, Université d'Antananarivo.

Rakotoarinivo, M. 2008. A remarkable *Ravenea* from the montane forest of Andilamena, Madagascar. *Palms* 52(1): 11–17.

Rakotoarinivo, M., and Dransfield, J. 2010. New species of *Dypsis* and *Ravenea* (Arecaceae) from Madagascar. *Kew Bulletin* 65: 279–303.

———. 2013. The history of palm exploration in Madagascar. *Scripta Botanica Belgica* 50: 184–191.

Rakotoarinivo, M., Blach-Overgaard, A., Baker, W., Dransfield, J., Moat, J., and Svenning, J.-C. 2013. Palaeo-precipitation is a major determinant of palm species richness patterns across Madagascar: A tropical biodiversity hotspot. *Proceedings of the Royal Society of London B: Biological Sciences* 280: 20123048.

Rakotoarinivo, M., Dransfield, J., Bachman, S. P., Moat, J, and Baker, W. J. 2014. Comprehensive Red List assessment reveals exceptionally high extinction risk to Madagascar palms. *PLoS One* 9(7): e103684.

Rakotoarivelo, N., Adriambololonera, S., Phillipson, P. B., and Callmander, M. W. 2014. Une espèce nouvelle du genre *Nesogordonia* Baill. (Malvaceae) endémique du nord de Madagascar. *Candollea* 69(2): 165–170. https://doi.org/10.15553/c2014v692a8.

Rakotoarivelo, N., Manjato, N., Andriamiarisoa, L., Bernard R., and Andriambololonera, S. 2020. Useful plants in the Park Bandro and its surroundings, in Lake Alaotra, Madagascar. *Madagascar Conservation and Development*.

Rakotobe, L., Mambu, L., Deville, A., Dubost, L., Jeannoda, V., Rakoto, D., and Bodo, B. 2010. Clerodane and 19-norclerodane diterpenoids from the tubers of *Dioscorea antaly*. *Phytochemistry* 71(8–9): 1007–1013.

Rakotomalala, N. H., Andriamanohera, M. A., Solofondranohatra, L. C., Ranaivojaona, A. E., Jeannoda, V., Ralimanana, H., and Vorontsova, M. S. 2021.

Grasses of the Isalo National Park, Madagascar—checklist, origins, and significance. *Madagascar Conservation and Development* 16(1): 14–24.
Rakotonasolo, F., and Davis, A. 2006. Six species of Madagascan *Genipa* transferred to *Hyperacanthus* (Rubiaceae-Gardenieae) and new data on general morphology, placentation and ovary structure in *Hyperacanthus*. *Taxon* 55: 387–396.
Rakotonirina, N., Rakouth, B., and Davis, A. P. 2012. A taxonomic revision of Madagascan *Gardenia* (Rubiaceae, Gardenieae). *Nordic Journal of Botany* 30: 712–728.
Rakoto Ratsimamanga, A., Boiteau, P., and Mouton M. 1969. *Eléments de pharmacopée malagasy*. Antananarivo: Société pour la Promotion de la Pharmacopée Malagasy.
Rakotozafy, B.F.L., Hanitrarivo, R. M., Ranirison, P., Tahinarivony, J. A., Edmond, R., and Gautier, L. 2013. Structure et composition floristique de la forêt sur faciès karstique de Beanka, Région Melaky, Ouest de Madagascar. In La forêt de Beanka, Région Melaky, Ouest de Madagascar, eds. S. M. Goodman, L. Gautier, and M. J. Raherilalao. *Malagasy Nature* 7: 105–125.
Ralainasolo, F., Ratsimbazafy, J., Lewis, R., and Andrianandrasana, H. 2013. Lake Alaotra. In *Lemurs of Madagascar. A strategy for their conservation 2013–2016*, eds. C. Schwitzer, R. A. Mittermeier, N. Davies, S. Johnson, J. Ratsimbazafy, J. Razafindramanana, E. E. Louis Jr., and S. Rajaobelina, pp. 65–66. Bristol: IUCN SSC Primate Specialist Group, Bristol Conservation and Science Foundation, and Conservation International.
Ralalaharisoa-Ramamonjisoa, Z. 1992. Etude du comportement de butinage de l'abeille *Apis mellifera* var. *unicolor* d'après les analyses polliniques dans la région des hauts-plateaux (Madagascar). PhD thesis, Université d'Antananarivo.
Ralimanana, H. 1994. Contribution à l'étude de l'apiculture et à la melissopalynologie dans le Parc National de Ranomafana. Mémoire de DEA, Université d'Antananarivo.
———. Systématique et biogéographie de *Phyllanthus* L. (Phyllanthaceae) de Madagascar. PhD thesis, Université d'Antananarivo.
———. 2017. Two new species of *Meineckia* Baill. (Phyllanthaceae) from Madagascar. *Kew Bulletin* 72(35). https://doi.org/10.1007/s12225-017-9709-2.
Ralimanana, H., and Cable, S. 2020. Taxonomic revision of *Phyllanthus* (Phyllanthaceae) in Madagascar and the Comoro Islands IV: Subgenus *Gomphidium* and *incertae sedis*. *Kew Bulletin* 75: 64. https://doi.org/10.1007/S12225-020-09910-7.
Ralimanana, H., and Hoffmann, P. 2011. Taxonomic revision of *Phyllanthus* (Phyllanthaceae) in Madagascar and the Comoro Islands I: Synopsis and subgenera *Isocladus*, *Betsileani*, *Kirganelia* and *Tenellanthus*. *Kew Bulletin* 66: 331–365.
———. 2014. Taxonomic revision of *Phyllanthus* (Phyllanthaceae) in Madagascar and the Comoro Islands II: subgenera *Anisonemoides* (Jean F. Brunel) Ralim. and Petra Hoffm., stat. nov. and *Menarda* (Müll. Arg.) Ralim. and Petra Hoffm. *Adansonia*, série 3, 36(2): 265–301.
Ralimanana, H., Hoffmann, P., and Rajeriarison, C. 2013. Taxonomic revision of *Phyllanthus* (Phyllanthaceae) in Madagascar and the Comoro Islands III: Subgenera *Swartziani*, *Afroswartziani* and *Emblica*. *Kew Bulletin* 68: 535–558.
Ramananjanahary, R., Frasier, C. L., Lowry II, P. P., Rajaonary, F. A., and Schatz, G. E., eds. 2010. *Madagascar's Endemic Plant Families. Species Guide*. Antananarivo: Missouri Botanical Garden Research and Conservation Program.
Ramiandrasoa, D. 2019. *Parcours d'un Aromatologue Malgache: L'aromathérapie essentiellement*. St. Denis: Editions Edilivre.
Ranarijaona, H. L. 1999. La flore des milieux lentiques (lacs, marais et étangs) de Madagascar: essais de typologie. PhD thesis, Université d'Antananarivo.
Ranarivelo, H. 2010. Systematics, phylogeny, and biogeography of the endemic Malagasy genus *Rousseauxia* (Melastomataceae). MSc thesis, San Francisco State University.
Ranarivelo, H., and Almeda, F. 2019. A new *Dichaetanthera* (Melastomataceae: Melastomateae) from Masoala National Park in Madagascar. *Candollea* 74: 131–136.
Ranarivelo, H. S., and Kotozafy, A. 2001. Etude de la structure et la composition floristique de la végétation dans les forêts de basse altitude (<1000 m) du couloir forestier entre le Parc National (PN) de Ranomafana et le PN d'Andringitra. In Inventaire biologique du Parc National de Ranomafana et du couloir forestier qui la relie au Parc National d'Andringitra, eds. S. M. Goodman and V. R. Razafindratsita. *Recherches pour le Développement, série Sciences Biologiques*, 17: 47–92.
Ranarivelo-Randriamboavonjy, T., Robbrecht, E., Rabakonandrianina, E., and De Block, P. 2007. Revision of the Malagasy species of the genus *Tricalysia* (Rubiaceae). *Botanical Journal of the Linnean Society* 155: 83–126.
Randriamalala, H. F., and Liu, Z. 2010. Rosewood of Madagascar: Between democracy and conservation. *Madagascar Conservation and Development* 5: 11–22.
Randriamiharisoa, M. N., Kuhlman, A. R., Jeannoda, V., Rabarison, H., Rakotoarivelo, N., Randrianarivony, T., Raktoarivony, F., Randrianasolo, A., and Bussmann, R. W. 2015. Medicinal plants sold in the markets of Antananarivo, Madagascar. *Journal of Ethnobiology and Ethnomedicine* 11: 60. https://doi.org/10.1186/s13002-015-0046-y.
Randrianaivo, R. 2013. Les Sapotaceae de Madagascar, deux nouvelles espèces du genre *Mimusops* L. *Madagascar Conservation and Development* 8: 69–72.
Randrianarivony, T. N., Randriatsivery, M. F., Andriamihajarivo, T., and Callmander, M. W. 2017a. Une nouvelle espèce de *Turraea* (Meliaceae) du Sud-Ouest de Madagascar. *Candollea* 72: 283–288.
Randrianarivony, T. N., Ramarosandratana, A. V., Andriamihajarivo, T. H., Rakotoarivony, F., Jeannoda, V. H., Randrianasolo, A., and Bussmann, R. W. 2017b. The most used medicinal plants by communities in Mahaboboka, Amboronabo, Mikoboka, southwestern Madagascar. *Journal of Ethnobiology and Ethnomedicine* 13(1): 19.
Randrianasolo, A. 1998. Systematics and evolution of three Malagasy genera of Anacardiaceae: *Micronychia* Oliv., *Protorhus* Engl. and *Rhus* section *Baronia* (Baker) H. Perrier. PhD thesis, University of Missouri at St. Louis.
———. 2000. A taxonomic revision of the Madagascar endemic genus *Micronychia* (Anacardiaceae). *Adansonia*, série 3, 22(1): 145–155.
———. 2003. Anacardiaceae. In *The Natural History of Madagascar*, eds. S. M. Goodman and J. P. Benstead, pp. 398–402. Chicago: University of Chicago Press.
Randrianasolo, A., and Lowry II, P. P. 2004. A new species of *Campnosperma* Thwaites (Anacardiaceae) from northeastern Madagascar. *Adansonia*, série 3, 26(2): 213–216.
———. 2006. *Operculicarya* (Anacardiaceae) revisited: An updated taxonomic treatment for Madagascar and the Comoro Islands, with descriptions of three new species. *Adansonia*, série 3, 28(2): 359–371.
———. 2009. Four new species and one new combination in the Malagasy endemic genus *Micronychia* Oliv. (Anacardiaceae). *Adansonia*, série 3, 31(1): 157–168.
———. 2015. A new species of *Operculicarya* H. Perrier (Anacardiaceae) from western dry forests of Madagascar. *Candollea* 70(1): 57–60.
Randrianasolo, A., and Miller, J. S. 1994. *Sarcolaena isaloensis*, a new species of Sarcolaenaceae from Isalo, south-central Madagascar. *Novon* 4: 290–292.
———. 1998. A revision of *Campnosperma* (Anacardiaceae) in Madagascar. *Adansonia*, série 3, 20(2): 285–293.
———. 1999a. A new species of *Poupartia* (Anacardiaceae) from Madagascar. *Novon* 9: 546–548.
———. 1999b. Taxonomic revision of the genus *Sarcolaena* (Sarcolaenaceae). *Annals of the Missouri Botanical Garden* 86: 702–722.
Randrianasolo, A., Lowry II, P. P., Schatz, G. E., Phillipson, P. B., and Wahlert, G. A. 2013. The lianescent species of *Grewia* L. (Malvaceae *s.l.*, formerly Tiliaceae) in Madagascar. *Adansonia*, série 3, 35(1): 73–85. https://doi.org/10.5252/a2013n1a7.
Randrianasolo, A., Lowry II, P. P., and Schatz, G. E. 2017. Taxonomic treatment of *Abrahamia* Randrian. and Lowry, a new genus of Anacardiaceae from Madagascar. *Boissiera* 71: 1–152.
Randrianjafizanaka, M. T., Autfray, P., Andrianaivo, A.P., Ratsimiala Ramonta, I., and Rodenburg, J. 2018. Combined effects of cover crops, mulch, zero-tillage and resistant varieties on *Striga asiatica* (L.) Kuntze in rice-maize rotation systems. *Agriculture, Ecosystems and Environment* 256: 23–33
Randriarisoa, A., Naciri, Y., and Gautier, L. 2020. A new Critically Endangered species in the Malagasy Region endemic genus *Labramia* (Sapotaceae). *Candollea* 75: 83–87.
Randriatafika, F., and Rabenantoandro, J. 2008. Correspondence between vernacular and scientific names of littoral forest plants in the Tolagnaro area. In SI/MAB series 11 *Biodiversity, Ecology and Conservation of Littoral Ecosystems in Southeastern Madagascar, Tolagnaro (Fort Dauphin)*, eds. J. U. Ganzhorn, S. M. Goodman, and M. Vincelette, pp. 95–117. Washington, DC: Smithsonian Institution.
Ranivo Rakotoson, J., and Razafimahatratra, P. M. 2018. Aspects légaux, juridiques et financiers des aires protégées à Madagascar: passé, présent et futur. / Legal, judicial, and financial aspects of Madagascar's protected areas: Past, present, and future. In *Les aires protégées terrestres de Madagascar: leur histoire, description et biote / The Terrestrial Protected Areas of Madagascar: Their History, Description, and Biota*, eds. S. M. Goodman, M. R. Raherilalao, and S. Wohlhauser, pp. 105–167. Antananarivo: Association Vahatra.
Rao, P. 2001. Taxonomic studies on *Cryphaea* (Cryphaeaceae, Bryopsida). 3. Revision of European, African, Australian and Oceanian, and American species. *Bryobrothera* 7: 37–111.

Rasoloarijao, T. M., Ramavovololona, P., Ramamonjisoa, R., Clemencet, J., Lebreton, G., and Delatte, H. 2019. Pollen morphology of melliferous plants for *Apis mellifera unicolor* in the tropical rainforest of Ranomafana National Park, Madagascar. *Palynology* 43: 292–320.

Rasplus, J.-Y., Harry, M., Perrin, H., Chassagnard, M. T., and Lachaise, D. 2003. Les *Ficus* (Moraceae) et l'entomofaune des figues (Hym. Agaonidae; Pteromalidae, Torymidae, Eurytomidae; Dipt. Drosophilidae; Col. Curculionidae) du Mont Nimba en Guinée. *Mémoires du Muséum National d'Histoire Naturelle* 190: 107–182.

Rasplus, J.-Y., Rodriguez, L. J., Sauné, L., Peng, Y.-Q., Bain, A., et al. 2020. Exploring systematic biases, rooting methods and morphological evidence to unravel the evolutionary history of the genus *Ficus* (Moraceae). *BioRxiv*. https://doi.org/10.1101/2020.04.15.042259.

Rauh, W. 1961. Weitere untersuchungen an Didiereaceen. 1. Teil. Beitrag zur kenntnis der wuchsformen der Didiereaceen, unter besonderer berücksichtigung neuer arten. *Sitzungsberichte der Heidelberger Akademie der Wissenschaften, Mathematische-Naturwissenschaftliche Klasse* 1960/61(7): 185–300.

———. 1963. Didieréacées. *Flore de Madagascar et des Comores* 121: 1–37.

———. 1979. *Euphorbia × lomi* Rauh (*E. lophogona × E. milii*). *Kakteen und Andere Sukkulenten* 30: 257–259.

———. 1995. *Succulent and xerophytic plants of Madagascar*, vol. 1. Mill Valley, California: Strawberry Press.

———. 1998. *Succulent and xerophytic plants of Madagascar*, vol. 2. Mill Valley, California: Strawberry Press.

———. 1999. *Euphorbia bemarahaensis* Rauh and Mangelsdorff, une nouvelle espèce du groupe *Euphorbia bosseri* Leandri et *Euphorbia platyclada* Rauh. *Succulentes* 21: 3–12.

Rauh, W., and Dittmar, K. 1970. Weitere untersuchungen an Didiereaceen. 3. Teil. Vergleichend anatomische untersuchungen an den sprossachsen und den dornen der Didiereaceen. *Sitzungsberichte der Heidelberger Akademie der Wissenschaften, Mathematische-Naturwissenschaftliche Klasse* 1969/70(4): 163–246.

Rauh, W., and Reznick, H. 1961. Zur frage der systematischen stellung der Didiereaceen. *Botanische Jahrbücher für Systematik, Pflanzengeschichte und Pflanzengeographie* 81: 94–105.

Rauh, W., and Schölch, H. F. 1965. Weitere untersuchungen an Didiereaceen. 2. Teil. Infloreszenz-, blutenmorphologische und embryologische untersuchungen mit ausblick auf die systematische stellung der Didiereaceen. *Sitzungsberichte der Heidelberger Akademie der Wissenschaften, Mathematische-Naturwissenschaftliche Klasse* 1965(3): 221–434.

Raunet, M. 1997. *Les Ensembles Morphopédologiques de Madagascar*. Montpellier: CIRAD-CA.

Ravaomanalina, H., and Razafimanahaka, J. 2016. *Adansonia grandidieri*. The IUCN Red List of Threatened Species 2016: e.T30388A64007143.

Raynal-Roques, A. 1980. Les plantes aquatiques (plantes à fleurs et Fougères). *Flore et Faune Aquatiques de l'Afrique Sahélo-Soudanienne* 44: 63–152.

Razafiarivony, M. 2006. Compter et réfléchir avec l'arbre dans la poésie orale traditionnelle malgache. In *L'Arbre et l'Homme, Recueil de textes sur la conception de l'arbre dans la culture malgache. Regards sur la Science*. Antananarivo: Institut des Civilisations.

Razafimamonjison, G., Léong Pock Tsy, J.-M., Randriamiarinarivo, M., Ramanoelina, P., Rasoarahona, J., Fawbush, F., and Danthu, P. 2017. Fatty acid composition of baobab seed and its relationship with the genus *Adansonia* taxonomy. *Chemistry and Biodiversity* 14: 1–9.

Razafimandimbison, S. G. 2002. A systematic revision of *Breonia* (Rubiaceae-Naucleeae). *Annals of the Missouri Botanical Garden* 89: 1–37.

Razafimandimbison, S. G., and Bremer, B. 2001. Tribal delimitation of Naucleeae (Cinchonoideae, Rubiaceae): Inference from molecular and morphological data. *Systematics and Geography of Plants* 71: 515–538.

———. 2002. Phylogeny and classification of Naucleeae *s.l.* (Rubiaceae) inferred from molecular (ITS, rBCL, and tRNT-F) and morphological data. *American Journal of Botany* 89(7): 1027–1041.

———. 2006. Taxonomic revision of the tribe Hymenodictyeae (Rubiaceae, Cinchonoideae). *Botanical Journal of the Linnean Society* 152: 331–386.

Razafimandimbison, S. G., and Manjato, N. 2019. First record of *Dentella repens* (Rubiaceae) from Madagascar. *Candollea* 74: 4345.

Razafimandimbison, S. G., Lantz, H., and Bremer, B. 2007. New combinations and names in *Peponidium* and *Pyrostria* (Rubiaceae, Vanguerieae). *Novon* 17: 516–521.

Razafimandimbison, S. G., Rydin, C., and Bremer, B. 2008. Evolutionary trends in the Psychotrieae alliance (Rubiaceae)—A rarely reported evolutionary change of many-seeded carpels from one-seeded carpels. *Molecular Phylogenetics and Evolution* 48: 207–223.

Razafimandimbison, S. G., Lantz, H., Mouly, A., and Bremer, B. 2009a. Evolutionary trends, major lineages, and new generic limits in the dioecious group of the tribe Vanguerieae (Rubiaceae): Insights into the evolution of functional dioecy. *Annals of the Missouri Botanical Garden* 96: 161–181.

Razafimandimbison, S. G., McDowell, T., Halford, D., and Bremer, B. 2009b. Molecular phylogenetics and generic assessment in the tribe Morindeae (Rubiaceae–Rubioideae): How to circumscribe *Morinda* L. to be monophyletic? *Molecular Phylogenetics and Evolution* 52: 879–886.

Razafimandimbison, S. G., Appelhans, M. S., Rabarison, H., Haevermans, T., Rakotondrafara, A., et al. 2010a. Implications of a molecular phylogenetic study of the Malagasy genus *Cedrelopsis* and its relatives (Ptaeroxylaceae). *Molecular Phylogenetics and Evolution* 57(1): 258–265. https://doi.org/10.1016/j.ympev.2010.06.023.

Razafimandimbison, S. G., McDowell, T. D., Halford, D. A., and Bremer, B. 2010b. Origin of the Pantropical and nutriceutical *Morinda citrifolia* L. (Rubiaceae): Comments on its distribution range and circumscription. *Journal Biogeography* 37: 520–529.

Razafimandimbison, S. G., Taylor, C. M., Wikström, N., Pailler, T., Khodabandeh, A., and Bremer, B. 2014. Phylogeny and generic limits in the sister tribes Psychotrieae and Palicoureeae (Rubiaceae): Evolution of schizocarps in *Psychotria* and origins of the bacterial leaf nodules of the Malagasy species. *American Journal of Botany* 101: 1102–1126.

Razafimandimbison, S. G., Kainulainen, K., Wikström, N., and Bremer, B. 2017. Historical biogeography and phylogeny of the Pantropical Psychotrieae alliance (Rubiaceae), with particular emphasis on the Western Indian Ocean Region. *American Journal Botany* 104: 1407–1423.

Razafimandimbison, S. G., Kainulainen, K., Senterre, B., Morel, C., and Rydin, C. 2020. Phylogenetic affinity of an enigmatic Rubiaceae from the Seychelles revealing a recent biogeographic link with Central Africa: gen. nov. *Seychellea* and trib. nov. Seychelleeae. *Molecular Phylogenetics and Evolution* 143: 10685.

Razafimandimby, H. 2011. Etudes écologique et ethnobotanique de *Tsiperifery* (*Piper* sp.) de la forêt de Tsiazompaniry pour une gestion durable. Mémoire de DEA, Ecole Supérieure des Sciences Agronomiques, Université d'Antananarivo.

———. 2017. Etudes de la diversité morphologique, biologique et écologique de *Tsiperifery* (*Piper* spp.) pour la gestion durable des ressources génétiques à Madagascar. PhD thesis, Ecole Doctorale Gestion des Ressources Naturelles et Développement, Université d'Antananarivo.

Razafimandimby, H., Benard, A. G., Andrianoelisoa, H., Leong J.-M., Touati, G., et al. 2017. *Tsiperifery*, the wild pepper from Madagascar, emerging on the international spice market whose exploitation is unchecked: current knowledge and future prospects. *Fruits* 72(6): 331–340.

Razafimandimby, H., Gautier, L., Bouvet, J. M., Danthu, P., and Ramamonjisoa, L. 2020. Characterization of the phenotypic diversity of *Tsiperifery* (*Piper* spp.), the wild pepper from Madagascar under-studied in spite of its international fame. *Acta Horticulturea* 1267: 39–44.

Razafindraibe, M., Kuhlman, A. R., Rabarison, H., Rakotoarimanana, V., Rajeriarison, C., et al. 2013. Medicinal plants used by women from Agnalazaha littoral forest (Southeastern Madagascar). *Journal of Ethnobiology and Ethnomedicine* 9(1): 73.

Razafindratsima, O. H. 2014. Seed dispersal by vertebrates in Madagascar's forests: Review and future directions. *Madagascar Conservation and Development* 9(2): 90–97.

Razafindratsima, O. H., and Dunham, A. E. 2016. Frugivores bias seed-adult tree associations through nonrandom seed dispersal: A phylogenetic approach. *Ecology* 97: 2094–2102.

Razafindratsima, O. H., Jones, T. A., and Dunham, A. E. 2014. Patterns of movement and seed dispersal by three lemur species. *American Journal of Primatology* 76: 84–96.

Razafindratsita, V., and Zack, S. 2009. Frugivory and facilitation of seed germination by the Velvet Asity, *Philepitta castanea* (Müller, 1776), in the rainforest understory of Ranomafana National Park, Madagascar. *Malagasy Nature* 2: 154–159.

Razanamaro, O., Rasoamanana, E., Rakouth, B., Randriamalala, J. R., Rabakonadrianina, E., Clément-Vidal, A., Léong Pock Tsy, J.-M., Menut, C., and Danthu, P. 2015. Chemical characterization of floral scents in the six endemic baobab species (*Adansonia* sp.) of Madagascar. *Biochemical Systematics and Ecology* 60: 238–248.

Razanameharizaka, J., Grouzis, M., Ravelomanana, D., and Danthu, P. 2006. Seed storage behaviour and seed germination in African and Malagasy baobabs (*Adansonia* species). *Seed Science Research* 16: 83–88.

RBG Kew. 2016. *The State of the World's Plants 2016*. Richmond: Royal Botanic Gardens, Kew.

Reeb, C., Marline, L., Rabeau, L., Andriamanantena, A., Andriamiarisoa, R. L., Ranarijaona, H. L., and Pócs, T. 2018. A survey of Marchantiales from Madagascar. *Acta Biologica Plantarum Agriensis* 6: 3–72.

Reeb, C., Letsara, R., Andriamiarisoa, R. L., Brinda, J. C., Abalo-Loko, G. A., et al. 2019. A pilot workshop on Bryophytes at the Antananarivo Herbarium (TAN) revealed the presence of seven additional species for Madagascar. *Candollea* 74: 145–150.

Reese, W. D. 1991. *Syrrhopodon armatissimus* sp. nov. from Madagascar, with comments on the Calymperaceae from the Madagascar region. *The Bryologist* 94: 217–220.

Reese, W. D., and Zander, R. H. 1987. Serpotortellaceae, a new family of mosses (Musci) from Madagascar and Réunion. *The Bryologist* 90(3): 230–236.

Refulio-Rodriguez, N. G., and Olmstead, R. G. 2014. Phylogeny of Lamiadae. *American Journal of Botany* 101: 287–299.

Renauld, F. 1897. *Prodrome de la flore bryologique de Madagascar, des Mascareignes et des Comores*. Monaco: Imprimerie de Monaco.

Renauld, F., and Cardot, J. 1915. Mousses. In *Histoire, physique naturelle et politique de Madagascar*, eds. A. Grandidier and G. Grandidier, vol. 9, pp. 1–560. Paris: l'Imprimerie Nationale.

Renner, S. S. 1989. A survey of reproductive biology in Neotropical Melastomataceae and Memecylaceae. *Annals of the Missouri Botanical Garden* 76: 496–518.

———. 1993. Phylogeny and classification of the Melastomataceae and Memecylaceae. *Nordic Journal of Botany* 13: 519–540.

———. 2004. Multiple Miocene Melastomataceae dispersal between Madagascar, Africa, and India. *Philosophical Transactions of the Royal Society of London B: Biological Sciences* 359: 1485–1494.

Renvoize, S. 2019. Graminées. In *Flore des Mascareignes. La Réunion, Maurice, Rodrigues* 203, eds. J. C. Autrey, J. Bosser, and I. K. Ferguson. Marseille: IRD Editions.

Renzaglia, K. S., Villarreal, J. C., and Duff, R. J. 2009. New insights into morphology, anatomy, and systematics of hornworts. In *Bryophyte Biology*, 2nd ed. eds. B. Goffinet and A. J. Shaw, pp. 139–171. Cambridge: Cambridge University Press.

Reveal, J. L. 2012. An outline of a classification scheme for extant flowering plants. *Phytoneuron* 2012–37: 1–221.

Richardson, I.B.K. 1980. Notes on *Diospyros* (Ebenaceae) in the Mascarene Islands. *Kew Bulletin* 34: 723–735.

Ridsdale, C. E. 1978a. A revision of *Mitragyna* and *Uncaria* (Rubiaceae). *Blumea* 24: 43–100.

———. 1978b. A revision of the tribe Naucleeae *s.s.* (Rubiaceae). *Blumea* 24: 307–366.

Riina, R., Peirson, J. A., Geltman, D. V., Molero, J., Frajman, B., et al. 2013. A worldwide molecular phylogeny and classification of the leafy spurges, *Euphorbia* subgenus *Esula* (Euphorbiaceae). *Taxon* 62: 316–342. https://doi.org/10.12705/622.3.

Rinaldo, D. 2020. Carbohydrate and bioactive compounds composition of starchy tropical fruits and tubers, in relation to pre and postharvest conditions: A review. *Journal of Food Science* 85: 249–259.

Riondato, I., Donno, D., Roman, A., Razafintsalama, V. E., Petit, T., et al. 2019. First ethnobotanical inventory and phytochemical analysis of plant species used by indigenous people living in the Maromizaha forest, Madagascar. *Journal of Ethnopharmacology* 232: 73–89.

Roalson, E. H., Prata, A. P., Mesterházy, A., Chase, M., Simpson, D. A., Thomas, W.W., and Larridon, I. 2019a. A broader circumscription of *Bulbostylis* as to include *Nemum* (Abildgaardieae: Cyperaceae). *Phytotaxa* 395: 199–208.

Roalson, E. H., Barrett, R. L., Wilson, K. L., Bruhl, J. J., and Larridon, I. 2019b. *Crosslandia setifolia* is a partly monoecious *Fimbristylis* (Abildgaardieae: Cyperaceae). *Phytotaxa* 399: 163–166.

Robbrecht, E. 1988. Tropical woody Rubiaceae. *Opera Botanica Belgica* 1: 1–271.

Robbrecht, E., and Manen, J.-F. 2006. The major evolutionary lineages of the coffee family (Rubiaceae, angiosperms): Combined analysis (nDNA and cpDNA) to infer the position of *Coptosapelta* and *Luculia* and supertree construction based on *rbcL*, *rps16*, *trnL-trnF* and *atpB-rbcL* data. A new classification in two subfamilies, Cinchonoideae and Rubioideae. *Systematics and Geography of Plants* 76: 85–146.

Robbrecht, E., Rohrhofer, U., and Puff, C. 1994. A survey of *Bertiera* (Rubiaceae), including a discussion of its taxonomic position. *Opera Botanica Belgica* 6: 101–141.

Rocha, M.J.R. da, Guimarães, P.J.F., Michelangeli, F. A., and Batista, J.A.N. 2018. Taxonomy of Marcetieae: A new Neotropical tribe of Melastomataceae. *International Journal of Plant Sciences* 179: 50–74.

Rodríguez-Echeverría, S., and Traveset, A. 2015. Putative linkages between below and above ground mutualisms during alien plant invasions. *AoB Plants* 7. https://doi.org/10.1093/aobpla/plv062.

Rodríguez-Echeverría, S., Fajardo, S., Ruiz-Díez, B., and Fernández-Pascual, M. 2012. Differential effectiveness of novel and old legume-rhizobia mutualisms: Implications for invasion by exotic legumes. *Oecologia* 170: 253–261.

Rogers, Z. S., and Thulin, M. 2012. *Peltophorum dasyrhachis* (Miq.) Kurz: A new record of a Southeast Asian species of Fabaceae (Caesalpinioideae) naturalized in northwestern Madagascar. *Candollea* 67(1): 145–147.

Rogers, Z. S., Malécot V., and Sikes, K. G. 2006. A synoptic revision of *Olax* L. (Olacaceae) in Madagascar and the Comoro Islands. *Adansonia* 28: 71–100.

Rogers, Z. S., Nickrent D. L., and Malécot, V. 2008. *Staufferia* and *Pilgerina*: Two new arborescent genera of Santalaceae from Madagascar. *Annals of the Missouri Botanical Garden* 95: 391–404.

Rose, J. P., Kleist, T. J., Löfstrand, S. D., Drew, B. T., Schönenberger, J., and Sytsma K. J. 2018. Phylogeny, historical biogeography, and diversification of angiosperm order Ericales suggest ancient Neotropical and East Asian connections. *Molecular Phylogenetics and Evolution* 122: 59–79

Rossi, G. 1973. Un Karst du domaine tropical sec: le plateau de l'Ankarana. *Bulletin de l'Association de Géographes Français* 410: 635–647.

———. 1977. Karst tropical et structure, l'exemple malgache. *Norois* 95 bis: 173–196.

———. 1980. *L'extrême nord de Madagascar*. Aix en Provence: Edissud.

Rowley, G. D. 1992. *Didiereaceae. "Cacti of the Old World"*. Richmond, UK: British Cactus and Succulent Society.

Ruhsam, M., and Davis, A. P. 2007. A taxonomic revision of the genus *Flagenium* Baill. (Rubiaceae–Octotropideae). *Botanical Journal of the Linnean Society* 155: 557–570.

Ryckewaert, P., Razanamaro, O., Rasoamanana, E., Rakotoarimihaja, T., Ramavovololona, P., and Danthu, P. 2011. Les Sphingidae, probables pollinisateurs des baobabs malgaches. *Bois et Forêts des Tropiques* 307: 55–68.

Rydin, C., Kainulainen, K., Razafimandimbison, S. G., Smedmark, J.E.E., and Bremer, B. 2009. Deep divergences in the coffee family and the systematic position of *Acranthera*. *Plant Systematics and Evolution* 278: 101–123.

Rydin, C., Wikström, N., and Bremer, B. 2017. Conflicting results from mitochondrial genomic data challenge current views of Rubiaceae phylogeny. *American Journal of Botany* 104: 1522–1532.

Safwat, F. M. 1962. The floral morphology of *Secamone* and the evolution of the pollinating apparatus in Asclepiadaceae. *Annals of the Missouri Botanical Garden* 49: 95–129.

Sakai, A., Wagner, W. L., and Mehrhoff, L. A. 2002. Patterns of endangerment in the Hawaiian flora. *Systematic Biology* 51: 276–302.

Salazar Allen, N. 1993. A revision of the Pantropical moss genus *Leucophanes* Brid. *Bryophytorum Bibliotheca* 46: 1–281.

Salmona, J., Olofsson, J. K., Hong-Wa, C., Razanatsoa, J., Rakotonasolo, F., Ralimanana, H., Randriamboavonjy, T., Suescun, U., Vorontsova, M. S., and Besnard, G. 2020. Late Miocene origin and recent population collapse of the Malagasy savanna olive tree (*Noronhia lowryi*). *Biological Journal of the Linnean Society* 129: 227–243.

Salomon, J.-N., and Pulina, M. 2005. Les karsts des régions climatiques extrêmes. *Karstologia Mémoires* 14: 1–220.

Samuel, R., Kathriarachchi, H., Hoffmann, P., Barfuss, M.H.J., Wurdack, K. J., Davis, C. C., and Chase, M. W. 2005. Molecular phylogenetics of Phyllanthaceae: Evidence from plastid *matK* and nuclear *PHYC* sequences. *American Journal of Botany* 92: 132–141.

Samyn, J. M. 1999. *Plantes utiles des hautes terres de Madagascar*. Antananarivo: Graphoprint.

Sanger, F., and Coulson, A. R. 1975. A rapid method for determining sequences in DNA by primed synthesis with DNA polymerase. *Journal of Molecular Biology* 94: 441–448.

Santesson, R. 1952. Foliicolous lichens I. A revision of the taxonomy of the obligately foliicolous, lichenized fungi. *Symbolae Botanicae Upsalienses* 22(1): 1–590.

Sass-Gyarmati, A. 2001. *Lopholejeunea leioptera* Gyarmati (Lejeuneaceae, subfam. Ptychanthoideae), une nouvelle espèce récoltée dans la Réserve Spéciale de

Manongarivo (Nord-Ouest de Madagascar). In Inventaire floristique et faunistique de la Réserve Spéciale de Manongarivo (NW Madagascar), eds. L. Gautier and S. M. Goodman. *Candollea* 56: 79–83.
———. 2017. *B. konratiana* sp. nov. (Marchantiophyta: Lepidoziaceae) from Madagascar. *Cryptogamie Bryologie* 38: 119–124.
Sass-Gyarmati, A., and Pócs, T. 2002. A second species of *Symbiezidium* from Africa. *Cryptogamie Bryologie* 23: 31–39.
Sato, H. 2012. Frugivory and seed dispersal by brown lemurs in a Malagasy tropical dry forest. *Biotropica* 44: 479–488.
Savolainen, V., Fay, M. F., Alback, D. C., Backlund, A., Van der Bank, M. et al. 2000. Phylogeny of the Eudicots: A nearly complete familial analysis based on *rbcl* gene sequences. *Kew Bulletin* 55: 257–309.
Sayre, R., Comer, P., Hak, J., Josse, C., Bow, J., et al. 2013. *A New Map of Standardized Terrestrial Ecosystems of Africa*. Washington, DC: Association of American Geographers.
Scales, I. R. 2011. Farming at the forest frontier: Land use and landscape change in western Madagascar, 1896–2005. *Environment and History* 17: 499–524.
Schatz, G. E. 1996. Malagasy/Indo-Austro-Malesian phytogeographic connexions. In *Biogéographie de Madagascar*, ed. W. R. Lourenço, pp. 73–83. Paris: Editions ORSTOM.
———. 2000. Endemism in the Malagasy tree flora. In *Biogeography of Madagascar*, eds W. R. Lourenço and S. M. Goodman, pp. 1–9. Paris: Société de Biogéographie.
———. 2001. *Generic Tree Flora of Madagascar*. Richmond and St. Louis: Royal Botanic Gardens, Kew and Missouri Botanical Garden.
Schatz, G. E., and Gautier, L. 1996. A new species and combinations in Malagasy *Chrysophyllum*. *Novon* 6: 426–428.
Schatz, G. E., and Lowry II, P. P. 2006. Endemic families of Madagascar. X. Two new species of *Rhopalocarpus* (Sphaerosepalaceae). *Adansonia*, série 3, 28(2): 329–336.
———. 2011. Nomenclatural notes on Malagasy *Diospyros* L. (Ebenaceae). *Adansonia*, série 3, 33: 271–281.
———. 2018. Taxonomic studies of *Diospyros* L. (Ebenaceae) from the Malagasy Region. III. New species from the island of Nosy Mangabe in the Bay of Antongil. *Novon* 26: 272–286.
———. 2020. Taxonomic studies of *Diospyros* L. (Ebenaceae) from the Malagasy region. IV. Synoptic revision of the Squamosa group in Madagascar and the Comoro Islands. *Adansonia*, série 3, 42(10): 201–218.
Schatz, G. E., Gereau, R. E., and Lowry II, P. P. 1999a. A revision of the Malagasy endemic genus *Chouxia* Capuron (Sapindaceae). *Adansonia*, série 3, 21: 51–62.
Schatz, G. E., Lowry II, P. P., and Wolf, A.-E. 1999b. Endemic families of Madagascar. II. A synoptic revision of Sphaerosepalaceae. *Adansonia*, série 3, 21: 107–123.
———. 2000. Endemic families of Madagascar. VI. A synoptic revision of *Rhodolaena* (Sarcolaenaceae). *Adansonia*, série 3, 22: 239–252.
———. 2001. Endemic families of Madagascar. VII. A synoptic revision of *Leptolaena* Thouars *sensu stricto* (Sarcolaenaceae). *Adansonia*, série 3, 23: 171–189.
Schatz, G. E., Gereau, R. E., and Lowry II, P. P. 2017. A revision of the endemic Malagasy genus *Beguea* (Sapindaceae). *Candollea* 72: 45–65.
Schatz, G. E., Lowry II, P. P., and Phillipson, P. B. 2020. Taxonomic studies of *Diospyros* L. (Ebenaceae) from the Malagasy region. V. Synoptic revision of the Bernieriana group in Madagascar and the Comoro Islands. *Candollea* 75: 203–218.
Schick, B. 1982. Zur morphologie, entwicklung, feinstruktur und funktion des translators von *Periploca* L. (Asclepiadaceae). *Tropische und Subtropische Pflanzenwelt* 40: 513–553.
Schill, R., and Leuenberger, B. A. 1972. Pollenmorphologie und cytotaxonomie der gattung *Pachypodium* Lindl. *Botanische Jahrbücher für Systematik, Pflanzengeschichte und Pflanzengeographie* 92: 169–177.
Schill, R., Rauh, W., and Wieland, H. P. 1974. Weitere untersuchungen an Didiereaceen. 4. Teil. Die chromosomenzahlen der einzelnen arten. *Tropische und Subtropische Pflanzenwelt* 11: 1–14.
Schmelzer, G. H., Gurib-Fakim, A., Arroo, R., Bosch, C. H., De Ruijter, A., et al. 2008. *Ressources végétales de l'Afrique tropicale* 11(1), *Plantes médicinales* 1. Wageningen: Fondation PROTA.
Schofield, W. B., and Crum, H. A. 1972. Disjunctions in Bryophytes. *Annals of the Missouri Botanical Garden* 59: 174.
Scholtus, G. 2017. Analyse de la distribution du poivre sauvage de Madagascar (*Voatsiperifery*) sur le marché européen. Mémoire de fin d'études, Université Paris-Sud.
Schrire, B. D. 2000. A synopsis of the genus *Philenoptera* (Leguminosae-Millettieae) from Africa and Madagascar. *Kew Bulletin* 55: 81–94.
———. 2008. The Madagascan genus *Vaughania* is reduced to synonymy under *Indigofera* (Leguminosae-Papilionoideae-Indigofereae). *Kew Bulletin* 63: 477–479.
Schrire, B. D., Lavin, M., Barker, N. P., Cortes-Burns, H., Von Senger, I., and Kim, J.-H. 2003. Towards a phylogeny of *Indigofera* (Leguminosae-Papilionoideae): Identification of major clades and relative ages. In *Advances in Legume Systematics 10, Higher Level Systematics*, eds. B. B. Klitgaard, and A. Bruneau, 269–302. Kew: Royal Botanic Gardens.
Schrire, B. D., Lavin, M., Barker, N. P., and Forest, F. 2009. Phylogeny of the tribe Indigofereae (Leguminosae-Papilionoideae): Geographically structured more in succulent-rich and temperate settings than in grass-rich environments. *American Journal of Botany* 96(4): 816–852.
Schultz, M., and Aptroot, A. 2008. Notes on crustose cyanobacterial lichens from wet tropical regions. *Sauteria* 15: 433–458.
Schumm, F., and Aptroot, A. 2010. *Seychelles Lichen Guide*. Beck: Süssen.
Schuurman, D., and Lowry II, P. P. 2009. The Madagascar rosewood massacre. *Madagascar Conservation and Development* 4: 98–102.
Schwarzbach, A. E., and McDade, L. A. 2002. Phylogenetic relationships of the mangrove family Avicenniaceae based on chloroplast and nuclear ribosomal DNA sequences. *Systematic Botany* 27(1): 84–98.
Scotland, R. W., and Vollesen, K. 2000. Classification of Acanthaceae. *Kew Bulletin* 55: 513–589.
Scott, K. D., McIntyre, C. L., and Playford, J. 2000. Molecular analyses suggest a need for a significant rearrangement of Rutaceae subfamilies and a minor reassessment of species relationships within *Flindersia*. *Plant Systematics and Evolution* 223: 15–27.
Seaward, M.R.D., and Aptroot, A. 2009. Checklist of lichens for the Seychelles group. *Bibliotheca Lichenologica* 99: 335–366.
Seelanan, T., Schnabel, A., and Wendel, J. F. 1997. Congruence and consensus in the cotton tribe (Malvaceae). *Systematic Botany* 22: 259–290.
Semmouri, I., Bauters, K., Léveillé-Bourret, E., Starr, J. R., Goetghebeur, P., and Larridon, I. 2019. The phylogeny and systematics of Cyperaceae, the evolution and importance of embryo morphology. *Botanical Review* 85: 1–39.
Sérusiaux, E. 1979. Contribution a l'etude des lichens du Kivu (Zaire), du Rwanda et du Burundi IV. Le genre *Stereocaulon* (Schreb.) Hoffm. *Revue Bryologique et Lichenologique* 45: 1–43.
Shanahan, M., So, S., Compton, S. G., and Corlett, R. T. 2001. Fig-eating by vertebrate frugivores: A global review. *Biological Reviews* 76: 529–572.
Shaw, J. 2001. Biogeographic patterns and cryptic speciation in bryophytes. *Journal of Biogeography* 28: 253–261.
Silva, C., Besnard, G., Piot, A., Razanatsoa, J., Oliveira, R. P., and Vorontsova, M. S. 2017. Museomics resolve the systematics of an endangered grass lineage endemic to north-western Madagascar. *Annals of Botany* 119: 339–351.
Sim, T. R., and Dixon, H. N. 1922. Bryophyta of Southern Rhodesia. *South African Journal of Science* 18: 294–335.
Simmen, B., Hladik, A., Ramasiarisoa, P. L., Iaconelli, S., and Hladik, C. M. 1999. Taste discrimination in lemurs and other primates, and the relationships to distribution of plant allelochemicals in different habitats of Madagascar. In *New Directions in Lemur Studies*, eds. B. Rakotosamimanana, H. Rasamimanana, J. U. Ganzhorn, and S. M. Goodman, pp. 201–219. New York: Kluwer Academic/Plenum Press.
Simmen, B., Sauther, M. L., Soma, T., Rasamimanana, H., Sussman, R. W., Jolly, A., Tarnaud, L., and Hladik, A. 2006. Plant species fed on by *Lemur catta* in gallery forests of the Southern Domain of Madagascar. In *Ringtailed Lemur Biology.* Lemur catta *in Madagascar*, eds. A. Jolly, R. W. Sussman, N. Koyama, and H. Rasamimanana, pp. 55–68. Boston: Springer.
Simões, A. O., Kinoshita, L. S., Koch, I., Silva, M. J., and Endress, M. E. 2016. Systematics and character evolution of Vinceae (Apocynaceae). *Taxon* 65: 99–122.
Simon, A., Goffinet, B., Magain, N., and Sérusiaux, E. 2018. High diversity, high insular endemism and recent origin in the lichen genus *Sticta* (lichenized Ascomycota, Peltigerales) in Madagascar and the Mascarenes. *Molecular Phylogenetics and Evolution* 122: 15–28.
Simon, M. F., Grether, R., de Queiroz, L. P., Särkinen, T. E., Dutra, V. F., and Hughes, C. E. 2011. The evolutionary history of *Mimosa* (Leguminosae): Toward a phylogeny of the sensitive plants. *American Journal of Botany* 98(7): 1201–1221.
Simpson, D. A., and Inglis C., A. 2001. *Cyperaceae of Economic, Ethobotanical and Horticultural Importance: A Checklist*. Richmond: Royal Botanic Gardens, Kew.
Singh, R. S., and Shahi, S. K. 2017. Diversity of medicinal plants of Ratanpur region of Bilaspur district (Chhattisgarh). *Journal of Medicinal Plants Study* 5: 276–281.
Sinou, C., Cardinal McTeague, W., and Bruneau, A. 2020. Testing generic limits in Cercidoideae (Leguminosae): Insights from plastid and duplicated nuclear gene sequences. *Taxon* 69(1): 67–86.

Sipman, H.J.M. 1983. A monograph of the lichen family Megalosporaceae. *Bibliotheca Lichenologica* 18: 1–241.

———. 1986. Additional notes on the lichen family Megalosporaceae. *Willdenowia* 15: 557–564.

———. 2004. Survey of *Lepraria* species with lobed thallus margins in the tropics. *Herzogia* 17: 23–35.

Skema, C. 2004. Plants at risk / Les plantes menaces. *Chaetocarpus rabaraba* Capuron. *Ravintsara* 2(4): 12–13.

———. 2012. Toward a new circumscription of *Dombeya* (Malvales: Dombeyaceae): A molecular phylogenetic and morphological study of *Dombeya* of Madagascar and a new segregate genus, *Andringitra*. *Taxon* 61(3): 612–628. https://doi.org/10.1002/tax.613010.

———. 2014. Reevaluation of species delimitations in *Dombeya* section *Hilsenbergia* (Dombeyaceae). *Systematic Botany* 39(2): 541–562. https://doi.org/10.1600/036364414X680717.

Skema, C., and Dorr, L. J. 2010. *Dombeya gautieri* (Dombeyaceae), a remarkable new species from Madagascar. *Kew Bulletin* 65(2): 305–310. https://doi.org/10.1007/s12225-010-9212-5.

———. 2011. *Nesogordonia tricarpellata* (Dombeyaceae), a new species from Madagascar that compels modification of the morphological circumscription of the genus. *PhytoKeys* 2: 9–15. https://doi.org/10.3897/phytokeys.2.747.

Sleumer, H. 1970. Révision du genre *Tisonia* Baill. (Flacourtiacées). *Adansonia*, nouvelle série, 10: 339–345.

———. 1971. Le genre *Casearia* Jacq. (*Flacourtiaceae*) en Afrique, à Madagascar et aux Mascareignes. *Bulletin du Jardin Botanique National de Belgique* 41: 397–426.

———. 1972a [publ. 1973]. Révision du genre *Calantica* Tul. (Flacourtiacées). *Adansonia*, série 2, 12: 539–544.

———. 1972b. Révision du genre *Ludia* Comm. ex Juss. (Flacourtiacées). *Adansonia*, série 2, 12: 79–102.

———. 1972c. A taxonomic revision of the genus *Scolopia* Schreb. (Flacourtiaceae). *Blumea* 20: 25–64.

———. 1973. Révision du genre *Homalium* Jacq. (Flacourtiacées) en Afrique (y compris Madagascar et les Mascareignes). *Bulletin du Jardin Botanique National de Belgique* 43: 239–328.

Smedmark, J.E.E., Razafimandimbison, S. G., Wikström, N., and Bremer, B. 2014. Inferring geographic range evolution of a Pantropical tribe in the coffee family (Lasiantheae, Rubiaceae) in the face of topological uncertainty. *Molecular Phylogenetics Evolution* 70: 182–194.

Smith, J. F., Stevens, A. C., Tepe, E. J., and Davidson, C. 2008. Placing the origin of two species-rich genera in the late Cretaceous with later species divergence in the Tertiary: A phylogenetic, biogeographic and molecular dating analysis of *Piper* and *Peperomia* (Piperaceae). *Plant Systematics and Evolution* 275(1–2): 9–30.

Snow, N. 2008. Studies of Malagasy *Eugenia* (Myrtaceae)—I: Two new species from the Masoala Peninsula and generic transfers from *Monimiastrum*. *Systematic Botany* 33: 343–348.

———. 2010. Studies of Malagasy *Syzygium* (Myrtaceae)—Two new species with small leaves and winged branchlets. *Harvard Papers in Botany* 15(1): 85–91.

———. 2011. Studies of Malagasy *Eugenia* (Myrtaceae)—II: Four new species, including one eaten by black lemurs on Nosy Be. *Systematic Botany* 36: 677–689.

Snow, N., and Callmander, M. W. 2016. Studies in Malagasy *Eugenia* (Myrtaceae)—V: *Eugenia quadriphylla*, a rare and unusual new species from the northeast. *Candollea* 71: 189–193.

Snow, N., McFadden, J., Evans, T., Salywon, A., Wojciechowski, M. F., and Wilson, P. G. 2011. Morphological and molecular evidence of polyphyly in *Rhodomyrtus* (Myrtaceae: Myrteae). *Systematic Botany* 36: 390–404.

Snow, N., Rabenantoandro, J., Randriatifika, F., Rabehevitra, D., Razafimamonjy, N. D., and Cable, S. 2012. Studies of Malagasy *Eugenia* (Myrtaceae)—III: Seven new species of high conservation concern from the eastern littoral forests. *Phytotaxa* 48: 39–60.

Snow, N., Callmander, M. W., and Phillipson, P. 2015. Studies of Malagasy *Eugenia* V: Seventeen new endemic species, one new combination, and three lectotypifications; with comments on emerging distributional, ecological and evolutionary patterns. *PhytoKeys* 49: 59–121.

Snow, N., Callmander, M. W., and Byng, J. W. 2020. Studies in Malagasy *Eugenia* (Myrtaceae)—VI: A new species with large leaves and coarsely and irregularly verrucose fruits. *Systematic Botany* 44(2): 274–276.

So, M. L. 2004. *Metzgeria* (Metzgeriaceae, Marchantiophyta) in Africa. *New Zealand Journal of Botany* 42: 271–292.

Söderström, L., Hagborg, A., Von Konrat, M., Bartholomew-Began, S., Bell, D., et al. 2016. World checklist of hornworts and liverworts. *PhytoKeys* 59: 1–828.

Solbreck, S. 2000. Ecology and biology of *Euphranta connexa* (Fabr.) (Diptera: Tephritidae)—a seed predator on *Vincetoxicum hirundinaria* Med. (Asclepiadaceae). *Entomologisk Tidskrift* 121: 23–30.

Soler, C., Schatz, B., Bessière, J.-M., and Hossaert-McKey, M. 2018. Geographic variation of fruit scents in a dispersion mutualism, the case of *Ficus lutea*. *Acta Oecologica* 90: 46–48.

Sollman, P. 2006. Studies of some Pottiaceous mosses from Africa, 2. *Tropical Bryology* 28: 1–3.

———. 2009. Studies of some Pottiaceous mosses from Africa, 4. *Tropical Bryology* 30: 15–16.

Solofondranohatra, C. L., Vorontsova, M. S., Hempson, G. P., Hackel, J., Cable, S., Jeannoda Vololoniaina, J., and Lehmann, C.E.R. 2020. Fire and grazing determined grasslands of central Madagascar represent ancient assemblages. *Proceedings of the Royal Society of London B: Biological Sciences* 287(1927): 20200598

Soltis, D. E., Soltis, P. S., Chase, M. W., Mort, M. E., Alback, D. C. et al. 2000. Angiosperm phylogeny inferred from 18S rDAN, *rbcl*, and *atpB* sequences. *Botanical Journal of the Linnean Society* 133: 381–461.

Sonnleitner, A., Rathbauer, J., Randriamalala, J. R., Raoliarivelo, L.I.B., Andrianarisoa, J. H., Rabeniala, R., and Ehrensperger, A. 2013. *Jatropha mahafalensis* oil from Madagascar: Properties and suitability as liquid biofuel. *Energy for Sustainable Development* 17(4): 326–330.

Soreng, R. J., Peterson, P. M., Romaschenko, K., Davidse, G., Teisher, J. K., Clark, L. G., Barberá, P., Gillespie, L. J., and Zuloaga, F. O. 2017. A worldwide phylogenetic classification of the Poaceae (Gramineae) II: An update and a comparison of two 2015 classifications. *Journal of Systematics and Evolution* 55: 259–290.

Soto Gomez, M., Pokorny, L., Kantar, M. B., Forest, F., Leitch, I. J., Gravendeel, B., Wilkin, P., Graham, S. W., and Viruel, J. 2019. A customized nuclear target enrichment approach for developing a phylogenomic baseline for *Dioscorea* yams (Dioscoreaceae). *Applications in Plant Sciences* 7: e11254.

Souto-Vilarós, D., Proffit, M., Buatois, B., Rindos, M., Sisol, M., et al. 2018. Pollination along an elevational gradient mediated both by floral scent and pollinator compatibility in the fig and fig-wasp mutualism. *Journal of Ecology* 106: 2256–2273.

Souza, E. R. de, Krishnaraj, M. V., and Queiroz, L. P. de. 2016. *Sanjappa*-—a new genus in the tribe Ingeae (Ingeae-Mimosoideae) from India. *Rheedia* 26(1): 1–12.

Sparrius, L. B. 2004. A monograph of *Enterographa* and *Sclerophyton*. *Bibliotheca Lichenologica* 89: 1–141.

Sponheimer, M., Alemseged, Z., Cerling, T. E., Grine, F. E., Kimbel, W. H., et al. 2013. Isotopic evidence of early hominin diets. *Proceedings of the National Academy of Sciences of the USA* 109: 10513–10518.

Staggemeier, V. G., Diniz-Filho, J.A.F., and Morellato, L.P.C. 2010. The shared influence of phylogeny and ecology on the reproductive patterns of Myrteae (Myrtaceae). *Journal of Ecology* 98: 1049–1421.

Staiger, B. 2002. Die flechtenfamilie Graphidaceae. *Bibliotheca Lichenologica* 85: 1–526.

Staiger, B., and Kalb, K. 1995. *Haematomma*-Studien I. Die glechtengattung *Haematomma*. *Bibliotheca Lichenologica* 59: 1–198.

Start, A. N. 1972. Pollination of the baobab (*Adansonia digitata* L.) by the fruit bat, *Rousettus aegyptiacus* E. Geoffroy. *East African Wildlife Journal* 10: 71–72.

Stauffer, F. W., Ouattara, D., Roguet, D., da Giau, S., Michon, L., Bakayoko, A., and Ekpe, P. 2017. An update to the African palms (Arecaceae) floristic and taxonomic knowledge, with emphasis on the West African region. *Webbia* 72(1): 17–30.

Stearn, W. T. 1971. A survey of the tropical genera *Oplonia* and *Psilanthele* (Acanthaceae). *Bulletin of the British Museum (Natural History), Botany*, 4(7): 259–323.

———. 1976. Union of *Chionanthus* and *Linociera* (Oleaceae). *Annals of the Missouri Botanical Garden* 63: 355–357.

———. 1980. African species of *Chionanthus* L. (Oleaceae) hitherto included in *Linociera* Swartz. *Botanical Journal of the Linnean Society* 80: 191–206.

Stenroos, S. 1991. Status of four species of *Cladonia* endemic to the Madagascan Region. *Annales Botanici Fennici* 28: 107–110.

Stephani, F. 1916. *Species hepaticarum* 5: 833–1008. Genève and Bale: George and Cie.

———. 1917. *Species hepaticarum* 6: 1–128. Genève and Bale: George and Cie.

Stewart, J., Hermans, J. and Campbell, B. 2004. *Angraecoid Orchids*. Portland: Timber Press.

Stizenberger, E. 1890. *Lichenaea Africana*. Vol. 2. Berichte de Thätigkeiten der St Gallenschen Naturforschungsverein, 1889–1890.

Stone, B. C. 1974. Towards an improved infrageneric classification in *Pandanus* (Pandanaceae). *Botanische Jahrbücher für Systematik* 94: 459–540.

Stone, J., and Cribb, P. 2017. *Lady Tankerville's Legacy. A Historical and Monographic Review of* Phaius *and* Gastrorchis. Kota Kinabalu: Natural History Publications.

Stone, J. R., and Davis, A. P. 2004. New taxa and nomenclatural notes on the flora of the Marojejy Massif, Madagascar. VI. Rubiaceae: A new species of *Lemyrea*. *Novon* 14: 119–123.

Stone, R. D. 2004. Phylogenetic systematics of Melastomataceae, subfamily Olisbeoideae. PhD thesis, Department of Integrative Biology, University of California, Berkeley.

———. 2006a. Phylogeny of major lineages in Melastomataceae, subfamily Olisbeoideae: Utility of nuclear glyceraldehyde 3-phosphate dehydrogenase (*GapC*) gene sequences. *Systematic Botany* 31: 107–121.

———. 2006b. New species of *Memecylon* L. and *Warneckea* Gilg (Melastomataceae) from Madagascar and Mayotte. *Adansonia*, série 3, 28: 337–358.

———. 2012. Endemism, species richness and morphological trends in Madagascan *Memecylon* (Melastomataceae). *Plant Ecology and Evolution* 145: 145–151.

———. 2014. The species-rich, Paleotropical genus *Memecylon* (Melastomataceae): Molecular phylogenetics and revised infrageneric classification of the African species. *Taxon* 63: 539–561.

———. 2017. Revised treatment of the genus *Lijndenia* (Melastomataceae, Olisbeoideae) in Madagascar. *Candollea* 72: 67–86.

———. 2018. *Lijndenia meeusei*, the correct name for the species previously known as *L. lutescens* (Melastomataceae, Olisbeoideae). *Candollea* 73: 257–259.

———. 2020. New species of *Memecylon* (Melastomataceae) from Madagascar, no 2: Treasures of TEF herbarium. *Candollea* 75: 219–239.

Stone, R. D., and Andreasen, K. 2010. The Afro-Madagascan genus *Warneckea* (Melastomataceae): Molecular systematics and revised infrageneric classification. *Taxon* 59: 83–92.

Stone, R. D., and Callmander, M. W. 2011. Two new combinations in *Memecylon* L. (Melastomataceae) of Madagascar. *Candollea* 66: 402–403.

Straka, H. 1975. Palynologie et différentiation systématique d'une famille endémique de Madagascar: les Didiereácées. *Boissiera* 24: 245–248.

Straub, S. C., Moore, M. J., Soltis, P. S., Soltis, D. E., Liston, A., and Livshultz, T. 2014. Phylogenetic signal detection from an ancient rapid radiation: Effects of noise reduction, long-branch attraction, and model selection in crown clade Apocynaceae. *Molecular Phylogenetics and Evolution* 80: 169–185.

Strid, D., Kearey, J., and Razafimandimbison, S. G. 2019. *Schismatoclada spathulata* (Rubiaceae), a new species from the Marojejy National Park (northeastern Madagascar). *Candollea* 74: 203–208.

Stride, G., Nylander, S., and Swenson, U. 2014. Revisiting the biogeography of *Sideroxylon* (Sapotaceae) and an evaluation of the taxonomic status of *Argania* and *Spiniluma*. *Australian Systematic Botany* 27: 104–118.

Strijk, J. S., Noyes, R. D., Strasberg, D., Cruaud, C., Gavory, F., Chase, M. W., Abbott, R. J., Thébaud, C., and O'Grady, P. 2012. In and out of Madagascar: Dispersal to peripheral islands, insular speciation and diversification of Indian Ocean daisy trees (*Psiadia*, Asteraceae). *PLoS One* 7: e42932.

Styger, E., Rakotoarimanana, J.E.M., Rabevohitra, R., and Fernandes, E.C.M. 1999. Indigenous fruit trees of Madagascar: Potential components of agroforestry systems to improve human nutrition and restore biological diversity. *Agroforestry Systems* 46: 289–310.

Su, H.-J., Hu, J.-M., Anderson, F. E., and Nickrent, D, L. 2015. Phylogenetic relationships of Santalales with insights into the origins of holoparasitic Balanophoraceae. *Taxon* 64: 491–506.

Sultan, A., Robertson, A. W., Callmander, M. W., Phillipson, P. B., Meyer, J.-Y., and Tate, J. A. 2019. Widespread morphological parallelism in *Korthalsella* (Santalaceae, tribe Visceae): A molecular phylogenetic perspective. *Taxon* 68: 1204–1218.

Swenson, U., and Anderberg, A. 2005. Phylogeny, character evolution, and classification of Sapotaceae (Ericales). *Cladistics* 21: 101–130.

Swenson, U., Richardson, J. E., and Bartish, I. V. 2008. Multi-gene phylogeny of the pantropical subfamily Chrysophylloideae (Sapotaceae): evidence of generic polyphyly and extensive morphological homoplasy. *Cladistics* 24: 1006–1031.

Swenson, U., Lowry II, P. P., Cornholm, B., and Nylander, S. 2020. Resolving the relationships of the enigmatic Sapotaceae genera *Beauvisagea* and *Boerlagella*, and the position of *Planchonella suboppositifolia*. *Taxon* 69(5): 998–1015.

SWG (*Syzygium* Working Group). 2016. *Syzygium* (Myrtaceae): Monographing a taxonomic giant via 22 coordinated regional revisions. *PeerJ Preprints*. https://peerj.com/preprints/1930/?td=wk.

Swinscow, T.D.V., and Krog, H. 1988. *Macrolichens of East Africa*. London: British Museum (Natural History).

Szabó, A., and Pócs, T. 2015. New or little known epiphyllous liverworts, XX. *Cololejeunea nosykombae* sp. nov. from Madagascar. *Journal of Bryology* 38: 302–307.

Takhtajan, A. [L.] 1987. *Systema Magnoliophytorum*. Leningrad: Izdatel'stvo, Nauka.

———. 1997. *Diversity and classification of flowering plants*. New York: Columbia University Press.

———. 1980. Outline of the classification of flowering plants (Magnoliophyta). *Botanical Review* 46: 225–359.

Tan, C. L. 1999. Group composition, home range size, and diet of three sympatric bamboo lemurs (genus *Hapalemur*) in Ranomafana National Park, Madagascar. *International Journal of Primatology* 20: 547–566.

Tardieu-Blot, M. L. 1952. Marsileacées. Flore de Madagascar et des Comores 10: 1–3.

Taylor, C. M. 2020. Overview of *Psychotria* in Madagascar (Rubiaceae, Psychotrieae), and of Bremekamp's foundational study of this group. *Candollea* 75: 51–70.

Taylor, C. M., and Rogers, Z. 2013. Six new species of *Danais* Vent. (Rubiaceae, Danaideae). *Candollea* 68: 167–180.

Taylor, C. M., Malcomber, S. T., and Schatz, G. E. 2014. Updated taxonomy of *Gaertnera* (Rubiaceae, Gaertnereae) in Madagascar, with sixteen new species. *Annals of the Missouri Botanical Garden* 99: 688–729.

Tehler, A., Ertz, D., and Irestedt, M. 2013. The genus *Dirina* (*Roccellaceae, Arthoniales*) revisited. *Lichenologist* 45: 427–476.

Tenza, N. P. 2015. Morphometric analysis of the *Warneckea sansibarica* species-complex (Melastomataceae, subfamily Olisbeoideae). BSc thesis, School of Life Sciences, University of KwaZulu-Natal, Pietermaritzburg, South Africa.

Terborgh, J. 1986. Keystone plant resources in the tropical forest. In *Conservation Biology*, ed. M. Soulé, pp. 330–344. Sunderland, Massachusetts: Sinauer Associates.

Terrazas, S. T. 1994. Wood anatomy of the Anacardiaceae: Ecological and phylogenetic interpretation. PhD thesis, University of North Carolina at Chapel Hill.

Thorén, S., Quietzsch, F., Schwochow, D., Sehen, L., Meusel, C., Meares, K., and Radespiel, U. 2011. Seasonal changes in feeding ecology and activity patterns of two sympatric mouse lemur species, the gray mouse lemur (*Microcebus murinus*) and the golden-brown mouse lemur (*M. ravelobensis*), in northwestern Madagascar. *International Journal of Primatology* 32: 566–586.

Thorne, R. F. 1992. Classification and geography of the flowering plants. *Botanical Review* 58: 225–327.

Thulin, M., and Razafimandimbison, S. G. 2016. *Ormocarpopsis anosyana* Thulin and Razafim. (Fabaceae), a new species from southern Madagascar and its phylogenetic position. *Candollea* 71(2): 281–286.

———. 2017. *Bourreria scabra* (Boraginaceae), a new species from southern Madagascar. *Candollea* 72: 345–350.

Thulin, M., Beier B.-A., Razafimandimbison, S. G., and Banks, H. I. 2008. *Ambilobea*, a new genus from Madagascar, the position of *Aucoumea*, and comments on the tribal classification of the frankincense and myrrh family (Burseraceae). *Nordic Journal of Botany* 26: 218–229.

Thulin, M., Phillipson, P. B., and Lavin, M. 2013. *Peltiera* (Fabaceae), the coming and going of an "extinct" genus in Madagascar. *Adansonia*, série 3, 35(1): 61–71.

Thulin, M., Nusbaumer, L., and Gautier, L. 2014. *Bauhinia darainensis* Thulin and Nusb. (Fabaceae), a new species from northern Madagascar. *Candollea* 69(2): 135–139.

Thureborn, O., Razafimandimbison, S. G., Wikström, N., Khodabandeh, A., and Rydin, C. 2019. Phylogeny of Anthospermeae of the coffee family inferred using clock and nonclock models. *International Journal of Plant Sciences* 180: 386–402.

Tibell, L., and Frisch, A. 2010. New data on crustose mazaediate lichens from tropical Africa. *Bibliotheca Lichenologica* 104: 323–332.

Tixier, P. 1977. Espèces nouvelles malgaches du genre *Diplasiolejeunea* (Spruce) Schiffn. (Hepaticae). *Lindbergia* 4: 117–125.

———. 1979a. La famille des Cololejeunoideae (Grolle) dans l'Ocean Indien occidental—Essai monographique. *Bulletin de l'Académie Malgache* 55(1–2): 173–247.

———. 1979b. A propos de quelques mousses nouvelles pour le Sud de Madagascar. *The Bryologist* 82(4): 598–599.

———. 1985. Contribution à la connaissance des Cololejeuneoides. *Bryophytorum Bibliotheca* 27: 1–439.

———. 1992. Deux espèces nouvelles malgaches du genre *Calymperopsis* (Musci). *The Bryologist* 95(3): 284–286.

———. 1993. Contribution à la connaissance du genre *Cololejeunea* (Lejeuneaceae, Hepaticeae) XI. De quelques *Pedinolejeunea* austraux. *Cryptogamie, Bryologie, Lichénologie* 14(4): 350–360.

———. 1995. Résultats taxonomiques de l'expédition BRYOTROP au Zaire et Rwanda. 30. Bryophytes épiphylles (récoltes de E. Fischer). *Tropical Bryology* 11: 11–76.

Tosh, J., Davis, A. P., Dessein, S., De Block, P., Huysmans, S., Fay, M. F., Smets, E., and Robbrecht, E. 2009. Phylogeny of *Tricalysia* (Rubiaceae) and its relationships with allied genera based on plastid DNA data: Resurrection of the genus *Empogona*. *Annals of the Missouri Botanical Garden* 96: 194–214.

Tosh, J., Dessein, S., Buerki, S., Groeninckx, I., Mouly, A., Bremer, B., Smets, E. F., and De Block, P. 2013. Evolutionary history of the Afro-Madagascan *Ixora* species (Rubiaceae): Species diversification and distribution of key morphological traits inferred from dated molecular phylogenetic trees. *Annals of Botany* 112: 1723–1742.

Touati, G. 2012. Etat des lieux de la filière du poivre sauvage de Madagascar—Un produit forestier non ligneux exploité pour la commercialisation. Mémoire de fin d'étude, Ecole supérieure d'Agro-Développement International, Cergy-Pontoise.

Touw, A. 1976. A taxonomic revision of *Thuidium*, *Pelekium* and *Rauiella* (Musci: Thuidiaceae) in Africa south of the Sahara. *Lindbergia* 3: 135–195.

———. 1993. *Bryowijkia madagassa* sp. nov. (Musci), a second species of a genus hitherto known from continental Asia. *Bulletin du Jardin Botanique National de Belgique* 6(2): 453–461.

———. 2001. A review of the *Thuidiaceae* (Musci) and a realignment of taxa traditionally accomodated in *Thuidium sensu amplo* (*Thuidium* Schimp., *Thuidiopsis* (Broth.) M. Fleisch. and *Pelekium* Mitt.) including *Aequatoriella* gen. nov. and *Indothuidium* gen. nov. *Journal of the Hattori Botanical Laboratory* 38: 123–128.

Trelease, W., and Yuncker, T. G. 1950. *The Piperaceae of Northern South America*, vol. 1. Urbana: University of Illinois Press.

Tripp, E. A. 2007. Evolutionary relationships within the species-rich genus *Ruellia* (Acanthaceae). *Systematic Botany* 32(3): 628–649.

Tripp, E. A., and Darbyshire, I. 2017. Phylogenetic relationships among Old World *Ruellia* L.: A new classification and reinstatement of the genus *Dinteracanthus* Schinz. *Systematic Botany* 42(3): 470–483.

———. 2020. *Mcdadea*: A new genus of Acanthaceae endemic to the Namib Desert of southwestern Angola. *Systematic Botany* 45: 200–211.

Tripp, E. A., and Manos, P. S. 2008. Is floral specialization an evolutionary dead-end? Pollination system transitions in *Ruellia* (Acanthaceae). *Evolution* 62: 1712–1737.

Tripp, E. A., and McDade, L. A. 2014. A rich fossil record yields calibrated phylogeny for Acanthaceae (Lamiales) and evidence for marked biases in timing and directionality of intercontinental disjunctions. *Systematic Biology* 63: 660–684.

Tripp, E. A., Daniel, T. F., Fatimah, S., and McDade, L. A. 2013. Phylogenetic relationships within Ruellieae (Acanthaceae) and a revised classification. *International Journal of Plant Sciences* 174: 97–137.

Turetsky, M. R., Mack, M. C., Hollingsworth, T. N., and Harden, J. W. 2010. The role of mosses in ecosystem succession and function in Alaska's boreal forest. *Canadian Journal of Forest Research* 40: 1237–1264.

Turk, D. 1995. *A Guide to Trees of Ranomafana National Park and Central Eastern Madagascar*. Antananarivo: USAID.

Turner, C. E, and Pemberton, R. W. 1989. Leaf domatia and mites: A plant protection-mutualism hypothesis. In *The Evolutionary Ecology of Plants*, eds. J. H. Bock and Y. B. Linhart, pp. 341–359. Boulder: Westview Press.

Ulloa, C. U., Nickrent, D. L., Whitefoord, C., and Kelly, D. L. 2010. *Hondurodendron*, a new monotypic genus of Aptandraceae from Honduras. *Annals of the Missouri Botanical Garden* 97: 457–467.

Ursch, E., and Leandri, J. 1954. Les euphorbes malgaches épineuses et charnues du Jardin Botanique de Tsimbazaza. *Mémoires de l'Institut Scientifique de Madagascar*, série B, *Biologie Végétale*, 5: 109–186.

Vainio, E. 1898. Lichenes quos in Madagascaria centrali Dr. C. Forsyth Major a. 1896 collegit. *Hedwigia* 37(2): 33–37.

Vanden Berghen, C. 1950a. Contribution à l'étude des espèces africaines du genre *Lopholejeunea* (Spruce) Schiffn. *Bulletin du Jardin Botanique National de Belgique* 20: 161–179.

———. 1950b. Révision des espèces africaines du genre *Frullania* Raddi, sous-genre *Meteoriopsis* Spruce. *Bulletin du Jardin Botanique National de Belgique* 20: 1–10.

———. 1951. Contribution à l'étude des espèces africaines du genre *Ceratolejeunea* (Spruce) Schiffn. *Bulletin du Jardin Botanique National de Belgique* 21: 61–81.

———. 1981. Le genre *Plagiochila* (Dum.) Dum. (Hepaticae) à Madagascar et aux Mascareignes, principalement d'après les récoltes de M. Onraedt. *Bulletin du Jardin Botanique National de Belgique* 51: 41–103.

———. 1984. Le genre *Lopholejeunea* (Spruce) Schiffn. (Lejeuneaceae, Hepaticae) en Afrique. *Bulletin du Jardin Botanique National de Belgique* 54: 393–464.

van den Boom, P.P.G., Brand, M., Ertz, D., Kalb, K., Magain, N., Masson, D., Schiefelbein, U., Sipman, H.J.M., and Sérusiaux, E. 2011. Discovering the lichen diversity of a remote tropical island: Working list of species collected on Reunion (Mascarene archipelago, Indian Ocean). *Herzogia* 24: 325–349.

Van der Laan, F. M., and Arends, J. C. 1985. Cytotaxonomy of the Apocynaceae. *Genetica* 68: 3–35.

Van der Veken, P. 1960. Anacardiaceae. *Flore du Congo Belge et du Ruanda-Urindi* 9: 5–108.

van der Werff, H. H. 1991. Studies in Malagasy Lauraceae I: Novelties in *Potameia*. *Adansonia*, nouvelle série, 13: 173–177.

———. 2003. A synopsis of the genus *Beilschmiedia* (Lauraceae) in Madagascar. *Adansonia*, série 3, 25: 77–92.

———. 2006. A revision of the Malagasy endemic genus *Aspidostemon* Rohwer and Richter (Lauraceae). *Adansonia*, série 3, 28: 7–44.

———. 2008. A new species and new combinations in *Cryptocarya* from Madagascar. *Adansonia*, série 3, 30: 41–46.

———. 2013a. A revision of the genus *Ocotea* Aubl. (Lauraceae) in Madagascar and the Comoro Islands. *Adansonia*, série 3, 35: 235–279.

———. 2013b. Nomenclatural notes on *Cryptocarya* R. Br. (Lauraceae) from Madagascar. *Candollea* 68: 303–306.

———. 2017. The genera of Lauraceae in Madagascar with nomenclatural novelties in *Cryptocarya*. *Candollea* 72: 323–328.

van Ee, B. W., Riina, R., and Berry, P. E. 2011. A revised infrageneric classification and molecular phylogeny of New World *Croton* (Euphorbiaceae). *Taxon* 60: 791–823.

van Ee, B. W., Forster, P. I., and Berry, P. E. 2015. Phylogenetic relationships and a new sectional classification of *Croton* (Euphorbiaceae) in Australia. *Australian Systematic Botany* 28: 219–233.

van Velzen, R., Wahlert, G. A., Sosef, M.S.M., Onstein, R. E., and Bakker, F. T. 2015. Phylogenetics of *Rinorea* (Violaceae): Elucidating infrageneric relationships using plastid and nuclear DNA sequences. *Systematic Botany* 40: 174–184.

van Welzen, P. C., Strijk, J. S., van Konijnenburg-van Cittert, J. H., Nucete, M., and Merckx, V. S. 2014. Dated phylogenies of the sister genera *Macaranga* and *Mallotus* (Euphorbiaceae): Congruence in historical biogeographic patterns? *PLoS One* 9(1): e85713.

van Welzen, P. C., Arias Guerrero, S., Arifiani, D., Bangun, T. J., Bouman, R. W., et al. 2020. *Weda*, a new genus with two new species of Euphorbiaceae-Crotonoideae from Halmahera (North Maluku, Indonesia) and phylogenetic relationships of the Australasian tribe Ricinocarpeae. *Journal of Systematics and Evolution* 59(5): 1000–1017. https://doi.org/10.1111/jse.12581.

van Zanten, B. O. 1959. *Trachypodaceae*. A critical revision. *Blumea* 9: 477–475.

———. 2003. First record of the tropical Asian-Pacific genus *Powellia* Racopilaceae, Bryopsida) for the East African Islands, *P. pocsii* Zanzen spec. nov. and *P. elliptica* (Renb.) Zanten comb. nov. *Acta Academiae Paedagogicae Agriensis, Sectio Biologiae* 24: 23–28.

Vary, L. B., Gillen, D. L., Randrianjanahary, M., Lowry II, P. P., Sakai, A. K., and Weller, S. G. 2011. Dioecy, monoecy, and their ecological correlates in the littoral forest of Madagascar. *Biotropica* 43: 582–590.

Vasavirama, K., and Upender M. 2014. Piperine: A valuable alkaloid from *Piper* species. *International Journal of Pharmacy and Pharmaceutical Sciences* 6(4): 8–34.

Vasconcelos, T.N.C., Proença, C.E.B., Ahmad, B., Aguilar, D. S., Aguilar, R., et al. 2017. Myrtaceae phylogeny, calibration, biogeography and diversification patterns: Increased understanding in the most species rich tribe of Myrtaceae. *Molecular Phylogenetics and Evolution* 109: 113–137.

Vasey, N. 2000. Niche separation in *Varecia variegata rubra* and *Eulemur fulvus albifrons*: I. Interspecific patterns. *American Journal of Physical Anthropology* 112: 411–431.

Veitch, N. C., Kite, G. C., and Lewis, G. P. 2008. Flavonol pentaglycosides of *Cordyla* (Leguminosae: Papilionoideae: Swartzieae): Distribution and taxonomic implications. *Phytochemistry* 69(12): 2329–2335.

Veranso-Libalah, M. C., Stone, R. D., Fongod, A.G.N., Couvreur, T.L.P., and Kadereit, G. 2017. Phylogeny and systematics of African Melastomateae (Melastomataceae). *Taxon* 66: 584–614.

Veranso-Libalah, M. C., Kadereit, G., Stone, R. D., and Couvreur, T.L.P. 2018. Multiple shifts to open habitats in Melastomateae (Melastomataceae) congruent with the increase of African Neogene climatic aridity. *Journal of Biogeography* 45: 1420–1431.

Veranso-Libalah, M. C., Stone, R. D., and Kadereit, G. 2020. Towards a complete phylogeny of African Melastomateae: Systematics of *Dissotis* and allies (Melastomataceae). *Taxon* 69(5): 946–991.

Verdcourt, B. 1976. Rubiaceae. pt. 1. In *Flora of Tropical East Africa*, eds. W. B. Turill and R. M. Polhill, pp. 1–414. Rotterdam: Balkema.

———. 1983. Notes on Mascarenes Rubiaceae. *Kew Bulletin* 37: 521–574.

Veress, M., Loczy, D., Zentai, Z., Toth, G., and Schlaffer, R. 2008. The origin of the Bemaraha tsingy (Madagascar). *International Journal of Speleology* 37: 131–142.

Veyrières, P. de, and Meritens, G. de. 1967. *Le Livre de la sagesse malgache*. Paris: Editions Maritimes d'Outre-mer.

Vězda, A. 2004. Neue foliicole Flechten III. *Acta Musei Richnoviensis* Sect. Natur. 11(2): 58–72.

Vidal-Russell, R., and Nickrent D. L. 2008a. Evolutionary relationships in the showy mistletoe family (Loranthaceae). *American Journal of Botany* 95: 1015–1029.

———. 2008b. The first mistletoes: Origins of aerial parasitism in Santalales. *Molecular Phylogenetics and Evolution* 47: 523–527.

Vieilledent, G., Cornu, C., Cuní Sanchez, A., Leong Pock-Tsy, J.-M., and Danthu, P. 2013. Vulnerability of baobab species to climate change and effectiveness of the protected area network in Madagascar: Towards new conservation priorities. *Biological Conservation* 166(1): 11–22.

Villarreal, J. C., Cargill, C., Söderström, L., Hagborg, A., and von Konrat, M. J. 2015. Notes on early land plants today. 70. Nomenclatural notes in hornworts (Anthocerotophyta). *Phytotaxa* 208: 92–96.

Virtanen, R. 1997. The genus *Breutelia* (Bartramiaceae, Musci) in Southeast Asia and Oceania. *The Bryologist* 100: 324–348.

Viruel, J., Segarra-Moragues, J., Raz, L., Forest, F., Wilkin, P., Sanmartín, I., and Catalán, P. 2016. Late Cretaceous–Early Eocene origin of yams (*Dioscorea*, Dioscoreaceae) in the Laurasian Palaearctic and their subsequent Oligocene–Miocene diversification. *Journal of Biogeography* 43: 750–762.

Viruel, J., Conejero, M., Hidalgo, O., Pokorny, L., Powell, R. F., et al. 2019. A target capture-based method to estimate ploidy from herbarium specimens. *Frontiers in Plant Science* 10: 937.

Vollesen, K. 1989. A revision of *Megalochlamys* and *Ecbolium* (Acanthaceae: Justicieae). *Kew Bulletin* 44: 601–680.

———. 1990. The identity of *Clerodendrum brunsvigioides* Baker. *Kew Bulletin* 45: 343–344.

———. 1992. The Old World species of *Stenandrium*. *Kew Bulletin* 47: 169–202.

———. 1994. Taxonomy, ecology and distribution of *Nelsonia* (Acanthaceae) in Africa. In *Proceedings 13th Plenary Meeting AETFAT*, eds. J. H. Seyani, and A. C. Chikuni, pp. 315–325. Zomba, Zambia: Association for the Taxonomic Study of the Flora of Tropical Africa.

———. 1997. Synopsis of the genus *Crossandra* (Acanthaceae) in Madagascar. *Kew Bulletin* 52: 379–415.

———. 2000. Blepharis*, a Taxonomic Revision.* Kew: Royal Botanic Gardens.

Vololona, J., and Goodman, S. M. 2019. Morphométrie des fruits et des graines de *Ficus* (Moraceae) de la forêt sèche de la Réserve Spéciale d'Ankarana, Madagascar. *Malagasy Nature* 13: 52–59.

Vololona, J., Ramavovololona, P., Noroalintseheno Lalarivoniaina, O. S., and Goodman, S. M. 2020. Fleurs visitées par *Rousettus madagascariensis* G. Grandidier, 1928 (Chiroptera: Pteropodidae) dans la Réserve Spéciale de l'Ankarana, Madagascar. *Bulletin de la Société Zoologique de France* 145: 49–67.

Von Teichman, I. 1992. Notes on the ovule and partially pachychalazal seed of *Opercularya decaryi* H. Perrier (Anacardiaceae) from Madagascar. *Botanical Bulletin of Academia Sinica* 33: 289–293.

Von Teichman, I., and Van Wyk, A. E. 1996. Taxonomic significance of pericarp and seed structure in *Heeria argentea* (Thunb.) Meisn. (Anacardiaceae), including reference to pachychalazal and recalcitrance. *Botanical Journal of the Linnean Society* 122: 335–352.

Vorontsova, M. S. 2013. Variable morphology of the Madagascar endemic *Aristida tenuissima* (Poaceae: Aristidoideae) and the absence of *Stipa* (Poaceae: Pooideae, Stipeae) from Madagascar. *Phytotaxa* 92: 55–58.

———. 2017. *Digitaria bosseri* (Poaceae: Panicoideae), a new species from Madagascar. *Kew Bulletin* 72: 29.

———. 2018. Revision of the group previously known as *Panicum* L. (Poaceae: Panicoideae) in Madagascar. *Candollea* 73: 143–186.

Vorontsova, M. S., and Hoffmann, P. 2008. A phylogenetic classification of the tribe Poranthereae (Phyllanthaceae, Euphorbiaceae *sensu lato*). *Kew Bulletin* 63: 41–59.

Vorontsova, M. S., and Rakotoarisoa, S. E. 2014. Endemic non-bambusoid genera of grasses (Poaceae) in Madagascar: Review of current knowledge. *Malagasy Nature* 8: 14–34.

Vorontsova, M. S., Hoffmann, P., Maurin, O., and Chase, M. W. 2007. Molecular phylogenetics of the tribe *Poranthereae* (Phyllanthaceae; *Euphorbiaceae sensu lato*). *American Journal of Botany* 94(12): 2026–2040.

Vorontsova, M. S., Ratovonirina, G., and Randriamboavonjy, T. 2013. Revision of *Andropogon* and *Diectomis* (Poaceae: Sacchareae) in Madagascar and the new *Andropogon itremoensis* from the Itremo Massif. *Kew Bulletin* 68: 193–207.

Vorontsova, M. S., Nanjarisoa, O. P., and Besnard, G. 2014. Three new grass records for Madagascar. In Notes on the flora of Madagascar 36, eds. M. Callmander and P. Phillipson. *Candollea* 69: 85–87.

Vorontsova, M. S., Haevermans, T., Haevermans, A., Razanatsoa, J., Lundgren, M. R., and Besnard, G. 2015. The genus *Sartidia* (Poaceae: Aristidoideae) in Madagascar. *Systematic Botany* 40: 448–453.

Vorontsova, M. S., Besnard, G., Forest, F., Malakasi, P., Moat, J., et al. 2016. Madagascar's grasses and grasslands: Anthropogenic or natural? *Proceedings of the Royal Society of London B: Biological Sciences* 283: 20152262.

Vorontsova M. S., Dransfield, S., Renvoize, S. A., Besnard, G., McRobb, A., Razanatsoa, J., Nanjarisoa, O. P., Rakotoarisoa, S. E., and Ralimanana, H. 2018. *Identification Guide to Grasses and Bamboos in Madagascar.* Kew: Royal Botanic Gardens.

Vorontsova, M. S., Besnard, G., Razanatsoa, J., and Hackel, J. 2019. The endemic "sugar canes" of Madagascar (Poaceae, Saccharinae: *Lasiorhachis*) are close relatives of sorghum. *Botanical Journal of the Linnean Society* 192: 148–164.

Vorontsova, M. S., Lowry II, P. P., Andriambololonera, S. R., Wilmé, L., Rasolohery, A., Govaerts, R., Ficinski, S. Z., and Humphreys, A. M. 2020. Inequality in plant diversity knowledge and unrecorded plant extinctions: An example from the grasses of Madagascar. *Plants People Planet* 3(15): 45-60. https://doi.org/10.1002/ppp3.10123.

Wahlert, G. A. 2010. Phylogeny, biogeography, and a taxonomic revision of *Rinorea* (Violaceae) from Madagascar and the Comoro Islands. PhD thesis, Ohio University, Athens.

———. 2016. Novelties from the northern mountains complex of Madagascar IV: A new *Rinorea* Aubl. (Violaceae) of restricted range from the Galoko and Kalabinono massifs. *Candollea* 71: 195–200.

Wahlert, G. A., and Ballard, H. E., Jr. 2012. A phylogeny of *Rinorea* (Violaceae) inferred from plastid DNA sequences with an emphasis on the African and Malagasy species. *Systematic Botany* 37: 964–973.

Wahlert, G. A., Nusbaumer, L., and Gautier, L. 2013. *Rinorea ranirisonii* Nusb. and Wahlert (Violaceae): A new species from the Daraina region of northern Madagascar. *Candollea* 68: 87–92.

Wahlert, G. A., Nusbaumer, L., and Ranirison, P. 2014. *Grewia gautieri* Wahlert and Nusb. (Malvaceae, Grewioideae): A new species from Madagascar. *Candollea* 69(2): 149–155. https://doi.org/10.15553/c2014v692a6.

Wahlert, G. A., Phillipson, P. B., and Lowry II, P. P. 2015. A new species of *Grewia* L. (Malvaceae, Grewioideae) from northeastern Madagascar. *Candollea* 70(2): 201–205. https://doi.org/10.15553/c2015v702a4.

Wahlert, G. A., Phillipson, P. B., Mabberley, D. J., and Lowry II, P. P. 2016. *Grewia hispidissima* Wahlert, Phillipson and Mabb., sp. nov. (Malvaceae, Grewioideae): A new species of restricted range from northwestern Madagascar. *Adansonia*, série 3, 38(1): 117–121. https://doi.org/10.5252/a2016n1a7.

Wahlert, G. A., Hoyos-Goméz, S. E., and Ballard, H. E., Jr. 2017. Systematic studies in Neotropical *Rinorea* (Violaceae): Two new sections and a new generic segregate. *Brittonia* 70: 140–147.

Wahlert, G. A., Phillipson, P. B., and Callmander, M. W. 2019. *Astrotrichilia leroyana*, sp. nov. (Meliaceae, Melioideae): A new species from northeastern Madagascar. *Adansonia*, série 3, 41(10): 91–96.

Wahlert, G. A., Gilland, K. E., and Ballard, H. E., Jr. 2020. Taxonomic revision of *Rinorea ilicifolia* (Violaceae) in Africa and Madagascar. *Kew Bulletin* 75: 12. https://doi.org/10.1007/s12225-020-9866-6.

Wallander, E., and Albert, V. A. 2000. Phylogeny and classification of Oleaceae based on *rps16* and *trnL-F* sequence data. *American Journal of Botany* 87: 1827–1841.

Walther, R. 1994. Pollenfracht als indikator für ressourcennutzung und einnischung bei madagassischen Schwärmern (Lepidoptera). PhD thesis, Friedrich-Alexander University, Erlangen-Nürnberg.

Wanasundera, J.P.D., and Ravindran, G. 1994. Nutritional assessment of yam (*Dioscorea alata*) tubers. *Plant Foods for Human Nutrition* 46: 33–39.

Wang, N., Yang, Y., Moore, M. J., Brockington, S. F., Walker, J. F., et al. 2018. Evolution of Portulacineae marked by gene tree conflict and gene family expansion associated with adaptation to harsh environments. *Molecular Biology and Evolution* 36: 112–126.

Wannan, B. S., and Quinn, C. J. 1990. Pericarp structure and generic affinities in the Anacardiaceae. *Botanical Journal of the Linnean Society* 102: 225–252.

———. 1991. Floral structure and evolution in the Anacardiaceae. *Botanical Journal of the Linnean Society* 107: 349–385.

Warren, B. H., Strasberg, D., Bruggemann, J. H., Robert P. Prys-Jones, R. P., and Thébaud, C. 2010. Why does the biota of the Madagascar region have such a strong Asiatic flavour? *Cladistics* 26: 526–538.

Wassel, A. C., and Applequist, W. L. 2020. A revision of *Homalium* sect. *Nisa* (Salicaceae) endemic to Madagascar. *Candollea* 75: 585–602.

Watling, M. C., and O'Shea, B. 2000. British Bryological Society expedition to Mulanje Mountain, Malawi. 11. A revision of the genus *Rhacopilopsis* Renauld and Cardot (Hypnaceae, Bryopsida). *Journal of Bryology* 22: 207–216.

Watson, D. M. 2001. Mistletoe—a keystone resource in forests and woodlands worldwide. *Annual Review of Ecology and Systematics* 32: 219–249.

Watson, D. M., and Herring, M. 2012. Mistletoe as a keystone resource: An experimental test. *Proceedings of the Royal Society of London B: Biological Sciences* 279: 3853–3860.

WCSP. 2020. World Checklist of Selected Plant Families. Facilitated by the Royal Botanic Gardens, Kew. Accessed 22 Apr. 2020. http://apps.kew.org/wcsp/.

Weber, O., Wilkin, P., and Rakotonasolo, F. 2005. A new species of edible yam (*Dioscorea* L.) from western Madagascar. *Kew Bulletin* 60(2): 283–291.

Weberling, F. 1989. *Morphology of flowers and inflorescences*. Cambridge: Cambridge University Press.

Webster, G. L. 1993. A provisional synopsis of the sections of the genus *Croton* (Euphorbiaceae). *Taxon* 42: 793–823.

———. 1994. Synopsis of the genera and suprageneric taxa of Euphorbiaceae. *Annals of the Missouri Botanical Garden* 81: 33–144.

———. 2014. Euphorbiaceae. In *The Families and Genera of Vascular Plants*, vol. XI. *Flowering plants. Eudicots. Malpighiales*, ed. K. Kubitzki, pp. 51–216. Berlin: Springer.

Weeks, A., and Simpson, B. B. 2007. Molecular phylogenetic analysis of *Commiphora* (Burseraceae) yields insight on the evolution and historical biogeography of an "impossible" genus. *Molecular Phylogenetics and Evolution* 42: 62–79.

Weeks, A., Daly, D. C., and Simpson, B. B. 2005. The phylogenetic history and biogeography of the frankincense and myrrh family (Burseraceae) based on nuclear and chloroplast sequence data. *Molecular Phylogenetics and Evolution* 35: 85–101.

Weeks, A., Zapata, A., Pell, S. K., Daly, D. C., Mitchell, J., and Fine, P.V.A. 2014. To move or to evolve: Contrasting patterns and climatic niche evolution in "Terebinthaceae" (Anacardiaceae and Burseraceae). *Frontiers in Genetics* 5: 1–20.

Weigend, M., Luebert, F., Gottschling, M., Couvreur, T.L.P., Hilger, H. H., and Miller, J. S. 2014. From capsules to nutlets—Phylogenetic relationships in the Boraginales. *Cladistics* 30: 508–518.

Weil, M., Descroix, F., Sing, A.S.C., Boulanger, R., Hoarau, M., Levesque, A., and Bohuon, P. 2014. Postharvest treatments of wild pepper (*Piper* spp.) in Madagascar. *Fruits* 69(5): 371–380.

WFO. 2020. World Flora Online. Accessed 16 Aug. 2020. http://www.worldfloraonline.org.

White, F. 1980. Notes on the Ebenaceae VIII. The African sections of *Diospyros*. *Bulletin du Jardin Botanique National de Belgique* 50: 445–460.

Whitlock, B. A., and Hale, A. M. 2011. The phylogeny of *Ayenia*, *Byttneria*, and *Rayleya* (Malvaceae *s.l.*) and its implications for the evolution of growth forms. *Systematic Botany* 36(1): 129–136. https://doi.org/10.1600/036364411X553216.

Whitlock, B. A., Bayer, C., and Baum, D. A. 2001. Phlyogenetic relationships and floral evolution of the Byttnerioideae ("Sterculiaceae" or Malvaceae *s.l.*) based on sequences of the chloroplast gene *ndhF*. *Systematic Botany* 26(2): 420–437.

Whitlock, B. A., Hale, A. M., Indorf, J. L., and Wilkins, C. F. 2011. Polyphyly of *Rulingia* and *Commersonia* (Lasiopetalae, Malvaceae *s.l.*). *Australian Systematic Botany* 24: 215–225. https://doi.org/10.1071/SB09030.

Wickens, G. E. 1983. The baobab: Africa's upside-down tree. *Kew Bulletin* 37: 173–209.

Wickens, G. E., and Lowe, P. 2008. *The Baobabs: Pachycauls of Africa, Madagascar and Australia*. London: Springer Science and Business Media.

Wiebes, J. T. 1963. Taxonomy and host plant preference of Indo-Australian fig wasps of the genus *Ceratosolen* (Agaonidae). *Tijdschrift voor Entomologie* 106: 1–112.

Wiens, D. 1975. Chromosome numbers in African and Malagasy Loranthaceae and Viscaceae. *Botanical Journal of the Linnaean Society* 71: 295–310.

Wiens, D., and Barlow, B. A. 1979. Translocation heterozygosity and the origin of dioecy in *Viscum*. *Heredity* 42: 201–222.

Wigginton, M. J. 2018. Checklist and distribution of the liverworts and hornworts of sub-Saharan Africa, including the East African Islands. *Tropical Bryology Research* 9(4): 1–138.

Wikström, N., Avino, M., Razafimandimbison, S. G., and Bremer, B. 2010. Historical biogeography of the coffee family (Rubiaceae, Gentianales) in Madagascar: Case studies from the tribes Knoxieae, Naucleeae, Paederieae and Vanguerieae. *Journal of Biogeography* 37: 1094–1113.

Wikström, N., Kainulainen, K., Razafimandimbison, S. G, Smedmark, J. E., and Bremer, B. 2015. A revised time tree of the asterids: Establishing a temporal framework for evolutionary studies of the coffee family (Rubiaceae). *PLoS One* 10: e0126690.

Wilbraham, J. 2016. Taxonomic notes on African Orthotrichaceae I. New synonymy in *Macromitrium*. *Journal of Bryology* 38: 1–7.

Wilding, N. 2016. Systematics, biogeography and morphological evolution in *Entosthodon* Schwägr. (Bryopsida, Funariaceae) with a revision of the genus in Africa. PhD thesis, University of Cape Town, South Africa.

Wilkie, P., Clark, A., Pennington, R. T., Cheek, M., Bayer, C., and Wilcock, C. C. 2006. Phylogenetic relationships within the subfamily Sterculioideae (Malvaceae/Sterculiaceae-Sterculieae) using the chloroplast gene *ndhF*. *Systematic Botany* 31(1): 160–170. https://doi.org/10.1600/036364406775971714.

Wilkin, P., Caddick, L. R., Foster, C., and Schols, P. 2000. A new species of *Dioscorea* (Dioscoreaceae) from eastern Madagascar and its pollen morphology. *Kew Bulletin* 55: 427–434.

Wilkin, P., Rakotonasolo, F., Schols, P., and Furness, C. A. 2002. A new species of *Dioscorea* (*Dioscoreaceae*) from western Madagascar and its pollen morphology. *Kew Bulletin* 57(4): 901–909.

Wilkin, P., Schols, P., Chase, M. W., Chayamarit, K., Furness, C. A., et al. 2005. A plastid gene phylogeny of the yam genus, *Dioscorea*: Roots, fruits and Madagascar. *Systematic Botany* 30(4): 736–749.

Wilkin, P., Hladik, A., Labat, J.-N., and Barthelat, F. 2007. A new edible yam (*Dioscorea* L.) species endemic to Mayotte, new data on *D. comorensis* R. Knuth and a key to the yams of the Comoro Archipelago. *Adansonia*, série 3, 29(2): 215–228.

Wilkin, P., Rajaonah, M. T., Jeannoda, V., Hladik, A., Jeannoda, V., and Hladik, C. M. 2008a. An endangered new species of edible yam (*Dioscorea*, *Dioscoreaceae*) from western Madagascar. *Kew Bulletin* 63(1): 113–120.

Wilkin, P., Andrianantenaina, W. P., Jeannoda, V., and Hladik A. 2008b. The species of *Dioscorea* L. (*Dioscoreaceae*) from Madagascar with campanulate tori, including a new species from eastern Madagascar. *Kew Bulletin* 63(4): 583–600.

Wilkin, P., Hladik, A., Jeannoda, V., and Weber, O. 2009a. The threatened edible yams of the *Dioscorea sambiranensis* R. Knuth species complex: A new species and subspecies. *Adansonia* 31(2): 249–266.

Wilkin, P., Weber, O., Hladik, A., Hladik, C. M., and Jeannoda, V. 2009b. A threatened new species of edible yam (*Dioscorea* L.) from northern Madagascar. *Kew Bulletin* 64(3): 461–468.

Wilkin, P., Kennerley, J. A., Rajaonah, M. T., Huckel, G. M., Rakotoarison, F., Randriamboavonjy, T., and Cable, S. 2017. A new species of critically endangered edible yam endemic to northern Madagascar, *Dioscorea irodensis* (Dioscoreaceae) and its conservation. *Kew Bulletin* 72: 15.

Wilkins, C. F., and Whitlock, B. A. 2011. A revision of *Commersonia* including *Rulingia* (Malvaceae *s.l.* or Byttneriaceae). *Australian Systematic Botany* 24: 226–283. https://doi.org/10.1071/SB10031.

Wilkins, C. F., and Whitlock, B. A. 2015. *Seringia* revised to include *Keraudrenia* (Lasiopetalae: Malvaceae *s.l.*). *Australian Systematic Botany* 28: 265–325. https://doi.org/10.1071/SB15028.

Wilmé, L., Goodman, S. M., and Ganzhorn, J. U. 2006. Biogeographic evolution of Madagascar's microendemic biota. *Science* 312(5776): 1063–1065. https://doi.org/10.1126/science.1122806.

Wilson, P. G. 2011. Myrtaceae. In *The Families and Genera of Vascular Plants*. Vol. X. *Flowering plants: Eudicots, Sapindales, Cucurbitales, Myrtaceae*, ed. K. Kubitzki, pp. 212–271. New York: Springer.

Wilson, P. G., O'Brien, M. M., Heslewood, M. M., and Quinn, C. J. 2005. Relationships within Myrtaceae *sensu lato* based on a *mat*K phylogeny. *Plant Systematics and Evolution* 251: 3–19.

Wink, M. 2020. Evolution of the Angiosperms and co-evolution of secondary metabolites, especially of alkaloids. In *Co-Evolution of Secondary Metabolites*, eds. J.-M. Mérillon and K. G. Ramawat, pp. 151–174, Cham: Springer International.

Winzer, L. F., Carnegie, A. J., Pegg, G. S., and Leishman, M. R. 2018. Impacts of the invasive fungus *Austropuccinia psidii* (myrtle rust) on three Australian Myrtaceae species of coastal swamp woodland. *Austral Ecology* 43: 56–68.

Wittle, P. M., and Davis, A. P. 2010. A revision of Madagascan *Bertiera* (Rubiaceae). *Blumea* 55: 105–110.

World Conservation Monitoring Centre. 1998. *Adansonia madagascariensis*. The IUCN Red List of Threatened Species 1998: e.T37681A10066258.

Wright, C. H. 1888. Mosses of Madagascar. *Journal of Botany* 26: 263–268.

Wright, P. C., Tecot, S. R., Erhart, E. M., Baden, A. L., King, S. J., and Grassi, C. 2011. Frugivory in four sympatric lemurs: Implications for the future of Madagascar's forests. *American Journal of Primatology* 73: 585–602.

Wurdack, K. J., and Davis, C. C. 2009. Malpighiales phylogenetics: Gaining ground on one of the most recalcitrant clades in the angiosperm tree of life. *American Journal of Botany* 96: 1551–1570.

Wurdack, K. J., Hoffmann, P., Chase, M. W., Samuel, R., De Bruijn, A. Y., and Van Der Bank, M. 2004. Molecular phylogenetic analysis of Phyllanthaceae (Phyllantideae *pro parte*, Euphorbiaceae *sensu lato*) using plastid *rbcL* DNA sequences. *American Journal of Botany* 91: 1882–1900.

Wurdack, K. J., Hoffmann, P., and Chase, M. W. 2005. Molecular phylogenetic analysis of uniovulate Euphorbiaceae (Euphorbiaceae *sensu stricto*) using plastid *rbcL* and *trnL-F* DNA sequences. *American Journal of Botany* 92: 1397–1420.

Xi, Z., Rhufel, B. R., Schaefer, H., Amorim, A. M., Sugumaran, M., et al. 2012. Phylogenomics and *a posteriori* data partitioning resolve the Cretaceous angiosperm radiation Malpighiales. *Proceedings of the National Academy of Sciences of the USA* 109: 17519–17524.

Yamada, K. 1975. Memoranda on the type specimens of *Radula* taxa from the Southeast Asia. *Journal of the Hattori Botanical Laboratory* 39: 71–84.

Yang, Y., Riina, R., Morawetz, J. J., Haevermans, T., Aubriot, X., and Berry, P. E. 2012. Molecular phylogenetics and classification of *Euphorbia* subgenus *Chamaesyce* (Euphorbiaceae). *Taxon* 61: 764–789.

Yoder, A. D., and Nowak, M. D. 2006. Has vicariance or dispersal been the predominant biogeographic force in Madagascar? Only time will tell. *Annual Review of Ecology, Evolution, and Systematics* 37: 405–431.

Yuncker, T. G. 1953. *The "Piperaceae" of Argentina, Bolivia and Chile*, vol. 27. Tucuman: Universidad Nacional de Tucuman, Instituto Miguel Lillo.

Zaborsky, J. G. 2009. *Hildegardia dauphinensis* (Malvaceae, Sterculioideae): A new species from southeastern Madagascar. *Adansonia* 31(1): 143–148. https://doi.org/10.5252/a2009n1a8.

Zander, R. H. 1972. Revision of the genus *Leptodontium* (Musci) in the New World. *The Bryologist* 75: 213–280.

Zemagho, L., Liede-Schumann, S., Sonké, B., and Dessein, S. 2016. Phylogenetics of tribe Sabiceeae (Ixoroideae, Rubiaceae) revisited, with a new subgeneric classification for *Sabicea*. *Botanical Journal of the Linnean Society* 182: 551–580.

Zhang, Q., Onstein, R. E., Little, S. A., and Sauquet, H. 2019. Estimating divergence times and ancestral breeding systems in *Ficus* and Moraceae. *Annals of Botany* 123: 191–204.

Zhang, Y. X., Ma, P. F., Haevermans, T., Vorontsova, M. S., Zhang, T., Nanjarisoa, O. P., and Li, D. Z. 2017. In search of the phylogenetic affinity of the temperate woody bamboos from Madagascar, with description of a new species (Bambusoideae, Poaceae). *Journal of Systematics and Evolution* 55: 453–465.

Zhou, Q., Lin, C.-W., Ng, W. L., Dai, J., Denda, T., Zhou, R., and Liu, Y. 2019. Analyses of plastome sequences improve phylogenetic resolution and provide new insight into the evolutionary history of Asian Sonerileae/Dissochaeteae. *Frontiers in Plant Science* 10: 1477. https://doi.org/10.3389/fpls.2019.01477.

Zhu, R. L., and Gradstein, S. R. 2005. Monograph of *Lopholejeunea* (Lejeuneaceae, Hepaticae) in Asia. *Systematic Botany Monographs* 74: 98.

Zhu, R. L., and Grolle, R. 2001. Notes on the taxonomy and distribution of *Acanthocoleus yoshinaganus* and *Lejeunea papilionacea* (Hepaticae, Lejeuneaceae). *Annales Botanici Fennici* 38(4): 329–336.

———. 2003. On the genus *Capillolejeunea* (Lejeuneaceae, Hepaticae) from the East African Islands. *Systematic Botany* 28(3): 467–470.

Zhu, R. L., and So, M. L. 2001. Epiphyllous liverworts of China. *Beiheft zur Nova Hedwigia* 121: 1–418.

Zizka, A., Carvalho-Sobrinho J. G., Pennington, R. T., Queiroz, L. P., Alcantara, S., Baum, D. A., Bacon, C. D., and Antonelli. A. 2020. Transitions between biomes are common and directional in Bombacoideae (Malvaceae). *Journal of Biogeography* 47(6): 1310–1321. https://doi.org/10.1111/jbi.13815.

Zjhra, M. L. 2006. New taxa of Coleeae (Bignoniaceae) from Madagascar. I. A collection from Masoala Peninsula. *Annales Botanici Fennici* 43: 225–239.

———. 2008. Facilitating sympatric species coexistence via pollinator partitioning in endemic tropical trees of Madagascar. *Plant Systematics and Evolution* 271: 157–176.

Zjhra, M. L., Sytsma, K. J., and Olmstead, R. G. 2004. Delimitation of Malagasy tribe Coleeae and implications for fruit evolution in Bignoniaceae inferred from a chloroplast DNA phylogeny. *Plant Systematics and Evolution* 245: 55–67.

Zomlefer, W. B. 1993. A revision of *Rigodium* (Musci: Rigodiaceae). *The Bryologist* 96: 1–72.

Zuloaga F. O., Salariato D. L., and Scataglini A. 2018. Molecular phylogeny of *Panicum s.str.* (Poaceae, Panicoideae, Paniceae) and insights into its biogeography and evolution. *PLoS One* 13: e0191529.

CHAPTER 9

INVERTEBRATES

INTRODUCTION TO INVERTEBRATES

B. L. Fisher

After a visit to Fort Dauphin (now Tolagnaro) in 1770, Philibert Commerson wrote a letter to the French astronomer and historian of science Joseph Jérôme Lefrançois de Lalande describing the island: "What an admirable country is Madagascar! It is the veritable Promised Land for naturalists. It is there that Nature seems to have retired as into a special sanctuary, to work there on other models than those to which she enslaved herself in other countries. The Dioscoride of the North [Linnaeus] would find there the stuff of ten revised and enlarged editions of his *Systema Naturae*, and would doubtless finish by avowing that merely a corner of the veil that covers the scattered productions of nature had been lifted" (Commerson 1772; translation by the author). These early proclamations on the uniqueness and richness of the island's biodiversity were the harbingers of what would become more clearly known after several centuries of biological exploration. This long history of discovery of the island's invertebrates, as well as many other groups of plants and animals, has shed light on their evolution, history of colonization, and speciation, and revealed astonishing levels of endemicity. Here I review many of those who made contributions toward lifting the veil on invertebrate diversity on the island, and conclude with a reflection on the future of invertebrate research.

EARLY COLLECTIONS

The scientific study of Madagascar's invertebrates commenced with the arrival of European visitors. Natural history had played a part (Pratt 2008) in most European-imperial voyages of discovery since the time of Linnaeus, whether or not an expedition was primarily scientific, or the traveler a trained scientist or natural historian (see Andriamialisoa and Langrand, pp. 1–38, for further details on this age of exploration specifically for vertebrates). Any traveler could contribute natural history findings as long as they had a notebook and a collecting bag. This is illustrated in a publication by Alfred Grandidier—an individual who was a major force in the advancement of different types of scientific research on the island—which provides a useful summary of visitors prior to 1890 who contributed to the understanding of Madagascar's biological wonders. Grandidier's review indicates where and what year the person visited, and whether each was primarily a naturalist, doctor, merchant, missionary, or government or colonial worker (Grandidier 1892: 206).

One of the first European naturalists to collect insects on Madagascar was Philibert Commerson, who visited the island from October 1770 to January 1771, principally around the Tolagnaro region. A portion of his collection made it to Paris in 1774 and was deposited in the Muséum National d'Histoire Naturelle (MNHN). Guillaume-Antoine Olivier (Olivier 1789) described a few of Commerson's Coleoptera (Scarabaeidae) specimens. At about the same time, Dru Drury (Drury 1773) described two iconic members of Lepidoptera from Madagascar (*Pharmacophagus antenor* and *Chrysiridia rhipheus*), although at the time, he made no indication that the collections were from Madagascar or who collected them. In 1829, Jules Prosper Goudot visited the island's east coast (see Andriamialisoa and Langrand, pp. 1–38 and Box 1, for a detailed profile of this naturalist-collector). Goudot's specimens were sold to Parisian merchants and later deposited in the MNHN in Paris, where many were described by Jean Baptiste Boisduval.

Thereafter, a steady stream of specimens from Madagascar began to arrive in European museums. The growing European knowledge-gathering enterprise was linked to the expanding search for resources to exploit and lands to colonize (Pratt 2008). In 1830, Henry Dupont visited the east coast of Madagascar to collect specimens of Lepidoptera and Coleoptera destined for the Berlin Museum; these were described by Johann Christoph Friedrich Klug (Klug 1833). In 1831, Gustave Poutier, a naval officer, sent back to the British Museum (Natural History) (BMNH; which would become the Natural History Museum, London) a considerable quantity of butterflies collected on La Réunion and at Tintingue, along Madagascar's central east coast. From 1831 to 1832, Victor Sganzin, a naval artillery captain and commander of Ile Sainte Marie (which France had annexed in 1821) sent to France a rich collection of butterflies and biological notes from Madagascar, La Réunion, and Mauritius. In 1834, Alphonse Charles Joseph Bernier, a surgeon with the French Navy who collected in Madagascar from 1831 to 1834, sent a diverse collection of Coleoptera specimens to the MNHN. Charles Coquerel, a naval surgeon, collected insects during his visits to Madagascar and La Réunion in 1846 and again in 1852. Louis Hyacinthe Boivin joined the Oise Expedition (1846–1852) and collected for MNHN. He suffered from malaria and died the day after his return to France. By the middle of the 19th century, a number of descriptions of Malagasy insects had been published by Boisduval, Klug, Achille Guenée, Félix Édouard Guérin-Méneville, and others.

In the latter half of the 19th century, a variety of commercial collectors, explorers, missionaries, and amateur naturalists continued to deliver specimens from Madagascar to European collections. These included James Caldwell, a member of General Montague Cholmeley Johnstone's British delegation to the 1862 coronation of King Radama II. He sent two shipments of insects from the area around Antananarivo to the BMNH, which were subsequently described by William Chapman Hewitson, Francis Walker, and Henry Walter Bates. Other British collectors, many associated with the London Missionary Society, included Reverends Robert Toy, George A. Shaw, and W. Deans Cowan, as well as Alfred Crossley (see Andriamialisoa and Langrand, pp. 1–38 and Box 2, for a detailed profile of this naturalist-collector), and Abraham Kingdon, who sent Lepidoptera specimens to Arthur Gardiner Butler. Between 1864 and 1867, François Paul Louis Pollen and Douwe Casparus van Dam visited La Réunion, Mayotte, and the northwestern part of Madagascar in the general Nosy Be region. Their material was sent back to the Rijksmuseum van Natuurlijke Historie in Leiden and subsequently studied by Dutch entomologists.

Carl Grevé (Figure 9.1c) was the son of a taxidermist at the museum in Saint Denis, La Réunion, and in 1864, he joined the Pollen and van Dam Dutch expedition to northwest Madagascar as a preparator. After the two-year expedition, he decided to remain on the island, marrying the daughter of a Sakalava chief and living in Taolampia, near Morondava. He was part of the network of collectors working with Alfred Grandidier and collected mostly plants but also insects and fossils. In 1895, he was captured by Hova soldiers and imprisoned in the Fort de Mahabo, then executed a few days later by the Hova as French troops arrived in Majunga (Mahajanga) (Grandidier 1895).

Johann Maria Hildebrandt was a traveler and naturalist whose extensive collections were sent to the Königliches Museum für Naturkunde in Berlin. He died in Antananarivo in 1881, and his grave can still be seen in the Norwegian cemetery in Ambatovinaky. Franz Sikora, an Austrian collector, spent long periods with Hildebrandt at the Protestant mission in Andrangoloaka, 70 km east of the capital. He also collected in Anosibe (Moramanga). His collections from the last decade of the 19th century are partly preserved at the Naturhistorisches Museum, Vienna, and the MNHN. Louis Besson, a doctor in the French Navy, was appointed *vice-résident* in Fianarantsoa in 1886. Before leaving in 1906, he made important collections in the Central Highlands.

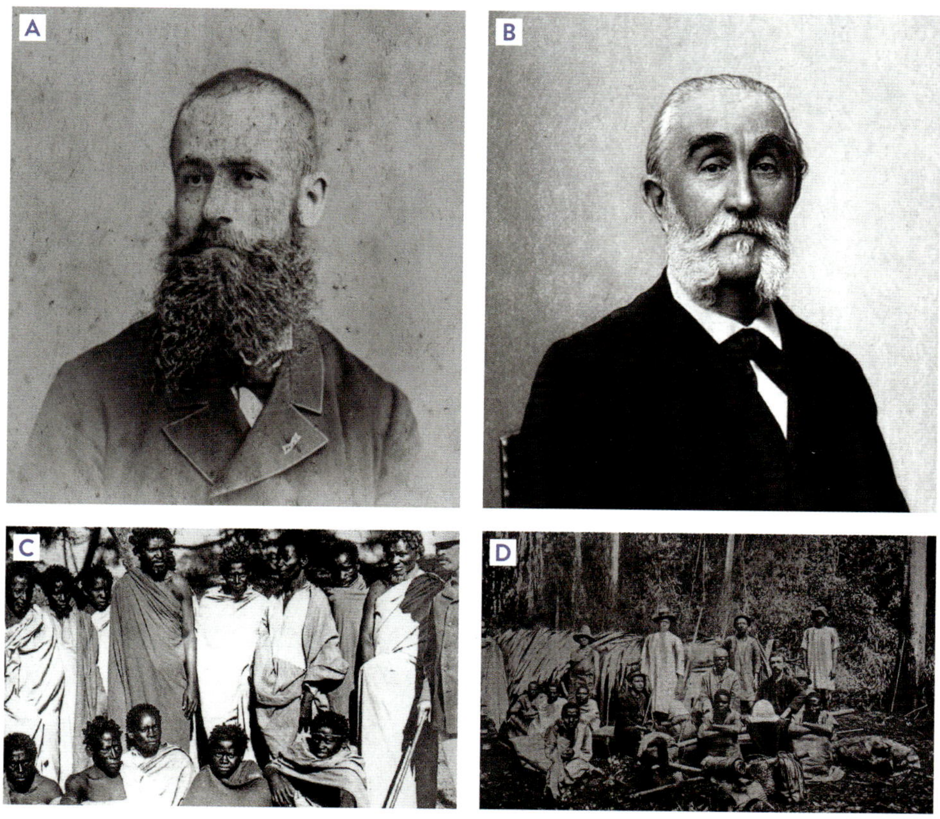

FIGURE 9.1 **Early collectors of invertebrates on Madagascar. A) Léon Joseph Henry Humblot (1852–1914) was a French naturalist. B) Alfred Grandidier (1836–1921), a French naturalist who traveled to Madagascar from 1865 to 1870. C) Carl Grevé (?–1895) (far right) visited Madagascar in the context of joining the Pollen and van Dam expedition in 1864 and collected for A. Grandidier until his death in 1895. His descendants still live in Morondava. D) The Perrot brothers' camp in Antsianaka, Lake Alaotra, January 1894. Edouard Perrot (1863–1903) is seated, holding the large white helmet.** (PHOTO A from BnF Gallica archive; B from Wikimedia; C from Actualites Morondava; and D from Vuillet 1911.)

William Henry O'Swald, whose father founded the commodity-trading company O'Swald & Co., expanded the firm's Zanzibar office to Madagascar and collected material from 1894 to 1889. His collections were deposited at the Musée de Hamburg (currently Zoologisches Institut und Museum der Universität, Hamburg, Germany, or ZMUH).

FRENCH COLONIZATION

In 1895, after the military intervention of the French led to the fall of the Merina kingdom, the French set up a colonial government in Madagascar. As French domination grew in Madagascar, more and more of the invertebrates collected on the island were funneled to the MNHN. Nosy Be, which France annexed earlier in 1841, was a frequent stop for colonial visitors and an important collecting locality. These collectors included Henri Pierron, a member of the municipal commission based in Diégo Suarez (Antsiranana), who made his living as a beef exporter and collected Lepidoptera specimens in both Nosy Be and the north of Madagascar in 1885; Edouard-Auguste Marie, a French civil servant on Nosy Be; and Jean Henri Jules Barre (referenced as Barre de Moussac), a port captain on La Réunion and Tamatave (to become Toamasina), who collected Lepidoptera.

In 1886, Conrad Keller collected specimens in all the French strongholds on Madagascar at the time: Diégo Bay (an important coal station), Nosy Be, Ile Sainte Marie, and Toamasina. Paul Camboué, a Jesuit priest, arrived in Madagascar in 1882 and spent 47 years working on the island. Most of his collections were made west of Antananarivo (Arivonimamo, Ambohibeloma) and Toamasina, and were sent to Charles Oberthur.

Léon Joseph Henry Humblot (Figure 9.1a) obtained specimens from the Lake Alaotra region, as well as the Comoro archipelago (specifically Grande Comore), where he died in 1914. Brothers Edouard and Benoni Perrot lived in Toamasina and collected along the north coast of Madagascar and many other localities starting in 1888 (see Andriamialisoa and Langrand, pp. 1–38, Box 3, on Charles Herschell-Chauvin for further details). The brothers ran a photography business in Toamasina and took images of people and habitats where they traveled (Figure 9.1d). Edouard Perrot also accompanied General Joseph Simon Gallieni as a photographer around Madagascar in the spring of 1898 (Anonymous 1901). Other missionary collectors in the late 1800s included Monsignor Jean-Baptiste Cazet, astronomer Edouard Elie Colin, and cartographer Désiré Roblet.

Toward the end of 19th century, the study of Madagascar's arthropods became more organized and focused. In 1875, Alfred Grandidier (Figure 9.1b), who had a keen interest in mammals and birds, began editing his monumental work, *Histoire physique, naturelle et politique de Madagascar* (see Andriamialisoa and Langrand, pp. 1–38, for more details). The series was based on the French scientist's fieldwork on the island in 1865, 1866, and 1868–1870, but also on the work of an extensive and loyal network of collectors that continued to funnel material to him and the MNHN after his return to France (Monnier 2017). Following his death, the series continued with a range of collaborators, including his son, Guillaume Grandidier, whom he had mentored from an early age. The series ultimately totaled 39 volumes in 57 parts published between 1885 and 1954. It includes two volumes on Lepidoptera (volumes 18 and 19), one volume on Hymenoptera (volume 20), two volumes on Coleoptera (volumes 21 and 22), one volume on Orthoptera (volume 23), and one volume on Myriapods (volume 27).

Charles Alluaud from the MNHN visited Madagascar three times in search of lepidopterans. His first voyage, in 1893, landed him in Diégo Suarez, Montagne des Français, and Montagne d'Ambre. Alluaud returned to Madagascar from 1900 to 1901 under the auspices of General Joseph Simon Gallieni and his adjunct, Louis Hubert Gonzalve Lyautey, who provided logistical support. They traveled throughout the south, collecting in areas never before sampled. Alluaud made one final trip to Madagascar on his way back from an expedition with Dr. René Jeannel to Kenya and Mount Kilimanjaro between 1911 and 1912. They stopped in Mahajanga, Nosy Be, Antsiranana, and Montagne d'Ambre. From 1904 to 1907, Martin François Geay made several trips to Madagascar for the MNHN, collecting in many areas of the country.

Albert Mocquerys was a merchant based in Antanambe, south of Antongil Bay. Some of his collections ended up at MNHN. During an extended trip to Madagascar and eastern Africa from 1903 to 1905, Alfred Voeltzkow, a German photographer, and his collaborators made extensive collections in different areas of the island, including the west (Menabe, Mahajanga, Soalala, Andranohinaly, and near Toliara), the east (Fenérive Est, Ile Sainte Marie, Ile aux Prunes, and Toamasina), and the Central Highlands (Lake Itasy and Fianarantsoa). These collections were deposited in the Zoologischen Museum, Berlin.

BETWEEN THE WORLD WARS

One of the most notable French invertebrate collectors was Raymond Decary. He was an administrator in the French Overseas Office who arrived in Antsiranana in 1916 and spent 27 years obtaining material that was deposited in the MNHN. In later years, he was stationed at Beloha in the far south and continued to collect and send specimens back to France until mobilized for military duty in 1942. In 1950, he published a book on the fauna of Madagascar (Decary 1950), which today is still a rich source of information.

Another important figure in Madagascar arthropod studies was André Seyrig, who moved to Madagascar in 1928. A mining engineer by training, he managed a mica mine at Ampandrandava near Betroka for 15 years. He was also interested in ichneumon wasps and was a corresponding member of the MNHN. He deposited in that institution many specimens of various orders from Betroka and Bekily, as well as from Montagne d'Ambre, Périnet (Andasibe), Anivorano (District de Brickaville), and Ankaratra, among other sites. In 1945, Seyrig was accused of spying in the service of Germany on the basis of his German-sounding surname and false testimony. He was arrested, imprisoned, and slaughtered by a fellow detainee who suspiciously was armed with a knife. After his tragic death, his young niece, Delphine Seyrig, dedicated her new theater career to the legacy of her murdered uncle and was instrumental in the production of one of the most significant theatrical works of the century, *Waiting for Godot*, by Samuel Beckett (Youngerman 2016).

By the early part of the 20th century, the substantial entomological holdings from Madagascar at the MNHN far surpassed those in any other European museum. As a result, Paris became the de facto source for reference materials on Madagascar's arthropods. Researchers from across Europe came to Paris to study the invertebrate fauna of "the Grand Island." For instance, the Spanish padre Longinos Navás described hundreds of species of Malagasy Neuroptera, Trichoptera, and Odonata from the MNHN's collections from 1910 to 1936.

AFTER WORLD WAR II

After World War II, reorganization of the collections at the MNHN made the Madagascar arthropod material easier to access for foreign scientists. Major advances in understanding the diversity of Malagasy arthropod fauna were made during this period. In 1947, the Institut de Recherche Scientifique de Madagascar (IRSM) was created as a department within the Office de la Recherche Scientifique et Technique Outre-Mer (ORSTOM), which many decades later became Institut de Recherche pour le Développement (IRD). With Jacques Millot as director and Renard Paulian as deputy director, the pace of Malagasy fauna studies markedly accelerated.

Three principal publishing outlets presented ORSTOM's scientific findings during this period, including those concerning the invertebrates of Madagascar. The *Faune de Madagascar* was launched by Renaud Paulian in 1956 as the principal vehicle to describe the island's fauna. In total, 94 volumes of the monograph series were published until the series was suspended in late 2011. Two other major publication series on the Madagascar arthropod fauna were *Le Naturaliste Malgache* and *Mémoires de l'Institut Scientifique de Madagascar*. The former was published by IRSM in 13 volumes between 1949 and 1962, while the latter was published in several series, two of which—série A, *Biologie animale*; and série E, *Entomologie*—contained articles on invertebrates. Série A was published in 14 volumes between 1948 and 1960, and série E was published in 13 volumes between 1952 and 1962.

André Peyriéras moved to Madagascar in 1954 with the idea to become a forester (see Andriamialisoa and Langrand, pp. 1–38, Box 5, for more details on this remarkable man). After meeting Jean Vadon in Maroantsetra, he changed his focus to collecting insects across the island. He adapted to economic and political changes in 1974 and started breeding rare and endangered insects and reptiles at a captive center near Mandraka.

Brian Stuckenberg, based at the Natal Museum in South Africa, traveled to Madagascar from December 1955 to January 1956, and again between November 1957 and April 1958. Though focused on collecting Diptera, he and his colleagues amassed a diverse array of invertebrate specimens. His second trip was assisted by Paul Griveaud and Renaud Paulian (see expedition itinerary in Kirk-Spriggs 2012).

In 1959, Edward S. Ross made an expedition to Madagascar from the California Academy of Sciences, San Francisco. He traveled throughout the country for two months and collected over 18,300 insect specimens (B. L. Fisher, unpublished data). From 1962 to 1963, a team of researchers from the Smithsonian Institution made an expedition to Madagascar, mostly to study small mammals, during which Everett D. (Tim) Cashatt captured some arthropods. Cashatt mostly obtained ectoparasites from birds and mammals but found time to do some general collecting during the day and some light trapping at night.

AFTER MADAGASCAR'S INDEPENDENCE

In 1960, Madagascar became an autonomous republic. It retained close ties to France for several more years. Political changes during the 1970s and 1980s, combined with disastrous economic policies, led to a disintegration of most scientific institutions and scientific training within the country. Foreign scientists relied even more heavily on the Malagasy collections maintained at the MNHN. A few advances continued to be made, many of which were published in the *Faune de Madagascar*. In addition, Pierre Viette published many works of broad interest concerning Madagascar, for example, two on naturalist collectors (Viette 1962, 1981) and another on principal historical collecting localities (Viette 1991).

In November 1966, a joint mission of ORSTOM (now IRD), the MNHN, and the French Army went to Tsaratanàna from Bealanana and then to the Maromokotra summit. With funding from Recherche Coopérative sur Programme (RCP), Paulian directed what is referred to as "RCP no. 225" to investigate three montane ecosystems: Andringitra, 1970–1971; Anosyenne Mountains and Ankaratra, 1971–1972; and Marojejy, Itremo, Ibity, 1972–1973. RCP 225 was noteworthy for collecting invertebrates from soil and litter communities. It was the first to extensively employ *lavage de terre* and Berlese methods in mountain ecosystems (Guillaumet et al. 2008). RCP no. 225 sparked a boom in high mountain research on Madagascar and brought foreign entomologists, including André Descarpentries, Jean-Marie Betsch, and André Peyriéras, together with young Malagasy entomologists being trained by IRSM.

Pierre Soga, originally from Andapa, was introduced to entomology by Jean Vadon in Maroantsetra. He participated in the RCP no. 225 expeditions to Andringitra, the Anosyenne Mountains, and Marojejy. IRSM trainees included Georges Randrianasolo (see Andriamialisoa and Langrand, pp. 1–38, Box 4, for more details), who studied birds but also collected insects; Edouard Razafimandimby, who accompanied Pierre Viette and Paul Griveaud; and Pierre Andria Robinson, who participated in almost all IRSM expeditions until his sudden death in 1961 in the Ambatondrazaka region at the age of 44. The Malagasy entomologists Gabriel Razafinarivo, Casimir Rafamantanantsoa, Ernest Raharizonina, and Jean Elie Randriamasy were also trained by IRSM.

The first Malagasy entomologist to publish a scientific paper was Jaonarivony Andrianasolo Ravoavy (Andrianasolo Ravoavy 1972), who received his PhD in 1970 at the Université Pierre-et-Marie-Curie in Paris. When the French left Madagascar in 1975, Andrianasolo Ravoavy was director of the Parc Botanique et Zoologique de Tsimbazaza (PBZT) and in charge of the collections at Tsimbazaza and Entomologie Agricole at Ambatobe, both in Antananarivo. Most of the specimens from these collections were taken to Paris (MNHN) and London (BMNH).

The late 1980s saw a change in Madagascar's political climate as well as an increasing national awareness that critical habitats were being irreversibly lost. The Malagasy began to recognize the urgency of documenting their fauna. Vincent Razafimahatratra received his

PhD in 1980 under Jack Lattin at Oregon State University, and was a specialist on Heteroptera but also started work on Ichneumonidae. As professor of entomology at the Université d'Antananarivo, he worked closely with Claire Kremen and trained a number of students, including Lantoniaina (Lanto) Andriamampianina. Lanto was one of the first Malagasy entomologists to apply patterns of species richness and endemism of insects (tiger beetles) to conservation planning (Andriamampianina et al. 2001). The early death of Professor Razafimahatratra in 1997 certainly cut short the important contribution he would make to Malagasy entomology.

In late 1986, Dan and John Polhemus, with John Wenzel, spent two months collecting aquatic insects, mostly specimens of Hemiptera and Coleoptera, as well as bees (Apoidea), at 67 different sites across the island. They tried to sample as many different habitats and river systems as possible. The aquatic hemipterans went to the Smithsonian Institution, the aquatic coleopterans to the California Academy of Sciences, and the bees to the University of Kansas (D. Polhemus, unpublished data).

Warren Steiner from the Smithsonian Institution, Washington, DC, made three trips to Madagascar in 1988, 1990, and 1993. On the first two trips, he collected approximately 141,000 specimens and on the last trip another 10,000. Most of the arthropods were collected at what is now Ranomafana National Park, but smaller collections were made at Toamasina, Morondava, Ifaty, and Antananarivo.

In the late 1980s, several nongovernmental conservation agencies began to organize biotic inventories of unknown or poorly known areas of the island, generally within native forests. Claire Kremen worked on butterfly distributions for the Xerces Society and Wildlife Conservation Society from 1988 to 1996 and helped obtain permits for visiting entomologists, such as Charles Griswold from the California Academy of Sciences, and Brian Fisher, then at the University of California, Davis. From this period through today, the Institute for the Conservation of Tropical Environments (ICTE) has helped organize the administrative (i.e., permits) and logistical aspects for numerous entomological collecting trips to Ranomafana National Park and elsewhere on the island.

LARGE-SCALE INVENTORIES

In the 1990s, two massive initiatives organized by French (presented here) and US institutions (see next section) began complementary large-scale systematic inventories of arthropods across the island. These efforts have returned the attention of taxonomists around the world to the diversity of Madagascar. In 1990, an inventory of the island's freshwater macroinvertebrates was begun by the Biodiversité et Biotypologie des Eaux Continentales Malgaches program (Biodiversity and Biotypology of Malagasy Fresh Waters), under the direction of Jean-Marc Elouard, jointly run by the Institut de Recherche pour le Développement (IRD) and the Centre National pour la Recherche sur l'Environnement (CNRE). Stream sampling, rearing of larvae, and light trapping were performed at 1000 sampling sites distributed at over 650 locations (Elouard and Gibon 2001; Benstead et al. 2003a). These efforts resulted in an impressive increase in the number of documented species and genera of aquatic insects. Using light traps to sample adult insects, this program discovered a bounty of new and endemic taxa, including hundreds of new caddisflies (Trichoptera) (see Gibon, pp. 1135–41) and mayflies (Ephemeroptera) (see Elouard et al., pp. 947–52). The collections made by this team have been important for documenting other invertebrate groups, such as crabs (see Cumberlidge, pp. 913–18). Together, these studies highlight a vast unknown diversity on the island and confirm high levels of microendemism. The group engaged a number of young Malagasy graduate students to take part in the field activities and work up different taxonomic groups (e.g., Désiré Randriamasimanana, Fabienne Ranaivoharindriaka, and Patricia Zoé Andriambelo); numerous publications resulted, many with Malagasy first authors.

FROM ZULU WOMEN WEAVERS TO MALAGASY PARATAXONOMISTS

In 1999, the California Academy of Sciences greatly expanded its arthropod research efforts on Madagascar to become one of the largest arthropod inventory programs ever undertaken on the island (Fisher 2005a). Fisher applied the parataxonomic training and specimen-processing model he developed while at the South African Museum (now Iziko Museums of South Africa) in Cape Town. Fisher trained Zulu women weavers, who have an important capacity to remember patterns, to sort thousands of leaf-litter, pitfall, and Malaise-trap samples and to mount specimens. Adept at fine hand movements, the textile workers were quick to learn the techniques for sorting and mounting insects. In 2000, Fisher trained a new team of parataxonomists on Madagascar (Figure 9.2) and in 2004, with support from donors in California, started construction of a new center in Antananarivo's Tsimbazaza park dedicated to entomological research and training (Figure 9.3). The Bibikely Biodiversity Center has trained a number of master of science (including the former system of DEA diplomas) and PhD students who have published taxonomic studies as first author, including Jean-Claude Rakotonirina, Andrianjaka Ravelomanana, Nicole Rasoamanana, Dimby Raharinjanahary, Eric Tsiriniaina Rajoelison, and Balsama Rajemison (Figure 9.2). Several of these individuals have been hired recently as lecturers and professors at the Université d'Antananarivo.

Since 2000, a field crew of Malagasy taxonomists from the center has inventoried 425 sites across the island, amassing >20,000 collections via leaf litter, beating samples, pitfall trap, light trap, Malaise trap, and hand collection. The aim of the Arthropod Inventory of Madagascar project was to maximize taxonomic group coverage by sampling the full range of habitats found on the island based on vegetation type, climate, elevation, and geological substrate. Specimens are first sorted at the Bibikely Center by the parataxonomists, then sent to the California Academy of Sciences for distribution to over 100 collaborating taxonomists around the world. Considerable additional support was obtained from the Schlinger Foundation for Malaise trapping and sorting. The approach emphasized speedily sharing specimens with active international taxonomists and training local scientists. As of October 2020, over the course of 20 years, an estimated 1500 species and 80 genera of invertebrates new to science have been described in over 375 scientific publications. The Arthropod Inventory of Madagascar project continues with a new initiative, Insects and People of the Southwest Indian Ocean (ipsio.org). This program monitors insect communities using metagenomic tools and

FIGURE 9.2 **Malagasy entomologists. A) Balsama Rajemison was the first student trained at the California Academy of Sciences as part of the Arthropod Inventory of Madagascar initiative. She now directs the Madagascar Biodiversity Center (MBC) in Tsimbazaza. B) Jean-Claude Rakotonirina received his MSc and PhD under the mentorship of the California Academy of Sciences and has authored a series of taxonomic works on the ants of Madagascar. He is one of the lead scientists at MBC and professor of entomology at the Université d'Antananarivo. C) Nicole Rasoamanana is finishing her PhD on ant systematics at the Université d'Antananarivo, in collaboration with MBC. D) Andrianjaka Ravelomanana is leading the research program at MBC on edible insects in the context of a project known as Insects and People and is professor of entomology at the Université d'Antananarivo. E) Chrislain Ranaivo is part of a team of collectors who have dedicated their careers to documenting the insect diversity of Madagascar. F) Tolotra Ranarilalatiana and Johannes Bergsten collecting aquatic insects on the summit of Marojejy.** (PHOTOS by B. L. Fisher.)

research on edible insects. The goal is to find candidate species for mass rearing to improve food security on the island (Van Itterbeeck et al. 2019; see Fisher and Hugel, pp. 218–30).

WHAT IS AND IS NOT INCLUDED IN THIS CHAPTER

Since the publication of Goodman and Benstead (2003), the precursor of the current volume, remarkable strides have been made in the working knowledge of the invertebrates of Madagascar. While many of these advances have been from the perspective of systematics and taxonomy, an increasing number of projects have focused on biology or ecology (see, for example, Dolch, pp. 853–56). When sending out invitations to potential contributors to this current book, Goodman and Fisher contacted slightly fewer than 100 invertebrate researchers. If few advances have been made for a group included in the 2003 book, these contributions were not invited to be revised herein. We have made a serious attempt to invite researchers who could write contributions on Malagasy invertebrates for groups that previously lacked broad syntheses, at least in English, such as Phasmatodea, as well as largely unknown groups, such as leeches.

THE FUTURE OF ENTOMOLOGY ON MADAGASCAR

In the precursor to the current volume (Goodman and Benstead 2003), a total of 36 contributions appeared in the chapter devoted to invertebrates. Several important changes have occurred in the interim period. Starting in the late 1980s, Madagascar opened its doors to foreign scientists with regulations for following research protocols to obtain government-issued permits, including the collection and exportation of specimens. In certain cases, the terms of the working relationship for these researchers, including entomologists, was to help mentor young Malagasy graduate students, which in turn gave rise to a rapid and dramatic increase in the number of working, homegrown entomologists.

The new regulations changed how research is done in the country. The conquest and possession approach to colonial research has been replaced with a collaborative model that encourages shared participation in science, exploration, and associated benefits. The development of Malagasy scientists is a bright spot in the future of entomology on Madagascar.

Deforestation and introduced species invasion are the two principal threats facing native wildlife on the island. An increasingly

FIGURE 9.3 **Entomology centers in the Parc Botanique et Zoologique de Tsimbazaza (PBZT), including A) Madagascar Biodiversity Center and B) the site of the entomological collection started by Institut de Recherche Scientifique de Madagascar (IRSM).** (PHOTOS by S. Andrianantenaina.)

unstable climate has only exacerbated these problems. Arthropods are at particular risk because they show high levels of microendemism, while island communities are more susceptible to invasion by exotic species.

How should entomologists respond to this threat? The "here today, gone tomorrow" (Raven and Miller 2020) rate of habitat loss should be a call to action to increase the pace at which the island's unique fauna is explored. At the same time, we must realize that taxonomic products, such as monographs and species lists, are not sufficient to ensure that biodiversity is protected. Entomologists must develop strong relationships with local conservation and government agencies and offer assistance to address systematic issues relating to forest loss. Efforts to document arthropod diversity across the island and rapidly apply the data to conservation projects will be aided by the development of a national arthropod collection and further training of Malagasy scientists in curation, species identification, taxonomy, and conservation biology. The training of Malagasy scientists to participate in land use decision-making in their country is the most effective means to ensure long-term conservation on this extraordinary island.

ACKNOWLEDGMENTS

Our fieldwork and taxonomic studies on the arthropods of Madagascar have been supported by the California Academy of Sciences and the National Science Foundation (most recently grant DEB-0072713). I thank our gracious Malagasy colleagues at the Bibikely Center in Parc Tsimbazaza, who share a community sense of enthusiasm for exploration and science.

Subject editor: Steven M. Goodman

INSECT–PLANT INTERACTIONS: THEIR IMPORTANCE FOR BIODIVERSITY AND ECOLOGICAL FUNCTIONING

R. Dolch

When the first version of this synopsis on insect–plant interactions on Madagascar was published (Dolch 2003), I hinted at the disproportionate amount of research on insects versus vertebrates. Although the amount of entomological literature published on Madagascar has multiplied enormously since that time, so has the number of publications on other taxa. The bottom line is that the disproportion remains. Not only do arthropods form the bulk of biodiversity and account for more than half of all known species across our planet (Stork 1991), but they shape our environment and provide some of the most important ecological services (e.g., E. O. Wilson 1987), not least because they often live in close relationships with plants.

Most of the entomological and botanical research undertaken on Madagascar focuses on the taxonomy, systematics, and biogeography of the group or species studied. We know alarmingly little about either the life history or the ecology of most of Madagascar's plants and insects. However, this is precisely the kind of research needed to better understand mutualisms as well as the ecological functioning of Madagascar's terrestrial environments. Razafimahatratra (1988) was one of the first to highlight the importance of studies on insect–plant relationships for better management of both natural and agricultural ecosystems on the island.

Malagasy plants and insects are both extremely diverse. More than 11,000 species of vascular plants occur, of which more than 80% are endemic (Callmander et al. 2011). Bryophytes are less diverse, with lower levels of endemism (see Marline et al., p. 510–20). In comparison to other tropical regions, some Malagasy forests exhibit intermediate levels of plant species diversity (Abraham et al. 1996), while others are floristically among the most diverse in the world (Dumetz 1999). The number of insect species on Madagascar can only be estimated but may comprise around 100,000 species, with high levels of endemism (Cassola and Andriamampianina 1998; Goodman and Benstead 2005), a significant proportion of which are thought to be still unknown to science. Aquatic (e.g., Sartori et al. 2000) and saprophytic (e.g., Betsch 2000a) insect communities have been surveyed on the island in what might be considered a partially comprehensive manner. In recent years, many new insects have been described from Madagascar (see Gaston 1994), and groups as diverse as mycalesine butterflies (Torres et al. 2001), dung beetles (Viljanen et al. 2010), diving beetles (Bukontaite et al. 2015), and orthopteroid insects (Krištín et al. 2019)—to name but a few—have been reviewed in detail. These also include many insect groups that are phytophagous or interact with plants in various ways.

Attempts have been made since about 2000 to identify the food plants of economically important herbivorous insect species, such as the wild silk moth *Antherina suraka* (Randrianandrasana et al. 2014), and gather information on the food plants of several other Malagasy members of Lepidoptera (D. Lees, unpublished data). Most insects depend on plants as resources, and together insects and plants account for almost three-quarters of all living organisms in the world (Strong et al. 1984). Moreover, the majority of the interactions between insects and plants are of critical importance for ecosystem functioning, since they encompass numerous mutualisms and ecological processes like pollination, seed dispersal, and herbivory. Still, our knowledge of insect–plant interactions on Madagascar remains surprisingly scant.

PLANT INSECTIVORY

One of the more uncommon but intriguing insect–plant interactions is plant insectivory (or carnivory). Some plants have evolved insectivory mainly as a way to cope with nitrogen-poor environments. Others, dubbed paracarnivorous, lack the ability to absorb nutrients from their prey. In recent years, the introduced silverleaf *Desmodium uncinatum* (family Fabaceae), native to South America, has been spreading dramatically along roadsides and other disturbed areas around Andasibe. The extremely sticky hairs on its stems and pods often trap and kill insects (as well as small vertebrates), making this para-carnivorous introduction a direct threat to native species. Most truly carnivorous plants on Madagascar grow in wet and ephemeral flush vegetation on inselbergs (Fischer and Theisen 2000; Seine et al. 2008; Rabarimanarivo et al. 2019), where nitrogen-rich topsoil cannot accumulate. These include five species of sundews (*Drosera* spp., family Droseraceae), only one of which, *D. humbertii* from Marojejy, is endemic (Keraudren-Aymonin 1982). The bladderworts (*Utricularia* spp., family Lentibulariaceae) often share the same habitat. Their eponymous bladders, which usually grow on the stolons, are only a few millimeters in size. They work like suction traps to capture small insects—a capture mechanism unique among carnivorous plants. The corkscrew plants (*Genlisea* spp., family Lentibulariaceae) are represented on Madagascar by only one species, *G. margaretae*, which also occurs in Africa (Fischer et al. 2000). The plant can be found in the surroundings of Antananarivo (Bosser 1958; Klotz and Kock 1991). *Genlisea* traps consist of cylindrical underground stems that form a structure that uses suction to trap small invertebrates. The stems' spiral arms are lined with hairs pointing inward, allowing the prey (tiny insects and other invertebrates) to go only forward into the trap.

Madagascar is also home to two endemic species of pitcher plants (*Nepenthes* spp., family Nepenthaceae). Whereas *N. masoalensis* appears to be restricted to the Masoala Peninsula and its surroundings (Schmid-Hollinger 1977), *N. madagascariensis* is more widespread along the nutrient-poor, sandy soils on the eastern littoral (Schlosser 2005; Rembold et al. 2010). Pitcher plants use their modified leaves as insect traps. The slippery rim of the pitchers causes invertebrate prey to fall and drown in the pitcher, which is filled with digestive liquid. In *N. madagascariensis*, the odor of the pitchers' liquid might additionally help to disorient the prey and cause it to fall into the trap (Ratsirarson and Silander 1996a). However, many arthropods manage to live and thrive in the pitchers, feeding on their host plant's less fortunate prey in a mutualistic relationship, providing the plant with nutrients from their feces (Ratsirarson and Silander 1996a; Adlassnig et al. 2010; Rembold et al. 2012). The most abundant inquilines of Malagasy *Nepenthes* appear to be dipteran larvae, including several species of *Uranotaenia* mosquitoes (Grjebine 1979). *Nepenthes madagascariensis* preys mostly on ants, which are even more likely to be caught in pitchers closer to the ground. Rembold et al. (2010) found that more than 80% of all arthropod prey in Malagasy *Nepenthes* were ants.

MUTUALISTIC RELATIONSHIPS BETWEEN PLANTS AND INSECTS

Many plants worldwide live in mutualistic relationships with ants. These myrmecophytes provide ants with food or shelter through the formation of special anatomical structures, including domatia, food bodies, and extrafloral nectaries (Buckley 1982; Beattie and Hughes 2002). In turn, the ants may benefit the plant by acting as pollinators, seed dispersers, or defenders against visiting herbivorous animals. In the Afro-Malagasy region, in comparison to Asia or South America, myrmecophytes are much less diverse and less adapted to ants (Jolivet 1998), and there is little evidence for myrmecophily in most Malagasy plants. Whereas the Malesian ant *Crematogaster borneensis* is completely dependent on certain species of *Macaranga* (family Euphorbiaceae) for survival (Fiala et al. 1991), the Malagasy species of this ant genus do not appear to show any similarly strong mutualism and do not appear to be strongly associated with plants. However, *C. dentata* has often been found in both dead and live plant parts (Blaimer and Fisher 2013). Dejean et al. (2010) found *Crematogaster* ants inhabiting living hollow branches of endemic chaste trees (*Vitex beraviensis*, family Lamiaceae) on the Masoala Peninsula, indicating that this plant could possibly be a myrmecophyte. Also, *Melissotarsus* ants on Madagascar were found to be obligatory inhabitants of bark cavities of living trees, which they actively enlarge to make galleries, and where they also guard and maintain armored scale insects (Ben-Dov and Fisher 2010). Among pteridophytes, most of the epiphytic staghorn ferns (*Platycerium* spp., family Polypodiaceae) tend to house ants (Hennipman and Roos 1982). The endemic *P. madagascariense* has shield fronds with a salient ruffled texture, which might offer ideal passageways for ants to live underneath (C. Lee, unpublished data), and it would be interesting to scrutinize whether such a mutualistic relationship does indeed exist.

SEED PREDATION BY INSECTS

Seeds of Malagasy plants are known to be predated upon by a large number of specialized coleopteran herbivores (Dolch and Tscharntke 2000). However, some ant species, in essence, contribute to secondary seed dispersal on Madagascar. The best-known case of such myrmecochory on the island is that of *Commiphora guillauminii* (family Burseraceae) in the central Menabe region. Ants disperse almost half of the seeds produced by this tree, with the endemic *Aphaenogaster swammerdami* accounting for most of the dispersal (Böhning-Gaese et al. 1996). Although the effectiveness of primary dispersers, such as birds and lemurs, seems to be higher than that of ants, the widespread occurrence and enormous diversity of ants (Fisher 1997; Fisher and Peeters 2019) makes them effective organisms for seed dispersal (Böhning-Gaese et al. 1999). When mammalian seed dispersers (and seed predators) are absent, *A. swammerdami* may also play a crucial role in dispersing the otherwise lemur-dispersed seeds of the tree *Strychnos madagascariensis* (family Loganiaceae) (Dausmann et al. 2008).

FOLIVORY BY INSECTS

If seeds are indeed successful in germinating and growing into seedlings, another insect–plant interaction may threaten their survival: folivory. Folivory is thought to be generally higher in the tropics than in temperate regions due to greater phytochemical diversity in tropical plants and higher specialization in tropical herbivores (Coley and Aide 1991; Coley and Barone 1996). Tree species diversity in tropical forests is in fact maintained by herbivory, since for a tree seedling, the risk of being killed is highest near the parent tree, where specialized herbivorous insects are naturally more abundant (Janzen 1970; Connell 1971). A study from Masoala, found that most of the damage inflicted on leaves by grazing insects was found to occur when leaf tissues are still tender and have not yet developed mechanical or chemical protection (Heatwole et al. 2013). The study also found that overall herbivory in Malagasy moist evergreen forests impacted up to 65% of all leaves (Heatwole et al. 2009).

INSECT POLLINATION

One of the most important insect–plant relationships in both agricultural and natural landscapes is pollination. It is estimated that worldwide up to 200,000 insect species serve as pollinators for 250,000 species of flowering plants (Abrol 2012). Vertebrates play a minor role in plant pollination, although some Malagasy plant species have been found to rely on vertebrates for pollination (Nilsson et al. 1993; Kress et al. 1994; Ratsirarson 1995; Birkinshaw and Colquhoun 1998). Systematic investigations of pollination ecology on Madagascar have been done mostly for baobabs (Baum 1995; Du Puy 1996) and some orchids (Nilsson et al. 1985a, 1986, 1987, 1992; Nilsson and Rabakonandrianina 1988; Pettersson and Nilsson 1993; Wasserthal 1997), showing the importance of insects as pollen vectors. Insect pollinators of both groups include hawkmoths (Lepidoptera, Sphingidae), which are characterized by their large, long proboscis and hovering behavior. Orchid pollination by hawkmoths seems to be a highly specialized mechanism (Nilsson et al. 1985a, 1987). The Malagasy baobab species (family Malvaceae) with short white flowers, specifically *Adansonia grandidieri* and *A. suarezensis*, depend on nocturnal mammals, including bats (see Andrianaivoarivelo et al., pp. 1911–16), for their pollination. *Adansonia za*, *A. perrieri*, *A. rubrostipa*, and *A. madagascariensis*, which all have elongate red or yellow flowers, depend largely on hawkmoths (Baum 1995, 1996; Ryckewaert et al. 2011).

Moths other than sphingids are also known to be important pollinators. They seem to be rather specialized, and some plant species appear to rely exclusively on them (Nilsson et al. 1990). Pollination by moths is likely in species with flowers that remain open at night, such as those of the genus *Delonix* (family Fabaceae) in western Madagascar (Du Puy et al. 1995). In Marojejy, pollination of two endemic species of Phyllanthaceae (*Phyllanthus marojejiensis* and *P. humbertii*) by gracillariid moths of the genus *Epicephala* was inferred from indirect observations (Kawakita 2010).

As elsewhere, different members of Hymenoptera are among the dominant diurnal pollinators on Madagascar, and bees have been found to be of considerable importance in the pollination of palms (Dransfield and Beentje 1995; Ratsirarson and Silander 1996b, 2003). Carpenter bees (*Xylocopa*) and stingless bees (*Liotrigona*) appear to be frequent visitors to—and important potential pollinators for—many plant species in Madagascar's dry deciduous forests (Waser et al. 2010). In Ambohitantely, bees of the genus *Pachymeles* were found to be the principal pollinators of the endemic *Plectranthus vestitus* (family Lamiaceae) (Nilsson et al. 1985b).

While open-flowered Malagasy species of *Dalechampia* (family Euphorbiaceae) are pollinated by pollen-feeding beetles and flies (Armbruster and Baldwin 1998, 2003), one lineage possesses closed flowers and thus restricts access to pollen to only a few specialist genera of bees that extract pollen by buzzing the flowers while vibrating their thoracic muscles (Armbruster et al. 2012; Plebani et al. 2015). Halictid bees of the genus *Lasioglossum*, which are suspected of pollinating a variety of different plants, have been identified as pollinators of orchids at Angavokely (Pettersson and Nilsson 1993). While the orchid *Brownleea coerulea*, also at Angavokely, showed specialization for pollination by long-tongued members of Diptera (Larsen et al. 2008), pollination of a variety of other orchids also appears to depend on hymenopteran pollinators. An interesting pollination system has been found in *Cymbidiella flabellata*, which has been studied in marshland areas near the town of Foulpointe. Despite the occurrence of a diverse local hymenopteran community, this orchid is pollinated only by two species of sphecid wasps, which use the marshes as a source of mud for nest construction (Nilsson et al. 1986).

Although flowers of *Commiphora guillauminii* in Kirindy Forest CNFEREF (Centre National de Formation, d'Etudes et de Recherche en Environnement et Foresterie) were found to be visited by at least 17 insect species (Hymenoptera, Lepidoptera, Diptera), fruit set was exceptionally low. Moreover, female trees had significantly lower visitation rates than male trees, suggesting that dioecy risks reducing pollination success (Farwig et al. 2004). A diverse assemblage of insect pollinators was also found in Malagasy Bignoniaceae of the tribe Coleeae. However, despite similar floral traits in the 13 sympatric Coleeae species on the Masoala Peninsula, the pollinator communities differ starkly between species. Pollinator partitioning is reached because different Coleeae species grow in different strata of the forest and have different flower phenologies and/or flowering durations (Zjhra 2008).

One of the most complex pollinating systems occurs in the Moraceae genus *Ficus* (Wiebes 1979; Dalecky et al. 2003; see Rasplus et al., pp. 617–34). The successful fruiting of figs depends on a complicated mutualism with fig wasps (Agaoninae, Hymenoptera). Each *Ficus* species generally has its own species of pollinating agaonine wasp. Other wasps of the same subfamily can be either parasitoids or gallers. The latter produce galls in the fig's ovules, which are in turn used as a food resource by the pollinating species. These complex interactions are further intensified by external herbivory on figs. Cushman et al. (1998) studied figs that were fed upon by members of Homoptera on Madagascar and in several African countries. The homopteran secretions attracted ants that considerably reduced the number of ovule gallers and parasitoids of the pollinating fig wasps, resulting in higher hatching rates of wasp eggs. Moreover, figs on Madagascar are eaten by a variety of vertebrates, although possibly to a lesser extent than elsewhere (Goodman and Ganzhorn 1997; Goodman et al. 1997a), which is thought to affect the insect communities of the figs and the ecological functions associated with them. Depending on the complexity or importance of their interactions with other organisms, some plant species can be characterized as keystone mutualists (Baum 1995; Du Puy 1996), and the *Ficus* example vividly demonstrates the ecological complexity of interactions between plants, insects, and other animals.

Deforestation and other pressures have resulted in a mosaic of highly fragmented natural habitats within a matrix of surrounding anthropogenic vegetation in Madagascar's landscapes. Biodiversity loss driven by fragmentation is known to significantly affect ecological functioning (Kruess and Tscharntke 1994; Naeem et al. 1994; Didham et al. 1996; Lawton et al. 1998). The interactions between two of the most species-rich organisms—insects and plants—are of major importance for ecological processes. The study of insect–plant interactions, therefore, is critical for understanding the effects of habitat fragmentation on Madagascar, which is likely to have severe consequences for both biodiversity and ecosystem functioning. However, in a study from the Androy Region, Bodin et al. (2006) demonstrated that even small remaining patches of natural habitat (often taboo forests, or *ala faly* or in other dialects *ala fady*) strewn throughout the landscape matrix can have a positive effect on ecological services, such as pollination by bees, thereby supporting the importance of landscape heterogeneity on ecological functioning (e.g., Kareiva and Wennergren 1995; Steffan-Dewenter et al. 2002). In the same area, the endangered palm *Dypsis decaryi* occurs only in an isolated fragment of suitable habitat where its survival is also directly linked to successful insect pollination (Ratsirarson and Silander 1996b). Habitat destruction and degradation, and the resulting fragmentation, profoundly affect all faunal and floral communities of Madagascar (Irwin et al. 2010). While research on the outcome of such habitat changes on Madagascar has largely focused on mammalian (e.g., Goodman and Rakotondravony 2000; Godfrey and Irwin 2007), avian (e.g., Langrand and Wilmé 1997), and amphibian (Vallan 2000) communities, the impact of anthropogenic disturbance on insects has been studied to a much lesser extent.

It has been estimated that deforestation since the 1950s has caused the extinction of almost a tenth of Madagascar's species (Allnutt et al. 2008), and given that insects often have restricted ranges and small population sizes, it has been postulated that many of the extinct species were insects (Irwin et al. 2010). Aquatic insects have been found to be sensitive to disturbance on Madagascar (Benstead et al. 2003b), and stream-dwelling rainforest specialists have disappeared following deforestation, most likely mediated by altered microclimate and increased sediment load (Elouard and Gibon 2003).

Among terrestrial insects, ants are probably one of the best-studied taxonomic groups on Madagascar (Fisher and Bolton 2016; Fisher and Peeters 2019), but our knowledge of how habitat change affects species and communities remains patchy even for ants (Irwin et al. 2010). Kremen et al. (2008) found that 15% of Madagascar's ant species and 11% of butterfly species occurred only in zones outside protected areas, highlighting the risk for further insect extinctions. Fonseca (2009) modeled extinction probabilities of herbivorous insects and found that, of all the world's biodiversity hotspots (Myers et al. 2000), the third-highest number of extinctions was predicted to occur on Madagascar. Insects, and phytophagous species in particular, are often assumed to be too diverse and difficult to sample, therefore discouraging much-needed research and hampering comprehensive assessments. For some Malagasy insect groups, barcoding (M. A. Smith et al. 2005) and other high-throughput DNA sequencing (Monaghan et al. 2009) have been shown to be promising methods for more rapid insect inventories in the future. However, if we want to know what shapes Madagascar's often hyper-diverse insect communities and their multifarious, highly complex interactions with plants, as well as how insects are affected by habitat change, we might have to resort to a more traditional approach. Ongoing studies from the rainforests of New Guinea show that almost complete sampling of phytophagous insects of different ecological guilds, along with their host plants, enables a comprehensive analysis of the highly complex interactions between insects and plants. These studies can be achieved by committed scientists with recourse to a large team of co-workers and para-taxonomists over many years (e.g., Novotny et al. 2010). A similarly thorough look at Madagascar's insect communities, their ecology, and their interactions with plants would dramatically increase our knowledge about these systems, including how ongoing habitat change affects these interactions, and how insect–plant relationships (or their disruption) determine ecosystem functioning at present and in the future.

Subject editors: Brian L. Fisher and Steven M. Goodman

SYSTEMATIC ACCOUNTS

ANNELIDA: HIRUDINEA, LEECHES, *DINTA, LINTA, DIMATIKA*

M. Fahmy and M. E. Siddall

Leeches are ectoparasitic and predatory hermaphroditic worms in the phylum Annelida, which also includes the oligochaetes, such as common earthworms, and the predominantly marine polychaetes. Of the 700 species of leeches known in the world, roughly 100 are marine, 90 are terrestrial, and the remaining are freshwater in habit (Sket and Trontelj 2008). Without a definitive fossil record for any leech group, ascertaining their origins and diversification is limited to biogeographic correlates (e.g., Borda et al. 2008), some of which are consistent with multiple hypotheses of vicariance and dispersal (Borda and Siddall 2011). Several families of leeches exhibit global distributions (Phillips et al. 2010), including the so-called medicinal leeches, typified by *Hirudo medicinalis* (family Hirudinidae), the European medicinal leech of bloodletting infamy, as well as proboscis-bearing leeches in the families Glossiphoniidae and Piscicolidae. Terrestrial and semiterrestrial groups tend to be more restricted in geographic ranges.

Sanguivory on vertebrate hosts appears to be not only the predominant but also the original life-history strategy for leeches (Borda and Siddall 2004). Nonetheless, blood feeding has been given up for a predatory mode of nutrition at least five times (Borda and Siddall 2011) and is a characteristic of several speciose groups, especially the erpobdelloid leeches that subsist on insect larvae and other aquatic invertebrates (Elliott 1973). The use of leeches in the practice of medicine, while dating at least to Galen's popularization of humoral theory, became widespread in phlebotomy in the early 19th century until their utility for managing disease was disproved (Morabia 1996). Nonetheless, they are still used in traditional medicine and have even found use as a medical device for the relief of venous congestion following flap and replantation surgery (Whitaker et al. 2004). Considerable attention has also been paid to the salivary anticoagulant repertoire leveraged by leeches, and whether that diversity reflects evolutionary constraints and host preferences (Siddall et al. 2011). The fact that many sanguivorous species can consume and retain many times their own weight in blood in a single feeding, has positioned leeches at the forefront of indirect vertebrate sampling through invertebrate DNA (iDNA) studies amplifiable from wild-caught individuals (Schnell et al. 2018).

CHARACTERISTICS OF LEECHES

Bodies of leeches are segmented, like those of all annelid worms, but in contrast to other annelids, leeches have no internal septa that define repeating metameric somites. In addition, these body somites are externally subdivided into multiple annuli (usually three or five annuli per mid-body somite) in a manner that is often useful for landmarking characteristics of taxonomic significance: position and separation of the male and female gonopores; number and arrangement of light-sensitive eyespots; and the internal shape and position of male and female median reproductive anatomy. The latter proves particularly informative in those groups of leeches that mate by copulation, which involves the insertion of a muscular penis into a corresponding vaginal sac (e.g., Hirudinidae, Haemadipsidae), as opposed to those that mate by traumatic insemination (injection into the body cavity) (e.g., Glossiphoniidae, Piscicolidae).

Unlike other annelid worms, leeches have a fixed number of body somites by virtue of the anterior and posterior suckers each possesses. The larger posterior or caudal sucker—a fusion of the last seven ganglia—is used for attachment and locomotion; in aquatic species, it functions much like a fluke for swimming, but it otherwise serves to facilitate a looping or "inchworm" action (Kristan 2019). The anterior oral sucker is associated with a ganglionic mass representing a fusion of the first six somatic ganglia through which the pharynx passes. The pharynx itself varies considerably among different leech groups, ranging from a simple muscular tube in some predatory species to a protrusible filiform proboscis in others. In the medicinal leeches, the pharynx forms a muscular "jaw" armed with sharp denticles that inflict a cutaneous incision, over which the powerful oral sucker applies strong negative pressure in order to suck a blood meal from its host.

LEECHES OF MADAGASCAR

The hungry hoards in the genus *Chtonobdella* (family Haemadipsidae) that plague visitors to the moist evergreen forests of eastern and northern Madagascar are the best-known and best-represented taxonomic group of leeches on the island. A single non-sanguivorous erpobdelloid, *Linta be*, can be found in southern wetlands (Westergren and Siddall 2004). The etymology of that genus name is a Malagasy word for leech: *linta* or *dinta*. *Linta* is closest to *lintah* in the language of the Barito people—a cultural group living in Borneo. Based on different lines of evidence, the Barito are among the people who colonized Madagascar several thousand years ago (Dahl 1951; see Wright and Rakotoarisoa, pp. 181–90). Overall, Madagascar is home to five known species of leeches: four in the genus *Chtonobdella* and *Linta be*, the only member of its genus (family Erpobdellidae).

Haemadipsidae is a family of sanguivorous terrestrial leeches distributed throughout the wet forests of the Indo-Pacific. Known colloquially as jungle leeches, this group had been traditionally divided by jaw morphology into duognathous (two-jawed) and trignathous (three-jawed) species groups. Trignathous jungle leeches represent the genus *Haemadipsa*, distributed exclusively across the Indian subcontinent and tropical Southeast Asia. The duognathous group includes Indo-Pacific endemics (Borda and Siddall 2011), many of which were classified under monotypic genera until their synonymy under the genus *Chtonobdella* (see Tessler et al. 2016).

Terrestrial leeches may have colonized Madagascar approximately 66 million years ago, during the early Cenozoic (Borda and Siddall 2011); they are unknown from other islands in the Malagasy Region (see exception below), all of which are in situ islands and of more recent date. Phylogenetic evidence suggests a single colonization event from the central Indo-Pacific, subsequent to Madagascar's split from the Mascarene Plateau. This was a period during which land vertebrates already existed on the island (see Samonds et al., pp. 73–78), there was a northern migration of the landmass to its current latitude in the tropics (between 12° and 25°S), and a suitable moist habitat for this group was formed (Borda and Siddall 2011). This kind of rare, but successful founder event is the best explanation for such a widespread Indo-Pacific distribution of species in the genus *Chtonobdella*: from Madagascar in the west to the Juan Fernandez Islands in the eastern Pacific, with a center of diversity in Oceania, their absence from Africa and South America, and a scattering of single endemics in isolated islands like Palmyra, Fiji, and Mahé (Tessler et al. 2016). Part of the success of the genus appears to be a relative lack of host-group specificity, allowing them to feed on any vertebrate (Fahmy et al. 2020), unlike the apparently mammalophilic genus *Haemadipsa* in southern and southeastern Asia. Indeed, *C. seychellensis* from the Seychelles (Mahé) appears to have even given up vertebrate blood altogether and has been observed feeding on snails (Richardson 1975; M. E. Siddall, unpublished data).

Classification and Diversity

The terrestrial leeches of Madagascar represent an understudied group, with Blanchard (1917) providing the earliest descriptions of three species, which he included in the genus *Haemadipsa*. Richardson (1975) placed these in their own genus, *Malagabdella*, in the subfamily Malagabdellinae, which Borda (2006) subsequently revised, adding a fourth species. Tessler et al. (2016) clarified the systematics of Haemadisipdae, finding the only consistent character for delimiting genera to be the presence of three jaws in *Haemadipsa* versus two in *Chtonobdella*. The following four species are known to exist on Madagascar: *C. fallax* (Blanchard 1917), which predominates south of 20°S; *C. vagans* (Blanchard 1917), which predominates in mid-latitudes; *C. morsitans* (Blanchard 1917), with an incompletely known distribution; and *C. niarchosorum* (Borda 2006), known only from Ranomafana National Park. This is certain to be a poor representation of the actual diversity and distributional limits of Malagasy terrestrial leeches, reflecting more of a history of limited collection efforts. Already there is morphological and genetic evidence of a third species resident in Ranomafana National Park, based on material collected in 2017.

Complicating this work is the degree of intraspecific variation in coloration and patterning in Madagascar's terrestrial leeches, as shown in Figures 9.4a and b: despite striking visual differences, these two leeches belong to the same species, *C. vagans*. As such, external patterning alone is insufficient for species determination (Figure 9.4c), especially after preservation in ethanol or other media. As with other groups of leeches, diagnostic morphological characteristics include morphology of the internal male and female median reproductive apparatus, including the position and orientation of female ovaries, oviduct, vaginal sac, male ejaculatory bulbs, and penis, as well as the number and arrangement of testisacs. Externally, the position of eyespots (Figure 9.4d), separation of gonopores, number of friction rays on the caudal sucker, and even the number of cutting denticles on the pair of muscular jaws, can be helpful across the genus *Chtonobdella* but are uniformly the same for the monophyletic group of species known from Madagascar (Borda 2006). While previously some evidence suggested species-specific information in the annulation of posterior somites near the "auricles" (openings next to the caudal sucker that probably serve to wet them), contemporary corroborating evidence of species delimitation involves reciprocal monophyly using molecular phylogenetic approaches (Tessler et al. 2016; Schnell et al. 2018) (Figure 9.4e).

Ecology and Behavior

Even equipped with adaptations to a terrestrial lifestyle, like copulatory internal fertilization and egg-laying in resistant cocoons, haemadipsid leech activity is spatiotemporally limited by soil water availability and temperature (Tan 2001). This constrains the distribution of Madagascar's terrestrial leeches to the limits of the eastern and northern moist evergreen forests, with anecdotal records as far north as the Montagne d'Ambre National Park and as far south as the southern limit of the Anosyenne Mountains (Borda 2006). This sensitivity to ecological factors such as rainfall, temperature, and sunlight, all of which are structured by canopy height and cover, predicts that terrestrial leech abundance is dictated by forest quality. Extensive surveys of both the Andasibe region and Ranomafana National Park corroborate this observation. In the vicinity of Andasibe, where years of logging and other types of habitat modification have degraded forests and decreased canopy cover, leeches are less abundant and less active, owing to greater insolation penetrating through to the forest floor. Although present, leeches in Andasibe (including the Analamazaotra protected area) are found exclusively along rivers, where the microclimate is more suitable for their survival than the open forest floors subject to regular drying cycles. This stands in stark contrast to abundant leech populations in segments of the forests in Ranomafana National Park where much of the canopy is intact and the understory remains dark and damp. This has led some to propose terrestrial leeches as indicator species, with their presence and numbers reflecting the overall health of a forest community (Drinkwater et al. 2019a).

Leeches seeking a blood meal rest anchored by their caudal sucker in a vertical, upright "questing" posture. Ground-questing leeches remain still until movement is detected, whereupon they quickly inch toward the vibrational source. Leaf-questing individuals will normally await the brushing past of a host, but they have also been filmed retracting their anterior followed by a forward thrust, in order to leap onto passing prospects. Once finding suitable skin or a mucous membrane, the looping locomotion slows to a stop and both suckers attach firmly in preparation for incision with the bilateral jaws. In artificial environments, haemadipsids will feed on rabbits, mice, frogs, chicks, and snakes (Keegan et al. 1969), but otherwise haemadipsid foraging preferences are not well studied. Host detection biases in ground-dwelling (*Haemadipsa sumatrana*) versus arboreal leech species (*H. picta*) in Borneo show *H. picta* feed on a wider range of mammals than does

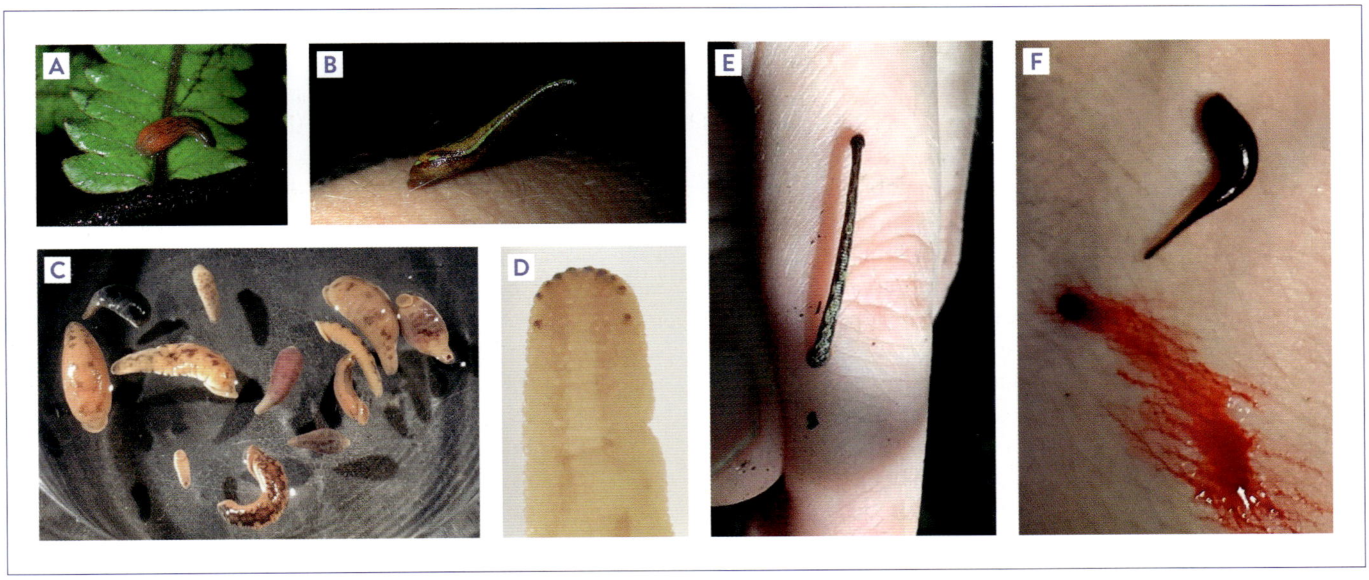

FIGURE 9.4 **Haemadipsids from Madagascar; note that the larger sucker is posterior and the thin end of the leech is anterior. A) and B) Two specimens of *Chtonobdella vagans*, both from Andasibe, demonstrating intraspecific variation in color; C) diversity of putative morphospecies from 1400 leeches collected in the "Lost Forest" near Ivohibe; D) parabolic arrangement of anterior eyespots typical of species of *Chtonobdella*; E) recently discovered, and as yet undescribed, new species of *Chtonobdella* from Ranomafana National Park; and F) leech engorged to more than five times its unfed weight.** (PHOTOS A, B, and D by M. E. Siddall; C and E by M. Fahmy; and F by R. B. Sulser.)

H. sumatrana (Drinkwater et al. 2019b). Leeches have been observed questing in close proximity to ripe fruit on the forest floor, which may be a strategy for finding and latching onto frugivorous terrestrial host species.

Until recently, data regarding natural hosts of the terrestrial blood-feeding leeches of Madagascar relied on incidental historical records of leeches feeding opportunistically on the limbs of investigators (Figure 9.4f), as well as on domestic and livestock species (Blanchard 1917). While generally thought to be mammalophilic, recent iDNA field collections of leeches from across Asia and Madagascar (Schnell et al. 2018) have revealed their capacity to feed on mammals, birds, reptiles, and amphibians, corroborating the findings of Rocha et al. (2012).

IDNA BIODIVERSITY MONITORING

Thorough biodiversity inventories that are needed to establish baseline measures of species richness for conservation initiatives are moving increasingly toward metagenomic noninvasive strategies. Although environmental DNA (eDNA) water sampling has received considerable attention, leech-derived iDNA has also seen extensive methodological treatment and refinement where terrestrial haemadispid leeches are abundant (Abrams et al. 2019). Terrestrial leeches are attractive candidates for iDNA surveys. Unlike blood-feeding dipterans and carrion flies (Kocher et al. 2017) with extensive home ranges, leeches retain residual host DNA within their guts for months (Schnell et al. 2012), and they maintain site fidelity, thus reflecting a portion of the local faunal diversity of the forest regions from which they were collected (Tessler et al. 2018). In direct comparison, iDNA from metabarcoding leech blood meals revealed local diversity and species composition comparable to camera trapping (Weiskopf et al. 2018) but with much higher efficiency with regard to the terrestrial fauna. In addition, iDNA leech surveys capture well-camouflaged, diminutive, and otherwise elusive taxa that routinely remain undetected by direct observation or camera traps (Fahmy et al. 2019, 2020).

Leeches collected from various forests on Madagascar have contributed to standardizing and expanding this novel technique and may provide crucial information on species occupancy required to safeguard certain forests. Through metabarcoding of multiple genetic loci targeting all terrestrial taxa (birds, mammals, reptiles, and amphibians) and residual eDNA, individual leeches have been shown to retain the DNA of up to four hosts (Fahmy et al. 2020). In an effort to reduce costs and improve efficiency, pooling individual leech tissue has been heralded as the preferred approach over Sanger's, sequencing individual leeches for each target gene. Strategies for pooling tissue include grouping together leeches of the same species collected from neighboring transects within each collection site. This allows for the identification of hosts partitioned by leech species and by locale, further elucidating potential feeding preferences and host distribution. In areas where leeches are scarce (e.g., degraded forests), nonrandom sampling along streams is appropriate for determining faunal diversity, as most taxa regularly visit sources of running water.

In Madagascar, iDNA biodiversity surveys have offered insight into the feeding behavior of terrestrial leeches, while simultaneously evaluating the presence of threatened species. iDNA has been shown to detect taxa spanning five classes, more than previously detected with any single monitoring method. The majority of overall host diversity detected with iDNA is represented by mammals and birds, yet those groups also constitute the highest proportion of ambiguous taxa on public reference databases, exposing a knowledge gap in genetic repositories. The method is only as precise and accurate as the mitochondrial DNA databases against which comparisons are made, which need to be based on sequences from vouchered specimens identified by specialists of the group concerned.

FUTURE RESEARCH DIRECTIONS

With the increasing interest in terrestrial leeches for biodiversity surveys, there remains much to be accomplished. Systematic and comprehensive surveys of leech diversity in the moist evergreen forests of Madagascar are needed in order to determine the geographic ranges and other limits to species of *Chtonobdella*. Haemadipsid species elsewhere segregate latitudinally and by elevation, as well as by host type—all parameters that need to be factored into iDNA results in order to avoid biases. Maximizing the information from individual blood meals should include evaluations of vertebrate blood parasites as well as the leeches' own gut microbiome (Siddall et al. 2019) and even zoonotic viral diversity (Briese et al. 2015).

While leech blood meals are an efficient tool for describing species richness within a sampled locality, they may be used alongside traditional surveying techniques to establish a more complete species assemblage. Leeches are also useful to identify the presence of introduced and invasive species, which has direct implications for conservation programs. Furthermore, iDNA presents an opportunity for community engagement whereby protected area managers may recruit local people to assist in the very simple strategy of leech collecting: a walk in the forest. Such efforts enable capacity building and foster stewardship among local communities, ensuring the sustainability of conservation programs. While current studies show promise, the future of iDNA for biodiversity monitoring is hampered by limits on populating and maintaining genetic databases of vertebrate taxa from Madagascar in order to generate valuable and reliable host determinations. Widespread surveys of vertebrates and leeches should proceed in a complimentary and coordinated manner.

Subject editors: Brian L. Fisher and Steven M. Goodman

GASTROPODA, TERRESTRIAL AND FRESHWATER MOLLUSCA (SNAILS), *SIFOTRA*

O. Griffiths and D. G. Herbert

TERRESTRIAL MOLLUSCA

Madagascar has a spectacular land snail fauna (including slugs), remarkable for its taxonomic breadth, endemism, and ancient affinities, and also for the gigantic size and extensive radiations of some genera (Emberton 1994a). In virtually any patch of relatively intact native forest on Madagascar, one can find snails. In some areas, they may occur in surprisingly large numbers, whereas in others, limited by poor soils, they may be quite rare. Introduced snail species predominate particularly in lowland urban areas, village gardens, and plantations. The only areas of Madagascar where indigenous snails are completely absent are the secondary grasslands of the Central Highlands.

The study of Malagasy nonmarine mollusks can be said to have started with the description of *Helix tricarinata* (now *Tropidophora tricarinata*) by the Danish scientist O. F. Müller in 1774. During the following 200 years, considerable numbers of additional species were described from Madagascar, culminating in two monographs on Malagasy snails by Edouard Fischer-Piette (1899–1988) and colleagues at the Muséum National d'Histoire Naturelle in Paris (Fischer-Piette et al. 1993, 1994). The authors brought together the species information available and described yet more species. In total, they discussed 511 species, excluding slugs but including a few introduced snails. Since 1990, fieldwork by Ken C. Emberton and colleagues that focused especially on smaller species resulted in much new data regarding the distribution, habitat, and ecology of Madagascar's snails, as well as the description of many new species. By 2000, the list of described species was up to 685, including 14 introduced species (Pearce 2003). By 2008, the number of described species had increased by 308 species to 993 (Griffiths and Herbert 2008). Since then a further 127 new species have been either fully described or at least noted in publications. Thus, at present, the island's land snail fauna is known to consist of 1123 species. It is clear, however, that a great many more species of Malagasy terrestrial Mollusca remain to be discovered and described.

Origins and Biogeographic Affinities with Africa and Asia

With the breakup of Gondwana during the Mesozoic era, Madagascar separated from Africa around 160 million years ago (Mya) and from India–Sri Lanka around 83–89 Mya (Reeves and de Wit 2000). Madagascar has thus been isolated for an extensive period of time, doubtless accounting for much that is unique about its biota (97% of terrestrial mollusk species and 29% of genera are endemic to the island). We know, however, that although Madagascar is rich in endemic species, the island's molluscan fauna has much in common with that of both continental Africa and Indo-Asia. To account for this, one must postulate either that the ancestors of the present-day fauna were present on the island when it parted company with the other Gondwanan fragments (vicariant events), or that they arrived subsequently through dispersal. Almost certainly both scenarios have occurred.

For families such as Acavidae, a Gondwanan connection undoubtedly seems the most plausible explanation, as this family and its close relatives have classic southern continental distributions. Nonetheless, not all potentially Gondwanan land snail groups have been found on Madagascar. The superfamily Orthalicoidea, for example, although recently shown to occur in Africa as well as South America and Australasia (Herbert and Mitchell 2004; Breure and Romero 2012), is not known on Madagascar or the Deccan Plateau region of India. Similarly, Malagasy snails once thought to belong to Rhytididae (Emberton 1990) have subsequently been shown to be referable to Acavidae (Herbert et al. 2015). Conversely, for families such as Urocyclidae, thought to be part of a Laurasian and post-Gondwanan radiation (Hausdorf 2000; Naggs and Raheem 2005), and others comprising mostly small or minute snails, dispersal events are more probable explanations. In most cases, these are likely to have been stochastic passive events mediated by rafting or aerial dispersal by wind and birds.

Although now somewhat dated in view of recent work by Emberton and colleagues, the biogeographic analysis of Madagascar's land snail fauna undertaken by Bruggen (1981) remains the most complete such study made to date, despite its African focus. An earlier study by Fischer-Piette and Blanc (1972) was more superficial. Bruggen noted that Madagascar shares more taxa with Africa than with any other part of the world (Bruggen 1980), with 33% of genera and 50% of species exhibiting African or Afro-Asian affinity. Of the 23 indigenous land snail families currently considered to occur on Madagascar (Pearce 2003), only Diplommatinidae and Acavidae are not represented in Africa. Emberton and Rakotomalala (1996) noted that 36% of Madagascar's land snail genera also occur in Africa, whereas only 20% occur in India and other portions of Asia. This predominantly African affinity of Madagascar's land snail fauna may be in part due to the fact that much of the biota of the Indian Plate would have been eliminated by the laval outpourings that created the Deccan Traps at the end of the Cretaceous during its northward journey after separation from Madagascar. Had this not occurred, the fauna of India and Sri Lanka might exhibit greater similarity with that of Madagascar (Naggs and Raheem 2005). Even so, clear links between the Malagasy and Indian–Sri Lankan land snail faunas are evident in the form of genera belonging to Acavidae, Ariophantidae (sometimes referred to as Helicarionidae), and Cyclophoridae. Recent work has tended to suggest that links with India and Sri Lanka may be even closer; Emberton and Rakotomalala (1996), for example, have postulated that the genera *Boucardicus* (Cyclophoridae) and *Kalidos* (Ariophantidae) are closely related, if not synonymous with Indo-Asian genera. This closer Indian affinity is also starting to be recognized for major components of the Mascarene fauna, including the snails (A. Cheke, unpublished data).

To date, biogeographic assessment of Madagascar's land snail fauna has largely been narrative and has been confounded by the limited extent and accuracy of available data, some of which has subsequently proven to be incorrect. Recent research, for example, has shown that the African cyclophorid genus *Chondrocyclus* should be excluded from the Malagasy fauna (Emberton 2004), and likewise the rhytidid snails mentioned above. Another study has shown that Malagasy snails traditionally referred to the Laurasian family Orculidae in fact belong to a separate and deeply divergent family, Fauxulidae, occurring only in southern Africa and Madagascar (Harl et al. 2017). More meaningful progress in this direction will require more robust data, critical to which will be the availability of well-supported phylogenetic statements for the groups under consideration.

CHARACTERISTICS OF THE SNAIL FAUNA AND MAJOR GROUPS

Table 9.1 lists the 115 species of snails described from Madagascar since Griffiths and Herbert (2008) and a further 12 new species that have not been formally named to date. Madagascar's snail species are distributed in 28 families, five of which are represented by only introduced species (Achatinidae, Bradybaenidae, Gastrodontidae, Limacidae, and Spiraxidae). Most of Madagascar's snail families consist of small species often overlooked by nonspecialists. The larger, more conspicuous snail species are distributed in only a few families, which are discussed below.

Eupulmonata

Family Acavidae, Bird's-egg Snails

The acavids are a Gondwanan relic group of medium-size to large snails, confined to Madagascar, the Seychelles, and Sri Lanka, with affinities to closely related groups in southern Africa, Australia, South America, and India (Emberton 1990; Stanisic 1998). On Madagascar, especially in the moist evergreen forests, they are the dominant snails, often occurring in very large numbers. Acavids are excellent burrowers, and many species spend the dry season buried deep in the leaf litter or soil. They occur in virtually all of Madagascar's habitat types, from the dry spiny thicket of the south to the summit region of the Andringitra Massif.

The island's biggest native snails all belong to this family, the largest of which, *Helicophanta farafanga*, has a shell than can reach a length of 11 cm and a width of 7 cm. Acavids are popularly known as "bird's-egg" snails because they produce very large eggs. Those of *H. gloriosa* can reach 34 mm in length and do indeed look like birds' eggs, complete with a solid calcified shell. On Madagascar, Acavidae is represented by three genera: *Helicophanta*; *Ampelita*, medium-size snails; and *Eurystyla*, smaller, brightly colored, and probably exclusively arboreal snails.

Family Clavatoridae, Cudgel Snails

Species of the genus *Clavator*, which until recently were considered to belong to Acavidae, are a group of deeply divergent acavoid snails with large, elongate, turriform shells that are now referred to a family of their own. Also perhaps referable to this family is the genus *Leucotaenius*, long considered to be an endemic representative of Achatinidae. Now, however, there is good morphological and molecular evidence to exclude *Leucotaenius* from Achatinidae, and strong evidence to indicate that it is another deeply divergent acavoid lineage perhaps related to *Clavator* (Mead 1985; Wade et al. 2001; Herbert et al. 2015). *Leucotaenius* comprises snails with relatively large, solid shells that occur in the dry spiny thicket of the southwest. In areas around Itampolo, the ground can be covered with thousands of empty shells of *L. favannii*. Estivating snails can be found buried up to 20 cm deep in the sand.

TABLE 9.1. **The land snail fauna of Madagascar described since Griffiths and Herbert (2008)**

SCIENTIFIC NAMES	LOCALITIES	ELEVATION (M)	YEAR COLLECTED	HABITAT
CYCLOPHORIDAE				
Acroptychia mahafinaritra Emberton et al., 2010	Andrantantely Massif, WNW Brickaville	302	2008	Moist evergreen forest
Boucardicus ambatoensis Emberton, 2009	NE Masoala	100	2007	Moist evergreen forest
B. anjarae Emberton et al., 2010	Andrantantely Massif, WNW Brickaville	290	2008	Moist evergreen forest
B. avo Emberton et al., 2010	Andrantantely Massif, WNW Brickaville	302	2008	Moist evergreen forest
B. capestensis Emberton et al., 2010	Cap Est, Masoala	1	2007	Moist evergreen forest
B. deltastoma Emberton, 2009	Cap Est, Masoala	1	2007	Moist evergreen forest
B. hetra Emberton et al., 2010	Andrantantely Massif, WNW Brickaville	302	2008	Moist evergreen forest
B. lalinify Emberton et al., 2010	Andrantantely Massif, WNW Brickaville	302	2008	Moist evergreen forest
B. lincolni Emberton, 2009	Mt. Ambohivohitra, WNW Antalaha	600	2007	Moist evergreen forest
B. mahavariana Emberton et al., 2010	Andrantantely Massif, WNW Brickaville	665	2008	Moist evergreen forest
B. matoatoa Emberton et al., 2010	Andrantantely Massif, WNW Brickaville	542	2008	Moist evergreen forest
B. menoi Emberton et al., 2010	Andrantantely Massif, WNW Brickaville	301	2008	Moist evergreen forest
B. paulayi Emberton, 2009	Mt. Anjiabe, NW Antalaha	200	2007	Moist evergreen forest
B. peggyae Emberton et al., 2010	Andrantantely Massif, WNW Brickaville	675	2008	Moist evergreen forest
B. pulchellus Emberton et al., 2010	Andrantantely Massif, WNW Brickaville	547	2008	Moist evergreen forest
B. slapcinskyi Emberton, 2009	Mt. Ambato, Masoala	300	2007	Moist evergreen forest
B. soniae Emberton, 2009	Mt. Ambohivohitra, WNW Antalaha	400	2007	Moist evergreen forest
B. tantelyae Emberton et al., 2010	Andrantantely Massif, WNW Brickaville	650	2008	Moist evergreen forest
B. thompsoni Emberton, 2009	Cap Est, Masoala	1	2007	Moist evergreen forest
Cyathopoma anjombona Emberton et al., 2010	Andrantantely Massif, WNW Brickaville	405	2008	Moist evergreen forest
C. hoditra Emberton et al., 2010	Andrantantely Massif, WNW Brickaville	590	2008	Moist evergreen forest
C. iridescens Emberton et al., 2010	Andrantantely Massif, WNW Brickaville	665	2008	Moist evergreen forest

SCIENTIFIC NAMES	LOCALITIES	ELEVATION (M)	YEAR COLLECTED	HABITAT
C. madio Emberton et al., 2010	Andrantantely Massif, WNW Brickaville	301	2008	Moist evergreen forest
C. matsoko Emberton et al., 2010	Andrantantely Massif, WNW Brickaville	468	2008	Moist evergreen forest
POMATIIDAE				
Tropidophora humbug Griffiths & Herbert, 2013a	Tsingy Beanka	380	2009	Dry deciduous forest
T. lincolni Emberton, 2009	Mt. Anjiabe, NW Antalaha	500	2007	Moist evergreen forest
T. sericea Griffiths & Herbert, 2013a	Tsingy Beanka	215	2010	Dry deciduous forest
ASSIMINEIDAE				
Omphalotropis sp. 1 Emberton, 2009	Mt. Ambato, NE Masoala	300	2007	Moist evergreen forest
Omphalotropis sp. 2 Emberton, 2009	WNW Antalaha	180	2007	Moist evergreen forest
FAUXULIDAE				
Anisoloma josephinae (Emberton & Griffiths, 2009a)	Mt. Ambohivohitra	500	2007	Moist evergreen forest
A. tsarakely (Emberton et al., 2010)	Andrantantely Massif, WNW Brickaville	547	2008	Moist evergreen forest
SUBULINIDAE				
Allopeas sp. 1 Emberton & Griffiths, 2009a	Mt. Anjiabe, NW Antalaha	200	2007	Moist evergreen forest
Allopeas sp. 2 Emberton & Griffiths, 2009a	S of Antsahanoro, WNW Antalaha	100	2007	Moist evergreen forest
CERASTIDAE				
Gittenedouardia randalanai (Griffiths & Herbert, 2013a)	Tsingy Beanka	450	2006	Dry deciduous forest
STREPTAXIDAE				
Fischerpietteus josephinae Emberton & Griffiths, 2009a	Mt. Ambohivohitra, WNW Antalaha	400	2007	Moist evergreen forest
Gulella andrantanteliae Emberton et al., 2010	Andrantantely Massif, WNW Brickaville	501	2008	Moist evergreen forest
G. kendrae Emberton & Griffiths, 2009a	Mt. Anjiabe, NW Antalaha	200	2007	Moist evergreen forest
G. lincolni Emberton & Griffiths, 2009a	Mt. Anjiabe, NW Antalaha	200	2007	Moist evergreen forest
G. thompsoni Emberton et al., 2010	Mt. Ambohivohitra, WNW Antalaha	302	2008	Moist evergreen forest
Gulella sp. 1 Emberton & Griffiths, 2009a	S of Antsahanoro, WNW Antalaha	180	2007	Moist evergreen forest
Gulella sp. 2 Emberton & Griffiths, 2009a	Mt. Anjiabe, NW Antalaha	200	2007	Moist evergreen forest

(continued overleaf)

TABLE 9.1. ***continued***

SCIENTIFIC NAMES	LOCALITIES	ELEVATION (M)	YEAR COLLECTED	HABITAT
Gulella sp. 3 Emberton & Griffiths, 2009a	Mt. Ambohivohitra, WNW Antalaha	400	2007	Moist evergreen forest
Parvedentulina andrantanteliae Emberton et al., 2010	Andrantantely Massif, WNW Brickaville	665	2008	Moist evergreen forest
P. benjamini Emberton et al., 2010	Andrantantely Massif, WNW Brickaville	300	2008	Moist evergreen forest
P. bitika Emberton & Griffiths 2009a	Mt. Anjiabe, NW Antalaha	560	2007	Moist evergreen forest
P. jeani Emberton et al., 2010	Andrantantely Massif, WNW Brickaville	468	2008	Moist evergreen forest
P. kendrae Emberton & Griffiths, 2009a	Mt. Ambato, Masoala	152	2007	Moist evergreen forest
P. lincolni Emberton & Griffiths, 2009a	Mt. Ambohivohitra, WNW Antalaha	640	2007	Moist evergreen forest
P. michellae Emberton & Griffiths, 2009a	Mt. Ambohivohitra, WNW Antalaha	400	2007	Moist evergreen forest
P. miova Emberton & Griffiths, 2009a	Mt. Ambohivohitra, WNW Antalaha	500	2007	Moist evergreen forest
P. paulayi Emberton et al., 2010	Andrantantely Massif, WNW Brickaville	590	2008	Moist evergreen forest
P. soa Emberton & Griffiths, 2009a	Mt. Anjiabe, NW Antalaha	200	2007	Moist evergreen forest
P. thompsoni Emberton et al., 2010	Andrantantely Massif, WNW Brickaville	244	2008	Moist evergreen forest
ACAVIDAE				
Ampelita andriamamonjyi Griffiths & Herbert, 2013a	Tsingy Beanka	330	2010	Dry deciduous forest
A. beanka Griffiths & Herbert, 2013a	Tsingy Beanka	380	2009	Dry deciduous forest
A. owengriffithsi Emberton et al., 2010	Andrantantely Massif, WNW Brickaville	65	2008	Moist evergreen forest
A. lindae Griffiths & Herbert, 2013a	Tsingy Beanka	230	2009	Riparian forest
Eurystyla ambatoensis (Emberton & Griffiths, 2009a)	Mt. Ambato, Masoala	100	2007	Moist evergreen forest
CHAROPIDAE				
Reticulapex michellae Emberton et al., 2010	Andrantantely Massif, WNW Brickaville	675	2008	Moist evergreen forest
R. stanisici Emberton & Griffiths, 2009b	Mt. Anjiabe, NW Antalaha	500	2007	Moist evergreen forest
Trachycystis masina Emberton & Griffiths, 2009b	WNW Antalaha	180	2007	Moist evergreen forest

SCIENTIFIC NAMES	LOCALITIES	ELEVATION (M)	YEAR COLLECTED	HABITAT
SUCCINEIDAE				
Succinea masoala Emberton & Griffiths, 2009a	Cap Est, Masoala	1	2007	Moist evergreen forest
EUCONULIDAE				
Microcystis albisuturalis Emberton et. al., 2010	Andrantantely Massif, WNW Brickaville	501	2008	Moist evergreen forest
M. celestinae Emberton & Griffiths, 2009b	Mt. Anjiabe, NW Antalaha	200	2007	Moist evergreen forest
M. fotsifotsy Emberton et al., 2010	Andrantantely Massif, WNW Brickaville	517	2008	Moist evergreen forest
M. josephinae Emberton & Griffiths, 2009b	Mt. Anjiabe, NW Antalaha	200	2007	Moist evergreen forest
M. kendrae Emberton & Griffiths, 2009b	WNW Antalaha	180	2007	Moist evergreen forest
M. michellae Emberton & Griffiths, 2009b	Mt. Ambato, Masoala	300	2007	Moist evergreen forest
M. soa Emberton & Griffiths, 2009b	Mt. Ambato, Masoala	200	2007	Moist evergreen forest
M. tsara Emberton & Griffiths, 2009b	Mt. Anjiabe, NW Antalaha	500	2007	Moist evergreen forest
M. vony Emberton et al., 2010	Andrantantely Massif, WNW Brickaville	547	2008	Moist evergreen forest
Microcystis sp. 1 Emberton & Griffiths, 2009b	Mt. Ambohivohitra, WNW Antalaha	500	2007	Moist evergreen forest
Sitala burchi Emberton et al., 2010	Andrantantely Massif, WNW Brickaville	675	2008	Moist evergreen forest
S. celestinae Emberton & Griffiths, 2009b	Mt. Ambato, Masoala	300	2007	Moist evergreen forest
S. hirsuta Emberton & Griffiths, 2009b	Mt. Anjiabe, NW Antalaha	200	2007	Moist evergreen forest
S. kendrae Emberton & Griffiths, 2009b	Mt. Ambohivohitra, WNW Antalaha	400	2007	Moist evergreen forest
S. lincolni Emberton & Griffiths, 2009b	Mt. Ambato, Masoala	300	2007	Moist evergreen forest
S. mavo Emberton et al., 2010	Andrantantely Massif, WNW Brickaville	665	2008	Moist evergreen forest
S. michellae Emberton & Griffiths, 2009b	Mt. Ambato, Masoala	100	2007	Moist evergreen forest
S. minuta Emberton & Griffiths, 2009b	Mt. Ambohivohitra, WNW Antalaha	400	2007	Moist evergreen forest
S. stanisici Emberton et al., 2010	Andrantantely Massif, WNW Brickaville	675	2008	Moist evergreen forest

(continued overleaf)

TABLE 9.1. ***continued***

SCIENTIFIC NAMES	LOCALITIES	ELEVATION (M)	YEAR COLLECTED	HABITAT
UROCYCLIDAE				
Chlamydarion celestinae Emberton & Griffiths, 2009b	WNW Antalaha	100	2007	Moist evergreen forest
C. michellae Emberton & Griffiths, 2009b	Mt. Anjiabe, NW Antalaha	400	2007	Moist evergreen forest
Chlamydarion sp. 1 Emberton & Griffiths, 2009b	Mt. Anjiabe, NW Antalaha	200	2007	Moist evergreen forest
Malagarion sp. 1 Emberton, 2010	Andrantantely Massif, WNW Brickaville	675	2008	Moist evergreen forest
Malagarion sp. 2 Emberton, 2010	Andrantantely Massif, WNW Brickaville	675	2008	Moist evergreen forest
Malagarion sp. 3 Emberton, 2010	Andrantantely Massif, WNW Brickaville	675	2008	Moist evergreen forest
VITRINIDAE				
Vitrina josephinae Emberton & Griffiths, 2009b	Mt. Ambohivohitra, WNW Antalaha	500	2007	Moist evergreen forest
ARIOPHANTIDAE				
Kalidos ambatoensis Emberton & Griffiths, 2009b	Mt. Ambato, Masolala	200	2007	Moist evergreen forest
K. ambraei Emberton, 2007	Montagne d'Ambre	1325	1995	Moist evergreen forest
K. analamerae Emberton, 2007	Analamerana	285	1995	Bamboo-dry deciduous thickets
K. angulorchidus Emberton, 2007	Pic des Orchidées	295	1995	Dry deciduous forest
K. avanalamerae Emberton, 2007	Analamerana Reserve	285	1995	Bamboo-dry deciduous thickets
K. beambrae Emberton, 2007	Montagne d'Ambre	1135	1995	Moist evergreen forest
K. betsaratae Emberton, 2007	Tsaratanàna	1100	1995	Moist evergreen forest
K. boriambrae Emberton, 2007	Montagne d'Ambre	1235	1995	Moist evergreen forest
K. capdambrae Emberton, 2007	Cap d'Ambre	40	1995	Dry deciduous forest
K. capestensis Emberton & Griffiths, 2009b	Cap Est, Masoala	1	2007	Moist evergreen forest
K. conorchidus Emberton, 2007	Pic des Orchidées, S. Cap d'Ambre	295	1995	Dry deciduous forest
K. dupuyi Verdcourt, 2006	Lake Tsimanampesotse	50	1989	Dry spiny thicket
K. etiambrae Emberton, 2007	Montagne d'Ambre	1325	1995	Moist evergreen forest
K. fisakambrae Emberton, 2007	Montagne d'Ambre	1235	1995	Moist evergreen forest
K. fisakus Emberton, 2007	Tsaratanàna	1100	1995	Moist evergreen forest
K. foitra Emberton, 2007	Montagne d'Ambre	1040	1995	Moist evergreen forest
K. gallorum Emberton, 2007	Montagne des Français	230	1995	Dry deciduous forest

SCIENTIFIC NAMES	LOCALITIES	ELEVATION (M)	YEAR COLLECTED	HABITAT
K. galokoae Emberton, 2007	Galoko Escarpment	980	1995	Secondary forest dominated by *Ravenala* and palms
K. globosus Emberton, 2007	Montagne d'Ambre	1475	1995	Moist evergreen forest
K. gora Emberton et al., 2010	Andrantantely Massif, WNW Brickaville	450	2008	Moist evergreen forest
K. josephinae Emberton & Griffiths, 2009b	Mt. Anjiabe, NW Antalaha	200	2007	Moist evergreen forest
K. ketronambrae Emberton, 2007	Montagne d'Ambre	1235	1995	Moist evergreen forest
K. mandamus Emberton, 2007	Analamerana	315	1995	Dry deciduous forest
K. manotrika Emberton et al., 2010	Andrantantely Massif, WNW Brickaville	547	2008	Moist evergreen forest
K. manta Emberton et al., 2010	Andrantantely Massif, WNW Brickaville	542	2008	Moist evergreen forest
K. maryannae Griffiths & Herbert, 2013a	Tsingy Beanka; Antsingimavo	345	2010	Dry deciduous forest
K. matoatoa Emberton, 2007	Analamerana	235	1995	Dry deciduous forest
K. minangulorchidus Emberton, 2007	Pic des Orchidées, S. Cap d'Ambre	295	1995	Dry deciduous forest
K. minorchidus Emberton, 2007	Pic des Orchidées, S. Cap d'Ambre	360	1995	Dry deciduous forest
K. morambrae Emberton, 2007	Montagne d'Ambre	1475	1995	Moist evergreen forest
K. namorokae Emberton, 2007	Tsingy de Namoroka	110	1995	Dry deciduous forest
K. orchidus Emberton, 2007	Pic des Orchidées, S. Cap d'Ambre	295	1995	Dry deciduous forest
K. pendutsaratae Emberton, 2007	Tsaratanàna	950	1995	Moist evergreen forest
K. platorchidus Emberton, 2007	Pic des Orchidées, S. Cap d'Ambre	295	1995	Dry deciduous forest
K. toisuarezensis Emberton, 2007	Cap d'Ambre	40	1995	Dry deciduous forest
K. tsarabe Emberton & Griffiths, 2009b	Mt. Ambato, Masoala	200	2007	Moist evergreen forest
K. tsaratae Emberton, 2007	Tsaratanàna	950	1995	Moist evergreen forest
K. vavaboriborius Emberton, 2007	Analamerana	285	1995	Bamboo dry deciduous thicket
CHRONIDAE				
Kaliella crandalli Emberton et al., 2010	Andrantantely Massif, WNW Brickaville	301	2008	Moist evergreen forest

Sources: This new compilation is based on the recent works of Emberton (2007, 2009), Emberton and Griffiths (2009a, 2009b), Emberton et al. (2010), Griffiths and Herbert (2013a, 2013b), and Verdcourt (2006).

Family Achatinidae, Agate Snails

This essentially African family includes two very large and widespread species: *Lissachatina immaculata* and *L. fulica*. Both were introduced to Madagascar in precolonial times. This we know indirectly from records of achatinid introductions in the Mascarenes. Férussac (1827) noted that "il paraît certain que cette espèce [*L. fulica*] a été importée à Bourbon. ... Mme Mothey, femme de l'intendant, étant attaquée d'une affection de poitrine, on lui ordonna du bouillon de limaçons; on fut obligé d'envoyer à Sainte-Marie pour en avoir" (it seems certain that this species [*L. fulica*] was imported to Bourbon. ... Mrs. Mothey, the steward's wife, being afflicated by a chest ailment, and he ordered snail broth; we had to send to Sainte-Marie to get some). These two species occur throughout the coastal and lowland areas of Madagascar. However, *L. immaculata* is the dominant species in drier areas, while *L. fulica* is the more common species along the east coast. It is interesting to note that the flesh of achatinid snails is a valuable export commodity, and one company in Toamasina annually collects, processes, and exports tons of fresh-frozen achatinid meat for the European restaurant trade.

Family Streptaxidae, Hunter Snails

This is a family of small to medium-size carnivorous snails that prey mostly on other snails. The family has a wide tropical and subtropical distribution. On Madagascar, there are four principal genera: the larger *Edentulina*, the smaller *Gulella*, and the small, generally elongate *Streptostele* and *Parvedentulina*. They are most abundant in the dry deciduous forests of the west and north, especially in limestone areas. However, they are almost completely absent from the moist evergreen forests. The shells are usually uniformly white or translucent, but the animal inside is usually brightly colored, often in shades of yellow, orange, or red. Two streptaxids have been introduced to Madagascar—*G.* (*Huttonella*) *bicolor*, which is a widespread species, probably accidentally introduced from India, and the eastern African snail *Tayloria quadrilateralis*, which was deliberately introduced to Madagascar and elsewhere in the region in the 1960s, along with the similarly carnivorous *Euglandina rosea*, from Florida, in a failed attempt at biological control of achatinid snails (Griffiths et al. 1993).

Family Ariophantidae

This is a family of small to large snails, mostly thin-shelled and lacking any thickening (lip) around the shell mouth. They range throughout parts of Africa, India, and Southeast Asia. On Madagascar, the main genera are *Kalidos* and the small, conical *Sitala*. Species of *Kalidos* range from tiny to the very large *K. griffithshauchleri*, with a diameter of up to 6.5 cm (see Figures 9.5a–c for images of live *Kalidos*). While *Kalidos* and *Sitala* occur all over Madagascar, they are most abundant and diverse in the dry deciduous forests of the lowland west, especially in limestone areas. Some authors refer *Sitala* and *Kalidos* to the family Helicarionidae (e.g., Pearce 2003). The limits between Ariophantidae and Helicarionidae have not been well established. In a molecular phylogeny of terrestrial pulmonates, both these families came out as polyphyletic, with some ariophantids nesting within Helicarionidae (Wade et al. 2001).

Family Veronicellidae

This family of tough, leathery slugs is somewhat dry to the touch and completely covered by a mantle shield (the notum). Veronicellids are widely distributed in tropical regions in South America, Africa, and southern Asia. Madagascar has a number of endemic species, especially in dry deciduous forests in the west and north. Two species have been introduced: *Laevicaulis alte* and *Semperula maculata*. The taxonomy of the group is poorly known, and many species show very similar external characteristics, differing only in the internal anatomy of the reproductive system.

Other Eupulmonate Snail Families

The bulk of the balance of Madagascar's eupulmonate land snails are relatively small and inconspicuous. These include representatives of 16 other families: Cerastidae, Charopidae, Chondrinidae, Chronidae, Euconulidae, Fauxulidae, Ferussaciidae, Helicarionidae, Punctidae, Pupillidae, Subulinidae, Succineidae, Urocyclidae, Valloniidae, Vertiginidae, and Vitrinidae.

Caenogastropoda

Family Pomatiidae, Shuffler Snails

All of Madagascar's pomatiids belong to either of two genera: *Tropidophora* or *Cyclotopsis*. All have flat to conical shells with a rigid, calcareous operculum. *Tropidophora* is a widespread genus, occurring also in southern Africa, the Seychelles, and the Mascarene islands, but reaches its greatest diversity and abundance on Madagascar. The taxonomy of the genus is complex, and phylogenetic relationships at the subgeneric level remain unresolved. Insights from molecular data suggest that diversity may be even greater than currently thought (Slapcinsky 2014). While *Tropidophora* species occur all over Madagascar, they are most common in the dry deciduous forests of the west and north and the dry spiny thickets of the south. The world's largest pomatiid snail is the spectacular *T. cuvieriana*, with a diameter of up to 65 mm. This snail is restricted to the *tsingy* (eroded limestone karst, often with needle-like columns) of the Ankarana Massif, where it lives on vertical rock faces, grazing on microalgae growing on and in the top layer of limestone. It is probably a significant eroder of the limestone (Middleton 1996). *Tropidophora* species in the moist evergreen forests are mostly arboreal (Figures 9.5d and e).

Family Cyclophoridae

This family has many large and spectacular species in the Old World tropics, and several genera occur on Madagascar. Unlike the pomatiids, cyclophorids all have a flexible, horny operculum. Most species on the island are very small, and they often have strangely shaped shell apertures. The principal genera of smaller species are *Cyclotus*, *Cyathopoma*, *Anosycolus*, and *Boucardicus*. The larger species belong to either *Hainesia*—small to medium-size elongate snails from the southeast—or *Acroptychia*, medium-size conical snails that occur in the west, north, and northeast. The most impressive of this group is *A. metableta*, from the moist evergreen forests of the north and east. Its shell forms a distinct lip after each period of estivation, and some shells can have up to 10 of these impressive ridges (see Figure 9.5f for another member of this genus).

FIGURE 9.5 **Some examples of Malagasy land snails. A) *Kalidos griffithshauchleri* (family Ariophantidae), Beanka (approximate shell diameter 60 mm); B) *K. oleatus*, Maromizaha Forest (30 mm); C) *Kalidos* species, Ansokosoko, near Antsingimavo (23 mm); D) *Tropidophora bicarinata* (family Pomatiidae), Maromizaha Forest (25 mm); E) *T. secunda*, Beanka (19 mm); and F) *Acroptychia bathiei* (family Cyclophoridae), Beanka (23 mm).** (PHOTOS by D. Herbert.)

Life History and Ecology

Like most snails and slugs the world over, Madagascar's terrestrial mollusks are mostly cryptic animals, shunning bright sunlight and hiding away from predators. Although some, such as *Tropidophora* and *Leucotaenius*, are capable of tolerating surprisingly dry conditions in the southwest, most species are found in well-vegetated habitats, particularly in moist evergreen forests of the east. The typical land snails of the Eupulmonata are hermaphrodite and generally reproduce by reciprocal fertilization, although self-fertilization is also possible in some groups. However, in the operculate caenogastropods such as *Tropidophora*, the sexes are always separate, and individuals are thus either male or female. Fertilized eggs are normally laid in clutches in leaf litter or loose earth, but some species retain eggs internally, up to and sometimes beyond hatching, "giving birth" to crawling young. Life span is variable, depending on adult size and environmental conditions. Obviously the larger species tend to be more long-lived—an age of 11.5 years has been recorded for *Helicophanta vesicalis*, based on an animal in captivity (Griffiths 2002)—but those living in dry habitats may also need to live for several years in order to avoid local extinctions during long periods of adverse conditions. In contrast, many of the smaller snails in the moist evergreen forests are probably annual.

Emberton (1994b) investigated the morphology and estivation behavior in some of Madagascar's acavid snails. He found that natural selection for estivation and crawling behavior seems to have dominated the evolution of external body morphology and shell thickness in that group.

Land snails and slugs are generally herbivorous, feeding on both living and decaying plant material, but the number of species that consume living green plant material may in fact be relatively few. Many of the smaller species are detritivores feeding on particulate organic material and microorganisms in soil and leaf litter. In addition to these, a number of snail families are primarily carnivorous, for example, members of Streptaxidae. In fact, very little is known of the biology and ecology of Madagascar's land snails, and much of what we do know is inferred from other regions. We clearly have much to learn in this regard.

Relationships with Other Species

Given their abundance and large size, it is not surprising that snails are an important food source for many other animals. In the Mascarenes, snails are a significant element in the diet of the introduced *Tenrec ecaudatus*, a Malagasy endemic (Mauremootoo et al. 2003). Snails have also been identified in the food remains of this same mammal in the dry deciduous forests of Kirindy Forest CNFEREF (Centre National de Formation, d'Etudes et de Recherche en Environnement et Foresterie) (Ade 1996). A number of rodent species also feed on snails. In so doing, they can become an intermediate host of *Angiostrongylus cantonensis* (Rat Lungworm), which is recorded from Madagascar (Alicata 1965). The worm develops in its primary snail host, which can be any one of a number of species. The worm is transmitted to the rodent when it eats an infected snail (Wallace and Rosen 1969). Further, rodents on Madagascar consume snail shells for a source of calcium.

In the Tsingy de Bemaraha, piles of smashed shells of *Tropidophora* and *Kalidos* may often be found under rock overhangs and next to suitable "anvils"—the work of rock-thrushes of the genus *Monticola*, as well as various locally occurring, largely ground-dwelling couas of the genus *Coua*. The extinct *C. delalandii*, apparently restricted to Ile Sainte Marie, was almost certainly a snail-eating specialist, based on firsthand accounts of its natural history (Ackerman 1841). In the southwest of Madagascar, a species of spider consistently uses an empty snail shell, which it hauls into the middle of its web as a refuge. It usually uses a shell of *Leucotaenius proctori* or a small *Kalidos*. In the Bemaraha, at least one species of lepidopteran (possibly of the family Psychidae) camouflages its larval case exclusively with empty snail shells. Fresh but empty snail shells are often found in the waste middens surrounding the nests of *Aphaenogaster* species (Formicidae), suggesting that these ants also feed on small snails. A range of beetles, including larval fireflies (family Lampyridae) feed on snails. Some fly species (family Sciomyzidae) lay an egg on a snail, and the developing maggot eats the snail's flesh and uses the eaten-out empty shell as a protected place to pupate.

FRESHWATER MOLLUSCA

In contrast to Madagascar's snail fauna, which is amazingly rich on a global scale, the freshwater molluscan fauna is surprisingly depauperate in terms of species diversity. There are only 44 recorded native species, 22 of which are endemic (Table 9.2), and only one endemic genus. Africa, by contrast, has over 400 species (Brown 1994). The rivers and wetlands associated with the *tsingy* of the Ankarana Massif have only 10 recorded species (Griffiths 1995), while the wetlands at the edge of the Bemaraha Massif have only 11 recorded species, with five species occurring on both massifs. Lacking from Madagascar's rivers are the large freshwater mussels so characteristic of rivers in the rest of the world. The only accepted records are those of the rare *Etheria elliptica* and the enigmatic *Germainaia geayi* (Graf and Cummings 2009). Why Madagascar's freshwater molluscan fauna is so poor, particularly at a higher taxonomic level, is not clear.

While the diversity of freshwater mollusks is generally low, abundance can be high. Some taxa, such as *Pila*, *Cleopatra*, and *Bulinus*, can be extremely abundant in many areas, such as in the ephemeral doline pans along the west coast. Similarly, there can be very high abundance of relatively large species (e.g., *Madagasikara*) in suitable habitat like the Mahavavy River.

A number of Malagasy freshwater snails are important from a human and livestock health perspective, since they may act as vectors of diseases; for example, the vectors of schistosomiasis (bilharzia) include *Bulinus* species and *Biomphalaria* species. Of the numerous species of *Schistosoma* parasites, only three have humans as an essential definitive host, and of these, two occur on Madagascar: *S. mansoni* and *S. haematobium* (Brown 1994). The common liver fluke has as an intermediate host, the mollusk *Radix natalensis* (Brown 1994).

DISTRIBUTION AND CONSERVATION

The distribution of land snail species on Madagascar varies greatly according to habitat type and, equally important, soil type. By far the greatest abundance in terms of the number of species occurs in the medium-altitude moist evergreen forests of the southeast and northeast—more than 80 species can be found in a very small area of the Vohimena Mountains north of Tolagnaro (Emberton 1997). The limestone (*tsingy*) areas of the west and north closely follow in terms of species diversity but have far greater abundance of individual snails. A preliminary survey of the Ankarana Massif yielded 40 species (Griffiths 1995). Similarly, preliminary surveys of two sites with *tsingy* habitat at Bemaraha produced 71 species (Griffiths 1997), and more intensive study of the smaller Beanka Massif recorded 77 species (Griffiths and Herbert 2013b).

The importance of soil type in regard to snail diversity and abundance is well known (Peake 1978). The poorest areas are within forests growing on quartz sands, such as those northwest of Ankerika (south of Analalava). Here, even in areas of intact dry deciduous forest, only three species have been recorded (two of which are introduced). Similarly, the ancient, poor, and highly eroded sandstone soils of Isalo support very few snail species. In contrast, soils derived from limestone rocks, even in the arid south, can support a considerable diversity of snail species with very high abundance (Griffiths 1998). Limestone is a rich source of calcium that, as calcium carbonate, is the major component of snail shells. A ready supply of calcium is also known to enhance fecundity and somatic growth in snails (Wäreborn 1979; Gomot et al. 1989).

The distribution of individual species also can vary enormously. Species with the smallest ranges tend to be those living in small, ecologically isolated, island-like habitats, such as tiny areas of *tsingy* or mountaintops. Significantly, there is at least an 80% difference in species in the two limestone karst areas of Bemaraha and Ankarana, separated by 750 km. Even within the Bemaraha there is a noticeable species turnover from south to north (Griffiths 1997). In the moist evergreen forests, some of the larger species have enormous geographic distributions: *Ampelita xystera* can be found from Antalaha

TABLE 9.2. **Madagascar's freshwater molluscan fauna**

SCIENTIFIC NAME	DISTRIBUTION	ENDEMISM
CAENOGASTROPODA		
Lanistes grasseti (Morelet, 1863)	South of Mahajanga to Toliara	Endemic
Pila cecillei (Philippi, 1849)	Widespread	Endemic
Cleopatra madagascariensis (Crosse & Fischer, 1872)	Widespread	Endemic
C. colbeaui (Craven, 1880)	Widespread, north	Endemic
C. grandidieri (Crosse & Fischer, 1872)	Central east, Toliara	Endemic
Melanoides tuberculata (Müller, 1774)	Widespread	Native
Madagasikara johnsoni (E. A. Smith, 1882)	Mahajanga Province	Endemic
M. madagascariensis (Grateloup, 1840)	Northern	Endemic
M. spinosa (Lamarck, 1822)	Widespread along east coast	Endemic
M. vazimba Köhler & Glaubrecht, 2010	Périnet	Endemic
M. vivipara Köhler & Glaubrecht, 2010	Central west	Endemic
M. zazavavindrano Köhler & Glaubrecht, 2010	Mahavavy River	Endemic
Thiara amarula (Linnaeus, 1758)	Widespread, coastal areas	Native
Clithon corona (Linnaeus, 1758)	Widespread, coastal areas	Native
C. coronatum (Leach, 1815)	Widespread, coastal areas	Native
C. madecassinum (Morelet, 1860)	Widespread along east coast	Native
C. spiniperda (Morelet, 1860)	Widespread, coastal areas	Native
Neritina pulligera (Linnaeus, 1767)	Widespread, coastal areas	Native
Vittina gagates (Lamarck, 1822)	Widespread	Native
Neripteron auriculata (Lamarck, 1822)	Widespread, coastal areas	Native
Septaria borbonica (Bory, 1804)	Widespread, coastal areas	Native
S. tessellata (Lamarck, 1816)	Marimbana River, east coast	Native
Neritilia rubida (Pease, 1865)	Widespread, coastal areas	Native
EUPULMONATA		
Radix natalensis (Krauss, 1848)	Widespread	Native
Physella acuta (Draparnaud, 1805)	Widespread	Introduced
Bulinus forskalii (Ehrenberg, 1831)	Widespread	Native
B. obtusispira (E. A. Smith, 1882)	Antananarivo	Endemic
B. liratus (Tristram, 1863)	Widespread	Endemic
Segmentorbis angustus (Jickeli, 1874)	Widespread	Native
Hovorbis crassilabrum (Morelet, 1860)	Widespread	Native
H. starmuehlneri (Brown, 1980)	Ankaratra Mountain	Endemic
Biomphalaria pfeifferi (Krauss, 1848)	Widespread	Native
Planorbella duryi (Wetherby, 1879)	Antananarivo	Introduced
Pettancylys modestus (Crosse, 1880)	Widespread	Native

(continued overleaf)

TABLE 9.2. ***continued***

SCIENTIFIC NAME	DISTRIBUTION	ENDEMISM
BIVALVIA		
Euglesa casertana (Poli, 1791)	Andriba, Antananarivo, Antsirabe, Andasibe, Betafo, Antsampandrano	Native
Pisidium betafoense Kuiper, 1953	Betafo	Endemic
P. johnsoni E. A. Smith, 1882	Betafo	Native
P. reticulatum Kuiper, 1966	Nosy Be, Maevatanana	Native
Sphaerium madagascariense (Tristam, 1863)	Antananarivo region, Betsileo region	Endemic
Eupera degorteri (Kuiper, 1954)	Cap Saint André, Sahondra, Morondava, Bemaraha, Antsiranana	Endemic
E. ferruginea (Krauss, 1848)	Morondava, Namoroka, Mahajanga, Antsohihy, Antsirabe	Native
Germainaia geayi (Germain, 1911)	Exact locality unknown	Endemic
Coelatura malgachensis[1] (Germain, 1911)	Exact locality unknown	Endemic
C. madagascariensis[1] (Sganzin, 1841)	Mahoupa River (river name as stated in original paper), Toamasina	Endemic
Etheria elliptica Lamarck, 1807	Betsika, northeast Madagascar	Endemic
Corbicula madagascariensis E. A. Smith, 1882	Antananarivo, Ikopa, Ambohitraimanitra Canal, Antsirabe; Mananara, Befotaka, Amboasary-Atsimo	Endemic

Sources: Based on publications by Starmühlner (1969), Fischer-Piette and Vukadinovic (1973), Brown (1994), Köhler and Glaubrecht (2010), and the authors' own unpublished records database from specimens in the collections of the Australian Museum. (Nomenclature updated according to MolluscaBase eds. 2020. Accessed 17 Feb. 2020. http://www.molluscabase.org.)

[1] Now considered a *nomen dubium*.

to Tolagnaro, and *Helicophanta amphibulima* from Nosy Be across to Marojejy and south to Farafangana (Fischer-Piette et al. 1994).

From a conservation standpoint, field survey work is still insufficient to provide meaningful information regarding the status of Madagascar's snails. The first attempt to do so listed the conservation status of nine species from southeastern Madagascar (Emberton and Pearce 2000). What is known is that most of Madagascar's native snails have a very low tolerance of forest disturbance. Secondary forests often contain very few snails, while intact forest even only a few meters away generally contains notably large numbers. Some species are able to survive, at least in the short term, in small native forest remnants, even if very degraded, as at Ambohimanga, near Antananarivo, where several small endemic species still occur. Given the extensive loss of native forest, it is probable that large numbers of snail species may have already disappeared, and many more are almost certainly threatened or endangered. Nonetheless, unlike in the Mascarenes, where many snail species are known to have become extinct (Griffiths 1996), none of Madagascar's described snail species are confirmed to have suffered this fate. Tucker Abbott (1989) listed one Malagasy snail species, *Tropidophora cuveriana*, and one morph, *T. tricarinata* morph *bicarinata*, as extinct, but both are in fact still surviving.

All but three of the Malagasy freshwater snail species are either nonendemic or, if endemic, are widespread, and thus they are not currently threatened. The status of the one restricted endemic, *Hovorbis starmuehlneri*, is Data Deficient (IUCN 2020). Similarly, while there is insufficient data to make any significant conclusions about the status of the Malagasy freshwater bivalves, other than the two aforementioned large mussel species (*Etheria elliptica* and *Germainaia geayi*), most species are widespread and are thus unlikely to be currently threatened.

ACKNOWLEDGMENTS

We are grateful to Tim Pearce for his assistance; Ken Emberton and Steve Goodman for help in obtaining literature; and Christian Albrecht for assistance with the freshwater fauna. We also acknowledge Aldus Andriamamonjy and Roger Randalana for information on various aspects of snail biology and distribution on Madagascar, and Judith Masters for discussions concerning Madagascar's historical biogeography.

Subject editors: Brian L. Fisher and Steven M. Goodman

SCORPIONES, SCORPIONS, *MAINGOKA*

W. R. Lourenço, P. O. Waeber, and L. Wilmé

Contributions to the knowledge of the scorpion fauna of Madagascar began with the description by Gervais (1844) of *Scorpio madagascariensis*, a species that was later transferred to the genus *Grosphus*. Pocock (1889) named a second species for the island, *Buthus limbatus*, which was also subsequently transferred to the genus *Grosphus*. In that same year, Pocock described *B. lobidens*, which later proved to be a synonym of *G. madagascariensis* (Kraepelin 1899). In 1890, Pocock named *Rhoptrurus baroni*, but he transferred it in 1893 to the genus *Tityobuthus*. At about the same time, several other species were described for the Malagasy fauna, with the contributions of Kraepelin (1894, 1896, 1901), Pocock (1896), and Birula (1903) particularly noteworthy.

At the beginning of the 20th century, the Malagasy scorpion fauna was considered to comprise two families: Scorpionidae (subfamily Ischnurinae, now Hormuridae), with two genera, *Opisthacanthus* and *Heteroscorpion*, with one species each; and Buthidae, with four genera: *Grosphus* with seven species, *Odonturus* (*Tityobuthus*) with one species, *Uroplectes* with one species, and the cosmopolitan species *Isometrus maculatus*. However, the record of the genus *Uroplectes* on Madagascar was based on a misidentification (Lourenço 1995, 1996a).

Fage (1929) produced the first monographic study of the island's scorpion fauna. He mainly considered previously described taxa and named a new variety, *G. limbatus annulata*. His publication was the first comprehensive work on Madagascar scorpions. In the following years, Roewer (1943) named an enigmatic new species, *Isometrus madagassus*, which remained of uncertain status for a long period. Soon thereafter, Fage (1946) described *Babycurus gracilis* (now *Troglotityobuthus gracilis*), a cave-dwelling scorpion. Over the course of the following 30 years, several syntheses were published on the Malagasy scorpion fauna, but few taxa were described (Millot 1948; Vachon 1969; Legendre 1972). The single new form named during this period was *G. griveaudi* (now *Neogrosphus griveaudi*) by Vachon (1969).

THE MODERN PERIOD AND ACCELERATED SPECIES DISCOVERY

From the mid-1990s, several papers were published by Lourenço (e.g., 1995, 1996b, 1996c) with the descriptions of three new genera and six new species. Information gathered to date on the scorpion fauna of the island was synthesized by Lourenço (1996a) in the *Faune de Madagascar*, and one new genus and nine new species were described therein as well. Furthermore, one new subfamily, Microcharminae, was created, and the subfamily Heteroscorpioninae was raised to the rank of family. After the publication of the scorpion monograph, faunal inventories in previously unknown or poorly known areas of the island led once again to new descriptions published between 1997 and 2010, including several new genera and a remarkable number of new species (Lourenço 2000a, 2000b; Lourenço and Goodman 1999a, 1999b, 2002, 2003, 2006a, 2006b, 2008; Lourenço et al. 2008; Lourenço and Ythier 2010). The subfamily Microcharminae was raised to the rank of family and confirmed by the discovery of several new species (Lourenço et al. 2006). The position of this family was subsequently rejected by other authors without much justification (Volschenk et al. 2008) but was reestablished again by Lourenço et al. (2019). After the publication of the Scorpiones contribution in *The Natural History of Madagascar* (Lourenço 2003), a remarkable number of new species from Madagascar were discovered and described (Lourenço 2014; Lourenço and Wilmé 2015a, 2015b, 2015c, 2019; Lourenço et al. 2015, 2016a, 2016b, 2016c, 2017, 2018a, 2018b, 2020).

The new synthesis presented here contradicts early statements by authors such as Fage (1929) and Millot (1948), who overestimated the extent of contemporary knowledge of Madagascar's fauna. Fage (1929; our translation) stated, "Since scorpion species are of large size and have been collected in all the regions of the island, it is possible to estimate that we know all the populations of the island as well as their relative density and distribution." Millot (1948: 137; our translation) followed up this statement by claiming, "Scorpions are the best known Arachnida of Madagascar. Because of their large size they can easily be observed and collected. Therefore, most of the species of the great island are certainly identified at present."

In fact, as with several animal groups, when the group is thought to be well known, there is subsequent discovery and description of smaller species, and the average body size of the group is reduced (Fenchel 1993; Blackburn and Gaston 1994). The recent discovery and description of several new genera, and in particular new species on Madagascar, refer in many cases to microscorpions whose existence had not previously been suspected. The discovery of small species depends upon the use of more sophisticated methods of collecting, which were not implemented when previous generations of researchers published their work (e.g., pitfall traps, Winkler extraction, or detection with ultraviolet light). Nevertheless, a remarkable number of new species of moderate and even large size have also been described since the start of the 21st century (see lists of references above). Consequently, it can be expected that, with continued fieldwork, the number of species on the island will continue to increase, bringing the total number of endemic scorpion species to well above 100.

MALAGASY SCORPION BIOGEOGRAPHY

The biogeographic peculiarities of Malagasy scorpions have attracted the attention of several researchers who have attempted to reach conclusions concerning the origins and affinities of this fauna. However, since the classical publications of Pocock (1894) and Kraepelin (1905), the biogeography of the scorpions of Madagascar has proved to be complex. As long ago as 1894, long before the notion of continental separation and the explicit sequence concerning Gondwana, Pocock suggested that Madagascar had been isolated from Africa for a very long period. Subsequent contributors (Fage 1929; Millot 1948; Paulian 1961a; Legendre 1972; Vachon 1979) proposed interpretations of the origins and especially of the affinities of Madagascar's fauna, but these lacked precise information on the phylogeny of Malagasy scorpions in relation to those of Africa and Asia. More recent attempts to define biogeographic patterns in relation to Madagascar's fauna are summarized by Lourenço (1996c, 2005) and Lourenço et al. (2015, 2016a, 2016b, 2018b).

DIVERSITY AND ENDEMISM OF THE MALAGASY SCORPION FAUNA

On the basis of an updated checklist of Malagasy scorpions (Table 9.3), it is possible to compare the diversity and endemicity of the island's fauna with other well-studied continental regions of the world, including those with comparable surface area to Madagascar (nearly 590,000 km^2) and those that are smaller or distinctly larger. When these values are compared, Madagascar appears to have a rather important scorpion fauna with respect to species diversity. The total number of native species (100) is superior to that of the state of Baja California, Mexico (about 71,500 km^2), with around 60 species, but inferior to that of the entire country of Mexico (nearly 2 million km^2), with more than 240 species. It is superior even to countries having a much bigger territorial surface, such as Brazil (8.5 million km^2), presenting around 170 species. In contrast, some countries with a smaller surface area, such as Ecuador (about 290,000 km^2), have a relatively elevated number of species—almost 50. In all these areas, it is almost certain that new taxa will be named in upcoming years. For example, on Madagascar, since the start of 1996, 88 species and six new genera have been described (Table 9.3). Further, at the generic level, with its 10 genera of scorpions, Madagascar is significant, especially when compared to Mexico or Brazil, with 38 and 20 genera, respectively (W. R. Lourenço, unpublished data).

The picture changes considerably when we look at endemicity. Madagascar is one of the regions of the world that possesses a remarkable level of endemic scorpion species and other taxa (see Paulian 1952). Without exception, all 100 native species of Malagasy scorpions are endemic. *Isometrus maculatus*, an introduced species probably from Asia, is occasionally found in some coastal areas and inland sites but is not counted among the native fauna. Of the 10 extant native genera on the island, eight are endemic. In fact, the genus *Opisthacanthus*, also present in Africa and tropical America, is represented on Madagascar by an endemic subgenus, *Monodopisthacanthus* (Lourenço 2001). The percentages of endemics are 90% for genera and 100% for species, the highest known in the world.

POSSIBLE AFFINITIES OF THE MALAGASY SCORPION FAUNA

African Affinities

For some time, different authors have accepted affinities between Malagasy and African scorpions (Fage 1929; Millot 1948; Vachon 1979), and the present configuration of the fauna certainly seems to support this conclusion. A few examples will be presented here. *Grosphus*, one of the Malagasy genera richest in species, and *Neogrosphus*, a genus that probably evolved more recently from *Grosphus*, clearly show affinities with the African genera *Odonturus* and, in particular, *Uroplectes*. These genera share very remarkable sexual dimorphism of the pectines (Fage 1929). The recently discovered and described genus *Pseudouroplectes* also shows affinities with the genus *Uroplectes*. However, the morphology of this new genus suggests a more primitive lineage when compared with both *Uroplectes* and *Grosphus*, which are more recent lineages. *Pseudouroplectes* is a primitive lineage that is still present on Madagascar but has vanished in other regions of the world.

Until recently, the genus *Tityobuthus* was phylogenetically poorly defined. The discovery of several new species, however, improves our knowledge of this group. Many clear affinities exist with the Gondwanan genus *Ananteris*, present today in West Africa and South America. *Ananteris* seems to have had its center of origin in the western portion of Gondwana, which corresponds today with the South American continent (Lourenço et al. 2016b, 2018c). These two genera present several primitive characteristics (e.g., small size and the absence of fulcra in the pectines; the absence of fulcra is observed in at least one species of *Tityobuthus*).

The genus *Opisthacanthus* is the most typical Gondwanan lineage observed today. Its present distribution ranges from Madagascar through Africa to South America, with one population on Hispaniola and another on Cocos Island in the Pacific. The center of origin of this genus is still a matter of debate (Lourenço 1996a; Lourenço et al. 2018a). Previous statements concerning the presence of *Opisthacanthus* in the Indo-Malaysian and Australian regions (Fage 1929; Millot 1948; Legendre 1972) have proved to be incorrect. As stated by Fage (1929) and by Millot (1948), the species of *Opisthacanthus* on Madagascar are closely allied to *O. davydovi*, of the Aru Islands in Indonesia. Subsequent studies, including of the type specimen of *O. davydovi* by Lourenço (1983), have revealed that this species in fact belongs to the genus *Liocheles*, which is common in the Indo-Malaysian and Australian regions and absent from Madagascar and Africa. *Opisthacanthus* also presents some affinities with the genera *Cheloctonus* from Africa and *Chiromachetes* from India. Affinities with the latter, however, have to be better established.

The recent discovery of the genus *Palaeocheloctonus* in the southwest of Madagascar (Lourenço 1996a) and its subsequent discovery in the north (Lourenço and Wilmé 2015a) provided material for character analysis, mainly spermatophore structure and disposition of granulations on chela fingers. This genus is closely associated with the South African genus *Cheloctonus* and represents a primitive lineage that probably survived on Madagascar after its separation from Africa.

Asian Affinities

With the discovery of the new genus *Himalayotityobuthus* in the Himalayas of India and Nepal (Lourenço 1997), a new affinity was established with the genus *Tityobuthus*, which is endemic to Madagascar. Both *Tityobuthus* and *Himalayotityobuthus* represent primitive lineages whose characteristics show that they are among

TABLE 9.3. **Checklist of the known Malagasy scorpion fauna**

FAMILY BUTHIDAE C. L. KOCH, 1837

Genus *Grosphus* Simon, 1880

G. madagascariensis (Gervais, 1844)
G. limbatus (Pocock, 1889)
G. hirtus Kraepelin, 1901
G. grandidieri Kraepelin, 1901
G. flavopiceus Kraepelin, 1901
G. bistriatus Kraepelin, 1901
G. annulatus Fage, 1929
G. feti Lourenço, 1996
G. intertidalis Lourenço, 1999
G. hirtus garciai Lourenço, 2001
G. ankarafantsika Lourenço, 2003
G. ankarana Lourenço & Goodman, 2003
G. darainensis Lourenço, Goodman & Ramilijaona, 2004
G. mahafaliensis Lourenço, Goodman & Ramilijaona, 2004
G. olgae Lourenço, 2004
G. simoni Lourenço, Goodman & Ramilijaona, 2004
G. mandena Lourenço, 2005
G. goudoti Lourenço, Goodman, 2006
G. polskyi Lourenço, Qi, Goodman, 2007
G. tavaratra Lourenço, Soarimalala & Goodman, 2009
G. bicolor Lourenço, 2012
G. rossii Lourenço, 2013
G. magalieae Lourenço, 2014
G. makay Lourenço & Wilmé, 2015
G. voahangyae Lourenço & Wilmé, 2015
G. eliseanneae Lourenço & Wilmé, 2016
G. ganzhorni Lourenço, Wilmé & Waeber, 2016
G. sabineae Lourenço & Wilmé, 2016
G. waeberi Lourenço & Wilmé, 2016
G. halleuxi Lourenço, Wilmé, Soarimalala & Waeber, 2017
G. rakotoariveloi Lourenço, Wilmé, Soarimalala & Waeber, 2017
G. ambre Lourenço, Wilmé & Waeber, 2018
G. bemaraha Lourenço, Wilmé & Waeber, 2018
G. mavo Lourenço & Rossi, 2020

Genus *Isometrus* Ehrenberg, 1828

I. maculatus (Degeer, 1778) = *I. madagassus* Roewer, 1943

Genus *Neogrosphus* Lourenço, 1995

N. griveaudi (Vachon, 1969)
N. blanci Lourenço, 1996
N. andrafiabe Lourenço, Wilmé & Waeber, 2015

Genus *Palaeogrosphus* Lourenço, 2000

P. copalensis (Lourenço, 1996)
P. jacquesi Lourenço & Henderickx, 2012

Genus *Pseudouroplectes* Lourenço, 1995

P. betschi Lourenço, 1995
P. pidgeoni Lourenço & Goodman, 1999
P. maculatus Lourenço & Goodman, 2006
P. lalyae Lourenço & Ythier, 2010
P. tsingy Lourenço, Wilmé & Waeber 2016

Genus *Tityobuthus* Pocock, 1893

T. baroni (Pocock, 1890)

FAMILY BUTHIDAE

T. guillaumeti Lourenço, 1995
T. pococki Lourenço, 1995
T. petrae Lourenço, 1996
T. parrilloi Lourenço, 1996
T. judsoni Lourenço, 1996
T. dastychi Lourenço, 1997
T. ivohibe Lourenço & Goodman, 1999
T. manonae Lourenço, 2000
T. griswoldi Lourenço, 2000
T. monodi Lourenço, 2000
T. darainensis Lourenço & Goodman, 2002
T. rakotondravonyi Lourenço & Goodman, 2003
T. antsingy Lourenço & Goodman, 2004
T. pallidus Lourenço, 2004
T. betschi Lourenço, Qi & Goodman, 2008
T. chelbergorum Lourenço, Qi & Goodman, 2008
T. mccarteri Lourenço, Qi & Goodman, 2008
T. lokobe Lourenço, Wilmé & Waeber, 2016
T. mariejeanneae Lourenço, Wilmé & Waeber, 2018

Genus *Troglotityobuthus* Lourenço, 2000

T. gracilis (Fage, 1946)

FAMILY MICROCHARMIDAE LOURENÇO, 1998

Genus *Microcharmus* Lourenço, 1995

M. cloudsleythompsoni Lourenço, 1995
M. hauseri Lourenço, 1996
M. sabineae Lourenço, 1996
M. jussarae Lourenço, 1996
M. fisheri Lourenço, 1998
M. madagascariensis Lourenço, 1999
M. pauliani (Lourenço, 2004)
M. p. namoroka Lourenço, Goodman & Fisher, 2006
M. p. ambre Lourenço, Goodman & Fisher, 2006
M. bemaraha Lourenço, Goodman & Fisher, 2006
M. confluenciatus Lourenço, Goodman & Fisher, 2006
M. duhemi Lourenço, Goodman & Fisher, 2006
M. maculatus Lourenço, Goodman & Fisher, 2006
M. variegatus Lourenço, Goodman & Fisher, 2006
M. violaceous Lourenço, Goodman & Fisher, 2006
†*M. henderickxi* Lourenço, 2009
M. andrei Lourenço, Waeber & Wilmé, 2019
M. antongil Lourenço, Waeber & Wilmé, 2019
M. djangoa Lourenço, Waeber & Wilmé, 2019

Genus *Neoprotobuthus* Lourenço, 2000

N. intermedius Lourenço, 2000

FAMILY HETEROSCORPIONIDAE KRAEPELIN, 1905

Genus *Heteroscorpion* Birula, 1903

H. opisthacanthoides (Kraepelin, 1895)
H. goodmani Lourenço, 1996
H. magnus Lourenço & Goodman, 2002
H. raselimanana Lourenço & Goodman, 2004
H. kraepelini Lourenço & Goodman, 2006
H. kaii Lourenço & Goodman, 2009

(*continued overleaf*)

TABLE 9.3. ***continued***

FAMILY HORMURIDAE LAURIE, 1896
Genus *Opisthacanthus* Peters, 1861
Subgenus *Monodopisthacanthus* Lourenço, 2001
Opisthacanthus madagascariensis Kraepelin, 1894
O. darainensis Lourenço & Goodman, 2006
O. lucienneae Lourenço & Goodman, 2006
O. maculatus Lourenço & Goodman, 2006
O. piceus Lourenço & Goodman, 2006
O. milloti Lourenço & Goodman, 2008
O. pauliani Lourenço & Goodman, 2008
O. ambanja Lourenço, 2014
O. andohahela Lourenço, 2014
O. antsiranana Lourenço, 2014
O. lavasoa Lourenço, Wilmé & Waeber, 2016
O. titanus Lourenço, Wilmé & Waeber, 2018
O. faillei Lourenço & Wilmé, 2019
Genus *Palaeocheloctonus* Lourenço, 1996
P. pauliani Lourenço, 1996
P. septentrionalis Lourenço & Wilmé, 2015

Notes: Total: four families, 11 genera (one fossil), and 103 species (excluding one fossil species (†) and one introduced species, *Isometrus maculatus*). Current extant endemics: two families (Heteroscorpionidae and Microcharmidae) = 50%; 10 genera (*Opisthacanthus* is the only genus occurring outside of Madagascar) = 90%; 100 species = 100%.

remaining lineages of living buthid scorpions. No other evidence is at present available to indicate affinities between Madagascar and the Indo-Malaysian or Asian regions, and no indication is known to suggest affinities between Madagascar and the Australian region (Lourenço et al. 2016b).

Biogeographic Conclusions

In summary, the main events that determined the biogeographic origin of the scorpion fauna of Madagascar at a paleogeographic scale were the fragmentation of Gondwana and subsequent continental drift, resulting in a Malagasy scorpion fauna mostly from African stock. Difficulties in explaining the patchy distribution of the endemic families Microcharmidae and Heteroscorpionidae point not only to the great geological age of these groups but also to the relict biogeographic patterns that they exhibit today.

SIGNIFICANT GAPS IN THE MALAGASY SCORPION FAUNA

As pointed out by Paulian (1952), the fauna of Madagascar has to be seen not only in connection with its remarkable uniqueness but also with respect to the gaps it presents. Even though two of the major lineages represented in Africa and the Indo-Malaysian region—the families Buthidae and Hormuridae—are also present on Madagascar, others are not. Two of these major gaps are the family Scorpionidae, which is present in Africa and the Indo-Malaysian region, and the family Chaerilidae, which occurs in the Indo-Malaysian region.

Already in 1894, Pocock had stated that the apparent absence from Madagascar of speciose African genera of Scorpionidae was significant, and he concluded that this was indicative of this family reaching central and southern Africa after the separation between Madagascar and Africa. In fact, Scorpionidae represents a more recent lineage than either Buthidae or Hormuridae. It probably evolved in some part of what is today Africa and later colonized the south and the east (via the Middle East), displacing Hormuridae. This is implied by biogeographic patterns observed today. By the

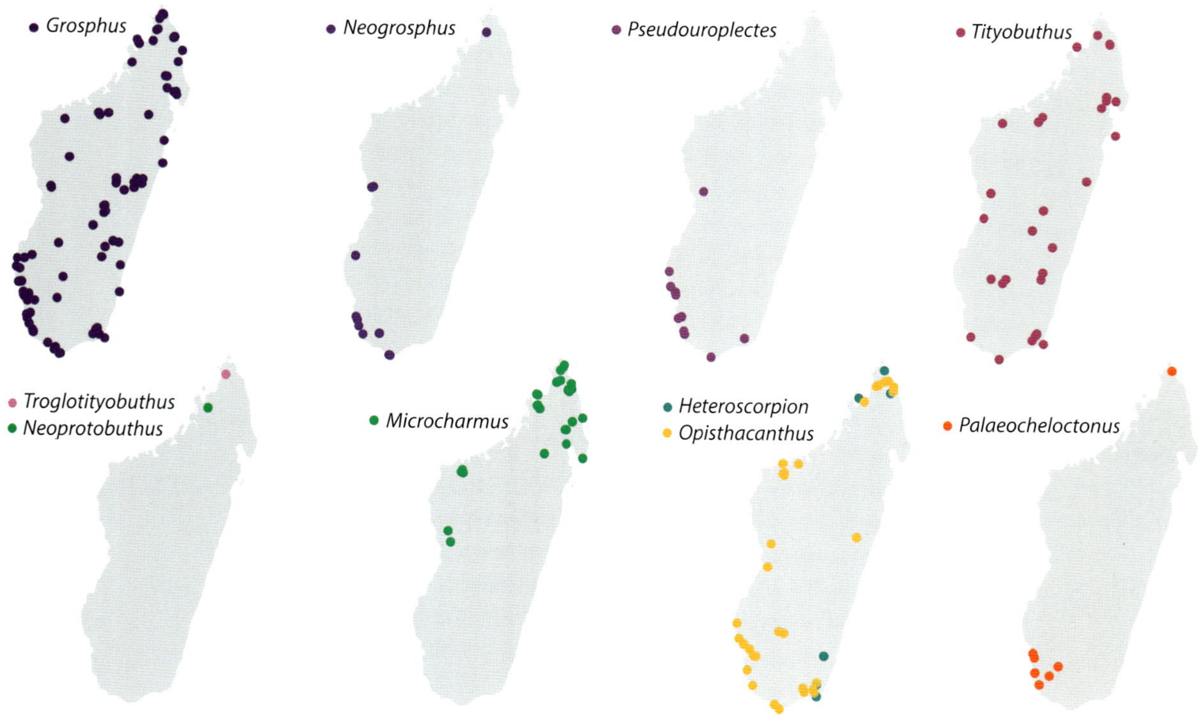

FIGURE 9.6 **Distribution of the 10 genera of scorpions recognized from Madagascar. Color patterns are defined in Figure 9.7.**

time Scorpionidae had colonized most of Africa, the separation of Madagascar had already taken place (Lourenço 1996c).

With regard to the family Chaerilidae, Lamoral (1980) proposed an explanation of its modern distribution. According to this author, the proto elements of the chaeriloids evolved in Laurasia, and the restriction of Chaerilidae to the Oriental faunal region suggests that it is a relict of an eastern Laurasian element that dispersed after the conjunction with India. The recent description of the new family Pseudochactidae from south-central Asia, which most certainly has affinities with Chaerilidae, brings some new evidence to this point. For this reason, it seems logical to assume that the family Chaerilidae does not exist on Madagascar.

DISTRIBUTION PATTERNS OF THE MALAGASY SCORPION FAUNA

On the basis of available information, many species of Malagasy scorpions have a patchy distribution. When examined at the generic level, the 10 genera show a range of distribution patterns (Figure 9.6). The highest number of species is encountered in the subhumid and humid forests, which are home to 43 species and six genera. In the western dry deciduous forests, 38 species and nine genera are recorded, and the southwestern dry spiny thicket and coastal bushland have 26 species and six genera (Figure 9.7). Several biogeographic patterns have been proposed to explain the currently known distribution of Malagasy scorpions, particularly those recently named and belonging to an ancient bradythelic group with slow evolution, based on geology and geomorphology, as well as paleoclimate oscillations (Lourenço and Wilmé 2015a, 2015c; Lourenço et al. 2015, 2016a, 2018a).

Madagascar's scorpion diversity (Figure 9.8) can, particularly for the humicolous microscorpions, be explained by the *Neogrosphus* rule (Lourenço et al. 2015, 2016a), which states that high species richness is explained by a low dispersal capability coupled with a great niche breadth of the ancestor taxon. In other words, we can expect a higher species richness in changing environments (e.g., where geographic barriers appear) if the species' dispersal ability is

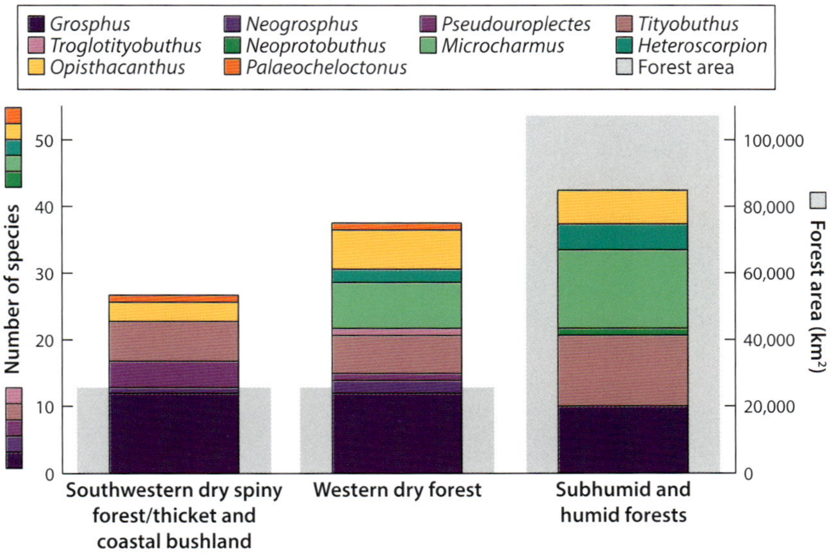

FIGURE 9.7 **Distribution of the scorpion species according to their genera in the main types of forests, which follows the classification defined by Moat and Smith (2007).**

FIGURE 9.8 **Some typical representatives of the Malagasy scorpion fauna in their natural habitats. A) *Grosphus ankarana* (female); B) *Palaeocheloctonus septentrionalis* (male); and C) *Opisthacanthus lucienneae* (female with brood).** (PHOTOS A and C by W. R. Lourenço, and B by E. Ythier.)

low and the ecological niche of the ancestor taxon is broad; while, in contrast, species richness is reduced if the dispersal capability is high or the niche breadth of the ancestor taxon is narrow.

CONCLUSIONS AND FUTURE DIRECTIONS

Although current knowledge on Malagasy scorpions can still be considered incomplete, the following characteristics of this fauna can be suggested:

- The majority of taxa found on Madagascar belong to primitive or archaic lineages that no longer exist in most other regions of the world.
- On the basis of current information, some genera are not very speciose. It is reasonable to expect the discovery of new species in genera composed of small species such as *Tityobuthus*, *Pseudouroplectes*, *Neoprotobuthus*, and *Microcharmus*, but also in genera with moderate to large species, such as *Opisthacanthus* and *Heteroscorpion*.
- The number of recorded species shows a moderate to high level of diversity for the island; however, many areas of the island have yet to be inventoried.
- Madagascar's total number of genera is significant, even when compared with other well-studied regions of the world.
- The most remarkable characteristic of the scorpion fauna of Madagascar is the impressive level of endemicity, both in species and in genera. This supports the hypothesis of very early isolation of the island from other landmasses.

Subject editors: Brian L. Fisher and Steven M. Goodman

ARANEAE, SPIDERS, *FOKA, FOKO, HALA*

H. M. Wood and C. E. Griswold

Spiders (order Araneae) are among the most conspicuous and abundant animals in all terrestrial ecosystems. Araneae is the seventh largest order of animals (Coddington and Levi 1991), and spiders may be the most important predators on insects and other small invertebrates. The study of spiders is flourishing, the order is completely cataloged in the World Spider Catalog (WSC) (2020), and spider biology and classification is summarized in several recent books accessible to the scientist and layperson alike, such as Jocqué and Dippenaar-Schoeman (2006) and Griswold and Ramírez (2017). A new work edited by Platnick et al. (2020) is perhaps the most useful to students of Madagascar spiders. As of mid-February 2020, the described world fauna was listed at 48,347 species (World Spider Catalog 2020), an increase of 10,000 species since the precursor of this book was published (Griswold 2003). Still, the current count may represent only 40–50% of the actual total. Previous reviews of Madagascar spiders have emphasized the endemism of the fauna and the inadequacy of our knowledge of it. Utilizing the WSC, we have tabulated the spiders occurring in Madagascar and referenced the most recent studies on their distributions, nearest relatives, and behavior. As of January 2020, 771 species in 58 families were reported from Madagascar (Table 9.4). This figure is certainly an underestimate of the total species—typically, revisions increase the known species by several fold. For example, since 2000, the Madagascar Archaeidae species count has increased from seven to 38 (Wood 2008; Wood and Scharff 2018). Since Griswold (2003), the described spider fauna of the island has nearly doubled, and true species richness may be in excess of 2000. Perusal of collections reveals that families Anapidae and Symphytognathidae, currently without named species, have rich faunas on Madagascar. The former family was illustrated by Griswold (2003: 585, Figure 8.8), and the latter was represented by an exemplar, "Symphytognathidae sp. Madagascar MR87," in the phylogenetic study of Wheeler et al. (2017). Accumulating evidence emphasizes the remarkable richness and endemism of Madagascar spiders. Whereas in 2003, much about Madagascar spider biology could only be predicted based on generalizations from other faunas, now a rich field record confirms, or refutes, what we had expected. In this contribution, we aim to review spider biology using examples from Madagascar; highlight exciting discoveries since c. 2003; summarize the character of the fauna, its history, and its relations to those of other areas; and provide a provisional checklist of the recorded families and described species.

ADVANCES SINCE c. 2003

Since the first version of this contribution was published over 20 years ago (Griswold 2003), three things have occurred that enhance and clarify our knowledge of the Madagascar spider fauna. First, beginning in the late 1990s and continuing to just a few years ago, the California Academy of Sciences, with generous support from the US National Science Foundation and the Schlinger Foundation, and in partnership with Parc Botanique et Zoologique de Tsimbazaza and Malagasy Institut pour la Conservation des Ecosystèmes Tropicaux (MICET), undertook an island-wide survey of arthropods.

TABLE 9.4. **Checklist of the modern families, genera, and valid species of spiders recorded from Madagascar**

AGELENIDAE, FUNNEL-WEB SPIDERS (ONE SPECIES, NOT ENDEMIC)

Tegenaria domestica (Clerck, 1757)

ANAPIDAE, ARMORED MICRO-ORB WEAVERS (UNDESCRIBED GENERA AND SPECIES)[1]

ARANEIDAE, ORB-WEB SPIDERS (83 SPECIES, 76% ENDEMIC)

Acantharachne madecassa Emerit, 2000
A. giltayi Lessert, 1938
A. milloti Emerit, 2000
Acrosomoides acrosomoides (O. Pickard-Cambridge, 1879)
Arachnura scorpionoides Vinson, 1863
Araneus isabella (Vinson, 1863)
A. kraepelini (Lenz, 1891)
A. lenzi (Roewer, 1942)
A. madagascaricus (Strand, 1908)
A. margitae (Strand, 1917)
A. nossibeus (Strand, 1907)*
A. pallescens (Lenz, 1891)
A. saccalava (Strand, 1907)*
A. sambava (Strand, 1907)
Argiope coquereli (Vinson, 1863)
A. ranomafanensis Bjørn, 1997
Augusta glyphica (Guérin-Méneville, 1839)
Caerostris almae Gregorič, 2015
C. bojani Gregorič, 2015
C. cowani Butler, 1882
C. darwini Kuntner & Agnarsson, 2010
C. ecclesiigera Butler, 1882
C. extrusa Butler, 1882
C. hirsuta (Simon, 1895)
C. mitralis (Vinson, 1863)
C. pero Gregorič, 2015
C. sexcuspidata (Fabricius, 1793)
C. wallacei Gregorič, Blackledge, Agnarsson & Kuntner, 2015
Chorizopes antongilensis Emerit, 1997
C. casictones Kallal & Hormiga, 2019
C. madagascariensis Emerit, 1997
Clitaetra episinoides Simon, 1889
C. perroti Simon, 1894
Coelossia trituberculata Simon, 1903
Cyclosa hova Strand, 1907*
C. sanctibenedicti (Vinson, 1863)
Cyphalonotus columnifer Simon, 1903
Cyrtarachne grubii (Keyserling, 1863)
C. ixoides (Simon, 1870)
C. madagascariensis Emerit, 2000
Cyrtophora citricola (Forskaal, 1775)
Exechocentrus lancearius Simon, 1889
E. madilina Scharff & Hormiga, 2012
Gasteracantha rhomboidea madagascariensis Vinson, 1863
G. rufithorax Simon, 1881
G. sanguinolenta andrefanae Emerit, 1974
G. s. bigoti Emerit, 1974
G. s. mangrovae Emerit, 1974
G. thorelli Keyserling, 1864
G. versicolor avaratrae Emerit, 1974

ANAPIDAE

G. v. formosa Vinson, 1863
Isoxya cowani (Butler, 1883)
I. mahafalensis Emerit, 1974
I. milloti Emerit, 1974
I. reuteri (Lenz, 1886)
Larinia tamatave (Grasshoff, 1971)
Madacantha nossibeana (Strand, 1916)
Nemoscolus waterloti Berland, 1920
Neoscona angulatula (Schenkel, 1937)
N. cereolella (Strand, 1907)
N. moreli (Vinson, 1863)
N. triangula mensamontella (Strand, 1907)
Nephila inaurata madagascariensis (Vinson, 1863)
N. komaci Kuntner & Coddington, 2009
N. pilipes malagassa Strand, 1907
N. senegalensis hildebrandti Dahl, 1912
Nephilingis livida (Vinson, 1863)
Paraplectana walleri (Blackwall, 1865)
Pararaneus uncivulva (Strand, 1907)
Parmatergus coccinelloides coccinelloides Emerit, 1994
P. c. ambrae Emerit, 1994
P. lens Emerit, 1994
Pasilobus antongilensis Emerit, 2000
P. capuroni Emerit, 2000
Poltys kochi Keyserling, 1864
P. reuteri Lenz, 1886
P. vesicularis Simon, 1889
Prasonica albolimbata Simon, 1895
P. seriata Simon, 1895
P. cavipalpis Grasshoff, 1971
Pronous tetralobus Simon, 1895
Pycnacantha fuscosa Simon, 1903
Thelacantha brevispina (Doleschall, 1857)

ARCHAEIDAE, PELICAN SPIDERS (38 SPECIES, 100% ENDEMIC)

Eriauchenius andriamanelo Wood & Scharff, 2018
E. andrianampoinimerina Wood & Scharff, 2018
E. bourgini (Millot, 1948)
E. fisheri (Lotz, 2003)
E. goodmani Wood & Scharff, 2018
E. harveyi Wood & Scharff, 2018
E. lukemacaulayi Wood & Scharff, 2018
E. mahariraensis (Lotz, 2003)
E. milajaneae Wood & Scharff, 2018
E. milloti Wood & Scharff, 2018
E. pauliani (Legendre, 1970)
E. rafohy Wood & Scharff, 2018
E. ranavalona Wood & Scharff, 2018
E. rangita Wood & Scharff, 2018
E. ratsirarsoni (Lotz, 2003)
E. rixi Wood & Scharff, 2018
E. sama Wood & Scharff, 2018

(continued overleaf)

TABLE 9.4. ***continued***

ARCHAEIDAE

E. workmani O. Pickard-Cambridge, 1881
E. wunderlichi Wood & Scharff, 2018
E. zirafy Wood & Scharff, 2018
Goleta peckhami Simon 1900
Madagascarchaea ambre (Wood, 2008)
M. anabohazo (Wood, 2008)
M. borimontsina (Wood, 2008)
M. fohy Wood & Scharff, 2018
M. gracilicollis (Millot, 1948)
M. griswoldi (Wood, 2008)
M. halambohitra (Wood, 2008)
M. jeanneli (Millot, 1948)
M. lavatenda (Wood, 2008)
M. legendrei (Platnick, 1991)
M. lotzi Wood & Scharff, 2018
M. moramora Wood & Scharff, 2018
M. namoroka (Wood, 2008)
M. rabesahala Wood & Scharff, 2018
M. spiceri (Wood, 2008)
M. tsingyensis (Lotz, 2003)
M. vadoni (Millot, 1948)
M. voronakely (Wood, 2008)

BARYCHELIDAE, BRUSH-FOOTED TRAPDOOR TARANTULAS (NINE SPECIES, 89% ENDEMIC)

Idioctis intertidalis (Benoit & Legendre, 1968)
Tigidia alluaudi (Simon, 1902)
T. bastardi (Simon, 1902)
T. dubia (Strand, 1907)
T. majori (Pocock, 1903)
T. mathiauxi (Simon, 1902)
T. processigera (Strand, 1907)*
T. typica (Strand, 1907)
Zophoryctes flavopilosus Simon, 1902

CHEIRACANTHIIDAE, YELLOW SAC SPIDERS (18 SPECIES, 67% ENDEMIC)

Cheiracanthium africanum Lessert, 1921
C. ambrense Lotz, 2014
C. ampijoroa Lotz, 2014
C. andranomay Lotz, 2014
C. anjozorobe Lotz, 2014
C. ashleyi Lotz, 2014
C. fisheri Lotz, 2014
C. foulpointense Lotz, 2014
C. furculatum Karsch, 1879
C. griswoldi Lotz, 2014
C. insulare (Vinson, 1863)
C. jocquei Lotz, 2014
C. leucophaeum Simon, 1897
C. ludovici Lessert, 1921
C. madagascarense Lotz, 2014
C. mahajanga Lotz, 2014
C. ransoni Lotz, 2014
C. rothi Lotz, 2014

CLUBIONIDAE, SAC SPIDERS (THREE SPECIES, 100% ENDEMIC)

Carteronius argenticomus (Keyserling 1877)
C. vittiger Simon, 1896
Clubiona hoffmanni Schenkel, 1937

CORINNIDAE, ANT-LIKE SAC SPIDERS (SIX SPECIES, 100% ENDEMIC)

Cambalida griswoldi Haddad, 2012
C. lineata Haddad, 2012
Castianeira majungae Simon, 1896
Copa auroplumosa Strand, 1907
C. lineata Simon, 1903
Corinna nossibeensis Strand, 1907

CTENIDAE, TROPICAL WOLF SPIDERS (SEVEN SPECIES, 100% ENDEMIC)[2]

Mahafalytenus fo Silva-Davila, 2007
M. fohy Silva-Davila, 2007
M. hafa Silva-Davila, 2007
M. isalo Silva-Davila, 2007
M. osy Silva-Davila, 2007
M. paosy Silva-Davila, 2007
M. tsilo Silva-Davila, 2007

CYATHOLIPIDAE, TREE SHEET-WEB SPIDERS (EIGHT SPECIES, 100% ENDEMIC)

Alaranea alba Griswold, 1997
A. ardua Griswold, 1997
A. betsileo Griswold, 1997
A. merina Griswold, 1997
Ulwembua antsiranana Griswold, 1997
U. nigra Griswold, 2001
U. ranomafana Griswold, 1997
Vazaha toamasina Griswold, 1997

DEINOPIDAE, NET-CASTING SPIDERS (TWO SPECIES, 50% ENDEMIC)

Deinopis madagascariensis Lenz, 1886
Menneus dromedarius Purcell, 1904

DESIDAE, LONG-JAWED INTERTIDAL SPIDERS (ONE SPECIES, NOT ENDEMIC)[3]

Desis crosslandi Pocock, 1903

DICTYNIDAE, MESH-WEB SPIDERS (ONE SPECIES, ENDEMIC)

Copaldictyna madagascariensis Wunderlich, 2004

DIPLURIDAE, SHEET-WEB MYGALOMORPHS (TWO SPECIES, 50% ENDEMIC)

Thelechoris rutenbergi Karsch, 1881
T. striatipes (Simon, 1889)

ERESIDAE, VELVET SPIDERS (TWO SPECIES, 50% ENDEMIC)

Stegodyphus mimosarum Pavesi, 1883
S. simplicifrons Simon, 1906

FILISTATIDAE, CREVICE WEAVERS (11 SPECIES, 100% ENDEMIC)

Andoharano decaryi (Fage, 1945)
A. grandidieri (Simon, 1901)

FILISTATIDAE

A. griswoldi Magalhães & Grismado, 2019
A. lehtineni Magalhães & Grismado, 2019
A. milloti Legendre, 1972
A. monodi Legendre, 1972
A. ramirezi Magalhães & Grismado, 2019
A. rollardae Magalhães & Grismado, 2019
A. simoni Magalhães & Grismado, 2019
A. woodae Magalhães & Grismado, 2019
A. zonsteini Magalhães & Grismado, 2019

GALLIENIELLIDAE, LONG-JAWED GROUND SPIDERS (10 SPECIES, 100% ENDEMIC)

Gallieniella betroka Platnick, 1984
G. blanci Platnick, 1984
G. mygaloides Millot, 1947
Legendrena angavokely Platnick, 1984
L. perinet Platnick, 1984
L. rolandi Platnick, 1984
L. rothi Platnick, 1995
L. spiralis Platnick, 1995
L. steineri Platnick, 1990
L. tamatave Platnick, 1984

GNAPHOSIDAE, FLAT-BELLIED GROUND SPIDERS (SEVEN SPECIES, 71% ENDEMIC)

Camillina fiana Platnick & Murphy, 1987
C. tsima Platnick & Murphy, 1987
Drassodes malagassicus (Butler, 1880)
Poecilochroa malagassa Strand, 1907*
Scotophaeus nossibeensis Strand, 1907*
Zelotes bastardi (Simon, 1896)
Z. madagascaricus (Strand, 1907)

HAHNIIDAE, COMB-TAILED SPIDERS (UNDESCRIBED GENERA AND SPECIES)

HERSILIIDAE, WHIRLIGIG SPIDERS, TWO-TAILED SPIDERS (SIX SPECIES, 83% ENDEMIC)

Hersilia eloetsensis Foord & Dippenaar-Schoeman, 2006
H. insulana Strand, 1907
H. madagascariensis (Wunderlich, 2004)
H. tamatavensis Foord & Dippenaar-Schoeman, 2006
H. vinsoni Lucas, 1869
Prima ansieae Foord, 2008

IDIOPIDAE, SPURRED TRAPDOOR SPIDERS (THREE SPECIES, 100% ENDEMIC)[4]

Genysa bicalcarata Simon, 1889
G. decorsei (Simon, 1902)
Hiboka geayi Fage, 1922

LINYPHIIDAE, HAMMOCK-WEB SPIDERS, DWARF SPIDERS (FIVE SPECIES, 80% ENDEMIC)

Helsdingenia extensa (Locket, 1968)
Microlinyphia simoni van Helsdingen, 1970
Thapsagus pulcher Simon, 1894
Thyreobaeus scutiger Simon, 1889
Tmeticides araneiformis Strand, 1907

LIOCRANIDAE, SPINY-LEGGED SAC SPIDERS (TWO SPECIES, 100% ENDEMIC)

Donuea collustrata Bosselaers & Dierick, 2010[5]
D. decorsei (Simon, 1903)

LYCOSIDAE, WOLF SPIDERS (17 SPECIES, 94% ENDEMIC)

Arctosa atroventrosa (Lenz, 1886)
Geolycosa nossibeensis (Strand, 1907)
Hognoides urbanides (Strand, 1907)
Katableps masoala Jocqué, Russell-Smith & Alderweireldt, 2011
K. perinet Jocqué, Russell-Smith & Alderweireldt, 2011
K. pudicus Jocqué, Russell-Smith & Alderweireldt, 2011
Lycosa madagascariensis Vinson, 1863
L. signata Lenz, 1886
Ocyale fera Strand, 1908
O. ghost Jocqué & Jocqué, 2017
Pardosa cinerascens (Roewer, 1951)
P. vinsoni (Roewer, 1951)
P. zorimorpha (Strand, 1907)
Tricassa madagascariensis Jocqué & Alderweireldt, 2001
Trochosa urbana hova (Strand, 1907)
Wadicosa jocquei Kronestedt, 2015
W. paulyi Kronestedt, 2017

MIGIDAE, RIDGE-FANGED TRAPDOOR SPIDERS, TREE TRAPDOOR SPIDERS (14 SPECIES, 100% ENDEMIC)

Micromesomma cowani Pocock, 1895
Paramigas alluaudi (Simon, 1903)
P. andasibe Raven, 2001
P. goodmani Griswold & Ledford, 2001
P. macrops Griswold & Ledford, 2001
P. manakambus Griswold & Ledford, 2001
P. milloti Griswold & Ledford, 2001
P. oracle Griswold & Ledford, 2001
P. pauliani (Dresco & Canard, 1975)
P. pectinatus Griswold & Ledford, 2001
P. perroti (Simon, 1891)
P. rothorum Griswold & Ledford, 2001
Thyropoeus malagasus (Strand, 1908)
T. mirandus Pocock, 1895

MIMETIDAE, PIRATE SPIDERS (THREE SPECIES, 100% ENDEMIC)

Ero lokobeana Emerit, 1996
E. madagascariensis Emerit, 1996
Mimetus madacassus Emerit, 1996

MYSMENIDAE, STARBURST ORB WEAVERS, MINUTE CLASPING WEAVERS (ONE SPECIES, NOT ENDEMIC)[6]

Microdipoena nyungwe Baert, 1989

NEMESIIDAE, WISHBONE TRAPDOOR SPIDERS (SIX SPECIES, 100% ENDEMIC)

Entypesa andohahela Zonstein, 2018
E. annulipes (Strand, 1907)*

(continued overleaf)

NEMESIIDAE

E. enakara Zonstein, 2018
E. fisheri Zonstein, 2018
E. nebulosa Simon, 1902
E. rastellata Zonstein, 2018

NESTICIDAE, CAVE COBWEB SPIDERS (TWO SPECIES, 100% ENDEMIC)

Nesticella baobab Lin, Ballarin & Li, 2016
N. griswoldi Lin, Ballarin & Li, 2016

OCHYROCERATIDAE, MIDGET GROUND WEAVERS (FOUR SPECIES, 100% ENDEMIC)

Speocera amber Li & Li, 2019
S. ankalana Li & Li, 2019
S. griswoldi Li & Li, 2019
S. tubularis Li & Li, 2019

OECOBIIDAE, STAR-LEGGED SPIDERS, DWARF ROUND-HEADED SPIDERS (FIVE SPECIES, 80% ENDEMIC)

Oecobius kowalskii Magalhães & Santos, 2018
O. marathaus Tikader, 1962
Paroecobius private Magalhães & Santos, 2018
P. rico Magalhães & Santos, 2018
P. skipper Magalhães & Santos, 2018

OONOPIDAE, GOBLIN SPIDERS (76 SPECIES, 89% ENDEMIC)

Heteroonops spinimanus (Simon, 1892)
Ischnothyreus peltifer (Simon, 1892)
I. serpentinum Saaristo, 2001
I. velox Jackson, 1908
Khamiscar ambi Platnick & Berniker, 2015
K. anta Platnick & Berniker, 2015
K. baly Platnick & Berniker, 2015
K. kiri Platnick & Berniker, 2015
K. maro Platnick & Berniker, 2015
K. tola Platnick & Berniker, 2015
Malagiella ambalavo Ubick & Griswold, 2011
M. andringitra Ubick & Griswold, 2011
M. fisheri Ubick & Griswold, 2011
M. goodmani Ubick & Griswold, 2011
M. nikina Ubick & Griswold, 2011
M. ranavalona Ubick & Griswold, 2011
M. ranomafana Ubick & Griswold, 2011
M. toliara Ubick & Griswold, 2011
M. valterova Ubick & Griswold, 2011
M. vohiparara Ubick & Griswold, 2011
Molotra katarinae Ubick & Griswold, 2011
M. milloti Ubick & Griswold, 2011
M. molotra Ubick & Griswold, 2011
M. ninae Ubick & Griswold, 2011
M. suzannae Ubick & Griswold, 2011
M. tsingy Ubick & Griswold, 2011
Noideattella amboa Alvarez-Padilla, Ubick & Griswold, 2012
N. assumptia (Saaristo, 2001)
N. famafa Alvarez-Padilla, Ubick & Griswold 2012
N. fantara Alvarez-Padilla, Ubick & Griswold, 2012

OONOPIDAE

N. farihy Alvarez-Padilla, Ubick & Griswold, 2012
N. gamela Alvarez-Padilla, Ubick & Griswold, 2012
N. lakana Alvarez-Padilla, Ubick & Griswold, 2012
N. mamba Alvarez-Padilla, Ubick & Griswold, 2012
N. omby Alvarez-Padilla, Ubick & Griswold, 2015
N. saka Alvarez-Padilla, Ubick & Griswold, 2012
N. sylvnata Alvarez-Padilla, Ubick & Griswold, 2015
N. tany Alvarez-Padilla, Ubick & Griswold, 2012
N. tsiba Alvarez-Padilla, Ubick & Griswold, 2012
Opopaea andranomay Andriamalala & Hormiga, 2013
O. andringitra Andriamalala & Hormiga, 2013
O. ankarafantsika Andriamalala & Hormiga, 2013
O. ankarana Andriamalala & Hormiga, 2013
O. antsalova Andriamalala & Hormiga, 2013
O. antsiranana Andriamalala & Hormiga, 2013
O. bemaraha Andriamalala & Hormiga, 2013
O. bemarivo Andriamalala & Hormiga, 2013
O. berenty Andriamalala & Hormiga, 2013
O. betioky Andriamalala & Hormiga, 2013
O. concolor (Blackwall, 1859)
O. foulpointe Andriamalala & Hormiga, 2013
O. itampolo Andriamalala & Hormiga, 2013
O. kirindy Andriamalala & Hormiga, 2013
O. mahafaly Andriamalala & Hormiga, 2013
O. manderano Andriamalala & Hormiga, 2013
O. manongarivo Andriamalala & Hormiga, 2013
O. maroantsetra Andriamalala & Hormiga, 2013
O. namoroka Andriamalala & Hormiga, 2013
O. sandranantitra Andriamalala & Hormiga, 2013
O. torotorofotsy Andriamalala & Hormiga, 2013
O. tsimaloto Andriamalala & Hormiga, 2013
O. tsimbazaza Andriamalala & Hormiga, 2013
O. tsimembo Andriamalala & Hormiga, 2013
O. tsingy Andriamalala & Hormiga, 2013
O. tsinjoriaky Andriamalala & Hormiga, 2013
O. vohibazaha Andriamalala & Hormiga, 2013
Silhouettella curieusei Benoit, 1979
S. perisalma Alvarez-Padilla, Ubick & Griswold, 2015
S. perismontes Alvarez-Padilla, Ubick & Griswold, 2015
Tolegnaro kepleri Alvarez-Padilla, Ubick & Griswold, 2012
T. sagani Alvarez-Padilla, Ubick & Griswold, 2012
Volborattella guenevera Saucedo, Ubick & Griswold, 2015
V. nasario Saucedo, Ubick & Griswold, 2015
V. paulyi Saucedo, Ubick & Griswold, 2015
V. teresae Saucedo, Ubick & Griswold, 2015
V. toliara Saucedo, Ubick & Griswold, 2015

OXYOPIDAE, LYNX SPIDERS (FIVE SPECIES, 20% ENDEMIC)

Hostus paroculus Simon, 1898
Oxyopes dumonti (Vinson, 1863)
O. pallidecoloratus Strand, 1906
Peucetia lucasi (Vinson, 1863)
P. madagascariensis (Vinson, 1863)

PALPIMANIDAE, PALP-FOOTED SPIDERS (TWO SPECIES, 100% ENDEMIC)

Diaphorocellus isalo Zonstein & Marusik, 2020
D. jocquei Zonstein & Marusik, 2020

PHILODROMIDAE, SMALL HUNTSMAN SPIDERS (TWO SPECIES, 100% ENDEMIC)

Philodromus niveus Vinson, 1863
Thanatus philodromicus Strand, 1916

PHOLCIDAE, DADDY-LONGLEGS SPIDERS (49 SPECIES, 90% ENDEMIC)

Artema mauriciana Walckenaer, 1837
Crossopriza francoisi Millot, 1946
C. nigrescens Millot, 1946
C. stridulans Millot, 1946
Leptopholcus griswoldi Huber, 2011
L. lokobe Huber, 2011
L. sakalavensis Millot, 1946
L. talatakely Huber, 2011
Micropolcus fauroti (Simon, 1887)
Ninetis toliara Huber & El-Hennawy, 2007
Paramicromerys betsileo Huber, 2003
P. coddingtoni Huber, 2003
P. combesi (Millot, 1946)
P. madagascariensis (Simon, 1893)
P. mahira Huber, 2003
P. manantenina Huber, 2003
P. marojejy Huber, 2003
P. megaceros (Millot, 1946)
P. nampoinai Huber, 2003
P. quinteri Huber, 2003
P. rabeariveloi Huber, 2003
P. ralamboi Huber, 2003
P. rothorum Huber, 2003
P. scharffi Huber, 2003
Pehrforsskalia conopyga Deeleman-Reinhold & van Harten, 2001
Smeringopus carli Lessert, 1915
S. elongatus (Vinson, 1863)
S. kalomo Huber, 2012
S. madagascariensis Millot, 1946
S. peregrinus Strand, 1906
Spermophora ranomafana Huber, 2003
S. vyvato Huber, 2003
Zatavua analalava Huber, 2003
Z. andrei (Millot, 1946)
Z. ankaranae (Millot, 1946)
Z. fagei (Millot, 1946)
Z. griswoldi Huber, 2003
Z. imerinensis (Millot, 1946)
Z. impudica (Millot, 1946)
Z. isalo Huber, 2003
Z. kely Huber, 2003
Z. madagascariensis (Fage, 1945)
Z. mahafaly Huber, 2003
Z. punctata Millot, 1946
Z. talatakely Huber, 2003
Z. tamatave Huber, 2003

PHOLCIDAE

Z. voahangyae Huber, 2003
Z. vohiparara Huber, 2003
Z. zanahary Huber, 2003

PHYXELIDIDAE, LACE-WEB WEAVERS (14 SPECIES, 100% ENDEMIC)[7]

Ambohima andrefana Griswold, Wood & Carmichael, 2012
A. antisinanana Griswold, Wood & Carmichael, 2012
A. avaratra Griswold, Wood & Carmichael, 2012
A. maizina Griswold, Wood & Carmichael, 2012
A. pauliani Griswold, 1990
A. ranohira Griswold, Wood & Carmichael, 2012
A. sublima Griswold, 1990
A. vato Griswold, Wood & Carmichael, 2012
A. zandry Griswold, Wood & Carmichael, 2012
A. zoky Griswold, Wood & Carmichael, 2012
Manampoka atsimo Griswold, Wood & Carmichael, 2012
Rahavavy fanivelona (Griswold, 1990)
R. ida Griswold, Wood & Carmichael, 2012
R. malagasyana (Griswold, 1990)

PISAURIDAE, NURSERY WEB SPIDERS, FISHING SPIDERS (18 SPECIES, 78% ENDEMIC)

Blandinia mahasoana (Blandin, 1979)
Caripetella madagascariensis (Lenz, 1886)
Dendrolycosa rossi Silva & Griswold, 2013
Dolomedes kalanoro Silva & Griswold, 2013
Hala impigra Jocqué, 1994
H. paulyi Jocqué, 1994
Hygropoda linearis (Simon, 1903)
H. madagascarica Strand, 1907*
H. tangana (Roewer, 1955)
Maypacius bilineatus (Pavesi, 1895)
M. vittiger Simon, 1898
Nilus esimoni (Sierwald, 1984)
N. leoninus (Strand, 1916)
N. majungensis (Strand, 1907)
Paracladycnis vis Blandin, 1979
Tallonia picta Simon, 1889
Thalassiopsis vachoni Roewer, 1955
Tolma toreuta Jocqué, 1994

SALTICIDAE, JUMPING SPIDERS (107 SPECIES, 88% ENDEMIC)

Aelurillus madagascariensis Azarkina, 2009
Asemonea ornatissima Peckham, Peckham & Wheeler, 1889
Bavia albolineata Peckham & Peckham, 1885
Beata lineata (Vinson, 1863)
Bianor paulyi Logunov, 2009
Brettus madagascarensis (Peckham & Peckham, 1903)
Carrhotus harringtoni Prószyński, 1992
Cyrba legendrei Wanless, 1984
Echinussa imerinensis Simon, 1901
E. praedatoria (Keyserling, 1877)
E. vibrabunda (Simon, 1886)
Evarcha madagascariensis Prószyński, 1992

(continued overleaf)

TABLE 9.4. **continued**

SALTICIDAE

Goleba lyra Maddison & Zhang, 2006
G. punctata Peckham, Peckham & Wheeler, 1889
Goleta peckhami Simon, 1900
G. workmani (Peckham & Peckham, 1885)
Harmochirus bianoriformis (Strand, 1907)
Heliophanus hamifer Simon, 1886
H. imerinensis Simon, 1901
H. innominatus Wesolowska, 1986
H. modicus Peckham & Peckham, 1903
H. mucronatus Simon, 1901
H. orchesta Simon, 1886
Hermosa volatilis Peckham & Peckham, 1892
Hispo cingulata Simon, 1886
H. frenata (Simon, 1900)
H. georgius (Peckham & Peckham, 1892)
H. macfarlanei Wanless, 1981
H. pullata Wanless, 1981
H. sulcata Wanless, 1981
H. tenuis Wanless, 1981
Hyllus albomarginatus (Lenz, 1886)
H. albooculatus (Vinson, 1863)
H. bifasciatus Ono, 1993
H. interrogationis (Strand, 1907)
H. lugubrellus Strand, 1908*
H. lugubris (Vinson, 1863)
H. madagascariensis (Vinson, 1863)
H. nossibeensis Strand, 1907*
H. vinsoni (Peckham & Peckham, 1885)
H. virgillus Strand, 1907*
Macopaeus spinosus Simon, 1900
Meleon insulanus Logunov & Azarkina, 2008
M. madagascarensis (Wanless, 1978)
M. raharizonina Logunov & Azarkina, 2008
M. russata (Simon, 1900)
M. tsaratanana Logunov & Azarkina, 2008
Microbianor deltshevi Logunov, 2009
M. madagascarensis Logunov, 2009
Myrmanu mahasoa (Wanless, 1978)
M. nubilis Wanless, 1978
Myrmapeni diegoensis (Wanless, 1978)
M. simplexella (Roewer, 1951)
Myrmarachne augusta (Peckham & Peckham, 1892)
M. cowani (Peckham & Peckham, 1892)
M. eumenes (Simon, 1900)
M. longiventris (Simon, 1903)
M. ransoni Wanless, 1978
Myrmele andringitra (Wanless, 1978)
M. electrica (Peckham & Peckham, 1892)
M. peckhami (Roewer, 1951)
M. rufescens (Simon, 1900)
Natta chionogaster (Simon, 1901)
Pachypoessa lacertosa Simon, 1902
Padilla armata Peckham & Peckham, 1894
P. astina Andriamalala, 2007
P. boritandroka Andriamalala, 2007

SALTICIDAE

P. cornuta (Peckham & Peckham, 1885)
P. foty Andriamalala, 2007
P. griswoldi Andriamalala, 2007
P. lavatandroka Andriamalala, 2007
P. maingoka Andriamalala, 2007
P. manjelatra Andriamalala, 2007
P. mazavaloha Andriamalala, 2007
P. mihaingo Andriamalala, 2007
P. mitohy Andriamalala, 2007
P. ngeroka Andriamalala, 2007
P. ombimanga Andriamalala, 2007
P. sartor Simon, 1900
Pandisus decorus Wanless, 1980
P. modestus (Peckham, Peckham & Wheeler, 1889)
P. parvulus Wanless, 1980
P. sarae Wanless, 1980
P. scalaris Simon, 1900
Pharacocerus ebenauensis Strand, 1908
P. sessor Simon, 1902
Phaulostylus furcifer Simon, 1902
P. grammicus Simon, 1902
P. grandidieri Simon, 1902
P. leucolophus Simon, 1902
Pochyta albimana Simon, 1902
Poessa argenteofrenata Simon, 1902
Portia africana (Simon, 1886)
P. schultzi Karsch, 1878
Salticus coronatus (Camboué, 1887)
Spadera unica Peckham & Peckham, 1894
Thyene inflata (Gerstäcker, 1873)
T. tamatavi (Vinson, 1863)
T. varians Peckham & Peckham, 1901
Tomobella andasibe (Maddison & Zhang, 2006)
T. fotsy Szűts & Scharff, 2009
Tomocyrba barbata Simon, 1900
T. berniae Szűts & Scharff, 2009
T. decollata Simon, 1900
T. griswoldi Szűts & Scharff, 2009
T. thaleri Szűts & Scharff, 2009
T. ubicki Szűts & Scharff, 2009

SCYTODIDAE, SPITTING SPIDERS (TWO SPECIES, 100% ENDEMIC)

Scytodes oswaldi Lenz, 1891
S. socialis Miller, 2006

SEGESTRIIDAE, TUBE-WEB SPIDERS (ONE SPECIES, 100% ENDEMIC)

Segestria madagascarensis Keyserling, 1877

SELENOPIDAE, FLATTIES (17 SPECIES, 88% ENDEMIC)

Anyphops benoiti Corronca, 1998
Garcorops madagascar Corronca, 2003
G. paulyi Corronca, 2003
Hovops antakarana Rodriguez & Corronca, 2014
H. betsileo Corronca & Rodriguez, 2011

SELENOPIDAE

H. ikongo Rodriguez & Corronca, 2014
H. legrasi (Simon, 1887)
H. lidiae Corronca & Rodriguez, 2011
H. madagascariensis (Vinson, 1863)
H. mariensis (Strand, 1908)
H. menabe Rodriguez & Corronca, 2014
H. merina Corronca & Rodriguez, 2011
H. pusillus (Simon, 1887)
H. vezo Rodriguez & Corronca, 2014
Selenops dufouri Vinson, 1863
S. ivohibe Corronca, 2005
S. vigilans Pocock, 1898

SPARASSIDAE, HUNTSMAN SPIDERS (41 SPECIES, 95% ENDEMIC)

Chrosioderma albidum Simon, 1897
C. analalava Silva-Davila, 2005
C. havia Silva-Davila, 2005
C. mahavelona Silva-Davila, 2005
C. mipentinapentina Silva-Davila, 2005
C. namoroka Silva-Davila, 2005
C. ranomafana Silva-Davila, 2005
C. roaloha Silva-Davila, 2005
C. soalala Silva-Davila, 2005
Damastes atrignathus Strand, 1908
D. coquereli Simon, 1880
D. c. affinis Strand, 1907
D. decoratus (Simon, 1897)
D. fasciolatus (Simon, 1903)
D. flavomaculatus Simon, 1880
D. grandidieri Simon, 1880
D. majungensis Strand, 1907
D. malagassus (Fage, 1926)
D. malagasus (Karsch, 1881)
D. masculinus Strand, 1908
D. nossibeensis Strand, 1907
D. oswaldi Lenz, 1891
D. pallidus (Schenkel, 1937)
D. sikoranus Strand, 1906
Eusparassus laterifuscus Strand, 1908
Heteropoda venatoria (Linnaeus, 1767)
Megaloremmius leo Simon, 1903
Olios coenobitus Fage, 1926
O. erraticus Fage, 1926
O. lamarcki (Latreille, 1806)
O. malagassus Strand, 1907
O. m. septifer Strand, 1908
O. mordax (O. Pickard-Cambridge, 1899)
O. nossibeensis Strand, 1907
O. pusillus Simon, 1880
O. subpusillus Strand, 1907
Palystes convexus Strand, 1907
P. spiralis Strand, 1907
Rhitymna hildebrandti Järvi, 1914
R. imerinensis (Vinson, 1863)
Staianus acuminatus Simon, 1889

SYMPHYTOGNATHIDAE, DWARF ORB WEAVERS, MICRO ORB WEAVERS (UNDESCRIBED GENERA AND SPECIES)[8]

SYNAPHRIDAE, MIDGET SPIDERS (THREE SPECIES, 100% ENDEMIC)

Africepheia madagascariensis Miller, 2007
Synaphris schlingeri Miller, 2007
S. toliara Miller, 2007

TETRABLEMMIDAE, ARMORED SPIDERS (ONE SPECIES, ENDEMIC)

Monoblemma browni Shear, 1978

TETRAGNATHIDAE, WATER ORB WEAVERS, LONG-JAWED SPIDERS (EIGHT SPECIES, 63% ENDEMIC)

Diphya pumila Simon, 1889
Leucauge lechei Strand, 1908
L. tetragnathella Strand, 1907*
L. undulata (Vinson, 1863)
Orsinome vorkampiana Strand, 1907*
Pachygnatha longipes Simon, 1894
Tetragnatha nitens (Audouin, 1826)
T. protensa Walckenaer, 1841

THERAPHOSIDAE, BABOON SPIDERS, TARANTULAS (THREE SPECIES, 100% ENDEMIC)

Encyocrates raffrayi Simon, 1892
Monocentropus lambertoni Fage, 1922
Phoneyusa bouvieri Berland, 1917

THERIDIIDAE, COMB-FOOTED SPIDERS, GUMFOOT WEB WEAVERS (55 SPECIES, 76% ENDEMIC)

Anelosimus andasibe Agnarsson & Kuntner, 2005
A. ata Agnarsson, Kuntner & Jencik, 2015
A. buffoni Agnarsson, Kuntner & Jencik, 2015
A. darwini Agnarsson, Kuntner & Jencik, 2015
A. decaryi (Fage, 1930)
A. hookeri Agnarsson, Kuntner & Jencik, 2015
A. huxleyi Agnarsson, Veve & Kuntner, 2015
A. lamarcki Agnarsson & Goh, 2015
A. may Agnarsson, 2005
A. moramora Agnarsson, Kuntner & Jencik, 2015
A. nazariani Agnarsson & Kuntner, 2005
A. sallee Agnarsson & Kuntner, 2005
A. salut Agnarsson & Kuntner, 2005
A. tita Agnarsson, Kuntner & Jencik, 2015
A. torfi Agnarsson, 2015
A. vondrona Agnarsson & Kuntner, 2005
A. wallacei Agnarsson, Veve & Kuntner, 2015
Argyrodes abscissus O. Pickard-Cambridge, 1880
A. argentata O. Pickard-Cambridge, 1880
A. meus Strand, 1907*
A. minax O. Pickard-Cambridge, 1880
A. sextuberculosus Strand, 1908
A. viridis (Vinson, 1863)
A. zonatus (Walckenaer, 1841)

(continued overleaf)

THERIDIIDAE
Asygyna coddingtoni Agnarsson, 2006
A. huberi Agnarsson, 2006
Crustulina ambigua Simon, 1889
Dipoena transversisulcata Strand, 1908
Latrodectus geometricus C. L. Koch, 1841
L. menavodi Vinson, 1863
L. obscurior Dahl, 1902
L. tredecimguttatus (Rossi, 1790)
Phoroncidia ambatolahy Kariko, 2014
P. aurata O. Pickard-Cambridge, 1877
P. quadrispinella Strand, 1907*
P. roseleviorum Kariko, 2014
P. rubroargentea Berland, 1913
P. vatoharanana Kariko, 2014
P. wrightae Kariko, 2014
Phycosoma excisum (Simon, 1889)
Theridion decemperlatum (Simon, 1889)
T. lacticolor Berland, 1920
T. quadrilineatum Lenz, 1886
T. rufipes Lucas, 1846
Theridula gonygaster (Simon, 1873)
T. perlata Simon, 1889
T. theriella Strand, 1907*
Thwaitesia argenteosquamata (Lenz, 1891)
T. aureosignata Lenz, 1891
T. pulcherrima Butler, 1883
Tidarren apartiolum Knoflach & van Harten, 2006
T. dasyglossa Knoflach & van Harten, 2006
T. ephemerum Knoflach & van Harten, 2006
T. horaki Knoflach & van Harten, 2006
T. obtusum Knoflach & van Harten, 2006

THERIDIOSOMATIDAE, RAY SPIDERS (UNDESCRIBED GENERA AND SPECIES)

THOMISIDAE, CRAB SPIDERS (47 SPECIES, 98% ENDEMIC)
Apyretina catenulata (Simon, 1903)
A. nigra (Simon, 1903)
A. pentagona (Simon, 1895)
A. quinquenotata (Simon, 1903)
A. tessera (Simon, 1903)
Cyriogonus fuscitarsis Strand, 1908
C. lactifer Simon, 1886
C. rutenbergi (Karsch, 1881)
C. simoni Lenz, 1891
C. triquetrus Simon, 1886
C. vinsoni (Thorell, 1875)
Diaea nakajimai Ono, 1993
Diplotychus longulus Simon, 1903
Emplesiogonus scutulatus Simon, 1903
E. striatus Simon, 1903
Firmicus bimaculatus (Simon, 1886)
Geraesta bilobata Simon, 1897
G. hirta Simon, 1889

THERIDIOSOMATIDAE
G. lehtineni Benjamin, 2011
G. octolobata (Simon, 1886)
Herbessus decorsei Simon, 1903
Heriaeus madagascar van Niekerk & Dippenaar-Schoeman, 2013
Iphoctesis echinipes Simon, 1903
Lampertia pulchra Strand, 1907
Phrynarachne clavigera Simon, 1903
P. pusiola Simon, 1903
P. rugosa (Walckenaer, 1805)
P. r. infernalis Strand, 1907
Plastonomus octoguttatus Simon, 1903
Pseudoporrhopis granum Simon, 1886
Pyresthesis laevis (Keyserling, 1877)
Runcinia oculifrons Strand, 1907
Soelteria nigra Dahl, 1907
Synema hildebrandti Dahl, 1907
S. lunulatum Dahl, 1907
S. obscurifrons Dahl, 1907
S. obscuripes Dahl, 1907
Tharrhalea cerussata Simon, 1886
T. semiargentea Simon, 1895
T. superpicta Simon, 1886
Thomisus boesenbergi Lenz, 1891
T. lamperti Strand, 1907
T. madagascariensis Comellini, 1957
T. m. pallidus Comellini, 1957
T. nossibeensis Strand, 1907*
Trichopagis manicata Simon, 1886
Xysticus hepaticus Simon, 1903

TITANOECIDAE, ROCK WEAVERS (ONE SPECIES, NOT ENDEMIC)
Pandava laminata (Thorell, 1878)

TRACHELIDAE, RUGGED SAC SPIDERS (NINE SPECIES, 100% ENDEMIC)
Cetonana aulifera (Strand, 1916)
Orthobula sicca Simon, 1903
Paccius angulatus Platnick, 2000
P. elevatus Platnick, 2000
P. griswoldi Platnick, 2000
P. madagascariensis (Simon, 1889)
P. mucronatus Simon, 1898
P. quinteri Platnick, 2000
P. scharffi Platnick, 2000

TROCHANTERIIDAE, SCORPION SPIDERS (FIVE SPECIES, 80% ENDEMIC)
Platyoides grandidieri Simon, 1903
P. mailaka Platnick, 1985
P. ravina Andriamalala & Ubick, 2007
P. vao Andriamalala & Ubick, 2007
P. velonus Platnick, 1985

UDUBIDAE, PRIMITIVE WOLF SPIDERS (FIVE SPECIES, 100% ENDEMIC)

Uduba dahli Simon, 1903
U. evanescens (Dahl, 1901)
U. madagascariensis (Vinson, 1863)
Zorodictyna inhonesta (Simon, 1906)
Z. oswaldi (Lenz, 1891)

ULOBORIDAE, HACKLED-BAND ORB WEAVERS (THREE SPECIES, 100% ENDEMIC)

Uloborus aureus Vinson, 1863
U. vanillarum (Vinson, 1863)
U. velutinus Butler, 1883

VIRIDASIIDAE, FALSE TROPICAL WOLF SPIDERS (SEVEN SPECIES, 100% ENDEMIC)[9]

Viridasius fasciatus (Lenz, 1886)
Vulsor isaloensis (Ono, 1993)
V. penicillatus Simon, 1896
V. quartus Strand, 1907*
V. quintus Strand, 1907*
V. septimus Strand, 1907
V. sextus Strand, 1907

ZODARIIDAE, BURROWING SPIDERS, ANT-EATING SPIDERS (18 SPECIES, 100% ENDEMIC)

Aschema madagascariensis (Strand, 1907)
A. pallida Jocqué, 1991
Diores anomalus Jocqué, 1990
D. milloti Jocqué, 1990
Omucukia angusta (Simon, 1889)
O. madrela (Jocqué, 1991)
Suffascar albolineatus Henrard & Jocqué, 2017
S. fianara Henrard & Jocqué, 2017
S. fisheri Henrard & Jocqué, 2017
S. fitzpatrickae Henrard & Jocqué, 2017
S. gigas Henrard & Jocqué, 2017
S. griswoldi Henrard & Jocqué, 2017
S. macromma Henrard & Jocqué, 2017
S. micromma Henrard & Jocqué, 2017
S. nonus Henrard & Jocqué, 2017
S. scutatus Henrard & Jocqué, 2017
S. sufficiens Henrard & Jocqué, 2017
S. tofti Henrard & Jocqué, 2017

Sources: Species list compiled from World Spider Catalog (2020); Natural History Museum Bern, online at http://wsc.nmbe.ch, accessed 15 Feb. 2020, doi: 10.24436/2. For tabulations, subspecies are counted as species. Most common names for families are from Jocqué and Dippenaar-Schoeman (2006).

Note: The types of many Madagascar spider species, especially those described by Embrik Strand, appear to have been tragically destroyed during World War II. Recently Nentwig et al. (2020) have declared 181 of Strand's names *nomina dubia*, including 19 species listed in the World Spider Catalog (WSC) from Madagascar. As of 15 Mar. 2020, the WSC accepted the opinion of Nentwig et al. (2020) on the validity of Strand's names. Nevertheless, we retain those names on our list because we believe that validity of names should be always be determined as part of a revision. The 19 names recently declared *nomina dubia* are marked with an asterisk (*). At least one of the criteria articulated by Nentwig et al. (2020), that the lost species have "never been recollected," is unsupported. For example, the species *Vulsor quartus* and *V. quintus* Strand, 1907 have been declared *nomina dubia*, yet numerous species of *Vulsor* have been collected since the start of the 20th century, and the revision is not yet complete, so it is impossible at this time to state that these species are not recognizable from among this new material. To declare these species as nonexistent would further distort our knowledge of Madagascar Viridasiidae.

[1] The web of an undescribed anapid was illustrated by Griswold (2003: 585, Figure 8.8).

[2] Although *Mahafalytenus* is placed in the Ctenidae by the World Spider Catalog (2020), Silva-Davila (2007: 59) refers to it as "a new genus of viridasiine spiders," which suggests that it belongs in Viridasiidae. There may be no true Ctenidae in Madagascar.

[3] *Ischalea incerta* (O. Pickard-Cambridge 1877) was described in *Ischalea*, which was formerly placed in Stiphidiidae (Griswold 2003) and now in Desidae (Wheeler et al. 2017; World Spider Catalog 2020). Examination of the original description of *Ischalea incerta* (O. Pickard-Cambridge 1877) reveals that this is not a true *Ischalea* but probably a pisaurid. Therefore, only one species of Desidae (*Desis crosslandi*) is listed from Madagascar, and the *Ischalea* species awaits positive identification.

[4] All Idiopidae species recorded from Madagascar belong in the subfamily Genysinae, which is also recorded from Sri Lanka and South America (Raven 1985). There also are undescribed species of the subfamily Idiopinae in collections.

[5] First described from subfossil material from copal/amber, *Donuea collustrata* Bosselaers and Dierick, 2010 was a short time later discovered alive (Bosselaers et al. 2010).

[6] Lopardo and Hormiga include several undetermined species as vouchers in their phylogeny of the family Mysmenidae (Lopardo et al. 2011; Lopardo and Hormiga 2015).

[7] All described species of Phyxelididae from Madagascar belong to the tribe Phyxelidini. A species of the tribe Vydoleini remains to be described.

[8] An undetermined species from Nosy Be in northwestern Madagascar was used as a Symphytognathidae voucher by Wheeler et al. (2017).

[9] *Mahafalytenus* listed in Ctenidae may instead belong in Viridasiidae.

The final count is yet untallied, but in the context of this large-scale inventory, as of 2010, more than 800,000 arthropod specimens have been collected, databased, and processed (Fisher 2005a). Further, these specimens were fast-tracked into the hands of scientists all over the world, creating an unprecedented resource for understanding Madagascar arthropods. By the end of 2010, 163 scientists had received 616 sets of specimens (loans) comprising 796,285 arthropod specimens. Coupled with this, we have attained numerous new observations on and images of Madagascar spiders and their biology. The Madagascar fauna, as well as that of surrounding landmasses, such as Africa and South Asia, are now much better surveyed than in the past, with numerous taxonomic papers published in the past few decades (World Spider Catalog 2020).

Second, there have been numerous careful, quantitative phylogenetic analyses utilizing morphological and/or molecular data, enabling a more precise picture of phylogenetic and biogeographic relations within the island and to other parts of the world (e.g., Griswold et al. 2005; Wheeler et al. 2017). These patterns may be tested for generality or used to corroborate or refute historical scenarios.

Third, utilizing molecular data, phylogenetic branching points may be dated within a margin of confidence, demonstrating consistence with, or refuting, dated historical scenarios. Molecular dating, especially when considered with fossil studies, sets a timeline for spider evolution and dispersal. We find Magalhães et al. (2020) to be the most useful work for understanding the timing of the evolution of spiders. This recent study incorporated dated molecular phylogenies together with a careful and critical study of spider fossils. Coupled with a more precise understanding of the environmental history of Madagascar and nearby lands, we can now rule out many vicariance scenarios—for example, continental drift—because, in most cases, the spiders are clearly too young for their distributions to have been the result of vicariance.

THE LIFESTYLES OF SPIDERS

Silk

All spiders are predators, and members of all but one family (Uloboridae, with three species present on Madagascar) use poison injected through hollow fangs to assist in subduing prey. Silk, produced in abdominal glands and issuing through spigots on abdominal spinnerets, characterizes spiders. Spiders produce eggs, which in most families are wrapped in silk and attached to the substrate or web, and then guarded or abandoned. However, members of Pholcidae, Pisauridae, and Scytodidae carry the egg sac with the chelicerae (equivalent to jaws or mandibles), while Lycosidae members attach it to the spinnerets. Not all spiders make webs, and not all web spinners make sticky webs. All spiders make at least some use of silk, particularly the dry type of fiber that may line a retreat or be played out behind a spider wherever it goes as a safety rope (dragline); some spiders use only this type of silk. At the other extreme, some female orb weavers may make five kinds of silk for spinning dry lines, attaching them, making a sticky snare, and protecting eggs. Spiders are prevented from becoming stuck in their own webs through dexterity, some sort of coating on their legs, and branched setae (Briceño and Eberhard 2012). Dry silk curtains or space webs serve to trip, block, or knock down potential prey, temporarily ensnaring or impeding them while allowing the spider to move speedily and surely on the web to capture the prey before it escapes. Such webs are found in members of Dipluridae and some members of Lycosidae and Pisauridae. Sheet and space webs made by Pholcidae may use glue from the anterior spinnerets (Platnick et al. 1991).

The most primitive form of sticky silk is cribellate silk, which entails a complex snare of dry foundation fibers and thousands of fine, curled fibrils that are teased and carded by a comb on the spider's fourth metatarsus. Although physically likened to Velcro, cribellate silk apparently also adheres by nonstructural forces, and the manner in which this works is still unknown (Opell 1995). Cribellate spiders are not a conspicuous part of the Madagascar fauna. Curtain, funnel, and sheet webs of cribellate silk are characteristic of Dictynidae, Eresidae, Filistatidae, Oecobiidae, Phyxelididae (Figures 9.9d and e), Titanoecidae, and some members of Udubidae (Figures 9.9a and b). The complex morphology and behavior responsible for making cribellate silk once led to these spiders being classified as a separate group, but it is now recognized that cribellate silk is primitive and has been lost many times. Indeed, within the genus *Uduba* (Udubidae), which is endemic to Madagascar, there are cases of closely related species that are cribellate or not cribellate (Polotow et al. 2015). Crevice weaver spiders (Filistatidae) have recently been revised for Madagascar (Magalhães and Grismado 2019). The genus *Andoharano*, endemic to Madagascar, increased from four to 11 species. These spiders were previously known only from caves (Legendre 1971); Magalhães and Grismado (2019) discovered seven new epigeal species. Interestingly, each of the cave-dwelling species is morphologically similar to a different epigeal species, suggesting repeated invasions of the subterranean realm.

Web-Building Spiders

Everyone recognizes the orb web—a point-symmetric structure comprising a frame and radii of dry silk and a sticky silk spiral for prey capture (Hormiga and Griswold 2014). Orb webs are built using homologous behaviors (Coddington 1986), but orbs are no longer considered monophyletic. They may be ancient and modified or lost in descendant lineages (Garrison et al. 2016) or may have even evolved in parallel (Fernández et al. 2018), although such a conclusion is controversial (Coddington et al. 2019). Planar orbs are typical of Araneidae, Symphytognathidae, Tetragnathidae, and Uloboridae. Members of Uloboridae spin orb webs utilizing cribellate silk; in all other orb builders, the sticky spiral is of gluey silk. The sticky spiral comprises a dry foundation that is coated with wet glue as it is extruded from spigots on the posterior spinnerets. Sticky, gluey orbs are conspicuous features of the Madagascar landscape. Webs of gasteracanthine Araneidae (e.g., *Augusta* and *Gasteracantha*) are commonly seen in daytime along paths, their occupants presumably protected from bird predation by sharp body spines. Many *Argiope* species decorate their orbs with silk crosses or zigzags (stabilimenta). The huge, golden silk orbs of *Nephila* may form striking aggregations in trees or wires, often near human habitations. One Malagasy member of this genus, *N. komaci*, is the world's largest web-building spider (Kuntner and Coddington 2009). Spectacular webs that span streams or small rivers with anchor and frame lines have long attracted comment (Griswold 2003). Recently the Malagasy orb-web builder *Caerostris darwini* (Darwin's Bark Spider) has been described. Its orbs may attain an area of 2.8 m^2, and anchor lines may bridge over 25 m, making these the largest webs ever observed (Kuntner and Agnarsson 2010) and the most striking case of spiderweb gigantism (Gregorič et al. 2015). Once considered the pinnacle of web design, planar orbs are now seen to have been variously modified by evolution (Dimitrov et al. 2017). Webs recognizable as modified orbs are most common in understories of damp forests. Individuals of Theridiosomatidae may pull their orb into a cone that is then quickly released to catch prey. Members of the Anapidae family leave out-of-plane radii that form a cone above the orb, and many Mysmenidae spiders make three-dimensional orbs with radii extending in all directions. Evolution has further modified orbs to the point that they could not be recognized as such except for the behaviors involved in making them, the type of sticky silk, and other evidence indicating the phylogenetic placement of their makers. Members of Deinopidae exhibit several typical orb-building behaviors in constructing their spreading net (retiarius) webs of cribellate silk (Coddington 1986). Other highly modified orbs include the sheet webs of Cyatholipidae and Linyphiidae and gumfoot webs of Nesticidae and Theridiidae, all of which use sticky, gluey silk for prey capture (Hormiga and Griswold 2014).

Hunting Spiders

Many spiders do not build webs to capture prey. Sit-and-wait predators remain motionless until alerted to nearby prey by cues such as substrate-borne vibration. Members of Nemesiidae, Segestriidae, and Theraphosidae lurk near the mouth of their silk-lined burrows. Most members of Barychelidae, Idiopidae, and Migidae close the opening of their retreat with a camouflaged door of silk and debris, hence the name "trapdoor spider." Most Migidae individuals place their trapdoor retreats on tree trunks. Thomisidae species characteristically wait on flowers or bark or in moss, the shape and markings of each species rendering it nearly invisible against the preferred backdrop. Members of Hersiliidae and their tiny relatives in Oecobiidae are known for racing in circles around their prey and tying it down with silk. Other spiders wander through the habitat in hopes of encountering prey. Members of Cheiracantheidae, Clubionidae, Corinnidae, Gallieniellidae, Gnaphosidae, Liocranidae, Oonopidae, Palpimanidae, Philodromidae, many Pisauridae, Selenopidae, Sparassidae, and Trochanteriidae, and some members of Udubidae (Figure 9.9a) and Zodariidae, are running hunters with poor eyesight that rely on touch or vibration to locate prey. The family Selenopidae (flatties) includes the fastest-running spiders and is richer in genera on Madagascar than anywhere else. Many species have been described and more remain. Crews (2011) and Zeng and Crews (2018) reported on their remarkable speed and turning ability, but perhaps Octavius Pickard-Cambridge (1876: 587) said it best when he wrote that they "run with unconceivable quickness ... legs extended flat ... [and can] glide in an instant through cracks and crevices so narrow as to have escaped observation until the Spider disappears." Spiders of the families Ctenidae, Viridasiidae, Lycosidae, Oxyopidae, and especially Salticidae rely on their good eyesight to locate prey from a distance. Members of Salticidae have exceptionally good eyesight, allowing them to stalk and pounce on their prey from a distance of several body lengths.

The goblin spiders (Oonopidae), which constitute a rich and until recently unknown fauna in Madagascar (more than 70 endemic species discovered since 2010), include many tiny (<2 mm), armor-plated spiders. Like beetles, these bulldoze through the leaf litter, hunting and eating cryptic prey. Goblin spiders have been recognized from the island since 1948 (Millot 1948), but no Malagasy species was formerly named or described until 2011 (Ubick and Griswold 2011a). Some 76 described species of Oonopidae have been recorded from Madagascar, and at least several new species of the cosmopolitan genus *Orchestina* and at least three new, endemic genera remain to be described, making the family the third largest known on the island. Recent research has recognized species described long ago from other parts of the world that occur on Madagascar as part of cosmotropical distributions—for example, *Heteroonops spinimanus*, *Opopaea concolor*, and *Ischnothyreus peltifer*—but all 70 species described since 2011 as part of the Goblin Spider PBI (Planetary Biodiversity Inventory) are thought to be endemic to Madagascar. The biotic surveys and inventories project carried out from 2000 to 2014 on the island by the California Academy of Sciences resulted in the collection of more than 10,000 oonopid specimens. Madagascar oonopids include both arboreal species (e.g., *Orchestina*) and terrestrial ones that are crucial components of the soil and leaf-litter fauna. The genus richest in described species from

FIGURE 9.9 **Spiders of Madagascar. A) A male of the genus *Uduba* (Udubidae) from Ranomafana National Park. B) A cribellate *Uduba* web from Ranomafana National Park. C) A female pelican spider of the genus *Eriauchenius* (Archaeidae) from Ranomafana National Park. The pelican spider has impaled an orb-weaving spider (Araneidae) with the fang at the tip of its extended chelicera. D) A male *Ambohima sublima* (Phyxelididae) from Ranomafana National Park. This spider was found waiting at the edge of a female's retreat. E) The web of *A. sublima*, in Anjozorobe-Angavo Forest.** (PHOTOS A and C by N. Scharff, Natural History Museum of Denmark; B by D. Lin; D by J. Miller; and E by J. Ledford.)

Madagascar is *Opopaea*, which was revised by Andriamalala and Hormiga (2013) based on nearly 4000 specimens. There are 27 named species of *Opopaea* on the island, of which 26 were newly described and 25 are apparently endemic. Andriamalala (2014) included a morphological phylogeny of world *Opopaea*. At least two clades occur in Madagascar, with their sister groups in each case found in Africa. Members of *Opopaea* have huge, swollen male palpal patellae, filled with muscles, which must function in some remarkable but yet unobserved mating behavior. The genus *Khamiscar*, with six Malagasy endemic species, also has African relatives (Platnick and Berniker 2015). Most other Madagascar goblin spiders demonstrate no close relationship to Africa. For example, the endemic genus *Malagiella* resembles *Opopaea* in that males of this genus also have a huge, swollen palpal patella, but this seems to be a case of parallel evolution, similar to the affinities of *Malagiella* to members of the *Ischnothyreus* group of Asia and Oceania (Ubick and Griswold 2011a). The oonopid fauna of Madagascar is exceptionally well represented by the *Silhouettella* complex, or silhouettelloids. A similar fauna was described by Saaristo (2001) from the adjacent Seychelles islands, where 10 of the 33 known species are silhouettelloids (of the *Lionneta* group). Our studies suggest that silhouettelloids are at least as well represented in the Madagascar fauna, currently numbering over 30 species (in various stages of analysis and description) of an estimated 100 total goblin spider species. New silhouettelloid genera include the beautiful, sparkling *Volborattella* (Saucedo et al. 2015), the rarely collected *Molotra* (Ubick and Griswold 2011b), and the abundant *Tolegnaro* and *Noideattella*, for which there are more than 2000 specimens available for study (Alvarez-Padilla et al. 2012). Additionally, two new species of *Silhouettella*, a genus otherwise scattered among the islands of the western Indian Ocean, have been added to the Malagasy fauna (Alvarez-Padilla et al. 2015). This silhouettelloid-pelecinoid group is richest in the Indian Ocean but not rich in Africa. Andriamalala (2014) and Alvarez-Padilla et al. (2015) suggest that the group's closest relatives are in Asia and Australia.

Mating

Male spiders are unique in using their pedipalps (second postoral appendages) as sperm transfer organs; the male inserts his pedipalpal tarsi in the female's genital opening on the underside of her abdomen. Understandably, for predators such as spiders, mating entails considerable risk, especially to the male. Mating is preceded by species-specific courtship behavior, which may involve vibratory communication via the substrate, perhaps chemical cues, and, at least in members of Lycosidae and Salticidae, visual cues. In salticids, courtship may involve an elaborate ritual, with the male displaying his beautiful decorations before the female through an intricate stereotyped dance. Such displays rival those of pheasants, grouse, and birds of paradise, although on a much smaller scale. Andriamalala (2007) provided a taxonomic and evolutionary study of the horned jumping spiders of the genus *Padilla*, so called because of the forward-pointing horns found on the male chelicerae of many species. She found a remarkable parallel evolution among species with similar ornaments. *Padilla* and other "modern" members of Salticidae are abundant on Madagascar (e.g., Azarkina 2009 and Logunov 2009), but the island is famous for a diversity of basal jumping spiders. The Salticidae subfamilies Lysomanninae (Maddison and Zhang 2006), Spartaeinae (Logunov and Azarkina 2008), and Hisponinae (Szűts and Scharff 2009) are conspicuously rich components of the fauna.

REMARKABLE LIFESTYLES OF MADAGASCAR SPIDERS

Madagascar has two marine intertidal spiders, *Idioctis intertidalis* (Barychelidae) and *Desis crosslandi* (Desidae), which hunt in rocks or reefs and spend high tide underwater, secured in silken tubes or cells beneath shells or within corals or stones (Legendre 1969). A particularly remarkable spider, *Olios coenobitus* (Sparassidae), has become famous for using discarded snail shells to make a safe, secure home. This spider hoists snail shells many times its own weight off the ground using a network of silk threads (Fage 1926). This sparassid, which lives in the dry spiny thickets of the southwest, has been featured by the naturalist David Attenborough in BBC broadcasts.

Many *Argyrodes* species (Theridiidae) are kleptoparasites, living in the webs of other spiders, especially large orb builders like *Nephila*, where they steal prey from their host (Legendre 1960; Kuntner and Agnarsson 2010). Spitting spiders (Scytodidae) spit sticky glue to a distance greater than their body length to trap prey. Cyrtarachnine araneids, many known as bolas spiders, have extraordinary prey-capture strategies. They make highly reduced webs (or none at all) and use aggressive chemical mimicry to lure their prey, typically lepidopterans (Stowe 1986). The Malagasy genus *Exechocentrus* is related to other cyrtarachnines, such as *Mastophora* (Emerit 1980; Scharff et al. 2020). We previously predicted that *Exechocentrus* could use pheromone mimicry to lure male moths as prey. Scharff and Hormiga (2012) observed *E. lancearius* near Ranomafana and photographed its highly modified "bolas" foraging web, which provides indirect evidence of aggressive chemical mimicry. Many spiders resemble ants or wasps in shape, color, and movement, and presumably gain protection from spider predators that mistake them for well-defended hymenopterans. Examples are *Castianeira*, *Gallieniella*, *Myrmarachne*, and *Diores*. *Diores*, at least, may also feed upon the ants it mimics (Jocqué 1990). Some spiders appear to prey exclusively on other spiders. Many of the elongate, wormlike theridiids of the Argyrodinae are araneophages (Agnarsson 2004; Su and Smith 2014). Spiders of the genus *Chorizopes* (Araneidae) have been observed to prey on other orb weavers, provoking them from the periphery of the web and attacking the web's occupant when they investigate (Eberhard 1982; Kallal and Hormiga 2019). Members of Mimetidae (pirate spiders) enter webs to prey on other spiders (Benavides et al. 2017).

The complete superfamily Palpimanoidea, popularly called assassin spiders (Griswold and Ramírez 2017), may be specialized to prey on other spiders. Palp-footed spiders (Palpimanidae) are common in collections from Madagascar, although it is only very recently that these specimens have begun to be formally documented and described. Among these, undescribed Madagascar species of *Diaphorocellus* have served as exemplars in phylogenetic studies (Wood et al. 2018), and recently Zonstein and Marusik (2020) described two new *Diaphorocellus* species. Palpimanids have been observed to use their comparatively large, powerful forelegs to enter the retreats of other spiders and eat the occupants (Pekar et al. 2011). Pelican spiders (Archaeidae), icons of Madagascar spiders, are close relatives to palpimanids but have an extremely unusual frontal region that they use to attack other spiders at a distance. Some archaeid species on Madagascar hunt from vegetation at night and have been found waiting at the edge of other spiders' webs, walking into webs, or hovering over webs in order to capture spider prey. Once in close proximity to their spider prey, they swing their greatly elongate chelicerae far out and spear their prey with the fang at the tip (Legendre 1961; Wood 2008). They leave their long chelicerae extended away from their body until their spider prey dies from the injected venom (Figure 9.9c), and only then do archaeids lower their chelicera to feed on the immobilized prey. Close relatives in Australia and South Africa are more cryptic; it is only in Madagascar that archaeids are easily observable in the vegetation at night while they are stalking spider prey.

Whereas most spiders are solitary, the orb builders *Nephila* and especially *Cyrtophora citricola* may form web aggregations containing dozens to hundreds of individuals, each in a separate but connected web. True group living is found in at least three different families of Madagascar spiders. Adults of both sexes and juveniles may occupy the same web, in which a few to hundreds of individuals reside in the same retreat and cooperate to maintain webs and mass attack prey. Unlike social bees and wasps, there is no apparent reproductive division of labor (i.e., there are no queens or workers), and all females probably have an opportunity to reproduce.

Species of *Stegodyphus* (Eresidae) have long been known to live in groups; at least three parallel examples of this behavior occur in South Asia (*S. sarisonorum*), Africa (*S. dumicola*), and Africa and Madagascar (*S. mimosarum*) (Miller et al. 2012). The rich fauna of inquilines and kleptoparasites known from African *S. mimosarum* (Griswold and Meikle 1990) seems to be absent from Madagascar. *Stegodyphus* may be common, conspicuous, and even abundant around the Parc Botanique et Zoologique de Tsimbazaza in the heart of Antananarivo, but Madagascar's other group-living spiders have been discovered only since the start of the 21st century, marking some of the most exciting revelations about the island's spider fauna. A new spitting spider (Scytodidae) was discovered in dry deciduous forest in the west (Miller 2006). *Scytodes socialis* lives alone or in colonies containing juveniles, females, and males; when in colonies, these spiders mass-attack large prey. A variety of social systems is found within spitting spiders, and this is the first species to show web-sharing sociality and cooperative prey capture. Further study of this and other Scytodidae species promises to enlighten our understanding of the evolution of sociality in spiders.

Perhaps the most thrilling new discovery is that Madagascar is a hotspot of social *Anelosimus* (Theridiidae) diversity. *Anelosimus* represents a diverse clade of spiders found worldwide in tropical to warm-temperate areas. Its members exhibit a variety of lifestyles from solitary to social, the latter trait typical of American species but until recently unknown elsewhere. In a phylogenetic analysis, Agnarsson and Kuntner (2005) discovered that the American *Anelosimus* and the Madagascar *Anelosimus* are close relatives. In subsequent expeditions to Madagascar, they discovered social *Anelosimus*, illustrating the utility of phylogenies as predictors of traits in species thus far unstudied. Their analysis documents monophyly of the Madagascar group and places it as sister to a clade containing the *eximius* lineage from the Americas and a pair of undescribed Tanzanian species. Six new species were found living sympatrically at Andasibe, and 10 additional new species (mostly single-forest endemics) were scattered around the island (Agnarsson et al. 2015). All 16 new species live in groups, representing a radiation stemming from a single colonization event. Remarkably, another *Anelosimus* species on Madagascar, the solitary *A. decaryi*, is related to a solitary American clade, implying duplicate colonizations from the Americas. Agnarsson and Kuntner (2005) have presented an inspiring picture of the importance of exploration and phylogenetic analysis of Madagascar spiders as keys to understanding historical biogeography and behavioral evolution.

THE MADAGASCAR FAUNA AND ITS BIOGEOGRAPHY

The past accounts of the Madagascar spider fauna (Millot 1948; Legendre 1972) emphasized its richness, endemism, strong affinity to Africa, and much weaker affinity to Asia and the Indo-Pacific. More recent summaries (Paulian and Viette 2003; Griswold et al. 2012) bear this out. Fifty-eight families are recorded from Madagascar, and all except Anapidae, Hahniidae, Symphytognathidae, and Theridiosomatidae are represented by described species. Currently, the World Spider Catalog (2020) describes 771 species in 247 genera from Madagascar (Table 9.4) (but see Nentwig et al. 2020). Knowledge has grown rapidly, with slightly less than half of the species (325) described since 2000. A high proportion of the species, 678 (88%), are endemic; generic endemism is lower (74 genera, 30%). Madagascar was formerly believed to harbor an endemic family, Halidae (Jocqué 1994), but this family has now been synonymized with Pisauridae (Polotow et al. 2015). No family is currently recognized as a Madagascar endemic.

Madagascar is geologically a Wallacean island (Griswold et al. 2012)—a fragment of a once larger, connected landmass—but in many ways the biota resembles that of a Darwinian island (Gillespie and Roderick 2002), which has always been separated by barriers from other landmasses. This is borne out in Madagascar's famously disharmonic terrestrial vertebrate biota (Carlquist 1965). Visiting the island, the birdwatcher familiar with Africa asks, "Where are the eagles, vultures, and cranes?"; these soaring birds are common in Africa, just 400 miles away. In contrast, Madagascar's spider fauna is not disharmonic and contains most of the families found in Africa and Asia. The arachnologist accustomed to Africa will find Madagascar very similar. The most striking differences might be the ease with which one can find large pelican spiders (*Eriauchenius*) in the vegetation at night and numerous crab spiders (Thomisidae) hanging from single lines at night, as well as the conspicuous daytime presence of bark spiders (*Caerostris*) and other large orb builders in their webs—these spiders are almost all nocturnal on the African mainland and hard to find.

Although the island is continental in origin, the great age of Madagascar's isolation, starting 140 million years ago (Mya) (Rabinowitz et al. 1983) and complete around 80 Mya (Krause et al. 2006), makes the study of the island's biota and its origin particularly intriguing. Had the spider fauna arrived through overwater dispersal during the Cenozoic? Do any spiders remain from the

Mesozoic? As Yoder and Novak (2006) have said for land vertebrates, Cenozoic dispersal appears to be the dominant pattern; however, as more understudied groups are examined, time will tell whether this pattern holds.

A recent study incorporating dated molecular phylogenies coupled with a careful and critical study of spider fossils (Magalhães et al. 2020) is notably insightful for understanding the timing of the evolution of spiders. This work shows that in the Mesozoic, the world's spider fauna consisted primarily of Mygalomorphae, Synspermiata, and other basal taxa with "haplogyne" genitalia (e.g., Palpimanoidea), reflecting an age of "haplogynes," as recognized by Wunderlich (2008). The most abundant modern spiders, including a diverse clade of wandering spiders (the RTA clade, so named for the retrolateral tibia apophysis on the male pedipalp) and most of the orb weavers and their relatives (Araneoidea), seem to have evolved or at least diversified after continental breakup, requiring long-distance dispersal over water as the most conceivable way for the ancestors of the bulk of Madagascar's spiders to have reached the island.

Agnarsson and Kuntner (2012) produced an extensive survey of the biogeography and phylogeography of the western Indian Ocean islands, emphasizing spiders and the importance of long-distance dispersal in crafting this island fauna. Their study of hermit spiders suggests that African lineages colonized Madagascar in the Cenozoic via dispersal and from there continued to colonize smaller islands like those in the Comoro and Mascarene archipelagoes (Kuntner and Agnarsson 2011), speciating as they island-hopped. Researchers at the California Academy of Sciences have focused on the taxonomy and biogeography of several diverse lineages of Madagascar spiders. Jumping spiders (Salticidae), cyatholipids, phyxelidids, and udubids may be too young for vicariance through continental drift, and each of these families shows a geographic pattern consistent with Cenozoic dispersal.

Andriamalala (2007) studied the horned jumping spiders of the genus *Padilla* (Salticidae). Using her data and those from Maddison and Hedin (2003) and Benjamin (2004), she recovered *Padilla* within the Ballinae and showed affinities to Asian relatives. Her dated phylogeny suggests *Padilla* origin as late as the Neogene, too late for Gondwanan vicariance, and suggests instead that *Padilla* reached Madagascar on island stepping-stones in the Indian Ocean. The discovery by Ledoux (2007) of typical *Padilla* on La Réunion reinforces the hypothesis of *Padilla* island-hopping. The araneoid family Cyatholipidae occurs today in Africa, Madagascar, Australia, and New Zealand, with possible fossils representing an extinct fauna in the Baltic region of Europe (Griswold 2001). Two cyatholipid clades in Madagascar (Griswold 1997), the genus *Alaranea* and some species of *Ulwembua*, show phylogenetic affinities to taxa in the eastern African mountains, exhibiting a pattern typical of Cenozoic dispersal. The family Phyxelididae (Figure 9.9d) occurs in eastern and southern Africa, the eastern Mediterranean, Madagascar, and Southeast Asia. A recent molecular phylogeny (Griswold et al. 2012) suggests that the three Madagascar genera of this family, *Ambohima*, *Manampoka*, and *Rahavavy*, form a monophyletic group that is related to African phyxelidids, again displaying a pattern typical of Cenozoic dispersal. The family comprises a few widely distributed species (e.g., *A. sublima* and *A. ranohira*), many narrowly distributed species, and at least two cases of sympatric sister species. The small *A. zandry* occurs in sympatry with the larger *A. avaratra* (its probable sister species) at Montagne d'Ambre in the far north, and the sister species *R. fanivelona* and *R. ida* occur in sympatry at Ranomafana. An undescribed member of the Asian genus *Vytfutia* adds a trans–Indian Ocean character to the fauna.

Polotow et al. (2015) proposed a total-evidence phylogenetic study of the wolf spiders and relatives, the "oval calamistrum clade." They described the new family Udubidae for the cryptic, terrestrial web-building or running spiders that make up a substantial part of the Madagascar fauna (Figures 9.9a and b). Relatives occur in Africa (*Raecius*; Griswold 2002) and Sri Lanka (*Campostichomma*; Polotow and Griswold 2017). Only five Madagascar species in two genera, *Uduba* and *Zorodictyna*, have been described, but at least 80 new species are in the process of revision. A few species are widespread, but most appear to be narrowly distributed. Thus, the majority of studies of Malagasy spiders to date suggest that most spiders are on Madagascar due to more recent dispersal after Madagascar was an isolated island.

In contrast to these probable Cenozoic dispersal patterns, there are a couple of spider lineages whose presence on Madagascar may be ancient and due to continental drift as Pangaea broke apart in the Mesozoic. The ancient trapdoor spiders of the family Migidae may show a vicariance pattern. Migids await a test from a dated molecular phylogeny, but their intercontinental biogeography is one of the most compelling cases of a Gondwanan distribution achieved through continental drift (Gillespie 2013). To fit a Gondwanan scenario, geographic relationships should conform to those predicted by continental drift. Madagascar, India, Sri Lanka, and the granitic Seychelles were the first fragments to separate from Gondwana (A. G. Smith et al. 1994), and so, if isolated by continental drift, Madagascar taxa should be the plesiomorphic relatives of those occurring elsewhere in Gondwana. Members of Migidae show this pattern; the three Malagasy genera form a monophyletic group that is the sister group of taxa occurring in Australia, New Zealand, South America, and Africa (Griswold and Ledford 2001). However, some migids are demonstrably capable of transoceanic dispersal. At least three species of African *Moggridgea* occur on oceanic islands: *M. nesiota* (Mohéli, Comoros), *M. socotra* (Socotra), and *M. occidua* (Príncipe) (Simon 1907; Griswold 1987). In a remarkable new discovery, ancestors of *M. rainbowi* have been shown to have dispersed from Africa to Kangaroo Island in Australia (Harrison et al. 2016). The migid biogeographic pattern (Griswold and Ledford 2001) and overall age of mygalomorphs (Magalhães et al. 2020) is consistent with a history forged by continental drift, but time will tell, as ongoing molecular phylogenetic studies of this family promise to corroborate or refute this extraordinary scenario.

The pelican spiders (Archaeidae) are another ancient group whose current distribution is likely due to the continental breakup of Pangaea. These spiders are true "Lazarus" taxa, initially discovered and known only from Baltic amber fossils of Eocene age (Koch and Berendt 1854) and presumed extinct, only to be discovered several decades later living on Madagascar (Pickard-Cambridge 1881). Since the initial discovery of these extant species on the island, more species have been discovered, but only from the Southern Hemisphere (Madagascar, Australia, and South Africa). Additional fossils have also been discovered, but only from the Northern Hemisphere, from Baltic, Bitterfeld, and Burmese amber (e.g., Wunderlich 2008), and even compression fossils from Mongolia of Jurassic age (Selden et al. 2008). To examine this enigmatic distribution, Wood et al. (2012) performed a phylogenetic analysis combining molecular data for living species and morphological data for both living and extinct species. Results showed strong support for a monophyletic southern extant clade due to several morphological synapomorphies present only in the living species. Furthermore, divergence dating analysis revealed that the split between the northern fauna and the southern fauna was consistent with the timing of Laurasia breaking with Gondwana, and the split between the Australian and Madagascar clades was consistent with that between eastern and western Gondwana (Wood et al. 2013). The South African clade was suggested to be a dispersal event from Madagascar to Africa, opposite to the typical pattern of dispersal from Africa to Madagascar (Yoder and Novak, 2006). The presence of Mesozoic archaeid spider fossils is evidence in itself that this family is ancient and existed prior to the Pangaean breakup. This research (Wood et al. 2013) offers further compelling evidence that this group existed on Madagascar before it became isolated and traveled with the landmass after separation.

Archaeid spiders, with their close relatives in Australia and southeastern Africa, have also been studied to understand how diversification has proceeded on Madagascar after isolation. During the Late Cretaceous, the landscape sustained extensive alteration as a result of volcanism and basalt flows associated with the separation of India and Madagascar (Wells 2003). Then in the Paleogene, Madagascar shifted in latitude after tectonic isolation and moved northward through the 30°S arid belt, after which it developed its modern ecogeographic regions. Thus, ancient lineages that have been on Madagascar since before isolation have experienced a number of vicissitudes as compared to more recent arrivals, as such lineages would have encountered dramatic geoclimatic shifts over long time periods.

Archaeids are morphologically and behaviorally bizarre due to their highly modified carapace and chelicerae, giving them the appearance of a "neck" and "head." This morphology directly relates to their unique predatory strategy of attacking other spiders at a distance with their long chelicerae (Legendre 1961; Wood et al. 2012) (Figure 9.9c). There is considerable interspecific morphological variation in the shape of the chelicerae, "neck," and "head." What is striking is that the Madagascar species appear to have greater amounts of morphological variation compared to their close relatives in South Africa and Australia. Another notable difference is that Madagascar species occur in sympatry, and it is possible to find up to eight different archaeid species in a single forest area. In contrast, species in Australia and South Africa tend to be allopatric (e.g., Lotz 2006; Rix and Harvey 2012). Wood et al. (2015) examined these patterns and confirmed that traits were diversifying at a faster rate in Madagascar archaeids. This study also found statistical correlation between endemicity and elevation; that is, montane areas had a greater amount of microendemics compared to lowland areas, where the species were more widespread. The implication of this research is that montane areas may have been important for building up the sympatric communities of archaeid spiders. Montane areas may have served as refugia when the forests expanded and contracted during geoclimatic events over long geologic timescales. Adaptive trait diversification then may have occurred to facilitate the coexistence of Madagascar species.

In contrast to Madagascar, South Africa and Australia experienced relatively stable geological and climatological environments until the more recent time period of the Miocene. In Australia, warm-temperate rainforests were widespread until the Miocene, when the climate became drier and seasonal (Crisp et al. 2004). In southeastern Africa, a warm, mesic climate pervaded and likely remained from the Cretaceous until the present day (Tyson and Partridge 2000). However, starting in the Miocene, geological changes fragmented the South African landscape due to uplift of the Great Escarpment (Tyson and Partridge 2000). It may be that more recent Miocene geological or climatic events contributed to distribution patterns in southeastern African and Australian archaeid species, whereas in Madagascar, different processes have been involved in shaping the diversity of the archaeids. Currently, population-level research is underway on the Madagascar species to closely examine these processes. As the island's fauna comes under increasing scrutiny, and cladistic analysis serves to clarify the relations of its components, the complex and varied history of the spider fauna will become clearer.

MADAGASCAR SPIDERS AND PEOPLE

Spiders, known as *foka* or *hala* in Malagasy, are widely admired for the beauty of their web architecture and fine silk. Madagascar was the site of a rare attempt to utilize spiders commercially for silk production (Petrunkevitch 1921). In the 19th century, *Nephila*, a huge orb weaver known for its strong, golden silk, was raised in special gardens. The spiders were periodically taken from their webs and placed in special racks, and silk was drawn from their spinnerets and wound on a reel. Beautiful garments of high quality were produced (Griveaud 1984). Nevertheless, the difficulties of procuring live insect food for these spinners made the production of their silk economically unviable.

A widespread perception of spiders is that their bites are dangerous to humans. Most spiders are far too small to deliver a bite to a person, others are nonaggressive, and many live in remote areas where encounters with people are unlikely. Nevertheless, at least the *menavody*, or "red-rump," may be dangerous (Lavauden 1933). This spider, *Latrodectus menavodi*, belongs to the nearly worldwide genus of "widow spiders," known for their neurotoxic venom, which may cause generalized pain and even death in rare cases (Brygoo 1982). Fear of the spiders by local people, however, appears unfounded. The crab spider *Phrynarachne rugosa* (family Thomisidae) is harmless (Vinson 1863). Huntsman spiders (Sparassidae) are probably also of no concern.

ACKNOWLEDGMENTS

Financial support for aspects of our research was supplied by the US National Science Foundation (NSF), the California Academy of Sciences (CAS), and the Schlinger Foundation. Jon Coddington provided valuable assistance with compiling the current list of species. We are especially grateful to our Madagascar research partners Parc Botanique et Zoologique Tsimbazaza (PBZT) and Malagasy Institut pour la Conservation des Ecosystèmes Tropicaux (MICET), and to H. (Rin'Ha) Rasolondalao of MICET, Balsama Rajemison of PBZT, and to Brian Fisher and members of the CAS Ant-Spider survey team.

Subject editors: Brian L. Fisher and Steven M. Goodman

IXODIDA, TICKS, *KONGONA*

H. Klompen and D. A. Apanaskevich

Ticks (Ixodida) form a distinct group of large (often >2 mm) mites (Acari) characterized primarily by their life history as obligate, nonpermanent blood feeders. Morphologically, the group is defined by its modified mouthparts: a pointed hypostome located at the anterior ventral part of the feeding apparatus (between the palps), covered ventrally with recurved teeth; and the transformation of the elongate chelicera (feeding mouthparts) into cutting, rather than the conventional biting, structures. All ticks feed on vertebrates, mostly mammals and birds but also reptiles and amphibians. They are best known for their ability to act as vectors for a range of pathogens causing diseases (see chapter 6).

SYSTEMATICS AND DEVELOPMENT CHARACTERS

Three extant families are currently recognized, two of which, Ixodidae (hard ticks) and Argasidae (soft ticks), occur on Madagascar. The two families are morphologically and biologically quite distinct. Soft ticks are generally secretive, spending most of their life in the burrow, nest, or roost of their hosts. The larvae of most soft tick species may feed for days and are the instar most commonly encountered on the host. In contrast to the larvae, the post-larval instars feed for only brief periods and are rarely found on the host. To locate these instars, burrows, nests, or roosts of appropriate hosts need to be examined. Development includes a six-legged larva, a variable number of eight-legged nymphs (usually at least three), and the adult. Nymphs and adults generally differ strikingly from the larva but can be distinguished from each other only by the presence and shape of the genital opening. Post-larval argasid ticks tend to be rather large and often fairly flat. The mouthparts are positioned ventrally, and they lack a dorsal shield and have a cuticle with smaller (granulate) or larger (mammillate) protuberances. The larvae usually have a dorsal shield, which is characteristically positioned in the middle of the dorsum.

In contrast to soft ticks, all instars of hard ticks generally feed on their host(s) for extended periods (days to weeks), and development includes only a single nymph. Larva, nymph, and female are all characterized by the presence of a distinct anterior dorsal shield, the scutum. Nymphs and females can be distinguished by the presence or absence of the genital opening in the sternal region of the venter. In males, a dorsal shield covers the entire dorsal surface. The soft cuticle is lightly striate, not mammillate or granulate as in argasids. The mouthparts are positioned anteriorly and are clearly visible in dorsal view. To attach themselves to their host, ixodids often rely on a glue-like "cement," secreted by the ticks, forming a small cone around the inserted mouthparts. The palps are relatively long and straight in *Ixodes* and *Amblyomma*, but short and broad in most *Haemaphysalis* and *Rhipicephalus*. Keys to the hard and soft ticks known from Madagascar are presented by Uilenberg et al. (1979). Although these keys do not include the species described in the past 40 years, they allow identification to genera for all instars and to most species for adults. Keys to the species for immature instars of Malagasy hard ticks are not yet available.

LIFE-HISTORY TRAITS

The life history of ticks in both families is characterized by long periods (often months) off the hosts interspersed with relatively brief feeding periods on a host. On-host time is often less than 5% of the total lifetime of a tick (Needham and Teel 1991). Hard tick larvae locate a host, feed to engorgement, drop off, and molt to the nymphal instar, which repeats the process. Finding a new host may involve active searching behavior (questing), with ticks crawling up twigs or blades of grass to increase the probability of encountering an appropriate host. Engorgement of immatures and females involves taking in an enormous blood meal, increasing their weight 10- to 100-fold (depending on the species and instar). After engorgement, nymphs drop off and molt to adults. Mating can be on or off the host. In those species in which mating occurs on the host, females will often not fully engorge until mated. Engorged, mated females drop off to lay a single large batch of eggs, after which they die. Exceptions to this pattern include one- or two-host ticks, such as some species of *Rhipicephalus*, which molt on the host without dropping off. In Argasidae species, mating is always off the host, and females can produce multiple but smaller batches of eggs, each proceeded by a bout of feeding.

FAUNISTICS, BIOGEOGRAPHY, AND HOST SPECIFICITY

The tick fauna of Madagascar is still poorly known. In an excellent review, Uilenberg et al. (1979) recorded seven species of Argasidae and 25 of Ixodidae. These numbers include two argasids, *Ornithodoros porcinus* and *Otobius megnini*, and three ixodids, *Amblyomma variegatum*, *Rhipicephalus sanguineus*, and *R. microplus*, that are associated with domestic animals. These tick species most likely were introduced relatively recently (Uilenberg et al. 1979). They are also the most important vectors of tick-borne pathogens causing diseases of humans and domestic animals on Madagascar (see Héraud et al., pp. 285–91).

Of the remaining "native" tick species recorded on Madagascar, the status of unidentified members of the "*Persicargas* group" of *Argas* (*Persicargas*) and the *Carios* species is unclear, but all other species are endemic. Since 1979 only two new species, *Amblyomma geochelone* and *Ixodes microgalei*, have been named from the island (Durden et al. 2002; Apanaskevich et al. 2013). Examination of recent tick collections obtained on Madagascar by Steven Goodman and colleagues and held in the Field Museum of Natural History, Chicago, revealed a diversity of new species.

TABLE 9.5. **Checklist of ticks recorded from Madagascar by host species**

HOST SPECIES	ARGAS (PERSICARGAS) SP.	A. (SECRETARGAS) ECHINOPS	A. (S.) HOOGSTRAALI	ORNITHODOROS GRENIERI	O. PORCINUS	OTOBIUS MEGNINI	CARIOS VESPERTILIONIS GROUP	C. SALAHI GROUP	IXODES (IXODES) LUNATUS	I. (AFRIXODES) ALBIGNACI	I. (A.) COLASBELCOURI	I. (A.) LEMURIS	I. (A.) MICROGALEI	I. (A.) NESOMYS	I. (A.) RANDRIANASOLOI	I. (AFRIXODES)	I. (SCAPHIXODES) DOMERGUEI	I. (ESCHATOCEPHALUS) SIMPLEX	HAEMAPHYSALIS (SHARIFIELLA) THEILERAE	H. (ORNITHOPHYSALIS) MADAGASCARIENSIS	H. (O.) SIMPLEX	H. (O.) SIMPLICIMA	H. (ORNITHOPHYSALIS)	H. (ELONGIPHYSALIS) ELONGATA	H. (E.) SUBELONGATA	H. (E.) TIPTONI	H. (RHIPISTOMA) LEMURIS	H. (R.) EUPLERES	H. (R.) FOSSAE	H. (R.) OBTUSA	H. (RHIPISTOMA)	H. (?) ANOPLOS	AMBLYOMMA CHABAUDI	A. GEOCHELONE	A. VARIEGATUM	RHIPICEPHALUS SANGUINEUS	R. MICROPLUS
OPLURIDAE (IGUANIDS)																																					
Oplurus fierinensis	–	–	L	–	–	–	–	–	–	–	–	–	–	–	–	–	–	–	–	–	–	–	–	–	–	–	–	–	–	–	–	–	–	–	–	–	–
Oplurus grandidieri	–	–	L	–	–	–	–	–	–	–	–	–	–	–	–	–	–	–	–	–	–	–	–	–	–	–	–	–	–	–	–	–	–	–	–	–	–
Oplurus quadrimaculatus	–	–	L	–	–	–	–	–	–	–	–	–	–	–	–	–	–	–	–	–	–	–	–	–	–	–	–	–	–	–	–	–	–	–	–	–	–
Testudinidae (Turtles)	–	–	–	–	–	–	–	–	–	–	–	–	–	–	–	–	–	–	–	–	–	–	–	–	–	–	–	–	–	–	–	–	–	–	–	–	–
Pyxis arachnoides	–	–	–	–	–	–	–	–	–	–	–	–	–	–	–	–	–	–	–	–	–	–	–	–	–	–	–	–	–	–	–	–	AI	–	–	–	–
Astrochelys radiata	–	–	–	–	–	–	–	–	–	–	–	–	–	–	–	–	–	–	–	–	–	–	–	–	–	–	–	–	–	–	–	–	A[1]	–	–	–	–
Astrochelys yniphora	–	–	–	–	–	–	–	–	–	–	–	–	–	–	–	–	–	–	–	–	–	–	–	–	–	–	–	–	–	–	–	–	–	A[2]	–	–	–
AVES (BIRDS)																																					
Centropus toulou		–	–	–	–	–	–	–	–	–	–	–	–	–	–	–	–	–	–	AI	–	–	–	–	–	–	–	–	–	–	–	–	–	–	I	–	–
**Gallus gallus*	AI	–	–	–	–	–	–	–	–	–	–	–	–	–	–	–	–	–	–	–	–	–	–	–	–	–	–	–	–	–	–	–	–	–	I	–	–
Artamella viridis	–	–	–	–	–	–	–	–	–	–	–	–	–	–	–	–	–	–	–	I	–	–	–	–	–	–	–	–	–	–	–	–	–	–	–	–	–
Coua reynaudii	–	–	–	–	–	–	–	–	–	–	–	–	–	–	–	–	–	–	–	I	–	–	–	–	–	–	–	–	–	–	–	–	–	–	–	–	–
Cyanolanius madagascarinus	–	–	–	–	–	–	–	–	–	–	–	–	–	–	–	–	–	–	–	–	–	–	–	–	–	–	I	–	–	–	–	–	–	–	–	–	–
Nelicurvius nelicourvi	–	–	–	–	–	–	–	–	–	–	–	–	–	–	–	–	A	–	–	–	–	–	–	–	–	–	–	–	–	–	–	–	–	–	–	–	–
Newtonia brunneicauda	–	–	–	–	–	–	–	–	–	–	–	–	–	–	–	–	A	–	–	–	–	–	–	–	–	–	–	–	–	–	–	–	–	–	–	–	–
Schetba occidentalis	–	–	–	–	–	–	–	–	–	–	–	–	–	–	–	–	–	–	–	–	–	–	–	–	–	–	I	–	–	–	–	–	–	–	–	–	–
MAMMALIA																																					
Carnivora																																					
Cryptoprocta ferox	–	–	–	–	–	–	–	–	–	–	–	–	–	–	–	–	–	–	–	–	–	–	–	–	–	–	–	–	–	A	–	–	–	–	–	–	–
Eupleres goudotii	–	–	–	–	–	–	–	–	–	–	–	–	–	–	–	–	–	–	–	–	–	–	–	–	–	–	–	A	–	A	–	–	–	–	–	–	–
Fossa fossana	–	–	–	–	–	–	–	–	–	–	–	–	–	–	–	–	–	–	–	–	–	–	–	–	–	–	–	–	A	AI	–	–	–	–	–	–	–
Galidia elegans	–	–	–	–	–	–	–	–	–	–	–	–	–	–	–	–	–	–	–	–	–	–	I[2]	–	–	–	–	A[2]	–	AI[2]	I[2]	–	–	–	–	–	–
Galidictis fasciata	–	–	–	–	–	–	–	–	–	–	–	–	–	–	–	–	–	–	–	–	–	–	–	I	–	–	–	–	–	A	–	–	–	–	–	–	–
**Viverricula indica*	–	–	–	–	–	–	–	–	–	–	–	–	–	–	–	–	–	–	–	–	–	–	–	–	–	–	–	–	A	AI	–	–	–	–	–	–	–
**Canis lupus*	–	–	–	–	–	I	–	–	–	–	–	–	–	–	–	–	–	–	–	–	–	–	–	–	–	–	–	–	–	A[1]	–	–	–	–	AI	AI	AI[1]
Perissodactyla																																					
**Equus asinus*	–	–	–	–	–		–	–	–	–	–	–	–	–	–	–	–	–	–	–	–	–	–	–	–	–	–	–	–	–	–	–	–	–	I	–	–

(continued overleaf)

HOST SPECIES	ARGAS (PERSICARGAS) SP.	A. (SECRETARGAS) ECHINOPS	A. (S.) HOOGSTRAALI	ORNITHODOROS GRENIERI	O. PORCINUS	OTOBIUS MEGNINI	CARIOS VESPERTILIONIS GROUP	C. SALAHI GROUP	IXODES (IXODES) LUNATUS	I. (AFRIXODES) ALBIGNACI	I. (A.) COLASBELCOURI	I. (A.) LEMURIS	I. (A.) MICROGALEI	I. (A.) NESOMYS	I. (A.) RANDRIANASOLOI	I. (AFRIXODES)	I. (SCAPHIXODES) DOMERGUEI	I. (ESCHATOCEPHALUS) SIMPLEX	HAEMAPHYSALIS (SHARIFIELLA) THEILERAE	H. (ORNITHOPHYSALIS) MADAGASCARIENSIS	H. (O.) SIMPLEX	H. (O.) SIMPLICIMA	H. (ORNITHOPHYSALIS)	H. (ELONGIPHYSALIS) ELONGATA	H. (E.) SUBELONGATA	H. (E.) TIPTONI	H. (RHIPISTOMA) LEMURIS	H. (R.) EUPLERES	H. (R.) FOSSAE	H. (R.) OBTUSA	H. (RHIPISTOMA)	H. (?) ANOPLOS	AMBLYOMMA CHABAUDI	A. GEOCHELONE	A. VARIEGATUM	RHIPICEPHALUS SANGUINEUS	R. MICROPLUS
*Equus caballi	–	–	–	–	–	I	–	–	–	–	–	–	–	–	–	–	–	–	–	–	–	–	–	–	–	–	–	–	–	–	–	–	–	–	A	–	AI
Artiodactyla																																					
*Bos taurus	–	–	–	–	–	I	–	–	–	–	–	–	–	–	–	–	–	–	–	–	–	–	–	–	–	–	–	–	–	–	–	–	–	–	AI	–	AI
*Bubalus bubalis	–	–	–	–	–	–	–	–	–	–	–	–	–	–	–	–	–	–	–	–	–	–	–	–	–	–	–	–	–	–	–	–	–	–		–	
*Capra hircus	–	–	–	–	–	–	–	–	–	–	–	–	–	–	–	–	–	–	–	–	–	–	–	–	–	–	–	–	–	–	–	–	–	–	AI	–	AI
*Ovis aries	–	–	–	–	–	I[1]	–	–	–	–	–	–	–	–	–	–	–	–	–	–	–	–	–	–	–	–	–	–	–	–	–	–	–	–	AI	–	AI
*Sus scrofa	–	–	–	–	AI		–	–	–	–	–	–	–	–	–	–	–	–	–	–	–	–	–	–	–	–	–	–	–	–	–	–	–	–	A	–	
Chiroptera																																					
Macronycteris commersoni	–	–	–	–	–	–	–	–	–	–	–	–	–	–	–	–	–	–	–	–	–	A[3]	–	–	–	–	–	–	–	–	–	–	–	–	–	–	–
Miniopterus sororculus	–	–	–	–	–	–	–	–	–	–	–	–	–	–	–	–	–	I[3]	–	–	–	–	–	–	–	–	–	–	–	–	–	–	–	–	–	–	–
Miniopterus majori	–	–	–	–	–	–	–	–	–	–	–	–	–	–	–	–	–	I[3]	–	–	–	–	–	–	–	–	–	–	–	–	–	–	–	–	–	–	–
Miniopterus manavi	–	–	–	–	–	–	–	–	–	–	–	–	–	–	–	–	–	AI[3]	–	–	–	–	–	–	–	–	–	–	–	–	–	–	–	–	–	–	–
Miniopterus egeri	–	–	–	–	–	–	–	–	–	–	–	–	–	–	–	–	–	I[3]	–	–	–	–	–	–	–	–	–	–	–	–	–	–	–	–	–	–	–
Mormopterus jugularis	–	–	–	–	–	–	I	–	–	–	–	–	–	–	–	–	–	–	–	–	–	–	–	–	–	–	–	–	–	–	–	–	–	–	–	–	–
Myotis goudoti	–	–	–	–	–	–	–	–	–	–	–	–	–	–	–	–	–	AI[3]	–	–	–	–	–	–	–	–	–	–	–	–	–	–	–	–	–	–	–
Rousettus madagascariensis	–	–	–	–	–	–	–	I	–	–	–	–	–	–	–	–	–	–	–	–	–	–	–	–	–	–	–	–	–	–	–	–	–	–	–	–	–
bat (unidentified)	–	–	–	–	–	–	–	I	–	–	–	–	–	–	–	–	–	–	–	–	–	–	–	–	–	–	–	–	–	–	–	–	–	–	–	–	–
Soricomorpha: Soricidae																																					
*Suncus murinus	–	–	–	–	–	–	–	–	–	A[2]	–	–	–	–	–	–	–	–	–	–	–	–	–	–	–	–	–	–	–	–	I[2]	–	–	–	–	–	–
Afrosoricida: Tenrecidae																																					
Echinops telfairi	–	L[2]	–	–	–	–	–	–	–	–	–	–	–	–	–	–	–	–	–	–	AI[2]	AI	I[2]	A[1]	A[1]	–	–	–	–	–	–	–	–	–	–	–	–
Geogale aurita	–	L[2]	–	–	–	–	–	–	–	–	–	–	–	–	–	–	–	–	–	–	–	A[3]	–	–	–	–	–	–	–	–	–	–	–	–	–	–	–
Hemicentetes nigriceps	–	–	–	–	–	–	–	–	–	–	–	–	–	–	–	–	–	–	–	–	–	–	–	A[3]	–	A	–	–	–	–	–	–	–	–	–	–	–
Hemicentetes semispinosus	–	–	–	–	–	–	–	–	A	–	–	–	–	–	–	–	–	–	–	–	–	–	–	A[2]I	A	A	–	–	–	I	–	–	–	–	–	–	–
Microgale cowani	–	–	–	–	–	–	–	–	I[2]	A[2]	A[3]	–	–	–	–	I[2]	–	–	–	–	–	–	–	–	–	–	–	–	–	–	–	–	–	–	–	–	–
Microgale drouhardi	–	–	–	–	–	–	–	–	–	AI[2]	–	–	–	–	–	–	–	–	–	–	–	–	–	–	–	–	–	–	–	–	–	–	–	–	–	–	–
Microgale gracilis	–	–	–	–	–	–	–	–	–	AI[2]	–	–	–	–	–	I[2]	–	–	–	–	–	–	–	–	–	–	–	–	–	–	–	–	–	–	–	–	–
Microgale monticola	–	–	–	–	–	–	–	–	–	AI[2]	–	–	–	–	–	–	–	–	–	–	–	–	–	–	–	–	–	–	–	–	–	–	–	–	–	–	–
Microgale parvula	–	–	–	–	–	–	–	–	–	–	–	–	A[2]	–	–	–	–	–	–	–	–	–	–	–	–	–	–	–	–	–	–	–	–	–	–	–	–

HOST SPECIES	ARGAS (PERSICARGAS) SP.	A. (SECRETARGAS) ECHINOPS	A. (S.) HOOGSTRAALI	ORNITHODOROS GRENIERI	O. PORCINUS	OTOBIUS MEGNINI	CARIOS VESPERTILIONIS GROUP	C. SALAHI GROUP	IXODES (IXODES) LUNATUS	I. (AFRIXODES) ALBIGNACI	I. (A.) COLASBELCOURI	I. (A.) LEMURIS	I. (A.) MICROGALEI	I. (A.) NESOMYS	I. (A.) RANDRIANASOLOI	I. (AFRIXODES)	I. (SCAPHIXODES) DOMERGUEI	I. (ESCHATOCEPHALUS) SIMPLEX	HAEMAPHYSALIS (SHARIFIELLA) THEILERAE	H. (ORNITHOPHYSALIS) MADAGASCARIENSIS	H. (O.) SIMPLEX	H. (O.) SIMPLICIMA	H. (ORNITHOPHYSALIS)	H. (ELONGIPHYSALIS) ELONGATA	H. (E.) SUBELONGATA	H. (E.) TIPTONI	H. (RHIPISTOMA) LEMURIS	H. (R.) EUPLERES	H. (R.) FOSSAE	H. (R.) OBTUSA	H. (RHIPISTOMA)	H. (?) ANOPLOS	AMBLYOMMA CHABAUDI	A. GEOCHELONE	A. VARIEGATUM	RHIPICEPHALUS SANGUINEUS	R. MICROPLUS
Microgale soricoides	–	–	–	–	–	–	–	–	–	–	–	–	A[2]	–	–	–	–	–	–	–	–	–	–	–	–	–	–	–	–	–	–	–	–	–	–	–	–
Microgale taiva	–	–	–	–	–	–	–	–	–	A[2]	–	–	–	–	–	–	–	–	–	–	–	–	–	–	–	–	–	–	–	–	–	–	–	–	–	–	–
Nesogale dobsoni	–	–	–	–	–	–	–	–	–	–	I?	–	A[2]	–	–	I[2]	–	–	–	–	–	–	–	–	–	–	–	–	–	–	–	–	–	–	–	–	–
Nesogale talazaci	–	–	–	–	–	–	–	–	–	AI[2]	I	–	–	–	A	I[2]	–	–	–	–	I	–	–	A[3]I	–	–	–	–	–	I	I[2]	–	–	–	–	–	–
Oryzorictes hova	–	–	–	–	–	–	–	–	–	AI[2]	–	–	–	–	–	–	–	–	–	–	–	–	–	–	–	–	–	–	–	–	–	–	–	–	–	–	–
Oryzorictes hova?	–	–	–	–	–	–	–	–	–	I	–	–	–	–	–	–	–	–	–	–	–	–	–	–	–	–	–	–	–	–	–	–	–	–	–	–	–
Setifer setosus	–	–	–	–	–	–	–	–	AI[2]	–	–	–	–	–	–	–	–	–	A	–	AI	AI	–	AI[1]		A[3] I[2]	–	–	–	–	I[2]	–	–	–	–	–	–
Tenrec ecaudatus	–	–	–	–	–	–	–	–	AI[2]	–	A	–	–	–	–	–	–	–	AI[2]	–	AI		–	AI[2]	AI[2]	AI[2]	–	–	–	–	I[2]	–	–	–	I	–	–
RODENTIA																																					
Muridae (rats)																																					
**Rattus rattus*	–	–	–	–	–	–	–	–		A[2]	AI	A	–	–	A[2]	–	–	–	–	–	I	–	–	–	I	–	–	–	–	I	I[2]	–	–	–	–	–	–
Nesomyinae (Malagasy rodents)																																					
Brachytarsomys albicauda	–	–	–	–	–	–	–	–	–	–	A[3]	–	–	–	–	–	–	–	–	–	–	–	–	–	–	–	–	–	–	–	–	–	–	–	–	–	–
Brachyuromys betsileoensis	–	–	–	–	–	–	–	–	–	–	A	–	–	–	–	–	–	–	–	–	–	–	–	–	–	–	–	–	–	–	–	–	–	–	–	–	–
Eliurus majori	–	–	–	–	–	–	–	–	–	A[2]	–	–	–	–	–	–	–	–	–	–	–	–	–	–	–	–	–	–	–	–	–	–	–	–	–	–	–
Eliurus tanala	–	–	–	–	–	–	–	–	–	A[2]	A[3]	–	–	–	–	–	–	–	–	–	–	–	–	–	–	–	–	–	–	–	–	–	–	–	–	–	–
Eliurus webbi	–	–	–	–	–	–	–	–	–	–	–	–	–	–	–	–	–	–	–	–	–	–	–	–	–	–	–	–	–	–	–	A[3]	–	–	–	–	–
Gymnuromys roberti	–	–	–	–	–	–	–	–	–	–	A[2]	–	–	–	–	–	–	–	–	–	–	–	–	–	–	–	–	–	–	–	–	–	–	–	–	–	–
Hypogeomys antimena	–	–	–	AI	–	–	–	–	–	–	–	–	–	–	–	–	–	–	–	–	–	–	–	–	–	–	–	–	–	–	–	–	–	–	–	–	–
Macrotarsomys bastardi	–	–	–	–	–	–	–	–	–	–	–	–	–	–	–	–	–	–	–	–	–	–	–	–	I	–	–	–	–	–	–	–	I[2]	–	–	–	–
Nesomys audeberti	–	–	–	–	–	–	–	–	A	–	–	–	–	–	–	–	–	–	–	–	–	–	–	–	–	–	–	–	–	–	–	–	–	–	–	–	–
Nesomys rufus	–	–	–	–	–	–	–	–	–	A[2]	A			A	–	–	–	–	–	–	A[2]	–	–	–	–	–	–	–	–	I		A	–	–	–	–	–
PRIMATES (LEMURS AND HUMANS)																																					
Cheirogaleus crossleyi	–	–	–	–	–	–	–	–	–	–	–	AI[2]	–	–	–	–	–	–	–	–	–	–	–	–	–	–	A[2]	–	–	–	–	–	–	–	–	–	–
Cheirogaleus sibreei	–	–	–	–	–	–	–	–	–	–	–	AI[2]	–	–	–	–	–	–	–	–	–	–	–	–	–	–	–	–	–	–	–	–	–	–	–	–	–
Eulemur fulvus	–	–	–	–	–	–	–	–	–	–	–	A	–	–	–	–	–	–	–	–	–	–	–	–	–	–	A[2]	–	–	–	–	–	–	–	–	–	–
Lemur catta	–	–	–	–	–	–	–	–	–	–	–	–	–	–	–	–	–	–	–	–	–	–	–	–	–	–	AI	–	–	–	–	–	–	–	–	–	–
Microcebus griseorufus	–	–	–	–	–	–	–	–	–	–	–	–	–	–	–	–	–	–	–	–	?I[2]	–	–	–	–	–	I[2]	–	–	–	–	–	–	–	–	–	–
Microcebus rufus	–	–	–	–	–	–	–	–	–	–	–	–	–	–	–	–	–	–	–	–	–	–	–	–	–	–	I[2]	–	–	–	–	–	–	–	–	–	–

(continued overleaf)

TABLE 9.5. ***continued***

HOST SPECIES	*ARGAS (PERSICARGAS)* SP.	*A. (SECRETARGAS) ECHINOPS*	*A. (S.) HOOGSTRAALI*	*ORNITHODOROS GRENIERI*	*O. PORCINUS*	*OTOBIUS MEGNINI*	*CARIOS VESPERTILIONIS* GROUP	*C. SALAHI* GROUP	*IXODES (IXODES) LUNATUS*	*I. (AFRIXODES) ALBIGNACI*	*I. (A.) COLASBELCOURI*	*I. (A.) LEMURIS*	*I. (A.) MICROGALEI*	*I. (A.) NESOMYS*	*I. (A.) RANDRIANASOLOI*	*I. (AFRIXODES)*	*I. (SCAPHIXODES) DOMERGUEI*	*I. (ESCHATOCEPHALUS) SIMPLEX*	*HAEMAPHYSALIS (SHARIFIELLA) THEILERAE*	*H. (ORNITHOPHYSALIS) MADAGASCARIENSIS*	*H. (O.) SIMPLEX*	*H. (O.) SIMPLICIMA*	*H. (ORNITHOPHYSALIS)*	*H. (ELONGIPHYSALIS) ELONGATA*	*H. (E.) SUBELONGATA*	*H. (E.) TIPTONI*	*H. (RHIPISTOMA) LEMURIS*	*H. (R.) EUPLERES*	*H. (R.) FOSSAE*	*H. (R.) OBTUSA*	*H. (RHIPISTOMA)*	*H. (?) ANOPLOS*	*AMBLYOMMA CHABAUDI*	*A. GEOCHELONE*	*A. VARIEGATUM*	*RHIPICEPHALUS SANGUINEUS*	*R. MICROPLUS*
Microcebus sp. cf. *rufus*	–	–	–	–	–	–	–	–	–	–	–	I[2]	–	–	–	–	–	–	–	–	–	–	–	–	–	–		–	–	–	–	–	–	–	–	–	–
Avahi laniger	–	–	–	–	–	–	–	–	–	–	–	–	–	–	–	–	–	–	–	–	–	–	–	–	–	–	A[2]	–	–	–	–	–	–	–	–	–	–
Indri indri	–	–	–	–	–	–	–	–	–	–	–	AI[2]	–	–	–	–	–	–	–	–	–	–	–	–	–	–	?[2]	–	–	–	–	–	–	–	–	–	–
Varecia variegata	–	–	–	–	–	–	–	–	–	–	–	–	–	–	–	–	–	–	–	–	–	–	–	–	–	–	A	–	–	–	–	–	–	–	–	–	–
Lepilemur mustelinus	–	–	–	–	–	–	–	–	–	–	–	AI[2]	–	–	–	–	–	–	–	–	–	–	–	–	–	–	A[2]	–	–	–	–	–	–	–	–	–	–
Lepilemur ruficaudatus	–	–	–	–	–	–	–	–	–	–	–	–	–	–	–	–	–	–	–	–	–	–	–	–	–	–	I	–	–	–	–	–	–	–	–	–	–
Lepilemur sp.	–	–	–	–	–	–	–	–	–	–	–	–	–	–	–	–	–	–	–	–	–	–	–	–	–	–	I	–	–	–	–	–	–	–	–	–	–
Prolemur simus	–	–	–	–	–	–	–	–	–	–	–	–	–	–	–	–	–	–	–	–	–	–	–	–	–	–	A[3]	–	–	–	–	–	–	–	–	–	–
Propithecus diadema	–	–	–	–	–	–	–	–	–	–	–	I[3]	–	–	–	–	–	–	–	–	–	–	–	–	–	–	A[2]	–	–	–	–	–	–	–	–	–	–
Propithecus verreauxi	–	–	–	–	–	–	–	–	–	–	–	–	–	–	–	–	–	–	–	–	AI	–	–	–	–	–	AI	–	–	–	–	–	–	–	–	–	–
**Homo sapiens*	–	–	–	–	AI	I[1]	–	–	–	–	–	–	–	–	–	–	–	–	–	–	–	–	–	I[1]	–	–	A[1]	–	–	–	–	–	–	–	I	–	AI

Sources: Most records are from Uilenberg et al. (1979), with host (and occasionally tick) classification updated; exceptions, including those from Klompen (2003), are noted.

Note: *, introduced host species; A, host for adults; I, host for immatures; L, host for larvae.

[1] Association uncommon, possibly accidental (Uilenberg et al. 1979).

[2] Additional records (not from Uilenberg et al. 1979), including those from Klompen (2003).

[3] New host record published in this contribution.

As a preliminary result, the junior author of this contribution identified one new species of *Haemaphysalis* and nearly a dozen new species of *Ixodes*, as well as recorded *I. simplex*, a bat parasite that is naturally shared with Africa and Asia.

The origin of the native tick fauna of Madagascar is mixed. Some species have clear African affinities (e.g., members of the genera *Ixodes*, *Amblyomma*, and *Carios*), but members of the most diverse genus, *Haemaphysalis*, appear to have their nearest relatives in India and Southeast Asia (Hoogstraal 1953). Particularly noteworthy in this respect is the presence on Madagascar of *H. theilerae*, a member of the "primitive" (*sensu* Hoogstraal and Kim 1985) *Haemaphysalis* subgenus *Sharifiella*. Most members of the remaining three "primitive subgenera" occur in India and in the overlap zone of the Palearctic and Oriental regions. The presence of a representative of that group on Madagascar is quite unexpected.

Other lineages within the genus *Haemaphysalis* have undergone a small radiation on Madagascar, with different subgenera (e.g., *Elongiphysalis* and *Ornithophysalis*) restricted to the island. The notion that the tick fauna of Madagascar is directly related to the fauna of nearby continental Africa is further weakened by the absence of native *Rhipicephalus* and *Hyalomma* on the island, and the presence of only two endemic species of *Amblyomma*. All three of these genera are very common and diverse on the African continent.

Within Madagascar, distribution patterns among the native species are much less resolved. This is largely due to still-inadequate sampling. Even so, it is clear that some ticks have quite specific ranges, most probably determined by combinations of climatic factors and host availability. Both *Argas* species and *Amblyomma chabaudi* have been recorded only from the relatively dry south and southwest. In contrast, the various *Ixodes* species are largely restricted to the areas of moist evergreen forests, including the Central Highlands. This fits with the overall distribution pattern of *Ixodes* species, which generally require relatively high humidity. The distribution of the *Haemaphysalis* species is more variable. Most records of *H. theilerae*, *H.* (*Elongiphysalis*) species, and the euplerid-associated *Haemaphysalis* (*Rhipistoma*) species are from the Central Highlands and moist evergreen forest areas of the east, but *H. simplex*, *H. simplicima*, and *H. lemuris* are largely restricted to the south and southwest.

Host specificity of the Malagasy ticks is also variable. All the more commonly collected species have been recorded from a number of different host species, but there appear to be some clear preferences. *Ixodes lunatus* is the most common *Ixodes* on larger tenrecs of the subfamily Tenrecinae (*Tenrec*, *Setifer*, and *Hemicentetes*); *I. albignaci* is common on many smaller tenrecs of the subfamily Oryzorictinae (*Microgale*, *Nesogale*, and *Oryzorictes*), and *I. colasbelcouri* occurs predominantly on endemic members of Nesomyinae and introduced murid rodents (Table 9.5). However, engorged *I. albignaci* and *I. colasbelcouri* have been found repeatedly on, respectively, rodents and tenrecs, demonstrating that host specificity is certainly not perfect. *Ixodes simplex*, a newly collected tick species on the island, is a specific parasite of various taxonomic groups of bats. Similar patterns are found in *Haemaphysalis*. *Haemaphysalis* (*Rhipistoma*) *lemuris* has been collected from a variety of lemurs, but the remaining three members of the subgenus *Rhipistoma* are associated with the Malagasy Carnivora, which are placed in their own endemic family, the Eupleridae (see Veron et al., pp. 1863–65). Each of the three species may occur on several host genera, with modest host preferences. Perhaps the best case for host specificity might be made for *Haemaphysalis* species associated with the larger spiny tenrecs. *Haemaphysalis theilerae* and *H. subelongata* are largely restricted to *Tenrec*, while *H. simplicima* has been found almost exclusively on *Echinops*. Other species occur on several host genera, such as *H. tiptoni* and *H. elongata* on *Tenrec*, *Hemicentetes*, and *Setifer*, and *H. simplex* on *Echinops* and *Setifer*. Hoogstraal (1953) argued that the differentially elongate coxal spines in species of *Haemaphysalis* were specific adaptations to the various preferred hosts, but this idea requires more testing.

Similar patterns in host associations can be found among the less diverse and less collected Argasidae. Most records of *Argas echinops* have been from the type host, *Echinops telfairi*, but a few recent collections included specimens from *Geogale aurita*, another tenrec placed in the subfamily Tenrecinae. The fact that these larvae were engorged suggests that this association may not be accidental. On the other hand, *A. hoogstraali* has been collected only from iguanids (*Oplurus* spp.; see Cadle et al., pp. 1502–05). Although the general patterns seem consistent with broad host specificity, it is quite likely that at least part of this pattern is due to off-host habitat, rather than true host specificity (Klompen et al. 1996).

The difficulty in identifying immatures, especially ixodid larvae, makes it hard to state definitively whether immatures and adults use different host ranges. Some species seem to use the same hosts in all instars. For example, larvae and nymphs of *Ixodes lemuris* have been found on lemurs (Blanco et al. 2013). Species associated with large-bodied hosts as adults may occasionally use smaller hosts as immatures. For example, larvae of both *Haemaphysalis* species and *I. lunatus*, commonly associated with large spiny tenrecs, have been found on small nonspiny tenrecs. In the most extreme example of this trend, *Haemaphysalis* larvae have been recovered from a wide range of hosts, including introduced *Rattus* and *Suncus*, and endemic *Microgale*, *Nesogale*, *Setifer*, *Tenrec*, as well as *Galidia*, which is the host of some *Haemaphysalis* adults. Larvae of *Amblyomma chabaudi*, a specific parasite of land tortoises, were found on the rodent *Macrotarsomys bastardi* (Ehlers et al. 2019).

For certain species, it is possible to provide some estimates of site specificity of these ticks on their hosts. On large spiny tenrecs, *Ixodes lunatus* is found most often in the region of the head and face, while *Haemaphysalis* species are found almost exclusively on the body and, less commonly, on the legs. However, another *Ixodes*, *I. albignaci* is found on all body parts of *Microgale* species, showing no obvious site specificity. In collections from the euplerid *Galidia elegans*, *H. eupleres* was collected from the face and anterior dorsal region, while *H. obtusa* was found in all body regions. Among the primate-associated species, males of *H. lemuris* were found most commonly in the nares of their hosts (Klompen et al. 2015). Data on the other species are still insufficient.

Subject editors: Brian L. Fisher and Steven M. Goodman

ATYIDAE AND PALAEMONIDAE, FRESHWATER SHRIMPS, *PATSA MENA*

J. W. Short

Madagascar has a rich and diverse fauna of freshwater decapod crustaceans, including shrimps (infraorder Caridea), crayfishes (infraorder Astacidea), and true crabs (infraorder Brachyura). Of these three groups, the caridean shrimps are the most diverse and widely distributed. Eight genera (two endemic) and 46 species (27 endemic) are presently known from the island (Tables 9.6 and 9.7).

The freshwater shrimps of Madagascar belong to two families—Atyidae and the Palaemonidae. Atyidae is predominantly a freshwater group but also includes a number of estuarine and anchialine species. The most speciose and widely distributed genus, *Caridina*, is found throughout tropical and subtropical regions of the world apart from the Americas, and currently contains over 300 species.

Members of Palaemonidae are more typically found in shallow marine habitats, particularly coral reefs, where many species form symbiotic relationships with other invertebrates. Of the few palaemonid genera that have colonized freshwater habitats, *Macrobrachium* is by far the most diverse and widely distributed. The genus is found in rivers, streams, and lakes throughout tropical and subtropical regions of the world, and currently includes over 250 species.

TABLE 9.6. **Checklist of the Atyidae (freshwater shrimps) of Madagascar**

SCIENTIFIC NAME	DISTRIBUTION
Atyoida serrata (Spence Bate, 1888)	Southwest Indian Ocean: South Africa, Madagascar, Comoros, Seychelles, Mauritius, and La Réunion
Caridina angulata Bouvier, 1905	Madagascar and Kenya
C. appendiculata Jalihal & Shenoy, 1998	Indo-West Pacific: Madagascar to Vanuatu
C. calmani Bouvier, 1919	Endemic, eastern headwater streams
C. crurispinata Gurney, 1984	Endemic, Grotte d'Antsatrobonko, Ankarana
C. edulis Bouvier, 1904	Endemic, Anantsahalankely (unknown locality)
C. gracilirostris De Man, 1892	Indo-West Pacific: Madagascar to Japan and Fiji
C. grandidieri Bouvier, 1904	Endemic, western drainages
C. hova Nobili, 1905	Endemic, Tolagnaro (Fort Dauphin) area
C. isaloensis Coutière, 1899	Endemic, southwestern drainages and Befotaka-Midongy du Sud, southeast
C. lamiana Holthuis, 1965	Endemic, Ampasindava Bay area, northwest to Ambahoabé area, northeast
C. lipalmaria Richard & Clark, 2010	Endemic, Betsiboka River basin
C. cf. *multidentata* Stimpson, 1860	Endemic, eastern drainages
C. natalensis De Man, 1908	Southwest Indian Ocean: eastern Africa, Madagascar, Comoros, Seychelles, and Mascarenes
C. cf. *nilotica* (P. Roux, 1833)	Endemic, widely distributed
C. norvestica Holthuis, 1965	Endemic, Mahajanga area and Mahajamba Lake
C. parvocula Gurney, 1984	Endemic, Grotte d'Antsatrobonko, Ankarana
C. petiti J. Roux, 1929	Endemic, Ambila-Lemaitso, eastern Madagascar
C. serratirostris De Man, 1892	Indo-West Pacific: Madagascar to the Ryukyus and Polynesia
C. steineri Cai, 2005	Endemic, Lakata Zafera, west
C. troglophila Holthuis, 1965	Endemic, Ambovonomby Cave, Tsingy de Namoroka
C. typus H. Milne Edwards, 1837	Indo-West Pacific: east Africa and Madagascar to Japan and Polynesia
C. unca Gurney, 1984	Endemic, Grotte d'Antsatrobonko, Ankarana
C. xiphias Bouvier, 1925	Endemic, eastern drainages
Elephantis jaggeri Klotz & De Grave, 2015	South Africa and Madagascar
Monsamnis carpolongus Richard, De Grave & Clark, 2012	Endemic, Ranomafana
Parisia dentata Gurney, 1984	Endemic, Grotte d'Andrafiabe, Ankarana
P. edentata Holthuis, 1956	Endemic, Tsingy de Bemaraha
P. macrophthalma Holthuis, 1956	Endemic, Grotte des Chauve-Souris, Ankarana
P. microphthalma (Fage, 1946)	Endemic, Grotte des Chauve-Souris, Ankarana
Typhlopatsa pauliani Holthuis, 1956	Endemic, Mitoho Cave, Tsimanampesotse

TABLE 9.7. **Provisional checklist of the Palaemonidae (freshwater shrimps) of Madagascar**

SPECIES	DISTRIBUTION
Macrobrachium australe (Guérin-Méneville, 1838)	Indo–West Pacific: Madagascar and the Comoros to Taiwan and French Polynesia
M. cf. *equidens* (Dana, 1852)	Indo–West Pacific: Madagascar and the Comoros to Taiwan and Fiji
M. glabrum Holthuis, 1995	Endemic, Kotomay, Mahajanga Province
M. hildebrandti (Hilgendorf, 1893)	Endemic, Ambatoharanana, Betsileo, east Imerina
M. idae (Heller, 1862)	Indo–West Pacific: east Africa and Madagascar to the Philippines, New Guinea, and the Admiralty Islands
M. idella (Hilgendorf, 1898)	Tanzania and Madagascar (?)
M. lar (Fabricius, 1798)	Indo–West Pacific: east Africa and Madagascar to the Ryukyus and French Polynesia
M. lepidactylus (Hilgendorf, 1879)	East Africa, Madagascar and La Réunion
M. patsa (Coutière, 1899)	East Africa and Madagascar
M. petiti (J. Roux, 1934)	Endemic, Vatomandry
M. rosenbergii (De Man, 1879)	South and southeast Asia (as far east as Borneo and Java in the Malay archipelago and eastward to Vietnam on the mainland). Introduced into Betsiboka River at Marovoay
M. rude (Heller, 1862)	Wide-ranging Indian Ocean: east Africa, Madagascar, India, and Sri Lanka
M. scabriculum (Heller, 1862)	Wide-ranging Indo–West Pacific: east Africa and Madagascar to New Guinea
M. therezieni Holthuis, 1965	Endemic, eastern drainages.
Palaemon concinnus Dana, 1852	Wide-ranging Indo–West Pacific: east Africa and Madagascar to Hong Kong and Fiji

Malagasy atyid shrimps are typically much smaller than freshwater palaemonids. One exception is the relatively robust species *Atyoida serrata*, which at a maximum size of 50 mm body length is similar to the smallest palaemonid species, *M. hildebrandti* and *M. lepidactylus*. In addition to a generally smaller body size, atyid shrimps are easily distinguished from palaemonids by the well-developed brushes of setae on the fingers of the first and second chelipeds (clawed legs).

BIOLOGY

Malagasy freshwater shrimps are found in a wide variety of permanent or seasonal habitats from near sea level to 1700 m elevation. Although the freshwater shrimps occurring on the island are unable to burrow to avoid desiccation, the juveniles of many species are highly mobile and quickly repopulate previously dry waterholes, pools, and lakes along seasonal watercourses during the monsoon season.

Atyid and palaemonid shrimps are often found together in the same habitats but show very different feeding strategies. In most atyid genera, the brushes of setae on the first and second chelae are used for gathering particulate organic matter, periphyton, and microbial films off the substrate. Filter-feeding genera, such as *Atyoida*, which prefer lotic habitats, use the long setae on the fingers of the chelae in a different way—the chelae are held wide open, and the setae are spread out like a fan to catch floating organic matter.

Most freshwater palaemonids are opportunistic omnivores. River shrimps of the genus *Macrobrachium* are polytrophic and are able to feed as detritivores, herbivores, scavengers, and predators of other invertebrates and small fish. Unlike atyids, the first and second chelipeds of *Macrobrachium* perform different functions during feeding. The smaller first chelipeds pick detritus and small food items from the substrate, whereas the enlarged second chelipeds are used to grab and tear apart large food items or to capture live prey.

Freshwater shrimps are generally more active at night and seek shelter during daylight to avoid predators. Atyids and juvenile *Macrobrachium* are often found in leaf-litter beds, among macrophytes, or in the root mats of riparian vegetation, where they are easily scoop netted. *Macrobrachium* adults prefer to shelter among tree roots or under fallen timber, ledges, boulders, rocks, and overhanging banks. Consequently, they are difficult to net and are more easily collected at night using baited traps. In mangrove areas and adjacent fresh waters, baited traps are also effective for the palaemonid *Palaemon concinnus*. When available, electrofishing is also a highly efficient technique for capturing a wide variety of freshwater shrimps during daylight, including adult *Macrobrachium*.

Both Palaemonidae and Atyidae have relatively simple reproductive biology and lack complex male and female reproductive structures. The male genital openings are located on the base of the fifth pereiopods, whereas the female genital openings are on the base of the third pair of legs. During mating, males deposit spermatophores onto the female sternum. The appendix masculinae on the second pair of male swimmerets (pleopods) assist in this process. After mating, females fertilize the eggs while they are being laid by rupturing the spermatophores attached to the sternum and releasing spermatozoa. The fertilized eggs are then transferred to the swimmerets for brooding.

After the brooding period, the eggs hatch as free-living larvae. Larval development shows considerable variation within both families, but is usually classified into two broad types—extended larval development (ELD) or abbreviated larval development (ALD). ELD is typically found in euryhaline species, which require marine influence to complete larval development. Generally, there are eight or more larval stages and a relatively long larval development period of at least 14 days. Some widely distributed, predominantly insular species have prolonged larval development and an oceanic, marine phase in their larval cycle (e.g., *M. lar*).

Euryhaline species with ELD typically incubate large broods of relatively small eggs (approximately 0.6–1.0 mm in length in *Macrobrachium*, 0.4–0.5 mm in *Caridina*). The eggs hatch as small, planktonic larvae (zoeae) and are released in the lower freshwater reaches or estuaries. The zoeal stages feed on microplankton until metamorphosis to a benthic larval form, variously referred to as the decapodid, megalopa, or postlarval stage.

Some euryhaline species with ELD are confined to estuaries or estuarine-inshore marine areas and are rarely found in fresh water beyond the upstream limit of tidal influence (e.g., *C. gracilirostris* and *M. equidens*). Others are primarily estuarine species but facultatively enter lowland, nontidal fresh waters (e.g., *Palaemon concinnus*). The majority of euryhaline species with ELD appear to be amphidromous (*sensu* McDowall 2007) and are found in fresh water only as adults (e.g., *A. serrata* and *M. lar*). Many amphidromous species release their larvae into the lower freshwater reaches and rely on river flow to transport the larvae to brackish or salt water. After larval development in tidal waters, juveniles then migrate en masse back into fresh water where they complete the life cycle and reproduce.

The transition from ELD to ALD has occurred independently in many lineages of freshwater shrimps (J. W. Short 2000, 2004; Murphy and Austin 2005; Wowor et al. 2009). Species with ALD complete their life cycle in fresh water and no longer require marine influence for larval development. Compared to species with ELD, they generally have smaller broods of relatively large eggs (approximately 1.0–2.0 mm length in *Macrobrachium*; 0.5–1.5 mm length in *Caridina*). The eggs hatch as well-developed, planktonic larvae or as benthic larvae resembling juveniles. The increased size of the eggs compared to species with ELD is largely because of an enlarged yolk sac and the transition from planktonotrophy (larvae feeding on plankton) to lecithotrophy (larvae obtaining nutrition from the yolk sac).

Some species with ALD have highly developed, benthic hatchlings that show only minor developmental changes through to the juvenile stage. Instead of free-swimming, these hatchlings immediately cling to vegetation, rocks, and other surfaces, and show limited dispersal behavior. Many of these species have a highly restricted, distributional range, such as the headwaters of a single river system, or a specialized habitat, such as a blackwater swamp or cave.

Although larval development of the endemic Malagasy species and many of the wide-ranging, nonendemic species have not yet been studied, in most cases the size of the eggs is presently known. For the purpose of this review, small-egged, widely distributed species are assumed to be euryhaline species with ELD, while large-egged endemics are considered to be oligohaline species with ALD.

TAXONOMY

The Malagasy Atyidae was last revised by Holthuis (1965a). Gurney (1984) described four new species and provided an updated key to species. Two new genera were added to the fauna by Richard et al. (2012) and Castelin et al. (2013a). Additional new species were described by Cai (2005) and Richard and Clark (2010a, 2012). Other studies that have resulted in changes to the taxonomy of the island's fauna include Cai and Ng (2007), Marquet and Keith (2008), Richard and Clark (2010b), Klotz and De Grave (2015), and de Mazancourt et al. (2019a, 2019b).

In general, the taxonomy of the Malagasy atyid fauna is well resolved (Table 9.6). Two species that were previously recorded in Holthuis (1965a) as *Caridina japonica* and *C. nilotica* are presently undescribed and reported here as *C.* cf. *multidentata* and *C.* cf. *nilotica* respectively. The two subspecies of *C. isaloensis* recognized by Holthuis (1965a), *C. i. isaloensis* and *C. i. grandidieri*, also require review. Distributional records of the two taxa show considerable geographic overlap. Both subspecies were also recorded from the Manambolo and Fandaramonona Rivers. Although the two taxa are highly similar, they do not appear to be geographically isolated and are provisionally treated here as full species.

A special mention should also be made of *C. edulis*, the least well-known and most elusive species of the Malagasy Atyidae. The original description of the species by Bouvier (1904) was based on two specimens from "Anantsahalankely" and a large series of cooked specimens obtained from an unspecified market. Although the species was apparently common enough to be sold at a market at that time, there have been no further records of the species. The location of "Anantsahalankely" within Madagascar also remains unknown.

Studies of the Malagasy freshwater palaemonid fauna commenced with Coutière (1899, 1900, 1901) and Roux (1934). Most of the wide-ranging species occurring on the island were revised by Holthuis (1950) in a report on the Palaemoninae collected by the Siboga and Snellius expeditions. New endemic *Macrobrachium* species were described by Holthuis (1965b, 1995). J. W. Short and Doumenq (2003) documented new distributional records of six species of *Macrobrachium* collected by the Laboratoire de Recherche sur les Systèmes Aquatique et leur Environnement (LRSAE) program. Hanamura et al. (2008) reported the introduction of the nonindigenous species *M. rosenbergii* into the Betsiboka River near Marovoay.

Compared to Atyidae, the taxonomy of the freshwater palaemonid fauna has received far less attention. Apart from the widely distributed euryhaline species *M. idae*, *M. lar*, and *M. lepidactylus*, the remaining Malagasy freshwater palaemonids are each known from just a few records. Several of the nominal species recorded from Madagascar (Table 9.7) may also be junior synonyms of other Malagasy species: *M. patsa* is a probable junior synonym of *M. lepidactylus*; *M. therezieni* is possibly a junior synonym of *M. petiti*; and *M. glabrum* appears to be based on a large, subordinate male with undeveloped second chelipeds and needs to be distinguished from the wide-ranging species *M. rude*.

The record of *M. idella* from Madagascar is probably a misidentification and is based on a juvenile specimen. The species was originally described from mainland Tanzania and reported as having large eggs, 1.25 mm in length, indicative of abbreviated larval development and a landlocked, freshwater life cycle. All records of the species outside mainland eastern Africa are therefore doubtful.

The taxonomy of the wide-ranging, Indo–West Pacific species *M. equidens* requires further study. Liu et al. (2007) reported high genetic divergence between a sequence from northern Singapore and material from Taiwan, Australia, and the Philippines. The species was originally described from Singapore Harbor.

Similarly, the wide-ranging *M. scabriculum* species complex requires review. Based on morphological characters, Cai and Ng (2002) split *M. scabriculum sensu lato* into three species, *M. dolichodactylus*, *M. lanatum*, and *M. scabriculum*. However, a 16S molecular phylogenetic study of the genus (J. W. Short, unpublished data) has revealed a low, intraspecific level of divergence between sequences of *M. scabriculum* and *M. lanatum* from Sri Lanka and Myanmar, respectively. Malagasy material is therefore provisionally assigned to *M. scabriculum sensu lato* until the three nominal species are studied in more detail using both morphological and molecular data.

TABLE 9.8. **Freshwater shrimp diversity in Madagascar compared to some well-known areas of the Indo–West Pacific region**

GEOGRAPHIC REGION	NUMBER OF GENERA	NUMBER OF SPECIES
Madagascar	8	46
Mozambique	3	10
Mascarenes	3	9
New Caledonia	7	34
Philippines	8	57
New Guinea	6	>48
Taiwan	5	34
Australia	10	>70
Sulawesi	6	63

EVOLUTION AND BIOGEOGRAPHY

Although Atyidae and Palaemonidae date back to at least the Early Cretaceous (Porter et al. 2005; von Rintelen et al. 2012; Jurado-Rivera et al. 2017), extant Malagasy genera such as *Atyoida*, *Caridina*, and *Macrobrachium* appear to have a much more recent Cenozoic origin (J. W. Short 2000, 2004; Murphy and Austin 2005; von Rintelen et al. 2012).

Among the remaining genera occurring on the island, the origin of the endemic, subterranean genus *Typhlopatsa* is possibly of greatest interest. As discussed by Jurado-Rivera et al. (2017), this genus shows a sister relationship with the anchialine Australian genus *Stygiocaris*. This sister relationship is mirrored in the obligate cave-dwelling fishes *Typhleotris* (Madagascar) and *Milyeringa* (Australia) from the same respective cave systems.

The Malagasy freshwater shrimp fauna includes a relatively high number of genera and species and is comparable to other well-known hotspots for freshwater shrimp diversity in the Indo–West Pacific region, including Australia, New Guinea, the Philippines, and Sulawesi (Table 9.8). Among these areas, only the continent of Australia surpasses Madagascar in the number of both genera and species.

Of the two shrimp families occurring in Malagasy fresh waters, Atyidae is more interesting from a biogeographic point of view and shows levels of diversity and endemicity more typical of a continental fauna—six genera (two endemic), 31 species (23 endemic, 74% endemicity) (Table 9.6). By comparison, the Malagasy freshwater Palaemonidae represents a more typical insular fauna and includes a high proportion of small-egged, euryhaline species with wide, extralimital distributions in the Indian Ocean or Indo–West Pacific region (Figure 9.10f; Table 9.7). Only a single, large-egged, oligohaline species, *M. hildebrandti*, is presently known (Figure 9.10a). The palaemonid fauna also has a much lower level of endemicity (27%).

The atyid fauna is also remarkable in terms of the high number of subterranean species, all endemic to the limestone karsts in the western half of the island (Figure 9.10c; Table 9.6). Six of these species are restricted to the Ankarana Massif, a hotspot for cave atyids. No subterranean examples of *Macrobrachium* are presently known from Madagascar.

The local distribution patterns of Malagasy freshwater shrimps are highly varied (Figure 9.10) and reflect the wide range of reproductive strategies, salinity tolerance, dispersal capabilities, and habitat preferences shown by different species. Regional differences in climate and topography within the island also appear to have a major influence on distribution patterns.

The most important topographic features in regard to the distribution of freshwater shrimps are the eastern escarpment, the drainage divide between western and eastern drainages, and the limestone massifs and plateaus in the western half of the island. Annual rainfall and seasonality of rainfall are the main climatic factors. The distribution of some upper catchment species may also be limited by physicochemical parameters such as water temperature, pH, and hardness.

The climatic and topographic factors affecting shrimp distributions are to a large degree well summarized by the scheme of freshwater ecoregions developed for freshwater fishes (see Sparks and Stiassny, pp. 1245–60) and subsequently utilized for the Malagasy freshwater fauna in general (Máiz-Tomé et al. 2018; FEOW 2019). One exception is the boundary between the eastern lowlands and eastern highlands ecoregions. Unlike freshwater fishes, which show a disjunction in species distributions at 200 m elevation, freshwater shrimps show an elevational disjunction much higher, at approximately 800 m elevation. This elevation largely corresponds to the upper eastern escarpment. Apart from the widely distributed species *M. lepidactylus*, euryhaline species are otherwise absent from eastern drainages above the eastern escarpment (Figure 9.11). The freshwater crayfish genus *Astacoides* is also largely restricted to the highlands above the eastern escarpment (Hobbs 1987).

Figure 9.11 presents a scheme of freshwater shrimp ecoregions based on the freshwater ecoregions in Máiz-Tomé et al. (2018) and FEOW (2019) but includes a redefined boundary between the eastern highlands and eastern lowlands. The new boundary, at

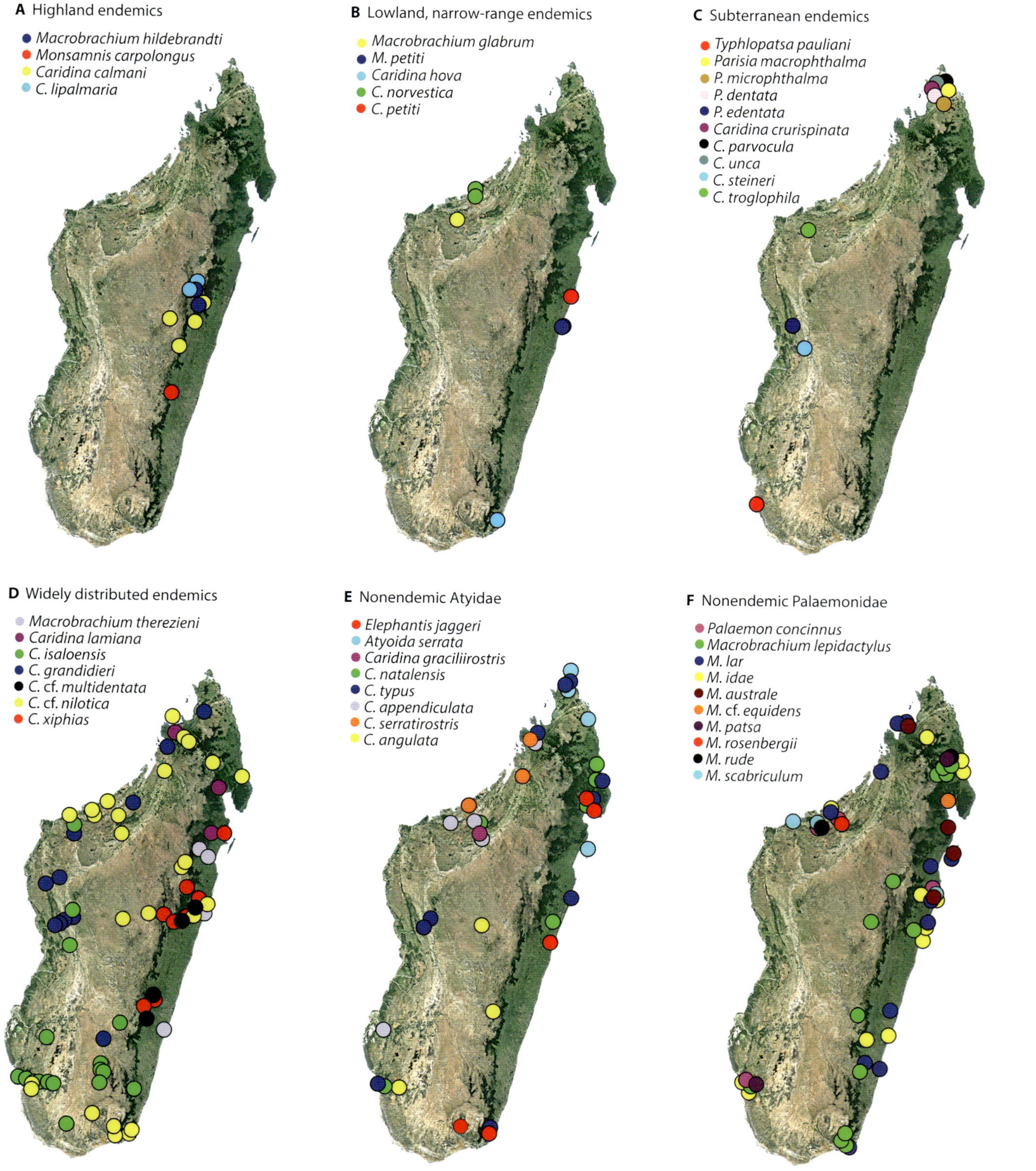

FIGURE 9.10 **Distribution maps of Malagasy freshwater shrimps.** (SOURCES: satellite image of Madagascar by Google Earth, 2018; data from SIO, NOAA, US Navy, NGA, GEBCO; image Landsat/Copernicus.)

approximately 800 m elevation, also corresponds to the division between eastern and central phytogeographic regions in Gautier and Goodman (2003). Freshwater shrimps occurring in each of the ecoregions are listed in Table 9.9. The ecoregions and their shrimp faunas are also briefly discussed below.

Northwestern Madagascar. This ecoregion receives the highest rainfall in the drier western half of the island and is the most diverse ecoregion for freshwater shrimps. Of the 24 species occurring in the region, eight are endemic, including seven subterranean species. Six of the endemic subterranean species are restricted to the Ankarana

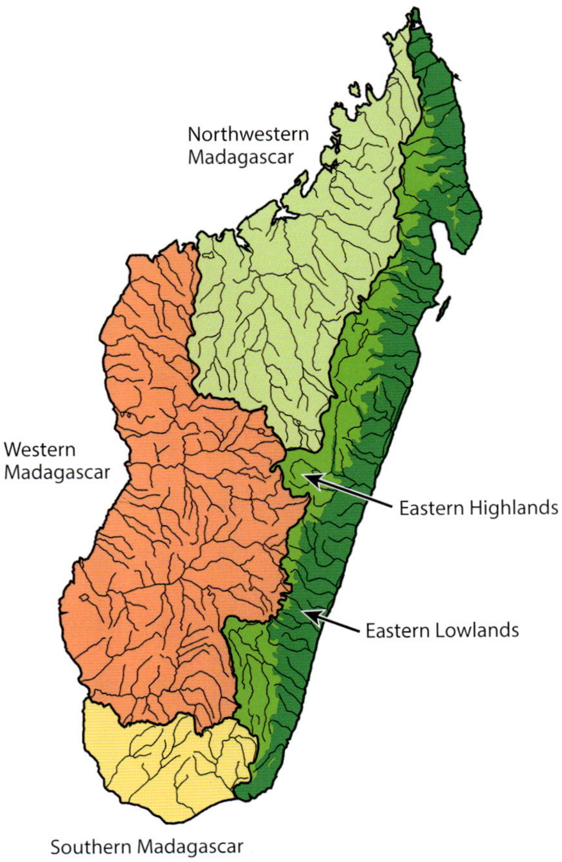

FIGURE 9.11 **Malagasy freshwater shrimp ecoregions.** (SOURCE: modified from the freshwater ecoregions of Máiz-Tomé et al. 2018; FEOW 2019.)

Massif. Three wide-ranging euryhaline species also appear to be restricted to the region: *Caridina gracilirostris*, *C. serratirostris*, and the introduced species *Macrobrachium rosenbergii*. Although the lowlands of this ecoregion have a high diversity of species, headwater streams draining the highlands contain only two species, *C.* cf. *nilotica* and *M. lepidactylus*.

Eastern lowlands. This perennially wet ecoregion has the most speciose epigeal fauna. Of the 22 species occurring in the region, at least five appear to be endemic: *Caridina hova*, *C.* cf. *multidentata*, *C. xiphias*, and *Macrobrachium petiti*. The wide-ranging euryhaline species *Atyoida serrata* also appears to be restricted to the region. Total species diversity is lower than in northwestern Madagascar, largely because of the lack of subterranean habitats.

Western Madagascar. This ecoregion receives less regular seasonal rainfall than northwestern Madagascar immediately to the north. It has a moderately impoverished fauna of 15 species. Three subterranean species, *Caridina steineri*, *C. troglophila*, and *Parisia edentata*, are endemic to the region.

Eastern highlands. This perennially wet ecoregion contains a restricted though highly distinctive shrimp fauna. Of the seven species occurring in the region, four are endemic: *Caridina calmani*, *C. lipalmaria*, *Monsamnis carpolongus*, and *Macrobrachium hildebrandti*. One euryhaline species, the wide-ranging *M. lepidactylus*, is known from the region. Two eurytopic, oligohaline species, *C.* cf. *nilotica* and *C. xiphias*, are found in both the eastern highlands and eastern lowlands ecoregions. The former species is also widely distributed across the island.

Southern Madagascar. This is the driest ecoregion and the most depauperate for freshwater shrimps. Only four species, all belonging to Atyidae, are presently known from the region. The subterranean *Typhlopatsa pauliani* is the only endemic to the region. Two of the remaining shrimps are widely distributed oligohaline species: *Caridina isaloensis* and *C.* cf. *nilotica*. The last species, *Elephantis jaggeri*, is widely distributed in eastern Madagascar and South Africa and is known only from the eastern part of the region bordering the eastern lowlands.

SHRIMPS AS FOOD ON MADAGASCAR

Freshwater shrimps are a highly popular part of the traditional Malagasy diet. Atyids are generally known as *patsa*, although the term may also be used for palaemonid shrimps. In the eastern portion of the island, *patsa* are collected using *filets carrelets* (a type of square net fixed at the end of a pole). The majority are dried and used to embellish sauces or added to broths. Dried *Caridina* is commercially marketed as either *patsa fotsy* ("white shrimp") or *patsa mena* ("red shrimp"). A highly popular dish using *patsa mena* is a mixture of sweet potato leaves with dried shrimp. *Ro patsa*, a stew of beef, potatoes, and *patsa mena* is also used as an aid for nursing mothers and as a general home remedy for illness. In the east of the island, a broth made of *patsa* is also used as a traditional drink for mothers who have just given birth, with the intent to augment milk production.

Large palaemonid shrimps are also regularly consumed throughout the island. Species of *Macrobrachium* are commonly referred to as *orana*, although the term is also used for freshwater crayfishes and to a lesser extent *Caridina* species.

Macrobrachium shrimps are collected by hand or using traps and are consumed fresh. The largest of the indigenous species, *M. lar*, reaches 195 mm in body length. The introduced, widely cultivated *M. rosenbergii* attains an even larger size of 320 mm in body length. In the Marovoay area it is referred to as *gamba*, a general name for prawn that is also used for the marine species *Penaeus monodon*. Holthuis (1980) also lists *M. australe*, *M. idae*, and *M. lepidactylus* as important to fisheries on Madagascar.

CONSERVATION STATUS

Although there are no freshwater shrimps on Madagascar currently listed in the threatened categories, or Near Threatened, on the International Union for Conservation of Nature (IUCN) Red List, almost half of the fauna (19 species) is presently categorized as Data Deficient. Among the Data Deficient species, all the narrow-range endemics occur within protected areas, apart from five species: *Caridina hova*, *C. lipalmaria*, *C. norvestica*, *C. petiti*, and *C. steineri* (Table 9.6). These species appear to be the most urgently in need of research on their population size and trends.

TABLE 9.9. **Freshwater ecoregion distribution of Malagasy freshwater shrimps**

SPECIES		SOUTHERN MADAGASCAR	EASTERN LOWLANDS	EASTERN HIGHLANDS	NORTHWESTERN MADAGASCAR	WESTERN MADAGASCAR
ATYIDAE						
Atyoida serrata		–	X	–	–	–
Caridina angulata		–	–	–	–	X
C. appendiculata		–	–	–	X	X
C. calmani	Endemic	–	–	X	–	–
C.389rurispinata	Endemic	–	–	–	X	–
C. edulis	Endemic	?	?	?	?	?
C. gracilirostris		–	–	–	X	–
C. grandidieri	Endemic	–	–	–	X	X
C. hova	Endemic	–	X	–	–	–
C. isaloensis	Endemic	X	X	–	–	X
C. lamiana	Endemic	–	X	–	X	–
C. lipalmaria	Endemic	–	–	X	–	–
C. cf. *multidentata*	Endemic	–	X	–	–	–
C. natalensis		–	X	–	X	X
C. cf. *nilotica*	Endemic	X	X	X	X	X
C. norvestica	Endemic	–	–	–	X	–
C. parvocula	Endemic	–	–	–	X	–
C. petiti	Endemic	–	X	–	–	–
C. serratirostris		–	–	–	X	–
C. steineri	Endemic	–	–	–	–	X
C. troglophila	Endemic	–	–	–	–	X
C. typus		–	X	–	X	X
C. unca	Endemic	–	–	–	X	–
C. xiphias	Endemic	–	X	X	–	–
Elephantis jaggeri		X	X	–	–	–
Monsamnis carpolongus	Endemic	–	–	X	–	–
Parisia dentata	Endemic	–	–	–	X	–
P. edentata	Endemic	–	–	–	–	X
P. macrophthalma	Endemic	–	–	–	X	–
P. microphthalma	Endemic	–	–	–	X	–
Typhlopatsa pauliani	Endemic	X	–	–	–	–

SPECIES		SOUTHERN MADAGASCAR	EASTERN LOWLANDS	EASTERN HIGHLANDS	NORTHWESTERN MADAGASCAR	WESTERN MADAGASCAR
PALAEMONIDAE						
Macrobrachium australe		–	X	–	X	–
M. cf. *equidens*		–	X	–	–	–
M. glabrum	Endemic	–	–	–	X	–
M. hildebrandti	Endemic	–	–	X	–	–
M. idae		–	X	–	X	X
M. lar		–	X	–	X	–
M. lepidactylus		–	X	X	X	X
M. patsa		–	X	–	–	X
M. petiti	Endemic	–	X	–	–	–
M. rosenbergii		–	–	–	X	–
M. rude		–	X	–	X	–
M. scabriculum		–	X	–	X	X
M. therezieni	Endemic	–	X	–	–	–
Palaemon concinnus		–	X	–	X	X

Note: For the ecoregions, see Figure 9.11.

Foreseeable threats to the freshwater shrimp fauna include habitat degradation, overfishing, pesticides, local climate change, rainwater acidification, and the introduction of non-native species (J. W. Short and Doumenq 2003; Cumberlidge et al. 2017). Of these threats, habitat degradation resulting from intensive deforestation is probably of greatest concern, particularly in the eastern portion of the island. Deforestation leads to increased variation in stream levels, higher rates of sedimentation, and increased turbidity through erosion. It also causes major changes in physicochemical parameters, such as dissolved oxygen, temperature, pH, and conductivity. The combined effect has been a modification of the composition of the aquatic flora and fauna as well as species abundance.

Overfishing is having a major impact on *Macrobrachium* populations and has led to the decline of stocks. Castelin et al. (2013b) reported anecdotal evidence from fishers of a substantial decline in Malagasy populations of *M. lar* over the previous decade. The impact of fishing on commercial species of *Caridina* also needs to be assessed.

Only one introduced freshwater shrimp species is presently known from Madagascar—the Asian species *M. rosenbergii*. Although the species has not yet been recorded outside the Betsiboka River in the Mahajanga Province, it shows a preference for large floodplain rivers and has the potential to become widespread in northwestern Madagascar. The impact of this species on the indigenous *Macrobrachium* fauna is presently unknown.

Subject editors: Brian L. Fisher and Steven M. Goodman

PARASTACIDAE: *ASTACOIDES*, FRESHWATER CRAYFISHES, *ORANA*, *ORAMBANONGA*, *ORAMBATO*

K. A. Crandall, J. P. G. Jones, and J. Rasamy Razanabolana

Freshwater crayfishes are a large group (over 670 species) of decapod crustaceans widely distributed around the world with the exception of Africa and the Indian subcontinent (Crandall and De Grave 2017). There is, however, an endemic freshwater crayfish genus, *Astacoides*, found on Madagascar. This fact has puzzled zoogeographers for years (Hobbs 1988) and makes the endemic crayfish fauna of Madagascar key to understanding both the evolutionary history of the group and the biogeographic history of the island.

The seven described species of *Astacoides* (Table 9.10) are known from relatively few locales in the southeastern region of Madagascar (Rabearisoa 1995; Rabearisoa et al. 1996; Boyko et al. 2005; J. P. G. Jones et al. 2007; Ravoahangimalala et al. 2007). Four species are considered vulnerable according to the International Union for Conservation of Nature's (IUCN) Red List (IUCN 2020) The bulk of what we know about the ecology of Madagascar's endemic crayfish species comes from Ranomafana National Park where, because of the importance of crayfish to the economy (Dixon 1992; J. P. G. Jones et al. 2006), their ecology has been studied in some detail (J. P. G. Jones et al. 2005, 2007; J. P. G. Jones and Coulson 2006). There was also a major national survey exploring their distribution in 2006 and 2010 (Ravoahangimalala et al. 2007; Rasamy Razanabolana 2010); however, there has been very little research in the decade since.

In this contribution, we review the phylogenetic position and uniqueness of the Malagasy crayfishes (*Astacoides*), their biogeography, and their known ecology. We summarize what is known about how people use them and then discuss crayfishes' conservation status, including the impact of overharvesting, habitat destruction, and introduction of invasive species.

PHYLOGENETIC POSITION

Freshwater crayfishes are a monophyletic group of freshwater decapod crustaceans with a sister relationship to marine clawed lobsters (Nephropidae) (Figure 9.12) (Crandall et al. 2000). Within the freshwater crayfishes, there are two superfamilies, Parastacoidea (Southern Hemisphere) and Astacoidea (Northern Hemisphere). The Southern Hemisphere crayfishes form a single family, Parastacidae (Crandall and DeGrave 2017). The family Parastacidae is further subdivided into 17 genera, 11 from Australia (the center of diversity for this family), three endemic to southern South America, one endemic to New Zealand, and *Astacoides*, which is endemic to Madagascar (Figure 9.12).

A comprehensive study of the relationships within the Southern Hemisphere family Parastacidae suggests a Gondwanan origin of the group (Toon et al. 2010). The Malagasy crayfishes fall phylogenetically basal to the entire Australian clade with an association to the endemic genera of New Zealand (*Paranephrops*) and Tasmania (*Spinastacoides* and *Ombrastacoides*) (Toon et al. 2010); however, the key nodes showing relationships among geographic groups are weakly supported (Figure 9.12), and this Malagasy clade moves around in other phylogenetic studies to the basal position of the New Zealand, Tasmania, and South America endemic genera (Owen et al. 2015). Nevertheless, all studies show the genus as a monophyletic group that is evolutionarily very distinct from other crayfish genera, diverging from them ~180–210 million years ago (Mya) (Toon et al. 2010; Bracken-Grissom et al. 2014).

BIOGEOGRAPHY

Another extremely interesting component of the Madagascar crayfish fauna is their biogeographic distribution relative to the other genera of the family Parastacidae. Several of the evolutionarily more recent faunas of Madagascar show clear biogeographic links to eastern Africa. However, as mentioned above, there is no evidence of freshwater crayfishes from the African continent. Instead, the Madagascar crayfishes show links to the South American, New Zealand, and Tasmanian crayfish fauna. It is clear that the major families of freshwater crayfishes are of ancient origin (Crandall et al. 2000). Fossilized burrows of freshwater crayfishes have been discovered in the western United States (Utah and Colorado) dating back to 265 Mya, demonstrating that crayfishes were established in the Permian and Early Triassic (Hasiotis and Mitchell 1993), before the breakup of Pangaea. The two major superfamilies of freshwater crayfishes show a clear split between the Northern and Southern Hemispheres, corresponding to the splitting of Pangaea into northern (Laurasia) and southern (Gondwana) landmasses ~185 Mya (Figure 9.12). However, a new fossil genus and species (*Aenigmastacus crandalli*) in Parastacoidea was recently discovered in British Columbia dating to the Eocene (Feldmann et al. 2011), which threw a wrench into our neat Pangaean interpretation of crayfish diversity as a whole. The association of the Madagascar crayfishes with the South American and Australian fauna also suggests an ancient origin for crayfishes on the island. Furthermore, the phylogenetic connection of the Southern Hemisphere crayfishes, represented in southern South America, Madagascar, and Australia, corresponds to the distribution patterns of the predatory dinosaur group Abelisauridae (Sampson et al. 1998). Likewise, other Early Triassic dinosaur groups show associations between Madagascar and South America (Flynn et al. 1999). Thus, the crayfishes offer further support for the hypothesis suggesting extended contact between these landmasses via Antarctica (Sampson et al. 1998) and the antiquity of the freshwater crayfish lineage (see Collins et al., pp. 45–51, for further discussion on these land connections).

TABLE 9.10. **Summary of geographic location and body size information for the seven species of freshwater crayfish known from Madagascar**

SPECIES	SEX	CARAPACE LENGTH	WEIGHT	LATITUDE	LONGITUDE
Astacoides betsileoensis Petit, 1923	F	33.8–61.3, μ = 47.16 (n = 42)	16–100, μ = 45.29 (n = 42)	19.08°–21.83°S	47.27°–48.36°E
	M	31–66.3, μ = 46.86 (n = 49)	13–109, μ = 43.57 (n = 49)	19.08°–21.28°S	47.36°–48.36°E
A. caldwelli (Spence Bate in Sclater, 1865)	F	8.9–55, μ = 41.22 (n = 38)	11–60, μ = 31.46 (n = 38)	19.28°–20.34°S	46.92°–47.63°E
	M	28.5–61.7, μ = 45.28 (n = 28)	8–96, μ = 38.04 (n = 28)	19.15°–20.34°S	46.92°–47.63°E
A. crosnieri Hobbs, 1987	F	19.4–43.4, μ = 31.73 (n = 31)	3–33, μ = 12.84 (n = 31)	21.25°–21.61°S	47.31°–47.4°E
	M	26.5–54.5, μ = 37.4 (n = 25)	5–57, μ = 21.29 (n = 26)	21.27°–21.61°S	47.31°–47.4°E
A. granulimanus Monod & Petit, 1929	F	22.4–57.2, μ = 39.86 (n = 89)	1.2–76, μ = 25.01 (n = 89)	20.32°–22.12°S	47.1°–47.62°E
	M	18.7–83.8, μ = 40.34 (n = 103)	1.6–126, μ = 29.27 (n = 103)	20.32°–22.12°S	47.1°–47.62°E
A. hobbsi Boyko, Ravoahangimalala, Randriamasimanana & Razafindrazaka, 2005	F	22–30.3, μ = 26.15 (n = 2)	4–11.2, μ = 7.6 (n = 2)	20.33°–20.33°S	47.63°–47.63°E
	M	24.5–46, μ = 31.59 (n = 8)	6–42, μ = 14.28 (n = 8)	20.33°–20.33°S	47.63°–47.63°E
A. madagascarensis (H. Milne Edwards & Audouin, 1839)	F	26.1–61.4, μ = 44.22 (n = 101)	7–110, μ = 39.73 (n = 101)	18.32°–18.44°S	47.94°–48.02°E
	M	27.5–64.4, μ = 44.71 (n = 78)	8–105, μ = 42.33 (n = 78)	18.32°–18.44°S	47.94°–48.02°E
A. petiti Hobbs, 1987	F	29.3–46.2, μ = 36.5 (n = 5)	–	–	–
	M	21.4–54.0, μ = 40.5 (n = 7)	–	–	–

Sources: Data from Rasamy Rosanabolana (2010), except for *A. petiti* from Hobbs (1987). A taxonomic key to the species is provided in Hobbs (1987).
Notes: F, female; M, male; μ, mean. Carapace length is the distance from the tip of the rostrum to the carapace-abdomen junction.

ECOLOGY

Crayfishes, as a rule, are temperate species, achieving their greatest diversity in the southern Appalachian Mountains in the eastern United States. Wherever crayfishes have been introduced and become invasive in the tropics, they tend to occur at higher elevations relative to their temperate relatives. On Madagascar, most known localities for these animals occur between 600 and 2000 m (although *Astacoides petiti* has been found down to 120 m).

J. P. G. Jones et al. (2007) provided information on the ecology of four of the seven known species (*A. betsileoensis*, *A. caldwelli*, *A. crosnieri*, and *A. granulimanus*) based on a detailed four-year study including a mark-and-recapture experiment involving more than 29,000 individual crayfishes. Little detailed information is available on the other three species not found in Ranomafana National Park, but what is known about the ecology of all species is summarized below.

Mark-and-recapture experiments reveal *Astacoides* to be slow growing. Growth rates of *A. granulimanus* and *A. crosnieri* are among the slowest of any known species of crayfish, with individuals living longer than 20 years (J. P. G. Jones et al. 2007). This longevity leads to large body sizes of many of these crayfishes (Table 9.10). Growth rates do not show density dependence; where population density is substantially lowered as a result of high fishing pressure, growth rates do not appear to be higher (J. P. G. Jones and Coulson 2006).

For the *Astacoides* species for which we have data, these crayfishes have been observed breeding just once a year, with a clear peak in the proportion of females bearing eggs between July and October. Eggs are carried for approximately four months, hatching in

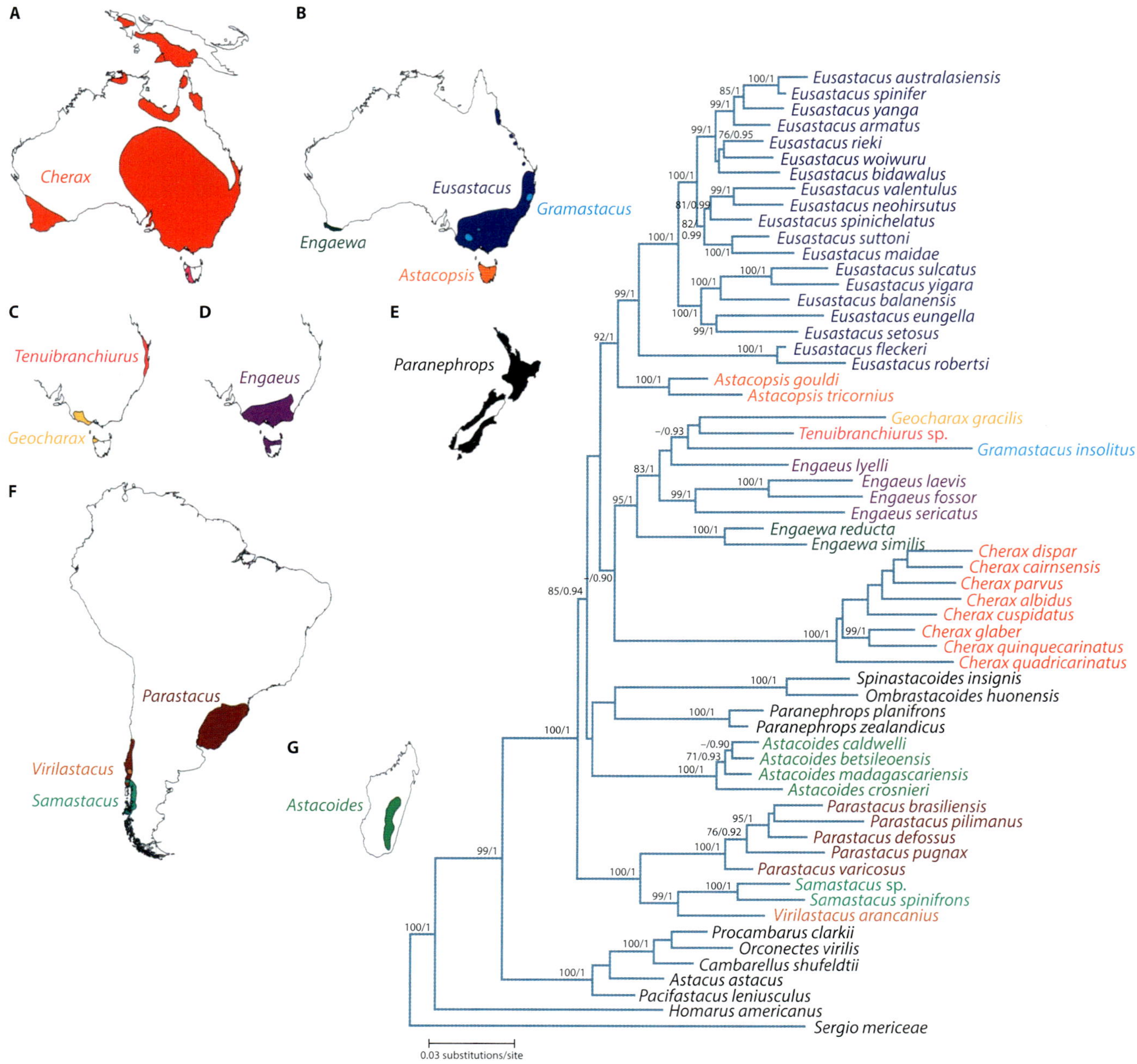

FIGURE 9.12 **Geographic range and phylogeny of Parastacidae.** (SOURCE: modified from Toon et al. 2007.)

October or November. All juveniles are independent by the end of January (J. P. G. Jones et al. 2007). There is a strong relationship between size and fecundity (because the number of eggs and the proportion of females bearing eggs varies with size). This relationship does appear to be density dependent; a higher proportion of females of a given size reproduced where fishing pressure had reduced the overall density (J. P. G. Jones and Coulson 2006).

Astacoides species have different but overlapping habitats. *Astacoides granulimanus* (and the similar but allopatric *A. madagascarensis*) is found mostly in small, clear, fast-flowing forest streams but can also be found in slower-flowing larger rivers (J. P. G. Jones et al. 2007). *Astacoides betsileoensis* is found mostly in deep, slow-flowing rivers above 1000 m, but occasionally in smaller tributaries where deep pools mimic the habitat offered by a larger river. This species spends time in rivers and is a secondary or tertiary burrower along riverbanks (*sensu* Hobbs 1981). It is found in burrows up to 1 m long, with extensive galleries running parallel to the bank (J. P. G. Jones et al. 2007). *Astacoides caldwelli* is found in large rivers at elevations ranging from 600 to over 1700 m (Boyko et al. 2005; Ravoahangimalala et al. 2007). This species has been observed in rivers draining the eastern slopes of Ranomafana National Park, in the Central Highlands site of Manjakatompo (Ankaratra), and in burrows near Tsinjoarivo (southeast of Ambatolampy) within the Onive River drainage (Ravoahangimalala et al. 2007). Deforestation has been extensive at low elevations, and many of the drainage areas had been cleared long ago of extensive natural forest. The catchment areas, however, often remain forested. *Astacoides caldwelli* is a tertiary burrower (*sensu* Hobbs 1981) but tends to make simpler burrows than *A. betsileoensis*. It has been observed under rocks and occasionally in rice canals (Ravoahangimalala et al. 2007). *Astacoides crosnieri* is always found in swampy habitat with a soft substrate. *Astacoides crosnieri* is a primary burrower (*sensu* Hobbs 1981), building a complex burrow system that seldom comes into contact with open water. *Astacoides hobbsi* is known only from the

Andranofotsiorana effluent of the Ranomadio River in the former province of Fianarantsoa, co-occuring with *A. granulimanus*, *A. betsileoensis*, and *A. caldwelli* (Boyko et al. 2005). *Astacoides hobbsi* was collected from the same river at 1440 m (Rasamy Razanabolana 2010). This species is found under large boulders and deadwood, as well as in burrows along riverbanks (Boyko et al. 2005). *Astacoides petiti* was collected at five sites inside Andohahela National Park in the far southeast. Unusually for *Astacoides*, *A. petiti* occurs in a very wide elevational range, from 120 to 1215 m (Ravoahangimalala et al. 2007).

Water quality associated with these species has been assessed in a few studies. Dixon (1992) found the dissolved oxygen ranged from 6.0 to 7.8 parts per million, pH from about 8 to 9, and temperature from 20° to 23°C. Rabearisoa et al. (1996) found a pH from 4 to 6 in crayfish-inhabited waters. Ravoahangimalala et al. (2007) carried out investigations at 52 stations from 20 sites and and recorded a pH from 6 to 7 and water temperature from 17°C to 23°C.

FIGURE 9.13 **Crayfishes are a Malagasy staple in many villages as both a food and a cash source. In some cases, their sale represents nearly 100% of the income for the village.** (PHOTO by J. Rasamy Razanabolana.)

USE OF CRAYFISHES ON MADAGASCAR

Many people around the world use freshwater crayfishes as a food source (and consequently an economic resource) (Figure 9.13). Madagascar's endemic freshwater crayfishes (*Astacoides*) are harvested by local people for both subsistence and small-scale trade (Dehgan 1990; Ferraro 2004; J. P. G. Jones et al. 2006; Ravoahangimalala et al. 2007). Through the use of local interviews to gain insights in harvesting trends (J. P. G. Jones et al. 2008a), J. P. G. Jones et al. (2006, 2007) studied crayfish exploitation in eastern Madagascar over four years. Subsistence use is widespread, particularly by children for whom crayfish meat may provide an important protein source. The existence of local taboos (*fady*) prevent commercial crayfish harvesting in some communities, particularly among the Tanala ethnic group (J. P. G. Jones et al. 2006, 2008b). Taboos also limit the collection of *A. petiti* by the local population in Ifanota, Tolagnaro (Ravoahangimalala et al. 2007). However, in some areas, the sale of crayfish catch to passersby or nearby markets provides vital income. In one harvesting village near Ranomafana, more than 50% of the 47 households were directly involved in the harvest, which contributed the equivalent of US$2,382 to the village economy in 2003–2004, an important sum in the context of local incomes (J. P. G. Jones et al. 2006). Sale of crayfishes continues to this day; informal observations made near Ranomafana in 2019 found many of the same individuals and their children still selling crayfishes at the same place along the road as nearly 20 years earlier.

In general, the minimum size of the harvested crayfishes and the annual collection period authorized by law are not respected (Ravoahangimalala et al. 2007), making management of crayfish populations particularly difficult. Illegal practices, such as applying extracts of toxic plants to the water (which has harmful effects on crayfishes and other aquatic animals), making nighttime torchlight collections, and crushing burrows to force crayfishes out, are sometimes used (Ravoahangimalala et al. 2007).

Crayfish harvesters have long complained about declining stocks (Ferraro 1994; Dehgan 1990). J. P. G. Jones et al. (2007) reported on interviews with 250 informants from 38 villages and small towns from 15 communes throughout the Fianarantsoa forest corridor. Informants commonly stated that crayfish populations (particularly *A. betsileoensis*, *A. caldwelli*, and *A. crosnieri*) were declining in their local area. They blamed a combination of overfishing (especially for the declines in *A. betsileoensis*) and habitat loss (which was blamed particularly for the loss of *A. crosnieri*). Respondents disagreed as to whether *A. granulimanus* was declining or not, and if it was indeed declining, they disagreed on the reason. It is interesting that an assessment (based on a major mark-and-recapture experiment) suggests that the harvest in Ranomafana National Park of *A. granulimanus* was, at least in the early 2000s, relatively sustainable (J. P. G. Jones et al. 2005). The study, based on mark-and-recapture experiments involving over 44,000 captures at 74 sites along a gradient of harvesting intensity, revealed that although harvesting changes the size and frequency distribution of crayfishes, density-dependent survival allowed sustainable harvest (J. P. G. Jones et al. 2005). This is in contrast to the harvest of *A. betsileoensis*, which was likely to be unsustainable partly because their large size at first reproduction meant that a smaller proportion of individuals of this species would have reproduced before being collected for sale (J. P. G. Jones et al. 2007). There may be opportunities to partner communities' harvesting needs with conservation, but this relationship can be complicated, as local peoples' mere willingness to contribute to monitoring may not be sufficient for it to be effective (Hockley et al. 2005).

CONSERVATION STATUS

Freshwater ecosystems in general (Groombridge and Jenkins 2000), and crayfishes in particular, tend to be vulnerable to human-induced change. More than 32% of the world's 660-plus species of freshwater crayfishes are considered threatened with extinction (Richman et al. 2015). Of the seven Malagasy species, four are classified as Vulnerable (*Astacoides betsileoensis*, *A. crosnieri*, *A. hobbsi*,

FIGURE 9.14 **Diversity and conservation status of the Malagasy crayfishes. I) Species listed by IUCN as Least Concern: A, B, C) *Astacoides madagascarensis*, with different carapace colors, Anjozorobe, and D) *A. granulimanus*, Sahavondronana. II) Species listed by IUCN as Vulnerable: A) *A. betsileoensis*, green type, Sahambaky, Lakato; B) *A. betsileoensis*, red type, Andragnaroa; C) *A. caldwelli*, Ramainandro; D) *A. crosnieri*, Sahavondrona; E) *A. hobbsi* (preserved specimen), Andranofotsiorana. *Astacoides petiti*, rated Data Deficient by IUCN, is not pictured.** (PHOTOS IA–C and IIB by J. Rasamy Razanabolana; and ID, IIA, and IIC–E by C. H. Ranaivoson.)

and *A. caldwelli*), two as Least Concern (*A. granulimanus* and *A. madagascarensis*), and one as Data Deficient (*A. petiti*) (Cumberlidge et al. 2017, 2018; Figure 9.14).

Overexploitation, as discussed above, is an important threat to *Astacoides* species; however, it is clear from recent studies that *Astacoides* species are vulnerable to loss of habitat as well (J. P. G. Jones et al. 2007; Cumberlidge et al. 2017, 2018). Around 37% of Madagascar's natural forest habitat was lost between 1973 and 2014 (Vieilledent et al. 2016). *Astacoides granulimanus* does show some tolerance of nonintact native forest, as it is found in highly disturbed natural forest to the west of Ranomafana National Park and plantation forest dominated by pine and eucalyptus near Mahasoabe (J. P. G. Jones et al. 2007). However, the banks of the rivers passing through these plantations retained natural vegetation. In Ranomafana, it is found at lower elevations in forested, rather than in deforested, streams and is almost never found in streams with banks cleared for agriculture. Timed searches for *A. crosnieri* in an area of suitable habitat that had been converted the year before to a rice field and an adjacent unconverted area, found only a handful of individuals in the cleared area but more than 90 in the adjacent uncleared area (J. P. G. Jones et al. 2007). This suggests that *A. crosnieri* is affected by habitat conversion, which is supported by interviews with local people who tend to associate its reduced population size with habitat loss more than overharvesting (J. P. G. Jones et al. 2007). *Astacoides caldwelli* is found predominantly in larger rivers at lower elevations but has been found in Manjakatompo, Ankaratra, at 1760 m and in Antanifotsy, Vakinankaratra, at 1740 m (Ravoahangimalala et al. 2007). Deforestation has been extensive at the lower elevations, and many of the rivers where deforestation has been observed are in areas long cleared of natural forest. However, this does not necessarily signal tolerance of habitat loss, as the catchments remain forested in all cases (J. P. G. Jones et al. 2007).

Conservation efforts for the endemic Malagasy crayfishes have been further complicated by the introduction of the invasive crayfish species *Procambarus virginalis*. This so-called marbled crayfish is a globally expanding, parthenogenetically reproducing crayfish (Lyko 2017) that was accidentally introduced into Madagascar in approximately 2005 (J. P. G. Jones et al. 2009). Although it was initially restricted to the area around Antananarivo, it spread rapidly, and surveys from 2019 reveal that it is now sympatric with *Astacoides* in the eastern moist evergreen forests (Andriantsoa et al. 2020). Anecdotal evidence shows it is now found in Ranomafana National Park—a stronghold for *Astacoides*. No research has been done to explore the impact of *Procambarus* on *Astacoides* or other elements of Madagascar's freshwater biodiversity. However, it is certainly a cause for concern, and research is urgently needed (Andriantsoa et al. 2020).

While the distribution of *Astacoides* species is not well known, most species are recorded from at least one protected area. For example, the stronghold for *A. petiti* appears to be the Andohahela protected area; *A. madagascarensis* is numerous in the Anjozorobe-Angavo protected area (Rakotonarivo 2004; Ravoahangimalala et al. 2007; Ranaivoson 2011); *A. crosnieri* is found in the Ambositra-Vondrozo forest corridor; and *A. caldwelli* in the Manjakatompo Ankaratra Massif protected area (Gardner et al. 2018). Three species are categorized as freshwater Key Biodiversity Area (KBA) trigger species: *A. crosnieri* in the KBA of Faraony Headwater, and *A. betsileoensis* and *A. caldwelli* in the KBA of Andasibe (Máiz-Tomé et al. 2018).

Subject editors: Brian L. Fisher and Steven M. Goodman

POTAMONAUTIDAE, FRESHWATER CRABS, *FOZA*

N. Cumberlidge

The 18 species of freshwater crabs found on Madagascar belong to nine genera. All are members of the Afrotropical family Potamonautidae, and all are endemic to the island. Freshwater crabs are found throughout Madagascar in inland water ecosystems, including rivers, streams, ponds, lakes, and marshes, or wherever fresh water collects. For example, *Madagapotamon humberti* (Figure 9.15) lives in erosion pools and crevices in limestone rock formations (Vuillemin 1970), *Skelosophusa prolixa* is found in caves, and all three species of *Malagasya* live in the water pools that collect in the leaf axils of screw-pine palms (*Pandanus*; see Callmander et al., pp. 452–64) (Cumberlidge et al. 2002, 2005, 2020). Marine crabs (e.g., Sesarmidae, Varunidae, Grapsidae) are also found in freshwater habitats together with freshwater crabs, but the former are limited to streams and rivers in the coastal regions because they need to return to salt water to breed.

The past few decades have seen a resurgence of interest in Madagascar's freshwater ecosystems, and biotic surveying of most groups of organisms has intensified throughout the island. Notably, substantial collections of freshwater crabs from many parts of the island are now available. The wealth of recent material has inspired long-term studies that have accelerated our knowledge of Malagasy species diversity by the author of this contribution and different colleagues (Cumberlidge and Sternberg 2002; Reed and Cumberlidge 2006; Cumberlidge et al. 2007, 2015, 2020; Cumberlidge and Meyer 2009; Meyer et al. 2014).

Even so, our present knowledge of the number of species and genera of freshwater crabs found on Madagascar is almost certainly an underestimate, because a recent study of the island's freshwater crab fauna indicates the presence of four new genera and 10 new species (Cumberlidge et al. 2020). Therefore, the estimated Malagasy freshwater crab diversity is more realistically at least 13 genera and 27 species, and all species are endemic (Cumberlidge and Sternberg 2002; Cumberlidge et al. 2015, 2020). Furthermore, it is highly likely that these numbers will continue to increase with more intensive collection efforts, particularly in unexplored areas, because the extensive evolutionary diversification of the freshwater crabs on Madagascar is only now being documented.

FIGURE 9.15 ***Madagapotamon humberti*** **on limestone** ***tsingy*** **in the Ankarana Massif, extreme northern Madagascar.** (PHOTO by H. Schütz.)

All Malagasy freshwater crabs belong to the same family as those found on the African mainland and associated islands (Cumberlidge 2008; Cumberlidge et al. 2008). Recent studies of the phylogenetic relationships of the Afrotropical fauna as a whole leave no doubt that Madagascar's freshwater crab fauna is monophyletic, that it originated from ancestral populations on the African mainland, and that its closest relatives live in eastern Africa and the Seychelles archipelago (Cumberlidge and Sternberg 2002; Daniels et al. 2006, 2015). At the genus level, however, the unique nature of Malagasy freshwater crabs becomes apparent, owing to the unusual combinations of morphological characteristics that set them apart from other members of the family. For example, some features of the first gonopod of Malagasy freshwater crabs are not seen in species from continental Africa nor in the African Potamidae in North Africa and Socotra Island (Cumberlidge 1999; Cumberlidge and Sternberg 2002). In addition, while characteristics such as a two-segmented mandibular palp unite the Malagasy freshwater crabs with the rest of the Afrotropical fauna, the unusually high incidence of long-legged, non-cave-dwelling species of freshwater crabs on Madagascar sets them apart from the rest of the family (Cumberlidge and Sternberg 2002).

TAXONOMY OF THE MALAGASY FRESHWATER CRABS

Earlier taxonomic treatments of Madagascar's freshwater crabs interpreted the striking differences in morphology of some species as evidence of paraphyly and assigned them to three different families or subfamilies, thereby linking them to species found in Africa, India, and the Middle East (Bott 1965; Ng et al. 1995). In contrast, all recent evidence supports the view that the entire freshwater crab fauna of Madagascar belongs to a monophyletic group that is endemic to the island and that belongs to a single family, Potamonautidae. The great diversity seen on this island appears to be the result of an extensive evolutionary radiation following the arrival of a single ancestral population from the African mainland between 37 and 16 million years ago (late Eocene to early Miocene) (Daniels et al. 2015). Cumberlidge and Sternberg (2002) established the modern taxonomy of the freshwater crabs of Madagascar. Those authors provided a comprehensive revision of the taxonomy of all the species that had been described from Madagascar up to that point, along with the first maps and identification keys to all the genera and species. This is the classification presented in the precursor of this book (Cumberlidge and Sternberg 2003).

Since then, molecular phylogenies of this group (Daniels et al. 2006, 2015; Cumberlidge et al. 2020) have provided support for Cumberlidge and Sternberg's (2002) classification, and have led to the description of several new taxa. The result has been a constant stream of additions to the fauna since 2002, bringing the number of Malagasy freshwater crabs currently known to 18 species and nine genera (Table 9.11; Cumberlidge et al. 2007, 2015, 2020; Reed and Cumberlidge 2006; Cumberlidge and Meyer 2009; Meyer et al. 2014). *Hydrothelphusa* is the most speciose Malagasy freshwater crab genus, with four species, while *Foza*, *Malagasya*, and *Skelosophusa* each have three species. Five genera (*Agora*, *Boreathelphusa*, *Glabrithelphusa*, *Madagapotamon*, and *Marojejy*) are monotypic.

FAMILY-LEVEL CLASSIFICATION OF THE MALAGASY FRESHWATER CRABS

Members of Potamonautidae are found only in sub-Saharan Africa and its associated islands, the largest of which is Madagascar (Cumberlidge et al. 2008). This family is divided into two subfamilies—Potamonautinae (with seven genera from continental Africa) and Deckeniinae (with 13 genera from Africa, the Seychelles, and Madagascar) (Cumberlidge et al. 2008; Ng et al. 2008; Cumberlidge and Ng 2009). Deckeniinae is divided into two tribes—Hydrothelphusini (with nine genera from Madagascar) and Deckeniini (with four genera from western and eastern Africa and the Seychelles). Like many other groups found on Madagascar, the freshwater crabs are unique but only at the generic level and below.

The Afrotropical freshwater crab fauna (which includes Madagascar) is monophyletic and endemic to this zoogeographic region at the family level. Diversification on the African continent since the Eocene has resulted in two distinct lineages (subfamilies), one of which included the ancestor of the freshwater crabs occurring on Madagascar. That is, the common ancestor of this fauna most likely lived in Africa, belonged to Deckeniinae (rather than Potamonautinae), and reached Madagascar from coastal eastern Africa rather than from the Seychelles archipelago or India.

BIOLOGY

Malagasy freshwater crabs spend their entire lives in fresh water, lay their eggs and rear their young independently of seawater, and are never found naturally in saltwater habitats. Although biologists first discovered freshwater crabs on Madagascar over 167 years ago, these crustaceans have been largely overlooked until recently. The result has been that even today, surprisingly little is known about most aspects of the biology of these animals. At a basic level, the absence of reliable and comprehensive identification keys has hampered our understanding of the diversity of Madagascar's freshwater crabs. Only now are we beginning to realize the unique nature of this fauna and its origins, and how they are related to other freshwater crabs found on the African mainland and the western Indian Ocean islands (Cumberlidge and Sternberg 2002; Cumberlidge 2008). Perhaps not surprisingly, more long-term field investigations of the ecology, distribution, and population levels of these crabs are badly needed to get a clear vision of their true diversity and their detailed phylogenetic relationships.

ECOLOGY

Freshwater crabs are found in all parts of Madagascar, from the eastern moist evergreen forests, to the drier and cooler Central Highlands, to the western dry deciduous forests. The high rainfall, notable humidity, and deep shade of the moist evergreen forests provides the favorable conditions that permit crabs to leave permanent water sources. Freshwater crabs are found in lakes, streams, and rivers, as well as in adjacent terrestrial habitats, where they feed on the vegetation and invertebrates on the forest floor, shelter in water-filled rocky crevices, and exploit water pools that collect in tree axils (Cumberlidge et al. 2002, 2005, 2020).

TABLE 9.11. **Checklist of the freshwater crabs (Potamonautidae: Deckeniinae) of Madagascar**

SCIENTIFIC NAMES	IUCN STATUS	RED LIST CRITERIA
Agora goudoti (H. Milne Edwards, 1853)	LC	
Boreathelphusa uglowi (Cumberlidge & Sternberg, 2002)	EN	B1ab(iii)
Foza ambohitra Cumberlidge & Meyer, 2009	LC	
F. manonae Cumberlidge, Klaus, Meyer & Koppin, 2015	DD	
F. raimundi Reed & Cumberlidge, 2006	LC	
Glabrithelphusa angene Meyer, Cumberlidge & Koppin, 2014	DD	
Hydrothelphusa agilis (A. Milne Edwards, 1872)	LC	
H. bombetokensis (Rathbun, 1904)	LC	
H. madagascariensis (A. Milne Edwards, 1872)	LC	
H. vencesi Cumberlidge, Marijnissen & Thompson, 2007	LC	
Madagapotamon humberti Bott, 1965	LC	
Malagasya antongilensis Rathbun, 1905	LC	
M. elvisshoes Cumberlidge, Soma, Leever & Daniels, 2020	NE	
M. goodmani (Cumberlidge, Boyko & Harvey, 2002)	DD	
Marojejy longimerus (Cumberlidge, Boyko & Harvey, 2002)	DD	
Skelosophusa eumeces Ng & Takeda, 1994	DD	
S. gollhardi (Bott, 1965)	DD	
S. prolixa Ng & Takeda, 1994	DD	

Sources: IUCN Red List categories from IUCN (2020). For an explanation of Red List Criteria see IUCN (2003).
Note: DD, Data Deficient; EN, Endangered; LC, Least Concern; NE, Not Evaluated; VU, Vulnerable.

The most common species (e.g., members of the genus *Hydrothelphusa*) are found in both montane forested areas and in more open country. Several genera (e.g., *Malagasya*, *Marojejy*, *Foza*, and *Madagapotamon*) have moved out of conventional aquatic ecosystems and colonized nearby terrestrial microhabitats in forests, grasslands, and even exposed rock formations. There is a general evolutionary trend in freshwater crabs to shift from a completely aquatic life toward an amphibious life, dividing their time between streams and adjacent land and breathing both water and air. For example, moist evergreen forest species in the genera *Malagasya*, *Marojejy*, and *Foza* are found not only in rivers, streams, and swamps but also in the shallow-water pools that collect in some parts of the vegetation (i.e., in phytotelmata). All three species of *Malagasya* are long-legged, tree-climbing crabs that inhabit water-filled leaf axils of the screw-pine (*Pandanus*) in the lower and mid-canopy forest levels in the moist evergreen forest. One of these species (*M. antongilensis*) has even been collected about 6.3 m above the forest floor in the moist evergreen forest on the Masoala Peninsula in the northeast. In drier areas of the island, the disappearance of surface waters during the dry season and accompanying low humidity have favored the evolution of burrow- or crevice-dwelling, semiterrestrial species such as *Madagapotamon humberti*.

Despite the wide distribution and great diversity of freshwater crabs on Madagascar, their ecological role in freshwater habitats is still poorly understood. Their large size and abundance indicate a significant biomass that would make them an important component of food webs in aquatic ecosystems, as has been demonstrated in Africa by Dobson (2004) and in the Neotropics by Williner et al. (2014). Malagasy freshwater crabs (like other freshwater crabs around the world) are omnivores that eat vegetable matter, live invertebrates, and even small vertebrates (Ng 1988; Cumberlidge et al. 2009; Wehrtmann et al. 2019). There is a single report of a species of freshwater crab (*Hydrothelphusa vencesi*) eating an adult Malagasy tree frog (Rosa et al. 2014). In continental Africa, freshwater crabs are preyed upon by mongooses, civets, otters, and crocodiles, but on Madagascar many of these large predators are absent, and the predators of crabs include *Cryptoprocta ferox* (Eupleridae), the largest carnivoran on the island (Goodman et al. 1997b). Despite the scarcity of reports, it is clear that freshwater crabs are an important link between aquatic and terrestrial ecosystems throughout their global range (Cumberlidge et al. 2009; Williner et al. 2014).

RESPIRATORY SYSTEMS

When in water, all freshwater crabs ventilate their gills by pumping a stream of water across the nine pairs of gills located in two gill chambers (one on each side of the body) formed by overlapping pieces of carapace wall. The move from fresh water onto land has, among other things, favored the development of freshwater crabs' ability to breathe air as well as water. When these crabs ventilate their gills with water, the respiratory streams enter the gill chambers through ventral inhalant openings and leave via a pair of openings on either side of the third maxillipeds that cover the mouth. When they breathe air, the respiratory streams enter the gill chambers via anterior openings to ventilate their "lungs" (vascularized membranes lining the upper regions of the gill chambers; known as pseudolungs, they function as the crustacean counterpart of lungs) (Cumberlidge 1991, 1999; Cumberlidge and Sternberg 2002). Pseudolungs are rare in continental African freshwater crabs but are found in several semiterrestrial Malagasy taxa, including species of *Madagapotamon*, *Marojejy*, *Malagasya*, and *Foza*.

DEVELOPMENT OF FRESHWATER CRABS

All potamonautid freshwater crabs exhibit direct development whereby their eggs hatch into juvenile crabs (hatchlings) without producing any free-living larval stages (as in marine crabs). Female freshwater crabs lay a few hundred large-diameter eggs at a time, as compared to the tens of thousands of small-diameter eggs produced by marine crabs. Freshwater crab hatchlings remain attached to the female's pleopods in the pleonal (abdominal) brood pouch for several weeks after hatching and are protected by their mother (Cumberlidge 1999). In contrast, marine crab eggs laid in seawater produce larvae that metamorphose through several stages in the plankton, developing into a juvenile crab that then inhabits the ocean floor, where it becomes an adult.

Not all crabs found in Madagascar's fresh waters are potamonautid freshwater crabs. For example, the marine crab *Varuna litterata* (Varunidae) spends extended periods of time in freshwater streams and rivers on the island, but differs from potamonautid freshwater crabs in its production of free-living brachyuran larval stages that must develop in seawater. Specimens of the tree-climbing sesarmid *Labuanium gracilipes* were collected (along with *Malagasya antongilensis*) from water pools in leaf axils of palm trees and in the moist evergreen forest canopy on the Masoala Peninsula (Cumberlidge et al. 2005).

IDENTIFICATION OF ADULT MALE AND FEMALE FRESHWATER CRABS

Adult male and female Malagasy freshwater crabs can be identified by examining the external parts of their reproductive systems. For example, the male pleon (abdomen) is slim and triangular, while the female pleon is broadly oval and shield-shaped; males have two pairs of uniramous, slim abdominal pleopods, while females have four pairs of biramous broad and feathery pleopods. Females bearing conspicuous egg masses or hatchlings under their pleon are obviously mature breeding adults, and so their body size (e.g., carapace width) can be used to infer that males of the same size are also adults.

GENERIC ACCOUNTS

Agora

This genus includes a single species, *Agora goudoti*, which was the first species of freshwater crab to be described from Madagascar (under the name *Thelphusa goudoti*). However, although this species has been recognized as distinct, its generic assignment has been far from stable, and it has been reassigned to eight different genera over the years. Its latest generic assignment to *Agora* is the first to be based not only on its distinctive morphology, but also on molecular data (Cumberlidge et al. 2020). This medium-size species (adult carapace width ~ 40 mm) can be recognized by its carapace proportions; it has the widest, longest, and most vaulted carapace of any species on the island. In addition, its carapace surface is almost completely smooth, its postfrontal crest completely crosses the carapace, and the carapace has two long cervical grooves that curve distally, forming the shape of cow horns. A redescription of this species, a map of its distribution, and identification keys are provided by Cumberlidge et al. (2020).

Boreathelphusa

This genus includes only one species, *Boreathelphusa uglowi*, which is a small-bodied crab with a transversely oval carapace and walking legs that are neither elongate nor shortened (Cumberlidge and Sternberg 2002). Although the mandibular palp of members of *Boreathelphusa* is similar to that of members of *Skelosophusa*, the two genera can be distinguished by characters of the ischium of the third maxilliped and the length of the walking legs (see *Skelosophusa* below). Otherwise the mandibular palp of *Boreathelphsua* (whose terminal segment is not bilobed but has a small, ledge-like anterior process) can be used to distinguish it from *Hydrothelphusa*, *Malagasya*, *Agora*, *Foza*, and *Glabrithelphusa* (whose mandibular palp is distinctly bilobed with a large anterior lobe), and *Madagapotamon* (whose mandibular palp has a simple, not bilobed, terminal segment). *Boreathelphusa* is known from Nosy Be off the northwest coast and from one locality on the mainland in the nearby DIANA Region (Cumberlidge and Sternberg 2002).

Foza

This genus of small-bodied freshwater crabs is characterized by a tube-shaped, first gonopod terminal article; fields of dense setae on the pterygostomial region of the carapace wall and the anterior sternopleonal cavity; conspicuous striae on the subhepatic region of the carapace wall; a single fused molar on the fixed finger (pollex) of the cheliped; and a mandibular palp with a distinctly bilobed terminal segment. The genus includes three species, *Foza raimundi*, *F. ambohitra*, and *F. manonae*, which are all small crabs (adult carapace width ~30 mm). Descriptions of these species, maps of their distributions, and identification keys are provided by Reed and Cumberlidge (2006), Cumberlidge and Meyer (2009), and Meyer et al. (2014). A fourth species (formerly known as *F. goudoti*) was recently reassigned to the genus *Agora* (Cumberlidge et al. 2020).

Glabrithelphusa

This genus includes only one species, *Glabrithelphusa angene*, which is a medium-size crab distinguished by its completely smooth carapace surface, smooth anterolateral margins lacking teeth or granules, and its mandibular palp, which has a distinct but short anterior lobe (smaller than in *Marojejy*, *Hydrothelphusa*, *Foza*, *Malagasya*, and *Agora* but larger than the small ledge of *Skelosophusa* and *Boreathelphusa*). This species is known from only a single locality that was unrecorded by the collectors, so we know nothing about its habitat and distribution, other than that it occurs on Madagascar (Meyer et al. 2014). This genus is not included in the molecular phylogenetic study of Cumberlidge et al. (2020) because no DNA from the species is available.

Hydrothelphusa

This is the most speciose genus of freshwater crabs on Madagascar, and its four species are the largest crabs found on the island (adult carapace width reaches 76 mm). Species of *Hydrothelphusa* are common stream- and river-living crabs, and this widespread genus is found in most parts of the island, except for the arid areas of the southwest. A detailed account of the species in this genus, along with distribution maps and identification keys to the species, are provided by Cumberlidge and Sternberg (2002) and Cumberlidge et al. (2007).

Hydrothelphusa agilis is a large, fairly common species, found in central Madagascar, whose unique characteristics make it easy to identify. The unusual frontal region of the carapace is horizontal, deeply indented, and has a toothed margin. The exorbital and epibranchial teeth consist of large pointed spines, and the suborbital margin is also strikingly toothed (Cumberlidge and Sternberg 2002).

Hydrothelphusa madagascariensis is one of the largest Malagasy freshwater crabs and is found in streams, rivers, lakes, and ponds throughout Madagascar, especially in the eastern area. This species can be easily distinguished by its carapace frontal region, which is only slightly deflexed but not horizontal, with a granulated (not toothed) margin; cheliped ischium and merus (which are heavily granulated); and a heavily granulated subhepatic region of the carapace wall (Cumberlidge and Sternberg 2002).

Hydrothelphusa bombetokensis is a large, widely distributed species found in most regions of the island. This species is recognized by its completely smooth carapace surface, large pointed exorbital and epibranchial teeth, and major cheliped, which has a large molariform cluster of three or four fused teeth on the immovable finger (pollex) (Cumberlidge and Sternberg 2002).

Hydrothelphusa vencesi is a large purple-brown crab from the Atsimo-Atsinanana Region, in the Mananara River basin that drains the mountainous forested region of the southeast, specifically the Vevembe Forest near Vondrozo. Individuals have conspicuous fields of large, beige-colored granules on the suborbital and pterygostomial regions of the carapace wall, and a distinctive, cone-shaped terminal article of the first gonopod, which has a broad, diamond-shaped dorsal membrane at the segment junction (Cumberlidge et al. 2007).

Madagapotamon

This genus includes only one species, *Madagapotamon humberti*, which is one of the most distinctive species of all Malagasy freshwater crabs. This yellowish-orange, long-legged species lives in rock crevices in caves and stands apart from all other freshwater crabs on the island (Figure 9.15). *Madagapotamon* is closest in appearance to *Malagasya*, which also has a small adult body size, a heart-shaped carapace, and elongate, slender walking legs. The two genera can be distinguished by the mandibular palp (simple in *Madagapotamon* and bilobed in *Malagasya*), and by the exopod of the third maxilliped (which lacks a flagellum in *Madagapotamon* but has a long flagellum in *Malagasya*). *Madagapotamon humberti* is a semiterrestrial, air-breathing, ecological specialist found in limestone areas in extreme northern Madagascar. During the rainy season, these crabs are found in dry deciduous forests, where they climb trees; in the dry season, if seen at all, they can be found crawling on limestone karst, where they live in the deep fissures and sinkholes (Vuillemin 1970; Cumberlidge and Sternberg 2002; Meyer et al. 2014; Cumberlidge et al. 2017, 2018).

Malagasya

This genus of small-bodied freshwater crab is characterized by a heart-shaped carapace, elongate walking legs, and a mandibular palp with a distinctly bilobed terminal segment. The genus includes three species (*Malagasya antongilensis*, *M. goodmani*, and *M. elvisshoes*), which all climb trees to reach water pools that collect in the leaf axils of *Pandanus* species. The carapace of *Malagasya* is elongate, vaulted, and widened, and has frontal and posterior margins that are notably narrow. *Malagasya antongilensis* can be distinguished from *M. goodmani* and *M. elvisshoes*; the latter two species have a band of dense, suede-like setae on the dactyli of all their walking legs that is missing in *M. antongilensis*. Each species has a distinctive geographic distribution, and their ranges do not overlap. *Malagasya antongilensis* is the most widespread and is known from northern and eastern Madagascar; *M. goodmani* is known from two regions (Analanjirofo and SAVA); *M. elvisshoes* is known only from the SAVA Region (Cumberlidge et al. 2000, 2020). Descriptions of *M. antongilensis* and *M. goodmani*, maps of their distributions, and identification keys are provided by Cumberlidge and Sternberg (2002), and the same information for *M. elvisshoes* is provided by Cumberlidge et al. (2020).

Marojejy

This genus includes only one species, *Marojejy longimerus*, a small-bodied, long-legged crab with a transversely oval carapace. Its unique characteristics include tapering eyestalks with very reduced corneas and a major cheliped merus that is extremely elongate (Cumberlidge et al. 2002; Cumberlidge and Sternberg 2002). *Marojejy* is known only from the upper elevations of the Marojejy Massif. A description of *M. longimerus*, a map of its distribution, and identification keys are provided by Cumberlidge et al. (2002) and by Cumberlidge and Sternberg (2002).

Skelosophusa

Skelosophusa is a genus of small-bodied, long-legged crabs with a transversely oval carapace that includes three species, *S. gollhardi*, *S. prolixa*, and *S. eumeces*, all found in northern Madagascar (Bott 1965; Ng and Takeda 1994; Cumberlidge and Sternberg 2002). At first sight, *Skelosophusa* is similar to *Hydrothelphusa*, *Boreathelphusa*, and *Marojejy*, but it can be distinguished from all of these by its distinctive mandibular palp (which has a small, ledge-like anterior process at the base of the terminal segment, unlike a well-developed anterior lobe in the other genera). Only one other genus (*Boreathelphusa*) has a mandibular palp that is similar to that of *Skelosophusa*, but the two genera can be distinguished as follows: *Skelosophusa* has a deep vertical sulcus on the ischium of the third maxilliped and slender, elongate walking legs, whereas the ischium of the third maxilliped of *Boreathelphusa* is smooth, and its walking legs are neither slim nor elongate. Descriptions of the species of *Skelosophusa*, maps of their distribution, and identification keys are provided by Ng and Takeda (1994) and Cumberlidge and Sternberg (2002).

CONSERVATION

The freshwater crab fauna in Madagascar is increasingly threatened by habitat disturbance, extreme fragmentation, poor land-use practice, introduced and invasive species, and overharvesting. Of the 18 species of freshwater crabs on Madagascar, the most recent extinction threat assessments based on the International Union for Conservation of Nature's (IUCN) Red List of Threatened Species (IUCN 2020) are as follows: one species (*Boreathelphusa uglowi*) is Endangered; nine are Least Concern and are therefore not currently threatened; seven are Data Deficient owing to a lack of basic information; and one (*Malagasya elvisshoes*) is newly described, and its conservation status has not yet been evaluated (Not Evaluated) (Table 9.11; Cumberlidge et al. 2017, 2018).

Boreathelphusa uglowi is the only species of Malagasy freshwater crab that is threatened with extinction, and its risk is worsening. Cumberlidge et al. (2017) uplisted this species from Vulnerable (Cumberlidge 2016a; Cumberlidge et al. 2009) to Endangered because of its restricted occurrence in just two locations (with an area substantially less than 5000 km^2) and the continuing decline in the extent and quality of its habitat.

On a more positive note, half of the Malagasy freshwater crab fauna (nine out of 18 species) is assessed as Least Concern. It is also encouraging that *Madagapotamon humberti* was downlisted from Vulnerable (Cumberlidge 2016b; Cumberlidge et al. 2009) to Least Concern (Cumberlidge et al. 2017, 2018), owing to the discovery of new populations at several localities in the far north and within protected areas (Ankarana, Montagne des Français, Oronjia, and Analamerana) (Cumberlidge et al. 2015).

The seven Data Deficient species (*Malagasya goodmani*, *Marojejy longimerus*, *Skelosophusa gollhardi*, *S. prolixa*, *S. eumeces*, *Foza manonae*, and *Glabrithelphusa angene*) lack sufficient information about their habitat, distributional range, population trends, and threats for an extinction risk assessment to be carried out (Meyer et al. 2014; Cumberlidge et al. 2015, 2017, 2018).

The remarkable diversity, richness, endemism, and phylogenetic uniqueness of Madagascar's freshwater crab fauna underlines the need to conserve these highly endemic decapods. Despite the apparent stability of Madagascar's freshwater crabs as a whole, these crustaceans inhabit freshwater habitats and associated land, especially in moist evergreen forests; these are among the most threatened ecosystems of all because they are especially vulnerable to rapid anthropogenic alterations. This means that a large proportion of the habitat of freshwater crabs (which includes most of the island's freshwater ecosystems) is threatened by the activities of a rapidly growing human population (Cumberlidge et al. 2018). The immediate nature of the potential threats to a large majority of the freshwater species found on Madagascar (including its freshwater crabs) make the protection of these animals for future generations a matter of the highest priority.

Subject editors: Brian L. Fisher and Steven M. Goodman

DIPLOPODA, MILLIPEDES, *MENAVETRAKA, ANKODAVITRA, ANKODIAVITRY, MAROTANANA, SAKOLAVITSY*

T. Wesener and H. Enghoff

Millipedes (Diplopoda) are a class of terrestrial arthropods with more than 11,000 described species. They occur in all non-Arctic regions but are particularly diverse in the tropics. With some tropical species growing to over 30 cm in length, they are in many places among the most conspicuous invertebrates. The vast majority of millipede species feed on leaf litter and other types of decaying plant material, but some attack living plants and may occasionally be significant pests on a variety of crops (e.g., potatoes, peanuts, cotton). In spite of the name, no known millipede has a thousand legs—the current record is 750. However, when newly hatched from the egg, most millipedes have only six legs; during their postembryonic growth, they add segments and legs, sometimes reaching a finite number, sometimes adding segments and legs indefinitely. Most millipedes are protected against predators by a heavy calcified cuticle and an ability to roll themselves into a ball (pill millipedes) or a spiral. Furthermore, many millipedes have a series of defensive glands from which they secrete substances like benzoquinones or hydrogen cyanide.

Like many other groups of living organisms, the millipedes are represented on Madagascar by a highly distinct and unbalanced assemblage of species. Only 20 out of approximately 120 known families of millipedes are represented on the island; five of these families (each with just one or two species recorded) are represented only by obviously introduced species, and a further seven families (also with one or two species each) have an uncertain native status. Therefore, only eight families of millipedes are currently recorded from Madagascar with indisputably indigenous species. In total, 266 species of millipedes are currently recognized from the island, including 227 endemics and 12 introduced tropical "tramp" species (Table 9.12). The described millipede fauna of Madagascar has thus grown by more than 60% since the precursor version of this contribution and checklist (Enghoff 2003).

Since Saussure and Zehntner's monumental monograph (1897, 1902), work on Malagasy millipedes has been focused mainly on three orders: Sphaerotheriida (Jeekel 1999a; Wesener and Wägele 2008; Wesener 2009; Moritz and Wesener 2017), Chordeumatida (Mauriès 1994, 1997), and Spirobolida (Jeekel 1971; Wesener et al. 2008, 2009a; Wesener and Enghoff 2009, Wesener et al. 2011). Knowledge of the large family Spirostreptidae was summarized by Krabbe (1982; see also Jeekel 1999c), but spirostreptids of Madagascar remain very poorly known although many species are large.

The rudimentary level of knowledge of the island's millipedes is perhaps best illustrated by the fact that as late as 1994, Mauriès described 13 species belonging to the new genus *Betscheuma*, the first Afrotropical representatives of an entire order of millipedes (Chordeumatida; see also Mauriès 1997), and in 2009, Wesener et al. (2009a) described 12 new genera of Spirobolida, in part including gigantic species, as well as 31 new species of Sphaerotheriida (Wesener 2009).

The present contribution adds another three families (Siphonophoridae, Siphonorhinidae, Spirobolellidae) not included in Enghoff's 2003 checklist—although it is not certain whether the species in the first two families are native to the island—as well as an additional family with a definitely introduced species (Cambalopsidae).

Several recent collections of Malagasy millipedes examined by the authors have revealed a large number of undescribed genera and species. Several of the undescribed, probably indigenous, species

TABLE 9.12. Number of endemic and nonendemic (including dubious) Malagasy millipede species

FAMILY	THE NUMBER OF SPECIES IN THE THREE MOST-THREATENED IUCN RED LIST CATEGORIES	INDIGENOUS TO MADAGASCAR	NUMBER OF KNOWN SPECIES IN MADAGASCAR	
			ENDEMIC	NONENDEMIC
Synxenidae	NE	Yes	–	1
Polyxenidae	NE	Yes	5	2
Lophoproctidae	NE	No	–	1
Arthrosphaeridae	19	Yes	84	–
Siphonotidae	NE	?	–	1
Siphonophoridae	NE	?	–	–
Siphonorhinidae	NE	?	–	–
Pygmaesomatidae	NE	Yes	18	–
Paradoxosomatidae	NE	No	–	2
Haplodesmidae	NE	?	–	1
Pyrgodesmidae	NE	No	–	1
Dalodesmidae	NE	Yes	7	–
Rhinocricidae	NE	?	–	1
Pachybolidae	25	Yes	57	3
Spirobolellidae	3	Yes	11	–
Pseudospirobolellidae	NE	No	–	1
Harpagophoridae	NE	?	–	1
Cambalopsidae	NE	No	–	1
Iulomorphidae	NE	?	–	1
Spirostreptidae	NE	Yes	45	21
Totals			227	38

Notes: Red List categories based on IUCN (2020). NE, Not Evaluated; ?, uncertain if indigenous to Madagascar.

were reported for the Colobognatha orders Polyzoniida (Wesener 2014a) and Siphonophorida (Wesener 2014b), but none has been named so far. Also, many described species are in dire need of revision. Extensive synonymy is to be expected among the nominal species of the large genus *Sechelleptus*, but no doubt the resulting loss of valid species will be more than balanced by new discoveries. Several Malagasy spirostreptid species are currently assigned to the nominal genus *Spirostreptus*, but since the true identity of *Spirostreptus* was clarified by Hoffman et al. (2001), these species are "orphaned"—that is, they cannot be assigned to a valid genus for the time being.

The scope of this contribution is to provide an up-to-date checklist of the millipedes of Madagascar, excluding islands and archipelagoes, such as the Seychelles (cf. Mauriès 1980; Golovatch and Korsós 1992), Mauritius (cf. Mauriès and Geoffroy 1999), the Comoros (cf. VandenSpiegel and Golovatch 2007), and La Réunion.

The information provided for each species is limited to the valid name; synonyms under which the species has been recorded in the literature dealing with Malagasy millipedes; Malagasy localities from which the species has been recorded, with references (earlier original papers are not cited if review references exist); the total distribution or an indication that the species is endemic to Madagascar; and, in some cases, miscellaneous notes. As 145 species of millipedes of the orders Sphaerotheriida and Spirobolida were recently evaluated for the International Union for Conservation of Nature's (IUCN) Red List (IUCN 2020), the Red List categories have also been added.

Quite a number of species are known only from the original description and have not been revised. Such species are indicated with quotation marks around the generic name. In many cases, a revision of these species may be impossible because the type specimen is juvenile or female. No major attempt has been made to study additional material, but a few records based on material in the Natural History Museum of Denmark and the Museum of Zoology and Natural History (La Specola), in Florence, Italy, are given, and an unpublished record kindly supplied by the late Dr. Richard Hoffman is also included.

COMPOSITION AND RELATIONSHIPS OF THE MALAGASY MILLIPEDE FAUNA

As is evident from the checklist of the known Malagasy millipede fauna (Table 9.13), the degree of endemism is very high indeed at the species level—of 266 species on the list, 227 are marked as endemic. Of the remaining 37 species, many are *species inquirendae* (mostly species originally described in the genus *Spirostreptus*). Most of the well-known, nonendemic species are very widespread and obviously synanthropic. These include *Orthomorpha coarctata*, *Oxidus gracilis*, *Dilophops bullatus*, *Rhinotus purpureus*, *Leptogoniulus sorornus*, *Trigoniulus corallinus*, and *Glyphiulus granulatus*. Twenty-one genera are endemic, and three are near-endemic (*Dactylobolus*, *Charactopygus*, and *Sechelleptus*).

The 20 millipede families represented in the Malagasy fauna are listed in Table 9.12, with an indication of their indigenousness and the number of known endemic and nonendemic species (including *species inquirendae*). In comparison with the eight families that are unquestionably native to Madagascar, the continental Afrotropical region, according to Hoffman (1980 [1979]), holds indigenous representatives of 23 families. Notable absences from the Malagasy fauna are the species-rich, endemic Afrotropical families Oxydesmidae, Gomphodesmidae, and Odontopygidae; the large, endemic Afrotropical subfamily Prepodesminae (family Chelodesmidae); as well as the very large, nearly cosmopolitan families Paradoxosomatidae, Trichopolydesmidae, and Pyrgodesmidae, which are represented only by a few well-known "tramp" species introduced to Madagascar. Members of the indigenous order Polydesmida, generally the most diverse group of millipedes (e.g., Hilgert et al. 2019, for Indonesia), occur very rarely on Madagascar, in terms of species and the range of habitats in which they occur.

For a proper elucidation of geographic relationships of the endemic Malagasy millipedes, one would need phylogenetic analysis, but such information is wanting, except for the Sphaerotheriida and two genera of Spirobolida. For the remaining groups, little more than the existing classification is therefore available for a preliminary estimate:

- The group taxonomy of Sphaerotheriida (giant pill-millipedes) was worked out by Jeekel (1974). Morphological and molecular phylogenies were constructed by Wesener and VandenSpiegel (2009) and Wesener et al. (2010a), respectively. The Malagasy genera were assigned to the family Arthrosphaeridae, together with the endemic Indian subcontinent genus *Arthrosphaera* (Wesener 2016). One of the three genera from Madagascar, *Sphaeromimus*, is more closely related to the Indian *Arthrosphaera* than to the other two genera from Madagascar, *Zoosphaerium* and *Microsphaerotherium* (Wesener et al. 2014). This suggests that the presence of Arthrosphaeridae in India is a result of colonization from Madagascar, with subsequent vicariance between *Sphaeromimus* and *Arthrosphaera*, but no molecular clock data are available, and thus any hypothesis definitely needs further substantiation.
- Pygmaesomatidae contains the endemic Malagasy genus *Betscheuma* and only one other genus, *Hendesonula* (= *Pygmaeosoma*), from the Indian subcontinent (Mauriès 1994; Enghoff et al. 2015).
- Dalodesmidae is a typical Gondwanan taxon, known from Australia, New Zealand, Madagascar, southern Africa, and southern South America. Hoffman (1974) noted that the endemic Malagasy genus *Dalodesmus* resembles some species from Chile, but no definite statement of relationship was made.
- Pachybolidae is a large family that is most diverse on Madagascar, followed by the continental parts of the Afrotropical and the Oriental regions (there are two Neotropical genera, however). Relationships within the family are largely unresolved. One Malagasy genus, *Madabolus*, clearly belongs to the tribe Pachybolini and is thus closely related to continental African genera (Wesener et al. 2008). One of the endemic Malagasy genera, *Spiromimus*, has been placed in a separate subfamily together with the Indian genus *Xenobolus*, but the justification for this is feeble at best (Wesener and Enghoff 2009).
- Spirobolellidae consists of mainly small species distributed in Australia, Oceania, Indonesia, Southeast Asia, India, and Madagascar (Enghoff et al. 2015). The family was only recently recorded from Madagascar with a single genus (*Hylekobolus*) and several species (Wesener et al. 2009a). The internal relationships of the family are unresolved (Pitz and Sierwald 2010; Enghoff et al. 2015).

TABLE 9.13. **Checklist of the millipedes of Madagascar with information on synonyms and geographic range**

SCIENTIFIC NAMES	MADAGASCAR RECORDS	IUCN STATUS	GENERAL DISTRIBUTION/NOTES
ORDER POLYXENIDA			
Family Synxenidae			
Phryssonotus capensis (Silvestri, 1923)	Tongobory (Marquet and Condé 1950); between Ambarimanitra and Andranovory (Marquet and Condé 1950)	–	Also South Africa (Marquet and Condé 1950)
Family Polyxenidae			
Saroxenus cf. *alluaudi* Brolemann, 1920	Fenoarivo-Atsinanana (Condé and Jacquemin 1962)	–	Also Rodriguez and La Réunion, *alluaudi* s.s.: east Africa (Condé and Jacquemin 1962)
Unixenus broelemanni (Condé & Jacquemin, 1962)	Fanovana	–	Endemic
Mauritixenus sakalavus (Marquet & Condé, 1950)	Nosy Mamoka (Ampasindava Bay) (Marquet and Condé 1950)	–	Endemic
Monographis sp.	Ambila-Lemaitso (Condé and Jacquemin 1962)	–	Probably an undescribed species (Condé and Jacquemin 1962)
Silvestrius brevipalpus Condé & Jacquemin, 1962	Ambila-Lemaitso (Condé and Jacquemin 1962)	–	Endemic
Pauropsxenus brachyartema silvestrii Marquet & Condé, 1950	Nosy Be, Hellville (Marquet and Condé 1950); Mahajanga (Condé and Jacquemin 1962)	–	Also east Africa, ssp. *silvestrii* endemic (Marquet and Condé 1950)
Propolyxenus crassisetosus Marquet & Condé, 1950	Bekily (Marquet and Condé 1950)	–	Endemic
Family Lophoproctidae			
Lophoturus madecassus (Marquet & Condé, 1950)	Toliara (Marquet and Condé 1950)	–	Circumtropical (Nguyen Duy-Jacquemin 1996)
ORDER SPHAEROTHERIIDA			
Family Arthrosphaeridae			
Microsphaerotherium anjozorobe Wesener, 2009	Andranomay (Anjozorobe) (Wesener 2009)	CR	Endemic
M. ivohibiense Wesener & VandenSpiegel, 2007	Ivohibe (Wesener and VandenSpiegel 2007)	LC	Endemic
Zoosphaerium actaeon (White, 1859)	Tolagnaro–Fianarantsoa–Antananarivo (Jeekel 1999a)	DD	Endemic
Z. alluaudi (Saussure & Zehntner, 1902)	Tolagnaro (Jeekel 1999a); Ambatotsirongorongo Mountain and Petriky (Wesener and Wägele 2007).	CR	Endemic
Z. album Wesener, 2009	Forêt de Vohibasia (Wesener 2009)	NT	Endemic
Z. amabile Wesener, 2009	Montagne d'Akirindro (Wesener 2009; Wesener et al. 2010b)	NT	Endemic
Z. ambrense Wesener, 2009	Montagne d'Ambre (Wesener 2009; Wesener et al. 2010b)	LC	Endemic
Z. analavelona Wesener, 2009	Forêt d'Analavelona (Wesener 2009)	NT	Endemic

(continued overleaf)

TABLE 9.13. ***continued***

SCIENTIFIC NAMES	MADAGASCAR RECORDS	IUCN STATUS	GENERAL DISTRIBUTION/NOTES
Z. anale (Saussure & Zehntner, 1897)	SW coast (Wesener and Wägele 2008)	DD	Endemic
Z. anomalum (Saussure & Zehntner, 1902)	Andohahela, Isaka-Ivondro (Wesener and Wägele 2008)	DD	Endemic
Z. arborealis Wesener & Sierwald, 2005	Mandena, Sainte Luce, Manantantely, Andringitra (Wesener and Sierwald 2005a; Wesener and Wägele 2007)	EN	Endemic
Z. aureum Wesener, 2009	Montagne d'Ambre (Wesener 2009)	LC	Endemic
Z. bambusoides Wesener & Bespalova, 2010	Betampona (Wesener et al. 2010b)	NT	Endemic
Z. bartolozzii Anilkumar & Wesener, 2020	Along the road between Ambositra and Fianarantsoa (Wesener and Anilkumar 2020)	–	Endemic
Z. bemanevika Sagorny & Wesener, 2017	Bemanevika (Sagorny and Wesener 2017)	–	Endemic
Z. bilobum Wesener, 2009	Forêt de Vohibasia (Wesener 2009)	NT	Endemic
Z. blandum (Saussure & Zehntner, 1902) [syn. *Z. stridulator* (Saussure & Zehntner, 1902)]	Andohahela, Col du Sakavalana–Andrahomana–Toliara (Wesener and Wägele 2008)	LC	Endemic
Z. broelemanni Wesener, 2009	Antananarivo (Wesener 2009)	DD	Endemic
Z. campanulatum (Saussure & Zehntner, 1897)	W coast (Wesener and Wägele 2008)	DD	Endemic
Z. coquerelianum (Saussure & Zehntner, 1897) [syn. *Heligmasoma errans* Chamberlin, 1921; *Z. amittum* Chamberlin, 1921]	"Madagascar" (Wesener and Wägele 2008)	DD	Endemic
Z. corystoides Wesener, 2009	Montagne d'Ambre (Wesener 2009)	LC	Endemic
Z. crassum (Butler, 1878)	Fianarantsoa (Jeekel 1999a)	DD	Endemic
Z. darthvaderi Wesener & Bespalova, 2010)	Ambohitantely (Wesener et al. 2010b)	CR	Endemic
Z. denticulatum Wesener, 2009	Andrombovato, Tatamaly River (Wesener 2009)	NT	Endemic
Z. discolor Wesener, 2009	Tsingy de Bemaraha, Forêt de Kirindy CNFEREF (Wesener 2009)	LC	Endemic
Z. elegans (Lenz, 1880)	Nosy Be (Jeekel 1999a)	DD	Endemic
Z. endemicum Wesener, 2009	Forêt d'Analavelona (Wesener 2009)	NT	Endemic
Z. fisheri Wesener, 2009	Mandraka (Wesener 2009)	NT	Endemic
Z. fraternarium Jeekel, 1999 [syn. *Sphaerotherium fraternum* Saussure & Zehntner, 1897, nom. praeocc.]	Forêt de l'Ikongo (Fort Carnot) (Wesener and Wägele 2008)	DD	Endemic
Z. glabrum (Butler, 1873)	"Madagascar" (Jeekel 1999a)	DD	Endemic
Z. haackeri Wesener, 2009	Cap Sainte Marie, Lavanono Beach, Mahafaly Plateau (Wesener 2009)	NT	Endemic
Z. heleios Wesener & Bespalova, 2010	Torotorofotsy (Wesener et al. 2010b)	CR	Endemic
Z. hippocastanum (Gervais, 1847)	Nosy Be (Wesener and Wägele 2008)	DD	Endemic
Z. ignotum Wesener, 2009	"Waterfalls of the Uamotna" (Wesener 2009)	DD	Endemic

SCIENTIFIC NAMES	MADAGASCAR RECORDS	IUCN STATUS	GENERAL DISTRIBUTION/NOTES
Z. immane (Karsch, 1881)	"Madagascar"–Nosy Be (Jeekel 1999a)	DD	Endemic
Z. isalo Wesener, 2009	Isalo (Wesener 2009)	NT	Endemic
Z. lambertoni (Brolemann, 1922)	Antananarivo (Jeekel 1999a)	DD	Endemic
Z. lamprinum (Butler, 1878)	Fianarantsoa (Jeekel 1999a)	DD	Endemic
Z. latum (Butler, 1872)	North (Jeekel 1999a)	DD	Endemic
Z. libidinosum (Saussure & Zehntner, 1897)	Toliara, Forêt d'Elakilaka, Ambovombe, Pays Mahafaly, Beloka, Andohahela, Ranohira-Isalo, Massif de l'Angona, Forêt de Vohimena, Forêt des Mikea, Forêt des Milua, Zombitse, Andrahomana, Faux Cap, Cap Sainte Marie, Antafoky, Forêt de Mahavelo, Forêt de Mité (Wesener and Wägele 2008)	LC	Endemic
Z. mangabense Wesener, 2020	Nosy Mangabe, Marojejy (Wesener and Anilkumar 2020)	–	Endemic
Z. micropiligerum Wesener, 2009	Andohahela: Col du Sedro, NW Eminiminy (Wesener 2009)	LC	Endemic
Z. minutus Sagorny & Wesener, 2017	Bemanevika (Sagorny and Wesener 2017)	–	Endemic
Z. mitoho Wesener, 2009	PN de Tsimanampesotse: Mitoho Cave (Wesener 2009)	NT	Endemic
Z. muscorum Wesener & Bespalova, 2010	Anjanaharibe-Sud (Wesener et al. 2010b)	NT	Endemic
Z. neptunus (Butler, 1872) [syn. *Z. digitale* (Saussure & Zehntner, 1897); *Z. pygidiale* (Saussure & Zehntner, 1897)]	Antananarivo, Moramanga, "Soanivrana," Fanovana, Manambato, Analamazaotra, Anderorante, Zahamena, Forêt de Betaolana, Marojejy, Manantenina (Wesener and Wägele 2008); Andasibe (Wesener and Schütte 2010); Betampona, Makira Plateau (Wesener et al. 2010b)	LC	Endemic
Z. piligerum (Saussure & Zehntner, 1897)	Andohahela, Andranomay (Wesener and Wägele 2008)	CR	Endemic
Z. platylabum (Saussure & Zehntner, 1897)	Antananarivo–Fianarantsoa (Jeekel 1999a); Andasibe (Wesener and Wägele 2008; Wesener et al. 2010b)	LC	Endemic
Z. priapus (Saussure & Zehntner, 1897)	Forêt d'Orangea (Wesener and Wägele 2008)	CR	Endemic
Z. pseudoblandum Wesener, 2009	Andohahela: Ebosika, Forêt Malio; Andrahomana (Wesener 2009)	NT	Endemic
Z. pseudopiligerum Wesener, 2009	Andohahela, Enakara (Wesener 2009)	LC	Endemic
Z. pseudoplatylabum Wesener, 2009	Forêt de Vinatelo, Andringitra (Wesener 2009); Ivohibe (Wesener et al. 2010b)	NT	Endemic
Z. pseudopriapus Wesener, 2009	Forêt de Bekaraoka (Wesener 2009); Forêt de Binara (Wesener et al. 2010b)	VU	Endemic
Z. pulchellum Wesener, 2009	Andohahela, 1500 m (Wesener 2009)	LC	Endemic
Z. reflexum (Brölemann, 1922)	Antananarivo? (Wesener and Wägele 2008)	DD	Endemic
Z. reticulatum (Butler, 1878)	"Madagascar" (Jeekel 1999a)	DD	Endemic

(continued overleaf)

TABLE 9.13. ***continued***

SCIENTIFIC NAMES	MADAGASCAR RECORDS	IUCN STATUS	GENERAL DISTRIBUTION/NOTES
Z. sakananum (Attems, 1910)	Sakana (Wesener and Wägele 2008)	DD	Endemic
Z. smaragdinum Wesener, 2009	Marojejy, 1875 m (Wesener 2009)	NT	Endemic
Z. solitarium Wesener, 2009	Montagne des Français (Wesener 2009)	EN	Endemic
Z. stigmaticum (Butler, 1873)	"Madagascar" (Jeekel 1999a)	DD	Endemic
Z. subreflexum Jeekel, 1999	Andringitra, 2000 m (Jeekel 1999a)	NT	Endemic
Z. tainkintana Wesener, 2009	Forêt de Binara, Forêt d'Antsahabe (Wesener 2009)	EN	Endemic
Z. taitii Anilkumar & Wesener, 2020	Zombitse (Wesener and Anilkumar 2020)	–	Endemic
Z. tampolo Wesener, 2009	Tampolo (Wesener 2009; Wesener et al. 2010b)	CR	Endemic
Z. testaceum (Olivier, 1792)	(Jeekel 1999a)	DD	Endemic
Z. tigrioculatum Wesener & Bespalova, 2010	Andringitra, Plateau d'Andohariana (Wesener et al. 2010b)	LC	Endemic
Z. trichordum Wesener, 2009	Forêt d'Ampondrabe, Forêt de Bekaraoka (Wesener 2009)	VU	Endemic
Z. tsingy Wesener, 2009	Tsingy de Bemaraha, Forêt de Tsimembo (Wesener 2009)	NT	Endemic
Z. villosum Wesener & Sierwald, 2005	Forêt de Tsianovoha (Wesenner and Wägele 2008); Betampona, Tampolo (Wesener et al. 2010b)	LC	Endemic
Z. viridissimum Wesener, 2009	Marojejy (Wesener 2009; Wesener et al. 2010b)	NT	Endemic
Z. voeltzkowianum (Saussure & Zehntner, 1897) [syn. *Z. globulus* (Saussure & Zehntner, 1902); *Z. imbecillum* (Saussure & Zehntner, 1897); *Sphaerotherium v.*]	Nosy Be, Lokobe (Wesener and Wägele 2008)	VU	Endemic
Z. xerophilum Wesener, 2009	Réserve Spéciale d'Ambre (Wesener et al. 2010b)	CR	Endemic
Sphaeromimus andohahela Wesener, 2014	Andohahela (Wesener et al. 2014)	NT	Endemic
S. andrahomana Wesener, 2014	Grotte d'Andrahomana (Wesener et al. 2014)	CR	Endemic
S. inexpectatus Wesener & Sierwald, 2005	Mandena (Wesener and Sierwald 2005b); Andohahela: Enato (Wesener and Wägele 2007)	EN	Endemic
S. ivohibe Wesener, 2014	Ivohibe (Wesener et al. 2014)	LC	Endemic
S. kalambatritra Moritz & Wesener, 2017	Kalambatritra (Moritz and Wesener, 2017)	–	Endemic
S. lavasoa Wesener, 2014	Ambatotsirongorongo: Petit Lavasoa and Grande Lavasoa (Wesener et al. 2014)	CR	Endemic
S. midongy Moritz & Wesener, 2017	PN Befotaka-Midongy du Sud (Moritz and Wesener 2017)	–	Endemic
S. musicus (Saussure & Zehntner, 1897)	Andohahela, Forêt d'Analavelona, Berenty (Wesener and Sierwald 2005b); Grotte d'Andrahomana, Bords du Fiheranana, Fort Dauphin (Wesener et al. 2014)	LC	Endemic
S. sainteluci Wesener, 2014	Sainte Luce (Wesener et al. 2014)	CR	Endemic

SCIENTIFIC NAMES	MADAGASCAR RECORDS	IUCN STATUS	GENERAL DISTRIBUTION/NOTES
S. splendidus Wesener & Sierwald, 2005	Sainte Luce (Wesener and Sierwald 2005b; Wesener et al. 2014)	CR	Endemic
S. titanus Wesener, 2014	Forêt de Manombo (Wesener et al. 2014)	CR	Endemic
S. vatovavy Wesener, 2014	Forêt de Tsianovoha (Fort Carnot) (Wesener et al. 2014)	DD	Endemic
ORDER POLYZONIIDA			
Family Siphonotidae			
Rhinotus purpureus (Pocock, 1893) [syn. *Rhinotus acuticonus* (Attems, 1910) "*Polyzonium*" *malagassum* Saussure & Zehntner, 1902]	Toamasina, Ile aux Prunes (Attems 1910); Nosy Be (Saussure and Zehntner 1902; Attems 1951); widespread in all moist evergreen forests (Wesener 2014a)	–	Introduced, synanthropic
ORDER CHORDEUMATIDA			
Family Pygmaesomatidae			
Betscheuma andringitrae Mauriès, 1994	Province Fianarantsoa: Massif d'Andringitra (Mauriès 1994); Province Toliara, Bemangidy, ~100 km N Tolagnaro (Mauriès 1997, aff. *andringitrae*)	–	Endemic
B. ankaratrae Mauriès, 1994	Province Antananarivo: Massif d'Ankaratra (Mauriès 1994); Tampoketsa d'Ankazobe (Mauriès 1994, aff. *ankaratrae*); Col du Manontongana (Mauriès 1997)	–	Endemic
B. anosyense Mauriès, 1994	Province Toliara, Anosyenne Mountains, northern massif (Mauriès 1994)	–	Endemic
B. bongolavae Mauriès, 1994	Province Antananarivo, W Tsiroanomandidy (Mauriès 1994)	–	Endemic
B. cornutum Mauriès, 1994	Massif de l'Ankaratra? (Mauriès 1994)	–	Endemic
B. franzi Mauriès, 1997	Province Toamasina: Maroantsetra Bay, Nosy Mangabe; environs of "Nanbasana" (Mauriès 1997)	–	Endemic
B. gruberi Mauriès, 1997	Province Toliara, Col du Manangotry (Mauriès 1997)	–	Endemic
B. itremoense Mauriès, 1994	Province Fianarantsoa, Massif de l'Itremo (Mauriès 1994)	–	Endemic
B. llinaresi Mauriès, 1994	Province Antananarivo, Massif d'Ankaratra; Province Toamasina/Province Antananarivo, La Mandraka (Mauriès 1994)	–	Endemic
B. majus Mauriès, 1994	Province Antananarivo, Massif d'Ankaratra (Mauriès 1994)	–	Endemic
B. marojezyae Mauriès, 1994	Province Antsiranana, Massif du Marojejy (Mauriès 1994)	–	Endemic
B. minutum Mauriès, 1997	Province Antsiranana, environs of "Antsimanara and of Atalongo" (Mauriès 1997)	–	Endemic
B. nigriantennae Mauriès, 1994	Province Antsiranana, Massif du Marojejy (Mauriès 1994)	–	Endemic

(continued overleaf)

TABLE 9.13. ***continued***

SCIENTIFIC NAMES	MADAGASCAR RECORDS	IUCN STATUS	GENERAL DISTRIBUTION/NOTES
B. orbatum Mauriès, 1994	Province Fianarantsoa, Massif d'Andringitra (Mauriès 1994)	–	Endemic
B. peranosyense Mauriès, 1997	Province Toliara, Bemangidy (Mauriès 1997)	–	Endemic
B. perinetense Mauriès, 1994	Province Toamasina: Périnet (Mauriès 1994); Analamazaotra Forest Station (Mauriès 1997)	–	Endemic
B. peyrierasi Mauriès, 1994	Province Antananarivo, Massif d'Ankaratra (Mauriès 1994)	–	Endemic
B. septentrionale Mauriès, 1997	Province Antsiranana: Montagne d'Ambre, Montagne du Petit-Lac (Mauriès 1997)	–	Endemic
ORDER POLYDESMIDA			
Family Paradoxosomatidae			
Chondromorpha xanthotricha (Attems, 1898)	Andasibe (Wesener and Anilkumar 2020)	–	Introduced, common tropical tramp (Likhitrakarn et al. 2017)
Orthomorpha coarctata (Saussure, 1860)	Nosy Be–Sakatia Island (Saussure and Zehntner 1902); Toamasina–Ile aux Prunes (Attems 1910)	–	Pantropical, anthropochorous
Oxidus gracilis (C.L. Koch, 1847)	Province Fianarantsoa: E coast, Fenoarivo-Atsinanana, Lake Alaotra, Ile Sainte Marie (Attems 1910); Province Toamasina: Périnet, near Andasibe 1000 m; Province Antsiranana: Montagne d'Ambre 1000 m (material in Natural History Museum of Denmark)	–	Almost cosmopolitan, anthropochorous
Family Haplodesmidae			
Prosopodesmus jacobsoni Silvestri, 1910, ssp. *hilaris* Brolemann, 1920	"Madagascar"	–	Zanzibar, nominate subspecies very widespread, synanthropic (Jeekel 1999b).
Family Pyrgodesmidae			
Dilophops bullatus Loomis, 1932	Lakata Zalera, Helmut Steiner leg. (Hoffman in litt.)	–	Quite widespread in the tropics (Jeekel 1999b)
Family Dalodesmidae			
Dalodesmus hamatus (Brandt, 1841)	Madagascar (Golovatch and Hoffman 1989)	–	Endemic
D. hova (Saussure & Zehntner, 1897)	Nosy Be (Saussure and Zehntner 1902); Périnet (Hoffman 1974); Sakatia Island (Golovatch and Hoffman 1989)	–	Endemic
D. odontopezus (Attems, 1898)	Nosy Be (Saussure and Zehntner 1902)	–	Endemic
D. orator Hoffman, 1974	Ambohimitombo (Hoffman 1974)	–	Endemic
D. voeltzkowi (Mesibov, Wesener & Hollier, 2018) [syn. *Polydesmus sakalava*; *Pterodesmus* s.; *Tubercularium* s.; *Eutubercularium* s.]	"Madagascar"–Nosy Be (Saussure and Zehntner 1902)	–	Endemic
D. tectus Cook, 1896	Central Madagascar (Cook 1896)	–	Endemic
Phymatodesmus sakalava (Saussure & Zehntner, 1897)	"Madagascar" (Saussure and Zehntner 1902)	–	Endemic

SCIENTIFIC NAMES	MADAGASCAR RECORDS	IUCN STATUS	GENERAL DISTRIBUTION/NOTES
ORDER SPIROBOLIDA			
Family Rhinocricidae			
"*Rhinocricus*" *collaris* Saussure & Zehntner, 1897	"Madagascar" (Saussure and Zehntner 1902)	DD	?
Family Pachybolidae			
Alluviobolus antanosy Wesener, 2009	Ambatotsirongorongo Mountain; Sainte Luce S8; Esetra: Mt. Mahermana; Andohahela: Isaka-Ivondro (Wesener et al. 2009a)	EN	Endemic
A. laticlavius Wesener, 2009	Petriky (Wesener et al. 2009a)	CR	Endemic
A. tsimelahy Wesener, 2009	Andohahela: Tsimelahy, Ebosika (Wesener et al. 2009a)	EN	Endemic
Aphistogoniulus aridus Wesener, 2009	Forêt de Mahavelo (Wesener et al. 2009b)	EN	Endemic
A. corallipes (Saussure & Zehntner, 1902)	Tolagnaro (Jeekel 1971); Manantantely (Wesener et al. 2009b)	CR	Endemic
A. cowani (Butler, 1882) [syn. *Aphisthogoniulus sanguinemaculatus* (Silvestri, 1897)]	Ankafana, Betsileo country (Jeekel 1971); Ranomafana, Ivohibe, Andringitra (Wesener et al. 2009b)	NT	Endemic
A. diabolicus Wesener, 2009	Midongy du Sud (Wesener et al. 2009b)	NT	Endemic
A. erythrocephalus (Pocock, 1893) [syn. *Aphisthogoniulus quadridentatus* (Attems, 1910)]	"Sakana" (Jeekel 1971); Anjanaharibe-Sud, Marojejy, Masoala, Nosy Be: Lokobe, Forêt de Betaolana, Daraina (Wesener et al. 2009b); Ambondrobe, "Forêt d'Ambanitaza" (Wesener et al. 2011)	LC	Endemic
A. hova (Saussure & Zehntner, 1897) [syn. *Aphisthogoniulus brolemanni* Jeekel, 1971; *Aphisthogoniulus polleni* Jeekel, 1971]	"Madagascar" (Jeekel 1971); Antananarivo (Jeekel 1971); Betampona, Ile Sainte Marie, Andasibe (Wesener et al. 2011)	EN	Endemic
A. infernalis Wesener, 2009	Sainte Luce S8, Andohahela: Isaka-Ivondro (Wesener et al. 2009b); Ambatotsirongorongo: Grand Lavasoa (Wesener et al. 2011); Andohahela parcel 1, NW Fort Dauphin, 300 m (Wesener and Anilkumar 2020)	EN	Endemic
A. jeekeli Decker & Wesener, 2011	Province Fianarantsoa: Forêt Classée Vatovavy and Réserve Speciale Manombo (Wesener et al. 2011)	EN	Endemic
A. rubrodorsalis Decker & Wesener, 2011	Marojejy (Wesener et al. 2011)	NT	Endemic
A. sakalava (Saussure & Zehntner, 1897)	Moramanga Forest (Jeekel 1971)	DD	Endemic
A. sanguineus Wesener, 2009	Ambohijanahary, Ambohitantely (Wesener et al. 2009b)	EN	Endemic
A. vampyrus Wesener, 2009	Andohahela: Col du Sedro, parcel 1, 1500 m (Wesener et al. 2009b)	LC	Endemic
Caprobolus andringitra Wesener, 2009	Andringitra; Forêt de Vevembe (Wesener et al. 2009a)	LC	Endemic
Colossobolus aculeatus Wesener, 2009	Forêt de Binara (Wesener et al. 2009a)	EN	Endemic

(continued overleaf)

TABLE 9.13. ***continued***

SCIENTIFIC NAMES	MADAGASCAR RECORDS	IUCN STATUS	GENERAL DISTRIBUTION/NOTES
C. giganteus Wesener, 2009	Ankarana (Wesener et al. 2009a)	NT	Endemic
C. litoralis Wesener, 2009	Forêt d'Orangea (Wesener et al. 2009a)	CR	Endemic
C. minor Wesener, 2009	Forêt d'Analabe (Wesener et al. 2009a)	CR	Endemic
C. oblongopedus Wesener, 2009	Forêt d'Analabe, Forêt d'Antsahabe, Manongarivo (Wesener et al. 2009a)	NT	Endemic
C. pseudoaculeatus Wesener, 2009	Forêt d'Ambre (Wesener et al. 2009a)	CR	Endemic
C. semicyclus Wesener, 2009	Forêt d'Antsahabe, Forêt de Binara, Daraina (Wesener et al. 2009a)	EN	Endemic
C. cruentus Wesener, 2009	Andohahela (Wesener et al. 2009a)	LC	Endemic
Dactylobolus bivirgatus (Karsch, 1881)	Mahajanga (Saussure and Zehntner 1902); Nosy Be: spiaggia Ambatoloaka (Wesener and Anilkumar 2020)	–	Also Comoros, Seychelles, and Pemba Island (Golovatch and Korsós 1992)
Flagellobolus pauliani Wesener, 2009	Andasibe, Andranomay (Wesener et al. 2009a)	EN	Endemic
Granitobolus andohahelensis Wesener, 2009	Andohahela: Mt. Vasiha, Malio; Manantantely (Wesener et al. 2009a)	NT	Endemic
G. endemicus Wesener, 2009	Ambatotsirongorongo Mountain (Wesener et al. 2009a)	CR	Endemic
Leptogoniulus sorornus (Butler, 1876) [syn. *Spirobolus naresi* Pocock, 1893]	"Alanana Island," Fenoarivo-Atsinanana, Toamasina (Shelley and Lehtinen 1999)	–	Pantropical with a strong predilection for islands (Shelley and Lehtinen 1999)
Madabolus maximus Wesener & Enghoff, 2008	Bemaraha, Ankarafantsika, Namoroka, Forêt Sakaraha (Wesener et al. 2008)	NT	Endemic
Ostinobolus montanus Wesener, 2009	Andohahela (Wesener et al. 2009a)	LC	Endemic
O. rufus Wesener, 2009	Andohahela: Malio, Isaka-Ivondro, Ivorona; Ambatotsirongorongo Mountain; Sainte Luce S9; Esetra: Mt. Mahermana; Manantantely; Vohimena Mountains (Wesener et al. 2009a)	NT	Endemic
O. stellaris Wesener, 2009	Andohahela (Wesener et al. 2009a)	LC	Endemic
O. subterraneus Wesener, 2009	Petriky, Ambatotsirongorongo Mountain (Wesener et al. 2009a); SE Tolagnaro: Spiaggia Libanona (Wesener and Anilkumar 2020)	CR	Endemic
Pseudocentrobolus aureus Wesener, 2009	Forêt de Beroboka, Forêt de Mikea, Lake Ranobe (Wesener et al. 2009a)	NT	Endemic
P. vohibasiensis Wesener, 2009	Forêt de Vohibasia (Wesener et al. 2009a)	NT	Endemic
Riotintobolus anomalus Wesener, 2009	Cap Sainte Marie, Mahafaly Plateau, Lake Ranobe (Wesener et al. 2009a)	NT	Endemic
R. aridus Wesener, 2009	Angavo, Antafiky (Wesener et al. 2009a)	EN	Endemic
R. mandenensis Wesener, 2009	Mandena (Wesener et al. 2009a)	CR	Endemic
R. minutus Wesener, 2009	Sainte Luce S9 (Wesener et al. 2009a)	CR	Endemic
Sanguinobolus maculosus Wesener, 2009	Montagne d'Ambre (Wesener et al. 2009a)	LC	Endemic
Spiromimus albipes Wesener & Enghoff, 2009	Réserve Spéciale d'Ambre (Wesener and Enghoff 2009)	CR	Endemic

SCIENTIFIC NAMES	MADAGASCAR RECORDS	IUCN STATUS	GENERAL DISTRIBUTION/NOTES
S. dorsovittatus Saussure & Zehntner, 1901	Nosy Be (Saussure and Zehntner 1902)	VU	Endemic
S. electricus Wesener & Enghoff, 2009	Montagne d'Ambre (Wesener and Enghoff 2009)	LC	Endemic
S. grallator Wesener & Enghoff, 2009	Anjanaharibe-Sud (Wesener and Enghoff 2009)	LC	Endemic
S. laticoxalis Wesener & Enghoff, 2009	Ankarafantsika, Forêt Sakaraha (Wesener and Enghoff 2009)	NT	Endemic
S. litoralis Wesener & Enghoff, 2009	Forêt d'Orangea, Andranomanitra Nord (Wesener and Enghoff 2009)	CR	Endemic
S. namoroka Wesener & Enghoff, 2009	Namoroka (Wesener and Enghoff 2009)	VU	Endemic
S. scapularis Wesener & Enghoff, 2009	Forêt de Binara (Wesener and Enghoff 2009)	CR	Endemic
S. simplex Wesener & Enghoff, 2009	Marojejy (Wesener and Enghoff 2009)	NT	Endemic
S. simplicicoxalis Wesener & Enghoff, 2009	Andringitra (Wesener and Enghoff 2009)	–	Endemic
S. triaureus Wesener & Enghoff, 2009	Ankarafantsika, Forêt de Tsimembo, Namoroka, Bemarivo (Wesener and Enghoff 2009)	NT	Endemic
S. univirgatus Saussure & Zehntner, 1897	Nosy Be (Saussure and Zehntner 1902); Ankarana (Wesener and Enghoff 2009)	NT	Endemic
S. voeltzkowi Saussure & Zehntner, 1901	Nosy Be, Sakatia (Saussure and Zehntner 1902)	VU	Endemic
Zehntnerobolus hoffmani Wesener, 2011	Ivohibe (Wesener 2011)	LC	Endemic
Z. rubripes (Saussure & Zehntner, 1897)	Andrangoloaka Forest [Mantasoa] (Saussure and Zehntner 1902)	NT	Endemic
Trigoniulus corallinus (Gervais, 1842) [syn. *Spirobolus goesii* (Porat, 1876); *Trigoniulus g*; *Spirobolus dorsopunctatus* Saussure & Zehntner, 1897]	Nosy Be (Shelley and Lehtinen 1999)	–	Pantropical with a strong predilection for islands (Shelley and Lehtinen 1999)
T. grandidieri Saussure & Zehntner, 1897	"Madagascar" (Saussure and Zehntner 1902)	DD	Endemic
T. olympiacus (Karsch, 1881)	Nosy Be (Saussure and Zehntner 1902)	DD	Endemic
T. sikorae Saussure & Zehntner, 1897	"Madagascar" (Saussure and Zehntner 1902)	DD	Endemic
Family Spirobolellidae			
Hylekobolus albicollaris Wesener, 2009	Andohahela: Ivorona, Isaka-Ivondro; Ambatotsirongorongo Mountain (Wesener et al. 2009a)	NT	Endemic
H. analavelona Wesener, 2009	Analavelona (Wesener et al. 2009a)	NT	Endemic
H. andasibensis Wesener, 2009	Andasibe (Wesener et al. 2009a)	CR	Endemic
H. anjanaharibe Wesener, 2009	Anjanaharibe-Sud (Wesener et al. 2009a)	LC	Endemic
H. brachiosauroides Wesener, 2009	Andohahela: Ivorona, Isaka-Ivondro; Ambatotsirongorongo Mountain (Wesener et al. 2009a)	NT	Endemic

(*continued overleaf*)

TABLE 9.13. ***continued***

SCIENTIFIC NAMES	MADAGASCAR RECORDS	IUCN STATUS	GENERAL DISTRIBUTION/NOTES
H. goodmani Wesener, 2009	Andohahela (Wesener et al. 2009a)	NT	Endemic
H. griseus Wesener, 2009	Andohahela: Enato, Malio; Sainte Luce S9; Mandena (Wesener et al. 2009a)	EN	Endemic
H. latifrons Wesener, 2009	Farafangana, Karianga (Wesener et al. 2009a)	CR	Endemic
H. marojejy Wesener, 2009	Marojejy (Wesener et al. 2009a)	NT	Endemic
H. montanus Wesener, 2009	Andohahela (Wesener et al. 2009a)	NT	Endemic
H. rufus Wesener, 2009	Midongy du Sud, Vohimena Mountain: Enato, Fort Carnot, Ranomafana (Wesener et al. 2009a)	NT	Endemic
Family Pseudospirobolellidae			
Pseudospirobolellus avernus (Butler, 1872)	Ranomafana (Wesener and Anilkumar 2020)	–	Introduced, widespread in tropics, originally from SE Asia (e.g., Golovatch and Korsós 1992)
ORDER SPIROSTREPTIDA			
Family Harpagophoridae			
Thyropygus vagabundus Saussure & Zehntner, 1897	"Madagascar" (Saussure and Zehntner 1902)	–	Also Sumatra (Saussure and Zehntner, 1902), introduced to Madagascar?
Family Iulomorphidae			
Iulomorpha sp.	Province Antananarivo: Ambohimanga, 1400 m; Andasibe; Ankarafantsika; Ranomafana; Ambohitantely (material in Natural History Museum of Denmark)	–	Introduced to Madagascar?
Family Cambalopsidae			
Glyphiulus granulatus (Gervais, 1847)	Nosy Be (Wesener and Anilkumar 2020)	–	Introduced, tropical tramp, also on Comoros (VandenSpiegel and Golovatch 2007) and Seychelles (Golovatch and Korsós 1992)
Family Spirostreptidae			
Charactopygus atratus (Karsch, 1881) [*Spirostreptus sepia* Brölemann, 1896; *Charactopygus* s.; *Spirostreptus hova*; Saussure and Zehntner, 1901	Nosy Be (Krabbe 1982)	–	Also Seychelles
C. betsilea (Saussure & Zehntner, 1902)	Western Madagascar (Krabbe 1982)	–	Endemic
?*C. bombifrons* Attems, 1914	Nosy Be, near Hellville on "Lake Kaiman" (Krabbe 1982)	–	Endemic
C. radamae (Saussure & Zehntner, 1902)	Antananarivo, Ankaratra, 2000 ft (Krabbe 1982)	–	Endemic
C. sakalavae (Saussure & Zehntner, 1897)	Western Madagascar (Krabbe 1982)	–	Endemic
?*C. tricolor* (Saussure & Zehntner, 1902)	"Madagascar" (Krabbe 1982)	–	Endemic

SCIENTIFIC NAMES	MADAGASCAR RECORDS	IUCN STATUS	GENERAL DISTRIBUTION/NOTES
C. trilobatus Attems, 1914	Nosy Be, Lokobe (Krabbe 1982)	–	Endemic
"*Diaporus*" *bigoti* Demange, 1969	Itampolo (Demange 1969)	–	Endemic
Doratogonus serpentinus Brolemann, 1923	"Madagascar" (Krabbe 1982)	–	?
Doratogonus stylifer (Peters, 1855)	"Madagascar" (Krabbe 1982)	–	Also Zanzibar, east Africa (Krabbe 1982); the Malagasy record perhaps due to a mislabeled specimen (R. L. Hoffman, in litt.)
Eumekius amplicollis Brölemann, 1923	"Madagascar" (Krabbe 1982)	–	Endemic
E. antimena (Saussure & Zehntner, 1901)	Nosy Be, Sakatia Island (Krabbe 1982); Nosy Be, Lokobe, Nosy Komba (Wesener and Anilkumar 2020)	–	Endemic
E. vermiculus (Saussure & Zehntner, 1897)	Western Madagascar (Krabbe 1982)	–	Endemic
Isophyllostreptus eyraudi (Brolemann, 1919)	Antsiranana (Krabbe 1982)	–	Endemic
I. fangaroka (Saussure & Zehntner, 1901)	Nosy Be (Krabbe 1982)	–	Endemic
"*Scaphiostreptus*" *politifrons* Attems, 1910	Ile aux Prunes (Krabbe 1982)	–	Endemic
"*Scaphiostreptus*" *marianus* Attems, 1910	Ile Sainte Marie	–	Endemic
Sechelleptus aberrans (Brolemann, 1923)	"Madagascar" (Krabbe 1982)	–	Endemic
S. anulatus (Attems, 1914) ssp. *nanus* (Attems, 1914)	"Tiherena" (Krabbe 1982)	–	Also Zanzibar (*S. a. anulatus*)
S. argus (Attems, 1896) [syn. *Spirostreptus ambulator* Saussure & Zehntner, 1897]	Imerina (Saussure and Zehntner 1902); "Sahana" (Krabbe 1982)	–	Also Zanzibar, Mauritius (Krabbe 1982)
S. betaminea (Saussure & Zehntner, 1897)	Moramanga Forest (Krabbe 1982)	–	Endemic
S. confusus (Attems, 1950) [syn. *Scaphiostreptus macilentus* sensu Attems (1914)]	"Madagascar" (Krabbe 1982)	–	Endemic
S. coriaceus (Saussure & Zehntner, 1901)	Nosy Be, Nosy Mitsio (Krabbe 1982)	–	Endemic
S. dauphini (Saussure & Zehntner, 1902)	Tolagnaro (Krabbe 1982)	–	Endemic
S. fulgens (Saussure & Zehntner, 1901) [syn. *Spirostreptus bicolor* Saussure & Zehntner, 1897]	La Mandraka, Tolagnaro, Imerina (Krabbe 1982); Andringitra (Enghoff 1996)	–	Endemic
S. gonospinosus (Attems, 1910)	Toliara (Krabbe 1982)	–	Endemic
S. kalobaptus (Attems, 1914)	"Bouririka, Amboo-natica" (Krabbe 1982)	–	Endemic
S. krabbae Jeekel, 1999	Andringitra (Jeekel 1999c)	–	Endemic

(*continued overleaf*)

TABLE 9.13. ***continued***

SCIENTIFIC NAMES	MADAGASCAR RECORDS	IUCN STATUS	GENERAL DISTRIBUTION/NOTES
S. lambertoni (Brölemann, 1923)	Antananarivo (Krabbe 1982)	–	Endemic
S. leprosus (Saussure & Zehntner, 1897)	Fianarantsoa (Krabbe 1982)	–	Endemic
S. lobifer (Attems, 1951)	Tolagnaro near Bezavona (Krabbe 1982)	–	Endemic
S. metazonalis (Saussure & Zehntner, 1902) [syn. *Scaphiostreptus leprosus* sensu Attems, 1914]	Col du Sakavalana (Krabbe 1982); Andringitra (Enghoff 1996)	–	Endemic
S. moramangae (Saussure & Zehntner, 1897)	Moramanga Forest (Krabbe 1982)	–	Endemic
S. multiporus (Attems, 1951)	Andzavibe [Anjavibe] near Ambanja (Krabbe 1982)	–	Endemic
S. nigritus (Saussure & Zehntner, 1897)	Antananarivo (Krabbe 1982)	–	Endemic
S. obscuratus (Attems, 1914)	"Forêts du Sud" (Krabbe 1982)	–	Endemic
S. obscurus (Attems, 1951)	Tolagnaro near Bezavona (Krabbe 1982)	–	Endemic
S. praepolitus (Attems, 1910)	North of Toliara-Mahafaly (Krabbe 1982)	–	Endemic
S. procerus procerus (Attems, 1951)	Tongobory (Krabbe 1982)	–	Endemic
S. procerus medius Demange, 1959	Toliara (Krabbe 1982)	–	Endemic
S. punctulatus (Attems, 1910)	Toliara (Krabbe 1982)	–	Endemic
S. pyrhozonus (Gerstäcker, 1873) [syn. *Spirostreptus hildebrandtianus* Karsch, 1881; *Spirostreptus alligans* Karsch, 1881; *Spirostreptus convolutus* Saussure & Zehntner, 1897; *Spirostreptus grandidieri* Saussure & Zehntner, 1897]	Nosy Be, northwest, north (Krabbe 1982)	–	Also Zanzibar
S. scabricollis (Saussure & Zehntner, 1897)	"Madagascar" (Krabbe 1982)	–	Endemic
S. seychellarum (Gervais, 1837) [syn. *Spirostreptus madecassus* Saussure & Zehntner, 1897]	Antsiranana (Krabbe 1982)	–	Also Seychelles
S. speculorbis (Attems, 1910)	Lake Alaotra (Krabbe 1982)	–	Endemic
S. sulcicollis (Saussure & Zehntner, 1897)	"Madagascar" (Krabbe 1982)	–	Endemic
"*Spirostreptus*" *amandus* Attems, 1914	Moramanga Forest (Krabbe 1982)	–	Endemic
"*S.*" *micromelas* Saussure & Zehntner, 1902	"Madagascar" (Krabbe 1982)	–	Endemic
"*S.*" *phthisicus* Saussure & Zehntner, 1902	Tolagnaro (Krabbe 1982)	–	Endemic
"*S.*" *pictus* Saussure & Zehntner, 1902	Antananarivo-Toamasina (Krabbe 1982)	–	Endemic
"*S.*" *sculptus* Saussure & Zehntner, 1902	"Madagascar" (Krabbe 1982)	–	Endemic

SCIENTIFIC NAMES	MADAGASCAR RECORDS	IUCN STATUS	GENERAL DISTRIBUTION/NOTES
"S." *versicolor* Saussure & Zehntner, 1897	Ile Sainte Marie, Toamasina, "Senbendrana-Moromango" (Krabbe 1982)	–	Endemic
"S." *bivalvis* Saussure & Zehntner, 1902	"Madagascar" (Krabbe 1982)	–	?
"S." *caelebs* Saussure & Zehntner, 1902	"Madagascar" (Krabbe 1982)	–	?
"S." *colossus* Saussure & Zehntner, 1902	West coast (Krabbe 1982)	–	?
"S." *corculus* Butler, 1882	Betsileo country: Ankafana (Butler 1882)	–	?
"S." *exaratus* Saussure & Zehntner, 1902	Summit of "Ivohitsombé" (Krabbe 1982)	–	?
"S." *fasciatus* Lenz, 1881	Nosy Be (Saussure and Zehntner 1902)	–	?
"S." *globiclunis* Saussure & Zehntner, 1897	"Madagascar" (Krabbe 1982)	–	?
"S." *labialis* Saussure & Zehntner, 1897	Nosy Be (Krabbe 1982)	–	?
"S." *madagascariensis* (Gervais, 1847)	Befasy Forest, south of Morondava (Krabbe 1982)	–	?
"*Spirostreptus*" 1	"Madagascar" (Saussure and Zehntner 1902)	–	?
"*Spirostreptus*" 2	Nosy Be (Saussure and Zehntner 1902)	–	?
"S." *spinipes* Saussure & Zehntner, 1897	"Madagascar" (Krabbe 1982)	–	?
"S." *trachydermus* Butler, 1882	Betsileo country: Ankafana (Butler 1882)	–	?
"S." *xanthopus* Saussure & Zehntner, 1901	Western Madagascar (Krabbe 1982)	–	?

Notes: See Viette (1991) for more information on toponyms. Some of the localities presented in this table are clearly misspelled or include transliteration errors from museum labels or field notes. PN, Parc National. IUCN status: CR, Critically Endangered; DD, Data Deficient; EN, Endangered; LC, Least Concern; NT, Near Threatened; VU, Vulnerable.

- Iulomorphidae is another Gondwanan group (Hoffman 1980 [1979]). The genus *Iulomorpha* is known from southern Africa only, in addition to the single Malagasy species, which may be introduced.
- Spirostreptidae is a very large family distributed in the Afrotropical and the Neotropical regions, with a few expansive taxa penetrating into the Holarctic region and one species (possibly introduced) reported from the Indian subcontinent. Relationships within the family are largely unresolved.
- Synxenidae was indicated by Hoffman (1980 [1979]) as being confined to Africa, excepting a fossil species from Baltic amber. According to Condé (1954), however, the family is much more widespread.

To sum up, the millipedes of Madagascar indicate connections with Gondwana in general (Dalodesmidae), the Indian subcontinent (Arthrosphaeridae, Pygmaesomatidae, Spiromiminae), and continental Africa (*Madabolus*). The connection with continental Africa is also represented by the genus *Iulomorpha*, if indeed the species found on Madagascar is indigenous. The continental Afrotropical spirostreptids are more likely candidates for closest relatives of the Malagasy millipedes than the Neotropical millipedes, although, so far, no phylogenetic analyses are available. One of the Malagasy spirostreptid species, "*Diaporus bigoti*," was described as belonging to a Neotropical genus, but this assignment was regarded as highly improbable (Krabbe 1982).

ACKNOWLEDGMENTS

We are grateful to Steve Goodman for inspiring this review, the late Richard Hoffman for providing unpublished information and comments on an earlier draft manuscript, and Sergei Golovatch for likewise commenting on an earlier draft. We are thankful for the numerous comments by the subject editors, which enhanced the quality of this work.

Subject editors: Brian L. Fisher and Steven M. Goodman

COLLEMBOLA, SPRINGTAILS

N. G. Cipola, G. C. Queiroz, and †J.-M. Betsch

Collembola is one of the most ancient hexapod groups. Its first appearance in the fossil record is in the mid-Devonian "old red sandstones" of Scotland; surprisingly, the overall morphology of the animals was conserved through to the current taxa (Hopkin 1997; Betsch 2003). Currently, the four springtail orders (Poduromorpha, Entomobryomorpha, Symphypleona, and Neelipleona) have together more than 9000 species in 712 genera and 29 families (Bellinger et al. 2020). The group's widespread distribution in different biogeographic domains is because of its success in occupying several terrestrial microhabitats and aquatic-surface ecosystems (Hopkin 1997).

These important edaphic arthropods are abundant in almost all soil types and occur on every continent; because of their reduced size—generally in a range of 0.5 to 2.0 mm—springtails are classified as soil microarthropods (Petersen and Luxton 1982; Hopkin 1997). Typically saprophagous, they feed on a broad array of resources, including fungi, bacteria, lichens, and soil debris, and although little is known about the biology of most of the described species, a preference for fungal hyphae seems to prevail (Gange 2000). As they feed directly on decomposer organisms, enabling population regulation of bacteria and fungi, they play an important role in the organic-matter decomposition process (Seastedt 1984; Gange 2000; Tordoff et al. 2008).

Springtails occupy a great variety of vertical microhabitats within the soil decomposition subsystem, from the upper litter deposits to deeper soil layers, as well as in suspended soils and canopies mainly in tropical forests. The morphological adaptations required to live in such disparate microhabitats have molded the different groups inhabiting them, allowing for classification according to their life-forms (Hopkin 1997; Petersen 2002). These distinct life-forms may also differ in their reproduction types and dispersal capabilities; eventually, such characteristics make them good bioindicators of ecosystem integrity (Petersen 2002; Ponge et al. 2006).

Jean-Marie Betsch was an important collembologist who, for over 40 years, contributed significant research to the Symphypleona of the world (Bellinger et al. 2020). For Madagascar, Betsch described 38 Symphypleona species, 10 genera, and one endemic family, and also made extensive collections that have been important for the advancement of Collembola systematics and studies of other insects. In addition, Betsch (2003) produced a summary of 50% (69 species) of the records of all springtails, including hypotheses regarding distribution and ecological factors, which provide considerable insight into endemism patterns on Madagascar. He restricted his regional work to the springtails of Madagascar and did not conduct parallel work on other islands in the Malagasy Region (explicitly the Comoro, Mascarene, and Seychelles archipelagoes). Over the past few decades, considerable field and taxonomic work has been conducted across the Malagasy Region, and this contribution is intended to provide an update on the Collembola fauna of the region.

TAXONOMIC HISTORY

The earliest information on Collembola from the Malagasy Region is the description of *Acanthurella braueri* from the Seychelles (Börner 1906). In the following year, the first four species from Madagascar were described, from the families Bourletiellidae, Isotomidae, and Entomobryidae (Börner 1907). Again in the Seychelles, Carpenter (1916) described 15 species of Entomobryomorpha and the first Poduromorpha from the Malagasy Region, all endemic. Denis (1929) was the first to record two *Seira* species in the region, which were originally described from the African continent, as well as from Java and Indonesia. In the late 1940s, the first endemic poduromorph from Madagascar, *Oudemansia dubia*, was described, and then three new species of *Salina* (Paronellidae), including a record of a species, *Salina insignis*, also known from Java (Denis 1947; Delamare-Deboutteville 1948, 1950).

Subsequently, two more species of Neanuridae were named by Delamare-Deboutteville and Massoud (1964), and Massoud and Betsch (1966a, 1966b) and Massoud (1967) described the only endemic species of Sminthurididae known to date from Madagascar, *Sminthurides sensillatus*, as well as naming the monotypic genus *Microfalcula delamarei* (Microfalculidae).

Starting in 1965, Betsch made six visits to Madagascar, totaling 30 months of fieldwork, prospecting microarthropod fauna (especially Collembola) at a large number of sites (Betsch 2003). This sizable amount of material was the basis for detailed studies of Symphypleona by Betsch (1970, 1974a, 1974b, 1974c, 1975, 1977, 1980, 2000b) and Betsch and Waller (1996), as well as of Neanurinae (Poduromorpha, Neanuridae) by Cassagnau and Deharveng (1980) and Cassagnau (1996). These taxonomic works on Malagasy Collembola brought the total number of described species at that time to 69 in 25 genera, of which 64 species and 10 genera were endemic: *Microfalcula* (Microfalculidae) and *Zebulonia* (Katiannidae), each with one species; *Richardsitas* (Sminthuridae), with two species; and seven Bourletiellidae genera—*Anjavidiella* and *Vatomadiella*, with five and three species, respectively, and *Bourletiellitas*, *Madecassiella*, *Massoudia*, *Parabourletiella*, and *Paulianitas*, all monotypic (Betsch 2003).

Since that period, additional endemic species have been revealed for Madagascar and the Malagasy Region; these discoveries also included several regional records of springtails living in coastal areas (Thibaud 2008a, 2008b, 2010a, 2010b, 2011, 2017). Recently, three new species of *Seira* (Seirinae), four of *Lepidocyrtinus* (Seirinae), and another of *Trogolaphysa* (Paronellinae) have been described for Madagascar; this last genus had not been previously

† Deceased (1939–2013).

recorded in the region (Cipola et al. 2018, 2020; Nguyen and Soto-Adames 2018).

However, the Collembola fauna of Madagascar and the Malagasy Region as a whole is incompletely known; probably only 20% of the fauna is named (Betsch 2003). This is because many species still remain to be described within at least 11 additional genera of Neanurinae (Betsch and Cassagnau 1996), pantropical genera (*Denisiella*, *Collophora*, *Afrosminthurus*, *Pararrhopalites*, *Calvatomina*, and *Papirioides*), or genera with broader distributions (*Sphaeridia*, *Sminthurinus*, and *Stenognathellus*) among the Symphypleona (Betsch 1980), as well as at least 10 new species of Seirinae (N. G. Cipola, unpublished data). Consequently, this deficit is in part due to the lack of specialists and/or taxonomic studies focused on exploring different vegetational domains and elevational zones of Madagascar and the other Malagasy Region islands.

SAMPLED SITES

Over the course of more than 100 years, at least 181 sites on 11 islands in the Malagasy Region have been sampled for Collembola specimens (Figure 9.16, Table 9.14). On Madagascar, 58 sites were sampled widely in the former provinces of Antananarivo (6), Antsiranana (13), Fianarantsoa (7), Mahajanga (7), Toamasina (13), and Toliara (12); field techniques included soil, litter, and moss sampling, and bush threshing (Betsch 2003). The sampled sites on adjacent islands include the Comoros (12 on Grande Comore and 43 on Mayotte) and the Mascarenes (18 on Mauritius, 26 on La Réunion, and 10 on Rodrigues), all on substrates from coastal environments (Thibaud 2008a, 2010a, 2010b, 2011, 2017). In the Seychelles, the sampled islands include Bird, Praslin, Malé, Silhouette, and the Aldabra Atoll, with a total of 14 sites sampled (Carpenter 1916).

FIGURE 9.16 **Collection sites (black dots) of Collembola on Madagascar and adjacent islands. The numbering on localities refers to records of each species, following Table 9.14.**

TABLE 9.14. **Checklist of the Collembola of the Malagasy Region**

	SCIENTIFIC NAMES	RECORD REGIONS	DISTRIBUTION	REFERENCES
	ENTOMOBRYOMORPHA			
	ISOTOMIDAE			
	Anurophorinae			
1	*Archisotoma madagascariensis* Thibaud, 2008	CO: Hantsindzi; MD: Antalaha, Tolagnaro,* Nosy Be, Toamasina; MU: Poste Lafayette	Endemic	Thibaud 2008a: 74; 2008b: 513; 2011: 9; 2015: 356
2	*A. mayotii* Thibaud, 2010	MY: Grande-Terre	Endemic	Thibaud 2010b: 115[1]
3	*A. vaoensis* Thibaud & Weiner, 1997	CO: Malé; MD: Antalaha, Tolagnaro, Nosy Boraha, Mahajanga, Manakara; widely in MU	PAN	Thibaud 2008a: 74; 2008b: 514; 2011: 10; 2015: 356
4	*Hemisotoma thermophila* (Axelson, 1900)	CO: Mitsamiouli; MD: Antalaha, Mahajanga, Mahavelona, Nosy Be, Nosy Boraha, Ramena, Sambava, Toamasina, Vatomandry; widely in MU	COS	Thibaud 2008a: 74; 2008b: 514; 2011: 10; 2015: 357
5	*H. subpontica* Thibaud, 2010	RE: Saint-Pierre*	Endemic	Thibaud 2010a: 27[1]
6	*Isotomiella nummulifer* Deharveng & Oliveira, 1990	SY: Bird, Mahé, Praslin	PAN	Deharveng and Fjellberg 1993: 125
7	*I. spinosa* Deharveng & Fjellberg, 1993	SY: Mahé*	Endemic	Deharveng and Fjellberg 1993: 121[1]
8	*I. symetrimucronata* (Najt & Thibaud, 1987)	SY: Mahé	PAN	Deharveng and Fjellberg 1993: 123
9	*Isotomodes buchardi* Thibaud, 2008	CO: Chindini; MD: Antalaha, Mahambo, Ramena,* Tolagnaro, Toamasina, Vatomandry; widely in MU; RE: Saint-Pierre	Endemic	Thibaud 2008a: 75; 2008b: 516; 2010a: 29; 2011: 11; 2015: 360
10	*Pauropygus caussaneli* (Thibaud, 1996)	CO: Chindini; MD: Antalaha, Mahajanga, Mahavelona, Nosy Boraha, Sambava, Tolagnaro, Toliara, Vohémar; MU: Poste Lafayette; MY: Grande-Terre; widely in RD	AFT	Thibaud 2008a: 74; 2008b: 514; 2010b: 116; 2011:10; 2015: 357; 2017: 300
	Isotominae			
11	*Axelsonia thalassophila* Börner, 1907	MD: Mananara; SY: Aldabra	Endemic	Börner 1907: 147; Carpenter 1916: 32
12	*Isotomurus obscurus* Carpenter, 1916	SY: Mahé, Silhouette	Endemic	Carpenter 1916: 34[1]
13	*Psammisotoma kingae* Greenslade & Deharveng, 1986	MD: Mahajanga, Nosy Boraha, Tolagnaro	AUS, PLT	Thibaud 2008b: 517; 2015: 360
	Proisotominae			
14	*Folsomides centralis* (Denis, 1931)	MD: Ramena	PAN	Thibaud 2008b: 515; 2015: 357
15	*F. parvulus* Stach, 1922	MD: Manakara, Nosy Boraha, Ramena, Vohémar; MU: west coast	COS	Thibaud 2008a: 75; 2008b: 515; 2015: 357

	SCIENTIFIC NAMES	RECORD REGIONS	DISTRIBUTION	REFERENCES
16	*Folsomina infelicia* Greenslade, 1999	MD: Mahavelona, Toamasina, Vatomandry	MR, ORT	Thibaud 2008b: 515; 2015: 357
17	*F. onychiurina* Denis, 1931	MD: Antalaha, Fenoarivo-Atsinanana, Mahajanga, Mahavelona, Manakara, Mahambo, Nosy Boraha, Ramena, Sambava, Tolagnaro, Toamasina, Vohémar, Vatomandry; widely in CO, MU, MY, RE and RD islands	COS	Thibaud 2008a: 75; 2008b: 515; 2010a: 29; 2010b: 116; 2011: 10; 2015: 357; 2017: 300
18	*Proisotoma tenella* Reuter, 1895	MD: Antalaha, Sambava, Toamasina, Vatomandry	COS	Thibaud 2008b: 516; 2015: 360
	ENTOMOBRYIDAE			
	Entomobryinae			
19	*Entomobrya seychellarum* Carpenter, 1916	SY: Mahé,* Silhouette	Endemic	Carpenter 1916: 37[1]
20	*Willowsia jacobsoni* (Börner, 1913)	MD: Toamasina	PAN	Denis 1929: 105; Betsch 2003: 629
	Heteromurinae			
21	*Dicranocentrus longicornis* (Carpenter, 1916)	SY: Mahé,* Silhouette	Endemic	Carpenter 1916: 36[1]
22	*D. reunionensis* Mari-Mutt, 1985	RE: Bébour*	Endemic	Mari-Mutt 1985: 299[1]
	Lepidocyrtinae			
23	*Acanthurella braueri* (Börner, 1906)	SY: Mahé, Silhouette	Endemic	Börner 1906: 176;[2] Carpenter 1916: 42
24	*Lepidocyrtus annulicornis* Carpenter, 1916	SY: Mahé*	Endemic	Carpenter 1916: 40[1]
25	*L. fryeri* Carpenter, 1916	SY: Mahé*	Endemic	Carpenter 1916: 40[1]
26	*L. gardineri* Carpenter, 1916	SY: Mahé*	Endemic	Carpenter 1916: 41[1]
27	*L. imperialis* Carpenter, 1916	SY: Mahé*	Endemic	Carpenter 1916: 41[1]
28	*L. obscuricornis* Carpenter, 1916	SY: Mahé*	Endemic	Carpenter 1916: 39; Jacquemart 1980: 2
29	*L. silvestris* Carpenter, 1916	SY: Mahé*	Endemic	Carpenter 1916: 39[1]
30	*L. stramineus* Carpenter, 1916	SY: Mahé*	Endemic	Carpenter 1916: 40[1]
	Seirinae			
31	*Lepidocyrtinus andevo* Cipola & Bellini, 2020	MD: Beravindravina*	Endemic	Cipola et al. 2020: 77
32	*L. betamponensis* Cipola & Bellini, 2020	MD: Ambodisira (Betampona Reserve)*	Endemic	Cipola et al. 2020: 89
33	*L. briani* Cipola & Bellini, 2020	MD: Daraina (Binara Forest)*	Endemic	Cipola et al. 2020: 84
34	*L. iego* Cipola & Bellini, 2020	MD: Moramanga (Andasibe-Mantadia National Park)*	Endemic	Cipola et al. 2020: 96

(continued overleaf)

TABLE 9.14. ***continued***

	SCIENTIFIC NAMES	RECORD REGIONS	DISTRIBUTION	REFERENCES
35	*L. voeltzkowi* (Börner, 1907) (Figure 9.17a)	MD: Ankarimbelo,* Ambalavao (Anja Reserve), Marofandilia	Endemic	Börner 1907: 152[1]
36	*Seira delamarei* Jacquemart, 1980	SY: not specified.	PAN	Jacquemart 1980: 9[2]
37	*S. lepidochaetosa* Cipola & Bellini, 2018	MD: Ambohimahavelona	Endemic	Cipola et al. 2018: 152[1]
38	*S. metafemurata* Cipola & Bellini, 2018	MD: Ambodisira (Betampona Reserve)*	Endemic	Cipola et al. 2018: 165[1]
39	*S. pseudocoerulea* Denis, 1924	MD: Toamasina	AFT	Denis 1929: 104; Betsch 2003: 629
40	*S. semicaerulea* Cipola & Bellini, 2018	MD: Ihosy (Anja Reserve)	Endemic	Cipola et al. 2018: 159[1]
	MICROFALCULIDAE			
41	*Microfalcula delamarei* Massoud & Betsch, 1966	MD: Ambaliha, Montagne d'Ambre*	Endemic	Massoud and Betsch 1966b: 4; Betsch and Massoud 1968: 901
	PARONELLIDAE			
	Cyphoderinae			
42	*Cyphoderus insularum* Carpenter, 1916	SY: Praslin,* Mahé	Endemic	Carpenter 1916: 47[1]
	Paronellinae			
43	*Cyphoderopsis madagascarensis* (Wilson, 1982)	MD: Ankarana*	Endemic	J. M. Wilson 1982: 222[1]
44	*Lepidonella flava* (Carpenter, 1916)	SY: Mahé*	Endemic	Carpenter 1916: 44; Jacquemart 1980: 8
45	*Salina insignis* (Handschin, 1928)	MD: Mantasoa (Mandraka)	AUS, PLT	Delamare-Deboutteville 1950: 107
46	*S. milloti* Delamare-Deboutteville, 1948 (Figure 9.17b)	MD: Moramanga (Analamazaotra Reserve)*	Endemic	Delamare-Deboutteville 1948: 40[1]
47	*S. nigra* Delamare-Deboutteville, 1948	MD: Ambatolampy (Manjakatompo)*	Endemic	Delamare-Deboutteville 1948: 41[1]
48	*S. pallida* Carpenter, 1916	SY: Mahé*	Endemic	Carpenter 1916: 45; Jacquemart 1980: 4[2]
49	*S. scotti* Carpenter, 1916	SY: Mahé*	Endemic	Carpenter 1916: 44[1]
50	*S. trilineata* Delamare-Deboutteville, 1948	MD: Ambatolampy (Tsiafajavona Ankaratra)*	Endemic	Delamare-Deboutteville 1948: 41[1]
51	*Troglobius coprophagus* Palacios-Vargas & Wilson, 1990	MD: Ankarana*	Endemic	Palacios-Vargas and Wilson 1990: 69[1]
52	*Troglopedetes caeruleus* Carpenter, 1916	SY: Mahé*	Endemic	Carpenter 1916: 43[1]

	SCIENTIFIC NAMES	RECORD REGIONS	DISTRIBUTION	REFERENCES
53	*Trogolaphysa judithnajtae* Nguyen & Soto-Adames, 2018	MD: Nosy Be*	Endemic	Nguyen and Soto-Adames 2018: 184[1]
	PODUROMORPHA			
	HYPOGASTRURIDAE			
54	*Acherontiella thibaudi* Barra 1994	MD: Antalaha, Fenoarivo-Atsinanana, Manakara, Mahajanga, Morondava, Nosy Be, Ramena, Sambava, Toamasina, Toliara, Vatomandry, Vohémar; widely in CO, MU, MY, RD and RE	AFT	Thibaud 2008a: 72; 2008b: 505; 2010a: 26; 2010b: 114; 2011: 7; 2017: 300
55	*Paraxenylla piloua* Thibaud & Weiner, 1997	MU: wide distribution on island; RE: Saint-Leu	PAN	Thibaud 2008a: 73; 2010a: 26
56	*Willemia nosyboraha* Thibaud, 2008	MD: Antalaha, Manakara, Nosy Boraha,* Ramena	Endemic	Thibaud 2008b: 505;[1] 2015: 354
57	*Xenylla stachi* Gama, 1966	MD: Sambava, Vohémar; MU: Roches Noires	AUS, PLT	Thibaud 2008a: 73; 2015: 354
58	*X. yucatana* Mills, 1938	MD: Mahajanga, Nosy Boraha, Vatomandry; RD: Port Mathurin	PAN	Thibaud 2008b: 506; 2015: 354; 2017: 300
	ISOTOGASTRURIDAE			
59	*Isotogastrura litoralis* Thibaud & Weiner, 1997	CO: Hantsindzi, Ourovéni; MY: widely on island	MR, AUS	Thibaud 2010b: 512; 2011: 8
60	*I. madagascariensis* Thibaud, 2008	MD: Antalaha, Ifaty, Tolagnaro*	Endemic	Thibaud 2008b: 512; 2015: 356
	NEANURIDAE			
	Frieseinae			
61	*Friesea mahajanga* Thibaud, 2008	MD: Mahajanga,* Nosy Be, Nosy Boraha, Ramena, Sambava; MU: Palmar; RE: Saint Pierre, Saint-Gilles	Endemic	Thibaud 2008a: 73; 2008b: 506; 2010a: 26; 2015: 354
62	*F. petiti* (Delamare-Deboutteville & Massoud, 1964)	MD: Mahajanga, Tolagnaro*	Endemic	Delamare-Deboutteville and Massoud 1964: 282; Thibaud 2008b: 507; 2015: 354
63	*F. versabilis* Barra, 1995	MD: Mahavelona	AFT	Thibaud 2008b: 507; 2015: 354
	Neanurinae			
64	*Afrobella mamillata* Cassagnau, 1996	MD: Andringitra*	Endemic	Cassagnau 1996: 157[1]
65	*A. scoparia* Cassagnau, 1996	MD: Andringitra*	Endemic	Cassagnau 1996: 158[1]
66	*Neanura sexoculata* (Carpenter, 1916)	SY: Mahé,* Silhouette	Endemic	Carpenter 1916: 29[1]
67	*Paleonura anosyennica* Cassagnau, 1996	MD: Andaza (Tandavan' Anosy),* Tranomaro	Endemic	Cassagnau 1996: 129[1]
68	*P. coalescens* Cassagnau, 1996	MD: Morafenobe (Bongolava)*	Endemic	Cassagnau 1996: 130[1]

(continued overleaf)

TABLE 9.14. ***continued***

	SCIENTIFIC NAMES	RECORD REGIONS	DISTRIBUTION	REFERENCES
69	*P. plumosa* Cassagnau, 1996	MD: Andaza (Tandavan' Anosy)*	Endemic	Cassagnau 1996: 130[1]
70	*Phylliomeria bebourensis* Cassagnau, 1984	RE: Bébour*	Endemic	Cassagnau 1984: 27[1]
71	*Pronura anjavicola* Cassagnau, 1996	MD: Andringitra*	Endemic	Cassagnau 1996: 142[1]
72	*P. caeca* Cassagnau, 1996	MD: Marojejy*	Endemic	Cassagnau 1996: 144[1]
73	*P. elegans* Cassagnau, 1996	MD: Andringitra*	Endemic	Cassagnau 1996: 144[1]
74	*P. laminata* Cassagnau, 1996	MD: Ambanja (Tsaratanàna Reserve)*	Endemic	Cassagnau 1996: 146[1]
75	*P. lemurica* Cassagnau, 1996	MD: Itremo,* Andaza, Andringitra, Mantasoa, Marojejy, Moramanga (Analamazaotra Reserve), Tolagnaro	Endemic	Cassagnau 1996: 146[1]
76	*P. madagascariensis* Cassagnau, 1996	MD: Andringitra*	Endemic	Cassagnau 1996: 148[1]
77	*P. prima* Cassagnau, 1996	MD: Manamby*	Endemic	Cassagnau 1996: 150[1]
78	*P. pumilio* Cassagnau, 1996	MD: Andaza (Tandavan' Anosy)*	Endemic	Cassagnau 1996: 150[1]
79	*P. setimigrans* Cassagnau, 1996	MD: Ambohimanga*	Endemic	Cassagnau 1996: 151[1]
80	*P. sphaeroculata* Cassagnau, 1996	MD: Analavelona*	Endemic	Cassagnau 1996: 151[1]
81	*P. straturata* Cassagnau, 1996	MD: Ambohimanga,* Ambohitantely, Moramanga, Ampijoroa (Ankarafantsika), Andringitra, Itremo	Endemic	Cassagnau 1996: 153[1]
82	*Travura betschi* Cassagnau & Deharveng, 1980	MD: Moramanga,* Mantasoa	Endemic	Cassagnau and Deharveng 1980: 6[1]
	Pseudachorutinae			
83	*Cephalachorutes masi* Thibaud, 2008	MD: Tolagnaro,* Nosy Boraha; CO: Malé	MR	Thibaud 2008b: 507; 2011: 7; 2015: 355
84	*Najtafrica riebi* (Barra, 1994)	MD: Tolagnaro	AFT	Thibaud 2008b: 508
85	*Oudemansia dubia* Denis, 1947	MD: Cap d'Ambre*	Endemic	Denis 1947: 31[1]
86	*O. petiti* Delamare-Deboutteville & Massoud, 1964	MD: Tolagnaro*	Endemic	Delamare-Deboutteville and Massoud 1964: 387[1]
87	*Pseudachorutes hodeberti* Thibaud, 2008 (Fig. 2C)	MD: Tolagnaro*; MY: Pamanzi	Endemic	Thibaud 2008b: 508; 2010b: 114
	ODONTELLIDAE			
88	*Axenyllodes comoriensis* Thibaud, 2011	CO: Mitsamiouli (Grande Comore)*	Endemic	Thibaud 2011: 7[1]
89	*Odontellina deharvengi* Barra 1995	MD: Toliara	AFT	Thibaud 2008b: 506

	SCIENTIFIC NAMES	RECORD REGIONS	DISTRIBUTION	REFERENCES
90	*Stachia folsomi* (Arlé, 1968)	MD: Toamasina	PAN	Thibaud 2008b: 506; 2015: 354
	ONYCHIURIDAE			
91	*Allonychiurus foliatus* (Rusek, 1967)	MD: Toamasina	MR, ORT	Thibaud 2008b: 509
92	*A. mariangeae* (Thibaud & Lee, 1994)	MD: Toamasina	MR, ORT	Thibaud 2008b: 509
	TULLBERGIIDAE			
93	*Fissuraphorura cubanica* Rusek, 1991	MD: Antalaha, Mahajanga, Mahambo, Nosy Boraha, Sambava, Toamasina, Vatomandry; RE: widely on island	PAN	Thibaud 2008b: 509; 2010a: 26; 2015: 355
94	*F. deharvengi* Rusek, 1991	MD: Antalaha, Nosy Boraha, Ramena, Tolagnaro, Vatomandry	MR, ORT	Thibaud 2008b: 509; 2015: 355
95	*Mesaphorura yosii* (Rusek, 1967)	MD: Antalaha, Ramena, Toamasina; MU: widely on island	COS	Thibaud 2008a: 74; 2008b: 510; 2015: 356
96	*M. subitalica* Thibaud, 1996	CO: Mitsamiouli (Grande Comore); MD: Tolagnaro	AFT, NEO	Thibaud 2011: 8; 2015: 355
97	*Psammophorura neocaledonica* Thibaud & Weiner, 1997	MD: Antalaha, Tolagnaro	AUS, MR	Thibaud 2008b: 510; 2015: 356
98	*Tullbergia tolanara* Thibaud, 2008	MD: Tolagnaro,* Mahavelona	Endemic	Thibaud 2008b: 510; 2015: 356
	SYMPHYPLEONA			
	BOURLETIELLIDAE			
	Bourletiellinae			
99	*Bovicornia greensladei* Massoud & Delamare-Deboutteville, 1967	MD: Maroantsetra (Nosy Mangabe)	MR, ORT	Betsch 1974a: 179;[1] 2003: 629
100	*Madecassiella ibityensis* Betsch & Waller, 1996	MD: Ibity*	Endemic	Betsch and Waller 1996: 414;[1] Betsch 2003: 629
101	*Massoudia griveaudi* Betsch, 1974	MD: Mampikony, Boriziny*	Endemic	Betsch 1974c: 7;[1] 2003: 629
102	*Paulianitas vietti* Betsch, 1977	MD: Marofandilia*	Endemic	Betsch 1977: 119;[1] 2003: 629
103	*Rastriopes amphigyus* Börner, 1907	MD: Andranovory*	Endemic	Börner 1907: 158;[1] Betsch 2003: 629
	Parabourletiellinae			
104	*Anjavidiella andoharianensis* Betsch, 1980 (Figure 19.17d)	MD: Andringitra*	Endemic	Betsch 1980: 182;[1] 2003: 629
105	*A. andringitrensis* Betsch, 1980	MD: Andringitra*	Endemic	Betsch 1980: 182;[1] 2003: 629
106	*A. anjavidilavensis* Betsch, 1980	MD: Andringitra*	Endemic	Betsch 1980: 182;[1] 2003: 629

(continued overleaf)

TABLE 9.14. ***continued***

	SCIENTIFIC NAMES	RECORD REGIONS	DISTRIBUTION	REFERENCES
107	*A. ankaratrensis* Betsch, 1974	MD: Ambatolampy (Tsiafajavona Ankaratra)*	Endemic	Betsch 1974b: 554;[1] 2003: 629
108	*A. vohidrayensis* Betsch, 1980	MD: Andringitra*	Endemic	Betsch 1980: 184;[1] 2003: 629
109	*Bourletiellitas imerinensis* Betsch, 1974	MD: Ambatolampy (Tsiafajavona Ankaratra)*	Endemic	Betsch 1974b: 547;[1] 2003: 629
110	*Parabourletiella mahafalensis* Betsch, 1975	MD: Ampanihy (Lembalemban'i Mahafaly)	Endemic	Betsch 1975: 478;[1] 2003: 629
111	*Vatomadiella descarpentriesi* Betsch, 1980	MD: Ibity*	Endemic	Betsch 1980: 185;[1] 2003: 629
112	*V. pauliani* Betsch, 1974	MD: Ambatolampy (Tsiafajavona Ankaratra)*	Endemic	Betsch 1974b: 560;[1] 2003: 629
113	*V. peyrierasi* Betsch, 1980	MD: Itremo*	Endemic	Betsch 1980: 184;[1] 2003: 629
	KATIANNIDAE			
114	*Papirinus ankaratrensis* Betsch, 1974	MD: Ambatolampy (Tsiafajavona Ankaratra)*	Endemic	Betsch 1974b: 530;[1] 2003: 629
115	*Zebulonia massoudi* Betsch, 1970	MD: Ambanja (Tsaratanàna Reserve)*	Endemic	Betsch 1970: 52;[1] 2003: 629
	SMINTHURIDAE			
	Sminthurinae			
116	*Richardsitas griveaudi* Betsch, 1977	MD: Marofandilia*	Endemic	Betsch 1977: 122;[1] 2003: 629
117	*R. najtae* Betsch, 1975	MD: Amboasary*	Endemic	Betsch 1975: 482;[1] 2003: 629
118	*Temeritas ambohitantelensis* Betsch, 2000	MD: Ambohitantely*	Endemic	Betsch 2000b: 334;[1] 2003: 629
119	*T. ambrensis* Betsch, 2000	MD: Montagne d'Ambre*	Endemic	Betsch 2000b: 330;[1] 2003: 629
120	*T. ampasimbensis* Betsch, 1980	MD: Ampasimbe,* Moramanga (Analamazaotra Reserve)	Endemic	Betsch 1980: 162;[1] 2003: 629
121	*T. andranobensis* Betsch, 2000	MD: Andriamena (Andranobe Forest)*	Endemic	Betsch 2000b: 334;[1] 2003: 629
122	*T. anjozorobensis* Betsch, 2000	MD: Anjozorobe (Vanjamanitra Forest)*	Endemic	Betsch 2000b: 325;[1] 2003: 629
123	*T. ankarafantsikensis* Betsch, 1980	MD: Ampijoroa (Ankarafantsika)*	Endemic	Betsch 1980: 159;[1] 2003: 629
124	*T. anosyennensis* Betsch, 1980	MD: Andaza (Tandavan' Anosy)*	Endemic	Betsch 1980: 164;[1] 2003: 629
125	*T. antongilensis* Betsch, 1980	MD: Antongil Bay,* Ambanizana, Maitsoarongana, Mananara (Ivontaka), Maroantsetra (Nosy Mangabe), Marojejy	Endemic	Betsch 1980: 159;[1] 2003: 629

	SCIENTIFIC NAMES	RECORD REGIONS	DISTRIBUTION	REFERENCES
126	*T. bergensis* Betsch, 1980	MD: Mampikony, Boriziny*	Endemic	Betsch 1980: 156;[1] 2003: 629
127	*T. iarakensis* Betsch, 2000	MD: Ambanizana (Iaraka)*	Endemic	Betsch 2000b: 330;[1] 2003: 629
128	*T. mahorensis* Betsch, 2000	MD: Ankarana, Analamerana (Mahory)*	Endemic	Betsch 2000b: 328; 2003: 629
129	*T. mananteninensis* Betsch, 1980	MD: Manantenina*	Endemic	Betsch 1980: 164; 2003: 629
130	*T. mantasoensis* Betsch, 1980	MD: Mantasoa*	Endemic	Betsch 1980: 164;[1] 2003: 629
131	*T. marojezensis* Betsch, 1980	MD: Marojejy*	Endemic	Betsch 1980: 161;[1] 2003: 629
132	*T. perinetensis* Betsch, 1980	MD: Moramanga (Analamazaotra Reserve,* Ankarongambe), Mantasoa (Mandraka)	Endemic	Betsch 1980: 162; 2003: 629
133	*T. sahafarensis* Betsch, 2000	MD: Ankarana, Ankitsakalaninaomby (Sahafary), Analamerana (Mahory)*	Endemic	Betsch 2000b: 326;[1] 2003: 629
134	*T. soalalensis* Betsch, 1980	MD: Soalala (Tongahibe Forest)*	Endemic	Betsch 1980:156;[1] 2003: 629
135	*T. tsaratananensis* Betsch, 2000	MD: Ambanja (Tsaratanàna Reserve)*	Endemic	Betsch 2000b: 332;[1] 2003: 629
	Sphyrothecinae			
136	*Sphyrotheca madagascariensis* Betsch, 1974	MD: Ambatolampy (Tsiafajavona Ankaratra)*	Endemic	Betsch 1974b: 539;[1] 2003: 629
	SMINTHURIDIDAE			
137	*Sminthurides sensillatus* Massoud & Betsch, 1966	MD: Maroantsetra*	Endemic	Massoud and Betsch 1966a: 582;[1] Betsch 2003: 629

Notes: Record regions (islands): CO, Union of the Comoros; MD, Madagascar; MU, Mauritius; MY, Mayotte; RD, Rodrigues; RE, La Réunion; SY, Seychelles; * type locality. Distribution (geographic regions): AFT, Afrotropical; AUS, Australian; COS, Cosmopolitan; MR, Malagasy Region; NEO, Neotropical; ORT, Oriental; PAN, Pantropical; PLT, Paleotropical. "Endemic" is in reference to the record region.

[1] Single record from original description.

[2] Exact locality date not specified.

DIVERSITY FROM MALAGASY REGION ISLANDS

In total, 137 species of Collembola in 65 genera and 14 families are known from the Malagasy Region, distributed among Entomobryomorpha (38%), Poduromorpha (33%), and Symphypleona (29%) (Figure 9.16, Table 9.14). Of these orders, Symphypleona has not been recorded on any regional island other than Madagascar, where 39 species are known.

Within Entomobryomorpha, Isotomidae has at least two species on almost all regional islands, while almost all members of Entomobryidae and Paronellidae occur only on Madagascar and the Seychelles. Regarding Poduromorpha, most species of Neanuridae have been documented on Madagascar, but at least three of them (Table 9.14, species nos. 61, 83, and 87), together with the Hypogastruridae (except *Willemia nosyboraha*), are shared among several islands with the exception of the Seychelles. Onychiuridae has been registered only on Madagascar, with two nonendemic species with a Paleotropical distribution. Odontellidae and Tullbergiidae are also poorly represented in the region, by species found on other islands or with a pantropical distribution. Finally, Isotogastruridae, although a relatively rare family, is represented by two species (59, 60) registered in the Malagasy Region, out of the 10 described in the world (Bellinger et al. 2020).

The families with the highest species richness are Neanuridae with 27 species, followed by Entomobryidae with 22, Sminthuridae with 21, and Isotomidae with 18. At the generic level, Isotomidae leads with 11 genera, followed by Neanuridae with 11, and Bourletiellidae with 9.

In the Malagasy Region as a whole, 15 of the recorded species are known from continents elsewhere in the world—five of these are cosmopolitan, four in Isotomidae (4, 15, 17, 18) and one in Tullbergiidae (95); and another 10 have a pantropical distribution, in Isotomidae (3, 6, 8, 14), Entomobryidae (20, 36), Hypogastruridae (55, 58), Odontellidae (90), and Tullbergiidae (93).

Madagascar has the highest species richness of the region, with 109 species in 51 genera, including all families recorded in the region. Currently 17 recognized Malagasy species, belonging to the following families, are also present on at least some regional islands: Isotomidae (1, 3, 4, 9–11, 15, 17), Hypogastruridae (54, 57, 58), Neanuridae (61, 83, 87), and Tullbergidae (93, 95, 96).

The Seychelles has the second-highest species richness of the Malagasy Region, with 22 species in 13 genera, 12 Entomobryomorpha genera and a single Poduromorpha genus (66). Out of this total, 11 species in five genera are members of Entomobryidae, seven of which are *Lepidocyrtus* (24–30). The other diverse genera are *Isotomiella*, with three species (6–8), and *Salina*, with two (48, 49). The greatest representativeness of this richness was on Mahé, with 20 species, seven of which were also recorded on Silhouette or Praslin (6, 12, 19, 21, 23, 42, 66).

The Mascarene islands have 17 species in 14 genera and five families, including 12 species on Mauritius, nine on La Réunion, and four on Rodrigues. Of this total, several are present on Madagascar, with five species shared in different combinations (9, 10, 17, 54, 61). The only species of Entomobryidae from the Mascarene islands has been recorded on La Réunion (22). Total species richness in the Comoro archipelago is 17 species, 11 of which occur in the Union of the Comoros and six on Mayotte—a single species for each recorded genus except for *Archisotoma*, with two species in the Union of the Comoros and one on Mayotte. Isotomidae represents the greatest species richness, with seven of these species, two of which (10, 17) are found on Grande Comore and Mayotte, as are one of Hypogastruridae (54) and Isotogastruridae (59).

Although Madagascar's species richness overall is superior to that of adjacent islands (109 out of 137 species), it is remarkable that so much of this diversity, except for members of Symphypleona and most members of Neanuridae (Poduromorpha) (totaling about 60 species), is shared across the Malagasy Region. Thus, only a small fraction of the Collembola fauna (~24%, or 32 species) from other continents is contributing additional richness to the archipelago.

FIGURE 9.17 **Habitus of some endemic Collembola species from Madagascar: A) *Lepidocyrtinus voeltzkowi* (Entomobryidae), B) *Salina milloti* (Paronellidae), C) *Pseudachorutes hodeberti* (Neanuridae), and D) *Anjavidiella andoharianensis* (Bourletiellidae).** (PHOTOS by N. G. Cipola.)

ENDEMISM

The Malagasy Region has a total of 104 endemic species in 47 genera, representing all the local families except Onychiuridae. Some of these endemics are shared among the islands, such as *Archisotoma madagascariensis*, *Isotomodes buchardi*, and *Axelsonia thalassophila* (Isotomidae), and *Friesea mahajanga* and *Pseudachorutes hodeberti* (Neanuridae) (Figure 9.17c). These species were found in the sand of intertidal zones of beaches (Börner 1907; Carpenter 1916; Thibaud 2008a, 2008b, 2010a, 2010b, 2011, 2015), suggesting that they are probably able to disperse via water and have certain physiological adaptations that support saline stress (Witteveen et al. 1987).

Exclusively on Madagascar, there are 76 endemic species in 30 genera, with an increase of 13 species since the last tabulation (Betsch 2003). Of the 10 endemic genera previously reported, nine are maintained, and one is not, since a new species of *Richardsitas* (Sminthuridae) from Australia has been described recently (Medeiros et al. 2020). Among the endemics, noteworthy genera include those of the family Bourletiellidae, including *Anjavidiella*, with five endemic species in the Central Highlands. *Anjavidiella andoharianensis* (Figure 9.17d) is one of the four species of its genus that has Andringitra as its type locality. Among the recent discoveries are *Isotogastrura madagascariensis* (Isotogastruridae) and *Willemia nosyboraha* (Hypogastruridae), both representing families recently recorded in Madagascar (Thibaud 2008b).

Symphypleona is a dominant component of the Madagascar endemics, with 38 species in 14 genera, 18 species of which are in the genus *Temeritas* (Sminthuridae), followed by Poduromorpha, with 23 species in nine genera, of which *Pronura* (Neanuridae) is the richest, with 11 endemic species. Finally, Entomobryomorpha is the group least surveyed taxonomically, but it has great potential. Betsch (2003) reported eight endemic species in five genera, of which three belong to *Salina*, among them *S. milloti* (Figure 9.17b), one of five species endemic to the Malagasy Region. *Salina* is the largest genus of the tribe Cremastocephalini, with 81 valid species, of which 30% are in the Neotropics (Oliveira et al. 2018; Bellinger et al. 2020). Subsequently, the Madagascar figures have increased to 15 species in seven genera of Entomobryoidea (Entomobryidae and Paronellidae), owing to the species descriptions of members of the genera *Trogolaphysa* (Nguyen and Soto-Adames 2018), *Seira* (Cipola et al. 2018), and *Lepidocyrtinus* (Cipola et al. 2020; Godeiro et al. 2020). *Lepidocyrtinus* is a pantropical genus, and Malagasy species are *L. voeltzkowi* (Figure 9.17a), *L. andevo*, *L. betamponensis*, *L. briani*, and *L. iegoi*. Isotomidae and three subfamilies of Entomobryidae (Entomobryinae, Heteromurinae, and Lepidocyrtinae) have few records and remain without endemic species on Madagascar.

The balance of the Malagasy Region has 28 or 29 endemic species of springtails, 18 of which are in the Seychelles, three on La Réunion, and one each in the Comoros and Mayotte. Most Seychelles endemics have not been reported on Madagascar, not even at the generic level. These mainly include members of Entomobryoidea, such as *Lepidonella*, which has a pantropical distribution; *Troglopedetes*, from the Old World; and *Cyphoderus* (Paronellidae), *Dicranocentrus*, *Entomobrya*, and *Lepidocyrtus* (Entomobryidae), with cosmopolitan ranges (Bellinger et al. 2020). Similarly, three Poduromorpha genera with endemic species in the Malagasy Region are unknown on Madagascar: *Neanura sexoculata* (Neanuridae) is endemic to the Seychelles, *Axenyllodes comoriensis* (Odontellidae) to the Comoros, and *Phylliomeria bebourensis* (Neanuridae) to La Réunion.

Analyzing the Malagasy Region as a whole, 77% of the species richness of Collembola is composed of endemic species, but once again, given our current level of knowledge, that figure represents only a fraction of the region's total Collembola diversity. This specific rate of endemism compared to its territorial area of 587,000 km^2 is extraordinarily high in relation to other pantropical regions with relatively similar vegetation types. The African continent, at 29,634,000 km^2 (50 times larger than Madagascar), has only 60% endemics (75 species of 124 recorded) (Janion-Scheepers et al. 2015). Brazil, for instance, with a territory of 8,511,000 km^2 (14.5 times larger than Madagascar), has a level of endemic species of 66% (264 species out of 400 recorded) (Zeppelini et al. 2020).

However, a comparison of levels of endemism of Malagasy Collembola with other tropical areas of the world poses several problems. The first is that springtails can occur in different biotopes of an ecosystem, some of which remain entirely unexplored (e.g., canopy, epiphytes, suspended soil). The other is that sampling methods (e.g., traps, soil or litter sifting, fauna extraction by drying) in different areas vary, and there is still no standardization in sampling techniques (Betsch 2003). Lastly, the period of the sampling effort at each site is also important with regard to extrapolations of species richness and must be minimally similar so that the number of species can be properly compared.

GEOGRAPHIC AND HABITAT DISTRIBUTIONS

Members of Collembola are saprophagous and depend on the quality of the dead plant matter they ingest. Consequently, they can be very abundant and represent a large part of the microarthropod-fauna-associated soil (e.g., litter, mosses). Soil-dwelling springtails, therefore, have remained dependent on soil conditions, while aboveground springtails have developed strategies allowing them to adapt to less-buffered hydric and thermal conditions. However, it is important to consider that some species found mainly on the ground during the dry season disperse to higher levels in the vertical vegetation in the wet season, as observed in the dry deciduous forests of western Madagascar (Rajaonarivelo et al. 2019).

In general, most noncavernicolous springtails—mainly members of Isotomidae, Sminthurididae, and Poduromorpha—are edaphic, inhabiting litter (epiedaphic), as well as some deep layers of soil (hemiedaphic and euedaphic), and those of this last category can be indirectly associated with vegetation and humus type. These taxa tend to have poorly developed (or reduced) appendages, which allows them to move among soil particles. Some euedaphic species (e.g., *Cyphoderus*, *Isotomiella*, *Isotomodes*) that live in dark environments (aphotic) may share characteristics with cave species, such as lack of pigment and absence of eyes.

Most species are epiedaphic and inhabit the shallow layers of soil and litter. However, some genera of Entomobryoidea, such as *Lepidocyrtinus* and *Salina* (Figures 9.17a and b), are also found on seedlings and/or low-elevation branches, and must certainly occur up to the canopy. Both genera have long appendages with morphological characteristics that make it possible to occupy these niches.

Occurrence and distribution of Collembola on Madagascar is dependent on geological history and lineage evolution since the breakup of Gondwana. The predominance of tropical rainforest, grasslands, and wooded savanna in the pantropical zone—including the grasslands of the Malagasy Region—provides similar conditions, including climate and vegetation types, for generalists to thrive. In this sense, pantropical genera (e.g., *Bovicornia*, *Pronura*, *Lepidocyrtinus*, *Salina*, *Seira*, *Sminthurides*) are not restricted to specific types of phytogeographic domains, precisely because they occur in different biomes on Madagascar and other continents; many of these genera may even occur at different elevations and climatic conditions. At the same time, progressive isolation of the Madagascar landmass also favored speciation and high levels of endemism of some genera and even a family (Microfalculidae).

At the species level, endemism is generally restricted to a single locale with specific climatic conditions and vegetation. Two limiting factors play an essential role in delimiting the distributions of many species of Collembola—the long-term average minimum of the coldest month and the annual hydric deficit. Among members of Neanurinae, speciation is well marked within the genus *Pronura*, which has a fairly restricted niche breadth and inhibits dry and subarid portions of the island. *Pronura* and *Paleonura* include at least three species that have a wide ecological distribution associated with their stable hypogean ecology in forest ecosystems, as is the case elsewhere in the pantropics (Bellinger et al. 2020; Zeppelini et al. 2020). *Pronura lemurica* and *P. straturata* are two species with broad distributions on Madagascar. *Paleonura anosyennica* is restricted to the southeast and is known from both moist evergreen forests at medium to high elevations and dry spiny thicket—two highly contrasting habitats with very different hydric conditions. Poduromorpha species, however, do not occur extensively across the western dry areas and southwestern and southern subarid environments.

Some genera of Poduromorpha (*Axenyllodes*, *Friesea*, *Willemia*, and *Isotogastrura*) and certain species of Isotomidae generally occupy different niches, but in the Malagasy Region, they seem to be limited to coastal areas, so endemism appears to be restricted to this habitat. Regardless, the ecomorphology of these taxa indicate intimate association with soil granulometry and humidity; therefore, sandy environments (such as beaches) are niches that offer resources for their ecological needs.

Epigeous Symphypleona and Entomobryoidea have colonized all bioclimatic zones of Madagascar, from the hottest to the coldest, from the most humid to the subarid, with species that have differentiated themselves in all possible niches (e.g., *Lepidocyrtinus*, *Seira*, *Salina*). Members of the Symphypleona, which rely especially on litter, are directly bound to plant formation types, specifically litter types, and have colonized the montane habitats of Madagascar as well as the dry and subarid bioclimatic zones. In many cases they are represented by endemic genera that are dependent on particular habitats—for example, *Zebulonia*, found in moist evergreen forest litter at medium elevation; *Bourletiellitas*, in montane moist evergreen forest litter; *Anjavidiella*, in montane ericoid thicket; *Madecassiella*, in the rocky substratum at ground level within montane ericoid thicket; *Vatomadiella*, in small rocky areas in montane grassland; *Richardsitas* and *Paulianitas*, in the litter of dry deciduous forests; and *Parabourletiella*, on the ground in dry spiny thicket.

Among members of Symphypleona, two genera, *Temeritas* and *Anjavidiella*, have undergone intense speciation. *Temeritas*, a pantropical genus found in humid and dry forest litter, includes 18 endemic species on Madagascar. It is important to mention that vast portions of the island (especially the west and the south) have not been properly prospected for these groups. Areas in the east, which are separated based on vegetational sectors (northern, central, and southern) as well as elevational zones, are also in need of more detailed field collections. For example, the central sector, at the latitude of Analamazaotra (Moramanga District), has three elevational levels, each occupied by a different species—*T. ampasimbensis*, at <900 m; *T. perinetensis*, at 900–1250 m; and *T. mantasoensis*, at 1250–1350 m. In the Anosyenne Mountains (southern sector), the strong topographical relief decreases the lower limit of *Temeritas* in the moist evergreen forest down to 100 m elevation.

The genus *Anjavidiella*, an endemic group dependent on montane ericoid thicket, is known from only the Andringitra and Ankaratra Massifs. On Andringitra, three species (*A. andoharianensis* [Figure 9.17d], *A. anjavidilavensis*, and *A. vohidrayensis*) occur in various portions of the ericoid zone just above the forest line (1900–2000 m) and on different slopes or in different ecological situations, while a fourth species (*A. andringitrensis*) is found in the summit zone, at 2500–2650 m, in a very cold subhumid bioclimate. On Ankaratra, the only described species, *A. ankaratrensis*, coexists with an undescribed species that occurs in different types of montane ericoid thicket, specifically of *Erica*.

AFFINITIES

The ancient origin of the Collembola—the oldest fossil record dates from the Devonian, distinctly before the breakup of Gondwana—makes it an interesting group for identifying the affinities of the Malagasy Region fauna (Betsch 2003). Madagascar originated from the fragmentation of an ancient continental landmass, and thus the source and evolution of its biota are expected to be more varied and dynamic than in mainland areas. The other islands in the Malagasy Region (the Comoros, Seychelles, and Mascarenes) are volcanic in origin and distinctly more recent, ranging from 0.01 million years ago (Mya) (Grande Comore) to 8–15 Mya (Rodrigues). In these latter cases, the terrestrial biota colonized via overwater dispersal mostly from Madagascar and from mainland Africa, but a small part may come from other continents (Agnarsson and Kuntner 2012).

In the Entomobryomorpha, *Lepidocyrtinus* probably has an Afrotropical origin, given that members of the genus occur on the African continent, Madagascar, and Brazil (Bellinger et al. 2020). *Seira* is a cosmopolitan genus of Seirinae, but three species (*S. lepidochaetosa*, *S. metafemurata*, and *S. semicaerulea*) have atypical modifications that are certainly restricted to Madagascar. Other genera of Entomobryidae, such as *Entomobrya* and *Lepidocyrtus*, are cosmopolitan, with larger diversity, but because of the difficulties in determining species limits among these taxa, there are almost certainly new species to be described from Madagascar. Recently, it was proposed that *Microfalcula* (Microfalculidae) is closer to *Salina* and *Akabosia* (not occurring in the Malagasy Region) than to other members of Entomobryomorpha (Zhang et al. 2019). If this is phylogenetically correct, then the origin of these taxa is the Old World, Madagascar for *Microfalcula* and Asia for *Salina* and *Akabosia*. This makes sense, since these last two taxa are a sister group (Oliveira et al. 2018).

Poduromorpha, specifically Neanurinae of Madagascar, contains Paleonurini, which includes a pantropical primitive set of genera (*Paleonura*, *Pronura*, and *Afrobella*) composed of Malagasy endemics very close to African and Asian species. Poduromorpha, which also includes an undescribed genus that should be named to replace *Travura betschi*, is derived from this primitive group (Cassagnau 1996).

The Malagasy Pseudachorutinae fauna seems to be much more closely related to the Asiatic fauna, mainly because of the presence of *Oudemansia*, a genus typical of that region. The more recently described *Cephalachorutes masi* reinforces the pantropical distribution of *Cephalachorutes*, although this genus is also highly diverse in the Oriental region. The subfamily's other two species are *Najtafrica riebi*, a monospecific genus closely related to the cosmopolitan genus *Stachorutes*, and *Pseudachorutes hodeberti*, which belongs to a cosmopolitan genus comprising about 110 species. *Pseudachorutes hodeberti* (Figure 9.17c) was described from Tolagnaro (Thibaud 2008b) and recorded on Pamanzi (found on beach sand in both locations), a nearshore island of Mayotte (Thibaud 2010b).

The remaining portion of the Poduromorpha fauna principally comprises species that inhabit intertidal sandy environments, many also known only in South Africa, which has the best-documented Collembola fauna of the African continent (see Janion-Scheepers et al. 2015). A special remark must be made regarding *Stachia folsomi*, an extremely small Odontellidae species widespread in South

America (mainly Brazil), from inland sites to sandy southern Atlantic beach environments, which has been identified from Madagascar at a Toamasina coastal site (Thibaud 2008b); a study of genetic variation of such widely separated populations would be highly informative from a phylogeographic point of view.

Worldwide, the Symphypleona group includes seven pantropical genera, four primitive ancient forest forms (*Collophora*, *Sphyrotheca*, *Pararrhopalites*, and *Temeritas*), and three more recently derived genera (*Calvatomina*, of secondary forest, and *Denisiella* and *Bovicornia*, of open habitats). Further, the Symphypleona includes two ancient genera present in Asia and Africa (*Papirinus* and *Afrosminthurus*); some cosmopolitan genera; an Oriental-region genus that has been introduced to Madagascar (*Papirioides*, with a nonendemic species occurring in secondary forest); one southern genus (*Rastriopes*); and nine genera endemic to Madagascar, six of which may have descended from a southern ancestor.

CONCLUSION

More than a hundred years since the first samples and species records were found, it is clear that the Collembola fauna of the Malagasy Region has a high level of species endemism and a lower level generic endemism. That is especially evident in relation to Symphypleona from Madagascar. However, the level of speciation varies between genera. It is, for example, well developed for one genus within Neanurinae, high for two Symphypleona genera (one pantropical and the other endemic), and relatively restricted for most other genera. In some cases, adjacent islands might also show a high level of endemism, although further studies are required to confirm whether that is the case.

The explanation for Madagascar's endemism is probably related to geographic isolation and highly heterogeneous environmental conditions that have an important relationship to speciation. Consequently, the speciation of certain Madagascar endemic genera occurred after the separation of Gondwana, because of the isolation of the island, either by the preexistence of some lineages or immigration from continental areas to the island. These genera include *Anjavidiella*, *Bourletiellitas*, *Madecassiella*, *Massoudia*, *Microfalcula*, *Parabourletiella*, *Paulianitas*, *Vatomadiella*, and *Zebulonia*. Other genera currently of pantropical distribution probably already inhabited Gondwana before its separation (e.g., *Lepidocyrtinus*, *Temeritas*, *Cephalachorutes*), and for that reason, today they coexist on disjunct continents, most likely because of similar environmental conditions (e.g., Africa, the Oriental region, South and Central America). Obviously, it cannot be ruled out that some species may have been introduced and/or developed adaptive mechanisms that facilitated their dispersion.

The Collembola fauna from the Malagasy Region is still very poorly known, owing to the lack of sampling in several regions and habitats, especially noncoastal habitats. While the efforts of Jean-Marie Betsch and his colleagues were extensive and admirable, most of the species documented on Madagascar are from coastal environments. Furthermore, before a more detailed synthesis can be presented, other areas need to be sampled, including western dry deciduous forests, the Central Highlands, and the dry spiny thickets. In addition, studies in the Malagasy Region are needed to better understand distribution patterns of Collembola and relationships of this fauna to other continents, as well as the evolutionary processes that occurred in the different Malagasy taxa.

Subject editors: Brian L. Fisher and Steven M. Goodman

EPHEMEROPTERA, MAYFLIES

J.-M. Elouard, J.-L. Gattolliat, and M. Sartori

Ephemeroptera, or mayflies, is among the most primitive order of winged insects. They retain several archaic features, such as unfolded wings, little reduction in wing venation, and an abdomen with 10 segments. This order was very diverse before the breakup of Gondwana and subsequently experienced a reduction in species diversity (Sartori and Brittain 2015). Larvae can be found in all types of standing and running waters. Life cycles last from a few weeks to three years. There is no pupal stage, and the adult stage is short, lasting from less than a few hours (Caenidae, Tricorythidae) to three days (Heptageniidae). The emergence stage, known as the subimago, molts into an imago that is able to mate. This intermediate subimago stage is unique among insects. The extremely short imago stage results in weak powers of dispersal from the emergence area. Consequently, gene flow between hydrological basins is low, and migration over long distances, such as the Mozambique Channel, appears difficult but not impossible, especially in the family Baetidae (Monaghan et al. 2005; Gattolliat et al. 2008; Rutschmann et al. 2014, 2017). The rate of species endemism on Madagascar is extremely high, approaching 100%.

Most species emerge at dusk or in the early hours of the night; however, members of the Caenidae typically emerge just before sunrise. Larvae are shredders, filterers, grazers, or collector-gatherers, and even a few predatory taxa are known. Some Malagasy mayfly groups are unusual in their large physical size (*Proboscidoplocia* and *Eatonica*), number of plesiotypic (ancestral or primitive) traits (*Madecassorythus* and *Spinirythus*), or diet (the predatory baetids), increasing the degree of uniqueness and interest in this fauna. Eleven families are present on the island (enumerated below).

Malagasy mayflies were almost unknown until the end of the 1980s, when a program known as Biodiversité et Biotypologie des Eaux Continentales de Madagascar commenced to document different groups of aquatic invertebrates based on island-wide trapping surveys and associated taxonomic studies (for other examples, see Gibon, pp. 1135–41; Cumberlidge, pp. 913–18). While a portion of the taxonomic advances of mayflies associated with this program was presented in *The Natural History of Madagascar* (Elouard et al. 2003), notable advances have been made, with more than 100 species new to science described since 1990 (Table 9.15). Further, the use of genetic tools, including work on Ephemeroptera, have brought new insights into the evolutionary history of this group and a range of different aspects associated with it systematics. Below we present a review of the Malagasy mayfly fauna by family.

EUTHYPLOCIIDAE

This family is represented on Madagascar by the single endemic genus *Proboscidoplocia*. Known previously in the 19th century as *Euthyplocia* (Vayssière 1891, 1937), it was assumed to be monospecific (Demoulin 1966; Fontaine 1968) until a recent revision showed that it comprised at least seven species (Elouard and Sartori 1997; Elouard et al. 1999). Members of this genus are noteworthy in several respects. They are the largest Malagasy representatives of the order and are in fact the largest mayflies in the world (Figure 9.18b). Their larvae are easily recognizable by their huge mandibular tusks, used to dig sand and other fine substrates on the bottom of stony streams. Some species are widespread and found in degraded areas in the east and the north of Madagascar (*P. ruffieuxae*), whereas others are restricted in distribution, such as *P. leplattenierae* (Montagne d'Ambre) and *P. mccaffertyi* (Andohahela). Adults exhibit synchronous emergence during a couple of weeks each year (April or November, depending on the species). At that time, they can be attracted in great numbers to light traps just after sunset.

PALINGENIIDAE

This family of burrowing mayflies is represented on Madagascar by the endemic and extraordinary genus *Cheirogenesia*. It was previously considered to be monospecific (Fontaine 1968), but subsequent studies showed that at least three species inhabit the island (Sartori and Elouard 1999). The larvae colonize the banks of slow-flowing streams and rivers, where they dig horizontal, U-shaped holes in fine silt and clay sediments. The emergence of adults is highly synchronous, lasting for no more than a couple of days, and always takes place before dawn. The most astonishing peculiarity of *Cheirogenesia* is that adults are brachypterous (with reduced wings) and do not fly but rather skim the water surface (Ruffieux et al. 1998). This is the only case of flightlessness ever reported in mayflies. Loss of flight appears to be a secondary adaptation to the lack of predatory fishes in the areas where these mayflies are found. Present in large rivers on both the eastern and western coasts of the island, the genus has a wide distribution. *Cheirogenesia decaryi* is the most common species, inhabiting rivers on the west coast (it is also present in the suburbs of Antananarivo). Other species have much more restricted distributions, including, for example, *C. edmundsi* (Figure 9.18f). Palingeniidae is the only family of mayflies present on Madagascar but absent in continental Africa, having mainly diversified in Asia.

EPHEMERIDAE

Eatonica is the only genus of Ephemeridae present on Madagascar (Demoulin 1969). Two more genera (*Afromera* and *Ephemera*) are found in addition to *Eatonica* in continental Africa. Three species of *Eatonica* are known from Madagascar, which is the same diversity as on Africa. Remarkable for its pink wings, *E. denysae* is the largest species of this genus in the world. The emergence of adults is synchronous, occurring in November at the beginning of the rainy season. Adults have been recorded from only two localities in the Central Highlands. However, unidentified larvae of this genus have been sampled in other forest localities. The larvae are burrowers, digging vertical U-shaped tunnels in silt; they mainly occur in small streams with low velocity in forest habitat.

BAETIDAE

This family is one of the most common and diverse throughout the world as well as on Madagascar, where at least 24 genera and 56 species occur. Currently, the baetids represent half of the species and genera described from the island, and more than 95% of these species have been described since 1997. However, there are still significant gaps in our knowledge, particularly for species living in standing waters, as well as for common genera such as *Afroptilum* and *Dicentroptilum* (Lugo-Ortiz and McCafferty 1998; Gattolliat et al. 1999). At present, the systematics are based mainly on the larval stage; it is generally not possible to identify the subimagos and the imagos to species or even genus level.

All the species but one, and a third of the genera, are endemic to Madagascar. The Malagasy fauna holds strong relationships with that of Africa. Except for the almost cosmopolitan *Cloeon* and *Labiobaetis* and the widely distributed *Nigrobaetis*, all genera are restricted to the Afro-Malagasy region (Lugo-Ortiz and McCafferty 1999; Gattolliat 2001a, 2004). In the Malagasy members of this family, the Oriental component is clearly of less importance (Sartori et al. 2000).

Baetidae is one of the most abundant mayfly families in every region of Madagascar. The Malagasy species show various distribution patterns. A few species occur across much of the island (e.g., *Dicentroptilum merina*, *Herbrossus edmundsorum*, *Labiobaetis fabulosus*). The majority of species are restricted to a single region. Finally, some species are restricted to a single hydrological basin (e.g., *Acanthiops namorona*; Gattolliat 2000) or even to a single locality (e.g., *Afrobaetodes lenae*; Gattolliat and Sartori 1999a). The overall diversity is much higher in the eastern and northern phytogeographic domains than in the western domain.

Members of Baetidae colonize all kinds of freshwater habitats, from standing waters to waterfalls and from small brooks to large rivers. They show the highest diversity in small, well-oxygenated streams. Most mayfly species found in ponds and rice paddies belong to Baetidae. Most baetids are considered to be collector-gatherers. However, some taxa possess highly modified mouthparts for feeding

TABLE 9.15. **Checklist of the described mayflies of Madagascar**

EUTHYPLOCIIDAE

Genus *Proboscidoplocia* Demoulin, 1966

P. auberti Elouard & Sartori, 1997
P. billi Elouard & Sartori, 1997
P. leplattenierae Elouard & Sartori, 1997
P. magdeleineae Elouard & Sartori, 1997
P. mccaffertyi Elouard & Sartori, 1999
P. ruffieuxae Elouard & Sartori, 1997
P. sikorai (Vayssière, 1895)
P. vayssierei Elouard & Sartori, 1997

PALINGENIIDAE

Genus *Cheirogenesia* Demoulin, 1952

C. decaryi (Navàs, 1926)
C. edmundsi Sartori & Elouard, 1999
C. laurencae Sartori & Elouard, 1999

EPHEMERIDAE

Genus *Eatonica* Navàs, 1913

E. denysae Elouard & Sartori, 1998
E. josettae Demoulin, 1969
E. luciennae Elouard & Oliarinony, 1998

BAETIDAE

Genus *Acanthiops* Waltz & McCafferty, 1987

A. delphinae (Gattolliat, 2000)
A. namorona (Gattolliat, 2000)
A. spinosum (Gattolliat, 2000)

Genus *Adnoptilum* Gattolliat & Monaghan, 2010

A. ottkei Gattolliat & Monaghan, 2010
A. thomasorum (Lugo-Ortiz & McCafferty, 1997)

Genus *Afrobaetodes* Demoulin, 1970

A. lenae Gattolliat & Sartori, 1999

Genus *Afroptilum* Gillies, 1990

A. confusum Lugo-Ortiz & McCafferty, 1998
A. gilberti Gattolliat & Sartori, 1999
A. lepidum Lugo-Ortiz & McCafferty, 1998
A. mathildae Gattolliat & Sartori, 1999

Genus *Bugilliesia* Lugo-Ortiz & McCafferty, 1996

B. mirandei (Lugo-Ortiz & McCafferty, 1997)

Genus *Cheleocloeon* Wuillot, 1993

C. madagascariense Gattolliat & Monaghan, 2009

Genus *Cloeon* Leach, 1815

C. cambouei Navàs, 1930
C. durani Navàs, 1926
C. emmanueli Lugo-Ortiz & McCafferty, 1998
C. smaeleni Lestage, 1924

Genus *Dabulamanzia* Lugo-Ortiz & McCafferty, 1996

D. concolorata Gattolliat, 2000
D. gigantea Gattolliat, 2000
D. gladius Gattolliat, 2000
D. improvida Lugo-Ortiz & McCafferty, 1997

Genus *Delouardus* Lugo-Ortiz & McCafferty, 1999

D. djabala Lugo-Ortiz & McCafferty, 1999

Genus *Demoulinia* Gillies, 1990

D. assimilis Gattolliat, 2003
D. insularis Lugo-Ortiz & McCafferty, 1998

Genus *Dicentroptilum* Wuillot & Gillies, 1994

D. merina Lugo-Ortiz & McCafferty, 1998

Genus *Edmulmeatus* Lugo-Ortiz & McCafferty, 1997

BAETIDAE

E. grandis Lugo-Ortiz & McCafferty, 1997

Genus *Guloptiloides* Gattolliat & Sartori, 2000

G. gargantua Gattolliat & Sartori, 2000

Genus *Herbrossus* McCafferty & Lugo-Ortiz, 1998

H. christinae Gattolliat & Sartori, 1998
H. edmundsorum McCafferty & Lugo-Ortiz, 1998
H. elouardi Gattolliat & Sartori, 1998

Genus *Labiobaetis* Novikova & Kluge, 1987

L. dambrensis Gattolliat, 2001
L. fabulosus Lugo-Ortiz & McCafferty, 1997
L. gilliesi Gattolliat, 2001
L. longicercus Gattolliat, 2001
L. nigrocercus Gattolliat, 2001
L. plumbago Lugo-Ortiz & McCafferty, 1997
L. punctatus Gattolliat, 2001
L. vulgaris Gattolliat, 2001

Genus *Madaechinopus* Gattolliat & Jacobus, 2010

M. giboni (Gattolliat, 2002)
M. minutus (Gattolliat, 2002)

Genus *Nesoptiloides* Demoulin, 1973

N. electroptera (Demoulin, 1966)

Genus *Nigrobaetis* Novikova & Kluge, 1987

N. cryptus Gattolliat, 2004

Genus *Potamocloeon* Gillies, 1990

P. bicoloratum (Gattolliat, 2001)
P. freitagae (Gattolliat, 2001)
P. portabile (Lugo-Ortiz & McCafferty, 1999)
P. pseudogladium (Gattolliat, 2001)

Genus *Pseudopannota* Waltz & McCafferty, 1987

P. camillae Gattolliat, 2002
P. vinckei (Demoulin, 1973)

Genus *Rheoptilum* Gattolliat, 2001

R. arni Gattolliat, 2001
R. lokohense Gattolliat, 2001

Genus *Scutoptilum* Gattolliat, 2002

S. verrucosum Gattolliat, 2002

Genus *Securiops* Jacobus, McCafferty & Gattolliat, 2006

S. mandrare Jacobus, McCafferty & Gattolliat, 2006

Genus *Xyrodromeus* Lugo-Ortiz & McCafferty, 1997

X. ambiguus Gattolliat, 2004
X. latipalpus Gattolliat, 2001
X. modestus Gattolliat, 2001
X. namarona Lugo-Ortiz & McCafferty, 1997
X. sartorii Gattolliat, 2001

OLIGONEURIIDAE

Genus *Madeconeuria* Demoulin, 1973

M. insulicola (Demoulin, 1966)

Genus *Rianilaneuria* Pescador & Peters, 2007

R. diminuta Pescador & Peters, 2007

HEPTAGENIIDAE

Genus *Notonurus* Crass, 1947

N. josettae (Sartori & Elouard, 1996)
N. matitensis (Sartori & Elouard, 1996)

(continued overleaf)

TABLE 9.15. ***continued***

LEPTOPHLEBIIDAE
Genus *Nesophlebia* Peters & Edmunds, 1964
N. adusta Peters & Edmunds, 1964
Genus *Petersophlebia* Demoulin, 1973
P. inaequalis (Demoulin, 1955)
P. insularis Demoulin, 1973
Genus *Polythelais* Demoulin, 1973
P. digitata Demoulin, 1973
Genus *Radima* Akers, Peters & Peters, 2003
R. edmundsorum Akers, Peters & Peters, 2003
Genus *Ulmerophlebia* Demoulin, 1955
U. succinea Demoulin, 1966
U. variegata Demoulin, 1966
TRICORYTHIDAE
Genus *Madecassorythus* Elouard & Oliarinony, 1997
M. hertui Elouard & Oliarinony, 1997
M. linae Elouard & Oliarinony, 1997
M. ramanankasinae Oliarinony & Elouard, 1997
M. raphaeli Oliarinony & Sartori, 2000
Genus *Ranorythus* Oliarinony & Elouard, 1998
R. langrandi Oliarinony & Elouard, 1998
R. violettae Oliarinony & Elouard, 1998
Genus *Spinirythus* Oliarinony & Elouard, 1998
S. colasi Elouard & Oliarinony, 1998
S. martini Oliarinony & Elouard, 1998
S. rosae Oliarinony & Raberiaka, 1998
Genus *Tricorythus* Eaton, 1868
T. ambinintsoae Oliarinony & Elouard, 1998
T. fyae Oliarinony & Raberiaka, 1998
T. goodmani Elouard & Oliarinony, 1998
T. jeannae Oliarinony & Elouard, 1998
TRICORYTHIDAE
T. pierrei Elouard & Oliarinony, 1998
T. rolandi Oliarinony & Raberiaka, 1998
T. sylvestris Oliarinony & Elouard, 1998
T. variabilis Oliarinony & Raberiaka, 1998
T. vulgaris Raberiaka & Oliarinony, 1998
CAENIDAE
Genus *Caenis* Stephens, 1835
C. gattolliati Malzacher, 2010
C. johannae Malzacher, 1995
C. namorona Malzacher, 1995
C. nausicaae Malzacher, 2010
C. rugosa Malzacher, 1995
C. rutila Malzacher, 1995
C. solida Malzacher, 2010
C. spinosa Malzacher, 1995
Genus *Callistellina* Sun & McCafferty, 2004
C. panda (Sun & McCafferty, 2002)
Genus *Madecocercus* Malzacher, 1995
M. bibulus Malzacher, 2006
M. tauroides Malzacher, 1995
Genus *Trichocaenis* Malzacher, 2009
T. inexperta Malzacher, 2009
TELOGANODIDAE
Genus *Manohyphella* Allen, 1973
M. keiseri Allen, 1973
PROSOPISTOMATIDAE
Genus *Prosopistoma* Latreille, 1833
P. variegatum Latreille, 1833

on varied food sources, for example aquatic vascular plants (*Edmulmeatus grandis* on *Hydrostachys*; Gattolliat and Sartori 2003); and scraping periphyton from stones (*Xyrodromeus*, Lugo-Ortiz and McCafferty 1997, Gattolliat 2002; *Rheoptilum*, Gattolliat 2001b; and some species of *Dabulamanzia*, Gattolliat and Sartori 2000a). Three endemic genera, *Guloptiloides* (Figure 9.18a), *Nesoptiloides*, and *Herbrossus*, were recognized as predators of other stream invertebrates (Gattolliat and Sartori 1998, 1999b, 2000b, 2001). A carnivorous diet is quite unusual among members of Baetidae.

OLIGONEURIIDAE

Oligoneuriidae is found worldwide. The first Malagasy species was described by Demoulin (1973) as *Elassoneuria* (*Madeconeuria*) *insulicola*, creating a new subgenus. Recently the subgenus *Madeconeuria* was elevated to the genus level (Massariol et al. 2019). Although a single species is currently described, this genus includes at least 15 additional putative species on Madagascar. Most of them have restricted distributions. This species richness seems high in comparison with the six *Elassoneuria* species present in Africa. Most of the species are distributed on the eastern slopes and in the Central Highlands. The new genus *Rianilaneuria* has been recorded only from the Mangoro River (Pescador and Peters 2007).

Adults of *Madeconeuria* emerge and fly at dusk, forming horizontal swarms in which males patrol to find females to mate with. The larvae are filter feeders and found in areas with fast water currents. They have additional sublabial gills that differentiate them from other mayfly larvae and are very sensitive to water quality and dissolved oxygen levels. Adults have geminated (subparallel arrangement of longitudinal and intercalary) wing veins. Male imagoes have large holoptic eyes (meeting along the median dorsal line of the head) while females have small, dichoptic (separated) eyes. The identification of larvae to species remains, for the time being, impossible.

On Madagascar, larvae of some species of *Madeconeuria* carry phoretic preimaginal instars of the black fly *Simulium* (Elouard 2003a). For example, *S. kiangarensis* is found on *Madeconeuria* in tributaries of the middle reaches of the Betsiboka River (Pilaka and Elouard 1999).

HEPTAGENIIDAE

Knowledge on the composition of this family on Madagascar is still fragmentary and has been the subject of much taxonomic confusion. Two species were described by Sartori and Elouard (1996), in two different genera: *Afronurus matitensis* and *Thalerosphyrus josettae*. Webb et al. (2006) recombined the latter in *Compsoneuria josettae*, which

FIGURE 9.18 **Malagasy members of Ephemeroptera at different life stages: A) Larva of *Guloptiloides gargantua*, one of the three carnivorous baetid genera endemic to Madagascar; B) larva of *Proboscidoplocia vayssierei*, one of the largest mayflies in the world; C) larva of *Radima edmundsorum*, one of the few described leptophlebiid species; D) larva of *Spinirythus martini*, males of which have large eyes, an unusual feature in the family Tricorythidae; E) larva of undescribed *Notonurus*, the most widespread species of Heptageniidae on Madagascar; F) male adult (above) and female adult (below) of *Cheirogenesia edmundsi*, endemic to the Mangoro River.** (PHOTOS A–D by M. Sartori, E by L. Vuataz, and F by Michel Krafft; repository of all images Museum of Zoology, Lausanne.)

was correct at that time, as *Thalerosphyrus* was found only in the Oriental realm. To resolve the origin and diversification of Malagasy Heptageniidae, a multiple gene phylogeny was proposed by Vuataz et al. (2013), including representatives of Africa and Southeast Asia. One of the main results indicated that Heptageniidae on Madagascar forms a monophyletic lineage, with the sister group being African. *Compsoneuria* is paraphyletic, and all Afrotropical "*Compsoneuria*" are now reallocated to the genus *Notonurus*. Although monophyletic, Malagasy *Notonurus* species are in two different clades currently known as "*Compsoneuria*-like" and "*Afronurus*-like." A species delineation model indicates that at least 14 species are at least present on the island, nine of *Compsoneuria*-like clades, and five of *Afronurus*-like clades. Distributional patterns are similar to those of other mayflies, with one widely distributed species in degraded areas and steppes, as well as an undescribed species of *Notonurus* (Figure 9.18e), and several others restricted to one or two basins in intact moist evergreen forests (e.g., Montagne d'Ambre, Namorona River, Rianila River). The larvae of *Compsoneuria*-like species are often found on deadwood in slow-flowing waters. Species of *Afronurus*-like clades have more restricted distributions and are mainly associated with the remnants of intact moist evergreen forests. *Afronurus*-like larvae are more rheophilic (preferring fast-flowing waters) than *Compsoneuria*-like larvae, and are predominantly found on the stony bottoms of cool brooks and streams.

LEPTOPHLEBIIDAE

Among mayflies, this family is one of the richest in species worldwide but the least-studied on Madagascar. At present, only seven species belonging to five genera are described from the island (Akers et al. 2003 and references therein). The only recent addition to the family is the description of the genus *Radima* (Figure 9.18c), known from all development stages (Akers et al. 2003). Although preliminary, our first investigations indicate that at least 15 genera and 100 species occur on the island.

Leptophlebiidae species are present in all kinds of watercourses. Although low current speeds are generally preferred, some genera are rheophilic. On Madagascar, this family has a very wide distribution. It is present in the eastern draining rivers, in the Central Highlands, as well as in western-draining river systems. Nevertheless, the majority of members of Leptophlebiidae are found in eastern moist evergreen forest streams at either low or high elevations. All genera are endemic. A phylogenetic study based on two nuclear genes (O'Donnell and Jockusch 2008) seems to indicate that Malagasy members of Leptophlebiidae belong to two different lineages: one is completely endemic to Madagascar, while the other forms a sister group with paleoaustral lineages from South America (e.g., *Meridialaris*, *Penaphlebia*), Australia (e.g., *Atalomicria*, *Koorrnonga*), and New Zealand (e.g., *Deleatidium*, *Zephlebia*), and a second sister group sharing relationships with southeast Asia and Papua New Guinea (*Thraulus* and *Choroterpes* lineages).

TRICORYTHIDAE

Madagascar seems to be the cradle of this family, given the presence of the most archaic forms. Four genera are present: *Madecassorythus*, *Spinirythus*, *Ranorythus*, and *Tricorythus*. The first three are treated by some authors as subgenera of *Tricorythus* (e.g., Kluge 2010); the first two are the most primitive genera in the family (Elouard and Oliarinony 1997; Oliarinony et al. 1998). *Tricorythus* is the only genus in this family that is nonendemic to Madagascar, occurring in Africa as well.

Madecassorythus and *Ranorythus* (Oliarinony and Elouard 1997) are found on the eastern slope, and species often show important levels of local microendemism. The monospecific genus *Spinirythus* (Figure 9.18d) has a wider distribution on the east coast and Central Highlands (Oliarinony et al. 1998). *Tricorythus* is widely distributed across the island (Oliarinony et al. 1997), and there are many microendemics. Only *T. variabilis* is widely distributed. These taxa are mainly characterized at the imaginal stage, and identification based on larvae is poorly known (but see Oliarinony et al. 2000)

Malagasy tricorythid larvae are rheophilic, living in medium to strong current speeds in all kinds of watercourses. Emergence occurs at dusk, but there is no mating swarm. In order to mate, males intercept females during upstream flight. Tricorythid adults have the shortest imaginal life among the mayflies, lasting less than an hour; the imaginal molt is only partial, serving only to free the genital apparatus of the male.

CAENIDAE

This family is represented on Madagascar by four described genera and 12 species (Sun and McCafferty 2002; Malzacher 1995, 2009, 2010). The cosmopolitan genus *Caenis* is the most abundant and diverse. It occurs in all regions of Madagascar, and its larvae are found mainly in rivers and large streams. Adults are often caught with light traps just before dawn. Some species exhibit a restricted range (*C. rutila*), but most have broad distributions and may be found in pseudosteppes and degraded secondary forests (e.g., *C. spinosa*). The endemic genus *Madecocercus* belongs to a primitive lineage (subfamily Madecocercinae) known from two described species (*M. tauroides* and *M. bibulus*) restricted to the east and Central Highlands, and is closely related to the Ethiopian genus *Afrocercus*. This genus is one example among many of an ancient lineage associated with intact moist evergreen forest. The larvae inhabit more fast-flowing watercourses than those of *Caenis*, and the adults have dawn and sunset activity patterns. The genus *Callistellina* seems to also be associated with intact moist evergreen forests, and the rare and atypical *Trichocaenis* has been reported only from the Namorona River basin.

TELOGANODIDAE

Teloganodidae is a relict Gondwanan family distributed mainly in southern South Africa (Pereira Da Conceicoa and Barber James 2013) and tropical Asia (Sartori et al. 2008); members of the family are rare on Madagascar (Allen 1973). The larvae are restricted to the coldest streams in montane areas, a distribution shared with Plecoptera (Elouard 2003b). On the island, this family is represented by the endemic genus *Manohyphella*, which has a single species, *M. keiseri*, that has been recorded from the Andringitra Massif, Ranomafana, and Andasibe areas; in the north, the species has been recorded from the higher tributaries of the Lokoho River basin. Known for a long time only from the imaginal female stage, the larva has been described by McCafferty and Benstead (2002) and the male imago by Oliarinony et al. (2016), who also reported its life cycle.

PROSOPISTOMATIDAE

The type species of this family, *Prosopistoma variegatum*, was described in 1833 from Madagascar (Barber-James 2010). Because the body of the larva is hidden under a bizarre form of a shield, this family was originally classified as a copepod crustacean (*Binoculus*; see Latreille 1833). This error was left uncorrected for almost a century. Adults have two pairs of wings without transversal veins. This monogeneric family is one of the most evolved among the mayflies and is present in Africa, Asia, Europe, and Australia.

Besides *P. variegatum* (Vayssière 1890a, 1890b), four undescribed species have been recorded on Madagascar; one large species is closely related to the type species, while the other three species are smaller and of the same size as those found in Africa. Members of *Prosopistoma* are distributed on the eastern slope and in the Central Highlands. The larvae are rheophilous and found in the rapid stretches of middle and large rivers in the same kinds of habitats in which members of Tricorythidae are found. Adults fly at dawn.

CONCLUSION

Excluding Leptophlebiidae (which likely represents at least 80 species), the balance of the Malagasy mayfly fauna encompasses more than 100 species belonging to more than 40 genera. This richness is quite high in comparison with what is found in Africa, even if we consider that large parts of Africa have not yet been explored for mayflies. The island's 120 million years of isolation from Africa has allowed the survival of several archaic (plesiomorphic) taxa, such as the Tricorythidae lineage, as well as other interesting forms (e.g., *Proboscidoplocia*).

The study of Madagascar's mayflies is far from complete. A remarkable number of species still await description in the families Baetidae, Prosopistomatidae, Oligoneuriidae, and Heptageniidae. Finally, the study of the largest family (Leptophlebiidae) has barely started, and we can estimate that at least 130 species are still to be discovered and described. Some areas of the island showing high degrees of endemism for other invertebrate groups, such as the Sambirano Region, the Masoala Peninsula, and the Tsaratanàna Massif, have not been properly prospected for mayflies, and many surprises remain to be discovered.

Combining molecular and morphological tools is an efficient method to estimate the biodiversity at different scales, allowing species delimitation and, as a final goal, taxonomical description. This approach has already been successfully applied to the family Heptageniidae (Vuataz et al. 2013) and should be more widely used for understudied lineages, such as the family Leptophlebiidae and some genera within Baetidae.

The digitalization of the mayflies from Madagascar housed in various European natural history museums (Museum of Zoology, Lausanne; Muséum National d'Histoire Naturelle, Paris; and the Natural History Museum, London), followed by the uploading of data to the GBIF (Global Biodiversity Information Facility) web portal, is of great importance for localizing available specimens, sharing metadata, and facilitating future research. This project included more than 4300 occurrence records representing around 74,000 specimens sampled between 1951 and 2017 (Podolak et al. 2019).

Subject editors: Brian L. Fisher and Steven M. Goodman

ODONATA, DRAGONFLIES, DAMSELFLIES, *ANGIDINA*

K.-D. B. Dijkstra

Dragonflies and damselflies are conspicuous freshwater insects that are sensitive to both aquatic and terrestrial habitat quality, making them among the best environmental sentinels (Darwall et al. 2011). Their amphibiotic life cycle, sensitivity to habitat quality (e.g., forest cover, water chemistry, river structure), and relative ease of identification make them well suited for evaluating ecological change above and below the water surface, in both the short term (conservation and monitoring) and long term (biogeography and climatology). Owing to their attractive appearance, they function as flagships for conservation not only in water-rich habitats, such as wetlands and rainforests, but also where water is scarce and therefore especially vital to the survival of life.

Odonata constitutes a relatively small insect order, with 6300-plus species described globally; its greatest species diversity is in the tropics. These insects are recognized by the slender abdomen, globular eyes that often make up a large portion of the head, short antennae, and long wings. The group is divided into the suborders Zygoptera (damselflies) and Anisoptera (true dragonflies), although "dragonflies" is used colloquially to refer to the entire order. All larvae live underwater and prey on small animals, taking a few weeks to several years to develop. Emergence takes place above the water on plants or the shore, after which the adult leaves to hunt and become sexually mature. The males return to the water to search for females or establish territories, whereas the females often return only to mate and lay their eggs (Suhling et al. 2015).

ODONATA OF MADAGASCAR

As of April 2020, 173 described species of Odonata are recognized on Madagascar (Table 9.16). Common African species whose reported presence on the island has not been verified are *Crocothemis sanguinolenta*, *Orthetrum brachiale*, *O. caffrum*, *O. chrysostigma*, *Palpopleura lucia*, *Sympetrum fonscolombii*, *Trithemis arteriosa*, *T. furva*, *T. stictica*, and *Zygonyx torridus*.

Reports from Madagascar of the Mascarene species *Gynacantha bispina* and *Hemicordulia virens* represent confusion with similar Malagasy species. Reports of *Ischnura hilli* (a synonym of the Ethiopian endemic *I. abyssinica*) and the Indian *Hemicordulia asiatica* by Legrand (2001a), and of the continental African *Proischnura subfurcata* (as *Enallagma subfurcatum*) and *Malgassophlebia bispina* by Donnelly and Parr (2003), are considered errors. Donnelly and Parr (2003) included possible records of the African species *Ceriagrion suave* and *Orthetrum austeni*, but this too could not be confirmed.

About 20 unnamed species are known to be present in collections. These include at least five species in *Nesolestes*, two in both *Protolestes* and *Tatocnemis*, one in *Proplatycnemis*, at least three in *Pseudagrion*, one in *Isomma*, two in *Nesocordulia*, and one in *Diplacodes*. *Archaeophlebia* and *Malgassophlebia* may include new species as well. An unknown species allied to *Anaciaeschna* is discussed below.

Considering these additions and that some of the unconfirmed species may yet prove to be present, the total number of species occurring on Madagascar is likely over 200. Almost 93% of the known species of Zygoptera are endemic to the island (over 100 in total), while 65% of the generally better-dispersing members of Anisoptera are endemic. The 35 additional species in the Malagasy Region, found in the Comoros (Anjouan, Grande Comore, Mayotte, and Mohéli), the Mascarenes (Mauritius and La Réunion), and the Seychelles (composed of numerous islands), are not treated in this contribution.

The Malagasy fauna is notably insular, with about half the species belonging to numerous unrelated African lineages (see below). These are widespread on the island but have not diversified or have barely done so there. The rest belong to a few lineages with more distant continental affinities, which radiated into numerous localized species. This dichotomy reflects the finding of Samonds et al. (2012; also see Samonds et al., pp. 73–78) that few poorly dispersing freshwater vertebrate groups arrived on Madagascar after the Cretaceous, while in the past 15 million years, only strong fliers reached the island.

The fauna's insularity is also reflected in the species' size and behavior. The local counterparts of the continental *Phaon iridipennis*, *Chalcostephia flavifrons*, *Diplacodes lefebvrii*, *Hemistigma albipunctum*, *Orthetrum abbotti*, and probably other species, are notably large, suggesting island gigantism. Endemics like *Anax tumorifer* and *Phyllomacromia trifasciata* perch more often than their patrolling relatives on the mainland. Indeed, most odonates appear more approachable on Madagascar. Also notable is that each of the three Malagasy genera in the family Gomphidae includes a relatively large species with a boldly black and yellow body and bright reddish abdominal tip. This striking appearance is shared with a number of more distantly related species (Figure 9.19). Such strong convergence is not seen outside Madagascar, but its cause or function (mimicry?) is unknown.

This contribution is based on the book *Dragonflies and Damselflies of Madagascar and the Western Indian Ocean Islands* (Dijkstra and Cohen 2021), and on chapters and reports on the order in Dijkstra et al. (2011) and Schütte et al. (2018), as well as a contribution from the precursor of this book (Donnelly and Parr 2003). Below, we present a review of the Malagasy Odonata fauna by family.

ZYGOPTERA

Lestidae

Of over 150 species in nine genera worldwide, only the cosmopolitan genus *Lestes* occurs in the Afrotropics, with nine species on the African continent and five on Madagascar. Of these rather dull and

TABLE 9.16. **Checklist of the Odonata species of Madagascar**

ZYGOPTERA SELYS, 1854

Lestidae Calvert, 1901

Lestes Leach, 1815

L. auripennis Fraser, 1955

L. ochraceus Selys, 1862—Also in Africa, but Madagascar subspecies *unicolor* McLachlan, 1895 often treated as a separate species, of which *aldabrensis* Blackman and Pinhey, 1967 from Aldabra (Seychelles) might be a subspecies or synonym.

L. pruinescens Martin, 1910—Synonymized with *L. simulatrix* by Schmidt (1951) and reinstated by Pinhey (1980) but overlooked by Donnelly and Parr (2003).

L. silvaticus (Schmidt, 1951)

L. simulatrix McLachlan, 1895—The masculine form *simulator* has also been used to match the gender of the genus name, but this is an unjustified emendation of a name that can be seen as a noun in apposition.

Argiolestidae Fraser, 1957

Nesolestes Selys, 1891—Genus is endemic to Madagascar and Comoros (Mohéli).

N. albicauda Fraser, 1952

N. albicolor Fraser, 1955

N. alboterminatus Selys, 1891

N. angydna Schmidt, 1951—Name spelled as *andygna* by Donnelly and Parr (2003); must refer to Malagasy word for dragonfly, *angidina*.

N. drocera Fraser, 1951

N. elisabethae Lieftinck, 1965—Name spelled as *elizabethae* by Donnelly and Parr (2003).

N. forficuloides Fraser, 1955

N. mariae Aguesse, 1968

N. martini Schmidt, 1951

N. pulverulans Lieftinck, 1965

N. radama Lieftinck, 1965

N. ranavalona Schmidt, 1951

N. robustus Aguesse, 1968

N. rubristigma Martin, 1902

N. tuberculicollis Fraser, 1949

Calopterygidae Selys, 1850

Phaon Selys, 1853

P. rasoherinae Fraser, 1949—Listed as the African *P. iridipennis* (Burmeister, 1939) by Donnelly and Parr (2003) and Legrand (2001a); see main text.

Protolestidae Dijkstra & Bybee, in Bybee et al. (2021)

Protolestes Förster, 1899—Genus is endemic to Madagascar.

P. fickei Förster, 1899

P. furcatus Aguesse, 1967

P. kerckhoffae Schmidt, 1949—Name spelled as *kerkhoffae* by Donnelly and Parr (2003).

P. leonorae Schmidt, 1949

P. milloti Fraser, 1949

P. proselytus Lieftinck, 1965—Schmidt (1951) erroneously described this species under the name *P. fickei*.

P. rufescens Aguesse, 1967

ZYGOPTERA

P. simonei Aguesse, 1967—Aguesse (1967) did not specify the identity or gender of the Simone after whom this species was named; therefore, the name should not be amended to *simoneae*.

Tatocnemididae Rácenis, 1959

Tatocnemis Kirby, 1889—Genus is endemic to Madagascar.

T. crenulatipennis Fraser, 1952

T. denticularis Aguesse, 1968

T. emarginatipennis Fraser, 1960

T. malgassica Kirby, 1889

T. mellisi Schmidt, 1951

T. micromalgassica Aguesse, 1968

T. olsufieffi Schmidt, 1951

T. robinsoni Schmidt, 1951

T. sinuatipennis (Selys, 1891)

T. virginiae Legrand, 1992

Platycnemididae Yakobson & Bianchi, 1905

Paracnemis Martin, 1902—Genus is endemic to Madagascar.

P. alluaudi Martin, 1902

P. secundaris (Aguesse, 1968)—Previously known as *Metacnemis secundaris*; see main text.

Proplatycnemis Kennedy, 1920—Genus is endemic to Madagascar, Comoros, and Pemba. All Malagasy species were previously placed in the Holarctic genus *Platycnemis* Burmeister, 1839.

P. alatipes (McLachlan, 1872)

P. aurantipes (Lieftinck, 1965)

P. hova (Martin, 1908)—Name spelled as *hove* by Donnelly and Parr (2003).

P. longiventris (Schmidt, 1951)

P. malgassica (Schmidt, 1951)

P. pallidus Aguesse, 1968—Described as a subspecies of *P. pseudalatipes*, but markings seem sufficiently distinct to consider it a good species.

P. protostictoides (Fraser, 1953)

P. pseudalatipes (Schmidt, 1951)

P. sanguinipes (Schmidt, 1951)

Coenagrionidae Kirby, 1890

Aciagrion Selys, 1891—See below; the Afrotropical *Aciagrion* species may not be closely related to the type from Asia. However, *Mombagrion* Sjöstedt, 1909 (of which *gracile* is the type) has precedence over *Millotagrion*.

A. inaequistigma (Fraser, 1953)—Previously placed in endemic genus *Millotagrion* Fraser, 1953, but so similar to *A. gracile* (Sjöstedt, 1909) from Africa that it seems best to place it in the same genus; see main text.

Africallagma Kennedy, 1920

A. rubristigma (Schmidt, 1951)—Previously placed in the Holarctic genus *Enallagma* Charpentier, 1840; see May (2002).

Agriocnemis Selys, 1877

A. exilis Selys, 1872—Also in Africa and Mascarenes, but reports from Comoros (Mayotte) may pertain to confusion with next species.

A. gratiosa Gerstäcker, 1891—Also in Africa and Comoros (Mayotte).

ZYGOPTERA

A. merina Lieftinck, 1965
Azuragrion May, 2002
A. kauderni (Sjöstedt, 1917)—Also in Comoros. Previously considered a subspecies of the African *A. nigridorsum* (Selys, 1876) and placed in the Holarctic genus *Enallagma* Charpentier, 1840; see May (1997a, 2002).
Ceriagrion Selys, 1876
C. auritum Fraser, 1951
C. glabrum (Burmeister, 1839)—Also in Africa, Comoros (Mayotte), Mascarenes, and Seychelles.
C. madagazureum Fraser, 1949
C. nigrolineatum Schmidt, 1951
C. oblongulum Schmidt, 1951
Ischnura Charpentier, 1840
I. filosa Schmidt, 1951
I. senegalensis (Rambur, 1842)—Also in Africa, Comoros, Aldabra, Mascarenes, Seychelles, and Asia.
Pseudagrion Selys, 1876
P. alcicorne Förster, 1906
P. ambatoroae Aguesse, 1968
P. ampolomitae Aguesse, 1968
P. apicale Schmidt, 1951
P. approximatum Schmidt, 1951
P. cheliferum Fraser, 1949
P. chloroceps Fraser, 1955—Replacement name for the species erroneously described as *P. igniceps* by Fraser (1953a); see Fraser (1955a).
P. deconcertans Aguesse, 1968
P. digitatum Schmidt, 1951—Described as a subspecies of *P. alcicorne*. Having seen Schmidt's manuscript, Fraser (1949) preemptively raised it to species level.
P. dispar Schmidt, 1951
P. divaricatum Schmidt, 1951
P. giganteum Schmidt, 1951
P. hamulus Schmidt, 1951
P. igniceps Fraser, 1953—Fraser (1955a) admitted to describing two different species by the same name; the true *P. igniceps* is that introduced by Fraser (1953b).
P. lucidum Schmidt, 1951—Name spelled as *lucidulum* by Donnelly and Parr (2003).
P. macrolucidum Aguesse, 1968—Name spelled as *macrolucidulum* by Donnelly and Parr (2003).
P. malgassicum Schmidt, 1951
P. sp. near *massaicum* Sjöstedt, 1909—*Pseudagrion massaicum* is an African species, but see main text.
P. mellisi Schmidt, 1951
P. merina Schmidt, 1951
P. nigripes Schmidt, 1951
P. olsufieffi Schmidt, 1951
P. pterauratum Aguesse, 1968—Name sometimes spelled as *pterauratus*, but *Pseudagrion* is neutral, hence *pterauratum*.
P. punctum Rambur, 1842—Also in Comoros (Mayotte) and Mascarenes.

ZYGOPTERA

P. renaudi Fraser, 1953—Name spelled as *ranaudi* by Donnelly and Parr (2003).
P. seyrigi Schmidt, 1951
P. simile Schmidt, 1951
P. stuckenbergi Pinhey, 1964—Name spelled as *stuchenbergi* by Legrand (2001a).
P. tinctipenne Fraser, 1951—Name sometimes spelled as *tinctipennis*, but *Pseudagrion* is neutral, hence *tinctipenne*.
P. trigonale Schmidt, 1951
P. ungulatum Fraser, 1951
P. vakoanae Aguesse, 1968
Teinobasis Kirby, 1890
T. alluaudi (Martin, 1896)—Also in Africa and Seychelles, with Madagascar population sometimes separated as subspecies *berlandi* Schmidt, 1951. Sometimes assigned its own genus, *Seychellibasis* Kennedy, 1920.

ANISOPTERA SELYS, 1854
Aeshnidae Leach, 1815
Anaciaeschna Selys, 1878
A. triangulifera McLachlan, 1896—Also in Africa.
Anax Leach, 1815
A. ephippiger (Burmeister, 1839)—Also in Africa, Comoros, Mascarenes, Seychelles, and Eurasia. Previously placed in genus *Hemianax* Selys, 1883; see Peters (2000).
A. imperator Leach, 1815—Also in Africa, Comoros, Mascarenes, and Eurasia.
A. mandrakae Gauthier, 1988
A. tristis Hagen, 1867—Also in Africa, Comoros, Aldabra, and La Réunion.
A. tumorifer McLachlan, 1885
Gynacantha Rambur, 1842
G. hova Fraser, 1956—Name spelled as *hove* by Donnelly and Parr (2003).
G. malgassica Fraser, 1962
G. radama Fraser, 1949
Gomphidae Rambur, 1842
Isomma Selys, 1892—Genus is endemic to Madagascar. Aside from paler face and smaller size, the type species of *Malgassogomphus* Cammaerts, 1987 (see below) is similar to the two named *Isomma* species (see Legrand 2003). An undescribed species is intermediate, so it seems best to merge the genera (K. Schütte, unpublished data).
I. elouardi Legrand, 2003
I. hieroglyphicum Selys, 1892
I. robinsoni (Cammaerts, 1987)—Previously placed in endemic genus *Malgassogomphus*; see above.
Onychogomphus Selys, 1854
O. aequistylus Selys, 1892—Donnelly and Parr (2003) assumed that *O. flavifrons* Selys, 1894 is a synonym of this species.
O. vadoni Paulian, 1960
Paragomphus Cowley, 1934
P. fritillarius (Selys, 1892)

(continued overleaf)

TABLE 9.16. ***continued***

ANISOPTERA

P. madegassus (Karsch, 1890)—Taxon must be revised relative to *P. genei* (Selys, 1841) from Africa and Comoros, as well as the next two species.

P. obliteratus (Selys, 1892)

P. z-viridum Fraser, 1955

Libelluloidea *incertae sedis*

Libellulosoma Martin, 1907—Genus is endemic to Madagascar.

L. minutum Martin, 1907—Name previously spelled as *minuta*, but *Libellulosoma* is neutral, hence *minutum* (Hyde-Roberts et al. 2019).

Nesocordulia McLachlan, 1882—Genus is endemic to Madagascar and Comoros (Mohéli).

N. flavicauda McLachlan, 1882

N. malgassica Fraser, 1956

N. mascarenica Fraser, 1948

N. rubricauda Martin, 1900

N. spinicauda Martin, 1902

Macromiidae Needham, 1903

Phyllomacromia Selys, 1878

P. trifasciata Rambur, 1842—Previously placed in the genus *Macromia* Rambur, 1842 from which the Afrotropical *Phyllomacromia* was split off (May 1997a).

Corduliidae Selys, 1850

Hemicordulia Selys, 1870

H. similis (Rambur, 1842)—Has been recorded from Mahé in the Seychelles, for which the name *delicata* Martin, 1896 is available.

Libellulidae Leach, 1815

Acisoma Rambur, 1842

A. ascalaphoides Rambur, 1842—This name was previously used to separate Afrotropical specimens as a subspecies of the Asian *A. panorpoides* Rambur, 1842. However, it pertains to an endemic species (Mens et al. 2016).

A. attenboroughi Mens et al., 2016—This taxon was previously considered to belong to the subspecies *ascalaphoides* of *A. panorpoides* (see above), but represents a second endemic species (Mens et al. 2016).

Aethiothemis Martin, 1908

A. modesta (Ris, 1909)—Previously placed in *Lokia* Ris, 1919; that genus is synonymous with *Aethiothemis* (Dijkstra and Clausnitzer 2014).

Aethriamanta Kirby, 1889

A. rezia Kirby, 1889—Also in Africa.

Archaeophlebia Ris, 1909—Genus is endemic to Madagascar.

A. martini (Selys, 1896)

Brachythemis Brauer, 1868

B. leucosticta (Burmeister, 1839)—Also in Africa.

Calophlebia Selys, 1896—Genus is endemic to Madagascar.

C. karschi Selys, 1896—Name spelled as *karschii* by Donnelly and Parr (2003). The name *interposita* Ris, 1909 refers to a clear-winged male form; see main text.

ANISOPTERA

Chalcostephia Kirby, 1889

C. flavifrons Kirby, 1889—Also in Africa, with Madagascar population sometimes treated as the subspecies *spinifera* Pinhey, 1962. The latter is a replacement name for *Libellula coronata* sensu Selys, 1869 nec Brauer, 1866.

Crocothemis Brauer, 1868

C. divisa Baumann, 1898—Also in Africa.

C. erythraea (Brullé, 1832)—Also in Africa, Comoros, and Eurasia.

C. striata Lohmann, 1981

Diplacodes Kirby, 1889

D. exilis Ris, 1911—Presence in Comoros (Mayotte) not confirmed. Name is sometimes erroneously spelled as *exul*.

D. lefebvrii (Rambur, 1842)—Also in Africa, Comoros (Mayotte), Aldabra, Mascarenes, Seychelles, and Eurasia. Name often spelled erroneously as *lefebvrei*. Notably large and dark on Madagascar and may refer to the taxon *tetra* Rambur, 1842 named from Mauritius.

Hemistigma Kirby, 1889

H. affine (Rambur, 1842)—Also in Comoros (Mayotte). Name often spelled as *affinis*, but *Hemistigma* is neutral, hence *affine*. Donnelly and Parr (2003) list *ouvirandrae* Förster, 1914 as a subspecies, but this a synonym as *H. affine* has no subspecies.

Macrodiplax Brauer, 1868

M. cora (Brauer, 1867)—Also in Africa, Mauritius, and Australasia.

Malgassophlebia Fraser, 1956

M. mayanga (Ris, 1909)

M. mediodentata Legrand, 2001

Neodythemis Karsch, 1889

N. arnoulti Fraser, 1955—Taxon must be revised relative to *N. pauliani* and *N. trinervulata*.

N. hildebrandti Karsch, 1889—Name spelled as *hilderbrandti* by Legrand (2001a).

N. pauliani Fraser, 1952

N. trinervulata (Martin, 1902)

Olpogastra Karsch, 1895

O. lugubris Karsch, 1895—Not previously listed for Madagascar, but records obtained by K. Schütte (unpublished data).

Orthetrum Newman, 1833

O. azureum (Rambur, 1842)—Subspecies *lugubre* Ris, 1915 in Comoros (Mayotte) seems distinct enough to be considered a valid species.

O. icteromelas Ris, 1910—Also in Africa, although somewhat distinct there from typical specimens from Madagascar and sometimes assigned to the subspecies *cinctifrons* Pinhey, 1970. Name often spelled erroneously as *O. icteromelan*.

O. lemur Ris, 1909

O. malgassicum Pinhey, 1970—Previously treated as a subspecies of the African *O. abbotti* Calvert, 1892, but may be considered a full species. Whether either species occurs in Comoros must be confirmed.

O. stemmale (Burmeister, 1839)—Also in Africa, Comoros, Mascarenes, and Seychelles; island records of *O. brachiale* (Palisot de Beauvois, 1817) are believed to refer to this species.

ANISOPTERA

O. trinacria (Selys, 1841)—Also in Africa, Comoros, Aldabra, and Eurasia.
Palpopleura Rambur, 1842
P. vestita Rambur, 1842
Pantala Hagen, 1861
P. flavescens (Fabricius, 1798)—Occurs worldwide.
Parazyxomma Pinhey, 1961
P. flavicans (Martin, 1908)—Also in Africa. Listed with doubt by Donnelly and Parr (2003) but presence now confirmed.
Rhyothemis Hagen, 1867
R. cognata (Rambur, 1842)
R. semihyalina (Desjardins, 1832)—Also in Africa, Comoros (Mayotte), Aldabra, Mascarenes, and Seychelles.
Tetrathemis Brauer, 1868—The genus name *Neophlebia* Selys, 1869 (of which *polleni* is the type) is available for the rather distinct Afrotropical member of this currently Paleotropical genus.
T. polleni (Selys, 1869)—Also in Africa.
Thermorthemis Kirby, 1889—Genus is endemic to Madagascar and Comoros.
T. madagascariensis (Rambur, 1842)—Name spelled *madagascarensis* by Donnelly and Parr (2003).
Tholymis Hagen, 1867
T. tillarga (Fabricius, 1798)—Also in Africa, Comoros (Mayotte), Mascarenes, Seychelles, and Asia.
Tramea Hagen, 1861—Legrand (2001a) placed the following species in *Trapezostigma* Hagen, 1848, but the name *Tramea* has been given precedence (Dijkstra et al. 2005).
T. basilaris (Palisot de Beauvois, 1817)—Also in Africa, Comoros, Aldabra, Mascarenes, and Asia.
T. limbata (Desjardins, 1832)—Also in Africa, Comoros (Mayotte), Aldabra, Mascarenes, Seychelles, and Asia. Legrand (2001a) listed the synonym *T. continentalis* Selys, 1878 separately.
Trithemis Brauer, 1868
T. annulata (Palisot de Beauvois, 1807)—Also in Africa, Mascarenes, and Eurasia. Sometimes treated as separate species *T. haematina* (Rambur, 1842) on Madagascar and Mascarenes, which was named from Mauritius; see main text. I have seen no evidence that the two species occur together, as suggested by Donnelly and Parr (2003).
T. hecate Ris, 1912—Also in Africa and Comoros (Mayotte).

ANISOPTERA

T. kirbyi Selys, 1891—Also in Africa, Comoros, and Eurasia. Afrotropical specimens are often treated as the subspecies *ardens* Gerstäcker, 1891. Donnelly and Parr (2003) additionally list the female color form *aurantiaca* Pinhey, 1970 as a subspecies. Madagascar males differ in coloration and may more likely represent an unnamed taxon; see main text.
T. persephone Ris, 1912
T. selika Selys, 1869—Subspecies *maia* Ris, 1915 in Comoros (Mayotte) seems distinct enough to be considered a good species.
Urothemis Brauer, 1868
U. assignata (Selys, 1872)—Also in Africa and Mayotte.
U. edwardsii (Selys, 1849)—Also in Africa, Comoros (Mayotte), and La Réunion. Name spelled as *edwardsi* by Donnelly and Parr (2003).
Viridithemis Fraser, 1960—Genus is endemic to Madagascar.
V. viridula Fraser, 1960—Male coloration was described almost half a century after the female was discovered (Crewe and Cohen 2009).
Zygonoides Fraser, 1957
Z. lachesis (Ris, 1912)—Previously placed in the genus *Olpogastra*, which is now limited to *O. lugubris* (Dijkstra et al. 2006).
Zygonyx Hagen, 1867
Z. elisabethae Lieftinck, 1963—Name spelled as *elizabethae* by Donnelly and Parr (2003).
Z. hova (Rambur, 1842)—Damaged holotype may be the same (and thus predate) the African *Z. torridus* (Kirby, 1889); see main text. The latter is known from the Mascarenes but not confirmed on Madagascar, despite being listed (with the erroneous spelling *torrida*) by Donnelly and Parr (2003) and Legrand (2001a).
Z. ranavalonae Fraser, 1949
Z. viridescens (Martin, 1900)

Notes: The families are listed in phylogenetic order (Dijkstra et al. 2013, 2014; Bybee et al. 2021), the genera and species within them are arranged alphabetically. The comments refer mostly to name changes relative to Legrand (2001a) and Donnelly and Parr (2003), while also indicating the distribution of nonendemic species and genera that are endemic to the region. Species mentioned for the Comoros, Mascarenes, or Seychelles are known from two or more of the main islands in those archipelagoes; if Aldabra or another individual island is listed, the species is known only from that specific island or immediate neighboring islands within the island group.

inconspicuous species, only the very common *L. ochraceus* occurs in Africa too, although it is much scarcer there. The taxonomic status of the Malagasy subspecies *L. o. unicolor*, which was treated as a valid species in the past, is therefore worth reevaluation. *Lestes pruinescens* and *L. simulatrix* are quite similar to species found at similar seasonal pools on the African mainland. Finally, the metallic green *L. auripennis* and *L. silvaticus* are confined to the moist semi-deciduous forests in the southwest (Analavelona Massif) and moist evergreen forests in the east, respectively, and appear more distinct morphologically. Further studies are needed to reveal their affinities within the genus.

Argiolestidae, Protolestidae, and Tatocnemididae

More than 40 genera and 300 species of forest-dwelling damselflies were previously assigned to the pantropical family Megapodagrionidae, with concentrations in Australasia, tropical America, and Madagascar. This assemblage was found to consist of multiple distantly related families (Dijkstra et al. 2014). Aside from three genera with over 30 species on Madagascar, the group is poorly represented in the Afrotropics. The monotypic genus *Allolestes* from the granitic Seychelles, two species of *Neurolestes* that range from southeastern Nigeria to western Congo, and the Malagasy

FIGURE 9.19 **Several unrelated Odonata species on Madagascar have a boldly black and yellow body with a bright reddish abdominal tip. A) *Protolestes kerckhoffae* belongs to the endemic family Protolestidae; and B) *Isomma hieroglyphicum*, C) *Onychogomphus aequistylus*, and D) *Nesocordulia malgassica* represent (probably) endemic genera. E) *Paragomphus fritillarius* and F) *Phyllomacromia trifasciata* are part of African radiations but show this same pattern. In contrast, the endemic G) *Viridithemis viridula* (male above, female below) has a green, red-tipped body that is unique worldwide but perhaps is another case of convergent coloration patterns.** (PHOTO A by C. Cohen, B and E by E. R. Nielsen, C and F by M. Post, D by D. Paulson, and G by K.-D. B. Dijkstra.)

Nesolestes species are now placed in the family Argiolestidae. Together with *Podolestes* from southeastern Asia, they form the subfamily Podolestinae, while the subfamily Argiolestinae ranges from the Philippines to Australia.

On Madagascar, multiple *Nesolestes* species can be found together at shaded seeps and streams, as well as on more open forested rivers. So far, 15 species have been named from Madagascar; *N. pauliani* was described from a male collected in 1947 on Mohéli in the Comoros but has not been found since. Many species probably await discovery, possibly making this odonate radiation (now second to that of *Pseudagrion*) the largest in the Malagasy Region. The taxonomy must be revised and can now only be pieced together from Schmidt (1951), Fraser (1955b), Lieftinck (1965), and Aguesse (1968).

The genera *Protolestes* and *Tatocnemis* have similar habits to *Nesolestes* but are restricted to the moist evergreen forests of northern and eastern Madagascar. Eight and 10 species have been named, respectively, but more await description, and taxonomic revision is badly needed. Schmidt (1951) remains the key reference, in addition to Lieftinck (1965) and Aguesse (1967) for *Protolestes*, and Fraser (1960), Aguesse (1968), and Legrand (1992) for *Tatocnemis*. The affinities of these two genera have long remained uncertain. Phylogenomic research indicates they are neither close to Argiolestidae nor what remains of Megapodagrionidae (now exclusively Neotropical), but together form a clade with another isolated Afrotropical group, the monogeneric Pentaphlebiidae from the rainforests of Cameroon, Gabon, and neighboring forested areas. However, differences between adults and larvae, as well as genetic differences, are sufficient to treat each genus as a separate family (Bybee et al. 2021). Protolestidae and Tatocnemididae are thus the first endemic odonate families to be recognized from Madagascar.

Calopterygidae

This family and the related Chlorocyphidae are represented by 17 and 43 species, respectively, in tropical Africa and even more in Asia, but both are (virtually) absent from Madagascar. Two species of the calopterygid genus *Phaon* occur in Africa, while *P. rasoherinae* is widespread along shaded streams and rivers across Madagascar; this is the largest damselfly on the island. Following Lieftinck (1965), *P. rasoherinae* was long treated as a subspecies or synonym of the African *P. iridipennis*, but it is sufficiently distinct to be considered a valid species (E. Insom and F. Terzani, unpublished data).

Platycnemididae

This morphologically diverse family, with some 470 species and 42 genera in the Old World, found mostly in flowing waters, was reclassified by Dijkstra et al. (2014). The group is notably rich in tropical Asia and New Guinea, while a sixth of the species is concentrated in the Afrotropics. Madagascar also has a good representation, but while the subfamilies Allocnemidinae and Disparoneurinae dominate in Africa, with well over 50 species combined, and extend to Arabia and Australia, respectively, neither has crossed the Mozambique Channel to Madagascar. In contrast, the subfamilies Onychargiinae and Platycnemidinae, which are found on Madagascar, are, respectively, absent and less diverse on the continent. The first is the sister group of remaining members of Platycnemididae and includes only four species, two in the genus *Onychargia* in tropical Asia and two others in the genus *Paracnemis* on Madagascar. They are unusual in preferring stagnant swampy habitats over streams. Known only from the holotype collected in 1960 at Beraty near the Manongarivo Special Reserve, *P. secundaris* was described as being in the South African genus *Metacnemis*. Its general appearance, however, suggests it is the western counterpart of *P. alluaudi* from the eastern moist evergreen forest (Dijkstra et al. 2014).

The subfamily Platycnemidinae is morphologically unusual, owing to the expanded and brightly colored legs of the males. Of 40 species worldwide, 10 are restricted to Madagascar and the Comoros. Formerly placed in the Palearctic genus *Platycnemis*, these are now classified in *Proplatycnemis*. A single species of the latter genus occurs on Pemba Island off the coast of Tanzania. This was discovered only in 2001 and was hypothesized to have reached the eastern African coast from Madagascar (Dijkstra et al. 2007a). However, Dijkstra et al. (2014) recovered it as the sister species of several sampled species of Malagasy *Proplatycnemis*, while that genus's sister group is the monotypic *Spesbona* from the Western Cape of South Africa (Figure 9.20). These genera could therefore represent the vestiges of an Afrotropical radiation that has largely disappeared from the continent (Dijkstra et al. 2011).

Coenagrionidae

With over 1350 species, this is the world's largest odonate family, although genetic research reveals two major clades that could be recognized as families (Dijkstra et al. 2014): "core coenagrionids" make up just over half of species diversity worldwide but 86% in the Afrotropics. That number is similar on Madagascar (88%), with

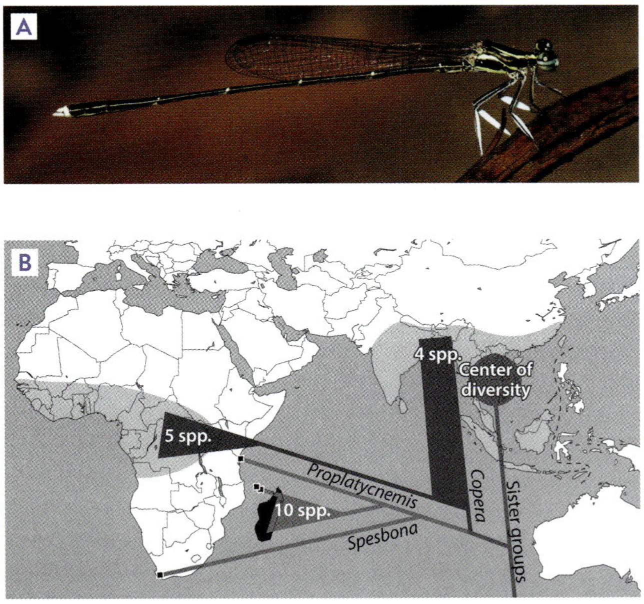

FIGURE 9.20 **With its bright and expanded legs, A) *Proplatycnemis malgassica* is a typical member of the Paleotropical tribe Coperini of the subfamily Platycnemidinae. B) Superimposing the tribe's phylogeny on its distribution, including sister-group relations with the Asian genus *Copera*, suggests that the genus *Proplatycnemis* on Madagascar, the Comoros, and Pemba (off Tanzania), and the monotypic *Spesbona* in South Africa, represent the vestiges of an Afrotropical radiation that has largely disappeared from the continent.** (SOURCE: modified from Dijkstra et al. 2011, 2014). (PHOTO by K. Schütte.)

most species belonging to *Pseudagrion*. Extending to Morocco, Japan, Australia, and the Pacific, *Pseudagrion* is among the largest genera in Odonata, with about 155 species. Over two-thirds of this diversity is Afrotropical and placed in three groups so distinct in morphology, genetics, ecology, and distribution that, in the future, they may be recognized as separate genera (Dijkstra et al. 2007b). The 46 species of the A-group are strictly continental, but two close relatives of the 25 species in the B-group occur in the Malagasy Region. *Pseudagrion punctum* is common on Madagascar, on Mayotte, and in the Mascarenes. The male *P. massaicum* that was reported from Ambohitra near Montagne d'Ambre by Fraser (1951) does not fully match members of that widespread African species and may also represent an endemic species. The third Afrotropical group (which has no published name but could be called the M-group for convenience) contains over 30 species from running waters (notably forest streams) on Madagascar and one species in the Comoros. This M-group is currently the island's largest radiation of Odonata (see *Nesolestes* above), but taxonomic revision is required, with Schmidt (1951), Pinhey (1964a, 1964b), and Aguesse (1968) remaining the main references.

Unlike *Pseudagrion*, most family members prefer open, standing waters. This is also true for the remaining Malagasy "core coenagrionids," which belong to genera that are common in mainland Africa. *Ischnura senegalensis* occurs throughout the warm parts of Africa and Asia, while *I. filosa*, *Africallagma rubristigma*, and *Azuragrion kauderni* are endemic and widespread in the Malagasy Region. The lattermost may be the most common damselfly on Madagascar and the Comoros. *Agriocnemis* species frequent marshes and temporary pools throughout the Old World (sub)tropics. They are among the tiniest odonates but can be good dispersers, with two widespread African species on Madagascar aside from *A. merina*, which is only known from collections made in 1958 near Maroantsetra. Similarly, the genus *Millotagrion* was described from northwestern Madagascar in 1953, with no definite records since (but see Lieftinck 1965). However, *M. inaequistigma* is so similar to the African *Aciagrion gracile* that it seems best to place it in the same genus. *Aciagrio inaequistigma* favors temporary habitats, as found in the poorly studied western part of Madagascar, and adults are most active at dusk, which may explain the dearth of records.

In the Malagasy Region, only *Ceriagrion* and *Teinobasis* belong to the family's second major clade. These are also most intriguing biogeographically. Most of the almost 80 species of *Teinobasis* are found on New Guinea and the Pacific Islands—from where the genus extends to the Philippines and the Malaysian Peninsula. A single species, *T. alluaudi*, inhabits swampy forest on Madagascar, the Seychelles, and (mostly coastal) eastern Africa. Being somewhat distinct morphologically, this species was awarded its own genus, *Seychellibasis*, by Kennedy (1920). While it may have arrived by westward transoceanic dispersal, as suggested for *Hemicordulia* by Dijkstra (2007), its similarity to *Teinobasis* may alternatively have arisen by convergence in an old radiation of African coenagrionids. These are now represented only by the superficially very disparate monotypic genera *Coryphagrion* and *Oreocnemis* from coastal east Africa and southern Malawi, respectively (Dijkstra and Clausnitzer 2014).

Of the over 50 species of *Ceriagrion* that occur from Africa through Eurasia to Australia, more than 20 are Afrotropical and most others Oriental. *Ceriagrion glabrum* is found at most open standing waters in Africa and extends to Madagascar, the Mascarenes, and the Seychelles. The Malagasy endemics *C. auritum* and *C. oblongulum* are similar to African species, but *C. nigrolineatum* and *C. madagazureum* differ in their startling neon green and blue coloration. Genetic data may reveal that they are a sister-species pair confined to eastern and western Madagascar, respectively, perhaps with Asian affinities.

ANISOPTERA

Aeshnidae

Worldwide, 55 genera and almost 500 species of this family are known, of which less than 10% occur in the Afrotropics. Madagascar has just nine species in three genera, but only the endemic *Anax tumorifer* is easily seen, found at almost any standing or slow-flowing water body. The similar but darker *A. mandrakae* of eastern Madagascar may prefer forested streams and rivers, but is hardly known (Gauthier 1988). The genus *Anax* is otherwise cosmopolitan, with over 30 species, of which 10 occur in tropical Africa, and three strong fliers extend to Madagascar and the Mascarenes.

Seven *Anaciaeschna* species range from southern Asia to the Pacific, but only *A. triangulifera* occurs in tropical Africa and Madagascar. Fraser (1962) described a larva with robust dorsal spines on the abdomen as belonging to this species. Such spines are highly unusual for an aeshnid, and Fraser's identification may well have been incorrect. This would suggest that an undiscovered genus is present on Madagascar. Adding to the intrigue, an adult female recalling *A. triangulifera* was recently found in Zahamena National Park (J. Bergsten, unpublished data). That, however, seems closest to the genus *Zosteraeschna*, which so far is known only from continental Africa.

Almost 100 species of *Gynacantha* are found across the world's tropics. The African species fall into three groups that may represent separate genera (Dijkstra 2005). Each of these has a single endemic species on Madagascar, while one has an endemic on each of the other western Indian Ocean archipelagoes as well. The Malagasy *G. radama* and *G. hova* are similar to *G. villosa* and *G. manderica* found on the adjacent African mainland. These belong to the *africana* and *bullata* groups, respectively, which combined have 13 species in Africa. By contrast, *G. malgassica* from Madagascar is morphologically very similar to several other species in the Malagasy Region, namely *G. bispina* from the Mascarenes, *G. comorensis* from the Comoros, *G. stylata* from the Seychelles, and the scarce and localized *G. immaculifrons* of eastern Africa. The distribution of this *bispina*-group recalls that of *Hemicordulia* in the western Indian Ocean, so it may have arrived by transoceanic dispersal from the east (see below).

Gomphidae

This family, with just over 100 genera and 1000 species (of which about 14% are Afrotropical) is the largest in Anisoptera after Libellulidae. Most species inhabit running water, seem to be weak fliers, and are thus absent or scarce even on larger islands. The family is indeed poorly represented on Madagascar, with a different composition than on the mainland. Possibly all species and probably two genera are endemic, while additional species likely await discovery. The subdivision of Gomphidae is not settled (see Carle 1986), but only two subfamilies occur on Madagascar, with the absence of Gomphinae (37 species in four genera in Africa) and Lindeniinae (14 species in four genera) being most notable. The subfamily Phyllogomphinae includes only the genera *Ceratogomphus* and *Phyllogomphus* in tropical Africa and *Isomma* on Madagascar. *Malgassogomphus* was created for *M. robinsoni*, known only from the holotype from Ile Sainte Marie (Cammaerts 1987), but it seems close enough to be placed into *Isomma* (cf. Legrand 2003).

The other species belong to Onychogomphinae, which is species-rich in the African and Asian tropics and extends across the Holarctic. Two Malagasy species assigned to *Onychogomphus* are unlikely to be related to this predominantly Eurasian genus. They appear more closely related to African rainforest genera, such as *Libyogomphus* and *Cornigomphus*, and most likely require their own endemic genus. *Paragomphus* is the dominant gomphid genus in the Afrotropics, with well over 30 species. Madagascar's most widespread gomphid is *P. madegassus*, although it has been confused with the presumed endemics *P. obliteratus* and *P. z-viridum*. All may be the same as the ubiquitous *P. genei* from mainland Africa and southwestern Eurasia; Levasseur (2007) described a subspecies of the latter from Anjouan in the Comoros, which, like *P. madegassus,* is darker. By contrast, *P. fritillarius* is distinctive and strictly limited to Madagascar, although its morphology suggests a close affinity to several species from tropical Africa.

Corduliidae, Macromiidae, and Similar Genera

Almost half of the world's members of Anisoptera belong to the superfamily Libelluloidea. About 70% of those species are in the family Libellulidae, discussed below. The remainder were once grouped as the family Corduliidae, but at least three separate families probably need to be recognized (Dijkstra et al. 2013). About 170 species remain in Corduliidae, placed mostly in Eurasian and North American genera, as well as in some tropical American groups. However, some 60 species in the closely allied genera *Hemicordulia* and *Procordulia* attain their greatest diversity in Australia and New Guinea. Of the former genus, the similar *H. virens* and *H. atrovirens* are restricted to Mauritius and La Réunion, respectively; *H. similis* is common on Madagascar and has been reported from the Seychelles, while the lookalike *H. africana* occurs sparsely across eastern and southern Africa. The group is also scarce on the Asian mainland but present on many Pacific islands, suggesting that the species disperse well but struggle to establish on continents, perhaps because of higher competition among the more diverse faunas there. Dijkstra (2007) therefore concluded that the presence of *Hemicordulia* in the western Indian Ocean represents transoceanic colonization from the east.

About 125 species ranging from Eurasia to North America, northern Australia, and Africa are now placed in Macromiidae. Most were once in the genus *Macromia*, but May (1997b) transferred the over 35 Afrotropical species to *Phyllomacromia*. The endemic *P. trifasciata* is unlike any other dragonfly on Madagascar (but see Figure 9.19), yet similar to its African relatives, implying that it arrived recently. Over 150 species found especially in Australia, New Guinea, New Caledonia, and tropical Asia and America may represent additional families.

Three genera from sub-Saharan Africa and the Malagasy genera *Libellulosoma* and *Nesocordulia* also belong to this unresolved group. Five named *Nesocordulia* species are endemic to Madagascar, while *N. villiersi* is known from a single male collected on Mohéli in 1955. The genus is in need of revision and, as one or two unnamed species are known, probably represents the region's largest anisopteran radiation. Based on larval morphology, *Nesocordulia* may be related to the elusive genus *Idomacromia* of equatorial Africa (Fleck and Legrand 2006). *Libellulosoma*, on the other hand, may be nearest to *Pentathemis* from Australia and *Aeschnosoma* from South America. Based on biogeography, the fossil record, and phylogeny, the genus might have been present on Madagascar already in the Early Cretaceous (Fleck and Legrand 2013). While described in 1907, the sole species, *L. minutum*, was known from only two specimens until it was rediscovered in littoral forest in southeastern Madagascar in 2016 (Hyde-Roberts et al. 2019).

Libellulidae

This is the largest anisopteran family, with 140 genera and 1040 species worldwide, of which over 23% are Afrotropical. They are often the most active and conspicuous dragonflies, especially at standing waters. While 16% of the world's odonate species are libellulids, in tropical Africa and on Madagascar, the figure is 27%. This higher percentage is explained by Africa's varied climatological history and Madagascar's relative isolation, as libellulids tend to be strong dispersers that fare well in dynamic environments. Many species on Madagascar are indeed African generalists (or close relatives) that favor seasonal or disturbed habitats. *Aethriamanta*, *Brachythemis*, *Olpogastra*, *Parazyxomma*, *Tetrathemis*, and *Urothemis* are each represented on Madagascar by only one or two species shared with Africa. The single species of *Macrodiplax*, *Pantala*, and *Tholymis* and two of *Tramea* occur in Asia as well, so they could also have come from there. Indeed, the annual migrations of *P. flavescens* between Africa and India are likely to reach Madagascar (Anderson 2009).

Other genera, however, diverged by varying degrees on Madagascar. *Chalcostephia* and *Hemistigma* are each represented on the island by an endemic (sub)species that differs little from its African counterpart. Six other genera have only one very distinctive endemic species each. For the strictly Afrotropical genera *Aethiothemis*, *Palpopleura*, and *Zygonoides*, these are the only representatives on the island. For the Paleotropical genera *Crocothemis*, *Diplacodes*, and *Rhyothemis*, the presence of additional species shared with the African mainland suggests a mainly western influence in the region too.

Few Malagasy genera shared with Africa have multiple endemic species on the island. *Orthetrum* and *Trithemis* both have over 50 species in the warmer parts of the Old World. They form the ecologically and taxonomically most diverse radiations in the Afrotropics, with repeated colonization and speciation events on Madagascar. Damm et al. (2010) suggest at least four separate arrivals on Madagascar of *Trithemis* from Africa, as the presence of several possibly shared species is unconfirmed. The endemics *T. persephone* and *T. selika* attest to substantial genetic divergence following two of these arrivals in the past 4 million years. Moreover, *T. annulata* from the Malagasy Region is large and dark (sometimes treated as the species *T. haematina*), while *T. kirbyi* males have red rather than black pterostigmas, suggesting that they diverged from their continental counterparts too. Madagascar's *Orthetrum* taxa are closest to African species as well, with the exception of *O. azureum*, which is possibly the island's most common dragonfly. Both *O. azureum* and the most widespread Malagasy *Trithemis* species have reached Mayotte and become sufficiently distinct to be recognized as species, with *O. lugubre* and *T. maia* replacing *O. azureum* and *T. selika*, respectively

The origins of *Zygonyx* on Madagascar may be similarly complex. The ubiquitous endemic *Z. elisabethae* is almost identical to *Z. natalensis* from Africa and an unnamed species from the Comoros (V. Nicolas, unpublished data), while the scarcer *Z. ranavalonae* recalls African species as well. The fragmented holotype of *Z. hova*, allegedly collected on Madagascar almost two centuries ago, may be the same as *Z. torridus* from Africa, adjacent Eurasia, and the Mascarenes (see Lieftinck 1963). The dark metallic *Z. viridescens* from waterfalls in Madagascar's moist evergreen forest and *Z. luctiferus* from the granitic Seychelles, however, recall the *Zygonyx* species of southern Asia.

Only for the genus *Acisoma* is there actual evidence of an Asian connection. Found widely across Madagascar, *A. attenboroughi* is morphologically and genetically closer to the Asian *A. panorpoides* than to two similar African species (Mens et al. 2016). Moreover, the sister group of the aforementioned complex is *A. ascalaphoides*, which is confined to eastern Madagascar's littoral forests, while the equatorial African *A. trifidum* is basal to all of them. The genus may thus have reached Asia via Madagascar, or reached Madagascar a second time from Asia (after the ancestor of *A. ascalaphoides* arrived, presumably from Africa). Either way, this colonizer may have pushed the earlier arrival into its coastal refuge.

Only five genera are either endemic to Madagascar or radiated on the island. Three were placed in the subfamily Tetrathemistinae owing to their small size, yellow-spotted bodies, and reduced wing venation (Donnelly and Parr 2003). Their similarity, however, is caused by convergent evolution in forest environments rather than shared ancestry (Fleck et al. 2008). Only two genera actually seem close to *Tetrathemis*, and all three are unusual for laying eggs on substrates overhanging shaded ponds (Clausnitzer and Lempert 1998)—two species of *Notiothemis* in tropical Africa and the monotypic *Calophlebia* on Madagascar. Eight species of *Tetrathemis* also occur in tropical Africa (with only *T. polleni* extending to Madagascar), while another five species range from southern Asia to northern Australia, suggesting the group has an Afrotropical origin.

The African species of the genera *Eleuthemis* and *Malgassophlebia* are genetically close and have similar larvae and ecology, laying eggs on leaves in (*Eleuthemis*) or above (*Malgassophlebia*) fast-flowing water. The two Malagasy species of *Malgassophlebia* appear similar (Legrand 2001b), as does the endemic and monotypic genus *Archaeophlebia*, but neither genus is well known on the island. Probably the three genera represent a modest Afrotropical radiation of forest stream dragonflies. Dijkstra et al. (2015) brought this group up from only three to at least eight species on the continent; further work on Madagascar is expected to have a similar effect.

Madagascar's most often seen tetrathemistines belong to the genus *Neodythemis*, as *N. hildebrandti* is found at most running waters, especially open rivers, but also near standing water. Other species occur at forested seeps and streams, but future taxonomic revision must determine whether *N. arnoulti*, *N. pauliani*, and *N. trinervulata* are synonymous or just very similar. Ten additional species occur in western and central Africa, while four species of the similar genus *Hylaeothemis* are present in southern Asia, suggesting this is yet another Malagasy group with African roots.

Ecologically, *Viridithemis viridula* is unlike any other endemic odonate on Madagascar, occurring in the dry deciduous forest of the west, rather than the mesic east. Here it survives the dry season as an adult, probably breeding in packs of leaf litter once temporary rivers begin to flow. Both the genus and species were named for the green body. This coloration is unusual in the family, while the male's combination of the green body with a red abdomen tip is entirely unique (Figure 9.19g). The nearest relatives are probably the monotypic *Cyanothemis* (named for its equally strange blue pigmentation) and the small genus *Porpax* from tropical Africa. The genus *Acisoma* (discussed above), the red *Rhodothemis* from Australasia, and the American *Erythemis* with red, green, black, and pruinose blue species are other gaudy members of the family's distinctive "erythemistine" clade (Fleck 2004).

The large-bodied *Thermorthemis madagascariensis*, finally, may be Madagascar's most iconic dragonfly. A male can be found guarding almost any sheltered pond on the island. The nearly identical *T. comorensis* occurs on Grande Comore and Anjouan, and has been seen on Mayotte. The genus recalls *Hadrothemis* of tropical Africa, females of which also rhythmically hit the water surface with their tail end while hovering, thus propelling eggs in drops of water onto the bank. This behavior is linked to a marked expansion of the abdomen close to its tip. While that feature may characterize a distinct group within the family, including its type genus *Libellula*, over 250 species seem involved, including *Aethiothemis*, *Neodythemis*, and *Orthetrum* on Madagascar. The closest relative of *Thermorthemis* will thus remain unknown until extensive phylogenetic work is done.

SUMMARY OF BIOGEOGRAPHY

Members of Odonata of Madagascar are distinctly unique, yet largely Afrotropical in origin. While only 17% of the over 190 known and confirmed species are shared with continental Africa, 79% of the 53 genera exist in both places. Nonetheless, members of families found broadly on the mainland, such as Calopterygidae, Chlorocyphidae, Gomphidae, and Macromiidae, as well as the subfamilies Allocnemidinae and Disparoneurinae of Platycnemididae, are not found or are poorly represented on Madagascar.

The most distinctive elements in terms of regional diversification and phylogenetic isolation are found in the suborder Zygoptera. The subfamilies Onychargiinae and Platycnemidinae of Platycnemididae are, respectively, absent and less diverse in Africa, while species placed formerly in Megapodagrionidae are overrepresented on Madagascar; on the African mainland, Argiolestidae has only two species in Lower Guinea, while the Malagasy families Protolestidae and Tatocnemidididae are only tentatively linked to the three species of Pentaphlebiidae found in the same region. The genera *Nesolestes*, *Protolestes*, *Tatocnemis*, and *Proplatycnemis* in these families, together with *Pseudagrion* in Coenagrionidae, represent the island's five main odonate radiations, with well over 80 species combined.

Madagascar's unique character is less pronounced in Anisoptera. The endemic genera in family Gomphidae and superfamily Libelluloidea are also largely restricted to moist evergreen forest steams and are suspected to have mostly African origins, but each has only one to seven known species. This difference may be due to the true dragonflies' greater dispersal capacity, leading to more exchange with the mainland and less isolation on certain parts of the island. However, adults of these taxa, which behave more furtively at the waterside, are also harder to find than damselflies. The scope for surprising discoveries is therefore greater, as exemplified by the mysterious aeshnids discussed above.

The remaining fifth or so of Madagascar's endemic species generally have even closer African affinities and probably derived from recent arrivals of grassland species, which have good dispersal capacity. Examples are *Paragomphus madegassus*, *Hemistigma affine*, and *Zygonyx elisabethae*, which are close relatives (if not synonyms) of *P. genei*, *H. albipunctum*, and *Z. natalensis*, respectively, on the mainland. These species occur across Madagascar in open, often anthropogenic, habitats.

The most likely exceptions to the general scenario that Madagascar's Odonata consists of ancient and recent African species are the genera *Teinobasis* and *Hemicordulia*, and the *bispina* group of *Gynacantha*. Each of these occurs only peripherally on the African continent; they are well represented on islands in the Malagasy Region and have potential relatives in Australasia, suggesting transoceanic arrival from the east. Not one of these cases, however, has been tested with molecular tools. Similarly, some endemic species of *Acisoma* and perhaps *Ceriagrion*, *Orthetrum*, and *Zygonyx* may have their nearest relatives in Asia rather than Africa, but currently there is little convincing evidence to support such speculation.

Finally, *Paracnemis* and *Libellulosoma* are the only endemic genera for which it seems quite certain that any surviving relatives are in Asia, Australia, or South America rather than Africa. However, many of the sister groups of Malagasy taxa that do persist in Africa are highly localized—for instance, in Lower Guinea or South Africa—suggesting that geographically closer relatives of those genera have simply become extinct (see Figure 9.20). Interestingly, the two occur together in swamp forest on Madagascar's eastern shore with the possibly relict *Acisoma ascalaphoides* (see above), emphasizing the importance of such rare lowland habitats for conservation and their potential for further discovery (Schütte and Razafindraibe 2007).

Other than this, little can be said of Malagasy odonate biogeography, as the necessary species-level research is simply wanting (see below). As expected with aquatic animals, diversity and endemism is heavily skewed toward the east and north. Therefore, perhaps one of the more interesting questions that remains is how distinct the fauna is from the drier west, which has been studied especially poorly. The unique endemic genus *Viridithemis* takes pride of place, but the presence of additional distinctive species, such as *Lestes auripennis*, *Ceriagrion madagazureum*, and *Crocothemis striata*, also makes the region worth exploring further.

RESEARCH AND CONSERVATION

While the study of Malagasy Odonata started more than 170 years ago (Rambur 1842), there has been little large-scale synthetic progress since the monographs by Schmidt (1951, republished in German in 1966) and Fraser (1956). Most endemics are restricted to forest, which has decreased in cover by 40% in the second half of the 20th century (Harper et al. 2007). Dijkstra and Clausnitzer (2004) estimated that two-thirds of species (more than 100, all endemic) may therefore be threatened. Clausnitzer et al. (2009) inferred, however, that over 70% of species had too few data to assess their status for the International Union for Conservation of Nature (IUCN) Red List of Threatened Species, with almost 40% known only from a single collection—the holotype or type series.

All of Madagascar's dragonflies were assessed in 2017, but only *Acisoma ascalaphoides* of the eastern littoral forests and *Lestes auripennis* from the southwestern Analavelona Forest were listed as threatened (Schütte et al. 2018). Data were still too deficient to make a fair assessment for 45% of the species (those remaining were considered of no immediate concern). Missing information most commonly relates to species' distribution and taxonomy. In total, more than 50 species have not been recorded since they were discovered, mostly between 1900 and 1950. This indicates that many more await discovery, while others may have become extinct before they became known.

Nowhere on earth is this discrepancy between habitat loss and lack of knowledge greater for Odonata than on Madagascar, underlining the need for an imminent and comprehensive reappraisal of these "lost sentinels" (Clausnitzer et al. 2009). On the African mainland, extensive fieldwork followed by a complete IUCN Red List (Clausnitzer et al. 2012), the publication of a handbook (Dijkstra and Clausnitzer 2014), and large-scale species descriptions (Dijkstra et al. 2015) allowed the development of a website with information on all the species (Dijkstra 2017), as well as a biotic index for environmental monitoring based on the species' status, range, and ecology (Vorster et al. 2020). Such advances in taxonomic and ecological research could be emulated on Madagascar, leading to Odonata species serving as examples for popularizing and protecting freshwater life.

Subject editors: Brian L. Fisher and Steven M. Goodman

BLATTODEA: TERMITOIDAE, TERMITES, *VITSIKAZO*, *VOTRY*

P. Eggleton

The termites of Madagascar are not well studied—only three substantial taxonomic works have been published (Cachan 1949, 1951; Paulian 1970), and nothing since. In addition, the island has been very patchily sampled, with the northern moist evergreen forest areas being especially poorly known. Our knowledge of the termites of the island has not advanced much since the contribution about them in the precursor of this book (Eggleton and Davies 2003). Since that time, there has been a detailed molecular study of Malagasy insects using the COII marker barcoding, which examined termites as one of the target groups (Monaghan et al. 2009). The other major paper (Nobre et al. 2009) deals with the fungus-growing Macrotermitinae of Madagascar. Members of the presently known fauna are listed in Table 9.17.

Termites are eusocial cockroaches (Blattodea: Termitoidae). They are one of only two orders of insects (the other being Hymenoptera) in which full sociality, with overlapping generations and divisions of labor into different castes, has evolved. They look and behave differently from most cockroaches, but their closest living relative, *Cryptocerus*, is an uncontroversial cockroach. Termite colonies generally have five kinds of individuals: a queen, a king, male and female alates (winged reproductives), soldiers, and workers. The queen's main purpose within the colony is egg-laying, although she also usually has some control over other aspects of colony organization, especially caste ratios, through the production of pheromones. The king mates regularly with the queen and contributes to pheromone production but seems to have no obvious other function. Soldiers defend the colony using a variety of strategies. Workers do all the remaining work, including foraging, larval feeding and care, and mound, nest, and tunnel construction.

Termites produce winged reproductives at regular times during the year, especially in response to the patterns of wet and dry seasons. In many cases (especially within Termitidae), alates fly right at the beginning of the rainy season, when it is easiest to burrow into the ground. After flight dispersal, alates form monogamous pairs; the majority of species burrow into the ground to form new colonies. The mated pair forms a small chamber underground, and workers are rapidly reared to allow the colony to feed itself and expand. Soldiers and new alates are produced later in the life of the colony.

NEST STRUCTURE AND DIET

Most Malagasy termites nest initially in the soil. However, a significant proportion (i.e., all members of Kalotermitidae) nest in deadwood. Malagasy termites generally do not make impressive aboveground nests of the kind found in other tropical biomes. Only species within *Microtermes*, *Microcerotermes*, *Coarctotermes*, and *Nasutitermes* form aboveground nests of any kind, and these

TABLE 9.17. **Checklist of the termites of Madagascar and associated coastal islands**

KALOTERMITIDAE
Bifiditermes madagascariensis (Wasmann, 1897)
Neotermes gracilidens Sjostedt, 1925
N. concavifrons Cachan, 1949
N. desneuxi (Sjostedt, 1904)
N. voeltzhowi (Wasmann, 1897)
N. laticollis (Holmgren, 1910)
Kalotermes isaloensis Cachan, 1949
K. delphinensis (Cachan, 1951)
Postelectrotermes amplus Sjostedt, 1925
P. howa (Wasmann, 1897)
P. longus (Holmgren, 1910)
Allotermes paradoxus (Wasmann, 1910)
A. papillifer Krishna, 1962
A. denticulatus Krishna, 1962
Cryptotermes parasitus Wasmann, 1911[1]
C. kirbyi Moszkowski, 1955
C. brevis (Walker, 1853)[1]
C. havilandi (Sjostedt, 1897)[1]
Glyptotermes scotti Holmgren, 1910[2]
Procryptotermes fryeri Holmgren, 1910

RHINOTERMITIDAE
Psammotermes voeltzhowi Wasmann, 1910
Prorhinotermes canalifrons (Sjostedt, 1910)
Coptotermes truncatus Wasmann, 1910[1]
Heterotermes philippinensis Light, 1921[1]

TERMITIDAE
MACROTERMITINAE
Microtermes kauderni Holmgren, 1909
M. sakalava Cachan, 1949
?*Microtermes* [undescribed species]

TERMITIDAE
TERMITINAE
Microcerotermes sikorae Silvestri, 1901
M. longiceps Cachan, 1949
M. subtilis Wasmann, 1897
M. unidentatus Cachan, 1949
M. subinteger (Cachan, 1951)
M. mandibularis (Cachan, 1951)
M. cachani (Eggleton, 2001)
M. minor (Cachan, 1951)
M. major (Cachan, 1951)
M. sakarahensis (Cachan, 1951)
Quasitermes incisus (Cachan, 1949)
Termes baculiformis (Holmgren, 1909)
Capritermes capricornis (Wasmann, 1893)

NASUTITERMITINAE
Malagasitermes milloti (Cachan, 1949)
"Nosytermes vulnerablus" [undescribed genus and species]
Nasutitermes salebrithorax (Sjostedt, 1904)
N. laticeps (Wasmann, 1897)
N. canaliculatus (Wasmann, 1897)
N. nigrita (Wasmann, 1897)
N. neonanus (Cachan, 1949)
N. vadoni Cachan, 1951
N. maheensis (Holmgren, 1912)
N. voeltzkowi (Wasmann, 1910)
Kaudernitermes kaudernianus (Sjostedt, 1914)
Coarctotermes clepsydra Sjoestedt, 1904
C. pauliani Cachan, 1949
C. beharaensis Cachan, 1949

[1] Species thought to be anthropochorous.
[2] Species of uncertain status.

are generally fairly amorphous rounded mounds. However, *C. clepsydra* forms extensive mound fields across derived grassland; *Microtermes kauderni* makes similar-looking mounds at forest edges and in forest fragments; and, perhaps most impressively of all, *C. beharaensis* forms highly characteristic conical mounds in dry deciduous forest and dry spiny thicket areas.

Termites generally feed on dead plant material at all stages of decay (e.g., deadwood, leaf litter, herbivore dung, humus-rich soil, humus-poor soil), as well as on some living plant materials (e.g., dry grass, tree microepiphytes). All feeding types are found on Madagascar, except for termites feeding on microepiphytes and those feeding on the most humus-poor soil. However, wood-feeders are the most species-rich group in all Malagasy biomes.

BIOGEOGRAPHY AND EVOLUTIONARY LINEAGES

Madagascar has, in some ways, the most biogeographically isolated of all major termite faunas (Eggleton 2000). There is no evidence to suggest that any termites (with the possible exception of *Psammotermes*; see below) were present on the island before the breakup of Gondwana. Indeed, the island has a relatively high proportion of pantropical genera that probably came to the island by rafting in deadwood sometime after the final split of Madagascar from India (~80 million years ago). In this sense, the island is oceanic and is in formal terms a neorefugium (Nekola 1999). However, what distinguishes it markedly from other oceanic islands is the apparently high level of cladogenesis that has occurred after the initial colonizing events. This means that Madagascar is, in termite terms, intermediate between an oceanic and a continental island, and is biogeographically unique.

Three main groups with unique evolutionary lineages within the island can be traced within Malagasy termites: *Allotermes* within Kalotermitidae; *Quasitermes* and *Capritermes* within Termitinae; and all endemic Malagasy genera within Nasutiterminae. It is possible that these three groups arose from just three colonization events by the three pantropical genera: *Procryptotermes* (Kalotermidae), *Termes* (Termitinae), and *Nasutitermes* (Nasutitermitinae). Malagasy Nasutitermitinae show this cladogenesis most clearly, with possibly six endemic genera having arisen from an initial colonization event. Considerable trophic diversification has occurred within this clade, with species specialized on soil, highly decayed deadwood, dry leaf litter, and grass. This trophic diversification is very similar to that of Nasutitermitinae in Southeast Asia (Gathorne-Hardy 2001).

Although Madagascar is geographically close to Africa, it has few termite genera that can definitely be said to have originated from an African ancestor. Even Macrotermitinae (i.e., the genus *Microtermes*), a subfamily that reached the island by dispersal flights across the Mozambique Channel (see below), is not unambiguously related to African species rather than Asian ones.

SPECIES DIVERSITY

Termite local diversity declines steeply with latitude, habitat fragmentation and isolation, elevation, and increased human disturbance. Madagascar is at a fairly high southerly latitude and is an ancient isolated island; a lot of its surface area is above 500 m, and much of the natural habitat is highly disturbed. Given all these factors, it is perhaps surprising that ecological surveys in Malagasy moist evergreen forests have shown local species richness levels at about what would be predicted for primary forest sites at the same latitude elsewhere in the world (P. Eggleton and D. Davies, unpublished data).

The main Malagasy biomes have about equal numbers of termite species (Table 9.18), although overall the moist evergreen forest areas are probably the richest. The dry spiny thicket is particularly interesting as it holds at least one endemic genus (*Allotermes*). This supports the general pattern, found throughout the world, of arid areas being important secondary diversity hotspots for termites (Eggleton 2000). Malagasy forests may be similar to very ancient tropical forests (i.e., those ~50 million years old) in their preponderance of phylogenetically old groups. Particularly striking is the presence of large numbers of members of Kalotermitidae in wet

TABLE 9.18. **Numbers of termite species within each genus for regions and major habitat types of Madagascar**

GENUS	NORTH	CENTRAL	SOUTH	SAMBIRANO TRANSITIONAL FOREST	DRY DECIDUOUS FOREST	DRY SPINY THICKET	GRASSLAND	*UAPACA* WOODLAND	MANGROVE/ COASTAL
Postelectrotermes	1	2	–	–	–	–	–	–	–
Bifiditermes	–	–	–	1	1	–	–	–	–
Neotermes	1	2	–	–	2	–	–	1	–
Kalotermes	–	–	1	–	–	–	–	–	–
Allotermes	–	–	–	–	1	2	–	–	–
Cryptotermes	–	–	–	–	–	1	–	–	1
Prorhinotermes	–	–	–	–	–	–	–	–	1
Coptotermes	–	–	–	–	1	–	–	–	1
Heterotermes	–	–	–	1	–	–	–	–	–
Psammotermes	–	–	–	–	–	1	–	–	–
Microtermes	1	1	1	–	1	1	1	–	–
Microcerotermes	1	1	2	4	4	4	1	3	–
Termes	–	–	–	–	1	1	–	–	–
Quasitermes	1	1	1	–	–	–	–	–	–
Capritermes	1	1	1	–	–	–	–	–	–
Nasutitermes	2	2	3	4	–	1	–	1	2
Malagasitermes	–	1	–	–	–	–	–	–	–
"Nosytermes"	–	1	1	–	–	–	–	–	–
Kaudernitermes	–	–	–	–	1	–	–	–	–
Coarctotermes	–	–	–	–	2	3	1	–	–
Totals	8	12	10	10	14	14	3	5	5

Note: Species recorded only in and around human settlements are not included.

wood on the forest floor, something that is unknown from other tropical zones.

THE MALAGASY TERMITE FAUNA

Kalotermitidae

Species of Kalotermitidae are wood feeders that nest in the usually very dry wood in which they feed. In most tropical forest systems, they are confined to deadwood in the canopy, although they are sometimes found in large trunks of hardwoods on the forest floor. They are the oldest of all termite groups found on Madagascar. In comparison with other biogeographic regions, Madagascar has an extraordinarily rich kalotermitid fauna (seven genera, one of which is endemic). The whole of sub-Saharan Africa, for example, has only eight genera, none endemic. The reason for this high diversity is probably related to Madagascar's position both geographically and palaeogeographically. Kalotermitidae species are known to raft across wide water gaps, and so the family is commonly one of a few groups that can colonize oceanic islands. Kalotermitidae species probably do relatively well on oceanic islands and at the edges of continents, possibly because they do not compete well with species of the family Termitidae in continental tropical biomes. On Madagascar, there is no abundant wood-feeding termitid fauna, and the very long coastline has promoted colonization (leaving aside the possibility of some kalotermitids having been present on the old Gondwanan landmass, which is possible but not proven). Where kalotermitids have colonized, therefore, they have been able to persist in niches where perhaps they would normally be excluded by competition. One consequence of this is that Malagasy species of the family are found in moist evergreen forest attacking wet wood on the forest floor—a microhabitat in which they have rarely previously been encountered.

Seven different genera of Kalotermitidae occur on the island. *Bifiditermes madagascariensis* is confined to deadwood in the dry deciduous forest and Sambirano floristic zones. *Postelectrotermes* has probably three species on the island, all confined to moist evergreen forest across a broad range of elevations. Individuals have been collected from sodden wood in montane forest and from a range of wood at different stages of decay in lowland and medium-altitude forest. It is a very common forest termite genus on Madagascar. *Neotermes* has apparently similar distributional and feeding habits to *Postelectrotermes*, although it may be slightly rarer. One species has been recorded from dry deciduous forest.

Cryptotermes species on Madagascar can be split into two groups. The first group consists of the endemic species *C. kirybi*, which is confined to the dry spiny thicket. The second group contains only species that have been introduced by humans; they are generally known only from Antananarivo and other larger cities. Among these is *C. brevis*, which has never been recorded from a natural environment and seems to be an entirely anthropogenic species. *Cryptotermes* species feed and nest in extremely dry wood and are dispersed extremely readily by human migrations. *Kalotermes* has two apparently rare species on the island, one from Isalo and the other from around Tolagnaro. *Allotermes* is endemic to Madagascar. Its biology is poorly known, but it is distributed only in dry deciduous forest and dry spiny thicket, while *Epicalotermes* is known only from spiny thicket around Toliara.

Rhinotermitidae

Rhinotermitids are all wood feeders with a range of nesting habits. This family on Madagascar has four different genera. *Psammotermes voeltzhowi* is an arid-zone termite with congeners in southern Africa and hot dry regions of the Palearctic and Oriental regions. On Madagascar, it has been recorded only from dry spiny thicket, where it appears to be common in sandy soils and feeds on deadwood and other dry, dead plant material. *Psammotermes* nests underground and is not known to raft or disperse by flight across water gaps. For these reasons, perhaps it is a genus that may have an ancient relict Gondwanan distribution.

Prorhinotermes canalifrons occurs in coastal regions of Madagascar. *Prorhinotermes* species are characteristically found on oceanic islands and along coastlines, nesting in wood and rafting readily. *Heterotermes philippinensis* appears to have been introduced by humans from Southeast Asia and has been recorded only from the northern coastal region, especially the Sambirano Region. *Coptotermes truncatus* is an extremely common pest of building timber. It is otherwise recorded only from dry deciduous forest and may also have been introduced to the island by humans.

Termitidae

Termitidae (the "higher termites") is presently split into eight subfamilies. A number of the subfamilies—the rather phylogenetically basal Foraminitermitinae, Sphaerotermitinae, and Apicotermitinae and the more derived Cubitermitinae and Syntermitinaeare—are absent from Madagascar. However, three other subfamilies, Termitinae, Macrotermitinae, and Nasutitermitinae, make up all the Malagasy termite species in Termitidae, using the classification of Engel and Krishna (2004).

Macrotermitinae

This subfamily, composed of fungus-growing termites, is an Old World group with apparently only three species, one undescribed, on Madagascar (although there are probably other undecribed species; see Thakur and Sen-Sarma 1978). This subfamily is unusual in having a mutualistic relationship with *Termitomyces*, a group of basidiomycete fungi. The fungi are cultivated in special chambers within the termatarium and are nourished by workers plastering fecal material onto the highly structured fungal vegetative body (the fungus comb). In turn, this comb provides a feeding substrate for the termite colony. The primary food of these termites varies—grass, litter, or wood—although how much of this variety of foodstuff is used by Malagasy Macrotermitinae is unknown. Some Macrotermitinae species build spectacular mounds, but although some Malagasy species have low-domed mounds, none reach the architectural complexity of African *Macrotermes*.

Macrotermitinae did not originate on Madagascar; they probably have an African humid forest origin (Aanen and Eggleton 2005) and do not raft on floating logs or vegetation mats, as many other termites are thought capable of (Bourguignon et al. 2016). However, they can cross moderately large water gaps. For example, they have colonized the Indonesian island Sulawesi, probably from Borneo, crossing the straits of Makassar, a water gap of 100 km (Gathorne-Hardy 2001). It is probable then that the present Macrotermitinae fauna of Madagascar is the result of one (or a very few) colonizations by pairs of winged reproductives. These colonization events are clearly most likely to have been across the Mozambique Canal, as this is the nearest source of Macrotermitinae (the subfamily does not occur on the string of islands connecting Madagascar with the Oriental region).

DNA studies have shown that all the confirmed Macrotermitinae of Madagascar are species within the genus *Microtermes* (Nobre et al. 2009). *Microtermes* termites are among the few fungus-growers that have vertical acquisition of the mutualistic fungi that they grow in their nests. This may have made it easier for them to colonize Madagascar as they could have brought the fungi with them.

Malagasy members of Macrotermitinae are very poorly known taxonomically and ecologically. *Microtermes sakalava* has been reported from deadwood in dry spiny thicket, but as yet there is no record of the structure of its nests or fungus combs. An apparently undescribed mound-building species also inhabits the Central Highlands, at least to the west of Antananarivo. In both cases, the present generic classification is not satisfactory; both fall morphologically somewhere between the genera *Odontotermes* and *Microtermes*, but DNA analyses suggest that they are probably best placed in *Microtermes*.

Termitinae

Microcerotermes, a member of this subfamily, is the most diverse genus on Madagascar, with possibly 11 species, and is placed taxonomically in the *Amitermes* group. These are arboreal-, ground-, or wood-nesting species that all feed on wood in an early stage of decay. The genus is pantropical, and wood-nesting species are known to colonize oceanic islands (Eggleton 2000). Almost certainly, the present Malagasy species are the result of one to a few colonization events by wood-nesting species, followed by speciation.

Within Madagascar, *Microcerotermes* is most species-rich in dry and dry-wet transitional zones. Within dry spiny thicket, dry deciduous forest, and the Sambirano Region there are four species, but only one to two species are present in moist evergreen forest areas. *Microcerotermes sikorae* forms distinctive, pyramid-shaped mounds in moist evergreen forest areas. Other *Microcerotermes* species appear to have only subterranean nests. There are a large number of apparently very similar species of *Microcerotermes* on Madagascar, with some even having been recorded in the nests of their congeners (something rarely recorded elsewhere). Further collecting and taxonomic studies will probably reduce the number of Malagasy species in this genus, although recent studies have suggested there may be a number of cryptic molecular species (Monaghan et al. 2009).

The genera *Termes*, *Quasitermes*, and *Capritermes* belong to the *Termes* group. *Termes baculiformis* feeds on soil or highly decayed wood and is apparently superficially similar to the eastern African *T. baculi*. It builds low-domed mounds in dry deciduous forests. *Quasitermes incisus* builds small round soil mounds within moist evergreen forests, especially at mid-elevations. It has also been found in the nests of *Microcerotermes* (and vice versa). It appears to be a soil feeder. *Capritermes capricornis* is the most common soil-feeding termite on Madagascar, recorded from moist evergreen forest, montane grassland, and moist semi-deciduous forest. It is found from sea level up to 2000 m, mostly in areas on and to the east of the Central Highlands where it is known to build low mounds (Paulian 1970), but in recent survey work, no mound structures were found (P. Eggleton and R. Davies, unpublished data). *Capritermes* is extremely variable in size, increasing in mean size with elevation. Krishna (1968) suggests that *Quasitermes* and *Capritermes* may be closely related.

Nasutitermitinae

This subfamily contains the snouted termites, so called because of the soldier's long, tubelike snouts, which are used to spray toxic defensive compounds at potential predators. Six genera are known from the island.

Nasutitermes is a common wood feeder across the wetter forested areas of Madagascar. Moist evergreen forest areas have the highest species richness of this genus, with apparent outlier species in dry deciduous forest and in *Uapaca* woodlands in the Isalo formation. Species nest arboreally in deadwood or in carton nests on the ground. Although globally *Nasutitermes* does not form a natural group, the Malagasy species are probably a single radiation and more closely related to other Malagasy members of Nasutitermitinae than they are to non-Malagasy *Nasutitermes*.

Kaudernitermes kaudernianus is superficially similar to the Asian genus *Bulbitermes*. It has so far been recorded only from dry deciduous forest in the north of Madagascar. Sands and Lamb (1975) suggest, from consideration of the worker mandibles, that *Kaudernitermes* may feed on soft rotten wood or decaying litter. However, no definite biological data exist for the genus.

Coarctotermes has three species found in grassland, dry deciduous forest, and dry spiny thicket, although Paulian (1970) states that it is not found in "dense forest." Two of the species are grass feeders (*C. clepysdra* and *C. pauliani*). *Coarctotermes clepsydra* is extremely abundant in grassland throughout the Central Highlands and western lowland regions of the island. It forms characteristic steeply conical carton nests on the ground, reaching densities of about 100 per ha. Inside each mound are numerous food stores of cut grass. *Coarctotermes pauliani* forms underground nests. Little is known about its biology.

Coarctotermes beharaensis is found within dry spiny thicket, where it forms steeply conical epigeal nests with a more fragile outer shell than those of most *Coarctotermes*. This species may best be placed in a separate genus; *Toliaratermes* was suggested in the precursor of this book (Eggleton and Davies 2003), although this name has no taxonomic validity, and this needs to be addressed in future studies. It is a predominantly leaf-litter-feeding species, as indicated by the presence of numerous, finely cut leaf-litter fragments inside the storage chambers of the carton nest. These termites construct subterranean foraging galleries lined with carton within the sand that forms the "soil" layer of the dry spiny thicket, not far below the surface. This rather striking nest structure appears to have been overlooked by previous authors.

There appear to be two soil-feeding Malagasy Nasutitermitinae genera: *Malagasitermes* and an undescribed new genus and species that has been provisionally named "Nosytermes." The biology and distributions of *Malagasitermes* and "Nosytermes" appear to be similar.

They are soil-feeding termites nesting in the ground within moist evergreen forest. The structure of *Malagsitermes* worker mandibles suggests a slightly more humidified feeding substrate than "Nosytermes."

CONCLUSIONS AND FUTURE DIRECTIONS

The termite fauna of Madagascar is still very poorly known, and there are whole areas of the island that have not been surveyed in any meaningful way for termites. Of special interest are the northern moist evergreen forests, including areas of the SAVA Region, sclerophyllous woodland in different zones of the central southwest, and the transitional forests, including the area to the west of the Anosyenne Mountains. Detailed survey work will have to precede new taxonomic revisions, as the existing collections are extremely meager. However, such survey work is likely to be particularly rewarding given the unique biogeographic interest of the Malagasy termite fauna.

Subject editors: Brian L. Fisher and Steven M. Goodman

ANOPLURA, SUCKING LICE, *HAO*

L. A. Durden

Sucking lice are blood-sucking ectoparasitic insects of eutherian mammals that spend their entire life cycle (egg, three nymphal instars, and adult male or female) on their hosts. They were previously assigned to their own order, Anoplura, but recent phylogenetic interpretations place Anoplura as a suborder together with three suborders of chewing lice in the order Phthiraptera, or with chewing lice and the nonparasitic bark lice and book lice in the order Psocodea (Durden 2019). Worldwide, almost 600 species of sucking lice have been described (Durden and Musser 1994; Durden 2019). Many species are host-specific to a single host species, but some species are known to parasitize a suite of closely related (usually congeneric) hosts (Durden and Musser 1994). Atypically for sucking lice, one species recorded from Madagascar, *Polyplax reclinata*, from the non-native *Suncus murinus* (House Shrew), is known to parasitize several species of shrews across Eurasia and the Afrotropical region (Durden and Musser 1994).

The Afrotropical region has the richest diversity of sucking lice (Kim and Ludwig 1978, Ledger 1980), but the sucking louse fauna of Madagascar has been poorly studied; undescribed species undoubtedly parasitize mammals that are endemic to Madagascar, notably lemurs and murine rodents. Conversely, some native Malagasy mammals, such as tenrecs, bats, and carnivorans, are not parasitized by sucking lice. Table 9.19 shows the host associations of the species of sucking lice that have been recorded from Madagascar, including undescribed species known to the author.

In addition to the sucking lice listed in Table 9.19, OConnor (1996, 1998, 2000) reported unidentified species of Anoplura from seven species of endemic nesomyine rodents, namely *Eliurus grandidieri*, *E. majori*, *E. minor*, *E. tanala*, *E. webbi*, *Gymnuromys roberti*, and *Nesomys rufus*. With the possible exception of the louse associated with *N. rufus*, these probably represent undescribed endemic species of sucking lice. Paulian (1961b) described *Polyplax nesomydis* from *Nesomys* sp. (species not determined), which may or may not be the same species reported from *N. rufus* by OConnor (1996, 1998).

At least four undescribed species of sucking lice are known to the author from endemic rodents or lemurs from Madagascar (Table 9.19), but adults of only one sex are currently available for each of these new species. It would be preferable to wait until both sexes are in hand before they are formally described. Females of a new species of *Phthirpediculus* have been collected from *Eulemur* sp. (Lemuridae). Similarly, males and nymphs of a new species of *Lemurpediculus*, have been collected from the recently described *Microcebus jonahi* (Jonah's Mouse Lemur). Also, a single specimen of an undescribed *Polyplax* louse is available from *Eliuris danieli* and another from *E. myoxinus*.

Some widespread species of sucking lice known elsewhere in the world are very likely present on the island, although I have not located records of them from livestock and pets on Madagascar. These include *Linognathus setosus* (Dog Sucking Louse), *Haematopinus asini* (Horse Sucking Louse), *L. stenopsis* (Goat Sucking Louse), *L. ovillus* (Sheep Face Louse), *L. pedalis* (Sheep Foot Louse), and *Solenopotes capillatus* (Little Blue Cattle Louse). Although *H. suis* (Hog Louse) has been recorded from Madagascar (Table 9.19), it has been reported from the introduced *Potamochoerus larvatus* (African Bush Pig; see Goodman and Andrianjakarivelo, pp. 2003–6) and not from its typical host, *Sus scrofa* (domestic pig/feral hog).

Only one of the two species of sucking lice (*Hoplopleura captiosa*) that parasitize the cosmopolitan *Mus musculus* (House Mouse) has been reported from Madagascar (Kim and Emerson 1974). The other species, *Polyplax serrata* (House Mouse Louse), also would be expected to occur on *M. musculus* on Madagascar. Similarly, both *H. pacifica* and *P. spinulosa* (Spined Rat Louse) commonly parasitize both *Rattus norvegicus* (Brown Rat) and *R. rattus* (Black Rat) in many parts of the world, but these louse species have been recorded with certainty from only the latter host species on Madagascar (Table 9.19).

In addition to sucking lice, some endemic mammals are parasitized by chewing lice in Madagascar. One notable species is *Trichophilopterus babakatophilus*, which interestingly has little apparent host specificity, having been recorded from the following six

TABLE 9.19. **Host associations of sucking lice recorded from endemic and non-native mammals of Madagascar**

SUCKING LICE	HOSTS	REFERENCES
FAMILY HAEMATOPINIDAE		
Haematopinus eurysternus Denny, 1842 (Short-nosed Cattle Louse)	Cattle	Kim and Emerson (1974)
H. quadripertusus Fahrenholz, 1916 (Cattle Tail Louse)	Zebu	Gretillat (1957); Meleney and Kim (1974)
	Cattle	Kim and Emerson (1974)
H. suis (Linnaeus, 1758) (Hog Louse)	*Potamochoerus larvatus* (African Bush Pig)[1]	Remy (1950)
FAMILY HOPLOPLEURIDAE		
Hoplopleura captiosa Johnson, 1960	*Mus musculus* (House Mouse)	Kim and Emerson (1974)
H. pacifica Ewing, 1924	*Rattus rattus* (Black Rat)	Kim and Emerson (1974); Ehlers et al. (2019)
FAMILY LINOGNATHIDAE		
Linognathus africanus Kellogg & Paine, 1911	Goat	Ehlers et al. (2019)
L. vituli (Linnaeus, 1758) (Long-nosed Cattle Louse)	Cattle	Ehlers et al. (2019)
FAMILY PEDICULIDAE		
Pediculus humanus capitis De Geer, 1778 (head louse)	Humans	Combescot et al. (1993); Amevigbe et al. (2000); Sangaré et al. (2014); Eremeeva et al. (2019)
P. h. humanus Linnaeus, 1758 (body louse)	Humans	Sangaré et al. (2014)
FAMILY POLYPLACIDAE		
Eulinognathus hypogeomydis Paulian, 1961	*Hypogeomys antimena* (Malagasy Giant Jumping Rat)	Paulian (1961b)
Lemurpediculus claytoni Durden, Blanco & Seabolt, 2017	*Cheirogaleus sibreei* (Sibree's Dwarf Lemur)	Durden et al. (2017)
L. madagascariensis Durden, Kessler, Radespiel, Zimmermann, Hasiniaina & Zohdy, 2018	*Microcebus murinus* (Gray Mouse Lemur)	Durden et al. (2018)
L. petterorum Paulian, 1958	*Lepilemur mustelinus*[2] (Weasel Sportive Lemur)	Paulian (1958)
L. robbinsi Durden, Blanco & Seabolt, 2017	*C. crossleyi* (Crossley's Dwarf Lemur)	Durden et al. (2017)
L. verruculosus (Ward, 1951)	*M. griseorufus*[3] (Gray-brown Mouse Lemur)	Ehlers et al. (2019)
	M. rufus (Rufous Mouse Lemur)	Ward (1951); Durden et al. (2010); Zohdy et al. (2012, 2017); Zohdy and Durden (2016)
Lemurpediculus sp. (close to *L. verruculosus*)	*M. griseorufus*	Rodriguez et al. (2012)
Lemurpediculus sp. nov.	*M. jonahi* (Jonah's Mouse Lemur)	Unpublished data
Lemurpediculus sp.	*M. ravelobensis* (Golden-brown Mouse Lemur)	A. Klein et al. (2018)
Phthirpediculus avahidis Paulian, 1960	*Avahi laniger* (Eastern Woolly Lemur)	Paulian (1960)
P. brygooi Clay, 1977	*Eulemur mongoz* (Mongoose Lemur)	Clay (1977)

(continued overleaf)

TABLE 9.19. ***continued***

SUCKING LICE	HOSTS	REFERENCES
P. propitheci Ewing, 1923	*Propithecus edwardsi* (Milne-Edwards' Sifaka)	Ewing (1923); Ferris (1932); Wright et al. (2009);[4] Leo (2009)[4]
Phthirpediculus sp. nov.	*Eulemur* sp.	Unpublished data
Polyplax brachyuromydis Kim & Emerson, 1974	*Brachyuromys betsiloensis* (Lesser Short-tailed Rat)	Kim and Emerson (1974)
P. nesomydis Paulian, 1961	*Nesomys* sp. (Red Forest Rat)	Paulian (1961b)
P. reclinata (Nitzsch, 1864)	*Suncus murinus* (Asian Musk Shrew)	Beaucournu and Houin (1967); Kim and Emerson (1974)
P. spinulosa (Burmeister, 1839)	*Rattus rattus* (Black Rat)	Kim and Emerson (1974); OConnor (1998)
	Rattus sp.	Kim and Emerson (1974)
Polyplax sp. nov. 1	*Eliurus danieli* (Daniel's Tufted-tail Rat)	Unpublished data
Polyplax sp. nov. 2	*E. myoxinus* (Western Tufted-tail Rat)	Unpublished data
FAMILY PTHIRIDAE		
Pthirus pubis (Linnaeus, 1758) (Pubic Louse)	Humans	IMAT (2020)

Note: sp. nov., new species; if there are more than one of these undescribed forms in a given genus, they are numbered.

[1] *Haematopinus latus* Neumann, 1909 is the louse that infests *P. larvatus* (family Suidae) in its native range in mainland Africa (Durden and Musser 1994). *Haematopinus suis* typically parasitizes domestic hogs and feral hogs, *Sus scrofa*.

[2] Paulian (1958) stated that the host of *Lemurpediculus petterorum* was "probably" *Lepilemur mustelinus* (family Lepilemuridae).

[3] Ehlers et al. (2019) reported *L. verruculosus* from *M. griseorufus*, but sucking lice of all other dwarf and mouse lemurs (family Cheirogaleidae) examined thus far have been host specific. Therefore, the louse of *M. griseorufus* could represent an undescribed species.

[4] Lice from *Propithecus edwardsi* (family Indriidae) were identified as *Phthirpediculus* sp. by Wright et al. (2009) and as a possible new species belonging to this genus by Leo (2009). See text for more explanation.

species of diurnal and social lemurs (Durden et al. 2017): *Indri indri* (Indri), *Propithecus diadema* (Diademed Sifaka), and *P. verreauxi* (Verreaux's Sifaka)—all family Indriidae; and *Eulemur coronatus* (Crowned Lemur), *E. macaco* (Black Lemur), and *E. mongoz* (Mongoose Lemur)—all family Lemuridae.

DISEASE AGENTS TRANSMITTED BY SUCKING LICE

The most important pathogens transmitted by sucking lice in Madagascar, as in other parts of the world, are transmitted to humans by the body louse *Pediculus humanus humanus* and possibly also by the head louse *P. h. capitis*. The body louse is a proven vector of the causative agents of at least three human pathogens: *Rickettsia prowazekii*, which causes epidemic (louse-borne) typhus; *Bartonella quintana*, which causes trench fever; and *Borrelia recurrentis*, which causes epidemic (louse-borne) relapsing fever (Durden 2019). Body lice can also be experimentally infected with other bacterial pathogens, such as *Acinetobacter baumannii* (Houhamdi and Raoult 2006), and may be a vector of this bacterium (LaScola and Raoult 2004). Although the head louse has commonly been considered unable to transmit any of these pathogens, some of them have recently been detected in head lice removed from humans in some parts of the world. On Madagascar, Sangaré et al. (2014) detected *B. quintana* in both head lice and body lice, and Eremeeva et al. (2019) detected *B. quintana* and *Acinetobacter* sp. in head lice. Therefore, the possible role of head lice as vectors of pathogens is being reconsidered. Plague, caused by the bacterium *Yersinia pestis*, also circulates on Madagascar, currently causing significant human morbidity and mortality (Ehlers et al. 2020). Certain species of fleas are recognized vectors of *Y. pestis*, but the body louse is also an efficient experimental vector, and it has been proposed that body lice are secondary plague vectors in Madagascar (Drancourt and Raoult 2018). Perhaps significantly, insecticide resistance has been documented in human lice on the island (Eremeeva et al. 2019).

Sucking lice of livestock and pets may also be vectors of pathogens on Madagascar, but more data are needed to be certain. Ehlers et al. (2020) detected *Rickettsia africae* (typically considered to be a tick-borne pathogen) in three species of livestock-associated sucking lice in Madagascar: *Haematopinus quadripertusus* and *Linognathus vituli* from cattle, and *L. africanus* from goats. They also reported *Bartonella* DNA in *H. quadripertusus*. Transmission experiments would need to be completed to determine if these lice are actually vectors of these bacterial pathogens. *Haematopinus suis* can transmit Swinepox Virus to hogs, but this virus can also be transmitted directly from hog to hog (Durden 2019). Regardless of pathogen transmission, large populations of lice can cause deleterious effects to livestock and pets, such as intense itching, allergic reactions, fur loss, suboptimal nutrition, and low weight gain.

Sucking lice of native Madagascar mammals are not known to be vectors of pathogens or parasites to their hosts, but again, more data are needed. Ehlers et al. (2020) detected *R. africae* and *Bartonella* sp. from *Lemurpediculus* lice from mouse lemurs (*Microcebus griseorufus*) in southwestern Madagascar, but as stated above, transmission experiments would be required to establish or refute lice as vectors of these pathogens. Some lemurs can be parasitized by pathogenic protozoans (including malaria parasites) or filarial worms; ticks and biting flies, rather than sucking lice, are the known or suspected vectors of these parasites (A. Klein et al. 2019; Ehlers et al. 2020).

LEMUR LICE AS INDICATORS OF HOST BIOLOGY

Some field studies on Madagascar have utilized sucking lice of mouse lemurs as tools to assess host traits such as physical contact between host individuals, host aggression, and socioecology. For example, Zohdy et al. (2012) individually marked *Lemurpediculus verruculosus* lice, replaced them onto their original host mouse lemur (*Microcebus rufus*), and then tracked their movements through the host population by recording lice on multiply recaptured lemurs. Host transfers of the lice demonstrated physical contacts between individual hosts that could not have been demonstrated by host data alone. It was also shown that transfer of lice to male hosts occurred mainly during the mating season and that many of the lice moved to the testes of reproductive male hosts. Zohdy et al. (2017) further showed that aggressive male hosts with high levels of testosterone and cortisol had most of the lice within the lemur population and were the main sources of lice to conspecific hosts. Also, A. Klein et al. (2018) demonstrated seasonal and socioecologcal aspects of *Lemurpediculus* infestations within populations of two other species of mouse lemurs (*M. murinus* and *M. ravelobensis*).

DESCRIPTIVE CORRECTION FOR *PHTHIRPEDICULUS PROPITHECI*

When Ewing (1923) described *Phthirpediculus propitheci*, he did not include accompanying illustrations, and he did not describe the female subgenital plate. Ferris (1932) provided diagnostic line drawings and a more detailed written description for adults of both sexes of this species. Unfortunately, in his drawing of the female subgenital plate, Ferris (1932), an overall excellent Anoplura taxonomist, misrepresented the shape of this plate, which is a diagnostic morphological character for female lice belonging to this genus. This misrepresentation led Leo (2009) to suggest that *Phthirpediculus* lice collected from *Propithecus edwardsi* (Milne-Edwards' Sifaka) in Ranomafana National Park might represent an undescribed species. Examination of those specimens by the current author initially appeared to confirm that assumption, but when they were compared with type specimens of *P. propitheci*, the lice matched, and the error by Ferris (1932) became apparent. Ferris (1932: 296, Figure 180) showed the female subgenital plate having a continuous bar anteriorly; however, there is actually a curved anteromedial extension on each side and no connecting bar. The anteromedial extensions can be seen clearly in Leo (2009: 263, Figure 11.3) and in Figure 9.21b (shown by the two arrows) herein.

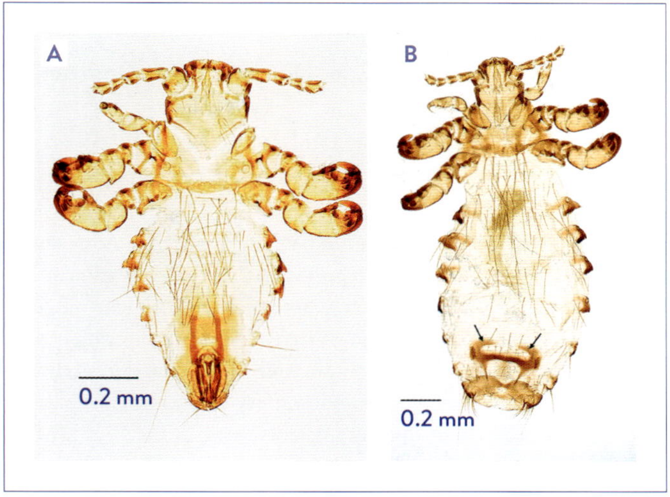

FIGURE 9.21 **Stacked images of cleared, slide-mounted male A) and female B) *Phthirpediculus propitheci* from *Propithecus edwardsi* collected in Ranomafana National Park. Arrows show anteriomedial extensions of the subgenital plate in the female.** (PHOTOS by L. Beati.)

CONSERVATION CONSIDERATIONS

Because many species of sucking lice on Madagascar are known to be host-specific parasites of endemic and, in some cases, endangered host species, conservation efforts for these hosts should also consider their parasites, including sucking lice. At the least, it is recommended that endangered hosts are not treated with parasiticides. Ectoparasites rarely cause life-threatening infestations to their hosts (transmission of pathogens or parasites by some species is an exception), and numerous studies have shown that parasite exposure promotes biodiversity, host genetic diversity, and other important biological traits in ecosystems and host populations (Michalakis et al. 1992). Except for lice of humans, sucking lice are not currently known to transmit any pathogens or parasites to their hosts on Madagascar.

ACKNOWLEDGMENTS

Several people have facilitated studies on Malagasy sucking lice, including (listed alphabetically): Lorenza Beati (Georgia Southern University, Statesboro, Georgia, USA), Marina Blanco (Duke Lemur Center, Durham, North Carolina, USA), David Furth (formerly, US National Museum of Natural History, Washington, DC, USA), Sharon Kessler (University of Stirling, Scotland), Anne Laudisoit (EcoHealth Alliance, New York, USA), Natalie Leo (formerly, Kyoto University, Japan), Ute Radespiel (University of Veterinary Medicine, Hannover, Germany), Elke Zimmermann (formerly, University of Veterinary Medicine, Hannover, Germany), and Sarah Zohdy (Auburn University, Alabama, USA, and Centers for Disease Control and Prevention, Atlanta, USA).

Subject editors: Brian L. Fisher and Steven M. Goodman

HEMIPTERA: CICADELLIDAE, LEAFHOPPERS

C. H. Dietrich, D. A. Dmitriev, S. M. Krishnankutty, and D. M. Takiya

Leafhoppers (Hemiptera: Cicadellidae) are among the most abundant herbivores in terrestrial ecosystems, ranging from tropical rainforest to grassland and desert, where they feed on plant vascular fluids or leaf cell contents using piercing-sucking mouthparts. A major source of food for vertebrate and invertebrate insectivores (Waloff 1980), they feed on a wide variety of plants, thus playing crucial roles in nutrient cycling (Wiegert and Evans 1967). Most dominant or subdominant perennial plant species have at least a few associated leafhopper species, and many specialize on a single genus or species of plants. Some individual forest trees in temperate North America have been reported to host more than 100 species of leafhoppers at a single locality, and these numbers are certainly higher in the tropics. Leafhoppers are excellent indicators of habitat quality and overall biodiversity because of their high species richness and abundance, the fidelity of many species to particular habitats and host plants, and ease of capture (Biedermann et al. 2005; Wallner et al. 2012).

Cicadellidae is the largest family of Hemiptera and one of the largest families of insects, currently comprising nearly 23,500 valid species worldwide, with an average of 200-plus new species discovered and described each year. It is presently classified as one of five families of superfamily Membracoidea, a well-supported monophyletic group. However, recent phylogenetic analyses indicate that Cicadellidae gave rise to a lineage that includes the three currently recognized families of treehoppers (Aetalionidae, Melizoderidae, and Membracidae) and is, therefore, paraphyletic (Dietrich et al. 2017). Membracidae, the largest and most widespread treehopper family, was recorded from Madagascar only once, by Signoret (1860). The record was based on the type specimen of *Anchon proximum*, a species more recently recorded from West Africa (Distant 1914; Capener 1968). Signoret's record is considered dubious, however, given that extensive recent collecting has failed to reveal the presence of any Membracidae on Madagascar. It seems likely that either Signoret's specimen was mislabeled or the record represents a short-lived, anthropogenic introduction of an African species.

Relationships among membracoid families and among recognized subfamilies of Cicadellidae are not yet sufficiently resolved to support a stable taxonomic classification, splitting Cicadellidae into additional, less inclusive monophyletic families. Thus, when considering the evolution of the leafhopper fauna in general, it is perhaps more appropriate to refer to Membracoidea, the lowest-ranking monophyletic taxon that includes all of the leafhoppers. Family Cicadellidae, as presently defined, comprises all known Malagasy species of Membracoidea. Cicadellids are easily distinguished from other members of Auchenorrhyncha (the hemipteran suborder that also includes planthoppers, spittlebugs, and cicadas) by the presence of rows of enlarged, spinelike setae (macrosetae) on the hind tibia. Genera and species of leafhoppers are distinguished by features of the head, wings, legs, and most importantly, male genitalia (Dietrich 2005).

ECONOMIC IMPORTANCE

Leafhoppers are important agricultural pests, injuring many crops through both direct feeding injury (Backus 1988) and transmission of viral and bacterial plant pathogens. Phloem-feeding leafhoppers, particularly Deltocephalinae, are the most important vectors of phytoplasmas, a widespread group of phloem-limited bacterial pathogens affecting many economically important plants (Weintraub and Beanland 2006). Sharpshooters (Cicadellinae), which feed preferentially on xylem, are the main vectors of *Xylella fastidiosa*, a xylem-limited bacterial pathogen that causes devastating diseases of grapevine, citrus, and stone fruits (Almeida et al. 2005). Green leafhoppers (*Nephotettix*), two species of which are recorded from Madagascar, are the main vectors of rice tungro and five other viral diseases of rice widespread in Asia (Hibino et al. 1979). So far, there do not appear to be any published records of bacterial or viral pathogens transmitted by leafhoppers on Madagascar, with the exception of Maize Streak Virus, which is widespread on the island; its known vectors, leafhoppers of the genus *Cicadulina*, have not yet been reported there but occur in the Mascarene and Seychelles archipelagoes.

DIVERSITY AND ENDEMISM

Recent studies of tropical faunas indicate that a majority of leafhopper species remain undescribed and suggest that the true diversity of Cicadellidae may exceed 100,000 species. The leafhopper fauna of Madagascar remains among the least studied tropical faunas worldwide. Historically, there have been no surveys specifically targeting leafhoppers on the island and only a handful of taxonomists have treated the Malagasy leafhopper fauna. Signoret (1860) listed 13 species, placing them in five genera previously described from other parts of the world. Evans (1953, 1959) recorded 111 species in 41 genera, 33 of which were considered endemic. Evans's work focused primarily on what he considered to be the unique or unusual elements of the fauna and entirely omitted the largest element, the microleafhopper subfamily Typhlocybinae. More recently, Dworakowska (1997) described 11 genera (four endemic) and 17 species (14 endemic) of Typhlocybinae from Madagascar based on the study of only two European collections. Her study remains the only attempt to treat the Malagasy fauna of that subfamily, which, as in other tropical regions, is highly diverse but remains almost entirely undocumented. Freytag and Knight (1966) reviewed Idiocerini on Madagascar, adding 13 new species to the three already recorded by Evans and placing five of these in a new endemic genus. They noted that while some species of this group from Madagascar "are closely related to the fauna of India and the Philippines," the Malagasy fauna also included unique elements with obscure relationships to the idiocerines of other parts of the world. Freytag and

Cwikla (1984) added two new species of the endemic genus *Nesocerus*. Subsequent authors studying specimens from museums added only 81 more species, mostly taxa of the sharpshooter subfamily Cicadellinae (Young 1986).

A recent terrestrial arthropod bioinventory led by entomologists at the California Academy of Sciences yielded a wealth of new leafhopper specimens from all parts of Madagascar. Studies of this material confirm that the leafhopper fauna is rich in species, highly endemic, and still largely undescribed. Since 2010, taxonomic papers based on this new material have included descriptions of 99 new endemic species and three new endemic genera. These have increased the numbers of known species in their respective genera or tribes from 60% to 90%. The recent survey indicates that many of the historically recorded species are still present on Madagascar, but some were not found.

The leafhopper fauna of the smaller islands of the Malagasy Region remain little studied, with the exception of the Aldabra Atoll group in the western Seychelles. Webb (1980) reported 33 species from these islands, of which 10 also occur in Africa, three are shared with other Seychelles islands, and 19 are endemic, including four apparently endemic genera. One of the latter has since been found on Madagascar (C. Dietrich, unpublished data), and it seems likely that many others eventually will be recorded on Madagascar because they belong to groups that have so far been poorly studied. Catalogs of the Hemiptera of La Réunion and Mauritius list only 31 and three cicadellid species, respectively, most of which are either widespread or also occur on Madagascar (Mamet 1957; Bonfils et al. 1994). One genus, *Mahellus* Nielson, is recorded only from southern India and the Seychelles, and other leafhoppers from the Seychelles islands also appear to have mixed Malagasy-Indian affinities (C. Dietrich, unpublished data).

UNIQUE ASPECTS OF THE MADAGASCAR FAUNA

The membracoid fauna of Madagascar is peculiar in several respects. Among the 103 genera recorded from Madagascar, 81 (78.6%) are endemic. Genus-level endemism is likely to increase once the fauna becomes better known and taxonomic studies further modernize genus-level classifications. Species-level endemism is even higher, with 278 of the 297 (93.6%) of recorded species restricted to Madagascar (Table 9.20).

Among the most noteworthy endemic groups is the soil-dwelling genus *Paulianiana*, represented by a single described species and at least two undescribed species (Figure 9.22i). These leafhoppers are flightless, have reduced compound eyes, lack ocelli, and coat themselves with soil such that they are highly cryptic. Hamilton (1999) suggested that they belong to a tribe (Sagmatiini) comprising two additional flightless, soil-dwelling genera endemic to northeastern Australia. However, a recent phylogenomic analysis placed *Paulianiana* in a clade with a representative of the subfamily Ledrinae (Australian sagmatiines have not yet been included in phylogenetic analyses). Other Ledrinae, an ancient subfamily that occurs on every other continent except Antarctica, have not been recorded from Madagascar.

Two endemic Malagasy genera, *Stenoledra* (Figure 9.22h) and *Ledracorrhis*, each represented by a single species, were initially placed in Ledrinae (Evans 1953, 1959), based on their strongly produced, spatulate heads with dorsal ocelli. Although these genera strongly resemble members of Ledrinae from other parts of the world, a morphology-based phylogenetic analysis (J. R. Jones and Deitz 2009) revealed that they are most closely related to Ulopinae and that their similarity to Ledrinae is superficial.

The largest leafhopper recorded from Madagascar, *Betsileonas marmorata* (Figure 9.22d) (~15–19 mm long), was also previously placed in Ledrinae, but in a revision of Ledrinae, J. R. Jones and Deitz (2009) treated the genus as unplaced within Cicadellidae. This species apparently belongs in the endemic tribe Platyjassini (subfamily Iassinae) (Dietrich et al. 2020). It is known only from three old female museum specimens. Platyjassini is also represented by four described species of the type genus, *Platyjassus* (Figure 9.22a). A recent taxonomic revision of this tribe has led to the discovery of 14 additional endemic genera and 54 new species (Dietrich et al. 2020; Figures 9.22b and c).

Several diverse groups of Membracoidea widely distributed in other parts of the world are conspicuous in being either absent or extremely rare on Madagascar. Treehoppers, which recent phylogenetic studies suggest arose in tropical America during the Cretaceous and dispersed into the Old World via the Bering Land Bridge during the Paleogene (Dietrich et al. 2017), are now diverse and abundant in tropical forests and savannas worldwide. But they apparently "missed the boat" and did not colonize Madagascar prior to its isolation from the other continents. Nevertheless, the leafhopper lineage that is sister to the treehoppers, comprising Ulopinae and Megophthalminae, includes at least seven endemic genera and 25 endemic species on Madagascar (Evans 1953; Viraktamath and Gonçalves 2013). These insects, which also feed on various trees and shrubs, include some peculiar treehopper analogues belonging to the ulopine tribe Coloborrhinini that have well-developed horns on the pronotum and/or scutellum (Figure 9.22g) and, in some cases, an undulate commissural margin of the forewing that gives the dorsum of the body an irregular shape in profile. These are unlike members of Ulopinae recorded from other parts of the world, which may be beetle-like or seed-like in appearance but lack treehopper-like modifications of the pronotum and forewing.

Evacanthinae is most diverse in the Indo-Malaysian region, but this subfamily also includes large endemic Afrotropical and Neotropical components. Molecular divergence time estimates place the origin of this group between ~89 and 123 million years ago (Mya) (Dietrich et al. 2017; Wang et al. 2017), but on Madagascar, this group appears to be represented by a single genus of Nirvanini, *Kana*, which also occurs in both Africa and the Indo-Malaysian region. The undescribed species of this genus present on Madagascar presumably represents a more recent (Paleogene or Neogene) colonization, but a phylogeny of the genus is needed to estimate the colonization date more precisely.

The subfamily Coelidiinae is abundant and diverse in tropical forests worldwide but appears depauperate on Madagascar. Nielson (1982) suggested that the single endemic genus, *Limentinus* (Figure 9.22m), has both Asian and African affinities, but a recent phylogeny of the subfamily based on combined molecular and morphological data placed this genus as sister to the endemic African genus *Afrolidia*, with a divergence date estimate of ~44 Mya (Wang 2018). This divergence date roughly corresponds to the time

TABLE 9.20. **Diversity of Cicadellidae on Madagascar, worldwide, and in the Afrotropical region (including Madagascar) based on previously described species**

SUBFAMILY	WORLD		AFROTROPICAL		MADAGASCAR		ENDEMIC TO MADAGASCAR	
	GENERA	SPECIES	GENERA	SPECIES	GENERA	SPECIES	GENERA	SPECIES
Aphrodinae	18	263	2	25	2	6	1	6
Bathysmatophorinae	15	49	0	0	0	0	0	0
Cicadellinae	339	2558	31	83	27	67	25	65
Coelidiinae	155	2570	31	122	2	8	1	7
Deltocephalinae	948	7080	222	929	27	49	18	37
Eurymelinae	177	1398	18	152	8	54	5	54
Evacanthinae	71	539	8	25	0	0	0	0
Hylicinae	13	40	2	11	0	0	0	0
Iassinae	151	2181	21	161	17	58	16	61
Ledrinae	64	421	9	31	0	0	0	0
Megophthalminae	80	738	6	16	2	9	1	7
Mileewinae	11	189	2	39	1	8	0	8
Neobalinae	9	64	0	0	0	0	0	0
Neocoelidiinae	33	181	0	0	0	0	0	0
Nioniinae	1	7	0	0	0	0	0	0
Signoretiinae	6	42	2	16	0	0	0	0
Tartessinae	37	145	0	0	0	0	0	0
Typhlocybinae	495	4926	100	599	10	19	8	15
Ulopinae	41	147	14	38	7	19	6	18
Total	2664	23538	468	2247	103	297	81	278

Sources: Data mostly from Dmitriev (2003). Subfamily classification follows Dietrich (2005) as updated from Dietrich et al. (2017) and more recent literature.

of origin of the clade of endemic Cicadellinae (Feng 2019) and the crown age of the endemic iassine tribe Platyjassini (Krishnankutty et al. 2016), suggesting that although the latter group originated much earlier, all of these groups began to diversify on Madagascar after orogenic processes during the late Paleocene–early Eocene led to the development of humid tropical forests prevalent in the eastern part of the island (Yoder and Nowak 2006). Interestingly, some endemic Malagasy genera and species previously assigned to Coelidiinae based on morphological similarities have been shown instead to be morphologically aberrant representatives of the deltocephaline tribe Acostemmini (Zahniser and Nielson 2012; Figure 9.221). This morphological convergence suggests that, in the forests of Madagascar, these members of Acostemmini occupy niches similar to those occupied by Coelidiinae in tropical forests elsewhere in the world. Signoretiinae and Hylicinae, two small but widespread Old World subfamilies known from the Indo-Malaysian and Afrotropical regions, appear to be absent on Madagascar.

BIOGEOGRAPHY AND EVOLUTION

Leafhoppers are part of an ancient lineage. The oldest undoubted cicadellid fossils are from the Early Cretaceous (~118 Mya) of Brazil and Australia, but recent molecular-divergence time estimates place the origin of the family in the Early Jurassic (~187 Mya). The superfamily Membracoidea is much older; fossils representing extinct lineages known from the Upper Triassic of Australia (~220 Mya) and molecular-divergence estimates place the origin of the lineage in the Early Triassic (~246 Mya) (reviewed by Dietrich et al. 2017). Thus, leafhoppers had ample opportunity to colonize Madagascar prior to its separation from other continental landmasses. Indeed, phylogenetic and biogeographic studies incorporating molecular and morphological data suggest that Madagascar is home to multiple ancient lineages of leafhoppers, each of which has diversified extensively and is now largely or entirely restricted to the island. These studies also indicate that multiple lineages of

FIGURE 9.22 **Endemic Madagascar representatives of Cicadellidae. Platyjassini: A) a new species of the type genus, *Platyjassus*; B) and C) representatives of two undescribed genera; D) *Betsileonas marmorata*, the largest leafhopper recorded from Madagascar, known only from old museum specimens. *Nesocerus*, one of the earliest diverging lineages of Eurymelinae: E) *N. latus*, F) *N. uniprocessus*. Ulopinae: G) *Pyrgophora enigma*, a treehopper analogue with projections on the pronotum and scutellum; H) *Stenoledra decorsei*, an ulopine showing strong morphological convergence with Ledrinae, a widespread subfamily apparently absent from Madagascar. I) *Paulianiana* sp., a flightless, soil-dwelling leafhopper morphologically convergent with the early-diverging membracoid family Myerslopiidae but apparently related to Ledrinae. Acostemmini, one of the earliest diverging lineages of Deltocephalinae: J) *Acostemma stilleri*; K) *Ikelibeloha cristata*; L) *Caelidioides tristis*, a species previously placed in Coelidiinae owing to strong morphological convergence. M) *Limentinus declinatus*, representing the only genus of true Coelidiinae recorded from Madagascar. Scale bars, 1.0 mm.** (PHOTOS A–C, E–H, and I by C. H. Dietrich; D by J. R. Jones; J–L by J. N. Zahniser; and M by X. Wang.)

leafhoppers colonized Madagascar more recently and have a mixture of affinities to other continents.

Krishnankutty (2012) used phylogenetic analyses to explore historical patterns in the biogeography of three different cicadellid lineages on Madagascar. Within Iassinae, whose members feed largely on trees and shrubs in forests and grasslands, the endemic tribe Platyjassini (Figures 9.22a–d) constitutes an early-diverging lineage sister to a clade comprising two exclusively New World tribes (Krishnankutty et al. 2016; Figure 9.23). The time of origin for Platyjassini was estimated, using molecular-divergence time methods, to be during the Cretaceous (~96–103 Mya), when Madagascar was joined with the Seychelles-Indian block (Krishnankutty et al. 2016; Dietrich et al. 2017). The ancestors of this tribe may have become isolated on Madagascar before it separated from the Indian block. The crown age of this endemic tribe is estimated to be 42 Mya, which suggests its diversification occurred on the island after initiation of orographic precipitation during the late Paleocene–early Eocene (Yoder and Nowak 2006). In contrast, the distantly related and more recently derived cosmopolitan iassine genus *Batracomorphus*, which is widespread in the Paleotropics, presumably colonized Madagascar during the Paleogene or Neogene. More detailed phylogenetic analyses will be needed to infer the geographic origin of the ancestors of the present-day Malagasy members of this genus.

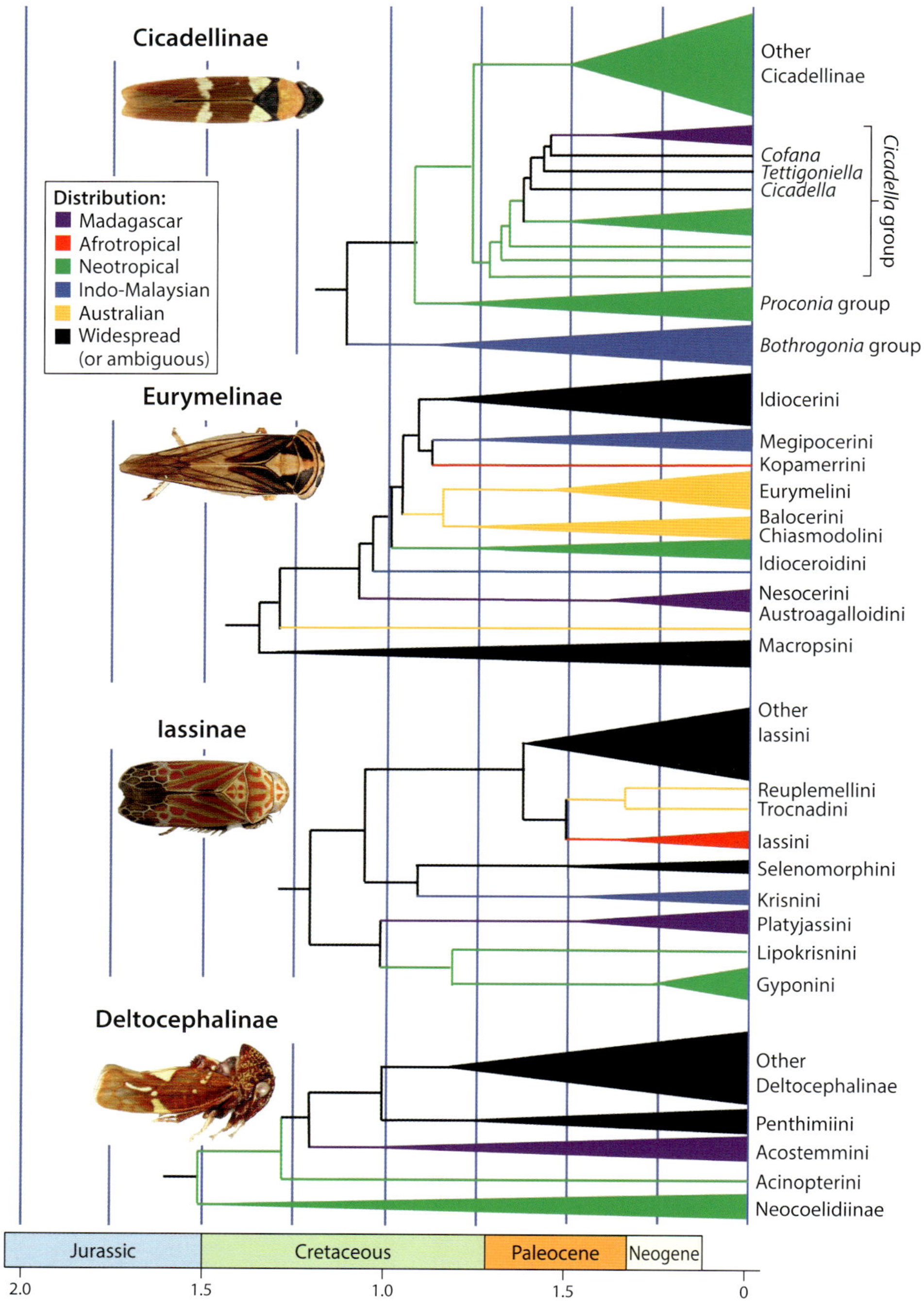

FIGURE 9.23 **Simplified molecular time trees showing relationships and times of origin of diverse endemic lineages of leafhoppers on Madagascar belonging to four globally distributed subfamilies. The endemic Malagasy lineages are indicated in purple. Note that three of the four originated during the Cretaceous. Among these four subfamilies, three (Eurymelinae, Iassinae, and Deltocephalinae) also include groups that colonized Madagascar more recently (not shown). Triangles toward branch tips indicate diversification of crown clades. The vertical bars indicate 25-million-year increments, and numbers on the horizontal axis are hundreds of millions of years.** (SOURCE: modified from Krishnankutty 2012; Krishnankutty et al. 2016 [Iassinae]; Dietrich et al. 2017; Feng 2019 [Cicadellinae]; and Xue et al. 2020 [Eurymelinae]. PHOTO of *Imadellana sikorae* [top] by J. Turner, National Museum of Wales.)

In the subfamily Eurymelinae, members of which also occur primarily on trees and shrubs, a similar pattern was observed (Figure 9.23). Here again, one of the earliest diverging lineages comprises a genus endemic to Madagascar, *Nesocerus* (Figures 9.22e and f). The time of origin for this clade was estimated at 90–104 Mya, and diversification of the crown group began at 34–25 Mya (Krishnankutty 2012)—both well within the 95% confidence intervals for the estimated origin and crown-group diversification of Platyjassini, suggesting that these two independent lineages arose at about the same time as a result of similar processes (Krishnankutty 2012). Phylogenetic analysis suggests that there were at least three additional colonizations of Madagascar by other lineages of Eurymelinae more recently, during the same time that *Nesocerus* began to diversify at the species level, and that these new colonists originated from either Africa or Asia, depending on the particular lineage. A more recent analysis of Eurymelinae that incorporated a broader sample of taxa from other continents and data from additional gene regions (Xue et al. 2020) corroborates these findings. A separate species-level phylogenetic analysis of *Nesocerus* placed the species in two sister clades—one largely restricted to the western dry deciduous forests and the other occurring mostly in the eastern moist evergreen forests (Krishnankutty and Dietrich 2011a). A similar pattern has been observed in some other endemic Malagasy arthropods (e.g., Wood et al. 2007).

In Cicadellinae (sharpshooters), whose members feed on xylem sap and occur primarily on herbaceous vegetation in forest understories and grasslands, the pattern is different. A recent comprehensive phylogenetic analysis of this subfamily recovered the Malagasy cicadelline fauna as monophyletic, indicating that it arose within a lineage comprising some widespread Old World genera of the *Cicadella* generic group, which also includes several New World genera (Figure 9.23) (Feng 2019). The divergence time estimate in this analysis places the origin of the Malagasy fauna at ~54 Mya and the origin of Old World lineages of the *Cicadella* group at ~71 Mya. This suggests that the Malagasy sharpshooter fauna is derived from a lineage that dispersed from the Neotropical region into the Old World tropics and subsequently colonized Madagascar during the Paleogene. Interestingly, phylogenetic analyses of both Cicadellinae and Iassinae have revealed possible relationships between the New World and Malagasy faunas (Figure 9.23), consistent with other studies that have reported possible faunal links between South America and Madagascar (Evans et al. 2008; Noonan and Chippendale 2006).

Detailed phylogenetic studies of other leafhopper groups occurring on Madagascar have not yet been undertaken. However, another endemic group with a diverse but largely undescribed fauna on the island, Acostemmini (Figures 9.22j–l), has been shown by phylogenetic analyses (e.g., Zahniser and Dietrich 2013; Dietrich et al. 2017) to be one of the earliest diverging lineages of Deltocephalinae, the largest leafhopper subfamily, with a mean divergence time estimate of 120 Mya (Dietrich et al. 2017; Figure 9.23). This clade includes one species recorded from eastern Africa and another from Sri Lanka and southern India, suggesting the possibility that the tribe arose prior to the separation of these three landmasses, although the non-Malagasy species may also represent recent colonizations. Other members of Deltocephalinae from Madagascar mostly belong to more recently derived lineages, including species of the forest-dwelling tribe Scaphoideini and the grass-specialist tribes Chiasmini, Hecalini, Paralimnini, and Stenometopiini. Some scaphoideine genera previously recorded in Africa (e.g., *Acastroma* and *Alemaia*) or in both Africa and the Indo-Malaysian region (e.g., *Phlogothamnus*), include several undescribed species from Madagascar, but most of the genera of this tribe occurring on the island appear to be endemic (and undescribed), suggesting that this tribe also colonized many millions of years ago.

Ujna, a genus of Mileewinae comprising species from Asia and Madagascar, provides evidence that some leafhopper lineages on Madagascar are derived from Asian ancestors (Krishnankutty and Dietrich 2011b). However, the Malagasy species are morphologically divergent from those inhabiting the Indo-Malaysian region, so phylogenetic analyses are needed to confirm their relationship.

The ulopine tribe Coloborrhinini, with most species endemic to Madagascar, includes two species that occur in Africa but no phylogenetic analysis of this group has been attempted. The aphrodine genus *Xestocephalus*, which includes many endemic species on Madagascar (most undescribed) is distributed worldwide, and the affinities of the Malagasy fauna remain to be determined.

SUMMARY AND SUGGESTIONS FOR FUTURE RESEARCH

The leafhopper fauna of Madagascar is rich and highly endemic but remains largely undescribed and unstudied from taxonomic, ecological, and phylogenetic perspectives. Recent sampling indicates that leafhoppers are abundant and diverse in habitats ranging from medium-altitude moist evergreen forest to dry deciduous forest, dry spiny thicket, and grassland. Nevertheless, some historically recorded species have not been documented in recent surveys, and their current status is not clear. Further efforts are needed to fully document the fauna and to delineate regions of endemism harboring diverse local faunas. Available data suggest that many species of Malagasy leafhoppers are restricted to particular regions and habitats, suggesting that they may be useful indicators of ecoregions and local biodiversity hotspots. Leafhoppers have been used elsewhere as indicators of habitat quality and ecological change, but their value in conservation and monitoring programs on Madagascar could be enhanced with additional data on the host and habitat preferences of individual species, in addition to the development of comprehensive and easily accessible tools for species identification.

To date, only one species-level phylogenetic analysis has been published for an endemic leafhopper genus (*Nesocerus*; Krishnankutty and Dietrich 2011a). Taxonomic revisions and phylogenies of several other highly diverse endemic leafhopper groups—including the microleafhoppers (Typhlocybinae), the relict deltocephaline tribe Acostemmini, and the highly speciose grass-feeding genus *Xestocephalus*—are needed to further elucidate the diversity of the Malagasy fauna and determine whether biogeographic patterns of diversification in these groups mirror those of other endemic animal lineages.

The biogeographic history of the leafhoppers of Madagascar is complex. The fauna includes ancient lineages that apparently were present prior to the separation of the island from other continental landmasses, as well as younger lineages that more recently colonized Madagascar from Africa, Asia, and possibly even South America. The iassine tribe Platyjassini, the eurymeline genus *Nesocerus*, and the deltocephaline tribe Acostemmini apparently represent relicts of ancient lineages that may have been widespread in Gondwana but have now been replaced by more recently derived groups everywhere except on Madagascar. The presence of these diverse, ancient, and unique faunal elements should amplify calls to strengthen preservation and protection of the biodiversity of Madagascar.

Scientific editors: Brian L. Fisher and Steven M. Goodman

HEMIPTERA, HETEROPTERA: REDUVIIDAE, ASSASSIN BUGS

C. Weirauch

Reduviidae, the assassin bugs, are the second-largest family within the hemipteran suborder Heteroptera, and most species are easily identified based on the strongly curved and robust, typically three-segmented labium (Schuh and Weirauch 2020). The group comprises about 7000 described species worldwide, almost all of which are predators of other arthropods, and it is morphologically diverse; species sizes range from only a few millimeters to more than 4 cm, and shapes vary from slender with long appendages to robust and heavily sclerotized body forms. Even though the biology and ecology for the great majority of species is poorly documented, published data make clear that members of Reduviidae show extraordinary diversity with respect to habitats, prey range, and predatory behaviors (Wignall and Taylor 2008; Forero et al. 2011). Although most speciose in wet tropical biomes, Reduviidae are also found in temperate climates, deserts, and high-elevation cloud forests, and in a wide range of microhabitats, including leaf litter, under stones, on vegetation, and under the bark of trees. In addition to including predatory groups that include beneficial natural enemies (Grundy and Maelzer 2000) as well as potentially harmful predators of pollinators (Masonick et al. 2019), Reduviidae also comprises subfamily Triatominae, the medically important vectors of Chagas disease (Lent and Wygodzinsky 1979). While species in some groups appear to hunt and feed on virtually any other insect in a given microhabitat, restricted dietary preferences have repeatedly evolved across Reduviidae, with species in certain groups feeding exclusively on termites, ants, or millipedes (Malipatil 1985; Gordon and Weirauch 2016; Forthman and Weirauch 2017).

DIVERSITY OF REDUVIIDAE ON MADAGASCAR

As in other groups of insects that are speciose in the tropics, Madagascar has a rich and largely endemic assassin bug fauna that continues to be described and documented (Figure 9.24). Current data indicate that 390 species of Reduviidae in 117 genera are known from the island (Table 9.21). Eleven of the 24 subfamilies of Reduviidae are documented in the literature (Maldonado Capriles 1990); summaries for these subfamilies are provided below. Several assassin bug subfamilies are restricted to the New World (e.g., Bactrodinae, Chryxinae, Hammacerinae), and their absence from Madagascar is therefore to be expected.

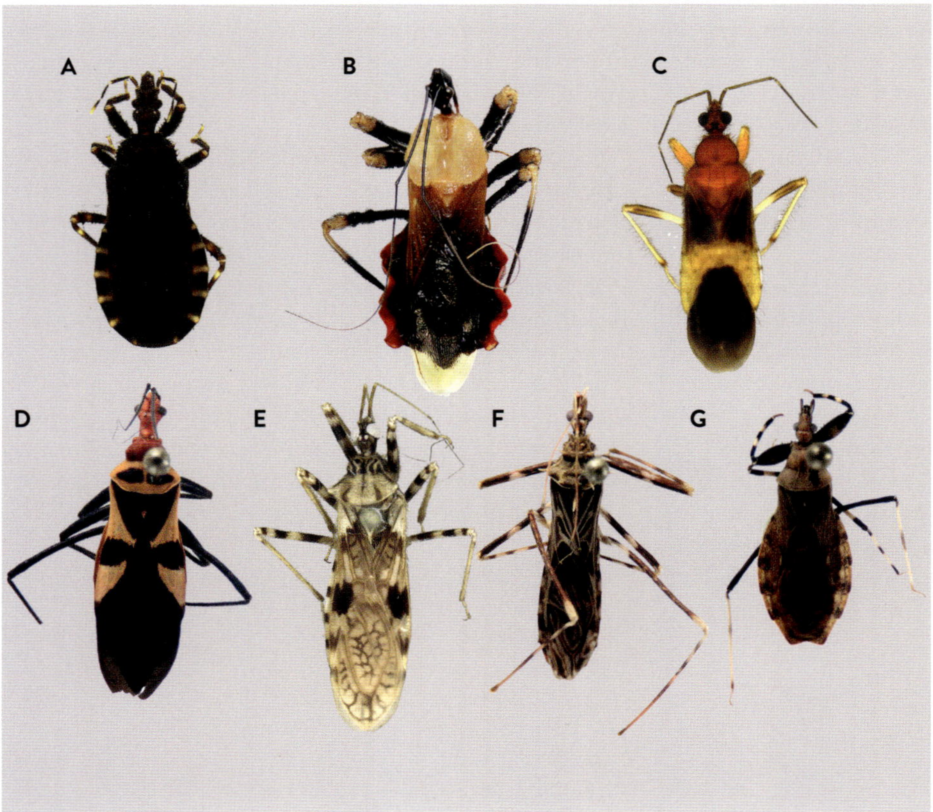

FIGURE 9.24 **Specimens of Malagasy Reduviidae, representing five of the 11 recorded subfamilies on the island. A) *Physoderoides annulipes* (Epiroderinae); B) undescribed species of *Ulpius* (Harpactorinae); C) *Bekilya tuleara* (Peiratinae); D) *Hoberlandtia cruciata* (Reduviinae); E) *Durevius tuberculatus* (Reduviinae); F) *Hendecacentrus adulterinus* (Stenopodainae); G) *Parawatsa rufina* (Stenopodainae).** (PHOTOS by former Weirauch lab undergraduate researchers S. Crum, G. Radabaugh, E. Potter, E. Ottero, and H. Thi; and by C. Weirauch.)

TABLE 9.21. **Checklist of the Reduviidae of Madagascar**

CETHERINAE

Cethera musiva (Germar, 1837)—NE: Madagascar, tropical Africa

ECTRICHODIINAE

Ectrichodiini

Distirogaster aenescens Horvath, 1914—E
D. proxima Horvath, 1914—E
D. tarsalis (Signoret, 1860)—E
D. tuberculifera Horvath, 1914—E
Gibbosella andasibe Forthman, Chlond & Weirauch, 2016—E
G. betampona Forthman, Chlond & Weirauch, 2016—E
G. brunalvus Forthman, Chlond & Weirauch, 2016—E
G. consimilis Forthman, Chlond & Weirauch, 2016—E
G. elongate Chlond, 2010—E
G. fulva Forthman, Chlond & Weirauch, 2016—E
G. mantilla Forthman, Chlond & Weirauch, 2016—E
G. megafrons Forthman, Chlond & Weirauch, 2016—E
G. mirabilis Chlond, 2010—E
G. nagocris Forthman, Chlond & Weirauch, 2016—E
G. nitida Forthman, Chlond & Weirauch, 2016—E
G. notoconica Forthman, Chlond & Weirauch, 2016—E
G. pallidacorium Forthman, Chlond & Weirauch, 2016—E
G. pallidalata Forthman, Chlond & Weirauch, 2016—E
G. planiscutum Forthman, Chlond & Weirauch, 2016—E
G. quadocris Forthman, Chlond & Weirauch, 2016—E
Glymmatophora carolae Forthman, Chlond & Weirauch, 2016—E
G. crassipes Forthman, Chlond & Weirauch, 2016—E
Maraenaspis bidens (Reuter), 1887—E
Marojejycoris auranticorium Forthman, Chlond & Weirauch, 2016—E
M. brevifrons Forthman, Chlond & Weirauch, 2016—E
M. francais Forthman, Chlond & Weirauch, 2016—E
M. notadichroa Forthman, Chlond & Weirauch, 2016—E
M. ranomafana Forthman, Chlond & Weirauch, 2016—E
Tanindrazanus amboasaricus Forthman, Chlond & Weirauch, 2016—E
T. andohahela Forthman, Chlond & Weirauch, 2016—E
T. anjozorobeus Forthman, Chlond & Weirauch, 2016—E
T. antananarivo Forthman, Chlond & Weirauch, 2016—E
T. bemaraha Forthman, Chlond & Weirauch, 2016—E
T. brunneus Forthman, Chlond & Weirauch, 2016—E
T. hannajagodae Forthman, Chlond & Weirauch, 2016—E
T. harinhali Forthman, Chlond & Weirauch, 2016—E
T. irwini Forthman, Chlond & Weirauch, 2016 —E
T. joffreyvillus Forthman, Chlond & Weirauch, 2016—E
T. kathrynae Forthman, Chlond & Weirauch, 2016—E
T. mahafalya Forthman, Chlond & Weirauch, 2016—E
T. marginatus Forthman, Chlond & Weirauch, 2016—E
T. marojejy Forthman, Chlond & Weirauch, 2016—E
T. nigripes Forthman, Chlond & Weirauch, 2016—E
T. notatus Forthman, Chlond & Weirauch, 2016—E
T. simulans Forthman, Chlond & Weirauch, 2016—E
T. tenebricus Forthman, Chlond & Weirauch, 2016—E
T. varicolor Forthman, Chlond & Weirauch, 2016—E
T. vohiparara Forthman, Chlond & Weirauch, 2016—E

ECTRICHODIINAE

Toliarus karinae Forthman, Chlond & Weirauch, 2016—E
T. trichrous Forthman, Chlond & Weirauch, 2016—E
Toxopus ambohitantely Forthman, Chlond & Weirauch, 2016—E
T. ampitavananima Forthman, Chlond & Weirauch, 2016—E
T. antsiranana Forthman, Chlond & Weirauch, 2016—E
T. basalis Forthman, Chlond & Weirauch, 2016—E
T. brucei Forthman, Chlond & Weirauch, 2016—E
T. farafangana Forthman, Chlond & Weirauch, 2016—E
T. fisheri Forthman, Chlond & Weirauch, 2016—E
T. griswoldi Forthman, Chlond & Weirauch, 2016—E
T. insignis Forthman, Chlond & Weirauch, 2016—E
T. italaviana Forthman, Chlond & Weirauch, 2016—E
T. melobrunneus Forthman, Chlond & Weirauch, 2016—E
T. miandritsara Forthman, Chlond & Weirauch, 2016—E
T. namoroka Forthman, Chlond & Weirauch, 2016—E
T. pallidus Forthman, Chlond & Weirauch, 2016—E
T. parkeri Forthman, Chlond & Weirauch, 2016—E
T. politus Bergroth, 1905—E
T. signoretii Reuter, 1887—E
T. simulans Forthman, Chlond & Weirauch, 2016—E
T. steineri Forthman, Chlond & Weirauch, 2016—E
T. tibialis Forthman, Chlond & Weirauch, 2016—E
T. toamasina Forthman, Chlond & Weirauch, 2016—E
T. toliara Forthman, Chlond & Weirauch, 2016—E
T. vazimba Forthman, Chlond & Weirauch, 2016—E

Tribelocephalini

Tribelocephala peyrierasi Villiers, 1970—E

EMESINAE

Collartidini

Stenorrhamphus barbiger (Weirauch, 2008)—E
S. orientalis (Villiers, 1970)—E
S. troglodytes (Chlond, Guilbert, Faille, Banar & Davranoglou, 2018)—E

Emesini

Gardena balachowskyae Villiers, 1971—E
G. dorstae Villiers, 1971—E
G. griveaudae Villiers, 1971—E
G. mauriciana Villiers, 1971—E
Gardenoides aymoninae Villiers, 1971—E
G. monsarratae Villiers, 1971—E
G. speluncarius Villiers, 1953—E
G. vadonae Paulian & Grjebine, 1971—E
Myiophanes kerzhneri Wygodzinsky, 1966—E
Stenolemus grandidieri Villiers, 1949—E
S. griveaudi Villiers, 1970—E
S. madagascariensis (Westwood, 1846)—E
S. seyrigi Villiers, 1949—E
S. vadoni Villers 1970—E

Leistarchini

Ambilobea fonsecae Villiers, 1971—E
Ambrinemesa blancae Villiers, 1971—E
Bettyella albignacae Wygodzinsky, 1971—E
B. edithae Villiers, 1971—E

(continued overleaf)

TABLE 9.21. ***continued***

EMESINAE

B. emmae Villiers, 1971—E
B. marita Wygodzinsky, 1966—E
B. marojejiensis Villiers, 1971—E
B. nicolae Villiers, 1971—E
B. perretae Villiers, 1971—E
B. scitula Villiers, 1966—E
B. tornatula Villiers, 1966—E
Laurenticoris inermiceps Villiers, 1975—E
Monicacoris elegantissima (Villiers, 1975)—E
Nesita annulosus Bergroth, 1906—E
Orthunga bicolorata Villiers, 1973—RE: Madagascar, Comoros
O. moheliana Villiers, 1973—E
O. octospinata Villiers, 1949—E
O. pantherina Villiers, 1973—E
O. rubronigra Villiers, 1973—E
O. seyrigi (Villiers, 1949)—E
O. sicardi Villiers, 1949—E
O. testacea Villiers, 1949—E
Ploiaria macrophthalma (Dohrn, 1949)—E
P. oculata (Villiers, 1949)—E
Tinna descarpentriesi Villiers, 1975—E
Tinnatunga olsufievi Wygodzinsky, 1966—E
Tinnunga descarpentriesi Villiers, 1975—E
T. macneilli Wygodzinsky, 1966—E
Voloina jouaninae Villiers, 1971—E

Metapterini

Bobba antanemora Wygodzinsky, 1966—E
Leptinoschidium madecassum (Villiers, 1966)—NE: Madagascar?, Cameroon
Schidium banianensis Villiers, 1979—E
S. inermiceps (Bergroth, 1906)—E
S. pelissieri Villiers, 1953—E
S. triangularis Villiers, 1979—E
S. vinsoni Villiers, 1979—E

Ploiariolini

Ademula comorensis Villiers, 1970—E
A. francinae Villiers, 1970—E
A. peregrine Wygodzinsky, 1966—E
Calphurnioides scalaris Villiers, 1970—E
Empicoris albatus Villiers, 1970—E
E. biannulatus Villiers, 1970—E
E. canaliculatus Villiers, 1960—E
E. cornutus Villiers, 1960—E
E. insularis Villiers, 1970—E
Sepimesos alexanderi Wygodzinsky, 1966—E

EPIRODERINAE

Befotaka granulosa Villiers, 1962—E
B. tumidicollis Villiers, 1962—E
Epiroderoides bicoloripes Villiers, 1962—RE: Mauritius, Madagascar
E. bipartitus Villiers, 1968—E
E. concoloripes Villiers, 1962—E
E. geniculatus Villiers, 1962—E
E. mauricensis Villiers, 1964—E

EPIRODERINAE

E. mirabilis Villiers, 1968—E
Henicocephaloides fulvescens Villiers, 1962—E
Maroantsetrana radula (Villiers 1962)—E
Mimoelasmodema depressa Villiers, 1962—E
Neophysoderes dubia Villiers, 1968—E
N. elongate Villiers, 1962—E
N. gigas Villiers, 1962—E
N. pandanophila Villiers, 1962—E
N. typical Miller, 1955—E
N. vadoni Villiers, 1968—E
Paraphysoderes crassa Villiers, 1962—E
P. peyrierasi Villiers, 1968—E
Paulianocoris alternatum (Signoret, 1860)—E
Physoderes brancsiki Bergroth, 1906—E
Physoderoides annulipes (Signoret, 1860)—E
P. browni Miller, 1955—E
Rodepirea lobate Villiers, 1962—E
R. ribesi Chlond, 2011—E
Tribelocephaloides gracilis Villiers, 1962—E

HARPACTORINAE

Diaspidiini

Cleontes dilatatus (Signoret, 1860)—E
C. laminatus Horvath, 1910—NE: Madagascar, Sri Lanka

Harpactorini

Anyttus sulcicollis (Signoret, 1860)—E
Aprepolestes cornutum Villiers, 1955—E
A. grandidieri Villiers, 1955—E
Callanocoris granulatus Villiers, 1960—E
C. hoberlandti Villiers, 1960—E
Cerellius nigricans Distant, 1903—E
C. typicus Distant, 1903—E
Chaetacantha excellens Bergroth, 1895—NE: Madagascar, Gabon
Coranus madagascariensis (Signoret, 1860)—E
C. nossibeensis Reuter, 1887—E
C rubripennis Reuter 1881—E
Endochus flavomarginatus Villiers, 1951—E
E. fuscus Villiers, 1951—E
E. meridionalis Villiers, 1951—E
E. seyrigi Villiers, 1951—E
E. villiersi Maldonado. 1951—E
Euagoras insipidus (Signoret, 1860)—E
Hammatoscelis annulipes Signoret, 1860—E
H. fasciatus (Signoret, 1860)—E
Hoplomargasus vicinus Horvath, 1914—E
Leptogaster flavipes Signoret, 1860—E
Margasus conifer Bergroth, 1895—E
M. elegans Varela, 1905—E
M. femoralis (Signoret, 1914)—E
M. luridus Distant, 1903—E
M. martini Varela, 1905—E
M. maurus Distant, 1903—E
M. nanus Varela, 1905—E
M. nitidus Varela, 1905—E
M. ornatus Varela 1905—E

HARPACTORINAE

M. spinosus Schouteden, 1909—E
M. varelai Schouteden, 1909—NE: Madagascar, Zaire
Myrmicella verticospinosa Chlond & Banar, 2013—E
Nagusta decorsei Villiers, 1951—E
Pantoleistes grandis Distant, 1879—E
Peyrierocoris gorvzycai Chlond, 2014—E
P. guilbert Chlond & Junkiert, 2010—E
P. herczeki Chlond, 2014—E
P. mirabilis Chlond & Junkiert, 2010—E
P. niger Chlond & Guilbert, 2012—E
P. seyrigi (Villiers, 1970)—E
P. wojciechowskii Chlond & Guilbert, 2012—E
Polididus longispinus Reuter, 1887—E
Rhynocoris fasciculatus (Bergroth, 1895)—E
R. gilviventris Bergroth, 1894—E
R. hovanus Kirkaldy, 1881—E
R. nigripes (Reuter, 1881)—E
Scoloponotus simulans Horvath, 1914—E
Sphedanolestes angularis Reuter, 1887—E
S. bastardi Villiers, 1969—E
S. bekiliensis Villiers, 1960—E
S. bicoloripes (Distant, 1881)—NE: Madagascar, Sri Lanka
S. bizonatus Villiers, 1969—E
S. callani Villiers, 1960—E
S. ivohibensis Villiers, 1969—E
S. keiseri Villiers, 1969—E
S. noualhieri Villiers, 1960—E
S. renaudi Villiers, 1969—E
S. seyrigi Villiers, 1960—E
S. subflaviceps (Signoret, 1865)—E
Sycanus harpactoides Signoret, 1860—E
Ulpius bicolor Distant, 1879—E
U. bigibbula Horvath, 1914—E
U. festivus Distant, 1879—E
U. grandituber Bergroth, 1906—E
U. guttiventris Horvath, 1914—E
U. nodosipes (Signoret, 1860)—E
U. obscurus Distant, 1879—E
U. tuberosus Horvath, 1914—E
U. tumidiceps Horvath, 1914—E
Velinus perfuga Bergroth, 1895—E
V. rotifer Bergroth, 1895—E

Rhapidosomini

Rhaphidosoma bastardi Jeannel, 1914—E
R. trituberculatum Bergroth, 1906—E

Tegeini

Lophocephala vicina Signoret, 1860—E

PEIRATINAE

Bekilya mahafalya Zhang & Weirauch, 2011—E
B. mira Villiers, 1949—E
B. tenebra Zhang & Weirauch, 2011—E
B. tricolor (Villiers, 1964)—E
B. tuleara Zhang & Weirauch, 2011—E

PEIRATINAE

Cleptocoris niger (Signoret, 1860)—E
C. perinetensis (Villiers, 1960)—E
C. strepitans (Rambur, 1855)—NE: Madagascar, Africa
Ectomocoris discoloripes (Reuter, 1881)—E
E. erebus (Distant, 1904)—NE: Myanmar, Madagascar?
E. grandidieri Villiers, 1964—E
E. laevicollis Villiers, 1964—E
E. pauliani Villiers, 1964—E
E. sculpticollis Villiers, 1964—E
Hovacoris bicolornotum Zhang & Weirauch, 2011—E
H. bipunctatus Villiers, 1964—E
H. melanoceps Zhang & Weirauch, 2011—E
H. rufiventris Zhang & Weirauch, 2011—E
Lestomerus hoberlandti Villiers, 1968—E
L. nigrotibialis Villiers, 1964—E
L. noctis (Distant, 1902)—E
L. piceipes Villiers, 1949—E
Peirates erebus Distant, 1903—E
Phalantus madecassus Villiers, 1949—E
Pseudolestomerus gracilis Villiers, 1964—E
Sirthenea atrocyanea Horvath, 1909—E
S. flaviceps (Signoret, 1860)—E

REDUVIINAE

Cargasdama noualhieri Villiers, 1950—E
Censorinus brancsiki Miller, 1953—E
C. dubius Villiers, 1950—E
C. ferrugineus Distant, 1903—E
C. geniculatus Villiers, 1962—E
C. karinae Chlond, 2010—E
C. monticolus Villiers, 1962—E
C. nigripes Villiers, 1968—E
C. peyrierasi Villiers, 1968—E
C. robinsoni Villiers, 1968—E
C. umbrosus Villiers, 1962—E
C. variegatus Villiers, 1950—E
Durevius cacao Hwang & Weirauch, 2010—E
D. galbeum Hwang & Weirauch, 2010—E
D. piceus Villiers, 1962—E
D. tuberculatus Villiers, 1950—E
D. usingeri Villiers, 1960—E
Hoberlandtia bipunctata Villiers, 1950—E
H. cruciate Villiers, 1962—E
H. fusca Villiers, 1962—E
H. grandidieri Villiers, 1950—E
H. hoberlandti Villiers, 1950—E
H. rufiventris Villiers, 1950—E
H. vadoni Villiers, 1968—E
Moramanga Formosa Villiers, 1962—E
Sphedanovarus comorensis Villiers, 1962—E
S. flavobasalis Villiers, 1962—E
S. sacalava Bergroth, 1903—E
S. vadoni Villiers, 1968—E

(continued overleaf)

TABLE 9.21. ***continued***

SAICINAE

Madecassosaica ornate Villiers, 1957—E
Polytoxus dlabolai Villiers, 1969—E
P. luridus Bergroth, 1906—E
P. mascarensis Miller, 1956—RE: Madagascar, Mauritius
P. mayottensis Villiers, 1979—E
P. mohelianus Villiers, 1957—E
P. pauliani Villiers, 1960—E
P. vadoni Villiers, 1979—E
Vadonocoris striatus Villiers, 1957—E

STENOPODAINAE

Anacanthiocnemis callani Villiers, 1960—E
Antanambeus funebris Villiers, 1948—E
A. marmoratus Chlond, 2011—E
A. pusillus Villiers, 1961—E
Beanana lineaticollis Villiers, 1960—E
Catala armata Villiers, 1961—E
C. flavipes Villiers, 1961—E
C. nigrina Villiers, 1961—E
C. roseonigra Villiers, 1951—E
Caunus seyrigi (Villiers, 1951)—E
Ceoncophalus funebris Villiers, 1961—E
C. viettei Villiers, 1968—E
Descarpentriesius depressus Villiers, 1961—E
Fitana alluaudi Villiers, 1948—E
F. orophila Villiers, 1961—E
F. vadoni Villiers, 1968—E
Gageus micropterus Villiers, 1961—E
Gallienius biounctatus Villiers, 1948—E
Griveaudicoris pulcher Villiers, 1961—E
Harpagochares decaryi Villiers, 1948—E
H. fusca Villiers, 1962—E
H. moheliana Villiers, 1962—E
Hendecacentrus adulterinus Bergroth, 1919—E
H. ligatus Villiers, 1961—E
H. mirabilis Villiers, 1961—E
H. monticolus Villiers, 1961—E
H. pauliani Villiers, 1961—E
H. seyrigi Villiers, 1951—E
H. simulans Chlond, 2011—E
H. transversus Villiers, 1961—E
Noualhierella longiceps Villiers, 1951—E
N. peyrierasi Villiers, 1968—E
Oncocephalus angulatus Reuter, 1882—RE: Madagascar, Mauritius
O. aurivillii Reuter, 1882—E
O. bastardi Villiers, 1948—E
O. milloti Villiers, 1948—E
O. ovatus Villiers, 1961—E
O. pauliani Villiers, 1961—E
O. subangulatus Villiers, 1961—E
Paraghesquierea lavaudeni Villiers, 1948—E

STENOPODAINAE

Parawatsa rufina Villiers, 1961—E
Perinetocoris lobatus Villiers, 1961—E
Planeocoris redeii Chlond, 2010—E
Pseudobeanana granulipennis Villiers, 1960—E
Pseudomuizonius milloti Villiers, 1961—E
Pygolampis robinsoni Villiers, 1961—E
P. secreta Villiers, 1961—E
P. albomaculata Villiers, 1961—E
P. bastardi Villiers, 1948—E
P. comorensis Villiers, 1968—E
P. griveaudi Villiers, 1961—E
P. lobate Villiers, 1948—E
P. madecassa Villiers, 1961—E
P. microcephala Villiers, 1968—E
P. perinetensis Villiers, 1961—E
P. piceipennis Villiers, 1961—E
P. stricticephala Villiers, 1961—E
P. vadoni Villiers, 1961—E
Renaudicoris laticollis Villiers, 1961—E
R. maculipennis Villiers, 1961—E
R. niger Villiers, 1961—E
R. trimaculatus Villiers, 1961—E
R. variegatus Villiers, 1961—E
R. viettei Villiers, 1961—E
Sastrapada incerta Signoret, 1860—E
S. madecassa Villiers, 1948—E
S. maroantsetrensis Villiers, 1962—E
S. meridionalis Villiers, 1962—E
S. noualhieri Villiers, 1962—E
S. pauliani Villiers, 1962—E
S. punctipennis Villiers, 1962—E
S. robinsoni Villiers, 1962—E
S. sogai Villiers, 1962—E
S. stricta Villiers, 1962—E
Thodelmus nigrispinosus Villiers, 1951—E:Madagascar
T. umbrosus Villiers, 1950—E
Xylinocoris depressus Miller, 1957—E
X. flavomaculatus Villiers, 1961—E
X. latipennis (Villiers, 1961)—E

TRIATOMINAE

Triatomini

Triatoma rubrofasciata (De Geer, 1773)—NE: Circumtropical

VISAYANOCORINAE

Carayonia milloti Villiers, 1960—E

Sources: Species described up until 1988 are listed based on the world catalog of Reduviidae by Maldonado Capriles (1990). Species described after 1988 are based on original publications referenced in the present chapter.
Note: E, species endemic to Madagascar; RE, regional endemic to Madagascar and Malagasy Region (Comoro, Mascarene, and Seychelles archipelagoes); NE, species not endemic to Madagascar and known from outside the Malagasy Region.

The lack of published records for three subfamilies widely distributed in the Afrotropical and Oriental regions is more surprising. Among these are Salyavatinae, a group of assassin bugs specialized to feed on termites. The subfamily includes many species in tropical Africa and the Oriental region, including the Indian subcontinent. Two salyavatine clades that are specialized on termites in the fungus-growing Macrotermitinae subfamily (a termite group found on Madagascar; see Eggleton, pp. 963–68) occur in both the Oriental and Afrotropical regions with estimated divergence times ~25 million years ago (Mya), a pattern similar to that of another assassin bug group that has colonized Madagascar multiple times (Gordon and Weirauch 2016). Phymatinae has the highest number of species in the New World (tribe Phymatini), but Themonocorini is restricted to Africa, and Macrocephalini has representatives in both the Afrotropical and Oriental regions, in addition to the New World. The group is old (divergences between the tribes were dated to 80–50 Mya), and its presumed absence from Madagascar is enigmatic (Masonick et al. 2017). There are also no published records from Madagascar for another old Reduviidae lineage, Holoptilinae, or feather-legged bugs. This group is widely distributed in the Afrotropical, Oriental, and Australian regions, with only one extant species known from the Neotropics (Weirauch et al. 2014). However, there is now evidence that Holoptilinae occurs on Madagascar; material collected from the Toliara area by the California Academy of Sciences contains one fifth-instar, immature, feather-legged bug specimen. Based on morphological features, the specimen can be attributed to the tribe Holoptilini but does not fit into current genus concepts within this tribe (C. Weirauch, unpublished data). Holoptilinae species are rarely collected, and this discovery suggests that additional sampling efforts are critical to reveal the diversity of Holoptilinae on the island. Similarly, Afrotropical and Oriental members of Phymatinae are rare in collections, and although certain species of Salyavatinae are readily collected at light traps, others are not. There is a possibility that representatives of both subfamilies have simply not been collected yet.

HISTORY OF DISCOVERY AND DOCUMENTATION

The early phase of documentation of reduviid biodiversity from Madagascar during the 19th and early 20th centuries was dominated by about 10 European authors. By 1916, 73 species of Reduviidae had been described from Madagascar. Victor Signoret (type material deposited in the Natural History Museum, Vienna), William Lucas Distant (type material mostly deposited in the Natural History Museum, London), and Ernst Evald Bergroth (type specimens in various European museums) contributed the bulk of the new species (Maldonado Capriles 1990).

The single most important figure in the discovery and description of Malagasy assassin bug diversity was André Villiers, who traveled widely in Africa and was based at the Muséum National d'Histoire Naturelle, Paris. In a series of taxonomic revisions and monographs published between 1948 and 1979, he described 206 species of Reduviidae from Madagascar, amounting to ~54% of the current species numbers (Villiers 1968, 1979). Many of these publications are comprehensive subfamily-level treatments with a review of existing taxa and description of new ones, published as part of a series on Reduviidae of Madagascar (e.g., Villiers 1951). These were synthesized into two contributions in the *Faune de Madagascar* series. The first summarized biodiversity information and provided identification keys for Peiratinae, Epiroderinae (then known as Physoderinae), Reduviinae, Cetherinae, Triatominae, and Stenopodainae (Villiers 1968); the second was on Emesinae, Saicinae, and Visayanocorinae, as well as the ectrichodiine tribe Tribelocephalini, then recognized as a separate subfamily (Villiers 1979). Villiers did not publish treatments for Ectrichodiinae or Harpactorinae, which is notable given that both show substantial genus and species-level diversity on Madagascar. Modern taxonomic work on members of Reduviidae on Madagascar started in the late 2000s after a gap of almost 30 years. Revisions and monographs of the past decade have built heavily on material collected by the California Academy of Sciences, as well as several European field researchers. The taxonomic focus has been on Ectrichodiinae; the monograph by Forthman et al. (2016) treats what amounts to 17% of the described species diversity of Malagasy reduviids, but attention has also been given to Harpactorinae (Chlond and Junkiert 2010; Chlond and Guilbert 2012; Chlond and Banar 2013; Chlond 2014), Stenopodainae (Chlond 2010a, 2016; Chlond and Junkiert 2011), Reduviinae (Chlond 2010b; Hwang and Weirauch 2010), Epiroderinae (Chlond 2011; Chlond et al. 2016), Emesinae (Chlond et al. 2018), and Peiratinae (Zhang and Weirauch 2011). The two worldwide catalogs for Reduviidae by Maldonado Capriles (1990) and Putshkov and Putshkov (1986) provide access to the bulk of the literature on Malagasy Reduviidae, while the modern literature, starting in 2008, is referenced above and below in the subfamily treatments.

REDUVIIDAE OF MADAGASCAR

Cetherinae

This small subfamily (six genera and ~23 species worldwide) is represented on Madagascar only by the widespread *Cethera musiva*, which is also widely distributed across tropical Africa (Villiers 1968). Recognized by globular—almost pedunculate—eyes, members of the Old World Cetherinae are often found on tree trunks with termites, but their biology is otherwise unknown.

Ectrichodiinae

Ectrichodiinae (millipede assassin bugs) is one of the four species-rich subfamilies on Madagascar, with currently 74 described species, all but one within the tribe Ectrichodiini. Recognized by the bifurcated scutellum and four- to six-segmented antennal flagellum in most species, many if not all members of Ectrichodiinae are specialized predators of toxic millipedes (Forthman and Weirauch 2012; see Wesener and Enghoff, pp. 918–33, for information on Malagasy millipedes). The group now also includes taxa that until recently were treated as the separate subfamily Tribelocephalinae (Forthman and Weirauch 2017). In addition to eight historical species descriptions by Bergroth, Signoret, Reuter, and Horvath in the late 19th and early 20th centuries, only two modern treatments have focused on Malagasy Ectrichodiinae (Chlond 2010c; Forthman et al. 2016).

Nine genera are recorded from Madagascar, six of which are endemic to the island, and all 75 species appear to be endemic. The island's fauna accounts for ~11% of the worldwide described species in this subfamily. The most speciose genera are *Gibbosella* (16 species), *Toxopus* (23 species), and *Tanindrazanus* (20 species). While most species in genera such as *Gibbosella* and *Marojejycoris* are restricted to the eastern part of the country, other genera (e.g., *Toxopus*, *Glymmatophora*) also show substantial diversity in the more arid regions of

Madagascar. Ectrichodiinae is the only group of Reduviidae for which a combination of phylogenetic hypotheses and historical biogeographic analyses provides insights into the evolutionary history of the group on Madagascar (Forthman and Weirauch 2016).

Emesinae

Emesinae (thread-legged bugs) includes more than 900 extant species worldwide in more than 90 genera. Among other features, Emesinae species are diagnosed by the slender habitus and long, thin appendages, and the often asymmetrical pretarsal claws (Weirauch et al. 2014). Species in several tribes are known or suspected to be associated with spiderwebs, either as kleptoparasites or as spider predators. The group is well represented in Madagascar, with 24 genera and 63 species, and is one of the four most species-rich subfamilies on the island. Emesinae species are associated with cryptic microhabitats, including living and dead vegetation and leaf litter. They are often delicate and are weak fliers. Nevertheless, thread-legged bugs have colonized remote islands, and four genera have worldwide distribution. Emesinae therefore appears to have substantial passive dispersal capabilities, possibly explaining both the subfamily's species richness on Madagascar and the relatively low genus-level endemism (46%). The only modern addition to the emesine fauna of Madagascar is the description of a new species of Collartidini (Chlond et al. 2018).

Epiroderinae (formerly Physoderinae)

Epiroderinae comprises small and cryptically colored species and represents one of the smaller reduviid subfamilies worldwide. Epiroderinae species are most commonly collected on Madagascar using leaf-litter extraction, suggesting that species live in leaf litter. Although only 26 species (all but one endemic to the island) are currently described from Madagascar, this number accounts for ~32% of described species in the world. Even more noteworthy is the high genus-level endemism; of the 12 recorded genera, 11 occur only on Madagascar and are characterized by substantial morphological diversity in a group that is otherwise fairly uniform. All endemic genera are monophyletic and therefore appear to be part of the same radiation (Hwang and Weirauch 2017). There is only one recent species-level addition to the epiroderine fauna of Madagascar (Chlond 2011; Chlond et al. 2016).

Harpactorinae

Harpactorinae consists of more than 2800 species in ~320 genera worldwide and is by far the largest assassin bug subfamily. Characterized by distinctive wing venation that includes a quadrate cell, Harpactorinae is among the most conspicuous subfamilies of Reduviidae because most species are diurnal and hunt on vegetation, including flowers (Weirauch et al. 2014). In addition to hand collecting, members of Harpactorinae are frequently collected using Malaise traps. With 77 recorded species, this group is one of the four largest subfamilies on the island. Interestingly, only eight of 25 genera are endemic (32%), while species-level endemism is almost as high as it is in other subfamilies, 73 of 77 species (95%). Published taxonomic revisionary work on the Malagasy fauna of this subfamily is far less comprehensive than it is for any other subfamily; for example, Villiers did not work intensively on members of the island's Harpactorinae, and modern revisionary work is restricted to several contributions by Chlond and co-workers, mostly focusing on the description and documentation of the two new endemic genera *Myrmicella* and *Peyrierocoris* (Chlond and Junkiert 2010; Chlond and Banar 2013).

Peiratinae

Peiratinae species, also known as corsairs, are characterized by the short posterior pronotal lobe. They are also known for inflicting the most painful bites among all assassin bugs. Of the ~34 genera worldwide, nine occur on Madagascar, with only three endemic at the genus level. Twenty-five of the 27 species recorded from the island are endemic. Surprisingly common in the collections assembled by the California Academy of Sciences—mostly from Malaise traps and leaf-litter extraction—this material allowed taxonomic revisions to the *Bekilya* genus group (Zhang and Weirauch 2011). Among the notable features in this group is strong sexual dimorphism that was not recognized by Villiers; apterous females in several species resemble mutilid wasps. The two species of *Sirthenea* have been shown to be derived from independent colonization events on the island (Chlond et al. 2019).

Reduviinae

Although still recognized in current classifications, Reduviinae has been shown to be polyphyletic, with species recovered in more than 10 separate clades (Hwang and Weirauch 2012). Of the approximately 140 genera described worldwide, only six have been recorded from Madagascar, with five of them being endemic. Only ~3% of the worldwide species diversity is recorded from Madagascar, where 29 species occur. The high level of endemism at the genus level (83%) is intriguing, even more so because the phylogenetic position of these genera among reduviine subgroups is unclear (e.g., *Cargasdama*, *Censorinus*, *Hoberlandtia*). *Durevius*, with five endemic Malagasy species (Hwang and Weirauch 2010), is likely a close relative of the cosmopolitan and very speciose genus *Reduvius*; the absence of *Reduvius* on Madagascar is nevertheless notable, given the prevalence of species in this genus in the Afrotropical, Oriental, and Palearctic regions.

Saicinae

Saicinae is closely related to Emesinae and Visayanocorinae; the three groups share small body size and a slender habitus with long appendages. Of the ~25 genera worldwide, only three occur on Madagascar (nine species total), with only the monotypic *Madecassosaica* and *Vadonocoris* being endemic (Villiers 1979). Similar to those in Emesinae, most specimens are collected at light traps, and most species are rarely collected.

Stenopodainae

With 79 species, Stenopodainae is currently the most speciose reduviid subfamily on Madagascar. Malagasy members of Stenopodainae account for ~10% of the worldwide described species in this group. Most are cryptically colored and recognized by a pentagonal or hexagonal cell on the forewing, prominent mandibular plates, and the antennal flagellomeres folded back underneath the proximal antennal segments.

The biology of this group is largely unknown; the great majority of specimens in collections have been collected at light traps. On Madagascar, specimens have also been hand collected from epiphyte-covered tree trunks (C. Weirauch, unpublished data). Nineteen of the 26 genera that occur in Madagascar (73%) are endemic. This group has been extensively worked on by Villiers, who recognized their morphological diversity on the island and described most of the endemic genera. Some genera with near worldwide distribution also have a number of representatives on Madagascar (e.g., *Pygolampis* and *Sastrapada*, with 13 and 10 species, respectively), while most endemic genera are currently monotypic (e.g., *Anacanthiocnemis* and *Parawatsa*) or known from only a few species (e.g., *Catala* and *Fitana*). The high level of genus-level endemism of Madagascar Stenopodainae is intriguing but may not be entirely surprising, given that Stenopodainae is one of the few groups of Reduviidae that are usually well represented on islands. Phylogenetic hypotheses of Stenopodainae are currently unavailable but will be essential to investigate the patterns and timing of the colonization of Madagascar. Recent additions to the fauna are by Chlond (2010a, 2011, 2016) and Chlond and Junkiert (2011).

Triatominae

Triatominae (kissing bugs) is represented on Madagascar by only the circumtropical species *Triatoma rubrofasciata* (Villiers 1968). The great majority of triatomine species are restricted to the New World, where they serve as arthropod vectors of the pathogen that causes Chagas disease in humans. The disease is not known to occur on Madagascar. *Triatoma rubrofasciata* is thought to have dispersed with humans via sea travel and in association with rats on ships (Gorla et al. 1997). Consistent with this hypothesis, *T. rubrofasciata* has been recorded only from coastal areas on Madagascar and is also recorded from La Réunion and Grande Comore (Villiers 1968).

Visayanocorinae

This small subfamily (two genera worldwide), which does not have a common name, is closely related to the more speciose Emesinae. Only *Carayonia milloti* is known from Madagascar, while other species in this genus occur in the Afrotropical, Oriental, and Australian regions. Species are small and delicate and are recognized by a very long second labial segment. Most specimens of these rarely collected assassin bugs have been obtained using light or flight intercept traps or have been recovered from leaf-litter extractions.

ORIGIN OF MALAGASY REDUVIIDAE

Origins of the assassin bug fauna of Madagascar are largely unclear. The described fossil record of Reduviidae is poor and no fossil assassin bugs have been described from Madagascar. Only four published phylogenetic studies for Reduviidae provide insights into possible historical biogeographic mechanisms and probable origins of the island's diversity. First, the focus of the molecular phylogenetic study by Hwang and Weirauch (2012) investigated relationships among the major clades within the group, but also provided divergence dating estimates across Reduviidae using fossil reduviid species from deposits around the world as calibrations. This study suggests that major radiations across the majority of Reduviidae, a clade known as Higher Reduviidae, started in the Late Cretaceous, with most major subfamilies diverging ~75–50 Mya. The split between Madagascar, Antarctica, and India from Africa and South America is dated to ~135 Mya, and the split between Madagascar and the Indian subcontinent to ~88 Mya (see Collins et al., pp. 45–51). Together with the fact that most Malagasy reduviid genera appear to be deeply nested within their respective subfamilies, this suggests that the extant assassin bug fauna of Madagascar is better explained by dispersal than vicariance.

Second, and as part of a broader phylogenetic study of the worldwide peiratine genus *Sirthenea*, Chlond et al. (2019) showed that the two Malagasy species included in their analyses are not closely related, suggesting independent dispersal events to Madagascar. Although not including a formal biogeographic analysis, one of these species, *Sirthenea flaviceps*, was shown to be nested within a clade that otherwise contains only Oriental taxa. Divergence estimates suggest that this species may have diverged from its Oriental ancestors during the Oligocene. Third, a morphology-based phylogenetic hypothesis for Epiroderinae inferred that most endemic Malagasy genera belong to a single radiation, but that one other lineage reached the island independently (Hwang and Weirauch 2017); no formal biogeographic analysis was conducted, but an Oriental or Australasian origin of this colonization appears likely.

The fourth study investigated the origins of the Malagasy clades of Ectrichodiinae based on a calibrated molecular phylogeny (Forthman and Weirauch 2016). It reconstructed at least two colonization events of Ectrichodiinae from the Oriental region and one from the Afrotropical region, all during the past 68 million years. The majority of species are contained in a clade that originated from one of the Oriental dispersal events, while *Gibbosella* is based on a separate colonization event from the Oriental region, and *Glymmatophora*, with only two species on Madagascar, originated from Africa. Representatives of *Maraenaspis*, another genus with numerous species restricted to Africa, was not included in the analysis, making a second colonization event from Africa likely.

The above suggests that members of Malagasy Reduviidae are derived largely from dispersal from the Afrotropical and Oriental regions. In the absence of phylogenies and biogeographic analyses for the remaining taxa, distribution patterns of nonendemic genera can provide some additional insights, assuming they are monophyletic. Of the 49 nonendemic genera, 27 have wide distribution ranges across multiple biogeographic regions, with some being worldwide (e.g., several Emesinae and the stenopodaines genera *Pygolampis* and *Oncocephalus*). Fifteen of the remaining genera are shared only between Africa and Madagascar (e.g., the emesine genera *Bobba* and *Orthunga*), while seven are shared only with the Oriental and/or Australian regions (all Harpactorinae and Epiroderinae). Future biogeographic research on any of these genera will refine our understanding of the patterns and timelines of the evolutionary history of Malagasy Reduviidae.

AREAS OF ENDEMISM

Areas of endemism on Madagascar are well established, based predominantly on the distribution ranges of plants, primates, birds, amphibians, and reptiles. In contrast, studies investigating endemism patterns based on insect distributions are comparatively rare. More than 2500 specimens of Reduviidae from Madagascar have now been digitized (C. Weirauch, unpublished data), the majority collected during the Terrestrial Arthropod Inventory of Madagascar Project under the direction of the California Academy of Sciences. These include distribution data for 254 described and undescribed assassin bug species in 78 genera. A total of 2360 of these records were geo-referenced and represent most reduviid subfamilies recorded from the island, though with substantial bias toward Ectrichodiinae (1760 of the total records). Only 54 of the currently 254 at least partially digitized species were represented by three or more geo-referenced localities, and these data were subjected to area of endemism analyses using NDM/VNDM software (Goloboff 2011). While these unpublished analyses are preliminary and will benefit from the inclusion of additional species and specimen data, they showed seven major areas of endemism for members of the island's Reduviidae that broadly overlap with endemism patterns seen in amphibian and reptiles (Brown et al. 2016). Among the best-supported areas are the northern half of the eastern mountain ranges, while several areas are overlapping in the northwest, and two smaller areas were recovered for the southwestern and southeastern regions. Compared to other parts of the world where Reduviidae shows fairly large-scale distribution patterns and that are therefore of little use for endemism studies (e.g., the Nearctic region; C. Weirauch, unpublished data), this preliminary result suggests that Reduviidae could provide insights into areas of endemism and historical biogeography of the Malagasy fauna.

UNDOCUMENTED BIODIVERSITY

Despite recent descriptive efforts and the already large number of documented species compared to the worldwide numbers of assassin bug species, current numbers of Reduviidae species on Madagascar are likely to be a dramatic underestimate. This may be particularly true for Harpactorinae, a subfamily that was not studied in detail by Villiers and that has received comparatively little recent attention beyond the documentation of two new genera (Chlond and Junkiert 2010; Chlond and Banar 2013). An ongoing taxonomic revision of the charismatic genus *Ulpius*, with species characterized by large size, strikingly contrasting color patterns, and lobes and processes on the thorax and abdomen, shows that in addition to the nine currently described species, there are at least four undescribed species, an addition of ~44% (G. Radabaugh and C. Weirauch, unpublished data). This pattern may be similar in other described genera of Harpactorinae, and there are likely genus-level taxa that remain to be named. Modern taxonomic revisions have shown that even groups that were treated by Villiers contain substantial unrecognized species-level diversity. Among these are the reduviine genus *Durevius*, which was originally based on three species but, after a recent revision, now contains five (Hwang and Weirauch 2010). Even more striking are numbers in the *Bekilya* genus group (Peiratinae), composed of the genera *Bekilya* and *Hovacoris*, for which a recent publication increased species numbers from two to nine (Zhang and Weirauch 2011). Using the average increase of these three taxonomic projects as a rough estimate for the potentially yet-to-be-discovered number of species in genera that Villiers proposed and studied fairly comprehensively, future fieldwork and taxonomic activity could see an increase of ~80%, equating to about 300 currently undocumented species.

ACKNOWLEDGMENTS

This synopsis of Malagasy Reduviidae would not have been possible without the more than three decades of dedicated research by André Villiers and the recent collecting and specimen-sorting efforts led by Brian Fisher and the late Norman Penny (California Academy of Sciences). I also thank previous members of my lab who have led or been involved with various taxonomic projects on assassin bugs in Madagascar: Michael Forthman, Wei Song Hwang, Guanyang Zhang, Grace Radabaugh, Steven Crum, and Elizabeth Romero. Three undergraduate research students, Emily Potter, Evangeleena Ottero, and Hao Thi, were involved in recent efforts to further document reduviid biodiversity in Madagascar and assisted with specimen imaging.

Subject editors: Brian L. Fisher and Steven M. Goodman

HEMIPTERA, FULGOROMORPHA: FLATIDAE, PLANTHOPPERS

D. Świerczewski and A. Stroiński

Flatidae is the fourth-largest family of planthoppers (infraorder Fulgoromorpha), with 296 genera and 1444 species worldwide (Bourgoin 2020), and is most common in the tropics. These insects can be recognized by two exclusive morphological characters: 1) a submarginal vein that parallels the wing margin, defining a series of marginal cells in the apical and the leading portion of the front wing, and 2) the presence of wax-bearing pustules in the claval region (Bartlett et al. 2014). Flatids are mostly macropterous, defined by the presence of a transversal row of five or six closed nodal cells, plus one complete distal row of open and closed postnodal cells (Bourgoin et al. 2015). Wings of adults often have a dusting of wax (Figure 9.25d), whereas nymphs are totally covered with flocculent wax (Figure 9.25b). The wax protects the insects against adverse abiotic (UV radiation and rain) and biotic factors (pathogenic fungi, parasitoids, and predators), as well as contamination with secreted honeydew (Lucchi and Mazzoni 2004). The family is divided into two easily distinguishable subfamilies: Flatinae and Flatoidinae, which can be readily distinguished from one another by body shape and wing position—the former flattened laterally, with wings tectiform, and the latter holding the wings horizontally (O'Brien 2002). Adults and immature stages feed on the aboveground portions of a wide variety of woody and semiwoody plants (Bartlett et al. 2018).

FLATIDAE OF MADAGASCAR

The island's Flatidae fauna has been of interest to natural historians for centuries and continues to be studied (Świerczewski and Stroiński 2013). The first member of this family was described in the first half of the 19th century, when French entomologist Félix Edouard Guérin-Méneville presented a short note with a drawing on *Flata malgacha* (currently in genus *Flatida*) and *Flatoides tortrix* in the work *Iconographie du règne animal* (Guérin-Méneville 1844). However, it was Victor Signoret who made the first real attempt to widen our knowledge of the Hemiptera fauna of Madagascar (Signoret 1860) by describing several additional species. Leopold Melichar, the preeminent worker on Hemiptera at that time, made a substantial contribution with his two-part monograph of the world fauna of Flatidae, describing and redescribing a number of species, including those restricted to Madagascar (Melichar 1901, 1902). This work was followed by a volume of *Genera insectorum* (Melichar 1923), also dedicated in part to Flatidae. Further species were described by Victor Lallemand and Jacques Auber. In 1956, Belgian entomologist Henri Synave gave an overview of Malagasy Flatinae, providing a key to all known species and illustrations of some morphological characters (Synave 1956). He also published a faunistic paper based on material collected in Madagascar during an

FIGURE 9.25 **Aspects of Madagascar Flatidae. A) Aggregation of *Flatida rosea* adults on a tree trunk at Saha Forest Camp, Anjozorobe; B) *F. rosea* nymph from Namoroka; C) Flatidae honeydew collected by ants of the genus *Technomyrmex* from Namoroka; and D) *Ulundia madagascariensis* from Namoroka.** (PHOTO A by B. L. Fisher, and B–D by G. Kunz.)

expedition organized by the Natural History Museum in Basel, which was in fact the last expedition dedicated to the island's flatids (Synave 1966). Currently, the Malagasy flatid fauna consists of 21 genera with 52 species of Flatinae and 11 genera with 41 species of Flatoidinae (Table 9.22).

Flatinae

Phromniini

This tribe on Madagascar is represented by three genera with 11 species. The genera *Ityrea* and *Flatida* are Afrotropical, whereas *Paraflata* is endemic to the island. Members of this tribe are fairly large flatids, with spectacular coloration of pink, red, green, or brown tegmina and a total body length of 16–30 mm. Individuals of the often very common *Flatida rosea* show a spectacular behavior, sitting on plants in clusters mimicking flowers and buds (Figure 9.25a). Their primary habitats are different types of moist evergreen forests; however, there are also records from dry spiny thickets and riparian forests.

The recently revised genus *Paraflata* (Świerczewski et al. 2016) is distributed mainly in the eastern and central part of Madagascar—*P. seminigra* (Figure 9.26a) on Nosy Be and in the eastern lowlands; *P. kingdomi* on the eastern slopes of the Ankaratra Massif; *P. dewalschei* on the northern slopes of the Ankaratra Massif and an isolated locality on the west coast; *P. masoalae* in the Masoala Peninsula; and *P. unispinosa* around Antongil Bay. The discontinuous distribution (mountain and coastal) reported for *P. dewalschei* is surprising but has already been recorded for other flatids, such as *Madoxychara unicornis* and *Perinetella flavomarginata*; all the mentioned cases, however, are still poorly understood. Further, several individuals of different *Paraflata* species are the hosts of ectoparasitic moth pupae of the family Epipyropidae (planthopper parasite moths). Although only three species of epipyropids are known from Madagascar—*Fulgoraecia grandidieri*, *F. malagassica*, and *F. radama*—identifying species parasitizing *Paraflata* based only on the pupal stage is not possible.

Sisciini

This tribe on Madagascar is represented by three genera—*Euryprosthius*, *Latois*, and *Phlebopterum* (Table 9.22)—and most species are brightly colored and medium-size. The majority belong to the endemic genus *Latois* (Figure 9.26c), most species (as of 2021) known only from littoral and moist evergreen forests of the east (Świerczewski and Stroiński 2012a). In contrast, *L. nigrolineata* is widely distributed in the western part of the island and associated with the vegetation of sandy areas near streams and rivers. This is the species in which the phenomenon of the erythraeid mite *Dambullaeus adonis* parasitizing a member of Flatidae was described for the first time (Mąkol et al. 2014). All larvae of this mite are found attached to the abdomen of the female host.

The Afrotropical flatid genus *Phlebopterum* includes three species confined to continental Africa as well as four from Madagascar—*P. angulatum*, *P. planicapitis*, *P. viridis*, and *P. tapiae*. The ranges of these taxa are associated with distinct vegetation types: *P. tapiae* is found in the tapia (*Uapaca*) woodlands of the Central Highlands (Świerczewski and Stroiński 2012b; see Kull and Birkinshaw, pp. 121–27); and *P. viridis* and *P. angulatum* in the moist evergreen forests in northern and northeastern areas. In contrast, *P. planicapitis* (Figure 9.26f) is limited to three localities in the northwest, one comprising coastal mangroves and the other two riparian forests (Świerczewski and Stroiński 2017).

Phantiini

Phantiini is a tribe of small flatids containing 13 genera with 36 species distributed worldwide. In the Afrotropical region, it is represented by seven genera and 12 species, and in Madagascar by three endemic genera and four species in total. The representatives of the tribe are usually short, globular insects, nearly as broad as long, with overall brown color, or rarely green, and body length not exceeding 6 mm (Medler 2001). For Madagascar, the first Phantiini record was *Soares testudinarius* (Figure 9.26k), occurring in the north (Stroiński and Świerczewski 2012a). Another described species is *Madoxychara unicornis* (Figure 9.26j), which is confined to the west and includes lowland and montane populations (Stroiński and Świerczewski 2013a). The genus *Griveaudus* includes two species, *G. issidiformis* and *G. tsarantananae*, both recorded from the Tsaratanàna Massif (Stroiński and Świerczewski 2014a).

Lawanini

Two genera known exclusively from Madagascar are *Flatopsis* and *Perinetella*. The two genera share the following characters: frons tricarinate with lateral carinae in the form of a horseshoe, pronotum with postocular eminences conical, mesonotum with three parallel carinae, ScP+RA and RP tegmen veins leaving the basal cell at one point.

The genus *Flatopsis* was named by Melichar (1902) for two species—*F. nivea* and *F. guttifera*: both can be easily distinguished by the presence of characteristic tegmina coloration, with numerous black dots in the latter species. Moreover, *F. nivea*, apart from the typical form without dots, comprises two color variations with single dots, *F. n. nigropunctata* and *F. n. basipunctata*, distributed abundantly across the island. Two other described species are *F. medleri*, associated with southeastern littoral forest (Świerczewski and Stroiński 2011), and *F. wojciechowskii* (Figure 9.26d), known from the northern part of Madagascar (Świerczewski and Stroiński 2015a). The genus *Perinetella* occurs in central portions of the island, mainly on the eastern slopes, comprising three species: *P. nigroflava* (Figure 9.26b) in moist evergreen forest, and two species, *P. fiedleri* and *P. flavomarginata*, occurring in more montane habitats (Świerczewski and Stroiński 2015b).

Ormenisini

On Madagascar, this tribe is represented by two Afrotropical genera—*Panormenis* and *Ulundia*. *Panormenis* includes five endemic Malagasy species and one other of continental Africa. These are small insects with body length not exceeding 6 mm and hyaline, oval wings with differentiated, mostly dark markings. They are associated with different types of forests. For example, *P. nigrocostata* (Figure 9.26g) was recently described from the moist evergreen forest of Ranomafana National Park (Stroiński and Świerczewski 2011). The genus *Ulundia* is represented on Madagascar by a widely distributed species, *U. madagascariensis* (Figure 9.25d).

TABLE 9.22. **Checklist of the known Flatidae of Madagascar**

FAMILY FLATIDAE SPINOLA, 1839
SUBFAMILY FLATINAE SPINOLA, 1839
TRIBE PHROMNIINI DISTANT, 1906
Genus *Ityrea* Stål, 1866
I. rubida Melichar, 1901 (E)
Genus *Flatida* White, 1846
F. malgacha (Guerin-Meneville, 1844) (E)
F. rosea (Melichar, 1901) (E)
F. flammicoma (Auber, 1954) (E)
F. coccinea (Auber, 1955) (E)
F. flosculina (Auber, 1955) (E)
Genus *Paraflata* Melichar, 1901
P. seminigra (Stål, 1866) (E)
P. kingdomi Distant, 1910 (E)
P. dewalschei Lallemand, 1933 (E)
P. masoalae Świerczewski et al., 2012 (E)
P. unispinosa Świerczewski et al., 2012 (E)

TRIBE SISCIINI MELICHAR, 1923
Genus *Euryprosthius* Karsch, 1890
E. latifrons Karsch, 1890 (E)
Genus *Latois* Stål, 1866
L. antica (Signoret, 1860) (E)
L. suturalis (Signoret, 1860) (E)
L. bicoloripes Karsch, 1890 (E)
L. frontalis Melichar, 1901 (E)
L. major Melichar, 1901 (E)
L. nigrofasciata Świerczewski & Stroiński, 2012 (E)
L. nigrolineata Świerczewski & Stroiński, 2014 (E)
Genus *Phlebopterum* Stål, 1854
P. angulatum Melichar, 1902 (E)
P. viridis Melichar, 1902 (E)
P. tapiae Świerczewski & Stroiński, 2012 (E)
P. planicapitis Świerczewski & Stroiński, 2017 (E)

TRIBE PHANTIINI MELICHAR, 1923
Genus *Griveaudus* Stroiński & Świerczewski, 2014
G. issidiformis Stroiński & Świerczewski, 2014 (E)
G. tsarantananae Stroiński & Świerczewski, 2014 (E)
Genus *Madoxychara* Stroiński & Świerczewski, 2013
M. unicornis Stroiński & Świerczewski, 2013 (E)
Genus *Soares* Stroiński & Świerczewski, 2012
S. testudinarius Stroiński & Świerczewski, 2012 (E)

TRIBE LAWANINI MELICHAR, 1923
Genus *Flatopsis* Melichar, 1902
F. nivea (Signoret, 1860) (E)
F. guttifera Melichar, 1902 (E)
F. medleri Świerczewski & Stroiński, 2011 (E)
F. wojciechowskii Świer. and Stroiń, 2015 (E)
Genus *Perinetella* Synave, 1956
P. nigroflava Synave, 1956 (E)
P. fiedleri Świerczewski & Stroiński, 2015 (E)
P. flavomarginata Świerczewski & Stroiński, 2015 (E)

TRIBE ORMENISINI MEDLER, 2001
Genus *Panormenis* Melichar, 1923
P. parvula (Melichar, 1902) (E)
P. impunctata (Schmidt, 1906) (E)
P. subclavata (Jacobi, 1917) (E)
P. keiseri Synave, 1966 (E)
P. nigrocostata Stroiński & Świerczewski, 2011 (E)
Genus *Ulundia* Distant, 1910
U. madagascariensis (Signoret, 1860) (AF)

TRIBE NEPHESISNI DISTANT, 1906
Genus *Pauliana* Lallemand, 1950
P. insignis Lallemand, 1950 (E)
Genus *Phaedolus* Karsch, 1890
P. quadripunctatus Karsch, 1890 (E)
P. varians Synave, 1956 (E)
Genus *Sogalabana* Stroiński & Świerczewski, 2014
S. ochracea Stroiński & Świerczewski, 2014 (E)

TRIBE SELIZINI DISTANT, 1906
Genus *Lembakaria* Świerczewski & Stroiński, 2019
L. mikeae Świerczewski & Stroiński, 2019 (E)
L. saintemarieae Świerczewski & Stroiński, 2019 (E)
Genus *Kelyflata* Świerczewski & Stroiński, 2019
K. capensis Świerczewski & Stroiński, 2019 (E)
K. ilakakae Świerczewski & Stroiński, 2019 (E)
Genus *Peyrierasus* Stroiński & Świerczewski, 2013
P. philippiae Stroiński & Świerczewski, 2013 (E)
Genus *Stenocyarda* Fennah, 1965
S. angustata (Melichar, 1902) (E)
Genus *Urana* Melichar, 1902
U. paradoxa Melichar, 1902 (E)
U. unica Stroiński & Świerczewski, 2012 (E)

SUBFAMILY FLATOIDINAE MELICHAR, 1901
Genus *Atracis* Stål, 1866
A. costalis Melichar, 1902 (E)
A. gibbosa Melichar, 1902 (E)
A. castaneiceps (Jacobi, 1917) (E)
Genus *Atracodes* Melichar, 1902
A. corrugata (Melichar, 1902) (E)
Genus *Dendrona* Melichar, 1923
D. verruculata (Stål, 1866) (E)
D. arcufera (Melichar, 1902) (E)
D. marmorata (Melichar, 1902) (E)
D. serena (Melichar, 1902) (E)
D. verruculata (Stål, 1866) (E)
Genus *Flatoides* Guérin-Méneville, 1844
F. tortrix Guérin-Méneville, 1844 (E)
Genus *Flatoidessa* Melichar, 1923
F. cicatricosa (Signoret, 1860) (E)
F. hyalinipennis (Signoret, 1860) (E)
F. sinuata (Signoret, 1860) (E)
F. vicina (Signoret, 1860) (E)
F. conspersa (Brancsik, 1893) (E)
F. breviceps (Melichar, 1902) (E)

(continued overleaf)

TABLE 9.22. ***continued***

SUBFAMILY FLATOIDINAE
F. demissa (Melichar, 1902) (E)
F. distanti (Melichar, 1902) (E)
F. fulva (Melichar, 1902) (E)
F. nossibeana (Melichar, 1902) (E)
F. signoreti (Melichar, 1902) (E)
F. sikorae (Melichar, 1902) (E)
F. turbata (Melichar, 1902) (E)
Genus *Flatosaria* Melichar, 1923
F. biplagiata (Brancsik, 1893) (E)
F. cyrta (Melichar, 1902) (E)
F. gibbula (Melichar, 1902) (E)
F. ignava (Melichar, 1902) (E)
F. longiceps (Melichar, 1902) (E)
F. marcida (Melichar, 1902) (E)
Genus *Lichena* Melichar, 1901
L. dealbata (Distant, 1881) (E)
Genus *Lichenopsis* Schmidt, 1912
L. incriminata (Schmidt, 1905) (E)
Genus *Melichitona* Metcalf, 1952
M. collaris (Jacobi, 1917) (E)
Genus *Paraflatoides* Melichar, 1923
P. angustata (Melichar, 1902) (E)
P. bimaculata (Melichar, 1902) (E)
P. divisa (Melichar, 1902) (E)
P. festiva (Melichar, 1902) (E)
P. punctulata (Melichar, 1902) (E)
P. undulata (Melichar, 1902) (E)
P. protea (Distant, 1917) (E)
Genus *Porophloeus* Melichar, 1902
P. handlirschi (Brancsik, 1893) (E)
P. fuscus Melichar, 1902 (E)

Note: (E), species endemic to Madagascar; (AF), Afrotropical, nonendemic species.

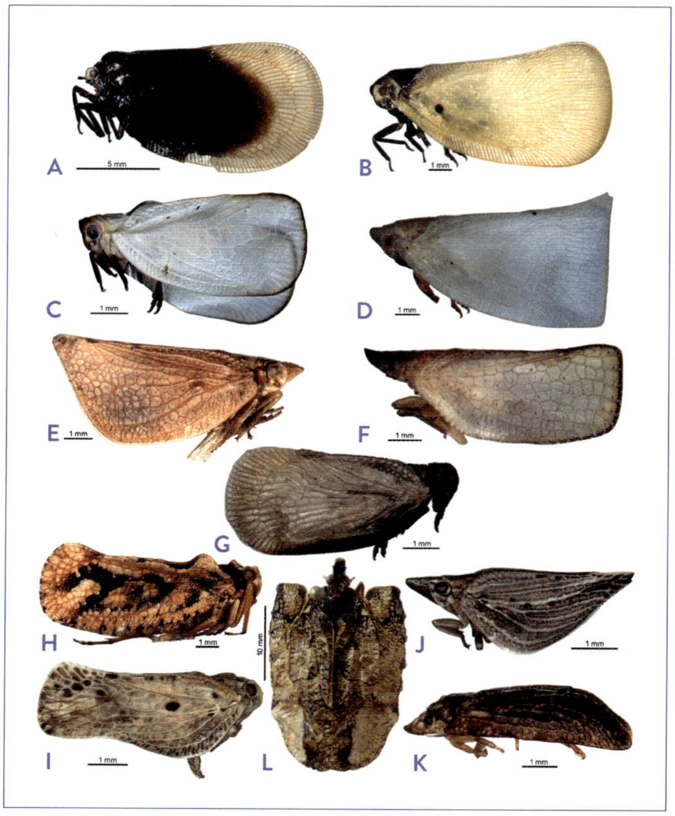

FIGURE 9.26 **Representatives of Madagascar Flatidae. A) *Paraflata seminigra* from Vohilava, B) *Perinetella nigroflava* from Analamazaotra, C) *Latois nigrofasciata* from Mahabo, D) *Flatopsis wojciechowskii* from Antsiranana, E) *Sogalabana ochracea* from Mangindrano, F) *Phlebopterum planicapitis* from Antrema, G) *Panormenis nigrocostata* from Vohiparara, H) *Urana paradoxa* from Andringitra, I) *Lembakaria saintemarieae* from Cap Sainte Marie, J) *Madoxychara unicornis* from Antananarivo, K) *Soares testudinarius* from Antsiranana, and L) *Lichena dealbata* from Ranomafana.** (PHOTOS by A. Stroiński.)

Nephesisni

This tribe covers three genera on Madagascar—*Pauliana*, *Phaedolus*, and *Sogalabana*—all endemic, medium-size, and brightly colored. The monotypic *Pauliana*, with *P. insignis*, is known only from Tolagnaro. The genus *Phaedolus* comprises two species: *P. quadripunctatus*, known from the southeast and *P. varians*, distributed across the east. The monotypic genus *Sogalabana* is represented by *S. ochracea* (Figure 9.26e), known from Tsaratanàna Massif (Stroiński and Świerczewski 2014b).

Selizini

This tribe includes small to medium-size flatids with brown coloration and distally narrowed wings with a sinuate costal margin. In some species, such as *Stenocyarda angustata*, tegmina are strongly constricted apically so that the insect's form mimics plant thorns. On Madagascar, the tribe is represented by five genera—*Urana*, *Peyrierasus*, *Lembakaria*, *Kelyflata* (all endemic), and *Stenocyarda* (Afrotropical)—containing eight species. The representatives of the genus *Urana*—*U. paradoxa* (Figure 9.26h) and *U. unica*—are distributed across north–south mountain ranges and related to the ecotone habitats of high-altitude to medium-altitude moist evergreen forest (Stroiński and Świerczewski 2012b). *Peyrierasus philippiae* is associated with montane ericoid thicket in the Anosyenne Mountains of the southeast (Stroiński and Świerczewski 2013b). Both species of *Lembakaria* (Figure 9.26i) occur in the extreme south and are associated with dry spiny thicket (Świerczewski and Stroiński 2019a), whereas *Kelyflata ilakakae* is confined to tapia woodlands (Świerczewski and Stroiński 2019b).

Flatoidinae

This subfamily covers fairly large insects with characteristic wings that are held horizontally. For example, one of the largest species, *Lichena dealbata*, reaches almost 30 mm in total length (Figure 9.26l). In this subfamily, there are 11 genera and 41 species recorded on Madagascar. Seven genera—*Dendrona*, *Flatoidessa*, *Lichena*,

Lichenopsis, *Melichitona*, *Paraflatoides*, and *Porophloeus*—are endemic to Madagascar. As *Atracis* is restricted to New Guinea and the Indo-Malaysian region (Medler 1988), the three species from Madagascar allocated to this genus probably represent a genus new to science. The representatives of the subfamily are collected mainly in moist evergreen, sclerophyllous, and littoral forests. Spending most of their lives on tree trunks and branches, they are usually brownish-green in coloration and blend with the bark, with some even mimicking arboricolous lichens and mosses. Most genera and species were described at the beginning of the 20th century exclusively on the basis of external characters; however, a preliminary analysis of genitalia shows that species diversity in this group is much higher.

NATURAL HISTORY

As members of Flatidae are phytophagous, they play an important role in ecosystem functioning through various ecological processes such as herbivory and interactions with their predators and parasitoids (e.g., *Paraflata* species parasitized by Epipyropidae moths or *Latois nigrolineata* parasitized by Erythraeidae mites). Moreover, extraordinary examples of interspecific trophobiotic relations are known between flatids (mainly *Flatida* spp.) and invertebrates, such as ants of the genus *Aphaenogaster* and *Technomyrmex* (Figure 9.25c), as well as vertebrates. In both cases, flatids provide food in the form of secreted honeydew. Interestingly, it has been reported that geckos induce flatids to excrete honeydew by head- nodding stimulus, and then they consume a drop of the liquid (Fölling et al. 2001). In mouse lemurs, honeydew represents a keystone resource during periods of food scarcity in highly seasonal environments (Joly-Radko and Zimmermann 2010). The honeydew clods known as *tantely sakondry* are collected and eaten by people in the southwest of Madagascar (Fisher and Hugel, pp. 218–30).

PATTERNS OF ENDEMISM

Current information suggests that the flatid fauna of Madagascar shows extremely high levels of species endemism (99%), and only *Ulundia madagascarensis* also occurs in the Afrotropics. Additionally, a large number of species reveal localized distributions, indicating a high level of regional speciation. This is probably related to a range of locally occurring niches as well as strongly contrasted topographic relief on the island. Most mountain zones have endemic genera, which include *Sogalabana*, *Peyrierasus*, *Griveaudus*, and *Urana*.

CONCLUSIONS

As one of the most abundant and easily collected groups of hemipterans on Madagascar (T. Bourgoin, unpublished data), Flatidae may be a useful tool in rapidly measuring patterns of species richness, species turnover, and endemism—all fundamental to current conservation efforts in Madagascar (see Fisher, pp. 847–53). Our research reveals that particular species are strictly limited to a given vegetational type, especially forests. For example, *Phlebopterum tapiae* and *Kelyflata ilakakae* are both characteristic of tapia formations, while other species such as *Flatopsis medleri* and *Latois nigrofasciata* are confined to littoral forest. Additionally, a cluster of *Lembakaria* species, together with *K. capensis*, is characteristic of dry spiny thickets. There is also a group of species known exclusively from moist evergreen forests.

Taking into account the direct relationship Malagasy flatids have with forest habitat specificity, it is not surprising that deforestation and habitat fragmentation seem to be the primary threat. Some of the species described recently that are based on 20th-century museum collections may already be extinct. Hence, the current protected area network of Madagascar and its strict conservation may be key factors to species survival.

Despite a long history of observation and investigation, the study of Madagascar's flatids is far from complete. A remarkable number of species still await description, and all the "older" taxa need redescription in terms of a modern taxonomic approach. Moreover, our knowledge of the biology of particular taxa, including life-history or host-plant preferences, is deeply unsatisfactory. Undoubtedly, further field collections, new discoveries, and revisional taxonomic publications will produce a fundamental change in the general views of the origin and relationships of Madagascar's flatid fauna.

Subject editors: Brian L. Fisher and Steven M. Goodman

HEMIPTERA: FULGORIDAE, LANTERNFLIES, *SAKONDRY*

J. Constant

The family Fulgoridae contains the largest and most spectacular planthoppers, known by entomologists and naturalists as lanternflies. Fulgoridae groups 142 genera and 772 species worldwide, mostly found in the tropics. The greatest diversity in terms of genera and species is found in the Neotropics and in Southeast Asia (Bourgoin 2020). They are phloem feeders at all stages, living mostly on tree trunks. Their posterior wings are usually brightly colored, but, as they are covered by the tegmina at rest, individual

TABLE 9.23. **Checklist of the Fulgoridae of Madagascar**

GENUS *ANTSALOVASIA* CONSTANT, 2004
Type species: *Antsalovasia hyalinipennis* Constant, 2004
A. hyalinipennis Constant, 2004
GENUS *BELBINA* STÅL, 1863
Type species: *Belbina falleni* Stål, 1863
B. bergrothi (Schmidt, 1911)
B. blotei Lallemand, 1959
B. bourgoini Constant, 2014
B. falleni Stål, 1863
B. foliacea Lallemand, 1950
B. laetitiae Constant, 2014
B. lambertoni Lallemand, 1922
B. madagascariensis Stål, 1866
B. nympha (Stål, 1866)
B. pionneaui Lallemand, 1922
B. recurva Lallemand, 1950
B. servillei (Spinola, 1839)
GENUS *LYNCIDES* STÅL, 1866
L. coquerelii (Signoret, 1860)
GENUS *RADAMANA* DISTANT, 1906
Type species: *Radamana varicolor* Distant, 1906
R. collarti Lallemand, 1950
R. varicolor Distant, 1906
GENUS *ZANNA* KIRKALDY, 1902
Type species: *Fulgora tenebrosa* Fabricius, 1775
Z. pauliani Lallemand, 1950
Z. tenebrosa (Fabricius, 1775)
f. *madagascariensis* (Signoret, 1860)
f. *nosibeana* Lallemand, 1959

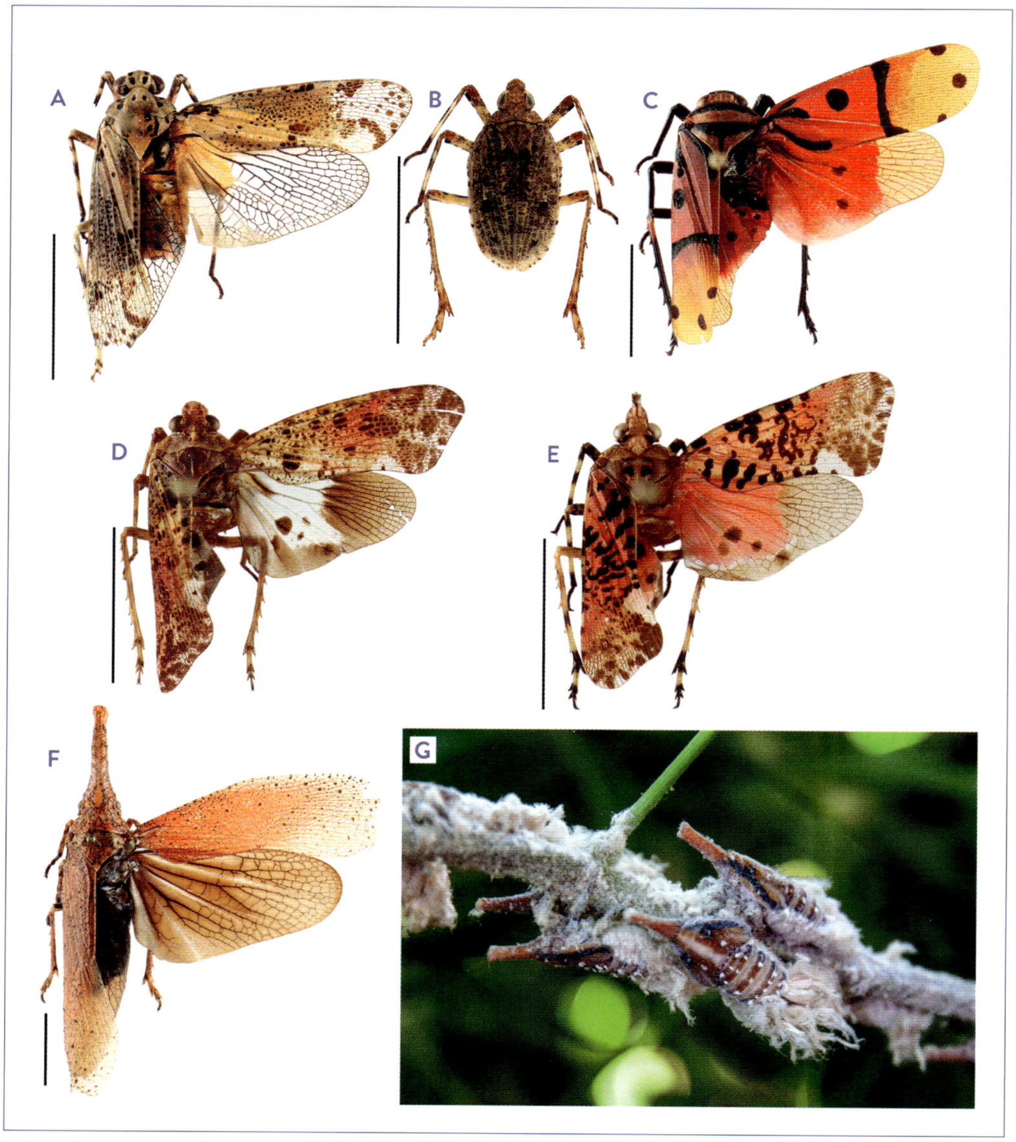

FIGURE 9.27 **Fulgoridae of Madagascar. A) *Antsalovasia hyalinipennis* from Andobo; B) *Lyncides* sp. from Tsingy de Namoroka; C) *Radamana varicolor* from Antongil Bay; D) *Belbina bourgoini* from Marojejy Massif; E) *B. bergrothi* from Marojejy Massif; F) *Zanna tenebrosa* from Marojejy Massif; and G) *Zanna* sp., nymphs, Toamasina. Scale bars, 10 mm.** (PHOTOS A–F by J. Constant and G by B. L. Fisher.)

animals tend to be well camouflaged when they sit on the bark of trees, where they hide in the cracks and crevices during the day (Jiaranaisakul et al. 2018). Many species are nocturnal, but a great portion of the taxa are not attracted to light traps commonly used by entomologists. The suprageneric classification within the family remains largely unresolved (Urban and Cryan 2009). Trophobiotic interactions were observed with other animals that collect the honeydew produced by the lanternflies, including ants, cockroaches, moths, geckos, and snails (Naskrecki and Nishida 2007; Constant 2015).

SYSTEMATICS

The Malagasy fulgorid fauna comprises 18 species in five genera (Table 9.23; Figure 9.27), representing about 2.3% of the world species and 3.5% of the genera. The most speciose genus is *Belbina*, with 12 species. The first Malagasy fulgorid species, *B. servillei*, was described in 1839 (Spinola 1839); the year after, Blanchard (1840) added the widely distributed Afrotropical species *Zanna tenebrosa* to the fauna of the island. Additional taxa were progressively described until the revision of the Afrotropical Fulgoridae by Lallemand (1959), which included all Malagasy taxa recognized at the time; he also added some species and proposed a number of taxonomic changes. More recently, a new genus and species were added (Constant 2004), the genus *Belbina* was revised (Constant 2014), and the occurrence of *Lyncides coquerelii* on Madagascar was confirmed (Gnezdilov 2015a). The infraspecific entities of *Z. tenebrosa*, as proposed by Lallemand (1959), require further study to confirm or refute their validity. Preliminary scrutiny of collections from Madagascar in several institutions revealed a number of undescribed taxa and confirmed the necessity of additional efforts concerning the alpha taxonomy in this family.

FAUNISTICS

The Malagasy species of Fulgoridae are largely endemic, with 16 of the 18 species unique to the island. The two nonendemic species are *Zanna tenebrosa*, widely spread across the Afrotropics, and *Lyncides coquerelii*, also recorded from Mayotte.

The genus *Zanna* is distributed in the Afrotropical and Oriental regions and forms a separate monogeneric subfamily, Zanninae, which should be separated from Fulgoridae, according to Urban and Cryan (2009). A separate monogeneric subfamily, Lyncidiinae, was also erected for the genus *Lyncides* and shows a distribution restricted to Madagascar and Mayotte. The genera *Belbina* and *Radamana* are endemic and placed in Aphaeninae, a subfamily distributed in all Old World tropics, close to, respectively, *Druentia* and *Metaphaena*, two Afrotropical genera (Lallemand 1959; Constant 2014). The placement and affinities of the genus *Antsalovasia* remain poorly understood and would benefit from further molecular studies. Distribution maps of all species of *Belbina* and *A. hyalinipennis* are available in Constant (2004, 2014).

BIOLOGY AND GASTRONOMY

Although lanternflies are actively sought by collectors, the biology and natural history—including host plants, nymphal stages, development, phenology, etc.—of all Malagasy species remain undocumented. The exception is *Zanna tenebrosa*, which was reported feeding on Lima Bean (*Phaseolus lunatus*, Fabaceae) (Gade 1985). Adults and larger nymphs of *Z. tenebrosa* are known by local people as *sakondry* and are eaten in rural areas, where they are sold in markets, often fried. Some farmers grow its cultivated host plants to attract and breed this insect (van der Heyden 2014; Randrianandrasana and Berenbaum 2015; Filou 2019).

CONCLUSION

The status of several Malagasy taxa, such as the two species of *Radamana* and the infraspecific entities of *Zanna tenebrosa*, require further research. Preliminary scrutiny of collection material has revealed the existence of a number of undescribed species, which may probably double the number of fulgorid species on Madagascar. Moreover, additional fieldwork should be conducted to document their life history and to make observations on the host plants and biology of these insects.

Subject editors: Brian L. Fisher and Steven M. Goodman

HEMIPTERA: CALISCELIDAE, PLANTHOPPERS

V. M. Gnezdilov

Caliscelidae is a small family of the Fulgoroidea (Insecta: Auchenorrhyncha), with around 75 genera and more than 230 species worldwide (Bourgoin 2019). Almost two-thirds of described genera are monotypic (Gnezdilov 2013a). These planthoppers are mainly small animals, with a total length (body with forewings) of 2–16 mm, reduced forewings (brachypterous) or forewings that barely cover the abdominal apex (subbrachypterous), and reduced hind wings. However, the members of the tribe Augilini and some members of Adenissini are distinguished by well-developed forewings and hind wings. Some members of Caliscelini and all of Peltonotellini are characterized by adult sensory pits, apparently a neoteny trait (larvalization). Accordingly, Gnezdilov (2015b) claimed that within Caliscelidae there are two main evolutionary trends—brachyptery and neoteny.

There is not much information on the biology and ecology of the family. Generally, Caliscelidae species are found mainly on grasses, and many taxa are associated with open, arid and subarid landscapes, as well as saline and dry habitats (Emeljanov 1969). Thus, for example, on and outside Madagascar, *Caliscelis wallengreni* is monophagous, feeding on *Phragmitis australis* (Poaceae), while *Ommatidiotus* species occur mainly on *Carex* (Cyperaceae) and sometimes on Poaceae in the mesophytic (neither particularly dry nor particularly wet) and hygrophytic (particularly wet) areas. *Bocra ephedrina* lives on *Ephedra* (Ephedraceae) in the mountains, and many Augilini species live on bamboo. In temperate areas, Caliscelidae species apparently have one generation and larval stages with five instars, and they hibernate in egg form (Logvinenko 1975). Members of the Dryinidae (Hymenoptera) parasitize imagoes and larvae of caliscelid species (Guglielmino et al. 2013).

Tropical Caliscelidae is not an easy group to collect when the host plants are unknown. Thus Malagasy brachypterous *Afronaso gryphus*, *Calampocus sphaeroides*, and *Campures pallens* were collected in pitfall traps, and long-winged *Cano merinus* in a Malaise trap. In other areas of the Old World, caliscelids are collected mainly by sweep netting grasses or even by nocturnal light traps.

The behavior of members of Caliscelidae and their potential predators is poorly known. Perhaps some species are myrmecophilous (having positive associations with ants). Thus, O'Brien (1988) mentioned that specimens of *Asarcopus palmarum* were found in India on *Caryota urens* (Arecaceae) being guarded by ants of the genus *Camponotus*. The species of the genus *Caliscelis* in the Palearctic apparently mimic jumping spiders (Salticidae) (A. F. Emeljanov, unpublished data), while the peculiar myrmecomorphic genus *Formiscurra*, with one Indian and one African species, is characterized by a ball-shaped process on the head, which apparently conceals the head of the planthopper behind a mask of an ant abdomen (Gnezdilov 2019).

SYSTEMATICS

Classification of Caliscelidae is well advanced (Gnezdilov 2013a, 2013b). The family comprises two subfamilies with five tribes—Caliscelinae (Caliscelini and Peltonotellini) and Ommatidiotinae (Ommatidiotini, Augilini, and Adenissini). The tribe Adenissini includes four subtribes: Adenissina, Bocrina, Coinquendina, and Pteriliina.

No phylogenetic analysis of the family has been conducted, but according to morphological data, the tribe Augilini and subtribe

TABLE 9.24. **Checklist of the Caliscelidae from Madagascar with distribution details**

SCIENTIFIC NAME	LOCALITY
FAMILY CALISCELIDAE AMYOT AND SERVILLE, 1843	
Subfamily Ommatidiotinae Fieber, 1875	
Tribe Augilini Baker, 1915	
Cano merinus Gnezdilov, 2011	Toliara Province: NW of Manombo, Mikea Forest
Signoreta victorina Gnezdilov and Bourgoin, 2009	Antananarivo Province: Périnet (Analamazaotra)
Subfamily Caliscelinae Amyot and Serville, 1843	
Tribe Caliscelini Amyot and Serville, 1843	
Afronaso gryphus Gnezdilov and Bourgoin, 2009	Fianarantsoa Province: Andringitra National Park
Afronaso malagasicus Gnezdilov and Bourgoin, 2009	Antananarivo Province: N Antananarivo, Ambohitantely Forest
Calampocus sphaeroides Gnezdilov and Bourgoin, 2009	Fianarantsoa Province: N Ranohira, Isalo National Park
Campures pallens Gnezdilov, 2015	Toliara Province: W Marovato, Réserve Spéciale Cap Sainte Marie
Issopulex gloriosus China and Fennah, 1960	Toliara Province: NE Morondava, Bereboka. Glorieuse archipelago
Madaceratops adelinae Gnezdilov, 2011	Toliara Province: Atsimo-Andrefana Region, in *Euphorbia* garden in Antsokay Arboretum
Patamadaga pauliani Gnezdilov and Bourgoin, 2009	Fianarantsoa Province: Andringitra National Park
Sphenax cuneus Gnezdilov and Bourgoin, 2009	Toliara Province: Atsimo-Andrefana Region, Ampanihy, Sakaraha

Note: Type localities listed for all species except *Issopulex gloriosus*, which was originally described from the Glorieuse archipelago and recorded on Madagascar later.

Pteriliina (Adenissini) may be treated as primitive, as the members of these groups have rather well-developed forewings and hind wings. Other tribes (and subtribes of Adenissini) are characterized by different levels of brachyptery and may be treated as advanced and specialized taxa. On the other hand, one of the most derived tribes is the Peltonotellini, as it is characterized by adult sensory pits that are apparently a neoteny characteristic (Gnezdilov 2015b).

MORPHOLOGY

Caliscelidae species are characterized by a narrow or wide metope (frons), often with intermediate carinae and sometimes with adult sensory pits. The lower part of the metope and upper part of the postclypeus form a proboscis in some species (e.g., of the genera *Afronaso*, *Sphenax*, *Ugandana*). The coryphe (vertex) is elongate or transverse, always without sensory pits. The pronotum has narrow paradiscal fields, sometimes with adult sensory pits. The forewings are well developed, surpassing the abdominal apex (Augilini; Adenissini: Pteriliina; macropterous pterodimorphic Caliscelini and Ommatidiotini), or from subbrachypterous to extremely brachypterous (Ommatidiotini; Adenissini: Adenissina, Bocrina; Caliscelini; Peltonotellini), sometimes saddle-shaped (e.g., *Caliscelis swazi*). Hind wings have well-developed remigium and vannus (Augilini; Adenissini: Pteriliina, some Coinquendina; macropterous forms of Caliscelini and Ommatidiotini) or are rudimentary (most species). The first metatarsomeres has latero-apical spines and sometimes an intermediate spine, or they lack any form of spine, in most Augilini. The Indo-African genus *Rhinogaster* is distinguished by the abdominal tergite 5 with large finger-shaped process (Fennah 1949). There are two types of the phallobase in the family—the "closed-tube" type (some Caliscelini, Adenissini, Augilini), which is possibly the primitive (ancestral) condition; and the "open-tube" type (the majority of Caliscelini and Peltonotellini), which may be treated as a derived condition (Gnezdilov 2015b). Genital styles have a large plate; the capitulum is often long and narrow, without a lateral tooth (Caliscelini), or sometimes small, with toothlike structures (Adenissini); in some Augilini species, the style plate has several processes (e.g., *Augilina namboina* from Vietnam). Gonoplacs are flat, rounded, or nearly triangular, without marginal teeth; anterior connective lamina of gonapophysis 8 are narrow, without comb, bearing one to nine large teeth; posterior connective lamina of gonapophysis 9 have wide and rounded apices and a convex median field Gnezdilov 2003).

DISTRIBUTION

The subfamily Caliscelinae has a broad distribution, with both tribes represented in the Old World and only Peltonotellini occurring naturally in the New World; the modern fauna of the subfamily Ommatidiotinae seems to be limited to the Old World and unknown in the Australasian region (Gnezdilov 2013a). Two Old World species of the tribe Caliscelini, *Caliscelis bonellii* and *Asarcopus palmarum*, have been introduced to the United States, specifically California (O'Brien 1988).

Malagasy members of the family Caliscelidae comprise 10 species in nine genera of the tribes Augilini and Caliscelini, many described in the last 10 years (Gnezdilov and Bourgoin 2009; Gnezdilov 2011a, 2011b, 2014, 2015c; see Table 9.24). Currently recognized species are known only from the former provinces of Antananarivo (two genera with two species), Fianarantsoa (three genera with three species), and Toliara (five monotypic genera). Nothing is known about this family in the northern portion of the island. All Malagasy species are endemic (Gnezdilov 2015c) with the exception of *Issopulex gloriosus*, which is also known from the Glorieuse archipelago (China and Fennah 1960) to the northwest of Madagascar. At the generic level, only the genus *Afronaso* is shared with continental Africa. The other eight genera are currently considered endemic to Madagascar and include *Calampocus* and *Issopulex*, which are close to the African genus *Savanopulex*. The presence on the island of two monotypic Augilini genera, *Signoreta* and *Cano*, is considered an important biogeographic aspect, as the tribe Augilini is present only in the Oriental region, outside Madagascar, with a fossil species, *Quizqueiplana alexbrowni*, closely related to the Oriental genus *Symplana*, which is known from early Miocene Dominican amber (Bourgoin et al. 2016). Thus, Malagasy Augilini can perhaps be treated as relicts of a former Old and New World distribution of this tribe (Gnezdilov 2015c).

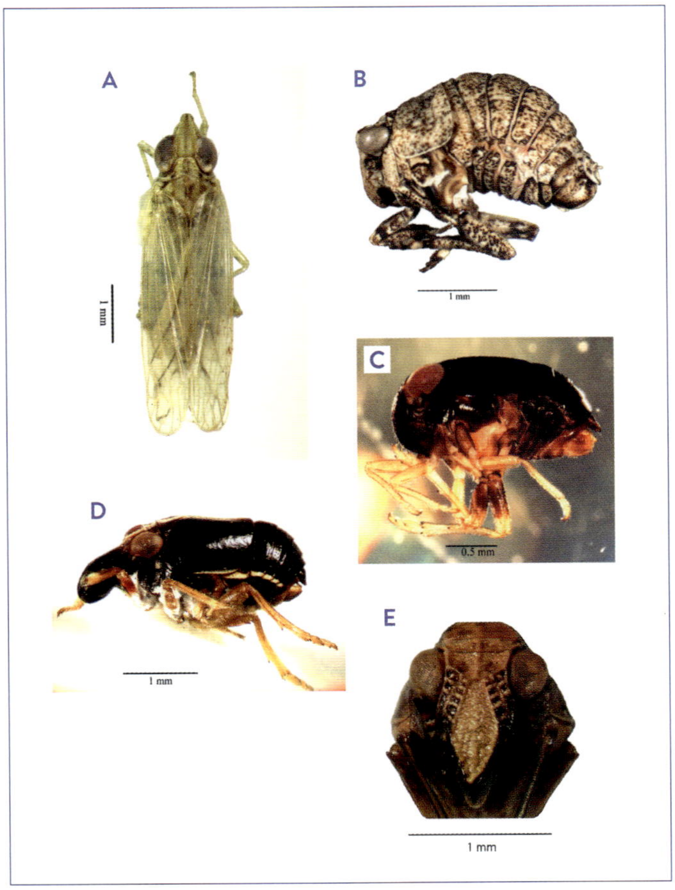

FIGURE 9.28 **Malagasy Caliscelidae: A) *Signoreta victorina*, female holotype, dorsal view; B) *Campures pallens*, female holotype, lateral view; C) *Calampocus sphaeroides*, male holotype, lateral view; D) *Afronaso malagasicus*, male holotype, lateral view; E) *Sphenax cuneus*, female holotype, frontal view.** (PHOTOS by V. M. Gnezdilov.)

Caliscelidae, with some other families of Fulgoroidea that are placed in the "issidoid" family group, may be treated as evolutionarily young taxa, having evolved at the Cretaceous–Cenozoic boundary and undergone a rapid diversification in the Eocene–Miocene (Gnezdilov 2013a). Southeast Asia may be considered the region of origin for Caliscelidae, as four of five tribes are present there. Colonization from Africa to Madagascar, as suggested for *Issopulex gloriosus* (Gnezdilov 2014), might best be explained by dispersal, and more specifically rafting of green islands of vegetation particularly associated with cyclones, rather than vicariance.

Key to Malagasy Caliscelidae

1.	Forewings and hind wings well developed. Coryphe (vertex) elongate and narrow (Ommatidiotinae, Augilini)	2
1a.	Brachypterous (Caliscelinae, Caliscelini)	3
2.	Forewings narrowing apically, with a nodal line distally	*Cano merinus*
2a.	Forewings not narrowing apically, without nodal line	*Signoreta victorina* (Figure 9.28a)
3.	Metope (frons) and postclypeus forming proboscis	7
3a.	Metope and postclypeus without proboscis	4
4.	Coryphe elongate medially, with median carina and acutely angulate anterior margin	*Patamadaga pauliani*
4a.	Coryphe transverse, without median carina; anterior margin nearly straight or trapezoidal	5
5.	Metope with distinct median and sublateral carinae. Generally pale	*Campures pallens* (Figure 9.28b)
5a.	Metope without intermediate carinae. Generally dark brown to black	6
6.	First metatarsomere with two latero-apical and one intermediate spine. Phallobase with large basal process. Ventral aedeagal hooks spirally curved	*Calampocus sphaeroides* (male) (Figure 9.28c)
6a.	First metatarsomere with only two latero-apical spines. Phallobase without basal process. Ventral aedeagal hooks weakly curved	*Issopulex gloriosus*
7.	Metope with sublateral carinae	9
7a.	Metope without sublateral carinae	8
8.	Generally brown or dark brown reddish, with yellowish forewing costal margins	*Afronaso gryphus*
8a.	Generally black, with white forewing costal margins and abdominal tergites laterally	*Afronaso malagasicus* (Figure 9.28d)
9.	Metope with two rows of granules (traces of larval sensory pits) between lateral margins and sublateral carinae. First metatarsomere with only two latero-apical spines	10
9a.	Metope without granules. First metatarsomere with two latero-apical and one intermediate spine	*Calampocus sphaeroides* (female)
10.	Metopial proboscis wide in lateral view	*Sphenax cuneus* (Figure 9.28e)
10a.	Metopial proboscis spine-shaped	*Madaceratops adelinae*

ACKNOWLEDGMENTS

This study was performed within the framework of the Russian State Research Project No. AAAA-A19-119020690101-6.

Subject editors: Brian L. Fisher and Steven M. Goodman

ORTHOPTERA: CAELIFERA AND ENSIFERA, GRASSHOPPERS, KATYDIDS, CRICKETS, *VALALA*, *ANGELY*

S. Hugel

The insect order Orthoptera includes the suborders Caelifera (grasshoppers and relatives) and Ensifera (katydids, crickets, and relatives). Members of Orthoptera are renowned for their ability to jump and their use of acoustic communication, although numerous exceptions to these characteristics apply, including on Madagascar. Humans have both strong and ambiguous relationships with Orthoptera. On the one hand, some species—mostly grasshoppers or "locusts" —are serious crop pests. On the other hand, orthopterans are a major source of insect protein consumed by humans.

TABLE 9.25. **Checklist of Orthoptera recorded in Madagascar**

ENSIFERA
GRYLLIDEA, MYRMECOPHILIDAE
Myrmecophilinae
Myrmecophilus americanus Saussure, 1877[1]

GRYLLIDEA, GRYLLOTALPIDAE
Gryllotalpinae, Gryllotalpini
Gryllotalpa africana Palisot de Beauvois, 1805[2]
G. parva Townsend, 1983 (Figure 9.29c)
G. ***madecassa*** (Chopard, 1920)

GRYLLIDEA, MOGOPLISTIDAE
Malgasiinae
Malgasia ***brevipalpis*** Chopard, 1952
M. ***chopardi*** Gorochov, 1984
M. ***decaryi*** (Chopard, 1946)
M. ***grisea*** Gorochov, 2014
M. ***longipes*** Chopard, 1948
M. ***madecassa*** Chopard, 1949
M. ***marmorata*** (Saussure, 1899)
M. ***microphthalma*** Chopard, 1951
M. ***milloti*** Chopard, 1949
M. ***minutissima*** Gorochov, 2014
M. ***pauliani*** Chopard, 1951
M. ***singularis*** Chopard, 1949
M. ***vicina*** Chopard, 1951
Mogoplistinae, Arachnocephalini
Cycloptiloides orientalis Chopard, 1925[3]
Mogoplistinae, Mogoplistini
Ectatoderus ***sikorai*** Gorochov, 1988
E. ***voeltzkowi*** Saussure, 1899

GRYLLIDEA, TRIGONIDIIDAE
Nemobiinae, Pteronemobiini
Pteronemobius (Pteronemobius) aethiops (Saussure, 1877)
P. (P.) heydenii ***madagascariensis*** Gorochov, 1984
P. (P.) ***maculosus*** (Saussure, 1899)
P. (P.) malgachus (Saussure, 1877)[4]
P. (Stilbonemobius) ***monochromus*** Chopard, 1955
Nemobiinae
Scottiola ***hirsuta hirsuta*** Chopard, 1952
S. ***obscura*** Chopard, 1952
S. ***silvicola*** Chopard, 1952
Trigonidiinae, Trigonidiini
Metioche (Metioche) ***bimaculata*** Chopard, 1952
M. (M.) ***ocularis*** (Saussure, 1899)
M. (M.) ***quadrimaculata*** Chopard, 1952
M. (M.) ***sexmaculata*** Chopard, 1952
Natula longipennis (Serville, 1838)[5]
Trigonidium (Trigonidium) cicindeloides Rambur, 1838[6]

GRYLLIDEA, PHALANGOPSIDAE
Paragryllinae, Paragryllini
Paragryllodes ***(Cortigryllus) andasibe*** Gorochov, 2015
P. **(C.)** ***annulicornis*** Kaltenbach, 1982
P. **(C.)** ***madecassus*** Chopard, 1927
P. **(C.)** ***raineri*** Gorochov, 2015
P. ***annulipes*** Chopard, 1952
Phalangopsinae
Prosecogryllus nossibianus Brancsik, 1893

GRYLLIDEA, GRYLLIDEA, PODOSCIRTIDAE
Euscyrtinae
Euscyrtus (Euscyrtus) ***madagascarensis*** Gorochov, 1988
E. (E.) bivittatus Guérin-Méneville, 1844[7]
E. (E.) bipunctatus Chopard, 1958[8]
Patiscodes ***hova*** (Brancsik, 1893)
Oecanthinae, Oecanthini
Oecanthus brevicauda Saussure, 1878
Podoscirtinae, Podoscirtini
Allotrella analogica Gorochov, 2006
Atruljalia ampla Gorochov, 2004
A. malgasa Gorochov, 1988
Eupodoscirtus affinis Gorochov, 2004
E. idoneus Gorochov, 2004
E. stolarczyki Gorochov, 2004
E. voeltzkowi Gorochov, 2004
Fryerius ***amplocellatus*** Gorochov, 2006 (Figure 9.29f)
F. ***congruens*** Gorochov, 2004
F. ***fowleri*** Gorochov, 2004
F. ***grandidieri*** (Saussure, 1878)
F. ***guichardi*** Gorochov, 2004
F. ***madecassus*** (Saussure, 1878)
F. ***magnus*** Gorochov, 2004
F. ***prudens*** Gorochov, 2004
Kilimagryllus (Brevitrella) ***madagascaricus*** Gorochov, 2004
Madasumma ***binotata*** (Brancsik, 1893)
M. ***hova*** (Brancsik, 1895)
M. ***reducta*** (Walker, 1869)
Malgasotrella robusta Gorochov, 2004
M. venosa Gorochov, 2004
Neozvenella ablata Gorochov, 2004
N. aucta Gorochov, 2004
N. bona Gorochov, 2004
N. hildebrandti Gorochov, 2004
N. modesta Gorochov, 2006
N. picta Gorochov, 2004
N. sikorai Gorochov, 2004
Ombrotrella beccalonii Gorochov, 2006
Paranaudus ***micropterus*** Chopard, 1952
Podoscirtus crocinus Serville, 1838
Posus mictiformis Bolívar, 1890
Spinotrella pulcherrima Gorochov, 2004
S. variegata Gorochov, 2004
Stenotrella lucens (Chopard, 1952)
S. sceleton (Gorochov, 2004)
S. seyrigi (Chopard, 1952)
Ultratrella gracilis Gorochov, 2004
Zvenellomorpha bella Gorochov, 2004
Z. recta Gorochov, 2006
Pentacentrinae, Homalogryllini
Astriduleva analamazaotra Gorochov, 2016[9]
Pentacentrinae, Pentacentrini
Orthoxiphus ***atriceps*** Saussure, 1899
Gryllinae, Gryllini
Acanthogryllus ***malgasus*** Gorochov, 1988
Brachytrupes ***grandidieri*** Saussure, 1877

(continued overleaf)

TABLE 9.25. ***continued***

GRYLLIDEA, GRYLLIDEA, PODOSCIRTIDAE

B. membranaceus ***colosseus*** Saussure, 1899
Cophogryllus ***sacalava*** (Brancsik, 1895)
Gialaia (Gialaia) ***africana*** Gorochov & Kostia, 1999[10]
Gryllodes sigillatus (Walker, 1869)
Gryllus (Gryllus) bimaculatus De Geer, 1773
G. (G.) ***madagascarensis*** Walker, 1869
Pezoloxoblemmus lativertex (Saussure, 1899)
P. obtusus (Saussure, 1899)
Scapsipedus ***limbatus*** Saussure, 1877
Modicogryllus conspersus (Shaum, 1853)[11]
Svercus palmetorum ***geonomes*** (Otte & Cade, 1984)[12]
Teleogryllus (Afroteleogryllus) ***lemur*** Gorochov, 1990
T. (Teleogryllus) afer (Saussure, 1877)[11]
Gryllinae
Regoza brevipennis Gorochov & Kostia, 1999[10]

TETTIGONIIDEA, STENOPELMATOIDEA, ANOSTOSTOMATIDAE

Anabropsinae, Anabropsini
Paterdecolyus ***chopardi*** (Karny, 1932)
Anabropsinae, Brachyporini
Brachyporus ***miser*** Griffini, 1913
B. ***pallidifrons*** Karny, 1930
B. ***personatus*** Brunner von Wattenwyl, 1888
B. ***spinulentus*** Gorochov, 2001
Anostostomatinae
Spizaphilus alatus (Butler, 1880)
S. cuniculator (Coquerel, 1848)
S. gigas Karny, 1932
S. kirbyi Griffini, 1912
S. ornatus (Brunner von Wattenwyl, 1888)
S. rothschildi (Griffini, 1912)
Unassigned Anostostomatidae
<u>*Hypocophus*</u> ***fortior*** Brunner von Wattenwyl, 1888
<u>*H.*</u> ***humilis*** (Brunner von Wattenwyl, 1888)
<u>*H.*</u> ***longicalcar*** (Karny, 1932)

TETTIGONIIDEA, STENOPELMATOIDEA, GRYLLACRIDIDAE

Gryllacridinae, Ametroidini
Pseuderemus exiguus (Brunner von Wattenwyl, 1888)
Gryllacridinae, Gryllacridini
<u>*Griffinigryllacris*</u> ***adelungi*** (Griffini, 1911)
Stictogryllacris ***conspersa brauni*** (Griffini, 1908)
S. <u>*conspersa conspersa*</u> (Brunner von Wattenwyl, 1888)
S. ***conspersa sikorae*** (Griffini, 1919)
S. ***difficilis*** (Karny, 1932)
S. ***madagassa*** (Karny, 1931)
S. ***pauliani*** (Chopard, 1952)
S. ***pittarellii*** (Giglio-Tos, 1907)
S. ***pungens*** (Griffini, 1911)
S. ***signoreti*** (Griffini, 1908)
Gryllacridinae, Progryllacridini
<u>*Karnygryllacris*</u> ***atriceps*** (Brunner von Wattenwyl, 1888)
<u>*K.*</u>-***grylloides*** (Karny, 1935)
<u>*K.*</u> ***humilis*** (Griffini, 1911)
<u>*K.*</u> ***occipitalis*** (Karny, 1932)

TETTIGONIIDEA, STENOPELMATOIDEA, GRYLLACRIDIDAE

<u>*K.*</u> ***scurra*** (Karny, 1932)
<u>*K.*</u> ***triocellata*** (Karny, 1932)
Hyperbaeninae, Phryganogryllacridini
<u>*Claudiagryllacris*</u> ***finoti*** (Karny, 1932)
<u>*C.*</u> ***lemur*** (Griffini, 1909)
<u>*C.*</u> ***stigmata*** (Brunner von Wattenwyl, 1888)
Echidnogryllacris sanguinolenta (Brunner von Wattenwyl, 1888) (Figure 9.29g)
<u>*Pissodogryllacris*</u> ***bedoti ambrens*** (Karny, 1932)
<u>*P.*</u> ***bedoti bedoti*** (Griffini, 1909)
<u>*P.*</u> ***mannae*** (Griffini, 1909)
<u>*P.*</u> ***nossibiana*** (Brancsik, 1895)
<u>*P.*</u> ***saussurei*** (Griffini, 1911)
<u>*P.*</u> ***silvestrii*** (Griffini, 1911)

TETTIGONIIDEA, TETTIGONIOIDEA, TETTIGONIIDAE

Conocephalinae, Agraeciini
Aethiomerus adelphus Redtenbacher, 1891
A. madagassus Redtenbacher, 1891
Allomenus bimacula Saussure, 1899
Centrocephalus viridis Brongniart, 1897
<u>*Cesacomora*</u> ***cucullata*** (Redtenbacher, 1891)
Dicranacrus furcatus Saussure, 1899
D. furcifer Redtenbacher, 1891
D. nasutus Saussure, 1899
D. piceus Redtenbacher, 1891
D. variegatus Redtenbacher, 1891
D. voeltzkowi Saussure, 1899
Episattus marmoratus Brongniart, 1897 (Figure 9.30g)
Gallienia elegans Brongniart, 1897
Oxycalypta plasoni Karny, 1914
Rhacoptera atra Karny, 1907
Subria ***microcephala*** Brongniart, 1897[13]
Conocephalinae, Conocephalini
Conocephalus (Anisoptera) iris (Serville, 1838)
C. (A.) ***affinis*** Redtenbacher, 1891[14]
C. (Megalotheca) ***marcelloi*** Gorochov & Llorente del Moral, 2004
C. (M.) ***nigrifrons*** (Chopard, 1952)
C. (M.) ***xiphidioides*** (Karny, 1907)
Enoplocephalacris brevipennis Chopard, 1952
Conocephalinae, Copiphorini
Apoecides madagascariensis Bolívar, 1914
Pedinostethus exiguus Redtenbacher, 1891
Poascirtus voeltzkowi Saussure, 1899
Pseudorhynchus hastifer (Schaum, 1853)[15]
Ruspolia ***abrupta*** (Walker, 1869)
R. differens (Serville, 1838)
R. madagassa (Redtenbacher, 1891)
Conocephalinae, Euconchophorini
Amblylakis inermis Redtenbacher, 1891
A. leprosipes Saussure, 1899
A. nigrolimbata Redtenbacher, 1891
Colossopus grandidieri Saussure, 1899
C. parvicavus Ünal & Beccaloni, 2017
C. redtenbacheri (Brongniart, 1897)

TETTIGONIIDEA, TETTIGONIOIDEA, TETTIGONIIDAE

Euconchophora infuscata Brongniart, 1897
E. spinigera (Redtenbacher, 1891)
E. subulata (Redtenbacher, 1891)
Malagasopus desutterae Ünal & Beccaloni, 2017
M. meridianus Ünal & Beccaloni, 2017
Odontolakis ***alluaudi*** Brongniart, 1897
O. ***armata*** Redtenbacher, 1891
O. ***bicolor*** Brongniart, 1897
O. ***brunneri*** Brongniart, 1897
O. ***hastata*** Redtenbacher, 1891
O. ***lantzi*** Brongniart, 1897
O. ***nigripes*** Redtenbacher, 1891
O. ***sexpunctata*** (Serville, 1838)
O. ***speculata*** Brongniart, 1897
O. ***spinifera*** Chopard, 1952
O. ***tibialis*** Redtenbacher, 1891
O. ***varia*** Redtenbacher, 1891
O. ***virescens*** Redtenbacher, 1891
Oncodopus brongniarti Ünal & Beccaloni, 2017
O. janetae Ünal & Beccaloni, 2017
O. saussurei Ünal & Beccaloni, 2017
O. soalalaensis Ünal & Beccaloni, 2017
O. zonatus Brongniart, 1897 (Figure 9.30f)

Conocephalinae

Elasmometopus madecassus Chopard, 1952
Paulianacris mirabilis Chopard, 1952[16]

Listroscelidinae

Paralistroscelis listrosceloides (Karny, 1907)

Meconematinae, Phisidini

Breviphisis robusta Gorochov, 2017
Longiphisis gracilis Gorochov, 2017
L. media Gorochov, 2017
Malagasyphisis maromizaha Hugel, 2012 (Figure 9.30b)
Poecilomerus saga Karny, 1907

Phaneropterinae, Amblycoryphini

Eurycorypha ***brevipennis*** Karsch, 1889
E. ***brunneri*** Brancsik, 1893
E. prasinata Stål, 1874[17] (Figure 9.30c)
Madagascarantia albolineata (Brunner von Wattenwyl, 1878)
Paraplangia sinespeculo Heller, 2018
Plangia ***guttatipennis*** Karsch, 1889
P. ***segonoides*** (Butler, 1878)

Phaneropterinae, Holochlorini

Holochlora biloba Stål, 1874[18]

Phaneropterinae, Phaneropterini

Agennis parallelinervis Brunner von Wattenwyl, 1891
Eucatopta heringi Karsch, 1889
Parapyrrhicia ***dentipes*** Saussure, 1899
P. ***leuca*** Hemp & Heller, 2019
P. ***longipodex*** Massa, 2017
P. ***madagassus*** (Karsch, 1889)
P. ***virilis*** Carl, 1914
Phaneroptera (Phaneroptera) sparsa Stål, 1857
Symmetroraggea depravata Massa, 2017
S. dirempta (Karsch, 1889)
Xenodoxus annulatus (Brunner von Wattenwyl, 1891)

TETTIGONIIDEA, TETTIGONIOIDEA, TETTIGONIIDAE

X. nobilis Carl, 1914

Phaneropterinae, Trigonocoryphini

Cosmozoma coelebs Carl, 1914
C. doenitzi Karsch, 1889
C. sikorae Brunner von Wattenwyl, 1891
C. vespertilio Carl, 1914
C. voluptaria Brunner von Wattenwyl, 1891
Megotoessa insulana Karsch, 1889
Trigonocorypha ***maxima*** Carl, 1914

Phaneropterinae, Tylopsidini

Tylopsis bilineolata (Serville, 1838)

Phaneropterinae

Anchispora appendiculata Brunner von Wattenwyl, 1891
Mimoscudderia longicaudata Heller & Kristín, 2019
M. modesta Carl, 1914
M. paulyi Massa, 2017
M. picta Carl, 1914
M. spinicercata Massa, 2017
Nesoscirtella polita Carl, 1914
Paracosmophyllum atrodelineatum Brunner von Wattenwyl, 1891
Paraphylloptera relicta Carl, 1914
Polygamus macropterus Carl, 1914
P. punctipennis Carl, 1914
Sikoriella bimaculata Carl, 1914

Pseudophyllinae, Aspidonotini

Aspidonotus spinosus Brullé, 1835 (Figure 9.29a)

Pseudophyllinae, Simoderini

Lonchitophyllum reticulatum Brunner von Wattenwyl, 1895
Parasimodera saussurei Carl, 1914 (Figure 9.30a)
Phyrama interjectum Karsch, 1889
P. laticolle Carl, 1914
P. majus Brunner von Wattenwyl, 1895
Simodera acutifolia Brunner von Wattenwyl, 1895
S. halterata Karsch, 1891
S. latifolia Chopard, 1952
Wattenwyliella dispar Carl, 1914

Tettigoniinae, Arytropteridini

Toliaridectes antsycurvis Hugel, 2019 (Figure 9.30d)
T. meridionalis Hugel, 2019
T. wendenbaumi Hugel, 2019

CAELIFERA

TRIDACTYLIDEA, TRIDACTYLIDAE

Tridactylinae

Afrotridactylus madecassus (Saussure, 1896) (Figure 9.31a)
Xya ***ancarafantsika*** Günther, 1982

ACRIDIDEA, TETRIGOIDEA, TETRIGIDAE

Cladonotinae, Xerophyllini

Morphopoides ***madagascariensis*** Günther, 1939

Cladonotinae

Epitettix ***spheniscus*** Günther, 1974
Microthymochares pullus Devriese, 1991
Thymochares bolivari Rehn, 1937
T. crassipes Rehn, 1937
T. delphini Günther, 1974
T. exiguus Günther, 1974

(continued overleaf)

TABLE 9.25. ***continued***

CAELIFERA
TRIDACTYLIDEA, TRIDACTYLIDAE
T. frontangulus Günther, 1974
T. galeatus Rehn, 1929
T. madagascariensis (Günther, 1959)
T. manjakatompo (Günther, 1974)
T. modestus (Günther, 1974)
T. pieraggii Devriese, 1995
T. rehni Günther, 1959
T. sambavana (Günther, 1974)
T. simplicior (Günther, 1974)
Metrodorinae, Cleostratini
Procytettix ***hova*** Rehn, 1937
P. ***robinsoni*** Günther, 1974
Rhynchotettix hancocki Bruner, 1910
R. rostratus Hancock, 1907
Metrodorinae
Andriana hancocki (Bruner, 1910)
A. intermedia Devriese, 1991
A. pyramidata Rehn, 1929
Arexion suavis Rehn, 1929
Bara turgida Rehn, 1929
Charagotettix longispinis (Günther, 1939)
C. lucubensis Brancsik, 1893
C. nannus Günther, 1974
C. sogai Günther, 1974
C. stenocnemis Günther, 1974
C. fanovana Günther, 1974
C. imerina Rehn, 1929
C. impennis Günther, 1939
C. insularis Günther, 1974
C. macrophthalmus Günther, 1974
C. similis Günther, 1974
C. spinilobus Hancock, 1900
Eurybiades cerastes Rehn, 1929
Holocerus lucifer (Serville, 1838)
H. devriesei Skejo et al., 2020
Hovacris undulata Rehn, 1929
Hybotettix camelus Devriese, 1991
H. humeralis Hancock, 1900
Isandrus ***cicatricosus*** Rehn, 1929
I. ***gibbosus*** Chopard, 1952
Notocerus cornutus Hancock, 1900
N. formidabilis Günther, 1974 (Figure 9.31b)
Ocytettix latihumerus Hancock, 1907
Oxytettix arius (Rehn, 1929)
O. cataphractus Rehn, 1937
O. hastatus (Hancock, 1900)
O. lathraeospanius (Günther, 1939)
O. macrocerus Günther, 1974
Pterotettix alluaudi Günther, 1939
P. andrei Bolívar, 1887
P. asmodaeus (Serville, 1838)
P. belphegor (Serville, 1838)
P. bigibbosus (Hancock, 1900)
P. humilis Günther, 1939

TRIDACTYLIDEA, TRIDACTYLIDAE
Tetriginae, Tetrigini
Hydrotetrix ***fallax*** Günther, 1974
Paratettix ***asbenensis*** Chopard, 1950
P. ***cinereus*** Bolívar, 1887
P. scaber (Thunberg, 1815)[19]
P. ***voeltzkowiana*** Saussure, 1899
Tetrix ***nanus*** Bruner, 1910
Tetriginae
Agkistropleuron simplex Bruner, 1910
Hedotettix pulchellus Bolívar, 1887
Unassigned Tetragidae
Lepocranus fuscus Devriese, 1991
Pseudosystolederus ***follvikae*** Devriese, 1995
P. ***sikorai*** Günther, 1939
Rehnitettix olsufieffi Günther, 1939
Silanotettix baroides Günther, 1974
S. notangulus Günther, 1959
S. strumiger Günther, 1959

ACRIDIDEA, PYRGOMORPHOIDEA, PYRGOMORPHIDAE
Orthacridinae, Caprorhinina
Dyscolorhinus squalinus Saussure, 1899
D. vittatus Kevan, Akbar & Singh, 1964
Orthacridinae, Geloiini
Geloius crassicornis Bolívar, 1905
G. nasutus Saussure, 1899
G. tanalanensis Wintrebert, 1972
Pseudogeloius affinis Kevan, 1965
P. decorsei (Bolívar, 1905)
P. fotadrevae Descamps & Wintrebert, 1966
P. marolintae Descamps & Wintrebert, 1966
P. relictus Dirsh, 1963
Orthacridinae, Gymnohippini
Gymnohippus marmoratus Bruner, 1910
Pyrgohippus pallidus Dirsh, 1963
P. productus (Descamps & Wintrebert, 1966)
Uhagonia depressa Dirsh, 1963
U. sphenarioides Bolívar, 1905
U. wintreberti Kevan, 1968
Orthacridinae, Malagasphenini
Malagasphena minor Kevan, Akbar & Singh, 1964
Orthacridinae, Orthacridini
Acropyrgus cadeti Descamps & Wintrebert, 1966
Ambositracris morati Kevan, Akbar & Chang, 1971
A. ornata Dirsh, 1963
Caprorhinus ***ambahitae*** Wintrebert, 1972
C. ***andohahelensis*** Wintrebert, 1972
C. ***anivoranensis*** Wintrebert, 1972
C. ***betrokae*** Wintrebert, 1972
C. ***cadeti*** Wintrebert, 1972
C. ***dechappei*** Descamps & Wintrebert, 1966
C. ***descampsi*** Wintrebert, 1972
C. ***donskoffi*** Wintrebert, 1972
C. ***fotadrevensis*** Kevan, Akbar & Chang, 1971
C. ***fusiformis*** Saussure, 1899
C. ***inflatus*** Wintrebert, 1972

ACRIDIDEA, PYRGOMORPHOIDEA, PYRGOMORPHIDAE

C. **isoanalae** Wintrebert, 1972
C. **kevani** Descamps & Wintrebert, 1966
C. **lavanonensis** Wintrebert, 1972
C. **mahabensis** Wintrebert, 1972
C. **major** Wintrebert, 1972
C. **malzyi** Wintrebert, 1972
C. **minor** Uvarov, 1929
C. **monclari** Wintrebert, 1972
C. **pauliani** Wintrebert, 1972
C. **puerisalbis** Wintrebert, 1972
C. **ralinoroi** Wintrebert, 1972
C. **ranohirae** Kevan, 1963
C. **rostratus** Uvarov, 1929
C. **seyrigi** Wintrebert, 1972
C. **tenikae** Wintrebert, 1972
C. **zolotarevskyi** Uvarov, 1929
Pseudosphena dispar (Dirsh, 1963)
Orthacridinae, Sagittacridini
Acanthopyrgus finoti (Bolívar, 1905)
A. longicornis Descamps & Wintrebert, 1966
Sagittacris malagassa Dirsh, 1963
Pyrgomorphinae, Atractomorphini
Atractomorpha acutipennis acutipennis (Guérin-Méneville, 1844)
Pyrgomorphella dicrostachyae Descamps & Wintrebert, 1966
P. madecassa Bolívar, 1904
P. minuta Dirsh, 1963
P. tulearensis Descamps & Wintrebert, 1966
Pyrgomorphinae, Schulthessiini
Buyssoniella madecassa Bolívar, 1905
Schulthessia biplagiata Bolívar, 1905
Pyrgomorphinae, Sphenariini
Rubellia nigrosignata Stål, 1875
Pyrgomorphinae, Chlorizeinini
Pseudorubellia brancsiki (Bolívar, 1904)
P. thoracica geniculata Dirsh & Descamps, 1968
P. t. thoracica Dirsh, 1963
Pyrgomorphinae, Phymateini
Phymateus ***madagassus*** Karsch, 1888[20]
P. ***saxosus*** Coquerel, 1861 (Figure 9.31c)

ACRIDIDEA, ACRIDOIDEA, ACRIDIDAE

Acridinae, Acridini
Acrida madecassa (Brancsik, 1893)[21]
Acrida ***subtilis*** Burr, 1902
Chromacrida brunneriana (Bolívar, 1893)
C. radamae (Saussure, 1899)
Acridinae, Calephorini
Calephorus ***ornatus*** (Walker, 1870)
Acridinae, Gymnobothrini
Gymnobothrus madacassus Bruner, 1910[22]
G. ***variabilis*** Bruner, 1910
Acridinae, Phlaeobini
Chlorophlaeobella tananarive (Dirsh, 1963)
Duronia chloronota chloronota (Stål, 1876)
Acridinae
Lemuracris longicornis Dirsh, 1966
Paracoryphosima betsileana Descamps & Wintrebert, 1966

ACRIDIDEA, ACRIDOIDEA, ACRIDIDAE

Pseudopargaella nigropunctata Descamps & Wintrebert, 1966
Vietteacris insularis Wintrebert, 1972
V. subfusca Descamps & Wintrebert, 1966
Calliptaminae
Acorypha ***decisa*** (Walker, 1870)[23]
Catantopinae, Allagini
Sauracris ***pigra*** (Carl, 1916)[24]
Catantops ***brevipennis*** Wintrebert, 1972
Catantopsis ***stenocrobyloides*** (Karny, 1907)[25]
C. malagassus (Karny, 1907)[26]
C. sacalava (Brancsik, 1893)[27]
Catantopinae, Mesambriini
Mesambria ***ferrugata*** Brancsik, 1893[28]
Catantopinae, Serpusiae
Serpusilla andringitra Wintrebert, 1972
S. erythropyga Chopard, 1952
S. glabra Dirsh, 1962
S. malagassa (Bruner, 1910)
S. manangotra Wintrebert, 1972
S. ochreopyga flavipes Descamps & Wintrebert, 1967
S. o. ochreopyga Dirsh, 1962
S. o. rubroornata Descamps & Wintrebert, 1967
S. o. viridipes Descamps & Wintrebert, 1967
Catantopinae
Ambrea acuticerca Dirsh, 1962
Calderonia biplagiata Bolívar, 1908
Cylindracris subaptera Descamps & Wintrebert, 1967
Dendrocatantops inauratus Descamps & Wintrebert, 1966
Descampsilla sambiranensis Wintrebert, 1972
Dirshilla antsingensis Wintrebert, 1972
Harantacris ambrensis Wintrebert, 1972
H. insulamagna Wintrebert, 1972
Mananara fasciata Dirsh, 1962
Parahysiella betsileana Wintrebert, 1972
P. curvicerca Descamps & Wintrebert, 1967
Paraserpusilla furcata Dirsh, 1962
Perineta bicolor Dirsh, 1962
Pseudofinotina keiseri Dirsh, 1962
Pseudohysiella inermis (Karsch, 1896)
P. pusilla Descamps, 1964
Serpusiacris alticola Descamps & Wintrebert, 1967
Serpusiformia malagassa Dirsh, 1966
Seyrigacris nigrofasciatus Bolívar, 1932
Vohemara hysielloides Dirsh, 1966 (Figure 9.31d)
Pamphagella comoroensis Bruner, 1910
P. **stenoptera** Descamps & Wintrebert, 1966
P. **suturalis** Descamps & Wintrebert, 1966
P. **thoracica** Descamps & Wintrebert, 1966
Cyrtacanthacridinae, Cyrtacanthacridini
Cyrtacanthacris tatarica tatarica (Linnaeus,1758)
Nomadacris septemfasciata (Serville, 1838) (Figure 9.31f)
Rhadinacris schistocercoides (Brancsik, 1893)[26]
Cyrtacanthacridinae
Finotina polychroma Descamps & Wintrebert, 1967
F. radama (Brancsik, 1893)

(continued overleaf)

TABLE 9.25. ***continued***

ACRIDIDEA, ACRIDOIDEA, ACRIDIDAE
F. ranavaloae (Finot, 1907)
Euryphyminae
Euryphymus exemptus (Walker, 1870)
Eyprepocnemidinae, Eyprepocnemidini
Eyprepocnemis ***brachyptera*** Bruner, 1910
E. smaragdipes Bruner, 1910[29]
Heteracris ***antennata*** (Bolívar, 1914)
H. ***concinnicrus*** Descamps & Wintrebert, 1966
H. finoti (Bolívar, 1914)[30]
H. ***nigricornis*** (Saussure, 1899)
H. ***nobilis*** (Brancsik, 1893)
H. ***reducta*** Dirsh, 1962
H. ***sikorai*** (Bolívar, 1914)
H. ***zolotarevskyi*** Dirsh, 1962
Eyprepocnemidinae
Malagacetrus rubripes (Chopard, 1919)
Tenebracris splendens Dirsh, 1962
Gomphocerinae
Gelastorhinus ***edax*** Saussure, 1899
Malagasippus andranomitae Descamps & Wintrebert, 1967
M. mikeus Descamps & Wintrebert, 1966
M. notabilis Descamps & Wintrebert, 1966
M. pullus Descamps & Wintrebert, 1966
M. quadratus quadratus Descamps & Wintrebert, 1966
M. q. reductus Descamps & Wintrebert, 1966
Salariacris panici Descamps & Wintrebert, 1966
Tanalanacris dechappei Descamps & Wintrebert, 1966
Hemiacridinae, Gergisini
Gergis minor Dirsh, 1962
G. pallidinervis Stål, 1875
Malagasacris rugosa Dirsh, 1962
M. strateia Rehn, 1944
Morondavia cephalica Dirsh, 1962
M. minor Dirsh, 1962
Pachyceracris fusca Dirsh, 1962
P. griveaudi Descamps & Wintrebert, 1966
Hemiacridinae, Leptacrini
Leptacris monteiroi ***hova*** (Karsch, 1896)
Hemiacridinae, Mesopserini
Xenippacris viridis Descamps & Wintrebert, 1966
Hemiacridinae
Acutacris tsaratananae Descamps & Wintrebert, 1967[31]
A. viridis Dirsh, 1965[31]
Euthymia bolivari Finot, 1903
E. fasciata (Walker, 1870)
E. polychroma Brancsik, 1893
Galideus elegans Dirsh, 1962
G. mocquerysi Finot, 1908
Hysiella flavovittata Dirsh, 1965
H. nigricornis (Stål, 1875)
Lopheuthymia brunneri (Finot, 1903)
Onetes fasciatus Dirsh, 1962
O. kraussi (Finot, 1903)
O. sanguinolentus Rehn, 1944
O. scudderi (Finot, 1903)
Paulianiobia ***hirsuta*** (Dirsh, 1962)

ACRIDIDEA, ACRIDOIDEA, ACRIDIDAE
Proeuthymia saussurei (Finot, 1903)
Pseudoserpusia flavocoerulipes Descamps & Wintrebert, 1967
P. polychroma Dirsh, 1962
Xenippoides elongatus Chopard, 1952
Oedipodinae, Acrotylini
Acrotylus ***aberrans*** Bruner, 1910
A. ***multispinosus*** Brancsik, 1893
A. patruelis (Herrich-Schäffer, 1838)
Oedipodinae, Epacromiini
Aiolopus thalassinus rodericensis (Butler, 1876)[32]
Paracinema tricolor tricolor (Thunberg, 1815)
Oedipodinae, Locustini
Gastrimargus africanus madagascariensis Sjöstedt, 1928 (Figure 9.31e)
G. verticalis verticalis (Saussure, 1884)[33]
Locusta migratoria migratorioides (Reiche & Fairmaire, 1849)
Oedaleus virgula (Snellen van Vollenhoven, 1869)[26, 31]
Oedipodinae, Sphingonotini
Conipoda calcarata Saussure, 1884[34]
Oedipodinae, Trilophidiini
Trilophidia ***cinnabarina*** Brancsik, 1893
Oedipodinae
Brancsikellus gracilis (Brancsik, 1897)
Pycnocrania grandidieri (Saussure, 1888)
Oxyinae, Oxyini
Oxya hyla Serville, 1831[35]
Spathosterninae, Spathosternini
Paraspathosternum ***andringitra*** Dirsh, 1962
Spathosternum ***malagassum*** Dirsh, 1962
Tropidopolinae, Tristriini
Tristriella malagassa Descamps & Wintrebert, 1967

ACRIDIDEA, EUMASTACOIDEA, EPISACTIDAE
Miraculinae, Heteromastacini
Heteromastax appendiculata (Chopard, 1951)
H. cuneata Descamps, 1965
H. stylifera Descamps, 1965
Miraculinae, Malagassini
Acronomastax butticerca (Saussure, 1903)
A. curvicerca Descamps, 1965 (Figure 9.31h)
A. dentata Descamps, 1965
Malagassa basidentata Chopard, 1952
M. bidens Descamps, 1969
M. coniceps Saussure, 1903
M. leptotes (Brancsik, 1893)
M. mucronata Descamps, 1965
M. tridens Rehn & Rehn, 1945
M. tsaratananae Descamps, 1969
Rhabdomastax blanci Descamps, 1969
R. cornuta (Descamps, 1965)
R. spinulosa (Descamps, 1965)
R. tenuis Descamps, 1974
Miraculinae, Miraculini
Miraculum mirificum Bolívar, 1903
Seyrigella notabilis Chopard, 1951

ACRIDIDEA, EUMASTACOIDEA, EUSCHMIDTIIDAE

Pseudoschmidtiinae, Apteropeoedini

Ambatomastax carinata Descamps & Wintrebert, 1965
Apteropeoedes ankarafantsika Descamps, 1971
A. betrokae Descamps, 1971
A. centralis Descamps, 1971
A. dentifer Descamps, 1971
A. elegans (Descamps, 1964)
A. himana Descamps, 1974
A. indigoferae (Descamps, 1964)
A. inermis Descamps, 1964
A. marmoratus (Descamps & Wintrebert, 1965)
A. monsarrati Descamps, 1971
A. nigroplagiatus Bolívar, 1903
A. pygmaeus Descamps, 1964
A. rostratus Descamps, 1971
A. tridens Descamps, 1974
A. variabilis maculatus Descamps, 1971
A. variabilis variabilis Descamps, 1971
A. wintreberti (Descamps, 1964)
Mastaleptea bongolava Descamps, 1971
M. maculifrons Descamps, 1971
M. viridis (Descamps & Wintrebert, 1965)
M. wintreberti Descamps, 1971
Tetefortina benetrixi Descamps & Wintrebert, 1965
T. curta Descamps, 1964
T. fotadrevoana Descamps & Wintrebert, 1965
T. gibbosa Descamps, 1964
T. hirsuta Descamps & Wintrebert, 1965
T. isaloana Descamps, 1971
T. lohenae Descamps & Wintrebert, 1965
T. maxima Descamps, 1964
T. media Descamps, 1964
T. sylvatica Descamps & Wintrebert, 1965
T. wintreberti Descamps, 1964

Pseudoschmidtiinae, Carcinomastacini

Acanthomastax alata (Bruner, 1910)
A. bifida Descamps, 1964
A. dentifera Descamps, 1971
A. maroantsetrae Descamps, 1971
Carcinomastax acutissima Descamps, 1964
C. minima Descamps, 1964
C. moralesi Descamps, 1971
C. nigrivalva Descamps, 1964
C. portentosa Rehn & Rehn, 1945
C. quadrispinosa Descamps, 1964
C. seyrigi Descamps, 1964
Sauromastax beieri Descamps, 1964
S. luteola Descamps & Wintrebert, 1965
S. sanctaemariae Descamps, 1964
S. tectifera Descamps, 1964
Teratomastax aberrans Descamps, 1964

Pseudoschmidtiinae, Cryptomastacini

Cryptomastax ***bicolor*** Descamps, 1971
C. ***rostrata*** Descamps, 1971
Dichromastax brunneoviridis Descamps, 1971

ACRIDIDEA, EUMASTACOIDEA, EUSCHMIDTIIDAE

Scleromastax brachypygia Descamps, 1974
S. luteifrons Descamps, 1971
S. ovatipennis Descamps, 1974
S. viridipes Descamps, 1971

Pseudoschmidtiinae, Dendromastacini

Acridomastax rehni (Descamps & Wintrebert, 1965)
A. tampolae Descamps, 1971
Dactulomastax gracilipes Descamps, 1971
Dendromastax cornuta Descamps, 1971
D. pectinifer Descamps, 1971
D. regressivalva Descamps & Wintrebert, 1965
D. spatulata Descamps & Wintrebert, 1965

Pseudoschmidtiinae, Lavanonini

Kratopodia andringitra Descamps, 1971
K. quadrifida Descamps, 1964
Lavanonia balachowskyi Descamps & Wintrebert, 1965
L. balmati Descamps & Wintrebert, 1965
L. itampolae Descamps, 1971
L. tenuipes Descamps, 1971
L. thalassina Descamps, 1964
Namontia crassipes Descamps, 1964
N. humilicrus Descamps, 1964
N. robusta Descamps, 1964

Pseudoschmidtiinae, Lobomastacini

Lobomastax angulata Descamps, 1964
L. hova (Saussure, 1903)
L. nana Descamps, 1971
L. recurva Descamps, 1964
L. tridens Descamps, 1971
Microlobia falcicerca Descamps, 1964
M. sanctaemariae Descamps, 1964
Wintrebertina ankarafantsika Descamps, 1971

Pseudoschmidtiinae, Micromastacini

Micromastax bosimavoana Descamps & Wintrebert, 1965
M. longivalva Descamps & Wintrebert, 1965
M. morondavae Descamps, 1974
M. salariensis Descamps, 1964
M. szumskii Descamps & Wintrebert, 1965
M. teteforti cavifrons Descamps, 1971
M. t. rectifrons Descamps, 1971
M. t. teteforti Descamps, 1964
M. truncata Descamps, 1964

Pseudoschmidtiinae, Parasymbellini

Parasymbellia bifida Descamps, 1964
P. crenulata Descamps, 1964
P. decorata Descamps & Wintrebert, 1965
P. grandis Descamps, 1971
P. inermis Descamps, 1964
P. mucronata Descamps, 1964
P. rubroornata Descamps, 1964
P. undulata Descamps, 1964
P. wintreberti Descamps, 1971

Pseudoschmidtiinae, Penichrotini

Harpemastax armata Descamps, 1964
H. cornuta boina Descamps, 1971

(continued overleaf)

TABLE 9.25. ***continued***

ACRIDIDEA, EUMASTACOIDEA, EUSCHMIDTIIDAE
H. c. cornuta Descamps, 1971
H. c. meridionalis Descamps, 1974
H. rubripes Descamps, 1971
H. spinifera Descamps, 1971
Penichrotes nudata Karsch, 1889
Raphimastax sylvatica Descamps, 1971
Rhinomastax acutifrons Descamps, 1971
R. ambreana Descamps, 1971
R. rostrata Descamps, 1971
Xenomastax miserabilis Descamps, 1964
X. wintreberti Descamps, 1964
Pseudoschmidtiinae, Pseudoschmidtiini
Amalomastax ambodirafiae Descamps, 1971
A. furcata Descamps, 1971
A. lambertoni Rehn & Rehn, 1945
A. maculata Descamps, 1971
A. moralesi Descamps, 1971
A. nigromarginata Descamps & Wintrebert, 1965
A. subaptera Descamps, 1971
Malagamastax dubiosa Descamps, 1971
M. spinulosa Descamps, 1964
Maroantsetraia finoti (Saussure, 1903)
Peoedes appendiculatus Karsch, 1889
Platymastax areolata Descamps, 1964
Pseudoschmidtia armata Descamps, 1964
P. biarcuata Descamps, 1964
P. carinata Descamps, 1964
P. complexa Descamps, 1971
P. curticerca Descamps, 1964
P. explanata Descamps, 1964
P. hyaletes (Rehn & Rehn, 1945)
P. incisa Descamps, 1964
P. integra Descamps, 1964
P. ligulata Descamps, 1964
P. lobipennis (Saussure, 1903)
P. meridionalis Descamps, 1971
P. parvipennis (Saussure, 1903)
P. quadridens Descamps, 1964
P. sakalava (Saussure, 1903)
P. sinuata Descamps, 1964
P. spatulata Descamps, 1964
P. subinvolvens Descamps, 1964
P. subovata Descamps, 1964
P. triangularis Descamps, 1964
P. tridens Descamps, 1964[36] (Figure 9.31g)
P. trilobata Descamps, 1964
P. versicolor (Saussure, 1903)
Pseudoschmidtiinae, Sphaerophallini
Descampsiella annulipes (Descamps, 1964)
Sphaerophallus durus Descamps, 1964
S. membranaceus Descamps, 1964
S. micropterus Descamps, 1971
Pseudoschmidtiinae, Symbellini
Isalomastax canaliculata Descamps & Wintrebert, 1965
Symbellia decempunctata Descamps, 1964
S. karschi Burr, 1899
ACRIDIDEA, EUMASTACOIDEA, EUSCHMIDTIIDAE
S. quadrata Descamps, 1964
S. viridipes Descamps, 1964
Tapiamastax bicoloripes Descamps & Wintrebert, 1965
Wintrebertella centralis Descamps, 1964
Pseudoschmidtiinae, Wintrebertini
Elutronuxia isolata Descamps, 1964
Exophtalmomastax lucicola Descamps, 1964
E. malzyi Descamps, 1964
Parawintrebertia armata Descamps & Wintrebert, 1965
P. discreta (Descamps, 1964)
P. gigantea (Descamps, 1964)
P. pauliani betrokae Descamps & Wintrebert, 1965
P. p. pauliani (Descamps, 1964)
P. polychroma Descamps, 1971
Wintrebertia ampanihi Descamps, 1964
W. angulata Descamps, 1964
W. arcuata arcuata Descamps, 1964
W. a. sakaveana Descamps, 1971
W. callosa Descamps, 1971
W. canaliculata Descamps, 1971
W. crassipes Descamps, 1971
W. denticulata bemokae Descamps & Wintrebert, 1965
W. d. denticulata Descamps, 1964
W. donskoffi Descamps & Wintrebert, 1965
W. inflatipes Descamps, 1971
W. itampolae Descamps, 1971
W. lavanoniae Descamps, 1971
W. nigromaculata Descamps, 1971
W. orientalis Descamps, 1971
W. pusilla Descamps, 1964
W. teteforti andranovatae Descamps & Wintrebert, 1965
W. t. teteforti Descamps, 1964
W. tsihombeana Descamps, 1971
W. tsivahae Descamps, 1971
W. tulearensis Descamps, 1964
W. zebra Descamps, 1971
Pseudoschmidtiinae
Macromastax infernalis Karsch, 1889
Pauromastax gracilipes Descamps, 1974
Trichoschmidtia ampulla Descamps, 1974
TAXA (AND POSSIBLE SYNONYMS) WITH DUBIOUS RECORDS FROM MADAGASCAR
Acrididea, Pyrgomorphidae, Pyrgomorphinae
Zonocerus elegans elegans (Thunberg, 1815)[37]
Acrididea, Acrididae, Oxyinae
Paracranae madagassa Ramme, ?[38]
Tettigoniidea, Tettigoniidae, Phaneropterinae
Plangia ovalifolia Bolívar, 1912[39]
Gryllidea, Trigonidiidae, Trigonidiinae
Trigonidium nigritum (Saussure, 1899)[40]
T. brevipenne Saussure, 1899[41]
Gryllidea, Gryllidae, Gryllinae
Platygryllus quadristrigatus (Saussure, 1877)[42]

Note: Taxa endemic to Madagascar are in **boldface type**; taxa endemic to the Malagasy Region are underlined.

[1] New record for Madagascar in Toamasina. This taxon also occurs in the Comoro and Mascarene archipelagoes in modified environments, always with *Paratrechina longicornis* (S. Hugel, unpublished data).

[2] Mentioned by Giglio-Tos (1907) from Moramanga; presence confirmed in Tsimbazaza, Antananarivo, and Ambodiforaha, Masoala (S. Hugel, unpublished data).

[3] This anthropophious species is now widespread in the Mascarenes and Comoros and has occurred in Ambohidempona, Antananarivo, since at least 2018 (S. Hugel, unpublished data).

[4] This species also occurs in the Mascarenes (S. Hugel, unpublished data).

[5] New record; the species is widespread in the Malagasy Region, mostly in modified environments.

[6] *Trigonidium brevipenne* (Saussure, 1899), described from immature specimens collected on Madagascar, is likely a synonym of *T. cicindeloides* Rambur, 1838. *Trigonidium nigritum* (Saussure, 1899) has the typical morphology of macropterous *T. cicindeloides* Rambur, 1838.

[7] Species widespread in the Malagasy Region; mentioned from Nosy Be by Saussure (1899).

[8] Described from the Comoros and mentioned by Gorochov (1988).

[9] *Astriduleva* and all crickets considered members of Landrevinae in Hugel (2009) belong to Pentacentrinae, as indicated by the shared characteristics of male genitalia with long and distinct ventral ectophallic sclerite and leg armature (S. Hugel, unpublished data). This is fully supported by molecular analysis (Chintauan-Marquier et al. 2016). *Astriduleva* and *Creolandreva* have genitalia very similar to that of *Homalogryllus depressus* Chopard, 1925 and are therefore recognized here to be in Homalogryllini within Pentacentrinae.

[10] Type locality originally in Africa; changed to Madagascar in Gorochov (2004b).

[11] Species mentioned from Madagascar in Giglio-Tos (1907).

[12] New record for Madagascar. This taxon also occurs in the Comoros and Mascarenes in modified environments.

[13] The author of this contribution concurs with Ingrish (pers. comm., 1996) that this species does not belong to *Subria* and deserves a new genus.

[14] In the Orthoptera Species File website (Cigliano et al. 2020), Braun (2008) indicates that in Otte (1997), *Conocephalus affinis* was apparently confused with *Xiphidion affine* Redtenbacher, 1891 and erroneously synonymized. The possible synonymy with *C. maculatus* (Le Guillou 1841) needs to be checked. Specimens morphologically similar to *C. maculatus* are found in Madagascar (S. Hugel, unpublished data; see also Krištín et al. 2019).

[15] Described from Mozambique; cited from Madagascar (Ragge 1969).

[16] The author of this contribution concurs with Maehr and Braun (2006) in Cigliano et al. (2020), suggesting that this species should probably be placed into Copiphorini.

[17] This species occurs also in the Comoros and on Mauritius (Chopard 1958; S. Hugel, unpublished data).

[18] This species occurs along the eastern coast of Madagascar in human-modified environments (mostly around Toamasina) and is identical to specimens from Mauritius, La Réunion, and Rodrigues, where it is encountered only in gardens and never in natural environments. The author of this contribution therefore considers *Holochlora mauritiana* Massa, 2017 to be synonymous with *H. biloba* Stål, 1874, n. syn., and has strong doubts that the species is native to Madagascar.

[19] According to Hendrik Devriese (in Hugel 2014; see also Massa 2009), the species redescribed by Günther (1974) under *Paratettix scaber* does not correspond to the type specimen described by Thunberg and should instead be considered *P. subpustulatus* (Walker, 1871).

[20] Dirsh and Descamps (1968) pointed out that *Phymateus madagassus* and *P. saxosus* are morphologically identical, differ only in coloration, and may be the same species, with *P. saxosus* having priority.

[21] Present on Juan de Nova (Parnaudeau et al. 2013).

[22] Present on all four islands in the Comoros (Bruner 1910; Chopard 1958; S. Hugel, unpublished data).

[23] *Caloptenus baliensis* Brancsik, 1893 from Malesia was synonymized under *Acorypha decisa* after the description of Brancsik (Dirsh 1962). Since the type is lost, and Brancsik's description does not allow *C. baliensis* to be distinguished from other *Acorypha*, the author of this contribution proposes to remove *C. baliensis* from synonymy and consider it *nomen dubium stat. nov.*

[24] This species was overlooked by Dirsh and Descamps (1968).

[25] Apparently, Jago (1984) forgot to consider this species in his revision of alate genera of African Catantopinae; since the species is very close to *Catantopsis malagassus* and *C. sacalava*, the author of this contribution proposes to transfer it to *Catantopsis* n. comb.

[26] Present on Glorieuses (Parnaudeau et al. 2013).

[27] The species *Catantops acuticercus* Bolívar, 1902 was synonymized under *C. sacalava* (Dirsh and Uvarov 1953), but it appears unlikely that *Catantopsis* from Madagascar and India are the same; since *C. sacalava* is present in the Comoros and Juan de Nova, the author of this contribution considers that species to be endemic to the Malagasy Region.

[28] Generic position of *Mesambria* needs to be reevaluated.

[29] Old records of *Eyprepocnemis plorans* from Madagascar may correspond to this species (see Dirsh and Descamps 1968), which also occurs in the Comoros and Mascarenes (Hugel 2014).

[30] May have existed on La Réunion (Hugel 2014).

[31] Wrongly placed in Eumastacidae by Cigliano et al. (2020).

[32] The subspecies *Aiolopus t. thalassinus* (Fabricius, 1781) is mentioned from time to time in the literature concerning Madagascar (e.g., Johnsen 1991), but the status of *Aiolopus* from the Malagasy Region has extensively and convincingly been addressed by Hollis (1968) and to my knowledge, all *Aiolopus* from these islands belong to *A. t. rodericensis*.

[33] Ritchie (1982) mentioned a single specimen of *Gastrimargus verticalis verticalis* (Saussure, 1884) from Antananarivo in Berlin (Museum für Naturkunde Humboldt-Universtät) and pointed out that this record needed confirmation.

[34] Present on the Glorieuses and likely synonym of *Conipoda aldabrae* Saussure, 1899 (Parnaudeau et al. 2013).

[35] *Oxya humeralis* (Walker, 1870) is a synonym of *Oxya hyla* (Hugel 2014).

[36] *Pseudoschmidtia tridens* was described from a female, and *P. polychroma* (Descamp, 1971) from a male. Mating specimens collected in Marojejy indicate that these are conspecific. The author of this contribution therefore considers *P. polychroma* to be synonymous with *P. tridens* n. syn.

[37] *Zonocerus hova* (Saussure, 1899) is a synonym of *Z. e. elegans* (Thunberg, 1815) (Dirsh 1961). The original description of *Z. hova* from a single female mentions the species from Madagascar. The specimen labeled as a holotype of *Z. hova* is a male and has no associated locality information (Cigliano et al. 2020). The author of this contribution concurs with Dirsh's opinion that the locality in Saussure's work is likely erroneous (see Dirsh 1961: 397).

[38] This name is recorded in the Orthoptera Species File website (Cigliano et al. 2020) as a *nomen dubium* (the name may never have been published). In this website, it is under Oxyini, but the example in the available picture is clearly not a member of Oxyini.

[39] This species is described from Aldabra. One specimen labeled *Plangia ovalifolia* is in the Natural History Museum, London (BMNH) collection but needs confirmation (Cigliano et al. 2020).

[40] *Trigonidium nigritum* (Saussure, 1899) has the typical morphology of macropterous *T. cicindeloides* Rambur, 1838.

[41] This species, described from immature specimens, is likely a synonym of *Trigonidium cicindeloides* Rambur, 1838.

[42] This species is mentioned by Giglio-Tos (1907) from Moramanga, but this identification is very unlikely to be correct, as the species is apparently restricted to Ghana.

Madagascar is renowned for its tremendous biodiversity, and although Orthoptera is far from being comprehensively known, current information indicates that the island's orthopterans have high levels of diversity and endemism. As shown in Table 9.25, a total of 742 named taxa (including some geographic forms) from 725 species of Orthoptera are currently recorded from the island, including new geographic records and synonyms. The number of of Malagasy Orthroptera species represents ~14% of the number known from Africa. Herein, the term "Malagasy Region" is defined as including Madagascar and the nearby Comoro, Mascarene, and Seychelles archipelagoes, as well as some other nearby islands.

A BRIEF HISTORY OF MALAGASY ORTHOPTEROLOGY

Reports of orthopterans from Madagascar are relatively ancient. In a letter from 1617, Father D'Azevedo mentions their consumption by Malagasy people, and similar reports by other occidental visitors followed (Decary 1937). The first formal description of a new genus and a new species from Madagascar, that of *Aspidonotus spinosus* by Gaspard Auguste Brullé, dates back to 1835 (Figure 9.29a). Since that first account, scattered descriptions of Malagasy Orthoptera have been regularly published in short articles or monographic works not necessarily focusing on the island's Orthoptera and often with a broader geographic perspective (Coquerel 1848, 1861; Brunner von Wattenwyl 1878; Butler 1880; Brunner von Wattenwyl 1888; Redtenbacher 1891; Griffini 1893; Brunner von Wattenwyl 1895). The first work listing species of Orthoptera on Madagascar was by Snellen van Vollenhoven and Selys-Longchamps (1869), which was followed by others examining Phaneropterinae specifically (Karsch 1889) and all members of Orthoptera (Saussure 1891a, 1891b, 1899). Saussure (1899) listed 18 Grylloidea, 19 Tettioniidea, and 26 Caelifera from Madagascar.

After a peak of new descriptions by the end of the 19th century, new Orthoptera species have been regularly named from Madagascar but at a slower pace (Figure 9.29b; Table 9.25). Regular publications on species from Madagascar have followed in the 20th century, mostly by authors working on restricted African or world groups of Ensifera, such as Bailey, Bolívar, Carl, Caudell, Chopard, Giglio-Tos, Griffini, Karny, and Ragge. The situation for Caelifera was very different (Figure 9.29b)—in addition to scattered publications examining various groups such as Tetrigoidea by Hancock and Rehn and other Acrididea by Bolívar, Brunner von Wattenwyl, Dirsh, Finot, Hollis, Rehn, Sjöstedt, Uvarov, and White, the three acridologists Marius Descamps, Vitaly Michailovich Dirsh, and Daniel Wintrebert focused on Malagasy Acrididea. Between 1962 and 1974, these authors provided extraordinary advances by describing 286 species or subspecies of Caelifera from Madagascar, corresponding to 35% of the island's fauna today. In addition, during that time, Klaus Günther's work on Tetrigidae and Keith Kevan's research on Acridoids further increased knowledge on Caelifera from Madagascar. By the end of the 20th century Henrik Devriese had started publishing on Malagasy Tetrigidae and Andrei V. Gorochov on Malagasy crickets.

The situation in the first portion of the 21th century slowly started to correct the apparent bias toward Caelifera, since most newly described Orthoptera during this period are in Ensifera (Gorochov 2001, 2004a, 2004b, 2005, 2006, 2014, 2015, 2017; Gorochov and Llorente 2004; Hugel 2012a, 2019; Massa 2017a, 2017b; Ünal and Beccaloni 2017; Heller et al. 2018, 2019).

DIVERSITY OF MALAGASY ORTHOPTERA

A total of 742 species and subspecies of Orthoptera have been recorded on Madagascar as of March 2020 (Table 9.25). Two thirds of these taxa belong to Caelifera (479), whereas one-third correspond to Ensifera (263). This larger species/subspecies diversity of Caelifera over Ensifera is quite unusual, as normally the world fauna of Orthoptera includes more Ensifera than Caelifera species (~55% vs. 45%, respectively; Cigliano et al. 2020), and the larger species diversity of Ensifera is even more pronounced in other areas of the Malagasy Region (S. Hugel, unpublished data). This apparent anomaly may be linked to the strong taxonomic coverage bias toward Caelifera resulting from the masterwork of Dirsh, Descamps, and Wintrebert (Figure 9.29b). Endemism of Malagasy Orthoptera is very high: 93% of the species are endemic to the island, and a few of those on the island occur elsewhere: 1.7% occur in the Malagasy Region, and 7% have a wider distribution in Africa and/or in the world (Table 9.26).

POSSIBLE ORIGINS OF ORTHOPTERA IN THE MALAGASY REGION

The diversity of species harbored on islands of the Malagasy Region is directly linked to the geological history of these landmasses. On the one hand, Madagascar and the granitic Seychelles are of continental origin as part of the Gondwana continent—Indo-Madagascar-Seychelles rifted from Africa during the Jurassic (~160–117 million years ago [Mya]), and this island conglomerate broke up into Madagascar, the Seychelles, and India around the Cretaceous-Paleogene boundary (~66 Mya) (Kusky et al. 2007). Therefore, species currently present on Madagascar and the Seychelles may descend either from those already present on these landmasses at Gondwana breakup, or from ancestors that dispersed overwater. On the other hand, the Mascarenes, Comoros, Iles Eparses, and outer islands of the Seychelles are volcanic in origin, the underlining basis for the growth of coral. These coralline islands are more recent, dating mostly to the Neogene and Quaternary (23 Mya to very recent). Species on these islands are certainly the result of overwater dispersal of their ancestors. For species on islands with low elevation, this dispersal cannot be older than the end of the last rise in sea level and the islands' associated last submersion, which dates to the Pleistocene interglacial period.

Fossils of the two suborders of Orthoptera have been recorded from the end of the Permian and Early Triassic periods (Jarzembowski 1999; Béthoux et al. 2002). A single fossil of Orthoptera has been described from Madagascar; it belongs to Elcanidea, an extinct group of Ensifera (Béthoux and Nel 2002). Although this fossil is not dated, it most likely pre-dates the breakup of Gondwana. The few ensiferan fossils (Cigliano et al. 2020) and analyses available (Vincente et al. 2017; Allegrucci and Sbordoni 2019)

FIGURE 9.29 **Orthoptera, taxonomic progress. A) The holotype of *Aspidonotus spinosus*, the first orthopteran formally described from Madagascar (repository: MNHN, Paris). B) Graph of the history of new species and subspecies descriptions on Madagascar. Note the peak of Caelifera descriptions was between 1960 and 1980. Ensifera, Gryllidea: C) the mole cricket *Gryllotalpa parva*, from Maroantsetra; D) undescribed cricket of genus *Malgasia* from Montagne d'Ambre; E) undescribed cricket of genus *Paragryllodes* from Montagne d'Ambre; F) the cricket *Fryerius amplocellatus* from Montagne d'Ambre. Ensifera, Stenopelmatoidea: G) the raspy cricket *Echidnogryllacris sanguinolenta*, from Marojejy; H) undescribed king cricket of genus *Spizaphilus* from Maromizaha.** (PHOTOS by S. Hugel.)

TABLE 9.26. **Orthoptera diversity and endemism on Madagascar**

SUBORDER	INFRAORDER, SUPERFAMILY	NUMBER OF SPECIES/+ SUBSPECIES	NUMBER OF SPECIES/+SUBSPECIES ENDEMIC TO MADAGASCAR	NUMBER OF SPECIES/+SUBSPECIES ENDEMIC TO SOUTHWESTERN INDIAN OCEAN ISLANDS
Caelifera	Acrididea, Tetrigoidea	74/74	72/72	0/0
	Acrididea, Acridomorpha	389/403	367/382	10/13
	Tridactylidea	2/2	1/0	0/0
Ensifera	Gryllidea	106/106	87/88	1/2
	Tettigoniidea	158/161	149/152	1/2

Note: Numbers indicate: number of species/number of species + subspecies.

suggest that diversification of some extant cricket families occurred mostly after Indo-Madagascar-Seychelles rifted from Africa. For Caelifera, ancient-most fossils of Eumastacidae are from the period of the Indo-Madagascar-Seychelles rift from Africa. The diversification of Acrididae occurred during the Cenozoic (Song et al. 2018), after the separation of Madagascar, the Seychelles, and India. The Gondwana breakup may therefore have isolated ancestors of extant higher-rank taxonomic groups to Madagascar. Molecular phylogenies focused on Orthoptera of the Malagasy Region are being conducted to reliably propose such biogeographic scenarios (B. Warren et al., unpublished data).

Species with Wide Geographic Distribution in Africa and/or the World

Some species of Orthoptera are common in artificial habitats or those modified by human activities. On Madagascar, the cosmotropical house cricket *Gryllodes sigillatus* is present in most cities and villages from Antananarivo to the coasts. The minute scaly cricket *Cycloptiloides orientalis* has recently spread in houses in the Malagasy Region; it was collected on La Réunion in 2002 by Jacques Rochat, is now known from the Comoros and the Mascarenes, and has been found in houses in Antananarivo (S. Hugel, unpublished data). A possibly distinct subspecies of the African field cricket *Gryllus bimaculatus* occurs on Madagascar in and close to agricultural areas from the Central Highlands to the coasts. The Trigonidinae crickets *Natula longipennis* and *Trigonidium cicindeloides* are very widespread at middle and low elevations in rice fields, as well as in modified marshes and estuaries; *T. cicindeloides* occurs in drier habitats as well.

Few taxa of grasshoppers having a wide distribution in Africa (and sometime in Asia too) occur on Madagascar; these are mostly species found in grasslands and never in forests, contributing to the issue of the antiquity of these habitats in the island (Bond et al. 2008; Vorontsova et al. 2016; see Lehmann et al., pp. 152–68). For example, the following species/subspecies occur in mesohydrophilic or hydrophilic habitats (Descamps and Wintrebert 1966; Dirsh and Descamps 1968; Braud et al. 2014): the plague locust *Nomadacris septemfasciata*, *Duronia chloronota chloronota*, *Paracinema tricolor tricolor*, and *Oxya hyla*. The last two are more hydrophilic and present around virtually all rice fields. The plague locust *Locusta migratoria migratorioides* occurs in mesophilic habitats (Braud et al. 2014). Molecular data suggest that the Malagasy Region populations of this species might be distinct (Chapuis et al. 2008; and see also discussion in Hugel 2014). The grasshoppers *Cyrtacanthacris tatarica tatarica* and *Acrotylus patruelis* occur in more xerophilous habitats of Madagascar.

All these species have wide distributions, at least in tropical Africa. It is therefore very difficult to define these taxa as introduced or not, since they may well have reached the island before the first human colonization; however, they have clearly benefited from human-driven habitat modifications. Importantly, this chapter does not address the following few species that are considered to have widespread distributions throughout Africa but occur in the Malagasy Region as endemic subspecies: *Brachytrupes membranaceus colosseus*, *Pteronemobius heydenii madagascariensis*, *Aiolopus thalassinus rodericensis*, *Gastrimargus africanus madagascariensis*, *Atractomorpha acutipennis acutipennis*, and *Leptacris monteiroi hova*. Should these taxa prove to be significantly distinct from their continental counterpart, that would be consistent with their initial colonization of the island before humans arrived.

Species/Subspecies with Wide Geographic Distribution in the Malagasy Region

Among the 742 species and subspecies of Orthoptera currently recorded on Madagascar, 12 have a distribution that includes only other islands in the Malagasy Region (Table 9.25). Some orthopterans, such as the highly variable grasshopper subspecies *Aiolopus thalassinus rodericensis*, occur on virtually all islands and islets of the Mascarene, Comoro, and Seychelles archipelagoes, as well as the Iles Eparses and Madagascar (Chopard 1957, 1958; Dirsh 1963; Dirsh and Descamps 1968; Hollis 1968; Matyot 1998; Parnaudeau et al. 2013; Hugel 2014). The grasshopper *Gastrimargus africanus madagascariensis* occurs in the Comoros, La Réunion, and Madagascar (Chopard 1958; Dirsh and Descamps 1968; Hugel 2014), mostly in grasslands maintained by fires. The bush cricket *Eurycorypha prasinata* is widespread on all four islands of the Comoros and Madagascar, as well as Mauritius, where it has settled in recent years (Brunner von Wattenwyl 1878; Karsch 1889; Chopard 1958; Massa 2017a, 2017c; Heller et al. 2019; Krištín et al. 2019; S. Hugel, unpublished data; Figure 9.30c).

Nevertheless, most of the species occurring on both Madagascar and other islands in the Malagasy Region have a distribution restricted to islands close to Madagascar, such as the Comoros and/or the Iles Eparses—*Catantopsis malagassus* and *C. sacalava* occur on Madagascar, the Comoros, and the Iles Eparses; *Conipoda calcarata*, *Oedaleus virgula*, *Acrida madecassa*, and *Rhadinacris schistocercoides* occur on Madagascar and the Iles Eparses; *Gymnobothrus madacassus*, *Pamphagella comoroensis*, and *Stictogryllacris conspersa* occur on Madagascar and the Comoros (Chopard 1958; Viette 1967; Dirsh and Descamps 1968; Parnaudeau et al. 2013; S. Hugel, unpublished data).

Taxa Endemic to Madagascar or the Malagasy Region

The rate of endemism of Malagasy Orthoptera is high: 93% of the species (674/724) are known only from the island. This rate reaches 94% when subspecies are taken into account (694/742). A total of 295 genera of Orthoptera are currently recorded from Madagascar, of which 75% are restricted to the Malagasy Region and 70% are endemic to Madagascar. Some groups contain only endemic genera. For example, all genera and species of Malagasy king crickets (family Anostostomatidae) are endemic to Madagascar, the Comoros, and the Iles Eparses. Some endemic genera contain a large number of species and subspecies, suggesting possible radiations. Six endemic genera of Caelifera and two of Ensifera include at least 10 species and subspecies each (Cigliano et al. 2020). Of the six, most of the Caelifera genera belong to the subfamily Pseudoschmidtiinae: *Tetefortina*, *Apteropeoedes*, *Wintrebertia*, and *Pseudoschmidtia* (Figure 9.31g); one belongs to the family Pyrgomorphidae: *Caprorhinus*; and one to Tetrigoidea: *Thymochares*. The two genera of Ensifera endemic to the Malagasy Region and comprising more than 10 species or subspecies each are the crickets *Malgasia* and the Euconchophorini katydids of the genus *Odontolakis*.

FIGURE 9.30 **Ensifera, Tettigoniidae: A) female of *Parasimodera saussurei* from Betampona; B) male holotype of *Malagasyphisis maromizaha*, from Maromizaha; C) male of *Eurycorypha prasinata* from Maroantsetra; D) paratype female of *Toliaridectes antsycurvis* in oviposition, from Toliara; E) *Odontolakis varia*, which lives mostly on Bambusoidea, from Marojejy; F) the large Euconchophorini *Oncodopus zonatus*, from the Makay; G) *Episattus marmoratus* from Marojejy. H) Spectrogram of a soundscape recording from the Marojejy Massif and Camp Mantella. In this sequence, the soundscape is dominated by the continuous call of *Aethiomerus madagassus* (peaking at 8 kHz) and short calls of *Episattus marmoratus* (peaking at 16 kHz).** (PHOTOS by S. Hugel.)

Consistent with its long isolation, Madagascar harbors endemic taxa of higher rank; these often include the above-mentioned species-rich genera. Within Caelifera, most of the tribes of Euschmidtiidae and the whole subfamily Miraculinae are endemic to Madagascar (Descamps 1965; Descamps and Wintrebert 1965; Descamps 1969, 1971).Within Ensifera, Malgasiinae contains only 15 species of *Malgasia* (Figure 9.29d; Chopard 1948, 1949, 1958; Gorochov 1984, 2014; Cigliano et al. 2020). Another clade of Ensifera, the tribe Euconchophorini, currently includes six genera known only from Madagascar and/or other islands in the Malagasy Region (Gorochov 1988; Ünal and Beccaloni 2017; Figures 9.30e and f).

Interestingly, many of these endemic subfamilies, tribes, or genera display reduced wings and might be regarded as a manifestation of an insularity syndrome. Indeed, species of Malgasiinae and Miraculinae are apterous, *Caprorhinus* are micropterous, Euschmidtiidae are at most brachypterous, and many members of Euconchophorini are apterous, micropterous, or brachypterous.

Taxa Apparently Lacking on Madagascar

Some Orthoptera species having a wide distribution, including some that are also present on certain islands of the Malagasy Region, are apparently lacking on Madagascar. This is the case, for example, for *Xipidiopsis lita*, which has rapidly colonized the Seychelles and the Mascarenes during the past 20 years (Hugel 2010). It is also the case for the large grasshopper *Afroxyrrhepes*

FIGURE 9.31 **Caelifera: A) the pygmy mole cricket *Afrotridactylus madecassus*, which lives near streams in the Makay; B) the pygmy grasshopper *Notocerus formidabilis*, from Marojejy; C) the milkweed grasshopper *Phymateus saxosus*, from Ankalalahana; D) the grasshopper *Vohemara hysielloides* feeding on Nolinoidea plants at Marojejy; E) the grasshopper *Gastrimargus africanus madagascariensis* at Ambohitantely; F) the plague locust *Nomadacris septemfasciata* at Ambohitantely; G) the monkey grasshopper *Pseudoschmidtia tridens*, Pseudoschmidtiinae, from Marojejy; H) mating pair of the monkey grasshopper *Acronomastax curvicerca*, Miraculinae, at Marojejy.** (PHOTOS by S. Hugel.)

procera, which occurs in continental Africa and the Comoros but is not recorded on Madagascar. The case of *Diabolocatantops axillaris saucius* is similar; it is present in continental Africa, the Iles Eparses, Aldabra, and all islands of the Comoros, and has probably settled temporarily on La Réunion in the past but is not recorded from Madagascar (Chopard 1958; Parnaudeau et al. 2013; Hugel 2014).

Some higher-ranking taxa with near worldwide distribution are unknown on Madagascar—for example, Rhaphidophoridae, which occurs in South Africa (Cigliano et al. 2020) and the Seychelles (A. Hochkirch, unpublished data). The apparent lack of Rhaphidophoridae on Madagascar is puzzling since that group is particularly diversified in the Southern Hemisphere, and this diversification is at least partly explained by the Gondwanan fragmentation (Allegrucci and Sbordoni 2019). Should the absence of the Rhaphidophoridae on Madagascar be real, it could be explained by the scenario proposed by Allegrucci and Sbordoni (2019) involving several regional extinctions.

The cricket subfamily Eneopterinae is also unknown from Madagascar, although the group occurs in the east of continental Africa, South America, Australia, and Asia (Cigliano et al. 2020). The current distribution of this subfamily is explained by vicariance after the breakup of Gondwana and more recent overwater dispersal (Vicente et al. 2017). Among African Caelifera, the families Lentulidae and Pneumoridae occur in southern Africa but are apparently absent on Madagascar.

Some ancient Orthoptera lineages are apparently restricted to young volcanic islands in the Malagasy Region and currently are unknown from Madagascar. These lineages must have evolved on other landmasses before the emergence of these volcanic islands. Therefore, this casts doubt on the possible occurrence of these lineages on Madagascar too, since it is currently the closest emerged landmass of continental origin. This is the case, for example, with the grasshopper family Pyrgacrididae, which diversified early from other members of Acridoidea (Leavitt et al. 2013) and contains only two species, both occurring in the Mascarenes (Descamps 1968; Hugel 2005, 2015). The presence of a Pyrgacrididae lineage on Madagascar as a source for ancestors of Mascarene species may therefore be expected. Interestingly, an alternative scenario involving now-submerged large landmasses of continental origin could explain these distributions and has been proposed for other groups such as the Dodo (*Raphus cucullatus*) and the Rodrigues Solitaire (*Pezophaps solitaria*) (Warren et al. 2010; Shapiro et al. 2002). Of course, the apparent absence of some taxa on Madagascar may simply be linked to insufficient sampling. For example, some members of the Tettigoniidae tribes, specifically Phisidini (Hugel 2012a; Figure 9.30b) and Arytropteridini (Hugel 2019; Figure 9.30d), were only recently found on the island (Hugel 2012a, 2019).

FAUNISTICS AND TAXONOMY OF MALAGASY ORTHOPTERA

A few research teams have published on Malagasy Orthoptera in recent decades, improving knowledge of some groups such as Podoscirtidae (see above section on History of Malagasy Orthopterology). As pointed out above, the currently known diversity of Malagasy Caelifera is greater than that of the Ensifera, likely owing to a bias in past taxonomic biases in field collecting and the research interests of systemacists but also resulting from a disproportionate amount of daytime collecting in nonpristine habitats. Since diversity in Ensifera is usually greater than in Caelifera, there may be a large number of ensiferans yet to be discovered on Madagascar. This is confirmed by unpublished data from numerous field surveys conducted since 2017 across the island (S. Hugel, unpublished data). It is worth mentioning that most of the undescribed species found during these inventories have been strictly nocturnal members of Ensifera living in intact forests and spotted with a headlamp. Most of these species are not attracted to light traps and are rarely collected using standard active methods conducted during the day hours. These field surveys, for example, revealed that Madagascar is a major center of diversity for Pentacentrinae crickets, with at least 20 species new to science yet to be described, whereas only two species are currently recorded on the island. Nocturnal Nemobiinae crickets are also distinctly more diversified on Madagascar than the eight species currently recorded would suggest, and tens of species are awaiting description, mostly from lowland and medium-altitude moist evergreen forests. Regarding Phalangopsidae and Gryllacrididae crickets, most forested areas harbor micropterous species that have been overlooked and possibly confused with subadults. Anostostomatidae also displays a very wide diversity, and several tens of species from this group remain to be named.

More general taxonomic issues on taxa of higher rank also need examination. Within Ensifera, the tribe Euconchophorini was erected within Conocephalinae to include five genera endemic to Madagascar and/or the Malagasy Region (Gorochov 1988), and a new, sixth genus (*Oncodopus*) was added in 2017 (Ünal and Beccaloni 2017). The genera currently included in Euconchophorini, as well as the criteria defining the tribe, need to be reviewed. Indeed, other Malagasy genera currently in different tribes, including Agraeciini, Conocephalini, and even Copiphorini, fit with the characters currently defining Euconchophorini. As pointed by out by Krištín et al. (2019), Agraeciini and Euconchophorini form a complex, and work is needed to understand the relationships between African, Oriental, Australian, and Malagasy species. Within Caelifera, the higher classification of some groups on Madagascar needs to be reviewed, for example, Hemiacridinae and Catantopinae, which have recently proven to be paraphyletic clades (Song et al. 2018).

Zoogeography of Malagasy Orthoptera

Zoogeography of Malagasy Caelifera has been very briefly discussed by various authors. For Caelifera, it has been pointed out that Madagascar harbors a quite distinct fauna when compared to both Africa and Oriental areas (Dirsh and Descamps 1968; Wintrebert 1972). Wintrebert pointed out that micropterous and brachypterous members of Catantopinae occurring in the northwest of Madagascar had clear African affinities (Wintrebert 1972). However, most authors mentioned Oriental affinities for many groups of Malagasy Caelifera, such as Hemiacridinae (Dirsh and Descamps 1968), and other members of Acridoidea (Dirsh and Descamps 1968; Wintrebert 1972). Within Caelifera, Paulian (1961a) considered members of Malagasy Tetrigoidea to have "Indo-African" affinities.

Few authors have discussed the zoogeography of Malagasy Ensifera. Gorochov (2005) proposed that at least nine out of the 15 genera of Malagasy Podoscirtidae descended from a single African colonist and that few other genera may have a more Oriental origin. Karny discussed the origins of Gryllacrididae, reaching similar conclusions—few Malagasy species groups or genera are shared with Africa, others are shared with the Oriental region, and all other groups are endemic to Madagascar or the Malagasy Region (Karny 1931). Paulian (1961a) was less balanced and considered the Oriental affinities of Malagasy Gryllacrididae as obvious. Few groups occur only in the Australian area and Madagascar, as is the case, for example, of leaf-mimicking katydids of the tribe Simoderini (Figure 9.30a). However, all these early works used morphological characters to discuss biogeographic affinities of Orthoptera from Madagascar with respect to other areas. Molecular phylogenies are required to test these hypothesis.

DISTRIBUTION OF ORTHOPTERA ON MADAGASCAR

Species Widely Distributed on Madagascar

Most of the Orthoptera species having a wide distribution in Africa and the Malagasy Region also have a broad distribution on Madagascar. This is particularly the case for synanthropic species living in and around human built structures—particularly cricket species—and species associated with agricultural areas, which are mostly grasshoppers. Some of these are considered to be ubiquitous species, such as the locust *Cyrtacanthacris tatarica*, which occurs across the island (Descamps and Wintrebert 1966).

Few endemic species are widely distributed on Madagascar—most have very narrow distributions with relatively low species overlap across sampling sites (Krištín et al. 2019; S. Hugel, unpublished data). Most endemic forms with broad distributions are grasshoppers associated with grasslands (Descamps and Wintrebert 1966; Dirsh and Descamps 1968; Braud et al. 2014). Their current distributions probably have been expanded by human activities associated with habitat degradation. Available data suggest that very few endemic forest-dwelling orthopteran species have broad geographic ranges on the island. Among grasshoppers, species with wide distributions across most habitats include *Finotina ranavaloae* and *F. radama*.

Species from Grasslands

Grasslands of various types are widespread in Madagascar, and their antiquity and the nature of certain types of formations have been subjects of considerable discussion (Bond et al. 2008; Crowley and Samonds 2013; Godfrey and Crowley 2016; Vorontsova et al. 2016). These grasslands harbor a diversity of grasshoppers, including species with a wide African distribution (e.g., *Locusta migratoria*, *Nomadacris septemfasciata*, *Paracinema tricolor*). Interestingly, some of these species occur on Madagascar and other areas in the Malagasy Region as distinct endemic subspecies (e.g., *Leptacris monteiroi hova*, *Gastrimargus africanus madagascariensis*, *Aiolopus thalassinus rodericensis*) or as populations genetically distinct from their continental counterpart (*Locusta migratoria*, see Chapuis et al. 2008). A significant proportion of grasshopper species from Malagasy grasslands are endemic species belonging to genera also occurring in Africa (e.g., *Acrotylus aberrans*, *Oedaleus virgula*, *Eyprepocnemis smaragdipes*, *Acrida subtilis*).

Finally, some genera are endemic to Madagascar (e.g., *Pycnocrania*, *Finotina*, *Rhadinacris*, *Chromacrida*), and their occurrence in grasslands would be consistent with the nonanthropogenic origin of some of these formations. However, many of these endemic taxa do not occur in fully open grasslands and clearly prefer Poaceae-dominated habitats scattered with shrubs and bushes (Descamps and Wintrebert 1966; Braud et al. 2014). Some of these endemic taxa are nevertheless clearly associated with open grasslands, including some maintained by fire. For example, *Leptacris monteiroi* occurs on Madagascar as an endemic subspecies (*L. m. hova*), and in South Africa the nominal subspecies is known to be associated with savannas maintained by artificial fires with low-intensity mesoherbivore grazing (van der Plas and Olff 2014). In the same manner, *Gastrimargus africanus* occurs on Madagascar as an endemic subspecies (*G. a. madagascariensis*, Figure 9.31e) that is able to display chromatic adaptations to burned environments (Rowell 1970). Although these observations might be consistent with a nonanthropogenic origin of grasslands, research is clearly needed for more reliable data on grasshoppers that could be overlaid with different types of grasslands. In this context, assessing the level of endemism of grasshoppers associated with fire-maintained versus grazing grasslands would be very interesting.

Patterns of Geographic Distribution

Although current knowledge on the distribution of Malagasy Orthoptera is far from comprehensive, occurrence and diversity of most groups appear to follow the well-defined ecoregions of Madagascar (Burgess et al. 2004). Many groups occur in all ecoregions, such as the Podoscirtidae crickets, the Phaneropterinae katydids, and Agraeciini and Euconchophorini (S. Hugel, unpublished data). By contrast, some groups seem less diverse or even absent from whole ecoregions. For example, the katydids of the tribes Phisidini and Simoderini are apparently restricted to humid and subhumid forest ecoregions. The Phalangopsidae crickets (Figure 9.29e) are also mostly diversified in these two ecoregions, with a few occurrences in the dry deciduous forest ecoregion. In leaf litter, the diversity of Nemobiinae crickets is high in humid forests and subhumid forest ecoregions and decreases in drier ecoregions—few species are found in dry deciduous forests, and even fewer in succulent woodland and spiny thicket ecoregions, where Nemobiinae is replaced by Mogoplistidae.

In contrast, some groups appear restricted to the succulent woodland and spiny thicket ecoregions, such as Arytropteridini bush crickets (Figure 9.30d; Hugel 2019). Among Euschmidtiidae grasshoppers, Descamps indicated that some tribes display very distinctive distributions: Lobomastacini is typical of eastern Madagascar; Cryptomastacini of dry deciduous forests, including in the Comoros; Symbellini of the north and the Comoros; and Wintrebertini of spiny thickets (Descamps 1971). He also pointed out that the proportion of species that are subapterous and/or have striated eyes was low in the east and high in the south and southwest (Descamps 1971); these characteristics may distinguish lineages and/or adaptations to distinct ecological conditions.

Associations with Plants

Various taxa of Orthoptera are frequently observed standing and/or feeding in the same plant types. For example, species of grasshoppers in the family Eumastacidae are often stenophagous—feeding on a limited number of plant types. Descamps and Wintrebert (1965) pointed out that food plants of Pseudoschmidtiinae species are often fragrant and/or gland-bearing. Although strict associations with a single plant species are uncommon in Orthoptera in the Malagasy Region (Hugel 2014; Warren et al. 2016), some taxa appear to be preferentially associated with monocots. This is the case, of course, for many Acrididea groups living in grasslands (Descamps and Wintrebert 1966). It is also the case for katydid forest species, such as most Euconchophorini genera with extended vertex, as well as some very close genera currently in Agraeciini. In Euconchophorini, all katydids of the genus *Odontolakis* occur on monocots, many on plants of the Palmacae and Pandanacae families, with species such as *O. sexpunctata* occurring on *Ravenala* and even on banana trees (Musaceae) in agroforestry areas (Chopard 1951; S. Hugel, unpublished data). The same holds true for *Odontolakis* in the Comoros. However, a few species are also found on bamboos (see Vorontsova et al., pp. 585–98), such as *O. varia* (Figure 9.30e) and the *Odontolakis* species from Mahé in the Seychelles. Within Euconchophorini, the large katydids of the genus *Amblylakis* are found mostly within large patches of *Ravenala*, and several species of *Euconchophora* are usually observed on bamboos.

Some grasshoppers are also found mostly on monocots—for example, certain genera of Hemiacridinae with long vertex (*Acutacris*, *Galideus*, etc.) can often be found in bamboo. Some genera currently included in Catantopinae, such as *Vohemara* (Figure 9.31d), are usually observed on Nolinoidea plants, such as *Dracaena*; and to a lesser extent, some species of *Procytettix*, placed in Metrodorinae, are often seen in understory bamboo. Some grasshopper groups, such as Pyrgomorphidae, are often observed on supposedly toxic plant species. For example, the colorful *Phymateus saxosus* (Figure 9.31c) feeds on various plant species, including milkweeds (family Apocynaceae), and is therefore expected to be toxic. In Malagasy this species is called the "dog's grasshopper" (*valalan'alika*), and a proverb states that "even dogs won't eat it."

CONTRIBUTION OF MALAGASY ORTHOPTERA TO SOUNDSCAPES

Very little has been published on bioacoustics of Malagasy Orthoptera (Heller et al. 2018; Hugel 2019), although this order is renowned for its extensive use of acoustic and/or vibratory communication. The Malagasy names for katydid, *kiangily*, and cricket, *sakoriri*, are often said to be onomatopoeic, mimicking the calls.

Interestingly, virtually no members of Caelifera on Madagascar produce stridulations. Even macropterous Malagasy members of Hemiacridinae, which elsewhere in Africa display a series of transverse stridulatory veinlets on the radial area of the forewings, lack or have strongly reduced specializations for sound production. Whereas many Old World members of Gomphocerinae use acoustic communication, I am not aware of calls produced by the few Malagasy representatives of this subfamily. Nevertheless, some grasshoppers produce a crepitation sound when escaping by flight (e.g., *Gastrimargus*, *Locusta*). Therefore, on Madagascar as on other islands of the Malagasy Region, virtually all singing orthopterans belong to Ensifera. Since the majority of Malagasy ensiferans are nocturnal, most singing members of Orthoptera call by night. However, *Eurycorypha prasinata* (Figure 9.30c), grassland species of Conocephalini, and many other cricket species from the leaf litter call by day too.

Some peculiarities of Madagascar's singing Ensifera are worth mention. Many tropical forests in the world harbor singing species of Nemobiinae in the leaf litter and of Trigonidiinae in higher plant strata; this is also the case in most Malagasy Region islands. By contrast, very few Nemobiinae on Madagascar have wings adapted for sound production (stridulation), and these animals are usually found on plant trunks and not on the ground. Very few members of Trigonidiinae occur on Madagascar, and the only species known to use acoustic communication is *Natula longipennis*, which occurs in modified wet environments and never in forests. Therefore, most species calling in leaf litter are Mogoplistidae and Gryllinae crickets.

At virtually all localities, few Gryllinae species call on or near the ground, and Podoscirtidae species call in elevated positions on plants. In moist evergreen forests with large trees, members of Phalangopsidae (*Paragryllodes*) call while standing on large trunks, often high in trees (Figure 9.29e). In sandy areas of the east, the large crickets of the genus *Brachytrupes* produce a loud song before and after sunset from the entrance of their burrow.

Curiously, it seems that there may be a tendency for the loss of acoustic communication in Malagasy crickets. For example, many species of Podoscirtidae are mute; very few forest species of Nemobiinae and no forest species of Trigonidinae are equipped for producing song; and many still-undescribed Phalangopsidae species are micropterous, having the appearance of juveniles and lacking sound-producing specializations. The calls of many katydids on Madagascar are in the range of ultrasound and out of human auditory capacity. This is the case for many members of Phaneropterinae, Phisidini (including *Malagasyphisis*, *Breviphisis*, and *Longiphisis*), and Listroscelidinae; and for most small species of Agraeciini and Euconchophorini with reduced wings (e.g., *Euconchophora*), and small species of Simoderini.

Over the past decade, systematic recordings of Malagasy Orthoptera, either directly in the field or in studio conditions, have captured the sounds of over 150 species (Figure 9.30h). These, together with systematic soundscape recordings across Madagascar, characterize singing orthopterans in the Malagasy soundscape, which in turn is a tool to monitor their populations in a noninvasive manner (S. Hugel, unpublished data).

ORTHOPTERA AND PEOPLE: AGRICULTURAL THREATS AND ENTOMOPHAGY

The grasshoppers known as locusts are among the few Malagasy Orthoptera species that represent a real threat to agriculture; two species of swarming locusts constitute a major threat: *Locusta migratoria* and *Nomadacris septemfasciata* (Braud et al. 2014; Figure 9.31f). These species display phase polymorphism—they can be either solitary or gregarious. These two forms display different morphologies and strikingly distinct behaviors. Swarms form only during the gregarious phase, resulting in damage to crops. For these locusts to switch from the solitary to the gregarious phases, a succession of peculiar climatic conditions and a high population density are required (Roy 1965; Darnhofer and Launois 1974; Lecoq and Mestre 1988). Other species of grasshoppers, specifically *Gastrimargus africanus* (Figure 9.31e) and *Paracinema tricolor*, can represent a moderate threat to agricultural crops. Interestingly, the bush cricket *Ruspolia differens* is renowned in continental Africa for swarming, its swarms flying during both day and night hours (McCrae 1982). The species, however, does not seem to swarm on Madagascar, although relatively high densities can sometimes be observed at night around lights at the Ivato airport.

Swarms of locusts have been reported on Madagascar by occidental visitors since the 17th century (Camboue 1886; Decary 1937). These reports also mentioned that locusts were eaten and prepared in various ways, often killed in boiling water and either directly consumed fried, or sun-dried and ground into a powder that was stored for future consumption.

Recent fieldwork by the team of the Madagascar Biodiversity Center documented 37 species of Orthoptera being consumed in different areas of the island (Van Itterbeeck et al. 2019; Golden et al., pp. 204–17; Fisher and Hugel, pp. 218–30). Most of the species eaten are members of Caelifera, but some Ensifera species are also consumed. For example, the large *Brachytrupes* are considered a delicacy, known as *sahobaka*, and are often sold in markets in the northeast of the island. Orthopterans are therefore culturally important for the Malagasy people and are mentioned in many local proverbs.

CONSERVATION AND USE OF ORTHOPTERA TO MONITOR HABITAT QUALITY

Up to now, members of Orthoptera have not been extensively used to monitor habitat quality on Madagascar. However, these insects can represent valuable bioindicators even in tropical habitats of the Southern Hemisphere. For example, they have been used in the southern tropics to assess grassland habitat quality (Andersen et al. 2001; Bazelet and Samways 2011), and mammalian predation pressure (Watts et al. 2017). Acoustic monitoring of Orthoptera has proven to be a useful tool for following the evolution of forest restoration schemes in the Malagasy Region (Hugel 2012b). On Madagascar, a study using mostly sweeping of low vegetation strata shows a significant association between habitat management and orthopteroid species rareness (Krištín et al. 2019). These observations should encourage the use of Malagasy Orthoptera, either directly or using acoustics, to monitor restoration schemes and habitat quality.

Little is known about the threat to Malagasy Orthoptera associated with habitat changes. Extinction risk assessments of 83 species of Orthoptera occurring on Madagascar have been performed (IUCN 2020). These were mostly assessments of Tetrigoidea by Danielczak, Devriese and Hochkirch, and of few other species with a wide African distribution by Bazelet and Naskrecki or Hochkirch. As is not unexpected, 21% of the assessed species are Data Deficient, underlying the strong need for further faunistic work on Madagascar; 10% were assessed as Critically Endangered.

Nevertheless, it is clear that comprehensive knowledge of taxonomy, distribution, biology, and ecology are needed to meaningfully assess threats and extinction risks of Malagasy Orthoptera. This further highlights the strong need for research in both the field and laboratory to improve our knowledge of Orthoptera in the Malagasy Region.

ACKNOWLEDGMENTS

All the field surveys conducted over the last years would not have been possible without the kind support of the Malagasy people and the team at the Madagascar Biodiversity Center. I particularly thank Brian Fisher, associated in part with the project Insect and People of the Southwest Indian Ocean (IPSIO), and the Malagasy authorities and organizations for allowing my research.

Subject editors: Brian L. Fisher and Steven M. Goodman

COLEOPTERA: CICINDELIDAE, TIGER BEETLES

J. Moravec

Tiger beetles (Cicindelidae) are distributed almost all over the world. A considerable amount is known about their evolutionary history, ecology, biogeography, and diversity. For a broad overview on this family see Pearson and Vogler (2001), whose estimate of 2300 species in the family has increased over the past decades.

The tiger beetles of the Malagasy Region were revised recently (Moravec 2002a, 2007, 2010) and their taxonomy, nomenclature, and distribution are now well known. The tiger beetle fauna of Madagascar, with 233 currently recognized species, is one of the richest in the world. Moreover, there are nine endemic genera, and all species except for two are endemic to the island. Together, they represent a unique and rich fauna.

NOTES ON SYSTEMATICS AND NOMENCLATURE

A number of earlier revisions have been conducted (Jeannel 1946a; Horn 1934; Olsoufieff 1934; Rivalier 1967, 1970). The taxonomy and nomenclature, as well as the distribution of Malagasy tiger beetles, have significantly changed since Cassola's (2003) contribution in the precursor of this book. The most speciose genera, *Pogonostoma* and *Physodeutera*, have been subjects of monographs (Moravec 2002a, 2007), and all other genera in the region have been revised as well (Moravec 2010). Consequently, Malagasy tiger beetle genera are among the most well known of the Cicindelidae.

It must be noted here that Cicindelidae is maintained as a separate family not only because of the differences in adult morphology but also based on larval morphology (Cassola 2001; Pearson and Vogler 2001; Putchkov and Cassola 2005). An important molecular study with a mitogenome phylogeny of Adephaga, published by Lopéz-Lopéz and Vogler (2017), reveals Cicindelidae as a separate (sister) family to Carabidae. The subdivision within Cicindelidae used by Cassola (2003) is maintained here, yet the authorships of the family-group names are changed according to International Commission of Zoological Nomenclature regulations.

FAUNAL ANALYSIS, DISTRIBUTION, AND ENDEMISM

The tiger beetle fauna of Madagascar is one of the richest in the world. The number of species has increased considerably since the start of the 21st century, from the 175 species tabulated by Cassola and Pearson (2000) to the 203 species by Cassola (2003) and the 228 species in the most recent taxonomic revisions (Moravec 2002a, 2007, 2010);

further, an additional five species have been subsequently described as new to science (Moravec 2004; Moravec and Vybíral 2010, 2018; Moravec and Razanajaonarivalona 2015). Descriptions of other new species are in preparation. Consequently, the recognized tiger beetle taxa (species and subspecies) occurring on Madagascar, including the nearshore islands of Nosy Be, Nosy Boraha (Ile Sainte Marie), Nosy Mangabe, and the Nosy Radama archipelago, now comprises 251 species-group taxa (233 species and 18 subspecies). Because of ongoing deforestation, the continued existence of many species known only from their types and other historical specimens is uncertain.

It must be emphasized here that some specimen locality labels clearly disagree with the known occurrence of a given species and were evidently (some of them quite certainly) mislabeled, usually by insect dealers (Moravec 2002a, 2007, 2010). Consequently, because of this problem the distribution of several species may be partially incorrect. All of this is further complicated by certain recorded locality names having various spellings, as well as a shift from French names to Malagasy. This problem is in part addressed by Viette (1991), particularly for entomological collection localities; however, many other names, as well as the system of administrative division presented by Viette (1991), have changed in the past years. Some of the problematic locality names are associated with type localities mentioned by historical authors in original descriptions and/or written on specimen labels. Some place names were misinterpreted or incorrectly transcribed by collectors or insect dealers, and certain place names (e.g., Ambodirafia, Ambongo, Andranobe, which were also on the labels of type specimens) are repeated in various parts the island.

All species (both of endemic and widespread genera) are endemic to the Malagasy Region, which includes the Comoros, the Seychelles, the Mascarenes, and other islands (Moravec 2010), and more specifically to Madagascar. The exceptions are as follows: two species of the genus *Myriochila* have subspecies distributed on regional islands, one of which, *M.* (*Myriochila*) *perplexa perplexa*, also occurs on La Réunion; *M.* (*M.*) *p. aldabrica* on the Comoros and the Seychelles; and *M.* (*M.*) *p. rodriguensis* on Rodrigues. *M.* (*M.*) *trilunaris trilunaris* is endemic to Madagascar, and *M.* (*M.*) *t. mauritiana* occurs on Mauritius. *Myriochila* (*M.*) *trilunaris* was previously (Cassola 2003) considered to be a subspecies of a widespread (also Palearctic) species, *Myriochila* (*M.*) *melancholica*, and was later elevated to its current species status (Moravec 2008). Another nearly cosmopolitan genus, *Cylindera*, is represented in the Malagasy Region by only three subgenera, two of which, *Ifasina* and *Eugrapha*, are widespread, and only subgenus *Cicindelina* is endemic to the Malagasy Region. The six species of *Ifasina* and a single species of *Eugrapha* are endemic to Madagascar, while one of the two species of subgenus *Cicindelina* also occurs on the Comoros. Other widespread genera, *Calomera*, *Lophyra*, *Habrodera*, and *Chaetodera*, occur also in Asia and Africa. However, their Malagasy Region species are endemic to Madagascar, except for *Lophyra* (*L.*) *abbreviata*, which may also occur on Grande Glorieuse (Glorieuse archipelago), situated 140 km from the northwestern promontory of Madagascar (provided that the single examined specimen was not mislabeled).

The following nine genera are endemic to Madagascar: *Pogonostoma* (111 species, eight subspecies), *Physodeutera* (68 species, six subspecies), *Calyptoglossa* (one species), *Peridexia* (four species, three subspecies), *Waltherhornia* (two species), *Stenocosmia* (one species), *Paraphysodeutera* (one species), *Ambalia* (two species), and *Chaetotaxis* (11 species, one subspecies).

Nonendemic genera are also included in Table 9.27. However, their species are endemic to Madagascar (except for the controversial occurrence of the abovementioned *Lophyra* [*L.*] *abbreviata*). The genus *Prothyma* (subtribe Prothymina) occurs also in Africa and Asia, and in the Malagasy Region it is represented by a single species endemic to Madagascar. The nine species of the genus *Hipparidium* occur on Madagascar (other species of the genus occur in Africa and one species in Indonesia).

MORPHOLOGICAL CHARACTERS

Owing to the notably heterogeneous characters of species, the most speciose genus, *Pogonostoma* (Figures 9.32a–f), was subdivided into two subgenera by Jeannel (1946a), into seven subgenera by Rivalier (1970), and recently into 16 subgenera by Moravec (2007). Adults of the largest species, *P.* (*Macropogonostoma*) *caeruleum* (Figure 9.32a) may reach 24.5 mm in length, while the adult of the smallest, *P.* (*Microstenocera*) *perexiguum* (Figure 9.32f), is only 4.7 mm long. The second-most speciose genus, *Physodeutera* (subtribe Prothymina), which is broadly distributed across Madagascar, with the exception of the extreme south, is subdivided into eight subgenera (three of which are illustrated in Figures 9.32g–i). Males of the monobasic genus *Paraphysodeutera* (Figure 9.33e), which was recently described (Moravec 2002b) from Tsingy de Bemaraha, have uniquely foliate-dilated terminal antennomeres, while another monobasic genus, *Stenocosmia*, which is endemic to the dry deciduous forests of the west, possesses a notably elongate and slim body (Figure 9.33a), and the elytral surface has a rasp-like appearance. The two species of *Waltherhornia* are characterized by their elytral surface covered with catoptric patches and humps or foveae (Figure 9.32j). The genus *Ambalia* (Figure 9.32k) and other genera belong to the subtribe Cicindelina. In contrast to the African species of *Hipparidium*, which are well-delimited by their reliably distinguishing characters, Malagasy species represent an example of the island's enormous biodiversity under continuous evolutionary forces (the type species is in Figure 9.33i).

PHYLOGENY

As speculated previously (Moravec 2007, 2010), some Malagasy genera, such as *Physodeutera* and the Neotropical genus *Pentacomia*, may be of Gondwanan origin, as previously addressed by Jeannel (1946a) for Malagasy *Pogonostoma*. However, there are fundamental differences in chaetotaxy and other characters between *Physodeutera* (subtribe Prothymina) and *Pentacomia* (subtribe Odontocheilina). As mentioned by Rivalier (1967) and summarized by Moravec (2010), the endemic genera of subtribe Prothymina, *Peridexia* and *Physodeutera*, may be closely related. However, *Peridexia* is also very similar to the Neotropical genus *Pometon* (subtribe Odontocheilina). Moreover, *Peridexia hilaris* and *P. fulvipes* mimic a pompilid wasp, *Pogonius venustipennis*, of the hymenopterous family Psammocharidae. This coexistence, first published by Jeannel (1946a), was observed on several occasions during field trips to Madagascar, and the wasp was recently illustrated (Moravec 2010).

TABLE 9.27. **Checklist of Malagasy taxa of the family Cicindelidae with areas of distribution and records confirming location**

FAMILY CICINDELIDAE LATREILLE, 1802

Subfamily Collyrinae Brullé in Audouin & Brullé, 1834

Tribe Ctenostomatini Laporte de Castelnau, 1834

Genus *Pogonostoma* Klug, 1834

Subgenus *Eupogonostoma* Moravec, 2007

- *E. cylindricum cylindricum* Fleutiaux, 1899—Northeast: Masoala to Antongil Bay
- *E. cylindricum filum* Jeannel, 1946—Central Highlands: Moramanga; East: S of Toamasina to Midongy du Sud
- *E. angustum* Fleutiaux, 1902—North: Montagne d'Ambre, Montagne des Français
- *E. aureovirescens* Moravec, 2007—Sambirano: Antseva Ambobako (SE of Ambanja)
- *E. brevicorne* W. Horn, 1898—Sambirano: Nosy Be; West; Central; East

Subgenus *Bathypogonum* Jeannel, 1946

- *B. levigatum levigatum* W. Horn, 1908—North: Montagne d'Ambre; Northeast: Vohémar; West: Maevatanana
- *B. levigatum lucens* Rivalier, 1970—Sambirano: Nosy Berafia, Ambanja to Bealanana (near Tsaratanàna, Sofia Region)

Subgenus *Neopogonum* Moravec, 2007

- *N. comptum* Rivalier, 1970—North: Montagne d'Ambre
- *N. surdum* Rivalier, 1970—Northeast: "Antsirabe" (65 km SW of Vohémar)
- *N. perrieri* Fairmaire, 1900—North: Antsiranana, Sahafary; West: Maevatanana
- *N. wiesneri* Moravec, 2003—Sambirano: Nosy Be
- *N. hirofumii* Moravec, 2003—West: Ankarafantsika
- *N. kraatzi* W. Horn, 1894—Sambirano: Nosy Be, Maevarano River (Tsaratanàna Massif)

Subgenus *Parapogonum* Moravec, 2007

- *P. sericeum* Klug, 1835—North: Antsiranana; East; Central; Central Highlands; Southeast

Subgenus *Polypogonostoma* Moravec, 2007

- *P. vestitum* Fairmaire, 1900—West: from Maevatanana ("Becodia") southward to Zombitse, Isalo
- *P. simplex* W. Horn, 1905—West: Soalala
- *P. simile* Jeannel, 1946—West: Ampijoroa, Antsohihy (Bora), Mandritsara, Ankirihitra
- *P. cyanescens* Klug, 1835—Northeast to central east: from Vohémar to Tampina
- *P. viridipenne* Jeannel, 1946—Sambirano: Maromandia, Maevarano; West: Antsohihy, Bora
- *P. septentrionale septentrionale* Fleutiaux, 1903—North: Antsiranana, Montagne d'Ambre, Ankarana; Northeast: Vohémar
- *P. septentrionale auripenne* W. Horn, 1909—Sambirano: Nosy Berafia, Ambanja, Ramena River, Tsaratanàna
- *P. violaceum* Fleutiaux, 1902—North: Montagne d'Ambre, Ankarana, Montagne des Français; Northeast: Vohémar
- *P.* ssp. *fulgidipenne* Lesne, 1911—Sambirano: Ramena, Tsaratanàna, Maromandia; West: ? Marovoay

Subgenus *Macropogonostoma* Moravec, 2007

- *M. caeruleum caeruleum* (Laporte & Gory, 1835)—North; Sambirano; Northwest; East; Central Highlands; Southeast
- *M. caeruleum cupripenne* Lesne, 1911—Sambirano: Ramena River, ? "Antsabetsienne"; West: ? Marovoay

FAMILY CICINDELIDAE

Subgenus *Pogonostoma s. str.*

- *P. affine* W. Horn, 1893—Central Highlands: Anjozorobe, Antsihanaka; Central east: Ranomafana; ? West
- *P. violaceolevigatum* W. Horn, 1927—North: Montagne d'Ambre
- *P. sambiranense* Rivalier, 1965—Sambirano: Manongarivo Massif
- *P. peyrierasi* Rivalier, 1970—East: Antongil Bay; Central: Antsihanaka; Southeast: Mananjary
- *P. malleatum malleatum* Rivalier, 1970—East: Antongil Bay
- *P. malleatum ambanjense* Rivalier, 1970—Sambirano: Beangona Ambevy ("Vallé d'Antremabe, 400 m")
- *P. perroti* Rivalier, 1970—Central Highlands: Moramanga, Ambalavao, Andringitra
- *P. globicolle* Rivalier, 1970—Central Highlands: Mantasoa, Moramanga eastward to Andasibe, Fianarantsoa
- *P. chalybaeum* Klug, 1835—East: Mount Antampona, Maroantsetra, S to Tolagnaro; Central Highlands
- *P. rugosoglabrum* W. Horn, 1923—East: Mananara-Nord to Fenoarivo-Atsinanana; Central Highlands: Moramanga to Andasibe
- *P. propinquum* Rivalier, 1970—Central Highlands: Fianarantsoa, Ambalavao; Central east: Ranomafana
- *P. spinipenne* (Laporte & Gory, 1835)—East: Antongil Bay to Ranomafana, Vondrozo; Central Highlands; South: Tolagnaro
- *P. subtile* W. Horn, 1904—North: Antsiranana, Montagne d'Ambre
- *P. andranobense* Moravec, 2007—Central: Andranobe (now burned forest SE of Ambatondrazaka), Didy
- *P. abadiei* Rivalier, 1965—Central: Andranobe (now burned forest SE of Ambatondrazaka)
- *P. hamulipenis* W. Horn, 1934—Central Highlands: mostly Moramanga area; South: ? Tolagnaro
- *P. tortipenis* W. Horn, 1934—Central Highlands: mostly Moramanga area; Central east; Ranomafana
- *P. densepunctatum* Rivalier, 1970—Southeast: Vondrozo
- *P. heteropunctatum* Moravec, 2000—Central Highlands east: Andranobe (destroyed forest SE of Ambatondrazaka), Didy
- *P. subtiligrossum subtiligrossum* W. Horn, 1934—West: Baly Bay
- *P. subtiligrossum rufomaxillaris* Cassola & Andriamampianina, 1998—West: Kirindy Forest CNFEREF (Morondava); Southwest: Andranohinaly
- *P. subtiligrossum pacholatkoi* Moravec, 2003—West: Katsepy (Mahajanga)
- *P. externespinosum* W. Horn, 1927—North: Montagne d'Ambre, Montagne des Français
- *P. impressum* Rivalier, 1970—Central Highlands: Fianarantsoa; Central east: Ranomafana
- *P. subgibbosum* Moravec, 2000—Central Highlands: Manankazo-Ankazobe; East: Maromizaha (Analamazaotra Forest)
- *P. srnkai* W. Horn, 1893—Central Highlands: Ambositra; South: Betroka

FAMILY CICINDELIDAE

P. gibbosum Rivalier, 1970—Central Highlands: Lakato (SE of Moramanga); Southeast: Vondrozo
P. densisculptum Moravec, 2003—Central Highlands: Manankazo near Ankazobe
P. elegans (Brullé in Audouin et Brullé, 1834)—North; East; Central; Central Highlands; Southeast up to Tolagnaro
P. alluaudi W. Horn, 1898—Sambirano: Nosy Be; North: Antsiranana; East: Masoala, Antongil Bay, Fenoarivo-Atsinanana
P. praetervisum Moravec, 2005—East: Fenoarivo-Atsinanana; Moramanga to Analamazaotra, Ranomafana; Tolagnaro
P. rivalieri Moravec, 2005—Central Highlands: Antsirabe, Andringitra
P. atrorotundatum W. Horn, 1934—Sambirano: Ambanja, Ankaramy; West: Boriziny up to Miandrivazo
P. litigiosum Rivalier, 1970—Sambirano: Nosy Be, Nosy Berafia; North: Antsiranana; Northeast
P. majunganum Jeannel, 1946—Sambirano: Nosy Be, Nosy Berafia; West: Antsohihy to Antsalova
P. brullei (Laporte de Castelnau & Gory, 1835)—"Madagascar" (exact locality unknown)
P. differens Cassola & Andriamampianina, 2001—East: Andriantantely (south of Toamasina)
P. sudiferum Rivalier, 1965—North: Antsiranana, Montagne d'Ambre, Sahafary
P. ankaranense Deuve, 1986—North: Ankarana
P. meridionale Fleutiaux, 1899—South: Bekily, Imanombo, Ambovombe, Berenty; South: Ampasimpolaka

Subgenus *Transstenocera* Moravec, 2007
T. sikorai W. Horn, 1894—East: Mount Antampona, Antongil Bay, Nosy Boraha; Central: Antsihanaka

Subgenus *Dipogonum* Moravec, 2007
D. anthracinum (Laporte de Castelnau & Gory, 1835)—North; Sambirano; East: Antongil Bay, Nosy Boraha; Central Highlands

Subgenus *Sexpogonum* Moravec, 2007
S. microtuberculatum W. Horn, 1934—North: Antsiranana; Sambirano: Nosy Be, Ambanja; East: Maroantsetra

Subgenus *Mitopogon* Rivalier, 1970
M. ovicolle W. Horn, 1893—North: Antsiranana; East: Antongil Bay; Central Highlands east: Moramanga area
M. ranomafanense Moravec, 2007—Central east: Ranomafana

Subgenus *Microstenocera* Jeannel, 1946
M. basidilatatum W. Horn, 1909—North; Sambirano; Northwest: up to Ampijoroa
M. deuvei Moravec, 2000—Sambirano: Nosy Be, Ankaramy Manongarivo
M. propripenis Moravec, 2000—North: Marotaolana (Ankarana); Sambirano: Ambanja
M. maculicorne W. Horn, 1934—North: Montagne d'Ambre (other localities were not confirmed)
M. dolini Moravec, 2007—Sambirano: Nosy Be, Nosy Berafia; West: Tsingy de Bemaraha
M. excisoclavipenis W. Horn, 1934—East: Antongil Bay; Central east: Andasibe

FAMILY CICINDELIDAE

M. andrei Moravec, 1999—Central Highlands: Andranobe, Didy, Moramanga; Central east: Analamazaotra Forest
M. juergenwiesneri Moravec, 2007—Central east: Ranomafana
M. humbloti Rivalier, 1970—Central Highlands: Antsihanaka (Ambatondrazaka)
M. schaumi W. Horn, 1893—Northeast: Sambava, Andapa, Maroantsetra, Antongil Bay
M. mathiauxi Jeannel, 1946—East: Mananara-Nord, Soanierana Ivongo
M. parallelum W. Horn, 1909—West: Antsohihy (Bora Forest), Ankarafantsika, Mahajanga, Marovoay
M. horni Fleutiaux, 1899—East: Sambava, Antongil Bay, Fenoarivo-Atsinanana, Andriantantely
M. skrabali Moravec, 2000—Central Highlands: Lakato (SE of Moramanga); Central east: Analamazaotra Forest
M. andreevae Moravec, 2007—Central east: Ranomafana
M. fleutiauxi W. Horn, 1905—North: Antsiranana, Montagne d'Ambre, Ankarana
M. globulithorax Jeannel, 1946—North: Montagne d'Ambre, Ankarana; Sambirano including Nosy Be; West: Maevatanana
M. basale Fleutiaux, 1899—East: Antongil Bay, Mananara-Nord
M. rugosiceps Rivalier, 1970—Southeast: Vondrozo
M. beananae Rivalier, 1963—East: Masoala, Beanana (Rantabe), Maroantsetra, Antakotako
M. moestum Rivalier, 1970—East: Belalona (30 km SW of Sambava)
M. pusillum (Laporte de Castelnau & Gory, 1835)—North: Montagne d'Ambre; East: Vohémar to Fenoarivo-Atsinanana; West: Antsohihy
M. vybirali Moravec, 2000—Central Highlands: Manankazo-Ankazobe, Andranobe to Didy, Mandraka, Moramanga
M. laportei W. Horn, 1900—Unknown: "base of eastern plateau"
M. dohnali Moravec, 2000—North: Ambohitra Mountains, Montagne d'Ambre, Anivorano-Avatra (Ankarana)
M. inerme Jeannel, 1946—West: Soalala, Marovoay, Ankarafantsika, Mahajanga, Maevatanana
M. flavomaculatum W. Horn, 1892—Central Highlands: Mandraka, Antsihanaka; Central east: Andasibe-Mantadia.
M. noheli Moravec & Vybíral, 2018—Central Highlands east: Lakato near Ankasoka (SE of Moramanga)
M. zombitsynense Moravec & Vybíral, 2010—Southwest: Zombitse Forest 10 km NE of Sakaraha;
M. sawadai Moravec, 2007—Central east: Ranomafana
M. minimum Fleutiaux, 1899—East: Antongil Bay area.
M. levisculptum W. Horn, 1934—East: Mananara-Nord, Andasibe-Analamazaotra
M. pliskai Moravec, 2003—Central east: Ranomafana
M. sicardi W. Horn, 1927—North: Montagne d'Ambre
M. perexiguum Moravec, 2000—North: Marotaolana (Ankarana); Sambirano: Ambanja
M. parvulum Rivalier, 1970—North: Ankarana, Benavony Circle, Mahamasina
M. geniculatum Jeannel, 1946—Sambirano: Tsaratanàna Massif (Ambanja)

(continued overleaf)

TABLE 9.27. ***continued***

FAMILY CICINDELIDAE

M. fabiocassolai Moravec, 2003—East: Sandranantitra (NE of Toamasina)
M. janvybirali Moravec, 2007—West: Ambodimanga, Bora near Antsohihy (now totally burned forest)
Subgenus *Mantistenocera* Moravec, 2007
M. nigricans Klug, 1835—East: Antongil Bay, Mantadia; Central Highlands: Mandraka, Moramanga, Lake Alaotra
M. pallipes Rivalier, 1970—Central Highlands: Antsihanaka to Lake Alaotra
M. mocquerysi Fleutiaux, 1899—East: Masoala, Antongil Bay, Mananara-Nord, Lake Alaotra
M. zasterai Moravec, 2003—Central east: Ranomafana, Talatakely
M. delphinense Jeannel, 1946—Southeast: Tolagnaro
Subgenus *Microgeniatum* Rivalier, 1970
M. pseudominimum W. Horn, 1934—East: Antongil Bay; Central Highlands east: Didy, Analamazaotra, Lake Alaotra
M. flavopalpale Jeannel, 1946—Southeast: "Piton Saint Louis" N of Tolagnaro
M. infimum Rivalier, 1970—North: Analamerana 50 km S of Antsiranana
Subgenus *Hornogeniatum* Moravec, 2007
H. gladiator W. Horn, 1934—North: Montagne d'Ambre
Subgenus *Leptopogonum* Rivalier, 1970
L. phalangioide Rivalier, 1970—East: Fenoarivo-Antsinanana, Sandranantitra (NE of Taoamasina)
Subfamily Cicindelinae Latreille, 1802
Tribe Cicindelini Latreille, 1802
Subtribe Prothymina W. Horn, 1910
Genus *Prothyma* Hope, 1838
Subgenus *Prothyma s. str.*
P. radama (Künckel, 1887)—North; West; Central Highlands; East: Nosy Boraha; Southwest; Southeast
Genus *Stenocosmia* Rivalier, 1965
S. tenuicollis (Fairmaire, 1904)—West: Katsepy; Soalala, Kirindy Forest CNFEREF (Morondava), Ambongo (Besalampy)
Genus *Waltherhornia* Olsoufieff, 1934
W. speculifera (W. Horn, 1934)—South: Ampandandrava, Bekily, Betroka
W. skrabali Moravec, 2008—South: Ranohira, Isalo, Zombitse; Central Highlands: Camp Catta (Ambalavao); Southwest: Toliara
Genus *Paraphysodeutera* Moravec, 2002
P. naviauxi Moravec, 2002—West: Antsalova and Tsingy de Bemaraha, Andranopasazy Forest
Genus *Physodeutera* Lacordaire, 1843
Subgenus *Homospila* Rivalier, 1967
H. gigantea gigantea (W. Horn, 1913)—East: Fenoarivo-Atsinanana
H. gigantea lebisi (Jeannel, 1946)—East: Beanana (25 km E of Rantabe), Antongil Bay
Subgenus *Coeliphora* Rivalier, 1967
C. megalommoides (W. Horn, 1896)—Sambirano: Nosy Be; East: Mount Antampona, Nosy Boraha, Toamasina to Moramanga

FAMILY CICINDELIDAE

C. belalonensis Deuve, 1987—East: Belalona (30 km SW of Sambava toward Andapa)
C. taniae Moravec, 2002—Central east: Ranomafana village area
Subgenus *Axinomera* Jeannel, 1946
A. flagellicornis (W. Horn, 1897)—East: Andranofotsy, Mount Antampona, Antongil Bay area, Nosy Boraha
A. skrabali Moravec, 1999—East: Nosy Boraha
A. rectipenis (W. Horn, 1934)—North: Montagne d'Ambre; Sambirano: Nosy Berafia, Ramena River N of Ambanja
A. boraensis Moravec, 2000—West: Bora Forest near Antsohihy
A. vybirali Moravec, 2000—West: Bora Forest near Antsohihy
A. antsalovensis Moravec, 1999 —West: Antsalova (Bemaraha Plateau)
A. andriai (Rivalier, 1965)—North: Analamerana (50 km SE of Antsiranana)
A. pseudotrimaculata (W. Horn, 1934)—Sambirano: Nosy Berafia, Ramena River SE of Ambanja
A. horimichioi Moravec & Razanajaonarivalona, 2015—West: Tsingy de Bemaraha, Melaky, Andranopasazy Forest
A. dorri (Fleutiaux, 1899)—West: Bora, Maevatanana, Katsepy, Soalala, Andriba; Northeast: Mandritsara
Subgenus *Microlepidia* Rivalier, 1967
M. centropunctata (W. Horn, 1934)—Sambirano: Nosy Berafia, Antseva Ambobako (near Ambanja)
M. biguttula (Fairmaire, 1903)—North: Montagne d'Ambre; ? East: Ambodirafia
M. marginemaculata (W. Horn, 1934)—North: Montagne d'Ambre, Montagne des Français; Ankarana; Sambirano: Nosy Be
M. peyrierasi Rivalier, 1967—North: Ankarana
M. bucephala (W. Horn, 1900)—East: Mount Antampona, Antongil Bay, Mananara-Nord to Fahitrosy
M. virgulata (Fairmaire, 1904)—West: Namaroka (Ambongo Plateau)
M. punctipennis (Fairmaire, 1903)—West: Mahajanga, Katsepy, Soalala, Ankirihitra (Ambato Boeni)
M. rectolabialis (W. Horn, 1913)—North: Montagne d'Ambre
M. longilabialis Moravec, 2000—North: Marotaolana (Ankarana); Sambirano: Nosy Be, Nosy Berafia.
Subgenus *Toxoma* Rivalier, 1967
T. sikorai (W. Horn, 1896)—East: Mount Antampona, Fenoarivo-Antsinanana, Lake Alaotra, Moramanga, Andasibe
T. breviformis (W. Horn, 1904)—East: Antalaha, Antongil Bay
T. dubia (Mařan, 1942)—Northeast: Ampanefena (70 km S of Vohémar)
T. conturbata Moravec, 2002—Sambirano: Antseva-Ambobako (15 km SE of Ambanja, Ramena River)
T. sulcoprothoracica (W. Horn, 1913)—North: Antsiranana, Montagne d'Ambre
T. subtilevelutina (W. Horn, 1934)—Central Highlands: Mandraka; Southeast: Mananjary, Vondrozo
T. lobicornis lobicornis Moravec, 2000—Sambirano: Ankaramy (Manongarivo Massif)

FAMILY CICINDELIDAE

T. lobicornis nosybensis Moravec, 2000—Sambirano: Nosy Be

Subgenus *Diarrhiza* Jeannel, 1946

D. viridicyanea (Audouin et Brullé, 1839)—East: Sambava, Antongil Bay, Toamasina, Lake Alaotra, Moramanga, Andasibe

D. maxima (Fleutiaux, 1899)—Central Highlands: Andranobe, Fianarantsoa

D. janthina (Fairmaire, 1903)—West: from Mahajanga coastal area to Antsalova

D. natalia (W. Horn, 1934)—Central Highlands: Mandraka, Antsihanaka (Lake Alaotra); East: Andasibe-Mantadia

D. catalai (Jeannel, 1946)—Southeast: Vohilava, Vondrozo

D. alluaudi (Fleutiaux, 1903)—South: Isaka-Ivondro (30 km NW of Tolagnaro)

D. ranomafanensis Moravec, 2002—Central east: Ranomafana village

D. murzini Moravec, 2004—Central Highlands: Andringitra

D. tricolorata (W. Horn, 1934)—South: Ampandandrava, Bekily, Betroka, Analavelona Forest (near Sakaraha)

Subgenus *Physodeutera s. str.*

P. adonis (Laporte de Castelnau, 1835)—West: Maevatanana; East: Fenoarivo-Atsinanana, Lake Alaotra

P. bellula (Fleutiaux, 1886)—East: Toamasina, Sandranantitra

P. consimilis Moravec, 2002—Central Highlands: Moramanga; East: Andasibe, Rogez, Ranomafana

P. parcepunctata (Jeannel, 1946)—East: Antongil Bay, Nosy Boraha, Toamasina; Central east: Ranomafana

P. didysilvae Cassola et Andriamampianina, 2001—Central Highlands east: Didy Forest near Antsevabe (Ambatondrazaka region)

P. truncatipenis Moravec, 2002—East: Mount Antampona, Antongil Bay, Mandritsara, Fahitrosy

P. uncifera uncifera (Jeannel, 1946)—East: Toamasina

P. uncifera sambiranensis (Jeannel, 1946)—Sambirano: Tsaratanàna Massif; West: Mahajanga

P. lateralis (Olsoufieff, 1934)—Northeast: Sambava, Marojejy, Andapa, Ambodirafia (Toamasina)

P. cassolai Moravec, 2002—Central Highlands east: Didy Forest near Antsevabe (Ambatondrazaka region)

P. subrufosignata Moravec, 2002—Northeast: Beanana village near Sambava

P. debilis Rivalier, 1967—East: Antalaha

P. trimaculata Fleutiaux, 1889—Northeast: Ampanefena, Marojejy, Masoala, Antongil Bay

P. sobrina Rivalier, 1967—Northeast: Ampanefena, Marojejy, Masoala, Maroantsetra

P. pokornyi pokornyi (Mařan, 1942)—Northeast: Ampanefena

P. pokornyi rivalieri Moravec, 1998—Northeast: Belalona (30 km SW of Sambava)

P. pokornyi perrieri Rivalier, 1967—Northeast: Antalaha

P. mocquerysi (Fleutiaux, 1899) —Northeast: Sambava to Antongil Bay, Mount Antampona

P. rufosignata (Audouin et Brullé, 1839)—North; Sambirano; East; Central Highlands; Southeast

P. uniguttata uniguttata (Fairmaire, 1871)—East: Nosy Boraha (Ile Sainte Marie)

FAMILY CICINDELIDAE

P. uniguttata smaragdina Rivalier, 1967—Northeast: Marojejy, Rantabe, Antongil Bay to Toamasina area

P. komorousi (Mařan, 1942)—Central Highlands: Manankazo, Mandraka; East: Rogez

P. fairmairei (W. Horn, 1899)—North: Ambilobe; Northeast up to Antongil Bay; Central Highlands: Ankazobe

P. punctum (Rivalier, 1951)—East: Ambohitsitondrona (Antongil Bay)

P. umbrosa Rivalier, 1967—East: Antakotako (Antongil Bay)

Subgenus *Minideutera* Moravec, 2002

M. cyanea (Audouin et Brullé, 1839)—East: "Ambodirafia" (70 km NE of Toamasina, 18°S)

M. minima (W. Horn, 1893)—East: Rogez, Anivorano (near Tampina); Central Highlands: Fianarantsoa

M. apicesignata Moravec, 1998—East: Analamazaotra; Central east: Mandraka, Toamasina area

M. vadoni (Rivalier, 1951)—East: Ambohitsitondrona (Antongil Bay); Central Highlands: Fianarantsoa

M. rubescens (Jeannel, 1946)—Southeast: Faraony, Vondrozo; Central Highlands: Fianarantsoa

M. pseudorubescens Deuve, 1987—East: "Forêt d'Ampasinambo" (district de Nosy Varika)

M. perroti Rivalier, 1967—East: Nosy Boraha

M. kamilmoravecii Moravec, 2004—East: Manakambahiny (Vavateniana prefecture)

Genus *Peridexia* Chaudoir, 1860

P. hilaris Fairmaire, 1883—Central Highlands: Mandraka; East: Andasibe; Ranomafana to Vondrozo

P. fulvipes fulvipes (Dejean, 1831)—North: Antsiranana, Antongil Bay; Central Highlands: Mandraka; East: Andasibe

P. fulvipes perroti Fleutiaux, 1899—Central Highlands: Ambalavao; East: Ranomafana, Vohilava, Faraony

P. fulvipes australis Alluaud, 1902—South: Tolagnaro, Isaka-Ivondro (near Tolagnaro), Manolo Forest

P. glaesariana glaesariana Jeannel, 1946—North: Montagne d'Ambre

P. glaesariana descarpentriesi Jeannel, 1946—Sambirano: Ambanja, Tsaratanàna and Manongarivo Massif, Andampy

P. ambanurensis (Brancsik, 1892)—Sambirano: Nosy Be, Nosy Berafia, Ambanja; West: Antsohihy-Bora, Antsalova

Genus *Calyptoglossa* Jeannel, 1946

P. frontalis (Audouin & Brullé, 1839)—East: Sambava, Antongil Bay, Nosy Boraha, Toamasina, Moramanga to Andasibe

Subtribe Cicindelina, Latreille, 1802

Genus *Chaetotaxis* Jeannel, 1946

C. macropus (W. Horn, 1915)—Central Highlands east: Mandraka, Moramanga, Didy, Zahamena; Central east: ? Ranomafana

C. descarpentriesi Deuve, 1987—West: Ampijoroa, Ankarafantsika

C. soalalae (Fairmaire, 1903)—West: Soalala, Ankirihitra (59 km SW of Ambato Boeni), Antsalova

C. leptographa Rivalier, 1965—Sambirano: Analalava (Maromandia)

C. serieguttata serieguttata (W. Horn, 1934)—Sambirano: Antseva-Ambobako (15 km SE Ambanja, Ramena River)

(*continued overleaf*)

TABLE 9.27. ***continued***

FAMILY CICINDELIDAE

C. serieguttata semiconfluens Rivalier, 1965—North: Montagne des Français

C. grandidieri (Künckel in Grandidier, 1887)—South: Isalo, Ankazotelo, Bekily, Ampandrandava, Imanombo

C. cicindeloides (W. Horn, 1905)—North: Montagne d'Ambre, Sakaramy

C. isaloensis Moravec, 2000—South: Isalo, area near Ranohira

C. rugicollis (Fairmaire, 1871)—East: Mount Antampona; West and Central (up to 20°S, absent in South)

C. katsepyana Moravec, 2009—West: Katsepy (Betsiboka River); Kirindy Forest CNFEREF (Morondava)

C. multifoveolata Moravec, 2008—Central Highlands; South: Isalo to Toliara and Tolagnaro; East: Manakara

Genus *Ambalia* Jeannel, 1946

A. aberrans (Fairmaire, 1871)—Throughout, absent on east coast with exception S of Manakara area

A. satura Rivalier, 1965—North: Montagne d'Ambre, Montagne des Français, Analamerana

Genus *Cylindera* Westwood, 1831

Subgenus *Cicindelina* Jeannel (1946)

C. pierroni (Fairmaire, 1880)—Throughout Madagascar (also in Comoros)

C. sakalava Cassola & Andriamampianina, 1998—West: Kirindy Forest CNFEREF, Ankilizato (Morondava)

Subgenus *Ifasina* Jeannel, 1946

I. fallax (Coquerel, 1851)—East: Antongil Bay, Toamasina; Central west; Central; Central east

I. constricticollis (W. Horn, 1913—Central Highlands: Tsiafajavona, Vatondrangy, Antsirabe, Ambositra

I. disjunctoides (Jeannel, 1946)—Central Highlands; South: Isalo, Betioky, Bekily, Betroka, Ambovombe

I. jeanneli Moravec, 2008—North-Central: Lembalemba Ambanin' Androna Plateau (Mandritsara)

I. umbratilis (Fairmaire, 1903)—West: Maevatanana area, Bora (Antsohihy); North: ? Ankarana

I. ramenensis Moravec, 2010—Sambirano: "Antsabetsienne," Ramena River (Ambanja)

Subgenus *Eugrapha* Rivalier, 1950

E. zaza (Alluaud, 1902)—South: Toliara coastal area, Ampasimpolaka, Lake Anony, Tolagnaro

Genus *Hipparidium* Jeannel, 1946

H. equestre (Dejean, 1826)—East: S of Toamasina; Central Highlands; Southwest; South

H. albosinuatum (Olsoufieff, 1934)—South: Betioky, Amboasary-Atsimo, Tranoroa, Ankobo, Ambovombe, Berenty

H. conturbatum Moravec, 2010—West: Katsepy (Mahajanga), Soalala, Antsalova

H. clavator (Jeannel, 1946)—Northeast including Nosy Boraha; Northwest; Central Highlands up to Ambositra

FAMILY CICINDELIDAE

H. obliqueclavatum Moravec, 2010—West: Amborovy "Cirque Rouge" near Mahajanga

H. micheli (Jeannel, 1946)—East: Maroantsetra, Mandritsara

H. osa (Alluaud, 1902)—Southeast: Farafangana, Vondrozo; South: Tolagnaro

H. perroti (Fairmaire, 1897)—North: Isokitra (Antsiranana); Northeast: Vohémar area, Maroantsetra

H. alluaudi Wiesner, 1992 (see Moravec 2010) —North: Montagne d'Ambre, Montagne des Français, Ankarana; Sambirano: Ambanja

Genus *Chaetodera* Jeannel, 1946

C. andriana (Alluaud, 1900)—Southwest: Morondava; South: from Sakaraha, Toliara to Tolagnaro

C. maheva (Künckel, 1887)—Sambirano: Maevarano River; West: up to Tsiribihina River (Belo)

Genus *Habrodera* Motschulsky, 1862

H. ovas (Bates, 1878)—East: S of Antongil Bay; West: Mahajanga to Morondava; South

H. truncatilabris (Fairmaire, 1897)—Throughout Madagascar but absent in northeast up to Farafangana

Genus *Calomera* Motschulsky, 1862

C. cristipennis (W. Horn, 1905)—Sambirano; West: Maevatanana; South (coastal or riversides)

Genus *Lophyra* Motschulsky, 1859

Subgenus *Lophyra s. str.*

L. perrieri (Fairmaire, 1897)—North; Sambirano; West up to Maevatanana; East: Antongil Bay

L. antatsima (Alluaud, 1902)—Southwest; Central Highlands; South (S from 20°S)

L. tetradia (Fairmaire, 1899)—West: Mahajanga to Maevatanana; South: from Toliara to Tolagnaro

L. abbreviata (Klug, 1832)—Throughout including Nosy Be (also on Grande Glorieuse island?)

L. vittula Rivalier, 1951—North-Central: Lembalemba Ambanin'Androna (Mandritsara)

L. quadraticollis (Chaudoir, 1835)—East: Beanana (near Antalaha), Antongil Bay

Genus *Myriochila* Motschulsky, 1857

Subgenus *Myriochila s. str.*

M. trilunaris trilunaris (Klug, 1832)—Throughout Madagascar including Nosy Be and Nosy Boraha

M. perplexa perplexa (Dejean, 1825)—North: Antsiranana; East: ? "Ste Marie" (also on La Réunion)

Notes: Original descriptions of some taxa by old authors are listed according to their inferred placement (in parentheses) and their recent locality names. ? indicates locality data uncertain; quotation marks indicate uncertainty associated with locality name. Geographical subdivisions basically follow Cassola (2003), but some locality names are presently known only from specimen labels.

Rivalier (1957) expressed a supposition that the Malagasy taxa of *Hipparidium* developed more recently from one common ancestor. Thus, the common ancestors of *Hipparidium* might have been only partly introduced from Africa and partly of Gondwanan origin but of a different lineage. Notwithstanding, it is very interesting that the internal sac within the aedeagi in *Hipparidium* possesses a remarkable structure very similar to that in the Neotropical genus *Phyllodroma*.

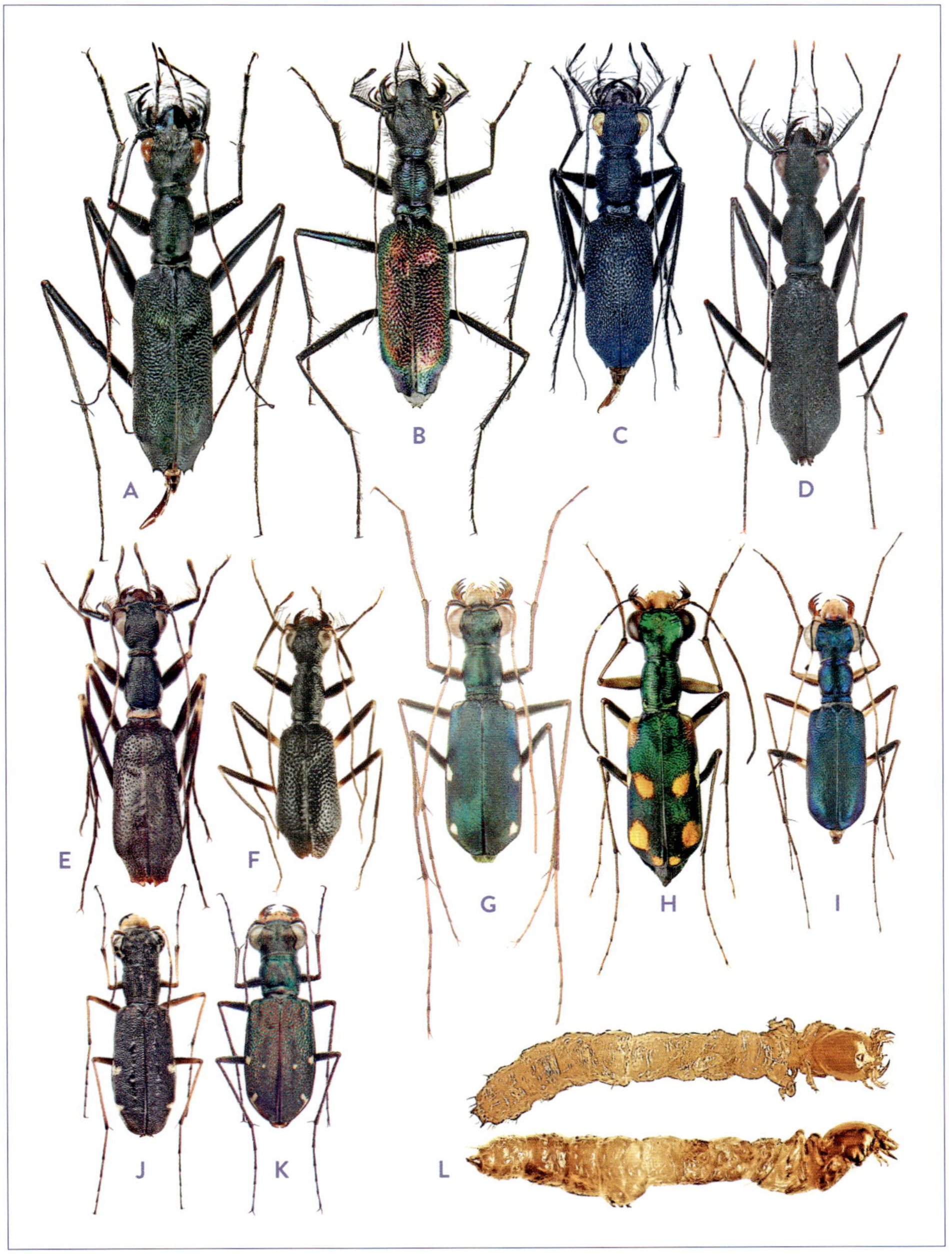

FIGURE 9.32 **Malagasy tiger beetles. A) *Pogonostoma (Macropogonostoma) caeruleum caeruleum*, male, Ranomafana; B) *P. (Polypogonostoma) septentrionale auripenne*, male, Ambanja; C) *P. (Pogonostoma) elegans*; D) *P. (Mitopogon) ranomafanense*, female (allotype), Ranomafana; E) *P. (Microstenocera) noheli*, female (allotype), Lakato; F) *P. (M.) perexiguum*, male (holotype); G) *Physodeutera (Axinomera) horimichioi*, male (holotype), Andranopasazy; H) *Ph. (Diarrhiza) murzini*, male (paratype), Andringitra; I) *Ph. (Toxoma) lobicornis nosybensis*, male (holotype), Nosy Be, Ambatozazavy; J) *Waltherhornia skrabali*, female (allotype), Isalo; K) *Ambalia satura*, female, Montagne d'Ambre; L) third instar larva, *Pogonostoma* sp. (probably of *P. elegans* species group), from tree trunk, Toamasina.** (PHOTOS modified in part from author's originals in Moravec 2002a, 2007, 2010; Moravec and Razanajaonarivalona 2015; and Moravec and Vybíral 2018.)

Alternatively, some Malagasy species of the genera *Habrodera*, *Chaetodera*, *Lophyra*, *Calomera*, *Cylindera*, and *Myriochila* may represent independent colonization events in geological time from eastern Africa. This possibility may be supported by the fact that external characters of several exclusively Malagasy species are remarkably similar to their eastern African relatives. *Habrodera ovas* is superficially barely distinguishable from the African *H. nilotica*; *Chaetodera andriana* is very similar to the African *C. regalis*; and *Cylindera* (*Ifasina*) *fallax* and *C.* (*I.*) *disjunctoides* closely resemble the African *C.* (*I.*) *disjuncta*.

Several tiger beetle genera endemic to Africa, such as *Manticora*, *Mantica*, *Dromica*, *Megacephala*, and *Neochila*, are unknown from Madagascar. This may also be interesting with regard to the hypotheses of the Gondwana breakup, because some of the significant genera of Carabidae occurring in eastern Africa (such as Anthiiae) are also absent from Madagascar (Jeannel 1946a).

The morphologically outstanding genus *Pogonostoma* is placed in the tribe Ctenostomatini together with the Neotropical genus *Ctenostoma*. This may indicate common Gondwanan ancestors, as suggested most recently by Cassola (2003), yet there are important mutual differences in morphology, male genitalia, and the behavior of adults.

The most recently published molecular studies may facilitate better knowledge of the origin of the ancestors of Malagasy tiger beetles. Nevertheless, the results are generally based only on sequences of individual samples per taxon and produce inconsistent results. For instance, the phylogenetic tree presented by Gough et al. (2018) possesses a number of discrepancies with dubious placements, whereby some morphologically, highly different, and geographically separated genera are nested within the same clade.

BIOLOGY

The genus *Pogonostoma* is the most remarkable, in both its habitus and habitat, and deserves extended remarks on the lifestyle and

FIGURE 9.33 **Malagasy tiger beetles. A) *Stenocosmia tenuicollis*, male (holotype of syn. *S. angusta*), Ampijora, Tsaramandroso; B) *Calyptoglossa frontalis* female, Moramanga; C) *Chaetotaxis macropus*, female, Moramanga; D) *Ch. grandidieri*, male, Ranohira, Isalo; E) *Paraphysodeutera naviauxi*, male (paratype), Antsalova; F) *Peridexia fulvipes fulvipes*, female, Moramanga; G) *P. ambanurensis*, male Ambodimanga; H) *Chaetodera maheva*, female, "Port Bergé"; I) *Hipparidium equestre*, male, Moramanga; J) *Habrodera ovas*, male, Saint Augustin; K) *Cylindera (Cicindelina) sakalava*, female, Ankilizato; L) *C. (Eugrapha) zaza*, male, Toliara; M) *C. (Ifasina) umbratilis*, female, Ambodimanga; N) *Lophyra (Lophyra) perrieri*, male, Maevatanana; O) *Calomera cristipennis*, female, Saint Augustin; P) *Myriochila (Myriochila) trilunaris trilunaris* (lectotype), "Madagascar."** (PHOTOS modified from author's originals in Moravec 2002a, 2007, 2010.)

biology of adults and larvae. All species of this endemic genus, whose taxa (including subspecies) represent ~50% of the tiger beetle species occurring on Madagascar, are forest dwelling and strictly arboreal, inhabiting both moist evergreen and dry deciduous forests. Only two species inhabit the sclerophyllous (*Uapaca*) woodland in the central south, as well as deciduous dry southern forests and scrubland in the southernmost portions of the island. Their hunting behavior and diet was partly described by Olsoufieff (1934) and Moravec (2002a). Their prey includes various kinds of generally small insects, such as ants and members of Diptera and Orthoptera (Mantodea), which have been observed in the mandibles of captured adults. Adults of large *Pogonostoma* species are occasional predators upon their much smaller relatives (mostly of subgenus *Microstenocera*) as they usually forage in the same trees (Moravec 2002a). Despite the mimesis mentioned by Jeannel (1946a), most species, with both black and colorful bodies, do not possess any remarkable crypsis, but some species imitate the behavior of ants. Several subspecies possess gold-green or reddish luster on their elytra (Figure 9.32b) and are immediately noticeable. As discussed previously (Moravec 2002a), many species, independent of their body size, inhabit both thin and large trees with smooth- or coarse-barked trunks. Adults of numerous species are very adept and fast fliers, but some adults (independent of species) rarely or never use their wings, although all species of *Pogonostoma* have well-developed thoracic wings. Instead, such adults can be found running quickly in a spiral direction along trunks or twigs. Some species are highly adaptable and inhabit introduced trees, such as large mango trees, but can also be found in coffee plantations. When disturbed, adults of certain species fly very quickly onto another tree or hide on the opposite side of the trunk; they might also fall or "jump" down and hide within the plant debris and vegetation near the trunk base. Adults of some species possess a peculiar behavior in that they do not try to hide but shake their head, imitating a similar behavior of ants (Moravec 2002a).

DEVELOPMENTAL STAGES

Little is known about the developmental stages of the endemic genera. Some characters of *Pogonostoma* larvae were described by Emden (1935), attributed tentatively by Jeannel (1946b) to *P. caeruleum*, *P. cyanescens*, or *P. chalybaeum*, all based upon larvae collected by Vadon, who described their ecology, behavior, breeding conditions, and rearing (Vadon 1935, 1946). The larvae were found in dead branches of soft wood, one of them in a thin, decaying branch. A synthesis of details known about *Pogonostoma* larval ecology was recently summarized (Moravec 2002a), including information and a description of second and third larval instars of *P. majunganum* (Putchkov and Dolin 2005). These authors, in contrast to Vadon, found the larval tunnels (3–4 cm long) with larvae mostly in tree trunks with wrinkled or grooved bark (acacia and mango). The larva (third instar) illustrated here in Figure 9.321, probably of the *P. elegans* species group, was recently collected by Czech entomologist O. Hovorka from a trunk in moist evergreen forest near Toamasina (see Moravec 2002a).

No larvae of other endemic genera are known. Olsoufieff (1934) speculated about a larval development of *Physodeutera* in dead branches of trees, similar to that of some Asian *Prothyma* species. Nevertheless, the larvae of *Megalomma* (*Megalomma*) *pierreorum* develop in bark of introduced *Eucalyptus robusta* on La Réunion, as first published by Deuve (1999) and demonstrated recently (Moravec 2010). Therefore, the silvicolous *Physodeutera* species may have similar development. However, despite very intense research, these details have not been confirmed. Cassola (2003) might be right in supposing that larval burrows should be found in the soil under low vegetation. This speculation is supported by the fact that the larvae of the Malagasy *Prothyma radama*, according to found larval tunnels, very probably develop in soil (Moravec 2007, 2010), similarly to larvae of *Peridexia*, as mentioned by Jeannel (1946a). We have observed mating pairs of *Physodeutera* (*Axinomera*) *skrabali*, which conspicuously preferred mossy decaying bark of fallen wood, suggesting that the larvae may develop under bark. Although all species of *Physodeutera* are silvicolous, considerable differences exist in their habitat and hunting behavior across the eight subgenera. Therefore, the larvae of different species of *Physodeutera* may also occupy various habitats, and at least those species whose adults are found on sandy soil of riverine forests may develop in soil under surrounding vegetation (Moravec 2007).

FURTHER RESEARCH AND CONSERVATION

Although the taxonomy of Malagasy tiger beetles has been thoroughly explored, immature stages of most indigenous genera are poorly known. As identification of a specific taxon's developmental stages requires continuous work at the same site, such research is suited to Malagasy scientists and students. Recently, young specialists from the Université d'Antananarivo (Faculté des Sciences, Département de Biologie Animale) and a Japanese research team from Kyoto University have been determining the immature stages of several species of *Physodeutera* and *Pogonostoma* and, at the moment, are preparing to publish the results (M. Hori, unpublished data).

Associated with ongoing deforestation, Malagasy tiger beetles, particularly those of the strictly arboreal genus *Pogonostoma* and other silvicolous genera, such as *Physodeutera* and *Peridexia*, are some of the most endangered creatures on the island. Some species of Cicindelidae have notably restricted geographic distributions that, in many cases, are not within protected areas. Some of these found refuge in small forest remnants, such as the now almost totally destroyed block near Ankazobe, northwest of Antananarivo. Many localities have been rapidly disappearing, literally in front of our eyes, over the few past years. For instance, the nonprotected evergreen hill forest near Antsahatsaka (4.5–5.5 km east of Moramanga), once full of tiger beetles, including some species described as new to science, was totally destroyed by fire between 2001 and 2006 (Moravec 2010; J. Vybíral, unpublished data). The same destiny was met by tiger beetles in the Andranobe Forest near Ambatondrazaka, which was destroyed by fire in 2002 (Moravec 2010). The destruction continues also in the Lakato Forest southeast of Moramanga, despite some official efforts to protect the area (Moravec 2010; Moravec and Vybíral 2018).

Therefore, Malagasy tiger beetles, as all other forest-dependent creatures, may be safe only in strictly protected areas. Andriamampianina et al. (2001) presented a set of 23 areas identified as priority foci for tiger beetle conservation, with six general regions of bioinventory priorities. Fortunately, 14 of the recommended areas are currently part of the Madagascar Protected Areas system, but the remaining nine conservation priority areas still fall outside the system. Besides some regional forests near major cities and towns, such as Fianarantsoa, Maevatanana, Maromandia, and Antalaha, these include important, mostly isolated sites, such as Ankazotelo, Sitampiky Ambongo, Menavava River, Vohilava-Faraony, and Sakaleona (Andriamampianina et al. 2001; L. Andriamampianina, unpublished data).

An important ongoing project in collaboration with the Université d'Antananarivo, Faculty of Sciences, Department of Entomology and Madagascar National Parks, is supervised by Miloš Trýzna of Czech Republic. This program of extensive field research has contributed to a better understanding of the current distribution of tiger beetles and other insects.

Subject editors: Brian L. Fisher and Steven M. Goodman

COLEOPTERA: DYTISCIDAE, DIVING BEETLES, *TSIKOVOKA*

J. Bergsten, M. Manuel, T. Ranarilalatiana, A. T. Ramahandrison, and J. Hájek

Diving beetles belong to the suborder Adephaga and are members of the largest family of aquatic beetles, with over 4500 species described worldwide (Nilsson and Hájek 2020). Phylogenetically, even with genomic data, it has been difficult to establish the exact relationships between diving beetles and the three closely related small dytiscoid families Aspidytidae, Amphizoidae, and Paelobiidae (= Hygrobiidae) (Vasilikopoulos et al. 2019; Gustafson et al. 2020). Dytiscid body size ranges from <1 mm to almost 5 cm. The family originated in the Jurassic and experienced an early burst in body-size evolution in the Cretaceous (Désamoré et al. 2018). Dytiscid body shape is almost always very streamlined but varies from globose to more elongate to dorsoventrally flattened (Figure 9.34). The color pattern is variable as well and, in many cases, has a likely cryptic function against different types of substrates (Miller and Bergsten 2016). All stages are aquatic except the pupal, and adults propel themselves through water with synchronous strokes using their oar-like, hair-lined hind legs (Balke and Hendrich 2016).

Together with fish, dragonflies, and aquatic bugs, diving beetles belong to the most diverse and ecologically important groups of generalist freshwater predators. Larvae are strictly predaceous and possess specialized grooved mandibles for sucking fluid from extraoral digestion (there are some exceptions, especially in the subfamily Copelatinae, where in lieu of grooved mandibles, serrated mandibles are present, likely for feeding on solid particles) (Kehl 2014; Miller and Bergsten 2016). Adults are also predaceous or partly scavengers, and larvae prey are largely correlated with body size (Nilsson 1996). Small species, such as members of

FIGURE 9.34 **Endemic diving beetles of Madagascar photographed in the field underwater (A–D) or at a hygropetric site at night (E and F). A) *Hydaticus nigrotaeniatus*, B) *Laccophilus isamberti*, C) *Madaglymbus* cf. *johannis*, D) *Hovahydrus* cf. *minutissimus*, E) *Africophilus* species with white epitrich ciliate outgrowths at lateral edges of the body, and F) *Africophilus* sp. larva capturing prey (Diptera larva).** (PHOTOS by J. Bergsten.)

hydroporines, may largely feed on microcrustaceans and early stages of oligochaetes and dipteran larvae; larger species, on aquatic insects such as Diptera larvae (e.g., chironomids, mosquitoes), corixids, dragonfly larvae, or even vertebrates, such as tadpoles and young fish (Culler et al. 2014). Dytiscids are themselves predated upon by fish, amphibians, snakes, waterfowl, small mammals, crustaceans, and aquatic insects, such as notonectids, belostomatids, and dragonfly larvae.

Diving beetles are currently classified into 11 subfamilies (Miller and Bergsten 2014, 2016), whose monophyly is generally well supported. Over half of the species belong to one subfamily, the Hydroporinae, which comprises small-bodied species. In tropical and subtropical regions, the subfamilies Laccophilinae and Copelatinae are also especially diverse groups. The phylogenetic relationship among subfamilies is still, to a large degree, uncertain (Miller and Bergsten 2014; Désamoré et al. 2018; Gustafson et al. 2020).

DIVING BEETLES OF MADAGASCAR

Six of the 11 subfamilies known worldwide are present on Madagascar: Colymbetinae (Figure 9.35a), Copelatinae (Figures 9.35b and c), Cybistrinae (Figure 9.35d), Dytiscinae (Figures 9.35e–h), Hydroporinae (Figures 9.35k–p and 9.36a–h), and Laccophilinae (Figures 9.36i–l). Klug (1833) described the first three diving beetles from Madagascar, and additional taxa were named by Aubé (1838), both based on material collected by the French naturalist Jules Prosper Goudot (see Andriamialisoa and Langrand, pp. 1–38). Klug's species included the first described Madagascar endemic diving beetle, namely *Laccophilus rivulosus*, and Aubé described several species of *Hydaticus*, one of which, *H. madagascariensis*, is, as of 2021, a very rare endemic species that we have found only a few times. Léon Fairmaire, David Sharp, Hermann Julius Kolbe, and Maurice Régimbart continued the description of

FIGURE 9.35 **Habitus of selected species representing the genera of subfamilies Colymbetinae, Copelatinae, Cybistrinae, Dytiscinae, and Hydroporinae (tribe Bidessini) present on Madagascar. A) *Rhantus manjakatompo*, B) *Copelatus owas*, C) *Madaglymbus fairmairei*, D) *Cybister tibialis*, E) *Rhantaticus congestus*, F) *Aethionectes oberthueri*, G) *Hydaticus ornatus*, H) *Eretes griseus*, I) *Hydroglyphus plagiatus*, J) *Liodessus luteopictus*, K) *Uvarus betsimisarakus*, L) *Bidessus longistriga*, M) *Pseuduvarus* sp., N) *Pachynectes* cf. *hygrotoides*, O) *Yola costipennis*, and P) *Clypeodytes concivis*.** (PHOTOS by M. Manuel.)

FIGURE 9.36 **Habitus of selected species representing the genera of subfamilies Hydroporinae (tribes Hydrovatini, Hygrotini, Hyphydrini, Laccornellini, Methlini, Pachydrini, and Vatellini) and Laccophilinae present on Madagascar. A) *Hydrovatus contumax*, B) *Hygrotus spadiceus*, C) *Hyphydrus separandus*, D) *Hovahydrus perrieri*, E) *Canthyporus reebae*, F) *Methles* sp., G) *Heterhydrus agaboides*, H) *Derovatellus marmottani*, I) *Africophilus nesiotes*, J) *Laccophilus complicatus*, K) *Neptosternus oblongus*, and L) *Philaccolus* cf. *elongatus*.** (PHOTOS by M. Manuel.)

dytiscids from Madagascar during the second half of the 19th century. At the onset of the 20th century, 95 species were known from the island, of which 62% were considered endemic (Alluaud 1900). In the 20th century, the very productive French doctor, naturalist, and coleopterist Félix Guignot described the bulk of new species from Africa and Madagascar up to 1960, when the island became independent. Guignot's African *magnum opus*, the three-volume *Révision des Hydrocanthares d'Afrique* (1959–1961), is still today the most useful single source of knowledge about diving beetles of Africa and Madagascar. This monograph does not include most taxa described by Guignot after 1954 (which, for Madagascar, is no fewer than 25 endemic dytiscid taxa today considered valid) in various publications (Guignot 1955a, 1955b, 1955c, 1955d, 1956, 1957, 1959a, 1959b, 1959c, 1959–1961, 1960). A large amount of the material used by Guignot was collected between 1947 and 1961 by Renaud Paulian, deputy director of the Institut de Recherche Scientifique de Madagascar and associated with the Office de la Recherche Scientifique et Technique Outre-Mer (ORSTOM), in areas difficult to access and, in many cases, previously not surveyed.

Only a handful of additional species were described following the Guignot era, before the most recent summary of Madagascar's fauna was published by Rocchi (1991), which listed 161 species with an endemism level of 69%. We now list 182 species currently known from Madagascar (Table 9.28), with an endemism level of 72% (78% when considering species endemic to Madagascar and one or more of the smaller western Indian Ocean islands). We include in this list, between brackets, a number of additional species that have been reported from Madagascar in the past but that, for various reasons, we consider doubtful; these are not included in the tally.

TABLE 9.28. **Checklist of diving beetle (Dytiscidae) species of Madagascar**

COLYMBETINAE
Colymbetini
Rhantus bouvieri Régimbart, 1900 (E)
R. latus (Fairmaire, 1869) (E[AF?])
R. manjakatompo Pederzani & Rocchi, 2009 (E)

COPELATINAE
Copelatini
Copelatus acamas Guignot, 1955 (E)
C. amphibius Ranarilalatiana & Bergsten, 2019 (E)
C. ankaratra Ranarilalatiana & Bergsten, 2019 (E)
C. andobonicus Guignot, 1960 (E)
C. baculiformis Guignot, 1955 (E)
C. befasicus Guignot, 1956 (E)
C. betampona Ranarilalatiana & Bergsten, 2019 (E)
[*C. collarti* Gschwendtner, 1936 (AF)]
C. distinguendus Régimbart, 1903 (E*)
C. erichsonii Guérin-Méneville, 1847 (AF)
[*C. guerini* Aubé, 1838) (E*)]
C. ilybioides Régimbart, 1895 (E)
C. insuetus Guignot, 1941 (E)
C. kely Ranarilalatiana & Bergsten, 2019 (E)
C. lineatipennis Guignot, 1955 (E)
C. mahajanga Pederzani & Hájek, 2005 (E)
C. marginipennis (Laporte, 1835) (E*)
C. monticola Guignot, 1951 (E)
C. owas Régimbart, 1895 (E)
C. polystrigus Sharp, 1882 (AF)
C. propino Guignot, 1960 (E)
C. pseudostriatus Ranarilalatiana & Bergsten, 2019 (E)
C. peridinus Guignot, 1955 (AF)
C. pulchellus (Klug, 1834) (AF)
C. ruficapillus Régimbart, 1895 (E)
C. safiotra Ranarilalatiana & Bergsten, 2019 (E)
C. scaphites Guignot, 1955 (E)
C. vigintistriatus Fairmaire, 1869 (E*)
C. vokoka Ranarilalatiana & Bergsten, 2019 (E)
C. zanatanensis Ranarilalatiana & Bergsten, 2019 (E)
Madaglymbus alutaceus (Régimbart, 1900) (E)
M. apicalis (Fairmaire, 1898) (E)
M. elongatus (Kolbe, 1883) (E)
M. fairmairei (Zimmermann, 1919) (E)
M. formosulus (Guignot, 1956) (E)
M. johannis (Wewalka, 1982) (E)
M. kelimaso Ranarilalatiana & Bergsten, 2019 (E)
M. mathaei (Wewalka, 1982) (E)
M. menalamba Ranarilalatiana & Bergsten, 2019 (E)
M. ruthwildae Shaverdo & Balke, 2008 (E)
M. semifactus Ranarilalatiana & Bergsten, 2019 (E)
M. strigulifer strigulifer (Régimbart, 1903) (E)
M. s. laevis (Guignot, 1955) (E)
M. unguicularis (Régimbart, 1903) (E)
M. xanthogrammus (Régimbart, 1900) (E)

CYBISTRINAE
Cybistrini
Cybister cinctus Sharp, 1882 (E)
C. dytiscoides Sharp, 1882 (E)
C. guignoti pseudosenegalensis Guignot, 1936 (E)

CYBISTRINAE
C. marginicollis Boheman, 1848 (AF)
C. operosus Sharp, 1882 (E)
C. owas Laporte, 1835 (AF)
C. senegalensis Aubé, 1838 (AF)
C. tibialis Sharp, 1882 (E)
[*C. tripunctatus* (Olivier, 1795) (OWT)]
C. vulneratus Klug, 1834 (AF)

DYTISCINAE
Aciliini
Aethionectes oberthueri (Régimbart, 1895) (E)
Rhantaticus congestus (Klug, 1833) (OWT)
Eretini
Eretes griseus (Fabricius, 1781) (OWT)
E. sticticus (Linnaeus, 1767) (COS)
Hydaticini
Hydaticus bivittatus Laporte, 1835 (AF)
H. dorsiger Aubé, 1838 (AF)
H. exclamationis Aubé, 1838 (AF)
H. intermedius Régimbart, 1895 (AF)
H. kolbei Branden, 1885 (E*)
H. limnetes Guignot, 1955 (E)
H. madagascariensis Aubé, 1838 (E)
H. nigrotaeniatus Régimbart, 1895 (E)
H. ornatus Kolbe, 1883 (E)
H. petitii Aubé, 1838 (E)
H. plagiatus Régimbart, 1895 (E)
H. saecularis Pederzani, 1982 (E)
H. servillianus Aubé, 1838 (AF)
H. sobrinus Aubé, 1838 (E*)

HYDROPORINAE
Bidessini
Bidessus apicidens Biström & Sanfilippo, 1986 (E)
B. ceratus Guignot, 1941 (AF)
B. complicatus Sharp, 1904 (AF)
B. longistriga Régimbart, 1895 (E)
B. nesioticus Guignot, 1956 (E)
[*B. ovoideus* Régimbart, 1895 (AF)]
B. perexiguus Kolbe, 1883 (E)
Clypeodytes concivis Guignot, 1955 (E)
C. insularis Guignot, 1956 (E)
[*C. meridionalis* Régimbart, 1895 (AF)]
C. sordidipennis Régimbart, 1903 (E)
[*Hydroglyphus apertus* Guignot, 1940 (AF)]
H. capitatus (Régimbart, 1895) (E*)
[*H. dakarensis* (Régimbart, 1895) (AF)]
H. farquharensis (Scott, 1912) (AF)
H. flavoguttatus (Régimbart, 1895) (AF)
H. geminodes (Régimbart, 1895) (AF)
H. plagiatus (Kolbe, 1883) (E)
[*H. strigicollis* (Fairmaire, 1880) (E*)]
Liodessus luteopictus (Régimbart, 1897) (E*)
Pachynectes costulifer (Régimbart, 1903) (E)
P. hygrotoides (Régimbart, 1895) (E)
P. mendax Guignot, 1960 (E)
Pseuduvarus vitticollis (Boheman, 1848) (OWT)

(*continued overleaf*)

TABLE 9.28. ***continued***

HYDROPORINAE

Bidessini

Uvarus alluaudi (Régimbart, 1895) (E)
U. betsimisarakus (Guignot, 1939) (E)
U. binaghii Pederzani & Sanfilippo, 1978 (E)
U. caprai Pederzani & Sanfilippo, 1978 (E)
U. gereckei Pederzani & Rocchi, 2009 (E)
U. laurentius Biström, 1995 (E)
[*U. peringueyi* (Régimbart, 1895) (AF)]
U. rivulorum (Régimbart, 1895) (E)
U. taitii Rocchi, 1991 (E)
Yola costipennis (Fairmaire, 1869) (E)

Hydrovatini

Hydrovatus acuminatus Motschulsky, 1859 (OWT)
H. badeni Sharp, 1882 (AF)
H. capnius Guignot, 1950 (AF)
H. confusus Régimbart, 1903 (E)
H. contumax Guignot, 1954 (AF)
H. crassicornis (Kolbe, 1883) (E)
H. cruentatus Kolbe, 1883 (E)
H. duponti Régimbart, 1895 (E)
H. madagascariensis Régimbart, 1903 (AF)
H. nefandus Omer-Cooper, 1957 (AF)
H. nigricans Sharp, 1882 (AF)
H. oblongus Omer-Cooper, 1957 (AF)
H. otiosus Guignot, 1945 (E)
H. parallelipennis Régimbart, 1895 (AF)
H. parvulus Régimbart, 1900 (AF)
H. pictulus Sharp, 1882 (AF)
H. singularis Guignot, 1956 (E)
H. sitistus Omer-Cooper, 1963 (AF)
H. testudinarius Régimbart, 1895 (E)
H. uniformis (Fairmaire, 1869) (E)

Hygrotini

Hygrotus assimilis (Régimbart, 1895) (E)
H. confusus (Régimbart, 1895) (E)
H. descarpentriesi (Peschet, 1923) (E)
H. goldschmidti (Pederzani & Rocchi, 2009) (E)
H. heros (Sharp, 1882) (E)
H. hyphoporoides (Régimbart, 1895) (E)
[*H. inquinatus* (Boheman, 1848) (AF)]
H. laticollis Fery, 2017 (E)
H. obsoletus (Régimbart, 1895) (E)
H. pauliani (Guignot, 1950) (E)
H. spadiceus (Sharp, 1882) (E)
H. travniceki (Šťastný, 2012) (E)
H. verticalis (Sharp, 1882) (E)

Hyphydrini

Hovahydrus minutissimus (Régimbart, 1903) (E)
H. perrieri (Fairmaire, 1898) (E)
H. praetextus (Guignot, 1951) (E)
H. sinapi (Guignot, 1955) (E)
Hyphydrus bigamus Guignot, 1956 (E)
H. cuppeni Biström, 1984 (E)
H. cycloides Régimbart, 1889 (AF)
H. distinctus Aubé, 1838 (E*)
H. impressus Klug, 1833 (AF)
H. madagascariensis Wehncke, 1877 (E)
[*H. scriptus* (Fabricius, 1798) (E*)]

HYDROPORINAE

H. separandus Régimbart, 1895 (E*)
[*H. signatus* Sharp, 1882 (AF)]
H. stipes Sharp, 1882 (E)
H. sylvester Guignot, 1955 (E)
H. trophis Guignot, 1955 (E)

Laccornellini

Canthyporus pauliani Guignot, 1951 (E)
C. reebae Manuel & Ramahandrison, 2017 (E)

Methlini

[*Methles cribratellus cribratellus* (Fairmaire, 1880) (AF)]
M. c. sparsepunctatus Guignot, 1956 (E)

Pachydrini

Heterhydrus agaboides Fairmaire, 1869 (E)

Vatellini

Derovatellus marmottani Guignot, 1940 (E)

LACCOPHILINAE

Laccophilini

Africophilus bartolozzii Rocchi, 1991 (E)
A. jaechi Bilardo & Rocchi, 2014 (E)
A. nesiotes Guignot, 1951 (AF)
A. pauliani Legros, 1950 (E)
Laccophilus addendus Sharp, 1882 (E*)
L. alluaudi Régimbart, 1900 (E)
L. comes Guignot, 1955 (E)
L. complicatus Sharp, 1882 (E)
L. flaveolus Régimbart, 1906 (AF)
L. furthi Biström, Nilsson & Bergsten, 2015 (E)
L. insularum Biström, Nilsson & Bergsten, 2015 (E)
L. isamberti Biström, Nilsson & Bergsten, 2015 (E)
L. lateralis Sharp, 1882 (E)
[*L. leonensis* Régimbart, 1895 (AF)]
L. luctuosus Sharp, 1882 (E)
L. mirabilis Guignot, 1956 (E)
L. morondavensis Guignot, 1957 (E)
L. olsoufieffi Guignot, 1937 (E[AF?])
L. pallescens Régimbart, 1903 (AF)
L. posticus Aubé, 1838 (E*)
L. pseustes Guignot, 1955 (E)
L. rivulosus Klug, 1833 (E)
L. ruficollis Zimmermann, 1919 (E)
L. seyrigi Guignot, 1937 (E)
L. transversovittatus Biström, Nilsson & Bergsten, 2015 (E)
Neptosternus alluaudi Régimbart, 1903 (E)
N. hedychrous Guignot, 1955 (E)
N. oberthueri oberthueri Régimbart, 1903 (E)
N. o. bilardoi Pederzani & Rocchi, 2009 (E)
N. oblongus Régimbart, 1895 (E)
N. ornatus Sharp, 1882 (AF)
Philaccolus elongatus (Régimbart, 1903) (E)
P. lepidus Guignot, 1949 (E)

Notes: E, endemic to Madagascar; E*, endemic to the Malagasy Region (Madagascar and the Comoro, Mascarene, and Seychelles archipelagoes); AF, Afrotropical; COS, cosmopolitan (located at least both in the New and Old Worlds); OWT, Old World Tropics; ?, uncertainy about geographic orgin. Species in brackets are reported from Madagascar in the literature, but their presence is doubtful.

Generally, the reasons we consider these doubtful are that modern taxonomic revisions based on studies of extensive material could not confirm those historical Madagascar records, and the species are also absent from our own modern samples. In most cases, these doubtful records are likely attributable to misidentifications but in other cases may represent undescribed species.

KNOWN DIVERSITY AND IDENTIFICATION

A collaboration between the Swedish Museum of Natural History and the Université d'Antananarivo to inventory, map, revise, and describe the water beetle fauna of Madagascar started in 2009 as a continuation of a DNA taxonomy project commenced in 2004 by the Natural History Museum in London (Monaghan et al. 2009). Throughout these 15 years, over 800 localities have been visited across Madagascar, and three PhD theses have been successfully presented (Isambert 2010; Bukontaite 2015; Ranarilalatiana 2020). A large number of new species have been discovered, leading to increased estimates of both the species diversity (now over 300, including not yet formally described species) and proportion of endemic species (now over 80%) (Table 9.29). We now have a solid basis of groups and habitats that can be expected to continue to reveal unknown diversity. For example, for Laccophilinae, Copelatinae, and Hydroporinae, we are still far from documenting the complete fauna, but for Colymbetinae, Cybistrinae, and Dytiscinae, we do not expect many additions. Both lotic (running-water) and lentic (standing-water) habitats are still yielding new species, but lotic habitats clearly have a higher potential. New species are found in all biomes, but humid and subhumid regions, including in the Central Highlands, are most productive. According to our experience, sampling efficiency is, on average, higher during the rainy season (especially for larvae) or immediately after, although less fieldwork has been carried out during the austral winter. Since the known number of endemic species has more than doubled over the last 15 years of sampling, it is reasonable to assume that we may currently know less than 75% of the fauna, thus the species number might be greater than 400 and the endemism level over 85%. About 50 species are nonendemic; this number has changed relatively little during the same period, compared to the number of endemic species.

Identification of members of Dytiscidae on Madagascar requires the use of multiple sources. Miller and Bergsten (2016) treated the world fauna with identification keys down to the genus level. Since then, the only genus-level changes affecting Madagascar's fauna are those resulting from a recent molecular phylogeny-based revision of the tribe Hygrotini (Villastrigo et al. 2017). Species previously treated in the genus *Herophydrus* are now included in *Hygrotus*, and the former endemic monotypic genus *Heroceras* also has fallen into synonymy with *Hygrotus*. Down to the species level, Guignot's (1959–1961) three-volume monograph on the African Dytiscoidea is the most useful single source. However, many species have been described since then, and for many genera, Guignot's monograph is outdated, especially in Hydroporinae, Laccophilinae, and Copelatinae. Therefore, for species identification, it is necessary to consult more recent publications (listed in Table 9.29), which include comprehensive modern revisions alongside many isolated species descriptions.

ECOLOGICAL DIVERSITY: TYPES OF HABITATS

Diving beetles occupy a range of aquatic habitats that vary in size from pools smaller than a footprint to the largest rivers and lakes of Madagascar. In larger water bodies, they are largely confined to the littoral zone. Diving beetles do not occur in the sea but can be found in marshes with brackish water (e.g., swamps associated with mangroves). They inhabit both lotic waters, such as streams and rivers, and lentic waters, such as marshes, pools, ponds, and lakes (Gioria 2014; Miller and Bergsten 2016).

The dichotomy between lentic and lotic waters has played an important role in understanding broad-scale distribution patterns of aquatic beetles and other insects (Ribera 2008). Lentic habitats are thought to be more ephemeral over evolutionary timescales; consequently, lentic species are expected to be stronger dispersers, more widespread and less geographically differentiated, along with several other predictions regarding speciation and extinction rates. This theory was tested across a set of adephagan water beetles on Madagascar (mainly members of Dytiscidae), and the study found lotic species to be indeed more geographically structured and with a higher degree of endemism as compared to lentic species (Hjalmarsson et al. 2015). This is in line with results obtained in nontropical environments, such as the European continent, for both aquatic beetles (Ribera 2008; Abellán et al. 2009) and aquatic invertebrates in general (Marten et al. 2006). The three Malagasy endemic genera are all associated with running-water bodies, as are most other intrageneric radiations on Madagascar (see below). Another important dichotomy in freshwater habitats is whether a habitat is temporary (seasonal) or permanent. Many dytiscids are good fliers and can rapidly colonize new, temporary habitats (Bilton 2014). In fact, after heavy rain in tropical regions, there is often an increase in flight activity of dytiscids seeking new habitats. However, habitats containing the highest specific diversity of dytiscids are usually permanent water bodies that allow the coexistence of opportunists, as well as more specialist species that rarely or perhaps never fly.

The importance of other biotic and abiotic factors, such as water chemistry (e.g., pH, conductivity, temperature), substrate, vegetation, and others, has previously not been investigated on Madagascar. However, it is being addressed in an ongoing project aimed at evaluating the impact on dytiscid assemblages of various anthropogenic disturbances affecting the surrounding terrestrial environment (e.g., deforestation and reforestation with exotic trees), as well as the water bodies themselves (e.g., eutrophication and frequent visits by zebu).

ENDEMIC RADIATIONS OF DYTISCIDAE ON MADAGASCAR

There are three endemic Dytiscidae genera on Madagascar: *Pachynectes* (Hydroporinae: Bidessini); *Hovahydrus* (Hydroporinae: Hyphydrini); and *Madaglymbus* (Copelatinae: Copelatini). *Madaglymbus* (Figures 9.34c and 9.35c) is likely the largest radiation, with 15 species described, but there are certainly over 30 species according to our unpublished data. It is a genus first and foremost associated with streams in intact lowland and medium-altitude moist

TABLE 9.29. **Checklist of Dytiscidae genera of Madagascar with number of described species, approximate known diversity including yet undescribed species, and distribution of each genus**

GENUS	DESCRIBED SPECIES	KNOWN SPECIES	DISTRIBUTION	IDENTIFICATION LITERATURE
COLYMBETINAE				
Rhantus	3	3	COS	Hjalmarsson et al. (2013)
COPELATINAE				
Copelatus	28	>50	COS	Nilsson et al. (1996); Bilardo and Rocchi (2015); Ranarilalatiana and Bergsten (2019); Ranarilalatiana et al. (2019)
Madaglymbus	14	>30	MAD*	Wewalka (1982); Shaverdo et al. (2008); Ranarilalatiana and Bergsten (2019)
CYBISTRINAE				
Cybister	9	9	COS	Bukontaite et al. (2015)
DYTISCINAE				
Aethionectes	1	1	AF	Bilardo and Rocchi (2017)
Eretes	2	2	COS	Miller (2002)
Hydaticus	14	14	COS	Guignot (1955a); Pederzani (1982); Bukontaite et al. (2015)
Rhantaticus	1	1	OWT	
HYDROPORINAE				
Bidessus	6	7	AF*	Biström (1985); Biström and Sanfilippo (1986); Ranarilalatiana (2020)
Canthyporus	2	3	AF	Biström and Nilsson (2006); Manuel and Ramahandrison (2017)
Clypeodytes	3	4	AF*	Biström (1988a)
Derovatellus	1	1	AF*	Biström (1979)
Heterhydrus	1	1	AF	Wewalka (1980a)
Hovahydrus	4	>10	MAD	Biström (1982a)
Hydroglyphus	5	9	OWT	Biström (1986)
Hydrovatus	20	23	COS	Biström (1997)
Hygrotus	12	12	COS	Biström and Nilsson (2002); Pederzani and Rocchi (2009); Šťastný (2012)
Hyphydrus	10	11	OWT	Biström (1982b, 1984)
Liodessus	1	1	AF-NW	Biström (1988b)
Methles	1	6	AF*	Guignot (1956)
Pachynectes	3	13	MAD	Biström (1987); Bukontaite (2015)
Pseuduvarus	1	3	OWT	Biström (1988c)
Uvarus	8	>30	COS	Biström (1988d, 1995); Rocchi (1991); Pederzani and Rocchi (2009)
Yola	1	1	AF*	Biström (1983)

GENUS	DESCRIBED SPECIES	KNOWN SPECIES	DISTRIBUTION	IDENTIFICATION LITERATURE
New genus 1		2	MAD	
New genus 2		1	MAD	
?New genus 3		1	?MAD	
LACCOPHILINAE				
Africophilus	4	>15	AF	Rocchi (1991); Franciscolo (1994); Bilardo and Rocchi (2014)
Laccophilus	20	34	COS	Biström et al. (2015)
Neptosternus	5	5	OWT	Bilardo and Rocchi (2012)
Philaccolus	2	3	AF	
Total species	182	~300		
Endemism	72%	83%		

Notes: AF, Afrotropical; AF*, genus is most diverse in the Afrotropical region but also exists, with fewer species, elsewhere; AF-NW, Afrotropical and New World (this concerns *Liodessus*, which is in need of considerable revision); COS, cosmopolitan; MAD, endemic to Madagascar; MAD*, endemic to Madagascar and the Comoros; OWT, mainly Old World Tropics; ?, uncertain taxonomic status or geographical locality. In the Described species and Known species columns, the listed figure is for Madagascar. In the Identification literature column, references given for species identification are in addition to Guignot's monograph (1959–1961).

evergreen forests. *Madaglymbus* also occurs in dry deciduous forests of the west, but with lower species diversity. Along streams, *Madaglymbus* does not occupy the actual running lotic sections, but rather leaf-choked side pools, rock pools, bays, and backwaters. Up to six different species of *Madaglymbus* have been found to co-occur in a single side pool. *Hovahydrus* (Figures 9.34d and 9.36d), a genus of small, ball-like animals, likewise inhabits small to medium-size streams in intact moist evergreen forests, but is seemingly even more sensitive to anthropogenic disturbance and therefore an excellent indicator of clean, pristine, or near-pristine forest streams. Individuals of this genus prefer the slowly flowing parts of streams rather than side pools, and they are notable specialists of backwaters, where they can be very numerous in places. The genus is most diverse in medium-altitude moist evergreen forests, but occurs from lowlands to the alpine zone >2000 m. Up to four different species have been found sympatrically in a single stream. Four species are described, but newly collected material will likely bring this number to more than 10. *Pachynectes* (Figure 9.35n) is also a radiation occurring in lotic habitats, but in contrast to *Madaglymbus* and *Hovahydrus*, these beetles also occupy medium to large streams and rivers, including in semi-open landscapes, and therefore are not restricted to intact forest sites. *Pachynectes* occurs all over Madagascar, including the dry spiny thicket in the south. In moist evergreen forests, this genus seems to be largely confined to rock pools. Three species are described, but over 13 are known to us, including some undescribed (Bukontaite 2015). Wang (2015) moved one of the three described species, *P. costulifer*, which was placed in *Pachynectes* (*Yoloides*), to the African genus *Yolina* based on microstructure characters. However, here we follow Miller and Bergsten (2016) and maintain *P. costulifer* in *Pachynectes* based on the molecular phylogenetic results of Bukontaite (2015) that show the subgenus *Yoloides* to be nested inside *Pachynectes sensu stricto*.

Apart from the above three endemic genera, there are a handful of similar-size radiations within some nonendemic genera. The hygropetric genus *Africophilus* (Figures 9.34e and f, and 9.36i) likely includes a species radiation around the smallest species with a simpler aedeagus shape (*A. bartolozzii*, *A. jaechi*, and a number of undescribed species). The *Laccophilus alluaudi* species group *sensu* Biström et al. (2015) is restricted to Madagascar and the Comoros, with five described and at least another eight awaiting description. This group is typical of small to medium-size forest streams, especially in low- and medium-altitude moist evergreen forests, but also in dry deciduous forests as well as montane grasslands in the alpine zones. The monotypic and endemic *L. isamberti* species group may be closely related (Figure 9.34b). *Copelatus* (Figure 9.35b) is currently the most diverse dytiscid genus on Madagascar following recent revisionary work (Ranarilalatiana et al. 2019; Ranarilalatiana and Bergsten 2019; T. Ranarilalatiana and J. Bergsten, unpublished data). A species group around *C. insuetus* was identified as a likely endemic radiation (Ranarilalatiana et al. 2019), and there is another one with some 20 species around *C. owas* (T. Ranarilalatiana and J. Bergsten, unpublished data).

What may well turn out to be the most species-rich radiation of Dytiscidae on Madagascar took place in the bidessine genus *Uvarus* (Figure 9.35k). This genus currently includes only eight Malagasy species, but at least three times more have already been collected, and new taxa are being constantly discovered. *Uvarus* on Madagascar have multiple origins but the majority of species seems to form a monophyletic island radiation (Holmgren 2015). *Uvarus* is not only diverse in species on the island, but its members have evolved to exploit a variety of aquatic ecological niches, including interstitial, hygropetric, and (partly) terrestrial niches (see below). If a subterranean and/or stygobiontic dytiscid were to be discovered on Madagascar, as known from elsewhere in both the New and Old World, odds are that it would belong to *Uvarus* as well. Other groups with potential small radiations in lotic environments include the *Hyphydrus separandus* (Figure 9.36c) species group *sensu* Biström (1982b) and the Afrotropical Laccophilinae genus *Philaccolus* (Figure 9.36l). In lentic environments, *Hydrovatus* (Figure 9.36a), *Hygrotus* (former *Herophydrus*) (Figure 9.36b), *Methles* (Figure 9.36f), and *Pseuduvarus* (Figure 9.35m) may include smaller endemic clades.

HABITAT SPECIALISTS

The hygropetric habitat is a specialized, two-dimensional aquatic environment consisting of a millimeter-thin water film on constantly wet rocks. These habitats may occur at seepages, along sides of waterfalls, or at sections of a stream often running over exposed bedrock. On Madagascar, these habitats house a range of specialized hygropetric water beetle taxa, such as *Incoltorrida* (Torridincolidae; see Bergsten, pp. 1047–49), *Hydroscapha* (Hydroscaphidae; see Bergsten, pp. 1050–51), *Madagaster* (Hydraenidae), *Tritonus* (Hydrophilidae) and other hydrophilids (e.g., *Coelostoma*), and hydraenids (e.g., *Hydraena*). Two genera of diving beetles on Madagascar can also be found in hygropetric habitats. Most common is the Afrotropical genus *Africophilus* (Laccophilinae) (Figures 9.34e and f, and 9.36i), with four described and many more undescribed species across the island. *Africophilus* are small (1.6–3.4 mm) diving beetles that are entirely black (apart from a pair of testaceous preapical elytral spots) and display phenomenal jumping capacities. Jumping is used to escape danger or to avoid or terminate mating interactions (J. Bergsten, unpublished data). Although the species is not yet described, we have also found a tiny (1.2 mm) hygropetric *Uvarus* species.

Diving beetles spend most of their time in water but may leave water for seasonal migration related to, for example, overwintering or when temporary aquatic habitats dry up. Recently, a specialized fauna of diving beetles was found in northeastern Madagascar, in an area with the highest annual level of precipitation; they apparently stay in forest-floor depressions even when dried up, waiting for rain (Ranarilalatiana and Bergsten 2019). Six new species of Copelatinae were described from these terrestrial-to-ephemeral aquatic habitats, three *Copelatus* and three *Madaglymbus*. They possess swimming hair-lined legs and therefore clearly are not truly terrestrial Dytiscidae (the latter are very rare globally, with only five minute species known in total). However, *M. menalamba* and *M. kelimaso* display some morphological characters, such as a more caraboid body shape and modified elytra that may have to do with terrestrial adaptations, as well as particularly efficient locomotion on land (Ranarilalatiana and Bergsten 2019). An *Uvarus* species was also found in the same habitats. Furthermore, a sixth truly terrestrial dytiscid species, a member of Bidessini, has recently been found on Madagascar (still undescribed: J. Bergsten and V. Grebennikov, unpublished data). Another kind of specialized ecology represented among Malagasy dytiscids is interstitial life among sand grains. An undescribed *Uvarus* species with reduced eyes and weak pigmentation was found along a forest stream in Manongarivo, digging extensively in a partly water-filled sandy side hole alongside a big forest stream with boulders (Holmgren 2015).

BIOGEOGRAPHY AND COLONIZATION

Diving beetles on Madagascar have contrasting colonization and speciation histories. Some groups are clearly endemic species radiations, whereas other groups have a history of multiple colonization and no significant speciation. Body size is generally positively correlated with dispersal capacity, and when the large-bodied genera *Hydaticus* (Figures 9.34a and 9.35g) and *Cybister* (Figure 9.35d) were investigated, the Malagasy species were clearly not monophyletic (Bukontaite et al. 2015). Both genera include endemic and nonendemic species, but the endemic species were also dispersed across the phylogeny, although several were "basal" in their respective species group. The large-bodied members of Aciliini (Figures 9.35e and f) and Eretini (Figure 9.35h) are likewise generally good fliers, three out of four species are nonendemic, and genera such as *Eretes* have fast larval development and can develop in very ephemeral aquatic habitats. In general, nonendemic dytiscid species are shared with the Afrotropics or are even more widely distributed.

Compared to the dytiscines and cybistrines, the situation is different for the large-bodied colymbetine genus *Rhantus* (Figure 9.35a). All three species are endemic taxa more or less restricted to the Central Highlands (Hjalmarsson et al. 2013), not shared with the three Mascarene islands of La Réunion, Mauritius, and Rodrigues, which each has its own endemic species; this southwest Indian Ocean island group forms a clade apart from *R. latus* (Morinière et al. 2016). The monophyly of the three endemic Dytiscidae genera—*Madaglymbus*, *Hovahydrus*, and *Pachynectes*—is not in question (except see discussion on *Pachynectes* and *Yolina* above), as each has a single origin on Madagascar followed by species radiation. *Hovahydrus* is interestingly a sister lineage to a species-poor radiation of five Hyphydrini genera endemic to the Cape region of South Africa (Ribera and Balke 2007). This Madagascar–Cape region faunistic link is also found in the Cape radiation of *Canthyporus* (Figure 9.36e), a genus that includes two known species on Madagascar (Manuel and Ramahandrison 2017), in addition to a few species in mountains of eastern Africa (Biström and Nilsson 2006). For *Pachynectes*, a close relationship with the Afrotropical *Yolina* has been invoked (Wang 2015) but not yet tested phylogenetically. This is of particular interest to test given the suggestion that the *Pachynectes* subgenus *Yoloides* is more closely related to *Yolina* (Wang 2015).

Madaglymbus was recently separated from the South American *Aglymbus* (Shaverdo et al. 2008), but recent phylogenetic analyses suggest that another Neotropical genus, *Agaporomorphus*, is its nearest relative (Bilton et al. 2015). This possible link between South America and Madagascar would be unique among Dytiscidae. Apart from *Madaglymbus* and the other two endemic genera, all other Dytiscidae genera on Madagascar also occur on mainland Africa. Some are exclusively Afrotropical-Malagasy—*Aethionectes* (Figure 9.35f), *Africophilus* (Figures 9.34e and f, and 9.36i), *Heterhydrus* (Figure 9.36g), *Canthyporus* (Figure 9.36e), and *Philaccolus* (Figure 9.36l)—and others have the majority of their species diversity in the Afrotropics (e.g., *Methles* [Figure 9.36f], *Derovatellus* [Figure 9.36h], *Bidessus* [Figure 9.35l], *Clypeodytes* [Figure 9.35p], *Yola* [Figure 9.35o], and the former *Herophydrus* group of *Hygrotus* [Figure 9.36b]). The remaining genera are mainly cosmopolitan or Old World tropics taxa; the exception is *Neptosternus* (Figure

9.36k), which has considerable species diversity in Asia, as well as roughly 20 species in Africa, including one possibly shared with Madagascar (Bilardo and Rocchi 2012). The *Neptosternus* species of Africa, Asia, and Madagascar would be interesting to assemble in a phylogenetic study to trace colonization origins.

MICROENDEMISM AND DISTRIBUTION

Microendemic distribution patterns have been analyzed by Bukontaite (2015) for the endemic river radiation of *Pachynectes*. Species formed three clades—a western, an eastern, and a "keeled" clade—and were clearly allopatrically or parapatrically distributed. For one pair of undescribed sister species, evidence points toward speciation along an elevation gradient. Some species exhibit microendemic distribution patterns, being confined, for instance, to the Isalo or Marojejy Massifs or the Central Highlands. The more widespread species were clearly not restricted to watersheds but rather to climatic regions, such as the eastern-escarpment humid region or the western deciduous region. *Pachynectes* has been collected at light sources at night, and diving beetles with flight capacity are rarely if ever watershed delimited. The Central Highlands fauna was recently investigated by Ranarilalatiana (2020) and A. T. Ramahandrison et al. (unpublished data) and is rich in endemics. There are also alpine species of dytiscids, which are known only from above 2000 m elevation, such as *Copelatus ankaratra* (endemic to Ankaratra), *Hygrotus* (formerly *Heroceras*) *descarpentriesi* (endemic to Andringitra), *Bidessus nesioticus* and *Canthyporus reebae* (both species present on Ankaratra and Andringitra, the latter also below 2000 m), and *Hovahydrus praetextus* and *Canthyporus pauliani* (both described from Tsaratanàna). The isolated patch of sclerophyllous woodland at the Isalo Massif is also a hotspot of microendemic dytiscids, such as *Copelatus acamas*, *Africophilus bartolozzii*, *Laccophilus pseustes*, and a new *Pachynectes* species, some extending north to the Makay Massif (M. Manuel, unpublished data).

LIFE-HISTORY DEVELOPMENT

Very little is known about the larval stages, life cycle, and phenology of most Madagascar dytiscids. Mainly, the work of Henri Bertrand has provided some descriptions of larvae from Madagascar (Bertrand 1928a, 1928b, 1949, 1963), as well as reports on larvae found during his fieldwork in 1960 (Bertrand 1968) and by ORSTOM (Bertrand 1971). Probably many species undergo larval development during the rainy season, but some can likely develop year-round, as we have found dytiscid larvae also outside of the rainy season. However, for most species, phenology data are unavailable, and identification of larvae to species level based on morphology is not a trivial matter. Bertrand (1968) reported collecting in 1960 larvae of the following genera during the rainy season (January–April): *Hyphydrus*, *Hydrovatus*, *Pachynectes*, *Herophydrus* (now *Hygrotus*), *Heterhydrus*, *Laccophilus*, *Africophilus*, *Philaccolus*, *Neptosternus*, *Copelatus*, *Rhantus*, *Hydaticus*, and *Cybister*. Of the three endemic genera, larvae of *Pachynectes* were described by Bertrand (1963). The yet undescribed larvae of *Hovahydrus* were recently collected during the rainy season at Marojejy, and a description is in preparation (Y. Alarie and J. Bergsten, unpublished data). Larvae of *Madaglymbus* are as yet undescribed but have also likely been collected during the rainy season in February (pending DNA matching). *Africophilus* is frequently found with larvae (Figure 9.34f) and adults together in hygropetric habitats (Bertrand 1968; J. Bergsten, unpublished data). Larvae of the *Laccophilus alluaudi* species group were collected rather abundantly, together with adults, during the rainy season in rock pools along a forest stream in Betampona.

ECOSYSTEM SERVICES

From a human perspective, the importance of diving beetles as predators of nuisance species—including vectors of human diseases—has been studied both in temperate-boreal ecosystems and in rice-agriculture settings (reviewed by Culler et al. 2014). Several studies have shown that dytiscids can reduce the density of mosquito larvae. They are known predators of malaria vector mosquitoes in their natural habitats (Culler et al. 2014). Even though the large dytiscids, such as *Cybister*, can prey upon small fish, the inverse trophic interaction—that is, fish predation upon dytiscids—is likely much more significant. There is, in general, a clear negative correlation between the presence of predatory fish and the diversity and abundance of dytiscids. The richest dytiscid habitats are free from fish, and in Madagascar, we have also noted a likely reduction in diving beetle abundance when large crustaceans (especially giant river shrimp, *Macrobrachium* spp.) are abundant. These crustaceans are likely significant predators of dytiscid larvae when abundant in streams and rivers.

Dytiscids are consumed as human food in rural communities, especially the larger *Cybister* species (Figure 9.35d) common in wetlands near villages (Randrianandrasana and Berenbaum 2015) but also *Hydaticus* species (Figure 9.35g) and *Rhantaticus congestus* (Figure 9.35e) (B. L. Fisher, unpublished data). In agricultural areas, farmers may capture *Cybister* in fish nets in rice fields and use them for food. In three out of five sites surveyed by Randrianandrasana and Berenbaum (2015), *Cybister* were among the top five most frequently consumed insects. *Cybister* is called *tsikovoka* in the official dialect of Malagasy as well as some other dialects. *Tsikovoka* is used in several traditional sayings (proverbs), such as *tsikovoka an-dobo: matavy tsy afahy*, meaning "a diving beetle in a pond: it fattens itself" (Veyrières and Méritens 1913). Other local names for *Cybister* are *tsikobogno*, *tsikoboka*, *tsimangovo*, *tsingovoka*, *kaity*, *kibihara*, and *behara*, although locally some of these may also be used for other water beetles such as hydrophilids (Randrianandrasana and Berenbaum 2015). Smaller dytiscids, noterids, and hydrophilids may be referred to by the nonspecific *voandrano*, which means "water beetle."

CONSERVATION AND FUTURE DIRECTIONS

The rapid pace of deforestation on Madagascar (Vieilledent et al. 2018) is extremely worrying for freshwater ecosystems and their inhabitants. A range of endemic Dytiscidae species and species radiations (e.g., *Hovahydrus*) are forest dwellers that are found only (or seldom) in aquatic habitats within intact native forests. Deforestation has a major impact on both biotic and abiotic factors for aquatic environments (Benstead et al. 2003a, 2003b; Benstead and Pringle 2004). A study comparing forested and peripheral open landscape sites at three separate protected areas of the Central Highlands found the aquatic Adephaga beetle communities to have a high degree of local uniqueness within forest fragments, but a more similar fauna in adjacent open landscapes (Ranarilalatiana 2020). Moreover, from fieldwork conducted over the last 15 years, the vast majority of new endemic species have been found in forested areas, and there is still no sign of the discovery curve leveling off. Extraordinary new dytiscid lineages not fitting any described genus have been discovered in both lowland and medium-altitude moist evergreen forests in the last few years (J. Bergsten, unpublished data).

A clear conclusion from analyses of an adephagan water beetle dataset (mostly dytiscids), with important consequences for the preservation of Madagascar biodiversity, is that maximum species diversity, maximum endemic diversity, and maximum phylogenetic diversity are different measures that can be used to rank areas for conservation priorities (Isambert et al. 2011). Rich communities of endemic species might come from few, sometimes shallow, radiations that yield a low phylogenetic diversity, but arguably these communities nevertheless deserve higher conservation priority than communities with a greater phylogenetic diversity resulting from more nonendemic species. As the knowledge of diversity and distribution of dytiscid species on the island increases, it will be possible to assess species using the International Union for Conservation of Nature (IUCN) Red List criteria, develop a set of indicator species of valuable freshwater sites, and identify Key Biodiversity Areas for freshwater invertebrates.

Apart from deforestation, eutrophication from practices of a growing human population, as well as from cattle, are also important factors affecting the fauna composition in freshwater habitats. Additional threats to dytiscid biodiversity include conversion of natural wetlands to agricultural lands (mainly rice fields) and the expansion of introduced and invasive fish (see Sparks and Stiassny, pp. 1045–60) and decapod crustaceans (see Crandall et al., pp. 908–12). Studies are greatly needed to assess the effects of all these anthropogenic factors on this group of generalist predators in freshwater environments on Madagascar.

In addition to inventories, a better understanding of trophic interactions, larval development and phenology, and the importance of various biotic and abiotic factors is also needed. The chemical ecology and biochemistry of the Madagascar dytiscid fauna, largely studied only for Northern Hemisphere taxa (Dettner 2014) is another area for future research. Diving beetles are known to produce an impressive array of steroids. Some can mimic vertebrate hormones, and several have tested positively as deterrents against fish predation. The green pigmentation of certain Laccophilinae species has been shown to be caused by a mixture of carotenoids with a special blue bile pigment, pterobiline, and is thought to be advantageous for species living among water plants (Dettner 2014). On Madagascar, however, *Philaccolus* specimens display this green coloration but occupy forest streams without any vegetation, which certainly calls for a different explanation.

Subject editors: Brian L. Fisher and Steven M. Goodman

COLEOPTERA: GYRINIDAE, WHIRLIGIG BEETLES, *FANDIORANO*

G. T. Gustafson, T. Ranarilalatiana, and J. Bergsten

The family Gyrinidae consists of approximately 900 species (A. Short 2018) with a nearly global distribution, absent only from arctic regions and with peak diversity in the tropics (Miller and Bergsten 2012). These aquatic beetles are unique among the extant Coleoptera in that adults are highly adapted for life on the surface of fresh water. The most notable adaptations include: eyes divided into two different subunits (Blagodatski et al. 2014), with a dorsal pair that sits above the waterline and a ventral pair situated below the water; unique antennal morphology consisting of an elongate pedicel equipped with a marginal fringe of setae and an enlarged Johnston's organ for detecting vibrations on the water's surface (Eggers 1926, 1927; Wilde 1941; Kolmes 1983); and, in most species, middle and hind legs that are strongly dorsoventrally flattened and widened into a paddle shape. These adaptations combined assist gyrinids in swimming on the water surface, detecting predators from both above and below, and locating struggling trapped prey. Claims that these beetles use a form of echolocation via surface-wave detection remain unsubstantiated (Voise and Casas 2013).

All known species of gyrinid are carnivorous, with adults feeding on terrestrial invertebrates that have become trapped on the water's surface and aquatic invertebrates that come to the surface for air (Kolmes 1983). Notably, adults form large aggregates, or rafts, of hundreds to thousands of individuals that can be composed of multiple species or genera (Realzola et al. 2007; Jäch et al. 2010). These aggregates function as a selfish herd for protection against predation (Vulinec and Miller 1989; Romey and Rossman 1995; Romey and Wallace 2007). The larval stage is also fully aquatic and carnivorous; however, larvae are equipped with lateral abdominal tracheal gills that allow them to remain submerged, removing the need to breathe atmospheric oxygen, unlike other larval aquatic beetles such as many Dytiscidae. The exact habitat occupied by Malagasy larval gyrinids remains unclear, with the exception of one *Dineutus* species found within fast-flowing water (Michat et al. 2017). The terrestrial pupal stage of gyrinids is spent under either stones or debris along the shore of aquatic environments within pupal chambers made of mud, as in the Dineutini (C. B. Wilson 1923; G. T. Gustafson, unpublished data). Alternatively, the pupal stage of gyrinids can resemble a cocoon, assembled using the mandibles and various materials (often plant matter) collected from the immediate environment; the pupa then attaches to emergent aquatic plants or other objects above the waterline, as in the Gyrinini (Butcher 1930; Balfour-Browne 1950; Colpani et al. 2020) and Orectochilini (Lesne 1902; G. T. Gustafson, unpublished data). Pupation and the immature stage of several key gyrinid taxa, such as *Heterogyrus* and *Spanglerogyrus*, remain unknown.

Madagascar is home to 25 different species of Gyrinidae, with all but one endemic to the island (Table 9.30). In terms of higher-level taxonomic diversity, the island contains two out of three subfamilies—Heterogyrinae (known only from Madagascar) and Gyrininae (nearly globally distributed)—and all three currently recognized tribes of Gyrininae: Gyrinini, Dineutini, and Orectochilini. Recent research suggests that Madagascar played a key role in unraveling the evolution of the family Gyrinidae by allowing the persistence of an exceptionally unique taxon that represents the oldest endemic plant or animal lineage currently known on the island.

EVOLUTIONARY HISTORY OF GYRINIDAE AND ORIGINS OF THE MALAGASY FAUNA

Using genomic data, the most recent estimates of the phylogeny of the beetle suborder Adephaga strongly support Gyrinidae as sister to all other adephagans, both aquatic and terrestrial (Baca et al. 2017a; Gustafson et al. 2020). Similarly, phylogenetic dating estimates using a tip-dating approach support the antiquity of this group (Gustafson et al. 2017a)—nearly 50% of the then-known unambiguous gyrinid fossil taxa were analyzed alongside 120 extant species using diverse morphological characters and five gene fragments. The results of this study (Figure 9.37) estimated that Gyrinidae diverged from other adephagan beetles during the late Permian, ~255 million years ago (Mya), with crown Gyrinidae occurring during the Triassic. The study also confirmed the relationships among the three subfamilies, Spanglerogyrinae, Heterogyrinae, and Gyrininae, as first proposed by Miller and Bergsten (2012).

Notably, the two currently monotypic subfamilies—Spanglerogyrinae and Heterogyrinae—were strongly supported as having fossil members. Examination of the fossil record, in combination with the tip-dated phylogeny, revealed that the dominant Mesozoic gyrinid fauna belongs to the subfamily Heterogyrinae, which is represented today by a single Malagasy species, *Heterogyrus milloti* (Gustafson et al. 2017a). Subsequent to the Cretaceous–Paleogene (K–Pg) extinction event, the Heterogyrinae was replaced by the subfamily Gyrininae as the dominant whirligig beetle fauna of the world; the fossil record showed a distinct transition following the K–Pg, in which all younger fossils belong to the Gyrininae. Presently, all known extant gyrinid species across the world but two belong to the subfamily Gyrininae.

While it is impossible to know exactly how and when the ancestor of *Heterogyrus* arrived on Madagascar, the estimated time of the divergence for the lineage containing *Heterogyrus* from its closest living relatives is ~206 Mya, a period when Madagascar was still firmly attached to Gondwana (Figure 9.37). Therefore, it is possible that the ancestors of *Heterogyrus* occurred on Madagascar, given that members of Heterogyrinae were widespread and abundant during the Mesozoic, and that as Madagascar rafted away from Africa, it took the ancestor of *Heterogyrus* with it. The resultant geographic isolation on Madagascar helps explain the persistence of *Heterogyrus* and its ancestors in comparison to their continental relatives; their replacement would be delayed following the end-Cretaceous mass extinction event, as members of Gyrininae mainly arrived on Madagascar in typical fashion during the Cenozoic through numerous independent oversea dispersal events. Only a single orectochiline lineage is estimated to have arrived prior to the Cenozoic (see discussion under Orectochilini). This proposed dispersal history also obviates the need for any additional ad hoc explanation of the subsequent dispersal of *Heterogyrus* to Madagascar from elsewhere. Such an island refugium scenario, while currently unprecedented for Madagascar, parallels that of the Tuatara (*Sphenodon punctatus*), a reptile of New Zealand, another sole surviving species from a formerly widespread Triassic–Jurassic lineage that was rescued from extinction by a microcontinental island (Carroll 1988). Future research into the phylogeny and times of divergence in other arthropods may reveal further examples of "paleoendemics" rescued from extinction via geographic isolation on Madagascar, similar to *Heterogyrus*.

HETEROGYRUS MILLOTI, MALAGASY STRIPED WHIRLIGIG, *FANDIORANO FAHAGOLA*

As the sole surviving member of the subfamily Heterogyrinae, *Heterogyrus milloti* (Figure 9.38e) is the hitherto oldest endemic lineage of animal or plant known from Madagascar (Gustafson et al. 2017a). Evidence for the highly relictual nature of this taxon can be seen in its distribution, habitat, and morphology (Gustafson et al. 2017b).

Heterogyrus seems to have a very limited distribution; it is known to date only from a few localities situated within the humid, medium-altitude moist evergreen forests of the eastern escarpment (Gustafson et al. 2017a, 2017b). The species was originally described from the upper Iantara River valley, with the type locality lying within or just outside the southeastern portion of the Andringitra National Park (Legros 1953; Gustafson et al. 2017b). The other known localities are similarly situated within protected areas like Pic d'Ivohibe and Ranomafana, with most records coming from the latter.

The known habitat of *H. milloti* was reviewed by Gustafson et al. (2017b) and is quite unusual for a whirligig beetle. *Heterogyrus* is found in small, often weakly trickling, forested streams with shallow pools and the surrounding area overgrown with vegetation. Interestingly, during fieldwork in 2014, no other gyrinid species were observed to coexist in habitats with *Heterogyrus*, despite a diversity

TABLE 9.30. **Checklist of Gyrinidae species of Madagascar**

SCIENTIFIC NAMES	SUBSPECIES	DISTRIBUTION	HABITAT	REFERENCE
HETEROGYRINAE				
Heterogyrus milloti Legros, 1953		C	Lotic in part	Gustafson et al. (2017a)
GYRININAE				
Dineutini				
Dineutus (*Cyclous*) *proximus* Aubé, 1838	*proximus*	N, C, E, W, S, Sa	Lotic	Legros (1951); Brinck (1955b)
	expansus Régimbart, 1892	W	Lotic	Brinck (1955b)
	kerhervei Ochs, 1926	N	Lotic	Brinck (1955b)
D. (*C.*) *sinuosipennis* Laporte, 1840	*sinuosipennis*	N, C, E, W, Sa	Lotic	Legros (1951)
	comorensis Régimbart, 1892	Comoros	Lotic	Legros (1951); Brinck (1955b)
		N, C, E, W, S, Sa	Lentic	Legros (1951)
D. (*C.*) *subspinsosus* (Klug, 1834)		N, C, E, W, S, Sa	Lentic	Legros (1951)
Gyrinini				
Gyrinus (*Gyrinus*) *ignitus* Régimbart, 1895		C, E	Lotolentic	Legros (1951); Brinck (1955b)
G. (*G.*) *madagascariensis* Aubé, 1838		C	Lotolentic	Legros (1951)
G. (*G.*) *superciliaris* Régimbart, 1892		C, S	Lotic	Legros (1951)
Aulonogyrus (*Afrogyrus*) *elegantissimus* Régimbart, 1883		C, E	Lotic	Legros (1951)
A. (*A.*) *carinipennis* Régimbart, 1895		E, C	Lotic	Legros (1951)
A. (*A.*) *cristatus* Régimbart, 1903		N, C, E, W, Sa	Lotic	Legros (1951)
A. (*A.*) *goudoti* Régimbart, 1883				
Orectochilini				
Orectogyrus (*Allogyrus*) *perrieri* Fairmaire, 1899		N, C, E, Sa	Lotic	Legros (1951); Brinck (1956)
O. (*Gonogyrellus*) *cyanicollis* (Aubé, 1838)		C, E	Lotic	Legros (1951); Brinck (1956)
O. (*G.*) *hastatus* Régimbart, 1892				
O. (*G.*) *pallidocinctus* (Fairmaire, 1880)	*pallidocinctus*	Sa	Lotic	Brinck (1956)
	attenuatus Régimbart, 1903	"Ampant-maizinoo"	Lotic	Brinck (1956)
	incertus Brinck, 1956	C, W	Lotic	Brinck (1956)
	leptomorphus Régimbart, 1907	N, C, E	Lotic	Legros (1951); Brinck (1956)

SCIENTIFIC NAMES	SUBSPECIES	DISTRIBUTION	HABITAT	REFERENCE
O. (*Meiogyrus*) *ornaticollis* (Aubé, 1838)	*ornaticollis*	N, C, E, W, S, Sa	Lotic	Legros (1951); Brinck (1956)
	incautus Guignot, 1955b	S	Lotic	Guignot (1955b)
		N, C, E, Sa	Lotic	Legros (1951)
O. (*M.*) *sedilloti* Régimbart, 1884		N, C, E	Lotic[1]	Legros (1951)
O. (*Nesogyrus*) *oberthueri* Régimbart, 1884		C, S	Lotic	Legros (1951)
O. (*N.*) *vestitus* Régimbart, 1892		C, E	Lotic	Legros (1951)
O. (*Orectogyrus*) *heros* Régimbart, 1884		N, C, E	Lotic	Legros (1951)
O. (*O.*) *madagascariensis* (Aubé, 1838)		N	Lotic	Legros (1951)
O. (*O.*) *vicinus* Régimbart, 1892		"Madagascar"	Lotic	Legros (1951)
O. (*O.*) *longitarsis* Régimbart, 1884				Legros (1951)
O. (*O.*) *purpureus* Régimbart, 1892	*purpureus*	N	Lotic	Legros (1951)
	meridionalis Régimbart, 1903	C, S	Lotic	Legros (1951); Brinck (1956)
		C, W	Lotic	Legros (1951)
O. (*Trichogyrus*) *grisescens* Fairmaire, 1899				

Notes: Distribution is based on references cited and in some cases new data. C, central; E, eastern; N, northern; S, southern; Sa, Sambirano; W, western; uncertain locality names or distribution are in quotation marks. This information is associated only with the distribution of a taxon in the Malagasy Region.

[1] Once found in numbers in a lentic habitat near Andasibe in 2011 (J. Bergsten, unpublished data).

of Gyrininae whirligigs found in the surrounding areas of Ranomafana at both lower and higher elevations. This situation is even stranger considering almost all other whirligig beetle species, including the sole surviving spanglerogyrine (*Spanglerogyrus* of North America), regularly co-occur in suitable habitats (Steiner and Anderson 1981), forming aggregates for predator avoidance. It may be that the occurrence of *Heterogyrus* in small trickling stream habitat is critical for the persistence of this relic taxon in light of potential competition with other Malagasy whirligigs. This could be determined by future observations of habitat and gyrinid species occurrence, potentially in combination with competitive exclusion experiments. Should this indeed be the case, specific conservation efforts should be considered to preserve these particular and potentially overlooked habitats for *Heterogyrus*. The maintenance of intact natural forests surrounding these habitats is likely of paramount importance, as the species has never been found in streams outside natural, moist-evergreen forest settings.

Much of the morphology of *Heterogyrus* is strongly conserved relative to fossil heterogyrines from the Mesozoic, particularly in relation to the elytra, pronotum, and features of the metaventrite (Gustafson et al. 2017a). As the only extant species of the sister lineage to Gyrininae, *Heterogyrus* preserves a suite of key intermediate features between the plesiomorphic states found in *Spanglerogyrus*—the taxon sister to all other members of Gyrinidae—and the derived features of Gyrininae (Figure 9.37). Such attributes were first discussed in Miller and Bergsten (2012), with a review of these and additional characters provided by Gustafson et al. (2017b). The anatomy of the head capsule and thorax was subsequently investigated by Beutel et al. (2017), and Beutel et al. (2018) revealed further transitional features. Other aspects of *Heterogyrus* morphology are unique to this taxon, such as the striking black-and-orange-striped appearance (Figure 9.38e). Additional autapomorphies include pubescent antennae with an array of different antennal sensillae; male adhesive setose palette fused into five distinct plates (one on each tarsomere); and metacoxae with a peg that likely serves as a friction hold for the metafemur, enabling *H. milloti* to jump powerfully (Gustafson et al. 2017b). Observing that *H. milloti* performs targeted jumps in a downstream manner, Gustafson et al. (2017b) suggested jumping as the insect's preferred means of locomotion when removed from water. This behavior and the aforementioned unique morphology may be adaptions to the habitat occupied by *Heterogyrus* (Gustafson et al. 2017b) and are thus indicative that this taxon has occupied such habitat for a considerable period of time. It could be that subsequent to the arrival of the bulk of Gyrininae during the middle Cenozoic, *Heterogyrus* was forced into marginalized trickling stream habitats devoid of other gyrinids, where it has since acquired unique associated adaptations aiding its persistence. The complete life history of *H. milloti* remains unknown, as do all of its juvenile stages.

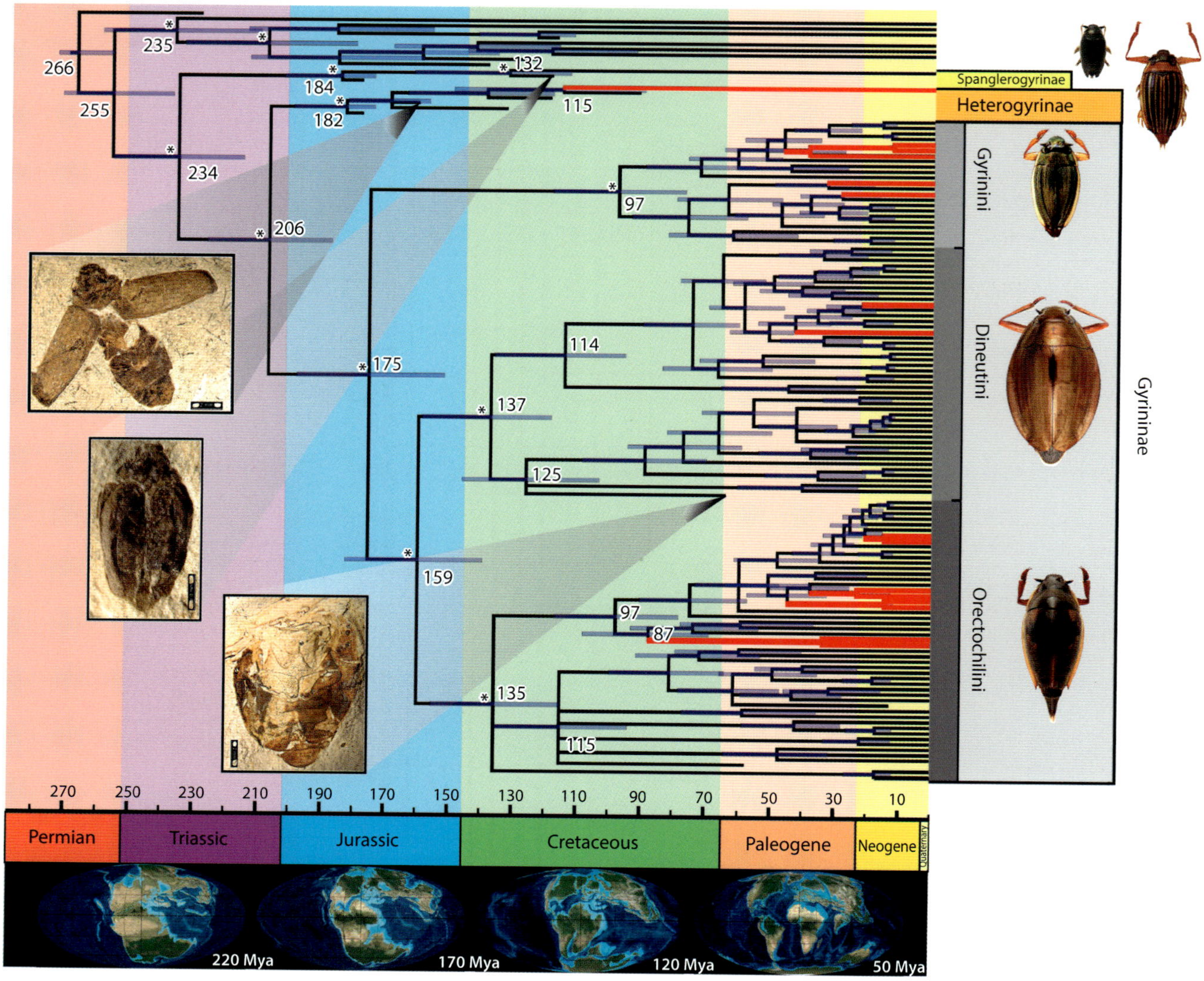

FIGURE 9.37 **Total evidence tip-dated phylogeny of Gyrinidae. Dates at selected nodes represent median posterior age estimate. Blue bars show the 95% highest posterior density age range. The asterisk above selected nodes indicates support at ≥0.95 posterior probability. Malagasy lineages are colored red. Fossils and imaged exemplars are not to scale.** (SOURCE: slightly modified from Gustafson et al. 2017a, originally published in *Scientific Reports* under a Creative Commons Attribution 4.0 International License https://creativecommons.org/licenses/by/4.0/.)

DINEUTINI

Worldwide, the tribe Dineutini comprises four genera, only one of which, *Dineutus*, can be found on Madagascar. Presently, three species of *Dineutus* are recognized on Madagascar (Table 9.30), all belonging to the subgenus *Cyclous* as redefined by Gustafson and Miller (2017). Two of the three species, *D. proximus* and *D. sinuosipennis*, are endemic to the Malagasy Region, while *D. subspinosus* (Figure 9.38f) is a widespread, primarily African species that can be found across the continent except in the extreme north and south (Brinck 1955a, 1955b). On Madagascar, it can be found across the island. It is encountered in open or disturbed environments, and unlike the two Malagasy Region endemic species of *Dineutus*, which are lotic, *D. subspinosus* is lentic and found in habitats such as ponds and temporary pools. The Mascarene islands, which are part of the Malagasy Region, also host two endemic species, *D. indus* and *D. picipes* (Brinck 1955b), which are not found on Madagascar despite prior erroneous records (Brinck 1955b).

Dineutus sinuosipennis is widespread across Madagascar and commonly encountered in slow recesses and pools within streams, as well as in human-disturbed habitats such as rice-field canals (Table 9.30). It can also be found on the Comoro islands, in a different geographic form from that on Madagascar (Guignot 1959a; Wewalka 1980b). All larval instars of *D. sinuosipennis*, in addition to their habitat, were described by Michat et al. (2017). The larvae are found among reeds and submerged aquatic vegetation directly within the current of fast-flowing rivulets adjacent to larger streams. In addition to forming surface aggregates, adults of *D. sinuosipennis* dive beneath the water's surface to swim in large swirling schools within the water column. This behavior was documented in several locations during 2014 fieldwork (G. T. Gustafson, unpublished data). It is not clear whether this behavior occurs outside of these beetles being disturbed by the presence of a potential predator (in

FIGURE 9.38 **Dorsal habitus images of selected Madagascar Gyrinidae species: A) *Gyrinus ignitus*, B) *G. madagascariensis*, C) *Aulonogyrus goudoti*, D) *A. elegantissimus*, E) *Heterogyrus milloti*, F) *Dineutus subspinosus*, G) *D. proximus*, H) *Orectogyrus cyanicollis* female, and I) *O. cyanicollis* male. Animals not depicted at an accurate relative scale.** (PHOTOS A–E, H, and I by G. Gustafson; and F and G by J. Bergsten.)

this case, a field researcher). Similar behavior has been described for only one other *Dineutus* species, the southeast Asian *D. indicus* (Wilkinson et al. 1995). *Dineutus proximus* was collected sympatrically at several of the localities where the schooling behavior was observed, but in far fewer numbers. Because of the mixed nature of aggregates and difficulty in discerning between actively swimming *D. sinuosipennis* and *D. proximus*, it remains unclear if *D. proximus* similarly engages in such behavior.

The other endemic Malagasy *Dineutus* species, *D. proximus* (Figure 9.38g), is considerably larger than *D. sinuosipennis*, with which it is commonly sympatric. *Dineutus proximus* is similarly widespread across the island (Table 9.30) but is unknown from the Comoros. The larvae of this species remain unknown; however, a very large *Dineutus* larva was collected during 2014 fieldwork from among vegetation submerged within a rapid in a stream that had *D. proximus* present. Therefore, similar to *D. sinuosipennis*, larvae of *D. proximus* may be found among submerged vegetation within fast-flowing currents of water. The protrochanter of adult *D. proximus* is sexually dimorphic; that of the male possesses a strange waxy region, the function of which remains unknown (Gustafson and Miller 2017). Two subspecies of *D. proximus*, *D. p. expansus* and *D. p. kerhervei*, have been described from mountain ranges within the northern portion of the island (Table 9.30) (Brinck 1955b). General Mixed Yule-Coalescent (GMYC) species delimitation analysis using cytochrome oxidase I (COI) sequence data showed structuring associated with geography, suggesting the potential presence of multiple cryptic species within *D. proximus* as currently defined (Isambert et al. 2011).

The most recent taxonomic work on the species of *Dineutus* of Madagascar is that of Brinck (1955b). All Malagasy species were included in the phylogenetic and biogeographic analysis of the tribe Dineutini by Gustafson and Miller (2017). Interestingly, *D. sinuosipennis* and *D. proximus* were recovered as being distantly related to one another. All three species of *Dineutus* known from Madagascar, or their direct ancestors, independently dispersed out of Africa to the island during the Cenozoic, with the earliest dispersal event being that associated with *D. sinuosipennis* during the Eocene.

GYRININI

The tribe Gyrinini consists of three genera worldwide, two of which occur on Madagascar: *Gyrinus* and *Aulonogyrus*. The Malagasy *Gyrinus* currently consists of three endemic species (Table 9.30) primarily found within the central region. A fourth species has been collected in the Central Highlands but is not yet described (G. T. Gustafson and J. Bergsten, unpublished data). *Gyrinus* species on the island are frequently encountered in lentic habitats such as ponds or temporary pools; however, they also occur in slow regions of streams, leading Hjalmarsson et al. (2015) to categorize *G. madagascariensis* as "lotolentic." Of the three species, *G. superciliaris* is relatively rare and has been collected only infrequently, while *G. ignitus* and *G. madagascariensis* (Figures 9.38a and b) are considerably more common; they are widely distributed across the island, primarily within the central region. The most recent taxonomic work on the genus is that of Brinck (1955b). A phylogenetic and biogeographic analysis of the genus is currently underway by the lead author of this contribution. The results show that, similar to other Malagasy gyrinid genera, there are two independent origins for the *Gyrinus* fauna. *Gyrinus ignitus* or its direct ancestor arrived on Madagascar independently of the common ancestor of *G. superciliaris* and *G. madagascariensis*. The latter two are recovered as sister taxa nested within a clade of African species, suggesting an African origin and in situ speciation.

Aulonogyrus of Madagascar includes four endemic species, all belonging to the subgenus *Afrogyrus* (Table 9.30) as recently redefined by Gustafson (2018). The phylogenetic and biogeographic analysis of Gustafson (2018) showed the Malagasy *Aulonogyrus* fauna to be the result of two independent out-of-Africa dispersal events. The first occurred during the Eocene via the common ancestor of *A. elegantissimus* (Figure 9.38d), *A. carinipennis*, and *A. cristatus*. The second occurred during the Oligocene by *A. goudoti* (Figure 9.38c) or its direct ancestor. Interestingly, *A. goudoti*, representing a more recent dispersal event, is quite unlike members of the clade originating from in situ speciation subsequent to earlier dispersal from a common ancestor. *Aulonogyrus goudoti* is among the most commonly encountered gyrinids found throughout most of the island, with the exception of the southern region. Furthermore, it appears to be a relatively hardy species inhabiting a variety of lotic habitats from pristine streams to relatively impacted ones situated within or near towns (G. T. Gustafson, unpublished data). *Aulonogyrus goudoti* has been observed swimming under water in a swirling school, forming a compact unit about the size of a football and including several hundred, perhaps over a thousand, individuals (J. Bergsten, unpublished data). This observation was made when the collectors arrived at a stream and therefore was likely not a result of disturbance from the collectors. The other Malagasy *Aulonogyrus* species are also lotic but are less common and more restricted in their distribution and habitat. The most recent taxonomic work for the species is that of Brinck (1955b) and Gustafson (2018) for the phylogeny and subgeneric classification.

ORECTOCHILINI

Orectochilini is the most speciose tribe of Gyrinidae, containing over 550 species distributed primarily within the New and Old World tropics. There are four genera currently recognized within Orectochilini (Miller and Bergsten 2012), of which only the African genus *Orectogyrus* occurs on Madagascar. *Orectogyrus* constitutes the most speciose genus on the island, currently comprising 14 species distributed among six subgenera (Table 9.30). Three of these subgenera are endemic to Madagascar: *Gonogyrellus*, *Meiogyrus*, and *Nesogyrus*.

Members of the Orectochilini, including *Orectogyrus*, are highly adapted to lotic habitats; the last three abdominal ventrites are tubular and extended into a "tail" (thus the *Gyrini caudati* of Ochs 1948, 1949, 1953). These abdominal ventrites, particularly 7 and 8 (sometimes 6) have a medial series of long, fine setae that form a keel (see Miller and Bergsten 2012 for a diagram). Most species are strongly laterally compressed and canoe-shaped in appearance. These adaptations combined allow the Malagasy *Orectogyrus* to move rapidly upstream, even through strong currents, and many species can be found on swiftly flowing streams or rivers outside of the sheltered and slow recesses occupied by *Dineutus*, *Gyrinus*, and *Aulonogyrus*. Larvae of Malagasy *Orectogyrus* have also been found in running water, such as small rivers, streams, and torrents (Bertrand 1968). Most species of *Orectogyrus*, including those on Madagascar, are distinctly sexually dimorphic, with males exhibiting a different pubescent patterning of the elytra. Some species, such as *O. sedilloti*, even have females with additional rough sculpturing of the elytra that is not present in males. Furthermore, some species exhibit considerable polymorphism with regard to female pubescent patterning and elytral sculpturing, resulting in the recognition of numerous subspecies (e.g., *O. pallidocinctus*, Table 9.30). Many of the Malagasy *Orectogyrus* species come in a variety of colors and are beautiful insects to behold; the most notable is *O. cyanicollis* (Figures 9.38h and i), which is bluish purple. Species of *Orectogyrus* can be found across the island, including endemics to the western dry deciduous forest area (e.g., *O. perrieri*, Table 9.30), unlike the other Malagasy gyrinid genera that do not currently have any known endemic species in the western dry deciduous forest area.

The last taxonomic treatment for the species of Malagasy *Orectogyrus* is that of Brinck (1956). However, there is evidence from COI molecular data using GMYC species delimitation that *O. cyanicollis* (Isambert et al. 2011) and other Malagasy *Orectogyrus* potentially have cryptic species within their current morphologically defined boundaries. The genus *Orectogyrus* has yet to be subject to an extensive phylogenetic analysis. The species included in the study by Gustafson et al. (2017a) show that the Malagasy fauna do not form a monophyletic clade but are nested throughout the tree. Interestingly, among the earliest diverging *Orectogyrus* lineages is the endemic subgenus *Gonogyrellus*, represented in the tree by *O. cyanicollis* and *O. hastatus*. These taxa are estimated to have diverged from their African sister *Orectogyrus* ~87 Mya, suggesting that the common ancestor of these taxa has potentially been in Madagascar since that time. Notably, this divergence time currently represents the earliest potential time for a member of the Gyrininae being present on the island. However, conclusions about the historical biogeography of *Orectogyrus*, such as whether this represents an out-of-Africa dispersal event, will require a more comprehensive phylogeny and associated biogeographic analysis. These further studies are especially needed, given that the current *Orectogyrus* phylogeny (Gustafson et al. 2017a) shows Malagasy species spread throughout the tree in a manner similar to the diving beetle genus *Hydaticus*; historical biogeographic reconstruction of *Hydaticus* supported out-of-Madagascar dispersal, rather than multiple dispersal events to Madagascar (Bukontaite et al. 2015). This proposed colonization scenario might have been due to skewed sampling of Malagasy versus mainland African taxa. Whether the origin of *Orectogyrus* could lie within Madagascar, rather than Africa, should be tested with thorough taxon sampling from both regions.

GYRINIDAE AND MALAGASY CULTURE

Members of Gyrinidae are well known in Madagascar and have several different Malagasy names depending on region and dialect. The most obvious and characteristic behavior of swirling around on the water surface has been the principal inspiration for local vernacular names. In the Merina dialect of Malagasy, gyrinids are known as *fandiorano*, or "cleaning water," referring to the thought that by swirling and creating small waves, they may clear away tiny floating objects on the water surface. This name is also used by several other groups, such as the Betsileo, Sihanaka, Antanosy, Antandroy, and Mahafaly. In other dialects, gyrinids are known by the names *velomiriorio*—"swirling around" or "to live in a whirlwind" (Sakalava); *velogno miriaria*—"to wander aimlessly" (Antankarana); *tsiriorion-drano*—"pretends to wander on water" (Antaifasy); *tsingiriviry* (Tsimihety) or *tsiverivery* (Betsimisaraka), which means something akin to "pretends to get lost." The large and conspicuous *Dineutus* species, especially the common *D. sinuosipennis*, are used for human consumption in some of the rural villages surveyed by Van Itterbeeck et al. (2019) (B. L. Fisher, unpublished data; also see Randrianandrasana and Berenbaum 2015).

FUTURE DIRECTIONS

The last revisionary taxonomic work on the Malagasy gyrinid fauna was that of Brinck (1955b, 1956). Since that time, molecular species delimitation methods have significantly advanced our ability to detect independently evolving lineages within widespread metapopulations currently considered to be a single species. Several gyrinid taxa, such as *Dineutus proximus*, *Gyrinus madagascariensis*, and *Orectogyrus cyanicollis*, show evidence of potentially having cryptic, species-level diversity within the current morphological definition of these species (Isambert et al. 2011). Additionally, molecular data can add evidence either for or against the distinct identity of the formally named subspecific taxa (Table 9.30). Therefore, the Malagasy gyrinid fauna would greatly benefit from future revisionary integrative taxonomic work (Dayrat 2005; Will et al. 2005; Schlick-Steiner et al. 2010).

As discussed above, *Heterogyrus milloti* represents a critical taxon for studying the evolution of Gyrinidae. Currently, the juvenile stages and entire life history of this species remain unknown. Efforts to describe and document these should be undertaken, as they will provide unique insights into broader gyrinid evolution. Additionally, the habitat and distribution of *H. milloti* require further investigation, not only for better understanding this key taxon but to generate data necessary for determining its IUCN (International Union for the Conservation of Nature) Red List status. Gustafson et al. (2017b) discussed some of the present and potential threats faced by *H. milloti,* in addition to highlighting the importance of conservation efforts specifically for this species, rather than relying upon insufficient "trickle-down" conservation (J. A. Clark and May 2002; Jenkins et al. 2013) through protected areas alone. Generating the aforementioned data will directly aid in these efforts. With its charismatic appearance and unique story of survival, *H. milloti* would serve well as a flagship species for freshwater conservation on Madagascar.

Subject editors: Brian L. Fisher and Steven M. Goodman

COLEOPTERA: HALIPLIDAE, CRAWLING WATER BEETLES

J. Bergsten

Haliplidae is a distinctive family of small-bodied (1.5–5.0 mm) water beetles of the suborder Adephaga, characterized by enlarged metacoxal plates. They are the sister lineage to the Dytiscoidea superfamily, according to phylogenomic analyses (Gustafson et al. 2020; McKenna et al. 2019). The general vernacular name "crawling water beetles" stems from the alternating hind-leg strokes when swimming, creating a somewhat wobbling form of locomotion. Haliplidae is a small family, with approximately 240 species distributed worldwide, but most diverse in the Northern Hemisphere (Vondel 2005, 2016).

There are only four genera in the family following a recent revision (Vondel 2019). *Peltodytes*, with about 37 species, occurs in North and Central America and the Old World except Australia. *Brychius* is a small Holarctic genus of five strictly lotic species. *Phalilus* was recently elevated to a separate genus and removed from *Haliplus* (Vondel 2019) to contain seven Australian and one New Caledonian species. As currently configured, *Haliplus* includes approximately 190 species in 11 subgenera (>130 in the subgenus *Liaphlus*) and has a global distribution.

Peltodytes is undoubtedly sister to the other three genera (Beutel and Ruhnau 1990; Gustafson et al. 2020; Vondel 2019). The genus maintains plesiomorphic states in both behavior and adult and larval morphology, such as nonendophytic egg laying (Beutel and Ruhnau 1990); the least developed (among Haliplidae genera) sub-metacoxal plate air-storing pit (Vondel 2019); and long, threadlike gills in larvae (Spangler 1991a). *Brychius* is sister to *Haliplus* and *Phalilus* (Vondel 2019). Resolution within *Haliplus* among the numerous subgenera needs further work. Fossils of both *Peltodytes* and *Haliplus* are known from the Lower Cretaceous (Prokin and Ponomarenko 2013), and the family is dated to the Early Jurassic (Hunt et al. 2007; McKenna et al. 2019).

Both adults and larvae are aquatic, but the last (third) larval instar pupates outside of water (Vondel 2016). Larvae breathe with elongate (*Peltodytes*) or microtracheal gills, whereas adults need to surface to replenish their air supply stored under the elytra and metacoxal plate. Larvae feed on filamentous algae or stonewarts, a form of green algae (Spangler 1991a; Vondel 2016). Adult feeding habits are often described as omnivorous but vary between species from a largely carnivorous diet to a diet of largely algae (Vondel 2016).

FIGURE 9.39 Type material housed in the Muséum National d'Histoire Naturelle in Paris of the two best-known Haliplidae species on Madagascar, collected by Charles Alluaud and described by Maurice Régimbart. A) *Haliplus alluaudi* (paralectotypes) and B) *Peltodytes quadratus* (paralectotype). (PHOTOS by J. Bergsten.)

MADAGASCAR DIVERSITY AND DISTRIBUTION

Representatives from two haliplid genera are present on Madagascar—*Peltodytes* with one species, and *Haliplus* with five species, all in the subgenus *Liaphlus*. The fauna was reviewed by Vondel and Bergsten (2012), who provide an identification key and habitus photos of all species. All are endemic to Madagascar or the Malagasy Region (including Mauritius). The latter applies to *H. alluaudi*, which is reported from Mauritius (Guignot 1959a; Gomy 2000) in addition to Madagascar, but the Mauritian record needs confirmation (Vondel and Bergsten 2012). A male of *P. quadratus* was once reported from South Africa (Gueorguiev 1967), but this is very likely a misidentification (Vondel 2010) and probably refers to the unnamed *Peltodytes* species in Perissinotto et al. (2016) from the same area. Both *P. quadratus* and *H. alluaudi* (Figure 9.39) are widespread and recorded from all six former provinces of Madagascar (Vondel and Bergsten 2012). Remaining species are distributed in the west of Madagascar: *H. gamma* (Soalala), *H. madagascariensis* (Beahitse), and *H. insularis* (Andobo), each of which is known only from a single locality and associated type specimen. *Haliplus incrassatus* was described from the offshore island Nosy Be, but based on the few known specimens available in collections, the western distribution stretches south to Ankavandra (east of Bemaraha) and Lambomakandro (northern portion of Zombitse-Vohibasia).

Haliplidae species of Madagascar

Haliplus alluaudi Régimbart, 1903 (E*) (TL: Madagascar Centre-Sud [environs de Fianarantsoa])
H. gamma Vondel and Bergsten, 2012 (E) (TL: Soalala)
H. incrassatus Régimbart, 1900 (E) (TL: Nossi-Bé [Nosy Be])
[*Haliplus aspilus* Guignot, 1957 (TL: Lambomakandro [Sakaraha])]
H. insularis Guignot, 1960 (E) (TL: Andobo, forêt Antsingy [Antsalova])
H. madagascariensis Vondel and Bergsten, 2012 (E) (TL: Beahitse)
Peltodytes quadratus Régimbart, 1895 (E) (TL: Lake Ambodinandohalo [Antananarivo])
Note: E, endemic to Madagascar; E*, endemic to Madagascar and Mauritius; TL, type locality.

PHYLOGENY AND EVOLUTION

The origin of the haliplid fauna on Madagascar is likely to be found in Africa. *Peltodytes quadratus* probably belongs with the African group of *Peltodytes*, subgenus *Peltodytes*. *Peltodytes alluaudi*, synonym of *P. speratus* following Vondel (2010), is known from Mauritius as well as several eastern African countries; if the identifications are correct, it confirms the dispersal capacity over the Mozambique Channel and beyond. Likewise, *Haliplus alluaudi* and *H. incrassatus* were placed in the African species group of *Haliplus*, subgenus *Liaphlus*, by both Zimmermann (1924: "*Groupe X*") and Guignot (1955c: "*9. Group africanus*"). Whether the Madagascar *Haliplus* species form a monophyletic clade within subgenus *Liaphlus* is not known as DNA sequence data is available only for *P. quadratus* and *H. alluaudi* of the Madagascar species.

BIOLOGY

The two widespread species *Haliplus alluaudi* and *Peltodytes quadratus* occur in both humid and dry regions. Both have been collected from sea level up to at least 1600 m elevation at Manjakatompo, Ankaratra Massif (*H. alluaudi*), and Andringitra (*P. quadratus*). Flight capacity is also documented for both species

FIGURE 9.40 **Sandy-bottomed Ivondro River, by the bridge of RN2 just south of Toamasina, in the east coast lowlands. *Peltodytes quadratus* was common in the river in mid-November 2011.** (PHOTO by R. Bukontaite.)

through black light catches at Analamazaotra (Vondel 2010). Interestingly, although most haliplids are assumed to be capable of flight, species in the tropics are much more often collected at light sources than temperate species, which are rarely collected while flying (Vondel 2016).

The most numerous specimen series of *P. quadratus* has been collected in rivers, which is presumed to be its preferred habitat, especially slow-flowing rivers with sandy bottoms (Figure 9.40). But *P. quadratus* seems to be a generalist species, which we know from vegetation-rich ponds, rice fields, and muddy waters near villages. Adults of *P. quadratus* have been reared from larvae collected in February (together with adults) among filamentous algae in a ditch at a marsh at the Station Agricole d'Ivoloina (Betrand 1963).

Although *H. alluaudi* is likewise widespread, the majority of records for the species are from the humid or subhumid regions. Actually, its presence in western Madagascar is based only on two single female records from Soalala and Bekopaka and not confirmed through examination of male genitalia. It is known from vegetation-rich ponds, as well as residual pools in temporary streams (Bertrand and Legros 1971). Remaining species in this genus are rare and all from the drier regions of Madagascar, including the Sambirano, but no habitat data are available in publications or on specimen labels. *Haliplus madagascariensis* is one of very few water beetle species endemic to the dry spiny thicket. The collecting locality coordinates point to the uppermost stretches of a seasonal tributary of the Linta River.

The diversity pattern for the family is unusual in that the highest diversity is to be found in the drier western parts of Madagascar. This region is also one of the most severely deforested, and the four species that occur only here are very rare, raising conservation concerns (Vondel and Bergsten 2012). Deforestation has a dramatic effect on aquatic habitats, leading to increased sediment load from erosion, increased insolation and water temperature, increased nutrient load, and changes in food web resources (Benstead et al. 2003a). No specimens have been found for *H. gamma*, *H. insularis*, or *H. incrassatus* in the past 60 years. It is possible that these species have suffered population declines, but it is also worth noting that tropical haliplids are very seasonal (Watts 2019). In tropical northern Australia, for instance, most adults have been collected during the wet season, and this may hold for Malagasy species as well. Hence, a dedicated search for the rare western species should be done during the wet season. The unique types of *H. madagascariensis* and *H. insularis* were both collected in February (Vondel and Bergsten 2012). Both active collecting with water nets as well as black-light traps near waters could be productive.

Subject editors: Brian L. Fisher and Steven M. Goodman

COLEOPTERA: NOTERIDAE, BURROWING WATER BEETLES

J. Bergsten and M. Manuel

Noteridae, the burrowing water beetles, is a rather small family of aquatic beetles with about 280 described species known worldwide (including those described since Nilsson 2011). The family is almost cosmopolitan, but its diversity is concentrated in tropical and subtropical regions (Nilsson 2005; Dettner 2016). Members of Noteridae belong to the Adephaga suborder of Coleoptera and superfamily Dytiscoidea, which also includes the diving beetles (Dytiscidae). The recently discovered monotypic family Meruidae from Venezuela is sister to Noteridae; together they form the sister clade to the remaining members of Dytiscoidea (Beutel et al. 2006; Gustafson et al. 2019; Vasilikopoulos et al. 2019). Molecular dating suggests a Jurassic origin for Noteridae (McKenna et al. 2019). Noterid species are placed in two subfamilies and three tribes, following Baca et al. (2017b). Phreatodytini, with the single subterranean Japanese genus *Phreatodytes*, is sister to *Notomicrus* and *Speonoterus* (Notomicrini) in Notomicrinae. The remaining 15 or so genera and >90% of all species belong to Noterinae, within the single tribe Noterini (Miller 2009; Baca et al. 2017b).

Both larvae and adults are aquatic, and most species occupy vegetation- or detritus-rich lentic habitats (standing waters). The name "burrowing water beetles" stems mainly from observations made of a few species of larvae burrowing in soft substrate around plant roots, and from extrapolations from the adult foreleg morphology of most Noterinae members (notably with a thick, curved distal spur on the protibia) (Miller 2009; Dettner 2016). Our knowledge of the diet and lifecycle of noterids is also very meager. Most observations stem from studies of temperate species in the Northern Hemisphere, especially the genus *Noterus*. Noterids are usually assumed to be predators of other aquatic invertebrates as both adults and larvae (Dettner 2016). However, dead arthropods and plant tissue may also be part of their diet (Spangler 1991b; Dettner 2016). Pupation has been observed to occur underwater (an exceptional trait among water beetles) in air-filled cocoons attached to aquatic plant roots. However, the life cycle and diet of most species are completely unknown.

MADAGASCAR DIVERSITY, DISTRIBUTION, AND BIOLOGY

On Madagascar, Noteridae is represented only by the subfamily Noterinae (no species of Notomicrinae are known from the Afrotropics). There is no endemic noterid genus on Madagascar, but all four genera include endemic species. Altogether, 19 species are known from four genera (species number in parentheses): *Neohydrocoptus* (3), *Synchortus* (2), *Sternocanthus* (5), and *Canthydrus* (9) (Guignot 1959a; Rocchi 1991; Nilsson 2005, 2011). *Hydrocanthus anthracinus* (type locality: "Madagascar") is a *nomen nudum* (unavailable and of unknown identity). The status of *C. biguttatus*, reported from Madagascar by Guignot (1960), is unclear. It has been presented as a synonym of *C. notula* (Nilsson 2005, 2011; synonymy established by Kolbe, 1902) but is considered a valid species by some previous authors (e.g., Peschet 1917; Guignot 1959a).

Noteridae species of Madagascar

Neohydrocoptus bradys (Guignot, 1955) (E) (TL, Namoroka)
N. placidus (Guignot, 1955) (E) (TL, Maroantsetra)
N. seriatus (Sharp, 1882) (AF) (TL, Madagascar)
Synchortus asperatus (Fairmaire, 1869) (E) (TL, Madagascar)
S. rugosopunctatus (Wehncke, 1876) (E) (TL, Madagascar)
Canthydrus concolor Sharp, 1882 (E) (TL, Madagascar)
C. andobonensis Guignot, 1960 (E) (TL, Andobo, forêt Antsingy, District Antsalova)
C. gibberosus Guignot, 1951 (E) (TL, Maroantsetra)
C. flavosignatus Régimbart, 1903 (AF) (TL, Fort Dauphin [Tolagnaro]; Pays Androy [extreme south]; Ankara [about 70 km SW of Maevatanana])
C. moneres Guignot, 1955 (E) (TL, Ambatoloana [misspelled "Ambatolaona"] east of Manjakandriana)
C. guttula (Aubé, 1838) (E*) (TL, La Réunion; Madagascar)
C. notula (Erichson, 1843) (AF) (TL, Angola)
C. biguttatus Régimbart, 1895 (AF) (TL, western Africa [multiple countries]) (according to some authors, synonym of *C. notula*; see text)
C. sellatus Régimbart, 1895 (E) (TL, Lake Ambodinandohalo [Antananarivo])
Sternocanthus constrictus (Régimbart, 1895) (AF) (TL, Antsianaka [east of Lake Alaotra])
S. delphinus (Guignot, 1942) (E) (TL, environs de Tananarive [Antananarivo])
S. fabiennae (Bameul, 1994) (E) (TL, Ambohimanatrika [about 40 km southeast of Ankarafantsika])
S. funebris (Fairmaire, 1869) (AF) (TL, Madagascar)
S. gracilis (H. J. Kolbe, 1883) (E) (TL, Madagascar, "S. inner part")
Note: E, endemic to Madagascar; E*, endemic to Madagascar and the Mascarenes; AF, Afrotropical; TL, type locality.

There has been no recent synthesis on the distribution patterns of Malagasy Noteridae species, but Alluaud (1900) summarized what was known at the time. In general, our knowledge of the distribution of the endemic noterid species on the island is very fragmentary, but some seem to be widespread, including in the lowlands, whereas others have a more or less restricted distribution. Most species are good fliers, resulting in broad distributions. Several occur in rice fields, wetlands, and marshes in open landscapes (Figure 9.41). Endemism for the family at the species level is relatively low at 66%, and there are only a few examples of microendemics. However, these numbers could change following modern revisions of the Afrotropical-Malagasy noterid fauna and new collecting efforts on Madagascar. For most of the species, virtually nothing is known about larval stages,

FIGURE 9.41 **A lentic habitat of temporary rainwater-filled pools with high Noteridae diversity near Mitsinjo and Lake Kinkony. This site housed the following noterid species in early December 2009: *Neohydrocoptus seriatus*, *Sternocanthus fabiennae*, *Canthydrus andobonensis*, *C. concolor*, and *C. guttula*.** (PHOTO by J. Bergsten.)

phenology, diet, trophic interactions, and other aspects of their biology. Potential larvae of *Canthydrus guttula* and *Hydrocanthus constrictus* were briefly described by Bertrand (1928a) from Antananarivo, but species-level identity is, in both cases, uncertain.

Neohydrocoptus

Neohydrocoptus seriatus (Figure 9.42a) is a very widespread and common nonendemic species across Madagascar. It is a good flier and often comes to light. It was described from Madagascar and also reported from Mauritius (Peschet 1917; Gomy 2000) and mainland Africa (Régimbart 1895), albeit the latter has been questioned pending genital examination (Guignot 1959a). The other two Malagasy species, both described by Guignot (1955a), are endemic but poorly known. *Neohydrocoptus placidus* was described based on a single male from Maroantsetra, later complemented with a female description from numerous specimens attracted to artificial light at the same locality (Guignot 1955b). Bameul (1984) reported this species from Ile Sainte Marie. *Neohydrocoptus bradys* was described from Namoroka and Betroka (Figure 9.42b). The type material needs to be consulted and newly collected material studied to clarify the species delimitation of the "*Neohydrocoptus bradys/placidus*" group or complex. New material of this group has been collected (north to south) from Anjanaharibe-Sud, Ankarafantsika, Andranofena, Manjakandriana, near Moramanga, Analamazaotra, Beroboka, Mananjary, Ranomafana, Sendrisoa, Maropaika, and Tolagnaro, and may include additional species. They have been collected in ponds, marshes, and lentic sections of rivers in both open and forested landscapes.

Synchortus

The two described *Synchortus* species on Madagascar are morphologically distinct and occur in different ecological niches. *Synchortus asperatus* is a widespread lowland species known in the east from near Toamasina; in several localities north up to Maroantsetra (Alluaud 1900; Guignot 1959a); and in the west from Ankarafantsika, Tsingy de Bemaraha, and Zombitse-Vohibasia. Flight capacity was documented in 2009 with a 22-watt black light placed on top of the *tsingy* (limestone formations) near Bekopaka. *Synchortus rugosopunctatus* (Figures 9.42c and d) is a central and eastern species known from elevations between 900 and 1700 m from Zahamena, Andasibe, Ankaratra Massif, Col de Tapia (between Antsirabe and Ambositra), and south to the Itremo Massif and Sendrisoa near Andringitra. Both species are lentic and inhabit swamps, marshes, and vegetation-rich ponds, or slow-flowing lentic sections at river edges. *Synchortus asperatus* can be found in anthropogenically disturbed habitats, such as rice fields and eutrophied wetlands frequented by zebu. A third species has recently been collected in a forest pond in Ranomafana but is not yet described. *Synchortus* species are sexually dimorphic, with large crescent-shaped punctures on elytra only in females (Figure 9.42d). The shape of punctures is diagnostic between the species, but there is also a large extent of intraspecific variation in their strength and density.

Canthydrus

The Afro-Malagasy members of this genus are in need of revision. A particular source of difficulty is intraspecific melanism variation, which in some species generates markedly different color patterns. The validity of some species, described merely based on pronotal and/or elytral coloration, needs to be reassessed. The brown-orange endemic *C. concolor* (Figure 9.42e) is a very widespread and common species both in the lowlands and the Central Highlands (Alluaud 1900) and is a good flier that often comes to light. *Canthydrus andobonensis* was described from Antsalova, and we have found it to be rather common in western Madagascar from Ankarafantsika to Tsingy de Bemaraha and Kirindy Forest CNFEREF (Centre National de Formation, d'Etudes et de Recherche en Environnement et Forestier), extending central-south to at least Analavoka (Ihorombe). The elytra

FIGURE 9.42 **Habitus images illustrating the four Noteridae genera of Madagascar. A) *Neohydrocoptus seriatus*, B) *N. bradys*, C) *Synchortus rugosopunctatus* male, D) *S. rugosopunctatus* female, E) *Canthydrus concolor*, F) *C. flavosignatus*, G) *C. guttula*, H) *Sternocanthus constrictus*, and I) *S. fabiennae*.** (PHOTOS by M. Manuel.)

color variation can range from five distinct yellow spots to just one distinct spot on each elytra or two longitudinal bands formed by the four anterior spots merging. This variation is very similar to that found in nonendemic *C. flavosignatus* (Figure 9.42f), and these species probably need reevaluation. A slightly darker series from Ranomafana possibly also belong to this species. *Canthydrus gibberosus* was described from Maroantsetra, and so far, we know it only from the lowland east coast south to Toamasina. It is probably close to *C. andobonensis* and *C. flavosignatus*. The *C. notula* group consists of several very similar species that are entirely black, apart from a variously extended anterior area on the head, the anterolateral pronotal corners, and a lateral and posteromedian testaceous spot on the elytron. On Madagascar, this group includes *C. notula*, *C. biguttatus* (possibly a synonym of *notula*, see above), and *C. guttula* (Figure 9.42g); the first two are nonendemic, while *G. guttula*, endemic to the Malagasy Region (Madagascar and the Mascarenes), is the most widespread and common on Madagascar. The endemics *C. moneres* and *C. sellatus* are poorly known, but according to available data, they seem confined to the Central Highlands, from where they were described.

Sternocanthus

Sternocanthus, previously a subgenus of *Hydrocanthus*, has recently been elevated to genus rank (Baca et al. 2017b). In this new classification, *Hydrocanthus* is distributed in the New World and *Sternocanthus* in the Afro-Malagasy, Oriental, and Australian regions. *Sternocanthus* species are the largest representatives of Noteridae in Madagascar in terms of body size. The five known Malagasy species are all entirely black and can be distinguished mainly by differences in habitus, punctation of the prosternal process surface, and shape of the median lobe of the male aedeagus. Like other noterids, they live mainly in lentic, well-vegetated habitats. The nonendemic *S. constrictus* (Figure 9.42h) is common and widespread in the lowlands, as well as in the Central Highlands up to an elevation of about 1800 m. The other two widespread species, *S. gracilis* (endemic) and *S. funebris* (nonendemic), inhabit the lowlands (but see below). The endemic *S. fabiennae* (Figure 9.42i) has been described from Ambohimanatrika (Mahajanga Province) (Bameul 1994) and seems to be a rather common species in the west, now known from Namoroka, Ankarafantsika, Mahavavy Kinkony, between Morafenobe and Ambohijanahary, and in diverse localities around Ranohira (Isalo), Zombitse-Vohibasia, and in the Makay. Finally, the enigmatic *S. delphinus* has been described from a single female specimen collected in Antananarivo. The holotype is morphologically very similar to *S. funebris*, from which it differs only by the more superficial punctation on the prosternal process (M. Manuel, unpublished data). We have specimens from Manjakatompo (Ankaratra Massif) that possibly belong to this species. More work is needed to determine whether *S. delphinus* is a valid species or represents only a variation characterizing isolated populations of *S. funebris* present in the Central Highlands.

PHYLOGENY AND EVOLUTION

It is clear that noterids have independently colonized Madagascar on multiple occasions, as none of the genera are endemic, and several of the species are widespread across the Afrotropics. *Synchortus*, together with *Renotus* (the only African genus not to have reached Madagascar), are the only noterid genera that do not occur outside the Afro-Malagasy region. Phylogenetically, *Synchortus* occupies a position as sister group to a clade with most other Noterinae genera of the world (Miller 2009; Baca et al. 2017b) and hence is likely to be rather old. *Neohydrocoptus*, *Sternocanthus*, and *Canthydrus* are distributed across the tropical and subtropical portions of the Old World. Colonization of Madagascar could potentially have been from either Asia or Africa, but given the distances of these two landmasses from the island and that the highest species diversity of all three genera is in the Afrotropics, it is likely that most Malagasy forms have ancestors from Africa. Strengthening this argument is the fact that all nonendemic noterid species on Madagascar also occur on Africa and none in Asia. Most of the Madagascar species have yet to be included in a phylogenetic analysis with congeners from Africa and Australasia, which is needed to allow researchers to draw stronger conclusions about colonization and the speciation history of Noteridae on the island.

Subject editors: Brian L. Fisher and Steven M. Goodman

COLEOPTERA: TORRIDINCOLIDAE, TORRENT BEETLES

J. Bergsten

Members of Torridincolidae, known as torrent beetles, are small, 1–3 mm long beetles currently consisting of seven genera and 52 described species across the New and Old Worlds. Additional undescribed species are known, especially from northern South America (Sampaio and Short 2018). The family is recorded from the Neotropics (Brazil, Paraguay, Venezuela, Suriname, and Guyana), Afrotropics (Democratic Republic of Congo, Zimbabwe, Namibia, South Africa, Madagascar, and Kenya; J. Bergsten, unpublished data), and Japan and southeastern China (Steffan 1964, 1973; Beutel and Vanin 2016; Sampaio and Short 2018). The greatest species diversity (34) is found in the Neotropics. Torrent beetles are aquatic in all life stages, including pupal, and larvae, pupae, and adults can be found together in the same habitat (Reichardt 1973). They are associated exclusively with running water and most of them with the hygropetric microhabitat where streams flow finely over bedrock at sides of waterfalls or at seepages. Most adult torridincolids breathe with plastron respiration, while larvae breathe with segmented tracheal gills (Hinton 1967; Beutel and Vanin 2016). Adults and larvae are assumed to feed on algae (Lawrence and Reichardt 1991). Adult beetles are thought to be involved in the pollination of a cascade-growing plant of the Podostemaceae family (Léonard and Dessart 1994). Larvae and adults of a South American species were also collected on the submerged leaves of a Podostemaceae at a waterfall (Pinto et al. 2011). Karyotype study of a South American torrid beetle of the genus *Ytu* gave a diploid chromosome number (2n = 20), with nine pairs of autosomes and a heteromorphic XY sex chromosome pair (Mesa and Fontanetti 1985). At least in some places, fish can be a predator of adult beetles, as evidenced by a species of Torridincolidae described from the gut contents of a characid fish (Reichardt and Costa 1967).

Torridincolidae was the fourth and last family of the beetle suborder Myxophaga to be described (Steffan 1964), and the monophyly is not in question (Beutel 1999; Beutel et al. 1999; Lawrence et al. 2011). Phylogenomic analyses resolve the position as a sister lineage to a clade with Sphaeriusidae and Lepiceridae (McKenna et al. 2019). Although it was the last family described, today it is the most diverse of the Myxophaga. The origin was estimated to the Triassic–Jurassic border by McKenna et al. (2019). Endrödy-Younga (1997) divided Torridincolidae into two subfamilies—Deleveinae, including Palearctic *Satonius* and southern African *Delevea*, and Torridincolinae. However, morphological phylogenetic analyses have shown that Deleveinae is paraphyletic, and *Delevea* is sister to all remaining genera, including *Satonius* (Beutel et al. 1999).

MADAGASCAR DIVERSITY AND DISTRIBUTION

On Madagascar, seven species of the endemic genus *Incoltorrida* are known (Figure 9.43). The family Torridincolidae was first reported from Madagascar by Steffan (1973), who erected the new genus *Incoltorrida* for *I. madagassica*. The description was based on material collected by Henri Bertrand in 1960 at both Cap Ambalasandra and in the Central Highlands between Antananarivo and Ambositra. The larvae and pupae, collected together with adults, were actually previously described and illustrated by Bertrand (1965) but noted as "genus *incertae sedis*" with unknown family affinity. Subsequently, Perkins and Bergsten (2019) described six additional species based on material collected between 2004 and 2018, and provided a determination key. The genus was delimited from African *Torridincola* mainly by the absence of parameres (Steffan 1973). However, the homologous apical setae of the parameres are present at the base, but the elongate paramere "stalks" present in *Torridincola* are absent in *Incoltorrida* (Perkins and Bergsten 2019). *Incoltorrida* species are known only from the lowland and medium-altitude moist evergreen regions of eastern, northern, and central Madagascar, including the Sambirano Region. *Incoltorrida magna* (Galoko Mountains), *I. galoko* (Galoko Mountains), *I. zahamena* (Zahamena), and *I. marojejy* (Marojejy) are known only from their respective type localities. *Incoltorrida madagassica*, *I. quintacostata*, and *I. benescultа* have wider distributions stretching from the Central Highlands to the northern parts of the island.

FIGURE 9.43 **Habitus of *Incoltorrida* species: A) *I. magna*, B) *I. marojejy*, C) *I. benesculpta*.** (PHOTOS from Perkins and Bergsten 2019; licensed under a Creative Commons Attribution License, http://creativecommons.org/licenses/by/3.0.)

Torridincolidae species of Madagascar

Incoltorrida benesculpta Perkins & Bergsten, 2019
I. galoko Perkins & Bergsten, 2019
I. madagassica Steffan, 1973
I. magna Perkins & Bergsten, 2019
I. marojejy Perkins & Bergsten, 2019
I. quintacostata Perkins & Bergsten, 2019
I. zahamena Perkins & Bergsten, 2019

PHYLOGENY AND EVOLUTION

Based on morphology, *Incoltorrida* is most closely related to mainland African *Torridincola* (Beutel 1999). Dense parallel incisions along the posterior margin of abdominal sternites were identified as a synapomorphy in adults (Beutel 1999), while larvae share dorsally situated spiracular gills on anterior abdominal tergites (Steffan 1964; Sampaio and Short 2018; Perkins and Bergsten 2019). Together, *Incoltorrida* and *Torridincola* are probably most closely related to a South American clade consisting either of *Iapir*, *Claudiella*, and *Ytu* (Beutel 1999), or only of *Iapir* and *Claudiella*, with which the larvae share the lack of lateral contact hairs on the thoracic terga (Beutel et al. 1999). *Iapir* and *Claudiella* larvae also seem to have at least two anterior spiracular gills situated more dorsally, although less so than in *Incoltorrida* and *Torridincola* (Vanin and Costa 2001; Reichardt 1973). The larvae of *Ytu* in turn share some similarities with *Satonius* (Hájek and Fikáček 2008). The alternative phylogenetic possibilities should be tested with molecular data. No dated phylogeny of Torridincolidae has yet been presented, and no crown-group age estimate is available.

Incoltorrida likely colonized Madagascar from mainland Africa, but timing for this presumed event is unknown. However, the family is undoubtedly an old lineage, and the distribution pattern of Torridincolinae is "typically Gondwanian" (Endrödy-Younga 1997), with the stem group estimated at 200 million years old (McKenna et al. 2019). The Neotropical *Iapir-Claudiella-*(*Ytu*) and Afrotropical *Torridincola-Incoltorrida* clades could be the result of vicariance as the south Atlantic opened (Granot and Dyment 2015), and the subsequent colonization of Madagascar would have been through overseas dispersal. Although not yet tested in a phylogenetic context, *Incoltorrida* is very likely a monophyletic island radiation. The species diversity of *Incoltorrida* is bound to increase as more hygropetric habitats are sampled across Madagascar.

BIOLOGY

In Madagascar, all torrent beetles have been collected in hygropetric habitats (see habitat photos in Perkins and Bergsten 2019). In the first report of these beetles from Madagascar, Bertrand (1965) describes the habitat as "les rochers suintants ou ruisselants" (oozing or dripping rocks). The hygropetric habitats have sometimes been associated with seepages of a fine water film onto rock surfaces that are not connected to streams, or with water seeping down from forest margins at the sides of streams. Alternatively, these beetles have been found in hygropetric habitats in streams

FIGURE 9.44 Locality of *Incoltorrida marojejy* on the Marojejy Massif, just above Camp Marojejia at around 775 m. This is the typical hygropetric habitat of *Incoltorrida*, consisting of a millimeter-thin water film slowly flowing over bedrock but offset from the main channel of a forest stream. (PHOTO by J. Bergsten.)

with a sometimes thicker and faster-flowing water film over exposed bedrock, either at the sides of waterfalls or on bedrock with a more gentle inclination (Figure 9.44). On Nosy Mangabe, *I. madagassica* was found in good numbers at forest-edge seepages onto sea cliffs, potentially exposed to saltwater splash. Up to three different species have been found to co-occur at a single locality (Galoko Mountains; Perkins and Bergsten 2019). At one site where *I. quintacostata* and *I. benesculpta* co-occurred, they occupied slightly different microhabitats 2 m apart, indicative of niche division and adaptive morphologies (Perkins and Bergsten 2019). The larger *I. quintacostata*, with a reduced number of elytral costae laterally, occupied a faster-flowing, thicker water layer in the central portions of the stream just before a small cascade. The smaller *I. benesculpta*, with a strongly sculptured dorsal surface, occupied a vertical seepage rock face at the side of the stream with a thinner more slowly flowing water film. In terms of elevation, *Incoltorrida* has been collected from sea level up to 1700 m in the Central Highlands. This is also the intraspecific elevation range for *I. madagassica* and *I. quintacostata*, which suggests a broad climatic niche envelope.

Very little is known about the flight capacity of torridincolids in general, but Hájek et al. (2011) reported from Asia a specimen of *Satonius kurosawai* caught in a flight intercept trap. In the same species, wing polymorphism was documented, with clearly flightless micropterous forms as well as macropterous forms with fully developed hind wings. With one exception, only one morph was found at a locality; moreover, there was a latitudinal trend, with only micropterous forms found at higher latitudes (Hájek et al. 2011). Most members of the family have fully developed wings but rarely fly, as noted by Endrödy-Younga (1997) at a Namibian site for *Delevea*. An unusual observation of a flying *Torridincola* among Podostemaceae plants at a waterfall was mentioned by Léonard and Dessart (1994). Steffan (1973) reported normally developed hindwings for *I. madagassica*, similar to wings illustrated for *Torridincola*. Perkins and Bergsten (2019) did not examine or describe wing development in the other six *Incoltorrida* species, but micro- or brachyptery has not been documented for any of the Malagasy species. To our knowledge, *Incoltorrida* has never been collected at light or with flight-intercept traps. If flight takes place in *Incoltorrida*, it is presumably uncommon and likely correlated with the relative stability of the habitat (Endrödy-Younga 1997), as in *Satonius kurosawai* (Hájek et al. 2011).

Larvae have been collected in association with adults for *I. quintacostata*, *I. marojejy*, and *I. madagassica*, and the first was illustrated with ventral and dorsal photos (Perkins and Bergsten 2019). The larvae are dorsoventrally flattened, with short crab-like legs ending in strong claws well adapted to cling to the substrate in a flowing water film. The last instar has four-segmented spiracular gills, but in earlier instars, they are three-segmented.

The urn-shaped lorica of sessile peritrich ciliates of the genus *Platycola* was documented on *I. madagassica* (Perkins and Bergsten 2019). Interestingly, Spangler (1980) described an epibiont of the same petritrich ciliate family, Vaginicolidae, on an *Ytu* species in Brazil. The details of the relationship between Vaginicolidae (epibiont) and Torridincolidae (basibiont) is not known in terms of their ecology or evolutionary history.

Subject editors: Brian L. Fisher and Steven M. Goodman

COLEOPTERA: HYDROSCAPHIDAE, SKIFF BEETLES

J. Bergsten

Members of Hydroscaphidae, known as skiff beetles, are minute, 1–2 mm long fusiform insects with truncated elytra and exposed, telescoping, terminal abdominal segments (Figure 9.45). The family includes four genera, three strictly Neotropical (*Confossa*, *Scaphydra*, and *Yara*), with three species each, and the widespread genus *Hydroscapha*, with 23 species, which is known from most biogeographic regions except Australia (A. Short et al. 2015). Interestingly, no species has yet been described from the mainland Afrotropics, but one specimen of unknown generic affinity, possibly *Hydroscapha*, is cited from Mpumalanga Province in South Africa (Villet and Endrödy-Younga 2007). These minute beetles are easily overlooked and could be more widespread in Africa and elsewhere. *Hydroscapha* was not known from South America until recently (Hall and Short 2010).

Hydroscaphidae belongs to the small beetle suborder Myxophaga, the fourth and last described suborder of beetles, erected by Crowson (1955). Myxophaga includes four families—two riparian (Lepiceridae and Sphaeriusidae) and two aquatic (Hydroscaphidae and Torridincolidae)—with around a hundred described species in the world combined. Except for Lepiceridae, which has an extant New World distribution, all are represented on Madagascar. Recent genomic analyses point to a sister-group relationship with the other tiny beetle suborder Archostemata and a Permian or Late Triassic origin of Myxophaga (Zhang et al. 2018; McKenna et al. 2019). Morphological analyses of the four myxophagan families have pointed to a sister-group relationship between Hydroscaphidae and Sphaeriusidae, with Lepiceridae forming a sister lineage to the remaining three families (Beutel and Haas 1998; Beutel 1999; Beutel et al. 1999; Lawrence et al. 2011). However, the latest genomic analyses place the families Lepiceridae and Sphaeriusidae as sister taxa and conclude with strong support that Hydroscaphidae is sister to the remaining three families with an inferred origin in the Triassic (McKenna et al. 2019).

FIGURE 9.45 **Habitus of *Hydroscapha andringitra*.** (PHOTOS from Perkins and Bergsten 2019; licensed under a Creative Commons Attribution License http://creativecommons.org/licenses/by/3.0.)

MADAGASCAR DIVERSITY AND DISTRIBUTION

Hydroscaphidae is represented on Madagascar by two species in the genus *Hydroscapha*. The family was first recorded from the island by Paulian (1949), who described *H. saboureaui* from near Miandrivazo in the central-west region ("60 km au sud d'Ankavandra, sur la piste de Miandrivazo" [60 km south of Ankavandra, on the trail to Miandrivazo]; Paulian 1949: 371). A second species, *H. andringitra*, was described by Perkins and Bergsten (2019) from Sendrisoa between Ambalavao and Andringitra National Park (Figures 9.45 and 9.46). Both species are known solely from their type localities. The two species can be identified based on the details presented in Perkins and Bergsten (2019), who also redescribed *H. saboureaui* and provided illustrations of genitalia and terminal segments of both sexes, which were not fully detailed by Paulian (1949).

Hydroscaphidae species of Madagascar

Hydroscapha andringitra Perkins and Bergsten, 2019
H. saboureaui Paulian, 1949

PHYLOGENY AND EVOLUTION

Hydroscapha is sister to a clade with the remaining three Neotropical genera of Hydroscaphidae (A. Short et al. 2015). As such, and given that Hydroscaphidae is inferred to be of Triassic origin, *Hydroscapha* has the potential to be a very old lineage. This is further supported by a lower Cretaceous impression fossil from China interpreted to belong to the extant genus (Cai et al. 2012). Neither of the two Malagasy species has yet been included in a phylogenetic context, and no DNA sequence is available.

FIGURE 9.46 **Hygropetric habitat and type locality of *Hydroscapha andringitra* near Sendrisoa, between Ambalavao and the northern limit of the Andringitra protected area; one of two known localities of *Hydroscapha* on Madagascar.** (PHOTO by J. Bergsten.)

Morphological characters were not interpreted to try to deduce a likely closest relative (Paulian 1949; Perkins and Bergsten 2019). Possible hypotheses as to the origin of *Hydroscapha* on Madagascar include a vicariant (or dispersal) origin from India–Southeast Asia or, if *Hydroscapha* indeed occur on the Afrotropical mainland, a later dispersal over the Mozambique Channel. The most diverse region for *Hydroscapha*—a characteristic often correlated with the origin of a group through the time-for-speciation effect (Wiens 2011)—is in fact Southeast Asia and in particular the region of India, Sri Lanka, and Nepal, with eight described species altogether (A. Short et al. 2015; Löbl 1994; Fikáček and Šípková 2009). India also houses the only documented localities with multiple syntopically co-occurring species of *Hydroscapha* (Fikáček and Šípková 2009). Based on what is currently known, evidence is perhaps leaning toward an Asian origin, and the age of the genus, according to fossil interpretation (Cai et al. 2012), does not preclude a possible Madagascar-India vicariance origin. Nevertheless, dedicated surveys in hygropetric habitats should be done in sub-Saharan Africa.

BIOLOGY

Hydroscaphidae beetles are associated with running water, and most species are from hygropetric habitats—a thin film of water flowing over rocks, often at the sides of waterfalls, at stream sections or seepages. In this habitat, the beetles are often found on algal films upon which adults and larvae presumably feed (Vanin et al. 2016). Species in North America are known from hot springs as well as colder rivers, and there are also some records of *Hydroscapha* collected under stones in fast-flowing streams at almost a meter's depth (Vanin et al. 2016).

Hydroscapha sabouraui was collected from a seepage forming a shallow pool with very warm water, and the adults were found crawling on an algal mat on the sand (Paulian 1949). The second Malagasy species was collected under similar circumstances—a small seepage with brownish water on a bare rock with parts of the seepage containing algal films—and in open sun-exposed landscape (Figure 9.46) (Perkins and Bergsten 2019). Open and exposed to the sun, hygropetric habitats with warm water and algal films are thus common features of both Madagascar localities. Miandrivazo is an area with dry deciduous and riparian forests, whereas *H. andringitra* was collected at an elevation of 1165 m in a medium-altitude moist evergreen forest region. Paulian (1949: 371) further observed flight capacity during daytime ("nous avons pu noter la facilité de leur envol en plein soleil" [we were able to note the ease of their flight in full sunlight]). Flight capacity has also been confirmed in the North American species *H. natans* (Löbl 1994; Vanin et al. 2016). A single large egg develops in the female, and pupation take place in the water within the last larval exuvia (Vanin et al. 2016). The larvae of *Hydroscapha* are fusiform, similar to adults, with posterior thoracic and abdominal tergites lined with setae, lateral long contact hairs and three pairs of spiracular, ballon-shaped gills (Vanin et al. 2016). Larvae of the two Malagasy species are not known.

Subject editors: Brian L. Fisher and Steven M. Goodman

COLEOPTERA: SCARABAEIDAE, MELOLONTHINAE, TRIBE ENARIINI, SCARAB BEETLES, *VOANGORY*

M. Lacroix and L. Andriamampianina

Scarab beetles are among the largest groups of Coleoptera in terms of species diversity. Scarabaeidae is a very diverse group, comprising insects of various forms and sizes, colonizing different types of habitats over a wide geographic range, and occupying various ecological niches. The feeding regimes of scarab beetles include forms that are phytophagous, saprophagous, necrophagous, and coprophagous. Other scarabs are parasites, including those that are myrmecophilous (living in ant nests) or termitophilous (living in termite mounds). The scarab beetle group treated here was also treated in the precursor to this book (Andriamampianina 2003).

The subfamily of Melolonthinae is among the well-represented scarab beetles in Madagascar, with six out of the eight tribes known worldwide, including: Rhizotrogini, Leucopholini, Schizonychini, Enariini, Pegylini, and Diplotaxini. In the Mascarenes, melolonthine beetles are represented only by the tribe Rhizotrogini (six genera and nine species), whereas on the Comoro islands only the tribe Enariini is represented (six genera and 16 species). According to Lacroix (1993), these six Comorian enariine genera are derived from Malagasy enariines. The Malagasy Region (Madagascar, the Comoros, and the Mascarenes) includes 260 species of Melolonthinae, all endemics and belonging to 49 genera.

TAXONOMY AND EVOLUTION

Enariini probably evolved sometime around the Miocene epoch (Lacroix 1993) and constitutes the only tribe of melolonthine beetle that is totally endemic to the Malagasy Region; excluding four forms known from the Comoro islands, the vast majority of species are found on Madagascar. The tribe Enariini is one of the best-known groups of scarab beetles in Madagascar and is distributed all over the country. Several studies of its members have been conducted on their biology and taxonomy. Olivier described the very first enariine species from the island, *Encya commersoni*, in 1789. Following several studies, including Klug (1833), Blanchard (1851), Künckel d'Herculais (1887), Alluaud (1900), Fairmaire (1883, 1889, 1901, 1903, 1905), and Moser (1919), 45 other species were described by the middle of the 20th century. When Dewailly created the tribe Enariini of the subfamily Melolonthinae in 1950, it was first divided into 10 genera and comprised 126 species. Between 1989 and 1993, the work of Lacroix greatly improved the state of knowledge of the enariines. The revision of the melolonthines by Lacroix (1989, 1993) resulted in the elevation of this group to the rank of family, whereas all the tribes of the former subfamily of Melolonthinae remained unchanged.

This revision of the melolonthine beetles has also led to the creation of several new genera. Thus, the genus *Encya* was divided into eight genera and *Enaria* into four genera. These changes were made to distinguish between groups based on characters that are unique to these genera. As a result of this revision, the size of the Enariini tribe increased to 30 genera and 164 species (Lacroix 1993). In this contribution, six of these genera are excluded (*Comencya*, *Djadjoua*, *Komrina*, *Humblotania*, *Mayataia*, and *Joziratia*), as they are found only in the Comoro archipelago. The tribe represents 63% of the Malagasy species of Melolonthinae.

MORPHOLOGICAL CHARACTERISTICS

Enariine beetles vary in size, color, and habits. The group is generally characterized by a heavy body, oval to elongate in shape and convex in profile, with each five-segmented tarsus ending with two tarsal claws that are either bifid or toothed. The powerful legs are armed with teeth or scalloped on the outer edge. The front tibiae are more or less dilated. The hind tibiae have two spurs that are very close to each other. The antennae are of the type lamellate, containing 10 segments, with the last three (rarely more) expanded into a platelike structure that may be spread apart or united to form a compact terminal club. The number of elements making up the antennal clubs is highly variable and is generally three but can be up to seven. In contrast to the other tribes of melolonthines, enariine beetles are characterized by the absence of any oculary canthus or internal spur on the front tibiae. The oculary canthus is a prolongation of the lateral part of the cheeks of beetles in front of or surrounding the eye. In addition, the sixth visible sternite is entire and not hidden under the fifth. The larvae are grub-like, with well-developed antennae and legs. They are typically C-shaped when immobile (Randriamanantsoa et al. 2010).

ECOLOGICAL CHARACTERISTICS

Adult enariines are hosts for some groups of insects such as Pyrgotidae flies (Diptera), whereas their larvae are hosts for a wide variety of other parasitoids, including the Hymenoptera families Scoliidae and Pelecenidae. They are also prey to some Asilidae and Tabanidae flies and even some Carabidae beetles (Dewailly 1950; Borror et al. 1976). Enariine species are mainly nocturnal or crepuscular and may fly to lights at night, but some are active during the day. The adults feed principally at night on plant materials, such as grasses, foliage, and probably flowers; some are serious pests of agricultural crops (e.g., corn, banana, sugarcane). The larvae or white grubs feed in the soil on grasses and other plant roots. They are destructive insects and can cause a lot of damage to crops such as rice, corn, other small grains, and potatoes, as well as to areas of pasture (Randriamanantsoa et al. 2010).

THE NATURAL HISTORY OF ENARIINE BEETLES BY GENUS

The entire tribe of Enariini is endemic to Madagascar and the Comoro islands (Dewailly 1950; Lacroix 1993). Geographic information used in this chapter was derived from the literature (mainly Lacroix 1993). Complementary data were obtained from the insect collections at the Parc Botanique et Zoologique de Tsimbazaza (PBZT), Antananarivo; the Entomology Department, the Natural History Museum (BMNH), London; the Muséum National d'Histoire Naturelle (MNHN), Paris; and the authors' own data based on recent fieldwork.

Given their feeding behavior (phytophageous), their distribution depends on the flora and type of vegetation. While most enariine beetles tend to be forest-dependent, members of this group are adapted to a wide range of habitats from the most natural forests, to agroforestry systems, to more anthropogenic areas including agricultural and pasture lands. On the basis of vegetation type and climates, five main regions are generally recognized: the humid, subhumid, montane, dry, and subarid (Schatz 2000). The same five ecological regions are used in this paper to describe the distribution of Enariini.

Enthora

In general, the eight species of this genus are quite large scarabs reaching up to 2 cm in length. They have a voluminous body shape and shiny metallic elytra. *Enthora* species are found in the eastern humid, subhumid, and montane regions. Except for *E. polita*, *E. ornata*, and *E. chlorodera*, which are broadly distributed all along the moist evergreen forest, the remaining species have very localized distributions. For example, *E. alluaudi* occurs only along the Angavo Escarpment; *E. miliaris* is confined to the area surrounding and to the north of the Antongil Bay; *E. lunata* is known only from the Tsaratanàna Massif; *E. atomaria* from near Antsiranana; and *E. catalai* in the forests near the Tantamaly Pass. The most broadly distributed forms are *E. chlorodera* and *E. ornata*, known from numerous collection sites. Females of these two species are rarely collected.

Encya

These big scarabs are generally more than 2 cm in length; the largest can measure up to 4 cm. Members of this genus are easily recognizable by their large size and the yellowish scales that color their elytra. The four species of this genus, *Encya commersoni*, *E. strigiscutata*, *E. sikorai*, and *E. albostriata*, occur in sympatry and are common in the eastern humid, subhumid, and montane regions. *Encya strigiscutata* is also very common in the Central Highlands and is a pest of various agricultural plants, such as corn and banana (Paulian 1950).

Bisencya

This genus contains eight species that vary in length from 2 to 3 cm and are generally brownish or reddish in color. In general, they occur in zones above 1000 m and tend to be geographically restricted to mountain groups. For example, *Bisencya catalai* occurs on the Andringitra Massif, and *B. viettei* is known only from the Anosyenne Mountains. Other species have distinctly broader geographic ranges. All members of the genus are found in eastern humid and subhumid regions, with the exception of *B. lacunosa*, which has been collected in the Bongolava area of the western limit of the subhumid region.

Globencya

Three species of the eastern moist evergreen forest compose this genus. They are elongate in body form, vary in size from 13 to 19 mm, and are brownish or reddish in color. *Globencya cribrata* occurs in the forests between Ranomafana National Park and Zahamena National Park; *G. farafanganae* is known only from low elevations near Farafangana; and *G. griveaudi* is from the forests of Manafiafy, near Tolagnaro.

Eutrichesis

Insects in this genus are big (24–45 mm), hairy, and reddish or fawn-colored. The three species of this genus—*Eutrichesis pilosicollis*, *E. bourgini*, and *E. punctatus*—are found across the humid, subhumid, and montane regions.

Anthrencya

The four species belonging to this genus are found in the moist evergreen forests. They are between 15 and 30 mm in length, elongate, and generally brownish. *Anthrencya anthracina* has a disjunct distribution, with a population found in the extreme north around Montagne d'Ambre and another population occurring in the region surrounding Toamasina. *Anthrencya castanipes* occurs at an elevation range of 400–2100 m and is found mainly in the subhumid region. *Anthrencya arrowi* occurs in the moist evergreen forests around Maroantsetra, whereas *A. lebisi* is known from the area of Moramanga.

Mucrencya

There are two species in this genus, but only *Mucrencya mucronata* occurs on Madagascar. The other species, *M. inermis*, is encountered only on Grande Comore. Individuals of this group vary from 18 to 30 mm in length. They are elongate and brownish, and the elytra are characterized by prominent longitudinal ridges and many circular whitish scales, with the apical angle extended as a point. *Mucrencya mucronata* occurs across a broad elevational gradient from sea level to 2300 m and is very common in different regions of Madagascar.

Varencya

Varencya is one of the largest genera, with 14 species found all over the eastern humid, subhumid, and montane regions. They are 13–25 mm in length, and the elytra have prominent irregular and projecting relief. Some species have broad geographic distributions, such as *V. varia*, which occurs across the eastern moist evergreen forest block and the subhumid Central Highlands. Other taxa have very limited ranges and are restricted to the summital zones of mountains—examples include *V. vittata*, *V. conspersa*, and *V. notata*, all three known only from the higher portions of the Marojejy Massif; and *V. intricata* and *V. tessellata*, both from the Tsaratanàna Massif.

Apicencya

Members of this genus, which is composed of nine species, measure from 15 to 25 mm in length and vary in coloration from yellowish to brown, with the apical calluses on smooth, widely striped elytra. *Apicencya* species occur across the island, including all types of bioclimatic regions, and several species have broad distributions. The subhumid central region has the greatest number of species with eight, followed by the western region with five species. The eastern moist evergreen forests have only three species, but none is a regional endemic. *Apicencya apicalis* is present across Madagascar.

Enaria

Enaria is the largest genus of the Enariini tribe, with 37 recognized species. They are medium-size, 10–20 mm long, with an elongate body shape slightly widened at the apex. Members of this genus occur in virtually all natural habitats on the island. Some are restricted to very specific habitats, such as *E. biapicata*, *E. grossepunctata*, and *E. androyensis*, found in the dry spiny thicket, and others have broad distributions across much of the island (e.g., *E. melanictera*). The western dry region has the greatest species diversity, with 19 species. The southern subarid region has 11 species, the central subhumid region has nine species, and the eastern humid region has six species. No species occurs across the island. Some members of this genus are also pests of agricultural crops. For example, adult *E. melanictera* attacks cacao, sugarcane, and *Eucalyptus*.

Cherbezatina

Cherbezatina constitutes the second-largest genus within the tribe Enariini, with 32 species. This genus is broadly distributed across the island in a variety of forest types in the humid, subhumid, montane, and dry regions. However, no representative of this genus has been observed in the subarid region. These beetles vary from 10 to 20 mm in length and are brownish or reddish to fawn in color. In general, most species have relatively small geographic ranges that seem to be allied to vegetation types and geographic zones. Members of this genus are principally concentrated in the central east of Madagascar, though some species occur in the north and west of the island. Some forms are restricted to offshore islands, such as *C. kalalaoensis*, known only from Ile Sainte Marie, and *C. marmorata*, only from Nosy Be.

Pseudenaria

This genus comprises eight species that are dark brown in color and of medium size (15–19 mm long). Males have antennal clubs with six parts. The protruding portions of elytra are strong. These beetles are all associated with moist evergreen forests. The different species are distributed in the humid, subhumid, and montane regions, but the highest diversity is observed on the massifs of Tsaratanàna, Marojejy, and Ankaratra, as well in the Moramanga area. Certain species have very localized distributions, such as *P. bidens*, known only from Manongarivo; *P. sogai*, from the highlands of Tsaratanàna and Marojejy; and *P. unguicularis*, from Andringitra. Others, such as *P. maculata*, have broad distributions across the Central Highlands.

Vadonaria

Vadonaria species vary from 13 to 18 mm in length and are brownish. Males have antennal clubs with seven parts. Members of this genus seem to be relatively rare and are not frequently collected. There are five species: *V. ambreensis*, found in the extreme north; *V. caliginosa*, from around Antongil Bay; *V. maxima*, localized in the high mountains of Andringitra; and *V. guilhoni* and *V. variegata*, from the Central Highlands.

Renaudiana

This genus comprises two species, *Renaudiana ranomandriensis* and *R. guttata*, that are brownish in color and about 13 mm in length. Both are confined to the Anosyenne Mountains.

Remaining Genera

Within this tribe are an additional 10 genera, all of which are monospecific, listed here with length, color, and distribution information.

- *Anenaria*, ~20 mm in length; very distinctive elongate, brownish, and hairy body; occurring in the central subhumid region and eastern moist evergreen forests from 50 to 1600 m elevation
- *Pseudencya*, ~2 cm in length; brown; known from ~1750 m elevation on the Marojejy Massif
- *Lebbea*, 2 cm in length; stout, oval, and brown; restricted to the high mountains of the Sambirano Region and northern Madagascar between 1000 and 2030 m
- *Semienaria*, ~10 mm in length; light brown; restricted to the subarid region of the south with sandy soil
- *Polyenaria*, one of the smallest species in the tribe, <1 cm in length; light brown; restricted to the central subhumid region
- *Ravautiana*, ~11 mm in length; yellowish brown; restricted to the southeast
- *Synenaria*, 7 mm in length; brownish but with the outer part of the pronotum and the inner part of the elytra much more whitish; restricted to Montagne d'Ambre
- *Pentaphylla*, ~11 mm in length; reddish brown; occurring in the subarid region in the southwest and in the central subhumid region around Antananarivo
- *Djafouna*, slightly less than 15 mm in length and distinctly elongate; light brown; restricted to the dry region near Maevatanana
- *Machala*, ~10 mm in length; yellowish brown; confined to the high mountains around the Tsaratanàna Massif

SUMMARY

Members of the Enariini tribe occur across Madagascar, with 148 species distributed in 24 genera (Table 9.31). Ten out of the 24 genera of Malagasy enariines are monospecific, and several others comprise just two or three species. These figures reflect the considerable morphological variety of the group.

In general, enariine beetles are predominantly forest dwelling. A considerable percentage occurs in the eastern moist evergreen forest and a lesser percentage in the remaining forested portions of the central subhumid region. The varied elevational gradient in the eastern portion of the island contains a wide assortment of habitats and microhabitats that in turn seem to have favored speciation in this group. A few genera, particularly *Semienaria*, *Pentaphylla*, and *Ravautiana*, are well adapted to the dry and subarid environments of the west and south of Madagascar.

A large number of species have very localized distributions, indicating a high level of regional speciation. Each portion of the island has at least one genus that is locally endemic: *Globencya*, *Pseudencya*, and *Renaudiana* in the east; *Djafouna* in the west; *Ravautiana* in the south; *Synenaria* in the north; *Machala* in the upper reaches of the Tsaratanàna Massif; and *Polyenaria* in the Central Highlands. At the species level, most scarab beetles tend to inhabit a special habitat type and seem to be sensitive to subtle changes in their habitats (Paulian 1988). A study on the scarab community within the forests of the Masoala Peninsula (Andriamampianina 1995) showed that members of this group, particularly the enariines, are distributed at a given locality along different gradients, such as elevation, latitude, and edge effects. Their responses generally comprise either a change in the species composition of the local community or a change in species abundance.

TABLE 9.31. **Checklist of Malagasy enariine scarab beetles and their distribution**

SCIENTIFIC NAME	DISTRIBUTION
***ENTHORA* ERICHSON, 1848**	
E. catalai Dewailly, 1950	Tantamaly Forest, southeast of Fianarantsoa
E. polita Waterhouse, 1878	All along eastern moist evergreen forest
E. alluaudi Dewailly, 1950	Moist evergreen forest on Angavo Escarpment
E. atomaria Fairmaire, 1905	Extreme north around Antsiranana and in Central Highlands around Antananarivo
E. miliaris Kolbe, 1894	Moist evergreen forest surrounding and north of Antongil Bay
E. lunata Lacroix, 1993	Moist evergreen forest of Tsaratanàna Massif
E. ornata Nonfried, 1891	Eastern moist evergreen forest
E. chlorodera Blanchard, 1851	Eastern moist evergreen forest
***ENCYA* DEJEAN, 1833**	
E. commersoni Olivier, 1789	Eastern moist evergreen forest
E. strigiscutata Fairmaire, 1883	Eastern moist evergreen forest and Central Highlands
E. sikorai Brenske, 1891	Eastern moist evergreen forest
E. albostriata Brenske, 1891	Eastern moist evergreen forest
***BISENCYA* LACROIX, 1993**	
B. bisignata Blanchard, 1851	Moist evergreen forest between Analamazaotra and Anjanaharibe-Sud
B. sogai Lacroix, 1993	Moist evergreen forest between Analamazaotra and Anjanaharibe-Sud
B. pyriformis Waterhouse, 1882	Region around Antongil Bay
B. invulnerata Waterhouse, 1882	Moist evergreen forest from east Antananarivo to east Fianarantsoa
B. gutticollis Waterhouse, 1882	Eastern moist evergreen forest
B. lacunosa Lacroix, 1993	Bongolava Region
B. catalai Dewailly, 1950	Andringitra Massif
B. viettei Lacroix, 1993	Anosyenne Mountains
***GLOBENCYA* LACROIX, 1993**	
G. cribrata (Waterhouse, 1882)	Moist evergreen forest between Ranomafana and Zahamena
G. farafanganae (Fairmaire, 1899)	Moist evergreen forest around Farafangana
G. griveaudi Lacroix, 1993	Moist evergreen forest around Manafiafy, Tolagnaro
***EUTRICHESIS* WATERHOUSE, 1882**	
E. pilosicollis Waterhouse, 1982	Moist evergreen forest from Fianarantsoa to Tsaratanàna
E. punctatus Waterhouse, 1882	Moist evergreen forest between east Antananarivo and east Fianarantsoa
E. bourgini Dewailly, 1950	Moist evergreen forest from Fianarantsoa to Tsaratanàna
***ANENARIA* LACROIX, 1993**	
A. rubiginea Dewailly, 1950	Moist evergreen forest from Vohilava Faraony to Marojejy; Central Highlands around Itremo Massif
***ANTHRENCYA* LACROIX, 1993**	
A. anthracina (Fairmaire, 1903)	Extreme north around Montagne d'Ambre and in central east around Toamasina

(continued overleaf)

TABLE 9.31. ***continued***

SCIENTIFIC NAME	DISTRIBUTION
A. castanipes Dewailly, 1950	Central Highlands and Sambirano near Ambanja
A. arrowi Dewailly, 1950	Northeast around Maroantsetra
A. lebisi Dewailly, 1950	Surroundings of Moramanga
***PSEUDENCYA* LACROIX, 1993**	
P. cinnabarina Lacroix, 1991	Northeast around Marojejy at high elevations (~1750 m)
***MUCRENCYA* LACROIX, 1993**	
M. mucronata (Klug, 1833)	Common all over the island
***LEBBEA* LACROIX, 1993**	
L. triangularis (Dewailly, 1950)	Northern portion of Madagascar and Sambirano Region, mountains above 1000 m
***VARENCYA* LACROIX, 1993**	
V. varia (Dewailly, 1950)	Common all along eastern moist evergreen forest and in Central Highlands
V. devillei (Dewailly, 1950)	Unknown distribution
V. tessellata Lacroix, 1993	High mountains of Tsaratanàna Massif
V. vittata Lacroix, 1993	High mountains of Marojejy Massif
V. variipennis (Blanchard, 1851)	Central Highlands and moist evergreen forest from Antongil Bay south to Midongy du Sud
V. picea Lacroix, 1993	Moist evergreen forest from Marojejy to Analamazaotra ~1000 m
V. homalophalla (Dewailly, 1950)	Central Highlands and moist evergreen forest from Antongil Bay south to Midongy du Sud
V. longiclava (Dewailly, 1950)	Moist evergreen forest around Antongil Bay
V. perinetensis (Dewailly, 1950)	Mid-latitude eastern moist evergreen forest from Analamazaotra to Ranomafana
V. mocquerysi (Dewailly, 1950)	Moist evergreen forest around Antongil Bay
V. conspersa Lacroix, 1993	High elevations of Marojejy Massif
V. notata Lacroix, 1993	High elevations of Marojejy Massif
V. montana (Moser, 1919)	Moist evergreen forest between Antsiranana and Antongil Bay
V. intricata Lacroix, 1993	Upper portions of Tsaratanàna Massif
***APICENCYA* LACROIX, 1993**	
A. apicalis (Blanchard, 1851)	East, south, and Central Highlands
A. pauliani (Dewailly, 1950)	Central Highlands
A. parva Lacroix, 1993	Northwest
A. plagulata (Fairmaire, 1901)	Extreme south around Betroka and Berenty
A. nuda Lacroix, 1993	Central Highlands
A. speculifera (Fairmaire, 1903)	Central Highlands
A. vadoni Lacroix, 1993	Central Highlands
A. calva (Waterhouse, 1882)	Central Highlands
A. waterloti (Dewailly, 1950)	Central Highlands

SCIENTIFIC NAME	DISTRIBUTION
***SEMIENARIA* DEWAILLY, 1950**	
S. descarpentriesi Dewailly, 1950	Sandy soil in dry southwest
***POLYENARIA* DEWAILLY, 1950**	
P. ciliata Dewailly, 1950	Central Highlands
***RAVAUTIANA* LACROIX, 1991**	
R. juncuda Lacroix, 1991	Southeast
***SYNENARIA* LACROIX, 1993**	
S. borealis Lacroix, 1993	Moist evergreen forest around Montagne d'Ambre
***PENTAPHYLLA* DEWAILLY, 1950**	
P. gieseckiei Dewailly, 1950	Central Highlands and central west
***DJAFOUNA* LACROIX, 1993**	
D. fairmairei (Dewailly, 1950)	Central west near Maevatanana
***MACHALA* LACROIX, 1993**	
M. transversa Lacroix, 1993	Upper elevations of Tsaratanàna Massif
***ENARIA* ERICHSON, 1848**	
E. perrieri Dewailly, 1950	Northwest around Soalala and Mahajanga
E. boissayei Dewailly, 1950	Central Highlands
E. grandidieri Dewailly, 1950	Southwest dry spiny thicket
E. melanictera (Klug, 1833)	All over the island
E. pauliani Lacroix, 1993	Around Morondava
E. fasciaria Lacroix, 1993	West and southwest
E. micantipennis (Blanchard, 1851)	Central Highlands and central east
E. rubescens Dewailly, 1950	Distribution unknown
E. cinerea (Blanchard, 1851)	Distribution unknown
E. speculifera Fairmaire, 1903	Northwest around Soalala and Mahajanga
E. biapicata Fairmaire, 1901	Arid south
E. squamata Lacroix, 1993	Southwest dry spiny thicket
E. scapulata Fairmaire, 1903	Central west near Maevatanana
E. tulearensis Dewailly, 1950	Southwest dry spiny thicket
E. eliei Lacroix, 1993	Central Highlands
E. granulosa Fairmaire, 1899	Central west near Maevatanana
E. grossepunctata Dewailly, 1950	Arid south
E. betiokensis Lacroix, 1993	Southwest dry spiny thicket
E. conspurcata (Klug, 1833)	Central west near Maevatanana; moist evergreen forest around Montagne des Français, Montagne d'Ambre, and Nosy Be
E. mathiauxi Dewailly, 1950	Northeast, from Marojejy to east of Antananarivo
E. scutellata Dewailly, 1950	Central Highlands and central east

(continued overleaf)

TABLE 9.31. ***continued***

SCIENTIFIC NAME	DISTRIBUTION
E. asperula Fairmaire, 1899	Central west near Maevatanana
E. barbieri Dewailly, 1950	Central west near Maevatanana
E. seyrigi Dewailly, 1950	Southwest dry spiny thicket
E. alluaudi (Dewailly, 1950)	Moist evergreen forest, extreme north
E. laeviscutata Fairmaire, 1899	Moist evergreen forest around Montagne des Français
E. antanala Künckel, 1887	Nosy Be
E. marginata Waterhouse, 1882	Southwest dry spiny thicket
E. orientalis Lacroix, 1993	Central Highlands and central east
E. crassa Fairmaire, 1899	Central west near Maevatanana
E. andriai Lacroix, 1993	Moist evergreen forest, extreme north
E. hepatica Lacroix, 1993	Central west around Morondava
E. limbalis Fairmaire, 1900	Central west near Maevatanana
E. reticulata Lacroix, 1993	Southwest dry spiny thicket
E. androyensis (Dewailly, 1950)	Arid south
E. ambalavaoensis Lacroix, 1993	Central Highlands
E. locellata Lacroix, 1993	Central Highlands
***CHERBEZATINA* LACROIX, 1993**	
C. micropunctata Lacroix, 1993	Northwest around Soalala; central west near Maevatanana
C. alluaudi (Dewailly, 1950)	Northwest around Soalala; central west near Maevatanana
C. bicolor Lacroix, 1993	Central west around Morondava
C. pinguis (Fairmaire, 1899)	Northwest around Soalala; central west near Maevatanana
C. dilutipes (Dewailly, 1950)	Central east moist evergreen forest
C. rufofulva (Fairmaire, 1880)	Central Highlands
C. maculata Lacroix, 1993	Montagne des Français, Lokobe Forest
C. kalalaoensis Lacroix, 1993	Ile Sainte Marie
C. fuliginosa Lacroix, 1993	Central Highlands
C. setigera (Dewailly, 1950)	Unknown distribution
C. apposita Lacroix, 1993	Northeastern moist evergreen forest around Antongil Bay
C. spadicea Lacroix, 1993	Southeastern moist evergreen forest
C. depressiuscula (Waterhouse, 1882)	Central Highlands
C. latifrons (Waterhouse, 1882)	Central east moist evergreen forest
C. marmorata Lacroix, 1993	Nosy Be
C. andriai Lacroix, 1993	Extreme north
C. integra Lacroix, 1993	High mountains of Andringitra
C. margiciliata Lacroix, 1993	Central Highlands
C. squamulosa Lacroix, 1993	Northwest around Soalala; central west near Maevatanana

SCIENTIFIC NAME	DISTRIBUTION
C. pierroni (Dewailly, 1950)	Extreme north
C. meridiana Lacroix, 1993	Southeastern moist evergreen forest
C. viossati Lacroix, 1993	Centtral east moist evergreen forest
C. oblongula (Fairmaire, 1903)	Extreme north
C. mandarina Lacroix, 1993	Central Highlands
C. livens (Dewailly, 1950)	Central Highlands
C. strigosa Lacroix, 1993	Central east moist evergreen forest
C. pilosa Lacroix, 1993	Moist evergreen forest around Antongil Bay
C. fanovanensis Lacroix, 1993	Central east moist evergreen forest
C. parallela (Dewailly, 1950)	Moist evergreen forest around Antongil Bay
C. laevis Lacroix, 1993	Southeastern moist evergreen forest
C. ferruginea Lacroix, 1993	Central Highlands
C. scrobiculata Lacroix, 1993	Central Highlands
***PSEUDENARIA* FAIRMAIRE, 1901**	
P. maculata (Moser, 1919)	Central Highlands
P. bidens Lacroix, 1993	High mountains in northeast
P. sogai Lacroix, 1993	High mountains in northeast
P. ornatipennis (Blanchard, 1851)	Moist evergreen forest around Antongil Bay
P. vadoni Lacroix, 1993	Moist evergreen forest from east Antananarivo to east Fianarantsoa
P. fairmairei (Dewailly, 1950)	Around Tolagnaro
P. catalai (Dewailly, 1950)	Moist evergreen forest from east Antananarivo to east Fianarantsoa
P. unguicularis (Moser, 1919)	Higher elevations on Andringitra Massif
***VADONARIA* DEWAILLY, 1950**	
V. guilhoni Dewailly, 1950	Central Highlands
V. ambreensis (Dewailly, 1950)	Moist evergreen forest in extreme north
V. maxima Lacroix, 1993	Moist evergreen forest at upper elevations of Andringitra Massif
V. variegata (Waterhouse, 1882)	Central Highlands
V. caliginosa Lacroix, 1993	Moist evergreen forest surrounding Antongil Bay
***RENAUDIANA* LACROIX, 1993**	
R. ranomandriensis Lacroix, 1993	Anosyenne Mountains
R. guttata Lacroix, 1993	Anosyenne Mountains

In general, there tends to be a decline in species richness with increasing elevation, but species occurring at higher elevations or away from the forest edge seem to be more specialized. Analysis of the species distribution patterns shows a high concentration of enariines species in the area around Analamazaotra (Périnet), whereas a mosaic of high-endemism areas are found dispersed around Madagascar and, in particular, in the Anosyenne Mountains, the Central Highlands, and the extreme north (Andriamampianina 1996). Finally, most of the data used in this review are rather old, and further field collections are necessary to update and better understand the current distribution of Enariini on Madagascar.

Subject editors: Brian L. Fisher and Steven M. Goodman

COLEOPTERA: ANTHRIBIDAE, FUNGUS WEEVILS

M. Trýzna

The family Anthribidae is part of the order Coleoptera, superfamily Curculionoidea (= Rhynchophora). At present, the family encompasses about 3800 species worldwide, representing roughly 1% of all known beetles. Anthribidae is diverse, particularly in tropical and subtropical regions. For their development, these insects require fungus-infested deadwood of predominantly deciduous trees, in relatively intact moist evergreen forests with a diverse number of tree species, and a relatively stable climate.

Within Curculionoidea, fungus weevils are considered primitive members. An apt characterization of the family's placement within the Curculionoidea system is provided by E. C. Zimmerman (1994: 20): "Anthribidae are atypical weevils. Their anatomical features are so unusual as to lead to the conclusion that they diverged from the mainstream of curculionid evolution and pursued an independent course a very long time ago. There appears to be no close nexus between them and Nemonychidae, which are among the oldest living members of the main stem of curculionid evolution. The Anthribidae appear to have come to a 'dead end.'"

MORPHOLOGY

The morphology of adults (imagos) within Anthribidae is relatively diverse. The beetles are generally characterized by a strongly sclerotized body covered with setae and scales; the head is often prolonged into a rostrum (with the exception of the subfamily Choraginae); the antennae of Malagasy species always have 11 segments, and unlike those of true weevils of the family Curculionidae, they are never elbowed and end in a more or less distinct three-segmented antennal club. All tarsi are five-segmented, with a very small tarsomere 4 covered by tarsomere 3, which is distinctly larger and deeply lobed. Malagasy species are highly diverse in size, ranging from *Choragus fasciger*, measuring a mere 1 mm, to the genus *Tophoderes* (e.g., *T. annulatus* and *T. murinus*), with the largest individuals over 32 mm in length. Sexual dimorphism tends to be exhibited by longer antennae in males.

BIOGEOGRAPHY AND SPECIES DIVERSITY

The extent of information on this family differs between geographic regions and is directly related to the degree of biological exploration. While knowledge of the number of species occurring in some areas is relatively comprehensive, there are regions of the world for which we have only rudimentary data. An overview of the species occurring in different geographic regions can be found in the *Illustrierter Katalog und Bibliographie der Anthribidae der Welt* (Rheinheimer 2004). As Rheinheimer states, the well-researched regions include Europe (56 species known to date), North America (91 species), Japan (177 species), New Zealand (61 species), and New Caledonia (58 species). In contrast, other regions have yielded only fragmentary information; for example, only 386 species are known from the entire South American continent, and 662 species from the African continent (Rheinheimer 2004).

Our knowledge of the distribution and biology of Malagasy species of Anthribidae is at the incipient stage. Rheinheimer (2004) listed 224 species occurring on Madagascar. At present 295 species have been described (Table 9.32), encompassing three subfamilies, 21 tribes, and 64 genera, including the genus *Triplodus* (*incertae sedis*), with a single species, *T. cuspis*, described from the island. The number of known species has increased significantly since Rheinheimer's catalog (2004) thanks to the different studies of R. Frieser (Frieser 2005, 2007, 2009, 2010) and M. Trýzna (Trýzna 2017; Trýzna and Baňař 2012, 2013a, 2013b, 2014a, 2014b, 2015a, 2015b, 2016, 2017a, 2017b, 2020; Trýzna and Andrianomenjanahary 2019).

SYSTEMATICS AND RESEARCH HISTORY ON MADAGASCAR

In the past, Anthribidae was classified into three subfamilies—Anthribinae, Choraginae, and Urodontinae (e.g., Alonso-Zarazaga and Lyal 1999). Trýzna and Valentine (2011) subsequently elevated tribe Apolectini to an independent subfamily, Apolectinae. Currently, the family comprises four subfamilies. The Urodontinae does not occur on Madagascar; its closest occurrence is South Africa. The Apolectinae is known from the island, with six genera, including the diverse *Caranistes* (Figure 9.47a), with 31 species, and *Dinephrius*, *Duplionistes*, *Phrynoidius*, *Protomerus*, and *Rhinoscopis*, each with a single species.

The first species described from Madagascar, *Uterosomus verrucosus*, was named by the French entomologist Guillaume-Antoine Olivier in 1795. The foundation for systematic studies of the Malagasy Anthribidae was laid by the French entomologist Léon Marc Herminie Fairmaire, who published descriptions of 12 genera and 37 species that are still considered valid. The German British entomologist Heinrich Ernst Karl Jordan described two genera and 17 species, while his German colleagues Paul Wolfrum and Robert Frieser described four genera and 75 species, and seven genera and 118 species, respectively. It is also noteworthy that these latter four aforementioned entomologists described a total of 246 species of the 295 species (83%) known today from the island. At present, Miloš Trýzna, in collaboration with Université d'Antananarivo and Madagascar National Parks, focuses on the study of Malagasy Anthribidae.

TABLE 9.32. **Checklist of Malagasy species of family Anthribidae and their distribution**

SCIENTIFIC NAMES	DISTRIBUTION
FAMILY ANTHRIBIDAE BILLBERG, 1820	
Subfamily ANTHRIBINAE Billberg, 1820	
Tribe PTYCHODERINI Jekel, 1855	
Genus *Phloeotragus* Schönherr, 1823	
**P. albicans* Fahraeus, 1839	North: Montagne d'Ambre; West: Andranofasika; East: Andasibe; South: Midongy du Sud
Tribe TOPHODERINI Lacordaire, 1865	
Genus *Sternocyphus* Wolfrum, 1961	
**S. atylus* (Jordan, 1925)	Northwest: Ambanja; Central: Moramanga; Southwest: Toliara, Sakaraha, Zombitse
**S. barbifer* Wolfrum, 1961	West: Ankarafantsika (Ampijoroa)
**S. ferranti* (Jordan, 1925)	South: Betioky
**S. quinquecarinatus* Frieser, 2000	Central: Moramanga; West: Morondava (Forêt de Kirindy), Ambodimanga
**S. stigma* (Klug, 1833)	East: Antalaha
Genus *Tophoderellus* Wolfrum 1959	
**T. aequalis* Wolfrum, 1961	North: Nosy Komba
**T. compactus* (Fairmaire, 1896)	"Madagascar" [no recent specimens]
**T. griseobrunneus* Wolfrum, 1961	West: Andobo, Antsalova
**T. insignis* Wolfrum, 1959	North: Androna Plateau (Mandritsara); East: Antakotako, Maroantsetra
**T. major* Wolfrum, 1961	North: Nosy Komba
**T. ovalimacula* Wolfrum, 1961	East: "forêt nord" of Anosibe
**T. ovalis* Wolfrum, 1959	North: Androna Plateau (Mandritsara); East: Antakotako, Maroantsetra, Navana
**T. parvus* Wolfrum, 1959	North: Androna Plateau (Mandritsara); East: Antakotako, Maroantsetra; West: Ampijoroa
**T. plagifer* Wolfrum, 1961	East: Ambatovosira (Andranomalaza)
**T. signatus* Wolfrum, 1961	Northeast: Sambava, Marojejy, Andasy
**T. viridis* Wolfrum, 1959	North: Androna Plateau (Mandritsara)
Genus *Tophoderes* Dejean, 1834	
**T. acarinulus* Wolfrum, 1959	North: Androna Plateau (Mandritsara)
**T. annulatus* Waterhouse, 1875	Central: Ambositra; East: Ranomafana
**T. banari* Trýzna, 2017	East: Ivohibe, Vondrozo
**T. ferrugatus* (Klug, 1833)	"Antananarivo"
**T. frenatus* (Klug, 1833)	East: Analamazaotra, Mantadia; Southeast: Midongy du Sud
**T. funebris* (Klug, 1833)	East: Toamasina (Alahakato)
**T. fuscoareatus* Wolfrum, 1959	Central: Moramanga, Antsianaka
**T. griseipes* Fairmaire, 1901	East: Anjiro
**T. griseovarius* Fairmaire, 1901	Southeast: Tolagnaro, Bezavona
**T. lidmilae* Trýzna & Baňař, 2015	North: Montagne d'Ambre
**T. murinus* Alluaud, 1899	Southeast: Ranomafana near Tolagnaro, Midongy du Sud; Southwest: Toliara

(continued overleaf)

TABLE 9.32. ***continued***

SCIENTIFIC NAMES	DISTRIBUTION
**T. nubeculosus* Fairmaire, 1888	East: Antongil Bay, Maroantsetra
**T. immaculatus* (Wolfrum, 1959)	East: Antsianaka
**T. sikorae* Jordan, 1895	"Antananarivo"; Central: Moramanga
**T. sinuatocollis* Jordan, 1895	"Antananarivo"; Central: Moramanga
Genus *Trachycyphus* Fairmaire, 1901	
**T. cottae* Fairmaire, 1901	East: Fenoarivo-Atsinanana, Alahakato, Vondrozo; Southeast: Tolagnaro
Genus *Uterosomus* Dejean, 1834	
**U. verrucosus* (Olivier, 1795)	North: "Ambre," Nosy Be; West: Mahajanga; East: Andasibe; Southeast: Midongy du Sud
Tribe DISCOTENINI Lacordaire, 1865	
Genus *Holophloeus* Jordan, 1928	
**H. loebli* Trýzna & Baňař, 2020	East: Analamazaotra, Ranomafana, Fenoarivo-Atsinanana; Central: Moramanga
**H. tuberosus* (Fairmaire, 1897)	North: Nosy Be, Montagne d'Ambre; Northeast: Antakotako
Tribe SINTORINI Lacordaire, 1865	
Genus *Anhelita* Jordan, 1895	
**A. aphanes* Wolfrum, 1959	East: Maroantsetra
**A. brevipes* Wolfrum, 1961	East: Andranomandevy, Didy
**A. distans* Wolfrum, 1959	North: Androna Plateau (Mandritsara)
**A. lineata* Jordan, 1895	East: Analamazaotra, Mantadia; Central: Moramanga
**A. unicarinata* Wolfrum, 1959	North: Androna Plateau (Mandritsara); East: Maroantsetra
Genus *Sintor* Schönherr, 1839	
**S. alternus* Frieser, 2000	Central: Moramanga
**S. conglobatus* Wolfrum, 1961	North: Montagne d'Ambre
**S. frenatus* Frieser, 2000	Central: Moramanga
**S. impressus* Frieser, 2000	Central: Moramanga
**S. ochraceus* Frieser, 2000	Central: Moramanga, Antsahatsaka
**S. paradistans* Wolfrum, 1961	North: Montagne d'Ambre
**S. sporadicus* (Wolfrum, 1959)	East: Analamazaotra, Maromizaha, Ranomafana; Central: Moramanga
Tribe CORRHECERINI Lacordaire, 1865	
Genus *Aneurhinus* Thomson, 1858	
**A. cylindricus* Jordan, 1895	Central: Moramanga
Genus *Apatenia* Pascoe, 1859	
**A. fallax* Frieser, 2010	East: Analamazaotra; Central: Moramanga
**A. longiclava* Wolfrum, 1955	North: Androna Plateau (Mandritsara); East: Maroantsetra
**A. mesostigma* Wolfrum, 1961	East: Ranomafana; Central: Moramanga
**A. oculifera* Frieser, 2000	East: Analamazaotra; Central: Moramanga
**A. quadristigma* Frieser, 1981	East: Fampanambo, Mananara

SCIENTIFIC NAMES	DISTRIBUTION
**A. sulcicollis* Frieser, 2000	Central: Moramanga
**A. stysi* Trýzna & Baňař, 2013	West: Andranofasika
Genus *Baseocolpus* Jordan, 1949	
**B. punctifer* Frieser, 2000	East: Mantadia, Maromizaha, Ranomafana; Central: Moramanga
Genus *Lemurisintor* Frieser, 1981	
**L. longiclava* Frieser, 1981	East: Ambodivoangy; North: Nosy Be
Genus *Pantorhaenas* Jordan, 1928	
**P. inornatus* Frieser, 2010	Central: Manankazo, Ambohitantely
Genus *Phaulimia* Pascoe, 1859	
**P. lemura* Wolfrum, 1961	East: Maroantsetra, Ambila, Fenoarivo-Atsinanana, Fampanambo
Genus *Ulorhinus* Sharp, 1891	
**U. lemurus* Wolfrum, 1959	East: Maroantsetra
Tribe TROPIDERINI Lacordaire, 1865	
Genus *Lemuricedus* Jordan, 1911	
**L. adhilaratus* Wolfrum, 1961	North: Androna Plateau (Mandritsara); East: Fampanambo
**L. argyrodes* Wolfrum, 1959	East: Antsianaka, Antongil Bay, Maroantsetra
**L. audouini* (Fahraeus, 1839)	East: Analamazaotra, Maromizaha, Ranomafana; Central: Moramanga
**L. brevirostris* Wolfrum, 1961	Central: Ivohibe
**L. cervinus* Jordan, 1911	East: Analamazaotra, Antongil Bay; Central: Moramanga
**L. dexius* Jordan, 1911	North: Antsiranana; East: Andasibe; Central: Ambohimahamasoa
**L. equulus* Wolfrum, 1961	East: Toamasina, Fananadra; Central: Moramanga
**L. guttulifer* Frieser, 2007	East: Mantadia; Central: Moramanga
**L. inferior* Frieser, 1981	East: Analamazaotra
**L. integer* Wolfrum, 1961	South: Marovato; Central: Moramanga
**L. lacer* Wolfrum, 1961	Central: La Mandraka
**L. longior* (Fairmaire, 1896)	"Madagascar" [no recent specimens]
**L. maculicollis* (Fairmaire, 1896)	East: Analamazaotra, Ranomafana; Central: Moramanga
**L. madagascariensis* (Faust, 1889)	North: Montagne d'Ambre; East: Analamazaotra, Ranomafana; Central: Moramanga
**L. microphthalmus* Wolfrum, 1961	North: Antsiranana, Montagne des Français; West: Andranofasika
**L. ochrus* Wolfrum, 1961	North: Tsaratanàna; Central: Moramanga
**L. punctatipennis* Frieser, 1959	North: Androna Plateau (Mandritsara); East: Maroantsetra
**L. subscutellatus* (Fairmaire, 1896)	North: Nosy Be
**L. torvus* (Jordan, 1895)	East: Analamazaotra, Ranomafana; Northeast: Vohémar
**L. vastus* Wolfrum, 1961	West: Ankarafantsika (Ampijoroa)
**L. verrucosus* (Jordan, 1895)	"Antananarivo"; East: Analamazaotra
Genus *Mecotarsus* Schönherr, 1839	
**M. longitarsis* (Fairmaire, 1903)	North: Montagne d'Ambre, Nosy Be; Central: Moramanga

(*continued overleaf*)

TABLE 9.32. ***continued***

SCIENTIFIC NAMES	DISTRIBUTION
**M. rosenschoeldi* Fahraeus, 1839	East: Toamasina (Alahakato), Fenoarivo-Atsinanana, Antongil Bay
Genus *Pseudocedus* Fairmaire, 1901	
**P. plagiatus* (Jordan, 1895)	South: Betioky, Imanombo, Androy, Mahafaly; Southeast: Tolagnaro
Genus *Sphinctotropis* Kolbe, 1895	
**S. celata* Frieser, 2007	North: Tsaratanàna, Montagne d'Ambre (Ambohitra)
**S. leucosticta* (Klug, 1833)	East: Maromizaha; West: Morondava
Genus *Tropideres* Schönherr, 1823	
**T. amoenus* Fairmaire, 1897	"Madagascar" [no recent specimens]
**T. grisescens* Fairmaire, 1897	"Madagascar" [no recent specimens]
**T. minor* Fairmaire, 1897	"Madagascar" [no recent specimens]
Tribe CAPPADOCINI Alonso-Zarazaga & Lyal, 1999	
Genus *Diastatotropis* Lacordaire, 1865	
**D. blazeji* Trýzna, 2019	Northeast: Toamasina (Ambohitsitondrona), Antsiranana (Andapa)
**D. clavigera* Frieser, 1992	East: Ranomafana; Central: Moramanga
**D. crassicornis* Waterhouse, 1882	"Madagascar" [no recent specimens]
**D. humeralis* Trýzna and Baňař, 2016	East: Analamazaotra, Mantadia
**D. irrorata* Lacordaire, 1865	East: Analamazaotra, Mantadia, Antongil Bay
**D. lepida* Trýzna and Baňař, 2016	Southeast: Anosyenne Mountains
**D. nitidipennis* Waterhouse, 1882	East: Antsianaka
**D. olivacea* Waterhouse, 1877	East: Analamazaotra; Central: Ambohitantely
**D. perrinae* Trýzna and Baňař, 2017	North: Montagne d'Ambre
**D. planifrons* Waterhouse, 1882	"Antananarivo"
**D. rubra* Frieser, 1992	East: Ambodivoangy
**D. rubricollis* (Fairmaire, 1892)	North: Antsiranana, Nosy Be; East: Antongil Bay
**D. tessellata* Fairmaire, 1897	North: Montagne d'Ambre, Nosy Be; East: Ranomafana
**D. tigrina* Lacordaire, 1865	East: Analamazaotra
Tribe STENOCERINI Kolbe, 1895	
Genus *Allandrus* LeConte, 1876	
**A. exul* (Fairmaire, 1897)	"Madagascar" [no recent specimens]
**A. ruficornis* (Wolfrum, 1961)	North: Antsiranana, Montagne des Français; East: Vohitrosa; Central: Manankazo
Genus *Plintheria* Pascoe, 1859	
P. trirudis (Wolfrum, 1961)	"Madagascar, Mohéli Fomboni" [?]; also from Comoros
Tribe ZYGAENODINI Lacordaire, 1865	
Genus *Blaberops* Jordan, 1904	
**B. exilloides* Frieser, 2000	East: Ambatondrazaka (Didy), Analamazaotra; Central: Moramanga
**B. korinae* Trýzna & Baňař, 2014	East: Analamazaotra

SCIENTIFIC NAMES	DISTRIBUTION
B. macrocerus Jordan, 1904	Northwest: Nosy Mitsio; East: Maroantsetra, Antalaha; also from S. Africa
Genus *Nistacares* Fairmaire, 1898	
**N. leucostictus* Fairmaire, 1898	West: Suberbieville (Maevatanana)
Genus *Noxius* Jordan, 1936	
**N. albisparsa* (Wolfrum, 1955)	East: Maroantsetra
**N. albomaculatus* Wolfrum, 1961	East: Maroantsetra, Ambodivoangy
**N. albopunctulatus* Frieser, 2000	North: Antsiranana
**N. basiensis* Wolfrum, 1961	West: Morondava (sud de Befasy)
**N. calvus* Frieser, 2000	Central: Moramanga
**N. circumcinctus* Frieser, 2000	Central: Moramanga
**N. circumflexus* Frieser, 2000	Central: Manankazo
**N. exiguus* Frieser, 2007	East: Analamazaotra
N. fallax (Fahraeus, 1839)	Southwest: Sakaraha; West: Morondava (Befasy); also S. Africa
**N. glaber* Frieser, 2000	Central: Moramanga
**N. indecorus* Frieser, 2007	East: Ambodidimaka, Andasibe
**N. ocellatus* Frieser, 2000	East: Ambohimanarivo (Ifanadiana); Central: Moramanga, Antsahatsaka
**N. producta* (Wolfrum, 1961)	West: Ankarafantsika (Ampijoroa)
**N. punctulifer* Frieser, 2007	East: Analamazaotra, Ranomafana; Central: Manankazo
**N. pupillata* (Wolfrum, 1961)	Northeast: Sambava, Marojejy
**N. serenus* Wolfrum, 1961	Southwest: Toliara
**N. tenebrosus* Frieser, 2010	North: Montagne d'Ambre (Ambohitra)
**N. undulatus* Frieser, 2000	Central: Betroka (Vohitrosa)
**N. urbanus* (Wolfrum, 1961)	Southwest: Sakaraha, Zombitse
**N. velatus* Frieser, 2000	Central: Manankazo
Genus *Rhaphitropis* Reitter, 1916	
**R. excisa* Wolfrum, 1962	"Madagascar" [no recent specimens]
Tribe ORMISCINI LeConte, 1876	
Genus *Hormiscops* Jordan, 1914	
**H. angustefasciatus* Frieser, 2010	North: Antsiranana District, Sambirano River, Marovato village
**H. blandus* Frieser, 2007	East: Analamazaotra, Ranomafana; Central: Moramanga
**H. brevior* Frieser, 2007	East: Analamazaotra, Maromizaha; Central: Moramanga
**H. bruneus* Frieser, 2007	East: Analamazaotra
**H. confluens* Frieser, 2010	East: Analamazaotra, Ranomafana (Vohiparara); Central: Ambositra
**H. comes* Frieser, 2007	East: Analamazaotra, Ranomafana; Central: Manankazo; North: Anjanaharibe
**H. frater* Frieser, 2007	East: Analamazaotra, Ranomafana, Ambondrombe; Central: Moramanga
ssp. **striolatus* Frieser, 2010	East: Analamazaotra, Ranomafana
**H. fraternus* Frieser, 2010	East: Analamazaotra

(continued overleaf)

TABLE 9.32. ***continued***

SCIENTIFIC NAMES	DISTRIBUTION
**H. granulatus* Frieser, 2007	Central: Moramanga
**H. inflexus* Frieser, 2007	East: Analamazaotra
**H. latus* Frieser, 2007	East: Analamazaotra, Ranomafana (Vohiparara)
**H. obtusus* Frieser, 2007	East: Analamazaotra
**H. quadrimaculatus* Wolfrum, 1961	East: Sandrangato
Tribe ECELONERINI Lacordaire, 1865	
Genus *Cenchromorphus* Fairmaire, 1892	
**C. barbicornis* Fairmaire, 1892	North: Antsiranana
**C. tuberosus* (Fairmaire, 1901)	South: Plateau de l'Androy; West: Ankarafantsika
Genus *Rawasia* Roelofs, 1880	
**R. rubroapicata* Frieser, 2009	Central: Ambositra
Tribe PLATYRHININI Bedel, 1882	
Genus *Basidissus* Fairmaire, 1897	
**B. bendai* Trýzna & Baňař, 2013	East: Analamazaotra
**B. cirrifer* Frieser, 2000	Central: Moramanga
**B. cristatus* Fairmaire, 1897	North: Antsiranana
**B. fulvitarsis* Frieser, 2007	Central: Moramanga
**B. incilis* Frieser, 2000	Central: Moramanga
**B. senilis* Frieser, 2000	Central: Moramanga
Genus *Pseudobasidissus* Trýzna & Baňař, 2014	
**P. barclayi* Trýzna & Baňař, 2014	Northeast: Marojejy; East: Ranomafana; Central: Anjozorobe-Angavo
Tribe PLATYSTOMINI Pierce, 1916	
Genus *Entaphioides* Fairmaire, 1896	
**E. albiguttatus* (Fahraeus, 1839)	East: Antsianaka
**E. brunneofasciata* Wolfrum, 1961	West: Ankarafantsika (Ampijoroa); North: Nosy Be
**E. discophora* Wolfrum, 1961	East: Analamazaotra, Mantadia, Fampanambo
**E. lacrymans* Fairmaire, 1896	East: Antongil Bay, Maroantsetra
Genus *Epitaphius* Fairmaire, 1898	
**E. adiacens* Wolfrum, 1961	West: Morondava (south of Befasy); Central: Ankaratra Massif
**E. albatus* Wolfrum, 1961	East: Fampanambo
**E. albopictus* Jordan, 1928	North: Antsiranana
**E. annulicornis* Fairmaire, 1898	West: Suberbieville (Maevatanana)
**E. cincticollis* Frieser, 2004	Central: Manankazo
**E. decoratus* (Jordan, 1895)	East: Anjiro
**E. fallax* Frieser, 2004	West: Mahajanga District, Ampatika

SCIENTIFIC NAMES	DISTRIBUTION
**E. geron* Wolfrum, 1961	Northeast: Marojejy (Ambinanitelo)
**E. gilvipes* Frieser, 2004	Central: Moramanga
**E. gravis* Frieser, 2004	Central: Manankazo, Moramanga
**E. griseatus* Wolfrum, 1961	Central: Moramanga
**E. inconspicuus* Wolfrum, 1959	East: Antsianaka
**E. litotropioides* Wolfrum, 1961	West: Morondava (south of Befasy)
**E. melanopictus* Frieser, 2004	East: Analamazaotra
**E. menoides* Wolfrum, 1959	East: Antsianaka
**E. piceopictus* (Fairmaire, 1902)	West: Ankirihitra
**E. pullatus* Wolfrum, 1961	Central: Moramanga
**E. rheinheimeri* Frieser, 2004	North: Montagne d'Ambre
**E. sugillatus* (Fahraeus, 1839)	North: Androna Plateau (Mandritsara)
**E. tetrastigma* (Fairmaire, 1903)	Southeast: Andrahomana
Genus *Gulamentus* Jordan, 1895	
**G. albinasus* Jordan, 1922	East: Antongil Bay
Genus *Litotropis* Fairmaire, 1880	
**L. areata* Wolfrum, 1961	East: Andranomandevy, Didy
**L. cirrata* Wolfrum, 1961	Southwest: Sakaraha, Lambomakanoro
**L. infucata* Frieser, 2000	Central: Antsahatsaka
**L. leuconota* (Fairmaire, 1896)	"Madagascar" [no recent specimens]
**L. marmorina* Wolfrum, 1961	East: Analamazaotra, Sandrangato
**L. provida* (Fahraeus, 1839)	North: Marovato, Ankarana
**L. pustulosa* Jordan, 1895	Central: Moramanga
**L. semipustulata* Frieser, 2000	Central: Moramanga, Antsahatsaka
Genus *Mentanus* Fairmaire, 1902	
**M. costulatus* Fairmaire, 1902	North: Montagne d'Ambre, Montagne des Français; Central: Bekily
Genus *Mylascopus* Fairmaire, 1901	
**M. pegasus* Valentine, 1994	East: Maroantsetra
**M. quagga* Valentine, 1994	East: Maroantsetra
**M. zebrinus* Fairmaire, 1901	Central: Andrangoloaka
Genus *Phloeobius* Schönherr, 1823	
P. gigas ssp. *cervinus* Klug, 1833	"Madagascar"; also from Comoros, Seychelles, Mauritius
**P. penicillus* Fairmaire, 1896	"Madagascar" [no recent specimens]
P. pustulosus Gerstaecker, 1871	North: Sambirano; Central: Moramanga; Southeast: Midongy du Sud; also from Africa
Genus *Pioenia* Pascoe, 1862	
**P. flavofasciata* Frieser, 1981	East: Maroantsetra

(*continued overleaf*)

TABLE 9.32. ***continued***

SCIENTIFIC NAMES	DISTRIBUTION
Tribe XYLINADINI Lacordaire, 1865	
Genus *Cercotaphius* Wolfrum, 1959	
**C. abnormis* Frieser, 2010	North: Ankarana (Mahamasina)
**C. nanos* Frieser, 2004	“Madagascar, Amboasari” [?]
**C. notabilis* Wolfrum, 1959	East: Antsianaka
ssp. **paululus* Frieser, 2004	North: Antsiranana District, Sambirano River, Marovato village
Tribe BASITROPIDINI Lacordaire, 1865	
Genus *Messalius* Fairmaire, 1903	
**M. puncticollis* (Jordan, 1895)	“SW Madagascar”; West: Ankarafantsika; Central: Moramanga, Isalo
Tribe ANTHRIBINI Billberg, 1820	
Genus *Opanthribus* Schilsky, 1907	
**O. albocingulatus* Frieser, 2004	East: Analamazaotra
**O. albosignatus* Frieser, 2004	East: Analamazaotra
**O. aureofasciatus* Frieser, 2004	East: Analamazaotra
**O. paraleuca* (Wolfrum, 1955)	East: Maroantsetra
**O. rubromaculatus* Frieser, 2004	East: Analamazaotra
**O. scolytinus* Frieser, 1981	East: Ambodivoangy; Central: Betroka (Vohitrosa), Manankazo
**O. scutatus* Frieser, 2004	East: Analamazaotra; Central: Manankazo
**O. scymnoides* Frieser, 1981	East: Ambodivoangy
**O. stillinus* (Wolfrum, 1961)	North: Montagne des Français
**O. submetallicus* (Wolfrum, 1961)	East: Sandrangato; Central: Moramanga
**O. undulatus* Frieser, 2004	East: Andasibe, Analamazaotra, Ranomafana
Tribe CRATOPARINI LeConte, 1876	
Genus *Pseudeuparius* Jordan, 1914	
**P. laticlava* Wolfrum, 1961	North: Antsiranana District, Analamerana
P. monoceros (Fahraeus, 1839)	Central: Manakazo, Moramanga; West: Ambodimanga; also from Africa
**P. tuberidorsis* (Fairmaire, 1897)	Central: Moramanga
Tribe MAUIINI Valentine, 1989	
Genus *Cleranthribus* Jordan, 1914	
**C. dyschirioides* Wolfrum, 1961	East: Maroantsetra, Ambodivoangy, Ambatovosira
Genus *Mauia* Blackburn, 1885	
M. subnotata (Boheman, 1859)	East: Ambila; also from Oriental and Australian regions
Subfamily APOLECTINAE Lacordaire, 1865	
Tribe APOLECTINI Lacordaire, 1865	
Genus *Caranistes* Schönherr, 1839	
**C. albofuscus* Wolfrum, 1959	“Madagascar” [no recent specimens]

SCIENTIFIC NAMES	DISTRIBUTION
*C. *bipartitus* Frieser, 2010	East: Analamazaotra; Central: Moramanga
*C. *cyphosis* Wolfrum, 1959	East: Antsianaka
*C. *deliciosus* Fairmaire, 1898	North: Antsiranana; West: Suberbieville (Maevatanana)
*C. *directus* Frieser, 2007	East: Analamazaotra
*C. *dubius* Frieser, 2007	Central: Manankazo
*C. *elegantulus* Wolfrum, 1959	North: Antsiranana; Central: Manankazo
*C. *filitarsis* (Fairmaire, 1897)	East: Analamazaotra, Antsianaka
*C. *fulvopictus* Fairmaire, 1898	East: Fenoarivo-Atsinanana
*C. *gibbosus* Frieser, 2007	East: Analamazaotra; Central: Moramanga, Betroka (Vohitrosa)
*C. *griseatus* Wolfrum, 1961	East: Analamazaotra; Central: Ambatolampy (Andranotobaka)
*C. *incultus* Frieser, 2007	East: Fenoarivo-Atsinanana
C. languidus Fahraeus, 1839	"Insulae Bourbon et Madagascar" [?] [no recent specimens]
*C. *laticollis* Frieser, 2007	North: Antsiranana District, Sambirano River, Marovato village
*C. *latifrons* (Fairmaire, 1901)	East: Fenoarivo-Atsinanana, Antakotako
*C. *lineatus* Fahraeus, 1839	"Madagascar" [no recent specimens]
*C. *marmorinus* Wolfrum, 1959	East: Analamazaotra, Mantadia, Ranomafana
*C. *nigroflavus* Frieser, 2007	Central: Moramanga
*C. *nitidus* Frieser, 2007	Central: Ambositra (Ambatofitoharanana)
*C. *nobilis* Frieser, 2007	Central: Moramanga
*C. *perrini* Frieser, 2007	East: Andasibe; Central: Moramanga, Antsahatsaka, Betroka (Vohitrosa)
*C. *rhanisus* Wolfrum, 1959	North: Ambohitra; East: Mantadia; Central: Ambohitantely, Moramanga
*C. *rufipes* Jordan, 1895	"Antananarivo"; North: Androna Plateau (Mandritsara)
*C. *senex* Frieser, 2007	Central: Betroka (Vohitrosa)
*C. *sonjai* Frieser, 2010	East: Analamazaotra
*C. *strenus* Frieser, 2007	East: Analamazaotra, Mananara
*C. *subvittatus* Frieser, 2007	East: Andasibe; Central: Manankazo
*C. *taeniatus* Frieser, 2007	North: Antsiranana
*C. *tenuiclavis* Fairmaire, 1897	North: Nosy Be
*C. *tenuilineatus* (Brancsik, 1893)	"Madagascar" [no recent specimens]
*C. *xanthographus* Wolfrum, 1959	North: Androna Plateau (Mandritsara)
Genus *Dinephrius* Jordan, 1924	
*D. *artifrons* Wolfrum, 1959	"Madagascar" [no recent specimens]
Genus *Duplionistes* Frieser, 2007	
*D. *robustus* (Wolfrum, 1959)	North: Montagne d'Ambre
Genus *Phrynoidius* Fairmaire, 1897	
*P. *raffrayi* Fairmaire, 1897	North: Androna Plateau (Mandritsara); East: Maroantsetra, Navana

(continued overleaf)

TABLE 9.32. ***continued***

SCIENTIFIC NAMES	DISTRIBUTION
Genus *Protomerus* Fairmaire, 1903	
**P. longitarsis* Fairmaire, 1903	Southeast: Tolagnaro
Genus *Rhinoscopis* Frieser, 2007	
**R. heissi* Frieser, 2007	Southeast: Tolagnaro (Cap Sainte Luce)
Subfamily CHORAGINAE Kirby, 1819	
Tribe ARAECERINI Lacordaire, 1865	
Genus *Adapterops* Frieser, 2010	
**A. cedrici* Trýzna & Baňař, 2015	North: Montagne d'Ambre (Ambohitra)
**A. dimbyi* Trýzna & Baňař, 2017	North: Ankarana
**A. hankae* Trýzna, 2012	East: Analamazaotra; North: Montagne d'Ambre (Ambohitra)
**A. mamyi* Trýzna & Baňař, 2017	North: Forêt d'Ambre
**A. nasalis* Frieser, 2010	East: Ambondrombe; Central: Ambohitantely
**A. festivus* Frieser, 2010	East: Analamazaotra; North: Montagne d'Ambre, Forêt d'Ambre
Genus *Araecerus* Schönherr, 1823	
A. fasciculatus (DeGeer, 1775)	Cosmopolitan
A. suturalis Boheman, 1839	North: Antsiranana District; East: Ranomafana; also Asia and Africa
Genus *Megatermis* Jordan, 1937	
**M. rugipennis* Frieser, 2000	East: Antananarivo, Ambodrona
Genus *Misthosimella* Jordan, 1914	
M. detracta Wolfrum, 1961	"Madagascar, Mohéli Fomboni" [?]; West: Ampijoroa; also Comoros
M. subgibba (Wolfrum, 1959)	East: Antakotako, Maroantsetra, Navana; North: Androna; also Comoros
Tribe CHORAGINI Kirby, 1819	
Genus *Allochoragus* Frieser, 2000	
**A. amictus* Frieser, 2004	East: Analamazaotra
**A. crux* Frieser, 2000	Central: Moramanga
**A. dentatus* Frieser, 2000	Central: Moramanga
**A. inarmatus* Frieser, 2000	Central: Betroka (Vohitrosa)
**A. rectimargo* Frieser, 2004	East: Analamazaotra
Genus *Choragus* Kirby, 1819	
**C. aethiops* Frieser, 2010	East: Analamazaotra
**C. attactus* Frieser, 2010	East: Analamazaotra
**C. cylindricollis* Frieser, 2004	"Madagascar, 30 km NW Maramag, Bagonongsilang" [?]
**C. ebeninus* Frieser, 2000	Central: Betroka (Vohitrosa)
**C. fasciger* Frieser, 2010	East: Analamazaotra
**C. femoralis* Frieser, 2010	East: Analamazaotra; Central: Moramanga
**C. flavofasciatus* Frieser, 2004	East: Andasibe

SCIENTIFIC NAMES	DISTRIBUTION
**C. fulvescens* Frieser, 2004	East: Analamazaotra
**C. interruptofasciatus* Frieser, 2004	East: Analamazaotra
**C. nitidus* Frieser, 2010	East: Analamazaotra
**C. othiodes* Frieser, 2004	Central: Moramanga
**C. spadiceus* Frieser, 2000	Central: Moramanga
**C. vicinus* Frieser, 2010	East: Analamazaotra
Genus *Dysnomelas* Frieser, 2007	
**D. alboscutatus* (Fairmaire, 1903)	West: Suberbieville (Maevatanana)
**D. melagris* Frieser, 1981	East: Ambodivoangy, Antalaha
Genus *Epichoragus* Frieser, 2010	
**E. acutus* Frieser, 2010	East: Analamazaotra
**E. externus* Frieser, 2010	East: Analamazaotra; Central: Moramanga
**E. politus* Frieser, 2010	East: Ranomafana
**E. tubericollis* Frieser, 2010	East: Analamazaotra
**E. variolosus* Frieser, 2010	East: Analamazaotra
**E. vulneratus* Frieser, 2010	East: Analamazaotra
Genus *Eudysnos* Frieser, 2010	
**E. pilicornis* Frieser, 2010	East: Analamazaotra
Genus *Perichoragus* Wolfrum, 1959	
**P. albicinctus* Frieser, 2004	East: Analamazaotra
**P. duplus* Frieser, 2004	Central: Manankazo
ssp. **inops* Frieser, 2004	East: Andasibe, Maromizaha; Central: Manankazo
**P. erotyloides* Frieser, 2004	East: Analamazaotra
**P. ovatus* Frieser, 2004	East: Maromizaha
**P. tetraspilotus* Frieser, 2004	Central: Manankazo
Incertae sedis	
Genus *Triplodus* Wolfrum, 1961	
**T. cuspis* Wolfrum, 1961	East: Andapa

Notes: *, endemic to Madagascar. The checklist contains confirmed and revised geographic data. Several published type localities of certain species have not been found or verified, and these are marked with a question mark in square brackets [?]. Details provided in Viette (1991) were used to identify certain ambiguous localities. It must be taken into consideration that older specimens, mainly from the 20th century and labeled "Antananarivo," may refer simply to Madagascar. These cases are presented between quotation marks. In cases when "Madagascar" was given as the type locality in the original description and no recent specimen is available, these are presented as "Madagascar" [no recent specimens].

FAUNAL ANALYSIS

Anthribidae fauna of Madagascar is characterized by a high level of endemism, which reaches over 96%. Out of the 295 presently known Malagasy species, 284 are clearly endemic, and only 11 taxa occur outside the island; for example, *Plintheria trirudis* is also known from the Comoros and *Noxius fallax* from South Africa. The other species known from Madagascar that have extralimital distributions are presented in Table 9.32. An unconfirmed species, *Blaberops macrocerus*, listed from Nosy Mitsio, Maroantsetra, and Antalaha by Wolfrum (1961), needs confirmation of its presence on the island (Trýzna and Baňař 2014a). Further, there are some errors in the literature about localities. For example, the type locality for *Opanthribus scolytinus* is published as "Zaire, Congo da

FIGURE 9.47 **A sampling of the diversity of Anthribidae beetles of Madagascar: A) *Caranistes* sp., Anjozorobe-Angavo, sexual behavior showing male protecting female with its antennae; B) *Diastatotropis irrorata*, Analamazaotra; C) *Litotropis pustulosa*, Zombitse; D) *Tophoderes frenatus*, Analamazaotra; E) *Holophloeus loebli*, Mantadia; and F) *Pseudobasidissus barclayi*, Anjozorobe-Angavo.** (PHOTOS by M. Trýzna.)

Lemba" by Frieser (1981) and repeated in Rheinheimer (2004), but the holotype label is "Madagascar, Ambodivangy."

In total, 22 genera are endemic to Madagascar, and within the subfamily Anthribinae, the most speciose endemic genera are *Diastatotropis* (14 species; Figure 9.47b), *Tophoderes* (14 species; Figure 9.47d), and *Tophoderellus* (11 species). Within the subfamily Choraginae, the most speciose endemic genera include *Adapterops* (six species), *Epichoragus* (six species), and *Allochoragus* (five species). About 200 of the recognized species from Madagascar occur in the band of moist evergreen forests running along the eastern length of the island. Many species have been described from a few locations, including the Andasibe (formerly Périnet) and the nearby sites of Analamazaotra and Mantadia. These forested areas are highly favorable for the occurrence of anthribids, but it is more likely that the high number of species known from this zone is associated with its easy access from the nation's capital. The surroundings of the nearby town of Moramanga represent an important collection area as well. Some species described from there, including *Epitaphius gilvipes* and *Litotropis infucata*, are known from only a single specimen. Sadly, forests surrounding this town have been largely destroyed during the past couple of decades, and the described species have not been re-collected, either here or in suitable nearby locations.

Another area with a high occurrence of species is the northern part of Madagascar, namely the medium-altitude moist evergreen forests in the Montagne d'Ambre National Park. Moreover, some species seem to be microendemics to this site, including *Tophoderes lidmilae*, *Sintor conglobatus*, *S. paradistans*, *Diastatotropis perrinae*, *Noxius tenebrosus*, *Duplionistes robustus*, and *Adapterops cedrici*.

On the basis of current information, many endemic anthribid species are rare and known from only single isolated locations. Extrapolation of the population data suggests they may be highly vulnerable to the destruction of the forest habitats where they have been found. Among such species is *Pantorhaenas inornatus*, whose occurrence in the Central Highlands is limited to several hectares of a tiny remnant of forest near the village of Manankazo, and the nearby Ambohitantely Special Reserve, which includes montane moist evergreen forests. Another example is two species—*Diastatotropis crassicornis* and *D. planifrons*—that Waterhouse described in the 19th century as from "Madagascar" and "Antananarivo," respectively, but not found since.

However, within this family, we can find some species that are still relatively common and widespread. For instance, *Phloeotragus albicans* occurs from the north (Montagne d'Ambre) to relatively far south (Befotaka–Midongy du Sud), as well as in the west (Andranofasika) and east (Andasibe). Other widespread and abundant species include: *Tophoderes frenatus* (Figure 9.47d), occurring in the moist evergreen eastern forests from Andasibe to Befotaka–Midongy du Sud; *Uterosomus verrucosus*, ranging from the nearshore island of Nosy Be to Befotaka–Midongy du Sud; and some species of *Lemuricedus* (*L. audouini*, *L. maculicollis*, and *L. madagascariensis*), which are common in the eastern forested zone.

During each field-collection mission to Madagascar conducted by the author of this contribution in collaboration with various colleagues, we have been able to find unknown species of anthribids, particularly in the less-explored areas. Such locations can be found in the dense moist evergreen forests surrounding Ivohibe, where the recently described *Tophoderes banari* was discovered (Trýzna 2017), and in the poorly known Anosyenne Mountains in the southeast, where newly described *Diastatotropis lepida* was found (Trýzna and Baňař 2016).

ECOLOGICAL NOTES

Remarkably few details have been published on the biology of Malagasy anthribids, including ecological notes on some species (Trýzna and Baňař 2020) and broader aspects of the family's biodiversity on the island (Trýzna and Baňař 2012). Anthribids can be found only in largely intact or well-preserved forests across a range of different elevations. They are typically saproxylic organisms, dependent on dead and decaying wood in which their larvae develop; it is also essential that the wood be infested with suitable fungi. Adults can be found on deadwood of various types of trees. Anthribids primarily prefer recent deadwood with intact bark that is often surrounded by dead leaves. As the wood mass gradually decays, the anthribid community decreases, and most species disperse to fresh deadwood, with some exceptions: both named species of the genus *Holophloeus* (Figure 9.47e) can be found on deadwood that is partly devoid of bark and in more advanced stages of decay (Trýzna and Baňař 2020). As far as is known, the adults are primarily fungivores.

The highest species diversity of anthribids on Madagascar can be found on wood in areas of forests that receive some sun exposure. In such places, local species diversity can reach up to 30 species (Trýzna and Baňař 2012, 2017a). The smaller species from subfamilies Choraginae (e.g., *Adapterops*, *Perichoragus*) and Anthribinae (e.g,. *Phrynoidius*, *Cleranthribus*) and particularly many still undescribed species of *Triplodus* can be found on freshly dying branches or twigs associated with dry leaves.

The majority of anthribids are good and nimble fliers. Only members of several larger species belonging to the genera *Phloeotragus*, *Tophoderes* (Figure 9.47d), and *Holophloeus* (Figure 9.47e) appear to be reluctant fliers, despite having fully developed wings. All anthribid species possess cryptic coloring (homochromy), and even larger species—such as those of the genera *Tophoderes*, *Litotropis* (Figure 9.47c), *Pseudobasidissus* (Figure 9.47f), and *Lemuricedus*—are very difficult to find with the naked eye in their natural environment.

I use a simple method for collecting anthribids on suitable deadwood, sweeping the underside of the twig, where the beetles are most often found, with an entomological net. Swift movement with the net is very important, as most Malagasy anthribids are generally very quick and nimble flyers. This method is effective for capturing small species, because their cryptic coloration and lack of movement while on bark makes them difficult to notice, and they move quickly if disturbed and can fly unnoticed out of a net (Trýzna and Baňař 2012).

CONCLUSION AND FURTHER DIRECTIONS

Beetles of the family Anthribidae are among Madagascar's little-explored invertebrate groups. Based on our studies of specimens in different entomological collections, as well as recent field missions, it is estimated that the currently recognized fungus weevil fauna of Madagascar, comprising 295 species, represents only about 30% of the island's total anthribid diversity. It is estimated that the anthribid fauna probably approaches 900 species.

The family's occurrence is strictly associated with native forest vegetation containing sufficient amounts of dead and decaying wood. Species of this family do not occur in places lacking such wood. The anthribid community of Madagascar is unique, endemic, and largely unexplored, despite the fact that many saproxylic organisms have been studied on the island over the past couple of decades. As deforestation of Madagascar continues, this family, which is bound to intact forest environments, will be one of the most rapidly disappearing organisms among the island's biodiversity.

No molecular studies have been published on the family Anthribidae that included material from Madagascar. Such research is critical to provide a better understanding of the evolutionary history of the island's fungus weevils, including colonization history and patterns of speciation. Nevertheless, it remains imperative to continue conducting field inventories, especially in protected areas but also in less-explored parts of the island, and to support the training of national entomologists.

ACKNOWLEDGMENTS

The research of the Anthribidae family has been conducted under a long-term project supervised by Miloš Trýzna. Our thanks to the Université d'Antananarivo, Faculté des Sciences, Département d'Entomologie; Madagascar National Parks; and Ministère de l'Environnement et des Forêts for allowing this work to be conducted.

Subject editors: Brian L. Fisher and Steven M. Goodman

SIPHONAPTERA, FLEAS, *PARASY*

J.-B. Duchemin, M. Harimalala, and J.-M. Duplantier

The order Siphonaptera includes approximately 246 genera and about 2600 species of fleas distributed across the world (Whiting et al. 2008). They have been studied from a medical point of view, mainly as vectors of plague, as well as from a zoological perspective to analyze the relationships between ectoparasites and their hosts.

Fleas are holometabolous (complete transformation during metamorphosis), wingless insects, adapted to jump, and adults of both sexes are hematophagous (blood-feeding). The female lays eggs on the ground or on the host, where the detritiphagous larvae develop, feeding on detritus from host fur or feathers or on dried fecal blood of adult fleas. The pupal stage is quiescent. Adults feed during painless bites on their warm-blooded vertebrate hosts, which are mainly mammals but also birds. Depending on the time the adult flea spends on its host, we distinguish the following categories:

- Nidicolous fleas, which are in contact with the host for a short time and feed when the host enters its nest or burrow (or when a human host enters a house). When not feeding, the adult, like the larva and pupa, is in the nest litter rather than remaining on the host.
- Pilicolous fleas, which are very mobile but spend the majority of their adult life in the host's fur (or human clothing).
- Fixed fleas, for which contact with the host is quasi-permanent, as they remain attached to the host by the mouthparts, like hard ticks. This category is rare among fleas.

These differences in behavior require special attention during sampling, as the number of potential hosts during a flea's lifetime depends on the host-parasite level of contact (amount of time on the host and number of host species in contact). Flea behavior also creates different risks of transmission of microbial—and sometimes pathogenic—agents within mammalian populations. In any case, terrestrial small mammals are good hosts for fleas, which find microclimatic conditions suitable for larval development in burrows. However, the patterns of host-flea associations must be carefully analyzed, since they are not necessarily the result of a linear evolutionary history (Beaucournu 1981). Several mechanisms of association can be observed: a direct phyletic origin, as found in bat fleas (see below); horizontal transfer from one host to another as a result of the sympatric occurrence of different small mammals; and particular microclimate requirements linked to burrows or nests in preadult stages.

FLEAS OF MADAGASCAR WITHIN A WORLD CONTEXT

Of the 15 families of Siphonaptera (Smit 1982; Whiting et al. 2008), only five are found on Madagascar, and four of these have broad global distributions (Table 9.33). Within these four families, there are endemic Malagasy species as well as, in two families, genera endemic to the island. Of the 49 species of fleas reported to occur on Madagascar, seven are introduced and commensal with humans either directly (*Pulex irritans*) or through domestic or commensal animals (Table 9.34). These non-native species have broad distributions, either cosmopolitan or tropical. Their arrival date on Madagascar is poorly documented but is certainly post human colonization of the island.

FLEA STUDIES ON MADAGASCAR

Early research on Malagasy fleas was primarily associated with plague and was conducted in epidemic zones (Robic 1937; Girard 1942). This work encompassed the description of the genus *Synopsyllus* and species *S. fonquerniei*, one of the two main local vectors of plague (Wagner and Roubaud 1932), as well as increased knowledge of its biology (Estrade 1935; J.-M. Klein and Uilenberg 1966a). Subsequent faunal studies provided specimens for descriptions of numerous species and a better understanding of the systematics of Malagasy fleas (Lumaret 1962; J.-M. Klein and Uilenberg 1966b; Beaucournu and Fontenille 1993).

Since 1998, collaborations between the Institut Pasteur of Madagascar, Institut de Recherche pour le Développement, WWF Madagascar, Association Vahatra, and the Field Museum of Natural History have led to intensive sampling efforts of a range of mammals in different forested areas of Madagascar. This resulted in considerable collections of fleas from known hosts and the subsequent description of several new endemic flea species, particularly those of the genus *Paractenopsyllus*. Combined with subsequent field surveys, the collaboration led to substantial new data on distribution and host range (Duchemin 2003a, 2003b, 2003c; Duchemin and Ratovonjato 2004; Hastriter and Dick 2009; Beaucournu and Goodman 2014; Beaucournu and Laudisoit 2014). The start of this new phase of information on the fleas of Madagascar coincided with the publication of Duchemin et al. (2003), the review of this subject in the precursor of this book. The current text is a notable update of that contribution. All this new information has also led to a better understanding of the biotopes in which transmission of plague may involve wild fauna (Duplantier et al. 2005). Further updated information on the sensitivity of fleas to insecticides is a critical component to vector-control programs (Coulanges et al. 1983; Boyer et al. 2014).

FAUNISTICS

Five families of fleas are found on Malagasy mammals—Ctenophthalmidae, Ischnopsyllidae, Ceratophyllidae, Tungidae, and Pulicidae

TABLE 9.33. **Distribution of Siphonaptera families around the world**

FAMILIES	GEOGRAPHIC REGIONS					
	AFROTROPICAL	ORIENTAL	AUSTRALIAN	NEOTROPICAL	NEARCTIC	PALEARCTIC
Ancistropsyllidae	–	X	–	–	–	–
Ceratophyllidae	X	X	X	X	X	X
Chimaeropsyllidae	X	–	–	–	–	–
Coptopsyllidae	–	–	–	–	–	X
Ctenophthalmidae	X	X	X	X	X	X
Hystrichopsyllidae	–	–	X	X	X	X
Ischnopsyllidae	X	X	X	X	X	X
Malacopsyllidae	–	–	–	X	–	–
Tungidae	X	–	–	X	X	X
Pulicidae	X	X	X	X	X	X
Pygiopsyllidae	X	X	X	–	–	X
Rhopalopsyllidae	X	–	–	X	–	–
Stephanocircidae	–	–	X	X	–	–
Vermipsyllidae	–	X	–	–	X	X
Xiphiopsyllidae	X	–	–	–	–	–

Sources: Modified from Lewis (1998) and Smit (in Beaucournu and Fontenille 1993).
Note: Families with names in **boldface type** occur on Madagascar.

(Table 9.33). For further information on rodent hosts (Nesomyidae and Muridae) and tenrec hosts (Tenrecidae), see Goodman and Soarimalala (pp. 1737–69); for endemic Carnivora hosts (Eupleridae), see Veron et al. (pp. 1863–65); and for bat hosts (represented by numerous families), see Goodman et al. (pp. 1894–911).

Ctenophthalmidae

The family Ctenophthalmidae is represented on Madagascar by a single Afrotropical subfamily, Dinopsyllinae, known only by the genus *Dinopsyllus* (Table 9.34), which is represented on Madagascar by three endemic species belonging to the subgenus *Dinopsyllus*. These fleas are large, dark brown, and characterized by a vertical genal comb with five teeth. When collected on hosts, they sometimes remain motionless.

In Africa, the majority of species in the genus *Dinopsyllus* have been collected in intact forest zones of relatively high elevation. Out of the 25 described species from the Rothschild collection (Hopkins and Rothschild 1966), the type specimens in nine cases come from elevations at or above 2000 m, in eight cases from between 1000 and 1999 m, and in three cases the mention of "mount" or "plateau" is associated with the type locality; the remaining five species are not necessarily species of elevations and are restricted to southern Africa. The three Malagasy species are found in the Central Highlands or on the Tsaratanàna Massif (Beaucournu and Fontenille 1993). With the exception of the type series of *D. brachypecten*, most specimens of this genus from Madagascar come from forested habitats.

Almost all the known hosts of *Dinopsyllus* in Africa are rodents, and Madagascar does not fully deviate from this rule. *Dinopsyllus flacourti* was described from specimens collected on the endemic rodent *Nesomys rufus*, family Nesomyidae (J.-M. Klein 1965a; see Carleton et al., pp. 2033–35), and this host is confirmed by more recent captures (Duchemin 2003a). Only the male of *D. tsaratananae* is known from its type specimen, captured on *Rattus rattus*, family Muridae (J.-M. Klein 1968). Another specimen was captured from the endemic rodent *Brachyuromys ramirohitra* near the Tsaratanàna Massif at 1600 m (Duchemin 2003a). *Dinopsyllus brachypecten* was described from specimens captured on *R. rattus* or dogs in human-modified habitats (Grenier and Klein 1965). To date, this species has not been recaptured on any endemic rodent, whereas specimens have been regularly collected on the endemic family Tenrecidae: *Tenrec ecaudatus* (J.-M. Klein and Uilenberg 1966b), *Hemicentetes* species, and *Microgale* species (Duchemin 2003a; Harimalala et al. 2018). Therefore, it seems likely that the host of *D. brachypecten* is an endemic tenrec, in contrast to the other species of the genus, including those occurring in Africa. Members of the genus *Dinopsyllus* have been suspected of being plague vectors in Tanzania and Angola (Ribeiro 1974; Kilonzo et al. 1992) and, more recently, on Madagascar (Duplantier et al. 2005).

TABLE 9.34. **Checklist of the fleas of Madagascar**

TUNGIDAE
Tunginae
Tunga penetrans (Linnaeus, 1758)—Trop
PULICIDAE
Pulicinae
Pulex irritans Linnaeus, 1758—COS
Echidnophaga gallinacean (Westwood, 1875)—Trop
Archeopsyllinae
Centetipsylla madagascariensis (Rothschild, 1900)—E
Ctenocephalides felis strongylus (Jordan, 1925)—COS
C. brygooi Beaucournu, 1975—E
Xenopsyllinae
Xenopsylla cheopis (Rothschild, 1903)—Trop
X. petteri Lumaret, 1962—E
X. brasiliensis (Baker, 1904)—Trop
Synopsyllus fonquerniei Wagner & Roubaud,1932—E
S. smiti Lumaret, 1962—E
S. estradei Klein, 1964—E
S. girardi Klein, 1966—E
S. robici Klein, 1966—E
CTENOPHTHALMIDAE
Dinopsyllinae
Dinopsyllus brachypecten Smit, 1951—E
D. flacourti Klein, 1966—E
D. tsaratananae Klein, 1968—E
CERATOPHYLLIDAE
Leptopsyllinae
Leptopsylla segnis (Schönherr, 1811)—COS
Paractenopsyllus kerguisteli Wagner, 1938—E
P. pauliani Lumaret, 1962—E
P. grandidieri Klein, 1965—E
P. petiti Klein, 1965—E
P viettei Klein, 1965—E
P. vauceli Klein, 1965—E
P. randrianasoloi Klein, 1968—E
P. albignaci Klein, 1968—E
P. goodmani Duchemin, 2003—E
CERATOPHYLLIDAE
Leptopsyllinae
P. rouxi Duchemin, 2004—E
P. ratovonjatoi Duchemin, 2004—E
P. duplantieri Duchemin, 2004—E
P. juliamarinus Duchemin, 2004—E
P. gemelli Duchemin, 2004—E
P. beaucournui Duchemin & Ratovonjato, 2004—E
P. oconnori Duchemin & Ratovonjato, 2004—E
P. raxworthyi Duchemin & Ratovonjato, 2004—E
P. madagascariensis Hastriter & Dick, 2009—E
P. exspectatus Beaucournu & Goodman, 2014—E
Tsaractenus grenieri Klein, 1968—E
T. rodhaini Duchemin, 2003—E
T. clavator Beaucournu & Laudisoit, 2014—E
ISCHNOPSYLLIDAE
Ischnopsyllinae
Araeopsylla martialis (Rothschild, 1903)—AFT & MR
A. goodmani Hastriter, 2016—E
Dampfia graham Waterston, 1915—Afr
Lagaropsylla incerta (Rothschild, 1900)—E
L. hoogstraali Smit, 1957—Afr
L. consularis Smit, 1957—Afr
L. idea Smit, 1957—Afr
L. makay Laudisoit, Prié & Beaucournu, 2012—E
Thaumapsyllinae
Thaumapsylla sp.—Afr & ORT

Sources: Data in this table are largely modified from Duchemin (2003a); Hastriter and Dick (2009); Beaucournu and Goodman (2014); Beaucournu and Laudisoit (2014); Beaucournu et al. (2015); and Hastriter (2016).

Notes: Distribution abbreviations: Afr, Africa/African region; AFT, Afrotropical; COS, Cosmopolitan; E, endemic to Madagascar; MR, Malagasy Region; ORT, Oriental region; Trop, tropical. The Malagasy Region is defined as Madagascar and neighboring archipelagoes (Comoros, Mascarenes, and Seychelles). The species not marked as endemic are presumed to be introduced, with the exception of those of the family Ischnopsyllidae (bat fleas), for which dispersal by their flying hosts makes the distribution designation a bit more difficult.

Ischnopsyllidae

Members of Ischnopsyllidae are fleas that are found strictly on bats. The two subfamilies, Thaumapsyllinae and Ischnopsyllinae, are found on two clades of bats, Pteropodiformes and Vespertilioniformes, respectively (see Goodman et al., pp. 1894–911). Beaucournu et al. (2015) provide a recent review of Malagasy bat fleas.

Thaumapsyllinae is known from the bat genera *Eidolon* and *Rousettus*, both represented on the island by endemic species and making their day roosts in caves. An as yet unidentified species of the genus *Thaumapsylla*, which is also present in the Afrotropical and Oriental regions and includes only three species, was reported on Madagascar from *E. dupreanum* (Brook et al. 2015; Table 9.34).

The Malagasy Ischnopsyllinae comprises three genera: *Araeopsylla*, *Dampfia*, and *Lagaropsylla* (Table 9.34). *Araeopsylla* is distributed in the Oriental and Afrotropical regions and Mediterranean subregion. The preferential hosts are Molossidae bats. Two species occur on Madagascar—*A. martialis* and *A. goodmani*. *Araeopsylla martialis* has been found on *Mormopterus jugularis* in the arid south, Ankarana, and Antananarivo (Duchemin 2003a), as well as on *Otomops madagascariensis* (Beaucournu et al. 2015). It is also present on La Réunion (Lumaret 1962). The second species, *A. goodmani*, has been found on another molossid bat, *Chaerephon jobimena*, at Isalo (Hastriter 2016). The second genus, *Dampfia*, is restricted to Africa and Madagascar, with only one species, *D. grahami*, and two subspecies. The unique Malagasy member of the genus, *D. g. grahami*, has been found on Madagascar not on a

Molossidae bat but on a bat of the family Vespertilionidae, *Neoromicia matroka*, at Andasibe (Hastriter 2016). This bat flea is also found in South Africa (Beaucournu et al. 2015; Hastriter 2016).

The third genus of Ischnopsyllinae, *Lagaropsylla*, is found on Madagascar and encompasses 22 species distributed in the Afrotropical, Oriental, and Australian regions. Fleas belonging to this genus are found preferentially on Molossidae bats. Five species occur on Madagascar (Table 9.34): *L. consularis*, also known from Africa, has been found on *Chaerephon atsinanana* in Andasibe (Beaucournu and Fain 1983); *L. hoogstraali*, another African species, was found on *Mops midas* (the main African host) and on *Mormopterus jugularis* and *Mops leucostigma* in the south (Lumaret 1962) and west (Duchemin 2003a) of Madagascar; *L. idae*, a third African species, is confirmed on Madagascar in the region of Toliara and found on *M. leucostigma* and *C. leucogaster* (Beaucournu et al. 2015); *L. incerta*, apparently endemic to Madagascar, has been collected on *Mormopterus jugularis* from Nosy Be and Lake Alaotra (Beaucournu et al. 2015); and *L. makay*, the second endemic species, was collected on *Otomops madagascariensis* in the Makay (Laudisoit et al. 2012).

Several other genera of Ischnopsyllidae known from elsewhere in the world have not been collected on Madagascar. These include genera that occur in the Neotropical, Australian, and Holarctic regions or that are strictly Afrotropical—*Allopsylla*, *Oxyparius*, and *Rhinolophopsylla* (the last genus also has a narrow extension in the Palearctic region).

Ceratophyllidae

Of the three recognized subfamilies of Ceratophyllidae in the world, only Leptopsyllinae is present on Madagascar, represented by three genera (Table 9.34). *Leptopsylla*, a mainly Palearctic genus, is represented by a single species on Madagascar, *L. segnis*—a widely distributed flea often associated with the introduced and often commensal rodents of the family Muridae, including *Mus musculus* (House Mouse) and the genus *Rattus* of urban or rural areas. A large number of Leptopsyllinae species are found in the Holarctic region (*Peromyscopsylla* and *Leptopsylla*) and only from mountains in other regions. An exception is *L. segnis*, mentioned above.

The two remaining genera, *Paractenopsyllus* and *Tsaractenus*, are endemic to Madagascar. The latter genus, described from a single male of *T. grenieri* collected from *R. rattus* on the Tsaratanàna Massif, has recently been obtained from several montane forests, especially in the Central Highlands. Two new species, *T. rodhaini* and *T. clavator*, both associated with *Microgale*/*Nesogale* hosts, have been described. They are large, dark fleas, morphologically close and genetically related to *Paractenopsyllus* (Duchemin 2003b; Harimalala et al. 2018), and all within a single clade representing a notable species radiation.

At a broader level, the phylogenetic tree of 205 species of fleas constructed by Zhu et al. (2015) shows that two *Paractenopsyllus* species (*P. raxworthyi* and *P. madagascariensis*) cluster together close to two *Mesopsylla* species; this latter genus of rodent parasites is present from Mongolia to the Urals and Iran, with one taxon found in Egypt. This potential relationship was peripherally mentioned by Beaucournu and Laudisoit (2014). Further, when he described *Tsaractenus*, J.-M. Klein (1968) mentioned morphological affinities with the Oriental *Cratynius*, and such relationships have also been mentioned by other authors (Beaucournu and Fontenille 1993; Duchemin 2003a, 2003b). Unfortunately, no material of *Cratynius* was included in the Zhu et al. (2015) study. The only African taxa in this subfamily belong to the genus *Leptopsylla*, which are morphologically closer to Palearctic genera than endemic Malagasy genera.

Paractenopsyllus currently comprises 19 species, all collected on small mammals (rodents and tenrecs) from montane forests of the Central Highlands or on massifs in the northern part of the island. Among the *Paractenopsyllus*, the monospecific subgenus *Consobrinopsyllus* was described by Duchemin (2003b). This assignment was then confirmed by phylogenetic studies placing it as the sister taxon of all other analyzed *Paractenopsyllus* species and differentiated from *Tsaractenus* (Harimalala 2018).

Outside of Madagascar, the usual hosts for members of Leptopsyllinae are rodents, with the exception of *Cratynius*, which is known to parasitize hedgehogs (family Erinaceidae), and two species of *Leptopsylla* occurring on shrews (family Soricidae). On Madagascar, members of *Paractenopsyllus* (Figures 9.48b and c)—in particular, *P. kerguisteli*, *P. duplantieri*, *P. juliamarinus*, *P. ratovonjatoi*, *P. albignaci*, and *P. raxworthyi*, as well as *P.* (*Consobrinopsyllus*) *goodmani* and *Tsaractenus rodhaini* (Figure 9.48d)—are almost exclusively captured on members of the Afrosoricida (represented on Madagascar by the family Tenrecidae, subfamilies Oryzorictinae and Tenrecinae; Table 9.35). On the other hand, some species, such as *P. grandidieri*, *P. gemelli*, *P. randrianasoloi*, and *P. madagascariensis*, are mostly collected on Nesomyinae rodents and are also known from forest-dwelling *R. rattus* (Muridae). The distributional range for some species of *Paractenopsyllus* and *Tsaractenus* is on the different main highland massifs (Duchemin 2003a). Also, some species, such as *P. duplantieri* and *P. juliamarinus*, share remarkable morphological and ecological traits and have allopatric montane distributions (Duchemin 2003c).

Tungidae

The origin of the family Tungidae is Neotropical. This family is found basal to the Siphonaptera (fleas) in the phylogeny proposed by Whiting et al. (2008) but recently was found more apically by Zhu et al. (2015). Therefore, the genus *Tunga* and family Tungidae are no longer considered part of the family Pulicidae. The single species occurring on Madagascar, *T. penetrans* (Figure 9.48a), was probably introduced from Africa—as indicated by its Malagasy name, *parasy lafrika*, (meaning "the flea from Africa")—and is found across the island (Brygoo 1972). It parasitizes people, pigs, and dogs. Once mature, the female digs in the skin, generally into the feet and particularly the toes in adults, but in children often in the head, which can be notably painful. Only the very end of its abdomen protrudes, allowing egg expulsion. The male, rarely caught, remains free and feeds on blood. As with other fleas, larvae live in soil, preferably fine grained. The total larval development time is around one month (Ratovonjato et al. 2008). The embedded female lesion is likely to become infected by contact with soil.

Pulicidae

The last family, Pulicidae, is represented on the island by three subfamilies: Pulicinae, Archeopsyllinae, and Xenopsyllinae. On

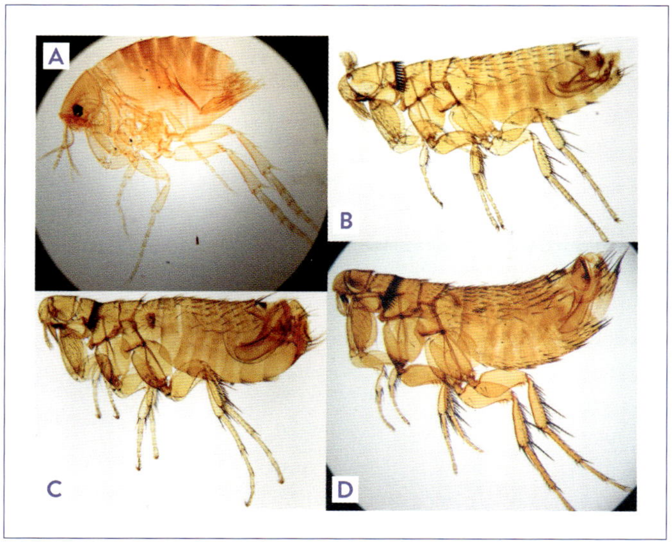

FIGURE 9.48 Images of Malagasy fleas: A) *Tunga penetrans* (male), B) *Paractenopsyllus duplantieri* (male), C) *P. goodmani* (male), and D) *Tsaractenus rodhaini* (male). Images are to the same scale. (PHOTOS by J.-B. Duchemin.)

Madagascar, the subfamily Pulicinae comprises two species: *Pulex irritans* and *Echidnophaga gallinacea*. *Pulex irritans* has a Neotropical origin. It invaded Africa via Europe through human migration. The flea parasitizes numerous commensal hosts (people, dogs, pigs, and, more rarely, rats). It has been implicated in small-scale plague epidemics in Africa (Democratic Republic of the Congo) and Brazil (Karimi et al. 1974). On Madagascar, Ratovonjato et al. (2014) reported the presence of plague bacilli DNA in nine specimens of *P. irritans* out of 230 collected inside houses during a plague outbreak. The presence of plague DNA within a flea provides evidence of its contact with mammalian plague carriers but does not demonstrate the role of the flea as a vector in plague transmission. *Echidnophaga gallinacea*, sometimes considered a primitive parasite of birds (poultry), is also found on commensal rodents and has also been collected on numerous animals in captivity—for example, lemurs (*Hapalemur griseus*). It has a geographic distribution in tropical regions. This flea lives almost permanently on its host and is simply fixed and not encysted in the skin.

The subfamily Archaeopsyllinae comprises two genera on Madagascar: *Centetipsylla* and *Ctenocephalides*. *Centetipsylla* is an endemic genus with a single species, *C. madagascariensis*, collected on *Tenrec ecaudatus* and once on *Rattus rattus*. Its range seems to be the eastern portion of the Central Highlands, but it has also been collected in Antananarivo (Brygoo and Rajenison 1959). This genus is morphologically close to Palearctic *Archaeopsylla*, a parasite of hedgehogs. Harimalala et al. (2018) confirmed the tenrec hosts *Tenrec ecaudatus* and *Setifer setosus* for *C. madagascariensis* and, based on a molecular study, placed this flea well within Pulicidae, in a basal position.

Ctenocephalides is a genus with Afrotropical origins and is secondarily Palearctic and Oriental (Beaucournu 1974). Two species are present on Madagascar: *C. brygooi* is an endemic species known only from the Antalaha area, where it was collected on an endemic carnivoran, *Fossa fossana* (family Eupleridae); and *C. felis strongylus*, which parasitizes mainly cats and dogs and sometimes captive animals and commensal rodents (J.-M. Klein and Uilenberg 1966b). The origin of the latter flea species is Afrotropical; it was imported to Madagascar by domesticated animals and is largely confined to human-modified habitats.

The subfamily Xenopsyllinae is represented on Madagascar by *Xenopsylla*, which has an almost worldwide distribution, and the endemic *Synopsyllus*. *Xenopsylla* comprises three species on the island: *X. cheopis*, *X. brasiliensis*, and *X. petteri*. *Xenopsylla cheopis* is an introduced flea common in human-modified habitats. It is collected mainly on *R. rattus* captured inside rural houses and on *R. norvegicus* in urban areas, and plays a major role in the transmission of plague. It was found to be abundant in Mahajanga, infesting the introduced shrew *Suncus murinus* (family Soricidae), the most important plague reservoir in that city during the local plague epidemics in the 1990s (Rahelinirina et al. 2017). It is very rarely captured on endemic mammals; for a recent example, see Harimalala et al. (2020). This flea has developed resistance to various insecticides (Coulanges and Randrianantoanina 1985; Boyer et al. 2014) and is the subject of careful monitoring and trials for new vector-control techniques (Rajonhson et al. 2017; Miarinjara et al. 2019). A genetics study showed that *X. cheopis* populations from Madagascar could be grouped into three genetic clusters with limited gene flow linked more to potential human-driven dispersal than that of *R. rattus* (Harimalala et al. 2017). Present on the Comoros and Mauritius (Hopkins and Rothschild 1953), *X. brasiliensis* was recently discovered on Madagascar, specifically in the Mandritsara District, infesting *R. rattus* captured in two villages investigated during a plague outbreak in 2013–2014 (Miarinjara et al. 2016). This species is a known plague vector, and its occurrence raises concerns about associated risk.

Xenopsylla petteri is an endemic species described from the Menabe area, where it parasitizes the endemic nesomyine rodent *Hypogeomys antimena*, whose extant range is limited to that area. This flea species is, for the time being, classified in the *hirsuta* group (Lumaret 1962), which contains five other species confined to extreme southwestern Africa (Hopkins and Rothschild 1953). The principal hosts of these five species are two rodents that occur in zones with loose, sandy, or alluvial soils, as is the case for *H. antimena*. There is no known role in plague transmission by this flea species; moreover, its distribution area is outside the known Malagasy plague foci.

The endemic genus *Synopsyllus* comprises five species on Madagascar. Its affinities are with the genera *Synosternus* (Afrotropical, Palearctic, and *pro parte* Oriental regions) and *Xenopsylla* from the *hirsuta* group (see above). *Synopsyllus fonquerniei* has a special importance in plague cycles on Madagascar (see Rasambainarivo and Zohdy, pp. 298–302). Indeed, its distribution coincides with that of human plague cases in rural areas of the Central Highlands. This distribution pattern seems to be coherent with its higher tolerance to low temperature than *X. cheopis* (Kreppel et al. 2016). This last characteristic could also explain the preferred outdoor environment of *S. fonquerniei*, in contrast to *X. cheopis*. According to Brygoo (1967), its capacity as a vector (i.e., its intrinsic capacity to transmit the plague bacillus) might be higher than that of *X. cheopis*.

Synopsyllus fonquerniei appears well adapted to *R. rattus*, particularly outside of commensal settings, such as in open habitats (rice

TABLE 9.35. **Checklist of endemic Malagasy Leptopsyllinae, with host species and elevation**

FLEA SPECIES	ORYZORICTINAE	TENRECINAE	NESOMYINAE	MURIDAE, PRINCIPALLY *RATTUS RATTUS*	ELEVATION (m)
Paractenopsyllus kerguisteli	*Oryzorictes hova, Nesogale dobsoni, Microgale cowani*	*Tenrec ecaudatus*		Yes	1600
P. pauliani	*N. talazaci, M. fotsifotsy, M. longicaudata, M. soricoides*	–	*Eliurus myoxinus*	(1)	800–1500
P. grandidieri	*M. fotsifotsy* (1), *N. dobsoni* (2)	–	*E. myoxinus* (?), *E. majori, E. tanala, Gymnuromys roberti, Nesomys rufus* (1), *E. minor* (1)	Yes	725–1400
P. petiti	*N. dobsoni, M. taiva, M. drouhardi, M. gymnorhyncha, M. thomasi, M. soricoides, M. parvula, M. pusilla, M. gracilis, M. longicaudata, M. cowani*	–	*N. rufus* (1), *E. minor* (1), *E. webbi* (1), *E. tanala* (2)	Yes (13)	600–1600
P. viettei	*N. dobsoni, M. cowani* (1), *M. thomasi* (1)	–	*Brachyuromys betsiloensis* (1)	Yes and *Mus musculus* (1)	1500–2050
P. vauceli	*N. dobsoni, M. gymnorhyncha, M. cowani, M. longicaudata, O. hova, M. gracilis, M. gracilis, M. parvula, M. soricoides, M. fotsifotsy, M. taiva, M. thomasi*	*H. nigriceps, H. semispinosus*	*N. rufus* (2), *E. majori* (1)	Yes (7)	1300–1875
P. randrianasoloi	*N. talazaci* (1), *M. thomasi* (1), *M. parvula* (2)	–	*E. tanala, E. ellermani, E. minor, E. grandidieri, E. majori, E. webbi, N. rufus* (1), *G. roberti* (1)	Yes	875–2000
P. albignaci	*Microgale* sp.	–	–	–	2400–2500
P. goodmani	*M. soricoides, M. cowani, M. fotsifotsy, M. longicaudata, M. gracilis*	–	*E. grandidieri* (1)	–	1025–1600
P. rouxi	*M. cowani* (1)	*H. nigriceps, Setifer setosus*	*E. majori, E. tanala*	Yes (2)	1200–1700
P. ratovonjatoi	*N. talazaci, N. dobsoni, M. taiva, M. cowani, M. gymnorhyncha, M. fotsifotsy*	–	–	–	1175–1450
P. duplantieri	*N. dobsoni, M. taiva, M. longicaudata, M. cowani, M. thomasi, M. drouhardi, M. fotsifotsy, M. soricoides, O. hova*	*S. setosus*	*E. majori* (1)	Yes (1)	1100–1400
P. juliamarinus	*M. cowani, M. longicaudata, N. dobsoni*	–	*E. grandidieri* (1)	–	1200–1600
P. gemelli		–	*E. myoxinus, E. grandidieri, E. ellermani, E. webbi*	–	810–1200
P. beaucournui		–		Yes (1)	1550
P. oconnori		–	*E. tanala* (1), *E. webbi* (1)	–	1000
P. raxworthyi	*M. brevicaudata* (1), *M. drouhardi* (2)	*T. ecaudatus* (1)	–	–	550–1000
P. madagascariensis	–	–	*E. tanala, E. majori, E. webbi, G. roberti, E. minor, N. rufus*	Yes (1)	650–1250
P. exspectatus	*M. cowani* (1)	–	–	–	1990
Tsaractenus grenieri	–	–	–	(1)	1500
T. rodhaini	*N. dobsoni, M. soricoides, M. thomasi, M. fotsifotsy, M. gracilis, M. cowani, M. gymnorhyncha, M. soricoides*	–	*E. tanala* (1)	–	1400–1650
T. clavator	*N. dobsoni*	–	–	–	1300–1600

Sources: Data presented herein are largely modifed from Duchemin (2003a); Hastriter (2009); Beaucournu and Goodman (2014); Beaucournu and Laudisoit (2014); and Goodman et al. (2015).

Note: Number of occurrences for rare associations are in parentheses.

fields and grasslands) and in certain moist evergreen forests of the Central Highlands. This flea has also been collected on tenrecs of the endemic subfamily Tenrecinae and on rodents of the endemic Nesomyinae (J.-M. Klein and Uilenberg 1966b), including different species of *Eliurus* and, rarely, on *Macrotarsomys bastardi* (Roubaud and Girard 1943). The report of this species from a *Microcebus* lemur is the only known record (Roubaud and Girard 1943) of a flea being captured on a wild lemur and probably is in error or a secondary infestation. Duchemin (2003a) reported notably high prevalence and loads of *S. fonquerniei* on two nesomyine rodents (*E. myoxinus* and *E. antsingy*) from the western dry, deciduous, low-altitude forests. The importance of *S. fonquerniei* in plague transmission has been studied in considerable detail (Brygoo 1967; Duplantier et al. 2005; Chanteau 2006), but its sensitivity to insecticides has been the subject of very few studies (Coulanges et al. 1983).

The other four species of *Synopsyllus* known from Madagascar are captured less often. According to Lumaret (1962), *S. smiti* is a flea occurring on *Macrotarsomys ingens*, a nesomyine rodent known only from the dry deciduous forests of Ankarafantsika (Duchemin 2003a). *Synopsyllus estradei* is found mainly on *R. rattus* (Goodman et al. 2015) in moist evergreen forests at elevations higher than 1000 m. It has also been collected on the nesomyine rodent *Nesomys rufus* and the oryzorictine tenrecs *Nesogale dobsoni* (J.-M. Klein and Uilenberg 1966b) and *N. talazaci*; *M. cowani* and other *Microgale* species; and, more rarely, on the tenrecine spiny tenrecs *Hemicentetes nigriceps*, *Tenrec ecaudatus*, and *Setifer setosus*. There are also recent records of this flea from other nesomyine rodents, namely *E. tanala*, *E. minor*, *E. grandidieri*, and *Gymnuromys roberti*, from montane areas generally between 1400 and 1600 m, rarely at lower elevations, and unknown below 850 m (Duchemin 2003a). *Synopsyllus girardi* was known only from its type series (two specimens) from the Anjozorobe region (J.-M. Klein 1965b), but more recently, it has been found in montane forests on the Manongarivo Massif and in eastern moist evergreen forests of Tsinjoarivo and Vatomikona (Duchemin 2003a). As in the type series, the hosts are mainly rodents of the genus *Eliurus*, including mostly *E. tanala/ellermani* (see Carleton et al., pp. 2014–22) and *E. majori*, and rarely on *M. gymnorhyncha* and *H. semispinosus* (Duchemin 2003a). *Synopsyllus robici* is represented by a few specimens found on the Ankaratra Massif and in the region of Ambositra at elevations of 1500 m or above (J.-M. Klein 1965c), with recent captures on *H. nigriceps* in the Central Highlands at 1670 m (Harimalala et al. 2018).

CONCLUSION

The role that fleas play in the transmission of plague on Madagascar has strongly influenced research on this group. Thus, while studies have focused on nonendemic fleas occurring on mammal hosts that have contact with humans, our knowledge of the flea fauna of endemic mammals is somewhat limited, as is information from zones of low elevation where the occurrence of plague is uncommon. Even with these limitations, current information suggests that the flea fauna of Madagascar demonstrates high levels of endemism (73%) compared to other hematophagous insects (see Robert et al., pp. 1089–98). The island's native flea fauna shows numerous host crossovers across mammalian families. The few cases of host specificity among Malagasy fleas might be directly related to their phylogenetic history. Among these are bat fleas but also *Synopsyllus smiti* and *Xenopsylla petteri*, each with a very narrow host spectrum among endemic rodents. The case of endemic Leptopsyllinae is more complex, with hosts distributed among either rodents or Tenrecinae. The Malagasy fleas also present interesting biogeographic patterns, with their affinities being largely African and to a lesser extent Oriental. The current observed distributional patterns of endemic fleas on the island, especially those occurring in zones of higher elevation, are perhaps associated with climatic vicissitudes in recent geological time and are of great importance to current plague epidemiology. Further, the zone of higher elevation has the highest diversity of small mammals (see Goodman and Soarimalala, pp. 1737–69). From both zoological and medical points of view, the Malagasy fleas deserve more detailed research.

Subject editors: Brian L. Fisher and Steven M. Goodman

DIPTERA: TEPHRITIDAE, FRUIT FLIES, *LALIBOANKAZO*

H. Rasolofoarivao, M. De Meyer, and H. Delatte

Tephritidae (Diptera), the true fruit flies, is one of the most diverse fly families, with approximately 4600 species described worldwide (Norrbom et al. 1999). Adults vary in size but can often be recognized by their patterned wings and the presence of a sclerotized ovipositor in females. Biologically, the majority are phytophagous in the larval stage, infesting the seed-bearing organs of a wide range of plants (White and Elson-Harris 1994). Two major groups can be recognized: those with larvae developing in fruits, and a second group with larvae living in flower heads, predominantly of Asteraceae. A minority are saprophagous, leaf or stem miners, or gall formers (Norrbom et al. 1999). Just before the start of the 21st century, the fruit-infesting, or frugivorous, group has received a lot of attention in Africa, mainly because its members attack a number of commercial crops, impacting not only horticultural production but also income and food security for rural populations (Ekesi et al. 2016). Their species recognition and identification has been the focus of taxonomic research over the last 25 years, and the ecology, developmental physiology, and management of several species of major economic significance have been studied in detail (Ekesi et al. 2016). The nonfrugivorous groups have received far less attention; although about 600 species are known from Africa, it is expected that numerous species remain to be described and named.

The tephritid fauna of Madagascar and the rest of the Malagasy Region (the Mascarenes, Seychelles, and Comoros) as a whole has received relatively little attention. It was the topic of a number of papers in the mid-1980s to early 1990s by D. L. Hancock, who presented a review for higher groups, including the description of several new species (Hancock 1984: Ceratitinae; Hancock 1985: Trypetinae; Hancock 1991a: Tephrellini). Since then, the Malagasy fauna has been dealt with only in papers focusing on the revision of particular genera (e.g., Freidberg and Hancock 1989; De Meyer 2000; White et al. 2003; De Meyer and Freidberg 2012). For the Malagasy Region, a review of the fruit flies of the Mascarenes and the Seychelles was presented by White et al. (2000). Since then, only the fauna of the Seychelles (De Meyer 2009) and the Comoro archipelago (De Meyer et al. 2012) have been the subject of taxonomic overviews.

In total, 75 species are recorded from Madagascar (Table 9.36), more than 30 of which appear to be frugivorous, while about one-third are considered flower-head infesters (for several species, the actual biology is unknown, and categorization into these groups is based on the known biology of congeners). The remaining species are either leaf miners, gall formers on stems or twigs, or presumably have multiple modes of larval development, while for some the biology is unknown. As in many other groups, the native fauna of Madagascar comprises a number of endemic fruit flies. Two-thirds of the known species are endemic to the island, while a few additional ones are endemic to the Malagasy Region. For some, a phylogenetic relationship could be established with taxa found on the African mainland. On the other hand, the region has also been the subject of a number of introduced infestations, including from Asia, which may have far-reaching consequences for the indigenous tephritid fauna, as well as for the horticultural industry. While the impact of introduced tephritids has been studied in detail on La Réunion and Mauritius (e.g., Sookar et al. 2012; Charlery et al. 2017), few studies have been conducted on Madagascar. Currently, surveys are being undertaken across Madagascar to evaluate the host range of tephritid fruit flies of economic importance. Between 2016 and 2018, six different ecological regions were inventoried (H. Rasolofoarivao et al., unpublished data). Information on the major tephritid groups is discussed below, including frugivorous and nonfrugivorous taxa. Records for frugivorous species obtained during recent fieldwork are incorporated in the respective subsections and the general discussion.

FRUGIVOROUS TEPHRITIDS

The indigenous Malagasy frugivorous fauna belongs mainly to four of the major pest genera: *Bactrocera*, *Dacus*, *Ceratitis*, and *Trirhithrum*. All these genera have representatives on the African mainland, while some have indigenous species on the Mascarenes. In addition, this group also comprises a pest species within the genus *Neoceratitis*.

Bactrocera is a mainly Asia-Pacific genus comprising more than 460 species (Norrbom et al. 1999), with only 13 representatives in Africa (White 2006) and three occurring on Madagascar. Of these, two are endemic to the island (*B. menanus* and *B. nesiotes*); the third has a much broader distribution (*B. dorsalis*), while another species is found on Mauritius and La Réunion (*B. montyanus*). They all belong to the subgenus *Daculus*, for which all other relatives are found on the African mainland. Very little is known about the Malagasy species as they are known from a limited number of type specimens. Other species in the same subgenus are known to feed on fruits of Oleaceae, Verbenaceae, and apparently Clusiaceae (White 2006).

Dacus is a predominantly African genus, with close to 200 species described from Africa, while 81 species are found in the Asia-Pacific region. The African representatives demonstrate a particular host-plant relationship with taxa associated or reared from three different host plant families: Cucurbitaceae, Apocynaceae, and Passifloraceae (White 2006). The host-plant association appears to be related to some extent to the phylogenetic relationships among the fruit flies, with clusters of species associated with the respective host families (Virgilio et al. 2009). Among the *Dacus* taxa, six are endemic to Madagascar: *D. amberiens*, *D. herensis*, *D. madagascariensis*, *D. melanaspis*, *D. quilicii*, and *D. xanthaspis*. The latter three species belong to a mainly Asia-Pacific subgenus comprising 23 species, contrary to the other faunal elements, which are more closely associated with the Afrotropical region. The host-plant association is unknown for these species, except for *D. xanthaspis*, which was recently reared from a wild cucurbit *Citrullus* sp., while *D. quilicii* was recorded as infesting the cucurbit *Luffa cylindrica* (H. Rasolofoarivao et al., unpublished data). In addition to the abovementioned endemic species, *D. demmerezi* is a species whose distribution is restricted to Madagascar, Mauritius, and La Réunion; it is also known as a pest on a number of cucurbit crops on these islands (White and Elson-Harris 1994).

Representatives of the African genus *Ceratitis* range from specialized fruit feeders to extreme polyphagous pests (De Meyer 2000). Of the 100 known species, five are endemic to Madagascar (De Meyer et al. 2012): *C. andranotobaka*, *C. argenteostriata*, *C. manjakatompo*, *C. sucini*, and *C. tananarivana*. In addition, *C. malgassa* is endemic to Madagascar but was also reported from the Comoros and Mauritius, where it is uncertain if these populations were introduced naturally or by humans. For these different species, the host range for *C. malgassa* is partially known and comprises a number of commercially grown crops (White and Elson-Harris 1994; H. Rasolofoarivao et al., unpublished data). For the other endemic *Ceratitis* species, host data are lacking, and most have been rarely encountered in the field. Only *C. argenteostriata* has an established host record with the native *Rubus myrianthus* at Ambatolampy (1556 m elevation).

The genus *Trirhithrum* is equally Afrotropical, with about 40 representatives. Host-plant associations are diverse, but a large group is known from Rubiaceae, including a number of coffee pests (White et al. 2003). Madagascar comprises four endemic species: *T. crescentis*, *T. iridescens*, *T. manganum*, and *T. resplendens*, while a fifth species, *T. argenteocuneatum*, is found on Madagascar and the Mascarenes. All share a common body characteristic of a bluish

TABLE 9.36. **Checklist of Tephritidae recorded from Madagascar, with Madagascar or Malagasy Region endemic status**

SCIENTIFIC NAME	ENDEMIC TO MADAGASCAR	ENDEMIC TO MALAGASY REGION	LOCATION OF LARVAL DEVELOPMENT
Acidoxantha bisinuata Hancock	Yes	–	(flowers)
Actinoptera tuckeri (Bezzi)	No	No	flowers
Bactrocera dorsalis (Hendel)	No	No	fruits
B. menanus (Munro)	Yes	–	(fruits)
B. nesiotes (Munro)	Yes	–	(fruits)
Carpophthoromyia speciose Hancock	Yes	–	(fruits)
Celidodacus madagascariensis Hering	Yes	–	(fruits)
Ceratitis andranotobaka Hancock	Yes	–	(fruits)
C. argenteostriata De Meyer & Freidberg	Yes	–	fruits
C. capitate (Wiedemann)	No	No	fruits
C. cosyra (Walker)	No	No	fruits
C. malgassa Munro	No	Yes	fruits
C. manjakatompo Hancock	Yes	–	(fruits)
C. pedestris (Bezzi)	No	No	fruits
C. punctate (Wiedemann)	No	No	fruits
C. sucini De Meyer	Yes	–	(fruits)
C. tananarivana Hancock	Yes	–	(fruits)
Coelopacidia madagascariensis Enderlein	Yes	–	stems
Coelotrypes hammersteini (Enderlein)	Yes	–	flowers
C. vittatus Bezzi	No	No	flowers
Cryptophorellia elongatula Freidberg & Hancock	Yes	–	(flowers)
C. madagascariensis Freidberg & Hancock	Yes	–	(flowers)
C. minuta Freidberg & Hancock	Yes	–	(flowers)
C. prairiensis Freidberg & Hancock	Yes	–	(flowers)
C. stenoptera Freidberg & Hancock	Yes	–	(flowers)
C. stuckenbergi Freidberg & Hancock	Yes	–	(flowers)
Dacus amberiens (Munro)	Yes	–	(fruits)
D. bivittatus (Bigot)	No	No	fruits
D. ciliates Loew	No	No	fruits
D. demmerezi (Bezzi)	No	Yes	fruits
D. herensis (Munro)	Yes	–	(fruits)
D. madagascariensis White	Yes	–	(fruits)
D. melanaspis (Munro)	Yes	–	(fruits)
D. punctatifrons Karsch	No	No	fruits
D. quilicii White	Yes	–	(fruits)
D. vertebratus Bezzi	No	No	fruits
D. xanthaspis (Munro)	Yes	–	(fruits)
Dectodesis comis (Munro)	Yes	–	flowers

SCIENTIFIC NAME	ENDEMIC TO MADAGASCAR	ENDEMIC TO MALAGASY REGION	LOCATION OF LARVAL DEVELOPMENT
D. spatiosa (Munro)	Yes	–	flowers
Gymnaciura austeni (Munro)	No	No	?(flowers)
Gymnosagena kakamega Freidberg & Merz	No[1]	No	(flowers)
Hemilea malgassa Hancock	Yes	–	(leaves)
Hoplandromyia madagascariensis Hancock	Yes	–	leaves
Malagaciura stuckenbergi Hancock	Yes	–	unknown
Metasphenisca grandidieri (Bezzi)	Yes	–	(flowers)
M. pallidifemur Hancock	Yes	–	(flowers)
Neoceratitis albiseta De Meyer & Freidberg	Yes	–	(fruits)
N. cyanescens (Bezzi)	No	Yes	fruits
Notomma munroi Hancock	Yes	–	(twigs)
Oedaspis inflate (Munro)	Yes	–	stems
O. nyx Freidberg & Kaplan	Yes	–	(stems)
O. pauliani (Munro)	Yes	–	stems
Paraciura perpicillaris (Bezzi)	No	No	?(flowers)
Parafreutreta mavoana Munro	Yes	–	?(flowers)
Paraspheniscoides binaries (Loew)	No	No	flowers
Philophylla andobana (Hancock)	Yes	–	(leaves/fruits)
P. inconspicua (Hancock)	Yes	–	(leaves/fruits)
P. mailaka (Hancock)	Yes	–	(leaves/fruits)
P. perineta (Hancock)	Yes	–	(leaves/fruits)
P. sandrangato (Hancock)	Yes	–	(leaves/fruits)
Pseudafreutreta diaphasis (Bigot)	No	No	(flowers)
P. guttatolimbata (Enderlein)	Yes	–	(flowers)
Pseudomyoleja tsaratanana (Hancock)	Yes	–	?(leaves/fruits)
Sphaeniscus sexmaculatus (Macquart)	No	No	flowers
Stephanotrypeta vittata Freidberg	No	No	?(flowers)
Taomyia pictipennis Hancock	Yes	–	(fruits)
Tephraciura flavimacula Hancock	Yes	–	(flowers)
T. tulearensis Hancock	Yes	–	(flowers)
Trirhithrum argenteocuneatum Hancock	No	Yes	fruits
T. crescentis Hancock	Yes	–	fruits
T. iridescens Hancock	Yes	–	(fruits)
T. manganum Munro	Yes	–	fruits
T. resplendens Hancock	Yes	–	(fruits)
Trupanea andobana Munro	Yes	–	?(flowers)
T. furcifera (Bezzi)	No	No	?(flowers)

Notes: Plant parts within parentheses refer to species for which information is lacking and inferred from congeneric species; a question mark (?) indicates that some ambiguity exists.

[1] Freidberg and Merz (2006) report that the Madagascar specimens differ morphologically from those of the African mainland but list them under this name.

metallic hue not observed in other representatives of the genus. However, White et al. (2003) pointed out that this is discordant with other observed characters and that it is likely to have evolved independently in response to a shared selection pressure, possibly mimicry. As with the other groups, specimen records are few, and there are rearings known from *Coffea* species only for *T. argenteocuneatum*, *T. crescentis*, and *T. manganum* (Munro 1954; S. Quillici, unpublished data; H. Rasolofoarivao et al., unpublished data).

Neoceratitis is a mainly African genus, with one representative from Central Asia and China (*N. asiataca*). Two species are reported from Madagascar. *Neoceratitis cyanescens* is considered a pest species of a number of solanaceous crops and one of the most abundant tomato pests across Madagascar. It is also recorded from the Comoros and the Mascarenes, and its presence on these islands is possibly the result of invasive populations, with first records from the 1950s on tomatoes (Hancock 1984). A second species, described as *N. albiseta*, is known only from type material collected on Madagascar from *Lycium* sp. (Solanaceae), which is known as the wild host for several other *Neoceratitis* species (De Meyer and Freidberg 2012).

In addition, a number of introduced species have been recorded over the last decades on Madagascar, and some have a major impact on the horticultural industry. The most important invader is undoubtedly *Bactrocera dorsalis*. This Asian species was detected for the first time on the African continent in Kenya in 2003, when it was described as a new species, *B. invadens* (Lux et al. 2003). Since then the species has spread throughout the whole of sub-Saharan Africa as well as to some of the western Indian Ocean islands, including Madagascar (De Meyer and Ekesi 2016). For several other species reported from Madagascar, the invasion history is poorly documented. Most of the records date back from the 1950s—for example, *Ceratitis cosyra* (1951), *Daca vertebratus* (1953), and *C. capitata* (1958). H. Rasolofoarivao et al. (unpublished data) reconfirmed the presence of these species in a recent survey but could not reconfirm the presence of others that have been recorded much more recently: *D. punctatifrons* (1998), *D. bivittatus* (2005), and *D. ciliatus* (2005).

In addition to representatives of these main frugivorous genera, there are also a number of species belonging to less important genera. *Carpophthoromyia speciosa* is the only representative of this Afrotropical genus in the Malagasy Region. It is restricted to Madagascar, and there are no host records, but confirmed hosts for other members of the genus are from *Drypetes* (Euphorbiaceae) (De Meyer 2006). There is one indigenous species on Madagascar of the Afrotropical genus *Taomyia*, *T. pictipennis*. While the host of this particular species is unknown, there are records of a related species, *T. marshalli*, reared from the fruits of *Dracaena* (Dracaenaceae) (Copeland et al. 2005). Two additional species are known from adjacent islands: *T. mauritiana* from Mauritius and *T. ocellata* from the Seychelles (Hancock 1991b; De Meyer 2009). Most likely the only Malagasy representative of the genus *Celidodacus*, *C. madagascariensis*, is also frugivorous, as other representatives of this genus are known to develop in Fabaceae (Copeland et al. 2005).

NONFRUGIVOROUS TEPHRITIDS

The nonfrugivorous tephritid fauna of Madagascar has been studied to a lesser extent. Most taxa were described by D. L. Hancock in his series on fruit flies from Madagascar and the Malagasy Region (Hancock 1985, 1991a) and a revision of the genus *Cryptophorellia* (Freidberg and Hancock 1989). The affinities of these taxa are largely with the African mainland where congeners are found for the majority of the species. Only the genera *Hemilea* and *Acidoxantha* have their closest relatives in the Indo-Australian fauna. One monotypic genus, *Malagaciura*, appears to be endemic to the island.

Not much is known about the biology of Malagasy Region taxa, but the mode of larval development can at times be deduced based on the known life history of congeneric species. Table 9.36 summarizes the available information on which part of the plant is used. In most cases, larvae appear to feed on flower heads of Asteraceae, such as the genera *Actinoptera*, *Dectodesis*, and *Gymnosagena* (Merz 1999; Freidberg and Merz 2006). Representatives of *Cryptophorellia*, in particular, are associated with the plant tribe Senecioneae (Freidberg and Hancock 1989). Some others may attack flowers of Acanthaceae (*Tephraciura*), Convolvulaceae (*Coelotrypes*), Lamiaceae (*Sphaeniscus* and possibly also *Gymnaciura*), or Verbenaceae (*Paraspheniscoides*) (Hancock 1991a; White et al. 2000). Also *Acidoxantha* could be infesting flower buds of different plant families, as is known to occur in several Oriental species (Hancock 1985). For some, the larval feeding behavior seems to differ within the genus. Representatives of the genus *Metasphenisca* are reported from seedpods or flower heads of Acanthaceae (Hancock 2010). Representatives of the genus *Oedaspis* can form galls on either the stems or on flower heads (Freidberg and Kaplan 1992). A minority are leaf miners of Rubiaceae (*Hoplandromyia*; see Hancock 1985) or possibly of Asteraceae (*Hemilea*; see Merz 1999), while others are stem borers (*Coelopacidia*; see Copeland et al. 2005). Representatives of the genus *Notomma* are reported to form galls on twigs of Leguminosae (Hancock 1985). For some genera, their biology is completely unknown or uncertain.

GENERAL DISCUSSION

Biogeographic associations of the Malagasy fauna appear to be mainly Afrotropical. For some genera, such as *Cryptophorellia* or *Ceratitis*, there is a distinct pattern of sublineages formed on the African mainland and islands of the Malagasy Region, respectively. According to Freidberg and Hancock (1989), this is probably because of vicariance associated with the split between Madagascar and Africa. An alternative hypothesis would be that species invaded the Malagasy Region at a later stage and evolved in isolation. A few groups show associations with the Asia-Pacific region. This is obvious in the subgenus *Dacus* (*Neodacus*), where the other representatives are found in the Oriental region. Also, *Acidoxantha*, *Hemilea*, and *Myoleja* (which is unknown from the Malagasy Region) have mainly Asia-Pacific congeners, with some Palearctic representatives (Norrbom et al. 1999). The degree of specific endemism is rather high, with more than two-thirds of species restricted to Madagascar or the Malagasy Region. However, endemism at higher taxonomic levels is limited; *Malagaciura* is the only endemic genus.

Distributional data on the island are too limited to draw any biogeographic conclusions and appear to be mainly a reflection of where collecting efforts have taken place. The only tendencies that could be discerned during recent studies (H. Rasolofoarivao et al., unpublished data) is that the polyphagous *Bactrocera dorsalis* and *Ceratitis malgassa* both show a similar distribution pattern, but *B. dorsalis* was distinctly more common at low elevations (below 500 m), while *C. malgassa* appeared to dominate at high elevations (above 1000 m). *Ceratitis capitata* was restricted to habitats in the eastern portion of the island, while *C. cosyra* occurred along the west and south coasts, where Mango (*Mangifera indica*) and Marula (*Pourpartia caffra*, treated as *Sclerocarya birrea* subsp. *caffra* by some authorities) are predominant.

Several frugivorous species are of economic significance, and the recent surveys by H. Rasolofoarivao et al. (unpublished data) have confirmed the host range and impact of some of these pest species. Five major species (*C. malgassa*, *Neoceratitis cyanescens*, *B. dorsalis*, *Dacus demmerezi*, and *D. vertebratus*) were associated with commercially produced fruit along elevation gradients (sea level to 1634 m) throughout all agroecological zones of Madagascar.

Throughout much of Africa, *B. dorsalis* has a very wide host range (e.g., Mwatawala et al. 2009; Goergen et al. 2011). A recent survey on Madagascar (H. Rasolofoarivao et al., unpublished data) confirmed 14 crops in 10 families as host plants for this species, only four of which are vegetables species (*Cucurbita pepo*, *Sechium edule*, *Solanum americanum*, and *S. lycopersicum*). Along the coast below 500 m, *B. dorsalis* was found in indigenous wild fruit, as well as in *Malleastrum* in the area of the Ankarafantsika National Park where introduced cultivated fruits were less abundant or absent. Other native species collected from urban areas, such as *Ficus polita*, were important host-plant reservoirs of *B. dorsalis*. *Mangifera indica* and fruit species belonging to the Myrtaceae and Rosaceae families were the most preferred among the cultivated host plants.

Of the pest species within the genus *Ceratitis*, recent surveys (H. Rasolofoarivao et al., unpublished data) reported *C. malgassa* as the most polypaghous, with hosts from 12 families and 23 plant species (showing extensive variation in fruiting phenology), but none from cultivated vegetables. Temperate fruits, such as apple (*Malus domestica*), pear (*Pyrus communis*), and peach (*Prunus vulgaris*), grown in the Central Highlands were the most infested. The two other polyphagous Tephritidae, *C. capitata* and *C. cosyra*, were found on a limited host spectrum. *Ceratitis capitata*, known as a highly polyphagous fruit fly in sub-Saharan Africa (De Meyer 2000), was restricted to the eastern portions of the island and not common in this survey; the hosts were *Mimusops coriacea* and *Terminalia catappa*. *Ceratitis cosyra*, also widespread and polyphagous throughout the African continent (Ekesi et al. 2016), was found associated mainly with *Mangifera indica* on Madagascar and a few wild fruits such as *Poupartia caffra* (*Sclerocarya birrea* subsp. *caffra*).

Among *Dacus*, two major cucurbit pests were recorded and several commercial and wild hosts confirmed. *Dacus vertebratus* and *D. demmerezi*, both widespread cucurbit feeders, were found on, respectively, six and 10 species of Cucurbitaceae. *Neoceratitis cyanescens* was recorded from 18 host plant species, of which four species of *Solanum* were the most preferred among the cultivated host plants.

In comparison to some older specimen records and published information from Madagascar, certain fruits were sampled, and no evidence of Tephritidae infestation was found. The distribution of different species on the other regional islands is even less known. Nevertheless, the number of recorded pest species and their economic impact, on the one hand, and the actual diversity with a high degree of endemism, on the other hand, will require more extensive sampling throughout Madagascar and neighboring islands in order to obtain a more accurate idea of the actual diversity of this group.

ACKNOWLEDGMENTS

This work was partially funded both by CIRAD, Union Européenne (FEDER INTERREG V), and Conseil Régional de La Réunion, under the EPIBIO-OI "EPIdémiosurveillance et BIOcontrole dans le Sud-Ouest de l'océan Indien" project. The authors are grateful to students from the Université d'Antananarivo who participated in the fruit sampling and assisted in the laboratory work.

Subject editors: Brian L. Fisher and Steven M. Goodman

DIPTERA: CONOPIDAE, THICK-HEADED FLIES

J.-H. Stuke

INTRODUCTION AND TAXONOMY

The family Conopidae consists of small to large flies (3–30 mm); three subfamilies occur on Madagascar, each with a very different habitus. Conopinae (Figure 9.49a) contains some of the largest dipterans on the island; they have a wasplike appearance, long antenna, a stylus-like arista situated at the top of the antenna, and the abdomen narrowed at the base; females also possess a ventral theca. Myopinae (Figures 9.49b and c) is represented by small, rather hunched-looking brown to black flies that can have an obvious metallic shimmer; females have a ventral sternite (theca, Figure 9.49b) toward the apex of the abdomen. Stylogastrinae (Figure 9.49d) consists of distinctive elongate brownish flies with long legs, a long proboscis geniculated (bent) at mid-length, and distinct setae; females have a unique ovipositor-like structure.

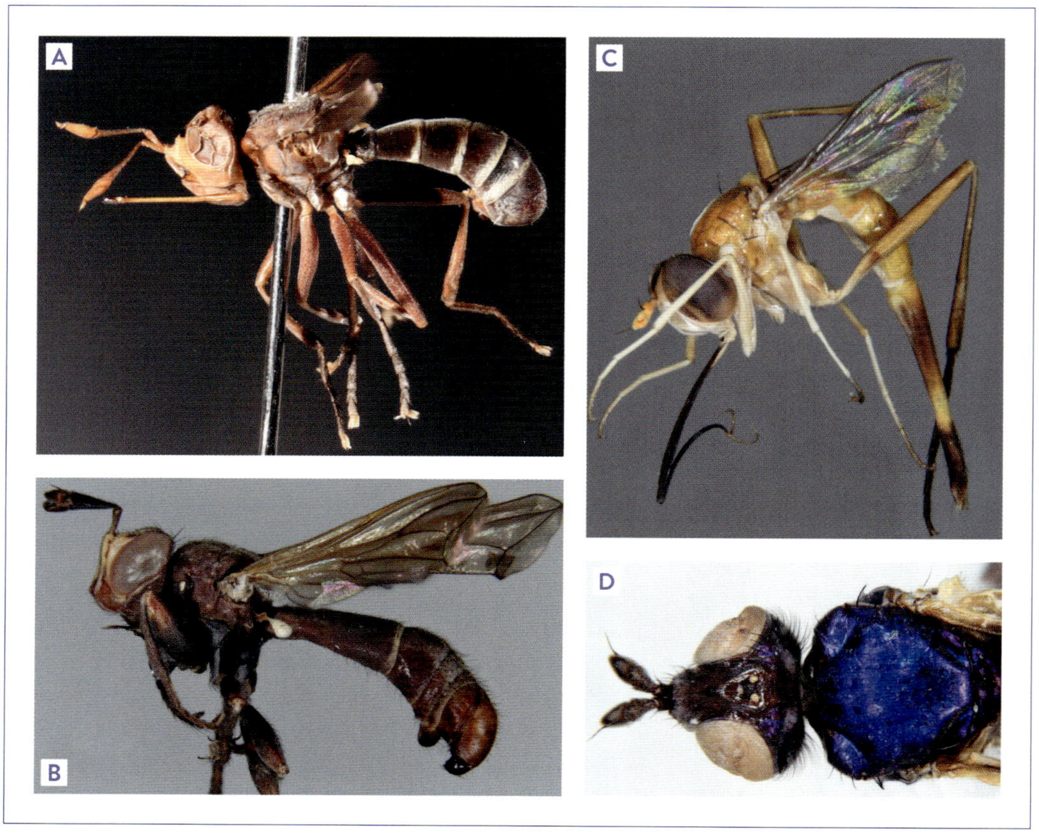

FIGURE 9.49 **Habitus of Malagasy Conopidae: A)** ***Conops unicolor*****; B)** ***Pseudoconops antennatus*****, female; C)** ***Thecophora metallica*****; and D)** ***Stylogaster pauliana*****.** (PHOTOS by J.-H. Stuke.)

The known larvae of all members of Conopidae, except Stylogastrinae, are endoparasitoides of Hymenoptera—mainly bees, wasps, and closely allied taxa (Hymenoptera: Aculeata). The larval biology of *Stylogaster* remains mysterious. On the African mainland, it is well documented that *Stylogaster* adults accompany army ants of the genera *Dorylus* (*Anomma*) during foraging raids (Stuckenberg 1963). There seems to be no close or direct relationship between *Stylogaster* and the ants, but *Stylogaster* females are known to inject their highly modified eggs into a range of other insects as they flee from the raiding ants. However, it is unclear whether the recorded oviposition behavior of the Malagasy forms is similar in Afrotropical *Stylogaster*. K. G. V. Smith and Cunningham–Van Someren (1985) reported three sympatric Afrotropical *Stylogaster* species that clearly differed regarding the insects on which their eggs are found: *S. varifrons* eggs were recorded only from cockroach nymphs (*Euloboptera* and possibly *Blatella*); *S. westwoodi* eggs were reported only from gryllid crickets (*Acanthogryllus*, *Gryllus*, and *Callogryllus*) and possibly also accidentally from spiders (Lycosidae); and *S. nitens* eggs are deposited in flies (Calliphoridae and Muscidae). Couri and Pont (2006) gave a recent overview of the members of Diptera on which *Stylogaster* eggs have been found. However, the only reports of Afrotropical *Stylogaster* larvae are from crickets, cockroach nymphs, and "des pupes des glossines" (the pupa of *Glossina morsitans*) (Berghe et al. 1956; K. G. V. Smith 1967; K. G. V. Smith and Cunningham–Van Someren 1985). Conopidae adults are well known for visiting flowers. If there is any specialization to particular flower species, however, this is most likely to be because of the presence of hymenopteran hosts, which are in turn restricted to specific flower types or species for the collection of nectar or pollen. Conopidae adults occur in a wide range of habitats wherever aculeate Hymenoptera is supported.

Some 775 conopid species belonging to 57 genera are recorded to date worldwide (Stuke 2017). The family is divided into one fossil and five recent subfamilies. There is a long-running debate as to whether or not Stylogastrinae, which contains the single large genus *Stylogaster*, represents a separate family, an idea that is supported both by the distinctive and consistent adult and larval morphology and also by the different host-group preferences of this genus. Another long-running debate concerns where to place Conopidae within Diptera. Conopidae is currently identified as an acalyptrate member of Diptera, but its precise position within Acalyptratae is unclear, and several conflicting hypotheses exist (Gibson et al. 2010).

HISTORY OF RESEARCH ON MALAGASY CONOPIDAE

As with most Diptera families, research on Conopidae of Madagascar is at an early stage, with the main focus still on finding new species and investigating their distribution. Knowledge of Malagasy conopids is relatively well developed, compared with other dipteran families, following an important period of research. The first conopids reported from Madagascar were *Conops unicolor* and *Physocephala madagascarensis* (= *P. antiqua*), which were described about 100 years ago by the Hamburg dipterologist Otto Kröber (1882–1969) in two of his large revisions of the family (Kröber 1915a, 1915b). Kröber obtained four of his specimens from "Fort

Dauphin" (Tolagnaro), in the collection of "K. K. Hofmus. Wien," together with one specimen from "Ambohimanga," in the collection of "Stettin." No further information about the collectors or the circumstances of collection is known. Additional species were subsequently described from Madagascar by Séguy (1932), Kröber (1939), and Janssens (1954). Sidney Camras was motivated by the large collections of Brian Roy Stuckenberg and Alfred Jakob Keiser, together with additional material from other collections, to provide a detailed overview of Malagasy Conopidae (Camras 1962). This fundamental taxonomic and faunistic work was later supplemented by Stuckenberg (1963), K. G. V. Smith (1984), and Camras (2007). A large amount of conopid material was also more recently collected in the Arthropod Survey of Madagascar's Protected Areas project initiated by Michael E. Irwin and the late Evert I. Schlinger (Kirk-Spriggs 2017), which formed the basis for the recent revisionary works of Stuke (2004, 2005, 2012, 2015, 2019) and Stuke and Clements (2019). In addition to faunistic and taxonomic research on the island's conopids, ecological research on the fascinating genus *Stylogaster* should also be highlighted: Stuckenberg (1963) provided observations of Malagasy *Stylogaster*, and subsequently Stuckenberg (1963) and K. G. V. Smith (1967) put forward important ideas concerning the biology of this genus. Couri and Pont (2006) and Couri and Silva Barros (2010) added records of Malagasy Diptera found carrying *Stylogaster* eggs, while Nilsson et al. (1985b) described the flower-visiting behavior of a *Stylogaster* species on the labiate *Plectranthus vestitus* in the Central Highlands.

TABLE 9.37. **Checklist of Conopidae of Madagascar**

CONOPINAE
Archiconops hova (Janssens, 1954)
A. insularis Kröber, 1936
A. niger Kröber, 1939
Conops stuckenbergi Camras, 1962
C. unicolor Kröber, 1915
Physocephala antiqua (Wiedemann, 1830)
MYOPINAE
Pseudoconops antennatus Camras, 1962
Thecophora clementsi Stuke, 2015
T. metallica Camras, 1962
T. obsoleta Stuke, 2015
T. submetallica Stuke, 2015
STYLOGASTRINAE
Stylogaster acanthocercus Stuke, 2012
S. amplicercus Stuke, 2012
S. camrasi Stuckenberg, 1963
S. clementsi Stuke, 2012
S. fanjae Stuke, 2012
S. fianarantsoensis Stuke, 2015
S. hauseri Stuke, 2012
S. hirsutifemora Stuke, 2012
S. irwini Stuke, 2012
S. kroeberi Stuke, 2012
S. latifrons Stuke, 2012
S. malaisei Stuke, 2015
S. malgachensis Camras, 1962
S. nilssoni Smith, 1984
S. parkeri Stuke, 2012
S. pauliana Camras, 1962
S. pseudofanjae Stuke, 2012
S. ranomafanensis Stuke, 2012
S. rinhaii Stuke, 2012
S. schachti Stuke, 2012
S. seguyi Camras, 1962
S. seyrigi Séguy, 1932
S. smithi Stuke, 2012
S. spinicercus Stuke, 2012
S. stuckenbergi Stuke, 2012

Sources: Modified from Stuke (2017), with additions from Stuke and Clements (2019).

BIOGEOGRAPHY OF CONOPIDS OF MADAGASCAR

Thirty-six species belonging to six genera of Conopidae are currently known from Madagascar (Table 9.37). All these species are seemingly endemic to the island with the exception of *Physocephala antiqua* and *Archiconops insularis*. *Conops unicolor* (Figure 9.49a) is widely distributed in Madagascar and has one obscure (and possibly erroneous) record from Mauritius (Herting and Simmonds 1977). The only endemic genus on Madagascar is the monotypic *Pseudoconops* (Figure 9.49b), and no other conopid genus is known from the island that is not also widely distributed in the Afrotropical and other biogeographic regions (Table 9.38). *Thecophora* and *Stylogaster* are the only genera showing notable species diversity on Madagascar as compared with the African continent. A group of *Thecophora* species occurring on the island has an unusual and obvious metallic habitus (Figure 9.49c), and the four known species almost certainly represent an endemic monophyletic group. *Stylogaster* (Figure 9.49d) is widely distributed in all tropical regions and has its highest diversity in the tropical Americas. Undescribed species of *Thecophora* and *Stylogaster*, in particular, are almost certainly to be discovered and described in the Malagasy fauna.

It is difficult to establish clear biogeographic patterns for Malagasy conopids because of the scarcity of reliable recent records. Only seven species have been reported from more than five locations to date. Figure 9.50 gives examples of the known distribution for some of these: *Conops stuckenbergi* has been recorded from the central area and southeast (Figure 9.50a); *C. unicolor* is found across much of the island (Figure 9.50b); *Pseudoconops antennatus* is restricted to the east (Figure 9.50c); and *Stylogaster pauliana* is widely distributed, with the exception of the east (Figure 9.50d). According to present knowledge, most conopid species appear to occur in eastern Madagascar, but this may easily be a collecting artifact.

BIOLOGY OF MALAGASY CONOPIDS

Research on Conopidae on Madagascar is at an early stage, and therefore information concerning its biology is poorly known.

TABLE 9.38. **Checklist and distribution of conopid taxa known from Madagascar**

	MADAGASCAR	AFROTROPICAL REGION	WORLD
Conopid species	36	156	775
Conopid genera	6	18	57
Conopinae species	6	95	458
Archiconops species	3	6	10
Conops species	2	30	120
Physocephala species	1	45	129
Myopinae species	5	17	108
Pseudoconops species	1	1	1
Thecophora species	4	10	40
Stylogastrinae species	25	42	125
Stylogaster species	25	42	125

Source: Modified from Stuke (2017).

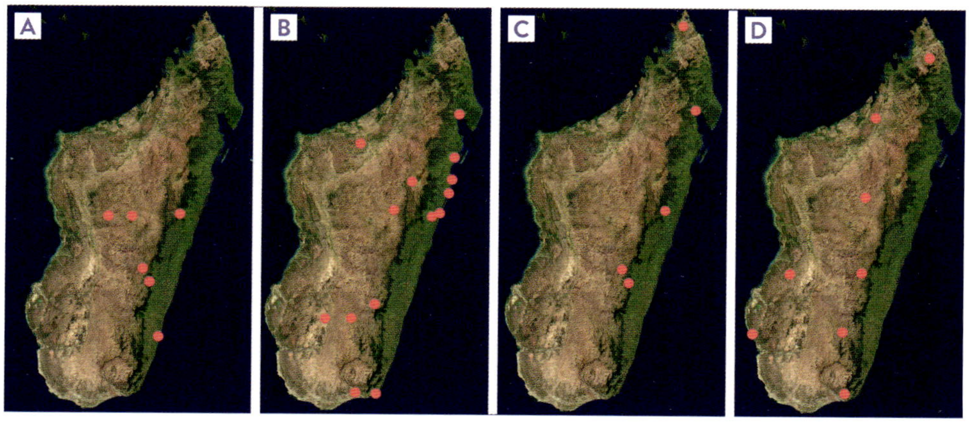

FIGURE 9.50 **Distribution of some Malagasy Conopidae, with confirmed records designated with dots: A) *Conops stuckenbergi*, B) *C. unicolor*, C) *Pseudoconops antennatus*, and D) *Stylogaster pauliana*.** (SOURCE: based on records presented by Camras 1962; Kröber 1915; and Stuke 2012, 2015, 2019.)

Hosts are currently documented only for *Conops unicolor*; Herting and Simmonds (1977), Moutia and Mamet (1946), and Stuke (2019) give records of this species reared from Scoliidae (Hymenoptera) of the genera *Micromeriella*, *Campsomeris*, *Cathimeris*, and *Scolia*. The only evidence of flower-visiting on the island is from *C. unicolor* at Mango (*Mangifera indica*) (Stuke 2019) and the *Stylogaster* at *Plectranthus vestitus* reported above (Nilson et al. 1985). No other ecological connections between Conopidae and particular plant species are thus far documented.

Just as it is difficult to identify distribution patterns of Conopidae species on Madagascar, the same holds true for their phenological patterns. Most records of adult conopids occur from October to February, although there are records of conopids in all months of the year. At least some Malagasy species appear to show year-round activity—for example, *Pseudoconops antennatus*, *Physocephala antiqua*, and *Stylogaster pauliana*.

ACKNOWLEDGMENTS

Fritz Geller-Grimm (Frankfurt) provided important literature. Martin Hauser (Sacramento) made the large conopid collection of the Arthropod Survey of Madagascar's Protected Areas project available for study. David Clements (Cardiff) provided comments on an earlier version of the manuscript and patiently checked the English.

Subject editors: Brian L. Fisher and Steven M. Goodman

DIPTERA: CULICIDAE, MOSQUITOES, *MOKA*

V. Robert, G. Le Goff, P. Boussès, and L. Tantely

Culicidae is a family of biting nematocerous dipterans commonly known as mosquitoes. This family belongs to the infraorder Culicomorpha, which otherwise includes biting flies, such as biting midges, blackflies, and frog-biting midges. The family is a sister group to Chaoboridae (phantom midges) and Corethrellidae (frog-biting midges; see Borkent and Robert, pp. 1132–34), which are traditionally included in the superfamily Culicoidea. Culicidae includes 3570 extant species classified in two subfamilies, Anophelinae and Culicinae.

Mosquitoes successively develop through aquatic and aerial stages. When the egg hatches, a larva emerges in the water, feeds on filtered alimentary particles, grows, and molts through four successive larval stages. The pupa is the last aquatic stage; it is mobile and unable to feed. The imaginal molt allows for the emergence of an adult, male or female, which is the sole aerial stage. Adult females have biting mouthparts and are mostly hematophagous, contrary to males, which do not take blood meals. After mating and egg laying, a new generation begins.

Mosquitoes are among the most studied insects for several main reasons. First, they include substantial species richness. Second, they are an important nuisance, owing to their biting behavior and associated injection of saliva that contains irritating and allergenic compounds, which in many vertebrates results in an allergic reaction. Finally, they act as vectors in the transmission of a variety of viruses, protozoans, and macroparasites, such as Yellow Fever Virus, malaria, and filarial nematodes, respectively (see Héraud et al., pp. 285–91).

Approximately two decades have passed since the precursor of this book (Duchemin et al. 2003), and many advances in our knowledge of the island's mosquitoes have been made. The present contribution highlights the level of advancements with respect to mosquitoes as insects, on one hand, and as vectors of different pathogens, on the other. Herein we provide updated information on taxonomy, systematics, endemism, vector bioecology, vector characterization, and the transmission of the agents of three major diseases: malaria, Rift Valley fever, and West Nile fever.

TAXONOMY, SYSTEMATICS, AND RATES OF ENDEMISM

Duchemin et al. (2003) enumerated 178 species of mosquitoes on Madagascar, of which 45% are endemic. The following year, Ramos and Brunhes (2004) published an extensive revision of the genus *Uranotaenia* in the southwest Indian Ocean area, including Madagascar and the Comoro, Mascarene, and Seychelles archipelagoes, as well as the Iles Eparses and the Chagos (this area herein is referred to as the Malagasy Region). This work encompassed 71 species, of which 48 were named as new to science. Subsequently, Boussès and Brunhes (2013) added three new *Uranotaenia* species to the Madagascar list. Tantely et al. (2016a) published a comprehensive annotated checklist of Malagasy mosquitoes, with 235 species belonging to 14 genera: *Aedeomyia* (3 species), *Aedes* (35), *Anopheles* (26), *Coquillettidia* (3), *Culex* (≥ 49 species), *Eretmapodites* (4), *Ficalbia* (2), *Hodgesia* (≥1 species), *Lutzia* (1), *Mansonia* (2), *Mimomyia* (22), *Orthopodomyia* (8), *Toxorhynchites* (6), and *Uranotaenia* (73). More recently, Brunhes et al. (2017) revised the subgenus *Diceromyia* of the genus *Aedes* and created the new genus *Paulianius*, along with the description of three new species in this genus, all endemic to Madagascar. These authors also considered *Diceromyia sylvaticus* as a junior synonym of *Paulianius madagascarensis*. Finally, Harbach (2018) states that *Aedes* (*Neomelaniconion*) *hylaius* is the *nomen novum* for *Ae.* (*Neo.*) *sylvaticum*.

As of April 2020, there are 237 known mosquito species on Madagascar (Table 9.39). All species are valid with the exception of one *Hodgesia*, which has not yet been formally described (see Tantely et al. 2016a, who specified "at least one species of *Hodgesia*"). Among these named species, a small number have been described based on very few specimens (sometimes a single individual) that have not been found for at least half a century, and in many cases, their natural habitats have suffered significant loss in the last decades. For these reasons, one may speculate that some species listed here are likely to be extinct.

The endemicity of Malagasy mosquitoes is 59.5% with respect to the island itself and 64.6% with respect to the Malagasy Region (Table 9.39). Considering the species that are not endemic to Madagascar (n = 85), 100% are also present in sub-Saharan Africa; 21% in the Palearctic region; and 5% on all continents (*Aedes aegypti*, *Ae. albopictus*, *Culex pipiens*, *Cx. quinquefasciatus*). The percentages of endemic species for Madagascar and the Malagasy Region are remarkably high and reach 100% across the region in several genera: *Orthopodomyia* (12 species), *Paulianus* (7), and *Toxorhynchites* (6); and subgenera: *Aedeomyia* (2 species), *Ochlerotatus* (3), *Skusea* (3), *Zavortinkius* (5), and *Pseudoficalbia* (56). By contrast, several genera do not have any species endemic to Madagascar: *Eretmapodites* (4 species), *Ficalbia* (2), *Lutzia* (1), and *Mansonia* (2). The genus *Culex* exhibits low endemism (23% for the 49 recognized species), but this genus has not been comprehensively studied to date, especially the mosquitoes living in phytotelmata, such as those in epiphytes and tree holes in screw-pines (*Pandanus*). All these observations are in agreement with the fact that the mosquito fauna of Madagascar, and more generally the Malagasy Region, shows a very strong biogeographic affinity to the Afrotropical area.

Interestingly, the focused efforts to inventory the mosquito fauna of Madagascar is not unique in the Indian Ocean. Inventories have also been conducted in the Seychelles (Le Goff et al. 2012), Mayotte (Le Goff et al. 2013, 2014), and La Réunion (Boussès et al. 2013). In the wider context of the Malagasy Region, the total number of mosquito species is 262 (Boussès et al. 2018).

TABLE 9.39. **Checklist of the 237 mosquito species present on Madagascar as of April 2020 and their geographic distribution**

SCIENTIFIC NAMES	A	B	C	D
Aedeomyia (Aedeomyia) madagascarica Brunhes, Boussès & Ramos, 2011	Y	–	–	–
Ad. (Ady.) pauliani Grjebine, 1953	Y	–	–	–
Ad. (Lepiothauma) furfurea (Enderlein, 1923)	–	–	–	Y
Aedes (Aedimorphus) albodorsalis Fontenille & Brunhes, 1985	Y	–	–	–
Ae. (Adm.) dalzieli (Theobald, 1910)	–	–	–	Y
Ae. (Adm.) domesticus (Theobald, 1901)	–	–	–	Y
Ae. (Adm.) durbanensis (Theobald, 1903)	–	–	–	Y
Ae. (Adm.) fowleri (de Charmoy, 1908)	–	–	–	Y
Ae. (Adm.) masoalensis Fontenille & Brunhes, 1985	Y	–	–	–
Ae. (Adm.) mathioti Fontenille & Brunhes, 1985	Y	–	–	–
Ae. (Adm.) natronius Edwards, 1932	–	–	–	Y
Ae. (Catageiomyia) argenteopunctatus (Theobald, 1901)	–	–	–	Y
Ae. (Coetzeemyia) fryeri (Theobald, 1912)	–	–	–	Y
Ae. (Fredwardsius) vittatus (Bigot, 1861)	–	–	–	Y
Ae. (Mucidus) mucidus (Karsch, 1887)	–	–	–	Y
Ae. (Muc.) scatophagoides (Theobald, 1901)	–	–	–	Y
Ae. (Neomelaniconion) albiradius (Le Goff, Boussès & Brunhes, 2007)	Y	–	–	–
Ae. (Neo.) belleci (Le Goff, Boussès & Brunhes, 2007)	Y	–	–	–
Ae. (Neo.) circumluteolus (Theobald, 1908)	–	–	–	Y
Ae. (Neo.) fontenillei (Le Goff, Boussès & Brunhes, 2007)	Y	–	–	–
Ae. (Neo.) hylaius Harbach, 2018	Y	–	–	–
Ae. (Neo.) nigropterum (Le Goff, Boussès & Brunhes, 2007)	Y	–	–	–
Ae. (Ochlerotatus) ambreensis Rodhain & Boutonnier, 1983	Y	–	–	–
Ae. (Polyleptiomyia) albocephalus (Theobald, 1903)	–	–	–	Y
Ae. (Skusea) cartroni (Ventrillon, 1906)	–	Y	–	–
Ae. (Sku.) lambrechti Van Someren, 1971	–	Y	–	–
Ae. (Sku.) moucheti Ravaonjanhary & Brunhes, 1977	Y	–	–	–
Ae. (Stegomyia) aegypti (Linnaeus, 1762)	–	–	–	Y
Ae. (Stg.) albopictus (Skuse, 1895)	–	–	–	Y
Ae. (Zavortinkius) brygooi Brunhes, 1971	Y	–	–	–
Ae. (Zav.) interruptus Reinert, 1999	Y	–	–	–
Ae. (Zav.) monetus Edwards, 1935	–	Y	–	–
Ae. (Zav.) phillipi van Someren, 1949	Y	–	–	–
Anopheles (Anopheles) coustani Laveran, 1900	–	–	–	Y
An. (Ano.) fuscicolor van Someren, 1947	Y	–	–	–
An. (Ano.) tenebrosus Dönitz, 1902	–	–	–	Y
An. (Cellia) arabiensis Patton, 1905	–	–	–	Y
An. (Cel.) brunnipes (Theobald, 1910)	–	–	–	Y
An. (Cel.) cydippis de Meillon, 1931	–	–	–	Y
An. (Cel.) flavicosta Edwards, 1911	–	–	–	Y
An. (Cel.) funestus Giles, 1900	–	–	–	Y
An. (Cel.) gambiae Giles, 1902	–	–	–	Y
An. (Cel.) grassei Grjebine, 1953	Y	–	–	–
An. (Cel.) grenieri Grjebine, 1964	Y	–	–	–
An. (Cel.) griveaudi Grjebine, 1961	Y	–	–	–
An. (Cel.) lacani Grjebine, 1953	Y	–	–	–
An. (Cel.) maculipalpis Giles, 1902	–	–	–	Y

SCIENTIFIC NAMES	A	B	C	D
An. (*Cel.*) *mascarensis* de Meillon, 1947	–	Y	–	–
An. (*Cel.*) *merus* Dönitz, 1902	–	–	–	Y
An. (*Cel.*) *milloti* Grjebine & Lacan, 1953	Y	–	–	–
An. (*Cel.*) *notleyi* van Someren, 1949	Y	–	–	–
An. (*Cel.*) *pauliani* Grjebine, 1953	Y	–	–	–
An. (*Cel.*) *pharoensis* Theobald, 1901	–	–	–	Y
An. (*Cel.*) *pretoriensis* (Theobald, 1903)	–	–	–	Y
An. (*Cel.*) *radama* de Meillon, 1943	Y	–	–	–
An. (*Cel.*) *ranci* Grjebine, 1953	Y	–	–	–
An. (*Cel.*) *roubaudi* Grjebine, 1953	Y	–	–	–
An. (*Cel.*) *rufipes* (Gough, 1910)	–	–	–	Y
An. (*Cel.*) *squamosus* Theobald, 1901	–	–	–	Y
Coquillettidia (*Coquillettidia*) *grandidieri* (Blanchard, 1905)	Y	–	–	–
Cq. (*Coq.*) *metallica* (Theobald, 1901)	–	–	–	Y
Cq. (*Coq.*) *rochei* (Doucet, 1951)	Y	–	–	–
Culex (*Culex*) *antennatus* (Becker, 1903)	–	–	–	Y
Cx. (*Cux.*) *argenteopunctatus* (Ventrillon, 1905)	Y	–	–	–
Cx. (*Cux.*) *carleti* Brunhes & Ravaonjanahary, 1971	–	Y	–	–
Cx. (*Cux.*) *comorensis* Brunhes, 1977	–	Y	–	–
Cx. (*Cux.*) *decens* Theobald, 1901	–	–	–	Y
Cx. (*Cux.*) *demeilloni* Doucet, 1950	Y	–	–	–
Cx. (*Cux.*) *duttoni* Theobald, 1901	–	–	–	Y
Cx. (*Cux.*) *grahamii* Theobald, 1910	–	–	–	Y
Cx. (*Cux.*) *guiarti* Blanchard, 1905	–	–	–	Y
Cx. (*Cux.*) *neavei* Theobald, 1906	–	–	–	Y
Cx. (*Cux.*) *perfidiosus* Edwards, 1914	–	–	–	Y
Cx. (*Cux.*) *perfuscus* Edwards, 1914	–	–	–	Y
Cx. (*Cux.*) *pipiens* Linnaeus, 1758	–	–	–	Y
Cx. (*Cux.*) *quasiguiarti* Theobald, 1910	–	–	–	Y
Cx. (*Cux.*) *quinquefasciatus* Say, 1823	–	–	–	Y
Cx. (*Cux.*) *scottii* Theobald, 1912	–	Y	–	–
Cx. (*Cux.*) *simpsoni* Theobald, 1905	–	–	–	Y
Cx. (*Cux.*) *sitiens* Wiedemann, 1828	–	–	–	Y
Cx. (*Cux.*) *striatipes* Edwards, 1941	–	–	–	Y
Cx. (*Cux.*) *theileri* Theobald, 1903	–	–	–	Y
Cx. (*Cux.*) *trifilatus* Edwards, 1914	–	–	Y	–
Cx. (*Cux.*) *tritaeniorhynchus* Giles, 1901	–	–	–	Y
Cx. (*Cux.*) *univittatus* Theobald, 1901	–	–	–	Y
Cx. (*Cux.*) *vansomereni* Edwards, 1926	–	–	–	Y
Cx. (*Cux.*) *ventrilloni* Edwards, 1920	Y	–	–	–
Cx. (*Cux.*) *watti* Edwards, 1920	–	–	–	Y
Cx. (*Cux.*) *weschei* Edwards, 1935	–	–	–	Y
Cx. (*Culiciomyia*) *cinerellus* Edwards, 1922	–	–	–	Y
Cx. (*Cui.*) *cinereus* Theobald, 1901	–	–	–	Y
Cx. (*Cui.*) *milloti* Doucet, 1949	Y	–	–	–
Cx. (*Cui.*) *nebulosus* Theobald, 1901	–	–	–	Y
Cx. (*Cui.*) *pandani* Brunhes, 1969	Y	–	–	–
Cx. (*Cui.*) *subaequalis* Edwards, 1941	–	–	Y	–
Cx. (*Eumelanomyia*) *brenguesi* Brunhes & Ravaonjanahary, 1973	Y	–	–	–

(*continued overleaf*)

TABLE 9.39. ***continued***

SCIENTIFIC NAMES	A	B	C	D
Cx. (*Eum.*) *chauveti* Brunhes & Rambelo, 1968	–	Y	–	–
Cx. (*Eum.*) *horridus* Edwards, 1922	–	–	–	Y
Cx. (*Eum.*) *insignis* (Carter, 1911)	–	–	–	Y
Cx. (*Eum.*) *kingianus* Edwards, 1922	–	–	–	Y
Cx. (*Eum.*) *rubinotus* Theobald, 1906	–	–	–	Y
Cx. (*Eum.*) *sunyaniensis* Edwards, 1941	–	–	–	Y
Cx. (*Eum.*) *wigglesworthi* Edwards, 1941	–	–	–	Y
Cx. (*Kitzmilleria*) *moucheti* Evans, 1923	–	–	–	Y
Cx. (*Maillotia*) *salisburiensis* Theobald, 1901	–	–	–	Y
Cx. (*Mai.*) *seyrigi* Edwards, 1941	Y	–	–	–
Cx. (*Oculeomyia*) *annulioris* Theobald, 1901	–	–	–	Y
Cx. (*Ocu.*) *aurantapex* Edwards, 1914	–	–	–	Y
Cx. (*Ocu.*) *bitaeniorhynchus* Giles, 1901	–	–	–	Y
Cx. (*Ocu.*) *giganteus* Ventrillon, 1906	Y	–	–	–
Cx. (*Ocu.*) *poicilipes* (Theobald, 1903)	–	–	–	Y
Eretmapodites oedipodeios Graham, 1909	–	–	–	Y
Er. plioleucus Edwards, 1941	–	–	–	Y
Er. quinquevittatus Theobald, 1901	–	–	–	Y
Er. subsimplicipes Edwards, 1914	–	–	–	Y
Ficalbia circumtestacea (Theobald, 1908)	–	–	–	Y
Fi. uniformis (Theobald, 1904)	–	–	–	Y
Hodgesia sp.	Y	–	–	–
Lutzia (*Metalutzia*) *tigripes* (de Grandpré & de Charmoy, 1901)	–	–	–	Y
Mansonia (*Mansonioides*) *africana* (Theobald, 1901)	–	–	–	Y
Ma. (*Mnd.*) *uniformis* (Theobald, 1901)	–	–	–	Y
Mimomyia (*Etorleptiomyia*) *martinei* (Doucet, 1951)	Y	–	–	–
Mi. (*Eto.*) *mediolineata* (Theobald, 1904)	–	–	–	Y
Mi. (*Ingramia*) *aurata* (Doucet, 1951)	Y	–	–	–
Mi. (*Ing.*) *bernardi* (Doucet, 1950)	Y	–	–	–
Mi. (*Ing.*) *beytouti* (Doucet, 1951)	Y	–	–	–
Mi. (*Ing.*) *brygooi* Grjebine, 1986	Y	–	–	–
Mi. (*Ing.*) *collessi* Grjebine, 1986	Y	–	–	–
Mi. (*Ing.*) *jeansottei* (Doucet, 1950)	Y	–	–	–
Mi. (*Ing.*) *levicastilloi* Grjebine, 1986	Y	–	–	–
Mi. (*Ing.*) *longicornis* Grjebine, 1986	Y	–	–	–
Mi. (*Ing.*) *marksae* Grjebine, 1986	Y	–	–	–
Mi. (*Ing.*) *mattinglyi* Grjebine, 1986	Y	–	–	–
Mi. (*Ing.*) *milloti* Grjebine, 1986	Y	–	–	–
Mi. (*Ing.*) *ramalai* Grjebine, 1986	Y	–	–	–
Mi. (*Ing.*) *roubaudi* (Doucet, 1950)	Y	–	–	–
Mi. (*Ing.*) *spinosa* (Doucet, 1951)	Y	–	–	–
Mi. (*Ing.*) *stellata* Grjebine, 1986	Y	–	–	–
Mi. (*Ing.*) *vansomerenae* Grjebine, 1986	Y	–	–	–
Mi. (*Mimomyia*) *hispida* (Theobald, 1910)	–	–	–	Y
Mi. (*Mim.*) *mimomyiaformis* (Newstead, 1907)	–	–	–	Y
Mi. (*Mim.*) *plumosa* (Theobald, 1901)	–	–	–	Y
Mi. (*Mim.*) *splendens* Theobald, 1903	–	–	–	Y
Orthopodomyia ambremontis Brunhes & Hervy, 1995	Y	–	–	–

SCIENTIFIC NAMES	A	B	C	D
Or. ankaratrensis Brunhes & Hervy, 1995	Y	–	–	–
Or. fontenillei Brunhes & Hervy, 1995	Y	–	–	–
Or. milloti Doucet, 1951	Y	–	–	–
Or. rajaonariveloi Brunhes & Hervy, 1995	Y	–	–	–
Or. ravaonjanaharyi Brunhes & Hervy, 1995	Y	–	–	–
Or. rodhaini Brunhes & Hervy, 1995	Y	–	–	–
Or. vernoni van Someren, 1949	Y	–	–	–
Paulianus ambremontis Brunhes & Boussès, 2017	Y	–	–	–
Pl. coulangesi (Rodhain & Boutonnier, 1983)	Y	–	–	–
Pl. grassei (Doucet, 1951)	Y	–	–	–
Pl. hirsutus Brunhes & Boussès, 2017	Y	–	–	–
Pl. madagascarensis (van Someren, 1948)	Y	–	–	–
Pl. rodhaini Brunhes & Boussès, 2017	Y	–	–	–
Pl. tiptoni (Grjebine, 1953)	Y	–	–	–
Toxorhynchites (Afrorhynchus) brunhesi Ribeiro, 2004	Y	–	–	–
Tx. (Afr.) fontenillei Ribeiro, 2004	Y	–	–	–
Tx. (Afr.) grjebinei Ribeiro, 2004	Y	–	–	–
Tx. (Afr.) lemuriae Ribeiro, 2004	Y	–	–	–
Tx. (Afr.) madagascarensis Ribeiro, 2004	Y	–	–	–
Tx. (Afr.) pauliani (Doucet, 1951)	Y	–	–	–
Uranotaenia (Pseudoficalbia) albimanus Ramos & Brunhes, 2004	Y	–	–	–
Ur. (Pfc.) albinotata Ramos & Brunhes, 2004	Y	–	–	–
Ur. (Pfc.) ambodimanga Ramos & Brunhes, 2004	Y	–	–	–
Ur. (Pfc.) antalahaensis Ramos & Brunhes, 2004	Y	–	–	–
Ur. (Pfc.) apicosquamata Ramos & Brunhes, 2004	Y	–	–	–
Ur. (Pfc.) bambusicola Ramos & Brunhes, 2004	Y	–	–	–
Ur. (Pfc.) belkini Grjebine, 1979	Y	–	–	–
Ur. (Pfc.) bicincta Ramos & Brunhes, 2004	Y	–	–	–
Ur. (Pfc.) bifasciata Ramos & Brunhes, 2004	Y	–	–	–
Ur. (Pfc.) bosseri Grjebine, 1979	Y	–	–	–
Ur. (Pfc.) boussesi Ramos & Brunhes, 2004	Y	–	–	–
Ur. (Pfc.) breviseta Ramos & Brunhes, 2004	Y	–	–	–
Ur. (Pfc.) brumpti Doucet, 1951	Y	–	–	–
Ur. (Pfc.) brunhesi Grjebine, 1979	Y	–	–	–
Ur. (Pfc.) cachani Doucet, 1950	Y	–	–	–
Ur. (Pfc.) carcinicola Ramos & Brunhes, 2004	Y	–	–	–
Ur. (Pfc.) combesi (Doucet, 1950)	Y	–	–	–
Ur. (Pfc.) contrastata Ramos & Brunhes, 2004	Y	–	–	–
Ur. (Pfc.) cornuta Ramos & Brunhes, 2004	Y	–	–	–
Ur. (Pfc.) damasei Grjebine, 1979	Y	–	–	–
Ur. (Pfc.) donai Ramos & Brunhes, 2004	Y	–	–	–
Ur. (Pfc.) douceti Grjebine, 1953	Y	–	–	–
Ur. (Pfc.) fulgens Ramos & Brunhes, 2004	Y	–	–	–
Ur. (Pfc.) grenieri Doucet, 1951	Y	–	–	–
Ur. (Pfc.) grjebinei Ramos & Brunhes, 2004	Y	–	–	–
Ur. (Pfc.) haddowi Ramos & Brunhes, 2004	Y	–	–	–
Ur. (Pfc.) hervyi Ramos & Brunhes, 2004	Y	–	–	–
Ur. (Pfc.) hirsuta Boussès & Brunhes, 2013	Y	–	–	–
Ur. (Pfc.) kraussi Grjebine, 1953	Y	–	–	–

(continued overleaf)

TABLE 9.39. ***continued***

SCIENTIFIC NAMES	A	B	C	D
Ur. (*Pfc.*) *laffosseae* Ramos & Brunhes, 2004	–	Y	–	–
Ur. (*Pfc.*) *lavieri* Doucet, 1950	Y	–	–	–
Ur. (*Pfc.*) *legoffi* Ramos & Brunhes, 2004	Y	–	–	–
Ur. (*Pfc.*) *longitubus* Ramos & Brunhes, 2004	Y	–	–	–
Ur. (*Pfc.*) *lousthei* Boussès & Brunhes, 2013	Y	–	–	–
Ur. (*Pfc.*) *madagascarensis* Ramos & Brunhes, 2004	Y	–	–	–
Ur. (*Pfc.*) *manakaraensis* Ramos & Brunhes, 2004	Y	–	–	–
Ur. (*Pfc.*) *nigricephala* Ramos & Brunhes, 2004	Y	–	–	–
Ur. (*Pfc.*) *nigripleura* Ramos & Brunhes, 2004	Y	–	–	–
Ur. (*Pfc.*) *pallidipleura* Ramos & Brunhes, 2004	Y	–	–	–
Ur. (*Pfc.*) *pauliani* Doucet, 1949	Y	–	–	–
Ur. (*Pfc.*) *pilosa* Ramos & Brunhes, 2004	Y	–	–	–
Ur. (*Pfc.*) *pseudoalbimanus* Ramos & Brunhes, 2004	Y	–	–	–
Ur. (*Pfc.*) *pseudoshillitonis* Ramos & Brunhes, 2004	Y	–	–	–
Ur. (*Pfc.*) *ravenalaphila* Boussès & Brunhes, 2013	Y	–	–	–
Ur. (*Pfc.*) *ravenalicola* Ramos & Brunhes, 2004	Y	–	–	–
Ur. (*Pfc.*) *scutostriata* Ramos & Brunhes, 2004	Y	–	–	–
Ur. (*Pfc.*) *spinitubus* Ramos & Brunhes, 2004	Y	–	–	–
Ur. (*Pfc.*) *spinosa* Ramos & Brunhes, 2004	Y	–	–	–
Ur. (*Pfc.*) *spiraculata* Ramos & Brunhes, 2004	Y	–	–	–
Ur. (*Pfc.*) *tricolor* Ramos & Brunhes, 2004	Y	–	–	–
Ur. (*Pfc.*) *tridentata* Ramos & Brunhes, 2004	Y	–	–	–
Ur. (*Pfc.*) *tsaratananae* Doucet, 1950	Y	–	–	–
Ur. (*Uranotaenia*) *alba* Theobald, 1901	–	–	Y	–
Ur. (*Ura.*) *alboabdominalis* Theobald, 1910	–	–	–	Y
Ur. (*Ura.*) *albocephala* Ramos & Brunhes, 2004	Y	–	–	–
Ur. (*Ura.*) *andavakae* Doucet, 1950	–	Y	–	–
Ur. (*Ura.*) *anopheloides* Brunhes & Razafindrasolo, 1975	–	Y	–	–
Ur. (*Ura.*) *argentipleura* Ramos & Brunhes, 2004	Y	–	–	–
Ur. (*Ura.*) *balfouri* Theobald, 1904	–	–	Y	–
Ur. (*Ura.*) *bidentata* Ramos & Brunhes, 2004	Y	–	–	–
Ur. (*Ura.*) *connali* Edwards, 1912	–	–	Y	–
Ur. (*Ura.*) *dumonti* Doucet, 1949	Y	–	–	–
Ur. (*Ura.*) *geniculata* Ramos & Brunhes, 2004	Y	–	–	–
Ur. (*Ura.*) *grassei* Ramos & Brunhes, 2004	Y	–	–	–
Ur. (*Ura.*) *hamoni* Grjebine, 1953	Y	–	–	–
Ur. (*Ura.*) *hebrardi* Ramos & Brunhes, 2004	Y	–	–	–
Ur. (*Ura.*) *joucouri* Ramos & Brunhes, 2004	Y	–	–	–
Ur. (*Ura.*) *lebiedi* Ramos & Brunhes, 2004	Y	–	–	–
Ur. (*Ura.*) *madagascarica* Ramos & Brunhes, 2004	Y	–	–	–
Ur. (*Ura.*) *mayottensis* Brunhes, 1977	–	Y	–	–
Ur. (*Ura.*) *moramangae* Ramos & Brunhes, 2004	Y	–	–	–
Ur. (*Ura.*) *neireti* Edwards, 1920	Y	–	–	–
Ur. (*Ura.*) *roberti* Ramos & Brunhes, 2004	Y	–	–	–
Total	140	12	5	80

Source: This listing follows Harbach (2018) for classification and abbreviations, except for the genus *Aedes*, which follows Wilkerson et al. (2015).
Note: A, endemic to Madagascar; B, endemic to the Malagasy Region (Madagascar and the Comoro, Mascarene, and Seychelles archipelagoes, Iles Eparses, Chagos); C, absent in the Malagasy Region, with the exception of Madagascar, but present in other parts of the world; D, present on different islands in the Malagasy Region and other parts of the world; Y, yes and present.

This area, excluding Madagascar, encompasses 28 tropical islands: four islands in the Comoros, five in the Iles Eparses, five in the Mascarenes, 11 in the Seychelles, and three in the Chagos. In total, the mosquito list excluding Madagascar presents 73 valid species, 10 of which belong to the subfamily Anophelinae and 63 to Culicinae. The mean number of mosquito species per island is 9.3, the median 4.5, and the highest number 45 (Mayotte). The number of species on the regional islands, compared with the total of 237 species on Madagascar, is an interesting comparison, clearly showing a much higher species richness for Madagascar. Twenty-five regional mosquito species are absent from Madagascar and present on at least one of the other regional islands.

VECTOR BIONOMICS

Tantely et al. (2016a) counted 64 species of Malagasy mosquitoes (27%) with a known medical or veterinary interest in the world, and various studies have provided a range of insights into these disease aspects. Genetic population structure of the primary malaria vector, *Anopheles funestus*, has been studied using microsatellite markers. Samples from Madagascar and the Comoros (Mohéli) evidenced significant genetic differentiation between the two islands, and the Madagascar samples showed no significant genetic difference between those collected on the east coast and those in the Central Highlands, while the west coast samples exhibited significant genetic differences (Ayala et al. 2006).

Other primary vectors of malaria in the Malagasy Region are members of the *An. gambiae* complex, composed of at least nine sibling species that are impossible to identify using morphological characters alone (Figure 9.51d). Some of them are excellent malaria vectors (*An. gambiae sensu stricto*), others are moderate malaria vectors (*An. arabiensis*), and others are strictly zoophilic (i.e., nonvector); thus identification at species and population levels is imperative and ordinarily performed using molecular markers on the rDNA. In this spirit, a large-scale sampling of *An. gambiae sensu lato* was carried out (2067 females at 38 sites) in all bioclimatic areas of Madagascar (Léong Pock Tsy et al. 2003a). Three species of the complex were identified: *An. gambiae*, *An. arabiensis*, and *An. merus*. The distribution of each species is largely related to bioclimatic area and to a lesser extent to elevation. *Anopheles arabiensis* is present in all bioclimatic zones, with the highest prevalence in the subhumid, dry, and subarid domains and up to 1515 m. The highest prevalence for *An. gambiae* is found in humid areas; it is found to a lesser extent in dry areas, is rare in subhumid areas, and is absent in subarid areas. *Anopheles merus* is restricted to the coastal fringe of the south and west. Twenty-one out of 38 sites had sympatry for at least two of the species, and two sites harbored all three species. The distribution of *An. merus* is wider than was previously known (Léong Pock Tsy et al. 2003a). Interestingly, despite the considerable environmental changes that have taken place on Madagascar, the distribution of *An. gambiae* and *An. arabiensis* appears unchanged for several decades, based on data from the periods 1964–1969 and 1996–2003, respectively (see Léong Pock Tsy et al. 2003a). However, Tantely et al. (2012) sampled *An. gambiae* and *An. arabiensis* between 2008 and 2010 near Anjozorobe in the Central Highlands at elevations close to 1200 m, suggesting the possible recent colonization by *An. gambiae* of areas at relatively high elevation. Similar population-level studies were performed on 35 *An. gambiae* specimens from Madagascar and on those collected at 10 localities on Mayotte and Grande Comore. The rDNA was sequenced, showing that the molecular form S and haplotype gIA were present in all individuals (Le Goff et al. 2006; Léong Pock Tsy et al. 2003b). These results are in agreement with the fact that the species of the *An. gambiae* complex and the population of *An. gambiae sensu stricto* of the Malagasy Region are similar to those found along the east coast of Africa.

Some species belonging to the genus *Aedes* and the subgenus *Neomelaniconion* play a role in the transmission of arboviruses. Certain advances in understanding patterns of transmission have not advanced as needed because females are difficult to identify morphologically (Le Goff et al. 2007). Sequence variation of rDNA in this subgenus was investigated to assess the validity of taxa that were defined based on morphological characters of male genitalia. Two taxonomic groups are distinguished: the first includes *Ae. belleci*, *Ae. nigropterum*, and *Ae. circumluteolus*, and the second group includes *Ae. hylaius*, *Ae. fontenillei*, and *Ae. albiradius*. These results also confirm the presence of *Ae. circumluteolus* on Madagascar (Kengne et al. 2009).

In the Malagasy Region, the primary vectors of Chikungunya Virus and Dengue Virus are two closely related species of the genus *Aedes*: *Ae. aegypti* and *Ae. albopictus*. In many parts of the world, *Ae. albopictus* is introduced and invasive, expanding its geographic distribution and in competition with *Ae. aegypti* (Raharimalala et al. 2012). The sampling of mosquitoes across the region was conducted from 2007 to 2009 in 15 localities with different climatic regimes. Phylogenetic analysis was done, and experimental infections with the Chikungunya Virus were performed to evaluate the vector competence of field-collected mosquitoes. *Aedes aegypti* was detected at only six sites in native forests. In contrast, *Ae. albopictus* was found at 13 of the 15 sites sampled. Phylogenetic analysis of *Ae. albopictus* distinguished haplotypes of invasive populations from South Asia and South America as compared to those of Madagascar, but the markers used were not discriminant enough to discern intra-Malagasy population differences. The experimental oral infection showed that *Ae. albopictus* populations of Montagne d'Ambre, Toamasina city, Ankazobe, and Antananarivo exhibited high-dissemination infection rates for Chikungunya Virus ranging from 95% to 100%. This study confirms that *Ae. albopictus* has extended its geographic distribution in Madagascar, whereas *Ae. aegypti* has become distinctly rarer and is a potential vector of Chikungunya Virus.

VECTORS OF *PLASMODIUM*, THE MALARIA AGENT

The Apicomplexa protozoa of the genus *Plasmodium* is the etiologic agent of malaria in a variety of mammals, birds, and reptiles. In humans, *P. falciparum* is the only species responsible for acute attacks that cause death. This species, *P. malariae*, and *P. vivax* are present in the Malagasy Region, the latter two with notably reduced prevalence as compared to *P. falciparum*. Three *Anopheles* vectors of primary importance, *An. funestus*, *An. gambiae*, and *An. arabiensis*, are responsible for the transmission of human malaria parasites on

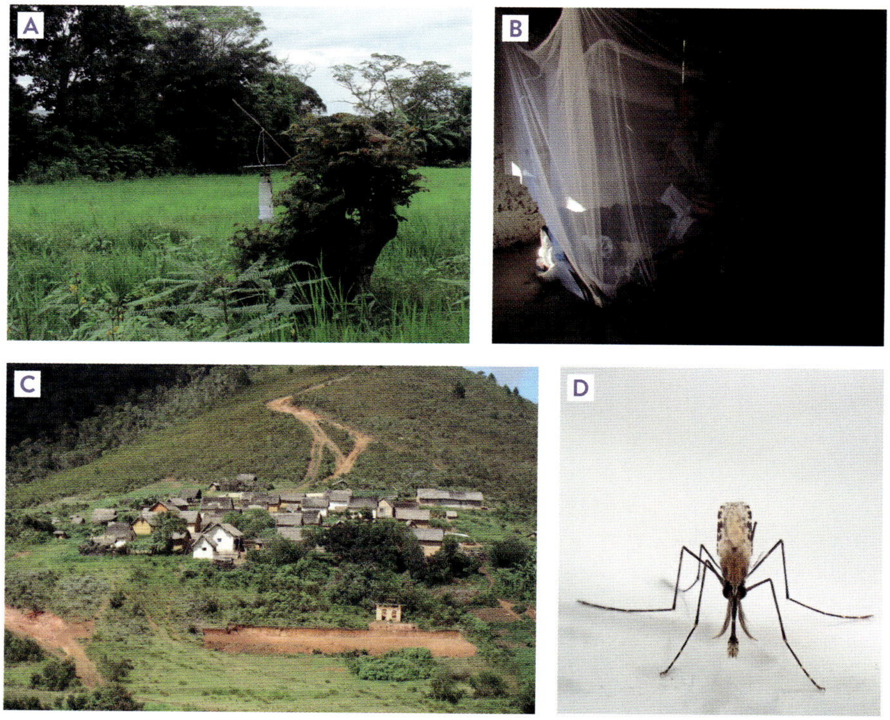

FIGURE 9.51 **Aspects of mosquitoes research on Madagascar. A) An attractive light trap, installed to capture mosquitoes overnight. B) System of a double mosquito net to capture aggressive mosquitoes searching for a blood meal, baited with a human who is protected by the internal net. C) Anorana village, Anjozorobe District, Analamanga Region, the setting of research on Rift Valley Fever Virus transmission (Tantely et al. 2013). D) *Anopheles gambiae* with the maxillary palpus ending in a club, indicating that the individual is a male. Because of their inability to penetrate through vertebrate skin, male mosquitoes are non-hematophagous and feed on a variety of vegetal liquids, such as nectar.** (PHOTOS A–C by L. Tantely, and D by P. Boussès.)

Madagascar. The species *An. mascarensis* is considered a vector of secondary importance on the east coast. Some species occurring on Madagascar have been shown to be nonvectors on the island but are known on the African continent to be vectors—for example, *An. tenebrosus*, *An. brunnipes*, *An. coustani*, *An. flavicosta*, and *An. merus* (see Duchemin et al. 2003; Tantely et al. 2016a). Subsequent to the contribution in the precursor of this book (Duchemin et al. 2003), three important aspects have been uncovered on secondary vectors. First, Le Goff et al. (2003) identified *An. mascarensis* as a secondary vector in two villages in the central west, Ambohimena (Mandoto District) and Fenoarivo (Ambohimananbola District). Second, Léong Pock Tsy et al. (2003a) pinpointed *An. merus* as a malaria vector in the southern subarid domain, with positive detection for *P. falciparum*. Third, Nepomichene et al. (2015a) identified *An. coustani* positive for *P. falciparum* and *P. vivax* in the Ankazobe District. These are the first indications that *An. merus* and *An. coustani* transmit *Plasmodium* to humans on Madagascar.

Several longitudinal studies on Madagascar were performed on malaria transmission and *Anopheles* in the context of malaria vector control campaigns using insecticides (DDT, then pyrethroids) for house spraying. Succinct summaries of five studies in the Central Highlands are provided here:

- Rajaonarivelo et al. (2004) worked for over two years in the village of Ambohimena (elevation 940 m) in the central west area. The total number of collected anophelines was 14,280. Two malaria vectors were identified: *An. funestus* and *An. arabiensis*, but the latter was very zoophilic (anthropophilic rate 8%) and therefore had only marginal importance for spreading malaria. Malaria transmission occurred from December to April. The annual entomological inoculation rate (i.e., the number of bites of infected anophelines per adult person and per year) from *An. funestus* alone, was 9.0 during the first year and 3.2 during the second year.
- Robert et al. (2006) worked for over two consecutive years in the village of Analamiranga (elevation 885 m) on the western edge of the Central Highlands. Of the 7480 aggressive mosquitoes collected on human subjects, 5790 were anophelines. Ten anopheline species were represented and three of these, *An. funestus*, *An. arabiensis*, and *An. mascarensis*, accounted for 59.2% of the mosquitoes collected. Among these three species, 4640 individuals were collected in resting places such as bedrooms, kitchens, holes in the ground, etc. The proportion of mosquitoes feeding on bovids—determined by blood analysis of engorged mosquitoes collected in resting places—was high, while the inverse of mosquitoes feeding on humans was especially low: 31%, 7%, and 1%, respectively, for *An. funestus*, *An. arabiensis*, and *An. mascarensis*. The only confirmed malaria vector was *An. funestus*, with a relatively low number of infective bites per person per unit of time, and with little variation over the two-year study.
- Ravoahangimalala et al. (2008) worked for two years in the capital city, Antananarivo (elevation 1100 m) at two sites: Ambohimiandra-Manakambahiny and Ambolokandrina. The collected mosquitoes belonged to the following genera (in order of abundance): *Culex*, *Mansonia*, and *Anopheles*. The only potential malaria vector was *An. arabiensis*. Its maximal abundance was observed in January, the wettest month of the austral summer (22 and 15 bites per person outdoors at night, at the two sites, respectively). This species bites indoors, but its aggressiveness was always higher outdoors. The absence of *An. gambiae* and *An. funestus* in the collections and the absence of *An. arabiensis* in-

fected by *P. falciparum* are important results of this study. The conventional entomological methods used in this case did not find evidence of malaria transmission. However, this does not contradict other observations of very low numbers of autochthonous malaria cases in Antananarivo (Rabarijaona et al. 2006).

- Andrianaivolambo et al. (2010) worked for one year in the village of Saharevo (elevation 900 m) on the eastern edge of the Central Highlands. Of the 5515 mosquitoes collected on humans, 3219 (58%) were anophelines, including *An. funestus*, *An. gambiae*, *An. arabiensis*, and *An. mascarensis*. Out of the 677 mosquitoes collected in bedrooms using pyrethrum spray catches and holes in the ground, 656 (97%) were anophelines belonging to the same four species. The proportion of female mosquitoes that fed on humans varied according to the mosquito species and the resting place: 86% of the *An. funestus* in bedrooms, whereas only 16% of *An. funestus* and 0% of *An. mascarensis* in holes in the ground. The annual rate of the number of infective bites per person per unit of time was relatively low. The transmission of malaria was mainly through *An. funestus* and was observed only in the second half of the rainy season, from February to May. Transmission by mosquitoes of the *An. gambiae* complex and *An. mascarensis* remained very low, although positive.
- An entomological survey performed by Jeffries et al. (2018a) during the winter season revealed infections in three *An. gambiae sensu lato* from Antafia (Maevantanana District), as well as in one *An. rufipes* and one *An. funestus* from Ambomiharina (Ambato Boeny District). *Plasmodium falciparum* infections were also detected in one pool of five *An. coustani* collected at the Ivato Airport and one pool of five *An. squamosus* in Ambohimarina, increasing the list of *Anopheles* species involved in *Plasmodium* transmission and questioning their designation as secondary malaria vectors.

Regarding bird endoparasites, Sadones et al. (2003), followed by Savage et al. (2009), published large-scale studies on roughly 1000 birds belonging to 26 families and 64 species collected in different areas of Madagascar. On the basis of blood smears, evidence was found in the samples of *Haemoproteus* (17.4%), microfilariae (11.0%), *Leucocytozoon* (9.4%), *Plasmodium* (1.9%), *Trypanosoma* (0.9%), and *Babesia* (0.2%). Species-level identifications confirmed the presence of 47 species of hemosporidians and trypanosomes, which is notably high and mirrors the diversity of their avian hosts. Eleven (23.4%) of these parasite species were new to science and thought to be endemic to Madagascar. Most of these were described at an alpha-taxonomic level by Geiner et al. (references in Savage et al. 2009). Because the vectors of these parasites on Madagascar were unknown, a study on mosquito transmission was carried out, focusing on mosquitoes that may be vectors of avian malaria parasites (*Plasmodium*, *Haemoproteus*, and *Leucocytozoon*) in the Maromizaha medium-altitude moist evergreen forest. A total of 418 mosquitoes belonging to at least 18 species were collected. *Haemoproteus* DNA was found in nine mosquitoes (2.15%), while *Plasmodium* DNA was found in 12 mosquitoes (2.87%). Five *Haemoproteus* lineages and seven *Plasmodium* lineages were detected. *Anopheles mascarensis* and *Uranotaenia* species (probably including an undescribed species) were identified for the first time as vectors of avian malaria on Madagascar (Schmid et al. 2017).

VECTORS OF RIFT VALLEY FEVER VIRUS (RVFV)

Rift Valley fever (RVF) is a viral zoonotic disease found throughout Africa, the Arabian Peninsula, and Madagascar. The disease is caused by a *Phlebovirus* (RVF Virus [RVFV]; see Héraud et al., pp. 285–91) and is transmitted to vertebrate hosts through the bite of infected mosquitoes, mainly *Aedes* and *Culex* species. The first circulation of RVFV on Madagascar was reported in 1979, based on its detection in mosquitoes and not within an epidemic episode. Subsequently, two outbreaks occurred: the first along the east coast and in the Central Highlands in 1990 and 1991, and the second along the north and east coasts and in the Central Highlands in 2008 and 2009. A total of 24 mosquito species present on the island have been potentially associated with RVFV transmission in the world (Tantely et al. 2015). To this list can be added *Cx. decens*, which was recently found RVFV-positive during interepidemic–epizootic periods in the western area of Madagascar (Jeffries et al. 2018b).

Four studies on Madagascar investigated the diversity, dynamics, and biology of potential RVFV vector species. The first three studies mentioned below clearly target *Culex* and *Anopheles* mosquitoes as potential vectors of RVFV in Madagascar. Nepomichene et al. (2018) reinforced this hypothesis through experimental vector competence studies with *Cx. antennatus* and *An. coustani*. Mosquito body parts and saliva of mosquitoes that fed on RVFV-infected blood were tested for RVFV using real-time quantitative polymerase chain reaction assays. Overall, viral RNA was detected in body parts and saliva at five days postinfection in both species, and transmission efficiencies were 4% (1/24) and 13% (5/38) in *Cx. antennatus* and *An. coustani*, respectively.

- Ratovonjato et al. (2011) worked in the Fianarantsoa I and II Districts in November 2008 and in the Ambalavao District in April 2009. A total of 12,785 adult mosquitoes belonging to five genera and 21 species were collected. After identification, unfed female mosquitoes were grouped in 319 monospecific pools, which were tested by real-time polymerase chain reaction. RVFV was detected in pools of *An. coustani*, *An. squamosus*, and *Cx. antennatus* (1, 5, and 2, respectively). The virus was isolated in mosquito cell lines in two out of five positive pools of *An. squamosus*. This study supports the assertion that *An. squamosus*, *An. coustani*, and *Cx. antennatus* may have been vectors in the RVFV outbreak of 2008–2009.
- Tantely et al. (2013) worked from November 2008 to July 2010 in the Anjozorobe District in two villages: Anorana, at the edge of the medium-altitude moist evergreen forest (Figure 9.51c), and Antanifotsy, in a grassland area. A total of 56,605 mosquitoes belonging to 35 species were collected. *Anopheles squamosus*, *An. coustani*, *Cx. antennatus*, *Cx. pipiens*, and *Cx. univittatus* were the most abundant during the rainy season and *Cx. univittatus* during the dry season. Cattle were the most attractive bait for all species, followed by sheep and poultry, and humans were the least attractive. Most of the 163 blood meals tested were from cattle. These results provide vectorial capacity parameters and imply that these abundant mosquito species might be involved in RVFV transmission in these areas.

- Nepomichene et al. (2015b) worked in six villages in subarid (Toliary II District) or subhumid (Mampikony District) bioclimatic zones, each with known RVFV transmission, between March 2011 and October 2011. *Culex tritaeniorhynchus* was the most abundant species, followed by *Cx. antennatus* and *An. squamosus* and/or *cydippis*. These three forms of mosquitoes comprised more than half of all mosquitoes collected. As expected, the highest diversity and abundance were observed in the subhumid site. No host preference was highlighted, except for *Cx. tritaeniorhynchus*, which showed a preference for zebu.
- During the winter season of 2016, Jeffries et al. (2018b) worked in five villages from five districts. Among the 704 collected mosquitoes, which belonged to species considered to be potential vectors of medically important arboviruses, RVFV was detected in one *Cx. decens* from Ambomiharina, one *Cx. decens* from Antafia, and 10 *Cx. tritaeniorhynchus* and five *Cx. antennatus* from Tsaramandroso (Ambato Boeny). This study provides evidence that there is a risk of RVF during the dry winter season.

VECTORS OF WEST NILE VIRUS (WNV)

West Nile fever (WNF) is a mosquito-borne zoonotic disease found nearly globally. Birds play a key role as they are reservoirs of the virus. In Madagascar, West Nile Virus (WNV) was first detected in 1978 in wild birds. The virus is currently distributed across the island, but no epidemic or epizootic period has been recorded. Studies described a high seroprevalence level in humans in different areas of the island, and a human fatal case of WNF was reported in 2011, suggesting a "tip of the iceberg" phenomenon on Madagascar. According to vector categorization (Tantely et al. 2015), 29 species were considered to be associated with WNV transmission. *Culex quinquefasciatus*, *Cx. univittatus*, *Cx. tritaeniorhynchus* and *Mansonia uniformis* were considered major WNV vectors. *Aedeomyia madagascarica*, *Aedes albocephalus*, *Ae. circumluteolus*, *Anopheles coustani*, *Cx. antennatus*, *Cx. decens*, and *Paulianus madagascarensis* were considered candidate vectors, and the balance of the 29 species were considered potential vectors (Tantely et al. 2016b).

Two studies explored the transmission of WNV:

- Maquart et al. (2016) investigated local mosquitoes and poultry for evidence of current infections in two rural zones endemic for WNV: the Mitsinjo District, close to Lake Kinkony, in November and December 2012, and the Antsalova District in July 2013. These two areas are close to lakes where domestic birds, populations of wild Palearctic-Africa migratory birds, and humans coexist. Domestic ducks (n = 343), chickens (n = 195), and turkeys (n = 43) comprised the majority of birds sampled. A total of 1037 mosquitoes were collected. West Nile Virus nucleic acid was detected in one chicken and in eight pools of mosquitoes, including *Aedeomyia madagascarica* and *An. pauliani*, both endemic to Madagascar. Neither species had been previously considered a candidate vector for WNV. Molecular analysis of WNV isolates showed that all viruses were part of lineage 2, the main lineage distributed in Africa.
- Tantely et al. (2017) continued the entomological work from February to December 2014 in the Mitsinjo District. A total of 2519 mosquitoes belonging to 21 different species were collected. The most abundant species was *Ad. madagascarica*, which made up 83% of all the mosquitoes collected. Mosquito abundance was associated with proximity to the lake. West Nile Virus RNA was detected in one pool of *Ad. madagascarica* and one pool of *An. pauliani*, confirming the results of the previous study and suggesting that these two species may be involved in the maintenance and/or transmission of WNV in Madagascar.

FUTURE DIRECTIONS

The present contribution succinctly focuses mainly on recent mosquito research showing major advances in taxonomy, systematics, vector ecology, and transmission of many pathogens to humans, domestic animals, and wildlife. With respect to culicidian diversity, more in-depth field inventories are needed at different sites, such as protected forested areas, to understand the levels of species richness in a more concrete manner and with precision. A parallel and complementary approach would be to use specimen material in the Collection ARIM (Arthropods of Medical Interest) housed at the Institut de Recherche pour le Développement (IRD) in Montpellier, France. This collection is the most important in the world for Malagasy mosquitoes, with more than 15,000 specimens belonging to 231 species among the 237 known from the island. This collection has been utilized for taxonomic and systematic revision of various genera (*Uranotaenia*, *Paulianus*) or subgenera (*Neomelaniconion*), and is currently being used for revising the subgenus *Culiciomyia* of *Culex*.

To date, taxonomic research on Malagasy Region mosquitoes has relied heavily on morphological characters. The use of molecular tools in these studies has not been extensive compared to other Malagasy Diptera, such as Phlebotominae (see Depaquit et al., pp. 1126–32). The integration of various types of data, including morphologic, morphometric, ecological, and molecular data, including DNA barcodes, will undoubtedly provide new insights into patterns of species richness, including the discovery and description of new species (Beebe 2018).

Subject editors: Brian L. Fisher and Steven M. Goodman

DIPTERA: NYCTERIBIIDAE AND STREBLIDAE, BAT FLIES

C. W. Dick

Bat flies (Nycteribiidae and Streblidae) are highly conspicuous bat ectoparasites and are found exclusively in association with bats (Dick and Patterson 2006). They are highly specialized for life on the bat's body (and, to some degree, in the bat's roosting environment) and as adults are obligate blood feeders. Among their morphological parasitic adaptations are body compression (often laterally or dorsoventrally); generally reduced eyes and, in some cases, wings; and setae that are modified into combs or spines. In addition, their life stages are reduced or "telescoped"—eggs are hatched and larvae develop inside the female fly. As a result, larval stages are more closely tied to the host bat. The only life stage that is conspicuous on the host is the adult, whereas the pupal stage may be found inside the bat's roosting habitat. There, gravid female flies extrude a mature pupa onto the roosting substrate, which immediately pupates. Development to the adult stage takes about 21 days, after which the adult fly emerges from the puparium and must then locate and colonize a host bat in order to feed and find mates (Overal 1980; Marshall 1981).

PHYLOGENY AND DIVERSITY OF BAT FLIES

In terms of evolutionary age, bat flies are likely not any older than bats themselves (early Eocene, or ~50 million years ago; Simmons et al. 2008). Bat flies have long been recognized as belonging to two families of calypterate Diptera, and along with Glossinidae (tsetse flies) and Hippoboscidae (louse or ked flies) comprise the superfamily Hippoboscoidea. However, phylogenetic proposals suggest that both families of bat flies are best relegated to subfamily status within Hippoboscidae. For the purpose of this treatment, we will continue referring to Streblidae and Nycteribiidae. On a worldwide basis, nycteribiids comprise about 280 species in 11 genera, while streblids comprise about 230 species in 33 genera (Dick and Patterson 2006). Although members of both families may be found in all continents, with the exception of Antarctica, species richness increases rapidly within subtropical and tropical regions. Moreover, species within the two families are unequally distributed between the hemispheres. Whereas nearly 70% of streblid species are found in the American tropics and subtropics, the reverse is true for nycteribiids, with over 80% of known species occurring in the Eastern Hemisphere tropics and subtropics. Nycteribiids are particularly rich in the Indo-Malaysian and Australasian regions, and somewhat less so on the African continent.

GENERAL BIOLOGY

Aside from the off-host roosting environment of the pupal stages, adult bat flies for the most part are limited to the exterior surfaces of their host's body. A bat's body offers two general habitats for ectoparasites—flight membranes and the furred parts of the trunk and head. There is evidence suggesting that bat flies possess morphological and behavioral characteristics corresponding generally to these habitats (Hiller et al. 2018). This phenomenon is referred to as ecomorphology. In terms of ecomorphology, species of the 11 known worldwide genera of Nycteribiidae are roughly similar in overall morphological appearance and vary mainly on the basis of size. However, among the 33 known genera of Streblidae, there is great variation in overall body plan, especially in relation to body shape, leg shape and length, and the degree of combs. Species of one genus (*Ascodipteron*, which is generally African and Asian in distribution and not known from Madagascar) become endoparasitic in that reproductively mature females detach their wings and legs and burrow beneath the skin of their hosts (Dick and Patterson 2006). Some bat flies, particularly Streblidae from the New World tropics, appear to have morphologies that correspond to various microhabitats and potentially grooming avoidance behavior. These morphological differences have been suggested to accommodate coexistence of multiple fly species on single host individuals and species (Tello et al. 2008).

Ecomorphological approaches to bat flies have been based on specificity of position or location on host-habitat, behavior, and the shape and structure of the legs. Three different such groups have been described to date (Haelewaters et al. 2018). These include a generalized morph that appears to be specialized for membranous regions of the host, and two more specialized morphs that appear to be adapted to living in the furred parts of the bat's body. These latter groups include one type that is compressed either laterally or dorsoventrally and that "swims" through the fur of the host, and another type typified by a broad flat sternal thorax and the presence of long hind legs. This latter morph appears to be adapted to "run" across the surface of the fur of the host bat. Selective pressure placed on bat flies via host grooming efforts (auto- or allo-grooming) is understood to be very high, and has been postulated to be the primary source of mortality for adult bat flies (Marshall 1981). A recent study by Ramanantsalama et al. (2018) demonstrated that grooming and consumption of adult bat flies by adult *Rousettus madagascariensis* may be very high, with up to 37 flies consumed per adult bat per day. In the specific bat colony studied at Ankarana, it was estimated that the 1908 *R. madagascariensis* roosting there may consume 57,905 ± 25,040 individual bat flies per day. These are remarkable mortality rates on an insect species that bears its offspring individually and portends strong selection on bat fly ecomorphology that would enable evasion of host grooming efforts. Although phylogenetic evidence is scant, it appears that these three ecological groups of flies are not natural but the result of convergent evolution. Given that nycteribiid flies all possess a relatively similar body shape and structures, it is unlikely that the ecomorphological groups witnessed in the Neotropics exist among nycteribiids. Instead, we can speculate that it

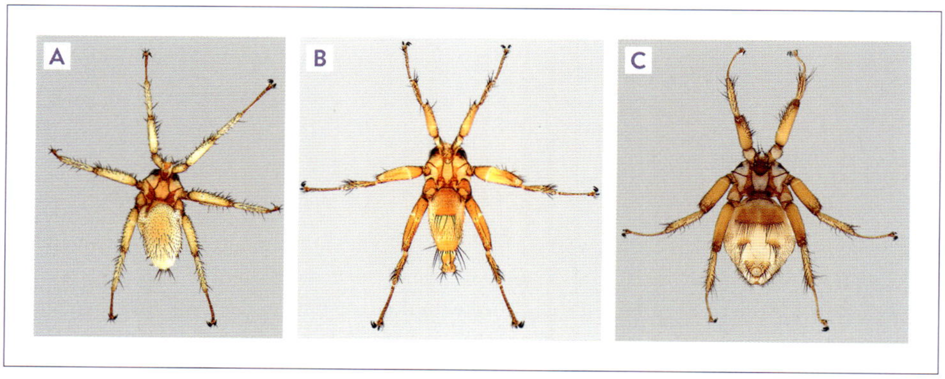

FIGURE 9.52 **Examples of bat fly genera from Madagascar: A) adult female *Eucampsipoda madagascarensis* from *Rousettus madagascariensis*, body length ~3.15 mm; B) adult female *Nycteribia stylidiopsis* from *Miniopterus gleni*, body length ~2.10 mm; and C) adult female *Penicillidia leptothrinax* from *Miniopterus* sp., body length ~3.25 mm. (Modified from Tortosa et al. 2013.)**

appears possible that patterns in insect size among co-occurring species may facilitate coexistence. Regarding host individuals or species parasitized by multiple fly species, with nycterbiids it is often the case that one large and one small fly species exist together, or, in cases of three, one large, one small, and one of intermediate size. These patterns, specifically among nycteribiid flies, need more attention.

ECOLOGY AND HOST ASSOCIATIONS

One intriguing emergent property of the parasite-host system is specificity of association. Specificity is the degree to which a parasite species is associated with a single host species. The spectrum of possibilities is broad, ranging from no specificity to complete host specificity (Dick and Dittmar 2014). Low host specificity might imply a broad immunological amplitude of host, parasite, or both. It may also imply a great deal of host-switching, which would preclude the expectation of any cophylogenetic structure among hosts and parasites. Conversely, high specificity might imply coevolved immunocompatability or extreme morphological specialization, and quite possible cospeciation of host and parasite lineages. Owing to their mobility and the fact that bat species often roost together in mixed arrangements (see Figure 6.5, chapter 6), in such cases, bat flies were historically understood to be of low host specificity (Jobling 1949; Theodor 1957; Wenzel et al. 1966).

Carefully controlled large field studies in the Neotropics have provided some evidence of remarkable host specificity, at least among streblid flies. As a general rule, evidence suggests that when nonspecific associations are found, the majority can be explained by simple human error (i.e., contamination upon sampling of the bats and bat flies; Dick 2007; Dick and Patterson 2007; Dick and Dittmar 2014). This and other evidence has led to a literature with many examples of demonstrated or assumed specificity. However, it is not yet clear whether a general rule of host specificity for bat flies can be extrapolated to nycteribiid flies or to streblids of the Eastern Hemisphere. There are indeed some notable exceptions to the rule of specificity. One is the African nycteribiid species *Penicillidia fulvida*. Theodor (1967) noted that this species apparently has a rather broad host distribution. Samples collected from Kenya (C. W. Dick, unpublished data) confirm what appear to be valid records of this species from at least 12 species of bats belonging to five genera and three families. Another example is found in the Southeast Asian

TABLE 9.40. **Checklist of Nycteribiidae and Streblidae bat fly species known from Madagascar and the Comoros with information on host species**

NYCTERIBIIDAE

Nycteribia stylidiopsis Speiser, 1908 (Figure 9.52b)
Known hosts: *Miniopterus gleni*, *M. griveaudi*, *M. majori*, *M. sororculus*, *Myotis goudoti*

Basilia (*Paracyclopodia*) *madagascarensis* Theodor, 1957
Known host: **Scotophilus* cf. *borbonicus*; most likely *S. robustus*

Basilia (*Paracyclopodia*) sp. nov. 1
Known host: **Scotophilus robustus*

Basilia (*Paracyclopodia*) sp. nov. 2
Known host: **Scotophilus marovaza*

Basilia (*Tripselia*) *blainvillii* Leach, 1917
Known host: **Taphozous mauritianus*

Basilia (*Basilia*) sp. nov. 1
Known host: **Pipistrellus hesperidus*

Basilia (*Basilia*) sp. nov. 2
Known host: **Laephotis matroka*

Penicillidia decipiens Theodor, 1957
Known hosts: *Coleura kibomalandy*, *Miniopterus griveaudi*, *M. majori*, *M. sororculus*, *Mormopterus jugularis*, *Myotis goudoti*, *Paremballonura atrata*, *P. tiavato*

Penicillidia leptothrinax Speiser, 1908 (Figure 9.52c)
Known hosts: *Miniopterus aelleni*, *M. ambohitrensis*, *M. brachytragos*, *M. gleni*, *M. mahafaliensis*, *M. majori*, *M. manavi*, *M. sororculus*, *Mormopterus jugularis*, *Myotis goudoti*, *Laephotis matroka*, *Paremballonura atrata*

Eucampsipoda theodori Hürka, 1964 (Comoros: Grande Comore, Anjouan)
Known host: *Rousettus* sp.; almost certainly **R. obliviosus*

Eucampsipoda madagascarensis Theodor, 1955 (Figure 9.52a)
Known hosts: **Rousettus madagascariensis*, *Miniopterus* sp., *Mormopterus jugularis*

Cyclopodia dubia Westwood, 1835
Known hosts: **Eidolon dupreanum*, *Mormopterus jugularis*, *Scotophilus robustus*

STREBLIDAE

Megastrebla wenzeli (Jobling, 1952)
Known host: **Rousettus madagascariensis*

Note: * indicates presumed primary host species.

nycteribiid *Cyclopodia horsfieldi*, which parasitizes three species of pteropodid bats across a geographic range exceeding 1000 km and which shows no population structuring among hosts or by isolation by distance based on three mtDNA markers (Olival et al. 2013).

Finally, molecular phylogenetic studies (Tortosa et al. 2013; Ramasindrazana et al. 2017) found somewhat variable results across bat fly taxa, including a number from Madagascar. Certain species (e.g., *Eucampsipoda* spp. from four species of *Rousettus*) showed relatively strong patterns of strict host specificity (Tortosa et al. 2013). However, the putative fly species *Nycteribia stylidiopsis* (Figure 9.52b) and *Penicillidia leptothrinax* (Figure 9.52c) showed little structuring across their known host species (up to eight or nine species, including *Myotis* and especially *Miniopterus*). A potential explanation for the observed polyxeny is based on roost sharing by these insectivorous bat species, which could facilitate these flies' use of multiple bat species as the "host" (Ramasindrazana et al. 2017). These cases of low specificity seen in Asia, Africa, and Madagascar contrast with the specific patterns emerging from work with Neotropical Streblidae. Thus, the reader is cautioned not to extend any general rule of host specificity in bat flies to all lineages and geographic regions.

Potentially relating to the issue of specificity is the impact of the host's roosting environment on the host associations and rates of parasitism. The host bat itself is the direct habitat only for the bat fly's adult stage. The life cycle of bat flies includes an off-host pupal stage that passes in the vicinity of the bat roost (Dick and Patterson 2006). During the reproductive cycle, the gravid female leaves the host to locate substrate within the immediate area, depositing a single larva and attaching it to the substrate (e.g., wall or ceiling of roost). The pupal stage typically lasts approximately three weeks. This is the critical time period during which the pupa is separated from the host. Once development is complete, the teneral adult emerges and must seek, find, and colonize a bat in order to feed and find mates. It follows that bats must visit roosts with a degree of fidelity to ensure that recently metamorphosed adult bat flies will be able to encounter and colonize a host. Bats roosting in ephemeral roosts, such as trees or under vegetation of different sorts, would disrupt this life cycle, lowering the intensity and prevalence of parasitism. Conversely, bats roosting in permanent roosts, such as caves, would reinforce these linkages between bat fly reproduction and parasitism. Studies of the effect of roost permanence on African or Malagasy bat flies have not yet been conducted, but a strong relationship has been found between the roosting ecology of Venezuelan bats and their streblids—those utilizing permanent roosts are more likely to be parasitized, have higher numbers of parasites, and be parasitized by more species of bat flies (Patterson et al. 2007). Bat species such as *Rousettus aegyptiacus* and *R. madagascariensis* are known to form large colonies inhabiting cave roosts, and these bats are frequently parasitized by high numbers of bat flies (see Figure 6.10, chapter 6).

In addition to the effects of roosting biology on parasitism rates, other aspects of the host-parasite association have been explored. These include variation in host body size and host sex and their effects on parasitism. On Madagascar specifically, one very common association is between the host *R. madagascariensis* and the nycteribiid *Eucampsipoda madagascarensis* (Figure 9.52a). This particular bat species is widespread on the island and shows little population structuring across the island (Goodman et al. 2010). Moreover, the species is a cave-rooster and forms large colonies (Andrianaivoarivelo et al. 2011). Research by Rajemison et al. (2017a, 2017b) found a positive correlation between bat body size and parasitism by *E. madagascarensis*. Moreover, male bats were generally more heavily parasitized than females, and for males, the degree of throat-gland development was positively correlated with abundance of the parasites. These general patterns with regard to parasitism rates and host body size have been shown in other systems and in other locations—for example, with 53 species of Venezuelan bats and parasite abundance (Patterson et al. 2008).

MALAGASY BAT FLIES

With respect to Madagascar and the Comoro archipelago, the list of known bat fly species is relatively short. Eight described species of nycteribiid and one species of streblid have previously been reported previously from these islands (Theodor 1957, 1967). There are an additional four likely new species from Madagascar (Table 9.40).

Subject editors: Brian L. Fisher and Steven M. Goodman

DIPTERA: TABANIDAE, HORSEFLIES, *FIHITRA, LALITR'OMBY, BOROA*

T. Zeegers

The family Tabanidae, or horseflies, consists of medium-size (seldom small) to very large flies. They are notorious for their bloodsucking behavior. Their medical importance as vectors of diseases is, however, of secondary importance compared to other vectors. Many species impress observers with their beautiful eyes, with stripes or other patterns, and sometimes with their patterned wings (Figure 9.53). The family is moderately large, with about 4500 described species worldwide (Morita et al. 2106), of which at least 700 are reported from the Afrotropical region (Chainey and Oldroyd 1980). Chainey (2017) provides the most recent overview over the Afrotropical horseflies.

FIGURE 9.53 **Habitus of female horseflies, dorsal. A) *Chrysops cervulus*, B) *Picromyza crocea*, C) *Tabanocella alveolata*, D) *Orgizomyia zigzag*, and E) *Oldroydiella oldroydi*. Scale bars, 1.0 mm.** (PHOTOS by T. Zeegers.)

BIOLOGY

Some species of horseflies are regular visitors of flowers, although little is known of this behavior for the tabanids of Madagascar. Most Malagasy horsefly species are found in forests, though *Aegophagamyia sensu stricto* and *Neavella* are restricted to coastal beaches. As in mosquitoes, only females of horseflies suck blood, mostly from mammals. In many parts of the world, ungulates (including livestock) are primary hosts. Given the historic paucity of ungulates on Madagascar until their introduction in historical times, female horseflies must have originally attacked other mammals on Madagascar and continue to do so. Lemurs are obvious candidates, and indeed horseflies are recorded attacking these animals (Maretti et al. 2010). *Neavella* is associated with turtles. Female horseflies also attack humans. The bite of several species is reported to be painful. Larvae of horseflies are predaceous. Generally, they have an aquatic or semiaquatic lifestyle, though some live in rot-holes of trees (some Rhinomyzini in the Afrotropical region). No records of larval stages are known from Madagascar.

TAXONOMY AND PHYLOGENY

Taxonomically, Tabanidae is placed in the infraorder Tabanomorpha. The small family Athericidae is considered its sister (Kerr 2010; Morita et al. 2016). Within the family of horseflies, traditionally three subfamilies are recognized: Pangoniinae, Chrysopsinae, and Tabaninae (Mackerras 1954). Recent molecular studies show that Pangoniinae and Tabaninae are monophyletic, but Chrysopsinae is paraphyletic (Turcatel 2014; Morita et al. 2016). Its three tribes, Bouvieromyiini, Chrysopsini, and Rhinomyzini, are recovered as monophyletic (though the first with exclusion of *Lilaea*). Rhinomyzini is found to be the sister of all Tabaninae (Turcatel 2014). In the subfamily Tabaninae, the traditional tribe Diachlorini is found to be paraphyletic (Morita et al. 2016). Its Old World species, including those from Madagascar, form the tribe Chasmiini (Bayless 2012). It must be pointed out that only very few Malagasy horseflies are included in the molecular studies. Several genera remain unsampled—*Aegophagamyia sensu stricto*, *Oldroydiella*, *Paulianomyia*, *Seguyiella*, and *Thriambeutes*—and the large genera *Tabanocella* and *Triclida* are, in general, notably undersampled.

Traditionally, many genera of Malagasy horseflies are recognized, especially in the tribe Rhinomyzini (Chainey 2017). I have argued that genera proposed by Dias (1955, 1956, 1966) and Quentin (1990) are based on highly plastic features (e.g., shape of third antennal segment) (Zeegers 2017). Their proposals do not lead to monophyletic genera. Therefore, *Alocella*, *Mackerresia*, *Orgizocella*, and *Tabanocellinus* are considered synonyms of *Tabanocella* (Zeegers 2017). A phylogenetic analysis of Rhinomyzini is hampered by the possible secondary loss of characters in some cases, leading to inconclusive results. Therefore, I have chosen to take a broad approach and combine *Jashinea* and *Seguytabanus* within the genus *Oldroydiella*.

On the other hand, within the tribe Bouvieromyiini, the genus *Triclida* is considered as valid next to *Aegophagamyia*, for the reasons already given by Oldroyd (1957). *Paulianomyia* is a clear candidate to be its sister. Study of the male genitalia of *Paulianomyia* confirms that this genus belongs in Bouvieromyiini, not Pangoniinae. *Rhinomyzopsis*, characterized by the long wing, is accepted as a valid genus. It contains all Malagasy species previously attributed to the genus *Rhigiglossa*. The latter is therefore absent from Madagascar. Also, the Diachlorini (perhaps best considered the Chasmiini) genus *Seguyiella* is considered valid and separate from *Limata*, a view already expressed by Chainey and Timmer (1986).

MALAGASY TABANIDAE FAUNA AND ENDEMISM

The Malagasy fauna (Table 9.41) differs significantly from the Afrotropical mainland. Nearly all species are endemic to Madagascar, with only four shared species (*Aegophagamyia pungens*, *Neavella albipectus*, *Atylotus agrestis*, and *Tabanus taeniola*). The last two might have been introduced by people. Five of the 15 currently recognized Malagasy genera are endemic, and *Triclida* is nearly endemic, with only a few species occurring on other islands in the Indian Ocean. The shared

TABLE 9.41. **Checklist of Malagasy Tabanidae and their distribution**

SCIENTIFIC NAME	DISTRIBUTION
SUBFAMILY PANGONIINAE	
Tribe Pangoniini	
Protosilvius inopinatus Zeegers, 2015[1]	Eastern moist evergreen forests: Moramanga
SUBFAMILY CHRYSOPSINAE	
Tribe Bouvieromyiini	
Aegophagamyia flava (Surcouf, 1909)	Strictly coastal; nearly all records on east coast[2]
A. pungens Austen, 1912	Strictly coastal, both west and east coasts; also east Africa
Paulianomyia rufa Oldroyd, 1957	Eastern moist evergreen forests
Rhinomyzopsis longipennis Séguy, 1950	Northern forest: Antsiranana
R. nigrita (Chainey & Oldroyd, 1980) comb. nov.	Eastern moist evergreen forests
R. seyrigi (Séguy, 1950) comb. nov.	Eastern moist evergreen forests
Rhinomyzopsis sp. nov.	North: Tsaratanàna
Triclida aurea (Oldroyd, 1957)	West: Befasy
T. basalis (Oldroyd, 1960)	Eastern moist evergreen forests: Andasibe-Mantadia (as Périnet)
T. bekilyana (Séguy, 1938)	Southern lowlands
T. bengalia (Séguy, 1938)	West coast: Nosy Voalavo (as Nossy-Volavo)
T. brunnea (Surcouf, 1909) [= *Aegophagamyia brunnipes* (Burger, 1992) syn. nov.][3]	Eastern moist evergreen forests
T. chaineyi (Burger, 1992)	Eastern moist evergreen forests, and one locality each in western and southern lowlands and Central Highlands
T. chopardi (Surcouf, 1913)	Eastern moist evergreen forests
T. cincta (Surcouf, 1909)	Predominantly found in southern lowlands[4]
T. completa (Oldroyd, 1957)	Western lowlands; once in southern lowlands
T. confusa (Surcouf, 1913)	North: Montagne d'Ambre
T. decaryi Séguy, 1950 stat. rev.	Eastern moist evergreen forests
T. grisea (Oldroyd, 1960)	Eastern moist evergreen forests; forests in western lowlands
T. hildebrandti (Enderlein, 1923)	"Central Madagascar"
T. keiseri (Oldroyd, 1960)	Eastern moist evergreen forests: Andasibe-Mantadia (as Périnet)
T. lata (Oldroyd, 1963)	Eastern moist evergreen forests and southern lowlands
T. longirostris (Séguy, 1950)	Predominantly in the eastern moist evergreen forests; some records from Central Highlands
T. lurida Enderlein, 1923	Central Highlands: Antananarivo
T. macrops (Séguy, 1950)	Southern lowlands: Ambovombe
T. mandrariana Séguy, 1950 stat. rev.	Southern lowlands: Ambovombe; Central Highlands: Mount Ibity (as Mont Bity)
T. nebulosa (Séguy, 1950)	Eastern moist evergreen forests
T. notata (Surcouf, 1909)	Eastern moist evergreen forests
T. proxima (Surcouf, 1909)	Eastern moist evergreen forests
T. pulchella (Austen, 1912)	Western lowlands and eastern moist evergreen forests.
T. seyrigi (Séguy, 1938)	Central Highlands: Antananarivo

(continued overleaf)

TABLE 9.41. ***continued***

SCIENTIFIC NAME	DISTRIBUTION
T. syrphoides (Enderlein, 1923)	Eastern moist evergreen forests
T. vadoni (Oldroyd, 1957)	Eastern moist evergreen forests
T. variegata (Surcouf, 1909)	Southern lowlands and aberrant record at Montagne d'Ambre[5]
T. xanthomera (Oldroyd, 1957)	Western lowlands and eastern moist evergreen forests
T. zeus (Oldroyd, 1957)[6]	Eastern moist evergreen forests: Fanovana
Tribe Chrysopsini	
Chrysops abaptistus Séguy, 1950[7]	Western lowlands; eastern moist evergreen forests, low elevations
C. aprugnus Austen, 1912	Eastern moist evergreen forests and adjacent Central Highlands
C. cervulus Séguy, 1950 (Figure 9.53a)	Southern lowlands and adjacent western lowlands
C. insulensis Austen, 1912	Eastern medium-altitude moist evergreen forests, above 1000 m
C. longirostris Zeegers, 2015	Eastern medium-altitude moist evergreen forests, above 1000 m; one record from southern lowlands
C. madagascarensis Ricardo, 1902, including *lloydi* Austen, 1912	Widespread
Picromyza addita (Oldroyd, 1957)	Southern edge of eastern medium-altitude moist evergreen forests: Andohahela, at 1800 m
P. burgeri Zeegers, 2015	Central Highlands: Ambohitantely, 46 km NE of Ankazobe
P. crocea (Séguy, 1950) (Figure 9.53b)	Abundant in eastern medium-altitude moist evergreen forests above 1000 m; some records from adjacent Central Highlands
P. hybrida Zeegers, 2015	Eastern moist evergreen forests: Ranomafana
P. infernalis Quentin, 1979	Southern part of eastern moist evergreen forests
P. lutea Zeegers, 2015	Eastern moist evergreen forests: Ranomafana
P. nigerrima Zeegers, 2015	Eastern moist evergreen forests: Ranomafana
P. oldroydi Zeegers, 2015	Eastern moist evergreen forests: Forêt d'Isaka, Fort Dauphin (Tolagnaro)
P. pauliani (Oldroyd, 1957)	Eastern moist evergreen forests
P. vittata Zeegers, 2015	Southeastern coast: Manombo Camp site, SSE of Farafangana, low elevation
Tribe Rhinomyzini	
Oldroydiella albocincta Zeegers, 2017[8]	Eastern moist evergreen forests: Ranomafana
O. expatriata (Oldroyd, 1957)	Eastern moist evergreen forests and adjacent Central Highlands
O. oldroydi (Paulian, 1962) (Figure 9.53e)	West
O. splendida (Oldroyd, 1963)	Eastern moist evergreen forests
Orgizomyia zigzag (Macquart, 1855) (Figure 9.53d)	Widespread
Orgizomyia sp. nov.	Western lowlands: Isalo National Park
Tabanocella alveolata (Surcouf, 1909) (Figure 9.53c)	Widespread
T. aurea Oldroyd, 1957	Eastern moist evergreen forests
T. bimaculata Zeegers, 2017	Southern lowlands; a few records from western lowlands and eastern moist evergreen forests
T. fenestrata (Séguy, 1934)	Eastern moist evergreen forests
T. hauseri Zeegers, 2017	Eastern moist evergreen forests; once from Central Highlands
T. longirostris (Bigot, 1859)	Northern part of eastern moist evergreen forests

SCIENTIFIC NAME	DISTRIBUTION
T. maculata (Surcouf, 1909)	Widespread, but lacking in the north
T. metallica Oldroyd, 1957	Eastern moist evergreen forests and one locality in Central Highlands
T. micromera Oldroyd, 1963	North: Montagne d'Ambre
T. mordosa (Austin, 1912)	Western lowlands and Central Highlands
T. quentini Zeegers 2017	North: Tsaratanàna
T. scirpea Oldroyd, 1957	Eastern moist evergreen forests
T. seguyi (Quentin, 1990)	Eastern moist evergreen forests
T. seyrigi Séguy, 1951 [= *Orgizocella pauliani* Quentin, 1990 (Zeegers 2017)]	Eastern moist evergreen forests and adjacent southern lowlands
T. simplicicornis (Austen, 1912)	West coast: Andranolava
T. sinuata Oldroyd, 1957	Eastern moist evergreen forests: Andasibe-Mantadia (as Périnet)
T. stigmatana (Séguy, 1934)	Central Highlands; once from southern coast
T. stuckenbergi Oldroyd, 1957	Northern part of western lowlands; one locality in Central Highlands
T. thoracica Séguy, 1951	Eastern moist evergreen forests
T. veittei (Quentin, 1990)	Northern part of western lowlands
Thriambeutes melanochrysa Zeegers, 2017	Southern lowlands
SUBFAMILY TABANINAE	
Tribe Diachlorini (perhaps best placed within the Chasmiini)	
Neavella albipectus (Bigot, 1859)	Eastern and southern, strictly coastal; also other islands in Indian Ocean and east coast of Africa
N. verstraeteni Leclercq, 1981	Western; strictly coastal
Seguyiella seyrigi (Séguy, 1955)	Lowlands
Seguyiella sp. nov.	Lowland forests in the northwest
Tribe Diachlorini	
Atylotus agrestis (Wiedemann, 1828)	Widespread, low elevations; also widespread on African mainland
Tabanus albitibialis Macquart, 1838	Widespread, but rare at higher elevations
T. bilorus Oldroyd, 1963	Central Highlands: Ankaratra Massif
T. haimovitchae Surcouf, 1909	Northern and neighboring western lowlands; once Central Highlands
T. obscurestigmatus Bigot, 1859	Eastern moist evergreen forests
T. silvanus Ricardo, 1908	Widespread
T. taeniola Palisot de Beauvois, 1807	Widespread; also on African mainland
Tabanus sp. nov. 1	Central Highlands
Tabanus sp. nov. 2	North: Tsaratanàna Massif

[1] Although the year of publication is given as 2014, it was actually published in 2015.

[2] Inland records are misidentifications of *Triclida aurea*.

[3] This new synonymy is established by investigation of the holotype in Paris. Burger (1992) correctly described a sibling species; however, he misinterpreted the concept of *brunnea*. Burger believed on authority of Oldroyd (1957) that *brunnea* had black legs and, therefore, the species with reddish-brown legs was new. However, Oldroyd (1957) described not the holotype male but a female in the Paris collection. It is already clear from the description of the male holotype of *brunnea* by Surcouf (1909) that the femora are reddish ("fauve rougâtre"), not black, as confirmed by the study of the holotype.

[4] Records in the literature are unreliable owing to confusion with an as yet undescribed species.

[5] Records in the literature are unreliable owing to confusion with an as yet undescribed species.

[6] At least 12 additional *Triclida* species are undescribed and new to science.

[7] According to Code article 30.1.4.3 (ICZN 2012), *Chrysops* should be treated as masculine.

[8] Although the year of publication is given as 2015, it was actually published in 2017.

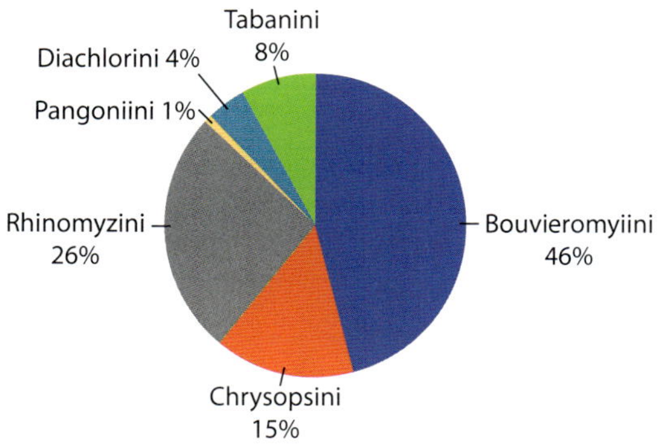

FIGURE 9.54 **Distribution of Malagasy species among the six tribes present on the island.**

distribution with the African east coast of the genera *Neavella*, *Aegophagamyia sensu stricto*, and several genera of Rhinomyzini illustrates an exchange between Madagascar and the African mainland.

At a tribal level, Bouvieromyiini and Rhinomyzini are rich in species on Madagascar (Figure 9.54), each with one large genus (*Triclida* and *Tabanocella*, respectively). Neither tribe shows such richness on the African mainland or any other region of the world. On the other hand, the tribe Tabanini is poorly represented on Madagascar, and the tribe Haematopotini, one of the major tribes in the Afrotropical region, is completely lacking. The presence of a Pangoniini genus on Madagascar is very interesting, since this tribe is virtually absent from the African mainland. The species is tentatively associated with the Neotropical genus *Protosilvius* and might reflect an ancient Gondwanan connection (Zeegers 2015). A common ancestry of Rhinomzyini from Madagascar and the Oriental region is possible (Zeegers 2017).

HISTORY OF STUDIES ON MALAGASY HORSEFLIES

The history of the study of Malagasy horseflies has been addressed by Chainey (2003). Since then, much more material has been collected, especially by a project run by the California Academy of Sciences, specifically H. (Rin'Ha) Rasolondalao, B. L. Fisher, M. E. Irwin, and F. Parker, who installed Malaise traps in many areas of the island, including various protected areas. Additional material has been collected by M. Hauser, A. Kirk-Spriggs, M. Kotrba, C. Schmid-Egger, and others. The total number of specimens collected since 2003 at least doubles the amount of material collected before that year. On Madagascar, collecting horseflies with Malaise traps proves to be superior to traditional net collecting. Many more specimens and a much broader species spectrum is found with Malaise traps. As a result of these efforts, the number of horsefly species known to the author of this contribution has risen from 75 to at least 105 (Table 9.42). Thirteen have recently been described (Zeegers 2015, 2017), and at least 17 are yet to be described; two are sunk into synonymy (Zeegers 2017), and two are revived from synonymy (*Triclida decaryi* and *T. mandrariana*; Table 9.41).

TABLE 9.42. **Number of currently known Tabanidae genera and number of species from Madagascar**

SCIENTIFIC NAMES	DESCRIBED SPECIES	UNDESCRIBED SPECIES
SUBFAMILY PANGONIINAE		
Tribe Pangoniini		
Protosilvius	1	0
SUBFAMILY CHRYSOPSINAE		
Tribe Bouvieromyiini		
Aegophagamyia	2	0
Paulianomyia	1	0
Rhinomyzopsis	3	1
Triclida	29	12
Tribe Chrysopsinae		
Chrysops	6	0
Picromyza	10	0
Tribe Rhinomyzini		
Oldroydiella	4	0
Orgizomyia	1	1
Tabanocella	20	0
Thriambeutes	1	0
SUBFAMILY TABANINAE		
Tribe Diachlorini		
Neavella	2	0
Seguyiella	1	1
Tribe Tabanini		
Atylotus	1	0
Tabanus	6	2

CONSERVATION

From an ecological point of view, forests, both lowland and at higher elevations, are strongholds for Malagasy tabanid biodiversity. Though some species flourish in secondary forests, more than half of all species are confined to intact forests, which are often associated with protected areas. Several species are known from only one or a few localities. Considering the rate of deforestation, many species can be expected to be threatened.

Subject editors: Brian L. Fisher and Steven M. Goodman

DIPTERA: MUSCIDAE, HOUSEFLIES, *LALITRA*

M. S. Couri and A. C. Pont

Muscidae is part of the Diptera infraorder Muscomorpha, which can be recognized by the presence of developed calypters; the absence of strong setae on the meron; straight and incomplete vein A_1+CuA_2, which does not reach the wing margin; the absence of hairlike setulae ventrally at tip of the scutellum; and the absence of abdominal spiracles 6 and 7 on the female ovipositor (spiracle 6 reacquired in one genus), this lattermost character being an autapomorphy or distinct feature of the family.

Although most species are not attracted to human habitats, the family is well known for at least two species: *Musca domestica*, a common and highly synanthropic species closely linked to human activities, and *Stomoxys calcitrans*, a hematophagous muscid known as the stable fly, which is of great economic and veterinary importance.

Muscidae is one of the more interesting families of Diptera, and the biology of the species is varied. Some species are of medical-veterinary importance, acting as vectors of certain etiological agents that can cause diseases in humans and other animals; others, such as members of the genus *Atherigona*, are of agricultural importance as pests of cereals, several crops of which are known to be of economic significance. Some other species are used in biological control as predators of other insects that can cause injury to humans and animals, such as *Coenosia attenuata*, currently unknown to occur on Madagascar, a voracious predator used to control leaf-mining pests in greenhouse plantations, and species of *Limnophora* and *Lispe*, which prey on mosquitoes (Culicidae) and blackflies (Simuliidae). Muscids are also one of the dominant families used in forensic investigations. Finally, adults of several genera are anthophilous, and in temperate areas, Muscidae is one of the most important families of pollinating Diptera. The larvae have varied habits. They may be coprophagous, saprophagous, phytophagous, carnivorous predators, and even parasites or parasitoids. Studies on the classification of the family Muscidae using molecular techniques (Kutty et al. 2014; Haseyama et al. 2015) have included a small number of Afrotropical taxa, but much work remains to be done on this group.

SYSTEMATICS AND BIOGEOGRAPHY

Members of this family occur in all biogeographic regions of the world, from sea level to high elevations, more commonly in forest regions and areas with high rainfall. They occur in a wide variety of habitats, except for the most arid ones.

As summarized in Couri et al. (2006), the Afrotropical Muscidae fauna has been dealt with in the comprehensive revisions by Emden (1939, 1940, 1941, 1942a, 1942b, 1943, 1951). Since Emden's work, new Afrotropical species have been described by Couri, Crosskey, Deeming, Dike, Kleynhans, Muller, Paterson, Peris, Pont, Snyder, Vikhrev, Zielke, and Zumpt, and keys have been published by Zumpt (1969) for *Aethiopomyia*; Paterson (1960) for *Alluaudinella*; Snyder (1953) for *Mydaea* (in part); Pont and Dear (1976) for *Ochromusca*; Pont (1974) for *Passeromyia*; Crosskey (1962) for *Pygophora*; Zielke (1971) for the tribe Muscini; Deeming (1971), Dike (1989, 1990), and Muller (2015) for the tribe Atherigonini; and Zumpt (1973) for the Stomoxyinae (summarized in Pont 1980) (see Couri et al. 2006).

Knowledge of the Malagasy Muscidae fauna, scattered throughout the publications of these authors, was cataloged by Pont (1980), who listed 78 species in 27 genera from Madagascar. After this catalog, species of *Atherigona* were added by Deeming (1987).

Couri et al. (2006) summarized the knowledge of Malagasy muscids, keyed all the genera and species recorded from Madagascar, described 23 new species, and recorded seven species and three genera that were new for the island. Almost 80% of the previously known Malagasy muscid fauna was recognized in their contribution, and replacement names were given for two homonyms. More recently, Vikhrev (2014, 2016) has dealt with some species groups of *Lispe* that include Malagasy species, and Deeming (2019) has described three new species of *Atherigona* together with an updated key to the island's members of this genus. Although there have been considerable advances in the knowledge of the taxonomy of these flies in recent years, many species in the Afrotropical region and on Madagascar are still to be described, and the fauna is certainly much richer than it appears to be at present. For speciose genera, such as *Atherigona*, there are still many species to be described.

The current number of Muscidae genera registered for Madagascar is 29, with 133 species, 50.4% of them endemic. Table 9.43 summarizes these records. Of the 29 genera, three are speciose: *Atherigona*, *Dichaetomyia*, and *Lispe*, with respectively, 26, 20, and 20 species each. Furthermore, 50% of the endemic species belong to these three genera, and of the 20 Malagasy *Dichaetomyia* species, only one is not endemic. The genus *Deltotus*, with its three species, is endemic to Madagascar, while all species recorded from *Helina* (five), *Phaonia* (two), *Pyrellia* (two), *Graphomya* (one), *Spilogona* (one), and *Cephalispa* (two) are also endemic.

One striking feature of the island's Muscidae is the occurrence of metallic shining green or blue species in genera that in other regions contain no species with this coloration: *Hydrotaea*, *Helina*, and especially *Dichaetomyia*. All species of the single endemic genus (*Deltotus*) are shining metallic green in color.

It is interesting to note that eggs of the genus *Stylogaster* (Diptera, Conopidae; see Stuke, pp. 1085–88) have been found impaled mainly in the eyes, mesonotum, and abdomen of some muscid specimens (Couri and Pont 2006; Couri and Barros 2010). Females of all species of *Stylogaster* oviposit their dart eggs on other insects, including calyptrate Diptera. Figure 9.55 illustrates some Malagasy muscid species impaled with *Stylogaster* eggs.

TABLE 9.43. **Checklist of genera and species of Muscidae recorded from Madagascar**

ATHERIGONINAE

Atherigona Rondani
A. addita Malloch
A. alaotrana Dike (E)
A. aster Emden
A. bedfordi Emden
A. bifurcata Deeming (E)
A. bimaculata Stein
A. clavata Deeming (E)
A. contrastiloba Deeming (E)
A. dikei Deeming (E)
A. erectisetula Muller
A. humeralis (Wiedemann)
A. laevigata (Loew)
A. lamina Deeming (E)
A. lineata (Adams)
A. madagascarensis Deeming (E)
A. marginifolia Emden
A. matilei Deeming
A. naqvii Steyskal
A. nigridorsalis Couri, Pont & Penny (E)
A. orientalis Schiner
A. pulla (Wiedemann)
A. quadriseta Couri, Pont & Penny (E)
A. soccata Rondani
A. trapezia Emden
A. variata Couri, Pont & Penny (E)
A. yorki Deeming

MUSCINAE

Muscini

Deltotus Séguy (E)
D. facetus Séguy (E)
D. stuckenbergi Zielke (E)
D. viola Zielke (E)
Morellia Robineau-Desvoidy
M. calyptrata Stein
M. nilotica (Loew)
Musca Linnaeus
M. confiscata Speiser
M. domestica Linnaeus
ssp. *calleva* Walker
ssp. *domestica sensu stricto*
M. sorbens Wiedemann
M. xanthomelaena Wiedemann
Neomyia Walker
N. albigena (Stein)
N. setulosa (Zielke) (E)
N. viridifrons (Macquart)
Pyrellia Robineau-Desvoidy
P. ampullacea Couri, Pont & Penny (E)
P. keiseri Zielke (E)

Stomoxyini

Stomoxys Geoffroy
S. calcitrans (Linnaeus)
S. niger Macquart

AZELIINAE

Azeliini

Azelia Robineau-Desvoidy
Azelia sp. nov. (E)
Hydrotaea Robineau-Desvoidy
H. bella Couri, Pont & Penny (E)
H. chalcogaster (Wiedemann)

Reinwardtiini

Fraserella Steyskal
Fraserella sp. nov. (E)

PHAONIINAE

Dichaetomyiini

Alluaudinella Giglio-Tos
A. bivittata (Macquart)
A. stuckenbergi Paterson (E)
Dichaetomyia Malloch
D. basialaris (Zielke) (E)
D. coerulea (Bigot) (E)
D. colorata Couri, Pont & Penny (E)
D. femoralis (Zielke) (E)
D. flabellifera Couri, Pont & Penny (E)
D. flavoscutellata (Stein) (E)
D. frontata Couri, Pont & Penny (E)
D. harlekini (Zielke) (E)
D. humeralis (Zielke) (E)
D. lucida Séguy (E)
D. madagascarensis Séguy (E)
D. nigra Couri, Pont & Penny (E)
D. ovata (Stein)
D. perineta Zielke (E)
D. rangeri (Zielke) (E)
D. scutellata (Séguy) (E)
D. seyrigi Séguy (E)
D. tricolorata Couri, Pont & Penny (E)
D. tristis (Zielke) (E)
D. zielkei Couri, Pont & Penny (E)

Phaoniini

Helina Robineau-Desvoidy
H. carpiae Couri, Pont & Penny (E)
H. cyanea (Stein) (E)
H. flavomaculata Couri, Pont & Penny (E)
H. grisella Couri, Pont & Penny (E)
H. insignis (Séguy) (E)
Phaonia Robineau-Desvoidy
P. plurivittata Couri, Pont & Penny (E)
P. univittata Couri, Pont & Penny (E)

MYDAEINAE

Dimorphia Malloch
D. cognata (Robineau-Desvoidy)
D. rossi (Zielke) (E)
Gymnodia Robineau-Desvoidy
G. differa (Couri, Pont & Penny) (E)
G. flexa (Wiedemann)
G. gentilis (Robineau-Desvoidy)
G. tonitrui (Wiedemann)

MYDAEINAE
G. versicolor (Stein)
Graphomya Robineau-Desvoidy
G. rossi Zielke (E)
Hebecnema Schnabl
H. humeralis Couri, Pont & Penny (E)
H. semiflava Stein
Myospila Rondani
M. bekilyana (Séguy) (E)
M. lenticeps (Thomson)
M. paradoxalis (Stein in Becker)

COENOSIINAE
Limnophoriini
Limnophora Robineau-Desvoidy
L. conversa Stein (E)
L. exigua (Wiedemann)
L. mesovittata Couri, Pont & Penny (E)
L. obsignata (Rondani)
L. quaterna (Loew)
L. rossi Zielke (E)
L. setalis Emden
L. stragula (Séguy)
L. triangularis Couri, Pont & Penny (E)
Lispe Latreille
L. argentata Couri, Pont & Penny (E)
L. bengalensis (Robineau-Desvoidy)
L. desjardinsii Macquart
L. dichaeta Stein
L. fulvitarsus (Snyder)
L. fulvitarsus ssp. *sensu stricto*
L. irvingi Curran
L. keiseri Zielke (E)
L. leucocephala Loew
L. leucostica Stein (E)
L. macfiei Emden
L. madagascariensis Zielke
L. medvedevi Vikhrev (E)
L. niveimaculata Stein
L. nuba Wiedemann
L. paraneo Zielke
L. pectinipes Becker
L. pennitarsis Stein
L. sexnotata Macquart
L. stuckenbergi Zielke
L. tuberculitarsis Stein
Ocypodomyia Pont
O. stuckenbergi Pont
Spilogona Schnabl
S. fulvipollinosa Couri, Pont & Penny (E)
Coenosiini
Anaphalanthus Loew
A. longicornis (Macquart)
Cephalispa Malloch
C. azurea Couri, Pont & Penny (E)

COENOSIINAE
C. curta Couri, Pont & Penny (E)
Coenosia Meigen
C. aberrans Couri, Pont & Penny (E)
C. madagascariensis (Séguy) (E)
C. nitidiventris Stein (E)
C. nova (Stein) (E)
C. strigipes Stein
C. strigipes ssp. *sensu stricto*
C. trichocnema Stein (E)
C. trina Wiedemann
Lispocephala Pokorny
L. mikii (Strobl)
L. pectinata (Stein)
Orchisia Rondani
O. costata (Meigen)
Pygophora Schiner
P. pallipalpis (Stein)

Note: E, Endemic to Madagascar

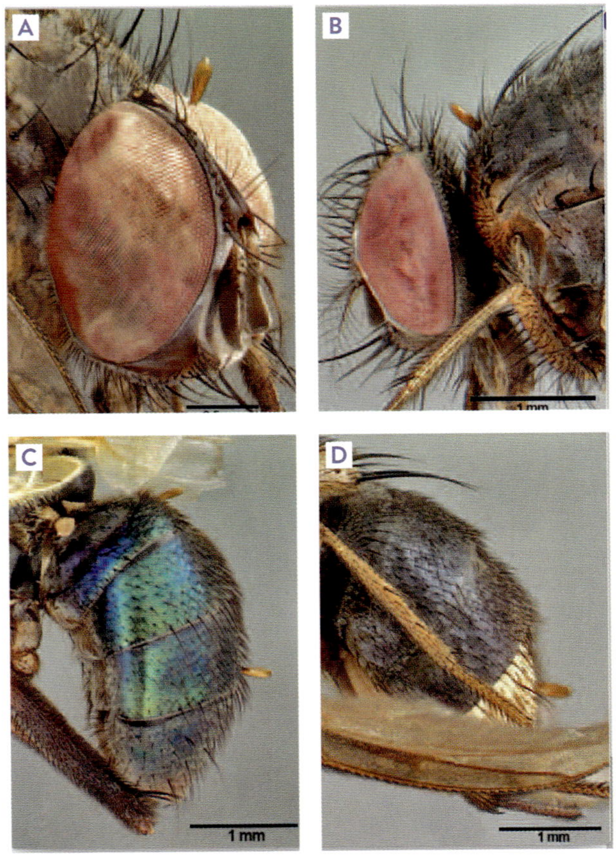

FIGURE 9.55 **Examples of *Stylogaster* (family Conopidae) dart eggs embedded in Muscidae flies. A) *Phaonia univittata*, male head; B) *Deltotus facetus*, female head and part of mesonotum, lateral view; C) *D. viola*, female abdomen, lateral view; and D) *D. facetus*, female abdomen, lateral view.** (PHOTOS modified from Couri and Pont 2006.)

FUTURE DIRECTIONS

The Malagasy Muscidae fauna is probably much richer than would appear at the present time, and there must be many species still to be discovered and described. More collections and inventories are needed, combined with molecular phylogenetic and biogeographic analyses. This new information will provide a better understanding of the systematics and faunal composition of the island's Muscidae fauna.

Subject editors: Brian L. Fisher and Steven M. Goodman

DIPTERA: DIOPSIDAE, STALK-EYED FLIES

H. R. Feijen and C. Feijen

Flies belonging to the family Diopsidae are commonly known as stalk-eyed flies. The adults carry the eyes and the antennae at the end of stalks. On the African mainland, the family also includes two genera of stalkless flies, *Centrioncus* and *Teloglabrus*. However, these stalkless genera, also referred to as Afromontane forest flies (Feijen 1983), are not known to occur on Madagascar. Diopsidae is placed in the paraphyletic Acalyptratae and is often referred to the superfamily Diopsoidea. The relation to other Schizophoran families has not yet been unambiguously established, but a close relation with the South American Syringogastridae seems likely (Marshall et al. 2009; Lonsdale 2020). Members of Diopsidae occur mainly in the Afrotropical and Oriental regions, along with a few species in the Nearctic, Palearctic, and Australasian regions. Worldwide, the stalk-eyed flies count 17 extant genera and one extinct genus. At present, 237 species are recognized, but a larger number of species awaits description. In the Afrotropical region, 12 genera and 157 species are presently recognized, of which five genera and 12 species occur on Madagascar. The stalk-eyed Diopsidae can be divided in the subfamilies Sphyracephalinae and Diopsinae, both of which occur on Madagascar.

MORPHOLOGY

The following description refers only to members of Diopsidae with eyestalks (Figure 9.56). The flies are small to medium-size. Body length is 3–13 mm and eye span (the distance between the tips of the eyes) 1.5–19 mm. The coloration is variable, most commonly grayish, blackish, or black with chestnut brown, more rarely yellowish brown. Species-specific pubescence patterns commonly occur on the thorax and/or abdomen. The eyestalks usually carry two pairs of setae, which are sometimes spinous. The arista of the antenna is tripartite in Sphyracephalinae and bipartite in Diopsinae. The thorax has a large and collar-like pronotum. Stalk-eyed flies can have a square basiliform prosternum or a precoxal bridge. The scutum usually carries 0–3 pairs of setae (presutural, supra-alar, and intra-alar), while dorsocentral and acrostichal setae are rarely present. All stalk-eyed flies count one pair of pleurotergal spines, while two Oriental genera have, in addition, one pair of supra-alar spines, and one Afrotropical genus has a pair of intra-alar spines. The scutellum has two posterior elongations, varying from small protuberances with long apical scutellar setae to strong spines without setae. The wing is slender, while an alula is present in Sphyracephalinae and absent in Diopsinae. Vein CuA+CuP extends beyond cell cua in Sphyracephalinae but not in Diopsinae. The wing pattern is variable, hyaline to infuscated with central, preapical or apical spots, or dark and irrorate with three bands of transparent spots. Front femora are often incrassate and have ventrally a double row of tubercles. The abdomen varies from long and slender to short and strongly clavate. In Sphyracephalinae, a syntergum 1–2 occurs, and in Diopsinae a syntergum 1–3. For more detailed descriptions of the morphology, including genitalia, see Peterson (1987), Feijen (1989), Hilger (2000), and Feijen and Feijen (2021).

The egg is elongate and striated in Diopsinae, but reticulated in Sphyracephalinae. The larva is fusiliform, tapering anteriorly, blunter posteriorly, and with anterior and posterior spiracles that are elaborately ornamented and often species-specific. Its cephalopharyngeal skeleton has paired mouth hooks of simple, curved form. The puparium is elongate and subcylindrical, with anterior and posterior spiracular stalks. More information on egg, larva, and puparium can be found in Descamps (1957), Feijen (1989), Meier and Hilger (2000), and Feijen et al. (2018a).

SPECIES DIVERSITY ON MADAGASCAR

Only a few papers describe members of Diopsidae from Madagascar. However, initial results were rather confusing as several species were assigned to Oriental genera (*Eurydiopsis*, *Cyrtodiopsis*, *Teleopsis*) now known to not occur in the Afrotropical region. The first diopsid described from Madagascar is the beautiful, yellowish *Madagopsina apollo* (Figures 9.56b and f). A major paper by Séguy (1949) described the endemic new genus *Cladodiopsis* (Figure 9.56c) and six new species in three genera. Vanschuytbroeck (1965) added two new species, which he placed in *Eurydiopsis*. Steyskal (1972) added to the confusion by reallocating four species to *Cyrtodiopsis*. Feijen and Feijen (2011) showed that *Teleopsis onopyxus* is a junior synonym of the Indian *T. sykesii*. The type locality "Madagascar" was based on the mislabeling of specimens collected in India. Feijen et al. (2018a) reviewed the Malagasy Diopsidae and described *Gracilopsina* (Figure 9.56d) and *Madagopsina* as new endemic genera. In addition, four new species were described, while two species were placed into synonymy. *Cladodiopsis* was listed as also occurring in the Comoros, so it became a near-endemic taxon.

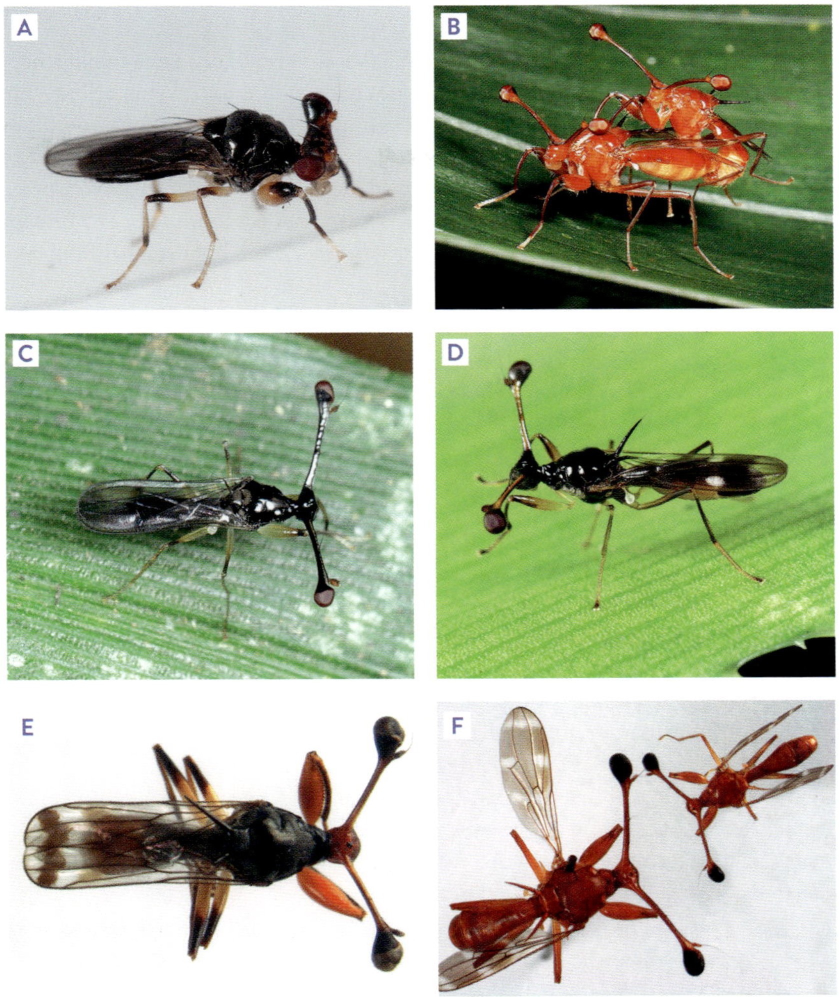

FIGURE 9.56 **Malagasy Diopsidae: A) *Sphyracephala beccarii*; B) *Madagopsina apollo*; C) *Cladodiopsis seyrigi*; D) *Gracilopsina sinespina*; E) *Diopsis nigrosicus*; F) *M. apollo* (left) and *M. parvapollina* (right), showing the difference in size.** (PHOTOS A, C, and D by S. A. Marshall; B by R. Krekels; and E and F by C. Feijen.)

As shown in the Table 9.44, 12 species, divided over five genera, are presently recognized for Madagascar. Sphyracephalinae is represented by *Sphyracephala beccarii* (Figure 9.56a) and three species of *Cladodiopsis*. Of the 12 Diopsidae species on Madagascar, only *S. beccarii* is not endemic. This very common fly occurs in the whole Afrotropical region and extends into the Palearctic region (Feijen et al. 2017). Diopsinae is divided among the genera *Diopsis* (one species), *Gracilopsina* (two species), and *Madagopsina* (five species). It is expected that a few species still need to be described in the genera *Cladodiopsis* and *Madagopsina*. The subfamilies and genera of Madagascar can be identified with the following key.

Key to the subfamilies and genera of Malagasy stalked-eye flies

1. Arista tripartite, alula present, vein CuA+CuP extending past cell cua, apical scutellar seta longer than scutellar spine, syntergum including terga 1 and 2 .... Sphyracephalinae: 2

1a. Arista bipartite, alula absent, vein CuA+CuP not extending past cell cua, apical scutellar seta shorter than scutellar spine or absent, syntergum including terga 1–3 .... Diopsinae: 3

2. Eyestalk stout (~0.80× the widest sagittal eye diameter), two pairs of strong scutal setae (intra-alar, presutural), apical scutellar seta more than 3× the scutellar spine length, alula well developed, vein CuA+CuP branching off near apex of cell cua .... *Sphyracephala*

2a. Eyestalk slender (0.25–0.40× the eye diameter), one pair of strong scutal setae (intra-alar, in one species also weak presutural setae), apical scutellar seta less than twice the scutellar spine length, alula reduced, vein CuA+CuP branching off well before apex of cell cua .... *Cladodiopsis*

3. Inner vertical seta (IVS) tiny and spinous, wing transparent with central infuscation and dark, curved preapical band, M_4 reaching wing margin, apical scutellar seta absent, syntergum 1–3 appearing as single sclerite, abdomen brown with black basal third .... *Diopsis*

3a. IVS distinct, wing brownish and irrorate with three bands of pale spots, M_4 not reaching wing margin, apical scutellar seta present, syntergum 1–3 with distinct seam between terga 2 and 3, abdomen uniformly yellowish or dark brown to blackish 4

4. Body glossy yellowish, scutum pollinose, IVS 0.8–2.3× stalk diameter, basiliform prosternum, pale preapical wing band a distinct continuous band with the section in cell r4+5 proximally hardly convex, terga 2 and 3 uniformly glossy or thinly pollinose, in some species with two posterolateral pollinose spots on tergum 3, surstyli with large apodeme and articulated — *Madagopsina*

4a. Body dark brown to blackish, scutum glossy black, IVS ≥ 2.9× stalk diameter, precoxal bridge, pale preapical wing band consisting of three spots with the spot in cell r4+5 proximally strongly convex, large mesal triangular pollinose spots on terga 2 and 3, surstyli without apodeme and fused to epandrium — *Gracilopsina*

ZOOGEOGRAPHIC RELATIONSHIPS OF MALAGASY DIOPSIDAE AND BIOLOGY

The subfamily Sphyracephalinae includes two genera, *Sphyracephala* and *Cladodiopsis*. Madagascar is the only country known where both genera occur. *Sphyracephala* has the widest distribution of all Diopsidae genera, as it occurs in the Holarctic, Afrotropical, Oriental, and Australasian regions. Based on molecular analysis, Kotrba and Balke (2006) placed *Cladodiopsis* unambiguously as the sister group of *Sphyracephala*. Also based on molecular analysis, this view was supported by another analysis (F. A. A. Feijen, unpublished data), though the author could not yet exclude the possibility that *Cladodiopsis* is embedded in *Sphyracephala*. The likely split between *Cladodiopsis* and *Sphyracephala* took place long ago, with an estimated age of the node ranging from 17 to 38 million years ago (Mya). The presence of *S. beccarii* on Madagascar is probably a relatively recent introduction from the African mainland.

The subfamily Diopsinae includes three genera on Madagascar. *Diopsis nigrosicus* (Figure 9.56e) is the sole Malagasy representative of the genus. Based on morphological characters, it can be placed in the *D. ichneumonea* species group (Feijen and Feijen 2009) of the Afrotropical region, though it is a distant representative of this group (Feijen et al. 2018b). As such, the ancestor of *D. nigrosicus* can be considered as originating from the African mainland. Molecular data are available for two species of the endemic genus *Madagopsina* (Feijen et al. 2018a). Analyses of nuclear gene regions place *Madagopsina* as the sister group of the Oriental *Eurydiopsis*. The likely divergence of these two genera took place 17–33 Mya. As far as the separation of the two *Madagopsina* species is concerned, this occurred more than 10 Mya. This notably old age is in line with the considerable differences in male genitalia within this genus (Feijen et al. 2018a). For the second endemic genus, *Gracilopsina*, no molecular data are yet available. However, principal component analysis of wing morphometry places it among the Oriental genera of the irrorate-wing group (the *Teleopsis* genus group).

TABLE 9.44. **Checklist of Diopsidae species known to occur on Madagascar**

SCIENTIFIC NAMES	DISTRIBUTION	MONTHS COLLECTED
SPHYRACEPHALINAE		
***Cladodiopsis* Séguy, 1949**		
C. leptophylla Séguy, 1949	Northern forests, Ranomafana	September–April
C. seyrigi Séguy, 1949	Northern and eastern forests	January–November
C. sicardi Séguy, 1949	Whole country	November–May
***Sphyracephala* Say, 1828**		
S. beccarii (Rondani, 1873)	Whole country	Year-round
DIOPSINAE		
Diopsis Linnaeus, 1775		
D. nigrosicus Séguy, 1949	From Makay to Montagne d'Ambre	June–August
***Gracilopsina* Feijen et al., 2018**		
G. sinespina Feijen et al., 2018	Tsaramamiandro, Périnet (Andasibe)	October–November
G. vadoni (Vanschuytbroeck, 1965)	Fampanambo, Ambodivoangy	February–July
***Madagopsina* Feijen et al., 2018**		
M. apographica (Séguy, 1949)	Eastern forests, Ambatolahy	September–July
M. apollo (Brunetti, 1928)	Northeastern forests	April, December
M. freidbergi Feijen et al., 2018	Eastern forests, Ambatolahy	February–April, August–November
M. parvapollina Feijen et al., 2018	Western forests	January–April, September–November
M. tschirnhausi Feijen et al., 2018	Montagne d'Ambre	January, May, September

Until recently, information on the biology of Diopsidae on Madagascar was scarce. For quite some time, it was assumed that the stalk-eyed flies were rare on Madagascar. Brian Stuckenberg, who extensively collected Diopsidae in the African mainland and also collected on Madagascar, and reported to the authors of the current contribution (personal communication) that he found it difficult to find Diopsidae on the island as compared to the mainland. Fred Keiser was the first to make a large collection of Malagasy Diopsidae in 1958, but the majority of his collection was unfortunately lost. In recent years, collecting records and photographic evidence showed that Diopsidae on Madagascar is relatively common after all. An exception seems to be for *Gracilopsina*, specifically. In *G. vadoni*, only the type series of 11 specimens is known, while Brian Stuckenberg collected an additional two specimens. For *G. sinespina*, only the holotype and some photographs are available.

The only nonendemic diopsid, *S. beccarii*, can be found year-round and in the whole country (Table 9.44). From the limited data available, it can be ascertained that this species can be found in the same habitat as in Africa. In the dry season, it concentrates in rocky places along rivers, while it disperses in the rainy season. Its well-known habit of clustering in the dry season (Feijen et al. 2017) has not yet been observed on Madagascar but is very likely to take place.

Of the three species of *Cladodiopsis*, two occur only in the northern and eastern forests, while *C. sicardi* can also be found in the southern and central regions. Most Malagasy members of Diopsidae are collected or observed between September and May and rarely, or not at all, between June and August. An exception is *D. nigrosicus*, which was collected only between June and August.

The two genera with irrorate wings, *Madagopsina* and *Gracilopsina*, occur in the northern and eastern forests. An exception is found for *M. parvapollina* (Figure 9.56f), which is known only from the western forests. For these two genera, information is available on the reproductive period. Females with eggs were collected in March, April, August, and November. These months correspond to the period outside the dry season in eastern coastal regions. On the African mainland, most members of Diopsidae are univoltine and start breeding toward the end of the dry season. In contrast, species in the Oriental genera *Cyrtodiopsis* and *Teleopsis* are often polyvoltine and breed more or less throughout the year. The question is whether *Madagopsina* and *Gracilopsina* are also polyvoltine. A curious characteristic was found for the eggs of *M. apographica*. Feijen et al. (2018a) stated that eggs of this species were extremely large: two eggs almost filled the abdominal cavity of a female. These eggs were, in volume, 10 times as large as those of other *Madagopsina* species, while the flies were only slightly smaller. It appears likely that the larvae of Malagasy Diopsidae are saprophagous, but this still needs to be proven. No links with particular plants are known for members of the Madagascar Diopsidae. In the African mainland, many species are linked to Poaceae and some species to Cyperaceae (see Descamps 1957; Feijen and Feijen 2013), while in Oriental genera, links to Araceae or Zingiberaceae are found. Whether a link exists between *G. sinespina* and *Pandanus* sp. (see Feijen et al. 2018a) remains to be investigated. An interesting observation was made in 2018 by Josiane Lips, who found stalk-eyed flies (*M. parvapollina*) in or at the entrance of the Namoroka caves (https://www.inaturalist.org/observations/37503778).

EYESTALK VARIATION

The functions of the eyestalks have, from early on, intrigued entomologists. In the past four decades, many studies have appeared on this subject. Research has concentrated especially on the aspects of sexual selection in species that are sexually dimorphic with regard to eye span. For an introduction to this research, the following studies can be suggested: Burkhardt and de la Motte (1987), Wilkinson and Dodson (1997), Wilkinson et al. (2005), David et al. (2000), Feijen (1989), and Feijen and Feijen (2009). Three aspects of the functions of the eyestalks have been proposed:

- improved spatial vision
- periscopic effect (watching from behind leaves or twigs)
- intraspecific behavior and sexual selection in dimorphic species

For research on sexual dimorphism, the relation between eye span and body length is studied. As a measure of dimorphism (D), the difference between males and females in the allometric slope for eye span on body length is used. A brief review of dimorphism in Diopsidae is given in Feijen and Feijen (2009). These levels of dimorphy used are: monomorphy $D < 0.25$; low dimorphy $D = 0.25–1$; moderate dimorphy $D = 1–2$; high dimorphy $D = 2–3$; very high dimorphy $D > 3$. Sexual dimorphism in eye span is clearly linked to genus and species groups. African mainland *Diopsina* and three species groups in *Diopsis* are, for instance, monomorphic, while *Diasemopsis* and three other species groups in *Diopsis* are dimorphic. In the Oriental region, *Cyrtodiopsis* is dimorphic, while *Eurydiopsis* and *Megalabops* are monomorphic.

A peculiar aspect of members of the endemic Madagascar Diopsidae concerns their level of sexual dimorphy with regard to eye span, as reported by Feijen et al. (2018b). The only nonendemic species on Madagascar, *S. beccarii*, is monomorphic. All endemic Malagasy species are dimorphic, while at least nine out the 11 species have monomorphic sister groups occurring elsewhere in the world. The moderately dimorphic *D. nigrosicus* is a distant representative of the uniformly monomorphic Afrotropical *D. ichneumonea* species group. The three *Cladodiopsis* species are moderately to highly dimorphic, but species of its sister genus *Sphyracephala* are mainly monomorphic, with only some species having low dimorphy. The moderately dimorphic *Madagopsina* is placed as the sister genus of the homomorphic Oriental genus *Eurydiopsis*. The phylogenetic position of the moderately to highly dimorphic *Gracilopsina* is not yet fully resolved, but it is likely to be related to the Oriental, basal homomorphic genera of the irrorate-wing group. This leads to the conclusion that at least nine out of 11 (probably all 11) endemic species have homomorphic sister groups in other regions. Worldwide, dimorphy is now known to have developed independently in at least 10 Diopsidae taxa. It appears that, on Madagascar, circumstances were optimal for development of dimorphy in the endemic Diopsidae species. This link between endemic species and the transition from monomorphy to dimorphy appears convincing. Feijen et al. (2018b) indicated this as perhaps a peculiar case of the disputed Foster's rule, in which size evolution is claimed to be governed by new biotic and abiotic conditions of an island.

Subject editors: Brian L. Fisher and Steven M. Goodman

DIPTERA: STRATIOMYIDAE, SOLDIER FLIES

M. Hauser, N. E. Woodley, and D. A. Fachin

The family Stratiomyidae includes 2842 species globally in nearly 367 genera (Woodley 2001, 2011; Hauser et al. 2017a, 2017b). The greatest diversity is found in the Neotropical region, with over a third of all species, while the Afrotropical region includes 377 described species and 87 genera. There are just under 90 species (and 11 synonyms) in 28 genera known from Madagascar (Figure 9.57), but many undescribed species are already on hand and awaiting description. Despite continental Africa being much larger than Madagascar, it has only three times the stratiomyid species diversity of the island. An updated summary of what is known about the Afrotropical fauna, with keys to genera and their biology, is presented in Hauser et al. (2017b). The Stratiomyidae fauna of Madagascar has close relationships to the African continent and only a few connections to India and the Oriental region. The fauna is unique, having relatively few genera, some of which have a rather large number of species, which would indicate dispersal events followed by a radiation on the island.

FIGURE 9.57 A selection of Stratiomyidae taxa from Madagascar. A) *Cardopomyia robusta*, B) *Keiseria* sp., C) *Allognosta* sp., D) *Odontomyia* sp., E) *Cephalochrysa lucens*, F–I) *Gongrosargus* species. Scale bars, 1.0 mm. (PHOTOS by M. Hauser.)

Key to Stratiomyidae genera of Madagascar

1.	Abdomen with segments 6 and 7 relatively undifferentiated, not retracted into abdomen; tergites 2–6 with distinctly impressed subapical grooves; mid-tibia with tiny apical spur (Beridinae)	*Allognosta* Osten Sacken
1a.	Abdomen with segments 6 and 7 reduced in size, usually retracted into abdomen, thus abdomen appearing 5-segmented; abdominal tergites lacking subapical grooves; mid-tibia without apical spur	2
2.	Wing with 3 median (M) veins	3
2a.	Wing with 4 median (M) veins	18
3.	Wing with m–cu crossvein connected to vein M_4 (Stratiomyinae [in part])	4
3a.	Wing with m–cu crossvein connected to vein M_{3+4} (Pachygstrinae and Stratiomyinae [in part])	6
4.	Delicate flies with abdomen elongate; lower calypter virtually linear, without lobe developed laterally; wing membrane almost entirely clothed in microtrichia; vein R_4 absent (Prosopochrysini [in part])	*Cyphoprosopa* James
4a.	Robust flies with abdomen rounded; lower calypter with a well-developed, conspicuous lobe arising laterally, mostly covered with long setulae; wing membrane largely devoid of microtrichia; wing vein R_4 present or rarely absent (Stratiomyini)	5
5.	Wing with discal cell (d) greatly reduced, small to absent; r–m crossvein absent as discal cell (d) broadly fused with radial sector (Rs) anteriorly; veins M_1 and M_2 absent or at most vein M_2 faintly discernible; vein CuP likewise very weak to absent beyond base, with cell cua undefined	*Oplodontha* Rondani
5a.	Wing with discal cell (d) reduced, not usually fused with radial sector (Rs) anteriorly; r–m crossvein distinct, sometimes punctiform; vein M_2 weak, but distinct, extending at least halfway to wing margin, usually longer; vein M_1 variable, occasionally absent, but usually ranging from a short stump vein near discal cell (d) to complete, sometimes basal portion reduced; vein CuP weak, but distinct, with cell cua defined	*Odontomyia* Meigen
6.	Scutellum with 2 marginal spines (Prosopochrysini [in part])	7
6a.	Scutellum without spines (Pachygastrinae)	11
7.	Hind femur strongly thickened, with large ventral tooth-like process near apex, mid-femur sometimes also conspicuously thickened	8
7a.	Mid- and hind femora unmodified, without armature, or with small spines	10
8.	Antennal flagellomeres 1–5 forming very short, conical complex; terminal flagellomere arista-like, >3× as long as complex; head and body black in color	*Lampetiopus* Lindner
8a.	Antennal flagellomeres 1–5 forming elongate cylindrical to elongate conical complex; terminal flagellomere in form of pubescent arista-like stylus 1–2× as long as complex; head yellowish, body color variable	9
9.	Mid-femur more strongly thickened than hind femur, both with only single, subapical tooth	*Madagascarina* Lindner
9a.	Mid-femur not nearly as strongly thickened as hind femur, without subapical tooth; hind femur with numerous denticles anterior to large, subapical tooth	*Madagascara* Lindner
10.	Antennal flagellum elongate, oblong-shaped, rounded apically; terminal flagellomere slightly tapering toward apex, but not arista-like; antenna much longer than head	*Keiseria* Lindner
10a.	Antennal flagellum not oblong-shaped, strongly tapered toward apex; terminal flagellomere arista-like; antenna at most as long as head	*Pachyberis* James
11.	Wing vein R_{2+3} arising distinctly beyond crossvein r–m, or if r–m absent, then beyond point where discal cell (d) is fused to radial sector (Rs)	12
11a.	Wing vein R_{2+3} arising before crossvein r–m, or close to fusion of discal cell (d) with radial sector (Rs)	13
12.	Terminal antennal flagellomere thickened, bilaterally flattened and vane-like, always black	*Argyrobrithes* Grünberg
12a.	Terminal antennal flagellomere slender, aristate, entirely white or at least apex white	*Cardopomyia* Kertész

13.	Terminal antennal flagellomere bilaterally flattened; invariably black in color	*Ptilinoxus* Lindner
13a.	Terminal antennal flagellomere arista-like, sometimes appearing thickened, but not bilaterally flattened, black or white in color	14
14.	Wing vein R_4 absent	*Zabrachia* Coquillett
14a.	Wing vein R_4 present	15
15.	Smaller species, <4 mm in length; head higher than long	16
15a.	Larger species, >4 mm in length; head longer than high (females) or round (males)	*Pseudoxymyia* Lindner
16.	Terminal antennal flagellomere arista-like, with short, dense, white pubescence	*Otionigera* Lindner
16a.	Terminal antennal flagellomere arista-like, thin, setula-like brown	*Pithomyia* Kertész
17.	Antennal flagellum with 8 discernible flagellomeres (flagellomere 7 may be minute and difficult to detect)	18
17a.	Antennal flagellum with 5, 6, or rarely 7 discernible flagellomeres	21
18.	Scutellum with 2 marginal spines (Clitellariinae)	19
18a.	Scutellum without spines; terminal antennal flagellomere oblong, laterally flattened, bladelike, with bristly setulae, especially ventrally; face with medial, ventrally directed conical process (Hermetiinae)	*Hermetia* Latreille
19.	Antennal flagellomeres 7 and 8 densely setulose, with setulae greater in length than diameter of flagellomeres; wing membrane yellowish with brownish markings; large flies, generally >15 mm in length	*Alopecuroceras* Lindner
19a.	Antennal flagellomeres 7 and 8 not densely setulose; wing membrane unicolorous; smaller flies, generally <15 mm in length	20
20.	Scutellum with spines as long as scutellum; eyes essentially bare, with only sparse, minute setulae, difficult to discern; abdomen widening posteriorly, widest at c. segment 4	*Ampsalis* Walker
20a.	Scutellum with spines about ⅓ as long as scutellum or less; eyes with distinct setulae although these may be sparse; abdomen elongate ovoid, widest at c. segments 2–3	Undescribed genus (to include *dichromata* James 1975)
21.	Scutellum with 2 marginal spines (Stratiominae [in part])	*Oxycera* Meigen
21a.	Scutellum without spines	22
22.	Face cone shape, with a distinct projection; proboscis long; small species <5 mm; wing crossvein m–cu connected to vein M_{3+4} (Nemotelinae)	*Nemotelus* Geoffroy
22a.	Face rounded, without cone shape projection; proboscis short; often much larger species; wing crossvein m–cu connected to vein M_4 (crossvein m–cu connected to M_{3+4} only in the genus *Gongrosargus*) (Sarginae)	23
23.	Median wing vein (M) present throughout entire length between cells bm and br	24
23a.	Median wing vein (M) weakly developed at base, only discernible distally	25
24.	Wing crossvein m–cu connected to vein M_{3+4}; female antenna with acute process on both inner and outer sides of pedicel, projecting into flagellum, male eyes holoptic	*Gongrosargus* Lindner
24a.	Wing crossvein m–cu connected to vein M_4; both sexes with acute process only on inner side of pedicel; male eyes dichoptic	*Ptecticus* Loew
25.	Wing veins M_1 and M_3 often weakly developed, as compared to veins M_2 and M_4; antenna with flagellar complex small, short-cylindrical to ovoid, about as long as or shorter than scape and pedicel; female head with very broad frons, strongly widening toward vertex	*Microchrysa* Loew
25a.	Wing veins M_1 and M_3 slightly (if at all) fainter than veins M_2 and M_4; antenna with flagellar complex variable, but often larger than described above; female head with frons shorter (broader in some *Cephalochrysa* Kertész and *Microptecticus* Lindner), frequently weakly developed toward vertex	26
26.	Lower calypter without projection or at most with very small rudimentary projection; male eyes dichoptic; smaller, more elongate species	*Microptecticus* Lindner
26a.	Lower calypter with distinct large projection; male eyes dichoptic or holoptic; often larger and broad species	27

27. Head with occiput with fringe of erect, posteriorly oriented setulae	*Sargus* Fabricius
27a. Head with occiput without fringe of erect, posteriorly oriented setulae	28
28. Abdomen broad; male eyes entirely holoptic, eyes with two different ommatidia sizes, smaller on ventral ½ and larger dorsally; lobe of calypter large, round; female antenna with inner side of pedicel without acute process	*Cephalochrysa* Kertész
28a. Abdomen often more elongate; male eyes virtually holoptic, eyes with only one size of ommatidia; lobe of calypter more oval-shaped; female antenna with inner side of pedicel often with acute process	*Ptectisargus* Lindner

TAXONOMIC HISTORY

As in many other groups of invertebrates, the fauna of Madagascar is not well understood, a fact that is reflected in the low number of specialists who study Malagasy Stratiomyidae; there have been 10 authors in total in over 200 years of exploration. Furthermore, only M. T. James (1905–1982) (Zack and Akre 1983) and E. Lindner (1888–1988) (Herting 1988) contributed significantly, with Lindner describing nearly 70% of all the known species on Madagascar. Lindner who was a prolific author and an expert in Stratiomyidae for many decades, was also very influential in continental Africa, with nearly 50% of the species described by him. Unfortunately, he did not study many types, his generic concepts were not very solid, and this led to many synonyms and name changes (Hauser et al. 2017a).

The history of Stratiomyidae research on Madagascar can be divided into three phases: an early phase (1805–1863), with Macquart, Loew, Bigot, and Rondani describing only a few isolated specimens; a peak period (1914–1979), with work by Enderlein, Kertész, Lindner, and James; and a modern phase (after 2000), in which one species was described by Schacht and Heuck (2006). The first and one of the most spectacular species of Stratiomyidae described from the Malagasy Region is *Chrysochlora amethystinus* (Hauser et al. 2017a: 927, Figure 29). The specimens were collected by D. K. Daldorff from Mauritius (listed under "Ile-de-France," the old name for Mauritius). The first species from Madagascar were described by Macquart in 1838 and included *Gongrosargus flavipennis*, *G. limbatus*, and *G. pallidus*, all three species originally described in the genus *Sargus*. Then Loew described *Ptectisargus flavomarginatus* (in *Chrysochroma*) in 1857 from Mauritius. Bigot in 1859 described five species: *Odontomyia limbifacies*, *O. bipunctata*, *Cephalochrysa australis* (in *Sargus*), *C. hovas* (in *Sargus*), and *G. glaucus* (in *Sargus*). He redescribed *G. flavipennis*, although it is clear from the description that he had a species of *Ptecticus* in front of him. Rondani only published *Ptecticus lateritius* in 1863 (in *Sargus*), and Enderlein in 1914 described *C. albisquama*. Kertész described the first Pachygastrinae in 1916, *Cardopomyia robusta* (Figure 9.57a). Lindner began his prolific series of publications in 1936 and described 218 Afrotropical species (181 of which are still valid) and 69 Malagasy species (58 are still valid) (Lindner 1936, 1959, 1966, 1967, 1968), while James described in the same period 31 Afrotropical species (29 are still valid), of which 11 are from Madagascar (James 1950, 1960, 1975, 1980).

Even though there has been only one new species described in the past 40 years, our understanding of Stratiomyidae has been growing steadily, for two reasons: first, we have never had more material on hand (over 10,000 specimens), owing to several collecting efforts, including Malaise traps, and second, because of examination of the majority of the type material, which led to several synonymies and new combinations (Hauser et al. 2017a).

KNOWN SPECIES DIVERSITY

Table 9.45 is a list of Stratiomyidae species found on Madagascar. Woodley (2001) lists *Chrysochlora amethystinus* for the island, but we have only seen material of this species from Mauritius. *Ptecticus posticus* is listed in Woodley (2001) as present in Madagascar and the Comoro islands, but the Malagasy specimens are clearly different from the continental specimens and not conspecific. *Lophoteles plumula* is also listed from Madagascar, but we could not find a specimen, nor could we find published records except for the Comoro islands (Lindner 1979) and the Seychelles (Kertész 1912; Woodley 2009a). *Ptectisargus flavomarginatus* was described from Mauritius but also recorded from Madagascar (Lindner 1936). We have not examined the type specimen and are therefore uncertain that this species occurs on both islands. *Tinda indica* is recorded from La Réunion and the Seychelles, while *T. javana* is known only from the Seychelles (Woodley 2009a). These records need to be confirmed, especially considering the poor taxonomic state of this genus. It is probable that only one species of *Tinda* is involved. The following species are recorded from the surrounding islands: *Cephalochrysa matilei*, *C. triste*, and *Ptectisargus argentipellitus* on the Comoros; *C. ranohira* on Mauritius and La Réunion; *Cardopomyia robusta* and *Microchrysa flaviventris* on the Comoros, La Réunion, and the Seychelles; *Argyrobrithes albopilosus* on La Réunion and the Seychelles; *Brachycara ventralis*, *Sargus seychellensis*, *Catatasis clypeata*, and *Odontomyia aequalis* on the Seychelles (Kertész 1912; Lindner 1979; Woodley 2001, 2009a).

CURRENT AND FUTURE RESEARCH

With a plethora of Malagasy Stratiomyidae material collected in the last 20 years and available to the authors, many new species are known now but are still undescribed. Several of these new taxa are available in long series, which facilitates our understanding of inter- and intraspecific variation and association of males and females. The fact that several are still known from a single specimen indicates that the number of species will increase when collections are made in new or poorly collected portions of the island.

The greatest taxonomic challenge is Pachygastrinae, because the limits of the genera are not well defined and it can often be difficult to place specimens in the correct genus. This is a general problem in this subfamily, which has a large number of monotypic genera

TABLE 9.45. **Checklist of the known Stratiomyidae fauna of Madagascar with taxonomic notes and locations**

SCIENTIFIC NAMES	TAXONOMIC AND LOCATION NOTES
SUBFAMILY BERIDINAE	
Allognosta sp. Osten Sacken, 1883	One undescribed species from Madagascar
SUBFAMILY PACHYGASTRINAE	
Argyrobrithes curtilamellatum (Lindner, 1966)	Originally described as endemic genus
Arthronemina Lindner, 1966.	*Lonchobrithes modestus* Lindner, 1968 is a synonym
Cardopomyia parvicornis (Lindner, 1959)	Originally described in *Pseudoxymyia* Lindner, 1959
C. robusta Kertész, 1916	*Physometopon minor* Lindner, 1968 is a synonym
C. vesicularis (Lindner, 1966)	Originally described in *Physometopon* Lindner, 1966
Otionigera acuticornis Lindner, 1966	
Pithomyia stuckenbergi James, 1975	
Pseudoxymyia flavitarsis Lindner, 1959	
Ptilinoxus fallax Lindner, 1966	
P. interruptum (Lindner, 1966)	Originally described in *Leucaron* Lindner, 1966
Zabrachia madagascariensis Lindner, 1959	Likely does not belong in this genus, which is otherwise only found in the Northern Hemisphere
SUBFAMILY CLITELLARIINAE	
Alopecuroceras atripluma James, 1960	
A. coloratum Lindner, 1936	
"*Ampsalis*" *dichromata* James, 1975	This species is not congeneric with *Ampsalis terminalis* and needs to be moved to a new genus
Ampsalis terminalis James, 1960	
SUBFAMILY HERMETIINAE	
Hermetia illucens (Linnaeus, 1758)	Introduced; New World in origin, now cosmopolitan
SUBFAMILY SARGINAE	
Cephalochrysa albisquama (Enderlein, 1914)	Originally described in *Microchrysa* Loew, 1855
C. australis (Bigot, 1859)	Originally described in *Sargus*; *Eulalia tabanoides* Lindner, 1936 is a synonym
C. bigoti (Lindner, 1968)	Originally described in *Chrysochroma*
C. flavum (Lindner, 1968)	Originally described in *Chrysochroma*
C. fortunatum (Lindner, 1966)	Originally described in *Chrysochroma*
C. hovas (Bigot, 1859)	Originally described in *Sargus*
C. lapidis (Lindner, 1966)	Originally described in *Chrysochroma*
C. latum (Lindner, 1966)	Originally described in *Chrysochroma*
C. lucens (Lindner, 1968)	Originally described in *Chrysochroma*
C. triste (Lindner, 1966)	Originally described in *Chrysochroma*
C. vadoni (Lindner, 1966)	Originally described in *Chrysochroma*
Gongrosargus flavipennis (Macquart, 1838)	Originally described in *Sargus*
G. glaucus (Bigot, 1859)	Originally described in *Sargus*; *Gongrosargus distinguendus* Lindner, 1966 is a synonym

SCIENTIFIC NAMES	TAXONOMIC AND LOCATION NOTES
G. lateritius (Lindner, 1968)	Originally described in *Dinosargus* Lindner, 1968
G. limbatus (Macquart, 1838)	Originally described in *Sargus*
G. maculipennis Lindner, 1936	Originally described in *Ptecticus*; *Gongrosargus imitans* Lindner, 1959 is a synonym
G. niveitarsalis Lindner, 1966	
G. pallidus Macquart, 1838	Originally described in *Sargus*; *Gongrosargus univittatus* Lindner, 1966 and *G. exclamationis* Lindner, 1968 are synonyms
G. pauliani Lindner, 1966	
G. stuckenbergi Lindner, 1959	
G. superpictus Lindner, 1966	
G. viridenotatus Lindner, 1966	
Microchrysa flaviventris (Wiedemann, 1824)	Originally described in *Sargus* and from the Oriental region but now known worldwide except for the Neotropical region
Microptecticus ambiguus Lindner, 1966	*Microptecticus clarus* Lindner, 1968 is a synonym
M. dimidiatus Lindner, 1936	
M. magnicornis (Lindner, 1936)	Originally described in *Ptecticus*
M. nigricoxa (Lindner, 1936)	Originally described in *Microchrysa*
Ptecticus breviunguis Lindner, 1966	
P. lateritius (Rondani, 1863)	Originally described in *Sargus*
Ptectisargus abditus Lindner, 1936	Originally described in *Ptecticus*; *Chrysochroma laetum* Lindner, 1966 and *Ptectisargus lucidus* Lindner, 1968 are synonyms
P. argentipellitus (Lindner, 1966)	Originally described in *Chrysochroma*
P. brunneus (Lindner, 1936)	Originally described in *Ptecticus*
P. cingulatum (Lindner, 1968)	Originally described in *Chrysochroma*
P. flavifrons (Lindner, 1968)	Originally described in *Chrysochroma*
P. flavomarginatus (Loew, 1857)	Originally described in *Chrysonotus* Loew, 1955
P. gracilipes (Lindner, 1936)	Originally described in *Ptecticus*
P. keiseri Lindner, 1966	Originally described in *Chrysochroma*
P. lindneri James, 1975	
P. longestylum (Lindner, 1966)	Originally described in *Chrysochroma*
P. punctum (Lindner, 1968)	Originally described in *Chrysochroma*
P. ranohira (Woodley, 2001)	New name for *Chrysochroma ptecticoides* Lindner, 1966, which is a homonym
P. unicolor (Lindner, 1968)	Originally described in *Chrysochroma*
Sargus sp.	One undescribed species in Madagascar
SUBFAMILY STRATIOMYINAE	
Tribe Oxycerini	
Oxycera adusta (Lindner, 1968)	Originally described in *Heraclina* Lindner, 1938
O. madagassica (Lindner, 1966)	Originally described in *Heraclina*

(continued overleaf)

TABLE 9.45. ***continued***

SCIENTIFIC NAMES	TAXONOMIC AND LOCATION NOTES
Tribe Prosopochrysini	
Cyphoprosopa lindneri James, 1975	
Keiseria amoena Lindner, 1966	
K. fasciata Lindner, 1966	
K. lunaris Lindner, 1968	
K. praescutellata Lindner, 1966	
K. rubicunda Lindner, 1966	
Lampetiopus umbrosus Lindner, 1936	
Madagascara seyrigi Lindner, 1936	
M. woodleyi Schacht & Heuck, 2006	
Madagascarina beyeri Lindner, 1967	
Pachyberis stigmaticalis James, 1975	
Tribe Stratiomyini	
Odontomyia bekily Woodley, 2001	New name for *O. rufifacies* Lindner, 1968, which is a homonym
O. bipunctata Bigot, 1859	
O. bulbifrons (James, 1950)	Originally described in *Eulalia* Meigen, 1800
O. elisabethae Lindner, 1966	
O. herbacea Lindner, 1966	
O. jamesi Lindner, 1968	
O. limbifacies Bigot, 1859	
O. longicornis Lindner, 1966	
O. pauliani James, 1975	
O. rhodaspis James, 1980	New name for *O. rufoscutellata* Lindner, 1966, which is a homonym
O. saphyrina Lindner, 1968	
O. seyrigi Lindner, 1968	
Oplodontha dispar (Macquart, 1838)	James (1980) mentioned in his Afrotropical catalog a record of this species from Madagascar. It is not clear whether this is an error; we have not seen specimens of this species from Madagascar, nor are there any published records of this species from Madagascar
O. pulchriceps (Loew, 1858)	*Hoplodontha madagascariensis* Lindner, 1936 was placed as a subspecies of *O. pulchriceps* by Lindner (1966) himself and was later synonymized by Woodley (2001); because of consistent differences to African specimens, this might be a valid species
SUBFAMILY NEMOTELINAE	
Nemotelus exsul James, 1960	
N. madagascarensis James, 1975	

worldwide, and the relationships among them are poorly understood. Most characters used to define genera are in fact species-specific characters, and with increasing understanding of the relationships in this subfamily, numerous genera will be synonymized in future. It is likely that most of the Madagascar species are results of a few dispersal events, with subsequent radiation. Only the genera *Cardopomyia* and *Argyrobrithes* are well defined, and both belong in the *Sternobrithes* group (including *Ageiton*, *Argyrobrithes*, *Berkshiria*, *Cardopomyia*, *Diademorphora*, *Gabaza*, and *Sternobrithes*), which are found in Asia and Africa. *Argyrobrithes* is also known from Africa and Asia, and *Cardopomyia* is endemic to Madagascar and nearby islands (Seychelles). Although *Cardopomyia* has only three described species, there are at least six additional species on hand, and *Argyrobrithes* has at least two more. The genus *Zabrachia*, described from the New World and defined mainly by the reduction of vein R_4, is very likely not represented in Madagascar (or the Afrotropical region), and several unrelated (and undescribed) species from Madagascar show a reduction of this vein. Therefore, the species *madagascariensis* will be moved eventually into a different genus. It is also not certain that the genus *Pithomyia*, originally described from South Africa, is represented on Madagascar.

Given that Pachygastrinae is such a difficult group, very likely molecular data is needed to clarify these relationships. Although *Otionigera*, *Pseudoxymyia*, and *Ptilinoxus* appear to be rather distinct, there are many undescribed species that cannot be placed in one of these genera with certainty, and these genera might be more closely related than is obvious at first glance. We have seen many new species of Pachygastrinae, mainly based on females, which await description. There seems to be a strong bias toward females when collecting with Malaise traps, while several of the hand-collected older types are males.

The genera of Clitellariinae have no obvious connection to the continental African fauna but do connect to the Australasian fauna. The genus *Ampsalis* was described from Indonesia, and the Malagasy species *dichromata* might not belong in this genus. However, it is related to the Asian species of *Ampsalis*, which form a group including the Asian genera *Eudmeta*, *Campeprosopa*, and the Australian genera, such as *Elissoma*, *Lagenosoma*, and *Pycnothorax*. We found several new species in nearly each genus of Malagasy Stratiomyidae, but only one species of *Allognosta* (Figure 9.57c) and no additional species of *Nemotelus* and *Oxycera*. The species with aquatic larvae (*Nemotelus*, *Oxycera*, *Odontomyia*, and *Oplodontha*) are not well represented, except for the genus *Odontomyia* (Figure 9.57d), which has 12 described species, while the species with larvae living under bark (Pachygastrinae) or in rotting plant material (Sarginae) are much more diverse. This might indicate that it is more difficult for the aquatic guilds to disperse over the ocean to Madagascar.

One of the most diverse radiations of Madagascar Stratiomyidae is in Sarginae, with several genera endemic to the island (*Microptecticus*, *Ptectisargus*, and two undescribed genera). The phylogenetically interesting genus *Gongrosargus*, which seems to be the sister to all other members of Sarginae, likely needs to be divided into several genera. The species often have a very different habitus. Strangely, some *Gongrosargus* species have a similar color pattern, but a very different head and antennal shape, which leads to the conclusion that they might be converging independently to a mimicry pattern (Figures 9.57f–i). While most Sarginae specimens are easy to identify to genus, a few specimens seem to be intermediate between the genera *Cephalochrysa* and *Ptectisargus*. It is unclear if the Nearctic and Australasian species of *Cephalochrysa* are really congeneric with the African species, and this needs further investigation.

The high generic diversity of Prosopochrysini, which is a not well-understood group that often occurs on islands, is also remarkable. It is quite possible that it is a relictual group, with only a fraction of its previous diversity and distribution. *Microchrysa flaviventris* is the only species (next to the introduced cosmopolitan *Hermetia illucens*) that is not endemic to Madagascar. It is very likely that this species was introduced to the island from Asia, but it is unclear whether this happened recently or in an early period of human dispersal to Madagascar. This species has a wide distribution from Russia through Asia and from India to Australia, and it has been recently introduced to the United States (Woodley 2009b). It seems likely that some aspects of its current distribution are also due to human activity. Of the 28 genera known to occur on Madagascar, 14 are endemic, while of the 13 also found outside Madagascar, two (*Hermetia* and *Microchrysa*) are likely to be introduced. These figures are almost certain to shift in the future toward more endemic genera, considering that there are two undescribed Sarginae genera and one Clitellariinae genus; that *Gongrosargus* could potentially be split into several endemic genera (there is at least one species of *Gongrosargus* in South Africa); and that *Zabrachia madagascariensis* could be moved into an endemic genus.

The high diversity and endemism of the Stratiomyidae fauna of Madagascar makes it unique and vulnerable to the drastic habitat loss caused by human activity. Continental Africa has more than 30 times the surface area of Madagascar but has less than four times the species diversity.

ACKNOWLEDGMENTS

The numerous curators and collectors who provided access to specimens used in this study are acknowledged, especially C. Daugeron, A. Freidberg, S. D. Gaimari, A. H. Kirk-Spriggs, E. McAlister, the late N. D. Penny, P. Tschorsnig, R. S. Zack, and J. Ziegler. Our colleagues and friends R. Rozkošný and F. Mason influenced this contribution through discussion, motivation, and their publications. The significant influx of new material was provided by B. L. Fisher, M. E. Irwin, F. D. Parker, H. (Rin'ha) Rasolondalao, Tiana Razafindratsita, the late E. Schlinger, and A. Ssysmank. For technical help with the preparation and sorting of the material, we thank D. Yu, D. Imes Kleeburg, and D. Woods for their careful work, and F. Rambeloson, D. Razafindratandra, B. Vavy, D. Wishon, and S. Letana for sorting insects from Malaise trap samples. We are also grateful to Fundação de Amparo à Pesquisa do Estado de São Paulo (FAPESP) grants #2014/05793–1, 2015/25736–5, and 2018/00788–0 to DAF.

Subject editor: Brian L. Fisher and Steven M. Goodman

DIPTERA: ACROCERIDAE, ENDOPARASITOID SPIDER FLIES

†E. I. Schlinger and J. P. Gillung

Acroceridae is a rather uncommon family of flies whose larvae attack and eventually kill spiders. They are worldwide in distribution (except for the polar regions and, in most cases, true volcanic islands) and presently consist of five extant subfamilies, 50 genera, and about 450 species (Gillung and Winterton 2019). The Malagasy fauna is represented by species in the subfamilies Ogcodinae and Philopotinae, while members of Acrocerinae, Cyrtinae, and Panopinae have not yet been found on the island.

Some acrocerids fly extremely fast and are thus hard to collect by netting, while others are very sluggish. They can also be caught in Malaise flight traps if placed in flyways. Many species are efficient pollinators, with mouthparts of variable length, and some species are very specific to one or a few forms of nectariferous flowers. Other species have reduced or no obvious mouthparts. Many acrocerids are brightly colored, often with metallic blue, purple, green, red, gold, orange, or yellow coloration, or they may be quite drab brown or black in color. Several species mimic the coloration and/or behavior of bees, wasps, or beetles, while others may be cryptic. These flies range in size from 2 to 20 mm in total length.

Species of Acroceridae exhibit remarkable variation in size, shape, and color, but despite their morphological dissimilarities, they can all be recognized by their large calypter, pulvilliform empodium, wing crossvein 2r-m, pleating of the wing membrane, and head mostly taken up by the eyes (Figures 9.58 and 9.59). For a complete worldwide description of the family, see Schlinger (1981), Winterton and Barraclough (2017), and Gillung and Winterton (2019). The most recent faunal summary of this family in Madagascar was that of Schlinger (2003), who recorded two subfamilies, six genera (two undescribed), and 22 species (13 undescribed) on the island (Table 9.46).

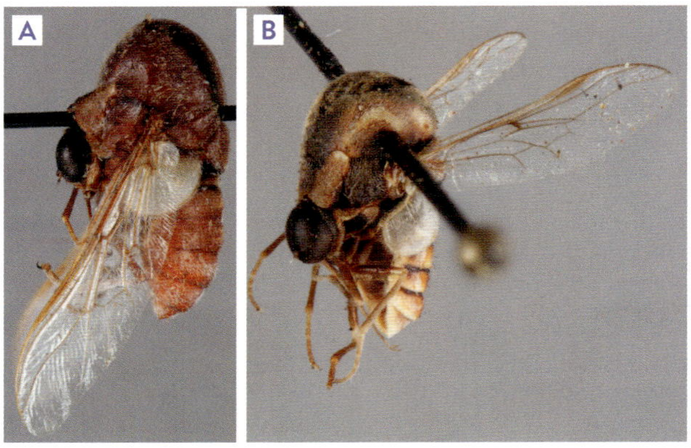

FIGURE 9.58 ***Thyllis advolitans*: A) female, lateral view; and B) female, anterolateral view.** (PHOTOS A and B by S. Winterton.)

FIGURE 9.59 **A representative of Malagasy Acroceridae: *Parahelle stuckenbergi*, lateral view.** (PHOTO by B. Dyer.)

GENERAL LIFE HISTORY OF ACROCERIDAE

Information known about acrocerids in different portions of the world shows that mating usually takes place in flight, after which the female begins to lay up to 5000 eggs and may continue to do so during the following 2–10 days. The minute, black, microtype, pear-shaped eggs are deposited either in flight or directly on the ground (*Eulonchus*), dead branches (*Ogcodes*), tree trunks (*Pterodontia*), or grass stems (*Acrocera*). Acrocerid eggs hatch in three to six weeks, giving rise to minute planidial larvae (the first instar mobile larva), which must seek out and locate their hosts.

Most species of acrocerids have planidia with well-developed hairs and spines, and move about in geometrid-like larval movements. Larvae of *Acrocera*, however, lack hairs and spines and exhibit a unique mode of entering the host, in which the planidium injects itself into the spider. The larvae firmly attach themselves to

† Deceased (1928–2014).

TABLE 9.46. **Checklist of Acroceridae species known to occur on Madagascar**

SCIENTIFIC NAMES	LOCALITY	MONTHS COLLECTED
PHILOPOTINAE		
Thyllis Erichson, 1840		
T. advolitans Séguy, 1962	Bekily	April
T. aerivaga Séguy, 1962	Fianarantosa	March
T. obesa Erichson, 1840[1]	Tolagnaro	–
T. philopotoides Schlinger, 1961	Madagascar: Sikora leg.	–
	Near Joffreville	January
T. splendens Brunetti, 1926	Antongil Bay	–
T. stenoptera Séguy, 1962	Rogez	April
T. torquata Séguy, 1962	Antsiranana	May
Thyllis sp. nov. 1	Ranomafana	April
Thyllis sp. nov. 2	Ranomafana	December
Thyllis sp. nov. 3	Ranomafana	April
Thyllis sp. nov. 4	Berenty Reserve	April
Thyllis sp. nov. 5	30 km SE of Farafangana	January
Parahelle Schlinger, 1961		
P. stuckenbergi Schlinger, 1961	Andringitra: Soaindrana Plateau (2000 m)	January
Parahelle sp. nov. 1	Ranomafana	December
Dimacrocolus Schlinger, 1961		
D. pauliani Schlinger, 1961	Forêt Est; Marovoay (920 m)	September
	Ranomafana	July
	Vohiparara	September
New genus 1, sp. nov. 1	Marojejy (1300 m)	December
New genus 2, sp. nov. 1	Bezà-Mahafaly	February
OGCODINAE		
Ogcodes Latreille, 1796		
Ogcodes sp. nov. 1	Isalo	March
Ogcodes sp. nov. 2	Marojejy	December
Ogcodes sp. nov. 3	Ranomafana	July
Ogcodes sp. nov. 4	20 km N of Vohipeno	December
Ogcodes sp. nov. 5	Montagne d'Ambre (1000 m)	January
Totals: 6 genera (4 known, 2 new); 22 species (9 known, 13 new)		

[1] E. I. Schlinger was unable to examine this specimen, and thus there is a doubt concerning authenticity of its designation. It was described from South Africa (see Schlinger 1960a).

the host's cuticle by their mouthparts, presumably feeding externally for about a week (Overgaard-Nielsen et al. 1999; Toft et al. 2012). Rather than entering the spider, the planidium subsequently molts, and the small, glabrous second instar is injected directly into the spider via the wound, leaving the exuvia of the ectoparasitic first instar covering the site of infection. It is unclear whether this mechanism is present in other Acroceridae lineages.

Either the proper host spider has to come into contact with the planidium, in which case the planidium attaches to the leg of the spider, or the larvae must seek out the host. This latter case occurs when a fossorial spider is involved. Eventually, all larvae end up in the book lung area of the spider and attach themselves in the air pockets between the lung lamellae, where they breathe outside air. The first instar planidium then apparently goes into a state of physiological diapause for several months (Acrocerinae and Cyrtinae) to 10 years (Panopinae) (Schlinger 1987), although there is very limited direct observational evidence to support this hypothesis, and further study is required.

The fourth instar, or mature larva, is the active feeding and destructive stage. About 24 hours prior to the active fourth instar's lethal attack on the host spider, the spider most often spins a protective molting web as if it is going to molt. It is within this web that the naked, mature, acrocerid larva has to locate and affix itself as it exits from the spider in order to successfully pupate. The ventral side of the parasitoid's abdomen contains a series of transverse rows of minute, hooked spines that likely facilitate the attachment of the larvae's heavy body to the premolting web. Adult flies usually emerge about two to three weeks after pupation.

All reported acrocerid larvae are endoparasitic, and while they are usually solitary, as many as 14 larvae may emerge from a single host spider. The only exception to this endoparasitic habit is the Chilean genus *Carvalhoa* (*Sphaerops*), which is reported to feed as an ectoparasitoid on its host spider for up to three weeks (Schlinger 1987).

THE SPIDER HOST RELATIONSHIPS OF ACROCERIDAE

Members of the family Acroceridae are unique in being the sole group of insect parasitoids to attack only spiders (Araneae). Records of spider flies parasitizing Acari are extremely rare, but two cases are known for both extant (Sferra 1986) and extinct taxa (Kerr and Winterton 2008). However, spider flies have never been reared from living mites to confirm or identify the fly species in question. The most recent review of the biology and host relationships of the world acrocerids was given by Gillung and Borkent (2017), in which 65 species of spider flies were recorded attacking 26 families of spiders.

Members of Acrocerinae, Ogcodinae, Cyrtinae, and Philopotinae attack araneomorph hosts, while species of Panopinae are associated with mygalomorph spiders (except for *Psilodera* and *Pterodontia*, which are recorded from araneomorph spiders) (Gillung and Borkent 2017; Gillung and Winterton 2019). Only the genera *Acrocera* and *Carvalhoa* (Acrocerinae) have been reared from Haplogynae spiders, while members of Philopotinae and Cyrtinae have only been recorded to attack Entelegynae. The cosmopolitan genera *Acrocera*, *Ogcodes*, and *Pterodontia* have been reared from numerous hosts in multiple spider families, but most geographically restricted and species-poor genera of spider flies tend to be more host-specific, generally attacking only a single spider family (Gillung and Borkent 2017). Strict host specificity between acrocerid and spider species is rare, and host preference generally follows spider guilds as opposed to spider lineages (Schlinger 1987; Cady et al. 1993).

Host records of Malagasy spider flies are available for only three species (see Wood and Griswold, pp. 878–93, for details on Madagascar spiders). These records were obtained from three different rearings, two of which are from Ranomafana National Park. An undescribed species of *Thyllis* (*Thyllis* sp. nov. 1) was reared from an immature phyxelidid spider, *Ambohima sublima*, by C. Griswold and D. Ubick. An undescribed species of *Ogcodes* (*Ogcodes* sp. nov. 3) was reared by Griswold and Ubick at Ranomafana from either an immature clubionid or miturgid spider. Finally, another undescribed species (*Ogcodes* sp. nov. 5) was reared by L. Boutin and E. I. Schlinger from an immature species of *Cheiracanthium* (Cheiracanthiidae) from Montagne d'Ambre.

TAXONOMY AND BIOGEOGRAPHY OF THE MALAGASY ACROCERIDAE

Spider flies are relatively rare insects seldomly collected in the field. Over the course of five decades, E. I. Schlinger accumulated a total of 33 specimens collected on Madagascar, representing 22 species (13 of which are still awaiting description) distributed in four described and two undescribed genera.

There is no identification key to the species and genera of spider flies of Madagascar, but a key to the Afrotropical genera of Acroceridae is presented in Winterton and Barraclough (2017). The Malagasy spider-fly fauna is represented by two subfamilies: Philopotinae and Ogcodinae. Philopotinae is the dominant acrocerid clade on Madagascar, representing five of the six genera and 17 of the 22 species. Ogcodinae consists of the genus *Ogcodes*, represented on Madagascar by five undescribed species (Table 9.46). In addition to the Malagasy species, in the western Indian Ocean region, this subfamily is known from one additional specimen collected on Mauritius, *O. guttatus* (Barraclough 1991a). The species is expected to also occur on Madagascar, as well as on other islands scattered throughout the western Indian Ocean. All Malagasy spider-fly species are endemic, with the possible exception of *Thyllis obesa*, which is also known from South Africa. In addition, four of the six genera that occur on Madagascar are endemic and/or native (Table 9.46). The two nonendemic Malagasy genera are *Thyllis* (South Africa) and *Ogcodes* (cosmopolitan) (Table 9.47).

The three described genera of spider flies in the subfamily Philopotinae (*Dimacrocolus*, *Parahelle*, and *Thyllis*) are closely related based on both morphological and molecular data (Winterton et al. 2007; Gillung and Winterton 2019). *Dimacrocolus* is a monotypic genus endemic to Madagascar and known from relatively few specimens. *Dimacrocolus pauliani* is a very distinct spider fly, with greatly elongate legs and specialized tufts of pile at the base of the wings in the male (Schlinger 2003: Figure 8.36). *Parahelle* is a genus endemic to Madagascar (Figure 9.58); at least one undescribed species has been identified by E. I. Schlinger (unpublished data). *Thyllis* contains 12 species distributed in the southern continental Afrotropics and Madagascar. Five undescribed species of *Thyllis* from Madagascar have also been identified by E. I. Schlinger (unpublished data). The Malagasy species *T. advolitans* (Figure 9.59) has one of the most extremely arched bodies of all acrocerids, with the head very close to the tip of the abdomen. *Thyllis splendens* (Schlinger 2003: Figure 8.35) is a relatively large, remarkable species endemic to Madagascar with metallic green-violet body coloration and lateral, spinelike processes on the abdomen. Two new philopotine genera have been identified by E. I. Schlinger (new genus 1 and 2, Table 9.47). However, these genera have not yet been published or included in an identification key, and their association to other spider flies is unclear.

TABLE 9.47. **Checklist of known and presumed Acroceridae genera occurring on Madagascar and their geographical distribution**

SCIENTIFIC NAMES	MADAGASCAR	AFROTROPICAL REGION	ORIENTAL REGION	AUSTRALIAN REGION	NEOTROPICAL REGION	PALEARCTIC REGION	NEARCTIC REGION
Acrocerinae	X	X	X	X	X	X	X
**Acrocera* Meigen	Unkn	X	X	Unkn	X	X	X
Cyrtinae	X	X	X	Unkn	X	X	X
**Meruia* Sabrosky	Unkn	X	Unkn	Unkn	Unkn	Unkn	Unkn
**Sabroskya* Schlinger	Unkn	X	Unkn	Unkn	Unkn	Unkn	Unkn
Ogcodinae	X	X	X	X	X	X	X
Ogcodes Latreille	X	X	X	X	X	X	X
Panopinae	Unkn	X	X	X	X	X	X
**Astomella* Latreille	Unkn	X	X	Unkn	Unkn	X	Unkn
**Corononcodes* Speiser	Unkn	X	Unkn	Unkn	Unkn	X	Unkn
**Psilodera* Gray	Unkn	X	Unkn	Unkn	Unkn	Unkn	Unkn
**Pterodontia* Gray	Unkn	X	X	X	X	X	X
**Stenopialea* Speiser	Unkn	X	Unkn	Unkn	Unkn	Unkn	Unkn
Philopotinae	X	X	X	X	X	X	Unkn
**Africaterphis* Schlinger	Unkn	X	Unkn	Unkn	Unkn	Unkn	Unkn
Dimacrocolus Schlinger	X	Unkn	Unkn	Unkn	Unkn	Unkn	Unkn
Parahelle Schlinger	X	Unkn	Unkn	Unkn	Unkn	Unkn	Unkn
Thyllis Erichson	X	X	Unkn	Unkn	Unkn	Unkn	Unkn
New genus 1	X	Unkn	Unkn	Unkn	Unkn	Unkn	Unkn
New genus 2	X	Unkn	Unkn	Unkn	Unkn	Unkn	Unkn
Total known genera	6	11	4	2	3	5	3

Notes: Genera marked with an asterisk (*) have the potential to occur in Madagascar along with probable spider host availability. See Schlinger (1961, 1971, 1972) for further details on these aspects. X indicates presence; X indicates inferred presence; Unkn indicates unknown to occur; and Unkn indicates unknown but possibly could occur.

Ogcodes is the sole extant member of the subfamily Ogcodinae and the fourth described genus recorded for Madagascar. Species in the genus are typically small to medium-size black and white-yellow flies with small spherical heads and a globose abdomen. The genus is the most species-rich lineage of spider flies, containing 114 species, and is virtually cosmopolitan, occurring in all zoogeographic regions, except Antarctica. Five new species have been identified from Madagascar by E. I. Schlinger, but they have not been published nor included in an identification key.

Members of Acrocerinae, Cyrtinae, and Panopinae have not yet been recorded from Madagascar, but they are present in other areas of the Afrotropics, including the Democratic Republic of Congo, Kenya, Malawi, Mozambique, Namibia, South Africa, Tanzania, and Zimbabwe. Their occurrence in southern and eastern Africa, as well as the presence of several suitable araneomorph and mygalomorph hosts on Madagascar (e.g., Dipluridae, Theraphosidae, Migidae, Lycosidae, Salticidae; see Wood and Griswold, pp. 878–93) may indicate that some of these spider-fly genera might also be found on the island. Likely candidates to be collected on Madagascar include species of *Acrocera*, *Astomella*, *Corononcodes*, *Psilodera*, *Pterodontia*, and *Stenopialea*.

Acrocera is the second-largest genus of Acroceridae, with 48 species recorded from all major zoogeographic regions except Australasia. Species in the genus exhibit a very characteristic body shape, with a large, round thorax, bulbous abdomen, and small, rounded head. The genus is likely to be found on Madagascar, as it contains eight species described from the Afrotropics, all from southern Africa (Barraclough 1984). *Astomella* is an Old World genus represented by seven species in the Afrotropics, known from Namibia, South Africa, and Tanzania (Barraclough 1984, 1991b). The genus is also likely to be present on Madagascar as its spider host, *Moggridgea crudeni* (Migidae), also occurs in the island. *Corononcodes*, in turn, is a distinctive panopine genus represented by four described species in South Africa. The genus is unique among panopine spider flies owing to its very small size, highly reduced wing venation, and greatly elevated ocellar tubercles. *Psilodera* is a genus endemic to southern Africa, with 10 described species from South Africa and Zimbabwe. The genus is likely to be found on

Madagascar, as it is relatively common and widespread in southern and eastern Africa. *Pterodontia* is a virtually cosmopolitan genus of 20 species occurring in all zoogeographic regions, except Antarctica. The genus is likely to also occur on Madagascar, since it is represented by two species in Ethiopia south to Mozambique. Finally, *Stenopialea* is a rare genus known only from four species from southern Africa (Barraclough 1985), but it may also be present on Madagascar.

ACKNOWLEDGMENTS

This contribution is dedicated to the late Dr. Evert I. Schlinger, both for his support and patronage of dipterology and for his invaluable contributions to the understanding of the taxonomy and natural history of the world Acroceridae.

Subject editors: Brian L. Fisher and Steven M. Goodman

DIPTERA, PSYCHODIDAE: PHLEBOTOMINAE, SANDFLIES

J. Depaquit, F. J. Randrianambinintsoa, and V. Robert

Phlebotomine sandflies are the vectors of *Leishmania*, protozoan parasites causing the zoonotic disease leishmaniasis. This disease, which infects humans, is distributed worldwide and affects nearly 100 countries across Europe, Africa, Asia, and North and South America (Burza et al. 2018). The Malagasy Region (the islands including Madagascar; the Comoro, Mascarene, and Seychelles archipelagoes; the Iles Eparses, and the Chagos) is free of leishmaniasis. For this reason, sandfly studies have until recently attracted little interest by the entomological community working on regional insects.

The first specimens from the Malagasy Region were recorded on Mauritius by Theodor (1931) and attributed to *Sergentomyia babu babu*. On Madagascar, the first Phlebotominae specimens were noted by Grandidier and Petit (1932). Unfortunately, these specimens were lost before they could be identified to a more precise level. Raynal and Le Gac (1937) recorded *Grassomyia squamipleuris* in and around Diégo Suarez (Antsiranana), while Le Gac demonstrated the role of mud dauber wasp nests as resting places for *G. squamipleuris* inside houses. Léger and Rodhain (1978) described the first anthropophilic sandfly on Madagascar based on one female caught by human landing capture in the Berenty Forest; the sandfly in question was *S. berentiensis*, which was later transferred to the genus *Phlebotomus* based on male morphology (Depaquit et al. 2004a). The second record of anthropophilic sandflies on Madagascar was documented when five specimens were captured by human-landing catches in the Andasibe (Périnet) moist evergreen forest at about 900 m elevation. These specimens were initially identified as *P. berentiensis*, but later, a reexamination of three of them found that they were misidentified and represented *P. fertei* (Depaquit et al. 2004a). Shortly after, at the same locality, a large number of specimens of this species were caught with US Centers for Disease Control (CDC) miniature light traps (Clerc et al. 1983). The most important contribution to knowledge on phlebotomine sandflies on Madagascar was led after 2000, resulting in the naming of 18 new species and six new subgenera (see below).

In the Seychelles, Cogan et al. (1971) recorded *Sergentomyia clydei* on Aldabra. In the Comoros, Randrianambinintsoa et al. (2012) recorded a new species and a new subspecies of *Sergentomyia*: *S. pessoni* and *S. goodmani comorensis*. They also recorded specimens of the genus *Grassomyia*.

The aim of this contribution is to consider the Malagasy Region and to summarize for the first time the systematics of sandflies, their distribution, biology, and role as a vector in disease transmission. Moreover, we provide some hypotheses on their biogeography and settlement.

RECORDS OF PHLEBOTOMINE SANDFLIES

Data regarding preimaginal stages (eggs, larvae, and pupae) are scarce in the literature; when available, they ordinarily originate from lab-reared colonies. On Madagascar, as well as other islands in the Malagasy Region, such data are lacking, and our complete knowledge of these insects comes from adult stages. Most sandflies have been collected with attractive traps, such as CDC miniature light traps. A minority of specimens come from UV light traps, sticky traps, and Malaise traps; the latter two are nonattractive interception traps. Recently, some sandflies have been collected using animal or human baits (Randrianambinintsoa et al. 2020a).

On Madagascar, the collections have mainly been performed by V. Robert and then by F. J. Randrianambinintsoa at sites scattered across the island. Special attention was paid to the three heavily eroded limestone massifs (Bemaraha, Namoroka, and Ankarana) of relatively recent origin and with classical *tsingy* formations, which harbor remarkable sandfly faunas, particularly rich in number of individuals as well as species diversity (Blavier et al. 2019). Other teams have also contributed to the collection of sandflies, especially the California Academy of Sciences, which graciously gave us permission to remove some specimens from material obtained from Malaise traps. Very recently, the Entomology Unit at the Institut Pasteur de Madagascar performed a number of collections currently under analysis (B. Ramasindrazana and L. Tantely, unpublished data). In the Comoro archipelago, the collections were made by

Robert (Grande Comore, Mohéli, and Mayotte), then by Randrianambinintsoa (Grande Comore and Anjouan). The Seychelles were prospected by Depaquit (Mahé, Praslin, and La Digue), then by Robert (Mahé, Praslin, La Digue, Aride, Aldabra, and Assumption).

SYSTEMATICS

Phlebotomine sandflies constitute a subfamily (Phlebotominae) of the family Psychodidae, in the order Diptera. The systematics of Malagasy sandflies rely on morphological characters linked to molecular nucleic sequences. Morphological characters constitute the basis of the systematics, which remain largely typological in this group. However, as much as possible, we generated molecular sequences for most of the studied material (including the type specimens) by using the insect body, once the heads and terminal parts of the abdomens containing the genitalia were preserved between slides and slip covers.

Several molecular markers were routinely used in taxonomy to define species of sandflies (Depaquit et al. 2014). These techniques allowed the pairing of males and females of a given taxonomic unit. Subsequently, phylogenetic trees were derived with more conserved genes. We thus derived 299 sequences of Madagascar sandflies (67 *Phlebotomus*, 229 *Sergentomyia*, and three *Grassomyia*), 21 sequences from the Comoros, specifically the Union of the Comoros (19 *Sergentomyia* and three *Grassomyia*), and 18 sequences from the Seychelles (18 *S. clydei*); all of these sequences have been deposited in GenBank (Figure 9.60). The imposed field constraints for the collection and preservation of specimens have not yet allowed us to initiate proteomic studies.

GENERA, SUBGENERA, AND SPECIES

The usual abbreviations used for genera and subgenera of sandflies are two and three letters, respectively (Marcondes 2007), but herein we use one letter for the genera and one or two letters for the subgenera. The sandfly fauna in the Malagasy Region includes 26 taxa grouped in three genera: *Phlebotomus*, *Sergentomyia*, and *Grassomyia* (Table 9.48). Their distribution per island is depicted in Figure 9.61.

Madagascar

Three genera are present on the island. The genus *Phlebotomus* includes six species that all belong to the subgenus *Madaphlebotomus* (Depaquit et al. 2015), endemic to Madagascar. All males exhibit ancestral characters, or symplesiomorphies (four spines on the

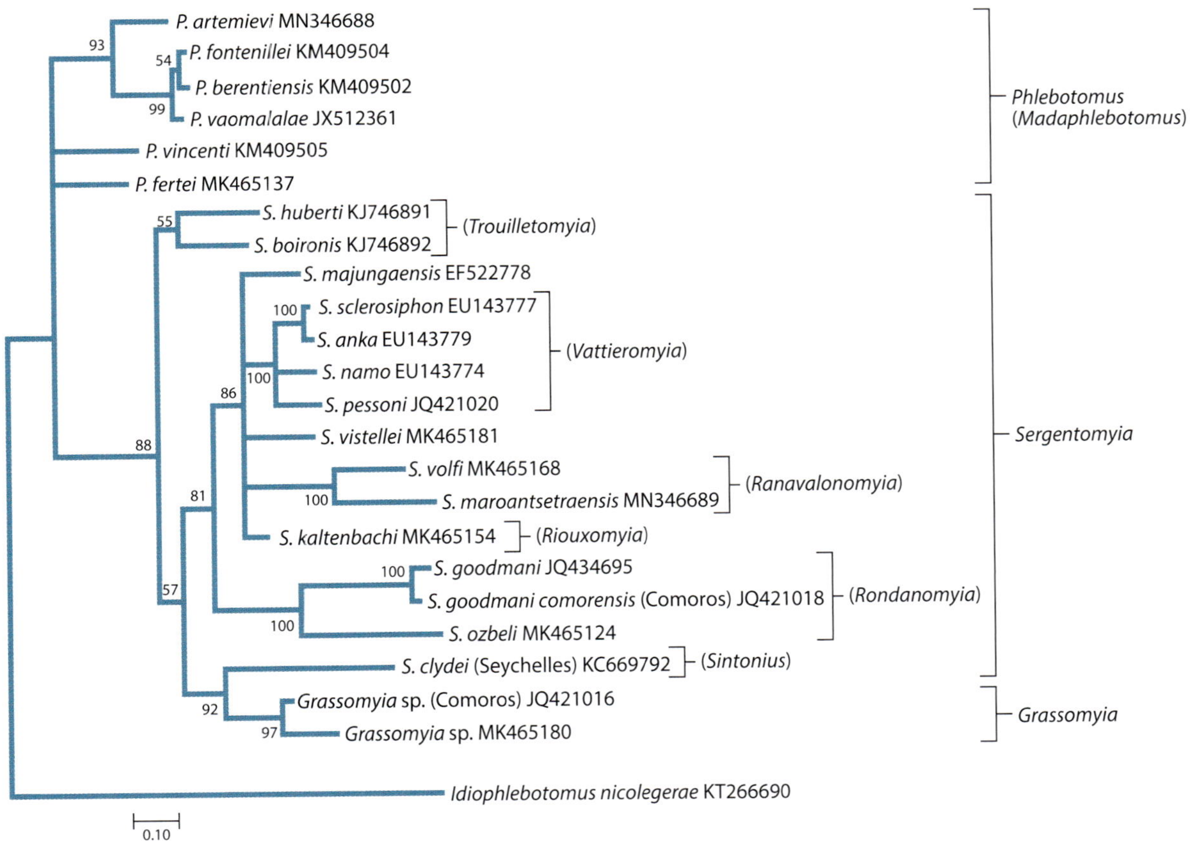

FIGURE 9.60 **Phylogenic relationships between the 23 taxa of phlebotomine sandflies recorded in the Malagasy Region. MrBayes tree (Huelsenbeck and Ronquist 2001) based on a 440 bp alignment of partial mtDNA cytochrome b sequences using the HKY85 substitution model. The percentages of probability are indicated on the nodes. The outgroup is *Idiophlebotomus nicolegerae*, a sandfly from the Oriental region. All the sandflies are from Madagascar, except those having an origin indicated in parentheses. No sequence for *Sergentomyia brunhesi* is available.**

TABLE 9.48. **Checklist of phlebotomine sandflies of the Malagasy Region**

ISLAND	SCIENTIFIC NAME	TYPE LOCALITY[1]	LOCATION IN MALAGASY REGION	BIOTOPE	MAIN REFERENCE
Madagascar	*Grassomyia madagascariensis* Abonnenc, 1969	Morombe	Toliara	Forest	Abonnenc (1969)
	G. squamipleuris Newstead, 1912	Khartoum, Sudan	Antsiranana (Diégo Suarez)	Savanna	Raynal and Le Gac (1937)
	Phlebotomus (Madaphlebotomus) artemievi Randrianambinintsoa & Depaquit, 2020	Antaravato	Maroantsetra	Forest edge	Randrianambinintsoa et al. (2020a)
	P. (M.) berentiensis (Léger & Rodhain, 1978)	Kaleta	Berenty	Forest	Léger and Rodhain (1978)
	P. (M.) fertei Depaquit, Léger & Robert, 2002	Androdroka-Bekopaka	Bemaraha	*Tsingy*	Depaquit et al. (2002)
	P. (M.) fontenillei Depaquit, Léger & Robert, 2004	Ambovonomby Forest	Namoroka	*Tsingy*	Depaquit et al. (2004b)
	P. (M.) vaomalalae Randrianambinintsoa, Léger & Depaquit, 2013	Abrahama-Jiloriaky	Mikea	Forest	Randrianambinintsoa et al. (2013)
	P. (M.) vincenti Randrianambinintsoa & Depaquit, 2013	Abrahama-Jiloriaky	Mikea	Forest	Randrianambinintsoa and Depaquit (2013)
	Sergentomyia (Ranavalonomyia) maroantsetraensis Randrianambinintsoa & Depaquit, 2020	Antaravato	Maroantsetra	Forest edge	Randrianambinintsoa et al. (2020a)
	S. (R.) volfi Depaquit, Blavier & Laroche, 2019	Ankarana	Ankarana	*Tsingy*	Blavier et al. (2019)
	S. (Riouxomyia) kaltenbachi Depaquit, Blavier & Randrianambinintsoa, 2019	Ankarana	Ankarana	*Tsingy*	Blavier et al. (2019)
	S. (Rondanomyia) goodmani Léger, Depaquit & Robert, 2005	Mandevy	Namoroka	*Tsingy*	Léger et al. (2005)
	S. (R.) ozbeli Depaquit, Blavier & Randrianambinintsoa, 2019	Ankarana	Ankarana	*Tsingy*	Blavier et al. (2019)
	S. (Trouilletomyia) boironis Randrianambinintsoa & Depaquit, 2014	Isalo	Isalo	Forest	Randrianambinintsoa et al. (2014)
	S. (T.) huberti (Depaquit, Léger & Robert, 2002)	Androdroka-Bekopaka	Bemaraha	*Tsingy*	Depaquit et al. (2002)
	S. (Vattieromyia) anka Depaquit, Léger & Robert, 2008	Andrafiabe	Ankarana	*Tsingy*	Depaquit et al. (2008)
	S. (V.) namo Depaquit, Léger & Robert, 2008	Ambovonomby Forest	Namoroka	*Tsingy*	Depaquit et al. (2008)
	S. (V.) sclerosiphon Depaquit, Léger & Robert, 2008	Ambovonomby Forest	Namoroka	*Tsingy*	Depaquit et al. (2008)

ISLAND	SCIENTIFIC NAME	TYPE LOCALITY[1]	LOCATION IN MALAGASY REGION	BIOTOPE	MAIN REFERENCE
	Ungrouped *Sergentomyia* (without subgenera): *S. brunhesi* Léger, Randrianambinintsoa & Depaquit, 2019	Ranomafana	Ranomafana	Forest	Randrianambinintsoa et al. (2020b)
	S. majungaensis Depaquit, Léger & Robert, 2007	Andiziabe	Namoroka	*Tsingy*	Depaquit et al. (2007)
	S. vistellei Depaquit, Randrianambinintsoa & Léger, 2019	Andringitra	Andringitra	Forest	Randrianambinintsoa et al. (2020b)
Comoros	*Grassomyia* sp.	Hamavouna	Mohéli (Mwali)	Wooded area	Randrianambinintsoa et al. (2012)
	Sergentomyia (*Rondanomyia*) *goodmani comorensis* Depaquit, Randrianambinintsoa & Léger, 2012	Zilimandzou	Grande Comore (Ngazidja)	Cave	Randrianambinintsoa et al. (2012)
	S. (*Vattieromyia*) *pessoni* Depaquit, Randrianambinintsoa & Léger, 2012	Ynambeni	Grande Comore (Ngazidja)	Cave	Randrianambinintsoa et al. (2012)
Mauritius	*Sergentomyia* (*Parrotomyia*) *babu babu* (Annandale, 1910)	India	Not specified	Not specified	Theodor (1931)
Seychelles	*Sergentomyia* (*Sintonius*) *clydei* (Sinton, 1928)	Pakistan	Aldabra	Coralline atoll	Cogan (1971); Depaquit et al. (2014)

[1] If no country is specified, type locality is on the associated island.

gonostyle, gonocoxite without basal lobe), shared with the subgenus *Anaphlebotomus*, which contains four species, two in continental Africa and two in Southeast Asia. By contrast, in Malagasy *Phlebotomus* (i.e., of the subgenus *Madaphlebotomus*), the unique architecture of an asymmetric spermatheca with a particular morphology (Figure 9.62) constitutes a derived character, or synapomorphy.

The genus *Sergentomyia*, which is widespread across the Old World, appears not to be monophyletic. It is well represented on Madagascar, with 13 species, 10 divided into five subgenera, and three ungrouped species (Table 9.48). Four subgenera are endemic to the Malagasy Region:

- *Ranavalonomyia*, grouping *S. volfi* and *S. maroantsetraensis*
- *Riouxomyia*, monospecific, with *S. kaltenbachi*
- *Vattieromyia*, grouping *S. anka*, *S. namo*, and *S. sclerosiphon*
- *Trouilletomyia*, grouping *S. huberti* and *S. boironis*

The fifth subgenus, *Rondanomyia*, which groups *S. goodmani* and *S. ozbeli*, is also recorded in Asia.

The other taxa have not been assigned in any subgenus and fall in the category of ungrouped *Sergentomyia*. When *S. majungaensis* was described, the authors (Depaquit et al. 2007) preferred to wait for a comprehensive revision of the *Sergentomyia* genus rather than create a subgenus for this single species. Today, it appears retrospectively that several unique characters of the female (smooth and narrow spermatheca, absence of ascoid on the first flagellomere, and antennal formula) strongly support the creation of a new subgenus, as was done for other subgenera endemic to Madagascar (Figure 9.62). The positioning of *S. brunhesi* and *S. vistellei* in the ungrouped *Sergentomyia* is justified by the rarity of examined individuals; indeed, these two species were both described from a single female, and the male remains unknown. The cibarium, which is the intermediate part between the mouthparts and the pharynx, of Malagasy *Phlebotomus* and *Sergentomyia* is useful as a species-specific character.

At least two species of the genus *Grassomyia* occur on Madagascar—*G. squamipleuris* and *G. madagascariensis*. The presence of this genus on the island is not surprising given its large distribution in the Old World from western Africa to Southeast Asia (Timor). However, the record of *G. squamipleuris* on Madagascar is, in our opinion, questionable. Collected many years ago near Antsiranana and reported by Raynal and Le Gac (1937), the specimens, to our knowledge, were not deposited in a museum collection, and it is not possible to verify the identification. Further, under the assumptions that the "*Grassomyia* sp." indicated on Figure 9.61d represents several different species and that these are endemic to Madagascar, another factor that brings the identification of the Malagasy material of *G. squamipleuris* into question is that this species would be the sole sandfly that is nonendemic to the Malagasy Region.

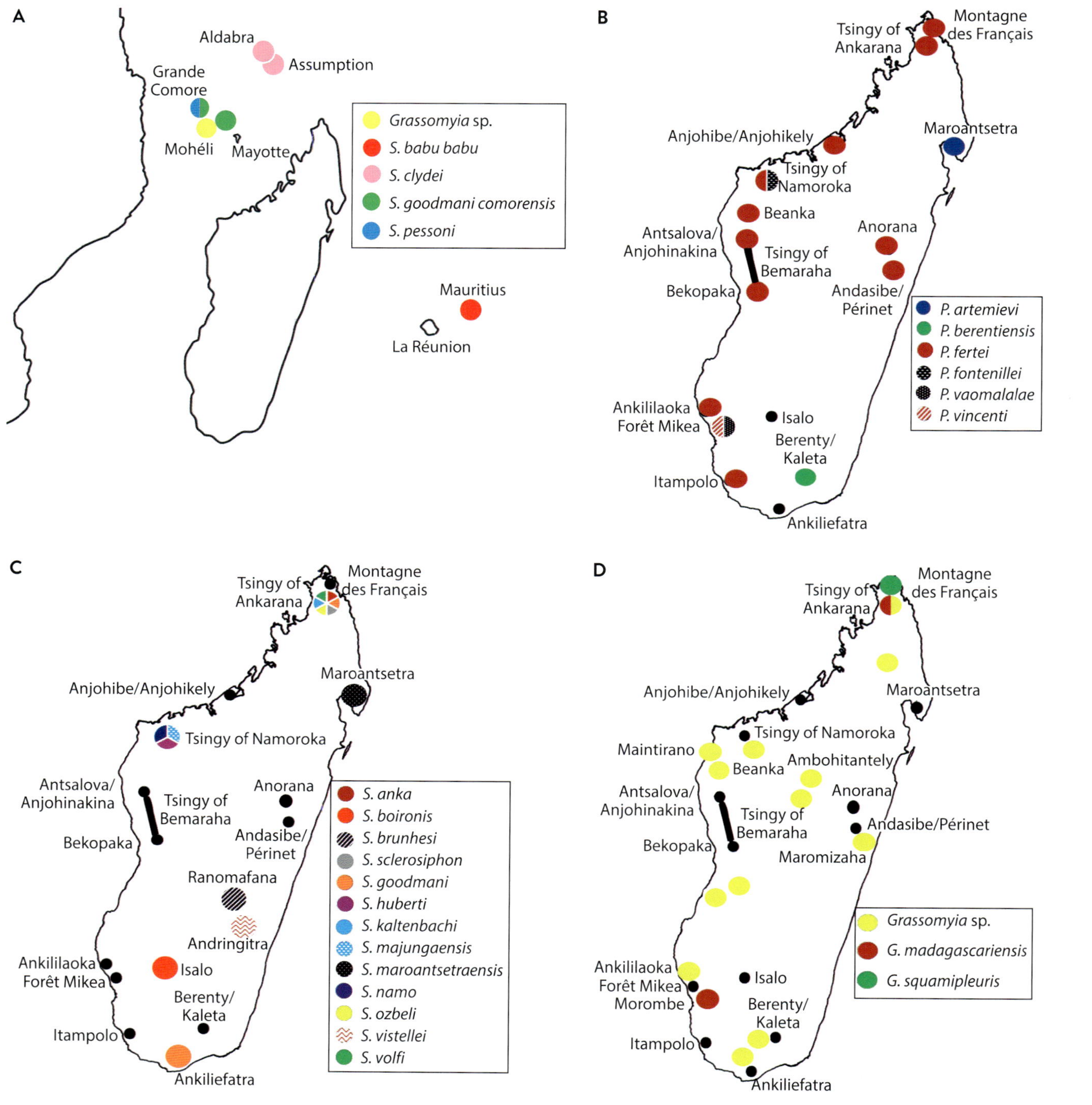

FIGURE 9.61 Distribution of phlebotomine sandflies in the Malagasy Region. A) Sandflies on the islands surrounding Madagascar; B) the genus *Phlebotomus* on Madagascar; C) the genus *Sergentomyia* on Madagascar; and D) the genus *Grassomyia* on Madagascar. (Drawings by J. Depaquit.)

Published information (Dhondt 2009; Randrianambinintsoa et al. 2012) and the authors' unpublished data indicate the existence of at least three populations in total, defined by the molecular biology of *Grassomyia* on Madagascar and on Mohéli. Taking into account the difficulty in systematics for this group—species exhibit notably homogeneous morphological characters that are often difficult to observe and sometimes with a large degree of uncertainty, such as overlapping number of cibarial teeth—we have cautiously postponed any description of Malagasy specimens falling in this genus. We think it is wiser to wait for a comprehensive revision of the genus across its Old World distribution and an integrative taxonomic approach combining molecular biology, ethology, and biogeography.

The Comoros

Three taxa have been recorded in the Comoro archipelago. *Sergentomyia pessoni* and *S. goodmani comorensis* are endemic to these islands, and their origin is clearly Madagascar, with dispersal occurring

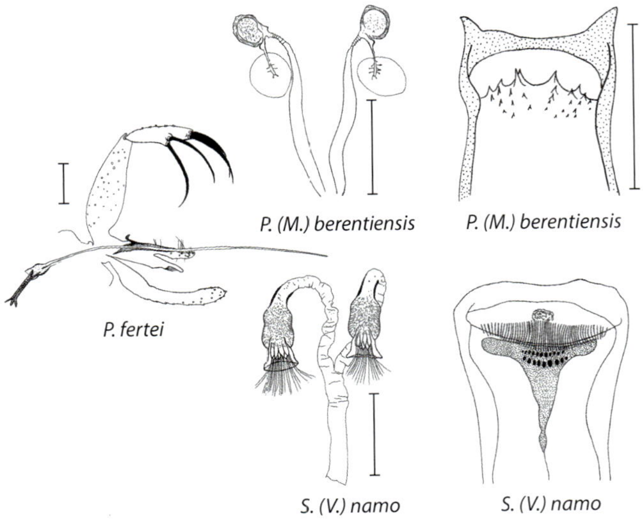

FIGURE 9.62 **Sexual-organ characters of three Madagascar endemic phlebotomine sandfly species. Genitalia of male *Phlebotomus (Madaphlebotomus) fertei* (scale bar, 100 μm). Spermathecae and cibarium of female *P. (M.) berentiensis* and *Sergentomyia (Vattieromyia) namo* (scale bars, 50 μm). (Drawings by J. Depaquit.)**

in recent geological time. The subspecies *comorensis* is closely related to *S. goodmani*, whereas *S. pessoni* shows a certain level of differentiation from the three Malagasy species belonging to the same subgenus, *Vattieromyia* (Figure 9.60). The recorded *Grassomyia* species has not been identified to species for the same reasons as mentioned above for the Madagascar members of the genus.

The Seychelles

We prospected some granitic islands in 1999 and 2008 (Mahé, Praslin, and La Digue), using CDC miniature light traps, but did not capture phlebotomine sandflies. However, we did obtain *Sergentomyia clydei* on the coral atoll of Aldabra, where it had been recorded previously (Cogan et al. 1971), as well as in the neighboring coral atoll of Assumption, which belongs to the Aldabra group. This species has a very wide distribution (from Senegal to Afghanistan), and we suggested that the arrival of this sandfly on these low-lying islands is of recent origin, despite noticeable molecular divergences (Depaquit et al. 2014).

Mauritius

One taxon has been recorded and identified as *Sergentomyia babu babu*, a species distributed in India and Pakistan (Lewis 1978; Ilango 2004). Taking into account that it is a very common species in India and there are many inhabitants of Indian origin on Mauritius, we hypothesize that its arrival to the island may be an indirect consequence of human activities in the recent past. Although sandflies are not at all prone to anthropogenic introduction, the occurrence of this species may be best explained in this manner. Further, to our knowledge, the species is known from only one older collection (Theodor 1931).

La Réunion

Important sampling efforts were performed on La Réunion to collect biting midges and sandflies (Desvars et al. 2015), and no sandflies were collected.

BIODIVERSITY AND GEOGRAPHIC DISTRIBUTION

The sandfly fauna of Mauritius and the Seychelles contains no endemic species; those present were probably introduced from elsewhere in the world. The *Sergentomyia* species of the Comoros are endemic and of Malagasy affinities. The Madagascar sandfly fauna exhibits remarkable levels of endemism: of the 21 recorded and identified to species, 20 are endemic to Madagascar, representing an endemism rate of 95%. When one excludes *Grassomyia squamipleuris*, whose presence is questionable (see above), and irrespective of the *comorensis* subspecies of *S. goodmani* on Grande Comore, all the Malagasy species are endemic. Among these species, 14 belong to subgenera that are themselves endemic: *Madaphlebotomus*, *Ranavalonomyia*, *Riouxomyia*, *Trouilletomyia*, and *Vattieromyia*. Of the remaining Malagasy species, two belong to the *Grassomyia* genus, which is widely distributed in the entire Old World, and two belong to the *Rondanomyia* subgenus, of Asian affinity. Finally, *S. majungaensis*, *S. brunhesi*, and *S. vistellei* are ungrouped endemic species.

Probably the most extensive sandfly inventories conducted to date on Madagascar have been in the limestone *tsingy* areas of Ankarana, Bemaraha, and Namoroka and with extensive trapping in caves occupied by bat colonies. Eight named species were recorded in the Ankarana, three species in the Bemaraha, and five in the Namoroka (Figure 9.61).

Grassomyia shows a large distribution across Madagascar, especially in open environments, in forests, or closer to human habitats. In contrast, *Phlebotomus berentiensis*, *P. vincenti*, and *P. vaomalalae* were collected only in forested areas. *Phlebotomus fertei* has a remarkably high abundance in the eroded limestone *tsingy* habitats, where it is in part cavernicolous, sharing areas around bat day-roost sites, as well as found in more open areas. It is also exceptional among Malagasy sandflies for its broad geographic distribution, known from the north (Montagne des Français) to the south (Itampolo), from east to west, and up to 1300 m of elevation (Anorana Forest; Figure 9.61). This wide range raises the question of possible multiple species, and this question needs to be addressed with morphological and molecular approaches.

Most Malagasy species are distributed in lowlands, but in addition to *P. fertei* at 1300 m, mentioned above, two *Sergentomyia* species, *S. brunhesi* and *S. vistellei*, are known at elevations of 1380 and 820 m, respectively (Randrianambinintsoa et al. 2020b). One *Grassomyia* species was recorded at 1300 m (Filalaovana village, 65 km northwest of Antananarivo), and another was recorded by Beza Ramasindrazana at 1550 m in the Ambohitantely Forest (Robert et al. 2014). The latter constitutes the Madagascar record in elevation for a phlebotomine sandfly. At elevations greater than 800 m, sandfly capture rates per trap are low.

The spermatheca architecture of Malagasy sandflies within the subgenus *Madaphlebotomus* is remarkable and unique within

Phlebotomus; it is probably an ancestral character state (plesiomorphic) associated with early colonization of Madagascar by this group. Further, the existence of a single type of spermatheca in *Madaphlebotomus* suggests probable monophyly or, in other words, a common ancestor from which all species of this subgenus have issued, which is strongly supported by molecular data (Depaquit et al. 2015; Figure 9.60). Several other subgenera recorded in eastern Africa (*Anaphlebotomus*, *Larroussius*, *Phlebotomus*, *Paraphlebotomus*, and *Synphlebotomus*) are not known from Madagascar.

In the absence of a family-wide phylogeny, specifically for *Sergentomyia*, it is not possible to speculate on the geographic origin for this genus. The *Rondanomyia* subgenus (*sensu* redefined by Léger et al. 2005) is the only one that presents a common distribution with Asia that would illustrate colonization of Madagascar through the Asian route, as described by Rage (1996), although this needs to be tested.

In the Malagasy sandfly fauna, the absence of the two genera *Idiophlebotomus* (restricted to southeast Asia) and *Spelaeophlebotomus* (restricted to sub-Saharan Africa) are noteworthy. Their absence is puzzling, and we hypothesize that with further field surveys, especially in geologically older caves, there is the possibility they might be found on the island.

BIOLOGY, NUISANCE, AND VECTORIAL ROLE

Few data are available on the blood-meal preferences of Malagasy sandflies. After many nights of trapping sandflies, we have never recovered an engorged female in CDC miniature light traps, despite the thousands of females collected. Could this observation be linked with an important ratio of autogenous females and the absence of *Leishmania* circulation in Madagascar? This question is difficult to answer, and new sampling methods are needed to understand this observation.

The only data related to blood-meal origin are the captures made on hosts. V. Robert caught a *Vattieromyia* female biting a gecko in the Bemaraha in November 2001. According to human-landing capture, two species are anthropophilic on Madagascar: *Phlebotomus fertei*, formerly identified as *Sergentomyia berentiensis*, from Andasibe (Clerc et al. 1983) and Berenty (Léger and Rodhain 1978), and *P. artemievi*, caught at the edge of the forest close to Maroantsetra (Randrianambinintsoa et al. 2020a).

Concerning the vectorial role of phlebotomine sandflies, a phlebovirus named Périnet Virus (Rhabdoviridae) was isolated from a batch of *P. fertei* (Clerc et al. 1983). *Leishmania* has not yet been detected on Madagascar. No case of human or animal (domestic or wild fauna) leishmaniasis has been reported from the island, except one case of imported canine leishmaniasis in 1950 (Buck et al. 1951). Consequently, no information is available regarding the potential vectorial role of phlebotomine sandflies for *Leishmania* species in Madagascar.

FUTURE RESEARCH DIRECTIONS

The knowledge of phlebotomine sandflies in the Malagasy Region has greatly increased during the past two decades. However, in our opinion, several research avenues remain open. The field inventories need to continue with special focus on forested areas and older geological formations with caves, and this work will most probably result in the discovery of new taxa. As previously underlined, the taxonomy of the genus *Grassomyia* needs revision, including specimens from the Malagasy Region, Africa, and Asia, coupling morphological and molecular approaches. The blood-feeding behavior of virtually all of Malagasy sandflies is unknown and presumed to be the usual vertebrate hosts known elsewhere in the world. For the Malagasy Region, cave-dwelling bats are presumably among potential hosts. Collecting methods using traps other than CDC light traps and targeting blood-feeding sandflies may generate new and valuable information. Finally, much remains to be done for detecting a possible vectorial role of sandflies in the transmission of arbovirus, proteobacteria such as *Bartonella*, and Trypanosomatida such as *Leishmania* or "*Leishmania*-like" in reptiles and bats. Finally, the evaluation of the ability of anthropophilic sandfly species to bite dogs and experiments on their ability to transmit *L. infantum* would be important to understand the possibility of the introduction of this pathogen in Madagascar.

Subject editors: Brian L. Fisher and Steven M. Goodman

DIPTERA: CORETHRELLIDAE, FROG-BITING MIDGES

A. Borkent and V. Robert

The family Corethrellidae, with its single genus *Corethrella*, is one of the more fascinating groups of flies. The adult females (Figure 9.63a) have biting mouthparts, and members of this family belong to the infraorder Culicomorpha, which otherwise includes biting flies such as mosquitoes, biting midges, and blackflies. The family is the sister group of Chaoboridae (phantom midges) + Culicidae (mosquitoes).

Unlike other biting nematocerous members of Diptera, which are initially attracted to their hosts by detecting CO_2 and by specific odors emitted by their vertebrate hosts, female *Corethrella* are attracted by the sound of calling anurans (male frogs and toads) and subsequently feed on them (Figures 9.63b and c). Due to the low number of specimens in collections, the group was once considered

FIGURE 9.63 **Adult female frog-biting midges of Corethrellidae: A) habitus of *Corethrella dicosimoae* female; B) *Corethrella* sp. females feeding on *Hyla rosenbergi*; and C) *C. mitra* females feeding on *Limnonectes leporinus* (note reddish abdomens of engorged females).** (Figure A ILLUSTRATED by J. A. Herrera and A. Brenes, PHOTO B by G. Kunz, and C modified from Borkent and Grafe 2012.)

a rare family until McKeever (1977) perceptively discovered the attraction to frogs and was able to collect hundreds in a single night by playing a taped call of a *Hyla* species in Georgia, United States (McKeever and Hartberg 1980). Female adults feed only at night and are able to hear and locate their hosts from substantial distances. Using this technique, A. Borkent was able to collect numerous new species in Costa Rica and then added the relatively small number of specimens of other species from elsewhere to produce a monograph of the entire family (Borkent 2008).

SYSTEMATICS

The genus consists of 113 extant species and 10 fossil species, and has a worldwide, more or less pantropical distribution between 50°N and 50°S, but with most species restricted to between 30°N and 30°S and below 1500 m in elevation. It is almost certain that many undescribed species await discovery. The oldest fossils are from 127-million-year-old Lebanese amber (Szadziewski 1995; Borkent 2008), showing, along with their phylogenetic position relative to other Culicomorpha (Borkent 2012), that the group is ancient.

A phylogenetic analysis of the genus, including its relationships to other Culicomorpha and those between the extant and fossil species of *Corethrella* on a worldwide basis, was provided by Borkent (2008, 2012), Borkent and Grafe (2012), and Baranov et al. (2016), showing that the earliest extant lineage lives in New Zealand, the same area with the earliest lineage of frogs. Further early lineages of *Corethrella* are restricted to the Old World (Borkent 2008).

Borkent (2017) summarized our knowledge of Afrotropical species, and Borkent (2008) provided a key to the five named Afrotropical species, none of which are known from Madagascar (with one possible exception). Robert and Borkent (2014) gave an overview of the first *Corethrella* species discovered on Madagascar, including a map of the collection sites and general habitats, reporting the presence of seven species, with at least six of these unnamed. These species remain undescribed, although their overall habitus, showing major differences, was presented. Males and females were collected with CDC light traps, and it seems likely that the use of a frog-call trap would increase this number of species, perhaps substantially. Considering the presence of more than 365 species of anurans in Madagascar, with more than 99% endemic (Glaw et al., pp. 1305–22), there are exciting opportunities to further study the interactions between the newly discovered species of *Corethrella* and their anuran hosts.

NATURAL HISTORY AND IDENTIFICATION

Adult females have never been observed feeding on frogs in Africa and Madagascar, but considering that African and Malagasy species have biting mouthparts and other modifications related to biting frogs (Figure 9.63), this lack of evidence is likely a result of insufficient research. Laboratory observations indicate that the occurrence of male swarming and mating pairs assume a venter-to-venter position (De Silva and Bernal 2013), but mating has never been observed in nature. Frog-call traps, using the playback of frog calls of less than 4 kHz, can be used to capture adult females at night (Grafe et al. 2019). In the New World tropics and Borneo, for example, the call of *Hyla gratiosa*, despite being a frog from the eastern United States, attracted many female adults (Borkent 2008; Borkent and Grafe 2012). This type of trap, essentially a speaker broadcasting a frog call and placed over a fan blowing into a collecting bag (Borkent 2008; McKeever and Hartberg 1980), has never been used in the Afrotropical region. Using frog calls successfully utilized in other regions, as well as those of local frogs (Carruthers and du Preez 2011; Meuche et al. 2016; Ambrozio-Assis et al. 2018), will likely result in fresh samples.

The larvae of species of *Corethrella* are also remarkable (Figure 9.64b). The aquatic larvae are predaceous ambush predators. When an insect, crustacean, nematode, or large rotifer is moving nearby, larvae either twist their bodies to bring their heads close to the prey (sometimes assuming a U-shaped position) or may slowly and stealthily extend their body length by about one-third its normal length for more distant prey. When the head is close enough, larvae lash at the prey and use their elongate antennae (Figure 9.64c) and mouthparts to ingest it. The larvae are able to anchor themselves to a substrate using robust spines on their respiratory siphon (Figure 9.64b), although the exact mechanism for doing so is not understood. This mechanism probably allows the larvae of some species to live in hyporheic habitats (within sediment beneath and alongside streams), even though most are found in lentic habitats, both in small ground pools and in various phytotelmata, which

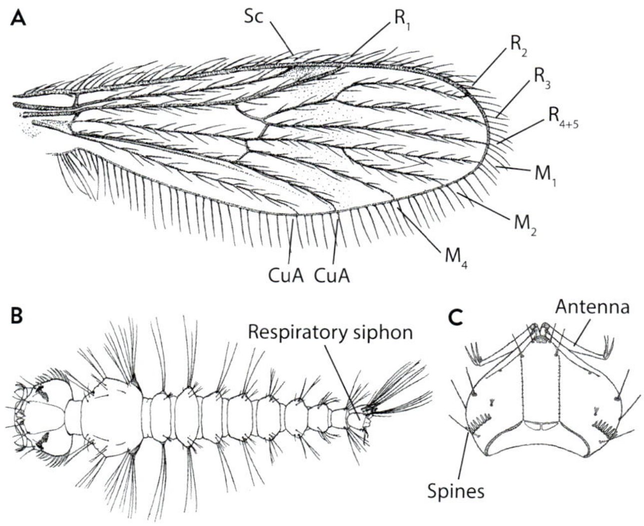

FIGURE 9.64 **Wing and larvae of Corethrellidae: A) wing of *Corethrella* sp.; B) larva of *C. calathicola*, dorsal view; and C) larva of *C. towadensis*, head, dorsal view.** (SOURCES: A modified from Cook 1981, B modified from Edwards 1930, and C modified from Okada and Hara 1962.)

include tree holes and *Nepenthes* (at least in southeast Asia) and other epiphytes.

Identifying specimens of *Corethrella* to genus is relatively straightforward. Larvae are unknown from the Afrotropical region, but species from elsewhere are mosquito-like in overall habitus, having a wide thorax and a respiratory siphon (Figure 9.64b), but are distinctive, with their long antennae originating medially and folded laterally against the head capsule when at rest (Figure 9.64c). In addition, the head capsule is unique in having a lateral row of strong spines. Considering the many studies of larvae of Afrotropical Culicidae, with none of these reporting the presence of *Corethrella*, it seems likely that *Corethrella* larvae in the Afrotropical region occur in unusual aquatic habitats, and hyporheic situations are a reasonable possibility.

Pupae are also unknown from the Afrotropical region and have the following combination of unique features: a well-developed, open-ended respiratory organ; the third leg curled beneath the wing sheath; the length of the cephalothorax (measured from the anterior margin to the apex of the wing sheath) about equal to the length of the remaining abdomen (posterior to the apex of the wing sheath); the apex of abdomen not curled under the thorax; and two pointed terminal processes, each with two subapical elongate setae (Figures 9.65c and d).

Adults have a mosquito-like wing venation (Figure 9.64a), with vein R four-branched, vein M three-branched, vein Cu two-branched, and veins R_{4+5} and M_1 virtually parallel to each other. However, unlike mosquitoes or phantom midges (family Chaoboridae), vein R_1 is either closer to vein Sc or lies nearly midway between veins Sc and R_2. Adults are also unique among nematocerous members of Diptera in having legs with the mid-femur thicker than both fore and hind femora (Figures 9.63a, 9.65a and b).

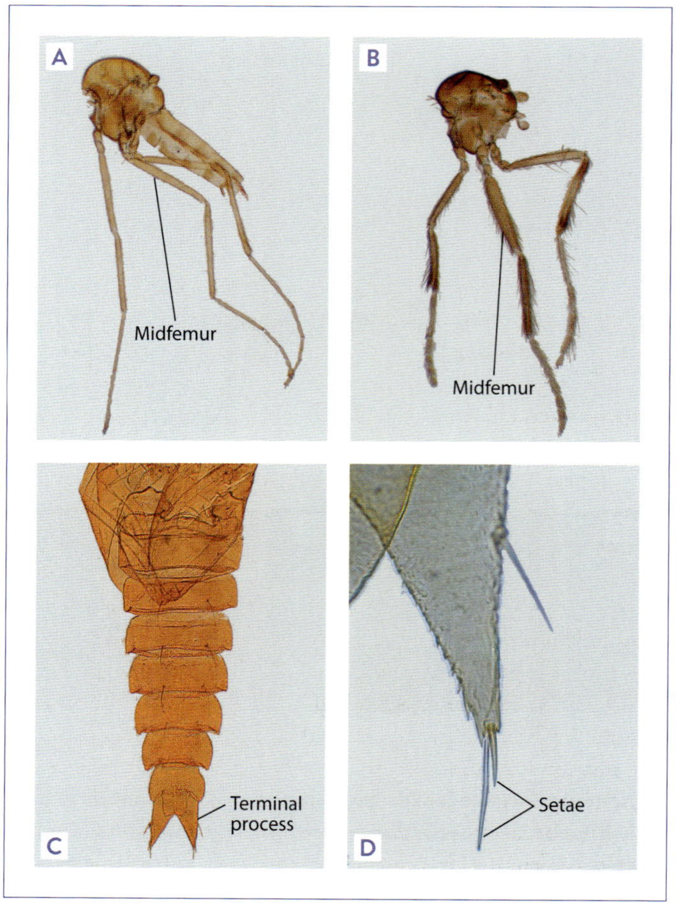

FIGURE 9.65 **Adult and pupal structures of Corethrellidae: A) thorax of *Corethrella harrisoni*, lateral view; B) thorax of *C. picticollis*, lateral view; C) pupal exuviae of *C. appendiculata*, dorsal view; D) apical portion of terminal process of pupal exuviae of *C. appendiculata*, dorsal view.** (SOURCE: images modified from Borkent 2008.)

VECTORS OF DISEASE AND FUTURE DIRECTIONS

Adult females of at least some *Corethrella* species are vectors of *Trypanosoma* between their male frog hosts (Johnson et al. 1993; Bernal and Pinto 2016). Based on phylogenetic patterns, the fossil record, and distribution patterns, it is likely that the association between *Corethrella*, frogs, and *Trypanosoma* is an ancient one, originating in the Jurassic period (Borkent 2008). Because Afrotropical species represent earlier lineages within the genus, and considering that nothing is known regarding their biology, it would be fascinating to study these interactions in this region. It is quite possible that the biting females of species of *Corethrella* have influenced the evolution of anurans' mating calls.

ACKNOWLEDGMENTS

Annette Borkent, Art Borkent's wife, is gratefully acknowledged for supporting this and many other taxonomic endeavors.

Subject editors: Brian L. Fisher and Steven M. Goodman

TRICHOPTERA, CADDISFLIES

F.-M. Gibon

Trichoptera, or caddisflies, is a small order of highly evolved insects. Related to Lepidoptera, caddisflies are holometabolous, undergo four life stages (egg, larva, pupa, adult), and with very few exceptions, the larval phase is aquatic. The adults, whose activity is essentially crepuscular, are often small, and with gray or beige coloration, they appear more elegant than remarkable. These flies are little known to the public outside the fly-fishing community. However, being common and abundant, they often constitute the major part of freshwater benthic animal biomass and are an essential element of these communities. The order is remarkable for its diversity of morphological, physiological, and behavioral adaptations. Caddisflies exploit most trophic resources and are able to colonize various freshwater environments, from high mountain streams to large rivers draining broad alluvial plains. Major advances in the systematics and distribution of this order, as well as some other aquatic invertebrate groups (see Elouard et al., pp. 947–52; Cumberlidge, pp. 913–18), have been made in the past decades largely as the result of large-scale field inventories and collections made through the program Biodiversité et Biotypologie des Eaux Continentales de Madagascar, which was under the direction of Jean-Marc Elouard and involved numerous other field and lab scientists. A total of 48 genera of Trichoptera are known from Madagascar (Table 9.49).

Trichoptera is the sister group of Lepidoptera. The key factor for their adaptive success in fresh water is the silk produced at the extremity of the labium of the larvae. The silk allows the construction of protective cases, shelters, sheaths, and capture or filtration nets, playing a decisive role in the fixation, movement, feeding, respiration, and protection of larvae and nymphs. In addition, these constructions, which incorporate various materials available in the environment, can modify, consolidate, or even build aquatic substrates, facilitating the presence and development of many other taxa. Caddisflies are often designated as the "underwater architects" (Wiggins 2005).

SYSTEMATICS AND EVOLUTIONARY GROUPS BASED ON SILK PRODUCTION

Various uses of the silk correspond to five distinct evolutionary trajectories:

I. Rhyacophiloidea: free-living larvae that construct a shelter immediately before the pupal stage. This superfamily is absent from the Afrotropics.
II. Glossosomatoidea: larvae build portable structures shaped like a saddle or turtle shell. These structures sometimes include small rocky fragments. This superfamily consists of a single family, Glossosomatidae. It is present but rare (four species) in the Afrotropics, where it is confined to the Cape Province and some high mountains along the Great Rift Valley. Two species were recently described from Madagascar in small forest torrents on the Andringitra and Andohahela Massifs (Gibon 2017).
III. Hydroptiloidea: larvae build protective, cocoon-shaped structures. These structures appear only at the fifth larval stage (stages one through four are free-living), principally in the family Hydroptilidae. Because of their small size, members of this group are often designated as "microcaddisflies" and are captured less frequently than individuals in other families. On Madagascar, where their study is much less advanced than that of other families, the main genera are *Catoxyethira* (Gibon and Ranaivoharindriaka 1995), *Orthotrichia* (Oláh and Johanson 2010a), *Hydroptila* (Botosaneanu 2002), and *Dhatrichia* (Kjaerandsen 2004). This fauna is similar to that of the African continent (some small genera are absent or have not yet been reported). Four species of *Stactobiella* were recently described, creating the first record of this genus on Madagascar and the Afrotropics in general (Gibon 2019).
IV. Philopotamoidea and Hydropsychoidea: larvae build shelters or galleries attached to the substratum. In some cases, these structures include rocky or organic fragments, and some lineages are associated with capturing nets that filter food particles carried by the water current.

The Philopotamoidea superfamily includes one family, Philopotamidae, which contains three subfamilies: Philopotaminae and Chimarrinae, both worldwide in distribution, and Rossodinae, which is endemic to Madagascar. For a long time, Rossodinae, considered the most archaic subfamily, was known only by two specimens from Tsaratanàna (Ross 1956). Today, 16 species are known, constituting a perfect example of microendemism, as they are strictly localized in pristine moist evergreen forests (Gibon 2013).

With around 900 species, the genus *Chimarra* is one of the few megagenera of the order. Two subgenera are Neotropical (with some Nearctic species), but the subgenus *Chimarra* is distributed worldwide. It is supposed to be of Neotropical origin, having colonized Madagascar from the Asiatic and African continents (Ross 1956). The African and Malagasy *Chimarra* are clearly polyphyletic, and important lineages (especially those resembling the archaic ones) are not included in the Ross analysis. Blahnik (1998) put forward the hypothesis of an African-Brazilian origin of *Chimarra* subgenus *Chimarra*. This idea is more consistent with the presence of Malagasy species with archaic characters, such as *C. goedefroitae* (Gibon 2016). A genetic study of Malagasy *Chimarra* would clarify this debate. There are more than 60 species on Madagascar, mostly unpublished, and of the 25 named species, 23 are endemic and two are shared with the African continent.

A. Hydropsychoidea is well represented on Madagascar by families that are present on the African continent:

TABLE 9.49. **Checklist of 48 genera of Trichoptera present on Madagascar**

Adicella McLachlan, 1877
Aethaloptera Brauer, 1875
**Afrorheithrus* Weaver, Gibon & Chvojka, 2008
Amphipsyche McLachlan, 1872
Anisocentropus McLachlan, 1863
Athripsodes Billberg, 1820
Blyzophilus Anderson, Kjaerandsen & Morse, 1999
Catoxyethira Ulmer, 1912
Ceraclea Stephens, 1829
Cheimacheramus Barnard, 1934
Cheumatopsyche Wallengren, 1891
Chimarra Stephens, 1829
Dhatrichia Mosely, 1948
Dipseudopsis Walker, 1852
Ecnomus McLachlan, 1864
Goera Stephens, 1829
Helicopsyche von Siebold, 1856
Homilia McLachlan, 1877
Hydroptila Dalman, 1819
Lepidostoma Rambur, 1842
Leptocerina Mosely, 1932
Leptocerus Leach, 1815
Leptonema Guerin-Meneville, 1843
Lype McLachlan, 1878
Macrostemum Kolenati, 1859
**Madagocerum* Johanson & Oláh, 2011
**Magadacerina* Malm & Johanson, 2013
Nyctiophylax Brauer, 1865
Oecetis McLachlan, 1877
Orthotrichia Eaton, 1873
Paduniella Ulmer, 1913
Parasetodes McLachlan, 1880
Petrothrincus Barnard, 1934
Pisulia Marlier, 1943
Polycentropus Curtis, 1835
Polymorphanisus Walker, 1852
‡*Potamyia* Banks, 1900
Pseudoneureclipsis Ulmer, 1913
**Ranarijaodes* Gibon, 2014
Rhoizema Barnard, 1934
**Rossodes* Oezdikmen & Darilmaz, 2008
Setodes Rambur, 1842
‡*Stactobiella* Martynov, 1924
Silvatares Navas, 1931
Synagapetus McLachlan, 1879
Tinodes Curtis, 1834
Triaenodes McLachlan, 1865
Wormaldia McLachlan, 1865

Note: * endemic to Madagascar; ‡ not recorded on African continent.

Psychomyiidae, Polycentropodidae, Dipseudopsidae, Ecnomidae, and Hydropsychidae. Psychomyiidae is a family with a worldwide distribution. There are few species, often confined to particular habitats, and found in low densities. Psychomyiidae includes three subfamilies, with two present in Madagascar: Paduniellinae, represented by the genus *Paduniella* (Johanson and Oláh 2010), and Psychomyiinae, represented by the genera *Tinodes* (Johanson and Oláh 2007; Chvojka and Gibon 2017) and *Lype* (which is present in collections but not yet studied).

B. Polycentropodidae has a worldwide distribution and includes two subfamilies. Pseudoneureclipsinae is represented on Madagascar by *Pseudoneureclipsis* (~10 species; Malicky 2015). Polycentropodinae is represented on Madagascar by *Nyctiophylax* (at least 16 species, three described by Oláh and Johanson 2010b) and *Polycentropus* (only one species, not yet described).

C. Dipseudopsidae is present in the tropical regions of the Old World. On Madagascar, it is represented by *Dipseudopsis*, which comprises 19 described species (Ross and Kingsolver 1959).

D. Ecnomidae is present in all faunal regions of the globe, with the exception of the Nearctic. At least 50 species are known from Madagascar, some of them recently described (Malicky 2015). It is interesting to note that most of the Malagasy species belong to the *Psychomyiellodes* species group. Previously considered unique to Africa, the genus *Psychomyiellodes* has been synonymized with *Ecnomus* but constitutes a monophyletic lineage endemic to the Afrotropics. This species group is much richer in species on Madagascar than on the continent. In contrast, *Ecnomus* species belonging to other species groups are common on Africa and comparatively few on Madagascar; most of these animals occur in open landscapes and not moist evergreen forests (Gibon 2018).

E. Hydropsychidae constitutes one of the dominant elements of running-water benthic communities of the world. Two subfamilies are present in Madagascar: Oestropsinae, including the genera *Aethaloptera*, *Polymorphanisus*, *Amphipsyche*, *Leptonema*, and *Macrostemum*, and Hydropsychinae, which includes the genera *Hydropsyche* (see below), *Potamyia*, and *Cheumatopsyche*. There are only two notable differences with the Afrotropic fauna. The first is the absence of the endemic African genus *Protomacronema*, which is sometimes abundant and broadly distributed on the continent. The second is the presence of the genus *Potamyia*, a small Asian, Siberian, and North American genus. *Potamyia* is absent from the African mainland, but eight species are abundant and extensively distributed on Madagascar (Oláh et al. 2006). Among Trichoptera are clear examples of colonization of Madagascar from the Indian subcontinent.

   1. *Hydropsyche* is the richest genus of the family. It is present in all faunal regions, with the exception of the Neotropics, but is less abundant in warm regions than in temperate and cold zones. Three species were previously named from Madagascar, but the descriptions are hardly usable. Only a few specimens were captured during the program Biodiversité et Biotypologie des Eaux Continentales de Madagascar; they were identified as *H. mauritiana*, originally described from

Mauritius. According to Mey (2005), the African species of *Hydropsyche* are the result of a single colonization event from the Palearctic. A secondary colonization movement reached Madagascar and subsequently Mauritius and La Réunion.

2. *Cheumatopsyche* is very well represented on Madagascar with 39 described species, slightly fewer than the known African members of this genus (Oláh et al. 2008). The genus is present across the whole island and is largely responsible for this family's general abundance. *Cheumatopsyche* has colonized the complete range of elevations and rivers, on both the western and eastern sides of Madagascar. *Polymorphanisus* occurs in tropical Asia, Africa, and Madagascar. It includes few species, six of which occur in Africa and one on Madagascar.
3. *Aethaloptera* is present in Asia, Africa, and Madagascar. It includes a small number of species that are taxonomically difficult to distinguish. Scott (1983) tentatively reported *A. dispar* from Madagascar. Specimens collected during the Biodiversité et Biotypologie des Eaux Continentales de Madagascar project were identified as *A. maxima*, a species widely distributed in southern Africa. This species, however, was rarely collected on Madagascar, occurring at low elevation and on large rivers (Figure 9.66). The rarity may be due to sampling technique, as it is likely that the heavy sediment loads in the larger Malagasy rivers clog the larval capture nets of this filter-feeding animal.
4. *Leptonema* has been recorded in South America, Africa, and Madagascar. Flint et al. (1987) either described or recorded seven species from Madagascar. Chvojka and Sykora (1998) subsequently described *L. aconicum*, and new forms are currently under study. The species richness of this genus is probably higher than currently recognized. *Leptonema* species are found on small rivers in areas with some topographic complexity and where forest cover is still at least partially present (Figure 9.66).
5. *Amphipsyche* is known from tropical Asia, Africa, and Madagascar. The Malagasy species, *A. pellucida*, is a close relative of *A. senegalensis*, widely distributed on the African continent. *Amphipsyche pellucida* is known from all areas of the island, with the exception of the eastern moist evergreen forests (Figure 9.66). The genus *Macrostemum* is one of the most frequently encountered in Malagasy streams and rivers.

V. The larvae of Limnephiloidea, Sericostomatoidea, and Leptoceroidea build portable protective cases or sheaths with silk and organic or mineral fragments. These structures also have a camouflaging and protective function; they are also used as ballast. More important, these structures, in combination with abdominal movements of the larvae, improve the animal's respiratory capacity.

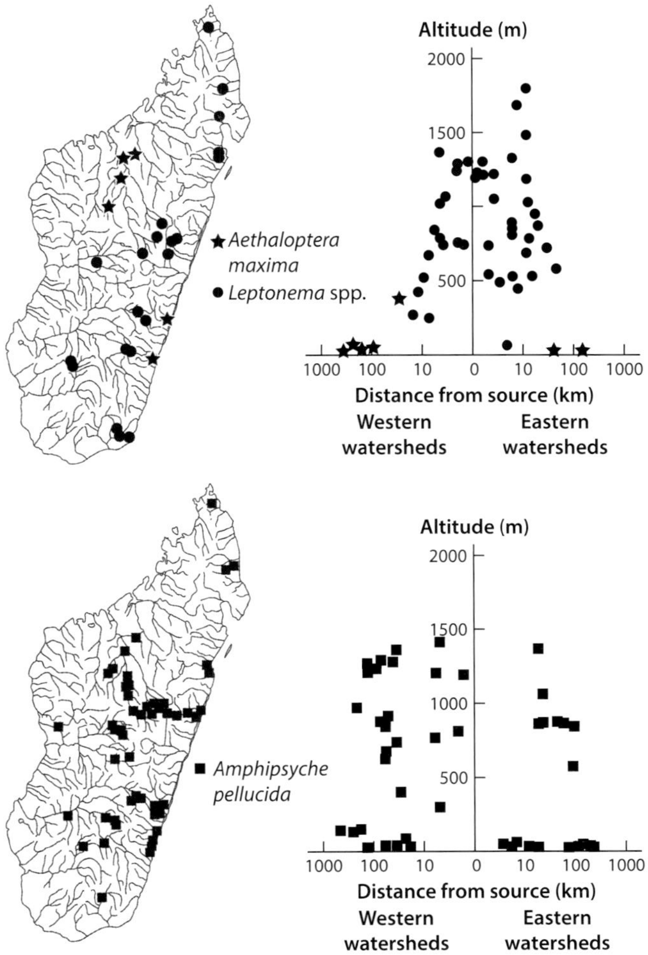

FIGURE 9.66 **Schematic distribution map and ecological profiles of *Aethaloptera maxima*, the genus *Leptonema*, and *Amphipsyche pellucida*. This analysis is discussed in detail by Randriamasimanana and Gibon (2001).**

A. On the basis of species richness, Limnephiloidea is one of the main groups of Trichoptera in the Palearctic and Nearctic zones. Ecologically, it dominates cold waters at high elevations and high latitudes. The family Limnephilidae, which is very diverse, is nearly absent from the Afrotropics, found only on a few mountaintops (Ethiopia). Three small families are present in Africa and on Madagascar: Pisuliidae (genera *Pisulia* and *Silvatares*), Lepidostomatidae (genus *Lepidostoma*), and Goeridae (genus *Goera*).
   1. Pisuliidae is a small family whose distribution is limited to the Afrotropics and Madagascar. Its members colonize small mountain rivers. The majority of species are known from eastern Africa, a few from South Africa, and one from Ghana. On Madagascar, the family is known by three species (Stoltze 1989; Johanson 2010). Around 20 additional species, all endemic, are currently under study, and once these are described, the Malagasy fauna will be richer in species than the entire African continent. Members of Malagasy Pisuliidae occur largely in moist evergreen forests.

2. Lepidostomatidae is a family with a broad distribution, though absent from the Australian and Neotropical regions. Particularly abundant in Asia, it also occurs in Africa and on Madagascar, where one genus, *Lepidostoma*, is restricted to montane areas. Eleven species are described from Madagascar (Weaver and Gibon 2007).
3. Goeridae is a family of minor importance with a worldwide distribution, absent only from Australia and the Neotropics. The family is overwhelmingly Oriental, but some species of the genus *Goera* are present in Africa, localized in the Cape Province and on some high mountains along the Great Rift Valley, and on Madagascar (Gibon et al. 1999; Johanson 2010), where they have been collected in pristine moist evergreen forests.

B. Members of Sericostomatoidea are rare and highly localized in continental Africa. Three families are present on Madagascar.
1. Petrothrincidae was established by Scott (1985) for three species described by Barnard (1934) in the genus *Petrothrincus*. Weaver (1997) described three species from the moist evergreen forests of Ranomafana. Today, 11 species are known from Madagascar, and more are under study.
2. The four Afrotropical genera belonging to Sericostomatidae were described as South African endemics (*Cheimacheramus*, *Rhoizema*, *Petroplax*, and *Aclosma*). They are geographically and phylogenetically distant from the other Holarctic and Oriental genera. Two of these were discovered on Madagascar: *Cheimacheramus* and *Rhoizema* (Johanson and Oláh 2006; Gibon 2014a).
3. Helicopsychidae is a medium-size cosmopolitan family with a largely tropical distribution; it is found mainly in the Neotropical and Oriental regions. It is rare in Africa, with 11 species described from Tanzania and the Democratic Republic of the Congo, and also present on Madagascar (Johanson 1997) and the Seychelles.

C. Leptoceroidea consists of a few small families, three of which are documented on Madagascar—Calamoceratidae, Odontoceridae, and Philorheithridae—as well as the large family Leptoceridae, one of the main caddisflies families in terms of specific richness worldwide and in the Malagasy Region.
1. Members of Calamoceratidae are present in all faunal regions. This family is essentially tropical and subtropical but poorly represented in the Afrotropics, with only one genus (*Anisocentropus*), including two species in the Democratic Republic of the Congo, two in eastern Africa, and two on Madagascar (Oláh and Johanson 2010b).
2. Philorheithridae is a small family, represented by nine genera, six from the Australian region, two from the temperate Neotropical region (southern Chile and Argentina), and one endemic to Madagascar (Weaver et al. 2008). This genus (*Afrorheithrus*) includes three species localized in pristine moist evergreen forests. Examples of Australian–South American Gondwanan distribution are not uncommon in Trichoptera. However, the extension of this distribution to Madagascar is exceptional.
3. Atriplectididae shows a similar distributional range and includes species in Australia, Bolivia, Brazil, and the Seychelles.
4. Odontoceridae is a small family that is almost cosmopolitan. The only record from the Afrotropical region is the genus *Madagocerum*, endemic to Madagascar (Oláh and Johanson 2011).
5. Leptoceridae is a large family, present in all faunal regions. It represents 13.7% of the Trichoptera world fauna, but in the Afrotropical region, this percentage rises to 30% (Morse et al. 2019). Eight tribes are recorded from the Afrotropical region, and only one (Mystacidini), whose presence in Africa is marginal (one species in Ethiopia), is absent from Madagascar.
   a) Oecetini (one genus): *Oecetis* is a large, polyphyletic genus with a worldwide distribution. In Madagascar, 23 species belong to five groups. Three groups have a worldwide distribution (*O. testacea*, *O. lais*, and *O. setodellina* species groups); and two are endemic to the island (*O. oliae* and *O. marojejyensis* species groups) (Randriamasimanana and Gibon 2000).
   b) Setodini: *Setodes* is another large, diverse, polyphyletic genus (Schmid 1987) and very rich in species. It is mainly widespread in Asia and on the African continent, but on Madagascar, it is represented only by a small and homogeneous group of five species close to *Trichosetodes* and probably of Asian origin (Randriamasimanana and Gibon 2001).
   c) Leptocerini: *Leptocerus* is a genus of Oriental and Afrotropical affinities, but it is also found in the Palearctic and is marginally present in the Nearctic. On Madagascar, seven species were described whose phylogenetic affinities are Asian (Gibon 2006).
   d) Triaenodini: *Triaenodes* has a vast distribution that excludes only the southern part of the Neotropical zone. Its presence on Madagascar has been known for a long time (four species described). *Adicella* is a small and homogeneous genus living in cold and well-oxygenated waters. On the African mainland, nine species are localized in mountainous areas. A few species were collected on Madagascar but are as yet undescribed.
   e) Nectopsychini: *Parasetodes* is very homogeneous in morphology and includes a small number of species, difficult to distinguish and generally with large geographic distributions. One species

is known on Madagascar, identified as *Parasetodes* cf. *sudanensis*, which is widely distributed across African savannas.

f) Blyzophilini: *Magadacerina* has been erected for one Malagasy species and is related to *Blyzophilus* (Malm and Johanson 2013).

g) Athripsodini: This tribe represents the main lineage of Malagasy Trichoptera with more than 130 recognized species and many still undescribed. For comparison, the South African fauna includes 42 species (de Moor 1993) and is considered to be unusually rich. Athripsodini includes two large and widely distributed genera, *Ceraclea* and *Athripsodes* (more precisely the *Athripsodes-Homilia* complex, with the two genera having been distinguished at certain periods, in particular in Africa), and five small and localized genera. These five genera and their distribution strongly indicate a Gondwanan origin centered on the Cape Province and Madagascar: *Axiocerina* (two species, Mauritius and La Réunion); *Leptecho* (three species, South Africa); *Leptoceriella* (one species, southern India); *Leptocerina* (18 species, Africa, Madagascar, Mauritius, and La Réunion); and *Neoathripsodes* (two species, Brazil). The complex *Athripsodes-Homilia*, with more than 100 species, is present in the Afrotropical, Oriental, and Palearctic regions (68% of the species are Afrotropical, half of them recorded from South Africa). Four species are described from Madagascar, but based on the existing collections, at least 90 species more are waiting description.

The genus *Ceraclea*, absent only from the Neotropical and Australasian regions, is divided into four subgenera, with *Ceraclea* subgenus *Ranaivodes* endemic to Madagascar (10 species described; Gibon and Randriamasimanana 2013). The description of a fifth subgenus endemic to Madagascar is in preparation, and molecular data indicates that it is probably the basal sister group of the remaining genera (F.-M. Gibon, unpublished data).

SPECIES RICHNESS

Trichoptera includes more than 16,000 species (Morse et al. 2019), making it the seventh-largest order of insects. Species are classified in 618 genera and 51 families. The highest species richness is recorded for the Oriental (more than 5800 species) and Neotropical (more than 3300 species) regions. With a little more than 1200 species, the Afrotropical region seems particularly poor relative to other regions, but this observation is presumably related to a much lower research effort.

As recently as 1991, only 52 described species were known from Madagascar. Bănărescu (1991) discussed this and proposed varied and sometimes contradictory explanations for this paucity—for example, cyclonic floods aggravated by the abrupt slopes in the east or drought in the west. In reality, the only reasonable factor to consider was the lack of entomological research or, more precisely, gaps in existing research.

The first Malagasy species of Trichoptera, *Macrostemum scriptum*, was described in 1842 by Rambur. Subsequently, a few species were described by different entomologists, including G. Ulmer, N. Banks, M. E. Mosely, and mainly L. Navas. During the 1940s and 1950s, important collections were made by R. Paulian and his collaborators of the IRSM (Institut de Recherche Scientifique de Madagascar). A few taxa were studied, including some philopotamids by Ross (1956) and the genus *Dipseudopsis* by Ross and Kingsolver (1959). The collection was then entrusted to J. Oláh, who published numerous articles in the 2000s, often with K. A. Johanson, who also produced a key to adults of known families and genera recorded from the island (2010).

During the 1990s, an inventory of the biodiversity of Malagasy fresh waters, Biodiversité et Biotypologie des Eaux Continentales de Madagascar, was carried out as part of a cooperation between the Institut de Recherche pour le Développement (IRD) and the Centre National pour la Recherche sur l'Environnement (CNRE). Trichoptera was studied by F.-M. Gibon and a group of Malagasy students (Désiré Randriamasimanana, Fabienne Ranaivoharindriaka, and Patricia Zoé Andriambelo). A first list of genera was published by Gibon et al. (1999), and a synthesis of this inventory resulted a few years later (Gibon 2001, 2003; Elouard and Gibon 2001). Other collections have subsequently been made—for example, at the biological station of the Ranomafana National Park.

Today, a little more than 300 species of Trichoptera are reported from Madagascar. However, our previous estimate of 700 species on the island (Gibon 2001) is still possible and compatible with the species accumulation curve of Trichoptera species described from Madagascar (Johanson 2010). This conclusion arises from the partially studied specimens containing undescribed taxa, as well as numerous areas of the island that remain not inventoried (e.g., Tsaratanàna Massif, Sambirano Region, Masoala Peninsula, and the forests surrounding the Antongil Bay and Mananara-Nord). Based on the described species only, the Malagasy fauna is exceptionally rich, with endemic species representing a quarter of the known Afrotropical fauna. To help put this into perspective, the caddisfly fauna of southern Africa (south of the Zambezi River, with a surface area twice that of Madagascar and equivalent geology and climatic diversity) is estimated at 200 species (de Moor 1993).

ENDEMISM

The rate of endemism at the species level exceeds 96%, and the balance—about 10 species—also occur on the African continent. Some of these shared species deserve comparative genetic studies to confirm their conspecific status (e.g., *Parasetodes sudanensis* and *Aethaloptera maxima*). Others are species that have a very wide geographic distribution, which is quite rare among Trichoptera (*Hydroptila cruciata*, *Catoxyethira mali*, and *Oecetis tripunctata*). The rate of generic endemism is much lower, at 9.5%, including *Afrorheithrus* (three species), *Magadacerina* (one species), *Madagocerum* (four species), *Ranarijaodes* (three species), and *Rossodes* (16 species).

GEOGRAPHIC DISTRIBUTION OF MALAGASY SPECIES

When one examines the distribution of caddisfly species on the island, one aspect is immediately apparent—the considerable faunal distinctness of the intact moist evergreen forests. Numerous families (Glossosomatidae, Goeridae, Helicopsychidae, Odontoceridae, Petrothrincidae, Philorheithridae, Pisuliidae, and Sericostomatidae), genera (*Afrorheithrus*, *Leptonema*, *Madagocerum*, *Ranarijaodes*, *Rossodes*, and *Wormaldia*), and most species known from this forest type are restricted to this habitat. Some species have small distribution areas, often reduced to a watershed, mountain range, or forest, which explains the high specific richness of the island. These taxa are mainly located toward the upper end of the lowland moist evergreen forests, but also on isolated forests of the Central Highlands, specifically the medium-altitude moist evergreen forests, or in relatively protected zones, such as Isalo. These observations show a clear latitudinal zonation of species (Gibon 2000), which in turn is best explained by the vicissitudes in recent geological time of drier and colder periods, when tropical forests were separated. Further, an important aspect is the low flight capacity of caddisflies living in moist evergreen forests. It is possible that there was concomitantly an elevation stratification of the species (as for the genus *Wormaldia* on Marojejy; Gibon 2014b).

In contrast, another group of taxa inhabit large and small rivers in open landscape areas (*Parasetodes*, *Setodes*, *Potamyia*, *Ecnomus* not belonging to the *Psychomyiellodes* group, *Aethaloptera*, and *Amphipsyche*). We assume that rivers subject to intermittent or seasonal drought are mainly recolonized from the lower courses that generally retain water. This phenomenon explains the absence or near lack of a species replacement following a longitudinal cline of this portion of the fauna along these watercourses. This second group constitutes the base of the fauna on the western lowlands, and many of these species, such as *Amphipsyche pellucida*, are also present on the eastern slope, downstream from forest areas (Figure 9.66). However, some species are confined to the western slope—for example, *Homilia andratina* (Figure 9.67) and *Chimarra goedefroitae* (Figure 9.68).

Besides these two large groups with different geographic distributions, there are others with different ecological profiles, which include those that occur in the open environments on the eastern coastal plain (for example, *Homilia* undetermined species "tsiraka"; Figure 9.67), species confined to high elevations (for example, *Chimarra* undetermined species "I"; Figure 9.68), or even on the deforestation front (*Chimarra* undetermined species "AN"; Figure 9.68).

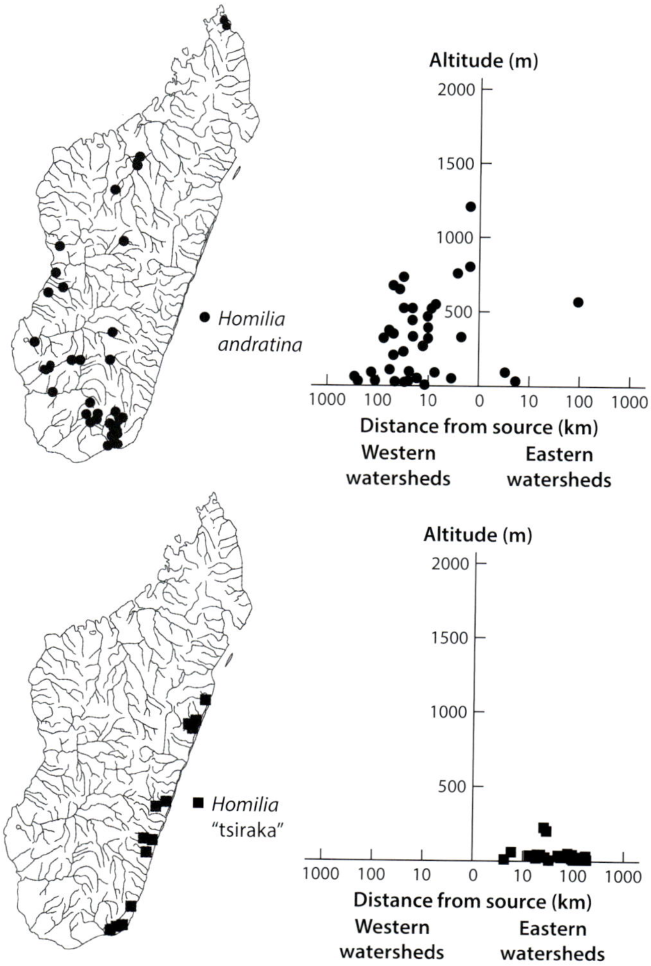

FIGURE 9.67 **Schematic distribution map and ecological profiles of *Homilia andratina* and *Homilia* undetermined species "tsiraka."**

ORIGINS OF THE MALAGASY FAUNA

The Malagasy trichopteran fauna is overall African. The fauna of the African mainland is rather homogeneous, with the exception of two notably richer areas—some high mountains along the Great Rift Valley, and the Cape Province. The Malagasy fauna includes most of the African genera, including those of the eastern mountains and the southern extremity. There are only a few gaps in the common fauna between Madagascar and these other two areas of Africa. The genera *Protomacronema* and *Ugandatrichia* and the main lineages of *Setodes* are the most noteworthy. A few genera of the high mountains along the Great Rift Valley (*Stenopsyche* and *Abaria*) and the Cape Province fauna (*Hydrosalpinx*, *Petroplax*, and *Aclosma*) are also missing, but these genera are seemingly rare and with low species diversity. In addition, some small archaic taxa are present on Madagascar and not on the continent (*Afrorheithrus*, *Madagocerum*, and *Rossodes*). In some exceptional cases, the hypothesis of colonization from Asia seems probable, specifically concerning potamic species inhabiting coastal, low-velocity waters rather than rhithric species inhabiting mountain waters. The probability of this event is reinforced by the size of the populations and the formation of huge swarms above large rivers. These conditions are verified for the genus *Potamyia*, which is unknown from Africa.

Most of the archaic elements belong to the fauna of moist evergreen forests, specifically small rivers, and their dispersal capacities are notably low. In contrast, the Trichoptera fauna of rivers in open

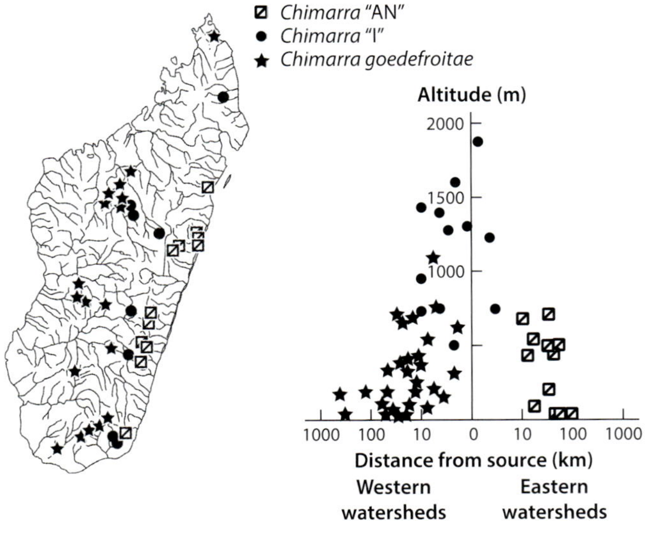

FIGURE 9.68 **Schematic distribution map and ecological profiles of *Chimarra* undetermined species "AN," *Chimarra* undetermined species "I," and *C. goedefroitae*.**

and anthropogenic habitats shows a strong homogeneity across the island, particularly below 1000 m. These widespread taxa have closer affinities with the African fauna, and their arrival on Madagascar would be after the breakup of Gondwana. The possibility of colonization of Africa from Madagascar needs to be considered.

Colonization events may have taken place when sea-level conditions were lower and the Seychelles Plateau was more emerged than today. There is a correlation between the biome type that a given caddisfly taxon occurs in and its level of endemism on Madagascar. The perennially stable nature of aquatic environments in moist evergreen forests does not provide selective pressure for the development of strong dispersal capabilities. Further, forest cover constitutes a considerable obstacle for the movements of adult Trichoptera. Thus, the limited genetic exchange between moist evergreen forest rivers presumably accelerates isolation and local speciation. Conversely, species that have successfully crossed the Mozambique Channel are adapted to low elevations and open habitats, and often have the ability to disperse long distances. In Madagascar, Trichoptera is consequently divided into two distinct groups. One group consists of a suite of forms that occur in the intact forests and tend to show high levels of endemism with localized populations. The second group includes taxa that are broadly distributed, often in open and human-modified habitats, and have probably colonized the island in recent geological time. These dominant patterns are not without exception, and in several highly endemic lines, species have adapted to western dry environments without developing a strong dispersal capacity that would have allowed them to colonize the continent or the deforested regions of the east coast.

Subject editors: Brian L. Fisher and Steven M. Goodman

LEPIDOPTERA, BUTTERFLIES AND MOTHS: SYSTEMATICS AND DIVERSITY

D. C. Lees and J. Minet

In 2003, we enumerated the Lepidoptera of Madagascar to contain (up to the end of 2001) 4528 valid described species, comprising 2829 "macrolepidopteran" moths and 311 butterflies (Lees and Minet 2003). At the end of 2005, Krüger (2007a) estimated for Madagascar only slightly more: 4589 described species, of which 340 were butterflies and 4249 moths (Figures 9.69 and 9.70). Most recently Lopez-Vaamonde et al. (2019), by accounting for data compiled on the Afromoths website (De Prins and De Prins 2011), estimated the total Malagasy fauna at 4900 species of Lepidoptera.

Since our last update on Malagasy Lepidoptera diversity (Lees and Minet 2003), which broke down Lepidoptera diversity essentially to family and subfamily level with an enumeration of genera and species, there have been some significant monographs adding dozens of new species for certain groups, notably satyrine nymphalids and pyralids, as well as epermeniids, nolines, acontiine noctuids, and boletobiine erebids (Gaedike 2004; Hacker et al. 2008, 2012; Hacker 2011, 2013, 2016, 2019; Hacker and Fibiger 2006; Lees 2016; P. Leraut 2000, 2002, 2004a, 2004b, 2005, 2006a, 2006b, 2006c, 2007, 2008, 2009a (2008), 2009b, 2009c, 2010, 2011a, 2011b, 2013, 2015, 2019; G. Leraut 2017, 2019a, 2019b). Many genera and even a few families have been added (Lees and Stonis 2007; Lopez-Vaamonde et al. 2019) or confirmed (Anikin 2019) for the fauna. In some groups that have been recently recorded from Madagascar (e.g., Micropterigidae and Opostegidae), no new species descriptions have been published so far (Lees and Minet 2003; Davis and Stonis 2007; Lopez-Vaamonde et al. 2019). It should be noted that for some families since our 2003 tabulation there are now comprehensive world catalogs (Sinev 2002, 2014; Gielis 2003; Brown 2005; De Prins and De Prins 2005; Baldizzone

FIGURE 9.69 **Some endemic Malagasy lepidopterans. A) Undescribed genus and species (Micropterigidae), Anjananaribe-Sud; B) *Euagophleps lambomakandro* (Tineidae: Scardiinae), station Périnet (Analamazaotra); C) *Tonza* sp. (Tonzidae), Vohitaly; D) *Microsynanthedon ambrensis* (Sesiidae), Montagne d'Ambre; E) *Boisduvalodes tamatavana* (Somabrachyidae), Ranomafana; F) *Beforona mirabilella* (Peleopodidae), near Moramanga; G) spinning moth (Gelechiidae: Dichomeridinae, possibly *Dichomeris*), near BOLD:ACV7974, Analamazaotra; H) *Smerina manoro* (Nymphalidae: Heliconiinae); and I) *Griveaudia charlesi* female (Callidulidae: Griveaudiinae), Andranovory.** (PHOTOS A, C–E, and G by D. C. Lees; B [NHMUK specimen] by L. Yang; F, H, and I [MNHN specimens] by J. Minet.)

et al. 2006; Sobczyk 2011; Schintlmeister 2013; Lewis and Sohn 2015; Nieukerken et al. 2016).

A more or less comprehensive and up-to-date synonymic checklist of the fauna, excluding butterflies (Papilionoidea), is incorporated in the Afromoths online database (De Prins and De Prins 2011), even though its systematic arrangement needs updating. Since the end of 2001 until the end of 2019, based on our count, 315 new species or replacement names and 10 subspecies have been introduced to the Madagascar Lepidoptera fauna. Our aim here is to provide an update of our previous count, down to tribal level where feasible, incorporating recent changes in higher-level classification, which should be comprehensive to the end of 2019. We emphasize in a series of comments appended to Table 9.50, the generic composition of certain families and subfamilies. Our current work enumerates 1418 genera and 5016 species of Lepidoptera described from Madagascar, or descriptions we regard as reliably recorded from the island—an increase of 107 genera and 488 species since Lees and Minet (2003).

The increase in number of genera would be higher, but here we take a conservative approach simply because of numerous species on Madagascar that have no direct or likely congeneric relationship with the type species of the respective genus. We have not included the genera for such taxa in our count (but there are at least 241 species with 105 of such false generic names). Undoubtedly, there are many more species that are also misplaced, but a comprehensive overhaul of this nature is beyond the scope of this work (and we have done no such revamp for some families, notably among Tortricoidea and many Pyraloidea). It is very useful for such assessment, nevertheless, when the type species of a genus has actually been included in molecular studies, and in many cases it is already the case that representatives of the type species have already been DNA-barcoded on BOLD (Barcode of Life Data System) (Ratnasingham and Hebert 2007; see also BOLD 2021). Indeed, the idea of using a short, standardized fragment of DNA (658 base pairs long) in the mitochondrial cytochrome oxidase I (COI) region has gained massive popularity

FIGURE 9.70 **Live endemic Malagasy moths. A) *Sindris sganzini* (Pyralidae: Pyralinae), Masoala; B) *Crocinis* near *viettei* (Drepanidae), Andasibe; C) *Caligatus splendissima* (Euteliidae: Euteliinae), Ankirindro, Makira; D) *Rothia zea* feeding on bird droppings (Noctuidae: Agaristinae), Kirindy Forest CNFEREF; E) *Thyrosticta pauliani* (Erebidae: Arctiinae: Syntomini), Kirindy Forest CNFEREF; F) "*Acripia*" *megalesia* (Erebidae: Anobinae), Zahamena; G) *Malagasanja palliatella* (Eupterotidae), Zahamena; and H) *Archichlora chariessa* (Geometridae: Geometrinae), Analamazaotra.** (PHOTOS by D. C. Lees.)

since the publication of Hebert et al. (2003). As a tool that was unavailable at the time of our previous work (Lees and Minet 2003), it is used primarily for identifying unknown samples, flagging potential new species, and matching early stages and adults. This new source of data is taken into account, allowing us to spot additional described taxa for the island. A more recent innovation (Ratnasingham and Hebert 2013) for uniquely numbering DNA barcode clusters (BINs, or barcode index numbers) means that it is now also possible to measure diversity by counting the number of these genetic clusters, which comprise crude surrogates for species. As an indication, we tabulate a summary of publicly available BINs for many higher taxa (these constitute only about 54% of the 2892 Lepidoptera BINs barcoded for Madagascar as of April 2020, according to the Public Data Portal of BOLD). The online supplementary data set of Lopez-Vaamonde et al. (2019) for micromoths adds 106 BINs identified to species level, whereas 1433 BINs are not identified to species. The database also includes a number of new genus and species records for the island, which we account for here.

In recent years, there have also been many changes at a higher systematic level. Since the publication by Nieukerken et al. (2011), it has been convenient to distinguish the clade Macroheterocera (comprising the superfamilies Bombycoidea, Drepanoidea, Lasiocampoidea, Geometroidea, and Noctuoidea) from other Lepidoptera. Within the butterflies, no longer arranged among members of this crown group as we had it in 2003, the above publication subsumed Hesperioidea within Papilionoidea.

TABLE 9.50. **Malagasy Lepidoptera: classification, principal genera and species, and number of public DNA barcode BINs**

CLADE	SUPERFAMILY / FAMILY	SUBFAMILY	TRIBE	GENERA	SPECIES	PUBLIC BINS	COMMENT	INCLUDED GENERA AND SPECIES
	Micropterigoidea							
	Micropterigidae			0	0	2+	1	See Figure 9.69a
HETERONEURA								
	Nepticuloidea							
	Opostegidae			2	0	5+	2	*Opostega*, *Pseudopostega* (undescribed species)
	Nepticulidae			3	1	28+	3	*Acalyptris* (undescribed species), *Fomoria scobleella* (Minet, 2004), *Stigmella* (undescribed species)
	Adeloidea							
	Adelidae			1	1	7+	4	*Nemophora gymnota* (Meyrick, 1912), comb. nov.
	Tischerioidea							
	Tischeriidae			1	1		5	*Coptotriche alavelona* Lees & Stonis, 2007
DITRYSIA								
	Tineoidea							
	Psychidae			10	20	23+		
		Naryciinae		2	2		6	*Narycia garrula* Meyrick, 1934, *Conoeca psammogona* (Meyrick, 1931)
		Typhoniinae		1	5		7	*Typhonia*
		Oiketicinae		5	11		8	*Acanthopsyche pauliani* Bourgogne, 1984, *Deborrea cambouei* (Oberthür, 1922), *Malgassopsyche viettei* Bourgogne, 1984, *Oiketicus saclavus* (Mabille, 1890)
		Psychidae *i.s.*		2	2		9	*Obtexocorytus schuettei* Sobczyk, 2009, *Sapheneutis pulchella* Sobczyk & Schutte, 2010
	Eriocottidae			2	9	12+		
		Eriocottinae		0	0		10	
		Compsocteninae		2	9		11	*Filiramifera naumanni* Mey, 2019, *Monachoptilos*
	Dryadaulidae			0	0	3+	12	
	Tineidae			27	33	159+	13	
		Hapsiferinae		4	4			*Callocosmeta eupicta* Gozmány, 1969, *Chrysocrata coruscans* Gozmány, 1969, *Cimitra horridella* (Walker, 1863), *Hapsifera nigraureella* Viette, 1968
		Setomorphinae		1	1		14	*Setomorpha rutella* (Zeller, 1852)
		Myrmecozelinae		5	3		15	*Ateliotum*, *Hilaroptera viettei* Gozmány, 1969, *Phthoropoea*, *Protaphreutis borboniella* (Boisduval, 1833), *Scalmatica insularis* Gozmány, 1969
		Siloscinae		1	1		16	*Tetanostola hexagona* Meyrick, 1931
		Harmaclonínae		1	3			*Harmaclona*
		Perissomasticinae		2	4		17	*Edosa cheligera* Gozmány, 1970, *Perissomastix* (3 spp.)
		Tineinae		3	2		18	*Ceratophaga vastellus* (Zeller, 1852), *Monopis*, *Praeacedes atomosella* (Walker, 1863)
		Erechthiinae		1	1		19	*Erechthias minuscula* (Walsingham, 1897)
		Hieroxestinae		3	8		20	*Amphixystis* (4 spp.), *Oinophila*, *Opogona* (4 spp.)
		Scardiinae		4	4		21	*Euagophleps brunneis* Viette, 1952, *E. lambomakandro* Viette, 1952 (Figure 9.69b), *Morophaga vadonella* (Viette, 1955), *Scardia*, *Ranohira silvestris* Viette, 1952
		Tineidae *i.s.*		2	2			*Ancystrocheira porphyrica* Gozmány, 1969, *Protagophleps masoala* Viette, 1954
	Gracillarioidea							
	Bucculatricidae			1	0	2	22	*Bucculatrix* (no described species)
	Gracillariidae			12	27	55+	23	
		Phyllocnistinae		1	1		24	*Phyllocnistis saligna* (Zeller, 1839)
		Ornixolinae		2	5		25	*Epicephala*, *Stomphastis* (5 spp.)
		Gracillariinae		4	8		26	*Aristaea* (2 spp.), *Callicercops* (3 spp.), *Caloptilia* (3 spp.)

CLADE	SUPERFAMILY	FAMILY	SUBFAMILY	TRIBE	GENERA	SPECIES	PUBLIC BINS	COMMENT	INCLUDED GENERA AND SPECIES
			Acrocercopinae		4	10		27	*Dialectica scalariella* (Zeller, 1850), *Acrocercops* (6 spp.), *Phodoryctis caerulea* (Meyrick, 1912), *Telamoptilia* (2 spp.)
			Lithocolletinae		1	3		28	*Phyllonorycter*
	Yponomeutoidea							29	
		Cemiostomidae			1	2	2	30	*Leucoptera*
		Bedelliidae			0	0	4+	31	
		Praydidae			1	3	2+	32	*Prays*
		Lyonetiidae			1	1		33	*Lyonetia clerkella* (Linnaeus, 1758)
		Argyresthiidae			1	9	5+		*Argyresthia*
		Yponomeutidae			5	10	2	34	*Niphonympha pauli* (Viette, 1968), *Swammerdamia villiersi* Gibeaux, 1984, *Yponomeuta* (6 spp.), *Zelleria kesslerioides* Gibeaux, 1985, *Xyrosaris secreta* Meyrick, 1912
		Ypsolophidae			1	1		35	*Phrealcia dolini* (Gershenson, 2003)
		Plutellidae			1	1		36	*Plutella xylostella* (Linnaeus, 1758)
		Glyphipterigidae			6	7	20+		
			Acrolepiinae		4	5		37	*Acrolepia dioscoreivora* Gibeaux, 1989, *Acrolepiopsis*, *Digitivalva* (3 spp.), *Iridostoma catatella* Viette, 1956
			Glyphipteriginae		2	2			*Chrysocentris eupepla* Meyrick, 1930, *Glyphipterix madagascariensis* Viette, 1951
		Tonzidae			1	0	1	38	*Tonza* (Figure 9.69c; undescribed species)
DITRYSIA *I.S.*					0	1		39	"*Adela*" *tsaratanana* Viette, 1954
APODITRYSIA									
	Alucitoidea								
		Alucitidae			1	4	3+	40	*Alucita*
	Pterophoroidea								
		Pterophoridae			34	65	19+	41	
			Macropiratinae		1	1			*Agdistopsis griveaudi* Gibeaux, 1994
			Agdistinae		1	2			*Agdistis*
			Ochyroticinae		1	1			*Ochyrotica rufa* Arenberger, 1987
			Deuterocopinae		1	0		42	*Deuterocopus* (no described species)
			Pterophorinae		30	61			
				Tetraschalini	1	2			*Titanoptilus*
				Platyptiliini	13	25		43	Main genera *Platyptilia* (8 spp.), *Sphenarches* (3 spp.)
				Exelastini	2	7		44	*Antarches tessmanni* (Strand, 1913), *Exelastis* (6 spp.)
				Oxyptilini	5	7		45	Main genus *Megalorhipida* (3 spp.)
				Oidaematophorini	8	16		46	Main genera *Crassuncus* (3 spp.), *Helpaphorus* (5 spp.)
				Pterophorini	1	4			*Pterophorus*
	Carposinoidea								
		Copromorphidae			2	1	5+	47	*Copromorpha*, *Rhynchoferella syncentra* (Meyrick, 1916)
		Carposinidae			2	2	3+	48	*Epicopistis*, *Meridarchis* (2 spp.)
	Epermenioidea								
		Epermeniidae			3	7	12+	49	*Epermenia* (5 spp.), *Mesepermenia malgachica* Gaedike, 2004, *Ochromolopis pallida* Gaedike, 2004
	Immoidea								
		Immidae			1	3	21+	50	*Moca humbertella* (Viette, 1956) and two others misplaced in Lecithoceridae but awaiting formal transfer
	Choreutoidea								
		Choreutidae			3	1	3+	51	*Anthophila*, *Brenthia*, *Tebenna micalis* (Mann, 1857)
	Galacticoidea								

(continued overleaf)

TABLE 9.50. ***continued***

CLADE	SUPERFAMILY / FAMILY	SUBFAMILY	TRIBE	GENERA	SPECIES	PUBLIC BINS	COMMENT	INCLUDED GENERA AND SPECIES
	Galacticidae			**1**	**1**	**3**	52	*Homadaula ravula* Mey, 2004
	Tortricoidea							
	Tortricidae			**119**	**331**	**150+**	53	
		Chlidanotinae		**3**	**4**			
			Polyorthini	1	1			*Ebodina lithoptila* (Diakonoff, 1960)
			Hilarographini	1	1			*Idiothauma malgassicella* Viette, 1958
			Chlidanotini	1	2			*Trymalitis*
		Tortricinae		**39**	**152**			
			Phricanthini	1	1			*Phricanthes flexilineana* (Walker, 1863)
			Archipini	30	138		54	Main genera *Cuspidata* (10 spp.), *Digitosa* (6 spp.), *Epichoristodes* (9 spp.), *Goniotorna* (33 spp.), *Pandemis* (31 spp.)
			Cnephasiini	0	1		55	"*Cnephasia*" *imitans* Diakonoff, 1948
			Schoenotenini	1	2			*Doridostoma*
			Tortricini	5	7		56	*Acleris* (2 spp.), *Eboda bryochlora* Diakonoff, 1960, *Panegyra* (2 spp.)
			Cochylini	2	3		57	*Chloanohieris comastes* Diakonoff, 1989, "*Cochylis*" *unicolorana* Mabille, 1900, *Oligobalia viettei* Diakonoff, 1988
		Olethreutinae		**77**	**175**			
			Microcorsini	1	2		58	*Cryptaspasma* (2 spp.)
			Olethreutini (= Bactrini)	29	58		59	Main genera *Bactra* (12 spp.), *Eccopsis* (4 spp.), *Lobesia* (10 spp.)
			Enarmoniini	3	4		60	*Aemulatrix notognatha* Diakonoff, 1988, *Dasybregma gypsodoxa* Diakonoff, 1983, *Tetramoera* (2 spp.)
			Eucosmini	25	75		61	Main genera *Epinotia* (7 spp.), *Plutographa* (29 spp.), *Xenosocia* (9 spp.)
			Grapholitini	19	36		62	Main genera *Cryptophlebia* (5 spp.), *Cydia* (6 spp.), *Thaumatotibia* (5 spp.)
	Cossoidea							
	Sesiidae			**13**	**31**			
		Sesiinae		**12**	**29**			
			Sesiini	4	5		63	*Hovaesia donckieri* (Le Cerf, 1912), *Lenyrhova heckmanniae* (Auriv-illius, 1909), *Madasphecia* (2 spp.), *Melittosesia flavitarsa* Bartsch, 2009
			Synanthedonini	8	24		64	Main genera *Camaegeria* (6 spp.), *Malgassesia* (7 spp.), *Microsynan-thedon* (3 spp.) (e.g., Figure 9.69d), *Tipulamima* (4 spp.)
		Tinthiinae		**1**	**2**		65	*Similipepsis*
	Brachodidae			**2**	**8**			
		Pseudocossinae		**1**	**6**		66	*Pseudocossus*
		Phycodinae		**1**	**2**	**1**	67	*Nigilgia*
	Dudgeoneidae			**1**	**1**		68	*Dudgeonea malgassa* Viette, 1958
	Metarbelidae			**1**	**2**			*Saalmulleria*
	Cossidae			**6**	**26**	**1+**		
		Cossinae		**3**	**16**		69	Main genus *Planctogystia* (13 spp.)
		Zeuzerinae		**3**	**10**		70	Main genus *Zeuzeropecten* (8 spp.)
	Zygaenoidea							
	Epipyropidae			**2**	**3**	**2+**	71	*Epipyrops*, *Fulgoraecia*
	Lacturidae			**1**	**9**	**1**		*Gymnogramma* (= *Eremothyris*)
	Zygaenidae	Procridinae		**4**	**5**		72	*Ankasocris striatus* Viette, 1965, *Ischnusia culiculina* (Mabille, 1879), *Madaprocris minetorum* Viette, 1978, *Sthenoprocris* (2 spp.)
	Somabrachyidae			**1**	**1**		73	*Boisduvalodes tamatavana* (Oberthür, 1922) (Figure 9.69e)
	Limacodidae			**26**	**67**	**10+**		

CLADE	SUPERFAMILY / FAMILY	SUBFAMILY	TRIBE	GENERA	SPECIES	PUBLIC BINS	COMMENT	INCLUDED GENERA AND SPECIES
		Chrysopolominae		1	1		74	*Vietteopoloma madagascariensis* Hering, 1961
		Limacodinae		24	65		75	Main genera *Ankijabe* (4 spp.), *Latoia* (12 spp.), *Marmorata* (5 spp.), *Parasa* (9 spp.), *Ximacodes* (4 spp.)
		Limacodidae *i.s.*		1	1		76	*Crothaema sericea* Butler, 1880
OBTECTOMERA								
	Gelechioidea							
	Stenomatidae			2	18	4+	77	*Amontes princeps* Viette, 1958, *Herbulotiana*
	Peleopodidae			13	61	131+	78	
		Peleopodinae		2	7		79	*Abychodes janineae* Viette, 1954, *Pseudepiphractis* (6 spp.)
		Oditinae		10	53		80	Main genera *Epimactis* (6 spp.), *Exoditis* (6 spp.), *Mnarolitia* (6 spp.), *Odites* (22 spp.)
		Peleopodidae *i.s.*		1	1		81	*Beforona mirabilella* Viette, 1956 (Figure 9.69f)
	Depressariidae			1	1	2+		*Agonopterix liesella* Viette, 1987
	Oecophoridae			5	15	28+		
		Oecophorinae	Metachandini	2	6			*Ancylometis isophaula* Meyrick, 1934, *Metachanda* (5 spp.)
		Oecophoridae *i.s.*		3	9		82	*Betroka* (3 spp.), *Plesiosticha practicodes* (Meyrick, 1918), *Psarolitia* (3 spp.), "*Scieropepla*" *minetorum* Viette, 1987
	Lecithoceridae			1	19	79+	83	*Lecithocera* s.s. (no described species), *Lecithocera* s.l. (18 spp.), *Adela janineae* (Viette, 1954)
	Xyloryctidae			3	9		84	*Eporycta pachnoscia* Meyrick, 1915, *Phracyps* (5 spp.), *Pseudoprocometis* (3 spp.)
	Autostichidae			1	1		85	*Encrasima insularis* (Butler, 1880) (but not "*Pachnistis*" *nigropunctella*)
	Cryptolechiidae			1	2		86	*Eutorna diluvialis* Meyrick, 1913, *E. punctinigrella* Viette, 1955
	Elachistidae			1	2	8+	87	*Elachista crocogastra* Meyrick, 1908, *Elachista merinaella* (Viette, 1956), comb. nov.
	Batrachedridae			0	0	4+	88	
	Coleophoridae			1	2		89	*Coleophora lastukhini* (Anikin, 2019), comb. nov., *C. leucobela* (Meyrick, 1934)
	Ethmiidae			1	19	1	90	*Ethmia* (19 spp., incl. *E. decaryanum* (Viette, 1954) formerly "*Trichocirca*")
	Momphidae			1	1		91	*Mompha millotella* Viette, 1955
	Blastobasidae			2	1	7+	92	*Blastobasis*, *Neoblastobasis ximeniaella* Adamski, 2010
	Scythrididae			3	5	14+	93	*Eretmocera* (2 spp.), *Haploscythris chloraema* (Meyrick, 1887), *Scythris* (2 spp.)
	Stathmopodidae			2	4	17+		*Phytophlops nigricella* Viette, 1958, *Stathmopoda* (3 spp.)
	Cosmopterigidae			12	13	59+		
		Chrysopeleiinae		3	0		94	*Ascalenia*, *Gisilia*, *Stilbosis* (no described species)
		Antequerinae		1	2		95	*Macrobathra antimeloda* Meyrick, 1930, *M. sikoraella* (Viette, 1956)
		Scaeosophinae		2	2		96	*Hyalochna malgassella* Viette, 1963, *Scaeosopha betrokensis* Sinev & Li, 2012
		Cosmopteriginae		6	9		97	*Anatrachyntis simplex* (Walsingham, 1891), *Cosmopterix* (2 spp.), *Falcatariella* (2 spp.), *Isidiella labathiella* (Viette, 1956), *Pyroderces ocreella* Viette, 1955, *Stagmatophora* (2 spp.)
	Gelechiidae			20	36	178+	98	
		Anacampsinae		6	11			
			Chelariini	2	5		99	*Anarsia* (3 spp.), *Hypatima* (2 spp.)
			Anacampsini	4	6		100	Main genera *Mesophleps* (2 spp.), *Stomopteryx* (2 spp.)
		Dichomeridinae		3	17		101	Main genus *Dichomeris* (14 spp.) (Figure 9.69g)
		Apatetrinae		2	2			
			Apatetrini	1	1			*Chrysoesthia stipelloides* (Janse, 1950)

(continued overleaf)

TABLE 9.50. ***continued***

CLADE	SUPERFAMILY / FAMILY	SUBFAMILY	TRIBE	GENERA	SPECIES	PUBLIC BINS	COMMENT	INCLUDED GENERA AND SPECIES
			Pexicopiini	1	1			*Pectinophora gossypiella* (Saunders, 1844)
		Thiotrichinae		**2**	**1**		102	*Polyhymno millotiella* Viette, 1954, *Thiotricha*
		Anomologinae		**2**	**1**		103	*Monochroa*, *Pycnodytis irrigata* Meyrick, 1918
		Gelechiinae		**3**	**2**			
			Gnorimoschemini	1	1		104	*Phthorimaea operculella* (Zeller, 1873)
			Litini	1	0		105	*Teleiopsis*
			Gelechiini	1	1			*Stegasta sattleri* Bidzilya & Mey, 2011 (see Mey 2011)
		Gelechiidae *i.s.*		**2**	**2**		106	*Idiophantis croconota* Meyrick, 1918, *Symbatica heimella* Viette, 1954
	Gelechioidea *i.s.*			**5**	**40**	**53+**	107	*Diocosma filinotella* Viette, 1958, "*Lecithocera*" *ojejyella* Viette, 1986, "*Macrobathra*" *auratella* Viette, 1958, "*Meleonoma*" *diehlella* Viette, 1955, "*Meleonoma*" *impulsa* Meyrick, 1934, 4 other false Lecithoceridae, "*Orophia*" *madagascariensis* (Viette, 1951), *Orygocera* (25 spp.), *Tyriograptis* (3 spp.), *Tyromantis metaxantha* Meyrick, 1918, *Xherocterys jeannelliella* Viette, 1954
	Papilionoidea							
	Papilionidae			**3**	**13**			
		Papilioninae		**3**	**13**			
			Leptocircini	1	3	**[3]**		*Graphium*
			Troidini	1	1	**[1]**		*Pharmacophagous*
			Papilionini	1	9	**7**		*Papilio*
	Hesperiidae			**19**	**57**			
		Coeliadinae		**3**	**6**	**[6]**	108	*Coeliades* (4 spp.), *Tekliades ramanatek* (Boisduval, 1833), *Pyrrhiades pansa* Hewitson, [1867]
		Tagiadinae		**3**	**7**	**1+**	109	
			Celaenorrhinini	1	3		110	*Celaenorrhinus*
			Tagiadini	2	4		111	*Eagris*, *Tagiades* (2 spp. each)
		Malazinae		**1**	**3**	**0**	112	*Malaza* (= *Manarina*)
		Heteropterinae	Heteropterini	**1**	**5**	**0**	113	*Hovala*
		Hesperiinae		**11**	**36**	**2+**	114	Main genera *Borbo* (4 spp.), *Fulda* (5 spp.), *Perrotia* (= *Miraja*) (15 spp.)
	Pieridae			**11**	**28**			
		Coliadinae		**2**	**6**	**0**		*Catopsilia* (2 spp.), *Eurema* (4 spp.)
		Pierinae		**9**	**22**		115	
			Leptosiaini	1	2	**1**		*Leptosia*
			Nepheroniini	1	1	**1**	116	*Nepheronia pauliani* Bernardi, 1958
			Teracolini	3	7	**7**	117	*Colotis* (5 spp.), *Gideona lucasi* (Grandidier, 1867), *Pinacopteryx mabillei* Aurivillius, [1899]
			Pierini	4	12	**2**		*Appias* (2 spp.), *Belenois* (6 spp.), *Dixeia charina* (Boisduval, 1836), *Mylothris* (3 spp.)
	Riodinidae			**1**	**4**			
		Nemeobiinae	Abisarini	**1**	**4**	**3**	118	*Saribia*
	Lycaenidae			**25**	**44**		119	
		Miletinae		**2**	**2**			
			Lachnocnemini	1	1			*Lachnocnema bibulus* (Fabricius, 1793)
			Spalgini	1	1	**0**		*Spalgis tintinga* (Boisduval, 1833)
		Theclinae		**5**	**12**			
			Iolaini	1	2	**0**		*Iolaus* (*Trichiolaus*)
			Deudorigini	1	5	**0**		*Deudorix*
			Hypolycaenini	3	5	**0**		*Hemiolaus* (3 spp.), *Hypolycaena philippus* (Fabricius, 1793), *Leptomyrina phidias* (Fabricius, 1793)

CLADE	SUPERFAMILY FAMILY	SUBFAMILY	TRIBE	GENERA	SPECIES	PUBLIC BINS	COMMENT	INCLUDED GENERA AND SPECIES
		Polyommatinae		**18**	**30**			
			Lycaenesthini	1	1	**0**		*Anthene princeps* (Butler, 1876)
			Polyommatini	18	29	**1**	120	Main genera *Eicochrysops* (3 spp.), *Euchrysops* (3 spp.), *Lepidochrysops* (5 spp.)
	Nymphalidae			**31**	**171**			
		Libytheinae		**1**	**2**	**0**		*Libythea*
		Danainae		**2**	**2**	**0**		*Amauris nossima* (Ward 1870), *Danaus chrysippus* (Linnaeus, 1758)
		Charaxinae	Charaxini	**1**	**10**	**9**	121	*Charaxes* (= *Euxanthe*, *Polyura*)
		Satyrinae		**4**	**100**			
			Melanitini	2	2	**0**		*Gnophodes betsimena* (Boisduval, 1833), *Melanitis leda* (Linnaeus, 1758)
			Satyrini	2	98	**56**	122	*Heteropsis* (63 spp.), *Strabena* (35 spp.)
		Heliconiinae		**5**	**22**			
			Acraeini	2	18	**3**	123	*Acraea* (7 spp.), *Telchinia* (11 spp.)
			Vagrantini	1	1	**0**		*Smerina manoro* (Ward, 1871) (Figure 9.69h)
			Argynnini	2	3	**0**	124	*Pardopsis punctatissima* (Boisduval, 1833), *Phalanta* (2 spp.)
		Limenitidinae		**5**	**9**		125	
			Cymothoini	1	2			*Cymothoe*
			Adoliadini	2	2	**0**		*Aterica rabena* Boisduval, 1833, *Euptera kinugnana* (Grose-Smith, 1889)
			Pseudacraeini	1	3	**3**		*Pseudacraea*
			Neptini	1	2	**1**		*Neptis*
		Biblidinae		**4**	**7**	**0**		
			Biblidini	3	4	**4**		*Byblia anvatara* (Boisduval, 1833), *Eurytela* (2 spp.), *Neptidopsis* (Boisduval, 1833)
			Eunicini	1	3	**2**	126	*Sevenia*
		Cyrestinae		**1**	**1**	**0**		*Cyrestis camillus*
		Apaturinae		**1**	**2**	**2**		*Apaturopsis*
		Nymphalinae		**7**	**16**			
			Nymphalini	2	2	**0**	127	*Vanessa cardui* (Linnaeus, 1758), *V. hippomene* (Hübner, [1823])
			Junoniini	5	14	**1**	128	*Hypolimnas* (5 spp.), *Precis* (2 spp.), *Protogoniomorpha duprei* (Vinson, 1863), *Salamis anteva* (Ward, 1870), *Junonia* (5 spp.)
	Thyridoidea							
	Thyrididae			**8**	**32**			
		Striglininae		**2**	**3**	**1**		*Striglina minutula* (Saalmüller, 1880), *Banisia* (2 spp.)
		Siculodinae		**6**	**29**	**1**	129	Main genera *Chrysotypus* (10 spp.), *Opula* (2 spp.), *Rhodoneura* (14 spp.)
	Whalleyanoidea							
	Whalleyanidae			**1**	**2**		130	*Whalleyana*
	Calliduloidea							
	Callidulidae			**2**	**4**			
		Pterothysaninae		**1**	**1**	**0**		*Helicomitra pulchra* (Butler, 1878)
		Griveaudiinae		**1**	**3**	**0**		*Griveaudia* (Figure 9.69i)
	Hyblaeoidea							
	Hyblaeidae			**1**	**3**		131	*Hyblaea*
	Pyraloidea							
	Pyralidae			**120**	**370**	**107+**	132	
		Galleriinae		**9**	**21**		133	Main genera *Lamoria* (3 spp.), *Perinetoides* (3 spp.), *Yxygodes* (9 spp.)

(continued overleaf)

TABLE 9.50. ***continued***

CLADE	SUPERFAMILY / FAMILY	SUBFAMILY	TRIBE	GENERA	SPECIES	PUBLIC BINS	COMMENT	INCLUDED GENERA AND SPECIES
		Phycitinae		**80**	**142**		134	
			Anerastiini	10	15		135	Main genera *Ematheudes* (2 spp.), *Emmalocera* (2 spp.), *Peoria* (2 spp.), *Polyocha* (4 spp.)
			Cryptoblabini	4	4		136	*Cantheleamima nygiella* Leraut, 2019, *Cryptoblabes gnidiella* (Millière, 1867), *Cryptozophera madegassalis* Leraut, 2019, *Xylia sophrosyne* Leraut, 2019
			Phycitini	66	123		137	Main genera *Acrobasis* (7 spp.), *Bahiria* (4 spp.), *Ctenomeristis* (3 spp.), *Epicrocis* (6 spp.), *Epischnia* (3 spp.), *Euzophera* (4 spp.), *Flabellobasis* (3 spp.), *Homoeosoma* (3 spp.), *Macrophycis* (5 spp.), *Malgachinsula* (5 spp.), *Morosaphycita* (5 spp.), *Mussidia* (3 spp.), *Phycita* (4 spp.), *Tsaraphycis* (3 spp.), *Veldticola* (3 spp.)
		Epipaschiinae		**9**	**13**		138	Main genera *Catalaodes* (3 spp.), *Macalla* (2 spp.), *Neopaschia* (2 spp.), *Salma* (2 spp.)
		Pyralinae		**22**	**194**		139	
			Endotrichini	**1**	**2**			*Endotricha*
			Hypotiini	**1**	**13**		140	*Hypotia*
			Pyralini	20	**179**		141	Main genera *Aglossa* (3 spp.), *Episindris* (3 spp.), *Goateria* (22 spp.), *Hypsopygia* (4 spp.), *Lophocera* (3 spp.), *Loryma* (7 spp.), *Nhoabe* (8 spp.), *Perula* (4 spp.), *Prosaris* (2 spp.), *Pyralis* (2 spp.), *Sacada* (2 spp.), *Sindris* (3 spp.) (Figure 9.70a), *Zitha* (107 spp.)
	Crambidae			**139**	**351**	**162+**		
		Cybalomiinae		**1**	**2**		142	*Goniophysetis* (2 spp.)
		Musotiminae		**4**	**16**			*Ambia* (11 spp.), *Neurophyseta* (2 spp.), *Panotima* (2 spp.), *Parthenodes ankasokalis* Viette, 1958
		Acentropinae		**11**	**32**		143	Main genera *Argyrophorodes* (5 spp.), *Cataclysta* (9 spp.), *Nymphicula* (3 spp.), *Parapoynx* (5 spp.)
		Schoenobiinae		**4**	**9**		144	Main genera *Patissa* (2 spp.), *Scirpophaga* (5 spp.)
		Lathrotelinae		**1**	**1**		145	*Sufetula nigrescens* Hampson, 1912
		Crambinae		**18**	**34**		146	
			Diptychophorini	**1**				*Glauchocharis*
			Ancylolomiini	**2**	**5**			*Ancylolomia* (4 spp.), *Prionapteryx texturella* Zeller, 1877
			Chiloini	**2**	**4**			*Chilo* (3 spp.), *Malgasochilo autarotellus* Bleszynski, 1970
			Haimbachiini	**1**	**1**			*Haimbachia leucopleuralis* (Mabille, 1900)
			Euchromiini	**1**	**3**			*Euchromius* (3 spp.)
			Calamotrophini	**2**	**5**			*Calamotropha* (4 spp.), *Pseudocatharylla berberichi* Bleszynski, 1970
			Crambini	**7**	**14**			*Alphacrambus prodontellus* (Hampson, 1919), *Angustalius* (4 spp.), *Crambus* (2 spp.), *Culladia achroellum* (Mabille, 1900), *Pediasia* (4 spp.), *Productalius tritaeniellus* Marion, 1954, *Sebrus amandus* Bleszynski, 1970
			Crambinae *incertae sedis*	**2**	**2**			*Charltona ariadna* Bleszynski, 1970, *Zacatecas ankasokellus* (Viette, 1960)
		Heliothelinae		**1**	**1**			*Heliothela ophideresana* (Walker, 1863)
		Scopariinae		**2**	**15**		147	*Eudonia* (13 spp.), *Scoparia* (2 spp.)
		Glaphyriinae		**1**	**1**			*Hellula undalis* (Fabricius, 1781)
		Evergestinae		**1**	**1**			*Crocidolomia pavonana* (Fabricius, 1794)
		Noordiinae		**1**	**2**		148	*Noorda* (2 spp.)
		Odontiinae		**6**	**23**			
			Eurrhypini	6	22		149	Main genera *Autocharis* (10 spp.), *Dicepolia* (4 spp.), *Mabilleodes* (4 spp.), *Viettessa* (2 spp.)
			Odontiini	0	1		150	"*Tegostoma*" *millotalis* (Marion, 1956)
		Pyraustinae		**20**	**34**		151	
			Euclastini	1	2			*Euclasta* (2 spp.)
			Portentomorphini	5	5		152	Main genus *Isocentris* (2 spp.)

CLADE	SUPERFAMILY FAMILY	SUBFAMILY	TRIBE	GENERA	SPECIES	PUBLIC BINS	COMMENT	INCLUDED GENERA AND SPECIES
			Pyraustini	11	23		153	Main genus "*Pyrausta*" (8 spp., plus 1 sp. true *Pyrausta*)
			Pyraustinae *i.s.*	3	4		154	Main genus *Euphyciodes* (2 spp.)
		Spilomelinae		**68**	**180**		155	
			Hydririni	1	1		156	*Hydriris ornatalis* (Duponchel, 1832)
			Udeini	1	1			*Udea ferrugalis* (Hübner, 1796)
			Lineodini	1	1		157	*Leucinodes raondry* (Viette, 1981), "*Lygropia*" (5 spp.)
			Agroterini	9	16		158	Main genera *Agrotera* (3 spp.), *Haritalodes* (4 spp.), *Notarcha* (2 spp.), *Patania* (2 spp.), *Ulopeza* (2 spp.)
			Margaroniini	28	61		159	Main genera *Agathodes* (2 spp.), *Analyta* (3 spp.), *Botyodes* (2 spp.), *Cirrhochrista* (3 spp.), *Dichocrocis* (3 spp.), *Glyphodes* (= *Agrioglypta*; 8 spp.), *Palpita* (4 spp.), *Parotis* (4 spp.)
			Spilomelini	3	10		160	Main genera *Cnaphalocrocis* (= *Marasmia*) (6 spp.), *Orphanostigma* (3 spp.)
			Herpetogrammatini	2	17		161	*Eurrhyparodes* (2 spp.), *Herpetogramma* (9 spp.), "*Pilocrocis*" (3 spp.)
			Hymeniini	2	2			*Hymenia perspectalis* (Hübner, 1796), *Spoladea recurvalis* (Fabricius, 1775)
			Asciodini	1	4		162	*Psara*
			Trichaeini	1	2			*Prophantis*
			Steniini	5	6		163	*Bradina admixtalis* (Walker, 1859), "*Bradina*" *macaralis* Walker, 1859, *Dolicharthria modestalis* (Saalmüller, 1880), *Duponchelia fovelialis* Zeller, 1847, *Hymenoptychis sordida* Zeller, 1852, *Metasia perfervidalis* (Hampson, 1913)
			Nomophilini	8	14		164	Main genus *Pardomima* (4 spp.)
			Spilomelinae *i.s.*	6	45		165	Main genera *Coptobasoides* (4 spp.), "*Lamprosema*" (10 spp.), "*Nacoleia*" (4 spp.), *Pycnarmon* (5 spp.), "*Syllepte*" (10 spp.)
MACROHETEROCERA								
	Drepanoidea							
	Drepanidae			7	22	0	166	
		Drepaninae						
			Nidarini	1	5			*Nidara*
			Oretini	6	17		167	Main genera *Crocinis* (10 spp.) (Figure 9.70b), *Epicampoptera* (4 spp.)
	Noctuoidea							
	Notodontidae			43	110		168	
		Scranciinae		**2**	**5**		169	*Malgadonta idioptila* (Bethune-Baker, 1916) (= *Dinotodonta nigripunctella* Viette, 1955), *Thacona* (= *Scrancia*)
		Pygaerinae		**4**	**26**		170	*Ambina* (9 spp.), *Analama* (3 spp.), *Antoraka* (1 sp.), *Eutrotonotus* (13 spp.)
		Dudusinae		**1**	**1**		171	*Ptilura* (= *Nesoptilura*) *malgassica* (Kiriakoff, 1960)
		Periergosinae		**5**	**6**		172	Main genus *Atrasana* (3 spp.)
		Spataliinae		**1**	**1**		173	*Rasemia descarpentrianum* (Viette, 1954)
		Phalerinae		**1**	**1**		174	*Rigema haasi* (Saalmüller, 1884)
		Thaumetopoeinae		**4**	**24**	2+	175	Main genus *Hypsoides* (20 spp.)
		Stauropinae		**7**	**14**		176	Main genera *Chlorocalliope* (= *Ochrocalliope*) (4 spp.), *Desmeocraera* (3 spp.), *Ochrosomera* (3 spp.)
		Neodrymoniinae		**3**	**8**		177	Main genera *Acroctena* (5 spp.), *Schedostauropus* (2 spp.)
		Notodontinae		**2**	**4**		178	*Antsalova* (3 spp.), *Stenostaura* (= *Platystaura*) *kiriakoffi* (Minet, 1982)
		Notodontidae *i.s.*		**13**	**20**		179	Main genera *Dasychoproctis* (3 spp.), *Pseudohypsoides* (3 spp.)
	Euteliidae			7	24			
		Euteliinae		**4**	**17**		180	Main genera *Caligatus* (2 spp.) (Figure 9.70c), *Eutelia* (= *Phlegetonia*, *Zobia*; 13 spp.)

(continued overleaf)

TABLE 9.50. ***continued***

CLADE	SUPERFAMILY / FAMILY	SUBFAMILY	TRIBE	GENERA	SPECIES	PUBLIC BINS	COMMENT	INCLUDED GENERA AND SPECIES
		Stictopterinae		**3**	**7**			*Gyrtona* (2 spp.), *Lophoptera* (3 spp.), *Stictoptera* (3 spp.)
	Nolidae			**26**	**115**		181	
		Risobinae		**2**	**3**		182	*Gigantoceras* (2 spp.), *Risoba* (1 sp.)
		Eligminae		**4**	**6**		183	*Axiopoeniella laymerisa* (Grandidier, 1867), *Eligma malgassica* Rothschild, 1896, *Iscadia* (= *Gadirtha*, *Ophiosema*) (Berio, 1955), "*Saaluncifera*" *uncinata* (Saalmüller, 1891), *Laelapia notata* Butler, 1879, "*Nyctennomos*" *ambitsha* Viette, 1976
		Westermanniinae		**5**	**11**		184	Main genera *Negeta* (3 spp.), *Plusiocalpe* (4 spp.)
		Nolinae		**6**	**71**		185	Main genera *Meganola* (57 spp.), *Nola* (10 spp.)
		Chloephorinae		**9**	**23**			
			Eariadini	3	9	2	186	*Earias* (4 spp.), *Lophocrama* (2 spp.), *Microzada* (3 spp.)
			Careini	1	7		187	*Maurilia* (7 spp.)
			Sarrothripini	5	7		188	*Blenina* (2 spp.), *Garella basalis* Berio, 1966, *Giaura*, *Nycteola mauritia* (Joannis, 1906), *Pardasena* (3 spp.)
		Nolidae *i.s.*		**0**	**1**		189	"*Pseudotolna*" *perineti* Viette, 1965
	Noctuidae			**153**	**534**		190	
		Plusiinae		**10**	**43**		191	Main genera *Ctenoplusia* (12 spp.), *Trichoplusia* (18 spp.), *Thysanoplusia* (12 spp.)
		Cuculliinae		**10**	**23**			
			Cuculliini	2	4		192	*Cucullia* (3 spp.), *Ectochela malagasy* (Viette, 1972)
			Cuculliinae *i.s.*	8	19		193	*Adaphaenura* (2 spp.), *Daphoenura fasciata* Butler, 1878, *Epicausis* (2 spp.), *Eudaphaenura* (3 spp.), *Fletcherea* (5 spp.), *Homonacna* (3 spp.), *Mydrodoxa* (2 spp.), *Tunocaria rubiginosa* Viette, 1961
		Oncocnemidinae		**2**	**3**		194	*Anedhella* (2 spp.), *Ethiopica befasy* (Viette, 1965)
		Pantheinae (= Thiacidinae)		**2**	**2**	1	195	*Sciatta delphinensis* (Viette, 1966), *Thiacidas alboporphyrea* (Pagenstecher, 1907)
		Eustrotiinae		**11**	**105**		196	Main genera *Deltote* (= *Eustrotia*, *Lithacodia*) (17 spp.), *Maliattha* (20 spp.), *Microplexia* (24 spp.), *Ozarba* (19 spp.), *Taraconica* (11 spp.)
		Acontiinae		**8**	**37**		197	Main genera *Acontia* (= *Cirrodes*, *Sculptifrontia*; 21 spp.), *Paracaroides* (8 spp.)
		Bagisarinae		**12**	**27**	1+	198	Main genera *Amyna* (3 spp.), *Bryophilopsis* (4 spp.), *Chasmina* (3 spp.), *Diadocis* (3 spp.)
		Amphipyrinae	Psaphidini	**3**	**4**		199	*Cetola phaleroides* Rothschild, 1924, *Lyncestis* (2 spp.), *Tanocryx pseudobamra* (Rothschild, 1924)
		Acronictinae		**4**	**7**	1+	200	*Amphia* (2 spp.), "*Fletcherea*" *minuscula* (Kenrick, 1917), *Madegalatha* (2 spp.), *Megalonycta mediovitta* (Rothschild, 1924), *Prototrachea leucopicta* (Kenrick, 1917)
		Agaristinae		**10**	**35**		201	Main genus *Rothia* (23 spp.) (Figure 9.70d)
		Aediinae		**4**	**8**	1	202	*Aedia* (5 spp.), *Ecpatia dulcistriga* (Walker, 1858), *Melanephia vola* Viette, 1971?, *Madecathymia cadoreli* Viette, 1968
		Condicinae		**4**	**14**			
			Condicini	3	6		203	*Acosmetia malgassica* Kenrick, 1917, *Condica* (3 spp.), *Perigea* (2 spp.)
			Leuconyctini	1	8		204	*Kenrickodes*
		Heliothinae		**6**	**11**		205	Main genera *Adisura* (2 spp.), *Helicoverpa* (2 spp.), *Heliothis* (4 spp.), *Timora* (2 spp.)
		Eriopinae		**1**	**14**		206	*Callopistria*
		Noctuinae		**51**	**183**			
			Hadenini	10	21		207	Main genus *Maghadena* (7 spp.)
			Eriopygini	3	8		208	Main genus *Elyptron* (6 spp.)
			Leucaniini	5	24		209	Main genera *Leucania* (7 spp.), *Mythimna* (14 spp.)
			Glottulini	3	4		210	Main genus *Brithys* (2 spp.)

CLADE	SUPERFAMILY FAMILY	SUBFAMILY	TRIBE	GENERA	SPECIES	PUBLIC BINS	COMMENT	INCLUDED GENERA AND SPECIES
			Apameini	5	18		211	Main genera *Acrapex* (5 spp.), *Apamea* (3 spp.), *Sciomesa* (3 spp.), *Sesamia* (6 spp.)
			Prodeniini	1	7			*Spodoptera*
			Caradrinini	2	42		212	Main genus *Athetis* (41 spp.)
			Dypterygiini	2	5	1+	213	*Callyna* (3 spp.), *Magusa* (2 spp.)
			Phlogophorini	5	17	1+	214	Main genera *Conservula* (4 spp.), *Phlogophora* (= *Parca*) (6 spp.), *Syrrhusis* (5 spp.)
			Xylenini	3	4		215	*Actinotia vadoni* (Viette, 1965), *Campydelta stolifera* (Saalmüller, 1891) (= *Lepidodelta*), *Neostichtis* (2 spp.)
			Noctuini	7	25		216	Main genera *Agrotis* (7 pp.), *Feleniopsis* (8 spp.), *Mentaxya* (3 spp.), *Ochropleura* (4 spp.)
			Noctuinae *i.s.*	5	8	2+	217	*Oedebasis* (3 spp.), *Syrrusoides viettei* Laporte, 1973, *Selenistis* (2 spp.), *Volazaha iridoplitis* Viette, 1971, *Xylostola punctum* Berio, 1956
		Noctuidae *i.s.*		**15**	**18**		218	*Anaphela stellata* (Guérin-Méneville, 1844), *Andobana duchesnei* (Viette, 1960), *Aucha tenebricosa* (Saalmüller, 1891), "*Bamra*" *cazeti* (Mabille, 1893), *Butleronea tsara* Viette, 1968, *Callicereon heterochroa* (Mabille, 1879), *Cyclopera gallienii* Viette, 1960, *Daula abscissa* Saalmüller, 1891, *Decarynodes ankasoka* Viette, 1961, *Iambia volasira* Viette, 1968, *Matopo* (= *Gigaglossa*) (3 spp.), *Nyeanella* "*Callicereon*" *mabillei* (Viette, 1965), *Prolyncestis biplagiata* Viette, 1971, *Phoperigea variegata* (Kenrick, 1917), *Protomeroleuca perlides* Berio, 1966, *Stenopterygia monostigma* (Saalmüller, 1891)
	Erebidae			**259**	**1250**		219	
		Scoliopteryginae		**2**	**13**		220	*Anomis* (12 spp.), *Argyphia arcifera* (Mabille, 1881)
		Rivulinae		**1**	**2**		221	*Rivula*
		Anobinae		**12**	**95**		222	Main genera *Hondryches* (4 spp.), *Marcipa* (10 spp., incl. "*Anoba*" *malagasy*), "*Anoba*"/"*Fodina*"/"*Parafodina*" (29 spp., incl. "*Mecodina*" *cataloxia* Viette, 1958), *Marcipopsis* (13 spp., incl. "*Deinopa*" *hiaraka* Viette, 1972), *Plecoptera* (7 spp.), *Paralephana* (= *Gaedonea*) (16 spp.)
		Hypeninae		**8**	**40**		223	Main genus *Hypena* (23 spp.)
		Lymantriinae		**55**	**260**		224	
			Leucomini	1	1			*Leucoma lechrisemata* Collenette, 1959
			Lymantriini	3	32		225	*Lymantica* (11 spp.), *Lymantria* (18 spp.), *Olapa* (3 spp.)
			Orgyiini	2	2			*Griveaudyria mascarena* (Butler, 1878), *Psalis punctuligera* (Mabille, 1880)
			Nygmiini	6	43	2+	226	*Euproctis* (~16 spp.), *Sphrageidus* (~10 spp.), *Noliproctis* (4 spp.), *Nolosia marmorata* Hampson, 1900, *Porthesaroa* (6 spp.), *Salvatgea* (6 spp.)
			Lymantriinae *i.s.*	43	182		227	Main genera *Collenettema* (14 spp.), *Eudasychira* (7 spp.), *Gallienica* (16 sp.), *Jabaina* (12 spp.), *Labordea* (5 spp.), *Masoandro* (5 spp.), *Mpanjaka* (37 spp.), *Pirgula* (6 spp.), *Rivotra* (7 spp.), *Stenaroa* (5 spp.), *Volana* (8 spp.)
		Pangraptinae		**9**	**24**		228	Main genera *Claterna* (4 spp.), *Egnasia* (5 spp.), *Pangrapta* (3 spp.)
		Herminiinae		**9**	**48**		229	Main genera *Coelophoris* (8 spp.), *Nodaria* (3 spp.), *Simplicia* (3 spp.)
		Aganainae		**4**	**10**	1+	230	*Asota* (2 spp.), *Hypsiforma* (5 spp.), *Mecodinops anceps* (Mabille, 1879), *Sommeria* (= *Digama*) (2 spp.)
		Arctiinae		**55**	**373**			
			Lithosiini	25	230		231	Main genera *Cyana* (5 spp.), *Eilema* (82 spp.), *Exilisia* (28 spp.), *Isorropus* (4 spp.), *Mimulosia* (21 spp.), *Ochrota* (8 spp.), *Parexilisia* (5 spp.), *Pelosia* (7 spp.), *Phryganopteryx* (20 spp.), *Viettesia* (24 spp.)
			Amerilini	1	2	1	232	*Amerila*
			Syntomini	15	98		233	*Fletcherinia decaryi* Griveaud, 1964, otherwise main genera *Dubianaclia* (4 spp.), *Maculonaclia* (30 spp.), *Melanonaclia* (6 spp.), *Stictonaclia* (9 spp.), *Thyrosticta* (24 spp.) (Figure 9.70e), *Tritonaclia* (5 spp.)
			Arctiini	14	43		234	Main genera *Fodinoidea* (6 spp.), *Madagascarctia* (3 spp.), *Nyctemera* (4 spp.), *Parachelonia* (4 spp.), *Spilosoma* (8 spp.), *Toulgarctia* (5 spp.), *Utetheisa* (4 spp.)

(continued overleaf)

TABLE 9.50. ***continued***

CLADE	SUPERFAMILY FAMILY	SUBFAMILY	TRIBE	GENERA	SPECIES	PUBLIC BINS	COMMENT	INCLUDED GENERA AND SPECIES
		Calpinae		**9**	**22**			
			Phyllodini	3	4		235	*Huebnerius dux* (Saalmüller, 1881), *Miniophyllodes* (2 spp.), *Miniodes discolor* Guenée, 1852
			Calpini	2	8			*Oraesia* (4 spp.), *Plusiodonta* (4 spp.)
			Ophiderini	2	6	1+	236	*Eudocima* (5 spp.), *Hemiceratoides hieroglyphica* (Saalmüller, 1891)
			Calpinae *i.s.*	2	4	1+	237	*Avitta* (3 spp.), *Khadira formosa* Griveaud & Viette, 1962
		Hypocalinae		**3**	**6**		238	*Antiophlebia griveaudi* Viette, 1966, *Hyperlopha* (4 spp.), *Hypocala florens* Mabille, 1880
		Eulepidotinae		**1**	**1**		239	*Anticarsia rubricans* Boisduval, 1833 [Panopodini]
		Toxocampinae		**1**	**2**			*Tathorhynchus*
		Tinoliinae		**2**	**3**	**1**	240	*Calesia nigriventris* Aurivillius, 1909, *Rhanidophora* (= *Melapera*) (2 spp.)
		Hypenodinae		**0**	**1**		241	"*Rhynchina*" *herbuloti* Viette, 1965
		Boletobiinae		**30**	**145**			
			Phytometrini	6	14		242	*Cycloprosopus strigifera* (Pagenstecher, 1907), *Epicerynea elegans* (Berio, 1959), *Gesonia* (2 spp.), *Loxioda* (= *Marca* [type species of]) (3 spp.), *Phytometra* (4 spp.), *Pleuronodes arida* (Hampson, 1902), "*Raparna*" (2 spp.)
			Araeopteronini	1	1		243	*Araeopteron papaziani* Guillermet, 2009
			Boletobiini	3	6		244	*Argyrolopha* (3 spp.), *Catalana* (2 spp.), *Parascotia trimacula* (Saalmüller, 1891)
			Eublemmini	17	121		245	Main genera *Andrianam* (= *Acremma*, syn. nov.) (14 spp.), *Cerynea* (14 spp.), *Corgatha* (incl. "*Pleurona*" *sirenia* Viette, 1956) (27 spp.), *Eublemma* (= *Autoba*) (29 spp.), *Hypobleta* (7 spp.).
			Boletobiinae *i.s.*	3	3		246	*Attonda adspersa* (R. Felder & Rogenhofer, 1875), *Homodes magnifica* Viette, 1958, *Macella euritiusalis* (Walker, 1865)
		Erebinae		**45**	**167**		247	
			Acantholipini	3	15		248	*Acantholipes* (2 spp.), *Cryptomeria mabillei* Saalmüller, 1880, "*Deinypena*" *ranomafana* Viette, 1966, *Hypospila laurentensis* Viette, 1966 "*Phlogochroa*" *madecassa* Viette, 1972, "*Phlogochroa*" *raketaka* Viette, 1972, "*Talariga*" *albomacula* (Kenrick, 1917), "*Thermesia*" *clarilinea* (Mabille, 1900), "*Ugia*" (7 spp.)
			Sypnini	1	1		249	*Sypnoides delphinensis* Viette, 1966
			Pandesmini	3	6		250	*Beriodesma* (2 spp.), *Pandesma* (2 spp.), *Polydesma* (2 spp.)
			Pericymini	5	12		251	*Calligraphidia tessellata* (Kenrick, 1917), *Lophotavia* (2 spp.), *Pericyma* (7 spp.), *Taveta eucosmia* Hampson, 1926, *Tavia nycterina* (Boisduval, 1833)
			Erebini	3	9	1+	252	*Cyligramma* (7 spp.), *Erebus walkeri* (Butler, 1875), *Sphingomorpha chlorea* (Cramer, 1777)
			Hypopyrini	2	6		253	*Entomogramma* (2 spp.), *Hypopyra* (4 spp.)
			Catocalini	2	8	1+	254	*Cerocala* (5 spp.), *Ulotrichopus* (3 spp.)
			Tachosini	1	1		255	*Tachosa acronyctoides* Walker, 1869
			Audeini	1	4		256	*Audea*
			Amphigoniini	1	1		257	*Lacera alope* (Cramer, 1780)
			Euclidiini	3	7		258	*Mocis* (4 spp.), *Remigiodes* (2 spp.), *Trigonodes hyppasia* (Cramer, 1779)
			Ercheini	1	2			*Ercheia*
			Hulodini	1	7			*Ericeia*
			Cocytiini	2	4		259	*Avatha saalmulleri* (Mabille, 1881, as "*Athyrma*"), *Serrodes* (3 spp.)
			Ophiusini	5	16		260	*Ophiusa* (= *Anua*) (9 spp.), *Stenopis* (2 spp.), *Plecopterodes* (2 spp.), *Thyas* (= *Dermaleipa*) (2 spp.), *Tytroca griveaudi* (Laporte, 1973)
			Poaphilini	9	61	6+	261	Main genera *Achaea* (30 spp.), *Dysgonia* (16 spp.), *Grammodes* (5 spp.).
			Erebinae *i.s.*	2	7		262	*Megalocephalomana* (3 spp.), *Maxera* (2 spp.), "*Thermesia*" *junctilinea* (Mabille, 1900), "*Zethes*" *sagittula* (von Heyden, 1891)

CLADE	SUPERFAMILY FAMILY	SUBFAMILY	TRIBE	GENERA	SPECIES	PUBLIC BINS	COMMENT	INCLUDED GENERA AND SPECIES
		Erebidae *i.s.*		**13**	**38**		263	*Caryonopera* (5 spp.), *Nyctennomos* (5 spp.), *Radara* (3 spp.), *Thausgea* (4 spp.), etc.
	Noctuoidea *i.s.*			**1**	**4**		264	"*Parasiccia*" (*Aemene*) *ochrorubens* (Mabille, 1900), *Tornoconia* (3 spp.)
	Lasiocampoidea							
	Lasiocampidae			**29**	**101**		265	Main genera: 6 spp. each of *Acosmetoptera*, *Borocera*, *Malacostola*; 4 spp. each of *Anchirithra*, *Ochrochroma*, *Raphipeza*, *Sunnepha*; *Closterothrix* (14 spp.), *Lechriolepis* (5 spp.), *Phoenicladocera* (11 spp.)
	Bombycoidea							
	Eupterotidae			**1**	**1**	**1**		
		Janinae		**1**	**1**			*Malagasanja palliatella* (Viette, 1954) (Figure 9.70g)
	Bombycidae			**2**	**2**	**1**		
		Bombycinae		**2**	**2**		266	*Bombyx mori* Linnaeus, 1758, *Ocinara malagasy* Viette, 1965
	Sphingidae			**28**	**64**	**>62**	267	
		Smerinthinae		**5**	**12**			
			Ambulycini	1	1			*Batocnema coquerelii* (Boisduval, 1875)
			Sichiini	1	6		268	*Gynoeryx*
			Leucophlebiini	1	3		269	*Malgassoclanis*
			Unplaced Smerinthinae	2	2		270	*Ceridia nigricans* Griveaud, 1959, *Pseudoclanis grandidieri* (Mabille, 1879)
		Sphinginae		**7**	**10**			
			Sphingini	7	10		271	Acherontiina: *Acherontia atropos* (Linnaeus, 1758), *Agrius convolvuli* (Linnaeus, 1758), *Coelonia* (3 spp.); Sphingina: *Lomocyma oegrapha* (Mabille, 1884); Cocytiina: *Panogena* (2 spp.), *Xanthopan morganii* (Walker, 1856); "*Psilogramma* Genus-Group": *Pantophaeasuffuscus* (Griveaud, 1959)
		Macroglossinae		**16**	**42**			
			Hemarini	1	3		272	*Cephonodes*
			Macroglossini	15	39		273	Main genera, Choerocampina: *Nephele* (4 spp.), *Temnora* (6 spp.); Macroglossina: *Hippotion* (11 spp.)
	Saturniidae			**5**	**26**	**>21**		
		Saturniinae		**5**	**26**			
			Saturniini	3	3		274	*Antherina suraka* (Boisduval, 1833), *Argema mittrei* (Guérin-Méneville, 1847), *Ceranchia apollina* Butler, 1878
			Bunaeini	1	1		275	*Bunaea aslauga* Kirby, 1877
			Urotini	1	22		276	*Maltagorea*
	Geometroidea							
	Uraniidae			**6**	**31**			
		Epipleminae		**3**	**19**		277	*Epiplema* (14 spp.), *Madepiplema* (2 spp.), *Phazaca* (3 spp.)
		Microniinae		**1**	**3**		278	*Acropteris*
		Uraniinae		**2**	**9**	**1+**	279	*Chrysiridia rhipheus* (Drury, 1773), *Urapteritra* (8 spp.)
	Geometridae			**115**	**709**			
		Sterrhinae		**13**	**144**	**1+**	280	
			Cosymbiini	3	63		281	*Chrysocraspeda* (54 spp.), *Cyclophora* (4 spp.), *Eois* (5 spp.)
			Timandrini	1	5		282	*Traminda*
			Rhodometrini	2	2		283	*Afrophyla vethi* (Snellen, 1886), *Rhodometra sacraria* (Linnaeus, 1767)
			Rhodostrophiini	1	3		284	*Metallaxis*
			Sterrhini	1	12		285	*Idaea*
			Scopulini	5	59		286	*Antitrygodes* (3 spp.), *Isoplenodia arrogans* Prout, 1932, *Problepsis* (2 spp.), *Scopula* (48 spp.), *Somatina* (5 spp.)

(*continued overleaf*)

TABLE 9.50. ***continued***

CLADE	SUPERFAMILY FAMILY	SUBFAMILY	TRIBE	GENERA	SPECIES	PUBLIC BINS	COMMENT	INCLUDED GENERA AND SPECIES
		Larentiinae		**20**	**73**			
			Trichopterygini	3	3		287	*Aposteira saurides* Prout, 1935, *Lobidiopteryx ecrinita* Herbulot, 1963, *Protosteira spectabilis* (Warren, 1899)
			Asthenini	1	9		288	*Asthenotricha*
			Melanthiini	1	2		289	*Horisme*
			Eupitheciini	6	35		290	Main genera *Chloroclystis* (3 spp.), *Eupithecia* (26 spp.), *Gymnoscelis* (3 spp.)
			Xanthorhoini	8	23		291	Main genera *Haplolabida* (4 spp.), *Mimoclystia* (6 spp.), *Parortholitha* (5 spp.)
			Larentiine *i.s.*	1	1		292	*Piercia viettei* Herbulot, 1954
		Desmobathrinae		**3**	**6**		293	*Brachytrita cervinaria* Swinhoe, 1904, *Conolophia* (2 spp.), *Derambila* (3 spp.)
		Geometrinae		**36**	**178**			
			Agathiini	1	1		294	*Agathia malgassa* Herbulot, 1978
			Comibaenini	1	2		295	*Comibaena*
			Pseudoterpnini	1	4	2+	296	*Pingasa*
			Hemitheini	22	151	5+	297	Main genera *Archichlora* (37 spp.) (Figure 9.70h) (= *Leptocolpia* syn. nov.), *Blechroneromia* (15 spp.), *Comostolopsis* (4 spp.), *Epigelasma* (23 spp.), *Heterorachis* (23 spp.), *Hypocoela* (17 spp.), *Maxates* (4 spp.), *Prasinocyma* (6 spp.)
			Geometrinae *i.s.*	11	20	1+	298	Main genera *Synclysmus* (5 spp.), *Syncollesis* (4 spp.), *Xanthodura* (2 spp.)
		Ennominae		**43**	**308**		299	
			Gonodontini	1	4			*Xenimpia*
			Ennomini	3	52		300	*Epigynopteryx* (19 spp.), *Mesothisa* (3 spp.), *Psilocerea* (30 spp.)
			Diptychini	1	11		301	*Idiodes* (= *Nopia*)
			Drepanogynini	1	35		302	*Drepanogynis*
			Hypochrosini	1	1		303	*Hypochrosis suffusata* Pagenstecher, 1907
			Caberini	1	2			*Cabera*
			Cassymini	3	15		304	*Heterostegane* (7 spp.), *Orbamia pauperata* Herbulot, 1966, *Zamarada* (7 spp.)
			Eutoeini	1	1		305	*Luxiaria pratti* Prout, 1925
			Macariini	4	33		306	Main genera *Chiasmia* (19 spp.), *Isturgia* (11 spp.)
			Boarmiini	12	82	1+	307	*Main genera Aphilopota* (7 spp.), *Cleora* (7 spp.), *Colocleora* (21 spp.), *Ectropis* (28 spp.), *Racotis* (5 spp.)
			Ennominae *i.s.*	15	72	3+	308	*Argyrophora trofonia* (Cramer, 1779), *Erastria* (= *Petrodava*; 4 spp.), *Herbulotides* (6 spp.), *Hylemera* (41 spp.), 4 spp. each of *Malgassapeira*, *Steganomima*, *Xenostega*, etc.
			TOTAL	1418	5016	>1569		

Notes: Genera: number of genera, except ones we regard as clearly misplaced (" "), that include described species. Species: number of described species. Both columns show numbers by family (gray), subfamily (boldface), or tribe (not boldface). Public BINs: approximate number of DNA barcode index numbers that are public and part of the Barcode of Life Systems (BOLD), which are designated with a BOLD number (e.g., "BOLD:ABC1234"). Included genera and species are specified only in certain cases (for the sake of clarity); otherwise see numbered comments; undescribed taxa are mentioned only for certain groups (notably those without any described species). Entries in table cells presented in brackets are uncertain and include inferred publication dates, taxonomic designations, and uncertain species counts. *Abbreviations:* auct., name used in the sense of subsequent authors; BIN, barcode index number, in a standard format, e.g., "BOLD:ABC1234"; comb. nov., *combinatio nova*; *i.s.*, *incertae sedis*; NJ, neighbor joining; n. sp., undescribed species; *q.v.*, *quod vide*; *s.a.*, *sensu auctorum*; *s.l.*, *sensu lato*; *s.s.*, *sensu stricto*; sp./spp., species (singular/plural); ssp., subspecies; t.s., type species; syn., synonym; syn. nov., *synonymum novum*. MNHN, Muséum National d'Histoire Naturelle, Paris; NHMUK, Natural History Museum, London; RMCA, Royal Museum for Central Africa, Tervuren, Belgium; ZSM, Zoologische Staatssammlung München.

Subfamilies or tribes are not mentioned where unnecessary (e.g., where they are the same as the family—except in cases where the mention of that unit has some special biogeographic interest—and in a few cases we also mention subtribes in the comments). Genera mentioned in quotation marks are not counted toward the generic total (while the corresponding species are counted toward the species total), even when distinct, because they are not genera that truly occur on Madagascar. Sometimes brief biological details are given in the comments for particular taxa of interest, such as introduced and invasive species or genera that have been instable in their systematic placement. In general, Table 9.50 and the comments mention all genera with the number of species, and most species singly representing their genus on Madagascar. Also detailed within each comment are those species additional to the count of Lees and Minet (2003), unless a genus is very large (e.g., *Zitha*). Lees and Minet (2003) contains additional information and many generic synonymies that are incorporated but not repeated here.

Table 9.50 does not fully take into account two articles that were published soon after the table was completed, namely Park et al. (2020) and Twort et al. (2021). According to the former, most Malagasy members of the Lecithoceridae belong to the Torodorinae—e.g., *Parkiana janineae* (Viette, 1954), erroneously described in Adelidae; "*Lecithocera*" *paulianella* Viette, 1955 and "*Idiopteryx*" *tananaella* Viette, 1985 belong to the genus *Dichomeris* (Gelechiidae); "*Idiopteryx*" *obitsyella* Viette, 1986 is an *Odites* (Peleopodidae); "*Lecithocera*" *ojejyella* Viette, 1986 can be placed in *Merocrates* (Gelechioidea *i.s.*); the endemic subfamily Adelomomphinae Minet & Park, 2020 (one species) must be added to the Malagasy Momphidae; and two false *Idiopteryx* (*I. descarpentriesella* Viette, 1954 and *I. marionella* Viette, 1954) actually belong to the genus *Moca* (Immidae). The family Whalleyanidae is now placed in the superfamily Calliduloidea (Twort et al. 2021).

Comments

In the comments, the word "recently" applies to additions since Lees and Minet (2003). For references to "Afromoths," see the corresponding online database by De Prins and De Prins (2011); for "GlobIZ," see the Pyraloidea database of Nuss et al. 2003. In comments 180–263, we propose a number of taxonomic innovations (D. Lees et al., unpublished data).

[1] The family Micropterigidae (see Figure 9.69a) has two undescribed genera on Madagascar (Gibbs 2014) and many undescribed species.

[2] Opostegidae occurs on the island, but there are no described species (Davis and Stonis 2007; Lopez-Vaamonde et al. 2019). Existing DNA barcode clusters for the supplementary data of the last paper have been referred to the genera *Opostega* (BOLD:ACS2986, BOLD:ACS4701) and *Pseudopostega* (BOLD:ACS7108).

[3] Only one nepticulid species is yet described from the island, which was renamed since our last update as *Ectoedemia scobleella* Minet, 2004 (see Minet 2004) and has most recently been referred by Nieukerken et al. (2016: 141) to the genus *Fomoria* Beirne, 1945. The family represents a major lacuna in taxonomic and faunal knowledge on the island, even though leaf mines can easily be found. Also, existing DNA barcode clusters are attributed to the genera *Acalyptris* (BOLD:ACS5438, BOLD: ACU4245, BOLD: ACT0910) and *Stigmella* (BOLD:ACT9600, BOLD:ACT6616, BOLD:ACU0718, BOLD:ACT3689, BOLD:ACV1961, BOLD:ACT3750, BOLD:ACS5439, BOLD:ACT7470, BOLD:ACU0628) (Lopez-Vaamonde et al. 2019: Supplementary data).

[4] There is only one true adelid described for the island, *Nemophora gymnota* (Meyrick, 1912) (see Paulian and Viette 1955: 145; Lees and Minet 2003: notes 2, 38, 80, concerning this species and taxa misplaced in Adelidae). All Malagasy adelids belong to the genus *Nemophora* (M. Kozlov, unpublished data). Several DNA barcode clusters exist for the fauna within this genus (BOLD:ACU1858, BOLD:ACU1958, BOLD:ABW0515, BOLD:ACU1980, BOLD:ACV6415, BOLD:ACU5348) (Lopez-Vaamonde et al. 2019: Supplementary data).

[5] The family Tischeriidae was recently recognized for the island (as *Coptotriche alavelona* Lees & Stonis, 2007, a tentative generic placement).

[6] The Naryciinae is characterized by a distinctive phallus, which is strongly arched, with the anterior region having an elongate ventral projection (Sauter and Hättenschwiler 1999: 270, Figure 4).

[7] *Typhonia bimaculata* Sobczyk & Schütte, 2010 was recently added to the typhoniine psychid fauna. *Typhonia decaryella* (Viette, 1955) was newly combined by Sobczyk and Schütte (2010) (see Paulian and Viette 1955: 147; as "*Melasina*"). *Melasina decaryella* Viette, 1955 (although placed in *Typhonia* by Sobczyk and Schütte, 2010) is here transferred to *Monachoptilas* (Eriocottidae; see comment 11), notably because its abdominal segments 2–7 have distinctive anterior bands of strong spines, as *M. decaryella* Viette, 1955 comb. nov.

[8] The psychid subfamily Oiketicinae contains *Acanthopsyche pauliani* Bourgogne, 1984, *Deborrea* (6 spp.), *Malgassopsyche viettei* Bourgogne, 1984, and *Oiketicus saclavus* (Mabille, 1890). *Oiketicus* has two spp. including *angulatus*, a species not mentioned by Afromoths for Madagascar but found in the checklist of Sobczyk and Schütte (2010), as well as *Pseudometisa alba* (Janse, 1917), a species also not mentioned by Afromoths. Although no specimen of the latter species has been found in the MNHN (among several from Africa and the Comoros), Viette, who was also very familiar with the Comoros fauna, had likely seen at least one *P. alba* from Madagascar after the publication of Bourgogne (1984) on Oiketicinae—a work omitted from the list of references in Sobczyk and Schütte (2010).

[9] We place in Psychidae *i.s.*: *Obtexocorytus schuettei* Sobczyk, 2009 and *Sapheneutis pulchella* Sobczyk & Schutte, 2010. *Obtexocorytus schuettei* was *i.s.* in the original description (Sobczyk 2009) but placed in Oiketicinae in the checklist of Sobczyk and Schütte (2010), which seems not convincing. Similarly, *S. pulchella* was placed ambiguously in either Naryciinae or Taleporiinae in the description by Sobczyk and Schütte (2010) but placed in Naryciinae in the checklist of the same publication. Taleporiinae is a subfamily not otherwise recorded for Madagascar. Unfortunately, as implored by Davis and Robinson (1998: 107), psychid subfamilies had not been characterized in "Sauter and Hättenschwiler 1991." Nevertheless, a key to subfamilies was proposed by Sauter and Hättenschwiler (1999). We can therefore be more definitive here. The subfamily Oiketicinae is thus characterized by 1) a strong reduction of the tibial spurs (see figures in Bourgogne 1984) and in the forewing; 2) a free anal vein (A_2) arising from the distal part of the "anal loop" or, usually, from the section of A_1 situated beyond the anal loop. None of these traits is present in *Obtexocorytus*, which, incidentally, does not have an "oiketicine habitus." With regard to *Sapheneutis*, its larval case, with triangular section, resembles that of the Naryciinae (also that of the Taleporiinae), but its pupa has at least two abdominal segments provided with two rows of teeth, one of which (the posterior row) is composed of anteriorly directed spines (an apomorphy found in *Typhonia* and "higher" Psychidae but not in Taleporiinae nor in Naryciinae. In the latter two subfamilies, the pupa has just one wide area of posteriorly directed teeth on the dorsal surface of each median abdominal segment). The phallus of *S. pulchella* is also completely different from that of the Naryciinae (comment 6, *q.v.*).

[10] Regarding Eriocottinae, see Lees and Minet (2003: 257, note 11); seven barcode BINs have been referred to this subfamily (see supplementary data set DS-MICROMA of Lopez-Vaamonde et al. 2019).

[11] The genus *Monachoptilas* Meyrick, 1934 is here transferred to Eriocottidae: Compsocteninae (from Tineidae). Also, the new species described by Mey (2019) is added to the list (*Filiramifera naumanni*), but its potential synonymy with *Monachoptilas* needs to be examined. All Malagasy members of Compsocteninae possess anterior bands of spines on most abdominal segments.

[12] For the presence of Dryadaulidae on Madagascar, see Lopez-Vaamonde et al. (2019: Supplementary file DS-MICROMA). So far, the family is recognized only tentatively for the Malagasy fauna on the basis of molecular placement of DNA barcodes (representing BINs BOLD:ACT5169, BOLD:ACT3317, and BOLD:ACU0466) from a Malaise trap sample, considering from online images that the vouchers are in very poor condition.

[13] Order of tineid subfamilies (not specified in Viette 1990) here largely follows Regier et al. (2015).

[14] Setomorphinae contains only *Setomorpha rutella* (Zeller, 1852), *fide* Paulian and Viette (1955: 146) and Viette (1990: 29), although the species is not mentioned in Afromoths for Madagascar (while it is for Seychelles and Mascarenes as well as Africa).

[15] We place in Myrmecozelinae *s.a.*, a polyphyletic group (Regier et al. 2015: Figure 3): *Hilaroptera viettei* Gozmány, 1969; *Protaphreutis borboniella* (Boisduval, 1833); and *Scalmatica insularis* Gozmány, 1969 (see also Lees and Minet 2003: 757, note 4; incidentally neither Meessiidae nor Meessiinae *s.a.*, where the species was previously placed, is presently known for Madagascar). Two other genera have been DNA barcoded: *Ateliotum* (BOLD:ACU0957, BOLD:ACS7898) and *Phthoropoea* (BOLD:ABV1745, BOLD:ABV1746) (Lopez-Vaamonde et al. 2019: Supplementary data).

[16] *Tetanostola hexagona* Meyrick, 1931 was transferred from Plutellidae to Tineidae (Lees and Minet 2003: 757, note 10). J. Minet has now examined the type of *T. hexagona* (including its genitalia slide: prep. Gibeaux no. 4237), and this suggests a placement in the Siloscinae. The forewing bears erect scales (not mentioned in the original description), uncus represented by two separate lobes, saccus rod-shaped and articulated, forewing with Rs_3 and Rs_4 long-stalked, hind wing with M_1 and M_2 long-stalked; M_3 and CuA_1 is also long-stalked. This genus is a close relative of *Organodesma*.
[17] *Perissomastix pauliani* Gozmány, 1970 was treated as a valid species in Viette (1990) but was synonymized with *P. atricoma* Meyrick, 1931 (Lees and Minet 2003: 757, note 7), a fact not mentioned in Afromoths.
[18] For Tineinae, the genus *Monopis* is also recorded for the island via DNA barcoding (BOLD:ACS7044) (Lopez-Vaamonde et al. 2019: Supplementary data).
[19] *Erechthias minuscula* (Walsingham, 1897) has been barcoded from Madagascar representing there the first recorded erecthiinae tineid (Lopez-Vaamonde et al. 2019). There is a large Indian Ocean island *Erechthias* fauna (e.g., Afromoths).
[20] Most of the more recently DNA barcoded tineids from Madagascar belong to undescribed species in the subfamily Hieroxestinae (Lopez-Vaamonde et al. 2019). Two of these (BOLD:ACU1695, BOLD:ACS0663) have been placed as true members of the genus *Oinophila* (in contrast to species now in *Amphixystis*: Lees and Minet 2003: 757, note 9).
[21] The species of *Euagophleps* (e.g., Figure 9.69b) and *Ranohira* are newly referred here to Scardiinae. The genus *Scardia* is also DNA barcoded for Madagascar (BOLD:ACY6159) (Lopez-Vaamonde et al. 2019: Supplementary data).
[22] The genus *Bucculatrix* has been DNA barcoded from the island (BOLD:ACT8413, BOLD:ACV2777; Lopez-Vaamonde et al. 2019: Supplementary data).
[23] For Gracillariidae we take into account the recent classification of Kawahara et al. (2017) for the arrangement of subfamilies (here preferring to place Phyllocnistinae first, considering also the antiquity of fossil leaf mines from the New World referred to the subfamily; Oecophyllembinae and Marmarinae are not yet recognized for the island), as well as the work by Bippus (2019), for the list of species recorded from Madagascar.
[24] Phyllocnistinae contains so far one introduced species, *Phyllocnistis saligna* (Zeller, 1839), but there are likely many native species.
[25] For Gracillariidae in the recently recognized subfamily Ornixolinae, Viette (1990: 30) mentioned five *Stomphastis* species; nevertheless, *S. conflua* is mentioned neither in Afromoths nor in Bippus (2019). The obligate Phyllanthaceae-pollinating genus *Epicephala* has been found in Marojejy (Kawakito and Kato 2009) and has also been DNA barcoded from Andasibe (BOLD:ACS4454) (Lopez-Vaamonde et al. 2019: Supplementary data).
[26] Concerning Gracillariinae, *Aristaea* has two species, including *A. bathracma* (Meyrick, 1912), according to Bippus (2019); *Caloptilia* has three species according to Viette (1990: 30) and Bippus (2019), but four according to Afromoths, and so we include here *C. prosticta* (Meyrick, 1909); see Triberti (1987).
[27] The also recently recognized gracillariid subfamily Acrocercopinae includes the introduced and invasive species *Dialectica scalariella* (Zeller, 1850), recently added based on a DNA barcoded specimen (BOLD:AAL3278; Lopez-Vaamonde et al. 2019), as well as *Phodoryctis caerulea* (Meyrick, 1912), added by Bippus (2019).
[28] For gracillariids in the subfamily Lithocolletinae, we add here *Phyllonorycter hibiscina* Vári, 1961, based on a DNA barcoded specimen (BOLD:AAC1747). It may be noted that the long-recognized species *P. lemarchandi* (Viette, 1951) and *P. madagascariensis* (Viette, 1949) have mines with a galling stage on *Solanum* and *Dombeya*, respectively (Paulian and Viette 1955; 157).
[29] See Sohn et al. (2013) for a phylogeny of Yponomeutoidea, which we largely follow for arrangement of higher taxa.
[30] We regard Cemiostomidae as a separate family from Lyonetiidae, considering particularly the high mtDNA divergence of *Leucoptera* from *Lyonetia* (here Lyonetiidae *s.s.*) (see also Sohn et al. 2013; Lopez-Vaamonde et al. 2019).
[31] Presence of Bedelliidae on Madagascar is so far based on DNA barcoded specimens (BOLD:ACS1680, BOLD:ACV2376, BOLD:ACU8214, and BOLD:ACZ4060; Lopez-Vaamonde et al. 2019: Supplementary data).
[32] In Praydidae we regard *Prays oleaeoides* Gibeaux, 1985 as a syn. of *P. citri* Millière, 1873 (see Lopez-Vaamonde et al. 2019: 119).
[33] Lyonetiidae so far contains only *Lyonetia clerkella* (Paulian and Viette 1955: 150, where an introduced species was mining on *Eucalyptus*; Viette 1990: 33). See also Cemiostomidae regarding *Leucoptera* (comment 30, *q.v.*).
[34] The Yponomeutinae count includes *Yponomeuta madagascariensis* Gershenson, 2013, as well as (added by Agassiz 2019) *Y. gnophera* and *Y. malagassella*.
[35] Ypsolophidae was recently introduced for the fauna based on *Phrealcia dolini* (Gershenson, 2003), which was described in *Rhabdocosma* Meyrick (as currently in Afromoths); see Sohn and Gershenson (2014) and Sohn (2015).
[36] Plutellidae is so far represented only by *Plutella xylostella* Linnaeus, a species with a vast cosmopolitan range, not found in all checklists (omitted from Afromoths), but it was mentioned by Lees and Minet (2003: 757, note 14), as well as several other sources for the island's fauna, such as Paulian and Viette (1955: 153) and Gershenson (2003).
[37] Concerning acrolepiine glyphipterigids, "*Iridostoma*" *catatella* Viette, 1956 was transferred to Yponomeutidae *i.s.* by Lees and Minet (2003), but more recently transferred to Acrolepiinae in Lopez-Vaamonde et al. (2019: 113) as *Acrolepia catatella* (as a comb. nov.); the genus *Acrolepiopsis* has also been barcoded from Madagascar (BOLD:ACU7673; Lopez-Vaamonde et al. 2019: Supplementary data).
[38] Regarding the newly described and so far monotypic family Tonzidae (Figure 9.69c), a *Tonza* species (representing BOLD:ACU1104) is known for Madagascar (as well as one from La Réunion and Africa) (Kobayashi et al. 2018), and D. Lees notes that a specimen in NHMUK collected by Camboué from Madagascar had previously been curated under *T. citrorrhoa* Meyrick, but that Oriental species does not occur on the island. The family is here placed after Glyphipterigidae, which is monophyletic as currently understood (Sohn et al. 2013), but aside from the existing DNA barcode, it remains to be analyzed in a molecular study.
[39] Not a member of Adelidae, "*Adela*" *tsaratanana* Viette, 1954 is currently *Ditrysia i.s.* (see Lees and Minet 2003: 757, 761 notes 2, 101).
[40] In Alucitidae, *Alucita meloui* and *A. murzini* were added by Ustjuzhanin and Kovtunovich (2017 [original descriptions 2016]).
[41] Our arrangement of Pterophoridae plume moths is based mainly on Gibeaux (1994, 1996) and Gielis (2003).
[42] The pterophorid subfamily Deuterocopinae is represented only by an undescribed *Deuterocopa* specimen without abdomen (Gibeaux 1994: 94–95).
[43] Additional smaller pterophorid genera and species in the Platyptiliini are: *Amblyptilia* (2 spp.); *Bigotilia* (2 spp.); *Bipunctiphorus dimorpha* (Fletcher, 1910); *Cnaemidophorus horribilis* Gibeaux, 1996; *Inferuncus nigreus* Gibeaux, 1994; *Lantanophaga pusillidactylus* (Walker, 1864); *Leesi masoala* Gibeaux, 1996; *Stenoptilia* (2 spp.); *Stenoptilodes taprobanes* (Felder & Rogenhofer, 1875); *Vietteilus stenoptilioides* Gibeaux, 1994; and the recently described *Xyroptila irina* Kovtunovich & Ustjuzhanin, 2006 (Kovtunovich and Ustjuzhanin 2006).
[44] Regarding pterophorids in the tribe Exelastini, "*pumilio*" is kept here in *Exelastis* (it is the t.s. of *Hepalastis*, but a syn. of *Exelastis*; see Gielis 2003: 57). The count includes one additional species of *Exelastis*, *E. pilum*, described by Gielis (2009).
[45] For Oxyptilini plume moths, the count comprises also *Buckleria madecassea* Gibeaux, 1994, *Eucapperia bullifera* (Meyrick, 1918), and *Stenodacma wahlbergi* (Zeller, 1852), plus the genus *Apoxyptilus*, recently introduced to the fauna by Gielis (2011), based on *A. steineri* Gielis, 2011.
[46] Oidaematophorini pterophorids comprise, additionally, *Adaina microdactyla* (Hübner, 1813), *Hellinsia* (2 spp.), *Paulianilus conyzae* Gibeaux, 1994, *Picardia betsileo* Gibeaux, 1994, *P. orchatias* (Meyrick, 1908), *Pselnophorus laudatus* Bigot, 1964, and *Setosipennula viettei* Gibeaux, 1994.
[47] Multiple representatives of the genus *Copromorpha* (BOLD:ACS8825, BOLD:ACV2318, BOLD:ACS7617, BOLD:ACV2958, BOLD:ACS7617)

have been DNA barcoded for the island (Lopez-Vaamonde et al. 2019: Supplementary data).

[48] The carposinid fruit-boring moth *Meridarchis scyrodes* Meyrick, 1916 is included here, as it was mentioned by Viette (1990: 71) although not listed for Madagascar by Afromoths (its type locality is India, but it is an economic pest). The genus *Epicopistis* is also recorded based on DNA barcoding (BOLD:ABW6776) (Lopez-Vaamonde et al. 2019: Supplementary data).

[49] Gaedike (2004) introduced Epermeniidae for the fauna, describing seven species in three genera (*Epermenia brevilineolata*, *E. griveaudi*, *E. maculata*, *E. mineti*, *E. minuta*, *Mesepermenia malgachica*, and *Ochromolopis pallida*).

[50] If one disregards two misplaced "lecithocerid" species (see Notes, above), just one named species was included by Viette (1990) in the Immidae. Nevertheless, Madagascar has a fairly rich immid fauna according to DNA barcodes (Lopez-Vaamonde et al. 2019).

[51] Although Madagascar has a rather rich choreutid diversity, the only named species recorded to date from the island is the widespread *Tebenna micalis* (Mann, 1857) (Lopez-Vaamonde et al. 2019), a taxon apparently misidentified by Viette (1990: *Tebenna "bjerkandrella"*). However, representatives of two other genera, *Anthophila* (BOLD:ABW1507) and *Brenthia* (BOLD:ACS7384), have been recorded via DNA barcoding (Lopez-Vaamonde et al. 2019: Supplementary data).

[52] Galacticidae was introduced to the fauna via *Homadaula ravula* Mey, 2004 (see Mey, 2004: 91–102).

[53] Our Tortricidae arrangement includes systematic information from Regier et al. (2012) and taxonomic information from Gilligan et al. (2018). It also takes into account unpublished data (J. Baixeras and J. Brown) and Afromoths.

[54] The tribe Archipini also contains the following smaller tortricine genera and species: *Adoxophyes* (3 spp.); *Anthophrys spectabilis* Diakonoff, 1960; *Bactrostoma cinis* Diakonoff, 1960; *Balioxena iospila* Meyrick, 1912; *Brachyvalva inoffensa* Diakonoff, 1960; *Clepsis* (2 spp.); *Cornusaccula periopa* Diakonoff, 1960; *Cosmiophrys* (2 spp.); *Diactora oxymorpha* Diakonoff, 1960; *Epichorista sicca* Meyrick, 1912; *Furcinula* (2 spp.); *Gephyraspis* (3 spp.); *Homona saclava* (Mabille 1900); *Homonoides euryplaca* (Meyrick, 1933); *Labidosa sogai* Diakonoff, 1960; *Midaellobes rubrostrigana* (Mabille, 1900); *Niphothixa* (3 spp.); *Paramesiodes* (2 spp.); *Peteliacma torrescens* Meyrick, 1912; *Platysemaphora rubiginosa* Diakonoff, 1960; *Procrica imitans* (3 spp.); *Vialonga* (2 spp.); *Viettea spectabilis* Diakonoff, 1960; and *Xenophylla megalogona* (Diakonoff, 1947).

[55] Representing Tortricinae: Cnephasiini, *"Cnephasia" imitans* is not a true *Cnephasia*, and the presence of this tribe on Madagascar needs to be reevaluated (see Gilligan et al. 2018).

[56] *Panegyra stenovalva* was recently added to Tortricini by Razowski (2005), and *Brachiolia amblopsis* (Meyrick, 1911) is also added to the fauna (based on a DNA barcoded specimen, representing BOLD:ACV3227; Lopez-Vaamonde et al. 2019: Supplementary data).

[57] Cochylini includes *Chloanohieris comastes* Diakonoff, 1989 and *Oligobalia viettei* Diakonoff, 1988 as well as *"Cochylis" unicolorana* Mabille, 1900 (see Gilligan et al. 2018).

[58] Regarding the olethreutine tribe Microcorsini, the otherwise African species *Cryptaspasma kigomana* Aarvik, 2005 (see Aarvik, 2005) was recently barcoded from Madagascar on BOLD but is not currently listed in Gilligan et al. (2018).

[59] Olethreutini also contains the following genera and species: *Acantheucosma trachyptila* Diakonoff, 1988; *Astronauta* (2 spp.); *Aterpia microchlamys* (Diakonoff, 1983); *Basigonia anisoscia* Diakonoff, 1983; *Bucephalacra* (2 spp.); *Celypha perfracta* Diakonoff, 1983; *Cosmopoda* (2 spp.); *Cosmorrhyncha ocellata* (Mabille, 1900); *Dolichohedya tripila* Diakonoff, 1970; *Dudua* (3 spp.); *Episimus selenosema* Diakonoff, 1963; *Eudemis polychroma* Diakonoff, 1981; *Hilaroptila mimetica* Diakonoff, 1970; *Hopliteccopsis* (2 spp.); *Megalomacha tigripes* Diakonoff, 1960; *Megalota antefracta* Diakonoff, 1981; *Mesocharis centrifuga* Diakonoff, 1981; *Metendothenia* (3 spp.); *Niphadophylax hemicycla* Diakonoff, 1992; *Olethreutes anisorrhopa* Diakonoff, 1983; *Phaecasiophora* (2 spp.); and *Xenopotamia radians* Diakonoff, 1983. Also, *Afroploce karsholti* and *Afrothreutes madoffei*, which were described by Aarvik (2004), were added to the fauna by Lopez-Vaamonde et al. (2019: Supplementary data), as was a member of the otherwise Oriental/Indo-Australasian genus *Sorolopha* (BOLD:ACU2380).

[60] Enarmoniini comprises the species *Aemulatrix notognatha* Diakonoff, 1988; *Dasybregma gypsodoxa* Diakonoff; 1983; *Tetramoera leptalea* Diakonoff, 1988; and *T. schistaceana* (Snellen, 1891).

[61] Eucosmini also comprises *Acroclita pertracta* Diakonoff, 1989; *Bascaneucosma magicopa* Diakonoff, 1989; *Cosmetra rythmosema* Diakonoff, 1992; *Crocidosema* (2 spp., including *lantana* Busck, 1910; Lopez-Vaamonde et al. 2019); *Eucosma bactromorpha* Diakonoff, 1992; *Gypsonoma penthetria* Diakonoff, 1992; *Icelita poliocycla* (Diakonoff, 1988); *Megaherpystis agmatophora* Diakonoff, 1989; *Neaspasia loxochlamys* Diakonoff, 1989; *Niphadostola* (3 spp.); *Notocelia* (2 spp.); *Penestostoma compsa* Diakonoff, 1992; *Potiosa vapulata* (Diakonoff, 1963); *Retinia mecynopus* Diakonoff, 1989; *Rhodotoxotis* (3 spp.); *Sociognatha oligoropa* Diakonoff, 1989; *Strepsicrates* (2 spp.); *Stygitropha funebris* Diakonoff, 1983; *Syngamoneura rubronotana* Mabille, 1900; *Syropetrova viridis* Diakonoff, 1970; *Thylacogaster rhodomenia* Diakonoff, 1988; and *Yunusemreia triangulum* (Diakonoff, 1970).

[62] Grapholitini also includes *Acanthoclita pectinata* (Diakonoff, 1988); *Coniostola stereoma* (Meyrick, 1912); *Dracontogena niphadonta* Diakonoff, 1970; *Eucosmocydia oedipus* Diakonoff, 1988; *Fulcrifera cirrata* Diakonoff, 1987; *Hyposarotis* (2 spp.); *Leguminivora glycinivorella* (Matsumura, 1898); *Microsarotis pauliani* Diakonoff, 1988; *Pammenitis calligrapha* Diakonoff, 1988; and *Stephanopyga legnota* Diakonoff, 1988. Also *Muhabbetina psymythistes* Diakonoff, 1988 was transferred from *Mesotes*. Recently added by Brown and Timm (2017) were *Celsumaria elongata*, *C. soror*, and *Grapholita mesosocia* Diakonoff, 1969 (based on a DNA barcode).

[63] Bartsch (2009) added the sesiine *Melittosesia flavitarsa*.

[64] After Bartsch and Berg (2012), the synanthedonine sesiids contain the recently described *Camaegeria lychnitis*, *C. polytelis*, *C. viettei*, and *C. xanthomos* (by Bartsch 2018); *Cinctosesia polistiformis* and *Nesosphecia mystica*; as well as *Epitarsipus rufitarsus* Le Cerf, 1922 and *Rodolphia humbergi* Le Cerf, 1911 (= *"Malgassesia" pauliani* Viette, 1955).

[65] Bakowski et al. (2008) introduced Tinthiinae to the sesiid fauna via *Similipepsis eumenidiformis* and *S. maromizaensis*.

[66] More recently described in Pseudocossinae are *Pseudocossus mineti* Yakovlev, 2011; *P. olsoufieffae* Yakovlev, 2011; *P. pljustchi* Yakovlev & Saldaitis, 2011; and *P. viettei* Yakovlev, 2011. The genus was included in the molecular phylogeny of Regier et al. (2013: Supplement S1, S2), confirming the phylogenetic position of this internally feeding genus (D. Lees, unpublished data) within Brachodidae and Cossoidea.

[67] The brachodid subfamily Phycodinae contains *Nigilgia*. See Kallies (2013) for an Afrotropical treatment of this Old World, day-flying, *Ficus*-feeding genus (figured in Staude et al. 2016: S246-S248 for an African species and there misidentified as a *Homadaula*, Galacticidae).

[68] There is only one dudgeoneid species on Madagascar (Viette 1990: 45). The website Afromoths erroneously mentions a second Malagasy species, *"Dudgeonea" locuples* (Mabille, 1879) (original combination: *Endagria locuples*), ignoring Whalley's (1967) designation of a neotype for the latter, thus now regarded as a senior syn. of the thyridid *Argyrotypus locuples* Butler, 1879 (Viette 1990: 71).

[69] Cossinae includes in addition: *Hirtocossus* (2 spp.); the recently described species *Planctogystia legraini* Yakovlev & Saldaitis, 2011; *P. lemur* Yakovlev, 2009; *P. olsoufieffae* Yakovlev, 2011; and *Rambuasalama augustasi* Yakovlev & Saldaitis 2008 (see Yakovlev 2009, 2011; Yakovlev and Saldaitis 2008).

[70] Cossidae: Zeuzerinae also contains *Phragmataecia itremo* Viette, 1974 and *Strigocossus* (2 spp.).

[71] Among Epipyropidae, a species of the genus *Fulgoraecia* has been DNA barcoded (BOLD:ACS3762) on Madagascar (Lopez-Vaamonde et al. 2019: Supplementary data).

[72] The Malagasy zygaenid species, including some undescribed diversity (Lees and Minet 2003: 758, note 23), likely belong to the tribe Artonini in Procridinae (S.-H. Yen, unpublished data).

[73] The peculiar moth *Boisduvalodes tamatavana* (Oberthür, 1922) (Figure 9.69e) was retained in Limacodidae in both Viette (1980, 1990: 65) and Afromoths, but see Lees and Minet (2003: 758, note 22) regarding its placement in Somabrachyidae.
[74] Chrysopolominae, tentatively maintained as a subfamily of limacodid slug moths, contains only *Vietteopoloma madagascariensis* Hering, 1961.
[75] Limacodinae also contains the smaller genera and species: *Ambaliha exsanguis* (Saalmüller, 1880); *Andaingo ecclesiastica* Hering, 1928; *Fletcherodes brunnea* (Viette, 1951); *Heringodes robinsoni* (Viette, 1965); *Heringocena* (3 spp.); *Heringyra* (3 spp.); *Lemuria gracilis* (Butler, 1882); *Lemuricomes* (2 spp.); *Macrosemyra tenebrosa* Butler, 1882; *Malgassica* (3 spp.); *Mandoto* (3 spp.); *Omocenops* (3 spp.); *Paryphantina argentifera* Hering, 1933; *Prosternidia metallica* Saalmüller, 1884; *Pseudolatoia* (3 spp.); *Pseudomocena albens* Hering, 1957; *Psythiarodes mahafaly* Viette, 1980; *Thliptocnemis* (3 spp.); and *Vietteiola viettei* Hering, 1957. *Lemuricomes vadoni* Viette, 1965 and *L. xerophyta* Viette, 1965, treated by Viette (1980: 15–16) as two subspecies of *Ambaliha vadoni*, are syns. of *Paryphantina argentifera* Hering, 1933 according to Afromoths, a genus and species strangely not mentioned by Viette (1980; but see 1990: 68). We treat these names here as a single species of *Paryphantina*. *Thliptocnemis robusta* (Kenrick, 1917) is a syn. of *T. barbipes* Mabille, 1900 according to Afromoths.
[76] Contains *Crothaema sericea* Butler, 1880, a taxon also present in South Africa. See comments by Viette (1980: 8–11); hence this taxon is Limacodidae *i.s.* The family-group name Crothaeminae Hering, 1955 is available.
[77] Stenomatidae (= Stenomidae) is an almost entirely Neotropical group, often treated as a subfamily (e.g., within the Depressariidae), containing on Madagascar a large radiation only of the robust-bodied genus *Herbulotiana*.
[78] Although hitherto not widely recognized as such, the Peleopodidae is a massive radiation on Madagascar (Lopez-Vaamonde et al. 2019, with many species known only from DNA barcode clusters), largely composed of Oditinae (see Wang and Li 2020 for a phylogeny).
[79] The genera *Abychodes* and *Pseudepiphractis* are here transferred from the Oecophoridae to the Peleopodinae. Indeed, these insects have in the male genitalia the typical spinose gnathos found in this subfamily (entire in *Abychodes* but divided in *Pseudepiphractis* as in, e.g., the genus *Durrantia*). Moreover, their hind-wing venation is also of peleopodine type.
[80] The peleopodine subfamily Oditinae, considered before to belong to Depressariidae or Lecithoceridae, also contains *Anoditica concretella* Viette, 1956; *Catanomistis loxophracta* Meyrick, 1933; *Ghuryx* (3 spp.); *Mexytocerus enigmaticus* Viette, 1989; *Mocquerysiella* (3 spp.); *Prothamnodes bathocentrella* Viette, 1968; and the additional four species mentioned below. Eight of the genera are here transferred from the Xyloryctidae to the Oditinae (previously restricted to *Odites* among Malagasy micromoths). In terms of recognition, like several members of the Australian Xyloryctidae, species of Oditinae have, on the dorsal surface of the hind wing, a fringe of piliform scales (pecten) along the lower edge of the discal cell. Nevertheless, they have a distinctive hind-wing venation (with short upper edge of the cell) and a downturned, pointed gnathos (occasionally lost), which resembles that found in the Lecithoceridae. We also place in Oditinae the following four species described by Pierre Viette in inappropriate genera: "*Cryptolechia*" *quadripunctella*; "*Cryptolechia*" *toulgoetianum*; *Odites nigropunctella* (Viette, 1955) comb. nov. (misplaced in *Pachnistis*, see comment 85); and "*Tanyzancla*" *oberthuerella* (see Notes, above).
[81] We tentatively place in Peleopodidae (thus *i.s.*) the monotypic genus *Beforona* (previously in Oecophoridae). Indeed, this very large and spectacular "micromoth" (Figure 9.69f) has no pecten to the scape (antenna) and possesses in its forewing venation two traits usually present in the Peleopodidae, namely a very large "anal loop" and the remoteness of veins Rs_1 and Rs_2.
[82] We assign to Oecophoridae (subfamily *i.s.*) *Betroka gibeauxella* (Viette, 1986), *B. malgassella* (Viette, 1956), and *B. peyrierasella* (Viette, 1986) (all three: comb. nov.) to the previously monotypic genus *Betroka* Viette, 1955 (t.s. *B. jacobsella*). These three species (described in "*Scieropepla*" or in "*Xylorycta*") are larger than *B. jacobsella* but share with it a similar habitus, a nearly identical wing venation, and strikingly similar male genitalia. We tentatively place *Betroka* in the Oecophoridae on account of its hind-wing veins R_5 and M_1, which are separate and parallel proximally (a plesiomorphy, nevertheless). Its robust, strongly sclerotized gnathos is fused to neither the uncus (unlike that of typical Xyloryctidae) nor the tegumen. However, the shape of this gnathos may suggest possible affinities with the Xyloryctidae. We place near *Betroka* the species "*Scieropepla*" *minetorum* Viette, 1987, which has similar male genitalia and differs from it only by its habitus and minor details. *Psarolitia maisongrossella* (Viette, 1955) comb. nov. is here transferred from *Lasiomactra* (absent from Madagascar) to the genus *Psarolitia* Viette, 1956 (Oecophoridae *i.s.*, erroneously described in Xyloryctidae). Indeed, its wing venation and male genitalia are strikingly similar to those of *P. albogriseella* Viette, 1956 (t.s. of *Psarolitia*).
[83] Among the 46 "lecithocerid" species listed by Viette (1990: 40–41), 29 are misplaced in this family (notably those 20 in *Odites*; also *Mexytocerus enigmaticus* Viette, 1989 and *Lecithocera ojejyella* Viette, 1968, as noted by Lopez-Vaamonde et al. 2019—see Gelechioidea *i.s.*, comment 107, and two in Immidae, comment 50). The described fauna contains no genuine members of the genera *Idiopteryx* and *Lecithocera*; hence the name *Lecithocera s.l.* for those species is used in our table. By contrast, as noticed by Lees and Minet (2003: 758, note 19), "*Adela*" *janineae* Viette, 1954 is a true Lecithoceridae, definitely not an Adelidae. Moreover, the following BINs are identified as *Lecithocera* in the online data set of Lopez-Vaamonde et al. (2019): BOLD:ACV2351, BOLD:ACS0308, BOLD:ACS4437, and indeed the lattermost is only 3.8% pairwise divergent to a potential representative of the t.s., *Lecithocera nigrana*, from Italy (see Notes above).
[84] In Xyloryctidae (*s.s.*) we assign to *Phracyps* Viette, 1952 two species described in "*Scieropepla*" (an Australian genus, which does not occur on Madagascar), namely *P. byblinopa* (Meyrick, 1925) comb. nov. and *P. nephelocentra* (Meyrick, 1933) comb. nov. These species are close relatives (if not senior synonyms) of, respectively, *P. longifasciella* and *P. lebisella*. Nevertheless, the genera *Eporycta*, *Phracyps*, and *Pseudoprocometis* are hardly distinct and may be synonymized when better studied. Their male genitalia (regarding *Eporycta*, see Mey 2011: 193) have an elongate, subtriangular/subconical juxta, which may represent a synapomorphy with *Opisina* (= *Nephantis*) and its relatives such as *Hylypnes* (taxa whose larvae live on monocots).
[85] The autostichid genus *Pachnistis* was erroneously recorded from Madagascar, leaving only *Encrasima insularis* (Butler, 1880) as a representative of the autostichid fauna. As mentioned above (comment 80), "*Pachnistis*" *nigropunctella* is an *Odites* belonging to a group of small species whose hind wings have lost vein M_2 (and whose male genitalia have lost the gnathos).
[86] Cryptolechiidae here comprises only *Eutorna diluvialis* Meyrick, 1913 and *E. punctinigrella* Viette, 1955. Viette (1990: 37) lists these two species in *Orophia*, with *Cryptolechia* as a syn., as well as "*Orophia*" *madagascariensis* (Viette, 1951), a species that we move to Gelechioidea *i.s.* Like Lvovsky (2012), we tentatively use the term "Cryptolechiidae" for the *Orophia* group (composed not only of *Orophia* and *Eutorna* but also *Cacochroa*). On the one hand, there is no obvious synapomorphy between *Cryptolechia* (t.s. *C. straminella* Zeller, 1852; "*Cryptolechia*" has been used by authors for various unrelated "oecophorid" species) and the monophyletic *Orophia* group, except perhaps for the parallel rows of spines present on the gnathos (see Lvovsky 2012: Figure 28, which shows the male genitalia of *C. straminella*). Indeed, it should be noted that such a gnathos (entire or divided) also occurs in several other groups of Gelechioidea (as a homoplasy). On the other hand, confusingly, the "*Cryptolechia*" species placed among Autostichidae in Figure 2 of Wang and Li (2020) are clearly misplaced in this genus, and their male genitalia (without gnathos) are of a quite different type. The Oriental species placed in Autostichidae in Wang and Li's Figure 2 have typical periacmine male genitalia (without gnathos). See also Lvovsky (2012), which illustrates the male genitalia of the t.s. of *Cryptolechia*. Regarding the above three "*Cryptolechia*" described by Viette, none actually belongs to the *Orophia* group, according to examination by J. Minet of the corresponding genitalia slides. Two belong to the Oditinae (*quadripunctella*; *toulgoetianum*; comment 80, *q.v.*) while the third one remains Gelechioidea *i.s.* (comment 107, *q.v.*; *madagascariensis*).

[87] Elachistidae (Elachistinae) contains *Elachista crocogastra* Meyrick, 1908 (Parenti, 2006) and "*Antispila*" *merinaella* (Viette, 1956), the latter a leafminer on Commelinaceae (Paulian and Viette 1955: 145). Now *E. merinaella* (Viette, 1956) comb. nov., this species was transferred by Nieukerken and Geertsema (2015: 43) from the Heliozelidae to the Elachistidae. It was in any case included in error as an "*Antispila*" by Lopez-Vaamonde et al. (2019), and although the last reference mentions leaf mines, we have been unable to otherwise verify the presence of Heliozelidae on Madagascar. D. Lees has reared an Elachistinae from a leaf mine on grasses on Madagascar, and species of *Elachista* can be abundant in Malaise trap samples (see Lopez-Vaamonde et al. 2019).

[88] The Batrachedridae were recently recognized for Madagascar based on DNA barcoding (Lopez-Vaamonde et al. 2019), but there is as yet no described species.

[89] *Coleophora lastukhini* (Anikin, 2019) comb. nov. has been described in *Casignetella* Strand, 1928, but this genus is usually regarded as a syn. of *Coleophora* Hübner, 1822. *Coleophora leucobela* (Meyrick, 1934) is confirmed also as a true Coleophoridae (see Anikin 2019).

[90] Enriching slightly the fauna of Ethmiidae (previously often regarded as a subfamily of either Depressariidae or Elachistidae; see nevertheless, e.g., Wang and Li 2020), "*Trichocirca*" *decaryanum* (Viette, 1954) (see also Lees and Minet: 758: note 14; 758: note 21) has been transferred to the genus *Ethmia* (Wei et al. 2007). The genus *Trichocirca* Meyrick, 1920 (Choreutidae) does not exist on Madagascar to our knowledge.

[91] According to the original description of *Mompha millotella* Viette, 1955, the larvae of this species make galls on Melastomataceae (see also Bruzzese et al. 2019).

[92] Blastobasidae contains the otherwise East African *Neoblastobasis ximeniaella* Adamski, 2010 (recognized from a DNA barcode, BOLD:ACL6083, as well as another exemplar of this genus, BOLD:ACS3752, and two representatives of the genus *Blastobasis*, BOLD:ACS4582, BOLD:ACS7341) (Lopez-Vaamonde et al. 2019).

[93] The Scythrididae count includes the addition to the fauna of *Scythris schouteni* by Bengtsson (2014).

[94] Adding the subfamily Chrysopeleinae to the cosmopterigid fauna, *Ascalenia* and *Gisilia* were recently identified from Madagascar based on DNA barcodes not identified to species, as was *Stilbosis*, BOLD:ABY7721 (Lopez-Vaamonde et al. 2019: Table 3 and Supplementary data).

[95] The cosmopterigid subfamily Antequerinae contains two species of *Macrobathra*: *M. antimeloda* Meyrick, 1930 and *M. sikoraella* (Viette, 1956). "*Macrobathra*" *auratella* Viette, 1958 is here excluded from true *Macrobathra* (t.s. *M. chrysotoxa* Meyrick, 1886 from Australia) and does not belong to Cosmopterigidae either. It is placed instead among Gelechioidea *i.s.* (see comment 107).

[96] Recently added to the Malagasy cosmopterigid fauna is *Scaeosopha betrokensis* Sinev & Li, 2012 (see H. Li et al. 2012). The subfamily Scaeosophinae belongs to Cosmopterigidae on molecular grounds also (Wang and Li 2020).

[97] Recently added to the Cosmopteriginae fauna from DNA barcoding is *Anatrachyntis simplex* (Walsingham, 1891) (Lopez-Vaamonde et al. 2019) as well as the recently described *Cosmopterix athesiae* Huemer & Koster, 2006. Removed from the cosmopterigid fauna are "*Meleonoma*" *diehlella* Viette, 1955 and "*Meleonoma*" *impulsa* Meyrick, 1934 (two species indisputably misplaced in *Meleonoma*, a genus not known to occur on Madagascar; cf. comment 107). Moreover *Meleonoma* Meyrick, 1914 (t.s. *Cryptolechia stomota* Meyrick, 1910) is no longer considered to be a cosmopterigid (Periacminae according to Lvovsky 2015; Autostichidae: Periacminae according to Wang and Li 2020). These species are here placed in Gelechioidea *i.s.* (comment 107, q.v.).

[98] The classification adopted here for the Gelechiidae is based on recently published molecular phylogenies, in particular on that of Karsholt et al. (2013). Nevertheless, various more recent phylogenies (e.g., Sohn et al. 2015; Wang and Li 2020) are to some extent in conflict with that study, e.g., in the position of Thiotrichinae.

[99] A member of the anacampsine tribe Chelariini, *Anarsia agricola* Walsingham, 1891, is now known to occur on Madagascar (cf. a publicly available DNA barcode).

[100] *Syncopacma sikoraella* Viette, 1957 is an addition to the fauna belonging to the tribe Anacampsini. *Aproaerema simplexella* (Walker, 1854) is also recognized for the island from DNA barcoding (BOLD:ACK6985; Lopez-Vaamonde et al. 2019).

[101] The dichomeridine gelechiids include *Brachmia* (2 spp.) as well as a large radiation of *Dichomeris* (see Figure 9.69g). "*Cymotricha*" *tepens* (Meyrick, 1923) and *Dichomeris* ("*Eporgastis*") *asaphocosma* (Meyrick, 1934) were synonymized with *Dichomeris* by Hodges (1986); see also Ponomarenko 2009: 258, 307; K. Sattler, unpublished data. Lopez-Vaamonde et al. 2019 added *D. acuminata* Staudinger in Kalchberg, 1876 to the fauna (as "*acuminatus*"). They also include *Helcystogramma metallica* (Walsingham, 1891). Note also that there currently exist two barcodes (belonging to BOLD:ACS8527) of a "*Tricyanaula*" species from Madagascar, 9.33% divergent to a barcode of *Tricyanaula* "*metallica*" (representing BOLD:AAJ8506) from Tanzania and two other East African BINs that are probably congeneric (BOLD:ACX6421, BOLD:ADU5939). *Tricyanaula* Meyrick, 1925 is a syn. of *Helcystogramma* according to Hodges (1998) (the t.s. of *Helcystogramma* is *Gelechia obseratella* Zeller, 1877, while that of *Tricyanaula* is *Strobisia aurantiaca* Walsingham, 1887, Sri Lanka). "*Tricyanaula*" indeed genitalically conforms to *Helcystogramma* (K. Sattler, unpublished data), although there might ultimately be reason to split up the last genus. Furthermore, it remains to be established if *H. metallica* really exists also on Madagascar (see Notes above).

[102] In Thiotrichinae, three representatives of the genus *Thiotricha* (BOLD:ACS4452, BOLD:ACV2086, BOLD:ACU8873) have been DNA barcoded from Madagascar (Lopez-Vaamonde et al. 2019: Supplementary data).

[103] Concerning the only species so far described from Madagascar in the gelechiid subfamily Anomologinae, the male genitalia of *Pycnoditis* t.s. (*P. erebaula* Meyr. from South Africa) are of the distinctive anomologine type; the hind-wing shape is also relatively characteristic (J. Minet, unpublished data). An additional genus, *Monochroa*, was added based on a DNA barcode (BOLD:ACV3124; Lopez-Vaamonde et al. 2019: Supplementary data).

[104] Mentioned by Viette (1990: 44) although not by Afromoths for Madagascar, the potato tuber pest *Phthorimaea operculella* (Zeller, 1873) is the only local representative of the tribe Gnorimoschemini.

[105] Representing Litini (= Teleiodini), multiple clusters belonging to the genus *Teleiopsis* have been DNA barcoded for the island (BOLD:ACS4761, BOLD:ACU2256, BOLD:ACV1969, BOLD:ACV2433, BOLD:ACU7617, BOLD:ACV6177, BOLD:ACV2735, BOLD:ACS6591, BOLD:ACU8874, BOLD:ACU4829) (Lopez-Vaamonde et al. 2019: Supplementary data).

[106] Regarding Gelechiidae *i.s.*, J. Minet (unpublished data) has examined the type of *Symbatica heimella* Viette, 1954 (t.s. *S. cryphias* Meyrick, 1910, from South Africa; not Lecithoceridae and possibly Autostichidae based on male genitalia in Janse [1960]; K. Sattler, unpublished data). Its female retinaculum (a row of scales along the upper edge of the discal cell) is clearly of the Gelechiidae type and does not pertain to Lecithoceridae. *Idiophantis* was historically in Meyrick's "group 4" (= Anacampsinae) (K. Sattler, unpublished data). The genus is widespread in the Afrotropics, and biological information can be attributed (see Afromoths; Staude et al. 2016: S7s, S74, rearings M679b, BM763b–c, here identified as *Idiophantis*, which were reared on *Sphedamnocarpus*, Malpighiaceae).

[107] A number of taxa cannot be definitively placed in the Gelechioidea. Among Gelechioidea *i.s.* are a number of species that remain misplaced at generic or family level: "*Lecithocera*" *ojejyella* Viette, 1986, suggested to be related to *Epichostis* (Lopez-Vaamonde et al. 2019: 113), an Oriental genus of unstable placement according to Wang and Li (2000); "*Macrobathra*" *auratella* Viette, 1958 (another possible *Epichostis* relative); "*Meleonoma*" *diehlella* Viette, 1955 and "*Meleonoma*" *impulsa* Meyrick, 1934 (the genus *Meleonoma*, which does not exist on Madagascar, was convincingly assigned to the Autostichidae: Periacminae by Wang and Li 2020); and "*Orophia*" *madagascariensis* (Viette, 1951). Although the radiation of *Orygocera* on Madagascar is impressive, the genus also occurs in Africa and in the Mascarenes. It was placed erroneously in Gelechiidae by Viette (1990: 43, where synonymized with *Epiphractis*,

Calliphractis, and *Rhozale*; see also Lees and Minet 2003: 758, note 21). Biological information can be attributed to this genus, with rearings on *Euclea*, Ebenaceae (Staude et al. 2016: S72, references M101 and M905, recognized by the habitus of the adults). We also place *Tyriograptis* (all three species) in Gelechioidea *i.s.* The male genitalia of the t.s. of *Tyriograptis* (*T. strepsaula*) was illustrated by Viette (1956a: Figure 9), clearly showing that this genus is a close relative of *Orygocera* (see Notes above).

[108] Regarding Coeliadinae, *Tekliades* Grishin, 2019 has been established for *T. ramanatek* (Boisduval, 1833), a species representing the oldest lineage of one of two groups within Coeliadinae, also occurring in the Comoros (see W. Li et al. 2019). Formerly also in *Coeliades* is *Pyrrhiades pansa* (Hewitson, [1867]) (= *Coeliades ernesti* (Grandidier, 1867); see Williams 2020).

[109] See W. Li et al. (2019: Supplementary T2). Tagiadinae now comprises Celaenorrhinini, Netrocoryini (which does not occur on Madagascar), and Tagiadini. Note also that Pyrginae is no longer recognized for Madagascar.

[110] In a revision of Afrotropical Celaenorrhinini (Libert 2014), one new Malagasy species was described in this tribe: *Celaenorrhinus landryi* Libert, 2014. Its type locality (Antananarivo) is unlikely.

[111] See W. Li et al. (2019) for systematic placement of the two Tagiadini genera on Madagascar.

[112] See Zhang et al. (2020) regarding this subfamily and its placement deep within essentially monocot-feeding lineages of skippers. Malazinae is the second Lepidoptera subfamily recognized as endemic to Madagascar (see also Griveaudiinae; Figure 9.69i).

[113] See W. Li et al. (2019) regarding tribal placement of Afrotropical Heteropterinae.

[114] Hesperiinae also includes *Acleros leucopyga* (Mabille, 1877); *Artitropa* (3 spp.); *Gegenes pumilio* (Hoffmannsegg, 1804); *Parnara naso* (Fabricius, 1798); *Pelopidas mathias* (Fabricius, 1798); *Ploetzia amygdalis* (Mabille, 1877); and *Xanthodisca ariel* (Mabille, 1878). For number of *Fulda* species, we follow Lees et al. (2003), except for the *F. bernieri* complex, in which, as in Viette (1956b), *bernieri* (Boisduval, 1833) = *lucida* Evans, 1937 = *gatiana* (Oberthür, 1923) = *pauliani* Evans, 1952. See Huang et al. (2019) regarding *Galerga*, following the original composition of Viette (1956b), whose species were placed in *Arnetta* in Lees et al. (2003). *Gegenes pumilio* (Hoffmannsegg, 1804) is recorded from a single museum specimen in Leiden (de Jong and Coutsis 2017). A tribal arrangement is awaited for the hesperiine fauna (see e.g., W. Li et al. 2019) but the Malagasy fauna includes Astictopterini (*Galerga* at least; Huang et al. 2019) as well as Baorini (*Borbo*, *Gegenes*, *Parnara*, and *Pelopidas*).

[115] Arrangement of pierine tribes and their generic composition follows Wahlberg et al. (2014). *Appias* belongs to subtribe *Appiadina*, while Aporiina comprises *Belenois*, *Dixeia*, and *Mylothris*; Madagascar has no Pierina.

[116] Uniquely representing Nepheroniini on Madagascar, *Nepheronia pauliani* Bernardi, 1958 was raised to species level by Nazari et al. (2011).

[117] *Gideona* is treated as a valid genus as in Wahlberg et al. (2014), not part of *Colotis* as in Lees et al. (2003). *Colotis* now has five species, and the tribe Teracolini also includes *Pinacopteryx mabillei* Aurivillius, [1899], the last raised to species level by Nazari et al. (2011).

[118] See Espeland et al. (2015) for tribal treatments within Riodinidae.

[119] Lycaenidae subfamilies and tribes are arranged according to Espeland et al. (2018). In the case of Polyommatini, that study suggests polyphyly of this tribe.

[120] Polyommatini (*s.l.*) also contains *Actizera* (2 spp.; *drucei* now regarded as a syn. of *A. atrigemmata* contrary to Lees et al. 2003; also see their note 100); *Azanus* (2 spp.); *Cacyreus darius* (Mabille, 1877); *Catachrysops scintilla* (Mabille, 1877); *Cupidopsis* (2 spp.); *Freyeria* (2 spp.); *Lampides boeticus* (Linnaeus, 1767); *Leptotes* (2 spp.); *Pseudonacaduba sichela* (Wallengren, 1857); *Uranothauma artemenes* (Mabille, 1880); *Zizeeria knysna* (Trimen, 1862); *Zizina antanossa* (Mabille, 1877); *Zizula hylax* (Fabricius, 1775); as well as the recently invasive *Chilades pandava* (Horsfield, [1829]) (see Wu et al. 2010); *Chilades* is distinct from *Freyeria*.

[121] Regarding Charaxinae, "*Euxanthe*" *madagascariensis* and "*Polyura*" *zoolina betsimisaraka* are here treated as members of *Charaxes* (i.e., subgenera at best) following Aduse-Poku et al. (2009).

[122] Satyrini contains *Heteropsis* (subtribe Mycalesina) and *Strabena* (Ypthimina), the two largest radiations of butterflies on Madagascar. Lees (2016) introduced 19 new species of *Heteropsis*. Although not affecting our count, *H. fraterna* (Butler, 1879) is treated as a full endemic species (Aduse-Poku et al. 2016).

[123] In Acraeini, past generic treatments differ widely for *Acraea*. Here, *Telchinia* is treated as a separate genus (Silva-Brandão et al. 2008). However, *Pardopsis* is now a member of Argynnini.

[124] The genera of Argynnini fall into two subtribes: Pardopsidina (*Pardopsis*) and Argynnina (*Phalanta*).

[125] See Dhungel and Wahlberg (2018) for a phylogeny and tribal treatment for Limenitidinae.

[126] We use Eunicini rather than Epicaliini for *Sevenia*, following Dias et al. (2019).

[127] See Wahlberg and Rubinoff (2011) regarding constitution of *Vanessa*.

[128] Junoniini contains the three genera *Precis*, *Protogoniomorpha*, and *Junonia*, following Wahlberg et al. (2005).

[129] *Chrysotypus* and *Argyrotypus* are included in Siculodinae (Argyrotypinae is a syn.; Minet 1991). The subfamily contains also *Cornuterus trivius* (Whalley, 1967), *Hapana milloti* (Viette, 1954), and *Symphleps seta* (Viette, 1958).

[130] Whalleyanidae is a valid endemic family whose sister group is now fairly well established (see Notes above).

[131] While Afromoths treats *Hyblaea apricans* (Boisduval, 1833) as a syn. of *H. puera* (Cramer, 1777) (described from Surinam), we follow Viette (1990) and regard it, at least provisionally, as an endemic Malagasy species. Indeed, on molecular evidence, *H. puera s.a.* is a widely distributed species complex, whereas the true *H. puera* would be a strictly Neotropical species (Buchsbaum et al. 2019).

[132] Arrangement of pyralid tribes and generic composition follows in part Mally et al. (2019) and GlobIZ (Nuss et al. 2003).

[133] Galleriinae also contains *Achroia grisella* (Fabricius, 1794); *Acracona pratti* (Kenrick, 1917); *Corcyra cephalonica* (Stainton, 1866); *Eldana saccharina* Walker, 1865; *Galleria mellonella* (Linnaeus, 1758); and *Paroxyptera filiella* (Saalmüller, 1880). While Viette (1990) includes eight species in *Yxygodes* Viette, 1989, we add a ninth species to this genus—indeed, taking into account an unpublished suggestion of the late M. Shaffer (see Beccaloni et al. 2003: "Lepindex"), "*Herculia*" *olapalis* (Viette, 1978) (described in "*Endorina*", i.e., *Eudorina*) is here formally transferred to the genus *Yxygodes* (as *Y. olapalis* (Viette, 1978) comb. nov.). The hymenopteran nest commensals *Achroia grisella* and *Galleria mellonella* are recognized from DNA barcoded specimens (BOLD)—see also Lees and Zilli (2019: 67) with regard to biology of *Acracona*.

[134] Phycitinae treatment largely follows G. Leraut (2019b).

[135] Phycitinae: Anerastiini includes *Ematheudes nigropunctata* (Legrand, 1966); *Maliarpha separatella* Ragonot, 1888; *Peoria nigricostalis* (Walker, 1863); *Polyocha flagrantella* Ragonot, 1901; *P. sanguinariella* (Zeller, 1848); *Saborma vicina* (Saalmüller, 1880); and *Saluria* (= *Pectinigeria*) *furvella* (Ragonot, 1888), as well as, after G. Leraut (2019b): *Ematheudes chryselephantinella*, *Emmalocera deprinsorum*, *E. incarnatella*, *Hypsotropha britomartis*, *Peoria legrandi*, *Polyocha heracleella*, *P. luteocuprella*, and *Polyochodes squalidella*. The genus *Comorta* (BOLD:ACV2205) was added by Lopez-Vaamonde et al. (2019: Supplementary data).

[136] Phycitinae: Cryptoblabini contains *Cryptoblabes gnidiella* (Millière, 1867), to which were added by G. Leraut (2019b): *Cantheleamima nygiella*, *Cryptozophera madegassalis*, and *Xylia sophrosyne*.

[137] Phycitini also contains also *Apomyelois ceratoniae* (Zeller, 1839); *A. subelutellum* (Ragonot, 1901); *Azanicola adspersa* Balinsky, 1991; *Cadra cautella* Walker, 1863; *C. rectivittella* (Ragonot, 1901); *Ceutolopha isidis* Zeller, 1867; *Cactoblastis cactorum* (Berg, 1885); *Conobathra saalmulleri* Ragonot, 1888; *Ecbletodes ethiopella* (Balinsky, 1991); *Edulica rufalis* Hampson, 1901; *Ephestia kuehniella* (Zeller, 1879); *E. elutella* (Hubner, 1796); *Etiella zinckenella* (Treitschke, 1832); *Faveria semiustella* (Hampson, 1901); *Gymnancyla africanella* (Balinsky, 1994); *Harraria diehlella* Marion & Viette, 1956; *Hypsipyla robusta* (Moore, 1886); *Insalebria kozhantschikovi* Filipjev, 1924; *Jakuarte martinalis* Viette, 1953; *Laomedonia grapholitella* (Ragonot, 1888); *Magiriamorpha superpalpia* Balinsky,

1994; *Megasis signatella* Pagenstecher, 1907; *Metoecis carnifex* (Coquerel, 1855); *Microthrix inconspicuella* (Ragonot, 1888); *Moitrelia serrata* (Balinsky, 1994); *Neojoannisia hypolepias* (de Joannis, 1927); *Nyctegretis inclinella* Ragonot, 1888; *N. malgassicola* Roesler, 1982; *Paralaodamia subdivisella* (Ragonot, 1893); *Pempelia funebrella* (Ragonot, 1893); *P. malgassicella* (Marion & Viette, 1956); *P. multicolorella* (Ragonot, 1893); *Phylebria paulianella* (Marion & Viette, 1956); *Plodia interpunctella* (Hübner, [1813]); *Pseudoceroprepes nosivolella* (Viette, 1964); *Psorosa biocellella* (Ragonot, 1893); *Roeslerinia lugubris* (Balinsky, 1994); *Selagiaforma sandrangatoella* Roesler, 1982; *Spatulipalpia ambahonella* Viette, 1964; *Syringia pectinatella* (de Joannis, 1915); *Tephris connexella* Ragonot, 1893; *Thylacoptila paurosema* Meyrick, 1885; *Tsaratanana attavella* (Viette, 1964); and *T. colorella* Roesler, 1982.

To these were added by G. Leraut (2019b): *Acrobasis cattella*, *A. hastella*, *Amphithrix alecto*, *Apomyelois vinosella*, *A. titan*, *Balinskyia apidis*, *Cathyalia pulchrotinctella*, *Ctenomeristis mammatella*, *C. nonnella*, *Duvernoisia argos*, *Epicrocis pulcherrissimella*, *E. strictella*, *Epischnia achatinella*, *Etiella ragonoti*, *E. behri*, *Eurhodope decludti*, *Euzophera mineti*, *Faveria conjugorum*, *Flabellobasis lynx*, *F. attis*, *Homoeosoma castella*, *H. lokoboeella*, *Hypochalcia peyrierasi*, *Laomedonia canescentella*, *Macrophycis andapella*, *M. calinagella*, *Malgachinsula delplanquei*, *M. perpropinquella*, *Micropteria felinella*, *Moitrelia helios*, *Morosaphycita c-album*, *M. dibursella*, *M. orthosiella*, *Nonphycita balinskyi*, *Phycita subsalitella*, *P. phryne*, *P. reductella*, *Phycitodes roesleri*, *Pseudosyria caligraphella*, *Selagia ardosiella*, *Sogaphycis cnephasiella*, [*Thylacoptila paurosema guillermeti*], *Tsaraphycis philippella napaella*, *T. oreadella*, *T. viettei*, *Tsaratanana colorella unicolorella*, and *Veldticola dividivalvella*. Also added was *Phycita demidovi* Guillermet, 2007. Additional generic records based on DNA barcoding are *Anabasis* (BOLD:ACK5713), a genus closely related to *Ctenomeristis*: *Aurana* (BOLD:ACS3383), *Lophothoracia* (BOLD:ACV3112), and *Ptyomaxia* (BOLD:ABX8157) (Lopez-Vaamonde et al. 2019: Supplementary data).

[138] Epipaschiinae contains also *Anexophana robinsonalis* Viette, 1960; *Lepipaschia inornata* Shaffer J. C. & Solis, 1994; *Noctuides griseoviridis* (Pagenstecher, 1907); *Omphalepia dujardini* Viette, 1967; and *Teliphasa andrianalis* Viette, 1960 (see G. Leraut 2019a).

[139] Pyralinae treatment largely follows the works of P. Leraut (2000, 2002, 2004a, 2004b, 2006a, 2006b, 2007, 2008, 2009a, 2009b, 2009c, 2010, 2011a, 2011b, 2013, 2015, 2019).

[140] The Hypotiini fauna comprises only the genus *Hypotia* Zeller, 1847 (syn. *Imerina* Ragonot, 1891 and *Marionodes* Viette, 1953), most species of which were recently described by P. Leraut (2004a, 2004b, 2006a, 2006b, 2006c, 2009a, 2009b, 2009c).

[141] Disregarding two previously misplaced species ("*Herculia*" *olapalis* and "*Philotis*" *gigantalis*; see comments 133 and 143), 79 species of Pyralinae were recorded by Viette (1990) from Madagascar, while the Malagasy Pyralinae now includes more than 190 species if one takes into account the numerous papers by P. Leraut listed in our comment 139. Most of these taxa belong to the tribe Pyralini (177 named species by the end of 2019), which also includes a number of genera that have, to date, just one described species in the limits of the Malagasy fauna, namely *Antisindris*, *Diloxia*, *Embryoglossa*, *Haplosindris*, *Mesosindris*, *Stemmatophora*, and *Synaphe*. By contrast, the genus *Zitha* Walker, [1866] (syn. *Tegulifera* Saalmüller, 1880; see P. Leraut 2000: 244) includes more than half of the species of Malagasy Pyralini.

[142] In Cybalomiinae *s.a.*, *Trichophysetis preciosalis* (Guillermet, 1996) is described from La Réunion, so that genus or others may also be expected on Madagascar.

[143] The subfamily Acentropinae (with aquatic larvae) also contains *Argyractis coloralis* (Guenée, 1854); *Elophila africalis* (Hampson, 1906); *Oligostigma* (2 spp.); *Stegothyris fasciculalis* (Zeller, 1852); *Symphonia* (2 spp.); *Theila fusconebulalis* (Marion, 1954); and *Thevitella alphalis* (Viette, 1958). Moreover, we transfer to the Acentropinae a large Malagasy species erroneously described in the Pyralinae, namely "*Philotis*" *gigantalis* Viette, 1960 (J. Minet, unpublished data). It should be noted that, in the absence of known type material (Viette 1990: 247), *Hydrocampa minimalis* Saalmüller, 1880 (from Nosy Be) remains an unidentified species (conventionally placed in *Elophila* on Afromoths).

[144] Schoenobiinae also contains *Adelpherupa terreus* (Zeller, 1877) and *Donacaula rufalis* (Hampson, 1919). Although South Africa is the type locality of *Patissa virginea* (Zeller, 1852), its presence on Madagascar is accepted on the basis of Viette (1990: 89) (not mentioned in Afromoths).

[145] See Minet (2015) regarding rehabilitation of the family group name Lathrotelinae.

[146] For the tribal composition of Crambinae we have followed GlobIZ and Léger et al. (2019). Only the essentially Neotropical tribe Argyriini is absent. Regarding inclusion of Diptychophorini, although no species have yet been formally described on Madagascar, multiple representatives of *Glaucocharis* have been DNA barcoded for the island (BOLD:ACT1042, BOLD:ACT0084, BOLD:ACT0405, BOLD:ACS0532, BOLD:ACV2682, BOLD:ACU2522, BOLD:ACS1536, BOLD:ACT9988, BOLD:ACU5479) (Lopez-Vaamonde et al. 2019: Supplementary data). Note also, *Bleszynskia* de Lattin 1961 was synonymized with *Angustalius* by Bleszynski (1965: 229).

[147] The scopariine genera *Dipleurinodes* Leraut, 1989; *Eudipleurina* Leraut, 1989; *Malageudonia* Leraut, 1989; *Vietteina* Leraut, 1989; and *Witlesia* Chapman, 1912 have all been synonymized with the genus *Eudonia* Billberg, 1820 (Léger et al. 2019; see also Nuss et al. 2003).

[148] For the Noordinae, here containing only *Noorda*, note that specimens identified as *N. blitealis* Walker, 1859 (the type locality is Ceylon [Sri Lanka]) represent four different barcode clusters on BOLD (BOLD:ABY4426, BOLD:ABY4426, BOLD:ADU8595, BOLD:AAK4370), and in the absence of DNA barcodes, it is not clear which of those BINs, if any, the Madagascar record might represent.

[149] Odontiinae: Eurrhypini also contains *Argyrarcha margarita* (Warren, 1892) and *Clupeosoma orientalalis* (Viette, 1954). See J. Hayden (2011: 239, 245) regarding *Mabilleodes alacralis* (replacement name due to junior secondary homonymy with *Mecyna catalalis* Viette, 1953) and *M. catalalis* treated as two different species in GlobIZ (Nuss et al. 2003). J. Minet has examined the male genitalia of *Mabilleodes catalalis*, and they correspond to typical Eurrhypini.

[150] In the tribe Odontiini, "*Tegostoma*" *millotalis* (Marion, 1956) is probably misplaced in this genus (prep. Marion 693), since the phallus has one very long cornutus.

[151] Arrangement of Crambidae: Pyraustinae tribes and their generic composition follows in part Mally et al. (2019) and GlobIZ (Nuss et al. 2003).

[152] Pyraustinae: Portentomorphini also contains *Cryptosara vadonalis* Marion, 1956; *Hyalobathra dictatrix* Meyrick, 1934; *Pioneabathra olesialis* (Walker, 1859); and *Uresiphita gilvata* (Fabricius, 1794). *Isocentris retinalis* is recorded based on a DNA barcoded specimen (BOLD), but this is a syn. of *I. filalis* (Maes 2014: 141). *Pioneabathra olesialis* is also accepted based on a DNA barcoded specimen on BOLD.

[153] Pyraustini may contain only one true *Pyrausta* on Madagascar, *P. phoenicealis* (Hübner, 1818) (= *panopealis* Walker, 1859); an additional eight species of "*Pyrausta*" need to be reassessed: *amelokalis* (Viette, 1958); *ankaratralis* Marion & Viette, 1956; *flavipunctalis* (Marion, 1954); *griveaudalis* Viette, 1978; *kandalis* Viette, 1989; *lambomakandroalis* Viette, 1954; *peyrieralis* Viette, 1978; *syntomidalis* Viette, 1960; and some at least probably belong to different genera. The tribe also contains *Achyra* (2 spp.); *Anania* (2 spp.); *Circobotys mabillealis* (Viette, 1953); *Crocidophora elongalis* Viette, 1978; *Crypsiptya viettalis* (Marion, 1956); *Loxostege decaryalis* Marion & Viette, 1956; *Ostrinia erythrialis* Marion & Viette, 1956; *Pagyda* (2 spp.); *Placosaris labordalis* Viette, 1958; and *Psammotis* (2 spp.). *Achyra nudalis* Hübner, 1796, a very widespread species, is accepted on the basis of the record of "*Loxostege*" *lacunalis* (Zeller, 1852) in Viette (1990: 96), but the species is not mentioned for Madagascar in Afromoths.

[154] Pyraustinae *i.s.* also contains the extraordinary-looking *Clatrodes squaleralis* Marion & Viette, 1953 (monotypic; according to the original description close to "*Thesiphisa*" Hb. (= *Mecyna* Gn. [i.e., now *Uresiphita* Hübner, 1825]); not, however, an intuitive placement). It also here includes *Stenochora lancinalis* (Guenée, 1854) (monotypic; [Australia], relevant BINs BOLD:ACR8335, shared with Seychelles, and BOLD:ABV2414 in Africa).

155 Arrangement of tribes and generic composition follows in part Mally et al. (2019) and GlobIZ (Nuss et al. 2003).
156 Hydririni contains *Hydriris ornatalis* (Duponchel, 1832, Sicily). It is likely that the species on Madagascar is not conspecific with European material (C. Guillermet could not find the type; Afromoths), although the only known BIN (BOLD:ACS8568) differs from that which predominates in Europe, Africa, and southwest Asia (BOLD:AAN4439). Whereas "*Lamprosema*" is placed in this tribe in GlobIZ, considering also the Neotropical t.s. (*L. lunulalis* Hübner, 1823; BOLD:AAG3078 applies; Neotropical), the "*Lamprosema*" taxa on Madagascar (e.g., in Afromoths) do not belong here and are likely to comprise more than one genus.
157 Lineodini contains *Leucinodes* (t.s. *L. orbonalis* Guenée, 1854). *L. raondry* occurs on Madagascar (Viette 1981) (see Mally et al. 2015; type not found in MNHN, but there newly combined from *Daraba*). For *Lygropia*, see Spilosominae *i.s.* (comment 165, *q.v.*).
158 Agroterini also contains *Diastictis capuronalis* Viette, 1966 and *Eretmopteryx flabelligera* (Saalmüller, 1880) (BIN: BOLD:ACS7648 applicable). The latter species was included in Pyraustinae on GlobIZ but linked by NJ (even though 7.6%+ distant) and external color characters to the Neotropical *Phostria* (e.g., *P. mapetalis*, BOLD:AAE0390 applies) (see also Lees and Zilli 2019: 126)—thus representing a potential Neotropical element in the fauna. It is not clear whether any true *Phostria* taxa occur in the fauna: regarding the *Phostria*-like "*Phryganodes*" *antongilensis* (Mabille, 1900), see Spilomelinae *i.s.*, comment 165, as for "*Phostria*" *gravitalis* (Saalmüller, 1880). Also, we place here "*Lamprosema*" *argyropalis* (Hampson, 1908), which has a similar wing pattern to *Haritalodes*. See P. Leraut (2006c) regarding the last genus, to which he added *H. barbuti* and *H. mineti*. Also, *Agrotera citrina* Hampson, 1899 is based on a DNA barcoded specimen on BOLD (BOLD:AAJ7038), but the generic assignment seems uncertain (according to NJ information on BOLD). Additional generic records DNA barcoded for Madagascar are *Chalcidoptera* (BOLD:ACS8316) and *Pleuroptya* (BOLD:ABZ2046) (Lopez-Vaamonde et al. 2019: Supplementary data).
159 Margaroniini also contains *Cadarena pudoraria* (Hübner, 1825); *Condylorrhiza zyphalis* (Viette, 1958); *Diaphania* (2 spp.); *Filodes* (2 spp.); *Megatarsodes baltealis* (Mabille, 1881); and *Obtusipalpis* (2 spp.) (monotypic; BIN: BOLD:ABA8768 applicable, 7%+ distant to East African *Filodes*; e.g., to BOLD:AAH4449), *Ghesquierellana hirtusalis* (Walker, 1859); *Glyphodella* (2 spp.); *Hodebertia testalis* (Fabricius, 1794); *Glauconoe subflavalis* (Warren, 1892) (DNA barcode, BIN: BOLD:AAM9196 places it close, at 4.6%+ distance, to *Hodebertia testalis*); *Maruca* (2 spp.); *Omiodes* (3 spp.) including "*Syllepte*" *glebalis* (Lederer, 1863); *Omphisa* (2 spp., *O. vaovao* Viette, 1973 and *O. alamotralis* (Viette, 1973) comb. nov. ["*Zagaridia*"]); *Parotis* (2 spp.); *Poliobotys ablactalis* (Walker, 1859) (monotypic); *Sinomphisa jeannelalis* (Marion & Viette, 1956); *Stemorrhages sericea* (Drury, 1773); *Synclera achatinalis* (Guenée, 1862) (misspelled "*achatinella*" in Viette 1990; here reinstated from synonymy with *S. traducalis*); *Synclera* "*traducalis*" (Zeller, 1852); *Terastia subjectalis* Lederer, 1863; and *Zebronia phenice* (Cramer, 1782). The presence of *S. traducalis* (Zeller, 1852; type locality South Africa) on Madagascar is tentatively accepted based on Viette (1990: 102; see also Viette 1957: 178). However, this may need to be reassessed, as BOLD:ADI0183 is a unique BIN for Madagascar within a complex, whereas South African material corresponds to BOLD:ABW0700. By contrast, another closely related species recently described is *Synclera seychellensis* J. C. Shaffer & Munroe, 2007, which has been DNA barcoded for Madagascar (where another representative of BOLD:ACU3680). Included here also are "*Polygrammodes*" *phyllophila* (Butler, 1878) and "*Polygrammodes*" *seyrigalis* Viette, 1953, which surely do not belong to that Neotropical genus (t.s. *Phalaena elevata* Fabricius, [1777]; Neotropical, exemplar BIN BOLD:ABW7384). These two species resemble *Condylorrhiza zyphalis* (BOLD:ACR8226 applies) in wing pattern, a genus apparently very close to *Botyodes*. Close to the last genus are *Endocrossis lanatalis* (Viette, 1960) comb. nov. (BOLD:AEB5658 applies) and *E. kenrickalis* (Viette, 1960) comb. nov. (BOLD:ADZ3573), which group together with several African BINs and share a similar pattern to the *Endocrossis* t.s. (*Botyodes flavibasalis* Moore, 1867; e.g., BOLD:ABA8743).
160 Spilomelini also contains *Aethaloessa floridalis* (Zeller, 1852) (t.s. of genus), *Orphanostigma abruptalis* (Walker, 1859) (t.s. of genus; BOLD:AAJ4002 applicable), and the cosmopolitan *O. haemorrhoidalis* Guenée, 1854 (BOLD:ACE4975 applies). Also, transferred from "*Syngamia*" (oddly in Nomophilini in GlobIZ: Nuss et al. 2003) is *O. latimarginalis* (Walker, 1859), [Sri Lanka], BOLD:ABV5333 applicable. The presence of the last genus and species, not mentioned for Madagascar by Afromoths but still in Viette (1990: 102) (with *jucundalis* Lederer, 1863 as a syn.), is confirmed by a DNA barcoded specimen (Lopez Vaamonde et al. 2019).
161 Among Herpetogrammatini spilomelines, which also include *Eurrhyparodes* (t.s. *E. stibialis* Snellen, 1880), the presence of *Herpetogramma basalis* (Walker, 1866) (t.s. of genus is *H. servalis* Lederer, 1863; Brazil) is based on a DNA barcoded specimen (representing BOLD:AAB6841, a BIN that occurs also in Africa and Asia). The type locality of "*basalis*" is presumed to be Sri Lanka, but the type has not been found. See also note on Afromoths, based on information from M. Shaffer in Guillermet (2009). Another genus on Madagascar is "*Pilocrocis*" (t.s. *P. ramentalis* Lederer, 1863 [Florida]; BOLD:AAA0334 applies). According to a DNA barcode of *P. rectilinealis* (Kenrick, 1917), the Malagasy species in this genus might belong to *Herpetogramma*. However, "*Herpetogramma*" *griseolineata* (Mabille, 1900) (BOLD:ACS8329 applicable) is here transferred to Spilomelinae *i.s.* (comment 165, *q.v.*).
162 The presence of the tribe Asciodini on Madagascar, a sister tribe to Hymeniini (see Mally et al. 2019 for discussion) is based on the genus *Psara*. Its t.s. is Neotropical (*P. pallicaudalis* Snellen, 1875; Colombia), so the status of the species in the genus may need reassessment.
163 Steniini contains *Bradina admixtalis* (Walker, 1859) (= *Spoladea avunculalis* Saalmüller, 1880, "*Syllepte*"; Vári et al. 2002: 101); "*Bradina*" *macaralis* Walker, 1859; *Dolicharthria modestalis* (Saalmüller, 1880); *Duponchelia fovealis* Zeller, 1847; *Hymenoptychis sordida* Zeller, 1852; and *Metasia perfervidalis* (Hampson, 1913). *Bradina admixtalis* is a true *Bradina* (BOLD:ACT2747 applicable, about 3% divergent from the t.s., *B. impressalis* Lederer, 1863 [India], BOLD:AAE8006 applies). *Dolicharthria modestalis* (Saalmüller, 1880) was listed as *Stenia modestalis* in Viette (1990: 247) as a species whose type is unknown, but it is here accepted as a Malagasy species based on its type locality and its currently accepted genus (see GlobIZ: Nuss et al. 2003 and Afromoths).
164 Nomophilini contains also *Bocchoris inspersalis* (Zeller, 1852) (t.s.); three species attributed to "*Bocchoris*": *gallienalis* (Viette, 1958), *isakalis* Viette, 1954, and *rufiflavalis* Hampson, 1912; *Diasemia monostigma* Hampson, 1913; *Diasemiopsis ramburialis* (Duponchel, 1834); *Epipagis quadriserialis* (Pagenstecher, 1907); *Nomophila noctuella* (Denis & Schiffermüller, 1775); *Sameodes cancellalis* (Zeller, 1852); and four species attributed to "*Syngamia*": *eos* Druce, 1902; *glebosalis* Viette, 1960; *jeanneli* (Viette, 1954); and *luteofusalis* Mabille, 1900. As regards the placement in this tribe of other "*Syngamia*" on Madagascar, the type of "*Syngamia*" *eos* Druce, 1902 cannot be located so is not verified; "*Syngamia*" *glebosalis* Viette, 1960 and "*Syngamia*" *luteofusalis* (Mabille, 1900) were provisionally assigned to "*Aethaloessa*" [Spilomelini] by M. Shaffer (unpublished data). The former may possibly be a member of Agroterini; the latter, however, is similar looking to "*Bocchoris*" *gallienalis*, BOLD:ADZ5622 (t.s. *Botys inspersalis* Zeller, 1852; BOLD:AAC5466 applicable, nearly 11% pairwise divergent). "*Syngamia*" *jeanneli* (Viette, 1954, described as *Dixoa*) also cannot be accurately assigned here. Transferred to Spilomelini, however (comment 160, *q.v.*), is "*Syngamia*" *latimarginalis* (Walker, 1859). Indeed, true "*Syngamia*" (t.s. *Phalaena florella* Stoll, 1781, [Neotropical]) apparently does not occur on Madagascar. The genus *Pessocosma* is represented by a DNA barcode (BOLD:ACS6129) (Lopez-Vaamonde et al. 2019: Supplementary data).
165 Spilomelinae *i.s.* also comprises here *Coptobasoides*, currently in Pyraustinae on GlobIZ (Nuss et al. 2003), but DNA barcodes connect this genus reasonably closely to other spilomeline genera (e.g., *Eulepte*) at 5.6%+ distance. Other spilomeline taxa that we cannot otherwise currently place are "*Lamprosema*" (t.s. Neotropical) (none Hydririni and probably not all congeneric); *Metoeca foedalis* (Guenée, 1854); "*Nacoleia*" *rubralis* (Hampson, 1898); *Nausinoe geometralis* (Guenée, 1854); *Piletocera hemiphaealis* (Hampson, 1907); "*Polythlipta*"

annulifera (Walker, 1866) (DNA barcode BIN BOLD:ADZ3657 applies, but its placement is not currently informative); *Phostria* (as "*Phryganodes*") *antongilensis* (Mabille, 1900) (t.s. *Phryganodes plicatalis* Guenée, 1854; BOLD:AAN7142 applicable); "*Phostria*" *gravitalis* (Saalmüller, 1880, as *Botys*) (type unknown but compared to *Omiodes cuniculalis* in appearance, and compare also representatives of BOLD:ABV9109, Lopez-Vaamonde et al. 2019: Supplementary data); and "*Prorodes*" *leucothyralis* (Mabille, 1900).

In Spilomelinae *i.s.* we currently also place *Pycnarmon cribrata* (Fabricius, 1794), for which BOLD:AAC5783 applies. Its t.s. is *Spilomela jaguaralis* Guenée, 1854; BOLD:AAY5180 applies. Afromoths attributes to this species the Madagascar record by Marion (1954) of "*caberalis* Guenée, 1854." According to recent mitogenomic phylogenies (e.g., Zhu et al. 2018: Supplement Figure S9), *Pycnarmon* does not fall in the same clade as *Nomophila*, so we do not place it in Nomophilini, although it does fall nearby (e.g., via NJ using a DNA barcode).

Regarding "*Syllepte*" (t.s. *S. incomptalis* Hübner, 1823 [Surinam?]), the 193 species worldwide that have been placed in "*Syllepte*" are in need of revision, and clarification of the group is problematic in the absence of a type specimen (see Mally et al. 2019: 187, for discussion of genera resembling spotting of the illustration in Hübner). Likely none of the Malagasy species belong there, nor do they form a monophyletic group, but there is nothing much practical we can do about it unless a neotype is designated; the genus is thus anyway cited in double quotation marks. However, transferred from "*Syllepte*" is *Pramadea ovialis* (Walker, 1859) (BOLD:ABV3925 applies) (t.s. *P. denticulata* Moore, 1888; see Kirti and Gill 2004: 180); also placed here are the very similar "*Herpetogramma*" *griseolineata* (Mabille, 1900) (BOLD:ACS8329 applies; 4.6%+ distant to the African "*Syllepte*" *purpurascens* Hampson, 1899, for which BOLD:ACN8356 is relevant), and "*Syllepte*" *sakarahalis* (Marion & Viette, 1956); "*Polygrammodes*" *faraonyalis* Viette, 1954; and "*Polygrammodes*" *griveaudalis* Viette, 1981 (type not checked). "*Syllepte*" *lanatalis* (Viette, 1960) and *kenrickalis* (Viette, 1960) are transferred to *Endocrossis* (Margaroniini, comment 159, *q.v.*). Otherwise (see also comments 157, 159), seven other "*Syllepte*" (see Mally et al. 2019) are relegated here and they are unlikely to form a natural group. These are three rather similar-looking species: "*Syllepte*" *pauperalis* (Marion, 1954) (BOLD:ADP5759 applies)—uninformatively placed by DNA barcode; "*Syllepte*" *aureotinctalis* (Kenrick, 1917); and "*Syllepte*" *mahafalalis* Marion & Viette, 1956, as well as "*Syllepte*" *posticalis* (Saalmüller, 1880) (type not checked). Unrelated-looking are "*Syllepte*" *malgassanalis* (Viette, 1954); "*Syllepte*" *stumpffalis* Viette, 1960; and "*Syllepte*" *rubrifucalis* (Mabille, 1900). Regarding "*Syllepte*" *hemichionalis* (Mabille, 1900), the genus is also not clear, but previously this species has been associated closely to "*Syllepte*" *vagans* (Tutt, 1890); see Mally et al. 2015: 150.

Another polyphyletic genus that causes problems here is *Lygropia* (t.s. *Asopia unicoloralis* Guenée, 1854 [Brazil]) (e.g., Mally et al. 2005). Described from Madagascar is "*Lygropia*" *vinanyalis* Viette, 1958 (BOLD:ACS7264 possibly applies), a potential congeneric of "*Lygropia*" *aureomarginalis* (Gaede, 1916) (see Mally et al. 2015: 149). Other species placed in this genus in Madagascar probably belong elsewhere. "*Lygropia*" *leucophanalis* (BOLD:ADZ1589 applies) is distant from other crambids (NJ connects nearest to *Pygospila marginalis*, Margaroniini, at 7.53% distance); it has a similar wing pattern, though, to specimens representing an "Australian" BIN, BOLD:AAO9130. Also doubtfully belonging to this genus are "*Lygropia*" *acosmialis* (Mabille, 1879) and "*Lygropia*" *ochracealis* (Saalmüller, 1880), although we have not been able to check the types.

166 Drepanidae, with just one subfamily on Madagascar (Drepaninae) and only two tribes, is arranged in reference to the "Ethiopian region" revision of Watson (1965).

167 Oretini also contains *Archidrepana saturniata* Warren; 1902, *Gonoreta bispina* Watson, 1965; *Gonoretodes timea* Watson, 1965; and *Oretopsis vohilava* (Viette, 1954) (Viette 1990: 103–104).

168 For one of the few molecular studies of Notodontidae relevant to our arrangement, see Kobayashi and Nonata (2016); see also Schintlmeister and Witt (2015) and Kiriakoff (1969).

169 Scranciinae was raised to subfamily status in Notodontidae by Schintlmeister (2008). See Schintlmeister and Witt (2015) regarding *Thacona* (= *Scrancia*). *Thacona leucopera* (Hampson, 1910) is included based on an RMCA record (see Afromoths). Some taxa of the *Scrancia* group of Kiriakoff (1969: 8) are not included here (*Antsalova* is placed in Notodontinae, *Paralerodes* is placed in Thaumetopoeinae, and *Romaleostaura* in Notodontidae *i.s.*).

170 Pygaerinae also contains *Antoroka munda* Kiriakoff, 1969. Of the four Malagasy genera that can be placed for now in Pygaerinae, only *Eutrotonotus*, representing a substantial endemic radiation of 14 described species, was included in the "*Clostera* group" of Kiriakoff 1969 (Pygaerinae). It may be noted that *Analama obliquifasciata* (Kenrick, 1917; *Scalmatica*) is misspelled both in Kiriakoff (1969: 133) and in Viette (1990: 149). We follow the treatment of *Ambina ochribasis* (Kiriakoff, 1960) as a good species by Viette (1990: 148) and Afromoths, despite its being regarded as a probable syn. of *A. ochreopicta* (Kenrick, 1917) by Kiriakoff (1969: 141–142). *Ambina*, *Analama*, and *Antoroka* ("*Scalmicauda* group" of Kiriakoff 1969: 8) are closely related to three genera placed in Pygaerinae by Schintlmeister and Witt (2015), namely *Janthinisca*, *Peratodonta*, and *Scalmicauda*. Nevertheless, these genera are probably misplaced in this subfamily (unlike *Eutrotonotus*, which is a close relative of *Clostera*).

171 Dudusinae is newly recognized for Madagascar.

172 Periergosinae, corresponding to only a part of the polyphyletic "*Chadisra* group" of Kiriakoff (1969), also contains *Artanasa viettei* Kiriakoff, 1960; *Nesochadisra protea* Kiriakoff, 1969; and *Stemmatophalera* (= *Acrasiodes*) *io* (Viette, 1954). Another species included here, *Pachycispia picta* Butler, 1882, seems to be a close relative of *Gangarides* (hence its tentative assignment to the Periergosinae; see Kobayashi and Nonaka 2016 for the composition of this subfamily). *Atrasana* (the larva of one African species illustrated in Staude et al. 2016: S232) has before been included in Dicranurinae, a subfamily not recognized here.

173 Spataliinae (= Ceirinae) is newly recognized for the fauna based on *Rasemia descarpentrianum* (Viette, 1954). Note that "*descarpentrianum* (Viette, 1954)" was counted twice on Afromoths (once as *Aprosdocetos*).

174 Phalerinae includes only *Rigema haasi* (Saalmüller, 1884) comb. nov. (previously in the genus *Antheua*). This is the only species of the "*Phalera* group" of Kiriakoff (1969: 8). We discount here country records in Afromoths for the South African species *R. ornata* Walker, 1865 (representing a probable misidentification of *R. haasi* from Butler, 1880: 389; see also Kiriakoff 1969: 76–77) and also a record that was on Afromoths of *Phalera lydenburgi* Distant, 1899 (based on a misidentification of *R. haasi*). Kiriakoff (1969: 181) then noted the endemism of Notodontidae as reaching 100% at species and 74% at generic level, but we can now accept the odd African species for the fauna based on occasional records (see comment 179 concerning *Galona*).

175 The processionary moth subfamily Thaumetopoeinae also includes *Anaphe aurea* Butler, 1892, *Nesanaphe* (2 spp.), and *Paralerodes albosparsatus* (Kenrick, 1914). *Paralerodes* is here transferred to this subfamily (e.g., from Notodontinae on Afromoths) based on: proboscis reduced, male antenna bipectinate to tip, female with a corethrogyne. It may be noted that *Hypsoides ambriensis* Poujade, 1903 is misspelled "*ambrensis*" by Kiriakoff (1969: 204) and Viette (1990: 153). Two genera previously placed in this subfamily, *Fanambana* and *Pseudohypsoides*, are here placed among Notodontidae *i.s.* (comment 179, *q.v.*).

176 Stauropinae also contains *Eramos viridissima* Kiriakoff, 1958, *Exantongila antongilensis* (Viette, 1955), *Italaviana griveaudi* Kiriakoff, 1960, and *Omocerina viettei* Kiriakoff, 1970. The subfamily is equivalent to "Stauropini" in Kobayashi and Nonaka 2016) and essentially corresponding to the "*Desmeocraera* group" of Kiriakoff (1969: 8).

177 Neodrymoniinae, newly recognized for Madagascar (= "Neodrymoniaini" in Kobayashi and Nonaka 2016), also includes *Griphocerura malgassica* (Kenrick, 1917).

178 In Notodontinae, *Antsalova* is closely related to *Helga*, *Leptolepida*, and *Psalisodes*, as evidenced by the morphology of its male genitalia (socii fused together; valvae short). We tentatively maintain these three African genera,

Antsalova, and *Stenostaura* (*S. kiriakoffi* (Minet, 1983) comb. nov., described in *Platystaura*) in the Notodontinae following Schintlmeister and Witt (2015), although they all lack the forewing apomorphy that we ascribe to the ground plan of the Notodontinae (*viz.* the "tooth" of the inner margin of the forewing).

[179] Notodontidae *i.s.* also includes *Dicranura malgassica* (Kiriakoff, 1960) comb. nov. (described in "*Iridoplitis*"); *Elaphrodes simplex* (Viette, 1955); *Epicerurina grisea* Kiriakoff, 1969; *Fanambana anomoeotina* Kiriakoff & Viette, 1969; *F. pyralidina* Kiriakoff & Viette, 1969; *Galona serena* Karsch, 1895 (a single record from Betioky: Minet 1983; *Galona* belongs to the *Harpyia* group); *Rhenea circumcincta* (Saalmüller, 1880); *R. mediata* (Walker, 1865) (doubtful record on Afromoths based on Beccaloni et al. 2003); *Rhynchophalerina inexpectata* Kiriakoff, 1969; *Romaleostaura insularis* Kiriakoff, 1960; *Tricholoba magnifica* Viette, 1955; *Vietteella madagascariensis* (Draeseke, 1937); *V. nigrilineata* Kiriakoff, 1969; *Zelomera imitans* Butler, 1882; and *Z. kiriakoffi* Viette, 1972. It should be noted that Staude et al. (2016: S236) illustrate a larva of the genus *Rhenea* Saalmüller, 1884.

The genus *Dasychoproctis* Hering, 1926 (3 spp.) was transferred to the Notodontidae by Minet (1983: 364), who tentatively placed it in the Thaumetopoeinae (a doubtful position in view of the absence of a corethrogyne at the extremity of the female abdomen). Previously placed in Thaumetopoeinae (e.g., Viette 1990) were the genera *Fanambana* Kiriakoff & Viette, 1969 (*i.s.* according to Schintlmeister 2013) and *Pseudohypsoides* Viette, 1960 (here excluded from the Thaumetopoeinae since the female lacks a corethrogyne).

[180] Euteliinae also includes *Marathyssa cuneata* (Saalmüller, 1891) and *Parelia albivirgula* Berio, 1957. *Eutelia gaedei* Hacker & Kobes, 2006 was added to the fauna by Hacker and Fibiger (2006).

[181] Order of nolid subfamilies and tribes follows largely Zahiri et al. (2013).

[182] Risobinae fauna so far recognized are only *Risoba* and two species of *Gigantoceras* (see Lees and Minet 2003: 760, note 77, but actually a valid genus).

[183] Concerning Eligminae, placement of *Iscadia* (= *Gadirtha*, *Ophiosema*) in Eligminae follows Zahiri et al. 2013 (*Iscadia* was placed in Collomeninae in Regier et al. 2017). Placed here is "*Saaluncifera*" *uncinata* (Saalmüller, 1891) (t.s. *Saaluncifera uncinata* Berio, 1966; Bekily). Berio himself stated in the original description that the last t.s. (described intentionally as "n. sp.") was probably the same as *Hypogramma uncinata* Saalmüller, 1891 (431: Figure 162) (it was in "Hadeninae" in Pitkin and Jenkins 2003). Also included here and probably congeneric is "*Nyctennomos*" *ambitsha* Viette, 1976 (Viette stated in the description that he was very doubtful of this species' generic placement). We also place here two closely related genera, *viz. Axiopoeniella* Strand, 1909 and *Laelapia* Butler, 1879 ("Arctiidae" in Viette 1990).

[184] Westermanniinae includes *Negeta*, following Zahiri et al. (2013), but also *Westermannia brillans* Viette, 1965 (as a species of *Plusiocalpe* in Viette 1990: 212). Tentatively, we also include *Paraxestis malagasy* Viette, 1988 (Chloephorinae in Staude et al. 2016: S226).

[185] To Nolinae, Hacker et al. (2012) added *Madanola efflucta*, *M. fuscocandida*, *M. kenrickialis*, *M. meloui*, *M. obliquivittata*, *M. parafuscatalis*, *M. subfuscigera*, *M. subpraefica*, *M. toulgoetiella*, and *Nola mineti*. *Nolidia* and *Vandamia* also belong here. See Hacker (2014) regarding *Evonima littoralis madagassalis*.

[186] In Chloephorinae: Eariadini, *Lophocrama* is placed due to similar habitus (green pigmentation) to *Earias*. Also placed here tentatively, based on presence of green pigments and DNA barcoding evidence, is the genus *Microzada* Hampson, 1912.

[187] Placement of *Maurilia* in Chloephorinae: Careini follows Zahiri et al. (2013) and Regier et al. (2017).

[188] Composition of Sarrothripini follows Zahiri et al. (2013), by subtribe: Bleninina (*Blenina*); Etannina (*Garella*, *Giaura* and *Pardasena*); and Sarrothripina (*Nycteola*). For the last subtribe, presence of *Giaura* on Madagascar is based on a DNA barcode

[189] Placed here is "*Pseudotolna*" *perineti* Viette, 1965 (the t.s. is *Methorasa eximia* Holland, 1894, bearing no obvious close relation to Viette's species).

[190] Arrangement of noctuid tribes and generic composition follows in part Holloway (1998) and Zahiri et al. (2013).

[191] Plusiinae also contains *Argyrogramma signata* (Fabricius, 1792); *Chrysodeixis* (2 spp.); *Eutheiaplusia pratti* (Kenrick, 1917); *Plusiopalpa* (2 spp.); *Plusiotricha livida* Holland, 1894; *Stigmoplusia* (2 spp.); and *Vittaplusia vittata* (Wallengren, 1856).

[192] In Cuculliinae: Cucullini, placed alongside *Cucullia* here is *Ectochela malagasy* (Viette, 1972), transferred to the last genus by Hacker (2004: 284) while synonymizing *Centrarthra* with *Ectochela* (Afromoths).

[193] In Cuculliinae *i.s.* we place *Adaphaenura*; *Daphoenura fasciata* Butler, 1878; *Epicausis*; and *Eudaphaenura*. These spectacular moths, representing a small radiation endemic to Madagascar, for which unfortunately there is still no genetic data, were placed in Pantheinae by Viette (1990: 217), but they have nothing to do with this subfamily, in which both *Panthea* and *Thiacidas* were included by Zahiri et al. (2013). Their genitalia are broadly of the cuculliine type (e.g., for species of *Eudaphaenura* on Afromoths), and indeed they were long placed in that subfamily (e.g., by Pitkin and Jenkins 2003). We also place in the same radiation the very spectacular genus *Mydrodoxa*; *M. sogai* Viette, 1965 and *M. splendens* Butler, 1880 were both collected only once as unique females in different parts of the Madagascar moist evergreen forest (see Minet and Thiaucourt 2018; Lees and Zilli 2019: 155) and are among the most spectacular noctuids on Madagascar. J. Minet has carefully examined the type of *M. sogai*. Cuculliinae *i.s.* also comprises *Fletcherea* but not "*Fletcherea*" *minuscula* (Kenrick, 1917) (Acronictinae, comment 200, *q.v.*), *Homonacna*, and *Tunocaria rubiginosa* Viette, 1961.

[194] Oncocnemidinae includes here *Anedhella* as well as *Ethiopica befasy* Viette, 1965 ("Hadeninae" in Pitkin and Jenkins 2003).

[195] Pantheinae includes *Thiacidas alboporphyrea* (Pagenstecher, 1907). Zahiri et al. (2013) synonymized Thiacidinae with Pantheinae (however, see Cuculliinae *i.s.*, comment 193, *q.v.*, regarding genera placed in Pantheinae in Viette 1990). Pantheinae also includes *Sciatta delphinensis* (Viette, 1966) (in Acronictinae on Afromoths), which was described from Tsaratanàna in *Schalidomitra* Strand, 1911 (Viette 1990: 220); this species is very similar to the t.s. of *Sciatta* Walker, 1869.

[196] Eustrotiinae also contains here the smaller genera *Acontiola* (2 spp.); *Aconzarba* (4 spp.); *Eulocastra* (2 spp.) (see Holloway 2011: 265); and *Pseudozarba aethiops* (Distant, 1898). *Micardia* (5 spp.) is also placed here (see Liang et al. 2019), a genus in "Acontiinae" in Pitkin and Jenkins 2003 but Boletobiinae in Afromoths. Likewise, we place here the *Ozarba*-like *Xanthomera leucogene* (Mabille, 1880). Also transferred here is the monotypic *Promionides obliqua* Berio, 1966 (Manjakatompo; Hadeninae on Afromoths and Pitkin and Jenkins 2003), which we consider congeneric with *Microplexia griveaudi* Berio, 1963 (*M. obliqua*, comb. nov.). "*Eustrotia*" *matercula* (Saalmüller, 1880) belongs to *Aconzarba* (it is similar to the recently added *A. goateri* Hacker, 2016). The other Malagasy species placed in *Eustrotia* Hübner, 1821 (see Han and Kononenko 2015) actually belong to *Deltote* R. L. [Reichenbach], 1817 (= *Eustrotia* Hübner, 1821, = *Lithacodia* Hübner, 1818). These include *D. albigutta* (Berio, 1959); *D. divisa* (Saalmüller, 1891); *D. hemicycla* (Berio, 1959); *D. manga* (Viette, 1982); *D. micardoides* (Berio, 1954); and *D. tsara* (Viette, 1988). This genus also includes here the otherwise monotypic *Cryphioides ocellata* Berio, 1964 (*D. ocellata*, comb. nov.; Boletobiinae on Afromoths but Acontiinae on Pitkin and Jenkins 2003). Berio considered the last species to be possibly conspecific with "*Bryophila*" *ocellata* Saalmüller, 1891, as stated also in Nye 1975. Also included here are *D. albannularis* Berio, 1954; *D. armilla* (Saalmüller, 1891); *D. cupreofuscoides* (Berio, 1954); *D. flavofimbria* (Saalmüller, 1891); *D. metachrysa* (Hampson, 1910); *D. monorbis* (Berio, 1959); *D. plurioculata* (Berio, 1964); *D. preapicilinea* (Berio, 1964); and *D. rubrilis* (Berio, 1954).

[197] The subfamily Acontiinae contains also *Eutelephia aureopicta* (Kenrick, 1917); *Procrateria malagassa* Viette, 1961; *Pseudelaeodes proteoides* (Kenrick, 1917); *P. sogai* Viette, 1969; and, newly transferred here, *Paracroria milloti* Viette, 1969, as well as tentatively (not related to *Eublemma* as on Afromoths), "*Tolpia*" *rufocastanea* (Rothschild, 1924). Here treated as closely related to *Paracroria* are also *Madathisanotia madagascariensis* (Rothschild, 1924) and *Zacthys biplaga*

Viette, 1973 ("Hadeninae" in Pitkin and Jenkins 2003). Five new *Acontia* species were introduced: *A. bollandi* Hacker, Legrain & Fibiger, 2008; *A. antica subtilis* Hacker, Legrain & Fibiger, 2010; *A. mineti* Hacker, 2011; *A.* (*Uracontia*) *viettei* Hacker, 2010; and *A. xanthochromata* Hacker, 2011 (see Hacker 2011). "*Sculptifrontia*" *arcuata* Berio, 1966 is treated here as a syn. of *A. laurenconi* (Viette, 1965) (as on Afromoths). *Xanthomera leucoglene* is moved, however, to Eustrotiinae (comment 196, *q.v.*).

[198] Smaller genera and species of Bagisarinae include: *Androlymnia malgassica* Viette, 1965; *Brevipecten* (2 spp.); *Honeyia* (2 spp., including *H. ankarana*, Hacker & Legrain, 2013); *Leocyma* (2 spp.); *Parangitia micrina* Berio, 1966 (see Minet et al. 2012: 146); *Pardoxia graellsii* (Feisthamel, 1837); *Xanthodes albago* (Fabricius, 1794); and *Xanthodesma rectangulata* Kenrick, 1917. Many of these taxa are specialized on Malvaceae (Staude et al. 2016: S190), but the presence of larval "appendiculate crochets" (Gardner 1947; Kitching and Rawlins 1998: 380) also connects them. See Zahiri et al. (2013) regarding inclusion of *Amyna* and *Parangitia*. Transferred here also on DNA barcoding evidence (from Hadeninae [e.g., Afromoths, Pitkin and Jenkins 2003] or from Nolidae: Chloephorinae in Holloway 2003: 226) is *Bryophilopsis* Hampson, 1894 (4 spp.). Note that "*Oglasa*" *dia* Viette, 1972 (original combination) and "*Honeyia*" *dia* are currently separate entries in different subfamilies on Afromoths, and so there counted twice although referring to the same species. It is possible that other Malagasy "*Oglasa*" (*trimacula*) *bergeri* Viette, 1987, and *ochreobrunneata* Viette, 1956) may also belong to *Honeyia* (but not "*O*". *auximena*; see Anobinae, comment 222).

[199] The Amphipyrinae: Psaphidini is newly recognized for Madagascar. *Cetola phaleroides* Rothschild, 1924 was established in Notodontidae but placed in "Hadeninae" in Pitkin and Jenkins 2003, but it connects to members of Psaphidini by DNA barcodes as does the genus *Tanocryx* (represented on Madagascar by *T. pseudobamra* Rothschild, 1924) and, on similar evidence, we also place here *Lyncestis grandidieri* (Viette, 1968) and *L. voeltzkowi* (Viette, 1965).

[200] Added to Acronictinae (here from Phlogophorini) is *Prototrachea leucopicta* (Kenrick, 1917) and "*Fletcherea*" *minuscula* (Kenrick, 1917) (transferred from Cuculliinae; possibly congeneric with the former). *Megalonycta mediovitta* (Rothschild, 1924), with a classically acronictine appearance and very close to the genus *Craniophora* by DNA barcoding, is placed, surprisingly, in Eriopinae currently on BOLD. See also Rota et al. (2015) for a phylogeny of Acronictinae.

[201] Agaristinae also contains *Ancarista laminifera* (Saalmüller, 1878); *Antigodasa rufodiscalis* (Rothschild, 1896); *Arctiopais ambusta* (Mabille, 1881); *Arrothia* (3 spp.); *Musurgina laeta* Jordan, 1921; *Pararothia* (3 spp.); *Pemphigostola synemonistis* Strand, 1909; *Pristoceraea eriopis* (Herrich-Schäffer, 1853); and *Schausilla obryzos* (Mabille, 1879). Contrary to Afromoths, Agaristinae does not include *Godasa sidae*, which is not a Malagasy species (Aganainae, comment 230, *q.v.*).

[202] Aediinae includes *Aedia nigropicta* (Saalmüller, 1880) (formerly "*Catephia*," a genus that does not exist on Madagascar) and *A. squamosa* (Wallengren, 1856), which was already transferred in Guillermet (2016). The subfamily was placed next to Condicinae in Zahiri et al. (2013). *Ecpatia dulcistriga* is here treated for convenience as a member of Aediinae, even though the placement of two species in the genus in Zahiri et al. (2011) is unresolved, and *Ecpatia* falls quite far from Aediinae as sister to (Bryophilinae + Noctuinae) in Keegan et al. (2019: Figure 2). *Ecpatia* shares with *Aedia* a lack of phragma lobes on the second abdominal tergite (Holloway 2005). *Madecathymia cadoreli* Viette, 1968 is also placed here, tentatively.

[203] Also included here in Condicini is *Perigea* (2 spp.); Condicinae in Kitching and Rawlins (1998: 381). *Acosmetia malgassica* Kenrick, 1917 is also moved here (Acronictinae on Afromoths, but the genus is close to *Condica* by DNA barcoding).

[204] Condicinae: Leuconyctini now contains the genus *Kenrickodes*, which is close by DNA barcoding to the North American genus *Leuconycta*.

[205] Heliothinae also includes *Heliocheilus multiradiata* (Hampson, 1902) and *Protadisura posttriphaena* (Rothschild, 1924) and here two species of *Timora* (*T. pauliani* Viette, 1961 and *T. prochaskai* Viette, 1958, as on Afromoths). Here retained in *Heliothis* is *epimethea* Viette, 1958 (Viette 1990: 185 had the last species as well as *prochaskai* Viette, 1958 in *Masalia*).

[206] Eriopinae is treated here at subfamily rather than tribal level (see Yen and Wu 2009). The count here does not include *Callopistria violascens* (Rothschild, 1924), which is counted as a species on Afromoths but is in Noctuidae *i.s.* in Viette 1990: 249. *Tanocryx pseudobamra* (Rothschild, 1924), treated as a member of Eriopinae by Fibiger and Lafontaine (2005) (along with *Mageochaeta*; see Hadenini), is placed here instead in Amphipyrinae: Psaphidini (comment 199, *q.v.*).

[207] Noctuinae: Hadenini also here contains *Cardepia mixta* (Pagenstecher, 1907); *Ethioterpia toulgoeti* Viette, 1961; *Odontestra malgassica* Viette, 1969; and 2 spp. each of *Berioana*, *Leumicamia*, *Mageochaeta*, *Nyodes*, *Rungsianea*, and *Saalmuellerana*.

[208] Noctuinae: Eriopygini, a tribe newly recognized for the fauna, here includes *Elyptron* (t.s. *E. cinctum* Saalmüller, 1891; Madagascar). The tribe also includes (tentatively, on DNA barcode evidence) *Dicerogastra madecassa* Viette, 1972 and *Omphalestra herbuloti* Viette, 1961 ("Hadeninae" in Pitkin and Jenkins 2003).

[209] Other members of Noctuinae: Leucaniini in our treatment are *Anapoma milloti* (Rungs, 1956); *Apospasta intricata* (Saalmüller, 1891); and *Vietteania torrentium* (Guenée, 1852). The first and last species were treated as "Hadeninae" in Viette (1990:187–188) and in Afromoths.

[210] Noctuinae: Glottulini also includes *Brithysana pauliani* Viette, 1967 and *Diaphone delamarei* Viette, 1963.

[211] Noctuinae: Apameini comprises *Apamea* in subtribe Apameina, the other genera in Sesamiina, also including *Carelis biluma* (Nye, 1959).

[212] Caradrinini contains essentially the genus *Athetis* on Madagascar. Representing, perhaps surprisingly, a genus not recorded for the island by Viette (1990), *Caradrina glaucistis* Hampson, 1902 was recognized for the fauna by Berio (1956).

[213] *Magusa* is included in Noctuinae: Dypterygiini based on DNA barcode evidence.

[214] Noctuidae: Phlogophorini also contains *Metappana crescentica* (Hampson, 1910) and *Tracheplexia debilis* (Butler, 1879). Included also, as a member of *Phlogophora* in Fibiger and Hacker (2007: 185), is *inusitata* Saalmüller, 1891, described in the monotypic genus *Parca*, which Nye (1975) transferred from Herminiinae to Acronictinae but Pitkin and Jenkins 2003 kept in Hadeninae (see African Moths website [Goff 2017], for its resting posture).

[215] Noctuidae: Xylenini has a very restricted sense here compared with the very large number of taxa currently in Xyleninae on Afromoths. Xylenini here includes only *Actinotia vadoni* (Viette, 1965) (the last genus that was in Noctuidae: Xylenini in Zahiri et al. 2013) and the closely related *Campydelta*, *Lepidodelta*, and *Neostichtis*.

[216] Noctuini also contains here *Amazonides confluxa* (Saalmüller, 1891); *Axylia annularis* Saalmüller, 1891; and *Mabilleana pudens* (Mabille, 1900).

[217] Among Noctuinae *i.s.*, we include three genera previously placed by Viette (1967 and 1990) in Amphipyrinae/Acronictinae (*s.l.*): *Selenistis* Hampson, 1908; *Syrrusoides* Laporte, 1973; and *Xylostola* Hampson, 1909; and also two genera erroneously regarded as "Ophiderinae auct." (i.e., erebids) by Viette (1990): *Oedebasis* Hampson, 1902 (now in Noctuinae: Guillermet 2016: 17), and *Volazaha* Viette, 1971 (here transferred to the Noctuinae on morphological evidence: frontoclypeus entirely scaled, pretarsus with an acute endodont [as in Minet et al. 2012: Figure 8], nodulus raised outward, tympanal hood reduced, etc.). It should be noted that the Amphipyrinae *s.a.* (e.g., Viette 1967; Poole 1989) corresponds to a noctuid assemblage without precise characteristics, most members of which were provisionally placed in "Hadeninae" by Kitching and Rawlins (1998) but are now assigned to the enlarged subfamily Noctuinae (although still in "Hadeninae" in Pitkin and Jenkins 2003).

[218] Among the taxa that we regard as Noctuidae *i.s.* are eight genera placed by Viette (1990) in the "Acronictinae" (i.e., "Amphipyrinae" *s.a.*): *Andobana*, *Aucha*, *Butleronea*, *Cyclopera*, *Iambia* (Noctuinae *i.s.* according to Holloway 1989,

2011), *Matopo*, *Phoperigea*, and *Stenopterygia*; one genus previously placed in the Acontiinae *s.a.*: *Protomeroleuca*; as well as *Callicereon heterochroa* (Mabille, 1879). *Aucha* (Acronictinae for Pitkin and Jenkins 2003) is a genus associated with mangrove plants (Robinson et al. 2010). The adults of *Cyclopera* have an unusual resting posture according to the African Moths website (Goff 2017). The genus *Decarynodes* Viette, 1961 ("Chloephorinae" in Viette 1990) is here transferred to the Noctuidae: its male retinaculum is squat, unlike that of most Nolidae, while it has a convex, scaled, well-sclerotized frontoclypeus, a trifid hind wing, an acute endodont (in pretarsus), and a raised nodulus between the tympanum and the conjunctiva. For similar reasons, three taxa are transferred from the "Ophiderinae auct." (Viette 1990; i.e., Erebidae) to the Noctuidae *i.s.*: "*Bamra*" *cazeti* (Mabille, 1893) and the genera *Daula* Saalmüller, 1891 and *Prolyncestis* Viette, 1971. Moreover, *Anaphela stellata* (Guérin-Méneville, [1844]), long placed in "Arctiidae," has been excluded from that group by Goodger and Watson (1995) (cf. Viette 1998). This rare, colorful, probably day-flying moth, which is endemic to Madagascar, is here tentatively assigned to the family Noctuidae.

[219] Erebidae classification is based on various sources, notably works by Holloway (2005), Homziak et al. (2019), Lödl (1998a), and Zahiri et al. (2012).

[220] Scoliopteryginae includes here the highly polymorphic *Argyphia arcifera* (Mabille, 1881), based on DNA barcode and morphological evidence (from Calpinae *s.l.*, as on Afromoths).

[221] Rivulinae contains only the genus *Rivula* (two described species according to Viette 1990: *R. cyclina* (Mabille, 1900) and *R. sororcula* (Saalmüller, 1880), although the identity of the former [without type locality] seems to be questionable). Species that were placed in "*Oglasa*" among rivulines are moved to Bagisarinae (comment 198, *q.v.*) and Anobinae (see comment 222).

[222] Anobinae here contains also the following smaller genera and species: "*Acripia*" *megalesia* Viette, 1965 (Figure 9.70f); *Agamana* (2 spp.); "*Anoba*" *auximena* Viette, 1958; *Attatha attathoides* (Karsch, 1896); *Baniana* (2 spp.); *Eublarginea argentifera* Berio, 1966; "*Parafodina*" *aldabrana iselaea* (Viette, 1958); "*Tathodelta*" *undilinea* Hampson, 1926; and tentatively, *Marojala* (3 spp.) as well as *Tephrialia silenalis* (Guenée, 1862) (= "*Hypena*" *glyptalis* Mabille, 1880, not in Herminiinae as suggested by Lees and Minet 2003: note 82), but not "*Fodina*" *decussis* (Saalmüller, 1891) (see Erebidae, *i.s.*, comment 263). Note that the original combinations of two species of *Marcipopsis*, "*Caradrina*" *asinina* Saalmüller, 1891 (although misspelled as "*asanina*") and "*Caradrina*" *pallidula* Saalmüller, 1891 were not counted separately, as currently for the respective species on Afromoths.

[223] In Hypeninae, the composition of "*Hypena*" is still not fully clarified—it includes "*Sarmatia*" *malagasy* (= *H.* (*Trichypena*) *malagasy* (Viette, 1968)) (see Lödl 1998b: 67–71) but not "*Hypena*" *mainty*; see Herminiinae (comment 229); neither does it include *H. fuscomaculalis* (Saalmüller, 1880: 289) nor "*Hypena*" *diakonoffi* Viette, 1976, see Erebidae, *i.s.* (comment 263). Placed here alongside *Hypena* are *Acidon* (including "*Aulocheta*" *parallelalis* Mabille, 1880: a syn. of *Acidon bigrammica* (Saalmüller, 1880)); *Catada* (2 spp.); *Dichromia nasuta* (Mabille, 1884) (but not "*Dichromia*" *rationalis* Viette, 1956 or "*Dichromia*" *sieglinde* Viette, 1979; see comment 229); *Maxia decora* Saalmüller, 1891; *Proluta deflexa* Saalmüller, 1891; "*Rhynchina*" *obliqualis* (Kollar, 1844) (see Mayerl and Lödl 1997); *Staga producta* Mabille, 1900; and *Zekelita*. For *Adrapsa*, see Herminiinae (comment 229). Note that "*Idia*" *serralis* (Mabille, 1880) (t.s. *Idia aemula* Hübner, 1813; BOLD:AAA2229 applies), considered a junior subjective syn. of *Hypena fusculalis* Saalmüller, 1880 by M. Lödl (1999: 68), which Viette (1990: 241–242) placed in *Epizeuxis* among Hypeninae (auct.), is a replacement name for *H. fuscomaculalis* Saalmüller, 1880: 288 (see Afromoths).

[224] For Lymantriinae classification we rely on the works of Griveaud (1977) and Schintlmeister (2004), as well as the molecular treatment of Wang et al. (2015) for tribal-level classification (see also Holloway 2011). Few early stages are known for Madagascar to guide tribal placement, hence the large number of *i.s.* genera, for which our list of genera does not differ essentially from that of Viette (1990).

[225] Lymantriini comprises *Lymantica* and *Lymantria* (= *Pyramocera*, = *Griveaudtria*) (subgenera in Schintlmeister 2004).

[226] In Nygmiini, probably many Malagasy "*Euproctis*" taxa belong to *Sphrageidus*, but a revision is awaited. Our placement here of *Salvatgea*, *Noliproctis*, and *Porthesaroa*, suggested by DNA barcodes, as well as *Nolosia*, remains tentative.

[227] In addition, Lymantriinae *i.s.* (see Viette 1990: 154–166) includes: *Abakabaka* (2 spp.); *Alina* (3 spp.); *Ankova* (2 spp.); *Aphomoeoma mesembrinum* Collenette, 1959; *Cadorela translucida* Griveaud, 1973; *Croremopsis argemma* (Mabille, 1900); *Erika analalava* Griveaud, 1976; *Fanala* (2 spp.); *Homoeomeria* (2 spp.); *Kintana ocellatula* (Hering, 1926); *Laeliolina* (2 spp.); *Lanitra* (2 spp.); *Naroma madecassa* Griveaud, 1971; *Nolosia marmorata* Hampson, 1900; *Numenoides* (3 spp.); *Orana* (3 spp.); *Peloroses praestans* (Saalmüller, 1884); *Radamaria* (4 spp.); *Rahona* (2 spp.); *Scaphocera* (2 spp.); *Sirana* (3 spp.); *Sychnacedes* (2 spp.); *Turlina punctata* Griveaud, 1976; *Varatra acosmeta* (Collenette, 1939); *Viettema* (2 spp.); *Vohitra* (2 spp.); and *Zavana* (2 spp.); as well as the whitish-transparent taxa *Eopirga* (3 spp.); *Leptepilepta* (3 spp.); *Madema viettei* Collenette, 1959; *Marbla divisa* (Walker, 1855); *Marblepsis flabellaria* (Fabricius, 1787); and *Ogoa* (2 spp.). Many of these genera probably belong to the Orgyiini, but at present we cannot give the exact composition of this tribe (more easily recognized on the basis of certain larval characters). The genus *Dasychoproctis* (3 spp.) belongs to the Notodontidae, as shown by its wing venation and tympanal morphology (Minet 1983); see comment 179.

[228] Pangraptinae also contains *Bareia incidens* Walker, 1858; *Cortyta remigiana* Hampson, 1913; *Episparis* (= *Episparina*) (2 spp.); *Gracilodes nysa* Guenée, 1852 (see Zahiri et al. 2012: Figure 4); *Taviodes virgata* Griveaud & Viette, 1962 (see Holloway 2005: 298; 2011: 201); and tentatively also *Aburina* (2 spp.), "*Euippodes*" *biplagula* (von Heyden, 1891), *Herpeperas* (2 spp.), and "*Zethes*" *humilis* Mabille, 1900. However, for "*Pangrapta*" *fauvealis* Viette, 1965 and "*Pangrapta*" *acolesis* Viette, 1958; see comment 229.

[229] Herminiinae contains also: "*Adrapsa*" (3 spp.); "*Dichromia*" *rationalis* Viette, 1956; "*Dichromia*" *sieglinde* Viette, 1979; "*Hypena*" *mainty* Viette, 1979; "*Idia*" *serralis* (Mabille, 1880); "*Macrochilo*" (2 spp.); "*Marca*" *univocalis* (Viette, 1956); "*Maxera*" *laportei* Viette, 1979; *Progonia* (2 spp., including, added by Orhant 2001, *P. matilei*); "*Sarmatia*" *ankasoka* Viette, 1979; "*Singara*" *humberti* Viette, 1966, and three "*Singara*" of "Viette, 1981" (*mantasoa*, *marojejy*, and *vaovalis*); and *Zethesides serangodes* Viette, 1956. Also, in the *Naarda* group of taxa, are "*Gesonia*" *elongalis* (Viette, 1954); "*Marca*" *griseonigralis* Viette, 1954; *Ipermarca monovittata* Berio, 1966; *Naarda ivelona* Viette, 1965; "*Nodaria*" *dubiefae* Viette, 1982; "*Ugiodes*" *vagulalis* Viette, 1965; and possibly "*Deinypeina*" *biplagialis* Viette, 1954. Other herminiines recognized here are the *Coelophoris*-like *Heteromala rougeoti* Viette, 1979; the *Chusaris*-like "*Hydrillodes*" *discoidea*, *incerta*, and *inversa* of Viette (1962) and "*Hydrillodes*" *pyraustalis* (Viette, 1954); *Hydrillodes uliginosalis* Guenée, 1854; "*Pangrapta*" *fauvealis* Viette, 1965, "*Pangrapta*" *acolesis* Viette, 1958; and tentatively, "*Radara*" *helcida* (Viette, 1962).

[230] Aganainae also here contains *Mecodinops anceps* (Mabille, 1879) but not "*Mecodina*" *cataloxia* (Viette, 1958) (Anobinae, comment 222, *q.v.*). *Hypsiforma* is transferred here tentatively (including *concolora* Swinhoe, 1903; in *Asota* in Afromoths). Previously placed in *Digama* (Viette 1990) are *Sommeria malgassica* (Toulgoët, 1954) and *S. septempuncta* (Hampson, 1910). Note that *Godasa sidae*, an aganaine as shown by its pupal morphology (but often misplaced in Agaristinae), has been erroneously recorded from Madagascar (Afromoths) based on a syn. ("*Aganais*" *mecynoides* Mabille, 1879) described in a work about Madagascar but in a footnote stating that it is an African taxon.

[231] *Phryganopteryx* uniquely represents the Phryganopterygina, a subtribe endemic to Madagascar, with 20 described species (Bendib and Minet 2000). The other Lithosiini taxa belong to the nonendemic subtribes Cistheniina, though apparently paraphyletic, and include *Siccia* (3 spp.) and *Thumatha* (2 spp.); see also comment 264 regarding "*Parasiccia*" *ochrorubens*; Nudariina for *Cyana*; and Lithosiina essentially, but the exact faunal composition of these tribes is still subject to revision (see Chialvo et al. 2018; Scott et al. 2014). Minor genera (and species) also include *Agylla madagascariensis* Toulgoët, 1960; *Alepista irregularis* Toulgoët, 1976, *Astacosia* (3 spp.); *Cristulosia* (2 spp.); *Metexilisia citrago* Toulgoët, 1958; *Microhyle* (4 spp.); *Novosia herbuloti* (Toulgoët,

1954); *Paraona* (2 spp.); *Paulianosia clathrata* Toulgoët, 1958; *Proxhyle* (2 spp.); *Pseudopelosia plumosa* (Mabille, 1900); *Spatulosia malgassica* Toulgoët, 1965; and *Turlinia phalaenoides* Toulgoët, 1976. *Cyana lobata* was added to the fauna by Karisch (2013).

232 See Zaspel et al. (2014) and references therein for placement of *Amerila* in the tribe Amerilini; see also Dowdy et al. (2020) for its phylogenetic placement.

233 In Syntomini, *Fletcherinia decaryi* is a relative of *Ceryx* in Africa falling with the "*Amata* clade" of Syntomini according to Przybyłowicz et al. (2019). The others form a monophyletic unit when the Mediterranean genus *Dysauxes* is included, an unusual biogeographic pattern. This last "*Dysauxes*" clade contains, in addition: *Micronaclia* (3 spp.); *Soganaclia* (3 spp.); *Tenuinaclia* (3 spp.); *Toulgoetinaclia obliquipuncta* (Rothschild, 1924); *Tsarafidynia* (2 spp.); *Tsirananaclia* (4 spp.); *Vadonaclia marginepuncta* Griveaud, 1964; and *Vitronaclia* (2 spp.).

234 Since there are no true Callimorphina taxa on Madagascar (a subtribe characterized by an extra verruca, near L3, of three abdominal segments of the larva; Bendib and Minet 1998: 1010; see also recently published molecular phylogenies: Zaspel et al. 2014, Zenker et al. 2016; also DaCosta and Weller 2005), the Malagasy Arctiini is here regarded as composed of four subtribes: Utetheisina, Nyctemerina, Spilosomina, and Euchromiina. In Utetheisina (characterized by a few long, white larval setae) we place *Amphicallia pratti* (Kenrick, 1914); *Alytarcha amanda* (Boisduval, 1847); *Argina astrea* (Drury, 1773); and *Utetheisa*. Malagasy Nyctemerina include *Galtara extensa* (Butler, 1880) and the clearly monophyletic genus *Nyctemera*, which can be divided into three subgenera (regarded as genera by Dubatolov 2006): *Chiromachla* (2 spp.: *gracilis* Saalmüller, 1884 and *insulare* (Boisduval, 1833); the presence of *pallescens* Oberthür, 1890, e.g., on Afromoths, is apparently incorrect), *Podomachla* (1 sp.: *virgo* (Strand, 1909)), and *Xylecata* (1 sp.: *biformis* (Mabille, 1879)). It should be noted that "*Xylecata*" *crassiantennata* (Oberthür, 1916) belongs in fact to the genus *Herbulotides* (Geometridae: Ennominae; see Viette 1990: 138; Lees and Minet 2003: 760, note 62). In Spilosomina (sister to Arctiina; e.g., Rönkä et al. 2016) we include "*Amsacta*" *duberneti* Toulgoët, 1968; *Creatonotos perineti* Rothschild, 1933; *Detoulgoetia virginalis* (Butler, 1878); *Madagascarctia* (*cellularis*, *femina*, *madagascariensis*); *Spilosoma*; *Toulgarctia* (*griveaudi*, *luteoradians*, *milloti*, *viettei*, *vieui*); and tentatively, *Fodinoidea* and *Parachelonia* (including *auremaculatus* (Rothschild, 1933), not in Viette 1990; a genus sometimes regarded as a syn. of *Neuroxena*). On Madagascar the subtribe Euchromiina includes only *Euchromia* (2 spp.); the alleged presence of *E. amoena* (e.g., on Afromoths) was based on Zerny (1912: 86), but we are unaware of any reliable record.

235 Phyllodini includes *Miniodes discolor* as a widespread Afrotropical species (in NHMUK there is one specimen from Madagascar and one from Mayotte) and, we suggest, *Huebnerius dux*.

236 Ophiderini includes *Hemiceratoides hieroglyphica* (see Hilgartner et al. 2007 regarding eye-frequenting behavior), currently regarded as a single species containing an additional subspecies, *vadoni* Viette, 1976 (Masoala). See Zahiri et al. (2012) for phylogenetic placement of the genus, and Staude et al. (2016: S170) for illustrations of the larvae of this species, which are similar to those of *Eudocima* but recorded as feeding on *Smilax* in Africa. *Eudocima salaminia* (Cramer, [1777]) was not included by Viette (1990); indeed, records for Madagascar are likely spurious (Zilli et al. 2017).

237 Calpinae *i.s.*: Calpinae classification is currently unsatisfactory for the fauna and, as currently treated in Afromoths, based essentially on the concept of Calpinae in Kitching and Rawlins (1998), which comprised "Calpini," probably including many Ophiderinae of Poole (1989) (at least what is now tribe Ophiderini, especially fruit-piercing taxa and all Scoliopteryginae (as Gonodontini and Anomini)). There was no list of genera in Kitching and Rawlins (1998), and the Calpinae consists of many (mainly erebid) taxa simply with fairly long and beak-like labial palps. Retaining the many Malagasy genera in Calpinae serves no useful purpose. The genus *Avitta* is one candidate for an additional calpine (see Holloway 2011: 399 and Hayashi 2003 regarding its larva). *Khadira formosa* Griveaud & Viette, 1962 is also placed here (in *Eudocima* on Afromoths, but not in Viette 1990: 232; Zilli and Hogenes 2002: 162 also considered it distinct).

238 *Hypocala deflorata* (Fabricius, 1794) we consider to be a misidentification of *H. florens* in Pagenstecher (1907: 112). Here we place other *Diospyros*-feeding taxa, *Antiophlebia* and *Hyperlopha* (see Holloway 2005: 210–211), based also on DNA barcoding evidence.

239 The subfamily Eulepidotinae, essentially Neotropical, contains *Anticarsia irrorata* (Fabricius, 1781) as a single representative of a Neotropical genus that is a legume pest species with a vast Paleotropical range (e.g., see Holloway 2011: 436). The species of *Anticarsia* on Madagascar is *rubricans* Boisduval, 1833, likely a different species from *irrorata* (Fabricius, 1781); see also Hacker et al. (2010: 23) and Hacker (2016: 283).

240 Tinoliinae include *Rhanidophora* (= *Melapera*; see also Lees and Zilli 2019: 105) and *Calesia nigriventris* Aurivillius, 1909 (see Holloway 2011: 225). The larvae are very characteristic semi-loopers, feeding on Acanthaceae vines (*Thunbergia*); see Staude et al. 2016: S168.

241 Following Mayerl and Lödl 1997, we recognize a hypenodine for the island's fauna belonging to the tribe Hypenodini (formerly "Strepsimaninae"): "*Rhynchina*" *herbuloti* Viette, 1965. Hypenodinae might include other described members on Madagascar (see Erebidae *i.s.*, comment 263).

242 In the Boletobiinae: Phytometrini, *Loxioda* includes two species of Viette, 1956 (*L. silvestralis* and *L. tristalis*) that were placed in *Marca* in Afromoths as well as *M. proclinata* Saalmüller, 1891 (see also Hacker 2019: 235, Plate 8). However, "*Marca*" *griseonigralis* and "*Marca*" *univocalis* belong in Herminiinae (comment 229, *q.v.*). We also place here *Cycloprosopus strigifera* (Pagenstecher, 1907) and *Pleuronodes arida* (Hampson, 1902) and retain here, tentatively, "*Raparna*" *confusa* and "*Raparna*" *didyma* of Mabille, 1900 (though not congeneric; Hacker 2019; t.s., *R. ochreipennis* Moore, 1882). The count includes recently added *Phytometra saecularia* Hacker, Fiebig & Stadie, 2019, but excluded here are the genera *Radara* and *Rhesala*, placed by Hacker (2019) in this tribe of Boletobiinae (without explicit justification); see Erebidae, *i.s.*, comment 263.

243 Araeopteronini contains *Araeopteron papaziani* (see Bippus 2018).

244 Concerning the fungus-feeding specialist Boletobiini (see Holloway 2005: 373 for generalities), we place here *Argyrolopha* and include *A. aviakala* (Bippus, 2018), based on DNA barcoding, and also "*Eudrapa*" *sogai* Viette, 1965 (close to *A. costibarbata* Hampson, 1914; see Hacker 2019, Plate 1: Figure 10a). We also include here the genus *Catalana* (Calpinae in Afromoths) based on DNA barcoding information.

245 Boletobiinae: Eublemmini contains also (see Hacker 2019): *Cautatha* (3 spp.); *Corgathalia* (2 spp.); *Eublemmoides apicimacula* (Mabille, 1880); *Honeyana* (3 spp.); *Hypersophtha* (3 spp.); *Lophoruza* (4 spp.); *Oediblemma leptinia* (Mabille, 1900); *Oruza tafana* (Viette, 1976); *Paragona auroviridis* Viette, 1958; *Syngatha geometriana* (Viette, 1981); and *Tegiapa* (4 spp.). We add here *Andrianam poinimerina* Viette, 1954; "*Maxera*" *nova* Viette 1956; and "*Pleurona*" *sirenia* Viette, 1956 (= *Corgatha elleni* Hacker, Fiebig & Stadie, 2019). The Eublemmini count includes the following new species recently named: *Eublemma aethiopica*, *E. baccatrix*, *E. ceresensis*, *E. madaphaea*, *E. poliochra*, *Honeyana aulombardi*, *H. pusillana*, and *Tegiapa catalai* all by Hacker, 2019; *Acremma chalcochra*, *A. clatrata*, *A. macrophaea*, *A. microphaea*, *A. rhodophaea*, *A. transalbipoda* (all *Andrianam*, comb. nov.), *Corgatha badia*, *C. sororcula*, *C. dobsoni*, *C. metachrosta*, *C. parvula*, *Corgathalia hirutae*, *Eublemmistis ramonafana* [*sic*], *Hypobleta biformis*, *H. pusillana*, and *Metachrostis marmoreata* all by Hacker, Fiebig & Stadie, 2019; and *Corgatha dirkstadiensis* and *C. ralffiebigi* both by by Hacker & Fiebig, 2019. From its description, *Ancistris saturnina* Mabille, 1898 is an available name potentially for a *Corgatha* species, perhaps *C. chopardi* (1954) (Viette 1990: 248 thought it to be possibly a Hypeninae), but its type is still unknown so we did not count the genus (in that case junior) or species.

246 Boletobiinae *i.s.* now contains a few taxa that might be placed either in Boletobiini or in Eublemmini. Placed here are *Attonda adspersa* (R. Felder & Rogenhofer, 1875) (a widespread Old World species, see Holloway 2011: 218, 337, where it is placed in the "*Saroba* group of genera") and *Homodes magnifica* Viette, 1958 (see Holloway 2011: 222; Zahiri et al. 2012: Figure 5; there without

tribe). Also belonging to Boletobiinae is *Macella euritiusalis* (Walker: 1865) (it is similar to "*Saroba*" ["*Capnodes?*"] *maculicosta* Walker (Indo-Australasian): Holloway 2005: 341, Plate 23, Figure 7).

[247] Arrangement of tribes and generic composition of Erebinae follows in part Zahiri et al. (2011, 2012) and Homziak et al. (2019).

[248] Regarding Erebinae: Acantholipini, see Zahiri et al. (2012: Figure 6) and Homziak et al. (2019) concerning the placement of these three genera. This tribe includes a range of taxa currently in inappropriate genera, as well as *Cryptomeria mabillei* Saalmüller, 1880 (monotypic): "*Deinypena*" *ranomafana* Viette, 1966 (but not "*Deinypeina*" *biplagialis* Viette, 1954; see Hermiininae, comment 229), "*Phlogochroa*" *madecassa* (Viette, 1972); "*Thermesia*" *clarilinea* (Mabille, 1900) (see also comment 262) and "*Ugia*" (Viette 1990: 240).

[249] The genus *Sypnoides* was included in Sypnini in Zahiri et al. (2011).

[250] For Erebinae: Pandesmini, see Holloway (2005) and Homziak (2016) regarding inclusion of *Polydesma*.

[251] For Erebinae: Pericymini, note that within *Pericyma*, "*viettei*" Laporte, 1975 is an unavailable name. See Homziak (2016) regarding placement here of *Lophotavia*. "*Tavia nycterina*" may be related to this genus, but only the illustration in Boisduval (1833) of this taxon seems to be available.

[252] Erebini here includes *Sphingomorpha* (not currently cited for Madagascar on Afromoths), due to a well supported relationship (Homziak et al. 2019: Figure 1).

[253] Regarding inclusion of *Entomogramma* in Hypopyrini, see Homziak et al. (2019). *Ophisma leucochiton* Mabille, 1884 may be regarded as a syn. of *Hypopyra allardi* (Oberthür, 1878).

[254] See Homziak et al. (2019) regarding placement in Catocalini of *Ulotrichopis*, but there is little doubt *Cerocala* belongs here also.

[255] Erebidae: Tachosini contains *Tachosa acronyctoides* Walker, 1869 (= *T. malagasy* Viette, 1966); see Homziak (2016: 74), who places Tachosini as sister to Audeini.

[256] Most recently described in Audeinae is *Audea jonasi* Kühne, 2005 (Kühne 2005).

[257] Regarding placement here in Erebinae: Amphigoniini of *Lacera*, see Homziak et al. (2019).

[258] Erebinae: Euclidiini contains *Mocis*, *Remigiodes*, and *Trigonodes* (Homziak 2016; Homziak et al. 2019). "*Remigia*" *frugalis* (Fabricius, 1775) is a misidentification of the Indo-Australian *Mocis frugalis* (Fabricius, 1775): Hacker et al. (2010: 21) and Zilli (2000).

[259] Erebinae: Cocytiini here includes *Avatha saalmuelleri* (Mabille, 1881) (as well as "*Athyrma*," but see Holloway 2011: 89–90) and *Serrodes* (see Zahiri et al. (2012: Figure 6; Homziak et al. 2019).

[260] For Erebinae: Ophiusini, see Zahiri et al. 2011 regarding placement here of *Thyas* (= *Dermaleipa*); *Tytroca griveaudi* (Laporte, 1973) also belongs here. Note that *Stenopis* (t.s. *reducta* Mabille, 1880) contains on Afromoths two Malagasy species usually placed in *Ophiusa* (*mabillei* (Viette, 1974) and *reducta* (Mabille, 1880)).

[261] For Erebinae: Poaphilini, see Holloway and Miller 2003 (concerning *Dysgonia*); Homziak 2016 and Homziak et al. 2019 (*Achaea*, *Bastilla javiana*, *Dysgonia*, and *Tolna*) and Zahiri et al. 2012 (*Bastilla* and *Chalciope*). We also place here *Buzara angularis* (Boisduval, 1883) (= *Caranilla*, Moore 1885), according to Holloway (2011: 345), as well as *Grammodes* and *Ogovia ebenaui* (Viette, 1965), based on DNA barcoding information.

[262] Currently, Erebinae *i.s.* contains the genus *Maxera* (including neither "*Maxera*" *laportei* [see Herminiinae, comment 229] nor "*Maxera*" *nova* Viette, 1956 [see Boletobiinae: Eublemmini, comment 245]). The Fabaceae-feeding larva of *M. marchalii* is illustrated by Staude et al. (2016: S168). Also relegated here is *Megacephalomana* Strand, 1943, a genus, however, probably near *Platyja* (tribe with *Ischyja* undefined in Homziak et al. 2019); "*Zethes*" *sagittula* (von Heyden, 1891) (see Bippus 2018: 14 and Plate 2 for resting posture); as well as "*Thermesia*" *junctilinea* Mabille, 1900. The tribe Thermesiini does not exist on Madagascar. The t.s. (*T. abadirina* Hübner, 1823, Surinam) is currently identified as a *Heteroblemma* according to Beccaloni et al. (2003: "Lepindex"). "*Thermesia*" *junctilinea* bears a passing resemblance in wing pattern to *Acantholipes trimeni*, but the abdomen and palps are longer, and its male antennae are bipectinate. For "*Thermesia*" *clarilinea* Mabille, 1900, however, see Acantholipini (comment 248).

[263] In Erebidae *i.s.*, we currently place the following genera and species: "*Antiblemma*" *acrosema* (Mabille, 1900); *Bamra jucunda* Griveaud & Viette, 1962; the three closely related genera *Caryonopera*, *Nyctennomos* (*ungulata* Berio, 1956 = *peratosema* Hampson, 1926, syn. nov.; see comment 183 regarding "*Nyctennomos*" *ambitsha* Viette, 1976, here transferred to Nolidae), and *Thausgea*; two species possibly members of Hypeninae or Hypenodinae, "*Colobochyla*" *mabillealis* (Viette, 1954) and "*Colobochyla*" *saalmuelleralis* (Viette, 1954); "*Elesmoides*" *malagasy* Viette, 1973 (a species misplaced in *Elesmoides* [Nolidae], and here transferred to Erebidae); "*Fodina*" *decussis* (Saalmüller, 1891); *Holoxanthina rhodotela* (Viette, 1958); "*Hypena*" *diakonoffi* Viette, 1976; "*Idia*" *pernix* (Townsend, 1958) (= *H. fuscomaculalis* (Saalmüller, 1880: 289) [unavailable name]); "*Ilyrgis*" *subsignata* Mabille, 1900; *Leucotelia ochreoplagata* (Kenrick, 1917); *Maronis rivosa* (Saalmüller, 1891); *Mepantadrea* (2 spp.); "*Paralephana*" *umbrata* Griveaud & Viette, 1962; *Prominea* (2 spp.; Erebidae *i.s.* according to Holloway 2011 and Guillermet 2016: 17); *Radara* (not including "*Radara*" *helcida*, transferred to Herminiinae); and *Rhesala* (2 spp.). The long-enigmatic (Lees and Minet 2003: 760, note 61) *Galtarodes ragonoti* (Mabille, 1880) (= "*Galtara*" *viettei* (Toulgoët, 1971)) is also included here. Also placed here is the low-growing-legume defoliator *Janseodes melanospila* (Guenée, 1852), which was arranged by Lafontaine and Schmidt (2010) in Phytometrinae and included even in *Raparna* by Franclemont and Todd (1983), but was transferred to the genus *Janseodes* by Poole (1989). However, it is not included or mentioned in Hacker (2019), even though in facies it is indeed similar to some *Phytometra*.

[264] Regarding Noctuoidea *i.s.*, currently unplaced noctuoids are *Tornoconia* (3 spp.) and "*Parasiccia*" (*Aemene*) *ochrorubens* (Mabille, 1900).

[265] Lasiocampidae arrangement is currently very unsatisfactory, based largely on interpretation of the groupings in Lajonquière (1972). Tribes are not yet clearly established. The lasiocampid fauna also includes *Apatelopteryx* (3 spp.); *Callopizoma* (3 spp. including *C. legraini*, added to the fauna by Basquin 2017); *Chionodiptera* (3 spp., including *C. xeros* Basquin, 2017); *Chrysium mesembrinus* Lajonquière, 1969; *Diaphoromorpha* (3 spp.); *Endacantha* (3 spp.); *Eupagopteryx* (2 spp.); *Europtera* (2 spp.); *Gastromega* (2 spp.); "*Gonometa*" *attenuata* Kenrick, 1914; *Hypotrabala regius* (Lajonquière, 1973); *Lamprantaugia* (2 spp.); *Lerodes fulgurita* (Saalmüller, 1880); *Melopla* (3 spp.); *Napta serratilinea* Guenée, 1865; *Ochanella hova* (Butler, 1882); *Phoberopsis ferox* (Kenrick, 1914); and *Pseudoborocera legrasi* Lajonquière, 1972.

Recently added by Zolotuhin and Prozorov (2010) was *Sonitha lila*. Among taxa we omit are *Braura truncata* (Walker, 1855), which is from another fauna (Africa), and *Gastromega sordida* Mabille, 1879, an unidentified species from a typological perspective (Viette 1990: 247, as *Bombyx*). *Bombyx* (*Artaxa*) cf. *fleurotii* Guérin-Méneville on *Cajanus* (Pigeon Pea) is possibly a syn. of a *Borocera* species (see Viette 1990: 247), and may indeed represent *cajani*, since that is the native species known as *landibe*, most widely used for sericulture on Madagascar. "*Lechriolepis*" *diabolus* Hering, 1928 and *Philotherma goliath* (Viette, 1962) are duplicated names in Afromoths for respective *Closterothrix* species.

[266] We mention two Bombycidae and not one as in Lees and Minet (2003: 754), because there we omitted to mention the domiciliary silkworm, which was introduced in the early 19th century onto the island, where it is known as *landikely*.

[267] Sphingidae higher classification is based on Kitching et al. (2018: Supplementary material 1).

[268] Concerning the Smerinthinae: Sichiini, there are more BINs on BOLD for some species of *Gynoeryx* than there are described species.

[269] See Pierre and Basquin (2017) regarding Smerinthinae: Leucophlebiini, *Malgassoclanis maculalis* and *M. rufus*.

[270] Regarding the "*Polyptychus* Genus-Group" of Kitching et al. (2018) that contains *Pseudoclanis*, we exclude the (African) species *P. postica*. The mention of "Madagascar" in Afromoths is based on an old paper (Kernbach 1955). Neither Griveaud (1959, in his revision) nor Viette (in 1990) have accepted this record.

[271] See also Haxaire and Minet (2017) regarding *Pantophaea suffuscus*. *Coelonia insularis* Basquin, 2018 is a *nomen nudum* (no repository).

[272] Concerning the Macroglossinae: Hemarini, an old record of "*Macroglossa*" *gyrans* for the island (as *bombus*; see Viette 1990: 249), is not reliable. Although it does not affect our count, *Cephonodes virescens* (Wallengren, 1865) has recently (Zolotuhin et al. 2019) been raised to species level (formerly *hylas virescens*).

[273] Macroglossini also contains, in Choerocampina: *Basiothia* (2 spp.), *Euchloron megaera* (Linnaeus, 1758), *Hyles* (2 spp.), *Rhagastis lambertoni* (Clark, 1923), and *Theretra orpheus* (Herrich-Schäffer, 1854); in Macroglossina: *Antinephele lunulata* Rothschild & Jordan, 1903, *Atemnora westermannii* (Boisduval, 1875), *Daphnis* (2 spp.; most recently described is *D. kitchingi*, by Haxaire and Melichar 2011), *Maassenia* (2 spp.), and *Macroglossum* (3 spp.).

[274] Note that according to morphological and DNA evidence, there is potentially subspecific level variation in both *Antherina suraka* (Randrianandrasana et al. 2016) and *Ceranchia apollina*. However, the name "*australis*" Griveaud, 1962 is unavailable (infrasubspecific in *A. suraka*) and in contrast to Lees and Minet (2003: 758, note 35), we regard *Ceranchia reticolens* Butler, 1882 as a probable syn. of *C. apollina* (the type locality of both taxa being in Betsileo region). Although "*Saturnia*" *mangiferae* Sganzin, 1833 (in Boisduval 1833: 89) has been regarded as a possible senior syn. of *C. apollina* Butler, 1878 (Griveaud, 1962), its identity remains uncertain in the absence of known type material (Viette 1990: 247). This is also because its description may suggest a pale form of *Bunaea aslauga*. Moreover, the possible host plant considered by Sganzin (*Mangifera*, Anacardiaceae) is among those reported for *B. alcinoe*, a close relative of *B. aslauga*, whereas *C. apollina* host plant(s) belong to the Apocynaceae.

[275] As for the sole representative of Bunaeini on Madagascar, we regard *Bunaea vulpes* Oberthür, 1916 as infraspecific.

[276] The Urotini count includes *Maltagorea basquini*, added by Rougerie (2003); *M. dubiefi*, added by Bouyer (2006); *M. pseudovulpina*, added by Basquin and Rougerie (2009); and *M. altivola*, *M. ambahona*, *M. mariae*, and *M. pseudomariae*, added by Basquin (2013).

[277] Epipleminae arrangement is based on Boudinot (1982).

[278] Among Uraniidae: Microniinae, *Micronia semifasciata* cannot be reliably identified as regards the missing type and in any case represents a genus otherwise typical of Indo-Australasia (Viette 1990: 248).

[279] *Urapteritra falcifera* occurs on Madagascar, where it is sympatric with *U. piperata*, according to Viette (1972).

[280] Sihvonen and Kaila (2004: Table 1) is very helpful for tribal placement of Sterrhinae.

[281] Sterrhinae: Cosymbiini contains *Eois* (*E. leighata*, based on a DNA barcode from Madagascar); the genus is mainly Neotropical (t.s. *E. russearia* Hübner, 1818; see also Strutzenberger et al. 2010), but the barcode of *E. leighata* pertains to a sizable group of species named *Eois* on BOLD; 15 Afrotropical species of this genus are recognized by Afromoths. The tribe also includes *Chrysocraspeda* (see Sihvonen and Kaila 2004: Table 1), and *Cyclophora* (see Murillo-Ramos et al. 2019: Supplementary data 3).

[282] In Sterrhinae: Timandrini, *Traminda* falls close to *Timandra* in Murillo-Ramos et al. (2019: Supplementary data 3) but is unplaced in the same work (Figure 2).

[283] *Rhodometra sacraria* falls not far from *Timandra* in Murillo-Ramos et al. (2019: Supplementary data 3). *Afrophyla vethi* is also placed in the same study in Rhodometrini.

[284] Regarding placement of *Metallaxis* in Rhodostrophiini, see Sihvonen and Kaila (2004: Table 1).

[285] For *Idaea* in Sterrhini, see Sihvonen and Kaila (2004: Table 1). Two species listed by Scoble (1999), *I. politata* (Hübner, 1793) ("*politaria*" was a *lapsus* in Lees and Minet 2003: 760, note 63) and *I. limbolata* (Mabille, 1900) (for the latter see Viette, 1990: 249), are not counted, as they do not reliably belong to the fauna.

[286] For these genera in Sterrhinae: Scopulini, see Sihvonen and Kaila (2004: Table 1).

[287] Regarding Larentiinae: Trichopterygini, *Lobidiopteryx* here is based on placement in the same clade as *Trichopteryx* in Murillo-Ramos et al. (2019: Supplementary data 3).

[288] Regarding Asthenini, *Asthenotricha* falls close to *Asthena* in Murillo-Ramos et al. (2019: Supplementary data 3). We follow Viette (1990: 248) and Afromoths rather than Lees and Minet (2003: 760, note 64) in not treating the Mascarene *Venusia distrigaria* (Boisduval, 1833) as reliably part of the Malagasy fauna.

[289] Larentiinae: Melanthiini contains *Horisme* according to Krüger (2007b) and based on its placement in Murillo-Ramos et al. (2019: Supplementary data 3). *Horisme minuata* (Walker, 1860), mentioned by Viette 1990, is currently omitted for Madagascar by Afromoths.

[290] Eupitheciini also contains *Collix foraminata* Guenée, 1858; *Mesocolpia nanula* (Mabille, 1900); and *Pasiphila derasata* (Bastelberger, 1905). See Õunap et al. (2016) for members of the tribe (e.g., *Collix*). *Chloroclystis consocer* Prout, 1937 and *Eupithecia festiva* Prout, 1916 are included here as they are mentioned by Viette (1990: 130–131), although currently omitted from Afromoths for Madagascar; however, in contrast to Lees and Minet (2003: 760, note 64), we count *E. hemistrigaria* Mabille, 1880, since the type locality is Madagascar (see also Afromoths).

[291] Larentiinae: Xanthorhoini also contains *Disclisioprocta natalata* (Walker, 1862); *Orthonama quadrisecta* Herbulot, 1954; *Polystroma subspissata* Warren, 1897; *Pseudolarentia* (2 spp.); and *Xanthorhoe* (3 spp.). For *Mimoclystia* and *Orthonama*, see placement in Murillo-Ramos et al. (2019: Supplementary data 3). For *Haplolabida* ("unplaced" but close to *Larentia* in Murillo-Ramos et al. 2019: Supplementary data 3) as well as *Pseudolarentia*, see Krüger (2007b). *Polystroma subspissata* Warren, 1897, although mentioned by Viette 1990: 133, is currently omitted by Afromoths for Madagascar.

[292] For the *Piercia* group of genera, see Krüger (2007b).

[293] Regarding the composition of Desmobathrinae, contrary to a suggestion in Lees and Minet (2003: 759, note 60), *Afrophyla vethi* is genuinely a Sterrhinae (see Sihvonen et al. 2011; Sihvonen and Staude 2011; Staude et al. 2016: S219 for the larva) and is put into Rhodometrini following Murillo-Ramos et al. (2019: Supplementary data 3).

[294] See Murillo-Ramos et al. (2019: Figure 5) for the "basal" placement of Geometrinae: Agathini.

[295] Murillo-Ramos et al. (2019: Figure 5) places the geometrine tribe Comibaenini tribe close to Nemoriini (a tribe not detected on Madagascar).

[296] Regarding Geometrinae: Pseudoterpnini, *Pingasa* falls next to *Pseudoterpna* and *Dysphania* in Murillo-Ramos et al. (2019: Supplementary data 3).

[297] Representatives of the following genera are included in Geometrinae: Hemitheini (Hemitheiti of Holloway, 1996: 147) in Murillo-Ramos et al. (2019: Supplementary data 3): *Comostolopsis*; *Hemistola hypnopoea* Prout, 1926; *Lophostola cara* Prout, 1913; *Maxates*; *Metallochlora* (2 spp.); *Mixocera* (2 spp.); *Phaiogramma stibolepida* (Butler, 1879); *Prasinocyma*; and *Thalassodes* (3 spp.). Furthermore, we consider also belonging in this tribe: *Acidromodes porphyretica* (Prout, 1925); *Archichlora* (= *Leptocolpia* syn. nov.) (e.g., Figure 9.70h); *Blechroneromia*; *Dryochlora cinctuta* (Saalmüller, 1891); *Dyschlorodes* (2 spp.); *Epigelasma*; *Eucrostes disparata* Walker, 1861; *Gelasmodes malagasy* Viette, 1978; *Heterorachis*; *Hypocoela*; *Microloxia ruficornis* Warren, 1897; *Mimandria* (3 spp.); and *Rhodesia* (2 spp.), owing to general habitus including general greenish or bluish pigment. However, on the one hand, *Prasinocyma pallidulata* (Mabille, 1880, as *Thalassodes*) is not included in our count, as it is mentioned by Viette (1990: 248) as unidentified, although it is treated as a member of the fauna by Afromoths and Scoble (1999); but on the other hand, *Rhodesia viridalbata* Warren, 1905, which is not mentioned in Viette (1990), was newly recorded from Madagascar based on a specimen in ZSM in Afromoths.

[298] Also relegated to Geometrinae *i.s.* are *Cancellalata fletcheri* Viette, 1979; *Chlorodrepana madecassa* Viette, 1971; *Doloma leucocephala* Prout, 1922; *Hydatopsis jaspidaria* Herbulot, 1968; *Lophorrhachia rubricorpus* (Warren, 1898); *Neromia picticosta* Prout, 1913; *Omphax* (3 spp.); and *Perithalera oblongula* Prout, 1922.

[299] See Murillo-Ramos et al. (2019) for several tribal placements and general arrangement.

[300] *Epigynopteryx* and *Mesothisa* (which might even be internal to *Epigynopteryx*) fall close to *Ennomos* in Murillo-Ramos et al. (2019: Supplementary data 3). *Psilocerea* is placed in Ennomini in Krüger (2007b).

[301] The fern-feeding group Diptychiini was formerly known as Lithinini.
[302] *Drepanogynis* is placed in its new tribe Drepanogynini by Murillo-Ramos et al. (2019), transferred from Nacophorini, e.g., in Krüger (2007b), which also includes *Argyrophora*; see comment 308. Lees and Minet (2003: 760, note 62) tentatively transferred *Diptychia rhodotenia* Mabille, 1898 to the genus *Drepanogynis* (as suggested by Viette 1990: 248), but here we regard this species, whose type is missing, as unidentified (or quite possibly a syn. of an existing species).
[303] Hypochrosini contains on Madagascar only *Hypochrosis suffusata* Pagenstecher, 1907, a species that is doubtfully a member of the genus (e.g., the forewings have a rounded rather than falcate apex, according to the illustration reproduced on Afromoths).
[304] *Zamarada* falls in clade "Cassymini I" in Murillo-Ramos et al. (2019).
[305] Regarding placement of *Luxiaria* in Eutoeini, see Murillo-Ramos et al. (2019).
[306] Regarding composition of Macariini, see Krüger (2007b) and Murillo-Ramos et al. (2019). Macariini also includes *Acanthovalva itremo* Krüger, 2001 (Krüger 2001) and *Semiothisa peyrierasi* Viette, 1975.
[307] Ennominae: Boarmiini also contains *Ascotis reciprocaria* (Walker, 1860); *Anticleora* (3 spp.); *Darisodes* (3 spp.); *Hypomecis* (2 spp.); *Rhodophthitus* (2 spp.); *Xylopteryx* (3 spp.); and *Zeuctocleora una* Prout, 1929. See also Murillo-Ramos et al. (2019), especially concerning the placement of *Aphilopota* (Supplementary file 3). See also Krüger (2007b) regarding *Colocleora* and *Xylopteryx*, as well as Fletcher (1978: 89) concerning the similar genitalia of *Xylopteryx* to *Rhodophthitus*, also related by DNA barcodes and by Jiang et al. (2017). The fauna also includes the genera *Ascotis*, *Cleora*, *Ectropis*, *Hypomecis*, and *Racotis* (Chainey and Karisch 2017).
[308] Also relegated to Ennominae *i.s.* are *Exeliopsis* (2 spp.); *Malgassothisa trifida* Herbulot, 1966; *Melinoessa* (2 spp.); *Milocera horaria* Swinhoe, 1904; *Negloides oceanitis* Prout, 1931; *Oaracta* (2 spp.); *Ochroplutodes hova* Herbulot, 1954; and *Sphyrocosta madecassa* (Viette, 1973). Concerning the unnamed *i.s.* group in Murillo-Ramos et al. (2019): *Argyrophora* falls close to the African genera *Mauna* and *Panhyperochia* rather than close to *Drepanogynis* (see Krüger 1999) in Murillo-Ramos et al. (2019: Supplementary data 3) (the last study does not include *Nacophora*). Regarding *Erastria* (= *Petrodava*, Lees and Minet 2003: note 62), see Murillo-Ramos et al. (2019: 13, Clade "Unnamed E6"), which revises Krüger's (2007b) placement of *Erastria* in Caberini.

The present work represents a substantial modernization of the systematic framework for the Lepidoptera fauna of Madagascar. It includes resolutions for numerous previously incorrectly placed taxa. We have been able to place many genera not only in families and subfamilies but in tribes, which have recently become very popular in molecular work—in particular for the large superfamilies Pyraloidea, Noctuoidea, and Geometroidea. There remain, though, numerous lacunae in the classification presented. For example, the current arrangements of Erebidae—Lymantriinae and Lasiocampidae—are very unsatisfactory. Among Noctuoidea in particular, we have been able to clean up many of these groups that were previously not much better than catchalls for unrelated taxa, such as Calpinae, Amphipyrinae, Hadeninae, and Xyleninae of different authors. Despite our attempts at tidying things up, there nevertheless remain dozens of genera in the *incertae sedis* (*i.s.*) category, notably within Noctuidae (15 genera and 18 species including those currently needing a valid genus); Erebidae (13 genera and 38 species); and Geometridae: Ennominae (15 genera and 72 species). Clearly, in-depth molecular treatments are called for to stabilize the systematics of the Malagasy fauna; these should also include exemplars, if not type species, of the relevant genera. DNA barcoding, even though certainly very limited in its phylogenetic resolution, has provided many useful hints or hypotheses for the placement of numerous taxa that can be confirmed by other data sets, particularly in morphology. The value of DNA barcoding is in its increasing comprehensiveness.

The fauna of Lepidoptera now exceeds 5000 described species. See Lopez-Vaamonde et al. (2019) regarding the large number of undescribed species, especially of micromoths (e.g., Tineoidea and Gelechioidea). The analysis of a combination of light trapping and Malaise sampling might suggest more than a doubling of the species total. A figure of 499 novel micromoth BINs sampled by Malaise trapping at Analamazaotra alone really stands out (Lopez-Vaamonde et al. 2019). Given continued problems with habitat modification on Madagascar and threats of extinction, there is very limited time to conduct a detailed census; an effort initiated in 2020 for a massive expansion of the Malaise trap program of up to 125 scattered sites on the island could yield an unprecedented appreciation of the true scale of the diversity of Madagascar's undescribed species.

There is still no accurate estimate for the level of endemism of the Lepidoptera fauna of Madagascar. It is clear though that this is widely variable among higher taxonomic groups. Krüger (2007a) calculated the relative endemism between the Malagasy and South African faunas for 50 families or subfamilies. The average species endemism of 24 families for Madagascar calculated by Krüger was 89.5%. Toward the lower end, G. Leraut (2019b) calculated more specifically for Pyralidae: Phycitinae, 65% (92 species) of 140 phycitines are endemic to Madagascar. At the upper end, for a large group such as Geometridae, in Krüger's analysis, 90.9% of Madagascar's fauna occurred only there rather than being shared with South Africa. It seems likely that species endemism of the Malagasy fauna will exceed 85% (it is nearly at this level for butterflies alone; Lees et al. 2003). Altogether, Krüger lists 453 shared species of Lepidoptera between those faunas. Therefore, considering only the presently known fauna (~5000 species) and not accounting for many additional nonendemics shared with other regional faunas, the level of species endemism on Madagascar should be below 90.4%. The total generic endemism is difficult to estimate at present and not a useful figure, as it will continue to change substantially as groups are comprehensively assessed.

ACKNOWLEDGMENTS

For access to barcoding data on Madagascar, as well as the Neotropics, we thank Carlos Lopez-Vaamonde, Christian Wieser, and Peter Huemer. Paul Hebert is credited for his great help in facilitating DNA barcoding of the Malagasy Lepidoptera. Colleagues at the Natural History Museum, London, are thanked for discussions, notably Ian Kitching, Geoff Martin, Klaus Sattler, Mark Sterling, and Alberto Zilli. For various other help, including bibliographic information, we also thank Jean Haxaire, Guillaume and Patrice Leraut, Kyu-Tek Park, Wolfgang Speidel, Niklas Wahlberg, and Linlin Yang. Photos are courtesy of the Muséum National d'Histoire Naturelle (MNHN) and the Trustees of the Natural History Museum, London (NHMUK) unless individually credited.

Subject editors: Brian L. Fisher and Steven M. Goodman

HYMENOPTERA: FORMICIDAE, ANTS, *VITSIKA*

B. L. Fisher

At some point during the Cretaceous, when dinosaurs dominated the land, the first ants walked the earth. We know little about the habits of these early ants, but it appears they were not abundant and did not form large colonies. Over the last 100 million years, these early ants gave rise to one of the most ecologically dominant animal lineages on the planet today.

At the same time, Madagascar was making its own journey toward isolation, separating first from Africa, along with the present-day Seychelles and India, and soon becoming an isolated evolutionary experiment. How this long-term isolation molded ant diversity on the island is a fascinating story of chance arrival, radiation, and convergent evolution. It is a story that is far from completely understood, but one that has intrigued ant researchers for several decades. I review here what we have learned to date about these remarkable and fascinating insects in a large-scale update to the parallel contribution that appeared in the precursor of this book (Fisher 2003).

EXPLORATION

Before the modern period of exploration, the last significant activity on Malagasy ants occurred a full century earlier, when Forel produced a couple of authoritative volumes (1891, 1892) that summarized, in part, the results of early explorers and collectors of ants on Madagascar, such as Alluaud, Camboué, Coquerel, Hildebrandt, Mocquerys, Perrot, Sikora, and Voeltzkow. My first trip to survey the ants of Madagascar was in 1993 to Andohahela near Tolagnaro. In 2000, I formed the Arthropod Inventory Team based at the Madagascar Biodiversity Center in Parc Botanique et Zoologique de Tsimbazaza. Together, as of March 2020, the team and I have visited over 400 field sites representing all major habitats and geological formations on the island (Fisher 2005a), as well as neighboring islands in the western Indian Ocean and southeastern Africa, which provide a regional perspective. Malagasy and international taxonomists have incorporated these field collections into their research programs, yielding more than 100 publications documenting the diversity, evolution, and biology of ants.

The boom in ant research on the island parallels a growing awareness of the threats facing Madagascar's natural splendors. The same threats facing the natural forests on Madagascar have certainly caused the loss of insect species (Allnutt et al. 2008). These threats have set off a race to document the diversity that remains, while simultaneously challenging field researchers to apply their knowledge to protect the remaining forests and link nature to human health. Though each new species and observation adds to the tale of the island's extraordinary ants, we must now also ensure that our discoveries can be applied to the challenge of conserving local landscapes.

DIVERSITY AND ENDEMISM: A TALLY OF NUMBERS

In total, 794 valid species and subspecies of ants are known on Madagascar, of which:

675 are endemic to Madagascar;
46 are endemic to the Malagasy Region (see definition below);
37 are shared with Africa;
36 are introduced "tramps."

The first native species described from Madagascar was the spectacularly beautiful *Odontomachus coquereli* (Figure 9.71a) in 1861, collected by Coquerel in Ambatomanjaka near Antananarivo. When I began researching the ants of Madagascar in 1993, 319 species (and subspecies) from 35 ant genera (according to the classification from that period) were known from the island (Fisher 1997). Today, 794 valid species and subspecies from 58 genera are recognized (AntCat 2020), with >500 morphospecies estimated as awaiting description, meaning that, in less than 30 years, the estimated known ant fauna has more than quadrupled to over 1,300 species. The surge in species descriptions since 1993 includes 472 new species (491 if we include nearby islands) and eight new endemic ant genera. Of the 472 new species from the island, 79 species were described by, or in collaboration with, Malagasy scientists. These are the first ants ever described by Malagasy scientists, an achievement that is a direct result of long-term investments in biodiversity training.

When discussing the ant diversity in the region, we refer to species on Madagascar as Malagasy species, while the Malagasy Region description refers to species known from Madagascar and nearby islands or archipelagoes (Anjouan, Europa Atoll, Grande Comore, Grande Glorieuse, Ile du Lys, Juan de Nova, Mauritius, Mayotte, Mohéli, La Réunion, and the Seychelles). Most of the currently valid ant species on Madagascar are restricted to the island or the Malagasy Region (Table 9.51). Of the native species on the island, only 37 also occur on continental Africa. The balance of the species awaiting description are all endemics: 495 morphotaxa are endemic to Madagascar, and all 505 morphotaxa are endemic to the Malagasy Region. With such high endemism at the species level, Madagascar and nearby islands are best classified as their own biogeographic Malagasy Region, not as a subset of the Afrotropical region.

OVERVIEW OF GENERA

Two recent books provide an overview of the ant fauna, including an illustrated key to genera of the Malagasy Region (Fisher and Bolton 2016) and to genera of Madagascar (Fisher and Peeters 2019). In addition, keys to genera based on the male caste are available for

FIGURE 9.71 **Aspects of Malagasy ants showing the considerable diversity of morphology and life-history traits. A) Trap-jaw ants like *Odontomachus coquereli*, shown here, are best known for phenomenally fast predatory strikes. In *O. coquereli*, unlike all other species in the genus, winged queens have been replaced by wingless reproductives. B) Some members of the genus *Eburopone* on Madagascar are similar in form to the Old World army ant genus *Aenictus*. The animal shown here is undescribed and is referred to by the confirmed candidate name *Eburopone* MG08. C) *Lioponera* returning to the nest after raiding a brood of *Pheidole*. D) *Metapone emersoni* worker. E) *Malagidris sofina*, found in the Sambirano Region near Ambanja, nests on cliff faces in natural rock alcoves or clay banks. Each nest has a funnel-like entrance, in the shape of an ear, projecting from the cliff face. F) Some species of *Mystrium*, such as *M. voeltzkowi*, have ergatoid (wingless) queens (the reddish individuals pictured). The workers have big mandibles and hunt outside. Only a few of the ergatoid queens mate and lay eggs, while virgin ergatoids stay inside and provide brood care.** (PHOTO A by A. Wild; B by E. Prado; C, E, and F by B. L. Fisher; and D by M. Esposito.)

genera in Amblyoponinae (Yoshimura and Fisher 2012), Dolichoderinae (Yoshimura and Fisher 2011), Ponerinae (Yoshimura and Fisher 2007), and Proceratiinae (Yoshimura and Fisher 2009).

Among the 72 genera known from the Malagasy Region are those known only from introduced species, and others known only from undescribed species in the region (Table 9.52). Five genera with the greatest native species diversity (>95 species per genus) contain slightly more than half the estimated ant species on Madagascar: *Camponotus*, *Hypoponera*, *Pheidole*, *Strumigenys*, and *Tetramorium*. These five genera are present across all habitats on the island. Even though these genera are diverse and easy to find, they do not always include the most locally abundant species. For example, the genera of the five most commonly collected species, in order of abundance, are as follows: *Monomorium*, *Anochetus*, *Bothroponera*, *Strumigenys*, and *Plagiolepis*.

Ten genera are endemic to the island: *Adetomyrma*, *Aptinoma*, *Eutetramorium*, *Lividopone*, *Malagidris*, *Pilotrochus*, *Ravavy*, *Royidris*, *Tanipone*, and *Vitsika*. One species of *Eutetramorium* is also known on Mohéli, in the Comoro archipelago. These endemic genera deserve special conservation consideration because of their potential importance for understanding ant evolution as a whole and the biogeography and origins of the Malagasy ants.

Nine genera are very difficult to find because they are actually rare or because they nest and forage in microhabitats that are difficult to survey: *Adetomyrma*, *Chrysapace*, *Discothyrea*, *Metapone*, *Parvaponera*, *Pilotrochus*, *Probolomyrmex*, *Stigmatomma*, and *Xymmer*. The following genera include only species accidentally introduced by humans to Madagascar: *Brachymyrmex*, *Erromyrma*, *Lepisiota*, *Ooceraea*, *Ponera*, and *Solenopsis*. See Table 9.52 for additional genera known only from introduced species in the Malagasy Region.

BIOGEOGRAPHIC AFFINITIES TO AFRICA AND ASIA

Our knowledge of the biogeographic affinities and origins of the Malagasy taxa has benefited from efforts to understand the phylogenetic history of the major lineages of ants (see Brady et al. 2014; Ward et al. 2015 and references therein). Though this research is ongoing, we can conclude that the ancestors of present-day ants arrived on Madagascar by chance via long-distance dispersal and were not present when the island separated from Africa. After arriving, these ancestral lineages subsequently experienced a wide range of novel ecological conditions, which over time led to the evolution of striking adaptive radiations on the island. In some cases, the radiations converged into forms morphologically similar to unrelated taxa in Africa. Most ancestors of present-day lineages on Madagascar arrived from Africa, which reflects a shared history with this nearby continent. Relatively few genera on Madagascar, such as *Ravavy*, *Aphaenogaster*, and *Chrysapace*, are closely related to species in southeast Asia, which suggests that their origin is linked with Indo-Malaysia and not Africa. The sister genus to the endemic *Ravavy* is *Loweriella*, which is restricted to Indo-Malaysia (Ward et al. 2010).

TABLE 9.51. **Checklist of the 794 valid species and subspecies of ants recorded on Madagascar as of March 2020**

Adetomyrma aureocuprea Yoshimura & Fisher, 2012 (E)
A. bressleri Yoshimura & Fisher, 2012 (E)
A. caputleae Yoshimura & Fisher, 2012 (E)
A. cassis Yoshimura & Fisher, 2012 (E)
A. caudapinnigera Yoshimura & Fisher, 2012 (E)
A. cilium Yoshimura & Fisher, 2012 (E)
A. clarivida Yoshimura & Fisher, 2012 (E)
A. goblin Yoshimura & Fisher, 2012 (E)
A. venatrix Ward, 1994 (E)
Anochetus boltoni Fisher & Smith, 2008 (E)
A. goodmani Fisher & Smith, 2008 (E)
A. grandidieri Forel, 1891 (E)
A. madagascarensis Forel, 1887 (MR: Anjouan, Mohéli, Mayotte)
Aphaenogaster friederichsi Forel, 1918 (E)
A. gonacantha (Emery, 1899) (E)
A. swammerdami Forel, 1886 (E)
A. s. clara (Santschi, 1915) (E)
A. s. curta Forel, 1891 (E)
A. s. spinipes Santschi, 1911 (E)
Aptinoma antongil Fisher, 2009 (E)
A. mangabe Fisher, 2009 (E)
Bothroponera cambouei Forel, 1891 (E)
B. comorensis (André, 1887) (E)
B. masoala (Rakotonirina & Fisher, 2013) (E)
B. perroti Forel, 1891 (E)
B. planicornis (Rakotonirina & Fisher, 2013) (E)
B. tavaratra (Rakotonirina & Fisher, 2013) (E)
B. vazimba (Rakotonirina & Fisher, 2013) (E)
B. wasmannii Forel, 1887 (MR: Anjouan)
Brachymyrmex cordemoyi Forel, 1895 (I)
Camponotus alamaina Rakotonirina et al., 2016 (E)
C. androy Rakotonirina et al., 2016 (E)
C. auropubens Forel, 1894 (AF-MR)
C. batesii Forel, 1895 (E)
C. bevohitra Rakotonirina et al., 2016 (E)
C. butteli Forel, 1905 (E)
C. cervicalis Roger, 1863 (MR: Mauritius, Mayotte)
C. c. gaullei Santschi, 1911 (E)
C. christi Forel, 1886 (E)
C. concolor Forel, 1891 (E)
C. darwinii Forel, 1886 (E)
C. d. rubropilosus Forel, 1891 (E)
C. d. themistocles Forel, 1910 (E)
C. descarpentriesi Santschi, 1926 (E)
C. dromedarius Forel, 1891 (E)
C. dufouri Forel, 1891 (E)
C. d. imerinensis Forel, 1891 (E)
C. echinoploides Forel, 1891 (E)
C. edmondi André, 1887 (MR: Anjouan, Grande Comore, Mayotte)
C. efitra Rakotonirina et al., 2017 (E)
C. ellioti Forel, 1891 (E)
C. e. relucens Santschi, 1911 (E)
C. ethicus Forel, 1897 (E)
C. foersteri Forel, 1886 (E)
C. galoko Rakotonirina et al., 2016 (E)
C. gerberti Donisthorpe, 1949 (E)
C. gibber Forel, 1891 (E)
C. gouldi Forel, 1886 (E)
C. grandidieri Forel, 1886 (AF-MR)
C. hagensii Santschi, 1922 (E)
C. heteroclitus Forel, 1895 (E)
C. hildebrandti Forel, 1886 (E)
C. h. dichromothrix Emery, 1920 (E)
C. hova Forel, 1891 (E)
C. h. becki Santschi, 1923 (E)
C. h. boivini Forel, 1891 (E)
C. h. fairmairei Santschi, 1911 (E)
C. h. hovahovoides Forel, 1892 (E)
C. h. hovoides Dalla Torre, 1893 (E)
C. h. mixtellus Dalla Torre, 1893 (E)
C. h. obscuratus Emery, 1925 (E)
C. h. radamae Forel, 1891 (E)
C. imitator Forel, 1891 (E)
C. immaculatus Forel, 1892 (E)
C. jodina Rasoamanana et al., 2017 (E)
C. karaha Rasoamanana et al., 2017 (E)
C. kelleri Forel, 1886 (E)
C. k. invalidus Forel, 1897 (E)
C. lamosy Rakotonirina & Fisher, 2018 (E)
C. legionarius Santschi, 1911 (E)
C. leveillei Emery, 1895 (E)
C. liandia Rakotonirina & Fisher, 2018 (E)
C. longicollis Rasoamanana et al., 2017 (E)
C. lubbocki Forel, 1886 (MR: Mayotte)
C. maculatus (Fabricius, 1782) (I)
C. maculiventris Emery, 1895 (E)
C. madagascarensis Forel, 1886 (E)
C. maintikibo Rakotonirina et al., 2017 (E)
C. mainty Rakotonirina & Fisher, 2018 (E)
C. manabo Rakotonirina & Fisher, 2018 (E)
C. matsilo Rakotonirina et al., 2016 (E)
C. mifaka Rakotonirina et al., 2016 (E)
C. mita Rakotonirina et al., 2017 (E)
C. mocquerysi Emery, 1899 (E)
C. nasicus Forel, 1891 (E)
C. nossibeensis André, 1887 (E)
C. orombe Rakotonirina et al., 2016 (E)
C. perroti Forel, 1897 (E)
C. p. aeschylus Forel, 1913 (E)
C. pulcher Forel, 1892 (E)
C. putatus Forel, 1892 (E)
C. quadrimaculatus Forel, 1886 (MR: Anjouan, Grande Comore, Mohéli, Mayotte)
C. q. opacatus Emery, 1925 (E)
C. q. sellaris Emery, 1895 (E)
C. radovae Forel, 1886 (E)
C. r. radovaedarwinii Forel, 1891 (E)
C. raina Rakotonirina & Fisher, 2018 (E)
C. reaumuri Forel, 1892 (E)

(*continued overleaf*)

TABLE 9.51. ***continued***

C. repens Forel, 1897 (E)
C. robustus Roger, 1863 (E)
C. roeseli Forel, 1910 (E)
C. sada Rakotonirina & Fisher, 2018 (E)
C. sikorai Emery, 1920 (E)
C. strangulatus Santschi, 1911 (MR: Grande Comore, Mohéli, Mayotte, Seychelles, Juan de Nova)
C. tafo Rakotonirina et al., 2016 (E)
C. tanosy Rakotonirina & Fisher, 2018 (E)
C. tratra Rakotonirina et al., 2016 (E)
C. ursus Forel, 1886 (E)
C. varatra Rakotonirina et al., 2016 (E)
C. voeltzkowii Forel, 1894 (E)
C. zavo Rakotonirina et al., 2016 (E)
Cardiocondyla cristata (Santschi, 1912) (E)
C. emeryi Forel, 1881 (I)
C. minutior Forel, 1899 (I)
C. neferka Bolton, 1982 (AF-MR)
C. shuckardi Forel, 1891 (AF-MR)
C. s. sculptinodis Santschi, 1913 (E)
C. wroughtonii (Forel, 1890) (I)
Carebara bara Azorsa & Fisher, 2018 (E)
C. berivelo Azorsa & Fisher, 2018 (E)
C. betsi Azorsa & Fisher, 2018 (E)
C. creolei Azorsa & Fisher, 2018 (MR: Mauritius, Seychelles)
C. demeter Azorsa & Fisher, 2018 (E)
C. dota Azorsa & Fisher, 2018 (E)
C. grandidieri (Forel, 1891) (MR: Anjouan, Mohéli, Mayotte)
C. hainteny Azorsa & Fisher, 2018 (E)
C. hiragasy Azorsa & Fisher, 2018 (E)
C. jajoby Azorsa & Fisher, 2018 (E)
C. kabosy Azorsa & Fisher, 2018 (E)
C. lova Azorsa & Fisher, 2018 (E)
C. mahafaly Azorsa & Fisher, 2018 (E)
C. malagasy Azorsa & Fisher, 2018 (E)
C. nosindambo (Forel, 1891) (E)
C. omasi Azorsa & Fisher, 2018 (E)
C. placida Azorsa & Fisher, 2018 (E)
C. raberi Azorsa & Fisher, 2018 (E)
C. salegi Azorsa & Fisher, 2018 (E)
C. sampi Azorsa & Fisher, 2018 (E)
C. tana Azorsa & Fisher, 2018 (E)
C. tanana Azorsa & Fisher, 2018 (E)
C. vazimba Azorsa & Fisher, 2018 (E)
Cataulacus ebrardi Forel, 1886 (MR: Mayotte)
C. intrudens (Smith, 1876) (AF-MR)
C. oberthueri Forel, 1891 (E)
C. porcatus Emery, 1899 (E)
C. regularis Forel, 1892 (E)
C. tenuis Emery, 1899 (E)
C. voeltzkowi Forel, 1907 (MR: Anjouan, Grande Comore, Mohéli, Mayotte)
C. wasmanni Forel, 1897 (E)
Crematogaster agnetis Forel, 1892 (E)
C. alafara Blaimer, 2013 (E)
C. bara Blaimer, 2013 (E)
C. castanea Smith, 1858 (AF-MR)
C. degeeri Forel, 1886 (E)
C. dentata Dalla Torre, 1893 (MR: Mauritius, Mayotte, Juan de Nova)
C. ensifera Forel, 1910 (E)
C. grevei Forel, 1891 (E)
C. hafahafa Blaimer, 2013 (E)
C. hazolava Blaimer, 2013 (E)
C. hova Forel, 1887 (E)
C. kelleri Forel, 1891 (MR: Seychelles)
C. lobata Emery, 1895 (E)
C. madagascariensis André, 1887 (E)
C. madecassa Emery, 1895 (E)
C. mafybe Blaimer, 2013 (E)
C. mahery Blaimer, 2010 (E)
C. maina Blaimer, 2013 (MR: Anjouan, Grande Comore, Mohéli, Mayotte)
C. malahelo Blaimer, 2013 (E)
C. malala Blaimer, 2010 (E)
C. marthae Forel, 1892 (E)
C. masokely Blaimer, 2013 (E)
C. mpanjono Blaimer, 2012 (E)
C. nosibeensis Forel, 1891 (E)
C. ramamy Blaimer, 2013 (E)
C. ranavalonae Forel, 1887 (E)
C. rasoherinae Forel, 1891 (MR: Anjouan, Grande Comore, Mohéli, Mayotte, Seychelles, Grande Glorieuse, Ile du Lys)
C. razana Blaimer, 2012 (E)
C. sabatra Blaimer, 2010 (E)
C. schencki Forel, 1891 (E)
C. sewellii Forel, 1891 (AF-MR)
C. sisa Blaimer, 2010 (E)
C. tavaratra Blaimer, 2013 (E)
C. telolafy Blaimer, 2012 (E)
C. tricolor Gerstäcker, 1859 (AF-MR)
C. tsisitsilo Blaimer, 2013 (E)
C. volamena Blaimer, 2012 (E)
Erromyrma latinodis (Mayr, 1872) (I)
Euponera agnivo (Rakotonirina & Fisher, 2013) (E)
E. antsiraka (Rakotonirina & Fisher, 2013) (E)
E. daraina (Rakotonirina & Fisher, 2013) (E)
E. gorogota (Rakotonirina & Fisher, 2013) (E)
E. haratsingy (Rakotonirina & Fisher, 2013) (E)
E. ivolo (Rakotonirina & Fisher, 2013) (E)
E. maeva (Rakotonirina & Fisher, 2013) (E)
E. mialy (Rakotonirina & Fisher, 2013) (E)
E. nosy (Rakotonirina & Fisher, 2013) (E)
E. rovana (Rakotonirina & Fisher, 2013) (E)
E. sikorae (Forel, 1891) (E)
E. tahary (Rakotonirina & Fisher, 2013) (E)
E. vohitravo (Rakotonirina & Fisher, 2013) (E)
E. zoro (Rakotonirina & Fisher, 2013) (E)

Eutetramorium mocquerysi Emery, 1899 (E)
E. monticellii Emery, 1899 (MR: Mohéli)
E. parvum Bolton & Fisher, 2014 (E)
Hypoponera grandidieri (Santschi, 1921) (E)
H. indigens (Forel, 1895) (MR: Anjouan, Grande Comore, Mohéli, Mayotte)
H. i. bellicosa (Forel, 1895) (E)
H. johannae (Forel, 1891) (MR: Anjouan, Mauritius, Mayotte, Seychelles)
H. ludovicae (Forel, 1892) (MR: Mohéli, Mauritius, La Réunion)
H. madecassa (Santschi, 1938) (E)
H. punctatissima (Roger, 1859) (I)
H. p. indifferens (Forel, 1895) (E)
H. sakalava (Forel, 1891) (E)
H. s. excelsior (Forel, 1892) (E)
Lepisiota canescens (Emery, 1897) (I)
Leptogenys acutirostris Santschi, 1912 (E)
L. alamando Rakotonirina & Fisher, 2014 (E)
L. alatapia Rakotonirina & Fisher, 2014 (E)
L. alluaudi Emery, 1895 (E)
L. ambo Rakotonirina & Fisher, 2014 (E)
L. andritantely Rakotonirina & Fisher, 2014 (E)
L. angusta (Forel, 1892) (E)
L. anjara Rakotonirina & Fisher, 2014 (E)
L. antongilensis Emery, 1899 (E)
L. arcirostris Santschi, 1926 (E)
L. avaratra Rakotonirina & Fisher, 2014 (E)
L. avo Rakotonirina & Fisher, 2014 (E)
L. barimaso Rakotonirina & Fisher, 2014 (E)
L. bezanozano Rakotonirina & Fisher, 2014 (E)
L. borivava Rakotonirina & Fisher, 2014 (E)
L. chrislaini Rakotonirina & Fisher, 2014 (E)
L. coerulescens Emery, 1895 (E)
L. diana Rakotonirina & Fisher, 2014 (E)
L. edsoni Rakotonirina & Fisher, 2014 (E)
L. falcigera Roger, 1861 (I)
L. fasika Rakotonirina & Fisher, 2014 (E)
L. fiandry Rakotonirina & Fisher, 2014 (MR: Mohéli)
L. fotsivava Rakotonirina & Fisher, 2014 (E)
L. gracilis Emery, 1899 (MR: Mohéli)
L. grandidieri Forel, 1910 (E)
L. imerinensis Forel, 1892 (E)
L. incisa Forel, 1891 (E)
L. johary Rakotonirina & Fisher, 2014 (E)
L. lavavava Rakotonirina & Fisher, 2014 (E)
L. lohahela Rakotonirina & Fisher, 2014 (E)
L. lucida Rakotonirina & Fisher, 2014 (E)
L. malama Rakotonirina & Fisher, 2014 (E)
L. mangabe Rakotonirina & Fisher, 2014 (E)
L. manja Rakotonirina & Fisher, 2014 (E)
L. manongarivo Rakotonirina & Fisher, 2014 (E)
L. maxillosa (Smith, 1858) (I)
L. namana Rakotonirina & Fisher, 2014 (E)
L. namoroka Rakotonirina & Fisher, 2014 (E)
L. oswaldi (Forel, 1891) (E)
L. pavesii Emery, 1892 (AF-MR)
L. pilaka Rakotonirina & Fisher, 2014 (E)
L. rabebe Rakotonirina & Fisher, 2014 (E)
L. rabesoni Rakotonirina & Fisher, 2014 (E)
L. ralipra Rakotonirina & Fisher, 2014 (E)
L. ridens Forel, 1910 (E)
L. sahamalaza Rakotonirina & Fisher, 2014 (E)
L. saussurei (Forel, 1891) (E)
L. suarensis Emery, 1895 (E)
L. tatsimo Rakotonirina & Fisher, 2014 (E)
L. toeraniva Rakotonirina & Fisher, 2014 (E)
L. truncatirostris Forel, 1897 (MR: Seychelles)
L. tsingy Rakotonirina & Fisher, 2014 (E)
L. variabilis Rakotonirina & Fisher, 2014 (E)
L. vatovavy Rakotonirina & Fisher, 2014 (E)
L. vitsy Rakotonirina & Fisher, 2014 (E)
L. voeltzkowi Forel, 1897 (E)
L. zohy Rakotonirina & Fisher, 2014 (E)
Lioponera kraepelinii (Forel, 1895) (E)
L. mayri (Forel, 1892) (E)
Lividopone livida (Brown, 1975) (E)
Malagidris alperti Bolton & Fisher, 2014 (E)
M. belti (Forel, 1895) (E)
M. dulcis Bolton & Fisher, 2014 (E)
M. galokoa Bolton & Fisher, 2014 (E)
M. jugum Bolton & Fisher, 2014 (E)
M. sofina Bolton & Fisher, 2014 (E)
Melissotarsus insularis Santschi, 1911 (MR: Mohéli, Mayotte)
Meranoplus cryptomys Boudinot & Fisher, 2013 (E)
M. mayri Forel, 1910 (E)
M. radamae Forel, 1891 (E)
M. sylvarius Boudinot & Fisher, 2013 (E)
Mesoponera ambigua (André, 1890) (AF-MR)
M. elisae (Forel, 1891) (AF-MR)
Metapone emersoni Gregg, 1958 (E)
M. madagascarica Gregg, 1958 (E)
M. vincimus Alpert, 2007 (E)
Monomorium bifidoclypeatum Heterick, 2006 (E)
M. chnodes Heterick, 2006 (E)
M. denticulum Heterick, 2006 (E)
M. dichroum Forel, 1902 (I)
M. exiguum Forel, 1894 (AF-MR)
M. flavimembra Heterick, 2006 (E)
M. floricola (Jerdon, 1851) (I)
M. hanneli Forel, 1907 (AF-MR)
M. lepidum Heterick, 2006 (E)
M. madecassum Forel, 1892 (AF-MR)
M. micrommaton Heterick, 2006 (AF-MR)
M. nigricans Heterick, 2006 (E)
M. pharaonis (Linnaeus, 1758) (I)
M. platynode Heterick, 2006 (E)
M. sakalavum Santschi, 1928 (E)

(continued overleaf)

TABLE 9.51. ***continued***

M. subopacum (Smith, 1858) (I)
M. termitobium Forel, 1892 (AF-MR)
M. versicolor Heterick, 2006 (E)
M. xuthosoma Heterick, 2006 (E)
Mystrium barrybressleri Yoshimura & Fisher, 2014 (E)
M. eques Yoshimura & Fisher, 2014 (E)
M. janovitzi Yoshimura & Fisher, 2014 (E)
M. labyrinth Yoshimura & Fisher, 2014 (E)
M. mirror Yoshimura & Fisher, 2014 (E)
M. mysticum Roger, 1862 (MR: Anjouan, Grande Comore, Mohéli, Mayotte)
M. oberthueri Forel, 1897 (E)
M. rogeri Forel, 1899 (MR: Mohéli)
M. shadow Yoshimura & Fisher, 2014 (E)
M. voeltzkowi Forel, 1897 (MR: Mayotte)
Nesomyrmex angulatus (Mayr, 1862) (AF-MR)
N. bidentatus Csősz & Fisher, 2016 (E)
N. brevicornis Csősz & Fisher, 2016 (E)
N. brunneus Csősz & Fisher, 2016 (E)
N. capricornis Csősz & Fisher, 2015 (E)
N. cingulatus Csősz & Fisher, 2016 (E)
N. clypeatus Csősz & Fisher, 2016 (E)
N. devius Csősz & Fisher, 2016 (E)
N. edentatus Csősz & Fisher, 2016 (E)
N. excelsior Csősz & Fisher, 2016 (AF-MR)
N. exiguus Csősz & Fisher, 2016 (E)
N. flavigaster Csősz & Fisher, 2016 (E)
N. flavus Csősz & Fisher, 2016 (E)
N. fragilis Csősz & Fisher, 2016 (MR: Mohéli)
N. gracilis Csősz & Fisher, 2016 (E)
N. hafahafa Csősz & Fisher, 2015 (E)
N. hirtellus Csősz & Fisher, 2016 (E)
N. longiceps Csősz & Fisher, 2016 (E)
N. madecassus (Forel, 1892) (E)
N. medusus Csősz & Fisher, 2015 (E)
N. minutus Csősz & Fisher, 2016 (E)
N. modestus Csősz & Fisher, 2016 (E)
N. nitidus Csősz & Fisher, 2016 (MR: Mayotte)
N. punctaticeps Csősz & Fisher, 2016 (E)
N. reticulatus Csősz & Fisher, 2016 (E)
N. retusispinosus (Forel, 1892) (E)
N. rugosus Csősz & Fisher, 2016 (E)
N. sellaris Csősz & Fisher, 2016 (E)
N. sikorai (Emery, 1896) (E)
N. spinosus Csősz & Fisher, 2015 (E)
N. striatus Csősz & Fisher, 2016 (E)
N. tamatavensis Csősz & Fisher, 2016 (E)
Nylanderia amblyops (Forel, 1892) (E)
N. a. rubescens (Forel, 1892) (E)
N. bourbonica (Forel, 1886) (I)
N. gracilis (Forel, 1892) (E)
N. humbloti (Forel, 1891) (E)
N. madagascarensis (Forel, 1886) (MR: Anjouan, Grande Comore, Mohéli, Mauritius, Mayotte, Ile du Lys)
N. m. ellisii (Forel, 1891) (E)
N. m. rufescens (Wheeler, 1922) (E)
N. sikorae (Forel, 1892) (E)
Odontomachus coquereli Roger, 1861 (E)
O. troglodytes Santschi, 1914 (AF-MR)
Ooceraea biroi (Forel, 1907) (I)
Paraparatrechina glabra (Forel, 1891) (MR: Anjouan)
P. myops LaPolla & Fisher, 2010 (E)
P. ocellatula LaPolla & Fisher, 2010 (E)
Parasyscia imerinensis Forel, 1891 (E)
Paratrechina ankarana LaPolla & Fisher, 2014 (E)
P. antsingy LaPolla & Fisher, 2014 (E)
P. longicornis (Latreille, 1802) (I)
Parvaponera darwinii madecassa (Emery, 1899) (E)
Pheidole aelloea Salata & Fisher, 2020 (E)
P. ala Salata & Fisher, 2020 (E)
P. andapa Salata & Fisher, 2020 (E)
P. ankerana Salata & Fisher, 2020 (E)
P. annemariae Forel, 1918 (E)
P. avaratra Salata & Fisher, 2020 (E)
P. bemarahaensis Salata & Fisher, 2020 (E)
P. bemarivoensis Salata & Fisher, 2020 (E)
P. bessonii Forel, 1891 (E)
P. binara Salata & Fisher, 2020 (E)
P. boribora Salata & Fisher, 2020 (E)
P. brevipilosa Salata & Fisher, 2020 (E)
P. curvistriata Salata & Fisher, 2020 (E)
P. decepticon Fischer & Fisher, 2013 (MR: Anjouan, Mauritius, Mayotte, Seychelles, Juan de Nova)
P. diakritos Salata & Fisher, 2020 (E)
P. ehazoara Salata & Fisher, 2020 (E)
P. ensifera Forel, 1897 (E)
P. ferruginea Salata & Fisher, 2020 (E)
P. fervens Smith, 1858 (I)
P. fisaka Salata & Fisher, 2020 (E)
P. fitarata Salata & Fisher, 2020 (E)
P. glabra Salata & Fisher, 2020 (E)
P. goavana Salata & Fisher, 2020 (E)
P. grallatrix Emery, 1899 (E)
P. indica Mayr, 1879 (I)
P. jonas Forel, 1907 (MR: Anjouan, Grande Comore, Mohéli, Mayotte)
P. lamperos Salata & Fisher, 2020 (E)
P. longipilosa Salata & Fisher, 2020 (E)
P. longispinosa Forel, 1891 (E)
P. lucida Forel, 1895 (E)
P. lutea Salata & Fisher, 2020 (E)
P. madecassa Forel, 1892 (E)
P. madinika Salata & Fisher, 2020 (E)
P. mahaboensis Salata & Fisher, 2020 (E)
P. maizina Salata & Fisher, 2020 (E)
P. makaensis Salata & Fisher, 2020 (E)
P. makirovana Salata & Fisher, 2020 (E)
P. manantenensis Salata & Fisher, 2020 (E)

P. mantadia Salata & Fisher, 2020 (E)
P. marieannae Salata & Fisher, 2020 (E)
P. masoala Salata & Fisher, 2020 (E)
P. mavesatra Salata & Fisher, 2020 (E)
P. megacephala (Fabricius, 1793) (I)
P. m. spinosa Forel, 1891 (E)
P. megatron Fischer & Fisher, 2013 (MR: Anjouan, Grande Comore, Mohéli)
P. miramila Salata & Fisher, 2020 (E)
P. moramanaensis Salata & Fisher, 2020 (E)
P. navoatrensis Salata & Fisher, 2020 (E)
P. nemoralis Forel, 1892 (E)
P. oculata (Emery, 1899) (E)
P. ocypodea Salata & Fisher, 2020 (E)
P. oswaldi Forel, 1891 (E)
P. o. decollata Forel, 1892 (E)
P. parviocula Salata & Fisher, 2020 (E)
P. petax Forel, 1895 (E)
P. podargea Salata & Fisher, 2020 (E)
P. praegrandis Salata & Fisher, 2020 (E)
P. punctulata Mayr, 1866 (AF-MR)
P. ragnax Fischer & Fisher, 2013 (MR: Mayotte)
P. ranohirensis Salata & Fisher, 2020 (E)
P. rugocephala Salata & Fisher, 2020 (E)
P. rugofitarata Salata & Fisher, 2020 (E)
P. scabrata Forel, 1895 (E)
P. sikorae Forel, 1891 (E)
P. s. litigiosa Forel, 1892 (E)
P. typhlos Salata & Fisher, 2020 (E)
P. vatovavensis Salata & Fisher, 2020 (E)
P. veteratrix Forel, 1891 (E)
P. v. angustinoda Forel, 1892 (E)
P. voasara Salata & Fisher, 2020 (E)
P. vohemarensis Salata & Fisher, 2020 (E)
P. zavamanira Salata & Fisher, 2020 (E)
Pilotrochus besmerus Brown, 1978 (E)
Plagiolepis alluaudi Emery, 1894 (AF-MR)
P. madecassa Forel, 1892 (MR: Anjouan, Grande Comore, Mohéli, Mauritius, Mayotte, La Réunion, Seychelles, Europa)
Platythyrea arthuri Forel, 1910 (MR: Anjouan, Mohéli, Mayotte)
P. bicuspis Emery, 1899 (E)
P. cribrinodis (Gerstäcker, 1859) (AF-MR)
P. mocquerysi Emery, 1899 (MR: Anjouan, Grande Comore, Mohéli, Mayotte, Europa)
Ponera swezeyi (Wheeler, 1933) (I)
Prionopelta descarpentriesi Santschi, 1924 (E)
P. laurae Overson & Fisher, 2015 (E)
P. subtilis Overson & Fisher, 2015 (E)
P. talos Overson & Fisher, 2015 (E)
P. vampira Overson & Fisher, 2015 (E)
P. xerosilva Overson & Fisher, 2015 (E)
Probolomyrmex curculiformis Hita Garcia & Fisher, 2014 (E)
P. tani Fisher, 2007 (E)
P. zahamena Hita Garcia & Fisher, 2014 (E)

Proceratium diplopyx Brown, 1980 (E)
P. google Fisher, 2005 (E)
Ravavy miafina Fisher, 2009 (E)
Royidris admixta Bolton & Fisher, 2014 (E)
R. anxietas Bolton & Fisher, 2014 (E)
R. clarinodis (Heterick, 2006) (E)
R. depilosa Bolton & Fisher, 2014 (E)
R. diminuta Bolton & Fisher, 2014 (E)
R. etiolata Bolton & Fisher, 2014 (E)
R. gravipuncta Bolton & Fisher, 2014 (E)
R. longiseta Bolton & Fisher, 2014 (E)
R. notorthotenes (Heterick, 2006) (E)
R. pallida Bolton & Fisher, 2014 (E)
R. peregrina Bolton & Fisher, 2014 (E)
R. pulchra Bolton & Fisher, 2014 (E)
R. robertsoni (Heterick, 2006) (E)
R. shuckardi (Forel, 1895) (E)
R. singularis Bolton & Fisher, 2014 (E)
Simopone consimilis Bolton & Fisher, 2012 (E)
S. dignita Bolton & Fisher, 2012 (E)
S. dux Bolton & Fisher, 2012 (E)
S. elegans Bolton & Fisher, 2012 (E)
S. emeryi Forel, 1892 (E)
S. fera Bolton & Fisher, 2012 (E)
S. grandidieri Forel, 1891 (E)
S. inculta Bolton & Fisher, 2012 (E)
S. mayri Emery, 1911 (E)
S. merita Bolton & Fisher, 2012 (E)
S. nonnihil Bolton & Fisher, 2012 (E)
S. rex Bolton & Fisher, 2012 (E)
S. sicaria Bolton & Fisher, 2012 (E)
S. silens Bolton & Fisher, 2012 (E)
S. trita Bolton & Fisher, 2012 (E)
S. victrix Bolton & Fisher, 2012 (E)
Solenopsis geminata (Fabricius, 1804) (I)
S. mameti Donisthorpe, 1946 (MR: Anjouan, Grande Comore, Mohéli, Mauritius, La Réunion)
Stigmatomma bolabola Esteves & Fisher, 2016 (E)
S. irayhady Esteves & Fisher, 2016 (E)
S. liebe Esteves & Fisher, 2016 (E)
S. roahady Esteves & Fisher, 2016 (E)
S. sakalava Esteves & Fisher, 2016 (E)
S. tsyhady Esteves & Fisher, 2016 (E)
Strumigenys abdera Fisher, 2000 (E)
S. actis Fisher, 2000 (E)
S. admixta Fisher, 2000 (E)
S. adsita Fisher, 2000 (E)
S. agra Fisher, 2000 (E)
S. alapa Fisher, 2000 (E)
S. alperti Fisher, 2000 (E)
S. ambatrix (Bolton, 2000) (E)
S. ampyx Fisher, 2000 (E)
S. apios Fisher, 2000 (E)

(continued overleaf)

TABLE 9.51. ***continued***

S. balux Fisher, 2000 (E)
S. bathron Fisher, 2000 (E)
S. bibiolona Fisher, 2000 (E)
S. bola Fisher, 2000 (E)
S. cabira Fisher, 2000 (E)
S. carisa Fisher, 2000 (E)
S. carolinae Fisher, 2000 (E)
S. charino Fisher, 2000 (E)
S. chilo Fisher, 2000 (E)
S. chroa Fisher, 2000 (E)
S. coveri Fisher, 2000 (E)
S. covina Fisher, 2000 (E)
S. deverra Fisher, 2000 (E)
S. dexis Fisher, 2000 (E)
S. dicomas Fisher, 2000 (MR: Anjouan, Grande Comore, Mayotte)
S. diota Fisher, 2000 (E)
S. diux Fisher, 2000 (E)
S. dolabra Fisher, 2000 (E)
S. dora Fisher, 2000 (E)
S. doxa Fisher, 2000 (E)
S. ection Fisher, 2000 (E)
S. emmae (Emery, 1890) (I)
S. epulo Fisher, 2000 (E)
S. erynnes (Bolton, 2000) (E)
S. europs Fisher, 2000 (E)
S. exiguaevitae Baroni Urbani, 2007 (E)
S. fanano Fisher, 2000 (E)
S. fautrix (Bolton, 2000) (E)
S. finator Fisher, 2000 (E)
S. fronto Fisher, 2000 (E)
S. glycon Fisher, 2000 (E)
S. gorgon Fisher, 2000 (E)
S. grandidieri Forel, 1892 (E)
S. hathor (Bolton, 2000) (E)
S. heliani Fisher, 2000 (E)
S. hilaris Fisher, 2000 (E)
S. inatos Fisher, 2000 (E)
S. ipsea Fisher, 2000 (E)
S. khakaura (Bolton, 2000) (E)
S. labaris Fisher, 2000 (E)
S. langrandi Fisher, 2000 (E)
S. levana Fisher, 2000 (E)
S. lexex Fisher, 2000 (E)
S. livens Fisher, 2000 (E)
S. luca Fisher, 2000 (E)
S. lucomo Fisher, 2000 (E)
S. ludovici Forel, 1904 (I)
S. lura Fisher, 2000 (E)
S. lutron Fisher, 2000 (E)
S. lysis Fisher, 2000 (E)
S. manga Fisher, 2000 (E)
S. maxillaris Baroni Urbani, 2007 (I)
S. membranifera Emery, 1869 (I)
S. micrans Fisher, 2000 (E)
S. milae Fisher, 2000 (E)
S. mola Fisher, 2000 (E)
S. nambao Fisher, 2000 (E)
S. norax Fisher, 2000 (E)
S. odacon Fisher, 2000 (E)
S. olsoni (Bolton, 2000) (E)
S. origo Fisher, 2000 (E)
S. peyrierasi Fisher, 2000 (E)
S. rabesoni Fisher, 2000 (E)
S. ravola Fisher, 2000 (E)
S. rogeri Emery, 1890 (I)
S. rubigus Fisher, 2000 (E)
S. schuetzi Fisher, 2000 (E)
S. scotti Forel, 1912 (AF-MR)
S. serket (Bolton, 2000) (E)
S. seti (Bolton, 2000) (E)
S. sphera Fisher, 2000 (E)
S. sylvaini Fisher, 2000 (E)
S. symmetrix (Bolton, 2000) (E)
S. tathula (Bolton, 2000) (E)
S. tegar Fisher, 2000 (E)
S. toma Fisher, 2000 (E)
S. vazimba Fisher, 2000 (E)
S. victrix (Bolton, 2000) (E)
S. wardi Fisher, 2000 (E)
Syllophopsis adiastolon (Heterick, 2006) (E)
S. aureorugosa (Heterick, 2006) (E)
S. cryptobia (Santschi, 1921) (AF-MR)
S. ferodens (Heterick, 2006) (E)
S. fisheri (Heterick, 2006) (E)
S. gongromos (Heterick, 2006) (E)
S. hildebrandti (Forel, 1892) (AF-MR)
S. infusca (Heterick, 2006) (E)
S. modesta (Santschi, 1914) (AF-MR)
S. sechellensis (Emery, 1894) (I)
Tanipone aglandula Bolton & Fisher, 2012 (E)
T. aversa Bolton & Fisher, 2012 (E)
T. cognata Bolton & Fisher, 2012 (E)
T. hirsuta Bolton & Fisher, 2012 (E)
T. maculata Bolton & Fisher, 2012 (E)
T. pilosa Bolton & Fisher, 2012 (E)
T. scelesta Bolton & Fisher, 2012 (E)
T. subpilosa Bolton & Fisher, 2012 (E)
T. varia Bolton & Fisher, 2012 (E)
T. zona Bolton & Fisher, 2012 (E)
Tapinoma melanocephalum (Fabricius, 1793) (I)
T. subtile Santschi, 1911 (MR: Anjouan, Grande Comore, Mohéli, Mauritius, Mayotte, La Réunion, Seychelles, Grande Glorieuse)
Technomyrmex albipes (Smith, 1861) (I)
T. anterops Bolton, 2007 (E)
T. curiosus Bolton, 2007 (E)
T. difficilis Forel, 1892 (AF-MR)
T. docens Bolton, 2007 (MR: Grande Comore)

T. fisheri Bolton, 2007 (E)
T. innocens Bolton, 2007 (MR: Mayotte)
T. madecassus Forel, 1897 (MR: Anjouan, Grande Comore, Mohéli, Mayotte)
T. mayri Forel, 1891 (E)
T. pallipes (Smith, 1876) (I)
T. vitiensis Mann, 1921 (I)
T. voeltzkowi (Forel, 1907) (AF-MR)
Terataner alluaudi (Emery, 1895) (E)
T. balrog Hita Garcia, 2017 (E)
T. foreli (Emery, 1899) (E)
T. nymeria Hita Garcia, 2017 (E)
T. rufipes Emery, 1912 (E)
T. steinheili (Forel, 1895) (E)
T. xaltus Bolton, 1981 (E)
Tetramorium adamsi Hita Garcia & Fisher, 2012 (E)
T. aherni Hita Garcia & Fisher, 2012 (E)
T. ala Hita Garcia & Fisher, 2012 (E)
T. alperti Hita Garcia & Fisher, 2014 (E)
T. ambanizana Hita Garcia & Fisher, 2012 (E)
T. ambatovy Hita Garcia & Fisher, 2012 (E)
T. andohahela Hita Garcia & Fisher, 2012 (E)
T. andrei Forel, 1892 (E)
T. ankarana Hita Garcia & Fisher, 2012 (E)
T. anodontion Bolton, 1979 (E)
T. artemis Hita Garcia & Fisher, 2012 (E)
T. aspis Hita Garcia & Fisher, 2014 (E)
T. avaratra Hita Garcia & Fisher, 2012 (E)
T. bessonii Forel, 1891 (E)
T. bicarinatum (Nylander, 1846) (I)
T. bonibony Hita Garcia & Fisher, 2012 (E)
T. bressleri Hita Garcia & Fisher, 2014 (E)
T. caldarium (Roger, 1857) (I)
T. camelliae Hita Garcia & Fisher, 2014 (E)
T. cavernicola Hita Garcia & Fisher, 2015 (E)
T. cognatum Bolton, 1979 (E)
T. coillum Bolton, 1979 (E)
T. dalek Hita Garcia & Fisher, 2014 (E)
T. degener Santschi, 1911 (E)
T. delagoense Forel, 1894 (AF-MR)
T. dysalum Bolton, 1979 (E)
T. electrum Bolton, 1979 (E)
T. elf Hita Garcia & Fisher, 2012 (E)
T. enkidu Hita Garcia & Fisher, 2014 (E)
T. freya Hita Garcia & Fisher, 2014 (E)
T. furtivum (Arnold, 1956) (AF-MR)
T. gilgamesh Hita Garcia & Fisher, 2014 (E)
T. gladius Hita Garcia & Fisher, 2014 (E)
T. gollum Hita Garcia & Fisher, 2014 (E)
T. hector Hita Garcia & Fisher, 2012 (E)
T. hobbit Hita Garcia & Fisher, 2014 (E)
T. humbloti Forel, 1891 (AF-MR)
T. ibycterum Bolton, 1979 (E)
T. isectum Bolton, 1979 (E)
T. isoelectrum Hita Garcia & Fisher, 2012 (E)
T. jedi Hita Garcia & Fisher, 2012 (E)
T. kali Hita Garcia & Fisher, 2012 (E)
T. kelleri Forel, 1887 (MR: Mayotte)
T. lanuginosum Mayr, 1870 (I)
T. latreillei Forel, 1895 (E)
T. mackae Hita Garcia & Fisher, 2012 (E)
T. mahafaly Hita Garcia & Fisher, 2011 (E)
T. malagasy Hita Garcia & Fisher, 2012 (E)
T. mallenseana Hita Garcia & Fisher, 2012 (E)
T. marginatum Forel, 1895 (AF-MR)
T. marojejy Hita Garcia & Fisher, 2012 (E)
T. mars Hita Garcia & Fisher, 2014 (E)
T. merina Hita Garcia & Fisher, 2014 (E)
T. monticola Hita Garcia & Fisher, 2014 (E)
T. muscorum Arnold, 1926 (AF-MR)
T. myrmidon Hita Garcia & Fisher, 2014 (E)
T. naganum Bolton, 1979 (E)
T. nassonowii Forel, 1892 (E)
T. nazgul Hita Garcia & Fisher, 2012 (E)
T. nify Hita Garcia & Fisher, 2012 (E)
T. noeli Hita Garcia & Fisher, 2012 (E)
T. norvigi Hita Garcia & Fisher, 2012 (E)
T. nosybe Hita Garcia & Fisher, 2012 (E)
T. obiwan Hita Garcia & Fisher, 2014 (E)
T. olana Hita Garcia & Fisher, 2012 (E)
T. orc Hita Garcia & Fisher, 2012 (E)
T. orientale Forel, 1895 (E)
T. phasias Forel, 1914 (AF-MR)
T. pleganon Bolton, 1979 (E)
T. plesiarum Bolton, 1979 (E)
T. popell Hita Garcia & Fisher, 2012 (E)
T. proximum Bolton, 1979 (E)
T. pseudogladius Hita Garcia & Fisher, 2014 (E)
T. quasirum Bolton, 1979 (E)
T. rala Hita Garcia & Fisher, 2014 (E)
T. ranarum Forel, 1895 (E)
T. robitika Hita Garcia & Fisher, 2012 (E)
T. rumo Hita Garcia & Fisher, 2014 (E)
T. ryanphelanae Hita Garcia & Fisher, 2012 (E)
T. sabatra Hita Garcia & Fisher, 2012 (E)
T. sada Hita Garcia & Fisher, 2012 (E)
T. sargina Hita Garcia & Fisher, 2012 (E)
T. schaufussii Forel, 1891 (MR: La Réunion)
T. scutum Hita Garcia & Fisher, 2014 (E)
T. scytalum Bolton, 1979 (MR: Anjouan, Grande Comore, Mohéli, Mayotte, Seychelles, Juan de Nova, Europa)
T. sericeiventre Emery, 1877 (AF-MR)
T. severini (Emery, 1895) (E)
T. shamshir Hita Garcia & Fisher, 2012 (E)
T. sikorae Forel, 1892 (E)
T. silvicola Hita Garcia & Fisher, 2012 (E)
T. simillimum (Smith, 1851) (I)

(continued overleaf)

TABLE 9.51. ***continued***

T. singletonae Hita Garcia & Fisher, 2012 (E)
T. smaug Hita Garcia & Fisher, 2012 (E)
T. steinheili Forel, 1892 (E)
T. tantillum Bolton, 1979 (E)
T. tenuinode Hita Garcia & Fisher, 2014 (E)
T. tosii Emery, 1899 (E)
T. trafo Hita Garcia &Fisher, 2012 (E)
T. tsingy Hita Garcia & Fisher, 2012 (E)
T. tyrion Hita Garcia & Fisher, 2012 (E)
T. valky Hita Garcia & Fisher, 2012 (E)
T. voasary Hita Garcia & Fisher, 2012 (E)
T. vohitra Hita Garcia & Fisher, 2012 (E)
T. vony Hita Garcia & Fisher, 2012 (E)
T. wardi Hita Garcia & Fisher, 2012 (E)
T. xanthogaster Santschi, 1911 (E)
T. yammer Hita Garcia & Fisher, 2012 (E)
T. zenatum Bolton, 1979 (E)
Tetraponera arrogans (Santschi, 1911) (E)
T. demens (Santschi, 1911) (E)
T. diana (Santschi, 1911) (E)
T. exasciata (Forel, 1892) (E)
T. fictrix (Forel, 1897) (E)
T. flexuosa (Santschi, 1911) (E)
T. grandidieri (Forel, 1891) (E)
T. hespera Ward, 2009 (E)
T. hirsuta Ward, 2009 (E)
T. hysterica (Forel, 1892) (E)
T. h. dimidiata (Forel, 1895) (E)
T. h inflata (Emery, 1899) (E)
T. inermis Ward, 2009 (E)
T. longula (Emery, 1895) (E)
T. manangotra Ward, 2009 (E)
T. mandibularis (Emery, 1895) (E)
T. merita Ward, 2009 (E)
T. morondaviensis (Forel, 1891) (E)
T. perlonga Santschi, 1928 (E)
T. phragmotica Ward, 2006 (E)
T. plicatidens (Santschi, 1926) (E)
T. rakotonis (Forel, 1891) (E)
T. sahlbergii (Forel, 1887) (E)
T. s. spuria (Forel, 1897) (E)
T. variegata (Forel, 1895) (E)
Trichomyrmex destructor (Jerdon, 1851) (I)
T. robustior (Forel, 1892) (AF-MR)
Vitsika acclivitas Bolton & Fisher, 2014 (E)
V. astuta Bolton & Fisher, 2014 (E)
V. brevis (Bolton & Fisher, 2014) (E)
V. breviscapa Bolton & Fisher, 2014 (E)
V. crebra Bolton & Fisher, 2014 (E)
V. disjuncta Bolton & Fisher, 2014 (E)
V. incisura Bolton & Fisher, 2014 (E)
V. labes Bolton & Fisher, 2014 (E)
V. manifesta Bolton & Fisher, 2014 (E)
V. miranda Bolton & Fisher, 2014 (E)
V. obscura Bolton & Fisher, 2014 (E)
V. procera Bolton & Fisher, 2014 (E)
V. producta (Bolton & Fisher, 2014) (E)
V. suspicax Bolton & Fisher, 2014 (E)
V. tenuis (Bolton & Fisher, 2014) (E)
V. venustas Bolton & Fisher, 2014 (E)

Note: Of these 794 species and subspecies, 37 are introduced (I) (757 native species); 36 are also known from Africa and elsewhere in the Malagasy Region (AF-MR); 675 (89% of native species) are endemic (E) to Madagascar; and 46 additional species are endemic to the Malagasy Region (MR) as defined within the text (721 species, 95%). For MR taxa, islands in addition to Madagascar are indicated. Full author citations are available from AntCat (2020).

The genus *Aphaenogaster* is absent in Africa, and the species on Madagascar are most closely related to those in Indo-Malaysia and Australasia (Branstetter et al. 2016). *Chrysapace* is known outside of Madagascar from only a few species in Indo-Malaysia and is absent in Africa. The history of the origin of the lineages on Madagascar will be further refined, with future work associated with a broad project known as the ant tree of life.

Dispersal has played out differently on each of the Malagasy Region archipelagoes. Although geographic position (proximity to Africa) predicts species similarity with that continent, and island size helps predict the number of species, one cannot calculate which lineages may have arrived on each of the island systems in the region. For example, though we can expect that ants dispersing from Africa would have a greater chance of colonizing the Comoro archipelago than those from Asia, we could not predict the discovery of the Afrotropical genera *Calyptomyrmex* and *Dicroaspis*, which are absent from the rest of the Malagasy Region. Likewise, we could not predict that we would encounter a radiation of *Adelomyrmex* in the Seychelles or of *Pristomyrmex* on Mauritius.

DISTRIBUTION ON MADAGASCAR

Macrohabitat, Elevation, and Vertical Stratification

Ants are most diverse in the moist evergreen forests of northeastern Madagascar, especially in the forest belt running from the lowlands of the Masoala Peninsula and Antongil Bay to the peaks of Marojejy, Tsaratanàna, and Manongarivo. One of the most diverse places to find ants on Madagascar is the second camp (now called Camp Marojejia) at 800 m in the Marojejy National Park. Species richness is lowest in the dry spiny thicket of the southwest and intermediate in the dry deciduous forests of the west. Species richness also varies along elevation gradients, peaking at medium altitude (600–800 m) and quickly declining above 1400 m (Fisher 1996, 1998, 1999a, 1999b, 2002). Few ant species call the montane portions of the medium-altitude moist evergreen forests above 1600 m home. Ants are thermophilic, and few species can tolerate foraging in cold, wet, and cloudy montane forests. The cold also slows larval development. Above tree line, however, where solar radiation reaches the ground, ants return in abundance though are not particularly rich in species.

TABLE 9.52. **Checklist of the 72 ant genera recorded in the Malagasy Region**

AMBLYOPONINAE (5)
- *Adetomyrma
- Mystrium
- Prionopelta
- Stigmatomma
- Xymmer +

DOLICHODERINAE (5)
- *Aptinoma
- Ochetellus* (La Réunion, Mauritius)
- *Ravavy
- Tapinoma
- Technomyrmex

DORYLINAE (8)
- Chrysapace +
- Eburopone +
- Lioponera
- *Lividopone
- Ooceraea*
- Parasyscia
- Simopone
- *Tanipone

FORMICINAE (9)
- Anoplolepis* (Mauritius, La Réunion, Seychelles)
- Brachymyrmex*
- Camponotus
- Lepisiota*
- Nylanderia
- Paraparatrechina
- Paratrechina
- Plagiolepis
- Tapinolepis +

MYRMICINAE (30)
- Adelomyrmex + (Seychelles)
- Aphaenogaster
- Calyptomyrmex + (Anjouan, Grande Comore, Mohéli)
- Cardiocondyla
- Carebara
- Cataulacus
- Crematogaster
- Cyphomyrmex* (La Réunion)
- Dicroaspis + (Anjouan)
- Erromyrma*
- Eurhopalothrix + (Mohéli)

MYRMICINAE (30)
- *Eutetramorium
- *Malagidris
- Melissotarsus
- Meranoplus
- Metapone
- Monomorium
- Nesomyrmex
- Pheidole
- *Pilotrochus
- Pristomyrmex (Mauritius)
- *Royidris
- Solenopsis*
- Strumigenys
- Syllophopsis
- Terataner
- Tetramorium
- Trichomyrmex
- *Vitsika
- Vollenhovia (Seychelles)

PONERINAE (11)
- Anochetus
- Bothroponera
- Brachyponera* (Mauritius)
- Euponera
- Hypoponera
- Leptogenys
- Mesoponera
- Odontomachus
- Parvaponera
- Platythyrea
- Ponera*

PROCERATIINAE (3)
- Discothyrea +
- Probolomyrmex
- Proceratium

PSEUDOMYRMECINAE (1)
- Tetraponera

Notes: The Malagasy Region (MR) herein comprises Madagascar, Comoros, Mauritius, Seychelles, and La Réunion; * before name of genus indicates endemic to Madagascar; + indicates genera known only from undescribed regional species; * after name of genus indicates known only from introduced species in the MR. (For genera with introduced or undescribed species occurring in the MR outside Madagascar, islands are given).

Ants are also surprisingly persistent in fragmented forest patches, presumably because of their small home-range size. Long after native rodents, carnivorans, and lemurs have disappeared from small forest blocks, native ants still survive. Thus, almost any patch of forest, big or small, especially in the rich moist evergreen forests, could harbor a largely functional ant community with species unknown to science.

Local species assemblages also change across macrohabitats and along elevational gradients. It takes a different kind of ant to survive in the dry spiny thicket limestone areas of the Mahafaly Plateau in the southwest than in the lowland moist evergreen forests of the Masoala Peninsula, or along the elevational gradient from the coast to the 2132 m summit of Marojejy. Likewise, notably different kinds of ants can be found in the trees versus on the ground. This vertical stratification is most pronounced in the closed canopy of lowland moist evergreen forests, where the ground receives little sunlight and never dries out, while the canopy is exposed and can be arid. On Madagascar, about 30% of ant species are restricted to arboreal habitats.

Leaf-Litter Ants

In the dry deciduous and moist evergreen forests of Madagascar, leaf-litter ant diversity is over twice that of arboreal ant communities. This is perhaps surprising because the leaf-litter microhabitat consists of only a thin layer below a voluminous canopy. With 90 described species on the island, the genus *Strumigenys* is an important leaf-litter specialist and dominant predator in the very small world of leaf-litter insects (Fisher 2000). Local diversity is also impressive. For example, in the Masoala Peninsula alone, 25 *Strumigenys* species have been recorded in broad sympatry (Fisher 1998). *Strumigenys* mostly rely on the trap-like action of their mandibles to secure food, and these structures are modified for a carnivorous lifestyle. Most of the striking differences between species reflect different techniques of prey seizure. Long-mandibled forms, such as *S. vazimba* (Figure 9.72c), use power-amplified mandibles to strike and stun, lift, and sting their prey, and are active hunters. By contrast, short-mandibled species such as *S. dexis* are more crypto-biotic and subterranean feeders that employ a strategy of luring or cautiously approaching prey, then gripping and stinging the struggling prey item.

Arboreal Ants

Genera specialized for arboreal habitats, especially nesting in dead, hollow twigs and branches, include *Camponotus*, *Cataulacus*, *Crematogaster*, *Nesomyrmex*, *Pheidole*, *Simopone*, *Teratuner*, and *Tetraponera*. Many arboreal species are generalist predators and scavengers, and collect honeydew and nectar from flowers. *Simopone* is a specialized doryline that I have observed raiding canopy *Teratuner* nests for their larvae. Most species of *Crematogaster* are arboreal; some construct large, conspicuous nests, composed of carton (chewed-up plant fibers), high on the trunks of large trees or hanging from branches (Figure 9.72d).

Some arboreal ants living in dead twigs use their heads to plug the entrance to their nest, a phenomenon called phragmosis. I have seen *Cataulacus* perform this action. *Tetraponera phragmotica*, a species from the dry deciduous forests of the northwest, has a specialized soldier caste with a strongly truncate head (Figure 9.72f); the mandibles and anterior portion of the clypeus have been transformed into a plug well suited for blocking the nest entrance of these twig-dwelling ants (Ward 2006). Cases of phragmosis are known in a few other ant genera, most notably *Colobopsis*, which is found in most bioregions but is notably absent from the Afrotropics and Malagasy Region. This phenomenon is especially striking since *Tetraponera* is the only case of phragmosis in the subfamily Pseudomyrmecinae. What led to its development on Madagascar and not in other regions is unknown. Do the soldiers provide protection from the dominant arboreal ants, like *Crematogaster*, or from *Simopone*, specialized predators of ant larvae?

TAXONOMIC GAPS

Madagascar's vertebrate fauna is often described as a friendlier assemblage than what is found in mainland Africa; the island hosts no venomous snakes or large predatory mammals. The ant fauna is no exception. Though no one can experience Madagascar without encountering ants, the island lacks two of the most aggressive groups found in Africa and Asia: the army ants (Dorylinae: *Aenictus*, *Dorylus*) that dominate the forest floor, and the weaver ants (*Oecophylla*) that dominate the forest canopy in the Afrotropical and Oriental tropical regions. Weaver ants, and especially army ants of the genus *Dorylus* (driver ants), are important predators of other ants and have been shown to influence ant population structure and the diversity of ant communities (Gotwald 1995). Army ants perform group predatory raids that provide a natural disturbance to ant and other insect communities. Driver ants have also been shown to be the most important predator of termites in Africa. Even the long legs and leaping ability of certain African shrews (family Soricidae) are suggested to be adaptations to escape driver ant attacks (Brosset 1988). Driver ants, because of their effect on populations of ants and other insects, have been labeled "keystone species." The absence of these ant groups from Madagascar suggests that the population dynamics of the island's ant communities may differ greatly from others in the Old World. A comparison of African and Malagasy ant community ecology might provide a natural setting to experimentally evaluate the effect of these dominant African ants on ant communities.

The absence on Madagascar of dominant genera found in Africa, such as *Oecophylla*, *Aenictus*, and *Dorylus*, offered unique opportunities to the island's ants. This distinctive evolutionary situation might have permitted certain older lineages to persist and others to radiate on the island. For example, the absence of army ants from Madagascar may have spurred the diversification of other genera in the subfamily Dorylinae, which are all thought to be specialized predators on the larvae of other ants. The evolution and radiation of the endemic genus *Tanipone*, which is restricted to the dry west and south and is predominantly ground-nesting, could be explained by the absence of army ants. Certain *Eburopone* species are morphologically convergent to the slender army ant genus *Aenictus* found in Africa (Figure 9.71b). The predatory behavior of *Lioponera* is the most easily observed of the doryline ants since the raids occur aboveground and the genus preys on the brood of other ants, especially *Pheidole* (Figure 9.71c). On Madagascar, *Lioponera* colonies can attain sizes of up to a few thousand workers. On other continents, *Lioponera* colonies are distinctly smaller. It is unclear whether the absence of army ants led to the diversification or large colony raiding behavior of *Lioponera* on the island, or simply permitted their persistence. Whether products of island radiation or relict taxa, these fascinating ants invite further study.

The absence of numerically and ecologically dominant genera on Madagascar may have also led to the persistence and diversification of amblyoponine genera such as *Adetomyrma*, *Mystrium*, *Stigmatomma*, and *Xymmer* (Ward and Fisher 2016). All amblyoponine species are specialized predators that are rarely encountered because they do not forage aboveground. Hypogaeic species, they are most often found in leaf litter and soil, sometimes very deep, but some species nest and forage in rotten wood (Esteves and Fisher 2016).

FIGURE 9.72 **Examples of ant–plant interactions, showing the considerable diversity of morphology and life-history traits in Malagasy ants. A) There are at least three known ant–plant interactions on Madagascar. Here *Vitsika breviscapa* leaves its specialized home in the swollen, hollow stem of the melastome *Gravesia*. The stem includes a weakened window that the ants can chew through to access the interior of the hollow stem. B) *Aphaenogaster swammerdami*, which is known to disperse *Commiphora guillauminii* seeds. C) *Strumigenys vazimba* is the largest member of this genus on Madagascar, which has 90 described species. Members of *Strumigenys* possess a remarkable biomechanical innovation: power-amplified trap-jaw mandibles that function much like a mousetrap, storing and releasing energy with a specialized trigger-and-latch mechanism that closes mandibles at tremendous speeds. D) Some ants such as *Aphaenogaster*, *Pheidole*, or more commonly *Crematogaster* (shown here) construct their nests out of carton (chewed plant material). E) Most *Tetraponera* species nest aboveground in dead hollow twigs. The brightly colored *grandidier* group species, however, all nest in decaying branches and wood on the forest floor. Shown here is *T. manangotra* from parcel 1 of the Andohahela protected area with a larva being transported between its legs. F) *Tetraponera phragmotica* is the only *Tetraponera* species on Madagascar with a major worker caste. The head of the worker illustrated here is truncated and used to plug the entrance of the nest, usually a dead twig of *Albizia*.** (PHOTO A by D. Ling; B, D, and E by B. L. Fisher; and C and F by A. Nobile.)

REMARKABLE LIFESTYLES OF MALAGASY ANTS

In Africa, many species are specialized predators of termites (see Eggleton, pp. 963–68), in particular many large ponerines. However, on Madagascar, only the genus *Metapone*, a myrmecine, is known to be a termite specialist. The three Malagasy *Metapone* species are found mostly in moist evergreen forests but also in dry deciduous forests, riparian forests, and dry spiny thicket in the west and southwest. Members of *Metapone* are morphologically distinct, their specialized features related to their association with their termite hosts, which live only inside fallen logs. The first collections of *Metapone* were by termite specialist Harold Kirby in June 1935. He collected *M. madagascarica* near Toliara in a stump with termites and *M. emersoni* (Figure 9.71d) three weeks later near Périnet (Andasibe). Alpert (2007) reported *Metapone* associations with *Cryptotermes kirbyi* (Kalotermitidae) and *Coptotermes truncatus* (Rhinotermitidae). When collecting *Metapone*, I have often noted paralyzed termites that were presumably stung by *Metapone* and kept alive inside the ant galleries as a food reserve. *Metapone emersoni* is a predator on *Cryptotermes*. Apparently young, newly mated *M. emersoni* queens must fly around until they locate fallen trees inhabited by the right termite species to found new colonies. In addition, the queen produces reproductive workers (gamergates) that can mate with brothers and reproduce. Though gamergates are highly unusual among myrmicines, this reproductive system allows them to occupy fully the valuable and long-lasting resource of a fallen tree. In addition, I have collected ergatoid males of *M. madagascarica*, which are wingless and morphologically similar to workers.

Melissotarsus insularis is restricted to the coastal regions of Madagascar and the dry spiny thicket in the southwest. Its minute workers dig narrow galleries in healthy wood under the bark of living trees. These galleries contain tens of thousands of yellow diaspidid scale insects (family Diaspididae) that are reared as obligate partners (Peeters et al. 2017). Workers are almost never seen outside host trees. The gait of living workers is peculiar; when walking, the fore and hind legs come in contact with the substrate, while the middle legs are elevated and in contact with the gallery walls. Workers struggle when walking on a flat surface, so they are restricted to foraging inside their tunnels. This implies that they must obtain all of their nourishment from scale insects. Workers' heads are huge and packed with muscles that power the mandibles, enabling them to tunnel through wood, while their antennae are very short and their eyes reduced. This odd morphology reflects a highly specialized, obligate lifestyle inside trees. Uniquely among ants, adult workers are able to produce silk using specialized glands in the head. Whenever breaches in the bark need to be sealed, silk is quickly spun and combined with wood shavings from inside the galleries to form a durable mesh. Nests of *Melissotarsus* can be located based on exterior markings on the tree bark.

The Hero Ant, *Malagidris sofina*, lives in the Sambirano Region and nests on cliff faces in natural rock alcoves or clay banks. Colonies are small, with about 60 workers and a single ergatoid (wingless) queen. Each nest has a funnel-shaped entrance projecting horizontally from the cliff face in the shape of an ear (Figure 9.71e). This funnel likely increases airflow within the nest (Helms et al. 2014). *Malagidris sofina* is the only cliff-dwelling ant known on Madagascar and also the only one that builds these large, funnel-shaped entrances. Workers display little aggression toward intrusion by several ant species, instead responding with an original form of nest defense: cliff jumping. Workers drop off the cliff face while clinging to invaders and then return to their nest.

Cardiocondyla species are widely distributed across Madagascar and can be quite common in human-modified (anthropogenic), open habitats, such as plantations and gardens. Even the native species *C. shuckardi* appears to be common in gardens in the Central Highlands, including that of the Madagascar Biodiversity Centre at Tsimbazaza, Antananarivo. Heinze et al. (2014) showed that *C. shuckardi* colonies are at least temporarily facultatively polygynous and that males are wingless. Queens mate in their natal nests with brothers and then disperse and seek adoption in other nests, in a manner similar to what has been observed in related species. Males have specialized morphology to attack and damage or kill male rivals.

Queens in many genera cannot fly and must disperse on foot, together with nestmate workers, to establish a new colony. Such ergatoid queens lack wing muscles, and their thorax is simplified and resembles that of wingless workers. Ergatoid queens are a common feature of Malagasy ants (Molet et al. 2009; Peeters and Fisher 2016). The following genera have at least one species with flightless queens: *Adetomyrma*, *Anochetus*, *Cardiocondyla*, *Eutetramorium*, *Hypoponera*, *Leptogenys*, *Lioponera*, *Lividopone*, *Malagidris*, *Mystrium*, *Odontomachus*, *Proceratium*, *Simopone*, *Strumigenys*, *Syllophopsis*, *Tanipone*, *Technomyrmex*, *Terataner*, and *Vitsika*. Since flightless queens disperse only a short distance by walking (colony division), their population structure shows high divergence, especially between isolated forest patches. M. A. Smith and Fisher (2009) showed deeper cytochrome oxidase1 (cox1 or CO1) divergences between different collection localities in the flightless *Odontomachus coquereli*, *Anochetus goodmani*, and *A. boltoni*, compared to similar species with winged queens. Graham et al. (2016) also compared the population structure of *Mystrium* winged queens against species having nonwinged queens. They found that reproductive strategies led to differences in female dispersal ability among species, and in some cases, they found microgeographic population structures that appear linked to localized habitat differences (*tsingy* limestone formations, littoral forests) on a scale much smaller than that found in vertebrates.

The life history of ergatoid queens has been studied extensively in *Mystrium* (Bouchet et al. 2013; Molet et al. 2007a, 2007b, 2009). In *M. voeltzkowi*, only a few mated ergatoid queens in each colony lay all the eggs, while virgin ergatoids behave as workers inside the nest (e.g., providing brood care) (Figure 9.71f). Only the workers have big mandibles and hunt outside.

ANT–PLANT AND ANT–ANIMAL INTERACTIONS

Unlike most tropical regions (Beattie 1985), Madagascar has only a few documented ant–plant associations (see Dolch, pp. 853–56, for a general review of insect–plant interactions). In the northeast, three species of *Gravesia* (family Melastomataceae) have ant associates. *Tetramorium silvicola* and *Vitsika breviscapa* nest only in the modified chambers of plants of the genus *Gravesia* (Figure 9.72a). Other ant species, such as *Monomorium chnodes*, appear to be opportunist nesters in *Gravesia*. In the southeast, *Nesomyrmex minutus* nests only in the stems of *Macphersonia gracilis* (Sapindaceae). *Macphersonia* and *Gravesia* ant–plant systems have not yet been studied in regard to possible benefits to the plants and ants.

Seed dispersal by ants has been documented in the dry deciduous forests of the west. The large, glossy, red ant *Aphaenogaster swammerdami* disperses the seeds of *Commiphora guillauminii* (Burseraceae) (Böhning-Gaese et al. 1996). The fruits of *C. guillauminii* are bicolored, with a fleshy red aril and a black seed. Ants carry the seeds into their colony, remove the arils, and discard the seeds undamaged on the refuse pile at the edge of the colony. Birds may be the primary seed disperser in this system, but ants serve as important secondary dispersers (Böhning-Gaese et al. 1999).

Throughout western Madagascar, *A. swammerdami* (Figure 9.72b) is famous for its association with snakes, most notably *Dromicodryas bernieri*, *D. quadrilineatus*, and *Madagascarophis colubrinus* (family Pseudoxyrophiidae) (Preston-Mafham 1991; Cadle 2003; see Cadle et al., pp. 1525–31). Oral tradition also notes this association between snakes and ants. According to people living in the vicinity of the Bezà-Mahafaly protected area, for example, *A. swammerdami* hosts a snake they call *rembitiky* (mother of ants). The story goes that the ants provide a nest for the snake and feed it during the cool dry season. The snake gets bigger and bigger, while the ants reduce the size of the entrance hole until the snake is no longer able to leave the nest. The ants then eat the fattened snake during the rainy season when it is supposedly difficult for the insects to forage outside. There is clear evidence of the ants eating the snake. *Aphaenogaster swammerdami* builds large and deep nests in the soil, which undoubtedly provide good habitat for large snakes seeking shelter. Jono et al. (2019) conclude that the association with *M. colubrinus* helps defend the ant-host larvae from predation by the blind snake *Madatyphlops decorsei*, a specialized predator of ant larvae (see Raxworthy, pp. 1532–34).

Ants are a common prey for frogs on Madagascar. For example, Woodhead et al. (2007) used analyses of frog stomach contents to show that in *Mantella aurantiaca* (family Mantellidae), ants comprise the bulk of the prey consumed. Ants, however, are more than just frog food. Similar to the convergent dendrobatid poison frog system in the Neotropics, Malagasy mantellids may sequester alkaloids from ant prey for their own chemical defense (V. C. Clark et al. 2005). Small ants are a good match for the active foraging diurnal *Mantella*, which captures prey mostly with the tongue.

INTRODUCED ANTS

Ants have probably hitched rides with humans since the dawn of history. At least 36 species of ants are thought to have been introduced to Madagascar. Many of these are restricted to urban and modified habitats and found in low numbers, but a few are known to be introduced and invasive species that pose a major threat to natural ecosystems. Combating invasive species is of particular importance on islands such as Madagascar, where habitat fragmentation is a key concern and provides the means for introduced species to colonize the forest edge and small forest parcels.

On Mauritius, where the area of original forest cover has been greatly reduced, introduced and invasive ants may have driven the entire lowland ant fauna to extinction (Fisher 2005b; M. A. Smith and Fisher 2009). The native ant species on Mauritius are limited to the humid forests at the highest elevations. On the smaller, granitic islands of the Seychelles, invasive ants, such as *Pheidole megacephala*, have already extirpated native ants and are now threatening nesting bird populations. Larger islands, such as Madagascar, where habitats are severely fragmented, can also be vulnerable to invasive ant species. While protected areas bolster the chances of survival among native species by protecting habitat, they cannot prevent aggressive introduced ants from driving native species locally extinct. In the littoral forests of the east, the presence of introduced ant species in disturbed and fragmented forest habitats is associated with the reduction of native ant populations (Fisher et al. 1998). Dejean et al. (2010) document that along a 4 km stretch of native littoral forest, the canopy is dominated by the invasive arboreal *Technomyrmex albipes*. The penetration of this species further inland seems likely given the low density of native arboreal ants able to limit its progression.

However, it can be tricky to determine if a given species is native or introduced. Since many species are undescribed on Madagascar and elsewhere in the world, identification is not always reliable. If the ant is mostly found in disturbed coastal habitats on Madagascar and is present across other, smaller islands in the region, it is likely an introduced species. This includes species that are described from the region, such as *Solenopsis mameti* (named from Mauritius), which has a distribution pattern that strongly suggests it was introduced to the Malagasy Region. Monitoring programs using pitfall traps or baits is one way to evaluate the colonization and population dynamics of introduced species. Such a system can be used on the edge of forest fragments but is also important for monitoring reforestation efforts. Introduced ant species could impede the return of healthy native forest processes.

ROLE IN CONSERVATION

Accurate and rapid measurement of patterns of species richness, species turnover, and endemism is important when planning and monitoring conservation efforts on Madagascar. The measurement of diversity is complex, and a single group or organisms cannot describe the full range of biodiversity at a site or between sites (Kremen et al. 2008). One approach is to sample taxa that are ecologically important, relatively easily collected in a standardized way, and diverse at a site; and, of course, they must supply detailed information for conservation planning. These ubiquitous insects are also the most behaviorally diverse social animals alive today. I consider ants the glue that holds ecosystems together.

Ants, particularly ground-dwelling ants, are a powerful conservation tool because they exhibit high levels of species turnover and thus delineate fine-scale patterns of diversity (M. A. Smith et al. 2005). Such fine-scale patterns provide information that can be used for conservation planning (Underwood and Fisher 2006). In Madagascar's eastern moist evergreen forests, ants showed consistently greater distinctness and species turnover between elevations and localities than, for example, birds (B. L. Fisher, unpublished data). The five most diverse ant genera, *Camponotus*, *Hypoponera*, *Pheidole*, *Strumigenys*, and *Tetramorium*, show high species richness and turnover patterns on the island and thus could provide a useful tool for habitat comparisons. These genera are also accurate indicators and predictors of total ant species richness at a locality and are useful for assessing patterns of similarity and diversity of ants among localities (Fisher 1999a).

The impacts of land use on ant species composition, richness, and behavior is not well studied and deserves more attention. In Kirindy Forest CNFEREF (Centre National de Formation, d'Etudes et de Recherche en Environnement et Foresterie), Dittmann et al. (2014) studied the impact of selectively logged forests on the behavior and ecology of a single species, *Aphaenogaster swammerdami*. They found that 20 years after selective logging, colony density was lower and colony size larger than at the two other unlogged forest sites. Fisher and Robertson (2002) compared ant communities in montane forests in the Central Highlands with those in adjacent grasslands. A surprising result was the discovery of 18 native ant species restricted to the grassland site, which suggests that this area once contained a mosaic of closed-canopy forests and perhaps wooded grasslands. In contrast, Ravelomanana and Fisher (2013) investigated the diversity of ants in burned and unburned grassland, as well as dry deciduous forests in the Beanka Reserve in the west. The scientists found a number of restricted-range species in the dry forests, while all grassland species had wide distributions and included 14 (42%) introduced species.

NEXT STEPS: THE FUTURE ROLE OF ANT RESEARCH

Despite the scale of the effort over the past three decades on Madagascar to know every ant species, knowledge of their habits, distribution, conservation status, and whether a given form is native or introduced remains far from complete. At current rates, it could take another two decades to complete the descriptions of the known but undescribed species of ants on the island. Given the breakneck speed of habitat destruction, however, we are running out of time to explore this remarkable portion of the island's diversity.

Though the taxonomic infrastructure is incomplete, future efforts need to prioritize translating what we already know into conservation tools. The ability of taxonomists to apply results to local conservation issues will determine whether the last two decades are viewed as the golden or the gold-plated age of exploration of Madagascar's arthropods (Fisher 2016). It could be called golden if taxonomists work together to uncover the biological diversity of Madagascar, and that information is used to help save the remaining natural landscapes. But it could just as easily be termed gold-plated if the boom in discovery was just a salvage mission to stock museums with specimens before they disappeared forever.

For ants, priorities should include the identification and impact of introduced ants, the role of ants as monitoring tools in landscape ecology, and the potential role of ants in forest restoration efforts. To achieve this, we need to direct taxonomic and ecological study efforts toward the introduced and invasive ant species, as well as the five ant genera with the greatest number of locally adapted species: *Camponotus*, *Hypoponera*, *Pheidole*, *Strumigenys*, and *Tetramorium*. Studies should also focus on the functional and ecological role of ants, including the documentation of life-history traits, nesting locations, diets, and reproductive phenology.

Little time remains to survey ants at all the island's remote forest fragments. In terms of priorities, isolated forest patches located considerable distances from already surveyed sites are predicted to harbor a considerable number of unknown ant species. Inventories should prioritize microhabitats, such as the soil and leaf litter, where undetected rare species are most likely to be found. Many discoveries await in the study of Malagasy ants, but they can take place only if we can find ways to protect the forests of this biodiversity stronghold. With these points in mind, I hope that, over the next decade or so, there will be many studies in which ants will be used in conservation monitoring, mapping, and management, and that sustainability studies will be applied to bolster the environmental and ecological health of Madagascar.

ACKNOWLEDGMENTS

Our knowledge of the ants of Madagascar is based on the collective efforts of a considerable number of dedicated ant collectors, as well as museum and laboratory technicians and scientists. In particular, the dedicated support of the Arthropod Inventory Team based at the Madagascar Biodiversity Center in Parc Botanique et Zoologique de Tsimbazaza: Pascal Rabeson, Jean-Jacques Rafanomezantsoa, Dimby Raharinjanahary, Balsama Rajemison, Valerie Rakotomalala, Jean-Claude Rakotonirina, Manoa Ramamonjisoa, Chrislain Ranaivo, Tantely Randriambololona, Clavier Randrianandrasana, Nicole Rasoamanana, Hanitriniana Rasoazanamavo, and Njaka Ravelomanana. I have joined this team over the past 20 years while it visited over 400 field sites on Madagascar. In addition to Malagasy taxonomists Jean-Claude Rakotonirina and Nicole Rasoamanana, we acknowledge the tremendous dedication of an international team that has described many new ant species from the island: Gary Alpert, Bonnie Blaimer, Barry Bolton, Brendon Boudinot, Sandor Csősz, Flavia Esteves, Georg Fischer, Francisco Hita Garcia, Brian Heterick, John Lapolla, Rick Overson, Sebastian Salata, Phil Ward, and Masashi Yoshimura. In addition, we would like to thank Steve Goodman for his long-term advice and collaboration since B. L. Fisher's first trip in 1993. Fieldwork and research on the ants of Madagascar was supported by National Geographic grant no. 8429–0, National Science Foundation grants no. DEB-0072713, -0344731, -0842395, -1655076, and the Critical Ecosystem Partnership Fund (CEPF). The Critical Ecosystem Partnership Fund is a joint initiative of l'Agence Française de Développement, Conservation International, the European Union, the Global Environment Facility, the Government of Japan, the MacArthur Foundation, and the World Bank. A fundamental goal is to ensure that civil society is engaged in biodiversity conservation.

Subject editor: Steven M. Goodman

PHASMATODEA, STICK AND LEAF INSECTS

N. Cliquennois and S. Bradler

Stick and leaf insects are a group of moderately diverse, large terrestrial insects of the order Phasmatodea, with currently a little more than 3000 described species (Bradler and Buckley 2018). They are abundant in tropical rainforests, where they generally exhibit their greatest diversity, but can also be found in xerophytic plant formations, such as dry forests, savannas, and scrubland, or in regions with more temperate climates, as well as at high elevations, up to 5000 m, in the tropics (Uvarov 1922; Murányi 2007). Being exclusively phytophagous, their modern forms largely coevolved with angiosperms, including astounding forms of camouflage, in order to protect themselves from predators. Members of Phasmatodea apparently have weak dispersal capabilities, but several transoceanic colonization events of remote islands have led to successful colonization and, in some cases, extensive species radiations (Buckley et al. 2010; Bradler et al. 2015).

THE PHASMATODEA OF MADAGASCAR

The island of Madagascar has a diverse stick insect fauna that is poorly known. Audinet-Serville (1838) described the first Malagasy stick insect under the name of *Cyphocrana punctipes* (currently *Achrioptera punctipes*) from a male specimen "coming from the coasts of Africa." Only 12 new species had been added by the end of the 19th century, including *Achrioptera fallax*, the first stick insect to have been explicitly described from Madagascar (Coquerel 1861). At the beginning of the 20th century, knowledge of Malagasy stick insects made significant progress with publication of the monographs by Brunner von Wattenwyl (1907) and Redtenbacher (1906, 1908), adding 53 species new to science and six new species for the island. However, because of mistakes in labeling of specimens, five of the six new species had been recorded from Madagascar erroneously, including *Macynia labiata* (Brock 2000) and four species belonging to Monandropterini (Cliquennois 2007). Two other species described from Madagascar also appear uncertain: *Heterophasma gaudichaudi* (N. Cliquennois and F. H. Hennemann, unpublished data) and *Parabactricia mirum*, of which type specimens are lost and for which two different ideas about its taxonomic position have been proposed: close to *Achrioptera* (Cliquennois 2005) or within Antongiliinae (Hennemann et al. 2016). For the balance of the 20th century, only 12 additional Malagasy species were described, all before 1952. Not until the 21st century were new taxa from Madagascar, ranging from species to family rank, proposed by Hennemann and Conle (2004), Zompro (2004), and Cliquennois (2005, 2006, 2008).

Currently, Madagascar's fauna comprises 78 valid phasmatodean species or subspecies, all endemic to the island, as well as three exotic species introduced by humans (Cliquennois 2012; Table 9.53). The native species are assigned to 24 genera and four major lineages, which together represent a monophyletic group based on recent molecular genetic studies (Figure 9.73); however, according to the traditional classification, they were viewed as being largely unrelated (Bradley and Galil 1977). In fact, the Malagasy stick insect fauna is morphologically very diverse, ranging from tiny wingless ground dwellers—some males in the *Pachymorpha madagassa* group (Figure 9.74b) (Antongiliidae) hardly reach 20 mm—to giant-winged likely canopy dwellers (female *Achrioptera manga*, 230 mm). Outside of molecular characters, no morphological trait is currently known that diagnoses the Madagascar radiation, although there are a number of plesiomorphic features. Originally classified into a tribe (Achriopterini), subfamily (Antongiliinae), or families (Anisacanthidae and Damasippoididae) (Bradley and Galil 1977; Zompro 2004), the recent phylogenetic analyses based on molecular data revealed the close relationship between these taxa (Simon et al. 2019) and subsequently prompted some rank escalations: Achriopterini became Achriopteridae; Antongiliinae became Antongiliidae; and all four families occurring on the island are now comprised under Anisacanthoidea (Cliquennois 2020). Antongiliidae and Damasippoididae are strictly endemic, whereas the Achriopteridae and Anisacanthidae are endemic to the Malagasy Region, comprising herein Madagascar and the Comoros, an archipelago with three valid species (Cliquennois 2018; Table 9.53).

Recent taxonomic research, albeit largely unpublished and predominantly based on morphological studies, has revealed a large and unexpected diversity. Currently, about 200 species, 40 genera, and several suprageneric taxa await formal scientific description (N. Cliquennois, unpublished data). In addition, molecular data has uncovered the existence of cryptic species that could not be distinguished based on superficial morphological examination (Glaw et al. 2019). Consequently, species with an apparently wide geographic distribution—for example, *Antongilia laciniata*, *A. muricata*, *Pseudoleosthenes irregularis*, and *Achrioptera punctipes*—might comprise a number of cryptic species as well.

PHYLOGENTICS OF MALAGASY PHASMATODEA

On the basis of transcriptomic analyses (Simon et al. 2019) and currently unpublished data, Phasmatodea of Madagascar and the Comoros appears to constitute a monophyletic group, Anisacanthoidea (Figure 9.73). This hypothesis is based purely on molecular data and initially was only partly supported (Bradler et al. 2015; Robertson et al. 2018). With increased sampling and more sequence data, this view now appears to be fully corroborated. The Malagasy stick insect ancestors most likely stem from Africa, and the presumed single colonization of Madagascar took place between 38 and 51 million years ago (Simon et al. 2019), long after Madagascar separated from Africa and later from India. Subsequently, the Malagasy lineage was able to colonize the Comoros. It is of considerable interest that the stick insects of the Mascarene and Seychelles archipelagoes are not derived from Madagascar but are of Asiatic origin (Bradler et al. 2015).

TABLE 9.53. **Checklist of valid Phasmatodea species recorded on Madagascar and the Comoros**

SCIENTIFIC NAMES	LOCATIONS AND HABITATS
ANTONGILIIDAE GÜNTHER, 1953	
Pseudodataminae, Pseudodatamini Zompro, 2004	
Cirsia Redtenbacher, 1906	Medium-altitude moist evergreen forest
C. finoti Redtenbacher, 1906	Probably east of Mantasoa
C. madegassa Redtenbacher, 1906	Probably north of Fianarantsoa
C. multilobata Chopard, 1952	Tsaratanàna
Paracirsia Cliquennois, 2006	Western dry deciduous forest and southern dry spiny thicket
P. distincta (Brunner von Wattenwyl, 1907)	Androy, Ambovombe
Pseudodatames Redtenbacher, 1906	Moist evergreen forest
P. alluaudi Redtenbacher, 1906	Col de Manangotry (Andohahela)
P. bicornutus Zompro, 2004	Probably east of Mantasoa
P. memorabilis Redtenbacher, 1906	Maroantsetra
Misplaced Pseudodatamini	
Antongilia annulicornis* Redtenbacher, 1906[1]	Nosy Be
A. pungens* Redtenbacher, 1906[2]	Probably north of Fianarantsoa
Canuleius delicatulus* Brancsik, 1898[3]	Nosy Be
Xylica madagassa* Redtenbacher, 1906[4]	Androy, Ambovombe
Pseudodataminae, *Pachymorpha madagassa* group	Moist evergreen forest
P. madagassa* Brunner von Wattenwyl, 1907[5]	Mahanoro
Pseudodataminae, *Spathomorpha*	Northern half of moist evergreen forest
Spathomorpha Cliquennois, 2005	
S. adefa Cliquennois, 2005[6]	Ambodiriana (Manompana)
S. lancettifer (Brancsik, 1893)	Nosy Be
Antongiliinae, long-legged Antongiliinae	
No described species to date	Ambodiriana (Manompana), Andasibe, Vohibola, Vohimana
Antongiliinae, *Phalces unilineatus* group	Moist evergreen forest from Zahamena to Tolagnaro
P. unilineatus* Redtenbacher, 1906[7]	Probably north of Fianarantsoa
Antongiliinae, *Antongilia madagassa* group	Northern Madagascar, moist evergreen forest
A. chopardi* Cliquennois, 2003[8]	Tsaratanàna
A. madagassa* (Brunner von Wattenwyl, 1907)[9]	Montagne d'Ambre
Onogastris pauliani* Chopard, 1952[10]	Tsaratanàna
Antongiliinae, Antongiliini Günther, 1953	
Antongilia Redtenbacher, 1906	Medium-altitude moist evergreen forest
A. laciniata Redtenbacher, 1906	Probably east of Mantasoa
Onogastris Redtenbacher, 1906	Southern moist evergreen forest
O. pardalina Redtenbacher, 1906	Col de Manangotry (Andohahela)

SCIENTIFIC NAMES	LOCATIONS AND HABITATS
Paronogastris Cliquennois, 2006	Moist evergreen forest from Maroantsetra to Andasibe
P. squamigera (Redtenbacher, 1906)	"Antongil" (Maroantsetra?)
Antongiliinae, Leprodini Cliquennois, 2006	Moist evergreen forest
Leprodes Redtenbacher, 1906	Southern moist evergreen forest
L. dicranocollis Redtenbacher, 1906	Isaka (Andohahela)
Pseudonogastris Cliquennois, 2006	Maroantsetra and Fianarantsoa area
P. aculeata (Redtenbacher, 1906)	Maroantsetra
Virgasia Cliquennois, 2006	
V. simplex (Redtenbacher, 1906)	Maroantsetra
Misplaced Leprodini	
Antongilia muricata* Redtenbacher, 1906[11]	Probably east of Mantasoa
A. quadrituberculata* Redtenbacher, 1906[12]	"Antongil" (Maroantsetra?)
A. unispinosa* Carl, 1913[13]	?
Leprodes gibbifer* Redtenbacher, 1906[14]	Probably north of Fianarantsoa
DAMASIPPOIDIDAE ZOMPRO, 2004	Moist evergreen forest
Damasippoides Brancsik, 1893	
D. albomarginatus Redtenbacher, 1906	Probably east of Mantasoa
D. erythropterus Redtenbacher, 1906	Maroantsetra
D. xanthostictus Brancsik, 1893	Nosy Be
Pseudoleosthenes Redtenbacher, 1906	
P. dubiosus Redtenbacher, 1906	Maroantsetra
P. irregularis Redtenbacher, 1906	Isaka (Andohahela)
P. scaberrimus Redtenbacher, 1906	Probably east of Mantasoa
ACHRIOPTERIDAE GÜNTHER, 1953	All forest types
Achrioptera Coquerel, 1861	
A. cliquennoisi Hennemann & Conle, 2004	Ambodiriana (Manompana)
A. fallax Coquerel, 1861	Northern dry deciduous forest
A. gracilis Hennemann & Conle, 2004	Ivohibe
A. griveaudi‡ Paulian, 1960	Mohéli (Comoros)
A. impennis Redtenbacher, 1908	Ambovombe (Androy)
A. lobipes (Rehn, 1940)	?
A. magnifica Hennemann & Conle, 2004	Anjozorobe, Manjakandriana, Maroantsetra, Montagne d'Ambre?
A. manga Glaw, Hawlitschek, Dunz, Goldberg & Bradler, 2019	Oronjia, Montagne des Français, Montagne d'Ambre
A. maroloko Glaw, Hawlitschek, Dunz, Goldberg & Bradler, 2019	Montagne des Français, Anjajavy?, Ankarafantsika?
A. punctipes (Audinet-Serville, 1838)	From Maroantsetra to Tolagnaro, moist evergreen forest
A. pygmaea Redtenbacher, 1908	"Antongil" (Maroantsetra?)
A. spinosissima (Kirby, 1891)	Morondava region

(continued overleaf)

TABLE 9.53. ***continued***

SCIENTIFIC NAMES	LOCATIONS AND HABITATS
Glawiana Hennemann & Conle, 2004	Southern dry spiny thicket
G. glawi Hennemann & Conle, 2004	Saint Augustin (south of Toliara)
ANISACANTHIDAE GÜNTHER, 1953	
Anisacanthinae Günther, 1953	Moist evergreen forest
Anisacantha Redtenbacher, 1906	Moist evergreen forest, from Marojejy to Mantadia
A. difformis Redtenbacher, 1906	Maroantsetra
Paranisacantha Cliquennois, 2008	Northern moist evergreen forest
P. poulaini Cliquennois, 2008	Marojejy
P. spinulosa (Chopard, 1952)	Tsaratanàna
Parectatosoma Wood-Mason, 1879	
P. cervinum Redtenbacher, 1906	Col de Manangotry (Andohahela)
P. echinus Wood-Mason, 1879	Fianarantsoa area
P. hystrix Wood-Mason, 1879	Fianarantsoa area
P. minus Chopard, 1952	Montagne d'Ambre
P. mocquerysi Finot, 1898	Maroantsetra
P. sakavalanum Redtenbacher, 1906	Col de Manangotry (Andohahela)
Somacantha Cliquennois, 2008	
S. kalolohai Cliquennois, 2008	Ambodiriana (Manompana)
Leiophasmatinae Cliquennois, 2008	
Adelophasma‡ Cliquennois, 2018	
A. anjouanense‡ Cliquennois, 2018	Anjouan (Comoros)
Amphiphasma Cliquennois, 2008	Moist evergreen forest
A. occipitale (Carl, 1913)	?
Leiophasma Uvarov, 1940	
L. adustum (Redtenbacher, 1906)	Mahanoro
L. brevivalvis (Redtenbacher, 1906)	"Antongil" (Maroantsetra?)
L. concolor (Redtenbacher, 1906)	?
L. flaviceps (Redtenbacher, 1906)	Maroantsetra
L. intermedium (Redtenbacher, 1906)	Montagne d'Ambre
L. lucubense (Brancsik, 1893)	Nosy Be
L. maculipes (Redtenbacher, 1906)	?
L. mayottense‡ Cliquennois, 2003	Mayotte (Comoros)
L. nigrolineatum (Stål, 1875)	?
L. nigrotuberculatum nigrotuberculatum (Redtenbacher, 1906)	Probably east of Mantasoa
L. n. modestum (Carl, 1913)	?
L. operculatum (Redtenbacher, 1906)	Maroantsetra
L. sohri (Brancsik, 1898)	Farafangana

SCIENTIFIC NAMES	LOCATIONS AND HABITATS
L. spinosum (Redtenbacher, 1906)	?
L. vaginatum (Redtenbacher, 1906)	Maroantsetra
Xerantherinae Cliquennois, 2008	Moist evergreen forest and northern dry deciduous forest
Archantherix Cliquennois, 2008	
A. tegminatus Cliquennois, 2008	"N.E. Madagascar, forest belt"
Cenantherix Cliquennois, 2008	
C. pauliani Cliquennois, 2008	Tsaratanàna
Parorobia Chopard, 1952	
P. lobiventris Chopard, 1952	Tsaratanàna
Xerantherix Brancsik, 1893	
X. albogeniculatus (Redtenbacher, 1906)	Ile Sainte Marie
X. nossibianus Brancsik, 1893	Nosy Be
X. parvipennis Redtenbacher, 1906	Maroantsetra
X. pinnatus Redtenbacher, 1906	?
Dubious species	
Heterophasma gaudichaudi Redtenbacher, 1908[15]	
Parabactricia mirum Redtenbacher, 1908[16]	
Introduced species	
Heteropterygidae, Heteropterygynae	
Heteropterix dilatata (Parkinson, 1898)[17]	Mantadia
Lonchodidae, Lonchodinae	
Carausius morosus Brunner von Wattenwyl, 1907	Central Highlands, from Anjozorobe to Ambohimahasoa
Necrosciidae, Necrosciinae	
Sipyloidea sipylus (Westwood, 1859)	Northwest region from Montagne d'Ambre to Mahajanga; east coast from Maroantsetra to Masomeloka; Central Highlands from Antananarivo, Andasibe to Tolongoina

Notes: The list includes three species that are introduced to Madagascar and three species (‡) endemic to the Comoros. The remaining 78 species are endemic to Madagascar. * after genus name indicates misplaced species, based on our unpublished information.

[1] Possible synonym of *Canuleius delicatulus*.

[2] Probably belongs in *Cirsia*; possible synonym of *C. madagassa*.

[3] *Paracirsia* or close to that genus.

[4] Probable *Paracirsia*; possible synonym of *P. distincta*.

[5] *Pachymorpha* Gray, 1835 (Phasmatidae) is an Australian genus.

[6] Resembles a species complex in its current definition.

[7] *Phalces* Stål, 1875 (Bacillidae) is a South African genus.

[8] Requires the erection of a new genus. This species may be congeneric with *A. madagassa*.

[9] Requires the erection of a new genus.

[10] Requires the erection of a new genus. This species is morphologically very different from the previous two.

[11] Belongs to a new genus close to *Virgasia*.

[12] Requires the erection of a new genus.

[13] Requires the erection of a new genus.

[14] This species is congeneric with *Antongilia unispinosa*.

[15] Likely a *Neohirasea* sp. (Necrosciidae) from Southeast Asia.

[16] Mysterious species and genus of unknown position (type specimens lost).

[17] Only one sighting, on a guava tree along the roadside.

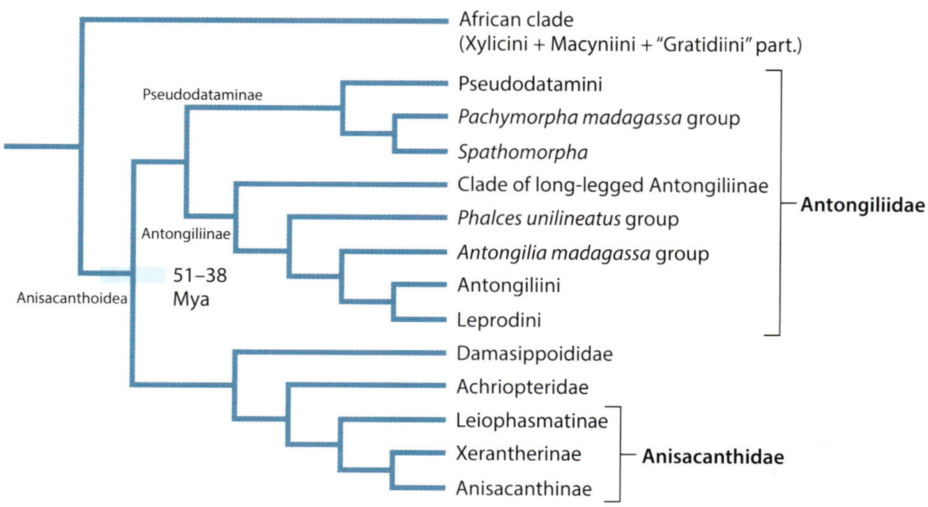

FIGURE 9.73 **Phylogeny of Malagasy Phasmatodea based on molecular data after various authors.** (SOURCES: Bradler et al. 2015; Glaw et al. 2019; Simon et al. 2019; and unpublished data of the authors.)

Anisacanthoidea is divided into two principal clades, one forming Antongiliidae, the other unnamed and composed of Damasippoididae, Achriopteridae, and Anisacanthidae. In recent years, molecular data have repeatedly corroborated a sister-group relationship of Achriopteridae + Anisacanthidae (Goldberg et al. 2015; Bradler et al. 2015; Glaw et al. 2019; Simon et al. 2019). Owing to the absence of the area apicalis in Achriopteridae and its presence in Anisacanthidae, both groups were formerly considered to be unrelated, with Achriopteridae traditionally ranked as a tribe within the predominantly Australasian Phasmatidae (Bradley and Galil 1977). No convincing synapomorphy for these two Malagasy groups has been detected so far, but a character, which is present in most of its members and lacking in all remaining members of Anisacanthoidea, is the elongate abdominal sternum 8 (subgenital plate) in the female. Members of both groups are either short-winged or even wingless in both sexes.

NATURAL HISTORY

The stick insects of Madagascar, as in the rest of the world, have their greatest diversity in moist evergreen forests, with, for example, about 40 species known from the Marojejy Massif (N. Cliquennois, unpublished data); the diversity found in the western dry deciduous forests and the dry spiny thickets of the southwest is much lower (generally no more than three species per locality). Stick insects are usually encountered in the vegetation at a height of ~1.5 m, but we can assume that they also inhabit the canopy. Certain species appear to prefer more open environments, like the forest edge or along river margins. They can also be found in forest litter and up to a height of a few meters, where they appear to be rarer or perhaps better camouflaged.

All Malagasy stick insects are nocturnal; consequently, the search for them in the forest is most fruitful during the night. In contrast, it is extremely difficult to detect them during the day due to their highly effective camouflage, which involves various techniques: remaining on the ground among dead leaves, pressed against a branch or mossy tree trunk, or in close proximity to a leaf, sometimes above or below. Further, aspects of camouflage are enhanced by their lack of movement, allowing stick insects to blend in with their surroundings. Some taxa adopt a particularly characteristic position: members of Xerantherinae (Figure 9.75e) and the "*Phalces*" *unilineatus* group in Antongiliidae press their legs in a characteristic form against the thorax or abdomen and let their body hang from the vegetation, thus perfectly imitating a dead branch. The diverse modes of perfecting this camouflage appear to be taxon-specific.

SYSTEMATICS

In the following section, we present details in a systematic order on the stick insects of Madagascar and, in some cases, the nearby Comoro islands.

Antongiliidae

This lineage represents the sister group of all remaining members of Anisacanthoidea and is divided into two principal clades, Pseudodataminae and Antongiliinae, each composed of few subgroups that are well-differentiated morphologically. Members of Antongiliidae are completely wingless and easily distinguished from other Malagasy stick insects by the presence of very short antennae (considerably shorter than the fore tibiae), most often composed of scapus and pedicellus—respectively, the first (basal) and second segments—and 12 flagellomeres (remaining segments that constitute the flagellum) in the female and 16 in the male, of which the first flagellomere is enlarged and modified for defensive stridulation. Members of Antongiliidae have various body forms, most often representing typically elongate stick insects with brown or green coloration and a rather smooth body, albeit also comprising some more massive forms with various spines and lobes, particularly in females. They generally have a modest size, measuring 5–7 cm in body length, but can also surpass 16 cm in few taxa (*Spathomorpha*, Figure 9.74c). The eggs, which resemble plant seeds and are usually laid singly and dropped to the ground, are of various shapes, mostly an ovoid capsule covered by a network of wrinkles and with many bristles (Cliquennois 2006). The surface of the egg lid (operculum) is similar to that of the capsule and lacks a capitulum, a knob-like structure. Only females of Pseudodatamini glue their eggs onto a suitable substrate like bark or twigs.

FIGURE 9.74 **Malagasy phasmids. Antongiliidae, Pseudodataminae: A) female, *Pseudodatames* sp., Vohibola littoral forest; B) male and female, *Pachymorpha madagassa* group, Lokobe Forest, Nosy Be; C) male and female, *Spathomorpha* sp., near Zahamena. Antongiliidae, Antongiliinae: D) male and female *Antongilia madagassa*, Montagne d'Ambre; E) female, *Antongilia* sp., Vohimana Forest. Damasippoididae: F) unidentified female, Ambodiriana (Manompana).** (PHOTOS A, B, D, E, and F by N. Cliquennois; and C by Y. Méléard.)

FIGURE 9.75 **Malagasy phasmids. Damasippoididae: A) unidentified male, Bevoloto Forest (Torotorofotsy). Achriopteridae: B) male *Achrioptera manga*, Montagne des Français; and C) male and female *Achrioptera* cf. *impennis*, Isalo. Anisacanthidae, Leiophasmatinae: D) male and female *Leiophasma intermedium*, Montagne d'Ambre. Anisacanthidae, Xerantherinae: E) male and female, *Xerantherix* sp., Ambodiriana (Manompana). Anisacanthidae, Anisacanthinae: F) male and female *Parectatosoma minus*, Montagne d'Ambre.** (PHOTOS A and C–F by N. Cliquennois; and B by S. Gombeer.)

Antongiliidae is a very diverse and common group of the moist evergreen forests, generally found between 0.5 and 1.5 m off the ground, most often on bushes belonging to Rubiaceae. In dry deciduous forests, only members of Pseudodatamini are known and with no more than one species per site.

Pseudodataminae

Pseudodataminae comprises three principal lineages: Pseudodatamini, *Spathomorpha*, and one clade yet to be named.

Pseudodatamini. Pseudodatamini exhibits a variety of body forms but is recognized by a pair of often well-developed spines on the head behind the antennae. *Pseudodatames* (Figure 9.74a) has a rough, brownish or blackish cuticle. Females are massive, with short legs; abdominal segments 5 and 6 laterally widened, with a pair of strong lobe-shaped outgrowths that are somewhat spiny; and a more or less strongly developed outgrowth on the mesonotum. Males are robust, with a body cylindrical in cross section, short-legged, and with outgrowths on the head. *Cirsia* is brownish or grayish, much more slender than *Pseudodatames*, with thin, elongate legs. Females have a pair of spiniform or lobuliform outgrowths on the head, triangular lobes on the edges of the femora, and widened abdominal terga 5 and 6 that form a triangle. Males have a pair of often massive spines on the head and, at the back of the head, four shorter thorns arranged in squares; they also have a pair of V-shaped spines at the back of the mesonotum and metanotum. *Paracirsia* is brownish, often beige, of the same general shape as *Cirsia* but with a prognathous head (unlike *Pseudodatames* and *Cirsia*, which have a head in a more orthognathous position) and legs that are shorter (the hind legs do not reach the end of the abdomen in females when stretched out backward) and thicker than those of *Cirsia*. The most characteristic feature of *Paracirsia* is the presence of two pairs of often well-developed spines between the eyes at the front of the head. The cuticle of the female is covered with numerous large granules and with a pair of outgrowths at the back of abdominal tergum 5, which is thickened; the male is less rough. Morphologically distinct forms exist, each represented by a single species, but the relationships with the three known genera remain unclear.

Members of Pseudodatamini display a unique feature among Malagasy phasmids: they glue their eggs onto a suitable surface, such as bark or twigs. Their eggs are elongate and have a strongly inclined operculum; they are neither reticulate nor setose, as is often the case in Antongiliidae. This group has the broadest distribution within Antongiliidae. *Pseudodatames* and *Cirsia* can be found in the moist evergreen forests (except Montagne d'Ambre). *Paracirsia* is found in the dry deciduous forests of the west, as far north as the Montagne d'Ambre, and in the south into the dry spiny thickets; this genus is the only member of Antongiliidae known to occur in this last vegetation type.

"*Pachymorpha madagassa*" group. This group (Figure 9.74b) does not yet have a formal taxonomic designation and so far contains a single recognized species, erroneously assigned to the unrelated Australian genus *Pachymorpha*. This group includes a very large number of undescribed species—at least one or two different per sampled site—and most with seemingly very limited geographic distributions. Females are often massive and have a moderate lengthened abdominal tergum 10 (anal segment), two to three times longer than abdominal tergum 9. Males are thinner, sometimes threadlike, with an asymmetrical vomer. Both sexes have a characteristic first antennary segment (scapus), of which the outer distal angle is extended in the form of a triangle. The group has a wide distribution, probably the largest besides the Pseudodatamini but, unlike the latter, is restricted to moist evergreen forests. Members of this group are found from the Sambirano Region to the northeast, south to the Tolagnaro area, and across the elevation range from the coast up to 2000 m; it is unknown from Montagne d'Ambre Massif. Unlike the majority of Malagasy stick insects, this group appears to be less sensitive to forest habitat degradation and fragmentation. Among the reasons members of this group remain so little known is their small size, rarely more than 5 mm in body length, and their ground-dwelling lifestyle. They are usually motionless, and their red to blackish-brown coloration allows them to blend perfectly with their surroundings. Occasionally, these insects can be observed at very low height on herbaceous plants or on rocks covered with low-growing vegetation. In captivity, they hide during the day among dead leaves of the litter, and their diet consists at least partially of dead leaves.

Genus *Spathomorpha*. The genus *Spathomorpha* (Figure 9.74c), with two described species, is unique among Antongiliidae in not having a triangular apical area on the ventral side of the tibia. *Spathomorpha* also contains the largest representative of Antongiliidae, *S. adefa*, the female of which measures 137–163 mm and the male 83–97 mm (Cliquennois 2005). The female is easily recognized by its extremely elongate anal segment (abdominal tergum 10), which measures between a quarter and a third of the total length of the abdomen, a unique trait among members of Phasmatodea. *Spathomorpha* species live in moist evergreen forests. *Spathomorpha lancettifer* is known only from Nosy Be, while *S. adefa* has been collected along the eastern side of the island, between 16.5° and 19° south latitude and across an elevation gradient from sea level to about 1000 m. However, on the basis of molecular data, *S. adefa* seems to include some cryptic species.

Antongiliinae

Antongiliinae comprises 1) a clade of long-legged members of Antongiliidae, 2) the *Phalces unilineatus* group, 3) the *Antongilia madagassa* group, 4) Antongiliini, and 5) Leprodini.

Long-legged Antongiliidae. The group constituting the long-legged Antongiliidae clade is devoid of males and reproduces asexually. The female is characterized by a very slender, smooth body, with very long, unarmed legs. It is known along the eastern moist evergreen forest of Ambodiriana (Manompana) and from the littoral forest of Loakankady (Ampanotoamaizina), as well as in moist evergreen forests in the region near Andasibe (Analamazaotra and Vohimana).

***Phalces unilineatus* group**. This group contains only one valid species to date, described from a male specimen and erroneously assigned to the South African genus *Phalces*. Members of the group include elongate, unarmed, or slightly prickly stick insects, which can be recognized by the black color of the lateral parts of the head in both sexes, but this mark is sometimes limited to a longitudinal postocular lateral line. The female has a secondary ovipositor formed by the elongation of the abdominal tergum 10 (anal segment) and the abdominal sternum 8 (subgenital plate). The two sexes also have two lateral carinae on the mesosternum, which converge forward; when in a resting position, the legs are pressed against the body and hidden in lateral dimples bordered by the carinae. Two main groups can be distinguished that will be described as new genera, including a few somewhat morphologically distinct species. The egg is typical of Antongiliidae: ovoid and elongate (more than twice as long as wide), reticulate and setose, with very short bristles, and brownish. This group lives in the moist evergreen forests, ranging from 800 to 1800 m in elevation, as well as in the littoral forests near Tolagnaro. It is not known north of 17.5°S latitude.

***Antongilia madagassa* group**. This group is known from three valid species, *A. madagassa* (Figure 9.74d), *A. chopardi*, and *Onogastris pauliani*, all assigned in error to two genera belonging to another group in Antongiliidae. The group comprises different forms, ranging from twig-like and almost unarmed stick insects to rather sturdy ones covered with numerous spines or other cuticular outgrowths. The group is diagnosed by a prominent female trait: the elongation of abdominal tergum 10 (anal segment) without any elongation of the sternum 8 (subgenital plate). The male is characterized by a lower number of antennal segments than the other Antongiliidae males, usually 9–14, including the scapus and pedicellus in this group, compared to the usual 18. Nearly 30 undescribed species have been identified to date (N. Cliquennois, unpublished data). The eggs are typical of Antongiliidae: ovoid, reticulate, setose, and brown. This group is endemic to northern Madagascar, where it is found in only moist evergreen forests (Sambirano, Montagne d'Ambre, Tsaratanàna, and Marojejy).

Antongiliini. This group consists of three well-defined genera: *Antongilia* (Figure 9.74e), *Onogastris*, and *Paronogastris*, each currently represented only by the respective type species, *A. laciniata*, *O. pardalina*, and *P. squamigera*. Certain species currently placed in *Antongilia* and *Onogastris* (Brock et al. 2020) need to be transferred to genera yet to be described (Cliquennois 2006) in order not to render those two genera polyphyletic.

Antongilia and *Onogastris* appear to be morphologically quite similar; both sexes have a rounded vertex, slightly orthognathous head, a smooth cuticle with numerous and quite sturdy outgrowths in females, and an enlarged abdomen in abdominal segments 3 to 6. Females can be distinguished based on specific outgrowths: *Antongilia* has relatively short spines and large medial spiny lobes arranged longitudinally on abdominal terga; *Onogastris* is devoid of lobes but bears many large and long spines, particularly dense and slightly finer on abdominal terga 4 and 5. Males are much more gracile than females and are rather similar in both genera, with the exception that *Antongilia* are spinier, with many triangular lobes on the femora and tibiae, while in *Onogastris*, these outgrowths are lacking. *Paronogastris* appears very different from the other two genera: it has a more elongate appearance (the mesonotum measures more than six times the length of the pronotum, compared to less than five times for *Antongilia* and *Onogastris*); it has no spines or lobes but instead has granules, black in females, white in males; and members of this genus do not have a dorsally rounded head. The female has a thorax about one and a half times longer than the abdomen, abdominal terga 5 and 6 generally widened and bulging, a pair of lobes on abdominal tergum 6, and many lobes on the ventral carinae of the fore and median legs.

These three genera were thought to be related because they have similar types of eggs that are very different from those of the other Antongiliidae (Cliquennois 2006). Notably, in *Onogastris* and *Paronogastris*, the capsule appears to have a hexagonal cross section, each surface smooth and delimited by long bristles; the operculum is oval, bearing a setose structure referred to as a "paracapitulum" (Cliquennois 2006) in its center. The *Antongilia* egg appears to morphologically resemble the classic Antongiliidae egg, as it is ovoid and reticulated, but it shares with the other two genera the beige or green coloration, the presence of a paracapitulum (albeit less developed), and a white and smooth micropylar plate (without a median carina). At present, no diagnostic morphological character common to these three genera has been identified.

The distribution of these three genera fall within distinct geographic areas: *Paronogastris* is known from coastal forests up to 1300 m, from Maroantsetra to the Moramanga areas (Andasibe and Mandraka); *Antongilia* occurs from Zahamena to Andringitra and across an elevational range from 800 to 2000 m; and *Onogastris* is distributed from Andringitra to the Tolagnaro area, falling within the elevational range from 50 to 2000 m. *Antongilia* is in geographic contact with *Paronogastris* in the north of its distribution and with *Onogastris* in the south of its distribution, but these latter two genera are not sympatric. *Antongilia* is morphologically very uniform, but molecular analyses (S. Bradler, unpublished data) indicate the existence of cryptic species, while the species boundaries within the genera *Onogastris* and *Paronogastris* appear well demarcated based on morphology. Molecular data for *Onogastris* are lacking.

Leprodini group. This group is currently known to contain seven species and three genera (*Leprodes*, *Pseudonogastris*, and *Virgasia*), but only three species—the type species of each of these genera—are correctly named; the other four species probably require the description of new genera (Cliquennois 2006). Like Antongiliini, Leprodini was characterized mainly based on the morphology of the egg (Cliquennois 2006). However, unlike the eggs of Antongiliini and Pseudophasmatini, the eggs of Leprodini appear to exhibit plesiomorphic (primitive) traits that prove useful for diagnosing this group. Molecular data, however, confirm the monophyly of this group.

They appear as the most classic Antongiliidae: stick-like, without noticeable outgrowths, a prognathous head, and terminalia without any notable feature. They often have a median outgrowth near the posterior edge of the pronotum, sometimes spiniform or bispiniform, females with rounded lobes on the dorsal carinae of the median and posterior femora, and the basal notch of the anterior femora colored red. Females have a rough cuticle, males a rather smooth one. Molecular data of this group, as currently sampled, indicate the existence of three subgroups: the *Leprodes* clade, the *Leprodes gibbifer* + *Antongilia unispinosa* clade, and the *Virgasia* clade.

Leprodes is known from the moist evergreen forests of the southeast from Andringitra to the Tolagnaro areas, and is the most stout and sturdy genus within Leprodini, with a mesonotum less than four times longer than the pronotum in the female, about four times in the male, and brown with a pair of more or less developed spines on the anterior margin of the pronotum. The subgroup *Leprodes gibbifer* + *Antongilia unispinosa* comprises the most slender members of Leprodini (mesonotum/pronotum ratio >5.5 in both sexes), with long and thin legs, almost unarmed, but the female bears dorsal lobes toward the base of the median and posterior femora. Further, in both sexes, there is a well-developed median outgrowth, often spiniform, near the posterior margin of the pronotum, the abdominal terga 4–6 in females is increasingly widening, and the abdominal tergum 6 is covered with large tubercles on its posterior half. This subgroup is known from the Andasibe region from around 800 to 1000 m and between Ambositra and Fianarantsoa from around 900 to 1800 m, with no data available for the area in between. The third subgroup is that of the genus *Virgasia*, comprising stick insects that have a general morphology similar to that of the previous subgroup, but they are slightly smaller (males 50–60 mm, females 70–80 mm) and a bit stockier, especially females. Males often have a median dorsal spine near the posterior edge of the three thoracic segments, sometimes double for the pronotum, and more or less blunt for the mesonotum and metanotum (*V. simplex*), exhibiting unarmed legs or otherwise a few small apical spines on the ventral carinae of the middle and hind femora. Females have finely granular, weakly spiny bodies, with a pair of poorly developed posterior spines on the head, a pair of submedian spines in the center of the pronotum, and, near the posterior margin of the pronotum, a median spine (*A. muricata*) or two V-shaped spines (*V. simplex*). *Antongilia muricata* also has some anterior spines on the mesonotum, some tubercles on the tergum 6, and some small dorsal lobes on the median and posterior femora.

These three subgroups represent five of the seven species described to date. The remaining two, or others closely related, likely to belong to other subgroups but have not been included to date in molecular analyses. The first of these species, *A. quadrituberculata*, is typical in morphology for Leprodini, as described above; it is similar to the subgroup *Virgasia* in its overall shape, but the female has a rough cuticle, as in *Leprodes*, a uniformly brown color, and legs provided with small lobes. The male is distinguished from all other Leprodini males by the number of antennal segments—14 instead of 18—which usually also appears to be the condition in the female.

The second of these species is *Pseudonogastris aculeata*, which appears atypical within Leprodini, and which has been placed within this taxon with reservation, based only on the egg morphology. Both sexes have an orthognathous head and a convex vertex, characters found in *Antongilia*, *Onogastris* (Antongiliini), *Pseudodatames*, and *Cirsia* (Pseudodatamini) and that are therefore believed to be unique within Leprodini. The somewhat massive general appearance of the females is reminiscent of that of *Antongilia* and *Onogastris* in the shape of the head, the somewhat enlarged abdomen, and the dorsal outgrowths. Less-developed features are spines and tubercles on the head and thorax, a pair of lobes on the abdominal terga 5 and 6, as well as legs equipped with many lobes, like those of *Antongilia*. The antennae of males consist of up of 13 segments instead of 18 or sometimes 19, as are found in male members of Leprodini and Antongiliini. The placement of the genus *Pseudonogastris* therefore remains uncertain. Its distribution appears to be disjunct and is known from the northeast (Marojejy, Maroantsetra area, the type locality of *P. aculeata*) and the south-central area (Andrambovato, Andringitra). It has not been observed in Ambodiriana (Manompana) or in the Andasibe area, regions that have been extensively explored.

Damasippoididae

This group comprises stick insects of medium size, with males 48–68 mm in body length and females 58–86 mm (Redtenbacher 1906). They exhibit striking sexual dimorphism: the females (Figure 9.74f) are larger and completely wingless, and the more slender males (Figure 9.75a) bear large functional wings, a unique character among Malagasy phasmids. Stick insects of this group are found exclusively in moist evergreen forests, generally at elevations above 800 m, where they appear to be not very abundant and difficult to find. Apparently, the taxon is rather diverse and thus more easily observable in the north. On the Marojejy Massif, at least eight species occur out of around 30 distinguishable species in the family (N. Cliquennois, unpublished data), of which only six have been described to date.

Members of this group are easily recognizable by an unusual morphological trait: the ventral surface of the thorax is smooth, flat, or concave, often blackish, with ventral bristles on the edge of the segments and the edges of the legs, often accompanied by lobes. In contrast, the dorsal body may be rough or smooth, with spines on the head and thorax, especially on the pronotum and the anterior part of the mesonotum. These characters are linked to the animals' daytime resting position, when they are pressed against a trunk or branch, sometimes with the abdomen raised. The female has a rounded head in dorsal view, sometimes with a bulge near the front margin of the mesonotum. The male is less thorny than the female. This group currently includes only two genera, *Damasippoides* and *Pseudoleosthenes*, each probably not monophyletic in its current delineation and both in need of revision. Their eggs are ovoid, more or less compressed laterally, with a usually reticulate capsule that is sometimes completely smooth. The operculum is the only one among Malagasy phasmids to possess a knob-like central structure (a "capitulum"), which is circled by another structure.

Achriopteridae

Individuals belonging to this group (Figures 9.75b and c) are often spectacular stick insects, both in size (the largest up to 164 mm long for the male and 238 mm for the female) (Hennemann and Conle 2004) and appearance, with impressive spination and striking coloration. Some males, like the radiantly blue males of *Achrioptera manga* (Figure 9.75b), exhibit bright colors probably associated with aposematism (a visual signal that warns predators about toxicity or distastefulness) as a defensive strategy (Glaw et al. 2019). The short wings of these insects appear to be useless for active flight, but might be used for gliding and are frequently deployed for a startling display, which also includes defensive stridulation against potential predators. The eggs of Achriopteridae are light brown, laterally compressed, oval in section, 1.5–2 times longer than wide, and have an opercular extension at both poles (Henneman and Conle 2004).

Members of Achriopteridae are widely distributed in both dry deciduous and moist evergreen forests up to 1500 m. The only two currently recognized genera within Achriopteridae are rather species-poor, comprising the monotypic *Glawiana* and *Achrioptera*, which contains 12 described species. The relationship between *Glawiana* and *Achrioptera* is not yet settled, with *Achrioptera* probably being paraphyletic (Glaw et al. 2019). The *A. impennis* group (Figure 9.75c) of the southern region (dry spiny thicket of the southwest and western dry deciduous forests from Isalo to the Morondava region) appears to be distantly related to the remaining *Achrioptera* species, probably sister to *Glawiana* (Glaw et al. 2019) of the southwest dry spiny thicket, or sister to all remaining Achriopteridae. The group is endemic to Madagascar and the Comoros, where it occurs on each of four islands in the archipelago (Cliquennois 2018), each perhaps representing a distinct species (N. Cliquennois, unpublished data). The only species described from the Comoros is *A. griveaudi* from Mohéli, whose phylogenetic position within Achriopteridae awaits elucidation.

Anisacanthidae

Recent phylogenetic analyses (Glaw et al. 2019; S. Bradler, unpublished data) corroborate monophyly of the three subfamilies of Anisacanthidae, as proposed by Cliquennois (2008), organized as follows: (Leiophasmatinae + [Anisacanthinae + Xerantherinae]). Its members have various body forms, ranging from elongate stick insects with a smooth and spineless body to a sturdy body with a rough cuticle carrying spiny or leaflike outgrowths. The eggs of this group are highly characteristic, exhibiting a number of unique features. They are ovoid, with a smooth capsule devoid of bristles and a very elongate micropylar plate extending from the opercular neck to the posterior pole, further extended by a crest that is simple in Anisacanthinae (but here also often absent) and in Xerantherine, double in Leiophasmatinae, as well as three lines imprinted on the ventral surface (Cliquennois 2008). Details on each of the three subfamilies are presented here.

Anisacanthinae

Anisacanthinae contains stick insects that are among the most commonly observed in the island's moist evergreen forests. They are also among the most remarkable and are therefore very popular among stick insect breeders. These phasmids are often very spiny, more or less massive, with a plump abdomen in females, thinner in males, and have a generally cone-shaped head, are usually short-winged, and, unlike members of Xerantherinae, have tegmina (forewings) in females. The legs often bear prominent lobes and spines. Currently, Anisacanthinae comprises 10 valid species placed in four genera: *Anisacantha* (one species), *Paranisacantha* (two species), *Parectatosoma* (six species), and *Somacantha* (one species).

Parectatosoma is recognized by the massive body of the female and, proportionally, of the smaller male, and its raised head that bears long spines and a pair of leaflike outgrowths on the vertex. It has shortened hind wings, which exceed the posterior edge of the first abdominal tergum (median segment), the abdominal tergum 10 (anal segment) is extended with posterior spines, and sternum 8 (subgenital plate) clearly exceeds the dorsal end of the abdomen. One can morphologically separate *Parectatosoma* into two groups based on whether the tegmina cover the metanotum (group *P. echinus* and *P. mocquerysi*) or do not cover it (group *P. hystrix*). In the latter case, the metanotum has developed a pair of long spines. *Somacantha* appears morphologically close to "hedgehog Anisacanthinae," a lineage still unnamed, and to the sister group to *Parectatosoma*. Stick insects of the genus *Somacantha* share similar female terminalia with *Parectatosoma* and can be distinguished by the shape of the body, which is less massive with a more slender mesonotum in *Somacantha* that is more than three times longer than the pronotum, versus just over twice as long in *Parectatosoma*. *Somacantha* and "hedgehog Anisacanthinae" are distinguished by spination, which is weakly developed in the former and strongly pronounced in the latter, particularly on the vertex, where the outgrowths are similar to those of *Parectatosoma*. *Anisacantha* and *Paranisacantha* are of similar body form as *Somacantha* but possess a vertex that is not raised but slightly domed (*Anisacantha*) or even flattened (*Paranisacantha*). The females exhibit very distinct terminalia: *Anisacantha* has a secondary ovipositor formed by the elongation of the abdominal tergum 10 and the sternum 8, while *Paranisacantha* has a short sternum 8 that does not extend beyond the dorsal end of the abdomen. *Parectatosoma minus* (Figure 9.75f) from Montagne d'Ambre appears to be the sister group of *Anisacantha* + *Paranisacantha*, and thereby distant from *Parectatosoma*, which renders this genus in its current form not monophyletic. The eggs are typical for Anisacanthidae, with the characteristic of having a circular dimple in the center of the operculum and sometimes a simple ridge at the posterior pole.

Leiophasmatinae

Members of Leiophasmatinae (Figure 9.75d) can be generally recognized, at first glance, by its elongate smooth body, without wings, and very long antennae. The female abdominal sternum 8 (subgenital plate) clearly protrudes from the remaining abdomen. Specimens with cuticular spines on the body are rare, and these are then circumscribed at the head, appearing exceptionally on the pronotum. Such spines are restricted to the head and pronotum in the genus *Amphiphasma*, from medium-altitude moist evergreen forests, and the taxa of the western lowland dry deciduous forests and the Comoros. An overall similar morphological condition prompted Redtenbacher (1906) to place all the species he had at his disposal in one single genus, *Orobia* (replaced since by the genus *Leiophasma* for reasons of homonymy). Since then, the genera *Amphiphasma* and the Comorian *Adelophasma* have been described (Cliquennois 2008, 2018). The subgroups identified in the molecular phylogeny remain to be characterized morphologically; for example, the genus *Leiophasma* is polyphyletic, since the genera *Adelophasma* and *Amphiphasma* are found nested within the former. More details on these relationships and associated morphological features will be presented in future publications. The egg of Leiophasmatinae is very characteristic in that it possesses a double crest at the posterior pole, which outlines the contours of what Sellick (1998) called a pseudoplate. Leiophasmatinae is the phasmid group with the widest distribution on Madagascar, since it is found in the moist evergreen forests from Montagne d'Ambre to the region of Tolagnaro as well as in the western dry decidious forests, but not in the southern dry spiny thicket. Furthermore, Leiophasmatinae dispersed to the Comoros, where it has diversified into a number of species yet to be determined, including the astonishing *Adelophasma anjouanense* Cliquennois, 2018.

Xerantherinae

Xerantherinae can be easily recognized by its camouflage coloration and morphology that make it resemble a dead branch. The body is gray or brown, sometimes with whitish spots and with many large granules or short blunt spines, found mostly on the pronotum and, more scattered, on the mesonotum. They generally have a bulging head with protruding eyes and moderately long antennae and short legs with enlarged anterior femora; they are devoid of forewings (except *Archantherix*) and hind wings, or have short or tiny wings. Sexual dimorphism is considerable, with rather massive females and much thinner males (Figure 9.75e). A very distinctive autapomorphic character is the shape of the metasternum (and often of the abdominal sterna 2 and 3), which is compressed laterally and provided with a median keel. This characteristic feature is linked to the diurnal resting position of species of Xerantherinae, which fold their middle and hind legs and huddle them against the body. This subfamily includes four described genera: *Archantherix*, *Cenantherix*, *Parorobia*, and *Xerantherix*. Each of these genera is known only from the type species, with the exception of *Xerantherix*, which includes four described species. *Archantherix* and *Cenantherix* have been described to contain morphologically highly distinct females with massive body forms and developed tegmina in *Archantherix*, and a rather slender and smooth body with abdominal tergum 8 strongly elongate in *Cenantherix*. The two other genera remain poorly characterized, and at best can be distinguished based on two character states: *Parorobia* species are wingless and have a flattened head, and *Xerantherix* species have short or tiny hind wings and a bulging head.

The Xerantherinae clade reveals three subclades, as currently sampled for molecular analyses (S. Bradler, unpublished data), which are missing certain taxa, for example, *Parorobia*, *Archantherix*, and *Cenantherix*. The first subclade includes species of the dry deciduous and moist semi-deciduous forests of the north (Forêt d'Ambre, Sakaramy, and Ankarana) that form the sister group to the remaining Xerantherinae. The second subclade contains species attributed to *Xerantherix*, including *X. nossibianus*, the type species of the genus. The third subclade represents a group of undescribed taxa with a very characteristic morphology, including long spines on the head and pronotum, males with white microwings, and females with a plump abdomen that resembles that of Anisacanthinae. These taxa are distributed in the central portion of the island from south of Ambositra to Andringitra, at elevations from about 1000 to 2000 m.

The eggs of Xerantherinae are ovoid and often slightly flattened, which gives them a lenticular shape, with a crest at the posterior pole and lacking any capitular structure on the operculum.

FUTURE DIRECTIONS

Efforts to reveal the diversity and evolution of Malagasy phasmids have just begun and have already led to some astounding findings, such as their geologically recent single colonization event and subsequent radiation. From the scientific side, the island's phasmids are very poorly known and merit more detailed field and laboratory studies, particularly with respect to their taxonomy and morphology, as well as genetic studies examining their phylogenetic and phylogeography patterns. New information from these studies will help to advance the description of what remains a largely unknown element of Madagascar's biodiversity.

Subject editors: Brian L. Fisher and Steven M. Goodman

REFERENCES

Aanen, D. K., and Eggleton, P. 2005. Fungus-growing termites originated in African rain forest. *Current Biology* 15(9): 851–855.

Aarvik, L. 2004. Revision of the subtribe Neopotamiae (Lepidoptera: Tortricidae) in Africa. *Norwegian Journal of Entomology* 51: 71–155.

———. 2005. Revision of African *Cryptaspasma* Walsingham, 1900 (Lepidoptera, Tortricidae). *Norwegian Journal of Entomology* 51: 193–201.

Abellán, P., Millán, A., and Ribera, I. 2009. Parallel habitat-driven differences in the phylogeographical structure of two independent lineages of Mediterranean saline water beetles. *Molecular Ecology* 18: 3885–3902.

Abonnenc, E. 1969. Sur *Phlebotomus squamipleuris* Newstead, 1912 et espèces voisines (Diptera: Psychodidae). *Cahiers de l'ORSTOM*, série *Entomologie Médicale et Parasitologie* 7(4): 307–323.

Abraham, J. P., Benja, R., Randrianasolo, M., Ganzhorn, J. U., Jeannoda, V., and Leigh, E. G. 1996. Tree diversity on small plots in Madagascar: A preliminary review. *Revue d'Ecologie (Terre et Vie)* 51: 93–116.

Abrams, J. F., Hörig, L. A., Brozovic, R., Axtner, J., Crampton-Platt, A., Mohamed, A., Wong, S. T., Sollmann, R., Yu, D. W., and Wilting, A. 2019. Shifting up a gear with iDNA: From mammal detection events to standardised surveys. *Journal of Applied Ecology* 56: 1637–1648.

Abrol, D. P. 2012. *Pollination Biology: Biodiversity Conservation and Agricultural Production*. Dordrecht: Springer.

Ackerman, M[onsieur]. 1841. Note sur le coua, *Famac-acora* des Malgaches, hache-escargot (Traduction littérale) ou casseur d'escargots. *Revue de Zoologie* 4: 209–10.

Ade, M. 1996. Examination of the digestive tract contents of *Tenrec ecaudatus* Schreber 1777 (Tenrecidae, Insectivore) from western Madagascar. In *Ecology and Economy of a Tropical Dry Forest in Madagascar*, eds. J. U. Ganzhorn and J.-P. Sorg. *Primate Report* 46–1: 233–249.

Adlassnig, W., Peroutka, M., and Lendl, T. 2010. Traps of carnivorous pitcher plants as a habitat: Composition of the fluid, biodiversity and mutualistic activities. *Annals of Botany* 107: 181–194.

Aduse-Poku, K., Vingerhoedt, E., and Wahlberg, N. 2009. Out-of-Africa again: A phylogenetic hypothesis of the genus *Charaxes* (Lepidoptera: Nymphalidae) based on five gene regions. *Molecular Phylogenetics and Evolution* 53: 463–478.

Aduse-Poku, K., Lees, D. C., Brattström, O., Kodandaramaiah, U., Collins, S. C., Wahlberg, N., and Brakefield, P. M. 2016. Molecular phylogeny and generic-level taxonomy of the widespread palaeotropical "*Heteropsis* clade" (Nymphalidae: Satyrinae: Mycalesina). *Systematic Entomology* 41: 717–731.

Agassiz, D.J.L. 2019. The Yponomeutidae of the Afrotropical region (Lepidoptera: Yponomeutoidea). *Zootaxa* 4600: 1–69.

Agnarsson, I. 2004. Morphological phylogeny of cobweb spiders and their relatives (Araneae, Araneoidea, Theridiidae). *Zoological Journal of the Linnean Society* 141(4): 447–626. doi:10.1111/j.1096-3642.2004.00120.x.

Agnarsson, I., and Kuntner, M. 2005. Madagascar: An unexpected hotspot of social *Anelosimus* spider diversity (Araneae: Theridiidae). *Systematic Entomology* 30: 575–592.

———. 2012. The generation of a biodiversity hotspot: Biogeography and phylogeography of the western Indian Ocean islands. In *Current Topics in Phylogenetics and Phylogeography of Terrestrial and Aquatic Systems*, ed. K. Anamthawat-Jónsson, pp. 33–82. Rijeka: InTech.

Agnarsson, I., Jencik, B. B., Veve, G. M., Hanitriniaina, S., Agostini, D., Goh, S. P., Pruitt, J., and Kuntner, M. 2015. Systematics of the Madagascar *Anelosimus* spiders: Remarkable local richness and endemism, and dual colonization from the Americas. *ZooKeys* 509: 13–52. doi:10.3897/zookeys.509.8897.

Aguesse, P. 1967. Nouveaux *Protolestes* Förster, 1899 de Madagascar (Odonata; Zygoptera). *Deutsche Entomologische Zeitschrift*, neue folge, 14: 277–284.

———. 1968. Zygoptères inédits de Madagascar [Odon.]. *Annales de la Société Entomologique de France*, nouvelle série, 4: 649–670.

Akers, A., Peters, W. L., and Peters, J. G. 2003. *Radima edmundsorum*, a new genus and species of Atalophlebiinae from Madagascar (Ephemeroptera: Leptophlebiidae). In *Research Update on Ephemeroptera and Plecoptera*, ed. E. Gaino, pp. 85–89. Perugia: University of Perugia.

Alicata, J. E. 1965. Occurrence of *Angiostrongylus cantonensis* in Madagascar, Mauritius, Ceylon and Sarawak. *Journal of Parasitology* 51(6): 937.

Allegrucci, G., and Sbordoni, V. 2019. Insights into the molecular phylogeny of Rhaphidophoridae, an ancient, worldwide lineage of Orthoptera. *Molecular Phylogenetics and Evolution* 138: 126–138.

Allen, R. K. 1973. New Ephemerellidae from Madagascar and Afghanistan. *Pan-Pacific Entomologist* 49(2): 160–164.

Allnutt, T. F., Ferrier, S., Manion, G., Powell, G.V.N., Ricketts, T. H., et al. 2008. A method for quantifying biodiversity loss and its application to a 50-year record of deforestation across Madagascar. *Conservation Letters* 1: 173–181.

Alluaud, C. 1900. Liste des insectes coléoptères de la région malgache. In *Histoire physique, naturelle et politique de Madagascar*. Vol. 21, *Histoire naturelle des Coléoptères*. Tome 1, text, pt. 1, ed. A. Grandidier, pp. 56–76. Paris: Imprimerie Nationale.

Almeida, R. P., Blua, M. J., Lopes, J. R., and Purcell, A. H. 2005. Vector transmission of *Xylella fastidiosa*: Applying fundamental knowledge to generate disease management strategies. *Annals of the Entomological Society of America* 98: 775–786.

Alonso-Zarazaga, M. A., and Lyal, C.H.C. 1999. *A World Catalogue of Families and Genera of Curculionoidea (Insecta: Coleoptera) (excepting Scolytidae and Platypodidae)*. Barcelona: Entomopraxis S.C.P.

Alpert, G. D. 2007. A review of the ant genus *Metapone* Forel from Madagascar. *Memoirs of the American Entomological Institute* 80: 8–18.

Alvarez-Padilla, F., Ubick, D., and Griswold, C. E. 2012. *Noideattella* and *Tolegnaro*, two new genera of goblin spiders from Madagascar, with comments on the gamasomorphoid and silhouettelloid oonopids (Araneae, Oonopidae). *American Museum Novitates* 3745: 1–76. doi:10.1206/3745.2.

———. 2015. Indian Ocean goblin spiders (Araneae, Oonopidae): Four new species of pelicinoids from Madagascar, with a redescription of the type species *Silhouettella curieusei* Benoit, 1979. *American Museum Novitates* 3835: 1–31. doi:10.1206/3835.1.

Ambrozio-Assis, A., Cortês Lopes, B., Amaral, A. P., Pinho, L. C., Peeters, E.T.H.M., and Neckel-Oliveira, S. 2018. Preferences for anuran calls in hematophagous corethrellids (Diptera: Corethrellidae) from southern Brazil. *Austral Entomology* 58: 622–628.

Amevigbe, M.D.D., Ferrer, A., Champorie, S., Monteny, N., Deunff, J., and Richard-Lenoble, D. 2000. Isoenzymes of human lice: *Pediculus humanus* and *P. capitis*. *Medical and Veterinary Entomology* 14: 419–425.

Andersen, A., Ludwig, J., Lowe, L., and Rentz, D. 2001. Grasshopper biodiversity and bioindicators in Australian tropical savannas: Responses to disturbance in Kakadu National Park. *Austral Ecology* 26: 213–222.

Anderson, R. C. 2009. Do dragonflies migrate across the western Indian Ocean? *Journal of Tropical Ecology* 25: 347–358.

Andriamalala, D. 2007. Revision of the genus *Padilla* Peckham and Peckham, 1894 (Araneae: Salticidae). Convergent evolution of secondary sexual characters due to sexual selection and rates of molecular evolution in jumping spiders. *Proceedings of the California Academy of Sciences* 58: 243–330.

———. 2014. Higher level systematics and evolution of the spider family Oonopidae (Araneae) and the genus *Opopaea* in Madagascar. PhD thesis, George Washington University. https://scholarspace.library.gwu.edu/etd/z890rt48c.

Andriamalala, D., and Hormiga, G. 2013. Systematics of the goblin spider genus *Opopaea* (Araneae, Oonopidae) in Madagascar. *Bulletin of the American Museum of Natural History* 380: 1–156. doi:10.1206/828.1.

Andriamampianina, L. 1995. Contribution à l'étude de la répartition et de la structure des peuplements des insectes Scarabeidae (Coléoptères) de la presqu'île de Masoala. Mémoire de DEA, Sciences Biologiques Appliquées, Université d'Antananarivo.

———. 1996. Biogeography of enariine (Melolonthidae) and cicindelid beetles in Madagascar. MS thesis, University of Kent, Canterbury.

———. 2003. Scarabaeidae: Melolonthinae: Tribe Enariini, scarab beetles. In *The Natural History of Madagascar*, eds. S. M. Goodman and J. P. Benstead, pp. 677–686. Chicago: University of Chicago Press.

Andriamampianina, L., Kremen, C., Vane Wright, R., Lees, D. C., and Razafimahatratra, V. 2001. Taxic richness patterns and conservation evaluation of Madagascan tiger beetles (Coleoptera: Cicindelidae). *Journal of Insect Conservation* 4: 109–128.

Andrianaivoarivelo, R. A., Andriafidison, D., Rahaingonirina, C., Raharimbola, S., Rakotoarivelo, A. A., Ramilijaona, O. R., Racey, P. A., and Jenkins, R.K.B. 2011. A conservation assessment of *Rousettus madagascariensis* (G. Grandidier, 1928, Pteropodidae) roosts in eastern Madagascar. *Madagascar Conservation and Development* 6: 78–82.

Andrianaivolambo, L., Domarle, O., Randrianarivelojosia, M., Ratovonjato, J., Le Goff, G., Talman, A., Ariey, F., and Robert, V. 2010. Anthropophilic mosquitoes and malaria transmission in the eastern foothills of the central highlands of Madagascar. *Acta Tropica* 116(3): 240–245. doi:10.1016/j.actatropica.2010.08.017.

Andrianasolo Ravoavy, J. 1972. Evolution des populations de *Gastrimargus africanus* (Sauss.) et *Cyrtacanthacris tatarica tatarica* (Linn.) sur le plateau de Betioky (Madagascar). *Annales de Zoologie et Ecologie Animale* 72–5: 159–188.

Andriantsoa, R., Jones, J.P.G., Achimescu, V., Randrianarison, H., Raselimanana, M., Andriatsitohaina, M., Rasamy, J., and Lyko, F. 2020. Perceived socio-economic impacts of the marbled crayfish invasion in Madagascar *PLoS One* 15(4): e0231773.

Anikin, V. V. 2019. A new species of the genus *Casignetella* (Lepidoptera: Coleophoridae) from Madagascar. *Zoosystematica Rossica* 28: 116–119.

Anonymous. 1901. *Voyage du général Gallieni: Cinq mois autour de Madagascar, progrès de l'agriculture, développement commercial, ressources industrielles, moyens de colonisation*. Paris: Hachette.

AntCat. 2020. An online catalog of the ants of the world. Accessed 18 Mar. 2020. https://antcat.org.

Apanaskevich, D. A., Soarimalala, V., and Goodman, S. M. 2013. A new *Ixodes* species (Acari: Ixodidae), parasite of shrew tenrecs (Afrosoricida: Tenrecidae) in Madagascar. *Journal of Parasitology* 99: 970–972.

Armbruster, W. S., and Baldwin, B. [G.] 1998. Switch from specialized to generalized pollination. *Nature* 394: 632.

———. 2003. Pollination and evolution of euphorb vines in Madagascar. In *The Natural History of Madagascar*, eds. S. M. Goodman and J. P. Benstead, pp. 391–393. Chicago: University of Chicago Press.

Armbruster, W. S., Lee, J., Edwards, M. E., and Baldwin, B. G. 2012. Floral paedomorphy leads to secondary specialization in pollination of Madagascar *Dalechampia* (Euphorbiaceae). *Evolution* 67: 1196–1203.

Attems, C. 1910. Myriopoden von Madagascar, den Comoren und den Inseln Ostafrikas. In *Reise in Ostafrika, Wissenschaftliche Ergebnisse*, ed. A. Voeltzkow, pp. 73–115. Stuttgart: E. Schweizerbartsche Verlagsbuchhandlung.

———. 1951. Myriapodes d'Afrique, de Madagascar et de La Réunion récoltés par le Pr. Paul Remy. *Mémoires de l'Institut Scientifique de Madagascar*, série A, 5: 173–186.

Aubé, C. 1838. *Species général des hydrocanthares et gyriniens; Pour faire suite au species général des coléoptères de la collection de M. le comte Dejean*. Paris: Méquignon Père et Fils.

Audinet-Serville, J. G. 1838 [1839]. *Histoire naturelle des insectes. Orthoptères*. Paris: Librairie encyclopédique de Roret.

Ayala, D., Le Goff, G. L., Robert, V., de Jong, P., and Takken, W. 2006. Population structure of the malaria vector *Anopheles funestus* (Diptera: Culicidae) in Madagascar and Comoros. *Acta Tropica* 97(3): 292–300.

Azarkina, G. 2009. Two new species of the genus *Aelurillus* Simon, 1885 (Araneae, Salticidae) from Africa. *Journal of Afrotropical Zoology* 5: 171–177.

Baca, S. M., Alexander, A., Gustafson, G. T., and Short, A.E.Z. 2017a. Ultraconserved elements show utility in phylogenetic inference of Adephaga (Coleoptera) and suggest paraphyly of "Hydradephaga." *Systematic Entomology* 42: 786–795.

Baca, S. M., Toussaint, E.F.A., Miller, K. B., and Short, A.E.Z. 2017b. Molecular phylogeny of the aquatic beetle family Noteridae (Coleoptera: Adephaga) with an emphasis on data partitioning strategies. *Molecular Phylogenetics and Evolution* 107: 282–292.

Backus, E. A. 1988. Sensory systems and behaviours which mediate hemipteran plant-feeding: A taxonomic overview. *Journal of Insect Physiology* 34: 151–165.

Bakowski, M., Bartsch, D., and Kallies, A. 2008. A review of the Similipepsini of the Afrotropical Region (Lepidoptera: Sesiidae: Tinthiini). *Annales Zoologici* 58: 785–797.

Baldizzone, G., van der Wolf, H. W., and Landry J.-F. 2006. *World Catalogue of Insects*. Vol. 8, *Coleophoridae, Coleophorinae (Lepidoptera)*, ed. B. Landry, pp. 1–215. Stenstrup: Apollo Books.

Balfour-Browne, F. 1950. *British Water Beetles*. London: Ray Society.

Balke, M., and Hendrich, L. 2016. Dytiscidae. In *Handbook of Zoology*. Vol. 4, *Arthropoda: Insecta*, pt. 38, *Coleoptera, Beetles*, vol. 1, *Morphology and Systematics (Archostemata, Adephaga, Myxophaga, Polyphaga partim)*, 2nd ed., eds. R. G. Beutel and R. B. Leschen, pp. 118–140. Berlin: Walter de Gruyter.

Bameul, F. 1984. Haliplidae, Noteridae, Dytiscidae et Gyrinidae capturés dans les Îles Mascareignes et à Madagascar par Yves Gomy (Coleoptera, Hydradephaga). *Nouvelle Revue d'Entomologie*, nouvelle série, 1: 87–103.

———. 1994. Un nouvel *Hydrocanthus* Say de Madagascar (Coleoptera Noteridae). *Bulletin Mensuel de la Société Linnéenne de Lyon* 63: 356–365.

Bănărescu, P. 1991. *Zoogeography of Fresh Waters*. Vol. 3, *Distribution and Dispersal of Freshwater Animals in Africa, Pacific Areas and South America*. Wiesbaden: Aula Verlag.

Baranov, V. A., Kvifte, G. M., and Perkovsky, E. E. 2016. Two new species of fossil *Corethrella* Coquillett from Late Eocene Rovno amber, with a species-level phylogeny for the family based on morphological traits (Diptera: Corethrellidae). *Systematic Entomology* 41: 531–540. doi:10.1111/syen.12172.

Barber-James, H. M. 2010. Neotype erection, redescription of the larva and first description of the winged stages of *Prosopistoma variegatum* Latreille, 1833 (Insecta: Ephemeroptera) from Madagascar. *Aquatic Insects* 32: 215–243.

Barnard, K. H. 1934. South African caddisflies (Trichoptera). *Transactions of the Royal Society of South Africa* 21(4): 291–394.

Barraclough, D. A. 1984. Review of some Afrotropical Acroceridae: With descriptions of eight new species from South Africa (Diptera: Brachycera). *Journal of the Entomological Society of South Africa* 47: 45–66.

———. 1985. Revision of *Stenopialea* Speiser, 1920 (Diptera: Acroceridae: Panopinae). *Journal of the Entomological Society of South Africa* 48: 169–177.

———. 1991a. First record of the family Acroceridae (Diptera) from an oceanic island. *Journal of the Entomological Society of South Africa* 54(1): 88.

———. 1991b. A review of the genus *Astomella* Lamark in southern Africa, with descriptions of two new species (Diptera: Acroceridae: Panopinae). *Journal of the Entomological Society of South Africa* 54(2): 163–172.

Bartlett, C. R., O'Brien, L. B., and Wilson, S. W. 2014. A review of the planthoppers (Hemiptera: Fulgoroidea) of the United States. *Memoirs of the American Entomological Society* 50: 1–287.

Bartlett, C. R., Dietz, L. L., Dmitriev, D. A., Sanborn, A. F., Soulier-Perkins, A., and Wallace, M. S. 2018. The diversity of the true hoppers (Hemiptera: Auchenorrhyncha). In *Insect Biodiversity: Science and Society*, vol. 2, eds. R. G. Foottit, and P. H. Adler, pp. 501–590. Chichester: Wiley Blackwell.

Bartsch, D. 2009. *Melittosesia*, a new genus of clearwing moths with a review of the Sesiinae Boisduval, 1828 in Madagascar (Lepidoptera: Sesiidae). *Entomologische Zeitschrift* 119: 9–16.

———. 2018. Taxonomic changes in Synanthedonini from Madagascar, with description of two new genera and species (Lepidoptera: Sesiidae). *Zootaxa* 4433: 174–186.

Bartsch, D., and Berg, J. 2012. New species and review of the Afrotropical clearwing moth genus *Camaegeria* Strand, 1914 (Lepidoptera: Sesiidae: Synanthedonini). *Zootaxa* 3181: 28–46.

Basquin, P. 2013. Contribution à la connaissance du complexe de *Maltagorea rostaingi* (Griveaud, 1961) à Madagascar (Lepidoptera, Saturniidae). *Saturnafrica* 15: 19–25.

———. 2017. Deux nouvelles espèces de Lasiocampides de Madagascar (Lepidoptera, Lasiocampidae). *Saturnafrica* 25: 5–10.

Basquin, P., and Rougerie, R. 2009. Contribution à la connaissance du genre *Maltagorea* Bouyer, 1993: Description d'une nouvelle espèce révélée par la combinaison de caractères morphologiques et de codes barres ADN (Lepidoptera, Saturniidae). *Bulletin de la Société Entomologique de France* 114: 257–263.

Baum, D. A. 1995. The comparative pollination and floral biology of baobabs (*Adansonia*-Bombacaceae). *Annals of the Missouri Botanical Garden* 82: 322–348.

———. 1996. The ecology and conservation of the baobabs of Madagascar. In *Ecology and Economy of a Tropical Dry Forest in Madagascar*, eds. J. U. Ganzhorn and J.-P. Sorg. *Primate Report* 46–1: 311–327.

Bayless, K. M. 2012. Evolutionary studies in Tabanomorpha (Diptera) with new classifications of Xylophagidae and Tabaninae. MS thesis, North Carolina State University.

Bazelet, C., and Samways, M. 2011. Identifying grasshopper bioindicators for habitat quality assessment of ecological networks. *Ecological Indicators* 11: 1259–1269.

Beattie, A. J. 1985. *The Evolutionary Ecology of Ant–Plant Mutualisms*. Cambridge: Cambridge University Press.

Beattie, A. J., and Hughes, L. 2002. Ant-plant interactions. In *Plant–Animal Interactions*, eds. C. M. Herrera and O. Pellmyr, pp. 211–235. Malden: Blackwell.

Beaucournu, J.-C. 1974. *Ctenocephalides brygooi* n. sp. (Siphonaptera, Pulicidae), parasite du viverridé endémique malgache *Fossa fossana* (Muller). *Bulletin de la Société de Pathologie Exotique et de ses Filiales* 67: 435–443.

———. 1981. Les Siphonaptères et leurs hôtes: Rapports phylétiques, convergences et déviations. *Mémoires du Muséum National d'Histoire Naturelle*, Paris, 123: 203–208.

Beaucournu, J.-C., and Fain, A. 1983. Notes sur les Ischnopsyllinae du Continent Africain (Siphonaptera). *Revue Zoologie Africaine* 97: 453–468.

Beaucournu, J.-C., and Fontenille, D. 1993. Contribution à un catalogue des puces de Madagascar (Insecta, Siphonaptera). *Archives de l'Institut Pasteur de Madagascar*, edition spéciale: 1–48.

Beaucournu, J.-C., and Goodman, S. M. 2014. Une nouvelle espèce de Puce du genre *Paractenopsyllus*, endémique de Madagascar (Siphonaptera, Ceratophyllidae, Leptopsyllinae). *Bulletin de la Société Entomologique de France* 119(4): 427–431.

Beaucournu, J.-C., and Houin, R. 1967. A propos de la présence á Madagascar de *Polyplax reclinata* (Nitzsch, 1864) sensu Johnson, 1960 (Insecta, Anoplura), parasite des musaraignes. *Archives de l'Institut Pasteur de Madagascar* 36: 67.

Beaucournu, J.-C., and Laudisoit, A. 2014. Une nouvelle espèce malgache de Puce du genre *Tsaractenus* (Siphonaptera, Ceratophyllidae, Leptopsyllinae). *Bulletin de la Société Entomologique de France* 119(3): 299–305.

Beaucournu, J.-C., Prié, V., Ramasindrazana, B., Goodman, S. M., and Laudisoit, A. 2015. Les puces de chauve-souris à Madagascar: Nouvelles données et clé d'identification illustrée actualisée (Siphonaptera, Ischnopsyllidae). *Bulletin de la Société Entomologique de France* 120(3): 323–334.

Beccaloni, G., Scoble, M., Kitching, I., Simonsen, T., Robinson, G., Pitkin, B., Hine, A., and Lyal, C., eds. 2003. The global Lepidoptera names index (LepIndex). World Wide Web electronic publication. Accessed Dec. 2019–Mar. 2020. https://www.nhm.ac.uk/our-science/data/lepindex/search/.

Beebe, N. W. 2018. DNA barcoding mosquitoes: Advice for potential prospectors. *Parasitology* 145(5): 622–633. doi:10.1017/S0031182018000343.

Bellinger, P. F., Christiansen, K. A., and Janssens, F. 2020. Checklist of the Collembola of the World. Accessed 3 Mar. 2020. http://www.collembola.org.

Benavides, L. R., Giribet, G., and Hormiga, G. 2017. Molecular phylogenetic analysis of "pirate spiders" (Araneae, Mimetidae) with the description of a new African genus and the first report of maternal care in the family. *Cladistics* 33(4): 375–405. doi:10.1111/cla.12174.

Bendib, A., and Minet, J. 1998. Female pheromone glands in Arctiidae (Lepidoptera): Evolution and phylogenetic significance. *Comptes Rendus de l'Académie des Sciences*, Paris, série 3, 321: 1007–1014.

———. 2000 (1999). Lithosiine main lineages and their possible interrelationships. I. Definition of new or resurrected tribes (Lepidoptera: Arctiidae). *Annales de la Société Entomologique de France*, nouvelle série, 35: 241–263.

Ben-Dov, Y., and Fisher, B. L. 2010. The mutualism of *Melissotarsus* ants and armoured scale insects in Africa and Madagascar: Distribution, host plants and biology. *Entomologia Hellenica* 19: 45–53.

Bengtsson, B. A. 2014. The Afrotropical Scythrididae. *Esperiana, Memoir* 7: 1–365.

Benjamin, S. P. 2004. Taxonomic revision and phylogenetic hypothesis for the jumping spider subfamily Ballinae (Araneae, Salticidae). *Zoological Journal of the Linnean Society* 142: 1–82.

Benstead, J. P., and Pringle, C. M. 2004. Deforestation alters the resource base and biomass of endemic stream insects in eastern Madagascar. *Freshwater Biology* 49: 490–501.

Benstead, J. P., de Rham, P. H., Gattolliat, J.-L., Gibon, F.-M., Loiselle, P. V., Sartori, M., Sparks, J. S., and Stiassny, M.L.J. 2003a. Conserving Madagascar's freshwater biodiversity. *BioScience* 53: 1101–1111.

Benstead, J. P., Douglas, M. M., and Pringle, C. M. 2003b. Relationships of stream invertebrate communities to deforestation in eastern Madagascar. *Ecological Applications* 13: 1473–1490.

Berghe, L.V.d., Lambrecht, F. L., and Christiaensen, A. R. 1956. Etude biologique et écologique des glossines dans la région du Mutara (Ruanda). *Académie Royale des Sciences Coloniales* 8(4): 1–101.

Berio, E. 1956. Contribution à l'étude des Noctuidae de Madagascar. *Mémoires de l'Institut Scientifique de Madagascar* (E) 6: 109–140.

Bernal, X. E., and Pinto, C. M. 2016. Sexual differences in prevalence of a new species of trypanosome infecting túngara frogs. *International Journal for Parasitology: Parasites and Wildlife* 5: 40–47.

Bertrand, H. 1928a. Les larves et nymphes des Dytiscides, Hygrobiides, Haliplides. *Encyclopédie Entomologique,* série A, 10: 1–366.

———. 1928b. Description sommaire de quelques larves de Dytiscides de Madagascar. *Faune des Colonies Française* 2: 361–381.

———. 1949. La larve des *Eretes* Cast. (Col. Dytiscidae). *Mémoires Institute Scientifique de Madagascar,* série A, 3: 330–340.

———. 1963. Contribution à l'étude des premiers états des Coléoptères aquatiques de la région Ethiopienne (5e note). Familles: Haliplidae, Dytiscidae, Gyrinidae (Hydrocanthares). *Bulletin de l'Institut Française d'Afrique Noire,* série A, 25: 389–466.

———. 1965. Contribution à l'étude des premiers états des Coléoptères aquatiques de la région éthiopienne (7e note). Familles diverses. Addenda et corrigenda. *Bulletin de l'Institut Française d'Afrique Noire*, série A, 27: 1336–1393.

———. 1968. Récolte de larves de Coléoptères aquatiques dans la région Ethiopienne: Madagascar (1960). *Bulletin du Muséum National d'Histoire Naturelle*, Paris, série 2, 40: 718–733.

———. 1971. Larves de Coléoptères aquatiques de Madagascar centre O.R.S.T.O.M. et mission Starmuhlner, 1958. *Cahiers de l'ORSTOM*, série *Hydrobiologie* 5: 251–261.

Bertrand, H., and Legros, C. 1971. Hydrocanthares (excl. Gyrinidae) recueillis à Madagascar (Mission Bertrand, 1960). *Cahiers de l'ORSTOM*, série *Hydrobiologie* 5: 241–249.

Béthoux, O., and Nel, A. 2002. Venation pattern and revision of Orthoptera sensu nov. and sister groups. Phylogeny of Palaeozoic and Mesozoic Orthoptera sensu nov. *Zootaxa* 96: 1–88.

Béthoux, O., Nel, A., Lapeyrie, J., Gand, G., and Galtier, J. 2002. *Raphogla rubra* gen. n., sp. n., the oldest representative of the clade of modern Ensifera (Orthoptera: Tettigoniidea, Gryllidea). *European Journal of Entomology* 99(1): 111–116.

Betsch, J.-M. 1970. Etude des Collemboles de Madagascar. I. Description d'un nouveau genre de Symphypléones: *Zebulonia*. *Revue d'Ecologie et de Biologie du Sol* 7: 51–70.

———. 1974a. Contribution à l'étude de la reproduction chez les Bourletiellinae (Collembola Symphypléones). *Pedobiologia* 14: 179–181.

———. 1974b. Etude des Collemboles de Madagascar. II. Principaux cadres génériques des Symphypléones de l'étage montagnard. *Bulletin du Muséum National d'Histoire Naturelle*, Paris, série 3, *Zoologie*, 147: 529–569.

———. 1974c. Etude des Collemboles de Madagascar. III. Un nouveau genre de Bourletiellidae (Symphypleona): *Massoudia griveaudi* n. g., n. sp. *Revue d'Écologie et de Biologie du Sol* 11(4): 561–567.

———. 1975. Etude des Collemboles de Madagascar. IV. Deux nouveaux genres de Symphypléones à dimorphisme sexuel important: *Parabourletiella* et *Richardsitas*. *Revue d'Ecologie et de Biologie du Sol* 12: 477–485.

———. 1977. Etude des Collemboles de Madagascar. V. Sur deux Symphypléones de la forêt sèche en secteur bioclimatique subaride. *Bulletin de la Société Entomologique de France* 82: 119–125.

———. 1980. Eléments pour une monographie des Collemboles Symphypléones (Hexapodes, Aptérygotes). *Mémoires du Muséum National d'Histoire Naturelle*, Paris, A 116: 1–227.

———. 2000a. Types de spéciation chez quelques collemboles Symphypleones Sminthuridae (Aptérygotes) de Madagascar. In *Diversité et endemisme à Madagascar/Diversity and Endemism in Madagascar*, eds. W. R. Lourenço and S. M. Goodman, pp. 295–306. Paris: Mémoires de la Société de Biogéographie.

———. 2000b. Etude des Collemboles de Madagascar. VII. Huit espèces nouvelles de *Temeritas* (Symphypléones, Sminthuridae). *Bulletin de la Société Entomologique de France* 105: 325–336.

———. 2003. Collembola, springtails. In *The Natural History of Madagascar*, eds. S. M. Goodman and J. P. Benstead, pp. 627–638. Chicago: University of Chicago Press.

Betsch, J.-M., and Cassagnau, P. 1996. Origine, différenciation locale et endémisme de quelques groupes de microarthropodes du sol et de la litière à Madagascar. In *Biogéographie de Madagascar*, ed. W. R. Lourenço, pp. 535–558. Paris: Editions de l'ORSTOM.

Betsch, J.-M., and Massoud, Z. 1968. Documents complémentaires sur *Microfalcula delamarei* (Collemboles Microfalculinae) de Madagascar. *Annales de la Société Entomologique de France*, nouvelle série, 4: 901–910.

Betsch, J.-M., and Waller, A. 1996. Etude des Collemboles de Madagascar. VI. *Madecassiella*, un nouveau genre de Symphypléones de l'étage montagnard. *Bulletin de la Société Entomologique de France* 101: 413–418.

Beutel, R. G. 1999. Phylogenetic analysis of Myxophaga (Coleoptera) with a redescription of *Lepicerus horni* (Lepiceridae). *Zoologischer Anzeiger* 237: 291–308.

Beutel, R. G., and Haas, A. 1998. Larval head morphology of *Hydroscapha natans* LeConte, 1874 (Coleoptera, Myxophaga, Hydroscaphidae) with special reference to miniaturization. *Zoomorphology* 118: 103–116.

Beutel, R. G., and Ruhnau, S. 1990. Phylogenetic analysis of the genera of Haliplidae (Coleoptera) based on characters of adults. *Aquatic Insects* 12: 1–17.

Beutel, R. G., and Vanin, S. A. 2016. 6.2. Torridincolidae Steffan, 1964. In *Handbook of Zoology*. Vol. 4, *Arthropoda: Insecta*, pt. 38, *Coleoptera, Beetles*, vol. 1, *Morphology and Systematics (Archostemata, Adephaga, Myxophaga, Polyphaga partim)*, 2nd ed., eds. R. G. Beutel and R. B. Leschen, pp. 67–70. Berlin: Walter de Gruyter.

Beutel, R. G., Maddison, D. R., and Hass, A. 1999. Phylogenetic analysis of Myxophaga (Coleoptera) using larval characters. *Systematic Entomology* 24: 171–192.

Beutel, R. G., Balke, M, and Steiner, W. E., Jr. 2006. The systematic position of Meruidae (Coleoptera, Adephaga) and the phylogeny of the smaller aquatic adephagan beetle families. *Cladistics* 22: 102–131.

Beutel, R. G., Yan, E. V., Richter, A., Büsse, S., Miller, K. B., Yavorskaya, M., and Wipfler, B. 2017. The head of *Heterogyrus milloti* (Coleoptera: Gyrinidae) and its phylogenetic implications. *Arthropod Systematics and Phylogeny* 75: 261–280.

Beutel, R. G., Yan, E. V., Yavorskaya, M., Büsse, S., Gorb, S. N., and Wipfler, B. 2018. On the thoracic anatomy of the Madagascan *Heterogyrus milloti* and the phylogeny of Gyrinidae (Coleoptera). *Systematic Entomology* 44: 336–360.

Biedermann, R., Achtziger, R., Nickel, H., and Stewart, A.J.A. 2005. Conservation of grassland leafhoppers: A brief review. *Journal of Insect Conservation* 9: 229–243.

Bilardo, A., and Rocchi, S. 2012. A revision of the African species of the genus *Neptosternus* Sharp, 1882 (Coleoptera Dytiscidae). *Memorie della Società Italiana di Scienze Naturali e del Museo Civico di Storia Naturale di Milano* 37: 3–48.

———. 2014. *Africophilus jaechi* sp.n. from Madagascar (Coleoptera: Dytiscidae). *Koleopterologische Rundschau* 84: 41–44.

———. 2015. A revision and synopsis of the African species of the genus *Copelatus* Erichson, 1832. The group *erichsonii*, subgroup *atrosulcatus* (Coleoptera Dytiscidae). *Memorie della Società Italiana di Scienze Naturali e del Museo Civico di Storia Naturale di Milano* 15: 3–38.

———. 2017. A taxonomic review of the Afrotropical genus *Aethionectes* Sharp, 1882 (Coleoptera Dytiscidae). *Memorie della Società Italiana di Scienze Naturali e del Museo Civico di Storia Naturale di Milano* 42: 1–26.

Bilton, D. T. 2014. Dispersal in Dytiscidae. In *Ecology, Systematics and the Natural History of Predaceous Diving Beetles (Coleoptera: Dytiscidae)*, ed. D. A. Yee, pp. 387–407. Dordrecht: Springer.

Bilton, D. T., Toussaint, E.F.A., Turner, C. R., and Balke, M. 2015. *Capelatus prykei* gen. et sp.n. (Coleoptera: Dytiscidae: Copelatinae)—a phylogenetically isolated diving beetle from the Western Cape of South Africa. *Systematic Entomology* 40: 520–531.

Bippus, M. 2018. New Erebidae from the Mascarene Islands and about some Madagascar Lepidoptera (Lepidoptera: Erebidae). *Phelsuma* 26: 10–43.

———. 2019. New records of Gracillariidae (Lepidoptera) from the islands of Madagascar, Mauritius and Réunion. *Phelsuma* 27: 18–35.

Birkinshaw, C. R., and Colquhoun, I. C. 1998. Pollination of *Ravenala madagascariensis* and *Parkia madagascariensis* by *Eulemur macaco* in Madagascar. *Folia Primatologica* 69: 252–259.

Birula, A. 1903. Sur une nouvelle espèce de scorpions provenant de l'île Madagascar. *Annals Museum Saint Petersburg* 7(1): 10–11.

Biström, O. 1979. A revision of the genus *Derovatellus* Sharp (Coleoptera, Dytiscidae) in Africa. *Acta Entomologica Fennica* 35: 1–28.

———. 1982a. *Hovahydrus* n. gen. from Madagascar (Coleoptera: Dytiscidae). *Entomologica Scandinavica* 13: 430–434.

———. 1982b. A revision of the genus *Hyphydrus* Illiger (Coleoptera, Dytiscidae). *Acta Zoologica Fennica* 165: 1–121.

———. 1983. Revision of the genera *Yola* Des Gozis and *Yolina* Guignot (Coleoptera, Dytiscidae). *Acta Zoologica Fennica* 176: 1–67.

———. 1984. *Hyphydrus cuppeni* n. sp., with taxonomic notes on the genus in Africa (Coleoptera: Dytiscidae). *Entomologische Berichten* 44: 182–184.

———. 1985. A revision of the species group *B. sharpi* in the genus *Bidessus* (Coleoptera, Dytiscidae). *Acta Zoologica Fennica* 178: 1–40.

———. 1986. Review of the genus *Hydroglyphus* Motschulsky (= *Guignotus* Houlbert) in Africa (Coleoptera, Dytiscidae). *Acta Zoologica Fennica* 182: 1–56.

———. 1987. Revision of the genus *Pachynectes* Régimbart (Coleoptera, Dytiscidae). *Annales Entomologici Fennici* 53: 48–52.

———. 1988a. Revision of the genus *Clypeodytes* Régimbart in Africa (Coleoptera: Dytiscidae). *Entomologica Scandinavica* 19: 199–238.

———. 1988b. Review of the genus *Liodessus* in Africa (Coleoptera, Dytiscidae). *Annales Entomologici Fennici* 54: 21–28.

———. 1988c. Generic review of the Bidessini (Coleoptera, Dytiscidae). *Acta Zoologica Fennica* 184: 1–41.

———. 1988d. Review of the genus *Uvarus* Guignot in Africa (Coleoptera, Dytiscidae). *Acta Entomologica Fennica* 51: 1–38.

———. 1995. *Uvarus laurentius* sp. n. and *Africodytes maximus* sp. n. and new faunistic records of other Bidessini (Coleoptera, Dytiscidae) from the Ethiopian region. *Entomologica Fennica* 6: 43–46.

———. 1997. Taxonomic revision of the genus *Hydrovatus* Motschulsky (Coleoptera, Dytiscidae). *Entomologica Basiliensia* 19(1996): 57–584.

Biström, O., and Nilsson, A. N. 2002. *Herophydrus* Sharp: Cladistic analysis, taxonomic revision of the African species, and world check list (Coleoptera: Dytiscidae). *Koleopterologische Rundschau* 72: 15–111.

———. 2006. Taxonomic revision of the Ethiopian genus *Canthyporus* (Coleoptera Dytiscidae). *Memorie della Società Entomologica Italiana* 85: 209–306.

Biström, O., and Sanfilippo, N. 1986. *Bidessus apicidens* sp. n., and faunistic notes on the genus from Africa (Coleoptera, Dytiscidae). *Annales Entomologici Fennici* 52: 46–47.

Biström, O., Nilsson, A. N., and Bergsten, J. 2015. Taxonomic revision of Afrotropical *Laccophilus* Leach, 1815 (Coleoptera, Dytiscidae). *ZooKeys* 542: 1–379.

Blackburn, T. M., and Gaston, K. J. 1994. Animal body size distributions: Patterns, mechanisms and implications. *Trends in Ecology and Evolution* 9(12): 471–474.

Blagodatski, A., Kryuchkov, M., Sergeev, A., Klimov, A. A., Shcherbakov, M. R., Enin, G. A., and Katanaev, V. L. 2014. Under- and over-water halves of Gyrinidae beetle eyes harbor different corneal nanocoatings providing adaptation to the water and air environments. *Scientific Reports* 4: 6.

Blahnik, R. J. 1998. A revision of the Neotropical species of the genus *Chimarra*, subgenus *Chimarra* (Trichoptera: Philopotamidae). *Memoirs of the American Entomological Institute* 59:1–318.

Blaimer, B., and Fisher, B. L. 2013. Taxonomy of the *Crematogaster degeeri*-species-assemblage in the Malagasy region (Hymenoptera: Formicidae). *European Journal of Taxonomy* 51: 1–64.

Blanchard, E. 1840. Homoptères. In *Histoire naturelle des insects Orthoptères, Névroptères, Hémiptères, Hyménoptères, Lépidoptères et Diptères*, vol. 3, ed. E. Blanchard, pp. 171–178. Paris: P. Duménil.

———. 1851. Ordre des Coléoptères. In *Catalogue de la collection entomologique: Classe des Insectes*, Tome 1, eds. M. Milne-Edwards, E. Blanchard, and H. Lucas, pp. 129–240. Paris: Gide et Baudry.

Blanchard, R. 1917. Monographie des hémadipsines (sangsues terrestres). *Bulletin de la Société de Pathologie Exotique* 10: 640–675.

Blanco, M. B., Elfawal, M. A., Durden, L. A., Beati, L., Xu, G., Godfrey, L. R., and Rich, S. M. 2013. Genetic diversity of ixodid ticks parasitizing eastern mouse and dwarf lemurs in Madagascar, with description of the larva, nymph, and male of *Ixodes lemuris* (Acari: Ixodidae). *Journal of Parasitology* 99: 11–18.

Blavier, A., Laroche, L., Randrianambinintsoa, F. J., Lucas, V., Gantier, J.-C., Léger, N., Robert, V., and Depaquit, J. 2019. Phlebotomine sandflies (Diptera: Psychodidae) from the Ankarana tsingy of northern Madagascar: Inventory and description of new taxa. *Parasite* 26: 38. doi:10.1051/parasite/2019039.

Bleszynski, S. 1965. Crambinae. In *Microlepidoptera Palaearctica*, 1 (2 vols.), eds. H. G. Amsel, F. Gregor, and H. Reisser, pp. 1–553; plates 1–133. Vienna: Georg Fromme.

Bodin, O., Tengö, M., Norman, A., Lundberg, J., and Elmqvist, T. 2006. The value of small size: Loss of forest patches and ecological thresholds in southern Madagascar. *Ecological Applications* 16: 440–451.

Böhning-Gaese, K., Burkhardt, J. F., and Schmid, J. 1996. Seed dispersal in the tree *Commiphora guillaumini*: A combination of ornithochory and myrmechory in a dry tropical forest in western Madagascar. In *Ecology and Economy of a Tropical Dry Forest in Madagascar,* eds. J. U. Ganzhorn and J.-P. Sorg. *Primate Report* 46–1: 305–310.

Böhning-Gaese, K., Gaese, B. H., and Rabemanantsoa, S. B. 1999. Importance of primary and secondary seed dispersal in the Malagasy tree *Commiphora guillaumini*. *Ecology* 80: 821–832.

Boisduval, J.B.A. 1833. *Faune entomologique de Madagascar, Bourbon et Maurice: Lépidoptères; Avec des notes sur les moeurs, par M. Sganzin*. Paris: Librairie Encyclopédique de Roret.

BOLD. 2021. The Barcode of Life Data System. Accessed Nov. 2021. http://v4.boldsystems.org.

Bond, W., Silander, J., Ranaivonasy, J., and Ratsirarson, J. 2008. The antiquity of Madagascar's grasslands and the rise of C4 grassy biomes. *Journal of Biogeography* 35: 1743–1758.

Bonfils, J., Quilici, S., and Reynaud, B. 1994. Les Hémiptères Auchénorhynques de l'île de La Réunion. *Bulletin de la Société Entomologique de France* 99: 227–240.

Borda, E. 2006. A revision of the Malagabdellinae (Arhynchobdellida: Domanibdellidae), with a description of a new species, *Malagabdella niarchosorum*, from Ranomafana National Park, Madagascar. *American Museum Novitates* 3531: 1–13.

Borda, E., and Siddall, M. E. 2004. Review of the evolution of life history strategies and phylogeny of the Hirudinida (Annelida: Oligochaeta). *Lauterbornia* 52: 25.

———. 2011. Insights into the evolutionary history of Indo-Pacific bloodfeeding terrestrial leeches (Hirudinida: Arhynchobdellida: Haemadipisdae). *Invertebrate Systematics* 24: 456.

Borda, E., Oceguera-Figueroa, A., and Siddall, M. E. 2008. On the classification, evolution and biogeography of terrestrial haemadipsoid leeches (Hirudinida: Arhynchobdellida: Hirudiniformes). *Molecular Phylogenetics and Evolution* 46: 142–154.

Borkent, A. 2008. The frog-biting midges of the world (Corethrellidae: Diptera). *Zootaxa* 1804: 1–456.

———. 2012. The pupae of Culicomorpha: Morphology and a new phylogenetic tree. *Zootaxa* 3396: 1–98.

———. 2017. Corethrellidae (frog-biting midges). In *Manual of Afrotropical Diptera*. Vol. 2, *Nematocerous Diptera and Lower Brachycera*, eds. A. H. Kirk-Spriggs and B. J. Sinclair, pp. 665–670. Suricata 5. Pretoria: South African National Biodiversity Institute.

Borkent, A., and Grafe, T. U. 2012. The frog-biting midges of Borneo—from two to eleven species (Corethrellidae: Diptera). *Zootaxa* 3279: 1–45.

Börner, C. 1906. Das system der Collembolen nebst Beschreibung neuer Collembolen des Hamburger Naturhistorischen Museums. *Mitteilungen aus dem Naturhistorischen Museum in Hamburg* 23: 147–188.

———. 1907. Collembolen aus Ostafrika, Madagaskar und Südamerika. In *Reise in Ostafrika in den Jahren 1903–1905*, vol. 2, ed. A. Voeltzkow, pp. 147–178. Stuttgart: Schweizerbart Science.

Borror, D. J., Delong, D. M., and Triplehorn, C. A. 1976. *An Introduction to the Study of Insects*. 4th ed. New York: Holt, Rinehart and Winston.

Bosselaers, J., Dierick, M., Cnudde, V., Masschaele, B., van Hoorebeke, L., and Jacobs, P. 2010. High-resolution X-ray computer tomography of an extant new *Donuea* (Araneae: Liocranidae) species in Madagascan copal. *Zootaxa* 2427: 25–35.

Bosser, J. 1958. Sur deux nouvelles Lentibulariacées de Madagascar. *Naturaliste Malgache* 10: 21–23.

Botosaneanu, L. 2002. A classical case of insular radiation: The *Hydroptila* species of La Réunion. In *Proceedings of the 10th International Symposium on Trichoptera*, Potsdam, Germany, July 30–Aug. 5, ed. W. Mey, pp. 323–330. Keltern: Goecke and Evers.

Bott, R. 1965. Die Süßwasserkrabben von Madagaskar. *Bulletin du Muséum National d'Histoire Naturelle*, Paris, 37(2): 335–350.

Bouchet, D. C., Peeters, C., Fisher, B. L., and Molet, M. 2013. Both female castes contribute to colony emigration in the polygynous ant *Mystrium oberthueri*. *Ecological Entomology* 38: 408–417.

Boudinot, J. 1982. Insectes Lépidoptères Epiplemidae. *Faune de Madagascar* 60: 1–55.

Bourgogne, J. 1984. Insectes. Lépidoptères Psychidae Oiketicinae. *Faune de Madagascar* 63: 1–57.

Bourgoin, T. 2019. FLOW (Fulgoromorpha Lists on the Web): A World Knowledge Base Dedicated to Fulgoromorpha. Accessed 10 Nov. 2019. https://flow.hemiptera-databases.org/flow/.

———. 2020. FLOW (Fulgoromorpha Lists on the Web): A World Knowledge Base Dedicated to Fulgoromorpha. Version 8, updated 30 Mar. 2020. https://flow.hemiptera-databases.org/flow/.

Bourgoin, T., Wang, R. R., Asche, M., Hoch, H., Soulier-Perkins, A., Stroiński, A., Yap, S., and Szwedo, J. 2015. From micropterism to hyperpterism: Recognition strategy and standardized homology-driven terminology of the forewing venation patterns in planthoppers (Hemiptera: Fulgoromorpha). *Zoomorphology* 134: 63–77.

Bourgoin, T., Wang, R.-R., and Gnezdilov, V. M. 2016. First fossil record of Caliscelidae (Hemiptera: Fulgoroidea): A new Early Miocene Dominican amber genus extends the distribution of Augilini to the Neotropics. *Journal of Systematic Palaeontology* 14(3): 211–218. doi:10.1080/14772019.2015.1032376.

Bourguignon, T., Lo, N., Sobotnik, J., Sillam-Dusses, D., Roisin, Y., and Evans, T. 2016. Oceanic dispersal, vicariance and human introduction shaped the modern distribution of the termites *Reticulitermes*, *Heterotermes* and *Coptotermes*. *Proceedings of the Royal Society of London B: Biological Sciences* 283(1827). doi:10.1098/rspb.2016.0179.

Boussès, P., and Brunhes, J. 2013. Trois nouveaux *Uranotaenia* Lynch Arribálzaga de Madagascar (Diptera, Culicidae). *Bulletin de la Société Entomologique de France* 118: 399–410.

Boussès, P., Dehecq, J. S., Brengues, C., and Fontenille, D. 2013. Inventaire actualisé des moustiques (Diptera: Culicidae) de l'île de La Réunion, océan Indien. *Bulletin de la Société de Pathologie Exotique* 106(2): 113–125. doi:10.1007/s13149-013-0288-7.

Boussès, P., Le Goff, G., and Robert, V. 2018. Inventaire des moustiques (Diptera: Culicidae) des îles du sud-ouest de l'océan Indien, Madagascar excepté: Une revue critique. *Annales de la Société Entomologique de France*, nouvelle série, 54(2): 89–110. doi:10.1080/00379271.2018.1429951.

Bouvier, E.-L. 1904. Crevettes de la famile des Atyidés: Espèces qui font partie des collections du Muséum d'Histoire Naturelle. *Bulletin du Muséum d'Histoire Naturelle* 10: 129–138.

Bouyer, T. 2006. Nouveaux Saturniidae de Madagascar et de Tanzanie (Lepidoptera). *Entomologia Africana* 11: 12–18.

Boyer, S., Miarinjara, A., and Elissa, N. 2014. *Xenopsylla cheopis* (Siphonaptera: Pulicidae) susceptibility to Deltamethrin in Madagascar. *PLoS One* 9(11): e111998.

Boyko, C. B., Ravoahangimalala, O. R., Randriamasimanana, D., and Razafindrazaka, T. H. 2005. *Astacoides hobbsi*, a new crayfish (Crustacea: Decapoda: Parastacidae) from Madagascar. *Zootaxa* 1091: 51–51.

Bracken-Grissom, H. D., Ahyong, S. T., Wilkinson, R. D., Feldmann, R. M., Schweitzer, C. E., et al. 2014. The emergence of lobsters: Phylogenetic relationships, morphological evolution and divergence time comparisons of an ancient group (Decapoda: Achelata, Astacidea, Glypheidea, Polychelida). *Systematic Biology* 63: 457–479.

Bradler, S., and Buckley, T. R. 2018. Biodiversity of Phasmatodea. In *Insect Biodiversity: Science and Society*, vol. 2, eds. R. G. Foottit and P. H. Adler, pp. 281–313 Hoboken: Wiley-Blackwell.

Bradler, S., Cliquennois, N., and Buckley, T. R. 2015. Single origin of the Mascarene stick insects: Ancient radiation on sunken islands? *BMC Evolutionary Biology* 15: 196.

Bradley, J. C., and Galil, B. S. 1977. The taxonomic arrangements of the Phasmatodea with keys to the subfamilies and tribes. *Proceedings of the Entomological Society of Washington* 79(2): 176–208.

Brady, S. G., Fisher, B. L., Schultz, T. R., and Ward, P. S. 2014. The rise of army ants and their relatives: Diversification of specialized predatory doryline ants. *BMC Evolutionary Biology* 14(93): 14.

Branstetter, M. G., Longino, J. T., Reyes-López, J., Schultz, T. R., and Brady, S. G. 2016. Into the tropics: Phylogenomics and evolutionary dynamics of a contrarian clade of ants. *BioRxiv*. 39966. doi:10.1101/039966.

Braud, Y., Franc, A., and Gay, P. E. 2014. *Les acridiens des formations herbeuses de Madagascar*. Rome: FAO.

Breure, A.S.H., and Romero, P. E. 2012. Support and surprises: Molecular phylogeny of the land snail superfamily Orthalicoidea using a three-locus gene analysis with a divergence time analysis and ancestral area reconstruction. *Archiv für Molluskenkunde* 141(1): 1–20.

Briceño, R. D., and Eberhard, W. G. 2012. Spiders avoid sticking to their webs: Clever leg movements, branched drip-tip setae, and anti-adhesive surfaces. *Naturwissenschaften* 99: 337–341.

Briese, T., Kapoor, A., Mischra, N., Jain, K., Kumar, A., Jabado, O. J., and Lipkin, W. I. 2015. Virome capture sequence enables sensitive viral diagnosis and comprehensive virome analysis. *mBio* 6(5): e01491–15.

Brinck, P. 1955a. A monograph of the whirligig beetles of southern Africa. In *South African Animal Life*, eds. B. Hanström, P. Brink, and G. Rudebeck, pp. 329–518. Stockholm: Almqvist Wiksel.

———. 1955b. A revision of the Gyrinidae (Coleoptera) of the Ethiopian region. I. *Acta Universitatis Lundensis.* nova series 51: 1–144.

———. 1956. A revision of the Gyrinidae (Coleoptera) of the Ethiopian region. II. *Acta Universitatis Lundensis.* nova series 52: 1–190.

Brock, P. D. 2000. Stick-insects (Phasmida) from the Cape Town area, South Africa. *Bulletin of the Amateur Entomologists' Society* 59: 2–13.

Brock, P. D., Büscher, T., and Baker, E. 2020. Phasmida Species File Online. Version 5.0/5.0. Accessed 1 Apr. 2020. http://Phasmida.SpeciesFile.org.

Brook, C. E., Bai, Y., Dobson, A. P., Osikowicz, L. M., Ranaivoson, H. C., Zhu, Q., Kosov, M. Y., and Dittmar, K. 2015. *Bartonella* spp. in fruit bats and blood-feeding ectoparasites in Madagascar. *PLoS Neglected Tropical Diseases* 10(2): e0003532.

Brosset, A. 1988. The community of rain forest Insectivora in northeast Gabon. *Revue d'Ecologie* (*Terre et Vie*) 43: 23–46.

Brown, D. S. 1994. *Freshwater Snails of Africa and Their Medical Importance*. 2nd ed. London: Taylor and Francis.

Brown, J. L., Sillero, N., Glaw, F., Bora, P., Vieites, D. R., and Vences, M. 2016. Spatial biodiversity patterns of Madagascar's amphibians and reptiles. *PLoS One* 11: e0144076.

Brown, J. W. 2005. *World Catalogue of Insects*. Vol. 5, *Tortricidae (Lepidoptera)*, ed. B. Landry, pp. 1–741. Stenstrup: Apollo Books.
Brown, J. W., and Timm, A. 2017. *Celsumaria*: A new genus of Grapholitini from the Afrotropical Region (Lepidoptera: Tortricidae). *Annals of the Ditsong National Museum of Natural History* 7: 97–108.
Bruggen, A. C. van. 1980. Gondwanaland connections in the terrestrial molluscs of Africa and Australia. *Journal of the Malacological Society of Australia* 4: 215–222.
———. 1981. The African element among the terrestrial molluscs of the island of Madagascar. *Proceedings of the Koninklijke Nederlandse Akademie van Wetenschappen*, ser. C, 84: 115–129.
Bruner, L. 1910. Acridoidea from Madagascar, Comoro Isl. and eastern Africa. In *Reise in Ostafrika in den Jahren 1903–1905*, ed. A. Voeltzkow, no. 2: 623–644.
Brunhes, J., Boussès, P., Tantely, L., and Kengne, P. 2017. Un nouveau genre de Culicidae (Diptera), Paulianius n. gen., avec la description de trois nouvelles espèces malgaches. *Annales de la Société Entomologique de France* 53: 344–373.
Brunner von Wattenwyl, C. 1878. *Monographie der Phaneropteriden*. Wien: K. K. Zoologisch-Botanischen Gesellschaft.
———. 1888. Monographie der Stenopelmatiden und Gryllacriden. *Verhandlungen der Zoologisch-Botanischen Gesellschaft Wien* 38: 247–394.
———. 1895. *Monographie der Pseudophylliden*. Wien: K. K. Zoologisch-Botanischen Gesellschaft.
———. 1907. *Die Insektenfamilie der Phasmiden. II. Phasmidae Anareolatae (Clitumnini, Lonchodini, Bacunculini)*. Leipzig: Verlag von Wilhem Engelmann.
Bruzzese, D. J., Wagner, D. L., Harrison, T., Jogesh, T., Overson, R. P., Wickett, N. J., Raguso, R. A., and Skogen, K. A. 2019. Phylogeny, host use, and diversification in the moth family Momphidae (Lepidoptera: Gelechioidea). *PLoS One* 14: e0207833.
Brygoo, E. R. 1967. Démonstration expérimentale du rôle de vecteur de *S. fonquerniei*. *Archives de l'Institut Pasteur de Madagascar* 35: 309–311.
———. 1972. Human diseases and their relationship to the environment. In *Biogeography and Ecology in Madagascar*, eds. R. Battistini and G. Richard-Vindard, pp. 703–725. The Hague: W. Junk.
———. 1982. Animaux venimeux de Madagascar. *Memoiras del Instituto de Butantan*. Sao Paulo 46: 15–17.
Brygoo, E. R., and Rajenison, S. 1959. Présence de *Centetipsylla madagascariensis* (Roth.), 1900, sur *Rattus rattus* d'Antananarivo. Observations sur les variations de la faune pulicidienne des rats d'Antananarivo. *Archives de l'Institut Pasteur de Madagascar* 27: 53–57.
Buchsbaum, U., Speidel, W., and Chen, M.-Y. 2019. *Hyblaea behouneki* sp. n. from West Papua (Indonesia) (Lepidoptera, Hyblaeidae): Studies of Hyblaeidae 3. *Mitteilungen der Münchner Entomologischen Gesellschaft* 109: 143–148.
Buck, G., Courdurier J., Dorel R., and Quesnel J. J. 1952. A propos de *Phlebotomus squamipleuris*. *Bulletin de la Société de Pathologie Exotique* 45: 696–697.
Buck, G., Courdurier, J., Dorel, R., and Quesnel, J. J. 1951. Premier cas de leishmaniose canine à Madagascar. *Bulletin de la Société de Pathologie Exotique* 44: 428–430.
Buckley, R. C. 1982. Ant-plant interactions: A world review. In *Ant-plant Interactions in Australia*, ed. R. C. Buckley, pp. 111–141. The Hague: W. Junk.
Buckley, T. R., Attanayake, D., Nylander, J. A., and Bradler, S. 2010. The phylogenetic placement and biogeographical origins of the New Zealand stick insects (Phasmatodea). *Systematic Entomology* 35(2): 207–225.
Bukontaite, R. 2015. Evolution of the biodiversity hotspot of Madagascar from the eye of diving beetles: Phylogeny, colonization and speciation. PhD thesis, Department of Zoology, Stockholm University.
Bukontaite, R., Ranarilalatiana, T., Randriamihaja, J. H., and Bergsten, J. 2015. In or out-of-Madagascar? Colonization patterns for large-bodied diving beetles (Coleoptera: Dytiscidae). *PLoS One* 10: e0120777.
Burger, J. F. 1992. Notes on some Tabanidae (Diptera) from Madagascar, with description of two new species of *Aegophagamyia* Austen, subgenus *Triclida* Enderlein. *Annales de la Société Entomologique de France,* nouvelle série, 28(3): 303–315.
Burgess, N., D'Amico Hales, J., Underwood, E., Dinerstein, E., Olson, D., Itoua, I., Schipper, J., Ricketts, T., and Newman, K. 2004. *Terrestrial Ecoregions of Africa and Madagascar: A Conservation Assessment.* World Wildlife Fund Ecoregion Assessments, 2nd ed. Washington, DC: Island Press.
Burkhardt, D., and de la Motte, I.. 1987. Physiological, behavioural and morphometric data elucidate the evolutive significance of stalked eyes in Diopsidae (Diptera). *Entomologia Generalis* 12: 221–233.
Burza, S., Croft, S. L., and Boelaert, M. 2018. Leishmaniasis. *Lancet* 392(10151): 951–970. doi:10.1016/S0140-6736(18)31204-2.
Butcher, F. G. 1930. Notes on the cocooning habits of *Gyrinus*. *Journal of the Kansas Entomological Society* 3: 64–66.
Butler, A. G. 1880. Description of a new species of Orthopteron of the genus *Anostostoma* from Madagascar. *Proceedings of the Zoological Society of London*
Bybee, S. M., Kalkman, V. J., Erickson, R. J., Frandsen, P. B., Abbott, J. C., et al. 2021. Phylogeny and classification of Odonata using targeted genomics. *Molecular Phylogenetics and Evolution* 160: 107115.
Cachan, P. 1949. Les termites de Madagascar. *Mémoires de l'Institut Scientifique de Madagascar* 3: 177–275.
———. 1951. Les termites de Madagascar. Supplement 1. *Mémoires de l'Institut Scientifique de Madagascar* 5: 1–18.
Cadle, J. E. 2003. Colubridae, snakes. In *The Natural History of Madagascar*, eds. S. M. Goodman and J. P. Benstead, pp. 997–1004. Chicago: University of Chicago Press.
Cady, A., Leech, R., Sorkin, L., Stratton, G., and Caldwell, M. 1993. Acrocerid (Insecta: Diptera) life histories, behaviors, host spiders (Arachnida: Araneida), and distributional records. *Canadian Entomologist* 125: 931–944.
Cai, C., Short, A.E.Z., and Huang, D. 2012. The first skiff beetle (Coleoptera: Myxophaga: Hydroscaphidae) from early Cretaceous Jehol Biota. *Journal of Paleontology* 86: 116–119.
Cai, Y. 2005. On a small collection of atyid shrimps from cave Lakata Zafera, western Madagascar, with a description of a new species (Decapoda: Atyidae). *Proceedings of the Biological Society of Washington* 118(2): 312–318.
Cai, Y., and Ng, P.K.L. 2002. The freshwater palaemonid prawns (Crustacea: Decapoda: Caridea) of Myanmar. *Hydrobiologia* 487: 59–83.
———. 2007. A revision of the *Caridina gracilirostris* De Man, 1892, species group, with descriptions of two new taxa (Decapoda; Caridea; Atyidae). *Journal of Natural History* 41(25–28): 1585–1602.
Callmander, M. W., Phillipson, P. B., Schatz, G. E., Andriambololonera, S., Rabarimanarivo, M., Rakotonirina, N., Raharimampionona, J., Chatelain, C., Gautier, L., and Lowry, P. P. 2011. The endemic and non-endemic vascular flora of Madagascar updated. *Plant Ecology and Evolution* 144: 121–125.
Camboué, R. P. 1886. Les sauterelles à Madagascar sur le riz malgache. *Bulletin Mensuel de la Société Nationale d'Acclimatation de France* 33: 168–172.
Cammaerts, R. 1987. Taxonomic studies on African Gomphidae (Anisoptera) 1. *Malgassogomphus robinsoni* gen. nov., spec. nov. from Madagascar. *Odonatologica* 16: 335–346.
Camras, S. 1962. The Conopidae of Madagascar (Diptera). *Mémoires de l'Institut Scientifique de Madagascar,* série E, 13: 179–187.
———. 2007. On the *Archiconops insularis*-group species of Madagascar. *Entomologist's Monthly Magazine* 143: 161–164.
Capener, A. L. 1968. The taxonomy of the African Membracidae. Pt. 2, The Centrotinae. *Republic of South Africa Department of Agricultural Technical Services Entomology Memoirs* 17: 1–124.
Carle, F. L. 1986. The classification, phylogeny and biogeography of the Gomphidae (Anisoptera). I. Classification. *Odonatologica* 15: 275–326.
Carlquist, S. 1965. *Island Life: A Natural History of the Islands of the World*. New York: Natural History Press.
Carpenter, G. H. 1916. The Apterygota of the Seychelles. *Proceedings of the Royal Irish Academy* 33(B): 1–70.
Carroll, R. L. 1988. *Vertebrate Paleontology and Evolution*. New York: W. H. Freeman.
Carruthers, V., and du Preez, L. 2011. *Frogs and Frogging in Southern Africa*, 2nd ed. Cape Town: Random Struik Nature.
Cassagnau, P. 1996. Collemboles Paleonurini primitifs de l'Afrique et de Madagascar. *Annales de la Société Entomologique de France*, nouvelle série, 32: 121–161.
Cassagnau, P., and Deharveng, L. 1980. Sur l'intérêt biogéographique et cytogénétique d'un nouveau genre de Collemboles Neanurinae: Le genre *Travura* n.g. *Travaux du Laboratoire d'Ecobiologie des Arthropodes Edaphiques*, Toulouse 2(2): 1–12.
Cassola, F. 2001. Studies of tiger beetles. CXXIII. Preliminary approach to the macrosystematics of the tiger beetles (Coleoptera, Cicindelidae). *Russian Entomology Journal* 10(3): 265–272.
———. 2003. Coleoptera: Cicindelidae, tiger beetles. In *The Natural History of Madagascar*, eds. S. M. Goodman and J. P. Benstead, pp. 669–677. Chicago: University of Chicago Press.
Cassola, F., and Andriamampianina, L. 1998. Deux espèces nouvelles de Cicindélides de Madagascar (Coleoptera, Cicindelidae). *Bollettino della Società Entomologica Italiana* 130: 47–54.
Cassola, F., and Pearson, D. L. 2000. Global patterns of tiger beetle species richness (Coleoptera: Cicindelidae): Their use in conservation planning. *Biological Conservation* 95: 197–208.

Castelin, M., Marquet, G., and Klotz, W. 2013a. *Elephantis*, a new genus for *Caridina natalensis* Bouvier, 1925 from eastern rivers of Madagascar. *Zootaxa* 3702: 573–586.

Castelin, M., Feutry, P., Hautecoeur, M., Marquet, G., Wowor, D., Zimmermann, G., and Keith, P. 2013b. New insight on population genetic connectivity of widespread amphidromous prawn *Macrobrachium lar* (Fabricius, 1798) (Crustacea: Decapoda: Palaemonidae). *Marine Biology* 160(6): 1395–1406.

Chainey, J. E. 2003. Tabanidae, horse flies. In *The Natural History of Madagascar*, eds. S. M. Goodman and J. P. Benstead, pp. 721–727. Chicago: University of Chicago Press.

———. 2017. Tabanidae (horse flies, deer flies and clegs). In *Manual of Afrotropical Diptera*. Vol. 2, *Nematocerous Diptera and Lower Brachycera*, eds. A. H. Kirk-Spriggs and B. J. Sinclair, pp. 893–913. Suricata 5. Pretoria: South African National Biodiversity Institute.

Chainey, J. E., and Karisch, T. 2017. A new species of *Racotis* Moore, [1887] from Madagascar (Lepidoptera: Geometridae: Ennominae). *Metamorphosis* 28: 49–53.

Chainey, J. E., and Oldroyd, H. 1980. Family Tabanidae. In *Catalogue of the Diptera of the Afrotropical Region*, ed. R. W. Crosskey, pp. 275–308, 1224, 1230. London: British Museum (Natural History).

Chainey, J. E., and Timmer, J. 1986. A new species of *Neavella* from Madagascar. *Entomologische Berichten* 46: 65–67.

Chanteau, S., ed. 2006. *Atlas de la peste à Madagascar*. Marseille: IRD Editions.

Chapuis, M. P., Lecoq, M., Michalakis, Y., Loiseau, A., Sword, G. A., Piry, S., and Estoup, A. 2008. Do outbreaks affect genetic population structure? A worldwide survey in *Locusta migratoria*, a pest plagued by microsatellite null alleles. *Molecular Ecology* 17: 3640–3653.

Charlery de la Masseliere, M., Ravigné, V., Facon, B., Lefeuvre, P., Massol, F., Quilici, S., and Duyck, P. F. 2017. Changes in phytophagous insect host ranges following the invasion of their community: Long-term data for fruit flies. *Ecology and Evolution* 7(14): 5181–5190.

Chialvo, C.H.S., Chialvo, P., Holland, J. D., Anderson, T. J., Breinholt, J. W., Kawahara, A. Y., Zhou, X., Liu, S., and Zaspel, J. M. 2018. A phylogenomic analysis of lichen-feeding tiger moths uncovers evolutionary origins of host chemical sequestration. *Molecular Phylogenetics and Evolution* 121: 23–34.

China, W. E., and Fennah, R. G. 1960. Fulgoroidea of the Iles Glorieuses. *Naturaliste Malgache* 12: 133–138.

Chintauan-Marquier, I. C., Legendre, F., Hugel, S., Robillard, T., Grandcolas, P., Nel, A., Zuccon, D., and Desutter-Grandcolas, L. 2016. Laying the foundations of evolutionary and systematic studies in crickets (Insecta, Orthoptera): A multilocus phylogenetic analysis. *Cladistics* 32: 54–81.

Chlond, D. 2010a. *Planeocoris*, a new genus of Stenopodainae (Hemiptera: Heteroptera: Reduviidae) from Madagascar. *Zootaxa* 2400: 41–48.

———. 2010b. A new species of the Madagascan genus *Censorinus* (Heteroptera: Reduviidae: Reduviinae). *Acta Entomologica Musei Nationalis Pragae* 50: 1–6.

———. 2010c. A new, remarkable genus and two new species of Ectrichodiinae (Hemiptera: Heteroptera: Reduviidae) from Madagascar. *Zootaxa* 2522: 61–68.

———. 2011. A new species of the Madagascan genus *Rodepirea* Villiers, 1962 (Hemiptera: Heteroptera: Reduviidae: Physoderinae). *Heteropterus Revista de Entomologia* 11: 235–240.

———. 2014. A review of the taxonomic position of *Vesbius seyrigi* Villiers, 1970, with a description of two new species of Peyrierocoris Chłond and Junkiert, 2010 (Hemiptera: Heteroptera: Reduviidae: Harpactorinae). *Zootaxa* 3785: 288–300.

———. 2016. A taxonomic revision of the Madagascan genus *Noualhierella* (Hemiptera: Heteroptera: Reduviidae: Stenopodainae). *Entomologica Americana* 122: 251–261.

Chlond, D., and Banar, P. 2013. *Myrmicella*, a new genus of Harpactorinae (Hemiptera: Heteroptera: Reduviidae) from Madagascar. *Zootaxa* 3718: 483–495.

Chlond, D., and Guilbert, E. 2012. *Sicardicoris*, a new Madagascan subgenus of Peyrierocoris Chłond and Junkiert 2010 (Hemiptera: Heteroptera: Reduviidae: Harpactorinae). *Zootaxa* 3313: 44–52.

Chlond, D., and Junkiert, L. 2010. *Peyrierocoris* a new genus of Harpactorinae (Hemiptera: Heteroptera: Reduviidae) from Madagascar. *Zootaxa* 2487: 33–42.

———. 2011. A new species of the Madagascan genus *Catala* Villiers, 1951 (Heteroptera: Reduviidae: Stenopodainae). *Genus* 22: 545–550.

Chlond, D., Redei, D., and Banar, P. 2016. A new species of the Madagascan genus *Physoderoides* (Hemiptera: Heteroptera: Reduviidae: Physoderinae). *Entomologica Americana* 122: 245–250.

Chlond, D., Guilbert, E., Faille, A., and Banar, P. 2018. A remarkable new species of cavernicolous Collartidini from Madagascar (Hemiptera: Heteroptera: Reduviidae). *Zootaxa* 4425: 372–384.

Chlond, D., Sawka-Gadek, N., and Zyla, D. 2019. Genetic data of museum specimens allow for inferring evolutionary history of the cosmopolitan genus *Sirthenea* (Heteroptera: Reduviidae). *PeerJ* 7: e6640. doi.org./10.7717/peerj.640.

Chopard, L. 1948. Les Orthoptères de Madagascar. *Mémoires de l'Institut Scientifique de Madagascar*, série A, 1: 121–135.

———. 1949. Les Orthoptèroides cavernicoles de Madagascar. *Mémoires de l'Institut Scientifique de Madagascar*, série A, 3: 41–56.

———. 1951. Notes sur les Orthopteroides de Madagascar. I. Orthopteroides palmicoles et pandanicoles; II., III. *Mémoires de l'Institut Scientifique de Madagascar*, série A, 5: 143–158.

———. 1957. La faune entomologique de La Réunion. Orthopteroides. *Mémoires de l'Institut Scientifique de Madagascar*, série E, 8: 31–56.

———. 1958. Les Orthopteroides des Comores. *Mémoires de l'Institut Scientifique de Madagascar*, série E, 10: 3–40.

Chvojka, P., and Gibon, F.-M. 2017. New species of *Tinodes* from Madagascar (Trichoptera, Psychomyiidae). *Zootaxa* 4318(2): 364–376.

Chvojka, P., and Sykora, J. L. 1998. Revision of the *Leptonema affine* group (Insecta: Trichoptera: Hydropsychidae) from Madagascar with the description of a new species. *Časopis Národniho Muzea* 167(1–4): 25–33.

Cigliano, M. M., Braun, H., Eades, D. C., and Otte, D. 2020. Orthoptera Species File. Version 5.0/5.0. Accessed 20 Mar. 2020. http://Orthoptera.SpeciesFile.org.

Cipola, N. G., Morais, J. W., and Bellini, B. C. 2018. Three new species of *Seira* Lubbock (Collembola, Entomobryidae, Seirinae) from Madagascar with *Lepidocyrtus*-like habitus. *Zootaxa* 4524(2): 151–173.

———. 2020. Review of *Lepidocyrtinus* Börner, 1903 (Collembola, Entomobryidae, Seirinae): The African species. *Zootaxa* 4898: 1–110.

Clark, J. A., and May, R. A. 2002. Taxonomic bias in conservation research. *Science* 297: 191–192.

Clark, V. C., Raxworthy, C. J., Rakotomalala, V., Sierwald, P., and Fisher, B. L. 2005. Convergent evolution of chemical defense in poison frogs and arthropod prey between Madagascar and the Neotropics. *Proceedings of the National Academy of Sciences of the USA* 102: 11617–11622.

Clausnitzer, V., and Lempert, J. 1998. Preliminary comparative approach of the reproductive behaviour of African Tetratheminae (Anisoptera: Libellulidae). *Journal of African Zoology* 112: 103–107.

Clausnitzer, V., Kalkman, V. J., Ram, M., Collen, B., Baillie, J.E.M., et al. 2009. Odonata enter the biodiversity crisis debate: The first global assessment of an insect group. *Biological Conservation* 142: 1864–1869.

Clausnitzer, V., Dijkstra, K.-D. B., Koch, R., Boudot, J.-P., Darwall, W.R.T., Kipping, J., Samraoui, B., Samways, M. J., Simaika, J. P., and Suhling, F. 2012. Focus on African freshwaters: Hotspots of dragonfly diversity and conservation concern. *Frontiers in Ecology and the Environment* 10: 129–134.

Clay, T. H. 1997. The genus *Phthirpediculus* Ewing (Anoplura, Phthiraptera, Insecta). *Bulletin du Muséum National d'Histoire Naturelle*, Paris, série 3, no. 457, *Zoologie* 320: 657–660.

Clerc, Y., Rodhain, F., Digoutte, J. P., Tesh, R., Heme, G., and Coulanges, P. 1983. Le virus Périnet, Rhabdoviridae, du genre *Vesiculovirus* isolé à Madagascar de Culicidae. *Annales de Virologie* (*Institut Pasteur*) 134E: 61–71.

Cliquennois, N. 2005. *Spathomorpha* n. gen: Un nouveau genre de Phasme de Madagascar (Phasmatodea, Anareolatae). *Bulletin de la Société Entomologique de France* 110(2): 113–124.

———. Révision partielle des Antongiliinae fondée sur l'étude des œufs, comprenant la définition d'une nouvelle tribu et de quatre nouveaux genres (Phasmatodea). *Bulletin de la Société Entomologique de France* 111(2): 157–172.

———. 2007. Aperçu général de la diversité des phasmes de Madagascar (Insecta, Phasmatodea). *Le Bulletin d'Arthropoda* 32: 3–16.

———. 2008. Révision des Anisacanthidae, famille de phasmes endémique de Madagascar (Phasmatodea: Bacilloidea). *Annales de la Société Entomologique de France* 44(1): 59–85.

———. 2012. Notes sur les espèces exotiques de phasmes à Madagascar (Insecta: Phasmatodea). *Cahiers Scientifiques de l'Océan Indien Occidental* 3: 1–10.

———. 2018. *Adelophasma anjouanense* n. gen., n. sp., Phasme énigmatique de l'île d'Anjouan, archipel des Comores (Phasmatodea). *L'Entomologiste* 74: 145–161.

———. 2020. Ordre des Phasmatodea (Phasmes). In *Les insectes du monde: Biodiversité; Classification; Clés de détermination des familles*, vol. 1, pp. 403–437 (text), and vol. 2, pp. 172–179 (figures), ed. H.-P. Aberlenc. Versailles, Montpellier and Plaissan: Quae and Museo Editions.

Coddington, J. A. 1986. Orb webs in "non-orb weaving" ogre faced spiders (Araneae: Deinopidae): A question of genealogy. *Cladistics* 2: 53–67.

Coddington, J. A., and Levi, H. 1991. Systematics and evolution of spiders (Araneae). *Annual Review of Ecology and Systematics* 22: 565–592.
Coddington, J. A., Agnarsson, I., Hamilton C.A., and Bond, J. E. 2019. Spiders did not repeatedly gain, but repeatedly lost, foraging webs. *PeerJ* 7: e6703. doi:10.7717/peerj.6703.
Cogan, B. H., Hutson, A. M., and Shaffer, J. C. 1971. Preliminary observations on the affinities and composition of insect fauna of Aldabra. *Philosophical Transactions of the Royal Society of London B: Biological Sciences* 260: 315–325.
Coley, P. D., and Aide, T. M. 1991. Comparison of herbivory and plant defenses in temperate and tropical broad-leaved forests. In *Plant-Animal Interactions: Evolutionary Ecology in Tropical and Temperate Regions*, eds. P. W. Price, T. M. Lewinsohn, G. Wilson-Fernandes, and W. W. Benson, pp. 25–49. New York: John Wiley and Sons.
Coley, P. D., and Barone, J. A. 1996. Herbivory and plant defenses in tropical forests. *Annual Review of Ecology and Systematics* 27: 305–335.
Colpani, D., Benetti, C. J., Hamada, N., Andrade-Souza, V., Schoeninger, K., and Michat, M. C. 2020. Description of the immature stages of the Neotropical whirligig beetle *Gyrinus* (*Neogyrinus*) *rozei* Ochs, 1953 (Coleoptera: Gyrinidae) and first report of the parasitoid wasp *Melanosmicra* sp. (Hymenoptera: Chalcididae) on a *Gyrinus* species. *Zootaxa* 4732: 99–116.
Combescot, M., Combescot-Lang, C., de Nadon, J., and Rasolofonirina, N. 1993. Scalp pediculosis and its treatment: Bioclinical trials of different pediculicides and repellents in Antananarivo. *Archives de l'Institut Pasteur de Madagascar* 61: 87–90.
Commerson, P. 1772. Lettre de M. Commerson à M. de Lalande, de l'Ile de Bourbon, le 18 avril 1771. In *Supplément au voyage de M. de Bougainville ou Journal d'un voyage autour du monde fait par MM. Banks et Solander, Anglois, en 1768, 1769, 1770, 1771*, by MM. Banks and Solander, pp. 251–286. Paris: Chez Saillant and Nyon Libraries.
Condé, B. 1954. Les Diplopodes Pénicillates de l'ambre et la faune actuelle. *Bulletin de la Société Zoologique de France* 79(1): 74–78.
Condé, B., and Jacquemin, M. 1962. Diplopodes Pénicillates de Madagascar et des Mascareignes. *Revue Française d'Entomologie* 29: 254–286.
Connell, J. H. 1971. On the role of natural enemies in preventing competitive exclusion in some marine animals and in rain forest trees. In *Dynamics of Populations*, eds. P. J. Den Boer and G. Gradwell, pp. 298–312. Wageningen: PUDOC.
Constant, J. 2004. Fulgoridae of Madagascar: Description of a new species representing a new genus, key to the genera and list of the species (Homoptera: Fulgoromorpha: Fulgoridae). *Bulletin de l'Institut Royal des Sciences Naturelles de Belgique* 74: 29–34.
———. 2014. Revision of the Malagasy lanternfly genus *Belbina* Stål, 1863, with two new species (Hemiptera: Fulgoromorpha: Fulgoridae). *European Journal of Taxonomy* 102: 1–37.
———. 2015. Review of the *effusus* group of the lanternfly genus *Pyrops* Spinola, 1839, with one new species and notes on trophobiosis (Hemiptera: Fulgoromorpha: Fulgoridae). *European Journal of Taxonomy* 128: 1–23.
Cook, E. F. 1981. 24. Chaoboridae. In *Manual of Nearctic Diptera*, vol. 1, coordinators J. F. McAlpine, B. V Peterson, G. E. Shewell, H. J. Teskey, J. R. Vockeroth, and D. M. Wood, pp. 335–339. Ottawa: Research Branch, Agriculture Canada, Monograph No. 27.
Cook, O. F. 1896. *Cryptodesmus* and its allies. In *Brandtia*, a series of occasional papers on Diplopoda and other Arthropoda, pp. 19–28. New York: Huntington.
Copeland, R. S., Okeka, W., Freidberg, A., Merz, B., White, I. M., De Meyer, M., and Luke, Q. 2005. A checklist of the Tephritidae (Diptera) of Kakamega Forest, Kenya. *Journal of East African Natural History* 94(2): 247–278.
Coquerel, C. 1848. Observations entomologiques sur divers insectes recueillis à Madagascar. *Annales de la Société Entomologique de France*, série 2, 6: 275–284.
———. 1861. Orthopthères de Bourbon et de Madagascar. *Annales de la Société Entomologique de France* 4(1): 495–500.
Coulanges, P., and Randrianantoanina, E. 1985. Résistance des puces pestigènes malgaches aux insecticides organochlorés, organophosphorés et aux carbamates. *Archives de l'Institut Pasteur de Madagascar* 51: 253–260.
Coulanges, P., Clerc, Y., and Randrianantoanina, E. 1983. Etude de *X. cheopis* et *S. fonquerniei*, puces pestigènes malgaches: Mise en évidence de leur résistance au DDT, Dieldrin et Malathion. *Archives de l'Institut Pasteur de Madagascar* 49: 171–191.
Couri, M. S., and Pont, A. C. 2006. Eggs of *Stylogaster* Macquart (Diptera: Conopidae) on Madagascan muscids (Diptera: Muscidae). *Proceedings of the California Academy of Sciences* 57: 473–478.
Couri, M. S., and de Silva Barros, G. P. 2010. Diptera hosts of *Stylogaster* Macquart (Diptera, Conopidae) from Madagascar and South Africa. *Revista Brasileira de Entomologia* 54: 361–366.
Couri, M. S., Pont, A. C., and Penny, N. D. 2006. Muscidae (Diptera) from Madagascar: Identification keys, descriptions of new species, and new records. *Proceedings of the California Academy of Sciences* 57: 799–923.
Coutière, H. 1899. Sur quelques macroures des eaux douces de Madagascar (Voyage de M. G. Grandidier). *Bulletin du Muséum d'Histoire Naturelle* 5(7): 382–383.
———. 1900. Sur quelques macroures des eaux douces de Madagascar. *Comptes rendu Hebdomadaire des Séances de l'Académie des Sciences* 130: 1266–1268.
———. 1901. Les Palaemonidae des eaux douces de Madagascar. *Annales des Sciences Naturelles*, Paris, série *Zoologie* 12: 249–342.
Crandall, K. A., and De Grave, S. 2017. An updated classification of the freshwater crayfishes (Decapoda: Astacidea) of the world, with a complete species list. *Journal of Crustacean Biology* 37: 615–653.
Crandall, K. A., Harris, D. J., and Fetzner, J. W. 2000. The monophyletic origin of freshwater crayfishes estimated from nuclear and mitochondrial DNA sequences. *Proceedings of the Royal Society of London B: Biological Sciences* 267: 1679–1686.
Crewe, M., and Cohen, C. 2009. *Viridithemis viridula* (Fraser, 1960): Discovery of the first known male. *Agrion* 13: 54–55.
Crews, S. C. 2011. A revision of the spider genus *Selenops* Latreille, 1819 (Arachnida, Araneae, Selenopidae) in North America, Central America and the Caribbean. *ZooKeys* 105: 1–182.
Crisp, M., Cook, L., and Steane, D. 2004. Radiation of the Australian flora: What can comparisons of molecular phylogenies across multiple taxa tell us about the evolution of diversity in present-day communities? *Philosophical Transactions of the Royal Society of London B: Biological Sciences* 359: 1551–1571.
Crosskey, R. W. 1962. A revision of the genus *Pygophora* Schiner (Diptera, Muscidae). *Transactions of the Zoological Society of London* 29: 393–551.
Crowley, B. E., and Samonds, K. E. 2013. Stable carbon isotope values confirm a recent increase in grasslands in northwestern Madagascar. *The Holocene* 23(7): 1066–1073.
Crowson, R. A. 1955. *The Natural Classification of the Families of Coleoptera*. London: Nathaniel Lloyd.
Culler, E. C., Ohba, S-y, and Crumrine, P. 2014. Predator-prey interactions of Dytiscidae. In *Ecology, Systematics and the Natural History of Predaceous Diving Beetles (Coleoptera: Dytiscidae)*, ed. D. A. Yee, pp. 363–386. Dordrecht: Springer.
Cumberlidge, N. 1991. The respiratory system of *Globonautes macropus* (Rathbun 1898), a terrestrial fresh-water crab from Liberia (Parathelphusoidea, Gecarcinucidae). *Crustaceana* 61(1): 69–80.
———. 1999. The freshwater crabs of West Africa. Family Potamonautidae. No. 35 of *Faune et Flore Tropicales*. Paris: Institut de Recherche pour le Développement.
———. 2008. Insular species of Afrotropical freshwater crabs (Crustacea: Decapoda: Brachyura: Potamonautidae and Potamidae) with special reference to Madagascar and the Seychelles. *Contributions to Zoology* 77(2): 71–81.
———. 2016a. *Boreathelphusa uglowi*. IUCN Red List of Threatened Species 2016: e.T134748A99452057. Accessed 13 Feb. 2020. https://dx.doi.org/10.2305/IUCN.UK.2016-2.RLTS.T134748A99452057.en.
———. 2016b. *Madagapotamon humberti*. IUCN Red List of Threatened Species 2016: e.T134826A87566246. Accessed 13 Feb. 2020. https://dx.doi.org/10.2305/IUCN.UK.2016-3.RLTS.T134826A87566246.en.
Cumberlidge, N., and Meyer, K. S. 2009. A new species of *Foza* Reed and Cumberlidge, 2006, from northern Madagascar (Decapoda, Brachyura, Potamoidea, Potamonautidae), with a redescription of *F. goudoti* (H. Milne Edwards, 1853) comb. N., and comments on *Skelosophusa prolixa* Ng and Takeda, 1994. *ZooKeys* 18: 77–89.
Cumberlidge, N., and Ng, P.K.L. 2009. Systematics, evolution, and biogeography of the freshwater crabs. In *Crustacean Issues: Decapod Crustacean Phylogenetics*, eds. J. W. Martin, K. A. Crandall, and D. L. Felder, pp. 491–504. Leiden: CRC.
Cumberlidge, N., and Sternberg, R. v. 2002. The freshwater crabs of Madagascar (Crustacea, Decapoda, Potamoida). *Zoosystema* 24(1): 41–79.
———. 2003. Potamonautidae, freshwater crabs. In *The Natural History of Madagascar*, eds. S. M. Goodman and J. P. Benstead, pp. 612–617. Chicago: University of Chicago Press.
Cumberlidge, N., Boyko, C. B., and Harvey, A. W. 2002. A new genus and species of freshwater crab (Decapoda, Crustacea, Potamoidea) from northern Madagascar, and a second new species associated with *Pandanus* leaf axils. *Journal of Natural History* 36(1): 65–77.

Cumberlidge, N., Fenolio, D. B., Walvoord, M. E., and Stout, J. 2005. Tree-climbing crabs (Potamonautidae and Sesarmidae) from phytotelmic microhabitats in rainforest canopy in Madagascar. *Journal of Crustacean Biology* 25(2): 302–308.

Cumberlidge, N., Marijnissen, S.A.E., and Thompson, J. 2007. *Hydrothelphusa vencesi*, a new species of freshwater crab (Brachyura: Potamoidea: Potamonautidae) from southeastern Madagascar. *Zootaxa* 1524: 61–68.

Cumberlidge, N., Sternberg. R. v., and Daniels, S. R. 2008. A revision of the higher taxonomy of the Afrotropical freshwater crabs (Decapoda: Brachyura) with a discussion of their biogeography. *Biological Journal of the Linnean Society* 93(2): 399–413.

Cumberlidge, N., Ng, P.K.L., Yeo, D.C.J., Magalhaes, C., Campos, M. R., et al. 2009. Freshwater crabs and the biodiversity crisis: Importance, threats, status, and conservation challenges. *Biological Conservation* 142: 1665–1673.

Cumberlidge, N., Klaus, S., Meyer, K. S., and Koppin, J. C. 2015. New collections of freshwater crabs from northern Madagascar, with the description of a new species of *Foza* Reed and Cumberlidge, 2006 (*Brachyura*, Potamonautidae). *European Journal of Taxonomy* 109: 1–15.

Cumberlidge, N., Rasamy Razanabolana, J., Ranaivoson, C. H., Randrianasolo, H. H., Sayer, C., Máiz-Tomé, L., Van Damme, D., and Darwall, W.R.T. 2017. Updated extinction risk assessments of Madagascar's freshwater decapod crustaceans reveal fewer threatened species but more data deficient species. *Malagasy Nature* 12: 32–41.

Cumberlidge, N., Rasamy Razanabolana, J., Ranaivoson, C. H., Darwall, W., and Màiz-Tomé, L. 2018. The status and distribution of freshwater decapod crustaceans. In *The Status of Freshwater Biodiversity in Madagscar and in the Indian Ocean Islands Hotspot*, eds. L. Màiz-Tomé, C. Sayer, and W. Darwall, pp. 42–58. Gland, Switzerland: IUCN.

Cumberlidge, N., Soma, J. B., Leever, E. M., and Daniels, S. R. 2020. New lineages within the Malagasy freshwater crab fauna: *Agora* n. gen. for *Thelphusa goudoti* H. Milne Edwards, 1853, and a phytotelmic new species of *Malagasya* Cumberlidge & Sternberg, 2002 (Brachyura: Potamonautidae: Deckeniinae). *Journal of Crustacean Biology* 40(5): 584–599. doi:10.1093/jcbiol/ruaa050.

Cushman, J. H., Compton, S. G., Zachariades, C., Ware, A. B., Nefdt, R.J.C., and Rashbrook, V. K. 1998. Geographic and taxonomic distribution of a positive interaction: Ant-tended homopterans indirectly benefit figs across southern Africa. *Oecologia* 116: 373–380.

DaCosta, M., and Weller, S. J. 2005. Phylogeny and classification of Callimorphini (Lepidoptera: Arctiidae: Arctiinae). *Zootaxa* 1025: 1–94.

Dahl, O. C. 1951. *Malgache et Maanjan. Une comparaison linguistique*. Oslo: Egede Instituttet.

Dalecky, A., Kerdelhué, C., Johnson, S., Razafindratsita, V. R., Grassi, C., Razafiarimalala, A. C., Overdorff, D., and Rasplus, J.-Y. 2003. Malagasy *Ficus* (Moraceae) and associated fauna. In *The Natural History of Madagascar*, eds. S. M. Goodman and J. P. Benstead, pp. 322–334. Chicago: University of Chicago Press.

Damm, S., Dijkstra, K.-D. B., and Hadrys, H. 2010. Red drifters and dark residents: The phylogeny and ecology of a Plio-Pleistocene dragonfly radiation reflects Africa's changing environment (Odonata, Libellulidae, *Trithemis*). *Molecular Phylogenetics and Evolution* 54: 870–882.

Daniels, S. R., Cumberlidge, N., Pérez-Losada, M., Marijnissen, S.A.E., and Crandall, K. A. 2006. Evolution of Afrotropical freshwater crab lineages obscured by morphological convergence. *Molecular Phylogenetics and Evolution* 40: 225–235.

Daniels, S. R., Phiri, E. E., Klaus, S., Albrecht, C., and Cumberlidge, N. 2015. Multi-locus phylogeny of the Afrotropical freshwater crab fauna reveals historical drainage connectivity and transoceanic dispersal since the Eocene. *Systematic Biology* 64(4): 549–567.

Darnhofer, T., and Launois, M. 1974. *L'Optimum pluviometrique du criquet migrateur malgache: Principe et applications; Etude globale de l'influence de la repartition spatio-temporelle des pluies sur les populations du criquet migrateur à Madagascar étude bio-météorologique*. Rome: Programme des Nations Unies pour le développement, Organisation des Nations Unies pour l'alimentation et l'agriculture.

Darwall, W.R.T., Holland, R. A., Smith, K. G., Allen, D. J., Brooks, E.G.E., et al. 2011. Implications of bias in conservation research and investment for freshwater species. *Conservation Letters* 4: 474–482.

Dausmann, K. H., Glos, J., Linsenmair, K. E., and Ganzhorn, J. U. 2008. Improved recruitment of a lemur-dispersed tree in Malagasy dry forests after the demise of vertebrates in forest fragments. *Oecologia* 157: 307–316.

David, P., Bjorksten, T., Fowler, K., and Pomiankowski, A. 2000. Condition-dependent signalling of genetic variation in stalk-eyed flies. *Nature* 406(6792): 186–188.

Davis, D. R., and Robinson, G. S. 1998. The Tineoidea and Gracillarioidea. In *Lepidoptera: Moths and Butterflies*. Vol. 1, *Evolution, Systematics and Biogeography*, ed. N. P. Kristensen, pp. 91–117. Handbuch der Zoologie, vol. 4, pt. 35. Berlin: Walter de Gruyter.

Davis, D. R., and Stonis, J. R. 2007. A revision of the New World plant-mining moths of the family Opostegidae (Lepidoptera: Nepticuloidea). *Smithsonian Contributions to Zoology* 625: 1–212.

Dayrat, B. 2005. Towards integrative taxonomy. *Biological Journal of the Linnean Society* 85: 879–886.

De Jong, R., and Coutsis, J. G. 2017. A re-appraisal of *Gegenes* Hübner, 1819 (Lepidoptera, Hesperiidae) based on male and female genitalia, with the description of a new genus, *Afrogegenes*. *Tijdschrift voor Entomologie* 160: 41–60.

de Mazancourt, V., Castelin, M., Renneville, C., Mlambo, M. C., Marquet, G., and Keith, P. 2019a. Revalidation of *Caridina natalensis* De Man, 1908 (Crustacea: Decapoda: Atyidae) in the South Western Indian Ocean. *Zootaxa* 4543(3): 375–387.

de Mazancourt, V., Klotz, W., Marquet, G., Mos, B., Rogers, D. C., and Keith, P. 2019b. The complex study of complexes: The first well-supported phylogeny of two species complexes within genus *Caridina* (Decapoda: Caridea: Atyidae) sheds light on evolution, biogeography, and habitat. *Molecular Phylogenetics and Evolution* 131: 164–180.

De Meyer, M. 2000. Systematic revision of the subgenus *Ceratitis* MacLeay s.s. (Diptera, Tephritidae). *Zoological Journal of the Linnean Society* 128: 439–467.

———. 2006. A systematic revision of the African fruit fly genus *Carpophthoromyia* (Diptera, Tephritidae). *Zootaxa* 1235: 1–48.

———. 2009. Family Tephritidae. In *Diptera of the Seychelles*, ed. J. Gerlach, pp. 321–326. Sofia: Pensoft.

De Meyer, M., and Ekesi, S. 2016. Exotic invasive fruit flies (Diptera: Tephritidae): In and out of Africa. In *Fruit Fly Research and Development in Africa: Towards a Sustainable Management Strategy to Improve Horticulture*, eds. S. Ekesi, S.A. Mohamed, and M. De Meyer, pp. 127–150. Berlin: Springer Verlag.

De Meyer, M., and Freidberg, A. 2012. Taxonomic revision of the fruit fly genus *Neoceratitis* Hendel (Diptera: Tephritidae). *Zootaxa* 3223: 24–39.

De Meyer, M., Quilici, S., Franck, A., Chadhouliati, A. C., Issimaila, M. A., Youssoufa, M. A., Barbet, A., Attié, M., and White, I. M. 2012. Frugivorous fruit flies (Diptera, Tephritidae, Dacini) of the Comoro Archipelago. *African Invertebrates* 53: 69–77.

De Moor, F. C. 1993. Factors influencing the distribution of Trichoptera in Southern Africa. In *Proceedings of the 7th International Symposium on Trichoptera*, Umea, Sweden, 3–8 Aug. 1992, ed. C. Otto, pp. 51–58. Leiden: Backhuys.

De Prins, J., and De Prins, W. 2011. Afromoths, online database of Afrotropical moth species (Lepidoptera). Accessed Mar. 2020. http://www.afromoths.net.

De Prins, W., and De Prins, J. 2005. *World Catalogue of Insects*. Vol. 6, *Gracillariidae (Lepidoptera)*, ed. B. Landry, pp. 1–502. Stenstrup: Apollo Books.

De Silva, P., and Bernal, X. E. 2013. First report of the mating behavior of a species of frog-biting midge (Diptera: Corethrellidae). *Florida Entomologist* 96(4): 1522–1529.

Decary, R. 1937. L'Entomophagie chez les indigènes de Madagascar. *Bulletin de la Société Entomologique de France* 42: 168–171.

———. 1950. *La faune malgache: Son rôle dans les croyances et les usages indigènes*. Paris: Payot.

Deeming, J. C. 1971. Some species of *Atherigona* Rondani (Diptera, Muscidae) from Northern Nigeria, with special reference to those injurious to cereal crops. *Bulletin of Entomological Research* 61: 133–190.

———. 1987. Some new and little known species of *Atherigona* Rondani (Diptera: Muscidae) from the Malagasian subregion. *Entomologist's Monthly Magazine* 123: 15–25.

———. 2019. Atherigonini (Diptera, Muscidae) from Madagascar. *Proceedings of the California Academy of Sciences* 66: 87–98.

Dehgan, A. O. 1990. Crayfish harvesting in the Ranomafana National Park. Ranomafana: Ranomafana National Park Project.

Deharveng, L., and Fjellberg, A. 1993. *Isotomiella* from Seychelles Islands (Insecta, Collembola, Isotomidae). *Spixiana* 16: 121–125.Dejean, A., Fisher, B. L., Corbara, B., Rarevohitra, R., Randrianaivo, R., Rajemison, B., and Leponce, M. 2010. Spatial distribution of dominant arboreal ants in a Malagasy coastal rainforest: Gaps and presence of an invasive species. *PLoS One* 5(2): e9319.

Delamare-Deboutteville, C. 1948. Collemboles de Madagascar (Note 1). *Bulletin de la Société Entomologique de France* 53 (3): 38–41.

———. 1950. *Salina insignis* (Handschin) Collembole commensal d'un Thysanoptère à Madagascar. *Naturaliste Malgache* 2: 107–109.

Delamare-Deboutteville, C., and Massoud, Z. 1964. Collemboles marins interstitiels des plages de Madagascar. *Vie et Milieu*, Supplément, 17: 381–392.

Demange, J. M. 1969. Myriapodes récoltés à Madagascar par M. L. Bigot. *Bulletin du Muséum National d'Histoire Naturelle*, Paris, série 2, 41(2): 484–489.

Demoulin, G. 1966. Contribution à l'étude des Euthyplociidae. (Ephemeroptera). IV, Un nouveau genre de Madagascar. *Annales de la Société Entomologique de France*, nouvelle série, 2(4): 941–949.

———. 1969. Le genre *Eatonica* Navàs (Ephemeroptera, Ephemeridae) existe-t-il à Madagascar? *Bulletin Institut Royal des Sciences Naturelles de Belgique* 45(6): 1–9.

———. 1973. Ephéméroptères de Madagascar. *Bulletin de l'Institut Royal des Sciences Naturelles de Belgique* 49: 1–20.

Denis, R. 1929. Sur deux Collemboles de Madagascar. *Bulletin du Muséum*, série 2, 1: 104–106.

———. 1947. XV. Collemboles. In Croisière du Bougainville aux îles australes françaises. *Mémoires du Muséum*, nouvelle série, 20: 31–52.

Depaquit, J., Léger, N., and Robert, V. 2002. Première mention de *Phlebotomus* à Madagascar (Diptera: Psychodidae). Description de *Phlebotomus (Anaphlebotomus) fertei* n. sp. et de *Phlebotomus* (*Anaphlebotomus*) *huberti* n. sp. *Parasite* 9(4): 325–331.

Depaquit, J., Léger, N., Ferté, H., and Robert, V. 2004a. Les phlébotomes de Madagascar (Diptera: Psychodidae). II, Description de la femelle de *Phlebotomus (Anaphlebotomus) fertei* Depaquit, Léger and Robert, 2002; Description du mâle et redescription de la femelle de *Phlebotomus* (*Anaphlebotomus*) *berentiensis* (Léger and Rodhain, 1978) comb. nov. *Parasite* 11(2): 201–209.

Depaquit, J., Léger, N., and Robert, V. 2004b. Les phlébotomes de Madagascar (Diptera-Psychodidae). III, Description de *Phlebotomus (Anaphlebotomus) fontenillei* n. sp. *Parasite* 11(3): 261–265.

———. 2007. Les phlébotomes de Madagascar (Diptera: Psychodidae). V, Description de *Sergentomyia majungaensis* n. sp. *Parasite* 14(3): 219–223.

———. 2008. Les phlébotomes de Madagascar (Diptera: Psychodidae). VI. Un sous-genre nouveau (*Vattieromyia*) avec trois espèces nouvelles: *Sergentomyia* (*V.*) *sclerosiphon*, *S.* (*V.*) *namo* et *S.* (*V.*) *anka*. *Parasite* 15(1): 15–26.

Depaquit, J., Randrianambinintsoa, F., Jaouadi, K., Payard, J., Bounamous, A., et al. 2014. Molecular and morphological systematics of the sandfly *Sergentomyia* (*Sintonius*) *clydei* Sinton, 1928 and questions about its record in the Seychelles. *Infection, Genetics and Evolution* 21: 41–53.

Depaquit, J., Léger, N., and Randrianambinintsoa, F. J. 2015. Paraphyly of the subgenus *Anaphlebotomus* and creation of *Madaphlebotomus* subg. nov. (Phlebotominae: *Phlebotomus*). *Medical and Veterinary Entomology* 29(2): 159–170.

Désamoré, A., Laenen, B., Miller, K. B., and Bergsten, J. 2018. Early burst in body size evolution is uncoupled from species diversification in diving beetles (Dytiscidae). *Molecular Ecology* 27: 979–993.

Descamps, M. 1957. *Recherches morphologiques et biologiques sur les Diopsidae du Nord-Cameroun.* Ministère de la France d'Outre-Mer, Direction de l'Agriculture, de l'Elevage et des Forêts, Section Technique d'Agriculture Tropicale, Bulletin Scientifique 7: 1–154.

———. 1965. Contribution à l'étude des Eumastacides Malgaches (Orthoptera-Eumastacidae). I, Révision des Miraculinae. *Mémoires du Muséum National d'Histoire Naturelle*, Paris, nouvelle série, série A, *Zoologie*, 34: 1–57.

———. 1968. Un Acridoide relique des Mascareignes (Orth. Acridoidea). *Bulletin de la Société Entomologique de France* 73: 31–36.

———. 1969. Eumastacides de Madagascar: Miraculinae (Acridomorpha Eumastacoidea). *Bulletin de la Société Entomologique de France* 74: 176–185.

———. 1971. Troisième contribution à l'étude des Pseudoschmidtiinae (Acridomorpha Eumastacidae). *Mémoires du Muséum National d'Histoire Naturelle*, Paris, nouvelle série, série A, *Zoologie*, 65: 1–252.

Descamps, M., and Wintrebert, D. 1965. Contribution à l'étude des Eumastacides Malgaches (Orthoptera-Eumastacidae). II—Pseudoschmidtiinae, Notes biologiques et espèces nouvelles. *Mémoires du Muséum National d'Histoire Naturelle,* Paris, nouvelle série, série A, *Zoologie*, 34: 59–187.

———. 1966. Pyrgomorphidae et Acrididae de Madagascar. Observation biologiques et diagnoses (Orth. Acridoidea). *Eos Revista Española de Entomologia* 42: 41–263.

Desvars, A., Grimaud, Y., Guis, H., Esnault, O., Allène, X., Gardès, L., Balenghien, T., Baldet, T., Delécolle, J.-C., and Garros, C. 2015. First overview of the *Culicoides* Latreille (Diptera: Ceratopogonidae) livestock associated species of Reunion Island, Indian Ocean. *Acta Tropica* 142: 5–19. doi:10.1016/j.actatropica.2014.10.018.

Dettner, K. 2014. Chemical ecology and biochemistry of Dytiscidae. In *Ecology, Systematics and the Natural History of Predaceous Diving Beetles (Coleoptera: Dytiscidae)*, ed. D. A. Yee, pp. 235–306. Dordrecht: Springer.

———. 2016. Noteridae Thomson, 1857. In *Handbook of Zoology.* Vol. 4, *Arthropoda: Insecta*, pt. 38, *Coleoptera, Beetles*, vol. 1, *Morphology and Systematics (Archostemata, Adephaga, Myxophaga, Polyphaga partim)*, 2nd ed., eds. R. G. Beutel and R. B. Leschen, pp. 98–107. Berlin: Walter de Gruyter.

Deuve, T. 1999. Description de *Megalomma pierreorum* n. sp., nouvelle Cicindèle de l'île de La Réunion (Coleoptera, Cicindelidae). *Bulletin de la Société Entomologique de France* 104(5): 409–411.

Dewailly, P. 1950. Coléoptères Melolonthini de Madagascar. *Mémoires de l'Institut Scientifique de Madagascar,* série A, 4(2): 209–454.

Dhondt, C. 2009. Analyse moléculaire des phlébotomes (Diptera, Psychodidae) de Madagascar. Pharmacy Doctorat, ref. 2009REIMP049, Reims.

Dhungel, B., and Wahlberg, N. 2018. Molecular systematics of the subfamily Limenitidinae (Lepidoptera: Nymphalidae). *PeerJ* 6: e4311.

Dias, F.M.S., Siewert, R. R., Freitas, A.V.L., Lamas, G., Magaldi, L. M., Mielke, O. H. H., and Casagrande M. M. 2019. An integrative approach elucidates the systematics of *Sea* Hayward and *Cybdelis* Boisduval (Lepidoptera: Nymphalidae: Biblidinae). *Systematic Entomology* 22: 226–250.

Dias, J.A.T.S. 1955. Denominação e definicão de um novo agrupamento génerica para a subfamilia Pangoniinae Loew, 1860 (Diptera, Tabanidae). *Memórias e Estudos do Museo Zoológico da Universidade de Coimbra* 237: 1–3.

———. 1956. Um novo género para a tribu Bouvieromyiini (Enderlein, 1922). *Boletim da Sociedade de Estudo de Moçambique* 98: 75–79.

———. 1966. Tabanídeos (Diptera—Tabanídae) de Moçambique. Contribuição para o seu conhecimento. Lourenço Marques [Maputo]: Universidade de Lourenço Marques.

Dick, C. W. 2007. High host specificity of obligate ectoparasites. *Ecological Entomology* 32: 446–450.

Dick, C. W., and Dittmar, K. 2014. Parasitic bat flies (Diptera: Streblidae and Nycteribiidae): Host specificity and potential as vectors. In *Bats (Chiroptera) as Vectors of Diseases and Parasites*, eds. S. Klimpel and H. Melhorn, pp. 131–155. Parasitology Research Monographs, vol. 5. Berlin: Springer-Verlag.

Dick, C. W., and Patterson, B. D. 2006. Bat flies: Obligate ectoparasites of bats. In *Micromammals and Macroparasites: From Evolutionary Ecology to Management*, eds. S. Morand, B. Krasnov, and R. Poulin, pp. 179–194. Tokyo: Springer-Verlag.

———. 2007. Against all odds: Explaining high host specificity in dispersal-prone parasites. *International Journal for Parasitology* 37: 871–876.

Didham, R. K., Ghazoul, J., Stork, N. E., and Davis, A. J. 1996. Insects in fragmented forests: A functional approach. *Trends in Ecology and Evolution* 11: 255–260.

Dietrich, C. H. 2005. Keys to the families of Cicadomorpha and subfamilies and tribes of Cicadellidae (Hemiptera: Auchenorrhyncha). *Florida Entomologist* 88: 502–517.

Dietrich, C. H., Allen, J. M., Lemmon, A. R., Moriarty Lemmon, E., Takiya, D. M., Evangelista, O., Walden, K.K.O., Grady, P.G.S., and Johnson, K. P. 2017. Anchored hybrid enrichment-based phylogenomics of leafhoppers and treehoppers (Hemiptera: Cicadomorpha: Membracoidea). *Insect Systematics and Diversity* 1: 57–72.

Dietrich, C. H., Magalhães, R. B., and Takiya, D. M. 2020. Revision of the endemic Malagasy leafhopper tribe Platyjassini (Hemiptera: Cicadellidae: Iassinae). *European Journal of Taxonomy* 695: 1–89.

Dijkstra, K.-D. B. 2005. Taxonomy and identification of the continental African *Gynacantha* and *Heliaeschna* (Odonata: Aeshnidae). *International Journal of Odonatology* 8: 1–33.

———. 2007. Gone with the wind: Westward dispersal across the Indian Ocean and island speciation in *Hemicordulia* dragonflies (Odonata: Corduliidae). *Zootaxa* 1438: 27–48.

———. 2017. African Dragonflies and Damselflies Online. http://addo.adu.org.za/.

Dijkstra, K.-D. B., and Clausnitzer, V. 2004. Critical species of Odonata on Madagascar. *International Journal of Odonatology* 7: 219–228.

———. 2014. The dragonflies and damselflies of eastern Africa: Handbook for all Odonata from Sudan to Zimbabwe. *Studies in Afrotropical Zoology* 298: 1–260.

Dijkstra, K.-D. B., and Cohen, C. 2021. *Dragonflies and Damselflies of Madagascar and the Western Indian Ocean Islands.* Antananarivo: Association Vahatra.

Dijkstra, K.-D. B., van Tol, J., Legrand, J., and Theischinger, G. 2005. *Tramea* Hagen, 1861: Proposed conservation (Insecta, Odonata). *Bulletin of Zoological Nomenclature* 62: 68–71.

Dijkstra, K.-D. B., Suhling, F., and Müller, O. 2006. Review of the genus *Zygonoides*, with description of the larvae and notes on "zygonychine" Libellulidae (Odonata). *Tijdschrift voor Entomologie* 149: 275–292.
Dijkstra, K.-D. B., Clausnitzer, V., and Martens, A. 2007a. Tropical African *Platycnemis* damselflies (Odonata: Platycnemididae) and the biogeographical significance of a new species from Pemba Island, Tanzania. *Systematics and Biodiversity* 5: 187–198.
Dijkstra, K.-D. B., Groeneveld, L. F., Clausnitzer, V., and Hadrys, H. 2007b. The *Pseudagrion* split: Molecular phylogeny confirms the morphological and ecological dichotomy of Africa's most diverse genus of Odonata (Coenagrionidae). *International Journal of Odonatology* 10: 31–41.
Dijkstra, K.-D. B., Boudot, J.-P., Clausnitzer, V., Kipping, J., Kisakye, J. J., et al. 2011. Dragonflies and damselflies of Africa (Odonata): History, diversity, distribution, and conservation. In *The Diversity of Life in African Freshwaters: Under Water, Under Threat; An Analysis of the Status and Distribution of Freshwater Species Throughout Mainland Africa*, eds. W.R.T. Darwall, K. G. Smith, D. J. Allen, R. A. Holland, I. J. Harrison, and E.G.E. Brooks, pp. 128–177. Gland: IUCN.
Dijkstra, K.-D. B., Bechly, G., Bybee, S. M., Dow, R. A., Dumont, H. J., et al. 2013. The classification and diversity of dragonflies and damselflies (Odonata). *Zootaxa* 3703: 36–45.
Dijkstra, K.-D. B., Kalkman, V. J., Dow, R. A., Stokvis, F. R., and van Tol, J. 2014. Redefining the damselfly families: A comprehensive molecular phylogeny of Zygoptera (Odonata). *Systematic Entomology* 39: 68–96.
Dijkstra, K.-D. B., Mézière, N., and Kipping, J. 2015. Sixty new dragonfly and damselfly species from Africa (Odonata). *Odonatologica* 44: 447–678.
Dike, M. C. 1989. A key for the identification of Afrotropical species of the shoot-fly subgenus *Atherigona* of *Atherigona* (Diptera: Muscidae), with a description of some new species from Africa. *Bulletin of Entomological Research* 79: 545–566.
———. 1990. Two new species of *Atherigona* from Nigeria with a key for the identification of Afrotropical species of the subgenus *Acritochaeta* (Diptera: Muscidae). *Systematic Entomology* 15: 297–303.
Dimitrov, D., Benavides, L. R., Arnedo, M. A., Giribet, G., Griswold, C. E., Scharff, N., and Hormiga, G. 2017. Rounding up the usual suspects: A standard target-gene approach for resolving the interfamilial phylogenetic relationships of ecribellate orb-weaving spiders with a new family-rank classification (Araneae, Araneoidea). *Cladistics* 33(3): 221–250. doi:10.1111/cla.12165.
Dirsh, V. M. 1961. Notes on Acridoidea of Africa, Madagascar and Asia (Orthoptera). *Eos Revista Espagnola de Entomologia* 37: 379–398.
———. 1962. Acridoidea (Orthoptera) collected by Dr. F. Keiser in Madagascar. *Verhandlungen der Naturforschenden Gesellschaft zu Basel* 73: 270–275.
———. 1963. The Acridoidea of Madagascar II. Acrididae. Acridinae. *Bulletin of the British Museum (Natural History), Entomology Series* 13: 243–286.
Dirsh, V. M., and Descamps, M. 1968. Insectes Orthoptères Acridoidea Pyrgomorphidae et Acrididae. *Faune de Madagascar* 26: 1–312.
Dirsh, V. M., and Uvarov, B. P. 1953. Tree locusts of the genus *Anacridium* (Orthoptera, Acrididae). *Eos Revista Española de Entomologia* 29: 1–69.
Distant, W. L. 1914. Homoptera (Membracidae and Jassidae) collected in the Lagos District by W. A. Lamborn. *Transactions of the Entomological Society of London* 1913: 515–520.
Dittmann, M., Dammhahn, M., and Kappeler, P. M. 2014. The impact of selective logging on behavior and ecology of *Aphaenogaster swammerdami* (Formicidae): 20 years later—a happy ant? *Malagasy Nature* 8: 35–48.
Dixon, H. M. 1992. Species identification and described habitats of the crayfish genus *Astacoides* (Decapoda: Parastacidae) in the Ranomafana National Park regions of Madagascar. Ranomafana, Ranomafana National Park Project.
Dmitriev, D. A. 2003. 3i: World Auchenorrhyncha Database. Accessed 9 Dec. 2019. http://dmitriev.speciesfile.org/search.asp?key=Erythroneura&lng=En.
Dobson, M. 2004. Freshwater crabs in Africa. *Freshwater Forum* 21: 3–26.
Dolch, R. 2003. Insect–plant interactions: Their importance for biodiversity and ecological functioning. In *The Natural History of Madagascar*, eds. S. M. Goodman and J. P. Benstead, pp. 386–387. Chicago: University of Chicago Press.
Dolch, R., and Tscharntke, T. 2000. Insect communities of Malagasy legumes (Fabaceae): Patterns of species richness, resource fragmentation, and tropical-temperate differences. In *Diversité et endemisme à Madagascar/Diversity and Endemism in Madagascar*, eds. W. R. Lourenço and S. M. Goodman, pp. 285–293. Paris: Mémoires de la Société de Biogéographie.
Donnelly, T. W., and Parr, M. J. 2003. Odonata, dragonflies and damselflies. In *The Natural History of Madagascar*, eds. S. M. Goodman and J. P. Benstead, pp. 645–654. Chicago: University of Chicago Press.
Dowdy, N. J., Keating, S., Lemmon, A. R., Lemmon, E. M., Conner, W. E., et al. 2020. A deeper meaning for shallow-level phylogenomic studies: Nested anchored hybrid enrichment offers great promise for resolving the tiger moth tree of life (Lepidoptera: Erebidae: Arctiinae). *Systematic Entomology* 45(4): 874–893. doi:10.1111/syen.12433.
Drancourt, M., and Raoult, D. 2018. Investigation of pneumonic plague, Madagascar. *Emerging Infectious Diseases* 24: 183.
Dransfield, J., and Beentje, H. 1995. *The Palms of Madagascar*. Kew: Royal Botanic Gardens and International Palm Society.
Drinkwater, R., Williamson, J., Swinfield, T., Deere, N. J., Struebig M. J., Clare, E. L., Coomes, D., and Rossiter, S. J. 2019a. Occurrence of blood-feeding terrestrial leeches (Haemadipsidae) in a degraded forest ecosystem and their potential as ecological indicators. *Biotropica* 52(2): 302–312.
Drinkwater, R., Schnell, I. B., Bohmann, K., Bernard, H., Veron, G., Clare, E., Gilbert, M.T.P., and Rossiter, S. J. 2019b. Using metabarcoding to compare the suitability of two blood-feeding leech species for sampling mammalian diversity in North Borneo. *Molecular Ecology Resources* 19: 105–117.
Drury, D. 1773. *Illustrations of Natural History*. London: White.
Du Puy, B. 1996. The baobabs of Madagascar. *Curtis's Botanical Magazine* 13: 86–95.
Du Puy, D. J., Phillipson, P. B., and Rabevohitra, R. 1995. The genus *Delonix* (Leguminosae: Caesalpinioideae: Caesalpinieae) in Madagascar. *Kew Bulletin* 50: 445–475.
Dubatolov, V. V. 2006. On the generic status of the Afrotropical *Nyctemera* species (Lepidoptera, Arctiidae). *Atalanta* 37: 191–205.
Duchemin, J.-B. 2003a. Biogéographie des puces de Madagascar. Thèse de Parasitologie, University of Paris XII, Val de Marne, Faculté de Médecine de Créteil.
———. 2003b. Two new fleas (Siphonaptera: Ceratophyllidae: Leptopsyllinae) of Madagascar: *Tsaractenus rodhaini* n. sp. and *Paractenopsyllus* (*Consobrinopsyllus* n. subgen.) *goodmani* n. sp. *Parasite* 10(4): 351–358.
———. 2003c. Leptopsyllines from Madagascar (Insecta: Siphonaptera: Ceratophyllidae): Description of five new species of *Paractenopsyllus* Wagner, 1938. *Parasite* 11(1): 59–70.
Duchemin, J.-B., and Ratovonjato, J. 2004. Description de trois nouvelles espèces de *Paractenopsyllus* (Siphonaptera: Leptopsyllinae) de Madagascar. *Parasite* 11(3): 253–360.
Duchemin, J.-B., Ramilijaona Ravoahangimalala, O., and Le Goff, G. 2003. Culicidae, mosquitoes, *moka gasy*. In *The Natural History of Madagascar*, eds. S. M. Goodman and J. P. Benstead, pp. 708–715. Chicago: University of Chicago Press.
Dumetz, N. 1999. High plant diversity of lowland rainforest vestiges in eastern Madagascar. *Biodiversity and Conservation* 8: 273–315.
Duplantier, J.-M., Duchemin, J.-B., Chanteau, S., and Carniel, E. 2005. From the recent lessons of the Malagasy foci towards a global understanding of the factors involved in plague reemergence. *Veterinary Research* 36(3): 437–453.
Durden, L. A. 2019. Lice (Phthiraptera). In *Medical and Veterinary Entomology*, eds. G. R. Mullen and L. A. Durden, pp. 79–106. London: Academic Press/Elsevier.
Durden, L. A., and Musser, G. G. 1994. The sucking lice (Insect, Anoplura) of the world: A taxonomic checklist with records of mammalian hosts and geographical distributions. *Bulletin of the American Museum of Natural History* 218: 1–90.
Durden, L. A., Keirans, J. E., and Smith, L. L. 2002. *Amblyomma geochelone*, a new species of tick (Acari: Ixodidae) from the Madagascan ploughshare tortoise. *Journal of Medical Entomology* 39: 398–403.
Durden, L. A., Zohdy, S., and Laakkonen, J. 2010. Lice and ticks of the eastern mouse lemur, *Microcebus rufus*, with descriptions of the male and third instar nymph of *Lemurpediculus verruculosus* (Phthiraptera: Anoplura). *Journal of Parasitology* 96: 874–878.
Durden, L. A., Blanco, M. B., and Seabolt, M. H. 2017. Two new species of sucking lice (Phthiraptera, Anoplura, Polyplacidae) from endangered, hibernating lemurs (Primates: Cheirogaleidae). *Journal of Medical Entomology* 54: 568–575.
Durden, L. A., Kessler, S. E., Radespiel, U., Zimmermann, E., Hasiniaina, A. F., and Zohdy, S. 2018. A new species of sucking louse (Phthiraptera: Anoplura: Polyplacidae) from the gray mouse lemur, *Microcebus murinus* (Primates: Cheirogaleidae), in Madagascar. *Journal of Medical Entomology* 55: 910–914.
Dworakowska, I. 1997. Typhlocybinae (Auchenorrhyncha, Cicadellidae) known to occur in Madagascar. *Annotationes Zoologicae et Botanicae* 220: 3–27.
Eberhard, W. G. 1982. Predatory behavior of an assassin spider, *Chorizopes* sp. (Araneidae), and the defensive behavior of its prey. *Journal of the Bombay Natural History Society* 79: 522–524.
Edwards, F. W. 1930. Notes on exotic Chaoborinae, with descriptions of new species (Diptera, Culicidae). *Annals and Magazine of Natural History* 10: 528–540.

Eggers, F. 1926. Die mutmaßliche Funktion des Johnstonschen Sinnesorgans bie *Gyrinus*. *Zoologischer Anzeiger* 68: 184–192.

———. 1927. Nähere Mitteilungen über das Johnstonsche Sinnesorgan und über das Ausweichvermögen der Taumelkäfer. *Zoologischer Anzeiger* 71: 136–156.

Eggleton, P. 2000. Global patterns of termite diversity. In *Termites: Evolution, Sociality, Symbiosis, Ecology*, eds. T. Abe, M. Higashi, and D. E. Bignell, pp. 25–51. Dordrecht: Kluwer Academic.

Eggleton, P., and Davies, R. G. 2003. Isoptera, termites. In *The Natural History of Madagascar*, eds. S. M. Goodman and J. P. Benstead, pp. 654–660. Chicago: University of Chicago Press.

Ehlers, J., Poppert, S., Ratovonamana, R. Y., Ganzhorn, J. U., Tappe, D., and Krüger, A. 2019. Ectoparasites of endemic and domestic animals in southwest Madagascar. *Acta Tropica* 196: 83–92.

Ehlers, J., Krüger, A., Rakotondranary, S. J., Ratovonamana, R. Y., Poppert, S., Ganzhorn, J. U., and Tappe, D. 2020. Molecular detection of *Rickettsia* spp., *Borrelia* spp., *Bartonella* spp., and *Yersinia pestis* in ectoparasites of endemic and domestic animals in southwest Madagascar. *Acta Tropica* 205: 105339.

Ekesi, S., De Meyer, M., Mohamed, S. A., Virgilio, M., and Borgemeister, C. 2016. Taxonomy, ecology and management of native and exotic fruit fly species in Africa. *Annual Review of Entomology* 61: 219–238.

Elliott, J. M. 1973. The diel activity pattern, drifting and food of the leech *Erpobdella octoculata* (L.) (Hirudinea: Erpobdellidae) in a Lake District stream. *Journal of Animal Ecology* 1: 449–459.

Elouard, J.-M. 2003a. Simuliidae, blackflies. In *The Natural History of Madagascar*, eds. S. M. Goodman and J. P. Benstead, pp. 715–721. Chicago: University of Chicago Press.

———. 2003b. Plecoptera, stoneflies. In *The Natural History of Madagascar*, eds. S. M. Goodman and J. P. Benstead, pp. 661–662. Chicago: University of Chicago Press.

Elouard, J.-M., and Gibon, F.-M. 2001. *Biodiversité et biotypologie des eaux continentales de Madagascar*. Montpellier: IRD.

———. 2003. Ecology of aquatic invertebrates. In *The Natural History of Madagascar*, eds. S. M. Goodman and J. P. Benstead, pp. 511–517. Chicago: University of Chicago Press.

Elouard, J.-M., and Oliarinony, R. 1997. Biodiversité aquatique de Madagascar. 6, *Madecassorythus* un nouveau genre de Tricorythidae définissant la nouvelle sous-famille des Madecassorythinae (Ephemeroptera, Pannota). *Bulletin de la Société Entomologique de France* 102(3): 225–232.

Elouard, J.-M., and Sartori, M. 1997. *Proboscidoplocia*, a singular plural (Ephemeroptera, Polymitarcyidae). In *Ephemeroptera and Plecoptera: Biology, Ecology and Systematics*, eds. P. Landolt and M. Sartori, pp. 439–448. Fribourg: MTL.

Elouard, J.-M., Sartori, M., Gattolliat, J.-L. and Oliarinony, O. 1999. *Proboscidoplocia* (Ephemeroptera, Polymitarcyidae) from the Réserve Naturelle Intégrale d'Andohahela and surrounding areas, with a description of a new species. In *A Floral and Faunal Inventory of the Réserve Naturelle Intégrale d'Andohahela, Madagascar: With Reference to Elevational Variation*, ed. S. M. Goodman. *Fieldiana: Zoology*, new ser., 94: 111–114.

Elouard, J.-M., Gattolliat, J.-L., and Sartori, M. 2003. Ephemeroptera, mayflies. In *The Natural History of Madagascar*, eds. S. M. Goodman and J. P. Benstead, pp. 639–645. Chicago: University of Chicago Press.

Emberton, K. C. 1990. Acavid land snails of Madagascar: Subgeneric revision based on published data (Gastropoda: Pulmonata: Stylommatophora). *Proceedings of the Academy of Natural Sciences of Philadelphia* 142: 101–117.

———. 1994a. Thirty new species of Madagascan land snails (Mollusca: Gastropoda). *Proceedings of the Academy of Natural Sciences of Philadelphia* 145: 147–189.

———. 1994b. Morphology and aestivation behaviour in some Madagascan acavid land snails. *Biological Journal of the Linnean Society* 53: 175–187.

———. 1997. Diversities and distributions of 80 land snail species in southeastern-most Madagascan rainforests, with a report that lowlands are richer than highlands in endemic and rare species. *Biodiversity and Conservation* 6: 1137–1154.

———. 2004. Madagascan *Georissa*, *Cyclotus*, *Omphalotropis* and so-called *Chondrocyclus*. *Archiv für Molluskenkunde* 133(1/2): 69–107.

———. 2007. Twenty-nine new land-snail species of the genus *Kalidos* from northern Madagascar (Pulmonata: Helicarionidae). *Archiv für Molluskenkunde* 136(2): 245–289.

———. 2009. Operculate land snails from three rainforest transects in northeastern Madagascar with descriptions of nine new species and one new sub species. *Archiv für Molluskenkunde* 138(1): 1–41.

Emberton, K. C., and Griffiths, O. L. 2009a. Pulmonate land mollusks from three rainforest transects in northeastern Madagascar: Pt. 1 of 2, with descriptions of 12 new species and one new subspecies. *Archiv für Molluskenkunde* 138(2): 137–167.

———. 2009b. Pulmonate land mollusks from three rainforest transects in northeastern Madagascar: pt. 2 of 2, with descriptions of 21 new species: (Gastropoda: Pulmonate: Stylommatophora). *Archiv für Molluskenkunde* 138(2): 169–203.

Emberton, K. C., and Pearce, T. A. 2000. Small high-spired pulmonates from Mounts Mahermana, Ilapiry, and Vasiha, southeastern Madagascar, with descriptions of a new genus, and with conservation statuses of 15 streptaxid species. *Veliger* 43: 126–135.

Emberton, K. C., and Rakotomalala, M. F. 1996. Madagascar's biogeographically most informative land-snail taxa. In *Biogéographie de Madagascar*, ed. W. R. Lourenço, pp. 563–574. Paris: Editions de l'ORSTOM.

Emberton, K. C., Slapcinsky, J., Campbell, C. A., Rakotondrazafy, J. A., Andramiarison, T. N., and Emberton, J. D. 2010. Terrestrial mollusks of Andriantantely Massif, eastern Madagascar, with descriptions of 36 new species. *Archiv für Molluskenkunde* 139(1): 71–141.

Emden, F. I. van. 1935. Description préliminaire d'une larve de Pogonostome. *Bulletin de l'Académie Malgache* 18: 150–151.

———. 1939. Muscidae: A—Muscinae and Stomoxydinae. *Ruwenzori Expedition* 1934–35(2): 49–89.

———. 1940. Muscidae: B—Coenosiinae. *Ruwenzori Expedition* 1934–35(2): 91–255.

———. 1941. Keys to the Muscidae of the Ethiopian Region: Scatophaginae, Anthomyiinae, Lispinae, Fanniinae. *Bulletin of Entomological Research* 32: 251–275.

———. 1942a. Keys to the Muscidae of the Ethiopian Region: *Dichaetomyia*-group [Part]. *Annals and Magazine of Natural History* (11) 9: 673–701.

———. 1942b. Keys to the Muscidae of the Ethiopian Region: *Dichaetomyia*-group [Concl.]. *Annals and Magazine of Natural History* (11) 9: 721–736.

———. 1943. Keys to the Muscidae of the Ethiopian Region: *Phaonia*-group. *Annals and Magazine of Natural History* (11) 10: 73–101.

———. 1951. Muscidae: C—Scatophaginae, Anthomyiinae, Lispinae, Fanniinae and Phaoniinae. *Ruwenzori Expedition* 1934–35(2): 325–710.

Emeljanov, A. F. 1969. Auchenorrhyncha (Homoptera). In *Rastitel'nye soobschestva I zhivotnoe naselenie stepey I pustyn' Tsentral'nogo Kazakhstana* [Plant and animal communities of the Central Kazakhstan steppe and deserts]. Pt. 1, *Biokompleksnye issledovaniya v Kazakhstane* [Biocomplex investigation in Kazakhstan], eds. L. V. Arnoldi and A. A. Yunatov, pp. 358–381. Leningrad: Nauka.

Emerit, M. 1980. *Exechocentrus lancearius* Simon, 1889: La redécouverte d'une araignée rare de Madagascar; Considérations sur les Exechocentreae. *Revue Arachnologique* 3: 13–23.

Endrödy-Younga, S. 1997. Active extraction of water-dissolved oxygen and descriptions of new taxa of Torridincolidae (Coleoptera: Myxophaga). *Annals of the Transvaal Museum* 36: 313–332.

Engel, M., and Krishna, K. 2004. Family-group names for termites (Isoptera). *American Museum Novitates* 3432: 1–9.

Enghoff, H. 1996. Millipedes (Diplopoda) from the eastern slopes of the Réserve Naturelle Intégrale d'Andringitra, Madagascar. In *A Floral and Faunal Inventory of the Eastern Slopes of the Réserve Naturelle Intégrale d'Andringitra, Madagascar: With Reference to Elevational Variation*, ed. S. M. Goodman, *Fieldiana: Zoology*, new ser., 85: 90–92.

———. 2003. Diplopoda, Millipedes. In *The Natural History of Madagascar*, eds. S. M. Goodman and J. P. Benstead, pp. 617–627. Chicago: University of Chicago Press.

Enghoff, H., Golovatch, S., Short, M., Stoev, P., and Wesener, T. 2015. Diplopoda. In *Treatise on Zoology: Anatomy, Taxonomy, Biology*, ed. A. Minelli. *The Myriapoda* 2(16): 363–453.

Eremeeva, M. E., Warang, S. S., Anderson, M. L., Capps, D., Zohdy, S., and Durden, L. A. 2019. Molecular survey for pathogens and markers of permethrin resistance in human head lice (Phthiraptera: Pediculidae) from Madagascar. *Journal of Parasitology* 105: 459–468.

Espeland, M., Hall, J.P.W., DeVries, P. J., Lees, D. C., Cornwall, M., et al. 2015. Ancient Neotropical origin and recent recolonization: Phylogeny, biogeography and diversification of the Riodinidae (Lepidoptera: Papilionoidea). *Molecular Phylogenetics and Evolution* 93: 296–306.

Espeland, M., Breinholt, J., Willmott, K. R., Warren, A. D., Vila, R., et al. 2018. A comprehensive and dated phylogenomic analysis of butterflies. *Current Biology* 28: 770–778.

Esteves, F. A., and Fisher B. L. 2016. Taxonomic revision of *Stigmatomma* Roger (Hymenoptera: Formicidae) in the Malagasy region. *Biodiversity Data Journal* 4: e8032.

Estrade, F. 1935. Observations relatives à la biologie de la *Xenopsylla cheopis* en Emyrne. *Bulletin de la Société de Pathologie Exotique* 28: 293–298.

Evans, J. W. 1953. Les Cicadellidae de Madagascar (Homoptères). *Mémoires de l'Institut Scientifique de Madagascar Tananarive (E)* 4: 87–137.

———. 1959. Quelques nouveaux Cicadellides (Homoptères) de Madagascar: Observations sur la signification évolutive de la spéciation dans le genre *Coloborrhis* Germar. *Mémoires de l'Institut Scientifique de Madagascar Tananarive (E)* 11: 481–507.

Evans, S. E., Jones, M.E.H., and Krause, D. W. 2008. A giant frog with South American affinities from Late Cretaceous of Madagascar. *Proceedings of the National Academy of Sciences of the USA* 105: 2951–2956.

Ewing, H. E. 1923. New genera and species of sucking lice. *Journal of the Washington Academy of Sciences* 13: 146–150.

Fage, L. 1926. Sur quelques araignées de Madagascar, nouvelles ou peu connues et sur leur curieuse industrie. *Archives de Zoologie Expérimentale et Générale* 65: 5–17.

———. 1929. Faune des colonies françaises 3. No. 637, Les scorpions de Madagascar. Paris: Société d'Editions Géographiques Maritimes Coloniales.

———. 1946. Complément à la faune des arachnides de Madagascar. *Bulletin du Muséum d'Histoire Naturelle*, Paris, série 2, 18(3): 256–267.

Fahmy, M., Ravelomanantsoa, N.A.F., Youssef, S., Hekkala, E., and Siddall, M. E. 2019. Biological inventory of Ranomafana National Park tetrapods using leech-derived iDNA. *European Journal of Wildlife Research* 65: 1–13.

Fahmy, M., Williams, K., Tessler, T., Weiskopf, S., Hekkala, E., and Siddall, M. E. 2020. Assessing iDNA metabarcoding on multilocus pooled sampling strategies from transcontinental terrestrial leech collections. *Journal of Parasitology* 106(6): 843–853.

Fairmaire, L. 1883. Diagnoses de coléoptères nouveaux de Madagascar. *Le Naturaliste* 46(5): 364–365.

———. 1889. Diagnoses de coléoptères madécasses. *Comptes-rendus des Séances de la Société Entomologique de Belgique* 33: vi–ix.

———. 1901. Note IX: Descriptions de quelques coléoptères recueillis par M. le Dr Decorse dans le sud de Madagascar, plateau de l'Androy. *Notes from the Leyden Museum* 23: 65–84.

———. 1903. Matériaux pour la faune coléoptérique de la région malgache, note 17. *Annales de la Société Entomologique de Belgique* 47: 358–380.

———. 1905. Matériaux pour la faune coléoptérique malgache, note 19. *Annales de la Société Entomologique de Belgique* 49: 114–138.

Farwig, N., Randrianirina, E. F., Voigt, F. A., Kraemer, M., and Böhning-Gaese, K. 2004. Pollination ecology of the dioecious tree *Commiphora guillauminii* in Madagascar. *Journal of Tropical Ecology* 20: 307–316.

Feijen, H. R. 1983. Systematics and phylogeny of Centrioncidae, a new Afromontane family of Diptera (Schizophora). *Zoologische Verhandelingen Leiden* 202: 1–137.

———. 1989. Diopsidae. Cyclorrhapha III (Schizophora other than Calyptratae). In *Flies of the Nearctic Region*, vol. 9, pt. 12, ed. G.C.D. Griffiths, pp. 1–122. Stuttgart: E. Schweizerbart.

Feijen, H. R., and Feijen, C. 2009. *Diopsis* (Diopsidae, Diptera) with unusual wing spots: Two new species from Malawi with a longer eye span in females than in males. *Zoologische Mededelingen Leiden* 83: 701–722.

———. 2011. On the biogeographic range of the genus *Teleopsis* Rondani (Diptera: Diopsidae), with redescription of *Teleopsis sykesii* from India and description of a new species from Borneo. *Zoologische Mededelingen Leiden* 85: 141–159.

———. 2013. A revision of the genus *Diopsina* Curran (Diptera, Diopsidae) with description of a new species from Guinea-Bissau. *Tijdschrift voor Entomologie* 156(2–3): 161–189.

———. 2021. 64. Diopsidae (stalk-eyed flies and Afromontane forest flies) (Diopsoidea). In *Manual of Afrotropical Diptera*. Vol. 3, *Brachycera: Cyclorrhapha, excluding Calyptratae*, eds. A. H. Kirk-Spriggs and B. J. Sinclair, pp. 1523–1543. Suricata 6. Pretoria: South African National Biodiversity Institute.

Feijen, H. R., Martin, R., and Feijen, C. 2017. The occurrence of stalk-eyed flies (Diptera, Diopsidae) in the Arabian Peninsula, with a review of cluster formation in the Diopsidae. *Tijdschrift voor Entomologie* 160 (2): 75–88.

Feijen, H. R., Feijen, F.A.A., and Feijen, C. 2018a. *Madagopsina* gen. n. and *Gracilopsina* gen. n. (Diptera: Diopsidae) from Madagascar with description of four new species. *Tijdschrift voor Entomologie* 160(3): 141–215.

———. 2018b. Biogeographical and allometric aspects of the Diopsidae of Madagascar. In *Abstracts Volume, 9th International Congress of Dipterology*, 25–30 Nov. 2018, Windhoek, Namibia, eds. A. H. Kirk-Spriggs and B. S. Muller, p. 77. Windhoek: John Meinert Printers.

Feldmann, R. M., Schweitzer, C. E., and Leahy, J. 2011. New Eocene crayfish from the Mcabee Beds in British Columbia: First record of Parastacoidea in the Northern Hemisphere. *Journal of Crustacean Biology* 31: 320–331.

Fenchel, T. 1993. There are more small than large species? *Oikos* 68: 375–378.

Feng, L. 2019. Systematic study on the subfamily Cicadellinae (Hemiptera: Cicadellidae). PhD thesis, Northwest A&F University, Yangling, Shaanxi, China.

Fennah, R. G. 1949. New exotic Fulgoroidea. *Annals and Magazine of Natural History* 20(12): 585–606.

FEOW. 2019. Freshwater ecoregions of the world: A global biogeographical regionalization of the Earth's freshwater biodiversity. World Wildlife Fund and Nature Conservancy. Accessed 10 Dec. 2019. https://www.feow.org/.

Fernández, R., Kallal, R., Dimitrov, D., Ballesteros, J., Arnedo, M., Giribet, G., and Hormiga, G. 2018. Phylogenomics, diversification dynamics, and comparative transcriptomics across the spider tree of life. *Current Biology* 28: 2190–2193. https://doi.org/10.1016/j.cub.2018.03.064.

Ferraro, P. 1994. Natural resource use in the southeastern rainforests of Madagascar and the local impacts of establishing the Ranomafana National Park. MS thesis, Duke University.

Ferris, G. F. 1932. Contributions toward a monograph of the sucking lice. Pt. 5, *Stanford University Publications University Series, Biological Sciences* 2: 271–413.

Férussac, A.E.J. d'Audebard de. 1827. Catalogue des espèces de mollusques terrestres et fluviatiles, recueillies par M. Rang dans un voyage aux Grandes-Indes. *Bulletin des Sciences Naturelles et de Géologie* 10: 298–307.

Fiala, B., Maschwitz, U., and Pong, T. Y. 1991. The association between *Macaranga* trees and ants in South-east Asia. In *Ant–Plant Interactions*, eds. C. R. Huxley and D. F. Cutler, pp. 263–270. New York: Oxford University Press.

Fibiger, M., and Hacker, H. H. 2007. Amphipyrinae, Condicinae, Eriopinae, Xyleninae (part). In *Noctuidae Europaeae*, vol. 9. Sorø: Entomological Press.

Fibiger, M., and Lafontaine, J. D. 2005. A review of the higher classification of the Noctuoidea (Lepidoptera) with special reference to the Holarctic fauna. *Esperiana* 11: 7–92.

Fikáček, M., and Šípková, H. 2009. New Asian Hydroscapha, with comments on male–female association of co-occurring species (Coleoptera, Myxophaga, Hydroscaphidae). *Zootaxa* 2286: 31–48.

Filou, E. 2019. Eat the insects, spare the lemurs. *Mongabay*, 11 July 2019. https://news.mongabay.com/2019/07/eat-the-insects-spare-the-lemurs/.

Fischer, E., and Theisen, I. 2000. Vegetation of Malagasy inselbergs. *Ecological Studies* 146: 259–276.

Fischer, E., Porembski, S., and Barthlott, W. 2000. Revision of the genus *Genlisea* (Lentibulariaceae) in Africa and Madagascar with notes on ecology and phytogeography. *Nordic Journal of Botany* 20: 291–318.

Fischer-Piette, E., and Blanc, F. 1972. Le peuplement de mollusques terrestres de Madagascar. In *Biogeography and Ecology of Madagascar*, eds. R. Battistini and G. Richard-Vindard, pp. 459–476. The Hague: W. Junk.

Fischer-Piette, E., and Vukadinovic, D. 1973. Sur les mollusques fluviatiles de Madagascar. *Malacologia* 12: 339–378.

Fischer-Piette, E., Blanc, C. P., Blanc, F., and Salvat, F. 1993. Gastéropodes terrestres prosobranches. *Faune de Madagascar* 80: 1–281.

———. 1994. Gastéropodes terrestres pulmones (excl. Veronicellidae et g. *Elisolimax*). *Faune de Madagascar* 83: 1–551.

Fisher, B. L. 1996. Ant diversity patterns along an elevational gradient in the Réserve Naturelle Intégrale d'Andringitra, Madagascar. In *A Floral and Faunal Inventory of the Eastern Slopes of the Réserve Naturelle Intégrale d'Andringitra, Madagascar: With Reference to Elevational Variation*, ed. S. M. Goodman. *Fieldiana: Zoology*, new ser., 85: 93–108.

———. 1997. Biogeography and ecology of the ant fauna of Madagascar (Hymenoptera: Formicidae). *Journal of Natural History* 31: 269–302.

———. 1998. Ant diversity patterns along an elevational gradient in the Réserve Spéciale d'Anjanaharibe-Sud and on the western Masoala Peninsula. In *A Floral and Faunal Inventory of the Réserve Spéciale d'Anjanaharibe-Sud, Madagascar: With Reference to Elevational Variation*, ed. S. M. Goodman. *Fieldiana: Zoology*, new ser., 90: 39–67.

———. 1999a. Improving inventory efficiency: A case study of leaf litter ant diversity in Madagascar. *Ecological Applications* 9: 714–731.

———. 1999b. Ant diversity patterns along an elevational gradient in the Réserve Naturelle Intégrale d'Andohahela, Madagascar. In *A Fauna and Flora Survey of the Réserve Naturelle Integrale d'Andohahela, Madagascar: With Particular Reference to*

Elevational Variation, ed. S. M. Goodman. *Fieldiana: Zoology*, new ser., 94: 129–147.

———. 2000. The Malagasy fauna of *Strumigenys*. In *The Ant Tribe Dacetini*, ed. B. Bolton. *Memoirs of the American Entomological Institute* 65: 612–710.

———. 2002. Ant diversity patterns along an elevational gradient in the Réserve Spéciale de Manongarivo, Madagascar. In *Inventaire floristique et faunistique de la Réserve Spéciale de Manongarivo*, Madagascar, eds. L. Gautier and S. M. Goodman. *Boissiera* 59: 311–328.

———. 2003. Ants (Formicidae: Hymenoptera). In *The Natural History of Madagascar*, eds. S. M. Goodman and J. P. Benstead, pp. 811–819. Chicago: University of Chicago Press.

———. 2005a. A model for a global inventory of ants: A case study in Madagascar. In *Biodiversity: A Symposium Held on the Occasion of the 150th Anniversary of the California Academy of Sciences*, 17–18 June 2003, ed. N. G. Jablonski. *Proceedings of the California Academy of Sciences* 56: 78–89.

———. 2005b. A new species of *Discothyrea* Roger from Mauritius and a new species of *Proceratium* from Madagascar (Hymenoptera: Formicidae). *Proceedings of the California Academy of Sciences* 56: 657–667.

———. 2016. Descriptive taxonomy: A golden or gold-plated age? *Ecology* 97: 1366–1367.

Fisher, B. L. and Bolton, B. 2016. *Ants of Africa and Madagascar: A Guide to the Genera*. Berkeley: University of California Press.

Fisher, B. L., and Peeters, C. 2019. *Ants of Madagascar: A Guide to the 62 Genera*. Antananarivo: Association Vahatra.

Fisher, B. L., and Robertson, H. 2002. Comparison and origin of forest and grassland ant assemblages in the high plateau of Madagascar (Hymenoptera: Formicidae). *Biotropica* 34: 155–167.

Fisher, B. L., and Smith, M. A. 2008. A revision of Malagasy species of *Anochetus* Mayr and *Odontomachus* Latreille. *PLoS One* 3(5): e1787.

Fisher, B. L., Ratsirarson, H., and Razafimandimby, S. 1998. Les fourmis (Hymenoptera: Formicidae). In *Inventaire biologique de la forêt littorale de Tampolo (Fenoarivo Atsinanana)*, eds. J. Ratsirarson and S. M. Goodman. *Recherches pour le Développement*, série *Sciences Biologiques* 14: 107–131.

Fleck, G. 2004. La larve du genre *Cyanothemis* Ris, 1915 (Odonata: Anisoptera: Libellulidae). Conséquences phylogénétiques. *Annales de la Société Entomologique de France,* nouvelle série, 40: 51–58.

Fleck, G., and Legrand, J. 2006. La larve du genre *Nesocordulia* McLachlan, 1882 (Odonata, Anisoptera, "Corduliidae"). Conséquences phylogénétiques. *Revue Française d'Entomologie* 28: 31–40.

———. 2013. Notes on the genus *Libellulosoma* Martin, 1906, and related genera (Odonata: Anisoptera: Corduliidae). *Zootaxa* 3745: 579–586.

Fleck, G., Brenk, M., and Misof, B. 2008. Larval and molecular characters help to solve phylogenetic puzzles in the highly diverse dragonfly family Libellulidae (Insecta: Odonata: Anisoptera): The Tetrathemistinae are a polyphyletic group. *Organisms, Diversity and Evolution* 8: 1–16.

Fletcher, D. S. 1978. Geometridae (Lepidoptera) collected by Dr. J. Szunyoghy in Tanzania. *Acta Zoologica Hungarica* 24: 41–105.

Flint, O. S., Jr., McAlpine, J. F., and Ross, H. H. 1987. A revision of the genus *Leptonema* Guérin (Trichoptera: Hydropsychidae: Macronematinae). *Smithsonian Contribution to Zoology* 450:1–193.

Flynn, J. J., Parrish, J. M., Rakotosamimanana, B., Simpson, W. F., Whatley, R. L., and Wyss, A. R. 1999. A Triassic fauna from Madagascar, including early dinosaurs. *Science* 286: 763–765.

Fölling, M., Knogge, C., and Böhme, W. 2001. Geckos are milking honeydew-producing planthoppers in Madagascar. *Journal of Natural History* 35: 279–284.

Fonseca, C. R. 2009. The silent mass extinction of insect herbivores in biodiversity hotspots. *Conservation Biology* 23: 1507–1515.

Fontaine, J. 1968. Contribution à l'étude des Éphémèroptères malgaches: La surperfamille des Ephemeroidea. *Bulletin Mensuel de la Société Linéenne de Lyon* 6: 228–242.

Forel, A. 1891. Les Formicides. In *Histoire physique, naturelle et politique de Madagascar*. Vol. 20, *Histoire naturelle des Hyménoptères*, 2 (fascicule 28), ed. A. Grandidier, pp. 1–231. Paris: Hachette.

———. 1892. Les Formicides. In *Histoire physique, naturelle et politique de Madagascar*. Vol. 20, *Histoire naturelle des Hyménoptères*, 2 (supplément au 28 fascicule), ed. A. Grandidier, pp. 229–280. Paris: Hachette et Cie.

Forero, D., Choe, D.-H., and Weirauch, C. 2011. Resin gathering in Neotropical resin bugs (Insecta: Hemiptera: Reduviidae): Functional and comparative morphology. *Journal of Morphology* 272: 204–229.

Forthman, M., and Weirauch, C. 2012. Toxic associations: A review of the predatory behaviors of millipede assassin bugs (Hemiptera: Reduviidae: Ectrichodiinae). *European Journal of Entomology* 109: 147–153.

———. 2016. Phylogenetics and biogeography of the endemic Madagascan millipede assassin bugs (Hemiptera: Reduviidae: Ectrichodiinae). *Molecular Phylogenetics and Evolution* 100: 219–233.

———. 2017. Millipede assassins and allies (Heteroptera: Reduviidae: Ectrichodiinae, Tribelocephalinae): Total evidence phylogeny, revised classification and evolution of sexual dimorphism. *Systematic Entomology* 42: 575–595.

Forthman, M., Chłond, D., and Weirauch, C. 2016. Taxonomic monograph of the endemic millipede assassin bug fauna of Madagascar (Hemiptera: Reduviidae: Ectrichodiinae). *Bulletin of the American Museum of Natural History* 400: 1–152.

Franciscolo, M. E. 1994. Three new *Africophilus* Guignot and new records of Gyrinidae and Dytiscidae from Sierra Leone (Coleoptera). *Problemi Attuali di Scienza e di Cultura* 267: 267–298.

Franclemont, J. G., and Todd, E. L. 1983. Noctuidae. In *Check List of the Lepidoptera of America North of Mexico*, eds. R. W. Hodges, T. Dominick, D. R. Davis, D. C. Ferguson, J. G. Franclemont, E. G. Munroe, and J. A. Powell, pp. 120–159. Cambridge: E. W. Classey Ltd. and the Wedge Entomological Research Foundation, Cambridge University Press.

Fraser, F. C. 1949. Odonata of Madagascar, Appendix I. *Mémoires de l'Institut Scientifique de Madagascar*, série A, 3: 21–40.

———. 1951. Appendix to the Zygoptera of Madagascar. *Mémoires de l'Institut Scientifique de Madagascar*, série A, 6: 407–417.

———. 1953a. Another new *Pseudagrion* from Madagascar [Odonata]. *Mémoires de l'Institut Scientifique de Madagascar*, série E, 3: 29–31.

———. 1953b. Odonates nouveaux de Madagascar. *Le Naturaliste Malgache* 5: 159–166.

———. 1955a. Additions à la faune des odonates de Madagascar. *Le Naturaliste Malgache*, 7: 39–44.

———. 1955b. Les *Nesolestes* de Madagascar [Odonates]. *Le Naturaliste Malgache*, 7: 45–52.

———. 1956. Insectes Odonates Anisoptères. *Faune de Madagascar* 1: 1–125.

———. 1960. A note on the classification of the genus *Tatocnemis* Kirby, with a key to the species and the description of a new species. *Le Naturaliste Malgache* 12: 65–69.

———. 1962. Report on the Austrian expedition to Madagascar, 1958. Order Odonata. *Memoires de l'Institut Scientifique de Madagascar,* série E, 13: 147–159.

Freidberg, A., and Hancock, D. L. 1989. *Cryptophorellia*, a remarkable new genus of Afrotropical Tephritinae (Diptera: Tephritidae). *Annals of the Natal Museum* 30: 15–32.

Freidberg, A., and Kaplan, F. 1992. Revision of the Oedaspidini of the Afrotropical Region (Diptera: Tephritidae: Tephritinae). *Annals of the Natal Museum* 33: 51–94.

Freidberg, A., and Merz, B. 2006. A revision of the *Gymnosagena* group of genera (Diptera: Tephritidae: Tephritinae). *Israel Journal of Entomology* 35–36: 367–422.

Freytag, P. H., and Cwikla, P. S. 1984. Two new species of idiocerine leafhoppers from Malagasy Republic (Homoptera: Cicadellidae). *Pan-Pacific Entomologist* 60: 341–344.

Freytag, P. H., and Knight, W. J. 1966. The Idiocerinae of Madagascar (Hom. Cicadellidae). *Annales de la Société Entomologique de France* 2: 75–103.

Frieser, R. 1981. Beitrag zur Kenntnis der Anthribiden (Coleoptera, Anthribidae). *Entomologische Arbeiten aus dem Museum G. Frey* 29: 249–258.

———. 2005. Betrag zur Kenntnis der Anthribiden (Coleoptera: Anthribidae). *Acta Coleopterologica* 21(2): 3–8.

———. 2007. Ein neuer Beitrag zur Kenntnis der Anthribiden Madagascars (Coleoptera: Anthribidae). *Acta Coleopterologica* 23(3): 33–56.

———. 2009. Beitrag zur Kenntnis der Anthribiden (Coleoptera: Anthribidae). *Acta Coleopterologica* 25(1): 46–70.

———. 2010. Teilergebnisse der entomologischen Expedition von Milos Tryzna auf Madagaskar in 2007 mit Genehmigung ANGAP (Coleoptera: Anthribidae). *Acta Coleopterologica* 26(1): 3–22.

Gade, D. W. 1985. Savanna woodland, fire, protein and silk in highland Madagascar. *Journal of Ethnobiology* 5(2): 109–122.

Gaedike, R. 2004. New genera and species of epermeniid moths from the Afrotropical Region (Lepidoptera: Epermeniidae). *Annals of the Transvaal Museum* 41: 41–59.

Gange, A. 2000. Arbuscular mycorrhizal fungi, Collembola and plant growth. *Trends in Ecology and Evolution* 15(9): 369–372.

Gardner, C. J., Nicoll, M. E., Birkinshaw, C., Harris, A., Lewis, R. E., Rakotomalala, D., and Ratsifandrihamanana, A. N. 2018. The rapid expansion of Madagascar's protected area system. *Biological Conservation* 220: 29–36.

Gardner, J.C.M. 1947. On larvae of the Noctuidae (Lepidoptera). III. *Transactions of the Royal Entomological Society of London* 98: 59–89.

Garrison, N., Rodriguez, J., Agnarsson, I., Coddington, J., Griswold, C., Hamilton, C., Hedin, M., Kocot, K., Ledford, J., and Bond, J. 2016. Spider phylogenomics: Untangling the spider tree of life. *PeerJ* 4: e1719.

Gaston, K. J. 1994. Spatial patterns of species description: How is our knowledge of the global insect fauna growing? *Biological Conservation* 67: 37–40.

Gathorne-Hardy, F. J. 2001. A review of the South-East Asian Nasutitermitinae (Isoptera: Termitidae) with descriptions of one new genus and a new species and including a key to the genera. *Journal of Natural History* 35: 1485–1506.

Gattolliat, J.-L. 2000. Three new species of *Afroptiloides* (Insecta: Ephemeroptera) and first report of this genus from Madagascar. *Mitteillungen der Schweizerischen Entomologischen Gesellschaft* 73: 305–315.

———. 2001a. Six new species of *Labiobaetis* Novikova and Kluge (Ephemeroptera: Baetidae) from Madagascar with comments on the validity of the genus. *Annales de Limnologie,* Toulouse 37: 97–123.

———. 2001b. *Rheoptilum*: A new genus of two-tailed Baetidae (Ephemeroptera) from Madagascar. *Aquatic Insects* 23: 67–81.

———. 2002. Three new Malagasy species of *Xyrodromeus* (Ephemeroptera: Baetidae) with the first generic description of the adults. *Revue Suisse de Zoologie* 109: 325–341.

———. 2004. First reports of the genus *Nigrobaetis* Novikova and Kluge (Ephemeroptera: Baetidae) from Madagascar and La Réunion with observations on Afrotropical biogeography. *Revue Suisse de Zoologie* 111: 657–669.

Gattolliat, J.-L., and Sartori, M. 1998. Two new Malagasy species of *Herbrossus* (Ephemeroptera: Baetidae) with the first generic description of the adults. *Annales de Limnologie*, Toulouse 34(3): 305–314.

———. 1999a. A new species of *Afrobaetodes* (Insecta: Ephemeroptera) and first report of this genus from Madagascar. *Annales de Limnologie*, Toulouse 35(3): 179–184.

———. 1999b. Revision of the Malagasy genus *Nesoptiloides* (Ephemeroptera: Baetidae). *Mitteillungen der Schweizerischen Entomologischen Gesellschaft* 72: 23–30.

———. 2000a. Contribution to the systematics of the genus *Dabulamanzia* (Ephemeroptera: Baetidae) in Madagascar. *Revue Suisse de Zoologie* 107(3): 561–577.

———. 2000b. *Guloptiloides*: An extraordinary new carnivorous genus of Baetidae (Insecta: Ephemeroptera). *Aquatic Insects* 22(2): 148–159.

———. 2001. Predaceous Baetidae in Madagascar: An uncommon and unsuspected high diversity. In *Trends in Research in Ephemeroptera and Plecoptera*, ed. E. Dominguez, pp. 321–330. New York: Kluwer Academic/Plenum.

———. 2003. An overview of the Baetidae of Madagascar. In *Research Update on Ephemeroptera and Plecoptera*, ed. E. Gaino, pp. 135–144. Perugia: University of Perugia.

Gattolliat, J.-L., Sartori, M., and Elouard, J.-M. 1999. Three new species of Baetidae (Ephemeroptera) from the Réserve Naturelle Intégrale d'Andohahela, Madagascar. In *A Floral and Faunal Inventory of the Réserve Naturelle Intégrale d'Andohahela, Madagascar: With Reference to Elevational Variation*, ed. S. M. Goodman. *Fieldiana: Zoology*, new ser., 94: 115–124.

Gattolliat, J.-L., Monaghan, M. T., Sartori, M., Elouard, J.-M., James, H., Derleth, P., Glaizot, O., de Moor, F., and Vogler, A. P. 2008. A molecular analysis of the Afrotropical Baetidae. In *International Advances in the Ecology, Zoogeography and Systematics of Mayflies and Stoneflies*, eds. F. R. Hauer, J. A. Stanford, and R. L. Newell, pp. 219–232. Berkeley: University of California Press.

Gauthier, A. 1988. Les *Anax* de Madagascar, avec la description d'une nouvelle espèce: *A. mandrakae* n. sp. (Odonata: Aeshnidae). *Bulletin de Société d'Histoire Naturelle de Toulouse* 124: 191–195.

Gautier, L., and Goodman, S. M. 2003. Introduction to the flora of Madagascar. In *The Natural History of Madagascar*, eds. S. M. Goodman and J. P. Benstead, pp. 229–250. Chicago: University of Chicago Press.

Gershenson, Z. S. 2003. Two new species of yponomeutoid moths (Lepidoptera, Yponomeutidae, Plutellidae) from Madagascar. *Vestnik Zoologii* 37: 93–95.

Gervais, P. 1844. Remarques sur la famille des scorpions. *Archives du Muséum d'Histoire Naturelle*, Paris 4: 201–240.

Gibbs, G. W. 2014. Micropterigidae (Insecta: Lepidoptera). *Fauna of New Zealand* 72: 1–127.

Gibeaux, C. 1994. Insectes Lépidoptères Pterophoridae. *Faune de Madagascar* 81: 1–137.

———. 1996. Pterophoridae de Madagascar (Lepidoptera). *Bulletin de la Société Entomologique de France* 101: 53–58.

Gibon, F.-M. 2000. Biologie de la conservation et singularité des cours d'eau: L'Exemple des Philopotamidae malgaches (Insecta, Trichoptera). In *Diversité et endemisme à Madagascar/Diversity and Endemism in Madagascar*, eds. W. R. Lourenço and S. M. Goodman, pp. 319–330. Paris: Mémoires de la Société de Biogéographie.

———. 2001. *Biotypologie des hydrosystèmes tropicaux: Exemples chez les Trichoptères africains et malgaches.* Montpellier: IRD.

———. 2003. Trichoptera, Caddisflies. In *The Natural History of Madagascar*, eds. S. M. Goodman and J. P. Benstead, pp. 740–748. Chicago: University of Chicago Press.

———. 2006. Le genre *Leptocerus* Leach, 1915 à Madagascar (Trichoptera, Leptoceridae). *Revue Française d'Entomologie* 28(4): 145–153.

———. 2013. Une sous-famille caractéristique des forêts humides primaires malgaches: Les Rossodinae (Trichoptera, Philopotamidae). *Zoosystema* 35(2): 151–174.

———. 2014a. Four new species of the genus *Cheimacheramus* Barnard, 1934 from Madagascar (Trichoptera: Sericostomatidae). *Aquatic Insects* 36(2): 79–92.

———. 2014b. Philopotaminae of Madagascar (Trichoptera: Philopotamidae). *Annales de la Société Entomologique de France* 50(3–4): 382–398.

———. 2016. Un nouveau *Chimarra*, à l'ouest de Madagascar (Trichoptera: Philopotamidae). *Bulletin de la Société Entomologique de France* 121(3): 323–328.

———. 2017. Presence of Glossosomatidae in Madagascar, with description of two species (Trichoptera). *Zootaxa* 4317(1): 174–178.

———. 2018. *Ecnomus* of Madagascar, species without modified spur (Trichoptera: Ecnomidae). *Annales de la Société Entomologique de France* 54(1): 1–16.

———. 2019. Le genre *Stactobiella* à Madagascar (Trichoptera, Hydroptilidae). *Bulletin de la Société Entomologique de France* 124(2): 177–182.

Gibon, F.-M., and Ranaivoharindriaka, F. 1995. Présence du genre *Catoxyethira* à Madagascar et descriptions des premières espèces (Trichoptera, Hydroptilidae. *Revue Française d'Entomologie* 17 (3): 107–114.

Gibon, F.-M., and Randriamasimanana, D. 2013. A new sub-genus of *Ceraclea* Stephens 1829: *Ranaivodes* n. s-g., endemic to Madagascar, with description of four new species (Trichoptera: Leptoceridae). *Annales de la Société Entomologique de France* 49(3): 257–266.

Gibon, F.-M., Andriambelo, P. Z., and Randriamasimanana, D. 1999. A study of the diversity and richness of the Malagasy Trichoptera. In *Proceedings of the 9th International Symposium on Trichoptera*, Chiang-Maï, Thaïlande, 5–10 Jan. 1998, eds. P. Chantaramongkol and H. Malicky, pp. 123–124. Chiang-Maï: Chiang-Maï University.

Gibson, J. F., Skevington, J. H., and Kelso, S. 2010. Placement of Conopidae (Diptera) within Schizophora based on mtDNA and nrDNA gene regions. *Molecular Phylogenetics and Evolution* 56: 91–103.

Gielis, C. 2003. *World Catalogue of Insects*. Vol. 4, *Pterophoroidea and Alucitoidea*, ed. B. Landry, pp. 1–198. Stenstrup: Apollo Books.

———. 2009. On a collection of Pterophoridae (Lepidoptera) from Haut-Katanga, Democratic Republic of the Congo. *Revue Suisse de Zoologie* 116: 223–256.

———. 2011. Notes on some African Pterophoridae, with description of new species (Lepidoptera). *Boletín de la Sociedad Entomológica Aragonese* 49: 33–36.

Giglio-Tos, E. 1907. Ortotteri di Madagascar. *Bollettino del Musei di Zoologia ed Anatomia Comparata della R. Università di Torino* 22: 1–8.

Gillespie, R. G. 2013. Biogeography. In *Spider Research in the 21st Century: Trends and Perspectives*, ed. D. Penney, pp. 154–185. Rochdale: Siri Scientific Press.

Gillespie, R. G., and Roderick, G. K. 2002. Arthropods on islands: Colonization, speciation and conservation. *Annual Review of Entomology* 47: 595–632.

Gilligan, T. M., Baixeras, J., and Brown, J. W. 2018. T@RTS: Online World Catalogue of the Tortricidae (Ver. 4.0). Accessed Dec. 2019–Mar. 2020. http://www.tortricid.net.

Gillung, J. P., and Borkent, C. J. 2017. Death comes on two wings: A review of dipteran natural enemies of arachnids. *Journal of Arachnology* 45: 1–19.

Gillung, J. P., and Winterton, S. L. 2019. Evolution of fossil and living spider flies based on morphological and molecular data (Diptera, Acroceridae). *Systematic Entomology* 44: 820–841.

Gioria, M. 2014. Habitats. In *Ecology, Systematics and the Natural History of Predaceous Diving Beetles (Coleoptera: Dytiscidae)*, ed. D. A. Yee, pp. 307–362. Dordrecht: Springer.

Girard, G. 1942. Le comportement de la puce *Synopsyllus fonquerniei* et son rôle dans la transmission de la peste. *Bulletin de la Société de Pathologie Exotique* 35: 177–181.

Glaw, F., Hawlitschek, O., Dunz, A., Goldberg, J., and Bradler, S. 2019. When giant stick insects play with colors: Molecular phylogeny of the Achriopterini and description of two new splendid species (Phasmatodea: Achrioptera) from Madagascar. *Frontiers in Ecology and Evolution* 7: 105.

Gnezdilov, V. M. 2003. Review of the family Issidae (Homoptera, Cicadina) of the European fauna, with notes on the structure of ovipositor in planthoppers. *Chteniya pamyati N. A. Kholodkovskogo (Meetings in Memory of N. A. Cholodkovsky), St. Petersburg* 56(1): 1–145 [in Russian with English summary].

———. 2011a. New genus and new species of the family Caliscelidae from southwestern Madagascar (Hemiptera: Fulgoroidea). *Revue Française d'Entomologie,* nouvelle série, 32(3–4): 181–183.

———. 2011b. New and little known planthoppers of the subfamily Ommatidiotinae (Homoptera, Fulgoroidea, Caliscelidae) from Madagascar and South Asia. *Entomologicheskoe obozrenie* 90(2): 329–334 [English translation in *Entomological Review* (2001) 91(6): 750–754].

———. 2013a. Modern system of the family Caliscelidae Amyot et Serville (Homoptera, Fulgoroidea). *Zoologichesky Zhurnal* 92(10): 1309–1311 [English translation in *Entomological Review* (2014) 94(2): 211–214]. doi:10.1134/S0013873814020092.

———. 2013b. Issidisation of fulgoroid planthoppers (Homoptera, Fulgoroidea) as an evidence of parallel adaptive radiation. *Entomologicheskoe obozrenie* 92(1): 62–69 [English translation published in *Entomological Review* (2013) 93(7): 825–830]. doi:10.1134/S001387381307004X.

———. 2014. First record of the genus *Issopulex* (Hemiptera: Fulgoroidea: Caliscelidae) from Madagascar. *Zoosystematica Rossica* 23(2): 234–237.

———. 2015a. Lost Madagascar. *Priroda* 10: 46–53 [in Russian].

———. 2015b. A new genus and new species of the family Caliscelidae (Hemiptera: Auchenorrhyncha: Fulgoroidea) from Thailand with notes on evolution of the family. *Proceedings of the Zoological Institute RAS* 319(1): 120–125.

———. 2015c. Madagascan Caliscelidae (Hemiptera, Fulgoroidea): Current knowledge and description of a new genus and species. *African Invertebrates* 56(3): 739–746.

———. 2019. A new species of the myrmecomorphic genus *Formiscurra* (Fulgoroidea: Caliscelidae) from Ethiopia. *Acta Entomologica Musei Nationalis Pragae* 59(1): 17–22. doi:10.2478/aemnp-2019-0002.

Gnezdilov, V. M., and Bourgoin, T. 2009. First record of the family Caliscelidae (Hemiptera: Fulgoroidea) from Madagascar, with description of new taxa from the Afrotropical Region and biogeographical notes. *Zootaxa* 2020: 1–36.

Godeiro, N. N., Pacheco, G., Liu, S., Cipola, N. G., Berbel-Filho, W. M., Zhang, F., Gilbert, M.T.P., and Bellini, B. C. 2020. Phylogeny of Neotropical Seirinae (Collembola, Entomobryidae) based on mitochondrial genomes. *Zoologica Scripta* 1: 2020.

Godfrey, L. R., and Crowley, B. E. 2016. Madagascar's ephemeral palaeo-grazerguild: Who ate the ancient C4 grasses? *Proceedings of the Royal Society of London B: Biological Sciences* 283: 20160360.

Godfrey, L. R., and Irwin, M. T. 2007. The evolution of extinction risk: Past and present anthropogenic impacts on the primate communities of Madagascar. *Folia Primatologica* 78: 405–419.

Goergen, G., Vayssières, J. F., Gnanvossou D., and Tindo, M. 2011. *Bactrocera invadens* (Diptera: Tephritidae), a new invasive fruit fly pest for the Afrotropical Region: Host plant range and distribution in West and Central Africa. *Environmental Entomology* 40: 844–854.

Goff, R. 2017. African Moths. https://www.africanmoths.com. Accessed Mar. 2020.

Goldberg, J., Bresseel, J., Constant, J., Kneubühler, B., Leubner, F., Michalik, P., and Bradler, S. 2015. Extreme convergence in egg-laying strategy across insect orders. *Scientific Reports* 5(1): 1–7.

Goloboff, P. 2011. NDM/VNDM programs for identification of areas of endemism. Version 3.0. Programs and documentation are available at: http://www.lillo.org.ar/phylogeny/endemism/.

Golovatch, S. I., and Hoffman, R. L. 1989. Identity of *Polydesmus hamatus* Brandt, 1841, a Malagasy milliped (Diplopoda Polydesmida Dalodesmidae). *Tropical Zoology* 2: 159–164.

Golovatch, S. I., and Korsós, Z. 1992. Diplopoda collected by the Soviet zoological expedition to the Seychelles Islands in 1984. *Acta Zoologica Hungarica* 38: 1–31.

Gomot, A., Gomot, L., Boukraa, S., and Bruckert, S. 1989. Influence of soil on the growth of the land snail *Helix aspersa*. An experimental study of the absorption route for the stimulating factors. *Journal of Molluscan Studies* 55: 1–7.

Gomy, Y. 2000. *Nouvelle liste chorologique des Coléoptères de l'Archipel des Mascareignes*. Saint-Denis: Société Réunionnaise des Amis du Muséum.

Goodger, D. T., and Watson, A. 1995. *The Afrotropical Tiger-moths: An Illustrated Catalogue, with Generic Diagnosis and Species Distribution, of the Afrotropical Arctiinae (Lepidoptera: Arctiidae)*. Stenstrup: Apollo Books.

Goodman, S. M., and Benstead, J. P., eds. 2003. *The Natural History of Madagascar*. Chicago: University of Chicago Press.

———. 2005. Updated estimates of biotic diversity and endemism for Madagascar. *Oryx* 39: 73–77.

Goodman, S. M., and Ganzhorn, J. U. 1997. Rarity of figs (*Ficus*) on Madagascar and its relationship to a depauperate frugivore community. *Revue d'Ecologie (Terre et Vie)* 52: 321–329.

Goodman, S. M., and Rakotondravony, D. 2000. The effects of forest fragmentation and isolation on insectivorous small mammals (Lipotyphla) on the Central High Plateau of Madagascar. *Journal of Zoology* 250: 193–200.

Goodman, S. M., Ganzhorn, J. U., and Wilmé, L. 1997a. Observations at a *Ficus* tree in Malagasy humid forest. *Biotropica* 29: 480–488.

Goodman, S. M., Langrand, O., and Rasolonandrasana, B.P.N. 1997b. The food habits of *Cryptoprocta ferox* in the high mountain zone of the Andringitra Massif, Madagascar (Carnivora, Viverridae). *Mammalia* 61(2): 185–192.

Goodman, S. M., Chan, L. M., Nowak, M. D., and Yoder, A. D. 2010. Phylogeny and biogeography of western Indian Ocean *Rousettus* (Chiroptera: Pteropodidae). *Journal of Mammalogy* 91: 593–606.

Goodman, S. M., Randrenjarison Andriniaina, H. R., Soarimalala, V., and Beaucournu, J.-C. 2015. The fleas of endemic and introduced small mammals in Central Highland forests of Madagascar: Faunistics, species diversity, and absence of host specificity. *Journal of Medical Entomology* 52(5): 1135–1143.

Gordon, E.R.L., and Weirauch, C. 2016. Efficient capture of natural history data reveals prey conservatism of cryptic termite predators. *Molecular Phylogenetics and Evolution* 94: 65–73.

Gorla, D. E., Dujardin, J. P., and Schofield, C. J. 1997. Biosystematics of Old World Triatominae. *Acta Tropica* 63: 127–140.

Gorochov, A. V. 1984. A contribution to the taxonomy of modern Grylloidea (Orthoptera) with a description of new taxa. *Zoologiceskij Zhurnal* 63: 1641–1651.

———. 1988. New and little known tropical Grylloidea (Orthoptera). *Trudy Zoologitscheskogo Instituta Akad Nauk SSSR* 178: 3–31.

———. 2001. New taxa of Anostostomatidae and Prophalangopsidae (Orthoptera). *Zoosystematica Rossica* 9[2000]: 299–315.

———. 2004a. Correction of geographic data for the types of *Regoza brevipennis* and *Gialaia africana* (Orthoptera: Gryllidae). *Zoosystematica Rossica* 12[2003]: 170.

———. 2004b. Taxonomy of Podoscirtinae (Orthoptera: Gryllidae). Pt. 3, Podoscirtini from Madagascar and nearest regions. *Zoosystematica Rossica* 12[2003]: 187–215.

———. 2005. Taxonomy of Podoscirtinae (Orthoptera: Gryllidae). Pt. 4, African Podoscirtini and geography of the tribe. *Zoosystematica Rossica* 13: 181–208.

———. 2006. Taxonomy of Podoscirtinae (Orthoptera: Gryllidae). Pt. 5, New Indo-Malayan and Madagascan Podoscirtini. *Zoosystematica Rossica* 15: 33–46.

———. 2014. New data on the genus *Malgasia* (Orthoptera: Mogoplistidae) from Madagascar and Seychelles. *Zoosystematica Rossica* 23: 210–218.

———. 2015. New and little-known crickets of the subfamily Phalangopsinae (Orthoptera, Gryllidae). 8. The genus *Paragryllodes* and notes on the subfamily classification. *Zoologichesky Zhurnal* 94: 905–916.

———. 2017. New taxa of the subfamily Meconematinae (Orthoptera: Tettigoniidae) from Africa and adjacent islands. *Proceedings of the Zoological Institute, Russian Academy of Sciences* 321: 32–64.

Gorochov, A. V., and Llorente, V. 2004. Remarks on the genus *Megalotheca* and new species of *Conocephalus* (Orthoptera Tettigoniidae). *Memorie della Societa Entomologica Italiana* 82: 397–402.

Gotwald, W. H., Jr. 1995. *Army Ants: The Biology of Social Predation*. Ithaca: Cornell University Press.

Gough, H. M., Duran, D. P., Kawahara, A. Y., and Toussaint, E.F.A. 2018. A comprehensive molecular phylogeny of tiger beetles (Coleoptera, Carabidae, Cicindelinae). *Systematic Entomology* 44(2): 305–321. doi:10.1111/syen.12324.

Graf, D. L., and Cummings, K. S. 2009. Actual and alleged freshwater mussels (Mollusca: Bivalvia: Unionoida) from Madagascar and the Mascarenes, with

description of a new genus, *Germainaia*. *Proceedings of the Academy of Natural Sciences of Philadelphia* 158: 221–238.
Grafe, T. U., Ahmad Sah, H. H., Ahmad, N., Borkent, A., Meuche, I., and Konopik, O. 2019. Studying the sensory ecology of frog-biting midges (Corethrellidae: Diptera) and their frog hosts using ecological interaction networks. *Journal of Zoology* 307: 17–27.
Graham, N. R., Fisher, B. L., and Girman, D. J. 2016. Phylogeography in response to reproductive strategies and ecogeographic isolation in ant species on Madagascar: Genus *Mystrium* (Formicidae: Amblyoponinae). *PLoS One* 11: e0146170.
Grandidier, A., ed. 1892. *Histoire physique, naturelle et politique de Madagascar*. Vol. 1, *Histoire de la géographie*. Paris: Imprimerie Nationale.
———. 1895. M. A. Grandidier annonce la mort de M. Grevé et donne les détails suivants sur ce triste événement. *Bulletin du Muséum d'Histoire Naturelle* 4: 138–140.
Grandidier, G., and Petit, G. 1932. *Zoologie de Madagascar*. Paris: Société d'Editions Géographiques, Maritimes et Coloniales.
Granot, R., and Dyment, J. 2015. The Cretaceous opening of the South Atlantic Ocean. *Earth and Planetary Science Letters* 414: 156–163.
Gregorič, M., Agnarsson, I., Blackledge, T. A., and Kuntner, M. 2015. Phylogenetic position and composition of Zygiellinae and *Caerostris*, with new insight into orb-web evolution and gigantism. *Zoological Journal of the Linnean Society* 175: 225–243. doi:10.1111/zoj.12281.
Grenier, P., and Klein, J.-M. 1965. Description complémentaire de *Dinopsyllus brachypecten* Smit, 1951 et de *Nosopsyllus ziarus* Klein, 1963 (Insecta, Siphonaptera). *Bulletin de la Société de Pathologie Exotique et de ses Filiales* 58: 297–305.
Gretillat, S. 1957. *Haematopinus palpebrae* n. sp. (Siphunculata), parasite du zébu á Madagascar. *Annales de Parasitologie Humaines et Comparée* 32: 167–172.
Griffini, A. 1893. Intorno a due Locustidi di Madagascar. *Bollettino del Musei di Zoologia ed Anatomia Comparata della R Universita di Torino* 8: 1–3.
Griffiths, O. [L.] 1995. Madagascar—Ankara Snail Survey. *Papustyla* 9: 1–7.
———. 1996. Summary of the land snails of the Mascarene Islands, with notes on their status. *Proceedings of the Royal Society of Art and Sciences of Mauritius* 6: 37–48.
———. 1997. A survey of the non-marine Mollusca of the central and northern parts of the Réserve Naturelle de Bemaraha in the central west of Madagascar. *Papustyla* 11: 4–14.
———. 1998. A survey of the non-marine molluscs of the Mahafaly limestone karst region in the southwest of Madagascar. *Papustyla* 12: 3–8.
———. 2002. A note on land snail longevity. *Australian Shell News* 116: 1.
Griffiths, O. L., and Herbert, D. G. 2008. Les mollusques terrestres et dulcaquicoles. In *Paysages naturels et biodiversite de Madagascar*, ed. S. M. Goodman, pp. 227–247. Paris: Muséum National d'Histoire Naturelle.
———. 2013a. New species of landsnails (Mollusca: Gastropoda) from two isolated karst formations in central west Madagascar: Tsingy Beanka and Antsingimavo, with additional notes on other regional endemics. *African Invertebrates* 54(1): 1–48.
———. 2013b. The non-marine molluscs of Tsingy Beanka, Melaky Region, western Madagascar. In *The Beanka Forest, Melaky Region, Western Madagascar*, eds. S. M. Goodman, L. Gautier, and M. J. Raherilalao. *Malagasy Nature* 7: 161–170.
Griffiths, O., Cook, A., and Wells, S. M. 1993. The diet of the introduced carnivorous snail *Euglandina rosea* in Mauritius and its implications for threatened island gastropod faunas. *Journal of Zoology*, London 229: 79–89.
Griswold, C. E. 1987. The African members of the trap-door spider family Migidae (Araneae: Mygalomorphae) 1: The genus *Moggridgea* O. P.-Cambridge, 1875. *Annals of the Natal Museum* 28: 1–118.
———. 1997. The spider family Cyatholipidae in Madagascar (Araneae, Araneoidea). *Journal of Arachnology* 25: 53–83.
———. 2001. A monograph of the living world genera and Afrotropical species of cyatholipid spiders (Araneae, Orbiculariae, Araneoidea, Cyatholipidae). *Memoirs of the California Academy of Sciences* 26: 1–251.
———. 2002. A revision of the African spider genus *Raecius* Simon, 1892 (Araneae, Zorocratidae). *Proceedings of the California Academy of Sciences* 53: 117–149.
———. 2003. Araneae, spiders. In *The Natural History of Madagascar*, eds. S. M. Goodman and J. P. Benstead, pp. 579–587. Chicago: University of Chicago Press.
Griswold, C. E., and Ledford, J. 2001. A monograph of the migid trap door spiders of Madagascar and review of the world genera (Araneae, Mygalomorphae, Migidae). *Proceedings of the California Academy of Sciences* 151: 1–20.
Griswold, C. E., and Meikle, T. C. 1990. Social life in a web. *Natural History* 89: 6–10.
Griswold, C. E., and Ramírez, M. 2017. Phylogeny of spiders. In *Spiders of North America: An Identification Manual*, 2nd ed., eds., D. Ubick, P. Paquin, P. E. Cushing, and V. Roth, pp. 17–29. Keene: American Arachnological Society.
Griswold, C. E., Ramírez, M. J., Coddington, J., and Platnick, N. 2005. Atlas of phylogenetic data for entelegyne spiders (Araneae: Araneomorphae: Entelegynae) with comments on their phylogeny. *Proceedings of the California Academy of Sciences* 56, supplement 2: 1–324.
Griswold, C., Wood, H., and Carmichael, A. 2012. The lace web spiders (Araneae, Phyxelididae) of Madagascar: Phylogeny, biogeography and taxonomy. *The Zoological Journal of the Linnean Society* 164: 728–810.
Griveaud, P. 1959. Insectes Lépidoptères Sphingidae. *Faune de Madagascar* 8: 1–161.
———. 1977. Insectes Lépidoptères Lymantriidae (pt. 1; pt. 2). *Faune de Madagascar* 43(1): 1–293; 43(2): 294–588.
———. 1984. The invertebrates. In *Key Environments: Madagascar*, eds. A. P. Jolly, P. Oberlé, and R. Albignac, pp. 75–88. Oxford: Pergamon Press.
Grjebine, A. 1979. Les moustiques des Nepenthes de Madagascar: Espèces nouvelles du genre *Uranotaenia* (Diptera, Culicidae). *Annales de la Société Entomologique de France* 15: 53–74.
Groombridge, B., and Jenkins, M. D. 2000. *Global Biodiversity: Earth's Living Resources in the 21st Century*. Cambridge, UK: World Conservation Monitoring Centre.
Grundy, P., and Maelzer, D. 2000. Assessment of *Pristhesancus plagipennis* (Walker) (Hemiptera: Reduviidae) as an augmented biological control in cotton and soybean crops. *Australian Journal of Entomology* 39: 305–309.
Gueorguiev, V. B. 1967. Coleoptera: Haliplidae. In *South African Animal Life: Results of the Lund Univ. Expedition in 1950–1951*, vol. 13, eds. B. Hanstrom, P. Brinck, and G. Rudebeck, pp. 9–14. Stockholm: Swedish Natural Science Research Council.
Guérin-Méneville, F. E. 1844. Insectes. In *Iconographie du règne animal*, ed. G.L.C.F.D. Cuvier, pp. 355–370. Paris: J. B. Baillière.
Guglielmino, A., Olmi, M., and Bückle, C. 2013. An updated host-parasite catalogue of world Dryinidae (Hymenoptera: Chrysidoidea). *Zootaxa* 3740(1): 1–113.
Guignot, F. 1955a. Nouveaux dytiscides de Madagascar (Coléoptères). *Le Naturaliste Malgache* 7: 139–144.
———. 1955b. Nouveaux Dytiscidés et Gyrinides du Congo Belge et de Madagascar. *Revue de Zoologie et de Botanique Africaines* 51: 190–196.
———. 1955c. Sur la systématique des *Haliplus* (Col. Haliplidae). *Mémoires de la Société Royale d'Entomologie de Belgique* 27: 289–296.
———. 1955d. Dytiscides et gyrinides nouveaux de Madagascar (Coléoptères). *Le Naturaliste Malgache* 7: 63–70.
———. 1956. Contribution à la connaissance de la faune dytiscidienne Malgache. *Le Naturaliste Malgache* 8: 75–80.
———. 1957. Un Haliplide et deux Dytiscides nouveaux de Madagascar. *Le Naturaliste Malgache* 9: 71–74.
———. 1959a. Révision des Hydrocanthares d'Afrique (Coleoptera Dytiscoidea), pt. 1, *Annales du Musée Royal du Congo Belge Tervuren (8) Sciences Zoologiques* 70: 1–313.
———. 1959b. Révision des Hydrocanthares d'Afrique (Coleoptera Dytiscoidea), pt. 2, *Annales du Musée Royal du Congo Belge Tervuren (8) Sciences Zoologiques* 78: 323–648.
———. 1959c. Dytiscidés et Gyrinides des Comores. *Mémoires de l'Institut Scientifique de Madagascar* 10(1958): 75–79.
———. 1959–1961. Révision des Hydrocanthares d'Afrique (Coleoptera Dytiscoidea), pts. 1–3. *Annales du Musée Royal du Congo Belge Tervuren (8) Sciences Zoologiques* 70, 78, 90: 1–995.
———. 1960. Haliplides et dytiscides nouveaux ou intéressants de Madagascar. *Le Naturaliste Malgache* 11(1959): 95–101.
Guillaumet, J.-L., Betsch, J.-M., and Callmander, M. W. 2008. Renaud Paulian et le programme du CNRS sur les hautes montagnes à Madagascar: Etage vs domaine. *Zoosystema* 30: 723–748.
Guillermet, C. 2009. Contribution à l'étude des Hétérocères de La Réunion: Trois nouveaux Tineidae et un nouveau Noctuidae (Lepidoptera). *L'Entomologiste* 65: 117–123.
———. 2016. *Les Hétérocères, ou papillons de nuit, de l'île de La Réunion*. Vol. 5, *Compléments aux volumes précédents: Familles des Gracillariidae, Oecophoridae, Cosmopterigidae, Gelechiidae, Tortricidae, Carposinidae, Pyralidae, Crambidae, Geometridae, Erebidae, Noctuidae.* Saint-Gilles-les-Hauts, La Réunion: Association N.D.P. (Nature, Découverte et Partage) and Parc National de La Réunion.

Günther, K. 1974. Beitrag zur Kenntnis der Tetrigoidea (Orthoptera, Caelifera) von Madagascar und von Mauritius. *Bulletin du Museum National d'Histoire Naturelle*, Paris, série 3, *Zoologie*, 236: 937–1031.

Gurney, A. R. 1984. Freshwater shrimp genera *Caridina* and *Parisia* (Decapoda: Caridea: Atyidae) of Madagascar, with descriptions of four new species. *Journal of Natural History* 18: 567–590.

Gustafson, G. T. 2018. Cenozoic out-of-Africa dispersal shaped diversification of the whirligig beetle genus *Aulonogyrus* (Coleoptera: Gyrinidae: Gyrinini). *Arthropod Systematics and Phylogeny* 76: 295–302.

Gustafson, G. T., and Miller, K. B. 2017. Systematics and evolution of the whirligig beetle tribe Dineutini (Coleoptera: Gyrinidae: Gyrininae). *Zoological Journal of the Linnean Society* 181: 118–150.

Gustafson, G. T., Prokin, A. A., Bukontaite, R., Bergsten, J., and Miller, K. B. 2017a. Tip-dated phylogeny of whirligig beetles reveals ancient lineage surviving on Madagascar. *Scientific Reports* 7: 8619.

Gustafson, G. T., Bergsten, J., Ranarilalatiana, T., Randriamihaja, J. H., and Miller, K. B. 2017b. The morphology and behavior of the endemic Malagasy whirligig beetle *Heterogyrus milloti* Legros, 1953 (Coleoptera: Gyrinidae: Heterogyrinae). *Coleopterists Bulletin* 71: 315–328.

Gustafson, G. T., Baca, S. M., Alexander, A. M., and Short, A.E.Z. 2020. Phylogenomic analysis of the beetle suborder Adephaga with comparison of tailored and generalized ultraconserved element probe performance. *Systematic Entomology* 45(3): 552–570. https://doi.org/10.1111/syen.12413.

Hacker, H. H. 2004. Nolidae and Noctuidae (excluding Catocalinae: Audeini and Tachosini) (Lepidoptera). In *The Lepidoptera of the Brandberg Massif in Namibia*, ed. W. Mey. *Esperiana Memoir* 1: 261–304.

———. 2010. Revision of the genus *Acontia* Ochsenheimer, 1816 and the tribus Acontiini Guenée, 1841 (Old World) (Lepidoptera: Noctuidae Acontiinae) by H. H. Hacker, A. Legrain and M. Fibiger (*Esperiana* 14: 7–533). Corrigenda and Supplementa (Plates 57, 64). *Esperiana* 15: 359–373.

———. 2011. Two new *Acontia* Ochsenheimer, 1816 species from Madagascar with an overview of the genus on Madagascar (Lepidoptera, Noctuidae, Acontiinae). *Esperiana* 16: 89–93.

———. 2013. Additions to several revisions of *Noctuid* genera revised from 2001 to 2011, with descriptions of nine new species and three new subspecies from Africa, Arabian Peninsula and Iran, with faunistic notes (Noctuioidea). *Esperiana* 18: 199–220.

———. 2014. Revision of the tribe Nolini of Africa and the Western Palaearctic Region (Lepidoptera, Noctuoidea, Noctuidae, Nolinae) Supplement 1. *Esperiana* 19: 121–179.

———. 2016. Systematic and illustrated catalogue of the Macroheterocera and Cossoidea Leach, [1815], Zygaenoidea Latreille, 1809, Thyridoidea Herrich-Schäffer, 1846 and Hyblaeoidea Hampson, 1903 of the Arabian Peninsula, with a survey of their distribution (Lepid.). *Esperiana* 20(1): 1–742, (2): 1–430.

———. 2019. *Biogeography: Boletobiinae (Erebidae). Moths of Africa*. Vol. 1, *Systematic and Illustrated Catalogue of the Heterocera (Lepidoptera) of Africa*. Bad Staffelstein: EsperianaVerlag.

Hacker, H. H., and Fibiger, M. 2006. Updated list of Micronoctuidae, Noctuidae (s.l.), and Hyblaeidae species of Yemen, collected during three expeditions in 1996, 1998 and 2000, with comments and descriptions of species. *Esperiana* 12: 75–166.

Hacker, H. H., Legrain, A., and Fibiger, M. 2008. Revision of the genus *Acontia* Ochsenheimer, 1816 and the tribus Acontiini Guenée, 1841 (Old World) (Lepidoptera: Noctuidae: Acontiinae). *Esperiana* 14: 7–533.

Hacker, H. H., Schreier H.-P., and Aistleitner, E. 2010. Noctuidae of Cape Verde Islands (Lepidoptera, Noctuidae). *Esperiana Memoir* 5: 7–96.

Hacker, H. H., Schreier H.-P., and Goater, B. 2012. Revision of the tribe Nolini of Africa and the Western Palaearctic Region (Lepidoptera, Noctuoidea, Noctuidae, Nolinae). *Esperiana* 17: 1–612.

Haelewaters, D., Hiller, T., and Dick, C. W. 2018. Bats, bat flies, and fungi: A case of hyperparasitism. *Trends in Parasitology* 34: 784–799.

Hájek, J., and Fikáček, M. 2008. A review of the genus *Satonius* (Coleoptera: Myxophaga: Torridincolidae): Taxonomic revision, larval morphology, notes on wing polymorphism, and phylogenetic implications. *Acta Entomologica Musei Nationalis Pragae* 48: 655–676.

Hájek, J., Yoshitomi, H., Fikáček, M., Hayashi, M., and Jia, F.-L. 2011. Two new species of *Satonius* Endrödy-Younga from China and notes on the wing polymorphism of *S. kurosawai* Satô (Coleoptera: Myxophaga: Torridincolidae). *Zootaxa* 3016: 51–62.

Hall, W. E., and Short, A.E.Z. 2010. A new species of *Hydroscapha* LeConte from northwestern Venezuela (Coleoptera: Myxophaga: Hydroscaphidae). *Zootaxa* 2358: 49–56.

Hamilton, K.G.A. 1999. The ground-dwelling leafhoppers Myerslopiidae, new family, and Sagmatiini, new tribe (Homoptera: Membracoidea). *Invertebrate Taxonomy* 13: 207–235.

Han, H. L., and Kononenko, V. S. 2015. A review of the genus *Deltote* Reichenbah, Leipzig, 1817 with description of a new species from China (Lepidoptera, Noctuidae: Eustrotiinae). *Zootaxa* 4007: 580.

Hanamura, Y., Koizumi, N., Morioka, S., Andriantsoa, M., and Rafalimanana, T. 2008. Occurrence of the non-indigenous freshwater prawn, *Macrobrachium rosenbergii* (De Man, 1879) (Decapoda, Caridea, Palaemonidae) in Madagascar. *Crustaceana* 81: 1143–1149.

Hancock, D. L. 1984. Ceratitinae (Diptera: Tephritidae) from the Malagasy subregion. *Journal of the Entomological Society of Southern Africa* 47: 277–301.

———. 1985. Trypetinae (Diptera: Tephritidae) from Madagascar. *Journal of the Entomological Society of Southern Africa* 48: 283–301.

———. 1991a. Tephrellini (Diptera: Tephritidae: Tephritinae) from Madagascar. *Journal of the Entomological Society of Southern Africa* 54: 173–184.

———. 1991b. Revised tribal classification of various genera of Trypetinae and Ceratitinae, and the description of a new species of *Taomyia* Bezzi (Diptera: Tephritidae). *Journal of the Entomological Society of Southern Africa* 54: 121–128.

———. 2010. A review of the fruit fly tribe Tephrellini (Diptera: Tephritidae: Tephritinae) in the Indo-Australian region. *Australian Entomologist* 37: 1–6.

Harbach, R. E. 2018. *Culicidepia: Species-group, Genus-group and Family-group Names in Culicidae (Diptera)*. Wallingford: CABI.

Harimalala, M., Telfer, S., Delatte, H., Watts, P. C., Miarinjara, A., Ramihangihajason, T. R., Rahelinirina, S., Rajerison, M., and Boyer, S. 2017. Genetic structure and gene flow of the flea *Xenopsylla cheopis* in Madagascar and Mayotte. *Parasites and Vectors* 10(1): 347.

Harimalala, M., Miarinjara, A., Duchemin, J.-B., Ramihangihajason, T., and Boyer, S. 2018. Species diversity and phylogeny of fleas of small terrestrial mammals in the forests of the Central Highlands of Madagascar. *Zootaxa* 4399(2): 181–196.

Harimalala, M., Rahelinirina, S., and Girod, R. 2020. Presence of the Oriental rat flea (Siphonaptera: Pulicidae) infesting an endemic mammal and confirmed plague circulation in a forest area of Madagascar. *Journal of Medical Entomology* 57(4): 1318–1323.

Harl, J., Haring, E., Asami, T., Sittenthaler, M., Sattmann, H., and Pall-Gergely, B. 2017. Molecular systematics of the land snail family Orculidae reveal polyphyly and deep splits within the clade Orthurethra (Gastropoda: Pulmonata). *Zoological Journal of the Linnean Society* 181(4): 778–794.

Harper, G. J., Steininger, M. K., Tucker, C. J., Juhn, D., and Hawkins, F. 2007. Fifty years of deforestation and forest fragmentation on Madagascar. *Environmental Conservation* 34: 325–333.

Harrison, S. E., Rix, M. G., Harvey, M. S., and Austin, A. D. 2016. An African mygalomorph lineage in temperate Australia: The trapdoor spider genus *Moggridgea* (Araneae: Migidae) on Kangaroo Island, South Australia. *Austral Entomology* 55: 208–216. doi:10.1111/aen.12172.

Haseyama, K.L.F., Wiegmann, B. M., Almeida, E.A.B., and de Carvalho, C. J. B. 2015. Say goodbye to tribes in the new house fly classification: A new molecular phylogenetic analysis and an updated biogeographical narrative for the Muscidae (Diptera). *Molecular Phylogenetics and Evolution* 89: 1–12.

Hasiotis, S. T., and Mitchell, C. E. 1993. A comparison of crayfish burrow morphologies: Triassic and Holocene fossil, paleo- and neo-ichnological evidence, and the identification of their burrowing signatures. *Ichnos* 2: 291–314.

Hastriter, M. W. 2016. Description of two new species of bat fleas of the genus *Araeopsylla* (Siphonaptera) from Kenya and Madagascar with notes on miscellaneous bat fleas. *ZooKeys* 15(572): 7–21.

Hastriter, M. W., and Dick, C. W. 2009. A description of *Paractenopsyllus madagascariensis* sp. n. and the female of *Paractenopsyllus raxworthyi* Duchemin and Ratovonjato, 2004 (Siphonaptera, Leptopsyllidae) from Madagascar with a key to the species of *Paractenopsyllus*. *ZooKeys* 13: 43–55.

Hausdorf, B. 2000. Biogeography of the Limacoidea *sensu lato* (Gastropoda: Stylommatophora): Vicariance events and long-distance dispersal. *Journal of Biogeography* 27: 379–390.

Hauser, M., Woodley, N. E., and Fachin, D. A. 2017a. Taxonomic changes in African Stratiomyidae (Diptera). *Zootaxa* 4263(1): 72–96.

———. 2017b. Stratiomyidae (soldier flies). In *Manual of Afrotropical Diptera*. Vol. 2, *Nematocerous Diptera and Lower Brachycera*. eds. A. H. Kirk-Spriggs and B. J.

Sinclair, pp. 919–979. Suricata 5. Pretoria: South African National Biodiversity Institute.

Haxaire, J., and Melichar, T. 2011. Description d'un nouveau Sphingidae de l'île de Madagascar *Daphnis kitchingi* sp. n. (Lepidoptera, Sphingidae). *The European Entomologist* 3: 189–195.

Haxaire, J., and Minet, J. 2017. The systematic position of *Pentateucha*, *Monarda* and a Malagasy taxon misplaced in Smerinthinae (Lepidoptera Sphingidae Sphinginae). *Antenor* 4: 102–113.

Hayashi, E. 2003. Larva and hostplant of *Avitta fasciosa* Moore (Noctuidae). *Japan Heterocerists' Journal* 224: 459–460.

Hayden, J. E. 2011. Revision of *Cliniodes* Guenée (Lepidoptera: Crambidae: Odontiinae). *Annals of Carnegie Museum* 79: 231–347.

Heatwole, H., Unsicker. S., Andriamiarisoa, L. R., and Lowman, M. D. 2009. Vicissitudes of leaves in a tropical rain forest in Madagascar. *Journal of Tropical Ecology* 25: 615–624.

Heatwole, H., Unsicker, S., and Lowman, M. 2013. Ontogeny of herbivory on leaves in a tropical rain forest in Madagascar. In *Treetops at Risk: Challenges of Global Canopy Ecology and Conservation*, eds. M. Lowman, S. Devy, and T. Ganesh, pp. 295–305. New York: Springer.

Hebert, P.D.N., Cywinska, A., Ball, S. L., and Dewaard, J. 2003. Biological identifications through DNA barcodes. *Proceedings of the Royal Society of London B: Biological Sciences* 270: 313–321.

Heinze, J., Schrempf, A., Wanke, T., Rakotondrazafy, H., Rakotondranaivo, T., and Fisher, B. L. 2014. Polygyny, inbreeding and wingless males in the Malagasy ant *Cardiocondyla shuckardi* Forel (Hymenoptera, Formicidae). *Sociobiology* 61: 300–306.

Heller, K.-G., Hemp, C., Massa, B., Kociński, M., and Warchałowska-Śliwa, E. 2018. *Paraplangia sinespeculo*, a new genus and species of bush-cricket, with notes on its biology and a key to the genera of Phaneropterinae (Orthoptera: Tettigonioidea) from Madagascar. *Journal of Orthoptera Research* 27(2): 143–153.

Heller, K.-G., Hemp, C., Massa, B., Rakotondranary, J., and Kristin, A. 2019. Notes on a small collection of phaneropterine bush-crickets (Insecta: Orthoptera: Tettigonioidea) from central and southern Madagascar with the description of two new species. *Zootaxa* 4563(2): 297–310.

Helms, J. A., IV, Peeters, C., and Fisher, B. L. 2014. Funnels, gas exchange and cliff jumping: Natural history of the cliff dwelling ant *Malagidris sofina*. *Insectes Sociaux* 61: 357–365.

Hennemann, F. [H.], and Conle, O. 2004. Revision of the tribe Achriopterini Bradley and Galil, 1977, with the description of a new genus, three new species and a new subspecies from Madagascar (Phasmatodea; Phasmatidae; Phasmatinae). *Mitteilungen der Münchner Entomologischen Gesellschaft* 94: 5–54.

Hennemann, F. H., Conle, O. V., and Perez-Gelabert, D. E. 2016. Studies on Neotropical Phasmatodea XVI: Revision of Haplopodini Günther, 1953 (rev. stat.), with notes on the subfamily Cladomorphinae Bradley and Galil, 1977 and the descriptions of a new tribe, four new genera and nine new species (Phasmatodea: "Anareolatae": Phasmatidae: Cladomorphinae). *Zootaxa* 4128(1): 1–211.

Hennipman, E., and Roos, M. C. 1982. *A Monograph of the Fern Genus Platycerium (Polypodiaceae)*. Amsterdam: North-Holland.

Herbert, D. G., and Mitchell, A. 2004. Phylogenetic relationships of the enigmatic genus *Prestonella*—the missing African element in the Gondwanan family Bulimulidae (Pulmonata). *World Congress of Malacology, Perth, Australia*. 11–16 July 2004.

Herbert, D. G., Moussalli, A., and Griffiths, O. L. 2015. Rhytididae (Eupulmonata) in Madagascar: Reality or conjecture. *Journal of Molluscan Studies* 81(2): 259–268.

Herting, B. 1988. Erwin Lindner 100 Jahre. *Jahrbuch der Gesellschaft für Naturkunde Württemberg* 143: 1–22.

Herting, B., and Simmonds, J. F. 1977. Hymenoptera. *A Catalogue of Parasites and Predators of Terrestrial Arthropods: Section A, Host or Prey/Enemy* 6: 119–120.

Hibino, H., Saleh, N., and Roechan, M., 1979. Transmission of two kinds of rice tungro-associated viruses by insect vectors. *Phytopathology* 69: 1266–1268.

Hilgartner, R., Raoilison, M., Büttiker, W., Lees, D. C., and Krenn, H. W. 2007. Malagasy birds as hosts for eye-frequenting moths. *Biology Letters* 3: 117–120.

Hilger, S. 2000. Family Diopsidae. In *Contributions to a Manual of Palaearctic Diptera*, vol. 4, eds. L. Papp and B. Darvas, pp. 335–343. Budapest: Science Herald.

Hilgert, M., Akkari, N., Rahmadi, C., and Wesener, T. 2019. The Myriapoda of Halimun-Salak National Park (Java, Indonesia): Overview and faunal composition. *Biodiversity Data Journal* 7: e32218. https://doi.org/10.3897/BDJ.7.e32218.

Hiller, T., Honner, B., Page, R. A., and Tschapka, M. 2018. Leg structure explains host site preference in bat flies (Diptera: Streblidae) parasitizing Neotropical bats (Chiroptera: Phyllostomidae). *Parasitology* 145: 1475–1482.

Hinton, H. E. 1967. On the spiracles of the larvae of the suborder Myxophaga (Coleoptera). *Australian Journal of Zoology* 15: 955–959.

Hjalmarsson, A. E., Bukontaite, R., Ranarilalatiana, T., Randriamihaja, J. H., and Bergsten, J. 2013. Taxonomic revision of Madagascan *Rhantus* (Coleoptera, Dytiscidae, Colymbetinae) with an emphasis on Manjakatompo as a conservation priority. *ZooKeys* 350: 21–45.

Hjalmarsson, A. E., Bergsten, J., and Monaghan, M. T. 2015. Dispersal is linked to habitat use in 59 species of water beetles (Coleoptera: Adephaga) on Madagascar. *Ecography* 38: 732–739.

Hobbs, H. H., Jr. 1981. The crayfishes of Georgia. *Smithsonian Contributions to Zoology* 318: 1–549.

———. 1987. A review of the crayfish genus *Astacoides* (Decapoda: Parastacidae). *Smithsonian Contributions to Zoology* 443: 1–50.

———. 1988. Crayfish distribution, adaptive radiation and evolution. In *Freshwater Crayfish: Biology, Management and Exploitation*, eds. D. M. Holdich and R. S. Lowery, pp. 52–82. Portland: Timber Press.

Hockley, N. J., Jones, J.P.G., Andriahajaina, F. B., Manica, A., Ranambitsoa, E. H., and Randriamboahary, J. A. 2005. When should communities and conservationists monitor exploited resources? *Biodiversity and Conservation* 14: 2795–2806.

Hodges, R. W. 1986. Gelechioidea, Gelechiidae (Part), Dichomeridinae. *Moths of America North of Mexico*. Fascicle 7.1, pp. 1–195. Washington, D.C.: Wedge Entomological Research Foundation.

———. 1998. The Gelechioidea. In *Lepidoptera: Moths and Butterflies*. Vol. 1, *Evolution, Systematics and Biogeography*, ed. N. P. Kristensen, pp. 131–158. Handbuch der Zoologie, vol. 4, pt. 35. Berlin: Walter de Gruyter.

Hoffman, R. L. 1974. Short studies on dalodesmid millipeds from South Africa and Madagascar (Diplopoda: Polydesmida). *The Wasmann Journal of Biology* 32: 221–246.

———. 1980 [1979]. *Classification of the Diplopoda*. Genève: Muséum d'Histoire Naturelle.

Hoffman, R. L., Golovatch, S. I., and Hamer, M. L. 2001. Identities of the millipede genera *Spirostreptus* Brandt, 1833 and *Spiropoeus* Brandt, 1833 (Diplopoda, Spirostreptida, Spirostreptidae). *Myriapodologica* 7(5): 35–47.

Hollis, D. 1968. A revision of the genus *Aiolopus* Fieber (Orthoptera: Acrididae). *Bulletin of the British Museum (Natural History), Entomology Series* 22: 307–355.

Holloway, J. D. 1989. The moths of Borneo (pt. 12): Family Noctuidae, trifine subfamilies; Noctuinae, Heliothinae, Hadeninae, Acronictinae, Amphipyrinae, Agaristinae. *Malayan Nature Journal* 42: 57–226.

———. 1996. The moths of Borneo (pt. 9): Family Geometridae, subfamilies Oenochrominae, Desmobathrinae and Geometrinae. *Malayan Nature Journal* 49: 147–326.

———. 1998. The classification of the Sarrothripinae, Chloephorinae, Camptolominae and Nolinae as the Nolidae (Lepidoptera: Noctuoidea). *Quadrifina* 1: 247–276.

———. 2003. Family Nolidae. In *The Moths of Borneo*, pt. 18, *Nolidae*. Kuala Lumpur: Southdene Sdn. Bhd.

———. 2005. The moths of Borneo (pts. 15 and 16): Noctuidae Catocalinae. *Malayan Nature Journal* 58: 1–528.

———. 2011. The moths of Borneo (pt. 2): Families Phaudidae, Himantopteridae, and Zygaenidae; revised and annotated checklist. *Malayan Nature Journal* 63: 1–548.

Holloway, J. D., and Miller, S. E. 2003. The composition, generic placement, and host plant relationships of the joviana-group in the *Parallelia* genus complex (Lepidoptera: Noctuidae, Catocalinae). *Invertebrate Systematics* 17: 111–128.

Holmgren, S. 2015. Phylogeny and diversity of the Madagascan *Uvarus*: A glimpse into the diving beetle tribe Bidessini (Coleoptera: Dytiscidae). MS thesis, Department of Zoology, Stockholm University.

Holthuis, L. B. 1950. The Decapoda of the Siboga Expedition. Part 10, The Palaemonidae collected by the *Siboga* and *Snellius* expeditions, with remarks on other species, pt. 1, Subfamily Palaemoninae. *Siboga-Expeditie*, Leiden 39(a9): 1–268.

———. 1965a. The Atyidae of Madagascar. *Mémoires Muséum National d'Histoire Naturelle*, nouvelle série, série A, *Zoologie*, 33(1): 1–48.

———. 1965b. A new fresh-water prawn of the genus *Macrobrachium* (Crustacea, Decapoda, Caridea) from Madagascar. *Zoölogische Mededeelingen* 40(30): 281–285.

———. 1980. FAO species catalogue. Vol. 1, Shrimps and prawns of the world: An annotated catalogue of species of interest to fisheries. *FAO Fisheries Synopsis* 1(125): 1–261.

———. 1995. Notes on Indo-West Pacific Crustacea Decapoda 3 to 9. *Zoölogische Mededeelingen* 69: 139–151.

Homziak, N. T. 2016. Systematics and phylogenomics of the Erebinae (Lepidoptera: Noctuoidea, Erebidae). PhD thesis, University of Florida, Gainesville.

Homziak, N. T., Breinholt, J. W., and Kawahara, A. Y. 2016. A historical review of the classification of Erebinae (Lepidoptera: Erebidae). *Zootaxa* 1489: 516–542.

Homziak, N. T., Breinholt, J. W., Branham, M. A., Storer, C. G., and Kawahara, A.Y. 2019. Anchored hybrid enrichment phylogenomics resolves the backbone of erebine moths. *Molecular Phylogenetics and Evolution* 131: 99–105.

Hoogstraal, H. 1953. Ticks (Ixodoidea) of the Malagasy faunal region (excepting the Seychelles): Their origins and host-relationships: With descriptions of five new *Haemaphysalis* species. *Bulletin of the Museum of Comparative Zoology, Harvard* 111(2): 37–113.

Hoogstraal, H., and Kim, K. C. 1985. Tick and mammal coevolution, with emphasis on *Haemaphysalis*. In *Coevolution of Parasitic Arthropods and Mammals*, ed. K. C. Kim, pp. 505–568. New York: John Wiley and Sons.

Hopkin, S. P. 1997. *Biology of the Springtails (Insecta: Collembola)*. New York: Oxford University Press.

Hopkins, G.H.E., and Rothschild, M. 1953. *An Illustrated Catalogue of the Rothschild Collection of Fleas (Siphonaptera) in the British Museum (Natural History)*. Vol. 1, *Tungidae and Pulicidae*. Cambridge: Cambridge University Press.

———. 1966. *An Illustrated Catalogue of the Rothschild Collection of Fleas (Siphonaptera) in the British Museum (Natural History)*. Vol. 4, *Hystrichopsyllidae*. Cambridge: Cambridge University Press.

Hormiga, G., and Griswold, C. E. 2014. Systematics, phylogeny and evolution of orb-weaving spiders. *Annual Review of Entomology* 59: 487–512.

Horn, W. 1934. Catalogue bibliographique et synonymique des Cicindélides de Madagascar (Coleoptera, fam. Carabidae, sbfam. Cicindelini). In *Les Cicindélides de Madagascar*, eds. W. Horn and G. Olsoufieff. *Mémoires de l'Académie Malgache* 1934: 7–28.

Houhamdi, L., and Raoult, D. 2006. Experimental infection of human body lice with *Acinetobacter baumannii*. *American Journal of Tropical Medicine and Hygiene* 74: 526–531. https://www.ajtmh.org/view/journals/tpmd/74/4/article-p526.xml?tab_body=pdf.

Huang, Z.-F., Chiba, H., Jin, J., Kizhakke, A. G., Wang, M., Kunte, K., and Fan, X.-L. 2019. A multilocus phylogenetic framework of the tribe Aeromachini (Lepidoptera: Hesperiidae: Hesperiinae), with implications for taxonomy and biogeography. *Systematic Entomology* 44: 163–178.

Huelsenbeck, J. P., and Ronquist, F. 2001. MRBAYES: Bayesian inference of phylogenetic trees. *Bioinformatics* 17(8): 754–755.

Hugel, S. 2005. Redécouverte du genre *Pyrgacris* à l'île de La Réunion: Description du mâle de *Pyrgacris descampsi* Kevan, 1975 (Orthoptera, Caelifera). *Bulletin de la Société Entomologique de France* 110: 153–159.

———. 2009. New Landrevinae from Mascarene Islands and little known Landrevinae from Africa and Comoros (Grylloidea, Landrevinae). *Annales de la Société Entomologique de France* 45: 193–215.

———. 2010. Présence de *Xiphidiopsis lita* aux Mascareignes et aux Seychelles (Orthoptera, Ensifera). *Bulletin de la Société Entomologique de France* 115: 167–173.

———. 2012a. New and little known Phisidini from Madagascar, Comoro and Seychelles (Ensifera: Meconematinae). *Zoosystema* 34: 525–552.

———. 2012b. Impact of native forest restoration on endemic crickets and katydids density in Rodrigues Island. *Journal of Insect Conservation* 16: 473–477.

———. 2014. Grasshoppers of the Mascarene Islands: New species and new records (Orthoptera, Caelifera). *Zootaxa* 3900: 399–414.

———. 2015. Endemic grasshoppers from the Mascarene Islands: A critically endangered island fauna. *Journal of Insect Conservation* 19: 87–96.

———. 2019. First record of shield-backed katydids in Madagascar with the description of a new genus and three new species (Orthoptera: Ensifera: Tettigoniidae: Tettigoniinae: Arytropteridini). *Zootaxa* 4706: 546–560.

Hunt, T., Bergsten, J., Levkanicova, Z., Papadopoulou, A., St. John, O., et al. 2007. A comprehensive phylogeny of beetles reveals the evolutionary origins of a superradiation. *Science* 18: 1913–1916.

Hwang, W. S., and Weirauch, C. 2010. Revision of the Malagasy *Durevius* Villiers with descriptions of two new species (Hemiptera: Reduviidae: Reduviinae). *Insect Systematics and Evolution* 41: 23–141.

———. 2012. Evolutionary history of assassin bugs (Insecta: Hemiptera: Reduviidae): Insights from divergence dating and ancestral state reconstruction. *PLoS One* 7: e45523.

———. 2017. Uncovering hidden diversity: Phylogeny and taxonomy of physoderinae (Reduviidae, heteroptera), with emphasis on *Physoderes* Westwood in the oriental and Australasian Regions. *European Journal of Taxonomy* 341: 1–118.

Hyde-Roberts, S., Barker, L., Chmurova, L., Dijkstra, K.-D. B., and Schütte, K. 2019. Rediscovery of *Libellulosoma minutum* in the littoral forests of southeast Madagascar (Odonata: Corduliidae). *Notulae Odonatologicae* 9: 125–133.

ICZN. 2012. International Code of Zoological Nomenclature, 4th ed. https://www.iczn.org/the-code/the-international-code-of-zoological-nomenclature/the-code-online/.

Ilango, K. 2004. A review of the *Sergentomyia babu* species complex (Diptera: Psychodidae: Phlebotominae) with description of a new species from India. *Oriental Insects* 38: 77–83.

IMAT. 2020. International Association for Medical Assistance to Travellers: Madagascar: Sexually transmitted infections. Accessed 21 Mar. 2020. https://www.iamat.org/country/madagascar/risk/sexually-transmitted-infections#.

Irwin, M. T., Wright, P. C., Birkinshaw, C., Fisher, B. L., Gardner, C. J., et al. 2010. Patterns of species change in anthropogenically disturbed forests of Madagascar. *Biological Conservation* 143: 2351–2362.

Isambert, B. 2010. The causes of insect endemicity with the example of Madagascar. PhD thesis, Imperial College London.

Isambert, B., Bergsten, J., Monaghan, M. T., Andriamizehy, H., Ranarilalatiana, T., Ratsimbazafy, M., Andriniainimanana, J. R., and Vogler, A. P. 2011. Endemism and evolutionary history in conflict over Madagascar's freshwater conservation priorities. *Biological Conservation* 144: 1902–1909.

IUCN (International Union for Conservation of Nature). 2003. *Guidelines for Application of IUCN Red List Criteria at Regional Levels*. Version 3.0. IUCN Species Survival Commission. Gland: IUCN.

———. 2020. IUCN Red List of Threatened Species. Version 2020–1. https://www.iucnredlist.org.

Jäch, M. A., Mazzoldi, P., Sharma, S., and Sharma, P. 2010. Remarkable cases of diurnal mass aggregations of Oriental species of *Orectochilus* subg. *Patrus* Aubé (Coleoptera: Gyrinidae). *Koleopterologische Rundschau* 80: 15–23.

Jacquemart, S. 1980. Collemboles récoltés par G. Marlier aux Iles Seychelles. *Bulletin de l'Institut Rroyal des Sciences Nnaturelles de Belgique, Entomologie* 52(27): 1–12.

Jago, N. D. 1984. The alate genera of East African Catantopinae (Orthoptera, Acridoidea) including revision of the genus *Catantops* Schaum. *Transactions of the American Entomological Society* 110: 295–387.

James, M. T. 1950. A new stratiomyid from Madagascar. *Proceedings of the Entomological Society of Washington* 52: 100–101.

———. 1960. Les Potamidinae et Hermetiinae de Madagascar (Diptera, Stratiomyidae). *Melanderia* 14: 1–22.

———. 1975. New taxa and records of Stratiomyidae from Madagascar (Diptera). *Annals of the Entomological Society of America* 68(3): 473–481.

———. 1980. 20. Stratiomyidae. In *Catalogue of the Diptera of the Afrotropical Region*, ed. R. W. Crosskey, pp. 253–274. London: British Museum (Natural History).

Janion-Scheepers, C., Deharveng, L., Bedos, A., and Chown, S. L. 2015. Updated list of Collembola species currently recorded from South Africa. *ZooKeys* 503: 55–88. doi:10.3897/zookeys.503.8966.

Janse, A.J.T. 1960. Gelechiadae [part]. *The Moths of South Africa*, vol. 6, pt. 2, ed. A. J. T. Janse, pp. 145–240. Pretoria: Transvaal Museum.

Janssens, E. 1954. Contribution a la faune diptérologique de Madagascar. *Bulletin de l'Institut Royal des Sciences Naturelles de Belgique* 30: 1–11.

Janzen, D. H. 1970. Herbivores and the number of tree species in tropical forests. *American Naturalist* 104: 501–528.

Jarzembowski, E. A. 1999. Arthropods 2: Insects. In *Fossils of the Rhaetian Penarth Group*, eds. A. Swift and D. M. Martill, pp. 149–160. London: Palaeontological Association.

Jeannel, R. 1946a. Coléoptères Carabiques de la Région Malgache (pt. 1). *Faune de l'Empire Français* 6: 1–372.

———. 1946b. Sur les larves de "Pogonostoma." *Revue Française d'Entomologie* 13: 124.

Jeekel, C.A.W. 1971. Notes on the genus *Aphistogoniulus* Silvestri (Diplopoda, Spirobolida, Trigoniulidae). *Bulletin Zoologisch Museum Universiteit van Amsterdam* 2: 33–38.

———. 1974. The group taxonomy and geography of the Sphaerotheriida (Diplopoda). *Symposia of the Zoological Society of London* 32: 41–52.

———. 1999a. A new pill-millipede from Madagascar, with a catalogue of the species hitherto described from the island (Diplopoda—Sphaerotheriida). In *Myriapod Memoranda I: A Collection of Papers and Notes on Systematics and Geography of Diplopoda and Chilopoda*, pp. 5–21. Oisterwijk: C.A.W. Jeekel.

———. 1999b. Records of millipedes from the West Indies. In *Myriapod Memoranda I: A Collection of Papers and Notes on Systematics and Geography of Diplopoda and Chilopoda*, pp. 23–43. Oisterwijk: C.A.W. Jeekel.

———. 1999c. A new *Sechelleptus* from Madagascar, with a key to the species of the genus (Diplopoda—Spirostreptida). In *Myriapod Memoranda I: A Collection of Papers and Notes on Systematics and Geography of Diplopoda and Chilopoda*, pp. 45–55. Oisterwijk: C.A.W. Jeekel.

Jeffries, C. L., Lawrence, G. G., Golovko, G., Kristan, M., Orsborne, J., et al. 2018a. Novel *Wolbachia* strains in *Anopheles* malaria vectors from sub-Saharan Africa. *Wellcome Open Research*. doi:10.12688/wellcomeopenres.14765.1.

Jeffries, C. J., Tantely, M. L., Raharimalala, F. N., Hurn, E., Boyer, S., and Walker, T. 2018b. Diverse novel resident *Wolbachia* strains in Culicine mosquitoes from Madagascar. *Scientific Report* 8: 17456. doi:10.1038/s41598-018-35658-z.

Jenkins, C. N., Guénard, B., Diamond, S. E., Weiser, M. D., and Dunn, R. R. 2013. Conservation implication of divergent global patterns of ant and vertebrate diversity. *Diversity and Distributions* 19: 1084–1092.

Jiang, N., Li, X., Hausmann, A., Cheng, R., Xue, D. Y., and Han, H. X. 2017. A molecular phylogeny of the Palaearctic and Oriental members of the tribe Boarmiini (Lepidoptera: Geometridae: Ennominae). *Invertebrate Systematics* 31(4): 427–441.

Jiaranaisakul, K., Makbun, N., and Constant, J. 2018. The lanternflies of the *Penthicodes* (*Ereosoma*) *atomaria*+ species group in Thailand: New records and host plants (Hemiptera: Fulgoridae). *Belgian Journal of Entomology* 71: 1–15.

Jobling, B. 1949. Host-parasite relationship between the American Streblidae and the bats, with a new key to the American genera and a record of the Streblidae from Trinidad, British West Indies (Diptera). *Parasitology* 39: 315–329.

Jocqué, R. 1990. A revision of the Afrotropical genus *Diores* (Araneae, Zodariidae). *Annales Musée Royal de l'Afrique Centrale, Sciences Zoologiques*, Tervuren, 260: 1–81.

———. 1994. Halidae, a new spider family from Madagascar. *Bulletin of the British Arachnological Society* 9: 281–289.

Jocqué, R., and Dippenaar-Schoeman, A. S. 2006. *Spider Families of the World*. Tervuren: Musée Royal de l'Afrique Centrale.

Johanson, K. A. 1997. Description of *Helicopsyche giboni* sp. n. from Madagascar (Trichoptera: Helicopsychidae). *Braueria* 24: 5–6.

———. 2010. Description of sixteen new species of Trichoptera with a key to adults of known families and genera recorded in Madagascar. *African Entomology* 18(2): 267–301.

Johanson, K. A., and Oláh, J. 2006. Eleven new species of Sericotomatoidea from Madagascar (Trichoptera: Helicopsychidae, Petrothrincidae, Sericostomatidae). *Zootaxa* 1205: 1–30.

———. 2007. Description of fourteen new *Tinodes* species from East Africa (Trichoptera: Psychomyiidae). *Insect Systematics and Evolution* 38: 377–404.

———. 2010. Descriptions of five new species of *Paduniella* from Madagascar (Trichoptera: Psychomyiidae). *Zootaxa* 2338: 54–62.

Johnsen, P. 1991. *Acridoidea of Botswana*. Pt. 2, *Acrididae: Catantopinae, Cyrtacanthacridinae, Acridinae*. Aarhus: Zoological Laboratory, Aarhus University.

Johnson, R. N., Young, D. G., and Butler, J. F. 1993. Trypanosome transmission by *Corethrella wirthi* (Diptera: Chaoboridae) to the green tree frog, *Hyla cinera* (Anura: Hylidae). *Journal of Medical Entomology* 30: 918–921.

Jolivet, P. 1998. *Interrelationship Between Insects and Plants*. Boca Raton: CRC Press.

Joly-Radko, M., and Zimmermann, E. 2010. Seasonality in gum and honeydew feeding in gray mouse lemurs. In *The Evolution of Exudativory in Primates*, eds. A. M. Burrows and L. T. Nash, pp. 141–153. New York: Springer-Verlag.

Jones, J.P.G., and Coulson, T. 2006. Population regulation and demography in a harvested freshwater crayfish from Madagascar. *Oikos* 112: 602–611.

Jones, J.P.G., Andriahajaina, F. B., Hockley, N. J., Balmford, A., and Ravoahangimalala, O. 2005. A multidisciplinary approach to assessing the sustainability of freshwater crayfish harvesting in Madagascar. *Conservation Biology* 19: 1863–1871.

Jones, J.P.G., Andriahajaina, F. B., Ranambinintsoa, E. H., Hockley, N. J., and Ravoahangimalala, O. 2006. The economic importance of freshwater crayfish harvesting in Madagascar and the potential of community-based conservation to improve management. *Oryx* 40: 168–175.

Jones, J.P.G., Andriahajaina, F. B., Hockley, N. J., Crandall, K. A., and Ravoahangimalala, O. R. 2007. The ecology and conservation status of Madagascar's endemic freshwater crayfish (Parastacidae; Astacoides). *Freshwater Biology* 52: 1820–1833.

Jones, J.P.G., Andriamarovololona, M. M., Hockley, N., Gibbons, J. M., and Milner-Gulland, E. J. 2008a. Testing the use of interviews as a tool for monitoring trends in the harvesting of wild species. *Journal of Applied Ecology* 45: 1205–1212.

Jones, J.P.G., Andriamarovololona, M. M., and Hockley, N. 2008b. The importance of taboos and social norms to conservation in Madagascar. *Conservation Biology* 22: 976–986.

Jones, J.P.G., Rasamy, J. R., Harvey, A., Toon, A., Oidtmann, B., Randrianarison, M. H., Raminosoa, N., and Ravoahangimalala, O. R. 2009. The perfect invader: A parthenogenic crayfish poses a new threat to Madagascar's freshwater biodiversity. *Biological Invasions* 11: 1475–1482.

Jones, J. R., and Deitz, L. L. 2009. Phylogeny and systematics of the leafhopper subfamily Ledrinae (Hemiptera: Cicadellidae). *Zootaxa* 2186: 1–120.

Jono, T., Kojima, Y., and Mizuno, T. 2019. Novel cooperative antipredator tactics of an ant specialized against a snake. *Royal Society Open Science* 6:190283. doi:10.1098/rsos.190283.

Jurado-Rivera, J. A., Pons, J., Alvarez, F., Botello, A., Humphreys, W. F., et al. 2017. Phylogenetic evidence that both ancient vicariance and dispersal have contributed to the biogeographic patterns of anchialine cave shrimps. *Scientific Reports* 7: 2852.

Kallal, R. J., and Hormiga, G. 2019. Evolution of the male palp morphology of the orb-weaver hunting spider *Chorizopes* (Araneae: Araneidae) revisited on a new phylogeny of Araneidae, and description of a third species from Madagascar. *Invertebrate Systematics* 33: 473–487. doi:10.1071/IS18061.

Kallies, A. 2013. The Brachodidae of sub-Saharan Africa (Lepidoptera, Cossoidea), with implications for the origin of the family. *Zootaxa* 4083: 1–39.

Kareiva, P., and Wennergren, U. 1995. Connecting landscape patterns to ecosystem and population processes. *Nature* 373: 299–302.

Karimi, Y., Eftekhari, M., and De Almeida, C. R. 1974. Sur l'écologie des puces impliquées dans l'épidémiologie de la peste et le rôle éventuel de certains insectes hématophages dans son processus au Nord-Est du Brésil. *Bulletin de la Société de Pathologie Exotique* 67: 583–591.

Karisch, T. 2013. Taxonomic revision of the African *Cyana*-species (Lepidoptera: Arctiidae, Lithosiinae). *Esperiana* 18: 39–198.

Karny, H. H. 1931. On the geographical distribution of the Indo-African and Mediterranean Gryllacrids. *Transactions of the Royal Society of South Africa* 19: 99–105.

Karsch, F. 1889. Orthopterologische Beiträge III. *Berliner Entomologische Zeitschrift* 32 (1888): 415–464.

Karsholt, O., Mutanen, M., Lee, S., and Kaila, L. 2013. A molecular analysis of the Gelechiidae (Lepidoptera, Gelechioidea) with an interpretative grouping of its taxa. *Systematic Entomology* 38: 334–348.

Kawahara, A. Y., Plotkin, D., Ohshima, I., Lopez-Vaamonde, C., Houlihan, P. R., et al. 2017. A molecular phylogeny and revised higher-level classification for the leaf-mining moth family Gracillariidae and its implications for larval host-use evolution. *Systematic Entomology* 42: 60–81.

Kawakita, A. 2010. Evolution of obligate pollination mutualism in the tribe Phyllantheae (Phyllanthaceae). *Plant Species Biology* 25: 3–19.

Kawakita, A., and Kato, M. 2009. Repeated independent evolution of obligate pollination mutualism in the Phyllantheae-*Epicephala* association. *Proceedings of the Royal Society of London B: Biological Sciences* 276: 417–426.

Keegan, H. L., Toshioka, S., and Suzuki, H. 1969. *Blood-sucking Asian Leeches of Families Hirudidae and Haemadipsidae: Biomedical Reports of the 406 Medical Laboratory 16.* United States Army Medical Command, Japan.

Keegan, K. L., Lafontaine, J. D., Wahlberg, N., and Wagner, D. L. 2019. Towards resolving and redefining Amphipyrinae (Lepidoptera, Noctuoidea, Noctuidae): A massively polyphyletic taxon; Towards resolving and redefining Amphipyrinae. *Systematic Entomology* 44: 451–464.

Kehl, S. 2014. Morphology, anatomy, and physiological aspects of Dytiscidae. In *Ecology, Systematics and the Natural History of Predaceous Diving Beetles (Coleoptera: Dytiscidae)*, ed. D. A. Yee, pp. 173–198. Dordrecht: Springer.

Kengne, P., Le Goff, G., and Fontenille, D. 2009. Molecular genetic investigation of morphological species of members of the *Neomelaniconion* subgenus (Diptera: Culicidae: Aedini) from Madagascar using ribosomal internal transcribed spacer 2. *Journal of Medical Entomology* 46(2): 403–407.

Kennedy, C. H. 1920. Forty-two hitherto unrecognized genera and subgenera of Zygoptera. *Ohio Journal of Science* 21: 83–88.

Keraudren-Aymonin, M. 1982. Droseraceae. *Flore de Madagascar et des Comores* 87: 53–62.

Kernbach, K. 1955. *Pseudoclanis postica* Walker und ihre Unterarten. *Revue de Zoologie et Botanique Africaines* 51: 27–32.

Kerr, P. H. 2010. Phylogeny and classification of Rhagionidae, with implications for Tabanomorpha (Diptera: Brachycera). *Zootaxa* 2592: 1–133.

Kerr, P. H., and Winterton, S. L. 2008. Do parasitic flies attack mites? Evidence in Baltic amber. *Biological Journal of the Linnean Society* 93: 9–13.

Kertész, K. 1912. The Percy Sladen Trust Expedition to the Indian Ocean in 1905, under the leadership of Mr J. Stanley Gardiner, M. A. Vol. 4, number 6, Diptera, Stratiomyiidae. *The Transactions of the Linnean Society of London*, ser. 2, *Zoology* 15(1): 95–99.

Kilonzo, B. S., Mbise, T. J., and Makundi, R. H. 1992. Plague in Lushoto district, Tanzania, 1980–1988. *Transactions of the Royal Society of Tropical Medicine and Hygiene* 86: 444–445.

Kim, K. C., and Emerson, K. C. 1974. A new *Polyplax* and records of sucking lice (Anoplura) from Madagascar. *Journal of Medical Entomology* 11: 107–111.

Kim, K. C., and Ludwig, H. W. 1978. The family classification of the Anoplura. *Systematic Entomology* 3: 249–284.

Kiriakoff, S. G. 1969. Insectes Lépidoptères Notodontidae. *Faune de Madagascar* 219: 1–230.

Kirk-Spriggs, A. H. 2012. Dedication: The life, career and major achievements of Brian Roy Stuckenberg (1930–2009). *African Invertebrates* 53: 1–34.

———. 2017. Introduction and brief history of Afrotropical dipterology. In *Manual of Afrotropical Diptera*. Vol. 1, *Introductory Chapters and Keys to Diptera Families*, eds. A. H. Kirk-Spriggs and B. J. Sinclair, pp. 1–67. Suricata 4. Pretoria: South African National Biodiversity Institute.

Kirti, J. S., and Gill, N. S. 2004. Revalidation and recharacterization of genus *Pramadea* Moore (Pyraustinae: Pyralidae: Lepidoptera). *Journal of Entomological Research* 28: 179–186.

Kitching, I. J., and Rawlins, J. E. 1998. The Noctuoidea. In *Lepidoptera: Moths and Butterflies*. Vol. 1, *Evolution, Systematics and Biogeography*, ed. N. P. Kristensen, pp. 355–401. Handbuch der Zoologie, vol. 4, pt. 35. Berlin: Walter de Gruyter.

Kitching, I. J., Rougerie, R., Zwick, A., Hamilton, C. A., St Laurent, R. A., Naumann, S., Ballesteros Mejia, L., and Kawahara, A. Y. 2018. A global checklist of the Bombycoidea (Insecta: Lepidoptera). Supplement material 1: Global Bombycoidea checklist. *Biodiversity Data Journal* 6: e22236.

Kjaerandsen, J. 2004. A revision of the Afrotropical genus *Dhatrichia* (Trichoptera, Hydroptilidae). *Zoologica Scripta* 33(2): 131–185.

Klein, A., Zimmermann, E., Radespiel, U., Schaarschmidt, F., Springer, A., and Strube, C. 2018. Ectoparasite communities of small-bodied Malagasy primates: Seasonal and socioecological influences on tick, mite and lice infestation of *Microcebus murinus* and *M. ravelobensis* in northwestern Madagascar. *Parasites and Vectors* 11: 459.

Klein, A., Strube, C., Radespiel, U., Springer, A., and Zimmermann, E. 2019. Differences in infection patterns of vector-borne blood-stage parasites of sympatric Malagasy primate species (*Microcebus murinus*, *M. ravelobensis*). *International Journal of Parasitology: Parasites and Wildlife* 10: 59–70.

Klein, J.-M. 1965a. Une nouvelle espèce de *Dinopsyllus* Jord. et Roth., 1913 de Madagascar, *D. flacourti* sp. n. (Insecta, Siphonaptera). *Bulletin de la Société de Pathologie Exotique et de ses Filiales* 58: 291–296.

———. 1965b. *Synopsyllus girardi* sp. n. (Insecta, Siphonaptera), nouvelle espèce de puce de la forêt orientale malgache. *Bulletin de la Société de Pathologie Exotique et de ses Filiales* 58: 306–311.

———. 1965c. *Synopsyllus robici* sp. n. (Insecta, Siphonaptera), une nouvelle puce de Madagascar, récolté au centre des Hauts Plateaux. *Bulletin de la Société de Pathologie Exotique et de Ses Filiales* 58: 553–559.

———. 1968. *Tsaractenus grenieri* n. gen., n. sp., nouvelle Puce de Madagascar. *Bulletin de la Société Entomologique de France* 73: 45–48.

Klein, J.-M., and Uilenberg, G. 1966a. Données écologiques et biologiques sur *Synopsyllus fonquerniei* Wagner et Roubaud 1932 (Siphonaptera) puce du rat péri-domestique, dans la région de Tananarive. *Cahiers de l'ORSTOM*, série *Entomologie Médicale* 4: 3–29.

———. 1966b. Données faunistiques et écologiques sur les puces de Madagascar (Siphonaptera). *Cahiers de l'ORSTOM*, série *Entomologie Médicale* 4: 31–60.

Klompen, H. 2003. Ixodida, ticks, *kongana*. In *The Natural History of Madagascar*, eds. S. M. Goodman and J. P. Benstead. pp. 588–593. Chicago: University of Chicago Press.

Klompen, H., Junge, R. E., and Williams, C. V. 2015. Ectoparasites of *Propithecus diadema* (Primates: Indriidae) with notes on unusual attachment site selection by *Haemaphysalis lemuris* (Parasitiformes: Ixodidae). *Journal of Medical Entomology* 52: 315–319.

Klompen, J.S.H., Black, W. C., IV, Keirans, J. E., and Oliver, J. H., Jr. 1996. Evolution of ticks. *Annual Review of Entomology* 41: 141–161.

Klotz, S., and Kock, U. V. 1991. Neufund von *Genlisea recurva* (Lentibulariaceae) auf Madagaskar. *Willdenowia* 20: 131–133.

Klotz, W., and De Grave, S. 2015. *Elephantis jaggeri*, a replacement name for *Elephantis natalensis* (Bouvier, 1925), a junior primary homonym of *Caridina nilotica* var. *natalensis* De Man, 1908. *Crustaceana* 88(12–14): 1463–1465.

Klug, J.C.F. 1833. *Bericht über eine auf Madagascar veranstaltete Sammlung von Insecten aus der Ordnung Coleoptera*. Berlin: Druckerei der Königlichen Akademie der Wissenschaften.

Kluge, N. J. 2010. Redescription of the taxon Tricorygnatha (Ephemeroptera, *Tricorythus* s.l.) based on new findings in Africa and Indonesia. *Russian Entomological Journal* 19: 79–104.

Kobayashi, H., and Nonaka, M. 2016. Molecular phylogeny of the Notodontidae: Subfamilies inferred from 28S rRNA sequences (Lepidoptera, Noctuoidea, Notodontidae). *Tinea* 23: 1–83.

Kobayashi, S., Matsuoka, H., Kimura, M., Sohn, J.-C., Yoshiyasu, Y., and Lees, D. C. 2018. Designation of a new family group name, Tonzidae fam. nov., for the genus *Tonza* (Lepidoptera, Yponomeutoidea), based on immature stages of *Tonza citrorrhoa*. *European Journal of Taxonomy* 443: 1–32.

Koch, C. L., and Berendt, G. C. 1854. Die im Bernstein befindlichen Crustaceen, Myriapoden, Arachniden und Apteren der Vorwelt. In *Die im Bernstein befindlichen organischen Reste der Vorwelt gesammelt in Verbindung mit Mehreren bearbeitetet und herausgegeben*, vol. 1, pt. 2, ed. G. C. Berendt, pp. 1–124. Berlin: Commission der Nicolaischen Buchhandlung.

Kocher, A., de Thoisy, B., Catzeflis, F., Valière, S., Bañuls, A. L., and Murienne, J. 2017. iDNA screening: Disease vectors as vertebrate samplers. *Molecular Ecology* 22: 6478–6486.

Kolbe, H. J. 1902. Koleopteren der Aldabra-Inseln. *Abhandlungen Herausgegeben von der Senckenbergischen Naturforschenden Gesellschaft* 26: 571–586.

Kolmes, S. A. 1983. Ecological and sensory aspects of prey capture by the whirligig beetle, *Dineutes discolor* (Coleoptera: Gyrinidae). *Journal of the New York Entomological Society* 91: 405–412.

Kotrba, M., and Balke, M. 2006. The systematic position of *Cladodiopsis* Séguy, 1949 and the origin of sexual dimorphism in stalk-eyed flies (Diptera: Diopsidae) inferred from DNA sequence data. *Molecular Phylogenetics and Evolution* 38: 843–847.

Kovtunovich, V. N., and Ustjuzhanin, P. Y. 2006. The genus *Xyroptila* Meyrick, 1908 in the world fauna: New species, new records and taxonomical comments. *Atalanta* 37(1–2): 249–276.

Krabbe, E. 1982. Systematik der Spirostreptidae (Diplopoda, Spirostreptomorpha). *Abhandlungen des Naturwissenschaftlichen Vereins in Hamburg*, neue folge, 24: 1–476.

Kraepelin, K. 1894. Revision der Scorpione. II. Scorpionidae und Bothriuridae. *Jahrbuch der Hamburgischen Wissenschaftlichen Anstalten* 11: 1–248.

———. 1896. Neue und weniger bekannte Scorpione evision der Scorpione. *Jahrbuch der Hamburgischen Wissenschaftlichen Anstalten* 13: 121–146.

———. 1899. Scorpiones und Pedipalpi. In *Das Tierreich No. 18*, ed. F. Dahl, pp. 1–265. Berlin: Friedländer Verlag.

———. 1901. Catalogue des scorpions des collections du Muséum d'Histoire Naturelle de Paris. *Bulletin du Muséum d'Histoire Naturelle*, Paris 7: 265–274.

———. 1905. Die geographische Verbreitung der Scorpione. *Zoologische Jahrbücher (Abteilung für Systematik, Ökologie und Geographie der Tiere)* 22: 361–364.

Krause, D. W., O'Connor, P. M., Rogers, K. C., Sampson, S. D., Buckley, G. A., and Rogers, R. R. 2006. Late Cretaceous terrestrial vertebrates from Madagascar: Implications for Latin American biogeography. *Annals of the Missouri Botanical Garden* 93: 178–208.

Kremen, C., Cameron, A., Moilanen, A., Phillips, S. J., Thomas, C. D., et al. 2008. Aligning conservation priorities across taxa in Madagascar with high-resolution planning tools. *Science* 320: 222–226.

Kreppel, K. S., Telfer, S., Rajerison, M., Morse, A., and Baylis, M. 2016. Effect of temperature and relative humidity on the development times and survival of *Synopsyllus fonquerniei* and *Xenopsylla cheopis*, the flea vectors of plague in Madagascar. *Parasites and Vectors* 9: 82.

Kress, W. J., Schatz, G. E., Andrianifahanana, M., and Morland, H. S. 1994. Pollination of *Ravenala madagascariensis* (Strelitziaceae) by lemurs in Madagascar: Evidence for an archaic coevolutionary system? *American Journal of Botany* 81: 542–551.

Krishna, K. 1968. Phylogeny and generic reclassification of the *Capritermes* complex (Isoptera, Termitidae, Termitinae). *Bulletin of the American Museum of Natural History* 138: 261–324.

Krishnankutty, S. M. 2012. Systematics and biogeography of leafhoppers in Madagascar. PhD thesis, University of Illinois Urbana-Champaign.

Krishnankutty, S. M., and Dietrich, C. H. 2011a. Taxonomic revision and phylogeny of the endemic leafhopper genus *Nesocerus* (Hemiptera: Cicadellidae: Idiocerinae) from Madagascar. *Zoological Journal of the Linnaean Society*. 162: 499–543.

———. 2011b. Review of mileewine leafhoppers (Hemiptera: Cicadellidae: Mileewinae) in Madagascar, with description of seven new species. *Annals of the Entomological Society of America* 104: 636–648.

Krishnankutty, S. M., Dietrich, C. H., Dai, W., and Siddappaji, M. 2016. Phylogeny and historical biogeography of leafhopper subfamily Iassinae (Hemiptera: Cicadellidae) with a revised tribal classification based on morphological and molecular data. *Systematic Entomology* 41: 580–595.

Kristan, W. 2019. Control of locomotion in annelids. In *The Oxford Handbook of Invertebrate Neurobiology*, ed. J. H. Byrne, pp. 451–470. Oxford: Oxford University Press.

Krištín, A., Heller, K. G., Zemko, M., Rakotondranary, S., and Jarčuška, B. 2019. Assemblages of orthopteroid insects along environmental gradients in central and southern Madagascar. *Journal of Orthoptera Research* 28: 155–166.

Kröber, O. 1915a. Die afrikanischen Arten der Gattung *Physocephala* Schin. *Archiv für Naturgeschichte, Abteilung A* 80: 81–99.

———. 1915b. Die afrikanischen Arten der Gattung *Conops*. *Archiv für Naturgeschichte, Abteilung A* 81: 35–68.

———. 1939. Beiträge zur Kenntnis der Conopiden. I. *Annals and Magazine of Natural History* 11(4): 362–395.

Kruess, A., and Tscharntke, T. 1994. Habitat fragmentation, species loss, and biological control. *Science* 264: 1581–1584.

Krüger, M. 1999. Revision of Afrotropical Ennominae of the *Drepanogynis* group III: The genera *Argyrophora* Guenée, *Pseudomaenas* Prout and *Microligia* Warren. *Annals of the Transvaal Museum* 36: 427–496.

———. 2001. A revision of the tribe Macariini (Lepidoptera: Geometridae: Ennominae) of Africa, Madagascar and Arabia. *Bulletin of the Natural History Museum* 70: 1–502.

———. 2007a. Composition and origin of the Lepidoptera faunas of southern Africa, Madagascar and Réunion (Insecta: Lepidoptera). *Annals of the Transvaal Museum* 44: 123–178.

———. 2007b. Composition and origin of the geometrid fauna (Lepidoptera) of the Sneeuberge, Eastern Cape, with descriptions of new taxa. *Annals of the Transvaal Museum* 44: 25–66.

Kühne, L. 2005. Revision und Phylogenie der Gattungsgruppe *Crypsotidia* Rothschild, 1901, *Tachosa* Walker, 1869, *Hypotacha* Hampson, 1913, *Audea* Walker, [1858] 1857 und *Ulotrichopus* Wallengren, 1869 (Lepidoptera, Noctuidae, Catocalinae). *Esperiana Memoir* 2: 7–220.

Künckel d'Herculais, J. 1887. In *Histoire physique, naturelle et politique de Madagascar*. Vol. 22, *Histoire naturelle des Coléoptères*, Tome 2, Atlas, pt. 1, ed. A. Grandidier. Paris: Imprimerie Nationale.

Kuntner, M., and Agnarsson, I. 2010. Web gigantism in Darwin's bark spider, a new species from Madagascar (Araneidae: *Caerostris*). *Journal of Arachnology* 38: 346–356.

———. 2011. Biogeography and diversification of hermit spiders on Indian Ocean islands (Nephilidae: *Nephilengys*). *Molecular Phylogenetics and Evolution* 59: 477–488.

Kuntner, M., and Coddington, J. A. 2009. Discovery of the largest orbweaving spider species: The evolution of gigantism in *Nephila*. *PLoS One* 4: e7516. doi:10.1371/journal.pone.0007516.

Kusky, T. M., Toraman, E., and Raharimahefa T. 2007. The Great Rift Valley of Madagascar: An extension of the Africa-Somali diffusive plate boundary? *Gondwana Research* 11(4): 577–579.

Kutty, S. N., Pont, A. C., Meier, R., and Pape, T. 2014. Complete tribal sampling reveals basal split in Muscidae (Diptera), confirms saprophagy as ancestral feeding mode, and reveals an evolutionary correlation between instar numbers and carnivory. *Molecular Phylogenetics and Evolution* 78: 349–364.

Lacroix, M. 1989. Insectes Coléoptères Melolonthidae (pt. 1). *Faune de Madagascar* 73: 1–302.

———. 1993. Insectes Coléoptères Melolonthidae (pt. 2). *Faune de Madagascar* 73: 303–875.

Lafontaine, J. D., and Schmidt, B. C. 2010. Annotated checklist of the Noctuoidea (Insecta, Lepidoptera) of North America north of Mexico. *ZooKeys* 40: 1–239.

Lajonquière, Y. de. 1972. Insectes Lépidoptères Lasiocampidae. *Faune de Madagascar* 34: 1–214.

Lallemand, V. 1959. Révision des espèces africaines de la famille Fulgoridae (Super-famille Fulgoroides—sous-ordre des Homoptères). *Publicaçoes culturais da companhia de diamantes de Angola* 41: 37–124.

Lamoral, B. H. 1980. A reappraisal of the suprageneric classification of recent scorpions and their zoogeography. In *Verhandlungen. 8. Internationaler Arachnologen—Kongress abgehalten ander Universität für Bodenkultur Wien*, 7–12 July 1980, ed. J. Gruber, pp. 439–444. Vienna: H. Egermannn.

Langrand, O., and Wilmé, L. 1997. Effects of forest fragmentation on extinction patterns of the endemic avifauna on the Central High Plateau of Madagascar. In *Natural Change and Human Impact in Madagascar*, eds. S. M. Goodman and B. D. Patterson, pp. 280–305. Washington, DC: Smithsonian Institution Press.

Larsen, M. W., Peter, C., Johnson, S. D., and Olesen, J. M. 2008. Comparative biology of pollination systems in the African-Malagasy genus *Brownleea* (Brownleeinae: Orchidaceae). *Botanical Journal of the Linnean Society* 156: 65–78.

LaScola, B., and Raoult, D. 2004. *Acinetobacter baumannii* in human body louse. *Emerging Infectious Diseases* 10: 1671–1673.

Latreille, P. A. 1833. Description d'un nouveau genre de crustacés. *Annales Muséum d'Histoire Naturelle de Paris,* série 3, 2: 23–34.

Laudisoit, A., Prié, V., and Beaucournu, J. C. 2012. Une nouvelle espèce de *Lagaropsylla* Jordan and Rothschild, 1921 de Madagascar (Insecta, Siphonaptera, Ischnopsyllidae). *Zoosystema* 34(4): 737–744.

Lavauden, L. 1933. Quelques expériences sur les propriétés venimeuses du *Latrodectus menavodi* Vinson (Araignée de Madagascar). *Travaux, V Congres International de l'Entomologie, Paris*.

Lawrence, J., and Reichardt, H. 1991. Torridincolidae (Myxophaga). In *Immature Insects*, vol. 2, ed. F. W. Stehr, p. 302. Dubuque: Kendall/Hunt.

Lawrence, J. F., Ślipiński, A., Seago, A. E., Thayer, M. K., Newton, A. F., and Marvaldi, A. E. 2011. Phylogeny of the Coleoptera based on morphological characters of adults and larvae. *Annales Zoologici* 61: 1–217.

Lawton, J. H., Bignell, D. E., Bolton, B., Bloemers, G. F., Eggleton, P., et al. 1998. Biodiversity inventories, indicator taxa and the effects of habitat modification in tropical forest. *Nature* 391: 72–76.

Le Gac, P. 1937. Rôle des Pélopées dans la création de gîtes à Phlébotomes à l'intérieur des habitations à Madagascar. *Bulletin de la Société de Pathologie Exotique* 30: 144–145.

Le Goff, G., Randimby, F. M., Rajaonarivelo, V., Laganier, R., Léong Pock Tsy, J.-M., Ceianu, C. S., Duchemin, J.-B., and Robert, V. 2003. *Anopheles mascarensis* de Meillon 1947, vecteur de paludisme dans le Moyen-Ouest de Madagascar? *Archives de l'Institut Pasteur de Madagascar* 69(1–2): 57–62.

Le Goff, G., Léong Pock Tsy, J.-M., and Robert, V. 2006. Molecular characterization of the malaria vector *Anopheles gambiae s.s.* in Madagascar. *Medical and Veterinary Entomology* 20(2): 259–260.

Le Goff, G., Boussès, P., and Brunhes, J. 2007. Révision des *Neomelaniconion* (Diptera: Culicidae) de Madagascar. Espèces présentes et description de cinq nouvelles espèces. *Annales de la Société Entomologique de France,* nouvelle série, 43(2): 187–200.

Le Goff, G., Boussès, P., Julienne, S., Brengues, C., Rahola, N., Rocamora, G., and Robert, V. 2012. The mosquitoes (Diptera: Culidae) of Seychelles: Taxonomy, ecology, vectorial importance, and identification keys. *Parasites and Vectors* 5: 207.

Le Goff, G., Brengues, C., and Robert, V. 2013. *Stegomyia* mosquitoes in Mayotte, taxonomic study and description of *Stegomyia pia* n. sp. *Parasite* 20: 31.

Le Goff, G., Goodman, S. M., Elguero, E., and Robert, V. 2014. Survey of the mosquitoes (Diptera: Culicidae) of Mayotte. *PLoS One* 9(7): e100696. doi:10.1371/journal.pone.0100696.

Leavitt, J. R., Hiatt, K. D., Whiting, M. F., and Song, H. J. 2013. Searching for the optimal data partitioning strategy in mitochondrial phylogenomics: A phylogeny of Acridoidea (Insecta: Orthoptera: Caelifera) as a case study. *Molecular Phylogenetics and Evolution* 67: 494–508.

Lecoq, M., and Mestre, J. 1988. *La surveillance des sauteriaux du Sahel*. La Haye/Montpellier: Ministère des Affaires Étrangères des Pays-Bas/CIRAD-GERDAT-PRIFAS.

Ledger, J. E. 1980. *The Arthropod Parasites of Vertebrates in Africa South of the Sahara*. Vol. IV, *Phthiraptera (Insecta)*. *Publications of the South African Institute for Medical Research*, no. 56.

Ledoux, J.-C. 2007. Araignées'de l'île de La Réunion: II. Salticidae. *Revue Arachnologique* 17: 9–34.

Lees, D. C. 2016. *Heteropsis* (Nymphalidae: Satyrinae: Satyrini: Mycalesina): 19 new species from Madagascar and interim revision. *Zootaxa* 4118: 1–97.

Lees, D. C., and Minet, J. 2003. Lepidoptera: Systematics and diversity. In *The Natural History of Madagascar,* eds. S. M. Goodman, and J. P. Benstead, pp. 748–761. Chicago: University of Chicago Press.

Lees, D. C., and Stonis, J. R. 2007. The first record of Tischeriidae (Insecta: Lepidoptera) from Madagascar, with description of *Coptotriche alavelona* sp. n. and an updated distributional checklist of Afrotropical Tischeriidae. *Zootaxa* 1645: 35–45.

Lees, D. C., and Zilli, A. 2019. *Moths: Their Biology, Diversity and Evolution.* London: Natural History Museum.

Lees, D. C., Kremen, C., and Raharitsimba, H. 2003. Classification, diversity and endemism of the butterflies (Papilionoidea and Hesperioidea): A revised species checklist. In *The Natural History of Madagascar,* eds. S. M. Goodman and J. P. Benstead, pp. 762–793. Chicago: University of Chicago Press.

Legendre, R. 1960. Quelques remarques sur le comportement des *Argyrodes* malgaches (Araignées, Theridiidae). *Annales des Sciences Naturelles,* Paris, série *Zoologie* 2: 507–512.

———. 1961. Etudes sur les *Archaea* (Aranéides). II. La capture des proies et la prise de nourriture. *Bulletin de la Société Zoologique de France* 86: 316–319.

———. 1969. Les araignées marines de Madagascar. *Revue de Zoologique et de Botanique Africaines* 80: 42–50.

———. 1971. Deux nouvelles araignées Filistatidae cavernicoles de Madagascar: *Andoharano milloti* n. sp. et *Andoharano monodi* n. sp. *Bulletin du Muséum National d'Histoire Naturelle,* Paris, 13: 645–650.

———. 1972. Les arachnides de Madagascar. In *Biogeography and Ecology in Madagascar,* eds. G. Richard-Vindard and R. Battistini, pp. 427–457. The Hague: W. Junk.

Léger, N., and Rodhain, F. 1978. *Sergentomyia berentiensis* n. sp. (Diptera, Psychodidae). Description à partir d'un exemplaire femelle récolté à Madagascar. *Bulletin de la Société de Pathologie Exotique* 71: 476–478.

Léger, N., Depaquit, J., and Robert, V. 2005. Les phlébotomes de Madagascar (Diptera: Psychodidae). IV. Description de *Sergentomyia* (*Rondanomyia*) *goodmani* n. sp. Rétablissement du sous-genre *Rondanomyia* Theodor. *Parasite* 12(1): 51–57.

Léger, T., Landry, B., and Nuss, M. 2019. Phylogeny, character evolution and tribal classification in Crambinae and Scopariinae (Lepidoptera, Crambidae). *Systematic Entomology* 44: 757–776.

Legrand, J. 1992. Un nouveau Zygoptère de Madagascar *Tatocnemis virginiae* n.sp. [Odonata, Megapodagrionidae]. *Revue Française d'Entomologie,* nouvelle série, 14: 25–28.

———. 2001a. Ordre des Odonates. In *Biodiversité et biotypologie des eaux continentales de Madagascar,* eds. J.-M. Elouard and F.-M. Gibon, pp. 113–130. Montpellier: IRD, CNRE, LRSAE.

———. 2001b. *Malgassophlebia mayanga* (Ris, 1909) et une nouvelle espèce du genre à Madagascar (Odonata, Anisoptera, Libellulidae). *Revue Française d'Entomologie,* nouvelle série, 23: 225–236.

———. 2003. Sur le genre malgache *Isomma, I. hieroglyphicum* Selys, male, femelle, larve et description d'une nouvelle espèce (Odonata, Anisoptera, Gomphidae, Phyllogomphinae). *Revue Française d'Entomologie,* nouvelle série, 25: 43–54.

Legros, C. 1951. Les gyrins de Madagascar (Coléoptères). *Le Naturaliste Malgache* 3: 117–123.

———. 1953. Un gyrinide nouveau de Madagascar (Coleoptera). *Le Naturaliste Malgache* 5: 63–67.

Lent, H., and Wygodzinsky, P. 1979. Revision of the Triatominae (Hemiptera, Reduviidae), and their significance as vectors of Chagas' disease. *Bulletin of the American Museum of Natural History* 163: 123–520.

Leo, N. 2009. Cryptic species and biodiversity of lice from primates. In *Primate Parasite Ecology: The Dynamics and Study of Host-Parasite Relationships,* eds. M. A. Huffman and C. A. Chapman, pp. 251–269, Cambridge: Cambridge University Press.

Léonard, J., and Dessart, P. 1994. Avis de recherché: Torridincolidés (Coleoptera) vivant en symbiose avec des Podostémacées (Podostématales). *Bulletin et Annales de la Société Royale Belge d'Entomologie* 130: 71–76.

Léong Pock Tsy, J.-M., Duchemin, J.-B., Marrama, L., Rabarison, P., Le Goff, G., Rajaonarivelo, V., and Robert, V. 2003a. Distribution of the species of the *Anopheles gambiae* complex and first evidence of *Anopheles merus* as a malaria vector in Madagascar. *Malaria Journal* 2: 33. https://doi.org/10.1186/1475-2875-2-33.

Léong Pock Tsy, J.-M., Elissa, N., Ouledi, A., Ariey, F., Duchemin, J.-B., and Robert, V. 2003b. Caractérisation moléculaire des moustiques du complexe *Anopheles gambiae* à Mayotte et à Grande Comore. *Parasite* 10(3): 273–276. Erratum *Parasite* 11(1): 74.

Leraut, G.H.C. 2017. Contribution à la connaissance des Epipaschiinae de Madagascar et des Mascareignes: Présence inédite de *Salma melapastalis* (Hampson, 1906) dans la Grande Ile et note sur *Lepipaschia inornata* Solis and Shaffer, 1994 (Lepidoptera Pyralidae). *L'Entomologiste* 75: 181–183.

———. 2019a. Contribution à l'étude des Pyrales de Madagascar et des Comores: Révision et inventaire des Pyralidae Epipaschiinae. *Antenor* 5: 171–182.

———. 2019b. Contribution à la connaissance des Pyralidae Phycitinae de Madagascar, des Comores et des Mascareignes. I. Révision et inventaire des Phycitinae des Comores et description de 2 genres, 8 espèces et une sous-espèce. *Revue Française d'Entomologie Générale* 1: 38–198.

Leraut, P. 2000. Contribution à l'étude du genre *Actenia* Guenée (Lepidoptera, Pyralidae, Pyralinae). *Revue Française d'Entomologie,* nouvelle série, 22: 239–244.

———. 2002. Contribution à l'étude des Pyralinae (Lepidoptera, Pyralidae). *Revue Française d'Entomologie,* nouvelle série, 24: 97–108.

———. 2004a. Contribution à l'étude du genre *Hypotia* Zeller (Lepidoptera, Pyralidae). *Revue Française d'Entomologie,* nouvelle série, 26: 77–96.

———. 2004b. Contribution à l'étude des genres apparentés à *Hypotia* Zeller (Lepidoptera, Pyralidae). *Revue Française d'Entomologie,* nouvelle série, 26: 97–108.

———. 2005. Etude de quelques genres et especes de Pyrales (Lepidoptera, Pyraloidea). *Revue Française d'Entomologie,* nouvelle série, 27: 21–44.

———. 2006a. Contribution à l'étude du genre *Hypsopygia* Hübner (Lepidopera, Pyralidae). *Revue Française d'Entomologie,* nouvelle série, 28: 5–30.

———. 2006b. Etude de quelques genres de Pyralinae (Lepidoptera, Pyralinae). *Nouvelle Revue d'Entomologie,* nouvelle série, 23: 57–74.

———. 2006c. Contribution à l'étude des genres *Pyralis* Linnaeus, *Pleuroptya* Meyrick et *Haritalodes* Warren (Lepidoptera, Pyraloidea). *Revue Française d'Entomologie,* nouvelle série, 28: 77–94.

———. 2007. Contribution à l'étude du genre *Zitha* Walker, 1859 (Lepidoptera, Pyralidae). *Bulletin de la Société Entomologique de France* 112: 485–498.

———. 2008. Nouvelles pyrales malgaches (Lepidoptera, Pyralidae). *Nouvelle Revue d'Entomologie,* nouvelle série, 24: 267–277.

———. 2009a (2008). Nouvelle contribution au genre *Zitha* Walker, 1859 (Lepidoptera, Pyralidae). *Nouvelle Revue d'Entomologie,* nouvelle série, 25: 33–44.

———. 2009b. Contribution à l'étude des genres *Hypotia* Zeller, 1847 et *Aglossodes* Ragonot, 1891 (Lepidoptera, Pyralidae). *Revue Française d'Entomologie,* nouvelle série, 30: 91–95.

———. 2009c. Note sur quelques genres de Pyralidae (Lepidoptera, Pyraloidea). *Revue Française d'Entomologie,* nouvelle série, 31: 69–79.

———. 2010. Etude d'un nouveau genre des pyrales (Lepidoptera, Pyraloidea). *Revue Française d'Entomologie,* nouvelle série, 31: 139–152.

———. 2011a. Nouvelles espèces et nouveau genre de Pyralidae Lepidoptera, Pyraloidea). *Revue Française d'Entomologie,* nouvelle série, 32: 33–58.

———. 2011b. Nouvelles pyrales de la sous-famille des Pyralinae (Lepidoptera, Pyraloidea). *Nouvelle Revue d'Entomologie,* nouvelle série, 27: 213–235.

———. 2013. Espèces et genres nouveaux de Pyralinae (Lepidoptera, Pyraloidea, Pyralidae). *Bulletin de la Société Entomologique de France* 118: 41–72.

———. 2015. Nouveaux Pyralinae d'Inde, d'Afrique et de Madagascar (Lepidoptera, Pyraloidea, Pyralidae). *Bulletin de la Société Entomologique de France* 120: 37–52.

———. 2019. Contribution à l'étude des Pyralinae d'Afrique et de Madagascar, avec description d'un genre nouveau et de 22 espèces nouvelles (Lep.: Pyraloidea, Pyralinae). *Revue Française d'Entomologie Générale* 1: 211–233.

Lesne, P. 1902. Contribution à l'étude des premiers états des Gyrinides [Col.]. *Bulletin de la Société Entomologique de France* 7: 85–88.

Levasseur, M. 2007. Odonates nouveaux pour l'île d'Anjouan, description d'une nouvelle sous-espèce de *Paragomphus genei* (Selys, 1841) (Archipel des Comores). *Martinia* 23: 115–126.

Lewis, D. J. 1978. The phlebotomine sandflies (Diptera: Psychodidae) of the Oriental Region. *Bulletin of the British Museum (Natural History), Entomology Series* 37(6): 217–343.

Lewis, J. A., and Sohn, J.-C. 2015. *World Catalogue of Insects.* Vol. 12, *Lepidoptera: Yponomeutoidea I (Argyresthiidae, Attevidae, Praydidae, Scythropiidae, and Yponomeutidae),* ed. B. Landry, pp. 1–253. Leiden: Brill.

Lewis, R. E. 1998. Résumé of the Siphonaptera (Insecta) of the World. *Journal of Medical Entomology* 35: 377–389.

Li, H., Zhang, Z., and Sinev, S. Y. 2012. Review of the genus *Scaeosopha* Meyrick, 1914 (Lepidoptera, Cosmopterigidae, Scaeosophinae) in the world, with descriptions of sixteen new species. *Zootaxa* 3322: 1–34.

Li, W., Cong, Q., Shen, J., Zhang, J., Hallwachs, W., Janzen, D. H., and Grishin, N. V. 2019. Genomes of skipper butterflies reveal extensive convergence of wing patterns. *Proceedings of the National Academy of Sciences of the USA* 116: 6232–6237.

Liang, Z.-W, Zhu, H.-B., Weng, Q., and Sun, C.-H. 2019. A new species of *Micardia* Butler, 1878 (Lepidoptera, Noctuidae, Eustrotiinae) from China. *Zootaxa* 4559: 593–597.

Libert, M. 2014. Sur la taxonomie du genre *Celaenorrhinus* Hübner en Afrique (Lepidoptera, Hesperiidae). Nairobi: African Butterfly Research Institute.

Lieftinck, M. A. 1963. The type of *Libellula hova* Rambur, 1842, with notes on the other species of *Zygonyx* Selys from Madagascar. *Verhandlungen der Naturforschenden Gesellschaft in Basel* 74: 53–61.

———. 1965. Notes on Odonata of Madagascar, with special reference to the Zygoptera and with comparative notes on other faunal regions. *Verhandlungen der Naturforschenden Gesellschaft von Basel* 76: 229–256.

Likhitrakarn, N., Golovatch, S. I., and Panha, S. 2017. The first record of the pantropical millipede, *Chondromorpha xanthotricha* (Attems, 1898) (Diplopoda: Polydesmida: Paradoxosomatidae), from Thailand. *Arthropoda Selecta* 26(4): 281–287.

Lindner, E. 1936. Stratiomyiiden von Madagaskar (Dipt.). *Konowia* 15: 33–50.

———. 1959. Stratiomyiidae de Madagascar [Diptera]. *Le Naturaliste Malgache* 10: 87–91.

———. 1966. Stratiomyiden von Madagaskar. *Stuttgarter Beiträge zur Naturkunde* 156: 1–26.

———. 1967. Eine neue Stratiomyiden-Gattung aus Madagascar (Diptera). *Stuttgarter Beiträge zur Naturkunde* 178: 1–2.

———. 1968. Madagassische Stratiomyiden aus dem Muséum National d'Histoire Naturelle, Paris (Diptera). *Stuttgarter Beiträge zur Naturkunde* 190: 1–18.

———. 1979. Diptera Stratiomyiidae von den Comoren aus dem Muséum National d'Histoire Naturelle, Paris. *Mémoires du Muséum National d'Histoire Naturelle*, Paris, nouvelle série, série A, *Zoologie*, 109: 307–310.

Liu, M.-Y., Cai, Y.-X., and Tzeng, C.-S. 2007. Molecular systematics of the freshwater prawn genus *Macrobrachium* Bate, 1868 (Crustacea: Decapoda: Palaemonidae) inferred from mtDNA sequences, with emphasis on east Asian species. *Zoological Studies* 46(3): 272–289.

Löbl, I. 1994. Les espèces asiatiques du genre *Hydroscapha* LeConte (Coleoptera, Hydroscaphidae). *Archives des Sciences (Genève)* 47: 15–34.

Lödl, M. 1998a. Checklist of the species of the genus *Hypena* Schrank, 1802 of the Ethiopian region and Madagascar (Lepidoptera: Noctuidae: Hypeninae). *Quadrifina* 1: 75–92.

———. 1998b. Zur Identität von *Hypena* (*Trichypena*) *malagasy* (Viette, 1968) [*Sarmatia*] comb.n. (Lepidoptera: Noctuidae: Hypeninae). *Quadrifina* 1: 67–71.

———. 1999. Die Homonymie und Synonymie von "*Hypena fuscomaculalis*," "*Hypena fusculalis*" und [*Helia*] *serralis* Mabille [1881] 1880: Ein skurriles nomenklatorisches Verwirrspiel (Insecta, Lepidoptera, Noctuidae, Herminiinae). *Senckenbergiana Biologica* 79: 63–70.

Logunov, D. V. 2009. Further notes on the Harmochireae of Africa (Araneae, Salticidae, Pelleninae). *ZooKeys* 16: 265–290. doi:10.3897/zookeys.16.227.

Logunov, D. V., and Azarkina, G. N. 2008. New species of and records for jumping spiders of the subfamily Spartaeinae (Aranei: Salticidae). *Arthropoda Selecta* 16: 97–114.

Logvinenko, V. N. 1975. Fulgoroidea. *Fauna Ukrainy* 20(2): 1–287 [in Ukrainian].

Lonsdale, O. 2020. Family groups of Diopsoidea and Nerioidea (Diptera: Schizophora): Definition, history and relationships. *Zootaxa* 4735(1): 1–177.

Lopardo, L., and Hormiga, G. 2015. Out of the twilight zone: Phylogeny and evolutionary morphology of the orb-weaving spider family Mysmenidae, with a focus on spinneret spigot morphology in symphytognathoids (Araneae, Araneoidea). *Zoological Journal of the Linnean Society* 173: 527–786.

Lopardo, L., Giribet, G., and Hormiga, G. 2011. Morphology to the rescue: Molecular data and the signal of morphological characters in combined phylogenetic analyses: A case study from mysmenid spiders (Araneae, Mysmenidae), with comments on the evolution of web architecture. *Cladistics* 27: 278–330.

Lopéz-Lopéz, A., and Vogler, A. 2017. The mitogenome phylogeny of Adephaga (Coleoptera). *Molecular Phylogenetics and Evolution* 7(114): 166–174. doi.org/10.1016/j.ympev.2017.06.009.

Lopez-Vaamonde, C., Sire, L., Rasmussen, B., Rougerie, R., Wieser, C., Allaoui, A. A., Minet, J., deWaard, J. R. J., Decaëns, T., and Lees, D. C. 2019. DNA barcodes reveal deeply neglected diversity and numerous invasions of micromoths in Madagascar. *Genome* 62: 108–121.

Lotz, L. N. 2006. Afrotropical Archaeidae: 3. The female of *Eriauchenius cornutus* and new species of *Afrarchaea* (Arachnida: Araneae) from South Africa. *Navorsinge van die Nasionale Museum Bloemfontein* 22: 113–126.

Lourenço, W. R. 1983. Considérations sur les genres *Liocheles*, *Ischnurus*, *Opisthacanthus*, *Hormurus*, *Hadogenes* et *Chiromachus* appartenant à la sous-famille des Ischnurinae (Scorpiones, Scorpionidae). *Annals of the Natal Museum* 25 (2): 403–411.

———. 1995. Description de trois nouveaux genres et quatre nouvelles espèces de Scorpions Buthidae de Madagascar. *Bulletin du Muséum National d'Histoire Naturelle*, Paris, série 4, *Zoologie* 17(1–2): 95–106.

———. 1996a. Scorpions (Chelicerata, Scorpiones). Faune de Madagascar 87: 1–102.

———. 1996b. A new species of *Tityobuthus* from Madagascar (Scorpiones, Buthidae). *Bolletino del Museo Regionale di Scienze Naturali di Torino* 14: 267–273.

———. 1996c. Origins and affinities of the scorpion fauna of Madagascar. In *Biogéographie de Madagascar*, ed. W. R. Lourenço, pp. 441–455. Paris: Editions de l'ORSTOM.

———. 1997. Description of a new genus and new species of Buthidae scorpion from the Himalayas of India and Nepal, with some new biogeographic implications. *Entomologische Mitteilungen aus dem Zoologischen Museum Hamburg* 12(156): 183–188.

———. 2000a. More about the Buthoidea of Madagascar, with special references to the genus *Tityobuthus* Pocock (Scorpiones, Buthidae). *Revue Suisse de Zoologie* 107(4): 721–736.

———. 2000b. Un nouveau genre de scorpion malgache, maillon possible entre les Microcharmidae et les Buthidae. *Comptes Rendus de l'Académie des Sciences, Paris, Sciences de la Vie* 323(10): 877–881.

———. 2001. Nouvelles considérations sur la phylogénie et la biogéographie des scorpions Ischnuridae de Madagascar. *Biogeographica* 77(2): 83–96.

———. 2003. Scorpiones, Scorpions. In *The Natural History of Madagascar*, eds. S. M. Goodman and J. P. Benstead, pp. 575–579. Chicago: University of Chicago Press.

———. 2005. Diversity and endemism in Malagasy scorpions. *Biogeographica* 80(1–4): 43–64.

———. 2014. Micro-endemic and vicariant populations of *Opisthacanthus* Peters, 1861 (Scorpiones: Hormuridae) in Madagascar, with descriptions of two new species. *Arthropoda Selecta* 23(4): 383–391.

Lourenço, W. R., and Goodman, S. M. 1999a. Taxonomic and ecological observations on the scorpions collected in the Réserve Naturelle Intégrale d'Andohahela, Madagascar. In *A Floral and Faunal Inventory of the Réserve Naturelle Intégrale d'Andohahela, Madagascar: With Particular Reference to Elevational Variation*, ed. S. M. Goodman. *Fieldiana: Zoology*, new ser., 94: 149–153.

———. 1999b. Taxonomic and ecological observations on the scorpions collected in the Forest of Ankazomivady-Ambositra and on the "RS d'Ivohibe," Madagascar. *Revista de Biología Tropical* 47(3): 475–482.

———. 2002. Scorpions from the Daraina region of northeastern Madagascar, with special reference to the family Heteroscorpionidae Kraepelin, 1905. *Revista Ibérica de Aracnologia* 6: 53–68.

———. 2003. Description of a new species of *Grosphus* Simon (Scorpiones, Buthidae) from the Ankarana Massif, Madagascar. *Revista Ibérica de Aracnologia* 7: 19–28.

———. 2006a. A reappraisal of the geographical distribution of the genus *Pseudouroplectes* Lourenço (Scorpiones: Buthidae) in Madagascar. *Comptes Rendus Biologies* 329: 117–123.

———. 2006b. Further considerations regarding the status of *Grosphus madagascariensis* (Gervais) and *Grosphus hirtus* Kraepelin, and description of a new species (Scorpiones, Buthidae). *Revue Suisse de Zoologie* 113(2): 247–261.

———. 2008. Scorpions of the Réserve Spéciale d'Ankarana, Madagascar, with particular reference to cave-dwelling animals and the description of two new species. *Zoosystema* 30(3): 665–679.

Lourenço, W. R., and Wilmé, L. 2015a. Micro-endemic populations of *Palaeocheloctonus* Lourenço, 1996 (Scorpiones: Hormuridae) in Madagascar: A new case of vicariance among Malagasy scorpions. *Arthropoda Selecta* 24(2): 189–195.

———. 2015b. Scorpions collected in the Makay Mountain range, Madagascar (Scorpiones: Hormuridae, Buthidae) and description of a new species. *Revista Ibérica de Aracnologia* 26: 55–61.

———. 2015c. Species of *Grosphus* Simon, 1880, associated to the group *madagascariensis/hirtus* (Scorpiones: Buthidae): Description of a peculiar new species from the humid eastern forests of Madagascar. *Entomologische Mitteilungen aus dem Zoologischen Museum Hamburg* 17(194): 207–223.

———. 2019. Scorpions from the Parc National du Tsingy de Namoroka, Madagascar and description of a new species of *Opisthacanthus* Peters, 1861 (Scorpiones: Hormuridae). *Revista Ibérica de Aracnologia* 34: 13–20.

Lourenço W. R., and Ythier, E. 2010. Another new species of *Pseudouroplectes* Lourenço, 1995 from Madagascar (Scorpiones, Buthidae). *ZooKeys* 48: 1–9.

Lourenço, W. R., Goodman, S. M., and Fisher, B. L. 2006. A reappraisal of the geographical distribution of the endemic family Microcharmidae Lourenço (Scorpiones) in Madagascar and description of eight new species and subspecies. *Proceedings of the California Academy of Sciences*, ser. 4, 57(26): 751–783.

Lourenço, W. R., Qi, J. X., and Goodman, S. M. 2008. The identity of *Tityobuthus baroni* (Pocock, 1890 (Scorpiones, Buthidae) and description of three new species from Madagascar. *Boletin de la Sociedad Entomológica Aragonesa* 42: 89–102.

Lourenço, W. R., Wilmé, L., and Waeber, P. O. 2015. More about the geographical distribution of the Malagasy genus *Neogrosphus* Lourenço, 1995 (Scorpiones: Buthidae) and description of a vicariant new species. *Comptes Rendus Biologies* 338: 768–776.

Lourenço, W. R., Wilmé, L., and Waeber, P. O. 2016a. More about the geographical pattern of distribution of the genus *Pseudouroplectes* Lourenço, 1995 (Scorpiones: Buthidae) from Madagascar. *Comptes Rendus Biologies* 339: 37–43.

Lourenço, W. R., Waeber, P. O., and Wilmé, L. 2016b. The geographical pattern of distribution of the genus *Tityobuthus* Pocock, 1890, a typical Ananterinae element endemic to Madagascar (Scorpiones: Buthidae). *Comptes Rendus Biologies* 339: 427–436.

Lourenço, W. R., Wilmé, L., and Waeber, P. O. 2016c. One more vicariant new species of *Grosphus* Simon, 1880, (Scorpiones: Buthidae) from Madagascar. *Revista Ibérica de Aracnologia* 29: 45–50.

Lourenço, W. R., Wilmé, L., Soarimalala, V., and Waeber, P. O. 2017. Species of *Grosphus* Simon, 1880 associated to *Grosphus simoni* Lourenço, Goodman and Ramilijaona, 2004 with description of two new species (Scorpiones: Buthidae). *Revista Ibérica de Aracnologia* 30: 61–69.

Lourenço, W. R., Wilmé L., and Waeber, P. O. 2018a. The genus *Opisthacanthus* Peters, 1861 (Scorpiones: Hormuridae), a remarkable Gondwanian group of scorpions. *Comptes Rendus Biologies* 341: 131–143.

Lourenço, W. R., Wilmé, L., and Waeber, P. O. 2018b. Two more new species of *Grosphus* Simon, 1880, associated to the "*Grosphus simoni* group" (Scorpiones: Buthidae) from the regions of the Bemaraha Tsingy and Montagne d'Ambre. *Revista Ibérica de Aracnologia* 32: 73–80.

Lourenço, W. R., Waeber, P. O., and Wilmé, L. 2018c. One more new species of *Tityobuthus* Pocock, 1890 (Scorpiones: Buthidae) from the SW of Madagascar with comments on the distributions of associated species. *Arachnida—Rivista Aracnologica Italiana* 18: 15–25.

Lourenço, W. R., Waeber, P. O., and Wilmé, L. 2019. Additions to the geographical distribution of the Malagasy family Microcharmidae Lourenço (Scorpiones: Buthoidea) and description of three new species of *Microcharmus* Lourenço. *Madagascar Conservation and Development* 14(1): 26–36.

Lourenço, W. R., Rossi, A., Wilmé, L., Raherilalao, M. J., Soarimalala, V., and Waeber, P. O. 2020. The remarkable diversity of the genus *Grosphus* Simon, 1880 (Scorpiones: Buthidae) in southern Madagascar and in particular in the region of Cap Sainte Marie. *Rivista Aracnologica Italiana* 27(1): 2–35.

Lucchi, A., and Mazzoni, E. 2004. Wax production in adults of planthoppers (Homoptera: Fulgoroidea) with particular reference to *Metcalfa pruinosa* (Flatidae). *Annals of the Entomological Society of America* 97: 1294–1298.

Lugo-Ortiz, C. R., and McCafferty, W. P. 1997. New Afrotropical genus of Baetidae (Insecta: Ephemeroptera) with bladelike mandibles. *Bulletin de la Société d'Histoire Naturelle de Toulouse* 133: 41–46.

———. 1998. The *Centroptiloides* complex of Afrotropical small minnow mayflies (Ephemroptera: Baetidae). *Annals of the Entomological Society of America* 91(1): 1–26.

———. 1999. Global biodiversity of the mayfly family Baetidae (Ephemeroptera): A generic perspective. *Trends in Entomology* 2: 45–54.

Lumaret, R. 1962. Insectes siphonaptères. *Faune de Madagascar* 15: 1–109.

Lux, S. A., Copeland, R. S., White, I. M., Manrakhan, A., and Billah, M. K. 2003. A new invasive fruit fly species from the *Bactrocera dorsalis* (Hendel) group detected in East Africa. *Insect Science and Its Applications* 23: 355–361.

Lvovsky, A. L. 2012. Comments on the classification and phylogeny of broad-winged moths (Lepidoptera, Oecophoridae sensu lato). *Entomological Review* 92: 188–205.

———. 2015. Composition of the subfamily Periacminae (Lepidoptera, Lypusidae) with descriptions of new and little known species of the genus *Meleonoma* Meyrick, 1914 from South, East, and South-East Asia. *Entomological Review* 95: 766–778.

Lyko, F. 2017. The marbled crayfish (Decapoda: Cambaridae) represents an independent new species. *Zootaxa* 4363: 544–552.

Mackerras, I. M. 1954. The classification and distribution of Tabanidae (Diptera). I. General review. *Australian Journal of Zoology* 3: 431–454.

Maddison, W. P., and Hedin, M. C. 2003. Jumping spider phylogeny (Araneae: Salticidae). *Invertebrate Systematics* 17: 529–549. doi:10.1071/IS02044.

Maddison, W. P., and Zhang, J. X. 2006. New lyssomanine and hisponine jumping spiders from Africa (Araneae: Salticidae). *Zootaxa* 1255: 29–35.

Magalhães, I.L.F., and Grismado, C. J. 2019. The Malagasy species of the crevice weaver genus *Andoharano* (Araneae: Filistatidae). *Bulletin of the Museum of Comparative Zoology* 162: 263–307. doi:10.3099/0027-4100-162.4.263.

Magalhães, I.L.F., Azevedo, G.H.F., Michalik, P., and Ramírez, M. J. 2020. The fossil record of spiders revisited: Implications for calibrating trees and evidence for a major faunal turnover since the Mesozoic. *Biological Reviews* 95: 184–217. https://doi.org/10.1111/brv.12559.

Máiz-Tomé, L., Sayer, C., and Darwall, W., eds. 2018. *The Status and Distribution of Freshwater Biodiversity in Madagascar and the Indian Ocean Islands Hotspot.* Gland: IUCN.

Mąkol, J., Moniuszko, H., Świerczewski, D., and Stroiński, A. 2014. Planthopper (Hemiptera: Flatidae) parasitized by larval erythraeid mite (Trombidiformes: Erythraeidae): A description of two new species from western Madagascar. *Journal of Insect Science* 14(194): 1–12.

Maldonado Capriles, J. 1990. Systematic catalogue of the Reduviidae of the world (Insecta: Heteroptera). *Caribbean Journal of Science*, special ed., 1–694.

Malicky, H. 2015. Trichopteren von Nosy Be (Madagaskar): Beschreibungen von neuen Arten und Kommentare zu bekannten. *Braueria* 42: 41–49.

Malipatil, M. B. 1985. Revision of Australian Holoptilinae (Reduviidae: Heteroptera). *Australian Journal of Zoology* 33: 283–299.

Mally, R., Korycinska, A., Agassiz, D.J.L., Hall, J., Hodgetts, J., and Nuss, M. 2015. Discovery of an unknown diversity of *Leucinodes* species damaging Solanaceae fruits in sub-Saharan Africa and moving in trade (Insecta, Lepidoptera, Pyraloidea). *ZooKeys* 472: 117–162.

Mally, R., Hayden, J. E., Neinhuis, C., Jordal, B. H., and Nuss, M. 2019. The phylogenetic systematics of Spilomelinae and Pyraustinae (Lepidoptera: Pyraloidea: Crambidae) inferred from DNA and morphology. *Arthropod Systematics and Phylogeny* 77: 141–204.

Malm, T., and Johanson, K. A. 2013. *Magadacerina*, a new genus of Leptoceridae (Trichoptera) from Madagascar. *Zootaxa* 3608(3): 215–220.

Malzacher, P. 1995. Caenidae from Madagascar (Insecta: Ephemeroptera). *Stuttgarter Beiträge zur Naturkunde, Serie A (Biologie)* 530: 1–12.

———. 2009. New larvae of Caeninae from Madagascar (Ephemeroptera: Caenidae). *Stuttgarter Beiträge zur Naturkunde* A, neue serie, 2: 177–194.

———. 2010. New *Caenis* species from Madagascar (Insecta, Ephemeroptera). *Mitteilungen der Schweizerischen Entomologischen Gesellschaft* 83: 207–226.

Mamet, J. 1957. A revised and annotated list of the Hemiptera (Heteroptera and Homoptera, excluding Sternorhyncha) of Mauritius. *Mauritius Institute Bulletin* 5: 31–81.

Manuel, M., and Ramahandrison, A. T. 2017. *Canthyporus reebae* sp. nov. from the Itremo and Andringitra mountains of central eastern Madagascar (Coleoptera: Dytiscidae: Hydroporinae). *Zootaxa* 4273: 131–140.

Maquart, M., Boyer, S., Rakotoharinome, V. M., Ravaomanana, J., Tantely, M. L., Héraud, J.-M., and Cardinale, E. 2016. High prevalence of West Nile virus in domestic birds and detection in 2 new mosquito species in Madagascar. *PLoS One* 11(1): e0147589. doi:v10.1371/journal.pone.0147589.

Marcondes, C. B. 2007. A proposal of generic and subgeneric abbreviations for phlebotomine sandflies (Diptera: Psychodidae: Phlebotominae) of the world. *Entomological News* 118: 351–356.

Maretti, G., Sorrentino, V., Finomana, A., Gamba, M., and Giacoma, C. 2010. Not just a pretty song: An overview of the vocal repertoire of *Indri indri*. *Journal of Anthropological Sciences* 88: 151–165.

Mari-Mutt, J. A. 1985. Eight new species of *Dicranocentrus* and redescription for *D. thaicus* and *D. pilosus* (Collembola: Entomobryidae: Orchesellinae). *Journal of Agriculture of the University of Puerto Rico* 69(3): 297–322.

Marquet, G., and Keith, P. 2008. Taxonomy and distribution of *Caridina similis* Bouvier, 1904 (Decapoda, Atyidae) from the Seychelles Islands. *Crustaceana* 81(8): 979–987.

Marquet, M. L., and Condé, B. 1950. Contribution à la connaissance des Diplopodes Pénicillates d'Afrique et de la région Madecasse. *Mémoires de l'Institut Scientifique de Madagascar*, série A, 4: 113–134.

Marshall, A. G. 1981. *The Ecology of Ectoparasitic Insects*. London: Academic Press.

Marshall, S. A., Buck, M., Skevington, J. H., and Grimaldi, D. 2009. A revision of the family Syringogastridae (Diptera: Diopsoidea). *Zootaxa* 1996: 1–80.

Marten, A., Brändle, M., and Brandl, R. 2006. Habitat type predicts genetic population differentiation in freshwater invertebrates. *Molecular Ecology* 15: 2643–2651.

Masonick, P., Michael, A., Frankenberg, S., Rabitsch, W., and Weirauch, C. 2017. Molecular phylogenetics and biogeography of the ambush bugs (Hemiptera: Reduviidae: Phymatinae). *Molecular Phylogenetic and Evolution* 114: 225–233.

Masonick, P., Hernandez, M., and Weirauch, C. 2019. No guts, no glory: Gut content metabarcoding unveils the diet of a flower-associated coastal sage scrub predator. *Ecosphere* 10: e02712.

Massa, B. 2009. New and less known Orthoptera (Insecta) from the island of Socotra (Yemen). *Zootaxa* 2132: 53–64.

———. 2017a. New taxa of Orthoptera (Insecta Tettigoniidae Phaneropterinae) from Madagascar. *Zootaxa* 4242: 299–312.

———. 2017b. Two new African and Madagascan species of the genus *Holochlora* (Orthoptera: Tettigoniidae, Phaneropterinae). *Fragmenta Entomologica* 49: 165–169.

———. 2017c. New data and taxa for Orthoptera Tettigoniidae and Acrididae from tropical Africa. *Annales de la Société Entomologique de France*, nouvelle série, 53: 236–255.

Massariol, F. C., Takiya, D. M., and Salles, F. F. 2019. Global classification and evolution of brushlegged mayflies (Insecta: Ephemeroptera: Oligoneuriidae): Phylogenetic analyses of morphological and molecular data and dated historical biogeography. *Zoological Journal of the Linnean Society* 187: 378–412.

Massoud, Z. 1967. Monographie des Neanuridae, Collemboles Poduromorphes a pièces buccales modifiées. In *Biologie de l'Amerique Australe*, vol. 3, eds. C. Delamare-Deboutteville and E. H. Rapoport, pp. 7–399. Paris: Editions du CNRS.

Massoud, Z., and Betsch, J.-M. 1966a. Considérations sur l'antenne des Sminthuridinae et description de deux nouvelles espèces de Collemboles interstitiels du genre *Sminthurides* Boerner, 1900 (Symphypléones). *Bulletin du Muséum National d'Histoire Naturelle*, Paris, série 2, 38: 574–585.

———. 1966b. Description de la nouvelle lignée de Collemboles Entomobryomorphes: Microfalculinae Massoud et Betsch. *Revue d'Ecologie et de Biologie du Sol* 3: 571–584.

Matyot, P. 1998. The orthopteroids of the Seychelles: A threatened island fauna. *Journal of Insect Conservation* 2: 235–246.

Mauremootoo, J. R., Watt, I., and Florens F.B.V. 2003. Mauritius biodiversity. In *The Biodiversity Hotspot of Mauritius, Past, Present and Future*, eds. V. Bachraz and R. Atkinson. Unpublished online report.

Mauriès, J. P. 1980. Contributions à l'étude de la faune terrestre des îles granitiques de l'archipel des Séchelles (Mission P. L. G. Benoit—J. J. Van Mol 1972). Myriapoda-Diplopoda. *Revue de Zoologie africaine* 94: 138–168.

———. 1994. Découverte de Diplopodes Craspedosomides à Madagascar: *Betscheuma* n. g. de la famille gondwanienne des Pygmaesomatidae Carl, 1941 (Myriapoda, Diplopoda). *Bulletin du Muséum National d'Histoire Naturelle*, Paris, série 4, section A, *Zoologie* 1: 55–86.

———. 1997. Matériel collecté par H. Franz, 1969 à Madagascar: Nouvelles données taxinomiques et chorologiques sur le genre *Betscheuma* Mauriès, 1994 (Diplopoda: Craspedosomatida). *Annalen des Naturhistorischen Museums Wien* 99B: 539–554.

Mauriès, J. P., and Geoffroy, J. J. 1999. Les Diplopodes édaphiques et souterrains de l'Ile Maurice (Myriapoda, Diplopoda). *Revue Suisse de Zoologie* 106: 69–79.

May, M. L. 1997a. The status of some species of *Enallagma* (Odonata: Zygoptera: Coenagrionidae). *Entomological News* 108: 77–91.

———. 1997b. Reconsideration of the status of the genera *Phyllomacromia* and *Macromia* (Anisoptera: Corduliidae). *Odonatologica* 26: 405–414.

———. 2002. Phylogeny and taxonomy of the damselfly genus *Enallagma* and related taxa (Odonata: Zygoptera: Coenagrionidae). *Systematic Entomology* 27: 387–408.

Mayerl, B., and Lödl, M. 1997. Checkliste aller Arten der Gattungen Zekelita WALKER, 1863 und *Rhynchina* GUENÉE, 1854 der paläarktischen und indo-australischen Region (Insecta: Lepidoptera: Noctuidae). *Annalen des Naturhistorischen Museums in Wien* 99B: 377–386.

McCafferty, W. P., and Benstead, J. P. 2002. Cladistic resolution and ecology of the Madagascar genus *Manohyphella* Allen (Ephemeroptera: Teloganodidae). *Annales de Limnologie* 38: 41–52.

McCrae, A.W.R. 1982. Characteristics of swarming in the African edible bush-cricket *Ruspolia differens* (Serville) (Orthoptera, Tettigonioidea). *Journal of the East Africa Natural History Society and National Museum* 178: 1–5.

McDowall, R. M. 2007. On amphidromy, a distinct form of diadromy in aquatic organisms. *Fish and Fisheries* 8: 1–13.

McKeever, S. 1977. Observations of *Corethrella* feeding on tree frogs (*Hyla*). *Mosquito News* 37: 522–523.

McKeever, S., and Hartberg, W. K. 1980. An effective method for trapping adult female *Corethrella* (Diptera: Chaoboridae). *Mosquito News* 40: 111–112.

McKenna, D. D., Shin, S., Ahrens, D., Balke, M., Beza-Beza, C., et al. 2019. The evolution and genomic basis of beetle diversity. *Proceedings of the National Academy of Sciences of the USA* 116: 24729–24737.

Mead, A. R. 1985. Anatomical studies transfer *Leucotaenius* from Achatinidae to Acavidae (Pulmonata: Sigmurethra). *Archiv für Molluskenkunde* 116: 137–155.

Medeiros, G. S., Greenslade, P., and Bellini, B. C. 2020. The rare *Richardsitas* Betsch (Collembola, Symphypleona, Sminthuridae): A new species from Australia with comments on the genus and on the Sminthurinae. *Insects* 11: 1–16.

Medler, J. T. 1988. Flatidae from the Taï Forest, Côte d'Ivoire, and taxonomic notes on the family in west Africa (Homoptera, Auchenorrhyncha, Fulgoroidea). *Revue Française d'Entomologie* 10: 117–148.

———. 2001. Review of Flatidae in southern Africa, with keys and descriptions of new species (Homoptera: Fulgoroidea). *Contributions on Entomology, International* 4: 323–375.

Meier, R., and Hilger, S. 2000. On the egg morphology and phylogenetic relationships of Diopsidae (Diptera, Schizophora). *Journal of Zoological Systematics and Evolutionary Research* 38(1): 1–36.

Meleney, W. P., and Kim, K. C. 1974. A comparative study of cattle-infesting *Haematopinus*, with redescription of *H. quadripertusus* Fahrenholz, 1916 (Anoplura: Haematopinidae). *Journal of Parasitology* 60: 507–522.

Melichar, L. 1901. Monographie der Acanaloniiden und Flatiden (Homoptera). *Annalen des K.K. Naturhistorischen Hofmuseums* 16: 178–258.

———. 1902. Monographie der Acanaloniiden und Flatiden (Homoptera) (Fortsetzung). *Annalen des K.K. Naturhistorischen Hofmuseums* 17: 1–253.

———. 1923. Homoptera, fam. Acanaloniidae, Flatidae et Ricaniidae. *Genera Insectorum*, Bruxelles, 182: 1–185.

Mens, L. P., Schütte, K., Stokvis, F. R., and Dijkstra, K.-D. B. 2016. Six, not two, species of *Acisoma* pintail dragonfly (Odonata: Libellulidae). *Zootaxa* 4109: 153–172.

Merz, B. 1999. Phylogeny of the Palearctic and Afrotropical genera of the *Tephritis* group (Tephritinae: Tephritini). In *Fruit Flies (Tephritidae) Phylogeny and Evolution of Behavior*, eds. M. Aluja and A.L. Norrbom, pp. 629–670. Boca Raton: CRC Press.

Mesa, A., and Fontanetti, C. S. 1985. The chromosomes of a primitive species of beetle: *Ytu zeus* (Coleoptera, Myxophaga, Torridincolidae) *Proceedings of the Academy of Natural Sciences of Philadelphia* 137: 102–105.

Meuche, I., Keller, A., Ahmadsah, H. H., Ahmad, N., and Grafe T. U. 2016. Silent listeners: Can acoustic preferences of blood-sucking eavesdroppers (Diptera: Corethrellidae) predict the parasitism risk of their anuran hosts? *Behavioral Ecology* 27: 995–1003.

Mey, W. 2004. Galacticidae (Ditrysia *incertae sedis*). In *The Lepidoptera of the Brandberg Massif in Namibia*, ed. W. Mey. *Esperiana Memoir 1*, pp. 91–102.

———. 2005. Genuine Africans or Tertiary immigrants? The genus *Hydropsyche* in the Afrotropical Region (Insecta, Trichoptera: Hydropsychidae). In *African Biodiversity*, eds. B. A. Huber, B. J. Sinclair, and K.-H. Lampe, pp. 141–150. Boston: Springer.

———. 2011. Basic pattern of Lepidoptera diversity in southwestern Africa. *Esperiana Memoir* 6: 1–316.

———. 2019. First report of Eriocottidae from Madagascar (Lepidoptera: Tineoidea). *Metamorphosis* 30: 30–32.

Meyer, S. K., Cumberlidge, N., and Koppin, K. C. 2014. A new genus and species of freshwater crab from Madagascar (Decapoda, Brachyura, Potamoidea, Potamonautidae). *Zootaxa* 3884(1): 65–72.

Miarinjara, A., Rogier, C., Harimalala, M., Ramihangihajason, T. R., and Boyer, S. 2016. *Xenopsylla brasiliensis* fleas in plague focus areas, Madagascar. *Emerging Infectious Diseases* 22(12): 2207–2208.

Miarinjara, A., Rahelinirina, S., Razafimahatratra, N. L., Girod, R., Rajerison, M., and Boyer, S. 2019. Field assessment of insecticide dusting and bait station treatment impact against rodent flea and house flea species in the Madagascar plague context. *PLoS Neglected Tropical Diseases* 13(8): e0007604.

Michalakis, Y., Olivieri, I., Renaud, F., and Raymond, M. 1992. Pleiotropic action of parasites: How to be good for the host. *Trends in Ecology and Evolution* 7: 59–62.

Michat, M. C., Gustafson, G. T., and Bergsten, J. 2017. Larval description and chaetotaxic analysis of *Dineutus sinuosipennis* Laporte, 1840, with a key for the identification of larvae of the tribe Dineutini (Coleoptera, Gyrinidae). *ZooKeys* 718: 95–114.

Middleton, G. 1996. Snails as karst geomorphological agents. *Journal of the Sydney Speleological Society* 40: 17–19.

Miller, J. A. 2006. Web-sharing sociality and cooperative prey capture in a Malagasy spitting spider (Araneae: Scytodidae). *Proceedings of the California Academy of Sciences* 57: 739–750.

Miller, J. A., Griswold, C. E., Scharff, N., Řezáč, M., Szűts, T., and Marhabaie, M. 2012. The velvet spiders: An atlas of the Eresidae (Arachnida, Araneae). *ZooKeys* 195: 1–144. doi:10.3897/zookeys.195.2342.

Miller, K. B. 2002. Revision of the genus *Eretes* Laporte, 1833 (Coleoptera: Dytiscidae). *Aquatic Insects* 24: 247–272.

———. 2009. On the systematics of Noteridae (Coleoptera: Adephaga: Hydradephaga): Phylogeny, description of a new tribe, genus and species, and survey of female genital morphology. *Systematics and Biodiversity* 7: 191–214.

Miller, K. B., and Bergsten, J. 2012. Phylogeny and classification of whirligig beetles (Coleoptera: Gyrinidae): Relaxed-clock model outperforms parsimony and time-free Bayesian analyses. *Systematic Entomology* 37: 705–746.

———. 2014. The phylogeny and classification of predaceous diving beetles. In *Ecology, Systematics and the Natural History of Predaceous Diving Beetles (Coleoptera: Dytiscidae)*, ed. D. A. Yee, pp. 49–172. Dordrecht: Springer.

———. 2016. *Diving Beetles of the World: Systematics and Biology of the Dytiscidae.* Baltimore: Johns Hopkins University Press.

Millot, J. 1948. Revue générale des arachnides de Madagascar. *Mémoires de l'Institut Scientifique de Madagascar*, série A, 1: 137–155.

Minet, J. 1983 (1982). Eléments sur la systématique des Notodontidae et nouvelles données concernant leur étude faunistique à Madagascar (Lep. Noctuoidea). *Bulletin de la Société Entomologique de France* 87: 354–370.

———. 1991. Tentative reconstruction of the ditrysian phylogeny (Lepidoptera: Glossata). *Entomologica Scandinavica* 22: 69–95.

———. 2004. Un nom de remplacement pour le premier Nepticulidae signalé de Madagascar (Lep., Nepticulina). *Bulletin de la Société Entomologique de France* 109: 366.

———. 2015. Lathrotelidae Clarke, 1971: A rehabilitated name deserving subfamily rank (Lepidoptera, Crambidae). *Bulletin de la Société Entomologique de France* 120: 109–112.

Minet, J., and Thiaucourt, P. 2018. The scientific publications of Pierre Viette: A chronological list. *Antenor* 5: 7–36.

Minet, J., Barbut, J., and Lalanne-Cassou, B. 2012. Les noctuelles: Classification et clef de détermination des familles (Lepidoptera: Noctuoidea). *Alexanor* 25: 131–151.

Moat, J., and Smith, P., eds. 2007. *Atlas of the Vegetation of Madagascar/Atlas de la végétation de Madagascar.* Kew: Royal Botanic Gardens.

Molet, M., Peeters, C., and Fisher, B. L. 2007a. Winged queens replaced by reproductives smaller than workers in *Mystrium* ants. *Naturwissenschaften* 94: 280–287.

Molet, M., Peeters, C., Follin, I., and Fisher, B. L. 2007b. Reproductive caste performs intranidal tasks instead of workers in the ant *Mystrium oberthueri*. *Ethology* 113: 721–729.

Molet, M., Fisher, B. L., Ito, F., and Peeters, C. 2009. Shift from independent to dependent colony foundation and evolution of "multi-purpose" ergatoid queens in *Mystrium* ants (subfamily Amblyoponinae). *Biological Journal of the Linnean Society* 98: 198–207.

Monaghan, M. T., Gattolliat, J.-L., Sartori, M., Elouard, J.-M., James, H., Derleth, P., Glaizot, O., de Moor, F., and Vogler, A.-P. 2005. Trans-oceanic and endemic origins of the small minnow mayflies (Ephemeroptera, Baetidae) of Madagascar. *Proceedings of the Royal Society of London B: Biological Sciences* 272: 1829–1836.

Monaghan, M. T., Wild, R., Elliot, M., Fujisawa, T., Balke, M., et al. 2009. Accelerated species inventory on Madagascar using coalescent-based models of species delineation. *Systematic Biology* 58: 298–311.

Monnier, J.-E. 2017. *Profession Explorateur: Alfred Grandidier, 1836–1921.* Rennes: Presses Universitaires de Rennes.

Morabia, A. 1996. PCA Louis and the birth of clinical epidemiology. *Journal of Clinical Epidemiology* 12: 1327–1333.

Moravec, J. 2002a. *Tiger Beetles of Madagascar 2. A Monograph of the Genus Physodeutera (Coleoptera: Cicindelidae).* Zlín, Czech Republic: Nakladatelství Kabourek.

———. 2002b. New or rare Madagascar tiger beetles—7. *Paraphysodeutera naviauxi* gen. n. et sp. n. (Coleoptera: Cicindelidae). *Folia Heyrovskyana* 10(1): 69–74.

———. 2004. New or rare Madagascar tiger beetles—9. Two new species of the genus *Physodeutera* Lacordaire, with revised keys to the species of subgenera *Diarrhiza* Jeannel and *Minideutera* Moravec (Coleoptera: Cicindelidae). *Zootaxa* 775: 1–12.

———. 2007. *Tiger Beetles of Madagascar 1. A Monograph of the Genus Pogonostoma (Coleoptera: Cicindelidae).* Zlín: Nakladatelství Kabourek.

———. 2008. New or rare Madagascar tiger beetles—12. Some new taxa and changes in taxonomy, nomenclature and classification. (Coleoptera: Cicindelidae). *Folia Heyrovskyana*, ser. A, 16: 9–28.

———. 2010. *Tiger Beetles of the Madagascan Region (Madagascar, Seychelles, Comoros, Mascarenes, and Other Islands: Taxonomic Revision of the 17 Genera Occurring in the Region (Coleopterea: Cicindelidae).* Lednice na Moravě, Czech Republic: Biosférická rezervace Dolní MoravaMadagascar (Coleoptera: Cicindelidae). *Folia Heyrowskyana*, ser. A, 23(1): 54–62.

Moravec, J., and Razanajaonarivalona, E. H. 2015. New or rare Madagascar tiger beetles—16. *Physodeutera (Axinomera) horimichioi* sp. nov. and a new record of *Paraphysodeutera naviauxi* from western gen. n. et sp. n. (Coleoptera: Cicindelidae). *Folia Heyrovskyana* 10(1): 69–74.

Moravec, J., and Vybíral, J. 2010. New or rare Madagascar tiger beetles—15. *Pogonostoma (Microstenocera) zombitsynense* sp. nov., a new species from southwestern Madagascar (Coleoptera: Cicindelidae). *Folia Heyrovskyana*, ser. A, 18(1–3): 95–102.

———. 2018. New or rare Madagascar tiger beetles—17. Description of *Pogonostoma (Microstenocera) noheli* sp. nov. and redescription of *P. (M.) flavomaculatum* W. Horn (Coleoptera: Cicindelidae). *Zootaxa* 4388(1): 76–88.

Morinière, J., Van Dam, M. H., Hawlitschek, O., Bergsten, J., Michat, M. C., Hendrich, L., Ribera, I., Toussaint, E.F.A., and Balke, M. 2016. Phylogenetic niche conservatism explains an inverse latitudinal diversity gradient in freshwater arthropods. *Scientific Reports* 6, 26340. doi.org/10.1038/srep26340.

Morita, S., Bayless, K. M., Yeates, D. K., and Wiegmann, B. M. 2016. Molecular phylogeny of the horse flies: A framework for renewing tabanid taxonomy. *Systematic Entomology* 41: 56–72.

Moritz, L., and Wesener, T. 2017. Integrative description of two new species of Malagasy chirping giant pill-millipedes, genus *Sphaeromimus* (Diplopoda, Sphaerotheriida, Arthrosphaeridae). *European Journal of Taxonomy* 381: 1–25. https://doi.org/10.5852/ejt.2017.381.

Morse, J. C., Frandsen, P. B., Graf, W., and Thomas, J. A. 2019. Diversity and ecosystem service of Trichoptera. *Insects* 10: 1–27.

Moser, J. 1919. Beitrag zur Kenntnis der Melolonthiden, (Col.) IX. *Stettiner Entomologische Zeitung* 80(1): 3–64.

Moutia, A., and Mamet, R. 1946. A review of 25 years of economic entomology in the Island of Mauritius. *Bulletin of Entomological Research* 36: 439–472.

Muller, B. S. 2015. Illustrated key and systematics of male South African *Atherigona s. str.* (Diptera: Muscidae). *African Invertebrates* 56: 845–918.

Munro, H. K. 1954. Note sur les Trypetides de Madagascar et description de nouvelles espèces cecidogènes (Diptera). *Mémoires de l'Institut Scientifique de Madagascar,* série E (1953) 4: 543–552.

Murányi, D. 2007. *Peruphasma marmoratum*, a remarkable new species of high montane Phasmatodea (Pseudophasmatidae: Pseudophasmatinae) from the Venezuelan Andes. *Zootaxa* 1398(1): 57–67.

Murillo-Ramos, L., Brehm, G., Sihvonen, P., Hausmann, A., Holm, S., et al. 2019. A comprehensive molecular phylogeny of Geometridae (Lepidoptera) with a focus on enigmatic small subfamilies. *PeerJ* 7: e7386.

Murphy, N. P., and Austin, C. M. 2005. Phylogenetic relationships of the globally distributed freshwater prawn genus *Macrobrachium* (Crustacea: Decapoda: Palaemonidae): Biogeography, taxonomy and the convergent evolution of abbreviated larval development. *Zoologica Scripta* 34(2): 187–197.

Mwatawala, M., De Meyer, M., Makundi, R., and Maerere, A. 2009. Host range and distribution of fruit-infesting pestiferous fruit flies (Diptera, Tephritidae) in selected areas of Central Tanzania. *Bulletin of Entomological Research* 99: 629–641.

Myers, N., Mittermeier, R. A., Mittermeier, C. G., da Fonseca, G. A., and Kent, J. 2000. Biodiversity hotspots for conservation priorities. *Nature* 403: 853–858.

Naeem, S., Thompson, L. J., Lawler, S. P., Lawton, J. H., and Woodfin, R. M. 1994. Declining biodiversity can affect the functioning of ecosystems. *Nature* 368: 734–737.

Naggs, F., and Raheem, D. 2005. Sri Lankan snail diversity: Faunal origins and future prospects. In *Pattern and Process in Land Mollusc Diversity*, eds. R. A. D. Cameron, J. C. Nekola, B. M. Pokryszko, and F. E. Wells. *Records of the Western Australian Museum*, Supplement 68: 11–29.

Naskrecki, P., and Nishida, K. 2007. Novel trophobiotic interactions in lantern bugs (Insecta: Auchenorrhyncha: Fulgoridae). *Journal of Natural History* 41(37–40): 2397–2402. doi.org/10.1080/00222930701633570.

Nazari, V., Larsen, T. B., Lees, D. C., Brattström, O., Bouyer, T., Van de Poel, G., and Hebert, P.D.N. 2011. DNA barcoding and phylogenetic relationships in *Colotis* and associated genera (Lepidoptera: Pieridae): Evolutionary and systematic implications. *Journal of Zoological Systematics and Evolutionary Research* 49: 204–215.

Needham, G. R., and Teel, P. D. 1991. Off-host physiological ecology of ixodid ticks. *Annual Review of Entomology* 36: 659–681.

Nekola, J. C. 1999. Paleorefugia and neorefugia: The influence of colonization history on community pattern and process. *Ecology* 80: 2459–2473.

Nentwig, W., Blick, T., Gloor, D., Jäger, P., and Kropf, C. 2020. How to deal with destroyed type material? The case of Embrik Strand (Arachnida: Araneae). *Arachnologische Mitteilungen* 59: 22–29. doi:10.30963/aramit5904.

Nepomichene, T.N.J.J., Tata, E., and Boyer, S. 2015a. Malaria case in Madagascar, probable implication of a new vector, *Anopheles coustani*. *Malaria Journal* 14: 475. doi:10.1186/s12936-015-1004-9.

Nepomichene, T.N.J.J., Elissa, N., Cardinale, E., and Boyer, S. 2015b. Species diversity, abundance, and host preferences of mosquitoes (Diptera: Culicidae) in two different ecotypes of Madagascar with recent RVFV transmission. *Journal of Medical Entomology* 52(5): 962–969. doi:10.1093/jme/tjv120.

Nepomichene, T.N.J.J., Raharimalala, F. N., Andriamandimby, S. F., Ravalohery, J. P., Failloux, A. B., Héraud, J.-M., and Boyer, S. 2018. Vector competence of *Culex antennatus* and *Anopheles coustani* mosquitoes for Rift Valley fever virus in Madagascar. *Medical and Veterinary Entomology* 32(2): 259–262. doi:10.1111/mve.12291.

Ng, P.K.L. 1988. *The Freshwater Crabs of Peninsular Malaysia and Singapore*. Singapore: Shing Lee.

Ng, P.K.L., and Takeda, M. 1994. *Skelosophusa* (Crustacea, Decapoda, Brachyura), a new genus of potamonautid freshwater crab from Madagascar, with descriptions of two new species. *Bulletin of the National Science Museum, Tokyo Series A (Zoology)*, 20(4): 161–172.

Ng, P.K.L., Stevcic, Z., and Pretzmann, G. 1995. A revision of the family Deckeniidae Ortmann, 1897 (Crustacea: Decapoda: Brachyura: Potamoidea), with description of a new genus (Gecarcinucidae: Gecarcinucoidea) from the Seychelles, Indian Ocean. *Journal of Natural History* 29: 581–600.

Ng, P.K.L., Guinot, D., and Davie, P.J.F. 2008. Systema Brachyurorum. Pt. 1, An annotated checklist of extant brachyuran crabs of the world. *Raffles Bulletin of Zoology*, Supplement 17: 1–286.

Nguyen, M., and Soto-Adames, F. N. 2018. Annotated checklist of Afrotropical *Trogolaphysa* Mills, 1938 (Hexapoda: Collembola: Paronellidae) and description of a new species from Madagascar. *Zoosystema* 40: 179–196.

Nguyen Duy-Jacquemin, M. 1996. Systématique et biogéographie des diplopodes pénicillates des Iles Canaries et du Cap Vert. *Mémoires du Muséum National d'Histoire Naturelle*, Paris 169:113–126.

Nielson, M. W. 1982. A revision of the subfamily Coelidiinae (Homoptera: Cicadellidae). 4. Tribe Coelidiini. *Pacific Insects Monographs* 38: 1–318.

Nieukerken, E. J. van, and Geertsema, H. 2015. A new leafminer on grapevine and *Rhoicissus* (Vitaceae) in South Africa within an expanded generic concept of Holocacista (Insecta, Lepidoptera, Heliozelidae). *ZooKeys* 507: 41–97.

Nieukerken, E. J. van, Kaila, L., Kitching, I. J., Kristensen, N. P., Lees, D. C., et al. 2011. Order Lepidoptera Linnaeus, 1758. In *Animal Biodiversity: An Outline of Higher-Level Classification and Survey of Taxonomic Richness*, ed. Z.-Q. Zhang. *Zootaxa* 3148: 212–221.

Nieukerken, E. J. van, Doorenweerd, C., Hoare, R.J.B., and Davis, D. R. 2016. Revised classification and catalogue of global Nepticulidae and Opostegidae (Lepidoptera, Nepticuloidea). *ZooKeys* 628: 65–246.

Nilsson, A. N. 1996. Coleoptera Dytiscidae, diving water beetles. In *Aquatic Insects of North Europe*, ed. A. N. Nilsson, pp 145–172. Stenstrup: Apollo Books.

———. 2005. *World Catalogue of Insects*. Vol. 7, *Amphizoidae, Aspidytidae, Haliplidae, Noteridae and Paelobiidae (Coleoptera, Adephaga)*, eds. A. N. Nilsson and B. J. van Vondel, pp. 87–153. Stenstrup: Apollo Books.

———. 2011. A world catalogue of the Family Noteridae, or the burrowing water beetles (Coleoptera, Adephaga), version 16.VIII.2011. http://www.waterbeetles.eu/documents/W_CAT_Noteridae.pdf.

Nilsson, A. N., and Hájek, J. 2020. A world catalogue of the family Dytiscidae, or the diving beetles (Coleoptera, Adephaga), version 1.I.2020. http://www.waterbeetles.eu/documents/W_CAT_Dytiscidae_2020.pdf.

Nilsson, A. N., Bilardo, A., and Rocchi, S. 1996. A check list of *Copelatus* Erichson 1832 species (Coleoptera Dytiscidae) from Afrotropical and Madagascan regions with a review of published penis drawings. *Tropical Zoology* 9: 11–148.

Nilsson, L. A., and Rabakonandrianina, E. 1988. Hawk-moth scale analysis and pollination specialization in the epilithic Malagasy endemic *Aerangis ellisii* (Reichenb. fil.) Schltr. (Orchidaceae). *Botanical Journal of the Linnean Society* 97: 49–61.

Nilsson, L. A., Jonsson, L., Rason, L., and Randrianjohany, E. 1985a. Monophily and pollination mechanisms in *Angraecum arachnites* Schltr. (Orchidaceae) in a guild of long-tongued hawk-moths (Sphingidae) in Madagascar. *Biological Journal of the Linnean Society* 26: 1–19.

———. 1985b. Pollination of *Plectranthus vestitus* (Lamiaceae) by trap-lining hovering bees in Madagascar. *Plant Systematics and Evolution* 150: 223–236.

———. 1986. The pollination of *Cymbidiella falbellata* (Orchidaceae) in Madagascar: A system operated by sphecid wasps. *Nordic Journal of Botany* 6: 411–422.

———. 1987. Angraecoid orchids and hawk-moths in central Madagascar: Specialized pollination systems and generalist foragers. *Biotropica* 19: 310–318.

Nilsson, L. A., Rabakonandrianina, E., Pettersson, B., and Ranaivo, J. 1990. "Ixoroid" secondary pollen presentation and pollination by small moths in the Malagasy treelet *Ixora platythyrsa* (Rubiaceae). *Plant Systematics and Evolution* 170: 161–175.

Nilsson, L. A., Rabakonandrianina, E., Razananaivo, R., and Randriamanindry, J. J. 1992. Long pollinia on eyes: Hawk-moth pollination of *Cynorkis uniflora* Lindl. (Orchidaeceae) in Madagascar. *Botanical Journal of the Linnean Society* 109: 145–160.

Nilsson, L. A., Rabakonandrianina, E., Pettersson, B., and Grunmeier, R. 1993. Lemur pollination in the Malagasy rainforest liana *Strongylodon craveniae* (Leguminosae). *Evolutionary Trends in Plants* 7: 49–56.

Nobre, T., Eggleton, P., and Aanen, D. K. 2009. Vertical transmission as the key to the colonization of Madagascar by fungus-growing termites? *Proceedings of the Royal Society of London B: Biological Sciences* 277: 359–365. doi.org/10.1098/rspb.2009.1373.

Noonan, B. P., and Chippindale, P. T. 2006. Vicariant origin of Malagasy reptiles supports Late Cretaceous Antarctic land bridge. *The American Naturalist* 168: 730–741.

Norrbom, A. L., Carroll, L. E., and Freidberg, A. 1999. Status of knowledge. In *Fruit Fly Expert Identification System and Systematic Information Database*, ed. F. C. Thompson, pp. 9–47. Leiden: Backhuys.

Novotny, V., Miller, S. E., Baje, L., Balagawi, S., Basset, Y., et al. 2010. Guild-specific patterns of species richness and host specialization in plant-herbivore food webs from a tropical forest. *Journal of Animal Ecology* 79: 1193–1203.

Nuss, M., Landry, B., Mally, R., Vegliante, F., Tränkner, A., et al. 2003. Global Information System on Pyraloidea [GlobIZ]. Accessed Mar. 2020. www.pyraloidea.org.

Nye, I.W.B. 1975. *Generic Names of the Moths of the World*. Vol. 1, *Noctuoidea (part): Noctuidae, Agaristidae, and Nolidae*. London: British Museum (Natural History).

O'Brien, L. B. 1988. Taxonomic changes in North American Issidae (Homoptera: Fulgoroidea). *Annals of the Entomological Society of America* 81(6): 865–869.

———. 2002. The wild wonderful world of Fulgoromorpha. *Denisia*, neue folge, 4: 83–102.

Ochs, G. 1948. Checklist of Neotropical Gyrinoidea (Col.). *Revista de Entomologia* 19: 565–567.

———. 1949. A revision of the Australian Gyrinidae. *Records of the Australian Museum* 22: 171–199.

———. 1953. Gyrinidae (Coleoptera Adephaga). *Exploration du Parc National de l'Upemba. Institut des Parcs Nationaux du Congo Belge. Mission G. F. de Witte* 16: 1–56.

OConnor, B. M. 1996. Parasitic and commensal arthropods of some birds and mammals of the Réserve Naturelle Intégrale d'Andringitra, Madagascar. In *A Floral and Faunal Inventory of the Eastern Slopes of the Réserve Naturelle Intégrale d'Andringitra, Madagascar: With Reference to Elevational Variation*, ed. S. M. Goodman. *Fieldiana: Zoology*, new ser., 85: 136–141.

———. 1998. Parasitic and commensal arthropods of some birds and mammals of the Réserve Spéciale d'Anjanaharibe-Sud, Madagascar. In *A Floral and Faunal Inventory of the Réserve Spéciale d'Anjanaharibe-Sud, Madagascar: With Reference to Elevational Variation*, ed. S. M. Goodman. *Fieldiana: Zoology*, new ser., 90: 73–78.

———. 2000. Parasitic and commensal arthropods of some birds and mammals of the Parc National de Marojejy, Madagascar. In *A Floral and Faunal Inventory of the Parc National de Marojejy, Madagascar: With Reference to Elevational Variation*, ed. S. M. Goodman. *Fieldiana: Zoology*, new ser., 97: 137–141.

O'Donnell, B. C., and Jockusch, E. L. 2008. Phylogenetic relationships of leptophlebiid mayflies as inferred by histone H3 and 28S ribosomal DNA. *Systematic Entomology* 33: 651–667.

Okada, K., and Hara, J. 1962. Notes on a new species of the genus *Corethrella*, from Japan (Diptera: Culicidae). *Bulletin of Physical Education* 5: 49–55.

Oláh, J., and Johanson, K. A. 2010a. Description of 46 new Old World Hydroptilidae (Trichoptera). *Folia Entomologica Hungarica* 71: 65–155.

———. 2010b. Generic review of Polycentropodidae with description of 32 new species and 19 new species records from Oriental, Australian and Afrotropical Biogeographical Regions. *Zootaxa* 2435: 1–63.

———. 2011. Description of a new endemic genus of Trichoptera from Madagascar (Odontoceridae). *Acta Zoologica Academiae Scientiarum Hungaricae* 57: 117–129.

Oláh, J., Barnard, P. C., and Malicky, H. 2006. A revision of lotic genus *Potamyia* Banks 1900 (Trichoptera: Hydropsychidae) with the description of eight new species. *Linzer Biologische Beiträge* 38(1): 739–777.

Oláh, J., Johanson, K. A., and Barnard, P. C. 2008. Revision of the Oriental and Afrotropical species of *Cheumatopsyche* Wallengren (Hydropsychidae, Trichoptera). *Zootaxa* 1738: 1–171.

Oldroyd, H. 1957. *The Horse-flies (Diptera: Tabanidae) of the Ethiopian Region*. Vol. 3, *Subfamilies Chrysopsinae, Scepsidinae and Pangoniinae and a Revised Classification*. London: British Museum (Natural History).

Oliarinony, R., and Elouard, J.-M. 1997. Biodiversité aquatique de Madagascar. 7—*Ranorythus* un nouveau genre de Tricorythidae définissant la nouvelle sous-famille des Ranorythinae (Ephemeroptera Pannota). *Bulletin de la Société Entomologique de France* 102(5): 439–447.

Oliarinony, R., Elouard, J.-M., and Raberiaka, N. 1997. Biodiversité aquatique de Madagascar. 19—Neuf nouvelles espèces de *Tricorythus* (Ephemeroptera, Pannota, Tricorythidae). *Bulletin de la Société Entomologique de France* 20(3): 73–90.

———. 1998. Biodiversité aquatique de Madagascar. 8—*Spinirythus* un nouveau genre de Tricorythidae (Ephemeroptera Pannota). *Bulletin de la Société Entomologique de France* 103(3): 237–244.

Oliarinony, R., Sartori, M., and Elouard, J.-M. 2000. Première description des larves et des oeufs du genre malgache *Madecassorythus* (Ephemeroptera, Tricorythidae). *Bulletin de la Société Entomologique Suisse* 73: 369–378.

Oliarinony, R., Elouard, J.-M., and Sartori, M. 2016. Complementary description of the genus *Manohyphella* Allen, 1973 (Insecta: Ephemeroptera: Teloganodidae), with some comments on its ecology in the Andasibe area (East Coast, Madagascar). *African Invertebrates* 57: 1–14.

Olival, K. J., Dick, C. W., Simmons, N. B., Morales, J. C., Melnick, D. J., Dittmar, K., Perkins, S. L., Daszak, P., and DeSalle, R. 2013. Lack of population genetic structure and host specificity in the bat fly, *Cyclopodia horsfieldi*, across species of *Pteropus* bats in Southeast Asia. *Parasites and Vectors* 6: 231.

Oliveira, F.G.L., Cipola, N. G., and Almeida, E.A.B. 2018. Systematics and biogeography of *Salina* MacGillivray (Collembola: Entomobryoidea), with emphasis on the species groups in the New World. *Insect Systematics and Evolution* 51: 81–138.

Olivier, G.-A. 1789. *Entomologie, ou histoire naturelle des insectes, avec leurs caractères génériques et spécifiques, leur description, leur synonymie et leurs figures enluminées*. Paris: Baudoin.

Olsoufieff, G. 1934. Essai de Révision systématique et Biologie des Cicindélides de Madagascar. In *Les Cicindélides de Madagascar*, eds. W. Horn and G. Olsoufieff. *Mémoires de l'Académie Malgache* 1934: 31–73.

Opell, B. D. 1995. Do static electric forces contribute to the stickiness of a spider's cribellate prey capture threads? *Journal of Experimental Zoology* 273: 186–189.

Orhant, G.E.R.J. 2001. *Progonia matilei* n. sp., espèce distincte de *P. oileusalis* (Walker) (Lepidoptera, Noctuidae, Herminiinae). *Revue Française d'Entomologie*, nouvelle série, 23: 124–126.

Õunap, E., Viidalepp, J., and Truuverk, A. 2016. Phylogeny of the subfamily Larentiinae (Lepidoptera: Geometridae): Integrating molecular data and traditional classifications. *Systematic Entomology* 41: 824–843.

Overal, W. L. 1980. Host-relations of the batfly *Megistopoda aranea* (Diptera: Streblidae) in Panama. *University of Kansas Science Bulletin* 52: 1–20.

Overgaard-Nielsen, B., Funch, P., and Toft, S. 1999. Self-injection of a dipteran parasitoid into a spider. *Naturwissenschaften* 86: 530–532.

Owen, C. L., Bracken-Grissom, H., Stern, D., and Crandall, K. A. 2015. A synthetic phylogeny of freshwater crayfish: Insights for conservation. *Philosophical Transactions of the Royal Society of London B: Biological Sciences*, 370: 20140009.

Pagenstecher, A. 1907. Lepidoptera Heterocera (Uraniidae, Geometridae, Noctuidae, Pyralidae, Thyrididae, Tortricidae, Tineidae, Pterophoridae) von Madagaskar, den Comoren und Ostafrika. In *Reise in Ostafrika in den Jahren 1903–1905, Wissenschaftliche Ergebnisse, Systematische Arbeiten*, vol. 2, pt. 2, ed. A. Voeltzkow, pp. 93–146. Stuttgart: E. Schweizerbartsche Verlagsbuchhandlung.

Palacios-Vargas, J. G., and Wilson, J. M. 1990. *Troglobius coprophagus*, a new genus and species of cave Collembola from Madagascar, with notes on its ecology. *International Journal of Speleology* 19: 67–73.

Park, K.-T., Koo, J.-M., and Minet, J. 2020. Review of the Malagasy lecithocerid species described by Pierre Viette and deposited in MNHN (Paris), with new generic combinations and descriptions of a new subfamily and genus of Momphidae (Lepidoptera: Gelechioidea). *Zootaxa* 4845: 151–190.

Parnaudeau, R., Rochat, J., Franck, A., Gasnier, S., Cazanove, G., and Hugel, S. 2013. Les Acrididae des Îles Eparses (Orthoptera, Caelifera). *Bulletin de la Société Entomologique de France* 118: 111–117.

Paterson, H. E. 1960. Notes on the genus *Allaudinella* G.-T. with the description of a new species and a key to the known species of the genus (Diptera, Muscidae). *Mémoires de l'Institut Scientifique de Madagascar*, série E, 11(1959): 355–367.

Patterson, B. D., Dick, C. W., and Dittmar, K. 2007. Roosting habits of bats affect their parasitism by bat flies (Diptera: Streblidae). *Journal of Tropical Ecology* 23: 177–189.

———. 2008. Parasitism by bat flies (Diptera: Streblidae) on Neotropical bats: Effects of host body size, distribution and abundance. *Parasitology Research* 103: 1091–1100.

Paulian, R. 1949. Recherches sur les insectes d'importance biologique de Madagascar. VI. Deux familles de Coléoptères nouvelles pour la faune Malgache. *Mémoires de l'Institut Scientifique de Madagascar*, série A, 3: 371–374.

———. 1950. *Insectes utiles et nuisibles de la région de Tananarive*. Antananarivo: Publications de l'Institut de Recherche Scientifique.

———. 1952. Esquisse du peuplement entomologique de Madagascar. *Mémoire de l'Institut Scientifique de Madagascar* 1(1): 1–22.

———. 1958. A propos des anoploures de lémuriens. *Mémoires de l'Institut Scientifique de Madagascar*, série E, *Entomologie* 9: 14–19.

———. 1960. Un nouvel anoploure de lémurien malgache. *Bulletin de la Société Entomologique de France* 65: 306–308.

———. 1961a. La Zoogéographie de Madagascar et des îles voisines. *Faune de Madagascar* 13: 1–475.

———. 1961b. Deux nouveaux anoploures de rongeurs malgaches et un mallophage de lémuriens. *Bulletin de la Société Entomologique de France* 66: 122–125.

———. 1970. The termites of Madagascar. In *Biology of Termites*, vol. 2, eds. K. Krishna, and F. M. Weesner, pp. 281–294. New York: Academic Press.

———. 1988. *Biologie des Coléoptères*. Paris: Lechevalier.

Paulian, R., and Viette, P. 1955. Essai d'un catalogue biologique des Lépidoptères Hétérocères de Tananarive. *Mémoires de l'Institut Scientifique de Madagascar*, série E, 6: 141–281.

———. 2003. An introduction to the terrestrial and freshwater invertebrates. In *The Natural History of Madagascar*, eds. S. M. Goodman and J. P. Benstead, pp. 503–511. Chicago: University of Chicago Press.

Peake, J. 1978. Distribution and ecology of the Stylommatophora. In *Pulmonates*, Vol. 2A, *Systematics, Evolution and Ecology*, eds. V. Fretter and J. Peake, pp. 429–526. London: Academic Press.

Pearce, T. A. 2003. Gastropoda, terrestrial snails. In *The Natural History of Madagascar*, eds. S. M. Goodman and J. P. Benstead, pp. 529–574. Chicago: University of Chicago Press.

Pearson, D. L., and Vogler, A. P. 2001. *Tiger Beetles, the Evolution, Ecology and Diversity of the Cicindelids*. Ithaca and London: Cornell University Press.

Pederzani, F. 1982. Notes on some Dytiscidae of the British Museum (Natural History) with descriptions of three new species (Coleoptera). *Bollettino della Società Entomologica Italiana* 114: 139–143.

Pederzani, F., and Rocchi, S. 2009. On some Madagascan Hydradephaga of the Natural History Museum, London, with the descriptions of five new species of Dytiscidae (Coleoptera Haliplidae, Dytiscidae, Noteridae). *Atti dell'Accademia Roveretana degli Agiati, Contributi della Classe di Scienze Matematiche, Fisiche e Naturali* (8) 8B (258) (2008): 81–100.

Peeters, C., and Fisher, B. L. 2016. Gamergates (mated egg-laying workers) and queens both reproduce in *Euponera sikorae* ants from Madagascar. *African Entomology* 24: 180–187.

Peeters, C., Foldi, I., Matile-Ferrero, D., and Fisher, B. L. 2017. A mutualism without honeydew: What benefits for *Melissotarsus emeryi* ants and armoured scale insects (Diaspididae)? *PeerJ* 5: e3599.

Pekar, S., Šobotník, J., and Lubin, Y. 2011. Armoured spiderman: Morphological and behavioural adaptations of a specialised araneophagous predator (Araneae: Palpimanidae). *Naturwissenschaften* 98: 593–603. doi:10.1007/s00114-011-0804-1.

Pereira-Da-Conceicoa, L. L., and Barber-James, H. M. 2013. Redescription and lectotype designation of the endemic South African mayfly *Lestagella penicillata* (Barnard, 1932) (Ephemeroptera: Teloganodidae). *Zootaxa* 3750: 450–464.

Perissinotto, R., Bird, M. S., and Bilton, D. T. 2016. Predaceous water beetles (Coleoptera, Hydradephaga) of the Lake St Lucia system, South Africa: Biodiversity, community ecology and conservation implications. *ZooKeys* 595: 85–135.

Perkins, P. D., and Bergsten, J. 2019. New myxophagan water beetles from Madagascar (Coleoptera: Torridincolidae, Hydroscaphidae). *Zootaxa* 4657: 57–96.

Pescador, M. L., and Peters, J. G. 2007. A new genus of Oligoneuriidae (Ephemeroptera) from Madagascar. *Annals of the Entomological Society of America* 100: 173–177.

Peschet, R. 1917. Coléoptères des Iles Mascareignes et Séchelles: Missions scientifique de MM. Ch. Alluaud (1892, 1893, et 1897) et P. Carié (1910–1913); Dytiscidae et Gyrinidae. *Annales de la Société Entomologique de France* 86: 1–56.

Peters, G. 2000. Unbekannte Bekannte: Die *Anax*-Species in Europa (Odonata: Aeshnidae). *Libellula* 19: 53–64.

Petersen, H. 2002. General aspects of collembolan ecology at the turn of the millennium. *Pedobiologia* 46: 246–260.

Petersen, H., and Luxton, M. 1982. A comparative analysis of soil fauna populations and their role in decomposition processes. *Oikos* 39(3): 288–388.

Peterson, B. V. 1987. 61. Diopsidae. In *Manual of Nearctic Diptera*, vol. 2, ed. J. F. McAlpine, pp. 785–789. Agriculture Canada Monograph 28. Quebec: Minister of Supplies and Services.

Petrunkevitch, A. 1921. Spider silk and its uses. *American Museum Journal* 21: 381.

Pettersson, B., and Nilsson, L. A. 1993. Floral variation and deceit pollination in *Polystachya rosea* (Orchidaceae) on an inselberg in Madagascar. *Opera Botanica* 121: 237–245.

Phillips, A. J., Arauco-Brown, R., Oceguera-Figueroa, A., Gomez, G. P., Beltrán, M., Lai, Y., and Siddall, M. E. 2010. *Tyrannobdella rex* n. gen. n. sp. and the evolutionary origins of mucosal leech infestations. *PLoS One* 5: e10057.

Pickard-Cambridge, O. 1876. Catalogue of a collection of spiders made in Egypt, with descriptions of new species and characters of a new genus. *Proceedings of the Zoological Society of London* 44: 541–630.

———. 1877. On some new species of Araneidea, with characters of two new genera and some remarks on the families Podophthalmides and Dinopides. *Proceedings of the Zoological Society of London* 1877: 557–578.

———. 1881. On some new genera and species of Araneidea. *Proceedings of the Zoological Society*, London 1881: 765–775.

Pierre, J., and Basquin, P. 2017. Nouveaux Sphinx de Madagascar (Lepidoptera, Sphingidae). *Bulletin de la Société Entomologique de France* 122: 479–483.

Pilaka, T., and Elouard, J.-M. 1999. Deux espèces nouvelles de simulies malgaches phorétiques (Diptera, Simuliidae). *Mitteillungen der Schweizerischen Entomologischen Gesellschaft* 72(1–2): 39–46.

Pinhey, E. 1964a. A revision of the African members of the genus *Pseudagrion* Selys (Odonata). *Revista de Entomologia de Moçambique* 7: 5–196.

———. 1964b. Dragonflies of the genus *Pseudagrion* Selys collected by F. Keiser on Madagascar. *Verhandlungen der naturforschenden Gesellschaft von Basel* 75: 140–149.

———. 1980. A revision of African Lestidae (Odonata). *Occasional Papers of the National Museum of Rhodesia (B)* 6: 328–479.

Pinto, V.A.B., da Fonseca C.R.V., and Hamada, N. 2011. *Iapir quadridentatus* sp. nov., a new torridincolid beetle from Brazil (Coleoptera: Myxophaga: Torridincolidae). *Zootaxa* 3031: 47–53.

Pitkin, B., and Jenkins, P. 2003. Butterflies and moths of the world: Generic names and their type-species. Accessed Mar. 2020. https://www.nhm.ac.uk/our-science/data/butmoth/.

Pitz, K. M., and Sierwald, P. 2010. Phylogeny of the millipede order Spirobolida (Arthropoda: Diplopoda: Helminthomorpha). *Cladistics* 26(5): 497–525.

Platnick, N. I., and Berniker, L. 2015. The goblin spider genus *Khamisia* and its relatives (Araneae, Oonopidae). *American Museum Novitates* 3837: 1–66.

Platnick, N. I., Coddington, J. A., Forster, R. F., and Griswold, C. E. 1991. Spinneret evidence and the higher classification of the haplogyne spiders (Araneae, Araneomorphae). *American Museum Novitates* 3016: 1–73.

Platnick, N. I., Hormiga, G., Jäger, P., Jocqué, R., Ramírez, M. J., and Raven, R. J. 2020. *Spiders of the World: A Natural History*. Princeton: Princeton University Press.

Plebani, M., Imanizabayo, O., Hansen, D. M., and Armbruster, W. S. 2015. Pollination ecology and circadian patterns of inflorescence opening of the Madagascan climber *Dalechampia* aff. *bernieri* (Euphorbiaceae). *Journal of Tropical Ecology* 31: 99–101.

Pocock, R. I. 1889. Notes on some Buthidae, new and old. *Annals and Magazine of Natural History*, ser. 6, 3(16): 334–351.

———. 1894. Scorpions and their geographical distribution. *Natural Science* 4(27): 353–364.

———. 1896. Notes on some Ethiopian species of Ischnuridae contained in the collection of the British Museum. *Annals and Magazine of Natural History*, ser. 6, 17: 312–319.

Podolak, M., Gattolliat, J.-L., Athanasiades, A., and Sartori, M. 2019. Indian Ocean Islands: Museum specimens of freshwater insect taxa. Version 1.1. Musée cantonal de zoologie, Lausanne–MZL. Metadata data set. Accessed Apr. 2020. https://doi.org/10.15468/pwhyes.

Polotow, D., and Griswold, C. 2017. Cleaning old cabinets: Revealing the taxonomy of Sri Lankan wolf spiders (Araneae, Udubidae and Zoropsidae). *Zootaxa* 4362: 51–74.

Polotow, D., Carmichael, A., and Griswold, C. E. 2015. Total evidence analysis of the phylogenetic relationships of Lycosoidea spiders (Araneae, Entelegynae). *Invertebrate Systematics* 29: 124–163. doi:10.1071/IS14041.

Ponge, J.-F., Dubs, F., Gillet, S., Sousa, J. P., and Lavelle, P. 2006. Decreased biodiversity in soil springtail communities: The importance of dispersal and landuse history in heterogeneous landscapes. *Soil Biology and Biochemistry* 38: 1158–1161.

Ponomarenko, M. G. 2009. *Gelechiid Moths of the Subfamily Dichomeridinae (Lepidoptera: Gelechiidae) of the World*. Vladivostok: Dal'nauka.

Pont, A. C. 1974. A revison of the genus *Passeromyia* Rodhain and Villeneuve (Diptera: Muscidae). *Bulletin of the British Museum (Natural History), Entomology Series* 30: 339–372.

———. 1980. Family Muscidae. In *Catalogue of the Diptera of the Afrotropical Region*, ed. R. W. Crosskey, pp. 721–761. London: British Museum (Natural History).

Pont, A. C., and Dear, J. P. 1976. A synopsis of the genus *Ochromusca* Malloch, 1927 (Diptera, Muscidae). *Annals of the Natal Museum* 22: 747–753.

Poole, R. W. 1989. Noctuidae. *Lepidopterorum Catalogus*, new ser., 118: 1–500 (pt. 1), 501–1014 (pt. 2), 1015–1314 (pt. 3). Leiden: E. J. Brill.

Porter, M., Pérez-Losada, M., and Crandall, K., 2005. Model-based multi-locus estimation of decapod phylogeny and divergence times. *Molecular Phylogenetics and Evolution* 37: 355–369.

Pratt, M. L. 2008. *Imperial Eyes: Travel Writing and Transculturation*. New York: Routledge.

Preston-Mafham, K. 1991. *Madagascar: A Natural History*. Oxford: Facts on File.

Prokin, A. A., and Ponomarenko, A. G. 2013. The first record of crawling water beetles (Coleoptera, Haliplidae) in the Lower Cretaceous of Mongolia. *Paleontological Journal* 47: 89–93.

Przybyłowicz, L., Lees, D. C., Zenker, M. M., and Wahlberg, N. 2019. Molecular systematics of the arctiine tribe Syntomini (Lepidoptera, Erebidae). *Systematic Entomology* 44: 624–637.

Putchkov, A. V., and Cassola, F. 2005. Tiger beetles deserve separate family status in suborder Adephaga (Coleoptera, Cicindelidae). *Bulletin de la Société Entomologique de France* 110: 281–293.

Putchkov, A. V., and Dolin, V. 2005. Description of the larva of the tiger beetle *Pogonostoma majunganum* (Coleoptera, Cicindelidae). *Vestnik Zoologii* 39: 35–38.

Putshkov, V. G., and Putshkov, P. V. 1986. *A Catalog of the Reduviidae (Heteroptera) of the World*, 6 vols. Lyubertsy: Vinity.

Quentin, R. M. 1990. Le Groupe de *Orgizomyia* de Madagascar (Diptera: Tabanidae: Chrysopsinae: Rhinomyzini). *Annales de la Société Entomologique de France*, nouvelle série, 26: 431–436.

Rabarijaona, L. P., Ariey, F., Matra, R., Cot, S., Raharimalala, A. L., Ranaivo, L. H., Le Bras, J., Robert, V., and Randrianarivelojosia, M. 2006. Low autochtonous urban malaria in Antananarivo (Madagascar). *Malaria Journal* 5: 27.

Rabarimanarivo, M. N., Ramandimbisoa, B., Rakotoarivelo, N.H., Phillipson, P. B., Andriambololonera, S., Callmander, M. W., and Porembski, S. 2019. The extraordinary botanical diversity of inselbergs in Madagascar. *Candollea* 74: 65–84.

Rabearisoa, B. S. 1995. Systématique, biogéographie et essais d'élevage des ecrevisses malgaches. Mémoire de fin d'études, Département Elevage, Ecole Supérieure des Sciences Agronomiques, Université d'Antananarivo.

Rabearisoa, B., Elouard, J.-M., and Ramanankasina, E. 1996. Biogéographie des ecrevisses malgaches (Decapoda: Parastacidae). In *Biogéographie de Madagascar,* ed. W. R. Lourenço, pp. 559–562. Paris: Editions de l'ORSTOM.

Rabinowitz, P. D., Coffin, M. F., and Falvey, D. 1983. The separation of Madagascar and Africa. *Science* 220: 67–69.

Rage, J. C., 1996. Le peuplement de Madagascar: Une composante venue de Laurasie est-elle envisageable ? In *Biogéographie de Madagascar*, ed. W. R. Lourenço, pp. 27–35. Paris: Editions de l'ORSTOM.

Ragge, D. R. 1969. A revision of the African species of *Pseudorhynchus* Serville (Orthoptera: Tettigoniidae). *Bulletin of the British Museum (Natural History), Entomology Series* 25: 169–190.

Raharimalala, F. N., Ravaomanarivo, L. H., Ravelonandro, P., Rafarasoa, L. S., Zouache, K., et al. 2012. Biogeography of the two major arbovirus mosquito vectors, *Aedes aegypti* and *Aedes albopictus* (Diptera, Culicidae), in Madagascar. *Parasites and Vectors* 5: 56. doi:10.1186/1756-3305-5-56.

Rahelinirina, S., Rajerison, M., Telfer, S., Savin, C., Carniel, E., and Duplantier, J.-M. 2017. The Asian house shrew *Suncus murinus* as a reservoir and source of human outbreaks of plague in Madagascar. *PLoS Neglected Tropical Diseases* 11(11): e0006072.

Rajaonarivelo, J. A., Raherilalao, M.-J., Andrianarimisa, A., and Goodman, S. M. 2019. Répartition verticale des arthropodes dans les forêts sèches occidentales Malgaches. *Bulletin de la Société Zoologique de France* 144(1): 3–39.

Rajaonarivelo, V., Le Goff, G., Cot, M., and Brutus, L. 2004. Les anophèles et la transmission du paludisme à Ambohimena, village de la marge occidentale des hautes-terres Malgaches. *Parasite* 11(1): 75–82.

Rajemison, F. I., Noroalintseheno Lalarivoniaina, O. S., and Goodman, S. M. 2017a. Parasitism by Nycteribiidae and Streblidae flies (Diptera) of a Malagasy fruit bat (Pteropodidae): Effects of body size and throat gland development on parasite abundance. *Journal of Medical Entomology* 54: 805–811.

———. 2017b. Bat flies (Diptera: Nycteribiidae, Streblidae) parasitising *Rousettus madagascariensis* (Chiroptera: Pteropodidae) in the Parc National d'Ankarana, Madagascar: Species diversity, rates of parasitism and sex ratios. *African Entomology* 25: 72–85.

Rajonhson, D. M., Miarinjara, A., Rahelinirina, S., Rajerison, M., and Boyer, S. 2017. Effectiveness of Fipronil as a systemic control agent against *Xenopsylla cheopis* (Siphonaptera: Pulicidae) in Madagascar. *Journal of Medical Entomology* 54(2): 411–417.

Rakotonarivo, A. L. 2004. Etudes des écrevisses (Parastacidae) dans la forêt d'Antsahabe-Est. Anjozorobe. Mémoire du DEA, Option Biologie, Ecologie et Conservation Animale, Université d'Antananarivo.

Ramanantsalama, R. V, Andrianarimisa, A., Raselimanana, A. P., and Goodman, S. M. 2018. Rates of hematophagous ectoparasites consumption during grooming by an endemic Madagascar fruit bat. *Parasites and Vectors* 11: 330.

Ramasindrazana, B., Goodman, S. M., Gomard, Y., Dick, C. W., and Tortosa, P. 2017. Hidden diversity of Nycteribiidae (Diptera) bat flies from the Malagasy region and insights on host-parasite interactions. *Parasites and Vectors* 10: 630.

Rambur, J. P. 1842. *Histoire naturelle des insectes, Névroptères*. Paris: Librairie encyclopédique de Roret Fain et Thunot.

Ramos, H. C., and Brunhes, J. 2004. Insecta Diptera Culicidae *Uranotaenia*. *Faune de Madagascar* 91: 1–463.

Ranaivoson, H. C. 2011. *Astacoides madagascariensis* (Edwards and Audouin, 1839) (Parastacidae) de la forêt d'Anjozorobe: Etude sur la biologie, l'écologie et les organismes associés. Mémoire du D.E.A., Option Biologie, Ecologie et Conservation Animale, Université d'Antananarivo.

Ranarilalatiana, T. 2020. Diversité de *Copelatus* Erichson, 1832 (Coleoptera, Dytiscidae) de Madagascar et des coléoptères Adephaga aquatiques dans les vestiges forestiers du haut plateau central particulièrement sur les aires protégées de Manjakatompo Ankaratra, d'Ambohitantely et d'Anjozorobe-Angavo. PhD thesis, Université d'Antananarivo.

Ranarilalatiana, T., and Bergsten, J. 2019. Discovery of a specialist Copelatinae fauna on Madagascar: Highly ephemeral tropical forest floor depressions as an overlooked habitat for diving beetles (Coleoptera, Dytiscidae). *ZooKeys* 871: 89–118.

Ranarilalatiana, T., Raveloson Ravaomanarivo, L. H., and Bergsten, J. 2019. Taxonomic revision of the genus *Copelatus* of Madagascar (Coleoptera, Dytiscidae, Copelatinae): The non-*erichsonii* group species. *ZooKeys* 869: 19–90.

Randriamanantsoa, R., Aberlenc, H.-P., Ralisoa, O. B., Ratnadass, A., and Vercambre, B. 2010. Les larves des Scarabaeoidea (Insecta, Coleoptera) en riziculture pluviale des régions de haute et moyenne altitudes du Centre de Madagascar. *Zoosystema* 32(1): 19–72.

Randriamasimanana, D., and Gibon, F.-M. 2000. Nouveaux *Oecetis* malgaches (Trichoptera, Leptoceridae). *Revue Française d'Entomologie* 22(1): 43–56.

———. 2001. Etude systématique, habitats et répartition géographique des *Setodes* (Trichoptera: Leptoceridae) de Madagascar. *Annales de Limnologie, International Journal of Limnolology* 37(2): 125–141.

Randrianambinintsoa, F. J., and Depaquit, J. 2013. Phleboyomine sand flies from Madagascar (Diptera: Psychodidae). VII. *Phlebotomus* (*Anaphlebotomus*) *vincenti* n. sp. *Bulletin de la Société de Pathologie Exotique* 106: 206–211.

Randrianambinintsoa, F. J., Depaquit, J., Brengues, C., Dhondt, C., Yahaya, I., Ouledi, A., Léger, N., and Robert, V. 2012. First record of phlebotomine sandflies (Diptera: Psychodidae) in the Comoros archipelago with description of *Sergentomyia* (*Vattieromyia*) *pessoni* n. sp. and *S.* (*Rondanomyia*) *goodmani comorensis* n. ssp. *Parasite* 19(3): 195–206.

Randrianambinintsoa, F. J., Léger, N., Robert, V., and Depaquit, J. 2013. Phlebotomine sand flies from Madagascar (Diptera: Psychodidae). VII. An identification key for *Phlebotomus* with the description of *Phlebotomus* (*Anaphlebotomus*) *vaomalalae* n. sp. *Parasite* 20: 6.

———. 2014. Paraphyly of the subgenus *Sintonius* (Diptera, Psychodidae, *Sergentomyia*): Status of the Malagasy species; Creation of a new subgenus and description of a new species. *PLoS One* 9(6): e98065.

Randrianambinintsoa, F. J., Depaquit, J., Martinet, J. P., Golden, C., Boyer, S., Robert, V., and Tantely, L. 2020a. Two new phlebotomine sandflies (Diptera: Psychodidae) at the edge of forest in Madagascar: The anthropophilic *Phlebotomus artemievi* n. sp. and *Sergentomyia maroensetrensis* n. sp. *Parasitology Research* 119(4): 1177–1199. doi:10.1007/s00436-020-06639-x.

Randrianambinintsoa, F. J., Robert, V., Blavier, A., Léger, N., and Depaquit, J. 2020b. Two new phlebotomine sandflies species (Diptera: Psychodidae) from the highlands of Madagascar. *Acta Tropica* 202: 105260. doi.org/10.1016/j.actatropica.2019.105260.

Randrianandrasana, M., and Berenbaum, M. R. 2015. Edible non-crustacean arthropods in rural communities of Madagascar. *Journal of Ethnobiology* 35(2): 354–383.

Randrianandrasana, M., Razafindraleva, H. A., and Berenbaum, M. R. 2014. Host plant records of *Antherina suraka* (Boisduval, 1833) (Saturniidae) in Madagascar. *Journal of the Lepidopterists' Society* 68: 130–140.

Randrianandrasana, M., Berlocher, S. H., Rougerie, R., and Berenbaum, M. R. 2016. Intraspecific variation in *Antherina suraka* (Lepidoptera: Saturniidae), an endemic resident of endangered forests in Madagascar. *Annals of the Entomological Society of America* 109: 384–395.

Rasamy Razanabolana, J. 2010. Malagasy crayfishes: Ecology, distribution, parasites and commensals. Project MacArthur Foundation: Advancement of Conservation Biology and Associated within the University of Antananarivo Community. Sous Projet 4245/HDR-2. Rapport final, non publié.

Ratnasingham, S., and Hebert, P.D.N. 2007. The barcode of life data system. *Molecular Ecology Resources* 7: 355–364. http://www.barcodinglife.org.

———. 2013. A DNA-based registry for all animal species: The Barcode Index Number (BIN) System. *PLoS One* 8: e66213.

Ratovonjato, J., Randriambelosoa, J., and Robert, V. 2008. *Tunga penetrans* (Insecta, Siphonaptera, Tungidae) à Madagascar: Une nuisance négligée. *Revue de Médecine Vétérinaire* 159(11): 551–556.

Ratovonjato, J., Olive, M.-M., Tantely, L. M., Andrianaivolambo, L., Tata, E., Razainirina, J., Jeanmaire, E., Reynes, J.-M., and Elissa, N. 2011. Detection, isolation, and genetic characterization of Rift Valley fever virus from *Anopheles* (*Anopheles*) *coustani*, *Anopheles* (*Anopheles*) *squamosus*, and *Culex* (Culex) *antennatus* of the Haute Matsiatra region, Madagascar. *Vector-Borne and Zoonotic Diseases* 11(6): 753–759. doi:10.1089/vbz.2010.0031.

Ratovonjato, J., Rajerison, M., Rahelinirina, S., and Boyer, S. 2014. *Yersinia pestis* in *Pulex irritans* fleas during plague outbreak, Madagascar. *Emerging Infectious Diseases* 20(8): 1414–1415.

Ratsirarson, J. 1995. Pollination ecology of *Aloe divaricata*, Berger (Liliaceae): An endemic plant species of south-west Madagascar. *South African Journal of Botany* 61: 249–252.

Ratsirarson, J., and Silander, J. A., Jr. 1996a. Structure and dynamics in *Nepenthes madagascariensis* pitcher plant micro-communities. *Biotropica* 28: 218–227.
———. 1996b. Reproductive biology of the threatened Madagascar triangle palm: *Neodypsis decaryi* Jumelle. *Biotropica* 28: 737–745.
———. 2003. Pollination ecology of plant communities in the dry forest of the southwest. In *The Natural History of Madagascar*, eds. S. M. Goodman and J. P. Benstead, pp. 272–275. Chicago: University of Chicago Press.
Ravelomanana, A., and Fisher, B. L. 2013. Diversity of ants in burned and unburned grassland, and dry deciduous forest in the Beanka Reserve, Melaky Region, western Madagascar, eds. S. M. Goodman, L. Gautier, and M. J. Raherilalao. *Malagasy Nature* 7: 171–183
Raven, P. H., and Miller, S. E. 2020. Here today, gone tomorrow. *Science* 370: 149–149.
Raven, R. J. 1985. The spider infraorder Mygalomorphae (Araneae): Cladistics and systematics. *Bulletin of the American Museum of Natural History* 182: 1–180.
Ravoahangimalala, R. O., Rasoamampionona Raminosoa, N., Razanabolana Rasamy, J., Andriamaro, L., and Randrianasolo, H. H. 2007. Les écrevisses de Madagascar. *Recherches Pour le Développement*, série *Sciences Biologiques* 25: 1–111.
Ravoahangimalala, R. O., Randrianambinintsoa, E. J., Tchuinkam, T., and Robert V. 2008. Paludisme en milieu urbain d'altitude à Antananarivo, Madagascar: Bioécologie d'*Anopheles arabiensis*. *Bulletin de la Société de Pathologie Exotique* 101(4): 348–352.
Raynal, J., and Le Gac, P. 1937. Phlébotomes dans le nord de Madagascar. *Phlebotomus squamipleuris* Newstead 1912. *Bulletin de la Société de Pathologie Exotique* 30: 76–90.
Razafimahatratra, V. 1988. La diversité des espèces d'insectes dans les écosystèmes forestiers et les écosystèmes agricoles. In *L'Equilibre des ecosystèmes forestiers à Madagascar*, eds. L. H. Rakotovao, V. Barre, and J. Sayer, pp. 38–40. Gland: UICN.
Razowski, J. 2005. Notes and descriptions of primitive Tortricini from tropical Africa, with a list of Asian taxa (Lepidoptera: Tortricidae). *Shilap, Revista de Lepidopterología* 33: 423–436.
Realzola, E., Cook, J. L., Cook, T. J., and Clopton, R. E. 2007. Composition of gyrinid aggregations in the east Texas primitive Big Thicket (Coleoptera: Gyrinidae). *The Coleopterists Bulletin* 61: 495–502.
Redtenbacher, J. 1891. Monographie der Conocephaliden. *Verhandlungen der Zoologisch-Botanischen Gesellschaft Wien* 41: 315–562.
———. 1906. *Die Insektenfamilie der Phasmiden. I. Phasmidae Areolatae.* Leipzig: Verlag von Wilhem Engelmann.
———. 1908. *Die Insektenfamilie der Phasmiden. III. Phasmidae Anareolatae (Phibalosomini, Acrophyllini, Necrosciini).* Leipzig: Verlag von Wilhem Engelmann.
Reed, S. K., and Cumberlidge, N. 2006. *Foza raimundi*, a new genus and species of potamonautid freshwater crab (Crustacea: Decapoda: Potamoidea) from northern Madagascar. *Proceedings of the Biological Society of Washington* 119(1): 58–66.
Reeves, C., and de Wit, M. 2000. Making ends meet in Gondwana: Retracing the transforms of the Indian Ocean and reconnecting continental shear zones. *Terra Nova* 12: 272–280.
Regier, J. C., Brown, J. W., Mitter, C., Baixeras, J., Cho, S., Cummings, M. P., and Zwick, A. 2012. A molecular phylogeny for the leaf-roller moths (Lepidoptera: Tortricidae) and its implications for classification and life history evolution. *PLoS One* 7: e35574.
Regier, J. C., Mitter, C., Zwick, A., Bazinet, A. L., Cummings, M .P., et al. 2013. A large-scale, higher-level, molecular phylogenetic study of the insect order Lepidoptera (moths and butterflies). *PLoS One* 8: e5856.
Regier, J. C., Mitter, C. Davis, D. R., Harrison, T. L., Sohn, J.-C., Cummings, M. P., Zwick, A., and Mitter, K. T. 2015. A molecular phylogeny and revised classification for the oldest ditrysian moth lineages (Lepidoptera: Tineoidea), with implications for ancestral feeding habits of the mega-diverse Ditrysia. *Systematic Entomology* 40: 409–432.
Regier, J. C., Mitter, C., Mitter, K., Cummings, M. P., Bazinet, A. L., Hallwachs, W., Janzen, D. H., and Zwick, A. 2017. Further progress on the phylogeny of Noctuoidea (Insecta: Lepidoptera) using an expanded gene sample. *Systematic Entomology* 42: 82–93.
Régimbart, M. 1895. Révision des Dytiscidae et Gyrinidae d'Afrique, Madagascar et îles voisines: En contribution à la faune entomologique du Congo. *Mémoires de la Société Entomologique de Belgique* 4: 1–244.
Reichardt, H. 1973. A critical study of the suborder Myxophaga, with a taxonomic revision of the Brazilian Torridincolidae and Hydroscaphidae (Coleoptera). *Arquivos de Zoologia*, São Paulo, 24: 73–162.
Reichardt, H., and Costa, C. 1967. *Ptyopteryx britskii*, a new Neotropical genus and species of the hitherto Ethiopian Torridincolidae (Coleoptera, Myxophaga). *Papéis Avulsos de Zoologia*, São Paulo, 21: 13–19.
Rembold, K., Fischer, E., Wetzel, M. A., and Barthlott, W. 2010. Prey composition of the pitcher plant *Nepenthes madagascariensis*. *Journal of Tropical Ecology* 26: 365–372.
Rembold, K., Fischer, E., Striffler, B. F., and Barthlott, W. 2012. Crab spider association with the Malagasy pitcher plant *Nepenthes madagascariensis*. *African Journal of Ecology* 51: 188–191.
Remy, P. A. 1950. Présence de l'anoploure *Haematopinus suis* L. sur le potamochère malgache. *Bulletin de la Société Entomologique de France* 55: 76–78.
Rheinheimer, J. 2004. Illustrierter Katalog und Bibliographie der Anthribidae der Welt (Insecta: Coleoptera). *Mitteilungen des Entomologischen Vereins Stuttgart* 39: 102–103.
Ribeiro, H. 1974. Sifonapteros de Angola (Insecta, Siphonaptera): Estudo sistematico e dados bioecologicos interessandoa epidemilogia da pestea. In *Parasitologia*, p. 202. Lisboa: Instituto de Higien e Medicina Tropical.
Ribera, I. 2008. Habitat constraints and the generation of diversity in freshwater macroinvertebrates. In *Aquatic Insects: Challenges to Populations*, eds. J. Lancaster and R. A. Briers, pp. 289–311. London: CAB International UK.
Ribera, I., and Balke, M. 2007. Recognition of a species-poor, geographically restricted but morphologically diverse Cape lineage of diving beetles (Coleoptera: Dytiscidae: Hyphydrini). *Journal of Biogeography* 34: 1220–1232.
Richard, J., and Clark, P. F. 2010a. A new species of *Caridina* H. Milne Edwards, 1837 (Decapoda, Caridea, Atyidae) from the Betsiboka River basin, Madagascar. In *Studies on Malacostraca: Lipke Bijdeley Holthuis Memorial Volume*, eds. C.H.J. M. Fransen, S. De Grave, and P.K.L. Ng. *Crustaceana Monographs* 14: 637–644.
———. 2010b. *Caridina* H. Milne Edwards, 1837 (Crustacea: Decapoda: Caridea: Atyoidae: Atyidae): Freshwater shrimps from eastern and southern Africa. *Zootaxa* 2372: 305–337.
Richard, J., De Grave, S., and Clark, P. F. 2012. A new atyid genus and species from Madagascar (Crustacea: Decapoda: Caridea). *Zootaxa* 3162: 31–38.
Richardson, R. L. 1975. A contribution to the general zoology of the land-leeches (Hirudinea: Haemadipsoidea superfam. nov.). *Acta Zoologica Academiae Scientiarum Hungaricae* 21: 119–152.
Richman, N. I., Böhm, M, Adams, S. B., Alvarez, F., Bergey, E. A., et al. 2015. Multiple drivers of decline in the global status of freshwater crayfish (Decapoda: Astacidea). *Philosophical Transactions of the Royal Society of London B: Biological Sciences*, 370: 20140060.
Ritchie, J. M. 1982. A taxonomic revision of the genus *Gastrimargus* Saussure (Orthoptera: Acrididae). *Bulletin of the British Museum (Natural History), Entomology Series* 44: 239–329.
Rivalier, E. 1957. Démembrement du genre *Cicindela* Linné. III. Faune africano-malgache. *Revue Française d'Entomologie* 24: 12–342.
———. 1967. Le genre *Physodeutera* Lacordaire (Col. Cicindelidae). Révision et description d'espèces nouvelles. *Annales de la Société Entomologique de France* 3: 261–296.
———. 1970. Le genre *Pogonostoma* (Col. Cicindelidae). Révision avec description d'espèces nouvelles. *Annales de la Société Entomologique de France* 6: 269–338.
Rix, M. G., and Harvey, M. S. 2012. Australian assassins. Pt. 3, A review of the assassin spiders (Araneae, Archaeidae) of tropical north-eastern Queensland. *ZooKeys* 218: 1–50.
Robert, V., and Borkent, A. 2014. First record of Corethrellidae (Diptera), the frog-biting midges, in Madagascar. *Malagasy Nature* 8: 49–53.
Robert, V., Le Goff, G., Andrianaivolambo, L., Randimby, F. M., Domarle, O., Randrianarivelojosia, M., Raharimanga, V., Raveloson, A., Ravaonjanahary, C., and Ariey, F. 2006. Moderate transmission but high prevalence of malaria in Madagascar. *International Journal for Parasitology* 36(12): 1273–1281.
Robert, V., Ramasindrazana, B., and Goodman, S. M. 2014. The species composition and distribution of insects collected by light-traps, with special reference to hematophagous groups, in and near cave systems of Madagascar. *Malagasy Nature* 8: 54–66.
Robertson, J. A., Bradler, S., and Whiting, M. F. 2018. Evolution of oviposition techniques in stick and leaf insects (Phasmatodea). *Frontiers in Ecology and Evolution* 6: 216.
Robic, J. 1937. Les caractéristiques de la peste à Madagascar. *Annales de Médecine et Pharmacie Coloniales* 35: 305–358.
Robinson, G. S., Ackery, P. R., Kitching, I. J., Beccaloni, G. W., and Hernández, L. M. 2010. HOSTS: A database of the world's lepidopteran hostplants. London:

Natural History Museum. Accessed Mar. 2020. https://www.nhm.ac.uk/our-science/data/hostplants/search/index.dsml.
Rocchi, S. 1991. Contributo alla conoscenza degli Haliplidae e dei Dytiscidae del Madagascar con descripzione di due nuove specie (Coleoptera). *Frustula Entomologica*, nuova serie, 14: 71–89.
Rocha, R., Borda, E., Andreone, F., and Rosa, G. M. 2012. First reports of leech parasitism in Malagasy anurans. *Comparative Parasitology* 79: 352–356.
Rodriguez, I. A., Rasoazanabary, E., and Godfrey, L. R. 2012. Multiple ectoparasites infest *Microcebus griseorufus* at Beza Mahafaly Special Reserve. Madagascar. *Madagascar Conservation and Development* 7: 45–48.
Roewer, F. C. 1943. Über eine neuerworbene Sammlung von Skorpionen des Natur-Museums Senckenberg. *Senckenbergiana* 26(4): 205–244.
Romey, W. L., and Rossman, D. S. 1995. Temperature and hunger alter grouping trade-offs in whirligig beetles. *American Midland Naturalist* 134: 51–62.
Romey, W. L., and Wallace, A. C. 2007. Sex and the selfish herd: Sexual segregation within nonmating whirligig groups. *Behavioral Ecology* 18: 910–915.
Rönkä, K., Mappes, J., Kaila, L., and Wahlberg, N. 2016. Putting *Parasemia* in its phylogenetic place: A molecular analysis of the subtribe Arctiina (Lepidoptera). *Systematic Entomology* 41: 844–853.
Rosa, G. M., Sabino-Pinto, J., Noël, J., and Andreone, F. 2014. Predation on the treefrog *Boophis rufioculis* (Anura, Mantellidae) by the freshwater crab *Hydrothelphusa* sp. (Decapoda, Potamonautidae) in Madagascar. *Crustaceana* 87(7): 890–894.
Ross, H. H. 1956. *Evolution and Classification of the Mountain Caddisflies*. Urbana: University of Illinois Press.
Ross, H. H., and Kingsolver, J. M. 1959. The Madagascan fauna of *Dipseudopsis* with speculations about the phylogeny and dispersal of the genus (Trichoptera). *Mémoires de l'Institut Scientifique de Madagascar*, série E, 11: 103–128.
Rota, J., Zacharczenko, B. V., Wahlberg, N., Zahiri, R., Schmidt, B. C., and Wagner, D. L. 2015. Phylogenetic relationships of Acronictinae with discussion of the abdominal courtship brush in Noctuidae (Lepidoptera). *Systematic Entomology* 41: 416–429.
Roubaud, E., and Girard, G. 1943. Observations sur deux pulicidés de la faune de Madagascar (*P. kerguisteli* et *S. fonquerniei*). *Bulletin de la Société de Pathologie Exotique* 36: 279–281.
Rougerie, R. 2003. Description d'une nouvelle espèce du genre malgache *Maltagorea* Bouyer, 1993 (Lepidoptera Saturniidae). *Bulletin de la Société Entomologique de France* 108: 177–180.
Roux, J. 1934. Macroures d'eau douce de Madagascar et des îles voisines (Palémonidés et Atyidés). *Faune des Colonies Françaises* 5: 529–547.
Rowell, C.H.F. 1970. Environmental control of coloration in an acridid, *Gastrimargus africanus* (Saussure). *Anti-Locust Bulletin* 47: 1–48.
Roy, J. 1965. La situation acridienne en 1964 en Afrique du Nord, Afrique occidentale et Madagascar. *L'Agronomie Tropicale*: 643–648.
Ruffieux, L., Elouard, J.-M., and Sartori, M. 1998. Flightlessness in mayflies and its relevance to hypotheses on the origin of insect flight. *Proceedings of the Royal Society of London B: Biological Sciences* 265: 2135–2140.
Rutschmann, S., Gattolliat, J.-L., Hughes, S. J., Baez, M., Sartori, M., and Monaghan, M. T. 2014. Evolution and island endemism of morphologically cryptic *Baetis* and *Cloeon* species (Ephemeroptera, Baetidae) on the Canary Islands and Madeira. *Freshwater Biology* 59: 2516–2527.
Rutschmann, S., Detering, H., Simon, S., Funk, D. H., Gattolliat, J.-L., Hughes, S. J., Raposeiro, P. M., DeSalle, R., Sartori, M., and Monaghan, M. T. 2017. Colonization and diversification of aquatic insects on three Macaronesian archipelagos using 59 nuclear loci derived from a draft genome. *Molecular Phylogenetics and Evolution* 107: 27–38.
Ryckewaert, P., Razanamaro, O., Rasoamanana, E., Rakotoarimihaja, T., Ramavovololoma, P., and Danthu, P. 2011. Les Sphingidae, probables pollinisateurs des baobabs malgaches. *Bois et Forêts des Tropiques* 307: 55–68.
Saaristo, M. I. 2001. Dwarf hunting spiders or Oonopidae (Arachnida, Araneae) of the Seychelles. *Insect Systematics and Evolution* 32: 307–358.
Sadones, H. L., Ariey, F., Goodman, S. M., Duchemin, J.-B., and Robert, V. 2003. Endoparasites of Malagasy birds. In *The Natural history of Madagascar*, eds. S. M. Goodman and J. P. Benstead, pp. 1067–1070. Chicago: University of Chicago Press.
Sagorny, C., and Wesener, T. 2017. Two new giant pill-millipede species of the genus *Zoosphaerium* endemic to the Bemanevika area in northern Madagascar (Diplopoda, Sphaerotheriida, Arthrosphaeridae). *Zootaxa* 4263(2): 273–294. https://mapress.com/zt/article/view/zootaxa.4263.2.4.
Samonds, K. E., Godfrey, L. R., Ali, J. R., Goodman, S. M., Vences, M., Sutherland, M. R., Irwin, M. T., and Krause, D. W. 2012. Spatial and temporal arrival patterns of Madagascar's vertebrate fauna explained by distance, ocean currents, and ancestor type. *Proceedings of the National Academy of Sciences of the USA* 109: 5352–5357.
Sampaio, B.H.L., and Short, A.E.Z. 2018. Chapter 15.1. Families Hydroscaphidae and Torridincolidae. In *Thorp and Covich's Freshwater Invertebrates*. Vol. 3, *Keys to Neotropical Hexapoda*, 4th ed., eds. N. Hamada, J. H. Thorp, and D. C. Rogers, pp. 519–525. San Diego: Academic Press.
Sampson, S. D., Witmer, L. M., Forster, C. A., Krause, D. W., O'Connor, P. M., Dodson, P., and Ravoavy, F. 1998. Predatory dinosaur remains from Madagascar: Implications for the Cretaceous biogeography of Gondwana. *Science* 280: 1048–1051.
Sands, W. A., and Lamb, R. W. 1975. The systematic position of *Kaudernitermes* gen. n. (Isoptera: Termitidae, Nasutitermitinae) and its relevance to host relationships of termitophilous staphylinid beetles. *Journal of Entomology*, ser. B, 44: 189–200.
Sangaré, A. K., Boutelis, A., Drali, R., Socolovschi, C., Barker, S. C., Diatta, G., Rogier, C., Olive, M.-M., Doumbo, O. K., and Raoult, D. 2014. Detection of *Bartonella quintana* in African body and head lice. *American Journal of Tropical Medicine and Hygiene* 91: 294–301.
Sartori, M., and Brittain, J. E. 2015. Order Ephemeroptera. In *Thorp and Covich's Freshwater Invertebrates*, Vol. 1, *Ecology and General Biology*, 4th ed., eds. J. H. Thorp and D. C. Rogers, pp. 873–891. New York: Academic Press.
Sartori, M., and Elouard, J.-M. 1996. Heptageniidae (Insecta, Ephemeroptera) of the Réserve Naturelle Intégrale d'Andringitra, Madagascar. In *A Floral and Faunal Survey of the Eastern Slopes of the Réserve Naturelle Intégrale d'Andringitra, Madagascar: With Reference to Elevational Variation*, ed. S. M. Goodman. *Fieldiana: Zoology*, new ser., 85: 121–130.
———. 1999. Biodiversité aquatique de Madagascar 30: Le genre *Cheirogenesia* (Ephemeroptera, Palingeniidae). *Revue Suisse de Zoologie* 106: 325–337.
Sartori, M., Gattolliat, J.-L., and Oliarinony, R. 2000. Biogeography of Malagasy mayflies (Insecta, Ephemeroptera): Preliminary results. In *Diversité et endemisme à Madagascar/Diversity and Endemism in Madagascar*, eds. W. R. Lourenço and S. M. Goodman, pp. 307–317. Paris: Mémoires de la Société de Biogéographie.
Sartori, M., Peters, J. G., and Hubbard, M. D. 2008. A revision of Oriental Teloganodidae (Insecta, Ephemeroptera, Ephemerelloidea). *Zootaxa* 1957: 1–51.
Saucedo, A. D., Ubick, D., and Griswold, C. E. 2015. The goblin spiders of the new genus *Volborattella* (Araneae, Oonopidae) from Madagascar. *American Museum Novitates* 3822: 1–71.
Saussure, H. de. 1891a. Orthoptera nova madagascarensia. 1. *Societas Entomologica* 6(2): 9–10.
———. 1891b. Orthoptera nova madagascarensia. 2. *Societas Entomologica* 6(3): 17.
———. 1899. Wissenschaftliche Ergebnisse der Reise in Madagaskar und Ostafrika in den Jahren 1889–95 von Dr. A. Voeltzkow. Orthoptera. *Abhandlungen der Senckenbergischen Naturforschenden Gesellschaft, Frankfurt/M* 21: 569–664.
Saussure, H. de, and Zehntner, L. 1897. Myriapodes de Madagascar. In *Histoire physique, naturelle et politique de Madagascar*, vol. 27, ed. A. Grandidier. Paris: Imprimerie Nationale.
———. 1902. Myriapodes de Madagascar. In *Histoire physique, naturelle et politique de Madagascar*, vol. 27, ed. A. Grandidier. Paris: Imprimerie Nationale.
Sauter, W., and Hättenschwiler, P. 1991. Zum System der palaearktischen Psychiden. (Lep. Psychidae). 1. Teil: Liste der palaearktischen Arten. *Nota Lepidopterologica* 14: 69–89.
———. 1999. Zum System der palaearktischen Psychiden (Psychidae). 2. Teil: Bestimmungsschlüssel für die Gattungen. *Nota Lepidopterologica* 22: 262–295.
Savage, A. F., Robert, V., Goodman, S. M., Raharimanga, V., Raherilalao, M. J., Andrianarimisa, A., Ariey, F., and Greiner, E. C. 2009. Blood parasites in birds from Madagascar. *Journal of Wildlife Diseases* 45(4): 907–920.
Schacht, W., and Heuck, P. 2006. Eine neue Art der Gattung *Madagascara* Lindner, 1936 von Madagaskar (Diptera, Stratiomyidae). *Entomofauna* 27(24): 293–296.
Scharff, N., and Hormiga, G. 2012. First evidence of aggressive chemical mimicry in the Malagasy orb weaving spider *Exechocentrus lancearius* Simon, 1889 (Arachnida: Araneae: Araneidae) and description of a second species in the genus. *Arthropod Systematics and Phylogeny* 70: 107–118.
Scharff, N., Coddington, J. A., Blackledge, T. A., Agnarsson, I., Framenau, V. W., Szűts, T., Hayashi, C. Y., and Dimitrov, D. 2020. Phylogeny of the orb-weaving spider family Araneidae (Araneae: Araneoidea). *Cladistics* 36: 1–21. doi:10.1111/cla.12382.

Schatz, G. E. 2000. Endemism in the Malagasy tree flora. In *Diversité et endemisme à Madagascar/Diversity and Endemism in Madagascar*, eds. W. R. Lourenço and S. M. Goodman, pp. 1–9. Paris: Mémoires de la Société de Biogéographie.
Schintlmeister, A. 2004. The taxonomy of the genus *Lymantria* Hübner, [1819] (Lepidoptera: Lymantriidae). *Quadrifina* 7: 1–248.
———. 2008. *Palaearctic Macrolepidoptera: Notodontidae*. Stenstrup: Apollo Books.
———. 2013. *World Catalogue of Insects*. vol. 11, *Notodontidae and Oenosandridae (Lepidoptera)*, ed. B. Landry, pp. 1–605. Leiden: Brill.
Schintlmeister, A., and Witt, T. J. 2015. The Notodontidae of South Africa including Swaziland and Lesotho (Lepidoptera: Notodontidae). *Proceedings of the Museum Witt*, Munich, 2: 1–288.
Schlick-Steiner, B. C., Steiner, F. M., Seifert, B., Stauffer, C., Christian, E., and Crozier, R. H. 2010. Integrative taxonomy: A multisource approach to exploring biodiversity. *Annual Review of Entomology* 55: 421–438.
Schlinger, E. I. 1981. Acroceridae. In *Manual of Nearctic Diptera*, coordinators, J. F. McAlpine, B. V. Peterson, G. E. Shewell, H. J. Teskey, J. R. Vockeroth, and D. M. Wood, pp. 575–584. Monograph No. 27. Ottawa: Research Branch, Agriculture Canada.
———. 1987. The biology of Acroceridae (Diptera): True endoparasitoids of spiders. In *Ecophysiology of Spiders*, ed. by W. Nentwig, pp. 319–327. Berlin: Springer-Verlag.
———. 2003. Acroceridae, spider fly endoparasitoids. In *The Natural History of Madagascar*, eds. S. M. Goodman and J. P. Benstead, pp. 734–740. Chicago: University of Chicago Press.
Schlosser, E. 2005. Notes on some little known carnivorous plants from Madagascar. *Carnivorous Plant Newsletter* 34(4): 100–105.
Schmid, F. 1987. Considérations diverses sur quelques genres leptocerins (Trichoptera, Leptoceridae). *Bulletin de l'Institut Royal des Sciences Naturelles de Belgique, Entomologie*, 57: 1–147.
Schmid, S., Dinkel, A., Mackenstedt, U., Tantely, M. L., Randrianambinintsoa, F. J., Boyer, S., and Woog, F. 2017. Avian malaria on Madagascar: Bird hosts and putative vector mosquitoes of different *Plasmodium* lineages. *Parasites and Vectors* 10(1): 6. doi:10.1186/s13071-016-1939-x.
Schmid-Hollinger, R. 1977. A new *Nepenthes* species from Madagascar, *Nepenthes masoalensis* sp. nov. *Botanische Jahrbücher für Systematik* 97: 575–585.
Schmidt, E. 1951. The Odonata of Madagascar, Zygoptera. *Mémoires de l'Institut Scientifique de Madagascar*, série A, 6: 116–283.
———. 1966. *Die Libellen der Insel Madagascar (Odonata). Teil 1, Zygoptera*. Bonn: Privately published.
Schnell, I. B., Thomsen, P. F., Wilkinson, N., Rasmussen, M., Jensen, L. R., Willerslev, E., Bertelsen, M. F., and Gilbert, T. P. 2012. Screening mammal biodiversity using DNA from leeches. *Current Biology* 8: R262–3.
Schnell, I. B., Bohmann, K., Schultze, S. E., Richter, S. R., Murray, D. C., et al. 2018. Debugging diversity: A pan-continental exploration of the potential of terrestrial blood-feeding leeches as a vertebrate monitoring tool. *Molecular Ecology Resources* 18: 1282–1298.
Schuh, R. T., and Weirauch, C. 2020. *True Bugs of the World (Hemiptera: Heteroptera): Classification and Natural History*, 2nd ed. Queensway: Siri Scientific Press.
Schütte, K., and Razafindraibe, P. 2007. Checklist of dragonflies of the littoral forests near Tolagnaro (Fort Dauphin). In *Biodiversity, Ecology and Conservation of Littoral Ecosystems in Southeastern Madagascar, Tolagnaro (Fort Dauphin)*, eds. J. U. Ganzhorn, S. M. Goodman, and M. Vincelette. *SI/MAB Series* 11: 163–165.
Schütte, K., Dijkstra, K.-D. B., Darwall, W., and Máiz-Tomé, L. 2018. The status and distribution of Odonata. In *The Status and Distribution of Freshwater Biodiversity in Madagascar and the Indian Ocean Islands Hotspot*, eds. L. Máiz-Tomé, C. Sayer, and W. Darwall, pp. 75–88. Gland: IUCN.
Scoble, M. J., ed. 1999. *Geometrid Moths of the World: A Catalogue*, vols. 1 and 2. Collingwood, Victoria: CSIRO.
Scott, C. H., Zaspel, J. M., Chialvo, P., and Weller, S. J. 2014. A preliminary molecular phylogenetic assessment of the lichen moths (Lepidoptera: Erebidae: Arctiinae: Lithosiini) with comments on palatability and chemical sequestration. *Systematic Entomology* 39: 286–303.
Scott, K.M.F. 1983. On the Hydropsychidae (Trichoptera) of Southern Africa with keys to African genera of imagos, larvae and pupae and species lists. *Annals of the Cape Province Museum, Natural History* 14(8): 299–422.
———. 1985. Order Trichoptera (Caddis Flies). In *Insects of Southern Africa*, eds. C. H. Scholz, and E. Holm, pp. 327–340. Durban: Butterworths.
Seastedt, T. R. 1984. The role of microarthropods in decomposition and mineralization processes. *Annual Review of Entomology* 29: 25–46.
Séguy, E. 1932. Trois Diptères nouveaux de Madagascar. *Bulletin de la Société Entomologique de France* 37: 160–163.
———. 1949. Diopsides de Madagascar. *Mémoires de l'Institut Scientifique de Madagascar,* série A, 3(1): 65–76.
Seine, R., Porembski, S., and Barthlott, W. 2008. A neglected habitat of carnivorous plants: Inselbergs. *Feddes Repertorium*: 106: 555–562.
Selden, P. A., Huang, D. Y., and Ren, D. 2008. Palpimanoid spiders from the Jurassic of China. *Journal of Arachnology* 36: 306–321.
Sellick, J.T.C. 1998. The micropylar plate of the eggs of Phasmida, with a survey of the range of plate form within the order. *Systematic Entomology* 23(3): 203–228.
Sferra, N. J. 1986. First record of *Pterodontia flavipes* (Diptera: Acroceridae) larvae in the mites *Podothrombium* (Acari: Trombidiidae) and *Abrolophus* (Acari: Erythraeidae). *Entomological News* 97: 121–123.
Shapiro, B., Sibthorpe, D., Rambaut, A., Austin, J., Wragg, G. M., Bininda-Emonds, O. R., Lee, P. L., and Cooper, A. 2002. Flight of the dodo. *Science* 295: 1683.
Shaverdo, H. V., Monaghan, M. T., Lees, D. C., Ranaivosolo, R., and Balke, M. 2008. *Madaglymbus*, a new genus of Malagasy endemic diving beetles and description of a highly unusual species based on morphology and DNA sequence data (Dytiscidae: Copelatinae). *Systematics and Biodiversity* 6: 43–51.
Shelley, R. M., and Lehtinen, P. T. 1999. Diagnoses, synonymies and occurrences of the pantropical millipeds, *Leptogoniulus sorornus* (Butler) and *Trigoniulus corallinus* (Gervais) (Spirobolida: Pachybolidae: Trigoniulinae). *Journal of Natural History* 33: 1379–1401.
Short, A.E.Z. 2018. Systematics of aquatic beetles (Coleoptera): Current state and future directions. *Systematic Entomology* 43: 1–18.
Short, A.E.Z., Joly, L. J., García, M., Wild, A., Bloom, D. D., and Maddison, D. R. 2015. Molecular phylogeny of the Hydroscaphidae (Coleoptera: Myxophaga) with description of a remarkable new lineage from the Guiana Shield. *Systematic Entomology* 40: 214–229.
Short, J. W. 2000. Systematics and biogeography of Australian *Macrobrachium* (Crustacea: Decapoda: Palaemonidae) with descriptions of other new freshwater Decapoda. PhD thesis, University of Queensland.
———. 2004. A revision of Australian river prawns, *Macrobrachium* (Crustacea: Decapoda: Palaemonidae). *Hydrobiologia* 525(1–3): 1–100.
Short, J. W., and Doumenq, E. 2003. Atyidae and Palaemonidae, freshwater shrimps. In *The Natural History of Madagascar*, eds. S. M. Goodman and J. P. Benstead, pp. 603–608. Chicago: University of Chicago Press.
Siddall, M. E., Min, G., Fontanella, F. M., Phillips, A. J., and Watson, S. C. 2011. Bacterial symbiont and salivary peptide evolution in the context of leech phylogeny. *Parasitology* 13: 1815–1827.
Siddall, M. E., Barkdull, M., Tessler, M., Brugler, M. R., Borda, E., and Hekkala, E. 2019. Ideating iDNA: Lessons and limitations from leeches in legacy collections. *PLoS One* 2: e0212226.
Signoret, V. 1860. Faune des hémiptères de Madagascar. Pt. 1, Homoptères. *Annales de la Société Entomologique de France*, série 3, 8: 177–206.
Sihvonen, P., and Kaila, L. 2004. Phylogeny and tribal classification of Sterrhinae with emphasis on delimiting Scopulini (Lepidoptera: Geometridae). *Systematic Entomology* 29: 324–358.
Sihvonen, P., and Staude, H. 2011. Geometrid moth *Afrophyla vethi* (Snellen, 1886) transferred from Oenochrominae to Sterrhinae (Lepidoptera: Geometridae). *Metamorphosis* 22: 102–113.
Sihvonen, P., Mutanen, M., Kaila, L., Brehm, G., Hausmann, A., and Staude, H. S. 2011. Comprehensive molecular sampling yields a robust phylogeny for geometrid moths (Lepidoptera: Geometridae). *PLoS One* 6: e20356.
Silva-Brandão, K. L., Wahlberg, N., Francini, R. B., Azeredo-Espin, A.M.L., Brown, K. S., Jr., Paluch, M., Lees, D. C., and Freitas, A.V.L. 2008. Phylogenetic relationships of butterflies of the tribe Acraeini (Lepidoptera, Nymphalidae, Heliconiinae) and the evolution of host plant use. *Molecular Phylogenetics and Evolution* 46: 515–531.
Silva-Davila, D. 2007. *Mahafalytenus*, a new spider genus from Madagascar (Araneae, Ctenidae). *Proceedings of the California Academy of Sciences* 58: 59–98.
Simmons, N. B., Seymour, K. L., Habersetzer, J., and Gunnell, G. F. 2008. Primitive Early Eocene bat from Wyoming and the evolution of flight and echolocation. *Nature* 451: 818–821.
Simon, E. 1907. Arachnides recueillis par L. Fea sur la côte occidentale d'Afrique. Pt. 1, *Annali del Museo Civico di Storia Naturale di Genova* 3: 218–323.
Simon, S., Letsch, H., Bank, S., Buckley, T. R., Donath, A., et al. 2019. Old World and New World Phasmatodea: Phylogenomics resolve the evolutionary history of stick and leaf insects. *Frontiers in Ecology and Evolution* 7: 345.

Sinev, S. Y. 2002. World catalogue of cosmopterigid moths (Lepidoptera: Cosmopterigidae). *Proceedings of the Zoological Institute,* St. Petersburg, 293: 1–184.

———. 2014. *World Catalogue of Blastobasid Moths (Lepidoptera, Blastobasidae).* St. Petersburg: Zoological Institute.

Sket, B., and Trontelji, P. 2008. Global diversity of leeches (Hirudinea) in freshwater. *Hydrobiologia* 595: 129–137.

Slapcinsky, J. 2014. Hypervariable or hyperdiverse, an independent assessment of the taxonomically confusing land snail genus *Tropidophora* (Pomatiidae: Littorinoidea: Caenogastropoda) in Madagascar. *American Malacological Bulletin* 32(2): 259–266.

Smit, F.G.A.M. 1982. Classification of the Siphonaptera. In *Synopsis and Classification of Living Organisms,* vol. 2, ed. S. P. Parker, pp. 557–563. New York: McGraw-Hill.

Smith, A. G., Smith, D. G., and Funnell, B. M. 1994. *Atlas of Mesozoic and Cenozoic Coastlines.* Cambridge: Cambridge University Press.

Smith, K.G.V. 1967. The biology and taxonomy of the genus *Stylogaster* Macquart, 1835 (Diptera: Conopidae, Stylogasterinae) in the Ethiopian and Malagasy regions. *Transactions of the Royal Entomological Society of London* 119: 47–69.

———. 1984. A new species of *Stylogaster* (Dipt., Conopidae, Stylogasterinae) from Madagascar. *Entomologist's Monthly Magazine* 120: 233–235.

Smith, K.G.V., and Cunningham–Van Someren, G. R. 1985. The larva of *Stylogaster varifrons* Malloch (Dipt., Stylogastridae). *Entomologist's Monthly Magazine* 121: 81–85.

Smith, M. A., and Fisher, B. L. 2009. Invasions, DNA barcodes, and rapid biodiversity assessment using ants of Mauritius. *Frontiers in Zoology* 6: 31.

Smith, M. A., Fisher, B. L., and Hebert, P.D.N. 2005. DNA barcoding for effective biodiversity assessment of a hyperdiverse arthropod group: The ants of Madagascar. *Philosophical Transactions of the Royal Society of London B: Biological Sciences* 360(1462): 1825–1834.

Snellen van Vollenhoven, S. C., and de Selys-Longchamps, E. 1869. Insectes. In *Recherches sur la faune de Madagascar et ses dépendances, d'après les découvertes de François P. L. Pollen et D. C. van Dam,* eds. J. K. Steenhoff, Leiden, No. 5(1): 1–25.

Snyder, F. M. 1953. Notes and descriptions of some Ethiopian Muscidae (Diptera). *American Museum Novitates* 1608: 1–21.

Sobczyk, T. 2009. *Obtexocorytus schuettei*—eine neue Gattung und Art der Psychidae aus Madagaskar (Lepidoptera). *Entomologische Zeitschrift* 119: 3–7.

———. 2011. *World Catalogue of Insects.* Vol. 10, *Psychidae (Lepidoptera),* ed. M. Nuss, pp. 1–467. Stenstrup: Apollo Books.

Sobczyk, T., and Schütte, K. 2010. Two new species, taxonomic notes and a checklist of bagworm moths from Madagascar (Lepidoptera: Psychidae). *Deutsche Entomologische Zeitschrift* 57: 59–68.

Sohn, J.-C. 2015. A taxonomic review of the genus *Phrealcia* Chrétien, 1900 with description of a new species from Korea (Lepidoptera: Ypsolophidae). *SHILAP Revista de Lepidopterología* 43: 428–437.

Sohn, J.-C., and Gershenson, Z. S. 2014. A taxonomic review of *Rhabdocosma* Meyrick (Lepidoptera, Ypsolophidae) with description of a new species from Japan. *Entomological Science* 17: 354–358.

Sohn, J.-C., Regier, J. C., Mitter, C., Davis, D., Landry, J.-F., Zwick, A., and Cummings, M. P. 2013. A molecular phylogeny for Yponomeutoidea (Insecta, Lepidoptera, Ditrysia) and its implications for classification, biogeography and the evolution of host plant use. *PLoS One* 8: 1–23.

Sohn, J.-C., Regier, J. C., Mitter, C., Adamski, D., Landry, J. F., et al. 2015. Phylogeny and feeding trait evolution of the mega-diverse Gelechioidea (Lepidoptera: Obtectomera): New insight from 19 nuclear genes. *Systematic Entomology* 41: 112–132.

Song, H. J., Marino-Perez, R., Woller, D. A., and Cigliano, M. M. 2018. Evolution, diversification, and biogeography of grasshoppers (Orthoptera: Acrididae). *Insect Systematics and Diversity* 2(4): 1–25.

Sookar, P., Alleck, M., Buldawoo, I., Khayrattee, F. B., Choolun, T., Permaloo, S., and Rambhunjun, M. 2012. Area-wide management of the melon fly, *Bactrocera cucurbitae* (Coquillett) (Diptera: Tephritidae). In *Actes du séminaire international de clôture GAMOUR Gestion Agroécologique des mouches des légumes à La Réunion,* 21–24 Nov. 2011, ed. J. P. Deguine, pp. 98–102. Saint Pierre: CIRAD.

Spangler, P. J. 1980. A new species of *Ytu* from Brazil (Coleoptera: Torridincolidae). *Coleopterists Bulletin* 34: 145–158.

———. 1991a. Haliplidae (Adephaga). In *Immature Insects,* vol. 2, ed. F. W. Stehr, pp. 311–312. Dubuque: Kendall/Hunt.

———. 1991b. Noteridae (Adephaga). In *Immature Insects,* vol. 2, ed. F. W. Stehr, pp. 314–315. Dubuque: Kendall/Hunt.

Spinola, M. 1839. Essai sur les Fulgorelles, sous-tribu de la tribu des Cicadaires, ordre des Rhyngotes. *Annales de la Société Entomologique de France* 8: 133–337. http://biodiversitylibrary.org/page/33710046.

Stanisic, J. 1998. Superfamily Acavoidea. In *Mollusca: The Southern Synthesis; Fauna of Australia,* vol. 5, pt. B, eds. P. L. Beesley, G.J.B. Ross, and A. Wells, p. 1093. Melbourne: CSIRO.

Starmühlner, F. 1969. Die Gastropoden der Madagassischen Binnengewasser. *Malacologia* 8: 1–434.

Šťastný, J. 2012. A new species of *Herophydrus* (Coleoptera: Dytiscidae) from Madagascar and notes on some poorly known species of the genus. *Klapalekiana* 48: 225–234.

Staude, H. S., Mecenero, S., Oberprieler, R. G., Sharp, A., Sharp, I., Williams, M. C., and Maclean, M. 2016. An illustrated report on the larvae and adults of 962 African Lepidoptera species: Results of the Caterpillar Rearing Group; A novel, collaborative method of rearing and recording lepidopteran life-histories. *Metamorphosis* 27: 46–59. Supplementary material. Knysna, South Africa: Lepidopterists' Society of Africa.

Steffan, A. W. 1964. Torridincolidae, coleopterorum nova familia e regione aethiopica. *Entomologische Zeitschrift (Stuttgart)* 74: 193–200.

———. 1973. Torridincoidarum tres novae species e regione aethiopica (Coleoptera: Sphaeroidea). *Revue de Zoologie et de Botanique Africaines* 87: 633–646.

Steffan-Dewenter, I., Münzenberg, U., Bürger, C., Thies, C., and Tscharntke, T. 2002. Scale-dependent effects of landscape context on three pollinator guilds. *Ecology* 83: 1421–1432.

Steiner, W. E., Jr., and Anderson, J. J. 1981. Notes on the natural history of *Spanglerogyrus albiventris* Folkerts, with a new distribution record (Coleoptera: Gyrinidae). *Pan-Pacific Entomlogist* 57: 124–132.

Steyskal, G. 1972. A catalogue of species and key to the genera of the family Diopsidae (Diptera: Acalyptratae). *Stuttgarter Beiträge zur Naturkunde, Serie A (Biologie),* 234: 1–20.

Stoltze, M. 1989. The Afrotropical caddisfly family Pisuliidae. Systematics, zoogeography, and biology (Trichoptera: Pisuliidae). *Steenstrupia* 15(1): 1–49.

Stork, N. E. 1991. Insect diversity: Facts, fiction and speculation. *Biological Journal of the Linnean Society* 35: 321–337.

Stowe, M. 1986. Prey specialization in the Araneidae. In *Spiders: Webs, Behavior and Evolution,* ed. W. Shear, pp. 101–131. Palo Alto: Stanford University Press.

Stroiński, A., and Świerczewski, D. 2011. A new species of the genus *Panormenis* Melichar, 1923 from Madagascar (Hemiptera, Fulgoromorpha: Flatidae). *Genus* 22(2): 191–203.

———. 2012a. *Soares testudinarius* gen. et sp. nov. (Hemiptera: Fulgoromorpha: Flatidae), a new representative of the tribe Phantiini from Madagascar. *Zootaxa* 3256: 38–50.

———. 2012b. Revision of an extraordinary Selizini genus *Urana* Melichar, 1902 from Madagascar (Hemiptera: Fulgoromorpha: Flatidae). *Journal of Natural History* 46(41–42): 2577–2593.

———. 2013a. *Madoxychara* gen. nov. (Hemiptera: Fulgoromorpha: Flatidae), a new genus of the tribe Phantiini Melichar from Madagascar. *Zootaxa* 3599(4): 377–389.

———. 2013b. *Peyrierasus* gen. nov.—a new genus of Flatidae (Hemiptera: Fulgoromorpha) from southeastern Madagascar. *Annales Zoologici* 63(2): 251–262.

———. 2014a. *Griveaudus* gen. nov. (Hemiptera: Fulgoromorpha: Flatidae) from Tsaratanana Massif supports the biodiversity of montane flatids in Madagascar. *Zootaxa* 3861(1): 61–75.

———. 2014b. *Sogalabana ochracea* gen. et sp. nov. from Tsaratanana massif in northern Madagascar (Hemiptera: Fulgoromorpha: Flatidae). *Journal of Natural History* 48(29–30): 1853–1865.

Strong, D. R., Lawton, J. H., and Southwood, T.R.E. 1984. *Insects on Plants: Community Patterns and Mechanisms.* Cambridge, MA: Harvard University Press.

Strutzenberger, P., Brehm, G., Bodner, F., and Fiedler, K. 2010. Molecular phylogeny of *Eois* (Lepidoptera, Geometridae): Evolution of wing patterns and host plant use in a species-rich group of Neotropical moths. *Zoologica Scripta* 39: 603–620.

Stuckenberg, B. R. 1963. A study on the biology of the genus *Stylogaster* with the description of a new species from Madagascar (Diptera: Conopidae). *Revue de Zoologie et de Botanique Africaines* 68: 251–275.

Stuke, J.-H. 2004. Revision der Gattung *Archiconops* Kröber, 1939 (Diptera: Conopidae). *Studia Dipterologica* 11: 33–50.

———. 2005. Der Status von *Conops hova* Janssens, 1954 (Diptera: Conopidae). *Studia Dipterologica* 12: 11–12.

———. 2012. A revision of Afrotropical species of *Stylogaster* Macquart (Diptera: Conopidae), with descriptions of twenty-one new species and an identification key. *African Invertebrates* 53: 267–354.

———. 2015. New conopid records from the Afrotropical Region (Diptera). Pt. 1, *Paramyopa* Kröber, *Pseudoconops* Camras, *Stylogaster* Macquart, *Thecophora* Rondani, and *Zodion* Latreille. *Zootaxa* 3963: 101–159.

———. 2017. *World Catalogue of Insects*. Vol. 15, *Conopidae (Diptera)*. Leiden: E. J. Brill.

———. 2019. New conopid records from the Afrotropical Region (Diptera: Conopidae). Pt. 2, Conopinae excluding Physocephalini. *Israel Journal of Entomology* 49: 277–349.

Stuke, J.-H., and Clements, D. K. 2019. New conopid records from the Afrotropical Region (Diptera). Pt. 3, Physocephalini. *Bonner zoologische Beiträge* 68: 209–273.

Su, Y.-C., and Smith, D. 2014. Evolution of host use, group-living and foraging behaviours in kleptoparasitic spiders: Molecular phylogeny of the Argyrodinae (Araneae: Theridiidae). *Invertebrate Systematics* 28: 415–431. doi:10.1071/IS14010.

Suhling, F., Sahlén, G., Gorb, S., Kalkman, V. J., Dijkstra, K.-D. B., and van Tol, J. 2015. Order Odonata. In *Thorp and Covich's Freshwater Invertebrates*. Vol. 1, *Ecology and General Biology*, eds. J. H. Thorp and D. C. Rogers, pp. 893–932. New York: Academic Press.

Sun, L., and McCafferty, W. P. 2002. *Callistina panda*, a striking new genus and species of Caeninae (Insecta: Ephemeroptera: Caenidae) from Madagascar. *Bulletin de la Société d'Histoire Naturelle de Toulouse* 137 (2001): 7–15.

Świerczewski, D., and Stroiński, A. 2011. *Flatopsis medleri* sp. n., a new flatid species from Madagascar (Hemiptera: Fulgoromorpha: Flatidae). *Acta Zoological Cracoviensia* 54B(1–2): 23–30.

———. 2012a. A new species of the genus *Latois* Stål, 1866 from Madagascar (Hemiptera: Fulgoromorpha: Flatidae). *Acta Zoological Cracoviensia* 55(1): 65–77.

———. 2012b. A new species of *Phlebopterum* Stål, 1854 (Hemiptera: Fulgoromorpha: Flatidae) from the tapia woodlands of Madagascar. *Annales Zoologici* (Warszawa) 62(4): 577–592.

———. 2013. Madagascar Flatidae (Hemiptera, Fulgoromorpha): State-of-the-art and research challenges. *ZooKeys* 319: 293–301.

———. 2015a. A new species *Flatopsis wojciechowskii* from Nosy-Komba and Madagascar (Hemiptera: Fulgoromorpha: Flatidae). *Polish Journal of Entomology* 84(4): 339–349.

———. 2015b. Revision of the endemic genus *Perinetella* (Hemiptera: Fulgoromorpha: Flatidae) from Madagascar. *Acta Entomologica Musei Nationalis Pragae* 55(2): 539–558.

———. 2017. A new species *Phlebopterum planicapitis* from Madagascar (Hemiptera: Fulgoromorpha: Flatidae). *Polish Journal of Entomology* 86(3): 275–291.

———. 2019a. *Lembakaria* gen. nov., a new genus of Selizini from Madagascar spiny forest ecoregion (Hemiptera: Fulgoromoprha: Flatidae). *Annales Zoologici* 69(3): 575–588.

———. 2019b. *Kelyflata* gen. nov. adds to Selizini flatids in Madagascar (Hemiptera: Fulgoromorpha: Flatidae). *Zootaxa* 4712(3): 434–444.

Świerczewski, D., Bourgoin, T., and Stroński, A. 2016. Revision of the Madagascan genus *Paraflata* (Hemiptera: Fulgoromorpha: Flatidae), with notes on planthopper hosts parasitized by Epipyropidae moths. *Annales Zoologici* 66(1): 57–82.

Synave, H. 1956. Les Flatidae de Madagascar (Hemiptera-Homoptera). *Mémoires de l'Institut Scientifique de Madagascar*, série E, 7: 197–217.

———. 1966. Homoptères de Madagascar. *Verhandlungen der Naturforschenden Gesellschaft in Basel* 77: 55–75.

Szadziewski, R. 1995. The oldest fossil Corethrellidae (Diptera) from Lower Cretaceous Lebanese amber. *Acta Zoologica Cracoviensia* 38: 177–181.

Szűts, T., and Scharff, N. 2009. Revision of the living members of the genus *Tomocyrba* Simon, 1900 (Araneae: Salticidae). *Contributions to Natural History* 12: 1337–1372.

Tan, E. 2001. The adaptation of leech (*Haemadipsa hainana*) to temperature and soil humidity. *Acta Ecologica Sinica* 21: 458–461.

Tantely, L., Rakotoniaina, J.-C., Tata, E., Andrianaivolambo, L., Fontenille, D., and Elissa N. 2012. Modification of *Anopheles gambiae* distribution at high altitudes in Madagascar. *Journal of Vector Ecology* 37(2): 402–406. doi:10.1111/j.1948-7134.2012.00244.x.

Tantely, L., Rakotoniaina, J.-C., Tata, E., Andrianaivolambo, L., Razafindrasata, F., Fontenille, D., and Elissa, N. 2013. Biology of mosquitoes that are potential vectors of Rift Valley Fever virus in different biotopes of the central highlands of Madagascar. *Journal of Medical Entomology* 50(3): 603–610.

Tantely, L., Boyer, S., and Fontenille, D. 2015. A review of mosquitoes associated with Rift Valley fever virus in Madagascar. *American Journal of Tropical Medicine and Hygiene* 92(4): 722–729. doi:10.4269/ajtmh.14-0421.

Tantely, L., Le Goff, G., Boyer, S., and Fontenille, D. 2016a. An updated checklist of mosquito species (Diptera: Culicidae) from Madagascar. *Parasite* 23: 20. doi:10.1051/parasite/2016018.

Tantely, L., Goodman, S. M., Rakotondranaivo, T., and Boyer, S. 2016b. Review of West Nile virus circulation and outbreak risk in Madagascar: Entomological and ornithological perspectives. *Parasite* 23: 49. doi:10.1051/parasite/2016058.

Tantely, L., Cêtre-Sossah, C., Rakotondranaivo, T., Cardinale, E., and Boyer, S. 2017. Population dynamics of mosquito species in a West Nile virus endemic area in Madagascar. *Parasite* 24: 3. doi:10.1051/parasite/2017005.

Tello, J. S., Stevens, R. D., and Dick, C. W. 2008. Patterns of species co-occurrence and density compensation: A test for interspecific competition in bat ectoparasite infracommunities. *Oikos* 117: 693–702.

Tessler, M., Barrio, A., Borda, E., Rood-Goldman, R., Hill, M., and Siddall, M. E. 2016. Description of a soft-bodied invertebrate with microcomputed tomography and revision of the genus *Chtonobdella* (Hirudinea: Haemadipsidae). *Zoologica Scripta* 45: 552–565.

Tessler, M., Weiskopf, S. R., Berniker, L., Hersch, R., Mccarthy, K. P., Yu, D. W., and Siddall, M. E. 2018. Bloodlines: Mammals, leeches, and conservation in southern Asia. *Systematics and Biodiversity* 16: 488–496.

Thakur, M. L., and Sen-Sarma, P. K. 1978. Macrotermitinae (Isoptera: Termitidae) from Madagascar, with remarks on the origin of the subfamily in Malagasy region. *Journal of Entomological Research* 2: 172–180.

Theodor, O. 1931. On African sandflies (Dipt.). *Bulletin of Entomological Research* 22: 469–478.

———. 1957. The Nycteribiidae of the Ethiopian region and Madagascar. *Parasitology* 47: 457–543.

———. 1967. *An Illustrated Catalogue of the Rothschild Collection of the Nycteribiidae (Diptera) in the British Museum (Natural History)*. London: Trustees of the British Museum.

Thibaud, J.-M. 2008a. Les Collemboles des sables littoraux de l'Ile Maurice. *Revue Française d'Entomologie* 30: 71–76.

———. 2008b. Les Collemboles des sables littoraux de Madagascar. *Annales de la Société Entomologique de France* 44: 503–519.

———. 2010a. Contribution à la connaissance des collemboles littoraux de l'île de La Réunion. *Revue Française d'Entomologie* 32: 25–31.

———. 2010b. Les collemboles des sables littoraux de l'île de Mayotte: Essai de synthèse sur les collemboles des sables littoraux d'îles de l'Océan Indien (zone ouest). *Revue Française d'Entomologie* 32: 113–121.

———. 2011. Les collemboles des sables littoraux de l'île de la Grande Comore. *Revue Française d'Entomologie* 33: 5–12.

———. 2015. Etude des collemboles des sables littoraux de la côte est de Madagascar (interstitiels terrestres). *Zoosystema* 37: 73–84.

———. 2017. Les Collemboles interstitiels des sables littoraux de l'île Rodrigues (Île Maurice). *Russian Entomological Journal* 26(4): 299–301.

Toft, S., Overgaard-Nielsen, B., and Funch, P. 2012. Parasitoid suppression and life-history modifications in a wolf spider following infection by larvae of an acrocerid fly. *Journal of Arachnology* 40: 13–17.

Toon, A., Pérez-Losada, M., Schweitzer, C. E., Feldmann, R. M., Carlson, M., and Crandall, K. A. 2010. Gondwanan radiation of the Southern Hemisphere crayfishes (Decapoda: Parastacidae): Evidence from fossils and molecules. *Journal of Biogeography* 37: 2275–2290.

Tordoff, G. M., Boddy, L., and Jones, T. H. 2008. Species-specific impacts of collembola grazing on fungal foraging ecology. *Soil Biology and Biochemistry* 40: 434–442.

Torres, E., Lees, D. C., Vane-Wright, R. I., Kremen, C., Leonard, J. A., and Wayne, R. K. 2001. Examining monophyly in a large radiation of Madagascan butterflies (Lepidoptera: Satyrinae: Mycalesina) based on mitochondrial DNA data. *Molecular Phylogenetics and Evolution* 20: 460–473.

Tortosa, P., Dsouli, N., Gomard, Y., Ramasindrazana, B., Dick, C. W., and Goodman, S. M. 2013. Evolutionary history of Indian Ocean nycteribiid bat flies mirroring the ecology of their hosts. *PLoS One* 8: e75215.

Triberti, P. 1987. Contributions to the knowledge of the Gracillariidae-fauna from Madagascan region. II. Genera *Macarostola* Meyrick and *Caloptilia* Hübner (Lepidoptera). *Revue Française d'Entomologie*, nouvelle série, 9: 120–126.

Trýzna, M. 2017. Description of a new species of the genus *Tophoderes* Dejean (Coleoptera: Anthribidae) from east Madagascar, with images of all Madagascan species of the genus. *Zootaxa* 4221(3): 377–385.

Trýzna, M., and Andrianomenjanahary, M. N. 2019. Description of a new species of the genus *Diastatotropis* Lacordaire (Coleoptera: Anthribidae) with strikingly elongated elytral apices from north-eastern Madagascar. *Zootaxa* 4563(3): 444–450.

Trýzna, M., and Baňař, P. 2012. New species of *Adapterops* (Coleoptera: Anthribidae) from east Madagascar with a key to species and notes on sexual dimorphism and biodiversity of the family. *Acta Entomologica Musei Nationalis Pragae* 52(2): 475–485.

———. 2013a. A new species of the genus *Apatenia* (Coleoptera: Anthribidae) from Madagascar with notes on female genitalia, redescription of the female of *Apatenia quadristigma* Frieser and list of Madagascan species. *Zootaxa* 3609(5): 504–512.

———. 2013b. A new species of the genus *Basidissus* (Coleoptera: Anthribidae) from east Madagascar, with a key to species. *Zootaxa* 3721(1): 71–78.

———. 2014a. A new species of the genus *Blaberops* (Coleoptera: Anthribidae) from east Madagascar, with a key to species. *Zootaxa* 3826(2): 386–392.

———. 2014b. Description of a new genus and species, *Pseudobasidissus barclayi* (Coleoptera: Anthribidae), from east Madagascar. *Zootaxa* 3869(2): 180–188.

———. 2015a. A new species of *Tophoderes* Dejean from northern Madagascar with a checklist of the species (Coleoptera: Anthribidae). *Zootaxa* 3905(2): 264–272.

———. 2015b. A new species of the genus *Adapterops* (Coleoptera: Anthribidae) from northern Madagascar, with a catalogue and key to species. *Zootaxa* 4052(4): 485–489.

———. 2016. Two new species of *Diastatotropis* Lacordaire (Coleoptera: Anthribidae) from east Madagascar with a key to species of the genus. *Zootaxa* 4161(3): 429–436.

———. 2017a. A new species of *Diastatotropis* Lacordaire (Coleoptera: Anthribidae) from Montagne d'Ambre National Park, northern Madagascar. *Zootaxa* 4221(5): 537–544.

———. 2017b. Two new species of *Adapterops* (Coleoptera: Anthribidae) from protected areas of northern Madagascar, with a key to species, and new faunistic data on the genus. *Zootaxa* 4231(2): 238–250.

———. 2020. A new species of *Holophloeus* Jordan (Coleoptera: Anthribidae) from eastern Madagascar with ecological notes on it and *H. tuberosus* (Fairmaire, 1897). *Zootaxa* 4732(1): 79–98.

Trýzna, M., and Valentine, B. D. 2011. Anthribidae. In *Catalogue of Palaearctic Coleoptera*. Vol. 7, *Curculionoidea*, eds. I. Löbl and A. Smetana, pp. 64–66, 90–107. Stenstrup: Apollo Books.

Tucker Abbott, R. 1989. *Compendium of Landshells*. Melbourne: American Malacologists.

Turcatel, M. 2014. A molecular phylogeny of deer flies and their closest relatives. PhD thesis, North Carolina State University, Raleigh.

Twort, V. G., Minet, J., Wheat, C. W., and Wahlberg, N. 2021. Museomics of a rare taxon: Placing Whalleyanidae in the Lepidoptera Tree of Life. *Systematic Entomology* 46(4): 926–937. doi:10.1111/syen.12503.

Tyson, P. D., and Partridge, T. C. 2000. Evolution of Cenozoic climates. In *The Cenozoic of Southern Africa*, vol. 40, eds. T. C. Partridge and R. R. Maud, pp. 371–387. Oxford: Oxford University Press.

Ubick, D., and Griswold, C. E. 2011a. The Malagasy goblin spiders of the new genus *Malagiella* (Araneae, Oonopidae). *Bulletin of the American Museum of Natural History* 356: 1–86.

———. 2011b. The Malagasy goblin spiders of the new genus *Molotra* (Araneae, Oonopidae). *American Museum Novitates* 3729: 1–69.

Uilenberg, G., Hoogstraal, H., and Klein, J.-M. 1979. Les tiques (Ixodoidea) de Madagascar et leur rôle vecteur. *Archives de l'Institut Pasteur de Madagascar, Numéro Spécial*, 1–153.

Ünal, M., and Beccaloni, G. W. 2017. Revision of the Madagascan genera *Oncodopus* Brongniart and *Colossopus* Saussure (Orthoptera: Tettigoniidae: Conocephalinae; Euconchophorini), with description of Malagasopus gen. nov. *Zootaxa* 4341: 193–228.

Underwood, E. C., and Fisher, B. L. 2006. The role of ants in conservation monitoring: If, when, and how. *Biological Conservation* 132: 166–182.

Urban, J., and Cryan, J. 2009. Entomologically famous, evolutionarily unexplored: The first phylogeny of the lanternfly family Fulgoridae (Insecta: Hemiptera: Fulgoroidea). *Molecular Phylogenetics and Evolution* 50: 471–484. doi.org/10.1016/j.ympev.2008.12.004.

Ustjuzhanin, P., and Kovtunovich, V. N. 2017. Two new species of the many-plumed moth genus *Alucita* Linnaeus (Lepidoptera, Alucitidae) from Madagascar. *Entomological Review* 96: 1115–1118 [original Russian text (2016) in *Entomologicheskoe Obozrenie* 95: 889–891].

Uvarov, B. P. 1922. Phasmid larvae from Mount Everest. *Entomologist's Monthly Magazine* 58: 277.

Vachon, M. 1969. *Grosphus griveaudi*, nouvelle espèce de Scorpion Buthidae Malgache. *Bulletin du Muséum National d'Histoire Naturelle*, Paris, série 2, 41(2): 476–483.

———. 1979. Remarques biogéographiques sur la faune des scorpions de Madagascar à propos de l'utilisation de caractères trichobothriotaxiques permettant la distinction des genres *Odonturus* Karsch, 1879 et *Tityobuthus* Pocock, 1893. In *Comptes-rendus du Vème Colloque d'Arachnologie d'Expression Française*, pp. 2117–2224. Barcelona: Ediciones de la Universidad de Barcelona.

Vadon, J. 1935. Note sur deux larves du genre *Pogonostoma* Klug. *Bulletin de l'Académie Malgache* 18: 149–150.

———. 1946. Sur les prémiers états des "Pogonostoma." *Revue Française d'Entomologie* 13: 122–124.

Vallan, D. 2000. Influence of forest fragmentation on amphibian diversity in the nature reserve of Ambohitantely, highland Madagascar. *Biological Conservation* 96: 31–43.

van der Heyden, T. 2014. *Flatida rosea* (Melichar, 1901) and *Zanna madagascariensis* Signoret, 1860, two bizarre and fascinating species of planthoppers from Madagascar (Hemiptera: Flatidae, Fulgoridae). *Arquivos Entomolóxicos* 10: 221–223.

van der Plas, F., and Olff, H. 2014. Mesoherbivores affect grasshopper communities in a megaherbivore-dominated South African savannah. *Oecologia* 175: 639–649.

Van Itterbeeck, J., Rakotomalala Andrianavalona, I. N., Rajemison, F. I., Rakotondrasoa, J. F., Ralantoarinaivo, V. R., Hugel, S., and Fisher, B. L. 2019. Diversity and use of edible grasshoppers, locusts, crickets, and katydids (Orthoptera) in Madagascar. *Foods* 8: 666. doi:10.3390/foods8120666.

VandenSpiegel, D., and Golovatch, S. I. 2007. The millipedes of the Comoro Islands (Myriapoda: Diplopoda). *Journal of Afrotropical Zoology* 3: 41–57.

Vanin, S. A., and Costa, C. 2001. Description of immature stages of *Claudiella ingens* Reichardt and Vanin, 1976 and comparative notes on other Torridincolidae (Coleoptera, Torridincolidae). *Aquatic Insects* 23: 1–10.

Vanin, S. A., Beutel, R. G., and Arce-Pérez, R. 2016. 6.4. Hydroscaphidae LeConte, 1874. In *Handbook of Zoology*. Vol. 4, *Arthropoda: Insecta*, pt. 38, *Coleoptera, Beetles*, vol. 1, *Morphology and Systematics (Archostemata, Adephaga, Myxophaga, Polyphaga partim)* 2nd ed., eds. R. G. Beutel and R. B. Leschen, pp. 71–75. Berlin: Walter de Gruyter.

Vanschuytbroeck, P. 1965. Description de deux Diptères Diopsidae nouveaux de Madagascar. *Revue de Zoologie et de Botanique Africaines* 71: 336–338.

Vári, L., Kroon, D. M., and Krüger, M. 2002. *Classification and Checklist of the Species of Lepidoptera Recorded in Southern Africa*. Chatswood: Simple Solutions.

Vasilikopoulos, A., Balke, M., Beutel, R. G., Donath, A., Podsiadlowski, L., et al. 2019. Phylogenomics of the superfamily Dytiscoidea (Coleoptera: Adephaga) with an evaluation of phylogenetic conflict and systematic error. *Molecular Phylogenetics and Evolution* 135: 270–285.

Vayssière, M. A. 1890a. Sur le *Prosopistoma variegatum* de Madagascar. *Compte Rendu de l'Académie des Sciences de Paris* 110: 95–96.

———. 1890b. Monographie zoologique et anatomique du genre *Prosopistoma* Latr. *Annales des Sciences Naturelles*, Paris, série *Zoologie* 9: 19–87.

———. 1891. Observations sur l'*Euthyplocia sikoraï*, type d'Ephéméridé de grande taille, provenant de l'île de Madagascar. *Compte Rendu de l'Association Française pour l'Avancement des Sciences Naturelles* 20: 243.

———. 1937. Description zoologique et anatomique de la larve nymphale et de la subimago F de l'*Euthyplocia Sikorai*, espèce d'Ephéméridé de Madagascar. *Annales de la Société des Sciences Naturelles*, Paris, série *Zoologie* 20(10): 73–98.

Verdcourt, B. 2006. Two new taxa of land snails of the genera *Kalidos* and *Ampelita* from Madagascar (Gastropoda, Pulmonata). *Basteria* 70: 103–108.

Veyrières, P. de, and Méritens, G. de. 1913. *Le livre de la sagesse Malgache: Proverbes, dictons, sentences, expressions figurées et curieuses.* Paris: Editions Maritimes et d'Outre-Mer.

Vicente, N., Kergoat, G., Dong, J., Yotoko, K., Legendre, F., Nattier, R., and Robillard, T. 2017. In and out of the Neotropics: Historical biogeography of Eneopterinae crickets. *Journal of Biogeography* 44(10): 2199–2210.

Vieilledent, G., Gardi, O., Grinand, C., Burren, C., Andriamanjato, M., et al. 2016. Bioclimatic envelope models predict a decrease in tropical forest carbon stocks with climate change in Madagascar. *Journal of Ecology* 104: 703–715. doi:10.1111/1365-2745.12548.

Vieilledent, G., Grinand, C., Rakotomalala, F. A., Ranaivosoa, R., Rakotoarijaona, J.-R., Allnutt, T. F., and Achard, F. 2018. Combining global tree cover loss data

with historical national forest cover maps to look at six decades of deforestation and forest fragmentation in Madagascar. *Biological Conservation* 222: 189–197.
Viette, P. 1956a (1954–1955). Etude des types de Microlépidoptères (Tineidae s. l.) malgaches de Meyrick du Muséum de Vienne. *Annalen des Naturhistorischen Museums in Wien* 60: 279–286.
———. 1956b. Insectes: Lépidoptères Hesperiidae. *Faune de Madagascar* 3: 1–85.
———. 1957. Lépidoptères (excepté les Tordeuses et les Géométrides). La Faune entomologique de l'île de La Réunion. I. *Mémoires de l'Institut Scientifique de Madagascar*, série E, 8: 137–226.
———. 1962. Noctuelles trifides de Madagascar, écologie, biogéographie, morphologie et taxonomie (Lep.). *Annales de la Société Entomologique de France* 131(1): 1–294.
———. 1967. Insectes Lépidoptères Noctuidae Amphipyrinae (part.) et Melicleptriinae. *Faune de Madagascar* 20: 491–531.
———. 1972. Contribution à l'étude des Lépidoptères Uraniidae malgaches. *Bulletin Mensuel de la Société Linnéenne de Lyon* 41: 182–193.
———. 1980. Insectes Lépidoptères Limacodidae. *Faune de Madagascar* 53: 1–162.
———. 1981. Les naturalistes à Madagascar. In *Madagascar: Un sanctuaire de la nature*, ed. P. Oberlé, pp. 98–104. Paris: Lechevalier.
———. 1990. Liste récapitulative des Lépidoptères Hétérocères de Madagascar (A provisional check-list of the Lepidoptera Heterocera of Madagascar). *Faune de Madagascar* Supplément 1: 1–264.
———. 1991. Principales localités où des Insectes ont été recueillis à Madagascar. *Faune de Madagascar*, Supplément 2: 1–88.
———. 1998. Critical notes on some species of the Madagascan zone in the Catalogue of "Goodger and Watson, 1995, the Afrotropical Tiger-Moths (Lepidoptera Arctiidae Arctiinae)." *Bulletin Mensuel de la Société Linnéenne de Lyon* 67: 222–225.
Vikhrev, N. E. 2014. Taxonomic notes on *Lispe* (Diptera, Muscidae), pts. 1–9. *Amurian Zoological Journal* 6: 147–170.
———. 2016. Taxonomic notes on *Lispe* (Diptera, Muscidae), pt. 13. *Amurian Zoological Journal* 8: 171–185.
Viljanen, H., Wirta, H., Montreuil, O., Rahagalala, P., Johnson, S., and Hanski, I. 2010. Structure of local communities of endemic dung beetles in Madagascar. *Journal of Tropical Ecology* 26: 481–496.
Villastrigo, A., Ribera, I., Manuel, M., Millán, A., and Fery, H. 2017. A new classification of the tribe Hygrotini Portevin, 1929 (Coleoptera: Dytiscidae: Hydroporinae). *Zootaxa* 4317: 499–529.
Villet, M. H., and Endrödy-Younga, S. 2007. Myxophaga. In *Guides to the Freshwater Invertebrates of Southern Africa*. Vol. 10, *Coleoptera*, eds. by R. Stals and I. J. de Moor, pp. 45–52. Pretoria: Water Research Commission.
Villiers, A. 1951. Les Reduviidae Malgaches. IV. Stenopoditae. Gen. *Hendecacentrus* Bergr., *Noualhierella* et *Catala* nov. *Mémoires de l'Institut Scientifique de Madagascar*, série A, 5: 255–261.
———. 1968. Insectes. Hémiptères Reduviidae (pt. 1). *Faune de Madagascar* 28: 1–198.
———. 1979. Insectes. Hémiptères Reduviidae (pt. 2). *Faune de Madagascar* 49: 1–202.
Vinson, A. 1863. *Aranéides des îles de La Réunion, Maurice et Madagascar*. Paris: Librairie Encyclopédique de Robert.
Viraktamath, C. A., and Gonçalves, A. C. 2013. Review of Madagascaran Agalliini (Hemiptera: Cicadellidae: Megophthalminae) with descriptions of a new genus and six new species. *Zootaxa* 3616: 1–21.
Virgilio, M., De Meyer, M., White, I. M., and Backeljau, T. 2009. African *Dacus* (Diptera: Tephritidae): Molecular data and host plant association do not corroborate morphology based classifications. *Molecular Phylogenetics and Evolution* 51: 531–539.
Voise, J., and Casas, J. 2013. Use of water wave propagation for echolocation in whirligig beetles: An unsubstantiated conjecture. In *Studying Vibrational Communication*, eds. R. Crocroft, A. Wessel, and M. Gogala, pp. 303–317. Berlin: Springer-Verlag.
Volschenk, E. S., Mattoni, C. I., and Prendini, L. 2008. Comparative anatomy of the mesosomal organs of scorpions (Chelicerata, Scorpiones), with implications for the phylogeny of the order. *Zoological Journal of the Linnean Society* 154: 651–675.
von Rintelen, K., Page, T. J., Cai, Y., Roe, K., Stelbrink, B., Kuhajda, B. R., Iliffe, T. M., Hughes, J., and von Rintelen, T. 2012. Drawn to the dark side: A molecular phylogeny of freshwater shrimps (Crustacea: Decapoda: Caridea: Atyidae) reveals frequent cave invasions and challenges current taxonomic hypotheses. *Molecular Phylogenetics and Evolution* 63: 82–96.
Vondel, B. J. Van. 2005. Family Haliplidae (Coleoptera, Adephaga). In *World Catalogue of Insects*. Vol. 7, *Amphizoidae, Aspidytidae, Haliplidae, Noteridae and Paelobiidae (Coleoptera, Adephaga)*, eds. A. N. Nilsson and B. J. Van Vondel, pp. 20–86. Stenstrup: Apollo Books.
———. 2010. Revision of the Haliplidae of the Afrotropical Region, including North Africa (Coleoptera). *Tijdschrift voor Entomologie* 153: 239–314.
———. 2016. Haliplidae Aubé, 1836. In *Handbook of Zoology*. Vol. 4, *Arthropoda: Insecta*, pt. 38, *Coleoptera, Beetles,* vol. 1, *Morphology and Systematics (Archostemata, Adephaga, Myxophaga, Polyphaga partim)*, 2nd ed., eds. R. G. Beutel and R. B. Leschen, pp. 89–98. Berlin: Walter de Gruyter.
———. 2019. Features of the metacoxal air-storage space as additional characters for reconstructing the phylogeny of Haliplidae (Coleoptera). *Tijdschrift voor Entomologie* 162: 13–32.
Vondel, B. J. Van, and Bergsten, J. 2012. Review of the Haliplidae of Madagascar, with descriptions of two new species (Coleoptera). *Tijdschrift voor Entomologie* 155: 57–66.
Vorontsova, M. S., Besnard, G., Forest, F., Malakasi, P., Moat, J., et al. 2016. Madagascar's grasses and grasslands: Anthropogenic or natural? *Proceedings of the Royal Society of London B: Biological Sciences* 283: 20152262.
Vorster, C., Samways, M. J., Simaika, J. P., Kipping, J., Clausnitzer, V., Suhling, F., and Dijkstra, K.-D. B. 2020. Development of a new continental-scale index for freshwater assessment based on dragonfly assemblages. *Ecological Indicators* 109: 105819.
Vuataz, L., Sartori, M., Gattolliat, J.-L., and Monaghan, M. T. 2013. Endemism and diversification in freshwater insects of Madagascar revealed by coalescent and phylogenetic analysis of museum and field collections. *Molecular Phylogenetics and Evolution* 66: 979–991.
Vuillemin, S. 1970. Observations écologiques et biologiques sur *Madagapotamon humberti* Bott, 1965 (Crustacé, Décapode, Potamonidé) du massif de l'Ankarana (Madagascar). *Annales de l'Université de Madagascar* 7: 245–266.
Vuillet, A. 1911. Bénoni et Edouard Perrot. *Insecta* 1(6): 113–118.
Vulinec, K., and Miller, M. C. 1989. Aggregation and predator avoidance in whirligig beetles (Coleoptera: Gyrinidae). *Journal of the New York Entomological Society* 97: 438–447.
Wade, C. M., Mordan, P. B., and Clarke, B. 2001. A phylogeny of the land snails (Gastropoda: Pulmonata). *Proceedings of the Royal Society of London B: Biological Sciences* 268: 413–422.
Wagner, J., and Roubaud, E. 1932. Sur un Pulicidé nouveau parasite des rats domestiques à Madagascar. *Bulletin de la Société de Pathologie Exotique* 25: 327–332.
Wahlberg, N., and Rubinoff, D. 2011. Vagility across *Vanessa* (Lepidoptera: Nymphalidae): Mobility in butterfly species does not inhibit the formation and persistence of isolated sister taxa. *Systematic Entomology* 36: 362–370.
Wahlberg, N., Brower, A.V.Z., and Nylin, S. 2005. Phylogenetic relationships of tribes and genera in the subfamily Nymphalinae (Lepidoptera: Nymphalidae) based on three gene sequences. *Biological Journal of the Linnean Society* 86: 227–251.
Wahlberg, N., Rota, J., Braby, M. F., Pierce, N. E., and Wheat, C. W. 2014. Revised systematics and higher classification of pierid butterflies (Lepidoptera: Pieridae) based on molecular data. *Zoologica Scripta* 43: 641–650.
Wallace, G. D., and Rosen, L. 1969. Studies on eosinophilic meningitis. Molluscan hosts of *Angiostrongylus cantonensis* on Pacific islands. *American Journal of Tropical Medicine and Hygiene* 18: 206–216.
Wallner, A. M., Molano-Flores, B., and Dietrich, C. H. 2012. Using Auchenorrhyncha (Insecta: Hemiptera) to develop a new insect index in measuring North American tallgrass prairie quality. *Ecological Indicators* 25: 58–64.
Waloff, N. 1980. Studies on grassland leafhoppers (Auchenorrhyncha, Homoptera) and their natural enemies. *Advances in Ecological Research* 11: 81–215.
Wang, H., Wahlberg, N., Holloway, J. D., Bergsten, J., Fan, X., Janzen, D. H., Hallwachs, W., Wen, L., Wang, M., and Nylin, S. 2015. Molecular phylogeny of Lymantriinae (Lepidoptera, Noctuoidea, Erebidae) inferred from eight gene regions. *Cladistics* 31: 579–592.
Wang, L.-J. 2015. *Yoloides* Guignot, 1960, a junior synonym of *Yolina* Guignot, 1936 with comments on the genera *Pachynectes* Régimbart, 1903 and *Yolina* Guignot (Coleoptera: Dytiscidae: Hydroporinae: Bidessini). *Japanese Journal of Systematic Entomology* 21: 325–329.
Wang, Q.-Y., and Li, H.-H. 2020. Phylogeny of the superfamily Gelechioidea (Lepidoptera: Obtectomera), with an exploratory application on geometric morphometrics. *Zoologica Scripta* 49: 307–328.
Wang, X. 2018. Systematic study on subfamily Coelidiinae (Hemiptera: Cicadellidae). PhD thesis, Northwest A&F University, Yangling, Shaanxi, China.

Wang, Y., Dietrich, C. H., and Zhang, Y. 2017. Phylogeny and historical biogeography of leafhopper subfamily Evacanthinae (Hemiptera: Cicadellidae) based on morphological and molecular data. *Scientific Reports* 7: 45387.

Ward, P. S. 2006. The ant genus *Tetraponera* in the Afrotropical Region: Synopsis of species groups and revision of the *T. ambigua*-group. *Myrmecologische Nachrichten* 8: 119–130.

Ward, P. S., and Fisher B. L. 2016. Tales of dracula ants: The evolutionary history of the ant subfamily Amblyoponinae (Hymenoptera: Formicidae). *Systematic Entomology* 41: 683–693.

Ward, P. S., Brady, S. G., Fisher, B. L., and Schultz, T. R. 2010. Phylogeny and biogeography of Dolichoderinae ants: Effects of data partitioning and relict taxa on historical inference. *Systematic Biology* 59: 342–362.

———. 2015. The evolution of myrmicine ants: Phylogeny and biogeography of a hyperdiverse ant clade. *Systematic Entomology* 40: 61–81.

Ward, R. A. 1951. Description of a new species of Anoplura (*Lemurphthirus verruculosus*) from a Madagascar lemur. *Entomological News* 62: 190–192.

Wäreborn, I. 1979. Reproduction of two species of land snails in relation to calcium salts in the foerna layer. *Malacologia* 18: 177–180.

Warren, B. H., Strasberg, D., Bruggemann, J. H., Prys-Jones, R. P., and Thebaud, C. 2010. Why does the biota of the Madagascar region have such a strong Asiatic flavour? *Cladistics* 26: 526–538.

Warren, B. H., Baudin, R., Franck, A., Hugel, S., and Strasberg, D. 2016. Predicting where a radiation will occur: Acoustic and molecular surveys reveal overlooked diversity in Indian Ocean island crickets (Mogoplistinae: *Ornebius*). *PLoS One* 11: e0148971.

Waser, N. M., Price, M. V., and TBA Kirindy Pollination Consortium. 2010. A preliminary early-season flower-visitation web for the Kirindy Forest, Madagascar. *Journal of Pollination Ecology* 2(1): 1–6.

Wasserthal, L. T. 1997. The pollinators of the Malagasy star orchids *Angraecum sesquipedale*, *A. sororium* and *A. compactum* and the evolution of extremely long spurs by pollinator shift. *Botanica Acta* 110: 343–359.

Watson, A. 1965. A revision of the Ethiopian Drepanidae (Lepidoptera). *Bulletin of the British Museum (Natural History), Entomology Series*, supplement 3: 1–178.

Watts, C.H.S. 2019. Haliplidae Aube, 1836. In *Australian Beetles*. Vol. 2, *Archostemata, Myxophaga, Adephaga, Polyphaga (part)*, eds. A. Slipinski and J. F. Lawrence, pp. 24–26. Melbourne: CSIRO.

Watts, C., Stringer, I., Innes, J., and Monks, J. 2017. Evaluating tree wētā (Orthoptera: Anostostomatidae: *Hemideina* species) as bioindicators for New Zealand national biodiversity monitoring. *Journal of Insect Conservation* 21: 1–16.

Weaver, J. S., III 1997. A new genus of Petrothrincidae (Trichoptera) from Madagascar with specialized modifications in the female terminalia for carrying the eggmass. In *Proceedings of the 8th International Symposium on Trichoptera*, Minneapolis, 9–15 July 1995, eds R. W. Holzenthal and O. S. Flint, Jr., pp. 467–474. Columbus: Ohio Biological Survey.

Weaver, J. S., III, and Gibon, F.-M. 2007. The Lepidostomatidae of Madagascar (Trichoptera). In *Proceedings of the 12th International Symposium on Trichoptera*, Mexico, 18–22 June 2006, eds. J. Bueno-Soria, R. Barba-Álvarez, and B. Armitage, pp. 335–348. Columbus: Caddis Press.

Weaver, J. S., III, Gibon, F.-M., and Chvojka, P. 2008. A new genus of Philorheithridae (Trichoptera) from Madagascar. *Zootaxa* 1825: 18–28.

Webb, J. M., Braasch, D., and McCafferty, W. P. 2006. Reevaluation of the genera *Compsoneuria* Eaton and *Trichogenia* Braasch and Soldán (Ephemeroptera: Heptageniidae). *Zootaxa* 1335: 55–68.

Webb, M. D. 1980. The Cicadellidae from Aldabra, Astove and Cosmoledo atolls collected by the Royal Society Expedition 1967–68. *Journal of Natural History* 14: 829–863.

Wehrtmann, I. S., Hernández-Díaz, D., and Cumberlidge, N. 2019. Freshwater crabs as predators and prey: The case of *Ptychophallus uncinatus* Campos and Lemaitre, 1999 (Brachyura, Pseudothelphusidae) from Costa Rica, Central America. *Latin American Journal of Aquatic Research* 47(1): 18–26.

Wei, C.-H., Kun, A., and Yen, S.-H. 2007. A preliminary analysis of the phylogeny of the Ethmiinae moths (Lepidoptera: Gelechioidea) with special reference to the evolutionary patterns of host use. *Acta Zoologica Academiae Scientiarum Hungaricae* 53 (Supplement 1): 61–100.

Weintraub, P. G., and Beanland, L. 2006. Insect vectors of phytoplasmas. *Annual Review of Entomology* 51: 91–111.

Weirauch, C., Berenger, J. M., Berniker, L., Forero, D., Forthman, M., et al. 2014. An illustrated identification key to assassin bug subfamilies and tribes (Hemiptera: Reduviidae). *Canadian Journal of Arthropod Identification* 26: 1–115.

Weiskopf, S. R., Mccarthy, K. P., Tessler, M., Rahman, H. A., Mccarthy, J. L., Hersch, R., Faisal, M. M., and Siddal, M. E. 2018. Using terrestrial haematophagous leeches to enhance tropical biodiversity monitoring programmes in Bangladesh. *Journal of Applied Ecology* 55: 2071–2081.

Wells, N. A. 2003. Some hypotheses on the Mesozoic and Cenozoic paleoenvironmental history of Madagascar. In *The Natural History of Madagascar*, eds. S. M. Goodman and J. P. Benstead, pp. 16–34. Chicago: University of Chicago Press.

Wenzel, R. L., Tipton, V. J., and Kiewlicz. 1966. The streblid batflies of Panama (Diptera Calypterae: Streblidae). In *Ectoparasites of Panama*, eds. R. L. Wenzel and V. J. Tipton, pp. 405–675. Chicago: Field Museum of Natural History.

Wesener, T. 2009. Unexplored richness: Discovery of 31 new species of giant pill-millipedes endemic to Madagascar, with a special emphasis on microendemism (Diplopoda, Sphaerotheriida). *Zootaxa* 2097: 1–134.

———. 2011. Re-discovery after more than a century: A redefinition of the Malagasy endemic millipede genus *Zehntnerobolus*, with a description of a new species (Diplopoda, Spirobolida, Pachybolidae). *Zootaxa* 3018: 21–26.

———. 2014a. Redescription of *"Polyzonium" malagassum*, a new synonym of *Rhinotus purpureus* (Pocock, 1894), with notes about the occurrence of the order Polyzoniida on Madagascar (Diplopoda). *Zootaxa* 3790(4): 587–594.

———. 2014b. First records of the order Siphonophorida from Madagascar and Mauriius (Diplopoda). *Revue Suisse de Zoologie* 121(3): 415–423.

———. 2016. The giant pill-millipedes, order Sphaerotheriida: An annotated species catalogue with morphological atlas and list of apomorphies (Arthropoda: Diplopoda). *Bonn Zoological Bulletin, Supplementum* 63: 1–104.

Wesener, T., and Anilkumar, P. A. 2020. The millipedes collected by the Museum "La Specola" on Madagascar 1989/1991, with the description of three new species of giant pill-millipedes (Diplopoda, Sphaerotheriida, Arthrosphaeridae). *ZooKeys*: 930: 3–35. doi:10.3897/zookeys.930.47620.

Wesener, T., and Enghoff, H. 2009. Revision of the millipede subfamily Spiromiminae, a Malagasy group with Indian connections? (Diplopoda Spirobolida Pachybolidae). *Tropical Zoology* 22(1): 71–120.

Wesener, T., and Schütte, K. 2010. Swarming behaviour and mass occurrences in the world's largest giant pill-millipede species, *Zoosphaerium neptunus*, on Madagascar and its implication for conservation efforts (Diplopoda: Sphaerotheriida). *Madagascar Conservation and Development* 5(2): 89–94.

Wesener, T., and Sierwald, P. 2005a. New giant pill-millipede species from the littoral forest of Madagascar (Diplopoda, Sphaerotheriida, *Zoosphaerium*). *Zootaxa* 1097: 1–60.

———. 2005b. The giant pill-millipedes of Madagascar: Revision of the genus *Sphaeromimus*, with a review of the morphological terminology (Diplopoda, Sphaerotheriida, Sphaerotheriidae). *Proceedings of the California Academy of Sciences*, ser. 4, 56(29): 557–599.

Wesener, T., and VandenSpiegel, D. 2007. *Microsphaerotherium ivohibiense*, a new genus and species of giant-pill millipedes from Madagascar (Diplopoda, Sphaerotheriida, Arthrosphaerinae). *Journal of Afrotropical Zoology* 3: 153–160.

———. 2009. A first phylogenetic analysis of giant pill-millipedes (Diplopoda: Sphaerotheriida), a new model Gondwanan taxon, with special emphasis on island gigantism. *Cladistics* 25: 545–573.

Wesener, T., and Wägele, J. W. 2007. Giant pill-millipedes (Diplopoda: Sphaerotheriida) in the littoral forest fragments of southeastern Madagascar. In *Biodiversity, Ecology and Conservation of Littoral Ecosystems in Southeastern Madagascar, Tolagnaro (Fort Dauphin)*, eds. J. Ganzhorn, S. M. Goodman, and M. Vincelette. *SI/MAB Series* 11: 145–151.

———. 2008. The giant pill-millipedes of Madagascar: Revision of the genus *Zoosphaerium* (Myriapoda, Diplopoda, Sphaerotheriida). *Zoosystema* 30(1): 5–85.

Wesener, T., Enghoff, H., and Wägele, J. W. 2008. Pachybolini, a tribe of giant Afrotropical millipedes: Arguments for monophyly and the description of a new genus from Madagascar (Diplopoda: Spirobolida: Pachybolidae). *Invertebrate Systematics* 22: 37–53. http://dx.doi.org/10.1071/IS07008.

Wesener, T., Enghoff, H., and Sierwald, P. 2009a. Review of the Spirobolida on Madagascar, with descriptions of twelve new genera, including three genera of "Fire Millipedes" (Diplopoda). *ZooKeys* 19: 1–128.

Wesener, T., Enghoff, H., Hoffman, R. L., Wägele, J. W., and Sierwald, P. 2009b. Revision of the endemic giant fire millipedes of Madagascar, genus *Aphistogoniulus* (Diplopoda, Spirobolida, Pachybolidae). *International Journal of Myriapodology* 3: 15–52.

Wesener, T., Raupach, M. J., and and Sierwald, P. 2010a. The origins of the giant pill-millipedes from Madagascar (Diplopoda: Sphaerotheriida: Arthrosphaeridae). *Molecular Phylogenetics and Evolution* 57: 1184–1193.

Wesener, T. Bespalova, I., and Sierwald, P. 2010b. Madagascar's living giants: Discovery of five new species of endemic giant pill-millipedes from Madagascar (Diplopoda: Sphaerotheriida: Arthrosphaeridae: *Zoosphaerium*). *African Invertebrates* 51(1): 133–161.

Wesener, T., Raupach, M. J., and Decker, P. 2011. Mountain refugia play a role in soil arthropod speciation on Madagascar: A case study of the endemic giant fire-millipede genus *Aphistogoniulus* (Diplopoda, Spirobolida, Pachybolidae). *PLoS One* 6(12): 1–15. http://dx.doi.org/10.1371/journal.pone.0028035.

Wesener, T., Le, D. M., and Loria, S. F. 2014. Integrative revision of the giant pill-millipede genus *Sphaeromimus* from Madagascar, with the description of seven new species (Diplopoda, Sphaerotheriida, Arthrosphaeridae). *ZooKeys* 414: 67–107. doi:10.3897/zookeys.414.7730.

Westergren, S., and Siddall, M. E. 2004. Two new species of salifid leeches (Arhynchobdellida: Erpobdelliformes: Salifidae) from South Africa and Madagascar. *American Museum Novitates* 3456: 1–6.

Wewalka, G. 1980a. Revision der afrikanischen Gattung *Heterhydrus* Fairm. (Coleoptera, Dytiscidae). *Annales Historico-Naturales Musei Nationalis Hungarici* 72: 97–101.

———. 1980b. Results of the Austrian Hydrobiological Mission, 1974, to the Seychelles-, Comores- and Mascarene Archipelagos. Pt. 7, Dytiscidae, Gyrinidae (Coleoptera). *Annalen des Naturhistorischen Museums in Wien* 83: 723–732.

———. 1982. Neue Copelatini aus Madagaskar und Afrika (Dytiscidae, Col.). *Koleopterologische Rundschau* 56: 127–133.

Whalley, P.E.S. 1967. Insectes Lépidoptères Thyrididae. *Faune de Madagascar* 24: 1–53.

Wheeler, W. C., Coddington, J. A., Crowley, L. M., Dimitrov, D., Goloboff, P. A., et al. 2017. The spider tree of life: Phylogeny of Araneae based on target-gene analyses from an extensive taxon sampling. *Cladistics* 33: 576–616. doi:10.1111/cla.12182.

Whitaker, I. S., Rao, J., Izadi, D., and Butler, P. E. 2004. Historical article: *Hirudo medicinalis*; Ancient origins of, and trends in the use of medicinal leeches throughout history. *British Journal of Oral and Maxillofacial Surgery* 2: 133–137.

White, I. M. 2006. Taxonomy of the *Dacina* (Diptera: Tephritidae) of Africa and the Middle East. *African Entomology Memoir* 2: 1–156.

White, I. M., and Elson-Harris, M. M. 1994. *Fruit Flies of Economic Significance: Their Identification and Bionomics*. London and Canberra: C.A.B. International and Australian Centre for International Agricultural Research.

White, I. M., De Meyer, M., and Stonehouse, J. 2000. A review of the native and introduced fruit flies (Diptera, Tephritidae) in the Indian Ocean islands of Mauritius, Réunion, Rodrigues and Seychelles. In *Proceedings of the Indian Ocean Commission, Regional Fruit Fly Symposium*, Mauritius, 5–9 June 2000. Indian Ocean Commission, Mauritius, eds. N. S. Price and I. Seewooruthun, pp. 15–21. Port Louis: Indian Ocean Commission.

White, I. M., Copeland, R. S., and Hancock, D. L. 2003. Revision of the Afrotropical genus *Trirhithrum* Bezzi (Diptera: Tephritidae). *Cimbebasia* 18: 71–137.

Whiting, M. F., Alison, S., Whiting, A. S., Hastriter, M. W., and Dittmar, K. 2008. A molecular phylogeny of fleas (Insecta: Siphonaptera): Origins and host associations. *Cladistics* 24(5): 677–707.

Wiebes, J. T. 1979. Co-evolution of figs and their insect pollinators. *Annual Review of Ecology and Systematics* 10: 1–12.

Wiegert, R. G., and Evans, F. C. 1967. Investigation of secondary productivity in grassland. In *Secondary Productivity in Terrestrial Ecosystems*, ed. K. Petrusewicz, pp. 499–518. Warsaw: Polish Academy of Science.

Wiens, J. J. 2011. The causes of species richness patterns across space, time, and clades and the role of "ecological limits." *Quarterly Review of Biology* 86: 75–96.

Wiggins, G. B. 2005. *Caddisflies: The Underwater Architects*. Toronto: University of Toronto Press.

Wignall, A. E., and Taylor, P. 2008. Biology and life history of the araneophagic assassin bug *Stenolemus bituberus* including a morphometric analysis of the instars (Heteroptera, Reduviidae). *Journal of Natural History* 42: 59–76.

Wilde, J. de. 1941. Contribution to the physiology of the Johnston organ and its part in the behavior of the *Gyrinus*. *Archives Néerlandaises de Physiologie de l'Homme et des Animaux* 25: 381–400.

Wilkerson, R. C., Linton, Y. M., Fonseca, D. M., Schultz, T. R., Price, D. C., and Strickman, D. A. 2015. Making mosquito taxonomy useful: A stable classification of tribe Aedini that balances utility with current knowledge of evolutionary relationships. *PLoS One* 10(7): e0133602.

Wilkinson, G. S., and Dodson, G. N. 1997. Function and evolution of antlers and eye stalks in flies. In *The Evolution of Mating Systems in Insects and Arachnids*, eds. J. Choe and B. Cresp, pp. 310–328. Cambridge: Cambridge University Press.

Wilkinson, G. S., Amitin E. G., and Johns, P. M. 2005. Sex-linked correlated responses in female reproductive traits to selection on male eye span in stalk-eyed flies. *Integrative and Comparative Biology* 45: 500–510.

Wilkinson, S. M., Rundle, S. D., Brewin, P. A., and Ormerod, S. J. 1995. A study of the whirligig beetles *Dineutus indicus* (Aubé) (Gyrinidae) in a Nepalese hillstream. *Entomologist* 114: 131–137.

Will, K. W., Mishler, B. D., and Wheeler, Q. D. 2005. The perils of DNA barcoding and the need for integrative taxonomy. *Systematic Biology* 54: 844–851.

Williams, M. C. 2020. Afrotropical butterflies. Online encyclopedia. Accessed Feb. 2020. http://www.lepsocafrica.org/?p=publications&s=atb.

Williner, V., Carvalho, D. A. Collins, P. A. 2014. Feeding spectra and activity of the freshwater crab *Trichodactylus kensleyi* (Decapoda: Brachyura: Trichodactylidae) at La Plata basin. *Zoological Studies* 53: 71.

Wilson, C. B. 1923. Water beetles in relation to pondfish culture, with life histories of those found in fishponds of Fairport, Iowa. *Bulletin of the Bureau of Fisheries* 39: 231–345.

Wilson, E. O. 1987. The little things that run the world (the importance and conservation of invertebrates). *Conservation Biology* 1: 344–346.

Wilson, J. M. 1982. A review of World Troglopedetini (Insecta, Collembola, Paronellidae) including an identification table and descriptions of new species. *Transactions British Cave Research Association* 9(3): 210–226.

Winterton, S. L., and Barraclough, D. A. 2017. Acroceridae. In *Manual of Afrotropical Diptera*, Vol. 2, *Nematocerous Diptera and Lower Brachycera*, eds. A. H. Kirk-Spriggs and B. J. Sinclair, pp. 981–993. Suricata 5. Pretoria: South African National Biodiversity Institute.

Winterton, S. L., Wiegmann, B. M., and Schlinger, E. I. 2007. Phylogeny and Bayesian divergence time estimations of small-headed flies (Diptera: Acroceridae) using multiple molecular markers. *Molecular Phylogenetics and Evolution* 43: 808–832.

Wintrebert, D. 1972. *Nouvelles contributions à l'étude des Acridoidea malgaches (Orthoptera)*. Tervuren: Musée Royal de l'Afrique Centrale.

Witteveen, J., Verhoef, H. A., and Letschert, J.P.W. 1987. Osmotic and ionic regulation in marine littoral Collembola. *Journal of Insect Physiology* 33: 59–66.

Wolfrum, P. 1961. Anthribiden aus dem Institut Scientifique de Madagascar. *Entomologische Arbeiten aus dem Museum G. Frey* 12: 291–325.

Wood, H. M. 2008. A revision of the assassin spiders of the *Eriauchenius gracilicollis* group, a clade of spiders endemic to Madagascar (Araneae, Archaeidae). *Zoological Journal of the Linnean Society* 152: 255–296.

Wood, H. M., and Scharff, N. 2018. A review of the Madagascan pelican spiders of the genera *Eriauchenius* O. Pickard-Cambridge, 1881 and *Madagascarchaea* gen. n. (Araneae, Archaeidae). *ZooKeys* 727: 1–96. doi:10.3897/zookeys.727.20222.

Wood, H. M., Griswold, C. E., and Spicer, G. S. 2007. Phylogenetic relationships within an endemic group of Malagasy "assassin spiders" (Araneae, Archaeidae): Ancestral character reconstruction, convergent evolution and biogeography. *Molecular Phylogenetics and Evolution* 45: 612–619.

Wood, H. M., Griswold, C. E., and Gillespie, R. 2012. Phylogenetic placement of pelican spiders (Archaeidae, Araneae), with insight into evolution of the "neck" and predatory behaviors of the superfamily Palpimanoidea. *Cladistics* 28, 598–626.

Wood, H. M., Matzke, N., Gillespie, R., and Griswold, C. E. 2013. Treating fossils as terminal taxa in divergence time estimation reveals ancient vicariance patterns in the palpimanoid spiders. *Systematic Biology* 62: 264–284.

Wood, H. M., Gillespie, R. G., Griswold, C. E., and Wainwright, P. C. 2015. Why is Madagascar special? The extraordinarily slow evolution of pelican spiders (Araneae, Archaeidae). *Evolution* 69: 462–481.

Wood, H. M., González, V., Lloyd, M., Coddington, J., and Scharff, N. 2018. Next-generation museum genomics: Phylogenetic relationships among palpimanoid spiders using sequence capture techniques (Araneae: Palpimanoidea). *Molecular Phylogenetics and Evolution* 127: 907–918. doi:10.1016/j.ympev.2018.06.038.

Woodhead, C., Vences, M., Vieites, D., Gamboni, I., Fisher, B. L., and Griffiths, R. A. 2007. Specialist or generalist? Feeding ecology of the Malagasy poison frog *Mantella aurantiaca*. *Herpetological Journal* 17: 225–236.

Woodley, N. E. 2001. A world catalog of Stratiomyidae (Insecta: Diptera). *Myia* 11: 1–475.

———. 2009a. Family Stratiomyidae. In *The Diptera of the Seychelles Islands*, ed. J. Gerlach, pp. 100–106. Sofia: Pensoft.

———. 2009b. *Microchrysa flaviventris* (Wiedemann), a new immigrant soldier fly in the United States (Diptera: Stratiomyidae). *Proceedings of the Entomological Society of Washington* 111(2): 527–529.

———. 2011. A world catalog of the Stratiomyidae (Insecta: Diptera): A supplement with revisionary notes and errata. *Myia* 12: 379–415.

World Spider Catalog. 2020. *World Spider Catalog*. Version 21.0. Natural History Museum, Bern. Accessed 15 Feb. 2020. doi:10.24436/2.

Wowor, D., Muthu, V., Meier, R., Balke, M., Cai, Y., and Ng, P.K.L. 2009. Evolution of life history traits in Asian freshwater prawns of the genus *Macrobrachium* (Crustacea: Decapoda: Palaemonidae) based on multilocus molecular phylogenetic analysis. *Molecular Phylogenetics and Evolution* 52(2): 340–350.

Wright, P. C., Arrigo-Nelson, S. J., Hogg, K. L., Bannon, B., Morelli, T. L., Wyatt, J., Harivelo, A. L., and Ratelolahy, F. 2009. Habitat disturbance and seasonal fluctuations of lemur parasites in the rain forest of Ranomafana National Park, Madagascar. In *Primate Parasite Ecology: The Dynamics and Study of Host-Parasite Relationships*, eds. M. A. Huffman and C. A. Chapman, pp. 311–330. Cambridge: Cambridge University Press.

Wu, L.-W., Yen, S.-H., Lees, D. C., and Hsu, Y.-F. 2010. Elucidating genetic signatures of native and introduced populations of the Cycad Blue, *Chilades pandava* to Taiwan: A threat both to Sago Palm and to native Cycas populations worldwide. *Biological Invasions* 12: 2649–2669.

Wunderlich, J., ed. 2008. Fossil and extant spiders (Araneae). *Beiträge zur Araneologie* 5: 1–870.

Xue, Q., Dietrich, C. H., and Zhang, Y. 2020. Phylogeny and classification of the leafhopper subfamily Eurymelinae (Hemiptera: Cicadellidae) inferred from molecules and morphology. *Systematic Entomology* 45: 687–702.

Yakovlev, R. V. 2009. New taxa of African and Asian Cossidae (Lepidoptera). *Euroasian Entomological Journal* 8: 353–361.

———. 2011. Catalogue of the family Cossidae of the Old World (Lepidoptera). *Neue Entomologische Nachrichten* 66: 1–129.

Yakovlev, R. V., and Saldaitis, A. 2008. *Rambuasalama augustasi* gen. nov. et spec. nov. of Cossidae from Madagascar (Lepidoptera, Cossidae). *Atalanta* 39: 401–403.

Yen, S.-H., and Wu, S. 2009. *Noctuoidea, Noctuidae, Eriopinae*. Biota Taiwanica, Hexapoda: Lepidoptera. Taipei: National Sun Yat-Sen University.

Yoder, A. D., and Nowak, M. D. 2006. Has vicariance or dispersal been the predominant biogeographic force in Madagascar? Only time will tell. *Annual Review of Ecology, Evolution and Systematics* 37: 405–431.

Yoshimura, M., and Fisher, B. L. 2007. A revision of male ants of the Malagasy region (Hymenoptera: Formicidae): Key to subfamilies and treatment of the genera of Ponerinae. *Zootaxa* 1654: 21–40.

———. 2009. A revision of male ants of the Malagasy region (Hymenoptera: Formicidae): Key to genera of the subfamily Proceratiinae. *Zootaxa* 2216: 1–21.

———. 2011. A revision of male ants of the Malagasy region (Hymenoptera: Formicidae): Key to genera of the subfamily Dolichoderinae. *Zootaxa* 2794: 1–34.

———. 2012. A revision of male ants of the Malagasy Amblyoponinae (Hymenoptera: Formicidae) with resurrections of the genera *Stigmatomma* and *Xymmer*. *PLoS One* 7(3): e33325.

Young, D. A. 1986. Taxonomic study of the Cicadellinae (Homoptera: Cicadellidae). Pt. 3, Old World Cicadellini. *North Carolina Agricultural Experiment Station Technical Bulletin* 281: 1–639.

Youngerman, D. 2016. Henri Seyrig ab ovo. *Syria* 3: 93–108.

Zack, R. S., and Akre, R. D. 1983. The scientific publications of Maurice T. James (1905–1982), with a list of proposed names. *Entomography* 2: 55–75.

Zahiri, R., Kitching, I. J., Lafontaine, J. D., Mutanen, M., Kaila, L., Holloway, J. D., and Wahlberg, N. 2011. A new molecular phylogeny offers hope for a stable family level classification of the Noctuoidea (Lepidoptera). *Zoologica Scripta* 40: 158–173.

Zahiri, R., Holloway, J. D., Kitching, I. J., Lafontaine, J. D., Mutanen, M., and Wahlberg, N. 2012. Molecular phylogenetics of the Erebidae (Lepidoptera, Noctuoidea). *Systematic Entomology* 37: 102–124.

Zahiri, R., Lafontaine, J. D., Schmidt, C., Holloway, J. D., Kitching, I. J., Mutanen, M., and Wahlberg, N. 2013. Relationships among the basal lineages of Noctuidae (Lepidoptera, Noctuoidea) based on eight gene regions. *Zoologica Scripta* 42: 488–507.

Zahniser, J. N., and Dietrich, C. H. 2013. A review of the tribes of Deltocephalinae (Hemiptera: Auchenorrhyncha: Cicadellidae). *European Journal of Taxonomy* 45: 1–211.

Zahniser, J. N., and Nielson, M. W. 2012. An extraordinary new genus and three new species of Acostemmini (Hemiptera: Cicadellidae: Deltocephalinae) from Madagascar with comments on the morphology and classification of the tribe. *Zootaxa* 3209: 28–52.

Zaspel, J. M., Weller, S. J., Wardwell, C. T., Zahiri, R., and Wahlberg, N. 2014. Phylogeny and evolution of pharmacophagy in tiger moths (Lepidoptera: Erebidae: Arctiinae). *PLoS One* 9: e101975.

Zeegers, T. 2015. Horseflies (Diptera: Tabanidae) of Madagascar. Pt. 1, Introduction, subfamily Pangoniinae and tribe Chrysopsini (Chrysopsinae). *Studia Dipterologica* 21(2) (2014): 301–334.

Zeegers, T. 2017. Horseflies (Diptera: Tabanidae) of Madagascar. Pt. 2, Subfamily Chrysopsinae, tribe Rhinomyzini. *Studia Dipterologica* 22(2) (2015): 259–304.

Zeng, Y., and Crews, S. 2018. Biomechanics of omnidirectional strikes in flat spiders. *Journal of Experimental Biology* 221: jeb166512. doi:10.1242/jeb.166512.

Zenker, M. M., Wahlberg, N., Brehm, G., Teston, J. A., Przybyłowicz, L., Pie, M. R., and Freitas, M.V.L. 2016. Systematics and origin of moths in the subfamily Arctiinae (Lepidoptera, Erebidae) in the Neotropical region. *Zoologica Scripta* 46: 348–362.

Zeppelini, D., Queiroz, G. C., and Bellini, B. C. 2020. Collembola in Catálogo Taxonômico da Fauna do Brasil. PNUD. Accessed 3 Mar. 2020. http://fauna.jbrj.gov.br/fauna/faunadobrasil/379.

Zerny, H. 1912. Syntomidae. In *Lepidopterorum Catalogus*, ed. H. Wagner, 7: 1–179. Berlin: W. Junck.

Zhang, F., Bellini, B. C., and Soto-Adames, F. N. 2019. New insights into the systematics of Entomobryoidea (Collembola: Entomobryomorpha): First instar chaetotaxy, homology and classification. *Zoological Systematics* 44(4): 249–278.

Zhang, G., and Weirauch, C. 2011. Matching dimorphic sexes and immature stages with adults: Resolving the systematics of the *Bekilya* group of Malagasy assassin bugs (Hemiptera: Reduviidae: Peiratinae). *Systematic Entomology* 36: 115–138.

Zhang, J., Lees, D. C., Shen, J., Cong, Q., Huertas, B., Martin, G., and Grishin, N. V. 2020. The mitogenome of a Madagascan butterfly *Malaza fastuosus* recovered from the holotype collected over 140 years ago adds support for a new subfamily of Hesperiidae. *Genome* 63: 195–202.

Zhang, S. Q., Che, L. H., Li, Y., Liang, D., Pang, H., Slipinski, A., and Zhang, P. 2018. Evolutionary history of Coleoptera revealed by extensive sampling of genes and species. *Nature Communications* 9(205): 1–11.

Zhu, Q., Hastriter, M. W., Whiting, M. F., and Dittmar, K. 2015. Fleas (Siphonaptera) are Cretaceous, and evolved with Theria. *Molecular Phylogenetics and Evolution* 90: 129–139.

Zhu, W., Yan, J., Song, J., and You, P. 2018. The first mitochondrial genomes for Pyralinae (Pyralidae) and Glaphyriinae (Crambidae), with phylogenetic implications of Pyraloidea. *PLoS One* 13: e0194672.

Zielke, E. 1971. Revision der Muscinae der aethiopischen Region. *Series Entomologica* 7: 1–199.

Zilli, A. 2000. African-Arabian and Asian-Pacific "*Mocis frugalis*": Two distinct species (Lepidoptera: Noctuidae). *European Journal of Entomology* 97: 419–426.

Zilli, A., and Hogenes, W. 2002. An annotated list of the fruit-piercing moth genus *Eudocima* Billberg, 1820 (sensu Poole) with descriptions of four new species (Lepidoptera: Noctuidae, Catocalinae). *Quadrifina* 5: 153–207.

Zilli, A., Brou, V. A. Klem, C., and Zaspel, J. 2017. The *Eudocima* Billberg, 1820 of the Australian Region (Lepidoptera: Erebidae). In *Biodiversity, Biogeography and Nature Conservation in Wallacea and New Guinea*, vol. 3, eds. D. Telnov, M. V. L. Barclay, and O.S.G. Pauwels, pp. 631–655. Riga: Entomological Society of Latvia.

Zimmerman, E. C. 1994. *Australian Weevils (Coleoptera: Curculionoidea)*. Vol. 1, *Orthoceri. Anthribidae to Attelabidae. The Primitive Weevils*. Melbourne: CSIRO.

Zimmermann, A. 1924. Die Halipliden der Welt. *Entomologische Blätter* 20: 1–16, 65–80, 129–144, 193–213.

Zjhra, M. L. 2008. Facilitating sympatric species coexistence via pollinator partitioning in endemic tropical trees of Madagascar. *Plant Systematics and Evolution* 271: 157–176.

Zohdy, S., and Durden, L. A. 2016. A review of ectoparasites in the Cheirogaleidae. In *The Dwarf and Mouse Lemurs of Madagascar: Biology, Behavior and Conservation Biogeography of the Cheirogaleidae*, eds. S. M. Lehman, U. Radespiel, and E. Zimmermann, pp. 220–232. Cambridge: Cambridge University Press.

Zohdy, S., Kemp, A. D., Durden, L. A., Wright, P. C., and Jernvall, J. 2012. Mapping the social network: Tracking lice in a wild primate (*Microcebus rufus*) population to infer social contacts and vector potential. *BMC Ecology* 12(1): 4.

Zohdy, S., Bisanzio, D., Tecot, S., Wright, P. C., and Jernvall, J. 2017. Aggression and hormones are associated with heterogeneity in parasitism and parasite dynamics in the brown mouse lemur. *Animal Behaviour* 132: 109–119.

Zolotuhin, V. V., and Prozorov, A. M. 2010. A review of the genera *Opisthodontia* Aurivillius, 1895, and *Stenophatna* Aurivillius, 1909, with erection of 8 new genera and description of 37 new species and 2 new subspecies (Lepidoptera, Lasiocampidae). *Atalanta* 41: 397–460.

FIGURE 13.14 **Additional aspects of seabirds in Malagasy waters. A and B) two of the Quatre Frères islands, Nosy Mitsio archipelago; C) flock of fishing *Sula leucogaster* (Brown Booby), Nosy Mitsio; D) roost of *Thalasseus bengalensis* (Lesser Crested Tern), Nosy Mitsio; E) two immature *S. leucogaster*, Nosy Mitsio; and F) the Quatre Frères hold an important roost of hundreds of *Fregata* spp. (frigatebirds).** (PHOTOS by C. Caumes.)

Although people fish in the marine area, no poaching or egg harvest has been recorded, likely because of the inaccessibility. It is not known whether introduced mammals, such as cats or rats, are present on the islets. Seabirds have been observed breeding in June and July (Polunin 1979; Turner and Dowsett 1988), but the complete annual breeding cycle is unknown.

5. Nosy Be and all the Islets between Nosy Be and Analalava—Northern Tip

This region includes the large, mountainous, inhabited island of Nosy Be and a number of smaller islands and islets, some of which are uninhabited. No complete seabird census has been conducted in the area, but there are reports of a colony of "a few dozen pairs"

of *Sula leucogaster* on Nosy Kasinjy (ZICOMA 2001), and 15 breeding pairs of *Phaethon lepturus* on Nosy Tanikely in July 1987 (Langrand 1990). Four breeding pairs of *P. lepturus* were recorded at this site in October 2019 (R. Rabarisoa, unpublished data). This island is heavily visited by tourists. In 2016, for example, 37,000 people visited the island (Madagascar National Parks, unpublished data), so human pressure is severe and may limit the breeding of seabirds. However, the area has at least 10 uninhabited islets, each less than 0.5 km^2, that could be suitable for seabirds, and it is likely that some species may still breed on these.

6. Iles Barren Archipelago (off Maintirano)—West Coast

This archipelago, located 10–30 km off Maintirano, is composed of nine islands and islets (Iles Barren, Nosy Marify, and several islets), most of them at least temporarily inhabited by nomadic fishermen, who harvest both adults and eggs of breeding seabirds. Large concentrations of bird guano suggest that the archipelago presumably once supported large populations of seabirds, but sustained human presence on the islands, the harvesting of eggs, and the introduction of rats have greatly decreased the populations (Cripps 2010). The archipelago is known to hold multispecies colonies of breeding terns, including a large colony of *Sterna dougallii* (1480 pairs in 1998), 100 pairs of *Onychoprion anaethetus*, and some *O. fuscatus* (ZICOMA 1999, 2001). The main breeding season of terns in this archipelago seems to be austral winter, but further data are needed.

In September 2007, Bemanaja visited all islands of the archipelago and counted 1750 pairs of *S. dougallii*, 500 pairs of *O. anaethetus*, and 25 pairs of *O. fuscatus* (Bemanaja 2009). He also conducted a survey to evaluate the use of seabirds by local people. He found that egg harvest and tern hunting were still very common and estimated that 200 to 400 eggs were harvested per day during the breeding season and 30 to 500 adults were hunted per day. The current status of the colony is not known, but it is likely that with such a high level of harvest and poaching, seabird populations would have declined on all islands in the archipelago.

Another important issue is the exploitation of seabird guano. The Iles Barren were mined for seabird guano in the 1990s and in 2009 and 2010 (at least), but no environmental impact assessment has been completed as far as we know (Cripps 2010). According to a recent statement by the extractive company Guanomad (cited in Cripps 2010), guano reserves are approximately 500,000 tons. Large-scale mining of this resource would have irreversible impacts on the islands and on neighboring marine ecosystems: destruction of island vegetation, coral reefs, and seagrass beds; and increased hunting and egg harvest by people who would live on the islands.

The archipelago has temporary protection status and is set to become a Marine Protected Area managed by local communities (Ministère de l'Environnement et du Développement Durable 2019). The guano extraction has been stopped but it is not currently clear whether there is a risk of reactivation despite the site's protection (Blue Ventures, unpublished information).

7. Islets off Morombe and Andavadoaka—West Coast

This region includes a group of 26 islands and islets off the coast of Morombe town and Andavadoaka village, and it holds the only breeding *Ardenna pacifica* (Wedge-tailed Shearwater) in Madagascar. No other seabird species are known to breed in the region, but further surveys are needed. Small breeding colonies, estimated to hold 100–125 nests, were discovered and described (Appert 1965). *Ardenna pacifica* breeds on rocky karstic islets where it has some protection because it typically nests in deep burrows and caves. However, it is heavily hunted by local fishermen who travel from the mainland specifically for this purpose. In April 2008, Bemanaja visited three islets that are known by local hunters to have breeding colonies of *A. pacifica*: Nosy Anjamanjiky Bé, Nosy Anjamanjiky Anivo, and Nosy Anjamanjiky Antimo (which correspond to the "Iles jumelles Jamanjaky" referred to by Appert 1965). He found nesting birds on the three islets (23 occupied nests, 21 empty nests that were recently used, and 28 empty burrows not recently used). He did not survey all the islets because of the difficulty of access, so the total population is unknown (Bemanaja 2008, 2009).

During this visit, Bemanaja found hunting to be intensive, and he joined a group of four hunters who showed him their techniques (Figures 13.13d and e). Shearwaters were captured in three different ways: with a harpoon, with nooses made from fishing line, or with local traps fabricated at the site from thorny and sticky plants. The hunters reported a catch rate of one to 12 birds per day during the breeding season. They usually sold their catch to a local woman who in turn sold it in a market on the mainland near Morombe (Figure 13.13f). Introduced rats are also present on the islets and are known to prey on eggs and unattended chicks of shearwaters (Bemanaja 2008). Although we lack any accurate data to properly describe the breeding season of *A. pacifica* in this archipelago, Appert's and Bemanaja's observations and census suggest a summer breeding regime, as on all other islands of the western Indian Ocean (Safford 2013m).

This unique colony is threatened by hunting and by invasive rats; urgent conservation measures are needed to protect it. We are not aware of any more recent surveys since Bemanaja's visit in 2008. Several conservation organizations are working in the region and could take up this opportunity for seabird conservation in the area.

8. Nosy Vé—West Coast

Nosy Vé is a small coralline island south of the town of Toliara and directly west of the village of Anakao. It is a sacred island where according to local *fady* (taboo) no hunting or animal harvest is allowed (Lilette 2006). The island hosts the only breeding colony of *Phaethon rubricauda* (Red-tailed Tropicbird) in Madagascar (Figure 13.13h). A small colony with fewer than 20 pairs was discovered in 1980 by Olivier Langrand (Langrand 1981). A report of a visit to the island 32 years earlier by Milon (1948a) interestingly did not mention any seabird colony. This suggests that the colonization of the island by *P. rubricauda* is relatively recent.

This site is the only seabird colony in Madagascar that has been regularly monitored. It was surveyed annually between 1991 and 1995 (Cooke and Randriamanindry 1996). Rats were eradicated in

July–August 2000 by Frontier-Madagascar, and the tropicbird population was monitored monthly between August 2000 and March 2003 (Rix et al. 2003) and regularly since 2004 by a research team from the University of La Réunion and Institut Halieutique et des Sciences Marines at the Université de Toliara (Le Corre and Bemanaja 2004; Bemanaja 2009; Le Corre 2019; M. Le Corre, unpublished data). Since rat eradication, and under the influence of local *fady*, the population of *P. rubricauda* has increased exponentially and is currently estimated at around 800 pairs. The breeding productivity is very high, with hundreds of fledglings produced annually, and many are then recruited into the breeding population at the age of three to five years (Gauchet and Piana 2019).

The population on Nosy Vé is expected to continue to grow in the future because a large area of suitable breeding habitat remains unoccupied. Breeding takes place year-round, with a clear seasonal peak of laying between March and July each year (Gauchet and Piana 2019). A *P. rubricauda* adult banded as a chick on 11 January 2006 at Sugarloaf Rock Nature Reserve, Western Australia, was found incubating on Nosy Vé on 20 April 2015 (M. Le Corre and G. K. Williams, Australian Bird and Bat Banding Scheme, unpublished data). This follows the recovery on La Réunion of a bird banded as a nestling in Western Australia (Le Corre et al. 2003a), further suggesting that populations across the Indian Ocean are connected.

Numerous ecological studies have been conducted on the Nosy Vé population, including population dynamics (more than 1000 birds have been banded since 2004; Gauchet and Piana 2019), population genetics, telemetry to investigate migration strategies and foraging behavior at sea (Le Corre et al. 2012; Hoarau 2019; A. Jaeger et al., unpublished data), foraging ecology and diet (Andriatahina 2019), and social perception and ecotourism value (Lilette 2006; Bemanaja 2009; Tsiebo 2019). Nosy Vé is popular with tourists, who visit the nearby village of Anakao (Figures 13.13j and k). Local guides and fishermen take tourists with traditional Vezo canoes for a day visit to the island, where they can observe the impressive aerial displays of hundreds of *P. rubricauda*. This form of ecotourism benefits the local community by providing a significant source of income and employment (Bemanaja 2009), as well as biodiversity through a ban on bird hunting. It is an excellent example of community-based conservation, and as far as we know, the only one of seabird ecotourism in Madagascar. It should serve as an example to other seabird sites in Madagascar to encourage a shift from poaching and egg harvesting to sustainable ecotourism. Although rat eradication was a great success, there is still a risk of reinvasion, as the island is visited daily by fishermen and tourists, with no specific biosecurity measure.

9. Nosy Manitra and Nosimborona—West Coast

Nosy Manitra and Nosimborona are two sandy islands located off the coastal village of Androka, in the extreme southwest of Madagascar. Tern colonies have been recorded on the islands since 1948, when Milon (1948b) found a multispecies colony on Nosy Manitra including 4000 pairs of *Sterna dougallii*, 100 pairs of *Onychoprion anaethetus*, and 100 pairs of *O. fuscatus*. He also found a colony of 25 pairs of *Hydroprogne caspia* on Nosimborona and a few *Larus dominicanus* (Kelp Gulls), possibly breeding. On both islands, terns were heavily hunted and eggs harvested. Bemanaja visited Nosimborona in August and September 2006. He found an active colony of *O. fuscatus* (thousands of birds), *O. anaethetus* (thousands of birds), and *S. dougallii* (hundreds of birds) (Bemanaja 2006).

No complete counts were conducted during Bemanaja's 2006 visit because the colony was being actively harvested (both eggs and adults) by local people (Figure 13.13b). Interviews with hunters revealed that one or two buckets of eggs were collected daily (approximately 50 to 100 eggs per day), in addition to the take of 40 to 600 adults. Hunters attract the adult terns by mimicking their call and then striking the flying birds using a long wooden pole to which a shorter piece of wood is attached with a rope; the swinging, short piece of wood strikes the birds. We are not aware of any field visit since Bemanaja's survey in 2006. Both Milon's and Bemanaja's observations suggest a winter breeding regime of the terns on these two islands.

As almost no chicks are produced annually because of this very high level of harvest, it is surprising that there were still so many terns attempting to breed on Nosimborona in 2006, nearly 60 years after the discovery of the colony in 1948. It is possible that this colony is connected to others in the region by immigration, although this requires further investigation.

NONBREEDING SPECIES: REGULAR MIGRANTS AND VAGRANTS

At least 47 species of nonbreeding seabirds are known to occur in Madagascar's EEZ (Table 13.16). This portion of the contribution is a synthesis of available information on these nonbreeding species. Data come from opportunistic observations from the coast and ships, from beaching events and ringing recoveries (mostly from Langrand 1990; Langrand and Sinclair 1994; Safford and Hawkins 2013), from at-sea surveys conducted during oceanic research cruises (for example, Jaquemet et al. 2005, 2014), and more recently from tracking studies (see references in Table 13.16).

Forty-three percent of the nonbreeding seabirds observed in Madagascar's EEZ (20 species) originate from Antarctica or sub-Antarctic islands. These include albatrosses (Diomedeidae), petrels (Procellariidae), and skuas (Stercorariidae) that generally frequent Malagasy waters during the austral winter (their nonbreeding season) but remain far out at sea, in the southern part of the EEZ. Some species pass through the Madagascar EEZ while on their way to wintering areas in the northern and eastern Indian Ocean (e.g., southern skuas [Weimerskirch et al. 2015] and several species of storm-petrels). Many of these species are threatened. The main pressure is at sea, from incidental mortality (bycatch) caused by large-scale fisheries, particularly long-line fisheries (Dias et al. 2019).

A second group of migrant seabirds is composed of 11 species originating from other islands of the tropical western Indian Ocean. This set includes species that breed on Madagascar but visit in larger numbers from populations elsewhere in the region, such as *Ardenna pacifica*, *Phaethon rubricauda*, *P. lepturus*, and several species of terns. Others include the Critically Endangered *Pseudobulweria aterrima* (Mascarene Petrel) and the Endangered *Pterodroma baraui* (Barau's Petrel), both endemic to La Réunion. Three pelagic marine

TABLE 13.16. **Nonbreeding seabirds recorded in the EEZ (exclusive economic zone) of Madagascar**

ORIGIN	SPECIES	OCCURRENCE	TYPE OF DATA	SOURCES
SA-A	*Stercorarius maccormicki*, South Polar Skua	Regular migrant	Tracking data	16
SA-A	*S. antarcticus lonnbergi*, Brown Skua	Regular migrant	Tracking data	5, 6, 13
TNH	*S. pomarinus*, Pomarine Jaeger	Vagrant	Observations at sea	6, 13
TNH	*S. parasiticus*, Parasitic Jaeger	Vagrant	Observations at sea	6, 13
TNH	*S. longicaudus*, Long-tailed Jaeger	Regular migrant	Tracking data	1, 2, 13
NIO	*Ichthyaetus hemprichii*, Sooty Gull	Vagrant	One observation from coast	12, 13
TRO-WIO	*Anous tenuirostris*, Lesser Noddy	Regular migrant	Observations at sea and from coast	6, 7, 13
TRO-WIO	*Gygis alba*, White Tern	Occasional migrant	Observations at sea	13
NIO	*Sternula saundersi*, Saunders's Tern	Regular migrant	Observations at sea and from coast	6, 7, 13
Co	*Gelochelidon nilotica*, Gull-billed Tern	Vagrant	Observations at sea and from coast	8, 13
TRO-WIO	*Sterna sumatrana*, Black-naped Tern	Occasional migrant	Observations at sea and from coast	6, 8, 13
TNH	*S. hirundo*, Common Tern	Regular migrant	Observations at sea and from coast	6, 7, 8, 13
TNH	*Thalasseus sandvicensis*, Sandwich Tern	Vagrant	Observations at sea and from coast	6, 8, 13
NIO	*T. bengalensis*, Lesser Crested Tern	Abundant migrant	Observations at sea and from coast	6, 7, 13
NIO	*Phaethon aethereus*, Red-billed Tropicbird	Vagrant	Observations at sea, beaching	8
SA-A	*Thalassarche carteri*, Indian Yellow-nosed Albatross	Regular migrant	Observations at sea, tracking data	6, 8, 13
SA-A	*T. cauta steadi*, White-capped Albatross	Regular migrant	Observations at sea, tracking data	6, 8, 13
SA-A	*T. melanophris*, Black-browed Albatross	Regular migrant	Observations at sea, beaching	2, 6, 7, 13
SA-A	*Phoebetria fusca*, Sooty Albatross	Regular migrant	Tracking data	2, 5, 13
SA-A	*Diomedea exulans amsterdamensis*, Wandering Albatross	Regular migrant	Tracking data	2
SA-A	*D. exulans exulans*, Wandering Albatross	Regular migrant	Observations at sea and from coast, tracking data	2, 4, 7, 13
SA-A	*Oceanites oceanicus*, Wilson's Storm-petrel	Regular migrant	Observations at sea, beaching	6, 7, 13
SA-A	*Pelagodroma marina*, White-faced Storm-petrel	Occasional migrant	Observations at sea	6, 8, 13
SA-A	*Fregetta grallaria*, White-bellied Storm-petrel	Vagrant	Observations at sea	6, 8
SA-A	*F. tropica*, Black-bellied Storm-petrel	Regular migrant	Observations at sea, beaching	6, 7, 13
PO	*Oceanodroma monorhis*, Swinhoe's Storm-petrel	Regular migrant	Observations at sea	6, 7, 13

ORIGIN	SPECIES	OCCURRENCE	TYPE OF DATA	SOURCES
SA-A	*Macronectes giganteus*, Southern Giant-petrel	Regular migrant	Observations at sea, beaching, ringing recoveries, tracking data	2, 7, 13, 14
SA-A	*M. halli*, Northern Giant-petrel	Regular migrant	Observations at sea and from coast, tracking data	2, 7, 13, 14
SA-A	*Daption capense*, Cape Petrel	Regular migrant	Observations at sea, beaching	6, 7, 8, 13
SA-A	*Pterodroma macroptera*, Great-winged Petrel	Vagrant	Observations at sea and from coast	8, 13
TRO-WIO	*P. arminjoniana/neglecta/heraldica*, Trindade/Kermadec/Herald Petrel[1]	Occasional migrant	Observations at sea, tracking	2, 13
SA-A	*P. mollis*, Soft-plumaged Petrel	Regular migrant	Observations at sea	2, 6, 8, 13
TRO-WIO	*P. baraui*, Barau's Petrel	Regular visitor	Tracking data	2, 8, 10, 11, 13
SA-A	*Pachyptila desolata*, Antarctic Prion	Vagrant	Beaching	13
SA-A	*P. belcheri*, Slender-billed Prion	Vagrant	Observations at sea, beaching	7, 8, 13
PO	*Bulweria bulwerii*, Bulwer's Petrel	Regular migrant	Observations at sea	6, 13
NIO	*B. fallax*, Jouanin's Petrel	Regular migrant	Observations at sea	6, 8, 13
TRO-WIO	*Pseudobulweria aterrima*, Mascarene Petrel	Occasional migrant	Tracking data	15
SA-A	*Procellaria aequinoctialis*, White-chinned Petrel	Regular migrant	Tracking data	2, 4, 6, 9, 13
PO	*Calonectris leucomelas*, Streaked Shearwater	Vagrant	One observation at sea	13
TNH	*C. diomedea borealis*, Cory's Shearwater	Regular migrant	Tracking data	2, 3, 8, 13
SA-A	*Ardenna carneipes*, Flesh-footed Shearwater	Regular migrant	Observations at sea	6, 8, 13
TRO-WIO	*Puffinus bailloni*, Tropical Shearwater	Regular migrant	Observations at sea	6, 13
TRO-WIO	*Fregata ariel*, Lesser Frigatebird	Regular visitor	Observations from coast and at sea, tracking data	2, 6, 7, 13
TRO-WIO	*F. minor*, Great Frigatebird	Regular visitor	Observations from coast and at sea, tracking data	2, 6, 7, 13, 17
TRO-WIO	*Sula dactylatra*, Masked Booby	Vagrant	Observations at sea	6, 8, 13
TRO-WIO	*S. sula*, Red-footed Booby	Regular visitor	Observations at sea and from coast	6, 7, 13
S-Af	*Morus capensis*, Cape Gannet	Vagrant	Ringing recovery	13

Notes: Origin: Co, cosmopolitan; NIO, northern Indian Ocean; PO, Pacific Ocean, SA-A, sub-Antarctic islands and Antarctica; S-Af, South Africa; TNH, temperate Northern Hemisphere; TRO-WIO, tropical western Indian Ocean.

Occurrence is defined in terms of abundance or regularity of occurrence, followed by the type of movements bringing birds into Malagasy waters. Terms are defined as follows. Abundant: large numbers known to migrate to Malagasy waters. Regular: regular at-sea or coastal observations, or tracking data showing that birds frequent Malagasy waters regularly. Occasional: occasional at-sea or coastal observations, or tracking data showing that birds frequent Malagasy waters occasionally. Migrant: bird occurring in Malagasy waters (EEZ) during immature or post-breeding migration. Visitor: bird occurring in Malagasy waters during its foraging trips, while breeding elsewhere in the western Indian Ocean. The single term *Vagrant* refers to both irregular and rare observations, probably of a few birds wandering out of their main range.

Key to sources: 1. van Bemmelen et al. (2017); 2. BirdLife International (2020b); 3. Campioni et al. (2020); 4. Delord and Weimerskirch (2011); 5. Delord et al. (2018); 6. Jaquemet et al. (2014); 7. Langrand (1990); 8. Langrand and Sinclair (1994); 9. Péron et al. (2010); 10. Pinet et al. (2011); 11. Pinet et al. (2012); 12. Renoult (2009); 13. Safford and Hawkins (2013); 14. Thiers et al. (2014); 15. LIFE+Petrels (unpublished data); 16. Weimerskirch et al. (2015); 17. Weimerskirch et al. (2017).

[1] A mixed-species, hybridizing population of *Pterodroma* petrels breeds on Round Island, Mauritius, including these three species, with *P. arminjoniana* in the majority; individual birds have been tracked in Madagascar's EEZ, but placing these to species requires caution.

Important Bird and Biodiversity Areas (IBAs) for *P. baraui* have been identified from tracking data (Figure 13.12), two southeast of Toamasina and one south of Ambovombe; all three are important foraging sites for *P. baraui* during its breeding period (November to April). Both species are threatened by introduced predators at breeding colonies (Faulquier et al. 2009) and by mass mortality induced by light pollution (Le Corre et al. 2002, 2003b). At-sea threats are not as well quantified, but static lights at night (e.g., ships, at-sea platforms) are known to be an issue for gadfly petrels in general (Dias et al. 2019). We are not aware of any other threats at sea except plastic pollution (Cartraud et al. 2019), which is a concern for almost all species of petrels and albatrosses worldwide, although the population-level impacts are yet to be quantified. The other taxa in this category (*Fregata* spp., *Sula* spp., *Anous tenuirostris*, and *Puffinus bailloni* [Tropical Shearwater] being the most common) breed on Europa Atoll or Seychelles and forage regularly in the EEZ of Madagascar.

The third group of seabird migrants includes six species that breed in the Northern Hemisphere and migrate to the Southern Hemisphere, going mostly to the southeast Atlantic, but some individuals regularly venture into the Indian Ocean. This group includes in particular *Sterna hirundo* (Common Tern), *Stercorarius longicaudus* (Long-tailed Jaeger), and *Calonectris diomedea* (Cory's Shearwater, of the subspecies *borealis*, treated as a species by some authorities); for the latter species there is differential movement of females to the western Indian Ocean (Perez et al. 2014). After *Thalasseus bengalensis* (Lesser Crested Tern) (see below; Figure 13.14d), *S. hirundo* is the most common migrant tern in the coastal area of Madagascar. Most observations are made in areas of mangrove, and around sandbars and mudflats in the western part of the island. The birds often roost in mixed groups with *T. bergii*. Large numbers are regularly reported (e.g., 2000 birds at Mahavavy River estuary in 2009), and observations suggest that some birds (presumably first-year birds) stay on Madagascar through the austral winter, so the species is present year-round (e.g., Safford 1993).

The fourth group of migrants consists of four species that breed in the northern Indian Ocean and disperse southward during their post-breeding migration. One of these, *T. bengalensis*, is the most abundant migrant seabird in Malagasy waters, with flocks of several thousand seen regularly, especially on the west coast. The major roosting places for this species are Nosy Chesterfield, Baly Bay, Mahavavy Delta, Tsiribihina estuary, Tambohorano wetlands, the coastal granitic islet of Sainte Luce (Manafiafy), and Nosy Vé (Anakao), among others (Safford 1993; ZICOMA 1999; Rabarisoa 2003, 2006; Rabarisoa et al. 2006; Le Corre 2019; R. Rabarisoa, unpublished data). The last group comprises three species that breed in the Pacific Ocean and migrate regularly (*Bulweria bulwerii*, Bulwer's Petrel; and *Oceanodroma monorhis*, Swinhoe's Storm-petrel), or very exceptionally in the western Indian Ocean (*Calonectris leucomelas*, Streaked Shearwater). These remarkable movements are almost entirely unstudied.

IMPORTANCE OF MALAGASY SEABIRD POPULATIONS IN A REGIONAL CONTEXT

In this section we discuss the importance of Madagascar's islets, coastal habitats, and EEZ for breeding and nonbreeding seabirds in the regional context of the western Indian Ocean (as defined in the introduction). In Figure 13.15 we present for each breeding species the proportion of the seabird population of Madagascar compared to the total known populations of the western Indian Ocean. This highlights the fact that among the 11 seabird species that breed on Madagascar, seven are significant for the region, as they represent at least 10% of the known population of the western Indian Ocean. These species are *Larus dominicanus* (100% of the regional population), *Thalasseus bergii* (88%), *Hydroprogne caspia* (87%), *Sterna dougallii* (27%), *Onychoprion anaethetus* (23%), *Sula leucogaster* (22%), and *Phaethon rubricauda* (11%). For three of these, *P. rubricauda*, *T. bergii*, and *Sterna dougallii*, populations on Madagascar may be at least 5% of the global totals estimated by Croxall et al. (2012); for the other breeding species, Malagasy populations are around 1% or less of the global number. The section below focuses on each of these seven species in order of importance. The Malagasy populations of the other four breeding species represent less than 1% of the western Indian Ocean populations, and these are not discussed.

Larus dominicanus (Kelp Gull)

Madagascar holds the only known breeding population of *L. dominicanus* among the western Indian Ocean islands. Furthermore, the species is represented by an endemic subspecies (*L. d. melisandae*; Jiguet 2002; Jiguet et al. 2012). The other nearest breeding populations are in temperate South Africa (subspecies *L. d. vetula*) and in the sub-Antarctic islands (Kerguelen and Crozet, subspecies *L. d. judithae*; Jiguet et al. 2012). In Malagasy waters, this species is restricted to the southern portion of the island. It can be seen along the coast from Tolagnaro to Toliara (Safford 2013n), usually on rocky shores, islets, sandy beaches, and lakes, with the highest concentrations in the southeast around Tolagnaro and more scattered or rare observations in the southwest. Recent records include 81 birds in 2005 along the coastal area between Sainte Luce (Manafiafy) and the estuary of Lake Sarisambo in Tolagnaro (Rabarisoa 2006), and

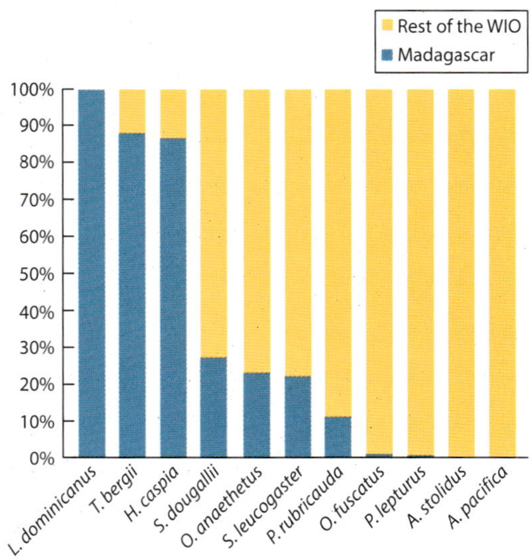

FIGURE 13.15 **Importance of the seabird populations of Madagascar in relation to other populations of the western Indian Ocean.**

17 birds at Lake Tsimanampesotse in 1998 (ZICOMA 1999). Along the southeastern coast, the northern limit is in the estuary of the Sandravinany River, about 120 km north of Tolagnaro (Rabarisoa 2007). The population of the locally occurring subspecies was estimated at fewer than 1000 individuals by F. A. Hawkins (Wetlands International 2006). Little is known about the breeding sites or population of this species on Madagascar.

Thalasseus bergii (Great Crested Tern)

Madagascar is very important for *T. bergii*, with breeding populations on at least five islands totaling 14,800 breeding pairs, 88% of the known population in the western Indian Ocean. All currently known colonies are around the northern tip of the island. Unlike other tern species breeding on Madagascar, *T. bergii* is now protected, resulting in little to no egg harvest or hunting, and the populations are probably increasing, although predation by introduced *Rattus rattus* remains a major problem on all islands. As in other parts of the world, *T. bergii* may change its breeding site from one year to another, making national population estimates difficult. Migration patterns are unknown, although the species is thought to disperse widely along the coasts of Madagascar and East Africa after breeding.

Hydroprogne caspia (Caspian Tern)

Hydroprogne caspia has a broad but patchy global distribution and is a rare breeding species in the western Indian Ocean. Unlike all other seabirds in the region, it is generally territorial and breeds solitarily or in small colonies. In the western Indian Ocean it breeds only on Madagascar, Europa, and Aldabra, typically on remote islets. There are six known breeding sites on Madagascar, with a recent total of 142 pairs, representing 87% of the western Indian Ocean population. It is likely that the species breeds on other remote islets that have yet to be surveyed. The largest colony of the species recorded in Madagascar and in the western Indian Ocean is that of Nosy Tsara (south of Oronjia), surveyed by Milon in 1947 (Milon 1950), although the current status of this colony is unknown. This tern is likely also threatened by egg harvest and poaching when it breeds in sympatry with other colonial tern species.

Sterna dougallii (Roseate Tern)

Sterna dougallii has an extremely broad distribution, breeding in Europe, North America, the Caribbean, eastern and southern Africa, Madagascar, Seychelles, Asia, and Australasia (Gochfield 1983). Kenya is the main stronghold for the species in the western Indian Ocean (Tree 2005), although Madagascar has some important breeding colonies. It has been found to breed on six islands in Madagascar, totaling 6700 pairs and representing 28% of the western Indian Ocean population. However, these figures should be interpreted with caution because the species frequently changes its breeding sites interannually. Furthermore, many of these colonies have not been surveyed recently and may have declined or completely disappeared; intense egg harvest and adult hunting is reported in four of the six known colonies. Thus, the species is at risk of local extirpation, and urgent actions are needed to control these threats.

Onychoprion anaethetus (Bridled Tern)

Onychoprion anaethetus is a tropical seabird with a very wide global distribution. In the western Indian Ocean, the main breeding locations are in Seychelles and Somalia, but four colonies have been recorded on Madagascar, totaling 1630 pairs (23% of the western Indian Ocean population). Three of the four Malagasy colonies are unprotected and are heavily exploited for eggs and poached animals. It is likely that some populations have declined or become locally extinct since they were last monitored. As for *S. dougallii*, there is an urgent need for effective seabird conservation to protect the last breeding colonies of this species on Madagascar.

Sula leucogaster (Brown Booby)

Sula leucogaster is a pantropical seabird generally feeding in inshore waters. It is relatively rare in the western Indian Ocean, with only five known colonies totaling 1115 pairs. The colony in the Nosy Mitsio archipelago, estimated to number around 250 pairs in 1979 and suspected to have increased since (ZICOMA 2001), is the second largest colony in the western Indian Ocean, after those of the Chagos archipelago (McGowan et al. 2008); its main breeding sites in the Nosy Mitsio archipelago are on inaccessible cliffs of a few rocky islets, affording the species some natural protection. The second largest Malagasy colony, on Nosy Kasinjy near Nosy Be, has never been properly surveyed, and its current status is unknown. New surveys around both Nosy Mitsio and Nosy Be are needed.

Phaethon rubricauda (Red-tailed Tropicbird)

Phaethon rubricauda is an Indo-Pacific tropical seabird. In the western Indian Ocean it breeds at nine sites, totaling more than 7000 pairs. The three largest colonies are on Round Island (Mauritius), Aldabra (Seychelles), and Europa (France). Round Island is an uninhabited island nature reserve (designated in 1957), with access restricted to authorized researchers and management staff, and lacking introduced mammals or poaching; the *P. rubricauda* population is increasing rapidly (V. Tatayah, unpublished data). On Aldabra and Europa, the species is heavily impacted by introduced *Rattus rattus*, which preys on eggs and unattended chicks. On these two islands the populations are declining rapidly. Nosy Vé is a relatively "new" population discovered in the early 1980s; after successful rat eradication and community-based conservation initiatives, the population of tropicbirds on Nosy Vé is increasing exponentially and the island may, like Round Island, become a major breeding colony for the species in the western Indian Ocean.

NONBREEDING SPECIES

Madagascar's coastal and oceanic habitats are very important for nonbreeding seabirds. There are several marine IBAs in Malagasy waters (Figure 13.12), most of them triggered by the presence of the endemic *Pterodroma baraui* of La Réunion. The southern EEZ of Madagascar is also very important because it has a series

of seamounts that attract seabirds (particularly from the Southern Ocean) and a range of large marine mammals (e.g., Le Corre et al. 2012; Fossette et al. 2014; Trudelle et al. 2016). When foraging at these seamounts, seabirds are in contact with industrial fisheries targeting tuna and swordfish (especially long-line fisheries). This represents a risk of bycatch, particularly for large petrels and albatrosses (Delord and Weimerskirch 2011).

Coastal habitats such as coral reefs, mudflats, sandbars, mangroves, estuaries, and islets are also very important for coastal migrant seabirds. This is particularly relevant for *Thalasseus bengalensis*, which probably originates from breeding colonies in the northern Indian Ocean or the Red Sea, although we are not aware of any band recoveries or tracking data. The proportion of the global population of *T. bengalensis* that winters on Madagascar is unknown but may be significant, as thousands are observed annually at numerous coastal sites.

CONCLUSIONS

Breeding seabirds on Madagascar are hunted or harvested at numerous breeding places, and the current diversity and population sizes presumably represent only a tiny fraction of what they could be, based on the number of available breeding and foraging sites. However, at a few localities, effective conservation projects, some of them community based, have led to rapid population recovery, showing the great potential for seabird conservation on Madagascar. Local communities benefit because seabird colonies are attractive for ecotourists, whose visits generate revenue. The case of Nosy Vé is remarkable and could be used as a regional model. However, numerous islands and islets have not been surveyed for several decades and others never have been, and few if any specific studies on the ecology of Malagasy breeding seabirds have been carried out.

Future seabird research and conservation on Madagascar should focus on updating population censuses and trends at seabird breeding sites, studying the species' ecology and breeding phenology, promoting awareness and education to gradually stop harvesting and hunting, and developing regulated, community-based seabird ecotourism including careful management of visitor numbers to avoid negative impacts on the birds.

For nonbreeding seabirds, studies are needed on the origin of the species that migrate to Madagascar, particularly *Thalasseus bengalensis*. This could be done through banding and tracking programs. Further studies should also focus on the importance of the seamounts south of Madagascar for the ecology and conservation of oceanic seabirds.

Subject editors: Roger J. Safford and Steven M. Goodman

ANATIDAE: *AYTHYA INNOTATA*, MADAGASCAR POCHARD, *ONJY, FOTSIMASO*

L.-A. Rene de Roland and H. G. Young

Aythya innotata (Madagascar Pochard) is endemic to Madagascar and belongs to a four-species clade of pochards, the "white-eyes," and while a relative occurs in Eurasia and Africa (*A. nyroca*, Ferruginous Duck) and has been recorded in Seychelles as a vagrant (Skerrett 1999), a molecular analysis suggests that the nearest relative is *A. australis* (Australian White-eye) (Livezey 1996; Sorenson and Fleischer 1996). All are diving ducks, with plumage largely in shades of dark mahogany brown, and they show moderate sexual dimorphism (Figure 13.16); the darker, brighter males have a pure white iris, which in the Madagascar species is attained in the first year (the pale iris becomes apparent before young males fledge at eight weeks old).

Aythya innotata has historically been considered almost exclusively restricted to Lake Alaotra and its environs (Wilmé 1994), and until 2006, records away from this relatively small area were rare (Collar and Stuart 1985; Wilmé 1994). Its rediscovery in 2006, when some authorities feared it extinct, was a momentous event, but it remains one of world's rarest birds and as such has been closely studied. Its status (including decline and rediscovery), biology, and conservation are reviewed here.

DISTRIBUTION AND REDISCOVERY

To date no subfossil material of *Aythya innotata* has been identified from Quaternary deposits on Madagascar, and no evidence can be mustered to understand the species' former distribution. Bone remains from the time of human arrival on La Réunion of an *Aythya* (Mourer-Chauviré et al. 1999) may represent dispersal events or the presence on this island of another, closely related, species. *Aythya innotata* was once quite common at Lake Alaotra (Webb 1936; Delacour 1966) and has never been recorded in large numbers anywhere else. However, it was last positively observed there in a free-living state in 1960 (Collar and Stuart 1985), despite several extensive searches in the area in the 1980s and 1990s (Young and Smith 1989; Wilmé 1994; Pidgeon 1996; Young and Kear 2006). Although reported in 1970 near Antananarivo (Salvan 1970), the species was not seen reliably anywhere after 1960 until a male was unexpectedly captured alive by a local trapper at Lake Alaotra in 1991 (Wilmé 1993)—perhaps a bird dispersing from the Bemanevika area (see below).

FIGURE 13.16 ***Aythya innotata* (Madagascar Pochard): A) adult male; B) adult female; and C) adult female with chick.** (PHOTOS by L.-A. Rene de Roland.)

Aythya innotata was considered extinct in 2006 by some authorities (Young and Kear 2006), until its rediscovery later the same year (Rene de Roland et al. 2007). The species formerly did well in captivity in Europe following export of live birds captured at Lake Alaotra during the Mission Zoologique Franco-Anglo-Américaine to Madagascar between 1929 and 1931 (Delacour 1932; Webb 1936), breeding in several collections (Delacour 1947), but only one bird, a male in the United Kingdom, survived the Second World War (Delacour 1947, 1959; P. Scott 1947).

In November 2006, *A. innotata* was rediscovered in the northwest of the island, specifically in the Sofia Region at Lake Matsaborimena, one of four small volcanic lakes (the others being Lakes Andriakanala, Matsaborimaitso, and Maramaratsalegy) at around 1650 m elevation in a forested area (Rene de Roland et al. 2007) that would become the Bemanevika protected area in 2015. The site is in the southern foothills of the Tsaratanàna Massif, 350 km north of Lake Alaotra.

The decline of *A. innotata* may have been ongoing since first human colonization of Madagascar (Young and Kear 2006), following extensive degradation and loss of wetlands throughout the Central Highlands (Woolaver et al. 2015). This species' rapid disappearance at Lake Alaotra, from being "common" in the 1930s to the last sighting in 1960, may have directly followed the introduction of carp (*Cyprinus*, Cyprinidae; see Sparks and Stiassny, pp. 1245–60) to Lake Alaotra between 1900 and 1926, and various cichlid fish (Cichlidae) between 1955 and 1960. These herbivorous fishes altered the floral structure of the lake and competed with waterbirds for food resources. Carp may have increased lake turbidity, making it difficult for diving waterbirds to find food (Woolaver et al. 2015).

Further, carnivorous fish (*Micropterus* and *Channa*; see Sparks and Stiassny, pp. 1245–60) have also been introduced to Alaotra; this took place after the pochard's presumed local extirpation but may prevent its recolonization at any lake where these fish are present (Young and Kear 2006).

At the time of its rediscovery in November 2006, nine adults and four young were noted, and 16 individuals were counted in January 2007 (Rene de Roland et al. 2007). From January 2010 to December 2012 simultaneous counts were undertaken across the four lakes, with the largest counts each year being 29 birds in 2010 (16 males and 13 females); 29 in 2011 (15 males and 14 females); and 21 in 2012 (13 males and nine females) (Bamford et al. 2015). From July to November, pochards were seen almost exclusively on Matsaborimena, with the largest counts always from this lake, except in March–April each year when Andriakanala had equal or larger numbers. Matsaborimaitso occasionally had small numbers (maximum of five). Pochards have never been seen on Maramaratsalegy. Counts across the lakes have continued and 64 were reported in December 2019 (The Peregrine Fund, unpublished data). Only Matsaborimena, with its limited marsh in one area, is used as a breeding site by pochards, although they will forage at Matsaborimaitso and Andriakanala.

SOCIAL BEHAVIOR AND FEEDING ECOLOGY

Aythya innotata has never been known to form flocks (congregations of unrelated conspecifics); pairs and families stay within quiet, well-vegetated areas of marsh, often among water lilies and other emergent vegetation (Young and Kear 2006). However, occasionally, mainly after the breeding season, *A. innotata* has been observed in mixed-species groups with *Anas melleri* (Meller's Duck), *A. erythrorhyncha* (Red-billed Duck), and *Tachybaptus pelzelnii* (Madagascar Grebe).

Food is obtained principally by diving, with individual dives lasting around 20–25 sec (longer in deeper water) (Bamford et al. 2015), and diving periods interspersed with inactive (loafing) periods of around 22 min (The Peregrine Fund, unpublished data). Stable isotope analysis of feathers and potential food items and examination of fecal samples provide evidence that adult pochards are insectivorous, favoring caddis fly (Trichoptera) larvae (Bamford et al. 2015).

BREEDING

Breeding of *Aythya innotata* was studied at Matsaborimena during the two breeding seasons in 2007 and 2008. During nest construction, the pair always stays together close to the nest territory, with

the female, who builds the nest, close to the nest during the day. She may go out to approach the male many times during this period, particularly when the male is aggressive to other males close to their nest territory. Based on genetic analysis of ducklings hatched from three clutches collected in 2009 (see below), each clutch had mixed parentage from several different males and females, highlighting parasitic egg laying (females laying in nests of others; e.g., Sorenson 1991) and possibly extra-pair mating, previously unrecorded in any species of *Aythya* (e.g., Anderson 1984). Hence, the three clutches collected in 2009 show contributions from more than six adults (three pairs), making genetic variation in captive populations greater than might have been expected.

In 2007, 14 nests were monitored among the 16 observed. Nests were placed 111 ± 98 cm (n = 12 nests) from the water's edge, and 30 ± 10 cm (n = 12 nests) above the water; nest diameter was 19 ± 3 cm (n = 12 nests). The number of eggs varied from seven to 11 per nest, with an average of 8.8 ± 1.1 eggs (n = 16 nests). Mean egg measurements from two nests were 51.6 ± 1.9 × 39.7 ± 1 mm, with a weight of 48.7 ± 3.7 g (n = 18 eggs).

There is no obvious breeding season, and birds may nest and rear young from May until February (Woolaver et al. 2015). Incubation was studied in September and October 2007–2008, and during 366 h of observation the female incubated 78% of the time (287 h) and was absent from the nest 22% of the time (79 h) for foraging (Sam 2011). Males never incubate the eggs but defend the territory from other males. The incubation period has been recorded as 25–27 days in the wild and 24–28 days in captivity (Woolaver et al. 2015). In 2007–2008, eight of 11 nests produced ducklings, but two nests were attacked by a predator (see next section), and one with eggs was abandoned (Sam 2011). From the first or second day after hatching, young follow the female on the lake.

SURVIVAL OF POCHARDS AND THREATS AT BEMANEVIKA

Nest success of *Aythya innotata* at Matsaborimena (76% in 2007–2008) and hatching success (89% in 2007–2008) are comparable to those of other *Aythya* species (Kear 2005), but fledging success (4% in 2011–2012) is extremely low. Duckling mortality rates peak between 14 and 21 days old, and starvation appears to be the major cause.

Macroinvertebrate density in the benthos of Matsaborimena is low, particularly in chironomid (Diptera: Chironomidae) larvae, an important food outside Madagascar for *A. fuligula* ducklings (Giles 1990); density at Matsaborimena of less than 500 m^2 is four times lower than energetic requirements of *A. fuligula* ducklings (Bamford et al. 2015). Similarly, poor macroinvertebrate levels were recorded at other selected Madagascar wetlands (Bamford and Razafindrajao 2012).

Water depths in the crater lakes at Bemanevika seem to present challenges to *A. innotata*, particularly ducklings, in finding enough food. Maximum water depths of the three lakes where this species has been recorded were 2.8 m at Matsaborimena, 14 m at Matsaborimaitso, and >80 m at Andriakanala (Bamford et al. 2015). The lakes are steep sided and Matsaborimena has a surface area of 36 ha, of which about 35.5 ha is >1.0 m deep, leaving only a very small area shallower than 1 m, and most of this is covered with emergent vegetation. Andriakanala was mostly too deep to measure, except for one bay that slopes from the shore to 40 m deep and contains a 0.5 ha area of submerged macrophytes at depths ranging from 1 to 5 m; this is the only lake with this type of vegetation. *Aythya innotata* was observed feeding in this shallow part of Andriakanala. Pochard ducklings cannot dive as deep as adults, reflected in shorter dive times, and even adult pochards stayed in the shallower parts of Matsaborimena when foraging. Ducklings were generally not observed diving until two weeks old, before which they fed at the surface. This switch in foraging method has been observed in other *Aythya* species and may occur because surface feeding no longer meets ducklings' energetic requirements (Hill and Ellis 1984). The depth of Matsaborimena may mean that two-week-old chicks cannot meet energy requirements by diving either, perhaps explaining the peak in mortality at between 14 and 21 days old (Bamford et al. 2015).

Bamford et al. (2015) concluded that these lakes are not good breeding habitat for *A. innotata*, and the species' persistence here and not elsewhere in its historical range is more owing to a lack of the human-induced habitat degradation impacting other wetlands on Madagascar. There are no fish, native or introduced, in the lakes. In the Bemanevika protected area, threats to pochards include the presence of *Circus macrosceles* (Madagascar Harrier), which can catch the young above the lake surface during the day (a whole brood was seen taken in October 2009), while other raptors and owls at the site may also be a threat. During nest monitoring in 2007, an introduced *Rattus* individual followed a trail from the forest edge to a nest and destroyed the eggs. A single *Crocodylus niloticus* (Nile Crocodile) of unexplained origin was known at Matsaborimena from 2006 until its disappearance in 2017, although the increase in pochard numbers after this date is possibly coincidental.

CONSERVATION

After the rediscovery of *Aythya innotata* in 2006, the Durrell Wildlife Conservation Trust, Wildfowl & Wetlands Trust, The Peregrine Fund, Asity Madagascar (conservation nongovernmental organizations [NGOs]), and the regional and national governments worked rapidly in close partnership to conserve the Madagascar Pochard. A collaborative project, Miaro Ny Fotsimaso (Saving the Madagascar Pochard) was established by a signed memorandum of understanding between the partners in 2008.

The wild *A. innotata* population at Lake Matsaborimena was provided protected status within the Bemanevika protected area in 2015: this protected area, totaling 35,605 ha, includes the lakes themselves (150 ha) and associated marshes (611 ha); the rest is moist evergreen forests and grasslands (Goodman et al. 2018). The lakes were designated by the Malagasy government as a Ramsar site in 2017 (Complexe des Zones Humides de Bemanevika). This protection does not include direct management of the pochard.

A captive population was established at a breeding center in Antsohihy (the closest city with governmental offices) in 2009, with 24 ducklings hatched from eggs collected at Lake Matsaborimena to establish a safety-net population, and a plan to release captive-bred birds in restored wetlands in the future. A Species Action Plan Workshop in 2013 brought together stakeholders from local

communities at Bemanevika, Lake Sofia (the site of a release program), the government, and local and international conservation NGOs in Antananarivo to develop a strategy for long-term restoration of this species. The Species Action Plan 2014–2024, the first IUCN plan for a Malagasy endemic bird, was published in 2015 (Woolaver et al. 2015).

The population's first captive-bred duckling hatched in 2011, the 100th in 2018, and by 2020 there were 117 ducks in captivity. The first steps to reestablishing a self-sustaining population in the wild, beyond the site where the species was rediscovered in 2006, were undertaken in 2018 when 21 captive-bred ducklings (11 males, 10 females) were released at 8–12 weeks old (fledging is typically at 8 weeks old; Young 2013) at Lake Sofia after four years of work with local communities, which was supported by a grant from the UK government's Darwin Initiative. The released birds receive supplementary food and are monitored throughout the year by local technicians. Unexpectedly, two females bred late in 2019 at just over 12 months of age. Eight ducklings successfully fledged in 2020. Further releases of captive-bred birds will be undertaken at this site in late 2020.

The captive-breeding centers are staffed entirely by Malagasy personnel including aviculturists, veterinarians, logistical support, and administration. Field staff at Bemanevika and Lake Sofia are all Malagasy. Training has been undertaken both on Madagascar and elsewhere by the Durrell Wildlife Conservation Trust and the Wildfowl & Wetlands Trust. Certain Durrell and Peregrine Fund Madagascar staff members have gone on to earn higher degrees (one a PhD) on the pochard, its decline, and restoration requirements (Sam 2011; Razafindrajao 2020).

Her Royal Highness The Princess Royal, Princess Anne (of the United Kingdom), and the former president of Madagascar, Hery Rajaonarimampianina, opened a second captive facility, also in Antsohihy, in 2017. This second center allows access to Malagasy visitors, local schools, and tourists and, with permanent signage and full-time educators, has the educational role of explaining the importance of wetlands and biodiversity to both local communities. Tourists are charged a small fee to visit the second center, and these funds are disbursed to Bemanevika village.

Subject editors: Roger J. Safford and Steven M. Goodman

MESITORNITHIDAE, MESITES

A. F. A. Hawkins, N. Seddon, and J. A. Tobias

Mesites are an ancient and strange group of birds endemic to Madagascar. According to the most recent systematic analyses based on molecular studies, they are considered a separate order, the Mesitornithiformes (Jarvis et al. 2014; Prum et al. 2015). The Mesitornithiformes form part of a clade including cuckoos, bustards, turacos, pigeons, and sandgrouse, the latter forming the sister group to the mesites. Estimated divergence times of the Mesitornithidae from sister groups differ between the two studies cited above, but they are over 50 million years. The same studies also identified the Cuckoo-roller (genus *Leptosomus*) as the sole member of another endemic order, the Leptosomiformes, with a similar divergence time.

The Mesitornithiformes consist of three extant species in two genera. They are terrestrial birds, in appearance a strange mix of rail, dove, and quail; hence their vernacular and scientific names, which come from the Greek for an intermediary or go-between. They have relatively long, wide tails, which they habitually flick upward while moving, short or medium-length legs, small heads, and soft, easily detached feathers. The predominant colors are browns, dull reds, and white. They search for food in the leaf litter, flicking leaves over or digging shallow pits in the substrate. For the most part, they subsist on invertebrates and small vertebrates such as lizards and chameleons, with a variable amount of seeds and small fruit depending on the season. They nest in shrubs 1–3 m above the ground, building a thin nest of twigs and laying one to three eggs (Evans et al. 1996). The downy young are speckled brownish and precocial (Safford 2013o). All three species are very strictly forest limited, rarely straying far outside primary or relatively intact forest vegetation.

SPECIES, DISTRIBUTION, AND BREEDING

The three extant species of Mesitornithidae are *Mesitornis variegatus* (White-breasted Mesite, *agolinala* or *tolohon'ala*), *M. unicolor* (Brown Mesite, *roatelo*), and *Monias benschi* (Subdesert Mesite, *naka*) (Figure 13.17). In their structure, colors, and habits, these three species are similar to one another, although *M. benschi* is classified in a separate genus because of its longer, more decurved bill, longer legs, and variation between the sexes in plumage coloration (dichromatism) (see Figures 13.17c and d). Genetic analyses found substantial molecular divergence between the two genera (Prum et al. 2015). The distributions of each of the three species are effectively limited to one of the three main forested regions of Madagascar: eastern, western, and southern. Quaternary subfossil remains recovered from a cave in northwestern Madagascar have been assigned to *Monias* sp. (Burney et al. 1997), which is far outside the modern range of this genus.

FIGURE 13.17 **Images of the three species of mesites. A) *Mesitornis variegatus* (White-breasted Mesite); B) *M. unicolor* (Brown Mesite); and C) male and D) female *Monias benschi* (Subdesert Mesite).** (PHOTOS by K. Behrens.)

Mesitornis unicolor is a resident of low and medium-altitude (0–1500 m) moist evergreen forests of the east, being widespread from the protected areas of Marojejy in the north to Andohahela in the south (A. Hawkins and Goodman 1999), but its density is often low and the species is difficult to find. It is mostly rufous brown, with a strange and variable white squiggle behind the eye, variable pinkish or whitish on the breast and head, and grayish on the crown. The legs and bill are grayish. Nesting is restricted to the rainy season, when platform nests made of twigs and lined with grass are constructed in the forks of sloping trees 1–2 m above the ground. The two nests that have been found contained single, relatively large eggs with a whitish ground and brownish spots (Evans et al. 1996).

Mesitornis variegatus is found in at least eight discrete forest areas in the north and west of Madagascar and at one site in the moist evergreen forests of the east. In the west, it is known from protected areas with dry deciduous forests, including Menabe Antimena, Ankarafantsika along with Ampijoroa, and nearby Bongolava (A. Hawkins 1994a, 2013a); in the northwest and north, it is in protected areas with dry deciduous and moist semi-deciduous forests, including Manongarivo (Raherilalao et al. 2002), Ankarana, Analamerana (A. Hawkins 1994a), Andrafiamena Andavakoera (A. Hawkins 2013a), and Loky Manambato (Daraina) (Evans et al. 1996); and in the east it is in the moist evergreen forests of Ambatovaky (Thompson and Evans 1992). A further report of the species in Betampona, also in the lowlands of the east, awaits full documentation. The records in the east are extremely surprising in that *M. unicolor* also occurs in the same area, which is primary lowland moist evergreen forest and very dissimilar to the western dry deciduous forest inhabited by *M. variegatus* elsewhere. This species is dark rufous brown above, grayer on the mantle, and darker on the crown, with a striking white supercilium and blue-gray orbital skin, a white breast variably marked with black crescents, and a narrow rufous breast band. The breast band is wider and more intense in the populations in the Menabe forests (A.F.A. Hawkins, unpublished data). Nesting is known from October to April, and two or three off-white eggs are laid in a nest composed of a few twigs laid across a clump of dead vegetation, 1–3 m up in the understory.

Monias benschi is endemic to an area of dry spiny thicket in the southwest, between the Fiherenana and Mangoky Rivers. It is found within this distinctly dry area in a range of habitats, including low-canopy spiny thicket on sand, coastal *Euphorbia* scrub, and degraded and intermediate forms of these thicket types. This bird is strongly sexually dichromatic, unlike the other two species. Males

are medium brown above, grayer on the crown, with a long white supercilium, and whitish underparts marked with irregular black crescents. Females are similar but have dense reddish blotches on the upper breast and flanks. Both sexes have longish decurved bills, reddish at the base, and red legs that are longer than those of the other two species. They can actively pursue large invertebrate prey items but mainly probe in the leaf litter and dig in the sand. Nesting occurs throughout the year, with groups producing no more than two clutches of one or two eggs annually. Eggs have a cream-colored ground, finely and evenly speckled medium to warm brown. Nests comprise loosely woven twigs forming a cup about 15 × 12 cm wide and 12 cm deep that is usually positioned around 1.5 m above the ground. Common nesting trees include *Securinega perrieri*, *Commiphora simplicifolia*, and *Euphorbia stenoclada*.

SOCIAL BEHAVIOR

In contrast to *Mesitornis variegatus* and *M. unicolor*, which live in pairs or small family groups (two to four, or rarely five in *M. variegatus*), *Monias benschi* resides in groups usually comprising four or five birds but occasionally containing as many as nine adults. While there are no available data on the size and configuration of *Mesitornis unicolor* territories, *M. variegatus* is known to inhabit stable, overlapping territories of 2–15 ha (A. Hawkins 1994a); territories are about 25% larger during the nonbreeding season, with greater overlap with neighboring territories (Gamero et al. 2013). Radio-tracking of several groups of *Monias benschi* at a site 32 km north of Toliara revealed that they inhabit larger, non-overlapping, multipurpose territories, the area of which (6–18 ha) does not appear to be related to the overall size of a given group, although it is correlated with the number of males in the group. As in members of the genus *Mesitornis*, this species maintains permanent territories that appear to be tightly packed, and the habitat is saturated with birds (Seddon et al. 2003).

Little is known about the breeding systems of the two *Mesitornis* species, although both are socially monogamous (Table 13.17). *Mesitornis variegatus* does not breed cooperatively; juveniles stay with adults for extended periods (up to 13 months) after fledging and are cared for by both adults, which in almost all cases are the parents (Gamero et al. 2013). A three-year investigation into the social behavior of *Monias benschi* revealed that it has a highly variable but essentially cooperative breeding system. In common with many other cooperatively breeding birds, there seems to be much variation in social organization, and a preliminary molecular examination of kinship hinted that this species has a flexible mating system. There was evidence of genetic monogamy and polygynandry, where groups had multiple male and female breeders and related helpers (Seddon et al. 2005). A male sex ratio bias was also recorded in the populations studied and may relate to slightly higher levels of dispersal and hence mortality in females. All group members appear to cooperate in the raising of offspring. Both males and females incubate, and all but the juvenile members of the group contribute to this activity. As in *Mesitornis variegatus*, males appear to carry out almost all the nocturnal incubation and seem to be the principal defenders of the precocial chicks. Interestingly, breeding in *Monias benschi* does not appear to be tied to rainfall, and reproduction occurs throughout the year, chicks having been recorded in the driest seasons (Seddon et al. 2003). This species differs in this respect not only from the other two mesites, in which breeding is limited to the rainy season, but also from all other bird species with which it shares the dry spiny thicket habitat. This suggests that *M. benschi* is able to either access a nonseasonal food resource or shift its diet and is therefore able to circumvent constraints usually imposed on breeding in the dry season.

The differences in the social systems adopted by the three mesite species may relate to fundamental differences in the structure and/or productivity of their respective habitats, factors that in turn influence dispersal. *Mesitornis variegatus* may have adopted a family-living but noncooperative breeding strategy owing to the costs to the parents of sustaining juveniles over long periods, leading to aggression toward last year's juveniles at the start of the breeding season. *M. variegatus* juveniles that learn foraging skills more slowly tend to stay with adults for longer periods, indicating the benefit

TABLE 13.17. **Summary of key differences and similarities in the basic ecology and breeding behavior of the three mesite species**

	MONIAS BENSCHI	*MESITORNIS VARIEGATUS*	*MESITORNIS UNICOLOR*
Main habitat	Open-canopy dry spiny thickets and coastal scrub	Closed-canopy dry deciduous and moist evergreen forests	Closed-canopy moist evergreen forests
Foraging mode	Digs in sand	Gleans in leaf litter	Gleans in leaf litter
Territories	6–18 ha, stable	2–15 ha, stable	Unknown
Breeding	Year-round	Rainy season only	Rainy season only
Clutch size	1–2	1–2 (3)	1– (?)
Group size	2–9	2–4 (5)	2
Social system	Multi-male, multi-female groups	Pairs plus recent offspring	Pairs plus recent offspring
Mating system	Variable	Monogamy*	Monogamy*
Sex differences	Dichromatic	Monomorphic	Monomorphic

* No genetic study has been carried out.

of extended parental care in this species (Gamero and Kappeler 2015a). Group cohesion in *M. variegatus* is linked to predator detection and vigilance, not to mate guarding, possibly limiting extra-pair copulation opportunities (Gamero and Kappeler 2015b). Lower levels of dispersal in *Monias benschi* are likely related to incentives to remain in or join a group, such as improved foraging efficiency in a habitat in which food is scarce or difficult to access. Alternatively, group living could provide protection from predators through vigilance or dilution effects in a semi-open habitat where there is minimal cover from arboreal or aerial predators. Such ecological constraints are likely to have played an important role in the evolution and maintenance of group living in this species (Seddon et al. 2005).

COMMUNICATION

Vocal communication plays a crucial role in the social systems of all three mesite species. For nonpasserines, they have relatively varied repertoires that include sex-specific songs and precisely synchronized duets. Duets in *Mesitornis variegatus* appear to be initiated by males and are thought to function primarily in territory defense (A. Hawkins 1994a). In *Monias benschi*, females initiate most duets, and these songs seem to serve multiple functions (Figure 13.18). Although these vocalizations are commonly used in territorial contexts, observational evidence and playback experiments carried out in 1998 suggested that they may also allow pairs and group members to maintain contact in a habitat where visibility is often impeded by dense understory (Seddon 2002).

Monias benschi also gives choruses involving up to five birds singing simultaneously and antiphonally with varying degrees of temporal precision. Playback experiments indicated that communal songs may allow groups to assess the number of individuals in intruding groups and hence their relative resource-holding potential. Specifically, the number of singing intruders significantly influenced the strength of response, with groups producing less aggressive but more collective responses to playback as the number of intruders increased. Groups appeared to modify their agonistic responses in relation to both their adult sex ratio and the number of males in their own group relative to the number of males in the intruding group. This discovery provided the first indication in birds of numerical assessment based on vocal cues (Seddon 2002; Seddon and Tobias 2003). Anecdotal observations indicate that these choruses may additionally function in inter- and/or intra-sexual assessment within groups and may be used in the establishment and maintenance of dominance hierarchies. Further fieldwork is required to investigate these ideas in more depth.

CONSERVATION

All three mesite species have been classified as Vulnerable based on their narrow geographic ranges and small, declining populations (BirdLife International 2020a). *Mesitornis unicolor* occurs over a relatively wide area but seems to be patchy in distribution and often very scarce. Eastern lowland moist evergreen forests, where this species occurs most commonly, are under extreme threat; relatively few protected areas have significant examples of this forest type that are not being rapidly degraded (Goodman et al. 2018). *Mesitornis variegatus* occurs in at least nine discrete areas, in between which are large zones of presumed suitable habitat that are apparently uninhabited by this species, for instance in Bemaraha. The Menabe population was estimated at 3000–19,000 individuals and that of Ankarafantsika at 6000–26,000 individuals in the early 1990s (A. Hawkins 1994a). Insufficient details are known about the other populations to estimate size, but few probably harbor more than a few hundred individuals. Densities and productivity are low in degraded habitats and areas near human habitation, the latter probably related to hunting pressure and predation by dogs (A. Hawkins 1994c). Recent intensive clearance of forest in the Menabe and Ankarafantsika forest areas (Zinner et al. 2014; Goodman et al. 2018) has undoubtedly had a major impact on the populations of *M. variegatus* in those areas.

FIGURE 13.18 **Group vocalizations play a vital role in the ecology of *Monias benschi*. Resident birds produce loud choruses during territorial disputes with neighbors and when establishing relationships within their own group. Two resident males are depicted here singing in synchrony with a perched resident female.** (ILLUSTRATED by R. Johnson, February 2001.)

Monias benschi has the smallest range of the three species, being confined to the Mikea Forest: a coastal strip 30–60 km wide and 200 km long between the Fiherenana and Mangoky Rivers. Within this small area, this species was once considered "extremely local" (Rand 1936). However, surveys throughout the Mikea Forest in late 1999 revealed it to be widespread and common. It occurs in a variety of habitat types from low-stature, open scrub within a kilometer of the coast to higher-stature, relatively closed-canopy dry forest 60 km inland. These surveys indicated that the total population of *M. benschi* lies in the region of 115,000 individuals (Tobias and Seddon 2002). Thus, this species would appear to far outnumber at least *Mesitornis variegatus*, which has been estimated to have a population of fewer than 50,000 (A. Hawkins 1994a). However, various factors indicate that, despite being relatively numerous, *Monias benschi* still warrants conservation concern (Seddon et al. 2000). Forest clearance continues across southwestern Madagascar (Vieilledent et al. 2018), and the creation of a protected area in the Mikea region does not seem to have reduced this. The main factors underlying deforestation in the Mikea are swidden maize cultivation in the north and charcoal production in the south, both of which have led to rapid rates of forest loss (Seddon et al. 2000). This alarming situation has prompted an initiative to protect the Mikea Forest, which also harbors a diverse assemblage of plants and reptiles, as well as the only population of another threatened bird species, *Uratelornis chimaera* (Long-tailed Ground-roller), which is estimated to number fewer than 15,000 individuals (Seddon and Tobias 2007).

Subject editors: Roger J. Safford and Steven M. Goodman

GRUIFORMES: SAROTHRURIDAE AND RALLIDAE, RAILS

R. J. Safford

CLASSIFICATION AND ENDEMISM

This contribution introduces the Malagasy members of the order Gruiformes. Until recently, this would have included the mesites (family Mesitornithidae), which are now recognized to form a separate and unrelated order (see A. Hawkins et al., pp. 1653–57), and *Turnix nigricollis* (Madagascar Buttonquail), which (along with the whole family Turnicidae) is now recognized to belong in the order Charadriiformes. This leaves only the birds generally referred to in English as rails, in the order Gruiformes, which on Madagascar includes two families: Sarothruridae, with four species in two genera (see below for an explanation of this relatively novel arrangement), and Rallidae, with eight species in six genera (see Table 13.1).

Thus, we immediately encounter an arrangement unsuspected 15 or more years ago, when all rails were placed in the single family Rallidae. Molecular studies unexpectedly found a deep phylogenetic split between the *Sarothrura* flufftails and the other rails, with the former found to be sister taxa to the very distinct finfoots of the family Heliornithidae (Prum et al. 2015). Acceptance that heliornithids should remain in their own family forced the recognition of the "new" family Sarothruridae for the flufftails, the remaining seven species of which are restricted to mainland Africa.

A further surprise was that *Mentocrex kioloides* (Madagascar Wood-rail) was grouped with the flufftails, while all other rails sampled worldwide remained in the Rallidae *sensu stricto* (García-R et al. 2014). A final clarification is needed, as García-R et al. (2014) placed *kioloides* as congeneric with the West African *Canirallus oculeus* (Gray-throated Rail), which they did not sample. Morphological and molecular evidence (Boast et al. 2019; Mayr 2019) now indicates that *C. oculeus* belongs in the true Rallidae, while *Mentocrex* is a Malagasy endemic genus in the Sarothruridae, not related to *Canirallus*.

The exclusively African and Malagasy distribution of the 11 species and two genera so far placed in the Sarothruridae is evident from the above; the true Rallidae comprise around 131 species in 31 genera worldwide. The only extinct "rail" species from Madagascar, *Hovacrex roberti* (see Safford et al., pp. 1553–602), known from bones, is in an endemic genus that is osteologically similar to a large gallinule and is probably a member of the Rallidae. Uncertainty attaches to the classification of *Sarothrura watersi* (Slender-billed Flufftail), which has several unusual features for *Sarothrura*, and an endemic genus, *Lemurolimnas*, has been proposed for it (Salomonsen 1934b; Penhallurick 2003); further study is needed to confirm the appropriate genus and family.

Of eight genera accepted here in the two families, two—*Mentocrex* and the extinct *Hovacrex*—are endemic to Madagascar, and a third, *Dryolimnas*, is restricted to the Malagasy Region. Such diversity at the genus level links to multiple colonization events of the island, involving at least four of the eight clades of the world's Rallidae (García-R et al. 2014). If valid, and whatever family it belongs to, *Lemurolimnas* would be another endemic genus. Six of the 12 species are endemic to Madagascar, and a seventh to the region (*Dryolimnas*), as is one distinctive endemic subspecies (*Gallinula chloropus pyrrorrhoa*, Common Moorhen).

GENERAL CHARACTERS

Members of both families are small to medium-size birds, with unspectacular but often attractive plumage, and sexes are often similar.

They may appear plump and slightly chicken-like in general shape, but their bodies are often narrow, helping them slip through dense vegetation; the wings are rounded, tail short, bill variable (long and slender to short and thick), legs fairly long, and toes usually long and slender. The downy young of nearly all species are black.

Generic morphological characters of members of the Sarothruridae that distinguish them from the Rallidae have not been identified, except for a morphological character of the hypotarsus bone (Mayr 2019). Overall, flufftails look remarkably like some small forest rails of the Asia-Pacific and Neotropical regions, while *Mentocrex* could, without molecular and skeletal evidence, still pass for an unremarkable, medium-size rallid.

Rails and flufftails are typically associated with marshes, particularly freshwater, but various species also use saltwater habitats, open water, the floor of forest and woodland (dry and moist evergreen), and secondary grassland and bushland. Most are omnivorous. A paradox concerns their apparently poor powers of flight, set against their evident success at colonizing islands rather distant from other land areas, including continents and islands in the western Indian Ocean. In this context, they demonstrate astonishing vagrancy; for example, *Porphyrio alleni* (Allen's Gallinule), which breeds only in mainland Africa and on Madagascar, has reached, among other places, the islands of Rodrigues, Ascension, St. Helena, and South Georgia. They are often notoriously difficult to see in their thickly vegetated habitat and prefer to walk or run away rather than fly but may be tame when eventually found. They swim well when the need arises and can also climb up vegetation. They are strongly vocal, with a wide repertoire, and so are often located by their voices.

SAROTHRURIDAE, FLUFFTAILS AND MALAGASY WOOD-RAILS

Sarothrura insularis (Madagascar Flufftail) is endemic to Madagascar, where it is widely distributed in the east and center, from sea level to high massifs such as Tsaratanàna, Marojejy, and Andringitra. It seems to be absent from the dry west and far northeast, although in the far north it is found in the mesic areas of Montagne d'Ambre, Daraina, and the Sambirano Region. It occurs in a wide range of degraded and intact habitats, both wet and dry: secondary brush, grassland at forest edges, forest clearings, and herbaceous marshes (Rand 1936; Keith 1973), and occasionally moist evergreen forests (Goodman et al. 1997c), usually but not exclusively close to the forest edge. They are often common, but very secretive and reluctant to leave thick vegetation, so that observers may get within meters or centimeters without seeing the bird. The usual sign of the bird is its song: one or two short trilled notes followed by several loud double notes, then a long series of single notes, accelerating and decreasing in pitch, becoming faint toward the end and almost insect-like; one rendition is *so-bir-ey biry biry bir bir ...* (Rand 1936), explaining the most common Malagasy name, *biry biry*. The whole sequence may run to 20–200 notes, and calling birds often set off their neighbors (Safford 2013p).

The diet is not well known but consists of insects and small seeds; gravel may also be ingested (Benson et al. 1976). No displays have been reported. The nest is a domed structure with a small side entrance, loosely assembled or woven of dried grass or similar plant fibers, and built on the ground, above the ground in a tussock, or up to 1.6 m up in bamboo vines in grassy fields or marshes (Rand 1936; Benson et al. 1976; Rene de Roland 2004). In the few observations to date of nest building, the female did most, but the male remained nearby and brought some material. Up to four milk-white eggs (the brown color sometimes noted is staining) are laid between September and March.

In contrast to the often abundant *S. insularis*, *S. watersi* (Slender-billed Flufftail) is rare. This species is restricted to herbaceous wetlands dominated by grasses (Poaceae) and sedges (Cyperaceae) in the highland areas of eastern Madagascar. Such habitat is widely distributed in (mostly) small patches over a broad forest zone, but this species has to date been found only between the Tsaratanàna and Andringitra Massifs at 900–1800 m (Safford 2013p). Few occupied sites are known, although many conceivably suitable sites remain unchecked; all are in forested regions, although the bird does not live in the forest itself. It is classified as Endangered on the IUCN Red List (BirdLife International 2020a) because its population is believed to be very small, fragmented, and declining as a result of the continuing exploitation of its habitat, mostly conversion to rice agriculture. The call is completely unlike that of *S. insularis*: simple sequences of medium- to low-pitched knocking or croaking sounds, given singly (repeated rapidly) or as doublets or triplets (Wilmé and Langrand 1990). The breeding habits and diet are essentially unknown.

Mentocrex kioloides is much larger than the flufftails, weighing around six times more. It is widespread and often common in the moist evergreen forests, from the Sambirano Region and Tsaratanàna Massif to the far southeast and from sea level to nearly 2000 m elevation, although most records come from below 1000 m. The typical call is a distinctive, long sequence of penetrating whistles lasting up to 30 seconds, sometimes longer. *Mentocrex kioloides* is a ground-dwelling moist evergreen forest bird, especially in undisturbed habitat, but it is also found in slightly degraded, contiguous second growth. Like most other birds with such habits, it can be elusive, although with patience it may reveal itself to be quite bold. Very little information on breeding exists; the nest has been reported to be a simple cup of fine grass stems, ferns, and tree leaves, built in a bush or among lianas 2–3 m above the ground (Milne Edwards and Grandidier 1879–1885; Milon et al. 1973), in which pale gray eggs with red and reddish-brown speckles are laid. However, in view of apparent confusion over the eggs of this and other, related species (Rabenandrasana and Safford 2013), both the nest and egg descriptions would be worth confirming.

The presence of a distinct-looking *Mentocrex* in a quite different area and habitat—dry deciduous forest on limestone karst or *tsingy* (see Bardot-Vaucoulon and Gautier, pp. 492–99) in central western Madagascar—had been known for some years before the birds concerned were formally recognized as a new species, *M. beankaensis* (Tsingy Wood-rail) (Goodman et al. 2011). Compared to the commoner species, it differs particularly in the much more extensive cinnamon rufous (and correspondingly less gray) on the head and neck, as well as in certain measurements (Figure 13.19); molecular analysis supports the distinction. Most of the range is the Bemaraha Massif, although the type locality is the nearby Beanka Massif, just to the north, the origin of the species name. Although the rugged terrain is to some extent a deterrent to forest conversion, the range is restricted

FIGURE 13.19 **About a decade ago a species of rail, *Mentocrex beankaensis* (Tsingy Wood-rail), was described as new to science. This species is known only from *tsingy* areas, specifically at Bemaraha, where this photo was taken, and at Beanka.** (PHOTO by K. Behrens.)

and the population likely to be declining, resulting in Near Threatened status on the Red List. Ramasinatrehina and Raherilalao (2013) found the species to be a locally common ground feeder taking invertebrates and seeds, but breeding habits remain unknown.

RALLIDAE, RAILS, CRAKES, GALLINULES, MOORHENS, AND COOTS

Rallus madagascariensis (Madagascar Rail) is a "classical" rallid, very reminiscent of members of the same genus in Africa, Eurasia, and the Americas: a medium-size secretive inhabitant of thick herbaceous vegetation of marshes and wetlands, typically dominated by grasses and sedges, where it is seldom seen but fairly often heard. It is restricted to, but widespread in, eastern Madagascar but is absent in the extensive reedbeds of the west. Despite its wide range, it is threatened by destruction and modification of its habitat. The breeding habits are almost unknown.

Dryolimnas cuvieri (White-throated Rail), also known as Cuvier's Rail, is by contrast a relatively bold and conspicuous species, as well as a notably robust one, surviving in disturbed wetlands even in urban areas, its presence announced by powerful whistling calls. Its main range is Madagascar and its offshore islands, but birds have reached Mayotte and Mauritius, seemingly as vagrants, and have colonized the Aldabra archipelago (with resulting loss of flying ability, but surviving on Aldabra Atoll itself as the subspecies, or species, *D. c. aldabranus*). Ancestors also colonized both Mauritius and La Réunion, resulting in an endemic species on each, both now extinct (Hume 2019). On Madagascar and its islands, White-throated Rails are widespread in a wide range of mainly wet habitats from sea level to the highest mountains; as well as typical natural and seminatural freshwater wetland types, these include rice paddies, and saline wetlands with vegetation cover including mangroves. In line with this catholic choice of habitats, they are adaptable in their feeding habits, wading, probing, picking animal prey from dry land, or grabbing larger items opportunistically; on Aldabra, where detailed studies have taken place, a range of vertebrates and invertebrates small and large, including crabs, are taken, and captive rails killed a *Rattus rattus* (Black Rat) that entered their enclosure (Wanless 2003; Wanless and Safford 2013). The nest is a bowl built on the ground in vegetation, the eggs off-white with maroon-brown speckling; otherwise the breeding biology on Madagascar is not well known.

Two small marshland species, formerly thought to be only distantly related, are now considered part of a widespread lineage of Old World rails (García-R et al. 2014) and placed in recent checklists in the same genus, *Zapornia*. *Zapornia olivieri* (Sakalava Rail) was until 2002 a very rarely recorded endemic species, strikingly unlike its abundant and presumed close relative *Z. flavirostra* (Black Crake) of Africa. However, since then it has been regularly found at a small number of freshwater sites in the west between Lakes Kinkony and Mandrozo, with an earlier record as far south as the lower Mangoky River. These records and associated studies (Rabenandrasana et al. 2009; Pruvot et al. 2017) have shown that this is indeed a rare bird, dependent on dense, flooded stands of reeds (*Phragmites mauritianus*) with other floating vegetation, in which it feeds on mainly small invertebrates. Like Madagascar's other rare rail, the Slender-billed Flufftail, it is treated as Endangered on the Red List, its habitats severely threatened by widespread and rapid degradation and conversion. The general habits are very typical of marshland rails, except for a remarkable tameness, often to the surprise of observers aware of the earlier decades with no sightings of the species. The nest is a simple platform in the marsh vegetation and the eggs are creamy white, freckled with reddish brown on grayish lilac.

The five remaining species are widespread in Africa and in some cases beyond. Malagasy information on all is summarized here from Safford (2013p). *Zapornia pusilla* (Baillon's Crake) is a widespread resident on Madagascar but, being another "classical," rarely observed marshland rail, is poorly known there; for example, its voice on the island is undocumented. However, its habits, as far as is known, do not differ from those elsewhere in its African range.

The large *Porphyrio madagascariensis* (African Swamphen) and the smaller but similarly colored *P. alleni* are widespread and often numerous in herbaceous freshwater marshes dominated by reeds (*Phragmites*), sedges (Cyperaceae), and bullrushes (*Typha*), and on lakeshores of the western lowlands; they are present but scarcer in the east below 800 m elevation. *Porphyrio madagascariensis*, despite its scientific name, also occurs in Egypt and sub-Saharan Africa. *Porphyrio alleni* is otherwise found only in Africa, although its movements, as discussed above, deserve much greater study. The elephantine trumpeting of the bold and conspicuous *P. madagascariensis* can be a characteristic sound of Malagasy wetlands, while *P. alleni* is far less obtrusive, foraging more often on floating aquatic plants with discreet and inconspicuous movements, in keeping with general shyness.

Gallinula chloropus (Common Moorhen) is an almost cosmopolitan species, but the birds on Madagascar (race *G. c. pyrrorrhoa*) are distinctive, having buff undertail coverts (not white as in all other races); whatever their color, these form a striking feature used in signaling conspecifics, as the birds flick their tails up frequently. Similar birds occur on Mauritius, La Réunion, and the Comoros. On Madagascar they are widespread, but generally not abundant, in a wide range of wetland habitats, primarily inland fresh waters with stretches of open water. Larger open-water habitats may be used by *Fulica cristata* (Red-knobbed Coot), another African and Malagasy species, but in this case without known geographic variation. It has been widely recorded on Madagascar up to 1500 m but is very localized, and absent from many localities that appear suitable based on habitats used in Africa; the largest numbers have been recorded in the west and south.

Subject editor: Steven M. Goodman

CHARADRIIDAE: *CHARADRIUS*, PLOVERS

S. Zefania and T. Székely

Madagascar has four resident breeding species of *Charadrius* plovers: *C. pecuarius* (Kittlitz's Plover), *C. thoracicus* (Madagascar Plover), *C. marginatus* (White-fronted Plover), and *C. tricollaris* (Three-banded Plover). After the pioneering observations of Otto Appert (Appert 1971), over the past decade the first three species have been the subject of focused fieldwork in the southwest (Andavadoaka in the Mikea region and Tsimanampesotse south of Anakao) and northwest (Namakia and Marambitsy Bays), as they inhabit many of the same coastal sites and habitats. This information is reviewed herein; *C. tricollaris* is ecologically rather distinct, and a short account based largely on other studies is added for completeness.

CHARADRIUS PECUARIUS, KITTLITZ'S PLOVER, *VOROMBATO*

Charadrius pecuarius is common and distributed broadly across much of the African continent and on Madagascar (Figure 13.20a). On the island, it can be found in a variety of aquatic habitats (Zefania and Székely 2013a), especially open wetland fringe habitats such as salt pans, along rivers, areas with short grass, rice fields, and mudflats. This species usually occurs in natural wetlands, although it can tolerate human-related activities such as salt extraction and livestock grazing.

Plumage and Body Size

Although *C. pecuarius* was previously considered sexually monomorphic (Zefania et al. 2010), the authors' own closer observations of many breeding birds have revealed slight sexual dimorphism in the black-and-white head markings and brightness of the belly color, these being, respectively, more sharply marked and rufous brown in females (Zefania and Székely 2013a, with further details from the authors' unpublished data). Plumage of the young is similar to that of adults, but without black bars on the head and no brown or rufous on the breast or belly. Downy chicks are generally brown with some white on the underparts.

In a field study involving measurements of 64 *C. pecuarius* individuals (30 male and 34 female, sexed using molecular techniques), no sexual size dimorphism in external measurements was found (Zefania et al. 2010; Zefania and Székely 2013a). The mean body mass of adult females was 34.4 g (range 27.3–42.0 g, n = 545) and of adult males was 33.1 g (range 27.8–40.6 g, n = 658); mean bill length of adult females was 16.5 mm (range 12.6–19.9 mm, n = 509) and of adult males was 16.5 mm (range 14.0–20.0 mm, n = 614); and mean tarsus length of adult females was 31.4 mm (range 27.2–35.5 mm, n = 529) and of adult males was 31.7 mm (range 26.5–37.0 mm, n = 645).

Distribution

On Madagascar, *C. pecuarius* occurs mainly in coastal and inland lowland areas but has been recorded up to 1400 m (Zefania and Székely 2013a). It is more common along the western and southern coasts than in other areas of the island. Open salt marsh habitats of the west constitute an important breeding habitat. At a local scale, its distribution can be influenced by rainfall, which provides standing water and presumably increased prey abundance. This species often nests close to the water's edge. The largest breeding populations found to date have been near Andavadoaka (2010 to 2019),

FIGURE 13.20 **Images of three of the four resident breeding species of *Charadrius* plovers on Madagascar. A) *Charadrius pecuarius* (Kittlitz's Plover) at Andavadoaka, presumed adult female based on the extensive white forehead and the relatively sharply defined black bands across the fore-crown and from the lore to behind the eye; B) *C. thoracicus* (Madagascar Plover) at Andavadoaka, presumed adult female based on the same sexual distinguishing marks as for A; and C) *C. marginatus* (White-fronted Plover) at Andavadoaka, presumed adult male based on the extensive black fore-crown and cap reaching above the eye and the extensive black ear coverts.** (PHOTOS A and B by K.-Y. Leong, and C by J. M. Tafitasoa.)

with a minimum of 100 to 300 individuals per breeding season, and Lake Tsimanampesotse (2004 to 2012), with a minimum of 50 to 70 individuals per breeding season (S. Zefania et al., unpublished data).

Food

No information on the diet of this species is available from Madagascar, but elsewhere in its range it is an animalivore, gleaning insects and other invertebrates off the ground in salt marshes, mudflats, and open grasslands (Zefania and Székely 2013a). On low-tide mudflats they probably consume a range of small invertebrates.

Breeding Ecology

Breeding period and laying dates: Breeding appears to peak during the rainy season, the timing of which varies between sites. In drought years, breeding activities are notably reduced or even absent. The number of nests per site is positively correlated with the amount of rainfall. For example, near Andavadoaka, breeding was recorded from February to June and from October to November (and egg laying noted in February, March, April, October, and November), with a wet season peak in March to April; at Tsimanampesotse the birds bred from January to July (egg laying in February to April); but around Namakia and Marambitsy Bay (Mahavavy Kinkony protected area) they did so from September to October. Evidently, breeding is not synchronized across the range, as is also shown by a nest with eggs in November, and a flightless chick in February, both in the lower Mangoky region (Appert 1971). The period between the first and second egg-laying dates was 2–4 days (mean 3.0 days, n = 17 nests).

Nest and eggs: The nest is a small scrape dug into dry soil and surrounded by vegetation and other materials (Zefania and Székely 2013a). When the incubating parent leaves the nest, it typically covers the eggs with loose soil by quick movements of its feet,

presumably to protect the eggs from predators and solar radiation (S. Zefania and T. Székely, unpublished data).

Mean egg length at Andavadoaka was 30.8 mm (range 27.3–34.6 mm, n = 1028) and width 21.6 mm (range 20.0–24.8 mm, n = 1597). Clutch size was typically two eggs (Zefania and Székely 2013a), with a mean of 1.9 ± 0.36 (n = 1019 nests). Out of 1019 examined nests, 151 had one egg and 868 had two eggs. One-egg clutches may be the result of partial predation.

Incubation and chick-rearing periods: Incubation usually commenced some days after the second egg laying and lasted between 22 and 28 days (mean 25 ± 2 days, n = 17 nests). Chick rearing lasted approximately four weeks.

Nesting Success and Survival of Young and Adults

In general, this species has low nesting success, and the main cause of nest failure is predation. For instance, at Andavadoaka, out of 883 nests followed, 27.5% produced at least one chick, and, based on inference or direct observation, the 72.5% losses were caused by predation (58.7%), abandonment (11.8%), flooding (0.1%), trampling (1.5%), or infertile eggs (0.5%) (S. Zefania and T. Székely, unpublished data). Predation was assumed to have occurred if the eggs disappeared before the expected hatching date or the banded parents were found without chicks on or just after the expected hatching date. Hence, high nest predation appears to be the limiting aspect in breeding success.

Chick survival is low, and out of 194 chicks monitored at Andavadoaka, 5.7% survived to near the fledgling stage at about 25 days of age, or a body mass of 20 g or more. Survival rates varied among sites and breeding seasons. For adults, maximum known survival is nine years, based on one adult female first captured and marked at Andavadoaka in 2009 and recaptured in 2017 (S. Zefania and T. Szekely, unpublished data). Nest and chick predators include *Corvus albus* (Pied Crow), *Felis silvestris* (Wild Cat), and *Falco newtoni* (Madagascar Kestrel).

Behavioral Ecology

Courtship and mating system: The mating system of this species can be pieced together from different observations and summarized as largely polygamous with male-only parental care (Parra 2014; Maher et al. 2017). Male adults provide brood care more often than females, which would imply polygamy (Eberhart-Phillips et al. 2018). Based on molecular testing, not a single brood out of 15 tested showed evidence of extra-pair parentage (Maher et al. 2017). There was no case of more than two adults being associated with a given nest. Changes of partners were found interannually: out of 26 pairs monitored at Andavadoaka, 62% changed partner once or twice between years and the remaining pairs did not change.

Nest and brood care: There is a cycle followed by the two attending adults. Based on passive integrated transponder (PIT) tags placed at five nests (four in 2015 and one in 2019), females incubated mostly during the day and males during the night, particularly from 22h until dawn (S. Zefania and T. Székely, unpublished data), similar to other plover species (Vincze et al. 2013). In some cases, the male took over from the female during the hot period of the day between 9h and 15h. In general, incubation was particularly intense between 10h and 15h (Vincze et al. 2017) to shade the eggs, and during the cold period, between 16h and 9h, to keep the eggs warm. Recorded images from 40 nests showed that at the beginning of the nesting period the female of the pair spent more time incubating (80%) than the male (20%); female participation then decreased progressively during the incubating period as compared to that of the male, which increased until the eggs hatched.

Male-biased brood care is common in *C. pecuarius* (Eberhart-Philips et al. 2018). Broods in this species, based on over 705 followed pairs and their broods at Andavadoaka, were cared for by the male in 83.1% of pairs/broods, and by the female in the rest (S. Zefania and T. Székely, unpublished data); biparental care of chicks has not been observed in this species (Parra 2014).

Movements and Dispersal

Marked *C. pecuarius* individuals were found to make local movements of a maximum of 15 km between study sites and years. However, this species almost certainly disperses over greater distances; the Madagascar population shows homogeneous genetic structure (Eberhart-Philips et al. 2015; J. Jackson et al. 2017), which would support broad dispersal patterns and facilitate gene flow through extensive social interactions (Cunningham et al. 2018). During the nonbreeding period this species occurs in groups, which forage in various wetland habitats.

Threats and Conservation

Charadrius pecuarius has a wide range and large population and uses a variety of habitats; on the IUCN Red List it is considered Least Concern (BirdLife International 2020a). Low breeding success appears to be an important factor limiting its population dynamics on Madagascar. This species shows a low prevalence of *Plasmodium* infection, with one (female) of 58 examined individuals infected by this blood parasite (Martínez-de la Puente et al. 2017).

CHARADRIUS THORACICUS, MADAGASCAR PLOVER, *VOROMBATO*

This species is endemic to Madagascar and its distribution is limited to the coastal area of the west (P. Long et al. 2008; Zefania et al. 2008) (Figure 13.20b). It breeds mainly in natural wetland habitats, ranging from open salt marshes to areas of short grassland or sandy beaches with some vegetation. It can tolerate some human activities such as fishing and salt extraction and often occurs close to footpaths.

Plumage and Body Size

Like *C. pecuarius*, breeding *C. thoracicus* was previously considered sexually monomorphic in plumage coloration (Zefania et al. 2010; Zefania and Székely 2013b), but we have subsequently found sexual differences, with the female showing sharper definition of the black-and-white crown and forehead patterns (S. Zefania et al., unpublished

data). Plumage of young birds lacks the black head band of adults, and the breast band is present but grayish brown. Downy chicks are generally pale brown on the back and white on the underside.

This species shows slight but significant (not discernible in the field; hence "cryptic") sexual size dimorphism in external measurements, females being heavier and longer winged than males, whereas males have longer tarsi (Zefania et al. 2010; Zefania and Székely 2013b). For birds sexed using molecular techniques, the mean body mass of adult females was 37.5 g (range 28.0–44.7 g, n = 349) and of adult males was 36.1 g (range 29.8–42.2 g, n = 287); mean bill length of adult females was 16.6 mm (range 15.0–19.2 mm, n = 276) and of adult males was 16.4 mm (range 14.5–19.3 mm, n = 238); mean tarsus length of adult females was 32.8 mm (range 28.9–38.4 mm, n = 346) and of adult males was 33.1 mm (range 29.5–36.5 mm, n = 282; and mean wing length of adult females was 109.5 mm (range 100–119 mm, n = 344) and of adult males was 108.5 (range 102–114 mm, n = 282).

Distribution, Habitat, and Population

Charadrius thoracicus is endemic to Madagascar and restricted largely to the western and southern coastal band, from just north of Mahajanga to the region around Tolagnaro. There are older records of this species in the eastern portion of the island and in the Central Highlands, the latter being particularly unusual and perhaps best explained by cyclone-caused vagrancy (Zefania and Székely 2013b). It occurs in sympatry with *C. pecuarius* in both foraging and breeding sites, particularly open salt marshes, as well as areas of open short grassland and sandy beach. As with *C. pecuarius*, the local distribution can shift as a function of rainfall patterns and associated distribution of water.

Breeding takes place in open grasslands and dry mudflats around mangroves and alkaline lakes, only rarely on sandy soil (Zefania and Székely 2013b), and generally close to the water's edge. The largest breeding populations known are near Andavadoaka (monitored between 2010 and 2019), with a minimum of 100 to 150 individuals per breeding season, and Lake Tsimanampesotse (2004 to 2012), with a minimum of 50 to 100 individuals per breeding season (S. Zefania et al., unpublished data). Based on predictive habitat modeling and population density estimation, P. Long et al. (2008) proposed a global population estimate of 3100 ± 396 (SE) individuals.

Food

No detailed data are available, but the species is presumed to be an animalivore, gleaning insects and other invertebrates off the ground in salt marshes, mudflats, and open grasslands (Zefania and Székely 2013b). On mudflats exposed at low tide, they probably consume a range of small invertebrates.

Breeding Ecology

Breeding period and laying dates: Breeding often but not always takes place during the rainy season and is often correlated with the start of rains (Zefania and Székely 2013b), but there is much inter-site variation across the island. Near Andavadoaka, birds breed during two periods from February to June, with a peak from March to April (recorded egg-laying dates from February to May) but also from October to December; at Tsimanampesotse, they breed from October to June (recorded egg-laying dates from December to April); and in the northwest around Marambitsy Bay, from April to May and November to December (with egg laying also recorded in August). The period between the first and second egg-laying dates was 3–4 days at four nests (mean 3.5 days). During the nonbreeding period, this species occurs in groups, foraging together in wetland habitats, often with other *Charadrius* species.

Nest and eggs: The nest is a small scrape dug into dry soil with both vegetation and other materials (Zefania and Székely 2013b). In a similar way to *C. pecuarius*, the incubating parent covers the nest when leaving it by movements of its feet (S. Zefania and T. Székely, unpublished data).

Mean egg length at Andavadoaka was 32.2 mm (range 27.7–35.6 mm, n = 927) and width 22.9 mm (range 20.2–25.6 mm, n = 925). From our sample of 895 nests, the modal clutch size was two eggs (Zefania and Székely 2013b), with a mean of 1.9 ± 0.36; 134 had one egg and 761 had two eggs. One-egg clutches might be the result of partial predation.

Incubation and chick-rearing periods: Egg incubation usually commenced some days after the second egg was laid, and the incubation period was between 28 and 32 days (mean 29 ± 1 days, n = 14 nests). The chick-rearing period was approximately four weeks.

Nesting Success and Survival of Young and Adults

Charadrius thoracicus has relatively low nesting success, and the main cause of nest failure is predation. For instance, at Tsimanampesotse, out of 270 nests followed, only 37.0% produced at least one chick, and based on inference or direct observation, the remaining 63.9% were lost to predation (37.4%), abandoned (10.7%), flooded (11.5%), trampled (1.3%), or had infertile eggs (3.0%) (S. Zefania and T. Székely, unpublished data). Chick survival is also low, and out of 390 chicks monitored at Andavadoaka, only 18.7% survived to near the fledgling stage at about 20 days of age or a body mass of 23.7 g or greater. There were slight differences in the survival rate among sites and breeding seasons. For adults, apparent annual survival rates were 80% determined using data from 176 banded adults from 2004 and 2007. Maximum known survival is 11 years, based on an adult male captured and marked at Andavadoaka for the first time in 2009 and recaptured 10 years later (S. Zefania and T. Szekely, unpublished data). Nest and chick predators are probably similar to those of *C. pecuarius*.

Behavioral Ecology

Courtship and mating system: Few details are known about the mating system of this species, but it is considered monogamous with biparental care (Zefania et al. 2008; Maher et al. 2017). Monogamy is suggested by both individuals of a pair providing nest and brood care (Eberhart-Phillips et al. 2018). Further, based on molecular testing, extra-pair paternity is rare, as not one out of 12 broods analyzed had young sired by another male (Maher et al. 2017). No example of more than two adults associated with a nest

was found. Changes of partners were found interannually: out of 72 pairs monitored at Andavadoaka, 56% changed partner once or twice between years.

Nest and brood care: Both adults take part in nest care, with females taking charge during the day (6h to 21h) and males from after dark to dawn (21h to 6h) (Vincze et al. 2013; S. Zefania and T. Székely, unpublished data). In some cases, the male took over during the hot period of the day between 9h and 15h. The function of nest incubation appeared to be to shade the eggs during the hottest period, mainly between 10h and 15h (Vincze et al. 2017), and to keep them warm during the cold period, between 16h and 9h. Based on recorded images from 18 nests, at the beginning of the nesting period the female spent more time incubating (80%) than the male (20%), but her participation decreased progressively as the male's increased, to 60% by the female and 40% by the male at the end of the incubation period.

Biparental brood care is common in *C. thoracicus* (Zefania and Székely 2013b; Eberhart-Philips et al. 2018): at Andavadoaka, in 83% of families (n = 464 nests), broods were cared for by both adults, while at Tsimanampesotse the corresponding figure was 69% (n = 363 nests) (S. Zefania and T. Székely, unpublished data). Male-only brood attendance increased with chick age (Parra 2014).

Movement and Dispersal

Adults seem to be largely sedentary. Marked *C. thoracicus* showed local movements of a maximum of 15 km between study sites and years. For juveniles, there is evidence of wider dispersal: an individual banded at Tsimanampesotse in March 2007 was found four months later at Ifaty, a distance of 100 km; another banded at Andavadoaka in April 2019 was located four months later near Morondava, a distance of about 250 km. Because adults are sedentary, their populations are poorly interconnected, resulting in a strong or heterogenetic population structure (Eberhart-Philips et al. 2015; J. Jackson et al. 2017).

Threats and Conservation

Charadrius thoracicus is classified as Vulnerable on the IUCN Red List (BirdLife International 2020a) based on its localized population, which is thought to be undergoing a continuous decline owing to pressures on its wetland habitats (see also Young et al., pp. 1627–36). Low breeding success appears to be the main population-limiting factor for this endemic species. It showed no evidence of *Plasmodium* infection in the 55 examined individuals (Martínez-de la Puente et al. 2017). A portion of the habitats and sites this species uses for feeding and breeding occur in the current protected area system, but additional inclusion of salt marshes in the network is still recommended.

CHARADRIUS MARGINATUS, WHITE-FRONTED PLOVER, *VOROMBATO*

Charadrius marginatus occurs (as three subspecies) in many coastal areas of Africa, as well as patchily inland; it is also found quite widely on Madagascar (*C. m. tenellus*), but as in Africa the main breeding zone is along the coast (Zefania and Székely 2013c). There are also observations of this species from Mayotte in the Comoros, but no evidence of breeding.

Plumage and Body Size

Breeding *C. marginatus* was thought to be sexually monomorphic (Zefania and Székely 2013c), but as with the previous two species, closer investigation has shown that the sexes can be differentiated based on plumage, with differences in crown, nape, and forehead patterns, as well as pigmentation patterns of the underside (Figure 13.20c). The plumage of the young differs from that of the adults in the poorly defined black band on the forehead and other markings on the head, subdued coloration on the nape, and white underside. Downy chicks generally have very pale plumage compared to congeners.

This species also shows low-level but significant (i.e., "cryptic") sexual size dimorphism in external measurements, females being slightly longer winged than males (Zefania et al. 2010; Zefania and Székely 2013c). For birds sexed using molecular techniques, the mean body mass of adult females was 37.1 g (range 30.5–42.5 g, n = 252) and of adult males was 36.0 g (range 26.5–45.5 g, n = 209); mean bill length of adult females was 14.9 mm (range 12.4–17.3 mm, n = 218) and of adult males was 15.0 mm (range 13.4–17.8 mm, n = 185); mean tarsus length of adult females was 26.3 mm (range 22.8–31.5 mm, n = 240) and of adult males was 26.7 mm (range 24.2–31.0 mm, n = 193); mean wing length of adult females was 105.6 mm (range 98–113 mm, n = 251) and of adult males was 105.3 (range 100–114 mm, n = 209).

Distribution and Habitat

On Madagascar, this species occurs mainly along the western and southern coastal zone, from Analalava to Tolagnaro (Zefania and Székely 2013c). The principal utilized habitats are open wetlands, including salt pans, sandy beaches, mudflats at low tide, and salt marshes, where it occurs in sympatry with *C. pecuarius* and *C. thoracicus*. Inland, most records are on wide, sandy rivers (Appert 1971). It usually occurs in natural wetland habitats but can tolerate some human activities such as salt extraction and cattle grazing.

The local distribution of *C. marginatus* can shift as a function of rainfall patterns and the associated amount of water, particularly in open salt marsh habitat. The breeding zones appear to be broadly distributed along the west coast but tend to be concentrated in salt marshes close to the water's edge. The largest breeding populations known are near Andavadoaka (monitored between 2010 and 2019), with a minimum of 50 to 100 individuals per breeding season, and Lake Tsimanampesotse (2004 to 2012), with a minimum of 30 to 50 individuals per breeding season (S. Zefania et al., unpublished data).

Food

A few data are available from Madagascar, including four stomachs containing marine crustaceans as well as fine stones (Goodman et al. 1997a). Field observations confirm an animalivorous diet, gleaning insects and other invertebrates, including crabs and other

crustaceans, from the ground in salt marshes, mudflats, and open grasslands (Zefania and Székely 2013c).

Breeding Ecology

Breeding period and laying dates: The breeding period in this species seems not to be highly seasonal; breeding takes place in both the rainy and dry periods and spans all months of the year. For example, near Andavadoaka nesting activities have been documented from February to November, with a peak between March and May (observed egg-laying dates recorded from February to May, and in November); at Tsimanampesotse breeding is from January to May (observed egg-laying dates recorded from January to April); and around Namakia and Marambitsy Bays from April to December. The time between the first and second egg laying was 2–5 days at three nests (mean 3.0 days) and between the second and third egg was 1–5 days at five nests (mean 3.0 days).

Nest and eggs: The nest is a small scrape dug into dry soil without cover or at most a few stones or seashell fragments (Zefania and Székely 2013c); unlike with *C. pecuarius* and *C. thoracicus*, when the incubating parent leaves the nest, it typically does not cover the eggs (S. Zefania and T. Székely, unpublished data).

Mean egg length at Andavadoaka was 30.7 mm (range 24.4–35.8 mm, n = 1377) and width 21.9 mm (range 19.0–24.9 mm, n = 1373). Modal clutch size was two eggs (Zefania and Székely 2013c), with a mean of 1.99 ± 0.61 (n = 832 nests). Out of 832 nests, 156 had one egg, 524 had two eggs, and 151 had three eggs; of the three species studied, only *C. marginatus* had some three-egg clutches. One-egg clutches might be the result of partial predation.

Incubation and chick-rearing period: Egg incubation usually commenced some days after the laying of the last egg in the clutch, and the incubation period was between 22 and 30 days (mean 27 ± 4 days, n = 6 nests). The chick-rearing period lasted approximately four weeks.

Nesting Success and Survival of Young and Adults

Like its relatives, *C. marginatus* has low nesting success, and the main cause of nest failure is predation. For instance, at Andavadoaka, out of 373 nests followed, 28.7% produced at least one chick; the rest were lost to predation (61.4%), abandoned (5.9%), flooded (2.1%), trampled (1.9%), or had infertile eggs (0.2%) (S. Zefania and T. Székely, unpublished data).

Chick survival is also low: out of 108 chicks monitored at Andavadoaka, 33.3% survived to near the fledgling stage at about 20 days of age or a body mass greater than 21 g; 8.3% of chicks reached the age of 25 days. There were differences in survival rate between sites and breeding seasons. Maximum known survival is 11 years, based on an adult male captured and marked at Andavadoaka for the first time in 2009 and recaptured in 2019 (S. Zefania and T. Szekely, unpublished data).

Behavioral Ecology

Courtship and mating system: The mating system of *C. marginatus* can be pieced together from different observations and summarized as monogamous and dominated by biparental nest and brood care (Parra 2014; Eberhart-Phillips et al. 2018). Based on molecular analysis, no evidence of extra-pair paternity was detected in 10 tested broods (Maher et al. 2017). No case of more than two adults associated with a nest was found. However, interannual changes of partners were found: out of 41 pairs monitored at Andavadoaka, 85% changed partner once or twice between years. During the nonbreeding period this species occurs in groups, sometimes with other *Charadrius* species, particularly *C. pecuarius* and *C. thoracicus*.

Nest and brood care: Incubation was investigated using PIT tags at Andavadoaka at six nests (two in 2015 and four in 2019): females incubated mostly during the day and males during the night (S. Zefania and T. Székely, unpublished data), particularly from 22h until dawn. In some cases, the male took over from the female during the hot period of the day between 9h and 15h. Nest incubation was most constant during the hot period (Vincze et al. 2017), between 10h and 15h, to shade the eggs, and during the cold period, between 16h to 9h, to keep the eggs warm. Recorded images from 40 nests indicate that early in the incubation period the female spent more time on the nest (60%) than the male (40%), but female participation increased slightly to 65% toward the later stages of the incubation period.

Based on over 545 followed broods at Andavadoaka, both parents cared for broods in 70.1% of cases, whereas at Tsimanampesotse this figure, based on 17 followed broods, was 58.8% (S. Zefania and T. Székely, unpublished data).

Movement and Dispersal

Records of local dispersal based on banded *C. marginatus* showed a maximal distance traveled of 15 km between study sites and years. Study of local dispersal in this species at Andavadoaka based on experimentally removed mates (Parra et al. 2014) found spatially discrete and less interconnected populations than in *C. pecuarius* on the breeding and feeding grounds (Cunningham et al. 2018). Genetic comparisons between *C. marginatus* populations showed little phylogeographic structure (Eberhart-Philips et al. 2015; J. Jackson et al. 2017), suggesting considerable dispersal and mixing.

Threats and Conservation

Charadrius marginatus has a large range and population and uses a variety of habitats; on the IUCN Red List it is considered Least Concern (BirdLife International 2020a). The Madagascar population, if considered separately, does not appear to be at great risk for the same reasons. Low breeding success appears to be an important population-limiting factor for this population. It shows a low prevalence of *Plasmodium* infection, with only one (female) of 55 birds examined infected (Martínez-de la Puente et al. 2017).

OTHER *CHARADRIUS* SPECIES ON MADAGASCAR

Charadrius tricollaris (Three-banded Plover, *vorombato* or *monditra*) occurs across much of sub-Saharan Africa and Madagascar but

is associated mainly with inland freshwater wetlands, particularly margins of streams and rivers, muddy ponds in open country, wet rice fields, and artificial lakes; it is not normally found on open coastlines but does use saline habitat at the edges of salt marshes, estuaries, or brackish inland lakes. The distinctive endemic race *C. t. bifrontatus* is widespread on Madagascar, although habitat for it is limited in the dry south and southwest, and it is largely absent from the Central Highlands. The species has not been studied in detail on Madagascar but behaviorally appears to be a typical small *Charadrius* (Appert 1971; Zefania and Székely 2013d).

Three more *Charadrius* species visit Madagascar's coastal wetlands as migrants from the Palearctic region: *C. hiaticula* (Common Ringed-plover); *C. leschenaultii* (Greater Sand-plover); and *C. mongolus* (Lesser Sand-plover) (see Young et al., pp. 1627–36). The latter two are difficult to distinguish, making their status somewhat uncertain, but all appear to be fairly common wherever appropriate sandy and muddy habitats, often intertidal, are found.

Subject editors: Roger J. Safford and Steven M. Goodman

JACANIDAE: *ACTOPHILORNIS ALBINUCHA*, MADAGASCAR JACANA, *TSIKIRANTA*, *PIRITRY*

J. D'Urban Jackson, S. Zefania, and T. Székely

Actophilornis albinucha (Madagascar Jacana) is endemic to Madagascar and distributed in freshwater wetlands in the west and north, mainly in lowland areas. It is found in wetlands with floating vegetation such as water lilies (*Nymphaea stellata* and *N. lotus*, family Nymphaeaceae) and also in lakes with the invasive water hyacinth (*Eichhornia crassipes*, family Pontederiaceae). This bird species occurs in natural and human-modified wetland habitats such as rice paddies, although the relative importance of these habitat types for the long-term persistence of *A. albinucha* is not known.

A recently published molecular phylogeny of extant Jacanidae species using mtDNA fragments indicates that *A. albinucha* is a sister species of *A. africanus* (African Jacana) (D'Urban Jackson et al. 2019). These species are the only two in the genus *Actophilornis*. No subspecies have been recognized for *A. albinucha*.

FIGURE 13.21 ***Actophilornis albinucha* (Madagascar Jacana) adult walking on lily pads (*Nymphaea stellata*), Lake Sariaka, Baly Bay protected area.** (PHOTO by L.-A. Rene de Roland.)

PLUMAGE AND SEXUAL SIZE DIMORPHISM

Adults of both sexes have a predominantly chestnut-brown back, belly, breast, and wings; white, black, or piebald (see below) hind neck and hind crown; and black underside of neck, with a pale blue frontal shield. Upper tail coverts can be white, rufous brown, or anything in between, and the middle tail feathers are black. The neck plumage is variable among adults: some individuals have almost entirely black necks with only white speckles on the hind neck, whereas others show a clear contrast between the black fore neck and largely white hind neck; some birds with white hind necks show golden plumage at the base of this area. Birds with more white on the hind neck, including golden coloration, tend to also have more white on the upper tail coverts; Figure 13.21 shows such a bird. Studies based on marked individuals through time have not been carried out, but this variation is thought to be age related (Safford 2013q; D'Urban Jackson et al. 2019). The legs and toes are gray to almost blackish, and toes are elongated, enabling these birds to walk across floating vegetation. Local people report that individuals undergo a simultaneous molt of primary feathers, making them flightless, during which time they swim when disturbed or avoiding predators.

Actophilornis albinucha displays reversed sexual size dimorphism, with females significantly larger than males. The following measurements are based on a sample of 13 females and 22 males unless stated

otherwise, and the sex of each individual has been confirmed with molecular methods (D'Urban Jackson et al. 2019): mass of females 240–285 g (266.2 g, n = 4), males 145–185 g (166.6 g, n = 8); tarsus length of females 64.3–80.1 mm (72.5 mm), males 62.7–71.02 mm (66.8 mm); wing length of females 180–190 mm (185.7 mm, n = 12), males 139–167 mm (161 mm); and shield length of females 46–58.8 mm (54.3 mm), males 47.3–54.7 mm (50.5 mm).

Immatures and juveniles have buffy plumage with the neck plumage colors reversed (black hind neck and hind crown and white underside). They have white cheeks with a black stripe from the beak across the eye to the hind crown, and a small gray shield. Their legs and toes are gray as in adults. During this life stage, their plumage is curiously similar to that of adult *A. africanus*, which in the distant past even led to erroneous reports of the latter species on Madagascar (Milne Edwards and Grandidier 1879–1885).

DISTRIBUTION AND POPULATION DENSITY

Recent surveys have found jacanas as far south as Lake Ihotry, at different localities toward the north, and in the northeast as far as Lake Sahaka (D'Urban Jackson et al. 2019). The surveys indicated that the distribution of this species is patchy. It was found at 22 of the 54 surveyed lakes, presumably reflecting the presence of suitable wetlands. Four of the 22 lakes with this species were east of the recently documented range by up to 113 km. In lakes where *A. albinucha* occurred, density was found to be on average 3.5 ± 0.74 individuals/ha. Repeated wetland bird surveys around Lake Mandrozo suggest that this area is a stronghold for this species, with 78–127 birds recorded between 2009 and 2015 (Razafimanjato et al. 2015). In addition, 80 individuals, together with a large diversity of wetland birds, were found in the Ambonara wetlands in the extreme south of the Boeny Region during wetland bird surveys in 2017 (Bamford et al. 2017).

Wetland bird surveys conducted by the Durrell Wildlife Conservation Trust and The Peregrine Fund Madagascar suggest that the number and density of *A. albinucha* at any given site vary widely throughout the year, potentially related to optimal environmental conditions for breeding but also associated with agricultural practices, notably the rice-growing season. Jacanas are often found alone or in small groups (Langrand 1990; Safford 2013q).

Historically *A. albinucha* was more widespread and common than today, occurring in the central east at Lake Alaotra into the 1990s (Safford 2013q). In the most recent survey, only three individuals were observed in the Lake Sahaka region (including Lake Anosy and Lake Ambinagny), which in 1998–1999 was occupied by slightly fewer than 70 individuals year-round (Safford 2000). Reports from local bird guides and repeated bird surveys from Lake Bemamba (Durrell Wildlife Conservation Trust, unpublished data) suggest a rapid decline in population size. The current global population estimate is 975–2064 birds (D'Urban Jackson et al. 2019).

BREEDING ECOLOGY AND SOCIAL BEHAVIOR

Actophilornis albinucha can presumably breed year-round. However, breeding records (including sightings of nests and downy young) fall between December and July, coinciding with wetter weather conditions (Rand 1936; Appert 2011; D'Urban Jackson et al. 2019).

Their nests consist of built-up vegetation floating above the water surface; a nest found by the authors (with eggs, in January 2016) was in an area largely covered by invasive *Eichhornia* mixed with (also invasive) *Pistia stratiotes*. Other jacana species in the world typically lay four eggs (Jenni 1996); only two clutches have been reported for *A. albinucha*: one with four eggs (Rand 1936) and the other with three eggs (D'Urban Jackson et al. 2019). The eggs are ovate and dark greenish brown, with a dense, dark pattern of lines and scribbles, similar to *A. africanus* eggs, and they measure 35.5 mm (± 1.8, n = 7) × 25.2 mm (± 0.4, n = 7) (Rand 1936; D'Urban Jackson et al. 2019).

High numbers of *A. albinucha* have been reported for some areas (see above). However, when they are looking after young, more solitary behavior has been observed. During breeding, female and male territorial aggression has been witnessed. In addition, aggression (vocalization and chasing) toward *Gallinula chloropus* (Eurasian Moorhen) and *Porphyrio alleni* (Allen's Gallinule) when coming into close contact has been observed (D'Urban Jackson et al. 2019).

Sex-role reversal behavior is assumed, which may include incubation and brood care by the male and polygamy by the female (Jenni 1996; Safford 2013q), based on breeding behavior and the extent of reversed sexual size dimorphism in *A. albinucha* being similar to that in the closely related *A. africanus* (D'Urban Jackson et al. 2019). However, breeding biology studies are needed in *A. albinucha* to confirm these assumptions, and virtually nothing is known about their breeding behavior or parental care. There is a single case of a molecularly sexed brooding adult male.

DIET AND ECOLOGY

No formal dietary study has been conducted on *A. albinucha*, but it has been observed foraging in floating vegetation by overturning leaves and eating small invertebrates, larvae, and aquatic plant seeds (Milne Edwards and Grandidier 1879–1885). These birds have also been seen foraging through piles of dried rice plants.

MOVEMENTS, GENE FLOW, AND GENETIC DIVERSITY

This species does not seem particularly keen to fly long distances; it takes short flights between vegetation patches when disturbed but otherwise tends to walk on floating vegetation (Rand 1936; Safford 2013q). A number of individuals have been banded, but no resightings of these birds have been recorded. Local dispersal or nomadic movements have been predicted based on high within-year fluctuations in their presence at Lake Bemamba and Lake Mandrozo, where repeated bird surveys are regularly conducted. Further, local people report that the species is at times absent from some breeding sites (D'Urban Jackson et al. 2019).

High gene flow has been found across the entire range of this species, and no barriers to gene flow have been identified, suggesting few or no barriers to their movements (D'Urban Jackson 2018).

This supports the prediction of widespread dispersal. Identical sequences of one mitochondrial gene (ND2) have been found in all 15 individuals that have been sequenced, representing a substantial part of their geographic range. Genomic data (RADseq) have shown that *A. albinucha* is less genetically diverse than *A. africanus* (D'Urban Jackson 2018).

THREATS AND CONSERVATION

In the 2020 revision of the IUCN Red List, *A. albinucha* was for the first time recognized as Endangered because its small population was undergoing a moderately rapid population decline through habitat degradation and hunting pressure (BirdLife International 2020a). The greatest threats suffered by this species are habitat loss and wetland conversion to rice paddies (Safford 2013q; D'Urban Jackson et al. 2019). It can tolerate low-level human disturbance and even uses flooded rice paddies for breeding and foraging. However, more generally the degradation of natural wetlands resulting from conversion to rice paddies, including the siltation of rivers and the use of pesticides, is likely contributing to declining wetland bird populations (Bamford et al. 2017). As with other waterbirds on Madagascar, illegal hunting also threatens this species (BirdLife International 2020a).

Subject editors: Roger J. Safford and Steven M. Goodman

ACCIPITRIFORMES AND FALCONIFORMES: HAWKS, EAGLES, KITES, AND FALCONS

L.-A. Rene de Roland and R. Thorstrom

Globally, diurnal birds of prey, or raptors, were formally placed in the order Falconiformes but are today considered best split into three separate orders. The Cathartiformes (New World vultures) and Accipitriformes (Secretarybird, Osprey, hawks, eagles, and kites) are sister to each other, while the order Falconiformes now contains only the falcons and caracaras and is not related to the other two orders (Prum et al. 2015). The Accipitriformes and Falconiformes are well represented on Madagascar. Owls, which are generally nocturnal, remain a separate order, Strigiformes.

Twelve (55%) of the 22 regularly occurring (i.e., excluding vagrants; see below) diurnal and nocturnal raptor species occurring on Madagascar are endemic, and three more are restricted to the Malagasy Region (see Table 13.1). Five resident species are widespread outside Madagascar, while two are regular migrant visitors. Within the Old World tropical region, Madagascar as a country has the highest percentage of predatory raptor species (Falconiformes and Strigiformes, excluding vultures, which are obligate scavengers) per the total known local avifauna: they make up slightly over 8.5% of the island's bird species (Goodman et al. 2018). Further, at least three diurnal birds of prey have disappeared from Madagascar in recent geological time, at least one of which was certainly endemic and is therefore now globally extinct (see Safford et al., pp. 1553–602).

Of Madagascar's 22 regularly occurring raptor species, according to the IUCN Red List, one is considered Critically Endangered, *Haliaeetus vociferoides* (Madagascar Fish-eagle); and two are Endangered, *Eutriorchis astur* (Madagascar Serpent-eagle) and *Circus macrosceles* (Madagascar Harrier). Although some more open-country species of Malagasy raptors have benefited from the degradation of forests (e.g., *Falco newtoni*, Madagascar Kestrel), most are forest species and have been adversely affected. Other causes of species declines have been modification of original wetland habitat, burning of grasslands, and persecution by humans for food, beliefs and practices related to superstitions or sorcery, and protection of poultry.

In this contribution, we provide information on the status, threats, habitat, and ecology of the island's 16 regularly occurring diurnal raptors. Three more species, *Pandion haliaetus* (Osprey), *Elanus caeruleus* (Black-winged Kite), and *Lophaetus occipitalis* (Long-crested Eagle) have occurred as vagrants (Safford and Hawkins 2013) and are not considered further.

ACCIPITRIFORMES

Eutriorchis astur, Madagascar Serpent-eagle, *Fandrasalambo*

Distribution and Status

The endangered, endemic *Eutriorchis astur*, in a monospecific genus, is one of the rarest birds of prey in the world (del Hoyo et al. 1994). An elusive raptor more often heard than observed, *Eutriorchis* is restricted to eastern moist evergreen forests (Rene de Roland 2013a), and 11 museum specimens were collected at seven sites in four different forested areas (Ampasimaneva, Analamazaotra, Fito, and Maroantsetra) between 1874 and the 1930s (Collar and Stuart 1985; Langrand 1990). After a sight record in 1988 at Marojejy (B. Sheldon and Duckworth 1990) and the discovery of carcass remains in 1990 at Ambatovaky (Raxworthy and Colston 1992), it has been only since 1993 (Thorstrom et al. 1995) that its distribution and habits have been confirmed by intensive fieldwork.

Presently, *Eutriorchis* is known from as far south as Ranomafana National Park (Karpanty 2010) to as far north as the Tsaratanàna Massif (ZICOMA 1999, 2001) and Sandrakana Forest in the Bemanevika protected area (Rabearivony et al. 2010). From 1993 to 1998, at least 15 individuals were repeatedly sighted and captured at nine different localities throughout the Masoala Peninsula (Thorstrom and Rene de Roland 2000), and studies have been carried out on the species' breeding biology there since 1993 (Thorstrom et al. 1995; Thorstrom and Watson 1997; Thorstrom and Rene de Roland 2000), and at Bemanevika from 2008 to 2019 (Rabearivony et al. 2010; Benjara et al. 2017; L.-A. Rene de Roland, unpublished data). The Masoala protected area covers about 230,000 ha of different habitats, including lowland moist evergreen and littoral forests with average annual rainfall of about 3000 mm, but in certain areas up to 6049 mm (Goodman et al. 2018). The forest has a canopy height of 30 m with emergent trees, high floristic diversity, and steep topography ranging from sea level to 1100 m. The second site, at Bemanevika, in the southern foothills of Tsaratanàna, received permanent protected area status in 2015 and is a 35,600 ha complex of medium-altitude moist evergreen forest across an elevational range of 1500–1750 m, with emergent trees of 25 m, wetlands including marshes and volcanic lakes, and grasslands. Annual rainfall ranges from 1600 to 2400 mm, most falling in the rainy season from November to March (Rabearivony et al. 2010).

Current information indicates that the elevational range of *E. astur* is from sea level on the Masoala Peninsula to approximately 1650 m at Bemanevika and 1860 m at Mahimborondro protected areas (L.-A. Rene de Roland, unpublished data). The large forest blocks in the protected areas of Masoala, Makira, and Ankeniheny-Zahamena are most likely the strongholds for this species.

Description

Eutriorchis astur is a medium-size forest raptor (head-to-tail length 60–66 cm and weight 700–1000 g), with short, rounded wings, long tail, and thick medium-length legs (Figure 13.22d). Adults vary from a medium to dark brown above, and underparts have brown barring across the breast, thighs, and undertail coverts. The dark brown head is thinly scalloped with white. The tail is dark brown and banded with six or seven narrow horizontal dark bars. The iris is yellow. The cere is gray and the prominent bill is long and stout. Legs are a yellowish horn color with special overlapping scales, an adaptation presumed to deflect the bites of reptiles. The immature is light brown above with feathers edged in white and has a white-gray iris and pale yellow tarsi and feet. One male had a wing length of 301 mm, several males had tail lengths from 280 to 292 mm, and unknown sexes had tarsus lengths from 90 to 92 mm (Brown and Amadon 1989). The unsexed *E. astur* captured in 1994 had a bill length of 30.9 mm, tail length of 296 mm, tarsus length of 79 mm, and weight of 770 g (Thorstrom et al. 1995). One adult female trapped in 2011 at Bemanevika weighed 850 g. We suspect that there is some degree of sexual dimorphism, but measurement data from known sexed individuals are insufficient.

The only Malagasy raptor that can be confused with *E. astur* is *Accipiter henstii* (Henst's Goshawk); these species occur in sympatry and are of similar size and plumage coloration, but the latter species has a prominent white eyebrow and breast and a more finely barred throat, black bars on the underparts, orange irises, more robust, longer legs, and a slightly shorter tail (del Hoyo et al. 1994). *Accipiter henstii* is very vocal and aggressive at its nest, contrasting with the secretive, nearly nonvocal *E. astur*. Away from the nest, *Eutriorchis* is shy and wary (Thorstrom and Rene de Roland 2000).

Breeding Behavior

During the breeding season, the territorial call is a moderately loud, barking *whaa whaa whaa whaa* given in the early morning and occasionally late afternoon prior to roosting. This call varies from three to 20 notes, averaging 1–1.5 sec between notes, depending on the behavior of the bird. During flight, this call changes to a shorter *wha* note. Nestlings and fledglings give a call similar to that of adults, but much softer and slower in tempo. Upon approaching the nest area with food, adults give another vocalization that consists of soft, squeaky chirps to alert the incubating and brooding bird.

All nests (n = 15) were built during September to October. The male delievered 70% and the female 30% of the nesting material (green twigs and leaves), and the female was largely responsible for arranging the nesting material. All nests on the Masoala Peninsula (n = 5, between 20 and 420 m elevation) and at Bemanevika (n = 10, between 1540 and 1860 m elevation) were in intact moist evergreen forest and built upon epiphytic ferns (*Asplenium nidus*), generally surrounded by vines and branches, 12–27 m above the ground in large mature trees. Nest trees occurred in flat terrain and on slopes up to 55%, often close to watercourses and several kilometers from human activity (Thorstrom and Rene de Roland 2000; Benjara et al. 2017, L.-A. Rene de Roland, unpublished data). The nest-building period lasted approximately 26 days.

Laying dates were late September to October at both sites. Clutch size varied from one (n = 8 nests) to two eggs (n = 7 nests). At one nest on Masoala, the female incubated 77% of the time and the male about 21%, and about 1% of the time the nest was without an incubating adult; incubation breaks lasted up to half an hour. The male delivered greenery (fresh twigs with leaves) 16 times and the female nine times during the incubation period. There was no food transfer at the nest; adults when not incubating fed themselves away from the nest. Incubation lasted approximately 42–46 days.

The nestling period was from late October to December, and the female was the sole attendant at the nest. The role of the male was only to deliver prey to the female and nestlings. Upon approaching the nest, the male made soft chirps to alert the female of his impending arrival. The female responded to these contact calls with a near-voiceless quivering of her mouth until prey delivery; thereafter she aggressively took the prey from the male and then fed herself and the nestling. The female brooded the nestling, fed it, and delivered greenery 16 times during the first few weeks of the nestling period (n = 1 nest). During this time, the male delivered greenery only once. The female left the nest for longer periods during the second week (nest attendance 93% and nest absence 7%) and began hunting and delivering prey items to her nestling when it was 18 days of age. At one nest site at Bemanevika, the male delivered 75% (n = 116) of prey items and the female 25% (n = 39) during the nine-week nestling period. Weekly prey delivery rates increased only slightly from the start of the nestling period, from 2.5 items/day to 2.8 at the end of the nestling period. One noticeable change in the development of the nestling was a change in iris color from brown as a nestling to light gray as a fledgling.

FIGURE 13.22 **Some of the Malagasy diurnal birds of prey. A)** ***Falco zoniventris*** **(Banded Kestrel); B)** ***Haliaeetus vociferoides*** **(Madagascar Fish-eagle); C)** ***Milvus aegyptius*** **(Yellow-billed Kite); D)** ***Eutriorchis astur*** **(Madagascar Serpent-eagle); E)** ***Aviceda madagascariensis*** **(Madagascar Cuckoo-hawk), juvenile; F)** ***F. newtoni*** **(Madagascar Kestrel); G)** ***Accipiter madagascariensis*** **(Madagascar Sparrowhawk); H)** ***Macheiramphus alcinus*** **(Bat Hawk); I)** ***F. peregrinus*** **(Peregrine Falcon); J)** ***F. concolor*** **(Sooty Falcon), juvenile; and K)** ***Circus macrosceles*** **(Madagascar Harrier), female.** (PHOTOS A, D, E, and I–K by R. Thorstrom; B, C, F, and G by L.-A. Rene de Roland; and H by G. Razafimanjato.)

Young fledged in late December or January, between 58 and 64 days of age. At one nest, after fledging the young roosted 20 m from the nest. At 76 days old, one fledgling was located 70 m from the nest tree. During the early post-fledging period, the young called and moved from treetop to treetop until an adult passed them a prey item. At one nest site a calling fledgling was charged by a lemur (*Varecia rubra*, Red Ruffed Lemur), which ran up the tree toward the young and flushed it from its perch, and in another case one young *E. astur* was struck and knocked off its perch by a *Buteo brachypterus* (Madagascar Buzzard) and fell 5 m until stopping in a treetop.

At 90 days of age, the young gradually began descending to the ground after feeding. One fledgling was observed capturing its first prey, a chameleon that was resting 30 cm above the ground in a small tree, at the age of 95 days. One fledgling was last noted at 112 days old.

The nesting attempts monitored, and their fates, are summarized as follows. From 1997 to 2007 at Masoala, three pairs were documented making five nesting attempts; six eggs were laid (mean 1.2 eggs per attempt), six nestlings hatched, and four young fledged, giving a productivity of 0.8 young fledged per nesting attempt. Between 2008 and 2019, three pairs were located and monitored at Bemanevika, including one pair from 2011 to 2019 (Benjara 2015; Benjara et al. 2017; L.-A. Rene de Roland, unpublished data). The three pairs were observed making 10 nesting attempts, 16 eggs were laid (mean 1.6 eggs per attempt), 14 nestlings hatched, and nine young fledged, giving a productivity of 0.9 young fledged per attempt. The nest trees were within the forest, from 590 to 2900 m from the edge, and several kilometers from villages.

Diet and Foraging

This species hunts from the ground up to the canopy, where it waits on a perch and scans up and down and side to side for 1–5 min, then moves to another perch about 50 m distant and continues scanning. It takes reptiles and amphibians out of trees and off the ground.

On Masoala, prey delivered to the first documented nest totaled 155 items, of which 133 were identifiable at last partially (if not to species). Prey delivered to the second nest included 226 items, of which 177 were recognizable. Prey was always transferred from the bill of the male to the bill of the female or nestling. All prey items delivered to the nests had already been decapitated prior to arrival. Of the identified prey items at two nests, 264 (85.1%) were chameleons (*Calumma* and *Furcifer* spp.) or leaf-tailed geckos (*Uroplatus* spp.), 41 (13.2%) were frogs (in the genera *Boophis* and *Mantidactylus*), two (0.7%) were snakes (*Stenophis*), two (0.7%) were bats (*Macronycteris commersoni*, Commerson's Leaf-nosed Bat), and one was an insect of an unknown taxon (0.3%). During the 2015 breeding season at Bemanevika, all 191 identified prey items were chameleons between 10 and 25 cm in length, even though *Uroplatus* occurs at this site.

At the 1997 nesting site on Masoala and during the post-fledging period, we observed seven prey items delivered: three *Uroplatus* sp., two chameleons, one bat, and one unidentified item. The fledgling from the 2000 nest at the same site was observed from 1 to 27 February catching eight prey items: five chameleons, one *Uroplatus* sp., one bat, and one insect.

Conservation

Eutriorchis astur has always been considered a rare and secretive raptor restricted to undisturbed and protected moist evergreen forests. It has a low productive output, laying one- or two-egg clutches and raising one or two young per breeding season, and has undoubtedly decreased in numbers in recent times with the loss of mature forest. At Bemanevika, the fragmentation of the remaining forest may have an impact on the presence of this species, as only blocks greater than 423 ha had nesting *E. astur* (Benjara 2015). The IUCN Red List classifies this species as Endangered, with a declining population (BirdLife International 2020a). Across its range, this bird of prey seems confined to the large remaining forest tracts that have not been drastically modified by human activity, many of which are in the protected area system; conservation of such forest areas is the key to the conservation of this and many other species.

Haliaeetus vociferoides, Madagascar Fish-eagle, *Ankoay*

Distribution and Status

Haliaeetus vociferoides is one of the most threatened birds of prey in the world (BirdLife International 2020a). Little was known about the species' biology until intensive studies by The Peregrine Fund began in 1991. After the launch of The Peregrine Fund's Madagascar Project, two protected wetland areas were established, in large part driven by research and conservation of this species: Tsimembo-Manambolomaty, near Antsalova; and Mandrozo, north of Maintirano. Both sites hold extensive freshwater aquatic ecosystems. Most research effort has been focused mainly on the wetlands of the Antsalova region—in order to understand aspects of the fish-eagle's natural history, particularly with the aim of developing a conservation program for the species and its habitat (R. Watson et al. 1993)—and at Lake Mandrozo in 2007.

Historically, naturalists described *H. vociferoides* as abundant during the 19th and most of the 20th centuries, and common along the northwest shoreline and up to 100 km inland (see Rabarisoa et al. 2003 for details). Surveys from 1991 to 1995 recorded a minimum of 222 adults at 105 sites, with the breeding population estimated at 99 pairs, and the southern limit was in the mangroves of Amboliboly, south of Morondava (Rabarisoa et al. 1997; Rabarisoa 1999a), but surveys in 2005–2006 did not find any sign of this species in this area (Razafimanjato et al. 2014). The current distribution is from Belo-sur-Tsiribihina in the south to Antsiranana in the north, and on lakes and rivers up to about 125 km inland (see Rabarisoa et al. 2003 for earlier references; Razafimanjato et al. 2014; D. Rasolonjatovo 2018). The last countrywide survey took place in 2005–2006 and recorded 287 individuals, including 280 adults, four subadults, and three juveniles (Razafimanjato et al. 2014). The two zones with the highest *H. vociferoides* populations were Tsimembo-Manambolomaty, with 64 individuals, and the mangroves of Sahamalaza National Park, with 33 individuals.

Haliaeetus vociferoides frequents marine and coastal habitat, and of the 287 birds recorded in the 2005–2006 surveys, 128 (44.6%) were observed on lakes; 116 (40.4%) in coastal areas, including 103 (35.9%) in mangroves and 13 (4.5%) in estuaries; 32 (11.2%) on marine islands; and 11 (3.8%) along rivers (Razafimanjato et al. 2014). In the central and southern part of the species' range, it

occurs most commonly on rivers and lakes. In these habitats, this species nests in large trees in undisturbed to moderately disturbed forest. Individuals living in freshwater habitats depend on large trees on the shoreline for perches and nesting sites and prefer deeper and clearer lakes (Berkelman et al. 1999a; R. Watson et al. 2000a).

In surveys at three coastal and six inland areas in 2005–2006 by Razafimanjato et al. (2014) and in 2017 by D. Rasolonjatovo (2018), 161 and 178 *H. vociferoides* individuals were recorded, respectively. The results of surveys in 2017 indicate a 10.6% increase in the number of individuals observed from more than a decade earlier at nine sites covered by both studies, with the number of birds increasing in two of the three coastal areas and three of the six inland areas. In 2017, a survey along the mangroves and river estuaries scattered along the coast of Madagascar from Ambavanankarana (coastal zone west of Ankarana) to Andranopasy (north of Morombe) recorded 62 individuals, and the southernmost distribution was at Belo-sur-Tsiribihina (D. Rasolonjatovo 2018).

Description

Haliaeetus vociferoides is the largest extant raptor on Madagascar, with a head-to-tail length of 70–80 cm and a wingspan of about 200 cm. The adult male weighs between 1500 and 2500 g, while the female weighs between 2000 and 3500 g. There is no sexual difference in plumage coloration. Adults are dark brown with rufous spangling on the breast (Figure 13.22b). The tail is white, sometimes with brown spots that may be a remnant of immature plumage in young adults. The head is brown, with a white cheek patch, brown streaking on the crown, nape, throat, and fore neck, and a narrow dark eye stripe. The eyes are dark brown, the bill dark gray to black, and the feet and legs pale gray. The juvenile plumage is a lighter brown than that of the adult, with a tawny brown head and chest, tan cheeks, and brown tail.

The call of *H. vociferoides* is a ringing yelp, *ko ko koy koy koy koy* (hence its Malagasy name *ankoay*), similar to that of *H. vocifer* (African Fish-eagle). The female's call is of a lower frequency than the male's, a difference most obvious when a pair duets in synchrony to produce a rapid sequence of calls that alternate from lower to higher pitch and can be heard for over 1 km.

Breeding Behavior

Haliaeetus vociferoides pairs occupy a territory, which they defend aggressively through the breeding season with vocalizations, prominent visibility, and attacks on intruders. The breeding season starts in May with courtship and nest building, and eggs are laid at the end of May. Nests are built in the fork of a tree (near rivers and lakes), on the top of mangrove trees, or directly on crags of rocky islands. In the freshwater wetlands of the Antsalova, Belo-sur-Tsiribihina, and Miandrivazo areas, *Tamarindus* (Fabaceae) and *Adansonia* (Bombacaceae) are the predominant tree species used by fish-eagles for nesting, although other tree species have also been recorded (*Alleanthus greveanus*, Hernandiaceae; *Neobeguea mahafaliensis*, Ptaeroxylaceae; and *Colvillea racemosa*, Fabaceae Fabaceae). Pairs typically nest 1.7 ± 1.0 km apart (R. Watson and Razafindramanana 1999).

Nest height varied from 12 to 24 m off the ground in trees along inland lakes (R. Watson et al. 2000a; D. Rasolonjatovo 2018), but in coastal mangroves and river estuaries nest height varied from 5 to 13 m (n = 11 nests), as they depended on the size of the mangrove trees (D. Rasolonjatovo 2018). Nests are also built in trees in littoral forests along the coast (near Anjajavy, Marimba, and Komanjara) and on crags on rocky islands, with or without vegetation, mainly in the north and northwest (Nosy Hara, Nosy Mitsio group, Nosy Be and its islets, and Nosy Radama group). Nest size varies from about 100 to 120 cm in diameter and 30 to 50 cm in depth. Nests are built by the pair and constructed of dead branches from 10 to 30 mm in diameter and from 30 to 60 mm in length (Razafindramanana 1995; R. Watson et al. 1999). The female typically lays a one- or two-egg clutch (but in 2003 a three-egg clutch was observed) between the end of May and mid-July, and incubation begins after the first egg is laid. Eggs measure 69.2 ± 0.8 mm in length, 52.6 ± 0.6 mm in width, and weigh 100.9 ± 3.4 g. Shells are white. Incubation lasts 37–43 days and is performed by both sexes, 71% and 22% of the time by the female and the male, respectively. Eggs are never left unattended for more than about 10 min. On rare occasions, replacement clutches are laid when the first is lost; this was recorded only three times at Tsimembo-Manambolomaty when the first clutch failed early during the incubation period (Rafanomezantsoa 1999).

Hatching occurs between the second week of July and September. Typically, for clutches of two eggs, both eggs hatch within two to three days of one another, but invariably only one nestling survives because of obligate siblicide. Siblicide generally occurs only when resources, specifically food sources, are scarce, and the surviving offspring benefits because it has now eliminated its competition for food (Mock et al. 1990). In obligate siblicide, the second-hatched nestling is either killed or displaced from the nest by the older nestling, usually within 10 days of hatching.

The nestling period ranges from 78 to 89 days, although nestlings start to move from the nest to nearby branches at 70 days of age. Fledging occurs in September or October, and productivity was calculated as 0.29 fledglings per territorial pair per year in the region of Antsalova from 1991 to 1997 (Rabarisoa 1999b). Failure to lay eggs, and human capture of nestlings to use for food or to keep in captivity, accounted for many of the breeding failures (R. Watson et al. 1999). From 2010 to 2015, in the same region, productivity per territorial pair was higher both inside (0.69) and outside (0.5) Tsimembo-Manambolomaty, most likely because of lower threats to this species and its habitat thanks to a community-based natural resource management system (Razafimanjato et al. 2014).

Juveniles disperse 14 to 28 weeks after fledging. They may visit areas outside the natal territory, using thermals to soar 60 km or more. At about 22 months of age, young individuals, still in juvenile plumage, return to the parental territory until the beginning of the next breeding season (Rafanomezantsoa 1998).

One or two subordinate, extra-pair adults were frequently (42% of nests) found at or around the nest of an established pair. They appeared to associate with the pair to contribute to breeding activities such as nest construction, incubation, and nestling feeding and shading during the absence of the parents (R. Watson et al. 1999). Behavioral studies and DNA fingerprinting analysis of genetic relatedness suggest that fish-eagles exhibit both cooperative polyandry and cooperative breeding (Tingay 2000). Nonbreeding juveniles (male and female) may adopt a delayed dispersal strategy, but there was no conclusive evidence to suggest that extra-pair

adults were progeny from previous years. In fact, adults attending the same nest were found to be less closely related to each other than they were to adults at other nests. In this molecular study, all extra-pair subordinate adults were identified as male, and all offspring were sired by subordinate males, who achieved four times more copulations than dominant males, although dominant males contributed the highest levels of parental investment at each nest (Tingay et al. 2002).

Diet and Foraging

Haliaeetus vociferoides feeds mainly on surface-dwelling fish and occasionally on crabs and young marine turtles in coastal areas. Fish selection depends on the relative abundance of species present in the eagle's territory and is typically dominated by four species of *Tilapia* (Cichlidae) and *Channa* cf. *striata* (Channidae), which are introduced to Madagascar, and *Megalops cyprinoides* (Megalopidae) and *Arius madagascariensis* (Ariidae), which are native (Berkelman et al. 1999b; Rasamoelina 2001). In the north and northwestern coastal area, *H. vociferoides* feeds on fish of the genera *Fistularia* spp. (Fistulariidae) and *Tylosurus* spp. (Belonidae). On rare occasions, eagles have attacked young domestic ducks (Berkelman et al. 1999b). Attacks on waterbirds have been recorded, such as *Anhinga rufa* (African Darter), *Microcarbo africanus* (Long-tailed Cormorant), *Ardea cinerea* (Gray Heron), *A. humbloti* (Madagascar Heron), *Dendrocygna viduata* (White-faced Whistling-duck), and *Platalea alba* (African Spoonbill), which may be associated with competition or territorial defense, as well as attempted predation.

Haliaeetus vociferoides typically perches in large trees or on overhanging rocks to watch for prey, and in mangroves it prefers sites adjacent to low-turbidity water that presumably facilitates spotting fish. It can observe fish near the surface from 100–200 m away. Once it sights prey, it takes to the air and glides to the proximity of the target fish before swooping down at a low angle to catch it in its feet, rarely becoming submerged (Berkelman et al. 1999b). Usually, it lifts a fish from the water and carries it back to a perch for consumption. Occasionally, if a prey item is too large to carry, an eagle may become immersed in the water for a few seconds before either lifting it from the water to carry it to shore, or swimming and dragging it there; in either case, the prey is then killed and consumed on the shore.

Conservation

The population of *Haliaeetus vociferoides* has declined dramatically in the past century (Langrand and Meyburg 1989; R. Watson et al. 2000b). The main causes of decline appear to be loss of habitat from deforestation, wetland conversion to rice paddies, and direct persecution by people who collect nestlings for pets or food, or hunt adults for sport or traditional sorcery-medicine uses. Collection of nestlings was frequent in the Antsalova region, with at least two nest trees cut down per year between 1992 and 1997 (Rabarisoa 1999b; R. Watson et al. 2000b), but this has not happened since then, presumably because of local public awareness and education programs conducted by The Peregrine Fund. In the same period mentioned above, three adults were found dead and another one alive, each with one foot missing. They were apparently the victims of traditional sorcery medicine in which the foot of a living eagle is used to bolster the strength of potions or spells.

The suspected recent impact of climate change has caused many wetlands in the Antsalova region, and other wetlands along the west coast of Madagascar, to become drier, and the water level in many permanent lakes has dropped, leading to a decline in the available fish stock in the lakes. In 2019, only one nest at the satellite lakes close to Tsimembo-Manambolomaty produced one young among the 23 nests monitored annually (L.-A. Rene de Roland, unpublished information). *Haliaeetus vociferoides* generally tolerates the presence of humans in its territory, but forest degradation (cutting large trees for dugout canoes and small trees for other types of construction and firewood) has destroyed much of the nesting habitat throughout its range (R. Watson and Rabarisoa 2000). Overfishing has depleted its food supply and affects annual productivity as well as survival. Erosion, mainly in wetlands outside protected areas associated with river drainages, from deforested areas upstream, has increased river turbidity, which inhibits fishing by eagles and has an indirect impact on their reproductive success.

As of January 2020, there were at least 44 breeding pairs in protected areas, of which 13 pairs were at Tsimembo-Manambolomaty, four at Mandrozo, 14 at Sahamalaza, seven on Nosy Hara, five at Baly Bay, three at Mahavavy Kinkony, and one at Ankarafantsika.

Improved public awareness and management of the wild population of *H. vociferoides* benefits the species by reducing the rate of population loss and eventually helping its recovery. In the Tsimembo-Manambolomaty protected area, The Peregrine Fund has successfully applied sibling rescue (removal of one nestling from a two-egg clutch before the youngest dies) with hacking (release back to the wild) to increase annual production and bolster the species' numbers in unoccupied areas (O'Daniel 1995; R. Watson et al. 1996). A community-based conservation project began in 1995 in this region, conducted in parallel with fish-eagle management, and control of overfishing by migrant fishermen and associated degradation of adjacent forest habitat began in 1997 (R. Watson and Rabarisoa 2000; R. Watson et al. 2000b). Currently, the Madagascar Fish-eagle is on the IUCN Red List as a Critically Endangered species with a declining population (BirdLife International 2020a).

Macheiramphus alcinus, Bat Hawk, *Hila*

Distribution and Status

Macheiramphus alcinus (Figure 13.22h) is rarely observed but is found throughout Madagascar. The subspecies *anderssoni* occurs across much of sub-Saharan Africa and Madagascar; the species also occurs in Southeast Asia to New Guinea. Few details are known about its population status on Madagascar, but densities are suspected to be extremely low throughout its range. Before the studies reported below, information was based almost entirely on one pair located near Antsalova in the early 1990s (The Peregrine Fund, unpublished data), and another nesting pair in the northeastern portion of the Masoala Peninsula in 1993 (Thorstrom and Watson 1997). The latter nest was in an isolated tree on a small hill surrounded by cleared land for subsistence agriculture. In addition, during the mid-1990s, several individuals roosted in the *Ficus* trees near the Queen's Palace (Rova de Manjakamiadana), Antananarivo, and at dusk fed on bats leaving roosts along nearby cliff faces (S. M. Goodman, unpublished data). Across the range of this secretive

species, it is mainly crepuscular and feeds primarily on small bats, with some birds and flying insects also taken (del Hoyo et al. 1994). It is difficult to ascertain its status, but forest felling may open up more habitat for it.

Breeding Behavior

Information on *Macheiramphus* breeding biology in the protected area of Mandrozo, north of Maintirano, is based on detailed studies from 2010 to 2017 (Razakaratrimo 2013, 2020). *Macheiramphus* was found in forest fragments near agricultural fields where there were fewer than 25 large, tall trees per ha, and local birds maintained fidelity to territories throughout the year. Nest sites were in fragmented forests with a few tall trees, especially *Pterygota perrieri* (Malvaceae). The breeding season began in January, with nest building and reconstruction by both adults delivering dry twigs and greenery. Egg laying was from January to May with one-egg clutches (n = 8 nesting attempts); eggs were white, and incubation was by both sexes, lasting 48 days. Adults and young were active during the crepuscular period; during full moon phases, adults were active at night and observed exiting and entering nest sites. Productivity at two nests sites was 0.75 young fledged per nesting attempt based on six young fledged from eight nesting attempts (Razakaratrimo 2013, 2020).

Diet and Foraging

Recent studies have provided new information and insight regarding the food habits of *Macheiramphus* on Madagascar. Food items identified from pellets collected at two sites in the west were composed almost exclusively of bats (58%) and birds (36%), with few reptiles and insects (6%) (Goodman et al. 2015). At five nesting sites in the same area, diet was predominantly bats (73%, 16 forms) and birds (27%, 10 species), with no difference between the prey taken in the dry and rainy seasons (Razakaratrimo et al. 2019).

Conservation

Macheiramphus alcinus is listed as Least Concern (not globally threatened) on the IUCN Red List, as it has a wide distribution and its population is not known to be declining (BirdLife International 2020a). On Madagascar, a study near the protected area of Mandrozo, recording 29 individuals and eight nesting attempts, is the most complete study of this species' breeding biology (Razakaratrimo 2020). The population status of the Malagasy population is difficult to ascertain, as this species has a large home range and crepuscular foraging habits, rendering it difficult to locate. Swidden agriculture is most likely the greatest threat to its habitat and nest sites throughout its range on Madagascar, although storms contribute to breeding failure.

Aviceda madagascariensis, Madagascar Cuckoo-hawk, Bobaka

Aviceda madagascariensis (Figure 13.22e) is endemic and sparsely distributed throughout Madagascar from sea level to 1800 m (Langrand 1990). It is found in all types of natural forest and is most often encountered at the edge of forests or around forest clearings. This species is easily overlooked because of its secretive behavior. Its nesting and breeding biology and diet are poorly known, but it appears to be a forest- or woodland-dependent species. *Aviceda* is easily confused with the common and widespread *Buteo brachypterus* (Madagascar Buzzard).

From 2004 to 2006, in the Ambatovaky protected area, two nesting pairs were studied (Randrianjafiniasa 2009; Rene de Roland 2013b). Pair formation began in August with aerial displays above the forest, followed by nest construction in September by both sexes; the two nests were placed near treetops. Eggs were laid in October and November. Both nests had two-egg clutches, and incubation was by both sexes, but predominantly by the female. Eggs hatched in November and December, and the young fledged in December and January, at approximately 43 days of age. The young did not return to the nest and became independent at 86 days of age.

From 2017 to 2019, in the Bemanevika protected area, in the southern foothills of the Tsaratanàna Massif, the breeding period was from October to December. One nesting pair discovered in 2017 nested in the same nest in 2017 and 2018, but in 2019, they nested 75 m from their previous nest. In 2019, a second nesting pair was located 2 km from the first nesting pair. All nesting attempts by the two pairs contained one- or two-egg clutches, all eggs hatched, and productivity was 1.25 young fledged per nesting attempt (n = 4 nesting attempts) (L.-A. Rene de Roland, unpublished data).

In a study of the dietary habits of *A. madagascariensis*, 989 identified prey items (Randrianjafiniasa 2009; Rene de Roland 2013b) consisted of predominantly arboreal and terrestrial frogs (50.3%), followed by large insects (cicadas, beetles, crickets, mantises, accounting for 43.2%), and chameleons and lizards (*Calumma/Furcifer*, *Uroplatus*, *Brookesia*, *Phelsuma*, *Zonosaurus*, accounting for 6.5%). Pellets recovered in the nest had beetles, mantises, and an unidentified nestling bird. *Aviceda* is not in any great danger overall, and it is recognized on the IUCN Red List as Least Concern, but declining forest cover is bound to affect it negatively (BirdLife International 2020a). Breeding areas need to be identified and habitat protected against human disturbance and degradation.

Milvus aegyptius, Yellow-billed Kite, Papango, Tsimalaho

Milvus aegyptius is a common species on Madagascar (Figure 13.22c). This species has recently been separated from *M. migrans* (Black Kite) (Wink and Sauer-Gürth 2000). It is found throughout the island in all habitat types, including urban areas from villages to cities, but avoids dense forests and spiny thickets. A gregarious and opportunistic species, it appears not to be threatened. People sometimes persecute it for its reputed habit of taking poultry.

The ecology of this species is not well known on Madagascar, except for a nesting biology study at the Tsimembo-Manambolomaty protected area from 2002 to 2003, which recorded 64 nesting attempts (Andriamalala et al. 2013). All nests were constructed of dry twigs, which formed the platform and lower layer, and an upper layer of an odd assortment of material collected from the ground (stones, chalky mud, plastic bags, rags, bryophytes, and dried dog and cattle dung). The odd nest materials were delivered to the nest 10 days prior to egg laying. The average time for building nests was 57 days, and the average distance between neighboring nests was 264 m (SD = 270.8, range = 26–1081 m, n = 33 nests).

This species wanders across Madagascar during the nonbreeding season, where it is attracted to grassland fires (L.-A. Rene de Roland, unpublished data). On the IUCN Red List, it is considered Least Concern because it has a wide distribution globally and occupies a variety of habitats (BirdLife International 2020a).

Polyboroides radiatus, Madagascar Harrier-hawk, *Fihiaka*

Polyboroides radiatus is an endemic and widespread species throughout much of Madagascar. It is found in intact to degraded forests, thickets, and wooded habitats and is frequently seen soaring above the forest canopy. Densities appear to be generally low across the island. Information on food habits suggests a generalist diet with items including carrion, invertebrates, frogs, lizards, snakes, nestling and adult birds, bats, rodents, tenrecs, and lemurs (Rand 1936; Rene de Roland et al. 1996; Karpanty and Goodman 1999; Thorstrom and La Marca 2000; Razarazafy 2015; see Goodman and Ganzhorn, pp. 1829–38). Humans probably persecute this species in areas where it preys on domestic fowl and livestock.

It lays one or two eggs, and in a two-egg clutch the first-hatched young shows siblicide behavior (see above under *Haliaeetus vociferoides*) toward its younger nest mate, resulting in the latter succumbing, and thus only one fledgling per nesting attempt (Thorstrom and La Marca 2000). A detailed study of nesting biology by Razarazafy et al. (2019) followed five nesting pairs in the Bemanevika protected area during the 2013 and 2014 breeding season. Pair formation and nest reconstruction (all pairs reused the nest from the previous season) began in August, and egg laying occurred in September and October, with a single egg laid per nest. Incubation averaged 38.7 ± 2.1 days (n = 3 nesting pairs); both sexes participated, with a rate of 53% by females, 43% by males, and 4% nest absence. Eggs hatched in November, with only the female brooding and feeding the young and the male hunting for and provisioning the female and young. Fledging occurred in December and January, with a productivity of 0.4 young fledged per nesting attempt (n = 8 nesting attempts). The inter-nest distance averaged 1.9 km (range 1.7–2.4 km). On the IUCN Red List, this species is considered Least Concern because it has a wide distribution throughout Madagascar in forested habitat, mainly in the western and eastern biogeographic regions (BirdLife International 2020a).

Circus macrosceles, Madagascar Harrier, *Fanindry, Kipanga, Fanintra*

Circus macrosceles (Figure 13.22k) is a Malagasy Region endemic that is uncommon and infrequently observed on Madagascar and poorly known from the Comoro islands (Grande Comore, Mohéli, and Anjouan). It has a broad distribution on Madagascar, extending about 1000 km north to south (Madagascar is about 1500 km in length) and east to west (Rene de Roland et al. 2009). Nearly 70% of the observations of *C. macrosceles* (n = 80 total individuals recorded) during a 16-month countrywide survey were made during the breeding season in Central Highlands marshes and grasslands above 1100 m in the former provinces of Mahajanga and Antananarivo. This harrier is usually seen coursing over fallow rice fields, marshes, and wetland habitats in the southwest to central west, Central Highlands, and eastern lowlands and may benefit from human agricultural practices that clear forested land and open fallow fields where it hunts and nests. In 2010 and 2011 a pair was observed in courtship flights at the Ambondrolava mangrove complex (Gardner et al. 2012), and in the same general area in 2015, two individuals were observed at marshes in Belalanda, 10 km north of Toliara (L.-A. Rene de Roland, unpublished data), most likely forming the southern limit of its distribution. In the Bemanevika protected area, a mosaic of wetlands, grasslands, and moist evergreen forests, 22 individual adults have been recorded, and the site holds the largest breeding population on the island.

The breeding season at Miadamankja (Paverne 1997) and Ambohitantely Special Reserve, both in the Central Highlands, and in the Bemanevika and Bealanana areas, both in the southern foothills of Tsaratanàna, is from August to December (Randriamanga 2000; Rene de Roland et al. 2004; L.-A. Rene de Roland, unpublished data). At Ambohitantely and Bemanevika, all nests were placed on the ground within marsh vegetation and 40 cm above water level. Egg laying occurred from mid-September to the end of October; clutch size varied from two to four eggs, averaging three. The incubation period was 32–34 days, young hatched in October and November, and fledging occurred at 42–45 days in November and December. Data from these sites indicate productivity rates of 0.9 young fledged per nesting attempt.

The diet of *C. macrosceles* is composed of insects, birds, reptiles, and small mammals. Prey biomass was dominated by birds (such as *Margaroperdix madagarensis*, Madagascar Partridge; *Eremopterix hova*, Madagascar Lark; and domestic chickens, *Gallus gallus*), reptiles (*Furcifer* and *Liopholidophis*), mammals (*Hemicentetes* and *Rattus*), and insects (*Nomadacris*, order Orthoptera) (Randriamanga 2000; Rene de Roland et al. 2004). Waterbird prey includes young *Ardeola idae* (Madagascar Pond-herons) taken from their nests, and ducklings of *Aythya innotata* (Madagascar Pochard) and *Anas erythrorhyncha* (Red-billed Duck) taken from the surface of lakes (L.-A. Rene de Roland, unpublished data).

The main threats to *Circus* are human caused and include grassland fires that usually occur during the dry period, which coincides with this species' breeding season; therefore nests are destroyed (n = 7 nests lost to fire in a study during 2005). Other threats include transformation of wetlands into rice fields (loss of nests and habitat in natural marshes), and human persecution by taking nestlings as a food source and killing adults to keep them from preying on domestic fowl (Paverne 1997; Randriamanga 2000; Rene de Roland et al. 2004, 2009).

Circus macrosceles is suspected to have seasonal movements, for example leaving its breeding areas in the Central Highlands at Ambohitantely Special Reserve during the rainy season (I. Randriamanga, unpublished data), and on the Ihorombe Plateau (L.-A. Rene de Roland, unpublished data), and moving toward lower-elevation grasslands—further studies are needed to determine whether such displacements indeed occur. The survival of this species is critically dependent on protecting the remaining natural marshes with bordering grasslands, which are an extremely limited and critically threatened habitat on Madagascar (Rene de Roland et al. 2009). The Madagascar Harrier is on the IUCN Red List as an Endangered species with an estimate of 100–249 mature individuals (BirdLife International 2020a).

Accipiter species

Distribution and Status

Three of the diurnal raptor species of Madagascar are members of the genus *Accipiter*: *A. francesiae* (Frances's Sparrowhawk, *firasa madinika, tsipera, perakibo, fandraokibo, tsiparahorovana*), *A. madagascariensis* (Madagascar Sparrowhawk, *firasa, firasa antonony, tsipara, pera*) (Figure 13.22g), and *A. henstii* (Henst's Goshawk, *firasabe, rehila, rehito*). The last two species are endemic to the island and distributed across much of the dry deciduous forests and moist evergreen forests; *A. madagascariensis*, but usually not *A. henstii*, is also in the dry spiny thickets. *Accipiter francesiae*, the smallest of the three species, is represented by four subspecies (del Hoyo et al. 1994), of which one, *A. f. francesiae*, is restricted to Madagascar and is rather common in a range of different forested habitats and open degraded zones; the other three subspecies are found on the Comoro islands.

Description

From a morphological viewpoint, *Accipiter francesiae* has marked sexual dimorphism. The two sexes are easy to distinguish from one another, as the dorsum of the male adult is dark blue, while that of the female is brown. *Accipiter madagascariensis* has a dark brown dorsum, brown ventrum, white barring, and a brown tail with horizontal dark bands. The subcaudal feathers are white, distinguishing it from *A. henstii*. *Accipiter henstii*, the largest of the three species, has upper parts entirely of brownish slate, with white below barred closely with dark brown, including the undertail region, a distinct yellow cere, large yellow tarsi and feet, and a brown tail with five or six darker bars. It is easily confused with the rare and Endangered *Eutriorchis astur* (Madagascar Serpent-eagle), and most reports of serpent-eagles by local villagers are goshawks. *Accipiter henstii* is extremely vocal during the breeding season.

Breeding Behavior

Based on our studies on the Masoala Peninsula, nest construction for *Accipiter henstii*, conducted by both adults, takes place from July to October, and nesting pairs reuse the structure from previous years until the nest tree falls down, unless they are disturbed by humans during the nest-building period; in the latter case, the pair may build a new nest some 300–500 m from the old nest. Neighboring nests in the interior of the Masoala Peninsula were approximately 7–12 km distant from one another (Rene de Roland et al. 1996). Each breeding season *A. madagascariensis* builds a new nest, constructed by both adults, generally from September to mid-October and averaging 2.5 km from the previous year's nest. All nests of *A. madagascariensis* and *A. henstii* were found in relatively intact secondary and primary forests. In the case of *A. francesiae*, nearly all pairs moved their nesting site by about 100 m each year, and nests were constructed by both adults during most of October (Rene de Roland 2000a, 2000b). This species nests in all types of wooded areas, including non-native tree plantations, and secondary and intact forests. Nest height averaged 13.9 m for *A. francesiae*, 24.3 m for *A. madagascariensis* (often hidden toward the top of a canopy tree), and 24.0 m for *A. henstii* (generally placed on the first main tree branch or large supporting branches in the canopy).

For *A. henstii* two or three eggs were laid per clutch, between mid-September and the first week of October. Incubation lasted 39–40 days and was conducted predominantly by the female. The average fledging period was 44 days for males and 47 days for females; the young became independent at 86 days for males and 89 days for females (Rene de Roland 2000c). For *A. madagascariensis* egg laying took place during the first week of October, and the number of eggs laid ranged from one to four. Incubation was 35 days, conducted only by the female. The period to fledging was 36 days for males and 39 days for females, and young became independent from 60 to 62 days for males and 65 to 67 days for females. For *A. francesiae* eggs were laid between the last week of October and the first week of November, with an average of 2.5 eggs per nest (range one to three). Incubation lasted 30 to 32 days and was conducted predominantly by the female. The fledging stage was reached on average in 26 days (range 25 to 27 days) for males and 28 days (range 27 to 29 days) for females. Young became independent at 46 days (range 44 to 48 days) for males and 50 days (range 48 to 51 days) for females (Rene de Roland 2000a). Of 14 nests studied on the Masoala Peninsula, 13 (93%) were successful in fledging at least one young.

Diet and Foraging

Food habits among these three species of *Accipiter* are associated with body size, foot morphology, and habitat. *Accipiter francesiae* feeds predominantly on *Phelsuma* geckos, small *Zonosaurus* plated lizards, and birds, but other prey taken includes snakes, frogs, rodents, and bats (Rene de Roland 2000a). Six bird species were identified as prey: *Hypsipetes madagascariensis* (Madagascar Bulbul), *Zosterops maderaspatanus* (Madagascar White-eye), *Cinnyris sovimanga* (Souimanga Sunbird), *Xanthomixis zosterops* (Spectacled Tetraka), *Bernieria madagascariensis* (Long-billed Tetraka), and *Neomixis tenella* (Common Jery). For *A. madagascariensis*, with a long middle toe adapted for taking birds, avian prey accounted for 97% of hunted animals—particularly doves and pigeons, such as *Nesoenas picturatus* (Madagascar Turtle-dove) and *Treron australis* (Madagascar Green-pigeon)—and 3% were lizards; it hunts in the upper canopy. For *A. henstii*, prey taken includes medium-size birds from the lower forest strata and ground, such as *Coua caerulea* (Blue Coua) and *C. serriana* (Red-breasted Coua), as well as mammals, such as lemurs, and rarely *Tenrec ecaudatus* (Tailless Tenrec). At a study site on Masoala, three lemur species were identified among prey remains, including the diurnal *Eulemur albifrons* (White-fronted Brown Lemur) and two nocturnal species, *Avahi mooreorum* (Masoala Woolly Lemur) and *Lepilemur scottorum* (Masoala Sportive Lemur) (Goodman et al. 1998). An analysis of prey taken by one nesting pair included 102 identified items made up of 84% birds and 26% mammals, but the smaller male delivered 76 (88%) of the total birds (n = 86), whereas the larger female delivered 22 (84%) of the total mammals (n = 26).

The three Malagasy *Accipiter* species have the same general hunting behavior as other members of this genus elsewhere in the world. They remain quiet on a horizontal branch while watching for potential prey. While there is overlap in the feeding ranges of the three Malagasy species, there seems to be little overlap in their diets.

Conservation

Accipiter francesiae is very common on Madagascar, and local villagers occasionally hunt this bird for food. *Accipiter henstii* is occasionally persecuted by local villagers for attacking poultry. Based on several factors, such as remaining habitat potentially utilized and reproductive rates, we estimated that on the Masoala Peninsula there might be as many as 25 pairs of *A. henstii*, 180 pairs of *A. francesiae*, and 30 pairs of *A. madagascariensis*. These last two species are on the IUCN Red List as Least Concern, whereas *A. henstii* was "uplisted" from Near Threatened to Vulnerable in 2020, with increasing recognition of its small population, estimated at 670–1500 mature individuals (BirdLife International 2020a).

Buteo brachypterus, Madagascar Buzzard, *Beririna, Bevorostse, Bobaka, Hindry, Bemanana*

Buteo brachypterus is an endemic and common raptor found in a range of forest types, forest clearings, and secondary vegetation, and it seems adaptable to a certain level of human modification of natural habitats. Its calls, soaring, and perching behavior are reminiscent of other *Buteo* species elsewhere in the world.

In a study on the Masoala Peninsula, Berkelman (1996) found a high breeding density of this species in the lowland moist evergreen forests. In the Bemanevika protected area, L. Raveloson (unpublished data) found a nesting density of 0.4 nest per km^2 (n = 32 nests), and inter-nest distance averaged about 950 m. At this site, *B. brachypterus* laid one or two eggs per clutch. Among the 15 studied nests with two-egg clutches, both eggs hatched in 11 cases, and in six of these facultative siblicide occurred, where the first-hatched young killed its sibling (Mock et al. 1990).

This species is an opportunistic hunter that feeds on a wide range of prey species including invertebrates, terrestrial crabs, lizards, snakes, birds, and rodents on the Masoala Peninsula in lowland moist evergreen forests (Berkelman 1994; Goodman and Langrand 1996). In medium-altitude moist evergreen forests at Bemanevika, the diet of *B. brachypterus* is composed predominantly of reptiles (mostly chameleons) and birds, followed by mammals (mainly *Rattus* and several lemurs), insects, and some amphibians (L. Raveloson, unpublished data). Local villagers occasionally hunt this raptor for food (L.-A. Rene de Roland, unpublished data). The Madagascar Buzzard is on the IUCN Red List as Least Concern (BirdLife International 2020a).

FALCONIFORMES

Falco newtoni, Madagascar Kestrel, *Hitsikitsike, Hitikitke*

Falco newtoni (Figure 13.22f) is the commonest and most widely distributed raptor species on Madagascar, inhabiting grasslands, croplands, secondary vegetation, and degraded woodland habitats, swidden agriculture clearings, and urban areas. This species nests in tree cavities and large hollows. It competes with *Eurystomus glaucurus* (Broad-billed Roller), *Hartlaubius auratus* (Madagascar Starling), the introduced and invasive *Acridotheres tristis* (Common Myna) (Robenarimangason 1999; Rene de Roland et al. 2005a), and other cavity nesters and acts aggressively toward these species during the nesting season.

On the Masoala Peninsula, egg laying takes place from mid-September to early October, with three to five eggs laid. The incubation period is 28 days, and only females incubate. Eggs hatch from mid-October to early November, and young fledge in late November at 23–24 days of age. For the studied pairs, 1.2 young fledged per nesting attempt (Robenarimangason 1999; Rene de Roland et al. 2005a). At this same site, the distance between neighboring nests averaged 675 m, and no agonistic behavior was observed between nesting pairs of *F. newtoni* and a nesting pair of *F. zoniventris* (Banded Kestrel) separated by 100 m (Robenarimangason 1999). Two weeks into their post-fledging period, young were observed catching insects and attacking larger prey, and they dispersed from their natal areas at 44–45 days of age. *Falco newtoni* feeds mainly on insects and lizards, and a few amphibians and birds captured from perches or hovering flights (Robenarimangason 1999; Rene de Roland et al. 2005a). This species is probably one of the few raptors on the island that has benefited from deforestation, cultivation, and urbanization. Apparently, it is doing well in altered and degraded forest habitat and grasslands across much of the island. This species is on the IUCN Red List as Least Concern, as it is common and widespread, with an increasing population (BirdLife International 2020a).

Falco zoniventris, Banded Kestrel, *Hitsiikitsik'ala*

Falco zoniventris (Figure 13.22a) is endemic to Madagascar and lives at forest edges and clearings in secondary and intact forests from the dry deciduous forests and dry spiny thickets of southern and western Madagascar to the moist evergreen forests of the north and east. It is apparently absent from the Central Highlands (Morris and Hawkins 1998). This species is about twice the weight of *F. newtoni*. *Falco zoniventris* is difficult to detect even during the breeding season because of its secretive and relatively nonvocal and nonaerial behavior.

The nesting season commences in the moist evergreen forests with the pair stamping out a nest in the center of an epiphytic fern situated in a large tree fork (Thorstrom 1999; Rene de Roland et al. 2005b); in the west it is known to use old nests of *Falculea palliata* (Sickle-billed Vanga) and roosting structures made by the nocturnal lemur *Mirza coquereli* (Coquerel's Giant Mouse Lemur) (Langrand 1990; Raveloson 2017). In both the humid and dry regions of Madagascar, breeding commences in September, egg laying in October, hatching in November, and fledging in December (Rene de Roland et al. 2005b; Raveloson 2017). Three nesting attempts by two nesting pairs on the Masoala Peninsula led to two clutches of three eggs and one of four eggs; the incubation period was approximately 29 days, and seven of the 10 eggs hatched. All of these young reached the fledgling stage, which gives a productivity of 2.3 young fledged per nesting attempt (Rene de Roland et al. 2005b). The one nest that failed was associated with the male disappearing during the incubation period, and the female could not complete the nesting cycle. Raveloson (2017) reported that in western Madagascar, three eggs were laid per clutch, incubation was 32 days, five of six eggs monitored hatched, and all the young died because of climatic conditions and/or predation. On the Masoala Peninsula, one pair nested 150 m

from the site of the previous year, and the distance between neighboring nests was 3.5 km (Rene de Roland et al. 2005b); in western Madagascar, inter-nest distance was 6.4 km (Raveloson 2017).

Prey of this species on the Masoala Peninsula was composed of chameleons, other types of lizards, insects (mainly katydids, Tettigoniidae; and mantises, Mantodea), birds, frogs, and snakes (Thorstrom 1999; Rene de Roland et al. 2005b), and in the dry deciduous forests at Tsimembo-Manambolomaty the diet was chameleons, katydids, and mantises (Raveloson 2017). *Falco zoniventris* employs predominantly a sit-and-scan hunting style from prominent perches, and when prey is spotted, the bird makes a fast direct flight, grabbing it with its feet from branches, bare limbs, and trunks, and sometimes even crashes into thick vegetation to capture it. It is considered Least Concern on the IUCN Red List; it has a stable population and is perhaps more abundant than previously thought owing to its secretive nature (BirdLife International 2020a).

Falco peregrinus, Peregrine Falcon, *Voromahery*

The subspecies found on Madagascar and the Comoro islands is *Falco peregrinus radama* (Figure 13.22i), which is patchily distributed on Madagascar mainly in the west, south, and Central Highlands. It nests on cliffs, offshore islands, rock walls, and escarpments. The only detailed studies (Razafimanjato et al. 2007) took place in the Central Highlands (one nest) and southwest (two nests). In these areas, the breeding season was June to October, and the nest was on a ledge inside a volcanic caldera. Eggs were laid in July and nestlings were present in August, but the nest failed in September when the nestlings disappeared. In the southwest, the breeding season was slightly later, from July to November, and nests were placed on escarpment shelves and holes in cliff faces. Eggs were laid in August, nestlings were present in September, and young fledged in November; they dispersed at 64 days of age. The two nests studied in the southwest were separated by 7 km. This species feeds on birds caught in flight, ranging from *Hypsipetes madagascariensis* (Madagascar Bulbul) to pigeons, and one nesting pair in the Central Highlands fed predominantly on chickens captured in local villages (Razafimanjato et al. 2007). It is considered Least Concern on the IUCN Red List (BirdLife International 2020a), but *F. p. radama* most likely has a small population and limited nesting sites.

Falco eleonorae, Eleonora's Falcon, *Firasambalala*

Falco eleonorae is a Palearctic-breeding species that migrates to Madagascar during the nonbreeding period, usually arriving in October to December and leaving in March and April. It is observed in groups or pairs feeding on large flying insects over open terrain, woodlands, and forests. It is common in the west soon after arriving on the island and in the north and east later in the season. On the Masoala Peninsula, this species appears to be less frequent, and it has been observed from December to April (L.-A. Rene de Roland, unpublished data). Nearly 50 years ago it was estimated that 80–90% of the world's population of this species wintered on Madagascar (Walter 1979).

Recent studies using satellite telemetry have added new information on migration routes and wintering habitat use of this species on Madagascar. Several satellite-tagged *F. eleonorae* individuals over two consecutive wintering years on the island showed a preference for degraded moist evergreen forests and cultivated lands in areas where largely intact moist evergreen forests were the most abundant habitat type, suggesting that the falcons were taking advantage of a spillover edge effect of insect prey into cultivated and more open areas close to forests (Mellone et al. 2012). In another study, four satellite-tagged falcons had variable wintering home ranges on Madagascar, but they were frequently recorded spending on average 146 days in the north, particularly in the northeast region of the island, and were associated with moist evergreen forest blocks (Kassara et al. 2012). Space-use analyses of satellite-tagged individuals at inter-colony breeding sites from five separated populations, making up most of the breeding range, demonstrated high within-individual home range overlap between consecutive years, suggesting strong winter site fidelity on Madagascar. Further, the inter-colony overlap was equal to or even exceeded in some cases the intra-colony overlap, suggesting that falcons from different colonies may aggregate during the wintering period and exploit the same areas (Kassara et al. 2017). In the central east and north of Madagascar, satellite-tagged individuals exhibited high site fidelity, moving from more open areas upon arrival toward moist evergreen forest areas with denser tree cover between December and February (rainy season), most likely in response to changes in food abundance (Hadjikyriakou et al. 2020).

Nocturnal hunting has been documented for satellite-tagged Eleonora's Falcons; it is more common than previously assumed and occurs preferably, but not exclusively, during above-average moon illumination on wintering grounds on Madagascar (Buij and Gschweng 2017). The importance of moist evergreen forests for Eleonora's Falcons seems to be high, and the current loss of this habitat on Madagascar is a cause for great concern with respect to the conservation of this long-distance migratory falcon species (Mellone et al. 2012). However, it is considered Least Concern on the IUCN Red List and has an increasing global population (BirdLife International 2020a).

Falco concolor, Sooty Falcon, *Firasambalala*, *Tomaimavo*

Falco concolor (Figure 13.22j) is a breeding species of the deserts of northeast Africa from eastern Libya and Egypt to Jordan and southeast along the coasts of the Red Sea and Arabian Gulf to southwestern Pakistan, where it feeds on migratory birds. It spends the northern winter on Madagascar, usually arriving in October to December and leaving in March and April. In 2008, a satellite-tagged *F. concolor* individual migrated on 1 November from its breeding site in the United Arab Emirates and arrived in the Mangoky River area of southwest Madagascar on 13 November, covering 5565 km in 13 days, and spent most of its time in this area before its return migration (Javed et al. 2012). On the wintering grounds, this species generally forages in groups, mostly on flying insects rather than on birds. It is common around Antananarivo during October to April (L.-A. Rene de Roland, unpublished data). In 2009, a group of two to eight individuals was observed from February to April foraging on insects in Ivandry, a suburb of Antananarivo (Boedts 2010). Up to 15 individuals have been noted foraging at dusk in the lights of the stadium in Antananarivo, even during football matches (S. M. Goodman, unpublished data). *Falco concolor* is more

common in the western and southern portions of the island than *F. eleonorae*.

The population size of *F. concolor* is not known with precision, but the number of wintering birds visiting Madagascar may have declined since the early 1990s. Based on estimates from nearly 50 years ago, 90–100% of the world's population of this species winters on Madagascar (Walter 1979). Satellite telemetry of three *F. concolor* individuals from Oman showed that they spent their nonbreeding season in southern and southwestern Madagascar, ranging over a large area, and in general moved rather nomadically across this region. In contrast, one satellite-tagged individual at Ivato airport had a small nonbreeding home range of about 1.1 km centered on the airport and moved mostly over an area of grasslands (Al Jahdhami et al., unpublished data). The species is considered Vulnerable on the IUCN Red List, with an estimated 2800–4000 mature individuals and decreasing population (BirdLife International 2020a).

Subject editors: Roger J. Safford and Steven M. Goodman

CORACIIFORMES: BRACHYPTERACIIDAE, GROUND-ROLLERS

O. Langrand

The family Brachypteraciidae of the order Coraciiformes is endemic to Madagascar, and based on DNA analysis, four extant genera and five species are recognized (Kirchman et al. 2001) (Figure 13.23); the same conclusion was reached based on osteological features (Mayr and Mourer-Chauviré 2000). Taxonomic work on the Coraciiformes has shown that this order is a heterogeneous assemblage. Cracraft (1971) suggested that three families have close relationships based on osteological characters: the Coraciidae, the Brachypteraciidae, and the Leptosomidae; hence the inclusion of "roller" in the English common name of all of them. However, it is likely that Coraciidae and Brachypteraciidae diverged after the Tertiary period (Kirchman et al. 2001; Mayr and Mourer-Chauviré 2003). It is worth noting that recent molecular studies concluded that the Leptosomidae falls outside the order Coraciiformes and is

FIGURE 13.23 The five species of the endemic family Brachypteraciidae. A) *Atelornis crossleyi* in Ranomafana National Park, November; B) *A. pittoides* in Mantadia National Park, November; C) *Geobiastes squamiger* in Masoala National Park, October; D) *Brachypteracias leptosomus* in Masoala National Park, October; and E) *Uratelornis chimaera* in the Ranobe PK32 protected area, December. (PHOTOS by L.-A. Rene de Roland.)

probably best considered in a distinct new order (Hackett et al. 2008; Prum et al. 2015).

The Brachypteraciidae consists of the genera *Brachypteracias* with one species (*B. leptosomus*, Short-legged Ground-roller, *fangadiovy, famakiakora, fandikalalana*), *Geobiastes* with one species (*G. squamiger*, Scaly Ground-roller, *fangadiovy*), *Atelornis* with two species (*A. pittoides*, Pitta-like Ground-roller, *fangadiovy, sakoka, tsakoaka*; and *A. crossleyi*, Rufous-headed Ground-roller, *voromboka, vorontotra*), and *Uratelornis* with one species (*U. chimaera*, Long-tailed Ground-roller, *tolohoranto*). The five species of Brachypteraciidae were described between 1833 and 1895 (Dresser 1896). Subfossil material dating from the Holocene and excavated at Ampoza in the southwest included an extinct species of Brachypteraciidae, *B. langrandi* (Goodman 2000).

The name Brachypteraciidae, from the Greek *brakhupteros*, meaning "short wing" (Jobling 2011), indicates a common morphological feature among the five species. Ground-rollers are secretive, largely terrestrial, socially monogamous, sexually monomorphic, diurnal-crepuscular, and animalivorous. They are of medium size, ranging from 26 to 38 cm in total body length (up to 47 cm for *U. chimaera*), with full tails, short wings, stout bills, and proportionately long legs adapted to cursorial habits. Their large heads, big eyes, short wings, strong legs, and stout bills typify the five species. The plumage, cryptic in appearance, shows some vivid coloration. They are forest dwellers found principally in moist evergreen forests, as well as in the dry spiny thickets (Langrand 2001, 2013).

As far as the etymology of the species names, *leptosomus* comes from Greek, a combination of *leptos*, "delicate," and *soma*, "body," and describes the Cuckoo-Roller (*Leptosomus discolor*) and is applied to *B. leptosomus* as a result of its apparent similarity with the former; *squamiger* comes from Latin and refers to the plumage scales on the bird's back; *pittoides* indicates a resemblance with a member of the genus *Pitta*, which designates a small ornament in the Telugu language (India); *crossleyi* refers to Alfred Crossley (1829–1888), a British bird collector who worked on Madagascar (see Andriamialisoa and Langrand, pp. 1–38); and *chimaera* comes from the Greek *khimaira*, a mythological creature made of the parts of different animals and by extension an implausible species (Jobling 2011; Beolens et al. 2014).

HABITAT

These species are found in a variety of native undisturbed or slightly disturbed forest types from sea level to 2000 m above sea level. Four of the five species (*Brachypteracias leptosomus*, *Geobiastes squamiger*, *Atelornis pittoides*, and *A. crossleyi*) inhabit the lowland and medium-altitude moist evergreen forests, with the two *Atelornis* species occurring in the upper reaches of this formation, notably the montane forest zone. *Atelornis pittoides* and *A. crossleyi* are generally allopatric based on their elevation ranges. The four ground-roller species that inhabit the various moist evergreen forest types have broad distributional ranges, all occurring in the north from the forests surrounding the Andapa Basin (Marojejy and Anjanaharibe-Sud) south to Andohahela, and along almost the entire eastern forest belt. *Atelornis pittoides* is also known from Montagne d'Ambre in the extreme north (Goodman and Raherilalao 2013; Langrand 2013; Goodman et al. 2018).

Brachypteracias leptosomus and *G. squamiger* tend to favor the lowland and medium-altitude moist evergreen forests, particularly undisturbed habitats with damp ground, closed canopy, moderately dense understory, and thick leaf litter. *Brachypteracias leptosomus*, which has an elevational range from 0 to 1500 m, tends to extend farther northeast and northwest than *G. squamiger*, which occurs between 0 and 950 m. *Atelornis pittoides*, the species with the broadest distribution, is adapted to all major types of natural moist evergreen forest, including the Sambirano in the northwest, and occurs from sea level to 2000 m. *Atelornis crossleyi* seems to prefer higher elevations, including montane formations from 800 to 2000 m, but is most common from 1250 to 1750 m (Langrand 2013).

Uratelornis chimaera has markedly different distribution and habitat choice, being geographically restricted to an area of between 3700 and 4100 km^2 in the dry spiny thickets of the southwest and across an elevational range of between 20 and 200 m. The distribution of this species is limited to a narrow coastal band between the Mangoky River to the north and the Onilahy River to the south. These areas are dominated by Euphorbiaceae and Didiereaceae growing on sandy soils. However, it seems to prefer lower-stature vegetation and is not directly associated with *Didierea madagascariensis*, as was previously believed. This unique xerophytic thicket receives an average annual rainfall of about 500 mm (Seddon and Tobias 2007; Goodman and Raherilalao 2013).

BEHAVIOR

The ground-rollers are largely diurnal species with a crepuscular tendency. The five species are active early in the morning, often calling before sunrise. In the case of *Uratelornis chimaera*, nocturnal activities have been reported, especially during full moon periods (Appert 1968; Langrand 1990). This species frequently calls at night, and counter-singing birds have been regularly reported.

Ground-rollers are terrestrial and forage for food in the forest or thicket leaf litter. However, they spend time perched in trees—*Brachypteracias leptosomus* shows strong arboreal tendencies—especially while giving territorial calls or wait-search prey spotting (Thorstrom and Lind 1999). All are burst flyers with short, direct, quick, and noisy flight. This species uses flight to reach prey, which is taken from the ground or vegetation. Most ground-rollers fly to and from their nests. They are generally found alone or in pairs during the reproductive season. After breeding, family groups can be observed together.

The behavior of ground-rollers is more thrush-like than that of true rollers (family Coraciidae). True rollers capture their prey in the air and do not have the anatomical features to uncover, pursue, and capture prey on the ground, as in the Brachypteraciidae (Cracraft 1971). The general foraging pattern is a wait-search ambush strategy. They silently pause for long periods, either on the ground or on horizontal branches 3–5 m off the ground (Langrand 1990). They catch prey on the ground or in the foliage after a quick sally or run. In the case of *B. leptosomus*, foraging can take place under the canopy up to 30 m off the ground. Prey searching often continues for an extended period (several minutes) in the leaf litter or in the foliage of a tree. When a potential item is spotted, it is pursued.

Forays toward prey can exceed 25 m, a considerable distance in a closed forest environment (Thorstrom and Lind 1999).

Members of the Brachypteraciidae usually feed on soil or litter invertebrates (insects, millipedes, snails, and slugs) and small vertebrates, such as amphibians, small reptiles, and shrew tenrecs (Goodman and Parrillo 1997; Langrand 2013). *Uratelornis chimaera* captures insects (Coleoptera, Blattidae, Orthoptera, and Lepidoptera) while foraging in leaf litter (Appert 1968). *Atelornis crossleyi* eats invertebrates, chiefly insects (Carabidae, Tenebrionidae, Curculionidae, and Formicidae), as well as beetle larvae and members of the Diplopoda and Gastropoda removed from rotten wood (Goodman and Parrillo 1997; Langrand 2013).

VOICE

Vocalizations are important in assessing the presence of ground-rollers at a site, particularly considering their secretive and terrestrial habits. Vocal communication seems to play an important role in the social behavior of these birds, especially to define territories. The four species inhabiting the moist evergreen forests have fairly similar calls that are emitted mostly in the early morning (often before sunrise) before and during the breeding season from September to February (Langrand 1990). Otherwise, they are more or less silent, making it difficult to assess their local occurrence at a site.

Brachypteracias leptosomus vocalizes very early in the morning, one of the first calls heard in the predawn chorus. The territorial vocalization consists of a single deep, low *boop* emitted with the head pushed downward. The call, given from a horizontal perch 5–30 m off the ground, is emitted for about 4 min at 1–5 sec intervals. Other individuals can be heard counter-singing with a similar *boop*, and territorial birds on adjacent territories may chase each other between song bouts. When pairs move around the forest, they use a specific call to maintain contact. This call is a single *boop* similar to the territorial call, but softer and emitted only once. The call may have a ventriloquial quality (Thorstrom and Watson 1997; Thorstrom and Lind 1999; Langrand 2013).

Geobiastes squamiger has a territorial call similar to that of *B. leptosomus*, but it is a higher-pitched, softer sort of *hooop*, slightly inflected upward and repeated every 5–10 sec. The call is given from a perch 0.1–5 m off the ground. The contact call is a single deep *hoop*, and a harsh *frrrret* is emitted when birds are excited. No evidence of counter-singing between territorial individuals has been found in this species (Langrand 1990; Rakotoarisoa and Be 2004).

Atelornis pittoides has a territorial vocalization similar to that of *G. squamiger*, but softer and shorter, and repeated every 4–10 sec. This territorial call is emitted from a stump or horizontal branch 0.5–5 m off the ground. The alarm call is a harsh hissing *kashhhhh*. Individuals respond to each other. *Atelornis crossleyi* has a territorial call of a series of clear *whoops* slightly inflected, repeated every 3–6 sec. This is the highest-pitched ground-roller vocalization. When calling, this species perches on a stump or a lower branch usually 1–2 m off the ground, but sometimes up to 10 m (Langrand 1990).

Uratelornis chimaera is fairly vocal and has a very distinct call, reminiscent of *Centropus toulou*, but softer and emitted more rapidly. The vocalization is a series of six to 10 soft, even notes, *booboobooboobo*, lasting from 10 to 40 sec and emitted from the ground or more often from a concealed perch 2–6 m off the ground. Calls are heard in the early morning, but also frequently at dusk and at night (Appert 1968; Langrand 1990). The hooting is emitted by only one individual of the pair, presumably the male, but both sexes emit abrupt popping notes. The call is audible to humans up to 200 m away (Tobias and Seddon 2003). A sound produced mechanically has been noted that is unique to this species. A cracking noise is produced with the wings, immediately following the typical soft hooting call, as the bird moves from the ground to a perch. This noise produced with the wings is similar to that of the wing cracking of the manakins (Pipridae) from the New World tropics (Tobias and Seddon 2003; Snow 2004).

BREEDING

Based on current information, ground-rollers spend all year in their breeding area. They are territorial and seem to hold stable territories (Thorstrom and Lind 1999). The five species are thought to be monogamous, but such details have not really been investigated. Individuals spend long periods calling to defend their territories during the breeding season from September to January.

During courtship, pairs move around their territory together. *Brachypteracias leptosomus* and *Geobiastes squamiger* males feed the females continuously. Females dropping their tail feathers during the nesting period have been documented for *B. leptosomus*, *G. squamiger*, and *Uratelornis chimaera*. It is not known whether this is the result of predator attacks or a natural tail molt developed as an antipredator strategy (Thorstrom and Lind 1999; Rakotoarisoa and Be 2004).

Ground-rollers lay one to four, usually two, globular white eggs between October and January (Langrand 1990). The principal egg-laying period appears to be in December. Except for *B. leptosomus* (below), eggs are deposited in a shallow depression (2 cm) dug in the soil and lined with dried leaves, in a chamber at the end of a tunnel 60–120 cm long. The entrance of the burrow is round and 7–10 cm in diameter (Appert 1968; Goodman 1994b). The incubation time for *G. squamiger* is 18 days (Rakotoarisoa and Be 2004). The only species that seems to be an arboreal breeder is *B. leptosomus*. The only two nests of this species ever reported by field workers were in tree hollows 20–30 m above ground level (Thorstrom and Lind 1999).

The division of parental care is poorly known. In *B. leptosomus* and *G. squamiger* only the female has been seen incubating, with the male occasionally bringing food to her. Males stay in the vicinity of the nest and give territorial calls (Thorstrom and Watson 1997; Rakotoarisoa and Be 2004). The incubation period for the other four species is not known exactly but probably exceeds 17 days. The time spent in the nest by the young before fledging is unknown. The age at sexual maturity has not been documented for any of the five species.

CONSERVATION

Natural climatic and associated habitat changes have been implicated in the extinction of some Malagasy animals, including one

species of ground-roller, *Brachypteracias langrandi* (Goodman 2000). Among the living ground-roller species, *B. leptosomus* is the most likely to be impacted by climate change, with the risk of losing 62% of its original ecological niche by 2050, while *Geobiastes squamiger* is more likely to adapt and keep 50% of its original niche (Andriamasimanana and Cameron 2013).

Human-induced changes to the island's environment have provoked a significant diminution in the natural forest cover, and most forest bird species are threatened as a result of this habitat destruction. Ground-rollers, forest-dependent species requiring large tracts of undisturbed forest, are particularly affected (Langrand and Wilmé 1997). Madagascar's forest cover went from 27% of the national territory in the 1950s to 16% in 2000, a 40% reduction in 50 years (Harper et al. 2007). In 2014 forest cover dropped to 15% of the island's surface area. The remaining forest cover is about 8.9 million ha, which includes 4.4 million ha of moist evergreen forest (50%) and 1.7 million ha of dry spiny thicket (19%) (Vieilledent et al. 2018). It is predicted that by 2050, if habitat destruction continues, forest cover will be reduced to 4 million ha, mostly in montane areas. This makes the future of ground-roller species, as well as any other bird species dependent on moist evergreen forests, appear pretty bleak. Deforestation is not the only element leading to species loss. Forest fragmentation is also affecting forest-dependent bird species like the ground-rollers, and it was estimated that in 2017, 46% of the remaining forests were within 100 m of a forest edge or an open area (Vieilledent et al. 2018).

Of the four ground-roller species found in moist evergreen forests, *Atelornis pittoides* appears to be the least sensitive to human disturbance, but *B. leptosomus*, *G. squamiger*, and *A. pittoides* are under some hunting pressure (Goodman and Raherilalao 2013). In the Ambohitantely protected area, *A. pittoides* occurs in forest fragments between 28 and 1250 ha (Langrand and Wilmé 1997). Further, it is also found in fairly degraded secondary forests of certain protected areas, such as portions of Ranomafana. At some sites, such as the Manambolo Forest just north of Andringitra, the density of *A. pittoides* is high, particularly in forested zones along stream courses that have been heavily degraded by cattle grazing.

Of the five ground-roller species, three are classified on the IUCN Red List as Vulnerable, one as Near Threatened, and one as Least Concern (i.e., not threatened). The four moist evergreen forest species are known to occur in numerous protected areas (*B. leptosomus*: 29 protected areas; *G. squamiger*: 21; *A. pittoides*: 34; and *A. crossleyi*: 25) (Goodman et al. 2018; Langrand and Kirwan 2020). *Uratelornis chimaera* is found in three protected areas: Mangoky Ihotry (IUCN Category V), Mikea (IUCN Category II), and Ranobe PK32 (IUCN category not defined) (Goodman et al. 2018; Langrand and Kirwan 2020). The global population of *U. chimaera* was estimated nearly 15 years ago at about 21,000 individuals (Seddon and Tobias 2007), and in the intervening period the forest habitat of this species has been under considerable human pressure.

Subject editors: Roger J. Safford and Steven M. Goodman

PSITTACIFORMES: *CORACOPSIS*, VASA PARROTS

J. M. M. Ekstrom and R. J. Safford

The genus *Coracopsis* contains two of the three parrot species on Madagascar, commonly known as Greater Vasa Parrot (*C. vasa*) and Lesser Vasa Parrot (*C. nigra*). These two species are largish, brownish-black parrots with long but rounded tails and stout bills. They are both endemic to Madagascar and the Comoro islands, although the birds usually treated as a subspecies of *C. nigra* on the Comoros probably deserve species rank (see under *C. nigra*, below).

Coracopsis parrots on Madagascar are relatively poorly known and surprisingly difficult to distinguish in the field, with rather similar plumage and a size difference that is far from easy to assess. However, recent studies (Böhning-Gaese et al. 1996, 1999; Hampe 1998; Ekstrom et al. 2003, 2013a, 2013b; Bollen and van Elsacker 2004) have begun to detail the complexity of their social and ecological relationships. The public popularity of Psittaciformes the world over is not mirrored in scientific knowledge of this bird order, and Madagascar's representatives are no exception. The difficulties of studying an intelligent, fast-flying, tropical treetop bird go a long way toward explaining the dearth of research on parrots. However, the bizarre nature of the *Coracopsis* social system and their sexual behavior make these species well worth the effort to study them.

CORACOPSIS VASA, GREATER VASA PARROT, *BOLOKY*, *BOLOKIBE*, *BOEZA BE*, *KIA*, *KOERA*, *VAZAMBE*

Three subspecies are recognized (Juniper and Parr 1998), all very similar: *C. v. vasa* of eastern Madagascar; *C. v. drouhardi* of western and southern Madagascar; and *C. v. comorensis* of the Comoro islands, on Grande Comore (Ngazidja), Mohéli (Mwali), and Anjouan (Ndzuani).

Coracopsis vasa is found in a wide variety of habitats and is probably restricted mainly by access to suitable nest holes in mature trees. It is found in moist evergreen and dry deciduous forests, coastal plains with coconut plantations, grasslands including those

dominated by *Bismarckia* palms, rice fields, mango plantations, and even dry spiny thickets. The species is not often recorded above 1000 m elevation, although it reaches 1875 m on massifs in eastern Madagascar and 2000 m on Grande Comore (Ekstrom 2013a; Goodman and Raherilalao 2013). Initial observations of a color-marked population by the first author in the Kirindy Forest CNFEREF (Centre National de Formation, d'Etudes et de Recherche en Environnement et Foresterie) (see Kappeler et al., pp. 127–33) suggest that the species is largely sedentary, making local movements for food. (All references in this text mentioning the Kirindy Forest refer to the CNFEREF block, rather than to Kirindy Mité south of Morondava.) However, females appear more site faithful than males, being frequently found near the habitual nest tree for much of the year.

No systematic study of their feeding ecology has been carried out. However, many food trees are already known. In his countrywide survey, Dowsett (2000) noted two genera of Burseraceae—*Canarium* sp. (pulp of large fruits) and *Commiphora* sp. (probably *C. guillaumini*, small fruit buds); Meliaceae—*Quivisianthe papinae* (flowers); Strelitziaceae—*Ravenala madagascariensis* (seeds); Tiliaceae—*Grewia cyclea* (seeds); Ulmaceae—*Trema orientalis* (unripe seeds); Anacardiaceae—introduced *Mangifera* (unripe mango fruits); Casuarinaceae—*Casuarina* sp. (seeds); and various palms. In the extreme south and southeast of Madagascar, Goodman et al. (1997a) noted foraging on seeds of *Tamarindus indica* and leaves of *Acacia* sp. (Fabaceae), fruits and seeds of *Ficus polita* (Moraceae), fruits and seeds of *Neotina isoneura* (Sapindaceae), and fruits and seeds of *Celtis gomphophylla* and *C. philippensis* (Ulmaceae). In the Kirindy Forest and near the Andranomena Special Reserve, it has been noted that this species consumes Caesalpiniaceae—*Cassia leandrii* (flowers) and *Delonix adansonioides* (fruit); Burseraceae—*Commiphora mafaidoha* (fruit); Rhamnaceae—*Berchemia discolor* (fruit); and Anacardiaceae—*Poupartia sylvatica* (fruit) and *Operculicarya gummifera* (fruit) (J. Ekstrom, unpublished data). Reviewing studies on frugivory by all species in the Kirindy and Sainte Luce forests, Bollen et al. (2005) considered this parrot to be a seed predator rather than disperser. *Coracopsis vasa* also commonly feeds outside the forest in cultivated areas, consuming a variety of crop plants. Groups of over 100 individuals have been observed in fields south of the Kirindy Forest and, not surprisingly, the species is regarded as a pest in some areas (Ekstrom 2003). At large food sources, such as groups of fruiting and flowering trees or ripe maize crops, *C. vasa* and *C. nigra* will commonly forage in mixed groups.

A remarkable facet of *C. vasa* behavior has been revealed in captive individuals: they are one of a small number of nonprimate animals to use tools, although these include some other large parrot species (M. Lambert et al. 2015). *Coracopsis vasa* is known for its tendency to explore and manipulate objects in captivity, and several individuals of a captive population spontaneously adopted a novel tool technique by using pebbles and date pits either as a scraper on the inner surface of seashells, subsequently licking the resulting calcium powder from the tool, or as a wedge to break off smaller pieces of the shell for ingestion. Tool use occurred most frequently just prior to the breeding season, when numerous instances of tool transfer were also documented. This may be the first report of a nonprimate using a tool for grinding, and similar behavior should be looked for in wild birds.

Coracopsis vasa breeds in the austral summer (October to January) (Langrand 1990; Ekstrom 2013a) and is a secondary tree-cavity nester, although in limestone karst areas, such as the Ankarana, it is known to nest on rock ledges over cave entrances (S. M. Goodman, unpublished data), and one nest was even found (with eggs) within a cave beyond the direct reach of sunlight (Middleton 2000). No nest material is added apart from some green foliage occasionally. For several years, anecdotes in the avicultural literature have suggested that *Coracopsis* parrots have a very unusual breeding system. In captivity, copulations lasting 100 min are common (Wilkinson and Birkhead 1995; L. Desborough, unpublished data), beginning with the male everting ("out-pocketing") a large (50–55 mm long by 40–45 mm wide), fleshy, bag-like protrusion from his cloaca (Figure 13.24); females also possess a cloacal protrusion, smaller than that of males but flexible. During copulation the male's cloacal protrusion completely enters the female's cloaca, allowing intromission of a phallus-like organ (5–15 mm in length) at its tip. Breeding females lose feathers specifically from the head and develop an orange color to the skin, which is apparently associated with a form of subcutaneous vascularization (Wilkinson and Birkhead 1995). Furthermore, females appear dominant over males, and in caged groups it is common for two males to feed a single brood (Wilkinson 1990; Blynn and Paul 1994).

A study in the Kirindy Forest has revealed a fascinating breeding system in the wild (Ekstrom 2003; Ekstrom et al. 2007). In this region, the social mating system of *C. vasa* is cooperative polygynandry, where several males provision each active nest. Females are behaviorally dominant over males throughout the breeding cycle and begin to solicit copulation and food from males at approximately four weeks before egg laying. Females forage little themselves during this period and cease to forage completely from egg laying onward (as in most psittacines). Two distinct forms of copulation occur. Protracted copulation (apparently similar to that described above for captive birds) lasts 5–114 min, involving intromission of the male phallus and vigorous pumping by the male. Such copulations are infrequent (approximately 0.3 per day per female) and occur only in the four weeks preceding egg laying. Copulation behavior changes with the commencement of egg laying, becoming short (1–3 sec) and very frequent (approximately 20–30 per day per female), sometimes with two or three males in rapid succession. Hence, sperm competition appears extremely intense. Copulations continue at a high rate throughout the incubation period; this may be because males are physically denied access to the nest hole by the female and therefore may not be able to assess the end of the female's fertile period. From egg laying onward a female is fed by at least three to six partners (most unmarked and presumed male), who provide all the resources for the growing chicks. Observations have shown that at least some of these provisioning individuals are the copulating males. However, the exact relationship between a male's copulation success and provisioning behavior remains unclear.

Female ranging and vocal behavior also change markedly at egg laying. The home range of breeding females contracts from approximately 15 ha before egg laying to just 1–2 ha around the nest hole once she has laid the first egg. Within this contracted area, the female uses particular tree perches (6–14), from which she sings. The songs are complex, multisyllabic vocalizations lasting 8–15 sec and

FIGURE 13.24 **During the breeding season, *Coracopsis vasa* males, prior to copulation, evert a large cloacal protrusion, which during copulation completely enters the female's cloaca, allowing intromission of a phallus-like organ at its tip. Here the enlarged structure can be seen.** (PHOTO by J. A. Tobias.)

are individually recognizable to the human ear. Females alternate incubation with singing and spend approximately 60% of their time singing during chick rearing. Female song may function to attract provisioning males, since the arrival rate of males is much higher during periods of song than during periods of quiet. Playback experiments have supported this hypothesis. However, since males are expected to use paternity cues to initiate their provisioning behavior, it is difficult to interpret female song further than its role in identification. In other words, it is difficult to suggest that a female's songs might sway the provisioning choices of males. Females defend small territories around the nest, but only during the chick-rearing period. Hence, territoriality is not associated with mate choice, as in most other birds. Resident females eject only intruding females (identified by head feather loss), who tend to be floaters rather than neighbors, an observation that has been amply supported by playback experiments. Territoriality may function in resource defense: intruding females sometimes manage to gain food from provisioning males, who therefore appear to occasionally feed nonresident females. This potential loss of valuable resources for a growing brood probably explains the unusual post-fertile territorial behavior.

Why does a cooperative breeding system exist in *C. vasa*? Answers to this interesting evolutionary question may be rooted in the rapid development of both eggs and chicks in this species. Comparative data show that *Coracopsis* parrots have some of the shortest incubation (15 days in *C. nigra*, 16 days in *C. vasa*) and chick-rearing periods (35 days in *C. nigra*, 45 days in *C. vasa*) of any Old World parrot, relative to their body size. The cause for this is unknown but may involve high nest ectoparasite loads or predation rates. Furthermore, *C. vasa* has a large brood size of three to five chicks given its body mass of approximately 500–600 g. Other parrots of similar size tend to have one or two chicks (Juniper and Parr 1998). The consequence of such reproductive anomalies is a high demand for food to fuel rapid growth of a large number of chicks. In this way, it may pay males to collaborate to raise the chicks of each nest, despite the costs of shared or uncertain paternity. Cooperation in this way would explain the lack of aggression between copulating and feeding males. However, the polygynandrous (rather than simply polyandrous) nature of this system adds further complexity to the *C. vasa* story.

During field studies in 1999–2000, the first sexual interactions were observed on 15 September and the first copulation was observed on 5 October. The first egg was laid on 18 October and the last known chick fledged on 15 January. Egg laying was very synchronous across females. Approximately 85% of females commenced egg laying within the same seven-day period, from the end of October to the beginning of November (n = 17 females). This is very unusual for a parrot, or indeed any tropical bird. No double clutches were recorded. Like most parrots, *C. vasa* is a secondary cavity nester, using a hollow in the trunk or large branch of a live or dead tree. A total of 55 nest holes previously used by *Coracopsis* spp. were located in the context of this research project; at least 38 holes were active with *C. vasa* during the 1999–2000 and 2000–2001 breeding seasons. Of these 38 nest holes, 18 were in living *Adansonia rubrostipa* (Malvaceae) baobabs, five in dead *A. rubrostipa*, 10 in living *Commiphora guillaumini*, three in dead *C. guillaumini*, one in a living *Poupartia silvatica*, and one in a dead *Cordyla madagascariensis* (Fabaceae). Nesting has also been recorded at different sites in other baobab species, *A. grandidieri* and *A. za*. Nest holes were located between 2 and 12 m high (canopy at 12–18 m), with a mean height of 8.2 ± 1.52 m, and cavity dimensions included a mean depth of 104 ± 41 cm (maximum 500 cm) and width of 14 ± 2 cm. Although most hole entrances were in the side of tree trunks, some were vertical and therefore facing toward the sky.

Three to seven white eggs per clutch have been recorded. In 1999, the rate of nest failure was high in comparison to other parrot

species. Of the 23 eggs laid, 18 eggs hatched, giving a hatching success rate (eggs hatched/eggs laid) of 78%. The causes of hatching failure were either infertility (two eggs) or failed development (three eggs). The fledging success was low (39%); only seven young fledged from a total of 18 hatchlings. Fledging success was low because of several unrelated factors; most important were predation of young chicks (suspected predators were *Tyto alba*, Barn Owl; and *Asio madagascariensis*, Madagascar Long-eared Owl) and death of mature chicks apparently caused by high ectoparasite loads inducing anemia. Human predation was responsible for the complete failure of two nests. The overall 1999 breeding success (chicks fledged/eggs laid) was 30.4%, with a mean of 1.2 fledglings per breeding pair.

On Madagascar, *C. vasa* and its congener can be freely persecuted and traded from 1 May to the first Sunday in October, although these restrictions are not widely known of or obeyed. At least in the Kirindy Forest area, the numbers of birds hunted for food by local people almost certainly exceed those captured for trade (J. M. Ekstrom, unpublished data), as previously noted by Fauré (1996). In the region surrounding the Bezà Mahafaly protected area, at least until a few decades ago, this species was extensively hunted as a crop pest when corn was ripening (S. M. Goodman, unpublished data). It survives well in some human-modified habitats. Survival probably depends on access to nest sites and therefore trees of sufficient age, as the species readily breeds in formerly forested areas now cleared for agricultural crops but retaining baobabs and a few scattered native woody trees. The destruction of large trees as part of wider deforestation, and particularly the loss of baobabs outside the forest for housing materials, seems very likely to have affected, and will continue to reduce, the breeding range of this species, at least in western Madagascar.

CORACOPSIS NIGRA, LESSER VASA PARROT, BOLOKY, KIA, KOERA, VAZA, BOLOKIKELY

On Madagascar, this species has been divided into two subspecies: the dark *Coracopsis n. nigra* in the east and north and the paler *C. n. libs* in the south and southwest. Additional morphological differences are mostly rather subtle; many individuals in the central west are hard to identify to subspecies (Ekstrom 2013b), and genetic analysis provided little support for separation of these forms (H. Jackson et al. 2016). So-called *C. n. sibilans* of the Comoro islands is a remarkable 25% smaller than Malagasy populations and forms a distinct genetic clade (Kundu et al. 2012; H. Jackson et al. 2016); it probably merits recognition as a species, as does (certainly, based on stronger genetic differentiation) another small, insular form, *C. barklyi*, on the granitic Seychelles.

Coracopsis nigra is known from moist evergreen and dry deciduous forests, mangroves, secondary woodland, and some grassland habitats. It appears more restricted to relatively intact forest than *C. vasa*, which is probably a function of their differing dietary regimes rather than inability to use nest holes outside forest. However, *C. nigra* has a wider elevational distribution, from sea level to about 1950 m (Goodman and Raherilalao 2013). It is believed to be sedentary, making daily movements in search of food (Juniper and Parr 1998).

Several bibliographic sources consider *C. nigra* to be more frugivorous than *C. vasa*, a belief that is corroborated by the former species' greater dependence on intact forest than its congener. However, it is difficult to make general assessments without comprehensive studies in which all major food items are identified year-round, and this appears to have been done in only one study, in the littoral forest of Sainte Luce, in the far southeast (Bollen and van Elsacker 2004). Here, of 40 food plant species taken, 68% were used as a source of seeds, 22% provided both seeds and pulp, and 10% flowers; one was non-native, the guava *Psidium guajava* (Myrtaceae), the rest native: *Poupartia chapelieri* (Anacardiaceae); *Polyalthia madagascariensis* (Annonaceae); *Cabucala madagascariensis* (Apocynaceae); *Polyscias* sp. and *Schefflera rainaliana* (Araliaceae); *Dypsis prestoniana* (Arecaceae); *Symphonia* sp. (Clusiaceae); *Terminalia fatraea* (Combretaceae); *Agelea pentagyna* (Connaraceae); *Vaccinium emirnense* (Ericaceae); *Erythroxylum buxifolium* and *E. nitidulum* (Erythroxylaceae); *Macaranga perrieri* and *Suregada baronii* (Euphorbiaceae); *Uapaca littoralis* (Phyllanthaceae); *Homalium louvelianum* and *Ludia antanosarum* (Salicaceae); *Apodytes dimidiata* (Metteniusaceae); *Bakerella ambongoensis* and *Bakerella* sp. (Loranthaceae); *Eugenia* sp. and *Syzygium* sp. (Myrtaceae); *Campylospermum obtusifolium* (Ochnaceae); *Jasminum kitchingi*, *Noronhia* cf. *lanceolata*, *Noronhia* sp., and *Olea* sp. (Oleaceae); *Cantium variistipula*, *Morinda* cf. *umbelluligera*, and *M. rigida* (Rubiaceae); *Vepris elliotii* and *V. fitoravina* (Rutaceae); *Tina thouarsiana* and *Tinopsis conjugata* (Sapindaceae); *Sideroxylon beguei* var. *saboureaui* (Sapotaceae); *Sarcolaena multiflora* (Sarcolaenaceae); *Rhopalocarpus coriaceus* (Sphaerosepalaceae); and *Ravenala madagascariensis*. Items taken included berries (31%), drupes (47%), and capsules and other fruit types (22%). Most fruits eaten had juicy pulp (70%), but fibrous fruits (8%) and fruits without pulp (22%) were also taken, one seeded or multi-seeded, with or without a hard protective kernel. Median fruit size was 12 mm and mass 0.6 g; median seed size was 7 mm and mass 0.1 g. Most fruits (70%) were eaten while unripe, giving enhanced dietary flexibility.

Elsewhere, observations are anecdotal and do not provide a full picture of the diet but still provide additional information of interest. Food plants listed by Dowsett (2000) for *C. nigra* across its range include fruits and seeds of *Commiphora mafaidoha*; young leaves of *Didierea madagascariensis* (Didiereaceae); seeds of *Foetidia asymetrica* and *F. retusa* (Lecythidaceae), *Ravenala madagascariensis*, and *Trema orientalis*; flowers of *Quivisianthe papinae*; fruits of *Ficus* spp., *Brochoneura* sp. (Myristicaceae), *Solanum mauritianum* (Solanaceae), *Psidium cattleyanum*, and mangos. Dowsett (2000) also noted the information of a reliable guide, who suggested that the seeds of *Albizia* sp. (Fabaceae), the flowers and fruits of *Macaranga* sp., and three liana species are also commonly eaten. Goodman et al. (1997a) reported *C. nigra* feeding on either the fruits or seeds of several other food species from southeastern Madagascar: the introduced *Agave rigida* (Agavaceae), *Hippocratea rubiginosa* (Celastraceae), *Alluaudia procera* (Didieraceae), *Croton* sp. and *Uapaca* sp., *Acacia farnesiana*, *Tamarindus indica*, *Melia azedarach* (introduced Meliaceae), *Neotina isoneura*, and *Celtis philippensis*. Hampe (1998), making observations in March at Kirindy, noted *Poupartia silvatica* (fruits and seeds), *Commiphora guillaumini* (fruits and seeds), *Breonia perrieri* (Rubiaceae, entire fruits), and the flowers of *Bivinia jalberti* (Flacourtiaceae), *Foetidia*

asymetrica, Capuronia madagascariensis (Lythraceae), and *Colvillea racemosa* (Caesalpiniaceae). Like its congener, *Coracopsis nigra* is commonly known as a pest of numerous agricultural crops (e.g., maize, cassava, and rice). In the Kirindy Forest area, reliable local guides have mentioned that *C. nigra* nestlings are fed large amounts of corn (Ekstrom 2003). As specialist and locally abundant frugivores, *Coracopsis* parrots may play important roles in forest ecology. In the studies at Kirindy and Sainte Luce, *C. nigra* has, like *C. vasa*, been found to be more of a seed predator than a seed disperser for many food species (Bollen et al. 2004b, 2005). However, despite a high seed predation rate, it was found to be the primary disperser of the tree *Commiphora guillaumini* at Kirindy by dropping a small proportion of intact fruits away from the source tree (Böhning-Gaese et al. 1999).

The breeding system of *Coracopsis nigra* in the wild is little known, but opportunistic observations in the Kirindy Forest area suggest it is significantly different from that of *C. vasa* (Ekstrom 2003): *C. nigra* females are less blatantly solicitous in seeking copulations from males, do not have complex songs during incubation or chick rearing, and are fed less frequently by males during the incubation period. Prior to nesting, groups of *C. nigra* fly and sexually interact together; this is markedly different from *C. vasa*, where females are frequently found on particular perches near their proposed nest tree, from which they solicit almost every male who passes by.

Bibliographic sources suggest that the breeding season of *C. nigra* is December to March, with egg laying recorded from October to January (e.g., Langrand 1990; Ekstrom 2013b). In the Kirindy Forest area, the chick-rearing period extends to April, and, in contrast to *C. vasa*, breeding does not appear synchronous across females of a population. *Coracopsis nigra* uses the nest hole of *C. vasa* after the latter has completed breeding. Opportunistic observations during fieldwork on *C. vasa* found few *C. nigra* nest holes in the Kirindy Forest area (n = 8). These were found in *Adansonia rubrostipa, Commiphora guillaumini* (living and dead), and *Tamarindus indica*. These cavities were 3–12 m off the ground, with an entrance diameter of 15–50 cm and cavity depth of 80–500 cm. Dowsett (2000) regarded *Coracopsis nigra* as more common than *C. vasa* in both eastern and western Madagascar. The former species is hunted and traded, like its congener (see above). At least in the Kirindy Forest area, the numbers of birds hunted for food by local people almost certainly exceed those captured for trade (Fauré 1996; J. M. Ekstrom, unpublished data). *Coracopsis nigra* is not threatened with extinction but is listed on Appendix II of CITES (see below for the significance of the CITES listing). Although this species has been observed nesting outside forest, this is probably less common than for *C. vasa*. For this reason, the species is more vulnerable to habitat modification.

TRADE IN *CORACOPSIS* VASA PARROTS WITHIN OR EXPORTED FROM MADAGASCAR

Neither *Coracopsis vasa* nor *C. nigra* has ever been considered to be threatened with extinction, both being Least Concern on the IUCN Red List of Threatened Species. Like many parrots, both species are traded, but this does not appear to be a major threat to either, as they are not popular as pets, presumably because of their drab plumage. Both are included on Appendix II of CITES, meaning that international trade may be allowed but is subject to permits issued by the government, in order to avoid utilization incompatible with survival. Numbers legally exported in the 1990s were in the hundreds annually, but exports of *C. vasa* from Madagascar have been suspended by CITES since 1995, so permitted exports of this species have dropped to zero (CITES 2020). *Coracopsis nigra* continued to be exported annually in the tens or low hundreds until 2006, but recorded trade in this species since then has also dwindled to near zero.

Nicoll and Langrand (1989) pointed out the contradiction between the national status of *C. vasa* as game (*gibier*) and international protection under CITES Appendix II, suggesting that the latter should have priority; listing on CITES Appendix I, banning all international trade, would be appropriate only if the species were considered globally threatened. The problems of enforcing trade restrictions for *Coracopsis* spp. on Madagascar were discussed by Dowsett (2000), who concluded that trade in these species should be fueled by captive-bred birds.

Domestic trade in *Coracopsis* parrots also takes place; free-living individuals seen in urban areas, such as Antananarivo, may well be escaped pets. A survey in 2016 in nine towns across Madagascar revealed widespread ownership: 37% of interviewees had seen captive birds and 8% had owned a *Coracopsis* parrot—it was estimated that close to 1300 individual *Coracopsis* parrots were held in captivity in the towns surveyed 1.5 years prior to the interviews (Reuter et al. 2019). In Malagasy towns, most captive *Coracopsis* parrots had been purchased or directly captured by the owner from the wild; when purchased, the price averaged a little over five US dollars (Reuter et al. 2017). The numbers of captive birds are modest for apparently common species, but it is not certain that current extraction rates are sustainable.

Subject editor: Steven M. Goodman

PASSERIFORMES: PHILEPITTIDAE, ASITIES AND SUNBIRD-ASITIES

R. O. Prum and V. R. Razafindratsita

The asities (Philepittidae) are a small but fascinating radiation of Malagasy endemic suboscine birds. The great radiation of perching birds (Passeriformes) includes over half the bird species in the world. The Passeriformes are composed of two main clades. The oscines, or true songbirds, are found throughout the world. The other group, the suboscines, includes more than a thousand New World species, but only 61 species in the Old World tropics. These include the pittas (Pittidae, 42 species), African and green broadbills (Calyptomenidae; six species), typical broadbills (Eurylaimidae, nine species), and asities (Philepittidae, four species) (F. Lambert and Woodcock 1996; Rasmussen and Donsker 2020). The asities are essentially broadbills endemic to Madagascar (Prum 1993) and are thus an isolated Malagasy lineage of this Old World clade. Although there are several larger radiations of passerine birds on Madagascar, including the major clade of Vangidae (see Reddy and Schulenberg, pp. 1621–26; Schulenberg, pp. 1694–99) and an eclectic assortment of passerines that have been shown to be monophyletic (and now referred to as the Bernieridae; see Reddy et al., pp. 1701–11), the asities are unique as the only suboscines on Madagascar. The asities include two very distinct genera with two species each (Table 13.1).

SYSTEMATICS AND PHYLOGENY

Like many biogeographically and systematically isolated groups, the asities have had a long and complex taxonomic history, including classification in no fewer than four different families. The genus *Philepitta* was variously placed in the starlings (Sturnidae) and birds of paradise (Paradisaeidae) before being recognized by its syringeal morphology as a suboscine and placed in its own family, the Philepittidae (Forbes 1880). The genus *Neodrepanis* was originally placed with the oscine sunbirds (Nectariniidae) in 1875. Seventy-five years later, following a tip from J. Delacour, Amadon (1951) examined the syringeal morphology of *N. coruscans* and identified it as suboscine, also discovering a host of morphological similarities shared between *Neodrepanis* and *Philepitta*. Amadon then transferred *Neodrepanis* to the Philepittidae.

The first phylogenetic analysis of the relationships of the asities by Raikow (1987) was based on hind limb myology (muscle) characters. Raikow concluded that the Old World suboscines (excluding the New Zealand wrens, Acanthisittidae) are monophyletic, that the pittas (Pittidae), broadbills (Eurylaimidae), and asities (Philepittidae) are each monophyletic, and that the asities and broadbills are sister groups.

Subsequently, Prum (1993) conducted a detailed phylogenetic analysis of the syringeal morphology of the broadbills and asities, based on numerous derived characters. He confirmed the monophyly of the asities and also concluded that asities share numerous derived morphological features with various broadbills, and that asities are actually embedded within the broadbills. Prum (1993) recommended that the asities be transferred to the subfamily Philepittinae within the Eurylaimidae.

Molecular systematic studies have confirmed the monophyly of the asities. After some variation in position, recent molecular studies have strongly supported their placement as the sister group to a clade including the Asian broadbills (without *Calyptomena*) and the central African *Pseudocalyptomena* (Moyle et al. 2006; Prum et al. 2015). The clade is currently given family status among multiple broadbill families.

DISTRIBUTION AND BIOGEOGRAPHY

The distributions of all four asity species are largely confined to well-established forest areas of endemism (Goodman and Raherilalao 2013; A. Hawkins 2013b). *Philepitta castanea* (Velvet Asity, *asity*) (Figures 13.25a –c) is distributed in primary and secondary moist evergreen forests of eastern and northern Madagascar between sea level and 1900 m from the extreme southeast near Tolagnaro, north to Loky Manambato and the forests of the Northern Highlands, and in the Sambirano Region in the northwest.

Philepitta schlegeli (Schlegel's Asity) (Figures 13.25d–f) is locally and patchily distributed in the more humid parts of deciduous dry and moist evergreen forests of the northwest, and in the central west as far south as the Menabe Antimena Protected Area (Goodman et al. 2018). *Philepitta schlegeli* "prefers humid forest in karst canyons ... [and] damp valleys ... [and] is absent from dry plateau sand-forest" (A. Hawkins 2013b), which is an unusual habitat preference among western Malagasy forest endemic birds. It is more common in the northern section of its range (from Ankarafantsika north) than to the south. *Philepitta schlegeli* has been found in local sympatry with *P. castanea* on the slopes of the Manongarivo Massif (Raherilalao et al. 2002).

Neodrepanis coruscans (Common Sunbird-asity) (Figures 13.25g and h) is distributed in moist evergreen forests between 400 and 1450 m from Andohahela (parcel 1) in the extreme south to Marojejy and Loky Manambato in the north (Goodman and Raherilalao 2013; A. Hawkins 2013b). It has also been reported once from the Central Highlands site of Ambohitantely (Andrianarimisa 1995); this record may well have been of a vagrant.

The distribution of *N. hypoxantha* (Yellow-bellied Sunbird-asity) (Figures 13.25i–k) was formerly very poorly known and the species was considered to be restricted to a few high-elevation forest localities in central Madagascar. As a result of avifaunal surveys of mountains throughout Madagascar, *N. hypoxantha* is now known to be widely distributed latitudinally, but locally restricted to medium-altitude moist evergreen and sclerophyllous forests between 1210 and 1990 m from the slopes of Andohahela in the south to at least Manongarivo in the north (Goodman and Raherilalao 2013).

FIGURE 13.25 **Different plumages and development of the caruncles in the four species of Philepittidae. A) *Philepitta castanea* (Velvet Asity) adult male near Andasibe in breeding plumage and with well-developed caruncle, B) adult female in the Andasibe-Mantadia protected area, and C) adult male at Analamazaotra in recently molted plumage with "scaly" appearance created by yellowish barb tips; D) *P. schlegeli* (Schlegel's Asity) adult male at Bemaraha in breeding plumage and with well-developed caruncle, E) adult female at Bemaraha, and F) young male at Bemaraha with developed and colorful caruncles before definitive plumage; G) *Neodrepanis coruscans* (Common Sunbird-asity) adult male at Ranomafana in breeding plumage and with well-developed caruncle, and H) presumed young male; I) *N. hypoxantha* (Yellow-bellied Sunbird-asity) adult male in breeding plumage and with well-developed caruncle, J) adult female at Ranomafana, and K) presumed young male at Ranomafana with slightly developed caruncle before definitive plumage, at a nest.** (PHOTOS A–C, E–G, J, and K by K. Behrens; D and H by M. J. Raherilalao; and I by H. Schütz.)

Throughout its range, *N. hypoxantha* is a high-elevation replacement of *N. coruscans*. At certain sites, including Marojejy and COMATSA Sud, the two species of *Neodrepanis* narrowly overlap in their elevational distribution. Goodman et al. (2000b) found that along an elevational transect of the Marojejy Massif the two species had abutting elevational ranges around 1250 m; *N. coruscans* was found at the lower end of this zone down to lowland moist evergreen forest and *N. hypoxantha* only at the upper end of this zone up to forest line at about 1775 m. Elevational migration of *N. hypoxantha* populations with seasonal variation in resources may also contribute to the variation in the lower elevational limit of the distribution.

Philepitta castanea, *N. coruscans*, and *N. hypoxantha* are all absent from the medium-altitude moist evergreen forests of Montagne d'Ambre in the extreme north, despite the presence of suitable habitat in the area. Goodman et al. (1996a) hypothesized that the generally depauperate avifauna of Montagne d'Ambre is the result of historic paleoclimatic isolation of this moist evergreen forest block from the originally contiguous portion of this formation.

PLUMAGE

The asities are sexually dimorphic in plumage color (Figure 13.25). In all species, females are variations of drab olive green, whereas males are some combination of bright or distinctive colors. *Philepitta castanea* has the most distinctive plumage in the clade. In breeding season (actually a worn basic plumage, see "Molt and Delayed Plumage Maturation" below), the definitive adult male is entirely velvet black (Figure 13.25a), with a small pair of yellow patches on the underwing marginal coverts (i.e., the inner surface of the wrist). Further, males have vivid green and blue caruncles, or wattle-like structures, over the eyes (see below). In the nonbreeding season (or fresh basic plumage), males have a distinctive "scaly" appearance created by the green or yellowish barb tips of the basally black contour feathers (Figure 13.25c). *Philepitta castanea* females and pre-definitive males are olive green above with markings above the eye, broad grayish and olive stripes on the breast, and a gray belly and undertail coverts (Figure 13.25b)

The definitive, alternate breeding plumage of *P. schlegeli* adult males is black on the head, olive green on the back and wings, and bright yellow below from the chin to the undertail coverts. In the breeding season, adult males have large, multilobed green caruncles with a bright blue vertical stripe around the eyes (Figure 13.25d). Females, subadult males, and basic, nonbreeding-plumaged males are olive green above, streaked broadly with gray and olive on the breast, and yellowish on the belly and undertail coverts (Figures 13.25e and f).

The breeding, alternate plumage of *N. coruscans* adult males is iridescent dark blue above and dull yellow below, with a lovely sky-blue and deep blue caruncle around the eye extending to the basal margin of the bill sheath (ramphotheca) (Figure 13.25g). Nonbreeding, basic-plumaged males and all females are generally olive green above and yellowish green below without a caruncle (Figure 13.25h).

Neodrepanis hypoxantha adult males in breeding, alternate plumage are iridescent dark blue above and bright, clear yellow below, with sky-blue and light green caruncles around the eyes (Figure 13.25i). Nonbreeding, basic-plumaged males are olive green above and bright yellow below (Figure 13.25k). Females resemble basic-plumaged males (Figure 13.25j).

The caruncles of *Neodrepanis* males differ significantly in shape and color (Prum et al. 1999; A. Hawkins 2013b). In *N. coruscans* males they are mostly light blue above the eye and deep, ultraviolet blue below the eye, with a fine lime-green eye-ring. The *N. coruscans* caruncles are also wedge shaped, with the broadest portion well above and behind the eye. In contrast, the caruncles of *N. hypoxantha* males are squarer, extend farther forward from the eye, and have a more conspicuous horizontal green panel in the center. However, photos reveal significant variation among individuals in caruncle shape and color. These same bright colors (which are structural; see below) extend several millimeters to the base of the bill under the ramphotheca.

MOLT AND DELAYED PLUMAGE MATURATION

Neodrepanis coruscans, *N. hypoxantha*, and *Philepitta schlegeli* have distinct basic and alternate plumages. However, in *P. castanea*, the breeding season plumage is a worn basic plumage (Prum and Razafindratsita 1997). In the first three species, the distinct alternate plumages are the result of a complete pre-alternate molt, whereas *P. castanea* males entirely lack the pre-alternate molt (Salomonsen 1965; Prum and Razafindratsita 1997). This distinct plumage has evolved through the loss of the pre-alternate molt in the asities (Prum and Razafindratsita 1997).

Both species of *Philepitta* also exhibit delayed plumage maturation. Males retain a female-like plumage for at least a year after reaching sexual maturity, and perhaps more (Benson et al. 1976; Goodman and Andrianarimisa 1995; Prum and Razafindratsita 1997). In *P. castanea*, pre-definitive males do not develop colorful caruncles, but young *P. schlegeli* males develop colorful, definitive caruncles before definitive plumage, creating a distinct pre-definitive appearance. It is possible that the all-green plumage and the green plumage with mature caruncles are two distinct age stages—years 1 and 2 (post-hatching)—in the sequences of plumage maturation of *P. schlegeli*, similar to Neotropical manakins (Pipridae), but this needs to be confirmed with observations of color-banded individuals.

Whether *Neodrepanis* has delayed plumage maturation is less clear. Some male specimens have green backs with a few isolated iridescent blue feathers, but it is not known whether these individuals are in molt or in a distinct, transitional plumage. Goodman et al. (1997a) reported an "immature" plumaged *N. hypoxantha* male with blue-fringed back feathers and a half-size wattle displaying to a female.

CARUNCLE ANATOMY AND STRUCTURAL COLOR PRODUCTION

Prum et al. (1994, 1999) described the anatomy, nanostructure (extremely fine structure), and biophysics of the colorful caruncles of male asities. The color of these caruncles is structural (i.e., the hues are the result of the interactions of light waves with the structure of the tissue rather than with pigment molecules in the tissue). The

caruncle hues include vivid green, sky blue, and, in *Neodrepanis*, a deep blue that is the first extensively ultraviolet color described from avian skin (Prum et al. 1999).

The color of the asity caruncles is created by coherent scattering (or constructive interference) of light waves by arrays of parallel collagen fibers. The diameter and distance between collagen fibers determine the hue. Larger fibers and greater distances between them will produce longer-wavelength light blue and green hues, whereas smaller fiber sizes and distances will produce deep blue and ultraviolet hues. The caruncles of male asities are unusual among birds in their annual growth and reabsorption.

The black plumage of breeding *Philepitta castanea* has been shown to incorporate microstructural features that enhance multiple scattering of ambient light among the surfaces of the barbules of individual contour feather barbs, which increases light absorption by melanin pigments in the feathers, producing a profoundly black appearance (McCoy and Prum 2019). First identified in birds of paradise (McCoy et al. 2018), "super-black" plumages constitute a form of structurally enhanced absorption and have now been described in at least 15 avian families. In all cases, super-black plumage patches are found adjacent to a highly saturated, brilliant plumage patch. The super-black appearance of *P. castanea* contour feathers is produced by dense dihedral arrays of vertically oriented, strap-shaped barbules on each side of the rachis. Light scattering within these vertical cavities between barbules leads to this profoundly black appearance, which is orders of magnitude darker than simply melanized feathers. The super-black male breeding plumage, which gives *P. castanea* its English name, Velvet Asity, is unusual in that it is associated with a brilliant, highly saturated fleshy caruncle instead of a plumage patch. *Philepitta castanea* is also unique in that the super-black effect is produced by the pigmented bases of the contour feathers; the greenish feather tips that give the fresh, nonbreeding plumage its scaly appearance have simple sparse barbules that are not arranged in a dihedral.

BILL SHAPE AND MASS

Asities exhibit substantial variation in bill shape. The bill of *Philepitta schlegeli* is the shortest, both actually and relative to body size (16.3 mm; Goodman and Andrianarimisa 1995). *Philepitta castanea* has a substantially longer bill (21.2 mm) that is also strikingly variable in length within populations. In *Neodrepanis*, the bill is longer and strongly decurved. In *N. hypoxantha*, the exposed culmen measures 18–22 mm (straight-line distance), whereas in *N. coruscans*, it measures 24–27 mm (F. Lambert and Woodcock 1996). The bill is also more strongly decurved in *N. coruscans* than in *N. hypoxantha*, but this difference can be very difficult to distinguish in the field (A. Hawkins 2013b). *Philepitta castanea* is significantly larger in body mass than *P. schlegeli*; likewise, the few data indicate the same for *N. coruscans* (see Faliarivola et al., pp. 1608–20).

DIET AND ECOLOGY

The diet of *Philepitta castanea* is the best known of the four species. In general, it consumes primarily fruit, and secondarily nectar and arthropods (Razafindratsita 1995; Goodman and Putnam 1996; Goodman et al. 1997a; Prum and Razafindratsita 1997; Rakotomanana and Hino 1998; Rakotomanana and Rene de Roland 2007; Razafindratsita and Zack 2009). *Philepitta castanea* has been documented feeding on a wide variety of fruit species from 15 plant families, with species of *Oncostemum* (Primulaceae) and *Psychotria* (Rubiaceae) apparently making up the largest proportion of the diet. In addition, it has been observed feeding on flower nectar of several plant species, especially *Bakerella* (Loranthaceae) and *Ditepalanthus* (Balanophoracae) (Safford and Duckworth 1990; Prum and Razafindratsita 1997).

At Ranomafana, Razafindratsita and Zack (2009) identified 23 plant species in the diet of *P. castanea*, nearly half of which were from the Rubiaceae and Myrsinaceae. During most months, eight or more different species contributed to the diet of *P. castanea*, but during July and August, only two to five fruit species were available. Rakotomanana (2007) documented that *P. castanea* forages mostly below 7.5 m high and spends the most time foraging between 2.5 and 5.0 m high.

The *Philepitta* species are two of the five predominantly frugivorous native bird species on Madagascar, which also include *Treron australis* (Madagascar Green-pigeon), *Alectroenas madagascariensis* (Madagascar Blue-pigeon), and *Hypsipetes madagascariensis* (Madagascar Bulbul) (Albert-Daviaud et al. 2018). The two pigeons and the bulbul are not forest dependent and can be found in degraded forest habitats and crossing open areas, and further, when in forest habitat the two pigeons tend to be confined to the canopy. These differences clearly underline the unique niche and critical role of *P. castanea* in seed dispersal and forest regeneration of plants in the understory, a subject in need of further research. Razafindratsita and Zack (2009) found that regurgitated seeds of *Piper* sp. (Piperaceae) and defecated seeds of *Aphloia theiformis* (Aphloiaceae) had higher germination rates than unprocessed seeds. However, the absence of this bird species from open areas or even forest edges (Rocha et al. 2015) may limit its importance for forest regeneration. Nonetheless, it may remain important to internal regeneration at tree falls, landslides, and other smaller disturbances. Although Salomonsen (1965) stated that the tongue of *P. castanea* is unspecialized for nectar foraging, Prum and Razafindratsita (1997) document that its tongue is bifid and divided into numerous brushy tips in an obvious adaptation for nectar feeding.

The diet of *P. schlegeli* is poorly known, but reports indicate that it is highly frugivorous but also takes nectar and arthropods (F. Lambert and Woodcock 1996). The only fruits so far identified are reddish-orange understory fruits of *Petchia* sp. (formerly *Cabucala*, Apocynacae) and small figs (*Ficus* sp.) (A. Hawkins 2013b). Nectar is taken from a range of reddish- and white-flowered plants, particularly *Albizia* sp. (Fabaceae) and *Combretum* sp. (Combretaceae) (F. Lambert and Woodcock 1996).

The diet of the sunbird-asities consists of nectar and insects (Langrand 1990; Goodman and Putnam 1996; Goodman et al. 1997a). As in *Philepitta castanea*, the predominant species foraged on by sunbird-asities include *Bakerella* spp. Goodman and Putnam (1996) reported *N. hypoxantha* eating a small green caterpillar. Good evidence of the importance of nectar feeding comes from observations of energetic, aggressive competition for access to floral

resources with nectarivorous sunbirds (e.g., *Cinnyris sovimanga*; Goodman et al. 1997a; R. O. Prum, unpublished data).

Few data are available about longevity. Woog et al. (2018) published the results of an eight-year banding study at Maromizaha. They established minimum ages of seven years for *P. castanea* and three years for *N. coruscans*. Given the low recapture rates (14.3% and 6.1%, respectively) for both species, these are likely to be significant underestimates. Prum and Razafindratsita (1997) color banded territorial *P. castanea* adult males at Ranomafana in 1993 and found at least two males occupying the same display territories five years later (R. O. Prum, unpublished data).

SONG

Although the syringeal morphology of asities includes a number of highly derived features (Prum 1993), the vocalizations of the asities are generally simple, low in volume, and weakly modulated in frequency. The advertisement vocalization of *Philepitta castanea* males consists of a high (4.8–6.3 kHz), thin, squeaky pair or short series of *weee-dooo* phrases, with a conspicuous emphasis on the *weee* syllable of each phrase (Prum and Razafindratsita 2003: Figure 12.25). This vocalization is inconspicuous and low in amplitude and can be difficult to detect from more than 15 m away. During male-male interactions, *P. castanea* gives a long series of rising notes similar to the initial syllable of the advertisement call, *weet* ... *weet* ... *weet* ... *weet*. A third, rare vocalization, a high thin *seeeeee* call, has also been reported. *Philepitta castanea* males make a pronounced, shuffling wing sound in flight that is distinctly audible and identifiable. The vocalizations of *P. schlegeli* have been described as "7–8 quiet but distinctive, uninflected and penetrating notes, first 4 or 5 rising and last 2 or 3 dropping, delivered from hidden perch or high in canopy: *hu-hu-hu-hi-hi-hu hu* lasting 1–1.5 s" (A. Hawkins 2013b). Squeaky calls have also been reported.

The primary vocalization of *N. coruscans* males consists of a rapid series of 3–10 simple, high, rising and falling (6–7.8 kHz) *seeet* notes that last 50–60 ms and are separated by 200–300 ms (Prum and Razafindratsita 2003: Figure 12.25). Female vocalizations are similar but less frequent. A. Hawkins (2013b) reports that the calls of *N. hypoxantha* are weaker, higher pitched, and less complex than those of *N. coruscans*.

Neodrepanis males also produce a pronounced mechanical wing sound in flight, which sounds like a rapid *whirr*. Spectrographic analysis of one recording of *N. coruscans* indicates that the sound consists of 10–12 incredibly brief, broad-frequency pulses repeated over 300 ms (Prum and Razafindratsita 2003: Figure 12.25). The production of these mechanical wing sounds is under the control of the individual, and they are produced most frequently in specific contexts around the nest and courtship (see below). The tip of the 10th, outermost primary in males is strongly pointed, or emarginate, in an apparent adaptation for mechanical sound production (Salomonsen 1934c).

The mechanical wing sounds of *N. hypoxantha* are reportedly louder and more pronounced than those of *N. coruscans* (A. Hawkins et al. 1997). Interestingly, this exaggerated mechanical sound production in *N. hypoxantha* is positively associated with the increased emargination of the 10th primary feathers.

Based on acoustic properties, C. Clark and Prum (2015) hypothesized that these mechanical wing sounds of *Neodrepanis* are produced by aeroelastic flutter of the 10th primary. However, direct experiments placing a 10th primary of *N. coruscans* in a wind tunnel were unable to elicit a sound with a frequency matching the recorded sounds of individuals in the wild. The precise mechanism of sound production remains to be identified.

BREEDING BEHAVIOR

Philepitta castanea is apparently unique among the birds of Madagascar, and the Old World suboscines, for its polygynous lek breeding system (Prum and Razafindratsita 1997), which constitutes only the 15th known independent derivation of lek behavior in the class Aves (Höglund and Alatalo 1995). However, on the Masoala Peninsula, Rakotomanana and Rene de Roland (2007) observed males participating in nest construction, and it would appear there may be significant plasticity to their breeding system.

At Ranomafana, *P. castanea* males occupy non-resource-based lek territories approximately 20–30 m in diameter that are distributed solitarily or in groups of up to five contiguous males. Males defend these territories from other males and perform elaborate secondary sexual displays. The same males occupy territories for more than five successive breeding seasons. Male display territories lack the food and nest site resources necessary for reproduction—an important feature of the definition of lekking (Höglund and Alatalo 1995).

The display repertoire of *P. castanea* males includes six or more distinct display elements, which are performed during male-female interactions, and intrasexual competitive elements, which are performed during male-male competitive interactions (Prum and Razafindratsita 1997). The most common intersexual display element is the erect posture in which a male extends its neck, elongates its body, and raises its caruncles into two vertical planes above its eyes like a tricornered hat, exposing the bright blue horizontal stripe on the vividly green caruncle (Figure 13.26a). Among the most striking of the intersexual display elements is the wing-flap pump display in which a male in erect posture pumps rhythmically up and down on its legs twice while the wings are conspicuously but briefly flapped open (Figure 13.26b). During the wing-flap pump display, the incongruous yellow spots on the inner surface of the "wrists" of the wings are conspicuously flashed like a pair of semaphore flags. In intrasexual interactions, males perform the hanging-gape display, in which the body falls forward and hangs from the perch while the head is held horizontal and the gape is held open (Figure 13.26c).

At Ranomafana, nest construction, incubation, and post-hatching parental care are conducted entirely by the female (Prum and Razafindratsita 1997). Males do not develop pair bonds with females during the breeding season. On several occasions, single adult males have been observed near nests in association with female-plumaged birds. These males were not consistently present at these nests and took no part in nest construction or parental care. Rakotomanana and Rene de Roland (2007) and other observers have reported two female-plumaged birds at nests during nest construction. Observations at several nests with banded birds indicate

FIGURE 13.26 **Display elements of *Philepitta castanea* males. A) The erect posture display, B) the wing-flap pump display, and C) the hanging-gape display.** (DRAWINGS by T. D. Pederson.)

that the second female-plumaged individuals observed accompanying the resident female at the nests were pre-definitive-plumaged males, which can be distinguished from females by the large whitish patch of thickened skin above the orbits that will mature later in the season into a supraorbital caruncle (R. O. Prum, unpublished data).

All other asities appear to have an established pair bond. A definitive-plumaged *P. schlegeli* male and a female have been observed together at a nest during construction (A. Hawkins 1994c), with both birds implied to be actively participating in nest construction. Other observations also report a consistent pair in attendance at a nest (A. Hawkins 2013b). Multiple calling males have been observed along a short stretch of trail, implying perhaps a non-resource-defense territoriality reminiscent of the *P. castanea* lek (A. Hawkins 1994c; P. Morris, unpublished data). A. Hawkins (1994c) reported a male displaying to a female with drooping wings and fluffed-up breast feathers, and it gradually raised its tail until it almost touched its back, while making a series of quiet squeaks. Photographs of *P. schlegeli* from Ankarafantsika deposited on eBird (2021) by Simon Lane (ML 134871811, 134871841) and David Bree (ML 24027691) show *P. schlegeli* adult males assuming exactly the same posture as the hanging-gape display of *P. castanea*. Further research is required to establish the breeding system in *P. schlegeli*.

We have observed nest construction and incubation at several nests of *N. coruscans*. The territory and nest were consistently attended and defended by a male and female with an apparently established and enduring pair bond, but the nest was constructed entirely by the female. No overt courtship other than frequent calling and mechanical wing whirs by the male was observed. Males have been observed feeding unfledged young in the nest (A. Hawkins et al. 1998).

The breeding behavior of *N. hypoxantha* is poorly known. As in *N. coruscans*, there appears to be a well-established pair bond, but nests are constructed entirely by the female, and males may visit the nest, as seen in Figure 13.25k (a presumably subadult bird). A. Hawkins observed several striking displays that are remarkably similar to the hanging-gape display and another around-the-perch somersault display of *P. castanea* (F. Lambert and Woodcock 1996; A. Hawkins 2013b). The striking derived similarity among them implies that they are homologous behaviors that first evolved in a common ancestor of the asities (Prum and Razafindratsita 2003: Figure 12.25).

The nests of all asities are characteristic hanging, spindle-shaped structures of woven leaves and plant fibers attached to a lower branch of a tree (Figure 13.25k). At Ranomafana, more than 15 nests of *P. castanea* were located in a single tree species, *Tambourissa obovata* (Monimiaceae), and only two were found in other broadleaf tree species. All four *N. coruscans* nests at Ranomafana were also in *T. obovata* trees. Many *P. castanea* nests have been observed hanging over streams.

We have observed the nest construction behavior of *P. castanea* and *N. coruscans* at Ranomafana and have documented a fascinating and (so far) unique manner of construction. In both species, females begin by hanging and wrapping plant fibers and spider web around a branch, forming a pendent orb that is conspicuously pointed at both ends. Then, after a substantial and nearly solid mass is complete, the female creates an opening in one side of the nest and makes the nest cavity and a slight "porch" or roof over the opening. The nest cavity is lined profusely with bamboo leaves. The nests of *P. schlegeli* (A. Hawkins 1994c) and *N. hypoxantha* (Goodman and Putnam 1996) have also been described. The nest of *P. schlegeli* is shorter, stouter, more broadly connected to the branch, and less pendent than the nest of *P. castanea*. Although all the broadbills (Eurylaimidae) build quite similar hanging nests, little has been reported about the method by which their nests are constructed (F. Lambert and Woodcock 1996).

The clutch of *P. castanea* consists of three smooth, white eggs (Rand 1936; Milon et al. 1973). Eggs are elongate ovate but not pointed; they measure 24.4–29.8 mm × 18.3–19.5 mm (n = 20) and have a very thin shell (0.08 mm) (Schönwetter 1960–62). The clutch size for *P. schlegeli* is unknown and the eggs undescribed. Clutch size in *Neodrepanis* is two. The only *Neodrepanis* egg known, in a museum, was also elongate ovate, white with no

gloss or speckling, measuring 15.5 × 10.7 mm (Schönwetter 1960–1962), and was probably from *N. hypoxantha* (A. Hawkins 2013b).

PARASITES

Asities have featured in an increasing number of surveys of avian ecto- and endoparasites on Madagascar. Price and Johnson (2006) report one species each of *Myrsidea* chewing lice (Phthiraptera: Menoponidae) from *Philepitta castanea* and *P. schlegeli*. Skoracki et al. (2016) report unidentified syringophilid mites (Acariformes: Syringophilidae) from *P. castanea*.

Atyeo (1966) described a "robust" new genus and species of proctophylloid feather mite, *Philepittalges rotundus* (Acariformes: Proctophyllodidae), from *Philepitta castanea*. Klimov et al. (2017) proposed that *Philepittalges rotundus*, and another undescribed species of *Philepittalges* from *Neodrepanis coruscans*, are the sister group to the *Nycteridocaulus* genus group that parasitizes New World suboscines (Tyrannides). They used this example of host-parasite codivergences to calibrate the dates of divergence in the proctophylloid radiation on passeriform birds.

Schmid et al. (2017) found two species of avian malaria (*Plasmodium*) in samples of *Philepitta castanea* from Maromizaha. However, these hemoparasites were not confined to this asity and were found in blood samples of numerous passerine birds at the same site. Savage (2004) described a new species of hematozoon, *Leucocytozoon greineri*, from *N. coruscans*, and hypothesized that it was the same species as an unnamed *Leucocytozoon* reported earlier from *P. castanea*. In a broader survey of avian blood endoparasites on Madagascar, Savage et al. (2009) confirmed the presence of *L. greineri* in *N. coruscans* and *P. castanea* and reported the observation of microfilariae (Nematoda) in *P. castanea* and *P. schlegeli*. Infection rates varied from 1/9 in *N. coruscans* to 1/2 in *P. schlegeli*.

EVOLUTION OF THE ASITY RADIATION

The asities constitute a modest but fascinating radiation of suboscine birds. Among the four species there are dynamic patterns of evolutionary change in diet, ecology, size, bill shape, plumage coloration, molt, secondary sexual ornamentation (i.e., caruncle color, shape, anatomy, and mobility), vocalizations, mechanical wing sounds, and breeding system (Prum and Razafindratsita 2003: Figure 12.25). Other features of asity biology exhibit little variation among the species, such as nest architecture and, perhaps, male courtship display.

The details of this pattern of radiation can best be understood in terms of the phylogeny of asities. Among the most striking features of this radiation are the correlated evolution in *Neodrepanis* of a shift in diet to primary nectarivory and the evolution of an elongate and decurved bill (Prum 1993). Another feature is the historical co-occurrence of lek behavior in *Philepitta castanea* and the evolution of numerous derived novelties in plumage coloration, molt, and caruncle anatomy and mobility. In contrast, several asity displays appear to be homologues plesiomorphic to the entire radiation. The evolution of lek polygyny found in at least some populations of *P. castanea* is strikingly convergent with other extralimital groups of birds such as manakins (Pipridae), cotingas (Cotingidae), birds of paradise (Paradisaeidae), and bowerbirds (Ptilonorhynchidae). This finding further supports Snow's (1976) hypothesis that frugivory can foster the release of males from parental care and the evolution of polygynous, female-choice, non-resource-defense breeding systems.

CONSERVATION

All the asities are common in some portion of their ranges, and none is currently highly threatened with extinction. *Philepitta castanea* and *Neodrepanis coruscans* are both common in moist evergreen forests along nearly the entire eastern length of the island and are classified as species of Least Concern by the IUCN. Densities of *N. coruscans* based on point-count data have been estimated at some sites to approach over 1000 individuals per km^2 (A. Hawkins et al. 1998). However, both species are forest dependent and have been found to be absent from forest patches smaller than 400 ha (Rakotoarisoa and Capparella 2013), so they are not entirely resilient to habitat change from human land use. *Philepitta schlegeli* is common in portions of northwestern Madagascar, including the Sambirano Region, though rather scarce in other parts of its range (F. Lambert and Woodcock 1996). It is currently considered Near Threatened by the IUCN.

Treated as Vulnerable on the IUCN Red List, *N. hypoxantha* is common only in high-elevation forests, reaching estimated densities based on point-count data of something on the order of 2650 individuals per km^2 (Goodman and Putnam 1996; Goodman et al. 1997a; A. Hawkins et al. 1998). However, mathematical modeling of the impact of climate change on the viability of Malagasy forest bird populations has identified *N. hypoxantha* as one of the five endemic bird species most vulnerable to climate change (Andriamasimanana and Cameron 2013). Given the documented sensitivity of other asities to forest fragmentation and the distribution of *N. hypoxantha* in higher-elevation forests, it should be considered a species of concern.

Fortunately, our growing knowledge of the distribution of asities has documented that healthy, sustainable populations of all four species remain intact. Madagascar's protected area network includes some 10 sites where one or more of the three moist forest species have been recorded, affording protection for all, and 11 where *P. schlegeli* is known (Goodman et al. 2018). The presence of *P. castanea* and *N. coruscans* in regenerating secondary forest less than 30 years old at a number of localities (e.g., Ranomafana) documents that at least these two species are able to expand into regenerating forest habitat.

Subject editors: Roger J. Safford and Steven M. Goodman

PASSERIFORMES: VANGIDAE, VANGAS

T. S. Schulenberg

The vangas (Vangidae) have traditionally been considered to constitute a radiation endemic to the Malagasy Region, with just one species (*Cyanolanius madagascarinus*, Blue Vanga) also occurring on the nearby Comoro islands (Grande Comore and Mohéli). Recent phylogenetic analyses have clarified that the Malagasy taxa are embedded within a broader radiation of shrike-like species found in both Africa and Asia, and so Vangidae is now expanded to include these species as well (see Reddy and Schulenberg, pp. 1621–26). The (expanded) Vangidae is therefore no longer treated as a family endemic to the Malagasy Region; however, from here on, I use the term "vangas" to refer exclusively to the Malagasy species unless otherwise stated.

These same phylogenetic studies, and others, all based on DNA sequence data (Figure 13.27), have also expanded the number of vanga species. This expansion has occurred in part through the inclusion of species previously classified in other families: newly confirmed as vangids are the five species of *Newtonia* (newtonias), *Mystacornis crossleyi* (Crossley's Babbler, now Crossley's Vanga) (Figure 13.28e), and *Pseudobias wardi* (Ward's Flycatcher, now Ward's Vanga) (Yamagishi et al. 2001; Johansson et al. 2008; Jønsson et al. 2012; Reddy et al. 2012). In addition, ongoing investigations of the population structure of Malagasy species have led to the description of a previously unknown species, *Newtonia lavarambo* (Lavarambo Newtonia) (Younger et al. 2018); this largely cryptic species was previously included within *N. amphichroa* (Dark Newtonia). Further, recent work has recognized the two subspecies of *Schetba* as separate species, *S. occidentalis* (Western Rufous Vanga) and *S. rufa* (Eastern Rufous Vanga) (Younger et al. 2019b). Therefore, the Vangidae of the Malagasy Region is an even larger and more diverse radiation than previously recognized.

DISTRIBUTION AND STATUS ON MADAGASCAR

Vangas are found throughout Madagascar in wooded habitats. Most species are widely distributed and are often fairly common in suitable habitat, although at the local scale some species are inexplicably scarce or absent. Two species, *Euryceros prevostii* (Helmet Vanga) (Figure 13.28a) and *Oriolia bernieri* (Bernier's Vanga), are confined to the northern half of the eastern lowland moist evergreen forest belt, a habitat that is under great pressure from subsistence agriculture and logging, and both are patchily distributed, often absent from sites with seemingly suitable habitat (Schulenberg et al. 2013). Although these two species are present in several protected areas, both are considered Endangered (BirdLife International 2020a). *Newtonia fanovanae* (Red-tailed Newtonia) is also largely confined to lowland forest in eastern Madagascar. Its distribution

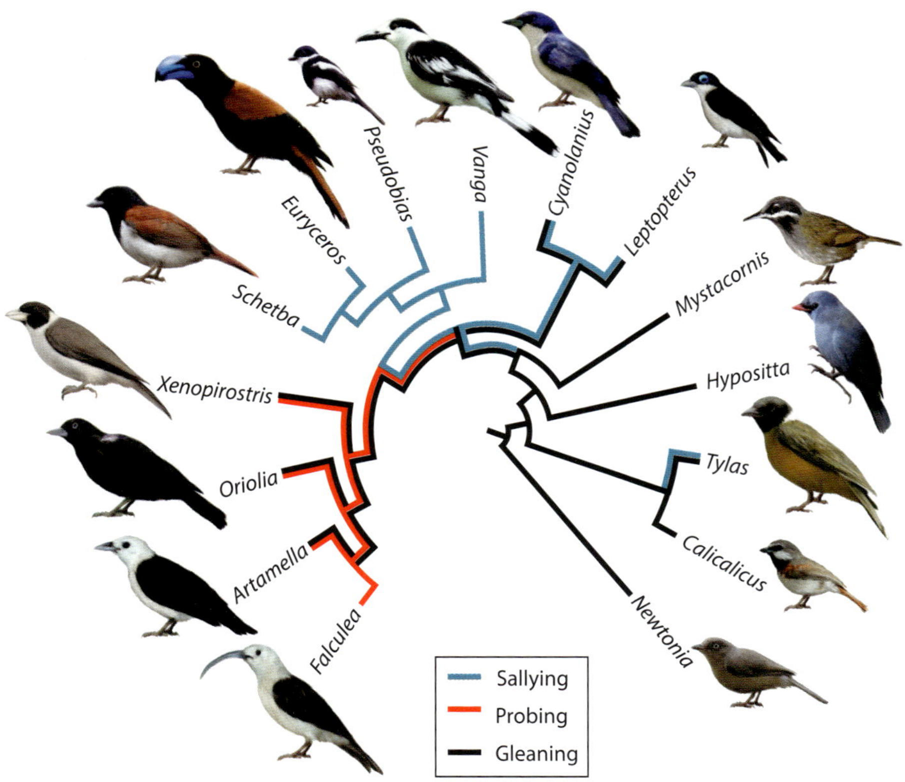

FIGURE 13.27 **Phylogeny of Malagasy vangas, also showing dominant foraging strategy for each genus.** (SOURCES: figure by Sushma Reddy, with illustrations of birds by Velizar Simeonovski; modified from Reddy et al. 2012.)

FIGURE 13.28 **The Vangidae of Madagascar, which forms a monophyletic group and is the result of the colonization of the island by a single ancestor, is one of the more spectacular adaptive radiations among the birds of the world. Within the group there is an assortment of body and bill forms, colors, and lifestyles, as seen in the images here. A) *Euryceros prevostii* (Helmet Vanga) on the Masoala Peninsula, B) *Calicalicus rufocarpalis* (Red-shouldered Vanga) south of Toliara at La Table, C) *Falculea palliata* (Sickle-billed Vanga) north of Toliara at Ifaty, D) *Newtonia brunneicauda* (Common Newtonia) at Anjozorobe, E) *Mystacornis crossleyi* (Crossley's Vanga) at Mantadia, and F) *Vanga curvirostris* (Hook-billed Vanga) at Ifaty.** (PHOTOS by K. Behrens.)

extends for most of the length of this forest type, from Anjanaharibe-Sud south to Andohahela, a zone that is under considerable anthropogenic pressure, and it is considered Vulnerable (BirdLife International 2020a). *Newtonia lavarambo* is restricted to the southern third of the eastern moist evergreen forests. *Xenopirostris polleni* (Pollen's Vanga) is more common in southeastern Madagascar than in seemingly suitable habitat in the northern part of the island (Goodman et al. 2000b), although it occurs north at least to Zahamena and the associated Sihanaka Forest (Lavauden 1932; A. Hawkins 1999); its status is assessed as Near Threatened (BirdLife

International 2020a). Two other species, *N. archboldi* (Archbold's Newtonia) and *X. xenopirostris* (Lafresnaye's Vanga), are restricted to the dry spiny thickets of the southwest, although both are fairly common within this region and are not considered to be at risk (BirdLife International 2020a).

Two vanga species, however, have extremely small distributions. The first of these, *X. damii* (Van Dam's Vanga), has been recorded in this century at only a few, widely separated areas in northern Madagascar. It is best known from Ankarafantsika (and the adjoining Ampijoroa Forestry Station), as well as the Bongolava protected area (Collar and Stuart 1985; Goodman et al. 2018), and was recently discovered north of Ankarafantsika, close to the coast, at Mariarano Forest (Rasamison et al. 2018). Farther north, there are smaller, disjunct populations at Ankazamborona (near the type locality; Woolaver et al. 2004) and at Analamerana (A. Hawkins et al. 1990), the latter of which is, like Ankarafantsika, a protected area. This species is locally common in dry deciduous forests and mangroves, although suitable habitat is distributed only very patchily within at least one of these protected areas (Ankarafantsika), and it is considered Endangered (BirdLife International 2020a). The second species with a highly restricted range is the recently described *Calicalicus rufocarpalis* (Red-shouldered Vanga) (Figure 13.28b; Goodman et al. 1997c), known from only a small area of southwestern dry spiny thickets, including three protected areas (Amoron'i Onilahy, Tsinjoriake, and Tsimanampesotse; Goodman et al. 2018). Based on the very limited known range, this species is considered Vulnerable (BirdLife International 2020a). There also remains considerable uncertainty regarding the status and distribution of *Tylas eduardi albigularis* (Tylas Vanga), which is known from only a very few observations in western Madagascar (A. Hawkins 1995; Appert 1996). Finally, *Hypositta perdita* (Bluntschli's Vanga) was described from two juvenile specimens collected in 1931 at a single locality in extreme southeastern Madagascar (Peters 1996). Molecular analysis of both specimens of "*H. perdita*" reveal that the two type specimens are juvenile *Oxylabes madagascariensis* (White-throated Oxylabes), a member of the family Bernieridae (Fjeldså et al. 2013).

Thirteen of the 17 genera of Vangidae are currently treated as monospecific; the exceptions are *Newtonia*, *Calicalicus*, *Schetba*, and *Xenopirostris*. The two species of *Calicalicus* and of *Schetba*, and the three species of *Xenopirostris*, are all allopatric from congeners. Two of the species of *Newtonia*, *amphichroa* and *lavarambo*, are probably parapatric, but their distributional limits remain to be clarified in the region of the southeastern moist evergreen forests where their ranges might approach one another. Otherwise, *Newtonia* represents the only vanga genus within which multiple species are syntopic. In eastern Madagascar, *N. brunneicauda* (Common Newtonia) (Figure 13.28d), *N. amphichroa/lavarambo*, and *N. fanovanae* may all be sympatric, although they each differ in habitat associations: *N. brunneicauda* occupies a broader range of forest types and elevational ranges than do the other species, and it is more tolerant of disturbed forest habitat, whereas *N. amphichroa/lavarambo* occurs in the understory of moist evergreen forests, and *N. fanovanae* is restricted to the middle and upper strata of lowland moist evergreen forests. Finally, *N. brunneicauda* and *N. archboldi* are locally syntopic in dry spiny thickets of the southwest.

DIET

The vangas are primarily insectivorous (Rand 1936; Benson et al. 1977; Goodman and Parrillo 1997; Faliarivola et al. 2020). The diets of few species are known in detail; however, most species appear to be dietary generalists. The most frequently noted prey items, across all vangas, are Blattodea (primarily cockroaches, also termites), Coleoptera (beetles), Hemiptera (true bugs, including cicadas and leafhoppers), Hymenoptera (primarily ants, also Apoidea bees and wasps), Lepidoptera (butterflies and moths, both caterpillars and adults), Orthoptera (of various families, most often katydids, Tettigoniidae; and crickets, Gryllidae), and Araneae (spiders) (Goodman and Parrillo 1997); less commonly reported invertebrates are Chilopoda (centipedes), Dermaptera (earwigs), Diplopoda (millipedes), Diptera (flies), Ephemeroptera (mayflies), Mantodea (mantises), Neuroptera (net-winged insects), Odonata (dragonflies and damselflies), Oniscidea (wood lice), Pseudoscorpiones (pseudoscorpions), Scorpiones (scorpions), and snails (Rand 1936; Benson et al. 1977; Safford and Duckworth 1990; Goodman and Parrillo 1997; Goodman et al. 1997a; Nakamura et al. 2009a, 2009b; Rakotomanana et al. 2009; Schulenberg et al. 2013).

As far as the insectivorous portion of the diet, members of this family seem to be generalists: most species are reported to consume five to eight orders of invertebrates. Of course, the different species have various foraging habits (see below), and presumably the diet of each species is also influenced by other factors, such as body size and prey availability. There is very little further information on dietary partitioning among vanga species. Yohannes and Woog (2020) investigated niche divergence in two syntopic species, *N. brunneicauda* and *N. amphichroa*, using stable isotope ratios. They found that the trophic niche of the two species did not differ; there were differences in the carbon sources in their diet, which is best explained by dissimilarities in foraging height.

Vangas also take vertebrate prey. *Vanga curvirostris* (Hook-billed Vanga) (Figure 13.28f) (weight about 70 g) is the most frequent predator of vertebrates. For example, Rand (1936) found remains of reptiles or amphibians in 43 out of 63 stomachs examined; similarly, Goodman and Parrillo (1997) found vertebrate remains in 11 out of 15 stomachs; and Rakotomanana et al. (2001) observed that a minimum of 65% of items provisioned to nestlings were vertebrates. *Vanga* is known to consume frogs (Rand 1936), geckos (Garbutt 1997; Goodman and Parrillo 1997; A. Hawkins et al. 1998), chameleons (Appert 1970; Goodman et al. 1997b), small birds (Goodman and Parrillo 1997), bird eggs (Ramiarison 1998), bats (A. Hawkins 1994b), and even young *Microcebus* mouse lemurs (see Goodman and Ganzhorn, pp. 1829–38). *Euryceros prevostii*, one of the largest species of Vangidae (weight about 98 g), also frequently consumes vertebrates. Rand (1936) noted that seven out of 24 stomachs examined contained vertebrate remains. Items specifically noted in its diet are frogs, geckos, chameleons, and perhaps other lizards (Rand 1936; Milon et al. 1973; Graetz 1991; Goodman and Parrillo 1997; Thorstrom and Watson 1997; La Marca and Thorstrom 2000).

There does not seem to be a direct correlation in the Vangidae between body size and predation on vertebrates. *Falculea palliata* (Sickle-billed Vanga) (Figure 13.28c) is slightly smaller than *Euryceros*, but reports of this species preying on vertebrates are rare

(possibly because its long but slender bill is less suited to subduing larger prey). Benson et al. (1977) reported consumption of a bird egg, and Nakamura et al. (2004) reported that small vertebrates (chameleons, geckos, and other lizards) constituted 7% of the items provisioned to nestlings.

Consumption of vertebrates, at least opportunistically, probably occurs in most if not all of the midsize to larger members of this family; taxa in which this has been reported to date include *Tylas* (Nakamura et al. 2009b), *Calicalicus madagascariensis* (Red-tailed Vanga) (Eguchi 1995; Rakotomanana et al. 2009), *Schetba* sp. (Schulenberg et al. 2013), *Oriolia bernieri* (Thorstrom and Rene de Roland 2001), *Artamella viridis* (White-headed Vanga) (Rand 1936), and *Xenopirostis xenopirostris* (Safford and Duckworth 1990). Of these, *Calicalicus* is the smallest-bodied species (mean weight 17 g).

A few species consume at least some fruit (e.g., *Cyanolanius madagascarinus*: Benson et al. 1977; *Leptopterus chabert*, Chabert Vanga: Appert 1970; Schulenberg et al. 2013; *Oriolia bernieri*: Schulenberg et al. 2013; *Artamella viridis*: Böhning-Gaese et al. 1995; Schulenberg et al. 2013; and *Xenopirostris xenopirostris*: Gardner and Jasper 2018), but fruit is not known to be a principal component of the diet of any species (also see Razafindratsima et al., pp. 142–52).

FORAGING BEHAVIOR

One of the most remarkable features of members of this family is the diversity in bill size and shape (Figures 13.27 and 13.28). In general, vangas may be categorized into three main groups with respect to the frequency of foraging maneuvers employed (but note that data on the foraging behavior of *Mystacornis*, which is largely terrestrial, are particularly sparse and anecdotal, so this species provisionally constitutes a fourth group):

Gleaning (including a variable contribution of short-range sallies): *Newtonia*, *Tylas*, *Calicalicus*, *Hypositta*, *Leptopterus*, and *Cyanolanius*
Sallying: *Vanga*, *Pseudobias*, *Schetba*, and *Euryceros*
Probing (including a variable amount of gleaning): *Oriolia*, *Falculea*, *Artamella*, and *Xenopirostris*
Mystacornis: The foraging behavior of this terrestrial species is not well known, but it relies on a mix of probing (and perhaps gaping?) of soft substrates (e.g., moss and epiphytes, but also rotted trunks) and gleaning

Gleaning among the vangas is typically directed at leaves or bark. Sallying by vangas may be to the ground or vegetation in most species, although *Pseudobias* specializes in capturing prey in midair, only rarely sallying to vegetation. Probing by vangas refers to foraging maneuvers directed at extracting prey from underneath bark or other woody substrates.

As discussed by Reddy et al. (2012), these foraging strategies are not randomly distributed across the vangas. Gleaning is the primary foraging strategy of all species that are basal within vangas (*Newtonia*, *Calicalicus*, *Tylas*, *Hypositta*, *Mystacornis*, *Leptopterus*, and *Cyanolanius*), although they do not form a single clade (Figure 13.27). The remaining species, however, form two well-defined clades, each of which consists of those that belong to one of the other two foraging strategies: those that sally (*Vanga*, *Pseudobias*, *Schetba*, and *Euryceros*) form one clade, whereas those that primarily probe (*Oriolia*, *Falculea*, *Artamella*, and *Xenopirostris*) form the second clade.

One implication of this pattern is that gleaning is the primitive condition within vangas. This would not be surprising, both because gleaning is a widespread foraging strategy in passerines in general (Remsen and Robinson 1990) and because it is prevalent in mainland members of the broader Vangidae, including in *Philentoma*, which may be the sister to the Malagasy species (Jønsson et al. 2012; Reddy et al. 2012; see Reddy and Schulenberg, pp. 1621–26). Sallying is also represented in mainland species of Vangidae (e.g., *Megabyas*, *Bias*, *Hemipus*), although it apparently evolved independently on Madagascar. Probing across Vangidae in the broad sense is restricted to the Malagasy species. As a foraging strategy, probing by vangas is basically similar to the strategies followed by some woodpecker species (Winkler and Christie 2002) in a family that does not occur on Madagascar. Some authors (e.g., Moreau 1966) recognized that *Falculea* could "fill" a "vacant" woodpecker "niche" on Madagascar, but it does not seem to have been recognized previously that not only *Falculea* but in fact a clade of vangas exhibit a foraging behavior that is essentially unknown in Old World continental passerines, regularly searching woody substrates in a superficially woodpecker-like manner. Most forest bird communities on the island contain two or three species of probing vangas, making up 5–14% of the passerine diversity in these forests. The contribution of probing species is greater in the less diverse communities in the dry deciduous forest and dry spiny thicket formations of the southwest and south.

Also, some of the most specialized bill morphologies among the vangas are found among the species of the probing clade. The bill of all three *Xenopirostris* species, for example, is deep and laterally compressed, with a sharply inflected gonys. This is a very unusual bill shape, shared by only a few other bird species worldwide, and is believed to be correlated with "chisel" motions in which the bill is used to dislodge bark (Remsen and Robinson 1990). Indeed, such motions constitute part of the foraging repertoire of *Xenopirostris* (Schulenberg et al. 2013).

Members of the family also regularly use two unusual prey-handling techniques, defined by G. Clark (1973) as "clamping" (when a bird places food between one or both feet and a perch) and "grasping" (when a food item is contained in a foot held off the perch). Clamping has been observed in *Cyanolanius madagascarinus*; in addition, in two instances of foot use (*Cyanolanius* once, *X. xenopirostris* once), it could not be ascertained whether food was grasped or clamped (Schulenberg 1995).

Grasping has been noted in 12 vanga species (Schulenberg 1995; the exceptions are *Newtonia* spp., *Calicalicus rufocarpalis*, *Hypositta*, *Mystacornis*, *Vanga*, and *Pseudobias*). The general pattern of prey acquisition and handling is the same across all species. After capturing prey with its bill, the bird perches on a horizontal limb and then lowers its head toward a foot, which is lifted slightly to receive the prey from the bill. Sometimes the foot is lifted upward and extended forward several times before it grasps the prey. Prey is grasped in the toes, while the tarsometatarsus rests on the perch, with the toes extended forward and down. Grasping typically occurs during the

handling of animal prey but is also used when feeding on fruit (Böhning-Gaese et al. 1995).

Vanga curvirostris, a species in which clamping or grasping has not been observed, anchors chameleons by wedging the head in a fork between two branches. Once prey is in place, the bird tears the suspended prey apart for consumption (Goodman et al. 1997a). Similar behavior is reported for *Artamella viridis*, which wedges the body of small chameleons in a horizontal fork and tears off body parts (Schulenberg et al. 2013).

SOCIAL BEHAVIOR

Most members of this family are encountered as singles or pairs that regularly associate with mixed-species foraging flocks composed of other insectivores (Rand 1936; Langrand 1990), although such flocking may be greatly reduced or not practiced at all when breeding (Appert 1970). Typical flock associates are other vanga species, including *N. brunneicauda*, as well as a wide range of other species, including *Coracina cinerea* (Madagascar Cuckooshrike), *Dicrurus forficatus* (Crested Drongo), *Terpsiphone mutata* (Madagascar Paradise-flycatcher), *Neomixis* spp. (jeries), *Nesillas* spp. (brush-warblers), *Hypsipetes madagascariensis* (Madagascar Bulbul), *Zosterops maderaspatanus* (Madagascar White-eye), *Cinnyris sovimanga* (Souimanga Sunbird), *Cinnyris notatus* (Madagascar Green Sunbird), and many others (Appert 1970; Thompson and Evans 1991; Eguchi et al. 1993; Goodman and Putnam 1996; A. Hawkins et al. 1998). *Newtonia amphichroa*, however, more often participates in understory flocks that may include *N. brunneicauda* but are dominated by members of the Bernieridae, such as *Oxylabes madagascariensis*, *Bernieria* spp., *Crossleyia xanthophrys* (Madagascar Yellowbrow), *Xanthomixis zosterops* (Spectacled Tetraka), and *X. cinereiceps* (Gray-crowned Tetraka) (Langrand 1990; Thompson and Evans 1992; Schulenberg et al. 2013). Similarly, common flock associates of *N. archboldi* are *Neomixis* spp., *Thamnornis chloropetoides* (Thamnornis), and, where their ranges overlap, *N. brunneicauda* (Appert 1997).

A few vangas are particularly gregarious. *Leptopterus chabert* often forages in flocks of up to 25 individuals (Rand 1936), which may be monospecific groups, or in association with other species such as *Neomixis* spp., *Newtonia* spp., and *Artamella viridis* (Schulenberg et al. 2013). Flocks of at least 25 *A. viridis* have been reported (Rand 1936), although usually this species is encountered in pairs or in small (family?) groups. Similarly, *Falculea palliata* forages in groups of up to 25 individuals, often in association with species such as *A. viridis* and *Dicrurus forficatus* (Rand 1936; Appert 1970). Even more remarkably, all three of these species roost communally, primarily when not breeding, in even larger aggregations of up to 60–80 *Leptopterus*, 10–20 *Artamella*, and 40–60 *Falculea* (Appert 1970; Eguchi et al. 2001). Such roosts may contain combinations of these species, such as *Artamella* and *Falculea*, and *Leptopterus* and *Falculea*.

At the other end of the spectrum are two species that apparently rarely if ever join flocks and are usually encountered only as singles or pairs, *Mystacornis crossleyi* (Rand 1936; Schulenberg et al. 2013) and *Vanga curvirostris* (Rand 1936; Eguchi et al. 1993; Goodman and Putnam 1996). *Schetba rufa* also associates with mixed-species flocks only rarely and is more often encountered in apparent family groups of four or five (Rand 1936; A. Hawkins et al. 1998). Rand (1936) reported similar behavior for *S. occidentalis*, although Hino (2002, 2009) found it to be a frequent member of mixed-species flocks.

A different type of association occurs between mesites and vangas. Groups of foraging *Monias benschi* (Subdesert Mesite) are occasionally followed by *Xenopirostris xenopirostris*, which presumably follows the group to capture arthropods flushed by the mesites (see A. Hawkins et al., pp. 1653–57). A similar association has been observed between *Mesitornis variegatus* (White-breasted Mesite) and *Vanga* (Gardner and Jasper 2018). This type of association is apparently rare among vangas, although it regularly occurs with *Dicrurus forficatus* and some other species.

The vocal behavior of vangas is similarly varied. Most species are quite vocal, and many have very distinctive sounds, perhaps best epitomized by one of the vocalizations of *Falculea*, a loud *kwaaahh* that strikingly resembles the cry of a human baby. Genera that are known to sing are *Newtonia* (Langrand 1990; Goodman and Schulenberg 1991), *Calicalicus* (Appert 1970; Schulenberg et al. 2013), *Tylas* (Appert 1970; Schulenberg et al. 2013), *Mystacornis* (Langrand 1990; Schulenberg et al. 2013), *Vanga* (Rand 1936; Appert 1970; Schulenberg et al. 2013), and *Euryceros* (Langrand 1990; La Marca and Thorstrom 2000). The two *Schetba* species are also very vocal (Rand 1936; Appert 1970), although the social functions of these vocalizations are not well understood (Schulenberg et al. 2013). On the other hand, songs have not been identified in *Leptopterus*, *Pseudobias*, and *Oriolia*, and a song is only tentatively known in *Cyanolanius*. Vanga songs are usually rather short and often consist of whistled notes or trills. But in some genera, such as *Leptopterus* and *Cyanolanius*, vocalizations are dominated by harsh, grating sounds (Langrand 1990; Schulenberg et al. 2013); and even in genera with whistled songs, other vocalizations may consist of harsh notes, as in *Calicalicus* (Schulenberg et al. 2013). Duets are reported in *Schetba* (Langrand 1990; Schulenberg et al. 2013). Mechanical sounds (bill clapping) are produced by *Leptopterus* and *Schetba* spp.

BREEDING BIOLOGY

The breeding biology of vangas is incompletely known. Courtship displays in particular are very poorly known in vangas. *Calicalicus madagascariensis* males display to females by opening and lowering the wings and tail and thrusting the head downward while calling (Schulenberg et al. 2013), but it is not known whether this display is related to pair formation, copulation, or perhaps both. Wing flicking, preceding courtship feeding, is described for *Tylas* (Goodman et al. 1997a), perhaps suggesting that wing flicking in *N. brunneicauda* (Schulenberg et al. 2013) may also be a courtship, rather than an agonistic, display. Apparent courtship feeding, immediately preceding copulation, is reported from *Euryceros* (La Marca and Thorstrom 2000). In contrast, in *Artamella* a female solicited copulation by fluffing the contour feathers and shivering the wings and tail, while the male simply watched (Nakamura et al. 2001b).

The function of some other reported displays or interactions by vangas is not clear. One of the most remarkable of these is the description of a *Mystacornis* pair that silently strutted around each

other in meandering circles with the tails cocked vertically; this activity lasted for 1–2 min, after which the members of the pair separated and resumed typical foraging (Safford and Duckworth 1990). In a display in *Falculea*, one adult chased a second bird into a tree, flapping its wings shallowly and fast after landing, while calling; next the wings were drooped and shivered slightly (Schulenberg et al. 2013). This may have been a solicitation display, although no copulation was observed.

There is only a single species, *N. fanovanae*, for which the nest is not documented, but for several other species information on breeding is quite limited. Nest building and egg laying of vangas is concentrated from September to December, although breeding activities such as nest building have been reported as early as July in *N. brunneicauda* (Schulenberg et al. 2013). The typical vanga nest is a cup, in most species a deep cup or bowl, usually placed on a sturdy branch or in the fork of two or more branches. One brief description, however, was of a nest, still under construction, of *Cyanolanius madagascarinus*, whose base appeared not to rest on a branch (Appert 1970). The few nests reported for *Hypositta corallirostris* were in vertical fissures or shallow cavities in a tree trunk (Schulenberg et al. 2013; Rakotomanana and Raveloson 2019).

Most vanga species are, or at least may be presumed to be, socially monogamous (Schulenberg et al. 2013). The better-documented species in this category are *Calicalicus madagascariensis* (Appert 1970; Rakotomanana et al. 2009; Nakamura et al. 2013), *Tylas eduardi* (Nakamura et al. 2009b), *Vanga curvirostris* (Rakotomanana et al. 2001), *Euryceros prevostii* (La Marca and Thorstrom 2000), *Xenopirostris polleni* (Putnam 1996), and *X. damii* (Mizuta et al. 2001).

Cooperative breeding has been reported in several vanga species; in contrast to the apparent association between phylogeny and foraging strategy (mentioned above), cooperative breeding appears to have evolved independently several times. The best-documented species is *Schetba occidentalis* (Yamagishi et al. 1995; Eguchi et al. 2002), the breeding of which has been examined during a long-term study at Ampijoroa. More than half (62%) of all breeding efforts are by male-female pairs, but across years, 24–47% of nests had one or more helpers. Cooperative breeding units may consist of a pair with a one-year-old female helper; a pair with an immature male; two adult males and a female; and two adult males, one female, and an immature male. Female helpers are very rare, since females are more likely to disperse from the natal territory, Males, in contrast, are philopatric but do not breed in their first year after hatching; most remain as helpers on their natal territories, although a few become helpers on non-natal territories. Helpers make little or no contribution to nest building, incubation, or brooding but assist in provisioning the young and in territorial defense (Yamagishi et al. 1995; Eguchi et al. 2002, 2009).

Cooperative breeding has also been documented in *Leptopterus chabert* and *Artamella viridis*. Nesting in *Leptopterus* may be undertaken by male-female pairs (Nakamura et al. 2013), but in other cases helpers are involved. Benson et al. (1977), for example, observed a group of three adults engaging in nest construction. Or, nests may be constructed by a pair, but one or two helpers assist in the provisioning of an incubating adult and nestlings and contribute to nest defense (Appert 1970; Nakamura et al. 2009b). Breeding attempts by *Artamella* again may consist of a pair or include one or two helpers; these helpers do not assist in incubation or in provisioning the nestlings but contribute to nest defense and allopreen the breeding pair. Finally, one out of four nests of *Oriolia bernieri* was attended by an immature male (Thorstrom and Rene de Roland 2001).

Perhaps the most interesting social system is that of *Falculea palliata* (Nakamura et al. 2001a), which is polyandrous: the female copulates with more than one male. Several males (and the female) participate in nest construction, incubation, and nestling care, but the males have a dominance hierarchy, and the socially dominant (alpha) male contributes the most to these activities. Of 10 nests under observation, six were attended by one or two extra males.

FINAL COMMENTS

Vangas are found throughout all natural forest habitats on Madagascar. They are conspicuous, and many species are regular members of mixed-species foraging flocks. As a well-known endemic "adaptive radiation," vangas have long been a "flagship" for Madagascar, emblematic of the special nature of the Malagasy fauna. The full scope of the vangid radiation is still coming into view, however. We only now recognize a range of morphological and behavioral diversity shown by this radiation that eclipses that of other insular passerine radiations worldwide, and ongoing research into the population structure suggests that species diversity remains underestimated. Many aspects of vangid biology remain poorly known. Basic natural history information such as territory, home range size, and population density is little known for most species. Such information is important not only in its own right but will also be necessary to address ongoing threats to the population viability of many vangas, not only from currently known threats (principally habitat loss or degradation from anthropogenic activities), but also from the looming specter of climate change. We also have only the broad outlines of information on topics such as habitat requirements and diet and foraging strategy, and we almost totally lack knowledge of resource partitioning among vangas. For several species the nesting biology and social behavior remain poorly documented, and even the best-known species have often been studied at only a single site; in particular, greater insight into the factors that promote cooperative breeding in some species would be welcome. We hope that this contribution, outlining what is known and more importantly what is not known about the vangas, will spur further interest in studying and conserving these fascinating birds.

Subject editors: Roger J. Safford and Steven M. Goodman

PASSERIFORMES, MONARCHIDAE: *TERPSIPHONE MUTATA*, MADAGASCAR PARADISE-FLYCATCHER, *REMALY, TSINGETRA, RENGETRA, SINGETRAKA, DADY, ANGETRY*

R. A. Mulder and R. Ramiarison

Terpsiphone mutata is a medium-size (13 g) monarch flycatcher of the family Monarchidae, endemic to Madagascar and the Comoro islands. It is found throughout Madagascar at elevations from sea level to 2100 m (Goodman and Raherilalao 2013) and is a common resident of most forest types, including secondary forest, plantations, and gardens. Most information on the species comes from two long-term studies at Bealoka (riparian forests surrounded by dry spiny thickets, southern Madagascar; R. Mulder) and Ampijoroa (dry deciduous forests, central western Madagascar; T. Mizuta).

MORPHOLOGY AND PHYLOGENY

The most visually striking aspect of *Terpsiphone mutata* is the dramatic variation in plumage coloration between the sexes and among males. Adult males in definitive plumage are highly ornamented and occur in two plumage phases; one black and white (Figure 13.29a) and the other predominantly rufous (Figure 13.29b). Both morphs possess a pair of elongated central tail feathers (streamers) of up to 27 cm in length, and a brilliant blue fleshy wattle (up to 3 mm in diameter) around the eye. Females (Figure 13.29d) are orange rufous, do not exhibit plumage dimorphism, and do not possess streamers, although in rare cases elongation of the central tail feathers (up to 6 cm beyond the normal tail length) has been observed. The orbital ring is dull purple and narrow (<1 mm).

Definitive adult plumage in males is not acquired until at least three years of age, and four different "transitional" phases can be recognized among younger males. Streamers may be present or absent in these males, and if present they may vary in length and color (a single feather may even include three colors). This has resulted in considerable confusion with respect to sex identification of non-definitive males.

We studied a population of color-banded flycatchers between 1993 and 2003 in the Bealoka Forest, an isolated 120 ha riverine forest bordering the Mandrare River in the southeast. In our population, definitive adult male plumage is indicated by the presence of elongated white streamers, and either predominantly rufous or predominantly white body plumage. In "rufous" males, the cap (including the crown and cheeks) is iridescent bluish black, and the wings are dark brown with wide white fringes to the coverts. In "white" males, the head and throat are entirely iridescent bluish black, the underparts white, the wings black with white fringes, and the tail feathers (other than the streamers) white inside and black outside the vane. The color of the back or mantle varies from pure white to black. Some authors recognize two Malagasy subspecies, *T. m. mutata* and *T. m. singetra*, based on differences in mantle color of white-morph males (Salomonsen 1933a, 1933b), and it is often stated that black-backed males are more common in the east and white-backed males more common in the west of Madagascar (Langrand 1990; Morris and Hawkins 1998). At Bealoka, most white males have white or mottled white-and-gray backs, but dark-backed males also occur, albeit less commonly. Given the lack of clear-cut geographic variation and the lack of genetic support for such races (Bristol et al. 2013), we and other authors (e.g., Goodman et al. 1997a) feel there is insufficient evidence to date to warrant recognizing subspecies based on mantle coloration.

Yamagishi et al. (1992) speculated that "rufous" morph males are younger and eventually become "white" morph males when they are older. This is based on the observation that nestlings, which are pale rufous, more closely resemble the rufous morph. However, our observations of individually recognizable (color-banded) males over several successive years (up to seven years for some individuals) indicate that this interpretation is incorrect. Instead, "white" and "rufous" are distinct and irreversible developmental pathways (Mulder et al. 2002); a subsequent study by Mizuta (2003) reached similar conclusions.

As noted by Yamagishi et al. (1992), all nestlings are pale rufous, and males of both morphs are identical in appearance in their first year. Immature plumage in both sexes closely resembles that of adult females, although a thicker and brighter blue orbital ring can generally distinguish juvenile males. Both sexes molt between January and March, and differences between the two male morphs first start to appear at this time, when males enter their second year. At the start of their second year, all males acquire broad white fringes to the wing coverts and tertials, and finer white bars on the leading edge of the primaries. However, two distinct transitional plumages can be recognized at this stage, which are reliable indicators of the male's eventual phenotype. Future white males are pale rufous with minor plumage imperfections such as occasional white feathers on the breast, back, or rump, or black feathers visible in the throat (Figure 13.29c), which indicate partial transition to the white phase. Males sporting this plumage in their second year generally do not have elongated tail feathers. They invariably molt into definitive white plumage in their third year, and at this time they also grow the extended white central tail feathers. Once the white plumage has been adopted, it is maintained from one season to the next and no further plumage changes occur during the bird's lifetime (Mulder et al. 2002; Mizuta 2003).

Future rufous males in their second year have darker plumage than transitional males, and there are no imperfections visible in the form of stray white or black feathers. Unlike white males, rufous males do not always acquire definitive plumage (white streamers) in their third year. They may remain rufous, often with slightly

FIGURE 13.29 **Images depicting a *Terpsiphone mutata* male in A) definitive white and B) rufous plumage; C) a second-year male in partial transition to the white phase; and D) a female feeding nestlings.** (PHOTOS A and C by R. A. Mulder, and B and D by C. Ruoso.)

elongated (15 cm) rufous streamers, for up to five successive years before eventually molting extended white streamers. Often this is accomplished over two successive seasons; in the initial season only one of the streamers may have changed to a full-length white feather (the other is shorter and remains rufous), but by the next year both streamers are full length and white. At Bealoka, individual males of known age acquired rufous plumage with white streamers at three, four, five, and six years of age. Once definitive rufous plumage has been acquired, no further plumage changes occur, as is true for the white morph (Mulder et al. 2002; Mizuta 2003).

Apart from plumage color, "white" and "rufous" phase males do not differ in any of a suite of morphological measures, including the length of the streamers, head and bill length, wing, tarsus, and tail length, and body mass (Mulder 2013). The streamers are lost each year when the birds molt, and a new pair is regrown over a period of about one month. The length of the streamers changes from season to season as a new pair is molted, but changes in length do not follow a systematic pattern, such as increased length with age. Frequently, one or both streamers are lost or broken before the next molt, and damage to the streamers from feather mites is also relatively common. *Terpsiphone mutata* is a known host of at least one species of syringophilid mite, *Pipicobia terpsiphoni* (Skoracki et al. 2016).

The biological significance of male color dimorphism remains unknown, but there is fascinating geographic variation in the prevalence of this phenomenon within this species and across the genus as a whole (Chapin 1948; Owen 1963). *Terpsiphone* includes 13 species distributed from Africa to East Asia. Among the 12 other species in the genus, only two others (*T. viridis* in Africa and *T. paradisi* in southeastern Asia) show plumage dichromatism (different color morphs) among the males. In most of the other species, males have elongated streamers and orbital wattles, but only a single morph is found. Ancestral character analyses by Fabre et al. (2012) indicate that the ancestral plumage form of the genus *Terpsiphone* probably resembled that of the Asian paradise-flycatcher *T. viridis*, although it remains unclear whether male dichromatism was part of this ancestral plumage condition.

The relative frequencies of the two definitive adult morphs appear to vary in populations across Madagascar. At Bealoka, where all adult males are color banded, the frequency of white-morph males relative to rufous-morph males averaged 62% over eight years (range 54–65% from 1996 to 2003). Similar frequencies are reported by Yamagishi et al. (1992) and Mizuta (2002a) at Ampijoroa (54%), but at other sites on Madagascar, particularly in the north (e.g., Ambohitantely; O. Langrand, unpublished data) and west (e.g., Kirindy Forest CNFEREF; A.F.A. Hawkins, unpublished data), the frequency of white-morph males appears to be much lower.

Different subspecies of *T. mutata* are recognized on each of the four Comoro islands—*T. m. vulpina* (Anjouan [Ndzuani]), *T. m. voeltzkowiana* (Mohéli [Mwali]), *T. m. pretiosa* (Mayotte [Maoré]), and *T. m. comorensis* (Grande Comore [Ngazidja])—but generally only one subspecies on Madagascar (*T. m. mutata*; see above). Both color morphs are found on Mayotte, the island nearest to Madagascar, but except for one sighting of a white male on Mohéli (Mulder 2013), only the rufous morph appears to occur on the remaining three islands in the Comoro archipelago (Benson 1960, 1971).

A molecular phylogeny of these and the other *Terpsiphone* paradise-flycatchers in the Malagasy Region (Bristol et al. 2013) suggests that there is a surprising degree of divergence among the *T. mutata* subspecies on Madagascar and Mayotte (which are closely related, forming a clade) and the three western Comoro islands. There is strong phylogenetic evidence for the existence of two other clades (populations from Grande Comore, and those of Mohéli and Anjouan), and the three clades are genetically almost as diverged from one another as they are from other, more morphologically and geographically differentiated *Terpsiphone* species. The *T. mutata* clades are thought to have had continuous evolutionary independence for around 1.5 million years. Phylogenetic analyses suggest an Asian origin for the Indian Ocean *Terpsiphone* species, though Madagascar and surrounding islands could have been colonized directly from Asia, via Africa, or a combination of both.

BEHAVIOR AND BREEDING

Terpsiphone mutata is a highly vocal and noticeable bird. Its call, a scolding *retret retret retretret*, and song, a series of melodious cascading whistled notes (sometimes followed by agitated chattering and squeaking), are distinctive and penetrating forest sounds. The birds also employ eye-catching aerobatics to capture insects in the lower to middle canopy, sometimes opportunistically joining mixed-species flocks passing through the territory (Hino 2000). Diet consists mainly of prey such as dragonflies, butterflies, moths, wasps, flies, crickets, ants, spiders, beetles, and an assortment of smaller flying insects (R. A. Mulder and R. Ramiarison, unpublished data; Goodman and Parrillo 1997; Faliarivola et al. 2020), which they generally hunt by hawking from a fixed perch. However, they are also frequently observed hovering beside webs to glean spiders or capturing beetles and caterpillars from branches or tree trunks. At Bealoka (n = 926 observations), sally gleaning was the most commonly employed foraging method (51%), followed by sallying/hawking (36%) and gleaning (13%); prey was captured at a mean height of 7.2 m above the ground (Mulder 2013).

It seems likely that male plumage variation plays an important role in female choice, but the mating system of *Terpsiphone* flycatchers is still not well understood, particularly the key question of whether females exhibit a preference for either morph. *Terpsiphone mutata* is sedentary and territorial, remaining in the same territories from year to year as socially monogamous pairs. Territory size at Bealoka is about 1.3 ha (90 pairs in 120 ha). At our study site, males of all ages, including first-year males in female-like plumage, pair with females. Goodman et al. (1997a) noted that males in this first-year plumage have fully ossified skulls and enlarged testes, and parentage analysis confirms that males are reproductively capable from their first year onward. However, separation of pair members and mate switching from one season to the next is common. Several females have been observed to switch from one male morph to the other between seasons. Intrusions by neighboring males are frequently observed during the breeding season. Lengthy chases involving two males are common, as well as spectacular confrontational displays in which two males revolve around each other in hovering flight while chattering and squeaking. Genetic

studies using microsatellite markers (Adcock and Mulder 2002) have shown that extra-pair fertilizations occur at high frequency (48.8% of 686 nestlings, 61.6% of 271 broods; R. A. Mulder, unpublished data). The percentage of extra-pair offspring is highest in clutches of first-year males in female-like plumage (69%), and lowest in clutches of males in definitive plumage (white morph 48%, rufous morph 42%). There is no predictable pattern in terms of the cuckolded/cuckolding morph: males of both morphs are cuckolded by other males of the same or different morph at frequencies comparable to their representation in the population.

The breeding season of *T. mutata* at Bealoka starts in mid-September and continues until mid- to late January, peaking in October and November. Mizuta (2006) found that the onset of breeding across two study sites at Ampijoroa was predicted by proximity to water; laying dates were earlier and insect abundance higher at the site closest to water. They are multi-brooded and may build up to six nests and successfully fledge up to two broods in a single season. The nest is a small demitasse cup-shaped structure (Figures 13.29b and d), about 70 mm high and 60 mm in diameter at the rim (Rand 1936). It is built from fine grasses bound together with silk and egg sacs from spider webs (giving it a white appearance) and takes between three days and a week to build. Nests are generally unconcealed and built in the juncture of vines or in the forks of fine twigs, at heights ranging from 50 cm to 15 m above the ground, but usually between 1 and 4 m high. At Bealoka, nests were built in over 50 plant species, but most often in *Capparis sepiaria* (25%)—Capparaceae, *Celtis philippensis* (20%)—Cannabaceae, *Rinorea greveana* (14%)—Violaceae, and *Tamarindus indica* (13%)—Fabaceae. Nest construction is rapid (one to seven days), but after completion the nest is often left unused for one to three weeks before the clutch is laid. A high proportion of nests (35% of 1598 with known fate at Bealoka) are abandoned before egg laying and for unknown reasons. Occasionally a pair will return to a previously abandoned and incomplete nest later in the breeding season, but previously active nests are never reused.

Both males and females contribute to nest construction, incubation, and the feeding of nestlings, although the female's contribution is typically larger. At Bealoka, males contributed building at 78% of nests and were responsible for 33% of building visits (range 5–65%, n = 50). They incubated at 93% of nests and were responsible for 29% of incubation time (range 2–79%, n = 84), contributing shorter incubation bouts than females (average 22 min vs. 50 min for females), and provisioned nestlings at 100% of nests, contributing 48% of nestling feeds. At Ampijoroa, feeding contributions of males and females were similar and scaled with brood size, so that the per capita feeding rate was similar across broods of different sizes (Mizuta 2005). There is no obvious difference between male morphs in the contribution to nest building, incubation, or nestling feeding. Although males incubate, only females develop a brood patch. Clutches contain between one and four eggs, though four-egg clutches are extremely rare (over 85% of clutches have three eggs and only 1% of clutches contain four eggs). The eggs are ivory or creamy white (dimensions: 12.9–14.9 mm × 16.7–20.2 mm, Mulder 2013; mass: 1.4–2.2 g, Mizuta 2002a) and speckled with fine reddish-brown spots, most heavily in the form of a ring near the blunt end of the egg. At Ampijoroa, egg mass increased as the season progressed, but this change was uncorrelated with precipitation and only weakly with insect abundance (Mizuta 2002b). Incubation starts with the laying of the second egg and continues for 14–16 days (at Bealoka, one infertile clutch was incubated for >35 days). Nestlings fledge after 10–11 days in the nest. Fledglings are fed by the parents for up to four weeks after leaving the nest. Fledglings continue to be seen regularly in their parents' territory until April. After this time they are rarely seen, and we assume that they undertake dispersal between May and October. First-year recruits to the population are generally first seen during November, more than six weeks after the start of the breeding season.

PREDATION AND OTHER ASPECTS

Nest predation is common (around 70% of clutches). Known nest predators include three birds, *Vanga curvirostris* (Hook-billed Vanga), *Accipiter francesiae* (Frances's Sparrowhawk), and *Centropus toulou* (Madagascar Coucal). *Vanga curvirostris* has been observed taking eggs (Ramiarison 1998), *A. francesiae* taking nestlings, and *C. toulou* taking both eggs and nestlings. Mammals including *Eulemur fulvus* (Brown Lemur) (Mizuta 2002c, 2007) and *Rattus* sp. (rat), and snakes such as *Madagascarophis colubrinus* (Mizuta 2007) also prey on nest contents; another snake species, *Ithycyphus miniatus*, has been seen to be mobbed and so is a likely predator (Gardner and Jasper 2018). At Ampijoroa, better-concealed nests and nests farther from the nearest tree experienced lower rates of predation (Mizuta 2009). Potential predators, particularly *C. toulou* and *A. francesiae*, are subjected to vigorous mobbing and alarm calling by both the male and female when near the nest. Interestingly, there is evidence that *T. mutata* alarm calls are exploited by an eavesdropping nonvocal lizard (*Oplurus cuvieri*), which is subject to predation by some of the same raptors and snakes that prey on *T. mutata*. This enhances the lizard's detection of predators and reduces its risk of predation (Ito and Mori 2010).

After predation of a nest, a pair will generally start building a new nest within a few days. Parasitism by cuckoos has not been observed at Bealoka. Although Langrand (1990) lists *T. mutata* as a regular host of *Cuculus rochii* (Madagascar Cuckoo), we have never observed a case of cuckoo parasitism in over 1500 studied nests at Bealoka.

Both males and females sing throughout the year, although singing activity peaks during the breeding season (particularly around sunrise and sunset), and female song is usually a shortened version of the male song. At Bealoka, songs were 0.7–2.5 s (mean 1.3 s) in duration and ranged in frequency from 1.3 to 4.1 kHz (van Dongen and Mulder 2006). Most males sing either a single song type (85%) or two song types (15%); these remain invariant for individuals within and between seasons. There are no obvious differences between the song types of rufous and white males, but white males appear to sing at a higher rate. In Bealoka, a 120 ha forest, seven distinct dialect types could be identified, differing in duration and mean maximum frequency. Song dialects were predictably associated with particular microhabitat types, with individuals occupying territories with denser habitat singing longer songs at lower frequencies (van Dongen and Mulder 2006).

Terpsiphone mutata adults can be long-lived; the oldest confirmed age for a male individual at Bealoka was nine years and

four months, and many males survived for at least seven years. The oldest female in the population was still alive at 10 years and two months and nested in 10 consecutive seasons. Similar maximum life spans (10 years) have been reported for *T. viridis* (African Paradise-flycatcher) (Hanmer 2001). Somewhat shorter life spans of five years have been reported for *T. mutata* from rainforest in eastern Madagascar (Maromizaha), based on a 14-year mark-recapture study (Woog et al. 2018). Survival of adults between seasons at Bealoka was high (60–70%), and long-term tracking of the survival of individually recognizable males found no difference between morphs in survival from birth to eight years of age. Likely predators of adults include *Accipiter francesiae*, which is abundant in many shared habitats.

Terpsiphone mutata occurs abundantly throughout Madagascar and is common at most forest sites, so this species is not threatened. Densities are likely to be higher in dry deciduous forest habitats than in moist evergreen forests, although for the latter, comparative data are not available. Densities of *T. mutata* in dry forests vary from around 0.5 pair/ha (Ampijoroa; Yamagishi et al. 1992) to 0.75 pair/ha (Bealoka; Mulder 2013). Surveys of moist evergreen forests indicate that this species is present in the highest numbers at lower to middle elevations (0–800 m). At higher elevations (above 1000 m), numbers of *T. mutata* rapidly dwindle (A. Hawkins and Goodman 1999).

Subject editors: Roger J. Safford and Steven M. Goodman

PASSERIFORMES, CORVIDAE: *CORVUS SPLENDENS*, HOUSE CROW, *GOAIKA VAHINY*

G. G. Meier, E. Raobson, B. A. Bezandry, and K. Freeman

Corvus splendens is a member of the family Corvidae native mainly to the Indian subcontinent, but extending to the west into the Middle East (Iran) and to the east into different areas of Asia. The species has developed a close relationship with people and has its highest populations concentrated in cities and densely populated areas.

Around the end of the 19th century, *C. splendens* was deliberately released in the three port cities of Klang (Malaysia), Aden (Yemen), and Zanzibar (Tanzania) (Lever 2005). The primary reported reason for these introductions was the desired impact of this crow on rodent and beetle control, although religious motivation cannot be ruled out. From Zanzibar, crows reached Mombasa in 1945, signaling that spread was truly under way. Meanwhile, initial records from Port Sudan (Kinnear 1942) likely resulted from the first ship-transported individuals—the mode the species has increasingly used over the past decades for transport among countries and continents. Such accidental introductions, most likely as vagabonds on freight ships (Davis 1951; Cheke 2008), to other areas of the Old World have become relatively frequent.

Since these introductions, *C. splendens* has become very abundant in many areas and is one of the most successful introduced bird species in the world (Lever 2005; Global Invasive Species Database 2020). However, the combination of superabundance in areas with native fauna and flora not adapted to its presence, and its highly generalist omnivorous habits has made it highly invasive, with a range of negative impacts. It was therefore a matter of serious concern when, as predicted (for example, Lever 2005), *C. splendens* recently reached Madagascar. This contribution explains this concern and describes the arrival and general habits of the crow on the island, as well as the attempts to eradicate the population and prevent its future establishment. Unless otherwise stated, in this chapter "crow" refers to *C. splendens*, not the native *C. albus* (Pied Crow).

NEGATIVE IMPACTS OF *CORVUS SPLENDENS* INTRODUCTIONS WORLDWIDE

The risks associated with introductions of *C. splendens* are varied and reported elsewhere in detail (Lever 2005; CABI 2020). Negative impacts have been cultural, economic (damaging livelihoods), environmental, and in relation to human health. Positive impacts of the introductions may be limited to religious and traditional beliefs as in the native range of this species. Any possible role in reducing local rodent populations is offset by likely transmission of different zoonotic diseases, and attacks on natural predators of rodents; in short, no net benefit has been demonstrated.

For human health, there is a risk of disease transmission, as the crows are known to carry pathogens and to host various zoonoses (Roy 1998; S. Khan et al. 2013), including avian influenza (Rahman et al. 2019), and they may also pollute drinking water sources (Al-Sallami 1991). Where crow populations are large, defecation and vocalization of thousands of birds in roost sites impact living conditions, degrade housing, and can be an air strike hazard. Tourism can be further affected where open-air restaurants become a food source, swimming pools are used for drinking and bathing, and these are sometimes defended by group attacks toward people (G. G. Meier, unpublished data).

Impacts on agriculture can include raiding of corn, wheat, vegetables, fruit, and other crops; these may be eaten directly or spoiled by investigation for insects. For subsistence farmers, this can be a

serious threat to livelihoods, but larger producers can be affected too (e.g., H. Khan 2003). For example, crows may attack young poultry such that chicken rearing may become impossible in open areas; larger animals can be affected by attacks on young, or wounding (leading to infection) by crows collecting parasites. Crows may also catch fish from ponds and streams. As scavengers, they steal landed catch and raid fish and meat market stalls, which can make open-air fish drying impossible and lead to closure of meat and fish markets (Stafford and Crouch 2009).

The main conservation threats concern predation and competition, although disease transmission to native fauna may also be a real and poorly documented problem. Native insectivorous birds have been particularly affected by predation (including nest contents) where crows have become common, as in East Africa (Ryall 1992), but they will eat any smaller animal, including amphibians, reptiles, and small mammals (Gupta 1969; Sivakumaran 2018); as well as invertebrates; impacts on native flora are possible, as they feed on flowers, fruits, and seeds.

DISCOVERY AND SPREAD OF *CORVUS SPLENDENS* ON MADAGASCAR

It is common for crows to arrive in ports, where impacts on native species are often not felt quickly, but populations may quickly become too large to prevent rapid population growth and expansion into the surrounding countryside. The next phase, often long after initial arrival, may involve invasion inland along roads, railways, rivers, or canals.

Corvus splendens reached the Malagasy Region at Mauritius around 1900, with a reported population of 100 birds there by 1976 (Feare and Mungroo 1990). Hence, its invasion of other western Indian Ocean islands was also expected. It was first recorded in Seychelles by 1977, where a small population developed on Mahé but was eradicated by 1994 (Safford 2013r; Rocamora and Henriette 2015). Single individuals continued to be recorded from time to time but were shot whenever possible (Rocamora and Henriette 2015); no ongoing population resulted. Records between 1995 and 2010 on La Réunion and Rodrigues were of only single birds that were soon eliminated (Safford 2013r); another arrived but was shot on La Réunion in 2019 (Kitundu 2019). On the Union des Comoros, the species was not found in 2010 (G. G. Meier, unpublished data), but visiting birdwatchers documented one bird on Anjouan (Ndzuani) in 2014; no breeding has been confirmed, and this aspect needs verification. Mayotte (Maoré) was searched in early 2020, but no *C. splendens* was found (C. J. Feare, unpublished data). The removal or prevention of colonization of *C. splendens* from these islands would be of obvious benefit locally but would also provide an important buffer and protection for Madagascar; a model predicted its arrival on the island, suggesting that the west and northwest coast were likely to be the first areas affected (Nyari et al. 2006).

In 2014 the first observations of *C. splendens* on Madagascar were made in the eastern port city of Toamasina (Linders and Langrand 2014). This is unsurprising, as Toamasina is by far the largest and busiest port in the country. Around one dozen birds were observed in the downtown area and in the immediate vicinity of the port. It is highly likely that the seed population arrived by ship around 2010, and the numbers found in 2014 were the result of two or even three successful breeding seasons. Often the species is first seen once it has increased in numbers, while the first pair to arrive often keep a low profile and blend in, for example in Africa and now Madagascar, among *C. albus* or where seabirds like Laridae gulls are present (G. G. Meier, unpublished data).

By April 2016, the total number of birds counted at Toamasina was around 25 (Goodman et al. 2017a) and still restricted to the port area, and by 2019, somewhat surprisingly, the number did not seem to have increased by more than a few individuals. The reasons for the seemingly low productivity of the population are not clear but are potentially related to founder effects (genetic characteristics of the first introduced, and thus dominant, crows), or the impact of parasites and diseases.

It was also necessary to assess any wider spread or other arrivals on Madagascar away from Toamasina, following reports of *C. splendens* at other ports on the island. Confirmation existed only for Nosy Be, where two individuals were seen and photographed in 2018, having been reported present since 2016 (Razafimanjato et al. 2020). Between October 2019 and February 2020, one of us (E. Raobson, unpublished data) surveyed 14 port cities and villages around Madagascar for further evidence of the presence of this invasive crow. The results were mostly negative, including on Nosy Be (no birds found), but three birds in Tolagnaro were newly confirmed (Figure 13.30a). One bird was known in Tolagnaro for around one year (S. Wohlhauser, unpublished data) before two more arrived and joined the single individual. These birds were still present in February 2020. The survey also showed that people often misidentify native *C. albus* as the invasive *C. splendens*, and therefore reports must be validated.

ECOLOGICAL OBSERVATIONS ON MADAGASCAR

The breeding period of *C. splendens* on Madagascar is between mid-October and early January, as in other southern latitudes invaded by the bird. It nests exclusively in trees, often large *Ficus benghalensis* (Moraceae, banyan) and *Mangifera indica* (Anacardiaceae, mango) trees, but also palms and casuarinas. The stable presence at previously identified nest sites allows control and eradication operations to take place.

The *C. splendens* population in Toamasina used an area in the city not exceeding 25 ha and within the city center and near the port. The only feeding site visited on a regular basis by a large portion of the local population was the Toamasina slaughterhouse, mostly in the later morning hours (Figures 13.30b and c). The night roost was left by all crows from 4h30 to 5h, when they spread around the immediate neighborhood to feed locally. Larger groups were seen feeding together only at the beach (washed-up items and crabs) and the slaughterhouse (pork remains), while individual birds were observed feeding in various locations (e.g., feeding on dog food, garbage, insects in fruit trees, and slaughtered animals in residential areas). Before roosting, the group assembled close to the roost trees and flew in mostly together, reaching their final positions not later than 17h30. The roost site was in the upper and central portion of

FIGURE 13.30 **Images of *Corvus splendens* on Madagascar. A) One of three individuals in Tolagnaro as of 19 January 2020. This bird is shown perched on an electric wire in an area near a school and with relatively dense stands of introduced *Araucaria* trees that were used as roosting sites. The crows spent a good portion of the day around the school and fed on food debris. B) One of the sites regularly visited by a good portion of the Toamasina population of *C. splendens* was the local slaughterhouse, a short distance from the principal roost site. Before descending to the ground, the crows looked from adjacent coconut trees for the presence of meat debris, and when this was present, C) they dropped to the ground to feed.** (PHOTOS by E. Raobson.)

the tallest *F. benghalensis* trees in Toamasina and visible from a considerable distance. Here between one and three nesting attempts were suspected to have been made, but no direct evidence was obtained because of the dense canopy.

Nest brooding was maintained by both partners in two-hour shifts. Because of the early stage of the breeding season, no feeding of juveniles was observed. In one case, two crows raided a nest after the nesting pair was shot, one of them taking an egg out of it and flying away. There are previous reports of cannibalistic predation by *C. splendens* (Greeshma and Jayson 2017), but intraspecific egg predation has not been reported.

Smaller birds like *Acridotheres tristis* (Common Myna) were attacked at the nest site, but they also showed antagonistic behavior toward the crows. Twice a *Falco newtoni* (Madagascar Kestrel) and a *Tyto alba* (Barn Owl) were observed being mobbed by two to five crows, while a group of 15 to 20 crows regularly attacked a domestic cat close to the roost site; such boldness did not continue when the population dwindled under the impact of the eradication.

TOWARD ERADICATION AND BIOSECURITY

Virtually no country in the world has attempted to target introduced, established *C. splendens* populations with the effort and duration needed to quickly and significantly reduce their numbers and allow eradication (Meier 2013). Annual population reductions with the use of poison, such as Starlicide/DRC-1339, as implemented by the National Parks and Conservation Service on Mauritius since 2003 (Gopal 2016), have reduced numbers temporarily. However, this species is still well established (Feare and Mungroo 1990; Puttoo and Archer 2004), and a recent count estimated 6500 birds on the island, the majority roosting near the port in Port Louis (Meier and Haverson 2016). On Seychelles and La Réunion, attempts have been made to shoot all observed *C. splendens*, as well as any new arriving individuals. Seychelles is thus free of this species at the moment (Rocamora and Henriette 2015), and a similar "shoot on sight" policy has been implemented since 2008 on La Réunion (G. G. Meier, unpublished data), where the most recent individual was shot in February 2019 (Kitundu 2019). Farther north in the western Indian Ocean, on Socotra (Yemen), a UNESCO World Heritage site, the entire population of this species, present there for at least 15 years, was eradicated in 2009 (Suliman et al. 2010).

For Madagascar, because the species is present in neighboring countries and islands, the risk of reinvasion, in the event of successful eradication, remains high. Hence, a policy to identify any new arrivals through a network of observers along all coasts, especially in port cities, and to rapidly kill any bird(s) with appropriate techniques is an important governmental procedure. Accordingly, plans were drawn up to eradicate *C. splendens* from Madagascar and to establish biosecurity measures to prevent its reestablishment. The Malagasy government and local and international organizations (Madagascar Fauna and Flora Group [MFG] in collaboration with Association Vahatra and Institut Supérieur de Sciences, Environnement et

Développement Durable, Université de Toamasina) formed a partnership to achieve this. In the absence of national experience in such an endeavor, international assistance was sought from a specialist invasive species control agency, which had achieved the eradication on Socotra, led by the first author. The initiative also had the support of the IUCN Invasive Species Specialist Group and BirdLife International.

Funds to implement the plan were secured in early 2019 from the Critical Ecosystem Partnership Fund, focusing initially on eradication of the estimated 25 individuals in Toamasina. Different types of traps placed near where the birds were observed did not result in successful capture, and nesting birds were targeted by shooting with a high-powered air gun, requiring considerable caution in the urban setting. A large proportion of nesting birds were destroyed in 2019, but the remaining nests that were not reachable successfully raised young, and numbers increased. The population in early 2020 was 32 individuals. These included many juveniles, which are more naive and hence easier to control. Continuing efforts in 2020 resulted in the near extermination of the Toamasina population, but the initiative was terminated in March 2020 as a result of the Covid-19 crisis. At that time, a single bird of the former population remained and was last seen alone in June 2020, often associated with a vasa parrot (*Coracopsis* sp.), presumed to be an escaped caged bird.

In June 2020 observations by the trained local staff of MFG found two apparently newly arrived *C. splendens* individuals, again using the area in downtown Toamasina, joining the single bird remaining after the eradication efforts. At the time of writing (August 2020), plans remain in place to resume the eradication as soon as conditions allow in Toamasina, as well as to eliminate the birds in Tolagnaro. In this way, we remain hopeful for a complete eradication of the Toamasina and Tolagnaro populations of this species from Madagascar, followed by biosecurity and rapid response protocols to prevent reestablishment, setting a precedent for protecting the island's unique biodiversity and natural resources against an invasive non-native species.

Subject editors: Roger J. Safford and Steven M. Goodman

PASSERIFORMES: BERNIERIDAE, TETRAKAS

S. Reddy, T. S. Schulenberg, and N. L. Block

One of the most dramatic modern discoveries of Malagasy biodiversity is that of a newly identified endemic bird family, the Bernieridae, comprising species previously thought to be, at various times, representatives of at least three different widespread passerine families. A series of papers (Cibois et al. 1999, 2001; Fjeldså et al. 1999) using genetic tools were able to show conclusively that a suite of Malagasy taxa formerly assigned to the Pycnonotidae, Timaliidae, and Sylviidae belonged together in a single Malagasy radiation, for which the name Bernieridae was proposed (Cibois et al. 2010). Interestingly, as early as the 1930s at least one bird systematist (Salomonsen 1934a) correctly inferred that the group, now commonly referred to as the tetrakas or Malagasy warblers, constituted an endemic radiation (although including a few additional taxa as well); this view was shared by only a few subsequent authorities (e.g., Milon et al. 1973; Olson 1989), and the "standard view" until very recently continued to partition most or all tetrakas into several different families (Table 13.18). Continued examination indicates that to our current knowledge, there are 13 species in this family (Block 2012; Younger et al. 2019a), which include *Bernieria* (3 species), *Xanthomixis* (3), *Crossleyia* (2), *Oxylabes* (1), *Hartertula* (1), *Thamnornis* (1), *Cryptosylvicola* (1), and *Randia* (1). The phylogeny of the group is presented briefly elsewhere (see Reddy and Schulenberg, pp. 1621–26), alongside that of the other Malagasy bird radiations. This current contribution provides further detail, focusing on biological and life history aspects of the Bernieridae.

A comprehensive phylogeny of the Bernieridae including all proposed members has only relatively recently been completed (Block 2012; Younger et al. 2019a). These studies show several intriguing relationships that help us understand the broad diversity of ecologies and features exhibited by this adaptive radiation. One striking conclusion is that some species that were formerly placed together in a family are not monophyletic—that is, all species formerly thought to be bulbuls (Pycnonotidae) are not monophyletic; those species formerly thought to be babblers (Timaliidae) are not each other's closest relatives; and the same is true for the taxa previously considered warblers (Sylviidae). This further indicates that these species diversified into these disparate forms via multiple evolutionary pathways. Additionally, the four species recently placed in *Xanthomixis* are not monophyletic, with *X. tenebrosa* (Dusky Tetraka) being more closely related to *Crossleyia* than its (presumed) congeners.

A number of widespread forms of tetrakas indicate the possibility of cryptic species, lineages that are morphologically similar but show distinct genetic signatures indicating potentially hidden species. In *Bernieria madagascariensis* (Long-billed Tetraka), what was previously considered to be a single widespread species has been shown to be three distinct evolutionary units (Block 2012; Younger et al. 2019a). An even more dramatic and complicated example is that of *Xanthomixis zosterops* (Spectacled Tetraka), a species distributed throughout the moist evergreen forests of eastern and northern Madagascar. Detailed genetic analysis shows deep

TABLE 13.18. Timeline showing the different classifications of the members of Bernieridae

SPECIES	SHARPE (1881)	SALOMONSEN (1934A)	DELACOUR (1943 AND 1946)	PETERS'S CHECKLIST[1]	SIBLEY AND MONROE (1990)
Cryptosylvicola randrianasoloi	(Described in 1996)	(Described in 1996)	(Described in 1996)	(Described in 1996)	(Described in 1996)
Thamnornis chloropetoides	–	–	–	Sylviidae	Sylviidae: Acrocephalinae
Oxylabes madagascariensis	Timaliidae	Endemic subfamily	Timaliidae (1943), Sylviidae (1946)	Timaliidae	Sylviidae: Timalinae
Bernieria madagascariensis	Timaliidae	Endemic subfamily	*Phyllastrephus*, Pycnonotidae	*Phyllastrephus*, Pycnonotidae	*Phyllastrephus*, Pycnonotidae
Hartertula flavoviridis	(described in 1924)	Endemic subfamily	*Neomixis*, Timaliidae	*Neomixis*, Timaliidae	*Neomixis*, Sylviidae: Timalinae
Xanthomixis zosterops	Timaliidae	*Oxylabes*, endemic subfamily	*Phyllastrephus*, Pycnonotidae	*Phyllastrephus*, Pycnonotidae	*Phyllastrephus*, Pycnonotidae
Xanthomixis apperti	(described in 1972)	(Described in 1972)	(Described in 1972)	(Described in 1972)	*Phyllastrephus*, Pycnonotidae
Xanthomixis cinereiceps	*Oxylabes*, Timaliidae	*Oxylabes*, endemic subfamily	*Phyllastrephus*, Pycnonotidae	*Phyllastrephus*, Pycnonotidae	*Phyllastrephus*, Pycnonotidae
Crossleyia tenebrosa	(described in 1925)	*Oxylabes*, endemic subfamily	*Phyllastrephus*, Pycnonotidae	*Phyllastrephus*, Pycnonotidae	*Phyllastrephus*, Pycnonotidae
Crossleyia xanthophrys	Timaliidae	*Oxylabes*, endemic subfamily	*Phyllastrephus*, Pycnonotidae	*Phyllastrephus*, Pycnonotidae	Sylviidae: Timalinae
Randia pseudozosterops	(described in 1931)	–	–	Sylviidae	Sylviidae: Acrocephalinae

[1] Rand and Deignan (1960), Deignan (1964), G. Watson et al. (1986).

mitochondrial differences between *X. zosterops* populations that likely started to diverge about 3.6 million years ago but have since become geographically and genetically more mixed, likely via hybridization, as evidenced by nuclear data (Block et al. 2015). This intriguing example of extreme mitochondrial divergence that is not matched in the biparentally inherited nuclear genome indicates that there are some complex patterns of past population divergences on Madagascar. The potential to discover other cryptic differentiation is high.

With comprehensive modern surveys and the use of genomic tools, we have new and considerable insights into the ecology and evolutionary history of this family. The tetraka species exhibit a great variety of bill shapes, wing and tail proportions, and tarsus lengths (Figure 13.31). This diversity in morphology may have concealed the monophyly of this endemic clade from ornithologists, since much of the traditional classification of birds is based on just morphological features.

HABITAT

Most tetraka species are forest dwellers. Otherwise, it is notable that most species are syntopic: up to seven species co-occur at the same site in moist evergreen forests in northern and eastern Madagascar, a pattern that has been observed at a number of locations. Furthermore, although there are some patterns of latitudinal and elevational zonation, up to five or six of these species may be found in the same mixed-species foraging flock. All tetraka species are largely insectivorous, but they do segregate to some extent by diet as well as by foraging stratum (A. Hawkins et al. 1998).

DISTRIBUTION AND STATUS ON MADAGASCAR

Tetrakas are largely restricted to intact forest, and most species rarely if ever occur in secondary forest. Furthermore, almost all species occur only in the moist evergreen forests of northern and eastern Madagascar; the sole exceptions are *Thamnornis chloropetoides* (Thamnornis) (Figure 13.31b), which occupies the dry spiny thickets of the southwest; *Xanthomixis apperti* (Appert's Tetraka) (Figure 13.31d), which occurs only in transitional dry deciduous forests and, at Alandraza Analavelo (Analavelona), in a particular formation that has been referred to as medium-altitude moist evergreen forest in south-central Madagascar; and members of the *Bernieria madagascariensis* complex, which occur both in the moist evergreen forests and in dry deciduous forests of the west (but not in the dry spiny thickets). Of the three species in *Bernieria*, however, one taxon (*incelebris*, Figure 13.31c) is restricted to dry deciduous forests of the west (and would be the only tetraka with such a distribution); one taxon (undescribed) is restricted to moist evergreen forests of the northeast (and so would have a relatively restricted distribution); and the third, *madagascariensis*, is widespread in central eastern and southeastern portions of the island.

Those species that are limited to the moist evergreen forests typically occupy the full range of this habitat belt along the eastern side of the island. Two species, however, have more restricted

FIGURE 13.31 **Images of different members of the family Bernieridae reflecting the considerable morphological variation in this endemic Malagasy adaptive radiation of birds. A) *Hartertula flavoviridis* (Wedge-tailed Tetraka) in the Ranomafana Forest; B) *Thamnornis chloropetoides* (Thamnornis) in the Ifaty Forest; C) *Bernieria incelebris* (Obscure Tetraka) in the Kirindy Forest CNFEREF; D) *Xanthomixis apperti* (Appert's Tetraka) in the Zombitse-Vohibasia Forest; E) *X. zosterops* (Spectacled Tetraka) in the Montagne d'Ambre Forest; F) *Oxylabes madagascariensis* (White-throated Oxylabes) in the Anjozorobe-Angavo Forest; G) *Cryptosylvicola randrianasoloi* (Cryptic Warbler) in the Mantadia Forest; and H) *Randia pseudozosterops* (Rand's Warbler) in the Ranomafana Forest.** (PHOTOS by K. Behrens.)

distributions. One of the most enigmatic and poorly known passerines on Madagascar, *Crossleyia* (formerly *Xanthomixis*) *tenebrosa*, occurs only in the northeast, from Marojejy (Goodman et al. 2000b) south to Moramanga (A. Hawkins et al. 2013). Furthermore, even within this region it is rarely encountered; its obscurity hinders a proper assessment of its conservation status, and it has been classified as Data Deficient (BirdLife International 2020a), the only endemic Malagasy passerine species thus categorized. *Xanthomixis apperti* has an estimated Extent of Occurrence of less than 3500 km^2 (Goodman and Raherilalao 2013); its IUCN Red List status is Vulnerable (BirdLife International 2020a). Fortunately, all sites from which this species is known fall within the current protected area system of Madagascar (Goodman et al. 2018). Most are in the interior (both main parcels of Zombitse-Vohibasia National Park: Langrand and Goodman 1997b; Mustoe et al. 1998; and Alandraza Analavelo: ZICOMA 1999), with a single record from near the coast at Salary Bay, within Mikea National Park (Langrand and von Bechtolsheim 2009). It is one of the most common understory birds at Alandraza Analavelo (S. M. Goodman and M. J. Raherilalao, unpublished data). Three of the less common species of moist forest are treated as Near Threatened on the Red List, based on their moderately small populations and expected declines owing to forest clearance and degradation (*Hartertula flavoviridis*, Wedge-tailed Tetraka; *X. cinereiceps*, Gray-crowned Tetraka; and *Crossleyia xanthophrys*, Madagascar Yellowbrow); the other species are treated as Least Concern, although *Bernieria* has been evaluated only as one widespread species, not three, as recently proposed by Younger et al. (2019a).

It is worth noting that only five of the 11 tetraka species were described before the 20th century (Table 13.18). *Hartertula flavoviridis* was described in 1924 (Hartert 1924); *Crossleyia tenebrosa* was described in 1925 (Stresemann 1925); *Bernieria (madagascariensis) incelebris* was described in 1926 (Bangs and Peters 1926); *Randia pseudozosterops* (Rand's Warbler) was discovered during the Mission Zoologique Franco-Anglo-Américaine à Madagascar of 1929–1931 (Delacour and Berlioz 1931); *Xanthomixis apperti* was

discovered in 1962 and described in 1972 (Colston 1972); *Cryptosylvicola randrianasoloi* (Cryptic Warbler) was described as recently as 1996 (Goodman et al. 1996b); and of the three species of the *Bernieria madagascariensis* complex, one taxon is in the process of being formally described (J. Younger et al., unpublished data). Of these, only *X. apperti* has a truly restricted distribution. Indeed, one of the most recently discovered species, *Cryptosylvicola*, is now known to be widely distributed in the moist evergreen forests from Manongarivo and Tsaratanàna in the north to Andohahela in the southeast. Perhaps no other family of Malagasy birds has such a large proportion of species that were not encountered during the initial explorations of the island. Why this is so is not clear, although the small body size of some Malagasy tetrakas, the occurrence of some in the tree canopy, and their relatively retiring habits may be contributing factors.

MORPHOLOGY

Tetrakas are small to medium-size passerines, ranging in average body mass from 8.1 (*Cryptosylvicola*) to 31.5 g (male *Bernieria madagascariensis*) (Faliarivola et al., pp. 1608–20). All have a generalized "warbler-like" aspect, with a slender bill and relatively short and rounded wings; the tail too is of medium length in most species, although it is quite short in *Crossleyia tenebrosa*. Sexes are similar in plumage, but the male is typically larger than the female; in most species this size difference is not particularly strong, but in *Bernieria* the bill of the male is 25% longer than in the female (A. Hawkins et al. 2013) (which suggests that there may be some level of dietary partitioning between the sexes). On the other hand, the juvenile plumage of several species is significantly different from that of the adult (e.g., *Crossleyia*, *Xanthomixis cinereiceps*, and *Oxylabes*); indeed, the juvenile of *Oxylabes* is so different from the adult that it was described as a separate species (see Schulenberg, pp. 1694–99).

DIET

Tetrakas are almost entirely insectivorous, although very little detail is known about their diet. Arthropods and other invertebrates are confirmed as prey items through examination of the stomach contents or fecal samples for seven species: *Oxylabes madagascariensis* (White-throated Oxylabes), *Bernieria madagascariensis*, *Cryptosylvicola randrianasoloi*, *Hartertula flavoviridis*, *Thamnornis chloropetoides*, *Crossleyia xanthophrys*, and *Xanthomixis zosterops* (Newton 1863; Benson et al. 1976; Goodman and Parrillo 1997; Goodman et al. 1997a; Faliarivola et al. 2020). Field observations also confirm arthropods as food for *C. tenebrosa* (Randriamanindry 1995), *Cryptosylvicola randrianasoloi* (Goodman et al. 1996b), and *Randia pseudozosterops* and *Oxylabes madagascariensis* (A. Hawkins et al. 2013). Therefore confirmation of insectivory is lacking only for *X. apperti* and *X. cinereiceps*, but there is no reason to doubt that they too are insectivorous, especially in view of their foraging behavior (described below). Additionally, *Bernieria* occasionally takes small vertebrates (Gekkonidae geckos) and plant seeds (Goodman and Parrillo 1997). *Bernieria* species, with a body mass ranging from 20.0 to 39.0 g (Faliarivola et al., pp. 1608–20), are the largest-bodied members of the family; it would interesting to know whether any of the medium-size species, such as *Crossleyia xanthophrys* or *C. tenebrosa*, also consume the occasional small vertebrate, or whether this behavior is unique to *Bernieria* within the tetrakas.

FORAGING BEHAVIOR

Most tetraka species forage in the understory, or even on the ground (*Crossleyia xanthophrys*, *C. tenebrosa*, *Xanthomixis apperti*, *X. cinereiceps*, and *O. madagascariensis*). Notable exceptions are two species that are restricted to the canopy, *Cryptosylvicola randrianasoloi* and *Randia pseudozosterops* (Figures 13.31g and h). The foraging behavior of most species is not described in detail, but tetrakas generally capture prey with gleans and short sallies; the substrates are typically leaf litter, branches, and leaves, but *X. cinereiceps* and *Bernieria* also frequently take prey from tree trunks. *Crossleyia*, which is primarily terrestrial, probes the leaf litter and ground cover (Langrand 1990; A. Hawkins et al. 2013). A few species have more specialized foraging strategies. *Xanthomixis cinereiceps* hops up slender tree trunks (generally less than 15 cm in diameter), ascending from near ground level to as high as 15 m; after an ascent, the bird flies to the base of another tree and resumes another ascent (Langrand 1990; Evans et al. 1992; Thompson and Evans 1992). Notable also is the foraging behavior of *R. pseudozosterops*, which occupies the canopy. This species advances along the upper surface of a branch while peering down to inspect the undersurface, pivoting from one side to the other as it gleans from moss and other epiphytes.

SOCIAL BEHAVIOR

Most tetraka species are regular and seemingly seasonal members of mixed-species flocks; in the case of *Bernieria*, their participation in such flocks declines markedly during breeding (Hino 2009), and the same is probably true in other species of the family. Frequent flock associates of species of the moist evergreen forests are other understory insectivores such as other tetraka species and various *Newtonia* species; less common flock associates include *Coracina cinerea* (Madagascar Cuckooshrike), *Calicalicus madagascariensis* (Red-tailed Vanga), *Artamella viridis* (White-headed Vanga), *Terpsiphone mutata* (Madagascar Paradise-flycatcher), *Zosterops maderaspatanus* (Madagascar White-eye), *Cinnyris sovimanga* (Souimanga Sunbird), *C. notatus* (Madagascar Green Sunbird), and *Nelicurvius nelicourvi* (Nelicourvi Weaver) (Langrand 1990; Thompson and Evans 1992; A. Hawkins et al. 1998; Morris and Hawkins 1998). Some, such as the two *Crossleyia* species, are also typically encountered as pairs or family groups apart from flocks (Evans et al. 1992; A. Hawkins et al. 2013). Flock associates of the canopy species, *Randia* and *Cryptosylvicola*, also include *Newtonia brunneicauda* (Common Newtonia), *Pseudobias wardi* (Ward's Vanga), *Neomixis* spp. (especially *N. striatigula*, Stripe-throated Jery), and *Zosterops* (Rand 1936; Goodman et al. 1996b). *Thamnornis* is most often encountered with *Newtonia archboldi* (Archbold's Newtonia), *N. brunneicauda*, *Neomixis striatigula*, *Calicalicus madagascariensis*, *Schetba occidentalis* (Western Rufous Vanga), and *Copsychus albospecularis* (Madagascar Magpie-robin) (Appert 1972; Langrand 1990). *Bernieria* has also been

observed foraging near the much larger-bodied terrestrial *Mesitornis variegatus* (White-breasted Mesite), perhaps to capture arthropods flushed by the larger species (A. Hawkins et al. 2013).

The vocalizations of most tetraka species are not particularly distinctive. *Crossleyia*, *Xanthomixis* spp., and *Hartertula*, for example, generally have thin, high-pitched, twittering songs (Langrand 1990; A. Hawkins et al. 2013). Songs of other species tend to be stronger and more chattering or fluting, as in *Thamnornis* and *Bernieria*. The songs of a few species are more distinctive, such as the short, rapid series of notes in the song of *Randia*, often given from an exposed perch in the canopy. The song of *Oxylabes* is a duet, each member of the pair apparently having a distinct, sex-specific song (Schulenberg 1991).

BREEDING BIOLOGY

The breeding biology of tetrakas is very poorly known. Based on seasonal patterns of singing, and from the dates of the few reported nests or of birds gathering nesting material, breeding in the moist evergreen forests of eastern Madagascar is probably primarily from August or September to December (A. Hawkins et al. 2013). Little is known about the phenology of *Thamnornis* breeding, but apparently eggs are laid in November or December (Rand 1936; Appert 1972).

For most species, the nest is a cup placed in the understory, generally 0.25–2.5 m above the ground (Appert 1972; Langrand 1990; Safford and Duckworth 1990; Randrianasolo 1996; Rene de Roland 1996; Goodman et al. 1997a; A. Hawkins et al. 1998, 2013; A. Hawkins and Goodman 2003; Sinclair et al. 2006; Temba et al. 2014; Ratsaralasy 2015). No nest has been reported for *Crossleyia tenebrosa* or *Randia*. In view of the foraging stratum of *Randia*, in the canopy of tall forest, its nest is probably not only arboreal, as surmised by Wilmé and Goodman (2003), but is likely to be placed much higher than 2 m above the ground. On the other hand, the only known nest of *Cryptosylvicola*, which also forages in the midstory and canopy, was only 1.5 m above the ground (M. Putnam, unpublished data). Finally, the only account of the nest of *Hartertula* (Langrand 1990) is based on a photograph of an individual sitting in a globular nest with a side entrance, which is different from the documented nests of other species of Bernieridae but is similar to the nests of sunbird-asities (*Neodrepanis*) or jeries (*Neomixis*); confirmation that this is the true nest form of *Harterula* would be desirable (A. Hawkins et al. 2013).

Surprisingly, the most widespread species, *Bernieria*, is one of the least known in terms of breeding biology. And beyond the basics of nest shape and placement, egg color, and clutch size, very little further information is reported about the breeding of any tetraka species, apart from the detailed study of *X. zosterops* by Temba et al. (2014). Most species presumably are socially monogamous, but there are several reports of three adults attending a nest or traveling with juveniles of *X. cinereiceps* (Goodman et al. 1997a; A. Hawkins et al. 1998).

DEMOGRAPHY

Very little is known about the demographic population structure of Malagasy passerines. Notable, then, are minimum longevity records, determined for a handful of tetrakas from mark-recapture rates, suggesting that these species are long-lived: *Hartertula* (4y 2m 15d); *Oxylabes* (5y 11m 17d); *Bernieria* (7y 0m 2d); *Xanthomixis zosterops* (7y 0m 4d); and *X. cinereiceps* (11y 2m 4d) (Woog et al. 2018).

All tetraka species are vulnerable to predation by raptors, carnivorous mammals, and perhaps snakes. *Xanthomixis zosterops* and *Bernieria* are both documented in the diet of *Accipiter francesiae* (Frances's Sparrowhawk) (Rene de Roland and Thorstrom 2003). The diet of *Tyto alba* (Barn Owl) on the island consists primarily of small mammals, but remains of *Thamnornis* have been identified in pellets from several sites in the southwest (Rasoma and Goodman 2007; Goodman and Griffiths 2009; Goodman et al. 2014). The Eupleridae carnivore *Galidia elegans* (Ring-tailed Vontsira) preys on nests and eggs of *X. zosterops* (Temba et al. 2014), and presumably on those of other members of the family as well. Two species, *X. zosterops* and *X. cinereiceps*, are reported as host species for the brood parasite *Cuculus rochii* (Madagascar Cuckoo) (A. Hawkins and Goodman 2003; Temba et al. 2014), and again the same is probably true for other tetraka species.

FINAL COMMENTS

This is an exciting period in research on the Malagasy avifauna. There are still many aspects of tetraka biology for which we lack information, pointing to an excellent opportunity to investigate the adaptive nature of this newly discovered radiation. In addition to the recently published studies cited above, a great deal of ongoing research should increase our understanding of the phylogeny and biogeographic histories of the different Malagasy bird lineages. We can also hope that the information now being gathered will lead to a more general understanding of the history of avian differentiation on Madagascar and will provide insights into some of the remaining mysteries.

Subject editors: Roger J. Safford and Steven M. Goodman

PASSERIFORMES, PLOCEIDAE: *NELICURVIUS NELICOURVI*, NELICOURVI WEAVER, *FODISAINA, FODIFETSY, FODY ALA*

A. J. F. K. Craig

Nelicurvius nelicourvi is endemic to Madagascar, occurring throughout the eastern section of the island from Sambava to Tolagnaro, and in the north from Montagne d'Ambre to Tsaratanàna and the Sambirano Region. It is locally common in moist evergreen forests and secondary forest habitats, from sea level to 2100 m (Safford 2013s). It is also known to occur in littoral forests on sandy soils, but except for the isolated population on Montagne d'Ambre, it seems to be absent from other patches of apparently suitable forest remote from the main moist forest block, such as Ambohitantely, Ambohijanahary, Analavelona, or Daraina.

In its social and breeding habits, *N. nelicourvi* strongly resembles some of the insectivorous African species like *Ploceus bicolor* (Dark-backed [Forest] Weaver) and *P. ocularis* (Spectacled Weaver). Morphological and biological information did not clearly support an African rather than Asian origin for this species (Craig 1999), but a recent molecular phylogeny shows the two Malagasy weavers as basal to the group, which includes all the African species formerly in the genera *Ploceus* and *Malimbus* (De Silva et al. 2019).

MORPHOLOGY

Male and female birds differ in appearance (Figure 13.32), but there may be no seasonal change in plumage, as seen in *N. sakalava* (Sakalava Weaver) (see Craig, pp. 1714–15); males in an apparent nonbreeding plumage with reduced black on the head could in fact be immature. Both sexes have a gray chest and belly, rufous undertail coverts, olive-green wings and back, and a brownish tail. The male has a yellow chin and throat, with a sharply defined yellow band extending around the nape of the neck; the forehead, crown, and cheeks are black, forming a well-marked cap. The female lacks this black cap and has more yellow on the head, except for a dark line from the bill to the eye, and a greenish patch on the crown, extending behind the eye and onto the ear coverts. In both sexes the bill is black, and the legs dark brown. The eyes are also brown, in the hand sometimes reddish brown, but this would not be distinguishable in the field. Young birds have a greenish head, with some yellow above the eye and on the throat, and are generally duller than the female. The bill is yellowish, often with black patches but probably uniformly pale in the youngest birds. The mass of adults is between 20.0 and 28.5 g (see Faliarivola et al., pp. 1608–20), with males having a mean mass of 24.6 g (n = 7) and females a mean mass of 20.9 g (n = 5) (Rakotomanana and Nakamura 2012).

BEHAVIOR AND BREEDING

This is a nongregarious species, usually encountered singly or in pairs, but *N. nelicourvi* will join mixed-species flocks foraging in the forest, exploring branches and leaf tangles (A. Hawkins et al. 1998). In these mixed flocks of insectivorous birds, *N. nelicourvi* is most often associated with *Bernieria madagascariensis* (Long-billed Tetraka) (Eguchi et al. 1993). These weavers are agile birds that will hang below twigs and creepers while probing crevices and move through the trees at various heights, from the canopy to lower levels. They feed primarily on insects and other arthropods (spiders, beetles, bugs, and grasshoppers have been reported in stomach contents or feces; Rand 1936; Goodman et al. 1997a; Faliarivola et al. 2020) but are likely to take small fruits as well. Nestlings were fed beetles, crickets, grasshoppers, stick insects, caterpillars, and even small chameleons (Rakotomanana and Nakamura 2012). Young birds at first form a family party with their parents; the age of sexual maturity is not known, and a long-term pair bond is likely. The full song, given while hanging from the nest, is rendered as *chiz ... chizz chswiriissssiszz*. Other calls include a rasping, high-pitched *chizz chizz chizz* when in feeding groups; also a medium-pitched *sit* or *chet*, a nasal *tiang tiang* (Langrand 1990), and a *tsrrrreee* alarm call at the nest (Rakotomanana and Nakamura 2012).

These weavers nest solitarily, suspending the beautifully woven nest from a branch 2–10 m above a stream, clearing, or path. The nest is built from grass and palm fibers, in one case from pine needles, attached at the base by a "stalk" 15–30 cm long, with an oval nest chamber and an extended entrance tunnel up to 20 cm long. Eggs are pale greenish blue, rarely with some spotting, and are laid in a clutch of two to four (most often three). The breeding season is September to December. There have been few observations at the nest. The male does most of the nest building (Benson et al. 1977), with the female contributing very little (Rakotomanana and Nakamura 2012). Leaves are stripped from branches around the nest, and only females were seen to incubate (Oschadleus 2008; Rakotomanana and Nakamura 2012). Both parents feed nestlings, brood them, and remove feces from the nest; they also both feed fledged young.

Nelicurvius nelicourvi was until recently placed in the genus *Ploceus*, which comprises more than 50 species in Africa, five in Asia and two on Madagascar (see Safford et al., pp. 1553–602). All have some yellow and black areas in the male breeding plumage, and they construct a woven nest that they enter from below. However, there is considerable variation in nest structure (e.g., presence or absence of a tunnel), in molts and plumages, and in social organization. Some species are gregarious, colonial, and polygynous, and sexually and seasonally dimorphic in appearance; *N. sakalava* appears to belong in this group, whereas *N. nelicourvi* shows characters that fit more into the group of monogamous, solitary breeders that remain in pairs throughout the year. In the latter case there is no seasonal change in plumage and there may be little or no sexual dimorphism.

FIGURE 13.32 **Images of *Nelicurvius nelicourvi*. A) An adult male at Ranomafana National Park, and B) an adult female at Anjozorobe-Angavo protected area.** (PHOTOS by K. Behrens.)

OTHER ASPECTS

Although *N. nelicourvi* is a forest-dwelling species, it can also be found at the forest edge, in secondary habitats a considerable distance from intact forests, and in gardens of villages close to forests. This species is currently not threatened, but it would clearly suffer habitat loss from forest clearing. It is well represented in numerous protected areas.

This species hosts various blood parasites including *Plasmodium*, *Leucocytozoon*, *Haemoproteus*, and microfilariae (Savage et al. 2009; Schmid et al. 2017; Ivanova et al. 2018; Musa et al. 2019). The impact of these organisms on their health and survival has not been studied. In the Maromizaha Forest, in the context of a long-term banding study, 86 *N. nelicourvi* individuals were marked and released, with recapture rates of 18.6% and birds recaptured up to seven years after originally being marked (Woog et al. 2018). This suggests site fidelity by individual birds, and reasonable life expectancy for a small passerine.

Subject editors: Roger J. Safford and Steven M. Goodman

PASSERIFORMES, PLOCEIDAE: *NELICURVIUS SAKALAVA*, SAKALAVA WEAVER, *FODISAHY, ZAKY, TSIAKA*

A. J. F. K. Craig

Nelicurvius sakalava is endemic to Madagascar and distributed from the northern coastal and lowland areas through the drier western and southern regions of the island. Southern birds are smaller and have been treated as a distinct subspecies, *N. s. minor*. This is a bird of open country, closely associated with habitats modified by human activity, though it does occur in relatively undisturbed dry spiny thicket areas and dry deciduous forests. It is confined to the lowlands, from the coast to 1150 m (Goodman and Raherilalao 2013), where it is common but often localized in its occurrence.

The colonial habits, sexual dimorphism, and seasonal plumage changes of *N. sakalava* parallel those of the granivorous ploceids of the African savannas. However, the bare skin around the eye is unique in the weaver family, and both the structure of the nest and the plumage of the male are similar to those of Asian species such as *Ploceus philippinus* (Baya Weaver). Data on carotenoid pigments in the plumage also suggested a link between *N. sakalava* and the Asian weavers (Craig 1999). However, despite the lack of similarity between *N. sakalava* and *N. nelicourvi*, a recent molecular phylogeny (see Craig, pp. 1712–13) confirms that they are sister species, basal to the major African *Ploceus/Malimbus* radiation.

MORPHOLOGY

This weaver shows both sexual and seasonal dimorphism in plumage coloration. Males in breeding plumage have a bright yellow head, forming a sharp line across the nape and chest (Figure 13.33). The bare skin around the eye is reddish, the bill blue gray. Wings and tail are dark brown, the back and rump gray, paler on the rump. The underparts are also gray, paling to dull white on the undertail coverts. The female is much duller and paler below, with a whitish throat and white undertail coverts, with some buff on the flanks. The head has three distinct brownish stripes above and below the eye, and a moustachial stripe from the corner of the lower mandible. Nonbreeding males resemble females but retain a broad pinkish area of bare skin around the eye. Their bills are pale gray. Juvenile birds are paler than females, particularly in the stripes on the head, and have pale horn-colored bills. Adults weigh between 18.0 and 28.5 g (see Faliarivola et al., pp. 1608–20).

BEHAVIOR AND BREEDING

Highly gregarious, this weaver forms flocks of more than 200 birds that feed on the ground, in rice paddies, or in trees. They consume primarily seeds but regularly take insects and other arthropods, particularly when feeding young. Stomach contents and fecal samples generally include insect remains, and the birds appear to take only waste rice, so they are not regarded as agricultural pests (Benson et al. 1977; Faliarivola et al. 2020). They have also been seen eating the flowers of *Alluaudia* (Didiereaceae).

When breeding, these weavers gather in colonies with 10–120 nests. These are usually placed in trees, including palms, baobabs (*Adansonia za*), and non-native *Gyrocarpus americanus*. Such colonies are often found within villages, and nests may also be suspended from thatched roofs. At one site, 18 nests were found under the roof of a veranda. Small colonies may also be found under the nests of *Corvus albus* (Pied Crow), *Buteo brachypterus* (Madagascar Buzzard), *Milvus aegyptius* (Yellow-billed Kite) (Rand 1936), and *Haliaeetus vociferoides* (Madagascar Fish-eagle) (Tingay and Gilbert 1999); 75 nests were counted below one *B. brachypterus* nest (Rene de Roland 2010). Avoidance of predation by *Polyboroides radiatus* (Madagascar Harrier-hawk) is a suggested explanation for this association with nesting raptors (Gardner et al. 2011).

The same colony sites are used in successive years. Nests may be within 1 m of the ground, or as high as 20 m. The nest is retort shaped, either woven directly onto twigs or attached by a short woven "rope." The nest entrance is extended into a tunnel, which varies in length from 17 to 40 cm. Often the mouth of the tunnel is "decorated" with strips of fresh material. Nests are woven from grass, leaf stems, and strips of palm leaf and finally lined with soft plant fibers. Depending on the material, they may appear tightly woven or quite scruffy. Both sexes are involved in nest building, and during the breeding period the birds sleep singly in unoccupied nests (Rand 1936).

At the colonies, males hanging from the nests produce a short high-pitched "swizzling" song, often in chorus. This is interspersed with low *chep*, *chup*, and *chrrrk* notes, as well as a buzzing *chee-chee-chee* song, while fluttering their wings (Rand 1936). Birds in flight call *treeyoo* (Langrand 1990). During courtship the male sometimes holds a piece of green vegetation or a grass seed head in its bill. Females quiver their wings when soliciting copulation. There is no clear evidence that males are polygynous, but it is likely that at least some individuals succeed in attracting more than one female. Breeding may be closely tied to rainfall rather than being strictly seasonal, especially in semiarid regions. However, nest building, in which subadult males also engage, is not itself a clear indication of breeding. In the north, colonies are active in September and October, in the west from November to April. In the southeast, breeding may be irregular, dependent on local rains, with nesting starting as early as August or as late as December (Goodman et al. 1997a), and given this information, this may be a widespread habit in this species, particularly in drier parts of its range. Eggs were noted from November to February (Appert 2011). The eggs are plain pale greenish blue, typically in a clutch of two to four. It appears that only the female incubates, but both sexes may feed the young.

FIGURE 13.33 ***Nelicurvius sakalava* adult male at Mandrare River Camp.** (PHOTO by K. Behrens.)

PREDATION AND OTHER ASPECTS

Sakalava Weavers have been reported as prey of *Tyto alba* (Barn Owl) from three sites in the south (Rasoma and Goodman 2007; Goodman and Griffiths 2009; Goodman et al. 2014). Adult birds may be caught by *Falco zoniventris* (Banded Kestrel), and nests are often robbed by *Polyboroides radiatus* (Madagascar Harrier-hawk). In general, people seldom molest *Nelicurvius sakalava*; in many dry areas of the island, weaver colonies in villages, especially those close to a house, are considered a sign of good fortune (Goodman et al. 1997a). However, at some localities these birds are collected as "bushmeat" (Ichino et al. 2018). Nevertheless, they are widespread and abundant in open country.

This colonially breeding weaver shows high levels of blood parasites such as *Plasmodium*, *Haemoproteus*, *Leucocytozoon*, *Trypanosoma*, and microfilariae (Savage et al. 2009, Ishtiaq et al. 2012), and in *N. sakalava* 75% of the 68 tested individuals were positive. Although the impact of such high levels of parasitism is unknown, it may well be associated with being highly colonial (Tella 2002).

Subject editors: Roger J. Safford and Steven M. Goodman

PASSERIFORMES, PLOCEIDAE: *FOUDIA*, FODY, *FODIMENA*, *FODIALA*

A. J. F. K. Craig

The fodies form a clearly defined group of small weavers that occur in the Malagasy Region, where each island or archipelago has an endemic species. Most are found in forest, but some, most notably *Foudia madagascariensis* (Madagascar Fody), are common in open country. Males of most *Foudia* species in breeding dress have bright red plumage around the head and extending over other parts of the body to a variable degree; some species have yellow instead of red. Currently seven species are generally recognized, on the Comoros, Aldabra, Seychelles, Mauritius, and Rodrigues, with two on Madagascar. There was another species on La Réunion, now extinct (Cheke and Hume 2008).

The genus *Foudia* has been linked to the African queleas (*Quelea*) and bishop birds (*Euplectes*) (Moreau 1960), which are small granivorous weavers with red areas in their plumage, and *Foudia* species build a nest with a side entrance near the top. This relationship is supported by skeletal characters, and by the carotenoid pigments in the feathers of these three genera (Craig 1999). A new molecular phylogeny confirms that *Foudia* is closest to *Quelea*, and part of a clade that includes *Euplectes*, the Asian species of *Ploceus*, and the African *Pachyphantes superciliosus* (De Silva et al. 2019).

Two species occur on Madagascar: *F. madagascariensis* and *F. omissa* (Forest Fody). The systematic relationship between the two was controversial for many years, as was the position of *F. omissa* in relation to other *Foudia* taxa; it was often treated as a subspecies of *F. eminentissima* with other races on the Comoros and Aldabra. A thorough (nuclear and mitochondrial) DNA analysis (Warren et al. 2012) found that *omissa* and the Aldabran form *aldabrana* were not closely related to the Comorian fodies, but results were consistent with peripatric divergence of *aldabrana* from ancestral *omissa*. On this basis it is reasonable to treat *F. omissa* as a species endemic to Madagascar and *F. eminentissima* as restricted to the Comoros. However, specimens morphologically intermediate between *F. madagascariensis* and *F. omissa* have been identified from Madagascar as interspecific hybrids (Benson et al. 1977), and the molecular data confirmed hybridization over a long period (millennia), with mitochondrial DNA suggesting it to be frequent between *F. madagascariensis* males and *F. omissa* females, but not between *F. omissa* males and *F. madagascariensis* females (Warren et al. 2012).

FOUDIA MADAGASCARIENSIS, MADAGASCAR FODY

Distribution and Habitat

Foudia madagascariensis is the commonest and most widespread native bird on Madagascar. It occurs in a variety of habitats and climatic regimes from the wettest to driest zones on the island (Safford 2013t) and has been found in mangroves (Gardner et al. 2012). During the 18th to 20th centuries it was also successfully introduced to other western Indian Ocean islands: La Réunion, Comoros (probably, although native status is not ruled out), Mauritius, Seychelles, Rodrigues, Glorieuses, Juan de Nova, and Chagos, and also to St. Helena (Atlantic Ocean) and Bahrain (Safford 2013t). Although this fody favors open areas, including grassland and cultivated areas, it may be found wherever seed is available, including towns and forest clearings, and on Madagascar it has been recorded up to 2750 m in elevation. However, it seems to stay out of intact forest. Flocks and roosts often hold several hundred birds, and this species is a serious pest in rice-growing areas. Traditional cage traps are used to catch birds in rice fields, and villagers also attempt to scare birds from the fields and to destroy nests; fodies are eaten regularly in some areas (Ichino et al. 2018). There have been trials with chemical avicides, though fortunately this method is not recommended, since secondary poisoning and other impacts on the environment would be unavoidable. Mist netting the birds at roosts has been suggested as a possible control measure (Zefania 1999).

Morphology

In breeding plumage, a *Foudia madagascariensis* male is a bright red bird, with a short black line through the eye, and black central streaks on the feathers of the mantle (Figure 13.34a). Wings and tail are olive brown, with paler edges to the feathers. The bill is black, the eyes dark brown, and the legs pale brownish. Occasional birds are more orange or even yellow instead of red. Female birds are olive brown on the upper parts, with faint central streaks on the head and nape feathers, dark streaking on the mantle, and an unstreaked rump, which is also paler in appearance. On the sides of the head there is a buffy stripe above, and often also below, the eye. The wings and tail are olive brown with paler edges, as in the male. The underparts are gray brown, paler on the belly, and dull white on the undertail coverts. The bill is horn colored, with the lower mandible much lighter in color than the upper mandible. Males in nonbreeding plumage and subadult birds resemble females but can be distinguished on measurements (Koenig 2005). From museum specimens, juvenile birds prior to the post-juvenile molt are much more buff in appearance, with broad buffy margins to many of their feathers. Adults have a body mass between 14.0 and 20.0 g (see Faliarivola et al., pp. 1608–20).

Diet, Behavior, and Breeding

Foudia madagascariensis subsists primarily on seeds, though it regularly takes arthropods such as caterpillars and spiders and feeds on the nectar of both native and introduced plants. On other islands this species has been observed in mixed-species flocks. In many areas of Madagascar, rice is the principal item in its diet, supplemented by seeds of grasses such as *Eragrostis maxima*, *Panicum maximum*, and

FIGURE 13.34 **The two species of *Foudia* occurring on Madagascar show some largely discrete plumage characters in males. A) *Foudia madagascariensis* in the Antsokay Arboretum, just south of Toliara; and B) *F. omissa* at Montagne d'Ambre National Park.** (PHOTOS by K. Behrens.)

Pennisetum setosum (Poaceae). Young are fed both seeds and insects, while adults regularly take nectar from plants such as *Grevillea* sp. (Proteaceae), *Phytolacca* sp. (Phytolaccaceae), *Lantana camara* (Verbenaceae), and *Nephelium litchi* (Sapindaceae). Flocks often roost in sugarcane or bamboo, and also in tall grasses such as *Panicum maximum*, in mangroves and other trees, and in reedbeds.

Both arrival at the roost in the evening and departure in the morning are well synchronized and occur over a short period; the timing varies with sunrise and sunset and is also influenced by weather conditions, so that birds go to roost earlier in overcast or rainy weather. Flocks containing immature birds have been recorded in October at Tolagnaro (Goodman et al. 1997a). *Foudia madagascariensis* often sunbathes early in the morning or in the late afternoon, or immediately after a rainstorm.

In contrast to many other gregarious granivorous weavers, *F. madagascariensis* leaves the flocks to breed, often as solitary pairs, but may also be polygynous with up to five females in a season (Rasamison and Andrianarimisa 2013). There is a protracted breeding season from September to May (Goodman et al. 1997a). Captive birds produced up to three broods in four months, so wild birds may be double brooded in good seasons. The nest is an oval structure woven of grass strips, with a side entrance near the top, and a projecting "porch" that may be extended into a short tunnel. Captive males each built several nests while the females contributed only lining material (Kleefisch 1981), and field observations indicate that nests are built largely by the male alone (Rasamison and Andrianarimisa 2013), although females may add lining material or make small adjustments. Nests may be built in reeds, tall grass, or shrubs within 1 m of the ground, in trees near the tips of branches, or attached to the midribs of palm leaves, as high as 8 m above the ground.

Foudia madagascariensis males defend a territory within a radius of about 20 m. From a prominent perch, the male gives a high-pitched trilling song, *trrr tree tree*, sometimes followed by short, wheezy phrases. Intruders are usually threatened and then displaced, but sometimes there are fights in which the birds may fall to the ground, locked together. In the threat display, the bird crouches and points the bill at the opponent, with the breast, back, and rump plumage ruffled and the wings slightly drooped. Females are initially treated as "intruders," but if they do not leave the territory, the male switches to an upright wing-beating display with loud *seer seer* calls. He then slowly flies to the nest, often gliding, and perches nearby, quivering his wings and giving the trilling song while the female inspects the nest. The female solicits copulation with *tsip* calls, with head raised and wings quivering. The male then approaches and mounts with all feathers ruffled, wings spread and drooped, and tail depressed (Crook 1961). A captive male frequently hovered over the female during this phase of courtship (Delacour 1933). The brightness of a male's plumage is positively correlated with body condition and clutch size, so it may be significant in sexual selection (Estep et al. 2006).

The eggs are plain pale blue green, typically in a clutch of two to four. Only the female incubates, while the male perches nearby, giving a *zi-ii-ii* call of five to eight notes. The alarm call is a sharp *tic-tic*. Nests may be destroyed by *Polyboroides radiatus* (Madagascar Harrier-hawk), and one nest was destroyed by a neighboring pair of *Acridotheres tristis* (Common Mynas), an introduced species on Madagascar (Ruempler and Ruempler 1996). Other nest predators include *Centropus toulou* (Madagascar Coucal), *Rattus rattus* (Black Rat), and *Microcebus* mouse lemur (Rasamison and Andrianarimisa 2013).

The incubation period is 11–14 days in captivity and 13–17 days in the field, and captive young leave the nest after 14–18 days (Brickell 2006). Both parents feed the young, and once the young leave the nest, in some cases the family may be divided, with each adult caring for some of the brood. Young males may not acquire

breeding plumage in their first year, which is the pattern in many other sexually dimorphic weavers.

FOUDIA OMISSA, FOREST FODY

Endemic to Madagascar from the northern region to the south of the island, *Foudia omissa* is restricted to the moist evergreen forests (Safford 2013u), where it may occur from sea level up to 2100 m (A. Hawkins 1999). It is present in some forest patches in the Central Highlands, such as Manjakatompo and Ambohitantely (Goodman and Putnam 1996).

Foudia omissa males in breeding plumage have forehead, crown, and nape red; mantle olive brown with dark central streaks (some feathers may be red tipped); rump red; wings and tail dark olive green, with narrow yellow edges to the remiges, and broad pale edges on the wing coverts; chin, throat, cheeks, and ear coverts red with a black ring around the eye and a dark patch behind the eye; upper breast red and lower breast, belly, flanks, thighs, and undertail coverts olive gray; iris dark brown; bill black; and legs brown (Figure 13.34b). Intensity of red is variable, and there is often a yellowish wash on the thighs and undertail coverts. Males in nonbreeding plumage and females are not distinguishable in appearance: forehead, crown, and nape are olive green with narrow central streaks; mantle olive green with much broader streaks, while rump is unstreaked; wings and tail dark olive green as in breeding males; cheeks and ear coverts olive green; underparts olive gray with some yellow streaking, palest on the chin and in the center of the belly; iris dark brown; bill brown; and legs brown. Juveniles resemble females, but upper parts are tinged brown rather than greenish, and wing coverts have buffy edges. There is a complete post-juvenile molt. Adult body mass is between 15.0 and 24.5 g, with males averaging slightly heavier than females (see Faliarivola et al., pp. 1608–20).

The song is described as a long sequence (20–60 sec) of very high, twittering and chirping notes, while the calls are apparently similar to those of *F. madagascariensis* (Safford 2013u). *Foudia omissa* feeds on seeds (e.g., *Sloanea*), insects, and nectar from flowers of *Strongylodon*, *Bakerella*, and *Symphonia* (Goodman et al. 1997a) and forages in small flocks of up to 15 birds, which may join mixed-species flocks in forests or flock with *F. madagascariensis* on the forest edge (Rand 1936).

Based on observations of seven nests of *F. omissa*, the clutch size is one to three eggs, and one case of polygyny was noted (Rasamison and Andrianarimisa 2013). In this species, only the female incubates, for 13 to 17 days.

PREDATION AND OTHER ASPECTS (BOTH SPECIES)

Foudia madagascariensis adults have been recorded as prey of *Tyto alba* (Barn Owl) at several sites (Rasoma and Goodman 2007; Goodman and Griffiths 2009; Goodman et al. 2014) and are even occasional prey of large chameleons (Garcia and Vences 2002). Both *Foudia* species may be hosts to blood parasites, including *Plasmodium*, *Haemoproteus*, *Leucocytozoon*, and microfilariae (Savage et al. 2009; Schmid et al. 2017; Ivanova et al. 2018; Musa et al. 2019). However, the impact of these parasites on *Foudia* populations has not been investigated.

As cultivation encroaches on forested areas, these two *Foudia* species are seldom effectively isolated, and *F. madagascariensis* does enter natural forest occasionally, for instance during periods of massive bamboo flowering when it feeds on the resulting seeds (S. M. Goodman, unpublished data). Thus, disrupting large tracts of intact forest might open more habitat for this species and lead to the disappearance of *F. omissa* through increased hybridization (Langrand 1990).

Large-scale banding of *Foudia* species has been conducted in the Maromizaha Forest (Woog et al. 2018). Of the more than 1000 *F. omissa* individuals marked and released, the recapture rate was very low (0.2%), and no birds were recorded after more than two years. In the case of *F. madagascariensis*, of the 233 individuals marked and released, the recapture rate was also low (1.3%), and one bird was retrapped four years after original capture.

Subject editors: Roger J. Safford and Steven M. Goodman

REFERENCES

Adcock, G. J., and Mulder, R. A. 2002. Polymorphic microsatellite loci for paternity analysis in the Madagascar paradise flycatcher *Terpsiphone mutata*. *Molecular Ecology Notes* 2: 287–289.

Albert-Daviaud, A., Perillo, S., and Stuppy, W. 2018. Seed dispersal syndromes in the Madagascan flora: The unusual importance of primates. *Oryx* 52: 418–426.

Ali, J. R., and Huber, M. 2010. Mammalian biodiversity on Madagascar controlled by ocean currents. *Nature* 463: 653–656.

Al-Sallami, S. 1991. A possible role of crows in the spread of diarrhoeal diseases. *Journal of the Egyptian Public Health Association* 66(3–4): 441–449.

Alström, P., Ericson, P.G.P., Olsson, U., and Sundberg, P. 2006. Phylogeny and classification of the avian superfamily Sylvioidea. *Molecular Phylogenetics and Evolution* 38: 381–397.

Alström, P., Fregin, S., Norman, J. A., Ericson, P.G.P., Christidis, L., and Olsson, U. 2011. Multilocus analysis of a taxonomically densely sampled dataset reveal extensive non-monophyly in the avian family Locustellidae. *Molecular Phylogenetics and Evolution* 58: 513–526.

Alström, P., Barnes, K. N., Olsson, U., Barker, F. K., Bloomer, P., Khan, A. A., Qureshi, M. A., Guillaumet, A., Crochet, P.-A., and Ryan, P. G. 2013. Multilocus phylogeny of the avian family Alaudidae (larks) reveals complex morphological evolution, non-monophyletic genera and hidden species diversity. *Molecular Phylogenetics and Evolution* 69: 1043–1056.

Alström, P., Cibois, A., Irestedt, M., Zuccon, D., Gelang, M., Fjeldså, J., Andersen, M. J., Moyle, R. G., Pasquet, E., and Olsson, U. 2018. Comprehensive molecular phylogeny of the grassbirds and allies (Locustellidae) reveals extensive non-monophyly of traditional genera, and a proposal for a new classification. *Molecular Phylogenetics and Evolution* 127: 367–375.

Amadon, D. 1947. An estimated weight of the largest known bird. *Condor* 49: 159–164.

———. 1951. Le pseudo-souimanga de Madagascar. *L'Oiseau et la Revue Française d'Ornithologie* 21: 59–63.

Andersen, M. J., McCullough, J. M., Mauck, W. M., III, Smith, B. T., and Moyle, R. G. 2017. A phylogeny of kingfishers reveals an Indomalayan origin and elevated rates of diversification on oceanic islands. *Journal of Biogeography* 170: 1–13.

Anderson, M. G. 1984. Parental investment and pair-bond behavior among canvasback ducks (*Aythya valisineria*, Anatidae). *Behavioral Ecology and Sociobiology* 15: 81–90.

Andersson, M. 1995. Evolution of reversed sex roles, sexual size dimorphism, and mating system in coucals (Centropodidae, Aves). *Biological Journal of the Linnean Society* 54: 173–181.

Andrews, C. W. 1897. On some fossil remains of carinate birds from central Madagascar. *Ibis*, seventh series, 3: 343–359.

Andriamalala, T., Rene de Roland, L.-A., Rakotondratsima, M., Razafimanjato, G., and Thorstrom, R. 2013. Nest characteristics of yellow-billed kites *Milvus aegyptius* in the Manambolomaty Lakes Complex, western Madagascar. *Ostrich* 84: 79–84.

Andriamampianina, J. 1976. Madagascar. In *Proceedings of International Conference on the Conservation of Wetlands and Waterfowl, Heiligenhafen, Federal Republic of Germany, 2–6 December 1974*, ed. M. Smart, pp. 125–126. Slimbridge: IWRB.

Andriamasimanana, R. H., and Cameron, A. 2013. Predicting the impacts of climate change on the distribution of threatened forest-restricted birds in Madagascar. *Ecology and Evolution* 3(4): 763–769.

Andriamasimanana, R. H., Rabenandrasana, M. N., Raminoarisoa, V., Sam, T. S., Virginie, M. C., Ratelolahy, F. J., and Rakotonirainy, E. O. 2001. Effets de la fragmentation de la forêt humide sur les populations d'oiseaux et de lémuriens dans le Corridor Mantadia-Zahamena. *Lemur News* 6: 18–22.

Andrianarimisa, A. 1992. Analyse fonctionnelle de l'écosystème forestier du massif d'Ankarafantsika et de ses stades de dégradation par l'étude du peuplement ornithologique. *Working Group on Birds in the Madagascar Region Newsletter* 2: 4–6.

———. 1995. A record of the sunbird-asity *Neodrepanis coruscans* in the Réserve Spéciale d'Ambohitantely. *Working Group on Birds in the Madagascar Region Newsletter* 5(2): 8–9.

Andrianarimisa, A., Bachmann, L., Ganzhorn, J. U., Goodman, S. M., and Tomiuk, J. 2000. Effects of forest fragmentation on genetic variation in endemic understory forest birds in central Madagascar. *Journal für Ornithologie* 141: 152–159.

Andriatahina, H. L. 2019. Ecologie alimentaire des pailles en queue à brins rouges (*Phaethon rubricauda*) de Nosy Vé, Anakao (sud-ouest de Madagascar). Rapport de stage de DEA en océanologie appliquée, Institut Halieutique et des Sciences Marines, Toliara.

Appert, O. 1965. Découverte de la nidification de *Puffinus pacificus* (Gmelin) près de la côte ouest de Madagascar. *L'Oiseau et la Revue Française d'Ornithologie* 35: 135–139.

———. 1968. Zur Brutbiologie des Erdracke *Uratelornis chimaera* Rothschild. *Journal für Ornithologie* 109: 264–275.

———. 1970. Zur Biologie der Vangawürger (Vangidae) Südwest-Madagaskars. *Ornithologische Beobachter* 67: 101–133.

———. 1971. Die Limikolen des Mangokygebietes in Südwest-Madagaskars. *Ornithologische Beobachter* 68: 53–77.

———. 1972. Beobachtungen über *Thamnornis* und die übrigen Sylviidae der Mangokygegend in Südwest-Madagascar. *Journal für Ornithologie* 113: 76–85.

———. 1996. A contribution to the ornithology of the region of Morondava, western Madagascar. *Working Group on Birds in the Madagascar Region Newsletter* 6(2): 18–54.

———. 1997. Zur Verbreitung und Biologie der Newtonien (Gattung *Newtonia*, Sylviidae) der Mangokyregion in Südwest-Madagaskar. *Ornithologische Beobachter* 94: 39–52.

———. 2011. Zur Brutsaison der Vögel im Mangokygebiet, Südwest-Madagaskar. *Ornithologische Beobachter* 108: 173–204.

Atyeo, W. T. 1966. Two new genera of feather mites (Acarina: Proctophyllodidae). *Journal of the Kansas Entomological Society* 39: 473–480.

Bamford, A. J., and Razafindrajao, F. 2012. A survey of the lakes and wetlands of the Madagascar plateau to assess potential sites for reintroduction of Madagascar pochard *Aythya innotata*. Unpublished report for the Wildfowl and Wetlands Trust and Durrell Wildlife Conservation Trust.

Bamford, A. J., Sam, T. S., Razafindrajao, F., Robson, H., Woolaver, L. G., and Rene de Roland, L.-A. 2015. The status and ecology of the last wild population of Madagascar pochard *Aythya innotata*. *Bird Conservation International* 24: 99–110.

Bamford, A. J., Razafindrajao, F., Young, R. P., and Hilton, G. M. 2017. Profound and pervasive degradation of Madagascar's freshwater wetlands and links with biodiversity. *PLoS One* 12: e0182673.

Bangs, O., and Peters, J. L. 1926. A new *Berneria* [*sic*] from Madagascar. *Proceedings of the New York Zoological Club* 9: 43–44.

Barker, F. K., Cibois, A., Schikler, P., Feinstein, J., and Cracraft, J. 2004. Phylogeny and diversification of the largest avian radiation. *Proceedings of the National Academy of Sciences of the USA* 101: 11040–11045.

Barré, N., and Barau, A. 1982. *Oiseaux de la Réunion*. St. Denis: Imprimerie Arts Graphiques Modernes.

Barthère, F.-M. 1915. Observations sur une hache en os, provenant des fouilles exécutées par l'Académie Malgache, à Ampasambazimba en 1908 (Madagascar). *Bulletin de la Société Préhistorique Française* 12: 358–361.

Battistini, R. 1965. Une datation au radio-carbone des oeufs des derniers *Aepyornis* de l'extrême-nord de Madagascar. *Comptes Rendus Sommaire des Séances de la Société Géologique de France* 5: 309.

Battistini, R., Vérin, P., and Rason, R. 1963. Le site archéologique de Talaky: Cadre géographique et géologique, premiers travaux de fouilles, notes ethnographiques sur le village actuel proche du site. *Annales de l'Université de Madagascar, Lettres*, 1: 111–153.

Beaujard, P. 2003. Les arrivées austronésiennes à Madagascar: Vagues ou continuum? (pt. 1, 2). *Etudes Océan Indien* 35–36: 59–147.

Becking, J. H. 1988. The taxonomic status of the Madagascar cuckoo *Cuculus (poliocephalus) rochii* and its occurrence on the African mainland, including southern Africa. *Bulletin of the British Ornithologists' Club* 108: 195–206.

Bemanaja, E. 2006. Rapport de missions réalisées à Nosimborona et Nosy Manitra (Androka) entre août et octobre 2006. Rapport interne ECOMAR / Institut Halieutique et des Sciences Marines.

———. 2008. Rapport de mission sur les ilots de Morombé, du 7 au 23 avril 2008. Rapport interne ECOMAR / Institut Halieutique et des Sciences Marines.

———. 2009. Les colonies d'oiseaux marins des futures aires protégées marines et côtières du sud-ouest, de l'ouest et du nord de Madagascar: Diagnostic écologique et socio-économique pour une exploitation durable de la ressource. PhD thesis, Institut Halieutique et des Sciences Marines, Université de Toliara.

———. 2013. Suivi écologique et conservation de la population d'oiseaux marins dans la région nord de Madagascar. Rapport interne Centre National de Recherches Océanographiques.

Benjara, A. 2015. Biologie et écologie de l'aigle serpentaire de Madagascar *Eutriorchis astur* (Sharpe, 1875) dans la nouvelle aire protégée de Bemanevika, District de Bealanana. Mémoire de DEA, Université de Toliara.

Benjara, A., Rene de Roland, L.-A., Rakotondratsima, M., Andrianarimisa, A., and Razafimanjato, G. 2017. Découverte de la construction du nid de l'aigle serpentaire de Madagascar (*Eutriorchis astur*) dans l'Aire Protégée de Bemanevika, nord-ouest de Madagascar. *Malagasy Nature* 12: 51–58.

Benson, C. W. 1960. The birds of the Comoro islands: Results of the British Ornithologists' Union Centenary Expedition 1958. *Ibis* 103b: 5–103.

———. 1971. Notes on *Terpsiphone* and *Coracina* spp. in the Malagasy region. *Bulletin of the British Ornithologists' Club* 91: 56–60.

Benson, C. W., Colebrook-Robjent, J.F.R., and Williams, A. 1976. Contribution à l'ornithologie de Madagascar. *L'Oiseau et la Revue Française d'Ornithologie* 46: 103–134, 209–242, 367–386.

———. 1977. Contribution à l'ornithologie de Madagascar. *L'Oiseau et la Revue Française d'Ornithologie* 47: 41–64, 168–191.

Beolens, B., Watkins, M., and Grayson, M. 2014. *The Eponym Dictionary of Birds*. London: Bloomsbury.

Beresford, P., Barker, F. K., Ryan, P. G., and Crowe, T. M. 2005. African endemics span the tree of songbirds (Passeri): Molecular systematics of several evolutionary enigmas. *Proceedings of the Royal Society of London B: Biological Sciences* 272: 849–858.

Berger, R., Ducote, K., Robinson, K., and Walter, H. 1975. Radiocarbon date for the largest extinct bird. *Nature* 258: 709.

Berkelman, J. 1994. The ecology of the Madagascar buzzard *Buteo brachypterus*. In *Raptor Conservation Today*, eds. B.-U. Meyburg and R. D. Chancellor, pp. 255–256. East Sussex: WWGBP/Pica Press.

———. 1996. Breeding biology of the Madagascar buzzard in the rain forest of the Masoala Peninsula. *Condor* 98: 624–627.

Berkelman, J., Fraser, J. D., and Watson, R. T. 1999a. Lake selection by Madagascar fish-eagles. *Auk* 116: 976–983.

———. 1999b. Madagascar fish-eagle prey preference and foraging success. *Wilson Bulletin* 111: 15–21.

Berlioz, J. 1948. Peuplement de Madagascar en oiseaux. *Mémoires de l'Institut Scientifique de Madagascar*, série A, 1: 181–192.

BirdLife International. 2020a. IUCN Red List for birds. http://www.birdlife.org.

———. 2020b. BirdLife International seabird tracking database. Accessed 15 May 2020. http://www.seabirdtracking.org/.

Block, N. L. 2012. Cryptic diversity and phylogeography in the Bernieridae, an endemic Malagasy passerine radiation. PhD thesis, University of Chicago.

Block, N. L., Goodman, S. M., Hackett, S. J., Bates, J. M., and Raherilalao, M. J. 2015. Potential merger of ancient lineages in a passerine bird discovered based on evidence from host-specific ectoparasites. *Ecology and Evolution* 5: 3743–3755.

Blynn, D., and Paul, B. 1994. Harper, Otis and Milo: A breeding trio of greater vasa parrots. *Bird Talk*, April 1994, 81–86.

Boast, A. P., Chapman, B., Herrera, M. B., Worthy, T. H., Scofield, R. P., Tennyson, A.J.D., Houde, P., Bunce, M., Cooper, A., and Mitchell, K. J. 2019. Mitochondrial genomes from New Zealand's extinct adzebills (Aves: Aptornithidae: *Aptornis*) support a sister-taxon relationship with the Afro-Madagascan Sarothruridae. *Diversity* 11(2): 24–21.

Boedts, B. 2010. Observations du faucon concolore *Falco concolor* dans les environs d'Antananarivo, Madagascar. *Bulletin of the African Bird Club* 17: 220–224.

Böhning-Gaese, K., Gaese, B. H., and Rabemanantsoa, S. B. 1995. Seed dispersal by frugivorous tree visitors in the Malagasy tree species *Commiphora guillaumini*. *Ecotropica* 1: 41–50.

Böhning-Gaese, K., Burkhardt, J. F., and Schmid, J. 1996. Seed dispersal in the tree *Commiphora guillaumini*: A combination of ornithochory and myrmecochory in a dry tropical forest in western Madagascar. In Ecology and economy of a tropical dry forest in Madagascar, eds. J. U. Ganzhorn and J.-P. Sorg. *Primate Report* (special issue) 46: 305–310.

Böhning-Gaese, K., Gaese, B. H., and Rabemanantsoa, S. B. 1999. Importance of primary and secondary seed dispersal in the Malagasy tree *Commiphora guillaumini*. *Ecology* 80: 821–832.

Bollen, A., and van Elsacker, L. 2004. The feeding ecology of the lesser vasa parrot, *Coracopsis nigra*, in south-eastern Madagascar. *Ostrich* 75: 141–146.

Bollen, A., van Elsacker, L., and Ganzhorn, J. U. 2004a. Relations between fruits and disperser assemblages in a Malagasy littoral forest: A community-level approach. *Journal of Tropical Ecology* 20: 599–612.

———. 2004b. Tree dispersal strategies in the littoral forest of Sainte Luce (SE-Madagascar). *Oecologia* 139: 604–616.

Bollen, A., Donati, G., Fietz, J., Schwab, D., Ramanamanjato, J.-B., Randrihasipara, L., van Elsacker, L., and Ganzhorn, J. 2005. An intersite comparison on fruit characteristics in Madagascar: Evidence for selection pressure through abiotic constraints rather than through co-evolution. In *Tropical Fruits and Frugivores: The Search for Strong Interactors*, eds. J. L. Dew and J. P. Boubli, pp. 92–118. Dordrecht: Springer.

Breman, F. C., Jordaens, K., Sonet, G., Nagy, Z. T., van Houdt, J., and Louette, M. 2013. DNA barcoding and evolutionary relationships in *Accipiter* Brisson, 1760 (Aves, Falconiformes: Accipitridae) with a focus on African and Eurasian representatives. *Journal of Ornithology* 154: 265–287.

Brickell, A. 2006. Collated data on the Madagascar fody *Foudia madagascariensis*. *Avicultural Magazine* 112: 169–173.

Bristol, R. M., Fabre, P.-H., Irestedt, M., Jønsson, K. A., Shah, N. J., Tatayah, V., Warren, B. H., and Groombridge, J. J. 2013. Molecular phylogeny of the Indian Ocean *Terpsiphone* paradise flycatchers: Undetected evolutionary diversity revealed amongst island populations. *Molecular Phylogenetics and Evolution* 67(2): 336–347.

Brodkorb, P. 1963. Catalogue of fossil birds. Part 1 (Archaeopterygiformes through Ardeiformes). *Bulletin of the Florida State Museum, Biological Sciences* 7(4): 181–293.

———. 1965. New taxa of fossil birds. *Quarterly Journal of the Florida Academy of Sciences* 28: 197–198.

Brown, L., and Amadon, D. 1989. *Eagles, Hawks, and Falcons of the World*. Secaucus: Wellfleet Press.

Buij, R., and Gschweng, M. 2017. Nocturnal hunting by Eleonora's falcons *Falco eleonorae* on their breeding and non-breeding grounds. *Acta Ornithologica* 52: 35–49.

Burney, D. A. 1999. Rates, patterns, and processes of landscape transformation and extinction in Madagascar. In *Extinctions in Near Time*, ed. R.D.E. MacPhee, pp. 145–164. New York: Kluwer Academic / Plenum Press.

Burney, D. A., James, H. F., Grady, F. V., Rafamantanantsoa, J.-G., Ramilisonina, Wright, H. T., and Cowart, J. B. 1997. Environmental change, extinction, and human activity: Evidence from caves in NW Madagascar. *Journal of Biogeography* 24: 755–767.

Burney, D. A., Burney, L. P., Godfrey, L. R., Jungers, W., Goodman, S. M., et al. 2004. A chronology for late prehistoric Madagascar. *Journal of Human Evolution* 47: 25–63.

Burney, D. A., Andriamialison, H., Andrianaivoarivelo, R., Bourne, S., Crowley, B., et al. 2019. Subfossil lemur discoveries from the Beanka Protected Area in western Madagascar. *Quaternary Research* 93: 187–203.

Burton, P.J.K. 1984. Anatomy and evolution of the feeding apparatus in the avian orders Coraciiformes and Piciformes. *Bulletin of the British Museum (Natural History) Zoology* 47: 331–443.

CABI. 2020. Invasive species compendium: *Corvus splendens* (house crow). Accessed 22 Aug. 2020. https://www.cabi.org/isc/datasheet/15463#toimpact.

Cadow, G. 1933. Magen und Darm der Fruchttauben. *Journal für Ornithologie* 81: 236–252.

Campera, M., Phelps, M., Besnard, F., Balestri, M., Eppley, T. M., Nijman, V., and Donati, G. 2019. Does forest management and researchers' presence reduce hunting and forest exploitation by local communities in Tsitongambarika, south-east Madagascar? *Oryx* 53: 677–686.

Campioni, L., Dias, M. P., Granadeiro, J. P., and Catry, P. 2020. An ontogenetic perspective on migratory strategy of a long-lived pelagic seabird: Timing and destination change progressively during maturation. *Journal of Animal Ecology* 89: 29–43.

Canning, G. 2011. Eradication of the invasive common myna, *Acridotheres tristis*, from Fregate Island, Seychelles. *Phelsuma* 19: 43–53.

Cartraud, A., Le Corre, M., Turquet, J., and Tourmetz, J. 2019. Plastic ingestion in seabirds of the western Indian Ocean. *Marine Pollution Bulletin* 140: 308–314.

Cauderay, H. 1931. Etude sur l'*Aepyornis*. *L'Oiseau et la Revue Française d'Ornithologie* 1: 624–644.

Chapin, J. P. 1948. Variation and hybridization among the paradise flycatchers of Africa. *Evolution* 2: 111–126.

Charles-Dominique, P. 1976. Les gommes dans le régime alimentaire de *Coua cristata* à Madagascar. *L'Oiseau et la Revue Française d'Ornithologie* 46: 174–178.

Cheke, A. S. 2005. Naming segregates from the *Columba–Streptopelia* pigeons following DNA studies on phylogeny. *Bulletin of the British Ornithologists' Club* 125: 293–295.

———. 2008. Seafaring behaviour of house crow *Corvus splendens*: A precursor to ship-assisted dispersal? *Phelsuma* 16: 65–68.

———. 2009. Was Mascarene grey white-eye *Zosterops borbonicus* introduced to Madagascar? *Bulletin of the British Ornithologists' Club* 129: 104–108.

Cheke, A. S., and Hume, J. 2008. *The Lost Land of the Dodo: An Ecological History of Mauritius, Réunion and Rodrigues*. London: T. and A. D. Poyser.

Chouteau, P. 2004. The impacts of logging on the microhabitats used by two species of couas in the western forest of Madagascar. *Compte Rendus Biologies* 327: 1157–1170.

———. 2007. The impact of burning on the microhabitat used by two species of couas in the western dry forest of Madagascar. *Ostrich* 78: 43–49.

Chouteau, P., Fenosoa, R., and Rakotoarimanana, V. 2004. Habitat selection and density of couas in Madagascar: Implication for their conservation. *Compte Rendus Biologies* 327: 37–50.

Cibois, A., Pasquet, E., and Schulenberg, T. 1999. Molecular systematics of the Malagasy babblers (Passeriformes: Timaliidae) and warblers (Passeriformes: Sylviidae), based on cytochrome b and 16S rRNA sequences. *Molecular Phylogenetics and Evolution* 13: 581–595.

Cibois, A., Slikas, B., Schulenberg, T. S., and Pasquet, E. 2001. An endemic radiation of Malagasy songbirds is revealed by mitochondrial DNA sequence data. *Evolution* 55: 1198–1206.

Cibois, A., David, N., Gregory, S.M.S., and Pasquet, E. 2010. Bernieridae (Aves: Passeriformes): A family-group name for the Malagasy sylvioid radiation. *Zootaxa* 2554: 65–68.

CITES. 2020. Convention on International Trade in Endangered Species of Wild Fauna and Flora Trade Database. Accessed 3 Feb. 2020. https://trade.cites.org/.

Clark, C. J., and Prum, R. O. 2015. Aeroelastic flutter of feathers, flight and the evolution of non-vocal communication in birds. *Journal of Experimental Biology* 218: 3520–3527.

Clark, G. A., Jr. 1973. Holding food with the feet in passerines. *Bird-Banding* 44: 91–99.

Clark, N. J., Ishtiaq, F., Olsson-Pons, S., and Clegg, S. M. 2015. Specialist enemies, generalist weapons and the potential spread of exotic pathogens: Malaria parasites in a highly invasive bird. *International Journal of Parasitology* 45(14): 891–899.

Clarke, S. J., Miller, G. H., Fogel, M. L., Chivas, R., and Murray-Wallace, C. V. 2006. The amino acid and stable isotope biogeochemistry of elephant bird (*Aepyornis*) eggshells from southern Madagascar. *Quaternary Science Reviews* 25: 2343–2356.

Clément, M., de Grissac, P., and Rolland, R. 2008. *Les oiseaux de Mayotte*. Mamoudzou: Naturalistes de Mayotte.

Clements, J. F., Schulenberg, T. S., Iliff, M. J., Billerman, S. M., Fredericks, T. A., Sullivan, B. L., and Wood, C. L. 2019. The eBird/Clements Checklist of Birds of the World. Version 2019. https://www.birds.cornell.edu/clementschecklist/download/.

Cloutier, A., Sackton, T. B., Grayson, P., Clamp, M., Baker, A. J., and Edwards, S. V. 2019. Whole-genome analyses resolve the phylogeny of flightless birds (Palaeognathae) in the presence of an empirical anomaly zone. *Systematic Biology* 68: 937–955. https://doi.org/10.1093/sysbio/syz019.

Collar, N. J. 2013a. Madagascar sacred ibis *Threskiornis bernieri*. In *The Birds of Africa*. Vol. 8, *The Malagasy Region*, eds. R. J. Safford and A.F.A. Hawkins, pp. 225–227. London: Christopher Helm.

———. 2013b. Madagascar magpie-robin *Copsychus albospecularis*. In *The Birds of Africa*. Vol. 8, *The Malagasy Region*, eds. R. J. Safford and A.F.A. Hawkins, pp. 692–695. London: Christopher Helm.

Collar, N. J., and Stuart, S. N. 1985. *Threatened Birds of Africa and Related Islands: The ICBP/IUCN Red Data Book*. Cambridge, UK: ICBP/IUCN.

Collin, A., and Collin, V. 1996. Contribution à l'étude de l'avifaune des Hauts Plateaux malgaches (axe Betafo-Miandrivazo). *Working Group on Birds in the Madagascar Region Newsletter* 6(1): 5–9.

Colston, P. R. 1972. A new bulbul from southwestern Madagascar. *Ibis* 114: 89–92.

Connell, J. H. 1978. Diversity in tropical rain forests and coral reefs. *Science* 199: 1302–1310.

Cooke, A., and Randriamanindry, J. J. 1996. Red-tailed tropicbird *Phaethon rubricauda* colony, Nosy Vé Islet, Toliara. *Working Group on Birds in the Madagascar Region Newsletter* 6: 2–6.

Cooper, A. 1997. Studies of ancient avian DNA: From Jurassic Park to modern island extinctions. In *Avian Molecular Evolution and Systematics*, ed. D. P. Mindell, pp. 345–373. San Diego: Academic Press.

Cowles, G. S., and Goodwin, D. 1959. Seed digestion by the fruit-eating pigeon *Treron*. *Ibis* 101: 253–254.

Cox, S. C., Prŷs-Jones, R. P., Habel, J. C., Amakobe, B. A., and Day, J. J. 2014. Niche divergence promotes rapid diversification of East African sky island white-eyes (Aves: Zosteropidae). *Molecular Ecology* 23: 4103–4118.

Cracraft, J. 1971. The relationship and evolution of the rollers: Families Coraciidae, Brachypteraciidae and Leptosomatidae. *Auk* 88: 723–752.

Craig, A.J.F.K. 1999. Weaving a story: The relationships of the endemic Ploceidae of Madagascar. In *Proceedings of the 22nd International Ornithological Congress, Durban*, eds. N. J. Adams and R. H. Slotow, pp. 3063–3070. Johannesburg: BirdLife South Africa.

Cripps, G. 2010. Feasibility study on the protection and management of the Barren Isles ecosystem, Madagascar. Blue Ventures conservation report to WWF.

Crook, J. H. 1961. The fodies (Ploceinae) of the Seychelles islands. *Ibis* 103a: 517–548.

Crowe, T. M., Bowie, R.C.K., Bloomer, P., Mandiwana, T. G., Hedderson, T.A.J., Randi, E., Pereira, S. L., and Wakeling, J. 2006. Phylogenetics, biogeography and classification of, and character evolution in, gamebirds (Aves: Galliformes): Effects of character exclusion, data partitioning and missing data. *Cladistics* 22: 495–532.

Crowley, B. E. 2010. A refined chronology of prehistoric Madagascar and the demise of the megafauna. *Quaternary Science Reviews* 29: 2591–2603.

Croxall, J. P., Butchart, S.H.M., Lascelles, B., Stattersfield, A. J., Sullivan, B., Symes, A., and Taylor, P. 2012. Seabird conservation status, threats and priority actions: A global assessment. *Bird Conservation International* 22: 1–34.

Cruaud, A., Raherilalao, M. J., Pasquet, E., and Goodman, S. M. 2011. Phylogeography and systematics of the Malagasy rock-thrushes (Muscicapidae, *Monticola*). *Zoologica Scripta* 40(6): 554–566.

Cunningham, C., Parra, J. E., Coals, L., Beltrán, M., Zefania, S., and Székely, T. 2018. Social interactions predict genetic diversification: An experimental manipulation in Malagasy shorebirds. *Behavioral Ecology* 29(3): 609–618.

Danckwerts, D. K., McQuaid, C. D., Jaeger, A., McGregor, G. K., Dwight, R., Le Corre, M., and Jaquemet, S. 2014. Biomass consumption by breeding seabirds in the western Indian Ocean: Indirect interactions with fisheries and implications for management. *ICES Journal of Marine Science* 71: 2589–2598.

Davis, M. 1951. Ocean vessels and the distribution of birds. *Auk* 68(4): 529–530.

Decary, R. 1962. Sur des introductions imprudentes d'animaux Mascareignes et à Madagascar. *Bulletin du Muséum National d'Histoire Naturelle*, Paris, série 2, 34: 404–407.

Dee, T. J. 1986. *The Endemic Birds of Madagascar*. Cambridge, UK: ICBP.

Deignan, H. G. 1964. Subfamily Timaliinae, babblers. In *Check-List of Birds of the World*, vol. 10, eds. E. Mayr and J. C. Greenway Jr., pp. 240–427. Cambridge, MA: Museum of Comparative Zoology.

de Kloet, R. S., and de Kloet, S. R. 2005. The evolution of the spindlin gene in birds: Sequence analysis of an intron of the spindlin W and Z gene reveals four major divisions of the Psittaciformes. *Molecular Phylogenetics and Evolution* 36: 706–721.

Delacour, J. 1931. Note sur les *Copsychus* malgaches. *L'Oiseau et la Revue Française d'Ornithologie* 1: 618–623.

———. 1932. Les oiseaux de la Mission Franco-Anglo-Américaine à Madagascar. *L'Oiseau et la Revue Française d'Ornithologie* 2: 1–96.

———. 1933. Le foudi rouge et son élevage *Foudia madagascariensis* (L.). *L'Oiseau et la Revue Française d'Ornithologie*, série 3, 2: 404–408.

———. 1943. A revision of the genera and species of the family Pycnonotidae (bulbuls). *Zoologica* 28: 17–28.

———. 1946. Les Timaliinés. *L'Oiseau et la Revue Française d'Ornithologie* 16: 7–36.

———. 1947. Waterfowl at Clères in 1947. *Avicultural Magazine* 6: 198–199.

———. 1959. *The Waterfowl of the World*. Vol. 3. London: Country Life.

———. 1966. *The Living Air*. London: Country Life.

Delacour, J., and Berlioz, J. 1931. Description d'oiseaux nouveaux de Madagascar. *L'Oiseau et la Revue Française d'Ornithologie* 1: 1–5.

del Hoyo, J., and Collar, N. J. 2014. *HBW and BirdLife International Illustrated Checklist of the Birds of the World*. Vol. 1, *Non-passerines*. Barcelona and Cambridge, UK: Lynx Edicions and BirdLife International.

———. 2016. *HBW and BirdLife International Illustrated Checklist of the Birds of the World*. Vol. 2, *Passerines*. Barcelona and Cambridge, UK: Lynx Edicions and BirdLife International.

del Hoyo, J., Elliot, A., and Sargatal, J. 1994. *Handbook of the Birds of the World*. Vol. 2, *New World Vultures to Guineafowl*. Barcelona: Lynx Edicions.

del Hoyo, J., Martínez-Vilalta, A., Motis, A., Collar, N., Kirwan, G. M., and Christie, D. A. 2020. Little Egret (*Egretta garzetta*), version 1.0. In *Birds of the World*, eds. S. M. Billerman, B. K. Keeney, P. G. Rodewald, and T. S. Schulenberg. Ithaca: Cornell Lab of Ornithology.

Delord, K., and Weimerskirch, H. 2011. New information on distribution of albatrosses and petrels breeding in the Indian Ocean and assessment of potential overlap with the IOTC fisheries. Indian Ocean Tuna Commission Working Party on Ecosystems and Byctach 07–38.

Delord, K., Cherel, Y., Barbraud, C., Chastel, Y., and Weimerskirch, H. 2018. High variability in migration and wintering strategies of brown skuas (*Catharacta antarctica lonnbergi*) in the Indian Ocean. *Polar Biology* 41: 59–70.

De Pietri, V. L. 2013. Interrelationships of the Threskiornithidae and the phylogenetic position of the Miocene ibis *"Plegadis" paganus* from the Saint-Gérand-le-Puy area in central France. *Ibis* 155: 544–560.

De Silva, T. N., Peterson, A. T., Bates, J. M., Fernando, S. W., and Girard, M. G. 2017. Phylogenetic relationships of weaverbirds (Aves: Ploceidae): A first robust phylogeny based on mitochondrial and nuclear markers. *Molecular Phylogenetics and Evolution* 109: 21–32.

De Silva, T. N., Peterson, A. T., and Perktaş, U. 2019. An extensive molecular phylogeny of weaverbirds (Aves: Ploceidae) unveils broad nonmonophyly of traditional genera and new relationships. *Auk* 136(3): 407–421.

Dewar, R. E. 1984. Extinctions in Madagascar: The loss of the subfossil fauna. In *Quaternary Extinctions: A Prehistoric Revolution*, eds. P. S. Martin and R. G. Klein, pp. 574–593. Tucson: University of Arizona Press.

Dewar, R. E., and Rakotovololona, S. 1992. La chasse aux subfossiles: Les preuves du onzième siècle au treizième siècle. *Taloha* 11: 4–15.

Diamond, J. M., and LeCroy, M. 1979. Birds of Karkar and Bagabag islands, New Guinea. *Bulletin of the American Museum of Natural History* 164: 467–531.

Dias, M. P., Martin, R., Pearmain, E. J., Burfield, I. J., Small, C., Phillips, R. A., Yates, O., Lascelle, B., Borboroglu, P. G., and Croxall, J. P. 2019. Threats to seabirds: A global assessment. *Biological Conservation* 237: 525–537.

Dickinson, E. C., and Christidis, L., eds. 2014. *The Howard and Moore Complete Checklist of the Birds of the World*. 4th ed. Vol. 2, *Passerines*. Eastbourne: Aves Press.

Dodman, T., and Diagana, C. 2007. Movements of waterbirds within Africa and their conservation implications. *Ostrich* 78: 149–154.

Dodman, T., Béibro, H. K., Hubert, E., and Williams, E. 1998. *African Waterbird Census 1998*. Dakar: Wetlands International.

Dorst, J. 1972. The evolution and affinities of the birds of Madagascar. In *Biogeography and Ecology in Madagascar*, eds. R. Battistini and G. Richard-Vindard, pp. 615–627. The Hague: W. Junk.

dos Remedios, N., Küpper, C., Székely, T., Zefania, S., Burns, F., Bolton, M., and Lee, P.L.M. 2020. Genetic structure among *Charadrius* plovers on the African mainland and islands of Madagascar and St Helena. *Ibis* 162: 104–118.

Dowsett, R. 2000. Le statut des perroquets vasa et noir *Coracopsis vasa* et *C. nigra* et de l'inséparable à tête grise *Agapornis canus* à Madagascar. Unpublished report, IUCN.

Dresser, H. E. 1896. Notes on some of the Madagascar rollers. *Antananarivo Annual* 20: 465–469.

D'Urban Jackson, J. 2018. Population genetic consequences of mating systems and dispersal. PhD thesis, University of Bath.

D'Urban Jackson, J., Zefania, S., Moehy, S., Bamford, A., Bruford, M. W., and Székely, T. 2019. Ecology, conservation, and phylogenetic position of the Madagascar jacana. *Ostrich* 90(4): 315–326.

Eberhart-Phillips, L. J., Hoffman, J. I., Brede, E. G., Zefania, S., Kamrad, M. J., Székely, T., and Bruford, M. W. 2015. Contrasting genetic diversity and population structure among three sympatric Madagascan shorebirds: Parallels with rarity, endemism, and dispersal. *Ecology and Evolution* 5(5): 997–1010.

Eberhart-Phillips, L. J., Carmona-Isunza, M. C., Vincze, O., Zefania, S., Kosztolányi, A., et al. 2018. Demographic causes of adult sex ratio variation and their consequences for parental cooperation. *Nature Communications* 9: 1651.

eBird. 2021. Schlegel's asity. Accessed 8 Aug. 2021. https://ebird.org/species/schasi1.

Eguchi, K. 1995. Community structure and adaptive radiation of Madagascar birds. *Japanese Journal of Ecology* 45: 259–275.

Eguchi, K., Yamagishi, S., and Randrianasolo, V. 1993. The composition and foraging behaviour of mixed-species flocks of forest-living birds in Madagascar. *Ibis* 135: 91–96.

Eguchi, K., Amano, H. E., and Yamagishi, S. 2001. Roosting, range use and foraging behaviour of the sickle-billed vanga, *Falculea palliata*, in Madagascar. *Ostrich* 72: 127–133.

Eguchi, K., Yamagishi, S., Asai, S., Nagata, H., and Hino, T. 2002. Helping does not enhance reproductive success of cooperatively breeding rufous vanga in Madagascar. *Journal of Animal Ecology* 71: 123–130.

Eguchi, K., Asai, S., and Yamagishi, S. 2009. Individual differences in the helping behaviors of cooperatively breeding rufous vangas. *Ornithological Science* 8: 5–13.

Ekstrom, J.M.M. 2003. The ecology of the greater vasa parrot *Coracopsis vasa*. PhD thesis, University of Sheffield.

———. 2013a. Greater vasa parrot *Coracopsis vasa*. In *The Birds of Africa*. Vol. 8, *The Malagasy Region*, eds. R. J. Safford and A.F.A. Hawkins, pp. 525–528. London: Christopher Helm.

———. 2013b. Lesser vasa parrot *Coracopsis nigra*. In *The Birds of Africa*. Vol. 8, *The Malagasy Region*, eds. R. J. Safford and A.F.A. Hawkins, pp. 531–534. London: Christopher Helm.

Ekstrom, J.M.M., Burke, T., Randrianaina, L., and Birkhead, T. 2007. Unusual sex roles in a highly promiscuous parrot: The greater vasa parrot *Coracopsis vasa*. *Ibis* 149: 313–320.

Endangered Wildlife Trust. 2018. Flamingo returns from two-year stay in Madagascar. https://endangeredwildlifetrust.wordpress.com/2018/08/03/flamingo-returns-from-two-year-stay-in-madagascar/.

Estep, L., Shawkey, M. D., and Hill, G. E. 2006. Carotenoid-based breast plumage colour, body condition and clutch size in red fodies (*Foudia madagascariensis*). *Ostrich* 77: 164–169.

Evans, M. I., Duckworth, J. W., Hawkins, A.F.A., Safford, R. J., Sheldon, B. C., and Wilkinson, R. J. 1992. Key bird species of Marojejy Strict Nature Reserve, Madagascar. *Bird Conservation International* 2: 201–220.

Evans, M. I., Hawkins, A.F.A., and Duckworth, J. W. 1996. Family Mesitornithidae (Mesites). In *Handbook of the Birds of the World*, vol. 3, eds. J. del Hoyo, A. Elliot, and J. Sargatal, pp. 34–43. Barcelona: Lynx Edicions.

Fabre, P.-H., Irestedt, M., Fjeldså, J., Bristol, R. M., Groombridge, J. J., Irham, M., and Jønsson, K. A. 2012. Dynamic colonization exchanges between continents and islands drive diversification in paradise-flycatchers (*Terpsiphone*, Monarchidae). *Journal of Biogeography* 39: 1900–1918.

Faliarivola, M. L. 2016. Distribution verticale des oiseaux du sous-bois de la péninsule de Masoala, Madagascar. Mémoire de Master, Mention Zoologie et Biodiversité Animale, Université d'Antananarivo.

Faliarivola, M. L., Raherilalao, M. J., Andrianarimisa, A., and Goodman, S. M. 2020. The diet of Malagasy dry forest understory birds based on faecal samples. *Ostrich* 91(1): 35–44.

Faulquier, L., Fontaine, R., Vidal, E., Salamolard, M., and Le Corre, M. 2009. Feral cats *Felis catus* threaten the endangered endemic Barau's petrel *Pterodroma baraui* at Réunion Island (western Indian Ocean). *Waterbirds* 32(2): 330–336.

Fauré, J.-C. 1996. Traditional utilisation of the forest. In Ecology and economy of a tropical dry forest in Madagascar, eds. J. U. Ganzhorn, and J.-P. Sorg. *Primate Report* (special issue) 46: 33–40.

Feare, C. J., and Mungroo, Y. 1990. Notes on the house crow in Mauritius. *Bulletin of the British Ornithologists' Club* 109: 199–201.

Feare, C. J., van der Woude, J., Greenwell, P., Edwards, H. A., Taylor, J. A., et al. 2017. Eradication of common mynas *Acridotheres tristis* from Denis Island, Seychelles. *Pest Management Science* 73: 295–304.

Ferraz, G., Nichols, J. D., Hines, J. E., Stouffer, P. C., Bierregaard, R. O., Jr., and Lovejoy, T. E. 2007. A large-scale deforestation experiment: Effects of patch area and isolation on Amazon birds. *Science* 315: 238–241.

Fjeldså, J., Goodman, S. M., Schulenberg, T. S., and Slikas, B. 1999. Molecular evidence for relationships of Malagasy birds. In *Proceedings of the 22nd International Ornithological Congress, Durban*, eds. N. J. Adams and R. H. Slotow, pp. 3084–3094. Johannesburg: BirdLife South Africa.

Fjeldså, J., Mayr, G., Jønsson, K. A., and Irestedt, M. 2013. On the true identity of Bluntschli's vanga *Hypositta perdita* Peters, 1996, a presumed extinct species of Vangidae. *Bulletin of the British Ornithologists' Club* 133: 72–75.

Flacourt, E. de. 1658 (repr. 1995). *Histoire de la Grande Isle Madagascar*. Edition présentée et annotée par Claude Allibert. Paris: INALCO-Karthala.

Fontoyont, M. 1909. Les gisements fossilifères d'Ampasambazimba. *Bulletin de l'Académie Malgache* 6: 3–8.

Forbes, W. A. 1880. On the anatomy of *Leptosoma discolor*. *Proceedings of the Zoological Society of London* 1880: 465–475.

Fossette, S., Heide-Jorgensen, M.-P., Jensen, M. V., Kiszka, J., Bérubé, M., Bertrand, N., and Vely, M. 2014. Humpback whale (*Megaptera novaeangliae*) post breeding dispersal and southward migration in the western Indian Ocean. *Journal of Experimental Marine Biology and Ecology* 450: 6–14.

Fregin, S., Haase, M., Olsson, U., and Alström, P. 2009. Multi-locus phylogeny of the family Acrocephalidae (Aves: Passeriformes): The traditional taxonomy overthrown. *Molecular Phylogenetics and Evolution* 52: 866–878.

Fritz-Vietta, N.V.M., Ferguson, H. B., Stoll-Kleemann, S., and Ganzhorn, J. U. 2011. Conservation in a biodiversity hotspot: Insights from cultural and community perspectives in Madagascar. In *Biodiversity Hotspots: Distribution and Protection of Conservation Priority Areas*, eds. F. E. Zachos and J. C. Habel, pp. 209–233. Berlin: Springer.

Frost, P.G.H. 1975. The systematic position of the Madagascan partridge *Margaroperdix madagascariensis* (Scopoli). *Bulletin of the British Ornithologists' Club* 9: 64–68.

Fuchs, J., Pons, J.-M., Pasquet, E., Raherilalao, M. J., and Goodman, S. M. 2007. Geographical structure of genetic variation in the Malagasy scops-owl inferred from mitochondrial sequence data. *Condor* 109: 408–418.

Fuchs, J., Parra, J. L., Goodman, S. M., Raherilalao, M. J., Vanderwal, J., and Bowie, R.C.K. 2013. Extending ecological niche models to the past 120 000 years corroborates the lack of strong phylogeographic structure in the crested drongo (*Dicrurus forficatus forficatus*) on Madagascar. *Biological Journal of the Linnean Society* 108: 658–676.

Fuchs, J., Johnson, J. A., and Mindell, D. P. 2015. Rapid diversification of falcons (Aves: Falconidae) due to expansion of open habitats in the Late Miocene. *Molecular Phylogenetics and Evolution* 82A: 166–182.

Fuchs, J., Lemoine, D., Parra, J. L., Pons, J.-M., Raherilalao, M. J., Prŷs-Jones, R., Thébaud, C., Warren, B. H., and Goodman, S. M. 2016. Long-distance dispersal and inter-island colonization across the western Malagasy Region explain diversification in brush-warblers (Passeriformes: *Nesillas*). *Biological Journal of the Linnean Society* 119: 873–889.

Gamero, A., and Kappeler, P. 2015a. Slow development of foraging skills and parental costs of family-living in a semi-precocial, non-cooperatively breeding bird. *Behavioral Ecology and Sociobiology* 26: 805–811.

———. 2015b. Always together: Mate guarding or predator avoidance as determinants of group cohesion in white-breasted mesites? *Journal of Avian Biology* 46: 378–384.

Gamero, A., Székely, T., and Kappeler, P. 2013. Delayed juvenile dispersal and monogamy, but no cooperative breeding in white-breasted mesites *Mesitornis variegatus*. *Behavioural Ecology and Sociobiology* 68: 73–83.

Ganzhorn, J. U., Ganzhorn, A .W., Abraham, J.-P., Andriamaro, L., and Ramanjatovo, A. 1990. The impact of selective logging on forest structure and tenrec populations in western Madagascar. *Oecologia* 84: 126–133.

Garbutt, N. 1997. Interesting ornithological observations made in Madagascar between October and December 1996. *Working Group on Birds in the Madagascar Region Newsletter* 7(1): 19–21.

Garcia, G., and Goodman, S. M. 2003. Hunting of protected animals in the Parc National d'Ankarafantsika, north-western Madagascar. *Oryx* 37: 115–118.

Garcia, G., and Vences, M. 2002. *Furcifer oustaleti* (Oustalet's chameleon) diet. *Herpetological Review* 33: 134–135.

García-R, J. C., Gibb, G. C., and Trewick, S. A. 2014. Deep global evolutionary radiation in birds: Diversification and trait evolution in the cosmopolitan bird family Rallidae. *Molecular Phylogenetics and Evolution* 81: 96–108.

Gardner, C. J. 2009. A review of the impacts of anthropogenic habitat change on terrestrial biodiversity in Madagascar: Implications for the design and management of new protected areas. *Malagasy Nature* 2: 2–29.

Gardner, C. J., and Davies, Z. G. 2014. Rural bushmeat consumption within multiple-use protected areas: Qualitative evidence from southwest Madagascar. *Human Ecology* 42: 21–34.

Gardner, C. J., and Jasper, L. D. 2011. Status of barn swallow *Hirundo rustica* in south-west Madagascar. *Bulletin of the African Bird Club* 18: 207–210.

———. 2018. Miscellaneous behavioural observations of Malagasy birds. *Madagascar Conservation and Development* 13: 70–74.

Gardner, C. J., Jasper, L. D., and Vincke, X. 2011. Sakalava weaver (*Ploceus sakalava*) nesting association with raptors: An alternative hypothesis. *Malagasy Nature* 5: 129–131.

Gardner, C. J., de Ridder, C., de Ridder, B., and Jasper, L. D. 2012. Birds of Ambondrolava mangrove complex, southwest Madagascar. *Check List* 8(1): 1–7.

Gardner, C. J., Jasper, L. D., Eonintsoa, C., Duchene, J. J., and Davies, Z. G. 2016. The impact of natural resource use on bird and reptile communities within multiple-use protected areas: Evidence from Madagascar. *Biodiversity and Conservation* 25: 1773–1793.

Gardner, C. J., Nicoll, M. E., Birkinshaw, C., Harris, A., Lewis, R. E., Rakotomalala, D., and Ratsifandrihamana, A. N. 2018. The rapid expansion of Madagascar's protected area system. *Biological Conservation* 220: 29–36.

Gauchet, L., and Piana, M. 2019. Dynamique des populations des pailles en queue à brins rouges de Nosy Vé, Madagascar. Rapport de stage de Master Biodiversité et Ecosystèmes Tropicaux, première année, Université de La Réunion.

Gauthier, N. E. 2018. Etude de la structure de la population et de la préférence en habitat de *Passer domesticus* et de *Foudia madagascariensis*, deux espèces d'oiseaux nuisibles dans la ville de Fénérive Est. Mémoire de Master, Institut Supérieur de Sciences, Environnement et Développement Durable, Université de Toamasina.

Geoffroy Saint-Hilaire, I. 1851. Notes sur des ossements et des oeufs à Madagascar dans les alluvions modernes et provenant d'un oiseau gigantesque. *Compte Rendus de l'Académie des Sciences*, Paris 32: 101–107.

Giles, N. 1990. Effects of increasing larval chironomid densities on the underwater feeding success of downy tufted ducklings *Aythya fuligula*. *Wildfowl* 41: 99–106.

Gilroy, J. J., and Edwards, D. P. 2017. Source-sink dynamics: A neglected problem for landscape-scale biodiversity conservation in the tropics. *Current Landscape Ecology Reports* 2: 51–60.

Global Invasive Species Database. 2020. Species profile: *Acridotheres tristis*. Accessed 24 Oct. 2020. http://www.iucngisd.org/gisd/speciesname/Acridotheres+tristis.

Gochfeld, M. 1983. The roseate tern: World distribution and status of a threatened species. *Biological Conservation* 25: 103–125.

Goodman, S. M. 1993. A reconnaissance of Ile Sainte-Marie, Madagascar: The status of the forest, avifauna, lemurs and bats. *Biological Conservation* 65: 205–212.

———. 1994a. Description of a new species of subfossil eagle from Madagascar: *Stephanoaetus* (Aves: Falconiformes) from the deposits of Ampasambazimba. *Proceedings of the Biological Society of Washington* 107: 421–428.

———. 1994b. A description of the ground burrow of *Eliurus webbi* (Nesomyinae) and case of cohabitation with an endemic bird (Brachypteraciidae, *Brachypteracias*). *Mammalia* 58: 670–672.

———. 1996. Description of a new species of subfossil lapwing (Aves, Charadriiformes, Charadriidae, Vanellinae) from Madagascar. *Bulletin du Muséum National d'Histoire Naturelle*, Paris, série 4, section C, 18: 607–614.

———. 1999. Holocene bird subfossils from the sites of Ampasambazimba, Antsirabe and Ampoza, Madagascar: Changes in the avifauna of south central Madagascar over the past few millennia. In *Proceedings of the 22nd International Ornithological Congress, Durban*, eds. N. J. Adams and R. H. Slotow, pp. 3071–3083. Johannesburg: BirdLife South Africa.

———. 2000. A description of a new species of *Brachypteracias* (family Brachypteraciidae) from the Holocene of Madagascar. *Ostrich* 71: 318–322.

———. 2003. *Leptosomus discolor*. In *The Natural History of Madagascar*, eds S. M. Goodman and J. P. Benstead, pp. 1121–1122. Chicago: University of Chicago Press.

———. 2012. *Les carnivora de Madagascar*. Antananarivo: Association Vahatra.

———. 2013. Genus *Coua*. In *The Birds of Africa*. Vol. 8, *The Malagasy Region*, eds. R. J. Safford and A.F.A. Hawkins, pp. 539–557. London: Christopher Helm.

Goodman, S. M., and Andrianarimisa, A. 1995. Morphological variation in *Philepitta* spp. (Aves: Euylaimidae). *Working Group on Birds in the Madagascar Region Newsletter* 5: 1–3.

Goodman, S. M., and Griffiths, O. 2009. Notes on the diet of the barn owl (Aves: Tytonidae: *Tyto alba*) from Zohin'Andavaka, Beahitse, extreme southwestern Madagascar. *Malagasy Nature* 2: 163–166.

Goodman, S. M., and Jungers, W. L. 2014. *Extinct Madagascar: Picturing the Island's Past*. Chicago: University of Chicago Press.

Goodman, S. M., and Langrand, O. 1996. Food remains found in a nest of the Madagascar buzzard (*Buteo brachypterus*) in the Vohibasia Forest. *Working Group on Birds in the Madagascar Region Newsletter* 6(2): 13–14.

Goodman, S. M., and Muldoon, K. M. 2016. A new subfossil locality for the extinct large Malagasy eagle *Stephanoaetus mahery* (Aves: Falconiformes): Implications for time of extinction and ecological specificity. *Holocene* 26(6): 985–989.

Goodman, S. M., and Parrillo, P. 1997. A study of the diets of Malagasy birds based on stomach contents. *Ostrich* 68: 104–113.

Goodman, S. M., and Putnam, M. S. 1996. The birds of the eastern slopes of the Réserve Naturelle Intégrale d'Andringitra, Madagascar. In A floral and faunal inventory of the eastern slopes of the Réserve Naturelle Intégrale d'Andringitra, Madagascar: With reference to elevational variation, ed. S. M Goodman. *Fieldiana: Zoology*, new series, 85: 171–190.

Goodman, S. M., and Raherilalao, M. J. 2003. Effects of forest fragmentation on bird communities. In *The Natural History of Madagascar*, eds. S. M. Goodman and J. P. Benstead, pp. 1064–1067. Chicago: University of Chicago Press.

———. 2013. Oiseaux ou classe Aves / Birds or the class Aves. In *Atlas d'une sélection de vertébrés terrestres de Madagascar / Atlas of Selected Land Vertebrates of Madagascar*, eds. S. M. Goodman and M. J. Raherilalao, pp. 63–168. Antananarivo: Association Vahatra.

Goodman, S. M., and Rakotozafy, L.M.A. 1995. Evidence for the existence of two species of *Aquila* on Madagascar during the Quaternary. *Geobios* 28: 241–246.

———. 1997. Subfossil birds from coastal sites in western and southwestern Madagascar: A paleoenvironmental reconstruction. In *Natural Change and Human Impact in Madagascar*, eds. S. M. Goodman and B. D. Patterson, pp. 257–279. Washington, DC: Smithsonian Institution Press.

Goodman, S. M., and Ravoavy, F. 1993. Identification of bird subfossils from cave surface deposits at Anjohibe, Madagascar, with a description of a new giant *Coua* (Cuculidae: Couinae). *Proceedings of the Biological Society of Washington* 106: 24–33.

Goodman, S. M., and Schulenberg, T. S. 1991. The rediscovery of the red-tailed newtonia *Newtonia fanovanae* in southeastern Madagascar with notes on the natural history of the genus *Newtonia*. *Bird Conservation International* 1: 33–45.

Goodman, S. M., and Thorstrom, R. 1998. The diet of the Madagascar red owl (*Tyto soumagnei*) on the Masoala Peninsula, Madagascar. *Wilson Bulletin* 110: 417–421.

Goodman, S. M., and Weigt, L. A. 2002. The generic and species relationships of the reputed endemic Malagasy genus *Pseudocossyphus* (family Turdidae). *Ostrich* 73: 26–35.

Goodman, S. M., and Wilmé, L. 2003. *Coua* spp., couas. In *The Natural History of Madagascar*, eds. S. M. Goodman and J. P. Benstead, pp. 1102–1108. Chicago: University of Chicago Press.

Goodman, S. M., Langrand, O., and Raxworthy, C. J. 1993a. The food habits of the barn owl *Tyto alba* at three sites on Madagascar. *Ostrich* 64: 160–171.

———. 1993b. Food habits of the Madagascar long-eared owl *Asio madagascariensis* in two habitats in southern Madagascar. *Ostrich* 64: 79–85.

Goodman, S. M., Andrianarimisa, A., Olson, L. E., and Soarimalala, V. 1996a. Patterns of elevational distribution of birds and small mammals in the humid forests of the Montagne d'Ambre, Madagascar. *Ecotropica* 2: 87–98.

Goodman, S. M., Langrand, O., and Whitney, B. M. 1996b. A new genus and species of passerine from the eastern rainforest of Madagascar. *Ibis* 136: 153–159.

Goodman S. M., Pidgeon, M., Hawkins, A.F.A., and Schulenberg, T. S. 1997a. The birds of south-eastern Madagascar. *Fieldiana: Zoology*, new series, 87: 1–132.

Goodman, S. M., Langrand, O., and Rasolonandrasana, B.P.N. 1997b. The food habits of *Cryptoprocta ferox* in the high mountain zone of the Andringitra Massif, Madagascar. *Mammalia* 61: 185–192.

Goodman, S. M., Hawkins, A.F.A., and Domergue, C. A. 1997c. A new species of vanga (Vangidae: *Calicalicus*) from southwestern Madagascar. *Bulletin of the British Ornithologists' Club* 117: 4–10.

Goodman, S. M., Rene de Roland, L.-A., and Thorstrom, R. 1998. Predation on the eastern woolly lemur *Avahi laniger* and other vertebrates by Henst's goshawk *Accipiter henstii* in Madagascar. *Lemur News* 3: 14–15.

Goodman, S. M., Tello, J. G., and Langrand, O. 2000a. Patterns of morphological and molecular variation in *Acrocephalus newtoni* on Madagascar. *Ostrich* 71: 367–370.

Goodman, S. M., Hawkins, A.F.A., and Razafimahaimodison, J.-C. 2000b. Birds of the Parc National de Marojejy, Madagascar: With reference to elevational variation. In A floral and faunal inventory of the Parc National de Marojejy, Madagascar: With reference to elevational variation. *Fieldiana: Zoology*, new series, 97: 175–200.

Goodman, S. M., Raherilalao, M. J., and Block, N. 2011. Patterns of morphological and genetic variation in the *Mentocrex kioloides* complex (Aves: Gruiformes: Rallidae) from Madagascar, with the description of a new species. *Zootaxa* 2776: 49–60.

Goodman, S. M., Raherilalao, M. J., and Muldoon K. M. 2013. Bird fossils from Ankilitelo Cave: Inference about Holocene environmental changes in southwestern Madagascar. *Zootaxa* 3750: 534–548.

Goodman, S. M., Mittermeier, J. C., Ramamonjisoa, J., and Rene de Roland, L.-A. 2014. The dietary habits of barn owls (*Tyto alba*) in the spiny bush of southwestern Madagascar. *Malagasy Nature* 8: 67–72.

Goodman, S. M., Razakaratrimo, S.V.J., and Rene de Roland, L.-A. 2015. An analysis of bat hawk *Macheiramphus alcinus* diet in the Melaky Region of lowland western Madagascar. *Ostrich* 87: 78–80.

Goodman, S. M., Raselimanana, A. P., Andriniaina, H. A., Gauthier, N. E., Ravaojanahary, F. F., Sylvestre, M. H., and Raherilalao, M. J. 2017a. The distribution and ecology of invasive alien vertebrate species in the greater Toamasina region, central eastern Madagascar. *Malagasy Nature* 12: 95–109.

Goodman, S. M., Anbdou, Y., Andriamiarantsoa, Y., Fisher, B. L., Griffiths, O., et al. 2017b. Results of a biological inventory of the Nosy Ankao island group, Parc National de Loky-Manambato, northeastern Madagascar. *Malagasy Nature* 11: 1–59.

Goodman, S. M., Raherilalao, M. J., and Wohlhauser, S., eds. 2018. *Les aires protégées terrestres de Madagascar: Leur histoire, description et biote / The Terrestrial Protected Areas of Madagascar: Their History, Description and Biota*. Antananarivo: Association Vahatra.

Gopal, V. S. 2016. The war against aliens: The case of crow control in the island of Mauritius. Report of a pilot project for post-graduate diploma on endangered species recovery. Unpublished program report to the Durrell Wildlife Conservation Trust, Jersey, UK.

Graetz, J. 1991. Nest observations of the helmet vanga *Euryceros prevostii*. *Working Group on Birds in the Madagascar Region Newsletter* 1(1): 2.

Grarock, K., Tidemann, C. R., Wood, J., and Lindenmayer, D. B. 2012. Is it benign or is it a pariah? Empirical evidence for the impact of the common myna (*Acridotheres tristis*) on Australian birds. *PLoS One* 7(7): e40622.

Grealy, A., Phillips, M., Miller, G., Gilbert, M.T.P., Rouillard, J.-M., Lambert, D., Bunce, M., and Haile, J. 2017. Eggshell palaeogenomics: Palaeognath evolutionary history revealed through ancient nuclear and mitochondrial DNA from Madagascan elephant bird (*Aepyornis* sp.) eggshell. *Molecular Phylogenetics and Evolution* 109: 151–163.

Greeshma, P., and Jayson, E. A. 2017. Scavenging by house crow *Corvus splendens* on its own species. *Journal of the Bombay Natural History Society* 114: 37.

Grimmett, R., Inskipp, C., and Inskipp, T. 1998. *Birds of the Indian Subcontinent.* London: Christopher Helm.

Griveaud, P. 1967. Le peuplement ornithologique de Madagascar: Origines-biogéographie. *Cahiers ORSTOM*, série *Biologie*, 4: 53–69.

Groombridge, J. J., Jones, C. G., Bayes, M. K., van Zyl, A. J., Carrillo, J., Nichols, R. A., and Bruford, M. W. 2002. A molecular phylogeny of African kestrels with reference to divergence across the Indian Ocean. *Molecular Phylogenetics and Evolution* 25: 267–277.

Gupta, S.N.S. 1969. The Indian house crow attacks five-striped squirrel. *Auk* 86(3): 556.

Hackett, S. J., Kimball, R. T., Reddy, S., Bowie, R.C.K., Braun, E. L., et al. 2008. A phylogenomic study of birds reveals their evolutionary history. *Science* 320: 1763–1768.

Haddad, N. M., Brudvig, L. A., Clobert, J., Davies, K. F., Gonzalez, A., et al. 2015. Habitat fragmentation and its lasting impact on Earth's ecosystems. *Science Advances* 1: e1500052.

Hadjikyriakou, T. G., Kassara, C., Rene de Roland, L.-A., Glokas, S., Tsiiopelas, N., Evangelidis, A., Thorstrom, R., and Kirshel, A.N.G. 2020. Phenology, variation in habitat use, and daily activity patterns of Eleonora's falcon overwintering in Madagascar. *Landscape Ecology* 35: 159–172.

Hampe, A. 1998. Field studies on the black parrot *Coracopsis nigra* in western Madagascar. *Bulletin of the African Bird Club* 5: 108–113.

Han, K.-L., Robbins, M. B., and Braun, M. J. 2010. A multi-gene estimate of phylogeny in the nightjars and nighthawks (Caprimulgidae). *Molecular Phylogenetics and Evolution* 55: 443–453.

Hanmer, D. B. 2001. Nine years in the Eastern Highlands of Zimbabwe. *Afring News* 30: 3–15.

Hansford, J. P., and Turvey, S. T. 2018. Unexpected diversity within the extinct elephant birds (Aves: Aepyornithidae) and a new identity for the world's largest bird. *Royal Society Open Science* 5: 181295.

Hansford, J. P., Wright, P. C., Rasoamiaramanana, A., Pérez, V. R., Godfrey, L. R., Errickson, D., Thompson, T., and Turvey, S. T. 2018. Early Holocene human presence in Madagascar evidenced by exploitation of avian megafauna. *Science Advances* 4: eaat6925.

Harper, G. J., Steininger, M. K., Tucker, C. J., Juhn, D., and Hawkins, F. 2007. Fifty years of deforestation and forest fragmentation in Madagascar. *Environmental Conservation* 34(4): 1–9.

Hartert, E. 1924. Dr. Ernest Hartert described a new bird from Madagascar. *Bulletin of the British Ornithologists' Club* 45: 35–36.

Hartlaub, G. 1877. *Die Vögel Madagascars und der benachbarten Inselgruppen: Ein Beitrag zur Zoologie der äthiopischen Region.* Halle: H. W. Schmidt.

Hawkins, A.F.A. 1994a. Density estimates and conservation status of the white-breasted mesite (*Mesitornis variegata*), a rare Malagasy endemic. *Bird Conservation International* 4: 279–303.

———. 1994b. Forest degradation and the west Malagasy forest bird community. PhD thesis, University of London.

———. 1994c. The nest of Schlegel's asity *Philepitta schlegeli*. *Bulletin of the African Bird Club* 1: 77–78.

———. 1995. Recent observations of the western tylas vanga *Tylas* (*eduardi*) *albigularis*. *Bulletin of the African Bird Club* 2: 13–15.

———. 1999. Altitudinal and latitudinal distribution of east Malagasy forest bird communities. *Journal of Biogeography* 26: 447–458.

———. 2013a. White-breasted mesite. In *The Birds of Africa*. Vol. 8, *The Malagasy Region*, eds. R. J. Safford and A.F.A. Hawkins, pp. 339–341. London: Christopher Helm.

———. 2013b. Family Philepittidae: Asities. In *The Birds of Africa*. Vol. 8, *The Malagasy Region*, eds. R. J. Safford and A.F.A. Hawkins, pp. 634–643. London: Christopher Helm.

Hawkins, A.F.A., and Goodman, S. M. 1999. Bird community variation with elevation and habitat in Parcels 1 and 2 of the Réserve Naturelle Intégrale d'Andohahela, Madagascar. In A floral and faunal inventory of the Réserve Naturelle Intégrale d'Andohahela, Madagascar: With reference to elevational variation, ed. S. M. Goodman. *Fieldiana: Zoology*, new series, 94: 175–186.

———. 2003. Introduction to the birds. In *The Natural History of Madagascar*, eds. S. M. Goodman and J. P. Benstead, pp. 1019–1044. Chicago: University of Chicago Press.

Hawkins, A.F.A., and Sartain, A. 2013. Family Bernieridae: Tetrakas or Malagasy warblers. In *The Birds of Africa*. Vol. 8, *The Malagasy Region*, eds. R. J. Safford and A.F.A. Hawkins, pp. 726–745. London: Christopher Helm.

Hawkins, A.F.A., and Wilmé, L. 1996. Effects of logging on forest birds. In Ecology and economy of a tropical dry forest in Madagascar, eds. J. U. Ganzhorn and J.-P. Sorg. *Primate Report*, special issue, 46-1: 203–213.

Hawkins, A.F.A., Chapman, P., Ganzhorn, J. U., Bloxam, Q.M.C., Barlow, S. C., and Tonge, S. J. 1990. Vertebrate conservation in Ankarana Special Reserve, northern Madagascar. *Biological Conservation* 54: 83–100.

Hawkins, A.F.A., Safford, R. J., Duckworth, J. W., and Evans, M. I. 1997. Field identification and status of the sunbird asities *Neodrepanis* of Madagascar. *Bulletin of the African Bird Club* 4: 36–41.

Hawkins, A.F.A., Thiollay, J.-M., and Goodman, S. M. 1998. The birds of the Réserve Spéciale d'Anjanaharibe-Sud, Madagascar. In A floral and faunal inventory of the Réserve Spéciale d'Anjanaharibe-Sud, Madagascar: With reference to elevational variation, ed. S. M. Goodman. *Fieldiana: Zoology*, new series, 90: 93–127.

Hawkins, [A.]F.[A.], Andriamasimanana, R., Sam, T. S., and Rabeony, Z. 2000. The sad story of Alaotra grebe *Tachybaptus rufolavatus*. *Bulletin of the African Bird Club* 7(2): 115–117.

Hawkins, A.F.A., Sartain, A., and Safford, R. J. 2013. Family Bernieridae: Tetrakas or Malagasy warblers. In *The Birds of Africa*. Vol. 8, *The Malagasy Region*, eds. R. Safford and A.F.A. Hawkins, pp. 726–745. London: Christopher Helm.

Hawkins, A.F.A., Safford, R. J. and Skerrett, A. 2015. *Birds of Madagascar and the Indian Ocean Islands*. London: Christopher Helm.

Hawkins, G. L., Hill, G. E., and Mercadante, A. 2012. Delayed plumage maturation and delayed reproductive investment in birds. *Biological Reviews* 87: 257–274.

Hedges, R.E.M., Pettitt, P. B., Bronk Ramsey, C., and Van Klinken, G. J. 1997. Radiocarbon dates from the Oxford AMS system: Archaeometry datelist 23. *Archaeometry* 39(1): 247–262.

Hill, D. A., and Ellis, N. 1984. Survival and age related changes in the foraging behaviour and time budget of tufted ducklings *Aythya fuligula*. *Ibis* 126: 544–550.

Hino, T. 2000. Intraspecific differences in benefits from feeding in mixed-species flocks. *Journal of Avian Biology* 31: 441–446.

———. 2002. Breeding bird community and mixed-species flocking in a deciduous broad-leaved forest in western Madagascar. *Ornithological Science* 1: 111–116.

———. 2009. Seasonality in the function of avian mixed-species flocks in Madagascar. *Ornithological Science* 8: 43–53.

Hoarau, V. 2019. Intérêt des oiseaux marins de l'ouest de l'océan Indien comme plateformes d'acquisition de données océanographiques. Rapport de stage M2BEST ALI, Université de La Réunion.

Höglund, J., and Alatalo, R. V. 1995. *Leks*. Princeton: Princeton University Press.

Hosner, P. A., Tobias, J. A., Braun, E. L., and Kimball, R. T. 2017 How do seemingly non-vagile clades accomplish trans-marine dispersal? Trait and dispersal evolution in the landfowl (Aves: Galliformes). *Proceedings of the Royal Society of London B: Biological Sciences* 284: 20170210.

Hume, J. P. 2011. Systematics, morphology and ecology of pigeons and doves (Aves: Columbidae) of the Mascarene islands, with three new species. *Zootaxa* 3124: 1–62.

———. 2019. Systematics, morphology and ecology of rails (Aves: Rallidae) of the Mascarene islands, with one new species. *Zootaxa* 4626(1): 1–107.

Ichino, S., Maehata, T., Rakotomanana, H., and Rakotondraporany, F. 2018. Forest vertebrate fauna and local knowledge among the Tandroy people in Berenty Reserve, southern Madagascar: A preliminary study. *African Study Monographs, Supplement* 54: 115–135.

Irestedt, M., Ohlson, J., Zuccon, D., Källersjö, M., and Ericson, P.G.P. 2006. Nuclear DNA from old collections of avian study skins reveals the evolutionary history of the Old World suboscines (Aves, Passeriformes). *Zoologica Scripta* 35: 567–580.

Ishtiaq, F., Beadell, J. S., Baker, A. J., Rahmani, A. R., Jhala, Y. V., and Fleischer, R. C. 2006. Prevalence and evolutionary relationships of haematozoan parasites in native versus introduced populations of common myna *Acridotheres tristis*. *Proceedings of the Royal Society of London B: Biological Sciences* 273: 587–594.

Ishtiaq, F., Beadell, J. S., Warren, B. H., and Fleischer, R. C. 2012. Diversity and distribution of avian haematozoan parasites in the western Indian Ocean region: A molecular survey. *Parasitology* 139: 221–231.

Ito, R., and Mori, A. 2010. Vigilance against predators induced by eavesdropping on heterospecific alarm calls in a non-vocal lizard *Oplurus cuvieri cuvieri* (Reptilia: Iguania). *Proceedings of the Royal Society of London B: Biological Sciences* 277: 1275–1280.

Ivanova, K., Zehtindjiev, P., Mariaux, J., Dimitrov, D., and Georgiev, B. B. 2018. Avian haemosporidians from rain forests in Madagascar: Molecular and morphological data of the genera *Plasmodium, Haemoproteus* and *Leucocytozoon*. *Infection, Genetics and Evolution* 58: 115–124.

Jackson, H. A., Bunbury, N., Przelomska, N., and Groombridge. J. J. 2016. Evolutionary distinctiveness and historical decline in genetic diversity in the Seychelles black parrot *Coracopsis nigra barklyi*. *Ibis* 158: 380–394.

Jackson, J. D., dos Remedios, N., Maher, K. H., Zefania, S., Haig, S., et al. 2017. Polygamy slows down population divergence in shorebirds. *Evolution* 71(5): 1313–1326. doi:10.1111/evo.13212.

Jaquemet, S., Le Corre, M., Marsac, F., Potier, M., and Weimerskirch, H. 2005. Foraging habitats of the seabird community of Europa Island (Mozambique Channel). *Marine Biology* 147: 573–582.

Jaquemet, S., Ternon, J.-F., Kaehler, S., Thiebot, J.-B., Dyer, B., Bemanaja, E., Marteau, C., and Le Corre, M. 2014. Contrasted structuring effects of mesoscale features on the seabird community in the Mozambique Channel. *Deep-Sea Research II: Topical Studies in Oceanography* 100: 200–211.

Jarvis, E. D., Mirarab, S., Aberer, A. J., Li, B., Houde, P. et al. 2014. Whole-genome analyses resolve early branches in the tree of life of modern birds. *Science* 346: 1320–1331.

Javed, S., Douglas, D. C., Khan, S., Shah, J. N., and Hammadi, A.A.A. 2012. First description of autumn migration of sooty falcon *Falco concolor* from the United Arab Emirates to Madagascar using satellite telemetry. *Bird Conservation International* 22: 106–119.

Jeanne, F., Laubin, A., Ousseni, M. B., Crémades, C., Pusinéri, C., and Lizot, P. 2015. *Bilan des ardéidés nicheurs et menacés de Mayotte*. Tsingoni: Groupe d'Etudes et de Protection des Oiseaux de Mayotte.

Jenni, D. A. 1996. Family Jacanidae. In *Handbook of the Birds of the World*. Vol. 3, *Hoatzin to Auks*, eds. J. del Hoyo, A. Elliot, and J. Sagatal, pp. 276–291. Barcelona: Lynx Edicions.

Jetz, W., Thomas, G. H., Joy, J. B., Hartmann, K., and Mooers, A. O. 2012. The global diversity of birds in space and time. *Nature* 491: 444–448.

Jetz, W., Thomas, G. H., Joy, J. B., Redding, D. W., Hartmann, K., and Mooers, A. O. 2014. Global distribution and conservation of evolutionary distinctness in birds. *Current Biology* 24: 919–930.

Jiguet, F. 2002. Taxonomy of the kelp gull *Larus dominicanus* Lichtenstein inferred from biometrics and wing plumage pattern, including two previously undescribed subspecies. *Bulletin of the British Ornithologists' Club* 122: 50–71.

Jiguet, F., Capainolo, P., and Tennyson, A. 2012. Taxonomy of the kelp gull *Larus dominicanus* Lichtenstein, revisited with sex-separated analysis of biometrics and wing tip patterns. *Zoological Studies* 51(6): 881–892.

Jobling, J. A. 2011. *The Helm Dictionary of Scientific Bird Names*. London: Christopher Helm.

Johansson, U. S., Bowie, R.C.K., Hackett, S. J., and Schulenberg, T. S. 2008. The phylogenetic affinities of Crossley's babbler (*Mystacornis crossleyi*): Adding a new niche to the vanga radiation of Madagascar. *Biology Letters* 4: 677–680.

Johnson, K. P., and Sorenson, M. D. 1999. Phylogeny and biogeography of dabbling ducks (genus: *Anas*): A comparison of molecular and morphological evidence. *Auk* 116: 792–805.

Johnson, K. P., Goodman, S. M., and Lanyon, S. M. 2000. A phylogenetic study of the Malagasy couas with insights into cuckoo relationships. *Molecular Phylogenetics and Evolution* 14: 436–444.

Johnson, K. P., de Kort, S., Dinwoody, K., Mateman, A. C., Cate, C., Lessells, C. M., and Clayton, D. H. 2001. A molecular phylogeny of the dove genera *Streptopelia* and *Columba*. *Auk* 118: 874–887.

Jønsson, K. A., Bowie, R.C.K., Nylander, J.A.A., Christidis, L., and Fjeldså, J. 2010. Biogeographical history of cuckoo-shrikes (Aves: Passeriformes): Transoceanic colonization of Africa from Australo-Papua. *Journal of Biogeography* 37(9): 1767–1781.

Jønsson, K. A., Fabre, P.-H., Fritz, S. A., Etienne, R. S., Ricklefs, R. E., et al. 2012. Ecological and evolutionary determinants for the adaptive radiation of the Madagascan vangas. *Proceedings of the National Academy of Sciences of the USA* 109: 6620–6625.

Juniper, T., and Parr, M. 1998. *A Guide to the Parrots of the World*. Robertsbridge: Pica Press.

Karpanty, S. M. 2010. Madagascar serpent eagle, Madagascar. In *The Eagle Watchers*, eds. R. E. Tingay and T. E. Katzner, pp. 67–72. Ithaca: Comstock.

Karpanty, S. M., and Goodman, S. M. 1999. Prey profile of the Madagascar harrier-hawk (*Polyboroides radiatus*) in southeastern Madagascar. *Journal of Raptor Research* 33: 313–316.

Kassara, C., Fric, J., Schweng, M., and Sfenthourakis, S. 2012. Complementing the puzzle of Eleonora's falcon (*Falco eleonorae*) migration: New evidence from an eastern colony in the Aegean Sea. *Journal für Ornithologie* 153: 839–848.

Kassara, C., Gangoso, L., Mellone, G., Hadjikyriakou, T. G., Tsiopelas, N., et al. 2017. Current and future suitability of wintering grounds for a long-distance migratory raptor. *Scientific Reports* 7: 8798.

Kear, J., ed. 2005. *Ducks, Geese and Swans*. Oxford: Oxford University Press.

Keith, S. 1973. The voice of *Sarothrura insularis* with further notes on members of the genus. *Bulletin of the British Ornithologists' Club* 93: 130–136.

———. 1980. Origins of the avifauna of the Malagasy Region. In *Proceedings IV Pan-African Ornithological Congress*, ed. D. N. Johnson, pp. 99–108. Johannesburg: Southern African Ornithological Society.

Kennedy, M., Seneviratne, S. S., Mendis, U. K., and Spencer, H. G. 2019. Sorting out the snakebirds: The species status, phylogeny, and biogeography of the darters (Aves: Anhingidae). *Journal of Zoological Systematics and Evolutionary Research* 57: 892–899.

Khan, H. A. 2003. Damage patterns of house crow (*Corvus splendens*) on some food crops in Faisalabad, Pakistan. *Pakistan Journal of Zoology* 6(2): 188–190.

Khan, S. U., Berman, L., Haider, N., Gerloff, N., Rahman, M. Z., et al. 2013. Investigating a crow die-off in January-February 2011 during the introduction of a new clade of highly pathogenic avian influenza virus H5N1 into Bangladesh. *Archives of Virology* 159(3): 509–518.

Kinnear, N. B. 1942. The introduction of the Indian house crow into Port Sudan. *Bulletin of the British Ornithologists' Club* 62: 55–56.

Kirchman, J. J., Hackett, S. J., Goodman, S. M., and Bates, J. M. 2001. Phylogeny and systematics of the ground rollers (Brachypteraciidae) of Madagascar. *Auk* 118: 849–863.

Kitundu, W. 2019. Action de lutte prècoce contre le corbeau (*Corvus splendens*). *Les Actus du GEIR* [newsletter of Groupe Espèces Invasives de la Réunion] 3: 1–2.

Kleefisch, T. 1981. Der Madagaskarweber *Foudia madagascariensis* (L. 1766). *Gefiederte Welt* 105: 123–125.

Klimov, P. B., Mironov, S. V., and OConnor, B. M. 2017. Detecting ancient codispersals and host shifts by double dating of host and parasite phylogenies: Application in proctophyllodid feather mites associated with passerine birds. *Evolution* 71: 2381–2397.

Koenig, P. 2005. Sexing Madagascar red fody *Foudia madagascariensis* in the non-breeding period. *Afring News* 34(1): 14–16.

Koparde, P., Mehta, P., Reddy, S., Ramakrishnan, U., Mukherjee, S., and Robin, V. V. 2018. The critically endangered forest owlet *Heteroglaux blewitti* is nested within the currently recognized *Athene* clade: A century-old debate addressed. *PLoS One* 13: e0192359.

Kruckenhauser, L., Haring, E., Pinsker, W., Riesing, M. J., Winkler, H., Wink, M., and Gamauf, A. 2004. Genetic vs. morphological differentiation of Old World buzzards (genus *Buteo*, Accipitridae). *Zoologica Scripta* 33: 197–211.

Kundu, S., Jones, C. G., Prŷs-Jones, R. P., and Groombridge, J. J. 2012. The evolution of the Indian Ocean parrots (Psittaciformes): Extinction, adaptive radiation and eustacy. *Molecular Phylogenetics and Evolution* 62: 296–305.

Kunz, F., Gamauf, A., Zachos, F. E., and Haring, E. 2019. Mitochondrial phylogenetics of the goshawk *Accipiter* [*gentilis*] superspecies. *Journal of Zoological Systematics and Evolutionary Research* 57: 942–958.

Kushlan, J. A., and Hafner, H. 2000. *Heron Conservation*. London: Academic Press.

Kushlan, J. A., and Hancock, J. A. 2005. *The Herons*. Oxford: Oxford University Press.

Kuussaari, M., Bommarco, R., Heikkinen, R. K., Helm, A., Krauss, J., et al. 2009. Extinction debt: A challenge for biodiversity conservation. *Trends in Ecology and Evolution* 24: 564–571.

La Marca, G., and Thorstrom, R. 2000. Breeding biology, diet and vocalization of the helmet vanga, *Euryceros prevostii*, on the Masoala Peninsula, Madagascar. *Ostrich* 71: 400–403.

Lambert, F., and Woodcock, M. 1996. *Pittas, Broadbills and Asities.* Robertsbridge: Pica Press.

Lambert, M. L., Seed, A. M., and Slocombe, K. E. 2015. A novel form of spontaneous tool use displayed by several captive greater vasa parrots (*Coracopsis vasa*). *Biology Letters* 11: 20150861.

Lamberton, C. 1934. Contribution à la connaissance de la faune subfossile de Madagascar: Lémuriens et ratites. *Mémoires de l'Académie Malgache* 17: 1–168.

Lambrecht, K. 1933. *Handbuch der Palaeornithologie*. Berlin: Verlag von Gebrüder Borntraeger.

Langrand, O. 1981. Nidification du paille en queue à queue rouge (*Phaethon rubricauda*) sur le territoire malgache. *L'Oiseau et la Revue Française d'Ornithologie* 51: 338–339.

———. 1990. *Guide to the Birds of Madagascar*. New Haven: Yale University Press.

———. 1994. The effects of forest fragmentation on forest dependent birds in Madagascar. *Working Group on Birds in the Madagascar Region Newsletter* 3: 8–10.

———. 1995. The effects of forest fragmentation on bird species in Madagascar: A case study from Ambohitantely Forest Reserve on the central high plateau. MS thesis, University of Natal, Pietermaritzburg.

———. 2001. Family Brachypteraciidae (ground-rollers). In *Handbook of the Birds of the World*. Vol. 6, *Mousebirds to Hornbills*, eds. J. del Hoyo, A. Elliott, and J. Sargatal, pp. 378–388. Barcelona: Lynx Edicions.

———. 2013. Family Brachypteraciidae: Ground-rollers. In *The Birds of Africa*. Vol. 8, *The Malagasy Region*, eds. R. J. Safford and A.F.A. Hawkins, pp. 616–626. London: Christopher Helm.

Langrand, O., and Goodman, S. M. 1995. Monitoring Madagascar's ecosystems: A look at the past, present, and future of its wetlands. In *Ecosystem Monitoring and Protected Areas*, eds. T. B. Herman, S. Bondrup-Nielson, J. H. Martin Wilson, and N.W.P. Munro, pp. 204–214. Wolfville: Science and Management of Protected Areas Association.

———. 1997a. Inventaire des oiseaux et des micro-mammifères des zones sommitales de la Réserve Naturelle Intégrale d'Andringitra. *Akon'ny Ala* 20: 39–54.

———. 1997b. Les oiseaux. In Inventaire biologique, Forêt de Vohibasia et d'Isoky-Vohimena, eds. O. Langrand and S. M. Goodman. *Recherche pour le Développement, Série Sciences Biologiques* 12: 131–143.

Langrand, O., and Kirwan, G. M. 2020. Long-tailed ground-roller (*Uratelornis chimaera*). In *Handbook of the Birds of the World Alive*, eds. J. del Hoyo, A. Elliott, J. Sargatal, D. A. Christie, and E. de Juana. Barcelona: Lynx Edicions. Accessed 21 Feb. 2020. https://www.hbw.com/node/55869.

Langrand, O., and Meyburg, B.-U. 1989. Range, status and biology of the Madagascar sea eagle *Haliaeetus vociferoides*. In *Raptors in the Modern World*, eds. B.-U. Meyburg and R. D. Chancellor, pp. 269–277. Berlin: World Working Group for Birds of Prey.

Langrand, O., and Sinclair, J. C. 1994. Additions and supplements to the Madagascar avifauna. *Ostrich* 65: 302–310.

Langrand, O., and von Bechtolsheim, M. 2009. New distributional records of Appert's tetraka (*Xanthomixis apperti*) from Salary Bay, Mikea Forest, Madagascar. *Malagasy Nature* 2: 172–174.

Langrand, O., and Wilmé, L. 1993. Protection des zones humides et conservation des espèces d'oiseaux endémiques de Madagascar. In Proceedings of the 8th Pan-African Ornithological Congress, ed. R. T. Wilson. *Annales Musée Royale de l'Afrique Centrale (Zoologie)* 268: 201–209.

———. 1997. Effects of forest fragmentation on extinction patterns of the endemic avifauna on the Central High Plateau of Madagascar. In *Natural Change and Human Impact in Madagascar*, eds. S. M. Goodman and B. D. Patterson, pp. 280–305. Washington, DC: Smithsonian Institution Press.

———. 2000. The effects of forest fragmentation on bird species abundance: A case study of the Central High Plateau of Madagascar. *Ostrich* 71: 315.

Lavauden, L. 1931. Animaux disparus et légendaires de Madagascar. *Revue Scientifique*, Paris 69: 297–308.

———. 1932. Etude d'une petite collection d'oiseaux de Madagascar. *Bulletin du Muséum National d'Histoire Naturelle*, Paris 4: 629–646.

———. 1937. Supplement to A. Milne Edwards and A. Grandidier (1879–1885), *Histoire physique, naturelle et politique de Madagascar.* Vol. 12, *Oiseaux*. Paris: Société d'Editions Géographiques, Maritimes et Coloniales.

Lavretsky, P., McCracken, K. G., and Peters, J. L. 2014. Phylogenetics of a recent radiation in the mallards and allies (Aves: Anas): Inferences from a genomic transect and the multispecies coalescent. *Molecular Phylogenetics and Evolution* 70: 402–411.

Le Corre, M. 2019. Etude des pailles en queue à brins rouges de Nosy Vé. Compilation des rapports des missions réalisées entre 2004 et 2018 par l'Université de La Réunion et l'Institut Halieutique et des Sciences Marines.

Le Corre, M., and Bemanaja, E. 2004. Etude des pailles en queue à brins rouges ou Vorompano (*Phaethon rubricauda*) de Nosy Vé, Anakao, Toliara, Madagascar. Mission du 19 au 26 janvier 2004. Rapport interne ECOMAR / Institut Halieutique et des Sciences Marines.

———. 2009. Discovery of two major seabird colonies in Madagascar. *Marine Ornithology* 37: 153–158.

Le Corre, M., Ollivier, A., Ribes, S., and Jouventin, P. 2002. Light-induced mortality of petrels: A 4-year study from Réunion Island (Indian Ocean). *Biological Conservation* 105: 93–102.

Le Corre, M., Salamolard, M., and Portier, M. C. 2003a. Transoceanic dispersion of the red-tailed tropicbird in the Indian Ocean. *Emu* 103: 1–2.

Le Corre, M., Ghestemme, T., Salamolard, M., and Couzi, F.-X. 2003b. Rescue of the Mascarene petrel, a critically endangered seabird of Réunion Island, Indian Ocean. *Condor* 105: 391–395.

Le Corre, M., Jaeger, A., Pinet, P., Kappes, M. A., Weimerskirch, H., Catry, T., Ramos, J. A., Russell, J. C., and Jaquemet, S. 2012. Tracking seabirds to identify potential marine protected areas in the tropical western Indian Ocean. *Biological Conservation* 156: 83–93.

Le Corre, M., Caumes, C., and Randriamoria, T. M. 2018. Seabird monitoring in Nosy Manampaho, Madagascar. Internal report, Island Conservation, Vahatra, UMR ENTROPIE, Madascarenes, Time and Tide Foundation, and Fanamby.

Leisler, B., and Winkler, H. 2015. Evolution of island warblers: Beyond bills and masses. *Journal of Avian Biology* 45: 1–9.

LeNoble, A. 1940. Etudes sur la géologie de Madagascar. Note 3: Le massif volcanique de l'Itasy. *Mémoires de L'Académie Malgache* 32: 43–80.

Lepage, D. 2020. Checklist of the birds of Kenya. Avibase, the world bird database. Accessed May 2020. https://avibase.bsc-eoc.org/checklist.jsp?region=KE.

Lerner, H.R.L., and Mindell, D. P. 2005. Phylogeny of eagles, Old World vultures, and other Accipitridae based on nuclear and mitochondrial DNA. *Molecular Phylogenetics and Evolution* 37: 327–346.

Lever, C. 2005. *Naturalised Birds of the World*. London: T. and A. D. Poyser.

Lewis, A., and Pomeroy, D. 1989. *A Bird Atlas of Kenya*. Rotterdam: A. A. Balkema.

Lilette, V. 2006. Mixed results: Conservation of the marine turtle and the red-tailed tropicbird by Vezo semi-nomadic fishers. *Conservation and Society* 4(2): 262–286.

Linders, T.E.W., and Langrand, O. 2014. First record of house crow *Corvus splendens* for Madagascar: Potential impacts and suggested management of an invasive bird species. *Bulletin of the African Bird Club* 21(2): 216–219.

Livezey, B. C. 1996. A phylogenetic analysis of modern pochards (Anatidae: Aythyini). *Auk* 113: 74–93.

———. 1997. A phylogenetic classification of waterfowl (Aves: Anseriformes), including selected fossil species. *Annals of Carnegie Museum* 66: 457–496.

Long, J. L. 1981. *Introduced Birds of the World*. London: David and Charles.

Long, P. R., Zefania, S., ffrench-Constant, R. H., and Székely, T. 2008. Estimating the population size of an endangered shorebird, the Madagascar plover, using a habitat suitability model. *Animal Conservation* 11: 118–127.

Lorenz, K. Z. 1941. Vergleichende Bewegungsstudien von Anatiden. *Journal fiir Ornithologie* 89: 194–294 (republished in Lorenz, K. 1971. *Studies in Human and Animal Behaviour*, vol. 2. London: Methuen).

Louette, M., and Herremans, M. 1985. Taxonomy and evolution of the bulbuls (*Hypsipetes*) on the Comoro islands. In *Proceedings of the International Symposium on African Vertebrates*, ed. K.-L. Schuchmann, pp. 407–423. Bonn: Museum Alexander König.

Louette, M., Herremans, M., Nagy, Z. T., Rene de Roland, L.-A., Jordaens, K., Van Houdt, J., Sonet, G., and Breman, F. C. 2011. Frances's sparrowhawk *Accipiter francesiae* (Aves: Accipitridae) radiation on the Comoro islands. *Bonner Zoologische Monographien* 57: 133–143.

Lovette, I. J., and Rubenstein, D. R. 2007. A comprehensive molecular phylogeny of the starlings (Aves: Sturnidae) and mockingbirds (Aves: Mimidae): Congruent mtDNA and nuclear trees for a cosmopolitan avian radiation. *Molecular Phylogenetics and Evolution* 44: 1031–1056.

Lowe, P. R. 1948. What are the Coraciiformes? *Ibis* 90: 572–582.

Maclean, G. L. 1984. Evolutionary trends in the sandgrouse (*Pteroclidae*). *Malimbus* 6: 75–78.

MacPhee, R.D.E. 1986. Environment, extinction, and Holocene vertebrate localities in southern Madagascar. *National Geographic Research* 2: 441–455.

MacPhee, R.D.E., Burney, D. A., and Wells, N. A. 1985. Early Holocene chronology and environment of Ampasambazimba, a Malagasy subfossil lemur site. *International Journal of Primatology* 6: 463–489.

Maher, K. H., Eberhart-Phillips, L. J., Kosztolányi, A., dos Remedios, N., Carmona-Isunza, M. C., et al. 2017. High fidelity: Extra-pair fertilisations in eight *Charadrius* plover species are not associated with parental relatedness or social mating system. *Journal of Avian Biology* 48(7): 910–920. doi:10.1111/jav.01263.

Manegold, A. 2008. Composition and phylogenetic affinities of vangas (Vangidae, Oscines, Passeriformes) based on morphological characters. *Journal of Zoological Systematics and Evolutionary Research* 46: 267–277.

Marine Protection Atlas. 2020. Marine Conservation Institute. Accessed 15 June 2020. http://www.mpatlas.org/map/mpas/.

Marks, B. D., and Willard, D. E. 2005. Phylogenetic relationships of the Madagascar pygmy kingfisher *Ispidina madagascariensis*. *Auk* 122: 1271–1280.

Marshall, J. T. 1978. Systematics of smaller Asian night birds based on voice. *Ornithological Monographs* 25: 1–58.

Martin, E. A., Ratsimisetra, L., Laloë, F., and Carrière, S. M. 2009. Conservation value for birds of traditionally managed isolated trees in an agricultural landscape of Madagascar. *Biodiversity and Conservation* 18: 2719–2742.

Martin, E. A., Viano, M., Ratsimisetra, L., Laloë, F., and Carrière, S. M. 2012. Maintenance of bird functional diversity in a traditional agroecosystem of Madagascar. *Agriculture, Ecosystems and Environment* 149: 1–9.

Martínez-de la Puente, J., Eberhart-Phillips, L. J., Carmona-Isunza, M. C., Zefania, S., Navarro, M. J., Kruger, O., Hoffman, J. V., Székely, T., and Figuerola, J. 2017. Extremely low *Plasmodium* prevalence in wild plovers and coursers from Cape Verde and Madagascar. *Malaria Journal* (2017) 16: 24. doi:10.1186/s12936-017-1892-y.

Martínez-Vilalta, A., Motis, A., and Kirwan, G. M. 2020. Black heron (*Egretta ardesiaca*), version 1.0. In *Birds of the World*, eds. J. del Hoyo, A. Elliott, J. Sargatal, D. A. Christie, and E. de Juana. Ithaca: Cornell Lab of Ornithology.

Matthews, T. J., Cottee-Jones, H. E., and Whittaker, R. J. 2014. Habitat fragmentation and the species-area relationship: A focus on total species richness obscures the impact of habitat loss on habitat specialists. *Diversity and Distributions* 20: 1136–1146.

Maurer, D., and Raikow, R. J. 1981. Appendicular myology, phylogeny, and classification of the avian order Coraciiformes (including Trogoniformes). *Annals of the Carnegie Museum of Natural History* 50: 417–434.

Mayr, G. 2008. The Madagascan "cuckoo-roller" (Aves: Leptosomidae) is not a roller: Notes on the phylogenetic affinities and evolutionary history of a "living fossil." *Acta Ornithologica* 43: 226–230.

———. 2019. Hypotarsus morphology of the Ralloidea supports a clade comprising *Sarothrura* and *Mentocrex* to the exclusion of *Canirallus*. *Acta Ornithologica* 54(1): 51–58.

Mayr, G., and Mourer-Chauviré, C. 2000. Rollers (Aves: Coraciiformes s.s.) from the Middle Eocene of Messel (Germany) and the Upper Eocene of the Quercy (France). *Journal of Vertebrate Paleontology* 20: 533–546.

———. 2003. Phylogeny and fossil record of the Brachypteraciidae: A comment on Kirchman et al. (2001). *Auk* 120(1): 202–203.

McCoy, D. E., and Prum, R. O. 2019. Convergent evolution of super black plumage near bright color in 15 families of birds. *Journal of Experimental Biology* 222: eb208140.

McCoy, D. E., Feo, T., Harvey, T. A., and Prum, R. O. 2018. Structural absorption by barbule microstructures of super black bird of paradise feathers. *Nature Communications* 9: 1.

McCullough, J. M., Moyle, R. G., Smith, B. T., and Andersen, M. J. 2019. A Laurasian origin for a pantropical bird radiation is supported by genomic and fossil data (Aves: Coraciiformes). *Proceedings of the Royal Society of London B: Biological Sciences* 286: 20190122.

McGowan, A., Broderick, A. C., and Godley, B. J. 2008. Seabird populations of the Chagos Archipelago, Indian Ocean: An evaluation of IBA sites. *Oryx* 42(3): 424–429.

Meier, G. G. 2013. House crow (*Corvus splendens*): An invasive bird travels to European cities. In *Invasive Alien Species: The Urban Dimension; Case Studies on Strengthening Local Action in Europe*, eds. C. van Ham, P. Genovesi, and R. Scalera, pp. 93–97. Brussels: IUCN European Union Representation Office.

Meier, G. G., and Haverson, P. J. 2016. The feasibility of eradicating invasive alien house crow from the Republic of Mauritius, Indian Ocean. Unpublished report to the government of Mauritius and Mauritian Wildlife Foundation.

Mellone, U., López-López, P., Limiñana, R., and Urios, V. 2012. Wintering habits of Eleonora's falcons *Falco eleonorae* in Madagascar. *Bird Study* 59: 29–36.

Miao, Y., Peng, M., Wu, G., Ouyang, Y.-N., Yang, Z.-Y., et al. 2013. Chicken domestication: An updated perspective based on mitochondrial genomes. *Heredity* 110: 277–282.

Middleton, G. J. 2000. Madagascar 1999: The Mangoky River Expedition. *Journal of the Sydney Speleological Society* 44: 301–309.

Mills, M.S.L., Boesman, P., and Collar, N. J. 2019. Species limits in the African palm swift *Cypsiurus parvus*. *Bulletin of the British Ornithologists' Club* 139: 75–82.

Milne Edwards, A., and Grandidier, A. 1879–1885. *Histoire physique, naturelle et politique de Madagascar*. Vol. 12, *Histoire naturelle des oiseaux*. Paris: Imprimerie Nationale.

———. 1895. Sur des ossements d'oiseaux provenant des terrains récents de Madagascar. *Bulletin du Muséum National d'Histoire Naturelle*, Paris 1: 9–11.

Milon, P. 1946. Nidification dans le nord de Madagascar de l'oiseau du tropique ou paille en queue à bec jaune. *Alauda* 14: 3–43.

———. 1948a. Note d'observation à Madagascar sur le paille en queue à brins rouges observé à l'île Europa. *Alauda* 16: 55–74.

———. 1948b. Visites à Nosy Mborono et à Nosy Manitra dans le sud-ouest de Madagascar. *Alauda* 16: 55–72.

———. 1950. Quelques observations sur la nidification des sternes dans les eaux de Madagascar. *Ibis* 92: 545–553.

———. 1951a. Les formes de *Saxicola torquata* à Madagascar. *Bulletin du Muséum National d'Histoire Naturelle*, Paris, série 2, 22: 705–708.

———. 1951b. Sur la distribution du martin à Madagascar. *Le Naturaliste Malgache* 3: 67–73.

Milon, P., Petter, J.-J., and Randrianasolo, G. 1973. Oiseaux. *Faune de Madagascar* 35: 1–263.

Ministère de l'Environnement et du Développement Durable. 2019. *Sixième rapport national sur la diversité biologique de Madagascar*. Antananarivo: Ministère de l'Environnement et du Développement Durable.

Mitchell, K. J., Llamas, B., Soubrier, J., Rawlence, N. J., Worthy, T. H., Wood, J., Lee, M.S.Y., and Cooper, A. 2014. Ancient DNA reveals elephant birds and kiwi are sister taxa and clarifies ratite bird evolution. *Science* 344(6186): 898–900. doi:10.1126/science.1251981.

Mizuta, T. 2002a. Breeding biology of the Madagascar paradise flycatcher *Terpsiphone mutata*, with special reference to plumage variation in males. *Ostrich* 73: 67–69.

———. 2002b. Seasonal changes in egg mass and timing of laying in the Madagascar paradise flycatcher, *Terpsiphone mutata*. *Ostrich* 73: 5–10.

———. 2002c. Predation by *Eulemur fulvus* on a nestling of *Terpsiphone mutata* (Aves: Monarchidae) in dry forest in north-western Madagascar. *Folia Primatologia* 73: 217–219.

———. 2003. The development of plumage polymorphism in male Madagascar paradise flycatcher *Terpsiphone mutata*. *African Journal of Ecology* 41: 124–130.

———. 2005. Parental care behavior in the monogamous, sexually dimorphic Madagascar paradise flycatcher: Sex differences and the effect of brood size. *Ecological Research* 20: 547–553.

———. 2006. Habitat difference in food abundance possibly causes within-population variation in the timing of breeding in the Madagascar paradise flycatcher (*Terpsiphone mutata*). *Canadian Journal of Zoology* 84: 817–822.

———. 2007. Identification of nest predator and time of predation on the Madagascar paradise flycatcher by use of temperature loggers. *Bird Research* 3: T21–T28 (in Japanese with English abstract).

———. 2009. Nest-site characteristics affecting the risk of predation on the Madagascar paradise flycatcher *Terpsiphone mutata*: Identification of predators and time of nest predation. *Ornithological Science* 8: 37–42.

Mizuta, T., Nakamura, M., and Yamagishi, S. 2001. Breeding ecology of Van Dam's vanga *Xenopirostris damii*, an endemic species in Madagascar. *Journal of the Yamashina Institute for Ornithology* 33: 15–24.

Mock, D. W., Drummond, H., and Stinson, C. H. 1990. Avian siblicide. *American Scientist* 78: 438–449.

Monnier, L. 1913. Les *Aepyornis*. *Annales de Paléontologie* 8: 125–172.

Monnier, L., and Lamberton, C. 1922. Note sur des ossements subfossiles de la région de Manajary. *Bulletin de l'Académie Malgache*, nouvelle série, 3: 211–213.

Moreau, R. E. 1957. Variation in the western Zosteropidae (Aves). *Bulletin of the British Museum (Natural History) Zoology* 4: 312–433.

———. 1960. The Ploceine weavers of the Indian Ocean islands. *Journal für Ornithologie* 101: 29–49.

———. 1966. *The Bird Faunas of Africa and Its Islands*. London: Academic Press.

Morris, P., and Hawkins, F. 1998. *Birds of Madagascar: A Photographic Guide*. New Haven: Yale University Press.

Mourer-Chauviré, C., Bour, R., Ribes, S., and Moutou, F. 1999. The avifauna of Réunion Island (Mascarene islands) at the time of the arrival of the first Europeans. In Avian paleontology at the close of the 20th century, ed. S. L. Olson. *Smithsonian Contributions to Paleobiology* 89: 1–38.

Moussu, G. 1933. Colonies françaises. In *L'aviculture dans le Monde: Etat de l'aviculture dans les pays extra-Européens*. Rome: Institut International d'Agriculture.

Moyle, R. G. 2006. A molecular phylogeny of kingfishers (Alcedinidae) with insights into early biogeographic history. *Auk* 123: 487–499.

Moyle, R. G., Chesser, R. T., Prum, R. O., Schikler, P., and Cracraft, J. 2006. Phylogeny and evolutionary history of the Old World suboscine birds (Aves: Eurylaimides). *American Museum Novitates* 3544: 1–22.

Moyle, R. G., Fuchs, J., Pasquet, E., and Marks, B. D. 2007. Feeding behavior, toe count, and the phylogenetic relationships among alcedinine kingfishers (Alcedininae). *Journal of Avian Biology* 38: 317–326.

Moyle, R. G., Filardi, C. E., Smith, C. E., and Diamond, J. 2009. Explosive Pleistocene diversification and hemispheric expansion of a "great speciator." *Proceedings of the National Academy of Sciences of the USA* 106: 1863–1868.

Mulder, R. A. 2013. Madagascar paradise flycatcher *Terpsiphone mutata*. In *The Birds of Africa*. Vol. 8, *The Malagasy Region*, eds. R. J. Safford and A.F.A. Hawkins, pp. 705–708. London: Christopher Helm.

Mulder, R. A., Ramiarison, R., and Emahalala, R. E. 2002. Ontogeny of male plumage dichromatism in Madagascar paradise flycatchers *Terpsiphone mutata*. *Journal of Avian Biology* 33: 342–348.

Muldoon, K. M., Crowley, B. E., Godfrey, L. R., Rasoamiaramanana, A., Aronson, A., Jernvall, J., Wright, P. C., and Simons, E. L. 2012. Early Holocene fauna from a new subfossil site: A first assessment from Christmas River, south central Madagascar. *Madagascar Conservation and Development* 7: 23–29.

Murphy, A., Kelly, M. J., Karpanty, S. M., Andrianjakarivelo, V., and Farris, Z. J. 2019. Using camera traps to investigate spatial co-occurrence between exotic predators and native prey species: A case study from northeastern Madagascar. *Journal of Zoology* 307: 264–273.

Musa, S., Mackenstedt, U., Woog, F., and Dinkel, A. 2019. Avian malaria on Madagascar: Prevalence, biodiversity and specialization of haemosporidian parasites. *International Journal for Parasitology* 49: 199–210.

Mustoe, S. H., Capper, D. R., Lowen, J. C., Leadley, J. D., and Rakotomalala, D. 1998. Zombitse-Vohibasia: A new national park in south-west Madagascar. *Bulletin of the African Bird Club* 5: 39–45.

Mwacharo, J. M., Bjørnstad, G., Han, J. L., and Hanotte, O. 2013. The history of African village chickens: An archaeological and molecular perspective. *African Archaeological Review* 30: 97–114. https://doi.org/10.1007/s10437-013-9128-1.

Mwema, M., and Razafindrajao, F. 2006. First pink-backed pelican *Pelecanus rufescens* sightings in Madagascar since 1960. *Bulletin of the African Bird Club* 13: 86–87.

Nakamura, M., Yamagishi, S., and Okamiya, T. 2001a. Breeding biology of the sickle-billed vanga *Falculea palliata*, which is endemic to Madagascar. In *Ecological Radiation of Madagascan Endemic Vertebrates with Special Reference to Coevolution between Birds and Reptiles*, eds. S. Yamagishi and A. Mori, pp. 48–52. Kyoto: Kyoto University.

Nakamura, M., Yamagishi, S., and Nishiumi, I. 2001b. Cooperative breeding of the white-headed vanga *Leptopterus viridis*, an endemic species in Madagascar. *Journal of the Yamashina Institute for Ornithology* 33: 1–14.

Nakamura, M., Okamiya, T., and Yamagishi, S. 2004. The diet of adult and nestling sickle-billed vangas *Falculea palliata*, a species endemic to Madagascar. *Journal of the Yamashina Institute for Ornithology* 35: 155–158.

Nakamura, M., Okamiya, T., Hasegawa, M., and Hasegawa, M. 2009a. Cooperative breeding in the endemic Madagascan Chabert's vanga *Leptopterus chabert*. *Ornithological Science* 8: 23–27.

Nakamura, M., Tateno, M., and Rakotomanana, H. 2009b. Breeding ecology of the tylas vanga *Tylas eduardi* in southeastern Madagascar. *Ornithological Science* 8: 15–22.

Nakamura, M., Rakotosoa, R. S., and Rakotomanana, H. 2013. Additional reports on the breeding ecology of Chabert's vanga *Leptopterus chabert* and red-tailed vanga *Calicalicus madagascariensis*. *Journal of the Yamashina Institute for Ornithology* 45: 53–58.

Ndang'ang'a, P. K., and Sande, E., compilers. 2008. International single species action plan for the Madagascar pond-heron (*Ardeola idae*). AEWA Technical Series No. 39. Bonn: Convention on Migratory Species.

Newton, E. 1863. Notes of a second visit to Madagascar. *Ibis* 5: 333–350, 452–461.

Nguembock, B., Fjeldså, J., Tillier, A., and Pasquet, E. 2007. A phylogeny for the Cisticolidae (Aves: Passeriformes) based on nuclear and mitochondrial DNA sequence data, and a re-interpretation of a unique nest-building specialization. *Molecular Phylogenetics and Evolution* 42: 272–286.

Nicoll, M. E., and Langrand, O. 1989. *Madagascar: Revue de la conservation et des aires protégées*. Gland: World Wide Fund for Nature.

Nyari, A., Ryall, C., and Peterson, A. T. 2006. Global invasive potential of the house crow (*Corvus splendens*) based on ecological niche modelling. *Journal of Avian Ecology* 37: 306–311.

Oatley, G., Simmons, R. E., and Fuchs, J. 2015. A molecular phylogeny of the harriers (*Circus*, Accipitridae) indicate the role of long distance dispersal and migration in diversification. *Molecular Phylogenetics and Evolution* 85: 150–160.

O'Daniel, D. 1995. Raising Cain ... and Abel. *Living Bird* 14(3): 30–35.

Oliveros, C. H., Field, D. J., Ksepka, D. T., Barker, F. K., Aleixo, A., et al. 2019. Earth history and the passerine superradiation. *Proceedings of the National Academy of Sciences of the USA* 116: 7916–7925.

Olson, S. L. 1989. Preliminary systematic notes on some Old World passerines. *Rivista Italiana di Ornitologia* 59: 183–195.

Olsson, U., Irestedt, M., Sangster, G., Ericson, P.G.P., and Alström, P. 2013. Systematic revision of the avian family Cisticolidae based on a multi-locus phylogeny of all genera. *Molecular Phylogenetics and Evolution* 66: 790–799.

Ó Marcaigh, F., Raveloson, B. A., Rakotomanga, G., Ratianarivo, A. N., Baddams, J., Rasamison, S., Neaves, J., Long, P., and Martin, T. E. 2020. The avifauna of Ankobohobo wetland, a neglected Important Bird Area in northwestern Madagascar. *Scopus* 40: 18–28.

Oschadleus, H. D. 2008. Nests of nelicourvi weaver *Ploceus nelicourvi* in central eastern Madagascar. *Ostrich* 79: 107–108.

Owen, D. F. 1963. The rufus and white forms of an Asiatic paradise flycatcher, *Terpsiphone paradisi*. *Ardea* 51: 230–236.

Owens, I.P.F., and Hartley, I. R. 1998. Sexual dimorphism in birds: Why are there so many different forms of dimorphism? *Proceedings of the Royal Society of London B: Biological Sciences* 265: 397–407.

Päckert, M., Martens, J., Wink, M., Feigl, A., and Tietze, D. T. 2012. Molecular phylogeny of Old World swifts (Aves: Apodiformes, Apodidae, *Apus* and *Tachymarptis*) based on mitochondrial and nuclear markers. *Molecular Phylogenetics and Evolution* 63: 606–616.

Parra, J. E. 2014. Brood attendance behaviour in three Malagasy plovers: Natural behaviours and experiments. PhD thesis, University of Bath.

Parra, J. E., Beltran, M., Zefania, S., dos Remedios, N., and Székely, T. 2014. Experimental assessment of mating opportunities in three shorebird species. *Animal Behaviour* 90: 83–90.

Pasquet, E., Pons, J.-M., Fuchs, J., Cruaud, C., and Bretagnolle, V. 2007. Evolutionary history and biogeography of the drongos (Dicruridae), a tropical Old World clade of corvoid passerines. *Molecular Phylogenetics and Evolution* 45: 158–167.

Paverne, L. 1997. Nidification et comportement de busard de Maillard (*Circus maillardi*) dans la région d'Ankazobe au nord-ouest d'Antananarivo. *Working Group on Birds in the Madagascar Region Newsletter* 7: 21–24.

Payne, R. B. 2005. *The Cuckoos*. Oxford: Oxford University Press.

Payne, R. B., and Sorenson, M. D. 2003. Museum collections as sources of genetic data. *Bonner zoologische Beiträge* 51: 97–104.

Pearson, D. L. 1975. The relation of foliage complexity to ecological diversity of three Amazonian bird communities. *Condor* 77: 453–466.

Penhallurick, J. 2003. Notes on some genera and subgenera of rails (Rallidae). *Bulletin of the British Ornithologists' Club* 123: 33–45.

Pereira, S. L., Johnson, K. P., Clayton, D. H., and Baker, A. J. 2007. Mitochondrial and nuclear DNA sequences support a Cretaceous origin of Columbiformes and a dispersal-driven radiation in the Paleogene. *Systematic Biology* 56: 656–672.

Perez, C., Granadeiro, J. P., Dias, M. P., Alonso, H., and Catry, P. 2014. When males are more inclined to stay at home: Insights into the partial migration of a pelagic seabird provided by geolocators and isotopes. *Behavioral Ecology* 25(2): 313–319.

Péron, C., Delord, K., Phillips, R. A., Charbonnier, Y., Marteau, C., Louzao, M., and Weimerskirch, H. 2010. Seasonal variation in oceanographic habitats and behaviour of white-chinned petrels (*Procellaria aequinoctialis*) from Kerguelen Island. *Marine Ecology Progress Series* 416: 267–284.

Peters, D. S. 1996. *Hypositta perdita* n. sp., eine neue Vogelart aus Madagaskar (Aves: Passeriformes: Vangidae). *Senckenbergiana Biologica* 76: 7–14.

Pidgeon, M. 1996. *An Ecological Survey of Lake Alaotra and Selected Wetlands of Central and Eastern Madagascar in Analysing the Demise of Madagascar Pochard* Aythya innotata. Antananarivo: Missouri Botanical Garden and World Wide Fund for Nature.

Pinet, P., Jaquemet, S., Pinaud, D., Weimerskirch, H., Phillips, R. A., and Le Corre, M. 2011. Migration, wintering distribution and habitat use of an endangered tropical seabird, Barau's petrel *Pterdroma baraui*. *Marine Ecology Progress Series* 423: 291–302.

Pinet, P., Jaquemet, S., Phillips, R. A., and Le Corre, M. 2012. Sex-specific foraging strategies throughout the breeding season in a tropical sexually monomorphic small petrel. *Animal Behaviour* 83: 979–989.

Polunin, N.V.C. 1979. *Sula leucogaster* and other species in the Iles Mitsio, Madagascar. *Bulletin of the British Ornithologists' Club* 99: 110–111.

Pons, P., and Wendenburg, C. 2005. The impact of fire and forest conversion into savanna on the bird communities of west Madagascan dry forests. *Animal Conservation* 8: 183–193.

Price, R. D., and Johnson, K. P. 2006. *Myrsidea willardi* Price and Johnson, a new species of chewing louse (Phthiraptera: Menoponidae) from Schlegel's asity (Passeriformes: Philepittidae). *Journal of the Kansas Entomological Society* 79: 267–271.

Projet ZICOMA. 1998. *Visite ornithologique de la Réserve Spéciale de Bemarivo (Besalampy)*. Rapport de mission. Antananarivo: BirdLife International Projet ZICOMA.

Provost, K. L., Joseph, L., and Tilston Smith, B. 2018. Resolving a phylogenetic hypothesis for parrots: Implications from systematics to conservation. *Emu* 118: 7–21.

Prum, R. O. 1993. Phylogeny, biogeography, and evolution of the broadbills (Eurylaimidae) and asities (Philepittidae) based on morphology. *Auk* 110: 304–324.

Prum, R. O., and Razafindratsita, V. R. 1997. Lek behavior and natural history of the velvet asity (*Philepitta castanea*: Eurylaimidae). *Wilson Bulletin* 109: 371–392.

———. 2003. Philepittinae, asities and sun-bird asities. In *The Natural History of Madagascar*, eds. S. M. Goodman and J. P. Benstead, pp. 1123–1130. Chicago: University of Chicago Press.

Prum, R. O., Morrison, R. L., and Ten Eyck, G. R. 1994. Structural color production by constructive reflection from ordered collagen arrays in a bird (*Philepitta castanea*: Eurylaimidae). *Journal of Morphology* 222: 61–72.

Prum, R. O., Torres, R. H., Kovach, C., Williamson, S., and Goodman, S. M. 1999. Coherent light scattering by nanostructured collagen arrays in the caruncles of the Malagasy asities (Eurylaimidae: Aves). *Journal of Experimental Biology* 202: 3507–3522.

Prum, R. O., Berv, J. S., Dornburg, A., Field, D. J., Townsend, J. P., Lemmon, E. M., and Lemmon, A. R. 2015. A comprehensive phylogeny of birds (Aves) using targeted next-generation DNA sequencing. *Nature* 526: 569–573.

Pruvot, Y. Z., Rene de Roland, L.-A., Razafimanjato, G., Rakotondratsima, M.P.H., Andrianarimisa, A., and Thorstrom, R. 2017. Nesting biology and food habits of the endangered Sakalava rail *Amaurornis olivieri* in the Mandrozo Protected Area, western Madagascar. *Ostrich* 89: 109–115.

Putnam, M. S. 1996. Aspects of the breeding biology of Pollen's vanga (*Xenopirostris polleni*) in southeastern Madagascar. *Auk* 113: 233–236.

Puttoo, M., and Archer, T. 2004. Control and/or eradication of Indian crows (*Corvus splendens*) in Mauritius. In *Proceedings of the Sixth Meeting of Agricultural Scientists, Réduit, Mauritius, 8–9 May 2003*, eds J. A. Lalouette and D. Y. Bachraz, pp. 299–309. Réduit: Food and Agricultural Research Council, Réduit, Mauritius.

Rabarisoa, R. 1999a. Nouveaux éléments sur la distribution du pygargue de Madagascar *Haliaeetus vociferoides* dans la région du sud-ouest de Madagascar. In *Projet de conservation des zones humides de Madagascar: Rapport d'avancement* 5, ed. A. Andrianarimisa, pp. 110–114. Antananarivo: Peregrine Fund.

———. 1999b. Productivité du pygargue de Madagascar *Haliaeetus vociferoides* dans la région d'Antsalova. In *Projet de conservation des zones humides de Madagascar: Rapport d'avancement* 5, ed. A. Andrianarimisa, pp. 133–139. Antananarivo: Peregrine Fund.

———. 2003. Madagascar. In *African Waterbird Census 1999, 2000 and 2001*, eds. T. Dodman and C. H. Diagana, pp. 296–300. Wetlands International Global Series No. 16. Wageningen: Wetlands International.

———. 2006. Madagascar. In *African Waterbird Census 2002, 2003 and 2004*, eds. T. Dodman and C. H. Diagana, pp. 225–230. Dakar: Wetlands International.

———. 2007. Inventories and assessment of wetlands between Andringitra and Andohahela National Parks, in the south-eastern region of Madagascar in order to get information on important wetlands which need conservation actions. Report for Ramsar Small Grants Fund, BirdLife International Madagascar.

———. 2018. New observation on the breeding of the crested tern (*Thalasseus bergii*) in Madagascar. *Indian Ocean Seabird Group Newsletter* 4: 10.

———. 2019. Status assessment and population trends of the glossy ibis *Plegadis falcinellus* in Madagascar between 1993 and 2016. *SIS [Stork, Ibis and Spoonbill] Conservation* 1: 60–64.

Rabarisoa, R. Watson, R. T., Thorstrom, R., and Berkelman, J. 1997. Status of the Madagascar fish-eagle *Haliaeetus vociferoides* in 1995. *Ostrich* 68: 8–12.

Rabarisoa, R., Rafanomezantsoa, S., and Watson, R. T. 2003. *Haliaeetus vociferoides*, Madagascar fish-eagle, *ankoay*. In *The Natural History of Madagascar*, eds. S. M.

Goodman and J. P. Benstead, pp. 1085–1087. Chicago: University of Chicago Press.

Rabarisoa, R., Rakotonomenjanahary, O., and Ramanampamonjy, J. 2006. Waterbirds of Baie de Baly, Madagascar. In *Waterbirds around the World*, eds. G. C. Boere, C. A. Galbraith, and D. A. Stroud, pp. 374–375. Edinburgh: Stationery Office.

Rabarisoa, R., Ramanampamonjy, J., Razafindrajao, F., Rene de Roland, L.-A., Jeanne, F., Bacar, O., Laubin, A., and Bignon, F. 2020. Status assessment and population trends of the Madagascar pond-heron (*Ardeola idae*) from 1993–2016. *Waterbirds* 43: 45–54.

Rabearivony, J., Thorstrom, R., Rene de Roland, L.-A., Rakotondratsima, M., Andriamalala, T.R.A., Sam, T. S., Razafimanjato, G., Rakotondravony, D., Raselimanana, A. P., and Rakotoson, M. 2010. Protected area surface extension in Madagascar: Do endemism and threatened species remain useful criteria for site selection? *Madagascar Conservation and Development* 5: 35–47.

Rabenandrasana, M. N., and Safford, R. J. 2013. Madagascar wood rail *Mentocrex kioloides*. In *The Birds of Africa*. Vol. 8, *The Malagasy Region*, eds. R. J. Safford and A.F.A. Hawkins, pp. 353–354. London: Christopher Helm.

Rabenandrasana, M. N., Zefania, S., Long, P. R., Sam, T. S., Virginie, M. C., Randrianarisoa, M., Safford, R. J., and Székely, T. 2009. Distribution, habitat and status of "Endangered" Sakalava rail of Madagascar. *Bird Conservation International* 19: 23–32.

Rafanomezantsoa, S. 1998. Contribution à l'étude des comportements et de la dispersion des jeunes pygargues de Madagascar *Haliaeetus vociferoides* dans le complexe des trois lacs d'Antsalova. Mémoire de DEA, Université d'Antananarivo.

———. 1999. Notes sur la ponte de remplacement chez le pygargue de Madagascar *Haliaeetus vociferoides*. *Working Group on Birds in the Madagascar Region Newsletter* 9(1): 20–21.

Raherilalao, M. J. 2001. Effets de la fragmentation de la forêt sur les oiseaux autour du Parc National de Ranomafana (Madagascar). *Revue d'Ecologie (La Terre et la Vie)* 56: 389–406.

Raherilalao, M. J., Gautier, F., and Goodman, S. M. 2002. Les oiseaux de la Réserve Spéciale de Manongarivo. In Inventaire floristique et faunistique de la Réserve Spéciale de Manongarivo, Madagascar, eds. L. Gautier and S. M. Goodman. *Boissiera* 59: 359–381.

Rahman, M., Mangtani, P., Uyeki, T. M., Cardwell, J. M., Torremorell, M., et al. 2019. Evaluation of potential risk of transmission of avian influenza A viruses at live bird markets in response to unusual crow die-offs in Bangladesh. *Influenza and Other Respiratory Viruses* 14: 349–352.

Rahobilalaina, S. S. 2017. Répartition écologique des Ardeidae des lacs satellites et des zones côtières du Complexe Mahavavy-Kinkony, Madagascar. Mémoire de Master, Mention Zoologie et Biodiversité Animale, Université d'Antananarivo.

Raikow, R. J. 1987. Hindlimb myology and evolution of the Old World suboscine passerine birds (Acanthisittidae, Pittidae, Philepittidae, Eurylaimidae). *Ornithological Monographs* 41: 1–86.

Rajaonarivelo, A., Andrianarimisa, A., Raherilalao, M. J., and Goodman, S. M. 2020. Répartition verticale des oiseaux dans les forêts de l'ouest de Madagascar (pt. 1). *Alauda* 88(3): 41–50 and 88(4): 271–280.

Rakotoarisoa, J.-E., and Be, B. 2004. Breeding and foraging behaviour and habitat characteristics of the scaly ground-roller *Geobiastes squamigerus* in Madagascar. *Ostrich* 75: 25–31.

Rakotoarisoa, J.-E., and Capparella, A. P. 2013. Forest-bird species assemblages in the lowland rainforest of Madagascar: The effects of forest fragmentation revisited. *Open Conservation Biology Journal* 7: 27–41.

Rakotomanana, H. [F.] 2007. Ecomorphology and foraging height in the Malagasy endemic velvet asity (*Philepitta castanea*). *Ostrich* 78: 305–307.

Rakotomanana, H. [F.], and Hino, T. 1998. Food preference in the velvet asity *Philepitta castanea* in a rain forest of Madagascar. *Japanese Journal of Ornithology* 47: 11–19.

Rakotomanana, H. [F.], and Nakamura, M. 2012. Breeding ecology of the Malagasy endemic nelicourvi weaver *Ploceus nelicourvi*. *Ornithological Science* 11: 39–46.

Rakotomanana, H. F., and Raveloson, B. A. 2019. *Ny vorontsika eto Madagasikara*. Bell Village: Précigraph.

Rakotomanana, H. [F.], and Rene de Roland, L.-A. 2007. Breeding ecology of the endemic, Madagascan, velvet asity *Philepitta castanea*. *Ornithological Science* 6: 79–85.

Rakotomanana, H. [F.], Nakamura, M., and Yamagishi, S. 2001. Breeding ecology of the endemic hook-billed vanga, *Vanga curvirostris*, in Madagascar. *Journal of the Yamashina Institute for Ornithology* 33: 25–35.

Rakotomanana, H. [F.], Tateno, M., and Nakamura, M. 2009. Breeding ecology of the Malagasy endemic red-tailed vanga *Calicalicus madagascariensis*. *Ornithological Science* 8: 29–35.

Rakotomavo, A. L. 2017. Diversité des oiseaux limicoles pendant la période postnuptiale dans les mangroves du Complexe Mahavavy-Kinkony, nord-ouest de Madagascar. Mémoire de Master, Mention Zoologie et Biodiversité Animale, Université d'Antananarivo.

Rakotozafy, L.M.A. 1996. Etude de la constitution du régime alimentaire des habitants du site de Mahilaka du XIè au XIVè siècle à partir des produits de fouilles archéologiques. Doctorat de Troisième Cycle, Université d'Antananarivo.

Rakotozafy, L.M.A., and Goodman, S. M. 2005. Contribution à l'étude zooarchéologique de la région du sud-ouest et extrême sud de Madagascar. *Taloha* 14–15. http://www.taloha.info/document.php?id=181.

Ramasinatrehina, N. S., and Raherilalao, M. J. 2013. Aperçu sur l'écologie de *Mentocrex beankaensis* (Aves, Rallidae) de la forêt sèche de Beanka, Région Melaky, ouest de Madagascar. *Malagasy Nature* 7: 237–244.

Ramiarison, N. 1998. Observations of predation on paradise flycatcher nests by hook-billed vanga. *Working Group on Birds in the Madagascar Region Newsletter* 8(1): 6–7.

Rand, A. L. 1936. The distribution and habits of Madagascar birds: Summary of the field notes of the Mission Zoologique Franco-Anglo-Américaine à Madagascar. *Bulletin of the American Museum of Natural History* 72: 153–499.

Rand, A. L., and Deignan, H. G. 1960. Family Pycnonotidae. In *Check-List of Birds of the World*, vol. 9, eds. E. Mayr and J. C. Greenway Jr., pp. 221–300. Cambridge, MA: Museum of Comparative Zoology.

Randriamanga, I. 2000. Contribution à l'étude de la biologie de la reproduction et écologie de busard de Madagascar *Circus macrosceles* dans le Tampoketsa d'Ankazobe. Mémoire de DEA, Université d'Antananarivo.

Randriamanindry, J.-J. 1995. The dusky greenbul *Phyllastrephus tenebrosus* in the Zahamena Strict Nature Reserve, Madagascar. *Working Group on Birds in the Madagascar Region Newsletter* 5(1): 1.

Randriamiharisoa, L. O. 2020. Stratégie d'adaptation et d'utilisation du milieu urbain d'Antananarivo, Madagascar par le martin triste (*Acridotheres tristis*, Linnaeus 1766). PhD thesis, Mention Zoologie et Biodiversité Animale, Université d'Antananarivo.

Randriamiharisoa, L. O., and Rakotomanana, H. 2019. Analysis of wetland uses by common mynas (*Acridotheres tristis*) in the urban environment of Antananarivo, Madagascar. *Madagascar Conservation and Development*. https://journalmcd.com/index.php/mcd/article/view/600/586.

Randriamiharisoa, L. O., Rakotondravony, D., Raherilalao, M. J., Ranirison, A., Wilmé, L., and Ganzhorn, J. U. 2015. Effects of transhumance route on the richness and composition of bird communities in Tsimanampesotse National Park. *Madagascar Conservation and Development* 10: 110–115.

Randrianasolo, H. H. 1996. Présence de *Newtonia fanovanae*, dans la forêt de Vevembe (Vondrozo) et note sur l'avifaune de cette région. *Working Group on Birds in the Madagascar Region Newsletter* 6(1): 14–18.

Randrianjafiniasa, D. R. 2009. Biologie de la reproduction du baza Malagache *Aviceda madagascariensis* (Smith, 1834), Accipitridae, dans la Réserve Spéciale d'Ambatovay. Mémoire de DEA, Université d'Antananarivo.

Raolihanintrasina, S. E. 2021. Etude de la biologie et du régime alimentaire de l'oiseau invasif, *Passer domesticus* (PLOCEIDAE) dans la ville de Toamasina, Madagascar. Mémoire de Masters II, Université d'Antananarivo.

Rasamison, S. A., and Andrianarimisa, A. 2013. First breeding survey of the endemic Madagascar red fody *Foudia madagascariensis* and forest fody *Foudia omissa* at Ranomafana National Park, Madagascar. *Vertebrate Zoology* 63(2): 233–240.

Rasamison, S., Raveloson, B. A., Palfrey, R. H., and Martin, T. R. 2018. Records of Van Dam's vanga *Xenopirostris damii* in Marianaro forest, north-west Madagascar. *Bulletin of the British Ornithologists' Club* 138: 275–277.

Rasamoelina, D. 2001. Impact de la pêche sur la ressource piscicole et la population de pygargue de Madagascar, *Haliaeetus vociferoides*, dans le complexe de Manambolotmaty, Antsalova, Madagascar. *Ostrich*, supplement 15: 210–214.

Rasmussen, P., and Donsker, D. 2020. IOC World Bird List (version 10.1). doi:10.14344/IOC.ML.10.1.

Rasmussen, P. C., Schulenberg, T. S., Hawkins, F., and Voninavoko, R. 2000. Geographic variation in the Malagasy scops-owl (*Otus rutilus* auct.): The existence of an unrecognised species on Madagascar and the taxonomy of other Indian Ocean taxa. *Bulletin of the British Ornithologists' Club* 120: 75–102.

Rasolonjatovo, D. 2018. Etude de la taille de population, de distribution et de l'écologie d'aigle pêcheur de Madagascar *Haliaeetus vociferoides*, dans la partie occidentale de Madagascar. Mémoire de DEA, Université de Toliara.

Rasolonjatovo, H.A.M., Muldoon, K. M., Ranivoharimanana, L., Rakotoarijaona, M., and Goodman, S. M. 2021. Subfossil birds from a submerged cave in southwestern Madagascar. *Malagasy Nature* 15: 128–140.

Rasoma, J., and Goodman, S. M. 2007. Food habits of the barn owl (*Tyto alba*) in spiny bush habitat of arid southwestern Madagascar. *Journal of Arid Environments* 69: 537–543.

Ratsaralasy, M. A. 2015. New information on the nest and eggs of long-billed tetraka *Bernieria madagascariensis*. *Bulletin of the African Bird Club* 22: 209–210.

Raveloson, L. 2017. Etude biologique et écologique de faucon à ventre raye *Falco zoniventris* (Peters, 1854) dans l'aire protégée (AP) complexe Tsimembo-Manambolomaty, centre ouest de Madagascar. Mémoire de DEA, Université d'Antananarivo.

Ravokatra, M., Wilmé, L., and Goodman, S. M. 2003. Bird weights. In *The Natural History of Madagascar*, eds. S. M. Goodman and J. P. Benstead, pp. 1059–1063. Chicago: University of Chicago Press.

Raxworthy, C. J., and Colston, P. R. 1992. Conclusive evidence for the continuing existence of the Madagascar serpent-eagle *Eutriorchis astur*. *Bulletin of the British Ornithologists' Club* 112: 108–111.

Razafimanjato, G., Rene de Roland, L.-A., Rabearivony, J., and Thorstrom, R. 2007. Nesting biology and food habits of the peregrine falcon *Falco peregrinus radama* in the south-west and central plateau of Madagascar. *Ostrich* 78: 7–12.

Razafimanjato, G., Sam, T. S., Rakotondratsima, M., Rene de Roland, L.-A., and Thorstrom, R. 2014. Population status of the Madagascar fish eagle *Haliaeetus vociferoides* in 2005–2006. *Bird Conservation International* 24(1): 88–99.

Razafimanjato, G., Razafimahatratra, B., Randrianjafiniasa, D., and Andriamalala, T. 2015. Suivi de la communauté aviaire aquatique dans la Nouvelle Aire Protégée Mandrozo, ouest de Madagascar. *Malagasy Nature* 9: 49–57.

Razafimanjato, G., Razafimahatratra, M., and Rene de Roland, L.-A. 2020. First sighting of the house crow *Corvus splendens* on Nosy Be. *Malagasy Nature* 14: 84–85.

Razafindraibe, H., Mobegi, V. A., Ommeh, S. C., Rakotondravao, M. L., Bjørnstad, G., Hanotte, O., and Jianlinb, H. 2008. Mitochondrial DNA origin of indigenous Malagasy chicken: Implication for a functional polymorphism at the *Mx* gene. *Annals of the New York Academy of Science* 1149: 77–79.

Razafindrajao, F. 2020. Etat des zones humides de haut plateau et de l'ouest et conservation des trois espèces d'Anatidae endémiques: *Aythya innotata* (Salvadori, 1894), *Anas bernieri* Hartlaub, 1860 et *Anas melleri*, Sclater, 1864. PhD thesis, Ecole des Sciences de la Vie et de l'Environnement, Université d'Antananarivo.

Razafindrajao, F., Young, H. G., and Bin Aboudou, I. A. 2012. Measurements and movements of Madagascar teal *Anas bernieri* captured and ringed at Lake Antsamaka in central-western Madagascar. *Wildfowl* 62: 165–175.

Razafindrajao, F., Bamford, A. J., Young, H. G., Andrianarimisa, A., Bin Aboudou, A. I., and Lewis, R. E. 2017. Reassessing the conservation outlook for Madagascar's endemic Anatidae following the creation of new protected areas. *Wildfowl* 67: 72–86.

Razafindramanana, S. 1995. Contribution à l'étude de la biologie de *Haliaeetus vociferoides*: Reproduction et domaine vital. Mémoire de DEA, Université d'Antananarivo.

Razafindratsita, V. R. 1995. Etude biologique et écologique de *Philepitta castanea* (Muller 1776): Son rôle dans la régénération du sous-bois forestier du Parc National de Ranomafana. Mémoire de DEA, Université d'Antananarivo.

Razafindratsita, V. R., and Zack, S. 2009. Frugivory and facilitation of seed germination by the velvet asity, *Philepitta castanea* (Müller, 1776), in the rainforest understory of Ranomafana National Park, Madagascar. *Malagasy Nature* 2:154–159.

Razakaratrimo, S.J.V. 2013. Contribution à l'étude des milans des chauves-souris *Macheiramphus alcinus anderssoni* (Gurney, 1866), famille des Accipitridae: Biologie, écologies. Mémoire de DEA, Université d'Antananarivo.

———. 2020. Population, biologie de la reproduction, écologie et conservation du milan des chauves-souris *Macheiramphus alcinus anderssoni* (Gurney, 1866), dans l'ouest de Madagascar. PhD thesis, Université d'Antananarivo.

Razakaratrimo, S., Goodman, S. M., Rene de Roland, L.-A., and Andrianarimisa, A. 2019. Caractéristiques de régime alimentaire du milan des chauves-souris *Macheiramphus alcinus* (Gurney, 1866) dans l'aire protégée de Mandrozo (ouest de Madagascar). *Bulletin de la Société Zoologique de France* 144: 107–119.

Razarazafy, D. 2015. Biologie de la reproduction de polyboroide rayé: *Polyboroides radiatus* (Scopoli, 1876), dans la Nouvelle Aire Protégée (N.A.P.) de Bemanevika (Bealanana). Mémoire de DEA, Université de Toliara.

Razarazafy, D., Rene de Roland, L.-A., Rakotondratsima, M., and Razafimanjato, G. 2019. Succès de la reproduction et comportements de polyboroide rayé (*Polyboroides radiatus*) dans l'Aire Protégée de Bemanevika, nord-ouest de Madagascar. *Malagasy Nature* 13: 97–104.

Reddy, S., Driskell, A. C., Rabosky, D. L., Hackett, S. J., and Schulenberg, T. S. 2012. Diversification and the adaptive radiation of the vangas of Madagascar. *Proceedings of the Royal Society of London B: Biological Sciences* 279: 2062–2071.

Reddy, S., Kimball, R. T., Pandey, A., Hosner, P. A., Braun, M. J., et al. 2017. Why do phylogenomic data sets yield conflicting trees? Data type influences the avian tree of life more than taxon sampling. *Systematic Biology* 66: 857–879.

Remsen, J. V., Jr., and Robinson, S. K. 1990. A classification scheme for foraging behavior of birds in terrestrial habitats. In *Avian Foraging: Theory, Methodology, and Applications*, eds. M. L. Morrison, C. J. Ralph, J. Verner, and J. R. Jehl Jr. *Studies in Avian Biology* 13: 144–160.

Rene de Roland, L.-A. 1996. Note sur la reproduction de l'oxylabe à gorge blanche *Oxylabes madagascariensis* sur la Presqu'ile Masoala. *Working Group on Birds in the Madagascar Region Newsletter* 6(2): 7.

———. 2000a. Breeding biology of Frances's sparrowhawk *Accipiter francesii* in a lowland rainforest of northeastern Madagascar. *Ostrich* 71: 332–335.

———. 2000b. Contribution à l'étude biologique, écologique et éthologique de trois espèces d'*Accipiter* dans la presqu'île de Masoala. Thèse de Doctorat de 3ème Cycle, Département de Biologie Animale, Université d'Antananarivo.

———. 2000c. Breeding biology of Henst's goshawk *Accipiter henstii* on Masoala Peninsula, northeastern Madagascar. In *Raptors at Risk*, eds. R. D. Chancellor and B.-U. Meyburg, pp. 107–112. Berlin: World Working Group on Birds of Prey.

———. 2004. Observations on nest building and courtship behavior of the Madagascar flufftail *Sarothrura insularis*. *Bulletin of the African Bird Club* 11: 42–43.

———. 2010. Madagascar buzzard (*Buteo brachypterus*) nest in association with the colonial-nesting Sakalava weaver (*Ploceus sakalava*). *Malagasy Nature* 4: 65–66.

———. 2013a. Madagascar serpent eagle *Eutriorchis astur*. In *The Birds of Africa*. Vol. 8, *The Malagasy Region*, eds. R. J. Safford and A.F.A. Hawkins, pp. 274–277. London: Christopher Helm.

———. 2013b. Madagascar cuckoo-hawk *Aviceda madagascariensis*. In *The Birds of Africa*. Vol. 8, *The Malagasy Region*, eds. R. J. Safford and A.F.A. Hawkins, pp. 263–265. London: Christopher Helm.

Rene de Roland, L.-A., and Thorstrom, R. 2003. *Accipiter* spp. goshawk and sparrowhawks. In *The Natural History of Madagascar*, eds. S. M. Goodman and J. P. Benstead, pp. 1091–1094. Chicago: University of Chicago Press.

Rene de Roland, L.-A., Thorstrom, R. T., and Watson, R. T. 1996. Breeding records and nestling predation of Henst's goshawks on Masoala Peninsula, Madagascar. *Ostrich* 67: 168–170.

Rene de Roland, L.-A., Rabearivony, J., Randramanga, I., and Thorstrom, R. 2004. Nesting biology and diet of the Madagascar harrier (*Circus macrosceles*) in Ambohitantely Special Reserve, Madagascar. *Journal of Raptor Research* 38: 256–262.

Rene de Roland, L.-A., Rabearivony, J., Robenarimangason, H., Razafimanjato, G., and Thorstrom, R. 2005a. Breeding biology and food habits of the Madagascar kestrel (*Falco newtoni*) in northeastern Madagascar. *Journal of Raptor Research* 39: 149–155.

Rene de Roland, L.-A., Rabearivony, J., Razafimanjato, G., Robenarimangason, H., and Thorstrom, R. 2005b. Breeding biology and diet of banded kestrels *Falco zoniventris* on Masoala Peninsula, Madagascar. *Ostrich* 78: 32–36.

Rene de Roland, L.-A., Sam, T. S., Rakotondratsima, M.P.H., and Thorstrom, R. 2007. Rediscovery of the Madagascar pochard *Aythya innotata* in northern Madagascar. *Bulletin of the African Bird Club* 14: 171–174.

Rene de Roland, L.-A., Thorstrom, R., Razafimanjato, G., Rakotondratsima, M.P.H., Andriamalala, T.R.A., and Sam, T. S. 2009. Surveys, distribution and current status of Madagascar harrier *Circus macrosceles* in Madagascar. *Bird Conservation International* 19: 1–14.

Renoult, J.-P. 2009. The sooty gull, *Larus hemprichii* (Aves: Laridae), on Nosy Ve: First records for Madagascar. *Malagasy Nature* 2: 174–176.

Reuter, K. E., Clarke, T. A., LaFleur, M., Rodriguez, L., Hanitriniaina, S., and Schaefer, M. S. 2017. Trade of parrots in urban areas of Madagascar. *Madagascar Conservation and Development* 12: 41–48.

Reuter, K. E., Rodriguez, L., Hanitriniaina, S., and Schaefer, M. S. 2019. Ownership of parrots in Madagascar: Extent and conservation implications. *Oryx* 53: 582–588. Rix, C. E., Woods-Ballard, A. J., and Fanning, E. 2003. Monitoring of the red-tailed tropicbird (*Phaethon rubricauda*) population, Nosy Vé. *Frontier Madagascar Environmental Research Report* 10: 1–10.

Robenarimangason, H. 1999. Contribution à l'étude biologique, écologique, et éthologique de la famille de Falconidae, faucon de Newton, *Falco newtoni*, et

faucon à ventre raye, *F. zoniventris*, dans la partie occidentale de la presqu'île Masoala. Mémoire de DEA, Université d'Antananarivo.

Rocamora, G., and Henriette, E. 2015. (Indian) house crow. In *Invasive Alien Species in the Seychelles: Why and How to Eliminate Them? Identification and Management of Priority Species*, eds. G. Rocamora and E. Henriette, pp. 270–272. Mèze: Biotope.

Rocha, R., Virtanen, T., and Cabeza, M. 2015. Bird assemblages in a Malagasy forest-agricultural frontier: Effects of habitat structure and forest cover. *Tropical Conservation Science* 8: 681–710.

Roux, F., and Bejoma, B. 2009. Les populations d'oiseaux aquatiques en périphérie d'une ferme de crevetticulture (OSO Farming). *Malagasy Nature* 2: 94–110.

Roy, P. 1998. Isolation of Newcastle Disease Virus from an Indian house crow. *Tropical Animal Health and Production* 30(3): 177–178.

Ruempler, U., and Ruempler, G. 1996. Im Lande der Lemuren und Chamäleons. *Zeitschrift des Kölner Zoo* 39 (3): 87–123.

Rush, C., and Hoddinott, D. 2014. First records of buff-breasted sandpiper *Calidris subruficollis* and red-necked phalarope *Phalaropus lobatus* for Madagascar. *Bulletin of the African Bird Club* 21: 224–226.

Ryall, C. 1992. Predation and harassment of native bird species by the Indian house crow *Corvus splendens* in Mombasa, Kenya. *Scopus* 16(1): 1–8.

Safford, R. J. 1993. The Madagascar teal *Anas bernieri*: A preliminary survey from Antsalova to Morondava. *Dodo* 29: 95–102.

———. 2000. *An Environmental and Ecological Study of Lac Sahaka, Madagascar.* Egham: Royal Holloway University of London.

———. 2013a. Genus *Nesoenas*. In *The Birds of Africa*. Vol. 8, *The Malagasy Region*, eds. R. J. Safford and A.F.A. Hawkins, p. 484. London: Christopher Helm.

———. 2013b. Namaqua dove *Oena capensis*. In *The Birds of Africa*. Vol. 8, *The Malagasy Region*, eds. R. J. Safford and A.F.A. Hawkins, pp. 500–502. London: Christopher Helm.

———. 2013c. Cuckoo-roller *Leptosomus discolor*. In *The Birds of Africa*. Vol. 8, *The Malagasy Region*, eds. R. J. Safford and A.F.A. Hawkins, pp. 627–631. London: Christopher Helm.

———. 2013d. Zebra dove *Geopelia striata*. In *The Birds of Africa*. Vol. 8, *The Malagasy Region*, eds. R. J. Safford and A.F.A. Hawkins, pp. 502–504. London: Christopher Helm.

———. 2013e. House sparrow *Passer domesticus*. In *The Birds of Africa*. Vol. 8, *The Malagasy Region*, eds. R. J. Safford and A.F.A. Hawkins, pp. 863–865. London: Christopher Helm.

———. 2013f. Common waxbill *Estrilda astrild*. In *The Birds of Africa*. Vol. 8, *The Malagasy Region*, eds. R. J. Safford and A.F.A. Hawkins, pp. 899–901. London: Christopher Helm.

———. 2013g. Madagascar buttonquail *Turnix nigricollis*. In *The Birds of Africa*. Vol. 8, *The Malagasy Region*, eds. R. J. Safford and A.F.A. Hawkins, pp. 345–348. London: Christopher Helm.

———. 2013h. Genus *Pachycoccyx* and genus *Cuculus*. In *The Birds of Africa*. Vol. 8, *The Malagasy Region*, eds. R. J. Safford and A.F.A. Hawkins, pp. 557–562. London: Christopher Helm.

———. 2013i. Order Podicipediformes. In *The Birds of Africa*. Vol. 8, *The Malagasy Region*, eds. R. J. Safford and A.F.A. Hawkins, pp. 108–114. London: Christopher Helm.

———. 2013j. Order Phoenicopteriformes. In *The Birds of Africa*. Vol. 8, *The Malagasy Region*, eds. R. J. Safford and A.F.A. Hawkins, pp. 234–238. London: Christopher Helm.

———. 2013k. Madagascar pratincole *Glareola ocularis*. In *The Birds of Africa*. Vol. 8, *The Malagasy Region*, eds. R. J. Safford and A.F.A. Hawkins, pp. 387–389. London: Christopher Helm.

———. 2013l. Common ringed plover *Charadrius hiaticula*, lesser sand plover *Charadrius mongolus*, greater sand plover *Charadrius leschenaultii*. In *The Birds of Africa*. Vol. 8, *The Malagasy Region*, eds. R. J. Safford and A.F.A. Hawkins, pp. 393–394, 403–406. London: Christopher Helm.

———. 2013m. Wedge-tailed shearwater *Puffinus pacificus*. In *The Birds of Africa*. Vol. 8, *The Malagasy Region*, eds. R. J. Safford and A.F.A. Hawkins, pp. 129–133. London: Christopher Helm.

———. 2013n. Kelp gull *Larus dominicanus*. In *The Birds of Africa*. Vol. 8, *The Malagasy Region*, eds. R. J. Safford and A.F.A. Hawkins, pp. 439–441. London: Christopher Helm.

———. 2013o. Family Mesitornithidae, mesites. In *The Birds of Africa*. Vol. 8, *The Malagasy Region*, eds. R. J. Safford and A.F.A. Hawkins, p. 337. London: Christopher Helm.

———. 2013p. Genus *Sarothrura*, Madagascar flufftail *Sarothrura insularis*, slender-billed flufftail *Sarothrura watersi*. In *The Birds of Africa*. Vol. 8, *The Malagasy Region*, eds. R. J. Safford and A.F.A. Hawkins, pp. 349–352. London: Christopher Helm.

———. 2013q. Madagascar jacana *Actophilornis albinucha*. In *The Birds of Africa*. Vol. 8, *The Malagasy Region*, eds. R. J. Safford and A.F.A. Hawkins, pp. 376–378. London: Christopher Helm.

———. 2013r. House crow *Corvus splendens*. In *The Birds of Africa*. Vol. 8, *The Malagasy Region*, eds. R. J. Safford and A.F.A. Hawkins, pp. 851–853. London: Christopher Helm.

———. 2013s. Nelicourvi weaver *Ploceus nelicourvi*. In *The Birds of Africa*. Vol. 8, *The Malagasy Region*, eds. R. J. Safford and A.F.A. Hawkins, pp. 868–871. London: Christopher Helm.

———. 2013t. Madagascar fody *Foudia madagascariensis*. In *The Birds of Africa*. Vol. 8, *The Malagasy Region*, eds. R. J. Safford and A.F.A. Hawkins, pp. 892–896. London: Christopher Helm.

———. 2013u. Forest fody *Foudia omissa*. In *The Birds of Africa*. Vol. 8, *The Malagasy Region*, eds. R. J. Safford and A.F.A. Hawkins, pp. 896–898. London: Christopher Helm.

Safford, R. J., and Duckworth, J. W., eds. 1990. *A Wildlife Survey of Marojejy Reserve, Madagascar*. ICBP Study Report No. 40. Cambridge, UK: International Council for Bird Preservation.

Safford, R. J., and Hawkins, A.F.A., eds. 2013. *The Birds of Africa*. Vol. 8, *The Malagasy Region*. London: Christopher Helm.

Salomonsen, F. 1933a. Les gobe-mouches de paradis de la région malgache. *L'Oiseau et la Revue Française d'Ornithologie* 3: 603–614.

———. 1933b. Remarks upon the Madagascar paradise flycatchers. *Bulletin of the British Ornithologists' Club* 53: 119–124.

———. 1934a. Revision of the Madagascar timaliine birds. *Annals and Magazine of Natural History*, 10th series, 14: 60–79.

———. 1934b. Four new birds and a new genus from Madagascar. *Ibis* (13)4: 382–390.

———. 1934c. Les *Neodrepanis*, genre particular de souimangas malgaches. *L'Oiseaux et la Revue Française d'Ornithologie* 4: 1–9.

———. 1965. Notes on the sunbird-asitys (*Neodrepanis*). *L'Oiseaux et la Revue Française d'Ornithologie* 35 (numéro speciale): 103–111.

Salter, J. F., Oliveros, C. H., Hosner, P. A., Manthey, J. D., Robbins, M. B., Moyle, R. G., Brumfield, R. T., and Faircloth, B. C. 2020. Extensive paraphyly in the typical owl family (Strigidae). *Auk* 137: 1–15.

Salvan, J. 1970. Remarques sur l'évolution de l'avifaune Malgache depuis 1945. *Alauda* 38: 191–203.

———. 1971. Une visite sur les ilots au sud de Tamatave (Madagascar). *Alauda* 34(3): 213–222.

———. 1972. Essai d'évaluation des densités d'oiseaux dans quelques biotopes malgaches. *Alauda* 2-1972: 163–170.

Sam, T. S. 2011. Etude bio-écologique et structural de la population de fuligule de Madagascar, *Aythya innotata* (Salvadori, 1894) dans le complexe lacustre de Bemanevika à Bealanana. Mémoire de DEA, Département de Biologie Animale, Université d'Antananarivo.

Samonds, K. E., Crowley, B. E., Rasolofomanana, T.R.N., Andriambelomanana, M. C., Andrianavalona, H. T., et al. 2019. A new late Pleistocene subfossil site (Tsaramody, Sambaina basin, central Madagascar) with implications for the chronology of habitat and megafaunal community change on Madagascar's Central Highlands. *Journal of Quaternary Science* 34(6): 379–392.

Sartain, A., and Hawkins, A.F.A. 2013a. Hamerkop *Scopus umbretta*. In *The Birds of Africa*. Vol. 8, *The Malagasy Region*, eds. R. J. Safford and A.F.A. Hawkins, pp. 218–220. London: Christopher Helm.

———. 2013b. Little egret *Egretta garzetta*. In *The Birds of Africa*. Vol. 8, *The Malagasy Region*, eds. R. J. Safford and A.F.A. Hawkins, pp. 202–204. London: Christopher Helm.

———. 2013c. Squacco heron *Ardeola ralloides*. In *The Birds of Africa*. Vol. 8, *The Malagasy Region*, eds. R. J. Safford and A.F.A. Hawkins, pp. 205–206. London: Christopher Helm.

Sauer, E.G.F. 1972. Ratite eggshells and phylogenetic questions. *Bonner zoologische Beiträge* 23: 3–48.

Savage, A. F. 2004. Hematozoa of the avian family Philepittidae (the asities and sunbird asities). *Journal of Parasitology* 90: 1473–1474.

Savage, A. F., Robert, V., Goodman, S. M., Raharimanga, V., Raherilalao, M. J., Andrianarimisa, A., Ariey, F., and Greiner, E. C. 2009. Blood parasites in birds from Madagascar. *Journal of Wildlife Diseases* 45: 907–920.

Schemske, D. W., and Brokaw, N. 1981. Treefalls and the distribution of understory birds in a tropical forest. *Ecology* 62: 938–945.
Schlegel, H. 1866. Contributions à la faune de Madagascar et des iles avoisinantes, d'après les découvertes d'observations de M. M. François Pollen et M.D.C. van Dam. *Nederlandsch Tijdschrift voor de Dierkunde* 3: 73–89.
Schlegel, H., and Pollen, F.P.L. 1868. Mammifères et oiseaux. In *Recherches sur la faune de Madagascar et de ses dépendances, d'après les découvertes de F.P.L. Pollen et D. C. van Dam*. Pt. 2. Leiden: E. J. Brill.
Schmid, S., Dinkel, A., Mackenstedt, U., Tantely, M. D., Randrianambinintsoa, F. J., Boyer, S., and Woog, F. 2017. Avian malaria on Madagascar: Bird hosts and putative vector mosquitoes of different *Plasmodium* lineages. *Parasites and Vectors* 10: 6. doi:10.1186/s13071-016-1939-x.
Schodde, R., Kirwan, G. M., and Porter, R. F. 2012. Morphological differentiation and speciation among darters (*Anhinga*). *Bulletin of the British Ornithologists' Club* 132: 283–294.
Schönwetter, M. 1960–1962. *Handbuch der Oologie*. Berlin: Akademie-Verlag.
Schulenberg, T. S. 1991. On the songs of *Oxylabes madagascariensis*. *Working Group on Birds in the Madagascar Region Newsletter* 1: 6–7.
———. 1995. Evolutionary history of the vangas (Vangidae) of Madagascar. PhD thesis, University of Chicago.
Schulenberg, T. S., Hawkins, A.F.A., Sartain, A., and Safford, R. J. 2013. Family Vangidae: Vangas. In *The Birds of Africa*. Vol. 8, *The Malagasy Region*, eds. R. Safford and A.F.A. Hawkins, pp. 802–841. London: Christopher Helm.
Scott, D., and Lubbock, J. 1974. Preliminary observations on waterfowl in western Madagascar. *Wildfowl* 25: 117–120.
Scott, D. M., Brown, D., Mahood, S., Denton, B., Silburn, A., and Rakotondraparany, F. 2006. The impacts of forest clearance on lizard, small mammal and bird communities in the arid spiny forest, southern Madagascar. *Biological Conservation* 127: 72–87.
Scott, P. 1947. The waterfowl registry. *Avicultural Magazine* 53(1): 30–34.
Seddon, N. 2001. The ecology, communication and conservation of the subdesert mesite *Monias benschi*. PhD thesis, University of Cambridge.
———. 2002. The structure, context and possible functions of solos, duets and choruses in the subdesert mesite (*Monias benschi*). *Behaviour* 139: 645–676.
Seddon, N., and Tobias, J. A. 2003. Communal singing in the cooperatively breeding subdesert mesite *Monias benschi*: Evidence of numerical assessment? *Journal of Avian Biology* 34: 72–80.
———. 2007. Population size and habitat associations of the long-tailed ground-roller *Uratelornis chimaera*. *Bird Conservation International* 17: 1–12.
Seddon, N., Tobias, J. A., Yount, J. W., Ramanampamonjy, J. R., Butchart, S.H.M., and Randrianizahana, H. 2000. Conservation issues and priorities in the Mikea Forest of south-west Madagascar. *Oryx* 34: 287–304.
Seddon, N., Tobias, J. A., and Butchart, S.H.M. 2003. Group living, breeding behavior and territoriality in the subdesert mesite *Monias benschi*. *Ibis* 145: 277–294.
Seddon, N., Amos, W., Adcock, G., Johnson, K., Kraaijeveld, K., Kraaijeveld-Smit, F.J.L., Lee, W., Senapathi, G. D., Mulder, R. A., and Tobias, J. A. 2005. Mating system, philopatry and patterns of kinship in the cooperatively breeding subdesert mesite *Monias benschi*. *Molecular Ecology* 14: 3573–3583.
Sganzin, V. 1840. Notes sur les mammifères et sur l'ornithologie de l'île de Madagascar (1831 et 1932). *Mémoires de la Société du Muséum d'Histoire Naturelle de Strasbourg* 3: 1–49.
Shapiro, B., Sibthorpe, D., Rambaut, A., Austin, J., Wragg, G. M., Bininda-Emonds, O.R.P., Lee, P.L.M., and Cooper, A. 2002. Flight of the dodo. *Science* 295: 1683.
Sharpe, R. B. 1881. On a new genus of Timaliidae from Madagascar, with remarks on some other genera. *Proceedings of the Biological Society of London B: Biological Sciences* 49: 195–197.
Sheldon, B. C., and Duckworth, J. W. 1990. Rediscovery of the Madagascar serpent-eagle *Eutriorchis astur*. *Bulletin of the British Ornithologists' Club* 110: 126–130.
Sheldon, F. H., Whittingham, L. A., Moyle, R. G., Slikas, B., and Winkler, D. W. 2005. Phylogeny of swallows (Aves: Hirundinidae) estimated from nuclear and mitochondrial DNA sequences. *Molecular Phylogenetics and Evolution* 35: 254–270.
Sheldon, F. H., Lohman, D. J., Lim, H. C., Zou, F., Goodman, S. M., Prawiradilaga, D. M., Winker, K., Braile, T. M., and Moyle, R. G. 2009. Phylogeography of the magpie-robin species complex (Aves: Turdidae: *Copsychus*) reveals a Philippine species, an interesting isolating barrier and unusual dispersal patterns in the Indian Ocean and Southeast Asia. *Journal of Biogeography* 36: 1070–1083.
Sibley, C. G., and Ahlquist, J. E. 1990. *Phylogeny and Classification of Birds*. New Haven: Yale University Press.
Sibley, C. G., and Monroe, B. L. 1990. *Distribution and Taxonomy of Birds of the World*. New Haven: Yale University Press.
Sinclair, I., and Langrand, O. 1998. *Birds of the Indian Ocean Islands*. Cape Town: Struik.
Sinclair, I., Langrand, O., and Andriamialisoa, F. 2006. *A Photographic Guide to the Birds of the Indian Ocean Islands: Madagascar, Mauritius, Seychelles, Reunion and the Comoros*. Cape Town: Struik.
Sivakumaran, M. S. 2018. Predation of Eurasian tree sparrow *Passer montanus* by house crow *Corvus splendens*. *BirdingASIA* 29: 102.
Skerrett, A. 1996. The first report of the Seychelles Bird Records Committee. *Bulletin of the African Bird Club* 3(1): 45–50.
———. 1999. Ferruginous duck *Aythya nyroca*: The first record for Seychelles. *Bulletin of the African Bird Club* 6: 148.
Skerrett, A., and Disley, T. 2011. *Birds of Seychelles*. London: Christopher Helm.
Skoracki, M., OConnor, B. M., Goodman, S. M., Marcinial, N., and Sikora, B. 2016. New species and records of syringophilid mites (Acariformes: Syringophilidae) associated with Malagasy birds. *Systematic and Applied Acarology* 21: 1534–1546.
Slotow, R. 1996. Black coucal *Centropus grillii* egg volume predicts their polyandrous mating system. *Journal of Avian Biology* 27: 171–173.
Snow, D. W. 1976. *The Web of Adaptation: Bird Studies in the American Tropics*. London: Collins.
———. 2004. Family Pipridae (manakins). In *Handbook of the Birds of the World*. Vol. 9, *Cotingas to Pipits and Wagtails*, eds. J. del Hoyo, A. Elliott, and D. A. Christie, pp. 110–169. Barcelona: Lynx Edicions.
Sorenson, M. D. 1991. The functional significance of parasitic egg laying and typical nesting in redhead ducks: An analysis of individual behaviour. *Animal Behaviour* 42: 771–796.
Sorenson, M. D., and Fleischer, R. C. 1996. Multiple independent transpositions of mitochondrial DNA control region sequences to the nucleus. *Proceedings of the National Academy of Sciences of the USA* 93: 15239–15243.
Sorenson, M. D., and Payne, R. B. 2005. A molecular genetic analysis of cuckoo phylogeny. In *The Cuckoos*, ed. R. B. Payne, pp. 68–94. Oxford: Oxford University Press.
Stafford, L., and Crouch, R. 2009. Feedback report of the house crow status assessment visit to Maputo and Inhaca, Mozambique. Unpublished report to InGrip-Consulting, Berlin, Germany.
Staub, F. 1976. *Birds of the Mascarenes and Saint Brandon*. Port Louis: Organization Normales des Entreprises.
Stresemann, E. 1925. Eine neue Vogelart aus Madagaskar: *Bernieria tenebrosa* sp. n. *Ornithologische Monatsberichte* 33: 150–151.
Suliman, A. S., Meier, G. G., and Haverson, P. J. 2010. Eradication of invasive house crow (*Corvus splendens*) from Socotra Island, Republic of Yemen: Lessons learned from 15 years of facing a bird invasion. *Proceedings of the Vertebrate Pest Conference* 24: 257–262. http://dx.doi.org/10.5070/V424110552.
Sylvestre, M. H. 2018. Etude de la structure de population et de la préférence en habitat de *Passer domesticus* et de *Foudia madagascariensis*, deux espèces d'oiseaux nuisibles dans la ville de Toamasina, Région Atsinanana. Mémoire pour l'obtention du Diplôme de Master, Institut Supérieur de Sciences, Environnement et Développement Durable, Université de Toamasina.
Tella, J. L. 2002. The evolutionary transition to coloniality promotes higher blood parasitism in birds. *Journal of Evolutionary Biology* 15: 32–41.
Temba, E. M., Cabeza, M., and Andrianarimisa, A. 2014. Breeding biology and reproductive success of the spectacled tetraka *Xanthomixis zosterops* (Bernieridae) in a rainforest of Madagascar. *Ostrich* 85: 119–123.
Terborgh, J. 1977. Bird species diversity on an Andean elevational gradient. *Ecology* 58: 1007–1019.
Thiers, L., Delord, K., Barbraud, C., Phillips, R., Pinaud, D., and Weimerskirch, H. 2014. Foraging zones of the two sibling species of giant petrels in the Indian Ocean throughout the annual cycle: Implication for their conservation. *Marine Ecology Progress Series* 499: 233–248.
Thompson, P. M., and Evans, M. I., eds. 1991. *A Survey of Ambatovaky Special Reserve, Madagascar*. London: Madagascar Environmental Research Group.
———. 1992. The threatened birds of Ambatovaky Special Reserve, Madagascar. *Bird Conservation International* 2: 221–237.
Thorstrom, R. 1999. A description of nests, diet and behaviour of the banded kestrel. *Ostrich* 70: 149–151.

Thorstrom, R., and La Marca, G. 2000. Nesting biology and behavior of the Madagascar harrier-hawk (*Polyboroides radiatus*) in northeastern Madagascar. *Journal of Raptor Research* 34: 120–125.

Thorstrom, R., and Lind, J. 1999. First nest description, breeding, ranging and foraging behaviour of the short-legged ground roller *Brachypteracias leptosomus* in Madagascar. *Ibis* 141: 569–576.

Thorstrom, R., and Rene de Roland, L.-A. 2000. First nest description, breeding behaviour and distribution of the Madagascar serpent-eagle *Eutriorchis astur*. *Ibis* 142: 217–224.

———. 2001. First nest descriptions, nesting biology and food habits for Bernier's vanga, *Oriolia bernieri*, in Madagascar. *Ostrich* 72: 165–168.

Thorstrom, R., and Watson, R. T. 1997. Avian inventory and key species of the Masoala Peninsula, Madagascar. *Bird Conservation International* 7: 99–115.

Thorstrom, R., Damary, B., Toto, F., Baba, M., Baba, V., and Watson, R. T. 1995. Repeated sightings and first capture of a live Madagascar serpent-eagle *Eutriorchis astur* confirms the survival of this species. *Bulletin of the British Ornithologists' Club* 115: 40–45.

Tingay, R. E. 2000. Sex, lies and dominance: Paternity and behaviour of extra-pair Madagascar fish eagle *Haliaeetus vociferoides*. MSc thesis, University of Nottingham.

Tingay, R. E., and Gilbert, M. 1999. Annotated list of the birds of Lacs Soamalipo, Befotaka and Ankerika ("Three Lakes") and surrounding Tsimembo Forest, western Madagascar. *Working Group on Birds in the Madagascar Region Newsletter* 9(1): 26–30.

Tingay, R. E., Culver, M., Hallerman, E. M., Fraser, J. D., and Watson, R. T. 2002. Subordinate males sire offspring in Madagascar fish-eagle (*Haliaeetus vociferoides*) polyandrous breeding groups. *Journal of Raptor Research* 36: 280–286.

Tobias, J. A., and Seddon, N. 2002. Estimating population size in the subdesert mesite (*Monias benschi*): New methods and implications for conservation. *Biological Conservation* 108: 199–212.

———. 2003. Vocalizations and display in the long-tailed ground-roller (*Uratelornis chimaera*). *Wilson Bulletin* 115(2): 193–196.

Torres, C. R., and Clarke, J. A. 2018. Nocturnal giants: Evolution of the sensory ecology in elephant birds and other palaeognaths inferred from digital brain reconstructions. *Proceedings of the Royal Society of London B: Biological Sciences* 285: 20181540. http://dx.doi.org/10.1098/rspb.2018.1540.

Tovondrafale, T. 1994. Contribution à la connaissance des Aepyornithidae: Etude de leurs œufs dans deux gisements de l'extrême sud de Madagascar et discussion comparatives sur leur éco-éthologie et les causes de leur disparition. Mémoire DEA d'Anthropologie, Université d'Antananarivo.

Tree, A. J. 2005. The known history and movements of the roseate tern *Sterna dougallii* in South Africa and the western Indian Ocean. *Marine Ornithology* 33: 41–47.

Trudelle, L., Cerchio, S., Zerbini, A. N., Geyer, Y., Mayer, F.-X., et al. 2016. Influence of environmental parameters on movements and habitat utilization of humpback whales (*Megaptera novaeangliae*) in the Madagascar breeding ground. *Royal Society Open Science* 3: 160616.

Tsiebo, M.V.J. 2019. Analyse de la valorisation écotouristique de l'ilot de Nosy Vé, Anakao, region sud-ouest de Madagascar. Rapport de stage de Master Biodiversité et Ecosystèmes Tropicaux, deuxième année, Université de La Réunion.

Turčoková, L., Kocian, L., Kürth, A., and Balázs, C. 2012. [The response of males belonging to the European subspecies of hoopoe to the playback of song of their own and foreign subspecies (*U. e. marginata*)]. *Tichodroma* 24: 11–17 (in Slovak with English abstract).

Turner, D. A. 2010. The *Egretta garzetta* complex in East Africa: A case for one, two or three species. *Scopus* 30: 59–63.

Turner, D. A., and Dowsett, R. J. 1988. Additions and corrections to Afrotropical and Malagasy avifaunas. 1. Western Indian Ocean islands. *Tauraco* 1: 130–138.

Urano, E., Yamagishi, S., Andrianarimisa, A., and Andriatsarafara, S. 1994. Different habitat use among three sympatric species of couas *Coua cristata*, *C. coquereli* and *C. ruficeps* in western Madagascar. *Ibis* 136: 485–487.

Uva, V., Päckert, M., Cibois, A., Fumagalli, L., and Roulin, A. 2018. Comprehensive molecular phylogeny of barn owls and relatives (family: Tytonidae), and their six major Pleistocene radiations. *Molecular Phylogenetics and Evolution* 125: 127–137.

van Bemmelen, R., Moe, B., Hanssen, S. A., Schmidt, N. M., Hansen, J., et al. 2017. Flexibility in otherwise consistent non-breeding movements of a long-distance migratory seabird, the long-tailed skua. *Marine Ecology Progress Series* 578: 197–211.

van Dongen, W.F.D., and Mulder, R. A. 2006. Habitat density, song structure and dialects in the Madagascar paradise flycatcher *Terpsiphone mutata*. *Journal of Avian Biology* 37: 349–356.

Vieilledent, G., Grinand, C., Rakotomalala, F. A., Ranaivosoa, R., Rakotoarijaona, J.-R., Allnutt, T. F., and Achard, F. 2018. Combining global tree cover loss data with historical national forest-cover maps to look at six decades of deforestation and forest fragmentation in Madagascar. *Biological Conservation* 222: 189–197. https://doi.org/10.1016/j.biocon.2018.04.008.

Vincze, O., Székely, T., Küpper, C., Alrashidi, M., Amat, J. A., et al. 2013. Local environment but not genetic differentiation influences biparental care in ten plover populations. *PLoS One* 8: e60998.

Vincze, O., Kosztolány, A., Barta, Z., Küpper, C., Alrashidi, M., et al. 2017. Parental cooperation in a changing climate: Fluctuating environments predict shifts in care division. *Global Ecology and Biogeography* 26(3): 347–358.

Voelker, G. 2002. Systematics and historical biogeography of wagtails: Dispersal versus vicariance revisited. *Condor* 104: 725–739.

Voous, K. H., and Payne, H.A.W. 1965. The grebes of Madagascar. *Ardea* 53: 36–39.

Walter, H. 1979. *Eleonora's Falcon: Adaptations to Prey and Habitat in a Social Raptor*. Chicago: University of Chicago Press.

Wang, M., Thakur, M., Peng, M., Jiang, Y., Frantz, L., et al. 2020. 863 genomes reveal the origin and domestication of chicken. *Cell Research* 30: 693–701.

Wanless, R. M. 2003. Flightless Aldabra rail (*Dryolimnas cuvieri aldabranus*) kills black rat (*Rattus rattus*). *Ostrich* 74: 134.

Wanless, R. M., and Safford, R. J. 2013. White-throated rail *Dryolimnas cuvieri*. In *The Birds of Africa*. Vol. 8, *The Malagasy Region*, eds. R. J. Safford and A.F.A. Hawkins, pp. 358–363. London: Christopher Helm.

Warren, B. H., Bermingham, E., Bowie, R.C.K., Prŷs-Jones, R. P., and Thébaud, C. 2003. Molecular phylogeography reveals island colonization history and diversification of western Indian Ocean sunbirds (*Nectarinia*: Nectariniidae). *Molecular Phylogenetics and Evolution* 29: 67–85.

Warren, B. H., Bermingham, E., Prŷs-Jones, R. P., and Thébaud, C. 2005. Tracking island colonization history and phenotypic shifts in Indian Ocean bulbuls (*Hypsipetes*: Pycnonotidae). *Biological Journal of the Linnean Society* 85: 271–287.

———. 2006. Immigration, species radiation and extinction in a highly diverse songbird lineage: White-eyes on Indian Ocean islands. *Molecular Ecology* 15: 3769–3786.

Warren, B. H., Strasberg, D., Bruggemann, J., Prŷs-Jones, R., and Thébaud, C. 2010. Why does the biota of the Madagascar region have such a strong Asiatic flavour? *Cladistics* 26: 526–538.

Warren, B. H., Bermingham, E., Bourgeois, Y., Estep, L. K., Prŷs-Jones, R. P., Strasberg, D., and Thébaud, C. 2012. Hybridization and barriers to gene flow in an island bird radiation. *Evolution* 66: 1490–1505.

Watson, G. E., Traylor, M. A., Jr., and Mayr, E. 1986. Family Sylviidae, Old World warblers. In *Check-List of Birds of the World*, vol. 11, eds. E. Mayr and G. W. Cottrell., pp. 3–294. Cambridge, MA: Museum of Comparative Zoology.

Watson, J.E.M., Whittaker, R. J., and Dawson, T. P. 2004a. Avifaunal responses to habitat fragmentation in the threatened littoral forests of south-eastern Madagascar. *Journal of Biogeography* 31: 1791–1807.

———. 2004b. Habitat structure and proximity to forest edge affect the abundance and distribution of forest-dependent birds in tropical coastal forests of southeastern Madagascar. *Biological Conservation* 120: 311–327.

Watson, R. T., and Rabarisoa, R. 2000. Sakalava fishermen and Madagascar fish eagles: Enhancing traditional conservation rules to control resource abuse that threatens a key breeding area for an endangered eagle. *Ostrich* 71: 2–10.

Watson, R. T., and Razafindramanana, S. 1999. Nearest neighbor nest distances, home range and territory area of the Madagascar fish-eagle (*Haliaeetus vociferoides*). *Journal of Raptor Research* 33: 335–338.

Watson, R. T., Berkelman, J., Lewis, R., and Razafindramanana, S. 1993. Conservation studies on the Madagascar fish eagle *Haliaeetus vociferoides*. In *Proceedings of the Eighth Pan-African Ornithological Congress*, ed. R. T. Wilson, pp. 192–196. Tervuren: Musée Royal de l'Afrique Centrale.

Watson, R. T., Thomsett, S., O'Daniel, D., and Lewis, R. 1996. Breeding, growth, development, and management of the Madagascar fish-eagle (*Haliaeetus vociferoides*). *Journal of Raptor Research* 30: 21–27.

Watson, R. T., Razafindramanana, S., Thorstrom, R., and Rafanomezantsoa, S. 1999. Breeding biology, extra-pair birds, productivity, siblicide and conservation of the Madagascar fish eagle. *Ostrich* 70: 105–111.

Watson, R. T., Berkelman, J., Rabarisoa, R., Thorstrom, R., and Watson, C.R.B. 2000a. Description of nesting and foraging habitat of the Madagascar fish-eagle *Haliaeetus vociferoides*: A conservation initiative. *Ostrich* 71: 336–340.

Watson, R. T., Andrianarimisa, A., Razandrizanakanirina, D., and Kalavah, L. 2000b. Madagascar fish-eagle *Haliaeetus vociferoides* and community-based wetland

conservation. In *Raptors at Risk*, eds. R. D. Chancellor and B.-U. Meyburg, pp. 333–342. Berlin: World Working Group on Birds of Prey and Hancock House.

Webb, C. S. 1936. Collecting waterfowl in Madagascar. *Avicultural Magazine* 5(1): 36–39.

Weimerskirch, H., Tarroux, A., Chastel, O., Delord, K., Cherel, Y., and Descamps, S. 2015. Population-specific wintering distribution of adult south polar skuas over three oceans. *Marine Ecology Progress Series* 538: 229–237.

Weimerskirch, H., Borsa, P., Cruz, S., de Grissac, S., Gardes, L., Lallemand, J., Le Corre, M., and Prudor, A. 2017. Diversity of migration strategies among great frigatebirds populations. *Journal of Avian Biology* 48: 103–113.

Wells, N. A. 2003. Some hypotheses on the Mesozoic and Cenozoic paleoenvironmental history of Madagascar. In *The Natural History of Madagascar*, eds. S. M. Goodman and J. P. Benstead, pp. 16–34. Chicago: University of Chicago Press.

Wetlands International. 2006. *Waterbird Population Estimates*. 4th ed. Wageningen: Wetlands International.

Wilkinson, R. 1990. Notes on the breeding and behaviour of greater vasa parrots *Coracopsis vasa* at Chester Zoo. *Avicultural Magazine* 96: 115–122.

Wilkinson, R., and Birkhead, T. R. 1995. Copulation behaviour in the vasa parrots *Coracopsis vasa* and *C. nigra*. *Ibis* 137: 117–119.

Wilmé, L. 1993. A recent record of the Madagascar pochard *Aythya innotata* in Lake Alaotra, Madagascar. *Bulletin of the British Ornithologists' Club* 113: 188–189.

———. 1994. Status, distribution and conservation of two Madagascar bird species endemic to Lake Alaotra: Delacour's grebe *Tachybaptus rufolavatus* and Madagascar pochard *Aythya innotata*. *Biological Conservation* 69: 15–21.

———. 1996. Composition and characteristics of bird communities in Madagascar. In *Biogéographie de Madagascar*, ed. W. R. Lourenço, pp. 349–362. Paris: Editions de l'ORSTOM.

Wilmé, L., and Goodman, S. M. 2003. Biogeography, guild scructure, and elevational variation in Madagascar forest birds. In *The Natural History of Madagascar*, eds. S. M. Goodman and J. P. Benstead, pp. 1045–1058. Chicago: University of Chicago Press.

Wilmé, L., and Langrand, O. 1990. Rediscovery of slender-billed flufftail *Sarothrura watersi* (Bartlett, 1879), and notes on the genus *Sarothrura* in Madagascar. *Biological Conservation* 51: 211–223.

Wiman, C. 1935. Über Aepyornithes. *Nova Acta Regiae Societatis Scientiarum Upsaliensis*, series 4, 9, no. 12.

Wink, M. 2008. Taxonomy and genetics: Phylogenetic and phylogeographic relationships. In *The Little Owl: Conservation, Ecology and Behaviour of* Athene noctua, eds. D. van Nieuwenhuyse, J.-C. Génot, and D. H. Johnson, pp. 38–44. Cambridge, UK: Cambridge University Press.

Wink, M., and Sauer-Gürth, H. 2000. Advances in molecular systematics of African raptors. In *Raptors at Risk*, eds. R. D. Chancellor and B.-U. Meyberg, pp. 135–147. Surrey: Hancock House.

Winkler, H., and Christie, D. A. 2002. Family Picidae (woodpeckers). In *Handbook of the Birds of the World*, vol. 7, eds. J. del Hoyo, A. Elliott, and J. Sargatal, pp. 296–555. Barcelona: Lynx Edicions.

Woog, F., Ramanitra, N., and Andrianarivelosoa, S. R. 2006. Effects of deforestation on eastern Malagasy bird communities. In *Proceedings of the German-Malagasy Research Cooperation in Life and Earth Sciences*, eds. C. Schwitzer, S. Brandt, O. Ramilijaona, M. Rakotomalala Razanahoera, D. Ackermand, T. Razakamanana, and J. U. Ganzhorn, pp. 203–214. Berlin: Concept Verlag.

Woog, F., Wink, M., Rastegar-Pouyani, E., Gonzalez, J., and Helm, B. 2008. Distinct taxonomic position of the Madagascar stonechat (*Saxicola torquatus sibilla*) revealed by nucleotide sequences of mitochondrial DNA. *Journal of Ornithology* 149: 423–430.

Woog, F., Ramanitra, N., Rasamison, A. S., and Tahiry, R. L. 2018. Longevity in some Malagasy rainforest passerines. *Ostrich* 89: 281–286.

Woolaver, L. G, Nichols, R., Razafindrajao, F., and Hawkins, A.F.A. 2004. Sighting of Van Dam's vanga (*Xenopirostris damii*) (Schlegel, 1866) in mangroves in north-west Madagascar. *Bulletin of the British Ornithologists' Club* 124: 69–71.

Woolaver, L. G., Young, H. G., Cranswick, P. A., Razafindrajao, F., Bamford, A. J., Mallon, D., Rakotobe, D., and Rabesihanaka, S. 2015. *Species Action Plan for the Conservation of the Madagascar Pochard 2014–2024*. St. Helier: Durrell Wildlife Conservation Trust and IUCN Species Survival Commission.

Yamagishi, S., ed. 2005. *Social Organization of the Rufous Vanga: The Ecology of Vangas; Birds Endemic to Madagascar*. Kyoto: Kyoto University Press.

Yamagishi, S., and Eguchi, K. 1996. Comparative foraging ecology of Madagascar vangids (Vangidae). *Ibis* 138: 283–290.

Yamagishi, S., Urano, E., Rakotoarison, N., Randriamahazo, H., and Randrianasolo, V. 1992. A possible significance of dichromatism in male Madagascar paradise flycatchers (*Terpsiphone mutata*). In *Social Structure of Madagascar Higher Vertebrates in Relation to Their Adaptive Radiation*, ed. S. Yamagishi, pp. 58–61. Osaka: Osaka City University.

Yamagishi, S., Urano, E., and Eguchi, E. 1995. Group composition and contributions to breeding by rufous vanga *Schetba rufa* in Madagascar. *Ibis* 137: 157–161.

Yamagishi, S., Honda, M., Eguchi, K., and Thorstrom, R. 2001. Extreme endemic radiation of the Malagasy vangas (Aves: Passeriformes). *Journal of Molecular Evolution* 53: 39–46.

Yohannes, E., and Woog, F. 2020. A multi-isotope and morphometric analysis to uncover ecological niche divergence in two endemic island birds from Madagascar: The dark and common newtonia (Vangidae). *Journal of Ornithology* 161: 137–147.

Yonezawa, T., Segawa, T., Mori, H., Campos, P. F., Hongoh, Y., et al. 2017. Phylogenomics and morphology of extinct paleognaths reveal the origin and evolution of the ratites. *Current Biology* 27(1): 68–77.

Young, H. G. 1995. Territoriality and reproductive behaviour of Meller's duck *Anas melleri*. *Dodo* 31: 82–94.

———. 1996a. The distribution and origins of wildfowl (Anatidae) of western Indian Ocean islands. In *Biogéographie de Madagascar*, ed. W. R. Lourenço, pp. 363–367. Paris: Editions de l'ORSTOM.

———. 1996b. Threatened Anatinae and wetlands of Madagascar: A review and evaluation. In Proceedings of the Anatidae 2000 Conference, Strasbourg, France, 5–9 December 1994, eds. M. Birkan, J. van Vessem, P. Havet, J. Madsen, B. Trolliet, and M. Moser. *Gibier Faune Sauvage / Game Wildlife* 13: 801–813.

———. 2006. Madagascar teal *Anas bernieri*: The ecology and conservation of a short distance migrant. In *Waterbirds around the World*, eds. G. C. Boere, C. A. Galbraith, and D. A. Stroud, pp. 252–254. Edinburgh: Stationery Office.

———. 2013. Order Anseriformes. In *The Birds of Africa*. Vol. 8, *The Malagasy Region*, eds. R. J. Safford and A.F.A. Hawkins, pp. 238–262. London: Christopher Helm.

Young, H. G., and Kear, J. 2006. The rise and fall of wildfowl of the western Indian Ocean and Australasia. *Bulletin of the British Ornithologists' Club* 126A: 25–39.

Young, H. G., and Rhymer, J. M. 1988. Meller's duck: A threatened species receives recognition at last. *Biodiversity and Conservation* 7: 1313–1323.

Young, H. G., and Smith, J. G. 1989. The search for the Madagascar pochard *Aythya innotata*: Survey of Lac Alaotra, Madagascar October–November, 1989. *Dodo* 26: 17–34.

Young, H. G., Sorenson, M. D., and Johnson, K. P. 1998. A description of the Madagascar teal *Anas bernieri* and an examination of its relationships with the grey teal *A. gracilis*. *Wildfowl* 48: 174–180.

Young, H. G., Lewis, R. E., and Razafindrajao, F. 2001. A description of the nest and eggs of the Madagascar teal *Anas bernieri*. *Bulletin of the British Ornithologists' Club* 121: 64–67.

Young, H. G., Razafindrajao, F., Lewis, R. E., and Bin Aboudou, A. I. 2006a. Distribution and status of Palearctic shorebirds in western Madagascar, September–November 2004. *Waterbirds* 29: 235–238.

Young, H. G., Safford, R., Hawkins, F., Rabarisoa, R., and Razafindrajao, F. 2006b. Madagascar white-backed duck: What is its true status? *Threatened Waterfowl Specialist Group Newsletter* 15: 38–40.

Young, H. G., Razafindrajao, F., and Lewis, R. E. 2013. Madagascar's wildfowl (Anatidae) in the new millennium. *Wildfowl* 63: 5–23.

Young, H. G., Young, R. P., Lewis, R. E., Razafindrajao, F., Bin Aboudou, A. I., and Fa, J. E. 2014. Patterns of waterbird diversity in central western Madagascar: Where are the priority sites for conservation? *Wildfowl* 64: 35–53.

Younger, J. L., Strozier, L., Maddox, J. D., Nyári, A. S., Bonfitto, M. T., Raherilalao, M. J., Goodman, S. M., and Reddy, S. 2018. Hidden diversity of forest birds in Madagascar revealed using integrative taxonomy. *Molecular Phylogenetics and Evolution* 124: 16–26.

Younger, J. L., Block, N. L., Raherilalao, M. J., Maddox, J. D., Wacker, K. S., Kyriazis, C. C., Goodman, S. M., and Reddy, S. 2019a. Diversification of a cryptic radiation, a closer look at Madagascar's recently recognized bird family. bioRxiv 825687. https://doi.org/10.1101/825687.

Younger, J. L., Dempster, P., Nyári, A. S., Helms, T. O., Raherilalao, M. J., Goodman, S. M., and Reddy, S. 2019b. Phylogeography of the rufous vanga and the role of bioclimatic transition zones in promoting speciation within Madagascar. *Molecular Phylogenetics and Evolution* 139: 1–11.

Zefania, S. 1999. Contribution à l'étude de la biologie et du comportement de *Foudia madagascariensis* (Linné 1766) dans la région de Tamatave. Mémoire DEA, Université d'Antananarivo.

Zefania, S., and Székely, T. 2013a. Kittlitz's plover *Charadrius pecuarius*. In *The Birds of Africa*. Vol. 8, *The Malagasy Region*, eds. R. J. Safford and A.F.A. Hawkins, pp. 397–399. London: Christopher Helm.

———. 2013b. Madagascar plover *Charadrius thoracicus*. In *The Birds of Africa*. Vol. 8, *The Malagasy Region*, eds. R. J. Safford and A.F.A. Hawkins, pp. 395–397. London: Christopher Helm.

———. 2013c. White-fronted plover *Charadrius marginatus*. In *The Birds of Africa*. Vol. 8, *The Malagasy Region*, eds. R. J. Safford and A.F.A. Hawkins, pp. 401–403. London: Christopher Helm.

———. 2013d. Three-banded plover *Charadrius tricollaris*. In *The Birds of Africa*. Vol. 8, *The Malagasy Region*, eds. R. J. Safford and A.F.A. Hawkins, pp. 399–401. London: Christopher Helm.

Zefania, S., ffrench-Constant, R., Long, P. R., and Székely, T. 2008. Breeding distribution and ecology of threatened Madagascar plover *Charadrius thoracicus*. *Ostrich* 79(1): 43–51.

Zefania, S., Razafimahatratra, E., Faria, P. J., Bruford, M. W., Long, P. R., and Székely, T. 2010. Cryptic sexual size dimorphism in Malagasy plovers *Charadrius* spp. *Ostrich* 79(2): 43–51.

Zehrer, W. 1997. Les oiseaux à risque de Madagascar. *Working Group on Birds in the Madagascar Region Newsletter* 7(1): 7–9.

ZICOMA. 1999. *Les zones d'importance pour la conservation des oiseaux à Madagascar*. Antananarivo: BirdLife International (Projet ZICOMA).

———. 2001. Madagascar. In *Important Bird Areas in Africa and Associated Islands*, eds. L.D.C. Fishpool and M. I. Evans, pp. 489–537. Newbury and Cambridge, UK: Pisces Publications and BirdLife International.

Zinner, D., Wygoda, C., Razafimanantsoa, L., Rasoloarison, R., Andrianandrasana, H. T., Ganzhorn, J. U., and Torkler, F. 2014. Analysis of deforestation patterns in the central Menabe, Madagascar, between 1973 and 2010. *Regional Environmental Change* 14: 157–166.

Zuccon, D., and Ericson, P.G.P. 2010a. The *Monticola* rock-thrushes: Phylogeny and biogeography revisited. *Molecular Phylogenetics and Evolution* 55: 901–910.

———. 2010b. A multi-gene phylogeny disentangles the chat-flycatcher complex (Aves: Muscicapidae). *Zoologica Scripta* 39: 213–224.

CHAPTER 14

MAMMALS

INTRODUCTION TO MAMMALS

S. M. Goodman and V. Soarimalala

The extant terrestrial mammal fauna of Madagascar is exceptional on a worldwide basis. First, without exception, all 174 indigenous and nonvolant mammal species known from the island are endemic (Table 14.1), as are the majority of the 46 bat species, of which a handful are known to occur in the Malagasy Region (including the archipelagoes of the Comoros and Mascarenes) and the African continent (see Goodman et al., pp. 1894–911). There is no other single island or restricted continental area on our planet with this level of combined species richness and endemism for mammals. Second, the diversity of body forms and life-history styles is largely without parallel in tropical mammal faunas across the world. In this chapter, we try to capture and explain some of the marvelous and exceptional aspects of the island's extant mammal fauna, as well as those mammals that have recently gone extinct (see Godfrey and Jungers, pp. 1824–28, for lemurs; Samonds et al., pp. 1859–62, for bats).

Since the publication of the introductory contribution to mammals in the precursor book on the natural history of Madagascar (Goodman et al. 2003a), major advances have been made to better understand the Malagasy mammals' evolutionary history, in part based on molecular studies (see Chikhi and Sgarlata, pp. 1769–98, for a broad review of mammal genetic studies). These aspects include the origins of their ancestors, insights as to how and the time period when they may have arrived on the island, and subsequent speciation patterns. On the basis of these studies, it is now clear that similarities in body form and morphological adaptations to continental forms can be explained in most cases by evolutionary convergence. On the other hand, there are some simply bizarre animals that have evolved on the island with unique suites of characters (e.g., *Daubentonia madagascariensis*, or Aye-aye, see Sterling et al., pp. 1975–78; or members of the genus *Myzopoda*, see Ralisata et al., pp. 1917–22). Another aspect that has led to major advances in our knowledge of the island's mammal fauna over the past decades is continued biological surveys of poorly known areas, with associated specimen documentation and samples for a considerable array of studies, including molecular genetics and more classical taxonomic studies.

Certainly, a major factor that needs to be considered in this introduction to better understand the very particular Malagasy mammal fauna, whether deep into geological history or the Quaternary, is the island's history, specifically earth tectonics. East Gondwana (Madagascar-Seychelles-India-Australia-Antarctica) separated from West Gondwana (Africa–South America) ~130 million years ago (Mya) (see Figure 6.1, in chapter 6), and isolation was completed with the split between Madagascar and India-Seychelles ~88 Mya (see Collins et al., pp. 45–51). On the basis of current knowledge of when modern mammal groups first appear in the fossil record, the evolution of the vast majority of these animals occurred after the breakup of the East and West Gondwanan landmass. Hence, by definition, extant groups of native Malagasy land mammals successfully colonized the island via swimming or rafting; it is important to underline that there are conflicting views on how some of these groups may have arrived to the island (cf. Samonds et al., pp. 73–78, and Masters et al., pp. 78–81). In any case, it is presumed that these successful colonizers found an assortment of unoccupied niches, which they occupied, and subsequently underwent adaptive radiations (A. D. Yoder and Nowak 2006). Finally, the long history of isolation and overwater colonization has meant that numerous mammal groups have not made it to Madagascar (Figure 14.1)—thus, the dichotomy that the fauna is exceptionally rich in some ways but depauperate in others.

TABLE 14.1. **Checklist of the extant and described nonvolant terrestrial mammals of Madagascar as of mid-November 2020**

SCIENTIFIC NAME	COMMON NAME (ENGLISH)	IUCN STATUS	OTHER/PAST SCIENTIFIC NAMES
AFROSORICIDA			**INSECTIVORA, LIPOTYPHLA**
Tenrecidae: Geogalinae (1)			
Geogale aurita Milne Edwards & A. Grandidier, 1872[1]	Large-eared Tenrec	LC	*Cryptogale australis*
Tenrecidae: Oryzorictinae (25)			
Microgale brevicaudata G. Grandidier, 1899	Short-tailed Shrew Tenrec	LC	*Microgale breviceps*, *M. occidentalis*, *Paramicrogale occidentalis*
M. cowani Thomas, 1882[2]	Cowan's Shrew Tenrec	LC	*M. cowani nigrescens*, *M. crassipes*, *M. longirostris*
M. drouhardi G. Grandidier, 1934	Drouhard's Shrew Tenrec	LC	*M. melanorrhachis*
M. dryas Jenkins, 1992	Dryad Shrew Tenrec	VU	
M. fotsifotsy Jenkins, Raxworthy & Nussbaum, 1997	Pale Shrew Tenrec	LC	
M. gracilis (Major, 1896)	Gracile Shrew Tenrec	LC	*Leptogale gracilis*
M. grandidieri Olson, Rakotomalala, Hildebrandt, Lanier, Raxworthy & Goodman, 2009	Grandidier's Shrew Tenrec	LC	
M. gymnorhyncha Jenkins, Goodman & Raxworthy, 1996	Naked-nosed Shrew Tenrec	LC	
M. jenkinsae Goodman & Soarimalala, 2004	Jenkins's Shrew Tenrec	EN	
M. jobihely Goodman, Raxworthy, Maminirina & Olson, 2006	Dark Shrew Tenrec	EN	
M. longicaudata Thomas, 1882[3]	Lesser Long-tailed Shrew Tenrec	LC	
M. majori Thomas, 1918	Major's Long-tailed Shrew Tenrec	LC	
M. mergulus (Major, 1896)	Web-footed Shrew Tenrec	VU	*Limnogale mergulus*
M. monticola Goodman & Jenkins, 1998	Montane Shrew Tenrec	VU	
M. nasoloi Jenkins & Goodman, 1999	Nasolo's Shrew Tenrec	VU	
M. parvula G. Grandidier, 1934	Pygmy Shrew Tenrec	LC	*M. pulla*
M. principula Thomas, 1926	Greater Long-tailed Shrew Tenrec	LC	*M. decaryi*, *M. sorella*
M. pusilla Major, 1896	Least Shrew Tenrec	LC	
M. soricoides Jenkins, 1993	Shrew-toothed Shrew Tenrec	LC	
M. taiva Major, 1896	Taiva Shrew Tenrec	LC	
M. thomasi Major, 1896	Thomas's Shrew Tenrec	LC	
Nesogale dobsoni (Thomas, 1884)	Dobson's Shrew Tenrec	LC	*M. dobsoni*
N. talazaci (Major, 1896)	Talazac's Shrew Tenrec	LC	*M. talazaci*
Oryzorictes hova (A. Grandidier, 1870)[4]	Hova Mole Tenrec	LC	*Oryzorictes talpoides*
O. tetradactylus Milne Edwards & G. Grandidier, 1882	Four-toed Mole Tenrec	DD	
Tenrecidae: Tenrecinae (5)			
Echinops telfairi Martin, 1838	Lesser Hedgehog Tenrec	LC	

SCIENTIFIC NAME	COMMON NAME (ENGLISH)	IUCN STATUS	OTHER/PAST SCIENTIFIC NAMES
Hemicentetes nigriceps Günther, 1875	Highland Streaked Tenrec	LC	
H. semispinosus (G. Cuvier, 1798)	Lowland Streaked Tenrec	LC	
Setifer setosus (Schreber, 1777)	Greater Hedgehog Tenrec	LC	*Dasogale fontoynonti*
Tenrec ecaudatus (Schreber, 1777)	Tailless Tenrec	LC	
SORICOMORPHA			**INSECTIVORA**
Soricidae			
**Suncus etruscus* (Savi, 1822)[5]	Etruscan Shrew	n/a	*Suncus madagascariensis*
**S. murinus* (Linnaeus, 1766)	Asian Musk Shrew	n/a	
PRIMATES			
Cheirogaleidae (41)			
Allocebus trichotis (Günther, 1875)	Hairy-eared Dwarf Lemur	EN	
Cheirogaleus andysabini Lei, McLain, Frasier, Taylor, Bailey, Engberg, Ginter, Nash, Randriamampionona, Groves, Mittermeier & Louis Jr., 2015	Sabin's Dwarf Lemur	EN	
C. crossleyi A. Grandidier, 1870	Crossley's Dwarf Lemur	VU	
C. grovesi McLain, Lei, Frasier, Taylor, Bailey, Robertson, Nash, Randriamanana, Mittermeier & Louis Jr., 2017	Groves' Dwarf Lemur	DD	
C. lavasoensis Thiele, Razafimahatratra & Hapke, 2013	Lavasoa Dwarf Lemur	EN	
C. major E. Geoffroy Saint-Hilaire, 1812	Greater Dwarf Lemur	VU	The recognition of *Cheirogaleus minusculus* as a distinct species is uncertain. We consider *C. ravus* a synonym of *C. major* (see Blanco, pp. 1922–26)
C. medius E. Geoffroy Saint-Hilaire, 1812	Fat-tailed Dwarf Lemur	VU	*C. adipicaudatus*
C. shethi Frasier, Lei, McLain, Taylor, Bailey, Ginter, Nash, Randriamampionona, Groves, Mittermeier & Louis Jr., 2016	Ankarana Dwarf Lemur	EN	
C. sibreei (Forsyth Major, 1896)	Sibree's Dwarf Lemur	CR	
C. thomasi (Forsyth Major, 1894)	Thomas' Dwarf Lemur	EN	
Microcebus arnholdi Louis Jr., Engberg, McGuire, McCormick, Randriamampionona, Ranaivoarisoa, Bailey, Mittermeier & Lei, 2008	Montagne d'Ambre Mouse Lemur	VU	
M. berthae Rasoloarison, Goodman & Ganzhorn, 2000	Madame Berthe's Mouse Lemur	CR	
M. bongolavensis Olivieri, Zimmermann, Randrianambinina, Rasoloharijaona, Rakotondravony, Guschanski & Radespiel, 2006	Bongolava Mouse Lemur	EN	
M. boraha Hotaling, Foley, Lawrence, Bocanegra, Blanco, Rasoloarison, Kappeler, Barrett, Yoder & Weisrock, 2016	Nosy Boraha Mouse Lemur	DD	
M. danfossi Olivieri, Zimmermann, Randrianambinina, Rasoloharijaona, Rakotondravony, Guschanski & Radespiel, 2006	Ambarijeby Mouse Lemur	VU	

(continued overleaf)

TABLE 14.1. ***continued***

SCIENTIFIC NAME	COMMON NAME (ENGLISH)	IUCN STATUS	OTHER/PAST SCIENTIFIC NAMES
M. ganzhorni Hotaling, Foley, Lawrence, Bocanegra, Blanco, Rasoloarison, Kappeler, Barrett, Yoder & Weisrock, 2016	Ganzhorn's Mouse Lemur	EN	
M. gerpi Radespiel, Ratsimbazafy, Rasoloharijaona, Raveloson, Andriaholinirina, Rakotondravony, Randrianarison & Randrianambinina, 2012	Gerp's Mouse Lemur	CR	
M. griseorufus Kollman, 1910	Gray-brown Mouse Lemur	LC	
M. jollyae Louis Jr., Coles, Andriantompohavana, Sommer, Engberg, Zaonarivelo, Mayor & Brenneman, 2006	Jolly's Mouse Lemur	EN	
M. jonahi Schüßler, Blanco, Salmona, Poelstra, Andriambeloson, Miller, Randrianambinina, Rasolofoson, Mantilla-Contreras, Chikhi, Louis Jr., Yoder & Radespiel, 2020	Jonah's Mouse Lemur	NE	
M. lehilahytsara Roos & Kappeler, 2005	Goodman's Mouse Lemur	VU	
M. macarthurii Radespiel, Olivieri, Rasolofoson, Rakotondratsimba, Rakotonirainy, Rasoloharijaona, Randrianambinina, Ratsimbazafy, Ratelolahy, Randriamboavonjy, Rasolofoharivelo, Craul, Rakotozafy & Randrianarison, 2008	Anjiahely Mouse Lemur	EN	
M. mamiratra Andriantompohavana, Zaonarivelo, Endberg, Randriamampionona, McGuire, Shore, Rakotonomenjanahary, Brenneman & Louis, 2006	Nosy Be Mouse Lemur	EN	
M. manitatra Hotaling, Foley, Lawrence, Bocanegra, Blanco, Rasoloarison, Kappeler, Barrett, Yoder & Weisrock, 2016	Bemanasy Mouse Lemur	CR	
M. margotmarshae Louis Jr., Engberg, McGuire, McCormick, Randriamampionona, Ranaivoarisoa, Bailey, Mittermeier & Lei, 2008	Margot Marsh's Mouse Lemur	EN	
M. marohita Rasoloarison, Weisrock, Yoder, Rakotondravony & Kappeler, 2013	Marohita Mouse Lemur	CR	
M. mittermeieri Louis Jr., Coles, Andriantompohavana, Sommer, Engberg, Zaonarivelo, Mayor & Brenneman, 2006	Mittermeier's Mouse Lemur	EN	
M. murinus (J. F. Miller, 1777)	Gray Mouse Lemur	LC	
M. myoxinus Peters, 1852	Peters' Mouse Lemur	VU	
M. ravelobensis Zimmerman, Cepok, Rakotoarison, Zietemann & Radespiel, 1997	Golden-brown Mouse Lemur	VU	
M. rufus (Lesson, 1840)	Rufous Mouse Lemur	VU	
M. sambiranensis Rasoloarison, Goodman & Ganzhorn, 2000	Sambirano Mouse Lemur	EN	
M. simmonsi Louis Jr., Coles, Andriantompohavana, Sommer, Engberg, Zaonarivelo, Mayor & Brenneman, 2006	Simmons' Mouse Lemur	EN	
M. tanosi Rasoloarison, Weisrock, Yoder, Rakotondravony & Kappeler, 2013	Anosy Mouse Lemur	EN	

SCIENTIFIC NAME	COMMON NAME (ENGLISH)	IUCN STATUS	OTHER/PAST SCIENTIFIC NAMES
M. tavaratra Rasoloarison, Goodman & Ganzhorn, 2000	Tavaratra Mouse Lemur	VU	
Mirza coquereli (Grandidier, 1867)	Coquerel's Giant Mouse Lemur	EN	
M. zaza Kappeler & Roos, 2005	Northern Giant Mouse Lemur	VU	
Phaner electromontis Groves & Tattersall, 1991	Montagne d'Ambre Fork-marked Lemur	EN	
P. furcifer (de Blainville, 1839)	Masoala Fork-marked Lemur	EN	
P. pallescens Groves & Tattersall, 1991	Pale Fork-marked Lemur	EN	
P. parienti Groves & Tattersall, 1991	Sambirano Fork-marked Lemur	EN	
Lepilemuridae (26)			
Lepilemur aeeclis Andriaholinirina, Fausser, Roos, Zinner, Thalmann, Rabarivola, Ravoarimanana, Ganzhorn, Meier, Hilgartner, Walter, Zaramody, Langer, Hahn, Zimmermann, Radespiel, Craul, Tomiuk, Tattersall & Rumpler, 2017	Antafia Sportive Lemur	EN	
L. ahmansoni Louis Jr., Engberg, Lei, Geng & Sommer, 2006	Tsiombikibo Sportive Lemur	CR	
L. ankaranensis Rumpler & Albignac, 1975	Ankarana Sportive Lemur	EN	
L. betsileo Louis Jr., Engberg, Lei, Geng, Sommer, Randriamampionona, Randriamanana, Zaonarivelo, Andriantompohavana, Randria, Prosper, Ramaromilanto, Rakotoarisoa, Rooney & Brenneman, 2006	Betsileo Sportive Lemur	EN	
L. dorsalis Gray, 1871	Gray's Sportive Lemur	EN	
L. edwardsi (Forsyth Major, 1894)	Milne-Edwards' Sportive Lemur	EN	
L. fleuretae Louis Jr., Engberg, Lei, Geng, Sommer, Randriamampionona, Randriamanana, Zaonarivelo, Andriantompohavana, Randria, Prosper, Ramaromilanto, Rakotoarisoa, Rooney & Brenneman, 2006	Andohahela Sportive Lemur	EN	
L. grewcockorum Louis Jr., Engberg, Lei, Geng, Sommer, Randriamampionona, Randriamanana, Zaonarivelo, Andriantompohavana, Randria, Prosper, Ramaromilanto, Rakotoarisoa, Rooney & Brenneman, 2006	Anjiamangirana Sportive Lemur	CR	
L. hollandorum Ramaromilanto, Lei, Engberg, Johnson, Sitzmann & Louis Jr, 2009	Mananara-Nord Sportive Lemur	CR	
L. hubbardorum Louis Jr., Engberg, Lei, Geng, Sommer, Randriamampionona, Randriamanana, Zaonarivelo, Andriantompohavana, Randria, Prosper, Ramaromilanto, Rakotoarisoa, Rooney & Brenneman, 2006	Zombitse Sportive Lemur	EN	
L. jamesorum Louis Jr., Engberg, Lei, Geng, Sommer, Randriamampionona, Randriamanana, Zaonarivelo, Andriantompohavana, Randria, Prosper, Ramaromilanto, Rakotoarisoa, Rooney & Brenneman, 2006	Manombo Sportive Lemur	CR	
L. leucopus (Forsyth Major, 1894)	White-footed Sportive Lemur	EN	
L. microdon (Forsyth Major, 1894)	Small-toothed Sportive Lemur	EN	

(continued overleaf)

TABLE 14.1. ***continued***

SCIENTIFIC NAME	COMMON NAME (ENGLISH)	IUCN STATUS	OTHER/PAST SCIENTIFIC NAMES
L. milanoii Louis Jr., Engberg, Lei, Geng, Sommer, Randriamampionona, Randriamanana, Zaonarivelo, Andriantompohavana, Randria, Prosper, Ramaromilanto, Rakotoarisoa, Rooney & Brenneman, 2006	Daraina Sportive Lemur	EN	
L. mittermeieri Rabarivola, Zaramody, Fausser, Andriaholinirina, Roos, Zinner, Marcel & Rumpler, 2006	Mittermeier's Sportive Lemur	CR	
L. mustelinus I. Geoffroy Saint-Hilaire, 1851	Weasel Sportive Lemur	VU	
L. otto Craul, Zimmermann, Rasoloharijaona, Randrianambinina & Radespiel, 2007	Ambodimahabibo Sportive Lemur	EN	
L. petteri Louis Jr., Engberg, Lei, Geng, Sommer, Randriamampionona, Randriamanana, Zaonarivelo, Andriantompohavana, Randria, Prosper, Ramaromilanto, Rakotoarisoa, Rooney & Brenneman, 2006	Petter's Sportive Lemur	EN	
L. randrianasoloi Andriaholinirina, Fausser, Roos, Zinner, Thalmann, Rabarivola, Ravoarimanana, Ganzhorn, Meier, Hilgartner, Walter, Zaramody, Langer, Hahn, Zimmermann, Radespiel, Craul, Tomiuk, Tattersall & Rumpler, 2006	Bemaraha Sportive Lemur	EN	
L. ruficaudatus Grandidier, 1867	Red-tailed Sportive Lemur	CR	
L. sahamalazensis Andriaholinirina, Fausser, Roos, Zinner, Thalmann, Rabarivola, Ravoarimanana, Ganzhorn, Meier, Hilgartner, Walter, Zaramody, Langer, Hahn, Zimmermann, Radespiel, Craul, Tomiuk, Tattersall & Rumpler, 2017	Sahamalaza Sportive Lemur	CR	
L. scottorum Lei, Engberg, Andriantompohavana, McGuire, Mittermeier, Zaonarivelo, Brenneman & Louis Jr., 2008	Masoala Sportive Lemur	EN	
L. seali Louis Jr., Engberg, Lei, Geng, Sommer, Randriamampionona, Randriamanana, Zaonarivelo, Andriantompohavana, Randria, Prosper, Ramaromilanto, Rakotoarisoa, Rooney & Brenneman, 2006	Seal's Sportive Lemur	VU	
L. septentrionalis Rumpler & Albignac, 1975	Sahafary Sportive Lemur	CR	
L. tymerlachsonorum Louis Jr., Engberg, Lei, Geng, Sommer, Randriamampionona, Randriamanana, Zaonarivelo, Andriantompohavana, Randria, Prosper, Ramaromilanto, Rakotoarisoa, Rooney & Brenneman Louis Jr., 2006	Nosy Be Sportive Lemur	CR	
L. wrightae Louis Jr., Engberg, Lei, Geng, Sommer, Randriamampionona, Randriamanana, Zaonarivelo, Andriantompohavana, Randria, Prosper, Ramaromilanto, Rakotoarisoa, Rooney & Brenneman, 2006	Wright's Sportive Lemur	EN	
Lemuridae (21)			
Eulemur albifrons (E. Geoffroy Saint-Hilaire, 1796)	White-fronted Brown Lemur	VU	
E. cinereiceps (Grandidier & Milne Edwards, 1890)	White-collared Brown Lemur	CR	*Eulemur albocollaris*
E. collaris (E. Geoffroy Saint-Hilaire, 1812)	Red-collared Brown Lemur	EN	

SCIENTIFIC NAME	COMMON NAME (ENGLISH)	IUCN STATUS	OTHER/PAST SCIENTIFIC NAMES
E. coronatus (Gray, 1842)	Crowned Lemur	EN	
E. flavifrons (Gray, 1867)	Blue-eyed Black Lemur	CR	
E. fulvus (E. Geoffroy Saint-Hilaire, 1796)	Brown Lemur	VU	
E. macaco (Linnaeus, 1766)	Black Lemur	EN	
E. mongoz (Linnaeus, 1766)	Mongoose Lemur	CR	
E. rubriventer (I. Geoffroy Saint-Hilaire, 1850)	Red-bellied Lemur	VU	
E. rufifrons (Bennett, 1833)	Red-fronted Brown Lemur	VU	
E. rufus (Audebert, 1799)	Rufous Brown Lemur	VU	
E. sanfordi (Archbold, 1932)	Sanford's Brown Lemur	EN	
Hapalemur alaotrensis Rumpler, 1975	Lake Alaotra Bamboo Lemur	CR	
H. aureus Meier, Albignac, Peyriéras, Rumpler & Wright, 1987	Golden Bamboo Lemur	CR	
H. griseus[6] (Link, 1795)	Gray Bamboo Lemur	VU	
H. meridionalis Warter, Randrianasolo, Dutrillaux & Rumpler, 1987	Southern Bamboo Lemur	VU	
H. occidentalis Rumpler, 1975	Western Bamboo Lemur	VU	
Lemur catta Linnaeus, 1758	Ring-tailed Lemur	EN	
Prolemur simus (Gray, 1870)	Greater Bamboo Lemur	CR	*Hapalemur simus*
Varecia rubra (E. Geoffroy Saint-Hilaire, 1812)	Red Ruffed Lemur	CR	
V. variegata (Kerr, 1792)[7]	Black and White Ruffed Lemur	CR	
Indriidae (19)			
Avahi betsileo Andriantompohavana, Lei, Zaonarivelo, Engberg, Nalanirina, McGuire, Shore, Andrianasolo, Herrington, Brenneman & Louis Jr., 2007	Betsileo Woolly Lemur	EN	
A. cleesei Thalmann & Geissmann, 2005	Bemaraha Woolly Lemur	CR	
A. laniger (Gmelin, 1788)	Eastern Woolly Lemur	VU	
A. meridionalis Zaramody, Fausser, Roos, Zinner, Andriaholinirina, Rabarivola, Norscia, Tattersall & Rumpler, 2006	Southern Woolly Lemur	EN	
A. mooreorum Lei, Engberg, Andriantompohavana, McGuire, Mittermeier, Zaonarivelo, Brenneman & Louis Jr., 2008	Masoala Woolly Lemur	EN	
A. occidentalis (Lorenz, 1898)	Western Woolly Lemur	VU	
A. peyrierasi Zaramody, Fausser, Roos, Zinner, Andriaholinirina, Rabarivola, Norscia, Tattersall & Rumpler, 2006	Peyriéras' Woolly Lemur	VU	
A. ramanantsoavani Zaramody, Fausser, Roos, Zinner, Andriaholinirina, Rabarivola, Norscia, Tattersall & Rumpler, 2006	Manombo Woolly Lemur	VU	
A. unicolor Thalmann & Geissmann, 2000	Sambirano Woolly Lemur	CR	

(continued overleaf)

TABLE 14.1. ***continued***

SCIENTIFIC NAME	COMMON NAME (ENGLISH)	IUCN STATUS	OTHER/PAST SCIENTIFIC NAMES
Indri indri (Gmelin, 1788)	Indri	CR	*Lichanotus mitratus*
Propithecus candidus Grandidier, 1871	Silky Sifaka	CR	
P. coquereli (Grandidier, 1867)	Coquerel's Sifaka	CR	
P. coronatus Milne Edwards, 1871	Crowned Sifaka	CR	
P. deckeni Peters, 1870	Decken's Sifaka	CR	
P. diadema Bennett, 1832	Diademed Sifaka	CR	
P. edwardsi Grandidier, 1871	Milne-Edwards' Sifaka	EN	
P. perrieri Lavauden, 1931	Perrier's Sifaka	CR	
P. tattersalli Simons, 1988	Tattersall's Sifaka	CR	
P. verreauxi Grandidier, 1867	Verreaux's Sifaka	CR	
Daubentoniidae (1)			
Daubentonia madagascariensis (Gmelin, 1788)	Aye-aye	EN	
CARNIVORA			
Eupleridae: Cryptoproctinae (1)			
Cryptoprocta ferox Bennett, 1833	Fosa	VU	
Eupleridae: Euplerinae (2)			
Eupleres goudotii Doyère, 1835	Falanouc	VU	Includes *Eupleres major* (see Rivera et al., pp. 1983–86)
Fossa fossana (Müller, 1776)	Spotted Fanaloka	VU	*Fossa fossa*, *F. daubentoni*, and *F. majori*
Eupleridae: Galidiinae (4)			
Galidia elegans I. Geoffroy Saint-Hilaire, 1837[8]	Ring-tailed Vontsira	LC	
Galidictis fasciata (Gmelin, 1789)[9]	Broad-striped Vontsira	VU	*Galidictis eximius*, *G. fasciatus*, *G. grandidiensis*, *G. grandidieri*, *G. ornatus*
Mungotictis decemlineata (A. Grandidier, 1867)[10]	Bokyboky	EN	
Salanoia concolor (I. Geoffroy Saint-Hilaire, 1837)[11]	Brown-tailed Vontsira	VU	*Salanoia durrelli*
Felidae			
**Felis silvestris* Schreber, 1777[12]	Feral and domestic cat	n/a	*Felis domesticus*, *F. sylvestris*
Canidae			
**Canis lupus* Linnaeus, 1758	Dog	n/a	*Canis familiaris*
Viverridae			
**Viverricula indica* (E. Geoffroy Saint-Hilaire, 1803)	Small Indian Civet	n/a	
ARTIODACTYLA			
Suidae: Suinae			
**Potamochoerus larvatus* (F. Cuvier, 1822)[13]	African Bush Pig	n/a	*Potamochoerus hova*

SCIENTIFIC NAME	COMMON NAME (ENGLISH)	IUCN STATUS	OTHER/PAST SCIENTIFIC NAMES
RODENTIA			
Caviidae: Caviinae			
**Cavia porcellus* (Linnaeus, 1758)	Guinea Pig	n/a	
Muridae: Murinae			
**Mus musculus* Linneaus, 1758	House Mouse	n/a	*Mus castaneus*, *M. domesticus*
**Rattus norvegicus* (Berkenhout, 1769)	Brown Rat	n/a	
**R. rattus* (Linneaus, 1758)	Black Rat	n/a	*Rattus alexandrinus*, *R. frugivorus*
Nesomyidae: Nesomyinae (28)			
Brachytarsomys albicauda Günther, 1875	White-tailed Tree Rat	LC	
B. villosa Petter, 1962	Hairy-tailed Tree Rat	VU	*Brachytarsomys albicauda villosa*
Brachyuromys betsileoensis (Bartlett, 1880)	Lesser Short-tailed Rat	LC	
B. ramirohitra Major, 1896	Greater Short-tailed Rat	LC	
Eliurus antsingy Carleton, Goodman & Rakotondravony, 2001	Tsingy Tufted-tail Rat	DD	
E. carletoni Goodman, Raheriarisena & Jansa, 2009	Carleton's Tufted-tail Rat	LC	
E. danieli Carleton & Goodman, 2007	Daniel's Tufted-tail Rat	LC	
E. ellermani Carleton, 1994	Ellerman's Tufted-tail Rat	DD	
E. grandidieri Carleton & Goodman, 1998	Grandidier's Tufted-tail Rat	LC	
E. majori Thomas, 1895	Major's Tufted-tail Rat	LC	*Eliurus myoxinus majori*
E. minor Major, 1896	Lesser Tufted-tail Rat	LC	
E. myoxinus Milne Edwards, 1885	Western Tufted-tail Rat	LC	
E. penicillatus Thomas, 1908	White-tipped Tufted-tail Rat	EN	*E. m. penicillatus*
E. petteri Carleton, 1994	Petter's Tufted-tail Rat	EN	
E. tanala Major, 1896	Tanala Tufted-tail Rat	LC	*E. m. tanala*
E. tsingimbato Jansa, Carleton, Soarimalala, Rakotomalala & Goodman, 2019	Rock-loving Tufted-tail Rat	NE	
E. webbi Ellerman, 1949	Webb's Tufted-tail Rat	LC	*E. m. webbi*
Gymnuromys roberti Major, 1896	Robert's Forest Rat	LC	*Gymnuromys bastardi*
Hypogeomys antimena A. Grandidier, 1869	Malagasy Giant Jumping Rat	EN	
Macrotarsomys bastardi Milne Edwards & G. Grandidier, 1898	Western Big-footed Mouse	LC	*Macrotarsomys occidentalis*
M. ingens Petter, 1959	Long-tailed Big-footed Mouse	EN	
M. petteri Goodman & Soarimalala, 2005	Petter's Big-footed Mouse	EN	
Monticolomys koopmani Carleton & Goodman, 1996	Koopman's Mountain-dwelling Mouse	LC	

(*continued overleaf*)

TABLE 14.1. ***continued***

SCIENTIFIC NAME	COMMON NAME (ENGLISH)	IUCN STATUS	OTHER/PAST SCIENTIFIC NAMES
Nesomys audeberti (Jentink, 1879)	Lowland Red Forest Rat	LC	*Nesomys rufus audeberti*
N. lambertoni G. Grandidier, 1928	Tsingy Red Forest Rat	EN	*N. r. lambertoni*
N. rufus Peters, 1870	Eastern Red Forest Rat	LC	
Voalavo antsahabensis Goodman, Rakotondravony, Randriamanantsoa & Rakotomalala-Razanahoera, 2005	Eastern White-tailed Mountain Mouse	EN	
V. gymnocaudus Carleton & Goodman, 1998	Northern White-tailed Mountain Mouse	LC	

Sources: Common names are from different sources: Tenrecidae, mostly IUCN (2020); Primates, Mittermeier et al. (2014) and other contributions in this chapter; Carnivora, Duckworth et al. (2014) and other contributions in this chapter; Rodentia, mostly IUCN (2020) and other contributions in this chapter. IUCN Red List conservation assessment status is taken from IUCN (2020) and previous assessments.

*Notes:*This list includes the 174 native, and in all cases endemic, nonvolant mammal species of Madagascar; this tally excludes those that are introduced to the island. Order and family: subfamily names are given. After the family or subfamily name, the total number of species for the group is presented in parentheses (for nonintroduced mammals). Introduced taxa are indicated with an asterisk (*) before the scientific name; excluding these species, all other taxa presented are endemic to Madagascar. We have avoided listing subspecies in the table, and in most cases such information is presented in footnotes. In some cases, most notably for lemurs, there is some debate on the validity of certain species; these details are presented in Tattersall and Cuozzo (2018), and in other cases are denoted within footnotes. IUCN Red List status abbreviations: CR, Critically Endangered; DD, Data Deficient; EN, Endangered; LC, Least Concern; NE, Not Evaluated; VU, Vulnerable. n/a, not applicable, as the species in question is introduced to Madagascar.

While there is some redundancy with other tables in this chapter, we considered it useful to have a complete list of all extant nonvolant terrestrial mammals in a single table. Many genera are dealt with in detail in other contributions in this chapter, and readers should reference these for other details on the taxonomy and delineation of taxa mentioned in this table. For a list of the bat fauna, see Goodman et al. (pp. 1894–911) and for marine mammals known from Malagasy waters see Cerchio et al. (pp. 411–24).

[1] The form *Geogale aurita orientalis* was described from coastal habitat near Fenoarivo-Atsinanana (Fénérive-Est). Fieldwork in this area since the late 20th century has not result in any additional local evidence of its presence.

[2] On the basis of molecular studies, it is clear that *Microgale cowani* as currently delimited comprises different and in some cases not closely related species (L. E. Olson et al., unpublished data), which resulted in the designation of confirmed candidate species in Goodman et al. (2018a) for animals previously identified as *M. cowani*.

[3] On the basis of a molecular analysis of long-tailed shrew tenrecs from different areas of the island, L. E. Olson et al. (2004) found a clade in the northern portion of the island separate from *M. longicaudata*, *M. majori*, and *M. principula*, which might be best referred to *M. prolixacaudata* G. Grandidier, 1937. See Jenkins et al. (pp. 1880–87) for further discussion of this point.

[4] Recent molecular evidence shows that *Oryzorictes hova* comprises several different species (Everson et al. 2018; see Everson et al., pp. 1888–91).

[5] Until 2011, it was thought that a native endemic form of Soricidae shrew, *Suncus madagascariensis*, occurred on Madagascar. On the basis of molecular work, it is clear that this species is introduced to the island, and it is now considered *S. etruscus* (Omar et al. 2011).

[6] Several different geographic forms have been recognized for *Hapalemur griseus* (see Tan et al., pp. 1947–52). These include *H. g. griseus* (Link, 1795) (Gray Bamboo Lemur), *H. g. gilberti* Rabarivola, Prosper, Zaramody, Andriaholinirina & Hauwy, 2007 (Beanamalao Bamboo Lemur), and *H. g. ranomafanensis* Rabarivola, Prosper, Zaramody, Andriaholinirina & Hauwy, 2007 (Ranomafana Bamboo Lemur).

[7] A range of geographic forms (subspecies) have been recognized for *Varecia variegata*, but recent molecular work indicates that this species shows little phylogeographic variation across its range, and no subspecific forms are recognized herein (Baden et al. 2014; see Vasey et al., p. 1957–63).

[8] On the basis of recent molecular work, this species shows distinct geographic populations, and in addition to the nominate form, two other subspecies are recognized, *G. e. dambrensis* and *G. e. occidentalis* (Veron et al. 2017; see Farris and Goodman, pp. 1989–92).

[9] Until recently, this genus was thought to comprise two distinct species, *Galidictis fasciata* and *G. grandidieri* Wozencraft, 1986. Recent molecular studies indicate relatively minor genetic differences between the two forms, and the latter is now ranked as a subspecies, *G. f. grandidieri* (Veron et al. 2017; see Farris and Goodman, pp. 1993–96).

[10] Genetic studies indicate that two subspecies should be recognized: *M. d. decemlineata* and *M. d. lineata* Pocock, 1915 (see Veron et al., pp. 1863–65; Kappeler et al., pp. 1996–98)

[11] Durbin et al. (2010) described "*Salanoia durrelli*" from the Lake Alaotra marshes, largely based on morphological studies. A recent genetic study indicates that this is not a valid species and should be considered a synonym of *S. concolor* (Veron et al. 2017; see Farris and Murphy, pp. 1999–2001).

[12] We follow Driscoll et al. (2007) in the taxonomy of feral and domestic cats.

[13] A recent genetic study shows that this species is introduced to Madagascar (Lee et al. 2020).

Research over the past few decades on the phylogeny and origin of the extant nonvolant land mammals of Madagascar has provided strong evidence that each of the four extant groups is derived from a single colonization event of the island, each being monophyletic with respect to Madagascar (Poux et al. 2005): lemurs (see Yoder, pp. 1821–24), Eupleridae carnivorans (see Veron et al., pp. 1863–65), Nesomyinae rodents (see Jansa and Carleton, pp. 1865–71), and tenrecs (Everson et al. 2016) (Figure 14.2). Some alternative hypotheses based on fossils from elsewhere in the Old World have been presented recently for multiple colonizations, specifically of lemurs (e.g., Gunnell et al. 2018), but the molecular data are in conflict with such scenarios (see Yoder, pp. 1821–24), and herein we maintain the hypothesis that each of the four named groups represents a single colonization of Madagascar. It is extraordinary that

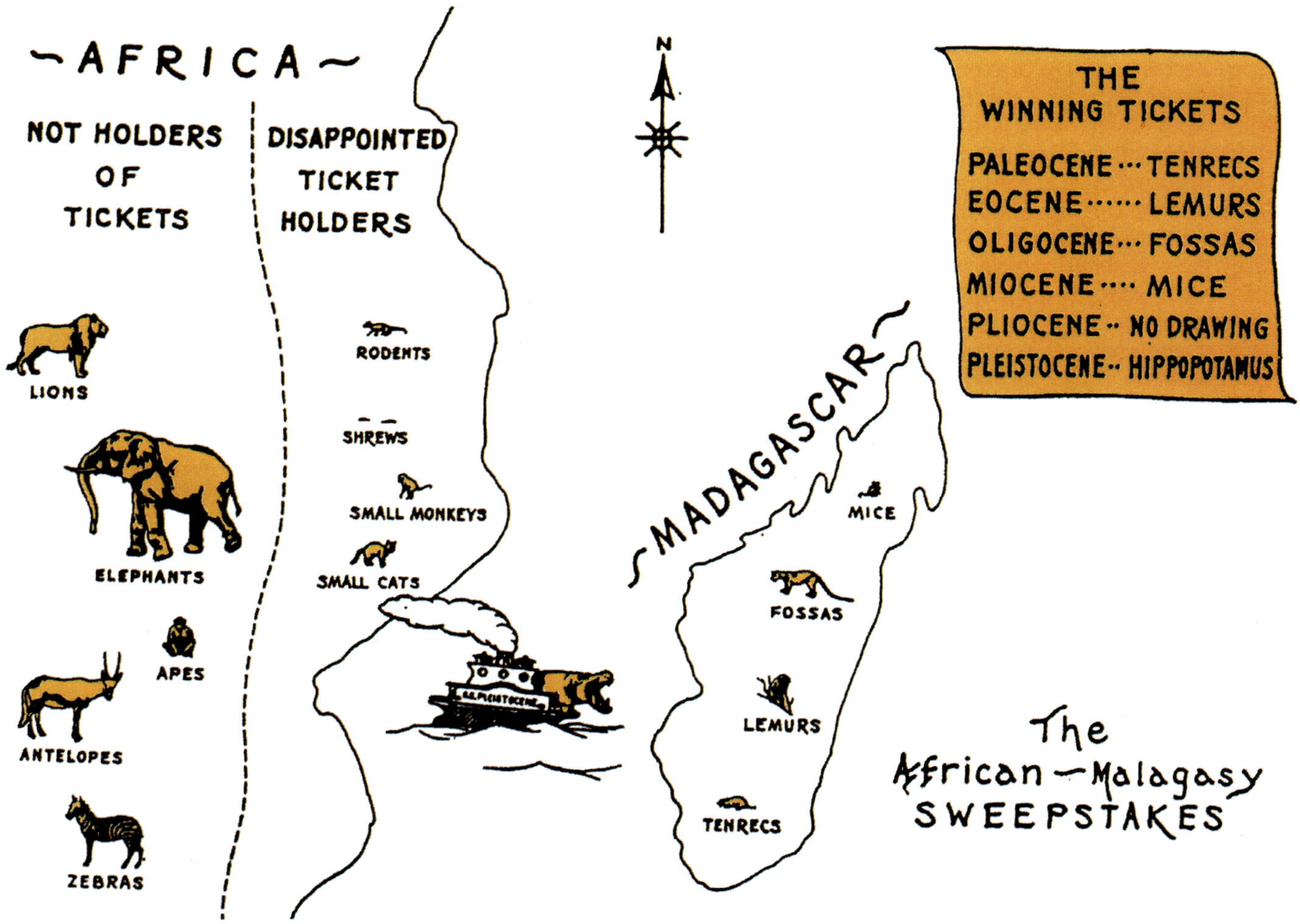

FIGURE 14.1 **A color-enhanced sketch drawn by paleontologist George Gaylord Simpson (1902–1984) depicting how he envisioned different Africa-to-Madagascar dispersal filters were in place during geological time, often referred to as the "sweepstakes model." Alternative hypotheses have been presented; see for example Stankiewicz et al. (2006).** (SOURCE: modified from Simpson 1940.)

the complete extant native land mammal fauna of Madagascar, amounting to 174 species at the time this contribution was written, appears to be derived from only four separate colonization events and, based on molecular-clock inference, during the Cenozoic. This would indicate that the Mozambique Channel is indeed an important barrier for mammal dispersal, and the probability of getting across this zone, spanning slightly more than 400 km, from Mozambique to the west coast of Madagascar was extremely low (Simpson 1952), or that the ability of certain mammal groups to successfully colonize the island after arriving on its shores was very limited.

RECENT DEVELOPMENTS IN KNOWLEDGE OF NATIVE MALAGASY LAND MAMMALS

Over the course of the past 20 years or so, since Goodman et al. (2003a), information on Malagasy mammals, including, for example, aspects of their origin, evolution, systematics, taxonomy, natural history, distribution, and physiology, has increased considerably. In part, this is due to numerous field projects, particularly the exploration of poorly known forested areas of the island in the context of biological inventories, focused studies on species and ecosystems, a range of different laboratory studies, particularly molecular research, and the creation and maintenance of field stations that have facilitated long-term research and prioritization of actions associated with protected areas. An excellent example of research advances through time at one research station, Kirindy Forest CNFEREF (Centre National de Formation, d'Etudes et de Recherche en Environnement et Foresterie), which has been active for close to 35 years, is discussed herein (see Kappeler et al., pp. 127–33). Another research site with an array of long-term studies that have provided a large number of new insights into mammal ecology is Ranomafana, while sites such as Ankarafantsika, Berenty, Bezà-Mahafaly, Kirindy Mité, and Tsimanampesotse have also contributed to a lesser extent. As discussed below, this work is disproportionately focused on lemurs, as compared to the other three endemic adaptive radiations of Malagasy mammals (tenrecs, carnivorans, and rodents). However, as demonstrated in this chapter, new generations of national and international students and researchers are broadening the taxonomic diversity of field and laboratory studies on terrestrial mammals, and

FIGURE 14.2 **The terrestrial nonvolant land mammals of Madagascar, numbering 174 species, are represented by four separate monophyletic groups: A) order Primates, here exemplified by *Allocebus trichotis* (Hairy-eared Dwarf Lemur), in the Lakato Forest; B) subfamily Nesomyinae, here represented by *Eliurus tanala* (Tanala Tufted-tail Rat), in the Befotaka–Midongy du Sud protected area; C) family Eupleridae, here characterized by *Galidictis fasciata grandidieri* (Broad-striped Vontsira), in the Tsimanampesotse protected area; and D) family Tenrecidae, *Geogale aurita* (Large-eared Tenrec), in the Kirindy Mité protected area.** (PHOTOS by V. Soarimalala and A. P. Raselimanana.)

the same pattern is readily apparent with marine mammals (see Cerchio et al., pp. 411–24).

Small Mammals

Compared to relatively large-bodied lemurs, particularly the diurnal species, terrestrial small-mammal species of Madagascar, including the endemic family Tenrecidae and the endemic subfamily Nesomyinae (for introductions to these groups, see Soarimalala and Goodman 2011; L. E. Olson 2013; and contributions that follow in this chapter), are difficult to study in the field with regard to their natural history. We are unaware of any long-term study conducted to date of marked individuals within a population of these two groups. In contrast, the substantial increase in the number of small-mammal specimens collected from the island over the past decades, particularly in native forest formations, and associated voucher and tissue samples has provided material for a large range of research projects.

The number of studies on parasites and diseases of Malagasy small mammals has increased dramatically since the precursor contribution (Goodman et al. 2003a), and these animals have been subjects of a range of epidemiological studies. Endoparasites, ectoparasites, and viral and bacterial pathogens have been examined in tenrecs and native and introduced rodents (family Muridae; see Introduced Mammals, below) (e.g., Durette-Desset et al. 2002a, 2002b; Duchemin 2003; Laakkonen et al. 2003; Raharivololona and Ganzhorn 2007; Apanaskevich et al. 2013; Beaucournu and Goodman 2014; Beaucournu and Laudisoit 2014; Dietrich et al. 2014, 2018; Reynes et al. 2014; Wilkinson et al. 2014; Lagadec et al. 2016; Ehlers et al. 2019, 2020; Apanaskevich and Goodman 2020a, 2020b; Kiene et al. 2020).

Tenrecidae

In the late 20th century, the period L. E. Olson and Goodman (2003) was written, there was considerable taxonomic change concerning tenrecs. The Tenrecidae had recently been transferred from the order Insectivora to the order Lipotyphla, made up of an assortment of groups including the families Tenrecidae and Chrysochloridae (golden moles), as well as Solenodontidae (solenodons), Erinaceidae (hedgehogs and gymnures), Talpidae (desmans and

moles), and Soricidae (true shrews). About this same time, a landmark paper was published, based on molecular research that uncovered that the tenrecs and golden moles were part of a completely different radiation of mammals, the superorder Afrotheria, and these two families were placed within the order Afrosoricida (Stanhope et al. 1998), which we follow herein. Subsequently, there have been different propositions to the higher-level systematics of this order and the order Tenrecoidea, composed of the Potamogalidae (African otter shrews) and the tenrecs (e.g., Mouchaty et al. 2000; Douady et al. 2002; Malia et al. 2002; Asher and Hofreiter 2006; Poux et al. 2008; Asher 2010).

The Tenrecidae comprises three subfamilies (Table 14.1): Geogalinae (long-eared tenrec), with a single species; Oryzorictinae (shrew and mole tenrecs), with 25 species; and Tenrecinae (spiny tenrecs), with five species. Members of the Geogalinae live in the southern dry spiny thickets and western dry deciduous forests. Members of the Oryzorictinae occur, for the most part, in the eastern and northern moist evergreen forests and show diverse body forms, with body weights ranging from about 3 to 40 g. Recent taxonomic changes in this group include the placement of the aquatic *Limnogale mergulus* (Web-footed Shrew Tenrec) in the genus *Microgale*, and *M. dobsoni* (Dobson's Shrew Tenrec) and *M. talazaci* (Talazac's Shrew Tenrec) in the genus *Nesogale* (Everson et al. 2016; see Jenkins et al., pp. 1880–87). Members of the Tenrecinae occur within the different natural vegetation formations of the island, as well as in anthropogenic habitats. This subfamily contains the largest members of the Tenrecidae, with *Tenrec ecaudatus* (Tailless Tenrec) reaching about 1 kg (see Goodman et al., pp. 1891–94). *Tenrec ecaudatus* has been introduced to several western Indian Ocean islands and is widely consumed on Madagascar and these other islands as bushmeat (see Golden et al., pp. 204–17). All members of this subfamily have spines, varying from short, in the hedgehog-like genera *Setifer* and *Echinops*, to the long spines of the genera *Tenrec* and *Hemicentetes*, which in the last genus are detachable and have small fishhook tips that adhere in the mouth and muzzle of would-be predators. *Hemicentetes* and young *Tenrec* have highly specialized stridulation organs on their back that are used for intraspecific communication. Further, *Hemicentetes* produces a tongue click that is probably a form of echolocation for locating prey (E. Gould 1965; Eisenberg and Gould 1970).

In our understanding of the evolutionary history and species diversity of the Tenrecidae, major advances have been made in the past few years (Everson et al. 2016). Further, there has been a clear refinement in the definition of species limits, particularly in shrew tenrecs of the genus *Microgale* (see Jenkins et al., pp. 1880–87). As a case in point, within shrew tenrecs there have been changes in generic allocations, and nine of the 21 (43%) currently recognized species have been described since 1992, while a considerable number of confirmed candidate species remain to be named (Everson et al. 2016; L. E. Olson et al., unpublished data). It has taken years of detailed inventories and associated molecular work to understand species delimitations within the Tenrecidae; many clades represent undescribed taxa, and the level of paraphyly is important (Everson et al. 2016; Goodman et al. 2018a; L. E. Olson et al., unpublished data).

Nesomyinae

The Nesomyinae shows a remarkable assortment of body forms and lifestyles and represents a rather interesting adaptive radiation. As currently understood, this subfamily comprises 28 species, placed in nine genera (Table 14.1). The most speciose genus is *Eliurus* (tufted-tail rats), which has been the subject of extensive alpha-taxonomic work based on specimens available from recent biological inventories and a reassessment of older museum specimens. Honacki et al. (1982) considered this genus to contain two species, but a generic revision and subsequent new descriptions have boosted the number of recognized species to 13 (see Carleton et al., pp. 2014–22). Members of this genus occur in all the natural forest types on the island, but species diversity is highest in the moist evergreen forests.

The results of molecular research on the evolutionary history of endemic Nesomyinae rodents is presented herein by Jansa and Carleton (see pp. 1865–71), and the reader is referred to that contribution for the finer details. In short, two new genera have been described since 1996, and of the 28 currently recognized species in the subfamily (Table 14.1), 11 (39%) have been named since 1994 (see additional contributions on this subfamily in this chapter).

Lemurs

Of all the different groups of mammals on the island, lemurs have been and continue to be the most intensively studied and the principal vertebrate focus from the conservation community. Further, a number of studies have been conducted on their evolutionary history and phylogenetic relationships (see Yoder, pp. 1821–24). These primates have been the subject of numerous monographic works, action plans, and guides (e.g., J.-J. Petter et al. 1977; Tattersall 1982; Mittermeier et al. 1992, 1994, 2010, 2014; C. Schwitzer et al. 2013, 2014, 2019), and several of the classic works in the study of behavior (ethology) concern lemurs (e.g., Jolly 1966; R. D. Martin 1972a, 1972b; Richard 1978). Madagascar Lemurs Portal (2017) is an interactive public website devoted to lemurs.

Since the late 20th century, there has been a considerable increase in the number of field studies looking at diurnal and nocturnal lemurs from ecological and evolutionary perspectives, and important insights have been gained into the natural history of most genera and many species (see the series of contributions herein). Several studies that commenced as dissertation topics for young primatologists of several decades ago have unfolded as long-term research projects for the person who initiated the work and cohorts of their students and grand-students. Such research programs provide important insight into population dynamics, genetic relationships, and behavioral ecology of these animals across generations, and knowledge of different parameters associated with life-history traits is a fundamental step for understanding the evolution of this group as a whole (e.g., Jolly 2012; Kappeler and Fichtel 2012; Sussman et al. 2012; P. C. Wright et al. 2012; Richard et al. 2016a).

The extant lemurs of Madagascar exhibit a wide variety of forms, ranging from the smallest extant primates in the world—such as *Microcebus berthae* (Madame Berthe's Mouse Lemur), with adult body mass averaging about 30 g (see Kappeler et al., pp. 1927–32)—to large species such as *Propithecus diadema* (Diademed Sifaka) and *Indri indri* (Indri), averaging 6.5 kg (see Gamba et al., pp. 1967–71). In contrast, among the lemur species that went extinct in recent geological time, body mass ranges from ~11 to ~160 kg (see Godfrey and Jungers, pp. 1824–28). The range of dietary regimes,

mating styles, reproductive strategies, and adaptations to deal with predators and other stressful aspects of the environment is most fascinating and is discussed in other contributions within this chapter.

Five families of lemurs occur on Madagascar today (Table 14.1): Cheirogaleidae, with 41 species, all largely nocturnal, in five genera; Lepilemuridae, with 26 species in a single genus; Lemuridae, with 21 species in five genera; Indriidae, with 19 species in three genera; and Daubentoniidae, with a single species. Two members of Lemuridae, *Eulemur fulvus* (Brown Lemur) and *E. mongoz* (Mongoose Lemur), also occur in the Comoro archipelago. It is generally accepted that these animals were introduced there (Mittermeier et al. 1994). Further support for this supposition is found in a molecular study of *E. f. fulvus* (from Madagascar) and *E. f. mayottensis* (from the Comoros), in which no genetic difference was found between these two forms (Pastorini et al. 1999).

An uncounted number of scientific papers and hundreds of theses and memoirs on lemurs have been published or completed since the last portion of the 20th century, including works on species for which basic aspects of how they live, what they eat, and how they divide up their world were previously unknown or poorly known. Many of these details and recent references are provided in the lemur contributions herein. It is important to underline that even given this wealth of information on the primates of the island, 50 of the 108 (46%) lemur species listed in Table 14.1 have been formally described as new to science since 2000. Hence, accordingly, there are still major gaps in knowledge on the natural history and distribution of many species. Further, a recent interest in the zoonotic diseases of lemurs (e.g., Sondgeroth et al. 2007; Rasambainarivo et al. 2013; Bublitz et al. 2015; Lim et al. 2015; Zohdy et al. 2015; Larsen et al. 2016; Wasimuddin et al. 2019; see chapter 6), as well as their ectoparasites (e.g., Blanco et al. 2013a; Ehlers et al. 2019; Kiene et al. 2020), has resulted in some remarkable findings.

Chiroptera

The past few decades has seen major advances on information concerning the bats of Madagascar. A broad review is presented herein, in Introduction to the Bats of Madagascar (see Goodman et al., pp. 1894–911), and we do not present the specific details in this contribution. Two more-detailed contributions are also presented herein, one on the family Pteropodidae (see Andrianaivoarivelo et al., pp. 1911–16) and the other on the genus *Myzopoda* (see Ralisata et al., pp. 1917–22).

Carnivora

Roland Albignac spent several years studying the endemic carnivorans of Madagascar, which are today placed in the endemic family Eupleridae (A. D. Yoder et al. 2003), and his work forms the basis for much of the current working knowledge on the natural history of these animals, which was summarized in a monograph (Albignac 1973). In many ways, mostly associated with technical difficulties in studying these wide-ranging and often nocturnal animals, until recently, there had been little improvement on information concerning their ecology. The advent of new technology, including radio collars and camera traps, since 2010 has fostered major progress in our understanding of a range of different life-history traits and human-imposed pressures on these animals. For example, the use of radio collars on the largest living euplerid, *Cryptoprocta ferox* (Fosa), has provided enlightening information concerning aspects of this animal's ecology, including social behavior and range capacity (e.g., Lührs and Kappeler 2013; see Gerber and Hawkins, pp. 1978–83). A substantial increase in the use of camera traps has brought many new insights into the community ecology of these carnivorans, their interactions with other forest vertebrates, and pressure from a range of different factors, particularly anthropogenic ones (see Farris et al., pp. 1806–11). There is considerable pressure on these animals from introduced carnivorans—of families Canidae (dogs) and Felidae (cats) as well as Viverridae (*Viverricula indica*, Small Indian Civet)—entering forest ecosystems, resulting in the decline of endemic euplerids (Farris et al. 2015a, 2015b, 2015c; see contributions in this chapter). In recent years, research has been conducted on the pathogens of endemic Malagasy carnivorans (e.g., Pomerantz et al. 2016; Rasambainarivo et al. 2017; Rasambainarivo and Goodman 2019; also see Rasambainarivo and Zohdy, pp. 298–302, and other contributions in chapter 6)

Previously, the native carnivorans of Madagascar were placed in two different families and three different subfamilies: family Herpestidae, subfamily Galidiinae, with five species in four genera; and family Viverridae, subfamily Cryptoproctinae, with one species, and subfamily Euplerinae, with two species in two genera (Wozencraft 1993); by inference, this would indicate multiple colonizations of the island. A subsequent molecular study (A. D. Yoder et al. 2003) found the native carnivorans to be a monophyletic group, indicating a single colonization of Madagascar, and these animals are now placed in the family Eupleridae, composed of seven species, each placed in a separate genus (Table 14.1). In 2010, one species new to science, *Salanoia durrelli* (Durbin et al. 2010), was described. However, more recent analyses indicate that it cannot be genetically differentiated from *S. concolor* (Brown-tailed Vontsira) (Veron et al. 2017). Further, the recognition of *Eupleres major* as a species distinct from *E. goudotii* (Falanouc) (Goodman and Helgen 2010) has been proposed, but recent molecular studies indicate that *Eupleres* is best considered a monospecific genus (Veron and Goodman 2018). Another important change based on molecular grounds has been that *Galidictis grandidieri*, of the extreme southwestern dry spiny thicket, is best considered a subspecies of *G. fasciata* (Broad-striped Vontsira), from moist evergreen forest formations (see Veron et al., pp. 1863–65).

THE FOSSIL AND SUBFOSSIL MAMMAL FAUNA

This section needs to start with two definitions: The term *fossil* is used here for rock that holds traces of a formerly living organism, such as shell, bone, tracks, etc. *Subfossils*, as we refer to them in this contribution, are the physical remains of mammals (bones or feces) without any significant degree of mineralization.

The vertebrate fossil record of Madagascar is notably incomplete. The earliest mammal fossils from the island date from the Mesozoic, specifically Middle Jurassic and Late Cretaceous (see Flynn et al., pp. 51–59, and Krause et al., pp. 59–68, respectively); not one of the lineages from these deposits is represented in the extant mammal fauna of the island. Excluding recent discoveries of

some very important Cenozoic deposits, including mammal remains from the Miocene (see Samonds, pp. 69–73), the next occurrences of land mammals in the geological record date from the Late Pleistocene. Sabatier and Legendre (1985) reported a possible Plio-cene-Pleistocene assemblage, but the dating of this deposit is unclear. Excluding the recent Miocene material mentioned above, the gap in fossil mammals of the island, spanning nearly 60 million years, from the Late Cretaceous to the Late Pleistocene, coincides with the period when colonization of ancestral lineages that led to modern forms took place. As mentioned in the previous section, successful colonization of Madagascar by terrestrial mammals was exceptional, and this aspect is underlined by the presence of 174 extant land mammals on the island (Table 14.1) from only four monophyletic groups, each representing a separate colonization event—a simply extraordinary indication of how rare successful colonization of the island was in geological history. It is anticipated that the recent discovery of Miocene mammal fossils will provide important new insights into the colonization and evolutionary history of mammals represented in the extant fauna.

In contrast to the relatively few mammal fossils available from the Mesozoic, reflecting the early history of mammals on the island, a variety of sites have yielded a considerable quantity of Quaternary subfossils. The study of these specimens provides a remarkable window into understanding the evolutionary history of recent Malagasy mammals, the previous richness of the fauna, and recent paleoecological changes that have taken place. Contrary to a notion presented in the literature, the subsequent Quaternary extinction events touched not only large-bodied mammals, often referred to as the megafauna, but also a number of smaller mammal forms, including shrew tenrecs and rodents (see below). The term *megafauna extinctions* is a misnomer when used in regard to Madagascar; as originally defined and used by P. S. Martin (1984), it was for animals greater than 44 kg, and hence, based on estimated body mass, not applicable to many mammals that have recently disappeared from the island (see, for example, Jungers et al. 2008 for body-mass estimates of extinct lemurs). The historical bias toward the study of large-bodied mammal subfossils has to do with excavation techniques and the specific interests of certain paleontologists. In any case, the vast majority of the Quaternary mammal subfossils recovered on the island date from the Holocene, while the oldest are from the Late Pleistocene (Crowley 2010). The study of these specimens with a variety of different techniques provides the means to tease apart natural change on an environmental or biome scale versus relatively punctuated anthropogenic change over the past millennium (Dewar 1984; Burney 1999; Crowley and Samonds 2013; Crowley et al. 2017; see Godfrey and Douglass, pp. 191–97).

Subfossil Site Types

Holocene subfossil sites can be divided into four different types of deposits (modified from Mahé 1965).

Caves: Such sites have yielded rich and varied faunal assemblages. Among the better-known cave sites are the karst limestone areas of Ankarana, Anjohibe, Ankilitelo, and Beanka, as well as some sites with smaller caves (E. L. Simons et al. 1990; Jungers et al. 1995; Burney et al. 1997, 2008, 2020a; Godfrey et al. 1997, 1999; Gommery et al. 1998, 2003, 2011), rock shelters (Dewar and Rakotovololona 1992; Dewar et al. 2013), and one small cave with rock art depicting what has been concluded to be animals that are extinct today (Burney et al. 2020b). Fieldwork commenced in earnest in 2014 in some submerged caves at Tsimanampesotse, when vast vertebrate bone deposits, including a range of mammals, were found and initially described by Rosenberger et al. (2015).

Marsh deposits in the Central Highlands: Several localities in former extensive marsh systems have been discovered that contain important concentrations of animal bones. Such sites are often associated with Central Highlands volcanic regions and where streams were dammed by lava flows, forming lakes or basins. Subsequent down-cutting of these dams resulted in the draining of the water body. Examples include the deposits of Ampasambazimba, to the west of Antananarivo, and several different deposits in the broad volcanic basins in the Vakinankaratra region (Jully 1898; G. Grandidier 1905a, 1905b; Standing 1906, 1909, 1910; MacPhee et al. 1985; Samonds et al. 2019).

Coastal marsh deposits: Along the coasts of Madagascar, most notably the west coast, numerous subfossil sites are known from interdunal swales in areas of currently low water tables (Burney 1999). Some of the more productive sites include Lamboharana, Ambolisatra, Belo-sur-Mer, and Itampolo (G. Grandidier 1905a; Burney 1999).

Riverine deposits: At several localities, most notably in southwestern Madagascar, there are subfossil sites along deep-cut riverine banks with considerable bone material. A good example of such a site is Ampoza, near Ankazoabo-Atsimo (E. I. White 1930; Jernvall et al. 2003). In this portion of the island are numerous localities—called *taolambiby* in Malagasy, meaning "place of animal bones"—which often have bone deposits in riverine sediment. Such sites, often with different processes of bone deposition (taphonomy), provide the means to study ecological change through time. One such site, Taolambiby near Betioky-Atsimo, first described by Raison and Vérin (1967), has yielded a considerable number of human-modified bones of then extant and now extinct mammals (Perez et al. 2005). A certain amount of controversy exists on the interpretation of the cut marks and other aspects of the site (Perez et al. 2005; Godfrey et al. 2011, 2019; cf. Anderson et al. 2018).

Mammal Subfossils

Mammals are generally one of the most common vertebrate groups recovered from subfossil sites, and currently 29 extinct species are recognized (Table 14.2, and see Godfrey and Jungers, pp. 1824–28). Subfossil material excavated during the late 19th century and early 20th century lacks stratigraphic control, and thus certain types of inferences associated with the reconstruction of temporal events are difficult to make. A considerable number of radiocarbon dates are available from extinct and extant mammal subfossils, which are tabulated by Burney et al. (2004) and Crowley (2010), and new dates continue to be published in more recent articles.

TABLE 14.2. **Species of nonprimate mammals identified from Quaternary deposits on Madagascar, including introduced feral species and extinct species**

CLASS MAMMALIA
†ORDER BIBYMALAGASIA (SEE MACPHEE 1994)
†*Plesiorycteropus germainepetterae* MacPhee, 1994
†*P. madagascariensis* Filhol, 1895
syn. *Hypogeomys boulei* Grandidier, 1912
syn. *Majoria rapeto* Thomas, 1915
syn. *Myoryctes rapeto* Major, 1908

ORDER AFROSORICIDA (DERIVED IN PART FROM SABATIER AND LEGENDRE 1985; BURNEY ET AL. 1997, 2008, 2020A; MULDOON ET AL. 2009; SAMONDS ET AL. 2010; GOMMERY ET AL. 2018)
Family Tenrecidae
Geogale aurita Large-eared Tenrec
syn. *Cryptogale australis* Grandidier, 1928
Microgale brevicaudata Short-tailed Shrew Tenrec
M. longicaudata Lesser Long-tailed Shrew Tenrec
†*M. macpheei* Goodman, & Burney, 2007[1]
M. cf. *majori* Major's Long-tailed Shrew Tenrec
M. nasoloi Nasolo's Shrew Tenrec
M. principula Greater Long-tailed Shrew Tenrec
syn. *M. decaryi* Grandidier, 1928
syn. *Paramicrogale decaryi* Grandidier & Petit, 1931
M. pusilla Least Shrew Tenrec
Nesogale talazaci Talazac's Shrew Tenrec
syn. *Microgale talazaci*
Oryzorictes sp. mole tenrec
Echinops telfairi Lesser Hedgehog Tenrec
Setifer setosus Greater Hedgehog Tenrec
Tenrec ecaudatus Tailless Tenrec
syn. *Centetes ecaudatus*

ORDER SORICOMORPHA (DERIVED IN PART FROM BURNEY ET AL. 2008; GOMMERY ET AL. 2018)
***Family Soricidae**
**Suncus etruscus* Etruscan Shrew
syn. *S. madagascariensis*
**S. murinus* Asian Musk Shrew

ORDER CHIROPTERA (DERIVED IN PART FROM SABATIER AND LEGENDRE 1985; BURNEY ET AL. 1997, 2008, 2020A; SAMONDS 2007; MULDOON ET AL. 2009; GOMMERY ET AL. 2018)
Family Pteropodidae
Eidolon dupreanum Madagascar Straw-colored Fruit Bat
Pteropus rufus Madagascar Flying Fox
syn. *P. edwardsi*
Rousettus madagascariensis Madagascar Rousette
syn. *Pelophilous madagascariensis*
Family Hipposideridae
†*Hipposideros besaoka* Samonds, 2007[2]
Macronycteris commersoni Commerson's Leaf-nosed Bat
syn. *Hipposideros commersoni*

ORDER CHIROPTERA
Family Rhinonycteridae
Paratriaenops furculus Trouessart's Trident Bat
syn. *Triaenops furculus*
†*Triaenops goodmani* Samonds, 2007[3]
T. menamena Rufous Trident Bat
Family Emballonuridae
Paremballonura atrata Peter's Sheath-tailed Bat
syn. *Emballonura atrata*
P. tiavato Rock-dwelling Sheath-tailed Bat
Taphozous sp. tomb bat
Family Molossidae
Chaerephon leucogaster Grandidier's Lesser Free-tailed Bat
Mops leucostigma Malagasy Large White-bellied Free-tailed Bat
M. midas Midas Free-tailed Bat
Mormopterus jugularis Peters' Goblin Bat
Otomops madagascariensis Malagasy Large-eared Free-tailed Bat
Family Vespertilionidae
Myotis goudoti Malagasy Mouse-eared Bat
Family Miniopteridae
Miniopterus gleni Glen's Long-fingered Bat
Miniopterus sp. (medium-size) long-fingered bat

ORDER CARNIVORA (DERIVED IN PART FROM GOODMAN ET AL. 2004A; MULDOON ET AL. 2009, 2012; SAMONDS ET AL. 2010; BURNEY ET AL. 2020A)
Family Eupleridae
†*Cryptoprocta spelea* G. Grandidier, 1902
syn. *C. antamba* Lamberton, 1939
C. ferox Fosa
Fossa fossana Spotted Fanaloka
Galidia elegans Ring-tailed Vontsira
Galidictis fasciata grandidieri Broad-striped [Grandidier's] Vontsira
Mungotictis decemlineata Bokyboky
***Family Felidae**
**Felis silvestris* Feral Cat
syn. *F. domesticus*
syn. *F. lybica*
syn. *F. sylvestris*
***Family Canidae**
**Canis lupus* Dog
syn. *C. familiaris*
***Family Viverridae**
**Viverricula indica* Small Indian Civet
syn. *Viverra fosa* Linneaus, 1793

ORDER ARTIODACTYLA (STUENES 1989; BURNEY ET AL. 1997, 2020A; FOVET ET AL. 2011; GOMMERY ET AL. 2011, 2018)

Family Hippopotamidae

†*Hippopotamus madagascariensis* Guldberg, 1883
syn. *Choeropsis madagascariensis*
syn. *Hexaprotodon madagascariensis*
syn. *Hippopotamus guldbergi* Fovet, Faure & Guérin, 2011
†*H. laloumena* Faure & Guérin, 1990
syn. *H. amphibius standini*
†*H. lemerlei* A. Grandidier, 1868

***Family Suidae**

**Potamochoerus larvatus African* Bush Pig
syn. *P. madagascariensis*

ORDER RODENTIA (DERIVED IN PART FROM SABATIER AND LEGENDRE 1985; BURNEY ET AL. 2008, 2020A; MULDOON ET AL. 2009; MEIN ET AL. 2010; GOMMERY ET AL. 2018)

***Family Muridae**

**Mus musculus* House Mouse
**Rattus rattus* Black Rat

Family Nesomyidae

†*Brachytarsomys mahajambaensis* Mein, Sénégas, Gommery, Ramanivosoa, Randrianantenaina & Kerloc'h, 2010
Brachytarsomys sp. tree rat[4]
Eliurus sp. tufted-tail rat
E. minor Lesser Tufted-tail Rat
E. myoxinus Western Tufted-tail Rat
E. tsingimbato Rock-loving Tufted-tail Rat
Hypogeomys antimena Malagasy Giant Jumping Rat
†*H. australis* G. Grandidier, 1903
Macrotarsomys bastardi Western Big-footed Mouse
M. petteri Petter's Big-footed Mouse
Monticolomys sp. mountain-dwelling mouse[5]
†*Nesomys narindaensis* Mein, Sénégas, Gommery, Ramanivosoa, Randrianantenaina & Kerloc'h, 2010
N. rufus Eastern Red Forest Rat

Notes: * introduced taxon; † extinct taxon; syn., synonym. For a list of extinct lemurs known from the same geological period see Godfrey and Jungers (pp. 1824–28, Table 14.6).

[1] Some subfossil material from Andrahomana Cave previously identified as *Microgale brevicaudata* (Burney et al. 2008) was used in the description of extinct species *M. macpheei* (Goodman et al. 2007a). Further, from sites on the Mahafaly Plateau in the extreme southwest, material from owl pellets was originally identified as *M. pusilla* (MacPhee 1986), which is probably referable to *M. jenkinsae*.

[2] Probably more appropriately placed in the genus *Macronycteris*, an aspect that will be resolved when DNA can be isolated from subfossil material.

[3] Since *Triaenops goodmani* was described, there have been changes in the generic allocation of Malagasy members of the family Rhinonycteridae, and its generic allocation needs to be reevaluated.

[4] Unidentified species allocated to this genus by Sabatier and Legendre (1985).

[5] Unidentified species allocated to this genus by Gommery et al. (2018).

A reexamination and new analyses of older subfossil material housed in museums and excavated over the past century or slightly earlier have provided many fresh insights into the recent history of the island's mammalian fauna, as well as inferences on human–animal interactions (see Godfrey and Douglass, pp. 191–97). In recent years, new techniques have been employed to address a range of different questions associated with mammal subfossils from Madagascar, including critical questions on the ecology of these animals, the possible causes of extinction, and the role humans may have played. For example, stable-isotope analyses of subfossil bone provide new insights and, when radiocarbon-dated specimens are employed in these studies, provide a finer time frame for pinpointing ecological shifts (e.g., Crowley et al. 2011, 2017; Crowley and Samonds 2013). Further, the use of stromium isotopes allows researchers to infer aspects of the ecology of extinct lemurs (Crowley and Godfrey 2019). Another technique employed uses nitrogen isotopes from amino acids collected in bones of extinct mammals (Nixon et al. 2018) as a means to separate natural landscape transformation, as compared to different forms of human interventions (hunting and habitat transformation), to explain the disappearance of these taxa.

Brief Review of Subfossil Mammals by Order

Bibymalagasia

In 1895, Henri Filhol described *Plesiorycteropus madagascariensis* from a fragmentary skull excavated by Monsieur Grevé at Belo-sur-Mer. On the basis of cranial characters, Filhol thought that this new genus and species was closely related to aardvarks (*Orycteropus*, family Orycteropodidae, order Tubulidentata). In a systematic review of the "Malagasy Aardvark" based on more extensive material, Lamberton (1946) noted that this genus differed from aardvarks in several osteological features and may represent a separate lineage of mammals. A subsequent analysis of *Plesiorycteropus*, along with other edentates (orders Xenarthra, Pholidota, and Tubulidentata), supported Lamberton's hypothesis (MacPhee 1994). To acknowledge the apparent uniqueness of *Plesiorycteropus*, MacPhee (1994), who also described a second species, erected a new order of mammals for the genus under the name Bibymalagasia, the etymology of which is derived from *biby* ("animal" in Malagasy) and *malagasia* (from Madagascar). Relatively recently, a molecular sequence from bone collagen was obtained from a *Plesiorycteropus* subfossil (M. Buckley 2013), which indicated that the animal was best placed within the order Afrosoricida, as defined herein, and that it might be a highly adapted member of Tenrecidae. We consider it best that further evidence be obtained before the genus *Plesiorycteropus* is transferred to the Afrosoricida.

As further evidence of the character complexity of *Plesiorycteropus* and the difficulty in diagnosing isolated elements referable to this genus (MacPhee 1994), a femur of this genus discovered at Ampasambazimba was described as that of a giant rodent, "*Hypogeomys boulei*" (G. Grandidier 1912), and a pelvis from Antsirabe was described as that of another large subfossil rodent, "*Myoryctes rapeto*" (Major 1908), which was subsequently changed to "*Majoria rapeto*" (Thomas 1915). Further, G. Grandidier (1901) named a new form of "edentate," "*Bradytherium madagascariense*," which is referable to the sloth-lemur genus *Palaeopropithecus* (Lamberton 1946). Although

numerous specimens of *Plesiorycteropus* have been excavated at paleontological sites, including posterior portions of crania, no dentary or maxillary has been found to date, and it is not known whether members of this genus had teeth or not.

Two species of *Plesiorycteropus* are currently recognized (Table 14.2): *P. germainepetterae*, from a subfossil site in the "Centre d'île" (Lamberton 1946), probably Ampasambazimba, and *P. madagascariensis*, from a variety of sites along the west coast from Belo-sur-Mer to Anjohibe Cave and inland at Ampasambazimba (MacPhee 1994; Burney et al. 1997, 2020a). If the provenance of the holotype of *P. germainepetterae* is indeed Ampasambazimba, then the two species of *Plesiorycteropus* were sympatric at this site. At the very least, both occurred in the Central Highlands. The only published radiocarbon date we are aware of for a member of this genus is from a specimen obtained at Masinandraina that yielded a date of 2154 cal BP ± 40 (cal BP: calibrated years before present) (Crowley 2010).

Afrosoricida

To our knowledge, the only described extinct and currently recognized species of Afrosoricida identified from Quaternary deposits on the island is *Microgale macpheei* (Table 14.2), presumed to be phylogenetically closely related to *M. brevicaudata* (Short-tailed Shrew Tenrec); it was described based on material recovered from Andrahomana Cave in the extreme southeast (Goodman et al. 2007a). G. Grandidier (1928) described *Cryptogale australis* based on skulls recovered from owl pellets in Andrahomana Cave; this material has subsequently been identified as the extant form *Geogale aurita* (Large-eared Tenrec) (Heim de Balsac 1972). G. Grandidier (1928) named another presumably extinct species, *M. decaryi*, from owl pellets obtained in the same cave, and Kaudern (1918) described *M. brevipes* based on material collected in a cave close to Mahajanga (MacPhee 1986). A broad analysis of the species limits of members of the genus *Microgale* found that *M. decaryi* is a synonym of *M. principula* (Greater Long-tailed Shrew Tenrec) and that *M. brevipes* is a synonym of *M. brevicaudata* (MacPhee 1987). Other extant species of *Microgale* have been reported from bone remains recovered in caves, the deposition of which was probably for the most part in the form of regurgitated bird of prey pellets (MacPhee 1986, 1987; Burney et al. 1997).

Andrahomana Cave is located at the western foothills of the Anosyenne Mountains of extreme southeastern Madagascar, in a remarkably abrupt dry-wet ecotonal zone, just on the arid side of a dramatic rain shadow. The natural modern flora of this region, located in close proximity to the Ankodida and Petriky protected areas, is transitional dry spiny thicket (Gautier et al. 2018), and the local mammal fauna is representative of this vegetation type (Goodman et al. 2018b). The discovery of subfossil material of *M. principula*, a species currently restricted to moist evergreen forests, in Andrahomana Cave, suggests that there has been a shift toward aridity in the local vegetational communities of this immediate region in recent geological time. Other organisms found in the cave support this conclusion (A. C. Walker 1967; Burney et al. 2008).

Soricomorpha

Bones of *Suncus murinus* and *S. etruscus*, species of Soricidae introduced to Madagascar (see Ramasindrazana et al., pp. 1872–80), were recovered in Anjohibe Cave (Burney et al. 1997) and Andrahomana Cave (Burney et al. 2008), respectively. These bones are presumed to have been deposited very recently.

Chiroptera

Later in this chapter, there is a contribution on fossil and subfossil bats (see Samonds et al., pp. 1859–62); this aspect is not discussed here.

Primates

A separate contribution in this book is devoted to subfossil lemurs (see Godfrey and Jungers, pp. 1824–28); details of this group are not presented here.

Carnivora

The only extinct member of the Carnivora of Madagascar, currently known from the Holocene, is *Cryptoprocta spelea*, a member of the endemic family Eupleridae. G. Grandidier (1902, 1905b) studied subfossils of this genus from the southwest and southeast, including Andrahomana Cave, and named this species *spelea* (meaning "cave"). Lamberton (1939) distinguished this species from its modern congener, *C. ferox* (Fosa) (see Gerber and Hawkins, pp. 1978–83), on the basis of the subfossil form's larger size, although a subsequent study of Savage (1978) considered these two to be conspecific. A more recent analysis of subfossil and modern skeletons of *Cryptoprocta* showed that there is a distinct separation in osteological measurements between *C. spelea* and *C. ferox* (Goodman et al. 2004a). At a few paleontological sites, both species are represented in the same deposits; however, owing to the lack of stratigraphic control, it is not known whether they were temporally sympatric. Analyses by Meador et al. (2019) confirm that the two species should be considered distinct, and they calculated that *C. spelea* had an estimated body mass of about 12.6 kg, as compared to a maximum of 9.9 kg in adult male *C. ferox* (Goodman 2012). They also found evidence of predation signs by *Cryptoprocta* on an assortment of extinct subfossil lemurs, the largest of which, *Megaladapis edwardsi*, weighed about 85 kg (Figure 14.3).

Throughout areas of the island, local people describe two forms of *Cryptoprocta*, or *fosa* in Malagasy, said to be living today—*fosa mainty*, or "black *Cryptoprocta*," and *fosa mena*, or "reddish *Cryptoprocta*"; the latter is said to be smaller than the former. All the modern specimens we have examined correspond to *fosa mena*. Given how poorly known certain forested areas of the island are, particularly for organisms such as carnivorans, it cannot be ruled out that two forms of *Cryptoprocta* exist on the island today and that the beast referred to as *fosa mainty* might be *C. spelea*—or simply based on local local folklore. The most recent radiocarbon date we are aware of for specimens identified as *C. spelea* is from material excavated at Andolonomby, which yielded a date of 1520 BP ± 25 (Crowley 2010).

Lamberton (1939) named the form *C. antamba* based on an oddly shaped mandible found at Tsiandroina. This specimen is probably a teratological individual of *C. spelea*. The name *antamba* was derived from a reputed animal living in southern Madagascar and described in Flacourt (1658 [repr. 1995]: 221): "C'est une bête grande comme un grand chien qui a la tête ronde et au rapport des Nègres, elle à la ressemblance d'un léopard, elle dévore les hommes

FIGURE 14.3 **A re-creation of two males of the carnivoran *Cryptoprocta spelea* and the *Pachylemur insignis* they have brought down—both species have gone extinct in recent geological time. There is physical evidence of *C. spelea* preying upon an assortment of lemurs that no longer exist, including *Megaladapis edwardsi*, which weighed about 85 kg (Meador et al. 2019).** (ARTWORK by V. Simeonovski.)

et les veaux. Elle est rare et ne demeure que dans les lieux des montagnes les moins fréquentés." (This is a beast of the size of a dog with a round head. According to local people it looks like a leopard and eats men and calves. It is rare and lives only in the most remote mountainous areas.)

Wozencraft (1986), based on older museum specimens, described what was presumed to be a living euplerid species, *Galidictis grandidieri* (Grandidier's Vontsira) (species name modified by Wozencraft 1987), from the region of Lake Tsimanampesotse. Subsequent molecular studies found it to be a geographic form of the moist-evergreen-forest-dwelling *G. fasciata* (Broad-striped Vontsira) (see Veron et al., pp. 1863–65). *Galidictis f. grandidieri*, which has a very limited distribution, has been discovered in subfossil remains from the Ankazoabo Cave, near Itampolo (Goodman 1996a). With the acumen typical of this remarkable paleontologist, Lamberton (1936: 18), who excavated Ankazoabo Cave, noted, "Mes récoltes comprennent aussi d'autres carnivores, j'ai notamment un crâne et divers os d'un *Galidictis*, voisin des espèces actuelles, et peut-être même identique." (My collections include also other carnivores. In particular I have a skull and various bones of a *Galidictis* that is closely related to the extant species and possibly even identical). Lake Tsimanampesotse and Itampolo are separated by about 50 km. Further, remains identified as "*Galidictis grandidieri*" have been found in Ankilitelo Cave, in the Mikoboka Mountains some 180 km north of Tsimanampesotse (Muldoon et al. 2009).

Subfossils of two other Eupleridae carnivorans, *Galidia elegans* (Ring-tailed Vontsira) and *Mungotictis decemlineata* (Bokyboky), have also been recovered in Ankilitelo Cave (Muldoon et al. 2009), neither species known today from this area of the southwest. The modern southern limit of *Mungotictis* is the dry deciduous forest in the southern portion of the Menabe Region, some 150 km farther north of the cave, and that of *Galidia* is about 400 km north of the cave in dry deciduous forest or 300 km to the east in the eastern moist evergreen forest. Thus, given that the radiocarbon dates for mammal subfossils from Ankilitelo Cave are about 500 BP, it is clear that the geographic distributions of these two euplerid members of the Carnivora, as well as *Galidictis f. grandidieri*, have changed in the very recent geological past.

Artiodactyla

At least three species of dwarf hippos occurred on Madagascar until recent geological time (Table 14.2). On the basis of modern radiocarbon techniques, the most recent well-substantiated date for hippos on the island is 1260 BP ± 25, from a bone excavated at Antsirabe (Crowley 2010); the published date of 980 BP ± 200 (Mahé and Sourdat 1972) is based on an older and more variable dating technique. Legends and stories of these animals remain part of the oral history in several regions of the island. On the basis of this line of evidence, hippos may have continued to exist on Madagascar into the late 19th century or even more recently (Godfrey 1986; Burney and Ramilisonina 1999).

The subfossil species of Malagasy dwarf hippos included *Hippopotamus lemerlei*, known from numerous sites in the southwest and west and northward, probably to the region of Mahajanga (Stuenes 1989; Burney et al. 1997); *H. laloumena*, identified from material collected along the east coast near Mananjary (Faure and Guérin 1990), previously named *H. amphibius standini* by Monnier and Lamberton (1922); and *H. madagascariensis*, excavated from several localities in the west and southwest (Stuenes 1989). On the basis of different arguments associated with naming priority and synonymy, it has been proposed that this last species should be called *H. guldbergi* (Fovet et al. 2011). J. M. Harris (1991) presented evidence that *H. madagascariensis* should be placed in the genus *Hexaprotodon*, the only living member of which (following certain authorities) is *H. liberiensis*, occurring in forests and marshes of

western Africa. In Table 14.2, we provisionally place all three species in the genus *Hippopotamus* and await the results of molecular studies to assess the phylogenetic and generic relationships of Malagasy hippos.

Hippopotamus madagascariensis and *H. lemerlei* had broad distributions across a good portion of Madagascar, excluding much of the east and extreme north. However, few appropriate subfossil sites are known from the central east and northeast, and it cannot be conclusively inferred that hippos did not occur in these zones. On the basis of osteological and cranial characters, *H. madagascariensis* was more terrestrial than *H. lemerlei* (Stuenes 1989; Rakotovao et al. 2014), and there was presumably some habitat segregation between them. At several sites, bone remains of these two species have been excavated from the same deposits (particularly on the Central Highlands), and it can be presumed that they lived contemporaneously and sympatrically (Stuenes 1989). However, most of the large collections of Malagasy subfossil hippo material were obtained at the end of the 19th and the early 20th centuries, and the associated excavations lacked stratigraphic control—hence, it is difficult to verify these aspects.

Notable bimodal variation in body size and canine length has been found in *H. lemerlei*, and this species probably showed sexual dimorphism (Stuenes 1991). This type of variation is comparable to that of the extant mainland African species *H. amphibius*. Numerous cranial remains of *H. lemerlei* show evidence of bone trauma (Stuenes 1991), and based on further extrapolation with the life-history traits of living *H. amphibius*, which also shows similar injuries associated with male-male competition for females, *H. lemerlei* may also have been polygynous. In contrast, *H. madagascariensis* shows reduced sexual dimorphism and incidence of cranial trauma, perhaps indicating a mating system with lower levels of sexual selection, such as monogamy.

In Anjohibe Cave, in an area of 2 m^2, Burney et al. (1997) excavated the partial skeletons of at least eight individuals of the genus *Hippopotamus*, including five adults, three immature animals of different ages, and one possible neonate or fetus. The bones of several of these individuals were partially superimposed upon one another (Figure 14.4). The excavators of the site concluded that these animals died contemporaneously and probably consisted of a herd that somehow got trapped in the cave. There was no sign of cut marks on

FIGURE 14.4 **When paleoecologist David Burney and colleagues worked in Anjohibe Cave, they recovered in an area of 2 m^2 the remains of at least eight individuals of the genus *Hippopotamus*—including five adults, three immature animals of different ages, and one possible neonate or fetus—partially superimposed upon one another. How the animals arrived deep in the cave is uncertain, but they were possibly washed in by a flash flood. The artist's rendition of the scene of what must have been complete pandemonium is depicted here, with bats flying around and the hippos knocking over stalagmites and defecating before they perished.** (ARTWORK by V. Simeonovski.)

the bones or other possible human implications in their death. Several broken speleothems were found in the sediments mixed with the bones, and these are probably the result of the animals thrashing about the site of their eventual death. One can only imagine the pandemonium of the scene.

Until a few decades ago, the earliest known evidence of humans on Madagascar was a hippo bone, recovered from Ambolisatra by Grandidier, with a distinct cut mark that was made when the bone was in a "green state." That is to say, the animal was dismantled with a knifelike object very soon after its death. On the basis of carbon-14 dating, using accelerator mass spectrometry (AMS) bone-collagen dating techniques, this hippo lived around 1970 BP ± 70 (MacPhee and Burney 1991). Subsequently, the date of first human presence on the island has been pushed deeper in time (see Wright and Rakotoarisoa, pp. 181–90). Further, from Anjohibe Cave, hippo bones with cut marks were recovered during a relatively recent excavation, and material in the associated fossiliferous layer yielded radiocarbon dates of 3819 BP ± 35 to 3275 BP ± 35 (Gommery et al. 2011). Other bones of hippos with butcher marks were recovered from Lamboharana and Belo-sur-Mer by Grandidier (MacPhee and Burney 1991).

Rodentia

Since the late 20th century, with the utilization of more precise excavation techniques at several paleontological sites, including washing and fine sieving of sediments, bones of small mammals, specifically rodents and tenrecs, have been recovered (MacPhee 1986; Burney et al. 1997, 2008, 2020a; Gommery et al. 2018). At certain cave sites, there are on occasion high concentrations of small-mammal bones, generally below ledges, which presumably represent places where cave-roosting owls dismantled prey and deposited pellets containing nondigested food remains. Little work has been conducted in a paleontological context with such material, although there are a number of modern studies on the diets of raptors (see Rene de Roland and Thorstrom, pp. 1668–79). Examination of such cave deposits in association with radiocarbon dating might provide some fine details with regard to faunal turnover through recent geological time and identification of periods when certain non-native small mammals (*Rattus* spp., *Mus musculus*, and *Suncus* spp.; see Ramasindrazana et al., pp. 1872–80) first colonized the island via human introductions.

Among Nesomyinae rodents, there are three named extinct species that have been recovered in Holocene deposits (Table 14.2). G. Grandidier (1903) described *Hypogeomys australis* on the basis of material obtained by C. Alluaud in Andrahomana Cave. Subsequent excavations conducted by F. Sikora in the same cave resulted in the recovery of more than 40 bones of this animal (Goodman and Rakotondravony 1996), and new material was recovered at the site during more recent work (Burney et al. 2008). The only living member of this genus is *H. antimena* (Malagasy Giant Jumping Rat), which is currently confined to the forest block north of Morondava and is threatened with extinction (see Sommer and Carleton, pp. 2025–27). The two species of *Hypogeomys*, with the extinct *H. australis* being the bigger of the two, are the largest known rodents to have occurred on Madagascar during the Quaternary. There is no evidence that these two species occurred in sympatry. G. Grandidier (1912) described a second subfossil species, *Hypogeomys boulei*, which has been subsequently identified as *Plesiorycteropus*, in the order Bibymalagasia (MacPhee 1994).

Subfossils of *Hypogeomys* from sites outside the modern distribution of *H. antimena* are known from the Beloha area in the extreme south (Lamberton 1946: Plate IIIf), from Tsirave (notably inland and near the Mangoky River), from Ampoza (not far from Ankazoabo-Atsimo and the Vohibasia Forest), and from a Central Highlands site near Antsirabe (Goodman and Rakotondravony 1996). The material from Antsirabe falls within the measurement range of *H. australis*, and the other bones are referable to *H. antimena*. Subfossils of *H. antimena* excavated at Ampoza, which is distinctly outside of this species' modern distribution, yielded a radiocarbon date of 1350 ± 60 BP (Goodman and Rakotondravony 1996), and the most recent radiocarbon date for *H. australis* is from Andrahomana Cave, at 1536 ± 35 BP (Burney et al. 2008). Further, bone remains of *H. antimena* presumed to be of Holocene age have been recovered from two different sites along the Mahafaly Plateau in the extreme southwest: Ankazoabo Cave near Itampolo (Lamberton 1936) and Mitoho Cave at the edge of Lake Tsimanampesotse (MacPhee 1986). On the basis of this information, it is clear that over the past few millennia, the distribution of *H. antimena* has greatly contracted, and *H. australis* went extinct.

During recent excavations in the zone to the north of Mahajanga, including the Narindra Peninsula, an assortment of rodent teeth were recovered from cave breccia. The material includes at least two new, recently described species of Nesomyinae rodents (Mein et al. 2010): *Brachytarsomys mahajambaensis* and *Nesomys narindaensis*. Morphologically similar specimens referable to *N. narindaensis* have been found in Anjohibe Cave and in the Ankarana karst complex, as well as other material referable to a large member of this genus (M. Carleton, unpublished data), and it seems to have been a relatively widespread species in northern and northwestern Madagascar. Further *Brachytarsomys* teeth have been excavated in the extreme southwest (Sabatier and Legendre 1985), and *Monticolomys* teeth in the Beloka Cave near Mahajanga, both records distinctly outside of the known modern distribution of these genera and presumably representing undescribed extinct subfossil species of Nesomyinae rodents.

Recently, a large species of *Macrotarsomys* from the Mikea Forest in the southwest of the island, to the north of Toliara, was named based on a single specimen obtained after extensive trapping effort (Goodman and Soarimalala 2005). Soon thereafter, remains of this species, *M. petteri* (Petter's Big-footed Mouse), were identified in subfossil remains collected in Andrahomana Cave (Goodman et al. 2006a). If the sequence of events had been reversed, and the subfossils were studied before the fieldwork in the Mikea Forest, this taxon would have been named as an extinct species. Further subfossils of a large species of *Macrotarsomys* have been identified from the Mahafaly Plateau in the southwest (Sabatier and Legendre 1985) that most likely represent *M. petteri*. In the recent geological past, this species had a distribution from the Mikea Forest south to the Mahafaly Plateau and then east to the western foothills of the Anosyenne Mountains. Subfossil material identified as *Eliurus myoxinus* (Western Tuft-tailed Rat) has been recovered from Andrahomana Cave (Goodman et al. 2006a) and from Ankilitelo Cave (Muldoon et al. 2009), both sites within the known range of living *E. myoxinus*.

INTRODUCED MAMMALS

Either accidentally or intentionally, a number of mammal species have been introduced to Madagascar. Some of these animals are human commensals that in several cases have invaded natural forest formations (e.g., *Rattus rattus*, *R. norvegicus*, *Mus musculus*, *Suncus etruscus*, and *S. murinus*; see Ramasindrazana et al., pp. 1872–80); others are introduced wild animals that have become naturalized (e.g., *Cervus timorensis* and *Dama dama*) or domestic animals (e.g., goat, sheep, pig, dog, and cat). More details of the role these animals play as vectors and reservoirs of disease are presented in chapter 6.

Rabbits, Order Lagomorpha, Family Leporidae

A variety of rabbits have been introduced to Madagascar (Dechambre 1951), mostly for meat production and to a much lesser extent for fur products. Rabbit meat continues to be consumed today and is appreciated by expatriates and Malagasy nationals in both towns and rural areas. Rabbit meat is available in supermarkets and many markets in Antananarivo. It is not uncommon for Malagasy families living in towns and cities to keep these animals, especially as pets for children.

Shrews, Order Soricomorpha, Family Soricidae

Elsewhere in this chapter, details are presented on members of this family that are introduced to Madagascar (see Ramasindrazana et al., pp. 1872–80), and only some summary details are presented here. Two shrew species have been unintentionally introduced by humans to the island. The tiny species *Suncus etruscus* (Etruscan Shrew), the Malagasy population of which was previously considered an island endemic, as *S. madagascariensis*, has been shown based on genetic research to be closely related to populations of *S. etruscus* from Sri Lanka and India (Omar et al. 2011; Meegaskumbura et al. 2012). On Madagascar this tiny shrew is largely forest dwelling and seems to be distinctly more common in the drier western and southern portions of the island than in the wetter east. The second species, *S. murinus* (Asian Musk Shrew), can be found as a human commensal in cities, towns, and villages in both the mesic east and dry west, as well as in natural forest formations. It or its parasites have been implicated as a vector of a variety of zoonotic diseases that are known to occur in humans, including bubonic plague (see chapter 6).

Carnivores, Order Carnivora

Cats, Family Felidae

The question of the occurrence of wildcats on Madagascar is intriguing. It is certain that cats, whether wild or domestic, were introduced to the island, but until recently the details of when and from where were unclear. Petit (1933) reported finding bones of cats in the context of subfossil deposits, but almost certainly these were relatively recent remains and do not reflect an ancient colonization of felids on the island. Flacourt (1658 [repr. 1995]: 220) noted, "*Saca* c'est un chat sauvage, il y en a de beaux. Ils s'accouplent avec les chats domestiques." (*Saca* is a wild cat, some of which are very handsome. They breed with domestic cats). Kerr (1792: 155) described "*Fel. Catus madagascarensis*" from the island and noted, "This is a beautiful variety, which inhabits the island of Madagascar." Subsequently this form has been synonymized with *F. silvestris*. A recent genetic study by Sauther et al. (2020) based on forest-dwelling "wild cats" showed that the analyzed individuals are descendants of domestic cats coming from different portions of the Arabian Sea region, which may have arrived to Madagascar on trade ships of the Islamic-era shipping network. However, no cat remains were recovered during excavations at Mahilaka (Rakotozafy 1996), a port city in the northwest of the island that flourished in 1050–1400 CE and was part of the Islamic trade network of that period (Radimilahy 1998; see Wright and Rakotoarisoa, pp. 181–90). Recently, the mystery of an unidentified carnivoran known in the northeast as *fitoaty* (Borgerson 2013) has been solved; it turned out to be a form of feral cat (*F. silvestris*) (Farris et al. 2016).

Dogs, Family Canidae

The other species of introduced carnivorans on Madagascar include *Canis lupus* (domestic dog) and *Viverricula indica* (Small Indian Civet). Dogs are common commensals across the island and in some places are used for hunting, particularly for terrestrial mammals such as *Tenrec* or *Setifer*. Further, feral dogs occur in disturbed habitats or at forest edges, prey on native mammals and birds, and are implicated in the transmission of different pathogens to endemic Eupleridae carnivorans (e.g., Rasambainarivo et al. 2017, Rasambainarivo and Goodman 2019). Recent genetic studies have shown that 90% of Malagasy dogs carry a haplotype that is present in dogs from sub-Saharan Africa (Ardalan et al. 2015).

Civets, Family Viverridae

The history of the introduction of *Viverricula* on the island was unclear until recently. There is no clear mention in Flacourt (1658 [repr. 1995]) of *Viverricula*, although the description and context of his "Falanouc" could be this species. Today, *V. indica* is widely distributed across much of the island, including the driest areas of the southwest, and often occurs close to human settlements and at the ecotone between forest and anthropogenic habitats. A recent genetic study of populations on western Indian Ocean islands (Socotra, Madagascar, Comoros, and Mafia) has shown that they are introduced from the Indian subcontinent and northern Indochina, presumably for feral rearing of animals for the production of its perianal gland secretion, used in different perfume products (Gaubert et al. 2017).

Odd-toed Ungulates, Order Perissodactyla

Horses and Donkeys, Family Equidae

The first record we are aware of that indicates the introduction of the horse (*Equus caballus*) on Madagascar is from 1817, when Robert Farquhar, governor of Mauritius, sent animals to Malagasy king Radama I (Dechambres 1951). During the French colonial era on the island, the breeding of horses was augmented, and an estimated 400 individuals in 1896 had grown to 3500 in 1935 (Deschamps 1960). Subsequently the numbers have notably been reduced, to about 300 individuals in 2010 (Cardinale et al. 2017), perhaps associated with rearing techniques or zoonotic diseases. A recent study by Cardinale et al. (2017) found that 46.2% of Malagasy

horses sampled had seroprevalence for West Nile Virus. Donkeys (*E. asinus*) have been imported on various occasions (Dechambres 1951) and today can be found in only a few areas of the island.

Even-toed Ungulates, Order Artiodactyla

Bush Pigs, Family Suidae

The question of the origin of bush pigs (*Potamochoerus*) on Madagascar is intriguing, and until recently it was unclear whether this animal was introduced and naturalized to the island or part of the native mammal fauna. This question has been resolved recently (Lee et al. 2020): bush pigs are introduced to Madagascar and are genetically closest to populations in southern Africa.

In many of the classic works on the mammals of Madagascar, bush pigs were considered indigenous, which at least in part is related to the naming of the species *P. larvatus* based on material collected on the island (Cuvier 1822). Decary (1950) classified it as an animal native to the island. Paulian (1961: 338n1) questioned this supposition and remarked, "Il paraît difficile de ne pas considérer le Potamochère malgache comme introduit à l'origine par l'homme, sans doute dans ce cortège de plantes et d'animaux ... qui entourait une population au stade de la cueillette ou de la culture itinérante." (It seems difficult not to believe that the Malagasy bushpig was introduced by man together with a variety of plants and animals ... which were associated with a population of hunters and gatherers). Subsequently, Paulian (1984: 152) stated the same idea in slightly different terms: "The lambo [Malagasy name for this animal] is very close to the African form. Man may have introduced it. In East Africa its congeners sometimes live in semi-liberty in the villages." In fact, we have found few records of African *Potamochoerus* breeding in captivity, and often the replenishment of captive village stock is through the capture of recently born wild animals (Boettger 1958).

Bone remains of *P. larvatus* have been found in caves in the context of subfossil remains, such as at Anjohibe (Burney et al. 1997) and Beanka (Burney et al. 2020a), but without a doubt very recent, and in midden remains at numerous archaeological sites (e.g., Rakotozafy and Goodman 2005; Radimilahy et al. 2013). The earliest evidence of it on the island in an archaeological context is at Rezoky, which dates from the 13th to the 15th centuries (Dewar and Wright 1993; Rakotozafy and Goodman 2005). The mid-17th-century writings of Etienne de Flacourt state, with regard to the Tolagnaro region (1658 [repr. 1995]: 219), "Il y a des porcs sangliers une grande quantité dans les bois qui font grand dommage aux vivres de ce pays." (Wild boar are abundant in the forests and cause substantial damage to the crops of the country). Thus, although it is negative evidence, we are inclined to interpret the lack of any trace of this species on the island until the 13th to 15th centuries to suggest that it was only recently introduced by humans and subsequently became feral. Bush pigs are now found in all the natural forest types on the island (see Goodman and Andrianjakarivelo, pp. 2003–6) and are widely consumed by non-Muslims in different areas of the island (Golden 2009; see Golden et al., pp. 204–17).

Deer, Family Cervidae

Two species of deer were introduced to Madagascar. Sometime between 1928 and 1932, individuals of *Dama dama* (Fallow Deer) and *Cervus timorensis* (Rusa or Timor Deer) were released on the island (Lever 1985). The first species was introduced in the upper portion of the Ankaratra Massif, and the latter species near the Analamazaotra Forestry Station (Périnet). Even though much of the natural forest on the Ankaratra Massif has been destroyed, a remnant naturalized population of *D. dama* still occurred in the area until at least a few decades ago. In 1996, during a biological inventory of the Nosiarivo Forest above Manjakatompo at about 2000 m, local people mentioned that even with continued hunting pressure, a population of *D. dama* still occurred locally (cf. Chapman and Chapman 1980), and ungulate footprints that may have belonged to deer were observed in the forest (S. M. Goodman and D. Rakotondravony, unpublished data). In the case of *C. timorensis*, the naturalized population was thriving in 1955 and perhaps into the early 1960s (Paulian 1961), but since then it has been exterminated as a result of poaching (Lever 1985). According to Lever (1985: 215), *C. nippon* (Sika Deer) was not introduced to Madagascar (cf. Whitehead 1972: 89).

Cattle, Family Bovidae

The actual date that cattle (subfamily Bovinae) and goats and sheep (subfamily Caprinae) were introduced to the island remains unclear. The place of origin of zebu (*Bos indicus*), known as *omby* in Malagasy, the most widespread form of cattle on the island, is almost certainly southern Asia (S. Chen et al. 2009). Zebu was subsequently brought to sub-Saharan Africa, and it is not clear whether it came to Madagascar directly from Asia or from introduced African populations (Souvenir Zafindrajaona and Lauvergne 1993), but in either case, its arrival may have been via the Comoro islands (Brucato et al. 2018). G. Grandidier (1900) described *Bos madagascariensis* on the basis of subfossil remains from Ambolisatra, which has been incorrectly interpreted to mean zebu is part of the ancient indigenous fauna of Madagascar (e.g., Poisson 1935); this is almost certainly an incorrect supposition.

Remains of zebu, goat, and sheep are represented in the Mahilaka bone middens (Rakotozafy 1996), a port city dating to 1050–1400 CE. Today, feral populations of zebu occur in forested areas of the island. A considerable literature exists on the relationship between Malagasy culture and zebu, the early history of their commercialization (e.g., G. Campbell 2020), and the role these animals play in environmental degradation (e.g., Fauroux 1989; Moizo 1997). Dechambre (1951) mentioned that feral zebu have a range of names and phenotypic characters—for example, *barias* refers to a form with a small or no hump.

Rodents, Order Rodentia

Guinea Pig, Family Caviidae

Cavia porcellus, in the form of the domestic Guinea Pig, has been introduced to Madagascar for meat production and as a household pet. This animal has not been very popular for consumption because of its small size and bad smell.

Rats and Mice, Family Muridae

A later contribution in this chapter presents a range of details on this family of rodents, which is introduced to the island (see

Ramasindrazana et al., pp. 1872–80), and another discusses the ecology of the genus *Rattus* (see Randriamoria et al., pp. 2006–8).

ELEVATIONAL VARIATION AND LEVELS OF SPECIES RICHNESS AND ENDEMISM

As mentioned earlier, the past decade has seen a dramatic increase in the number of forest sites surveyed for mammals on Madagascar. Considerable new information is available about elevational variation among most terrestrial mammals, and it is now possible to derive a relatively accurate estimate of species richness for certain forested areas, updating the information presented in Goodman et al. (2003a).

Several mountains in the moist evergreen forest formation have been the subject of small-mammal inventories along an elevational gradient, and these massifs span the complete latitudinal breadth of the island, from Montagne d'Ambre in the north to Andohahela in the south. The study techniques used and work efforts expended during these different surveys are comparable with regard to documentation of the local presence of tenrecs and rodents, and we confine our comparisons to these two groups. Studies associated with other mammalian orders, specifically Primates, Chiroptera, and Carnivora, are not as consistent with regard to survey effort, and these groups are not reviewed here. In Table 14.3, we list the known elevational ranges for species of tenrecs and rodents from seven different mountains in the moist evergreen forest, all of which are part of the protected area system (Figure 14.5): Montagne d'Ambre (12°S), Tsaratanàna (14°S), Manongarivo (14°S), Marojejy (14°S), Anjanaharibe-Sud (15°S), Andringitra (22°S), and Andohahela, parcel 1 (25°S). The last site falls south of the Tropic of Capricorn. The range of elevations surveyed on each of these massifs spans the remaining intact forest zones on Madagascar.

Several points need to be mentioned about the elevational distribution data. First, for most species of tenrecs and rodents, the elevational zone that has been recorded on these different massifs is relatively consistent. Several species of small mammals are found from lowland forest zones to the montane forest. Zonation specificity is indicated in the data by only two species, *Oryzorictes tetradactylus* (Four-toed Mole Tenrec), known only from montane ericoid thicket, and another species, *Microgale brevicaudata* (Short-tailed Shrew Tenrec), from lowland moist evergreen forest on certain of these massifs and also occurring in western dry deciduous forests. A few species on a given massif are absent from a mid-elevational band and in such cases are known only in lowland and upper-elevation portions of the moist evergreen forest. This pattern is probably artificial and associated with reduced chance of capture for species with low abundance or that are difficult to trap. As a general rule, a large percentage of the species are found from mid- to upper-elevational forested zones of the different massifs. There are few examples of animal species found on one massif only in the lowlands and on another massif only in the montane forest. Some variation in elevational distribution occurs within certain species of Tenrecidae. For example, *Oryzorictes hova*, as currently defined (see Everson et al. 2016), shows some substantial differences in elevational distribution between massifs. Two explanations can be offered: 1) it is largely a fossorial species that is more active on the ground surface after rains, and the likelihood of capturing it decreases during dry spells—hence our presence-absence data do not reflect its real elevational distribution; or 2) this species is polyphyletic with at least three candidate species that are geographically separated (see Everson et al., pp. 1888–91), and perhaps each form has different elevational distributions.

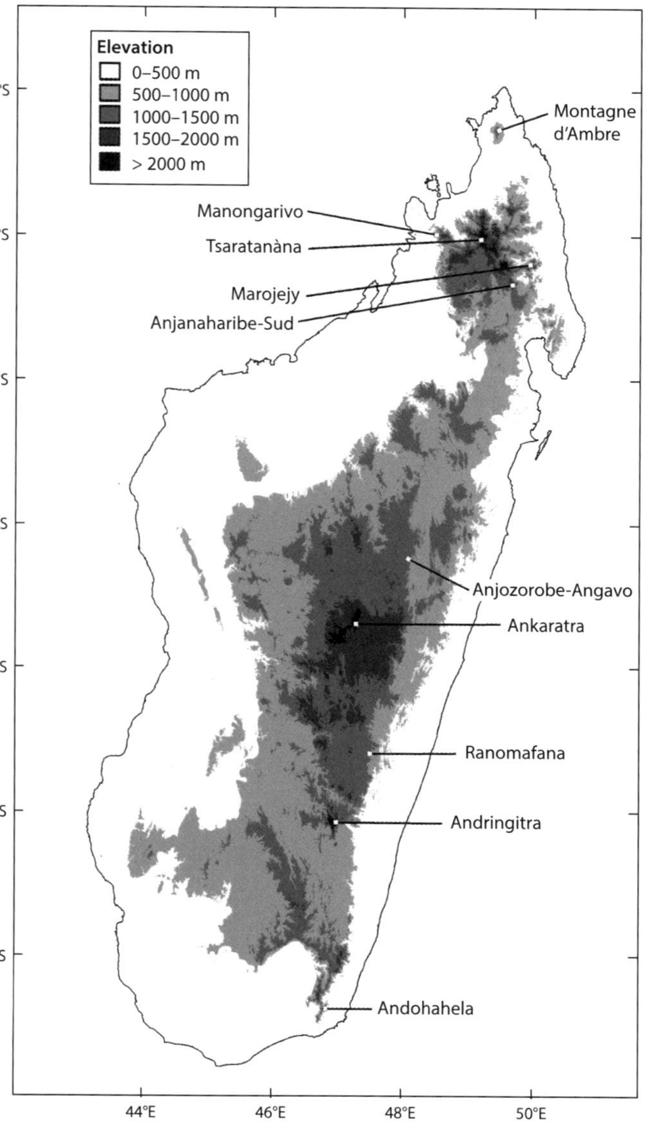

FIGURE 14.5 **Map showing most of the major moist-evergreen-forest sites that have been extensively surveyed for small mammals, including seven different massifs that have been the subject of elevational transects on these animals.**

Second, in general, a good proportion of these mammals have broad geographic distributions and are found along nearly the complete length of the latitudinal swath of the seven massifs. Twelve of the 25 tenrecs recorded from the different sites were censused on at least five of seven massifs. Of endemic rodents, only four of the 15 species were found on five of the seven massifs.

Third, along a north–south gradient, there is no clear pattern of a decrease in the lower limit of the elevational zone in which a given species occurs. Based on arguments of the potential dampening effect of latitudinal gradients and the fact that our transect covers 13°

TABLE 14.3. **Elevational distribution of tenrecs and rodents (small mammals) of Madagascar on mountains with moist evergreen forests and all sites within protected areas**

	MONTAGNE D'AMBRE[1]	TSARATANÀNA[2]	MANONGARIVO[3]	MAROJEJY[4]	ANJANAHARIBE-SUD[5]	ANDRINGITRA[6]	ANDOHAHELA[7]
Elevation range sampled (m)	340–1350	730–2500	0–1600	450–1875	875–1950	720–2450	440–1875
Latitude (°S)	12	13–14	14	14	15	22	25
AFROSORICIDA							
Family Tenrecidae							
Hemicentetes nigriceps	–	–	–	–	–	2050	–
H. semispinosus	–	1420–2050	–	775–810	–	810	–
Microgale brevicaudata	350–650	730–1150	–	450–810	–	–	–
M. cowani	–	1430–2500	1600	††1175–1875	–	810–2450	1200–1875
M. drouhardi	1000–1350	1430–2500	1240–1600	810	–	720–810	–
M. dryas	–	–	–	–	1200	–	–
M. fotsifotsy	650–1150	1590–2500	1240	1175–1225	1200–1600	720–1990	440–1500
M. gracilis	–	–	–	1175–1875	1200	1210–1990	1500–1875
M. gymnorhyncha	–	1430–2500	–	1250–1625	1260–1600	1210–1990	810–1875
M. longicaudata	650–1350	1430–2500	785–1240	1175–1625	1260–1950	720–1990	440–1875
M. majori	–	–	785–1240	–	–	720–1625	1200–1875
M. mergulus	–	–	–	–	–	720	–
M. monticola	–	–	–	1625–1875	1550–1950	–	–
M. parvula	1150–1350	1430–2050	–	450–1625	1260–1950	720–1990	440–1875
M. principula	–	–	–	1225–1875	875–1550	1600	440–1200
M. pusilla	–	–	–	–	–	2050	–
M. soricoides	–	1430–2500	1600	1175–1625	1260–1600	1210–1990	810–1875
M. taiva	–	1430–2500	–	1175–1250	875–1950	720–1990	–

(continued overleaf)

TABLE 14.3. ***continued***

	MONTAGNE D'AMBRE[1]	TSARATANÀNA[2]	MANONGARIVO[3]	MAROJEJY[4]	ANJANAHARIBE-SUD[5]	ANDRINGITRA[6]	ANDOHAHELA[7]
Family Tenrecidae *continued*							
M. thomasi	–	1430–2500	–	1250	–	720	440–1200
Nesogale dobsoni	1050	1430–2500	1600	810–1625	1260	1210–2450	810–1875
N. talazaci	650–1350	1150–1300	785–1240	450–1625	1260–1550	720–1990	810
Oryzorictes hova	–	1590–2050	1240–1600	450–1625	1200	1625–1990	1500–1875
O. tetradactylus	–	–	–	–	–	2050–2450	–
Setifer setosus	650	1420–2050	785–1240	450–775	875–1200	810	810–1200
Tenrec ecaudatus	1000–1350	–	785	450–775	875–1260	720–810	440–1200
Total number of species of Tenrecidae	9	15	11	19	15	22	15
Total number of species of *Microgale*	5	10	6	13	10	14	10
Soricidae							
**Suncus murinus*	100–1350	–	785–1240	–	–	–	–
RODENTIA							
Subfamily Murinae							
**Mus musculus*	–	2500	–	–	–	1960–2050	–
**Rattus rattus*	340–1350	1150–2500	785–1600	1250–1625	875–1950	810–2450	810–1875
Subfamily Nesomyinae							
Brachytarsomys albicauda	–	–	–	1250	875	–	1875
B. villosa	–	1430–2050	–	–	1600	–	–
Brachyuromys betsileoensis	–	–	–	–	–	1960–2450	–
B. ramirohitra	–	–	–	–	1600	1210–1960	1500

	MONTAGNE D'AMBRE[1]	TSARATANÀNA[2]	MANONGARIVO[3]	MAROJEJY[4]	ANJANAHARIBE-SUD[5]	ANDRINGITRA[6]	ANDOHAHELA[7]
Eliurus ellermani	1000	–	785–1240	775–810	1260	–	–
E. grandidieri	–	1590	1600	1250–1875	1260–1600	–	–
E. majori	1000–1350	1300–2500	1600	1250–1875	1260–1950	1210–1990	1200–1500
E. minor	1000	1300–2050	1240–1600	1250–1625	875–1260	720–1960	440–1875
E. myoxinus	–	730	400	810	–	–	–
E. tanala	–	730–1600	–	–	–	810–1625	810–1875
E. webbi	650–1000	–	785–1240	450–775	875	720–810	440–810
Gymnuromys roberti	–	–	–	1250	1260	720–1625	1200
Monticolomys koopmani	–	1590–2050	–	–	–	1210–1990	1875
Nesomys rufus	–	1300	785–1600	810–1250	1260–1950	720–1990	810–1200
Voalavo gymnocaudus	–	–	–	1250–1875	1600	–	–
Number of species of Nesomyinae	4	8	7	10	11	9	9
Total number of species of small mammals[8]	15	25	20	30	27	33	25
Total number of species of native small mammals	13	23	18	29	26	31	24

Notes: * introduced species, † extinct species, †† species listed is based on the field identification, and subsequent molecular work has shown the taxon is a confirmed candidate species. Introduced species are preceded by an asterisk (*)

[1] Data for tenrecs are from Raxworthy and Nussbaum (1994), Goodman et al. (1996a, 2013), P. D. Jenkins et al. (1997), and Association Vahatra (unpublished data); for rodents, Raxworthy and Nussbaum (1994), Goodman et al. (1996b, 1997a, 2013), and Association Vahatra (unpublished data).

[2] Data for tenrecs and rodents are from Maminirina et al. (2008).

[3] Data for tenrecs and rodents are from Goodman and Soarimalala (2002).

[4] Data for tenrecs are from Goodman and Jenkins (2000) and Soarimalala and Goodman (2003a); for rodents, Carleton and Goodman (2000) and Soarimalala and Goodman (2003a).

[5] Data for tenrecs are from Goodman and Jenkins (1998) and Soarimalala and Goodman (2003a); for rodents from Goodman and Carleton (1998) and Soarimalala and Goodman (2003a).

[6] Data for tenrecs and rodents are from Goodman and Rasolonandrasana (2001) and Association Vahatra (unpublished data).

[7] Data for tenrecs are from Goodman et al. (1999a); for rodents from Goodman et al. (1999b). Data is only for parcel 1 of Andohahela, composed of moist evergreen forest.

[8] Counts include native and introduced species.

of latitude, it might be expected that, related to potential shifts in vegetational communities across this zone, there would be clinal variation in the elevational range of mammals on these mountains. This pattern is not apparent in the data set.

The species richness of these two groups of mammals varies among the seven massifs. This is most notable on Montagne d'Ambre, where both tenrecs and rodents have distinctly lower species richness than on the other six mountains. Located in the extreme far north of the island, Montagne d'Ambre experienced considerable volcanic activity during the Quaternary (Battistini 1965), and significant portions of the massif at the elevations of our trapping sites (1000 and 1350 m) were considerably impacted less than 8000 years ago. Possible evidence of the effect of this volcanic activity, and of the associated inference that many of the mammal species had to recolonize the forest after it was heavily damaged, is that there is no highly specialized small mammal known from the massif, such as the semi-fossorial *Microgale gracilis* or *M. gymnorhyncha*. The vast majority of small mammals found on Montagne d'Ambre occur throughout much of the moist evergreen forest. With regard to the other six massifs, some variation in species richness occurs among these two small-mammal groups; the number of native species varies from a low of 18 in moist evergreen forests on Manongarivo to a high of 31 species on Andringitra.

A number of other surveyed sites on Madagascar have important levels of mammalian diversity. In the Tsinjoarivo Forest, to the east of Ambatolampy, an inventory of the elevational zone between 1400 and 1550 m found an exceptionally large number of small mammals at two different sites within a close distance of each other (Goodman et al. 2000). Twenty-four species of small mammals were found in this forest block, consisting of 16 tenrecs (including 11 *Microgale*/*Nesogale* spp.) and eight rodent species (two introduced). On the basis of current information, the small-mammal community at Tsinjoarivo is the richest known within a narrow elevational range for any site on the island. It is the only place both species of *Hemicentetes* occur in sympatry (Goodman et al. 2000). As a point of comparison, the richest known site on the African continent for shrews (family Soricidae) is the Bwindi Impenetrable National Park in southwestern Uganda, with 19 species (Kasangaki et al. 2003). It is important to mention that the Bwindi forest includes a wide variety of habitat types across a broad elevational gradient, while two sites at about the same elevation and with similar forest types were surveyed at Tsinjoarivo.

Since the late 20th century, dry deciduous forests of the west and dry spiny thickets of the south have been the focus of biological surveys, and the results for native small mammals confirm that relatively intact habitat has notably lower species richness than intact moist evergreen forests of the east and north (Goodman and Wilmé 2008). However, these different inventories have uncovered species that are restricted to the dry deciduous forests of the west and/or dry spiny thickets, including some taxa with very localized distributions. Among small mammals, for example, *Microgale jenkinsae* (Jenkins's Shrew Tenrec) and *Macrotarsomys petteri* (Petter's Big-footed Mouse) are found only in the Mikea protected area; *M. ingens* (Long-tailed Big-footed Mouse) in the Ankarafantsika protected area; *Hypogeomys antimena* (Malagasy Giant Jumping Rat) in Kirindy Forest CNFEREF within the Menabe Antimena protected area; and *Nesomys lambertoni* (Tsingy Red Forest Rat) in the Bemaraha protected area. For lemurs, of the 43 species found in dry deciduous forests, nine have very limited distributions and are locally endemic, such as *Avahi cleesei* (Bemaraha Woolly Lemur) in Bemaraha, *Lepilemur mittermeieri* (Mittermeier's Sportive Lemur) in Ampasindava, and *L. sahamalazensis* (Sahamalaza Sportive Lemur) in Sahamalaza (Mittermeier et al. 2014). The best-known deciduous forest sites on the island are Bemaraha, Ankarafantsika, and the Kirindy Forest CNFEREF. Bemaraha and Kirindy each have a total of 19 known species of tenrecs, rodents, and lemurs, and Ankarafantsika has 17 species. Mammalian species richness is even lower in the dry spiny thickets of the south and southwest. For example, in this habitat in Andohahela (parcel 2), 14 species of land mammals (10 native) have been recorded: three tenrecs, one nesomyine, one murid (introduced), four carnivores (three introduced), and five lemurs (Feistner and Schmid 1999; Goodman and Pidgeon 1999; Goodman et al. 1999a, 1999b). The number of species in this vegetation type decreases with latitude, and sites farther south have a low number of species of the three groups (tenrecs, rodents and lemurs): 11 at Bezà-Mahafaly, 10 in Tsimanampesotse, and six in Cap Sainte Marie (Goodman et al. 2018b).

LEVELS OF SPECIES RICHNESS AND ENDEMISM AT AN ISLAND AND CONTINENTAL LEVEL

All 174 native species of nonvolant terrestrial mammals of Madagascar are found nowhere else on earth (Table 14.1). This level of species endemism, at 100%, combined with species richness is without parallel for any single island in the world, although only four native nonvolant mammalian orders occur on the island. In this section, we examine in some detail how levels of ordinal and species richness and endemism on Madagascar compare with those in other regions of the world.

For comparative purposes, we have tabulated levels of mammalian species richness and endemism (grouped by order) for two other tropical Old World islands, Borneo (757,000 km^2) and New Guinea (808,500 km^2), both of which are larger than Madagascar (594,000 km^2). Borneo holds a rich fauna, with 102 species of land mammals from 11 different orders, and about one-third of the species are endemic to the island (Payne and Francis 1998). Thus, there are close to 60% more mammal species on Madagascar than Borneo but more than double the number of orders on Borneo. There are some remarkable differences in group representation between the two islands. The tenrec and primate radiations on Madagascar contain 31 and 109 named species, respectively, as compared with the seven shrews (the ecological equivalent of tenrecs) and 13 primate species on Borneo. On the other hand, for two other orders, Carnivora and Rodentia, the species diversity on Borneo is two to three times greater than on Madagascar.

The total nonvolant mammalian fauna of New Guinea, at 138 species (Flannery 1995), is slightly greater than that of Borneo, but New Guinea has 36 fewer species than Madagascar (slightly under 25%). The level of land mammal endemism on New Guinea is high, at about three-quarters of species. One notable difference between the land mammal faunas of these two islands is the presence of

several orders on New Guinea that are part of the Australasian region. Convergence in the niches occupied by different orders on New Guinea and Madagascar is rather prevalent. For example, on New Guinea, some of the Diprotodontia (composed of kangaroos and cuscuses) replace folivorous primates (e.g., Lemuridae). Other species of Diprotodontia, particularly possums and pygmy possums, seem to have a diet similar to members of the Malagasy Cheirogaleidae (A. P. Smith and Ganzhorn 1996).

When one turns to comparisons between Madagascar and continental countries along the eastern side of Africa—regions the ancestors of extant Malagasy mammals may have come from—some very striking differences are notable. Ethiopia-Eritrea (1,023,000 km^2) and Tanzania (939,800 km^2) have land mammal faunas nearly double the size of Madagascar's, but these countries also have nearly double the surface area. When a factor of number of land mammal species per unit area (in this case 1000 km^2) is calculated, the following patterns emerge with regard to species richness—Madagascar (0.29), Tanzania (0.25), New Guinea (0.17), Ethiopia-Eritrea (0.17), and Borneo (0.14). Thus, on the basis of these comparisons, the modern land mammal fauna of Madagascar is richer in number of species overlaid on surface area than the other island and continental comparisons made. Needless to say, these comparisons do not take into account mammal species in these different areas, particularly islands, that disappeared after human colonization.

Many groups are missing from Madagascar as compared with continental Africa. These include elephants (Proboscidea), ungulates (Perissodactyla and Artiodactyla; the extant species occurring on Madagascar are introduced), hyrax (Hyracoidea), aardvarks (Tubulidentata), pangolins (Philidota), rabbits (Lagomorpha; the extant species on Madagascar is introduced), and elephant shrews (Macroscelidea). For virtually all of these groups, there is no evidence from the fossil and subfossil record that they ever occurred on Madagascar, with the exception of several species of dwarf hippos (Artiodactyla) that existed on the island until recent times (see review of subfossil mammals, above). Thus, there is no evidence of several orders of African mammals colonizing Madagascar. The absence from Madagascar of certain groups, such as the Artiodactyla, which contain important diversity and an enormous amount of biomass in eastern Africa, has important implications for the evolution of ecological systems on the island.

ADVANCEMENT OF MALAGASY MAMMALOGISTS IN THE 21ST CENTURY

We suggest that an important measure of scientific advancement associated with the study of Malagasy mammals, as well as an engagement of nationals in conservation actions, is the number of national students and researchers participating in scientific studies associated with this group of vertebrates (Figure 14.6). Here we review the evolution of a few of these facets over the past 30 years or so, examining advances in publication patterns, which reflect engagement and inclusion in the international scientific community; and the number of people obtaining higher university degrees, directly associated with the level of interest in studies related to mammalogy.

Publications

The 21st century, particularly the second decade, has seen a considerable increase in the number of books, chapters in books, and papers in international journals published by Malagasy mammalogists, comprising professors and researchers as well as younger scientists about to or having finished their higher university degrees. These publications span a diverse range of topics including mammalian ecology, taxonomy, parasites, molecular systematics, and zoonotic diseases. To simplify comparisons of changes through time, we have compiled figures from the current volume and the precursor book (Goodman and Benstead 2003).

As can be appreciated by the figures presented in Table 14.4, there has been a net augmentation in the Malagasy mammalogists contributing to the two versions of this book. Over the course of this period, contributions with Malagasy coauthors have increased from 11.8% of the total to 45.1%, along with a less pronounced increase from 5.9% to 9.8% in the number of Malagasy first-authored contributions. We suggest that the increase in the number of Malagasy researchers engaged and publishing on the island's mammals is indicative of the number of nationals working in the field of Malagasy mammalogy and carrying out dedicated research programs in this field. Further, there has been a notable increase in collaborative studies, and the current chapter has a total of 34 Malagasy coauthors, and several contributions have multiple Malagasy coauthors, as compared to the 2003 book, with six Malagasy coauthors.

Graduate Studies at Universities and Other National Institutions

Within Madagascar's national university system, which has campuses in each of the six former provincial capitals, there are graduate students working in departments with research interests related to the field of zoology, specifically mammalogy. These different university departments, under the direction of the Ministère de l'Enseignement Supérieur et de la Recherche Scientifique, include (listed in alphabetic order by city): Mention Zoologie et Biodiversité Animale (MZBA; formerly Département de Biologie Animale, or DBA) and Mention Anthropologie Biologique et Evolution, Université d'Antananarivo; Faculté des Sciences, Mention Science de la Nature et de l'Environnement, Université d'Antsiranana (UNA); Institut des Sciences et Techniques de l'Environnement (ISTE), Université de Fianarantsoa; Ecole Doctorale Ecosystèmes Naturels (EDEN), Université de Mahajanga; Institut Supérieur de Sciences, Environnement et Développement Durable (ISSEDD, ex GRENE), Université de Toamasina; and Ecole Doctorale de Biodiversité et Environnements Tropicaux, Université de Toliara. Additionally, other departments at these universities have extensive programs in fields related to mammalogy. Two of several examples at the Université d'Antananarivo are the Mention Sciences Animales, Ecole Supérieure des Sciences Agronomiques (ESSA-Forêts), and Mention Médecine Vétérinaire, Faculté de Médecine, both of which have important research and pedagogic programs associated with mammals.

In 2014, before the Malagasy national university structure shifted toward the Anglophone *licence-master-doctorat* (LMD) system,

A
B
C
D
E
F
G

TABLE 14.4. **Comparisons of Malagasy authorship of contributions to the Mammals chapter in *The Natural History of Madagascar* (Goodman and Benstead 2003) and the current book**

CATEGORY	GOODMAN AND BENSTEAD (2003)	CURRENT BOOK
Number of contributions to Mammals chapter	51	51
Number of contributions with a Malagasy coauthor[1]	6 (11.8%)	23 (45.1%)
Number of contributions with Malagasy first author or single author	3 (5.9%)	5 (9.8%)
Total number of Malagasy coauthors[2]	6	34

[1] The tally indicates that at least one Malagasy coauthor was involved in a given contribution but does not reflect the number of Malagasy nationals per contribution.
[2] The tally includes the total number of Malagasy authors involved in the Mammals chapter, with certain contributions having more than one Malagasy coauthor.

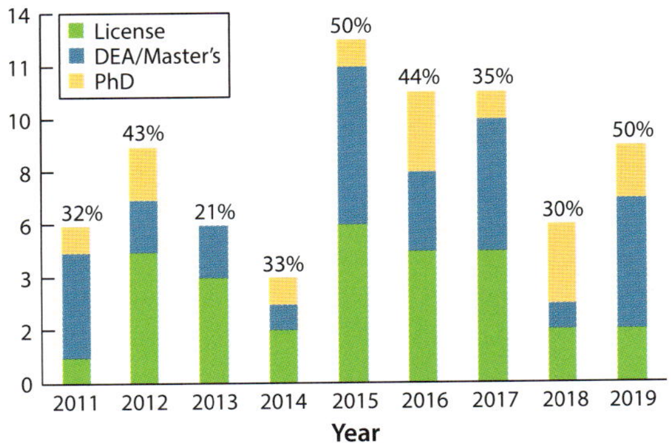

FIGURE 14.7 **The numbers of higher degrees in fields related to mammalogy for which Association Vahatra scientific staff members acted as directors or jury members between 2011 and 2019. The figure at the top of each annual bar graph is the percentage of the total related to mammology, relative to other disciplines.**

the higher degrees included *diplôme d'études approfondies* (DEA), *thèse de troisième cycle*, and *thèse d'état*, and after the transition period in 2015–2016, these became to a large extent master's, PhD, and *habilitation à diriger des recherches* (HDR), respectively. In the 21st century, there has been a considerable increase in the number of Malagasy students doing graduate studies in fields related to mammalogy. Using data from annual reports of Association Vahatra listing the intervention of its four scientific members in the Malagasy university system, we extracted details on the number of diplomas presented between 2011 and 2019 in domains related to mammalogy, including bats and marine mammals (Figure 14.7).

MAMMALIAN CONSERVATION AND THE FUTURE

The majority of native Malagasy land mammals are forest dwelling, and a large portion of research studies and associated conservation programs have been conducted in different forest ecosystems on the island. However, it is important to point out that the vast majority of mammal surveys and different research projects over the past decades have been conducted in areas of natural forest, and until recently, little was known about the native animals occurring in more open natural habitats, such as marshes and native grasslands, as well as anthropogenic settings. Starting a few years back, a number of field projects were undertaken in nonforested habitats, and perhaps to the surprise of certain mammalogists, a variety of endemic mammals were found (e.g., Randriamoria et al. 2015; Randriamoria 2017; see Eppley and Goodman, pp. 1818–21). While this shows that the previous notion that Malagasy land mammals largely or exclusively live in natural forests is not 100% accurate, it is important to mention that the number of forest-dwelling species occurring in open or anthropogenic settings is relatively small, and, in many cases, these sites

OPPOSITE: FIGURE 14.6 **Since the end of the 20th century, mammalogy on Madagascar has made important strides, and several generations of mammalogists have emerged. A) Field schools for starting university students provide an important first step to initiate young mammalogists. Here, in the context of a joint field school at Tsimanampesotse for students from the universities of Antananarivo, Fianarantsoa, and Toliara, participants are learning how to manipulate traps. B) José Ralison (standing at right), a primatologist, and research assistants in Ambatovy Forest during a nocturnal lemur survey. C) The study of zoonotic diseases of wild small mammals has been an important course of inquiry in recent years; here, in the Ankazomivady Forest, Tojo Ramihangihajason and Lalaina Arivony Nomenjanahary (seated, left to right) from Institut Pasteur de Madagascar, and students from the Université de Fianarantsoa take samples for laboratory research; D) Tamby Nasaina Ranaivoson just outside the Marojejy National Park collecting small-mammal ectoparasites. E) Steve Goodman and Voahangy Soarimalala (left to right) during a biological inventory of the Mikea National Park, collecting samples from a *Tenrec ecaudatus* (Tailless Tenrec). F) Zafimahery Rakotomalala and Landryh Ramanana (left to right) during a small-mammal inventory in the upper portion of the Andringitra Massif, close to tree line at Anjavidilava, a zone composed of montane ericoid thicket. G) The use of pitfall traps during surveys, which result in the capture of considerable numbers of terrestrial small mammals, particularly of the family Tenrecidae, has revolutionized working knowledge on Malagasy small mammals; here, Voahangy Soarimalala and Soavololonirina Ferdinette (front to back) install a pitfall line in the Ankazomivady Forest.** (PHOTOS by V. Soarimalala).

were in close proximity to natural forest. Notable exceptions include all five species of spiny tenrecs (subfamily Tenrecinae), which also occur in open grassland areas and in heavily degraded forest zones; a few species of oryzorictines (subfamily Oryzorictinae), most notably *Microgale pusilla* (Least Shrew Tenrec; see Jenkins et al., pp. 1880–87) and *Oryzorictes hova* (Hova Mole Tenrec; see Everson et al., pp. 1888–91), which have been found in open areas including marshes and rice fields (Goodman et al. 1997b; S. M. Goodman and V. Soarimalala, unpublished data); and a few Nesomyinae rodents that appear equally at home in forest or marsh ecosystems, most notably *Brachyuromys betsileoensis* (Lesser Short-tailed Rat; see Jansa et al., pp. 2011–13). Among lemurs, a handful of species are able to adapt to open habitats and different types of tree plantations (see Eppley and Goodman, pp. 1818–21), and certain species, such as members of the genera *Microcebus* and *Cheirogaleus*, can have higher population densities in slightly disturbed habitats than in intact natural forest (Ganzhorn et al. 1997). Despite this certain level of adaptability for a few species to nonforested habitats, the continued existence of much of the mammalian diversity on Madagascar depends on the maintenance and conservation of forested zones large enough, but not necessarily perfectly pristine, to sustain viable populations. Given the continued levels of deforestation on the island (see Grinand and Nourtier, pp. 105–13) and other forms of human pressure such as hunting (see Golden et al., pp. 204–17), and that most mammal species are affected by habitat fragmentation (see Steffens et al., pp. 1812–17), there is a growing view that the long-term future for certain mammals is rather bleak.

Considerable world attention has been drawn to the island's primates, and biologists and conservationists have used these animals as a "flagship" for the plight of Madagascar's unique and endangered biota (see different contributions in this chapter). Among mammals, several nonprimate species are advancing toward extinction in the wild. One example is *Hypogeomys antimena* (Malagasy Giant Jumping Rat), the largest extant rodent on the island, now restricted to a small area north of Morondava (see Sommer and Carleton, pp. 2025–27). A combination of factors has resulted in the demise of this animal, including 1) high levels of deforestation and fragmentation of the remaining dry deciduous forests, which have contributed to reduced dispersal and genetic bottlenecks, and 2) heavy predation by native carnivorans (*Cryptoprocta*) and introduced dogs, significantly reducing population sizes and recruitment into the breeding population.

Given that in the east, a considerable portion of the diversity of small mammals is in the upper portion of the medium-altitude moist evergreen forests, a zone currently facing relatively low levels of human threat, the continued existence of these mammals is much less threatened than that of groups occurring in lowland moist evergreen forests. Most notable among these lowland animals are several of the largest remaining lemurs, such as *Indri indri* (Indri), *Propithecus diadema* (Diademed Sifaka), *Varecia variegata* (Black and White Ruffed Lemur), and *V. rubra* (Red Ruffed Lemur). Perhaps it is also reasonable to place lowland forest rodents in the same group of threatened species—such as *Eliurus petteri* (Petter's Tufted-tail Rat), known from a few sites with high levels of deforestation and associated forest habitat fragmentation. Among small mammals, those confined to particular habitats and in certain cases with limited distributions include *Macrotarsomys petteri* (Petter's Big-footed Mouse), *Microgale nasoloi* (Nasolo's Shrew Tenrec), and *M. jenkinsae* (Jenkins's Shrew Tenrec), as well as the largely aquatic *M. mergulus* (Web-footed Shrew Tenrec); all are threatened by habitat destruction.

Hunting for lemurs, carnivorans, bats, and spiny tenrecs continues at significant levels (see Golden et al., pp. 204–17). Further, organized lemur-hunting parties utilizing firearms, slings, and blowguns are known from many areas of the island. In certain portions of Madagascar, there is heavy hunting pressure on spiny tenrecs, particularly *Tenrec ecaudatus* (Tailless Tenrec) and perhaps to a lesser extent *Setifer setosus* (Greater Hedgehog Tenrec). The flesh of *T. ecaudatus* is highly prized by many people, particularly toward the end of the rainy season and before the animal enters hibernation, when large fat reserves make it particularly succulent. In some areas of the island, such as in and around the Menabe Region and specifically the Kirindy Forest CNFEREF, spiny tenrecs are extensively hunted by local people, often using dogs. Along national roads leading to and from the nation's capital, Antananarivo, live *T. ecaudatus* is sold by the roadside. However, at least until the first decade or so of the 21st century, even with this pressure, these animals remained relatively common in forest parcels exploited for timber extraction, nonexploited forest parcels, and at the forest-grassland ecotone (Ganzhorn et al. 1990, 1996; Raharivololona 1996; although see Goodman et al., pp. 1891–94). In the Mikea Forest, where protein sources are limited, as well as numerous other areas around the island, mammals have been the subject of considerable hunting pressure, including *Microcebus* species (mouse lemurs) that weigh some tens of grams (Goodman et al. 2004b).

Local cultural taboos (*fady*) have both positive and negative effects on certain species. For several ethnic groups, based on local dictates, the consumption of lemur flesh is forbidden, and these animals are therefore not hunted. However, in many areas these taboos are in the process of breaking down through local sociocultural change or often are not respected by immigrants of other ethnic groups from elsewhere on the island and with different taboos (C. Schwitzer et al. 2014). Further, in periods of ecological crises, such as drought and associated famine, these customs are notably relaxed.

One example of a taboo that has negative impacts on a mammal species concerns *Daubentonia madagascariensis* (Aye-aye; see Sterling et al., pp. 1975–78). Among certain ethnic groups living in the west and northwest, this lemur species is considered extremely dangerous because it is reputed to attack, kill, and consume chickens living in the villages. Further, it is rumored to enter houses during the night through thatched roofs and murder sleeping human occupants by cutting the aortic vein with its elongated finger. It is for this reason, as a harbinger of evil misfortune, that different ethnic groups kill Aye-ayes when they have the chance. The appearance of this species in a village is a divination of the death of a villager, unless the animal can be killed.

With increased survey work on Madagascar and collection of associated specimens for taxonomic research and molecular studies, mammalogists are learning how little we really know about the fauna of the island. The level of discovery of previously unrecognized species or unnamed clades is simply extraordinary, and we leave it up to the reader to learn about these advances in the different contributions that follow in this chapter. Given the remarkable

rate of new mammal species being described from the island on the one hand and the continued destruction of the remaining habitat of these animals on the other, it is possible that certain mammal species may become extinct before they are known to science. It is for these reasons, among others, that continued faunal surveys are needed, to document what exists now and may not in the relatively near future. At the very least, data from these surveys have important archival value, and it is hoped that this information can be used to reinforce conservation programs and priorities through management plans at a range of different sites, saving this national and international natural patrimony for the prosperity of this island nation.

CONCLUSION

Since the start of the 21st century, there has been an important augmentation in working knowledge of the mammals of Madagascar. Substantial advances have been made in understanding aspects of colonization history and subsequent diversification patterns, species limits, phylogeny, biogeography, physiology, and zoonotic diseases. The island's known levels of mammal species richness will certainly increase. For example, several confirmed candidate species are currently in the process of being written up, and it is certain that further exploration of the island in the form of mammal surveys and resulting voucher specimens will yield additional new taxa and more detailed ecological information on Malagasy mammals.

Even given the important advances in systematic studies, it is remarkable that the natural history of most of the island's mammalian fauna remains poorly understood. With the exception of several lemurs (see subsequent contributions) and a smattering of rodents (e.g., *Nesomys*, *Hypogeomys*), carnivores (e.g., *Cryptoprocta*), and tenrecs (e.g., *Tenrec*), little research has been done on the diet, reproduction, social behavior, and other aspects of the natural history of the island's mammals. These major voids should be the focus of future studies.

Subject editors: Jörg U. Ganzhorn and Steven M. Goodman

GENETICS OF MALAGASY MAMMALS: AN OVERVIEW

L. Chikhi and G. M. Sgarlata

The aim of this contribution is to review the use and interpretation of genetic and genomic data generated since the end of the 20th century on Malagasy mammals and provide an overview of this rich and diverse literature. We explain most, but not all, terminology and technical topics in separate boxes. While we argue that genetic studies are too limited in number, we still could not do justice to the wide-ranging literature and have limited ourselves to work focusing principally on species diversity. Our review addresses phylogeographic and phylogenetic studies only superficially, as they are treated in detail in other contributions herein.

Genetic data are increasingly used across a wide range of taxa and disciplines, from ecology to taxonomy, evolution, anthropology, biodiversity, and conservation (Goldstein and Chikhi 2002; Steiner et al. 2013; Leitwein et al. 2020; see Box 1). For Malagasy organisms, genetic data have also been used to address a wide variety of questions (e.g., A. D. Yoder 2013; Lawler 2018). Research teams interested in behavioral ecology have used genetic data to clarify patterns of diversity and relatedness at a local scale and to quantify sex-biased dispersal rates (e.g., Radespiel et al. 2001; Wimmer et al. 2002; Lawler et al. 2003). At a larger temporal and geographic scale, other researchers have investigated complex and sometimes controversial phylogenetic relationships between species that diversified over tens of millions of years and across a wide variety of environments within the island (A. D. Yoder et al. 1996a, 2003; Jansa et al. 1999; Douady et al. 2002; Everson et al. 2016). For instance, genetic studies have played a central role in our understanding of the relationships between lemurs and other primates and in the demonstration of their monophyly (e.g., A. D. Yoder et al. 1996a). Genetic data have clarified former controversial phylogenetic questions and have established the now well-accepted scenario of ancient arrival of the lemuriform clade and its diversification on Madagascar. Similar genetic studies on other terrestrial Malagasy mammals—Tenrecidae, Eupleridae, and Nesomyinae—have also helped to firmly establish that the colonization events of these three groups were each unique and that these groups diversified in Madagascar (A. D. Yoder et al. 2003; Poux et al. 2005; Everson et al. 2016). More recently, ancient DNA studies have provided a fascinating and unique perspective on extinct subfossil lemur species (K. P. Karanth et al. 2005; see Godfrey and Jungers, pp. 1824–28), showing, for instance, that genetic diversity of two extinct species was relatively low compared to that of extant lemur species (Kistler et al. 2015).

At an intermediate geographic and temporal scale (i.e., between phylogenetic and behavioral ecology studies), genetic studies have also been conducted on Malagasy mammals for more than two decades. For instance, Leipoldt et al. (1996) compared genetic diversity among *Lepilemur mustelinus ruficaudatus* (now *L. ruficaudatus*; see Radespiel et al., pp. 1935–40), sampled in different forests of Kirindy Forest CNFEREF (Centre National de Formation, d'Etudes et de Recherche en Environnement et Foresterie) in the central west. Similarly, Rabarivola et al. (1996) compared genetic diversity among populations of *Eulemur macaco* sampled on two nearshore islands, Nosy Be and Nosy Komba, as well as the mainland, in the northwest (see Johnson

BOX 1 MEASURES OF GENETIC DIVERSITY AND DEFINITIONS

NUMBER OF ALLELES (n_A): The number of recognized variants observed in a sample of individuals for a specific locus (or stretch of DNA). It is the simplest measure of genetic diversity, but it does not account for the relative frequencies of alleles and is strongly influenced by the sample size.

SNP (single-nucleotide polymorphism): SNPs are genetic variants observed at the level of a single nucleotide. SNPs were called *segregating sites* in classical population genetics studies, but the term *SNP* is now dominant. In many cases SNPs are assumed to have only two alleles, one considered ancestral and the other one derived.

Observed heterozygosity (H_{obs}): The proportion of actual heterozygotes in the sample averaged across the loci that have been genotyped. H_{obs} varies between 0 and 1 and can be computed only if the observed genotypes for the sampled (diploid) individuals are known. It is thus a measure of *individual* diversity averaged across the loci and sampled individuals. Contrary to a common belief, it is not necessarily a reliable measure of *population* diversity because it is influenced by the mating system. It can thus be very low even when there are many alleles in the sample or population and, therefore, even when genetic diversity is high. An extreme example would be one in which all individuals are homozygous for different alleles at the same locus: H_{obs} would be zero, since no heterozygotes would be observed, but H_{exp} (see below) would be maximal.

Expected heterozygosity (H_{exp}): The proportion of heterozygotes one would observe in a sample if the observed alleles were distributed randomly within the sampled diploid individuals. This is thus the proportion of heterozygotes that one expects under random mating (or at Hardy-Weinberg equilibrium)—i.e., under panmixia. In other words, H_{obs} and H_{exp} should be equal under random mating. Differences between H_{exp} and H_{obs} are usually interpreted in terms of departures from Hardy-Weinberg equilibrium. H_{exp} is also called *gene diversity* and varies between 0 and 1. It can be computed, if the observed *allele* frequencies (p_i) are known, as $H_{exp} = 1 - \Sigma p_i^2$. Genotypes are thus not necessary. This is why it can be computed for haploid markers (mtDNA data) and is then called *haplotype diversity*.

Expected heterozygosity under mutation-drift equilibrium ($H_{exp\text{-}eq}$): This is the value expected for H_{exp} when a random mating population has reached mutation-drift equilibrium (see Box 3). At mutation-drift equilibrium, Ewens (1972) has shown that we can predict the expected frequencies of observed alleles (p_{i_eq}) by knowing only their number (n_A), the sample size (k), and the population mutation rate (the product of the population size, N, and per-locus mutation rate, u). Ewens's results thus allow the computation of $H_{exp\text{-}eq} = 1 - \Sigma(p_{i\_eq})^2$ without using the actual, observed allele frequencies (p_i), which are required for H_{exp}. By comparing H_{exp} and $H_{exp\text{-}eq}$, we can thus test whether the population is at mutation-drift equilibrium (assuming random mating) or not (see Box 3). When testing for mutation drift-equilibrium (see Box 3), H_{exp} is thus considered as the *observed* H_{exp} because its computation requires *observed* allele frequencies (p_i).

Allele frequency spectrum (AFS): Assuming that we have genotyped a large number of independent bi-allelic loci for a sample of size k, and that we can identify an ancestral and a derived allele, the AFS (also known as site frequency spectrum, or SFS) is a histogram with k + 1 values obtained by counting the number of loci having either 0, 1, 2, ... or k copies of the derived allele in the sample. It is thus a genomic description of the frequencies of SNPs. Theoretical studies have shown how the shape of the AFS changes with the demographic history of species. The AFS can thus be used as a summary of genomic data to detect population size changes (Excoffier et al. 2013; X. Liu and Fu 2015) or population structure (Excoffier et al. 2013). The two-dimensional AFS can also be computed as a matrix for two populations, and in models with two populations it can be used to infer parameters such as splitting times (Gutenkunst et al. 2009; Excoffier et al. 2013).

Mismatch distribution, or distribution of pairwise differences: Histogram obtained for a sample of k sequences of the same locus by computing the number of differences (substitutions) for all k*(k-1)/2 possible pairwise comparisons. The shape of the mismatch distribution is influenced by the demographic history of species and can be used to detect departures from mutation-drift equilibrium. Under panmixia and neutrality it can be used to detect and date bottlenecks and expansions.

F_{ST}: Used as a measure of genetic differentiation, it actually measures fixation of different alleles in different populations. It varies between 0 (when the allele frequencies are identical between populations) and 1 (when populations have lost genetic diversity and are fixed for different alleles).

Effective population size (N_e): Real populations exhibit complex features such as different numbers of males and females, variation in the reproductive success of individuals from the same of from different sexes, or variation in population size through time. The effective population size is the size of an ideal population (constant size, same number of males and females, and a Poisson variation in the number of offspring) that would have the same properties as the real population from the point of view of some genetic measure such H_{exp}. The concept of N_e is central in population genetics, as it measures the importance of genetic drift.

Ascertainment bias: This is a statistical bias due to the nonrandom discovery of genetic markers. For instance, to minimize genotyping costs, microsatellites developed in one species are typically selected as a function of their variability in the initial sample. Typing the same markers in other populations or species will lead to an overestimation of genetic diversity in the initial sample and an underestimation in the other samples, even within the same species. Ascertainment bias is not necessarily problematic to identify genetic clusters (population structure), but it is problematic for demographic inference, because it biases the representation of genomic diversity and the AFS.

et al., pp. 1941–46, for details on this genus). Phylogeographic studies linking population genetic and phylogenetic analyses have also helped to clarify the relationships between closely related species and test hypotheses concerning species diversification (e.g., A. L. Russell et al. 2007 on bats). For example, Markolf and Kappeler (2013) inferred gene flow between *Eulemur* sister species that are now separated by rivers and thus suggested that rivers may not always have been a major factor promoting reproductive isolation between sister taxa.

Despite this large diversity of genetic studies across time, space, and taxonomic groups, the associated literature devoted to mammals is highly biased toward lemurs. Out of the >210 articles that we identified on this subject, >170 focused on lemurs. Assuming there are ~220 mammal species on Madagascar, of which ~100–110 are lemurs, this suggests that lemurs represent ~40% of mammal species but ~80% of all studies. If, as some authors consider, there are only ~50 lemur species (Tattersall and Cuozzo 2018), and thus ~150 mammal species, the overrepresentation of lemurs is even more dramatic. Within lemurs a bias can also be observed toward four genera (*Microcebus*, *Lepilemur*, *Propithecus*, and *Eulemur*). Among nonprimate mammals, rodents and bats are the most represented. Interestingly, outside lemurs, the most studied mammal species is the introduced and invasive Black Rat (*Rattus rattus*; see Ramasindrazana et al., pp. 1872–80), the subject of at least seven genetic studies, which have generally focused on aspects associated with the transmission of plague on Madagascar (e.g., Hingston et al. 2005; Tollenaere et al. 2010; see Tortosa, pp. 265–67).

This overview suggests that although important genetic studies have been published, much more work is needed. We have almost no population genetics data on several lemur genera, such as *Phaner*, *Allocebus*, *Prolemur*, or *Cheirogaleus*. Even the emblematic *Indri indri* (see Gamba et al., pp. 1967–71) and *Varecia variegata* (see Vasey et al., pp. 1957–63) are subjects of relatively few studies each (e.g., Louis et al. 2005; Nunziata et al. 2016; Bonadonna et al. 2019; Baden et al. 2020). Beyond lemurs the situation is even more striking. Most species are either not represented at all or represented by only a couple of studies, as can be seen with *Cryptoprocta ferox* (see Gerber and Hawkins, pp. 1978–83) and *Mungotictis decemlineata* (see Kappeler et al., pp. 1996–98), both in the Eupleridae family of the order Carnivora (Veron et al. 2018). It would thus be fair to say that we have today nearly no understanding of the genetic diversity hosted by most Malagasy mammals. There is an absolute and urgent need to document this unique diversity across the island and across all species, in the hope that such studies will contribute to their conservation.

While our understanding of the genetic diversity of Malagasy mammals is indeed still very limited, the number of Malagasy and international teams developing high-quality projects to document that diversity and to identify the corresponding evolutionary processes has increased since 2010, even if not rapidly enough. The move from population genetics studies, using a limited number of independent genetic markers, to population genomic studies, in which tens of thousands of markers or whole genomes are used, is now well underway, also for Malagasy mammals. Some examples are the recent genetic studies that have analyzed whole mitochondrial genomes and have thus expanded phylogenetic or phylogeographic work (e.g., Lei et al. 2017). While mitogenomic studies do not actually use large numbers of independent markers, they are often included among genomic studies because they analyze much larger sequence data sets (~16,000 base pairs [bp]) than classical mitochondrial DNA (mtDNA) studies (typically fewer than 1000–2000 bp). Other genomic studies have used full genome sequences for an increasing number of species and individuals. For instance, next-generation sequencing (NGS) technologies (see Box 2) have allowed researchers to investigate old questions in new ways, such as those concerning the diet of *Propithecus tattersalli* (Quéméré et al. 2013) or the adaptive immune system of *P. coquereli* (Larsen et al. 2014; see Lawler and Richard, pp. 1971–74, for details on this genus); the demographic histories of *Eulemur flavifrons* and *E. macaco* (Meyer et al. 2015), *P. coquereli* and *Prolemur simus* (M. T. R. Hawkins et al. 2018), or *Microcebus* species (Poelstra et al. 2021; see Kappeler et al., pp. 1927–32); the evolution of sensory receptor genes in *Microcebus* species (Hunnicutt et al. 2020); speciation and admixture in shrew tenrecs (*Microgale* species; Everson et al. 2020a; see Jenkins et al., pp. 1880–87); or ancient admixture in *Cheirogaleus* species (Williams et al. 2020; see Blanco, pp. 1922–26, for details on the genus).

In addition, the statistical analyses of genomic (see Box 2) and genetic (see Box 3) data from Malagasy mammal species has become increasingly sophisticated, with new modeling approaches being applied to genetic (Olivieri et al. 2008; N. Schneider et al. 2010; Salmona et al. 2017) or genomic (M. T. R. Hawkins et al. 2018; Poelstra et al. 2021; Williams et al. 2020) data. Some of the new methods allow researchers to better describe patterns of genetic diversity and differentiation, while others allow the reconstruction of ecological or evolutionary processes, including the identification of major events in the recent evolutionary history of these animals. The distinction between the description of patterns and the reconstruction of evolutionary processes is not always clear-cut, as we will discuss below, but this distinction helps us organize this review in the next two sections. We will also discuss several issues related to taxonomy without entering into much detail, since phylogenetic research is discussed for different mammal groups elsewhere in this chapter (see, for example, Goodman et al., pp. 1894–911, for bats; Yoder, pp. 1821–24, for lemurs; Veron et al., pp. 1863–65, for endemic carnivorans; Jansa and Carleton, pp. 1865–71, for endemic rodents).

GENETICS AT DIFFERENT SCALES: FROM SOCIAL AND LOCAL TO LANDSCAPE AND SPECIES-WIDE PATTERNS

Early Genetic Studies: A Diversity of Molecular Approaches but Few Population Studies

The earliest genetic studies of Malagasy mammals, while limited in number and in taxonomic diversity, used a surprisingly varied set of molecular approaches, demonstrating an early interest of researchers in the molecular methods of their times (see Box 2 for definitions of some methods). The techniques used included immunodiffusion (Dene et al. 1976, 1980), karyotypes (Rumpler and Dutrillaux 1976; Rumpler et al. 1985), DNA-DNA hybridization (Bonner et al. 1980), restriction fragment-length polymorphism (RFLP) (Crovella and Rumpler 1992; Jung et al. 1992), repetitive DNA (Montagnon et al. 1993; Crovella et al. 1994), random amplification of polymorphic DNA (RAPD) (Leipoldt et al. 1996; Neveu et al. 1998), nuclear gene sequences (Koop et al. 1989), and mtDNA sequences

BOX 2 GENETIC MARKERS

HERE WE EXAMINE in detail aspects of polymorphism and sex-linked markers, specifically the diversity of genetic markers and the use of genetic markers. One of the first steps in population genetics studies is to describe patterns of genetic diversity and differentiation at different geographic scales. This can be done with different genetic markers that can differ by their variability or by their transmission mode. Allozymes and (nuclear) microsatellites both inform on nuclear diversity and are both transmitted by males and females, but they differ in their respective levels of variability. Mitochondrial DNA is transmitted only by females, and Y chromosome data only by males, and therefore they can provide unique information on female- and male-specific behavior, such as dispersal or demographic history. However, important differences exist between mtDNA and Y chromosome data. Mitochondrial DNA data can be collected from both males and females, whereas only males have Y chromosomes. Also, the molecular mechanism generating mutations and the mutation rate in the genetic markers that can be obtained from mtDNA (DNA sequences that vary in mutation rates along the mtDNA molecule) and Y chromosome (DNA sequences and linked microsatellites) data can be rather different. They also differ from autosomes in that their effective population size (N_e; see Box 1) is much smaller than that of nuclear loci, and they are therefore more subject to genetic drift. X chromosomes are transmitted by both males and females, but since there is only one copy in males, the effective size of X chromosome is smaller than that of autosomes.

While we are not aware of studies examining Y or X chromosome diversity in Malagasy mammals, recent genomic studies suggest that it may now become possible to extract both Y and X chromosome data from ongoing sequencing projects that have produced full-genome sequences (Meyer et al. 2015 for *Eulemur macaco* and *E. flavifrons*; M. T. R. Hawkins et al. 2018 for *Prolemur simus*; Williams et al. 2020 for several *Cheirogaleus* spp.). Finally, most genetic studies have usually focused on genetic markers thought to behave neutrally, but a number of genetic studies have also focused on regions thought to be under selection (Sommer et al. 2002a on *Hypogeomys antimena*; Schwensow et al. 2007 on *C. medius*; Hunnicutt et al. 2020 for *Microcebus*). The genetic markers that have been used to study Malagasy mammals have varied over time.

Immunodiffusion: Immunodiffusion consists in comparing the antigens (proteins, lipids, saccharides, etc.) of different taxa to quantify their genetic divergence. It is based on a reaction between antibodies and antigens diffused in an agarose gel. Patterns observed in the gels allow researchers to determine whether antigens are identical, similar, or dissimilar. It is then possible to build similarity matrices and species trees (e.g., Dene et al. 1976, 1980).

Cytogenetics: Cytogenetic studies quantify chromosomal differences across taxa (differences in number of chromosomes, centromere position, rearrangements such as inversions, etc.). Metaphase chromosomes (condensed chromatin) are stained with special dyes that reveal the unique banding pattern of chromosome pairs. This had been used extensively for phylogenetic studies, taxonomy, and hybridization studies before DNA sequencing became more accessible to researchers. One of the main advantages of this technique is that it allows researchers to easily detect large chromosomal rearrangements and investigate the role of these rearrangements as reproductive barriers between taxa. Today, new techniques use fluorescently labeled probes and, more recently, genomic data to identify chromosomal rearrangements (e.g., Rumpler and Dutrillaux 1976; Eisfeldt et al. 2019).

Allozymes: General term used to identify protein variants from the same locus that can be separated on a agar gel. Allozymes revolutionized population genetics as they allowed population geneticists to easily identify large amounts of single-locus polymorphisms (Hubby and Lewontin 1966). They have been rarely used with Malagasy mammals.

PCR (polymerase chain reaction): Molecular technique that produces a very large number of copies of a short, prespecified region of DNA. A thermo-resistant enzyme (DNA polymerase) synthetizes new DNA fragments that are complementary to the region of interest, delimited by a pair of oligonucleotides (short artificial DNA fragments called primers) flanking the region to be amplified, each of which is complementary to one of the two DNA strands. The primers are used to initiate DNA synthesis. The PCR technique is widely used and recognized as a revolutionary method that makes use of small amounts of tissue and DNA (e.g., fecal samples).

RAPD (random amplification of polymorphic DNA): PCR-based technique used to detect polymorphism in the genome. While a PCR typically needs two primers (see *PCR*, above), each binding on either side of the DNA fragment to be amplified, RAPD uses only one short primer. If this primer is short enough, it is expected that it will randomly bind in a very large number of genomic regions. When pairs of locations are close enough to each other to be effectively amplified by PCR, a band will be produced. RAPDs thus focus on the banding patterns across individuals or populations. On Madagascar, since the early 1990s, RAPDs often have been used to quantify genetic diversity or differentiation between populations.

RFLP (restriction fragment-length polymorphism): Polymorphism based on the presence or absence of short sequences (typically between four and eight nucleotides) called

restriction sites. These sequences are recognized by restriction enzymes that cut the DNA, hence generating DNA fragments of variable length. This approach has been used extensively to produce banding patterns that are visualized through gel electrophoresis. Variation in banding patterns across individuals from different species or populations can then be used for evolutionary inference.

Sanger sequencing: DNA sequencing approach based on the incorporation of nucleotides labeled with a fluorescent dye that can be detected easily by a sequencing machine. Sanger sequencing typically delivers sequences of between a few hundred base pairs and ~1 Kbp (kilobase pair, or 1000 base pairs). The Sanger method has been the dominant approach for decades and is still used for the analysis of small (in number of loci) data sets (e.g., Everson et al. 2016; Sgarlata et al. 2019). This method has also been used for sequencing mitogenomes (~16 Kbp) in several lemur species, mainly *Microcebus* and *Lepilemur* species (Louis and Lei 2016; Lei et al. 2017). It has been particularly useful in studies that aim at characterizing target genomic regions, such as major histocompatibility complex (Schad et al. 2005; de Winter et al. 2019), vomeronasal receptors (Hohenbrink et al. 2017), or opsin genes (Veilleux et al. 2013); or identifying microbe communities within mammal hosts, such as viruses (Wasimuddin et al. 2019), bacteria (Gomard et al. 2016), and parasites (Kiene et al. 2020).

Microsatellite: A microsatellite locus is a DNA sequence composed of several repetitions of the same two- to eight-nucleotides-long motif. Microsatellites became a marker of choice in conservation genetics because they are highly variable, noncoding, likely neutral, have genome-wide distribution, and could be polymorphic even in species with small population sizes. They also can be obtained from minute noninvasive samples, such as feces (e.g., Quéméré et al. 2010b; Bertoncini et al. 2017). Most conservation genetics studies, in Madagascar and elsewhere, typically use between five and 20 microsatellites, even if studies with more than 20 loci exist. Microsatellite loci identified in one species can often be used in other species, but this can typically generate strong biases in demographic inference (see *ascertainment bias*, Box 1).

Next-generation sequencing (NGS): These are DNA-sequencing technologies that provide genomic data at relatively low cost, thanks to the parallel and massive production of relatively short sequences. Depending on the NGS technique, short sequences are then assembled to build larger DNA fragments from a few hundred to tens of millions of base pairs. The advent of NGS methods allows researchers to address questions that could not be investigated rapidly with Sanger sequencing. For example, one of the widely used NGS machines in 2010 (Illumina HiSeq 2000) was able to sequence DNA 10,000 times faster and 0.0001 times more cheaply than Sanger sequencing (Glenn 2011). This is a field in constant evolution, and new NGS approaches can now obtain long sequences (~1 Mbp [megabase pair, or 1 million base pairs]), which facilitate the assembly of complex genomic regions (e.g., highly repetitive sequences) or the study of chromosomal-scale evolution. These technologies can be adapted to target specific genomic regions, acquire large-scale data on the transcription of thousands of genes, or rapidly sequence whole genomes. Working with genomic data has major challenges related to 1) the computational power needed to assemble massive amounts of data into reliable genomic information, 2) the capacity for storing large amounts of processed data, and 3) the identification of the best parameters to be used in the genomic-data-processing pipelines.

For Malagasy mammals, NGS approaches have been used to sequence DNA extracted from fecal samples to study the diet of *Propithecus tattersalli* (Quéméré et al. 2013) and different bat species (Kemp et al. 2019) and to characterize the gut microbial community of several lemurs (A. Springer et al. 2016; Greene et al. 2019; Perofsky et al. 2019). Few studies have explored profiles of gene transcription in Malagasy mammals, but examples are the studies of Faherty et al. (2016, 2018), which have used NGS technology to investigate the gene-expression profile of adipose tissue in *Cheirogaleus crossleyi* during hibernation.

Restriction-site-associated DNA sequencing (RAD-seq): A next-generation sequencing method that produces a massive amount of short DNA sequences flanking a specific restriction site (see *RFLP*, above). The genomic information retrieved represents a nonrandom sample of the whole genome (typically less than 1%), since only regions around the restriction sites are sequenced. There are several variants of the RAD-seq technique, which differ mainly in the number of restriction enzymes used to digest the genome, the adaptor ligation, and the barcoding and size selection of the ideal DNA fragment length used for sequencing (K. R. Andrews et al. 2016). RAD-seq is particularly well adapted for classical population genetics studies of nonmodel organisms, because it does not require prior knowledge of the genome of the species of interest and provides a large amount of population genomic data at a reasonable cost. (Model organisms such as mice, humans, and *Drosophila* have extremely good genetic and genomic resources, including reference genomes that are necessary to statistical analyses of population genomic data with limited coverage.) The number of independent DNA fragments and their coverage (the number of times the same fragment is read, which represents a measure of genotyping reliability) depends also on the frequency of the restriction-enzyme cutting site, and it is typically on the order of 10^3–10^6 (locus size is 30–500 bp). The term *ddRAD* is used when two different restriction enzymes are used (e.g., A. D. Yoder et al. 2016, on *Microcebus*), typically leading to reduction in the total number of loci. These data can be used to study population diversity and differentiation; they can also be summarized using the AFS (see Box 1) for demographic inference (Excoffier et al.

(continued overleaf)

BOX 2 GENETIC MARKERS *continued*

2013) or examined for detecting loci under selection (Hohenlohe et al. 2010). So far, few Malagasy mammal species have been studied with RAD-seq data; studies include Salmona et al. (2015) on *Microcebus* and *Lepilemur*, and A. D. Yoder et al. (2016) and Poelstra et al. (2021) on *Microcebus*.

Whole-genome sequencing (WGS): Next-generation sequencing approaches have opened a new avenue for WGS, the sequencing of full genomes, even for wild nonmodel organisms. WGS has two main challenges; it requires 1) the acquisition of sequence data spread across the whole genome, and 2) the assembly of these sequences to compose chromosomal-scale contiguous sequences. The fast evolution of sequencing technologies has allowed for the possibility of sequencing both short reads (~150 bp) and long reads (~10 Kbp) and combining the information of these two different types of approaches for the assembly of a full genome. Among many parameters that quantify the quality of a genome, two are widely used: coverage, which defines the number of reads representing a given genomic region; and N50 scaffold/contig, which is a standardized measure of sequence contiguity of the assembled genome. In lemurs, the first draft-genome assemblies became available in the early 2010s, with the release of *Microcebus murinus* (coverage: ~1.9×, N50 scaffold: 140 Kbp; Lindblad-Toh et al. 2011) and *Daubentonia madagascariensis* (coverage: ~19×, N50 scaffold: ~14 Kbp; Perry et al. 2012a) draft genomes. The cost of WGS has subsequently decreased, and it is now possible to obtain sequencing data from nonmodel organisms with a 20–30× coverage and N50 scaffold/contigs of 10–30 Kbp for US$550–1700 per individual.

(Hasegawa et al. 1990; Del Pero et al. 1995). However, with the exception of the study of Arnaud et al. (1992), past genetic studies, including most of those mentioned above, were not about population diversity but rather aimed at answering taxonomic and phylogenetic questions. As we will see throughout this contribution, this is still the case for most genetic studies on Malagasy mammals several decades later. This does not mean that all taxonomic and phylogenetic studies address the same questions; some, for instance, aimed to clarify lemur taxonomy (Rumpler and Albignac 1978; Crovella and Rumpler 1992; see Yoder, pp. 1821–24, for further details), whereas others examined the relationships of lemurs with primate groups outside Madagascar (Dene et al. 1976; Dutrillaux 1979; M. Goodman et al. 1994).

Population studies were thus uncommon, and they usually estimated genetic differences between groups of individuals sampled in different but geographically close locations. The main questions were: 1) whether genetic diversity varied across locations, 2) whether individuals sampled from different locations could be considered to be from the same or different populations (or different species, in Bachmann et al. 2000), and 3) whether some identified populations had lower diversity and were thus possibly isolated. For instance, Arnaud et al. (1992) compared the genetic diversity of captive and wild samples of *Eulemur macaco*. Leipoldt et al. (1996) used RAPDs on *Lepilemur ruficaudatus* and detected departures from random mating but no major differences in genetic diversity across populations. Tomiuk et al. (1997) used allozymes on the same populations and confirmed strong departures from random mating with significant deficits in heterozygotes (see Boxes 1 and 3). Bachmann et al. (2000) extended these studies by using allozymes, RAPDs, and karyotypic analyses, the lattermost for species validation. Similar population genetics studies were carried out by Rabarivola et al. (1996) on *E. macaco*, by Fausser et al. (2000) on *E. m. flavifrons* (now *E. flavifrons*), and by Hafen et al. (1998), Neveu et al. (1998), and Tomiuk et al. (1998) on *Microcebus murinus*.

Population genetics studies concerning Malagasy mammals mainly used two types of genetic markers (see Box 2). Leipoldt et al. (1996), Hafen et al. (1998), and a few others used RAPDs, whereas Rabarivola et al. (1996) and Tomiuk et al. (1997) used allozymes. This is notable because allozymes had been used extensively in many regions of the world and were probably the dominant class of genetic markers typed to study diversity in many taxa from insects to birds, fish, and mammals during this early phase of genetic studies (for a review, see Allendorf 2017). However, most genetic markers were rapidly replaced by microsatellite and mtDNA loci in studies of Malagasy mammals. From a practical point of view, the mtDNA and microsatellite markers had several advantages. Minute quantities of samples, from an ear or a tail or noninvasive samples such as hair or feces, could be used to obtain mtDNA or microsatellite data (Taberlet et al. 1996; Goossens et al. 2000, 2011). These techniques were also important for researchers working on elusive, rare, or endangered species that were difficult to approach or capture. However, we remark that genetic studies using noninvasive samples have not been notably frequent in Malagasy mammal research, with a few exceptions (e.g., Quéméré et al. 2010a, 2010b, 2012, studying *Propithecus*; Salmona et al. 2015, 2017, *Propithecus*; Bertoncini et al. 2017, *E. collaris*).

It is important to stress that all the early genetic studies discussed in this section were focused on lemurs. For nonprimate Malagasy mammals, little seems to have been done in this period. Jansa et al. (1999) analyzed mtDNA sequences to reconstruct the phylogeny of Malagasy rodents, and Douady et al. (2002) studied the phylogeny of tenrecs using mtDNA and nuclear gene sequences. We did not find any published population genetics studies from this early period.

Microsatellites and mtDNA: The First Studies on Social and Population Structure

When microsatellites started to be adopted by researchers working on Malagasy mammals, there was a change of focus. Instead of

BOX 3 DEMOGRAPHIC INFERENCE AND COALESCENT THEORY

MUTATION-DRIFT EQUILIBRIUM: Mutation-drift equilibrium is reached when mutations (which create new alleles) and genetic drift (which randomly eliminates alleles) balance each other. Ewens (1972) has shown that at mutation-drift equilibrium it is possible to predict the *expected* frequencies of alleles observed in a sample (p_{i_eq}) under the Wright-Fisher model (constant size, nonoverlapping generations, and neutrality). This equilibrium is very different from Hardy-Weinberg equilibrium (HWE). HWE is reached after only one generation of random mating, whereas mutation-drift equilibrium is an evolutionary equilibrium that may never be reached. The results of Ewens (1972) were published in a period of controversy between neutralists and selectionists. As a consequence, a departure from mutation-drift equilibrium was interpreted as a possible sign of selection (Watterson 1978) and led to the classical Ewens-Watterson test, based on the comparison of homozygosity values (i.e., $1\text{-}H_{exp}$). However, Ewens clearly stated that his results were obtained under an evolutionary set of models that made several assumptions, such as the infinite allele mutation model, neutrality, panmixia, constant size, and no population structure. Thus, departures from *any* of these assumptions or combinations thereof could potentially explain a statistically significant result. In the 1980s–1990s the population genetics community started to be interested in population size changes, and new statistics were developed to detect departures from mutation-drift equilibrium. Some were presented as detecting selection, while others were introduced as detecting population size changes (Tajima 1989a, 1989b; Fu 1997). Theoreticians were aware of these interpretation issues and knew that they were in reality proposing improvements on the original Ewens-Watterson test. For instance, Tajima (1989a) developed the D statistic (now Tajima's D) as a way to test neutrality. He also showed, however, that the D statistic was also influenced by population size changes (Tajima 1989b).

Mutation models and mutation-drift equilibrium: Demographic inference depends on assumptions on the mutation model. The analytical results of Ewens (1972) were developed for the infinite allele model. Simulations have shown that significant departures from mutation-drift equilibrium could also be detected not because of selection or population size change but because the wrong mutation model was assumed

Population structure and mutation-drift equilibrium: Since 2000 there has been an increasing recognition that population structure and the sampling strategy can generate signals in the genetic data that can be interpreted as population size changes under the assumption of local panmixia and the absence of connectivity with other populations (Chikhi et al. 2010; Heller et al. 2013; Mazet et al. 2016).

Selection: We have focused mainly on neutral processes but do not wish to minimize the likely effects of selection. There are, however, many types of selection, and it is not clear how important they have been in shaping patterns of genomic diversity. One general argument used by population geneticists is that neutral forces shape the whole genome in a similar way, whereas loci under selection are expected to exhibit different signals, since they are subject to different types of selection. For several decades it was a common assumption that neutral loci represent thus the core of genetic data, and loci under selection were a minority that could be detected once we could predict the expected neutral patterns (Cavalli-Sforza 1966; Beaumont and Nichols 1996; Goldstein and Chikhi 2002). However, an increasing number of studies are now considering that some forms of selection, such as background selection, may directly or indirectly influence major parts of the genome (Comeron 2017; Pouyet et al. 2018) to the point that Comeron (2017) recently defended the view that the null model for genome evolution should include background selection. In addition, other molecular processes such as recombination, biased gene conversion, etc., may play an important role in shaping patterns of diversity at the level of genomes.

Coalescent theory, strength, and limitations: The coalescent theory was developed in the 1980s and 1990s to study the statistical properties of gene trees (Kingman 1982). The standard coalescent theory assumes that we have a nonrecombining and neutral DNA fragment (a locus) for which several copies (genes) have been sampled. It is typically assumed that the size of the population, N, is constant and that the population is panmictic and isolated from other populations. The coalescent theory is a retrospective method, as it starts with the sample (which could be present-day material, or museum or ancient DNA specimens) and then goes backward until the MRCA (most recent common ancestor) of the sample is reached, at a time called T_{MRCA}. The coalescent theory allows population geneticists to better understand the very large variance associated with gene trees. Under the same evolutionary assumptions, two loci can exhibit different gene trees with very different T_{MRCA}. This is why it is difficult to draw strong conclusions regarding the demographic history inferred from a limited number of loci. This is particularly true for mtDNA, which is a notably large set of linked loci and thus behaves as a single locus. The coalescent theory thus differs from the theoretical work done before the 1980s, a period in which theoreticians tended to use a forward-looking approach, starting from a particular situation and predicting various possible outcomes, such as the fate of advantageous or deleterious mutations. Forward-looking theory is population-based, since whole populations need to be modeled or simulated. The coalescent theory is sample-based, as it focuses on the properties of the sample. These properties are a function of the whole population (or populations in structured models), but coalescent simulations are computationally much more efficient as they depend mainly on the size of the sample, not the size

(continued overleaf)

of the population. This explains why they became extremely popular and have been at the heart of population genetics for three decades (taking Hudson's 1990 review article as a possible start for its widespread use). The coalescent theory is extremely important, but it also has limitations. First, it typically assumes that the sample size (k) must be much smaller than the population size (N), which is assumed to be very large ($k << N$). For rare species, which are often endangered, this is rarely true. How good the approximation is depends on many factors that are little discussed. For instance, the coalescent theory also assumes that the probability to have several coalescent events is very small. In species with social units and a high variance in the reproductive success, this is unlikely to be true.

In the 1990s several studies showed that the shape of gene trees is influenced by demographic events such as bottlenecks and expansions, hence allowing us to detect, quantify, and date such events. Most theoretical work is, however, dependent on the standard coalescent theory, which assumes panmixia. This means that two important levels of population structure have often been ignored. The first is the within-population structure, since the consequences of social structure generating variance in reproductive success have not been very much studied. Second, the existence of gene flow and connectivity among populations has also been ignored. The coalescent theory allows one to account for population structure (Herbots 1994; Wakeley 1999), but not all methods account for it, as we discuss in the main text.

Likelihood-based and Bayesian methods: The objective of likelihood-based approaches is to compute the probability P_M(Data | Param) of generating the observed data under a predefined demographical model M, defined by a set of parameters: Param = (Par_1, ... , Par_k). The vertical bar represents a conditional probability and means "given that." While this is a probability, it is crucial to stress that in a likelihood framework, we compare probabilities across parameter values. We thus do not compare probabilities of alternative outcomes (for one specific set of parameter values), which would then sum to one. For instance, we may want to compute the probability that a migrant individual originated from a specific source population based on its genotype and allele frequencies in that population. Let us call this probability P_M(Genotype | Pop Origin). If there are three potential source populations with similar allele frequency, we may find that the three probabilities are similar and close to, say, 50%. In that case, the sum would be >100%. We might also find that the probabilities are small, say less than 1%, and in that case the sum would be <<100%. Likelihoods are thus probabilities that are seen as functions of the model parameters (Param) and therefore of the model. Importantly, the model M is assumed to be true and the data are observed. For a likelihood (L) probability, P_M(Data | Param) is typically rewritten as either L_M(Param | Data), by inverting the order of Param and Data, or simply L(Param) (implicitly, we mean "given the observed data"). Likelihood methods are used to find the parameter values that maximize the function L(Param). These maximum likelihood estimates (MLE) are then used as the best estimates explaining the observed data. Other likelihood-based methods may use a Bayesian perspective and estimate probability density functions for these parameters (rather than a point estimate like the MLE). To do that, they require the use of *prior* distributions of the parameters P_M(Param) that specify the values that the parameters can take and with which probability. For instance, we could state *a priori* that the three source populations have the same *prior* probability, or we may have some prior information suggesting that the first population has a higher probability. This allows the Bayesian analysis to compute a *posterior* distribution, which is obtained using the Bayes formula: P_M(Params | Data) = P_M(Param) * P_M(Data | Param) / P_M(Data). Note that the prior and posterior distributions are both probabilities of the parameters. One can be seen as the probability before we see the data and the other after we see the data, and they are both conditional on the model M that we assumed was true.

Approximate Bayesian computation (ABC): General simulation-based approach used to infer parameter values of a demographic model when the likelihood function is difficult or impossible to evaluate. This is particularly useful to compare complex models with changes in connectivity or population size, as there is no simple way to compute the likelihood for such models. Here, the idea is to approximate the likelihood function and the data. The first step requires a summary of the data by a limited number of summary statistics (such as n_A or H_{exp}, see Box 1; or Tajima's D, above). Thus, instead of computing or estimating the full likelihood P_M(Data | Param), the objective is to estimate P_M(SummData | Param), where SummData is a vector of summary statistics. In order to estimate this probability, a very large number of simulations are carried out (usually $>10^5$–10^6) and the summary statistics used to represent the data are computed for each single simulation. The simulations producing summary statistics closest to the observed ones (for the real data) are selected (usually the 1% or 0.1% best). Then the parameter values corresponding to these "optimal" simulations are kept for inference. There are thus two levels of approximation: the data are approximated by summary statistics, and the fit to the data is approximated by the closest simulations. The term *approximate Bayesian computation* was introduced by Beaumont et al. (2002), but the principle had been independently used by several authors (Beaumont et al. 2002; see Chikhi and Beaumont 2005; Beaumont 2010 for reviews). The ABC framework has been particularly useful in population genetics, thanks to the coalescent theory and simulation software such as ms (Hudson 2002), which simulate genetic data very efficiently. On Madagascar, the ABC framework has been used in only a limited number of studies (Brouat et al. 2014; Salmona et al. 2017) but could be important to the development of comparative studies across species and regions.

replacing allozymes and other markers in the analysis of populations, microsatellites were mainly used with mtDNA sequences to study processes on a much more local scale. In the period between 2000 and 2005, most of these studies were carried out by research teams that had established field stations and were interested mainly in using highly polymorphic markers to identify individuals and study local (possibly sex-biased) migration patterns, differences in male and female behavior, and the details of mating systems. These sociogenetic studies sometimes established aspects suspected or expected from behavioral or comparative data from other mammal species. For instance, in general, higher migration rates were expected in males compared to females based on data collected across mammals (Greenwood 1980). In other cases, genetic data allowed researchers to identify behaviors that were difficult to observe or were expected to be rare or absent. Outside of lemurs, such sociogenetic studies have been applied to very few other mammals; exceptions are one study on *Cryptoprocta ferox* (Lührs et al. 2013) and two studies on *Mungotictis decemlineata* (T. C. Schneider and Kappeler 2014; T. C. Schneider et al. 2016). As the next section will show, sociogenetic studies have offered remarkable insights into the behavioral ecology of lemurs, yet there are still no such studies on rodents, tenrecs, or bats.

Around the same period, but at a much slower pace, microsatellite and mtDNA data started being used to study genetic diversity at the population level. The number of population genetics studies remained limited for several years. The first of such studies was that of Mayor et al. (2002) on several species of the *Propithecus* genus. These authors provided and tested genetic markers for future population genetics studies, but did not actually carry out population genetics analyses. Three years later, Louis et al. (2005) provided the first example in which genetic variation was analyzed across populations. The authors developed 25 microsatellite markers for *Varecia variegata* and compared populations from four different locations, which encompassed most of the species' distribution in the moist evergreen forests of eastern Madagascar. It would take another few years before other population genetics studies would be carried out addressing questions related to population-level genetic diversity and differentiation.

The next two subsections examine both sociogenetics and population structure studies in greater detail, and underline the progress done in our understanding of social organization and genetic diversity in Malagasy mammals.

Sociogenetic Studies

Genetic data have been used for decades to study various aspects of social systems and have helped to elucidate details of the social organization of many species (see reviews by Sugg et al. 1996; Di Fiore 2003). Sociogenetic studies have typically focused on kin composition, parentage analysis, inbreeding patterns, and sex-biased dispersal. While a few studies have stressed one particular aspect of social organization, most studies have typically investigated several components of social systems. Fietz et al. (2000) developed and applied microsatellite data to examine the mating system of *Cheirogaleus medius* in central-west populations and provided the first estimates of genetic diversity for this species. In *Microcebus murinus* from Ankarafantsika, Radespiel et al. (2001) found that females from the same sleeping group were genetically more closely related than females from different sleeping groups (*rco-sleep* = 0.362; *rnot co-sleep* = 0.006). In *Hapalemur griseus alaotrensis* (now *H. alaotrensis*; see Tan et al., pp. 1947–52, for details on this genus), Nievergelt et al. (2002) found that individuals of the same social group were genetically much more related to each other than individuals from different social groups were (*rsame* = 0.327 and *rbetween* = 0.054). They also found that the individuals of the same social group were all sharing the same mtDNA haplotype. Interestingly, Nievergelt et al. (2002) used microsatellites developed for *Eulemur mongoz* and *E. rufus* one decade earlier by Merenlender (1993). In the southwest, Lawler et al. (2003) measured relatedness in *Propithecus verreauxi* and found that females from the same social group had higher levels of genetic relatedness than males (*rfemales* = 0.1–0.27; *rmales* = 0.04–0.14). Wimmer and Kappeler (2002) observed a similar pattern in populations of *E. fulvus rufus* (now *E. rufifrons*) in the central west (*rfemales* = 0.26–0.70; *rmales* = 0.10–0.27).

Nuclear (usually microsatellites) and sex-specific markers (mtDNA and Y-linked genes), together with spatial patterns of diversity and relatedness, can provide complementary information on sex-biased dispersal and kinship composition. For example, Wimmer and Kappeler (2002) found in *E. rufifrons* a few instances of high average relatedness among adult males of a social group, while observing high mtDNA diversity, suggesting that those individuals were relatives but were not maternally related. Using highly variable mtDNA D-loop (displacement-loop) sequences, Wimmer et al. (2002) assessed the matrilineal structure of a *M. murinus* population in a restricted area (~4.5 ha) of the Kirindy Forest CNFEREF. They found that 80% of the female mouse lemurs were sharing only one haplotype, whereas males exhibited most of the mtDNA diversity of the population. Given that males inherit their mtDNA from their mothers and cannot transmit it, this suggests notably higher dispersal rates in males, specifically recent migration from other local populations or social groups. Moreover, females with distinct haplotypes formed distinct spatial clusters with little overlap, suggesting a hierarchical social organization in which females form groups with their kin (social unit) and the associated matrilineal structure sharing the same mtDNA haplotype above the social unit (matrilines). Overall, these findings were thus strong evidence that females were philopatric and that males were the dispersing sex, as is usually observed in mammals (Greenwood 1980; Trochet et al. 2016). In a later study, Fredsted et al. (2004) examined the same population but at a larger spatial scale (~1200 ha, ~250 times larger). They confirmed that the matrilineal structure of *M. murinus* and male-biased dispersal were consistent even at a much larger geographic scale (Figure 14.8). In the sympatrically occurring *M. berthae*, Dammhahn and Kappeler (2005) found that females were more related than males (*rfemales* = 0.049; *rmales* = −0.007), confirming male-biased dispersal also in this mouse lemur species, although with lower values of relatedness than those mentioned above in *M. murinus*. A similar conclusion was drawn by Nievergelt et al. (2002) in *H. alaotrensis*, where most genetic diversity (nuclear and mitochondrial) was brought by reproducing males, thus suggesting male-biased dispersal.

Other quantitative estimates of sex-specific dispersal patterns (e.g., distance) can be obtained by comparing genetic relatedness and geographic distance between individuals of the same sex.

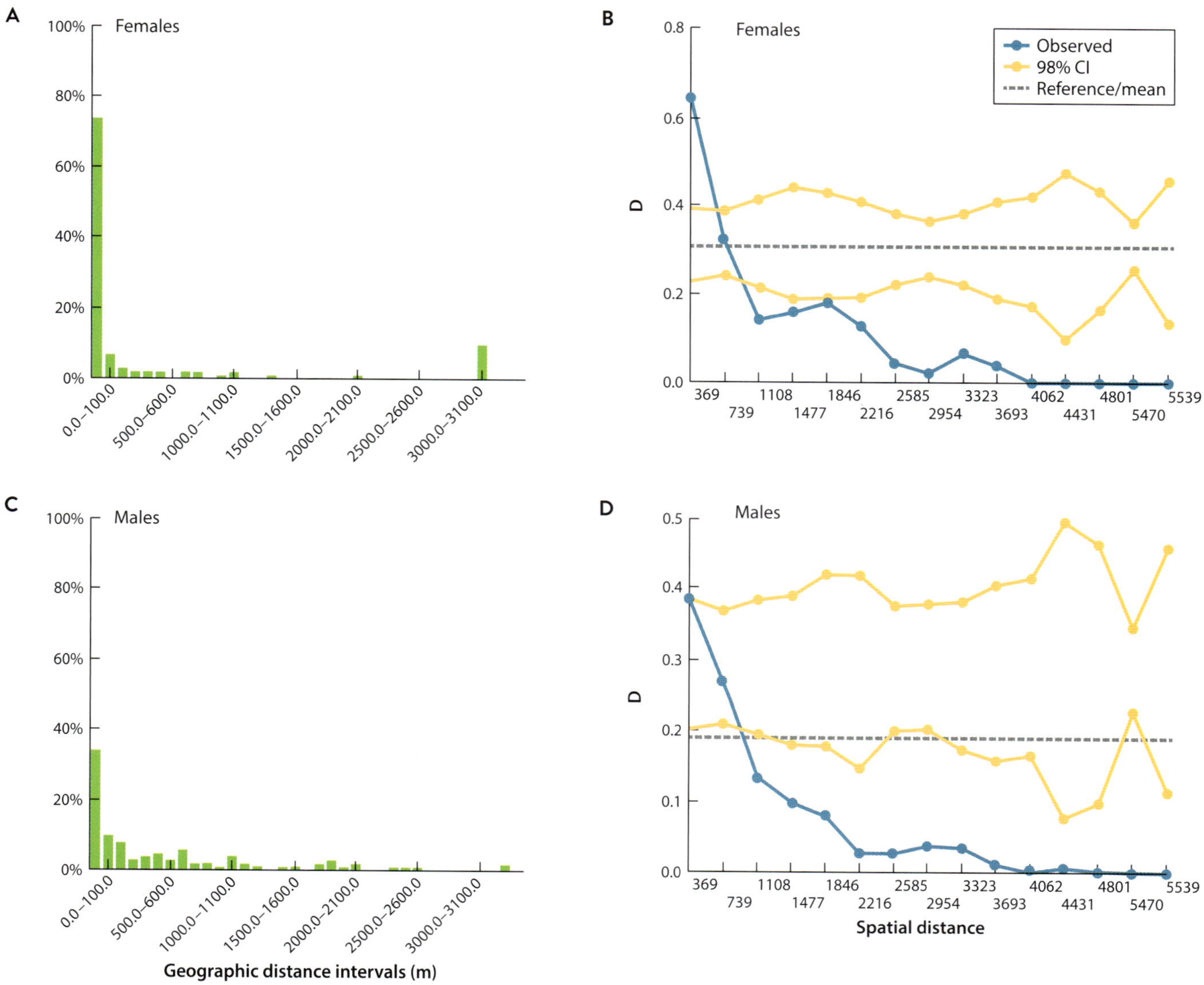

FIGURE 14.8 **Sociogenetic analysis performed on *Microcebus murinus* individual females (A, B) and males (C, D) from the Kirindy Forest CNFEREF, central-western Madagascar. *Left:* Distribution of the geographic distances to nearest individual with the same haplotype (%), for A) females and C) males. *Right:* Spatial "autocorrelation" analysis performed on measures of genetic similarity (mean number of haplotypes in common of individuals belonging to a given distance class), separately, for B) females and D) males.** (SOURCE: modified from Fredsted et al. 2004.)

For instance, Radespiel et al. (2003) computed the geographic distances between closely related female or male dyads ($r = 0.5$) in *M. murinus* populations from the northwest. (Dyads are individuals sharing the same home range.) They found that interindividual distances were on average smaller between closely related females than between males (100 and 400 m, respectively). This, together with the results on co-sleeping individuals mentioned above, suggested that *M. murinus* males move away from their natal group, while females establish a hierarchical social organization together with their kin. Kappeler et al. (2002) studied the social structure of *Mirza coquereli*, a solitary lemur species, individuals of which forage alone and rarely share nests with other adults (see Kappeler, pp. 1932–34, for details on this genus). Since no social groups are formed in this species, these authors investigated sex-biased dispersal by quantifying the mean distance between centers of activity of either male or female dyads sharing or not a mtDNA haplotype. They found that maternally related females were significantly clustered in space ($dist_{same\text{-}hap}$ = 90–250 m; $dist_{different\text{-}hap}$ = 350–380 m), whereas males did not show this pattern ($dist_{same\text{-}hap}$ = 240–440 m; $dist_{different\text{-}hap}$ = 320–340 m), thus suggesting that also in *M. coquereli* males are the dispersing sex.

Other approaches that explicitly model dispersal can be used to estimate more precisely dispersal distances in males and females, such as spatial autocorrelation analysis (see Box 4). However, accurate estimates can be obtained only if certain criteria are met. For instance, Vekemans and Hardy (2004) noted that the sampling area should be neither too large nor too small in relation to the species' mean dispersal distance. Specifically, they suggested a sampling area on the order of 10 to 50 times σ^2 (population variance), where σ^2 is proportional to the area where dispersal takes place (see Box 4).

BOX 4 SPATIAL GENETICS

ISOLATION BY DISTANCE

A pattern known as isolation by distance (IBD) can be observed when dispersal and reproduction are limited by geographic distance (S. Wright 1943). Theoretical work has shown that IBD patterns can be informative on several species-specific parameters, such as the mean squared axial parent-offspring distance (σ^2) and the neighborhood size ($4\pi De\sigma^2$), where *De* is the effective population density. For instance, Rousset (1997) demonstrated that in a homogeneous two-dimensional habitat, accurate estimates of the neighborhood size can be obtained by computing the inverse of the slope of the regression between genetic and geographic distance between pairs of populations, namely between F_{ST} / (1-F_{ST}) and *ln*(d), the natural logarithm of the geographic distance. Similar theoretical results have also been found by computing the average kinship between pairs of individuals separated by geographic distances that fall within a set of distance classes (Vekemans and Hardy 2004). Using estimates of effective population density (*De*), one could, in principle, derive from the estimated neighborhood size ($4\pi De\sigma^2$) an estimate of the area of gene dispersal (σ^2), thus an estimate of the effective dispersal distance (σ). This approach has been implemented in the software SPAGeDI (Hardy and Vekemans 2002) and has been applied to microsatellite data across various taxa outside Madagascar but not yet on the island. One main limitation of this approach is that effective population density and effective dispersal distance cannot be inferred at the same time, which means that it is necessary to estimate one of the two in an "independent" manner.

However, Ringbauer et al. (2017) have recently developed a method that does not require an independent estimate of *De* or σ^2 but uses the length distribution of identical genome tracts shared between pairs of individuals (identity-by-descent blocks) with known geographic location to accurately infer both *De* and σ, and recent changes in *De*. This method is probably just one among many that will likely be used in the next years. It requires either dense genome-wide data or whole-genome sequences from a few dozen individuals of a given species and a linkage map. This type of data is currently difficult to obtain for most nonmodel organisms, but we hope that the situation will change on Madagascar and that appropriate genomic data will become more common in the future (e.g., Hunnicutt et al. 2020; Williams et al. 2020).

FROM IBD TO ISOLATION BY RESISTANCE AND ISOLATION BY ENVIRONMENT

Unlike the approaches described in the section above, which assume homogeneous *De* and σ across the continuous habitat of the complete study region, several other methods have been proposed to actually identify environmental features (biotic and abiotic) that influence dispersal and may thus represent either barriers to gene flow or corridors at the scale of the landscape (Hendry 2004; Nosil et al. 2008; Sexton et al. 2014). For instance, Cushman (2006) proposed *causal modeling* (CM) as an approach to identify the most important landscape features (rivers, roads, agricultural lands, etc.) influencing gene flow. The idea is to build a resistance map based on these features and identify the least-cost path connecting every sampled pair. Genetic differentiation and least-cost-path distances are then correlated across all samples. The features showing significant relationship with genetic distance are then considered to be those having higher impact on dispersal. CM analysis, like many landscape genetics methods, is difficult to validate, as it would require heavy spatial simulations that, to our knowledge, have not yet been carried out. It also requires an *a priori* list of landscape features to compute the least-cost path of dispersal. Finally, it considers only this least-cost path between sample pairs rather than multiple dispersal pathways. McRae (2006) proposed a solution to the problem of multiple dispersal pathways by developing a model called *isolation by resistance* (IBR), which incorporates all possible paths and improves predictions of genetic differentiation. It also allows researchers to estimate a surface of connectivity among samples (called *current map*), determining the areas that facilitate or restrict gene flow (Anantharaman et al. 2020). In these two approaches, however, it is impossible to separate the effects of geographically limited dispersal and environmental variables on gene flow. Thus, some authors have gone further and proposed the concept of *isolation by environment* or *by ecology* (IBE), allowing researchers to assess the relative contribution of an environmental variable and geographic distance in limiting species gene flow (I. J. Wang and Summers 2010; I. J. Wang and Bradburd 2014; Bradburd et al. 2013). If IBE is widespread, it could be studied to help us better understand the ecology of local adaptation (e.g., Bolnick and Otto 2013), to provide evidence for incipient ecological speciation (e.g., Shafer and Wolf 2013), or to identify biased dispersal resulting from preference for a particular environment (Davis and Stamps 2004). While IBE patterns are potentially interesting, it is unclear whether they are informative about ecological speciation or adaptation, but Madagascar could be an appropriate place to test such theories.

IDENTIFYING CHANGES IN CONNECTIVITY OVER TIME

In the way they are currently used, IBD, IBR, and IBE models assume that genetic patterns have reached equilibrium, meaning that they will not change over time and that they reflect the effect of present landscape features on gene flow. Present-day genetic diversity may actually be significantly influenced by past landscape structure. This is because certain genetic measures may take some time before showing

(continued overleaf)

BOX 4 SPATIAL GENETICS *continued*

significant changes (e.g., Landguth et al. 2010). Recently, Bradburd et al. (2016) have introduced a method that implicitly infers historical rates of dispersal between locations. In contrast to previous methods, its aim is to identify changes in connectivity and possible regions of expansion over long periods of time. This method uses genome-wide data and an IBD model to build a geogenetic map, in which population locations reflect genetic rather than geographic proximity. Its objective is to distinguish the genetic signals of local and nonlocal dispersal. The underlying reasoning states that if populations show a level of genetic similarity that is high compared to what would be expected given their geographic distance, this could be interpreted as a signature of admixture. Similarly, if two populations have a lower level of genetic similarity compared to their geographic distance, this would suggest the presence of a barrier to dispersal between the two populations. The method then draws arrows on the inferred geogenetic map to indicate possible sources and targets of admixture. Note that although the approach of Bradburd et al. (2016) is useful to represent and visualize historical migration patterns, it cannot really distinguish events that have occurred at different time intervals in the past. This is because the information used from these genetic data represent a summary of many historical events over timescales that are not always easy to separate. Other studies that we will not detail here (e.g., Al-Asadi et al. 2019) have proposed new ways to retrieve fine-scale information from genomic data, identifying how dispersal rate and population size vary in space and in recent times. This suggests that we will probably see the development of new models and methods that will better tease apart the effects of space and time on genetic patterns, allowing us to improve our inference of the changes in landscape connectivity over time.

Otherwise, relative rather than absolute values of dispersal parameters may be estimated. For instance, Fredsted et al. (2005) used 10 microsatellite loci from 167 *Microcebus murinus* individuals (83 males, 83 females, and one individual not sexed) across an area ~12 km^2 in the Kirindy Forest CNFEREF. They computed the mean number of shared alleles between individual pairs within the same distance interval for males and females, separately. The results showed no significant departure in the number of shared alleles across all distance classes for males, even if a higher value was observed for the first distance class. For females, however, a significant and positive value was observed for the first distance class (up to ~250 m). The results, hence, suggested longer dispersal distances in males than in females. Similar results were obtained on the same population using mitochondrial D-loop sequences (Fredsted et al. 2004; see Figure 14.8).

Genetic parentage analyses have been used to quantify reproductive skew (i.e., variance in the reproductive success) and extra-group reproduction (i.e., the frequency of offspring sired by individuals outside the social group), components of social organization that are not necessarily easy to study without genetic data. Evidence of male reproductive skew in *E. rufifrons* was shown by Wimmer and Kappeler (2002), who found that within four social groups, only one or two reproductively successful males were siring offspring, even though each group contained several adult males. For two social groups, there was additional behavioral data, which showed that three out of four (75%) and three out of five (60%) offspring, respectively, were sired by one single male, suggesting an average male reproductive skew of 67% (six out nine offspring). Gachot-Neveu et al. (1999) used RAPD markers (see Box 2) to determine paternity in two social groups of captive *E. fulvus mayottensis* (now *E. fulvus*) during a four-year study. In one group, the socially dominant male sired 100% of seven infants, whereas in the second group, a subordinate male sired two out of five infants (40%). Pronounced male reproductive skew was also observed in a population of *P. verreauxi* at Kirindy Forest CNFEREF by Kappeler and Schäffer (2008). During the mating seasons, in which social groups contained multiple males, they found that 31 out of 34 offspring (~90%) were sired by the dominant male of the different groups.

Both these studies suggest that, in these species, the resident males and females were generally the genetic parents of the offspring. However, they also showed cases in which other males had managed to reproduce in the group. Genetic studies on several pair-living and group-living lemur species have shown that a non-negligible proportion of offspring can indeed be sired by a male from outside the social unit, typically defined as extra-group paternity (EGP), which includes also extra-pair paternity in the case of pair-living species. For instance, in a recent study, Bonadonna et al. (2019) investigated genetic monogamy in *Indri indri*, a lemur species known to be socially monogamous, although individuals have been observed engaging in extra-pair copulation (Bonadonna et al. 2014). Using genetic parentage analysis, Bonadonna et al. (2019) demonstrated that EGP occurs at a rate of ~8% in *I. indri*. Similar rates were reported for *H. alaotrensis* (8.5%; Nievergelt et al. 2002) and *E. rubriventer* (~5%; R. L. Jacobs et al. 2018), whereas much higher rates of EGP were found in other lemur species such as *Cheirogaleus medius* (40%; Fietz et al. 2000), *Lemur catta* (3/14 offspring, or 21%; and 3/9 offspring, or 30%; Parga et al. 2016), and *Phaner furcifer* (75%, n = 4; Schülke et al. 2004). Also, studies on the same species but carried out in different locations may generate different results. For instance, Lawler (2007) reported that in *Propithecus verreauxi*, 29 out of 52 males (56%) sired offspring outside their resident group, a number that is very different from the 10% observed by Kappeler and Schäffer (2008).

Other genetic studies have reported cases of mixed paternity, in which some of the offspring of a social unit appeared to have been sired by males that entered the group temporarily. For instance, Kappeler et al. (2002) found in a population of *Mirza coquereli* that no resident male could be assigned as the genetic father of four out

of 13 offspring from known mothers. They interpreted these results as evidence for mixed paternity, suggesting that those four offspring were sired by males that entered in the study area for only a short period of time. A genetic study on two social groups of *L. catta* living in natural habitat enclosures showed that two immigrant males introduced in the forest enclosure did sire offspring with resident females. Interestingly, even in presence of resident males, all estrous females were engaging in sexual encounters with immigrant males, and the females attracted exclusively to the immigrants reproduced with them (Pereira and Weiss 1991).

We found only two studies on the sociogenetics of nonprimate Malagasy mammals, both in endemic euplerid Carnivora. One measured relatedness of 22 *Cryptoprocta ferox* adult males (Lührs et al. 2013) captured over 9 km^2 in the Kirindy Forest CNFEREF, showing that four out of six dyads were composed of litter mates ($r \geq 0.40$). The other, T. C. Schneider et al. (2016), was the first population genetics and sociogenetics study in *Mungotictis decemlineata*, characterizing its social organization and mating system. In this species, males and females form separate social units with either one to three females or two to four males (T. C. Schneider and Kappeler 2016). T. C. Schneider et al. (2016) showed that mtDNA diversity was significantly higher in males than females ($h_{males} = 0.818$, $h_{females} = 0.714$) and that average pairwise relatedness was higher in female social units than in most male associations ($r_{female} = 0.25–0.54$, $r_{male} = 0–0.32$), suggesting that 1) female units may be formed by mothers and their offspring, and 2) *M. decemlineata* males disperse farther away from their natal unit than females. Parentage analyses pointed to a mildly promiscuous mating system and low levels of reproductive skew. However, the authors observed that the infants surviving the first year of life (28%) were all born from the dominant female of the social unit, leading to the hypothesis that postpartum mechanisms might be involved in regulating reproductive skew in female *M. decemlineata*.

The consequences of social structure and mating systems on patterns of genetic or genotypic diversity are still not fully understood, despite early theoretical work (not directly related to Madagascar) by pioneers such as Prout (1981) and Chesser (1991). Population geneticists have tended to ignore social structure, either modeling social groups as small populations or simply ignoring them. In other words, it was assumed that social groups were unlikely to have major effects on global genetic patterns, and that such effects, if they existed, would be ephemeral, with limited consequences on allelic frequencies and thus negligible from an evolutionary perspective (e.g., Storz 1999). Recent theoretical work suggests that this may not be that simple (Parreira and Chikhi 2015). First, genotypic changes may be important for genes under selection affecting the overall fitness of individuals and populations. Secondly, social structure may be crucial if we want to understand data such as patterns of inbreeding at the genomic scale. For example, behavioral ecologists have tended to interpret heterozygosity excess within social groups as an indication of inbreeding avoidance. This interpretation has been criticized, as an increasing number of field studies have demonstrated that inbreeding tolerance and preference exist in wild populations (Szulkin et al. 2013). Parreira and Chikhi (2015) explicitly simulated social groups and found that social structure may naturally generate excesses in heterozygosity (i.e., $H_{obs} > H_{exp}$; see Box 1), without the need to incorporate inbreeding-avoidance behaviors. These and other results suggest that in order to understand patterns of genotypic diversity at the genomic level, it may be necessary to consider social structure, mating systems, and other details of social systems. Thus, instead of interpreting "outbreeding" as a consequence of inbreeding avoidance, we should test whether the measured "outbreeding" could be the result of how social systems are organized and connected, and whether an appropriate neutral model that incorporates social structure and connectivity could be used to predict the observed genotypic diversity patterns (Di Fiore and Valencia 2014; Parreira and Chikhi 2015).

Parreira and Chikhi (2015) also found that when social groups are ignored and pooled for genetic analyses, the heterozygote excess decreases and eventually disappears as the number of pooled samples increases. This gives the misleading impression that the (pooled) sample is at Hardy-Weinberg equilibrium when, actually, mating strongly departs from random mating (see Boxes 1 and 3). Now, returning to Madagascar, there are still too few empirical studies on inbreeding. Lawler et al. (2003) measured within-social-group inbreeding in a study on *Propithecus verreauxi*, revealing an excess of heterozygosity in offspring but not as much in reproductive adults. They attributed this result to female philopatry and male-biased dispersal. Quéméré et al. (2010b) measured heterozygosity (H_{obs} and H_{exp}) within social groups of *P. tattersalli* and found extremely high heterozygosity excesses in some social groups but did not interpret them. Recently, Parreira et al. (2020) applied the model of Parreira and Chikhi (2015) to genetic and genotypic data from *P. tattersalli*, finding that the results published by Quéméré et al. (2010a) could also be a simple consequence of the social structure, mating system, and sampling scheme. Taken together, these studies stress the importance of both field observations and models to improve our understanding of genetic and genotypic data. More work on Malagasy mammals is needed to integrate sociogenetics work and population genetics studies and modeling.

Population Studies of Diversity and Differentiation: From Early to Recent Studies

As noted above, population genetics studies of Malagasy mammals took several years, after those of Mayor et al. (2002) and Louis et al. (2005), to appear in the literature. Many of these early studies were descriptive and looked at genetic diversity and differentiation within single species. This was the case of the two companion articles of Ramanamahefa et al. (2009a, 2009b) on *Eulemur coronatus* and *E. sanfordi* living sympatrically in the same forests of northern Madagascar, that of Ranaivoarisoa et al. (2010) on *E. collaris* in the southeast, that of Razakamaharavo et al. (2010) on *Varecia rubra* in the northeast, and those of Quéméré et al. (2010a, 2010b) on *Propithecus tattersalli*.

Interestingly, the first population genetics studies performed on a nonprimate group of Malagasy mammals focused on the introduced *Rattus rattus* (Hingston et al. 2005; Gilabert et al. 2007; Loiseau et al. 2008; Tollenaere et al. 2010). Beyond rats, most genetic studies of Malagasy mammals, including recent ones (e.g., Rakotoarivelo et al. 2019, on the bat *Macronycteris commersoni*), are based on mtDNA analyses. There are exceptions, such as that of Andrianaivoarivelo et al. (2009), which identified and typed 22 microsatellite loci in one southern population of the endemic bat *Rousettus madagascariensis*,

and Goodman et al. (2010a), which analyzed the genetic structure of the same species using mtDNA sequence data and six microsatellites developed for another *Rousettus* species, *R. leschenaultii*, from southeastern Asia (Hua et al. 2006). Goodman et al. (2010a) found very low levels of genetic differentiation (F_{ST} ~0.004; see Box 1) between Malagasy populations distributed across the island, and they also studied diversity of the closely related species *R. obliviosus* from the nearby Comoro islands.

Using mtDNA sequence data, several authors have looked at the genetic structure of other bat species. Ratrimomanarivo et al. (2009a) observed limited genetic differentiation at the level of the island for the endemic *Mormopterus jugularis*, and Chan et al. (2011) reported low genetic differentiation for two *Pteropus* species, one occurring within Madagascar (*P. rufus*) and the other elsewhere in the Malagasy Region (*P. seychellensis comorensis*), showing results parallel to those of Goodman et al. (2010a) on *Rousettus*. The limited genetic differences described by Chan et al. (2011) at the island level were not always small. For instance, they reported large Phi_{ST} values (0.18 or 0.25) (Phi_{ST} is similar to F_{ST} [see Box 1] but for DNA sequences) between Miandrivazo (central-west Madagascar) and two other Malagasy populations (northwest and west), which suggests that genetic differentiation is not limited and needs further investigation in *P. rufus*. Similarly high and even higher Phi_{ST} values were found in the endemic *Myotis goudoti* (Weyeneth et al. 2011a), suggesting ancient and regional diversification in some bat species. Finally, the recent study of Rakotoarivelo et al. (2019) suggests that there may be rather high levels and possibly ancient genetic differentiation in populations of *Macronycteris commersoni*, a Madagascar endemic. We wish to stress that results suggesting limited differentiation at a wide geographic scale, as in *Mormopterus jugularis* or *R. madagascariensis* do not mean that it will be impossible to detect the effect of local genetic differentiation when comparing populations of variable size between geographically close localities. Given the high level of allelic diversity observed in *Rousettus* microsatellites (Andrianaivoarivelo et al. 2009), one could potentially carry out very fine-scale studies of local genetic differentiation. There are currently no such studies for Madagascar bats. Clearly, the bats of Madagascar, which represent nearly 30 independent colonization events of the island (see Goodman et al., pp. 1894–911), remain understudied, even as they appear to exhibit a range of species-specific patterns that need to be studied in more detail and play important ecological roles that are increasingly recognized (see Kemp et al. 2019 and Box 5).

The early population genetics studies reported so far for Madagascar looked at population structure from the point of view of the sampled locations; that is, groups of individuals sampled in different locations, called populations, were compared as we have mentioned above. However, an important shift happened with Pritchard et al. (2000), who turned the question upside down (in a study not related to Madagascar mammals). Their idea was to ignore the sampling locations of the groups of individuals (the "populations") and use only the genotypic information to identify "hidden genetic structure." They used a Bayesian approach and implemented it in their STRUCTURE software, which has become one of the most widely used programs in the field since 2000.

Since then, turning back to Madagascar, a Bayesian approach has been used across different taxa to ask a range of questions. Brenneman et al. (2016), using STRUCTURE, showed that there was no relation between genetic structure and the phenotypes that were associated with putative subspecies of *Indri indri*. Pastorini et al. (2009) used the method to identify putative hybrids between *Eulemur fulvus* and *E. mongoz*. Markolf et al. (2013) employed this method, as well as others, to study *E. fulvus*, the brown lemur complex, which includes seven taxa regarded as either subspecies or species by various authors, and concluded that species status could be confirmed. In most genetic studies, however, the authors were interested in identifying the potential effects of habitat fragmentation within species and in identifying putative populations that could possibly need to be protected (Olivieri et al. 2008; Ramanamahefa et al. 2009a, 2009b; Quéméré et al. 2010a).

In the first of such studies, Olivieri et al. (2008), a Bayesian method was applied to three mouse lemurs, *Microcebus ravelobensis*, *M. bongolavensis*, and *M. danfossi*, from northwestern Madagascar. For *M. ravelobensis*, the authors obtained samples from eight locations, four located in the Ankarafantsika National Park (area: ~1000 km^2) and the others from four forest fragments (areas: 4–37 km^2). They identified two main clusters. The first consisted mainly of individuals from Ankarafantsika and the two forest fragments closest (but not connected) to the protected area today: Tsiaramaso, at a distance of ~20 km from Ankarafantsika, and Sainte Marie, at a distance of 1 km and probably connected in the recent past. The other genetic cluster corresponded to the two remaining lowland forests, located around 80 km from the protected area. In a further analysis, the authors also found that the first cluster could be further subdivided into three sub-clusters, corresponding to Ankarafantsika, Sainte Marie, and Tsiaramaso. Finally, they also identified an isolation-by-distance pattern (see Box 4) across all sampled populations, including those located in forest fragments, hence suggesting a recent fragmentation of forest habitats in this region. *Microcebus bongolavensis* was sampled in three forest fragments, with one location >50 km away from the other two. Despite the large geographic distance, the absence of a continuous forest, and the lack of connectivity among locations, only one genetic cluster could be identified. *Microcebus danfossi* individuals were sampled at seven sites corresponding to forest fragments (areas 1.5–37 km^2). The authors found higher levels of genetic differentiation in this species than in *M. ravelobensis* but no correlation between genetic and geographic distances. Despite the similarly large geographic distances between some *M. danfossi* samples compared to *M. ravelobensis* and the lack of a large continuous forest habitat, *M. danfossi* individuals grouped mainly in one genetic cluster, with the exception of one forest fragment that formed a second cluster.

The first non-lemur studies using STRUCTURE were those of Brouat et al. (2013, 2014) on introduced *Rattus rattus* (see Ramasindrazana et al., pp. 1872–80), which implemented broad sampling across the island. Their results showed that these animals belong to two genetic clusters with distinct distributions. One set of genetic samples clustered around Antsiranana (Diégo Suarez) in the very north of Madagascar, whereas nearly all other samples belonged to a second cluster. They also found a few locations where individuals belonged to one of the two clusters or were possibly admixed. In a very recent study on two shrew tenrec species (see Jenkins et al., pp. 1880–87), *Microgale fotsifotsy* and *M. soricoides*, Everson et al. (2020a) used

BOX 5 MISCELLANEOUS GENETIC STUDIES ON MALAGASY MAMMALS

THE TOPICS ADDRESSED in the main text of this contribution provide a review of many of the genetic studies carried out on Madagascar mammals. However, there have been additional studies that could not be easily integrated into the different sections but deserve to be mentioned here. While their numbers are still limited, this may change in the future, as the use of NGS technologies will allow researchers to address questions that before the genomic era involved work that was technically challenging, time-consuming, and expensive, including the detection of bacteria and viruses in wild or captive Malagasy mammals (see chapter 6) and analyses of their diets or microbiotas.

One rather isolated example is the study of Han and Worobey (2012), who reanalyzed whole-genome shotgun sequences (~38× coverage) to identify foamy-virus-like insertions within the *Daubentonia madagascariensis* genome. Using comparative phylogenetic analyses with foamy virus (family Retroviridae, genus *Spumavirus*) sequences inserted in other primates, they found a strong correlation between the foamy virus and primate phylogeny, hence suggesting that foamy viruses might share an ancient coevolutionary history with primates, as observed for other retroviruses (e.g., Cornelis et al. 2014; Katzourakis et al. 2014).

Several studies have used genetic data to detect and classify viruses and bacteria in wild and captive Malagasy mammals, but we will focus here on the former. Using classical Sanger sequencing, Reynes et al. (2014) assessed the presence of a hantavirus across several potential hosts of Malagasy mammals and found that the Thailand Orthohantavirus (THAIV) species, typically found in Asia and recently identified in Africa, was also present on Madagascar. They identified a new genetic variant in both introduced *Rattus rattus* (92 out of 231) and endemic Malagasy rodent *Eliurus majori* (n = 1). More recently, Raharinosy et al. (2018) studied the prevalence of hantaviruses in urban and rural areas across the island. They sampled 1242 individual mammals across a larger number of taxa (introduced rodents: *R. rattus*, *R. norvegicus*, *Mus musculus*; introduced shrews: *Suncus murinus*; and endemic tenrecs: *Setifer setosus*, *Tenrec ecaudatus*, and *Hemicentetes semispinosus*). Interestingly, they found evidence of hantavirus infection only in *R. rattus* (12.4%) and *M. musculus* (1.6%).

Recent molecular studies have also examined the prevalence of ecto- and endoparasites in Malagasy mammals. For example, Blanco et al. (2013a) used molecular data (COI mitochondrial gene) to identify *Ixodes* tick species in *Microcebus rufus*, *M. lehilahytsara*, *Cheirogaleus sibreei*, and *C. crossleyi* sampled at two sites, one in the east (Ranomafana) and the other in the Central Highlands (Tsinjoarivo). They found the same *Ixodes* species (*I. lemuris*) in three of the lemur species (all except for *M. rufus*). Similarly, Kiene et al. (2020) have used genetic data to identify lice and tick species sampled across several lemur and rodent taxa (*M. murinus*, *M. ravelobensis*, *Eliurus myoxinus*, and *Rattus rattus*) and investigated the effect of habitat loss and fragmentation on the composition of ectoparasite communities in those small mammals. They observed differences in parasite prevalence between host species and a reduction in parasite prevalence in proximity to forest edges.

A. Klein et al. (2018) used molecular approaches to identify ectoparasite species in two sympatric mouse lemur species (*M. murinus* and *M. ravelobensis*), aiming at assessing the abiotic factors that best correlate with parasite prevalence. They showed a significant contribution of season on parasite infection. Interestingly, they also found differences in parasite prevalence between the two sympatric host species. They suggested that they could be related to species-specific differences in sleeping-site ecology. A study by Schwensow et al. (2010a) investigated the host genetic determinants of parasite infection in wild Malagasy mammals. They genotyped a fragment of the major histocompatibility complex class II DRB locus (MHC-DRB), for which evidence of parasite-driven selection has been reported (Schwensow et al. 2007, 2010b). They sequenced MHC-DRB from 149 *Cheirogaleus medius* and 180 *M. murinus* individuals and tested for the association between specific MHC-DRB alleles and the intensity of infection with certain intestinal parasites. In both species, they found significant positive association between a specific MHC allele and infection with helminths of the genus *Ascaris* and suggested a functional link between MHC-DRB sequence and parasite infection. A similar association study was carried out by Tollenaere et al. (2010) on *Rattus rattus* in relation to plague (*Yersinia pestis*) infection, aiming to determine the genetic markers associated with plague resistance in this species. They found 22 loci with high differentiation between resistant and susceptible populations, two of which were confirmed to be associated with survival in an experimental challenge performed by injecting *Y. pestis* in individuals caught from resistant or susceptible populations.

Using NGS technology, A. Springer et al. (2016) have investigated the transmission of *Escherichia coli* (a commensal gut bacterium) among 39 individuals of *Propithecus verreauxi* from Kirindy Forest CNFEREF and found that *E. coli* sharing reflected *P. verreauxi* group membership and, in part, intergroup interaction and sharing of space. Perofsky et al. (2017) have carried out high-throughput 16S rRNA sequencing on fecal samples collected from seven social groups of *P. verreauxi* living in Kirindy Forest CNFEREF (group size ranging from four to nine individuals) to characterize their gut microbiome composition and assess the relative contribution of social structure, diet, habitat overlap and relatedness on gut microbiota sharing among individuals. They found that social group membership was the most significant factor explaining gut microbiota similarity, when controlling for other factors. More recently, Greene et al. (2019) observed that *P. coquereli* showed significant shifts in microbiota

(continued overleaf)

BOX 5 MISCELLANEOUS GENETIC STUDIES ON MALAGASY MAMMALS *continued*

composition even with small changes in diet. Wasimuddin et al. (2019) carried out high-throughput sequencing of the v4 region of the ribosomal 16S on DNA extracted from fecal samples of wild *Microcebus griseorufus* to study how natural infection by an adenovirus (AdV) can induce significant changes in the gut microbiota. They found a decrease in microbial diversity and microbial interactions (positive and negative), and abundance of specific bacterial taxa in AdV-positive individuals (n = 44) compared to AdV-negative individuals (n = 116).

Similar high-throughput sequencing approaches have also been applied to study the diet of Malagasy mammals. Quéméré et al. (2013) carried out the first of such studies among Malagasy mammals, focusing on *P. tattersalli* individuals sampled across the species' entire range (Loky Manambato region). The objective of this study was to assess the influence of habitat type on diet composition. They sequenced part of *trnL* intron (plast gene), using DNA extracted from fecal samples obtained during the dry season, and compared the sequenced DNA with a database of *trnL* sequences from plants sampled in the same region, together with public sequence databases. They found a large dietary diversity in *P. tattersalli*, including ~80 plant genera and 49 families, consistent with the only known previous study, based on feeding behavior observations (88 genera; Meyers 1993).

Recently, Kemp et al. (2019) used a similar DNA metabarcoding approach to detect insect pest species present in the diet of six Malagasy bat species (*Chaerephon atsinanana*, *Mops leucostigma*, *Mormopterus jugularis*, *Myotis goudoti*, *Miniopterus manavi*, and *M. majori*) occurring in proximity of five villages near Ranomafana National Park. They extracted genomic DNA from 58 fecal samples and sequenced part of the COI mitochondrial locus. The DNA metabarcoding analysis showed that all bat species fed on arthropods of 11–13 orders, with Coleoptera being the most represented. They identified six known insect pest species and 17 potential pest taxa, among which two are known rice pests (*Spodoptera mauritia* and *Herpetogramma licarsisalis*) that were found in three out of six investigated bat species, thus demonstrating the role of bats in pest control. Bats also likely play an important role in controlling insects known to transmit diseases, but this was not explicitly mentioned in this study.

Genetic data from wild Malagasy mammals have been also used to study the evolution of certain phenotypic traits considered to be of relevance for present species diversity and ecology. For instance, Veilleux et al. (2013) sequenced the *OPN1SW* gene (associated to dichromatic color vision, ideal under light exposure) from 106 nocturnal lemurs belonging to 19 different species from five genera (*Microcebus*, *Avahi*, *Lepilemur*, *Phaner*, and *Cheirogaleus*). They found that the *OPN1SW* gene of most species living in open-canopy forests (spiny thickets and seasonally open dry deciduous forests) had stronger signature of purifying selection (less likely to have deleterious mutations in the gene) compared to species from closed-canopy moist evergreen forest. In an earlier study, Larsen et al. (2014) made use of published gene-expression data from several primates, including lemurs (*Daubentonia madagascariensis*, *Varecia variegata*, *Eulemur mongoz*, and *Propithecus coquereli*), to characterize antibody diversity across wild-caught primate species. They found high similarity in the type of antibodies expressed across studied species, and more specifically between haplorrhines and strepsirrhines, suggesting a "baseline" similarity between the adaptive immune systems of the two main clades of primates.

In a much earlier study, Sommer et al. (2002a) had studied the diversity of two MHC class II loci (involved in the adaptive immune system) in three endemic Malagasy rodents, *Eliurus myoxinus*, *Macrotarsomys bastardi*, and *Hypogeomys antimena*, the first with a promiscuous mating system and the other two with a monogamous mating system. They tested the hypothesis that monogamous species may have lower diversity in MHC class II genes than promiscuous species. They found indeed that the two monogamous species, *H. antimena* and *M. bastardi*, hold significantly lower MHC class II variation in the DQA gene (two and three alleles, respectively) than the promiscuous species, *E. myoxinus* (DQA: 11 alleles), suggesting a possible link between mating system and MHC class II genetic diversity.

Hunnicutt et al. (2020) have recently used genomic data of four *Microcebus* species (*M. griseorufus*, *M. ravelobensis*, *M. mittermeieri*, and *M. tavaratra*), two *Cheirogaleus* species (*C. sibreei* and *C. medius*), one *Mirza* species (*M. zaza*), and other primates to study the diversity of pheromone receptor class 1 family (V1R) across lemurs. The comparative genomic approach shows significantly higher diversity of V1R receptors in nocturnal compared to diurnal primates. Important differences in V1R diversity were identified even between diurnal and nocturnal lemurs, the latter showing higher variation within individuals. For instance, nocturnal lemurs such as *Microcebus mittermeieri* and *M. murinus* had as many as 146 and 102 intact V1R genes, respectively, compared to the ~20 genes found in *Propithecus coquereli* or *Prolemur simus*.

---

the fineStructure method (Lawson et al. 2012), similar to STRUCTURE but adapted to manage genomic data. They obtained ~2500 highly conserved loci for 18 individuals and identified two genetic clusters within *M. fotsifotsy* and a possible admixture between *M. soricoides* and the southernmost *M. fotsifotsy* cluster.

Whereas most of the articles mentioned above looked mainly at genetic differentiation and tried to identify homogeneous genetic clusters, Quéméré et al. (2010b) went further and tried to quantify for *Propithecus tattersalli* the relative importance of various landscape features in the Loky Manambato region, such as the presence

of open habitats and the potential barrier role of the Manankolana River and the national road crossing the region. These authors first identified two main genetic clusters corresponding to individuals sampled on the two sides of the Manankolana River, hence suggesting that the river was the main landscape feature in this region shaping genetic diversity in this species (see Figure 14.9). The national road did not appear as a significant barrier. In a later study based on 15 microsatellites from *Microcebus tavaratra* sampled in the same region, Aleixo-Pais et al. (2019) found that the Manankolana River was not the main factor correlated to genetic differentiation. They, rather, identified populations in the two most humid and southern forests as clustering together and apart from all other samples. Three other studies based on mtDNA have been carried out in the Loky Manambato region, the first two on Nesomyinae rodents *Eliurus carletoni* and *E. tanala* (now *E. ellermani*; Jansa et al. 2019) (J.-E. Rakotoarisoa et al. 2013a, 2013b) and the second on *M. tavaratra* (Sgarlata et al. 2018). Both studies found that the

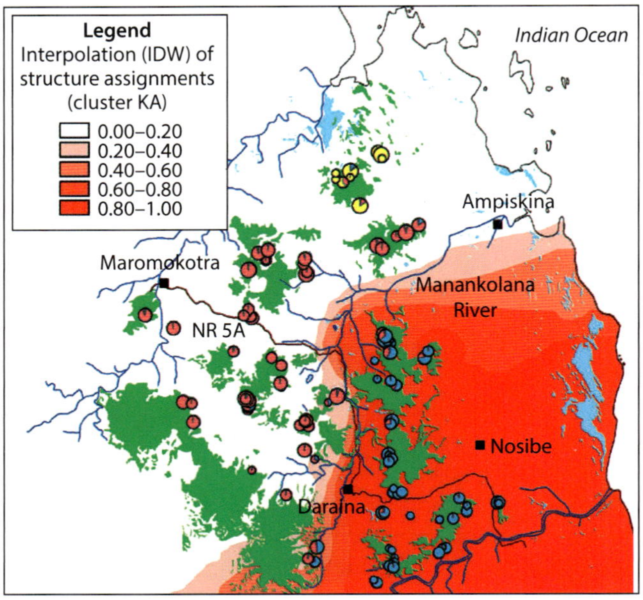

FIGURE 14.9 Population genetics structure in *Propithecus tattersalli* across its fragmented distribution range, in the Loky Manambato region in the north of Madagascar. Pie charts represent social groups of *P. tattersalli*. Their size is proportional to the number of sampled individuals. The colors indicate the average membership coefficients to each of the three genetic clusters (blue, red, and yellow) inferred using the STRUCTURE software. The red gradient illustrates the interpolated membership coefficients of the blue cluster across the study area, showing that the main genetic discontinuity overlaps with the location of the Manankolana River. Green areas are remaining forest parcels. IDW, inverse distance weighted, applies to the interpolation function used for the membership coefficients to the first genetic cluster; KA corresponds to the first of the three identified genetic clusters, which is composed of individuals located east of the Manankolana River (and is represented by the red area in the map and the blue color in the pie charts); and NR 5A is the National Road 5A. (SOURCE: modified from Quéméré et al. 2010b.)

Manakolana River did not have a strong effect on the genetic structure of these species. Hence, the results of landscape genetics studies carried out in the Loky Manambato region on *Microcebus*, *Eliurus*, and *Propithecus* identified different effects of landscape configuration on genetic differentiation and diversity, and they demonstrate that studying only one species in a given region is not sufficient to draw general conclusions about the effects of landscape features on genetic variation.

Genetic results suggest that even congeneric species within the same or neighboring regions can exhibit very different population genetics patterns, as presented by Olivieri et al. (2008) for *Microcebus* species. This pattern can also be seen in the companion studies carried out in the north by Ramanamahefa et al. (2009a, 2009b) on *Eulemur coronatus* and *E. sanfordi*. These studies sampled individuals at the same locations over a large region between Montagne d'Ambre in the extreme north and the Binara Forest in the southern part of the Loky Manambato region. The authors detected significant genetic differentiation between populations (using a classical sample-based approach) in both species. However, they identified only one genetic cluster in *E. coronatus* and two in *E. sanfordi*, despite the rather large geographic distances and the absence of continuous habitat today between samples. In contrast, they found several clusters in the Loky Manambato region for *P. tattersalli* and *M. tavaratra*. Differences between the two *Eulemur* species could be due to different colonization histories or to behavioral or ecological differences between the species.

These examples show that multispecies studies carried out in the same regions or across regions are urgently needed on the island if we are to understand how and whether natural or anthropogenic landscape features such as rivers, agricultural lands, or open habitats affect different species in similar or different ways. Generation time, dispersal ability, population size, social structure, and many other factors, including the level of forest dependency and anthropogenic pressure, will likely be crucial in that respect. The more we are able to study multiple species from the same or different regions using similar and comparable genetic markers, the less our conclusion will be taxon-biased (see Avise 2000 for general phylogeographic principles; Everson et al. 2020b for a comparative analysis of genetic data across mammal and reptile species). This underlines the importance of studies developing or testing markers across species, such as those of Edward E. Louis Jr. and colleagues at Omaha's Henry Doorly Zoo and Aquarium, Nebraska, United States. Among others following the same approach we can identify, for example, the study of G. Rakotoarisoa et al. (2006) on *Propithecus coquereli*, Tokiniaina et al. (2009) on *Eulemur cinereiceps*, Bailey et al. (2016) on *Propithecus* species, Andrianaivoarivelo et al. (2009) on bats, and Vogler et al. (2009a) on *Cryptoprocta ferox*. Genomic data will also contribute to such efforts if similar markers are used across species. For instance, Poelstra et al. (2021) used a standardized approach on *Microcebus* species, hence making their data comparable. Among the early population genetics studies, Olivieri et al. (2008) was probably the first comparative population genetics study on Madagascar, quantifying and dating population size changes in the three species of *Microcebus* occurring in the northwest.

What these genetic studies tell us about ancient habitat or population connectivity is not always clear, because they identify *patterns* based on genetic structure (or lack of) but do not necessarily

aim at identifying the *processes* responsible for the observed patterns. It is tempting and probably justified to suggest that the forested habitats currently occupied by *E. sanfordi* and *E. coronatus* in the north or *M. ravelobensis* in the northwest were continuous in the recent past, but without proper spatial and temporal modeling, as well as paleoecological data, it is difficult to clarify what is meant by "recent." A number of studies have tried to link patterns and processes by inferring the demographic history of Malagasy species for which spatial patterns had been identified and linked to habitat change—for example, the work of Olivieri et al. (2008) on the three species of *Microcebus* from northwestern Madagascar, Craul et al. (2009) on *Lepilemur edwardsi* from the same region, and Quéméré et al. (2012) on *P. tattersalli* in the Loky Manambato region. As we will present below, many of the methods developed to infer demographic history (historical processes) conversely tend to ignore space (population structure) and thus the associated patterns. But before moving to methods developed to infer the demographic history of species, we need to examine the interplay between landscape and spatial genetics approaches and how some methods have been applied to Malagasy mammals in an attempt to link spatial features and processes.

Investigating Spatial Processes in Malagasy Mammals: Toward the Estimation of Present-Day Dispersal Distances Based on Isolation-by-Distance (IBD) Patterns

In most species, dispersal is limited by geographic distance, and most individuals will reproduce at a relatively short distance from where they were born. This produces a pattern known as *isolation by distance* (IBD), in which individuals geographically close are genetically more similar than individuals far apart (S. Wright 1943). This pattern is often visualized by plotting pairwise genetic distances (between individuals or populations) against the corresponding geographic distance. Theoretical work has shown that the correlation between these geographic and genetic distances is informative about parameters such as species-specific dispersal distances (see Box 4). Similarly, such demographic parameters can also be estimated if one computes the average relatedness (e.g., kinship) between pairs of individuals separated by geographic distances that fall within a set of distance classes (Vekemans and Hardy 2004). For instance, Fredsted et al. (2005) genotyped 83 males and 83 females of *Microcebus murinus* across an area of ~12 km^2. They then computed pairwise geographic distances between all males and all females, separately. They created distance classes that had similar and sufficiently large numbers of pairs and computed the number of shared alleles across microsatellite loci as a measure of relatedness between pairs of individuals for each distance class. They plotted the average number of shared alleles for the increasing distance classes and found that this number was higher and significant for females from the first distance class (<250 m). For males, even if relatedness was higher in the first than in other distance classes, it was not significantly different from the average number of shared alleles across the sampled area. Thus, although the authors did not estimate absolute values of effective dispersal distance, their results suggest relatively longer dispersal distances in males than in females (e.g., Figure 14.8).

Theoretical studies suggest that one could go further than these semiquantitative analyses. For instance, data from studies such as Fredsted et al. (2005) could in principle be used together with estimates of population density to derive an estimate of the effective dispersal distance (σ) (see Box 4). This approach has been implemented in the software SPAGeDI (Spatial Pattern Analysis of Genetic Diversity) (Hardy and Vekemans 2002) and has been applied to microsatellite data across various taxa outside Madagascar and could thus be used to improve our understanding of dispersal patterns in Malagasy mammals. Information on mammal dispersal can also shed light on broader aspects of the ecology of a given species. Brouat et al. (2013) studied the spatial genetic structure of introduced *Rattus rattus* in four regions (each in an area ~150–200 km^2, with 2–6 subpopulations ~2 km apart) in which human plague epidemics are regularly reported. They tested whether plague dissemination correlated with the effective dispersal of *R. rattus*, the fleas of which are the main reservoir of the disease on the island. These authors genotyped 910 individuals at 14 nuclear microsatellite loci and correlated genetic differentiation (F_{ST}) and differences in plague seroprevalence levels between pairs of populations within two of the four surveyed regions. They found significant relationship between these two variables in only one of the two sites, suggesting that *R. rattus* dispersal is important but not sufficient to explain plague dissemination in all regions of the island.

Studies Identifying Recent and Ancient Environmental Features That Influence Species Dispersal

Environmental features (biotic and abiotic) can influence species dispersal, representing either barriers to gene flow or corridors at the scale of the landscape (Hendry 2004; Nosil et al. 2008). Several approaches nowadays allow researchers to test hypotheses on the factors limiting or favoring species dispersal (see Box 4). Quéméré et al. (2010b) have used causal modeling (CM), in addition to other methods, to study effects of geographic distance, roads, river, and forest canopy on the dispersal of *Propithecus tattersalli*. This technique identified the Manankolana River crossing the Loky Manambato region as the main barrier to dispersal in this species, in agreement with other landscape genetics approaches. In addition, a significant effect of geographic distance was detected, implicitly suggesting that the state of habitat fragmentation of the region might not disrupt gene flow significantly in this species. In the moist evergreen forests of the east, Baden et al. (2019) have used the approach known as *isolation by resistance* (IBR; see Box 4) to identify areas that facilitate or restrict gene flow among sampled *Varecia variegata* individuals and to investigate the impact of landscape heterogeneity on this species' dispersal. They tested effects of rivers, topography, roads, habitat cover, and proximity to human activity on genetic differentiation (measured by F_{ST}) to identify the landscape variables that significantly affect *V. variegata* dispersal in the fragmented habitat of eastern Madagascar. The study used 10 microsatellite loci for 200 adults sampled from 18 localities over an area of ~64,000 km^2. The authors identified a significant effect of geographic distance on gene flow, hence suggesting an IBD pattern (explaining 28.2% of the genetic structure). However, they also found other, more important effects in their model comparisons; in particular, habitat cover and distance to nearest village had the

highest explanatory inference (~52%), as compared to habitat cover only (~25%), distance to nearest village only (~22%), and IBD only (~1%). Considering the high rate of deforestation in eastern Madagascar since 1960 or so and the large effect of anthropogenic-related variables on the genetic differentiation of *V. variegata*, Baden et al. (2019) proposed that rapid land-cover modification by humans has driven changes in genetic structure of this species.

The CM and IBR approaches rely on *a priori* knowledge of the landscape features that may influence dispersal, which can be difficult to obtain. An interesting method that does not require prior information on landscape structure was recently proposed by Tang et al. (2020) and applied to the *P. tattersalli* genetic data set from Quéméré et al. (2010a). They computed resistance maps, which represent how easy or difficult it is for genes to cross a particular area of the sampled region. For that they quantified deviations of pairwise genetic differentiation between all sampled locations from expected differentiation under a simple IBD model (i.e., under the assumption of a continuous and homogeneous landscape). The deviations are presented on the resistance map together with the sampled individuals and thus help identify areas that are easier or more difficult to cross. In this approach, habitat features such as rivers or roads are not explicitly tested, and their contribution is not explicitly quantified. However, a qualitative comparison between the mapped resistance and landscape structure can help identify putative barriers to dispersal. For instance, Tang et al. (2020) identified several sections of the Manankolana River where resistance to gene flow was high and others where it was low, suggesting that the river per se is not a barrier in *P. tattersalli*. Similarly, some areas of currently nonforested habitat appeared to represent a high resistance to dispersal whereas others did not. In Madagascar, where habitats are increasingly fragmented, this kind of approach could help visualize fine-scale resistance maps for different species across regions. This type of analysis helps identify whether it is useful to consider a whole river or nonforested habitats as barriers and then test with other approaches the relative contribution of such landscape features on species genetic structure. Indeed some methods mentioned here tend to use categorical approaches where features such as "open habitat" or "river" are considered and identified or not as potential barriers to gene flow. A finer approach might be more useful and needs to be tested and implemented across more Malagasy mammals and regions.

How we interpret genetic patterns from natural populations can depend significantly on the assumptions of the model used to analyze the data. For example, one important limitation of the two statistical approaches mentioned above (CM and IBR) is that the relative contribution of geographic and environmental distance cannot be separated. Some authors working outside of Madagascar have thus proposed the concept of *isolation by environment* or *by ecology* (IBE; see Box 4), which allows them to assess the relative contribution of an environmental variable compared to geographic distance in limiting species gene flow (I. J. Wang and Summers 2010; Bradburd et al. 2013). Madagascar, with its diversity of habitats and environmental conditions, should provide a wealth of study cases to which researchers could apply these methods. This is exactly what Scheel et al. (2015) did with *Microcebus griseorufus* populations occurring in three neighboring vegetation types within a continuous landscape. They applied the IBE model to test whether distinct genetic characteristics attributable to habitat-type preference would be observed and would thus favor the hypothesis of ecological adaptation and incipient speciation. Specifically, they genotyped 76 *M. griseorufus* individuals at nuclear loci (amplified fragment-length polymorphism, or AFLP, 793 fragments of 50–400 bp) and the mitochondrial D-loop (~690 bp) over an area of ~3 km^2. The sampled individuals were spread along two parallel 2.5 km–long transects, each with the same three vegetation formations. They quantified the relative contribution of environmental distance (IBE) on the observed genetic structure of *M. griseorufus*, controlling for the effect of geographic distance (IBD). The mtDNA D-loop data did not show a significant effect of habitat ecology when controlling for geographic distance, while geography could explain ~11% of genetic variance. The nuclear loci results were consistent, suggesting that environmental differences did not reduce gene flow in this species, at least at the geographic scale of the study. As a result, they found that habitat types did not have a significant effect on the genetic structure of the studied *M. griseorufus* populations, thus rejecting the hypothesis of incipient ecological adaption.

Whereas the studies mentioned above looked at the landscape features that affect present species dispersal, it is becoming increasingly important, on Madagascar and elsewhere, to also understand past habitat connectivity. For instance, A. D. Yoder et al. (2016) studied five *Microcebus* species occurring in several habitat types across the island: *M. mittermeieri* and *M. rufus* in moist evergreen forests of the east, *M. myoxinus* and *M. berthae* in dry deciduous forests of the west, and *M. lehilahytsara* in moist evergreen forests of the Central Highlands. They genotyped 30 individuals at ~7000 SNPs (single nucleotide polymorphisms, or segregating sites) using double-digest restriction-site-associated sequencing (ddRAD) (see Box 2), and analyzed mitochondrial data (cytochrome oxidase 2, or cox2; and cytochrome b, or cyt b) of 332 individuals from 25 different described *Microcebus* species. The aim of the study was to use spatial genomic patterns to test three hypotheses on past landscape changes in the Central Highlands: 1) forest hypothesis: 90% of the island was covered by primary forest before human arrival; 2) grassland hypothesis: Central Highlands grasslands were present long before human arrival; 3) mosaic hypothesis: the Central Highlands were characterized by a mixture of wooded grassland and closed-canopy forest. They built a "geogenetic" map for each studied species by drawing arrows pointing in the direction of hypothesized genetic history and admixture, using the method of Bradburd et al. (2016) (see Box 4). A. D. Yoder et al. (2016) found a stronger geogenetic relationship between *M. rufus* and *M. berthae*, which occur, respectively, in the moist evergreen forests of the east and dry deciduous forests of the west, than between species of the same ecoregion (*M. myoxinus* and *M. berthae*). The higher genetic distance between *M. myoxinus* and *M. berthae* was interpreted as evidence for the presence of a biogeographic barrier (Tsiribihina River). The surprising geogenetic proximity and the estimated divergence time of *M. rufus* and *M. berthae* suggested that forest-dwelling species such as *Microcebus* could have dispersed across the Central Highlands throughout the Pleistocene until ~55,000 years ago. In addition, the geogenetic map of *M. lehilahytsara* showed that subpopulations of this species occupied two distinct geogenetic clusters, interpreted as an indication that

the Central Highlands might have experienced cyclic events of fragmentation and reconnection. Overall, their genomic data pointed toward a mosaic hypothesis of pre-human-arrival vegetation in the Central Highlands characterized by a mosaic of forests and wooded grassland. This is in agreement with other studies (e.g., Quéméré et al. 2012) that have increasingly shown that the forest hypothesis is unlikely to have been correct and that natural forces have driven patterns of forest fragmentation even long before the arrival of humans.

Studies Investigating Spatial Processes in the Recent Past

The geogenetic study of A. D. Yoder et al. (2016) provided fascinating insights into the recent past. Another approach was followed by N. Schneider et al. (2010), who used spatially explicit simulations to study the demographic history of *Microcebus murinus* in northwestern Madagascar (Figure 14.10). They sampled 195 individuals from 15 populations (in Ankarafantsika National Park and forest fragments from two inter-river systems). They sequenced the mitochondrial D-loop (455 bp) and used, among various methods, mismatch-distribution analysis to infer the demographic history (see Reconstructing the Demographic History of Species, below, and Boxes 1 and 3). The results of the demographic analyses supported a complex model with two spatial expansions rather than one. Identifying this complex model was made possible with the SPLATCHE software (Currat et al. 2004, 2019), allowing researchers to carry out spatially explicit simulations, the results of which suggested that two recent expansions took place in *M. murinus*, one before and one after the Last Glacial Maximum (LGM, ~21,000 years ago). Besides evidence of a recent range expansion, the authors have also shown that IBD patterns computed using populations separated by open habitat (fragmented populations) were significantly different from those obtained using only populations sampled in continuous habitat, such as in the Ankarafantsika protected area. In particular, they found that, for the same geographic distance, genetic differentiation was significantly increased across fragmented populations compared to continuous populations. They postulated that these fragments might have been connected in the recent past, hence explaining the IBD pattern, but that recent genetic drift had increased genetic differentiation, hence explaining the IBD differences between connected and fragmented populations. They thus noted that 1) genetic data might maintain memory of the relatively recent pre-fragmentation past, and 2) differences in IBD might hold information on how and when fragmentation occurred.

In addition to *M. murinus*, several genetic studies have suggested that range expansions might have taken place for many Madagascar species, such as *M. tavaratra* (Sgarlata et al. 2018) or different endemic bats (*Rousettus madagascariensis*, Goodman et al. 2010a; *Mormopterus jugularis*, Ratrimomanarivo et al. 2009a). A well-known example of recent range expansion on the island is the introduced and often human-commensal rodent *Rattus rattus*. The distribution of genetic variation in this species across the island has been investigated in part to reconstruct the colonization histories of this species and of humans (Hingston et al. 2005; Tollenaere et al. 2010). Brouat et al. (2014) used genetic data from 672 *R. rattus* individuals sampled from 35 locations widely distributed across the

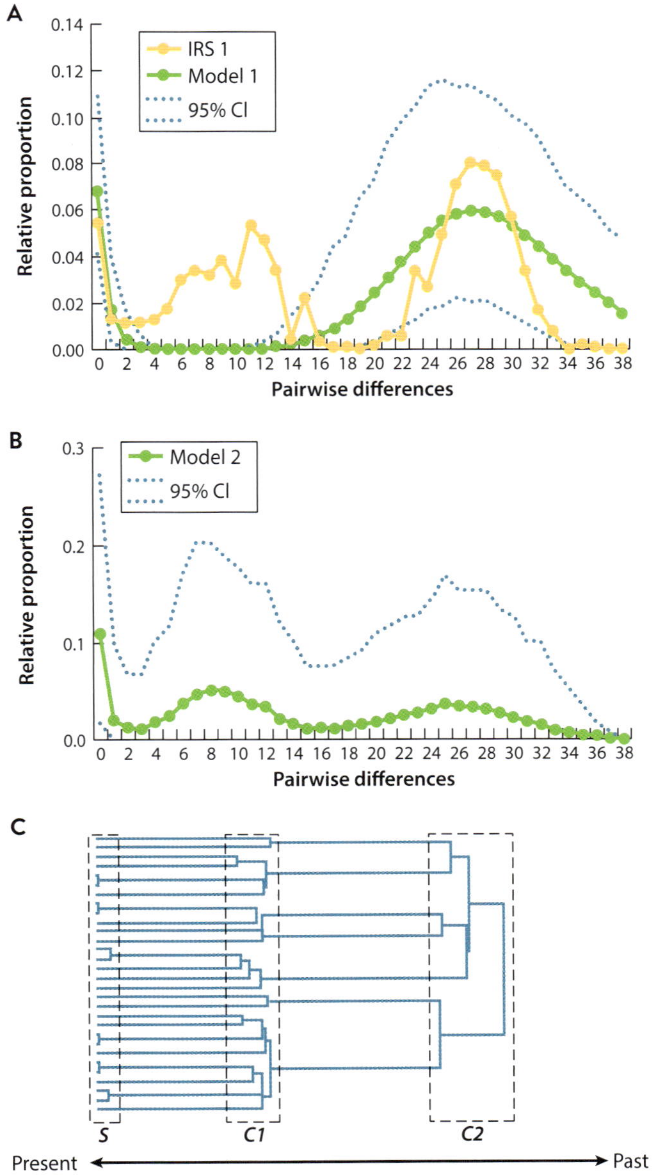

FIGURE 14.10 **Inferred spatial expansion in *Microcebus murinus* from northwestern Madagascar in two inter-river systems (IRS). A) Comparison of the mismatch distributions obtained from real data (mtDNA sequences sampled in the first river system, IRS 1) against data simulated under a scenario with a single expansion (Model 1). B) Mismatch distribution obtained by simulating genetic data under a model with two independent spatial expansions (Model 2). C) One typical gene genealogy obtained under Model 2, highlighting the three main phases of coalescence (S, C1, and C2, corresponding to the so-called scattering and collecting phases; Wakeley 1999), which explain the three modes in the mismatch distribution.** (SOURCE: modified from N. Schneider et al. 2010.)

island. The genetic data consisted of 17 nuclear microsatellite and two mitochondrial (partial D-loop and cyt b) loci. Population-structure clustering and phylogenetic analyses identified two major genetic groups (north vs. rest of Madagascar). Since range expansion of any species in a relatively homogeneous habitat should result in a

decrease of genetic diversity as it moves away from the origin of expansion, Brouat et al. (2014) tested for the rats several putative origins of expansion in Madagascar by computing, for each of them, a linear regression between genetic diversity (H_e; see Box 1) and geographic distance from the candidate sites. Two sampled sites in the southeast (Sainte Luce and Mandena) showed the strongest negative relationship between H_e and geographic distance (r ~12%), suggesting that southern Madagascar is the most likely region of introduction of *R. rattus*. The estimated area of first colonization was further corroborated by its close proximity to areas in which archaeological data suggest well-established human settlements around 1000–1500 years ago.

Taken together, these studies indicate how spatial patterns can be better understood by integrating time and simple processes representing the demographic history of species. Reconstructing history is often difficult and requires specific methods. The application of such methods to Malagasy mammals is the center of interest of the next section.

RECONSTRUCTING THE DEMOGRAPHIC HISTORY OF SPECIES FROM GENETIC DATA

Detecting Changes in Population Size in Malagasy Mammals, and First Dating Attempts

Besides the study of population structure, genetic data increasingly have been used since the mid-1980s to detect, date, and quantify past demographic events such as population expansions, bottlenecks, changes in connectivity, and admixture (Goldstein and Chikhi 2002; Lawler 2018). This became possible when population geneticists realized that some demographic events could potentially leave specific signatures in the genome of present-day populations (Ewens 1972; Nei et al. 1975). For instance, Nei et al. (1975) showed that when a stationary population goes through a bottleneck, the number of alleles (n_A) and the expected heterozygosity (H_e) will exhibit different temporal trajectories during and long after the bottleneck. In other words, after a bottleneck, a population will deviate from mutation-drift equilibrium (see Boxes 1 and 3). It is this type of signature that Brenneman et al. (2011) looked for in *Eulemur cinereiceps* in southeastern Madagascar. They used 26 microsatellite loci and tested for departures from mutation-drift equilibrium using the Bottleneck software (Cornuet and Luikart 1996; Piry et al. 1999). They found a significant departure in only one of the three sampled populations, which was more fragmented and impacted by human activities and cyclones. They were, however, unable to firmly conclude the existence of a recent or ancient bottleneck in this species of lemur.

In a similar study, carried out with eight microsatellite loci on *Lemur catta* (see Sauther and Cuozzo, pp. 1952–56, for details on this species) in the southwest of the island, Parga et al. (2012) investigated departures from equilibrium using an additional method developed by Garza and Williamson (2001). They also found contrasting results, depending on the population tested, with significant departures for some samples under certain mutation models. Parga et al. (2012) concluded that the bottleneck signal could potentially be due to real changes in population size, but they noted that the results might also be confounded by population structure, as suggested by several theoretical studies (see Boxes 1 and 3). Using the same approaches, Razakamaharavo et al. (2010) genotyped 15 microsatellite loci in two populations of *Varecia rubra* from Masoala Peninsula in the northeast and found significant departures from mutation-drift equilibrium in one of the two populations. Taken together, these and other studies did not provide clear signals of population bottlenecks in several lemur species. One likely reason for this is that these early approaches were not sufficiently powerful and required either a very strong bottleneck or a large number of variable loci. In other words, the statistics used were not particularly informative. Despite these limitations, there have also been cases in which the results were strong and significant, such as in Quéméré et al. (2012), which detected clear departures from equilibrium in *Propithecus tattersalli* using the same methods.

While this general approach was an important step in population genetics, it mainly allowed researchers to detect departures from stationarity. It did not easily allow them to quantify or date the putative changes in population size. The quantification and dating of population size change events with genetic data took place thanks to theoretical work carried out in the 1990s and implemented in various approaches. These include mismatch distributions (Slatkin and Hudson 1991; Rogers and Harpending 1992) and the Bayesian skyline plots (BSP; Drummond et al. 2005), which have been extensively used on Malagasy taxa. Other approaches were based on the development of likelihood-based and Bayesian demographic inference methods (Felsenstein 1992; Beaumont 1999; Box 3), which have been less used in studies of Malagasy mammals.

Ratrimomanarivo et al. (2009a) computed the mismatch distribution for the endemic bat *Mormopterus jugularis* using mtDNA D-loop sequences. They found a unimodal distribution compatible with a population expansion, estimated to have taken place between 120,000 and 230,000 years ago. Goodman et al. (2010a) carried out a similar analysis based on cytochrome b sequence data for the two western Indian Ocean *Rousettus* species (*R. madagascariensis*, endemic to Madagascar, and *R. obliviosus*, endemic to the Comoro islands). They found a clear unimodal distribution for *R. madagascariensis* and inferred a demographic expansion, which was poorly dated between 115,000 and 580,000 years ago. For *R. obliviosus*, the mismatch distribution was multimodal, and it was not clear whether the species had been stationary or subject to a more complex demographic history. The authors also tried to estimate the date of a putative expansion; the results had an even larger uncertainty.

Weyeneth et al. (2011a) also used mtDNA sequence data (D-loop and cyt b) from the endemic bat *Myotis goudoti*, applying spatial and demographic analyses. They identified three genetic clusters spatially distributed from the north to the south. They performed mismatch-distribution analysis on the three genetic clusters, each exhibiting unimodal distributions associated with demographic expansions of decreasing age from 123,000 years ago in the north-central cluster to 66,000 and 14,000 years ago in the southern and most southwesterly populations, respectively. Finally, in a more sophisticated study, N. Schneider et al. (2010) used several approaches to reconstruct the demographic history of *Microcebus murinus* from two inter-river systems in northwestern Madagascar (Figure 14.10). They computed two statistics that are known to be

sensitive to departures from mutation-drift equilibrium (namely Tajima's D [see Box 3] and Fu's *Fs*; Tajima 1989a; Fu 1997), and they also plotted the mismatch distribution. What is particularly worth stressing is that the authors used spatially explicit simulations to fit the observed mismatch distribution. This is important because most studies mainly try to fit a sudden or exponential increase under the assumption of total panmixia (Rogers and Harpending 1992). To do that, N. Schneider et al. (2010) used the SPLATCHE software (Currat et al. 2004, 2019) to simulate scenarios of expansion of mouse lemurs over tens of thousands of years and found that they needed to simulate two spatial expansions to explain the complex bimodal mismatch distributions found in *M. murinus*.

Bayesian skyline plots (Drummond et al. 2005) have also been used on several Malagasy mammals, from shrew tenrecs (*Microgale* spp., L. E. Olson et al. 2009) to mole tenrecs (*Oryzorictes* spp., Everson et al. 2018), bats (*Chaerephon* spp., Lamb et al. 2012; *Macronycteris* spp., Rakotoarivelo et al. 2019), endemic rodents (*Eliurus* spp., J.-E. Rakotoarisoa et al. 2013a, 2013b; see Carleton et al., pp. 2014–22, for details on this genus), and lemurs (*Propithecus coronatus*, Sgarlata et al. 2016; *Microcebus* spp., Blair et al. 2014, Sgarlata et al. 2018). Like mismatch distributions, BSP plots have been obtained mainly for nonprimate species, probably because BSP is typically used with sequence data and was thus applied to species for which mtDNA data were the main source of genetic information. BSP plots are attractive because they visually represent the demographic history as a sequence of population size increases or decreases that is not fixed *a priori*. In other words, the method does not try to fit the model with only one or two predefined size changes but to find the best number of changes that explain the data. This is different from the Beaumont methods discussed in the next section, which are able to extract more information from the data but assume models with a single monotonic size change. One of the first Malagasy studies to publish BSP plots was that of L. E. Olson et al. (2009) on two sister species of shrew tenrecs, *Microgale brevicaudata*, from the northern and central western areas of the island, and *M. grandidieri*, from the central west. They found that the two species had different demographic histories. *Microgale grandidieri* exhibited a continuous but slow decrease in population size that accelerated in the recent past, and *M. brevicaudata* showed a very stationary population that exhibited a sharp increase in the recent past.

Lamb et al. (2012) also used mtDNA sequences (cyt b and D-loop) to infer the history of population size changes in two bat species, *Chaerephon atsinanana* and *C. leucogaster*. They used both mismatch distributions and BSP plots. Whereas BSP plots suggested a recent population decrease in both species, the mismatch distributions were very different. For *C. atsinanana* they found a ragged distribution that could indicate either a stationary population or a complex history, possibly with population structure. For *C. leucogaster* they identified a recent population increase. There was thus disagreement with the BSP plots. One possible interpretation is that BSP and mismatch distribution may lead to different results because the different methods use different parts of the genetic information (see Box 1). J.-E. Rakotoarisoa et al. (2013a) used BSP on mtDNA (cyt b and D-loop) sequences from *Eliurus carletoni*, distributed in the low-elevation forests of the Loky Manambato region. They found a clear signal for an ancient stationary population that was subjected to a recent decline, possibly as a consequence of recent climate change and habitat fragmentation. These results were confirmed in another study (J.-E. Rakotoarisoa et al. 2013b), in which the authors also studied *E. tanala* (now the local population considered *E. ellermani*; Jansa et al. 2019), distributed in the same region but in higher-elevation forest, and found that *E. ellermani* exhibited a different history with no clear signal of population size change and perhaps a slight continuous increase.

These results thus appeared to confirm the idea that long-term habitat change during the Holocene has led to an expansion of the distribution of *E. ellermani* and a reduction and fragmentation of the distribution of *E. carletoni*. The authors also used mismatch distributions, which confirmed a possible ancient expansion for *E. ellermani*. However, for *E. carletoni* the distributions were ragged, as in the bat *C. atsinanana* (Lamb et al. 2012)—hence making it difficult to make strong conclusions, despite the connection between inferred population size changes and recent Holocene habitat changes. Also, the results were in agreement with results suggesting that *Propithecus tattersalli* living in the same region, or the neighboring species *P. perrieri*, had experienced recent changes in connectivity (as detailed in the next section). Genetic data can be difficult to interpret and compare across species. Sgarlata et al. (2018) obtained a bimodal mismatch distribution for *Microcebus tavaratra*, also sampled in the Loky Manambato region. This bimodal distribution is consistent with one or several past expansions, as N. Schneider et al. (2010) found for *M. murinus* from northwestern portions of the island (Figure 14.10). However, the BSP plots of *M. tavaratra* were flat, indicating no signal whatsoever of population size change. Similarly, flat BSP plots were found by Sgarlata et al. (2016) in *P. coronatus* in the northwest. Blair et al. (2014), who used three nuclear genes and two mtDNA loci on *M. griseorufus* in the southern and southwestern areas, obtained BSP plots suggesting a recent population increase for *M. murinus* sampled in the southwest. This is in partial agreement with the work of N. Schneider et al. (2010) (see Figure 14.10) on this same species, which had recovered the signal for two expansions rather than one in the northwest. Finally, Everson et al. (2018) used extended BSP (EBSP; Heled and Drummond 2008), an extension of the BSP to multi-locus data, in a study of *Oryzorictes hova* (Hova Mole Tenrec). They identified a signal of long-term increase until around 250,000 years ago, followed by a decrease since then. This species is distributed in the moist evergreen forests of Madagascar, and the authors identified three genetically distinct clades, noting that they could possibly represent divergent populations in the process of speciation. The same demographic trend was found in the three clades, but the cause of the decrease could not be identified, the authors pointed out, owing to the large uncertainty on the EBSP plots and their inability to detect changes in the recent (Holocene) past.

Despite their limitations, the BSP and mismatch-distribution approaches have provided important insights into the demographic history of many taxa for which mtDNA sequences were the main genetic data available. Consistent expansion signals have been detected independently in *M. murinus* in the south and northwest but also in *M. tavaratra* in the far north. In other cases, the signals were contradictory for the same species depending on the method used. In some cases, differences observed between species living in the same region might indicate different ecological requirements. This might be the case for *E. ellermani* and *E. carletoni*, which

appear to prefer dissimilar forest types and elevational zones, and these differences might be related to different demographic histories. Further, if we compare these rodents to *M. tavaratra*, they may have recently arrived in the Loky Manambato region. There is a need to bring all these studies together and perhaps construct a comparative framework, even if some of the data are preliminary at this stage. This should become increasingly possible, as certain regions of the island, including Ankarafantsika, Kirindy Forest CNFEREF, and the Loky Manambato region, are starting to have sufficient data thanks to long-term studies. In the next section, we bring together studies that have used more advanced methodologies for demographic inference.

DATING PAST POPULATION SIZE CHANGES IN MALAGASY MAMMALS IN RELATION TO NATURAL HABITAT CHANGE AND ANTHROPOGENIC ACTIVITIES

Demographic inference significantly changed after the article of Felsenstein (1992), who argued that by using summary statistics calculated from genetic data, population geneticists were throwing away most of the information available in the genealogy of genes. He noted that if information could be extracted from the data using likelihood-based methods, it would significantly increase our ability to infer the evolutionary history of species (Boxes 1 and 3). Olivieri et al. (2008) were the first to apply likelihood-based methods to lemurs, specifically the methods of Beaumont (1999) and Storz and Beaumont (2002), which were used to detect and date population size changes in orangutans (Goossens et al. 2006). Olivieri et al. (2008) identified, dated, and quantified a major bottleneck in three *Microcebus* species from northwestern Madagascar, which suggested that the three species had a much larger population in the recent past, possibly as a result of significant habitat loss and fragmentation. The best-supported estimate suggested a major demographic event in the past 500–900 years. The three species showed similar results despite their nonoverlapping distributions and differences in terms of population structure. In a similar study carried out in the same region, Craul et al. (2009) also found a strong and recent bottleneck signal for *Lepilemur edwardsi*, which most likely started during the past 1000 years. The generation time assumed for mouse lemurs by Olivieri et al. (2008) was one year, whereas recent studies (Radespiel et al. 2019a) suggest that a more realistic value might be between two and three years (see also A. D. Yoder et al. 2016). Despite the complexities of determining a consistent measure of generation time—a problem no doubt related to poorly known life-history strategies—the dating of the demographic event detected in these *Microcebus* species could thus be older than dates suggested originally by Olivieri et al. (2008). Nonetheless, the age would still be reasonably recent, likely within the past 1000–3000 years.

Taken together, these two studies strongly suggested that the signal for a bottleneck found in four species from the northwest was possibly related to major habitat changes in the recent past, possibly as a consequence of human activities (see Godfrey and Douglass, pp. 191–97, for further details on habitat change in this area of Madagascar). This appears to be the first clear genetic indication that humans might have been responsible for habitat loss generating a massive reduction in lemur population sizes. These results should also be integrated with the results of N. Schneider et al. (2010) suggesting two major population expansions of *M. murinus* in the same region but in a much more ancient period and on the basis of mtDNA data.

In northern Madagascar, genetic studies seem to indicate a rather different scenario, with evidence of more ancient habitat loss and fragmentation compared to the northwest. In a study carried out in the Loky Manambato region, Quéméré et al. (2012) used the same likelihood-based methods on genetic data of *Propithecus tattersalli*. They also detected a bottleneck signal but with strong support for an ancient and likely pre-human-arrival habitat change, possibly between 4000 and 10,000 years ago. Since it has been shown that population genetic structure can confound demographic inference (Chikhi et al. 2010; see Box 3), Quéméré et al. (2012) also tested the effect of population structure on *P. tattersalli* results, concluding that population structure was unlikely to have generated the detected bottleneck signal, even if it might have contributed to it. Additionally, by analyzing satellite pictures, they found that forested habitats had decreased by only 2% in the previous 50–60 years in the Loky Manambato region. Therefore, they concluded that the fragmented habitat of the Loky Manambato region, which is topographically and geologically complex (Goodman et al. 2018b), was likely natural and ancient, making this region rather different from other areas of the island, where deforestation has clearly been very high in the recent past (Vieilledent et al. 2018). There is increasing evidence that humans arrived in Madagascar much earlier than was thought when these studies were performed (see Wright and Rakotoarisoa, pp. 181–90; Godfrey and Douglass, pp. 191–97).

In a more recent study, Salmona et al. (2017) extended the work of Quéméré et al. (2012) by applying several methods of demographic inference to *P. tattersalli* and to *P. perrieri*, the latter of which lives in the neighboring Andrafiamena region. The distribution of *P. perrieri* is currently notably smaller and more fragmented than that of *P. tattersalli*. The results of this study are too complex to summarize here because of the large number of methods used, but they are generally consistent with one another, although not always in agreement regarding the dating of events. Again, this is likely due to the fact that the methods used make different assumptions and summarize genetic information in different ways. Salmona et al. (2017), following the same methods as Quéméré et al. (2012), found a major signal for a bottleneck that started at least 3000 years ago and possibly even before 10,000 years ago, depending on the generation time assumed. The results were thus consistent with Quéméré et al. (2012), strengthening the conclusions of the previous study. However, Salmona et al. (2017) were uncertain whether the timing was the same in the two species, given the uncertainties of the generated dates. What makes this study unique is its use of ABC (approximate Bayesian computation; see Box 3) framework to compare a large number of alternative models that incorporated both population size change and fragmentation. All together these authors compared 14 demographic models with and without population size change, with and without ancient population structure, and with and without recent changes in connectivity. They found that the best model explaining the genetic data for *P. perrieri* was one in which populations were structured in the past

and underwent an increase in habitat loss and fragmentation in more recent geological time. In the case of *P. tattersalli*, the same model best explained the recovered patterns but could not distinguish it from a model in which habitat had been more continuous in the past. The authors could thus identify an increase in fragmentation in both species, but for *P. tattersalli* the habitat might have been more continuous than for *P. perrieri*. Because of the imprecise dating and the pushing of the date of human arrival on the island deeper into time, they were unable to exclude human activities as a possible cause of the recent increase in habitat fragmentation. Thus Salmona et al. (2017) provided the first study in which complex demographic histories, incorporating population size changes, population structure, and changes in habitat connectivity, could be compared together.

The population genetics studies discussed above are important because they provide insights on the relatively recent evolutionary history of species, which in turn have important implications for conservation purposes. They are based on the implicit or explicit idea that one could in principle study past changes in habitat by inferring the demographic history of the species living today in these habitats. Currently, the genetics studies suggest that regions in the northwest of the island, specifically Ankarafantsika and neighboring areas, likely have had different histories of habitat fragmentation from those of the northeast, namely the Loky Manambato and Andrafiamena regions. In the first case, genetic data suggest a recent and major loss of habitats, whereas in the second case, habitats may have been fragmented over much longer periods, and humans may have contributed in only a limited way to that process (excluding recent decades). This second scenario is in agreement with the geogenetic study of A. D. Yoder et al. (2016) discussed above.

Interpreting genetic data must be done with caution. Linking population sizes estimated by some methods to changes in the dynamics of habitat connectivity is not simple. For instance, most methods that infer population size changes explicitly assume that population structure can be ignored (see Box 3). An implicit assumption is that if we detect, say, a 10-fold change in population size, it will seem unlikely that population structure could be responsible for a change of such magnitude. There are two problems with that assumption. First, there is an increasing recognition that population structure can actually generate major signals of change in population size even without any real change in population size. In other words, our intuition is simply not good enough and most methods aiming at detecting population size changes, while ignoring population structure (Beaumont 1999; Drummond et al. 2005; Li and Durbin 2011), may actually be misleading (Beaumont 2004; Chikhi et al. 2010; Mazet et al. 2016). Second, if we wish to understand how human activities or environmental factors, such as natural climate change, have influenced ancient patterns of habitat fragmentation in Madagascar, we need also to understand how changes in population connectivity influence genetic diversity, differentiation, and demographic inference. Thus, ignoring population structure is unlikely to be correct for many species.

This does not mean that the results presented above are incorrect and that no population size changes took place in the presented case examples. It only means that the interpretation of genetic data is more challenging than often assumed, and that the same data may be explained by rather different scenarios. It is difficult to imagine a method that would account for all the complexities of demographic histories, including population and social structure, population size changes, changes in gene flow, and possible population splitting or extinction. It seems thus important to be modest and instead base our conclusions on the comparison of alternative scenarios relying on meaningful biological, ecological, paleoclimatological, and archaeological data. This is where ABC methods (see Boxes 1 and 3; Beaumont et al. 2002; Beaumont 2010) provide one possible solution, as we have seen with the Brouat et al. (2014) and Salmona et al. (2017) studies. The great advantage of ABC is that it can be applied to nearly any demographic model of interest. As a consequence, ABC can be used for model choice, although it can be computationally demanding, with detailed genomic data and very complex models.

Finally, another word of caution is necessary when interpreting genetic data. An important but too often neglected issue is that of sampling. Many population genetics methods assume that the samples analyzed are taken from an isolated random-mating population. However, obtaining samples from rare and threatened species is not a simple matter. Moreover, as we have seen for many Malagasy mammals, genetic samples can be obtained in different portions of the island, based on a limited number of individuals from nonadjacent locations. This means that some of the mismatch distributions or BSP plots discussed above were generated by pooling samples from distant locations. It is increasingly recognized that sampling methodologies can generate significant signals of demographic changes in genetic data (Wakeley 1999; Chikhi et al. 2010, 2018; Heller et al. 2013; Mazet et al. 2016) or in the analysis of genetic diversity—see *ascertainment bias* in Box 1.

STUDIES USING GENOMIC DATA TO DETECT AND DATE ANCIENT EVOLUTIONARY EVENTS

The pairwise sequentially Markovian coalescent (PSMC) method of Li and Durbin (2011) is probably the most popular method, both in and outside Madagascar, of using genomic data to detect and date ancient evolutionary events. It allows researchers to reconstruct a history of population size change from the genome of a single individual, and it is thus well adapted to Malagasy and other nonmodel species for which full genomes can be obtained for only a limited number of individuals. The method has already been applied to several lemur species, such as *Eulemur macaco* and *E. albifrons* (Meyer et al. 2015), *Prolemur simus*, *Microcebus murinus*, *Propithecus verreauxi* (M. T. R. Hawkins et al. 2018), *Cheirogaleus* species (Williams et al. 2020), and *Microcebus* species (Poelstra et al. 2021).

In Figure 14.11, we show the PSMC plots obtained for *Cheirogaleus* species, which are known to hibernate, and analyzed by Williams et al. (2020). The figure also shows patterns of diversity as measured by heterozygosity along the genome in the four individuals representing the different species. The four PSMC curves are different from each other, suggesting that the demographic histories of each taxon are also different from one another. For instance, Williams et al. (2020) interpreted the curves as representing changes in effective population size through time and noted that whereas

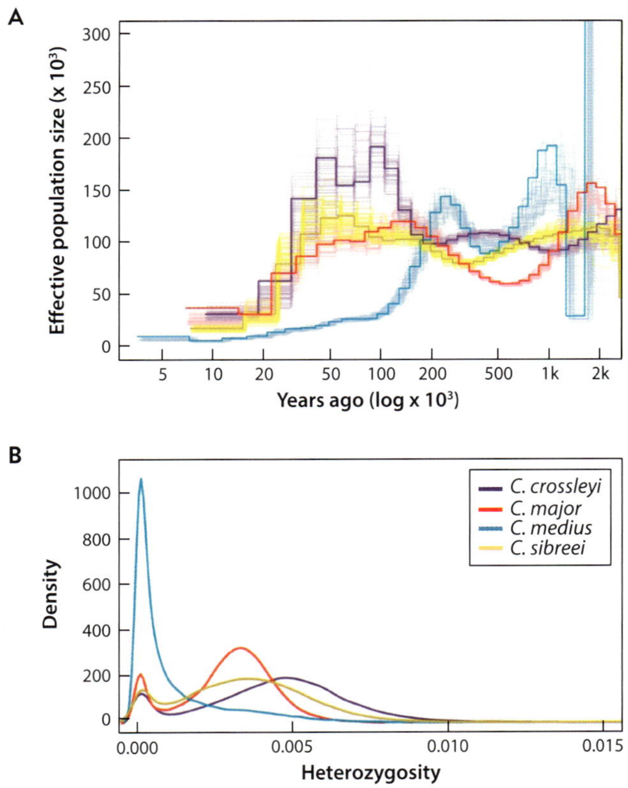

FIGURE 14.11 Demographic inference and genome-wide heterozygosity distribution of individuals of *Cheirogaleus* species. A) Inferred population size changes (N_e) using single diploid genome (PSMC method; see main text) of each studied species (see legend in panel B). For each species, bold lines indicate the inferred population size, whereas thinner lines correspond to bootstrapped PSMC curves. B) Genome-wide distribution of heterozygosity, computed across the genome over 100-kb windows. (SOURCE: modified from Williams et al. 2020.)

three curves suggest large population sizes in the past 200,000 years, this was not the case for the *C. medius* (blue) PSMC plot. This can also be seen by the fact that the heterozygosity distribution shows a strong bias toward low values. *Cheirogaleus major* (red) and *C. medius* (blue) have very large geographic distributions, whereas the other two species are known from only a few locations. A further complication is that the genotyped *C. medius* individual was sampled in a small forest within the distribution of *C. major*, outside the previously known range of *C. medius*. Finally, these curves could also be interpreted in a population structure framework (Mazet et al. 2016), suggesting perhaps an increase in fragmentation rather than major changes in population size across the complete distribution of these taxa. While much work is needed to analyze more samples from other regions, we stress that this is the first study of its kind, as it also tried to detect potential admixture events between the sampled species. The results suggested that there may have been an admixture event between *C. medius* and both *C. major* and *C. sibreei* around 4 million years ago (Mya). The authors also suggested that genes involved in hibernation might have been introduced between these species during the admixture events, but the proportion of such genes among the introgressed genes was low.

We are still in a period in which such methods are experimental and results are preliminary. The important aspect is that the Williams et al. (2020) study was the first one that tried to use a rather complex set of inference methods. A subsequent publication by Poelstra et al. (2021) went further in the sense that these authors not only described a new species (*Microcebus jonahi*) but also used a variety of methods to recover the demographic history of *Microcebus* species from eastern Madagascar. Some of the methods used were based on restriction-site-associated DNA sequencing (RAD-seq; see Box 2) data and used the allele frequency spectrum (AFS; see Box 1), but the authors also used the PSMC method. They found an apparent decrease in population size using both the PSMC and AFS-based methods (Gronau et al. 2011).

The PSMC method assumes that the individual was sampled in a nonconnected panmictic population and that population structure is negligible. However, Mazet et al. (2016) have shown that the PSMC is profoundly influenced by population structure and that even if population size is constant, population structure will unavoidably generate a major signal of population decrease in the recent past. In addition, they showed that if migration rates (connectivity) changed in the past, this should necessarily generate humps similar to those found in real PSMC curves, such as those represented in Figure 14.11 and those observed in other lemurs (Meyer et al. 2015; M. T. R. Hawkins et al. 2018). Given that habitats have been subjected to complex cycles of connectivity and disconnection, and that these have also been accompanied by changes in population size, it is difficult to determine the extent to which the genomic patterns uncovered with the PSMC method should be interpreted as indicating changes in connectivity. Chikhi et al. (2018) proposed a general framework allowing researchers to construct alternative models of great complexity with both population size changes and changes in connectivity, but this framework does not allow them to automatically infer the models. There is still no simple manner to identify the best model.

While these comments may seem technical, they are sufficiently general to be mentioned. Data on a genomic scale are just starting to be applied toward a better understanding of Madagascar's biodiversity, and the methods adapted to the corresponding large data sets are being developed as we write this contribution. The advantage of genomic data is that they provide large amounts of information and thus allow researchers to infer demographic parameters with statistical confidence. However, this also comes at a cost. First, the analysis of genetic data is computationally expensive and technically challenging, making it difficult for people outside the field to contribute critically to the interpretation of the data. Second, this selects for new types of students who will be less and less able to physically conduct fieldwork, as they will become increasingly tied to the computers required to manipulate the large text files needed to analyze the data. Third, the complexity of the many program scripts required to analyze and filter the data is such that it is very difficult to test and validate properly the results obtained by increasingly specialized computational biologists. Fourth, using large amounts of data under the wrong model may generate very precise estimates of potentially misleading parameters.

A common saying in statistics is that "all models are wrong, but some are useful." The reason for this is that models are simplified

versions of reality, stressing one or several aspects of that reality. They are constructed for what is hoped to be a clear goal and should be used beyond that only if it can be proven that they are indeed applicable. Unfortunately, scientists working in these and other domains tend to believe very strongly that the methods they use and the underlying models are correct. They often forget the assumptions that were required for the cherished conclusions to be properly substantiated. Genetic and genomic data, together with models and inference methods, are fundamental to help make sense of a complex world and to make the best use of the data. However, models and data need to be interpreted with an open mind and in an increasingly comparative framework. There are still few published studies and PhD theses using genomic data from Malagasy mammals and aimed at reconstructing the demographic history of species.

TAXONOMY, MAMMAL SPECIES DIVERSITY, AND HYBRIDIZATION STUDIES

Taxonomy and Mammal Species Diversity

Genetic data have significantly changed our understanding of Malagasy mammals, not just at the local, landscape, or species scale, as we have seen in the previous sections. These data have been increasingly used, often with morphological and fossil data, to reconstruct evolutionary relationships among Malagasy mammals, clarifying the phylogenetic position of diverse mammals at different taxonomic levels, such as the family allocation of *Daubentonia madagascariensis*; identifying the Malagasy Carnivora as a radiation unique to the island and showing remarkable morphological convergence with other members of the order found elsewhere in the world; determining the monophyly of all Malagasy land mammal orders; and dating speciation events or periods of diversification. These issues are discussed in other contributions herein and will thus be presented only briefly here.

While molecular data have generally helped answer important evolutionary questions, they have also generated controversies, particularly regarding the number of lemur species that have been identified since 2000. For instance, Tattersall (2007) questioned the validity of many of these new taxa, noting that the number of lemur species had increased from 36 to 83 since 1982, even though few new populations of lemurs had been discovered during that period. A few years later, Markolf et al. (2011) made a similar statement, noting that the number of newly described species had been on the order of 4.5 per year for the period 2006–2011, and pointed out that in too many instances the new species had been described on the basis of a few individuals. These authors suggested that genetic differences between individuals from different species were in some cases smaller than between individuals within a previously defined species. For instance, they noted that Louis et al. (2008) estimated a 3.7% divergence between D-loop sequences of individuals of *Microcebus margotmarshae* and *M. mamiratra*, while Fredsted et al. (2004) had identified much higher divergence (~8.2%) between the most divergent sequences within the *M. murinus* clade. It is important to note that *M. murinus* has the widest distribution of any member of this genus, and Hotaling et al. (2016) later described two new *Microcebus* species from individuals previously identified as *M. murinus* (*M. ganzhorni* and *M. manitatra*) (see Kappeler et al., pp. 1927–32, on this genus).

The tendency to split species has continued since 2010 and has been criticized by Tattersall and Cuozzo (2018), who deemed that about half of the currently identified species should possibly be merged with previously described species. The number of recognized *Microcebus* (mouse lemur) species has significantly increased from only two species in the 1990s (*M. rufus* and *M. murinus*) to ~25 today (J.-J. Petter 1962; Poelstra et al. 2021). Similarly, there are currently 26 recognized *Lepilemur* (sportive lemur) species (Louis et al. 2006a; Lei et al. 2017), while only one species, with six subspecies, was accepted by Tattersall (1982). Other genera, such as *Propithecus*, have seen not a proliferation of new species but rather former recognized subspecies being elevated to full species (Mittermeier et al. 2006). Markolf et al. (2013) have defended the idea that the subspecies of the brown lemur (*Eulemur fulvus*) complex should be considered different species, justifying this decision by the significant morphological and genetic differences identified among them.

The regular increase in the number of lemur species is probably the result of different factors, among which genetic data played a major role. First, a certain number of new species are actually the result of populations or subspecies already known being redescribed as new species (see Tattersall 2007). Second, the increased use of molecular data (mainly mtDNA) and the application of the "phylogenetic species concept" (*sensu* Cracraft 1989) have led to the identification of monophyletic groups, which were often not diagnosable based only on morphological data. Those monophyletic groups that could not be allocated to recognized taxa were considered to be new species. Third, from a conservation point of view, the International Union for the Conservation of Nature (IUCN) currently recognizes the species as the basic unit of conservation. It is possible, though difficult to determine with certainty, that a form of conservation politics (and perhaps a cautionary principle) might have led to the "upgrade" of divergent populations, to further stress the critical need to preserve Malagasy forests. It is certainly better to upgrade a subspecies or divergent population now and merge taxa later than to realize, once it is too late, that the taxon or population in question indeed represents a now extinct species.

In some cases, genetic information have not always led to an increase in the number of recognized species. Brenneman et al. (2016) used genetic data and concluded that the *Indri indri* should not be divided into subspecies, as suggested on the basis of pelage differences. Recently, Poelstra et al. (2021) used genomic data together with complex demographic analyses, as well as morphological data (Schüßler et al. 2020), to identify a putative new *Microcebus* species in eastern Madagascar, named *M. jonahi*. Specifically, Poelstra et al. (2021) used criteria based on the multispecies coalescent to test whether the newly discovered lineage was a species or a divergent population. While the criteria allowed them to describe *M. jonahi* as a new species, the same criteria also suggested that two currently identified species (*M. mittermeieri* and *M. lehilahytsara*) might actually be divergent populations of the same species. Applying this general multispecies coalescent framework to all mouse lemur and sportive lemur species described between 2000 and 2020 might be a useful test to confirm their taxonomic status or their synonymy, as

suggested by Tattersall and Cuozzo (2018). There is a serious need to develop methods that can help determine more objectively whether divergent lineages should or should not be identified as new species—a process that has important consequences for conservation priorities.

During the first two decades of the 21st century, field surveys and museum-based research have greatly contributed to a better understanding of the biodiversity of the Malagasy endemic rodents (subfamily Nesomyinae), with two new genera being described (see Goodman and Soarimalala, pp. 1737–69). Genetic data have now well established that Malagasy rodents came from Africa during a single colonization event (see Jansa and Carleton, pp. 1865–71), and these data have also been used to describe new species or clarify taxonomy (e.g., Jansa et al. 1999, 2019).

The Malagasy Carnivora, belonging to the endemic family Eupleridae, currently includes seven genera with seven species (see Veron et al., pp. 1863–65). Because of their morphological resemblance to other carnivorans elsewhere in the world, there have been debates on whether or not these animals are monophyletic and the result of a single colonization event. In the first comprehensive genetic study of these animals, A. D. Yoder et al. (2003) investigated their molecular phylogeny using four genetic loci (two mtDNA and two nuclear loci) and provided clear evidence of their monophyly. However, the taxonomy within Malagasy Carnivora is still debated, mostly owing to the limited sampling of certain putative forms (Veron et al. 2017, 2018). For example, Durbin et al. (2010) described a new species, *Salanoia durrelli*, as sister species of *S. concolor* (see Farris and Murphy, pp. 1999–2001), on the basis of morphological divergence, despite a low level of cyt b genetic divergence (0.8%). In a later study, Veron et al. (2017) increased the number of *S. concolor* sampled individuals, while having access to only one sample of *S. durrelli*, and used a higher number of genetic markers (two mtDNA loci and one nuclear locus). They confirmed the generally low levels of genetic divergence between *S. durrelli* and *S. concolor* (0.2%–1.2%) and concluded that the two taxa should be merged. In the same study, two species of the genus *Galidictis* (see Farris and Goodman, pp. 1993–96) were also merged when the authors found similarly low levels of cyt b divergence (1.1%–1.2%). Veron et al. (2018) also noted considerably low levels of genetic divergence (0%–1.4%) between specimens allocated to *Eupleres major* and *E. goudotii* (see Rivera et al., pp. 1983–86), two previously described species differentiated based on morphology (Goodman and Helgen 2010). Overall, these examples show that more work, sampling, and morphological and genetic data are still needed to robustly validate the species diversity within the endemic family Eupleridae.

Until about 2000, members of the family Tenrecidae, generally referred to as tenrecs, were originally associated with shrews, moles, and other insectivores (ex-order Lipotyphla), and previously the order Insectivora, owing to their apparent morphological similarities. Molecular studies have played a major role in clarifying their evolutionary history and taxonomy, showing that tenrecs are genetically closer to other African mammals belonging to the superorder Afrotheria than to the two orders to which they have been previously placed (M. S. Springer et al. 1997; Stanhope et al. 1998; Mouchaty et al. 2000; Meredith et al. 2011). Everson et al. (2016), in the most recent and the largest molecular phylogenetic study of Tenrecidae, with samples from all species, used 11 nuclear genes (~9600 bp). They suggested placing the *Limnogale* within *Microgale* and placing two species (*M. dobsoni* and *M. talazaci*) in *Nesogale*. Tenrecs have thus exhibited a species-discovery rate of about one new species every two years since 1992, with nine species, out of the 31 Malagasy species recognized, having been described during this period.

Hybridization Studies

Most of the articles mentioned in the previous sections assume that species are clearly identified and represent taxonomic units that are reproductively isolated from other related taxa. As a consequence, most studies tend to measure genetic differentiation between populations from the same and supposedly clearly identified species or compute genetic distances and phylogenetic relationships between well-separated species. However, several studies have also identified areas of putative hybridization within some Malagasy genera, such as *Eulemur* (Rabarivola et al. 1991; Lehman and Wright 2000; Wyner et al. 2002; Pastorini et al. 2009). At this stage, and given the major changes that have happened in the taxonomy of lemurs since 2000 and the fact that genetic studies are still taxonomically and geographically limited, we can fairly say that hybridization analyses are very limited.

Wyner et al. (2002) worked at Andringitra in the south-central portion of the island, where most individuals from one *Eulemur* population were identified as hybrids between *E. albocollaris* (now *E. cinereiceps*) and *E. fulvus rufus* (now *E. rufus*). Gligor et al. (2009) and Hapke et al. (2011) identified and studied a hybrid zone in the south between *Microcebus murinus* and *M. griseorufus*. Pastorini et al. (2009) identified hybridization between *E. fulvus* and *E. mongoz* using microsatellite and mtDNA data in the northwest, and they identified six *E. mongoz* individuals with putative *E. fulvus* alleles introgressed in their genotype and one *E. mongoz* individual with the mtDNA haplotype of *E. fulvus* (Figure 14.12). More recently, Williams et al. (2020) used full-genome sequences from dwarf lemurs (*Cheirogaleus medius*, *C. major*, *C. crossleyi*, and *C. sibreei*) and identified putative events of ancient admixture, about 4 Mya, between *C. medius* and both *C. major* and *C. sibreei*. They interpreted these admixture events as being related to adaptation to hibernation. However, they also noted that hibernation was ancestral in *Cheirogaleus* (which diverged from a common ancestor ~18 Mya) and that there was no particular high representation of hibernation genes in the genomic regions that appeared to be introgressed. This would definitely need further research. Another recent study by Everson et al. (2020a) also claimed to have identified ancient admixture events between two shrew tenrec species (*Microgale soricoides* and *M. fotsifotsy*).

In addition, putative hybridization has been described for other species but was not necessarily supported by genetic data. Hybrids between *Eulemur f. fulvus* and *E. f. rufus* were documented by Lehman and Wright (2000). *Propithecus coronatus* and *P. deckeni* are thought to hybridize in central-western portions of the island (Thalmann et al. 2002; Rakotonirina et al. 2014), and *E. macaco* and *E. flavifrons* are thought to hybridize in some forest fragments in the northwest (Rabarivola et al. 1991). We may also mention the meiotic study of Djelati et al. (1997), carried out on seven male hybrids of different *Eulemur* species, three of which were infertile.

Hybridization studies of Malagasy mammals are notably limited, and this line of research needs a more solid theoretical basis, as well

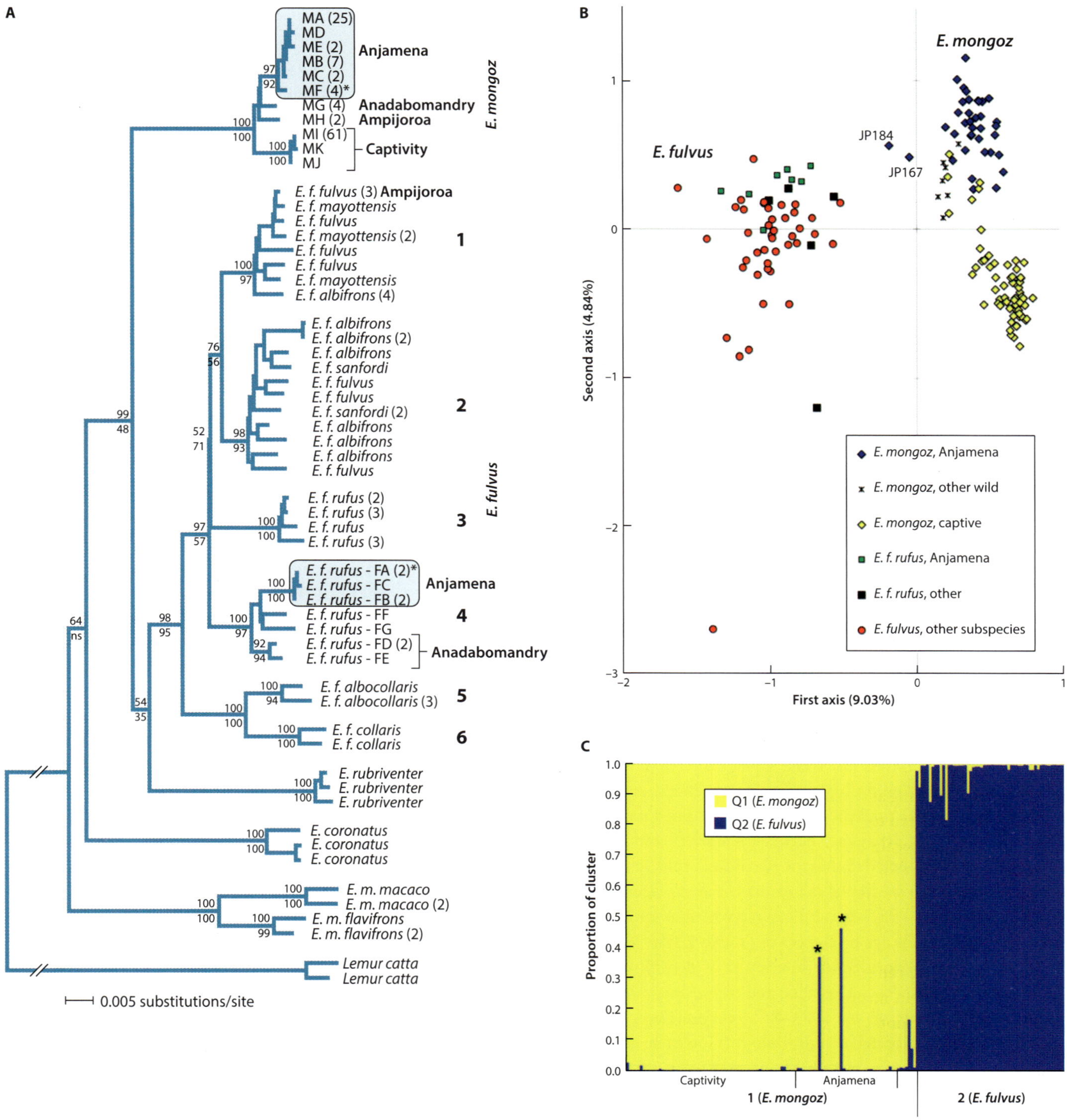

FIGURE 14.12 **Hybridization analysis on *Eulemur mongoz* and *E. fulvus* sampled at Anjamena, western Madagascar. Note that species and subspecies names are those of the original study and are now outdated (see Johnson et al., pp. 1941–46, for details on this genus). A) Phylogenetic tree inferred from the mitochondrial DNA D-loop and ND4 loci (subspecies names in the tree are as in the original). MA, MD, etc., and FA, FC, etc., refer to mtDNA haplotype IDs in the original study, with parenthetical numbers specifying the observed absolute frequency of the haplotypes. Asterisks (*) indicate the two mtDNA haplotypes that were found in both species. The 1–6 numbering on the right indicates the six mtDNA clades identified within *E. fulvus*. Small numbers on the tree nodes are the bootstrap values obtained with neighbor-joining (above) and maximum parsimony (below) analyses. One node was not shown in the parsimony tree topology and is indicated by "ns." B) Principal component analysis of individual *E. mongoz* and *E. fulvus* genotypes highlighting the two hybrids (JP167 and JP184) between *E. mongoz* and *E. fulvus*. C) Admixture analysis of *E. mongoz* and *E. fulvus* sampled individuals. The two hybrids (JP167 and JP184), marked with *, show mixed genetic ancestry with each of the two *Eulemur* species.** (SOURCE: modified from Pastorini et al. 2009.)

as more fieldwork if we want to understand the distribution of hybridization in Malagasy mammals. Hybridization events, whether recent or ancient, are by nature dynamic and require questions to be posed about species identity, taxonomy, and phylogeny. Clarifying the evolutionary processes taking place in contact zones between closely related or diverging taxa would be very important for evolutionary biologists and also for conservation programs. The very rapid habitat changes taking place in the forests of the island will likely change the distribution of many species, and in some cases reduce interspecies secondary contact (and thus hybridization), but may also generate new zones of contact between animals of closely related species. For instance, in a theoretical sense, if conspecifics are rare within an isolated forest fragment, it is not necessarily far-fetched to imagine that such a situation could favor hybridization between sympatric closely related species.

CONCLUSION

In this contribution, we summarized insights that have been gained on Malagasy mammals based on recent genetic studies. Other contributions in this chapter look in greater detail at certain groups and at different taxonomic levels. However, while this current contribution is extensive, it was not possible to address all the different developments over recent decades. For example, we have acknowledged the importance of karyological studies in early taxonomic and phylogenetic studies and in more recent research (e.g., Andriaholinirina et al. 2006). While not much has been presented herein about karyological studies, we would not be surprised if they made a comeback in the next few years as our understanding of structural variants increases for nonmodel species. We have also given little space to studies aiming at detecting selection or adaptation (but see Box 5) or those related to developing technical aspects of noninvasive sampling (e.g., fecal samples) for genetic studies. Nevertheless, we have tried to mention some of these studies, which represent a minority of research studies but may become more common in the future as the importance of linked selection is better understood.

Considering that there are 200–250 native mammal species living on the island, we can state that most have not yet been properly studied genetically. In most other groups of Malagasy vertebrates, invertebrates, and plants, the situation is even less advanced, but research teams are actively working to rectify the situation. For most mammal species for which genetic data are available, they are often limited to mtDNA sequences that were used to address taxonomic or phylogenetic questions, and these are sometimes pooled to carry out demographic inference studies.

We would like to highlight the fact that we are in a very exciting period in which genomic data are increasingly easy to obtain. The recent work of Blanco et al. (2020), for instance, is an interesting case in which it was shown that the possibility of next-generation methods could in principle be used in the field for research on Madagascar. Similarly, Guevara et al. (2018) developed a simple and cheap (economically and ecologically) protocol to carry out genetic typing in the field and tested it on *Propithecus verreauxi* fecal samples from the southwest of the island. It is too early to make strong claims about such studies and their use in a larger context of biodiversity loss, but it is important to stress that there is a need to move the analyses of genetic data from outside to within Madagascar. From the perspective of conservation, we should also reflect on the fact that many research activities that rely on laboratory analyses or computing work, including genetic and genomic studies, are typically polluting with respect to required chemicals and electronic resources, which can unfortunately be important. There is thus a need for our community to perhaps balance the gains and the costs that our activities generate.

Our review also showed that the statistical methods used to analyze genetic data are becoming increasingly sophisticated, hence allowing us to ask more complex questions. However, we have also stressed that genetic and genomic data are not always easy to use and interpret. The information brought forth by these associated techniques is often counterbalanced by their magnitude and complexity. Nowadays, genomic analyses require users to go through various filtering and computation programs that cannot be validated by hand. This means that errors are likely to be published, as fewer and fewer people are able to analyze, check, and test the results. Also, the interpretation of data remains a crucial issue for which there is no simple solution. Training students to analyze the new (big) genomic data sets will be a major challenge that requires understanding the theory and the assumptions behind the models. In a recent review, Allendorf (2017: 26) wrote that population genetics had moved from a period in which there was a lot of theory and limited data to a period in which we have loads of data and too little theoretical understanding. "Current training focuses too much on technique," he added, and "even the most basic aspects of population genetics theory are commonly misunderstood or overlooked." We have tried to avoid overinterpretation of the genetic data but cannot guarantee that we did not fail. We hope that we have managed to provide tools for students to look critically at such data and reinterpret for themselves the results obtained by others.

Genetic data are often seen as being more objective than other types of data. It may be true to some extent, since we do understand how genes are transmitted from generation to generation. However, there are often several competing interpretations or models that could explain the same genomic data, even when authors discuss only one of them. The danger with genomic data is that they tend to convey a misleading overconfidence on statistically significant signals. For instance, Chikhi et al. (2010) showed that with simulated genetic data under a model of population structure and constant size, the detection, dating, and quantification of population size changes will increase with increasing data, even though no population size change was simulated. In other words, the more data we analyze, under a model whose assumptions are not met, the more confident (and precise) we will be on the inference of a demographic event that may never have taken place (see also Philippe et al. 2011 on similar issues in phylogenetics). The PSMC plots discussed above are an example of demographic inference based on genomic data that could either identify very clear and indisputable population size changes under one model (no population structure) or actually be generated under a model with changes in connectivity and absolutely no change in population size. These two interpretations are simplistic, but the point is that they are profoundly different and difficult to separate.

Conservation genetics has contributed to the development of theoretical population genetics, and as such it has enriched the theory of evolution. For instance, this field of research played a major role in the study of small and isolated populations (Lynch et al.

1990), where deleterious mutations are expected to accumulate as a consequence of genetic drift and inbreeding. The observation of genetic defects in various endangered species that went through serious bottlenecks (e.g., Roelke et al. 1993; Munson et al. 1996; Madsen et al. 1999), and the genetic restoration of some of these isolated populations by the reintroduction of individuals from other areas, have demonstrated that the theory could be used successfully for practical short-term conservation projects (Madsen et al. 1999; Hostetler et al. 2012). Unfortunately, we are not aware of solid research in these areas carried out in Madagascar, while we may soon be in the situation where we will need people able to analyze genetic data from species with increasing genetic defects.

However, we strongly defend the use of genetic data, despite their current limitations. Genetic data have played and will continue to play a central role in clarifying major questions related to Malagasy biodiversity across geographic and temporal scales. They will definitely do so for some time to come, and the next few years will, without any doubt, bring exciting new insights into an increasing number of mammals. We need these data if we are to say anything of relevance regarding Malagasy biodiversity.

ACKNOWLEDGMENTS

We are grateful to the government of Madagascar for permission to conduct research on the island and specifically to the Direction Générale du Ministère de l'Environnement et des Forêts de Madagascar (Région SAVA), Comité Ad Hoc pour la Faune et la Flore et le Comité Organisationel pour la Recherche Environnementale (CAFF/CORE), the Département de Biologie Animale et Ecologie de l'Université de Mahajanga, the Mention Zoologie et Biodiversité Animale de l'Université d'Antananarivo, the Département de Biologie de l'Université d'Antsiranana, and the NGO Fanamby for their support over the years. We also would like to thank Guillaume Besnard, Filipa Borges, Jörg Ganzhorn, Steve Goodman, Richard Lawler, Beatriz Mourato, Bárbara Parreira, Ute Radespiel, Jordi Salmona, Rémi Tournebize, and Anne Yoder for their constructive and useful comments that significantly helped us improve the manuscript. This work was supported by the Fundação para a Ciência e Tecnologia (PTDC-BIA-EVL/30815/2017 to LC; PD/BD/114343/2016 to GMS), the 2015–2016 BiodivERsA COFUND with the national funders ANR (ANR-16-EBI3–0014) and the Fundação para a Ciência e Tecnologia ref. Biodiversa/0003/2015 and PT-DLR (01LC1617A), the LABEX entitled TULIP (ANR-10-LABX-41 and ANR-11-IDEX-0002–02), the LIA BEEG-B (Laboratoire International Associé–Bioinformatics, Ecology, Evolution, Genomics and Behaviour), and the Investissement d'Avenir grant of the Agence Nationale de la Recherche (CEBA: ANR-10-LABX-25–01).

Subject editors: Jörg U. Ganzhorn and Steven M. Goodman

HETEROTHERMY IN MALAGASY MAMMALS

K. H. Dausmann, S. Reher, and J. Bethge

Madagascar is an island of multifaceted climates and associated vegetation formations, ranging from the dry, very unpredictable conditions in the dry spiny thickets of the south to the moist evergreen rainforests of the east and extreme north. All land species have to adapt to the varying conditions of their habitats, as the local environmental vicissitudes govern the performance and energy use and ultimately the abundance and distribution of the organism concerned (L. B. Buckley et al. 2018). Therefore, they have to cope with these differing conditions and changes, whether these are daily, seasonal, or unpredictable (e.g., extreme weather events, fires, cyclones). The seasonal changes concomitant with the cool dry season are especially challenging for Malagasy animals, as ambient temperatures are low, rainfall is virtually absent in some regions, and food availability (leaves, fruits, flowers, insects and other invertebrates) is markedly reduced (Donque 1972). For mammals in particular, this period is also energetically costly, as it requires an increased energy uptake to sustain high, endothermic body temperature (i.e., regulation via endogenous generation of heat). To cope with demanding times, Malagasy mammals have developed a variety of different responses, such as sunbathing in the cool mornings, employed by certain diurnal lemurs (e.g., *Lemur catta*, see Sauther and Cuozzo, pp. 1952–56; *Propithecus* spp., see Lawler and Richard, pp. 1971–74), social thermoregulation by huddling (e.g., *Hapalemur meridionalis*; Eppley et al. 2017a), or choice of suitable microclimates by smaller nocturnal species (e.g., *Triaenops menamena*; Reher et al. 2019). Moreover, some species shift their food choices and activity patterns across seasons (Hemingway and Bynum 2005; Andriatsimietry et al. 2009; Farris et al. 2015a). Beyond these more obvious adaptations, Malagasy mammals have mastered the art of responding flexibly to challenging conditions with exceptional physiological adaptations.

Most notably, members of at least three orders of Malagasy land mammals (Afrosoricida, Chiroptera, Primates; Figure 14.13) abandon mammalian endothermy at least occasionally and become torpid, displaying a hitherto unknown extent of flexibility for endotherms, ranging from almost daily use of heterothermy to very rare employment, from extremely short bouts of only a few minutes to continuous hibernation over many months. Hibernation, prolonged torpor, and daily torpor (all three included in the term

FIGURE 14.13 **Different species of Malagasy mammals that undergo some seasonal change in their ecophysiology. A) *Echinops telfairi* becomes torpid every day, regardless of season and ambient temperature, when not reproductively active. B) *Macronycteris commersoni* retreats to the warmest cave within the Tsimanampesotse National Park cave system as a resting site throughout the year, practically negating the need for active thermoregulation during the daily resting phase in the rainy season and keeping body temperature high despite heterothermy in the rainy and the cool dry seasons. C) *Macronycteris commersoni* tolerates hyperthermic body temperatures of up to 42.9°C when resting in open vegetation on hot days during the warm rainy season. Note the temperature-sensitive collar transmitter. D) *Microcebus griseorufus* uses heterothermy as a very flexible response to current internal and external conditions, and daily torpor, prolonged torpor, and hibernation are shown at the same time within the same population and the same habitat. Note the base of the tail is slightly enlarged. E) *Cheirogaleus medius* is an obligate hibernator, and all individuals enter continuous hibernation over several months during the dry season. Body temperature patterns during hibernation can be diverse, from almost constant to highly fluctuating, depending on the insulation capacities of individual hibernacula. F) Species of the genus *Lepilemur*, in this case *L. edwardsi*, maintain one of the lowest general metabolic rates of all placental mammals and shift their thermal neutral zone to cope with the low efficiency of their food and seasonality of their habitats.** (PHOTOS A, D, and E by K. Dausmann; B and C by S. Reher; and F by A. Wulff.)

heterothermy) are physiological states of controlled interruption of normal maintenance of body temperature (normothermia) via an active depression of metabolic rate and virtually all bodily functions and an extension of the range of tolerated body temperature (Geiser 2004; Heldmaier et al. 2004). Daily torpor is limited to short bouts of less than 24 hours; prolonged torpor bouts last for several days; hibernation consists of a series of approximately one- to two-week-long torpor bouts, usually totaling several months, punctuated by normothermic spontaneous arousals (i.e., phases with active heat production; Geiser 2004; Heldmaier et al. 2004). The function of these energy-demanding arousals remains enigmatic, but they seem to be necessary for the maintenance of vital bodily functions in hibernators with permanently low body temperatures (Humphries et al. 2003).

Body temperature during heterothermy often approximates ambient temperature, especially during deep torpor (Ruf and Geiser 2015). This suspension of active thermoregulation allows high savings in energy and water. Notably, for torpor use during periods of extended aridity or high ambient temperatures, water conservation might play the even more decisive role (e.g., Schmid and Speakman

2000; Bondarenco et al. 2013). When metabolic rate is reduced, water turnover is generally lowered, and additional water-depleting processes such as respiration, urine production, and defecation are down-regulated or even absent (Levin et al. 2015). Given even more advantages such as, for example, avoidance of predation or parasite pressure, heterothermy provides mammals with a very efficient strategy to cope with demanding environmental conditions (Lyman et al. 1982). Heterothermy is best known in arctic and temperate climates, but it also occurs in the tropics (McKechnie and Mzilikazi 2011; Dausmann et al. 2012; Ruf and Geiser 2015; Nowack et al. 2020).

The previous version of this book included a contribution on what was known on the ecophysiology of Malagasy mammals at that time (Schmid and Stephenson 2003). Over the intervening years, different techniques have been developed to study how mammals change their metabolism, and herein we provide a review of what has been learned about certain groups occurring on the island in the past nearly two decades. We focus on three separate orders of mammals: tenrecs, insectivorous bats, and lemurs.

TENRECS: MASTERS OF LIFE ON A LOW FLAME

The masters of keeping life on a low flame are some of the Malagasy tenrecs (family Tenrecidae). They may be reminiscent of basal placental mammals (Lovegrove 2019) and have been termed protoendotherms (*sensu* Grigg et al. 2004) because of their highly labile thermoregulation. With their often reptilian-like patterns of body temperature, they might represent relicts of the transition from ectothermy to homeothermic endothermy (Levesque et al. 2014). Indeed, tenrecs have some of the lowest, generally less than 35°C, and most highly variable body temperatures, as well as one of the lowest basal metabolic rates, of any eutherian mammal (Stephenson and Racey 1995).

Tenrecs have experienced a tremendous adaptive radiation that resulted in species that are terrestrial, arboreal, fossorial, and even aquatic (see Goodman and Soarimalala, pp. 1737–69; Jenkins et al., pp. 1880–87), with a multitude of lifestyles and presumably many unique physiological adaptations. However, the physiology of only a few species of tenrecs has been studied so far, and even fewer in the field, where animals show the complete spectrum of their behavioral and physiological capacity. Besides their already generally low metabolic rates, many tenrec species have been reported to be highly heterothermic and seem to defend a stable body temperature throughout the day only when they are pregnant or lactating (Thompson and Nicoll 1986). Showing an even more pronounced adaptation, several tenrec species are known to hibernate to bridge the unfavorable dry and cold season (E. Gould and Eisenberg 1966; Levesque et al. 2014; Dausmann et al. 2020).

The spiny tenrec species (subfamily Tenrecinae) best studied in regard to physiological adaptations are *Echinops telfairi*, *Tenrec ecaudatus*, and *Setifer setosus*. *Echinops telfairi* (Figure 14.13a) has one of the lowest reported normothermic body temperatures even within the tenrecs (around 31°C) and is highly thermally labile (Lovegrove and Génin 2008; Dausmann et al. 2020). It becomes torpid every day regardless of season and ambient temperature when not reproductively active. In the warm season, *E. telfairi* uses daily fluctuations in ambient temperature to rewarm passively from daily torpor, which leads to decreased energy expenditure as well as exhibits synchrony in the activity phases and torpor bouts among individuals (Dausmann et al. 2020). This exogenous, mainly passive reheating from torpor bouts is known from several tropical heterotherms (e.g., bats, lemurs; discussed below) and makes rewarming comparatively energetically inexpensive, with 60–100% reduction as compared to active, endogenous warming (e.g., Ortmann et al. 1997; Geiser and Drury 2003; Bondarenco et al. 2013). This might explain why daily torpor is common in sunny regions and might occur more frequently at low latitudes than hitherto believed (Geiser and Drury 2003). Nevertheless, functional brown adipose tissue, necessary for active endogenous heat production, has been recorded in *E. telfairi* (Oelkrug et al. 2013). During the hibernation period, which is the cool dry season, this species hibernates for several months, almost regardless of the level and extent of fluctuations of (naturally occurring) ambient and respective body temperature.

Interestingly, *E. telfairi*'s energy expenditure during the much shorter daily torpor bouts in the warm season can be as low as during the hibernation bouts in the cold season. Both are initiated by active metabolic inhibition and reach levels of the most competent arctic hibernators, such as Arctic Ground Squirrel (*Spermophilus parryii*) (Buck and Barnes 2000), despite *E. telfairi* having an approximately 10°C higher body temperature (Dausmann et al. 2020), possibly a consequence of the already low active metabolic rate. However, there seems to be a lower limit for hibernation at about 12°C, below which *E. telfairi* shows difficulties arousing from hibernation bouts (Scholl 1974; Dausmann et al. 2020). Although temperatures do drop below 10°C within the range of *E. telfairi* during the coldest nights of the cold dry season, this does not occur very frequently and is buffered even in hibernacula (space an animal seeks refuge during hibernation) with low insulation capacities (tree hollows, dead trees, and under leaf litter). More importantly, even on those coldest days, ambient temperature will usually increase to above 20°C in the tenrecs' habitats, ensuring passive rewarming. Thus, the 10°C threshold is presumably rarely problematic in natural environments (Lovegrove and Génin 2008; Dausmann et al. 2020).

Tenrec ecaudatus shows the same extreme plasticity in thermoregulation and metabolism as *E. telfairi*. During the wet warm season, the animal enters daily torpor, and during the cold dry season, *T. ecaudatus* enters hibernation for up to nine months (Lovegrove et al. 2014a), at a great range of ambient and body temperatures, but the depth of torpor may vary. *Tenrec ecaudatus* uses small underground burrows for hibernation (see Goodman et al., pp. 1891–94) and possibly hibernates in groups. Field data on hibernating *T. ecaudatus* demonstrated that body temperature follows soil temperature for the duration of the hibernation season, and showed no evidence of arousals, which is very exceptional among hibernators (Lovegrove et al. 2014b). Indeed, one of the most surprising discoveries from warm-climate hibernators is that periodic arousals, thought to be essential to proper functioning during hibernation, are not necessarily needed. To date, the only other mammal not to exhibit these arousals outside Madagascar is American Black Bear (*Ursus americanus*), which hibernates at body temperatures above 30°C (Tøien et al. 2011). Moreover, when body temperature drops below 20°C during hibernation in *T. ecaudatus*, individuals may

suspend breathing for up to 45 minutes (Treat et al. 2018). This mechanism might allow efficient gas exchange in environments that become hypoxic and hypercapnic (with elevated carbon dioxide levels), such as underground burrows. Additionally, it might help to conserve water under dry conditions, which is likely critical during the pronounced dry season of southern and southwestern Madagascar. Unlike the general patterns of hibernators, the end of the hibernation season seems to be a gradual transition in *T. ecaudatus* and occurs over a couple of weeks, at least in captivity (Treat et al. 2018). Remarkably, even when tenrecs are being active, their body temperature may range from about 12°C to 34°C, fluctuating passively throughout the day. Metabolic rate can be very low in *T. ecaudatus* even while active, sometimes reaching torpid levels, despite higher body temperatures. Thus, body temperature does not necessarily dictate metabolism, and tenrecs seem to be able to modify heat retention and conductance independent of metabolism. Contrary to *E. telfairi*, *T. ecaudatus* females show variable body temperatures during gestation without apparent effects on embryonic development and experience more stable body temperatures above 20°C only after parturition (Treat et al. 2018).

As with the other two spiny tenrec species discussed so far, *Setifer setosus* shows a large degree of heterothermy and enters hibernation for five to seven months during the cold dry season. Only reproductive females have slightly higher and less variable body temperatures (Levesque and Lovegrove 2014). There is anecdotal evidence that *S. setosus* females become torpid for prolonged periods during lactation, but this needs further investigation (Levesque et al. 2013). Resting sites in this species can be below- or aboveground (in hollow logs or under leaf litter), thus fully or partially exposed to environmental conditions, and *S. setosus* individuals hibernating in variable ambient temperatures show no evidence of periodic arousals (Figure 14.14a; Levesque et al. 2014). Since *S. setosus* can be

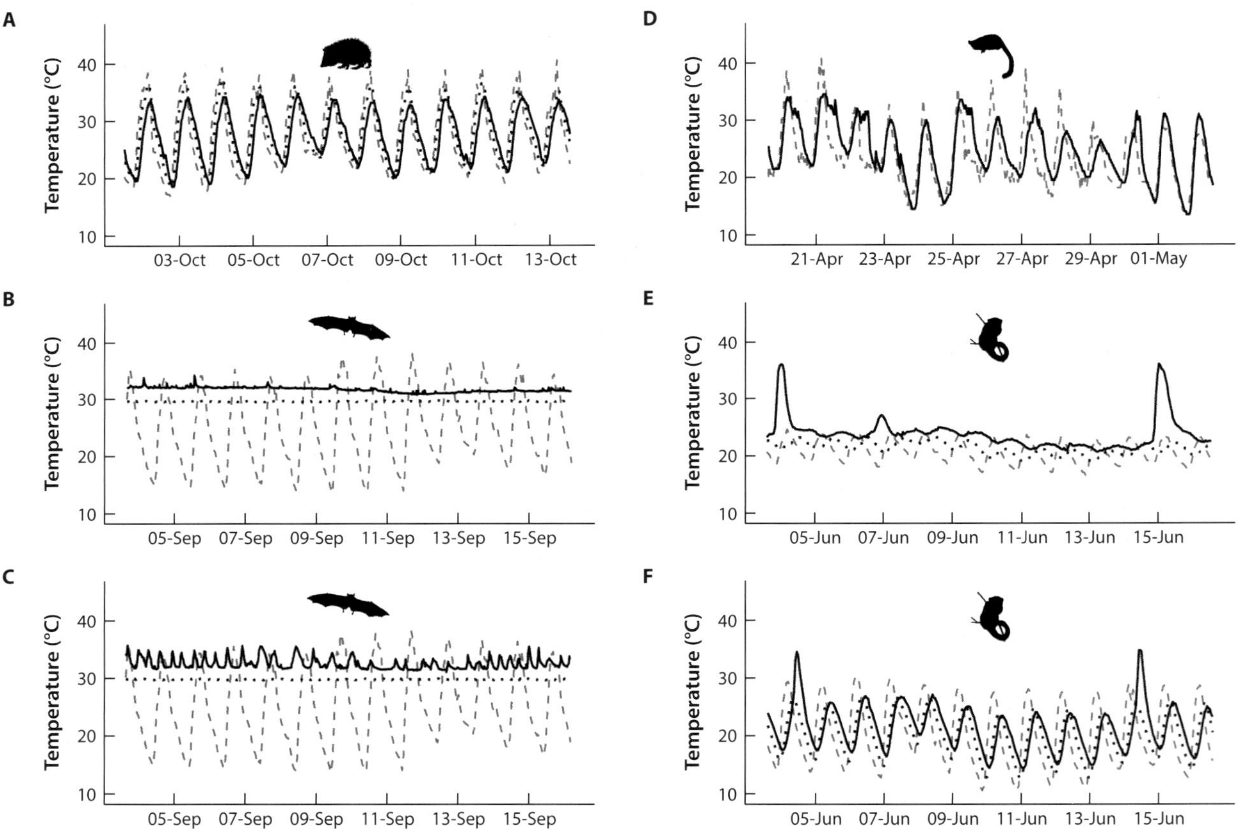

FIGURE 14.14 **Body temperature of free-ranging individuals from three Malagasy mammalian orders during the dry season. Black solid line: body temperature; black dotted line: temperature at the resting site; gray dashed line: ambient temperature. During heterothermy, body temperature closely tracks the temperature of the resting site with its daily rise and fall, depending on insulation capacities. A) Continuous hibernation bout of a *Setifer setosus* in a poorly insulated hibernaculum showing strongly fluctuating body temperature. B) Continuous hibernation bout of a *Macronycteris commersoni* in a cave with very stable resting site temperature, resulting in very stable body temperature. C) Body temperature of a *M. commersoni* in the same cave with very stable resting site temperature and at the same time but employing daily torpor. D) Body temperature of a *Microcebus griseorufus* showing diverse patterns of heterothermy. For the first three days, this individual entered daily torpor, still being active at night; this was followed by two days of prolonged torpor and then by a hibernation bout with fluctuating body temperature. E) Continuous hibernation bout of a *Cheirogaleus medius* in a well-insulated tree hollow, with almost constant body temperature; notice the two spontaneous, active arousals. F) Continuous hibernation bout of a *C. medius* in a more poorly insulated tree hollow, with strongly fluctuating body temperature; notice the two spontaneous, active arousals.** (SOURCES: A, E, and F redrawn from Nowack et al. 2020; B and C from S. Reher et al., unpublished data; and D redrawn from Kobbe et al. 2011.)

active at body temperatures as low as 28°C (Eisenberg and Gould 1970), active rewarming is virtually dispensable, as activity itself may be used for heat production. Consequently, *S. setosus* relies on ambient temperature to regulate body temperature, with little energetic costs of thermoregulation, and thermolability is the norm (Levesque et al. 2014).

Tenrecs are surprisingly intolerant to ambient temperature extremes, considering their generally flexible implementation of mammalian thermoregulation. As they are capable of sustaining stable body temperature when reproductively active, this flexibility is clearly not a lack of ability for precise thermoregulation (Thompson and Nicoll 1986). General plasticity in thermoregulation reduces general energy expenditure; however, it also limits the ambient temperature range over which an organism can function (Treat et al. 2018). For many spiny tenrec species, temperatures at the high end of the spectrum may be problematic. *Echinops telfairi*, for example, lives in the hottest and driest portions of the island but can survive temperatures above 36°C only with sufficient supply of water, as the animals need to drink and wet their bodies (Scholl 1974), and *T. ecaudatus* pants and breathes irregularly above 34°C, although inhabiting the whole island (Kayser 1961; Treat et al. 2018). Torpor, on the other hand, might counterbalance this disadvantage, broadening the temperature niche, if temperatures do not consistently drop below 10–12°C. Indeed, torpor use has been found to lower the risk of extinction in highly variable and quickly changing environments (Geiser and Turbill 2009; Liow et al. 2009).

Tenrecs have clearly not read the classical physiology textbooks, when it comes to thermoregulation. They seem to be essentially ectotherms and become endothermic only when they breed (Lovegrove 2019). As most species have not yet been studied, there might be more surprises ahead, possible elucidating the evolution of endothermy.

BATS: TORPOR WHIZ MASTERS

The shortest, regular torpor bouts of any mammal studied so far are shown by the Malagasy bat *Macronycteris commersoni* (family Hipposideridae; Figures 14.13b and c). During the resting phase in warm but not extremely hot conditions (24–34°C), it routinely shuts down metabolism repeatedly for micro-torpor bouts of only several minutes, still enjoying energy and water savings while remaining alert and normothermic (Reher and Dausmann 2021). However, individuals of this species also enter hibernation over several weeks when caves are available as roosting options. Thus, within a single population of this species, individuals span the whole spectrum of heterothermic responses endotherms are capable of and exemplify the amazing flexibility with regard to thermoregulation in Malagasy mammals.

Macronycteris commersoni is relatively widespread on the island. In Madagascar's dry spiny thickets, it gains massive fat deposits by the end of the wet season and does not actively forage for several months during the dry season (Goodman 2006; Rakotoarivelo et al. 2007; Reher et al. 2019). Only a few juveniles, which most likely have not managed to build up a sufficiently large fat store to overcome the long dry season without foraging breaks, are occasionally found outside the cave. Interestingly, in Tsimanampesotse National Park in the extreme southwest, *M. commersoni* overwinters in large colonies in the hottest and most humid cave in the region (≥32°C and 95% relative humidity year-round) with body temperatures closely following cave temperature (Figures 14.13b and 14.14b), although less warm caves are available. These colder caves are frequently used by other bat species and would possibly allow higher energy savings during torpor because of generally lower nightly temperatures (allowing lower metabolic rates and body temperatures), as they are less buffered, resulting in greater fluctuations in temperature and relative humidity (Reher et al. 2018, 2019). Why *M. commersoni* prefers the hot cave remains unknown; however, it is feasible that stable temperatures in the thermal neutral zone (i.e., the temperature range where no additional energy expenditure to sustain high endothermic body temperature is needed) and high humidity, reducing overall water loss, are more advantageous compared to fluctuating conditions.

Even in the very predictable, constant conditions of the hottest cave in Tsimanampesotse National Park, different individuals of *M. commersoni* show very different physiological responses during the cool dry season, when arthropod food resources are low. Whereas some enter hibernation with single bouts lasting up to 16 days between arousals (Figure 14.14b), others employ daily torpor and prolonged torpor (Figure 14.14c; Reher et al. 2018). Surprisingly, even the individuals in prolonged torpor completely cease foraging flights, although their metabolic rate is at an active level at night. This suggests that either the habitat does not offer enough food to make foraging profitable, and/or the accumulated fat combined with a favorable microclimate (high humidity and ambient temperature presumably in the thermal neutral zone) is sufficient to get these animals through the dry season in a form of inactivity but not necessarily continuous hibernation.

Triaenops menamena (family Rhinonycteridae) lives in the same region as *M. commersoni* but has adapted physiologically to the cold dry season in a very different manner. Instead of long-term hibernation, it regularly enters daily torpor and forages at night. Contrary to *M. commersoni*, *T. menamena* utilizes day-roost sites with very different degrees of ambient condition buffering (including the hot cave) during the cold dry season (Reher et al. 2019). The greater the roost's fluctuations in temperature and humidity over the course of the day, the higher the probability of individuals entering torpor and accordingly lower daytime energy expenditure. This makes less-buffered sites the energetically more efficient choice for daytime rest (Remmers 2020). Nevertheless, individuals shift their roosting preferences toward the hot cave for the cold dry season (Reher et al. 2019), indicating that the stable, hot and humid microclimate is also beneficial for *T. menamena*, possibly because it negates the need for torpor (Reher et al. 2018; Remmers 2020).

Two more bat species rest in the hot cave in Tsimanampesotse along with *M. commersoni* and *T. menamena*: *Paratriaenops furculus* (family Rhinonycteridae) and *Miniopterus mahafaliensis* (family Miniopteridae). No physiological data is available for the latter, but *P. furculus* repeatedly enters prolonged torpor bouts lasting up to seven days (Reher et al. 2019; H. Rabarison et al., unpublished data). Prolonged torpor is an intermediate torpor response, combining the flexibility of daily torpor with higher energy savings. Most importantly, animals are active after or between prolonged torpor bouts and carry on foraging, which eliminates the need for

depositing fat as energy stores and allows for sustained social interactions during active hours. Indeed, *T. menamena* and *P. furculus* forage in between torpor bouts, and *M. mahafaliensis* is frequently trapped during the dry season. All three species feed primarily on lepidopterans, supplemented by small coleopterans in the dry season, whereas *M. commersoni* relies entirely on coleopterans (Ramasindrazana et al. 2012). This might be the reason *M. commersoni* has to resort to continuous inactivity during the dry season, a period in which beetles are scarce, to support activity, whereas the more generalist bat species can shift feeding regimes, depending on availability.

All four species are also resident in the same habitat in the warm rainy season, with greater availability of food resources (Ramasindrazana et al. 2012; Reher et al. 2019). Physiological data of the rainy season is available only for *M. commersoni* and *T. menamena*. Both species also enter torpor during this period. In addition to daily torpor, *M. commersoni* also enters prolonged torpor on occasion (Reher et al. 2018); while the exact triggers remain elusive, individuals may remain normothermic or enter torpor bouts lasting up to six days (sometimes coinciding with cyclonic rains). In both species, torpor is used more opportunistically during the warm rainy season than during the cool dry season and appears to be linked to environmental and internal factors that are assessed daily, like an insufficient foraging flight or generally low body mass (S. Reher et al., unpublished data).

As mentioned above, *M. commersoni* is widespread across the island, occupying different habitat types. In the western dry deciduous forest at Kirindy Forest CNFEREF (Centre National de Formation, d'Etudes et de Recherche en Environnement et Foresterie), it responds very differently to thermoregulatory challenges. Here, caves do not occur, and individuals roost solitarily in understory shrubs offering no protection from daytime climatic extremes during the hot and wet season (Figure 14.13c). While being exposed to unbuffered high temperature and low humidity during the day, the bats respond in two different ways. In the cooler morning hours and generally on cooler rainy days (~33°C at noon), they switch between normometabolic resting and very short micro-torpor bouts lasting 3–53 minutes throughout the daily resting phase. If temperatures increase above a critical threshold (~37°C at noon), however, they extend their torpor bouts until the late afternoon and tolerate hyperthermic body temperatures near or exceeding normothermia, up to 42.9°C, without initiating cooling mechanisms (Reher and Dausmann 2021). By accumulating heat instead of trying to dump it, no water is "wasted" via evaporative cooling, which is the only option for actively regulating body temperature at ambient temperatures higher than normothermia, analogous to the "camel strategy" (Schmidt-Nielsen et al. 1956). Consequently, while the key to cope with the unpredictable environment in the southwest appears to be the selection of a highly predictable cave year-round, in the seasonal west *M. commersoni* tolerates hyperthermia in the rainy season and either hibernates or migrates to more suitable habitats during the dry season (Rakotondramanana and Goodman 2011; S. Reher et al., unpublished data).

Apart from the handful of species mentioned above, little is known on the physiological adaptations of Madagascar's bats (Racey et al. 2010; Goodman 2011). For example, fruit bats have been reported to enter torpor, but to date no physiological data are available. Consequently, we expect that more Malagasy bat species are heterothermic or make use of further physiological adaptations, such as shifts in the thermal neutral zone, intensive passive rewarming, or mechanisms that we currently do not know.

LEMURS: SLEEPING BEAUTIES AND THE DWARFS

In the field of heterothermy in Malagasy mammals, perhaps the most surprising discovery was that of hibernation lasting several months long within our own order, Primates, in the lemurs (J.-J. Petter et al. 1977; Petter-Rousseaux 1980; Dausmann et al. 2004). However, heterothermy in lemurs seems to be restricted to one family, Cheirogaleidae (Figures 14.13d and e). Throughout the island, members of Cheirogaleidae become torpid during the Malagasy cool dry season, although depth and duration of torpor bouts vary considerably, depending on species, locality, habitat, sex, and individual condition.

As far as is known, all mouse lemur species (*Microcebus* spp.) enter daily torpor, usually within their tree hollows in the cool hours of the early mornings of the dry season; however, all individuals of a population do not necessarily undergo torpor, and not every day (Dausmann 2014). Occurrence of torpor episodes can be regular, irregular, or daily; various patterns are often found within the same population and within one season. Thus, torpor is used as a very flexible response to current internal and external conditions. Physiological studies have verified daily torpor for *M. griseorufus* (Kobbe and Dausmann 2009; Figure 14.13d), *M. murinus* (Schmid 2000), *M. lehilahytsara* (Karanewsky et al. 2015; captive population), *M. rufus* (Randrianambinina et al. 2003), *M. ravelobensis* (Randrianambinina et al. 2003), and *M. berthae* (the study population is now considered to be *M. myoxinus*; Ortmann et al. 1997). Metabolic rate can decrease to about 15% of resting metabolic rate (*M. murinus*; Schmid 2000; Schmid et al. 2000); and body temperature during daily torpor can be as low as 6.8°C, depending on ambient temperature (*M. berthae*; Schmid et al. 2000). Maybe even more importantly, in the dry deciduous forests and dry spiny thickets, water requirements are drastically reduced during torpor (Schmid and Speakman 2000).

Additionally, some species utilize prolonged torpor or months-long hibernation, such as *M. griseorufus* (Figures 14.13d and 14.14d; Kobbe and Dausmann 2009; Kobbe et al. 2011) and *M. murinus* (Schmid and Kappeler 1998; Schmid 2000). The frequency and duration of torpor bouts increases with increasing body condition in *M. griseorufus* (Kobbe et al. 2011), and entry into hibernation is determined by age and body mass, with older (heavier) females being more likely to go into hibernation in *M. murinus* (Schmid and Kappeler 1998; Faherty et al. 2017). Whereas prolonged torpor is more an extension of daily torpor but with increased energy savings, employed flexibly depending on current internal and external conditions, hibernation requires preparation and can be employed only by individuals with sufficient body condition and fat reserves. *Microcebus berthae*, the smallest species of extant primate in the world (~30 g), uses solely daily torpor, as its body mass, which changes little throughout the year, does not support the accumulation of sufficient fat reserves to fuel months-long

hibernation (Schmid et al. 2000). Just as the tenrecs and bats, these lemurs use the daily rise in ambient temperature to warm up passively at the end of daily torpor or hibernation bouts, before endogenous heat production kicks in, to reduce the costs of these arousals. Indeed, this two-step arousal was first described in *M. murinus* (Ortmann et al. 1997).

The environmental cues that trigger torpor use in *Microcebus* species are not fully understood. Studies on a captive population of *M. murinus* identified light and food availability as potential zeitgeber triggering heterothermy (Perret and Aujard 2001a, 2001b). For example, when exposed to food restriction, *M. murinus* entered torpor earlier and increased the depth and length of torpor even during gestation and lactation (Giroud et al. 2008; Canale et al. 2011, 2012). However, the decrease in body mass in food-restricted and lactating females resulted in delayed growth in the offspring (Canale et al. 2012).

Additionally, as has been shown in *M. griseorufus*, mouse lemurs may shift their thermal neutral zone to cooler temperatures during the cold dry season, to physiologically adjust to changing environmental conditions when staying normothermic (Kobbe et al. 2014). Armed with this suite of flexible responses, mouse lemurs are able to respond in very individualized ways to changing and challenging climatic situations, availability of food and water, and body condition.

While *Microcebus* species utilize all or a combination of the different heterothermic strategies, the most extreme extent of heterothermy within the lemurs is shown by the dwarf lemurs (*Cheirogaleus* spp.). All species of this genus are obligate hibernators, and all individuals enter continuous hibernation over several months during the dry season (J.-J. Petter et al. 1977; Dausmann et al. 2004; Blanco and Rahalinarivo 2010). The length of the hibernation season is variable in the different regions, longer in the dry forests (six to eight months) than in the moist evergreen forests (three to five months), and influenced by rainfall and forest productivity (Lahann and Dausmann 2011). To fuel life during the hibernation period, *C. medius* (Figure 14.13e) almost doubles its body mass by storing monounsaturated oleic acids (synthesized from dietary carbohydrates, e.g., sugary fruits), mainly in their tails, prior to hibernation (Fietz et al. 2003; Fietz and Dausmann 2006). Interestingly, the complex physiological underpinnings of hibernation in *C. medius* seem to be activated not by a unique set of genes but by differential expression of genes that are present in all mammals and are involved in metabolic pathways, feeding behavior, and circadian rhythms (Faherty et al. 2016). *Cheirogaleus medius* and *C. major* hibernate in tree hollows of various insulation capacities, depending on height and thickness of the trees, and are thus exposed to differing climatic conditions (Dausmann et al. 2004). In contrast, *C. crossleyi* and *C. sibreei*, in the Central Highlands as well as in lower-elevation moist evergreen forest sites, hibernate buried underground in cool but quite stable surroundings (J.-J. Petter et al. 1977; Blanco et al. 2013b). As body temperature usually approximates ambient temperature during hibernation, the different species' flexibilities in choice of hibernacula are also reflected in their body temperature profiles. Dwarf lemurs hibernating in well-insulated tree hollows or underground show fairly constant body temperatures between about 10°C and 20°C, depending on the environmental temperature of the habitat, and undergo regular, active arousals about once a week (Figure 14.14e; Dausmann and Blanco 2016). However, individuals hibernating in more poorly insulated tree hollows, as studied in *C. medius*, experience (and tolerate) daily body temperature fluctuations of up to 25°C or more (Figure 14.14f). Body temperature can drop below 10°C in the cool early mornings, but *C. medius* also continues to hibernate when being passively warmed during the day, with body temperatures reaching 30°C or above. Most notably, if these fluctuating body temperatures are passively increased above 30°C at least occasionally, expensive arousals with endogenous heating are abandoned, as in *Echinops telfairi*, and the individuals remain "ectothermic" and torpid for several months (Dausmann et al. 2004, 2005). Thus, dwarf lemurs hibernate continuously not despite daily recurrent high ambient temperatures but precisely because of them. These largely passive patterns also mean that huddling during hibernation does not provide energetic benefits, and *C. medius* individuals indeed hibernate mostly solitarily, although spending most of their daily resting phases in family groups during the rainy season (Dausmann and Glos 2015). Interestingly, despite these differences in physiological modi operandi, the different patterns yield the same level of energy savings, about 70%, as resting metabolic rate, which probably explains the apparent lack of preference of *C. medius* for a specific choice of hibernaculum (Dausmann et al. 2009).

Whether hibernation in tree hollows or underground is the more original form in dwarf lemurs remains unsolved. In the Central Highlands, temperatures occasionally drop below 0°C, possibly entailing a freezing risk for lemurs in poorly insulated tree hollows (Dausmann and Blanco 2016). In the western dry forests, on the other hand, the ground might simply be too hard or friable for dwarf lemurs to dig themselves into, and aboveground temperatures never drop to life-threatening levels. No dwarf lemurs are known from the dry spiny thickets in the far south.

No physiological studies are available for the genera *Mirza* and *Allocebus*, also members of the family Cheirogaleidae, but the lemurs of these genera are assumed to respond in a way similar to *Microcebus* species. For example, *Mirza coquereli* has been found curled up and cold to the touch in traps during the dry season, clearly in a torpid state (Dausmann 2014), and *Allocebus trichotis* in captivity is less active during the dry season, and a body temperature of 26.2°C has been measured in one individual at an ambient temperature of 11°C (Meier and Albignac 1991; Rakotoarison et al. 1997). The notable exception within the Cheirogaleidae is the genus *Phaner*, which seems to remain normothermic throughout the year. However, *Phaner* is most distantly related to the other Cheirogaleidae genera and relies on a very specialized diet (tree exudates) that is available independent of season (Schülke 2003; see Blanco, pp. 1922–26).

Apart from heterothermy, another physiological way to save energy and water and thus to cope with hot and arid habitats, or habitats with (seasonally) sparse food availability, is to maintain a generally low metabolic rate. Many mammals living in hot and arid habitats have a basal metabolic rate 20–40% lower than would be expected for their body size (Lovegrove 2003). A low basal metabolic rate reduces energy requirements and the production of metabolic heat, which in turn allows a higher rate of heat accumulation before expensive, water-consuming active cooling is necessary

(Swanson et al. 2017). Moreover, species can adapt to seasonal changes by shifting their thermal neutral zone (e.g., *M. griseorufus*, as noted above).

Members of the family Lepilemuridae do both. Bethge et al. (2017) found that *Lepilemur leucopus* (the study population is now considered to be *L. petteri*; see Radespiel et al., pp. 1935–40) living in the dry spiny thickets of southern Madagascar not only has a very low general metabolic rate (about 50% of what would be expected for its size, similar to tenrecs) but also shifts its thermal neutral zone seasonally. In contrast to the shift in *M. griseorufus*, and in a seemingly counterintuitive direction, the thermal neutral zone shifts upward, to higher temperatures, in the cooler dry season. *Lepilemur petteri* feeds mainly on leaves containing high concentrations of potentially toxic plant secondary metabolites. One interpretation of this shifted thermal neutral zone is that plant secondary metabolites can be processed more efficiently at ambient temperatures just below the thermal neutral zone (Dearing 2013), enabling sufficient uptake of energy for the high thermoregulatory costs during the cool dry season. Alternatively, the hot daytime temperatures might be more critical for *L. petteri* during the scarce dry season, especially along with increased evaporative water loss, and the upward shift of the thermal neutral zone might thus counterbalance decreased energy and water content of its food (Bethge et al. 2017). *Lepilemur ruficaudatus* (Schmid and Ganzhorn 1996; K. Dausmann et al., unpublished data), *L. edwardsi* (J. Bethge et al., unpublished data; Figure 14.13f), and *L. petteri* in Tsimanampesotse (Magdziak 2017) also have exceptionally low metabolic rates, and this is likely the case for all *Lepilemur* species. Whether *Lepilemur* also becomes heterothermic remains unsolved (partly owing to the difficulties of distinguishing between already extremely low resting rates and torpid metabolic rates), but heterothermy does not seem to be a regular, essential response. A relatively low resting metabolic rate seems to be a general characteristic of lemur physiology, as it has been found in most lemur species studied to date, diurnal and nocturnal alike (e.g., *M. murinus*, Perret 1998; *Eulemur fulvus*, Daniels 1984, Simmen et al. 2010; *Lemur catta*, Simmen et al. 2010; *Propithecus verreauxi*, Richard and Nicoll 1987).

CONCLUSION

Heterothermy is not known to occur in the other Malagasy mammalian orders. However, given the small number of species that have been physiologically studied, and even smaller numbers in the field, it is conceivable that heterothermy will be detected in additional species. For example, *Eupleres goudotii* (Falanouc, family Eupleridae; see Rivera et al., pp. 1983–86), a highly specialized carnivoran that feeds on soft-bodied invertebrates such as earthworms, apparently can store more than 20% of its body weight as fat in its tail and is said to "go to sleep" for two to three months during the cold dry season (Lovegrove 2019). Scientific evidence is still lacking, but this might suggest that *Eupleres* hibernates to get through the period when earthworms are scarce.

The cornucopia of physiological responses found in Malagasy terrestrial mammals enables them to respond individually and flexibly to the often challenging environments of Madagascar and changes within them (Dewar and Richard 2007). Heterothermy seems to be an important component in the physiological tool kit, enabling survival in unfavorable times in numerous orders and species of mammals on the island. Moreover, the range of basic physiological approaches within the Malagasy mammals is amazing: from bats, metabolic super performers while active but appearing to jump at every possibility to enter torpor, sometimes even extremely short bouts, to temporarily decrease their high metabolic demands and even tolerating hyperthermia close to lethal levels; to spiny tenrecs, which take the completely opposite path and keep metabolism low most of the time, except when reproductive activities prohibit this, resembling protoendotherms in their thermoregulatory patterns. Whether the comparatively high proportion of heterothermic species within Malagasy mammals reflects concentrated scientific efforts on this topic, or whether Madagascar's unique evolutionary and geological history and challenging environment has led to selective pressures favoring this physiological response, remains a question of debate.

In contrast to arctic or temperate regions, where low temperatures and low seasonal availability of food promote heterothermy, the ultimate triggers of tropical heterothermy might be less straightforward and more multifaceted. For example, studies in other tropical areas showed that besides the vital need of water conservation, extreme weather events as well as environmental disasters (cyclones, droughts, storms, floods) can elicit heterothermic responses in small mammals (reviewed in Nowack et al. 2020). As climatic extremes in general and temperatures in particular are predicted to continue to increase with global climate change, with Madagascar being no exception (Hannah et al. 2008), Malagasy animals could be pushed to the edge of their limits. Malagasy mammals are vulnerable to extremes on either side of the climatic continuum. For example, *Echinops telfairi* might succumb when temperatures stay continuously below the temperature threshold that enables it to return to normothermia after torpor bouts during cold spells. *Macronycteris commersoni*, on the other hand, might perish during heat waves, when its body temperature is driven above the lethal level during passive hyperthermic torpor episodes, and *Lepilemur petteri* might suffer from generally elevated temperature levels because of increased toxicity of its food plants. Nevertheless, heterothermy, especially flexible shorter torpor bouts, might be a useful tool to help many Malagasy mammals overcome more dire and unpredictable environmental pressures.

Subject editors: Jörg U. Ganzhorn and Steven M. Goodman

CAMERA TRAPPING ON MADAGASCAR

Z. J. Farris, B. D. Gerber, A. Murphy, and E. Wampole

BACKGROUND ON CAMERAS AND THEIR USE

A camera trap is a digital camera connected to an infrared sensor that can "see" warm objects, such as animals, moving in front of it. When an animal moves past the sensor it causes the camera to activate, recording an image or video to the memory card within the device for later retrieval. Camera traps can be left in the field to continuously watch an area for weeks or even months, recording the rarest events that occur in nature. These devices have revolutionized biodiversity science and conservation of many wild animals. Their use is now commonplace in wildlife studies, especially those focused on terrestrial mammals. In Africa alone, the number of camera-trapping studies has increased from a handful prior to 2008 to over 60 per year by 2017 (Agha et al. 2018). The scale of a camera-trapping study can range from a few cameras used over a small local area for a short period of time to thousands of cameras deployed worldwide over many years. While there are many camera-trap models and types, the fundamental element of the data they record is imagery (photograph or video) of an animal at a known place and time. For more in-depth information on choosing the appropriate camera and on active versus passive camera triggers, as well as guidelines and recommendations for establishing and positioning cameras, the authors have created and will maintain for the foreseeable future an online database designed for Madagascar wildlife and ecosystems (Camera Trapping Madagascar, https://sites.google.com/view/ct-madagascar/).

Evaluating the reliability of a camera model should ideally be done prior to the study. This can be done by consulting with colleagues using cameras in a similar environment or consulting online resources that provide critical reviews (Trailcampro 2020). It is also important to evaluate camera-trap models based on their hardware and software features. Notable aspects to consider are the trigger speed, image quality and resolution, video capability, type of flash (infrared or white flash), battery life and allowable types (rechargeable, alkaline, lithium-ion), allowable SD cards (based on read and write speeds between the camera sensor and the card), camera design and durability, and price. Price may be the determining factor for most studies. A reliable active-passive camera trap can be purchased for ~US$150–$200 (e.g., Browning Strike Force Pro XD).

It is perhaps surprising that the basic information provided by a camera trap can help researchers learn so much about species that we would otherwise rarely observe (O'Connell et al. 2010). Simply, a camera trap provides evidence of the detection of an animal at a specific place and time. Conversely, if an image of the animal was not taken (assuming the camera can detect the species), it can be concluded that the species was either not present or went undetected. By summarizing these detections and nondetections at camera traps in differing locations, we can use occupancy modeling to account for sampling biases, such as imperfect detection of a species, and estimate species' distributions (Linkie et al. 2013) and habitat use (Gerber et al. 2012a). By combining population estimates with changes in habitat across meaningful time periods, such as climatic seasons or years, we can estimate the dynamics (e.g., colonization or extirpation) of habitat use (Farris et al. 2017a). Of course, even in studies targeting a single species, many species are often detected, and by aggregating detection and nondetection across a zone, we can estimate species richness and other aspects of the local community (Zipkin et al. 2009).

An intuitive extension of whether a species was there or not is to ask how often we detected the species at each camera-trap location. Dividing this number by a measure of sampling effort (e.g., operating camera days) provides a photographic rate for the species, which can be compared across camera traps, seasons, or species. This measure is sometimes interpreted as a relative abundance index (RAI) (T. G. O'Brien et al. 2003). However, it should be done cautiously, as the RAI is influenced not only by the abundance of a species but also by the rate and pattern of movements, the habitat, and the camera setup (Sollmann et al. 2013). Disentangling these effects and isolating and comparing measures of abundance require additional information. A more natural interpretation of the photographic rate is as an index of animal activity, with this measure increasing because there are 1) more individuals that use the area and/or 2) individuals that use that site more often.

To estimate animal abundance or density from camera traps, individual animals, ideally, can be identified based on unique coloration or markings without error from each photograph. By aggregating the detections of individuals by species over a short time period, when it is assumed that the population is closed to demographic or geographic changes (births, deaths, immigration, and emigration), it is possible to estimate abundance or density using capture-recapture models (Gerber et al. 2012a). By linking these data over multiple sampling periods, such as seasons or years, we can estimate population dynamics, including survival and recruitment (K. U. Karanth et al. 2006). Camera traps can also be used to identify and quantify unique animal behavior that otherwise might go unobserved (Bridges and Noss 2011) or be difficult to obtain. This can include behaviors such as feeding and foraging (Razafindratsima 2017), predation events (Karpanty 2006), and antipredator behavior or general activity patterns (Farris et al. 2015a; Merson et al. 2019a).

CAMERA-TRAP USE ON MADAGASCAR

Overview of Camera-Trapping Surveys to Date

Camera-trapping survey work on Madagascar to date has centered primarily on surveying, monitoring, and/or estimating rare, elusive members of the order Carnivora (including both endemics of the family Eupleridae [see Veron et al., pp. 1863–65] and introduced species of three different families [see Goodman and Soarimalala,

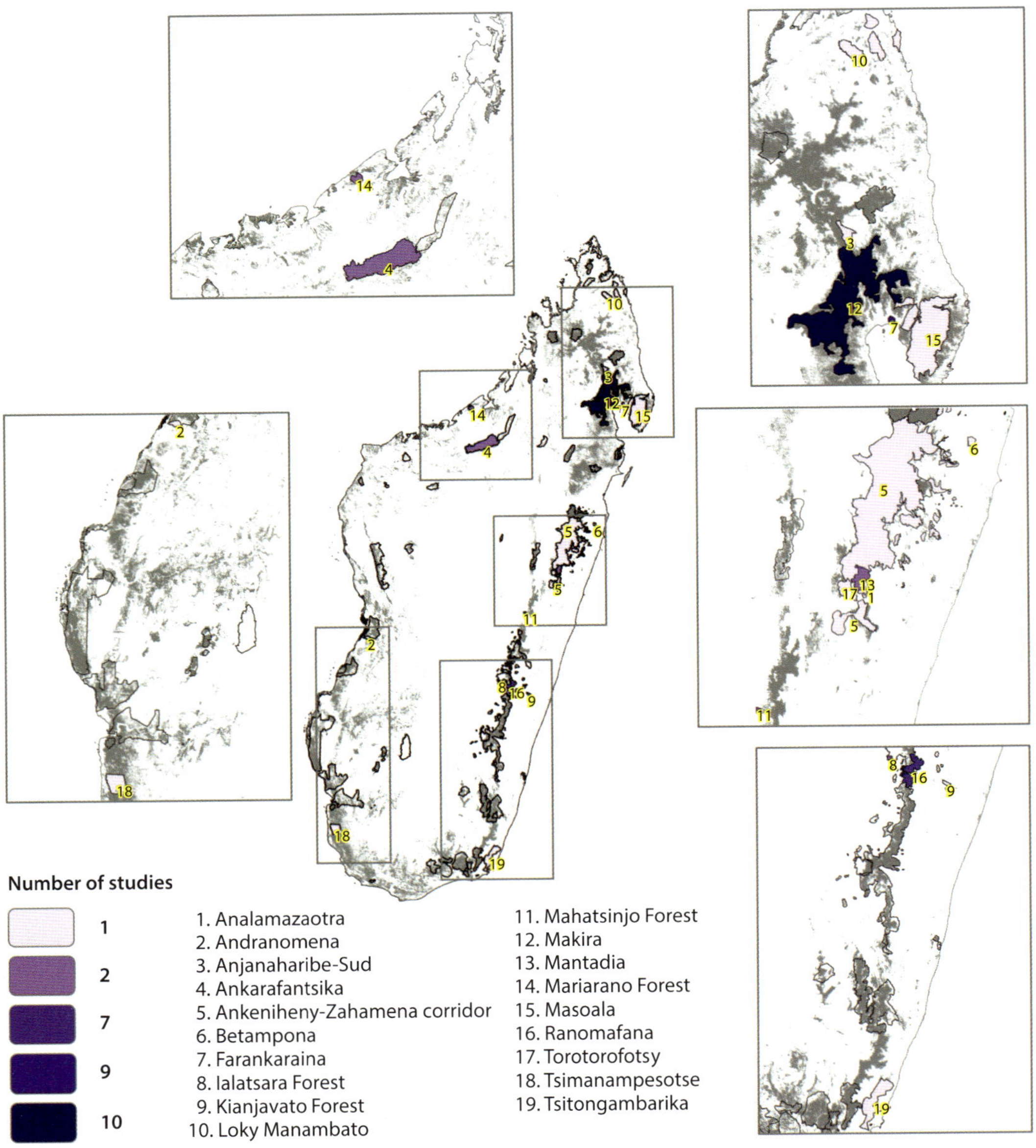

FIGURE 14.15 Map of sites of camera-trapping research throughout Madagascar, including number of studies or publications and name of protected area where research was conducted.

pp. 1737–69]), particularly those occupying eastern moist evergreen forest (Figure 14.15). Two moist evergreen forest protected areas have been the focus for the majority of the camera-trapping surveys to date: Ranomafana and Makira (Table 14.5). However, in the past five years (2015–2019), we have seen an expansion of camera-trapping surveys of carnivoran populations across eastern moist evergreen forest protected areas, including Andasibe [Analamazaotra]–Mantadia, Anjanaharibe-Sud, Betampona, and Torotorofotsy. Camera-trapping surveys of carnivoran populations in other vegetation formations have also been carried out in the past several years, including those in Loky Manambato (Daraina region) in the northeast (P. Ross and B. Semel, unpublished data), Mariarano in the northwest (Evans et al. 2013; Mann et al. 2016), and Ankarafantsika and Andranomena in the west (Merson et al. 2017, 2019a, 2019b). Given the lack of individual identifiable markings for the majority of Madagascar's carnivorans, population-level estimates have focused primarily on occupancy (probability of site use) estimation, including single-season, multiseason, and co-occurrence modeling. However, for some populations and/or protected areas, density estimations of *Fossa fossana* (Spotted Fanaloka) and *Cryptoprocta ferox* (Fosa) have been achieved (see examples below, as well as Kerridge et al., pp. 1886–89; Gerber and Hawkins, pp. 1978–83). Additionally, camera surveys have provided data that will allow researchers to explore sustainability of hunting and poaching rates (Farris et al. 2015b), species interactions (Farris et al. 2015c, 2020), species distributions (Beaudrot et al. 2018), and disease transmission (Rasambainarivo et al. 2017).

Despite the strong focus on Carnivora populations, camera-trapping surveys in Madagascar have also been used to estimate population parameters for other taxa, including birds (Murphy et al. 2017a) and small mammals (Murphy et al. 2017b), and also investigate rodent behavior (Razafindratsima 2017) (Table 14.5). Camera-trapping surveys of carnivorans have been combined with line-transect sampling of lemur populations to investigate lemur-predator interactions (Farris et al. 2014; see example below). Using camera traps to study lemur populations remains limited to date. Researchers have used camera traps to confirm the presence of rare lemur species

TABLE 14.5. **Summary of camera-trapping surveys conducted across Madagascar**

	STUDY	TAXA	NUMBER OF LOCATIONS/ TRAP NIGHTS	TOPIC OR ANALYSIS	SITE
1	Gerber (2010)	*Fossa fossana*	26/1586	*F. fossana* density estimation	Ranomafana
2	Gerber et al. (2012b)	Carnivora	31/1612	Carnivoran activity patterns	Ranomafana, Ialatsara Forest, Mahatsinjo Forest
3	Gerber et al. (2012a)	Carnivora	111/5565	*Cryptoprocta ferox* and *Fossa fossana* density; carnivoran single-season occupancy	Ranomafana, Ialatsara Forest, Mahatsinjo Forest
4	Farris et al. (2012)	*Salanoia concolor*	25/2910	*S. concolor* distribution and trap rates	Makira
5	E. R. Olson et al. (2012)	*Prolemur simus*	7/231	*P. simus* presence rapid assessment	Ankeniheny-Zahamena corridor
6	Evans et al. (2013)	Carnivora	7/227	Carnivoran rapid assessment	Mariarano Forest
7	Farris et al. (2014)	Lemurs, Carnivora	96/8717	Lemur-Carnivora co-occurrence	Makira, Farankaraina Forest
8	LaFleur et al. (2014)	*Lemur catta*	34/915	Temporal activity patterns	Tsimanampesotse
9	Farris et al. (2015b)	Carnivora	152/8854	Hunting/poaching rates; carnivoran single-season occupancy	Makira, Farankaraina Forest
10	Farris et al. (2016)	*Felis silvestris*	152/14,045	Free-ranging cat occupancy and distribution	Makira, Farankaraina Forest
11	Farris et al. (2015a; 2015c)	Carnivora	152/15,253	Temporal activity patterns; spatial co-occurrence	Makira, Farankaraina Forest
12	Farris et al. (2017b)	Carnivora	25/6662	Multiseason occupancy	Makira, Farankaraina Forest
13	Mann et al. (2016)	*Cryptoprocta ferox*	20/517	*C. ferox* observation and assessment	Mariarano Forest
14	Brown et al. (2016)	Amphibians, Carnivora	198/79,200	Ecological niche modeling of invasive Asian toad and native carnivorans	Eastern, moist evergreen forest
15	Farris et al. (2017a)	Carnivora	108/41,499	Multiseason co-occurrence and spatial distribution	Ranomafana
16	Rasambainarivo et al. (2017)	Carnivora	30/2589	Spatial interactions with emphasis on disease transmission	Betampona
17	Razafindratsima (2017)	Small-mammal community	10/140	Seed dispersal by small mammals	Ranomafana
18	Murphy et al. (2017b)	Small-mammal community	293/8793	Single-season occupancy and habitat use	Makira, Farankaraina Forest
19	Murphy et al. (2017a)	Ground-dwelling bird community	348/18,056	Single-season occupancy and habitat use	Makira, Farankaraina Forest
20	Merson et al. (2019a)	Carnivora	160/8730	Carnivoran temporal activity patterns	Ankarafantsika, Andranomena

	STUDY	TAXA	NUMBER OF LOCATIONS/ TRAP NIGHTS	TOPIC OR ANALYSIS	SITE
21	Merson et al. (2017)	*Eupleres goudotii*	80/6320	*E. goudotii* observations and assessment	Ankarafantsika
22	Murphy et al. (2019)	Introduced carnivorans, native small mammals and birds	148/8793	Spatial co-occurrence between introduced carnivorans and native species	Makira, Farankaraina Forest
23	Murphy et al. (2018)	*Cryptoprocta ferox*	341/17,204	*C. ferox* density estimation	Makira, Farankaraina Forest
24	Beaudrot et al. (2018)	Mammal community	60/10,800	Species distributions	Ranomafana
25	B. Semel et al. (unpublished data)	Carnivora	60/~360	Carnivoran single-season occupancy	Loky Manambato
26	P. Ross et al. (unpublished data)	Carnivora	35/3270	Carnivoran single-season occupancy	Anjanaharibe-Sud
27	Z. J. Farris et al. (unpublished data)	Carnivora	24/120	Carnivoran single-season occupancy	Analamazaotra (Andasibe) Forestry Station (Mitsinjo)
28	T. Eppley et al. (unpublished data)	Lemur, carnivoran communities	20/1800	Species richness, single-season population estimates	Tsitongambarika, Masoala
29	P. Narváez-Torres et al. (unpublished data)	Lemur community	60/1800	Occupancy, functional diversity, and community assembly	Ranomafana, Kianjavato Forest
30	E. Wampole et al. (unpublished data)	Carnivora	80/9396	Carnivoran density, occupancy, and spatiotemporal interactions	Andasibe-Mantadia, Torotorofotsy
31	N. Guthrie and S. Johnson (unpublished data)	*Microcebus jollyae*	70/na	Presence/absence in reforestation areas	Kianjavato Forest
32	DeSisto et al. (2020)	Frugivorous birds and lemurs	02/28	Frugivore assemblage on *Psidium cattleyanum* (Strawberry Guava)	Ranomafana
33	N. N. Raoelinjanakolana and O. H. Razafindratsima (unpublished data)	Frugivorous birds and lemurs	05/1209	Plant-frugivore networks	Torotorofotsy-Ihofa

(L. E. Olson et al. 2012) and have used photographic sampling to bolster behavioral sampling of *Lemur catta* (Ring-tailed Lemur; see example below). However, robust, arboreal camera-trap grids designed to monitor and estimate population parameters of entire lemur communities have only recently been initiated. These arboreal camera surveys are being carried out in Ranomafana National Park and Kianjavato Forest (Figure 14.15), including surveys of reforested fragments with the aim of investigating occupancy, functional diversity, and community assembly (S. Johnson et al., unpublished data). Additionally, camera traps are currently being used to survey for *Daubentonia madagascariensis* (Aye-aye) populations and co-occurring lemur species within the protected areas of Masoala and Tsitongambarika (T. Eppley, unpublished data).

Examples of Camera-Trapping Research Projects

Density Estimation and Predictive Modeling: Cryptoprocta *and* Fossa

To effectively assess the conservation and management needs of a target species, accurately estimating population size is of vital importance. While the original capture-mark-recapture (CMR)

method of estimating population size required researchers to physically trap and mark animals, K. U. Karanth et al. (2006) pioneered the use of CMR population estimation using individually identifiable marks (stripes and spots) naturally found on certain species (e.g., Tiger) that are recorded during camera-trapping surveys. Recent innovations now allow researchers to directly estimate density by incorporating spatial information from individual movement between camera locations using spatially explicit capture-recapture models (i.e., requiring camera-trap spacing that is close enough to allow individuals to be detected at multiple locations). Additional criteria must also be met, including the assumptions that the population being estimated remains "closed" demographically (no births or deaths) and geographically (no emigration or immigration), individuals are not missed, and their marks do not change during the survey. However, recently developed spatial mark–resight models have made it possible to estimate the population density of naturally unmarked species by picking up other individually distinguishing characteristics throughout their life (i.e., scars, other forms of injuries, ear notches).

These approaches have been used in Madagascar to estimate the density of two threatened carnivoran species: *Cryptoprocta ferox* (Figure 14.16e) and *Fossa fossana*. In Ranomafana National Park, Gerber (2010) and Gerber et al. (2012a) used spatially explicit capture-recapture models to provide the first population density estimates for both species using the unique stripe-spot patterns and natural scars present on individuals of each species. *Fossa* density, at 3.19 ind/km^2 (individuals per square kilometer) in intact forest and 1.38 ind/km^2 in selectively logged forest, showed a negative relationship to habitat degradation, whereas *Cryptoprocta* density was similar between the two types of forest (0.12 and 0.09 ind/km^2, respectively). Using *Cryptoprocta* estimates from intact and selectively logged areas, Gerber et al. (2012a) predicted an island-wide *Cryptoprocta* population of 8626 adults, with only the Makira-Masoala and Zahamena-Mantadia moist evergreen forest complexes large enough to hold >300 adults. Additionally, Murphy et al. (2018) used 15 camera-trapping surveys and spatial mark–resight models to estimate *Cryptoprocta* density at 0.20 adults/km^2 (95% highest posterior density interval: 0.12–0.34) in the Makira-Masoala complex, providing a population estimate of 1061 (596–1780) in these protected areas.

Predator-Prey Dynamics: Lemur and Carnivoran Spatial Interactions

Farris et al. (2014) used camera-trapping survey data in a novel fashion by overlaying straight-line transects for lemur surveys inside existing camera-trap grids. By recording the location of both diurnal and nocturnal lemur species inside the camera grid, they were able to investigate how lemurs and multiple endemic and introduced carnivoran species overlapped in space use, thus exploring the potential for predator-primate interactions (Figures 14.16b and c). Using two endemic euplerids (*Cryptoprocta ferox* and *Galidia elegans* [Ring-tailed Vontsira]), two introduced carnivorans (*Canis lupus* [dog] and *Felis silvestris* [cat]), and nonresearcher humans as potential predator foci, and three lemur species (*Avahi laniger* [Eastern Woolly Lemur], *Microcebus rufus* [Rufous Mouse Lemur], and *Eulemur albifrons* [White-fronted Brown Lemur]) as potential prey foci, they investigated spatial interactions across contiguous and fragmented forest sites. They found that free-ranging cats demonstrated the highest number of interactions for any predator species. Nocturnal *M. rufus* demonstrated "avoidance" with all predator species across contiguous forest, and diurnal *E. albifrons* showed "attraction" with both cats and humans in contiguous forest. This sampling and modeling approach allowed researchers to combine two noninvasive surveying approaches to investigate predator-primate interactions for rare, difficult to study species across moist evergreen forest habitat.

Behavior Sampling: *Lemur catta* Activity Patterns

While most camera-trapping research focuses on detection/nondetection data used for estimating population parameters, it is possible to use camera traps to explore behavior in a wide range of taxa (e.g., Figure 14.16a). LaFleur et al. (2014) used camera traps to study Ring-tailed Lemur populations in the dry spiny thickets of southern Madagascar, specifically at Tsimanampesotse (Figure 14.15) by combining photographic sampling with behavioral observations to explore daily activity patterns. Using only a small number (four to six) of individual camera traps, the researchers were able to effectively use the camera traps' continuous, 24-hour monitoring capabilities to observe the lemurs' nest sites and quantify their activity budgets, arboreal versus terrestrial activity, and temperature-related activity patterns, as well as predator presence. The researchers documented nocturnal activity throughout the year and found that nocturnal activity was driven by nighttime temperatures and provided further understanding into the mechanisms of daily activity patterns in the local Ring-tailed Lemur population.

Disease Ecology: Introduced and Native Carnivoran Interactions at Betampona

Using noninvasive, continuous monitoring provided by camera traps, Rasambainarivo et al. (2017) investigated the frequency and spatial distribution of interactions between native carnivorans and free-ranging dogs (Figure 14.16f) and cats. They identified more than 200 interactions between native and introduced carnivorans and, using land-cover data in Betampona (Figure 14.15), found the highest density of short-interval interactions between native and introduced carnivorans occurred near the local research station, just outside the limit of the protected area. While the research team found no direct interactions (native and introduced present at exact space and time), they found 70% of the camera locations had some level of indirect interaction (e.g., introduced carnivoran visit followed by native carnivoran visit). Using estimated survival times for relevant, transmittable carnivoran pathogens, they highlighted potential risks of disease transmission from introduced animals to natives, including Canine Parvovirus and Canine Distemper Virus (see Rasambainarivo and Zohdy, pp. 298–302). This novel approach provided insights into the little-studied relationship(s) between habitat alternations, animal interactions, and disease transmission.

Long-term Estimation: Carnivore Multiseason Trends

The majority of published research globally involving camera-trapping data comes from single-season or single-year surveys, which provide snapshot estimates of wildlife populations. Multiseason or multiyear surveys allow researchers to investigate shifts in species occurrence and/or population parameters across years (e.g.,

FIGURE 14.16 **Collection of camera-trap photos from Madagascar-related research projects, including: A) *Propithecus candidus* (Silky Sifaka) demonstrating geophagia behavior in the Makira protected area; *Felis silvestris* (cat) predation on B) on *Eulemur fulvus* (Brown Lemur) and C) *Leioheterodon* cf. *geayi* snake; D) *Eupleres goudotii* (Falanouc) observed near the end of the cool, wet, lean season inside Makira; E) single, male *Cryptoprocta ferox* (Fosa) captured in Mantadia; and F) *Canis lupus* (dog) group traveling through the Mantadia Forest.** (PHOTOS A, D, and E by Z. J. Farris; B and C by S. Merson; and F by E. Wampole.)

survival, recruitment, extirpation), as these modeling approaches eliminate critical assumptions between survey periods associated with single-season, "closed" populations (without, for example, birth, death, immigration, and emigration). Despite the usefulness of such long-term, dynamic population trends or estimates, multiseason surveys and resulting occurrence estimates are not very common in the literature. Multiseason monitoring and estimation requires repeat surveys of the same wildlife population(s) across the same survey area(s) for at least two years. On Madagascar, these long-term or multiyear surveys have been carried out and occurrence dynamics estimated in only two protected areas: Ranomafana (Farris et al. 2017a) and Makira (Farris et al. 2017b) (Figure 14.15). In Ranomafana, the Tropical Ecology and Assessment Monitoring (TEAM) network and ValBio research staff have carried out camera-trapping surveys across three sampling grids inside the park from 2010 to the present. Farris et al. (2017a) used these multiseason survey data to estimate occupancy trends over time for five endemic euplerid carnivores (*C. ferox*, *Eupleres goudotii* [Falanouc], *F. fossana*, *Galidia elegans*, and *Galidictis fasciata* [Broad-striped Vontsira]), free-ranging dogs, and nonresearcher humans. They found that *C. ferox* and *G. elegans* decreased their spatial distribution (occupancy) by 50% over this six-year period, resulting in a probability of local extirpation of 0.44 and 0.60, respectively, while humans increased spatial distribution across the protected area by 25%. Additionally, they used multiseason co-occurrence models to demonstrate that both *C. ferox* and *G. elegans* had strong positive space use (occurring together more than at random; species interaction factor >1.0) with free-ranging dogs. These multiyear assessments, while rare, are critical to improve our understanding of dynamic changes occurring within wildlife populations occupying threatened ecosystems across Madagascar.

HOW CAMERA TRAPS CAN ADVANCE CONSERVATION ON MADAGASCAR

Camera traps have yet to be used to their full potential in biodiversity studies on Madagascar. We anticipate two advances in the coming years: 1) a broader use of camera traps by researchers asking more varied questions on a more diverse set of taxa, and 2) the scaling-up of ecological inference over space and time by integrating multiple, small-scale surveys into a broader monitoring network to better understand biodiversity changes island-wide over a temporal scale. We believe the first may be accomplished simply by researchers recognizing that camera traps can be used to answer many types of ecological questions (O'Connell et al. 2010). Furthermore, there are a number of in-depth practical guides to camera trapping, which are quite useful for designing a study and analyzing data (see Wearn and Glover-Kapfer 2017). The second can be accomplished through collaboration and sharing of data via a centralized database, such as eMammal (www.emammal.si.edu) or Wildlife Insights (www.wildlifeinsights.org). It is by combining our shared knowledge that we will be able to understand better the truly complex ecology of Madagascar's threatened wildlife and how to effectively manage and conserve it.

Subject editor: Steven M. Goodman

THE EFFECTS OF FOREST LOSS AND FRAGMENTATION ON NONVOLANT MAMMALS

T. S. Steffens, M. S. Ramsay, F. Mercado Malabet, and S. M. Lehman

Deforestation through habitat loss and fragmentation is the leading threat to mammals in Madagascar (C. Schwitzer et al. 2014). Since the 1950s, Madagascar has lost approximately 44% of its total forest. Of the remaining forests, 46% are 100 m from a forest–degraded area ecotone (Vieilledent et al. 2018). Forest loss and fragmentation are largely a result of small-scale forest removal for rice production, commercial wood exploitation, swidden agriculture, and the creation of pasture for grazing cattle (Bloesch 1999; Harper et al. 2007). Climate change is expected to have further negative effects on Madagascar's remaining forests. Morelli et al. (2020) modeled the effects of deforestation and climate change on moist evergreen forests of the island. In 2014, they estimated an approximate cover of 45,680 km^2 of moist evergreen forest, of which 66% (30,220 km^2) was considered interior forest (i.e., forest habitats free from edge effects). If deforestation continues at the same rate inside and outside protected areas, they estimated, 84% of current forest cover would be lost by 2070. The situation is somewhat improved when deforestation was modeled to occur only outside protected areas, where forest cover is predicted to decline only 51% by 2070. It is likely that overall forest cover and interior forest habitats will continue to decline in other habitats of Madagascar, such as the western and transitional dry forests (Figure 14.17a).

Forest loss tends to reduce the amount of habitat a species can occupy, resulting in reduced population size of a single species (Craul et al. 2009) and lowering species diversity within communities (Turner 1996). Many species also have minimum habitat area requirements and can then be extirpated from fragments as they decrease in size (Rösch et al. 2015). This general pattern has been noted in nonvolant mammals (hereafter simply named as mammals), with species richness tending to decline linearly with habitat area (A. H. Harcourt and Doherty 2005). A similar pattern holds for the distribution-abundance relationships these species exhibit, which describes a positive relationship between local abundance of species and the size of their ranges within a region. Habitat area is certainly an important variable in conserving mammal populations

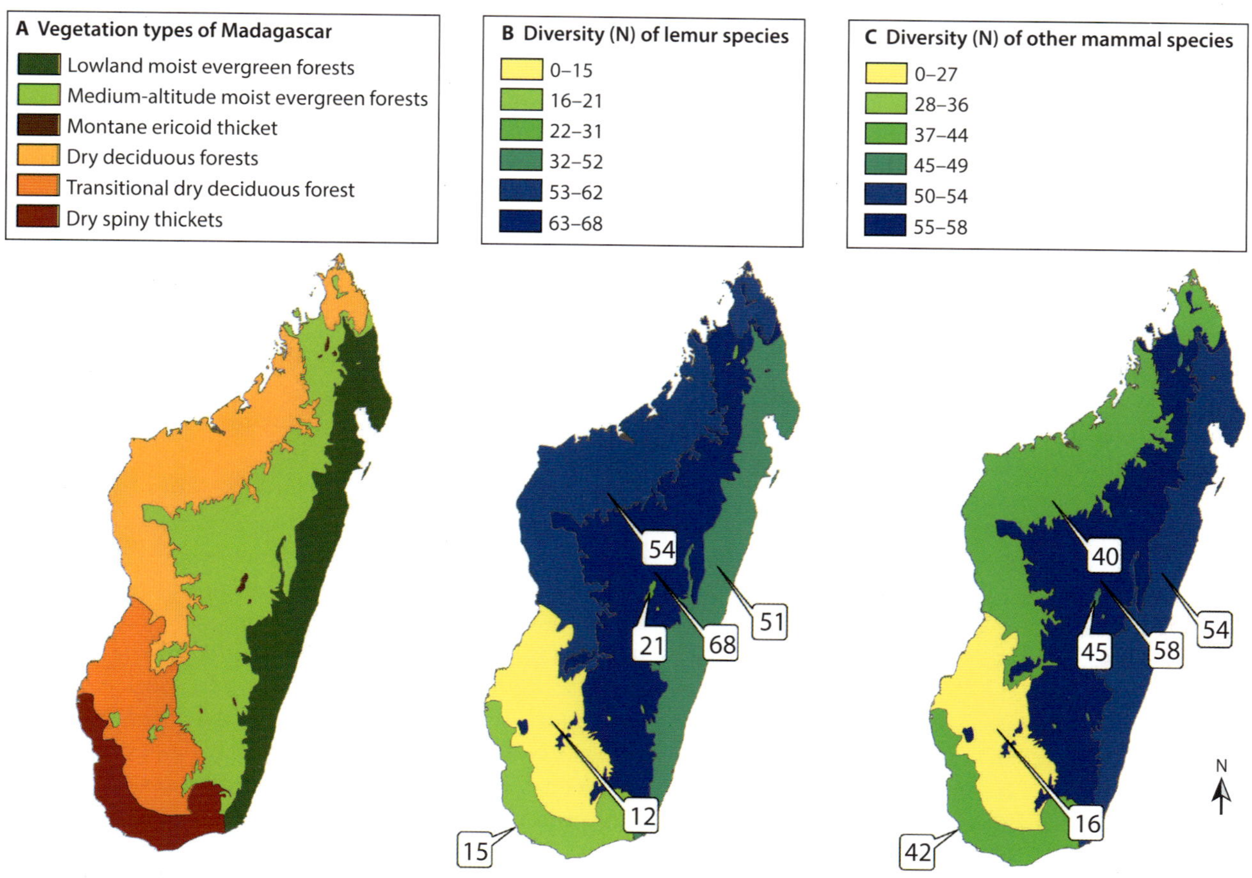

FIGURE 14.17 **Maps showing A) six vegetation types on Madagascar; and total species diversity of B) lemurs and C) other mammals, across these regions.** (SOURCES: modified from Gautier et al. 2018; geographic range data based on Red List species maps, IUCN 2020.)

in fragmented landscapes, but researchers must also be cautious to not let species-area or distribution-abundance models overshadow the impact of other variables such as habitat isolation on species persistence (Matthews et al. 2016). For instance, mammals experiencing forest fragmentation may form subpopulations within fragments that show temporal and spatial variations in occupancy and connectivity (i.e., metapopulation dynamics; Hanski 1994), which affect their viability across fragmented landscapes.

Adding to these issues is the fact that deforestation results in the creation of forest edges and subsequent edge effects—the abiotic and biotic interactions that occur at the boundary of two or more habitats, such as the interface between forest and grassland (Murcia 1995). In fact, the study of forest loss and fragmentation ultimately involves edge effects, because these effects are confounded with fragment-area (patch-size) effects (Laurance 2000). For example, mammal populations in a series of small fragments may be subjected to higher extinction probabilities than conspecifics in relatively larger fragments (MacArthur and Wilson 1967); moreover, these smaller fragments actually have a higher proportion of edge-modified habitats that reduce the amount of habitat a species can occupy. Put differently, forest loss and fragmentation can synergistically produce a greater proportion of edge habitats in shrinking fragments, which confounds using area as a main determinant of species diversity and abundance (Malcolm et al. 2017). If some species prefer or require "core area," then they may be extirpated from smaller or narrower fragments composed predominantly of edge habitats. Thus, edge effects are an inevitable outcome of forest loss and fragmentation, and it is imperative that we work to understand how mammals respond to varying intensities and scales of edge effects.

In the contribution on this subject published in the precursor to this book, by Ganzhorn et al. (2003), the authors found a positive effect of fragment size on mammal species richness, supporting a species-area model as a determinist method for predicting lemur responses to deforestation in Madagascar. Since 2003, the knowledge of the natural history and taxonomic diversity of many Malagasy mammals has been greatly expanded. Thus, the question that arises today is whether or not more recent data continue to support a species-area model for mammals in the fragmented landscapes of Madagascar. The purposes of this contribution are to update information presented in Ganzhorn et al. (2003) with regard to the effects of forest loss and fragmentation on mammals and, more specifically, to describe which species are known to be susceptible to these deforestation processes and edge effects.

LEMUR CONSERVATION BIOGEOGRAPHY AND FOREST FRAGMENTATION

The combination of high levels of biodiversity and endemism with landscape-scale deforestation has, in many ways, resulted in Madagascar becoming a natural laboratory for fragmentation research (Eppley et al. 2020). Of the 174 native nonvolant mammals currently recognized in the IUCN Red List as occurring on Madagascar, 62.1% (n = 108) are lemurs, 16.1% (n = 28) are rodents, 17.8% (n = 31) are tenrecs, and 4.0% (n = 7) are carnivorans (IUCN 2020). The highest diversity of lemur species is found, respectively, in the medium-altitude moist evergreen, dry deciduous, and lowland moist evergreen forest vegetation types of the island (Figure 14.17a). In comparison, vegetation types in the southern regions (i.e., transitional dry deciduous forests and spiny thickets) and montane forests exhibit lower levels of lemur species diversity (Figure 14.17b). As for the other mammals observed on the island (i.e., rodents, tenrecs, and carnivorans), the majority occur in the eastern vegetation types—lowland and medium-altitude moist evergreen and montane forests (Figure 14.17c). Western vegetation areas in contrast, exhibit lower numbers of species.

Given their abundance and dominance in fragmentation research, we begin our review with a focus on lemurs. Of the 108 species that have been assessed by the IUCN, currently, 31.4% (n = 33) of lemur species are listed as Critically Endangered, 41.7% (n = 45) as Endangered, and 23.2% (n = 25) as Vulnerable; only two taxa are listed as Least Concern. Lemur extinction risks relate to a complex mix of anthropogenic factors, with the most relevant threats arising from various deforestation processes (e.g., agriculture, logging, fires) and hunting. A meta-analysis of the effects of anthropogenic habitat modification on primate community structure indicated that lemur communities were more negatively affected by habitat disturbance than any other primate community at the global level (Almeida-Rocha et al. 2017). Lemurs are particularly sensitive to deforestation given that almost all species prefer forest habitats, although there have been suggestions that lemur behavioral and ecological flexibilities somehow mitigate the deleterious effects of deforestation (Curtis and Donati 2012).

Kling et al. (2020) and Eppley et al. (2020) recently published reviews of lemur responses to forest fragmentation across Madagascar. Both papers provide general patterns that can then be explored in more detail for specific taxa and various research sites. Kling et al. (2020) noted a fourfold increase from 2000 to 2019 in papers on the responses of lemurs to forest fragmentation. They also noted a strong regional bias in research, with most studies being undertaken in moist evergreen and littoral forests in eastern Madagascar. Kling et al. (2020) also summarized results from matrix use by lemurs, finding that 22 lemur species used matrix habitats in different regions of the island. In accordance with these findings, we have separated the impacts of fragmentation into three subsections: fragment area, fragment isolation, and edge effects.

Lemur Responses to Fragment Area Effects

Kling et al. (2020) noted that fragment area was the most consistent feature associated with lemur responses to forest fragmentation, in that larger fragments tended to support a higher abundance of lemur populations, higher species richness, and animals with overall better health. Other studies on species-area relationships in lemurs provide further support that area is the strongest factor predicting species richness (Andriatsitohaina et al. 2019; T. S. Steffens and Lehman 2019). For example, T. S. Steffens and Lehman (2019) found that the number of lemur species increased as fragment size increased at the fragmented site of Ambanjabe, and that some species occurred in even the smallest fragments (e.g., 0.23 ha). These authors suggested that the existence of some lemurs in fragments seemingly too small to support animals on a medium- to long-term basis was due to the ability of resident small-bodied *Microcebus*

species to tolerate edge habitats and/or disperse across the nonforest matrix, including estimated distances of up to 250 m (Radespiel et al. 2003). This case demonstrates the importance of natural history research in determining the impacts of fragmentation, as *Microcebus* dispersal distances were essential in the building of these predictive models.

Kling et al. (2020) cautioned that the forces behind species-area relationships in lemurs likely represent a complex mix of natural and anthropogenic causes of forest fragmentation, which will vary because of spatial heterogeneity in topography, climate, and forest characteristics. To better understand how forest loss and fragmentation impact mammals beyond species-area relationships, it is critical that researchers investigate how connectivity, independent of habitat loss, affects occurrence patterns. Eppley et al. (2020) pursued similar questions on how functional traits relating to lemur's natural history, such as feeding ecology and distribution, are associated to habitat fragmentation characteristics (e.g., patch size, edge density, landscape configuration) to determine how lemurs respond to forest fragmentation. Of the 32 species in their study, 10 showed positive responses to increased habitat area, whereas 14 showed negative responses to forest fragmentation. It is important to note that forest fragmentation causes the breaking apart of continuous forest into smaller, more numerous fragments, which can divide a once continuous animal population into many smaller populations. Five taxa showed no responses to habitat area, fragmentation, or landscape connectivity, including rare species such as *Eulemur mongoz* and *Propithecus coronatus*. The researchers found that only folivore-frugivores demonstrated flexibility/variability when faced with forest fragmentation. They also determined that habitat area had a strong positive effect on the distribution of many species, particularly species in the genera *Eulemur* and *Propithecus*.

Lemur Responses to Fragment Isolation Effects

Isolation of remaining forest patches following deforestation and connectivity between these patches can also impact the persistence of lemurs (Kling et al. 2020). For instance, distribution patterns of *Microcebus murinus* and *M. ravelobensis* in northwestern Madagascar can be at least partially explained by their different dispersal abilities between forest fragments and across biogeographic barriers (Radespiel 2016). Metapopulation dynamics offers a method for determining the population viability of taxa that exist in a fragmented forest landscape. Put simply, a metapopulation is a group of spatially separated populations of the same species that interact via dispersal between fragments; thus, a knowledge of an organism's natural history (in particular dispersal ability) is vital (Hanski 1994). T. S. Steffens and Lehman (2018) investigated metapopulation dynamics in six lemur species (*Propithecus coquereli*, *M. murinus*, *M. ravelobensis*, *Lepilemur edwardsi*, *Cheirogaleus medius*, and *Eulemur fulvus*) within a fragmented forest landscape at Ankarafantsika. Of these species, only four (*M. murinus*, *M. ravelobensis*, *C. medius*, and *E. fulvus*) formed metapopulations. The associated models and simulations of future deforestation indicated that fragment area was the main determinant of survival for the four species forming metapopulations, while isolation had a lower and species-specific effect on survival.

The modeling of gene flow and determination of population genetic health allows researchers to assess whether isolation is negatively impacting lemur populations. Fragment isolation effects seem to have little impact on the genetic diversity of *M. ganzhorni* in fragmented forests of southern Madagascar, as gene flow is possible between isolated fragments (Montero et al. 2019). Research in the fragmented forests in northern Madagascar also found unexpectedly high levels of genetic diversity in *P. tattersalli* and *M. tavaratra*, despite the fragmented nature of their forest habitats (Aleixo-Pais et al. 2019; Quéméré et al. 2010a). Thus, fragment isolation effects seem to have a lower impact on lemur species than fragment area effects.

Lemur Responses to Edge Effects

Understanding how mammals respond to edge effects is crucial for conservation planning and for understanding their natural history in Madagascar. Studies of forest fragmentation consider two interrelated aspects of edge effects: small forest patches tend to have small population sizes and high extinction probabilities (MacArthur and Wilson 1967), and small patches also have a high ratio of fragment perimeter to area, resulting in a higher proportion of edge habitats in these patches (Gascon et al. 2000). The relative proportion of edge habitat will increase with any further reduction in the size or change in the shape of a forest patch (Malcolm et al. 2017). Consequently, small or narrow forest patches are composed predominantly of edge habitats with little or no interior habitat. If mammals are not able to respond to increasing edge effects, then they may become extirpated from small patches, or they may have to increase their movement and dispersal patterns between patches in a fragmented landscape (Ries et al. 2017). However, as the majority of Malagasy mammals covered in this review are thought to be forest-dependent, they have reduced ability to cross nonforested habitat.

Lemur responses to edge effects have been investigated either directly or as part of community ecology studies in Madagascar. Research specific to edge effects has focused largely on line-transect surveys for the purpose of modeling species abundance, distribution, and/or diversity; to a lesser extent, research on edge effects has addressed the behavioral ecology and population genetics of lemurs. Much of the initial research of edge effects on lemurs took place in the eastern and northern portions of the island. Based primarily on density estimates collected as part of line-transect surveys, five lemur species (*Avahi laniger*, *Eulemur rubriventer*, *Hapalemur griseus*, *Microcebus rufus*, and *Lepilemur edwardsi*) exhibited no spatial patterns of density in response to edge effects, but in edge habitats in Vohibola III forest in the southeast, *M. rufus* and *Propithecus edwardsi* showed higher densities (Lehman et al. 2006a). Conversely, the more frugivorous *Cheirogaleus major* and *E. rufifrons* avoided edge habitats in Vohibola III (Lehman et al. 2006b). Farris et al. (2019) studied habitat use in some of the same lemur species in Ranomafana, which is about 55 km south of the Vohibola III site worked by Lehman et al. (2006b). Although their sample sizes were low (6–12 observations per species), occupancy models indicated that only *P. edwardsi* showed a negative response to edge effects, with the detection probability increasing with distance from the forest edge. This variation between sites is difficult to explain with

ecological parameters alone but could be due to differences in human encroachment and associated activities like hunting, with edges acting as gateways to inaccessible forest habitat.

Other survey-based research in the Corridor Ankeniheny-Zahamena revealed that frugivorous *Varecia variegata* avoided edge habitats, whereas the more folivorous *Indri indri* had relatively more sightings nearer forest edges (Seaman et al. 2018). These interspecific differences in density estimates are thought to be associated with edge-related variations in food abundance and quality. Although there are few data on feeding ecology of lemurs in edge habitats, Irwin (2008) found that *P. diadema* in forest fragments preferred to feed on plants found at edge habitats, whereas conspecifics in nearby, continuous forests tended to avoid edges altogether. Another example has been observed at Ankarafantsika, where a major road bordering dry deciduous forest bisects the protected area. This forest road was found to operate as an edge, and thus limited road-crossing movements in female but not male *M. ravelobensis* (Ramsay et al. 2019). These patterns of edge responses in lemurs should, in theory, also influence their population dynamics and genetic diversity.

More recently, the application of genetics as a tool to determine population dynamics has been used to investigate the importance of edge effects in lemurs. Quéméré et al. (2010a) noted that patterns of genetic population clustering of *P. tattersalli* near forest edges suggested that it is capable of moving between isolated fragments in the Loky Manambato region in the north, a zone with considerable heterogeneity with regard to vegetation types and geological substrates. These interactions between edge effects and animal dispersal have until recently been a largely unstudied aspect of conservation genetics. In the first study of its kind in Madagascar, Radespiel et al. (2019b) genotyped, using seven nuclear microsatellites, *M. ravelobensis* in one edge and two interior habitats in close proximity to each other within a continuous forest region of Ankarafantsika. They found that overall genetic diversity—measured via allelic richness, heterozygosity, haplotype richness, and nucleotide diversity—was lower for *M. ravelobensis* in the edge habitat than in conspecifics in the two interior sites. Moreover, there was very little genetic exchange among the mouse lemurs occurring at the edge, 600 m from the edge, and in interior forest sites. Taken together, these results suggest that the mouse lemurs exhibited distinct habitat preferences and an unexpected level of genetic isolation, despite each of the trapping sites being only 500–1400 m apart and not separated by any obvious barriers to dispersal (e.g., no interior edges, forest clearings, roads, etc.). These results indicate that there is a molecular edge effect influencing *M. ravelobensis*. Thus, edge effects likely play a major role in determining the distribution and abundance of lemurs. However, the specific causative factors driving variations in these patterns have yet to be determined.

NON-LEMUR CONSERVATION BIOGEOGRAPHY AND FOREST FRAGMENTATION

While lemurs make up the majority of described mammal species in Madagascar, it is important to consider how other taxa are impacted by forest fragmentation. These animals interact with lemurs as potential competitors, predators, and prey but also contribute to the functioning of different ecosystems overall. While natural history research and ecological modeling of most non-lemur mammal species is lacking in Madagascar, in parallel to studies on forest fragmentation in lemurs, studies on the other mammals of Madagascar have found mixed effects of fragmentation. Below we examine the impact of fragmentation and edge effects specifically on non-lemur mammals.

Non-Lemur Responses to Fragmentation

Given the importance of habitat area in the distribution of lemur species, it stands to reason that this is also an important factor in the distribution of other species of mammals. Three protected areas in the northeast—Masoala, Marojejy, and Anjanaharibe-Sud—have been the centers of studies of small-mammal ecology, including those seeking to determine which factors, such as habitat characteristics, influence species diversity and distribution across the landscape. At Ambohitantely in central Madagascar, Goodman and Rakotondravony (2000) used pitfall trapping to determine that the number of Tenrecidae species declined with decreasing forest fragment area. In the Masoala-Makira protected area complex, Murphy et al. (2016) used camera trapping and habitat data to test various occupancy models for *Eliurus* rodents. They found that detection probabilities in these rodents were weakly related only to habitat patchiness—which can be seen as an indirect measure of forest fragmentation—but not with any of the other habitat covariates, including distance to nearest forest edge or other dendrometric measures. At two regions in the northwest, Andriatsitohaina et al. (2019) used live-trapping data to determine ecological fragmentation effects on *E. myoxinus*, finding that neither habitat size nor isolation affected the abundance of this species at two dry deciduous forest sites. Both Ganzhorn (2003), working in western dry forests, and Ramanamanjato and Ganzhorn (2001), in littoral dry forests, noted higher capture rates for *Eliurus* species in larger forest patches. Although species identification of *Eliurus* was difficult to determine in some of these studies, and elevation differences between the regions may impact the comparative results, taken as a whole, these data support the idea that different species of *Eliurus* may exhibit regional or even site-specific responses to forest fragmentation.

The best-studied species of the Malagasy carnivoran family, Eupleridae, with respect to habitat loss and fragmentation, is *Cryptoprocta ferox*. Density estimates for this species in the Kirindy Forest CNFEREF (Centre National de Formation, d'Etudes et de Recherche en Environnement et Foresterie) (C. E. Hawkins and Racey 2005) are higher than those reported in eastern Madagascar (Gerber et al. 2010) but still lower than what is predicted for tropical carnivorous mammals (C. E. Hawkins and Racey 2005). Research in both the moist evergreen forests and the dry deciduous forests suggests that *Cryptoprocta* is tolerant of habitat loss and can survive in human-modified landscapes, although low detection rates remain a methodological issue (Murphy et al. 2018; Wyza et al. 2020). This species is most likely impacted by secondary impacts of fragmentation such as encroachment of humans. For example, in Ankarafantsika National Park, respondents to interviews have reported killing *Cryptoprocta* for food and to protect livestock (Borgerson et al. 2019a).

Woolaver et al. (2006) found that another euplerid carnivoran, *Mungotictis decemlineata*, was found only in larger patches of dry deciduous forest but suggested this may be due to confounding anthropogenic factors, such as the presence of human hunters or dogs, rather than habitat area. Gerber et al. (2010) found that the species richness of native carnivores did not appear to be related to anthropogenic disturbance in continuous forest, in that density estimates were similar between continuous undisturbed and selectively logged areas. However, in a later, expanded study, Gerber et al. (2012a) found that although species richness of native carnivorans in moist evergreen forest was similar in continuous intact and selectively logged forest, the number of native species decreased in forest fragments. In contrast, species richness of introduced species showed the inverse relationship. Gerber et al. (2012a) also found that the probability of occupancy of the euplerid *Galidictis f. fasciata* increased with fragment area. They suggest that habitat loss and fragmentation synergistically interact to create a situation that has negative effects on native carnivoran occurrence but positive effects on the occurrence of introduced species. In the Masoala-Makira landscape, Farris et al. (2015c) found a similar relationship, noting that increased forest degradation resulted in decreased encounter rates and occupancy in euplerids, while introduced carnivoran species' occupancy and encounter rates increased.

Taken together, it seems likely that area is also an important factor for the abundance of some non-lemur mammal species, but in other species, data are inconclusive or forest area is not driving responses to habitat fragmentation. The cryptic nature of these species combined with low detection rates and methodological constraints further confuse the ability of researchers to draw firm conclusions. However, it is clear that differing natural histories of these diverse species is driving some of these differences in response to the impact of habitat fragmentation.

Non-Lemur Responses to Edge Effects

There are fewer studies of edge effects on non-lemur mammals in Madagascar, and most of these studies used distance to forest edge as a proxy for determining the depth and intensity of edge effects. At Ranomafana, Farris et al. (2017b) used occupancy models to study co-occurrence patterns in native and introduced carnivorans. They found that detection of dogs (*Canis lupus*) increased with distance from the forest edge within the park, whereas *Cryptoprocta ferox* had higher occupancy in degraded edge forest outside the park. They linked these patterns of edge effects to the spatial distribution of human-made trails in forests. Some species, such as the introduced *Viverricula indica* and the endemic *Galidia elegans*, make use of edge habitats, although doing so placed them under increased levels of hunting by people (Farris et al. 2015b). Thus, for these two species, expansion of edge habitats may result in a sort of increasing ecological trap, which happens when animals exploit habitats characterized by relatively low reproductive fitness compared to other habitats as a result of rapid environmental change (Hale and Swearer 2016).

Rodent responses to edge effects have been studied using a variety of ecological and isotopic methods. Andriatsitohaina et al. (2019) studied the endemic *Eliurus myoxinus* at a series of dry deciduous forest sites in the northwest to gain insight into this rat's response to forest edge. They found that this species had lower abundance in edge habitats compared to core habitats, similar to the introduced *R. rattus*, which appeared to prefer interior forests in Ankarafantsika and the Mariarano Forest. Using camera-trapping methods, Murphy et al. (2017b) examined local distribution of four endemic rodent species in two different genera (*Eliurus* spp. and *Nesomys* spp.) and two endemic tenrecs (*Setifer setosus* and *Tenrec ecaudatus*), in protected areas in the Masoala-Makira region. They found that of the four taxa, only in *Nesomys* did edge proximity have a negative impact on occupancy patterns. At Ambohitantely in the Central Highlands, Crowley et al. (2018) used stable isotopes to examine the ecology and dispersal patterns of *Eliurus* species, *R. rattus*, and *Mus musculus* in and near a large (1250 ha) forest fragment. They found that *Eliurus* species exploited forest interior and edge habitats, that *M. musculus* preferred marsh habitat and local human habitations, and that *R. rattus* was generally ubiquitous. Their data did not support regular movement of rodents between the forest edge and interior. In another study, this one at Ranomafana, the probability of the presence of *R. rattus* and *N. rufus* increased with decreasing distance from forest edge, whereas the distribution of *E. tanala* showed no response to the proximity of the forest edge (Lehtonen et al. 2001). Although once again taxonomic issues and methodological differences exist among the cited studies, as they did for fragmentation effects, the data do provide support to a hypothesis that *Eliurus* species and *R. rattus* have habitat responses to edge effects.

Interspecific Interactions

Non-lemur mammals have received relatively little attention in fragmentation research, but competition between mammals is an important area of research in Madagascar. Species in the genera *Eliurus*, *Rattus*, and *Microcebus* in particular have been studied for their interspecific interactions in response to deforestation and fragmentation in differing biogeographic regions on the island (Ramanamanjato and Ganzhorn 2001; Ganzhorn 2003; Muldoon and Goodman 2010; J.-E. Rakotoarisoa et al. 2013a, 2013b). Each of these mammals is nocturnal, relatively small-bodied compared to sympatric lemurs, and a largely solitary forager, making these taxa ideally suited to studies to determine whether they exhibit either a species-specific or regionally specific response to forest fragmentation. Using a combination of trapping and line-transect surveys, R. Rakotondravony and Radespiel (2009) documented a negative relationship between the abundance of *M. murinus* and that of *M. ravelobensis* in continuous forest in Ankarafantsika. Conversely, T. S. Steffens et al. (2016) used data from line-transect surveys and found a positive relationship for the same taxa in a fragmented forest landscape within the park. Using capture data, Andriatsitohaina et al. (2019) found no relationship between these two species in Ankarafantsika. These somewhat conflicting results showcase the complexity of studying interspecific interactions in fragmented and anthropogenic landscapes. While methodological differences (survey and trapping) could be leading to different results, it is also plausible that across the ecological gradient of Ankarafantsika, especially between highly fragmented and continuous forests, interspecific interactions change. Additionally, as forest fragmentation and human impacts on forests are both

dynamic processes, interactions between these species in this region may change over time.

In western dry deciduous forests, Ganzhorn (2003) and Andriatsitohaina et al. (2019) both found no significant relationship between the abundance of introduced *R. rattus* and endemic *E. myoxinus* and *Microcebus* species, suggesting that despite overlapping body sizes, ranges, and diets, introduced rodents are not a primary conservation concern in terms of Malagasy small mammals. At Bezà-Mahafaly, Youssouf Jacky and Rasoazanabary (2008) captured high numbers of introduced rodents (*M. musculus* and *R. rattus*) and very few endemic species (*E. myoxinus* and *Macrotarsomys bastardi*) in degraded riparian forest habitats. However, neither introduced nor endemic rodents were captured inside nearby dry spiny thicket habitat, suggesting habitat preference was a more important factor than competition. *Rattus rattus* has the potential to transmit diseases and parasites to endemic wildlife, especially in human-disturbed forests (Ehlers et al. 2019), although habitat fragmentation can also lead to a decrease in ectoparastic infection (Kiene et al. 2020). The degree to which *R. rattus* has had an ecological impact on endemic mammals in Madagascar remains an open question.

SUMMARY

In this contribution, we sought to update information presented in Ganzhorn et al. (2003) with regard to the effects of forest loss and fragmentation on nonvolant mammals. Since the original contribution was published, deforestation has accelerated on Madagascar, producing a landscape of tracts of continuous forest surrounded by fragments of varying sizes. Climate change will further reduce the size and extent of forest habitats on the island, placing considerable pressure on mammals that prefer or are dependent on forests rather than nonforest matrix or grasslands. These predictions are only for moist evergreen forests, as no extensive comparable data exist for other forest formations on the island. Irrespective of these gaps, all remaining natural forest types are suffering from ongoing and accelerating fragmentation, reduction of forest-block size, and increased edge effects. Many nonvolant mammals of Madagascar are threatened with extinction (IUCN 2020).

We found convincing evidence for species-area relationships as an effective model for determining lemur species diversity in the fragmented forest landscapes of Madagascar. Although there is considerably less comparable data for non-lemur mammals, available information indicates that the diversity of many small mammals and carnivorans is higher in larger forested areas, with notable exceptions. However, we also documented considerable variations in intraspecific responses of nonvolant mammals to forest fragmentation and loss as well as edge effects. These differences are driven by underlying ecological differences between organisms such as feeding ecology, dispersal, and life history, which highlights the need to understand an organism's natural history in the context of forest loss and fragmentation.

FUTURE DIRECTIONS

Given that deforestation is ongoing and the underlying factors contributing to deforestation are not improving (J. P. G. Jones et al. 2019), research will no doubt continue in the fragmented landscapes of Madagascar. Based on the research presented in this contribution, we see several important future directions for research on forest fragmentation in Madagascar: greater use of landscape-level studies, more basic research on non-lemur animals, and the integration of anthropogenic and ecological data into models of fragmentation.

The high regional variability in mammalian responses to fragmentation makes it crucial that more studies investigate fragmentation at the landscape level and investigate biases in methodology that might be impacting comparability between studies. The majority of fragmentation studies in Madagascar are occurring at the patch level or across a single or small number of landscapes (Kling et al. 2020). A landscape-level approach examines fragmentation across multiple landscapes, using the landscape, not the patch, as the unit of analysis (Fahrig 2003). Fragmentation is a landscape-level process, and in order to answer ecological and conservation questions, we must examine these questions at the appropriate scale.

Central to the feasibility of landscape-level modeling is the need for high-quality basic natural history data. As presented above, the mammals of Madagascar can respond to fragmentation in positive, negative, and neutral ways. Yet, in many Malagasy mammalian species, especially non-lemurs, we are missing vital natural history data such as dispersal, diet, or reproductive behavior. This leads to a lack of predictive power in quantitative analyses and thus a lack of useful conservation outcomes from fragmentation research. In order to determine the impacts of fragmentation on communities of mammals, these basic data need to be reliably collected for all members of communities in given landscapes.

Lastly, integration of anthropological data is crucial for ecological models on the impacts of fragmentation on Malagasy animals, especially if these models are being used to inform conservation. Researchers need to incorporate the unique anthropological and economic factors (e.g., taboo [*fady*], immigration, socioeconomic status) in Madagascar, which will greatly improve their analyses of fragmentation. Those researchers working on fragmentation research need to find innovative ways to incorporate these different types of data, which will require collaboration between social and natural scientists and crucially collaboration with Malagasy scientists.

Subject editors: Jörg U. Ganzhorn and Steven M. Goodman

NON-NATIVE HABITAT USE BY ENDEMIC TERRESTRIAL MALAGASY MAMMALS

T. M. Eppley and S. M. Goodman

It has been estimated that approximately 1200 introduced vascular plant species exist on Madagascar (Kull et al. 2012), compared to the conservative approximation of 11,220 native vascular plants (Callmander et al. 2011). Though 8.9% of these—slightly more than 100 species—are considered invasive (Kull et al. 2014), many introduced plants constitute elements of habitat and food resources for endemic animals, and in some cases the plants are used by local people; according to Gérard et al. (2015), 100 endemic vertebrate species on Madagascar have been identified as using introduced plant species.

Since 1953, approximately 44% of Madagascar's forest cover was lost, and 46% of remaining forest habitat is less than 100 m from a forest edge (Vieilledent et al. 2018). Further, numerous forest-dependent land vertebrates, including 95% of lemur species (C. Schwitzer et al. 2014), are threatened with extinction, and as their natural habitats disappear, degraded areas are often (at least initially) colonized by introduced plant species, some of them invasive (Kull et al. 2013). As such, it is important to understand the role of introduced plants and associated habitats, as well as agroecosystems, in lemur and other endemic mammal survival. The purpose of this contribution is to summarize what is known about endemic Malagasy nonvolant mammals, specifically lemurs, tenrecs, and nesomyine rodents, using non-native habitats, which includes what we consider anthropogenic grasslands and degraded formerly forested areas.

ORDER PRIMATES

Families Cheirogaleidae, Lepilemuridae, Lemuridae, Indriidae, and Daubentoniidae

There are an estimated 108 recognized lemur species, all endemic to Madagascar (see Goodman and Soarimalala, pp. 1737–69), many of which occupy and utilize a variety of different habitat types. Given the widespread diversity of both lemur and introduced plant species, we examine herein lemur use of these non-native habitats.

In terms of cash-crop plantations, it was recently confirmed that a number of lemur species utilize *Theobroma cacao* (Cacao) plantations, at least occasionally, near Ambanja (Webber et al. 2020). These plantations are grown under both native and introduced shade trees, which commonly include introduced *Albizia* species (silk trees), *Artocarpus heterophyllus* (Jackfruit), and *Cananga odorata* (Ylang-ylang). Among the lemur species recorded in these plantations are *Lepilemur dorsalis* (Gray's Sportive Lemur), *Mirza zaza* (Northern Giant Mouse Lemur), *Phaner parienti* (Sambirano Fork-marked Lemur), *Microcebus* species (mouse lemurs), and *Cheirogaleus* species (dwarf lemurs). There were also local reports mentioned in the Webber et al. (2020) study of *Eulemur macaco* (Black Lemur) and *Hapalemur* species (bamboo lemurs) moving through this non-native woody plant habitat, though the authors were unable to confirm this.

Cash-crop plantations are becoming more common throughout eastern Madagascar, where many lemur species have also been observed in plantations of *Vanilla planifolia* (Bourbon Vanilla), including *E. coronatus* (Crowned Lemur), *M. tavaratra* (Tavaratra Mouse Lemur), *C. shethi* (Ankarana Dwarf Lemur), *C. crossleyi* (Crossley's Dwarf Lemur), and *C. major* (Greater Dwarf Lemur) (Hending et al. 2018). These plantations are often within a few hundred meters of, or sometimes within, native forest fragments, thus possibly acting as corridors and forest habitat extensions. Similarly, shade-grown *Coffea* (coffee) plantations, which often mix native and introduced plant species, have been shown to provide habitat for *M. rufus* (Rufous Mouse Lemur; Deppe et al. 2007) and *Prolemur simus* (Greater Bamboo Lemur; P. C. Wright et al. 2008).

Other agricultural areas, especially those in close proximity to native forest, are well known to provide habitat to several lemur species. Degraded forests dominated by *Mangifera indica* (Mango) in different portions of the island are frequently inhabited by lemurs, including *Cheirogaleus major* (J.-J. Petter et al. 1977), *Mirza coquereli* (Coquerel's Giant Mouse Lemur; Kappeler 2003), *Lepilemur edwardsi* (Milne-Edwards' Sportive Lemur; Ganzhorn 1987), *Daubentonia madagascariensis* (Aye-aye; J.-J. Petter et al. 1977), *Propithecus coquereli* (Coquerel's Sifaka; Ganzhorn and Abraham 1991), and *P. edwardsi* (Milne-Edwards' Sifaka; Lehman and Mayor 2004). *Litchi chinensis* (Lychee) has been recorded as habitat for *Microcebus rufus* (Deppe et al. 2007), *C. major* (J.-J. Petter et al. 1977), and *D. madagascariensis* (J.-J. Petter et al. 1977), and noted as frequently visited by *Eulemur collaris* (Red-collared Brown Lemur) along the periphery of native forest (Eppley et al. 2017b). *Eulemur rubriventer* (Red-bellied Lemur) and *Hapalemur griseus* (Gray Bamboo Lemur) have been observed utilizing habitat largely consisting of *Psidium cattleyanum* (Strawberry Guava) in degraded forested areas of Ranomafana National Park (Overdorff 1988; Grassi 2006), while *E. collaris* often utilizes this introduced species in the southeast (Eppley et al. 2017b).

Among other recorded non-native habitat–lemur associations, unspecified citrus trees can provide habitat to *M. rufus* in the southeast near Ranomafana (Deppe et al. 2007), while the introduced *Syzygium aromaticum* (Clove) is used as a regular nesting site by *M. rufus* (J.-J. Petter et al. 1977). Heavily degraded forest dominated by *Anacardium occidentale* (Cashew) in the west is utilized regularly by *Mirza coquereli* (Kappeler 2003). Both *Cocos nucifera* (Coconut) and *Terminalia catappa* (Indian Almond) are occasionally used as nest-site habitat by *D. madagascariensis* (J.-J. Petter et al. 1977). In agricultural fields adjacent to Masoala National Park, both *Miconia crenata* (Soapbush, previously known as *Clidemia hirta*) and *Oryza sativa* (rice) are utilized by *H. occidentalis*

(Western Bamboo Lemur; Martinez 2008). In the southwest, cultivated crop habitat of *Ipomoea batatas* (Sweet Potato) is heavily relied upon by *Lemur catta* (Ring-tailed Lemur; LaFleur and Gould 2009). *Tamarindus indica* (Tamarind) has been recorded as a reputed habitat for *Propithecus verreauxi* (Verreaux's Sifaka; Yamashita 2002) and extensively recorded being used by populations of *L. catta* in the riparian forests of Bezà-Mahafaly (L. Gould et al. 2011) and Berenty (Mertl-Millhollen et al. 2011). *Tamarindus* does not have any invasive properties, and recent phylogeographic studies across its tropical range indicate that it is probably native to Madagascar (Diallo et al. 2007).

Timber plantations occur in different areas of the island and, despite being utilitarian, are well known to provide vertical structure, enabling many lemur species to travel arboreally more easily. Among the most widespread timber trees are species of *Eucalyptus* (Gérard et al. 2015). In the dry west near Kirindy Forest CNFEREF (Centre National de Formation, d'Etudes et de Recherche en Environnement et Foresterie), *Eucalyptus* has been observed to provide habitat for *Microcebus murinus* (Gray Mouse Lemur), *Cheirogaleus major*, *Mirza coquereli*, and *Phaner pallescens* (Pale Fork-marked Lemur; Ganzhorn et al. 1999a; Ganzhorn 2003). In the north, *Eucalyptus* plantations have been inhabited by *Microcebus arnholdi* (Montagne d'Ambre Mouse Lemur), *C. andysabini* (Sabin's Dwarf Lemur), *P. electromontis* (Montagne d'Ambre Fork-marked Lemur), and *E. sanfordi* (Sanford's Brown Lemur) (Ganzhorn et al. 1997). In the central east, these introduced plantations were used by *Lepilemur mustelinus* (Weasel Sportive Lemur; Ganzhorn 1988), *Avahi laniger* (Eastern Woolly Lemur; Ganzhorn 1987), *E. rubriventer* (Overdorff 1988), and *Indri indri* (Indri; Ganzhorn 1987), while in the southeast they were used by *A. meridionalis* (Southern Woolly Lemur; Scobie et al. 2017). Old, sometimes abandoned *Eucalyptus* plantations often have an understory overgrown with other introduced plants, including *Miconia crenata* and *Lantana camara*, which are utilized by *M. lehilahytsara* (Goodman's Mouse Lemur), *Cheirogaleus major*, *E. fulvus* (Brown Lemur), and *H. griseus*. These plantations occasionally have an understory dominated by introduced *Bambusa* (bamboo) species, utilized by both *H. griseus* and *C. major* (Ganzhorn 1987).

Similar plantations consist of *Acacia* species and *Cassia siamea*, which are used by *M. murinus*, *M. rufus*, *Mirza coquereli*, and *P. pallescens* (Ganzhorn et al. 1999a; Ganzhorn 2003). Corridors of *A. mangium* are used by *Microcebus ganzhorni* (Ganzhorn's Mouse Lemur) to travel between littoral forest fragments in the southeast (Andriamandimbiarisoa et al. 2015). Plantations of *Araucaria araucana* (Monkey Puzzle Tree) provide habitat for *Cheirogaleus andysabini*, *P. electromontis*, *E. coronatus*, and *E. sanfordi* (Ganzhorn et al. 1997).

Additional introduced utilitarian trees that provide potential habitat for lemurs include *Aucoumea klaineana* (Okoumé), used by *Avahi laniger* near littoral forests in the central east (Ratsirarson and Ranaivonasy 2002); and *Ceiba pentandra* (Kapok), the flowers and fruits of which provide >80% of the diet of *E. mongoz* (Mongoose Lemur), as reported by J.-J. Petter et al. (1977). At Manombo, in the southeast, *Varecia variegata* (Black and White Ruffed Lemur) was recorded to heavily rely on two introduced and invasive plant species, *Cecropia peltata* (Trumpet Tree) and *Miconia crenata* (Ratsimbazafy et al. 2002).

In the southeast, *Melaleuca quinquenervia* (Broad-leaved Paperbark Tree) has invaded many wetland areas along the coast. Though invasive, this tree is harvested for timber by local people. The littoral forests within this region are highly fragmented, and *Melaleuca* provides both structural habitat, which certain lemurs use as corridors to travel between fragments, and occasional food, specifically the tree's fragrant flowers (Figure 14.18). Among the species that have been observed utilizing *M. quinquenervia* are *Microcebus ganzhorni*, *Cheirogaleus medius* (Fat-tailed Dwarf Lemur), *A. meridionalis*, *E. collaris*, and *Hapalemur meridionalis* (Southern Bamboo Lemur) (Bollen 2003; Eppley et al. 2015a). Additionally, the introduced grass *Stenotaphrum dimidiatum* grows well in partially exposed areas within *Melaleuca* woodlands and forms a foraging habitat frequently used by *H. meridionalis* (Eppley et al. 2017b).

Another introduced plant, *Argemone mexicana* (Mexican Poppy), is heavily utilized by *Lemur catta* in and around Bezà-Mahafaly in the southwest and can constitute a large portion of this animal's annual diet, especially during drought (LaFleur and Gould 2009).

ORDER RODENTIA

Family Nesomyidae

A few species of rodents belonging to the endemic subfamily Nesomyinae, most of which are considered forest-dependent, have been documented in different types of introduced or non-natural

FIGURE 14.18 ***Hapalemur meridionalis*** **(Southern Bamboo Lemur) foraging on flowers of the introduced tree** ***Melaleuca quinquenervia*** **in the Mandena littoral forest, southeast Madagascar.** (PHOTO by T. M. Eppley.)

plant habitats. Two different nesomyine species have been found in fallow rice fields in close proximity to relatively intact moist evergreen forest near Ranomafana National Park and the corridor linking this site to Andringitra National Park: *Nesomys rufus* (Eastern Red Forest Rat) and *Brachyuromys betsileoensis* (Lesser Short-tailed Rat; Jansa and Carleton 2003a; S. M. Goodman and V. Soarimalala, unpublished data). In the region of Moramanga, at a site about 12 km from the nearest natural moist evergreen forest block, Randriamoria et al. (2015) found *B. betsileoensis* in an area of grassland in close vicinity to a dispersed planting of *Pinus* and a recently harvested rice field. Among the nesomyine rodents, this species is exceptional in that it lives in non-native forest formations and has also been documented in marsh areas of the east and montane ericoid thicket.

In heavily degraded littoral forest of the lowlands of the central east, D. Rakotondravony et al. (1998a) found *Eliurus webbi* (Webb's Tufted-tail Rat) associated with a plantation of *Aucoumea klaineana* in close proximity to natural forest. In northern Madagascar, around the medium-altitude moist evergreen forest of Montagne d'Ambre, *E. minor* (Lesser Tufted-tail Rat) has been associated with *Eucalyptus* plantations (Goodman et al. 1997a). Highly degraded monocultures of *Ziziphus mauritiana* (Indian Jujube) bordering partially disturbed dry deciduous forest in the central west are used as habitat by tufted-tail rats (*Eliurus* sp.; Ganzhorn 2003). In an area of montane forest on the Ankaratra Massif that is reputed to be replanted with native *Weinmannia* trees and includes numerous introduced and invasive plant species dominated by *Pinus*, the nesomyine rodent *Monticolomys koopmani* (Koopman's Mountain-dwelling Mouse) was trapped in largely non-native woody vegetation (Goodman et al. 1996a).

ORDER AFROSORICIDA

Family Tenrecidae

Members of this family compose three different subfamilies: Oryzorictinae, which is largely forest-dependent, and Tenrecinae and Geogalinae, which occur in natural forest, degraded formations, and grassland habitats. In the case of the Tenrecinae, numerous documented cases record its members' occurrence outside natural forest formations (Deppe et al. 2007; Soarimalala and Goodman 2011), and this subfamily is not discussed here.

One rather exceptional oryzorictine is the aquatic *Microgale mergulus* (Web-footed Shrew Tenrec; formerly placed in the genus *Limnogale*), known to occur in streams and small rivers passing through areas outside natural moist evergreen forests, including *Pinus* plantations (Benstead and Olson 2003). *Oryzorictes hova* (Hova Mole Tenrec) is found in rice fields and open marshy habitats as well as natural forest formations, while *O. tetradactylus* (Four-toed Mole Tenrec) is found in native montane ericoid thicket above forest line (Goodman 2003a).

Over the past decades, much of the field research on Malagasy small mammals has focused on natural forest habitats and to a large extent has not provided insight into members of this family, particularly Oryzorictinae, occurring outside these formations. Recent work by Randriamoria et al. (2015), however, affords new insights into species that are not necessarily forest-dependent. At different trapping localities in the Moramanga District, the authors found five species of shrew tenrecs of the genus *Microgale* occurring outside natural moist evergreen forest. An individual of *M. cowani* (Cowan's Shrew Tenrec) was found in an area dominated by sugarcane, bananas, and the introduced *Lantana camara*, and another individual in herbaceous vegetation in close proximity to a rice field; the maximum straight-line distance of these trapping localities to natural forest was less than 500 m. Two individuals of *M. majori* (Major's Long-tailed Shrew Tenrec) were trapped in *savoka* (regenerating humid forest habitat) dominated by Asteraceae (*Psiadia altissima* and *Helichrysum cirrhosum*) and other non-native vegetation, including *L. camara*. Other individuals of this species were trapped in plantations of introduced *Eucalyptus*. The direct distance between sites where these animals were trapped and native forest was 775 m to 3 km. Another species, *M. pusilla* (Least Shrew Tenrec), which was previously known to occur in marsh areas outside of natural forest (Soarimalala and Goodman 2011), was trapped in a variety of settings: near a rice field, in areas of *savoka* with *L. camara*, *Psidium cattleyanum*, *Psiadia altissima*, and *H. cirrhosum*. The last shrew tenrec captured outside the forest by Randriamoria et al. (2015) was *M. thomasi* (Thomas's Shrew Tenrec), which was in *savoka* dominated by *Psidium cattleyanum* and *L. camara*, and the site was about 100 m from natural forest.

In an area of medium-altitude moist evergreen forest on the Ankaratra Massif reputedly replanted with *Weinmannia* and numerous introduced plant species, some of them invasive, dominated by *Pinus*, the shrew tenrec *M. thomasi* was captured in largely non-native woody vegetation (Goodman et al. 1996a). At another site in the Central Highlands, in this case Ankazomivady, *M. cowani* was found in secondary grasslands about 100 m from a native medium-altitude moist evergreen forest fragment (S. M. Goodman and V. Soarimalala, unpublished data). This species, like some other members of this genus, is also known from natural montane ericoid thicket above forest line on different massifs, such as Marojejy and Andringitra, confirming that it is not strictly forest-dependent (Langrand and Goodman 1997; Goodman and Jenkins 2000).

Remarkably little is known about the natural history of the Geogalinae, specifically *Geogale aurita* (Large-eared Tenrec), which is reputed to show a marked preference for termites (Stephenson 2003). A survey near Ampoza of the organisms occurring in what is presumed to be secondary grasslands found *G. aurita* in areas of secondary grasslands and at the grasslands–dry spiny thicket ecotone (Tingle et al. 2003).

CONCLUSION

Though it is difficult to measure the contribution of introduced and invasive plant species to habitats used by Malagasy native nonvolant mammals, it would appear that in some cases, under specific conditions at certain sites, these plants play an important role (Gérard et al. 2015). Although the ultimate survival of all forest-dwelling mammal species, which has been extensively discussed in the literature for lemurs, should be considered precarious because of a multitude of anthropogenic and climatic pressures (C. Schwitzer et al. 2014), the observations that certain lemur and other small mammal

species are able to cope with some habitat degradation should be seen as positive. However, it is important to underline that in most cases, sites with non-native habitat where these mammal species have been found are in close proximity to native forest, which in virtually all cases serve as the critical corridor or buffer zone to allow the dispersal of certain mammal species into the non-native formations. We suspect that if the native blocks are severely degraded or disappear, this system will break down, and for largely forest-dependent mammal species, the non-native plant areas will no longer serve as critical habitat for their continued existence.

Subject editors: Jörg U. Ganzhorn and Steven M. Goodman

PHYLOGENETIC OVERVIEW OF THE LEMURIFORMES

A. D. Yoder

It is astonishing to reflect upon how much has changed in phylogenetic methods and theory since this contribution was written for the precursor of this book close to 20 years ago (A. D. Yoder 2003). Leading up to that time, the subject of lemuriform origins was considered controversial. The most essential aspect of this controversy was the question of whether or not lemurs constitute a clade. Early in the period of phylogenetic systematic investigation, a number of researchers focused on morphological characters of the basicranium, concluding that certain unusual aspects of the arterial and bony morphology shared by Malagasy dwarf lemurs (Cheirogaleidae) and Afro-Asian lorises indicate a cladistic relationship between the two that excludes other Malagasy lemurs (Szalay and Katz 1973; Cartmill 1975). Because cheirogaleids and lorisiforms share certain characteristics of carotid circulation and related cranial morphology that are unique within living and known fossil primates, these authorities concluded that lorises and dwarf lemurs form a clade that excludes the remaining Malagasy primates. There is no doubt that the lorisiforms are the closest relatives of the Malagasy lemuriforms, and that the two groups together form the suborder Strepsirrhini (i.e., the tooth-combed primates), but the idea that lorisiforms and cheirogaleids share a relationship that excludes other lemurs was initially considered a radical departure from traditional thinking. The phylogenetic position of *Daubentonia madagascariensis* (Aye-aye) (see Sterling et al., pp. 1975–78) was also considered problematic. Its bizarre morphology and unusual ecological specializations made phylogenetic placement based on morphology within the Strepsirrhini very difficult, and consequently at least two mutually exclusive hypotheses were proposed in the literature. Various authors considered *Daubentonia* to be either a specialized indriid (J. H. Schwartz and Tattersall 1985) or the monotypic sister group to all remaining strepsirrhines (Groves 1989). Conversely, molecular phylogenetic hypotheses were nearly unanimous in finding that living Malagasy primates constitute a clade (Dene et al. 1976; A. D. Yoder 1994; Porter et al. 1995).

Subsequent investigation of this question using phylogenomic methods has served to confirm and strengthen these early molecular phylogenetic studies, finding that all living Malagasy nonhuman primates, including the Aye-aye, constitute a clade with strong statistical support (DelPero et al. 2006; Horvath et al. 2008; dos Reis et al. 2018). Fantastically, the same revolutions in genomic technologies have allowed for the inclusion of the subfossil lemurs (see Godfrey and Jungers, pp. 1824–28) in phylogenetic analysis, conclusively finding that they are members of the same clade as the living lemurs (K. P. Karanth et al. 2005; Kistler et al. 2015), with a single colonization of Madagascar occurring sometime in the early Cenozoic (A. D. Yoder et al. 1996b; dos Reis et al. 2018; Figure 14.19). One important implication of this phylogenetic result that we emphasize here is that the spectacular array of lemuriform morphologies, behaviors, ecotypes, and physiologies all derive from a single ancestral primate type that colonized Madagascar via overwater dispersal. And as implausible as this colonization may seem, given the rigors of an assumed transoceanic dispersal event from Africa to Madagascar, recent and sophisticated climatological models that have reconstructed the likely direction and magnitude of Indian Ocean currents have provided credible mechanisms by which early strepsirrhines (and other terrestrial Malagasy vertebrates) could have been relatively rapidly transported from the west to the east across the Mozambique Channel (Ali and Huber 2010; see Samonds et al., pp. 73–78). Further, if patterns observed in the present, as described by Krause et al. (pp. 59–68), were also true for the early Cenozoic, ancestral lemurs might easily have been transported on large island rafts torn from the riverbanks of eastern Africa, perhaps aided by metabolic mechanisms of "emergency" torpor (Kappeler 2000a).

The only subsequent kink in this otherwise consistent story of lemur origins can be found in a recent reanalysis of the 20-million-year-old fossil primate *Propotto* from Africa (Gunnell et al. 2018). Based on a variety of morphological characteristics, the authors concluded that *Propotto* was actually a basal Aye-aye, implying that there were two rather than one lemuriform dispersal event from Africa to Madagascar. Given that essentially *all* published molecular-phylogenetic studies have identified *Daubentonia* as the basal-most lineage in the lemuriform radiation (e.g., Horvath et al. 2008; Matsui et al. 2009; dos Reis et al. 2018), this conclusion not only upends the idea that nonhuman Malagasy primates constitute a clade, it also has profound implications for the geological age of the radiation. If the early Miocene *Propotto* was indeed an ancestral

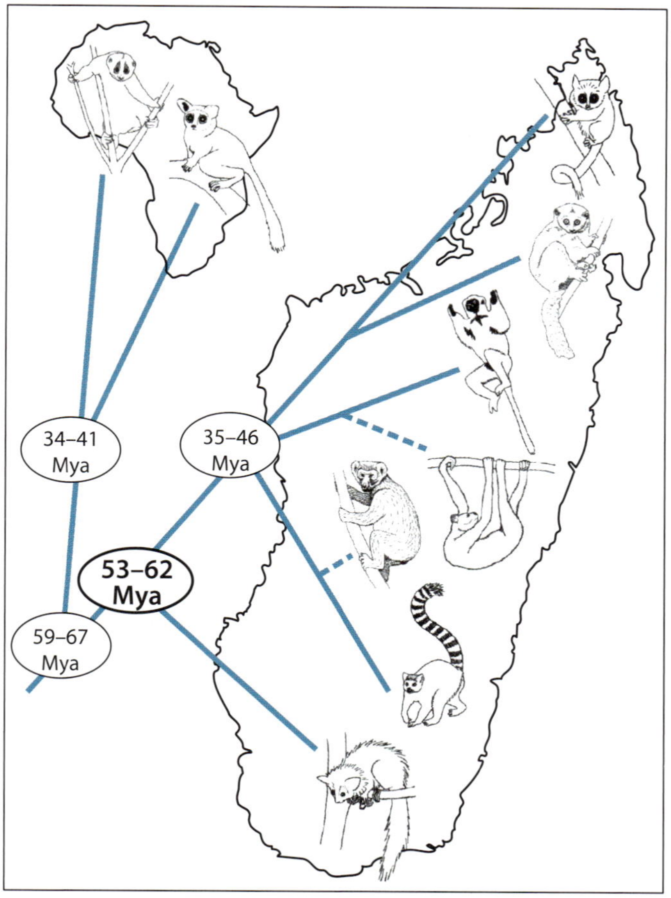

FIGURE 14.19 **Schematic phylogeny depicting single origin of Malagasy primates. Ancestral lemur is estimated to have colonized Madagascar sometime between 53 and 62 million years ago (Mya) (dos Reis et al. 2018). All phylogenomic studies agree that *Daubentonia* is the basal taxon in lemuriform phylogeny and that genus *Lepilemur* (family Lepilemuridae) is the sister lineage to the mouse and dwarf lemur clade (family Cheirogaleidae). Otherwise, there is a general lack of consensus regarding the phylogenetic relationships among the Indriidae, Lemuridae, and Cheirogaleidae plus *Lepilemur* lineages (see text for details).**

Daubentonia, this would suggest a far more recent colonization of lemurs to Madagascar—implying that lemurs did not arrive in Madagascar until about 20 million years ago (Mya). In this author's view, this seems highly unlikely given, that the divergence age of the lorisiform clade has been demonstrably shown with fossil data to be about 40 Mya (Seiffert et al. 2003). As shown in Figure 14.19, the age of the ancestral lorisiform radiation is roughly equivalent to the secondary radiation of the lemuriform clade, which in turn is considerably more recent than the inferred age of the *Daubentonia* lineage from other lemurs. Thus, the conclusions of Gunnell et al. (2018)—fascinating as they are—are in fundamental conflict with both phylogenomic patterns and the fossil calibrations from the lorisiform clade. Instead, the skeleton phylogeny depicted in Figure 14.19 continues to provide an essential framework for comparative evolutionary studies of lemurs, representing a spectacular array of primate diversity.

TAXONOMIC PROLIFERATION AND FAMILY-LEVEL PHYLOGENETICS

One of the most remarkable developments in the area of lemuriform systematics has come in the form of a massive expansion in the number of recognized species (see Goodman and Soarimalala, pp. 1937–69; Table 14.1). Since the previous contribution on lemur phylogeny (A. D. Yoder 2003), there have been, as of April 2020, at least 48 new species named, and astonishingly, all but one of these belongs to a nocturnal lineage. Why is this so?

The answer is not absolute, and though related to the phylogenomics revolution of the past decade, the explanation is multifaceted. First, the extreme bias toward nocturnal species must relate to the fact that the depth of their respective evolutionary divergence as measured by external morphological characters, which was the basis of early taxonomic work on this group, is largely obscured to human eyes. Whereas diurnal species tend to advertise their evolutionary diversity via differences in coloration as a mechanism for mate recognition (e.g., sifaka populations [genus *Propithecus*; see Lawler and Richard, pp. 1771–74], show distinct color patterns that correlate with their disjunct geographic distributions), the same is not true for nocturnal species. Within their respective clades, dwarf lemurs (*Cheirogaleus*; see Blanco, pp. 1922–26), mouse lemurs (*Microcebus*; see Kappeler et al., pp. 1927–32), sportive lemurs (*Lepilemur*; see Radespiel et al., pp. 1935–40), and woolly lemurs (*Avahi*; see Donati et al., pp. 1963–66) tend to look essentially the same, regardless of where they are geographically distributed; in other words, they are regarded as being morphologically "cryptic." It is only via the mechanism of genetic testing that the depth of their evolutionary relationships can be readily revealed. Thus, a combination of expanded geographic and population sampling, paired with genetic characterization, has led to a bonanza of taxonomic advances. There are differing opinions as to the validity of this approach, with some authors cautioning that genetic data alone, and not meeting certain specifications, are insufficient for the delineation of new species (Tattersall 2007; Markolf et al. 2011; Tattersall and Cuozzo, 2018). This cautionary advice is being increasingly adopted, with some investigators advocating an integrated taxonomy approach that combines genetic data with phenotypic, ecological, and geographic information (e.g., Zimmermann and Radespiel 2014).

A considerable portion of the taxonomic expansion described above has focused on the *Microcebus* clade (for an overview, see Kappeler et al., pp. 1927–32). Similarly, there has been an extraordinary proliferation of species designations within the genus *Lepilemur*, with no fewer than 18 species recognized since 2006 (see Radespiel et al., pp. 1935–40), up from eight recognized species before the work of Andriaholinirina et al. (2006). Accordingly, numerous studies have focused on relationships within four of the five primary lemuriform lineages, currently described as families (the family Daubentoniidae is at present monotypic, containing only one living species, *Daubentonia madagascariensis*). Prior to 2003, the bulk of this work had concentrated on the diurnal family Lemuridae (e.g., Crovella et al. 1993; Pastorini et al. 2002). Subsequently, there has been more intensive investigation of the Indriidae (Rumpler et al. 2011; Brenneman et al. 2016), Lepilemuridae (Andriaholinirina et al. 2006; Rumpler et al. 2008; Lei et al. 2017), and Cheirogaleidae (Rasoloarison et al. 2013; Setash et al. 2017; Sgarlata et al. 2019).

Figure 14.20 illustrates an overview of intrafamily-level phylogenomic resolution. The study from which these phylogenies are taken (dos Reis et al. 2018) is currently the most comprehensive phylogenomic analysis undertaken for lemurs (and other primates), and as such, it has merit for illuminating the relationships among species and clades. Even so, it should be interpreted with some caution, and I urge the reader to also take into account any notable disagreements with the molecular phylogenetic studies summarized above. Despite the undoubted power of phylogenomics to resolve the evolutionary relationships among lemurs and other organisms, the intricacies of genomic evolution combined with the complexities of computational analysis still leave room for conflicting results and nuanced interpretation (L. Liu et al. 2017; Leache et al. 2019).

RECONSIDERING ECOLOGICAL BARRIERS

By virtue of the historical perspective provided by molecular phylogenetic analysis, such studies can go beyond the limited testing of taxonomic boundaries and potentially reveal the impact (or lack thereof) of ecological barriers for promoting and maintaining species diversity. As we initially discovered in a first foray into examining species boundaries in mouse lemurs (A. D. Yoder et al. 2000),

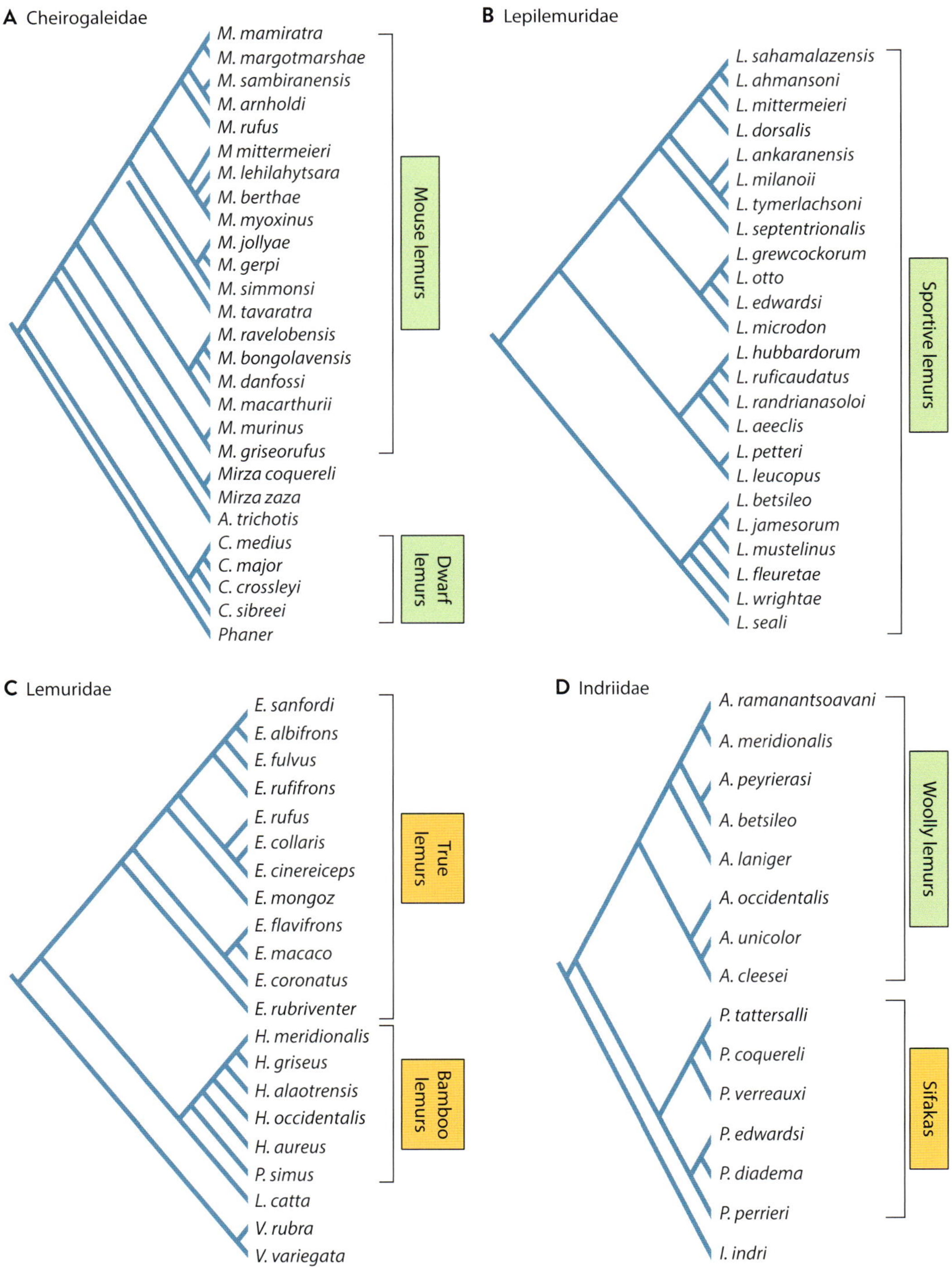

FIGURE 14.20
Phylogenetic summaries of intrafamilial relationships within A) Cheirogaleidae (*top to bottom*: *Microcebus*, *Mirza*, *Allocebus*, *Cheirogaleus*, *Phaner*), B) Lepilemuridae (*Lepilemur*), C) Lemuridae (*Eulemur*, *Hapalemur*, *Prolemur*, *Lemur*, *Varecia*), and D) Indriidae (*Avahi*, *Propithecus*, *Indri*). Nocturnal groups are highlighted in gray, and diurnal species in yellow. Phylogenetic relationships are depicted as they were resolved in dos Reis et al. (2018). That study is based on a data set of 372 taxa (367 primates and 5 outgroups, 3.4 million aligned base pairs) that includes nine primate genomes, and as such, might be considered to be quasi-definitive. That said, there are at least a few questionable placements of species within the phylogeny (e.g., the position of *Microcebus murinus* in the mouse lemur clade), and it should therefore be considered with at least some degree of uncertainty.

the assumption that eastern *Microcebus rufus* would be the sister group to all the western species under investigation was completely overturned. Prior taxonomy had recognized a single moist-evergreen-forest-adapted species in the east, *M. rufus*, and a dry-adapted species in the west, *M. murinus* (R. D. Martin 1972a). Thus, in many people's minds—certainly my own—the ecological conditions of the east and west would have imposed constraints on mouse lemur distributions that would have been reflected in their phylogenetic history. Instead, it turned out that the two eastern moist-evergreen-forest populations in our study (one from Ranomafana and one from Tampolo) nested within the western radiation. This implied that the previously assumed ecological and biogeographic divide between eastern wet-adapted and western dry-adapted populations did not follow the evolutionary history of the genus based on phylogenetic inference. Instead, it appeared that the fundamental geographic split within the mouse lemur clade was between northern and southern clades, with the biogeographic barrier separating them corresponding to the Tsiribihina River (A. D. Yoder et al. 2000: Figure 4).

Much progress has been made in the intervening years toward understanding the role that Madagascar's major rivers have played in driving and maintaining species diversity within the lemuriforms. Notably, Pastorini et al. (2003), following on the seminal paper by R. D. Martin (1972b), explored the extent to which rivers serve to define the regions of endemism and boundaries among and between lemur species, finding that whereas some rivers do (e.g., the Tsiribihina and the Betsiboka), others do not (e.g., the Mahavavy). Shortly after Pastorini's study reignited biogeographic interest in Madagascar's rivers, an influential paper was published proposing a mechanistic model wherein river catchments served to create "retreat and dispersion" (Wilmé et al. 2006). Based on this model, the elevation of riverine headwaters and the climatic cycles of the Quaternary would have created pulses of forest connectivity, during warm and wet periods, alternating with forest contraction during periods of drying and cooling. In turn, these cycles of connection and fragmentation would have served to power speciation in lemurs and other endemic vertebrates. This model has served to drive yet further interest and attention to the role of rivers as barriers to gene flow in lemurs (Craul et al. 2008; Markolf and Kappeler 2013), largely supporting the conclusions of Pastorini et al. (2003). The extent to which this phylogeographic hypothesis holds up will depend upon a variety of factors, including, but not limited to, increased geographic sampling and detailed investigation of species limits within all five lemuriform lineages.

Subject editors: Jörg U. Ganzhorn and Steven M. Goodman

SUBFOSSIL LEMURS

L. R. Godfrey and W. L. Jungers

At least 17 large-bodied lemur species became extinct on Madagascar during the late Holocene. These subfossil (or recently extinct) species belong to five families (Table 14.6), three of which (the Palaeopropithecidae, or sloth lemurs; the Archaeolemuridae, or monkey lemurs; and the Megaladapidae, or koala lemurs) have no living members. Two extant lemur families, the Lemuridae and Daubentoniidae, also have extinct representatives, which are the largest species in each family. An additional three families of Malagasy lemurs (the Indriidae, Cheirogaleidae, and Lepilemuridae) have no known extinct members but are represented in the subfossil record. Because all extinct lemurs were larger in adult body mass than the largest of extant species, they are sometimes called the "giant" lemurs of Madagascar. They ranged in body mass from ~11 to ~160 kg (Figure 14.21).

THE SUBFOSSIL LEMUR FAUNA

Madagascar's subfossil sites often contain remains of both extinct and extant animals. Most are Holocene (i.e., 11,650 years old or younger), but some extend back tens of thousands of years. Subfossil marsh, cave, and stream-bank sites bearing primate fossils have been found in all ecogeographic zones of the island—except the east and the Sambirano Region—from the northern to the southern tips of the island. Despite the lack of subfossil sites in the east and Sambirano, there is no reason to believe that the extinct lemurs, most of which were well adapted for living in forested habitats, were absent from Madagascar's moist evergreen forests. Indeed, when Etienne de Flacourt traveled to Madagascar in the mid-1600s, he recorded stories of a giant lemur (the "tretretretre," likely *Palaeopropithecus*) living in the mountains just north of Fort Dauphin (see Andriamialisoa and Langrand, pp. 1–38). Although some of the giant lemurs are known to have survived well into the last millennium, there is strong evidence of rapid population decline between 1250 and 1050 years before present (BP) (Godfrey et al. 2019). There is no question that this was after human colonization of Madagascar, although the question of how long afterward is still debated (Douglass et al. 2019).

We are beginning to understand spatial and temporal changes in the distribution of the megafauna (herein referring to extinct animals larger than their living counterparts) over the past 30,000 years, which includes the last glacial period (>17,000 cal BP, or calibrated years before present), the deglaciation period (between ~17,000 cal BP and the beginning of the Holocene at 11,650 cal

TABLE 14.6. **Taxonomy of extinct lemurs**

SUBORDER STREPSIRRHINI E. GEOFFROY SAINT-HILAIRE, 1812
INFRAORDER LEMURIFORMES GREGORY, 1915
Family Palaeopropithecidae Tattersall, 1973
Genus *Mesopropithecus* Standing, 1905
M. globiceps (Lamberton, 1936)
M. pithecoides Standing, 1905
M. dolichobrachion Simons, Godfrey, Jungers, Chatrath & Ravaoarisoa, 1995
Genus *Babakotia* Godfrey, Simons, Chatrath & Rakotosamimanana, 1990
B. radofilai Godfrey, Simons, Chatrath & Rakotosamimanana, 1990
Genus *Palaeopropithecus* G. Grandidier, 1899
P. ingens G. Grandidier, 1899
P. maximus Standing, 1903
P. kelyus Gommery, Ramanivosoa, Tombomiadana-Raveloson, Randrianantenaina & Kerloc'h, 2009
Genus *Archaeoindris* Standing, 1909
A. fontoynontii Standing, 1909
Family Archaeolemuridae G. Grandidier, 1905
Genus *Archaeolemur* Filhol, 1895
A. majori Filhol, 1895
A. edwardsi (Filhol, 1895)
Genus *Hadropithecus* Lorenz von Liburnau, 1899
H. stenognathus Lorenz von Liburnau, 1899
Family Megaladapidae Forsyth Major, 1894
Genus *Megaladapis* Forsyth Major, 1894
M. edwardsi (G. Grandidier, 1899)
M. grandidieri Standing, 1903
M. madagascariensis Forsyth Major, 1894
Family Lemuridae Gray, 1821
Genus *Pachylemur* (Lamberton, 1948)
P. insignis (Filhol, 1895)
P. jullyi (G. Grandidier, 1899)

INFRAORDER CHIROMYIFORMES ANTHONY & COUPIN, 1931
Family Daubentoniidae Gray, 1863
Genus *Daubentonia* E. Geoffroy Saint-Hilaire, 1795
D. robusta (Lamberton, 1934)

FIGURE 14.21 **A mouse lemur representing Madagascar's smallest extant lemur genus, *Microcebus*, sits on top of a skull of the extinct *Megaladapis edwardsi* (one of Madagascar's largest extinct lemur species).** (ARTWORK by Dao Van Hoang, 2015, www.daovanhoang.com. Printed with permission.)

BP), and the Holocene itself. Today the Central Highlands have only a few pockets of forest with remaining populations of lemurs (e.g., A. D. Yoder et al. 2016), and the megafauna (including the large-bodied lemurs) is gone everywhere. But we know from subfossil sites that in the not-too-distant past, the former forested portions of the Central Highlands offered an important corridor between the east and west through which lemurs could disperse.

During the glacial period, Madagascar was probably, like South Africa, ~6°C colder on average than it is today. There is palynological evidence that Central Highlands sites above 1500 m were dominated by wetlands and heathlands, and inhospitable to most terrestrial vertebrates except waterbirds. We have remains only of *Archaeolemur*, one of the most terrestrial of extinct lemurs, at Ampasambazimba (~1000 m) during the glacial period, and no primates at higher-elevation sites such as Tsaramody, Antsirabe, or Masinandraina at that time. Low-elevation forests were, however, hospitable to arboreal primates during the glacial period (Samonds et al. 2019). Near the end of the glacial period, a rich megafaunal community of hippopotamuses, crocodiles, and elephant birds occupied elevations over 1500 m. As Madagascar warmed during the deglaciation period and the Holocene, highland sites became more forested, and more arboreal species including lemurs spread across them (up to ~1500 m), only to disappear altogether or retreat to the lowlands toward the late Holocene, at the time of the megafaunal crash (Goodman and Jungers 2014).

There is continued debate over the degree to which climate change (as opposed to human activities) triggered megafaunal extinction. Some regional variation in rainfall has been documented (most recently using stalagmite analysis) as far back as the Last Glacial Maximum (21,000 years ago) and onward (e.g., Scroxton et al. 2017, 2019; Voarintsoa et al. 2017); there were wet and dry spells lasting sometimes hundreds of years. Periodic droughts could have caused local extirpations of particular species such as freshwater birds. However, stable nitrogen isotope ($\delta^{15}N$) values measured on radiocarbon-dated subfossils show no systematic directional change in habitat moisture over the past 10,000 years (Crowley et al. 2017). Ecogeographic differences that exist today (e.g., from the subarid south and southwest to the dry deciduous forests of the northwest and the subhumid Central Highlands) appear to have existed throughout the Holocene. We also know that, beginning near the end of the first millennium CE, major changes in habitat (from woodland or forest to grassland) occurred without concomitant aridification, thus signaling burning by humans (Burns et al. 2016; Railsback et al. 2020). Palynological data confirm that there have been dramatic changes in plant species composition during the past 1000 years, with declines and extinctions of endemic tree species in a variety of habitats (e.g., Virah-Sawmy et al. 2016). Debate on the role of climate continues, but it appears that these changes occurred without widespread increases in local aridity and without changes in the trophic levels of most megafauna (Crowley et al. 2017; Hixon et al. 2018).

With few exceptions, the subfossil lemurs were forest-adapted, as are their living relatives. In view of their much larger body masses, however, it can be expected that virtually all of the subfossil species also frequented the ground, if only to travel between trees, and at least one group, the archaeolemurids, was more terrestrial than any living lemur. We now have indirect evidence that even the most arboreal species at least periodically descended to the ground: crocodiles were formidable ground predators of giant lemurs across a wide variety of habitats, particularly larger-bodied lemurs such as *Palaeopropithecus* and *Megaladapis* (Meador et al. 2019). These were not the most terrestrial of extinct lemurs, but they were certainly the least agile. Judging from predation traces on the bones of extinct lemurs, crocodile predation was most common at lake and marsh sites, including those in more arid and open habitats, such as the dry spiny thicket. This suggests that, even in open environments where giant "arboreal" lemurs may have been most vulnerable to ground predators, large lemurs descended to the ground not merely to travel between trees but to drink water at lakes, ponds, and streams.

At the species level, high regional endemicity characterizes the primate communities of the recent past as well as today (Godfrey et al. 1999). The primate paleocommunities were speciose; some regions that are today devoid of lemurs once harbored more than 20 lemur species, ranging in body size from under 100 g to over 150 kg. Strong niche differentiation (as, for example, occurs among bamboo lemurs; see Tan et al., pp. 1947–52) seems to have allowed numerous closely related species to thrive in sympatry (Godfrey et al. 1999). About half of the extant genera have representatives in every major ecogeographic zone of the island, and this was probably also true of the extinct genera (Albrecht et al. 1990). Recent exploration of subfossil sites near Maintirano in the central west has resulted in range extensions for both extant (*Prolemur simus*) and extinct (*Babakotia radofilai*) primates (Burney et al. 2020a).

ADAPTIVE DIVERSITY

The extinct lemurs have been compared to large-bodied anthropoids (orangutans, gelada and savanna baboons, even hominins), but in many ways they were much more similar to their smaller-bodied relatives. Their orbits lacked a postorbital plate and were bordered instead by a postorbital bar. Their brains were considerably smaller than those of like-size anthropoids (Jungers 1999). Like their extant relatives, the extinct lemurs exhibited little or no sexual size or canine dimorphism (Godfrey et al. 1993). It is clear that the common ancestor of the Megaladapidae, Archaeolemuridae, and Palaeopropithecidae had a grooming claw and dental traits (such as reduced medial incisors in the maxilla and a toothcomb in the mandible) associated with grooming, as do extant strepsirrhines. The entire grooming complex was lost in the Archaeolemuridae but retained in the Megaladapidae and in some but not all species of the Palaeopropithecidae (Jungers et al. 2002).

P. C. Wright (1999) argued that living lemurs have adaptations to minimize energy expenditure, maximize energy intake from foods of varying quality, and survive episodes of food scarcity whether seasonal or due to environmental resource unpredictability. The same was clearly true of the extinct lemurs. Evidence of this is preserved in the morphology, histology, and chemistry of bones and teeth. For example, strontium isotope ratios vary spatially in rocks; strontium ions are leached from rocks and taken up by plants that are then consumed by animals. Because Madagascar is geologically diverse, the variability in the strontium ratios in animal tissue reveals animal mobility. Low variance can be inferred to mean small ranges (Crowley and Godfrey 2019). Further confirmation of reduced activity levels in extinct lemurs can be gleaned from their skeletal adaptations (Jungers et al. 2002; Shapiro et al. 2005) and the relative size of the semicircular canals in their ears (Spoor et al. 2007; A. Walker et al. 2008). Their dental microstructure and precocious dental development can probably be understood in the context of low activity levels (Hogg et al. 2015). In living indriids, and apparently in palaeopropithecids (G. T. Schwartz et al. 2002), dental precocity is associated with a rapid absolute pace of postnatal dental eruption, early replacement of the deciduous teeth, and a relatively low body mass. New weanlings are well equipped to process tough and fibrous, low-quality foods. They thus attain ecological independence well before they are either sexually mature or fully grown. This lowers the energetic demands made on lactating mothers and increases the probability that the mothers will survive the stressful period of lactation under low resource availability. C. A. Andrews et al. (2016) reconstructed the common ancestor of all Lemuriformes (without *Daubentonia*) as highly folivorous. Strong dependence on foliage consumption distinguishes extant Lemuriformes from primates on all other continents (Fleagle and Reed 1996; Kappeler and Heymann 1996), and the same appears to be true of extinct species (Jungers et al. 2002). When necessary, folivores can survive on less-desirable foods of low "quality."

In Table 14.7, we summarize our inferences about subfossil lemur genera via thumbnail portraits. There are consistent and sometimes very obvious differences between the extinct and living lemurs of Madagascar. The smallest subfossil taxa (e.g., *Pachylemur*, *Mesopropithecus*, *Daubentonia robusta*) are all larger than the biggest extant lemurs (*Indri* and *Propithecus diadema*; R. J. Smith and Jungers 1997), and the largest subfossil species are among the largest primates to evolve anywhere in the world (e.g., *Archaeoindris fontoynontii*, *Megaladapis edwardsi*). Correlated with this pervasive difference in body size, none of the subfossil taxa exhibit any adaptations for the well-known leaping prowess of many living lemurs. Conversely, the extreme morphological specializations for suspensory behaviors seen in the sloth lemurs are absent in extant species, although indriids and *Varecia* do engage in hang-feeding behaviors. Even though some living species frequent the ground to varying degrees (e.g., *Lemur*, *Hapalemur*), none of them display the derived, semiterrestrial anatomies of the archaeolemurids. Most of the extinct species have been reconstructed as diurnal on the basis of their small orbit sizes, although there is some indirect evidence that *Pachylemur*, like other lemurids, may have been cathemeral (Vasey and Godfrey, forthcoming). Extrapolations to body sizes beyond the upper limit of extant species in the same family are always fraught with difficulties, but we suspect that some of the extinct taxa were not strictly diurnal despite having relatively small orbits (Jungers et al. 2002), and that visual acuity of most was decidedly lower than anthropoids of comparable body size (Kay and Kirk 2000; C. F. Ross 2000).

On the basis of anatomical evidence from the vertebral column, limb proportions, articular morphology, and phalangeal curvature (Jungers et al. 2002), the palaeopropithecids appear to have

TABLE 14.7. **Portraits of extinct lemurs**

TAXON (NUMBER OF EXTINCT SPECIES)	BODY WEIGHT (kg)	DIET	INFERRED ACTIVITY AND POSITIONAL BEHAVIOR; SALIENT CHARACTERISTICS
Palaeopropithecidae (8)	11–160	Leaves, fruits, and seeds	Slow climbers with varying degrees of quadrupedal suspension; elongate, hook-like hands and feet, long curved phalanges, reduced pollex and hallux. Poor day vision; relatively small brains; short tails.
Archaeolemuridae (3)	18–35	For *Archaeolemur*: fruits, seeds, foliage, small animals, structurally defended resources. For *Hadropithecus*: CAM leaves, succulent plants.	Semiterrestrial quadrupeds; better day-vision than other lemurs; relatively large brains (given body size). Heavy-bodied with short, robust limbs, long tails, and short, relatively flat digits. Robust jaws with buccolingually expanded molars, and anterior teeth modified into chisel-like cutting devices not used in grooming. Molar enamel thick and heavily decussated.
Megaladapidae (3)	46–85	Mainly tree foliage	Vertical climbers with poor day vision, long forelimbs, enormous pincerlike feet, long and divergent halluces, and short tails. No permanent upper incisors. Toothcomb reduced but used in grooming.
Pachylemur (2)	11–13	Primarily fruits	Deliberate climbers with *Varecia*-like dentition but distinctly different postcranial (especially vertebral) features.
Daubentonia (1)	14	Structurally defended resources	Robust quadruped with ever-growing central incisors and an elongated, filiform third manual digit.

Source: Body weight estimates from Jungers et al. (2008).

exhibited a continuum of arboreal locomotor adaptations, from slow climbing and suspension (*Mesopropithecus* and *Babakotia*) to extremely derived, sloth-like hanging (*Palaeopropithecus*). Even the enormous sloth lemur *Archaeoindris* (~160 kg) preserved some scansorial capabilities. Members of the palaeopropithecid-indriid clade also share dental developmental traits (including tooth loss) associated with very rapid dental eruption (G. T. Schwartz et al. 2002). This unusual combination of rapid dental and slow reproductive developmental traits has been interpreted as related to early ecological competence of young individuals (coupled with late reproductive maturation) (e.g., Godfrey et al. 2004). The life-history trajectories of members of this group can be described as simultaneously very fast and very slow, owing to the decoupling of ecological and reproductive development.

Megaladapis species were also well designed for arboreality (Jungers 1980); as a percentage of total limb length, both hands and feet were enormous and sported huge, powerful pincerlike thumbs and big toes (Wunderlich et al. 1996). As very large folivores with elongated crania atypical for primates, they resembled their smaller-bodied relatives in having relatively small brains and life-history characteristics typical for lemurs (G. T. Schwartz et al. 2005; Hogg et al. 2015).

Although neither *Archaeolemur* nor *Hadropithecus* displayed bona fide cursorial adaptations, they had digital modifications best suited for travel on the ground (e.g., digital shortening, greater dorsal excursions at the metapodial-phalangeal joints). On balance, archaeolemurids are best regarded as semiterrestrial quadrupeds (Lemelin et al. 2008). They were short-limbed and possessed massive torsos. *Archaeolemur* likely consumed mechanically challenging foods (such as hard seeds or fruits with hard or tough pericarps) as well as a variety of other foods. It appears to have had a more eclectic diet than did *Hadropithecus*, which likely specialized on the leaves of certain succulent plants (Crowley and Godfrey 2013; Godfrey et al. 2016).

Pachylemur was a larger, more robust version of *Varecia*, a quadrupedal genus that engages in substantial amounts of hind-limb suspension (Jungers et al. 2002). Like *Varecia*, it was predominantly frugivorous and presumably an important seed disperser and was likely the most important disperser of large seeds in the primate communities.

On the basis of a shared suite of specialized anatomical features linked to extractive foraging (including ever-growing central incisors and a long, filiform third digit of the hand; E. L. Simons 1994), we infer that the positional repertoire of *Daubentonia robusta* was similar in most respects to that of the living member of this genus, *D. madagascariensis*. The extinct species likely exploited structurally defended resources such as hard-coated seeds and wood-boring insect larvae.

PHYLOGENY

Our understanding of the phylogenetic relationships among lemurs, and particularly the relationships of extinct to extant lemurs, has changed since the end of the 20th century with advances in molecular phylogeny (particularly, improved techniques for studying ancient DNA), although uncertainties remain with regard to both topology and divergence dates for major groups (see Yoder, pp. 1821–24). Researchers are beginning to generate nuclear paleogenome sequences

for extinct lemurs (Marciniak et al. 2020), which should prove to be very useful in testing phylogenetic hypotheses. To date, however, there are a limited number of molecular phylogenetic studies that have included subfossil lemurs, and only two that have endeavored to resolve sister-taxon relationships and divergence dates for all three extinct families (Kistler et al. 2015; Herrera and Dávalos 2016). Of these, one relied solely on ancient DNA (Kistler et al. 2015), while the other employed a "total evidence" approach, embracing molecular and morphological data simultaneously (Herrera and Dávalos 2016). Despite some differences, a general consensus is building around certain aspects of subfossil lemur topology. We first review points of general agreement and then issues that remain unresolved.

It has long been clear on morphological grounds that the extinct *Daubentonia robusta* is a large-bodied congener of the living *D. madagascariensis* (Aye-aye) (E. L. Simons 1994). Size and robusticity serve to distinguish the two, but they are remarkably similar overall. However, higher-rank relationships of Daubentoniidae to other lemurs (indeed other strepsirrhines) has been the subject of intense debate and disagreement. Because Groves (1989) viewed the phylogenetic relationship of the Daubentoniidae to other strepsirrhines as uncertain, he placed this family in its own infraorder (the Chiromyiformes, of equal status to Lemuriformes and Lorisiformes), following Anthony and Coupin (1931). Molecular data generally support the view, articulated by A. D. Yoder (1997), that *Daubentonia* is the sister taxon to all other lemurs, extinct and extant, but closer to other lemurs than to the lorises of continental Africa and Asia (Kistler et al. 2015; Herrera and Dávalos 2016).

Although *Megaladapis* is much larger in body size than *Lepilemur*, until the end of the 20th century, morphologists viewed the two as sister taxa on the basis of their similarities in the form of the molars, the loss of the upper incisors in adults, and the development of particular aspects of skull morphology (Jungers 1980; Wall 1997). This view shifted as molecular data, including a recent analysis of the nuclear genome of *Megaladapis* (Marciniak et al. 2020), failed to corroborate it (A. D. Yoder et al. 1999; K. P. Karanth et al. 2005). Instead, a sister-taxon relationship for the Lepilemuridae and the Cheirogaleidae is supported by molecular studies (see review by Masters et al. 2013). There is increasing consensus that *Megaladapis* and *Lepilemur* are distantly related; morphological similarities are likely convergences related to similar diets. Within the Megaladapidae, a close relationship between *M. grandidieri* and *M. madagascariensis*, which form a clade that is sister to *M. edwardsi*, is supported by both dental and especially postcranial evidence (Vuillaume-Randriamanantena et al. 1992).

In contrast with the lack of concordance between morphological and genetic data for the Megaladapidae, data from ancient DNA has broadly confirmed earlier phylogenetic inferences based on the morphology of the Palaeopropithecidae (A. D. Yoder et al. 1999). The palaeopropithecids were long considered the sister to the extant Indriidae, given a suite of shared craniodental traits (Tattersall 1982; G. T. Schwartz et al. 2002). While these two families differ markedly in postcranial adaptations (as palaeopropithecids are primarily suspensory and indriids are well adapted for leaping), there are nevertheless some postcranial features that link the two. Within the sloth lemurs, *Palaeopropithecus* and *Archaeoindris* share unusual cranial characters, and cranial anatomy also links *Mesopropithecus* and *Babakotia* to the other sloth lemurs. Postcranial anatomy firmly links *Mesopropithecus* and *Babakotia* to the other sloth lemurs, with *Babakotia* more derived in the *Palaeopropithecus*-*Archaeoindris* direction (Jungers et al. 1991, 2002; E. L. Simons et al. 1995).

Cranial, dental, and postcranial synapomorphies (e.g., dental formula, aspects of dental morphology, postcranial adaptations for semiterrestrial locomotion) clearly unite *Archaeolemur* and *Hadropithecus*, but higher-rank relationships of the archaeolemurids to other lemur families have been difficult to resolve on morphological grounds alone. Molecular data have confirmed that the family Archaeolemuridae is the sister to the palaeopropithecid-indriid clade (Kistler et al. 2015; Herrera and Dávalos 2016).

Finally, it is now widely accepted on the basis of molecular data that *Pachylemur* is the sister genus to *Varecia* and that this clade is the sister to all other Lemuridae (Kistler et al. 2015; Herrera and Dávalos 2016). A sister-taxon relationship for *Pachylemur* and *Varecia* was long supported by morphologists on the basis of similarities in craniodental characteristics (Szalay and Delson 1979; Tattersall 1982), although a number of divergent postcranial characters, indicative of less flexibility in the back of the larger-bodied genus (Shapiro et al. 2005), distinguish the two.

Still poorly resolved is the issue of higher-rank relationships for the Daubentoniidae and Megaladapidae. The view that *Daubentonia* may be related to extinct African genera including *Plesiopithecus* has been defended recently by Godinot (2006) and Gunnell et al. (2018), challenging the notion that all Malagasy lemurs descend from a single colonization. Karyological data are enigmatic and have been interpreted as supporting a sister-taxon relationship of *Daubentonia* to all other Strepsirrhini (e.g., Picone and Sineo 2012).

With regard to the Megaladapidae, two views are current: Kistler et al. (2015) and others support a sister-taxon relationship for *Megaladapis* and the Lemuridae as well as a sister-taxon relationship for the aforementioned megaladapid-lemurid clade and a clade comprising all other lemuriform families. In contrast, Herrera and Dávalos (2016) consider *Megaladapis* to be the sister to all other Lemuriformes, including the Lemuridae. The nuclear genome of *Megaladapis* lends support to the first interpretation (Marciniak et al. 2020).

Also poorly resolved is the timing of the origin of the Lemuriformes (again, without the Daubentoniidae). According to Kistler et al. (2015), members of the Lemuriformes share a last common ancestor from ~31 Mya. That study's point estimate for diversification of Lemuriformes agrees with certain other estimates (e.g., M. S. Springer et al. 2012), and places the initial diversification of Lemuriformes within the Eocene–Oligocene transition, a period of global cooling, forest reduction, and forest fragmentation. In contrast, Herrera and Dávalos (2016) place the initial diversification of Lemuriformes in the mid-Eocene (at ~42 Mya), when the global climate was considerably milder. Their point estimate for the initial diversification of Lemuriformes is closer to those generated by certain other authors (e.g., Horvath et al. 2008).

Understanding when the Lemuriformes began radiating on Madagascar is important if we are to identify the selective regime under which traits that distinguish this clade evolved. Are the traits that characterize the Lemuriformes (and pointedly not the Chiromyiformes) adaptations to a climate shift that occurred during the Eocene–Oligocene transition?

Subject editors: Jörg U. Ganzhorn and Steven M. Goodman

PREDATION ON LEMURS

S. M. Goodman and J. U. Ganzhorn

Until the early 1990s, there was little evidence that nonhuman predation pressure played a major role in the population dynamics of lemurs. Thus, it was not certain whether predation was or is an important factor in the evolution of lemur behavior, other adaptive aspects of their life-history traits, or even their physiology. A few reports had been published in the literature of that period about acts of predation (e.g., Albignac 1976; J.-J. Petter et al. 1977; Richard 1978), but no quantitative information was available on species of prey and predator, frequency of predation, or age- or sex-related aspects of predatory pressure. Thus, the underlying assumption was that predation has a much less important role in the molding of the primate communities on Madagascar than in other areas in the world (e.g., van Schaik and van Hooff 1983).

On the basis of subsequent research and observations, it is now clear that predation has and continues to play an important role in the evolution of lemur behavioral ecology and population dynamics (Goodman 2003b; Gursky and Nekaris 2007; Meador et al. 2019). A number of experiments have shown that assorted diurnal and cathemeral (active day or night) lemurs react to the presence and vocalizations of predators (Macedonia and Polak 1989; Macedonia 1990, 1993a; Macedonia and Yount 1991; Fichtel and Kappeler 2002; Fichtel 2007; Karpanty and Wright 2007; Rahlfs and Fichtel 2010). Subsequently, as reported in this contribution, based on long-term field studies on lemurs at different sites on Madagascar, an ever-increasing number of naturalists visiting forest areas and witnessing acts of predation, and expanded studies of carnivorous animal prey remains, it has become clear that predation by a variety of raptors, carnivorans, and snakes on both nocturnal and diurnal lemurs is not uncommon.

Animals that have been documented or inferred to feed on lemurs include several euplerid and introduced carnivorans, lemurs themselves, diurnal birds of prey, nocturnal owls, crocodiles, and snakes (Table 14.8; Figure 14.22). Another important aspect that has unfolded over the past decades is the discovery of several extinct subfossil birds of prey on Madagascar, which disappeared in the late Holocene, as well as remains of an extinct *Cryptoprocta*, distinctly bigger than the extant species and with a relatively broad distribution, that exerted predation pressure on lemurs (Goodman and Jungers 2014; Meador et al. 2019).

Further, it has recently come to light that behavioral ecology studies of euplerid carnivorans have shown that several use communal hunting to capture lemurs (e.g., Deppe et al. 2008; Lührs and Dammhahn 2010). On the flip side, several lemurs have been documented to fend off would-be predators through group intraspecific efforts (e.g., Eberle and Kappeler 2008; Dausmann 2010; Mandl et al. 2017). In both of these situations, such behavior has important bearing on adaptations to predator-prey interactions (Crofoot 2012).

The purposes of this contribution are to update information presented in Goodman et al. (1993a) and Goodman (2003b) with regard to what is known about predation on lemurs, evolutionary responses to predation pressure, and possible consequences on population dynamics.

WHO FEEDS ON WHOM?

On the basis of a tabulation of information available as of August 2019 in the form of published reports or unpublished data on predators that feed on lemurs (Table 14.9), it is clear that there is predation pressure on all lemur species. All predators prey on the smallest lemur species of the genus *Microcebus*. Predation pressure, estimated as the number of predator species, decreases with increasing size of the lemur species (Scheumann et al. 2007; Figure 14.23).

The small nocturnal lemurs, particularly of the genus *Microcebus*, adults of which weigh between 30 and 90 g (Mittermeier et al. 2010), undergo high levels of predation by owls. The level of predation pressure by owls on the next largest group of nocturnal lemurs, the genus *Cheirogaleus*, is much lower than for *Microcebus*. The only definitive evidence of owl predation pressure on *Cheirogaleus* species is by *Asio madagascariensis* (Madagascar Long-eared Owl), the largest strigiform on the island, and this is limited to *C. medius*, an animal weighing 130 g on average. The larger species *C. major*, which weighs between 350 and 600 g (Mittermeier et al. 2010), is currently not known to be taken by nocturnal birds of prey. However, diurnal birds of prey, such as *Accipiter henstii* (Henst's Goshawk) and *Polyboroides radiatus* (Madagascar Harrier-hawk), and a variety of carnivorans, particularly *Cryptoprocta ferox* (Fosa), feed on *Cheirogaleus major* as well as *C. medius* (Table 14.9). In the dry deciduous forests of Ankarafantsika, *Cryptoprocta* predation pressure on *C. medius* is higher during the dry season, when this lemur is hibernating, as compared to the wet season. This might imply that this carnivoran digs torpid lemurs out of burrows rather than hunting actively moving animals (Dollar et al. 2007). Yet, this pattern was not seen in the dry deciduous forest of Kirindy Forest CNFEREF (Centre National de Formation, d'Etudes et de Recherche en Environnement et Foresterie), indicating different hunting strategies or different availabilities of prey (C. E. Hawkins and Racey 2008). Differences in prey composition might be driven by the availability of *Tenrec ecaudatus*, which is consumed in large quantities during the wet season when it is active. During this species' hibernation period, *Cryptoprocta* compensates for the lack of tenrecs by feeding more on lemurs (C. E. Hawkins and Racey 2008; Kappeler and Fichtel 2012).

For larger nocturnal lemurs, such as species of *Phaner* and *Mirza*, which weigh 350–500 g and 275–330 g (Mittermeier et al. 2010), respectively, predation pressure is restricted largely to diurnal birds of prey. There is documentation of *M. coquereli* being taken by *Asio madagascariensis*, *Buteo brachypterus* (Madagascar Buzzard), and two species of carnivorans. The genus *Lepilemur*, with average body mass varying from 500 to 1100 g (Mittermeier et al. 2010), is preyed

FIGURE 14.22 **A wide assortment of predators are known to take lemurs. A) The largest living carnivoran on Madagascar is *Cryptoprocta ferox* (here shown at Kirindy Forest CNFEREF), and at certain localities, 75% or more of the biomass it consumes is lemur prey. B) The decomposed remains of a white-furred *Propithecus candidus*, including the skull in the middle of the image, found at Marojejy; based on different lines of inference, this lemur was probably dispatched by *Cryptoprocta ferox* (Patel 2005). A range of diurnal birds of prey feed on lemurs, and *Accipiter henstii* (C–E) is one of the principal predators (Goodman et al. 1998a): C) an adult consuming a *Microcebus* cf. *murinus* at Kirindy Forest CNFEREF; D) distal limbs of an *Avahi* that had been taken and dismantled on the Masoala Peninsula; and E) a subadult starting to consume a *Lepilemur ruficaudatus* at Kirindy Forest CNFEREF. F) Snakes, particularly boas, are known to take lemurs. Here is shown an *Acrantophis dumerili* at Mandena, the site of a study of radio-collared *Hapalemur meridionalis*. After one marked individual disappeared, the radio signal was followed to the snake, and the bulge in the lower abdomen provided the telltale sign of the act of predation (Eppley and Ravelomanantsoa 2015).** (PHOTO A by K. Behrens; B by E. R. Patel; C by J. Henke-von der Malsburg; D by R. Thorstrom; E by M. Markolf; and F by T. M. Eppley.)

TABLE 14.8. **List of predatory animals documented or proposed to feed upon lemurs**

SCIENTIFIC NAME	VERNACULAR NAME
BIRDS	
Aviceda madagascariensis	Madagascar Cuckoo-hawk
Eutriorchis astur	Madagascar Serpent-eagle
Polyboroides radiatus	Madagascar Harrier-hawk
Accipiter henstii	Henst's Goshawk
Buteo brachypterus	Madagascar Buzzard
Tyto soumagnei	Red Owl
T. alba	Barn Owl
Asio madagascariensis	Madagascar Long-eared Owl
Vanga curvirostris	Hook-billed Vanga
CARNIVORANS	
Cryptoprocta ferox	Fosa
Galidia elegans	Ring-tailed Vontsira
Galidictis fasciata grandidieri	Broad-striped [Grandidier's] Vontsira
Mungotictis decemlineata	Bokyboky
**Canis lupus*	Domestic dog
**Felis silvestris*	Wild or domestic cat[1]
**Viverricula indica*	Small Indian Civet
LEMURS	
Eulemur "fulvus"	brown lemur group[2]
Mirza coquereli	Coquerel's Giant Mouse Lemur
REPTILES	
Sanzinia madagascariensis	Eastern Madagascar Tree Boa
S. volontany	Western Madagascar Tree Boa
Acrantophis dumerili	Dumeril's Ground Boa
A. madagascariensis	Madagascar Ground Boa
Ithycyphus miniatus	
Madagascarophis colubrinus	Malagasy Cat-eyed Snake
Crocodylus niloticus	Nile Crocodile

Note: Introduced species are marked with an asterisk (*).

[1] Recent genetic studies have determined that samples of "wild cats" from forested areas of Bezà-Mahafaly, Ankarafantsika, Makira, and Masoala indicate that they are genetically related to domestic cats and were introduced to the island from populations from the Arabian Sea (Sauther et al. 2020).

[2] In older literature on animal predation dating before the revisions of the genus *Eulemur*, some records are referred to the "*E. fulvus* group" or the "brown lemur complex," which we have used here.

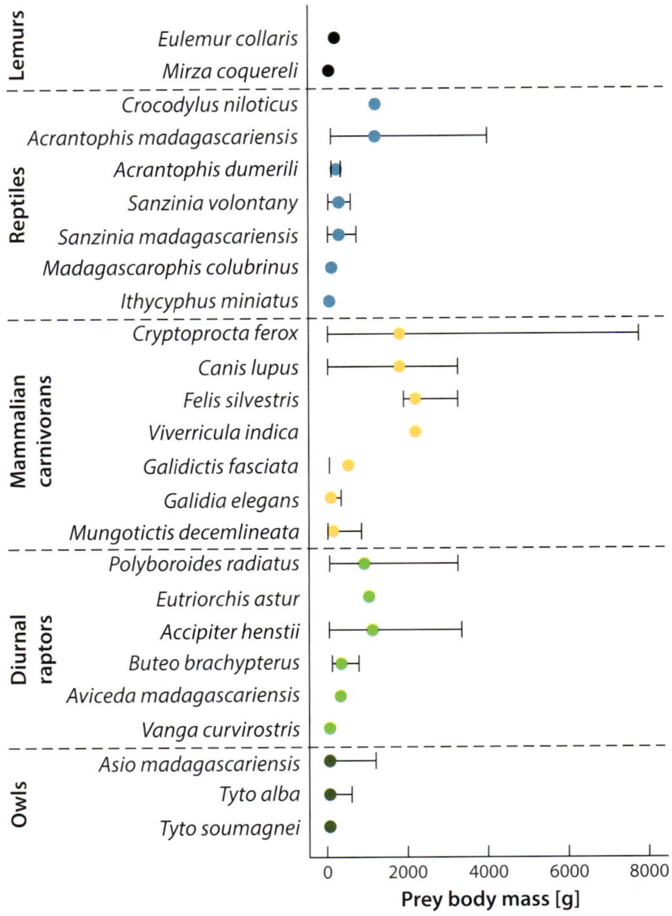

FIGURE 14.23 **Predators on lemurs in relation to lemur body mass; predators within the same taxonomic or ecological group are arranged with increasing body mass from left to right.**

upon largely by diurnal birds of prey and carnivorans. *Lepilemur petteri*, one of the smallest species in the genus, has been reported to be taken by *Tyto alba* (Barn Owl) (Goodman et al. 1993a, 1993c), and *L. ruficaudatus* by *A. madagascariensis* (Rasoloarison et al. 1995). *Cryptoprocta ferox* regularly takes members of the genus *Lepilemur* in areas of dry deciduous forest, where predation rates differ between the wet and dry seasons, and rarely takes them in moist evergreen forests (Goodman et al. 1997c; Dollar et al. 2007). Finally, *Avahi* species which weigh between 700 and 1600 g (Mittermeier et al. 2010), are taken by diurnal birds of prey, and there is one possible record of remains of *Avahi laniger* in the pellets of *Asio madagascariensis*. On the Masoala Peninsula, members of this genus are commonly taken by *Accipiter henstii*. Of the bone remains collected at the nests and prey-dismantling sites of this raptor, *Avahi* remains composed 31.5% of the minimum number of individual animals identified and 65.4% of the total biomass (Goodman et al. 1998a). Thus, in general, owls tend to feed much more extensively on nocturnal lemurs weighing in the range of 100 g or less, while the upper limit for diurnal birds of prey is considerably heavier.

Predation upon the larger diurnal or cathemeral lemur species is largely limited to a variety of hawks and to a greater extent carnivorans, particularly *C. ferox* (Table 14.9). For some of the large lemur species, acts of predation have yet to be documented, but

TABLE 14.9. **A summary of different types of predators feeding on various species of lemurs**

	BIRDS	CARNIVORANS	OTHERS
Cheirogaleus[1] *major*	*Accipiter henstii* Karpanty and Wright (2007)	*Galidia elegans* Goodman et al. (1993a); P. C. Wright and Martin (1995)	*Sanzinia madagascariensis*[2] P. C. Wright and Martin (1995)
	Buteo brachypterus Goodman et al. (1993a)	*Cryptoprocta ferox* Goodman et al. (1997c); Karpanty and Wright (2007)	*Acrantophis dumerili* Lahann (2008)
	Polyboroides radiatus Karpanty and Wright (2007)	–	–
C. medius	*Polyboroides radiatus* M. Gilbert and Tingay (2001); Dausmann (2010)	*Cryptoprocta ferox* Rasoloarison et al. (1995); Rasamison (1997); Dollar et al. (2007); C. E. Hawkins and Racey (2008); Dausmann (2010)	*Acrantophis madagascariensis*[2] Dausmann (2010)
	Buteo brachypterus Goodman and Langrand (1996a); Dausmann (2010)	?*Galidia elegans* P. Razafy et al. (unpublished data)	*Sanzinia volontany*[2] Dausmann (2010)
	Asio madagascariensis Rasoloarison et al. (1995); Dausmann (2010)	*Mungotictis decemlineata* Rabeantoandro (1997); Dausmann (2010); Rasolofoniaina et al. (2019)	*Madagascarophis colubrinus* Dausmann (2010)
	?*Tyto alba* Fietz and Dausmann (2003)	–	–
C. thomasi	–	–	*Acrantophis dumerili* Lahann (2008)
Microcebus[3] *berthae*	*Asio madagascariensis* Rasoloarison et al. (1995)[4]	*Mungotictis decemlineata*[5] Rasolofoniaina et al. (2019)	–
M. ganzhorni	*Asio madagascariensis* Goodman et al. (1991, 1993b)	–	–
	Vanga curvirostris Goodman et al. (1993c)	–	–
M. griseorufus	*Tyto alba* Goodman et al. (1993a, 1993c, 2014a); Rasoloarison et al. (2000); Rasoma and Goodman (2007); Goodman and Griffiths (2009)	*Galidictis fasciata grandidieri* Andriatsimietry et al. (2009)	–
	Asio madagascariensis Goodman et al. (1993b); Rasoloarison et al. (2000)	–	–
M. lehilahytsara	*Tyto alba* Goodman et al. (1993c)	–	–
	Asio madagascariensis Langrand and Goodman (1996)	–	–
M. mittermeieri	*Tyto soumagnei* Goodman and Thorstrom (1998)	–	–
M. murinus	*Accipiter henstii* Rand (1935)	*Cryptoprocta ferox* R. J. Russell (1977); Rasoloarison et al. (1995);[4] Dollar et al. (2007); S. M. Goodman and C. E. Hawkins (unpublished data)	*Ithycyphus miniatus* Richard (1978)
	Polyboroides radiatus Karpanty and Goodman (1999)	–	*Sanzinia volontany* Randrianarivo (1979); Fish (2010)
	Tyto alba Langrand (1990); Goodman et al. (1993c); Rasoloarison et al. (1995);[4] Goodman and Griffiths (2006); Rasoma and Goodman (2007)	*Mungotictis decemlineata* Albignac (1976); Goodman et al. (1993a); Rabeantoandro (1997)	*Mirza coquereli* Schliehe-Diecks et al. (2010); U. Schmid (unpublished data)

	BIRDS	CARNIVORANS	OTHERS
	Asio madagascariensis Rasoloarison et al. (1995);[4] U. Schmid (unpublished data)	*Mirza coquereli* Schliehe-Diecks et al. (2010)	–
M. myoxinus	*Tyto alba* Rasoloarison et al. (1995)[4]	–	–
M. ravelobensis	–	*Cryptoprocta ferox* Dollar et al. (2007)	–
M. rufus	*Accipiter henstii* Karpanty and Wright (2007)	*Cryptoprocta ferox* Karpanty and Wright (2007); S. M. Goodman and L. Dollar (unpublished data)	*Sanzinia madagascariensis* P. C. Wright et al. (2012)
	Polyboroides radiatus Goodman et al. (1993a); P. C. Wright (1998); Thorstrom and La Marca (2000); Karpanty and Wright (2007)	*Galidia elegans* J.-J. Petter et al. (1977); Karpanty and Wright (2007); Deppe et al. (2008)	–
	Asio madagascariensis Sterling and McFadden (2000)	–	–
M. sambiranensis	–	*Canis lupus* Goodman et al. (1993a)	–
M. simmonsi	–	*Galidia elegans* P. Razafy et al. (unpublished data)	–
M. tavaratra	*Tyto soumagnei* Cardiff and Goodman (2008)	–	–
Mirza coquereli	*Aviceda madagascariensis* Goodman et al. (1993a)	*Cryptoprocta ferox* Rasoloarison et al. (1995); Kappeler (1997a);[6] Rasamison (1997); S. M. Goodman and C. E. Hawkins (unpublished data)	?*Sanzinia volontany* Schülke (2001)
	Buteo brachypterus Goodman et al. (1993a); Goodman and Langrand (1996a)[7]	–	–
	Asio madagascariensis Rasoloarison et al. (1995)	*Mungotictis decemlineata* Kappeler (1997a);[6] Rabeantoandro (1997)	–
Phaner furcifer[8]	*Aviceda madagascariensis* Charles-Dominique and Petter (1980)	*Cryptoprocta ferox* Rasolonandrasana (1994); Rasoloarison et al. (1995); S. M. Goodman and C. E. Hawkins (unpublished data)	?*Sanzinia volontany* Schülke (2001)
	Buteo brachypterus Goodman et al. (1993a); Goodman and Langrand (1996a)[7]	–	–
Eulemur albifrons	–	–	*Acrantophis madagascariensis* Goodman et al. (1993a)
E. collaris	–	*Cryptoprocta ferox* Donati et al. (2007a)	–
E. coronatus	–	*Cryptoprocta ferox* J. M. Wilson et al. (1989); Rasolonandrasana (1994)[9]	*Crocodylus niloticus* J. M. Wilson et al. (1989)
	–	–	*Acrantophis madagascariensis* K. J. E. Steffens and J. Sanamo (unpublished data)
E. flavifrons	*Polyboroides radiatus* Randriatahina and Volampeno (2012)	*Cryptoprocta ferox* Randriatahina and Volampeno (2012)	–
E. fulvus	–	*Cryptoprocta ferox* Dollar et al. (2007)	–
	–	*Felis silvestris* Merson (2017)	–

(continued overleaf)

TABLE 14.9. ***continued***

	BIRDS	CARNIVORANS	OTHERS
E. macaco[10]	–	–	–
E. mongoz	–	*Cryptoprocta ferox* Dollar et al. (2007)	–
	–	*Cryptoprocta ferox* or *Canis lupus* D. I. Curtis (1997)	–
E. rubriventer	*Accipiter henstii* Karpanty and Wright (2007)	*Cryptoprocta ferox* Overdorff and Strait (1995); P. C. Wright et al. (1997); P. C. Wright (1998); Karpanty and Wright (2007)	–
E. rufifrons	*Accipiter henstii* Goodman et al. (1993a); Karpanty and Wright (2007)	*Cryptoprocta ferox* Goodman et al. (1993a); P. C. Wright et al. (1997); P. C. Wright (1998); Karpanty and Wright (2007); Irwin et al. (2009); Schnoell and Fichtel (2011–2012)	?*Acrantophis madagascariensis* Pyritz and Andrianjanahary (2010)
E. rufus	*Accipiter henstii* Schwab (1999)	*Cryptoprocta ferox* Goodman et al. (1993a); Rasoloarison et al. (1995); C. E. Hawkins and Racey (2008)	–
E. sanfordi	–	*Cryptoprocta ferox* Rasolonandrasana (1994)[9]	–
Hapalemur aureus[10]	–	–	–
H. griseus	*Accipiter henstii* Karpanty and Wright (2007)	*Cryptoprocta ferox* Goodman and Pidgeon (1999); Sterling and McFadden (2000); Karpanty and Wright (2007)	*Sanzinia madagascariensis* Goodman et al. (1993a); D. Rakotondravony et al. (1998b)
	?*Buteo brachypterus* Andrianandrasana et al. (2018)	–	–
	Polyboroides radiatus Karpanty and Wright (2007)	–	–
H. meridionalis	?*Asio madagascariensis* Goodman et al. (1993b)	–	*Acrantophis dumerili* Eppley and Ravelomanantsoa (2015)
Prolemur simus	*Accipiter henstii* Karpanty and Wright (2007)	*Cryptoprocta ferox* P. C. Wright et al. (1997); P. C. Wright (1998); Karpanty and Wright (2007)	–
Lemur catta	*Polyboroides radiatus* Ratsirarson (1987); Goodman et al. (1993a); L. Gould and Sauther (2007)	*Cryptoprocta ferox* Richard et al. (2016a)	*Eulemur "fulvus"* Pitts (1995)
	?*Accipiter* sp. Koyama (1992)[11]	*Viverricula indica* Goodman et al. (1993a); L. Gould and Sauther (2007)	–
	–	*Felis silvestris*[12] Goodman et al. (1993a); Ratsirarson et al. (2001); L. Gould and Sauther (2007)	–
	–	*Canis lupus* L. Gould and Sauther (2007)	–
Varecia rubra	?*Buteo brachypterus* Goodman et al. (1993a)	–	–

	BIRDS	CARNIVORANS	OTHERS
V. variegata	*Accipiter henstii* Karpanty and Wright (2007)	*Cryptoprocta ferox* Britt et al. (2000)[13]; Karpanty and Wright (2007); Sefczek et al. (2018)	–
Lepilemur[14] *dorsalis*	*Accipiter henstii* Goodman et al. (2014b)	–	–
L. edwardsi	–	*Cryptoprocta ferox* Dollar et al. (2007)	–
L. leucopus[15]	–	–	–
L. microdon	*Accipiter henstii* Goodman et al. (1998a)	–	–
L. mustelinus	*Polyboroides radiatus* Thorstrom and La Marca (2000)	*Cryptoprocta ferox* Rasoloarison et al. (1995); Goodman et al. (1997c); Irwin et al. (2009)[16]	–[17]
L. petteri[15]	*Tyto alba* Goodman et al. (1993a, 1993c)	–	*Sanzinia volontany* Fish (2010)
	Buteo brachypterus Ratsirarson and Emady (1999)	–	–
L. ruficaudatus	*Asio madagascariensis* Rasoloarison et al. (1995)	*Cryptoprocta ferox* Rasamison (1997); S. M. Goodman and C. E. Hawkins (unpublished data)	–
	Polyboroides radiatus Goodman et al. (1993a); Schülke and Ostner (2001)	*Mungotictis decemlineata* Rabeantoandro (1997)	–
L. sahamalazensis	*Buteo brachypterus* Randriatahina and Volampeno (2012)	–	–
L. septentrionalis	–	–	–[17]
Avahi laniger	*Accipiter henstii* Goodman et al. (1998a, 2014b)	*Cryptoprocta ferox* Irwin et al. (2009)[16]	–
	Polyboroides radiatus Karpanty and Wright (2007)	–	–
	?*Asio madagascariensis* Goodman et al. (1993b)	–	–
A. occidentalis	–	*Cryptoprocta ferox* Dollar et al. (2007)	–
A. peyrierasi	*Accipiter henstii* Goodman et al. (1993a); P. C. Wright (1998); Karpanty and Wright (2007)	*Cryptoprocta ferox* Karpanty and Wright (2007)	–
	?*Eutriorchis astur*[18] P. C. Wright (1998); Karpanty and Wright (2007)	–	–
	Polyboroides radiatus Karpanty and Wright (2007)	–	–
Indri indri[10]	–	–	–
Propithecus candidus	–	*Cryptoprocta ferox* Patel (2005)	–
P. coquereli	–	*Cryptoprocta ferox* Dollar et al. (2007)	*Acrantophis madagascariensis* Burney (2002); Gardner et al. (2015)
P. coronatus	*Buteo brachypterus* Goodman et al. (1993a)	*Cryptoprocta ferox* Goodman et al. (1993a)	–

(continued overleaf)

TABLE 14.9. ***continued***

	BIRDS	CARNIVORANS	OTHERS
P. deckeni	–	*Cryptoprocta ferox* Goodman et al. (1993a)	–
P. diadema	–	*Cryptoprocta ferox* P. C. Wright (1998); Irwin et al. (2009)	–
P. edwardsi	–	*Cryptoprocta ferox* P. C. Wright et al. (1997); P. C. Wright (1998); Karpanty and Wright (2007); Irwin et al. (2009)	–
P. tattersalli[10]	–	–	–
P. verreauxi	*Polyboroides radiatus* Rasoanindrainy (1985a, 1985b); Goodman et al. (1993a); Karpanty and Goodman (1999); Brockman (2003)	*Cryptoprocta ferox* Richard (1978; Richard et al. 1991, 2016a); Goodman et al. (1993a); Rasoloarison et al. (1995); Rasamison (1997); Dollar et al. (2007); C. E. Hawkins and Racey (2008); Lührs and Dammhahn (2010)	–
	Buteo brachypterus Goodman et al. (1993a)	*Canis lupus* L. Gould and Sauther (2007)	–
	–	*Felis silvestris* Brockman et al. (2008)	–
Daubentonia madagascariensis[19]	–	*Cryptoprocta ferox* J.-J. Petter (1977)[20] Sefczek et al. (2018)[21]	–

Notes: The taxonomy of lemurs and predators follows different contributions in Goodman et al. (2018b). "?" before a predator's name indicates that the identity of the animal was uncertain or an attempted attack was made without successful capture of the prey.

[1] The species delimitations of *Cheirogaleus* are in a state of flux, and the names assigned in this table may in some cases be incorrect (see Blanco, pp. 1922–26, for more details on the taxonomy of this genus).

[2] *Sanzinia madagascariensis*, including what is now recognized as *S. volontany*, has been called by some authors *Boa manditra*, and *Acrantophis madagascariensis* has been called *B. madagascariensis* (see Raxworthy and Glaw, pp. 1522–25, for details on taxonomy).

[3] Recent taxonomic work on *Microcebus* has demonstrated that this genus is much more speciose than previously understood (see Kappeler et al., pp. 1927–32). It is now known that in numerous areas of the west two species of *Microcebus* occur in sympatry, and previous reports of predation on *Microcebus* may in certain cases not have been assigned to the correct species.

[4] Samples from predators obtained at Kirindy Forest CNFEREF by Rasoloarison et al. (1995) were reported as two different *Microcebus* species: *M. myoxinus* (= *M. berthae*; Rasoloarison et al. 2000) and *M. murinus*.

[5] Identified food remains from this predator were identified as *Microcebus* sp.; could also be *M. murinus*.

[6] Predation took place while the lemur was inside a trap.

[7] Bone remains found in a nest of this species were identified as *Mirza coquereli* or *Phaner furcifer*.

[8] The species delimitations of *Phaner* are in a state of flux, and we have lumped cases of confirmed predation of members of this genus under *P. furcifer*.

[9] Bone remains from scats were reported to genus but were of either *E. coronatus* or *E. sanfordi*.

[10] There are several reports of attempted predation on this species (Goodman et al. 1993a), but to our knowledge no documented cases.

[11] An attack on a young *L. catta* was attributed to *A. francesiae* by Koyama (1992). However, this seems unlikely as, at least on the Masoala Peninsula, this relatively small raptor feeds on small prey and rarely on mammals and is not known to take lemurs (Rene de Roland 2000). We assume that the raptor in question was possibly *A. madagascariensis* or *A. henstii*.

[12] On the basis of recent genetic analyses, the wild forest cats of Madagascar are derived from domestic cats that we name as *Felis silvestris* (Sauther et al. 2020).

[13] A former captive individual released into a natural forest setting was taken by a *Cryptoprocta* (Britt et al. 2000).

[14] The taxonomy of the genus *Lepilemur* is complex (see Radespiel et al., pp. 1935–40), and we have not in all cases followed the different recent species designations.

[15] According to changes in the distributional ranges of *Lepilemur leucopus* and *L. petteri*, the observations previously assigned to *L. leucopus* are now attributed to *L. petteri*.

[16] Remains found in scats were identified as *L. mustelinus* or *Avahi laniger*.

[17] There are a number of reports of *Sanzinia madagascariensis* and other snakes feeding on *L. mustelinus* and *L. septentrionalis* (Ratsirarson 1986; R. J. Russell 1977), but to our knowledge no confirmed cases.

[18] *Eutriorchis astur* was reported to feed on *Avahi*. During a study of a nesting pair conducted on the Masoala Peninsula (Thorstrom and Rene de Roland 2000), no evidence was found that the species feeds on primates. We suspect that the predator reported by P. C. Wright (1998) and Karpanty and Wright (2007) might have been *Accipiter henstii*.

[19] Dehgan (2003) found evidence of predation on *Daubentonia*, but the predator was not identified.

[20] J.-J. Petter (1977: 55) mentioned, "the cryptoprocte (*Cryptoprocta ferox*), is capable of killing an aye-aye at night in the trees." However, whether an act of predation was actually documented is not clear.

[21] Sefczek et al. (2018) documented an attempted *Cryptoprocta* predation on a juvenile *Daubentonia* and found remains of this lemur in scats attributed to *Cryptoprocta*.

there is inferential data that they fall to a variety of predators. On the basis of observed foiled attempts by predators, as well as the antipredator behavior by the lemur species in question, most notably for *Indri indri*, it is assumed that at the very least young lemurs of these species are occasionally taken. Within the Lemuridae, species of the genera *Eulemur* and *Hapalemur* are extensively taken by a range of predators (Table 14.9).

Apart from predation by expected predators, there are cases of unsuspected predators of lemurs, such as *Mirza coquereli* feeding on *Microcebus murinus* (Schliehe-Diecks et al. 2010) and *Eulemur* feeding on infant *Lemur catta* (Pitts 1995).

GEOGRAPHIC AND SEASONAL VARIATION IN THE DIETARY REGIMES OF LEMUR PREDATORS

There is a growing database of information from several sites on Madagascar associated with seasonal or geographic variation in the diets of animals that feed on lemurs. In a sample of pellets collected at Bezà-Mahafaly below a *Tyto alba* roost site on a biweekly basis over the course of a year, there was considerable variation in the number of *Microcebus griseorufus* individuals taken (see Richard et al. 2016b for details on the species of *Microcebus* occurring at this site), from a maximum of 17 individuals (five subadults and 12 adults) during the month of May to an absence from the samples collected in January, October, and November (Goodman et al. 1993c). In the Kirindy Forest CNFEREF area, *M. murinus* shows a broad season of inactivity, ranging in general from early April to late October, with some daily variation in torpor during this period (Schmid 1999, 2000). At Bezà-Mahafaly, nearly three-quarters of the *Microcebus* lemurs consumed by *Tyto* on a yearly basis were obtained during these months (Goodman et al. 1993c), a period when there is probably a substantial reduction in prey available for raptors in general. There is significant geographic, temporal, and individual variation in the level of seasonal inactivity in *Microcebus* (cf. Schmid 1999; Schmelting et al. 2000; Lahann et al. 2006; Kobbe et al. 2011). While periods of inactivity have been interpreted at least in part as a response to reduce high levels of predation in small nocturnal species (P. C. Wright and Martin 1995; Schmid and Kappeler 1998; Schmid 1999), there is little evidence that being inactive actually helps in reducing predation pressure, neither when measured from the perspective of the prey (Kraus et al. 2008) nor the perspective of the predator (Dollar et al. 2007; C. E. Hawkins and Racey 2008).

In dry spiny thicket and gallery forest near Bezà-Mahafaly, *M. griseorufus* represented 5.7% of the total individual prey items taken by *T. alba* and 22.9% of the biomass (Goodman et al. 1993c). By comparison, pellets of this same owl species obtained in the village of Andasibe (at the edge of the Analamazaotra Special Reserve) and at a site near a *Eucalyptus* plantation contained remains of very few *Microcebus*, which by total prey items or biomass represented less than 2.5% of the animals consumed (Goodman et al. 1993c).

Collections of *Asio madagascariensis* pellets were obtained at a lowland moist evergreen forest site near Nahampoana (Tolagnaro) and in riverine forest near Bezà-Mahafaly (Goodman et al. 1993b). At the former site, *M. tanosi* comprised 7.2% of the total individuals taken and 4.4% of the biomass, and at Bezà-Mahafaly, *M. griseorufus* comprised 20.5% and 21.5%, respectively. In moist evergreen forests, where *Rattus rattus* dominates the small-mammal community, this introduced animal is much more commonly taken by this owl species than *Microcebus* (Langrand and Goodman 1996).

A study of the diet of *Buteo brachypterus* in lowland moist evergreen forest on the Masoala Peninsula found no evidence that this diurnal raptor fed upon lemurs (Berkelman 1994). In contrast, prey remains that were found near the nest of this species in the transitional dry deciduous forest of Vohibasia included several species of lemurs (Goodman and Langrand 1996a). Further, *B. brachypterus* has been noted to feed on a variety of lemurs, generally in dry forest formations (Table 14.9).

On the basis of scat analyses, data are available from several different sites and habitats on the prey choices of *Cryptoprocta ferox* (Table 14.10). In the western dry deciduous forests, including Kirindy Mité, Kirindy Forest CNFEREF, and Ankarafantsika, the lemur diet of this carnivoran ranged from 39.1% to 61.9% of total individuals and 57.0% to 82.1% of biomass. In the medium-altitude moist evergreen forests of Montagne d'Ambre and Andringitra, lemurs represented only 3.7% to 5.4% of the food items taken by *Cryptoprocta* (based on a minimum number of 36 identified prey remains). However, given that many of the other prey items were small mammals and frogs, the total representation of lemurs was between 31.4% and 39.8% of biomass. At Ranomafana, most lemur species have been found to be preyed upon by *Cryptoprocta* (Karpanty and Wright 2007). Overall, there appears to be considerable geographic and temporal variation in the diet of *Cryptoprocta* that is certainly related to aspects of the local potential prey community, seasonal shifts in prey abundance, and perhaps idiosyncratic differences between individuals.

PREDATION EFFECTS ON LEMUR POPULATIONS

Several forest sites have been the subject of long-term study, particularly by primatologists, and provide detailed baseline data that can be used to compare known lemur densities to different measures of predation pressure. In the dry deciduous forest of Kirindy Forest CNFEREF, more than half the prey animals taken by *Cryptoprocta* are lemurs, and annual offtakes, measured as the estimated percentage of the population consumed each year, include: *Microcebus*, 18%; combined *Lepilemur*/*Phaner*/*Mirza*, 16%; *Propithecus*, 13%; *Cheirogaleus*, 7%; and *Eulemur*, 4% (C. E. Hawkins and Racey 2008); predation rates of *Propithecus* show seasonal differences, with most being predated upon between June and October (Kappeler and Fichtel 2012).

In the moist evergreen forests of Ranomafana, field studies closely following individual groups of *P. edwardsi* provide detailed information of kill rates of these lemurs by *Cryptoprocta* (Karpanty and Wright 2007). In this case, on an annual basis, there was a 23.3% chance of a group losing an individual and a 5.7% chance of a given individual being taken. In the medium-altitude moist evergreen forests of Tsinjoarivo, concerning *P. diadema*, the annual rate of a group losing an individual was 18.2%, and the individual take rate was 7.3% (Irwin et al. 2009). Predation pressure on lemurs by birds of prey in Ranomafana has been estimated to range widely, but when

TABLE 14.10. **Comparison of the dietary regime of *Cryptoprocta ferox* at several different sites on Madagascar**

	MONTAGNE D'AMBRE (n = 36)[1]	ANDRINGITRA, ABOVE FOREST LINE (n = 57)	KIRINDY FOREST CNFEREF (n = 37)	KIRINDY FOREST CNFEREF (n = 19)	KIRINDY FOREST CNFEREF (n = 554)	KIRINDY MITÉ (n = 63)	ANKARAFANTSIKA (n = 311)
Frogs	7/19.3%/0.3%[2]	–	–	–	–	–	1/0.3%/0%
Reptiles	–	3/3.7%/0.8%	5/13.5%/2.0%	2/10.0%/0.9%	72/13.0%/1.4%	5/7.9%/0.9%	39/12.5%/1.3%
Birds	5/13.7%/11.7%	8/9.8%/32.8%	1/2.7%/0.5%	1/5.0%/0.2%	11/2.0%/0.3%	5/7.9%/6.7%	61/19.6%/15.1%
Tenrecids	5/13.8%/19.9%	27/32.9%/16.4%	3/8.1%/2.7%	2/10.0%/0.6%	77/13.9%/11.0%	13/18.8%/17.7%	13/4.2%/2.2%
Rodents	16/44.4%/17.4%	16/19.5%/19.3%	5/13.5%/12.7%	5/30.0%/11.7%	45/8.1%/4.5%	12/17.4%/2.0%	50/16.1%/1.3%
Lemurs	2/5.4%/39.8%	3/3.7%/31.4%	20/54.0%/57.0%	8/40.0%/81.6%	343/61.9%/82.1%	27/39.1%/72.4%	137/44.1%/79.6%
Other mammals	1/2.7%/10.8%	–[3]	3/8.1%/23.8%	1/5.0%/5.0%	6/1.1%/0.7%	1/1.4%/0.2%	10/3.2%/0.5%
Data source	Rasolonandrasana (1994)	Goodman et al. (1997c)	Rasolonandrasana (1994)	Rasamison (1997)	C. E. Hawkins and Racey (2008)	L. Dollar et al. (unpublished data)	Dollar et al. (2007)

[1] The figure presented for each site (n) is the total minimum number of individuals identified from the scats.

[2] Figures are presented as minimum number of individuals/% total representation/% total biomass. Biomass figures do not include invertebrates.

[3] Remains of *Bos indicus* (zebu) were also found in these scats. However, it is presumed that this material was scavenged, and it is not included in these calculations.

these estimates are combined with the predation pressure by mammalian carnivores, the annual offtake seems substantial (Karpanty and Wright 2007). Predation has become a problem for the survival of lemur populations in isolated forest remnants where predators can bridge the nonforested matrix while prey species cannot.

At Bezà-Mahafaly, it has been calculated that over 500 mouse lemurs are consumed per year by the estimated nine or 10 pairs of *Tyto alba* inhabiting the reserve (Goodman et al. 1993c). Further, other species of owls, particularly *Asio madagascariensis*, and other potential predators (snakes, carnivorans, and diurnal birds of prey) that are also known from the area would add to this already high predation pressure on *Microcebus* populations. At Ranomafana it is estimated that diurnal raptors take about 4.5% of the local *Microcebus* population on an annual basis (Karpanty 2003), and there is notable variation among the raptor species in the number of mouse lemurs in their diets (Karpanty and Wright 2007). While mouse lemurs might be able to compensate for the loss, populations of lemur species with slower life histories can collapse under unusual predation pressure, as may occur when groups of possibly dispersing *Cryptoprocta* adolescents roam through an area. This situation has led almost to the extinction of *Eulemur collaris* in littoral fragments of Mandena (Donati et al. 2007a) and has raised concerns for *Propithecus* species in Ranomafana and Tsinjoarivo (Irwin et al. 2009). Estimating the effects of predation on populations is difficult, as predation especially by *C. ferox* seems to be concentrated in space and time and may be dictated by the availability of prey (C. E. Hawkins and Racey 2008; Irwin et al. 2009). The large number of individuals killed under conditions of locally high prey density might result in inflated estimates of predation effects when extrapolated over large areas and populations as a whole. However, at least at certain times, the offtake can be considerable.

SUMMARY

Since the last years of the 20th century a major shift has occurred in the interpretation of the role of predation in different aspects of lemur evolution. It is now clear that predation has played, and continues to play, a major role in selection pressures that are related to the evolution of lemur ecology and behavior. The data available on predation on lemurs has increased from a handful of anecdotal observations to numerous detailed and quantified information on predator-prey interactions. Virtually every genus of extant lemur is known to experience some predation pressure.

Subject editors: Claudia Fichtel and Steven M. Goodman

LEMUR FOOD PLANTS

T. M. Eppley, K. J. E. Steffens, I. C. Colquhoun, and C. R. Birkinshaw

Research on lemur diets began with J.-J. Petter's landmark 1956–1957 survey of lemur ecology (J.-J. Petter 1962), and further information accumulated steadily over the subsequent decades. Of the nearly 110 lemur species currently recognized, 61 lemur species have been the subject of at least one dietary study that has provided information on the taxa and parts of plants exploited for food. Building on Birkinshaw and Colquhoun (2003), published in the precursor of this book, and updating it with recent lemur-ecology studies, K. J. E. Steffens (2020) assembled a database of food plants exploited by lemurs, aggregating published lists and updating the taxonomy of plants following the online Catalogue of the Plants of Madagascar (Madagascar Catalogue 2020), which is part of the plants database Tropicos. The current contribution builds on this with additional unpublished data sets, limiting our scope to plants, both native and introduced, rather than other types of food items lemurs consume (e.g., arthropods, eggs, soil, etc.).

The 61 lemur species were documented to exploit foods from species in 155 vascular plant families (including introduced) and from species in 147 of 239 native vascular plant families. Currently, five plant families are recognized as endemic to Madagascar—Asteropeiaceae, Barbeuiaceae, Physenaceae, Sarcolaenaceae, and Sphaerosepalaceae—and lemurs have been recorded exploiting all of these except for Barbeuiaceae. The families that are exploited by the greatest numbers of lemur species are Rubiaceae (exploited by 50 species), Fabaceae (45 species), Moraceae (43 species), Malvaceae (42 species), and Apocynaceae (39 species). These families, with the exception of Moraceae, contain several hundred species that grow in a wide array of different vegetation types (Schatz 2001). Moraceae is a small family, with 42 native Malagasy species currently recognized. Its widespread utilization can be accounted for by the huskless, small-seeded fruits of most of the constituent genera (which are thus accessible to a wide range of lemur species, as well as frugivorous birds and bats) and the asynchronous fruit maturation among individuals of *Ficus*, both between species and to a certain extent within the same species (thus providing a more or less continuous supply of fruits throughout the year, including periods when other fruits are rare, particularly the dry season; see Rasplus et al., pp. 617–34). It might be expected that lemurs would avoid exploiting families whose plants contain latex, glycosides, and alkaloids (Simmen et al. 1999), but this does not seem to be the case, and such families are well represented in lemur diets (e.g., Apocynaceae, Clusiaceae, Moraceae, Sapotaceae).

Given the mainly arboreal lifestyle of lemur species, most of the exploited plants are trees, shrubs, and lianas. Notable exceptions are seen in *Hapalemur* species and *Prolemur simus*, which are recorded to exploit terrestrial herbs of the Poaceae and Cyperaceae families (Figure 14.24c; see Larridon et al., pp. 580–85), and *Lemur catta*, which exploits herbs in a diversity of families (see Sauther and Cuozzo, pp. 1952–56). Most lemurs exploit an array of food items (e.g., leaves, fruits, flowers), whereas relatively few lemur species would be considered strictly frugivorous. It is suggested that protein is a limiting factor for primate species (Ganzhorn et al. 2017), ultimately affecting life-history traits, and may have potentially led to a paucity of strictly frugivorous lemurs (Donati et al. 2017).

In general, lemur species inhabit every major habitat type on Madagascar; yet, relatively few records exist of them in mangroves (Gardner 2016). Only a few observations have been made of lemurs exploiting species from the mangrove genera *Avicennia*, *Rhizophora*, or *Sonneratia*. This may be related to the unpalatability of mangrove plant species, as most are rich in tannin and polyphenolic content (Donati et al. 2019), but also to a lack of research owing to the difficulty in accessing this habitat type. Similarly, the overall rarity of ferns in lemur diets is probably explained by a combination of factors, including the terrestrial habitat of most fern species; their lack of flowers, fruits, and seeds; their cyanogenic components; and the low palatability of tannin-rich fern fronds (May 1978). The unusual exploitation of ferns by *Propithecus diadema* may reflect the high tolerance to tannins by this genus compared to other lemur species (Simmen et al. 1999).

Given the large number of studies and observations of lemur feeding ecology that have been published over the past couple decades, we present information on exploited food plant families by lemur species from each of the five extant families. For a more detailed review, consult the database in K. J. E. Steffens (2020). The tables presented here indicate the plant part(s) within a given botanical family exploited by different lemur species. Eight different food-type classes are recognized. Some of these classes include the more precise food types distinguished by some researchers: in particular, leaf tips, new leaves, and petioles are included here in the class **leaves**; piths, shoots, and stems in the class **piths**; saps and gums in the class **exudates**; flowers, flower buds, and petals in the class **inflorescences** (note: **nectar** is in its own specific class); unripe and ripe fruits in the class **fruits** (note: **seeds** are in their own specific class when they are uniquely the consumed item). This has been done to simplify the general overview presented here and because the more precise food-type classes are inconsistently applied among researchers.

CHEIROGALEIDAE

The Cheirogaleidae family includes *Allocebus trichotis*, *Microcebus* species (see Kappeler et al., pp. 1927–32), *Cheirogaleus* species (see Blanco, pp. 1922–26), *Mirza* species (see Kappeler, pp. 1932–34), and *Phaner* species; feeding data are available for representatives of all five genera. There are currently 41 recognized species within Cheirogaleidae, and 18 of these have been recorded to exploit foods from 82 plant families (Table 14.11). *Cheirogaleus major* exploits foods from 49 plant families, while other species with high plant family diversity in their diets include *Microcebus griseorufus* (35 families), *C. thomasi* (34 families), *M. ganzhorni* (34 families), and *M. ravelobensis*

FIGURE 14.24 **Lemurs and their food plants. A) *Eulemur fulvus* feeding on fruits of introduced *Solanum mauritianum* (Solanaceae) in Analamazaotra; B) *Lepilemur tymerlachsonorum* shortly after feeding on the flowers of *Ceiba pentandra* (Malvaceae), with the anterior portion of its body covered with the pollen, near Lokobe, Nosy Be; C) *Hapalemur meridionalis* feeding on the pith/stem of *Cyperus* sp. (Cyperaceae) in Mandena; D) *Microcebus murinus* feeding on exudate of an unidentified tree species in Ankarafantsika; E) *Lemur catta* feeding on the leaves of *Aloe* sp. (Asphodelaceae) in Ifotaka; F) *Cheirogaleus thomasi* feeding on nectar from *Vaccinium emirnense* (Ericaceae) in Sainte Luce; G) *Propithecus diadema* feeding on the fruit of *Decarydendron* sp. (Monimiaceae) at Maromizaha; H) *Indri indri* feeding on the leaves of *Bakerella* sp. (Loranthaceae) in Mitsinjo Reserve, Andasibe.** (PHOTOS A and C by T. M. Eppley; B by S. H. Roberts; D by E. Zimmermann; E by B. P. Semel; F by E. Račevska; G by M. Lutz; and H by M. A. Semel.)

(27 families). Though *C. major* is one of the most widespread species within this lemur family, the high diversity of families recorded in its diet seems to be more a result of the number of studies focused on it, and this is also likely the case with the range-restricted *M. ganzhorni*. Among the plant families most exploited by Cheirogaleidae species are Rubiaceae (exploited by 15 species), Combretaceae (11 species), and multiple plant families (native and introduced taxa) exploited by 10 lemur species each, including Anacardiaceae, Celestraceae, Fabaceae, and Malvaceae. For most of these, Cheirogaleidae species tend to focus on exploiting fruits, inflorescences, nectar (Figure 14.24f), and exudates (Figure 14.24d), with the highest diversity exploiting the genera *Terminalia* (Combretaceae), *Canthium* (following Schatz 2001), *Gaertnera*, and *Hyperacanthus* (Rubiaceae).

DAUBENTONIIDAE

The Daubentoniidae family includes only one extant species, *Daubentonia madagascariensis* (Aye-aye) (see Sterling et al., pp. 1975–78), which exploits foods from 13 different plant families (Table 14.12). Among the frequently exploited plant items are *Canarium* (Burseraceae) fruits and seeds, *Terminalia* (Combretaceae)

FIGURE 14.24 *continued*

seeds, and *Ravenala* (Strelitziaceae) nectar; it is well known that *D. madagascariensis* is insectivorous and thus focuses its diet on invertebrates; fruits, seeds, and nectar are largely supplemental (Sterling et al. 1994; Randimbiharinirina et al. 2018; Sefczek et al. 2020a).

LEPILEMURIDAE

There are currently 26 recognized species within the family Lepilemuridae, all in the genus *Lepilemur* (see Radespiel et al., pp. 1935–40), but as most of these nocturnal lemur taxa are largely unstudied, feeding ecology data are available for only eight species. Despite the limited number of studies, *Lepilemur* species are known to exploit foods from 59 plant families (Table 14.13). Longer-term studies showed that seven different *Lepilemur* species each exploit between 16 and 22 families, with *L. mustelinus* exploiting the highest diversity, 22 families. Among the most frequently exploited plants, those of the Malvaceae (Figure 14.24b), including introduced species, are utilized by eight *Lepilemur* species; the Fabaceae by seven *Lepilemur* species; Rubiaceae by six species; and Apocynaceae, Euphorbiaceae, Phyllanthaceae, and Sapindaceae by five species each. As folivores, Lepilemuridae species feed mostly on leaves, most frequently exploiting those of the genera *Albizia* (Fabaceae), *Canthium* (Rubiaceae), *Commiphora* (Burseraceae), *Diospyros* (Ebenaceae), *Grewia* (Malvaceae), *Strychnos* (Loganiaceae), and *Terminalia* (Combretaceae).

LEMURIDAE

The family Lemuridae consists of 21 currently recognized species, and dietary data are available for all. Lemuridae species exploit food items from 136 plant families (Table 14.14). While some genera focus mostly on leaves and piths (*Hapalemur* spp., *Prolemur simus*; see Tan et al., pp. 1947–52 for general details on these genera), the genera *Eulemur* (see Johnson et al., pp. 1941–46) and *Varecia* (see Vasey et al., pp. 1957–63) tend to focus more heavily on ripe fruits

TABLE 14.11. **Plant parts consumed by different members of the Cheirogaleidae**

PLANT FAMILIES EXPLOITED	CHEIROGALEIDAE SPECIES																	
	ALLOCEBUS TRICHOTIS	*CHEIROGALEUS CROSSLEYI*	*C. MAJOR*	*C. MEDIUS*	*C. THOMASI*	*MICROCEBUS BERTHAE*	*M. GANZHORNI*	*M. GRISEORUFUS*	*M. JOLLYAE*	*M. LEHILAHYTSARA*	*M. MURINUS*	*M. MYOXINUS*	*M. RAVELOBENSIS*	*M. RUFUS*	*M. TANOSI*	*MIRZA COQUERELI*	*M. ZAZA*	*PHANER PALLESCENS*
Acanthaceae	–	–	L	–	–	–	–	–	–	–	–	–	–	–	–	–	–	–
Anacardiaceae	–	–	F	F	F		F	F L E X	–	–	E	–	F L E	–	F	–	–	E
Anacardiaceae (introduced)	–	F	F	–	–	–	–	–	–	–	–	–	I	–	–	–	–	–
Annonaceae	–	–	F	–	F	–	F	–	–	–	–	–	L	–	F	–	–	–
Aphloiaceae	–	–	F L	–	F	–	F	–	–	F	–	–	–	F	F	–	–	–
Apocynaceae	–	–	F L	F	F	–	F	F E	–	–	–	–	F L I	–	F	–	–	–
Aquifoliaceae	–	–	–	–	–	–	–	–	–	–	–	–	–	F	–	–	–	–
Araliaceae	–	–	I	–	–	–	–	–	–	–	–	–	–	–	–	–	–	–
Arecaceae	–	–	F	–	F	–	F	–	F	–	–	–	–	F	F	–	–	–
Asparagaceae	–	–	F	–	F	–	F	F	–	–	–	–	–	–	F	–	–	–
Asparagaceae (introduced)	–	–	–	–	I	–	–	N	–	–	–	–	–	–	–	–	–	–
Asteraceae	–	–	–	F I	–	–	–	–	–	–	–	–	–	–	–	–	–	–
Asteropeiaceae	–	–	F I	–	F I	–	F I	–	–	–	–	–	–	–	F	–	–	–
Bignoniaceae	–	–	F	F	–	–	–	F E X	–	–	–	–	–	–	–	–	–	–
Boraginaceae	–	–	–	–	–	–	–	F	–	–	–	–	–	–	–	–	–	–
Burseraceae	–	–	–	–	–	–	–	F L E	–	–	E	–	E	–	–	–	–	E
Cactaceae	–	–	–	–	–	–	–	–	–	–	–	–	–	F	–	–	–	–
Cactaceae (introduced)	–	–	–	–	–	–	–	E	–	–	–	–	–	–	–	–	–	–
Calophyllaceae	–	–	F	–	–	–	–	–	–	–	I E	–	L	–	–	–	–	–
Canellaceae	–	–	–	–	–	–	–	–	–	–	–	–	E	–	–	–	–	–
Capparaceae	–	–	–	–	–	–	–	F N	–	–	F	–	–	–	–	–	–	N
Celastraceae	–	–	F I	F I	F I	–	F I	E	–	–	F N E	–	E	–	F	–	–	I
Chrysobalanaceae	–	–	–	–	–	–	–	–	–	–	–	–	L	–	–	–	–	–
Clusiaceae	–	–	L	–	–	–	–	–	–	F	F E	–	–	–	–	–	–	–
Combretaceae	E	–	F	F I	F	–	F	F L I E	–	–	E	–	L I E	–	F	E	–	E
Connaraceae	–	–	–	–	–	–	–	–	–	–	–	–	L	–	–	–	–	–
Convolvulaceae	–	–	–	–	–	–	–	X	–	–	–	–	–	–	–	–	–	–
Cucurbitaceae	–	–	–	–	–	–	–	F	–	–	–	–	–	–	–	–	–	–
Cunoniaceae	–	–	L	–	–	–	–	–	–	–	–	–	–	–	–	–	–	–
Cyperaceae	–	–	–	–	–	–	–	–	I	–	–	–	–	–	–	–	–	–
Dichapetalaceae	–	–	–	–	–	–	–	–	–	–	–	–	L	F	–	–	–	–
Didiereaceae	–	–	–	–	–	–	–	X	–	–	–	–	–	–	–	–	–	–
Dilleniaceae	–	–	F	–	F	–	F	–	–	–	–	–	–	–	–	–	–	–
Dioscoreaceae	–	–	–	–	–	–	–	–	–	–	F	–	–	–	–	–	–	–
Ebenaceae	–	–	F	F X	–	–	–	F	–	–	–	–	E	–	–	–	–	–

PLANT FAMILIES EXPLOITED	CHEIROGALEIDAE SPECIES																	
	ALLOCEBUS TRICHOTIS	*CHEIROGALEUS CROSSLEYI*	*C. MAJOR*	*C. MEDIUS*	*C. THOMASI*	*MICROCEBUS BERTHAE*	*M. GANZHORNI*	*M. GRISEORUFUS*	*M. JOLLYAE*	*M. LEHILAHYTSARA*	*M. MURINUS*	*M. MYOXINUS*	*M. RAVELOBENSIS*	*M. RUFUS*	*M. TANOSI*	*MIRZA COQUERELI*	*M. ZAZA*	*PHANER PALLESCENS*
Ericaceae	–	–	F	–	FI	–	FI	–	–	–	–	–	–	–	F	–	–	–
Erythroxylaceae	–	–	F	F	F	–	F	–	–	–	E	–	–	–	–	–	–	–
Euphorbiaceae	–	–	FL	–	F	–	F	FL EX	–	–	E	–	–	–	–	–	–	–
Fabaceae	–	–	LIX	I	I	–	I	FLIN EX	–	–	FE	–	FE	–	–	N	–	E
Gentianaceae	–	–	F	–	–	–	–	–	–	–	–	–	–	F	F	–	–	–
Hernandiaceae	–	–	–	–	–	–	–	FLE	–	–	–	–	–	–	–	–	–	–
Hypericaceae	–	–	F	–	F		F	–	–	FI	–	–	–	F	F	–	–	–
Lamiaceae	–	–	F	F	F		F	FE	–	–	N	–	–	–	–	–	–	–
Lauraceae	–	–	FI	–	F		F	–	–	–	–	–	–	–	F	–	–	–
Loganiaceae	–	–	–	FS	–	F	–	FE	–	–	F	–	FL	–	–	–	–	–
Loranthaceae	–	–	FI	–	FI		FI	F	–	–	–	–	–	F	F	–	–	–
Lythraceae	–	–	–	F	–		–	–	–	–	–	–	–	–	–	–	–	–
Malpighiaceae	–	–	–	–	–		–	F	–	–	–	–	–	–	–	–	–	–
Malvaceae	–	–	F	FIE	F	F	–	FLI EX	–	–	F	–	E	–	–	E	–	INE
Malvaceae (introduced)	–	–	–	–	–	–	–	–	–	–	N	–	–	–	–	–	–	–
Melastomataceae	–	–	–	–	–	–	F	–	–	F	–	–	–	F	–	–	–	–
Melastomataceae (introduced)	–	–	–	–	–	–	–	–	F	F	–	–	–	–	–	–	–	–
Meliaceae	–	–	F	–	F	–	F	FE	–	–	E	–	LE	–	–	–	–	E
Meliaceae (introduced)	–	–	–	–	–	–	–	E	–	–	–	–	–	–	–	–	–	–
Menispermaceae	–	–	F	–	F	–	F	–	–	–	–	–	–	F	–	–	–	–
Metteniusaceae	–	–	F	–	F	–	–	–	–	–	–	–	–	–	F	–	–	–
Monimiaceae	–	–	F	–	–	–	–	–	–	–	–	–	–	F	F	–	–	–
Moraceae	–	–	FL	–	F	–	F	–	F	–	E	–	LIE	F	F	–	–	–
Myrtaceae	–	–	FL	–	F	–	F	–	–	–	–	–	L	–	F	–	–	–
Myrtaceae (introduced)	–	–	FI	–	FI	–	FI	–	–	F	–	–	–	F	–	–	–	–
Ochnaceae	–	–	F	F	F	–	F	–	–	–	–	–	–	–	–	–	–	–
Olacaceae	–	–	–	–	–	–	–	FEX	–	–	–	–	F	–	–	–	–	–
Oleaceae	–	–	F	I	F	–	F	–	–	–	FE	–	FLE	–	F	–	–	–
Orchidaceae	–	–	I	–	–	–	–	–	–	–	–	–	–	–	–	–	–	–
Passifloraceae	–	–	–	–	–	–	–	F	–	–	–	–	F	–	–	–	–	–
Phyllanthaceae	–	–	FL	F	F	–	FL	FLIE	–	–	FE	–	–	–	F	–	–	–
Physenaceae	–	–	–	–	–	–	–	FE	–	–	–	–	–	–	–	–	–	–
Poaceae (introduced)	–	–	L	–	–	–	–	–	–	–	–	–	–	–	–	–	–	–
Primulaceae	–	–	FL	–	F	–	F	–	–	F	–	–	–	F	–	–	–	–
Putranjivaceae	–	–	–	–	–	–	–	–	–	F	–	–	–	–	–	–	–	–

(continued overleaf)

TABLE 14.11. ***continued***

PLANT FAMILIES EXPLOITED	CHEIROGALEIDAE SPECIES																	
	ALLOCEBUS TRICHOTIS	*CHEIROGALEUS CROSSLEYI*	*C. MAJOR*	*C. MEDIUS*	*C. THOMASI*	*MICROCEBUS BERTHAE*	*M. GANZHORNI*	*M. GRISEORUFUS*	*M. JOLLYAE*	*M. LEHILAHYTSARA*	*M. MURINUS*	*M. MYOXINUS*	*M. RAVELOBENSIS*	*M. RUFUS*	*M. TANOSI*	*MIRZA COQUERELI*	*M. ZAZA*	*PHANER PALLESCENS*
Rhamnaceae	–	–	–	F	–	–	F	F	–	–	–	F	–	–	–	–	–	F
Rhizophoraceae	–	–	–	–	–	–	–	–	–	–	–	–	E	–	–	–	–	–
Rosaceae	–	–	L	–	–	–	–	–	–	–	–	–	–	–	–	–	–	–
Rosaceae (introduced)	–	–	L	–	–	–	–	–	–	–	–	–	–	–	–	–	–	–
Rubiaceae	–	I	F L I	F X	F	F	F I	F E	F	F I	F I N E	–	F L I E	F	F	–	F	E
Rubiaceae (introduced)	–	–	F	–	–	–	–	–	–	–	–	–	–	–	–	–	–	–
Rutaceae	–	–	F	–	F	–	F	L E X	–	–	E	–	L E	–	F	–	–	E
Salicaceae	–	–	F L	–	F	–	F	–	–	–	E	–	F E	–	F	–	–	–
Salvadoraceae	–	–	–	–	–	–	–	F L E X	–	–	–	–	–	–	–	–	–	–
Santalaceae	–	–	–	–	–	–	–	F	–	–	–	–	–	F	–	–	–	–
Sapindaceae	–	–	F	F	F	–	F	–	–	–	F	–	L	–	F	–	–	–
Sapotaceae	–	–	F	–	–	–	–	F	–	–	–	–	–	–	–	–	–	–
Sarcolaenaceae	–	–	F I	–	F I	–	F I	–	–	–	–	–	–	–	F	–	–	–
Smilacaceae	–	–	F	–	F	–	F	–	–	–	–	–	–	–	–	–	–	–
Sphaerosepalaceae	–	–	–	–	–	–	–	F E	–	–	E	–	E	–	–	–	–	–
Stilbaceae	–	–	–	–	–	–	–	–	–	–	–	–	–	F	–	–	–	–
Strelitziaceae	–	I	N	–	–	–	–	–	–	–	–	–	–	–	–	–	N	–
Talinaceae	–	–	–	–	–	–	–	F X	–	–	–	–	–	–	–	–	–	–
Verbenaceae	–	–	–	–	–	–	–	–	–	–	I	–	–	–	–	–	–	–
Verbenaceae (introduced)	–	–	F I	–	–	–	–	–	–	F	–	–	–	–	–	–	–	–
Violaceae	–	–	–	F	–	–	–	–	–	–	–	–	–	–	–	–	–	–
Vitaceae	–	–	–	–	–	–	–	–	–	–	–	–	–	F	–	–	–	–
References	3	13	6, 13, 14, 22, 23, 28, 35, 47	2, 8, 11, 12, 15, 20, 40	6, 23, 38	9	23, 25, 26	5, 17, 18, 32–34, 43	31	13, 14, 36	9, 16, 18, 20, 21, 24, 26, 29, 30, 37, 41, 43–45	10	19, 29, 30, 37, 45, 46	1, 31	6	20, 27	4, 39	2, 7, 9, 18, 40, 42, 43

Notes: Plants introduced to Madagascar are noted. Key to plant parts exploited: B, bark; E, exudates; F, fruits; I, inflorescences; L, leaves; N, nectar; P, piths and/or stems; S, seeds; X, no data available on which plant part was exploited.

Key to references: 1. Atsalis (1999a); 2. Baum (1995); 3. Biebouw (2009); 4. Birkinshaw and Colquhoun (1998); 5. Bohr et al. (2011); 6. Bollen et al. (2004a); 7. Charles-Dominique and Petter (1980); 8. D. J. Curtis and Zaramody (1998); 9. Dammhahn and Kappeler (2008a); 10. Dammhahn et al. (2009); 11. Fietz and Ganzhorn (1999); 12. Fietz et al. (2003); 13. Ganzhorn (1987); 14. Ganzhorn (1988); 15. Ganzhorn and Kappeler (1996); 16. Génin (2003); 17. Génin and Rambeloarivony (2018); 18. Génin et al. (2010); 19. Hagenah (2001); 20. Hladik et al. (1980); 21. Joly-Radko and Zimmermann (2010); 22. Kress et al. (1994); 23. Lahann (2007b); 24. Lutermann (2001); 25. R. D. Martin (1972a); 26. R. D. Martin (1973); 27. Pagès (1980); 28. J.-J. Petter et al. (1977); 29. Radespiel et al. (2006); 30. M. Rahelinirina (2002); 31. Ramananjato et al. (2020); 32. Randrianarimalalasoa (2008); 33. Rasoazanabary (2011); 34. Rasoazanabary and Godfrey (2016); 35. Ratsirarson and Ranaivonasy (2002); 36. O. H. Razafindratsima (unpublished data); 37. Reimann (2002); 38. S. H. Roberts (unpublished data); 39. Rode-Margono et al. (2016); 40. Scharfe and Schlund (1996); 41. Schmelting (2000); 42. Schülke (2003); 43. A. C. Smith (2010); 44. Sussman (1978); 45. Thorén et al. (2011); 46. Weidt (2001); 47. P. C. Wright and Martin (1995).

TABLE 14.12. Plant parts consumed by *Daubentonia madagascariensis* (Daubentoniidae)

PLANT FAMILIES EXPLOITED	PLANT PART
Anacardiaceae (introduced)	F
Arecaceae	F S
Arecaceae (introduced)	F
Burseraceae	F S B
Combretaceae	S
Euphorbiaceae	I
Fabaceae	F I B
Moraceae	X
Moraceae (introduced)	F S
Musaceae (introduced)	F N
Pandanaceae	X
Passifloraceae (introduced)	F
Poaceae (introduced)	L
Sapindaceae (introduced)	F
Strelitziaceae	N
References	1–15

Notes: Plants introduced to Madagascar are noted. Key to plant parts exploited: B, bark; E, exudates; F, fruits; I, inflorescences; L, leaves; N, nectar; P, piths and/or stems; S, seeds; X, no data available on which plant part was exploited.

Key to references: 1. Ancrenaz et al. (1994); 2. Andriamasimanana (1994); 3. Gardner (2009); 4. Goodman et al. (1996c); 5. Iwano (1991); 6. Iwano and Iwakawa (1988); 7. Lhota et al. (2008); 8. J.-J. Petter et al. (1977); 9. Pollock et al. (1985); 10. Randimbiharinirina et al. (2018); 11. Sefczek et al. (2017); 12. Sefczek et al. (2020a); 13. Sterling (1994a); 14. Sterling and McCreless (2006); 15. Sterling et al. (1994).

and seeds. Though considered frugivores, both genera have been observed to rely on leaves and flowers during resource-limited seasons (Martinez and Razafindratsima 2014; Sato et al. 2016). *Lemur* is perhaps the most flexible of the lemurid genera, known to exploit a variety of food items (e.g., fruits, leaves, flowers, etc.) throughout its broad geographic distribution. In fact, *L. catta* (Figure 14.24e) exploits the highest diversity (94 families) of any lemur species, but it is important to note that this is also the most intensively studied species. Among the other species displaying a large food plant diversity are *V. variegata* (72 plant families), *E. rufifrons* (64 families), *E. coronatus* (63 families), and *E. collaris* (60 families). The plant families most frequently exploited by Lemuridae species are Moraceae (20 species), Rubiaceae (18 species), and—with 16 species each—Apocynaceae, Arecaceae, Fabaceae, and Malvaceae. Examples of frequently exploited genera include, for fruits, *Canarium* (Burseraceae), *Canthium* (Rubiaceae), and *Cryptocarya* (Lauraceae); and for fruits and leaves, *Diospyros* (Ebenaceae), *Erythroxylum* (Erythroxylaceae), *Eugenia*, *Syzygium* (Myrtaceae), *Ficus* (Moraceae), and *Grewia* (Malvaceae).

Among the more unusual foods of lemurid species are aquatic plants; the stems of *Nymphaea lotus* (Nymphaeaceae) and the introduced and invasive *Eichhornia crassipes* (Pontederiaceae) are consumed by *H. alaotrensis* (Mutschler 1999). Presumably other lemurs rarely, if ever, exploit such aquatic plants, as normally they occupy habitats in which such plants are inaccessible to them. Furthermore, a number of Lemuridae species have been observed consuming fungi, but relatively few studies identify the fungi to finer taxonomic levels. For example, fungi of the families Auriculariaceae (two species) and Polyporaceae (unidentified genera) are regularly consumed by *H. aureus*, *H. griseus*, *H. meridionalis*, and *P. simus* (C. L. Tan 1999; Eppley et al. 2011, 2016a), while *V. variegata* frequently consumes Polyporaceae fungi at Manombo in the southeast (Ratsimbazafy et al. 2002).

INDRIIDAE

The family Indriidae consists of 19 currently recognized species, and plant-food data are available for 13 of them, mostly concerning diurnal *Indri indri* (see Gamba et al., pp. 1967–71) and *Propithecus* species (see Lawler and Richard, pp. 1971–74), as the feeding ecology of species in the nocturnal genus *Avahi* (see Donati et al., pp. 1963) has been less explored. From these studies, 100 plant families have been recorded as food sources for Indriidae species (Table 14.15). *Propithecus verreauxi* exploits foods from 55 plant families, while other species with high plant family diversity in their diets include *P. tattersalli* (54 families), *P. diadema* (43 families; Figure 14.24g), *A. meridionalis* (38 families), and *P. candidus* (35 families). *Indri indri* exploits foods, mostly young leaves and some fruits, from 33 plant families. Among the plant families exploited by most Indriidae species are Anacardiaceae, Moraceae, and Sapotaceae (all exploited by 12 species); and Apocynaceae, Fabaceae, and Rubiaceae (11 species each). Indriidae species include both fruits and leaves in their diet (Figures 14.24g and h, respectively), frequently exploiting genera such as *Ocotea* (Lauraceae), *Oncostemum* (Primulaceae), *Protorhus* (now considered best placed in the genus *Abrahamia*; Anacardiaceae), *Symphonia* (Clusiaceae), *Syzygium* (Myrtaceae), and *Diospyros* (Ebenaceae). In areas where both *I. indri* and *Propithecus diadema* are sympatric, they exhibit little dietary overlap, with the former consuming mostly young leaves, and the latter consuming fruits, seeds, and flowers. The most unusual plants consumed within Indriidae are the fungus-like terrestrial inflorescences of the root parasites *Cytinus* (Cytinaceae) and *Langsdorffia* and *Ditepalanthus* (Balanophoraceae), all without chlorophyll, which have been reported to be exploited by *P. candidus* and *P. diadema*.

INTRODUCED PLANTS

Plant species from at least 114 botanical families have been introduced to Madagascar via human migration, trade, and agricultural experimentation, though a large number of introduced tree species belong to only a small group of botanical families—for example, Myrtaceae, Fabaceae, Pinaceae, and Meliaceae (Kull et al. 2012).

TABLE 14.13. **Plant parts consumed by different members of the Lepilemuridae**

PLANT FAMILIES EXPLOITED	LEPILEMURIDAE SPECIES							
	LEPILEMUR EDWARDSI	*L. FLEURETAE*	*L. MUSTELINUS*	*L. PETTERI*	*L. RUFICAUDATUS*	*L. SAHAMALAZENSIS*	*L. SEPTENTRIONALIS*	*L. TYMERLACHSONORUM*
Anacardiaceae	X	L	–	–	–	L	–	–
Anacardiaceae (introduced)	–	–	–	–	–	L	L I	–
Annonaceae	X	–	L	–	–	–	L	–
Aphloiaceae	–	–	L	–	–	–	–	–
Apocynaceae	L	L	–	L X	–	L	L	–
Araliaceae	–	–	L	–	–	–	–	–
Asteraceae	–	–	–	–	–	L	–	–
Bignoniaceae	X	–	–	X	F L I	–	–	–
Burseraceae	–	–	–	L X	–	–	–	–
Buxaceae	–	–	–	–	F	–	–	–
Capparaceae	–	–	L	L X	–	–	–	–
Cardiopteridaceae	–	–	L	–	–	–	–	–
Celastraceae	L	–	–	X	F L	–	L	–
Chrysobalanaceae	–	–	–	–	–	L	–	–
Clusiaceae	X	L	L	–	–	L	–	–
Combretaceae	–	L	–	–	F S L	L	–	–
Connaraceae	–	L	–	–	–	–	L	–
Convolvulaceae	–	L I	–	L X	–	–	–	–
Cucurbitaceae	–	–	–	F L X	–	–	–	–
Cyperaceae	X	–	–	–	–	–	–	–
Dichapetalaceae	–	–	L	–	–	–	–	–
Didiereaceae	–	–	–	L I X	–	–	–	–
Dilleniaceae	–	F	–	–	–	–	–	–
Ebenaceae	X	–	–	–	F L	L	–	–
Erythroxylaceae	L	–	L	–	–	L	–	–
Euphorbiaceae	–	–	L	L	L	L	L I	–
Fabaceae	L X	L I	L	L I X	F L I B	L	F L	–
Fabaceae (introduced)	–	–	–	–	–	–	F L	–
Hernandiaceae	–	–	–	X	–	–	–	–
Hypericaceae	–	–	F	–	–	L	–	–
Lamiaceae	L X	–	–	X	–	–	–	–
Lauraceae	–	–	L	–	–	–	–	–
Lecythidaceae	–	–	L	–	L	–	–	–
Loganiaceae	X	–	–	–	F L	L	L	–

PLANT FAMILIES EXPLOITED	LEPILEMURIDAE SPECIES							
	LEPILEMUR EDWARDSI	*L. FLEURETAE*	*L. MUSTELINUS*	*L. PETTERI*	*L. RUFICAUDATUS*	*L. SAHAMALAZENSIS*	*L. SEPTENTRIONALIS*	*L. TYMERLACHSONORUM*
Malvaceae	L X	L	F	L X	F L I X	L	F L	–
Malvaceae (introduced)	–	–	–	–	–	–	–	I
Melastomataceae	–	–	L	–	–	–	–	–
Menispermaceae	–	–	–	X	–	L	–	–
Moraceae	–	–	–	–	–	F L	F L	–
Moringaceae (introduced)	–	–	–	–	–	–	L	–
Myristicaceae	–	L	–	–	–	–	–	–
Myrtaceae	–	F	F L	–	–	–	L	–
Ochnaceae	L	–	–	–	–	–	–	–
Olacaceae	–	–	–	X	–	L	L	–
Oleaceae	L X	–	–	–	L	–	–	–
Phyllanthaceae	–	L	L	X	F L	L	–	–
Poaceae (introduced)	–	–	–	–	–	L	–	–
Polygalaceae	–	–	–	X	–	–	–	–
Primulaceae	–	–	L	–	–	–	–	–
Putranjivaceae	L X	–	–	–	–	–	–	–
Rhamnaceae	–	–	–	–	F	–	L	–
Rhizophoraceae	–	–	–	–	–	L	–	–
Rubiaceae	L X	F L	F L	L X	F L I	–	L	–
Rutaceae	X	–	–	–	L	–	–	–
Salicaceae	–	L	–	–	–	–	–	–
Salvadoraceae	–	–	–	L	–	–	–	–
Sapindaceae	L	–	L	–	L	L	L	–
Sapotaceae	–	L	–	–	–	–	–	–
Sarcolaenaceae	–	–	F	–	–	–	L	–
Scrophulariaceae	–	L	–	X	–	–	–	–
Sphaerosepalaceae	–	–	–	–	–	–	L	–
Violaceae	X	–	L	–	–	–	–	–
References	6, 7, 15, 19	2	6, 13, 14	3, 5, 10, 12	1, 5, 8, 9, 11, 17	18	4	16

Notes: Plants introduced to Madagascar are noted. Key to plant parts exploited: B, bark; E, exudates; F, fruits; I, inflorescences; L, leaves; N, nectar; P, piths and/or stems; S, seeds; X, no data available on which plant part was exploited.

Key to references: 1. Baum (1996); 2. Campera (2018); 3. Charles-Dominique and Hladik (1971); 4. Dinsmore et al. (2016); 5. Dröscher and Kappeler (2014a); 6. Ganzhorn (1988); 7. Ganzhorn (1993); 8. Ganzhorn (2002); 9. Ganzhorn and Kappeler (1996); 10. Hladik and Charles-Dominique (1974); 11. Hladik et al. (1980); 12. Nash (1998); 13. Ratsirarson and Ranaivonasy (2002); 14. O. H. Razafindratsima (unpublished data); 15. Razanahoera (1988); 16. S. H. Roberts (unpublished data); 17. Scharfe and Schlund (1996); 18. Seiler (2012); 19. Thalmann (2001).

TABLE 14.14. **Plant parts consumed by different members of the Lemuridae**

PLANT FAMILIES EXPLOITED	LEMURIDAE SPECIES																						
	EULEMUR ALBIFRONS	*E. CINEREICEPS*	*E. COLLARIS*	*E. CORONATUS*	*E. FLAVIFRONS*	*E. FULVUS*	*E. MACACO*	*E. MONGOZ*	*E. RUBRIVENTER*	*E. RUFIFRONS*	*E. RUFUS*	*E. SANFORDI*	*HAPALEMUR ALAOTRENSIS*	*H. AUREUS*	*H. GRISEUS*	*H. MERIDIONALIS*	*H. OCCIDENTALIS*	*LEMUR CATTA*	*PROLEMUR SIMUS*	*V. RUBRA*	*V. VARIEGATA EDITORUM*	*V. VARIEGATA SUBCINCTA*	*V. VARIEGATA VARIEGATA*
Acanthaceae	–	FL	–	FLI	–	L	FL	–	FLI	FLI	–	FL	–	F	FL	–	–	LX	–	–	F	S	–
Aizoaceae	–	–	–	–	–	–	–	–	–	–	–	–	–	–	–	–	–	L	–	–	–	–	–
Amaranthaceae	–	–	–	–	–	–	–	–	–	–	–	–	–	–	–	–	–	LX	–	–	–	–	–
Amaranthaceae (introduced)	–	–	–	–	–	–	–	–	–	–	–	–	–	–	–	–	–	LIX	–	–	–	–	–
Anacardiaceae	F	FL	F	FSI	F	F	FLI	L	FX	F	–	–	–	–	–	–	–	FL IX	–	X	FLX	F	FLI
Anacardiaceae (introduced)	–	–	–	F	FL	–	FLI EB	F	–	–	–	F	–	–	–	–	–	FX	F	–	–	–	–
Anisophylleaceae	–	F	–	–	–	–	F	–	–	–	–	–	–	–	–	–	–	–	–	L	FL	–	F
Annonaceae	–	FL	FL	FLI	FL	FSL	FI	–	F	L	–	F	–	–	–	–	–	–	–	FL IX	FLX	F	FL
Annonaceae (introduced)	–	–	–	FI	–	–	FI	–	–	–	–	–	–	–	–	–	–	F	X	–	–	–	–
Aphloiaceae	–	–	–	LI	–	L	F	–	FL	FLI	–	FL	–	–	–	–	–	X	–	F	F	–	FL
Apiaceae	–	–	–	–	–	–	–	–	–	–	–	–	–	–	–	L	–	L	–	–	–	–	–
Apocynaceae	FL	FL	I	FL	FL	FL	FL	FL	FLI NX	FL	–	F	–	–	FL	LP	–	FL IP BX	–	F	FX	F	F
Aquifoliaceae	–	–	–	–	–	L	–	–	FX	–	–	–	–	–	–	–	–	–	–	–	X	–	–
Araceae	L	–	FL	–	–	–	–	–	–	–	–	–	–	–	–	LP	–	P	–	–	–	–	–
Araceae (introduced)	–	–	–	–	–	–	L	–	–	–	–	–	–	–	–	–	–	–	–	–	–	–	–
Araliaceae	–	F	F	FN	–	L	–	–	LI	–	–	F	–	–	–	–	–	–	–	–	FLI	–	–
Arecaceae	–	FI	F	F	F	F	FI	–	F	FL	–	F	–	F	F	FLP	–	FP X	FLI	F	FL IE	–	F
Arecaceae (introduced)	–	–	–	–	–	–	F	–	–	–	–	–	–	–	–	–	–	–	–	–	–	–	–
Aristolochiaceae	–	–	–	–	–	–	–	–	–	F	–	–	–	–	–	–	–	LX	–	–	–	–	–
Asclepiadaceae	–	–	L	–	–	–	–	–	–	–	–	–	–	–	–	–	–	–	–	–	–	–	–
Asparagaceae	–	L	FI	FLI	FI	–	F	–	–	–	–	FI	–	–	–	F	–	–	–	FL	–	–	F
Asparagaceae (introduced)	–	–	–	–	–	–	–	–	–	–	–	–	–	–	–	–	–	FL IX	–	–	–	–	–
Asphodelaceae	–	–	–	–	–	–	–	–	–	–	–	–	–	–	–	LP	–	LIX	–	–	–	–	–
Aspleniaceae	–	–	–	–	–	–	–	–	–	L	–	–	–	–	–	–	–	–	–	–	L	–	–
Asteraceae	–	FL	L	–	–	–	–	–	FLX	FL	–	–	–	–	L	LP	–	FL IX	–	–	F	–	–
Asteraceae (introduced)	–	–	–	–	–	–	–	–	–	–	–	–	L	–	–	–	–	LX	–	–	–	–	–
Asteropeiaceae	–	X	F	–	–	–	–	–	–	–	–	–	–	–	–	–	–	X	–	FL	–	–	–
Bignoniaceae	F	FI	F	–	–	–	F	–	–	FI	–	–	–	–	–	–	–	FL IX	–	F	–	–	–
Bignoniaceae (introduced)	–	–	–	–	–	–	–	N	–	–	–	–	–	–	–	–	–	I	–	–	–	–	–
Boraginaceae	–	–	–	F	–	–	FLI	FSL	–	FLI	–	–	–	–	–	–	–	FL IX	–	–	–	–	–
Brassicaceae	–	–	F	–	–	–	–	–	–	–	–	–	–	–	–	–	–	–	–	–	–	–	–
Bromeliaceae (introduced)	–	–	–	–	–	–	L	–	–	F	–	–	–	–	–	–	–	–	–	–	–	–	–
Burseraceae	F	–	F	F	FL	–	F	F	F	F	–	F	–	–	–	–	–	FLX	–	FLI	FX	F	FL

PLANT FAMILIES EXPLOITED	LEMURIDAE SPECIES																					
	EULEMUR ALBIFRONS	*E. CINEREICEPS*	*E. COLLARIS*	*E. CORONATUS*	*E. FLAVIFRONS*	*E. FULVUS*	*E. MACACO*	*E. MONGOZ*	*E. RUBRIVENTER*	*E. RUFIFRONS*	*E. RUFUS*	*E. SANFORDI*	*HAPALEMUR ALAOTRENSIS*	*H. AUREUS*	*H. GRISEUS*	*H. MERIDIONALIS*	*H. OCCIDENTALIS*	*LEMUR CATTA*	*PROLEMUR SIMUS*	*V. RUBRA*	*V. VARIEGATA EDITORUM*	*V. VARIEGATA SUBCINCTA*	*V. VARIEGATA VARIEGATA*
Burseraceae (introduced)	–	–	–	–	–	I	–	–	–	–	–	–	–	–	–	–	–	–	–	–	–	–	–
Buxaceae	–	–	–	–	–	–	–	–	–	–	–	–	–	–	–	–	–	F	–	–	–	–	–
Cactaceae	–	–	–	–	–	–	–	–	F	–	–	–	–	–	–	–	–	–	–	–	–	–	–
Cactaceae (introduced)	–	–	–	–	–	–	–	–	–	–	–	–	–	–	–	–	–	FLI EX	–	–	–	–	–
Calophyllaceae	–	FL	F	–	–	F	FI	–	FLI	FI	–	–	–	–	–	–	–	–	–	FLX	FIX	–	F
Canellaceae	–	F	F	F	–	F	–	–	FL	F	–	F	–	–	–	–	–	–	–	–	F	–	–
Cannabaceae	–	–	–	FL	–	–	–	–	–	FLI	–	FLI	–	–	–	–	–	FL IX	–	–	F	–	–
Capparaceae	–	–	F	F	–	–	–	–	–	F	–	–	–	–	–	–	–	FL IX	–	–	–	–	–
Caricaceae (introduced)	–	–	–	–	–	–	FLI	–	–	–	–	–	–	–	–	–	–	F	F	–	–	–	–
Casuarinaceae	–	–	–	–	–	–	–	–	–	–	–	–	–	–	–	–	–	L	–	–	–	–	–
Celastraceae	–	I	FLI	FLI	–	FL	FL	–	–	F	–	I	–	–	–	N	–	LIX	–	FL	F	–	–
Chrysobalanaceae	–	–	–	–	FI	–	FLI	–	–	–	–	–	–	–	–	–	–	–	–	–	L	–	–
Clusiaceae	F	FLI	FLI	FN	FL	FL	F	–	FLI NX	FS LI	–	FL	–	–	–	–	–	–	–	FL IN	FLI	F	FLI
Colchicaceae	–	–	–	–	–	–	–	–	–	–	–	–	–	–	–	–	–	LI	–	–	–	–	–
Combretaceae	F	FL	FI	F	FL	F	FL	FL N	L	FL IE	–	–	–	–	–	–	–	FLI EX	–	FI	F	–	F
Commelinaceae	–	–	–	–	–	–	–	–	–	–	–	–	–	–	–	–	–	LX	–	–	–	–	–
Connaraceae	FL	–	–	–	–	–	–	–	FL	F	–	–	–	–	–	–	–	–	–	–	L	–	–
Convolvulaceae	–	–	–	–	–	–	–	F	–	–	–	–	LP	–	–	–	–	FLI NX	–	–	F	–	–
Crassulaceae	–	–	–	–	–	–	–	–	–	–	–	–	–	–	–	–	–	LX	–	–	–	–	–
Cucurbitaceae	–	–	–	–	–	FSL	F	–	L	FL	–	–	–	–	–	–	–	FLX	–	F	–	F	–
Cucurbitaceae (introduced)	–	–	–	–	–	F	–	–	–	–	–	–	–	–	–	–	–	LX	–	–	–	–	–
Cunoniaceae	–	–	–	–	–	L	–	–	FIN	FLI	–	–	–	–	–	–	–	–	–	–	FIX	–	–
Cyperaceae	–	–	–	–	–	–	–	–	–	–	–	–	LIP	L	–	LIP	X	IP	L	–	F	–	–
Davalliaceae	–	–	–	–	–	–	–	–	–	–	–	–	–	–	–	–	–	–	–	L	–	–	–
Dennstaedtiaceae	–	L	–	–	–	–	–	–	–	–	–	–	–	–	–	–	–	–	–	–	–	–	–
Dichapetalaceae	–	–	FL	F	–	FI	FL	–	FL	FL	–	F	–	–	–	–	–	L	–	F	F	–	F
Didiereaceae	–	–	–	–	–	–	–	–	–	–	–	–	–	–	–	–	–	FL IX	–	–	–	–	–
Dilleniaceae	–	–	FLI	–	–	–	–	–	–	–	–	–	–	–	–	I	–	–	–	L	–	–	I
Dioscoreaceae	–	–	F	FS	–	–	–	–	–	–	–	–	–	–	–	–	–	LX	–	–	–	–	–
Ebenaceae	FL	FL	FI	FSI	FI	FL	FI	L	F	F	–	F	–	–	–	F	–	FX	–	FL	L	F	FL
Elaeocarpaceae	–	–	F	–	–	–	–	–	FX	FL IN	–	F	–	–	–	–	–	–	–	–	FLX	–	–
Ericaceae	–	–	F	–	–	–	–	–	IX	–	–	–	–	–	–	F	–	X	–	–	–	–	–
Erythroxylaceae	–	FL IX	F	FL IX	L	FL	–	–	LX	FL	–	FLI	–	F	–	F	–	F	–	IN	FL	–	FL
Euphorbiaceae	–	FLI	FI	–	F	FL	FI EB	N	F	FL	–	–	–	L	–	–	X	FLI EX	–	FLI N	FL	–	FL

(continued overleaf)

TABLE 14.14. *continued*

PLANT FAMILIES EXPLOITED	LEMURIDAE SPECIES																						
	EULEMUR ALBIFRONS	*E. CINEREICEPS*	*E. COLLARIS*	*E. CORONATUS*	*E. FLAVIFRONS*	*E. FULVUS*	*E. MACACO*	*E. MONGOZ*	*E. RUBRIVENTER*	*E. RUFIFRONS*	*E. RUFUS*	*E. SANFORDI*	*HAPALEMUR ALAOTRENSIS*	*H. AUREUS*	*H. GRISEUS*	*H. MERIDIONALIS*	*H. OCCIDENTALIS*	*LEMUR CATTA*	*PROLEMUR SIMUS*	*V. RUBRA*	*V. VARIEGATA EDITORUM*	*V. VARIEGATA SUBCINCTA*	*V. VARIEGATA VARIEGATA*
Euphorbiaceae (introduced)	–	–	–	I	–	–	–	–	–	–	–	–	–	–	–	–	–	LI	–	–	–	–	–
Fabaceae	FLI	FLI	FLI	FSL IN	FLI	FLI	FSL IN	FS LI	FLI N	FLI NE BX	–	FI	–	–	FI	L	–	FS LIE BX	–	FLI N	FLI N	I	FL
Fabaceae (introduced)	–	–	–	FI	–	I	FLI	I	–	LIE	–	–	–	–	–	–	–	FSL IX	X	–	F	–	–
Flacourtiaceae	–	–	FE	–	–	–	–	–	–	–	–	–	–	–	–	F	–	F	–	–	–	F	–
Flagellariaceae	–	–	–	–	–	–	–	FLI	–	–	–	–	–	–	–	L	–	–	–	–	–	–	–
Gentianaceae	–	F	F	–	–	–	–	–	FLX	F	–	–	–	–	–	–	–	–	–	F	I	–	F
Hernandiaceae	–	–	–	–	–	–	–	–	–	–	–	–	–	–	–	–	–	FL IX	–	–	–	–	–
Hypericaceae	–	F	–	FI	FLI	–	FI	–	F	F	–	FL	–	–	–	–	–	X	–	–	FX	–	–
Icacinaceae	F	F	F	–	–	–	F	–	L	–	–	–	–	–	–	–	–	X	–	–	–	–	–
Lamiaceae	–	F	F	L	–	F	FI	–	X	FL	–	X	–	–	–	FI	–	FL IX	–	–	FL	–	–
Lauraceae	FL	FL	FL	FL	F	FSL	FI	–	FL IX	FLI	–	F	–	–	L	–	–	X	–	FL IN	FLX	FL	FL
Lauraceae (introduced)	–	–	–	F	–	–	–	–	–	–	–	–	–	–	–	–	–	–	–	–	–	–	–
Liliaceae	–	–	–	–	–	–	–	–	–	–	–	–	–	–	–	–	–	–	–	L	–	–	–
Linaceae	–	F	–	–	–	–	–	–	–	–	–	–	–	–	–	–	–	–	–	–	F	–	–
Loganiaceae	FL	–	F	F	F	F	F	F	–	F	–	FI	–	–	–	–	–	FLX	–	FL	F	–	F
Loranthaceae	–	L	FL	FS LI	–	–	F	–	FLI NX	FLI	–	FL	–	–	–	–	–	L	–	L	FLI	–	–
Lygodiaceae	–	–	–	–	–	–	L	–	–	–	–	–	–	–	–	–	–	–	–	–	–	–	–
Lythraceae	–	–	–	FI	–	–	L	–	–	FL	–	–	–	–	–	–	–	FL	–	–	–	–	–
Malpighiaceae	–	–	–	–	–	–	–	–	–	–	–	–	–	–	–	–	–	L	–	–	X	–	–
Malvaceae	F	FLI	–	F	F	FI	FL	FL	FLI NX	FLI	F	FI	–	F	F	–	–	FL IX	–	FLI NX	FL IX	FS	F
Malvaceae (introduced)	–	–	–	–	–	–	FLI N	FN	–	–	–	–	–	–	–	–	–	–	–	–	–	–	–
Melastomataceae	F	F	F	F	–	FL	F	–	F	FLI	–	–	–	F	F	F	–	F	–	IN	FL	F	F
Melastomataceae (introduced)	–	F	F	–	–	F	–	–	–	–	–	–	–	–	F	–	FX	–	–	F	F	–	–
Meliaceae	FL	F	F	FL IN	–	F	–	–	FX	LI	–	FLI	–	–	–	–	–	FL IX	–	FL	FLI	FLI	–
Meliaceae (introduced)	–	–	–	–	–	–	–	–	–	F	–	–	–	–	–	–	–	FL IX	–	–	–	–	–
Menispermaceae	–	F	F	F	F	F	F	–	F	–	–	–	–	–	–	–	–	LX	–	–	F	S	
Metteniusaceae	–	FL	F	–	–	–	–	–	F	–	–	–	–	–	–	–	–	FL	–	–	F	–	–
Molluginaceae	–	–	–	–	–	–	–	–	–	–	–	–	–	–	–	–	–	L	–	–	–	–	–
Monimiaceae	–	F	F	F	–	FL	F	–	FL	FL	–	F	–	–	–	–	–	–	–	–	FLX	–	F
Moraceae	F	F	FLI	FLX	FLI	FSL	FL	FS LI	FLX	FLI	FL	FLI	–	F	FL	F	FX	FLX	FX	FLI	FL X	F	FL
Moraceae (introduced)	–	–	–	F	–	–	FLI	–	–	–	–	–	–	–	–	–	X	–	FX	–	–	–	–
Musaceae (introduced)	–	–	–	–	–	–	FI	–	–	–	–	–	–	–	–	–	–	F	FX	–	–	–	–

PLANT FAMILIES EXPLOITED	LEMURIDAE SPECIES																						
	EULEMUR ALBIFRONS	*E. CINEREICEPS*	*E. COLLARIS*	*E. CORONATUS*	*E. FLAVIFRONS*	*E. FULVUS*	*E. MACACO*	*E. MONGOZ*	*E. RUBRIVENTER*	*E. RUFIFRONS*	*E. RUFUS*	*E. SANFORDI*	*HAPALEMUR ALAOTRENSIS*	*H. AUREUS*	*H. GRISEUS*	*H. MERIDIONALIS*	*H. OCCIDENTALIS*	*LEMUR CATTA*	*PROLEMUR SIMUS*	*V. RUBRA*	*V. VARIEGATA EDITORUM*	*V. VARIEGATA SUBCINCTA*	*V. VARIEGATA VARIEGATA*
Myricaceae	–	–	–	–	–	–	–	–	–	–	–	–	–	–	–	–	–	X	–	–	–	–	–
Myristicaceae	F	–	F	–	–	–	–	–	–	–	–	–	–	–	–	–	–	–	–	FL	–	–	L
Myrtaceae	F	FL	FI	F	–	FL	F	–	FL IX	FL	–	F	–	–	–	F	–	FIX	–	FL IX	FL IX	FL	FL
Myrtaceae (introduced)	–	F	F	F	–	I	FI	–	FI	F	–	–	–	F	F	N	–	FIX	–	–	–	–	–
Nyctaginaceae	–	–	–	–	–	–	–	–	–	–	–	–	–	–	–	–	–	LIX	–	–	–	–	–
Nyctaginaceae (introduced)	–	–	–	–	–	–	–	–	–	–	–	–	–	–	–	–	–	LIX	–	–	–	–	–
Nymphaeaceae	–	–	–	–	–	–	–	–	–	–	–	–	LP	–	–	–	–	–	–	–	–	–	–
Ochnaceae	–	–	F	–	–	L	–	–	F	FL	–	–	–	–	–	–	–	–	–	L	–	–	–
Olacaceae	–	–	–	F	FL	F	–	–	–	–	–	–	–	–	–	–	–	FX	–	–	–	–	–
Oleaceae	F	FLI	FL	FL		FL	F	–	FX	FL	–	FLI	–	–	–	FLP	–	FLX	–	F	F	–	F
Opiliaceae	–	–	–	–	–	–	–	–	–	–	–	–	–	–	–	–	–	LX	–	–	–	–	–
Orchidaceae	–	–	–	I	–	L	–	–	X	–	–	I	–	FLI	FLI	I	–	LI	–	LX	–	–	–
Pandanaceae	F	FLI	FL IP	F	–	–	FL	–	FI	F	–	–	–	–	–	FLP	–	P	–	F	F	–	–
Papaveraceae (introduced)	–	–	–	–	–	–	–	–	–	–	–	–	–	–	–	–	–	LIX	–	–	–	–	–
Passifloraceae	–	–	–	FL	–	F	–	F	–	F	–	–	–	–	–	–	–	L	–	–	–	–	–
Phyllanthaceae	–	FL	F	FI	I	FL	F	F	FX	F	–	FL	–	–	–	FL	–	FL IX	–	FL	FL	F	F
Physenaceae	–	–	–	F	–	–	–	–	–	–	–	F	–	–	–	–	–	FLX	–	–	–	–	–
Pinaceae (introduced)	–	–	–	L	–	LI	–	–	–	–	–	–	–	–	–	–	–	–	–	–	–	–	–
Piperaceae	–	–	–	FLI	–	–	–	–	–	–	–	LI	–	–	–	–	–	–	–	–	–	–	–
Piperaceae (introduced)	–	–	–	–	–	–	F	–	–	–	–	–	–	–	–	–	–	–	–	–	–	–	–
Pittosporaceae	–	–	–	F	–	–	–	–	F	FL	–	F	–	–	–	–	–	–	–	–	X	–	–
Poaceae	–	L	–	LI	–	FI	–	–	L	–	–	FI	LP	LP	LIP	LP	LPX	LIX	LIP	–	–	–	–
Poaceae (introduced)	–	–	–	–	–	–	L	–	–	–	–	–	–	–	FLI	L	X	LI	FLX	–	–	–	–
Podocarpaceae	–	–	–	–	–	F	–	–	–	–	–	–	–	–	–	–	–	–	–	–	–	–	F
Polygonaceae	–	–	–	–	–	–	–	–	–	–	–	–	L	–	–	–	–	L	–	–	–	–	–
Pontederiaceae (introduced)	–	–	–	–	–	–	–	–	–	–	–	–	IP	–	–	–	–	–	–	–	–	–	–
Primulaceae	–	FLI	F	FL	–	FS LI	F	–	FL IX	FL	–	FLI	–	L	F	F	–	FX	–	–	FLX	F	F
Proteaceae	–	–	–	–	–	–	–	–	FL IX	–	–	–	–	–	–	–	–	–	–	–	FLX	–	–
Putranjivaceae	–	–	F	FLI	–	–	–	–	–	–	–	FLI	–	–	–	–	–	–	–	F	–	–	–
Rhamnaceae	–	–	–	FL	–	F	–	FL NB	F	F	F	I	–	–	–	–	–	FL IX	–	FL	–	–	–
Rhizophoraceae	–	–	–	FL	F	L	F	–	–	–	–	F	–	–	–	–	–	–	–	–	F	–	–
Rosaceae (introduced)	–	–	–	F	–	–	–	–	–	–	–	FL	–	–	–	–	–	–	X	–	–	–	–
Rubiaceae	FLI	FLI	FLI	F	F	FSL	F	FSL	FL IX	FL IX	–	FI	–	F	F	F	–	FL IX	–	FLI NX	FLX	FI	FI
Rubiaceae (introduced)	–	–	–	F	–	–	F	–	–	–	–	L	–	–	–	–	–	–	X	FL	F	–	F

(continued overleaf)

TABLE 14.14. ***continued***

PLANT FAMILIES EXPLOITED	LEMURIDAE SPECIES																						
	EULEMUR ALBIFRONS	*E. CINEREICEPS*	*E. COLLARIS*	*E. CORONATUS*	*E. FLAVIFRONS*	*E. FULVUS*	*E. MACACO*	*E. MONGOZ*	*E. RUBRIVENTER*	*E. RUFIFRONS*	*E. RUFUS*	*E. SANFORDI*	*HAPALEMUR ALAOTRENSIS*	*H. AUREUS*	*H. GRISEUS*	*H. MERIDIONALIS*	*H. OCCIDENTALIS*	*LEMUR CATTA*	*PROLEMUR SIMUS*	*V. RUBRA*	*V. VARIEGATA EDITORUM*	*V. VARIEGATA SUBCINCTA*	*V. VARIEGATA VARIEGATA*
Rutaceae	–	L	F	FLI	–	L	–	–	F	FLI	–	FI	–	F	–	F	–	FLIX	–	–	FL	–	F
Rutaceae (introduced)	–	–	–	FI	–	–	FLI	–	F	–	–	–	–	–	–	–	–	–	–	–	–	–	–
Salicaceae	–	FLX	FI	FI	F	FL	F	–	F	FL	–	FLI	–	–	F	–	–	FLX	–	FL	F	–	F
Salvadoraceae	–	–	–	FL	–	–	–	–	–	FL	–	–	–	–	–	–	–	FLIBX	–	–	–	–	–
Santalaceae	–	–	–	–	–	–	–	–	F	–	–	–	–	–	–	–	–	–	–	–	–	–	–
Sapindaceae	–	FL	F	FSLIX	I	FLI	FLI	–	FSLX	FSI	–	FL	–	–	–	F	–	FLX	–	FLI	FLX	–	FL
Sapindaceae (introduced)	–	–	–	–	–	F	–	S	–	–	–	–	–	–	–	–	X	–	X	–	L	–	–
Sapotaceae	FL	FL	FI	FSI	–	F	FL	–	FL	F	–	FLI	–	–	–	–	–	–	–	FLX	FLINX	FSN	FL
Sarcolaenaceae	–	F	FI	–	–	L	F	–	–	F	–	–	–	–	–	FN	–	FI	–	–	FN	–	FS
Scrophulariaceae	–	–	–	–	–	F	–	–	–	–	–	–	–	–	–	–	–	X	–	–	–	–	–
Smilacaceae	L	F	FL	FL	–	–	FL	–	FLX	FL	–	FL	–	L	FL	LP	–	P	–	–	–	–	–
Solanaceae (introduced)	–	F	–	FI	–	–	–	–	–	–	–	F	–	–	–	–	–	FIX	–	–	–	–	F
Sphaerosepalaceae	F	L	F	S	–	F	–	–	–	L	–	–	–	–	–	–	–	X	–	F	F	–	F
Stemonuraceae	–	–	–	FLI	–	–	–	–	–	–	–	FLI	–	–	–	–	–	–	–	–	–	–	–
Stilbaceae	–	F	–	–	–	–	–	–	F	–	–	–	–	–	–	–	–	X	–	–	–	–	–
Strelitziaceae	FN	IN	I	–	–	–	FIN	–	–	L	–	–	–	–	–	IN	–	I	LIX	FLINX	FIN	FN	IN
Taccaceae	–	–	FP	–	–	–	–	–	–	–	–	–	–	–	–	–	–	–	–	–	–	–	–
Talinaceae	–	–	–	–	–	–	–	–	–	–	–	–	–	–	–	–	–	FLX	–	–	–	–	–
Thelypteridaceae	–	–	–	–	–	–	–	–	–	–	–	–	L	–	–	–	–	–	–	–	–	–	–
Torricelliaceae	–	–	–	–	–	–	–	–	F	F	–	–	–	–	–	–	–	–	–	–	–	–	–
Urticaceae	–	–	–	–	–	–	–	L	L	F	–	–	–	L	L	–	–	L	–	–	–	–	–
Urticaceae (introduced)	–	F	–	–	–	–	–	–	–	–	–	–	–	–	–	–	–	–	–	–	F	–	–
Velloziaceae	–	–	–	–	–	–	–	–	–	–	–	–	–	–	–	–	–	I	–	–	–	–	–
Verbenaceae	–	–	FI	F	–	–	–	–	–	–	–	–	–	–	–	–	–	L	–	–	–	–	–
Verbenaceae (introduced)	–	F	–	FLI	–	–	–	–	–	–	–	FI	–	–	–	–	–	F	–	–	F	–	–
Violaceae	–	–	–	F	–	–	LI	FI	–	F	–	–	–	–	–	–	–	FLIX	–	–	–	–	–
Vitaceae	–	–	–	FSLI	–	–	F	FLN	F	FL	–	F	–	–	L	–	–	FLX	–	–	F	F	–
Ximeniaceae	–	–	–	–	–	F	–	–	–	–	–	–	–	–	–	–	–	FS	–	–	–	–	–
Zingiberaceae	F	F	–	–	–	–	F	–	–	–	–	–	–	–	–	–	X	–	LX	–	–	–	–
Zygophyllaceae	–	–	–	–	–	–	–	–	–	–	–	–	–	–	–	–	–	FLI	–	–	–	–	–

PLANT FAMILIES EXPLOITED	LEMURIDAE SPECIES																						
	EULEMUR ALBIFRONS	*E. CINEREICEPS*	*E. COLLARIS*	*E. CORONATUS*	*E. FLAVIFRONS*	*E. FULVUS*	*E. MACACO*	*E. MONGOZ*	*E. RUBRIVENTER*	*E. RUFIFRONS*	*E. RUFUS*	*E. SANFORDI*	*HAPALEMUR ALAOTRENSIS*	*H. AUREUS*	*H. GRISEUS*	*H. MERIDIONALIS*	*H. OCCIDENTALIS*	*LEMUR CATTA*	*PROLEMUR SIMUS*	*V. RUBRA*	*V. VARIEGATA EDITORUM*	*V. VARIEGATA SUBCINCTA*	*V. VARIEGATA VARIEGATA*
References	31, 47, 62, 71, 98, 128–130	3, 59, 88	11, 14, 28, 29, 38, 112	15, 41, 46, 47, 66, 97, 120, 133	131	42–44, 50, 95, 103–106, 111, 127	1, 8–10, 17, 18, 83, 84, 116, 117	5, 20, 123	22, 24, 30, 51, 75–79, 81, 87, 100, 101, 113, 126, 135	24, 25, 27, 40, 45, 51, 59, 77–79, 81, 89, 100, 101, 109, 114, 119, 121, 122, 135	21	16, 41, 66, 133	74, 84	39, 49, 69, 124, 139	39, 44, 49, 56, 57, 80, 84, 95, 124, 134, 139	33–38	67, 82	13, 19, 32, 36, 47, 48, 52–55, 60, 61, 63–65, 70, 75, 85, 86, 91, 92, 94, 107, 108, 113, 114, 115, 118, 122, 135–138, 140	2, 26, 39, 49, 69, 90, 96, 124, 125, 139	68, 71, 98, 99, 102, 128–130	6, 7, 23, 24, 40, 51, 58, 73, 93, 100, 101, 132	72	4, 12, 110

Notes: Plants introduced to Madagascar are noted. Key to plant parts exploited: B, bark; E, exudates; F, fruits; I, inflorescences; L, leaves; N, nectar; P, piths and/or stems; S, seeds; X, no data available on which plant part was exploited.

Key to references: 1. J. R. Andrews and Birkinshaw (1998); 2. Andriaholinirina et al. (2003); 3. Andriamaharoa et al. (2010); 4. Andrianarisata (1994); 5. Andriatsarafara (1988); 6. Balko (1998); 7. Beeby and Baden (2021); 8. Birkinshaw (1999); 9. Birkinshaw (2001); 10. Birkinshaw and Colquhoun (1998); 11. Bollen et al. (2004a); 12. Britt (2000); 13. Budnitz and Dainis (1975); 14. Campera (2012); 15. K. S. Chen et al. (2015); 16. K. S. Chen et al. (2016); 17. Colquhoun (1993); 18. Colquhoun (2005); 19. Crawford et al. (2015); 20. D. I. Curtis (1997); 21. D. J. Curtis and Zaramody (1998); 22. Dague and Petter (1988); 23. Day et al. (2009); 24. Dew and Wright (1998); 25. de Winter et al. (2013); 26. Dolch et al. (2008); 27. Donati et al. (1999); 28. Donati et al. (2007b); 29. Donati et al. (2011); 30. DuBour (2018); 31. Duckworth et al. (1995); 32. Ellwanger and Gould (2011); 33. Eppley et al. (2011); 34. Eppley (2015); 35. Eppley et al. (2015a); 36. Eppley et al. (2015b); 37. Eppley et al. (2016a); 38. Eppley et al. (2017a); 39. Eppley et al. (2017b); 40. Erhart et al. (2018); 41. Freed (1996); 42. Ganzhorn (1985); 43. Ganzhorn (1987); 44. Ganzhorn (1988); 45. Ganzhorn and Kappeler (1996); 46. Gardner (2009); 47. Gardner (2016); 48. Gemmill and Gould (2008); 49. Glander et al. (1989); 50. Goodman et al. (1996c); 51. Goodman et al. (1997c); 52. L. Gould and Gabriel (2014); 53. L. Gould et al. (2009); 54. L. Gould et al. (2011); 55. L. Gould et al. (2015); 56. Grassi (2002); 57. Grassi (2006); 58. Holmes et al. (2016); 59. Johnson (2002); 60. Jolly (1966); 61. Kelley (2011); 62. Kress et al. (1994); 63. LaFleur (2012); 64. LaFleur and Gould (2009); 65. LaFleur and Sauther (2015); 66. Marrocoli et al. (2013); 67. Martinez (2008); 68. Martinez and Razafindratsima (2014); 69. Meier and Rumpler (1987); 70. Mertl-Millhollen et al. (2003); 71. Mogilewsky (2020); 72. Morland (1991a); 73. Moses and Semple (2011); 74. Mutschler (1999); 75. O'Mara (2012); 76. Overdorff (1988); 77. Overdorff (1992); 78. Overdorff (1993); 79. Overdorff and Strait (1998); 80. Overdorff et al. (1997); 81. Overdorff et al. (2002); 82. Patel et al. (2014); 83. J.-J. Petter (1962); 84. J.-J. Petter et al. (1977); 85. Pinkus et al. (2006); 86. S. V. Rakotoarisoa (1999); 87. Rakotonirina et al. (2010); 88. Ralainasolo et al. (2008); 89. Ralisoamalala (1996); 90. Randriahaingo et al. (2014); 91. Rasamimanana (1999); 92. Rasamimanana and Rafidinarivo (1993); 93. Ratsimbazafy et al. (2002); 94. Ratsirarson (1987); 95. Ratsirarson and Ranaivonasy (2002); 96. Ravaloharimanitra et al. (2011); 97. Ravelomalala (2015); 98. Razafindratsima (2009); 99. Razafindratsima and Razafimahatratra (2010); 100. Razafindratsima et al. (2014); 101. O. H. Razafindratsima (unpublished data); 102. Rigamonti (1993); 103. Sato (2012); 104. Sato (2013a); 105. Sato (2013b); 106. Sato et al. (2014); 107. Sauther (1992); 108. Sauther and Cuozzo (2009); 109. Scharfe and Schlund (1996); 110. Schmidt et al. (2010); 111. Semel (2015); 112. Serra (2011); 113. Simmen et al. (1999); 114. Simmen et al. (2003); 115. Simmen et al. (2006); 116. Simmen et al. (2007); 117. Snow (2011); 118. Soma (2006); 119. Spehn and Ganzhorn (2000); 120. K. J. E. Steffens (unpublished data); 121. Sussman (1975); 122. Sussman (1977a); 123. Sussman and Tattersall (1976); 124. C. L. Tan (1999); 125. C. L. Tan (2006); 126. Tecot (2008); 127. Valenta (2014); 128. (1997a); 129. Vasey (2000a); 130. Vasey et al. (2018); 131. Volampeno (2009); 132. F. J. White et al. (1995); 133. J. M. Wilson et al. (1989); 134. P. C. Wright (1986); 135. Yamashita (1996); 136. Yamashita (2002); 137. Yamashita (2003); 138. Yamashita (2008); 139. Yamashita et al. (2009); 140. Yamashita et al. (2015).

TABLE 14.15. **Plant parts consumed by different members of the Indriidae**

PLANT FAMILIES EXPLOITED	INDRIIDAE SPECIES: *AVAHI LANIGER*	*A. MERIDIONALIS*	*A. OCCIDENTALIS*	*A. PEYRIERASI*	*INDRI INDRI*	*PROPITHECUS CANDIDUS*	*P. COQUERELI*	*P. CORONATUS*	*P. DIADEMA*	*P. EDWARDSI*	*P. PERRIERI*	*P. TATTERSALLI*	*P. VERREAUXI*
Acanthaceae	F L	–	–	–	L	–	–	–	L	L	–	–	L
Amaranthaceae (introduced)	–	–	–	–	–	–	–	–	–	–	–	–	L
Anacardiaceae	–	X	L X	L	L	F L I	F L I X	L I	F S L I	F S L	L	F S L I X	F L I B X
Anacardiaceae (introduced)	–	–	–	–	–	–	F L B	–	–	–	I	F S L I X	–
Anisophylleaceae	–	L	–	–	F L	–	–	–	–	–	–	–	–
Annonaceae	L	L	X	–	F L I	L I	X	–	L	S	–	X	X
Annonaceae (introduced)	–	–	–	–	–	–	–	–	–	–	–	F S X	–
Aphloiaceae	–	L	–	–	–	L	–	–	L	L	–	–	–
Apocynaceae	–	L	X	L	L	F L I	–	L	F L I	F L	S L	F S L X	F L I X
Apocynaceae (introduced)	–	–	–	–	–	–	–	–	–	–	–	–	L
Araceae	–	–	–	–	–	–	–	–	–	–	–	X	–
Araliaceae	–	–	–	–	L	F L I	–	–	F L I	F S L	–	X	–
Arecaceae	–	–	–	–	–	–	–	–	–	–	–	F	–
Aristolochiaceae	–	–	–	–	–	–	–	–	–	–	–	–	L
Asclepiadaceae	–	–	–	–	–	–	–	–	–	–	–	–	F L P
Asparagaceae	–	X	–	–	–	–	–	–	–	–	–	X	L
Asteraceae	–	–	–	–	–	–	–	–	–	–	–	X	L
Asteropeiaceae	–	X	–	–	–	–	–	–	–	–	–	–	–
Balanophoraceae	–	–	–	–	–	I	–	–	I	–	–	–	–
Balsaminaceae	–	–	–	–	–	–	–	–	L	–	–	–	–
Bignoniaceae	–	–	–	–	–	–	L I	–	–	–	–	–	X
Blechnaceae	–	–	–	–	–	L	–	–	–	–	–	–	–
Boraginaceae	–	–	–	–	–	–	–	–	–	–	–	F	L
Burseraceae	–	X	X	–	L	F L	B	F L	–	–	–	F X	F S L I B X
Buxaceae	–	–	–	–	–	–	–	–	–	–	–	–	F
Calophyllaceae	–	–	–	–	S L I	F L I	X	–	F L I	F S	–	L X	–
Canellaceae	–	X	–	–	–	–	–	–	–	–	–	–	–

PLANT FAMILIES EXPLOITED	INDRIIDAE SPECIES												
	AVAHI LANIGER	*A. MERIDIONALIS*	*A. OCCIDENTALIS*	*A. PEYRIERASI*	*INDRI INDRI*	*PROPITHECUS CANDIDUS*	*P. COQUERELI*	*P. CORONATUS*	*P. DIADEMA*	*P. EDWARDSI*	*P. PERRIERI*	*P. TATTERSALLI*	*P. VERREAUXI*
Cannabaceae	–	–	–	–	–	–	–	–	–	–	–	–	F L
Capparaceae	–	–	–	–	–	–	X	–	–	–	–	X	L
Celastraceae	–	L X	L	–	–	–	–	–	F S	–	–	X	F S L
Clusiaceae	F L	L X	X	–	F S L I B	F L I	X	–	F S L I	F S L I	–	S L I	–
Combretaceae	–	–	–	–	L	–	–	L	–	–	–	F S L X	F L I X
Connaraceae	–	–	–	–	–	–	–	–	L	–	–	X	–
Convolvulaceae	–	–	–	–	–	–	–	–	–	–	–	X	L
Cucurbitaceae	–	–	–	–	–	F L I	–	–	L	–	–	X	L I
Cunoniaceae	–	L	–	–	–	F L I	–	–	–	–	–	–	–
Cyatheaceae	–	–	–	–	–	–	–	–	L	–	–	–	–
Cytinaceae	–	–	–	–	–	I	–	–	L I	–	–	–	–
Dennstaedtiaceae	–	–	–	–	–	–	–	–	L	–	–	–	–
Dichapetalaceae	L	–	–	–	–	F L I	–	–	–	F S	–	–	–
Didiereaceae	–	–	–	–	–	–	–	–	–	–	–	–	I
Dilleniaceae	–	F	–	–	L	–	–	–	–	–	–	–	–
Dioscoreaceae	–	–	X	–	–	–	–	–	–	–	–	–	L
Dryopteridaceae	–	–	–	–	–	L	–	–	–	–	–	–	–
Ebenaceae	–	X	X	–	L	F L	–	L	–	–	L	I X	F S L X
Erythroxylaceae	L I	X	L	L	L	F L I	X	–	F S L I	F S L X	–	F I X	–
Euphorbiaceae	–	L	–	–	L	F L I	–	–	F S L I X	S L	–	X	F L I P X
Euphorbiaceae (introduced)	–	–	–	–	–	–	I	–	–	–	–	–	–
Fabaceae	–	L X	X	–	L I	F L I	F L X	L I	S L	F S L I X	F L I	F S L I X	F S L I P B X
Fabaceae (introduced)	–	–	–	–	–	–	–	–	–	–	–	X	F L I X
Flacourtiaceae	–	–	–	–	–	–	–	–	–	–	–	–	L
Gentianaceae	–	–	–	–	L	–	–	–	–	–	–	–	–
Hamamelidaceae	–	X	–	–	–	–	–	–	L	–	–	–	–
Hernandiaceae	–	–	–	–	–	–	–	–	–	–	–	–	L

(continued overleaf)

TABLE 14.15. ***continued***

PLANT FAMILIES EXPLOITED	INDRIIDAE SPECIES												
	AVAHI LANIGER	*A. MERIDIONALIS*	*A. OCCIDENTALIS*	*A. PEYRIERASI*	*INDRI INDRI*	*PROPITHECUS CANDIDUS*	*P. COQUERELI*	*P. CORONATUS*	*P. DIADEMA*	*P. EDWARDSI*	*P. PERRIERI*	*P. TATTERSALLI*	*P. VERREAUXI*
Hypericaceae	L	L	X	L	–	–	–	–	–	F	–	–	–
Icacinaceae	–	–	–	–	–	L	–	–	–	–	–	–	L
Lamiaceae	–	–	X	–	–	–	X	L	–	F	–	F	F L
Lamiaceae (introduced)	–	–	–	–	–	–	–	–	–	–	–	X	–
Lauraceae	L	X	–	L	F S L I B	F L I	–	–	F S L	F S L	–	X	–
Lecythidaceae	–	–	–	–	–	–	–	–	–	–	–	X	L X
Loganiaceae	–	–	–	–	–	–	F I	–	–	–	–	–	F L X
Loranthaceae	–	–	–	–	L	F L I	–	–	F S L I	F L	–	X	–
Lygodiaceae	–	–	–	–	–	–	–	–	L	–	–	–	–
Lythraceae	–	–	–	–	–	–	–	–	–	–	–	–	F L
Malvaceae	L	L	L X	L	F L B	F L I	F L X	–	–	–	–	F S I X	F L I X
Malvaceae (introduced)	–	–	–	–	–	–	L	–	–	–	–	–	–
Melastomataceae	L	–	–	–	L B	F L I	–	L	F	F	–	F X	–
Meliaceae	–	L	L	–	–	–	X	–	F S L	S	–	I X	L I
Meliaceae (introduced)	–	–	–	–	–	–	–	–	–	–	–	–	F L I X
Metteniusaceae	–	X	–	–	–	–	–	–	–	–	–	–	L
Monimiaceae	–	L X	–	–	F I	F L	–	–	F L	F	–	–	–
Montiniaceae	–	–	–	–	–	–	–	–	–	–	–	X	–
Moraceae	L	L X	X	–	F L	F L I	F	F L	F S L	F S X	F	L X	F L
Musaceae (introduced)	–	–	–	–	–	–	–	–	–	–	–	X	–
Myristicaceae	–	L X	–	–	F S L I B	–	–	–	–	F	–	–	–
Myrtaceae	L	L X	–	L	F L I	F L I	–	–	F S L	F S L	–	X	–
Myrtaceae (introduced)	–	–	–	–	–	–	–	–	F	–	–	–	L
Nyctaginaceae (introduced)	–	–	–	–	–	–	–	–	–	–	–	–	L
Ochnaceae	L	L X	–	–	–	–	–	–	F L	–	–	L	–
Olacaceae	–	–	L	–	–	–	–	L	L	–	L	L I X	F L I
Oleaceae	–	X	X	–	L	–	–	L	–	F	–	X	F X

PLANT FAMILIES EXPLOITED	INDRIIDAE SPECIES												
	AVAHI LANIGER	*A. MERIDIONALIS*	*A. OCCIDENTALIS*	*A. PEYRIERASI*	*INDRI INDRI*	*PROPITHECUS CANDIDUS*	*P. COQUERELI*	*P. CORONATUS*	*P. DIADEMA*	*P. EDWARDSI*	*P. PERRIERI*	*P. TATTERSALLI*	*P. VERREAUXI*
Opiliaceae	–	–	–	–	–	–	–	–	–	–	–	–	L
Pedaliaceae	–	–	–	–	–	–	–	–	–	–	–	X	–
Phyllanthaceae	L	L X	X	–	F L I B	–	–	–	F L	F	–	X	F L I X
Physenaceae	–	–	–	–	–	–	–	–	–	–	–	L X	L
Pittosporaceae	L	–	–	–	–	F L I	–	–	F S L	F L	L	X	–
Plantaginaceae	–	–	–	–	–	–	–	–	–	–	–	X	–
Poaceae (introduced)	–	–	–	–	–	–	–	–	–	–	–	X	–
Primulaceae	L	–	–	L	L	F L I	–	–	F S L	F L X	–	X	–
Proteaceae	–	L	–	–	–	–	–	–	–	–	–	–	–
Putranjivaceae	–	–	–	–	–	–	X	–	F L I	–	–	F X	–
Rhamnaceae	–	–	–	–	–	L I	X	F L	–	–	–	F X	F S L I X
Rhamnaceae (introduced)	–	–	–	–	–	–	–	–	–	–	–	–	L
Rhizophoraceae	L	–	–	–	L	–	–	–	–	–	–	–	–
Rubiaceae	L	L X	L X	L	F L	F L	I	–	L	F	–	F S X	F L I X
Rubiaceae (introduced)	–	X	–	–	–	–	–	–	–	–	–	X	–
Rutaceae	L	–	L X	–	–	–	X	–	L I	F L	–	X	F L I X
Salicaceae	–	L X	–	–	L	F L I	–	–	L	–	–	X	F L X
Salvadoraceae	–	–	–	–	–	–	–	–	–	–	–	–	F L
Sapindaceae	L	L X	–	L	F L	F L I	X	L I	F S L I	F S L	–	S L X	F S L B X
Sapindaceae (introduced)	–	–	X	–	–	–	–	–	–	–	–	X	–
Sapotaceae	F L	L	L	L	–	F L I	L X	F L	S L	F S	L I	L X	F X
Sarcolaenaceae	–	X	–	–	L	F L I	–	–	I	–	–	F S I	F X
Scrophulariaceae	–	L	–	–	–	–	–	–	–	–	–	–	–
Simaroubaceae	–	L	–	–	–	–	–	–	–	–	–	–	I
Smilacaceae	–	–	–	–	–	–	–	–	L	F L	–	–	–
Solanaceae (introduced)	–	–	–	–	–	–	–	–	F	F L	–	X	F L I
Sphaerosepalaceae	–	–	X	–	–	–	X	F L	–	–	–	F X	F L

(continued overleaf)

TABLE 14.15. ***continued***

PLANT FAMILIES EXPLOITED	INDRIIDAE SPECIES												
	AVAHI LANIGER	*A. MERIDIONALIS*	*A. OCCIDENTALIS*	*A. PEYRIERASI*	*INDRI INDRI*	*PROPITHECUS CANDIDUS*	*P. COQUERELI*	*P. CORONATUS*	*P. DIADEMA*	*P. EDWARDSI*	*P. PERRIERI*	*P. TATTERSALLI*	*P. VERREAUXI*
Strelitziaceae	–	–	–	–	L	–	–	–	–	–	–	–	–
Talinaceae	–	–	–	–	–	–	–	–	–	–	–	F	L I
Theaceae	–	–	–	–	–	–	–	–	F	–	–	–	–
Violaceae	–	–	X	–	–	–	–	–	–	–	–	–	F L I X
Vitaceae	–	–	–	–	–	–	–	–	–	F	–	–	L
References	15, 19, 51	2, 38	15, 16, 53, 61	13, 22	6, 15, 43, 44, 46–48, 52, 62	20, 41, 56	14, 17, 43, 54	36, 45	9, 27, 29, 28, 30, 47, 48, 52	1, 10, 12, 21, 23–26, 39, 40, 64	32	35, 49, 58, 60	3–5, 7, 8, 11, 18, 31, 33, 34, 37, 42, 50, 55, 57, 59, 63–67

Notes: Plants introduced to Madagascar are noted. Key to plant parts exploited: B, bark; E, exudates; F, fruits; I, inflorescences; L, leaves; N, nectar; P, piths and/or stems; S, seeds; X, no data available on which plant part was exploited.

Key to references: 1. Arrigo-Nelson (2006); 2. Balestri (2018); 3. Baum (1995); 4. Baum (1996); 5. Böhning-Gaese et al. (1995); 6. Britt et al. (2002); 7. Carrai et al. (2003); 8. Charrier et al. (2007); 9. Day et al. (2009); 10. Dew and Wright (1998); 11. de Winter et al. (2013); 12. Erhart et al. (2018); 13. Faulkner and Lehman (2006); 14. Ganzhorn (1987); 15. Ganzhorn (1988); 16. Ganzhorn (1993); 17. Ganzhorn and Abraham (1991); 18. Ganzhorn and Kappeler (1996); 19. Ganzhorn et al. (1985); 20. Ganzhorn et al. (2017); 21. Goodman et al. (1997c); 22. C. Harcourt (1991); 23. Hemingway (1995); 24. Hemingway (1996); 25. Hemingway (1998); 26. Hemingway (1999); 27. Irwin (2008); 28. Irwin and Ravelomanantsoa (2004); 29. Irwin et al. (2007); 30. Irwin et al. (2014); 31. Jolly (1966); 32. Lehman and Mayor (2004); 33. Markham (2014); 34. Markham and Gould (2018); 35. Meyers (1993); 36. P. Müller (1997); 37. Norscia et al. (2006); 38. Norscia et al. (2012); 39. Overdorff and Strait (1998); 40. Overdorff et al. (2002); 41. Patel (2012); 42. Perofsky et al. (2017); 43. J.-J. Petter (1962); 44. J.-J. Petter et al. (1977); 45. Pichon et al. (2010); 46. Pollock (1977); 47. Powzyk (1997) (in Irwin 2006); 48. Powzyk and Mowry (2003); 49. Quéméré et al. (2013); 50. Ralisoamalala (1996); 51. Ratsirarson and Ranaivonasy (2002); 52. O. H. Razafindratsima (unpublished data); 53. Razanahoera (1988); 54. Richard (1974); 55. Richard (1977); 56. Sato et al. (2016); 57. Scharfe and Schlund (1996); 58. B. P. Semel and M. A. Semel (unpublished data); 59. Simmen et al. (2003); 60. E. L. Simons (1988); 61. Thalmann (2001); 62. Thalmann et al. (1993); 63. Veilleux et al. (2016); 64. Yamashita (1996); 65. Yamashita (2002); 66. Yamashita (2003); 67. Yamashita (2008).

Plant species from 42 of these introduced plant families have been identified as being exploited for food by lemurs. The highest diversity of introduced food plants is exploited by Lemuridae (35 plant families), followed by Indriidae (17 families), Cheirogaleidae (11 families), Daubentoniidae (seven families), and Lepilemuridae (five families). The plant families with introduced species exploited by the highest number of different lemur species include, in decreasing order, Myrtaceae, Anacardiaceae, Fabaceae, Rubiaceae, and Poaceae. Introduced plants exploited by the largest diversity of lemur species include, for their fruits, *Mangifera indica* (Anacardiaceae), *Psidium* spp. (Myrtaceae), *Miconia crenata* (previously known as *Clidemia hirta*; Melastomataceae), and *Solanum mauritianum* (Solanaceae; Figure 14.24a). While these fruits typically constitute only small proportions of lemur diets, *Daubentonia madagascariensis* exhibits a relatively high diversity of introduced species in its diet, including fruits from *Cocos* sp. (Arecaceae), *Artocarpus* sp. (Moraceae), and *Litchi* sp. (Sapindaceae). However, this is more likely a reflection of the nature of vegetation at the study sites (i.e., to a greater or lesser extent anthropogenic) than the predilection of the species.

In areas of Madagascar where agricultural areas are intermixed with forested zones, different crop plants are incorporated in the diets of various lemur species. Further, invasive plant species, those exhibiting varying abilities to colonize and thrive in

disturbed habitats (Kull et al. 2012), are also consumed by several lemur species. Food items of the latter type include the fruits of *Psidium cattleyanum* and *P. guajava* (Myrtaceae), *Lantana camara* (Verbenaceae), and *Miconia crenata*; and fruits, leaves, and flowers of *Pithecellobium dulce* (Fabaceae). As humans impact natural habitats, introduced plant species become increasingly abundant (Kull et al. 2013), and so the high diversity of non-native food plants utilized by lemur species might be best explained by the conversion of Madagascar's forests into more anthropogenic vegetation types within the last century (Vieilledent et al. 2018). Additionally, it could be due to the tendency of researchers to select more accessible field sites within close proximity to the forest edge ecotones. The data presented here appear to support the general idea that at some sites introduced plants can be an important component of lemur diets (Gérard et al. 2015).

CONCLUSION

It is clear that lemurs exploit a significant proportion (>62%) of the island's woody flora (both native and introduced). Nevertheless, some taxa are clearly more important than others in terms of the number of different lemur species that exploit them, the number of different plant parts exploited, and their abundance in species' diets. With the exclusion of the family Poaceae (see Vorontsova et al., pp. 585–98), nonwoody taxa, especially aquatic plants, are found rarely in lemur diets, with the notable exception being the flexible diet of *Lemur catta*. Still, the large number of plant taxa and plant parts exploited by all the lemur species whose feeding ecologies have thus far been studied reflects the remarkable plasticity in their dietary regimes.

Yet, despite the increase in lemur dietary studies since c. 2000, approximately 50 lemur species have never been the focus of feeding-ecology research, and among some species whose feeding ecology has been studied, this research was conducted in largely anthropogenic vegetation with abundant introduced flora, and complementary research is required in more natural habitats. Given that an understanding of species ecology is vital to creating effective conservation programs, dietary studies of these species should be considered high priority. Beyond general feeding-ecology descriptions, future directions should look to expand our understanding of 1) daily or seasonal macronutrient and micronutrient balancing (e.g., Irwin et al. 2014); 2) potential pharmacopeia use (e.g., Huffman 2003); and 3) the role of food traits such as visual and olfactory cues and specifically how lemurs may help shape these (e.g., Valenta and Nevo 2020). In summary, advances in lemur dietary research will ultimately help to reshape our understanding of the role of these animals within this unique island ecosystem, as well as inform the design of effective and urgently required initiatives to restore lemur habitat to Madagascar's sadly degraded landscapes.

Subject editors: Jörg U. Ganzhorn and Steven M. Goodman

FOSSIL AND SUBFOSSIL BATS

K. E. Samonds, S. M. Goodman, J. L. Alumbaugh, and N. B. Simmons

Madagascar's living bats, totaling 46 species, show a high level of endemicity and possess considerable ecological and morphological diversity (see Goodman et al., pp. 1894–911). While species endemism in Malagasy bats is lower than that of most other groups of terrestrial vertebrates, endemism is considerably higher than on other similar-size landmasses, and 80% of Malagasy bat species are known from nowhere else in the world. One of the nine chiropteran families that inhabit Madagascar is endemic to the island, Myzopodidae (see Ralisata et al., pp. 1917–22).

Madagascar was isolated by about 90 million years ago (Mya) (Storey et al. 1995), before the origin and evolution of modern bats (Teeling et al. 2005), and most groups are thought to have colonized the island by flying ~400 km across the Mozambique Channel from Africa, the closest available source (Goodman 2011; Rakotoarivelo et al. 2015; Foley et al. 2017). One notable exception is *Pteropus* (Pteropodidae), a taxon not known from continental Africa, whose ancestor likely came from Asia (Almeida et al. 2014). Some bat lineages have molecular divergence times within the Paleogene (Teeling et al. 2005), but most are thought to have colonized the island more recently, many probably during the past 5 million years (Goodman 2011; Rakotoarivelo et al. 2015; Foley et al. 2017). Most extant Malagasy bat species have been the subject of molecular phylogenetic studies, and it seems likely on the basis of biogeography and divergence patterns that the modern bat fauna of the island represents 28 or 29 different colonization events by different bat lineages (see Goodman et al., pp. 1894–911).

Triaenops/Paratriaenops (Rhinonycteridae) may have had either two separate dispersal events to the island or a dispersal event from Madagascar to Africa (A. L. Russell et al. 2007), and *Scotophilus* (Vespertilionidae) may have had at least two separate dispersal events to Madagascar (Truijillo 2005).

The fossil record of the Cenozoic, a critical interval for interpreting the origin and evolution of most of the island's fauna, including bats, is unfortunately poorly represented in Malagasy formations (see Samonds et al., pp. 1859–62). The Madagascar fossil record is richest in two time periods: 1) Middle–Late Triassic to Late Cretaceous (Krause et al. 1997), which is too old to provide relevant context for distinctly more modern groups such as extant bats; and

2) Late Pleistocene and Holocene, which provides a "subfossil" record (see Godfrey and Douglass, pp. 191–97). Work in Late Pleistocene–Holocene deposits historically has focused on larger land vertebrates, while small vertebrate remains, though recovered from subfossil sites (e.g., Sabatier and Legendre 1985; Ravoavy 1986; Burney et al. 1997), have rarely been systematically identified or described. As a result, less is known about the history of small mammals such as bats than is known about the larger mammals of the island.

Madagascar's fossil bat record is sparse, especially compared to better-known and more heavily studied taxa such as primates and elephant birds (e.g., Godfrey and Jungers 2003; Hansford and Turvey 2018). The bat fossil record is restricted to a small collection from the Miocene plus a considerable number of specimens representing Late Pleistocene and Holocene species (Table 14.16). Known bat fossils represent 19 different taxa, including 17 extant genera and in some cases species in six families (Hipposideridae, Miniopteridae, Molossidae, Pteropodidae, Rhinonycteridae, and Vespertilionidae) (Gunnell and Simmons 2005; Samonds 2007; Gunnell 2010; Figure 14.25; Table 14.2). In addition, there are two extinct Malagasy endemics in the record: *Hipposideros besaoka*

TABLE 14.16. **Occurences and ages of Malagasy fossil and subfossil Chiroptera**

SPECIES	LOCATION	AGE	METHOD	LOCALLY EXTANT	AGE INFORMATION SOURCE
Eidolon dupreanum	Vintany Cave	Unknown	–	Yes	Alumbaugh (2019)
E. dupreanum	Anjohibe Cave	≤10,000 BP	U/Th, associated stalagmite	No	Samonds (2007)
Rousettus madagascariensis	Anjohibe Cave	69,600 ± 7300 to 86,800 ± 7800 BP	U/Th, associated stalagmite	Yes	Samonds (2007)
†*Hipposideros*[1] *besaoka*	Anjohibe Cave	≤10,000 BP	U/Th, associated stalagmite	No	Samonds (2007)
Hipposideros sp.[1]	Nosy Makamby	Early late Miocene (early Tortonian, ~10 Mya)	Strontium isotopes of sediment	–	K. Samonds et al. (unpublished data)
Macronycteris commersoni	Mitoho Cave	≥8000 BP	U/Th, associated stalagmite	Yes	L. Godfrey (unpublished data)
M. commersoni	Vintany Cave	1855 ± 70 cal BP	Direct ^{14}C dating	Yes	L. Godfrey (unpublished data)
M. commersoni	Andranolovy Cave	≤1000 cal BP	^{14}C of associated subfossil	Yes	L. Godfrey (unpublished data)
M. commersoni	Anjohibe Cave	69,600 ± 7300 to 86,800 ± 7800 BP	U/Th, associated stalagmite	Yes	Samonds (2007)
Minopterus gleni	Ankilitelo Cave	510 ± 40 to 630 ± 50 BP	^{14}C dating of associated subfossils	Yes	Muldoon et al. (2009)
Miniopterus sp.	Nosy Makamby	Early late Miocene (early Tortonian, ~10 Mya)	Strontium isotopes of sediment	–	K. Samonds et al. (unpublished data)
Mormopterus jugularis	Vintany Cave	1855 ± 70 cal BP	^{14}C dating of associated subfossil	Yes	L. Godfrey (unpublished data)
M. jugularis	Ankilitelo Cave	510 ± 40–630 ± 50 BP	^{14}C dating of associated subfossils	Yes	Muldoon et al. (2009)
Myotis sp.	Nosy Makamby	Early late Miocene (early Tortonian, ~10 Mya)	Strontium isotopes of sediment	–	K. Samonds et al. (unpublished data)
Otomops madagascariensis	Ankilitelo Cave	510 ± 40 to 630 ± 50 BP	^{14}C dating of associated subfossils	Yes	Muldoon et al. (2009)
†*Triaenops goodmani*	Anjohibe Cave	≤10,000 BP	U/Th, associated stalagmite	No	Samonds (2007)
T. menamena	Mitoho Cave	Unknown (recent)	–	Yes	Alumbaugh (2019)

Notes: † extinct species; BP, years before present; cal BP, calibrated years before present; Mya, million years ago; U/Th, uranium-thorium dating; ^{14}C, carbon-14 dating.
[1] This taxon is perhaps best placed in the genus *Macronycteris* (see Table 14.2).

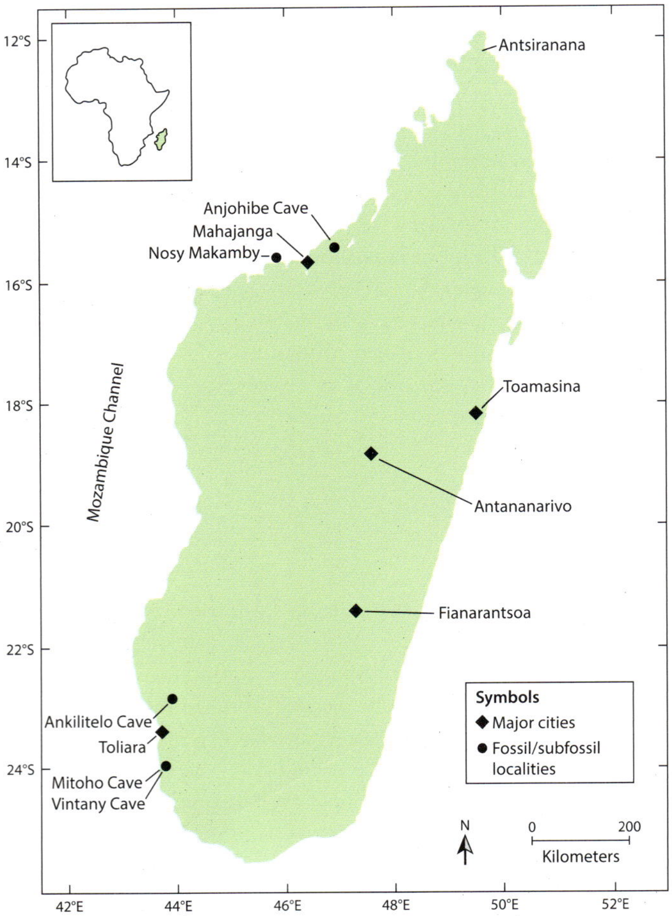

FIGURE 14.25 **Map of bat fossil and subfossil localities and major cities.**

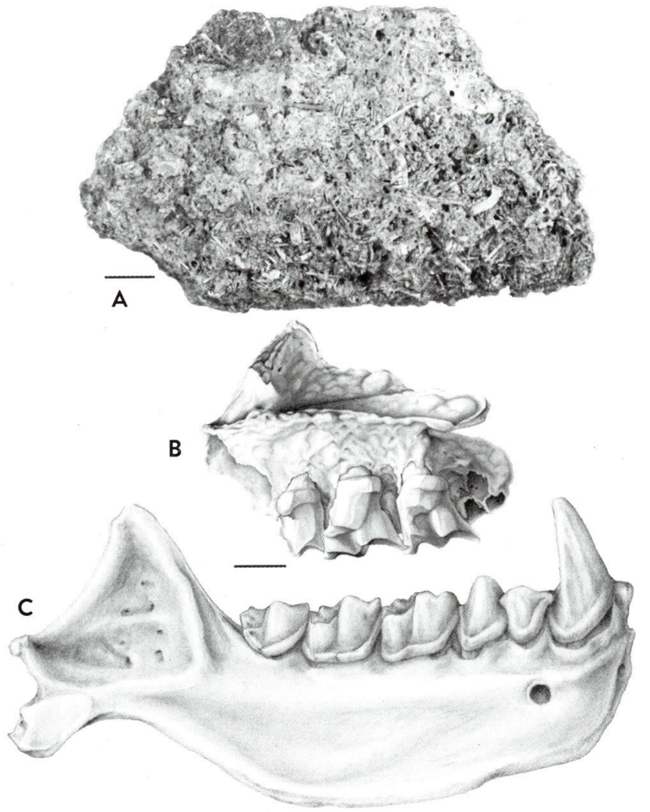

FIGURE 14.26 **Malagasy bat fossils. A) Example of preservation and concentration of bat fossils in cave breccia, Anjohibe Cave; note, all the small structures in this image are bat bones (scale bar 2 cm). B) Miocene *Hipposideros* bat maxilla with teeth, from Nosy Makamby. C) *Hipposideros besaoka*, subfossil bat, from Anjohibe Cave (scale bar 2 mm).** (PHOTO A by K. Samonds, image B by M. Woodall, and image C by C. Lodge and modified from Samonds 2007.)

(Hipposideridae, perhaps best placed in the genus *Macronycteris*; see Table 14.2 and Foley et al. 2017) and *Triaenops goodmani* (Gunnell and Simmons 2005; Samonds 2007; Gunnell 2010). Compared to many other landmasses, this is a relatively small number of endemic fossil taxa; however, the fossil record of African Cenozoic bats is similarly sparse, although it includes representatives from the families Pteropodidae, Emballonuridae, Hipposideridae, Megadermatidae, Molossidae, †Philisidae, Rhinolophidae, Myzopodidae, and Vespertilionidae (Gunnell 2010; Gunnell et al. 2014).

MIOCENE FOSSIL BATS

A small collection of Miocene bat fossils is reported from Nosy Makamby, an offshore island in northwestern Madagascar (see Samonds, pp. 69–73; Figure 14.25). Fossils recovered at Nosy Makamby include multiple upper and lower jaws of what is currently considered a member of the genus *Hipposideros* but might be best places in the genus *Macronycteris*, a small lower molar referable to *Myotis* (Vespertilionidae), and a distal humerus referable to *Miniopterus* (Miniopteridae) (K. Samonds et al., unpublished data; Figure 14.26b). All three of the families represented currently inhabit Madagascar today. The fossiliferous deposits at Nosy Makamby consist of medium to coarse sandstones representing a coastal plain/nearshore marine environment, perhaps similar to the warm tropical environment interpreted for Riversleigh, a mid- to late Cenozoic locality in Australia that is famous for its rich diversity of bats (about 30 species; see Archer et al. 2006). Riversleigh has produced a remarkable diversity and abundance of both hipposiderid and rhinonycterid bats, with at least 22 species from the two families (Hand and Archer 2005; L. A. B. Wilson et al. 2016); in fact, high hipposiderid and rhinonycterid diversity appears to be the signature of the early and middle Tertiary Old World tropics and temperate regions (Gunnell and Simmons 2005). The global fossil record of hipposiderids is extensive, encompassing the middle Eocene to early Pliocene of Europe, the early Miocene to Recent of Africa, the early Pleistocene to Recent of Asia, and the Late Pleistocene to Recent of the East Indies, Australia, and New Guinea (Gunnell and Simmons 2005), suggesting that there were few geographic or climatic barriers to dispersal of this group across the Paleotropics during these different geological periods.

The Nosy Makamby bat fossils extend the Cenozoic record of Madagascar back to the late Miocene; recent work on strontium isotopes suggests that some of the sediments may be as late as early

Tortonian in age (about 10 Mya) (Samonds and Fordyce 2019). This material represents the oldest nonmarine fossil collection from within the island's 80-million-year fossil gap (K. Samonds et al., unpublished data). As these fossils represent our first glimpse into this unknown time period, they can continue to help refine our understanding of the timing of specific biogeographic events.

LATE PLEISTOCENE AND HOLOCENE BAT FOSSILS AND SUBFOSSILS

Madagascar's bat fossil record is more extensive in the Late Pleistocene and Holocene than earlier Cenozoic time periods (Table 14.2), a pattern that is common for bats (Gunnell and Simmons 2005). Pleistocene–Holocene specimens are typically preserved as subfossils—skeletal remains that are not permineralized and may be hundreds to thousands of years old (Table 14.16). Bat subfossils are typically recovered from caves and vary widely in their quality of preservation, ranging from fragmentary bones preserved in fluvially transported breccias to complete crania in submerged cave deposits (Table 14.16; Figure 14.25). Quaternary material usually consists of fragmentary skulls, isolated teeth, and postcrania. Several living species have inhabited the same areas and roosts for multiple millennia, as evidenced by their Quaternary subfossil record in known roosting sites as well as overall distributions of fossils and species ranges. These data reinforce the conclusion that particular caves are critical habitats for bat conservation, just as subfossil records have informed the conservation tactics targeting bats in the southeastern United States (Toomey et al. 2002; Jansky et al. 2016). Unfortunately, bat fossils have been rarely described despite being abundant at multiple localities.

Anjohibe Cave in northwestern Madagascar contains subfossils of the only two species of extinct bats known from the island—*Hipposideros besaoka* and *Triaenops goodmani*—robust species that are represented by dental and mandibular material from breccia deposits dated to ≤10,000 years before present (BP) (Samonds 2007; Figure 14.26). Contemporaneous subfossils representing extant species include specimens referable to *Eidolon dupreanum* (Pteropodidae) and *Macronycteris commersoni*, the latter of which also occurs with *Rousettus madagascariensis* (Pteropodidae) in breccia dated to ≥60,000 BP. Unknown-age subfossils of *Myotis goudoti* have also been found within the cave. *Macronycteris commersoni*, *Myotis goudoti*, and *Rousettus madagascariensis* are current residents of Anjohibe Cave (Goodman 2011).

Subfossil bats in southern Madagascar come from two areas: Ankilitelo Cave and Tsimanampesotse National Park (Mitoho Cave and Vintany Cave) (Figure 14.25). Subfossils from Ankilitelo Cave have been directly dated to ≥500 BP, and represent a diverse array of taxa including *Miniopterus gleni*, *Mormopterus jugularis*, and *Otomops madagascariensis* (Molossidae) (Muldoon et al. 2009). Bat subfossils from Tsimanampesotse have also been recovered from cave sites, in this case two submerged caves, Vintany Cave and Mitoho Cave (Alumbaugh 2019). Species include *M. jugularis* and *E. dupreanum* from Vintany Cave; *Triaenops menamena* from Mitoho Cave; and *M. commersoni* from both caves (Alumbaugh 2019; L. Godfrey et al., unpublished data). Preliminary dating at Mitoho Cave suggests the presence of two distinctly aged deposits, one dated to ≥8000 years ago, and a younger, time-averaged assemblage beneath an active *Macronycteris* roost. *Macronycteris* from both of the latter deposits differ morphologically from local modern samples, which may be indicative of recent shifts in community structure (Alumbaugh 2019).

Sabatier and Legendre (1985) reported four species of subfossil bats from Tsimanampesotse: *Macronycteris commersoni*, *Mormopterus jugularis*, *Paratriaenops furculus*, and *Paremballonura* cf. *tiavato* (Emballonuridae). The lattermost species was initially identified as *Emballonura* (*Paremballonura*) *atrata* but more likely represents *Paremballonura tiavato*, which occurs on the western side of the island and to the north of Tsimanampesotse (Goodman et al. 2006b). These subfossils were described as Pliocene to Pleistocene in age (Sabatier and Legendre 1985), although the accuracy of this age determination is uncertain and warrants review.

SYNTHESIS

While recent collections of bat fossils from the Miocene and subfossils from the Quaternary of Madagascar provide new insights into the geological history of Malagasy Chiroptera, there are notable limitations on what can be gleaned from current information. Miocene material provides clear evidence of the presence of three families of modern bats (Hipposideridae, Vespertilionidae, and Miniopteridae) on the island, but it is not possible to infer that these three colonization events gave rise to the modern representatives of these families. The Quaternary record provides a window into the presence of bats in the recent geological past that are still extant today, as well as two recognized subfossil species that are extinct (*Hipposideros besaoka* and *Triaenops goodmani*). With the exception of the subfossil record of *Paremballonura tiavato* mentioned in the previous section, and the subfossil record of *Eidolon dupreanum* from Anjohibe Cave (which has been extirpated in this cave system within the past few decades; Samonds 2007), there are no other published examples of range extensions or contractions among bats having been found by overlaying the distributions of subfossil and extant species in Madagascar. This is surprising given the notable changes in other vertebrate groups, such as lemurs, between the Holocene and Recent eras (see Godfrey and Jungers, pp. 1824–28; Table 14.6), but likely reflects the general lack of study of bats compared to other larger-bodied groups.

ACKNOWLEDGMENTS

We thank the government of Madagascar for permission to conduct this research and the Mention Bassins Sédimentaires Evolution Conservation, Université d'Antananarivo, for its collaboration and joint fieldwork. Special thanks to David Burney for providing some of the original subfossil cave breccia. Illustrations were done by Colleen Lodge (*Hipposideros besaoka*) and Melissa Woodall (Miocene *Hipposideros*). Fieldwork was performed under a collaborative accord between Northern Illinois University and the Université d'Antananarivo. Thanks to Jean-Luc Raharison, Mitchell Irwin, and the organization Sadabe Madagascar for logistical support.

Subject editors: Paul A. Racey and Steven M. Goodman

ORIGIN AND DIVERSIFICATION OF THE MALAGASY CARNIVORA

G. Veron, M. Michaud, and S. M. Goodman

The native Malagasy members of the order Carnivora are placed in the endemic family Eupleridae. They represent an extraordinary case of morphological diversification, ranging from the felid-like *Cryptoprocta ferox*, which is equally agile on the ground and in trees; the invertebrate eater *Eupleres goudotii*; the civet-like *Fossa fossana*; and several mongoose-like species (*Galidia elegans*, *Galidictis fasciata*, *Mungotictis decemlineata*, and *Salanoia concolor*). This diversity, and cases of convergence with Carnivora elsewhere in the world, led early taxonomists to place these species in different families than in the modern classification.

TAXONOMIC HISTORY

Cryptoprocta ferox has a catlike dentition and a Puma-like external morphology, while its plantigrade feet with wide plantar pads are similar to those of the Asian palm civets (family Viverridae, subfamily Paradoxurinae) (Pocock 1916; Veron 1994). E. T. Bennett (1833) described *Cryptoprocta* as a member of Viverridae on the basis of its bare feet and retractile claws. Milne Edwards and Grandidier (1867) suggested that its general morphology and cranial features pointed to a close relationship to the family Felidae. Based on the dentition, the shape of the tympanic bullae, and the disposition of the basicranial foramina, Flower (1869) instead placed *Cryptoprocta* in a separate family, the Cryptoproctidae, which he believed was close to both the Viverridae and Felidae. Mivart (1882) and Gregory and Hellman (1939) concluded that this genus shared traits with the family Herpestidae (which includes mongooses and kin)—the presence of an anal pouch, the absence of perineal glands, and the size of the baculum—that differentiate them from the Viverridae. Gregory and Hellman (1939) decided that *Cryptoprocta* was a "little modified survivor of *Proailurus*" (an Oligocene–Miocene felid; Hunt 1989), and they placed it in the subfamily Cryptoproctinae within the Felidae. Somewhat thereafter, Simpson (1945) included *C. ferox* in the Viverridae. Wozencraft (1989) placed this genus in the subfamily Cryptoproctinae within the Viverridae. *Cryptoprocta* has thus been placed in the Viverridae, the Felidae, and its own separate family, the Cryptoproctidae.

Using DNA-DNA hybridization experiments, Veron and Catzeflis (1993) suggested that *C. ferox* was closer to the Herpestidae than to the Viverridae. A phylogenetic morphological analysis (Veron 1994; 1995) highlighted that *Cryptoprocta* and the Felidae share many dental characters. However, when fossils were included in the analysis, it was confirmed that these dental features, which are an adaptation to hypercarnivory, are convergent between *Cryptoprocta*, the Felidae, and the Hyaenidae. In fact, *C. ferox* shares derived features with the Herpestidae (the reduction of the presylvian sulcus) and also with the Herpestidae and Hyaenidae (the presence of an anal pouch) (Veron 1994, 1995).

Eupleres goudotii was first described as an insectivore (Doyère 1835) on the basis of its long, thin snout and very reduced and sharp teeth. However, it was soon thereafter placed in the Viverridae (Gray 1864), and thought to be close to the subfamily Hemigalinae, because of similarities in its skull and teeth and its foot morphology with *Chrotogale owstoni* (Thomas 1912; Gregory and Hellman 1939). Gregory and Hellman (1939), however, placed *Eupleres* in a separate subfamily, the Euplerinae, while Simpson (1945) placed it in the subfamily Hemigalinae. More recently, Wozencraft (1989) placed this genus in the subfamily Cryptoproctinae within the Viverridae.

Fossa fossana displays a general morphology similar to that of the terrestrial civets, has a viverrid-like basicranium, and was included in the Viverridae (Mivart 1882). Gregory and Hellman (1939) suggested affinities with the Hemigalinae, while Pocock (1915a) pointed out some shared characteristics with the linsangs (*Poiana* and *Prionodon*, both in the family Viverridae then; now *Prionodon* is in the Prionodontidae). *Fossa* was placed either in its own subfamily, the Fossinae (Pocock 1915b; Gregory and Hellman 1939); in the Hemigalinae (Simpson 1945); or in the Euplerinae, together with *Eupleres* (Wozencraft 1993). G. Petter (1974) highlighted shared morphological features between *Fossa* and *Eupleres* and suggested that similarities between these taxa and the Hemigalinae species were the result of convergence.

The mongoose-like Malagasy species (*Galidia elegans*, *Galidictis fasciata*, *Mungotictis decemlineata*, and *Salanoia concolor*) were all grouped in the subfamily Galidiinae within the Viverridae, along with the mongooses (subfamily Herpestinae) by Gray (1864). The Herpestinae were later placed in a separate family, the Herpestidae (Gregory and Hellman 1939; Wozencraft 1989), within which the Galidiinae was included (Pocock 1915b). However, on the basis of soft anatomy features, Gregory and Hellman (1939) suggested that the mongoose-like Malagasy species were an "offshoot from the base of the viverrid stem where it joins the herpestid branch" and placed them in the subfamily Galidiinae, but this time within the Viverridae.

The diversity of morphotypes of Malagasy carnivorans and their placement in different families suggested multiple origins and multiple dispersal events for their colonization of Madagascar. A. D. Yoder et al. (2003) analyzed two mitochondrial genes and two nuclear genes and found the extraordinary result that the native Malagasy carnivorans form a monophyletic group—placed in the family Eupleridae—that is the sister group to the Herpestidae. The divergence of the Malagasy carnivorans from their African relatives was estimated to have occurred 18–24 million years ago (Mya) (A. D. Yoder et al. 2003), which was congruent with the divergence date for Herpestidae-*Cryptoprocta*, estimated at 24 Mya, inferred from DNA-DNA hybridization results (Veron and Catzeflis 1993); another estimate of this divergence, 26–19 Mya, was obtained from the analysis of three nuclear genes (Poux et al. 2005).

This means that an African mongoose ancestor colonized Madagascar about 18–26 Mya and then diversified on the island into an extraordinary diversity of animals, ranging from the mongoose-like to the civet-like to the catlike. Such diversification was made possible by the absence of any other carnivorans on the island, leaving empty niches for the new invaders to fill (Goodman 2009; J. B. Yoder et al. 2010).

The close relationship of the Malagasy carnivorans to the Herpestidae was then confirmed by many other molecular studies (e.g., Veron et al. 2004; Eizirik et al. 2010; Nyakatura and Bininda-Emonds 2012; Zhou et al. 2017; Slater and Friscia 2019). The morphological features considered diagnostic to include the Malagasy civet-like species in the Viverridae were either plesiomorphic characters or convergences. In fact, it was shown that the Malagasy civet-like forms share no synapomorphy with the Viverridae (Gaubert et al. 2005). The catlike dentition of *C. ferox* can be considered as adaptive to predation, which occurred by convergence in *C. ferox*, the Felidae, and the Hyaenidae (G. Petter 1974; Veron 1994, 1995). Also, the Malagasy civet-like species exhibit several primitive features (such as a viverrid-like basicranium; Hunt 1974, 1987; Veron 1994, 1995), which were incorrectly interpreted to place them in the Viverridae.

The Malagasy carnivorans were then placed in a separate family, the Eupleridae, with two subfamilies, the Euplerinae (*Cryptoprocta*, *Eupleres*, and *Fossa*) and the Galidiinae (*Galidia*, *Galidictis*, *Mungotictis*, and *Salanoia*) (Wozencraft 2005).

TOWARD A RESOLUTION OF EUPLERIDAE SYSTEMATICS

The relationships of the species within the Eupleridae were partially resolved by A. D. Yoder et al. (2003), which showed the monophyly of the Galidiinae, but the position of *Eupleres* was ambiguous, owing to the lack of samples for genetic studies. Poux et al. (2005) included genetic data for this genus, but the relationships between the genera *Cryptoprocta*, *Fossa*, and *Eupleres* remains unresolved.

The carnivoran supertree of Nyakatura and Bininda-Emonds (2012) proposed a sister relationship for *Eupleres* and *Fossa*, and *Cryptoprocta* as sister to the remaining six euplerid genera. Zhou et al. (2017) did not include *Eupleres*, but their mitochondrial data analyses also suggested *Cryptoprocta* as sister taxon to the remaining Eupleridae genera. The results by Michaud (2019), based on three mitochondrial markers and four nuclear markers, confirmed the existence of three lineages (Figure 14.27): 1) Galidiinae, 2) *Fossa* + *Eupleres*, and 3) *Cryptoprocta*. However, the position of *Cryptoprocta* remains unclear. It was found by Michaud (2019) to be sister to the Galidiinae but with very poor support; the same relationship was found by Slater and Friscia (2019). These results should be viewed as preliminary, as the internode for the *Cryptoprocta* branch was very short, and its position not stable. This almost certainly highlights a fast early diversification of the three Eupleridae lineages. Further molecular data should be gathered to try to solve the position of *Cryptoprocta*. The absence of fossils of early Eupleridae

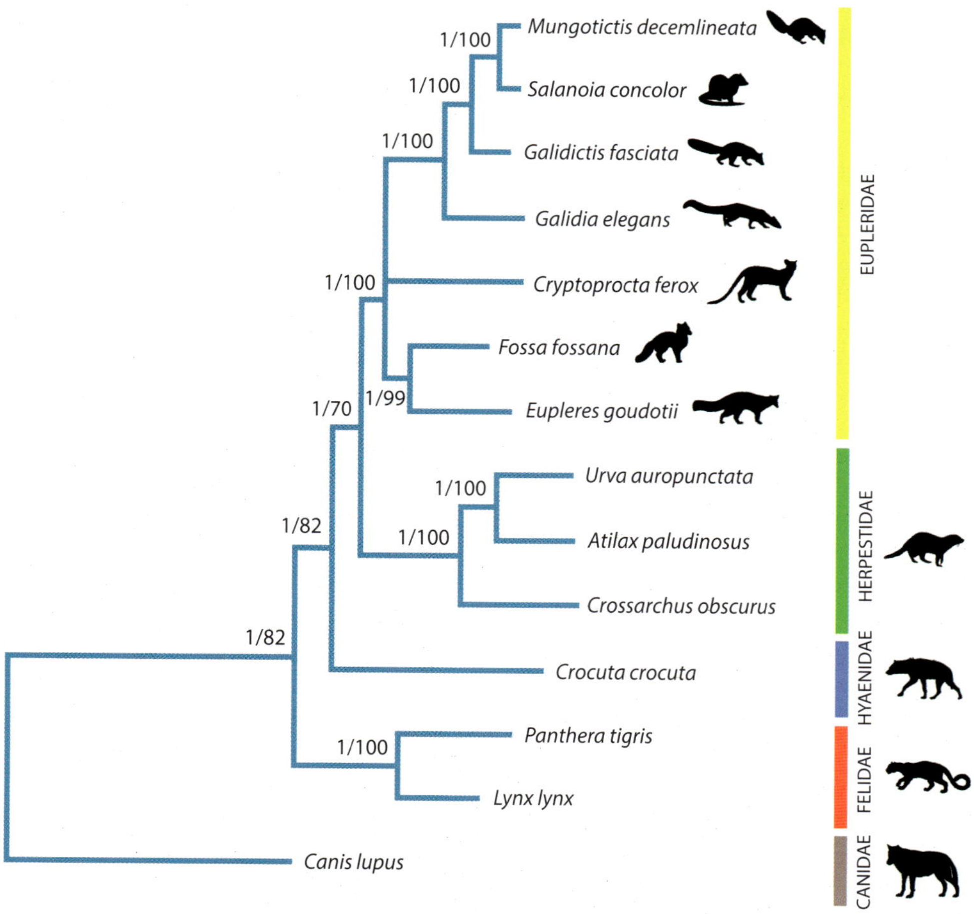

FIGURE 14.27 **Phylogenetic relationships of the Eupleridae and other families of Carnivora. Bayesian inferences tree computed using a combined data set of mitochondrial and nuclear markers (COI + Cyt b + ND2 + FGB + IRBP + TTR + vWF; see Michaud 2019). Values at the nodes represent: Bayesian posterior probabilities/ML (maximum likelihood) bootstrap values; the node with posterior probabilities <0.99 is shown as a polytomy. New sequences have been deposited in GenBank: accession nos. MT048533–MT048549.**

forms contributes to the difficulty in understanding the evolutionary history of this lineage.

In the view of the recent phylogenetic results, the three lineages should be considered separate subfamilies (instead of two, as in recent classifications by Wozencraft 2005 and Goodman 2009): 1) Cryptoproctinae (*Cryptoprocta*), 2) Euplerinae (*Fossa* and *Eupleres*), 3) Galidiinae (*Galidia*, *Galidictis*, *Mungotictis*, and *Salanoia*).

Within the Galidiinae, a molecular study by Veron et al. (2017), based on two mitochondrial markers and one nuclear marker, suggested that *Galidia* was sister to the three other genera, and *Galidictis* was sister to a clade formed by *Mungotictis* and *Salanoia*. This study also examined intrageneric genetic variation in order to verify the taxonomic status of some newly described species. Based on these results, Veron et al. (2017) proposed the recognition of four species in the Galidiinae, rendering each genus monospecific. Genetic structure and polymorphism suggest the recognition of three subspecies in *Galidia elegans* (*G. e. dambrensis*, *G. e. elegans*, and *G. e. occidentalis*), two subspecies in *Mungotictis decemlineata* (*M. d. decemlineata* and *M. d. lineata*), and two subspecies in *Galidictis fasciata* (*G. f. fasciata* and *G. f. grandidieri*; the latter was described several decades ago as a distinct species). Further, the results of this study suggest that *Salanoia durrelli*, recently described from a few individuals from the marshlands around Lake Alaotra (Durbin et al. 2010), should be treated as a junior synonym of *S. concolor*. Indeed, the individuals of *S. durrelli*, including the type specimen, are closer to one haplotype of *S. concolor*, than haplotypes of *S. concolor* are to each other (Veron et al. 2017).

Genetic polymorphism has also been studied in the genus *Eupleres*. Thanks to the sequencing of DNA from museum specimens identified, based on morphological characters, as *E. goudotii* and *E. major*, Veron and Goodman (2018) showed that the level of polymorphism within *Eupleres* is not in agreement with the recognition of two species. This result is in conflict with and does not support the conclusion of Goodman and Helgen (2010), who raised *E. g. major* to the level of species.

Veron et al. (2018) studied the genetic polymorphism within *Cryptoprocta ferox* by sequencing three mitochondrial markers and one nuclear marker. Measures of polymorphism were low within the species, probably related to its dispersal capacity, and some geographic genetic structure was observed, possibly associated with geographic barriers, such as large rivers. In order to provide insight into the management of captive-breeding programs of *Cryptoprocta*, the genetic diversity of the captive animals was also studied. The results showed that the captive population encompasses a considerable proportion of the genetic diversity of the species, presumably the consequence of frequent imports of wild animals into zoos from different areas of Madagascar. No distinct lineages require a separate management in captive-breeding programs.

Subject editors: Jörg U. Ganzhorn and Steven M. Goodman

SYSTEMATICS AND PHYLOGENETICS OF MADAGASCAR'S NATIVE RODENTS (NESOMYIDAE: NESOMYINAE)

S. A. Jansa and M. D. Carleton

Knowledge of the diversity, systematics, and phylogeny of Madagascar's native rodents has grown dramatically since the late 1990s, thanks to extensive field inventories, renewed museum-based research, and large-scale phylogenetic studies. Nevertheless, our picture of the group as a remarkably diverse assemblage of rodents has remained constant. Notwithstanding the recognition of six new species since 2001, Madagascar's native rodent fauna comprises only 28 species in nine genera (Table 14.17), a relatively impoverished assemblage given its probable age and the island's geological and ecological complexity. What sets this radiation apart from other insular rodent radiations is the degree of morphological and ecological diversity exhibited among the genera, which is partly reflected in their habits and the common names given to each genus: the saltatorial, gerbil-like big-footed mouse (*Macrotarsomys*), the vole-like short-tailed rat (*Brachyuromys*), the giant jumping rat (*Hypogeomys*), and the arboreal tufted-tail rat (*Eliurus*). This unusual pattern of substantial diversity observed among few genera has prompted considerable debate over the origin of Madagascar's rodents and their status as a monophyletic group. Indeed, Carleton and Musser (1984: 343) mused that "each of the genera could stand as a separate tribe or subfamily were it not for the centripetal taxonomic influence provided by their common distribution on Madagascar."

Jansa and Carleton (2003b) previously consolidated the history of nesomyine descriptions and classifications and discussed attendant implications for evolutionary interpretations of their diversity, whether arising from an insular radiation or from multiple independent invasions of the island. The nomenclatural foundation of the subfamily Nesomyinae, *sensu* Musser and Carleton (2005), and past classifications of nesomyine genera are summarized in Tables 14.17 and 14.18, respectively. In this contribution, we emphasize the substantial molecular phylogenetic work that has occurred since about 2000 that bears on our understanding of nesomyine origins and evolution. The appearance of broad-scale, phylogenetic studies on muroid rodents has convincingly settled the debate surrounding nesomyine diversification: Madagascar's native rodents are a monophyletic group (Jansa and Weksler 2004; Steppan et al.

TABLE 14.17. **The taxonomy of Madagascar's native rodents**

NESOMYINAE MAJOR, 1897

Nesomyinae Major, 1897. *Proceedings of the Zoological Society of London* 1897: 718 (Brachytarsomyes Ellerman, 1941: 6; Gymnuromyinae Ellerman, 1941: 8; Brachyuromyes Ellerman, 1941: 8; Eliurini Ellerman, 1941: 9).

Brachytarsomys Günther, 1875

B. albicauda Günther, 1875. *Proceedings of the Zoological Society of London* 1875: 80.

B. villosa Petter, 1962. *Mammalia* 26: 570 (named as a subspecies of *B. albicauda*; acknowledged as a species by Carleton and Schmidt 1990: 20).

Brachyuromys Major, 1896

B. betsileoensis (Bartlett, 1880). *Proceedings of the Zoological Society of London* 1879 [1880]: 770 (named as species of *Nesomys*; generic reallocation by Major 1896a: 322).

B. ramirohitra Major, 1896. *Annals and Magazine of Natural History*, ser. 6, 18: 323.

Eliurus Milne Edwards, 1885

E. antsingy Carleton, Goodman & Rakotondravony, 2001. *Proceedings of the Biological Society of Washington* 114: 974.

E. carletoni Goodman, Raheriarisena & Jansa, 2009. *Bonner Zoologische Beiträge* 56: 136.

E. danieli Carleton & Goodman, 2007. *American Museum Novitates* 3547: 3.

E. ellermani Carleton, 1994. *American Museum Novitates* 3087: 39.

E. grandidieri Carleton & Goodman, 1998. *Fieldiana: Zoology*, new ser., 90: 165.

E. majori Thomas, 1895. *Annals and Magazine of Natural History*, ser. 6, 16: 164.

E. minor Major, 1896. *Annals and Magazine of Natural History*, ser. 6, 18: 462.

E. myoxinus Milne Edwards, 1885. *Annales des Sciences Naturelles, Zoologie et Paléontologie*, Paris, 20: Art. 1 bis.

E. penicillatus Thomas, 1908. *Annals and Magazine of Natural History*, ser. 8, 2: 453.

E. petteri Carleton, 1994. *American Museum Novitates* 3087: 37.

E. tanala Major, 1896. *Annals and Magazine of Natural History*, ser. 6, 18: 462.

E. tsingimbato Jansa, Carleton, Soarimalala, Rakotomalala & Goodman, 2019. *Bulletin of the American Museum of Natural History* 430: 31.

E. webbi Ellerman, 1949. *The Families and Genera of Living Rodents*, vol. 3, app. 2: 163 (named as subspecies of *E. myoxinus*; elevated to species by Carleton 1994: 33).

Gymnuromys Major, 1896

G. roberti Major, 1896. *Annals and Magazine of Natural History*, ser. 6, 18: 324.

Hypogeomys A. Grandidier, 1869

H. antimena A. Grandidier, 1869. *Revue et Magasin de Zoologie* Pure et Appliquée, Paris, série 2, 21: 339.

Macrotarsomys Milne Edwards & G. Grandidier, 1898.

M. bastardi Milne Edwards & G. Grandidier, 1898. *Bulletin du Muséum National d'Histoire Naturelle*, Paris, série 1, 4: 179.

M. ingens Petter, 1959. *Mammalia* 23: 140.

M. petteri Goodman & Soarimalala, 2005. *Proceedings of the Biological Society of Washington* 118: 453.

Monticolomys Carleton & Goodman, 1996

M. koopmani Carleton & Goodman, 1996. *Fieldiana: Zoology*, new ser., 85: 235.

Nesomys Peters, 1870

N. audeberti (Jentink, 1879). *Notes from the Leyden Museum* 1879: 107 (described as type species of *Hallomys*; generic synonymy effected by Major 1897a: 712).

N. lambertoni G. Grandidier, 1928. *Bulletin de l'Académie Malgache*, nouvelle série, 11: 95.

N. rufus Peters, 1870. *Sitzungsberichte der Gesellschaft naturforschender Freunde*, Berlin, 1870: 55.

Voalavo Carleton & Goodman, 1998

V. antsahabensis Goodman, Rakotondravony, Randriamanantsoa & Rakotomalala-Razanahoera, 2005. *Proceedings of the Biological Society of Washington* 118: 865.

V. gymnocaudus Carleton & Goodman, 1998. *Fieldiana: Zoology*, new ser., 90: 182.

2004; Jansa et al. 2009; Fabre et al. 2012; Steppan and Schenk 2017) and most likely arrived on the island during the middle Cenozoic (Poux et al. 2005; Crottini et al. 2012; Steppan and Schenk 2017). Herein, we consider that pivotal literature and discuss related questions pertaining to the diversification of Madagascar's native rodents.

PLACING MADAGASCAR'S RODENTS IN THE RODENT TREE OF LIFE

When we last reviewed the systematics of Madagascar's native rodents (Jansa and Carleton 2003b), only two molecular phylogenetic studies had addressed the placement of nesomyine species within the broader context of muroid rodent evolution (DuBois et al. 1996; Jansa et al. 1999). DuBois et al. (1996) used complete nucleotide sequences from the mitochondrial 12S rRNA gene and DNA-DNA hybridization data to assess the monophyly of Nesomyinae; Jansa et al. (1999) used parsimony analysis of the mitochondrial cytochrome b gene to address the same question. Although innovative for their time, both studies were flawed and gave incomplete or erroneous pictures of nesomyine phylogeny. DuBois et al. (1996) included only three nesomyine genera and a limited number of other muroids, thus their test of nesomyine monophyly was necessarily limited by taxon sampling. Jansa et al. (1999) employed parsimony analysis of a rapidly evolving mitochondrial gene, which failed to recover nesomyine monophyly and yielded weak support for basal relationships among muroid lineages.

Subsequent studies adopted more slowly evolving nuclear loci for phylogenetic insight and more sophisticated probabilistic methods

TABLE 14.18. **Five influential classifications of Madagascar's indigenous rodents (nesomyine genera indicated in boldface)**

A. ALSTON (1876)
- **Family Muridae**
- **Subfamily Sminthinae**
  - *Sminthus* [= *Sicista*]
- **Subfamily Hydromyinae**
  - *Hydromys*
- **Subfamily Platacanthomyinae**
  - *Platacanthomys*
- **Subfamily Gerbillinae**
  - *Gerbillus*, *Mystromys*, *Otomys*, *Dasymys*
- **Subfamily Phloeomyinae**
  - *Phloeomys*
- **Subfamily Dendromyinae**
  - *Dendromys* [= *Dendromus*], *Steatomys*, *Lophuromys*
- **Subfamily Cricetinae**
  - *Cricetus*, *Saccostomus*, *Cricetomys*
- **Subfamily Murinae**
  - *Mus*, *Pelomys*, *Echinothrix*, *Uromys*, *Hapalotis* [= *Conilurus*], *Acomys*, ***Nesomys***, ***Brachytarsomys***, *Holochilus*, *Hesperomys* [= *Calomys*], *Ochetodon* [= *Reithrodontomys*], *Reithrodon*, *Sigmodon*, *Neotoma*
- **Subfamily Arvicolinae**
  - *Fiber* [= *Ondatra*], *Arvicola*, *Myodes* [= *Lemmus*]
- **Subfamily Siphneinae**
  - *Ellobius*, *Siphneus* [= *Myospalax*]

B. WINGE (1923)
- **Family Muridae**
  - Rhizomyini
    - Cricetodontes (fossil)
      - *Cricetodon*, *Eumys*
    - Rhizomyes
      - ***Nesomys***, ***Brachytarsomys***, ***Gymnuromys***, ***Eliurus***, ***Brachyuromys***, *Tachyoryctes*, *Rhizomys*
  - Cricetini
    - Criceti
      - *Cricetus*, *Calomyscus*, *Lophiomys*, *Myospalax*
    - Hesperomyes
      - New World cricetines [= Sigmodontinae]
    - Arvicolae
      - Arvicolines
  - Murini
    - Mures
- Murines (including cricetomyines, dendromurines, and otomyines)
  - Gerbilli
    - *Gerbillus*, *Rhombomys*
  - Hydromyes
    - *Xeromys*, *Crunomys*, *Hydromys*, *Chrotomys*, *Celaenomys*

C. ELLERMAN (1941)
- **Family Muridae**
  - **Subfamily Murinae**
    - ***Eliurus***
    - Murines
  - **Subfamily Dendromyinae**
    - *Petromyscus*
    - Dendromurines
  - **Subfamily Cricetinae**
    - ***Nesomys***, ***Hypogeomys***, ***Macrotarsomys***, *Calomyscus*, *Mystromys*
    - Old World cricetines
    - New World cricetines [= Sigmodontinae]
  - **Subfamily Gymnuromyinae**
    - ***Gymnuromys***
  - **Subfamily Tachyoryctinae**
    - ***Brachyuromys***
    - *Tachyoryctes*
  - **Subfamily Microtinae**
    - ***Brachytarsomys***
    - Arvicolines

D. SIMPSON (1945)
- **Superfamily Muroidea**
  - **Family Cricetidae**
    - **Subfamily Cricetinae**
    - **Subfamily Nesomyinae (all seven genera)**
    - **Subfamily Lophiomyinae**
    - **Subfamily Microtinae**
    - **Subfamily Gerbillinae**
  - **Family Spalacidae**
  - **Family Rhizomyidae**
  - **Family Muridae**
    - **Subfamily Murinae**
    - **Subfamily Dendromurinae**
    - **Subfamily Otomyinae**
    - **Subfamily Phloeomyinae**
    - **Subfamily Rhynchomyinae**
    - **Subfamily Hydromyinae**

E. LAVOCAT (1978)
- **Superfamily Muroidea**
  - **Family Cricetodontidae**
    - **Subfamily Afrocricetodontinae**
  - **Family Nesomyidae**
    - **Subfamily Nesomyinae (all seven genera)**
    - **Subfamily Lophiomyinae**
    - **Subfamily Mystromyinae**
    - **Subfamily Tachyoryctinae**
    - **Subfamily Gerbillinae**
    - **Subfamily Otomyinae**
  - **Family Muridae**
    - **Subfamily Dendromurinae**
    - **Subfamily Murinae**

for phylogenetic inference. Using the IRBP (also known as RBP3) gene and a broad sampling of muroid rodents, including representatives of all nine Malagasy genera, Jansa and Weksler (2004) recovered three well-supported clades of native Malagasy rodents (Figure 14.28a), but analyses of the IRBP gene alone did not strongly support these three clades as a monophyletic group. A contemporaneous study (Steppan et al. 2004) used more nuclear loci but only five genera of Malagasy rodents and recovered the monophyly of the nesomyines sampled as the sister group to a diverse clade of endemic African muroids (Figure 14.28b). A follow-up study (Jansa

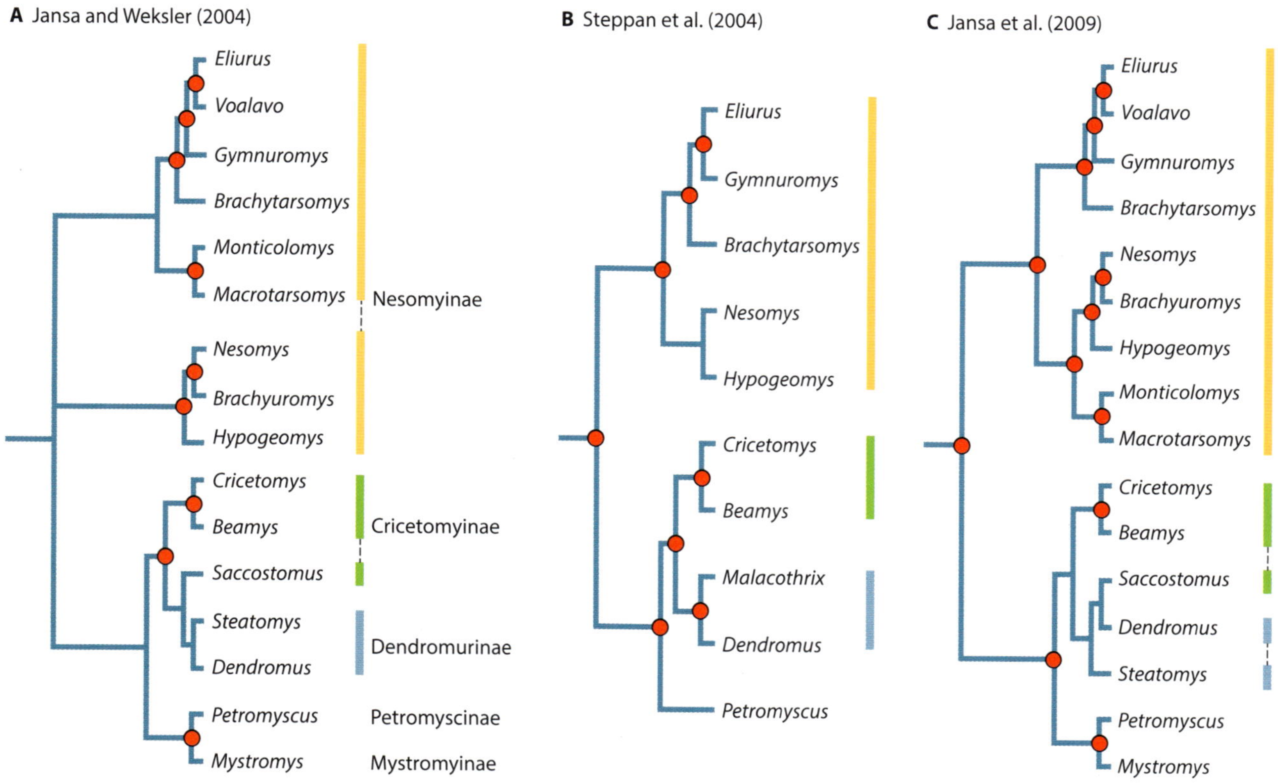

FIGURE 14.28 **Three phylogenies of Malagasy native rodents (Nesomyidae: Nesomyinae) derived from analyses of nuclear gene sequences: A) Jansa and Weksler (2004), based on analysis of the nuclear IRBP gene; B) Steppan et al. (2004), based on analysis of four nuclear genes; and C) Jansa et al. (2009), based on analysis of the nuclear GHR and IRBP genes combined. Orange bars bracket genera of Nesomyinae; green bars those of Cricetomyinae; and blue bars those of Dendromurinae. Dashed lines between bars indicate that subfamilial monophyly was not supported. Red dots indicate nodes that were well supported by bootstrap values, posterior probabilities, or both.**

et al. 2009) added the GHR locus to the existing IRBP sequences and recovered strong support for a monophyletic group comprising all nine Malagasy genera that was sister to the same clade of endemic African muroids identified by Steppan et al. (2004) (Figure 14.28c). Collectively, this inclusive clade is now formally recognized as the family Nesomyidae (Musser and Carleton 2005), comprising the native Malagasy subfamily Nesomyinae along with the African muroid subfamilies Cricetomyinae, Dendromurinae, Delanymyinae, Petromyscinae, and Mystromyinae.

The repeated demonstration of nesomyine monophyly thus establishes that rodents can join lemurs, carnivores, and tenrecs as one of the four extant mammalian adaptive radiations unique to Madagascar.

DATING THE NESOMYINE RADIATION

The sister-taxon relationship of Malagasy rodents and rodent groups from mainland Africa indicates that the founding rodent stock arrived from Africa, not from Asia. Although some Holocene remains of rodents have been discovered (Goodman and Rakotondravony 1996; Muldoon et al. 2009; Mein et al. 2010), the fossil record of terrestrial vertebrates on Madagascar for the most part pre-dates the Cenozoic (but see Samonds, pp. 69–73), the era when modern mammals likely colonized the island (Samonds et al. 2012). Thus, the current paleontological record can provide no direct evidence about when rodents first arrived from Africa. Researchers have therefore turned to molecular phylogenies that have been time-scaled using a relaxed molecular clock (Thorne et al. 1998; Drummond et al. 2006), calibrated against the fossil record documented outside the nesomyine radiation (Table 14.19).

Nesomyine rodents must have arrived on Madagascar between the time they split from their African sister clade (the stem age for Nesomyinae) and their initial diversification on the island (the subfamily's crown age) (Table 14.19). Estimates of stem age derived from the various time-scaled phylogenies range widely from 48.1 to 12.5 million years ago (Mya), and crown-age estimates vary nearly as much, from 28.8 to 10.9 Mya. These inferred dates frame important questions for understanding the evolution of nesomyine rodents: When did a founding population disperse to Madagascar; what geo-climatic events facilitated this dispersal; how quickly did the initial nesomyine radiation transpire after arrival; and what role did extinction play in shaping the subfamily's present diversity? For example, the estimate for the latest arrival time falls between 12.5 Mya and 10.9 Mya (Steppan and Schenk 2017; Table 14.19), which implies that nesomyines would have had no more than 1.6 million years to begin their initial diversification and that extinction may have played a minor role in their early diversification. By contrast,

TABLE 14.19. **Estimated divergence times (in millions of years) for Nesomyinae based on selected molecular phylogenetic studies**

STUDY	NESOMYINAE STEM AGE	NESOMYINAE CROWN AGE
Poux et al. (2005)	23.5 (18.2–29.6)	20.1 (15.4–25.7)
Bininda-Emonds et al. (2007)	48.1 (43.8–52.4)	28.8 (21.0–36.6)
Fabre et al. (2012)	25.8	21.4
Crottini et al. (2012)	28 (17–42)	-
Hedges et al. (2015)	30 (18–48)	21.4 (15.3–28.6)
Steppan and Schenk (2017)	12.5 (11.7–13.4)	10.9 (9.5–12.1)
Upham et al. (2019)	26.5	21.1

Note: The values in the two age columns are median divergence time and 95% credible interval (in parentheses when available) for the divergence time between Nesomyinae and their African relatives (stem age) and the basal divergence within the Malagasy radiation (crown age).

if one accepts the oldest stem-age and crown-age estimates, 48.1 Mya and 28.8 Mya, respectively (Bininda-Emonds et al. 2007), then 19 million years elapsed between nesomyine colonization and the group's initial diversification, a lengthy interval that would have allowed extinction to play a larger role in shaping its present diversity. Clearly, very different biogeographic and evolutionary processes could be inferred from these widely disparate chronological estimates.

The chronological signposts estimated from molecular phylogenies rely heavily on the fossil calibrations employed, the analytical methods used, and the underlying data, including the evolutionary rates of the genes analyzed. For the studies summarized in Table 14.19, those that have a broader taxonomic scope—vertebrates (Poux et al. 2005; Crottini et al. 2012; Hedges et al. 2015), all mammals (Bininda-Emonds et al. 2007; Upham et al. 2019), or all rodents (Fabre et al. 2012)—tend to infer much earlier dates of nesomyine origin than those that focus on just Muroidea (e.g., Steppan and Schenk 2017). In particular, the stem-age estimates derived from a supertree of all mammals (Bininda-Emonds et al. 2007) are quite old (median: 48.1 Mya; 95% credibility interval: 43.8–52.4 Mya), which partly reflects the lack of resolution among major lineages of muroid rodents apparent in this phylogeny. Even when omitting this study, stem-age estimates for Nesomyinae range from 30 Mya to 12.5 Mya, which covers portions of two epochs, late Oligocene to middle Miocene, and a corresponding diversity of paleoclimatic and geological events that could have facilitated or impeded dispersal from Africa (Samonds et al. 2012; see Samonds et al., pp. 73–78) and subsequent patterns of diversification on Madagascar. Although several studies now place the arrival of nesomyines sometime between the late Oligocene and middle Miocene, the pattern and timing of their early diversification on the island remain open questions.

In view of the current understanding informed by time-scaled molecular phylogenies (Table 14.19), René Lavocat, former paleontologist at the Muséum National d'Histoire Naturelle in Paris, deserves posthumous plaudits. Lavocat (1973, 1978) postulated the entry of ancestral nesomyines into Madagascar by overwater dispersal from eastern Africa sometime in the early Miocene, 18–23 Mya. Lavocat (1973) based his hypothesis on the Kenyan lower-Miocene fossil *Protarsomys*, a member of the archaic Afrocricetodontinae (see discussion in Carleton and Goodman 1996: 246–249, 251–252). The early Miocene, or earlier, antiquity of Nesomyinae, as adduced by Lavocat, comfortably falls within the confidence intervals derived for many crown-age estimates. Lavocat's conceptual framework was formalized in the novel reclassification of Muroidea by Chaline et al. (1977) and expanded by Carleton and Musser (1984: 344–345), and has received convincing support in recent genetic studies (Jansa and Weksler 2004; Poux et al. 2005; Jansa et al. 2009; Steppan and Schenk 2017).

Finally, we emphasize that most evidence for relationships among nesomyine species and the timing of their diversification issues from relatively little data. To date, only one gene—the mitochondrial cytochrome b—has been sequenced for all species represented in current phylogenies (Figure 14.29), which in turn represent only 75% of the current known diversity of Nesomyinae (Table 14.17). Thus, a complete, species-level phylogeny derived from multiple loci, time-scaled within the context of global rodent diversification, remains a pressing research need for understanding the diversification of this endemic subfamily. Such a robust phylogenetic framework holds tremendous promise for integrating comparative analyses of the morphology, genomics, and ecology of nesomyine rodents and for developing fuller comprehension of their fascinating adaptive radiation within its insular setting.

RELATIONSHIPS AMONG GENERA OF NESOMYINAE

Certain stable relationships among the Malagasy genera have emerged from the above-mentioned phylogenetic studies. Concatenated phylogenetic analysis of the GHR and IRBP genes (Jansa et al. 2009) has depicted living nesomyines in two main lineages: one comprising *Brachytarsomys*, *Gymnuromys*, and *Eliurus-Voalavo*; the other *Macrotarsomys-Monticolomys*, *Hypogeomys*, and *Brachyuromys-Nesomys* (Figure 14.28c). This division is consistent with some well-supported relationships recovered through phylogenetic analysis of the mitochondrial gene cytochrome b (Jansa et al. 1999) and with the expansive study of Muroidea based on nuclear and mitochondrial genes (Steppan and Schenk 2017; Figure 14.29). These corroborated genus-level groupings are briefly summarized below and expanded where necessary.

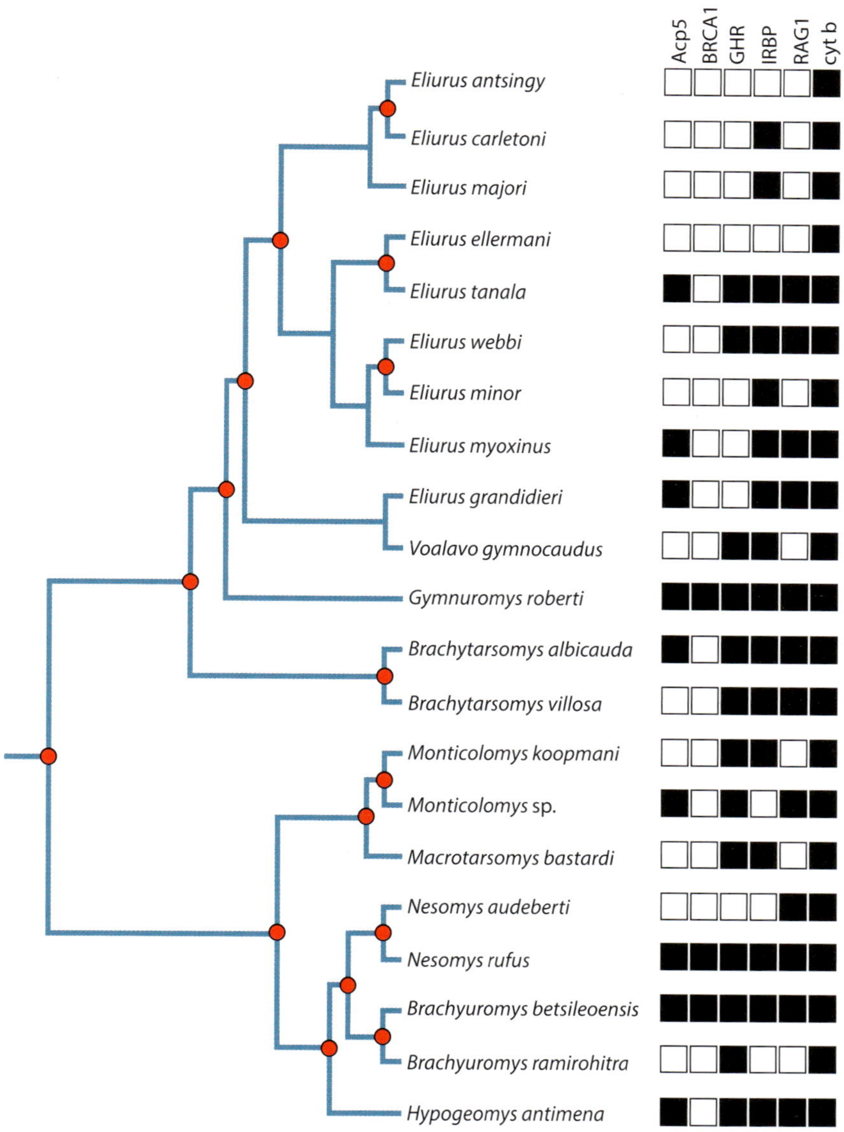

FIGURE 14.29 **The phylogeny of Nesomyinae extracted from a larger study of muroid relationships (Steppan and Schenk 2017). The six genes included in the study's broader analysis are shown in the table to the right of the tree: black squares indicate that the gene was sampled for the corresponding taxon; white squares mean the gene was not sequenced.**

Macrotarsomys-Monticolomys

Carleton and Goodman (1996) identified five discrete character-state transformations of the molars and skull that indicated a sister-group relationship between *Macrotarsomys* and *Monticolomys*. While acknowledging that these few transformations were not uniquely synapomorphic within Muroidea, they concluded that "a hypothesis of cognate affinity warrants attention at this formative stage of phylogenetic understanding among nesomyines" (Carleton and Goodman 1996: 250).

Subsequent molecular data and broader taxon sampling have provided a critical test of their hypothesis. Cytochrome b sequences overwhelmingly supported a sister-group relationship between *Macrotarsomys* and *Monticolomys* (Jansa et al. 1999); in fact, this grouping was the most stable clade apparent in the cytochrome b tree and was also recovered in separate analysis of the nuclear loci IRBP and GHR as well as concatenated analyses of these genes. Other molecular studies have also recovered *Macrotarsomys* and *Monticolomys* as the closest generic kin among the nesomyines surveyed (Jansa and Weksler 2004; Steppan and Schenk 2017; see Figures 14.28a and 14.29). However, relationships among the three species of *Macrotarsomys* (Goodman and Soarimalala 2005; Jansa et al. 2008) and the taxon's monophyly with respect to populations of *Monticolomys* have yet to be rigorously evaluated.

Brachyuromys-Nesomys

Although the short-tailed, small-eared members of *Brachyuromys* superficially resemble voles of the Holarctic Arvicolinae (Cricetidae), early authors stressed the taxon's dental similarities to various mole rats (Spalacidae), whether of the subfamily Tachyoryctinae (Major 1897a; Ellerman 1941) or Spalacinae (F. Petter 1961). Molecular phylogenetic analyses have convincingly rejected these improbable relationships and firmly anchor *Brachyuromys* among Nesomyinae, namely as the sister taxon to *Nesomys* (Jansa and Weksler 2004; Jansa et al. 2009; Steppan and Schenk 2017; see Figures 14.28a and c, and 14.29). Jansa et al. (1999) first recovered this alliance with moderate support from analysis of cytochrome b sequences; subsequent analyses of nuclear genes GHR and IRBP also recovered this group with very strong support (Jansa et al. 2009).

Eliurus-Voalavo

Molecular phylogenetic studies incorporating broad taxonomic sampling have provided the best evidence for grouping the nine genera of native rodents as monophyletic and have robustly depicted their interrelationships. Still, such studies have not included dense sampling of nesomyine species per se, particularly from the species-rich genus *Eliurus*. The first molecular phylogenetic study to include more than one *Eliurus* species brought into question the monophyly of the genus (Jansa et al. 1999). Its cytochrome b analyses disclosed a sister-taxon relationship between *E. grandideri* and *Voalavo gymnocaudus* that excluded seven other *Eliurus* species. Carleton and Goodman (1998) had described *V. gymnocaudus* and arranged its genus as closely related to, but distinct from, *Eliurus* based on morphological characteristics. Although the molecular sequences contradicted this generic distinction, Jansa et al. (1999) refrained from formally synonymizing these taxa, because the apparent paraphyly of *Eliurus* rested on a single mitochondrial gene and conflicted with the available morphological evidence. Nonetheless, a subsequent study including nuclear genes also supported a sister-taxon relationship of *E. grandidieri* and *Voalavo* (Steppan and Schenk 2017; Figure 14.29); these authors advised removal of *E. grandidieri* from *Eliurus* and placement in *Voalavo*. Formal resolution of this taxonomic problem is clearly amenable through more comprehensive analysis of species relationships, especially including *E. petteri*, and integrating analyses of morphological and molecular data.

PATTERNS OF SPECIATION WITHIN *ELIURUS*

Aside from the issue of *Voalavo*, current taxonomy recognizes 13 species of *Eliurus* (Table 14.17); however, the number of species considered valid has continued to grow since the early explorations of the island (see Jansa et al. 2019: Figure 1). Although Madagascar's small mammals exhibit a certain degree of microendemism (Wilmé et al. 2006), we doubt that many new species of *Eliurus* remain to be discovered through field inventories, given the ample coverage of geographic and bioclimatic zones by small-mammal surveys conducted since 1990; this expectation contrasts with that concerning other vertebrate groups, such as frogs (see Glaw et al., pp. 1305–22), that show considerable levels of microendemism. Rather, data from existing museum specimens of *Eliurus* should be brought to bear on testing the limits of described species, refining our current understanding of geographic ranges, and identifying cryptic lineages. For example, strong phylogeographic structure within *E. myoxinus* (Shi et al. 2013) and among some of the Central Highlands endemic species (Everson et al. 2020b) suggests that certain specific definitions remain composites. Conversely, multi-gene approaches to species delimitation (Jansa et al. 2019) suggest that some recognized species may be better considered as geographically isolated populations than as distinct species.

With the continuing description of new species, Carleton and Goodman (2007) identified several morphological themes among the 11 then-known species of *Eliurus* and distilled these as five provisional species groups: 1) the *E. majori* group (*E. majori*, *E. penicillatus*, and *E. danieli*); 2) the *E. antsingy* group (*E. antsingy*); 3) the *E. myoxinus* group (*E. myoxinus* and *E. minor*); 4) the *E. petteri* group (*E. petteri* and *E. grandidieri*); and 5) the *E. tanala* group (*E. tanala*, *E. ellermani*, and *E. webbi*). Subsequent species descriptions clearly allied *E. carletoni*, a species endemic to the northern reaches of the island, with the *E. antsingy* group from western dry forests (Goodman et al. 2009a). A recent revision of the *E. tanala* group based on molecular and morphological data from hundreds of museum specimens identified a new species, *E. tsingimbato*, from the western karst-associated forests (Jansa et al. 2019). The authors provided additional evidence that *E. tanala* and *E. ellermani*, both from eastern moist evergreen forests, should be retained as separate species and questioned the association of *E. webbi* with the *E. tanala* species group. Focused revisionary work of this nature has advanced understanding of the deeper relationships within *Eliurus*, but clearly, the genus invites additional research employing an integrated taxonomic approach that densely samples both populations and species.

RESOLUTION OF THE PHYLETIC PLACEMENT OF *BRACHYTARSOMYS*, *GYMNUROMYS*, AND *HYPOGEOMYS*

The morphological definition and taxonomic circumscription of these three genera have posed no problems since their original descriptions in the 1800s. Nevertheless, their phyletic placement in the nesomyine radiation has elicited some confusion, as evidenced by their earlier allocation to different tribes and subfamilies of other muroid groups (e.g., Ellerman 1941; see Tables 14.17 and 14.18c). Early molecular phylogenies utilizing only cytochrome b offered little resolution for placement of these taxa, due largely to the rapid evolution of this mitochondrial gene and attendant difficulties in rooting the phylogeny (Jansa et al. 1999). Although this phylogeny provided weak support for linking *Hypogeomys* with the clade comprising *Macrotarsomys* and *Monticolomys*, the relationship seemed improbable at first impression given their morphological distinctiveness. Similarly, the placement of *Gymnuromys* and *Brachytarsomys* outside the core Nesomyinae, as implicated by this tree, was unlikely.

Recent phylogenetic studies have considerably expanded taxonomic representation of Muroidea and sampled both mitochondrial and nuclear genes. In all studies that use nuclear genes (Jansa and Weksler 2004; Steppan et al. 2004; Jansa et al. 2009; Steppan and Schenk 2017), *Gymnuromys* and *Brachytarsomys* join the *Eliurus-Voalavo* clade as sequential sister taxa with strong support; these phylogenies also provide robust support for grouping *Hypogeomys* with the clade comprising *Brachyuromys* and *Nesomys* (Figures 14.28c and 14.29). Finally, these same nuclear-gene analyses provided novel and robust support for uniting this latter clade with the *Macrotarsomys-Monticolomys* sister group (Figures 14.28c and 14.29). This large clade includes one of the smallest (*Monticolomys*) and the largest (*Hypogeomys*) members of Nesomyinae, along with species that live at the tops of mountains (*Monticolomys*), in marshy wetlands (*Brachyuromys*), in moist evergreen forests (*Nesomys*), and in dry deciduous forests and dry spiny thickets (*Macrotarsomys* and *Hypogeomys*). Such pronounced ecomorphological diversity makes this assemblage—and indeed the whole of Nesomyinae—a particularly compelling example of mammalian adaptive radiation, one that has unfolded within a confined geography, that is ripe for further study.

Subject editor: Steven M. Goodman

INTRODUCED TERRESTRIAL SMALL MAMMALS

B. Ramasindrazana, T. M. Randriamoria, S. Rahelinirina, J.-B. Duchemin, J.-M. Duplantier, V. Soarimalala, and S. M. Goodman

As one of the world's biodiversity centers, Madagascar represents a cradle of unique vertebrate species, and terrestrial mammals represent a good example. Of the nonvolant small mammal species occurring on the island, including 28 species of the endemic subfamily of rodents, Nesomyinae, and 31 species of the endemic family Tenrecidae (see Goodman and Soarimalala, pp. 1737–69), only three rodent species of the order Rodentia (family Muridae) and two shrew species of the order Soricomorpha (family Soricidae) have been unintentionally introduced by humans (Figure 14.30). The three rodent species are *Rattus rattus* (Black Rat), *R. norvegicus* (Brown Rat), and a member of the *Mus musculus* complex (House Mouse). The two shrews are represented by *Suncus etruscus* (Etruscan Shrew) and *S. murinus* (Asian Musk Shrew). There is no evidence to date for the introduction of *R. tanezumi* (Tanezumi Rat) on Madagascar.

Another rodent was intentionally introduced to Madagascar as a farm animal—*Cavia porcellus* (Guinea Pig, family Caviidae). This introduction had no negative ecological consequences for endemic species, but it had implications for public health. Brygoo (1966) mentioned several plague epizootics concerning this species between 1926 and 1952 on small farms around Antananarivo, Moramanga, and Manjakandriana, and proposed that these incidents should have been taken as warning signals in order to prevent human cases.

Introduced small mammal species were transported by humans to Madagascar and thereafter colonized different environments, including natural forests, and represent a threat not only to the native and endemic biodiversity of the island but also to public health. The earliest known presence of *Rattus* and *Mus* on the island is based on archaeological remains from a 10th- to 14th-century site near Ambanja and associated with a Middle Eastern–East African maritime trading network (Rakotozafy 1996). Little information is available about the date of the introduction of the two *Suncus* species to western Indian Ocean islands (Hutterer and Tranier 1990; Fuller and Boivin 2009), but it can be presumed to be contemporary with the Islamic period. Coinciding with their successful colonization of the island, these small mammals introduced their own micro- and macro-parasites. Since the start of the 21st century, these mammal species have been extensively screened for different pathogens threatening possible zoonotic disease transfer not only to the endemic small-mammal fauna of the island but also to its human inhabitants (see chapter 6 for details on this subject).

In the precursor of this book, a contribution appeared in the Human Ecology chapter entitled "Human Diseases and Introduced Small Mammals" (Duplantier and Duchemin 2003a). Since that time, a considerable amount of fieldwork has been conducted on the small mammals of Madagascar, much of it in different types of native forests but also in secondary habitats and in close proximity to human habitations and agricultural areas. During these field operations, endemic and introduced rodents and shrews were captured. Our intent herein is to review different aspects of what is known about the five species of unintentionally established small mammals on Madagascar, with special emphasis on their initial introduction to the island, distribution, ecology, and invasive capacity, and brief mention of their role as known or possible reservoirs for different zoonotic diseases. Detailed information on their ectoparasites is presented elsewhere in this book (for fleas, see Duchemin et al., pp. 1074–80; for ticks, Klompen and Apanaskevich, pp. 894–99).

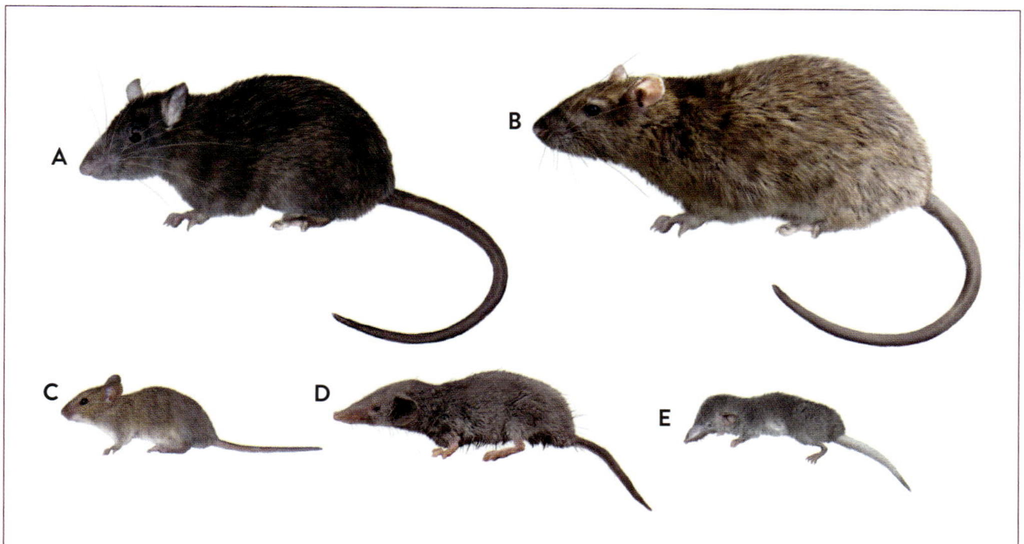

FIGURE 14.30 **Five species of small mammals introduced to Madagascar occur in urban, rural, and native forest areas. Rodents of the family Muridae: A) *Rattus rattus*, B) *R. norvegicus*, and C) *Mus musculus*. Shrews of the family Soricidae: D) *Suncus murinus*, and D) *S. etruscus* (the Madagascar population of which was previously considered an endemic species, *S. madagascariensis*).** (ARTWORK by V. Simeonovski.)

RATTUS RATTUS, BLACK RAT, ALSO KNOWN AS SHIP RAT, ROOF RAT, HOUSE RAT, *VOALAVO*

Origin and Systematics

Rattus rattus is native to the southern part of the Indian Peninsula (Aplin et al. 2011; Figure 14.30a). This species employed different human maritime movements at various points in history to spread beyond its original distribution. Based on archaeological remains, the earliest evidence of this genus on Madagascar dates from the 10th to 14th century from Mahilaka (Rakotozafy 1996; Radimilahy 1998; see Wright and Rakotoarisoa, pp. 181–90), which is the earliest known town on the island and was an entrepôt for a Middle Eastern and East African sea-trading network. Microsatellite and mitochondrial analyses support the hypothesis of two independent introductions of *R. rattus* to Madagascar. One of these was in the island's north and the other in the south, both probably from the same ancestral source population (Arabian Peninsula) and estimated to have taken place in the 10th century (Brouat et al. 2014); the samples used in this genetic analysis include in part those obtained in and around modern Malagasy ports. Given all the haplotypic variations of *R. rattus* around world (e.g., Tollenaere et al. 2010; Aplin et al. 2011; Bastos et al., 2011), it is rather surprising that no evidence of other genetic forms has been found on the island. In contrast, in southern Africa, for example, seven different haplotypes of *R. rattus* have been identified (Bastos et al. 2011). This difference can probably be best explained by a lower level of shipping exchanges, including containers, in the ports of Madagascar compared to those of South Africa and/or by competition with preexisting *R. rattus* populations. This question merits further research.

Two different karyotypes have been identified in the "*R. rattus*" group, now separated as distinct species (Baverstock et al. 1983). Animals with the karyotypic form 2n = 38–40 correspond to *R. rattus* and constitute the most widespread species in the world. Lineages with 2n = 42 represent *R. tanezumi*, the natural populations of which are limited to Southeast Asia and the Pacific Ocean, while introduced populations occur in and around ports of the Indian Ocean, eastern and southeastern coastal Africa, and the Pacific coast of North America (Aplin et al. 2011). On Madagascar, only the 2n = 38 karyotype has been identified in animals phenotypically identified as *R. rattus* (Capanna and Civitelli 1971; Duplantier et al. 2003; Hingston et al. 2005). Further, different genetic studies have found no evidence of *R. tanezumi* on the island (Tollenaere et al. 2010; Brouat et al. 2014). Given the very recent arrival of this species in harbors of all continents, *Rattus* in the main Malagasy harbors should be monitored in the future to document its possible arrival on the island.

Distribution

Based on a comparison of the results of zoological expeditions over the past 120 years, some changes in the presence and distribution of *R. rattus* can be traced. Major (1896b), who collected numerous endemic Nesomyine rodents in the eastern moist evergreen forests in 1895 and 1896, did not report capturing any specimens of *Rattus* but did mention the capture of other introduced small mammals. Webb (1954: 256), who trapped small mammals at Périnet (Analamazaotra), noted that introduced rats (*Rattus* spp.) "have multiplied at an alarming rate. The eastern forests are now swarming with them, even in the most isolated regions." Some of the earliest specimens of *R. rattus* on Madagascar in museum collections were taken in Mahanoro (1895); Manjakatompo, at the base of the Ankaratra Massif (1929); Andrafiavelo Forest, near Maintirano (1930); Montagne d'Ambre (1932); and Bemangidy, north of Tolagnaro (1948).

Nowadays, *R. rattus* is widespread and occurs in virtually all natural and anthropogenic habitats on the island, including as a human commensal, in secondary habitat, agricultural areas, and degraded and intact forests from sea level up to 2500 m (Goodman 1995; Andrianjakarivelo et al. 2005; Duplantier et al. 2005; Maminirina et al. 2008; Soarimalala 2008). It has been captured in remote forest areas up to 20 km from the nearest village (Soarimalala and Goodman 2011). To our knowledge, Madagascar is the only country in the world completely and almost uniformly covered by *R. rattus*.

In general, this species occurs in areas with mesic microclimates, which, in a synanthropic context, include burrows and galleries in and around buildings, irrigated agricultural areas, and water evacuation networks, including sewers and different forms of canals. In the context of native forest formations, this species is broadly distributed in the moist evergreen forests of eastern and northern Madagascar, and at certain intact forest sites it can be captured with greater frequency than endemic Nesomyinae rodents. A number of elevational transects have been conducted on different mountains in the moist evergreen forests, and in almost all cases the density of *R. rattus* is highest in areas of mid-altitude (e.g., Goodman and Carleton 1998; Soarimalala et al. 2001, 2007; Goodman and Soarimalala 2002, Soarimalala and Goodman 2003a; Maminirina et al. 2008). One possible explanation for this observed pattern is that at lower elevations on these massifs there is a more pronounced dry season than at mid-altitude, where food resources are more seasonally available, or in a more general sense, the mid-altitude zone better fits the bioclimatic niche of the animal. In this same context, capture rates in drier natural forest formations, specifically dry deciduous forests (e.g., Soarimalala 2008), are dramatically lower, with the same trapping effort, than in moist evergreen forests, which correspond with its primary habitat—moist forests of southern India (Aplin et al. 2011). Further, in the dry spiny thicket, which has a dry season approaching or surpassing 10 months, *R. rattus* numbers are very low, except near natural water sources or human-dug wells (Goodman et al. 2002; Soarimalala 2008). Hence, this species' ability to colonize forest areas appears to be directly related to the presence of water sources, and in moist evergreen forest habitats, it is more abundant along streams, which in turn are presumed to act as dispersal corridors from lowland human habitations and agricultural fields to higher elevational ranges.

Ecology and Biology

Under favorable environmental conditions, *R. rattus* can reproduce throughout the year (Duplantier and Rakotondravony 1999), and is a precocious and prodigious breeder (see Randriamoria et al., pp. 2006–8). Therefore, theoretically, a female can produce hundreds of descendants in a year and millions in three years. In forests and agricultural fields, breeding is discontinuous and rather favored

during the rainy season, when food resources are more abundant (Duplantier and Rakotondravony 1999; Soarimalala and Goodman 2011).

This species is mainly nocturnal and has an omnivorous diet. In forested and anthropogenic sites in the central east (Moramanga District), based on stable isotope analyses, Dammhahn et al. (2017) observed that *R. rattus* has an extremely broad dietary profile, including several trophic levels and encompassing the isotopic space of the complete locally occurring endemic forest-dwelling small-mammal community; this broad overlap indicates significant levels of possible competition. Further, these authors found that the stable isotope signal of *R. rattus* tended to change seasonally and differed between natural forests and anthropogenic habitats, indicating plasticity in feeding niches. Moreover, in this same study, on the basis of differences in stable isotope signatures from the same individuals of *R. rattus*, at the level of months (derived from fur) and hours (obtained from feces), evidence of dispersal movements at a very local level between natural forest and anthropogenic habitats could be identified.

Local dispersal movements of *R. rattus* between different types of anthropogenic habitats have also been demonstrated through other field methods. For example, based on trapping studies at two east coast sites, this species showed marked seasonal displacement to villages, particularly around houses, during the period of rice harvest or food scarcity in secondary forested habitat (Rasolozaka 1998). In the Central Highlands, seasonal displacements between habitats and different zones depend on phenological stages of possible food sources—for example, in agricultural and synanthropic settings, on ripening of crops such as rice, maize, cassava, and sugarcane; and within forest habitats or secondary habitats, on the production of fruits, particularly during the rainy season (D. Rakotondravony 1986). Using rhodamine B as a marker, S. Rahelinirina et al. (2010a) demonstrated that, in the Central Highlands, individuals of this species move regularly between houses, adjacent sisal plantations, and irrigated rice fields, traveling up to 350 m over a three-month period. Within the same study, movements of this species according to season were likely associated with food availability but also with its breeding season and with the human plague season.

Invasion Capacity

Rattus rattus is considered among the top 100 of the world's worst invasive organisms (Lowe et al. 2000). On Madagascar, it is known as one of the largest contributors to public health problems (see different contributions in chapter 6 for the diseases in which it is a major reservoir, including plague), a threat to endemic species (Goodman, 1995), and a crop pest (e.g., G. Rasamoelina et al. 1997; FAO and PAM 2013; Soarimalala et al. 2019). It causes significant damage to standing or stored rice stocks as well as other crops such as cassava, sweet potatoes, tomatoes, corn, and beans (Duplantier and Rakotondravony 1999; FAO and PAM 2013); such data for Madagascar were until recently not well documented as compared to those for continental sub-Saharan Africa (Swanepoel et al. 2017). This species is known to be a serious crop pest in the following regions of Madagascar: Boeny, Atsimo Atsinanana, Vatovavy Fitovinany, Atsinanana, Analanjirofo, and Haute Matsiatra (FAO and PAM 2013). At certain localities, damage caused by rats can reach 15–20% of the anticipated rice harvest. In the Boeny Region, for example, damage caused by rats on irrigated rice plots is estimated at around 1.2% of the standing crop, which corresponds to the equivalent harvest of 10,000 ha of rice fields (G. Rasamoelina et al. 1997). In the Lake Alaotra area, the average value of preharvest damage was slightly less than 100 kg of nonthreshed rice per hectare of rice field (Salvioni 1991). In a study conducted in anthropogenic habitats in the central and eastern areas of the island, it was documented that *R. rattus* damages crops (rice, cassava, pineapple, banana, and sugarcane), soils and consumes food stocks, and gnaws holes in clothes and different types of household utensils (Soarimalala et al. 2019).

In medium-altitude moist evergreen forest and introduced-tree plantations of Montagne d'Ambre in the far north, during trapping sessions conducted in April for three consecutive years (1994–1996), *R. rattus* accounted for between 64% and 90% of small mammals captured, and in certain forest types this figure exceeded 95%. The native forests of this protected area are infested with rats. In addition, in areas outside of natural forest in the central east, this species was the most abundant introduced rodent (Duplantier and Rakotondravony 1999; Randriamoria 2017; Soarimalala et al. 2019). In zones where *R. rattus* has colonized natural habitats, which range from degraded to intact forests, there is an apparent concordant decline in endemic Nesomyine rodents (Goodman 1995), which are largely forest dwelling. This situation is evident in the case of degraded forest fragments, as at Ambohitantely Special Reserve (Goodman and Rakotondravony 2000), and degraded littoral forest (D. Rakotondravony et al. 1998a). However, direct evidence of causality for this relationship has been difficult to assess, partly owing to a lack of information on possible dietary overlap. A comparison of external and craniodental morphology of *R. rattus* and some endemic rodents found broad overlap in certain species in "ecomorphological space," providing possible inference of competition (Miljutin and Lehtonen 2008). Extrapolation from stable isotope analyses of sympatric species of small mammals in a medium-altitude moist evergreen forest near Moramanga showed notable overlap and showed that *R. rattus* occupied a dietary niche equivalent to that of all endemic rodent and tenrec species in the complete small-mammal community (Dammhahn et al. 2017). Further, there is increasing evidence of the role *R. rattus* has played in the introduction of a wide range of zoonotic diseases to native small mammals.

Ectoparasites and Zoonotic Diseases

Rattus rattus is known as a host of different ectoparasites (see Duchemin et al., pp. 1074–80, for fleas, and Klompen and Apanaskevich, pp. 894–99, for ticks) and a number of zoonotic diseases (see chapter 6) that can be transmitted to endemic taxa; few data are available on the pathogenicity of these diseases to their hosts. For example, at a forested site in the Central Highlands, *Yersinia pestis* (the plague bacterium) was isolated from the endemic tenrec *Hemicentetes nigriceps* (Duplantier et al. 2005) and endemic rodent *Eliurus tanala* (S. Rahelinirina, unpublished data), even though the role of these species as a reservoir is not yet confirmed. Movements of *R. rattus* between different habitats might also increase the probability of disease transmission. In some areas of Madagascar, this species is a documented reservoir of bubonic plague (Duchemin

2003; Andrianaivoarimanana et al. 2013) and is considered the principal rodent involved in the rural plague cycle, and two fleas, the introduced *Xenopsylla cheopis* and endemic *Synopsyllus fonquerniei*, are known as the primary vectors (Duchemin 2003).

RATTUS NORVEGICUS, BROWN RAT, ALSO KNOWN AS COMMON RAT, STREET RAT, SEWER RAT, NORWAY RAT, *VOALAVO, VOALAVO SIEDOA*

Origin and Systematics

On the basis of molecular studies, Zeng et al. (2018) revealed that *R. norvegicus* (Figure 14.30b) originated from southeastern Asia as previously proposed (Aplin et al. 2003), then spread into the Middle East (about 3100 years ago), then to eastern Africa (about 2000 years ago), and then Europe (about 1800 years ago). These dates are much older than those previously inferred from historical and archaeological records and should be treated with some caution, and the spread of this species beyond its natural distribution should be still considered as more recent than that of *R. rattus* (Aplin et al. 2003). The earliest *R. norvegicus* museum specimen record we are aware of on Madagascar is 1929, an animal trapped at Manjakatompo at the foothills of the Ankaratra Massif. Further and, in contrast to *R. rattus*, no clear archaeozoological record is known for this species (Rakotozafy 1996; Radimilahy 1998). Across its non-native range, *R. norvegicus* lives as a human commensal and is generally considered less common in tropical zones than *R. rattus*.

Distribution

On Madagascar, the distributional range of *R. norvegicus* is largely in cities, towns, and villages in the eastern lowlands and Central Highlands, up to 1500 m (Malzy 1964; Soarimalala and Goodman 2011). In these areas of the island, it is not uncommon to capture a few individuals of *R. norvegicus* in rural areas within synanthropic settings or close to fields (rice or other agricultural crops), but it is rarely captured in native disturbed or relatively intact forest (Randriamoria 2016, 2017; Soarimalala et al. 2019; B. Ramasindrazana, unpublished data). This species lives predominantly in areas with relatively humid meteorological conditions, presumably associated with its need to have access to drinking water. Some isolated individuals have been captured away from the immediate vicinity of human settings, including transitional dry–moist evergreen forest in parcel 3 of the Andohahela protected area (Goodman et al. 1999a). It is worth mentioning that in a large-scale survey of small mammals living in the greater Moramanga area, with nearly 12,000 nights of trapping, across habitats spanning human habitation, agricultural areas, and degraded forest, this species was not captured (Randriamoria 2017). On Madagascar, *R. norvegicus* is distinctly an animal of urban and to a lesser extent agricultural areas, while *R. rattus* is the more common in rural and forested zones, particularly at higher elevations. Curiously, the exact opposite pattern is found on La Réunion, where *R. rattus* is the dominant commensal and urban species, and *R. norvegicus* is the more abundant of the two in rural and upland forested zones (Guernier et al. 2014).

Ecology and Biology

Rattus norvegicus is largely a terrestrial species but also occurs in semiaquatic habitats. It is mainly nocturnal and has an omnivorous diet. With sufficient food resources, this species can breed throughout the year, with higher rates between October and March (D. Rakotondravony 1986). Reproductive females give birth three to nine times per year, with up to 10 young per birth (M. Rasamoelina and Andriamalala 1999; Soarimalala and Goodman 2011), sexual maturity is reached at 50–60 days, and gestation period is 20–22 days. We are not aware of any precise published details on the ecology of this species on Madagascar. Understanding more about its natural history in urban areas is clearly a line of research that is critical for future work, particularly at the interface of zoonotic diseases and public health.

Invasive Capacity

The period of the initial colonization of Madagascar by *R. norvegicus* remains unclear. Nonetheless, it is presumed that this species arrived on the island more recently than *R. rattus*. Petit (1934) demonstrated that previous references to *R. norvegicus* on Madagascar, including in works by Kaudern, Perrier de la Bâthie, and Carougeau, were not credible and resulted from confusion between the different morphotypes of *R. rattus* already present on the island. Kaudern (1915) suggested it should be looked for close to major maritime ports. In 1941, Robic reported the capture of four individuals of *R. norvegicus* in the Toamasina port (Blanchy 1995). Brygoo (1966) noted the capture of one *R. norvegicus* in Antananarivo by the Bureau Municipal d'Hygiène. However, by 1983, the number of *R. norvegicus* individuals captured in Antananarivo was higher than that of *R. rattus*, and by 1987, based on trapped individuals, *R. norvegicus* was dominant over *R. rattus* (Blanchy 1995). In parallel to these results, starting in the early 1980s, A. D. S. Rakotondravony (1992) noted that *R. norvegicus* represented more than 80% of the captures in Antananarivo, and more recently, *R. norvegicus* constituted 60–98% of the rodents trapped in the capital (S. Rahelinirina, unpublished data).

Because of its scarcity in natural forests in Madagascar, invasive impacts of *R. norvegicus* on endemic biodiversity are undocumented and perhaps not measurable. Available information is mainly from rural and anthropogenic areas. *Rattus norvegicus* is also recognized as crop pest in Madagascar (FAO and PAM 2013), but the associated citation is based on interviews, and it is possible that the interviewees confused the two species of *Rattus*. In the central east of Madagascar, attacks on young poultry have been reported for *R. norvegicus* (Soarimalala et al. 2019). Based on stable isotope analyses in the same region, it was found that *R. norvegicus* consumes more animal protein than *R. rattus* (Dammhahn et al. 2017). Further, *R. norvegicus* has negative impacts on human goods in houses, including damage to clothes and different household items. Despite the lack of published data on the various impacts caused by this species, it is presumed that it is a potential invasive species in Madagascar as in other countries worldwide (CABI 2019).

Ectoparasites and Zoonotic Diseases

Given the close synanthropic association of *R. norvegicus*, it has been shown to be an important vector of a variety of zoonotic diseases with direct impact on public health. Many of these aspects are reviewed in chapter 6, and only an overview is presented here. The bacteria responsible for leptospirosis are shed by this rat, and at some localities close to half of the animals test positive for *Leptospira* (S. Rahelinirina et al. 2010b; also see Dietrich et al., pp. 268–77). Further, different viruses have been detected in this rat (Rollin et al. 1986; also see Hoarau et al., pp. 277–85). The vast majority of fleas collected on *R. norvegicus* are the introduced *Xenopsylla cheopis* (J.-B. Duchemin, unpublished data). The impact of plague on *R. norvegicus* and *R. rattus*, and their role in the transmission of this disease to humans, are different. *Rattus rattus* is highly sensitive to plague and during local epidemics dies in large numbers. This results in the fleas living on these rats to abandon the dead animal and to find another mammalian host, such as a human being, to feed on, a mechanism through which they transmit plague bacteria. On the contrary, in at least Antananarivo, *R. norvegicus* is more resistant to plague (Rahalison et al. 2003), and most individuals do not succumb to this disease, keeping infected fleas in their fur. Hence, this species and its associated fleas are not a regular mechanism for the transmission of fleas to people and instead act as a maintenance reservoir between human epidemics.

MUS MUSCULUS, HOUSE MOUSE, *TOTOZY*

Origins and Systematics

The original distribution of the *Mus musculus* complex (Figure 14.30c) is the Indian subcontinent, but the dispersal history is complicated (Boursot et al. 1996; Din et al. 1996). These different authorities recognized three different lineages or subspecies: *Mus musculus domesticus* in western Europe and the Mediterranean basin; *M. m. musculus* in central Europe and China; and *M. m. castaneus* in southeastern Asia and the Indian subcontinent. Subsequently, Prager et al. (1998) distinguished another lineage on the Arabian Peninsula (Yemen), which they named "*gentilulus*."

Genetic analyses concerning only mitochondrial DNA (Duplantier et al. 2002) and performed on *M. musculus* from 13 different localities across Madagascar, demonstrated that the populations on the island are genetically homogeneous and closely related to the *gentilulus* lineage from the Arabian Peninsula. Sakuma et al. (2016) also confirmed this *gentilulus* affinity, using mitochondrial DNA from a small sample of *Mus* from Antananarivo. However, at about the same time, Hardouin et al. (2015) analyzed the nuclear DNA of *Mus* from Asia, Africa, and Europe, as well as specimens from Madagascar (same individuals used in the Duplantier et al. 2002 study), and concluded that the Malagasy animals belong to the *castaneus* lineage; they suggested that this should be considered a subspecies of *M. musculus*. Throughout the book we use *M. musculus* for the species introduced to Madagascar, which simplifies the taxonomy but does not reflect the complex's evolutionary history.

Archaeological bone remains on Madagascar include *M. musculus* material excavated from Mahilaka, an Islamic port site south of Ambanja (Radimilahy 1998) dating from 1050–1400 CE. As with *Rattus*, material of which was identified from the same midden remains, the introduction of these animals to Madagascar was probably associated with their being stowaways in cargo boats of Arab traders moving between eastern Africa, islands in the western Indian Ocean, and the Middle East (see Beaujard 2012 for further details on trade routes across the Indian Ocean between the 7th and 10th centuries). The earliest *M. musculus* museum specimens from Madagascar we are aware of include those collected at Vinanitelo (1908), Antsiranana (1910), Forêt d'Ikongo (1928), Manjakatompo (1929), Andrafiavelo (1930), and Ambovombe (1932).

Distribution

Mus musculus can be found almost everywhere on Madagascar, living mostly as a human commensal but also found in natural ecosystems, including montane habitats. In studies associated with work on zoonotic diseases, this rodent is one of the most or the most common in the trap captures in surveys of small mammals living in urban areas. For example, during a 2014 inventory of Antananarivo, of the 114 small mammals trapped, all introduced, *M. musculus* made up more than 50% of the captures (S. Rahelinirina et al. 2019). In urban areas, the importance of *M. musculus* could have been previously underestimated, as the organization in charge of rodent control (Bureau Municipal d'Hygiène) used only large multiple-capture traps well adapted for large species (e.g., *Rattus*) but rather ineffective for small *M. musculus*. In the countryside, it is regularly captured in agricultural areas (beans, cassava, corn, and sugarcane) and in peridomestic situations within or close to human habitation (Randriamoria 2017; Soarimalala et al. 2019). In the moist evergreen forests of the east and north, this species is rarely captured (Soarimalala and Goodman 2003a; Soarimalala et al. 2001, 2007; Maminirina et al. 2008; Randriamoria 2017), and it is unknown to occur in some sites, such as Montagne d'Ambre, with extensive surveys across years with live traps and pitfalls (Goodman et al. 1997a). However, in mountainous zones toward the upper limit of forest cover or above, including montane ericoid thicket and montane grasslands, it can be rather common (Langrand and Goodman 1997; Goodman and Rasolonandrasana 2001). This species has been trapped in the summit zone of Tsaratanàna (2550 m), the highest massif on the island (Maminirina et al. 2008). *Mus musculus* can be found also in dry deciduous forests in the west and central west (Soarimalala 2008; Z. Rakotomalala and Goodman 2010).

Ecology

In general, this species is nocturnal and granivorous, although it can be seen and captured during crepuscular hours. In extreme temperature conditions, such as those of the montane grassland of the Andohariana Plateau (Andringitra), at over 2000 m, which during the winter months can have regular temperatures below freezing, this species can be partially diurnal (Langrand and Goodman 1997). The rarity of this species in the dry spiny thicket might be related to its need for sufficient water to survive (Soarimalala 2008) or perhaps some form of interspecific competition. We are not aware of any specific studies conducted on the ecology of this species on Madagascar.

Ectoparasites and Zoonotic Diseases

Given the peridomestic habits of *M. musculus*, it has been shown to be implicated as a possible vector of a variety of zoonotic diseases that have direct impact on public health. Many of these aspects are reviewed in chapter 6, and only an overview is presented here. DNA from pathogenic *Leptospira* was identified from this rodent but generally not at high prevalence rates (S. Rahelinirina et al. 2010b, 2019; also see Dietrich et al., pp. 268–77). Further, a range of different viruses has been detected in Malagasy populations of *M. musculus* (Raharinosy et al. 2018; also see Hoarau et al., pp. 277–85). *Yersinia pestis*–specific antigens have been detected in *M. musculus* (S. Rahelinirina 2009).

SUNCUS MURINUS, ASIAN MUSK SHREW, *VOALAVONARABO*, *VOALAVO FOTSY*

Origins and Systematics

This large shrew is Asian in origin and native across a broad area from Pakistan to Japan (Figure 14.30d). It has colonized areas of western Asia, the Arabian Peninsula, the eastern African coast (see distribution map in Duplantier 2013), and islands of the Indian Ocean, at least in part the result of human transportation and, specifically the last two zones, via early maritime commerce, particularly during the Islamic period (Hutterer and Tranier 1990; Fuller and Boivin 2009). In continental Africa, there is no evidence that any population is firmly established, and it seems that only individuals are introduced from time to time, and these breed and survive during short periods around harbors and along trade routes (Duplantier 2013). *Suncus murinus* may have reached Madagascar via an eastern African route (Hutterer and Tranier 1990; Duplantier et al. 2003), but this hypothesis still needs zooarchaeological evidence (Fuller and Boivin 2009). The Malagasy name for this shrew, *voalavonarabo*, or "Arab mouse," seems to support the notion that Arab traders introduced it to the island. The populations of *S. murinus* from the Arabian Peninsula and Africa show considerable morphological variability, and therefore it is presumed that they were the result of multiple introductions from diverse sites (Hutterer and Tranier 1990). Nevertheless, phylogenetic analysis showed that *S. murinus* individuals from Madagascar clustered with those from the Comoros (Ohdachi et al. 2016), which would be anticipated, given the hypothesis of introduction in the context of trade during the Islamic period.

Distribution

Suncus murinus occurs as a human commensal in cities, towns, and villages in both the humid east and dry west. In eastern areas of the island currently or formerly with moist evergreen forest vegetation, it occurs in natural forests, in some cases partially degraded, in *savoka* (regenerating humid forest habitat), and in and around agricultural areas, including rice fields and fruit orchards at elevations up to 1500 m (Duplantier and Duchemin 2003b; Soarimalala and Goodman 2011; Soarimalala et al. 2013; Randriamoria 2017; B. Ramasindrazana, unpublished data). This species also occurs in dry deciduous forests but seems to be absent from dry spiny thickets with the exception of areas immediate to water sources (Ganzhorn et al. 1996; Goodman et al. 2002; Soarimalala 2008). It occurs across an elevational gradient from near sea level to 1600 m.

Ecology

To our knowledge, no specific details on the natural history of this species are available for the introduced Madagascar population. For general information about its ecology in Asia, see Motokawa (2018). Heim de Balsac (1972) proposed that given this species' ability to colonize forest habitat and its aggressive behavior, it might pose a threat via competition to small tenrec shrews of the genus *Microgale* (family Tenrecidae). A half century later, there are some data to address this point, and numerous moist evergreen forest inventories have found this shrew and what seems to be a full complement of shrew tenrecs (Goodman and Rakotondravony 2000; Soarimalala et al. 2007).

Ectoparasites and Zoonotic Diseases

Given the synanthropic habits of *S. murinus*, it has been implicated as a possible vector of a variety of zoonotic diseases that are known to occur in humans, several of which are discussed in chapter 6. For example, the bacteria responsible for leptospirosis, *Leptospira*, have been isolated from this shrew; depending on the population, incidence rates varied from 0% to slightly more than 40% (S. Rahelinirina et al. 2010b, 2019; also see Dietrich et al., pp. 268–77). Classically on Madagascar, it was thought that *Rattus* species and their fleas were responsible for the transmission of bubonic plague. A notable exception to this "rule" seems to occur in Mahajanga, where the introduced flea *Xenopsylla cheopis*, the main plague vector typically found on *R. rattus*, is also abundant on *S. murinus*. Antibodies against *Yersinia pestis*, the bacterium responsible for plague, have been regularly detected in samples from this shrew during and between human plague epidemics, including several different strains (S. Rahelinirina et al. 2017).

SUNCUS ETRUSCUS, ETRUSCAN SHREW, *VOALAVO FOTSY*

Origins and Systematics

In the literature before 2010, Madagascar was thought to have an endemic species of the family Soricidae, *Suncus madagascariensis*. Recent phylogenetic analyses based on a mitochondrial marker revealed that specimens referred to as *S. madagascariensis* are genetically nested within *S. etruscus* from Sri Lanka and India (Omar et al. 2011; Meegaskumbura et al. 2012; Figure 14.30e). These studies show that the taxonomic status of other insular or isolated minute *Suncus* "species" have to be reconsidered, and populations within a discontinuous, patchy distribution from the Philippines to the Mediterranean basin, including Madagascar, are best referred to as *S. etruscus* (Sheftel 2018). The studies' authors suggested that the Madagascar population recently colonized the island, its founding animals originating from the Indian subcontinent or in a larger sense southeastern Asia, presumably transported by maritime travelers. As with *Rattus*, *Mus*, and *S. murinus*, the original arrival of *S. etruscus* on Madagascar is probably associated with trade vessels dating from

the Islamic period. To date, we are unaware of any archaeological remains of this species on Madagascar, but given its minute size, the lack of material is not surprising. On Mayotte, in the Comoros, there is another small shrew that is considered endemic, *S. coquereli*, but it probably has a parallel history to *S. madagascariensis* and is actually introduced *S. etruscus*; this needs to be verified with molecular analysis, as insularity can lead to morphological differences relative to mainland individuals of the same species.

Distribution

This species has a broad distribution on Madagascar, which includes synanthropic situations in villages and rural communities and occurrence in a range of different natural vegetation formations, often in sympatry with *S. murinus*. In the east it is known from rural villages, modified open areas, and moist evergreen forests (Goodman and Rakotondravony 2000; Soarimalala and Raheriarisena 2010; Randriamoria 2017), but it is distinctly more common in the drier portions of the island, found in a variety of dry deciduous formations (Soarimalala 2008) as well as dry spiny thicket (Goodman et al. 1999b, 2002; Soarimalala 2008). The two species of *Suncus* occur in sympatry in dry deciduous habitats, but *S. murinus* drops out in the dry spiny thicket. *Suncus etruscus* occurs across an elevational gradient from near sea level to 1580 m.

Ecology

Suncus etruscus is the smallest land mammal on the island (Soarimalala and Goodman 2011). Little is known about its ecology and behavior, both on Madagascar and in the other parts of its distribution area, owing to the difficulty of observing it in the wild and the near impossibility of keeping it in captivity. Work by Fons (1975), conducted on animals in Mediterranean habitats of southern France and in captivity, is probably the most complete, and often the only available, concerning different aspects of the biology of this species.

Invasive Capacity

Suncus etruscus has been able to colonize a range of anthropogenic habitats and natural forest habitats on the island. Particularly in dry forest formations, it can be relatively common. We are unaware of any data that indicates that it has a negative impact on the native forest biota of the island.

Ectoparasites and Zoonotic Diseases

We are unaware of any tick or flea species collected on Malagasy populations of *S. etruscus*.

ECTOPARASITES OF THE INTRODUCED SMALL MAMMALS

Fleas

Different species of fleas are known ectoparasites of introduced small mammals on Madagascar (Table 14.20). Most are introduced fleas, among which are *Xenopsylla cheopis* and *Leptopsylla segnis* (rat fleas), *Echidnophaga gallinacea* (hen fleas), and more rarely *Ctenocephalides felis strongylus* (cat and dog fleas) and *Pulex irritans* (human fleas) (see Duchemin et al., pp. 1074–80). However, endemic fleas, including those of the genera *Paractenopsyllus* and *Synopsyllus*, are documented on *Rattus rattus* collected in natural forests, as highlighted in a study from Ambohitantely (Goodman et al. 2015a). Obviously, these latter genera of endemic fleas are also found on native mammals. Based on the literature and recent work, *R. rattus* is parasitized by a variety of fleas (see Table 9.35).

Ticks

Hard and soft ticks are known from introduced mammals, particularly *Rattus rattus*, but their primary hosts are endemic rodents and tenrecs (Uilenberg et al. 1979; see Klompen and Apanaskevich, pp. 894–99). However, recent fieldwork and associated captures have shown that different species of native ticks, such as species of *Ixodes* and *Haemaphysalis*, may parasitize introduced small mammals (Rakotomanga et al. 2017; B. Ramasindrazana, unpublished data). Randriamoria (2016) identified several taxa of ticks parasitizing introduced small mammals, with five taxa on *R. rattus* (*Haemaphysalis* sp., *H. simplex*, *H.* aff. *simplicima*, *Ixodes* sp., and *Ixodes* aff. *albignaci*); one on *R. norvegicus* (*Haemaphysalis* sp.); one on *Mus musculus* (*H. simplex*); and one on *Suncus murinus* (*Haemaphysalis* sp.). Detailed study on ticks (larvae, nymphs, and adults) infesting introduced small mammals is needed in order to futher our understanding of the diversity of ticks infesting these animals.

Lice

Duplantier and Duchemin (2003b) reported that *Polyplax reclinata* was found on *Suncus murinus* trapped on Madagascar. This louse was also collected on several African shrews (*Crocidura* spp.), but to our knowledge has never been found on an endemic Malagasy tenrecid (Beaucournu and Houin 1967). A louse, *P. spinulosa*, was collected on *Rattus rattus* occurring on the Anjanaharibe-Sud and Andringitra Massifs (OConnor 1996, 1998). Other lice, not identified to the species level, were collected on endemic nesomyine rodents of the genera *Eliurus* and *Voalavo* (OConnor 1998, 2000). Since the compilation of data presented in Duplantier and Duchemin (2003b), little additional information on lice infecting introduced small mammals has become available, but these ectoparasites are suspected to play a role in the transmission of the pathogenic bacterium *Bartonella* on Madagascar (Brook et al. 2017).

CONSEQUENCES OF INTRODUCED SMALL MAMMALS

Introduced murid rats and mice (*Rattus* and *Mus*) and soricid shrews (*Suncus*) on Madagascar have been shown to be associated not only with different zoonotic diseases within the endemic small-mammal community but also a range of socioeconomic and public health aspects. In terms of agriculture, *Rattus*, particularly *R. rattus*, is responsible for considerable damage to standing crops and food storages

TABLE 14.20. **Flea ectoparasites of introduced small mammals on Madagascar**

FLEA SPECIES	*RATTUS RATTUS*	*R. NORVEGICUS*	*MUS MUSCULUS*	*SUNCUS MURINUS*	*S. ETRUSCUS*	*REFERENCES*
Centetipsylla madagascariensis	+	–	–	–	–	J.-M. Klein and Uilenberg (1966); Duchemin (2003)
Ctenocephalides felis	+	–	–	–	–	J.-M. Klein and Uilenberg (1966); Duchemin (2003)
Dinopsyllus brachypecten	+	–	–	–	–	J.-M. Klein and Uilenberg (1966); B. Ramasindrazana (unpublished data)
Echidnophaga gallinacea	+	–	+	–	–	J.-M. Klein and Uilenberg (1966); Duchemin (2003)
Leptopsylla segnis	+	–	+	–	–	Goodman et al. (2015a)
Paractenopsyllus duplantieri	+	–	–	–	–	Harimalala et al. (2018)
P. goodmani	+	–	–	–	–	Goodman et al. (2015a); Harimalala et al. (2018)
P. kerguisteli	+	–	–	–	–	Duchemin (2003)
P. pauliani	+	–	–	–	–	Duchemin (2003)
P. petiti	+	–	–	–	–	Duchemin (2003); Harimalala et al. (2018)
P. randrianasoloi	+	–	–	–	–	Duchemin (2003)
P. rouxi	+	–	–	–	–	Duchemin (2003); Harimalala et al. (2018)
P. vauceli	+	–	–	–	–	Duchemin (2003); Harimalala et al. (2018)
P. viettei	+	–	+	–	–	Goodman et al. (2015a); Harimalala et al. (2018)
Pulex irritans	+	–	–	–	–	J.-M. Klein and Uilenberg (1966); B. Ramasindrazana (unpublished data)
Synopsyllus estradei	+	–	+	–	–	J.-M. Klein and Uilenberg (1966); Duchemin (2003); Goodman et al. (2015a); Harimalala et al. (2018)
S. fonquerniei	+	+	+	+	–	J.-M. Klein and Uilenberg (1966); Duchemin (2003); Harimalala et al. (2018); B. Ramasindrazana (unpublished data)
S. robici	+	–	–	–	–	J.-M. Klein and Uilenberg (1966)
Tsaractenus grenieri	+	–	–	–	–	Duchemin (2003)
T. rodhaini	+	–	–	–	–	Harimalala et al. (2018)
Xenopsylla brasiliensis	+	–	–	–	–	Miarinjara et al. (2016)
X. cheopis	+	+	+	+	–	Duchemin (2003)
Total	**22**	**2**	**6**	**2**	**0**	

(FAO and PAM 2013; Soarimalala et al. 2019). The different forms of damage significantly affect the livelihoods of local people, specifically in rural areas, as agriculture production is often the main source of income and subsistence. Further, damage to household items can be very significant in certain circumstances.

In terms of diseases, introduced small mammals and their ectoparasites are reservoirs of different zoonoses and in some cases the source of transmission. Plague is the first disease that comes to mind. In fact, *R. rattus*, *R. norvegicus*, and *S. murinus* are the main plague reservoirs on Madagascar. While the two rodent species are widely distributed and in some areas reach important levels of prevalence (Andrianaivoarimanana et al. 2013; Ramasindrazana et al. 2017a), in Mahajanga, *S. murinus* is the main reservoir of plague (S. Rahelinirina et al. 2017, 2019). Within the Afro-Malagasy region, Madagascar is the most important plague focus area. Plague reached the Toamasina harbor in 1898 and the Central Highlands in 1921, and subsequently, epidemics of this disease reappear every year in the central part of the island above 800 m (Brygoo 1966; Chanteau 2006), but plague also has been recorded in lowland areas such as Mahajanga. Besides plague infection, *Rattus* species are reservoirs of various zoonotic bacteria with different etiology and epidemiology, such as *Leptospira* species (Dietrich et al. 2018), *Bartonella* species (Brook et al. 2017), and *Rickettsia* species (Rakotonanahary et al. 2018). Further, introduced rodents are also reservoirs and presumably vectors of different viruses such as hantavirus (Reynes et al. 2014; Raharinosy et al. 2018) and paramyxoviruses (Wilkinson et al. 2014).

Since their introduction to Madagascar, these non-native small mammals have continued to colonize different habitats. Most of them live as human commensals in urban and rural areas. These introduced animals and particularly *R. rattus* constitute major socioeconomic and public health problems on the island. Within natural forest, the impact of introduced small mammals is poorly documented, but they are clearly having a deleterious impact on the native flora and fauna.

Subject editor: Steven M. Goodman

SYSTEMATIC ACCOUNTS

TENRECIDAE: *MICROGALE* AND *NESOGALE*, SHREW TENRECS

P. D. Jenkins, L. E. Olson, K. M. Everson, V. Soarimalala, and S. M. Goodman

As their common name implies, these tenrecs (Tenrecidae, Oryzorictinae) are shrewlike in appearance, general ecology, and behavior. The pelage is short, dense, and soft, lacking spiny hair; the body is long; the head is elongated, with a tapering rostrum, numerous vibrissae, and small eyes; the tail is often subequal to head-and-body length; the limbs are short, with five digits; a cloaca (common intestinal, genital, and urinary opening) is present in both sexes; and testes remain abdominal throughout life. The dental formula in adults is: incisors 3/3, canines 1/1, premolars 3/3, molars 3/3 (× 2) = 40. There is no obvious sexual dimorphism in external appearance or size. Adults of the genus *Microgale* range in body measurements from the very small *M. parvula* (head-and-body length [HBL] 42–65 mm, tail length [TL] 47–66 mm, weight [Wt] 2.0–4.7 g, n = 43–47) to moderately large species such as *M. soricoides* (HBL 63–103 mm, TL 80–112 mm, Wt 14.22 g, n = 42–53), and the very large *M. mergulus* (HBL 116–170 mm, TL 128–161 mm, Wt 60–110 g, n = 9–15), which, until recently, was placed in the monotypic genus *Limnogale*. The two species of *Nesogale*, formerly included in the genus *Microgale*, are larger than the largest species of *Microgale* with the exception of *M. mergulus*. *Nesogale dobsoni* is on average smaller (HBL 79–130 mm, TL 89–128 mm, Wt 20.5–47.5 g, n = 90–133) than *N. talazaci* (HBL 105–189 mm, TL 120–162 mm, Wt 24.3–56.2 g, n = 22–68). Although morphologically and ecologically very different, *N. talazaci* is comparable in size to some of the smaller endemic rodents such as *Eliurus minor* (see Carleton et al., pp. 2014–22).

Most species of shrew tenrecs are forest dwelling, occupying the moist evergreen, dry deciduous, and karstic *tsingy* zones, while a few species are known from the gallery forest and dry spiny thicket in the extreme south and southwest. Some species have also been found in secondary degraded forest areas and montane grassland (e.g., *M. cowani*), and a few others are known from marshland habitats (e.g., *M. pusilla*). Over the past two decades—and since the publication of P. D. Jenkins (2003) in the precursor of this book—a considerable amount of new information on shrew tenrecs has been obtained. Here we provide updates and add new information from field and laboratory studies on these animals.

SPECIES DIVERSITY, MORPHOLOGY, AND CHROMOSOMES

The genus *Microgale* is the most speciose of the Tenrecidae, with 21 extant and one extinct species currently recognized (Table 14.21). They are superficially similar in external appearance; most are brown or gray brown, and in many species the tail is subequal to the head-and-body length (Figure 14.31). Nevertheless, some species are more distinctive (see Soarimalala and Goodman 2011; P. D. Jenkins 2003, 2018): *M. drouhardi* has a dark middorsal stripe (Figure 14.31d), *M. parvula* is usually very dark brown, and *M. nasoloi* is pale gray (Figure 14.31b). The tail of *M. brevicaudata*

TABLE 14.21. **Checklist of currently recognized species of shrew tenrecs**

TENRECIDAE GRAY, 1821: 301
Oryzorictinae Dobson, 1882b: 71
Microgale Thomas, 1882: 319
M. brevicaudata G. Grandidier, 1899: 349
M. dryas Jenkins, 1992: 53
M. fotsifotsy Jenkins, Raxworthy & Nussbaum, 1997: 2
M. gracilis (Major, 1896: 321)
M. grandidieri Olson, Rakotomalala, Hildebrandt, Lanier, Raxworthy & Goodman, 2009: 1097
M. gymnorhyncha Jenkins, Goodman & Raxworthy, 1996: 211
M. jenkinsae Goodman & Soarimalala, 2004: 251
M. jobihely Goodman, Raxworthy, Maminirina & Olson, 2006: 384
M. longicaudata Thomas, 1882: 320
†*M. macpheei* Goodman, Vasey & Burney, 2007: 367
M. majori Thomas, 1918: 304
M. mergulus[1] (Major, 1896: 318)
M. monticola Goodman & Jenkins, 1998: 149
M. nasoloi Jenkins & Goodman, 1999: 156
M. parvula G. Grandidier, 1934: 476
M. principula Thomas, 1926: 250
M. pusilla Major, 1896: 462
M. soricoides Jenkins, 1993: 2
M. taiva Major, 1896: 461
M. thomasi Major, 1896: 318
Nesogale Thomas, 1918: 303
Nesogale dobsoni[2] (Thomas, 1884: 337)
Nesogale talazaci[2] (Major, 1896: 318)

Sources: Based on Everson et al. (2016) and Goodman et al. (2018b).
Notes: In total, 23 species of extant members of the genera *Microgale* and *Nesogale* are currently recognized. †, extinct species, known from Quaternary subfossils from Madagascar.
[1]Formerly *Limnogale*.
[2]Formerly *Microgale*.

(Figure 14.31a) and *M. grandidieri* is approximately half the head-and-body length, while that of *M. longicaudata*, *M. majori*, and *M. principula* (Figure 14.31g) is one and a half to more than two times as long as head-and-body length; these three species also have lengthened hind limbs. *Microgale gracilis* and *M. gymnorhyncha* (Figure 14.31c) have a dense, velvety pelage, small eyes and ears, an elongated rostrum and rhinarium (tip of snout), and short forelimbs with stout claws. As reviewed by Benstead and Olson (2003), the semiaquatic *M. mergulus* is most strikingly distinguished from all other species of *Microgale* by several features (Figure 14.31i): its dense, soft pelage has long guard hairs, and the dark brown dorsal pelage contrasts with the pale, silvery ventral pelage; the head is short and broad, the muzzle blunt, with pronounced mystacial vibrissae on each side; the nostrils are dorsolaterally positioned, and there is a well-developed philtrum (shallow groove above upper lip); the eyes and ears are small and nearly concealed in the pelage; the distal region of the tail is laterally compressed; and the feet are extensively webbed, with a fringe of stiff hairs on the hind feet. Other than size, there is little to distinguish *Nesogale* species externally from the larger species of *Microgale*, but the tail of *N. dobsoni* (Figure 14.31h) becomes seasonally incrassated, unlike that of the slightly larger *N. talazaci*.

The diploid number of chromosomes is 30 (2n = 30) in *N. dobsoni* and *N. talazaci* (Hsu and Benirschke 1970) and three species of *Microgale* (*M. longicaudata*, *M. majori*, and *M. principula*); 2n = 32 in *M. fotsifotsy*, *M. parvula*, *M. soricoides*, and *M. taiva*; 2n = 38 in *M. cowani*; and 2n = 56 in *M. thomasi* (C. Gilbert et al. 2007).

TAXONOMY AND EVOLUTIONARY HISTORY

Microgale and *Nesogale* belong to the subfamily of nonspiny tenrecs (Oryzorictinae) in the family Tenrecidae (see Goodman et al., pp. 1891–94). An early revision of shrew tenrecs (Thomas 1918) recognized three distinct genera on the basis of morphology: *Nesogale*, containing *dobsoni* and *talazaci*; *Leptogale* for *gracilis*; and *Microgale* for seven other species then recognized. Many species of *Microgale* had been described by the time the genus was revised by Heim de Balsac (1972), who considered *Limnogale* and *Leptogale* to be separate genera but *Nesogale* a subgenus of *Microgale*. In his exhaustive revision, MacPhee (1987) subsumed *Leptogale* and *Nesogale* into *Microgale* but did not consider *Limnogale* in his review. MacPhee, who examined the majority of specimens available at that time in the major museums in the United States and Europe, demonstrated the marked differences in tooth form and morphology between deciduous and permanent dentitions and showed that, because of a failure among many earlier authors to distinguish between age classes, many of the available names were designated as synonyms of species with priority that had been described based on specimens with permanent dentitions. MacPhee divided the 10 species he considered valid into six morphological groups based on body proportions, dental variation, and other characters, but he explicitly made no attempt at phylogenetic interpretation. This phenetic method has proved useful for subsequent comparative and descriptive work but has obvious disadvantages in failing to indicate possible relationships. This situation has been redressed recently by phylogenetic analyses (Olson and Goodman 2003; Poux et al. 2008; Everson et al. 2016).

The taxa accepted as valid by MacPhee (1987) had been discovered and named between 1882 and 1934. It was not until the late 1980s that intensive surveys and refinements in capture techniques—including the use of pitfall traps, which have captured 86% of the oryzorictine tenrecs collected since the late 1980s (L. E. Olson, unpublished data)—provided a wealth of new information on the distribution and ecology of *Microgale*, *Nesogale*, and *Oryzorictes* (see Everson et al., pp. 1888–91). The resulting series of specimens has allowed more rigorous assessment of intra- and interspecific variation, allowing further taxonomic changes, including the description of eight new extant species since MacPhee's (1987) revision (P. D. Jenkins 1992, 1993; P. D. Jenkins et al. 1996, 1997; Goodman and Jenkins 1998; P. D. Jenkins and Goodman 1999; Goodman and Soarimalala 2004; Goodman et al. 2006c; L. E. Olson et al. 2009) and one extinct species based on Quaternary remains (Goodman et al. 2007a).

Molecular phylogenetic and phylogeographic studies have provided new insights into the diversity and evolutionary history of tenrecs. A molecular study of the Tenrecidae including all

FIGURE 14.31 **The body forms of shrew tenrecs of the genera *Microgale* and *Nesogale* are rather diverse, as exemplified by the following photos: A) *M. brevicaudata* in the Kirindy Forest CNFEREF, B) *M. nasoloi* in the Kirindy Forest CNFEREF, C) *M. gymnorhyncha* in the Ambatovy Forest, D) *M. drouhardi* in the Ambatovy Forest, E) *M. cowani* in the Bemanevika Forest, F) *M. taiva* in the Ambatovy Forest, G) *M. principula* in the Befotaka–Midongy du Sud Forest, H) *N. dobsoni* in Anjozorobe-Angavo Forest, and I) *M. mergulus* in Ranomafana.** (PHOTOS A–H by V. Soarimalala, and I by S. Zack.)

then-known species of *Microgale* showed that the genus comprises several separate clades, and that *Limnogale* nests deeply within *Microgale* (Olson and Goodman 2003). Evidence for a close relationship between *Limnogale* and *Microgale* was also supported by morphological similarities in placental structure (Enders et al. 2007). Subsequent studies (Asher and Hofreiter 2006; Poux et al. 2008) provided additional molecular evidence for a clade containing *Limnogale* within *Microgale* but conflicted with morphological results that continued to favor a relationship between *Limnogale* and the African genera *Potamogale* and *Micropotamogale* (known as otter shrews) exclusive of other tenrecs (Asher 1999; Asher and Hofreiter 2006). However, differences in functional anatomy of the fore and hind limb between *Limnogale* and otter shrews suggested that the resemblance in morphological traits was an example of convergent evolution due to similarities in the shared semiaquatic lifestyle (Salton and Szalay 2004; Salton and Sargis 2008, 2009).

More recently, a molecular phylogenetic analysis of all known species of Tenrecidae (Everson et al. 2016) revealed that all genera are monophyletic, with the exception of *Microgale sensu* MacPhee (1987). Furthermore, Everson et al. (2016) demonstrated that the clade containing *M. dobsoni* and *M. talazaci* was sufficiently separate and morphologically distinct from other *Microgale* to represent a distinct genus, for which the name *Nesogale* was already available and defined by the same morphological characters of the original diagnosis. The morphologically and ecologically distinctive *Limnogale* was recovered as deeply nested within *Microgale* and, surprisingly, sister to the diminutive species *M. parvula*. The observation that the largest and smallest shrew tenrecs are each other's closest relative is a perplexing enigma and exemplifies the morphological diversification within the genus.

While solving some taxonomic problems, molecular approaches have highlighted others. For example, L. E. Olson et al. (2004) revealed the presence of cryptic species among the long-tailed shrew tenrecs and the difficulties of resolving the nomenclature of some of these taxa, which includes a distinct clade in the north to which the name *M. prolixacaudata* has been presumed but not formally

proposed to apply, pending further ongoing research. Another recent study using a large multi-locus data set suggested that *M. fotsifotsy* is likely to represent two species, one broadly distributed in the eastern moist evergreen forests and another restricted to forests in the far north (Everson et al. 2020a). Furthermore, mitochondrial DNA representing 12 shrew tenrec species from the moist evergreen forests (Everson et al. 2020b) as well as unpublished data from a large assortment of additional species (L. E. Olson et al., unpublished data) strongly suggest that numerous currently unrecognized candidate species await formal description.

DISTRIBUTION AND HABITAT

Most species of shrew tenrecs occur exclusively in the northern, eastern, central, and southeastern moist evergreen forests of Madagascar. Three species (*Microgale jenkinsae*, *M. nasoloi*, and *M. grandidieri*) are known only from dry formations in the west and south. *Nesogale dobsoni* is known from the dry deciduous forest of Montagne des Français in the extreme north. Five species—*M. parvula*, *M. longicaudata*, *M. fotsifotsy*, *N. dobsoni*, and *N. talazaci*—extend over the latitudinal length of the moist evergreen forests from Montagne d'Ambre (12°S) in the extreme north to Andohahela (25°S) in the far south (Raxworthy and Nussbaum 1994; P. D. Jenkins et al. 1997; Goodman et al. 1999b, 2013). *Microgale longicaudata* also occurs in dry western deciduous forests (L. E. Olson et al. 2004). Three species—*M. cowani* (Figure 14.31e), *M. drouhardi*, and *M. taiva* (Figure 14.31f)—have a slightly less extensive range. An additional four species—*M. gracilis*, *M. gymnorhyncha*, *M. principula*, and *M. soricoides*—have been recorded in a range spanning over 10° latitude, from the north in the mountains ringing the Andapa Basin (protected areas of Marojejy and Anjanaharibe-Sud) to the far south in and around Andohahela (P. D. Jenkins et al. 1996; Goodman and Jenkins 1998, 2000; Goodman et al. 2013; P. D. Jenkins 2018).

Within these mesic forests, shrew tenrecs occur in lowland moist evergreen forest (0–800 m), through the medium-altitude moist evergreen forest (800–1950 m), to montane ericoid thicket and montane grassland (1900–2300 m). Some species have a broad elevational range, such as *M. parvula* and *N. talazaci*, which occur from lowland forest to ericoid thicket, and *M. cowani*, found on the Andringitra Massif from the lowlands to 2450 m, above the tree line in montane grassland. In contrast, *M. monticola* was initially thought to be restricted to a rather narrow elevational band of medium-altitude moist evergreen in the Northern Highlands sites of Marojejy and Anjanaharibe-Sud (1550–1950 m) (Goodman and Jenkins 1998, 2000) but subsequently has been found at 500–720 m in the Makira protected area (S. M. Goodman and V. Soarimalala, unpublished data). *Microgale mergulus* occurs in and along rivers in moist evergreen forest and also in degraded forest and rivers bordering non-native tree plantations. *Microgale pusilla* is known from scattered localities in the east and the Central Highlands and in littoral forests near Tolagnaro (MacPhee 1987; Goodman et al. 1997b).

Microgale brevicaudata occurs in more varied forest habitats in several protected areas ranging from intermediate dry deciduous forests on Montagne des Français and Montagne d'Ambre (lower portions; Goodman et al. 1996b), extending along the western coast, to slightly more moist evergreen forests of Manongarivo and dry deciduous forests of Ankarafantsika as far south as Kirindy Mité, but also into lowland moist evergreen forest in Marojejy and Masoala. *Microgale grandidieri* occurs in relatively intact and secondary riparian forest and limestone *tsingy* formations from the Namoroka Massif to the Onilahy River in western and southwestern Madagascar (L. E. Olson et al. 2009; Goodman et al. 2013). The rarely captured *M. nasoloi* has been recorded in dry deciduous forests of the Menabe Region of the central west and isolated transitional moist evergreen–dry deciduous forests of Zombitse-Vohibasia and Alandraza Analavelo (Analavelona) in the southwest (P. D. Jenkins and Goodman 1999; Soarimalala and Goodman 2008). *Microgale jenkinsae* has been recorded only in the Mikea of the southwest in transitional dry deciduous forest–dry spiny thicket (Goodman and Soarimalala 2004). *Microgale jobihely* is known from three disjunct populations: one in medium-altitude moist evergreen forest on the southern slopes of the Tsaratanàna Massif in the northwest; another in medium-altitude moist evergreen forest at Analamay and Ambatovy, in the central east; and the third in Ambohitantely in the Central Highlands (Goodman et al. 2006c; Soarimalala et al. 2010; S. M. Goodman and V. Soarimalala, unpublished data).

Although most species are believed to be primarily forest dwelling, several are recorded from other habitats, suggesting that they may not be particularly sensitive to certain types of environmental disturbance. *Microgale pusilla*, *M. cowani*, *N. dobsoni*, *M. brevicaudata*, and rarely *M. majori* occur in ecotonal areas between relatively intact and degraded moist evergreen forests, and agricultural and nonforested zones of the east, while the first three species are also recorded from vestigial fragmented forest and marshlands in the Central Highlands (MacPhee 1987; Goodman et al. 1997b; V. Soarimalala and S. M. Goodman, unpublished data).

Subfossils of *M.* cf. *jenkinsae*, originally identified as *M. pusilla*, are known from owl pellets at currently arid sites of Anjohimpaty (northeast of Lake Tsimanampesotse) and Lelia (Mahafaly Plateau) in the extreme southwest. Subfossil remains of *M. pusilla* have been recovered from Lavajaza, near Antsirabe, far from current forested regions (MacPhee 1986, 1987). Other species found as subfossils include *M.* cf. *brevicaudata*, from Lelia, and *M. brevicaudata* and *N. talazaci*, from caves north of Antsiranana (MacPhee 1986, 1987; Dewar and Rakotovololona 1992). A subfossil species, *M. macpheei*, was described from Andrahomana Cave in the extreme southeast and has been allied with the *M. brevicaudata* group based on overall cranial morphology (Goodman et al. 2007a). *Microgale brevicaudata*, *M. nasoloi*, and *M.* cf. *majori* have been reported based on subfossils recovered in Ankilitelo Cave in the southwest (Muldoon et al. 2009). Cranial remains of *M. brevicaudata*, *M. grandidieri*, and *N. talazaci* have been reported from the caves of Beanka in the central west; the lattermost species is not known to occur in this region today (Noromalala 2016; Burney et al. 2020a).

NATURAL HISTORY

Feeding and Foraging Habits

Shrew tenrecs generally forage among leaf litter, fallen branches, and roots on the forest floor, but several also appear to be scansorial

or possibly even semiarboreal. Indications of this stem from the trapping of a few individuals of *N. dobsoni*, *N. talazaci*, *M. cowani*, *M. fotsifotsy*, *M. longicaudata*, *M. monticola*, *M. nasoloi*, *M. principula*, *M. soricoides*, *M. taiva*, and *M. thomasi* on 2–20 cm diameter horizontal branches at 1–2.5 m above the ground (P. D. Jenkins 2003; S. M. Goodman et al., unpublished data). *Microgale longicaudata*, with its very long and distally prehensile tail (Goodman et al. 1996d; Goodman and Jenkins 1998) and elongated hind feet and digits, has been considered to be at least scansorial and possibly occasionally arboreal. Observations of captive *M.* cf. *longicaudata* showed that the tail was used for balance and stability while foraging and feeding, with the elongated hind feet also aiding stability (Hilgartner 2005). However, a subadult *M.* cf. *longicaudata* live-trapped near Grande Lac in Montagne d'Ambre exhibited none of these proclivities when released onto horizontal branches ranging up to ~0.75 cm in diameter and instead appeared rather helpless (L. E. Olson, unpublished data). Specimens of *M.* cf. *principula* were reported to show good climbing ability when released from traps, leaping short distances between branches and using their tails to balance and coil around thin branches; one animal made its way up the vertical trunk of a large forest tree to about 7 m above the ground (P. D. Jenkins 2003).

Microgale mergulus spends most of its active time swimming and diving in fast-flowing streams. In a short study of a captive animal, the hind limbs provided the main propulsive force, with the tail acting mainly as a rudder (Benstead et al. 2001). Anatomical studies corroborated the significant role of the hind limb in propulsion, whereas the forelimbs are used mainly for paddling and steering and perhaps also for digging in stream banks (Salton and Sargis 2008, 2009). This species preys predominantly on aquatic invertebrates—including crayfish, crabs, and shrimps, but especially on insect larvae—such as those of Ephemeroptera, Odonata, and Trichoptera—and tadpoles. Small aquatic vertebrates were found in the stomach contents in one study (Malzy 1965) but, despite their presence in local streams, were not found in a later analysis of fecal pellets (Benstead et al. 2001).

Analyses of stomach contents of *Microgale* specimens collected at Ranomafana (Soarimalala and Goodman 2003b) found that members of Orthoptera were most commonly consumed, followed by Hymenoptera and Coleoptera. In captivity, orthopterans were preferred, while frogs were consumed by *N. dobsoni*, and *N. talazaci* and were eaten occasionally by *M. drouhardi* (Eisenberg and Gould 1970; Stephenson et al. 1994). There is evidence from pitfall trapping that *N. talazaci*, *N. dobsoni*, *M. soricoides*, *M. thomasi*, and *M. taiva* consume their smaller congeners that fall into the same buckets (although in these circumstances this may not be natural behavior). For example, *M. cowani*, *M. longicaudata*, *M. majori*, *M. principula*, and *M. taiva* were eaten by *N. dobsoni*. Observations of captive *N. talazaci* and *N. dobsoni* showed that prey was detected by scent and sound as well as by foraging, digging, and nosing among leaf debris and under fallen branches and roots. Prey was seized with the mouth, and the forepaws were used to pin down but not to manipulate prey (Eisenberg and Gould 1970).

Specific behavioral and ecological variation, such as dietary differences in prey size, diversity, and density, may be correlated with marked differences in body size and anatomical adaptations. There is evidence that *M. soricoides*, with its enlarged incisors, as well as *N. dobsoni* and *N. talazaci*, include vertebrate prey in their diet, while *M. parvula* is presumably confined to smaller invertebrate prey than that of medium-size species of *Microgale*. Interestingly, stable isotope studies at Tsinjoarivo indicate that the very small *M. parvula* is principally a secondary consumer, preying mainly on plant-eating invertebrates, whereas the slightly larger *M. pusilla* is a tertiary consumer, with a large proportion of predatory insects in its diet and feeding at a higher trophic level than most of the sympatric shrew tenrecs at that locality (Dammhahn et al. 2013). Furthermore, despite the similar size of the two *Nesogale* species, the seasonal fat storage shown by *N. dobsoni* suggests its physiological and ecological strategies differ from those of *N. talazaci*.

Shrew Tenrecs as Prey

Small nonspiny tenrecs such as *Microgale* species, which lack obvious defenses other than concealment and escape behavior, are potential prey for the larger reptilian, avian, and mammalian predators of Madagascar. Limited data exist on predation of shrew tenrecs. An unidentified species of *Microgale* was found in the stomach of a snake (*Pseudoxyrhopus*), and an *M. drouhardi* was dispatched and partially consumed by a large centipede (Scolopendromorpha) (S. M. Goodman, unpublished data). *Microgale cowani*, *M. brevicaudata*, *M. drouhardi*, *M. dryas*, *M. jobihely*, *M. fotsifotsy*, *M. longicaudata*, *M. majori*, *M. thomasi*, *Nesogale dobsoni*, and *N. talazaci* were found in pellets of *Tyto soumagnei* (Red Owl) (Goodman and Jenkins 1998; Goodman and Thorstrom 1998; Cardiff and Goodman 2008; Ramamonjisoa 2014), and *M. pusilla* in pellets of *T. alba* (Barn Owl) (Goodman et al. 1997b). *Geobiastes squamiger* (Scaly Ground-roller) was seen feeding on a large shrew tenrec, thought to be *N. talazaci* (J.-E. Rakotoarisoa and Be 2004). In the Bemanevika Forest, analysis of *T. soumagnei* pellets showed that *Microgale* species represented 87.5% of the minimum number of individuals identified (J. Ramamonjisoa et al., unpublished data). Cranial fragments of *M. drouhardi* and a humerus of *N.* cf. *talazaci* were recorded in scats of the euplerid carnivoran *Cryptoprocta ferox* (Fosa) (Goodman et al. 1997c; see Gerber and Hawkins, pp. 1878–83). In Ankarafantsika, scat of *C. ferox* contained a large number of *M. brevicaudata* remains (Rakotomanana 2009). An analysis of scats of another euplerid, *Fossa fossana* (Spotted Fanaloka) (see Kerridge et al., pp. 1986–89), collected near Vondrozo revealed that it consumes a variety of small shrew tenrecs, ranging in size from *M.* cf. *pusilla* to *N. dobsoni*, which form a relatively greater component of the diet during the cool, dry season than the wet season (Goodman et al. 2003b).

Interannual Population Fluctuations and Density

Few long-term field studies have been conducted to understand population dynamics in *Microgale* and *Nesogale*. There is some evidence of interannual variation in population size in *M. drouhardi* at the same sites and season over three consecutive years (using the same trapping effort) in late March and April on the Montagne d'Ambre Massif (Goodman et al. 1997a), with 15 individuals recorded in 1994, 48 in 1995, and 80 in 1996. Data pertaining to long-term trends in effective population size (i.e., over thousands

or millions of years) based on modeling of genetic data are also limited. One such study estimated that the population trajectory of *M. brevicaudata* has recently increased, whereas *M. grandidieri* exhibited signatures of a recent demographic decline (L. E. Olson et al. 2009).

Surveys along elevational transects on several massifs with continuous moist evergreen forest—including Andringitra (Goodman et al. 1996d), Anjanaharibe-Sud (Goodman and Jenkins 1998), Andohahela (Goodman et al. 1999b), and Marojejy (Goodman and Jenkins 2000)—using the same field protocols, have allowed for estimates of relative population densities. *Microgale cowani* was recorded as the most common shrew tenrec species at three of the four sites, forming 25% of the total individuals of 11 species trapped at Marojejy, 39% of nine species at Anjanaharibe-Sud, 52% of 10 species at Andohahela, and 20% of nine species at Andringitra, where it was replaced as the most common species by *M. taiva* (40%). *Microgale parvula* comprised 5% of the individuals captured at Andohahela, 8% at Anjanaharibe-Sud, 13% at Marojejy, and 14% at Andringitra. *Microgale gymnorhyncha*, although found at these four sites, is apparently relatively rare, at least based on the trapping techniques employed, comprising less than 5–6% of the total individuals captured. On Montagne d'Ambre (Raxworthy and Nussbaum 1994), where *M. cowani* has not been recorded, the most common species was *M. drouhardi*, forming 70% of the captures of six shrew tenrec species. In any shrew tenrec species assemblage at the five above-mentioned sites, while medium-size species (such as *M. cowani*, *M. drouhardi*, or *M. taiva*) were ubiquitous, and the very small *M. parvula* was also comparatively common, the largest species (*Nesogale dobsoni* and *N. talazaci*), perhaps because of their greater energy requirements, usually formed a smaller proportion of captures.

These patterns are not consistent across inventoried sites, even when using parallel trapping techniques. On the Befotaka–Midongy du Sud Massif in the southeast, the most commonly trapped species were *M. taiva* and *N. dobsoni*, comprising 24.3–25.4% of the 12 shrew tenrec species, with *M. principula* also common (18.6% trap captures) and *M. cowani* notably rarer than at the aforementioned sites (6.8% trap captures) (V. Soarimalala, unpublished data). In the Anjozorobe-Angavo Forest of the Central Highlands, shrew tenrec species showed largely consistent representation across surveyed localities, with the following 12 species captured at seven medium-altitude moist evergreen forest sites (percentage captured in parentheses): *M. fotsifotsy*, *M. majori*, *M. principula*, *M. gymnorhyncha*, and *M. cowani* were recorded at low density (less than 1%); *M. parvula*, *M. soricoides*, *N. dobsoni*, and *N. talazaci* were common (9%, 10%, 12%, and 9%, respectively); *M. longicaudata* and *M. thomasi* were captured at slightly high density (4% each); and *M. taiva* was the most common (20%) (Soarimalala et al. 2007). A mid-elevational peak in species richness and diversity of *Microgale* is evident in moist evergreen forests, and a correlation with invertebrate diversity has been documented at Andringitra (Goodman et al. 1996d). This mid-elevational peak in species richness varies according to the massif, from five species at 1150 m on Montagne d'Ambre to 10 at 1250 m on Anjozorobe-Angavo.

In the moist evergreen forests, nine to 11 species of shrew tenrecs routinely occur in sympatry; core species include *M. cowani*, *M. fotsifotsy*, *M. gymnorhyncha*, *M. longicaudata*, *M. parvula*, and *M. soricoides*. In a relatively small (<1250 ha) forest block at Tsinjoarivo, to the east of Ambatolampy, 11 species of *Microgale* plus *N. dobsoni* were found together (Goodman et al. 2000; Dammhahn et al. 2013). In the more extensive and ecologically complex area of Tsaratanàna, 12 species of *Microgale* and both species of *Nesogale* have been recorded (Maminirina et al. 2008). Of these species, however, not one was found over the whole elevational range of the transect (730–1740 m); three species of *Microgale* and *N. talazaci* were rarely recorded in association with other species of shrew tenrecs, while eight species of *Microgale* and *N. dobsoni*, in contrast, were routinely found together, although not at all elevations. In the medium-altitude moist evergreen forest of Marojejy at 1225 m, for example, very small species such as *M. parvula* occur with medium-size *M. cowani*, *M. fotsifotsy*, *M. monticola*, and *M. soricoides*, and the large *N. dobsoni* and *N. talazaci*, but also with medium-size *M. gymnorhyncha* and *M. longicaudata*.

Reproduction

Based on captive animals captured in the wild and held in Antananarivo (nearly 19°S), the breeding season for *N. dobsoni*, *N. talazaci*, and *M. drouhardi* started during September–October with an increased display of aggression toward members of the same sex. Most births occurred from November to January in the first year but after the end of January in the second year (Stephenson et al. 1994). In the moist evergreen forest, parturition in many species of shrew tenrecs generally occurs from late October to early February, coinciding with the start and advancement of the rainy season (P. D. Jenkins and Goodman 1999; V. Soarimalala and S. M. Goodman, unpublished data) and the time of maximum food availability. In *M. brevicaudata*, *M. cowani*, and *N. talazaci*, the breeding period is more extended, across the period from September to April (V. Soarimalala and S. M. Goodman, unpublished data). Malzy (1965) observed that parturition in *M. mergulus* appeared to occur from December to January, when the relative water temperature of rivers was highest. During this period, a nest of a postpartum and lactating female contained two infants. The gestation period of *N. dobsoni* in captivity was approximately 62 days (n = 2); females made a nest of leaves and paper strips for litters of one to five infants, born naked and with their eyes and ears closed (Eisenberg and Gould 1970; Stephenson et al. 1994). Litter size in shrew tenrecs, as liberally estimated by placental scars (which may represent multiple parturitions) or embryo counts (which do not account for those subsequently resorbed), is generally two or three but may range from one to seven (Table 14.22). Available records suggest litter size variation within and between species—for example, two to seven embryos in *N. dobsoni*, one to six in *N. talazaci*, one to five in *M. cowani*, and for well-sampled species a reduced range, such as one to three in *M. taiva* and two to four in *M. brevicaudata*. One *M. monticola* and one *N. talazaci* female each were recorded as pregnant and lactating at the same time (Goodman and Jenkins 2000; L. E. Olson, unpublished data), the only examples so far recorded in shrew tenrecs. Among other genera of tenrecs, the phenomenon of animals being pregnant and lactating at the same time has been documented in the dry-forest-dwelling *Geogale* (subfamily Geogalinae). In captivity, infants of *N. dobsoni* began to leave the nest and forage actively shortly after their eyes opened, at 22–27

TABLE 14.22. **Potential litter size of *Microgale* and *Nesogale* species**

SPECIES	LITTER SIZE							R	X
	1	2	3	4	5	6	7		
M. brevicaudata	–	23	–	1	–	–	–	2–4	2.1
M. cowani	3	13	31	14	2	–	–	1–5	2.5
M. drouhardi	1	4	1	–	–	–	–	1–3	2.0
M. dryas	1	1	–	–	–	–	–	1–2	1.5
M. fotsifotsy	–	–	6	1	–	–	–	3–4	3.1
M. gracilis	–	5	1	–	–	–	–	2–3	2.2
M. grandidieri	–	1	1	–	–	–	–	2–3	2.5
M. gymnorhyncha	2	3	1	–	–	–	–	1–3	1.8
M. longicaudata	3	7	5	2	–	–	–	1–4	2.4
M. majori	–	–	3	–	–	–	–	1–4	3.0
M. monticola	–	3	–	–	–	–	–	2	
M. parvula	1	6	2	1	–	–	–	1–4	2.3
M. principula	2	6	–	–	–	–	–	2–4	1.8
M. soricoides	–	7	6	1	–	–	–	1–3	2.6
M. taiva	3	18	5	–	–	–	–	1–3	2.1
M. thomasi	1	6	5	1	–	–	–	1–4	2.5
N. dobsoni	–	12	9	9	15	1	3	2–7	4.6
N. talazaci	3	13	9	1	–	2	–	1–6	2.6
Generic totals	20	128	85	31	17	3	3	1–7	2.5

Notes: R, range of potential litter sizes recorded based on embryo and placental scar counts from 298 collected specimens of *Microgale* and *Nesogale* (V. Soarimalala and S. M. Goodman, unpublished data); X, mean of potential litter size.

days; however, suckling continued beyond this date, and age of weaning was difficult to determine. Individuals of this species appeared to reach full adult size at 50–65 days, and the molt to adult pelage was complete by day 95 (Eisenberg and Gould 1970).

Stephenson et al. (1994) noted only one litter per year for *N. dobsoni* in captivity, while a single individual of *N. talazaci* had one litter during her first year in captivity but two in the second year, ranging in size from two to three infants, whose eyes opened at 28 days. There is limited evidence from Andringitra that females of *M. cowani* and *M. thomasi* (and males of *M. taiva*) may become reproductively mature while retaining some of their deciduous dentition (P. D. Jenkins et al. 1996; Goodman et al. 1999b).

It is assumed that adult shrew tenrecs are usually solitary, although in captivity *N. talazaci*, *N. dobsoni*, and *M.* cf. *cowani* were kept in male-female pairs, and most pairs shared nests (Stephenson and Racey 1993). When Eisenberg and Gould (1970) introduced two males of *N. dobsoni* to a cage together, they usually interacted offensively before ignoring each other. Offensive behavior included mouth gaping, squealing, or biting, while defensive animals usually fled to cover. Male and female *N. dobsoni* and *N. talazaci* were observed to scent mark by repeatedly dragging the cloacal region over the same surface.

PHYSIOLOGY

Stephenson and Racey (1993) reported that the resting metabolic rate and body temperature of adult males and nonreproducing females of *N. talazaci*, *N. dobsoni*, and *M.* cf. *cowani* were higher than those recorded in other members of Tenrecidae, which in general have a low metabolic rate and a low body temperature that fluctuates with the ambient temperature. Furthermore, these three species showed elevated levels of resting metabolic rate during pregnancy and lactation as well as improved thermoregulation during pregnancy. Smaller species apparently maintained a relatively higher body temperature than larger species: *M.* cf. *cowani* maintained almost constant homeothermy; *N. talazaci* showed greater variation; and *N. dobsoni* maintained a lower mean body temperature and showed greater fluctuation in body temperature. Limited evidence in Stephenson and Racey (1993) suggested that

M. drouhardi was similar in thermoregulation to *M. cowani*. A single adult male *M. mergulus* kept in captivity for six weeks maintained a relatively constant body temperature 3°C above ambient temperature, thus the resting metabolic rate and body temperature was comparable to those of other *Microgale* and *Nesogale* species (Stephenson 1994a). Such a situation is unusual for an aquatic mammal, most of which normally maintain a higher body temperature and resting metabolic rate relative to body mass to compensate for the greater heat loss in water. Stephenson (1994a) suggested that heat production may be increased periodically by bouts of activity or food ingestion and that large body mass may provide thermal inertia rather than increased metabolic rate. As the taxonomy of *Microgale* has changed considerably since the time of that research, and voucher specimens of the individual animals used in the laboratory experiments were not saved, some questions remain about the species involved.

Nesogale dobsoni is apparently unique among tenrecs in its seasonal accumulation of fat reserves in the tail, which in animals in captivity increased body weight by a factor of one and a half to nearly two. In captivity, presumably also in Madagascar, Eisenberg and Gould (1970) found a tendency for the seasonal fluctuation in weight to continue, increasing from May to a maximum in November–December (the start of the rainy season) and thereafter declining until May. In contrast to *Microgale* species inhabiting moist evergreen forests, *M. grandidieri* occurring in dry spiny thickets, and more specifically riverine forests along the Onilahy River in the southwest, showed seasonal activity. In surveys carried out for more than a year, this species was trapped only during the warm season, and it was suggested that it may estivate (become torpid) for extended periods during the cold dry season, when food availability is drastically reduced (L. E. Olson et al. 2009).

PARASITES AND DISEASES

The parasites and diseases of shrew tenrecs are poorly known, although the number of studies on this subject has increased dramatically since the *Microgale* account of P. D. Jenkins (2003) was published. This is thanks in part to advances in molecular genetics and new material from continued sampling of these animals in the field.

Known shrew tenrec ectoparasites include fleas of the genera *Paractenopsyllus*, *Synopsyllus*, and *Tsaractenus* (see Duchemin et al., pp. 1074–80); mites of the genera *Microgalobia*, *Limnogalobia*, and *Madamyobia* (Fain 1994; OConnor 2003); and ticks of the genus *Ixodes* (see Klompen and Apanaskevich, pp. 894–99). Endoparasites include nematodes in the genus *Trichuris* (Eisenberg and Gould 1970) and gut apicomplexans in the genus *Eimeria* (Couch et al. 2011). Shrew tenrecs were also recently found to be a vector for *Leptospira*, a bacterial pathogen capable of infecting humans that has emerged as a public health problem globally, including on Madagascar (Dietrich et al. 2014; Lagadec et al. 2016). Screening for paramyxoviruses, a group of viruses that produce a range of diseases in people, showed that among the sampled animals, the majority represented by *M. cowani* and *N. dobsoni* from Ankazomivady Forest had notably high detection rates (Wilkinson et al. 2014). A number of other zoonotic diseases of shrew tenrecs are discussed in chapter 6.

CONSERVATION

All named shrew tenrec species are known from at least one protected area (Goodman et al. 2018b), and this affords some level of protection, but the stability of their populations depends on the conservation of these forested habitats and the reduction of pressures from different human-related activities. While a few species of *Microgale* occupy diverse forest and degraded habitats and seem capable of adjusting to anthropogenic changes (e.g., *M. cowani*, *M. longicaudata*, *M. brevicaudata*), based on current knowledge it appears that most species are far less adaptable, and indeed there is evidence that apparently rare species (such as *M. dryas* and *M. monticola*) or those believed to be confined to particular habitats (such as *M. nasoloi* and *M. jenkinsae*) are almost certainly threatened by habitat destruction. In the latest conservation status assessment using the IUCN (International Union for Conservation of Nature) Red List criteria, four species of *Microgale*—*M. dryas*, *M. mergulus*, *M. monticola*, and *M. nasoloi*—were considered to be Vulnerable; and two species—*M. jenkinsae* and *M. jobihely*—were listed as Endangered (Stephenson et al. 2021).

In contrast to the above list, *N. dobsoni* appears to be not particularly sensitive, at least in the short-term, to certain ecological change and habitat disturbance, as it dominates degraded moist evergreen forests in the Central Highlands such as Ankazomivady and Anorana (Anjozorobe-Angavo), and Ambohitantely. The relatively high reproduction rate for this species (as noted above) might explain its local dominance. Also, at these three sites, *Microgale* species richness is still high, but density is low. *Microgale longicaudata* and *M. fotsifotsy* were found in areas of burned montane ericoid thicket on the Andringitra Massif, adjacent to relatively intact thicket parcels and where sufficient numbers of soil invertebrates had recolonized after the passage of fire (Rasolonandrasana and Goodman 2006).

CONCLUSION

Much remains to be learned about the biology and ecology of the diverse and fascinating shrew tenrecs. The marked diversity of this group and recent discovery of so many new species, as well as a considerable number of undescribed cryptic species (Everson et al. 2016; Goodman et al. 2018b), have important implications for conservation, especially in view of the past and present forest habitat destruction on the island. Finally, because of this ongoing taxonomic fluidity, any new information that cannot be confidently associated with voucher material is almost certain to lose validity over time; we therefore encourage the continued proportionate collection and curation of well-documented voucher specimens with associated tissue samples whenever it is possible and, of course, following national laws and permit regulations.

Subject editor: Steven M. Goodman

TENRECIDAE: *ORYZORICTES*, MOLE TENRECS

K. M. Everson, S. M. Goodman, and L. E. Olson

The genus *Oryzorictes* is one of the more distinctive groups of non-spiny tenrecs (subfamily Oryzorictinae). Two species are currently recognized: *O. hova* (which includes *O. talpoides*, as a junior synonym) and *O. tetradactylus*. Thomas (1918) transferred *O. tetradactylus* to the monotypic genus *Nesoryctes*, but Heim de Balsac (1972) subsequently returned it to *Oryzorictes*. A recent study (Everson et al. 2018) revealed several "cryptic" candidate species currently ascribed to *O. hova*, although confusion surrounding type specimens (discussed below) has thus far precluded any formal taxonomic revision or description. Hereafter, *O. hova* refers to *O. hova sensu stricto*.

Oryzorictes hova is broadly distributed in the moist evergreen forest zone of the island, as well as in bottomlands outside of forests, including natural marshes and those converted to rice paddies (hence, one common name, "rice tenrec" has been proposed; see below). *Oryzorictes tetradactylus* is known from far fewer localities and appears to be confined largely to montane areas of the central eastern portion of the Central Highlands.

DESCRIPTION

As their other common name, mole tenrec, implies, members of *Oryzorictes* superficially resemble true moles in the family Talpidae. All species of mole tenrecs are characterized by distinctly robust bodies; adults weigh between 28 and 55 g (Table 14.23). Their pelage is very soft, dense, and silky, with a slight iridescence. They are easily differentiated from other oryzorictines (*Microgale* and *Nesogale*) by their stout and robust forelimbs with elongate claws; short and slightly robust hind limbs with broad footpads and relatively short claws; broad naked nose; and small ears and eyes. There is considerable variation in the fur color of members of this genus, particularly *O. hova*, which can have a dark blackish-brown to light tan-brown dorsum and a dark brown to buffy-white ventrum. On Nosy Mangabe, in the Antongil Bay, albinism is apparently not rare in the local *O. hova* population (Figure 14.32). *Oryzorictes tetradactylus* has largely dark-brown fur that is often mixed or mottled with lighter brown, particularly on the dorsum. Both species are approximately equal in external dimensions, and in *O. hova* the length of the short naked tail is approximately half that of the head and body, while in *O. tetradactylus* the tail is proportionally shorter (Table 14.23). Both species fit the model of a semi-fossorial mammal, with modifications to the limbs for digging. *Oryzorictes tetradactylus* and *O. hova* can be readily distinguished from one another by the presence of either four or five digits on the forelimbs, respectively.

Members of this genus have several cranial characteristics that set them apart from other oryzorictines. The skull is relatively robust, the premaxilla is flared dorsolaterally, and the braincase is short and wide with well-defined lamboid crests. The canines are well developed and distinctly longer than any other tooth, including the first incisor. In contrast to their superficial size similarities, *O. hova* is significantly larger than *O. tetradactylus* in 26 of 36 craniomandibular measurements (Everson et al. 2018).

DISTRIBUTION AND HABITAT PREFERENCES

Oryzorictes tetradactylus is known from only a few, largely high-elevation areas at the eastern central edge of the Central Highlands. Many specimens were collected in forested areas and, in part, above tree line. On the Andringitra Massif, *O. tetradactylus* has been collected along the Andohariana Plateau at 2050 m in a vast area of montane ericoid thicket and in a small marshy area with montane grassland at about 2450 m near the foot of Pic Boby (2658 m), the second-highest summit on Madagascar (Goodman and Rasolonandrasana 2001). It is also represented in older collections from near Antsirabe and Vinanitelo.

TABLE 14.23. **External measurements for species of adult *Oryzorictes***

SPECIES	HBL (mm)	TL (mm)	HFL (mm)	EL (mm)	WT (g)
O. hova	108.3 ± 7.1	50.3 ± 4.7	16.9 ± 1.3	11.5 ± 1.4	40.0 ± 6.5
	85–122	39–60	13–21	6–16	28–55
	(n = 57)	(n = 66)	(n = 67)	(n = 70)	(n = 66)
O. tetradactylus	117.0 ± 4.4	47.4 ± 5.3	18.0 ± 2.1	15.0 ± 1.9	32.2 ± 3.4
	114–122	42–57	15–20	12–17	29.5–36
	(n = 3)	(n = 7)	(n = 7)	(n = 7)	(n = 3)

Notes: HBL, head-and-body length; TL, tail length; HFL, hind-foot length (not including claw); EL, ear length; WT, weight. Sample statistics include the mean ± one standard deviation, the minimum–maximum range, and the number (n) of measured individuals.

FIGURE 14.32 **Photo of albinistic *Oryzorictes hova* from Nosy Mangabe.** (PHOTO by H. Schütz.)

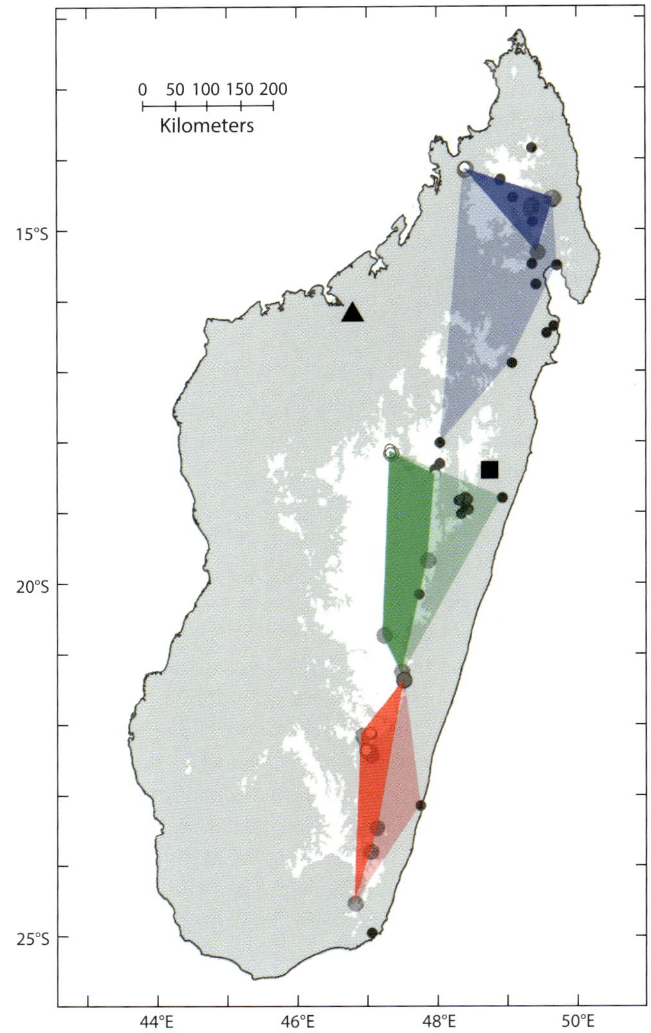

FIGURE 14.33 **Geographic ranges of the three candidate species of the *Oryzorictes hova* complex identified by Everson et al. (2018). Individual specimens used in this study were associated with sequence data and morphology data (gray circles), sequence data alone (white circles), or morphology data alone (black circles). The type localities of *O. hova* and *O. talpoides* are indicated by a square and a triangle, respectively. Colors represent the ranges of the three candidate species; darker colors show the extents using only genetically confirmed specimens, while lighter colors expand on these regions by showing inferred clade memberships using the larger, morphometric data set.**

Oryzorictes hova has been trapped across much of the eastern forest zone and in different forms of moist evergreen forest from Ambatotsirongorongo in the south to the Maroantsetra area in the north, including Makira, Rantabe, Nosy Mangabe, and the Masoala Peninsula, across an elevational gradient from near sea level to 1990 m (Goodman et al. 2013). It is also known from different areas of the Northern Highlands and associated southern extensions (Marojejy, Anjanaharibe-Sud, Tsaratanàna, and COMATSA [Corridor Marojejy–Anjanaharibe-Sud–Tsaratanàna]). Extensive survey work in the extreme north on Montagne d'Ambre did not find evidence of *O. hova*. This species can be found in a range of forest formations from lowland moist evergreen forest to *Erica*-dominated montane ericoid thicket near tree line. Further, *O. hova* is known from isolated forests in the Central Highlands such as the Ambohitantely Special Reserve (Goodman and Rakotondravony 2000). This species is forest dwelling, but there are records from the forest-edge ecotone, notably disturbed areas with little natural woody vegetation, and open marshy areas at least in part associated with rice fields (Randriamoria 2017).

MOLECULAR GENETICS AND TAXONOMY

A recent study using a combination of molecular and morphometric data from museum specimens assigned to *O. hova* identified the presence of three cryptic lineages that the authors concluded to be candidate species (Everson et al. 2018). These three reciprocally monophyletic groups are restricted to the northern, central, and southern regions of Madagascar's moist evergeen forests (Figure 14.33), and there is no evidence of gene flow among clades despite the presence of two potential contact zones around 18°S (northern and central clades) and 21.5°S (central and southern clades). While the genetic evidence for three distinct species is strong, morphometric support is relatively weak. To date, no character has been identified that can be used to diagnose the three candidate species, although it is possible that morphological differences between these groups exist that were not uncovered by Everson et al. (2018).

The three candidate species have yet to be formally described, owing in large part to confusion surrounding the type specimens and taxonomic history of *O. hova*, as discussed in detail by Goodman et al. (1999b) and Everson et al. (2018) and briefly summarized here. In 1870, A. Grandidier described this genus and species based on a specimen probably originating from the Sihanaka region of eastern Madagascar, indicated by a square on the map shown in Figure 14.33; no mention was made of this specimen's disposition, nor was it identified by a collector or museum catalog number. Among the characters Grandidier noted for his new beast were forefeet with four digits—three of which were tipped with large and strongly recurved claws—and a dental formula of incisors 3/3,

canines 1/1, premolars and molars (combined) 6/6. However, the specimen cataloged as the type specimen clearly has five digits on the front limbs. Furthermore, although A. Grandidier (1870) clearly stated that the type specimen had an upper third incisor, there is no evidence of this tooth on the specimen. A final point of discrepancy between the characters noted in the description of *O. hova* and the purported type specimen is that the latter includes two fluid-preserved neonates, which A. Grandidier (1870) failed to mention. Considering all these anomalies, Everson et al. (2018) called into question the authenticity of the purported *O. hova* holotype.

Another species in this genus, *O. talpoides*, was described by G. Grandidier and Petit (1930) after *O. hova*. The holotype of *O. talpoides* was taken in the rice fields near Marovoay, east of Mahajanga, indicated by a triangle in Figure 14.33. The primary characters proposed to differentiate *O. hova* and *O. talpoides* were the absence of the third incisor in the latter and differences in the size of the pollex (G. Grandidier and Petit 1930; Genest and Petter 1975). However, Goodman et al. (1999b) determined both characters to be specious and inadequate for diagnosing the two species, and *O. talpoides* was therefore synonymized with *O. hova*. Nonetheless, *O. talpoides* remains an available name, which might be given to one of the three candidate species identified by Everson et al. (2018).

Assigning names to the three candidate species identified in Everson et al. (2018) is challenging for several reasons. First, the two type specimens bearing available names were collected from geographic areas that are either between (*O. hova*) or extralimital to (*O. talpoides*) the candidate species' ranges (Figure 14.33). Second, both type specimens could not be unambiguously assigned to a clade based on morphometrics, and genetic data from these specimens have thus far been unattainable. Given the described peculiarities in both range and morphology, another possibility is that additional species exist in this complex beyond the three that were proposed by Everson et al. (2018). Notably, recent surveys in the dry deciduous forest of the Ankarafantsika region, not far from the type locality of *O. talpoides*, did not result in the capture of a mole tenrec (D. Rakotondravony et al. 2002; Ito et al. 2013), although the sampled habitats were very different from marsh areas and rice fields near Marovoay. Hence, it is not known whether or not any mole tenrec population still exists near the *O. talpoides* type locality. We expect that additional taxonomic work in the coming years—including DNA sequence data from type specimens—will provide clarity.

FIELD SURVEYS AND NATURAL HISTORY

Pitfall trapping during extensive small-mammal field surveys across Madagascar's forested regions since the early 1990s has significantly increased the number of sites from which *Oryzorictes hova* has been recorded. Mole tenrecs are more commonly taken in these trap devices than the more standard live traps such as the Sherman trap (79 out of 89 specimens for which we have tabulated trap type were captured in pitfalls). Semi-fossorial oryzorictines—including *O. hova*, *Microgale gracilis*, and *M. gymnorhyncha*—are captured far less frequently than nonfossorial taxa. They are more often captured after periods of moderate to heavy rain than during dry periods. It is presumed that this is related to flooding of their living spaces, which might be in part underground, or perhaps to greater surface activity of soil invertebrates, their presumed food, after rain. As a consequence, when mammal surveys are conducted during dry periods, the absence of these species from pitfall or other trap captures cannot be used as evidence that they do not occur at the site.

Very little is known about the natural history of *Oryzorictes*. Between two and four embryos have been recorded from specimens trapped in January, March, October, and November (n = 8). Females have two or three sets of mammae (n = 8). Like other male tenrecids, males in reproductive condition retain the testicles in an abdominal position, but specimens with enlarged testes and convoluted epididymes indicative of active sperm production have been collected in January, March, April, September, October, November, and December; interestingly, of 41 specimens with epididymis condition recorded, 39 were observed to be convoluted, and this gives the impression that adult males are in reproductive condition throughout the year. None of the craniodental or external measurements evaluated in *O. hova* by Everson et al. (2018) showed any evidence of sexual dimorphism. Virtually nothing is known about the feeding habits of *O. hova*. The stomach contents of three specimens of animals assigned to *O. hova* collected by C. S. Webb contained insects (including grasshoppers), earthworms, and vegetable matter (Eisenberg and Gould 1970). In captivity, this species readily feeds on earthworms (Stephenson 1994b).

The generic name *Oryzorictes* is derived from the Greek and means "rice burrower," hence, the often-used common name "rice tenrec." On numerous occasions during small-mammal surveys in the eastern moist evergreen forest, our local collaborators from nearby villages recognized *O. hova* when it was captured. They mention that it is an animal that lives in rice fields, and they often disturb its burrows when tilling the ground. It is commonly believed that this species causes damage to rice crops by burrowing in the earth and uprooting the young sprouts. Apparently, in some rice fields these tenrecs reach high densities.

In the hand, live individuals of both species of *Oryzorictes* show surprising forelimb strength. Like golden moles (Chrysochloridae)—but unlike true moles (Talpidae)—mole tenrecs appear to use dorsoventral rather than lateral extension of their forelimbs when digging (Figure 14.32). Although mole tenrecs rarely bite when handled, their large canines powered by impressive jaw muscles can inflict serious and deep wounds to mammalogists who do not pay attention.

A few different types of predators are known to consume *O. hova*. On the Masoala Peninsula, *Tyto soumagnei* (Red Owl) preys on this species, which represented less than 6%, by total individuals or estimated biomass, of the remains identified from regurgitated pellets (Goodman and Thorstrom 1998). Skeletal remains of *O. hova* have been recovered from owl pellets collected in the Maroantsetra area (Heim de Balsac 1972). The cadaver of one of these mole tenrecs was found in the digestive system of a fossorial snake of the genus *Pseudoxyrhopus* captured in parcel 1 of Andohahela (Goodman et al. 1999b).

CONSERVATION

Given that *Oryzorictes* species occur outside of forested zones, they are presumably less impacted by current levels of deforestation than

many other species of forest-dependent small mammals. Further, they have been found to survive in islands of forest that have been isolated for considerable periods of time (Goodman and Rakotondravony 2000). Thus, members of this genus are probably amongst the small set of endemic Malagasy mammals that are not seriously threatened by current levels of habitat destruction. Nonetheless, *O. tetradactylus* is classified as Data Deficient by the IUCN (Stephenson et al. 2016), as little is known about the extent of its occurrence or population trends, and most specimens of this species were collected more than 100 years ago. Furthermore, the predicted areas of occupation of the three candidate species of the *O. hova* complex identified by Everson et al. (2018) range in size from 20,071 km^2 (south) to 53,813 km^2 (north). All three candidate species are, therefore, close to the 20,000 km^2 threshold set by the IUCN Species Survival Commission to classify a species as Threatened. If the candidates are elevated to full species status, this action will necessitate a reassessment of conservation concerns.

Subject editor: Steven M. Goodman

TENRECIDAE: *TENREC ECAUDATUS*, TAILLESS TENREC, *TANDRAKA, TRANDRAKA, KELORA*

S. M. Goodman, L. E. Olson, and †M. E. Nicoll

Tenrec is a monotypic genus, represented by *T. ecaudatus*, the largest member of Tenrecidae, a family entirely endemic to Madagascar. The genus is one of four in the subfamily Tenrecinae, a grouping of five species (see Goodman and Soarimalala, pp. 1737–69) that exhibit varying degrees of spinescence, with adult *T. ecaudatus* being the least spiny (Stankowich and Stensrud 2019). All of the 31 or so species in Tenrecidae occur naturally on Madagascar, the majority in forest formations. *Tenrec ecaudatus* is found in most habitats across the island. A considerable amount of new research has been conducted on this rather remarkable beast, and herein we update the contribution of Nicoll (2003) that appeared in the precursor of this book.

DESCRIPTION

The general body form of *Tenrec* is somewhat like that of a New World opossum, *Didelphis virginiana*, but it is completely tailless, as is indicated by the specific epithet *ecaudatus*. The snout is long and pointed, the ears are short and rounded, and the head is distinctly more slender in females and young males than in adult males. Dorsally, the head broadens and domes in older males, specifically the area associated with muscle attachments to the sagittal crest. The gape spans up to 10 cm in large individuals, and the snapping defensive bite can inflict serious wounds as the canines may be up to 15 mm in length. Middorsal skin thickness increases with age in males, and the back in such individuals often shows signs of bite marks.

Overall color of adults is brown; males are paler owing to a broad, light band in the individual dorsal hairs. The pelage of both sexes darkens with age; western and southern individuals are generally paler than those in the east. Flexible and sparse spines are concentrated around the nape and crown but also occur on the back to the mid-dorsum, and their density decreases with age (Nicoll 1982). The nape spines form a small group that is associated with scent glands. The rigid spines are believed to favor bacterial growth that forms a crust on the spines, and females rub their forefeet over them to scent mark. This form of scent marking has been recorded when females encounter sites already marked by other females. Males have not been observed to do this, and the scent-gland spines are generally less encrusted by exudate and/or bacterial growth. A second set of specialized spines, found in the middorsal region of juveniles, forms the stridulating organ used to communicate within family groups. The ribbed spines vibrate together to produce noise spanning a range from just audible to humans to ultrasonic (E. Gould and Eisenberg 1966). The organ is not functional in adults, and the spines lose their motility and become less numerous and more spaced. Juveniles have striped, black and yellowish-white spines that have a relatively higher proportion of barbs than those of adults. Molt to adult pelage begins at around 35 days and is completed at 60–70 days (Eisenberg and Gould 1970; Nicoll 1982, 1983).

GEOGRAPHIC AND ELEVATIONAL DISTRIBUTION

Tenrec ecaudatus has a broad distribution on Madagascar and is perhaps the most widely occurring native terrestrial mammal on the island. It occurs in all natural forest types, secondary forest formations, wooded grasslands, anthropogenic grasslands, and even at the edge of urban areas (E. Gould and Eisenberg 1966; Eisenberg and Gould 1970). In the dry deciduous forests of the west and the moist evergreen forests of the north and east, this species tends to be common, or at least this was the case until the early 21st century (see Hunting and Conservation, below), and in the dry spiny thickets of the southwest it has lower population densities. This observation is

† Deceased (1954–2020).

consistent with species-distribution models that suggest the distribution of *Tenrec* can be explained largely by vegetation type and precipitation (Goodman et al. 2013). It is known from close to sea level to about 1700 m and is absent from the upper reaches of the highest mountains on the island.

Tenrec ecaudatus is the only Malagasy tenrecid known to have been introduced to other islands in the western Indian Ocean. On the basis of the archaeological record, the earliest evidence of it on Mayotte (Maoré) in the Comoros dates from the eighth century (Allibert 1989; Allibert and Vérin 1996), in the Mascarenes (Mauritius and La Réunion) from the first portion of the 18th century, and slightly later in the Seychelles, apparently around 1880 (Racey and Nicoll 1984; Cheke 2010). The species was presumably introduced to serve as a local source of animal protein food, as other than fruit bats, there are no native mammals on these islands for consumption by people. Furthermore, in the case of Mayotte, some of the island's settlers are Sakalava from western Madagascar, an ethnic group for which the consumption of *Tenrec* is widespread and popular. These mammal introductions were also associated with the establishment of some public health problems, specifically leptospirosis (see below).

ECOLOGY, BEHAVIOR, AND REPRODUCTION

Tenrec is an omnivore that varies its food habits with season and reproductive activity. It is generally nocturnal, but different sex and age classes may be partly diurnal (Nicoll 1982, 1983). A major part of the tenrec's diet is soil-inhabiting invertebrates. A study conducted in March (end of the wet season) in a dry deciduous forest in western Madagascar found that beetle larvae are the most important elements, but other invertebrates such as termites, ants, larval lepidopterans, and centipedes—and occasionally fruit—are also taken (Ade 1996; Soarimalala and Goodman 2003b). These observations agree with food habits recorded in the Seychelles, in that terrestrial and soil invertebrates are the most significant prey of the tenrec (Nicoll 1982). *Tenrec* has a limited ability to catch small vertebrates, but this was occasionally observed in the Seychelles, as was consumption of small snail species (Nicoll 1982). Ade (1996) considers feeding within the upper soil strata characteristic of this animal. The snout is used to probe and open up the soil to expose prey.

Wild animals live up to four to five years in the Seychelles (Nicoll 1982; Nicoll and Racey 1985). Seasonal cycles of reproduction, shifts in foods consumed, and thermoregulation are marked and largely consistent within a given population (Eisenberg and Gould 1970; Nicoll 1982). Seasonal torpor begins in the austral autumn after a period of fattening that commences after the breeding season. Body mass may be double that of lean weight by the start of torpor (Nicoll 1985). Individuals excavate a burrow and seal it from the inside before spending five to six months in hibernation, which in southwestern Madagascar may extend to nine months. Males reemerge in spring one month ahead, on average, of females. Details on the ecophysiological adaptations of this species are presented in detail by Dausmann et al. (pp. 1798–805).

Some work has been conducted on the home ranges of *T. ecaudatus* on Madagascar, including a study of 10 radio-collared individuals in the Kirindy Forest CNFEREF (Centre National de Formation, d'Etudes et de Recherche en Environnement et Foresterie) (Randriamahady 2012). The collars of three tagged adult females functioned long enough to calculate home ranges, which averaged 2.93 ha (based on 95% minimum convex polygon), and the range was from 1.7 to 5.3 ha. The home ranges of two of the three females overlapped considerably. Similar data are available from the Seychelles (Nicoll 1985), where home ranges overlap and individuals typically cover approximately 1 ha during a given night's activity. However, there is considerable seasonal variation, at least in part associated with the reproductive state of a given individual and food availability, and the nightly displacement can become at least two to three times more extensive.

The male reproductive tract is already active at emergence from hibernation, and males devote time to searching for females during much of the first half of the active season. Females mate several days after emergence and give birth two months later (Nicoll 1985). Receptive females reduce their nightly ranges from ~1.0 ha to smaller than 0.1 ha, moving very little and remaining close to the sleeping site. This is believed to favor the concentration of the female's scent in a small area and facilitate the male's ability to locate her (Nicoll 1982). It may also favor intermale competition for access, as several males may cross the reduced home range at the same time, leading invariably to conflict and dominance by one individual. The male will attempt to mate with the female once contact is established. If the male is relatively large, it will stay with the female and attack or chase any other male that approaches. Smaller males will also stay until driven off by a larger individual.

Larger males may periodically leave the female (usually, if not always, in a burrow) for up to one to two hours to seek other females. Where the species is common, this usually means that smaller roving males will find the female and mate with her if time permits. Smaller males that are discovered by the returning larger male are invariably attacked and driven off. It thus appears that the female's strategy is to reduce movement, possibly to concentrate scent cues, and mate with any male that is able to reach and stay with her. The male strategy appears to be dependent on size. All males seek receptive females, but only larger males are capable of defending access to a female for the two to four days that she is receptive.

On Madagascar between latitudes of 12°S and 25°S, the birth season appears to peak in January in the east and slightly later in the west (Rand 1935; Eisenberg and Gould 1970). The male reproductive tract becomes inactive at around this time, corresponding with a regression of the testes and cessation of sperm production (Nicoll 2003). The offspring remain with the mother for up to 55 days. They emerge from the nest at 18–20 days and forage as a group with the mother (Figure 14.34a). At about 35 days, they may forage without her or in smaller and looser groups until they are solitary (Eisenberg and Gould 1970; Nicoll 1983, 1985). Females draw upon nearly the entirety of stored energy held as fat during reproduction, with the highest energy demands presumably occurring during lactation, and residual fat from the previous winter torpor season is critical to successful reproduction in the following summer. Healthy males do not deplete their entire fat reserves during seasonal activity.

Tenrec is capable of producing very large litters; the maximum embryo count is 34, the maximum number of infants per litter is 32, and more than 20 infants is not unusual (Eisenberg and Gould

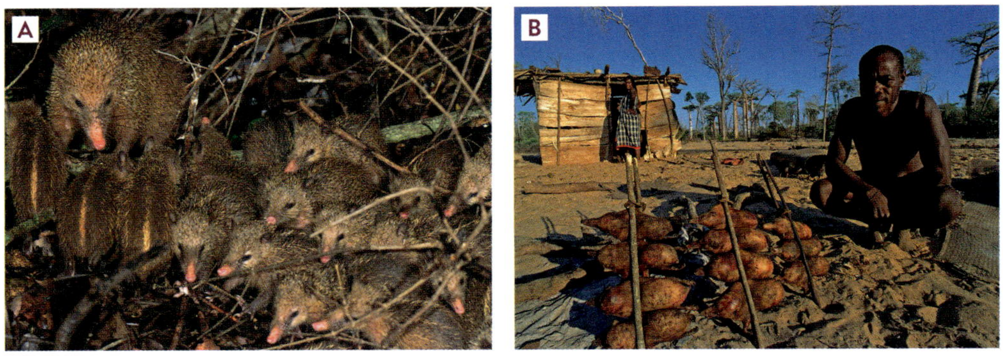

FIGURE 14.34 Different aspects of *Tenrec ecaudatus* on Madagascar: A) female in the Ankarana protected area with a number of young in tow; B) roasting of large and fatty individuals at the outskirts of the Kirindy Mité protected area for consumption by local people. (PHOTOS by H. Schütz.)

1970; Nicoll 1983; Nicoll and Racey 1985). However, litter size is related to age and appears to vary geographically. On the basis of a small number of museum and published records it appears that litter size in dry deciduous forests of the west is often around 25 and in the less seasonal moist evergreen forests usually around 20.

While there are likely to be environmental factors influencing litter size, some intrinsic features of female *Tenrec* reproduction are also implicated. Seychelles populations for which such data are available showed a clear decline in litter size with maternal age (Nicoll 1985). Females in their first breeding season (at one year old) consistently had the highest number of ovulated ovarian follicles, implantation sites, and surviving postnatal offspring. The number declined until the third or fourth breeding season when fetal survival was severely reduced, and most individuals failed to rear young successfully.

Field studies of *Tenrec* demonstrate that females during late pregnancy and lactation are active during both the night and the day (Nicoll 1983). Once they are old enough to accompany the mother outside of the burrow, the juveniles follow the same activity pattern, which persists until around the time of their molt to adult pelage. The darker brown color of females may serve as partial crypsis, as they must forage for part of the year during the daytime, while the juveniles have a more marked, striped cryptic coloration associated with the need to forage during daylight hours for all of the preadult molt period of their life.

Among the few predators known to feed on *Tenrec*, the most important—other than humans—is the endemic carnivoran *Cryptoprocta ferox* (Eupleridae), the largest living member of the family (see Gerber and Hawkins, pp. 1978–83). Several studies have been conducted on the diet of this predator in the dry deciduous forests of the west. In the Kirindy Forest CNFEREF of the Menabe Antimena protected area, this euplerid more frequently predated on *Tenrec* during the rainy season, when the prey animal is more active (C. E. Hawkins and Racey 2008). The same general pattern was found in the Ankarafantsika Forest, farther to the north (Dollar et al. 2007). *Cryptoprocta* dispatches *Tenrec* with a slap of its strong front foot, perhaps to avoid a mouthful of spines, or a neck bite, and then opens the carcass from the ventral side, where spines are reduced or absent. Other euplerids are too small to take adult *T. ecaudatus*, although introduced dogs roaming the forest do depredate subadults and adults. Owls are not known to feed on *Tenrec*. Among diurnal raptors, the largest species, such as *Polyboroides radiatus* (Madagascar Harrier-hawk), and *Buteo brachypterus* (Madagascar Buzzard) do take *Tenrec* (Goodman and Langrand 1996a; Karpanty and Goodman 1999).

ZOONOTIC DISEASES AND ECTOPARASITES

A notable amount of recent research has been conducted on zoonotic diseases of *T. ecaudatus*; several of these aspects are discussed in detail in chapter 6 and are mentioned here only briefly. Of particular note is the disease leptospirosis, which is caused by different bacteria in the genus *Leptospira*, which is discharged in water via mammal urine and transmitted by different members of the Tenrecidae—including *T. ecaudatus*—as well as other mammals. Leptospirosis is a disease of public health concern on islands in the western Indian Ocean. A new species of *Leptospira*, *L. mayottensis* was described from Mayotte based on human clinical cases (Bourhy et al. 2014), and fieldwork on the island found introduced *T. ecaudatus* as one of the reservoirs of the bacterium (Lagadec et al. 2016). Fieldwork on Madagascar has uncovered different species of *Leptospira*, including *L. mayottensis*, in the Tenrecidae and in some cases *T. ecaudatus* (see Dietrich et al., pp. 268–77). This bacterium is native and presumably endemic to Madagascar and was most likely brought to Mayotte with the introduction of *T. ecaudatus*. On La Réunion, introduced *T. ecaudatus*, based on serological analysis, has a high prevalence of *Leptospira* (Sigaud et al. 2009).

Tenrec ecaudatus is known to host a range of ectoparasites, including an assortment of ticks (see Klompen and Apanaskevich, pp. 894–99) and fleas (Duchemin 2003; see Duchemin et al., pp. 1074–80). The latter include several introduced species as well as two endemic species, *Synopsyllus fonquerniei* and *Dinopsyllus brachypecten*, which are known or implicated in the transmission of bubonic plague. *Tenrec* has been shown to be seropositive for plague, and its fleas are considered vectors of the disease (e.g., Andrianaivoarimanana et al. 2013). Little is known about the role of *Tenrec* ticks in the transmission of human zoonotic diseases, and this is an area needing further research.

HUNTING AND CONSERVATION

Individuals of *Tenrec* are commonly hunted and represent an important traditional food source on Madagascar (see Golden et

al., pp. 204–17; Figure 14.34b), although for people from certain ethnic groups and religious orientations eating them is taboo (*fady*) (Reuter and Sewall 2016). Based on archaeological midden remains, consumption of these animals is a practice that dates at least as far back as the 9th–10th centuries (Radimilahy 1998). In certain areas of the island, these animals add an important nutritional contribution for individuals and families living a subsistence lifestyle and are readily consumed (Golden et al. 2014). Ganzhorn et al. (1990) found that in the dry deciduous forest of central western Madagascar, selective logging had little measurable impact on population density of this species, and the most important impact was offtake by humans in the form of hunting. Such pressure appears to have greatly reduced numbers or to have caused extirpation of some populations, as their collection for food is common in many parts of the country. In the northeast, specifically in and around the Makira protected area, levels of *Tenrec* exploitation at current levels appear sustainable, but in other portions of this zone, such as the Masoala Peninsula, the offtake is too high, and populations are declining (Annapragada et al. 2021).

In the central west, hunters construct temporary forest camps and use trained dogs to search out *T. ecaudatus* in burrows or other types of resting sites and, once located, often use spears to subdue and kill animals. The dogs used in these hunting parties also kill and consume a range of animals, including other spiny tenrecs (Tenrecinae) of different sorts, as well as species classified on the IUCN Red list as Endangered, such as the endemic rodent *Hypogeomys antimena* (see Sommer and Carleton, pp. 2025–27). On occasion, these hunting dogs escape, become feral, and hunt forest animals. In certain places, such as the central west, the hunted *T. ecaudatus*, rather than being consumed by the hunter group, are sold in neighboring villages in formal and informal markets. The price per unit weight of *Tenrec* was at least twice the cost of other types of domestic or wild meat in markets of this region (Randrianandrianina et al. 2010).

Hunting is widely practiced on the Mascarene islands, particularly by local people of African descent (Creoles) or Malagasy descent, and on the Comoro islands, particularly on Mayotte, by recent colonizers from Madagascar. Collection of *T. ecaudatus* for food is no longer practiced in the Seychelles (Rocamora and Henriette 2015), but animals are killed as garden pests because of damage to sprouting plants while foraging (Nicoll 2003). The lack of natural predators in the Seychelles might be why *T. ecaudatus* population densities may reach locally 15 adults/ha, far higher than any noted on Madagascar or the Mascarene islands, where the animal is exploited.

In relatively intact to pristine forest sites that have been surveyed for small mammals since the last portion of the 20th century, the number of *T. ecaudatus* has drastically declined since about the 2010s. An example is Ambohitantely, in the Central Highlands (S. M. Goodman and V. Soarimalala, unpublished data), a forest zone known to have a continuous cycle of bubonic plague, a disease that might be having an impact on local *Tenrec* populations. Nearly annual surveys were conducted at this site between 2015 and 2019, and only a few *Tenrec* individuals were captured, as compared to higher trap rates in the 1990s. These recently trapped individuals had internal organs riddled with nematodes causing damage; these same types of infestations, although rarer and not as severe, have been found in other species of Tenrecidae at this site and elsewhere in the Central Highlands. Neither the identity of these nematodes and their origin nor the impact they may be having on *T. ecaudatus* populations is known as of this writing. Whether the reduction in *T. ecaudatus* at Ambohitantely is associated with zoonotic diseases, increased level of endoparasites, illicit human hunting, or a combination of these factors is in need of further research.

Tenrec ecaudatus is well represented in many protected areas on Madagascar (Goodman et al. 2018b). The IUCN lists the conservation status of this species as Least Concern, noting that it is widespread in native forest formations as well as disturbed habitats, with stable population trends, and that "anecdotal" accounts of hunting pressure may be increasing in certain areas. In contrast, sufficient data are indeed available that *T. ecaudatus* offtake for bushmeat is on the increase and is affecting certain populations (Annapragada et al., unpublished data). More research on the impact diseases and hunting are having on this species is urgently needed to better understand population trends.

Subject editors: Jörg U. Ganzhorn and Steven M. Goodman

BATS OF MADAGASCAR

S. M. Goodman, B. Ramasindrazana, and M. C. Schoeman

The most recent phase of intensive research on the bats of Madagascar commenced at the beginning of the 21st century. This was about the same time an overview to the bats of the island was published in *The Natural History of Madagascar* (Eger and Mitchell 2003), which was to a large extent an extension of a monograph published some years earlier (Peterson et al. 1995). In addition to this was a project started in 2000 by the University of Aberdeen, Scotland, and Malagasy colleagues and students, under the name Lamin'asa Fiarovana Ramanavy (Project to Conserve Bats). This project, which would lead to the creation of the organization Madagasikara Voakajy, focused initially on Pteropodidae bats, and some of its initial survey and research findings were presented in the 2003 precursor to this

book (MacKinnon et al. 2003) and also by Racey et al. (2010). Another long-term research program that included work on the bats of Madagascar was commenced by researchers and students of the Ecology Training Program (ETP), WWF Madagascar, and in collaboration with the Field Museum of Natural History (FMNH); this WWF project in 2007 became Association Vahatra (see Andriamialisoa and Langrand, pp. 1–38). Hence, as clear evidence of the considerable progress that has been made in the past two decades on available information concerning Malagasy bats, the Eger and Mitchell (2003) contribution is now out of date, and a completely new contribution is presented herein. In contrast, the previous contributions on Pteropodidae and Myzopodidae have been revised by some of the original and new contributors (see, respectively, Andrianaivoarivelo et al., pp. 1911–16, and Ralisata et al., pp. 1917–22). One of the outstanding outcomes of these past decades concerning Malagasy bats is the number of national students and researchers working on this group of animals. This aspect is exemplified by the references cited in the 2003 bat contributions, which, among the 49 references cited, included only one published citation coauthored by a Malagasy bat biologist (2% of the total), while in this contribution the figure is 97 out of 178 references (+50%).

Coincidental with the work conducted on the bat fauna of Madagascar, the past couple of decades have seen major changes in the higher systematics of bats (order Chiroptera) in general. On the basis of largely molecular insights, the former higher-level systematics of bats—dividing them into the two suborders, Megachiroptera, including the family Pteropodidae, and Microchiroptera, including the balance of bat families—has been completely revamped (M. S. Springer et al. 2001; G. Jones and Teeling 2006; Tsagkogeorga et al. 2013). Two suborders are currently recognized: the Pteropodiformes (Figure 14.35), also referred to as the Yinpterochiroptera, which on Madagascar comprises the Pteropodidae, Hipposideridae, and Rhinonycteridae; and the Vespertilioniformes (Figure 14.36), also referred to as the Yangochiroptera, which on Madagascar comprises the Emballonuridae, Myzopodidae, Molossidae, Vespertilionidae, and Miniopteridae (Table 14.24).

ADVANCES ON MALAGASY BATS SINCE 2003

Using the summary on Malagasy bats presented in the precursor of this book as the point of comparison (Eger and Mitchell 2003), the past decades have seen significant growth in scientific studies on Malagasy bats. In the initial phase of these programs, the foci were largely on three different aspects. The first was associated with field inventories and a simple drive to better understand faunistic aspects, and this included the collection of specimens and associated tissue samples as well as fecal material, stomach contents, and ectoparasites. On the basis of morphological and genetic research, a large-scale reevaluation of the systematics and species delimitations of most species of Malagasy bats was conducted in a series of studies, and many taxa have also been the subject of phylogeographic research. The different findings led to the descriptions of numerous bats new to science, and the fauna increased from 26 recognized species on the island (62% endemic) in Peterson et al. (1995) to 30 species (60% endemic) in Eger and Mitchell (2003) to 46 species (36 endemic) herein (Table 14.24). (This measure of species richness includes *Scotophilus* cf. *borbonicus*, whose occurrence on Madagascar is called into question.) On the basis of recent research, the type specimens of *Nycteris madagascariensis* (family Nycteridae) thought to have been collected on Madagascar are indeed of African origin, and this taxon has been removed from the Madagascar bat list (Demos et al. 2021). These different advancements are discussed in detail in this contribution by family under the Systematics subheadings. The numerous published papers addressing different topics in the taxonomy and systematics of Malagasy bats led to Madagascar's emergence as a country having one of the best-known chiropteran faunas of the Afro-Malagasy region. Synthesis publications from this period include a general book in French on the island's bats (Goodman 2011) and a portion of a recent vertebrate atlas dedicated to their distribution (Goodman and Ramasindrazana 2013).

The second direction associated with 21st-century renewed interest in Malagasy bats focused on different ecological aspects of these organisms, including different members of the suborders

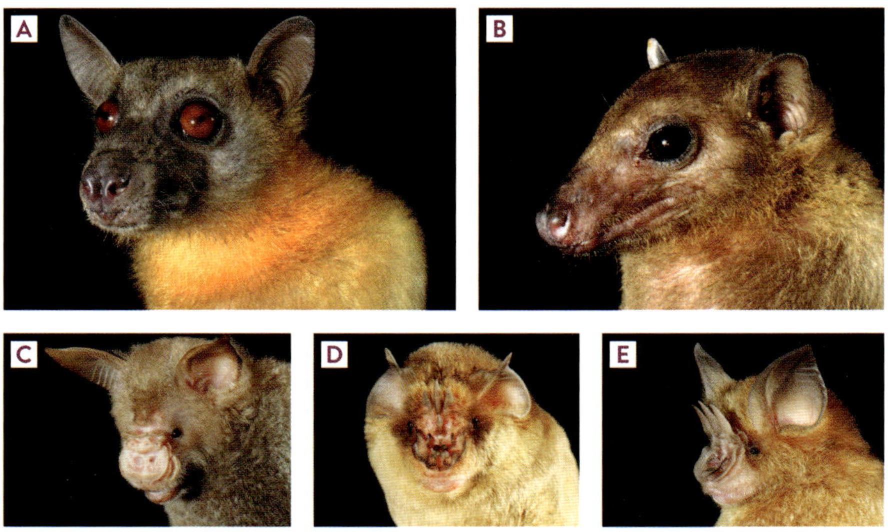

FIGURE 14.35 **Portraits of different bats of the order Pteropodiformes (Yinpterochiroptera) from Madagascar. Pteropodidae: A) *Eidolon dupreanum* at Ankarana and B) *Rousettus madagascariensis* at Ranomafana; Hipposideridae: C) *Macronycteris commersoni* at Ankarana; and Rhinonycteridae: D) *Triaenops menamena* at Ankarana and E) *Paratriaenops auritus* at Ankarana.** (PHOTOS by Merlin Tuttle/ Bat Conservation International.)

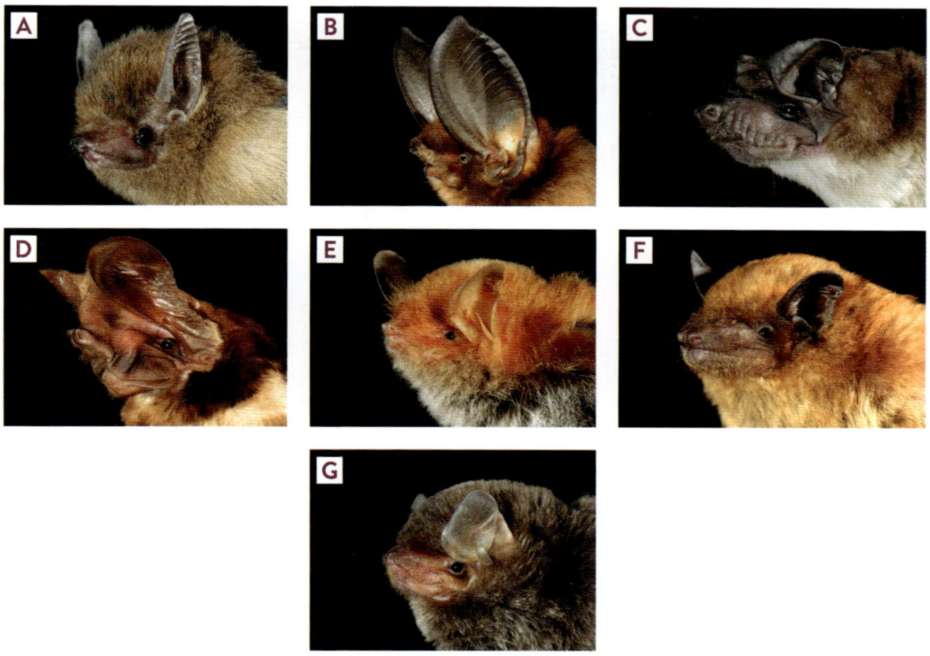

FIGURE 14.36 **Portraits of different bats of the order Vespertilioniformes (Yangochiroptera) from Madagascar. Emballonuridae: A) *Paremballonura tiavato*, described as new to science in 2006, at Ankarana; Myzopodidae: B) *Myzopoda aurita* at Kianjavato; Molossidae: C) *Mops leucostigma* at Kianjavato and D) *Otomops madagascariensis* near Sarodrano; Vespertilionidae: E) *Myotis goudoti* at Isalo and F) *Pipistrellus raceyi*, described as new to science in 2006, at Kianjavato; and Miniopteridae: G) *Miniopterus aelleni*, described as new to science in 2009, at Ankarana.** (PHOTOS by Merlin Tuttle/Bat Conservation International.)

Pteropodiformes and Vespertilioniformes. While certain of these aspects are presented in other portions of this contribution and other sections of this book, these include (presented here in a summary fashion, to provide a window into the advancements):

dietary aspects (Bollen and Van Elsacker 2002; Raheriarsena 2005; Razakarivonjy et al. 2005; Andriafidison et al. 2006a, 2007; Andrianaivoarivelo et al. 2006; Long and Racey 2007; Picot et al. 2007; Rakotoarivelo et al. 2007, 2009; Ratrimomanarivo 2007);
roosting behavior (Andriafidison et al. 2007; Kofoky et al. 2007; Raharinantenaina et al. 2008; Ralisata et al. 2010, 2015; Ramanantsalama et al. 2019);
ecomorphology (e.g., Ranivo and Goodman 2007a);
reproductive ecology, placenta development, and baculum morphology (Andriafidison et al. 2007; A. M. Carter et al. 2008; Rakotondramanana and Goodman 2017);
bioacoustics and associated evolutionary aspects (Russ et al. 2003; Kofoky et al. 2009; Ramasindrazana et al. 2011);
ecology and taxonomy of ectoparasites (Laudisoit et al. 2012; Tortosa et al. 2013; Beaucournu et al. 2015; Hastriter 2016; Wilkinson et al. 2016; F. I. Rajemison et al. 2017a, 2017b; Ramasindrazana et al. 2017b; Ramanantsalama et al. 2018; see also Dick, pp. 1099–101);
population dynamics and trends (Noroalintseheno Lalarivoniaina et al. 2018, 2019; Brook et al. 2019); and
conservation, including bats as bushmeat (Goodman et al. 2005a; Cardiff 2006; Goodman 2006; Randrianandrianina et al. 2006; R. K. B. Jenkins et al. 2007, 2011; R. K. B. Jenkins and Racey 2008; Golden 2009; Cardiff et al. 2009; Cardiff and Jenkins 2016).

The third direction of new interest in the island's bat fauna, particularly since about 2005, has been on zoonotic diseases and aspects of possible transfer to humans in the form of emerging diseases. Such research, which includes studies on viruses, bacteria, fungi, and parasites, is a growing field of investigation on Madagascar; details are presented not in this chapter but in different portions of chapter 6.

Now that the stage of resolving the taxonomy of Malagasy bats is well advanced, the needed foundation is in place to launch in a proper manner new directions of research on these organisms. For example, in recent years new questions are being addressed about Malagasy bats, concerning, for example:

insights into their evolutionary history via chromosome research (Richards et al. 2010, 2016);
fossils dating from the Late Pleistocene and the Holocene (Samonds 2007; see Samonds et al., pp. 1859–62);
aspects of tropic niches and microhabitat utilization, in part based on stable isotope research (Dammhahn and Goodman 2013; Dammhahn et al. 2015; Rakotondramanana et al. 2015);
patterns of species diversification and community assembly (Schoeman et al. 2015);
understanding roost selection of synanthropic species (Lopéz-Baucells et al. 2017);
bats' role in reducing populations of insect crop pests and disease vectors (Raharinjatovo Ny 2012; Kemp et al. 2019); and
new questions related to conservation concerns and the changing cultural dictates of the Malagasy people (Cardiff and Jenkins 2016; Fernández-Llamazares et al. 2018).

These past decades of advancing fieldwork and different forms of laboratory research on the island's bats have led to many new potential questions that we propose need to be considered. Some of these include:

the refinement of a comprehensive bioacoustics dictionary, with barcodes of recorded individuals for taxonomically difficult groups;

TABLE 14.24. **The modern chiropteran fauna of Madagascar as of 1 September 2019**

SCIENTIFIC NAME (INFERRED ORIGIN)	ENGLISH COMMON NAME	FRENCH COMMON NAME	DISTRIBUTION	IUCN STATUS
PTEROPODIFORMES				
Pteropodidae				
**Eidolon dupreanum* (Afr)	Madagascar Straw-colored Fruit Bat	Roussette pailée de Madagascar	Madagascar	VU A2ad
**Pteropus rufus* (As)	Madagascar Flying Fox	Renard volant de Madagascar	Madagascar	VU A2acd
**Rousettus madagascariensis* (As)	Madagascar Rousette	Roussette de Madagascar	Madagascar	VU A2d
Hipposideridae				
**Macronycteris commersoni* (Afr)	Commerson's Leaf-nosed Bat	Phyllorhine de Commerson	Madagascar	NT
**M. cryptovalorona* (Afr)	Madagascar Cryptic Leaf-nosed Bat	Phyllorhine cryptidue de Madagascar	Madagascar	NE
Rhinonycteridae				
**Paratriaenops auritus* (Afr)	Golden Trident Bat	Triénope doré	Madagascar	VU B1ab(iii)
**P. furculus* (Afr)	Trouessart's Trident Bat	Triénope de Trouessart	Madagascar	LC
**Triaenops menamena* (Afr)	Rufous Trident Bat	Triénope roussâtre	Madagascar	LC
VESPERTILIONIFORMES				
Emballonuridae				
**Coleura kibomalandy* (Afr)	Madagascar Sheath-tailed Bat	Emballonure de Madagascar	Madagascar	DD
**Paremballonura atrata* (Unc)	Peter's Sheath-tailed Bat	Emballonure de Peters	Madagascar	LC
**P. tiavato* (Unc)	Rock-dwelling Sheath-tailed Bat	Emballonure rupestre	Madagascar	LC
Taphozous mauritianus (Unc)	Mauritian Tomb Bat	Taphien de Maurice	Madagascar, Africa, and western Indian Ocean islands	LC
***Myzopodidae**				
**Myzopoda aurita* (Unc)	Eastern Sucker-footed Bat	Chauves-souris à ventouses de Madagascar	Madagascar	LC
**M. schliemanni* (Unc)	Schliemann's Sucker-footed Bat	Chauves-souris à ventouses de Schliemann	Madagascar	LC
Molossidae				
**Chaerephon atsinanana* (Afr)	Malagasy Eastern Free-tailed Bat	Molosse de l'est malgache	Madagascar	LC
**C. jobimena* (Afr)	Malagasy Western Free-tailed Bat	Molosse de l'ouest malgache	Madagascar	LC
C. leucogaster (Afr)	Grandidier's Lesser Free-tailed Bat	Molosse de Grandidier	Madagascar, Africa	LC

(continued overleaf)

TABLE 14.24. ***continued***

SCIENTIFIC NAME (INFERRED ORIGIN)	ENGLISH COMMON NAME	FRENCH COMMON NAME	DISTRIBUTION	IUCN STATUS
***Mops leucostigma* (Afr)	Malagasy Large White-bellied Free-tailed Bat	Grand molosse malgache	Madagascar, Comoros	LC
M. midas (Afr)	Midas Free-tailed Bat	Molosse de Midas	Madagascar, Africa	LC
**Mormopterus jugularis* (Unc)	Peters' Goblin Bat	Tadaride de Madagascar	Madagascar	LC
**Otomops madagascariensis* (Afr)	Malagasy Large-eared Free-tailed Bat	Molosse à grandes oreilles de Madagascar	Madagascar	LC
Tadarida fulminans (Afr)	Malagasy Large Free-tailed Bat	Tadaride de Thomas	Madagascar, Africa	LC
Vespertilionidae				
**Laephotis malagasyensis* (Afr)	Isalo Serotine	Sérotine de l'Isalo	Madagascar	VU B1ab(iii)+2ab(iii)
**L. matroka* (Afr)	Malagasy Serotine	Sérotine de Madagascar	Madagascar	LC
**L. robertsi* (Afr)	Robert's Serotine	Sérotine de Robert	Madagascar	DD
**Myotis goudoti* (Afr)	Malagasy Mouse-eared Bat	Murin de Madagascar	Madagascar	LC
**Neoromicia bemainty* (Afr)	Dark Madagascar Pipistrelle	Pipistrelle sombre de Madagascar	Madagascar	LC
Pipistrellus hesperidus (Afr)	Dusky Pipistrelle	Pipistrelle sombre	Madagascar, Africa	LC
**P. raceyi* (Unc)	Racey's Pipistrelle	Pipistrelle de Racey	Madagascar	DD
P. rueppellii (Afr)	Rueppell's Pipistrelle	Pipistrelle de Rueppell	Madagascar, Africa	LC
Scotophilus cf. *borbonicus* (Unc)	La Réunion House Bat	Scotophile de la Réunion	Madagascar, La Réunion	DD
**S. marovaza* (Afr)	Marovaza House Bat	Scotophile de Marovaza	Madagascar	LC
**S. robustus* (Afr)	Malagasy Large House Bat	Grande scotophile de Madagascar	Madagascar	LC
**S. tandrefana* (Afr)	Malagasy Western House Bat	Scotophile de l'ouest de Madagascar	Madagascar	DD
Miniopteridae				
***Miniopterus aelleni* (Afr)	Aellen's Long-fingered Bat	Minioptère d'Aellen	Madagascar, Comoros	LC
**M. ambohitrensis* (Afr)	Malagasy Northern Long-fingered Bat	Minioptère du Nord de Madagascar	Madagascar	LC
**M. brachytragos* (Afr)	Short-tragus Long-fingered Bat	Minioptère à tragus court	Madagascar	LC
**M. egeri* (Afr)	Eger's Long-fingered Bat	Minioptère d'Eger	Madagascar	LC
**M. gleni* (Afr)	Glen's Long-fingered Bat	Minioptère de Glen	Madagascar	LC
**M. griffithsi* (Afr)	Griffiths' Long-fingered Bat	Minioptère de Griffiths	Madagascar	DD
***M. griveaudi* (Afr)	Griveaud's Long-fingered Bat	Minioptère de Griveaud	Madagascar, Comoros	DD

SCIENTIFIC NAME (INFERRED ORIGIN)	ENGLISH COMMON NAME	FRENCH COMMON NAME	DISTRIBUTION	IUCN STATUS
**M. mahafaliensis* (Afr)	Mahafaly Long-fingered Bat	Minioptère Mahafaly	Madagascar	LC
**M. majori* (Afr)	Major's Long-fingered Bat	Minioptère de Major	Madagascar	LC
**M. manavi* (Afr)	Manavi Long-fingered Bat	Minioptère manavi	Madagascar	LC
**M. petersoni* (Afr)	Peterson's Long-fingered Bat	Minioptère de Peterson	Madagascar	DD
**M. sororculus* (Afr)	Small Sister Long-fingered Bat	Minioptère petite sœur	Madagascar	LC

Notes: Scientific names preceded by a single asterisk (*) are species and in one case a family endemic to Madagascar; those preceded by a double asterisk (**) are endemic to Madagascar and Comoros. On the basis of phylogenetic analyses, the geographic origins of most taxa can be inferred: Afr, Africa; As, Asia; Unc, uncertain; references associated with these inferences are mentioned in the family summaries under the Systematics subheadings. It should be noted that in several cases the question of the origin of a given species should be considered provisional, as published phylogenies do not necessarily have complete genera and species coverage from different geographical areas of the Old World. IUCN Red List status abbreviations: DD, Data Deficient; LC, Least Concern; NE, Not Evaluated; NT, Near Threatened; VU, Vulnerable. Of the 46 species recognized here, 36 (78%) are endemic to Madagascar and 39 (85%) are endemic to Madagascar and Comoros. The occurrence of *Scotophilus* cf. *borbonicus* on Madagascar is uncertain (see main text), and this taxon is included in the 46 species total. Information on the broad geographical distribution for each species are presented. IUCN Red List category from IUCN (2020).

the impact of habitat fragmentation on forest-dependent and forest-nondependent species;
the role of bat ectoparasites in the transmission of zoonotic diseases;
the impacts of ambient night illumination, pesticides, and heavy metal pollution in urban areas;
the effects of climatic change on the distribution, ecology, and reproduction of endemic species;
the quest to obtain more precise details on annual cycles of fruit and insect phenology overlaid on food types consumed by bats;
studies on ecophysiology, particularly of cave-dwelling species; and more details on the ecosystem services bats provide, including agricultural pest control, seed dispersal, tree regeneration, and pollination of forest plants and particularly fruits of economic importance.

SUBORDER PTEROPODIFORMES (YINPTEROCHIROPTERA)

Family Pteropodidae, Fruit Bats

Systematics

Three monospecific genera of the family Pteropodidae are known from Madagascar (Table 14.24), as compared to southern Africa, with 21 species in 11 genera (Monadjem et al. 2020a). From the perspective of the systematics of Malagasy pteropodids, no changes have taken place in the recent past decades, with the exception of the higher classification of the genus *Eidolon*, which is now placed in its own subfamily, Eidolinae (Almeida et al. 2016).

Recent molecular studies have provided insight into the colonization history of the three endemic species of Malagasy pteropodids. *Eidolon dupreanum* (Figure 14.35a) was derived from the African mainland lineage of *E. helvum*, and despite both species showing considerable panmixia across their respective geographic distributions, divergence occurred after colonization of Madagascar, estimated to have taken place in the mid- to late Miocene (Shi et al. 2014). Hence, in this genus, the geographic distance between the eastern African mainland and neighboring offshore islands to Madagascar was apparently sufficient to prevent subsequent exchanges between these two areas. The Malagasy endemic *Pteropus rufus* is part of the *P. vampyrus* group, with constituent species occurring in southeastern Asia and across islands in the Indian Ocean to Madagascar and the Comoro archipelago; these different taxa are poorly differentiated based on genetic data, and there may have been multiple dispersal-colonization events from Asia to Indian Ocean islands (J. O'Brien et al. 2009; Almeida et al. 2014). The origin of *Rousettus madagascariensis* (Figure 14.35b), as to whether it derived from Africa (*R. aegyptiacus*) or Asia (*R. leschenaultii*), was previously unresolved (Goodman et al. 2010a), but based on a recent multi-locus study, its colonization of the island appears to have been of Asiatic origin (Stribna et al. 2019). Hence, each of the three genera of Malagasy pteropodids represents an independent colonization event of the island, *E. dupreanum* from Africa, and the other two species, *P. rufus* and *R. madagascariensis*, from Asia.

General Ecology

This aspect of the Pteropodidae is treated in detail in another contribution (see Andrianaivoarivelo et al., pp. 1911–16). Aside from human consumption of fruit bats, other forms of predation have been documented in recent years. Remains of a *P. rufus* were found

at Berenty with signs that the animal had been dispatched by a *Polyboroides radiatus* (Madagascar Harrier-hawk), which presumably is not very frequent (Goodman and Pidgeon 1992). In contrast, *Tyto alba* (Barn Owl) feeds regularly on *R. madagascariensis* (Goodman and Griffiths 2006).

Vocalizations

Although vision and olfaction are assumed to be the dominant sensory mechanisms for orientation and foraging in Pteropodidae, fruit bats of the genus *Rousettus* use tongue clicks to navigate the caves where they roost (Holland et al. 2004; Yovel et al. 2010). In fact, click-based echolocation in bats is as effective as the biosonar used by whales and dolphins (Yovel et al. 2011a); *R. aegyptiacus* performed equally well in obstacle negotiation tests as laryngeal echolocators (Yovel et al. 2011b). *Rousettus madagascariensis* produces echolocation clicks in pairs that are about 30 milliseconds (ms) apart, with paired clicks at about 115 ms intervals (Russ et al. 2003). It remains to be tested whether the click-echolocation capacity of *R. madagascariensis* is as sophisticated as that of *R. aegyptiacus*. *Eidolon dupreanum* prefers to roost in caves with high and wide entrances, within sight of the entrance. There is evidence that it uses different calls for social communication, and echo clicks in a sensory context, perhaps as a form of incipient echolocation to navigate dark caves (Schoeman and Goodman 2012).

Roosting Habitats

The three Malagasy members of this family have different roosting habitats. *Pteropus rufus* makes its day-roost sites in introduced and native trees, both within and outside closed-canopy forest (Goodman 2011; Goodman and Ramasindrazana 2013). *Eidolon dupreanum* is found mainly in caves, crevices, and sometimes in dense foliage of *Raphia* palm trees (Arecaceae). The third Malagasy member of this family, *R. madagascariensis*, is found mainly in caves and rock overhangs.

Family Hipposideridae, Leaf-nosed Bats

Systematics

In the family Hipposideridae, two species in a single genus are now recognized from Madagascar (Table 14.24), as compared to southern Africa, with six species placed in three genera (Monadjem et al. 2020a). A recent study by Foley et al. (2015) showed that Hipposideridae, as previously classified, was paraphyletic and Malagasy species in the genera *Paratriaenops* and *Triaenops* belonged to a separate family, which was named the Rhinonycteridae (see next family account). Further, based on this same study and then a more detailed analysis (Foley et al. 2017), the genus *Hipposideros* is paraphyletic, and members of the *H. commersoni* group occurring on Madagascar and Africa have been placed in the resurrected genus *Macronycteris*. A cryptic species of the *commersoni* group has recently been named from southwestern Madagascar, *M. cryptovalorona*, which occurs in sympatry with *M. commersoni* at a few localities (Goodman et al. 2016a; Rehrer et al. 2018). Contrary to expectations, the two species of *Macronycteris* occurring on the island do not form a monophyletic species pair, and there is evidence of two separate colonizations of this genus (Rakotoarivelo et al. 2015; Foley et al. 2017).

Within *M. commersoni* (Figure 14.35c), there is considerable genetic structure, in part associated with bioclimatic zones, and individuals from dry forests in the north form a monophyletic clade, and a second, more widespread and nonoverlapping (western) clade occurs in other portions of this vegetation type, including the southwest (Rakotoarivelo et al. 2015, 2019). This pattern may be best explained by Pleistocene climatic fluctuations, with the northern and western areas acting as refugia during cooler and drier periods in recent geological history. These general patterns show parallels across western Madagascar in aspects of external and craniodental morphology and bioacoustic variation (Ranivo and Goodman 2007b; Ramasindrazana et al. 2015).

General Ecology

Several studies have been conducted on the dietary regime of Malagasy *Macronycteris*. At Bemaraha, *M. commersoni* specializes on relatively large members of Coleoptera (Carabidae and Scarabaeidae) and secondarily Hemiptera (Rakotoarivelo et al. 2007). In other dietary studies of this species, coleopterans were the most common prey taken, but the taxonomic range of prey items at the family level was often more diversified than shown in the Rakotoarivelo et al. (2007) study, whether based on stomach contents (Razakarivony et al. 2005) or fecal pellets (Ramasindrazana et al. 2012; Rakotondramanana et al. 2015; Rabarison 2016). Even given the considerable level of sexual size dimorphism in *M. commersoni*, with males being larger than females (Ranivo and Goodman 2007b), at the level of identified prey families, few differences were found in insects taken by the different sexes (Ralisata 2005; Rakotondramanana et al. 2015). At Tsimanampesotse, with a notably long dry period of 9–10 months, *Macronycteris* species showed notable seasonal dietary variation based on percentage by volume of prey remains identified from feces, with the wet period being dominated by Coleoptera (93%), Homoptera (4%), and Hymenoptera (3%), as compared to the dry season, with Coleoptera (72%), Dictyoptera (25%), Homoptera (2%), and Hymenoptera (1%) (Ramasindrazana et al. 2012).

Members of the genus *Macronycteris* have been found in the food remains of different bird and mammal predators. These include nocturnal birds of prey, specifically *Asio madagascariensis* (Madagascar Long-eared Owl) (Goodman et al. 1993b; see Rene de Roland and Thorstrom, pp. 1668–79), and a nocturnal carnivoran of the family Eupleridae, *Galidictis fasciata grandidieri* (Broad-striped Vontsira) (Andriatsimietry et al. 2009; see Farris and Goodman, pp. 1993–96).

Some details are available on the home ranges of *M. commersoni* in the littoral forest near Tampolo (lowland central east) based on the movements of radio-collared individuals. Razafimanahaka et al. (2016) had more than 50 fixes for nine of the 22 bats they fitted with radio collars, and these nine individuals had a calculated mean home range (minimum convex polygon) across the study periods of 31.8 ha for males and 41.7 ha for females. Core areas, defined as the zone in which 85% of the fixes were registered, encompassed 15.2 ha for males and 32.3 ha for females. Males showed little home-range overlap, while this was not necessarily the case for certain females, which demonstrated broad overlap in home-range core area.

Individuals of *Macronycteris* species are known to increase their body mass substantially before the start of the austral winter via

deposition of body fat, before they "disappear" from different sites (Goodman 2006; Rakotoarivelo et al. 2007). At least in the dry deciduous forests of the central west, *M. commersoni*, which presumably uses vegetation or hollow trees for day-roost sites, is apparently seasonally present. For example, in the Kirindy Forest CNFEREF, during systematic trapping at the end of the dry season (between 5 September and 9 October 2010), a single adult *M. commersoni* was netted, while during the start of the wet season (between 14 November and 17 December 2010), 42 adult *M. commersoni* were captured (Rakotondramanana and Goodman 2011). Interpretation of these results indicates that at the start of the wet season, a period of higher insect abundance, there was an influx into the area of *M. commersoni* individuals. This extrapolation is supported by observed dispersal movements of numerous animals of this species during the same period not too far from the Kirindy Forest CNFEREF (Ranivo and Goodman 2007b). Parallel results from an even more extreme and seasonally dry area of the southwest, at Tsimanampesotse, found the same general pattern, with the vast majority of netted individuals of *Macronycteris* species captured during the rainy season, but in this case most were juveniles (Rehrer et al. 2019).

Research at Tsimanampesotse on the ecophysiology of members of this genus in caves with high ambient temperatures found that individual bats showed extreme differences in torpor patterns, including short bursts (lasting on average 20 minutes) at remarkably low metabolic rates, even though the skin temperature was high, followed by metabolic rate peaks (Rehrer et al. 2018; see Dausmann et al., pp. 1798–805). More remarkable is that during a dry-season period of 10 weeks, no individual was captured leaving the cave study site, although roosting individuals were known to be in the cave. Hence, members of this genus are physiologically capable of entering torpor at high ambient temperatures and rapidly alternating in short bursts between torpid and normothermic metabolic rates. These results call into question previous axioms on aspects of the metabolism in heterothermic mammals. Further, these observations provide a clear explanation as to the manner certain populations "disappear"—rather than undergoing some form of migration, at certain cave day-roost sites, particularly in areas with extreme dry weather conditions, they remain in the roost sites for extended periods of more than two months.

Another aspect is that in portions of western and southwestern Madagascar, the period when members of this genus are depositing body fat coincides with local food shortages for human populations, and the bats are subject to nonsustainable exploitation for bushmeat (Racey et al. 2010). Further, in different portions of the island, including the southwest and the northwest (Fernández-Llamazares et al. 2018; S. M. Goodman, unpublished data), classical notions of certain caves being sacred, and thus excluded from the exploitation of bats, have been the subject of cultural relaxation, and the caves no longer serve as refuges for *Macronycteris* against different local human pressures.

Vocalizations

Hipposideridae emit high duty-cycle, narrowband, and long constant-frequency echolocation calls (HD-CF) that terminate with brief frequency-modulated (FM) elements. The terminal FM sweep may be more broadband when the bat is close to an object, for example insect prey (Russ et al. 2003). The calls consist of a maximum of three harmonics, with most of the energy in the fundamental or second harmonic (Kofoky et al. 2009). The largest insectivorous bat on Madagascar, *M. commersoni*, emits calls with peak frequency (PF) at ~66.6 kHz and long duration of ~20 ms, yet there is evidence of sexual and geographic variation in frequency of calls (Ramasindrazana et al. 2015). The PF of the larger male *M. commersoni* is at 68.6 kHz, while that of the smaller female is at about 72.9 kHz. Females from the far north of Madagascar (Ankarana) significantly deviate from the allometric relationship between PF and body size by emitting echolocation calls lower than predicted by their size. To our knowledge, the echolocation calls of *M. cryptovalorona* have not been recorded.

Roosting Habitats

The genus *Macronycteris* generally uses caves and rock crevices as day-roosting sites, particularly in limestone karstic areas (Goodman 2011), mostly found on the western side of the island. However, in the eastern portion of the island, *Macronycteris* is found during the day hanging singly on tree branches in areas with closed canopy (Goodman et al. 2014c; Razafimanahaka et al. 2016). Such roosting behavior is also known from closed-canopy dry deciduous forest areas in immediate vicinity to caves (S. M. Goodman, unpublished data). Two Malagasy species are recognized within this genus, and at a few localities in the central west and southwest both occur in the same day-roost sites, but few details are available.

Family Rhinonycteridae, Trident Bats

Systematics

The recently recognized family Rhinonycteridae, which comprises genera formerly placed in the Hipposideridae (Foley et al. 2015), includes three species in two different genera on Madagascar, as compared to two species in two genera in southern Africa (Monadjem et al. 2020a). The three species on Madagascar, all endemic to the island, were formerly placed in the genus *Triaenops* (Peterson et al. 1995). Goodman and Ranivo (2009) showed that the type specimen of *T. rufus* (from the Latin, meaning "reddish") was not collected on Madagascar but in continental Africa, which resulted in the Malagasy species being renamed *T. menamena* (from the Malagasy for "reddish"; Figure 14.35d).

Research by Benda and Vallo (2009) on different forms placed in the genus *Triaenops* across their geographic distribution uncovered that two Malagasy species, *T. auritus* and *T. furculus*, formed a separate group that was phylogenetically distant from other *Triaenops*, and for these two species, they created the genus *Paratriaenops*. Using phylogenetic analyses of mitochondrial DNA sequence data for Malagasy and eastern African species of *Triaenops* and *Paratriaenops* overlaid on different genetic methods, A. L. Russell et al. (2007, 2008a) showed support for two independent and unidirectional dispersal events from Africa to Madagascar. The first colonization led to *T. menamena*, and the second to the two species making up the genus *Paratriaenops*.

General Ecology

Different studies conducted on the dietary habits of Malagasy insect-eating bats have shown some divergent results in this family.

On the basis of fecal remains of *Triaenops menamena* and *Paratriaenops furculus* collected in the central-western deciduous forest areas (Bemaraha), Rakotoarivelo et al. (2007) found for both species decreasing mean percentage volume for the following insect orders: Lepidoptera (greater or close to 50%), Hemiptera, Dictyoptera, and Diptera. These two bat species showed broad dietary overlap but some differences in microhabitat use. In another study at the same site, based on food remains identified from stomach contents, Razakarivony et al. (2005) did not find a dominance of Lepidoptera in the diet of *T. menamena*. Slightly farther south in the same habitat, at a site only with *T. menamena*, Rakotondramanana et al. (2015), based on proportional volume in scat remains, found that it feeds predominantly on Lepidoptera and secondarily on different insect orders. Further, although sample size for males was reduced, there was some evidence of sexual differences in the types of prey consumed. Finally, in the extreme southwest, in a zone with a notably long dry season, the diets of these two species averaged across the year were dominated by Lepidoptera (+65%) and Coleoptera (+27.0%), were notably similar at the level of family, and showed broad niche overlap (Ramasindrazana et al. 2012). In contrast, when the data are segregated by the dry and wet seasons, there was a reduced level of dietary overlap between the two species. Another study, at Saint Augustin in the southwest, also found important levels of dietary overlap between the two species (Bambini et al. 2011).

Remains of *P. furculus* have been identified in *Macheiramphus alcinus* (Bat Hawk) pellets (Goodman et al. 2016b; Razakaratrimo et al. 2019). Further, boid snakes have been observed predating on *T. menamena* (Cardiff and Jenkins 2016).

Some details are available on the home ranges of *P. furculus* in the Saint Augustin area from research employing radio collars. Manjaoazy (2018) followed six different individuals, and the mean home range (minimum convex polygon) of their displacements was 47.9 ha (range 24.5–107.9 ha).

The activity patterns of *P. furculus* and *T. menamena* at a cave roost site with an estimated 10,058 and 41,021 individuals (respectively) were monitored by researchers using mist nets and observing their direction of capture. For both species there was large-scale exit after dusk, a marked increase in returning bats after 2100 h, augmentation of activity from 0000 h to 1000 h, and decreasing movements before dawn (Olsson et al. 2006). There were also sexual differences in the activity patterns of both species, with males on average returning before females.

Vocalizations

Bats of the family Rhinonycteridae emit high duty-cycle, narrowband, and relatively short constant-frequency echolocation calls (HD-CF) that terminate with brief frequency-modulated (FM) elements (Russ et al. 2003). The calls consist of a maximum of three harmonics, with most of the energy in the second harmonic (Kofoky et al. 2009). Male *Paratriaenops auritus* (Figure 14.35e) and *P. furculus* exhibit reversed sexual dimorphism, in which the smaller males emit higher PF calls (107.8 and 113.1 kHz, respectively) than the larger females (95.6 and 98.2 kHz, respectively) (Ramasindrazana et al. 2013). By contrast, *Triaenops menamena* shows typical patterns of sexual size dimorphism, with the larger males emitting lower PF calls (82.3 kHz) than the smaller females (93.5 kHz). When segregated by sex, there was a strong allometric relationship between body size and the PF in these three species, as well as two African hipposiderids (*T. afer* and *Cloeotis percivali*), but *P. auritus* males and both sexes of *P. furculus* deviate from this allometric relationship (Ramasindrazana et al. 2013). Echolocation calls of *P. auritus*, *P. furculus*, and *T. menamena* were respectively 61.4%, 91.5%, and 97.1% correctly classified by multiple discriminant function analysis (Kofoky et al. 2009); whereas Bambini et al. (2011) identified Rhinonycteridae with PF >97 kHz as *P. furculus*, and those with PF ≤97 kHz as *T. menamena*.

Roosting Habitats

The three species within this family are cave roosting. While *Triaenops menamena* is present throughout the country, *Paratriaenops auritus* and *P. furculus* have more restricted distributions. *Paratriaenops auritus* is present in the northern and northwestern portions of Madagascar and roosts sympatrically in caves with *T. menamena*. *Paratriaenops furculus* replaces *P. auritus* from the northwest to the extreme south and generally shares the same roosts with *T. menamena*. This lattermost species also occurs in areas where there is no exposed sedimentary rock (i.e., with no caves), and it presumably roosts in tree hollows.

SUBORDER VESPERTILIONIFORMES (YANGOCHIROPTERA)

Family Emballonuridae, Sheath-tailed Bats

Systematics

On Madagascar in this family, four species in three genera are recognized (Table 14.24), as compared to southern Africa, with seven species in three genera (Monadjem et al. 2020a). Goodman et al. (2006d), based on molecular and morphological analyses, named a species new to science, *Emballonura tiavato*, found in the dry western portion of the island. Subsequent studies found the genus *Emballonura* to be paraphyletic, and the two Malagasy taxa were placed in a separate genus, *Paremballonura* (Goodman et al. 2012a; Ruedi et al. 2012).

The genus *Coleura* was first discovered on Madagascar in 2004 and tentatively identified as the Afro-Arabian species *C. afra* (Goodman et al. 2008a). However, subsequent bioacoustic, morphological, and molecular research found the Malagasy population distinct from the Afro-Arabian form, and it was described as a species new to science, *C. kibomalandy* (Goodman et al. 2012a). As the genus *Paremballonura*, with two sister species, is endemic to Madagascar, and the other two genera (*Coleura* and *Taphozous*) are phylogenetically distinct from one another (Ruedi et al. 2012; Shi and Rabosky 2015), the extant members of this family occurring on the island represent three separate colonization events.

General Ecology

Little information is available on the diet of species of this family occurring on Madagascar. The remains from the stomach of one *Paremballonura tiavato* captured at Loky Manambato contained Lepidoptera (Razakarivony et al. 2005). In contrast, fecal remains from five individuals of *P. atrata* netted near Kianjavato included,

by percentage of volume: Diptera (40.9%), Hymenoptera (31.3%), Coleoptera (26.7%), and Hemiptera (12.0%) (Rasoanoro et al. 2015). Detailed analyses were completed on the diet of *Taphozous mauritianus* by Razafimalala (2017) in the lowland west, and the principal orders consumed based on percentage by volume were: Hymenoptera (45%), Lepidoptera (30%), and, to a much lesser extent, Coleoptera, Homoptera, Diptera, Orthoptera, and Odonata. In this same study no significant difference was found in the diets of adult males and females, but sexually immature individuals disproportionately consumed more Lepidoptera than adults.

There are some documented cases of Malagasy Emballonuridae being the subject of raptor predation. *Taphozous mauritianus* was found in pellet remains of *Tyto alba* in the southwest (Goodman et al. 1993c). Remains of both *T. mauritianus* and *C. kibomalandy* have been identified from *Macheiramphus alcinus* food remains in the central west (Goodman et al. 2016b; Razakaratrimo et al. 2019). In the Ankarana, *T. alba* has been documented to feed on *C. kibomalandy* (Goodman et al. 2008a)

Vocalizations

Bats of the family Emballonuridae emit low duty-cycle, short constant-frequency or quasi-constant echolocation calls (LD-CF or LD-QCF) that terminate with frequency-modulated (FM) elements (Russ et al. 2003). The calls comprise up to five harmonics with most of the energy in the fundamental or second harmonic (Kofoky et al. 2009). The PFs of *P. tiavato* and *P. atrata* (54.2 and 52.9 kHz, respectively) show some overlap, and a discriminant function analysis of calls of these two species correctly assigned 80.0% and 68.4%, respectively, of cases (Kofoky et al. 2009). The distress calls of *P. atrata* exhibit broad FM components, with PF ~55 kHz, and short interpulse duration (Russ et al. 2004). The PF, bandwidth, and duration of calls of *C. kibomalandy* (33.8 kHz, 2.9 kHz, and 4.3 ms, respectively) appear to be markedly lower, broader, and longer, respectively, than those of *C. seychellensis* (39.2 kHz, 0.5 kHz, and 4.4 ms) in the eastern Seychelles, but there was no significant differences in echolocation call parameters between *C. kibomalandy* and *C. afra* from Kenya (33.4 kHz, 6.2 kHz, and 4.5 ms, respectively) (Goodman et al. 2012a). No published information on echolocation calls of *T. mauritianus* on Madagascar has been presented, but in southern and central Africa this species produces calls with a low PF (25.9 kHz), narrow bandwidth (2.8 kHz), and intermediate duration (7.4 ms) (Monadjem et al. 2020a).

Roosting Habitats

The family Emballonuridae comprises four species with different roosting habits. *Coleura kibomalandy* roosts in deep caves (Goodman 2011). The genus *Paremballonura* uses caves and shallow rock shelters as roosting sites. *Paremballonura tiavato* (Figure 14.36a) in the western portion of the island generally roosts in caves, whereas *P. atrata* in the eastern areas roosts in rock shelters, mine shafts, holes in tree trunks, and largely abandoned buildings. *Taphozous mauritianus* on Madagascar uses vertical tree trunks for roosting sites. In Maintirano, this species was found head down on tops of coconut trees (*Cocos nucifera*, Arecaceae) (Rakotondramanana et al. 2017), and in Tsimembo-Manambolomaty complex, it was found roosting on *Tamarindus indica* (Fabaceae) trunks (Ravelomanantsoa et al. 2019).

[Family Nycteridae, Slit-faced Bats

Systematics

Only a single species of this family has been reported from Madagascar, as compared to nine currently recognized species from southern Africa (Monadjem et al. 2020a). The form reported from Madagascar, *Nycteris madagascariensis*, was described by G. Grandidier (1937) based on two specimens collected in "la vallée du Rodo," which has been interpreted previously as the Irodo River valley, presumably in or close to the Analamerana Special Reserve. *Nycteris* is the only genus of bat reported from Madagascar that has not been recaptured on the island since its original description.

In the context of a recent molecular study of African members of this genus, a short mitochondrial sequence was obtained from the holotype of *N. madagascariensis* (Demos et al. 2019, 2021), and this sample was found to be nested within African mainland populations of *N. macrotis*. Given that members of this genus are poor long-distance flyers, rarely colonizing offshore islands near the African mainland, as well as the results of the molecular analysis, there is firm doubt that the two specimens named *N. madagascariensis* were obtained on Madagascar. Until further evidence of this genus and family on the island is available, it should not be considered as occurring on the island.]

Family Myzopodidae, Sucker-footed Bats

Systematics

The Myzopodidae, which is represented by a single genus, *Myzopoda*, is endemic to the island. Fossils referred to this family have been identified from the late Eocene and early Oligocene of Egypt (Gunnell et al. 2014), and tentatively from the early Pleistocene of Tanzania (Butler 1978; see Ralisata et al., pp. 1917–22). The factors that led to the extinction of this family on the African continent are unknown, as is its colonization history from the mainland to Madagascar. However, given that the two extant species of *Myzopoda* form a monophyletic group, it can be assumed that they have a common ancestor and Madagascar was colonized once.

Contrary to the statement of Dorst (1947), that this genus is rare on Madagascar, fieldwork on the island over the past few decades has found *M. aurita* (Figure 14.36b) to be relatively common in lowland wetland areas and degraded forest, particularly those dominated by a tree in the genus *Ravenala* (Strelitziaceae) (see Ralisata et al., pp. 1917–22). Further, a western population was discovered and based on morphology and molecular genetics named as a new species, *M. schliemanni* (Goodman et al. 2007b; A. L. Russell et al. 2008b). At certain localities, particularly in *Bismarckia* (Arecaceae) palm grasslands near marsh areas, *M. schliemanni* can be very common (Ravelojaona 2017; A. F. Kofoky and S. M. Goodman, unpublished data).

General Ecology

This aspect is treated in detail in another contribution (see Ralisata et al., pp. 1917–22). In the central west, *M. schliemanni* has been identified from prey remains of *Macheiramphus alcinus* (Bat Hawk) (Goodman et al. 2016b; Razakaratrimo et al. 2019).

Vocalizations

The echolocation calls of *M. aurita* are distinct and consist of very shallow, almost constant-frequency (CF) sweeps, often broken up into a series of components, that terminate with frequency-modulated (FM) elements (Gopfert and Wasserthal 1995; Russ et al. 2003). The low duty-cycle echolocation calls have long duration (23 ms), with the PF at about 42 kHz (Russ et al. 2003). The first harmonic is dominant, but the fundamental harmonic can occasionally be seen at around 21 kHz. The distress call consists of a series of "trills" (Gopfert and Wasserthal 1995). The echolocation calls of *M. schliemanni* exhibit complex structures similar to those of *M. aurita*, with PF at about 45.6 kHz (A. F. Kofoky and S. M. Goodman, unpublished data).

Roosting Habitats

Myzopoda aurita utilizes pads on the wrists and ankles to stay head up on uncurled *Ravenala* leaves that are used as day-roost sites (Ralisata et al. 2010), whereas *M. schliemanni* uses *Bismarckia nobilis* leaves (A. F. Kofoky, unpublished data). Further information on the roosting habits of the two species of *Myzopoda* is presented elsewhere herein (see Ralisata et al., pp. 1917–22).

Family Molossidae, Free-tailed Bats

Systematics

This family is represented on Madagascar by eight species placed in five genera (Table 14.24), as compared to southern Africa with 20 species in seven genera (Monadjem et al. 2020a). All of the Malagasy species have been included in phylogenetic studies, and a few have been the subjects of detailed phylogeographic analyses. Two species endemic to Madagascar have been described in recent years, *Chaerephon jobimena* and *C. atsinanana* (Goodman and Cardiff 2004; Goodman et al. 2010b).

Recent phylogenetic research on Afro-Malagasy members of the family (Lamb et al. 2011), as well as across the Old and New World geographic range of this family (Ammerman et al. 2012), indicate cases of paraphyly, particularly in the genera *Chaerephon*, *Mops*, and *Tadarida*. The results indicate that *C. jobimena* is separated from other members of this genus and is closely related to *T. aegyptiaca*, and the generic placement of this species pair is unresolved but probably best fits in the latter genus. Further, on the basis of mitochondrial markers, the forms *C. leucogaster* and *C. atsinanana* are poorly differentiated, despite distinct morphological characters (Ratrimomanarivo et al. 2009b; Goodman et al. 2010b).

The three western Indian Ocean species of *Mormopterus*, with one each on the islands of Madagascar, La Réunion, and Mauritius, form a species group (Goodman et al. 2008b). On the basis of different morphological and molecular data, these different group members are separate from a range of New World forms placed in this genus, as well as several species from the Australian region that are now in different subgenera (Lamb et al. 2011; Reardon et al. 2014). These results and the fact that *jugularis* was the first species placed in the genus *Mormopterus*, indicate the genus name is best applied to the western Indian Ocean members of the species group, and that these animals are endemic to the Malagasy Region, rather than those in the Australian region or the New World.

On the basis of different published phylogenies of Afro-Malagasy molossids, it can be extrapolated that this family has colonized Madagascar on seven occasions (Lamb et al. 2011; Ammerman et al. 2012)—the genera *Mops*, *Chaerephon*, and *Tadarida*, as currently defined, represent five different colonization events (*M. midas*, *M. leucostigma*, *C. leucogaster*/*atsinanana*, *C. jobimena*, and *T. fulminans*), and the monospecific genera *Mormopterus* and *Otomops* had separate arrivals.

As mentioned earlier, different species of Malagasy molossids have been the subject of phylogeographic studies using mitochondrial markers, and show different patterns of genetic variation. The first pattern is of species *M. leucostigma* (Figure 14.36c), *Mormopterus jugularis*, and *O. madagascariensis* (Figure 14.36d), all with broad distributions on Madagascar and in some cases neighboring islands and demonstrating genetic panmixia or little genetic variation related to geography (Lamb et al. 2008; Ratrimomanarivo et al. 2008, 2009a). The second pattern, represented by *Mops midas*, shows little differentiation between South African and Malagasy populations, and this can be explained by its recent colonization of Madagascar and/or continued movements across the Mozambique Channel (Ratrimomanarivo et al. 2007). A third pattern, found in *C. atsinanana*, shows considerable geographic genetic structure along latitudinal and altitudinal gradients in eastern Madagascar, which has been proposed as the result of refuge-retreat areas during Pleistocene climatic vicissitudes that led to partial differentiation (Lamb et al. 2012). The last pattern is found in *C. leucogaster*—based on sampling from Madagascar, the Comoros (Mayotte or Maoré), and the Tanzanian offshore island of Pemba, and using the cytochrome b marker, these populations show little differentiation. In contrast, for a D-loop marker, the Pemba and Mayotte populations were differentiated from Madagascar and some structure was found in Malagasy populations (Ratrimomanarivo et al. 2009b); the addition of a nuclear marker (Rag2) provided no further differentiation within the species complex of *C. pumilus*/*atsinanana*/*leucogaster*, with *C. pumilus* occurring in Africa (Naidoo et al. 2016). These different patterns in Afro-Malagasy molossids were compared for different estimators of molecular diversity against variables associated with wing loading and body size; F_{ST} values were negatively correlated with wing loading, an estimation of their dispersal ability (P. J. Taylor et al. 2012).

General Ecology

Details are available on the prey taken by Malagasy Molossidae from different areas. In the east, the diet of *C. atsinanana* based on percentage by volume is largely dominated by Coleoptera (44.0%), Lepidoptera (25.4%), Homoptera (19.0%), and other insect orders (Rasoanoro et al. 2015). In another study in the general Antananarivo and Moramanga areas, Raharinjataovo Ny (2012) found the principal orders of insects consumed include Coleoptera, Hemiptera, Diptera, and Lepidoptera. On the basis of a few *Mops leucostigma* fecal samples from the central eastern lowlands, using percentage by volume, Rabarison (2016) found that it feeds predominantly on Coleoptera (67.0%) and then, in descending order of importance, Hemiptera, Hymenoptera, Lepidoptera, Diptera, Ephemeroptera, and Trichoptera. For this same species, but at a site near Moramanga and in close proximity to the forest, Raharinjatovo Ny (2012) found that coleopterans of the families Scarabaeidae, Coccinelidae,

Dermestidae, Hydrophilidae, and Chrysomelidae were dominant prey, followed by Hemiptera and Diptera (Culicidae, Tipulidae). Data on the diet of *Mormopterus jugularis* at sites around Antananarivo and Moramanga indicate that Coleoptera makes up more than 50% of the diet, followed by Diptera, Lepidoptera, and Hemiptera (Raharinjatovo Ny 2012). Tsibara (2011), using a considerable number of fecal samples of *Otomops madagascariensis* collected in the west at Bemaraha and near Saint Augustin, and based on percentage by volume, found that this species feeds almost equally on Lepidoptera (43.5%) and Coleoptera (38.9%), followed in decreasing importance by Diptera, Hemiptera, Heteroptera, and Ephemeroptera. This same study found notable seasonal differences in the prey taken by *Otomops* at the two sites, particularly at Saint Augustin, which is characterized by a longer dry season, but no measurable difference in the diets of males and females.

A wide assortment of molossid bats are known to be preyed upon by *Tyto alba* and *Macheiramphus alcinus*, including *C. leucogaster*, *Mops leucostigma*, *M. midas*, *Mormopterus jugularis*, and *O. madagascariensis* (Goodman and Griffiths 2009; Goodman et al. 1993b, 1993c, 2016b; Rasoma and Goodman 2007; Razakaratrimo et al. 2019). Seasonal differences were found in the prey taken by *Macheiramphus alcinus* at a site in the central west, with *C. leucogaster* being disproportionately more common during the wet season as compared to the dry season (Razakaratrimo et al. 2019). Members of this family make up by number more than 10% of the prey taken by this raptor.

Vocalizations

Bats of the family Molossidae emit low duty-cycle, constant-frequency (LD-CF) or quasi-constant (LD-QCF) echolocation calls. Most species use calls with low frequencies, and at least one species, *O. madagascariensis*, echolocates within the hearing range of humans (<20 kHz). To date, echolocation calls of only four molossid species have been recorded on Madagascar (Russ et al. 2003; Manjoazy 2018). Two species, *C. leucogaster* and *Mops leucostigma*, exhibit overlap in PF (32.0 and 32.8 kHz, respectively), but their calls differ in bandwidth (31.2 vs. 20.7 kHz) and duration (9.0 vs. 5.9 ms) (Manjoazy 2018; also see Russ et al. 2003). The echolocation calls of *Mormopterus jugularis* are often variable: in open habitats the LD-QCF calls have a PF of ~24 kHz, whereas in closed habitats calls show a relatively steep FM sweep (Russ et al. 2003). *Otomops madagascariensis* produces echolocation calls with a low PF (15.0–16.4 kHz), intermediate bandwidth (31.4 kHz), and intermediate duration (8.7 ms) (Russ et al. 2003; Manjoazy 2018). Distress calls of this species consist of a series of low-frequency FM sweeps repeated at regular intervals (Russ et al. 2003). Given the little genetic differentiation between South African and Malagasy *Mops midas* populations (Ratrimomanarivo et al. 2007), the echolocation calls of the different populations are probably similar; South African *M. midas* produces LD-CF and LD-QCF echolocation calls with low PF (16.1 kHz), narrow bandwidth (5.1 kHz), and long duration (20.1 ms) (M. C. Schoeman, unpublished data). Although to the best of our knowledge the echolocation calls of *Tadarida fulminans* have not been recorded on Madagascar, on mainland Africa it produces LD-QCF calls with low PF (17 kHz), narrow bandwidth (13 kHz), and long duration (15 ms) (Monadjem et al. 2020a).

Roosting Habitats

Malagasy members of the family Molossidae use a variety of sites for day roosts and are well known on the island in synanthropic settings. In many coastal areas and the Central Highlands, the distinct musk odor of different molossid colonies, particularly of the genera *Chaerephon*, *Mops*, and *Mormopterus*, is common in the attics of houses and public buildings in villages, towns, and major cities. *Mormopterus jugularis*, *O. madagascariensis*, and *C. jobimena* are generally found in caves or narrow rock crevices (Goodman 2011). There are numerous examples of multiple species occurring in the same roost sites. Rakotondramanana (2011) reported *Mops midas*, *M. leucostigma*, and *C. leucogaster* occurring together in a cavity of a *Commiphora* tree (Burseraceae) in the Kirindy Forest CNFEREF region. In the same general area of Madagascar, but slightly farther south, Andriafidison et al. (2006b) found *M. midas* and *M. leucostigma* co-occurring in the hollow of a baobab (*Adansonia*, Malvaceae) tree.

Family Vespertilionidae, Vespertilionid Bats

Systematics

As currently understood, Madagascar has 12 recognized species of vespertilionids, belonging to five genera (Table 14.24), as compared to southern Africa, with 34 species in 11 genera (Monadjem et al. 2020a). The systematics of Afro-Malagasy vespertilionid taxa still remains partially unresolved with regard to generic allocations, as well as naming unrecognized cryptic species (e.g., Kearney 2005; Koubínová et al. 2013). Recent bat inventories in different portions of Africa and Madagascar have provided important reference material to advance studies to help resolve the taxonomy of regional members of this family (Decher et al. 2015; Goodman et al. 2015b, 2017a; Hutterer et al. 2019; Monadjem et al. 2020b).

An important point of progress for the Malagasy taxa was the study of Bates et al. (2006), who recognized the following species occurring on the island: *Hypsugo anchietae*, *Neoromicia matroka* (previously considered a member of the genus *Eptesicus*), *N. malagasyensis*, *N. melckorum*, *Pipistrellus hesperidus*, and *P. raceyi* (named as new to science; Figure 14.36f). Some years thereafter, using molecular and morphological data, certain species identifications were revisited, and the Malagasy material previously assigned to the African species *H. anchietae* was described as an endemic species, *H. bemainty* (Goodman et al. 2015b), but see below for details on its generic allocation. In a parallel manner, the Malagasy specimens formerly identified as *N. melckorum*, an African species often considered a junior synonym of *N. capensis* (Monadjem et al. 2010), were named as an endemic species to the island, *N. robertsi* (Goodman et al. 2012b).

The phylogenies produced by Goodman et al. (2015b, 2017a) using two mitochondrial genes, placed *H. anchietae* and *H. bemainty* within the *Neoromicia* clade, and this relationship is supported by morphological aspects of the male reproductive organ (Kearney 2005; Monadjem et al. 2020a, 2020b), as well as cranial characters separating these two species from Eurasian *Hypsugo* (Hutterer et al. 2019). Hence, what was previously considered *H. anchietae* and by extrapolation *H. bemainty* is best placed in the genus *Neoromicia* (Monadjem et al. 2020a), a generic allocation

followed here. A recent integrative taxonomic study by Monadjem et al. (2020b) employing molecular genetics, baculum characters, and craniodental morphology of Afro-Malagasy vespertilionids has brought new insights into the evolutionary history of these animals and proposed the following taxonomic changes for the Malagasy species: *H. bemainty* is indeed best placed in the genus *Neoromicia*; *N. malagasyensis*, *N. matroka*, and *N. robertsi* are now members of the genus *Laephotis*; and the three *Pipistrellus*, *P. hesperidus*, *P. raceyi*, and *P. rueppellii*, are retained in that genus—this is the arrangement we follow herein for these species.

Another group of vespertilionids that has posed considerable difficulties in our understanding of the number of species occurring on Madagascar, as well as the African continent, is the genus *Scotophilus* (Robbins et al. 1985). Specimens collected over the past decades have helped to resolve certain aspects of the taxonomic delimitations of this genus, and phylogenies are available for most Afro-Malagasy members (Trujillo et al. 2009; Demos et al. 2018). A relatively recent review of Malagasy members of this genus recognized the following species (Goodman et al. 2005b): *S. robustus*, *S. tandrefana* (described as a new species), and *S.* cf. *borbonicus*. Subsequently, using new specimen material, an additional species, *S. marovaza* was described, which is endemic to Madagascar (Goodman et al. 2006d). On the basis of cytochrome b sequence data, *S. marovaza* and *S. tandrefana* show little differentiation (Trujillo et al. 2009), but until further specimen and genetic data are available are considered distinct species. *Scotophilus borbonicus* was named based on material reportedly from La Réunion, and the skull of the lectotype, the only known specimen of the genus from that island, is in poor condition. Hence, it was not possible for Goodman et al. (2005b) to verify that the Madagascar specimen tentatively named *S.* cf. *borbonicus* could be confidently assigned to this taxon. Goodman et al. (2020) isolated a short DNA sequence from the lectotype of *S. borbonicus*, which was found to fall within eastern African individuals of *S. trujilloi*, and it would appear that the specimen reputed to be from La Réunion was not collected on that island.

On the basis of different published phylogenies of Malagasy vespertilionids, this family has colonized Madagascar on at least eight separate occasions—the genera *Laephotis*, *Neoromicia*, and *Pipistrellus* represent six different colonization events (*L. matroka*, *L. malagasyensis*/*robertsi*, *N. bemainty*, *P. hesperidus*, *P. raceyi*, *P. rueppellii* based on Goodman et al. 2015b, 2017a; Hutterer et al. 2019; Monadjem et al. 2020b), and there have been one colonization of *Myotis*, which is African in origin (Patterson et al. 2019) and at least two separate events for the genus *Scotophilus* (*S. robustus* and *S. marovaza*/*tandrefana*, based on Demos et al. 2018).

General Ecology

A number of studies have been conducted on the diet of smaller Malagasy vespertilionids in different portions of the island. At Kianjavato in the southeast, Coleoptera was the principal prey based on percentage by volume for *Myotis goudoti* (43.7%) and *Laephotis matroka* (53.4%) (Rasoanoro et al. 2015). At another lowland site in the central east, *M. goudoti* fed (based on percentage by volume) predominantly on Coleoptera (61.5%), followed by Lepidoptera (19.3%), and then, in order of descending importance, on Hemiptera, Arachnida, Diptera, Trichoptera, and Neuroptera (Rabarison 2016). At a montane site in the Anjozorobe-Angavo Forest in the eastern Central Highlands, sympatrically occurring *L. matroka* and the slightly larger *L. robertsi* had diets dominated by Coleoptera followed by Hymenoptera, and at this level of taxonomic resolution they showed broad overlap in consumed prey (Rakotondramanana et al. 2015). At Kianjavato, *Pipistrellus raceyi* consumed predominantly Coleoptera (32.5%), Diptera (28.9%), Lepidoptera (16.3%), and Homoptera (11.7%), as compared to a site in the central lowland west, where the diet included Isoptera (30.0%), Coleoptera (27.8%), Lepidoptera (26.1%), and Hymenoptera (12.5%) (Rakotondramanana et al. 2015; Rasoanoro et al. 2015). In the vicinity of Lake Mandrozo, central western lowlands, on the basis of percentage by volume, *Pipistrellus* species, mostly *P. hesperidus*, fed on Coleoptera (53.6%), Hymenoptera (21.3%), Lepidoptera (19.1%), Hemiptera (3.6%), and Homoptera (2.4%); based on one fecal sample from the same site, *P. rueppellii* consumed Lepidoptera and Hymenoptera nearly equally (Ravelojaona 2017; R. N. Ravelojaona, unpublished data). On the basis of stomach contents of *M. goudoti* (Figure 14.36e) from different sites in western Madagascar, this species did not show notable interlocality differences, and the two dominant orders at Bemaraha and Namoroka were Isoptera and Coleoptera (Razakarivony et al. 2005). At Kirindy Forest CNFEREF, *N. bemainty*, based on percentage by volume in fecal samples, fed predominantly on Isoptera (52.0%), followed by Lepidoptera (18.6%), Coleoptera (14.1%), and Hymenoptera (12.0%) (Rakotondramanana et al. 2015). The presence of Isoptera in the diet of these different bats is almost certainly highly periodic, specifically during the wet season, and associated with the consumption of alates. The capacity of vespertilionids, particularly those living in areas with extended dry seasons, to modify the type of prey consumed with respect to what is available is indicative of their generalist diet.

Scotophilus robustus, the largest member of Vespertilionidae on Madagascar, shows considerable variation in its diet. Based on proportional volume, near Anjozorobe, its most commonly consumed prey were Lepidoptera (50.0%), Dictyoptera (27.5%), and Coleoptera (15.5%); in the *Bismarckia* grassland around Lake Mandrozo, Coleoptera (73.8%), Blattodea (8.9%), and Hemiptera (6.6%); and at Kianjavato, Coleoptera (73.0%), Lepidoptera (9.1%), and Hymenoptera (8.7%) (Rakotondramanana et al. 2015; Rasoanoro et al. 2015; Ravelojaona 2017). For *S. marovaza* some dietary information is available from the Lake Mandrozo area and based on proportional volume, the following groups make up the most frequently taken prey: Coleoptera (70.9%), Hemiptera (15.0%), Lepidoptera (9.8%), and Hymenoptera (2.7%) (Ravelojaona 2017).

In the central west, different vespertilionids are known to be predated on by *Macheiramphus alcinus*, including *P. hesperidus*, *P. raceyi*, *Pipistrellus* sp., *S. marovaza*, *S. robustus*, *N. bemainty*, and *Myotis goudoti* (Goodman et al. 2016b; Razakaratrimo et al. 2019). Seasonal differences were found in this raptor's consumption of bats of the genera *Pipistrellus* and *Neoromicia*, with both more common prey during the dry season as compared to the wet season. Members of this family make up about half of the prey items by number consumed by this raptor in central western Madagascar.

Vocalizations

Members of the family Vespertilionidae emit low duty-cycle, frequency-modulated (LD-FM), quasi-constant frequency (LD-QCF),

or constant-frequency (LD-CF) echolocation calls. Their adjustable echolocation calls allow most vespertilionid bats to display flexible foraging behavior, switching between open-air and clutter-edge habitat space (Fenton 1990). Echolocation parameters of six vespertilionids belonging to two genera—*Laephotis malagasyensis*, *L. matroka*, *L. robertsi*, *N. bemainty*, *P. hesperidus*, and *P. raceyi*—show marked overlap: PF 57.9, 57.5, 53.0, 50.2, 54.0, 56.1 kHz; bandwidth 32.5, 37.0, 32.1, 47.6, 48.6, and 78.3 kHz; and duration 1.6, 2.0, 2.7, 2.4, 2.7, 2.7 ms, respectively (Goodman et al. 2015b). However, a principal component (PC) analysis of call parameters of these three genera revealed some differences between species: the projection of PC1 versus PC2 showed overlap between *L. matroka*, *L. malagasyensis*, and *P. raceyi*, while *N. bemainty* and *P. hesperidus* formed separate clusters; whereas projections of PC2 versus PC3 and PC1 versus PC3 showed overlap between *P. hesperidus*, *P. raceyi*, and *N. bemainty*, while *L. malagasyensis* and, to a lesser degree, *L. matroka*, formed separate clusters (Goodman et al. 2015b). *Myotis goudoti* produces calls with a high PF (64.4 kHz), very broad bandwidth (75.8 kHz), and short duration (3 ms) (Russ et al. 2003; Kofoky et al. 2009). The distress calls of *M. goudoti* are distinct from its echolocation calls, with a PF of ~40 kHz and bandwidth of ~25 kHz (Russ et al. 2004). PFs of calls of two *Scotophilus* species, *S. tandrefana* and *S. marovaza*, show limited overlap (48.2 and 45.9 kHz, respectively), with bandwidth (48.3 and 26 kHz, respectively) and duration (3.0 and 6.4 ms, respectively) of their calls more distinct; discriminant function analysis of call parameters correctly identified 83.3% and 71.4% of individuals, respectively (Kofoky et al. 2009). By contrast, *S. robustus* emits echolocation calls with a 35–38 kHz PF, 32.5 kHz bandwidth, and 5 ms duration, and 92.9% of individuals were correctly classified to species in a discriminant function analysis of call parameters (Russ et al. 2003; Kofoky et al. 2009).

Roosting Habitats

Except for *Myotis goudoti*, which is known to roost in caves, crevices, and rock shelters (Goodman 2011), and *Scotophilus marovaza*, which roosts in palm leaves as well as house roofs made of this same material (Ratrimomanarivo and Goodman 2005; Goodman et al. 2006d), information on the roosting ecology of the Malagasy members of this family is limited. Nonetheless, *Laephotis matroka*, *Pipistrellus hesperidus*, *P. raceyi*, and *S. robustus* have been found in synanthropic settings (Goodman 2011; Goodman et al. 2014c). Natural roost sites of the others members are not yet documented.

Family Miniopteridae, Long-fingered Bats

Systematics

Currently, 12 species of long-fingered bats, all in the genus *Miniopterus*, are recognized from Madagascar, two of which also occur in the Comoro islands (Table 14.24), as compared to four species in southern Africa (Monadjem et al. 2020a). The past years have seen considerable advances in the systematics and species delimitations of Malagasy members of this family, but these aspects are still not completely resolved. In a monograph on the bats of Madagascar published by Peterson et al. (1995), four species were recognized on the island: *M. fraterculus*, shared with Africa; the endemic *M. gleni*, described as new to science; *M. majori*, also reputed to also occur in the Comoros; and *M. manavi*, a widespread endemic species with notable geographic variation in size and morphology.

In subsequent publications from the 21st-century period of bat research on Madagascar mentioned in the introduction, specimens previously assigned to *M. fraterculus* were demonstrated, using morphological and genetic data, to be different from African populations and separated into two new endemic species: *M. sororculus* (Goodman et al. 2007c) and *M. petersoni* (Goodman et al. 2008c); these two species are morphologically similar but phylogenetically not closely related (Christidis et al. 2014). Further, studies on *M. gleni* showed it to be genetically homogeneous across most of its extensive range, with the exception of a distinct population in the extreme southwest, described as *M. griffithsi* (Goodman et al. 2010c).

On the basis of relatively recent fieldwork conducted in the Comoro archipelago, no evidence was found of a medium-size *Miniopterus* similar to *M. majori* (Goodman et al. 2010d). This aspect combined with uncertainty about the reputed collection site of this species on Grande Comore (Ngzuani) has resulted in its occurrence in that archipelago being called into question (Goodman and Maminirina 2007). Hence, until further evidence is available, *M. majori* is considered endemic to Madagascar.

The case of *M. manavi* is notably more complex and not completely resolved. Peterson et al. (1995) mentioned considerable morphological variation in specimens they assigned to this species. After the death of Randolph Peterson in 1989, when his co-authors of the 1995 monograph were preparing the manuscript for publication, several new species of *M. manavi* were proposed, but for different reasons these descriptions were excluded from the publication (J. Eger, unpublished data). The first steps in resolving the taxonomy of this presumed species group was sorting sequenced specimens overlaid on their clade allocation and to identify consistent morphological traits. This resulted in the restriction of animals referable to *M. manavi sensu stricto* to central eastern Madagascar, based on sequence data from the original type series, and the description of three new species—*M. aelleni* (Figure 14.36g), *M. brachytragos*, and *M. mahafaliensis*—as well as the elevation of *M. manavi griveaudi* to a full species rank (Goodman et al. 2009b). Two of these taxa, *M. aelleni* and *M. griveaudi*, also occur in the Comoros (Goodman et al. 2009c; Weyeneth et al. 2011b) and thus are endemic to the Malagasy Region. Subsequent molecular work in combination with morphological analyses resulted in the description of *M. egeri* (Goodman et al. 2011) and the separation of *M. aelleni* into two separate species, the second being the new taxon *M. ambohitrensis* (Goodman et al. 2015c).

On the basis of a large-scale mitochondrial DNA analysis, Christidis et al. (2014) presented a phylogeny of *Miniopterus* occurring on Madagascar and the Comoros, which appears to represent a monophyletic radiation with respect to Malagasy species. A total of 18 clades were recovered, which included five primary lineages: 1) *M. griveaudi*; 2) *M. mahafaliensis*, *M. sororculus*, and an unnamed clade (X3); 3) *M. majori*, *M. gleni*, and *M. griffithsi*; 4) *M. brachytragos*, *M. aelleni* A (*M. aelleni sensu stricto*), and *M. aelleni* B (subsequently renamed *M. ambohitrensis*); and 5) *M. manavi* and *M. petersoni* as sister species, which were in turn linked to a group comprising *M. egeri* and five genetically distinct populations (P3, P4, P5, P6, and P7). The question of monophyly in the Malagasy Region species has

not been supported by other analyses (Agnarsson et al. 2011; Shi and Rabosky 2015; Demos et al. 2020). In a multi-locus nuclear gene tree presented by Demos et al. (2020), 11 of the 12 named regional taxa are monophyletic, but *M. griffithsi* falls outside this clade, and based on cytochrome b, it would appear that this genus colonized Madagascar from Africa at least on two or perhaps three separate occasions. Certain aspects of the species limits of this genus on Madagascar remain to be evaluated, probably best accomplished by a genomic approach with extensive sampling to resolve its speciation history and the resulting phylogeny overlaid on morphological characters to determine the number of recognizable species.

General Ecology

Given taxonomic changes at the species level of Malagasy members of *Miniopterus* since the 2010s, in certain cases it is not clear from some published dietary analysis papers which species were studied, particularly for *M. manavi sensu lato*. Stomach content remains have been analyzed of "*M. manavi*," from sites in the dry deciduous forests of the west and transitional vegetational formations: in Bemaraha, the diet, mostly of individuals of *M. griveaudi*, showed a dominance of Isoptera, for which alates were undergoing nuptial flights during the field visit, followed by Hymenoptera; in Daraina (Loky Manambato), probably *M. griveaudi*, it consisted largely of Coleoptera followed by Isoptera and Hemiptera; in Ankarana, probably *M. griveaudi* and perhaps a few individuals of *M. aelleni*, the diet was dominated by Lepidoptera, then Hymenoptera, Coleoptera, and Orthoptera; and in Namoroka, presumably several different *Miniopterus* species, the principal group consumed was Hymenoptera, followed by Coleoptera and Isoptera (Razakarivony et al. 2005). Other dietary analyses from Bemaraha, based on percentage by volume from fecal remains, presumably of *M. griveaudi*, found that the diet was dominated by Coleoptera (33.9%) and Hemiptera (30.7%), followed by Lepidoptera (23.0%) (Rakotoarivelo et al. 2007), which is notably different from the results presented above based on stomach contents. These data indicate that there is considerable variation in the diet of small *Miniopterus* species, giving the impression that certain members of the genus are not dietary specialists on specific insect orders, and differences between studies and sites may be linked to local and seasonal availability, as well as the type of analyzed remains.

Data are available on dietary preferences for a few other Malagasy *Miniopterus* species. Rasoanoro et al. (2015) found that based on percentage by volume in fecal samples collected in lowland areas of the southeast, *M. egeri* feeds predominantly on Coleoptera, followed by Lepidoptera and Isoptera. In the dry spiny thickets of the extreme southwest, based on percentage by volume of insects recovered from fecal pellets of *M. mahafaliensis*, 47.5% of the identified food remains were Lepidoptera, followed by 39.9% Coleoptera (Ramasindrazana et al. 2012). As is to be anticipated in an area such as the dry spiny thicket, which is subject to a long dry season, and with *M. mahafaliensis* present throughout the year (Reher et al. 2019), there were dramatic shifts in the insect orders consumed during the dry and wet seasons (Ramasindrazana et al. 2012).

Few details are available on diurnal or nocturnal predators of *Miniopterus* species. Remains of a form referred to as *M.* cf. *griveaudi* were identified from *Macheiramphus alcinus* pellets recovered from a site in the lowland central west (Razakaratrimo et al. 2019). *Athene superciliaris* (White-browed Owl) was seen feeding on a small *Miniopterus* just after dusk at the entrance of a cave at Ankarana (V. Soarimalala, unpublished data).

Vocalizations

Miniopterus bats emit low duty-cycle, frequency-modulated echolocation calls (LD-FM). Peak frequency (PF) of species ranges between 40.1 and 134.8 kHz, whereas duration ranges between 2.1 and 5.0 ms (Russ et al. 2003; Ramasindrazana et al. 2011; Goodman et al. 2015c). Two species deviated significantly from the allometric relationship between PF and body size; PF of *M. sororculus* was higher than expected from its body size, while that of *M. aelleni* was lower than expected from body size (Ramasindrazana et al. 2011). Discriminant function analysis correctly identified 75.8% of the calls of 11 *Miniopterus* species; those of *M. griffithsi*, *M. majori*, *M. manavi*, and *M. petersoni* were 100% correctly identified, whereas calls of *M. griveaudi* were only 49.0% correctly identified (Ramasindrazana et al. 2011). The distress calls of *M. majori* and *M. "manavi"* are distinct from their echolocation calls, with PFs of ~30 and 35 kHz, respectively; steep FM bandwidths of ~50 and 60 kHz, respectively; and very short interpulse durations (Russ et al. 2004).

Roosting Habitats

Generally, Malagasy species of *Miniopterus* roost in caves, narrow crevices, and rock shelters (Goodman 2011; Goodman and Ramasindrazana 2013). Several species roost together in strict sympatry or in syntopy within the same cave.

COLONIZATION HISTORY OF THE EXTANT BATS OF MADAGASCAR

The extant native land mammals of Madagascar (Table14.1), all of which are endemic and comprise 31 species of tenrecs (Tenrecidae), seven species of carnivorans (Eupleridae), 28 species of

TABLE 14.25. **Number of estimated colonization events of Malagasy bats at the family level**

FAMILY	EVENTS
Pteropodidae	3
Hipposideridae	2
Rhinonycteridae	2
Emballonuridae	3
Myzopodidae	1
Molossidae	7
Vespertilionidae	>8
Miniopteridae	>2
Total	>28

Note: Events: the number of estimated colonization events to Madagascar. The details on the derived figures are summarized in the respective texts under Systematics for each family.

TABLE 14.26. **Bat species recorded at different sites on Madagascar**

SITE	ANKARANA	ANJOHIBE	ANKARAFANTSIKA	NAMOROKA	BEMARAHA	MENABE ANTIMENA	KIRINDY MITÉ	ZOMBITSE-VOHIBASIA	ISALO	TSINJORIAKE	TSIMANAMPESOTSE	MASOALA	ANALAMAZAOTRA-MANTADIA	TAMPOLO/IVOLOINA	RANOMAFANA	TOLAGNARO AREA
Protected area	Yes	No	Yes	Yes	Yes	Yes	Yes	Yes	Yes	Yes	Yes	Yes	Yes	Portions	Yes	Portions
PTEROPODIDAE																
**Eidolon dupreanum*	X	X	X	X	X	X	–	X	X	–	X	–	–	–	X	X
**Pteropus rufus*	X	X	X	X	X	X	X	–	X	X	–	X	X	X	X	X
**Rousettus madagascariensis*	X	X	X	X	X	–	X	–	X	–	–	X	X	X	X	X
HIPPOSIDERIDAE																
**Macronycteris commersoni*	X	X	X	X	X	X	X	X	X	X	X	X	X	X	X	X
**M. cryptovalorona*	–	–	–	–	–	–	–	–	X	–	X	–	–	–	–	–
RHINONYCTERIDAE																
**Paratriaenops auritus*	X	–	–	–	–	–	–	–	–	–	–	–	–	–	–	–
**P. furculus*	–	X	–	X	X	X	X	–	–	X	X	–	–	–	–	–
**Triaenops menamena*	X	X	X	X	X	X	X	–	X	X	X	X	–	–	–	X
EMBALLONURIDAE																
**Coleura kibomalandy*	X	–	–	–	–	–	–	–	–	–	–	–	–	–	–	–
**Paremballonura atrata*	–	–	–	–	–	–	–	–	–	–	–	X	X	–	–	X
**P. tiavato*	X	X	–	X	X	–	–	–	–	–	–	–	–	–	–	–
Taphozous mauritianus	–	X	X	X	X	–	–	X	–	X	–	X	–	X	–	X
MYZOPODIDAE																
**Myzopoda aurita*	–	–	–	–	–	–	–	–	–	–	–	X	X	X	X	X
**M. schliemanni*	–	–	X	X	–	–	–	–	–	–	–	–	–	–	–	–
MOLOSSIDAE																
**Chaerephon atsinanana*	–	–	–	–	–	–	–	–	–	–	–	X	X	X	X	X
**C. jobimena*	X	–	–	–	–	–	–	X	X	–	–	–	–	–	–	–
C. leucogaster	X	X	X	X	X	X	X	X	–	X	–	–	–	–	–	–
***Mops leucostigma*	X	–	X	X	X	X	X	X	–	X	X	X	X	X	X	–
M. midas	–	–	–	X	–	X	X	X	–	–	–	–	–	–	–	X
**Mormopterus jugularis*	X	–	–	–	–	X	–	X	X	X	X	X	X	–	X	X
**Otomops madagascariensis*	X	X	–	X	X	–	–	–	X	X	–	–	–	–	–	–
Tadarida fulminans	–	–	–	–	–	–	–	–	X	–	–	–	–	–	–	X

(continued overleaf)

TABLE 14.26. ***continued***

SITE	ANKARANA	ANJOHIBE	ANKARAFANTSIKA	NAMOROKA	BEMARAHA	MENABE ANTIMENA	KIRINDY M ITÉ	ZOMBITSE-VOHIBASIA	ISALO	TSINJORIAKE	TSIMANAMPESOTSE	MASOALA	ANALAMAZAOTRA-MANTADIA	TAMPOLO/IVOLOINA	RANOMAFANA	TOLAGNARO AREA
VESPERTILIONIDAE																
**Myotis goudoti*	X	X	–	X	X	X	X	–	X	X	X	X	X	X	X	X
**Neoromicia bemainty*	–	–	–	–	–	X	X	X	–	X	–	–	–	–	–	–
**Laephotis malagasyensis*	–	–	–	–	–	–	–	–	X	–	–	–	–	–	–	–
**L. matroka*	–	–	–	–	–	–	–	–	X	–	–	–	X	–	X	–
**L. robertsi*	–	–	–	–	–	–	–	–	–	–	–	–	X	–	–	–
Pipistrellus hesperidus	–	X	X	X	–	X	X	–	–	X	–	–	–	–	–	–
**P. raceyi*	–	X	–	–	–	X	–	–	–	X	–	–	–	X	–	–
**Scotophilus marovaza*	–	X	X	–	–	X	X	–	–	–	–	–	–	–	–	–
**S. robustus*	–	X	–	X	X	X	–	X	–	–	–	X	X	–	X	X
**S. tandrefana*	–	–	–	–	X	–	–	–	–	X	–	–	–	–	–	–
MINIOPTERIDAE																
***Miniopterus aelleni*	X	X	–	X	X	–	–	–	–	–	–	X	–	–	–	–
**M. brachytragos*	–	–	–	X	X	–	–	–	–	–	–	X	–	–	–	–
**M. egeri*	–	–	–	–	–	–	–	–	–	–	–	X	–	–	–	
**M. gleni*	X	X	X	X	X	X	–	–	X	X	–	X	–	–	–	X
**M. griffithsi*	–	–	–	–	–	–	–	–	–	–	X	–	–	–	–	–
***M. griveaudi*	X	X	X	X	X	–	–	–	–	–	–	X	–	–	–	–
**M. mahafaliensis*	–	–	–	–	–	–	X	–	X	X	X	–	–	–	–	–
**M. majori*	–	X	–	–	–	–	–	–	–	–	–	–	X	–	X	X
**M. manavi*	–	–	–	–	–	–	–	–	–	–	–	–	–	–	X	–
**M. petersoni*	–	–	–	–	–	–	–	–	–	–	–	–	–	–	–	X
Total number of species	17	19	13	20	18	16	13	10	15	16	10	17	13	9	13	17

Notes: Sites aregenerally arranged from north to south. * endemic to Madagascar; ** endemic to Malagasy Region. Some taxa known from the island are not listed, as their geographical ranges do not cover the sites mentioned. Some synanthropic species are also listed when they are known to occur in, or in close vicinity of, a given site.

rodents (Nesomyinae), and 108 species of lemurs (Primates), all represent monophyletic clades (Poux et al. 2005). What is simply extraordinary is that this remarkable diversity of approximately 175 species of land mammals can be explained by only four asynchronous colonizations of the island, further indicating that such successful events were very rare in geological history.

As mentioned in the introduction to this contribution, the bats of Madagascar have been the subject of a considerable number of phylogenetic studies, and data are available to estimate the number of independent colonization events of the island's extant fauna (Table 14.25). For the eight families evaluated for this aspect, 28 or perhaps 30 independent colonization events are represented, which is in marked contrast to that of the land mammal fauna. All three species of the families Pteropodidae and a large proportion of the 12 Vespertilionidae occurring on the island represent separate colonizations. With a few exceptions among the 46 species

recognized to occur on the island (see Table 14.24), there are not many cases of congeneric species being sister taxa and representing local speciation, and well over 50% of the species represent unique colonization events. The principal exception is the Miniopteridae, specifically the genus *Miniopterus*, in which a number of species form monophyletic clades and were the subject of local speciation events.

DISTRIBUTION AND SITE SPECIES DIVERSITY OF THE EXTANT BAT FAUNA

Bat inventories since the late 20th century and associated taxonomic work on collected species provide insights into distribution patterns and species diversity at well-known or reasonably well-known sites (Table 14.26). In general, sites in western Madagascar associated with limestone karst habitat and representing areas with eroded rock and caves and crevices that form protected day-roost sites have the highest species diversity. Such sites falling within the dry deciduous forest regions of the island include (number of known bat species in parentheses): Namoroka (20), Anjohibe (19), Bemaraha (18), Ankarana (17), and Tsinjoriake (16). In contrast, the limestone karst site of Tsimanampesotse (10) in the extreme southwest, with dry spiny thicket habitat and a much extended dry season, has a reduced species diversity. Other western sites with dry deciduous forest but without exposed sedimentary rock have lower species diversity, which is presumed to be associated with the lack of cave and crevice roost sites: Menabe Antimena (16), Ankarafantsika (13), and Kirindy Mité (13). Transitional dry to moist evergreen habitat types show intermediate levels of diversity with the sandstone Isalo Massif (15), containing some caves and rock crevices, having higher species diversity than Zombitse-Vohibasia (10), without exposed sedimentary rock.

In the east, including areas with moist evergreen forest and no exposed sedimentary rock, species diversity is important, but as a general trend, is lower or equal to the western limestone karst zones: Masoala Peninsula (17), Tolagnaro area (17), Analamazaotra-Mantadia (13), Ranomafana (13), and Tampolo/Ivoloina (9). Hence, measures of species diversity at these latter sites are not too far behind those in the west with limestone karst, and it is clear that the local bat fauna has found different solutions to finding local day-roost sites.

There are many areas of the island that remain unknown or poorly known with regard to the local bat fauna. Further inventories are needed to better document measures of species diversity at these localities, and captured bats should have at least wing punches saved along with external measurements and photographic images before an animal is released. With advancements of species delimitations and molecular research, a large percentage of these individuals can be identified in the hand, and the final determination based on barcoding techniques. However, it is almost certain that unrecognized cryptic species remain on the island, and in cases of doubt with regard to field identifications, we suggest collection of specimens with detailed information, and associated material (e.g., ectoparasites, blood samples for zoonotic disease research, bacula, etc.) be saved.

Subject editors: Paul A. Racey and Steven M. Goodman

PTEROPODIDAE, FRUIT BATS, *FANIHY*, *ANGAVO*

R. Andrianaivoarivelo, D. Andriafidison, J. H. Razafimanahaka, N. Razafindrakoto, R. Z. Oleksy, and P. A. Racey

The frugivorous species of the suborder Pteropodiformes (Yinpterochiroptera) occur in Africa, tropical Asia, and Indo-Australia and include the family Pteropodidae (formerly classified as Megachiroptera), comprising approximately 170 species. All are herbivores, feeding on fruit, nectar, pollen, and leaves. Their large eyes, with reflective tapeta, distinguish them from the insect-feeding bats of the suborder Vespertilioniformes (Yangochiroptera), as well as several families with this dietary habitat within the Pteropodiformes. Members of Pteropodidae navigate and find their food by sight and olfaction (Acharya et al. 1998; Luft et al. 2003), although one genus, *Rousettus*, has evolved a precise form of echolocation enabling it to navigate deep into caves, where it has day roosts (Waters and Vollrath 2003; Yovel et al. 2011a; for further information see Goodman et al., pp. 1894–911). Certain Old World fruit bats are large, weighing up to 1.5 kg, with wingspans reaching to almost 2 m.

All three of Madagascar's pteropodid bat species are endemic to the island (Figure 14.37). *Pteropus*, the genus containing the largest species, originates from Asia and has spread to the islands of the western Indian Ocean and African islands off Tanzania but not as far as the mainland; it is represented on Madagascar by *P. rufus*. *Eidolon*, the genus with the middle-size species, is found only in Africa, its offshore islands, and Madagascar. The Malagasy species, *E. dupreanum*, is derived from the African species, *E. helvum* (Shi et al. 2014). *Rousettus*, the genus containing the smallest species, is found in Africa, the Middle East, and Asia, as well as Madagascar and the Comoros, and it is now clear that the African and western Indian Ocean island populations are derived from Asian descendants (Stribna et al. 2019). Madagascar thus holds a unique assemblage of fruit bats, representing a mixture of those of African and Asian origin.

FIGURE 14.37 **Different types of day-roost sites for Malagasy members of the family Pteropodidae. A) *Pteropus rufus* (Madagascar Flying Fox) roosting in a tree within the Analalava protected area; B) *Eidolon dupreanum* (Madagascar Straw-colored Fruit Bat) roost in a cave in the Ankarana protected area; C) *Rousettus madagascariensis* (Madagascar Rousette) colony in a cave in Antsahahety, Anosibe An'Ala.** (PHOTO A by Madagasikara Voakajy; B by M. Tuttle/Bat Conservation International; and C by R. A. Andrianaivoarivelo.)

PTEROPUS RUFUS, MADAGASCAR FLYING FOX, *FANIHY*, *FANIHY MENA*, *FANIHY BE*, *ANDREHY*

IUCN status: Vulnerable
Legal status: *animaux gibiers* (game)

Description

Pteropus rufus is notably large among the world's bats and is the largest bat on Madagascar. In adults, total length is 23.0–31.8 cm, forearm 14.0–17.8 cm, wingspan 100–125 cm, and weight 245–749 g (Goodman 2011). Its yellow or orange head and upper body contrast with its very dark mid- and lower back. The wings are dark gray or black, and the underparts are beige. A study of the retina suggests the species has polychromatic vision (B. Müller et al. 2007). Roosting bats are easily disturbed during the day and can often be seen circling above the roost, calling loudly. *Pteropus rufus* is also very vocal in interactions with nearby roosting conspecifics. This is especially true during mating, which peaks in April and May, when males pursue females around the roost. Young are born mainly in October and November. Females usually have only one young a year but occasionally produce twins.

Roosting Ecology

Pteropus typically roosts in large trees, often near rivers and in mangroves (Figure 14.37a). It is most commonly found in the lowlands within 100 km of the coast and on offshore islands, but some roosts have also been found in the Central Highlands. Roosts are conspicuous and noisy, and their populations range in size from 10 to 10,000 individuals, although large roosts are now rare. The largest roost recorded to date was in Ambondrombe (Menabe Region), with up to 10,000 individuals in 2009. This roost and its surrounding area has been classified as a protected area since 2015 (Goodman et al. 2018b). A total of 114 occupied roost sites were surveyed in different areas of Madagascar from April 1999 to December 2000 (MacKinnon et al. 2003), and the median roost size was 250 individuals. Well-known roosts include those at Berenty and Nosy Tanikely. Twenty-seven out of 154 sites (17.5%) visited were reported to have been abandoned within the previous 10 years.

Between 2006 and 2008, a second survey (Madagasikara Voakajy, unpublished data) was carried out involving a further 92 roosts, 54 (58.7%) of which were occupied by *P. rufus*, while 38 (41.3%) were reported to have been abandoned. The median roost size was smaller than that of previous surveys. During interviews, local people were asked when they last observed *P. rufus* at the abandoned roosts. The years reported ranged from 1981 to 2006, and 45% of the roosts had been abandoned between 2001 and 2006.

In the Central Highlands, the proportion of deserted sites is much higher (five out of seven, or 70%), probably owing to the demand for wood from remaining forest fragments where trees can serve as roost sites. The two remaining roosts located in this region were small (approximately 50 and 250 animals) and are unlikely to survive for more than a few years. Fire and deforestation are ubiquitous threats to bat colonies in central eastern Madagascar (R. K. B. Jenkins et al. 2007).

At all deserted sites, local villagers were asked why the bats had left, and the most common explanation cited throughout the whole country was hunting with shotguns.

In a few cases, desertion of roost sites was natural because cyclones had knocked over the roost trees. In another two cases, desertion was due to a destructive hunting method, used in the southeast, in which the hunters cut through the tree trunk during the day, leaving just enough intact so that the tree remains standing. They return the next day, quickly make the final cuts so that the tree falls, full of bats, which are then beaten to death with sticks. This was the case in Ambakoana, a roost that contained up to 2000 individuals in 2004–2006 and has been abandoned since 2015 (D. Andriafidison, unpublished data).

Hunting and Conservation

Hunting of *P. rufus* is common throughout most of its range, and this appears to be the main cause of both reductions in population size and desertion of roosts, as described above. The decline in bat populations is caused not only by the local consumption of bat meat at the village level but also especially by the commercialized restaurant and market trade. In the northeast, *P. rufus* is eaten widely by individual households at the local community level and is the most expensive meat sold, exceeding the price of most domestic livestock meat (Golden 2009). It is among the preferred foods in roadside restaurants (*hotelys*) in different portions of the island. In the Menabe Region of the central west, specifically in Morondava, *P. rufus* meat in restaurants was priced the same as eel and a little lower than *Tenrec ecaudatus* (R. K. B. Jenkins and Racey 2008). In the Mahavavy-Kinkony area of the northwest, a *P. rufus* roost was reported to be severely threatened by regular hunting (Rakotoarivelo and Randrianandrianina 2007), with teams of up to eight men visiting the roost on a regular basis and catching up to 100 bats on each occasion. Similarly, overhunting seems to be common in the Menabe Region (Oleksy et al. 2015a).

Traditional beliefs limit human pressures on bats in some areas. The eating of bats is taboo for members of the Mahafaly and Antandroy cultural groups, and bat roosts in these areas are therefore relatively well protected. However, the large numbers of immigrants from other cultural groups are responsible for at least some hunting of bats in almost all roost sites surveyed in these regions. It is also taboo for Muslims to eat bats, and hence bat roosts in the north of Madagascar, particularly in the region of Antsiranana, tend to suffer less hunting pressure than elsewhere. In many areas there are also local taboos that restrict people from hunting in the roost site. For example, bats roosting in sacred forests or near tombs are not disturbed. In the Melaky Region (Antsalova), people reported that hunting is taboo when female bats are pregnant and lactating.

Unpublished fieldwork by Madagasikara Voakajy found fewer *Pteropus* roosts in unprotected sites than in protected sites. Sites were considered "protected" if they were in a region where it is taboo to eat bats and there is no hunting, if they were in an officially protected area, or if the roosts were within sacred areas where hunting was not permitted. Our analysis indicates that bat populations outside protected areas would likely be negatively affected by disturbance or hunting. During the original surveys (MacKinnon et al. 2003), we knew of only five *P. rufus* roost sites within protected areas: Nosy Atafana in Mananara-Nord, Zahamena, Masoala, Ibity, and in the private reserve of Berenty. Several more roosts have since been discovered in protected areas: Analalava, Ampanangandehibe-Behasina, Mangabe-Ranomena-Sahasarotra, Ambositra-Vondrozo, Tsitongambarika, Antrema, Mahavavy-Kinkony, Namoroka, and Tsimembo-Manambolomaty (Goodman et al. 2018b). However, some of these roosts are currently visited by hunters. Furthermore, many traditional taboos are being ignored, and hunting now sometimes occurs in sacred sites (Rahaingondrahety et al. 2008), such as the Tsiandrora roost on the western side of Beanka, where hunting materials (long wooden poles used to erect nets) were found (R. Andrianaivoarivelo, unpublished data).

In 2015, three new protected areas, designated partly for *P. rufus* roost conservation, were created in Ambatondrazaka District: Mahialambo, Ampanangandehibe-Behasina, and Analalava. In these now-protected areas, *P. rufus* populations were monitored on a monthly basis between 2008 and 2018 (Brook et al. 2019). Population size fluctuated between 200 and 4000 individuals across these areas. Our count data on the Tsiandrora population from 2015 to 2017 demonstrated decreasing numbers of bats, from approximately 560 to 460 individuals (R. Andrianaivoarivelo, unpublished data).

Population

The total *P. rufus* population is still relatively large. Approximately 100,000 individuals were counted during our surveys, which covered approximately one-half of the area of Madagascar that has suitable habitat (Madagasikara Voakajy, unpublished data). Assuming that half the population was not counted because of undercounting in roost sites and incomplete coverage of the survey areas, the total population of *P. rufus* in 2019 is extrapolated to be approximately 200,000 individuals. This represents a reduction of one-third since the surveys conducted some 20 years ago (MacKinnon et al. 2003), and this decline is a cause of concern.

Pteropus rufus was listed by the IUCN as Vulnerable in 2004. Data on roost sizes and hunting levels suggest that this species has experienced a 20% decline in 10 years, which confirms it as a Vulnerable species (criterion A2acd) (Racey 2016). We anticipate comparable or greater rates of decline in coming years.

In Malagasy legislation, *P. rufus* is classified as a game species and can be hunted from May to August (Durbin 2007). Existing regulations are ineffective in protecting this species from overhunting. In fact, hunting should not be carried out at night when the bats are foraging, and use of guns during the day is allowed only with a permit (Rakotoarivelo et al. 2011). However, these regulations are poorly enforced and cases of night hunting and hunting with guns at the roosts have been observed and reported (R. K. B. Jenkins et al. 2007; Rahaingondrahety et al. 2008).

EIDOLON DUPREANUM, MADAGASCAR STRAW-COLORED FRUIT BAT, *ANDREHY*, *ANGAVO*, *ANGOAVY*, *FANIHY VATO*

IUCN status: Vulnerable
Legal status: *animaux gibiers* (game)

Description

Eidolon dupreanum was until recently classified as a subspecies of *E. helvum*, which is found on the Arabian Peninsula and throughout sub-Saharan Africa. In 1995, *E. dupreanum* was reinstated as a separate species (Peterson et al. 1995), and recent molecular genetics work supports this conclusion (Shi et al. 2014). In adults, total length is 21.8–22.9 cm, forearm 12.8–13.8 cm, wingspan 75.0–95.0 cm, and weight 288–392 g (Goodman 2011). This fruit bat may be distinguished from *Pteropus rufus* by its duller coloration, the long, narrow shape of its wings, and its short tail. Adult males tend to be 10% larger than females, and the reddish-cinnamon collar around the neck is more conspicuous in males than in females. Most of the body is a medium gray brown, though the upperparts may be a dull yellow, and the underparts an olive beige. The wings are dark brown-black and often have a distinct white patch. The head is more pointed than that of other Malagasy fruit bats, and the face anterior to and beneath the eyes is furless. Schoeman and Goodman (2012) found evidence of incipient echolocation in this species.

Roosting Ecology

Eidolon roosts on crags and river cliffs, in caves (Figure 14.37b), and in the canopies of dense trees (in the dense crowns of palms around the island, including in the Parc Botanique et Zoologique de Tsimbazaza in Antananarivo) and in baobab hollows in the Morondava area. Colonies typically contain between 10 and 500 individuals, although there are larger roosts in Ankarana. There is also a well-known roost at Lake Tritriva near Antsirabe. This species is found throughout Madagascar and may often be seen roosting in clefts of the crags of the Central Highlands. In the congener *E. helvum*, there is a postmating delay of several months in the implantation of the embryo, followed by four months of post-implantation development (Mutere 1967; Fayenuwo and Halstead 1974). Females of *E. dupreanum* on Madagascar give birth to a single young in December or January.

The median roost size for *E. dupreanum* is 200. Three roosts of over 1000 individuals are known, all of them in the Ankarana region. *Eidolon* roosts appear to be occupied throughout the year. Nevertheless, those in the forests of the southwest have fewer bats during the dry months, when fruits are scarce, which suggests that some animals may migrate. Evidence for this is the recovery of an individual marked in Ankarana and recovered near Daraina; some 35–40 km separates the two localities (S. M. Goodman, unpublished data).

Hunting and Conservation

The most common method of hunting *Eidolon* in cliff faces is to smoke them out of their roosts in rock fissures (Ranivo 2001). This method apparently often leads to desertion of the roost, of which there is a high incidence—18 out of 60 or ~30%. However, anecdotal evidence from hunters suggests that the roosts are reoccupied after a few years. Another hunting method is undertaken by specialists who either access roosts with wooden ladders or light fires directly underneath the roosts and net or hit flying bats with wooden sticks as they emerge. Alternatively, a hunter descends the cliff on a rope and hits the bats with a stick as they exit (R. K. B. Jenkins and Racey 2008). The continued survival of *Eidolon* in the Central Highlands, even in areas that have been completely deforested and where few other native vertebrates survive, suggests that this species will persist even with continued moderate hunting pressure. However, roost sizes in the Central Highlands are generally small (only two appear to consist of over 100 animals), and so the contribution of this species to pollination and seed dispersal in this part of Madagascar is limited.

Population

There are insufficient data to quantify declines in *Eidolon* populations. Although exploitation levels are relatively high, this species appears to have survived such pressures for a long time. At current levels of hunting, it does not appear to be threatened with extinction. In 2015, a new protected area was created in the Anosibe An'Ala District, at Ampotaka-Ankorabe, designated for *E. dupreanum* roost conservation. Here, *E. dupreanum* was monitored monthly between 2016 and 2018. Population size fluctuated between 100 and 180 individuals. In terms of conservation, the viability of this species at this site is good. The challenge is to maintain this state by ensuring that this roost site continues to be undisturbed.

ROUSETTUS MADAGASCARIENSIS, MADAGASCAR ROUSETTE, *ANDREHY, BEMAINTY, FANIHY VATO, MATAVIKELY, NANAVIROVANA*

IUCN status: Vulnerable
Legal status: *animaux gibiers* (game)

Description

Rousettus madagascariensis is the smallest of Madagascar's fruit bats, formerly grouped by some authorities as a subspecies of the larger African form, *R. lanosus* (Hayman and Hill 1971), and by others as conspecific with *R. lanosus* (Kingdon 1974). Recent molecular work indicates that these taxa are best considered as full species (Goodman et al. 2010a). Bats of the genus *Rousettus* emit high-pitched sounds (with an audible buzz) by clicking their tongues in a form of echolocation (Waters and Vollrath 2003), which is no longer regarded as a primitive form of sonar (Yovel et al. 2011a).

The total average length of *R. madagascariensis* is 12.0 cm (MacKinnon et al. 2003); forearm length for adult male and female averages 72.0 and 70.0 cm, respectively; and adult male and female weights average 70 g and 58 g, respectively (Andrianaivoarivelo 2012). The upper body is gray-brown, and the underparts are a paler gray-brown. The ears are relatively short, and the wings broad. This bat seems not to have color vision (B. Müller et al. 2007). When flying, this species might be mistaken for a vespertilioniform (yangochiropteran) bat, but its eyeshine in torchlight and its direct flight distinguish it from insectivorous bats, which lack eyeshine and have a back-and-forth flight.

Morphological differences and reproductive phenology were examined in 3198 adult individuals of *R. madagascariensis* captured across five geographic areas of the island (east, north, northwest, west, and southeast) and four elevational ranges (0–300 m, 301–500 m, 501–1000 m, and >1000 m) from January 2001 to February 2010 (Andrianaivoarivelo 2012). Forearm and body mass measurements revealed evidence of sexual dimorphism, with males being larger (also see Goodman et al. 2017b). There were morphological differences according to geographic sites and elevation. Individuals from eastern and high-elevation colonies (>500 m) tend to have higher body mass, as well as shorter forearms, than bats in colonies at low elevations located in the west, north, and northwest. These phenotypic differences are inconsistent with molecular results, which concluded that genetic differences from microsatellite DNAs between geographically distant colonies are insignificant. The studied samples were taken from the same sites for genetic and morphometric studies. Due to its wide distribution, this relatively small frugivorous animal has been described as a species with significant dispersal capacity (Andrianaivoarivelo et al. 2012a). Goodman et al. (2010a) also found no evidence of genetic differentiation between *R. madagascariensis* populations across Madagascar.

Roosting Ecology

Rousettus madagascariensis roosts in caves, beyond the twilight zone (Figure 14.37c), and well-known roosts include those in caves in Bemaraha, Ankarana, and Anjohibe (near Mahajanga). It is also present on the neighboring islands of Nosy Be, Nosy Komba, and Ile Sainte Marie. Roosts can typically consist of several thousand animals. From different observations and other published records it seems likely that *Rousettus* is widely associated with forests, particularly in areas of caves (Andrianaivoarivelo et al. 2011a). It is unknown from the dry spiny thickets of the southwest and appears to be absent from the deforested portions of the Central Highlands (Goodman and Ramasindrazana 2013). In the eastern portion of the island, females have been observed with single young, especially during the austral summer (December–February) but also in a few circumstances during the winter (Andrianaivoarivelo 2012).

Feeding Ecology

Rousettus madagascariensis uses forested and fragmented habitats and agropastoral lands, and has a stronger preference for fruits of forest and pioneer plant species than for commercially important fruits (Andrianaivoarivelo et al. 2012a, 2012b). At least 12 introduced plant species and 10 native plant species are part of its diet (Andrianaivoarivelo 2012). Fruits of introduced plants are available seasonally, and most of the marketable fruits (e.g., *Litchi chinensis*, Sapindaceae; *Diospyros kaki*, Ebenaceae; *Syzygium malaccense*, Myrtaceae) from the east are ripe during the wet season. Other forest fruits or pioneer species sometimes found in degraded habitat (e.g., *Zizyphus mauritiana*, Rhamnaceae, from the northwest) provide continuous food for this bat species, especially during the dry season. The survival of *R. madagascariensis* depends at least in part on intact natural forest or at least secondary formations with their pioneer species and not exclusively on introduced plants. Thus, we assume that the magnitude of the damage to commercial fruit depends inversely on the range size of natural feeding sites. The disappearance of natural habitats is likely to lead to the decline of *R. madagascariensis* populations. In a study of population size and survival of *R. madagascariensis* in the dry deciduous *tsingy* forest of the Ankarana, Noroalintseheno Lalarivoniaina et al. (2019) concluded that the health and stability of the population relies heavily on individual survival, which underlines the negative effect of hunting.

Hunting and Conservation

The main threat to this species is hunting in its roost caves (Rakotonandrasana and Goodman 2007; R. K. B. Jenkins and Racey 2008; Andrianaivoarivelo et al. 2011a) and occasionally at feeding sites during the night, especially when the bats feed on economically important fruits (e.g., Andrianaivoarivelo et al. 2007). Hunting in cave roosts is very destructive, as a few hunters can collect hundreds of bats in a short time, and that may cause the bats to permanently desert the roost. The exploitation is mainly for domestic consumption, and no record has been found of *R. madagascariensis* sold alive in markets or served in restaurants.

In 2015, the new protected area of Ambatofotsy, designated partly for *R. madagascariensis* roost conservation, was created in the Anosibe An'Ala District. The cave where this species roosts is difficult to access and may be better protected than most, although there is recent (2008–2010) evidence of hunting. However, since the bats are used by local communities as a protein source, their exploitation must be managed to prevent excessive disturbance to the colony.

THE ROLE OF MALAGASY FRUIT BATS IN SEED DISPERSAL AND POLLINATION

Many of Madagascar's forest plants may be dependent on fruit bats for pollination and seed dispersal. Pollen or fruit remains from 114 plant species of 60 genera have been identified from the feces and ejecta of the three species of Malagasy fruit bats. For 80% of 20 plant species so far tested, seeds recovered from bat feces were more likely to germinate within four to six weeks than those of the same species taken from intact fruit (Oleksy 2014; Oleksy et al. 2017). *Pteropus rufus* can travel nightly distances of up to 34 km between roost and feeding sites (Long 2001; Oleksy et al. 2015b), and this species may thus disperse seeds between distant and isolated patches of forest. However, in certain cases adult females may travel nightly distance of up to 40 km between roosts during the mating season (April–June). In the moist evergreen forest, the average distance between the roost and feeding sites is 3.3 km, and this indicates the presence of preferred foods around the permanent roost sites.

Pteropus rufus shows a preference for foraging in native habitat or agroforest, such as an overgrown sisal plantation at Berenty, where it had a narrow dietary breadth, relying heavily on sisal pollen (Long and Racey 2007). This habitat was used more frequently than others available, regardless of the density of flowering sisal plants. This suggests that agroforestry on the island can in certain cases have a positive impact on fruit bat populations, but as explained above, *P. rufus* requires continuous food availability in its

home range. For a single colony over a period of three months, the total cumulative home-range area was 58,500 ha, but the curve had not reached an asymptote, and the area is presumed to be larger (Oleksy et al. 2015b). The females tend to make nightlong foraging trips, and they often vary their feeding sites while seeking fruit containing nutrients essential for gestation and lactation.

Pollen from 26 plant species and the remains of fruit from 40 species have been found in *Pteropus* feces and ejecta (Bollen and Van Elsacker 2002; Long and Racey 2007). Fourteen plant taxa were identified in the diet of *Eidolon dupreanum*, although seeds from a further 16 plant species were unidentified (Picot et al. 2007). From 150 fecal samples collected from one *Eidolon* roost, at Lake Tritriva, evidence of 22 plant species (from 21 genera) was found in a zone surrounded primarily by grasslands and *Eucalyptus* (Myrtaceae) plantations (Ratrimomanarivo 2007). The feces were collected over an eight-month period, so the total number of plant species visited throughout the year may be higher. From 958 fecal samples collected from four *Pteropus* roosts in Moramanga, evidence of 19 species (from nine plant genera) was found in a zone surrounded by forest fragments where the families Moraceae and Myrtaceae are most commonly represented (Andriafidison 2016). The plants most consumed by *P. rufus* in the Moramanga study are *Aphloia theiformis* (Aphloiaceae), *Eucalyptus* spp., *Harungana madagascariensis* (Hypericaceae), and *Ficus politoria* (Moraceae). Ratrimomanarivo (2007), based on the Lake Tritriva study, found that the diet of *E. dupreanum* in the Central Highlands consists mainly of introduced plants, which are the result of anthropogenic activity leading to a change in the flora over time.

About 20% of the plants identified in the diet of Malagasy pteropodids are economically significant. Two studies of Kapok (*Ceiba pentandra*, Malvaceae) have shown that pteropodids contribute to its pollination, and studies on two baobab species (*Adansonia suarezensis* and *A. grandidieri*, Malvaceae) suggest that bats are the main pollinators (Andriafidison et al. 2006a). *Eidolon dupreanum* visited these two *Adansonia* species and came into contact with the flowers' reproductive parts. In Kirindy Mité, *P. rufus* also visited *A. grandidieri*. In the case of *A. suarezensis*, no other vertebrate species is known to pollinate this baobab, while in the case of *A. grandidieri*, two species of lemurs also visited flowers but only those of trees situated in forest. Lemurs cannot enter flowering mature baobabs from the ground, as their trunks are too broad to climb. It is likely therefore that isolated *A. grandidieri* trees are pollinated only by fruit bats.

A study of bat damage to mango and lychee crops indicated that Malagasy fruit bats have little economic impact on these crops. The damage caused is much less than is widely believed and few fruit harvesters try to deter bats from eating their fruits. Lychee fruit damage was recorded in Tolagnaro and the western part of Anosibe An'Ala (Raharimihaja et al. 2016). In the case of mangoes in the Mahajanga region, a seasonal glut of fruit ensures that a much larger proportion of the crop is left unharvested than is taken by bats. In the case of lychees harvested on the east coast, bats were considered a problem in the past, such that deterrents were developed by Raharimihaja et al. (2016). However, in 2000, in only three villages of the dozen studied were bats considered to be a significant pest. Most respondents to a survey considered bats visiting their fruit trees to be more important as sources of meat than as pests.

Recent studies demonstrated that *R. madagascariensis* feeds more intensively on flowers than on fruits. In Maromizaha, the feces were composed mostly of leaves or unripe fruit, as well as pollen. This species was captured in Kirindy Mité feeding on *Ceiba pentandra* flowers (Andriafidison et al. 2006a). Seeds of six native forest plant species were found in the feces, and *Ficus* seeds were recorded especially during the rainy season. *Rousettus madagascariensis* swallows and is capable of dispersing seeds less than 2.5 mm in diameter. Ripe fruit of *F. rubra* was observed in native forest, and its seeds were present in *Rousettus* feces, in February 2005 (Andrianaivoarivelo et al. 2011a, 2011b). Given the significant time this species has spent in banana plantations in eastern Madagascar, it is likely that banana flowers extensively supplement its diet. Its intense feeding activity on banana and *Ceiba pentandra* flowers during periods of food scarcity would likely contribute to their pollination in substantial areas of eastern and western Madagascar, respectively.

In Maromizaha, no evidence of introduced invasive plant species (e.g., *Lantana camara*, Verbenaceae; *Miconia crenata*, previously known as *Clidemia hirta*, Melastomataceae) was observed in the feces of *R. madagascariensis*, and the use of luminescent light tags revealed that the average straight-line distance traveled between roost and foraging sites was 8.1 km (Andrianaivoarivelo et al. 2011a). At the same site, *F. rubra* seeds that had passed through the gut of *R. madagascariensis* germinated significantly faster than those extracted from the intact fruits, whereas germination percentage was similar across treatments.

In Ankarana, 13 plant taxa were identified from pollen swabs taken from the rostra of captured *R. madagascariensis* returning to the cave roost site in the early morning (Vololona et al. 2020). The most common plant species visited were *Parkia madagascariensis* (Fabaceae) and *Eucalyptus* species. It is assumed that the bats pollinated these species. An assortment of other pollen types was identified from the feces of captured *Rousettus*.

The role that *R. madagascariensis* plays as a pollinator and seed disperser is expressed by the fact that it has a very diverse diet that allows it to adapt to different habitats and even to disperse to different regions of the island and nearshore islets with different vegetation types. The ability of this species to move between natural and human-modified forest environments (agricultural fields or secondary formations) indicates its capacity to adapt to a mosaic of habitats. The large distributional range of some introduced plants, such as *Ziziphus jujuba* (Rhamnaceae) (Andrianaivoarivelo et al. 2011b, 2012a, 2012b) and *Ceiba pentandra*, as well as indigenous plants such as *F. sakalavarum*, all consumed by this bat species, is thought to facilitate the regional dispersal of the bats in western Madagascar during the dry season—while it pollinates flowers and disperses seeds across the zone. *Rousettus madagascariensis* eats fruits, leaves, nectar, and pollen. The bats are extremely mobile and are capable of flying considerable distances to exploit seasonal food resources. These long flights may be associated with fruit rarity in natural Malagasy forests at certain times of the year associated with irregular fruiting phenology (Canale et al. 2011). A quick and direct flight from the roost located at the Maromizaha forest edge to the flowering banana field 8 km away is an example of such a long night flight.

Subject editor: Steven M. Goodman

MYZOPODIDAE: *MYZOPODA*, OLD WORLD SUCKER-FOOTED BATS, *KAPITY LAVASOFINA, KIPOTIPOTY LAVASOFINA*

M. Ralisata, S. M. Goodman, A. F. Kofoky, P. A. Racey, and H. Schliemann

The evolutionary history and the systematic position of the genus *Myzopoda* has often been debated by bat taxonomists. In their original description of the genus based on material collected on Madagascar, Milne Edwards and Grandidier (1878) made no clear family designation except to say that it was not a vespertilionid genus and was best placed in a higher taxonomic category. Thomas (1904) reviewed the anatomy of the genus and created a new family, Myzopodidae, for the single species known at that time. This designation has generally since been followed, but the phylogenetic position of the Myzopodidae has remained ambiguous until recent molecular analyses clarified its relation to another family of bats possessing sucker-like structures, the Thyropteridae of the New World tropics, as well as the evolutionary history and origin of this enigmatic genus (Teeling et al. 2005, 2012).

The second important question resolved recently is the systematic position of the Myzopodidae in relation to other bat families and its higher relationships at the superfamily level. The Myzopodidae was previously placed in the superfamily Vespertilionoidea and in 1998 was considered part of the superfamily Nataloidea (Simmons 1998). Subsequent work by different research groups, largely based on molecular research, has shown that the Myzopodidae, most probably is the sister group of all members of the superfamily Noctilionoidea (Teeling 2005, 2012). However, the structure of the female reproductive tract and the placenta of *Myzopoda* are similar to those in the Emballonuridae, when compared with noctilionoid or vespertilionoid lineages (A. M. Carter et al. 2008).

The first clear evidence of the potential origin of the Myzopodidae was from a fossil humerus recovered in Pleistocene deposits of the Olduvai Gorge (Tanzania) that was tentatively placed in the genus *Myzopoda* and named *M. africana* (Gunnell et al. 2015). Further, two new fossil species allocated to the Myzopodidae were obtained from Paleogene deposits of the Fayum (Egypt); these include *Phasmatonycteris phiomensis* from the early Oligocene formation at Jebel Qatrani and *P. butleri* from the late Eocene formation at Birket Qarun (Gunnell et al. 2014). Hence, this family dates to at least 36 million years ago and is presumably African in origin but is today restricted to Madagascar. The Myzopodidae, which is represented by a single genus, *Myzopoda*, is endemic to the island. Fossils referred to this family have been identified from the late Eocene and early Oligocene of Egypt (Gunnell et al. 2014), and tentatively from the early Pleistocene of Tanzania (Butler 1978). The factors that led to the extinction of this family on the African continent are unknown, as is its colonization history from the mainland to Madagascar, but it is clear that the two extant species are derived from a common ancestor.

DISTRIBUTION AND SPECIES

With the recent wave of bat studies on Madagascar in the 21st century, *Myzopoda aurita* was considered to be an extremely rare and largely unknown mammal species that was represented by only a few museum specimens (Schliemann and Maas 1978; Figure 14.38a). More recently, based largely on expanded programs of biological inventories on Madagascar, including bat surveys, information on the geographic range and the ecology of this species has increased considerably.

Up until 2003, virtually all the known specimens of *Myzopoda* had come from Madagascar's east coast, except for a single report from Mahajanga (Majunga) (Schliemann and Goodman 2003). Eastern sites where this species has been captured, delineated in Goodman and Ramasindrazana (2013: 184), range across most of the latitudinal range of the moist evergreen forest from the Masoala Peninsula south to just north of Tolagnaro, and an elevational swath from near sea level to just under 1000 m. Further, on the basis of echolocation recordings, this species has been reported from Nosy Mangabe, an island in the Bay of Antongil (Russ and Bennett 1999).

Until recently, with the exception of a single *Myzopoda* specimen from the northwest (Mahajanga), all collected individuals of this genus were obtained as delineated above from the eastern moist evergreen forests of the island and associated with the name *M. aurita*. In 2003, an individual of *Myzopoda* with distinctly light pelage coloration was captured in dry deciduous forest at Ankarafantsika in the northwest and, shown to be morphologically different from eastern populations of *M. aurita*, was described as *M. schliemanni* (Goodman et al. 2007b; Figure 14.38b). Subsequently, a phylogeographic analysis based on samples of both forms from different localities on the island, found genetic corroboration for *M. schliemanni* being a separate species from *M. aurita* (A. L. Russell et al. 2008b). *Myzopoda schliemanni* is now known from numerous localities in the northwest, from north of Maintirano (Mandrozo) to just south of Antsohihy and across an elevational range from about 10–200 m above sea level (Goodman and Ramasindrazana 2013: 185).

MORPHOLOGY

Two unique morphological features easily distinguish *Myzopoda* from other genera of bats: first, a mushroom-shaped process, partly closing the outer auditory meatus, or ear opening (Thomas 1904; Figure 14.38a); and second, the conspicuous horseshoe-like, sessile adhesive disks on the thumb and sole (Figure 14.39). Further, the ears are large and separate, the upper lip extends beyond the lower, the tail is long and extends beyond the well-developed uropatagium (a web of skin extending between the hind legs and enclosing the tail), and the thumb has a small vestigial claw. The dental formula is incisors 2/3, canines 1/1, premolars 3/3, molars 3/3 (× 2) = 38. The second digit is reduced to the metacarpal, and the toes are united along the proximal half of the first phalanx and are distally free

FIGURE 14.38 **Since the last years of the 20th century, there have been considerable advancements in information on the natural history of members of the family Myzopodidae, which is endemic to Madagascar. A) *Myzopoda aurita* was previously known from a handful of specimens, and few details were available on its natural history. Recent field and laboratory studies have uncovered many intriguing details, including how its suckers function. B) A second species in the genus, *M. schliemanni*, was described in 2007 from Ankarafantsika, in the west, and the individual shown here was used as the type specimen. One of the remarkable windows into the ecology of both species has been their roosting ecology. Day-roost sites have been located by attaching radio collars to netted individuals captured during the night and following the signals to the sites, which for C) *M. aurita* are largely in *Ravenala* leaves and for D) *M. schliemanni* in *Bismarckia* leaves.** (PHOTO A by C. Lee, B by S. M. Goodman, C by M. Ralisata, and D by A. F. Kofoky.)

but closely approximated. There are only two phalanges to each toe, the mesosternum is slightly keeled, and there is no fusion of vertebrae (with the exception of the sacrum). The trochiter of the humerus (tuberculum majus) forms a very well-developed secondary articulation with the dorsal side of the scapula. The shoulder joint of *Myzopoda* is very similar in its details to that found in Vespertilionidae and Molossidae, although in these families the secondary shoulder joint is developed further (Schliemann 1997; Schliemann and Schlosser-Sturm 1999).

Whereas these remarkable features of the locomotor apparatus and the unique characters mentioned above (mushroom-shaped process and adhesive disks) show *Myzopoda* to be a rather specialized animal, this does not apply to the skeleton as a whole or to the dentition. Nearly 100 years ago Thomas (1904) and G. S. Miller (1907) had already drawn attention to this fact: *Myzopoda* shows a mixture of basal and specialized features. Details of the skull, the dentition, and the postcranial skeleton of *M. aurita* can be found in the publications of Dobson (1878), Thomas (1904), and G. S. Miller (1907), and craniodental aspects of *M. schliemanni* in Goodman et al. (2007b). External measurements of both species are provided in Table 14.27. For *M. aurita*, other skull measurements and illustrations of the skull, portions of the postcranial skeleton, and head can also be found in Thomas (1904).

Adhesive Disks

In the past, the adhesive disks of *Myzopoda* and those of *Thyroptera* (Thyropteridae, New World sucker-footed bat) have been described as structurally similar or perhaps even showing a common phylogenetic origin. It is now clear that in both genera these organs are very sophisticated but show completely different morphological structures and are independently derived. Some decades ago little was known about the morphology of the adhesive disks of *Thyroptera* and nothing about those organs in *Myzopoda* (Dobson 1876; Schliemann 1970, 1971; Wimsatt and Villa-R. 1970). They clearly serve a role in the roosting biology of members of these two genera. Although there is much information on the roosting sites and behavior of *Thyroptera*, allowing for interpretation of how these animals make use of their adhesive organs (Schliemann 1970; Findley and Wilson 1974), until recently there has been little information about the roosting sites of *Myzopoda* and how their adhesive disks might be employed. Because of the presumed functional significance of the adhesive organs of *Myzopoda*, their very interesting morphology, and the rarity of such organs in mammals, some details of their structure are presented here.

The adhesive organs of *Myzopoda* (Figure 14.39) are flat, disk-shaped sessile skin accessories becoming thinner distally and

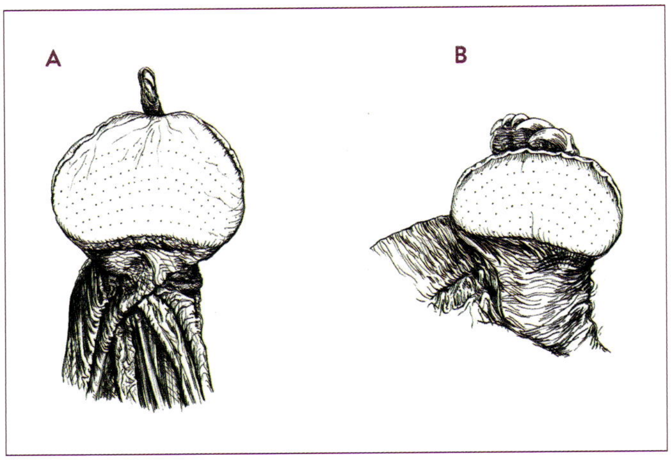

FIGURE 14.39 **Ventral views of the adhesive organs of *Myzopoda aurita*. Left: adhesive organ of the left anterior extremity; right: adhesive organ of the left posterior extremity. Note the linear arrangement of the integument pores.** (DRAWING by A. Schulz.)

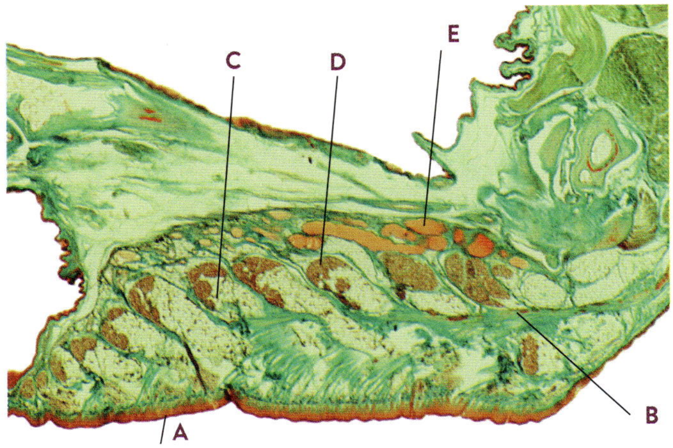

FIGURE 14.40 **Longitudinal cross section through the adhesive organ of the anterior extremity of *Myzopoda aurita*: A) thickened ventral epithelium; B) tendons of musculus palmaris longus; C) adipose tissue in cylindrical compartments; D) skin glands; E) venous plexus.** (MODIFIED from Schliemann and Goodman, 2011.)

laterally. They are situated ventrally on the thumb (underneath the proximal phalanx and the base of the distal phalanx) and ventrally on the sole (underneath the distal three-quarters of the metatarsals and the bases of the proximal phalanges). The outlines of these organs can be described as roughly horseshoe-shaped, the organ on the sole being especially extended in a transversal direction. The organ on the thumb is 6.5 mm wide and 4.0 mm long, and that on the sole 5.0 mm wide and 3.0 mm long. The ventral surface is essentially even and smooth, with conspicuous openings of skin glands arranged in curved lines, which are visible in the older alcohol-preserved material. This surface shows less pigmentation than other dermal portions of specimens, and in recently collected material, it is translucent.

These organs consist mainly of adipose tissue, collagenous connective tissue, tendons, glands, and numerous venous vessels (Figure 14.40). The adipose tissue is subdivided in cylindrical compartments lying in transverse and slightly concave lines, corresponding exactly with that of the gland openings on the ventral epithelium, since each adipose tissue compartment contains one of these glands. The compartments are orientated in an oblique manner extending from the dorsal side of the organs (and distally) to its ventral side (and proximally).

Strong bundles of collagenous fibers pass through the ventral half of the organs. The passage of the fiber bundles through each organ is rather complicated: they enter the organ proximally, splitting up over the whole breadth of the organ, and then envelop the ventral half of the adipose tissue compartments along an undulating course. At the same time the fiber bundles run in an arcuate manner to the ventral epithelium. Here they are divided into smaller bundles, which are fixed in the cleft-like dermal papillae between the cone-shaped epithelial projections into the corium. All the tendinous tissue originates from a tendinous membrane near the proximal rim of the organs. This membrane is connected with the musculus palmaris longus (of the forelimb) and with the musculus flexor tibialis (of the hind limb).

The dorsal half of the adipose tissue compartments is not enveloped by these strong tendinous fibers but instead by more delicate connective tissue associated with elastic fibers. In the most dorsal portion of each compartment, the body of the skin gland is localized and connected to the ventral epithelium by a long excretory duct. A vast number of venae forming plexuses are found dorsal to the adipose tissue compartments and beside small arteries, nerves, and Vater-Pacini corpuscles. It is assumed that these venae function as erectile tissue,

TABLE 14.27. **External measurements and weights of *Myzopoda aurita* and *M. schliemanni* adult specimens**

SPECIES	TOTAL LENGTH (mm)	TAIL LENGTH (mm)	HIND-FOOT LENGTH (mm)	EAR LENGTH (mm)	FOREARM LENGTH (mm)	WEIGHT (g)
M. aurita (n = 18)	113.4 ± 1.01	49.1 ± 0.64	5.5 ± 0.22	33.1 ± 0.17	48.4 ± 1.38	8.9 ± 0.57
	106–120	43–54	4–7	32–34	46–51	8.0–8.9
M. schliemanni (n = 27)	109.1 ± 0.63	46.3 ± 0.51	4.9 ± 0.08	33.2 ± 0.25	47.5 ± 0.27	8.0 ± 0.14
	100–118	42–54	4–6	30–36	45–51	6.5–9.9

Notes: All field measurements made by the same field worker. Sexes combined. Measurements presented as mean ± standard deviation, and minimum–maximum range.

helping to stabilize the adhesive disks, which are otherwise not supported by any skeletal structure. Further, they would help to extend or stretch out the disks, which would be necessary to bring the ventral epithelium in contact with the surface to which the animal clings.

The ventral epithelium and the glands of the adhesive organs are also remarkable, since they differ widely from what is known in other mammals (Schliemann 1970). The ventral epithelium, which is exposed to mechanical stress due to contact with the surface, is thickened compared to the other epithelia of the bat's body. Histologically, it is a multilayered, cornified squamous epithelium. Its inner surface bordering the corium is formed mainly by very unusual cone-shaped protrusions into the corium, the tips of which lie close to the network of elastic fibers. As already mentioned, tendinous fiber bundles surround these cones and terminate in the cleft-like distal parts of the papillary layer between the epidermal cones. In scanning-electron micrographs, the whole surface of the adhesive epithelium is seen to be unusually characterized by pegs, ridges, pits, and troughs; all these structures measure less than 1 μm, a topography notably different from the surface of the stratum corneum elsewhere on the organ. This surface is ideally suited to create and maintain a liquid film, which is a requirement for the functional mode of wet adhesion (see below).

The glands consist of a long excretory duct and a secretory part, situated mainly in a dorsal position of the cylindrical compartments and arranged in acini, consisting of secretory cells with numerous apical secretory granules. The morphology of the glands suggests that their secretion is a thin, watery fluid. These glands are similar to those of the mouth cavity and do not show any resemblance to skin glands of other mammals.

It has been proposed by several authors that the disks are sucking organs or that there might be a gluing effect or a combination of these functional modes (Schliemann 1970; Schliemann and Maas 1978; Thewissen and Etnier 1995, Göpfert and Wasserthal 1995). However, recent investigations have proven that the pads work by wet adhesion, facilitated by the continuous glandular secretion described above (Riskin and Racey 2010). These latter authors investigated the adhesive performance of 28 living individuals of *M. aurita*. They found that the adhesive force of the wrist pads was more than ninefold weaker when lifted perpendicular to the surface than when pulled parallel to it, and further attachment performance was not affected by the presence or absence of a seal around the pad–surface interface. Both findings are characteristic for wet adhesion. With these findings, all other considerations about the function of the adhesive organs are obsolete. The morphological details of the adhesive disks (Schliemann and Goodman 2011) are in accordance with this functional mode; this species is also known to roost on smooth cave walls (Kofoky et al. 2006).

Riskin and Racey (2010) also found when pushing the wrist pads anteriorly that they peel more easily from the surface than when they are pushed in the opposite direction. This observation is due to the deformation of the pads by a longitudinal fold forming at the center, facilitating detachment during crawling, even along vertical surfaces. Hence, if the bat roosted head down it would cause passive detachment of the pads. Schliemann and Goodman (2011) explained the formation of the longitudinal fold on the pads associated with the collagenous fiber bundles, which are moved dorsally by contraction of the aforementioned muscles. The functional mode of wet adhesion and the morphological features of the pads provide an ecomorphological explanation of the head-up roosting behavior reported in these bats.

VOCALIZATIONS

Recent work on echolocation calls of *M. aurita* by Ralisata (2018) confirms earlier observations of Göpfert and Wasserthal (1995) and Russ and Bennett (1999). This species emits distinct complex frequency-modulated (FM) echolocation calls, with two to four elements of increasing amplitude and long call duration. The call structure is notably variable, due to the different number of elements, with up to four harmonics, and the frequency decreasing from the first to the last element. For example, the second harmonic, generally the strongest element, has a maximum energy that decreases from 42 to 28 kHz and a shallow FM sweep of about 1 kHz/ms. Individuals recorded in flight cages produce calls of shorter duration and inter-pulse intervals than those free-flying. The vocalizations of *M. schliemanni* are also complex and composed of four elements with decreasing frequency (A. F. Kofoky, unpublished data). The dominant frequency is about 46.5 kHz, and its echolocation call consists of a short constant frequency, followed by a shallow FM sweep, and terminates with quite steep FM. When leaving and entering its roosts, *M. aurita* emits six recognizable social calls with lower frequencies than echolocation calls (Ralisata 2018).

ECOLOGY, SOCIAL BEHAVIOR, AND REPRODUCTION

In an ecological study of *M. aurita* in a coffee research station at Kianjavato in the southeast, now part of the Ambositra-Vondrozo protected area, 593 individuals were caught—229 unique captures and 364 recaptures, exclusively males (Figure 14.38c). Such sexual segregation in such a relatively small study area is unique among bats and maybe among mammals (Ralisata et al. 2015). No female was recorded at the study area during the seven years of research. However, Goodman et al. (2014c), at sites within 4 km of Kianjavato and at lower elevations, captured females shortly after the termination of the Ralisata et al. study. Analysis of the sex ratio of specimens in museum collections also reveals a strong male bias (P. A. Racey, unpublished data).

In a parallel study in the Andranomanitsy Forest, north of Besalampy in western Madagascar, a site composed of dry deciduous forest and associated palm grassland, A. F. Kofoky (unpublished data) established that *M. schliemanni* roosted exclusively within dead and attached leaves of *Bismarckia nobilis* (family Arecaceae; Figure 14.38d) within the palm grassland. No bats were found in the other palm species available in the grassland nor in *Ravenala* (family Strelitziaceae) in nearby marshlands. Two types of day-roost groups were identified: breeding/maternity colonies, which contain exclusively females, either pregnant or lactating, and offspring; and male bachelor colonies. Mixed colonies were found during the transition between the seasons, from October to

December. The bachelor colonies were observed during the dry and cool season. In July 2008, a bachelor colony was found with more than 30 individuals.

At Kianjavato, *M. aurita* roosted in the partially unfurled central leaves of *Ravenala*, and no bat was found in any other roosting situation (Ralisata et al. 2015). Leaves took between three and 25 days to unfurl, and roosts became available between one and 19 days after unfurling commenced and were then occupied for between one and 12 days. *Myzopoda aurita* was more likely to occupy roosts on taller trees, whereas *M. schliemanni* roosted between 2.5 and 4 m from the ground. No ectoparasite was ever found on *M. aurita*, and this may reflect the smooth and clean nature of the roosting surface inhibiting the pupae and instar development of different invertebrates, as well as frequent roost switching. In contrast, bat flies (see Dick, pp. 1099–101) were found on *M. schliemanni* (S. M. Goodman, unpublished data), but these have yet to be identified.

The size of roosting groups of *M. aurita* varied between one and 36 individuals and of *M. schliemanni* between one and 32. Movements of *M. aurita* between roosts were recorded on 35 occasions, and between two and nine individuals found in one roost were subsequently found together in a different roost. Russ and Bennett (1999) examined over 200 *Ravenala* leaves in a zone near where they recorded *Myzopoda*. About 5% were furled, and none contained this bat. In *M. schliemanni*, individual bats changed roost sites every one to seven days and utilized the same roost on average for 2.8 consecutive days (A. F. Kofoky, unpublished data).

To date, we are unaware of any individual of *Myzopoda* captured in deep forest. The vast majority of recently netted individuals have been found in either extensive marshlands, generally dominated by *Ravenala* and *Typhonodorum* (family Araceae), another plant with massive broad leaves, or in secondary forest habitat, often in close vicinity to marshlands, including those converted to rice paddy. *Ravenala* does particularly well in secondary zones and is often one of the principal colonists after extensive habitat alteration. In the Tampolo Forest a single individual of *M. aurita* was captured at the edge of an extensive marsh system and within 50 m of an extensive *Eucalyptus* plantation (S. M. Goodman, unpublished data). Near Maroantsetra and on the Masoala Peninsula, its calls were recorded over old rice paddies and villages (Russ and Bennett 1999). Thus, in general, *M. aurita* appears to make extensive use of marshlands and degraded habitats, presumably when foraging. It is thus probably one of the few endemic mammals to Madagascar that has benefited from anthropogenic habitat modifications in eastern Madagascar.

Radio-tracking at Kianjavato revealed that *M. aurita* foraged preferentially in coffee plantations, degraded moist evergreen forest, wooded grassland, and over rice fields (Ralisata 2018; Ralisata et al. 2010). The home range of tagged individuals was up to 148 ha and the maximum recorded distance between the tagging site and the foraging site was 1.8 km. In *M. schliemanni*, the foraging range varied from 15 to 205 ha, and individual bats when foraging traveled up to 3.6 km from their day roost. The most preferred foraging areas in this species were open *Bismarckia* grasslands (A. F. Kofoky, unpublished data).

Both species of *Myzopoda* are seasonal breeders. In *M. aurita* at Kianjavato, juveniles were captured only from February to March and October to November. For this species, the pseudo-scrotum of 83 males examined between October and November appeared to be larger than at other times (Ralisata 2018). In *M. schliemanni*, during the transitional dry and humid seasons (late October–mid-December), 54% of the individuals captured were pregnant females. One female in a day-roost site gave birth to a single baby on 28 November 2008, and on 1 December 2007 a captured female was lactating and carrying a neonate (A. F. Kofoky, unpublished data). It is presumed that both species breed once per year and have a litter size of one.

DIET

A number of studies have been conducted on the prey consumed by *M. aurita*. On the basis of fecal samples from 12 individuals captured in the central eastern lowlands at Ivoloina, the three principal insect orders consumed are in order of importance: Lepidoptera, Coleoptera, and Blattodea; Araneae was also identified (Ramasindrazana et al. 2009). Lepidoptera had the highest mean percentage by volume and was identified in all samples. In a study of this species at Kianjavato, based on the pellets of five individuals, the following orders were identified (percentage by volume in parentheses): Lepidoptera (40.1%), Coleoptera (26.7%), Araneae (15.4%), Hymenoptera (8.4%), Neuroptera (5.5%), Diptera (3.6%), and Homoptera (0.3%) (Rasoanoro et al. 2015). In another dietary study at Kianjavato, Lepidoptera and Coleoptera were the principal invertebrates consumed by *M. aurita*, and there were statistically significant seasonal differences in the proportions of these two orders consumed (Ralisata et al. 2010; Ralisata 2018). Rabarison (2016), working in the central eastern lowland moist evergreen forest of Betampona, found, based on percentage by volume in fecal samples, that this species fed predominantly on Lepidoptera (82.4%), followed in descending importance by Coleoptera, Arachnida, Diptera, Ephemeroptera, Hemiptera, Dictyoptera, and Orthoptera.

Analysis of the diet of *M. schliemanni*, based on scat samples from 18 individuals captured in the Andranomanitsy Forest, found Lepidoptera to be the most common prey type, consumed by 89% of the individuals, followed by Blattodea, consumed by 78% of the animals, and a notably smaller representation of Coleoptera and Hymenoptera (A. F. Kofoky and S. M. Goodman, unpublished data); parallel results were obtained in another study from the same site (B. Rajemison and Goodman 2007). Another study of fecal pellets of *M. schliemanni* collected at Mandrozo in central western Madagascar (Ravelojaona 2017) found Lepidoptera made up 64.3% of the insect remains, followed by Coleoptera 22.8%, Hymenoptera 11.4%, Blattodea 1.0%, and Orthoptera 0.1%; traces of Trichoptera were also identified. No significant differences were found in the diets of males and females in the percentages of the six orders of insects consumed.

CONSERVATION

Until recently, little was known about the distribution and conservation status of *Myzopoda* species. In the 1988 IUCN Red List assessment, *M. aurita* was designated as Insufficiently Known and

then, in the 1990, 1994, and 1996 assessments, as Vulnerable. Subsequently, and associated with a period during which extensive bat inventories found this species to be common at certain localities, its IUCN status was reduced to Least Concern in 2008 and has remained as such since. In a parallel fashion, *M. schliemanni* was given the conservation status Least Concern in 2008, and this is currently maintained.

As the principal roosting sites of *M. schliemanni*, in the west, are in the fronds of *Bismarckia*, and those of *M. aurita*, in the east, are in the leaves of *Ravenala*, both of which are used by local people for house thatching and different construction purposes, the exploitation of these materials may have an impact on the roosting sites of these two species. Members of this genus have not been found roosting in any human-built structures or in unfurling banana leaves.

Even given the different conservation problems Madagascar is facing, particularly concerning the loss of native forest, the Least Concern status is well justified for both species, as they have large geographic distributions and can be found in highly modified habitats. In fact, these two species are among the few endemic mammals that have benefited from anthropogenic habitat modifications in Madagascar.

Subject editor: Steven M. Goodman

CHEIROGALIDAE: *CHEIROGALEUS*, DWARF LEMURS, *TSITSIHY*, *MATAVY RAMBO*

M. B. Blanco

The dwarf lemurs of Madagascar (genus *Cheirogaleus*), akin to other members of the family Cheirogaleidae, are small-bodied, nocturnal, and heterothermic (the genus *Phaner* being the only non-heterothermic member of the family; see Dausmann et al., pp. 1798–805, for further details). Dwarf lemurs are able to variably reduce metabolism for hours, days, or weeks, and they are the only known obligate hibernators within the order Primates. As far as is documented, all nine of the currently recognized species of dwarf lemurs, across a range of habitats, hibernate between three and seven months per year (Dausmann 2014; Blanco et al. 2018). The use of this extreme metabolic strategy requires dwarf lemurs to deposit large amounts of body fat to sustain metabolism during hibernation. These cycles between activity and hibernation shape the behavior, ecology, physiology, and life histories of dwarf lemurs in unique ways. Herein, a review is provided of what is known about this rather remarkable genus of lemurs, specifically since the precursor of this book (Fietz 2003), with a certain emphasis on ecophysiology.

TAXONOMY

The taxonomic history of *Cheirogaleus* shows an unusual trajectory in the "waxing and waning" of recognized species in recent years that is related to a number of different taxonomic issues, and changes in systematists' perspectives in using a few diagnostic genetic markers over traditional morphological characters and ecological attributes (see Yoder, pp. 1821–24, for further details on this subject).

Dwarf lemurs were originally classified as two main morphotypes, a smaller, gray western type (*C. medius*) and larger, brownish-reddish eastern type (*C. major*). In the 1970s, distinctions within the eastern lineage by J.-J. Petter et al. (1977) led to the recognition of two subspecies within the eastern type, the "brown" form, *C. m. major*, and the "red" form, *C. m. crossleyi*, with the former primarily found in lower-elevation moist evergreen forests, and the latter frequently observed in degraded habitats (J.-J. Petter et al. 1977; Hapke et al. 2005). At the turn of the century, Groves (2000) published a revision of the genus based on museum specimens and increased the number of species to seven, naming *C. adipicaudatus* as a new species in the *medius* group, and *C. ravus*, *C. sibreei*, *C. crossleyi*, and *C. minusculus* in the *major* group. As Groves relied exclusively on morphological characters, such as dental traits and fur coloration, to diagnose these new species, based mostly on older museum specimens, it was difficult for field researchers to identify animals captured during field studies to these species.

Almost a decade later, in an ambitious attempt to reconcile information from museum specimens with samples from field locations across Madagascar, Groeneveld et al. (2009) undertook a taxonomic revision of the genus *Cheirogaleus* based on morphological and genetic characters. They concluded that some of the species identified by Groves were best treated as synonyms: *C. ravus* was subsumed in *C. major* and *C. adipicaudatus* in *C. medius*. On the basis of samples available to them, Groeneveld et al. (2009) recognized three lineages deserving species recognition: *C. medius*, *C. crossleyi*, and *C. major*, leaving the status of *C. sibreei* unresolved and deeming that of *C. minusculus* inconclusive. This reduction in the number of recognized species highlighted that morphological variation alone was inadequate to define species among this genus of lemur. For example, the reddish versus silvery fur coloration found in the *major* lineage did not match genetic variation that warranted species status. In a subsequent publication, Groeneveld et al. (2010) confirmed the presence of a fourth independent lineage, *C. sibreei*, when samples were included in the analysis from a population at

Tsinjoarivo, a medium-altitude moist evergreen forest in central eastern Madagascar. The presence of this species had been indicated in a previous work based on morphology (Blanco et al. 2009).

As of 2020, nine species of *Cheirogaleus* are recognized: *C. medius*, *C. shethi*, and *C. thomasi* (within the *medius*-like group); *C. crossleyi*, *C. lavasoensis*, *C. andysabini*, and *C. grovesi* (within the *crossleyi*-like group); *C. major*; and *C. sibreei* (Frasier et al. 2016; Lei et al. 2014; McLain et al. 2017; Thiele et al. 2013).

ABUNDANCE

Pioneering studies during the 1980s and 1990s showed relatively high abundance of fat-tailed *Cheirogaleus medius* in the western dry deciduous forests of Madagascar. For instance, Hladik et al. (1980) estimated population densities of about 350 ind/km^2 (individuals per square kilometer) in Marosalaza, 50 km north of Morondava, and Fietz (1999) provided similar assessments of between 280 and 360 ind/km^2 for the years 1996 and 1998 at Kirindy Forest CNFEREF, a nearby and similar type of forest. Due to ramping deforestation rates in the Menabe Region since the start of the 21st century (Zinner et al. 2014), there is growing concern that the area of occupancy of dwarf lemurs has been severely reduced, though updated density numbers are lacking. As far as the eastern species are concerned, early assessments showed that *C. major* was frequently sighted at a lowland moist evergreen forest block near Mahambo, about 60 km north of Toamasina, with densities estimated between 75 and 110 ind/km^2 (Pollock 1979). More recent studies at Vohibola III, a southeastern medium-altitude moist evergreen forest, estimated densities for *C. major* of between four and 60 ind/km^2 and observed this species showing negative edge effects, with lowest density levels toward the edge of the forest (Lehman et al. 2006b). More recent density estimates by Herrera et al. (2018) in the medium-altitude moist evergreen forest at Ranomafana range from two to >12 ind/km^2 for *C. sibreei* and two to >50 ind/km^2 for *C. crossleyi*.

Eastern dwarf lemurs have lower densities than western dwarf lemurs, which may be the result of a habitat bias, because these nocturnal lemurs are more difficult to see in the eastern closed-canopy moist evergreen forest environments compared to the western dry deciduous forests. This trend, however, is not limited to the genus *Cheirogaleus* and has been noted for the genus *Microcebus* (Setash et al. 2017). Somewhat surprisingly, recent lemur surveys conducted in the SAVA Region in the northeast showed high mean encounter rates (number of individuals/transect length) for dwarf lemurs in secondary forests with vanilla plantations compared to low-altitude moist evergreen forest fragments and fallow-derived vanilla sites (F. Ravelomandrato, unpublished data). The presence of dwarf lemurs, highly frugivorous species, in small fragments specialized for vanilla cultivation may be indicative of sinking, rather than thriving populations. Anecdotal data from Tsinjoarivo, where *C. sibreei* and *C. crossleyi* live in sympatry, show a progressive decline in trapping success for both species since 2006, from a handful of individuals captured per day to almost no lemurs captured every two weeks, when keeping trap numbers and the time of the year relatively constant. This pattern is particularly pronounced for *C. sibreei*, which is rarely captured or seen anymore at similar surveyed locations at Tsinjoarivo (M. Blanco, unpublished data).

LIFE HISTORY

The complex life-history strategies of dwarf lemurs cannot be understood without considering their status as obligate hibernators (also see Dausmann et al., pp. 1798–805). Dwarf lemurs of all species and across different habitat types hibernate, although the timing and duration are highly variable. At the Duke Lemur Center in the United States, where *C. medius* is maintained under constant temperatures and offered daily food, dwarf lemurs express short torpor bouts, and they continue to eat every day, or every few days, during the "torpor season." A recent study, however, showed that the same lemurs can hibernate for weeks at the time, without feeding, when controlling for lower temperatures and restricting food (M. Blanco, unpublished data).

Hibernation has shaped the life history of dwarf lemurs in unique ways. For instance, compared to similar-size strepsirrhine primates, such as bush babies (e.g., *Galago moholi*), dwarf lemurs display shorter gestation periods, of about 60 days, as compared to about 120 days in bush babies. The relatively short pregnancy and lactation periods allow adult *Cheirogaleus* females sufficient time to fatten in preparation for hibernation. In the wild, juvenile dwarf lemurs have the strictest of schedules, as they must grow, achieve independence, and prepare for hibernation during a window of five months or less. To do so, infants exhibit fast growth rates, achieving ~85% of body length and ~90% of head measurements during the first three to four months of life. By this time, most of the molars are already in place (Blanco and Godfrey 2014). Soon after weaning, young dwarf lemurs begin depositing fat stores that will be used to fuel metabolism during their first hibernation season.

When young individuals are captured right before and after hibernation, they show the same dental status—with deciduous third and fourth premolars still in place—and the same overall size, demonstrating that somatic growth and dental development are halted during hibernation. In the weeks following emergence from hibernation, juvenile dwarf lemurs continue to grow and attain dental maturation, though sexual maturity is generally achieved only during the second year of life. For instance, females may show evidence of vaginal swelling at the end of their first year, but they generally do not have their first offspring until they are two or three years old (A. E. Müller 1999; Blanco and Godfrey 2014). This stepwise trajectory of relatively fast growth and development and "delayed" reproduction is unique among primates. In captivity, because hibernation expression is attenuated by mild environmental conditions, this trajectory is softened, and juvenile dwarf lemurs grow more gradually and achieve sexual reproduction during the first year of life (Blanco and Zehr 2015).

Wild *Cheirogaleus* females mate soon after they come out of hibernation, between October and December, and generally give birth to a single litter per year, with one to four offspring per litter (Lahann and Dausmann 2011; Blanco and Godfrey 2014). Males generally come out of hibernation two to four weeks earlier than do females, and during this time their testes enlarge and they secure territories (A. E. Müller 1999). Reproduction may be irregular in some dwarf lemur populations. For instance, *C. thomasi* (formerly lumped together with *C. medius*) from the littoral forest of Mandena reproduces every year, whereas *C. medius* from dry deciduous

forest of Kirindy Forest CNFEREF generally produces offspring every other year (Lahann and Dausmann 2011). Currently, the data are insufficient to determine whether variation in reproductive parameters is species-specific, shaped by the environment, or both.

PHYSIOLOGICAL ECOLOGY

Mammals thermoregulate by producing heat to maintain homeostasis (see Dausmann et al., pp. 1798–805, for further details on ecophysiology of lemurs). During the active period, dwarf lemurs behave like other endotherms and actively maintain body temperature within narrow limits. During hibernation, however, the body temperature of dwarf lemurs approximates that of the immediate environment, and the degree of energy savings (or expenditure) depends on the thermic properties of the hibernaculum. Thus, the type of tree hole selected becomes critical for successful hibernation, because larger trees can provide greater insulation to buffer external temperature variation (Dausmann et al. 2009; Blanco et al. 2013b). Not only do the temperature extremes of a hibernaculum (how cold or hot it gets) determine the rate of fat depletion, but so too does the temperature variability (e.g., in poorly insulated tree holes daily temperature fluctuation can be more than 20°C). Both temperature features of a given hibernaculum will further determine whether or not the dwarf lemurs need to internally produce heat to arouse, or if they can passively achieve euthermy (i.e., body temperature over 30°C) by tracking hibernaculum temperatures. The inextricable relationship between metabolism and hibernaculum selection is based on the fact that cellular enzymatic reactions are temperature-dependent, and metabolic rates will increase, or decrease, as the temperature of the hibernaculum rises, or falls. For animals like dwarf lemurs that rely on fat storage for fuel, warmer temperatures mean faster rates of depletion. However, if individuals can passively warm up to achieve euthermy, fat stores can be maintained for longer periods. This can lead to very different thermic profiles during hibernation: dwarf lemurs experiencing stable temperature during torpor bouts and undergoing periodic arousals versus dwarf lemurs passively warming up and cooling down during torpor without undergoing energetically expensive arousals. Although these physiological patterns would look very different, energetic savings would be comparable in these contrasting conditions (Dausmann et al. 2009).

There is variation in hibernation "styles" not only within field sites but also across habitats. One fascinating aspect of *Cheirogaleus* ecophysiology is that dwarf lemurs, unlike more traditional temperate hibernators, inhabit a great range of forest types, each with unique temperature profiles during hibernation season. For example, dry deciduous forests such as Kirindy Forest CNFEREF are subjected to dramatic daily temperature fluctuations, ranging from about 10°C to 32°C (Fietz and Dausmann 2006). In contrast, montane moist evergreen forests like Tsinjoarivo experience colder but less fluctuating temperatures, ranging from 9°C to 17°C, though absolute values can drop close to freezing on occasion (Dausmann and Blanco 2016).

In addition to temperature variation in their environment, these animals vary in size depending on the species, with body mass of about 150 g for *C. medius*, 250 g for *C. sibreei*, 350 g for *C. crossleyi*, and 450 g for *C. major*. Those values significantly increase during pre-hibernation fattening. The interplay between habitat (temperature profiles) and species (body mass related to metabolic demands) determines the animal's metabolic profiles. For instance, small dwarf lemurs, by virtue of having relatively higher metabolic rates per unit of body mass, benefit the most by hibernating. Furthermore, dwarf lemurs inhabiting colder environments achieve greater reductions in metabolic rates than do those living in warmer habitats. *Cheirogaleus medius* is able to save up to 70% energy during hibernation in dry forests like Kirindy Forest CNFEREF, whereas the slightly larger *C. sibreei* can save up to ~90% while hibernating at colder, stable temperatures (Dausmann and Blanco 2016). *Cheirogaleus medius* in western Madagascar exclusively hibernates inside tree holes, whereas eastern species such as *C. sibreei* and *C. crossleyi* hibernate underground in medium-altitude moist evergreen forests (Figure 14.41d). There is some evidence that eastern species like *C. major*, or even *C. crossleyi* in lower-elevation moist evergreen forests, may hibernate inside tree holes or in nest-like structures, at least during a portion of the hibernation season (J.-J. Petter et al. 1977; Blanco et al. 2018).

HABITAT USE AND SOCIAL SYSTEMS

Dwarf lemurs are found in a variety of habitats, from western dry deciduous forests to moist evergreen forests. The only ecoregion where they are conspicuously absent is the dry spiny thicket of the south. However, subfossil bones attributed to *C. medius* have been recovered from the Ankilitelo Cave in the northern portion of the southwest, along with a diverse assemblage of extant taxa absent from the region today (Muldoon et al. 2009). That dwarf lemurs were present at Ankilitelo in the past millennia suggests they underwent a significant geographic-range contraction, perhaps due to a combination of natural climate change and human-induced forest fragmentation.

Dwarf lemurs form small groups that share common territories. For instance, Fietz (1999) showed that family units (see below) of *C. medius* at Kirindy Forest CNFEREF had overlapping home ranges of about 1.5 ha. A. E. Müller (1998), at Ampijoroa, in dry deciduous forest of the northwest, estimated home ranges for *C. medius* to be between 1.0 and 2.4 ha. Similar estimates of about 2.0 ha were given for *C. thomasi* in the southeastern littoral forests of Mandena (Lahann 2007a). Preliminary data from eastern *Cheirogaleus* species indicate larger home ranges, though there is much variation. Lahann (2007a) estimated home ranges for *C. major* at Mandena, when it lives in sympatry with *C. thomasi*, to be between 3.3 and 4.8 ha. In medium-altitude moist evergreen forests, home-range estimates for *C. crossleyi* are between 1.0 and 10.0 ha (Ambatovy), and between 1.0 and 17.0 ha (Tsinjoarivo). *Cheirogaleus sibreei*, sympatric with *C. crossleyi* at Tsinjoarivo, had smaller ranges, between 2.0 and 5.0 ha (Domoinaharivelo 2014; M. Blanco, unpublished data). At this site, both species showed smaller home ranges post-hibernation compared to pre-hibernation (Domoinaharivelo 2014).

Although most species use tree holes as sleeping sites, it is not always the case. Whereas *C. medius* exclusively occupies tree holes (Figure 14.41a), *C. major* can occasionally use nest-like structures

FIGURE 14.41 **Different aspects of *Cheirogaleus* use of tree holes and hibernacula: A) *C. medius* from the low-altitude moist evergreen forest at Tsihomanaomby in the northeast; B) *C. sibreei* occupying tree hole in the medium-altitude moist evergreen forest fragment at Tsinjoarivo; C) *C. crossleyi* occupying tree hole in a forest fragment at Tsinjoarivo; and D) *C. crossleyi* in underground hibernaculum in medium-altitude moist evergreen forest at Ambatovy.** (PHOTOS by M. Blanco.)

in Marojejy and Tsihomanaomby in the northeast (M. Blanco, unpublished data). Nests vary from simple entangled vines and leaves to more complex structures (Blanco and Godfrey 2014). At Tsinjoarivo, *C. crossleyi* uses a variety of sleeping sites, including tree holes (Figure 14.41c), nest-like structures, naked branches, and so forth, unlike their sympatric congener, *C. sibreei*, which exclusively uses tree holes (Figure 14.41b). The number of sleeping sites known per individual is also larger in the former compared to the latter (M. Blanco, unpublished data), and there seems to be more fidelity of tree hole use in *C. sibreei* compared to *C. crossleyi*. The differentiation in sleeping site use between sympatric dwarf lemur species may contribute to niche separation, allowing *C. crossleyi* to occupy areas that are more degraded and depauperate of suitable tree holes. This pliability in space use is consistent with feeding flexibility, also observed in this species at Tsinjoarivo (Domoinaharivelo 2014).

Social systems are better known for *C. medius*, but opportunistic data from eastern species confirm general findings. Dwarf lemurs form monogamous pairs, and pair-bonding is maintained until one of the individuals dies. *Cheirogaleus medius* showed long-term relationships among pairs, despite high levels of extra-pair copulations (Fietz et al. 2000). Adult males play an important role in raising offspring, and mortality rates for juveniles are higher without paternal help (Fietz and Dausmann 2006). Offspring generally live with their parents until the second year of life. *Cheirogaleus* lemurs tend to forage solitarily during the night, although infants are generally accompanied by an adult parent during those feeding trips. It is because single individuals are generally seen during night surveys that members of the genus were thought to be solitary animals. This perception, however, has changed as more observations have revealed complex social dynamics among members of family units (Fietz 1999; A. E. Müller 1999; A. E. Müller and Thalmann 2002). Contrary to reports from *C. medius* from the west, where adult individuals often forage alone, Lahann (2007a) reported that *C. major* individuals from the same family group forage, rest, and move together almost 50% of the (tracking) time.

DIETARY PREFERENCES

Cheirogaleus medius living in dry deciduous forest is highly frugivorous, though its diet also includes gums, insects, and spiders, all resources that vary seasonally (Fietz and Ganzhorn 1999; A. E. Müller and Thalmann 2002). This species feeds preferentially on fruits with high sugar content prior to hibernation. Sugars from such fruits are readily converted to fats that are accumulated primarily in the tails of these animals (Fietz and Ganzhorn 1999). We know less about the diets of eastern species, but similar patterns emerge, with dramatic increases in body mass occurring in the months prior to hibernation. Data from sympatric *C. sibreei* and *C. crossleyi* from Tsinjoarivo show a high percentage of fruit intake and no detectable animal prey in their diets. Insect captures may be difficult to see, particularly in closed-canopy moist evergreen forests. Notably, both species consumed a relatively large proportion of unripe fruits. Moreover, *C. crossleyi* had a more diversified diet than *C. sibreei* and spent more time feeding during the pre-hibernation period (Domoinaharivelo 2014).

The pre-hibernation period is characterized not only by a switch in food preference but also by a period of hyperphagia (excessive

eating), during which dwarf lemurs spend a lot of time foraging to maximize fattening. Interestingly, in the weeks prior to the immersion into hibernation, the dwarf lemurs' activity levels are reduced (Fietz and Dausmann, 2006), and they maintain or even reduce body mass (Blanco and Klopfer 2013). This transitional period may require internal metabolic adjustments, including so-called test drops, where they "practice" torpor bouts for a short period before their long hibernation season begins.

Dwarf lemurs are important seed dispersers. For instance, *Cheirogaleus* lemurs from medium-altitude moist evergreen forests (e.g., Tsinjoarivo) and dry deciduous forests (e.g., Kirindy Forest CNFEREF) disseminate seeds (e.g., *Bakerella*, family Loranthaceae, at Tsinjoarivo), a resource abundantly consumed by many species of lemurs and particularly critical for dwarf lemurs before and after hibernation (Ganzhorn and Kappeler 1996; Blanco 2010) (Figure 14.42).

BIOMEDICINE

In recent years there has been a renewed interest in research on *Cheirogaleus* associated with the biomedical relevance of primate hibernation. Unlocking the mechanisms of hibernation, including cellular mechanisms to fight oxidative stress and reverse natural conditions that are associated with diseases and syndromes in humans, is a goal reaching into multiple disciplines and fields. Of particular interest is the fact that *Cheirogaleus* may become virtually "pre-diabetic" during the fattening phase when high-sugar fruits are readily converted to fats. That state is reversed when fats are depleted during hibernation. Understanding the mechanisms responsible for metabolic switches and their regulation in these lemurs can be potentially informative to help ameliorate problems of diabetes in humans (Blanco et al. 2018).

FIGURE 14.42 ***Cheirogaleus sibreei* feces showing germinating seeds of the mistletoe *Bakerella clavata* in medium-altitude moist evergreen forest at Tsinjoarivo.** (PHOTO by M. Blanco.)

CONSERVATION

At the 2018 IUCN lemur species assessment workshop (IUCN 2020), one dwarf lemur species was categorized as Critically Endangered (*C. sibreei*), four as Endangered (*C. andysabini*, *C. lavasoensis*, *C. shethi*, and *C. thomasi*), three as Vulnerable (*C. crossleyi*, *C. major*, and *C. medius*), and one as Data Deficient (*C. grovesi*). These assessments are imprecise because of the lack of intensive ecological studies to delineate geographic ranges but also because species assignations remain difficult in the field, without including genetic data. In any case, the major threats for *Cheirogaleus* include continuous habitat loss, fragmentation, and other forms of habitat degradation, and hunting.

CONCLUSION

Despite new information from the field, members of the genus *Cheirogaleus* fall behind *Microcebus* in terms of accrued genetic, ecological, and behavioral data. In some ways, we have only just scratched the surface of *Cheirogaleus* eco-biogeography, with baseline behavioral, ecological, and physiological data being available for only a few populations. We know that certain species tend to be associated with certain environments and that some species tend to be more generalist than others.

Because hibernation expression and climate change may be inextricably linked, identifying species, their ecological requirements, and their physiological flexibility can provide clues to assert long-term survival prospects. Ultimately, because temperature-related changes due to climate change can have strong effects on *Cheirogaleus* species and their survivorship, they may be good indicators of what is to come before it happens to the rest of the ecosystem.

It is worth repeating that all *Cheirogaleus* species are threatened and that research strategies, in the wild and in captivity, should employ novel and potentially minimally invasive ways to advance studies and experiments. Only then, can dwarf lemurs emerge as a great animal model to study health, senescence, and disease.

Subject editors: Jörg U. Ganzhorn and Steven M. Goodman

CHEIROGALIDAE: *MICROCEBUS*, MOUSE LEMURS, *TSIDY*, *TSY-TSY*

P. M. Kappeler, U. Radespiel, R. M. Rasoloarison, J. Salmona, and A. D. Yoder

Mouse lemurs (*Microcebus* spp.) are the smallest (30–90 g) living members of the family Cheirogaleidae and of the order Primates.[1] The number of recognized species of these nocturnal lemurs has increased from two to about two dozen since the early 1990s (Figure 14.43). Mouse lemurs have a cryptic lifestyle and have colonized all suitable Malagasy forest habitats, where they forage alone on fruits and animal matter at night. Some species have the remarkable ability (for primates) to enter torpor and hibernation during the austral winter and form stable sleeping groups during the day. While mouse lemurs are almost ubiquitous on Madagascar and can be very abundant where they occur, most species have notably limited geographic distributions, putting many of them at serious risk of extinction. Detailed genetic analyses have proven to be essential for understanding the evolutionary history, biogeography, socio-ecology, and conservation risk of each member of this speciose radiation.

TAXONOMY

The genus *Microcebus* is notable for having undergone extreme taxonomic splitting. The number of recognized species of mouse lemurs has gone from two, as recently as 1993, to 25 at the time this contribution was finalized (early 2020). The two-species taxonomy was established by R. D. Martin (1972a), wherein he made note of the differing habitats and ecological constraints defining the two species: *M. murinus* (Figure 14.43f), inhabiting dry deciduous forest and dry spiny thicket and specializing in insectivory, and *M. rufus*, inhabiting moist evergreen forest and showing dietary tendencies toward omnivory. This taxonomic view was first modified with the resurrection of a previously synonymized species, *M. myoxinus*, measurably smaller than *M. murinus*, from the dry deciduous forests of central western Madagascar (Schmid and Kappeler 1994), and the naming of a fourth species, *M. ravelobensis* (Figure 14.43d), identified from northwestern Madagascar (Zimmermann et al. 1998).

The pace accelerated abruptly with the increase in field efforts in remote areas of Madagascar together with the introduction of genetic data into the species discovery process, which proved to be a powerful tool, revealing the largely cryptic species diversity within *Microcebus*. With the combined efforts of a morphological team lead by Rasoloarison et al. (2000) and a genetics team led by A. D. Yoder et al. (2000), another five new species were described. Along with the revised taxonomy of a portion of the animals once identified as *M. myoxinus*, now recognized as *M. berthae* (Figure 14.43e), so began an era of taxonomic proliferation (Kappeler et al. 2005; Andriantompohavana et al. 2006; Louis et al. 2006b; Olivieri et al. 2007; Louis et al. 2008; Radespiel et al. 2008, 2012; Rasoloarison et al. 2013; Hotaling et al. 2016; Sgarlata et al. 2019), with much of this based primarily, if not entirely, on small DNA data sets that were mostly of mitochondrial origin. Not surprisingly, there have been several calls for greater circumspection and a more evidence-based approach (Tattersall 2007; Markolf et al. 2011; Tattersall and Cuozzo 2018).

It is our prediction that the coming years will reflect the call for a more careful evaluation of supporting information, including genetic, morphological, and ecological data when describing or refining mouse lemur taxonomy. Rapid advances in genomic technologies with data analyzed within the multispecies coalescent framework (e.g., Flouris et al. 2019) should prove to be powerful for this endeavor, perhaps leading to as many species sunk as those to be newly described. Thus, though we confirm that the genus *Microcebus* is notably and justifiably speciose relative to other genera of lemurs, a lasting taxonomic framework is still a work in progress.

ABUNDANCE

Throughout their ranges, mouse lemurs are among the most abundant land mammals of their respective local communities, occupying almost all native and in some cases degraded forest types (Knoop et al. 2018), but comprehensive estimates of their abundance are difficult to obtain. Two distinct methods have been used to assess their densities: nocturnal census walks and various trapping regimes (R. Rakotondravony and Radespiel 2009), both of which are combined with diverse statistical approaches (e.g., Meyler et al. 2012), therefore introducing variability into density estimates. While long-term trapping sites tend to be established in areas with high densities, trapping success seems strongly influenced by habitat type, resource availability, and the local torpor regime, with overall high versus low trapping success in dry deciduous and moist evergreen forests, respectively (Evasoa et al. 2019). Visual surveys are affected by torpor regime and by microhabitat structure (i.e., visibility) and are of limited use for species identification in areas of sympatry, given the cryptic nature of mouse lemurs (R. Rakotondravony and Radespiel 2009; Schäffler et al. 2015; T. S. Steffens and Lehman 2018). Furthermore, a large portion of mouse lemur visual surveys have used nonrecommended statistical approaches to estimate density from distance sampling data (Sterling and Ramaroson 1996; Meyler et al. 2012), thus limiting our ability to confidently include most published data in meta-analyses (Setash et al. 2017).

This methodological variability is further increased by local heterogeneity on at least two scales. First, several mouse lemur populations appear to be clumped on a small spatial scale, and such population nuclei are surrounded by hectares of intact forest with few or no mouse lemurs (R. D. Martin 1972a; Fredsted et al. 2004;

1 This contribution is dedicated to the memory of Elke Zimmermann (1958–2019), a pioneer of mouse lemur research.

FIGURE 14.43 **Mouse lemur diversity. Representatives of mouse lemurs inhabiting Madagascar's western dry deciduous forests. A) *Microcebus bongolavensis*, B) *M. danfossi*, C) *M. mamiratra*, D) *M. ravelobensis*, E) *M. berthae*, and F) *M. murinus*.** (PHOTOS A and B by B. Randrianambinina, C by E. Zimmermann, D by U. Radespiel, and E and F by J. Henke-von der Malsburg.)

Dammhahn and Kappeler 2008b). Second, there is additional heterogeneity on a larger spatial scale, among different parts, say a few kilometers apart, of the same forest (Schäffler and Kappeler 2014; A. Miller et al. 2018). Accumulating evidence suggests that some of this heterogeneity may be related to differences in habitat structure or disturbance (Ganzhorn 1995; Ganzhorn and Schmid 1998; Rendigs et al. 2003; Schäffler and Kappeler 2014; A. Miller et al. 2018), competition (R. Rakotondravony and Radespiel 2009), and predation avoidance (Schäffler et al. 2015).

As a result of this variation, after 40 years of nocturnal surveys and trapping, population density data vary by a factor of nearly 200, with most species reaching local density estimates of more than 100 ind/km^2 (individuals per square kilometer) (Randrianambinina et al. 2010; Setash et al. 2017). Part of this variation is perhaps additionally due to individual variation in detection ability among different researchers. Moreover, at the island level, the factors influencing mouse lemur densities, such as seasonality, torpor regime, and number of sympatric species, appear to vary distinctly between dry and humid regions (Setash et al. 2017). Species living in dry deciduous forests generally exhibit higher densities than those in moist evergreen forests, a likely result of the seasonal magnitude of resource fluctuations, favoring mouse lemurs in dry deciduous forests for their ability to cope with environmental changes and resource paucity (Knoop et al. 2018).

Surprisingly, at a lower spatial scale, forest area seems to have very limited if any effect on mouse lemur densities (Salmona et al. 2014a; T. S. Steffens et al. 2016; but see Andriatsitohaina et al. 2019), again pointing out mouse lemurs' exceptional ability to survive in small forest patches and to cope with challenging environmental conditions. While listing specific density values is of limited use, any given method, applied consistently, provides useful relative density estimates that allow comparisons over time (e.g., Hladik et al. 1998; Setash et al. 2017). Overall densities (Setash et al. 2017) indicate that mouse lemurs are among the most abundant lemurs wherever they occur and likely the most abundant primates in general. Given these densities, mouse lemurs must play important ecological roles, for instance, as seed dispersers and/or as prey for vertebrate predators (Rasoloarison et al. 1995; Scheumann et al. 2007; Génin and Rambeloarivony 2018; also see Goodman and Ganzhorn, pp. 1829–38).

In addition to field censuses, the effective population size (N_e) and demographic fluctuations of mouse lemurs have been inferred using genetic data (see Salmona et al. 2017: Table S10). Although molecular-based estimates also face limitations, they have allowed investigators to identify small declining populations that are geographically restricted, locally endemic, and of high conservation concern (Olivieri et al. 2008; Montero et al. 2019). Population genetics analyses also revealed that the geographically most widespread species (*M. murinus*) harbors signals of recent population expansions (N. Schneider et al. 2010), whereas the geographic distributions of *M. griseorufus* and *M. tavaratra* have remained relatively stable over the past millennia (Blair et al. 2014; Sgarlata et al.

2018), suggesting that dry deciduous forest–inhabitating mouse lemurs with large distributions may have a particular ability to cope with habitat change.

HABITAT USE

Microcebus species have colonized all forest habitats on Madagascar, including formations such as mangroves (Gardner 2016). Despite their geographic distribution across much of the island, including a wide variety of vegetation types, all species of mouse lemur appear to use their habitat in similar ways despite having species-specific (micro-) habitat preferences (Rendigs et al. 2003; R. Rakotondravony and Radespiel 2009; Rakotondranary and Ganzhorn 2011; Schäffler et al. 2015). They can use all forest strata, but seem to prefer the lower strata and even come regularly to the ground to hunt insects in the leaf litter (Radespiel et al. 2006; Siemers et al. 2007; Lahann 2008). Because of their small body size they can exploit what R. D. Martin (1972a) called the "fine-branch niche"—that is, they also exploit resources in dense shrubs or liana tangles. They move quadrupedally, typically in rapid bursts, and can also leap considerable distances in pursuit of animal prey or during regular locomotion. Some species seem to prefer forest edges (e.g., *M. ravelobensis* in Ankarafantsika; Burke and Lehman 2013), whereas others seem to be attracted to smaller open spaces, such as along trails or tree-fall gaps, which may offer more profitable food (e.g., *Microcebus* spp.; Ganzhorn 1988, 1995). Despite this high flexibility in habitat requirements, there seem to be structural and associated food and shelter limitations that prohibit the occurrence of mouse lemurs in degraded forests (K. J. E. Steffens et al. 2017).

During their nocturnal periods of activity, individual *Microcebus* females use home ranges of 0.26–2.7 ha: *M. murinus*, 0.26 ha (Dammhahn and Kappeler 2009) to 2.6 ha (Radespiel 1998); *M. berthae*, 1.2 ha (Schwab 2000) to 2.5 ha (Dammhahn and Kappeler 2005); *M. ravelobensis*, 0.5 ha (Weidt et al. 2004) to 2.7 ha (Ehresmann 2000); *M. lehilahytsara*, 0.3–0.7 ha (Randrianambinina 2001); *M. griseorufus*, 0.43–0.9 ha (Génin 2008); *M. ganzhorni*, 0.5–0.7 ha (Lahann 2008); *M. sambiranensis*, 0.87–1.15 ha (Hending et al. 2017). Male ranges are slightly larger in some species and exhibit a pronounced seasonal increase during the mating season (discussed below). Home-range size estimates, however, are no doubt vulnerable to some of the same observational limitations described above for census counts.

Habitat use within the home range appears to be partly determined by food availability (Corbin and Schmid 1995; Dammhahn and Kappeler 2009; Joly and Zimmermann 2011). During the day, mouse lemurs stay inside tree holes, self-constructed nests, or other natural shelters (Radespiel 2006; Génin 2010; Karanewsky and Wright 2015; Hending et al. 2017), which buffer them from daily temperature fluctuations and help protect them from predators. Suitable tree holes, in particular, are therefore important structural resources that may influence habitat use by mouse lemurs (Lutermann et al. 2010; Hending et al. 2017). For example, each *M. murinus* in one study site in Ankarafantsika, Jardin Botanique A (JBA), used three to nine different tree holes, which were shared with variable numbers of conspecifics and used for two to five days in a row (Radespiel et al. 1998). By choosing trees with particular insulation capacities and by sharing tree holes with conspecifics, *M. murinus* enjoys considerable energetic advantages, which further increase energetic savings during periods in which it undergoes daily or seasonal torpor (Schmid 1998a, 2000). Regular changes of tree holes appear to be motivated by hygienic benefits (Poirotte and Kappeler 2019).

COMMUNITY ECOLOGY

Within a given local lemur community, *Microcebus* species, based on the modern taxonomy of this genus, always have the most diverse diet and are omnivorous throughout the year. They feed on fruits when available, but they also regularly hunt small arthropods, exploit gum, and feed on insect secretions (R. D. Martin 1972a; Ganzhorn 1988; Corbin and Schmid 1995; Dammhahn and Kappeler 2008a, 2010; Thorén et al. 2011). In addition, they also visit flowers, where they feed on nectar and may therefore act as pollinators (Radespiel et al. 2006; Génin and Rambeloarivony 2018). Because of their high biomass, mouse lemurs may also be quantitatively important seed dispersers for some of their food tree species (Lahann 2007b; Génin and Rambeloarivony 2018). Across an annual cycle, the relative composition of their diet is highly variable and largely reflects seasonal changes in food availability (e.g., Dammhahn and Kappeler 2008a, 2010; Thorén et al. 2011).

At several sites, two species of mouse lemurs occur sympatrically and potentially compete for similar resources. At least seven such cases of *Microcebus* species coexistence have been documented, five of which involve *M. murinus* and one other local congener in southern, western, and northwestern Madagascar (Dammhahn and Kappeler 2008b; Radespiel 2016); the other cases are *M. macarthurii* and *M. mittermeieri* coexisting in the Makira region (Radespiel et al. 2008), and *M. tavaratra* coexisting with a yet undescribed species only in the upper reaches of the Binara Massif (Loky Manambato) (Sgarlata et al. 2019). At most other sites, mouse lemurs share their habitat with at least one other cheirogaleid species, which may have similar feeding and resting preferences (Hladik et al. 1980) but is always higher in body mass than the sympatric mouse lemurs by a factor of two to 12 (L. A. Taylor and Schwitzer 2012). In addition, several species of endemic rodents, particularly of the genus *Eliurus* (subfamily Nesomyinae, see Carleton et al., pp. 2014–22), occupy a similar forest stratum and may compete with mouse lemurs over fruit and tree holes (Andriatsitohaina et al. 2019). The mechanisms that mediate coexistence among (mouse) lemur taxa include body size, structural microhabitat characteristics, and food (Ganzhorn 1988, 1989a). Species also differ in their response to habitat disturbance and fragmentation, which again indicates different habitat requirements and behavioral and ecological plasticity in habitat use (Andriatsitohaina et al. 2019).

Because of their high densities, *Microcebus* lemurs are important prey items for several predators (Scheumann et al. 2007). Analyses of regurgitated pellets of owls revealed that mouse lemurs may make up nearly half of all prey items in some areas (Goodman et al. 1993a, 1993b, 1993c). Mouse lemur remains have also been found in the feces of *Cryptoprocta ferox*, and attacks have been documented by other carnivorans, birds of prey, and large snakes (see Goodman and Ganzhorn, pp. 1829–38). It has been estimated that about 25% of a

mouse lemur (mostly *M. griseorufus*) population in and around the Bezà-Mahafaly is taken annually by a single species of owl alone (Goodman et al. 1993a, 1993c), and in the Kirindy Forest CNFEREF, total annual mortality due to predation is as much as 50% (Kraus et al. 2008). *Microcebus murinus* has adaptive behavioral responses to different types of predators (Rahlfs and Fichtel 2010), including mobbing (Eberle and Kappeler 2008), but nocturnal predators are probably difficult to detect and avoid, although olfactory predator recognition has been demonstrated in naive and wild mouse lemurs (Sündermann et al. 2008; Kappel et al. 2011).

PHYSIOLOGICAL ECOLOGY

An important determinant of temporal variation in abundance of some *Microcebus* species, and presumably even at the population level, is their response to seasonal variation in ambient temperature and food availability. During the austral winter, individuals may enter periods of inactivity, ranging in duration from hours (daily torpor) to weeks (hibernation; Bourlière and Petter-Rousseaux 1966; Petter-Rousseaux 1980; Ortmann et al. 1997; also see Dausmann et al., pp. 1798–805). This metabolic flexibility, which has been described for several species of *Microcebus*, has most likely evolved in response to pronounced seasonal variation in temperature and food availability in central and southern Madagascar, but its distribution, manifestation, and ecological causes remain to be determined in more detail (Blanco et al. 2018).

Daily and seasonal torpor are effective mechanisms to conserve energy. First, body temperature during torpor can be lowered to levels close to ambient temperature, which saves energy otherwise needed for heat production. Body temperatures as low as 7°C were measured both in the laboratory (Andriantsiferana and Rahandraha 1974) and the field (Ortmann et al. 1996; Schmid 2000; Schmid et al. 2000). Second, this drop in body temperature is accompanied by a substantial reduction in oxygen consumption and, thus, metabolic rate (Aujard et al. 1998; Schmid et al. 2000). Furthermore, arousal from daily torpor is coupled with largely passive exogenous heating fueled by the daily increase in ambient temperature. Together, these mechanisms reduce daily energy expenditure by almost 40% and may enhance survival during the cool dry season, which is associated with reduced food availability.

These physiological adaptations to seasonality drive pronounced cycles in body mass and fat content, which in turn have an impact on activity budgets, feeding behavior, and ultimately life-history tactics of *Microcebus*. During several months of hibernation, mouse lemurs lose about one-third of their pre-hibernation body mass (Schmid and Kappeler 1998; Atsalis 1999b), which is a particular burden on adult females, because they have to gestate and wean their young during the season of food abundance while they also have to replenish their energy reserves for the upcoming cool season. The constraints imposed by thermoregulatory needs are also manifest by intraspecific variation in body mass, reproductive rates, and life expectancy of *M. murinus* along a north–south gradient across their distributional range (Lahann et al. 2006).

Sex differences in reproductive effort may partly explain important interpopulation modifications in activity between the sexes. At Ampijoroa, in an area of dry deciduous forest, *M. murinus* males and females exhibit daily but not seasonal torpor (Zimmermann 1998). In the Kirindy Forest CNFEREF and the same vegetation type, both sexes show daily torpor, and most adult females hibernate for several weeks to five months per year (Schmid 1998; Schmid and Kappeler 1998). Adult males, in contrast, remain inactive for a few days at a time at the most, and are all active weeks before females reemerge from hibernation (Fietz 1998; Schmid and Kappeler 1998; Rasoazanabary 2006). At Kirindy Forest CNFEREF, both sexes in the sympatrically occurring *M. berthae* use daily but not prolonged torpor (Schmid et al. 2000). In the Ranomafana moist evergreen forest, *M. rufus* males and females increase body fat and disappear during part of the cool season (Atsalis 1999b), which has also been documented for *M. lehilahytsara* in the same vegetation type as Ranomafana (Randrianambinina 2001; Blanco et al. 2017). In the dry spiny thicket of the Tsimanampesotse National Park, *M. griseorufus* exhibits individual energy-saving strategies at the beginning of the dry season, including irregular short torpor bouts, regular daily torpor, prolonged torpor of a few days, and hibernation over several weeks (Kobbe et al. 2011), indicating that species and sex differences alone are insufficient to explain the existing variation in heterothermy (Vuarin et al. 2015).

SOCIAL SYSTEM

The social system of mouse lemurs is characterized by predominantly solitary activity embedded in some higher-order social complexity, especially in terms of sleeping arrangements. Solitary foraging may be necessitated by the nature of food sources, such as animal prey or gum sites, which can typically be exploited by only a single individual, because these food items typically cannot be shared (Dammhahn and Kappeler 2009). Note, however, that gum trees can be used sequentially and tend to attract in particular *M. murinus*, individuals of which were more likely to be trapped in their vicinity (Génin 2003). Social complexity is most clearly manifested in the size and composition of daytime sleeping groups, as well as in social interactions at night, which may consist of direct interactions or of vocal and olfactory signals exchanged among the members of a local neighborhood (R. D. Martin 1972a; Zimmermann 1995; Buesching et al. 1998; Hafen et al. 1998).

The first information on *Microcebus* social organization became available from studies by R. D. Martin (1972a). He found that mouse lemurs in littoral forest at Mandena (*M. ganzhorni*), just north of Tolagnaro, occur in population nuclei, whose cores were defined by overlapping home ranges of adult females. Home ranges of so-called central males encompassed those of several adult females in the core area, whereas several smaller adult males occupied the periphery, resulting in a female-biased sex ratio in the center of nuclei. Two brief radio-tracking studies of *M. murinus* in dry deciduous forest at Ampijoroa (Barre et al. 1988; Pagès-Feuillade 1988) revealed that female ranges overlap less than those of males, and that the ranges of all members of a neighborhood overlap in a central area. Male ranges were found to be almost twice as large as those of females, but there was no evidence for biased sex ratios or differences among males in size or ranging behavior (Radespiel 2000). In addition, the larger size of male ranges was shown to be temporary and limited to the mating season. However, none of the

males managed to exclude others from access to females (Radespiel 2000; but see Schmelting et al. 2007). In the Kirindy Forest CNFEREF, a radio-tracking study of *M. murinus* revealed that male home ranges approximately tripled in size during the mating season (Eberle and Kappeler 2002), whereas female ranges showed no seasonal variation in size, and they overlapped year-round with those of on average five other females. Genetic analyses from the same site indicated that these females are organized into spatial clusters of closely related individuals (Wimmer et al. 2002), and a radio-tracking study revealed that most males emigrate several home-range diameters away from their natal ranges when they are only a few months old (Schliehe-Diecks et al. 2012).

Patterns of shelter use provide a glimpse into additional social complexity at the level of sleeping groups. Mouse lemurs monitored by R. D. Martin (1972a) at Mandena appeared to undergo seasonal changes in sleeping-group composition. After the mating season, females most commonly nested with three other females, whereas males typically nested singly or in pairs, but the ages of the individuals were not known in this short-term study. A male was found with several females in only 7% of nests. During and immediately after the breeding season, a much higher proportion of nests (45%; n = 47) at the same site contained at least one male and female (R. D. Martin 1973). Furthermore, the median number of females per nest was reduced from four to three. Most *M. murinus* nests monitored at Ampijoroa after the breeding season contained individuals of the same sex. Female nests were spatially clumped and typically used by two or three females at a time. Males slept alone or in pairs; only one of 14 nests contained a male-female pair (Pagès-Feuillade 1988). Another study at this same site confirmed that most females sleep in stable groups and that most males sleep alone (Radespiel et al. 1998). In the Kirindy Forest CNFEREF, an analysis of long-term sleeping-group composition data of the *M. murinus* population there also confirmed this pattern (Eberle and Kappeler 2002).

Relatively little is yet known about the social systems of some of the other *Microcebus* species whose social systems have been studied at all. The results of a trapping study at Ranomafana indicated that *M. rufus* individuals occupy overlapping home ranges, and males may have larger ranges and, relative females, more pronounced migratory activity (Atsalis 2000). This species also spends the day in nests close to the ground (P. C. Wright and Martin 1995) in small groups of same- or mixed-sex individuals (Karanewsky and Wright 2015). Among *M. berthae* at Kirindy Forest CNFEREF, male ranges are larger than those of females, and this difference increases during the mating season (Schwab 2000). This species' ranges are bigger than those of sympatric *M. murinus*, despite the fact that *M. berthae* is only about half the size (Dammhahn and Kappeler 2005). *Microcebus berthae* individuals were always found to sleep in tangles of vegetation, and all sex combinations of sleeping groups were regularly observed. In *M. griseorufus* in the riparian forests of the extreme south (Berenty Private Reserve), female home ranges overlapped with, on average, three male home ranges, whereas male home ranges overlapped with those of five females (Génin 2008), and same-sex sleeping groups of two females or two males were observed most often (Génin 2010). The home ranges of *M. ravelobensis* at Ankarafantsika are small relative to those of other species and populations, and do not vary seasonally in size, and overlap with those of one to three other adults of either sex (Weidt et al. 2004). This species' sleeping groups consist of either females or up to five members of both sexes and are based on close genetic relatedness within matrilines (Radespiel et al. 2009). Finally, in *M. sambiranensis* in Anabohazo Forest at Sahamalaza–Iles Radama National Park, home ranges are about 1 ha in size and overlap with those of a few members of both sexes; sleeping groups were not stable and included members of both sexes (Hending et al. 2017).

Mating in mouse lemurs is highly seasonal and coincides with the end of the austral spring, where it is locally fine-tuned by local climate (Evasoa et al. 2018). Interestingly, the timing of reproduction in sympatric species pairs was not closely synchronized, indicating the existence of additional determinants of reproductive activity, such as phylogenetic proximity, ambient temperature, or rainfall. Female receptivity is as short as several hours (Eberle and Kappeler 2004a, 2004b; Eberle et al. 2007; Huchard et al. 2012). Mating is promiscuous, with *M. murinus* females mating with as many as seven males up to 11 times total in one night, resulting in intense sperm competition (Eberle and Kappeler 2004b). Inbreeding in *M. murinus* is avoided, despite high home-range overlap, through male-biased natal dispersal (Radespiel et al. 2003; Schliehe-Dieck et al. 2012; Huchard et al. 2017), and mate choice (possibly based on MHC [major histocompatibility complex] genotype) occurs despite promiscuous mating (Huchard et al. 2013). After two months of gestation, females of this species give birth to one to three altricial young, with some litters exhibiting mixed paternities (Radespiel et al. 2002; Eberle and Kappeler 2004a). Where adult females of *Microcebus* share nests, as in *M. murinus*, young can be raised communally (Eberle and Kappeler 2006).

LIFE HISTORY AND POPULATION DYNAMICS

The dynamics of individual *Microcebus* populations have not yet been studied systematically, and long-term demographic data for life-history analyses are available only for *M. murinus*. Females of this species begin reproducing within their first year of life (i.e., when they are about 10 months old), but the generation time, recently estimated as the average age of parents in the Ampijoroa population, is about 2.5 years (Radespiel et al. 2019a). They generally give birth only once a year, but second litters, born one to two months after the majority of other births, have been observed. Average reproductive life span for individual females can vary between populations and is two years in Kirindy Forest CNFEREF, because their average life span is only 3.4 years—seven months longer than that of males (Hämäläinen et al. 2014). The main known cause of death is predation (see Goodman and Ganzhorn, pp. 1829–38), but body condition showed a terminal decline in the season before disappearance (Hämäläinen et al. 2014). Indeed, hair cortisol levels, which reflect the magnitude of long-term stress responses, were negatively correlated with survival (Rakotoniaina et al. 2017). Because newborn infants spend the first weeks of their life in tree holes or other shelters, levels of early infant mortality are unknown. However, one study showed that adult survival was higher in females co-sleeping with their mothers or daughters than in those sleeping alone (Lutermann et al. 2006). Hibernation has no intrinsic survival benefits, as males and females survive the austral winter

equally well, but males suffer increased mortality during the mating season (Kraus et al. 2008).

One study has documented important differences in the population dynamics of *M. murinus* as a function of habitat quality (Ganzhorn and Schmid 1998). In a secondary forest with few large trees with holes, this species had reduced body mass and less opportunity to engage in energy-saving torpor. This apparent stress may have increased the population's mortality rates as well, as there were no recaptures of marked individuals between years, but a more recent study in the same region (Kirindy Forest CNFEREF) found no effects of habitat disturbance on health and parasitism (Rakotoniaina et al. 2016). In contrast, forest degradation and fragmentation had marked effects on the level of parasitism in *M. murinus* inhabiting southern littoral forests (Raharivololona and Ganzhorn 2009); and in Ranomafana, *M. rufus* that had both high numbers of parasite species as well as high prevalence of ectoparasites and gastrointestinal parasites had even better body condition (Rafalinirina et al. 2015). Thus, habitat modification may have dramatic effects on entire populations of mouse lemurs, highlighting the potential risk of extinction for several of the species with small known geographic ranges.

CONCLUSION

Though thousands of hours of field effort, behavioral observation, and genetic analyses have been applied toward understanding the biological complexity of mouse lemurs, the details of their ecological roles, their species diversity, and the evolutionary forces that have driven their diversification remain elusive. We hope that advances in genomic and field technologies can be applied in the coming years to bring us closer to understanding the biological conditions that drive and maintain species diversity in this fascinating primate clade.

Subject editors: Jörg U. Ganzhorn and Steven M. Goodman

CHEIROGALIDAE: *MIRZA*, GIANT MOUSE LEMURS

P. M. Kappeler

The lemur genus *Mirza* (Gray, 1870) is represented by two recognized species: *M. coquereli* (Grandidier, 1867), or Coquerel's Giant Mouse Lemur (Figure 14.44a), and *M. zaza* (Kappeler and Roos, 2005), or Northern Giant Mouse Lemur (Figure 14.44b). Originally considered a separate genus by Gray, and subsequently classified as one of either the dwarf (*Cheirogaleus*) or mouse lemurs (*Microcebus*), *Mirza* was resurrected by Tattersall (1982) because of its larger size and various behavioral and morphological differences with mouse lemurs.

Mirza is a medium-size member of the family Cheirogaleidae with an average adult body mass of around 300 g. Striking external features include the long bushy tail, which exceeds head-and-body length, and relatively large ears. Giant mouse lemurs are covered with short gray-brown fur that turns creamy gray ventrally and black at the tip of the tail. *Mirza zaza* is generally smaller than *M. coquereli*, but *M. zaza* males have relatively larger testes (Kappeler et al. 2005; Rode-Margono et al. 2016). In fact, *M. zaza* males have the relatively largest testis size of any primate species (Rode-Margono et al. 2015). Significant variation in body size and proportions between two populations of *M. zaza* has also been reported (Rode-Margono et al. 2016). Hind limbs are slightly longer than forelimbs in *Mirza* species, so that these lemurs move in a quadrupedal fashion, sometimes interspersed by short leaps and bounds. Giant mouse lemurs are excellent climbers and use all levels of the forest. They typically travel and forage at a height of 5–10 m. However, they can also come briefly to the ground, typically headfirst on small trunks, to hunt insects in the leaf litter or to traverse short distances.

DISTRIBUTION

Giant mouse lemurs are restricted to western lowland forests. There is a gap between the two species' ranges spanning several hundred kilometers. However, neither the exact limits of remaining population centers nor the actual and historical presence or absence of *Mirza* in the intermediate regions are known (J.-J. Petter et al. 1977; Tattersall 1982). *Mirza zaza* is found in the Sambirano Region, with the Mahavavy River as a possible northern boundary and the Maeverano River as a southern boundary of this species' range (Markolf et al. 2008). *Mirza coquereli* is known to occur in the Zombitse-Vohibasia National Park (Ganzhorn 1994; Goodman et al. 1997e), and the southern limit of its distribution is probably somewhere north of the Onilahy River (Gardner and Jasper 2009). Further, *M. coquereli* is known to occur in other protected areas, including Bemaraha and Menabe Antimena. It appears to tolerate a fair amount of habitat disturbance, so that the species is most threatened by complete loss of natural forest habitat (Schäffler et al. 2015).

NATURAL HISTORY

The first detailed description of the natural history of *M. coquereli* can be found in J.-J. Petter et al. (1971), who collected opportunistic observations during a study of *Phaner* near Beroboka, north of Morondava. A study by Pagès (1978, 1980) focused on the social

FIGURE 14.44 The two *Mirza* species: A) *M. coquereli* in the Massif du Makay; B) *M. zaza* at Ambato, near the Hotel Ermitage, north of Ambanja; C) *M. coquereli* feeding on insect secretions of homopteran larvae at Kirindy Forest CNFEREF; and D) *M. coquereli* feeding on a tree trunk gouged out by *Phaner pallescens* (Pale Fork-marked Lemur) at Kirindy Forest CNFEREF. (PHOTOS by M. Markolf.)

organization and feeding ecology of a population in Marosalaza Forest, north of Morondava. Finally, studies in Kirindy Forest CNFEREF, north of Morondava, also focused on social organization (Kappeler 1997a), genetic structure (Kappeler et al. 2002), and mating behavior (Markolf and Kappeler 2020). Andrianarivo (1981) conducted a study of the ranging and social behavior of what would become *M. zaza* on the Ampasindava Peninsula, during which several individuals were also radio-tracked. Studies on a population of *M. zaza* in Ankarafa Forest on the Sahamalaza Peninsula focused on nesting behavior (Rode et al. 2013) and habitat use (Rode-Margono et al. 2016). The largest captive population of this genus, specifically *M. zaza*, at the Duke Lemur Center, was the subject of several behavioral and physiological studies (Stanger 1993, 1995; Stanger et al. 1995; Seiler et al. 2019).

Population estimates for giant mouse lemurs are sparse. In the Marosalaza Forest, the population density was estimated to range from 50 to 210 ind/km^2 (individuals per square kilometer) (J.-J. Petter et al. 1971; Hladik et al. 1980). Near Ambanja, 385 individuals were estimated to inhabit 1 km^2 of heavily degraded forest dominated by mango and cashew nut trees (Andrianarivo 1981). One extensively studied population in the Kirindy Forest CNFEREF maintained densities of around 120 ind/km^2 for several years (Kappeler 1997a), followed by a rapid and steady decline, the causes of which remain unknown. Even within the Kirindy Forest population, however, local densities vary substantially, with distinctly fewer animals found in more open parts of the forest.

Giant mouse lemurs are exclusively nocturnal. They spend the day in self-constructed nests. These nests are built with short twigs that are chewed off nearby trees by the animals. Only adult females have been observed building nests (Sarikaya and Kappeler 1997), for up to an hour at a time, but the behavior has been observed so rarely that this potential sex difference needs to be confirmed in a focused study. The resulting nests are up to 0.5 m in diameter and are typically located high in the canopy (Rode et al. 2013). Some nests are surrounded by one or several others in the same or adjacent trees (Andrianarivo 1981; Sarikaya and Kappeler 1997). Most nest sites are overgrown by lianas, which may make it difficult for certain potential predators to reach nests (also see Goodman and Ganzhorn, pp. 1829–38).

Nesting behavior differs fundamentally between the two species. *Mirza coquereli* virtually always sleeps alone (except for mother-offspring dyads). Each individual uses up to 10–12 nests, among which it rotates in intervals of several days. Some nests are also shared among neighboring *Mirza* lemurs or used by *Phaner pallescens* and *Rattus rattus*. In contrast to most sympatrically occurring nocturnal lemurs, *M. coquereli* virtually never uses tree holes as daytime shelters. *Mirza zaza*, however, spends the day in small stable groups of two to eight individuals (Kappeler et al. 2005; Rode et al. 2013). It appears to use fewer nests (one to three; Rode et al. 2013) than *M. coquereli*, but it has not yet been studied in undisturbed forest. Notably, several *M. zaza* adult males have been observed in different study sites to share a nest. Such unusual male tolerance is not exclusively due to kinship, as unrelated males also shared a nest (Rode et al. 2013).

Around sunset, *M. coquereli* leaves the nest and spends several minutes in the immediate vicinity, often grooming and stretching.

It begins its typically solitary activities in the final moments of dusk and returns to one of its nests just before dawn (see also Rode et al. 2013). During the cold winter months, it may reduce its activity and return to the nest during the second half of the night. However, in contrast to most closely related sympatric cheirogaleids, *Mirza* species remain active year-round and are not known to enter daily or seasonal torpor.

Mirza species are omnivorous. Their diet consists mainly of fruit, but they have been observed to hunt and feed on several vertebrates and invertebrates, including rodents, snakes, chameleons, and large insects (Hladik et al. 1980; Pagès 1980; Schliehe-Diecks et al. 2010). There is circumstantial evidence suggesting that *Mirza* species may even prey opportunistically on other small lemurs, such as *Microcebus*. During the dry season, sugary secretions of homopteran larvae (Figure 14.44c) and tree exudates (Figure 14.44d) may also contribute significantly to their diet (J.-J. Petter et al. 1971; Hladik et al. 1980; Rode-Margono et al. 2016).

After about 90 days of gestation, *Mirza* females give birth, typically to two young or more irregularly one. The young are poorly developed, with a birth mass of around 12 g, and therefore spend about the first three weeks of life in their mother's nest (Pagès 1978; Petter-Rousseaux 1980; Stanger et al. 1995). They are transported between nests in their mother's mouth. After several weeks, infants are parked in the vegetation while the mother forages nearby. Infants grow quickly and begin to travel and forage independently during their third month (Pagès 1983). Females of *M. coquereli* may start reproducing as early as 10 months of age. Mating for this species in the Morondava area is restricted to a few weeks in November (Pagès 1978, 1980; Kappeler 1997a), while for *M. zaza* at Ambanja, mating takes place in August (Kappeler et al. 2005). Members of a captive population of *M. zaza* reproduced year-round (Stanger et al. 1995), and females advertised their estrus vocally (Seiler et al. 2015). Once reproductively active, females may reproduce every year; postpartum estrus has been observed in captivity (J.-J. Petter and van der Sloot 2000). The longevity of *Mirza* individuals, and thus their reproductive life span, remains unknown, but they probably rarely exceed five or six years of age in the wild.

Adult males and females of *M. coquereli* inhabit individual home ranges of about 1–4 ha. Home ranges among neighboring animals overlap to various degrees, and home-range exclusivity varies between 1% and 99%, with zero to eight neighbors (Kappeler 1997a). Male home ranges in the Kirindy Forest CNFEREF more than quadruple in size around the mating season, whereas those of females remain constant in size and stable in location, in some cases over years. Adults typically forage alone throughout the night. On the basis of radio-tracking and direct observations at Analabe, Pagès (1978, 1980) suggested that individual males and females form pair-bonds. At Ankarafa, *M. zaza* individuals occupied home ranges of about 1 ha that largely overlapped, especially with those of nest mates (Rode-Margono et al. 2016), but this study was only a few weeks long, and estimates of several home ranges did not reach an asymptote. Thus, by combining all this information, it appears that the social organization of *Mirza* is highly flexible, exhibiting all basic types reported for nocturnal primates.

Genetic analyses of the Kirindy Forest CNFEREF population revealed that females have one or two surviving infants per year. Variation in male reproductive success varied from zero to three infants sired by individual males in a given year. Several females had litters with mixed paternity (Kappeler et al. 2002). The facts that males have relatively large testes, that they roam widely beyond their typical ranges during the mating season, and that litters with mixed paternities occur support the hypothesis that these lemurs engage in scramble-competition polygyny (Kappeler 1997a). Analyses of mitochondrial DNA (mtDNA) indicated that some males disperse from their natal ranges at around two years of age, whereas others remain in their natal ranges for several years (Kappeler et al. 2002). The mating systems in other populations remain unstudied.

The patterns of solitary adult female activity and nesting behavior of *M. coquereli* in the Kirindy Forest CNFEREF obscured a spatial organization of females along genetic markers that was not evident from behavioral observations (Kappeler et al. 2002). In the 60-ha study area, three common female mitochondrial haplotypes were found. Females sharing a haplotype were highly clumped in space. The sizes of these matrilines and the genetic distances between their members indicate that their borders must be actively maintained. These matrilineal clusters also contained subadults of both sexes and some adult males. The presence of a few adult males with rare haplotypes not represented by other individuals in that population indicated that they migrated over considerable distances and are primarily responsible for gene flow. Whether other *Mirza* populations are also organized into such matrilines remains unknown.

Social interactions among *Mirza* adults are very rare and most often occur during the second part of the night (Pagès 1978, 1980; Kappeler 1997a). Agonistic interactions, which involved repeated chases, were observed between two females and between males and females. Around the mating season, injuries, such as bites to the head and pulled-out hair on the head and shoulders, have been observed and are almost certainly indicative of male-male aggression. Allogrooming between adults occurs at even lower frequencies (Rode-Margono et al. 2016).

Vocalizations are a prominent mechanism of social behavior. Some individuals emit "loud calls," especially soon after the onset of their nightly activity, and also almost constantly utter soft *hon* calls, which may signal the sender's position and movements to neighbors. A number of other vocalizations have been described in a study of captive *M. zaza* (Stanger 1993), including sex-specific advertisement calls with different functions (Seiler et al. 2019). Finally, olfactory signals, especially saliva, urine, and anogenital secretions, are used to mark small branches and other objects in the environment (J.-J. Petter and van der Sloot 2000). They may have a territorial function, which remains to be demonstrated.

Subject editors: Jörg U. Ganzhorn and Steven M. Goodman

LEPILEMURIDAE: *LEPILEMUR*, SPORTIVE LEMURS

U. Radespiel, S. Rasoloharijaona, and E. E. Louis Jr.

Sportive lemurs, of the genus *Lepilemur*, are medium-size (0.54–1.19 kg, Louis et al. 2006a), nocturnal, arboreal lemurs that are categorized as vertical clingers and leapers (Warren and Crompton 1996; Blanchard et al. 2015). They are generally a brownish-grayish color, often lighter on the belly than on dorsal or lateral parts of the body. They are monomorphic in pelage coloration (with the possible exception of *L. wrightae*; Louis et al. 2006a) and show no clear sexual size dimorphism in most species, despite some evidence for a female-biased body mass in *L. aeeclis* and *L. mustelinus* and a male-biased body mass in *L. microdon* (Taylor and Schwitzer 2012). In line with this rather inconspicuous outer appearance, species cannot be easily visually distinguished from each other.

TAXONOMY

Currently, *Lepilemur* is the only genus within the family Lepilemuridae and is the sister clade to the family Cheirogaleidae (Horvath et al. 2008; Perelman et al. 2011; Veilleux et al. 2013). However, other studies have presented contradictory evidence of the monophyly of Lepilemuridae and its relationship with the family Cheirogaleidae; although they confirmed the phylogenetic relationships of four genera in Cheirogaleidae (*Cheirogaleus*, *Allocebus*, *Microcebus*, and *Mirza*), Chatterjee et al. (2009), Fabre et al. (2009), and M. S. Springer et al. (2012) found that *Phaner* (Cheirogaleidae) and *Lepilemur* clustered together as a clade, thus challenging the phylogenetic position of *Phaner* with respect to the genus *Lepilemur*. Furthermore, Masters et al. (2006) suggested that the taxonomic status of the family Lepilemuridae is not warranted and *Lepilemur* should be included within Cheirogaleidae. However, incomplete data and/or insufficient sampling may be contributing to ongoing controversy about the phylogenetic relationships of Cheirogaleidae and Lepilemuridae (Louis and Lei 2016).

The genus *Lepilemur* has undergone an impressive cryptic radiation, most likely within the Miocene (Herrera and Dávalos 2016; Lei et al. 2017; cf. Horvath et al. 2008). Sportive lemurs were originally classified as two species: *L. mustelinus*, from the eastern moist evergreen forests, and *L. ruficaudatus*, from the western dry deciduous forests and southern dry spiny thickets (Schwarz 1931; Hill 1953). As scientific technological methodology has advanced, the taxonomy of this genus has been revised repeatedly (J.-J. Petter and Petter-Rousseaux 1960; Rumpler and Albignac 1975; J.-J. Petter et al. 1977; Tattersall 1982; Groves 2001). The most recent revisions, using cytogenetic (Rumpler and Albignac 1975; Andriaholinirina et al. 2005, 2006), molecular, and/or morphological data (Andriaholinirina et al. 2006; Louis et al. 2006a; Rabarivola et al. 2006; Craul et al. 2007; Lei et al. 2008; Ramaromilanto et al. 2009), have identified remarkable cryptic diversity within this genus, which has expanded to 26 species (Figure 14.45). This marked increase in sportive lemur species has been attributed to a better comprehensive sampling across the entire range of the genus as well as the advancement of molecular tools that are well suited to detecting cryptic biodiversity (Lei et al. 2017). However, as researchers have used different combinations of mtDNA sequence data, from fragments to entire mitogenomes, direct comparisons between the various data sets cannot be made without significantly truncating data (Lei et al. 2017). Lastly, the expansion of certain sportive lemur species has not been universally accepted, owing to 1) disagreements about the unconfirmed locality of valid and synonymized holotypes within the distributions of proposed species; 2) a lack of nuclear-sequence data and further phenotypic or ecological attributes as additional independent data sources for species delimitation; or 3) the lack of consistent parameters or criteria in describing these species (Tattersall 2007; Zinner et al. 2007; Tattersall and Cuozzo 2018). For instance, Lei et al. (2017) found no evidence to support the separation of *L. mittermeieri* from *L. dorsalis*. Thus, the syntypes, held in the British Museum (Natural History) (now the Natural History Museum, London) of *L. dorsalis* should be evaluated with next-generation sequencing platform technology to genetically characterize the reference specimens for this species and determine whether more recently described sportive lemurs are synonyms of *L. dorsalis*.

In conjunction with the expansion of species diversity in *Lepilemur* and other lemur genera, several hypotheses have been proposed to explain the distribution of endemism areas across the island. Multiple scenarios have rivers acting as significant barriers to gene flow, which was also confirmed for *Lepilemur* (to be subsequently referred to as "river barrier hypothesis"; R. D. Martin 1972b; Craul et al. 2007). Craul et al. (2008) tested a biogeographic model in which "centers of endemism" were defined based on the isolation effects of paired rivers for *Lepilemur* in a specific region in northeastern Madagascar. Here, at least one exception was found to rivers acting as a major driver of speciation, and this concerned *L. seali*, which occurs on both sides of the large Antainambalana River; it was hypothesized that this species may be able to traverse the river at higher elevations, if suitable forest habitat persisted at the headwaters. Ganzhorn et al. (2006) also described the importance of rivers as corridors based on cytogenetic reconstructions of the genus, specifically the sister relationship of the western *L. edwardsi* and the eastern *L. microdon* (Ishak et al. 1992). Current phylogenetic reconstructions from sequence-based data of the genus have substantiated this finding (Lei et al. 2017).

Two other models incorporate climatic factors to explain biogeographic centers of endemism. The retreat–dispersion hypothesis (also known as the watershed hypothesis; Wilmé et al. 2006) overlays the locations of rivers with Quaternary climate shifts to document zones of speciation/endemism, whereas the current climate hypothesis identifies 14 climatic regions from clustering analysis of 19 bioclimatic variables to explain species partitioning (Pearson and Raxworthy 2009). Using present distribution data of *Lepilemur* species, Lei et al. (2017) performed an ancestral area reconstruction and ecological vicariance analysis to trace the history of diversification

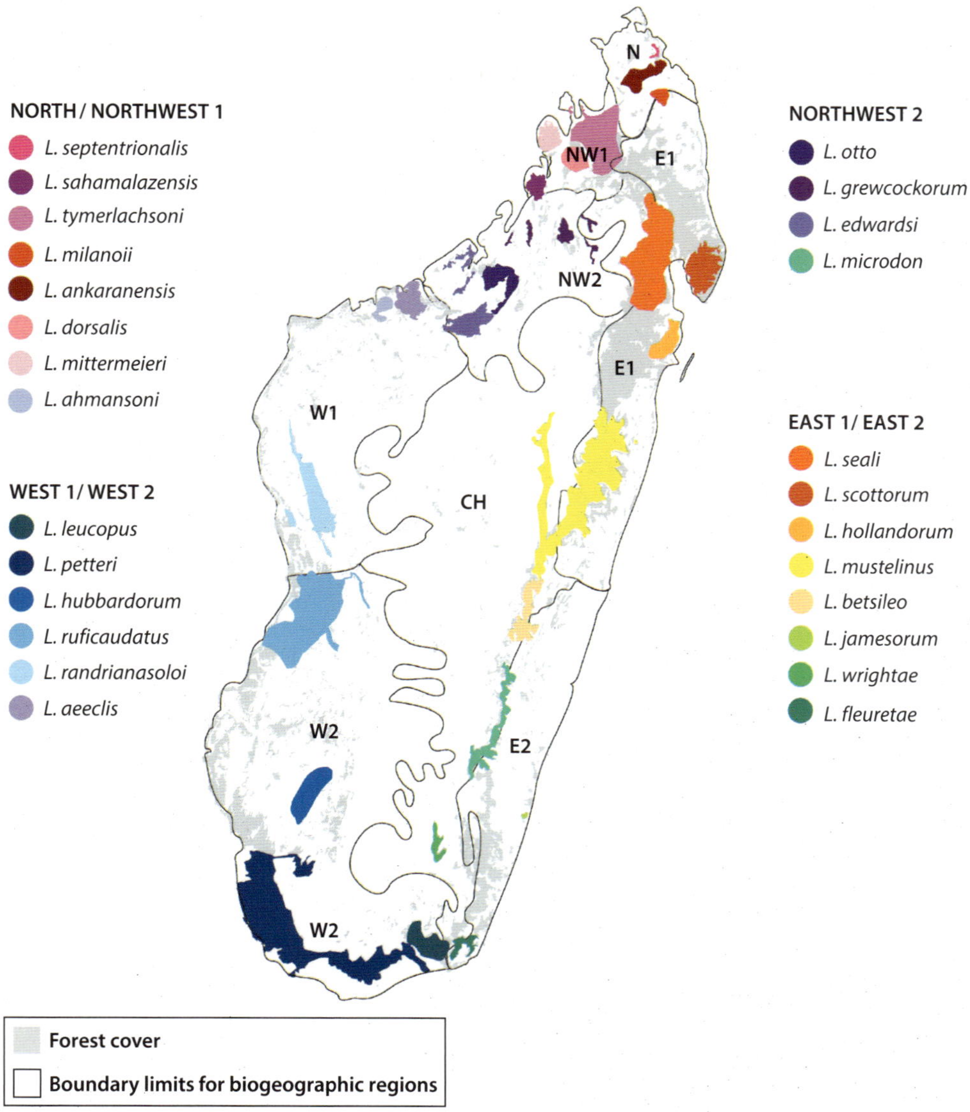

FIGURE 14.45 **Map summarizing the available knowledge on the geographic distribution of all recognized *Lepilemur* species and phytogeographic regions. For the delimitation of the biogeographic regions, we have used the criteria proposed by R. D. Martin (1972a, 1995). CH: Central Highlands.** (MAP generated by B. A. D. Robertson and T. M. Sefczek.)

and to test these biogeographic hypotheses. They estimated the initial split between the eastern and western *Lepilemur* clades to have occurred in the Miocene, with the divergence of most sportive lemur species occurring from the Pliocene to the Pleistocene. Furthermore, these authors found that the biogeographic patterns recovered were best explained with a combinatorial approach that included climate, watershed, and river hypotheses. The authors found that current climate and watershed hypotheses performed better for western and eastern clades, but the speciation of northern clades was not adequately explained by the underlying ecological factors.

Lei et al. (2017) partitioned sportive lemur taxa, based on an ancestral reconstruction analysis of mitogenomic data, into four geographic groups, but these groupings do not inclusively place geographically adjacent species into one area of endemism, thus, clustering taxa into east clades 1 and 2; west clades 1 and 2; north clade; and northwest clade 1 and 2 (as shown in Figure 14.45). For instance, the phylogenetic position of *L. microdon* challenges the east–west biogeographic division among sportive lemurs, as this species is geographically found in the east (E2) but phylogenetically is closely related to the *L. grewcockorum*, *L. otto*, and *L. edwardsi* clade, all endemic to the northwest (NW2). This relationship could be an example of riparian forest corridors acting as a link between the two regions during past climatic conditions, as described in the watershed hypothesis (Wilmé et al. 2006). Furthermore, the ancestral reconstruction analyses in Lei et al. (2017) postulated evidence of movement north from either the west coast or the Central Highlands (CH), exemplified by the *L. septentrionalis* clade (sister to the *L. microdon* group) being found in N, and *L. ahmansoni* distributed in W1. Thus, multiple mechanisms likely contributed to the speciation and distribution patterns in the genus *Lepilemur*.

HABITAT USE

Until now, only seven of the 26 described species of *Lepilemur* have been studied in some detail regarding aspects of their ecology, reproduction, social organization, and behavior, including communication (see below). One comment is warranted about *Lepilemur* from the southwest, including Berenty: available genetic results suggest that almost all studies published so far on *L. leucopus* concern *L. petteri* (Figure 14.45; Louis et al. 2006a; Lei et al. 2017), and for clarity, the latter species name will be used throughout this contribution.

The better-studied species are therefore *L. petteri* (southern dry spiny thicket, Berenty), *L. ruficaudatus* (western dry deciduous forest, Kirindy Forest CNFEREF), *L. edwardsi* (northwestern dry deciduous forest, Ankarafantsika), *L. sahamalazensis* (northwestern semi-deciduous forest, Sahamalaza–Iles Radama), *L. mittermeieri* (northwestern lowland moist evergreen forest, Ampasindava Peninsula), *L. septentrionalis* (northern dry deciduous forest, Montagne des Français), and *L. mustelinus* (eastern medium-altitude moist evergreen forest, Mantadia) (Figure 14.46; Mittermeier et al. 2010). These taxa will be referred to most often in the subsequent sections. It should be emphasized that further information about the other species is urgently needed to allow researchers to fully comprehend and acknowledge the ecological and behavioral diversity that may be present within this genus.

Average home-range sizes are variable among the seven studied species and partly between the sexes, and values range between 0.18 ha (female *L. petteri*) and 2.01 ha (*L. mittermeieri*) (Table 14.28). It has to be emphasized, however, that the methods employed to calculate home-range sizes also varied between species: these methods were the 95% kernel (*L. petteri*, Dröscher and Kappeler 2013; *L. ruficaudatus*, Hilgartner et al. 2012; *L. mittermeieri*, Wilmet et al. 2019; *L. septentrionalis*, Dinsmore et al. 2016), the 99% kernel (*L. sahamalazensis*, Mandl et al. 2018), and the minimum convex polygon (*L. edwardsi*, Rasoloharijaona et al. 2006). Variation in home-range size may therefore be partly attributed to dissimilarities in resource availability in different habitats and partly to methodological details of the various studies.

FIGURE 14.46 **The better-studied *Lepilemur* species: A) *L. sahamalazensis* at Sahamalaza, B) *L. edwardsi* at Mariarano, C) *L. ruficaudatus* at Kirindy Mité, D) *L. mittermeieri* at Ampasindava Peninsula, E) *L. mustelinus* at Mantadia, F) *L. petteri* at Bezà-Mahafaly, and G) *L. septentrionalis* at Montagne des Français.** (PHOTOS A, B, and G by E. E. Louis Jr.; C and F by R. Randriamampoinona; D by L. Wilmet; and E by R. Mittermeier. PHOTO collage generated by B. A. D. Robertson.)

TABLE 14.28. Available information on home-range size, preferred sleeping sites and associations, and social system of the better-studied *Lepilemur* species

PARAMETER	SEX	*L. SEPTENTRIONALIS*	*L. MITTERMEIERI*	*L. SAHAMALAZENSIS*	*L. EDWARDSI*	*L. RUFICAUDATUS*	*L. PETTERI**	*L. MUSTELINUS*
Home-range size	Male	n/a	2.01 ha[2]	0.67 ha[3]	1.01 ha[4]	0.99 ha[5]	0.33 ha[6]	n/a
	Female	1.91 ha[1]			0.98 ha[4]	0.66 ha[5]	0.18 ha[6]	n/a
Preferred sleeping sites		n/a	n/a	Tangles of lianas/trees, palm leaves[3,7]	Tree holes[8]	Tree holes[9,10]	Confluences of branches[6]	Tree holes[11]
Sleeping association		n/a	n/a	n/a	51.8%[8] (0–100%)[8]	26.3%[9] (1.7–83.3%)[9]	0.0%[6] (no variation)[6]	7.0%[11] (0–100%)[11]
Social system		n/a	n/a	Largely solitary[12]	Dispersed pairs[4]	Dispersed pairs or polygyny[5]	Dispersed pairs or polygyny[6]	n/a

Notes: Sleeping association indicates frequency, with mean %, range in parentheses. n/a, not available. * Based on genetics, the *Lepilemur* population from Berenty Reserve belongs to *L. petteri* and is therefore named accordingly throughout this contribution on *Lepilemur*.

[1] Dinsmore et al. (2016).
[2] Wilmet et al. (2019).
[3] Mandl et al. (2018).
[4] Rasoloharijaona et al. (2006).
[5] Hilgartner et al. (2012).
[6] Dröscher and Kappeler (2013).
[7] Seiler et al. (2013a).
[8] Rasoloharijaona et al. (2003).
[9] Zinner et al. (2003).
[10] E. J. Rakotomalala et al. (2017).
[11] Rasoloharijaona et al. (2008).
[12] Mandl et al. (2019a).

Many species have been reported to sleep in shelters during daytime, which may provide thermoregulatory benefits but can also help them to avoid detection by predators. Tree holes are the preferred shelter in three studied species, *L. edwardsi*, *L. ruficaudatus*, and *L. mustelinus* (Table 14.28). In contrast, *L. sahamalazensis* occupies dense tangles of trees/lianas and palm leaves, whereas *L. petteri* uses confluences of branches, mainly of *Alluaudia* (Didiereaceae). Two comparative studies on parasite loads of *L. edwardsi* and *Avahi occidentalis* in Ankarafantsika revealed that sleeping in tree holes (*L. edwardsi*) conveys higher rates of tick and mite infection, as well as oxyurid nematodes, than sleeping in the open vegetation (*A. occidentalis*) (Hokan et al. 2017, 2018), suggesting a link between sleeping site ecology and health (see also Donati et al., pp. 1963–66). Similar differences in parasite load were detected between *L. mustelinus* and *A. laniger* at Ambatovy (Junge et al. 2017). Tree holes are typically located 3–11 m above the ground (Rasoloharijaona et al. 2003, 2008; Seiler et al. 2013a; E. J. Rakotomalala et al. 2017) and are used by single individuals but also by pairs with dependent offspring in various proportions in different species; whereas *L. edwardsi* was observed sleeping in male-female pairs on an average of 51.8% of the days, sleeping associations were formed only on an average of 26.3% of the days in *L. ruficaudatus*, and on 7.0% of the days in *L. mustelinus*, but pair partners never shared sleeping sites in *L. petteri* (Table 14.28). These patterns suggest varying levels of sociality in different *Lepilemur* species, but co-sleeping varies also considerably between individual pairs in all studied species, with the exception of *L. petteri*, and the reasons for this high plasticity are still not understood.

DIET

Lepilemur species are mainly folivorous but complement their diet with fruits, flowers, and buds in varying amounts across the year. For example, whereas in *L. edwardsi* leaves accounted for 100% of the diet in April–May, at the end of rainy season, the proportion dropped to almost 50% in October–November, at the end of dry season (Thalmann 2001). Variation in food composition and food selectivity has been explained by the seasonal availability of young leaves and other food items, leaf chemistry, and the presence or absence of potential competitors. Whereas mature leaves are available year-round, the production of young leaves peaks in the rainy season, and it was shown that *L. ruficaudatus* individuals are more selective in leaf choice toward leaves of high quality (i.e., higher protein concentration) during the rainy season than during the dry season (Ganzhorn 2002). Some unusual food items were recorded in two cases of spider consumption, one case of beetle consumption, and one extensive episode of *L. sahamalazensis* licking and feeding on a spiderweb (Seiler et al. 2014). Lowin (2010) recorded the consumption of tree exudates by *L. ankaranensis* on several occasions but also confirmed a predominantly folivorous diet during his short-term study. In an earlier study, *L. petteri* in Berenty was reported to reingest its own feces (Charles-Dominique and Hladik 1971), but this behavior (caecotrophy) has not been confirmed in a recent study that reported results from 337 hours of feeding observations of this species at the same site (Dröscher and Kappeler 2014a).

COMMUNITY ECOLOGY

All *Lepilemur* species have allopatric distributions but typically share their habitat with 5–13 other lemur genera (Ganzhorn et al. 1999b). Among those genera co-occurring with *Lepilemur* species on a regular basis, *Avahi* species are the most similar in body size and feeding ecology to *Lepilemur* species. It was shown across four study sites containing four different *Lepilemur* species that, when sharing their habitat with *Avahi* species, which are also mainly folivorous, they eat leaves with a lower ratio (by percentage) of extractable protein to acid detergent fiber (i.e., lower-quality leaves) than in areas where they are not in strict sympatry with *Avahi* species (Ganzhorn 1993). These results suggest some form of interspecific feeding competition between these two genera, which at Ankarafantsika seems to be counteracted by a seasonal avoidance of feeding niche overlap between *L. edwardsi* and the sympatric *A. occidentalis* (Thalmann 2001). Niche separation between these two genera was also recently reported on a temporal scale between *L. fleuretae* and *A. meridionalis* in the southeast (Campera et al. 2019).

Sportive lemurs have various predators (birds of prey, carnivorans, and snakes), most of which are native (reviewed in Goodman et al. 1993a; Burnham et al. 2012; see Goodman and Ganzhorn, pp. 1829–38), but some are introduced (e.g., *Felis silvestris*; Dröscher and Kappeler 2014a). Several antipredator strategies have so far been described in sportive lemurs besides sleeping in shelters during daytime. First, *L. sahamalazensis* has shown an active antipredator behavior—mobbing against snakes (Mandl et al. 2017). Second, *L. ruficaudatus* produces instant alarm calls that may be mainly directed toward the predator but may also warn kin or pair partners (Fichtel 2007). Third, *L. sahamalazensis* shows increased vigilance behavior to detect predators when exposed to predator vocalizations (Seiler et al. 2013b).

PHYSIOLOGICAL ECOLOGY

Lepilemur ruficaudatus was described as having one of the lowest resting metabolic rates known for any folivorous mammal in the world, and it was hypothesized that such low rates may allow *Lepilemur* to subsist on leaves with a high frequency of potentially toxic allelochemicals (Schmid and Ganzhorn 1996; Bethge et al. 2017). Such a mechanism may be important, as *Lepilemur* species are generalist folivores. More specifically, *L. edwardsi* was shown to use at least 25 tree and five liana species as food sources (Thalmann 2001); Seiler et al. (2014) described the consumption of at least 42 different tree species by *L. sahamalazensis* and confirmed this species' predominantly folivorous diet (98.9%); and Dröscher and Kappeler (2014a) observed *L. leucopus* feeding on at least 32 tree species and 16 liana species, showing an overall average of 90.1% folivory.

SOCIAL SYSTEM

Lepilemur species live either 1) in dispersed pairs (*L. edwardsi*, *L. ruficaudatus*, and *L. petteri*), in which male and female partners forage solitarily but share large parts of their respective home range; 2) in dispersed polygyny (*L. ruficaudatus* and *L. petteri*), with some male home ranges overlapping with those of two adult females; or 3) largely solitarily, though with partly overlapping home ranges between the sexes in *L. sahamalazensis* (Table 14.28). In all cases, adult intrasexual home-range overlap is minimal in both sexes, and female resource competition has been suggested as the main driver of these dispersed social structures.

Sharing larger parts of the home range with a pair partner, however, does not necessarily imply frequent affiliative encounters between the pair members. A detailed study on *L. ruficaudatus* revealed that pair partners stay on average 43.5 m (range: 0–180 m) from each other—that is, out of sight (Hilgartner et al. 2012). Proximity (<10 m distance) was rarely observed (15% of time) and occurred more often during the pre-mating and mating season (25.7%), interpreted as mate guarding, than during the non-mating season (8.8%). Even though pair partners were mostly separated from each other, they met between 1.6 times/6 hr (non-mating season) and 3.5 times/6 hr (mating season), and about half of all encounters involved agonistic behaviors. Fichtel et al. (2011) noted that general behavioral activities such as resting, foraging, and locomotion were significantly synchronized among the partners. The authors suggested, however, that the observed patterns of coordinated space use and behavioral synchronization may result from harmonization of endogenous activity rhythms that may serve an active mutual avoidance of pair partners in order to minimize intersexual feeding competition (Hilgartner et al. 2012). Dröscher and Kappeler (2013) also noted that affiliative interactions among pair partners of *L. petteri* were virtually absent, and partners met very rarely (0.14 interactions/hr), despite a considerable proportion of home-range overlap between them. In contrast to these two species of rather low pair sociality, vocal duetting was observed in the species with the highest rates of pair sleeping, *L. edwardsi*, and this behavior was shown to directly increase behavioral synchronization within the pair and was suggested to strengthen the pair-bond between the partners and to facilitate cooperative resource defense against neighbors (Méndez-Cárdenas and Zimmermann 2009). It is well known, however, that social monogamy does not necessarily imply a monogamous mating system. Indeed, Hilgartner et al. (2012) observed in *L. ruficaudatus* nonagonistic encounters between male and female neighbors on a regular basis and witnessed one extra-pair copulation. However, parentage data have not been published for any of the studied *Lepilemur* species, and mating systems are therefore not well understood.

Regulating and coordinating dispersed-pair activities and space use among neighbors requires intraspecific communication. Interestingly, to coordinate the dispersed pairs or to signal resource ownership, some *Lepilemur* species employ extensive vocal repertoires and high vocal activity: *L. edwardsi* (Rasoloharijaona et al. 2006, 2010), *L. sahamalazensis* (Seiler et al. 2015), and *L. otto* (Mahaboubi et al. 2015); while other members of this genus seem to rely more on olfactory communication: *L. mustelinus* (Rasoloharijaona et al. 2010) and *L. petteri* (R. J. Russell 1977; Dröscher and Kappeler 2014b).

From northwestern to northern Madagascar, Méndez-Cárdenas et al. (2008) demonstrated that two loud-call types, the *ouah* and the high-pitched call, carry species-specific acoustic signatures. Up to 12 different call types have been identified in highly vocal species: *L. edwardsi*, with nine call types, 1.31 calls/hr (Rasoloharijaona et al. 2006, 2010); and *L. sahamalazensis*, with 12 call types, 0.91 calls/hr (Seiler et al. 2015; Mandl et al. 2019b). In the regularly pair-sleeping *L. edwardsi*, behavioral contexts range from affiliative contacts (n = 15) or

agonistic encounters (n = 13) at feeding sites, affiliative contacts (n = 23) or agonistic encounters (n = 25) at sleeping sites, and solitary situations at sleeping sites (n = 13) to traveling (n = 4) (Rasoloharijaona et al. 2006). Both sexes differed in acoustic repertoire in this species. In *L. sahamalazensis*, Mandl et al. (2019b) discriminated between "targeted calls" (emitter <10 m from another individual) and "broadcast calls" (emitter >10 m from other individuals) and noted that 1) eight of 12 call types were emitted in both situations (total: 392 assigned calls); 2) the relatively rare squeak (n = 4), high-pitched call (n = 2), and growl (n = 5) were used only in proximity to other individuals; and finally that 3) the squeal (n = 14) was used only as "broadcast calls." Whereas the call rate differed among seasons (higher in pre-mating and mating season) and between sexes (males more vocal than females), no evidence for sex-specific calls was found in this species. These findings indicate a high vocal plasticity within and between some *Lepilemur* species (e.g., *L. edwardsi*, *L. sahamalazensis*), which is remarkable given that some other species, such as *L. mustelinus*, only very rarely emit loud calls at all (Rasoloharijaona et al. 2010).

Active tree gouging was observed instead of loud calling in *L. mustelinus* in the moist evergreen forests of Mantadia, mostly in the early evening after individuals were leaving the tree hole or in the early morning. This behavior was interpreted as a resource defense strategy, which may have evolved in species living in low population densities, when acoustic signals may not actually reach a potential receiver. Olfactory signals last much longer than calls and may convey occupancy information to a neighboring individual even after the signaler has left the sleeping site. This hypothesis is still awaiting formal testing once information becomes available on population densities, vocal activity, and olfactory communication for many more members of this genus. *Lepilemur petteri* was shown to establish jointly used latrines to deposit urine and feces, mostly within the core area of each pair home range (Dröscher and Kappeler 2014b), and it was suggested that these latrines mainly announce the presence of a group member to the mate or other family members and thereby facilitate familiarity and social bonding within social units, but do probably not serve to defend mates, territories, or resources, or to advertise the reproductive state of the depositor. Latrine use was also observed in *L. petteri* at Bezà-Mahafaly, in *L. wrightae* at Kalambatritra, *L. jamesorum* at Manombo, and *L. ruficaudatus* at Kirindy CNFEREF (reviewed in Irwin et al. 2004), but the latrines' use and function has not been studied in these taxa.

LIFE HISTORY AND POPULATION DYNAMICS

Many *Lepilemur* species inhabit highly seasonal environments and are therefore seasonal breeders, like most other lemurs, and this seasonality is expressed in both sexes. For example, a detailed study on reproduction in *L. edwardsi* revealed that male testes are largest in May–June and decrease significantly afterward (Randrianambinina et al. 2007). Estrous females were observed between May and July, and small infants were observed only in October and November, indicating a gestation length of four to five months. Similarly, the mating season of *L. ruficaudatus* lies between May and June, but gestation is much longer than expected for a lemur of its size (151–190 days, Hilgartner et al. 2008). Although reproductive schedules can differ between species by up to two months, reproductive seasonality characterizes all other species studied so far, specifically *L. petteri* (Dröscher and Kappeler 2013) and *L. sahamalazensis* (Mandl et al. 2019a).

Lepilemur females give birth to singletons, which are transported in the mother's mouth but are also parked in tree holes or vegetation (Randrianambinina et al. 2007; Hilgartner et al. 2008). One case of infanticide has been observed in *L. edwardsi* (Rasoloharijaona et al. 2000). In *L. ruficaudatus*, parental care is provided entirely by the mother, but infants start to forage and leave the nest independently at an age of 50 days and are weaned at about two months (Hilgartner et al. 2008). The typical inter-birth interval of *L. ruficaudatus* females is one year, but in *L. edwardsi* offspring continue to grow during their first year of life and do not reach sexual maturity before the second mating season following their birth (Randrianambinina et al. 2007).

CONSERVATION

While all Malagasy lemurs face the threat of extinction, with 95% of the taxa in the top three threatened categories of the IUCN Red List of Threatened Species, some species within the genus *Lepilemur* represent the most endangered primates in the world: nine species are listed as Critically Endangered, 15 as Endangered, and two as Vulnerable, (IUCN 2020). Two of the 26 sportive lemur species, *L. septentrionalis* and *L. jamesorum*, have total populations of fewer than 100 known individuals. Of critical importance, the folivorous diet and predilection for new-growth leaves of *L. septentrionalis* complicates any attempts or plans to maintain it in captivity. Currently, there are no records of any sportive lemurs held in zoological parks, and all known attempts to maintain them in captivity have failed, with animals dying, on average, within one week of being brought into captivity (E. E. Louis Jr., unpublished data). Therefore, in situ conservation actions in combination with local community-based programs are the only viable solutions. Besides suffering heavily from habitat loss across their rather local small geographic distributions, *Lepilemur* species are under direct threat from hunting, owing to their use of holes and branch tangles as sleeping sites during daylight, which make them easy to capture (see Golden et al., pp. 204–17). Given this precarious conservation situation, it is also of utmost importance to firmly establish clear delimitations between recognized species limits and to properly document their distributional ranges, as this information is lacking for most of the *Lepilemur* species (IUCN 2020).

CONCLUSION

Next-generation sequencing data using previously used DNA technologies should be utilized on all 26 recognized species of *Lepilemur*, including all available museum holotype or paratype specimens, to clarify remaining taxonomic uncertainties within the genus associated with naming the different clades. This information is critical to the development of efficient conservation management plans. In order to complement this work, expanded field studies are urgently needed that will provide the lacking census and natural history information on the vast number of understudied lineages within the genus.

Subject editors: Jörg U. Ganzhorn and Steven M. Goodman

LEMURIDAE: *EULEMUR*, TRUE LEMURS

S. E. Johnson, S. R. Tecot, F. B. Ralainasolo, J. H. Ratsimbazafy, D. J. Overdorff, and G. Donati

The true lemurs (genus *Eulemur*) represent a diverse and widespread species group (Figure 14.47). Our understanding of their species-level diversity has increased substantially in recent years through taxonomic changes. The members of this genus have varied diets, habitat use, diel patterns, reproductive biology, and social organization, denoting a high degree of flexibility and adaptation to local environmental conditions. Nonetheless, flexibility has its limits in the face of ongoing habitat loss, degradation, and hunting, and nearly all true lemur species face elevated risks of extinction.

TAXONOMY

Like many lemur groups, members of the genus *Eulemur* have undergone major taxonomic revisions in recent years, resulting in a significant increase in the number of recognized species (e.g., Mittermeier et al. 2008, 2010), though these changes are not without controversy (Tattersall 2007; Tattersall and Cuozzo 2018). However, in contrast with other lemur genera, in *Eulemur* nearly all of this growth has derived from elevating recognized subspecies to species. The genus *Eulemur* was described by E. L. Simons and Rumpler (1988), who suggested that these species should be removed from *Lemur* based on behavioral, anatomical, and karyotypic evidence. *Eulemur* is a monophyletic group (Markolf et al. 2013) containing 12 species: *E. mongoz* (Mongoose Lemur), *E. coronatus* (Crowned Lemur), *E. rubriventer* (Red-bellied Lemur; Figure 14.47b), *E. macaco* (Black Lemur), *E. flavifrons* (Blue-eyed Black Lemur), *E. fulvus* (Brown Lemur), *E. sanfordi* (Sanford's Brown Lemur), *E. albifrons* (White-fronted Brown Lemur; Figure 14.47c), *E. rufus* (Rufous Brown Lemur), *E. rufifrons* (Red-fronted

FIGURE 14.47 **True lemurs (all males). A) *Eulemur collaris*, Tsitongambarika protected area; B) *E. rubriventer*, Ranomafana National Park; C) *E. albifrons*, Masoala National Park; and D) *E. rufifrons*, Kirindy Forest CNFEREF.** (PHOTO A by J. Chambler, B by S. Tecot, C by T. Eppley, and D by E. Račevska.)

Brown Lemur; Figure 14.47d), *E. collaris* (Red-collared Brown Lemur; Figure 14.47a), and *E. cinereiceps* (White-collared Brown Lemur) (Mittermeier et al. 2008; IUCN 2020).

Until recently, the black lemurs, *E. macaco* and *E. flavifrons*, were considered subspecies of *E. macaco*, while the members of the so-called brown lemur species complex (*E. fulvus*, *E. sanfordi*, *E. albifrons*, *E. rufus*, *E. rufifrons*, *E. collaris*, and *E. cinereiceps*) were subspecies of *E. fulvus*. Initially, evidence based on meiotic study of hybrids (Djelati et al. 1997) and population aggregate analysis of mtDNA (Wyner et al. 1999a) indicated that *E. collaris* and *E. cinereiceps* warranted consideration as full species. A further division of *E. cinereiceps* and *E.* "*albocollaris*" (the previously accepted nomenclature for gray-headed lemurs) suggested by Groves (2001) was not supported by evidence from mtDNA or ground surveys (Johnson et al. 2008), the name *E. cinereiceps* was considered to have priority and has been adopted for this species (Johnson et al. 2008; Mittermeier et al. 2008; IUCN 2020). More recently, a comprehensive assessment based on the general lineage species concept and using nuclear and mtDNA markers, vocalizations, skull morphology, and pelage traits supported species-level designation for each of the brown lemur taxa (Markolf et al. 2013)—confirming what has become standard taxonomy for *Eulemur* (Mittermeier et al. 2010). The existence of natural hybridization across several *Eulemur* species (Rabarivola et al. 1991; Pastorini et al. 2001a; Delmore et al. 2013) does not decisively support nor confound this taxonomy, as interfertility among true lemur species aligns poorly with evolutionary relationships. For example, *E. collaris* × *E. cinereiceps* hybrids are sterile (Djelati et al. 1997), while *E. rufifrons* and *E. cinereiceps* form a broad, stable hybrid zone with multiple generations of backcrossing (Delmore et al. 2013).

Changes in taxonomy in *Eulemur* have coincided with efforts to clarify the evolutionary relationships within the genus. Phylogenetic analyses using primarily genetic markers have produced some consensus, notably that the two black lemurs and the seven brown lemurs respectively form monophyletic, recently diverged clades, and that *E. collaris* and *E. cinereiceps* form a distinct group within the brown lemurs (Markolf et al. 2013). However, the relationships among the true lemurs are otherwise ambiguous, and there is a lack of agreement regarding sister relationships or basal position for *E. mongoz*, *E. coronatus*, and *E. rubriventer* (Horvath et al. 2008; Markolf et al. 2013). Several recent investigations have estimated divergence times for the *Eulemur* genus and subsequent splits among species (Horvath et al. 2008; Markolf and Kappeler 2013); these place the origin of the genus anywhere between the early Miocene, c. 20 million years ago (Mya) (Horvath et al. 2008), and the Pliocene, 4.5 Mya (Markolf and Kappeler 2013), while some currently recognized species may have diverged as early as 9 Mya (when *E. rubriventer* split from other true lemurs; Horvath et al. 2008) and as recently as 0.09 Mya (*E. albifrons*–*E. sanfordi* division; Markolf and Kappeler 2013). This lack of consensus makes it difficult to draw firm inferences regarding the biogeographic and climatic context for *Eulemur* evolution, though Markolf and Kappeler (2013) found general support for the importance of river catchments during Pleistocene drying cycles (Wilmé et al. 2006) for much recent speciation in this group.

HABITAT USE

Cathemerality (activity day and night) is characteristic of *Eulemur*. It is unusual in primates but common in other mammals (Curtis and Rasmussen 2006). All *Eulemur* species studied to date appear to be active during day and night, although the activity profile over 24 hours may vary substantially among species, sites, and seasons (Donati and Borgognini-Tarli 2006; Curtis 2007). Cathemeral activity in *Eulemur* is best documented in *E. collaris* (Donati et al. 2016), *E. flavifrons* (N. Schwitzer et al. 2007), *E. fulvus* (M. A. Rasmussen 1999), *E. macaco* (J. R. Andrews and Birkinshaw 1998), *E. mongoz* (Curtis et al. 1999; M. A. Rasmussen 1999), and *E. rufifrons* and *E. rubriventer* (Overdorff and Rasmussen 1995; Kappeler and Erkert 2003), which has allowed some general hypotheses to be developed regarding the evolution of this activity. Three patterns of cathemerality have been described (M. A. Rasmussen 1999). Pattern A species switch activity seasonally from a fairly strict diurnality to nocturnality (*E. mongoz*, see Curtis et al. 1999; M. A. Rasmussen 1999). Pattern B species also seasonally switch to nocturnal activity, or they increase nocturnal activity while continuing to remain active during the day (*E. collaris* and *E. rufifrons* × *E. collaris* hybrids, see Donati et al. 2009, 2016; *E. fulvus*, see M. A. Rasmussen 1999; and *E. rufifrons*, see Kappeler and Erkert 2003). Pattern C species are active across the 24-hour period throughout the year (*E. flavifrons*, see N. Schwitzer et al. 2007; *E. macaco*, see Colquhoun 1998, J. R. Andrews and Birkinshaw 1998; and *E. rufifrons* and *E. rubriventer*, see Overdorff and Rasmussen 1995).

The mechanisms underlying cathemerality are increasingly understood, and a variety of proximate factors (photoperiod, moon phase, temperature, and rainfall) and ultimate factors (food quality and availability, reduction of predation risk, and reduction of interspecific competition) have been shown to play a role. Increased moonlight, for example, triggers increased nocturnal activity in most species (Curtis et al. 1999; Kappeler and Erkert 2003; Donati et al. 2009) but not in some (Overdorff and Rasmussen 1995; Freed 1996). One of the first hypotheses for why cathemerality evolved in *Eulemur* proposed that true lemur species need to extend their activity around the clock to maximize nutrient extraction from fibrous food, owing to their nonspecialized gut and fast food-passage rate (Engqvist and Richard 1991). This idea has been supported by several studies (Donati et al. 2007b, 2009, 2016), and Overdorff and Rasmussen (1995) found that unripe fruit might place similar pressures on *E. rufifrons*. A second explanation is that cathemeral species are using exposed feeding sources at night to avoid predation by diurnal raptors (Curtis et al. 1999). Finally, given the degree of sympatry among different *Eulemur* species, it has also been suggested that cathemerality may minimize interspecific competition by varying activity across a 24-hour period (Curtis and Rasmussen 2006). It is clear that there is no single ecological factor driving this inherently flexible behavior, but the adaptive nature of cathemerality is strongly supported by the intermediate visual morphology of these species, allowing them to cope with a range of light conditions (Kirk 2006) and by comprehensive phylogenetic analyses (Santini et al. 2015).

DIET

Eulemur species are predominantly frugivores, despite the wide range of habitats they occupy. For the species that have been observed over at least one annual cycle, fruit comprises between 64.3% and 99.8% of their diet (Sato et al. 2016 and references therein). However, a large coefficient of variation has been recorded between the eastern and western populations. In the western dry deciduous forests, *Eulemur* species are more folivorous (see Eppley et al., pp. 1839–59), with leaves accounting for between 17% (*E. mongoz*) and 89% (*E. rufifrons*) of their diets (Sussman 1977a; Curtis et al. 1999). In the moist evergreen forests, where *Eulemur* densities are lower (Johnson and Overdorff 1999), fruit is always a major component of the diet, and leaves comprise 0–23% (Overdorff 1993; Andriamaharoa et al. 2010). However, monthly leaf eating can be extremely variable, and very high when fruit is scarce (e.g., >50% in *E. rubriventer*; Tecot 2008). These figures suggest that, despite tooth morphology comparable to that of folivorous lemurs (Overdorff and Rasmussen 1995), *Eulemur* species are constrained by their simple digestive system and can afford limited dietary shifts (J. H. Campbell et al. 2000). This hypothesis is supported by the fast food-passage rate (Overdorff and Rasmussen 1995) and the low fiber digestibility reported for *Eulemur* (J. H. Campbell et al. 2004).

Western populations of *Eulemur* tend to have lower dietary diversity relative to species living in the northern and eastern moist evergreen forests. In dry deciduous forests, *E. rufifrons* feeds on only 11–30 species of plants (Sussman 1977a; Ganzhorn and Kappeler 1996), and *E. macaco* consumed plant parts from only 31 species across a 12-month period (Colquhoun 1993). In the southern gallery forest of Berenty, *E. rufifrons* × *E. collaris* hybrids fed on 48 plant species year-round (Donati et al. 2009). Although *E. mongoz* and *E. fulvus* sampled food from over 100 plant species, 15 or fewer species contributed to the bulk (>50%) of their monthly diet (M. A. Rasmussen 1999; Sato 2012). A similar pattern is seen in the north and the east: *Eulemur* species can exploit food from 80 (*E. rufifrons*) to more than 120 plant species (*E. collaris* and *E. rubriventer*), but they concentrate their feeding time on only five to 15 plant species each month (Overdorff 1993; Donati et al. 2007b; Tecot 2008).

Flowers appear to be an important supplementary food source for *Eulemur* species, particularly during the dry season. Although flowers account for only 3–5% of the total annual diet of *E. mongoz*, the total percentage of time spent feeding on flower nectar can be over 60% on a monthly basis (Curtis 1997; M. A. Rasmussen 1999). The fact that *Eulemur* species concentrate some proportion of their feeding on nectar seasonally may have important implications for their role as potential nonflying pollinators for particular plant species (Kress 1993).

Evidence is available to indicate that *Eulemur* species are crucial as seed dispersers in Malagasy forests (see Razafindratsima et al., pp. 142–52). In Ranomafana, composed of moist evergreen forest, *E. rubriventer* and *E. rufifrons* disperse seeds at mean distances of 120 and 96 m, respectively, and this is suggested to result in local clustering of tree distributions (Razafindratsima et al. 2014). Both *E. rufifrons* and *E. rubriventer* eat fruit from plant genera that no other lemur species appears to exploit (P. C. Wright et al. 2011). In the Ankarafantsika dry deciduous forest, 23 large-seeded plants have been shown to be dependent on *E. fulvus* for seed dispersal (Sato 2018), while in the littoral forest, *E. collaris* appears to be the only disperser of seeds larger than 12.5 mm in length (Bollen et al. 2004a). Ganzhorn et al. (1999a) demonstrated that the absence of *E. rufifrons* from fragments of dry deciduous forest in the Kirindy Forest CNFEREF area has a negative impact on regeneration of lemur-dispersed plant species. *Eulemur* species also have been shown to exhibit some degree of flexibility to anthropogenic habitats, with non-native plant species sometimes prevalent in the diet. In secondary forests of northwestern Madagascar, *E. macaco* can meet its nutritional requirements by including in the diet fruits from introduced species and old cash-crop plantations (Simmen et al. 2007). A general ability to cope well with secondary forests was also observed in *E. flavifrons* (N. Schwitzer et al. 2007) and *E. collaris* (Donati et al. 2009, 2020). However, this is not the case for all species; for example, *E. rubriventer* in secondary forest responds less flexibly to environmental change (including food availability) than its congeners in intact forest (Tecot 2008, 2013).

RANGING PATTERNS

The ranging patterns in *Eulemur* can be extremely variable, as would be expected for a group that is present in all forested habitats of Madagascar. Home ranges in dry deciduous forest vary in size from >1 ha, for *E. rufifrons* in the west, to 16 ha, for *E. fulvus* and *E. coronatus* in the north and northwest (Sussman 1977a; Freed 1996; M. A. Rasmussen 1999). In moist evergreen forests, *Eulemur* species, especially those formerly classed as *E. fulvus* subspecies (i.e., the brown lemur species complex; see Taxonomy, above), have been recorded to reach the largest home ranges, 85–113 ha (Overdorff 1993; Vasey 1997b; Campera et al. 2014). However, exceptions to these general size ranges have been observed. In the dry deciduous forest of Kirindy Forest CNFEREF, home ranges of *E. rufifrons* can reach 324 ha as a consequence of seasonal water scarcity (Scholz and Kappeler 2004). These large seasonal variations are not unusual for *Eulemur* species, as they are known to travel several kilometers when food is scarce. Temporary shifts from familiar areas have been recorded in *E. rufifrons* (Overdorff 1993), *E. fulvus* (Sato 2012), and *E. collaris* (Campera et al. 2014). This extreme ranging flexibility also allows some species to survive in fragmented and/or secondary forests (N. Schwitzer et al. 2007; Donati et al. 2011; Campera et al. 2014). Despite this flexibility, however, ecological niche models strongly indicate that most *Eulemur* species exhibit substantially reduced distributions under anthropogenic impact (Kamilar and Tecot 2016).

ABUNDANCE

Eulemur is among the most widespread of all lemur genera, with one or more species found across nearly all remaining forest habitats on Madagascar, while introduced populations have naturalized the nearby Comoro islands (Tattersall and Sussman 1998; Mittermeier et al. 2010). Populations of *E. mongoz*, *E. macaco*, *E. flavifrons*, *E. coronatus*, and *E. rubriventer* can be found around the

perimeter of Madagascar and are allopatric. Additionally, each of these species is usually sympatric with one or more species from the brown lemur species complex. The distributions of eastern and western populations of *E. rufifrons* and *E. fulvus* were at one time contiguous (Tattersall and Sussman 1998), thus having occupied the mosaic habitats of the Central Highlands.

Although these lemurs are ubiquitous in forests across Madagascar, there is considerable variation in the abundance of *Eulemur* species and individual populations. Most dramatically, population densities in dry deciduous forests can be an order of magnitude higher than those in moist evergreen forests, including conspecifics (from ~0.07 to >1 ind/ha; Sussman 1974; Tattersall and Sussman 1998; Irwin et al. 2005; Herrera et al. 2011; Brenneman et al. 2012). This pattern might be explained by regional differences in the predictability of food resources or by relaxed competition, as lemur species richness is lower in the west (Ganzhorn et al. 1999b; Mittermeier et al. 2010; Razafindratsima et al. 2013); as western populations and species also tend to be smaller than eastern counterparts (Gordon et al. 2016), there may also be a trade-off between body mass and population density, though overall lemur biomass remains higher in the west (Ganzhorn et al. 1999b). Even within biomes, there can be striking differences in relative abundance. For example, population densities in the *Eulemur rufifrons* × *E. cinereiceps* hybrid zone on the Andringitra Massif are considerably higher than those in either parental species' range (Johnson 2007; Herrera et al. 2011; Brenneman et al. 2012). The higher densities may be due in part to the apparently higher availability of fig trees in the hybrid zone and the heavy reliance by hybrids on *Ficus* as a fallback food (Johnson 2007).

Anthropogenic disturbance such as forest fragmentation and hunting pressure can have variable impacts on true lemur populations; densities are typically lower in more disturbed areas (Lehman 2007; Herrera et al. 2011; Brenneman et al. 2012), though the reverse (de Winter et al. 2018) and no effect have been observed (Lehman et al. 2006b). Preferences in some true lemurs (e.g., *E. albifrons*, *E. collaris*, *E. rufifrons*) for lower-elevation forests, often subjected to high levels of disturbance, could accelerate population declines (Campera et al. 2020). Those species with the lowest abundances may also have highly restricted geographic ranges (i.e., compound rarity). Such risks are reflected in the elevated conservation status of such species as *E. cinereiceps*, *E. mongoz*, and *E. sanfordi* (IUCN 2020).

COMMUNITY ECOLOGY

Several long-term studies on *Eulemur* have focused on evaluating the degree of niche separation between sympatric *Eulemur* species. In most of the comparisons between sympatric pairs, both species have much in common, including overall diet (Sato et al. 2016) and general activity (Donati et al. 2016). However, subtle distinctions in diet and habitat use may help to explain how these animals coexist (Ganzhorn 1989a; Tattersall and Sussman 1998). Sympatric species potentially avoid each other by feeding and resting at different times of the day or night, using different levels of the forest canopy when feeding and traveling, and feeding on different parts of the same plant (Freed 1996; M. A. Rasmussen 1999). While mixed-species associations are rare, they were observed in northern Madagascar between *E. coronatus* and *E. sanfordi* with some regularity during the wet season, when food resources were more available (Freed 1996). Due to niche similarities, competition may also take place between true lemurs and other sympatric lemurids, especially the ecologically similar *Lemur catta*. Dietary overlap has been shown to be high between *L. catta* and *E. rufifrons* × *E. collaris* hybrids in Berenty during the dry season (Simmen et al. 2003). During these periods, *Eulemur* individuals appear to compensate for a low-quality diet by increasing the amount of food eaten (Simmen et al. 2003) and by using cathemeral activity (Donati et al. 2009). Curiously, *E. rufifrons* showed positive spatiotemporal associations with both *E. rubriventer* and *Varecia variegata* in fragmented forests in southeastern Madagascar (Holmes et al. 2019). This suggests that these species may be drawn to similar food sources in this degraded environment despite the potential for competitive interactions; alternatively, there may be coincident habitat use due to similar antipredator strategies.

SOCIAL SYSTEM

One of the striking aspects of *Eulemur* social structure is that group sizes are quite small compared to those of haplorrhine primates (Kappeler and Heymann 1996). The composition of *Eulemur* groups fall into two categories: small pair-bonded family groups (*E. mongoz* and *E. rubriventer*) and larger multi-male and multi-female groups (all other *Eulemur* species). Phylogenetic reconstructions indicate that pair-living likely evolved from group-living species at least once within the *Eulemur* clade (Kappeler and Fichtel 2016). Both *E. mongoz* and *E. rubriventer* appear to function as classic pair-living, pair-bonded species. They are territorial, and in both species, group cohesion is high, the breeding adult male and female seem to prefer each other as nearest neighbors, and offspring of both sexes migrate from their natal group at between two and three and a half years of age (Curtis and Zaramody 1998; Overdorff and Tecot 2007; Tecot et al. 2016). In one case, in which a female was observed to conceive an offspring in her natal group, the fetus was aborted (Curtis et al. 2000). Though to our knowledge, copulations have been directly observed in *E. rubriventer* only twice, despite many years of observation, paternity tests on *E. rubriventer* groups suggest that they have a monogamous mating system (Merenlender 1993; R. L. Jacobs et al. 2018). New group formation is also rarely observed in *E. rubriventer*, but groups seem to form through the addition of new adult females, usually after the resident female has died or disappeared; males have not been observed to replace resident males (Overdorff and Tecot 2007).

Multi-male and female *Eulemur* groups range in size from five to 12 individuals (mean group size is approximately eight to nine) (Kappeler and Fichtel 2016) to as many as 29 individuals, although groups of *E. rufifrons* in the east appear to fission permanently along matrilines when reaching maximum group size (Overdorff et al. 1999). Groups contain multiple reproductive males and females, and adult sex ratio is variable, but usually even or male-biased (Kappeler 2000b). While some species remain spatially cohesive year-round (for example, western *E. rufifrons*, see Sussman 1977a; *E. albifrons*, see Vasey 1997b), fission-fusion has been observed

either regularly or seasonally in other species. *Eulemur cinereiceps* groups regularly undergo fission-fusion, although *E. cinereiceps* × *E. rufifrons* hybrids do not appear to do so (Johnson 2007). Groups of *E. macaco* and *E. coronatus* formed daily subgroups during the dry season (Freed 1996). In other cases, fission-fusion may occur only under extraordinarily harsh conditions. During a long-term study of eastern *E. rufifrons*, groups remained stable for many years but in 1995 formed subgroups regularly during the early dry season, when fruit abundance was abnormally low that year (D. J. Overdorff and S. G. Strait, unpublished data). Stable groups with rare events of fission-fusion have been also observed in *E. collaris* over an 18-year period (Donati et al. 2020).

Within larger groups, males and females form opposite-sex dyads more often than with members of the same sex. For example, male *E. sanfordi* had a female nearest neighbor for more than 70% of the time regardless of season (Freed 1996). Even in larger social groups, strong affiliative relationships have been observed between specific males and females, which some researchers have labeled as pair-bonds (Jolly 1998) or as "special relationships" (Pereira and McGlynn 1997). Possible explanations for this pattern include decreased infanticide risk (Jolly et al. 2000) or increased foraging efficiency by females due to the presence of a male dyad partner (Overdorff 1998). However, detailed social data from wild populations are limited, and current work suggests that male-female dyads are not necessarily stable or common in all *Eulemur* species. For example, Colquhoun (1993) noted that there is no evidence for pair-bonding in *E. macaco*. Patterns also vary within species; in eastern *E. rufifrons*, certain males in their physical prime appear to function as preferred social partners for females, but females do not mate exclusively with their partner, preferred partners can change, and older males are socially peripheral to the main group (Overdorff 1998). In the western dry deciduous forests, all *E. rufifrons* females socialize with one central male, who may have a "special relationship" with multiple females (Ostner and Kappeler 1999), and there is high male reproductive skew (Wimmer and Kappeler 2002). Similar patterns have been observed in wild *E. rufifrons* populations in the east (Merenlender 1993). Female relationships may be more agonistic, involving targeted aggression, eviction from the natal group, and even infanticide (e.g., *E. rufifrons*, Jolly et al. 2000).

A model of female power, with components of female dominance (based on agonistic interactions) and female leverage (e.g., access to resources), might provide a useful way to view intersexual relationships in *Eulemur* species (Lewis 2020). The phenomenon of female dominance over males has been little studied in the wild, but there is enough evidence from captivity and short-term field studies to suggest that female superiority in aggressive interactions is not characteristic of most *Eulemur* species (Pereira et al. 1990). Nonetheless, females from several *Eulemur* species do seem to have leverage over males in some contexts. For example, female agonism is rare in wild *E. macaco*, but females have first access to food and water, can displace males, and commonly lead group movements (Colquhoun 1993). Females in species such as *E. rubriventer*, *E. rufifrons*, and *E. flavifrons* also often lead group movements between food resources; however, leadership success is not consistently related to dominance status, and *E. rubriventer* and *E. rufifrons* are egalitarian in the wild (Erhart and Overdorff 2008a; Tecot and Romine 2012; Sperber et al. 2019). Aggression is extremely rare in wild *E. rubriventer*, occurring mostly within conflict between mothers and offspring in a weaning context (Overdorff and Tecot 2007); similarly, *E. mongoz* has very little intersexual aggression (Curtis and Zaramody 1999), and *E. rufifrons* females do not consistently win in agonistic encounters with males (Erhart and Overdorff 1999). As suggested by Pereira et al. (1999), *Eulemur* females probably employ different strategies to mitigate the costs of reproduction than species with true female dominance, particularly in light of variable and unpredictable patterns of food availability on Madagascar (P. C. Wright 1999).

LIFE HISTORY

Eulemur species generally reach sexual maturity between 20 and 24 months, though some species are estimated to reach maturity between 36 and 48 months in the wild, and first reproduction occurs between 29 and 57 months (Colquhoun 1993; Merenlender 1993; Curtis 1997; Overdorff et al. 1999). Both males and females may leave their natal groups, sometimes before and sometimes after reproducing, and whether they disperse or are evicted can vary by sex (e.g., *E. rufifrons*; see Erhart and Overdorff 2008b; Kappeler and Fichtel 2016). *Eulemur* females reproduce every one to two years, with a mean inter-birth interval of 15 months (Tecot et al. 2013). Gestation is approximately 120–130 days, and offspring are weaned around four to five months after birth (D. T. Rasmussen 1985; Colquhoun 1993; Freed 1996; Curtis 1997; Zehr et al. 2014). It can be difficult to observe nursing and measure milk transfer in the wild, and more precise measures are needed. *Eulemur* females have one or two infants at a time, and twinning occurs relatively frequently in *E. collaris* and *E. rubriventer* and occasionally in other species, both in the wild and in captivity (D. T. Rasmussen 1985; Freed 1996; Mittermeier et al. 2010; Tecot 2010; Volampeno et al. 2011). They have highly seasonal breeding periods, lasting from two to six weeks (P. C. Wright 1999; Curtis et al. 2000; Ostner and Kappeler 2004), and breeding seasonality is largely entrained by photoperiod (D. T. Rasmussen 1985).

Food availability may play a role in shaping the strict timing of reproductive events. In the northeast, *E. albifrons* females give birth during a period of resource abundance (Vasey 1997b), and in the southeast, infants are weaned at the time when resource abundance is most likely to occur (P. C. Wright 1999). In *E. rubriventer*, reproduction is timed such that there is maximum overlap throughout the entirety of reproduction (conception through weaning) with food abundance (Tecot 2010). There is some flexibility, however. For example, *E. rubriventer* has been observed giving birth in eight different months, and this research demonstrated that there is very strong selection for strictly timed breeding, as no infants survived outside of the birth peak. Infants are primarily carried ventrally and are weaned between six and seven months of age (Tecot et al. 2013). Direct care of infants has been documented by grandmothers in *E. collaris* (Kesch 2009), by adult males in *E. mongoz* (Curtis and Zaramody 1999), and by adult males and presumed siblings in *E. flavifrons* and *E. rubriventer* (Volampeno et al. 2011; Tecot et al. 2013). However, allomaternal care is facultative and not obligate, as has been documented in callitrichid monkeys. As in callitrichids, in *E. rubriventer* paternal estradiol levels elevate during a mate's

gestation in anticipation of the infant's birth (S. R. Tecot et al., unpublished data), and variation in allomaternal care behavior is associated with androgen levels (Tecot and Baden 2018), suggesting hormonal mechanisms underlying allomaternal care. Infanticide by both males and females has been observed (e.g., *E. rufifrons* × *E. collaris* hybrids; see Jolly et al. 2000), but it is rare, and infanticide risk is low in the genus, despite considerable variation in social organization and mating system (Kappeler and Fichtel 2016).

The presence of female dominance in species such as *Lemur catta*, which is closely related to members of the genus *Eulemur*, has historically been explained by increased "female need" during reproduction. Recent evidence suggests that this may not be the whole story, particularly since female dominance is not as widespread among the Lemuridae as was once thought. Based on several recent studies regarding metabolic strategies and energy expended while reproducing, it appears that *Eulemur* females do not expend any more energy during reproduction than other strepsirrhines such as lorisoids. While lemurs generally have high fetal growth rates (Kappeler 1996), the highest growth rates are in lemur species that park their infants (e.g., *Varecia*; see Tecot et al. 2012). Moreover, females produce low-quality milk, and postnatal investment in offspring may not in fact be energetically expensive (Tilden and Oftedal 1995). Females, however, may still face some measure of ecological stress, given that plant phenological patterns are unpredictable, especially supra-annually; food patches are uniformly smaller relative to forest habitats outside of Madagascar; and there is a shortage of keystone resources (Ganzhorn et al. 1999b; P. C. Wright 1999). Consequently, *Eulemur* females may avoid some of this stress by physiologically preparing for the lean season by increasing hair growth, food intake, and body fat, as seen in captive individuals (Pereira et al. 1999). High levels of cortisol metabolites were recorded during gestation in females of *E. collaris* in a degraded fragment of littoral forest and in females of *E. rubriventer* in secondary moist evergreen forest. Since gestation is occurring during the lean season in both of these areas of southeastern Madagascar, these results may reflect a combination of ecological and reproductive pressures as well as the development of the fetal adrenal glands (Tecot 2008, 2013; Balestri et al. 2014).

CONSERVATION

Like most lemurs, *Eulemur* species are primarily threatened by a reduction in forest area and increasing fragmentation of suitable habitats (Eppley et al. 2020; see Steffens et al., pp. 1812–17). The flexibility of these species appears to provide them some ability to persist, despite the small available habitat area and reduced canopy cover (for *E. collaris*, see Donati et al. 2011), or to cross the matrix between forest fragments (T. S. Steffens and Lehman 2018). However, highly fragmented areas with significant edge effects invariably cause a negative response, suggesting a threshold of habitat degradation beyond which these species disappear (Eppley et al. 2020). This vulnerability to fragmentation is also supported by genetic data that show a highly structured population and low diversity within subpopulations in forest fragments in comparison to continuous blocks of forest (Brenneman et al. 2012; Bertoncini et al. 2017). This vulnerability to habitat degradation has also been demonstrated in secondary forest within a protected area, where *E. rubriventer* was less behaviorally and physiologically flexible and experienced higher infant mortality compared to groups in more intact moist evergreen forest (Tecot 2008, 2013).

The threat of habitat loss is exacerbated in some species and in areas of the island by hunting, the pet trade, and extermination of these lemurs as agricultural pests (Reuter et al. 2018). Hunting in particular represents a serious threat, as *Eulemur* species are often the primary target of this activity (Randriamanalina et al. 2000; Borgerson 2015). Hunting may affect sex ratios in *Eulemur* species, because 1) females often lead foraging parties, making them more vulnerable to snare hunting (Bollen and Donati 2006); and 2) males are more vulnerable to pursuit hunting because they show sentinel behaviors toward ground-based predators, including humans (Nadhurou et al. 2017).

While all *Eulemur* species receive CITES (Convention on International Trade in Endangered Species) Appendix I protection, and all are threatened, they vary in degree of present extinction threat. With large distributions (which include protected areas) and often relatively high densities, *E. albifrons*, *E. fulvus*, *E. rubriventer*, *E. rufifrons*, and *E. rufus* are classified as Vulnerable on the IUCN Red List (IUCN 2020). At the other extreme, owing to highly restricted distributions and/or severely fragmented habitats, *E. cinereiceps*, *E. flavifrons*, and *E. mongoz* are listed as Critically Endangered. *Eulemur cinereiceps* also has relatively low population densities in much of its range (Johnson and Overdorff 1999; Brenneman et al. 2012). The balance of the species in this genus, *E. collaris*, *E. coronatus*, *E. macaco*, and *E. sanfordi*, are listed as Endangered (IUCN 2020). The presence of hybrid zones with less vulnerable *Eulemur* species may also threaten the maintenance of distinct populations of both *E. cinereiceps* and *E. flavifrons* (Delmore et al. 2013).

CONCLUSION

We conclude by dedicating this chapter to the memories of Dr. Robert W. Sussman and Hubert E. Andriamaharoa. Across a storied career, Dr. Sussman made brilliant, foundational contributions to our understanding of behavior, ecology, and evolution across primates—from true lemurs to humans. He has also left an enduring legacy through his training of generations of eminent lemur biologists. Though his life was tragically brief, Mr. Andriamaharoa was no less dedicated to true lemurs, especially in his remarkable efforts to ensure the survival of some of the most threatened populations and their unique habitats in southeastern Madagascar. He was an inspiring leader to the people he served—the communities whose livelihoods are intertwined with that of Madagascar's spectacular and fragile biodiversity.

Subject editors: Jörg U. Ganzhorn and Steven M. Goodman

LEMURIDAE: *HAPALEMUR* AND *PROLEMUR*, BAMBOO LEMURS

C. L. Tan, J. A. Norosoarinaivo, R. M. Randrianarison, and T. Mutschler

Members of the family Lemuridae, bamboo lemurs (*Hapalemur* and *Prolemur*) are known for their dietary specialization on monocotyledonous plants. With a few exceptions, they are predominantly bamboo eaters, mirroring the ecological niche occupied by the Giant Panda (*Ailuropoda melanoleuca*, family Ursidae) and the Red Panda (*Ailurus fulgens*, family Ailuridae) (C. L. Tan 2006). Early accounts about the bamboo lemurs are based largely on museum and zoo specimens. Dubbed "le petit maki gris" by Buffon (1789), the first bamboo lemur species was placed in the genus *Lemur* and given the name *L. griseus* by Link (1795). I. Geoffroy Saint-Hilaire (1851) subsequently established a new genus, *Hapalemur*, to distinguish this "small gray lemur" from other *Lemur* species known at the time. In 1870 Gray identified a significantly larger specimen that he described as *Hapalemur simus*. Since then, additional bamboo lemur taxa have been discovered, prompted by the field studies of Jean-Jacques Petter and colleagues (J.-J. Petter and Petter-Rousseaux 1958; J.-J. Petter and Peyriéras 1970a). Though the systematics of this lemur group has continued to undergo taxonomic reappraisal (e.g., Rabarivola et al. 2007), the present contribution follows the nomenclature proposed by Tattersall and Cuozzo (2018). Specifically, the bamboo lemurs comprise five species of *Hapalemur* (*H. griseus*, *H. alaotrensis*, *H. occidentalis*, *H. meridionalis*, and *H. aureus*) and one species of the monotypic genus *Prolemur* (*P. simus*). The generic separation of *Prolemur* from *Hapalemur* is supported by Beddard (1884), Pocock (1917), and more recently Groves (2001). The phylogenetic relationships of bamboo lemurs to one another, as well as their close affinities to *Lemur catta*, have been substantiated by a range of studies (e.g., Rumpler and Dutrillaux 1978; Macedonia and Stanger 1994; Stanger-Hall 1997; McLain et al. 2012; Finstermeier et al. 2013).

HAPALEMUR GRISEUS, GRAY BAMBOO LEMUR, BOKOMBOLO, KOTRIKA, ALOKOTEHA, KONTÈ

Ranging in eastern central, southeastern central, western central, and northwestern Madagascar, *H. griseus* has a wide but disjunct distribution. This species can be found in lowland and medium-altitude moist evergreen forests mixed with bamboo and in dry to moist semi-deciduous forests and riparian forests where bamboo may or may not exist (C. L. Tan 2006; Goodman et al. 2018b).

On the basis of the current taxonomic arrangement of this species, three different subspecies are recognized (*H. g. griseus*, *H. g. gilberti*, and *H. g. ranomafanensis*) and largely differentiated based on cytogenetics (Rabarivola et al. 2007). Cytogenetic analyses have detected five *H. griseus* karyotypes; their diploid chromosome number (2n) differs, from 2n = 54 in the Mantadia-Andasibe-Maromizaha-Vatateza (Tsinjoarivo) populations, to 2n = 52 in the Beanamalao population, to the polymorphic 2n = 54, 55, and 56 in the Ambolomavo-Ranomafana-Kianjavato-Vatoalatsaka-Bemaraha populations (Rumpler et al. 2002; Rabarivola et al. 2007). Despite subtle pelage color differences, varying from gray to olivaceous to rust brown, each of these progressively darker and more reddish over the head and around the shoulders, all *H. griseus* individuals have a gray face with a short muzzle as well as small ears (Figure 14.48a). Wild adults weigh on average 0.88 kg (n = 54; range: 0.68–1.10 kg), with no sexual dimorphism in size (C. L. Tan 2006; Rabarivola et al. 2007).

The behavioral ecology of *H. griseus* is best known from long-term studies conducted in the eastern moist evergreen forests, particularly at Ranomafana National Park and Maromizaha (C. L. Tan 1999, 2006; Andrianandrasana 2019; C. L. Tan and R. M. Randrianarison, unpublished data). Although *H. griseus* is known to consume over 100 plant species, bamboos and grasses (family Poaceae; see Vorontsova et al., pp. 585–98) are its principal food plants. At Talatakely, Ranomafana, approximately 75–80% of the annual diet comprised young leaves and shoots of the bamboos *Cathariostachys madagascariensis*, *Sokinochloa brachyclada* (formerly *Cephalostachyum* cf. *perrieri*), *S. chiataniae* (formerly *Cephalostachyum* sp.), *Nastus elongatus*, and *Nastus* sp., as well as leaves and stems of the grass *Poecilostachys baronis*—species that *H. griseus* shares with sympatric *H. aureus* and *Prolemur simus*. Elsewhere within the park the bamboo "*Arundinaria ambositrensis*" is also a food plant. At Maromizaha, 51–77% of the lemur's recorded diet consisted of bamboos and grasses: *Cathariostachys* sp., "*Arundinaria*" spp., *Sokinochloa* spp., *Panicum* spp., and *Poecilostachys* sp. A cyanogenic glycoside (dhurrin), a secondary compound commonly found in certain Poaceae plants, was detected in the growing parts of *C. madagascariensis*, *N. elongatus*, and a *Panicum* species. However, the feeding behavior of *H. griseus* suggests that individuals may potentially limit their cyanide intake by selecting plants and parts that contain little or no cyanide. Depending on availability, young leaves, fruits, flowers, and fungi were eaten also. For example, at Talatakely, opportunistic frugivory was observed in March–April during the ripening of the fruits of the introduced and invasive Strawberry Guava (*Psidium cattleyanum*, Myrtaceae). In *H. griseus*, fruit consumption could be as high as 28% during the wet season.

Based on studies involving direct observation and camera traps, *H. griseus* is active during the day, with a tendency toward crepuscular activity (C. L. Tan 2006; C. L. Tan and R. M. Randrianarison, unpublished data). In fact, continuous 24-hour follows of focal groups carried out over a year by Tan and her colleagues further confirmed that *H. griseus* is active only during the day. On an annual basis, males and females spent 41% of their time budget resting, 48% feeding, and 9% traveling. They were mainly arboreal and tended to travel in the lower forest strata. The mean height occupied by *H. griseus* varied from 2.6 to 5.5 m above the ground, depending on the site. On average, individuals traveled 662 m a day (daily path length range: 377–1075 m). The home-range size of a group was between 5 and 20 ha.

FIGURE 14.48 **Bamboo lemur taxa: A) adult *Hapalemur griseus* feeding on mature leaves of *Ficus* at Maromizaha; B) adult *H. alaotrensis* in the marsh of Lake Alaotra; C) adult *H. meridionalis* in *Melaleuca* swamp habitat in Mandena; D) adult *Prolemur simus* feeding on bamboo shoot of *Cathariostachys madagascariensis* in the Ranomafana National Park; and E) subadult *H. aureus* in the Ranomafana National Park.** (PHOTO A by R. M. Randrianarison; B by Durrell Wildlife Conservation Trust; C by T. Eppley; and D and E by C. L. Tan.)

Hapalemur griseus groups are generally small, each containing two to seven individuals. However, larger groups of up to 11 members have been observed (Pollock 1986a; C. L. Tan 1999, 2006). A group may consist of either a breeding pair or one male and multiple breeding females, and their young. Females are dominant over males in feeding and other contexts. The adults of both sexes are known to actively defend their territories against conspecifics. Scent marking, vocal display, and chasing are common territorial defense behaviors (C. L. Tan 2006; C. L. Tan and R. M. Randrianarison, unpublished data). At Talatakely, *H. griseus* seemed

indifferent to sympatric *H. aureus* and *Prolemur simus* when they were in close proximity (C. L. Tan 2006). Characteristic use of latrine sites in *H. griseus* has been documented at Analamazaotra (Irwin et al. 2004).

Both male and female *H. griseus* are known to disperse from their natal groups, sometimes even as adults (C. L. Tan 2006). Mating typically occurs in June–July. After a gestation period of 137–140 days, infants are born in October–November, but births have been noted as late as January (J.-J. Petter and Peyriéras 1970a; Pollock 1986a; C. L. Tan 2006). Mothers are the primary caretakers. During the first two weeks after birth, infants are orally transported before they are able to cling to their mothers. Mothers are known to "cache and carry," parking their infants nearby while they forage. Infants begin to taste and eat solid foods at three and six weeks of age, respectively, and are weaned at four months old (C. L. Tan 2006). *Hapalemur griseus* individuals, particularly infants, are vulnerable to a number of natural predators. Direct and indirect evidence suggests their known predators include *Polyboroides radiatus* (Madagascar Harrier-hawk), *Accipiter henstii* (Henst's Goshawk), *Buteo brachypterus* (Madagascar Buzzard), *Asio madagascariensis* (Madagascar Long-eared Owl), *Sanzinia madagascariensis* (Eastern Madagascar Tree Boa), and *Cryptoprocta ferox* (Fosa) (Karpanty 2006; see Goodman and Ganzhorn, pp. 1829–38).

HAPALEMUR ALAOTRENSIS, LAKE ALAOTRA BAMBOO LEMUR, *BANDRO*

Described by J.-J. Petter and Peyriéras (1970a), *H. alaotrensis* (2n = 54) is confined to Lake Alaotra and its neighboring marshes, some of which do not have bamboo (Mutschler et al. 1995; Waeber et al. 2019a). This species has darker and denser fur and is considerably larger than *H. griseus* (Figure 14.48b). The mean body mass of wild adults is 1.24 kg (n = 73; range: 1.00–1.60 kg); there is no significant difference in weight between females and males (Mutschler et al. 2000; Waeber and Hemelrijk 2003).

Hapalemur alaotrensis is almost exclusively folivorous with a narrow dietary breadth. Mutschler (1999) documented 11 food plant species, and over 95% of the lemur's feeding time was spent on only four species belonging to two families (Cyperaceae and Poaceae). Specifically, portions of papyrus stems (*Cyperus papyrus madagascariensis*), tender reed shoots (*Phragmites australis*), and surface grasses (*Echinochloa* sp. and *Leersia hexandra*) were the most important food items.

Hapalemur alaotrensis has a cathemeral activity pattern. Although predominantly active during daylight hours, this species also exhibits substantial nighttime activity. During all nighttime observations, *H. alaotrensis* showed a minimum of one activity bout, each lasting 30 minutes or more (Mutschler et al. 1998). Short-term surveys conducted in the dry season (May–August) found little activity between 0830 h and 1600 h (Guillera-Arroita et al. 2010), confirming the conclusions of J.-J. Petter and Peyriéras (1970a).

Groups are known to maintain small (0.6–8.0 ha) and largely exclusive territories that members actively defend (Nievergelt et al. 1998). The typical group size is three, but occasionally that number can reach 12 or 13. Membership appears stable throughout the year (Mutschler et al. 2000; Waeber and Hemelrijk 2003). About 50% of the groups studied were families with one breeding pair and their offspring, but a substantial proportion (35%) contained two breeding females. Additionally, groups with up to three full-grown males were observed, though genetic data revealed only a single breeding male. Because *H. alaotrensis* is not consistently organized in monogamous groups, it is best to describe this species as living in small one-male groups (Mutschler et al. 2000; Nievergelt et al. 2002). Moreover, females are dominant over males (Waeber and Hemelrijk 2003).

The dispersal patterns showed that both sexes disperse. Whereas females tend to leave their natal groups as subadults, males appear to delay dispersal and migrate as adults. The birth season in *H. alaotrensis* starts in early September and continues until February. In both wild and captive populations, a high occurrence of twinning (40%) has been observed (Mutschler et al. 2000). Predation on this lemur species, especially on infants, by *vontsira* (reported as "*Galidia elegans*" but presumably *Salanoia concolor*) and *Sanzinia madagascariensis* has been reported (J.-J. Petter and Peyriéras 1970a).

HAPALEMUR OCCIDENTALIS, WESTERN BAMBOO LEMUR, *BEKOLA*, *ANKOMBA'VALIHA*, *KINTRONTRO*

Hapalemur occidentalis (2n = 58) is lighter in its pelage color than *H. griseus*; it is also slightly larger, weighing 1.0 kg on average (n = 6) (Rabarivola et al. 2007). Largely resulting from the cytogenetic analyses of Rumpler et al. (2002) and Rabarivola et al. (2007), it known that *H. occidentalis* includes populations from three geographic regions: part of the northwest (east of Betsiboka River), the north, and the northeast (north of Onibe River). These lemurs can be found in moist evergreen and dry to moist semi-deciduous forests with or without bamboo, ranging from about sea level to over 1600 m (Goodman et al. 2018b).

Hapalemur occidentalis has not been studied extensively to date, although short-term observations suggest this species is highly adaptive to varied habitat conditions. In the Maroantsetra area, individuals were located in patches of bamboo in a degraded and partially flooded forest (J.-J. Petter and Peyriéras 1970a). They were sighted at all hours of the day but were most active early in the morning and late in the afternoon into the evening, showing a crepuscular propensity. At Fampotobe, an unprotected part of the Masoala Peninsula, groups were found living in secondary forest fragments intermixed with agricultural fields and villages. There, *H. occidentalis* spent 37% of its time feeding and exhibited two peak feeding periods: 0500–0800 h and 1700–2100 h (Martinez 2008). In the Sambirano River valley (northwest), Mutschler (2000) observed several groups living in habitat fragments that were completely surrounded by cacao plantations and without any connection to pristine or secondary forests. Observations during the dry season (July–September) showed the animals usually began moving at 1630 h and remained mostly active throughout the night. At Ambato, also part of the Sambirano Region, *H. occidentalis* was described as diurnal (Colquhoun 1993).

When bamboo is available, *H. occidentalis* has been observed to feed on new growth, including young leaves, pseudo-petioles, and shoots (J.-J. Petter and Peyriéras 1970a; Mutschler 2000; Martinez

2008). Because the giant bamboo *Cathariostachys madagascariensis* had been planted at Fampotobe, 89% of the feeding records were young pseudo-petioles of this bamboo, and the remaining 11% were ripe fruits of an introduced shrub, *Miconia crenata* (previously known as *Clidemia hirta*, Melastomataceae), and two other plant species. In human-altered landscapes, *H. occidentalis* habitually traveled low to the ground, moving from one patch of vegetation to the next.

In general, *H. occidentalis* groups are small, ranging from two to five individuals each. A group typically consists of one adult male, one or two adult females, and their young. Infants were observed in January and February at Maroantsetra (J.-J. Petter and Peyriéras 1970a). Predation by *Sanzinia madagascariensis* and *Cryptoprocta ferox* has been documented at Tampolo and Marojejy, respectively (D. Rakotondravony et al. 1998b; Sterling and McFadden 2000; see Goodman and Ganzhorn, pp. 1829–38).

HAPALEMUR MERIDIONALIS, SOUTHERN BAMBOO LEMUR, *HALO*

First located at the Mandena Forestry Station, approximately 10 km north of Tolagnaro, *H. meridionalis* (2n = 54) was identified as separate from *H. griseus* based on karyotype and morphological characteristics (Warter et al. 1987). Relative to *H. griseus*, its overall coat color is darker, its body slightly larger, and its tail shorter (Figure 14.48c). The average weight of adults is 0.98 kg (n = 27) (Rabarivola et al. 2007; Eppley et al. 2015b). There is no noticeable size difference between the sexes.

Besides Mandena, *H. meridionalis* populations are present at several sites in southeast Madagascar, including Ambatotsirongorongo, Andohahela, Tsitongambarika, Befotaka–Midongy du Sud, Kalambatritra, and Ambalavero, and possibly even farther north along the Vondrozo–Midongy forest corridor to the Mananara River (Goodman et al. 2018b). Within this geographic range, they are found from near sea level to 1500 m, inhabiting different forest types that may or may not have bamboo.

Most of the available information about this lemur is based on observations from Mandena. Although bamboo does occur there, it is extremely patchy. The forest contains a mosaic of habitats, including swamps that had been invaded by *Melaleuca quinquenervia* (Broad-leaved Paperbark Tree, Myrtaceae). Despite the fragmented landscapes and presence of introduced and invasive plant species, *H. meridionalis* is able to persist and has been shown to use not only the littoral forest but also the littoral swamp as well as the *Melaleuca* swamp (Eppley et al. 2015a; see Eppley and Goodman, pp. 1818–21).

Hapalemur meridionalis is known to consume 72 different plant species. Of these, monocots (Poaceae, Cyperaceae, and Strelitziaceae) represented almost 40% of its diet (based on total feeding records), with the majority (32.3%) being grasses. Specifically, *Trichanthecium parvifolium* (Poaceae) was the most frequently consumed species. In addition, fruits, nectar, and flowers, including those of *M. quinquenervia*, were eaten. Its diet during the austral winter months has been shown to be of relatively low nutritional quality (Eppley 2015; Eppley et al. 2011, 2016a).

As a consequence of feeding on grasses, lianas, forbs, fungi, and even fallen fruit, *H. meridionalis* is notably terrestrial. The average daily percentage of terrestrial feeding was 31% during months of food abundance versus 53% during months of food scarcity. The home-range size of groups varied from 6.6 to 18.4 ha, with minimal overlap between groups. The mean daily path length was 904 m (range: 227–2224 m) (Eppley et al. 2015b, 2016a). At Mandena, *H. meridionalis* spent 41–45% of its time feeding, 35–44% resting, and 10% traveling. Its activity showed a cathemeral pattern, peaking immediately after sunrise and before sunset; additionally, its nighttime activity was positively associated with moon luminosity (Eppley et al. 2015a, 2015b).

Similar to *H. griseus*, *H. meridionalis* exhibits latrine behavior, which has been suggested to aid intergroup communication while reducing the likelihood of direct conflict between groups (Eppley et al. 2016b). Up to nine individuals can be found in a group; each comprises several adult females and adult males. The mating season in this species is in June–July; accordingly, newborns have been observed in mid-November. Individual dispersals, both emigration and immigration, can occur throughout the year except during the mating season (Eppley et al. 2015b). There is evidence supporting female dominance in *H. meridionalis* (T. Eppley, unpublished data). Both adults and infants can fall prey to a number of terrestrial and aerial predators. *Cryptoprocta ferox* and *Acrantophis dumerili* (Dumeril's Ground Boa) have been established as definitive predators of *H. meridionalis* (Eppley and Ravelomanantsoa 2015; see Goodman and Ganzhorn, pp. 1829–38).

HAPALEMUR AUREUS, GOLDEN BAMBOO LEMUR, *VARIBOLOMENA, BOKOMBOLOMENA*

Hapalemur aureus (2n = 62) was discovered in 1986 in an area now designated as Ranomafana National Park (Meier et al. 1987). Currently, its geographic range is restricted to the eastern moist evergreen forests. Direct sightings and indirect evidence that has yet to be confirmed suggest a patchy distribution along the forest corridors from south of the Onive River (Ambohimiadana) to about the Befotaka–Midongy du Sud protected area (Marovato) (Goodman et al. 2018b). *Hapalemur aureus* has distinctive reddish-brown fur on the dorsal side and golden-yellow fur framing the face and covering the underparts (Figure 14.48e). On average, adults weigh 1.45 kg (n = 12; range: 1.30–1.60 kg) (C. L. Tan 2006). Females and males are sexually monomorphic.

Much of what is known about the natural history of *H. aureus* comes from long-term studies conducted at Talatakely, Ranomafana, where this species is sympatric with *H. griseus* and *Prolemur simus*. *Hapalemur aureus* is diurnal; it is active from about 0500 h to 1900 h, except 0900–1300 h. Continuous 24-hour observation of focal groups did not detect nocturnal activity. The overall proportion of time spent in major activities was 50–60% resting, 22–37% feeding, and 8–14% traveling, depending on the season. The mean home-range size of study groups was 26 ha, and their mean daily path length was 582 m (range: 276–941 m) (C. L. Tan 1999, 2006; C. L. Tan, unpublished data).

Close to 90% of the diet of *H. aureus* was bamboo—the staple being the giant bamboo *Cathariostachys madagascariensis*, which has been shown to contain high concentrations of cyanide (C. L. Tan 1999, 2006; Ballhorn et al. 2009). Besides *C. madagascariensis*,

the lemur also consumed other bamboo species such as *Sokinochloa brachyclada*, *S. chiataniae*, *Nastus* sp., *N. elongatus*, "*Arundinaria*" sp., and "*A. ambositrensis*."

Hapalemur aureus generally maintains small family groups. At Talatakely, the majority of the study groups (80%) contained a breeding pair; however, one group of up to eight individuals had two breeding females. Members are extremely territorial, and adults produce complex, sex-specific vocal duets as a form of advertisement and intergroup territorial defense. There is no clear dominance hierarchy between the sexes. Both females and males are known to disperse from their natal groups at about three years old. Mating events were observed in July–August, with births occurring in late November–December. The gestation length is approximately 138 days, and females give birth to a single infant once a year. Infants are born in an altricial state; they are sheltered in nest-like dense vegetation for the first 10–14 days. Like *H. griseus* mothers, *H. aureus* mothers practice infant parking and transport them orally. Infants begin to show interest in solid foods as early as six weeks old, and start ingesting bamboo and other plants after 10 weeks of age. At six months, they are weaned (C. L. Tan 2006). Though no predation events have been observed, *H. aureus* individuals are known to emit distinct aerial and terrestrial predator alarm calls in the presence of *Polyboroides radiatus*, *Accipiter henstii*, *Buteo brachypterus*, *Galidia elegans*, and free-ranging domestic dogs (*Canis lupus*). *Cryptoprocta ferox* can be a potential threat also (see Goodman and Ganzhorn, pp. 1829–38).

PROLEMUR SIMUS, GREATER BAMBOO LEMUR, *VARIBOLO*, *VARIKOVOKA*, *RENIBEN'NY KOTRIKA*, *KOTRIKABE*, *GODROKA*, *GODROGODROKA*, *HALOGODRO*, *BOKOMBOLOBE*, *ALAKOTO*, *HALOKOTO*, *TALEMBARIKA*

Prolemur simus is found only in the eastern region, where direct and indirect evidence and local knowledge suggest extensive but patchy distribution from north to south, ranging from Antohakalava to Antanimora and potentially to the east of the Kalambatritra protected area. At some locations, this species exists in sympatry with other bamboo lemurs (*H. occidentalis*, *H. meridionalis*, or *H. griseus*, or both *H. griseus* and *H. aureus*) (Goodman et al. 2018b). *Prolemur simus* seems to prefer mid- to high-altitude intact moist evergreen forests associated with large-culmed bamboos; however, it can be found in lowland degraded forest fragments with little or no bamboo (C. L. Tan 2006; King et al. 2013). Museum and zoo collection records and subfossil finds indicate that *P. simus* once had a much more extensive geographic distribution on the island, living in habitats similar to those occupied by extant populations (Muldoon et al. 2017; Burney et al. 2020a).

Prolemur simus (2n = 60) is easily distinguished from members of the genus *Hapalemur* by appearance and size. It features a broad nose, blackish muzzle/face, and white ear tufts (Figure 14.48d). Overall, its coat color is sooty gray, with a rusty-brown pygal patch (Tattersall 1982). The mean body mass of wild adults is 2.66 kg (n = 50, range: 2.15–3.55 kg); males are about 10% heavier than females (C. L. Tan 2006; Fraiser et al. 2015).

Prolemur simus has a highly specialized diet consisting of primarily woody bamboos (C. L. Tan 1999, 2006; Yamashita et al. 2009). Long-term research at Ranomafana showed that *Cathariostachys madagascariensis* represented 95% of the animal's annual diet. Individuals were observed eating mostly ground shoots (90–98% of monthly feeding records) in the warm, wet season (December–March), which coincides with shoot availability. In the cool, dry season (July–November), *P. simus* focused on eating the pith inside the hollow culms and mature leaves of the bamboo, as well as a number of other plant species. Remarkably, *C. madagascariensis* has anti-herbivore defense properties that can pose serious challenges for its consumers. Mechanical tests performed on the bamboo showed that the culms are both tough and stiff, requiring considerable force to perforate the surface in order to access the inner pith (Vinyard et al. 2008; Yamashita et al. 2009). Moreover, high levels of hydrogen cyanide (68.7–328.5 µmol HCN per gram dry weight) found in the bamboo suggest that, on a daily basis, *P. simus* consumes >50 times the average lethal cyanide dose for a mammal of its size (Glander et al. 1989; C. L. Tan 2006; Ballhorn et al. 2016). The consumption of cyanogenic bamboo has been linked to high protein intake by the lemur as a strategy to offset the energy required to help detoxify the cyanide (Eppley et al. 2017c). The mechanism by which *Prolemur* and *Hapalemur* manage to prevent cyanide poisoning has yet to be determined, though some cyanide and its metabolites are excreted in their urine (Yamashita et al. 2010).

Besides feeding on *C. madagascariensis*, *P. simus* at Talatakely and elsewhere is known to eat other bamboos, including: *C.* cf. *capitata*, *Sokinochloa brachyclada*, *S. chiataniae*, *Nastus* sp., *N. elongatus*, "*Arundinaria*" sp., "*A. ambositrensis*," *Valiha diffusa*, and *Bambusa vulgaris*. The latter two species are the principal food of populations living in low-elevation and degraded forests. At locations near human settlements, *P. simus* has been observed to consume a variety of monocot and dicot plants, such as flowers of *Ravenala* (Strelitziaceae); leaves and stems of *Aframomum angustifolium* (Zingiberaceae) and of *Oryza* spp., *Cenchrus clandestinus*, and *Saccharum* sp. (Poaceae); and fruits of *Annona squamosa* (Annonaceae), *Artocarpus* spp. and *Ficus* sp. (Moraceae), *Carica papaya* (Caricaceae), *Coffea* spp. (Rubiaceae), *Dypsis* spp. (Arecaceae), *Litchi chinensis* (Sapindaceae), *Mangifera indica* (Anacardiaceae), and *Musa* sp. (Musaceae) (Meier and Rumpler 1987; C. L. Tan 2006; King et al. 2013).

Though active during daytime, *P. simus* exhibits a cathemeral activity pattern throughout the year, which may reflect an adaptation to energetic and/or nutritional stress associated with a specialized diet (C. L. Tan 1999, 2006). Diurnal activity data showed that individuals spent 48–60% of the time resting, 31–41% feeding, and 6–17% traveling. Furthermore, *P. simus* is notably terrestrial, spending on average about 9% of its time on the ground and as much as 30% during the warm, wet season (C. L. Tan 2000, 2006; Rakotoarinivo et al. 2017; Mihaminekena et al. 2018).

The home range of *P. simus* groups has been reported to be as small as 3.5 ha and up to nearly 100 ha (C. L. Tan 1999, 2006; Dolch et al. 2008; Andrianandrasana et al. 2013). Such striking variation likely is influenced by ecological and anthropogenic factors. At Talatakely, the study group had a mean daily path length of 647.9 m (range: 162–1561 m) (C. L. Tan, unpublished data). Group members concentrated their activities within core areas

(20% of their 62-ha home range) for about two weeks at a time. Specifically, areas dominated by *Cathariostachys madagascariensis* were heavily utilized, whereas other areas were used mostly during travel between bamboo patches (C. L. Tan 1999).

Prolemur simus may exhibit fission-fusion dynamics. Individual groups vary from three to 55 individuals, and within them there can be multiple adult females, one or more adult males, and their offspring (C. L. Tan 2006; Frasier et al. 2015; Rakotoarinivo et al. 2017). Subadult males disperse when they are about three and a half years old, whereas females remain in their natal group. There is evidence supporting male dominance, particularly during feeding (C. L. Tan 2006). The mating season in *P. simus* is from the end of April to June. After a gestation period of about 149 days, infants are born in September–November. Females give birth to singletons, and the interbirth interval is one year (C. L. Tan 2006; Frasier et al. 2015). Mothers are the primary caretakers; they do not practice infant parking and continue to carry their young for the first four months. Infants begin to feed on bamboo at eight weeks but continue to suckle until they are eight months old (C. L. Tan 2006). High infant mortality (up to 54.5%) was reported in groups living in degraded forests (Frasier et al. 2015). However, the specific causes of these deaths are unclear. Several aerial and terrestrial predators could be responsible. Specifically, *Cryptoprocta ferox* and *Accipiter henstii* are known to prey on extant and subfossil *P. simus* (Karpanty and Wright 2007; Muldoon et al. 2017; see Goodman and Ganzhorn, pp. 1829–38).

CONSERVATION

The bamboo lemurs of the genera *Hapalemur* and *Prolemur* are vulnerable to severe habitat fragmentation and are potentially threatened by a lack of suitable areas for dispersal. Of paramount conservation concern is large-scale habitat loss. Within bamboo lemurs, the conservation outlook is most dire for *H. alaotrensis* because of its restricted geographic range. J.-J. Petter and Peyriéras (1970a) recognized that the ultimate threat to this species is humans. The fires and hunting they witnessed at Lake Alaotra in October 1969 are still a regular occurrence. Indeed, the continuous conversion of land into rice fields, the extensive burning of marsh vegetation, and the hunting of *H. alaotrensis* for food and live capture for pets have led to the population's precipitous decline. Fewer than 2000 individuals remain, representing a decrease of >80% from population estimates obtained in the 1990s (Mutschler and Feistner 1995; Waeber et al. 2019b). Without well-planned, coordinated conservation efforts involving multiple stakeholders and the buy-in from the local community, *H. alaotrensis* will become extinct in the near future (Rendigs et al. 2015).

On the basis of their current geographic distribution, *H. griseus* and *P. simus* appear to exhibit broader environmental tolerances than species such as *H. aureus*, although all bamboo lemurs may be living in less than optimal conditions resulting from anthropogenic and climate-induced change. Most bamboos and grasses have invasive habits and thrive in open spaces, and it has been shown that fire even stimulates the growth of some species (e.g., Franklin et al. 2010; M. Smith and Nelson 2011). Moreover, in Fampotobe and Maromizaha, *Hapalemur* species have been observed to recolonize abandoned *tavy* areas that were replanted with native bamboos (Martinez 2008; C. L. Tan et al., unpublished data). Ostensibly, these animals may fare better than some lemur taxa that are more sensitive to habitat disturbance. Nevertheless, because bamboo lemurs can be found near human settlements and are known to raid crops, hunting is a threat to their viability, especially *P. simus* (Meier and Rumpler 1987; Martinez 2008; Ravaloharimanitra et al. 2011).

Madagascar is one of the poorest nations in the world (Stocker et al. 2019). Any conservation strategy designed to protect bamboo lemurs must incorporate long-term solutions to reduce human poverty. Creating alternative livelihood opportunities to help local people generate sustainable revenue should be a top priority. One potential opportunity could involve the cultivation of bamboos and grasses, which are known to have great economic value to people as food and building material, and can provide forage for livestock. Even using the introduced and invasive water hyacinth (*Eichhornia crassipes*) as a raw material for making local handicrafts can be an economic solution for the people at Lake Alaotra (T. F. Rakotoarisoa et al. 2016). Moving forward, it is essential to further develop partnerships across a spectrum of local and international stakeholders to generate win-win strategies that benefit *Hapalemur* and *Prolemur* and the people who live alongside them.

Subject editors: Jörg U. Ganzhorn and Steven M. Goodman

LEMURIDAE: *LEMUR CATTA*, RING-TAILED LEMUR, *MAKY*, *HIRA*

M. L. Sauther and F. P. Cuozzo

With its raccoon-like facial coloration, svelte gray fur, and above all, its black-and-white-ringed tail, *Lemur catta* (Ring-tailed Lemur) is Madagascar's most iconic endemic animal. Indeed, it is often seen as Madagascar's trademark, appearing on signs, storefronts, and past currency (Sauther et al. 2015) and has also been featured in the popular media, such as 21st-century animated films. Yet, despite its familiarity, this species is far from being a typical lemur. Whether sauntering together down a gallery-forest path, tails held like

swaying question marks over their backs, or climbing down limestone rocks in dry spiny thickets to cuddle together in small caves, tails over their shoulders like feather boas, these lemurs continue to challenge researchers with their ecological flexibility. They are the most terrestrial of all extant species, live in the largest social groups, and tolerate a variety of extreme habitats.

With a head-and-body length of 385–455 mm and tail length of 560–624 mm (Tattersall 1982), *L. catta* is roughly the size of a big domestic cat. Adult wild animals in the dry deciduous forests at Bezà-Mahafaly weigh an average of 2.17 kg (Singleton et al. 2015). Those in the limestone spiny thickets at Tsimanampesotse weigh far less, an average of 1.99 kg (Dutton et al. 2003). This species is not sexually dimorphic in body mass (Singleton et al. 2015) but does exhibit male-biased canine-height dimorphism (Sauther and Cuozzo 2008).

DISTRIBUTION AND HABITAT

As a single species, *L. catta* has a dramatic geographic distribution that links to its strong ecological plasticity (Figure 14.49). It ranges across southern Madagascar from the west coast eastward to the "rainfall fault line," where transitional dry deciduous forest gives way to moist evergreen forest. Its northern limits are south of Morondava in the west and the mountains near Ambalavao in the east. Assemblages of recent subfossil remains of *L. catta* are found only within the historical and current range of the species (Godfrey et al. 1999). These lemurs persist in a variety of habitats, including dry spiny thickets that receive as little as 30–50 cm annual rainfall. Here they gain liquid only from dew and succulent plants, including endemic aloes (*Aloe*) and introduced prickly-pear (*Opuntia*) (Kelley 2013), and in some areas sleep in caves (Sauther et al. 2013). They also live in dry deciduous forests, anthropogenically altered grasslands, scrub and brush lands, and rocky outcrop environs (Sauther et al. 2015). Groups of *L. catta* even live up to 2600 m in the summit zone of the Andringitra Massif, above forest line, with seasonal frost, scaling nearly vertical rock outcrops and sleeping in caves (Goodman and Langrand 1996b; Goodman et al. 2006e). However, within this wide geographic distribution, a number of *L. catta* groups occur in disconnected and patchy forest fragments (Gabriel et al. 2018), essentially dependent on remaining forests now set in a stressed landscape (L. Gould and Andrianomena 2015; L. Gould and Cowen 2020). On Madagascar, the survival of even such hardy animals cannot be taken for granted.

POPULATION DENSITIES AND DEMOGRAPHIC TRENDS

Anthropogenic Effects

Population density of *Lemur catta* varies from 6.2 to 0.017 ind/ha, and this span is driven by habitat type and degree of habitat fragmentation (L. Gould and Sauther 2016). In forest fragments such as Anja Community Reserve near Ambalavao, populations are more crowded (L. Gould and Andrianomena 2015), while in

FIGURE 14.49 ***Lemur catta*** **(Ring-tailed Lemur) A) individual at Bezà-Mahafaly Special Reserve; B) group sunning in the early morning for thermoregulation and to maintain body temperature at Tsimanampesotse National Park.** (PHOTO A by M. L. Sauther, and B by M. LaFleur).

degraded dry spiny thicket habitat such as that at Cap Sainte Marie, the absence of water and shade results in very low densities (Kelley 2013). Recent demographic data by researchers who conduct in-depth studies of this species indicate a dramatic population decline since the original chapter on this species in the precursor of this book (Jolly 2003). Throughout its range, *L. catta* is in decline (Sussman et al. 2006; Kelley et al. 2007; L. Gould and Andrianomena 2015; L. Gould and Sauther 2016; LaFleur et al. 2017a). Among the 34 sites where *L. catta* is or was recently extant, 12 of the sites have populations numbering 30 or fewer individuals, and at 15 sites this species is either locally extirpated or lives in such small isolated forest fragments that long-term survival is unlikely. Only three known sites (Berenty Private Reserve, Bezà-Mahafaly Special Reserve, and Anja Community Reserve) contain more than 200 individuals. Not without controversy (Murphy et al. 2017c; LaFleur et al. 2018), the IUCN Red List rating of this species has been changed from Near Threatened to Endangered (C. Schwitzer et al. 2013), and in 2017 it was listed as one of the 25 most endangered primates in the world (LaFleur et al. 2017b). In addition to habitat destruction and the bushmeat trade (Reuter et al. 2016), continued threats to the species include illegal trade of wild-captured individuals (LaFleur et al. 2019).

Stochastic Environmental Effects

Population numbers are also affected by the stochastic nature of Madagascar's environment. At Bezà-Mahafaly 80% of infants and 20% of adult females died during and after the 1992 drought (L. Gould et al. 1999); at Berenty the birth rate and juvenile survival were reduced in the aftermath of a drought and reduction of fruit resources (Jolly et al. 2002); and in Tsimanampesotse National Park the proportion of infants in the population dropped markedly in years without rain (Kasola et al. 2020). L. Gould et al. (1999) concluded that *L. catta* is a relatively *r*-selected primate, reproducing quickly and at high rates and thus adapted to boom-and-bust fluctuations in its arid habitat. In more normal years, over 80% of wild females give birth to an infant, but first-year mortality varies from about 25% to 50% (Sussman 1991; Sauther and Sussman 1993; Sauther et al. 1999; Koyama et al. 2001; Jolly et al. 2002).

ECOLOGY

Feeding Ecology and Activity Patterns

Much of *Lemur catta* behavior, ecology, biology, and evolution has been summarized recently in scientific articles (Sauther et al. 1999) and books (Jolly et al. 2006; Sauther et al. 2015). In terms of general ecology, these lemurs can be seen as flexible edge or weed species (Sussman 1977b; L. Gould et al. 1999; Sauther et al. 1999). They live in highly seasonal habitats and are opportunistic frugivores/folivores, consuming a diverse number of plants (146 species from 50 families; also see Eppley et al., pp. 1839–59), as well as parts of termite galleries and soil (Simmen et al. 2006). Given the seasonal change in food resources, their diet can be dominated by a few species during certain times of the year when other foods are not available (Sauther and Cuozzo 2009). In southern riparian forests, the fruits and leaves of *Tamarindus indica* are important resources, especially during the dry season (LaFleur and Sauther 2015), while in dry spiny thickets the introduced *Opuntia* cactus is a key plant food resource year-round (Kelley 2013; L. Gould et al. 2015). *Lemur catta* rarely (but avidly) consumes both invertebrate and vertebrate prey such as locusts, cicadas, and even chameleons (Oda 1996; Ichino 2011).

This species has blue-yellow but not red-green color vision (G. H. Jacobs and Deegan 1993), and it retains a reflective tapetum but also has adaptations to daylight, including a fovea-like *area centralis* in the retina (Pariente 1979). In some habitats this species is cathemeral (Donati et al. 2013; LaFleur et al. 2014), which may relate to thermoregulation and antipredation strategies.

Predation

Lemur catta is susceptible to a variety of endemic and introduced predators, the endemics including *Polyboroides radiatus* (Madagascar Harrier-hawk), different snakes such as *Sanzinia madagascariensis* and *Leioheterodon madagascariensis*, and *Cryptoprocta ferox* (Fosa), Madagascar's largest extant predator (see Goodman and Ganzhorn, pp. 1829–38; Gerber and Hawkins, pp. 1978–83). Nonendemic predators include *Viverricula indica* (Small Indian Civet), and free-ranging *Felis silvestris* (cat), and *Canis lupus* (dog) (see Goodman and Ganzhorn, pp. 1829–38). *Lemur catta* engages in both predator-sensitive foraging strategies (Sauther 2002; L. Gould and Sauther 2007) and "representational signaling," with specific vocalizations for certain classes of predators (Jolly 1966; Sauther 1989; Macedonia 1990).

BIOLOGY

Health

Health and physiological data from a variety of habitats have been published, providing important baseline health information for *Lemur catta* (Dutton et al. 2003; D. S. Miller et al. 2007). Anthropogenic and weather effects have significant impacts on this species' physiology, health, and demography. Groups living in human-degraded habitat with less access to standing water have lower hydration values than those in forest environs (Singleton et al. 2015). Such studies are also revealing the impact of Madagascar's hypervariable climate of droughts and cyclones on this species' ability to respond to environmental stress. Hair-cortisol values and body-weight data demonstrate negative effects of drought as well as of cyclones, with immature lemurs more negatively impacted by such extreme weather events (Fardi et al. 2018). Glucocorticoid values are higher in groups that are atypically large or small (Pride 2005) and are also higher in populations living in more fragmented habitats that experience intense crowding and higher resource defense (Gabriel et al. 2018).

Longitudinal studies of wild lemur health have also revealed age differences in immune system function, with older individuals experiencing immunosenescence (Singleton et al. 2018), as well as significant age differences in gut microbiota that may be linked to social and reproductive factors (G. Bennett et al. 2016). Studies of *L. catta* dental ecology indicate that in some environments the overemphasis of hard and tough fallback foods like the ripe fruit of

Tamarindus indica can lead to severe tooth wear (Cuozzo and Sauther 2006). Dental-wear variation in this species starts at an early age and reflects sex, habitat, diet, and levels of anthropogenic disturbance (Cuozzo et al. 2010, 2014; Yamashita et al. 2016).

Genetics

With the establishment of important microsatellite data for this species (Pastorini et al. 2005), genomic studies have provided new insight into dispersal, reproductive strategies, and genetic health. Baseline population genetics data reveal moderate levels of genetic diversity in some areas (Clarke et al. 2015) but also that some populations may have experienced a historical genetic population bottleneck (Parga et al. 2012). While the species is thought to be female philopatric, mothers may sometimes disperse with daughters in some habitats (Koyama et al. 2002; Parga et al. 2015). Genetic data reveal that female mate selection and the females' tendency to mate with multiple males result in varying male paternity skew (Parga et al. 2016). Genetic data are also providing important captive genetic husbandry information as well as insights on the geographic origin of captive founders (Pastorini et al. 2015; Grogan et al. 2017).

Communication

Olfactory communication in *Lemur catta* is complex but highly stereotyped (Jolly 1966): females scent mark branches with the vulva, males with both wrist and scrotal glands. Males mark their tails with wrist and shoulder glands and have ritualized "stink fights" of tail waving and branch marking. Patterning of female scent marking may reflect territoriality and resource defense (Mertl-Milhollen 2006) and/or be a form of advertisement of their reproductive status (Kappeler 1998a; Drea and Scordato 2008). Male scent marking may reflect dominance status relative to other males (Scordato and Drea 2007; Drea and Scordato 2008). The chemical composition of various secretions may also be used to identify individuals (Palagi and Dapporto 2006; Drea and Scordato 2008), genetic quality and relatedness (Charpentier et al. 2008), and injury status (R. L. Harris et al. 2018).

Vocalizations include meows (group movement, contact), clicks (movement, alarm), purring (soft clicks during contact and grooming), spat calls (submissive squeak series), predator alarm yaps and screams, and infant distress peeps, with many variants within each category (Macedonia 1993b). There is individuality in contact calls (Macedonia 1986), and calls appear to maintain social cohesion and social relationships (Odo 1996; Kulahci et al. 2015; Bolt and Tennenhouse 2017).

SOCIAL SYSTEM AND REPRODUCTIVE BIOLOGY

Lemur catta lives in multi-male, multi-female social groups, usually comprising six to 24 animals, although groups above 30 occasionally occur. Large groups eventually fission, usually along matrilines (Jolly et al. 1993; Ichino and Koyama 2006). The core of the group is female matrilines. Males emigrate at maturity and frequently again as adults (K. D. Jones 1983; Sussman 1992). Life span in the wild can exceed 15 years—the oldest individuals at Bezà-Mahafaly die at 21 years of age; in captivity, life span can exceed 30 years (Cuozzo et al. 2010). The reproductive success and life cycle of this species is highly dependent on environmental conditions. Overall, females are pregnant during the cooler dry season of lower food availability and give birth, lactate, and wean their infants when resources are in greater abundance (Sauther 1998). In exceptionally good years in the wild, age of maturation is earlier, and birth rate and infant survival are much higher, compared to years with severe environmental conditions such as drought (L. Gould et al. 2003; Kasola et al. 2020). Females are sexually receptive for one to two days each year, and estrus may be as short as six to 24 hours (Van Horn and Resko 1977; Sauther et al. 1999). Due to ovarian synchronicity, all adult females in a habitat are in estrus at roughly the same period (Sauther 1998). The breeding season lasts between seven and 21 days, and both males and females have multiple mates (Pereira 1991; Sauther 1991; Sussman 1991). The mating season varies across different study sites in southern Madagascar, but is concentrated in April at Berenty and May at Bezà-Mahafaly (Sauther et al. 1999).

Males compete for females by year-round dominance status, by a few hours of mate-guarding, and by intense "jump fights," in which the rivals leap in the air, slashing downward with their upper (maxillary) canines (Jolly 1966). Gestation lasts from 135 to 145 days, and females almost always give birth to singletons, though groups living in harsh envirnoments have higher fecundity (Koyama et al. 2001; Sauther 1991; L. Gould et al. 2003). Rates of multiple births, including twins and triplets, are higher in captivity than in the wild (Sussman 1991). Between 75% and 80% of the adult females in a population give birth each year (Koyama et al. 2001; Jolly et al. 2002; L. Gould et al. 2003). Such high rates of reproduction allow populations of this species to rebound after years of high mortality associated with environmental stress (L. Gould et al. 2003).

For the first three weeks of life, the mother is the primary caregiver to her new infant, but she is tolerant of other females in the group, especially siblings of the infant and other mothers (Hosey and Jacques 1994). In the first days of life, *L. catta* infants cling ventrally to the mother, but by day three, they are able to move actively on her body and can climb onto another female (Jolly 1966). By the age of one month, infants ride dorsally on their mothers and begin to explore their surroundings independently, spending about 16% of their time off their mothers. Other female members of the group, including those with their own new infants, are attracted to newborns and approach mother-infant pairs frequently, attempting to lick or groom infants, especially in the first month of life (Jolly 1966; L. Gould 1990; Nakamichi and Koyama 2000) (Figure 14.50). In addition to licking and grooming new infants, members of the social group provide varying degrees of infant care for the mother, a behavior called alloparenting, and this may include allonursing (Jolly 1966; L. Gould 1992).

In adulthood, *L. catta* is a female-dominant species (Sauther et al. 1999). In competition over space or food, and even during mating, males are inhibited from attacking females, while females supplant, cuff (i.e., slap), or chase males with impunity. This is true in spite of the continuing, and sometimes violent, status disputes males engage in among themselves and the fact that the canines of

FIGURE 14.50 Infant *Lemur catta* with mother and "aunt" at Bezà-Mahafaly Special Reserve. (PHOTO by M. L. Sauther.)

males are longer than those of females (Kappeler 1996; Sauther and Cuozzo 2008). Throughout the year, males compensate for their exclusion from favored foods by feeding faster and less selectively (Rasamimanana 1999). Female dominance in this species could relate to female reproductive costs attributable to the metabolic pressures of rapid infant growth in a seasonal environment (Sauther 1993). However, it seems that, at least under laboratory conditions, the growth rate and milk supply in *L. catta* differ little from those of the male-dominant lorisoids and do not support a thesis of extraordinary female need (Kappeler 1996; Tilden and Oftedal 1997).

Although female dominance over males still does not have a satisfactory adaptive explanation, several hypotheses have been suggested. The energy conservation hypothesis (ECH) (P. C. Wright 1999) posits that lemur traits are part of an adaptive complex selected to enable lemurs to conserve and extract energy from their seasonally and stochastically resource-poor environments. Some support for this hypothesis has been found in the challenging dry spiny thicket habitats at Tsimanampesotse (LaFleur 2012). *Lemur catta* females are unusual among mammals in exhibiting masculinized genitalia, and recent hormonal studies implicate hormone levels as important drivers for the ontogeny of female dominance in lemurs (Petty and Drea 2015). Considerable female–female competition occurs in *L. catta* and, at least in captivity, can result in lethal aggression toward other females (Kittler and Dietzel 2016) as well as others' infants (Charpentier and Drea 2013). It has been suggested that male-caused infanticide could be a male reproductive tactic (Pereira and Weiss 1991), but the reproductive biology of this species does not support this, as reproduction is strictly seasonal and females usually breed in consecutive years (Sauther et al. 1999; Charpentier and Drea 2013). Female-caused infanticide could be a form of female–female competition (Jolly et al. 2000; Charpentier and Drea 2013; Kittler and Dietzel 2016). Episodic targeting aggression, where several lemurs follow and attack several troop mates over a period of days and even months, occurs in this species and may be a tactic to reduce reproductive competition, as it can result in the eviction of entire matrilines (Vick and Pereira 1989). Troops and their descendant daughter troops have apparently maintained the same home ranges over many decades, even in some cases keeping the same scent-marked frontiers (Jolly and Pride 1999; Mertl-Millhollen 2000). Highly developed female resource defense could thus underlie the relation of individual, troop, and habitat and, ultimately, the survival of the individual and her descendants.

CONCLUSION

As we noted at the start of this contribution, *Lemur catta* is well known across the world and often seen as the emblematic animal ambassador of Madagascar. Despite its ecological plasticity, at the time of the writing of this chapter, this iconic species is under serious threat from a variety of sources. This is reflective of all constituents of Madagascar's endemic biota, and the survival of this "plastic" (i.e., highly adaptable, ecologically flexible) primate species is not certain. In many ways, this species may be serving as the "canary in the coal mine" in terms of the rapid loss of Madagascar's remaining natural habitats. Let us hope that this trend can be reversed.

ACKNOWLEDGMENTS

We write this chapter in honor of the late Dr. Alison Jolly, building upon the framework of her contribution on *Lemur catta* in the precursor of the current book (Jolly 2003). Portions of our work discussed herein were supported by the US National Science Foundation (BCS 0922465) and the University of Colorado, among other funding sources. We thank the many Malagasy and international assistants and collaborators who contributed to our decades of research on *Lemur catta* on the ground in Madagascar.

Subject editors: Jörg U. Ganzhorn and Steven M. Goodman

LEMURIDAE: *VARECIA*, RUFFED LEMURS, *VARIKANDANA*, *VARIJATSY*

N. Vasey, A. L. Baden, and J. H. Ratsimbazafy

Varecia (family Lemuridae) occurs at low to medium elevations, under 1350 m, throughout most of Madagascar's eastern moist evergreen forest corridor and on the Masoala Peninsula. Despite having an extensive latitudinal range, populations are patchily distributed (Vasey 1997a; Irwin et al. 2005; Lehman et al. 2006c) and vary in density (Table 14.29). Two species are currently recognized, *V. variegata* (Black and White Ruffed Lemur) and *V. rubra* (Red Ruffed Lemur) (Figure 14.51). Gray (1863) proposed this taxonomy when he first introduced the genus *Varecia*, but the genus name was not immediately accepted, and nearly 100 years elapsed before the generic distinction between *Lemur* and *Varecia* was reintroduced (J.-J. Petter 1962; Tattersall 1982). For much of the 19th and 20th centuries, *V. rubra* was considered a variant or subspecies of *V. variegata* (known during that time as *Lemur varius*). Subsequently, a geographic divide between the two forms was identified, the Antainambalana River in northeastern Madagascar (J.-J. Petter et al. 1977). *Varecia rubra* occurs east of the Antainambalana River and on the Masoala Peninsula, with the northernmost records ~30 km south of Andapa in the Besariaka forest corridor (Ranorovelohanta 1996) and at the Antohakalava private reserve (E. Patel, unpublished data). *Varecia variegata* has a much larger latitudinal range, extending from west of the Antainambalana River (J.-J. Petter et al. 1977; Lindsay and Simons 1986; H. J. Simons and Lindsay 1987) to south of the Mananara River, with the southernmost records at Ambalavero in the Vondrozo–Midongy du Sud forest corridor and in the Vohitrambo and Marakopila Forests in the commune of Bevata (Vasey and Tattersall 2002; Rakotonirina et al. 2013; I. Tattersall, unpublished data).

TABLE 14.29. **Population densities of *Varecia variegata* and *V. rubra* in continuous versus isolated forests (i.e., surrounded by nonforest matrix) by elevation**

SITE	SPECIES/VARIANT	ELEVATION (m)	DENSITY (ind/km)[1]	REFERENCE
CONTINUOUS FORESTS				
Nosy Mangabe	*V. v. subcincta*[2]	0–331	29–43	Morland (1991a)
Andranobe (Masoala)	*V. rubra*	110–260	31.2–53.4	Vasey (1997a)
Ambatonakolahy Forest	*V. rubra*	450–650	21.5–23.2	Rigamonti (1993)
Mangevo (Ranomafana)	*V. v. editorum*	800–1200	24.3	Baden (2011)
Analamazaotra	*V. v. variegata*	800–1300	<4	Pollock (1975a)
Valohoaka (Ranomafana)	*V. v. editorum*	1200–1300	6	Balko (1998)
Vatoharanana (Ranomafana)	*V. v. editorum*	1200–1300	3	Balko (1998)
ISOLATED FOREST FRAGMENTS				
Manombo	*V. v. editorum*	0–137	0.4–2.5	Ratsimbazafy (2002)
Kianjavato Forests[1]	*V. v. editorum*	70–390	0.11–0.18	Narváez-Torres (2018); P. R. Narváez-Torres et al. (unpublished data)
Vatovavy Forest	*V. v. editorum*	100–322	32	Balko (1992)
Betampona	*V. v. variegata*	275–650	1.6–2.2	Welch and Katz (1992)
Betampona	*V. v. variegata*	275–650	2.5–3.1	Britt (1997)
Antanamalaza Classified Forest	*V. v. variegata*	600–700	10–15	Britt et al. (1999)

[1] Density estimate represents the combined densities of five forest fragments in 2014, 2015, and 2016; the fragments include Vatovavy, Sangasanga (also known as Kianjavato), and Tsitola.

[2] *V. v. subcincta* was introduced to Nosy Mangabe in the 1930s (Kuhn 1972). As it is a small island (520 ha), it is not easily classified as either a continuous forest or an isolated fragment. Ecologically, the forest is relatively intact.

FIGURE 14.51 **The two species of *Varecia*. A) *Varecia variegata* in the forest canopy at Mangevo, Ranomafana National Park. This individual expresses the "editorum" coat pattern (see text). B) A mixed-age subgroup of *Varecia rubra* individuals in the forest canopy at Andranobe, Masoala National Park. The animals are actively feeding on *Lepidotrichilia* sp. (Meliaceae). Markings shown include a white ankle band (top left individual) and white patches on the dorsum (the two individuals below).** (PHOTO A by F. Bendell, and B by N. Vasey.)

Since the precursor of this book, which contained a contribution on *Varecia* (Vasey 2003), a considerable amount has been learned about this genus of lemur, summarized herein.

TAXONOMY

The variegated coat patterns of *V. variegata* and of *Varecia* hybrids (captive and wild-caught), coupled with incomplete information on the geographic distribution of pelage variants, have long prevented taxonomists from arriving at a firm consensus concerning specific and subspecific variation in the genus (Vasey and Tattersall 2002). Since at least 1868, the two *Varecia* species have hybridized in menageries and zoological gardens and were assumed to do so in the wild. Largely on this basis, by the mid- to late 19th century, the Red Ruffed Lemur was downgraded to a variant or subspecies of *Lemur varius* (Schlegel 1866; Pollen 1868; Schwarz 1931; Hill 1953). This fueled queries about the existence of a natural hybrid zone. Based on local reports of a rufous-brown form north of the Bay of Antongil (Tattersall 1977) and study of museum holdings and collection records (Tattersall 1982; Buettner-Janusch and Tattersall 1985), it was suggested that the black-and-white and red forms are in secondary contact between the confluent Vohimaro and Antainambalana Rivers. A review and synthesis of historical documents and illustrations, taxonomic literature, museum collections, and survey work indicated a more widespread hybrid zone, extending across two additional river drainages farther east (the Andranofotsy and the Mahalevona), but one in which hybridization is rare (Vasey and Tattersall 2002).

In the late 19th and early 20th centuries both Black and White and Red Ruffed Lemurs were collected near Maroantsetra, as were a handful of hybrids from two localities within the three watersheds (Bevato and Malewo). Sightings have since accumulated of *Varecia* individuals with "hybrid" coat patterns east of the Antainambalana River at Ambodivoangy in 2008 (R. Kramer, unpublished data) and farther north at Antohakalava in 2009, 2012, and 2019, and at Maherivaratra in 2018 (E. Patel, unpublished data). However, within the same time frame, long-term demographic records on the Masoala Peninsula (Andranobe Forest) document a small number of *V. rubra* individuals with similarly unusual coat patterns (N. Vasey, unpublished data). This casts open, once again, the question as to whether a hybrid zone exists; the unusual coat patterns may alternatively represent rare, previously undocumented pelage variations attributable to genetic drift and/or reduced gene flow.

Lemur trapping and extensive swidden agriculture have led to habitat fragmentation and the partial or complete isolation of *Varecia* populations north of the Bay of Antongil (Lindsay and Simons 1986; H. J. Simons and Lindsay 1987; Hekkala et al. 2007). Near the Mahalevona River in the northwestern reach of the Masoala Peninsula (in the Ambatoledama forest corridor), the *V. rubra* population has recently undergone a genetic bottleneck (Razakamaharavo et al. 2010). Population and habitat surveys are currently underway to determine the extent of the geographic range of *Varecia* in northeastern Madagascar, to document the pelage patterns therein, and importantly, to obtain tissue samples suitable for comparative genomic analysis to be paired with those from San Diego Zoo's Frozen Zoo. Such analyses using samples gathered across the entire extant range of *Varecia* should resolve the question of species delimitations and allow examination of in situ and ex situ population health. Herein we treat the two forms as distinct species and discuss the question of variants defined by pelage below.

It is important to know the number of taxonomic units we aim to protect and their geographic distribution. To determine specific and subspecific divergence, less emphasis on pelage and more

reliance on craniometry (which is notably lacking) and neutral genetic variation are warranted. Sequence variation in the mtDNA control region suggests that *V. variegata* contains two geographic forms: a southern unit, based on samples from the protected areas of Manombo and Ranomafana, and a northern unit, based on samples from Betampona (Wyner et al. 1999b). Population structure inferred from microsatellites and mtDNA from samples spanning the geographic range of *V. variegata* (19 sites) similarly indicates two subspecies, separated by the largest river in eastern Madagascar, the Mangoro (Baden et al. 2014). These different data call into question the generally accepted three subspecies of *V. variegata* (as listed in Table 14.29).

PHYSICAL FEATURES

Varecia species are the largest members of the family Lemuridae (wild adult weights: *V. rubra*, 2.1–3.6 kg, n = 25, Vasey 2003, Dutton et al. 2008; *V. variegata*, 2.5–4.8 kg, n = 98, Baden et al. 2008), and the sexes show no difference in pelage coloration or size. The long, lavishly furred tail of these species slightly exceeds body length, averaging about 60 cm. The rest of its coat is also long and luxuriant. Both species have black fur on the ventrum, tail, manus, pes, crown, forehead, and face. Surrounding the face and ears is a ruff of long fur, white in *V. variegata* and red or honey blond in *V. rubra*. Consistency in coat color and pattern ends there. In *V. rubra* the dorsum is typically a single color but varies in any given individual from dark blood red to red orange to honey blond. The nape bears a large distinct patch of white fur, and white or honey-blond fur may encircle the base of the tail or appear in a patch on the dorsum. The tarsus, metatarsus, and pedal digits often have bands of white fur in these otherwise black areas. White fur may also appear on the lateral aspect of the ankle or extend up to the knee or midthigh. In comparison, individuals of *V. variegata* show highly personalized patches or bands of white or light fur on the dorsum and appendages (Figure 14.51).

Three principal variants of *V. variegata* have long been recognized (e.g., Geoffroy Saint-Hilaire 1851). While the overall amount of black in the dorsal pelage seems to be reduced in favor of white in the southern part of the species' geographic range, there is no straightforward north–south cline (J.-J. Petter et al. 1977; Tattersall 1982), and dark regions are not always pure black but may grade into or be light brown or dark brown. In the lightest form ("variegata") the dorsal fur is white, with black restricted to the shoulder, upper arm to elbow, and front of thigh; whereas in the darker form known from the north ("subcincta"), the dorsum is mainly black, with two variably thick bands of white fur—one band encircles the torso and sometimes extends longitudinally toward the nape of the neck, and the other band extends across the rump, down the posterior aspect of the thigh, and onto the lateral surface of the lower leg. In another form ("editorum") the black shoulder patches extend onto the dorsum, forming a black mantle across the back and shoulders. In addition to these three variants, others have been described. J.-J. Petter et al. (1977) described eight forms based on museum specimens and field observations. I. Tattersall (unpublished data) recognized as many as 10 repeated variants, and based on those, with associated provenance in combination with field observations, Vasey and Tattersall (2002) illustrated broad areas within which more than one pelage variant is found. In the absence of any clear geographic patterning across the latitudinal range in which the Black and White Ruffed Lemur occurs, these authors view *V. variegata* as a species embracing multiple largely discrete pelage patterns rather than one that is divisible, based upon pelage, into discrete geographic subspecies. Thus, while the IUCN currently recognizes three subspecies of *V. variegata* based on the three principal pelage variants (*V. v. variegata*, *V. v. editorum*, and *V. v. subcincta*), following Groves (2001), we do not concur. It may prove more profitable to study the pied and patterned pelage variation in *V. variegata* in terms of why it is so attractive (i.e., conspicuous), a question of adaptation as opposed to taxonomy. An adaptive role has recently been proposed, in that the pelage of the different forms of *Varecia*, as measured from museum specimens, is correlated with tree cover and precipitation, suggesting that countershading may be useful in the dense moist evergreen forest its populations inhabit (Spriggs 2017).

LIFE HISTORY AND POPULATION DYNAMICS

Varecia species have an unusual set of reproductive traits for medium-size, gregarious, day-active primates, including the bearing of litters, nesting of altricial young, and an absentee parenting system (which consists in the oral transport of nonclinging young combined with "infant stashing"; Vasey 2007). Only a handful of small-bodied, nocturnal strepsirrhines share this suite of traits. Uniquely, however, *Varecia* nests are built exclusively to care for young, whereas those of nocturnal litter-bearing strepsirrhines are also used throughout the year for sleeping (Kappeler 1998b; Bearder et al. 2003). *Varecia* reproductive traits were first documented in captivity, and study is ongoing (Dechambre 1935; Zehr et al. 2014 and references therein). Though fewer in number, long-term field studies have contextualized *Varecia* reproduction in the wild.

The mating season occurs between May and July, and infants are born from September to early November (Morland 1990; Vasey 2007; Baden et al. 2013). In captivity, gestation averages 102 days (D. T. Rasmussen 1985), interbirth interval is one year, and age at sexual maturity is 18–20 months for females and 36–48 months for males (Foerg 1982). In the wild, gestation is 102–109 days (Vasey 2007; Baden 2019), interbirth interval varies considerably (see below), and female age at sexual maturity is 32 months (Morland 1991a). *Varecia* species bear litters of two to three infants in the wild (averages are 2.1 in *V. rubra*, Vasey 2007; and 2.7 in *V. variegata*, Baden et al. 2013), and each infant at birth weighs just under 100 g (averages are 98.2 g in *V. rubra*, and 87.2 g in *V. variegata*; Brockman et al. 1987). Locomotor independence occurs at 10 weeks, intake of solid food at 5–8 weeks, and weaning at 3–4 months, though suckling may continue as late as 7–8 months (Morland 1990, 1991a; Vasey 2007). Relatively altricial young grow extremely rapidly, attaining 70% of adult weight at four months of age (Pereira et al. 1987).

Mothers nurse on schedule versus on demand, producing milk that is higher in dry matter, fat, protein, and gross energy (kcal/g) than that of other lemurids, with protein concentrations similar to those of lorisoid milks, which are more concentrated in nutrients

than the milks of any other group of primates (Tilden and Oftedal 1995, 1997). Despite being the largest living lemurid, *Varecia* has shorter gestation periods, larger litters, more rapidly developing infants, and richer milk than other members of its family. Thus, its prenatal (A. L. Young et al. 1990) and perhaps also postnatal energetic investment in reproduction is greater than in any other primate.

Field observations of mating and parenting behavior, and a synthesis of data on captive animals, demonstrate that *Varecia* species mate polygamously and exhibit extensive alloparenting behavior (Morland 1990; Vasey 2007; Baden et al. 2013). In combination with absentee parenting, alloparenting mitigates the very high maternal reproductive costs in *Varecia*, allowing lactating females to range great distances from stashed young (Vasey 2006). Mothers sometimes cache their litters in a single communal nest or stash site—a crèche—or with a male affiliate (Vasey 2007; Baden et al. 2013; Baden 2019). These mothers may be kin or nonkin. Although this behavior is facultative (i.e., not all females use crèches), females that place their infants in crèches are able to spend more time away from their young feeding and foraging, and their infants experience lower mortality (Baden et al. 2013). On this basis, *Varecia* is characterized as having a cooperative, or alternatively, a communal, breeding system.

Newborns are kept in a nest made by the mother (the natal nest; Baden et al. 2013) for three to 22 days and then periodically transported orally to other arboreal sites (Vasey 2007; Baden et al. 2013; Baden 2019). At Mangevo (Ranomafana National Park), gestating females of *V. variegata* individually construct multiple nests (n = 8) in the cruxes of trees (near the trunk) by chewing off branches and carrying them orally to drop among lianas and/or previously collected nesting material (Baden 2019). At Andranobe, nest and stash sites also occur in tree crowns, where they are often concealed and sheltered by dense foliage and old-growth woody vines (Vasey et al. 2018). Nests take on the form of platforms or shallow bowls just over 1 m wide (Morland 1990; Vasey 2007; Baden 2019). At Mangevo, nest and stash trees (average ~34 per female) are spread throughout each female's home range in proximity to feeding trees that are used throughout the year (Baden 2019). For *V. rubra* at Andranobe, nest and crèche trees (average ~40 per female) are clustered in different adjacent valleys within seasonally nonoverlapping core areas, and just 12 genera (24 species) make up 73% of trees used, all of which are known food species (Vasey et al. 2018). At this site, nest and crèche trees are the largest trees in the forest, even larger than those used for feeding (mean dbh [diameter at breast height] of nest and stash trees: 75.8 cm; mean dbh of feeding trees: 55.3 cm; Vasey et al. 2018).

Birth rates and infant mortality vary widely from year to year, both within and among populations of both species. For *V. variegata* on Nosy Mangabe, birth rate varied from 0.20 to 0.86 over two annual cycles, and infant mortality rate was 0.64 in one of those years (Morland 1990). For *V. rubra* at Andranobe, birth rate was 0.86 in one year, and there was no infant mortality over two annual cycles (Vasey 2007). At the other end of the spectrum, *Varecia* populations of both species collectively abandon reproduction for years at a time in the aftermath of major cyclones that reduce plant productivity (Ratsimbazafy 2002; Vasey and Borgerson 2009; Baden et al. 2013); interbirth intervals between one and six years are documented. These demographics may in part underlie variations in density (Table 14.29) and contribute to the ruffed lemurs' patchy distribution. Dramatic population growth can occur in adequate habitat and/or in productive fruiting years, especially given the capacity of these lemurs to produce litters. Such population growth potential may buffer them from local extinction in years or sequences of years when, owing to natural reasons, birth rate is low (or nil) and infant mortality is high. However, the patchy distribution of *Varecia* today is more complex, factoring in anthropogenic impacts (see Conservation, below).

HABITAT USE AND DIET

Varecia species show a similar microhabitat profile across many intact moist evergreen forest sites, regardless of other sympatric lemur species present. Members of this genus use mainly mid- to upper forest strata and relatively large feeding trees, and are active primarily by day (Vasey 2000b and references therein). Both species spend most of their time in tree crowns (94% of time on an annual basis) but show seasonal departures and daily rhythms during the hot seasons attributable to predator-avoidance tactics, reproduction, and thermoregulation (Vasey 2000b, 2004; Vasey et al. 2018; Beeby and Baden 2021). Locomotion and posture are cost-efficient for a high-canopy dweller; quadrupedal spring leaping allows *Varecia* species to travel through the often-discontinuous upper canopy without descending to seek out continuous arboreal pathways, and suspension allows access to plant foods located in the crown periphery (Britt 1997, 2000). Given the similarity in microhabitat use across studies, *Varecia* species appear to have relatively inflexible ecological requirements (Vasey 2000b). This ecological inflexibility has undoubtedly contributed to their vulnerability when faced with habitat alteration and loss, as *Varecia* species have fewer dispersal and habitat options than other lemurs (only *Eulemur rubriventer* is similarly both highly frugivorous and limited to eastern rain forests). Both *Varecia* species rarely come to the ground (Vasey 2002; Vasey et al. 2018) and are unlikely to traverse large open areas. Thus, habitat fragmentation and fragment isolation pose some of the most significant dispersal barriers to the genus (Holmes et al. 2013; Baden et al. 2014). Indeed, anthropogenic landscape features (i.e., habitat quality and human habitation) impede *V. variegata* gene flow more than natural barriers to gene flow such as rivers (Baden et al. 2019).

Yet, in degraded habitat where both lemurs and forest have fallen under protection, *Varecia* species have proven to be somewhat resilient, at least in the short term. At Manombo, an isolated forest fragment where *V. variegata* group sizes were halved and 85% of the canopy lost due to the unbuffered effects of a large-scale cyclone, the population rallied by broadening its diet, including more leaves and the fruits of two introduced, light-loving pioneer plants (*Miconia crenata* [previously known as *Clidemia hirta*], Melastomataceae; and *Cecropia peltata*, Urticaceae), which totaled 38% of their diet. They had no option but to use lower forest strata and began to reproduce again after a hiatus of four years (Ratsimbazafy 2002, 2006). In the Ambatoledama forest corridor of Masoala, a restoration site designed to connect wildlife populations separated by agricultural land and deforestation, *V. rubra* not only foraged in the recently planted corridor, dispersing native seeds, but also came to

the ground frequently to feed on the ubiquitous *Miconia crenata* (Martinez 2010; Martinez and Razafindratsima 2014). Even in intact habitat, *Varecia* species show some degree of attraction to natural disturbance in that they are more frequently observed in close proximity to canopy gap edges created by cyclone-driven tree-fall gaps. At these tree-fall gaps, vegetative regrowth increases the quantity of fruit and young leaves at the canopy level (Mogilewsky 2020). Given the regularity of cyclones making landfall on Madagascar, co-adaptation to natural disturbance makes evolutionary sense for a canopy-dwelling frugivore such as *Varecia*.

Varecia species are among the most frugivorous living lemurs, spending 61–96% of feeding time on fruit. Mature leaves (0–17%), young leaves (2–6%), flowers (0–37%), and nectar (0–21%) are consumed less often (percentages are drawn from studies that sampled across all seasons over one or more annual cycles: Morland 1991a; Balko 1998; Vasey 2000b, 2002; Ratsimbazafy 2006; Erhart et al. 2018; Beeby and Baden 2021). At the highly disturbed sites of Kianjavato and Vatovavy, *Ravenala* (Strelitziaceae) flowers and nectar compose a large portion of the diet of *V. variegata* (23–34% annually; Holmes et al. 2016). At Andranobe, *V. rubra* fruit intake does not drop below 75% in any season and reaches 100% when females are neither gestating nor lactating, during the resource-scarce cold seasons (Vasey 2000b, 2002). At Mangevo, in contrast, frugivory in *V. variegata* reaches 100% in some months during the warm, wet, resource-rich season and dips as low as 25% in the cool, lean season. Leaf consumption is equally variable across years and seasons here, reaching 56% in some lean-season months (Beeby and Baden 2021), notably higher than that at other sites. Foliage intake, even in small proportions, may confer benefits at key times. During lactation, when protein requirements are greatest, *V. rubra* females at Andranobe show a daily rhythm, feeding more often on young leaves late in the day, when soluble carbohydrates in leaves peak, and before ensuing night-time inactivity, during which the leaves' protein and other nutrients can be slowly extracted (Vasey 2004). Moreover, compared to males, pregnant and lactating females more often diversify their diets with seasonally available young leaves and flowers, presumably low-fiber protein items (Vasey 2000b, 2002). These sex differences are attributed to high reproductive costs of *Varecia* females, as are sex differences in activity budgets and distances traveled between food patches (Vasey 1997b, 2005a).

At Mangevo and Andranobe, intact moist evergreen forest sites, *V. variegata* and *V. rubra* consumed the parts of 111 and 132 different plant species from 19 and 36 plant families, respectively (Vasey 2000a; Beeby and Baden 2021). Over a three-year period, dietary diversity of *V. variegata* was lower than that of *Propithecus edwardsi* or *Eulemur albifrons* (Erhart et al. 2018), as is common for frugivorous primates. Rigamonti (1993), Balko (1998), Ratsimbazafy (2006), and P. C. Wright et al. (2011) provide lists of plant species eaten by *Varecia* species. Plant taxa frequently consumed at most sites include *Canarium* (Burseraceae), *Chrysophyllum* (Sapotaceae), *Cryptocarya*, *Ocotea*, and *Ravensara* (Lauraceae), *Eugenia* (Myrtaceae), and *Ficus* (Moraceae). Some of these taxa are viewed as fallback foods, as they are eaten over a protracted period in times of relative resource scarcity (Vasey 2000a; Balko and Underwood 2005; Beeby and Baden 2021). Balko and Underwood (2005) note that areas of Madagascar that contain high tree-species richness (e.g., Masoala and Nosy Mangabe) also support some of the highest densities of *Varecia* species (Table 14.29). They speculate that these lowland moist evergreen forests, which experience a lot of natural disturbance, can support elevated densities of *Varecia* because high tree-species richness increases the probability of year-round fruit availability, which buffers the effects of asynchrony in the fruiting phenology of Malagasy forests.

SOCIAL SYSTEM AND RANGING PATTERNS

Wild *Varecia* populations of both species exhibit considerable behavioral variation. A wide array of community (or group) sizes, social structures, social organizations, and home-range sizes, as well as differences in territorial behavior, have been documented. On the basis of surveys at Analamazaotra, Fanovana, and Ambodiriana (in July and October) and of short-term observations at several other localities, early field reports suggested that members of this genus live in cohesive, territorial family groups of two to four individuals (J.-J. Petter 1962; J.-J. Petter et al. 1977; Pollock 1979). A two-month study during the austral winter at Ranomafana reported that two *V. variegata* individuals lived as a cohesive, monogamous pair in an enormous home range of 197 ha (F. J. White 1991). A subsequent longer-term study in the same region documented cohesive, territorial, multi-female and/or multi-male groups of four to nine animals, in home ranges of 100–150 ha (Balko 1998), that grew dispersed over the course of several years (Balko and Underwood 2005). In an eight-month-long study in Betampona, *V. variegata* was found in dispersed monogamous groups of two to five individuals (an adult pair and presumed offspring) in home ranges of 28.9–43.1 ha (Britt 1997).

In all other long-term-study populations, both species of *Varecia* live in multi-female and/or multi-male communities with a fission-fusion type of social organization that has both daily and seasonal components (Nosy Mangabe, Morland 1991a, 1991b; Ambatonakolahy Forest on Masoala, Rigamonti 1993; Andranobe Forest on Masoala, Vasey 2006; Mangevo at Ranomafana, Baden et al. 2016; Kianjavato Forest, Holmes et al. 2016). Subgroup transitions (either fissions or fusions) occur on average every 90 minutes, on the same order of magnitude as in the highly dynamic fission-fusion social systems of chimpanzees, bonobos, and spider monkeys (Baden et al. 2016). Yet, compared to these haplorrhine taxa, both species of *Varecia* form smaller subgroups, have dramatically lower rates of social interaction (solitary 48% of the time), and have a female-centered social organization (Morland 1991a, 1991b; Baden et al. 2016). Interestingly, neither social associations nor social preferences in *Varecia* can be explained by kinship; rather, associations are best explained by shared range use (Baden et al. 2021). Some, though not all, of the behavioral variation found in different populations of members of this genus may be an artifact of short-term observations in early studies and a lack of sampling during the hot rainy season, when fission-fusion dynamics are elevated and it is possible to clearly discern that small aggregations (i.e., two to four individuals) are part of a larger community network (Vasey 2003, 2006). Low population density and its underlying causes (e.g., resource distribution and floristic diversity, hunting pressure, presence of other day-active frugivorous lemurs) may also contribute to

the formation of stable, cohesive groups at some sites (Table 14.29; Vasey 2006; Baden et al. 2016).

The *V. variegata* population on Nosy Mangabe communally defends food resources but is not territorial (Morland 1991a, 1991b), whereas at Mangevo, Andranobe, and (possibly) Ambatonakolahy, members of this genus are territorial, communally defending exclusive home-range boundaries (Rigamonti 1993; Vasey 2006; Baden et al. 2016). Females play the most active role in defending food resources and/or home-range boundaries, and despite the variation in territorial behavior, all four populations mentioned above are similar in their seasonal ranging patterns and, concomitantly, their fission-fusion social organization. For example, in these studies *Varecia* communities are formed of core groups with discrete core areas; core groups disperse into separate core areas in the food-scarce cold season, and individuals travel shorter daily distances in cold versus hot months. Shifts in ranging correspond with seasonal food distribution and/or reproductive stages, albeit to a much larger extent in females than in males (Vasey 2006; Baden et al. 2021). Thus, the ranging pattern of both species of *Varecia* appears to be the outcome of its reproductive pattern combined with its reliance on a spatiotemporally patchy diet of ripe fruit, flowers, and young leaves (Vasey 1997a, 2006). This co-adapted interaction between reproduction and foraging ecology may necessitate flexibility in its social behavior. In turn, flexible social behavior appears to provide the means for maintaining ecological similarity across sites (see Habitat Use and Diet).

COMMUNICATION

Like other diurnal lemurs, ruffed lemurs use vocal, visual, and olfactory modes of communication. Little research on *Varecia* communication has accumulated since the precursor of this contribution, so we refer readers to that review (Vasey 2003) and limit our discussion to a few notable traits. Female greeting displays are spectacular, involving anogenital scent marking of each other's backs, jumping over one another in a leapfrog fashion, writhing together, and emitting soft squealing sounds (Morland 1991a; Vasey 2006). These displays occur during the hot season, when female ranges overlap extensively and fission-fusion dynamics are elevated (Vasey 2006). *Varecia* is further distinguished by its highly aggressive antipredator behavior that involves mobbing accompanied by loud calls that continue long after the stimulus (i.e., predator) has departed. Ground predators evoke "pulsed squawks," while aerial predators elicit the contagious "abrupt roar." These antipredator tactics are seen in part as an effect of larger body size but also as a consequence of having young bound to nest and crèche sites, which prevents adults from fleeing predators without risking reproductive loss (Macedonia 1993a). Field observations suggest that the "roar/shriek chorus" (a group-advertisement loud call) facilitates dispersed intra-community communication within large home ranges by permitting, for example, coordination of individual schedules during infant-stashing season via vigilance displays (Vasey 2007) and time-sharing of highly prized masting fruit trees by subgroups during certain times of year (Vasey 2000b). Another remarkable trait is that some *Varecia* females possess trichromatic vision—those that are heterozygous at the X-linked M/L opsin gene locus (Y. Tan and Li 1999; G. H. Jacobs and Deegan 2003). These females may have an advantage in detecting young leaves that flush red against a background of mature green foliage (Dominy and Lucas 2001; Vasey 2004). The vocal, visual, and olfactory communication systems of *Varecia* clearly warrant further research.

CONSERVATION

Both *V. rubra* and *V. variegata* are classified as Critically Endangered (IUCN 2020). Hunting and anthropogenic habitat loss (e.g., due to swidden agriculture and logging) have reduced their numbers in many areas of their range (Rigamonti 1996; Lehman et al. 2006c; Hekkala et al. 2007). These factors quite likely increase the naturally patchy distribution of *Varecia* species and make demographic declines permanent (Vasey 2005b). Many *Varecia* populations have been reduced to living in physically and genetically isolated forest fragments surrounded by periodically burned agricultural land (e.g., Manombo, Louis et al. 2005; Vatovavy Forest, Holmes et al. 2013). Isolated forest fragments have poor prospects for recovery after natural cyclone damage, as fires can rage unchecked, consuming fallen trees, and the influx of animal-dispersed seeds or pollen can be greatly reduced. Degraded forest seems unable to support top frugivores such as *Varecia* species, and these lemurs' numbers are greatly diminished or absent in such areas (Table 14.29). Habitat fragmentation has had a strongly negative effect on the occurrence of *V. variegata* in particular (Eppley et al. 2020).

Although total remaining population size is unknown, it is clear that the occurrence of *Varecia* is tied to the presence of moist evergreen forest habitat. Deforestation is projected to eliminate *Varecia* habitat before 2080 and therefore presents the most immediate threat to their survival, surpassing the projected adverse effects of climate change (Morelli et al. 2020). What makes *Varecia* species especially vulnerable is their need for numerous exceptionally large trees in which to nest and stash their litters, leading Vasey et al. (2018) to propose that logging directly precipitates local extinctions by impeding these lemurs' ability to reproduce. Indeed, *V. rubra* is negatively impacted by altered habitat even more than by hunting, as compared to the sympatric *Eulemur albifrons* (Borgerson 2015). Nonetheless, *Varecia* is intentionally trapped for food (Golden 2009; Borgerson 2016) and for the bushmeat and pet trades (Vasey 1996; Reuter et al. 2019), even in protected areas, and harvest rates are not sustainable, putting the genus at significant extinction risk (Golden 2009; Brook et al. 2018).

Varecia rubra has been afforded protection within Madagascar's two largest protected areas, Masoala and Makira, whereas *V. variegata* occurs in at least 17 protected areas throughout Madagascar's eastern moist evergreen forest corridor (Goodman et al. 2018b). Both species are the subjects of reintroduction and translocation projects: a captive-to-wild reinforcement effort for *V. variegata* at Betampona (e.g., Britt et al. 2004); a translocation of wild *V. variegata* to Analamazaotra, where the species had been locally extinct since 1976 (Day et al. 2009); and a translocation of wild *V. rubra* to Fanankaraina reserve (a private holding managed by a local NGO, Antongil Conservation; GERP 2016), where the species has been locally extinct for several decades (T. Alexis, unpublished data).

Both species of *Varecia* are flagship taxa for conservation efforts. Their habitat requirements are strict, such that they disappear early in the process of anthropogenic habitat degradation; they have large home ranges that encompass a myriad of other plant and animal taxa; and lastly, they are charismatic, beautiful animals that scientists and nonscientists alike can appreciate. Bust-boom reproduction is a defining life-history trait of *Varecia*, and the genus is thereby equipped to rebound after natural catastrophes. Moreover, in degraded habitats where both lemurs and forest have fallen under protection, *Varecia* has proven to be somewhat ecologically resilient, at least in the short term. Should we be successful in maintaining the protected area network and connecting populations of this genus throughout eastern Madagascar, it will benefit the larger mission of biodiversity conservation on Madagascar as a whole.

Subject editors: Jörg U. Ganzhorn and Steven M. Goodman

INDRIIDAE: *AVAHI*, WOOLLY LEMURS, *FOTSY-FE*, *TSARAFANGITRA*, *DADINTSIFAKY*

G. Donati, I. Norscia, M. Balestri, A. Zaramody, E. E. Louis Jr., and U. Thalmann

The woolly lemurs, *Avahi* species, are the only nocturnal members of the family Indriidae, which also includes *Propithecus* species and *Indri indri*. The English vernacular name refers to the curly, woolly appearance of the dense fur, whereas the genus name is a transcription of its typical high-pitched and rapid, loud call (*wo-he, va-hií, vou-hií*). In southeastern and eastern Madagascar, *Avahi* species are usually called *fotsy-fe* ("white thigh" in Malagasy), reflecting the white fur coloration on the inner backside of their thighs. In the west of the island, lemurs of this genus have locally varying names. For example, in the region of Mahajanga they are called *tsarafangitra*, meaning "well-dressed hair" in Malagasy, while in the central western region they are called *dadintsifaky*, which translates to "grandparent [or ancestor] of the *sifaka*" (*Propithecus*).

TAXONOMY

As has happened in other lemur groups, particularly nocturnal genera, the taxonomy of the monophyletic genus *Avahi* was significantly revised in recent years, resulting in the current identification of nine species (IUCN 2020). These species are: *A. betsileo* (Betsileo Woolly Lemur; Figure 14.52f), *A. cleesei* (Bemaraha Woolly Lemur; Figure 14.52a), *A. laniger* (Eastern Woolly Lemur; Figure 14.52e), *A. meridionalis* (Southern Woolly Lemur; Figure 14.52i), *A. mooreorum* (Masoala Woolly Lemur; Figure 14.52d), *A. occidentalis* (Western Woolly Lemur; Figure 14.52b), *A. peyrierasi* (Peyriéras' Woolly Lemur; Figure 14.52g), *A. ramanantsoavani* (Manombo Woolly Lemur; Figure 14.52h), and *A. unicolor* (Sambirano Woolly Lemur; Figure 14.52c) (Thalmann and Geissmann 2005; Zaramody et al. 2006; Andriantompohavana et al. 2007; Lei et al. 2008). For well over a century, *A. laniger* was considered to be the only species in the genus. Rumpler et al. (1990) demonstrated that western and eastern populations should be distinguished from one another based on cytogenetic characters and suggested the recognition of two different species: *A. occidentalis* and *A. laniger*. As for the western forms, *A. unicolor* and more recently *A. cleesei* were later identified as separate species from *A. occidentalis* based on morphological differences and vocalizations (Thalmann and Geissmann 2000, 2005). As for the eastern forms, on the basis of mtDNA analyses, *A. meridionalis* and *A. peyrierasi* were first identified as different species from *A. laniger* (Zaramody et al. 2006), and this was followed by a further split from *A. peyrierasi* of *A. betsileo*, *A. ramanantsoavani* (Andriantompohavana et al. 2007), and *A. mooreorum* (Lei et al. 2008).

An analysis of complete mitochondrial genome indicates that within the Indriidae, the nocturnal *Avahi* and the diurnal *Propithecus* separated about 13 Mya (Finstermeier et al. 2013). Chromosomal and molecular analyses suggest that the genus *Avahi* first diverged in an eastern group and a separate western group followed by differentiation on the mitochondrial level but without any chromosomal changes (Rumpler et al. 2011). Within the western region, the Betsiboka River seems to constitute a major geographic barrier separating northern from southern taxa. Within the eastern region, the main barrier between the northern and the southern forms appears to be the Mangoro-Onive River system (Rumpler et al. 2011). Based on an illustration from Sonnerat (1782), *A. laniger* was described by Gmelin in 1788. Sonnerat's itineraries would place the most plausible type locality of *A. laniger* in northeastern Madagascar, specifically the Maroantsetra region (Zaramody et al. 2006).

ACTIVITY

It has been hypothesized that *Avahi* is secondarily nocturnal and that its gregarious lifestyle is retained from a former diurnal activity pattern (Ganzhorn et al. 1985; A. E. Müller and Thalmann 2000). Both *A. laniger* and *A. occidentalis* have been described as mainly nocturnal, with a decrease in activity in the central hours of the night and a correlation between night length and overall amount of activity (Ganzhorn 1985; Thalmann 2006). A more recent study,

FIGURE 14.52 The nine species of woolly lemurs: A) *Avahi cleesei*, B) *A. occidentalis*, C) *A. unicolor*, D) *A. mooreorum*, E) *A. laniger*, F) *A. betsileo*, G) *A. peyrierasi*, H) *A. ramanantsoavani*, and I) *A. meridionalis*. (PHOTO A by U. Thalmann, B by T. M. Eppley, C and D by E. E. Louis Jr., E by E. Patel, F by J. R. Zaonarivelo, G by A. Randrianarijaona, H by R. Randriamampionona, and I by G. Donati.)

using accelerometers attached to radio collars, reported *A. meridionalis* to be predominantly nocturnal with peaks of activity at twilights, but consistent bouts of activity during the day were also recorded (Campera et al. 2019). This flexible activity, varying from strict nocturnality to an even distribution of activity during night and day, has been recently defined as a cathemerality *sensu lato*. Evidence of diurnal activity in woolly lemurs (mainly vigilance) was also reported in *A. occidentalis* (Warren and Crompton 1997; Thalmann

2001). These findings support a diurnal ancestor for the Indriidae and consolidate the hypothesis of a secondary nocturnality for *Avahi* (Ganzhorn et al. 1985; Roos et al. 2004). Secondary nocturnality is also supported by the visual adaptations of this genus, such as the maintenance of dichromacy with visual pigments optimally adjusted to detect young green leaves (Veilleux et al. 2014). This retention of color-based detection appears to provide advantages under certain luminosity conditions and may help to explain the lunarphilia (increased activity during nights with brighter moon) observed in *A. meridionalis* (Campera et al. 2019). The importance of luminosity levels is also suggested by the stronger selection to maintain short-wavelength-sensitive cones in the open-canopy species *A. occidentalis* and *A. cleesei* compared to the closed-canopy species *A. laniger* and *A. peyrierasi* (Veilleux et al. 2013).

DIET

Field studies showed very similar behavioral and ecological patterns for *A. laniger* (Ganzhorn et al. 1985; Ganzhorn 1988; C. Harcourt 1991; Roth 1996), *A. occidentalis* (Warren 1994; Thalmann 2001), *A. peyrierasi* (Faulkner and Lehman 2006), and *A. meridionalis* (Norscia et al. 2012; Balestri 2018). With body weights in the range of 700–1600 g, *Avahi* species are exceptionally small for specialized folivores (R. D. Martin 1990). On average, over 70% of their diet consists of mature and young leaves, and during certain seasons they are almost exclusively folivorous (Thalmann 2003). The non-leaf part of their vegetarian diet consists of small plant items such as flowers (especially petals, for *A. meridionalis*) and leaf buds or young leaf shoots. A field study of *A. occidentalis* in the deciduous forest of Ampijoroa revealed a highly selective diet (Thalmann 2001). This species feeds predominantly on plants that are highly underrepresented in the forest relative to their consumption. *Avahi meridionalis* is moderately specialist and integrates high proportions of uncommon resources in its diet (Norscia et al. 2012; Balestri 2018). In the eastern littoral forest, Norscia et al. (2012) observed *A. meridionalis* to feed on 125 trees belonging to 43 species and 26 plant families from June to December. The top two species that it consumed accounted for 41% of the total feeding time and the six most preferred feeding species accounted for about 60% of the total feeding time. In the lowland moist forest of Tsitongambarika, *A. meridionalis* has an annual diet that includes 43 plant species (Balestri 2018).

As for the nutritional content of the diet, Ganzhorn (1985, 1988) found high concentrations of protein and sugar but no alkaloids in 18 out of 36 food items eaten by *A. laniger* in the medium-altitude moist evergreen forest of Analamazaotra. Similarly, alkaloids were present in only one food item out of a total of 43 eaten by *A. meridionalis* in the lowland moist evergreen forest of Tsitongambarika (Balestri 2018) and were absent in 11 food items analyzed from the dry deciduous forest of Ampijoroa (Ganzhorn 1993). Conversely, in the eastern littoral forest, the same species has been observed to ingest intermediate level of phenolics and alkaloids in about half of the food plants (Norscia et al. 2012). Thus, some dietary flexibility likely driven by environmental constraints is present in the genus, which may lead either to avoidance of certain secondary compounds or ingestion of small amounts of different secondary substances (Ganzhorn 1989b).

HABITAT USE

The ranging pattern in *Avahi* can be remarkably variable between dry deciduous forest species and moist evergreen forest species. During a typical night, the mean horizontal path length of *A. occidentalis* in the dry deciduous forest of Ampijoroa has been estimated at 740 ± 187 m (n = 12; Thalmann 2006) and 1175 ± 347 m (Warren and Crompton 1997). Home ranges have been estimated at 0.95 ± 0.12 ha (n = 4; Thalmann 2006) and 1.59 ± 0.42 ha (n = 4; Warren and Crompton 1997) at the same site. In *A. occidentalis* there is little overlap between home ranges of neighboring groups, and the areas remained stable in size and location over consecutive years (Thalmann 2006). In the lowland moist evergreen forest of Tsitongambarika, the mean horizontal path length of *A. meridionalis* was 640.7 ± 27.6 m during the season of food abundance and 498.8 ± 36.4 m during the lean season (Balestri 2018). At the same site, the home range of several pairs varied between 4.53 and 10.39 ha (n = 4). In the littoral moist forest of Sainte Luce, *A. meridionalis* has home ranges of 2.23–2.81 ha (n = 4) (Norscia and Borgognini-Tarli 2008). *Avahi meridionalis* has been shown to rely on a time-minimizing strategy, reducing the horizontal path length, the time spent feeding, and the number of feeding trees during the lean season (Norscia et al. 2012; Balestri 2018).

The genus shows seasonal variation in the selection and use of sleeping sites. During the dry season, *A. occidentalis* uses a small number of sleeping sites and preferentially rests in the middle part of trees, while it shows no preference during the rainy season (Ramanankirahina et al. 2012). This is interpreted as an antipredator and thermoregulatory strategy when the vegetation cover is low and there are fewer suitable locations. Sleeping on branches and frequently changing sleeping sites seems to reduce parasite infection and transmission in *A. occidentalis* compared to individuals that use tree holes (Hokan et al. 2018). In this study, fecal samples of *A. occidentalis* contained nematode eggs (family Strongylidae), with a prevalence of 20.7% (n = 29 individuals), while no protozoal stages were detected (Hokan et al. 2018). At Tsitongambarika, *A. meridionalis* selects sleeping trees that do not significantly diverge from random trees in terms of size and height but generate a microclimate with lower mean temperatures compared to the forest average (Cooper 2017).

SOCIAL SYSTEM AND COMMUNICATION

Avahi species are pair living, with female dominance (*A. meridionalis*; Norscia and Palagi 2016). Despite their predominantly nocturnal activity period, lemurs of this genus can move and feed as a cohesive family group containing an adult pair and one to three offspring (Thalmann 2003), although in *A. meridionalis* the adult female and male have been found to spend a variable amount of time together or in proximity (6–45%, depending on the season; Norscia and Borgognini-Tarli 2008). Furthermore, unlike most other nocturnal strepsirrhines, the female *Avahi* carries her single newborn continuously during active periods, instead of parking it (Norscia 2006). Occasional grooming has been observed in *A. meridionalis* when the male, the female carrying infants, and/or the subadult

offspring rest together during the day (Norscia 2006). However, no direct parental care (e.g., infant carrying) has ever been observed in males, but indirect parental care has been hypothesized (Thalmann 2003). Indeed, occasional rapid excursions to the range border suggesting range defense by the male have been observed in *A. occidentalis* (Thalmann 2001). In the southeastern littoral moist forest, males of *A. meridionalis* were found to travel longer distance and have larger home ranges than females (Norscia and Borgognini-Tarli 2008). Moreover males increased the time spent in proximity to the females during the night activity after birth. This further supports Thalmann's hypothesis of possible indirect parental care via resource defense.

A single offspring is usually born in August–October, after mating has taken place in March–May, depending on regions (Thalmann 2003; Norscia 2006). In *A. occidentalis*, offspring remain with their parents over the next breeding season before leaving the family. Although rarely, in *A. meridionalis* up to three immature individuals have been seen sleeping with the parental pair (group size = 5; Norscia 2006). As the female often carries an infant and/or cares for other young offspring of different ages, she may not be involved in territory defense (Thalmann 2003).

Along with their inconspicuous pelage coloration, *Avahi* species also generally display cryptic behavior, especially when vocalizing. Besides the above-mentioned loud call starting with *wo-he*, which has been interpreted in the context of territorial behavior and alarm calls (C. Harcourt 1991), further vocalization types include whistles, chirps, and growls (Thalmann 2003; Ramanankirahina et al. 2016). The whistles are unmodulated notes of long duration and pure tone. According to C. Harcourt (1991), these single-frequency whistles serve as means of communication between individuals, particularly members of a pair, enabling them to locate one another. In *A. occidentalis* the loud call is used primarily during locomotion in the noncore areas of home ranges (Ramanankirahina et al. 2016). The chirps are hypothesized to be closely related to the whistles and serve similar functions. The main difference is that the chirps are not of a pure tone, and some modulation is present (Thalmann 2003). Growls are low-intensity vocalizations and seem to occur mainly before animals leave a feeding locality but also in other contexts. They also serve as means of intragroup communication and group coordination (Ramanankirahina et al. 2016).

ABUNDANCE AND CONSERVATION

Like most lemurs, *Avahi* species are threatened by the destruction and fragmentation of their natural forest habitat (IUCN 2020). In addition to this ubiquitous threat throughout Madagascar, conservation of this genus is complicated by the fact that these lemurs combine a highly specialized diet (selective folivory) with a highly specialized locomotion (vertical climbing and leaping). As a result, *Avahi* species heavily rely on vertical supports and to date have not been successfully kept in captivity.

Surveys conducted in eastern littoral forest fragments showed that the abundance of *A. meridionalis* (0.0–2.6 ind/ha) correlated with the density of large trees, whereas birth rate was sensitive to fragment size (Ganzhorn et al. 2007; Norscia 2008). At Ranomafana National Park, encounter rates for *A. peyrierasi* are higher in intact moist evergreen forest than in logged habitats, and the species' abundance is positively related to canopy height (Herrera et al. 2011). A similar pattern was observed in Masoala National Park for *A. mooreorum* (Sawyer et al. 2017). Minimum area requirements, limited numbers of large trees, and hunting pressure have also been cited to explain the absence of *A. occidentalis* in the forest fragments within the western portion of Ankarafantsika National Park (T. S. Steffens and Lehman 2018). On the other hand, in northeastern moist evergreen forests there was no difference in density estimates of *A. laniger* between intact, intermediately degraded, and degraded forest sites (Murphy et al. 2016) or between mature and secondary forest (A. Miller et al. 2018). In the lowland moist forest of Tsitongambarika, *A. meridionalis* showed a neutral edge response, with higher encounter rates between 250 and 750 m from the edge, and a preference toward areas with small adult trees (Balestri 2018). At Mandena, the same species has been seen using *Eucalyptus* plantations for moving and resting in close proximity to littoral forest (Scobie et al. 2017). *Avahi peyrierasi* also appears to be edge tolerant in the southeastern moist forest of Vohibola (Lehman et al. 2006b). In summary, the genus shows some variability in terms of tolerance toward edges and sensitivity to logging and other disturbance, but tree size and forest vertical structure appear critical for its presence (Ganzhorn 1989a; Warren 1994). Thus, it is of utmost importance to protect the different *Avahi* populations in natural habitats with mature structure.

With large distributions (which include protected areas) and often relatively high densities, some of the eastern species—*A. laniger*, *A. peyrierasi*, and *A. ramanantsoavani*—are classified as Vulnerable (IUCN 2020). In contrast, the other three eastern species, *A. betsileo*, *A. meridionalis*, and *A. mooreorum* are distributed over much smaller areas and are considered Endangered. The western species *A. occidentalis* is listed as Vulnerable, and *A. cleesei* and *A. unicolor* as Critically Endangered, due to highly restricted distributions and severely fragmented habitats.

CONCLUSION

Compared to other lemur genera, *Avahi* has been relatively understudied, and most species are still poorly known. This is partly due to the difficulties of tracking and observing these cryptic nocturnal primates, especially in moist evergreen forest habitats. We hope that the fast, recent development of miniaturized tracking equipment will help to fill this gap in the next few years. As we illustrated in this contribution, *Avahi* species are characterized by several traits that make them unique among primates both from an ecological and from a behavioral perspective. Since members of *Avahi* cannot be kept in captivity, and several species have very limited distribution areas, we conclude this review by emphasizing again the importance of conserving these elusive lemurs in their natural habitats. This is especially relevant in western Madagascar, owing to dramatic agriculture shifts irreversibly changing the landscape.

Subject editors: Jörg U. Ganzhorn and Steven M. Goodman

INDRIIDAE: *INDRI INDRI*, INDRI, *BABAKOTO*

M. Gamba, V. Torti, J. Powzyk, U. Thalmann, L. Miaretsoa, R. M. Randrianarison, and C. Giacoma

The distinctive black-and-white pelage and a long, loud call make the Indri one of Madagascar's best-known lemurs (Figure 14.53). This species, a member of the family Indriidae, is a denizen of moist evergreen forests of the east and known from an elevation range from close to sea level to about 1500 m (J.-J. Petter et al. 1977). *Indri indri* has not been successfully managed in captivity, but viewing of wild groups at the Analamazaotra Special Reserve (Périnet) has been ongoing for nearly 50 years. As with many lemur species, the Indri is under pressure from extensive habitat loss (Mittermeier et al. 1994) and hunting (Harper et al. 2007). This species does receive limited protection from native taboo (*fady*) traditions that prohibit its consumption by certain ethnic groups, owing to its resemblance to the sacred ancestors of the Malagasy, as the only lemur lacking a long tail. A popular legend passed down orally across generations tells of a young boy, living in the forests of eastern Madagascar, who climbed high into a tree to gather honey and got trapped, unable to climb back down. However, when it seemed that his fate was sealed, an *Indri* came through the trees and

FIGURE 14.53 **Aspects of *Indri indri*: A) a subadult female at Analamazaotra (Andasibe-Mantadia National Park); B) an adult male, showing the characteristic darker pelage pattern, in the Anjozorobe-Angavo protected area; C) a solitary-ranging female in the Andasibe Forestry Station (Mitsinjo); D) a young male "ricochet leaping," a species-typical behavior, in the Maromizaha Forest; E) an adult female at Maromizaha feeding in the typical vertical clinging posture; and F) an adult emitting a song unit at Maromizaha.** (PHOTOS A, B, and C by V. Sorrentino; and D, E, and F by F. Carugati.)

helped him descend from the canopy. That is the reason the Malagasy name for the species is *Babakoto*, meaning "ancestor of humans." Several versions of this legend can be heard across the eastern portion of the island, and for centuries the local people considered hunting *Indri* a strict taboo.

The Indri has long been considered the largest of the extant Malagasy lemurs, based solely on visual estimates. However, fieldwork has shown that this species shares this title with *Propithecus diadema* (see Lawler and Richard, pp. 1971–74). *Indri indri* adults captured in the Mantadia National Park averaged 6.5 kg in body weight (n = 4), and those of the sympatric *P. diadema* also averaged 6.5 kg (n = 11). When sexes were compared, *I. indri* females averaged 7.1 kg (n = 2), and males averaged 5.8 kg (n = 2); *P. diadema* females averaged 6.5 kg (n = 6), and males averaged 6.5 kg (n = 5) (Powzyk 1997; Glander and Powzyk 1998). Therefore, it is more accurate to describe *P. diadema* and *I. indri* as the two largest lemurs, and when sexes are compared, *Indri* females are the heaviest among all extant lemurs. Some of the largest body weights of *Indri* were recorded at Marotandrano, where mean body weight was 8.1 kg (n = 8) (Zaonarivelo et al. 2007).

TAXONOMY

The first description of *Indri indri* was based on a specimen brought to Europe by Sonnerat and illustrated in the account of his journey (Sonnerat 1782: Plate 88). The type specimen is almost entirely black except for the white pygal patch (Figure 14.53b). Having the outer portions of its arms and legs black, it resembles animals from the northernmost population (Thalmann et al. 1993: 363, Figure 3a). Peters (1872) described a second species as "*Lichanotus mitratus*." This particular specimen had a different coloration from that of the Sonnerat type: the top and the back of the head were white, extending downward behind the ears and forward onto the throat. The outer side of the upper and lower hind limbs and the outer side of the lower arms were gray. Milne Edwards and Grandidier (1875) doubted the existence of two different *Indri* species, reporting that light and dark individuals occurred together in the same troops (also see Pollock 1975b; Powzyk 1997). Hence, they concluded that this lemur is highly variable in pelage coloration, and that all individuals belong to the same species, correctly named *I. indri*.

Schwarz (1931) believed that the type specimen of *Lichanotus mitratus* (= *I. indri*), collected by Crossley, came from the east of the Antongil Bay (i.e., Masoala Peninsula), but recent findings may indicate that the specimen could have been collected near Nosivola (mentioned as "Nossi Vola"), southeast of Lake Alaotra (Carleton et al. 2014), presumably in close vicinity to the current Zahamena protected area of today and thus within the documented distribution of the species.

A closer examination of specimens of known origin confirmed the highly differing pelage coloration but also revealed that there might be a geographic pattern to this variation. *Indri* individuals from the northernmost part of the range conform with Sonnerat's mostly black type, whereas the southern individuals usually exhibit those of Peters's *L. mitratus*. A pronounced transformation of these two pelage coloration patterns occurs at approximately the latitude of Mananara-Nord, where intermediate forms are found (Thalmann et al. 1993). Groves (2001) considered the two extreme color variants different subspecies, but more recent molecular analysis of mitochondrial markers shows no clear genetic separation across the latitudinal distribution of *Indri* to support the recognition of geographic forms (Brenneman et al. 2016). Hence, the two major color forms are best explained as a clinal variation.

DIET

As a member of the folivorous guild, *Indri indri* shows a clear preference for immature leaves (72%), with a reduced emphasis on fruit seeds or whole fruits (16%) and flowers (7%) (Powzyk 1997). This species feeds by plucking off the preferred plant part with its teeth or by pulling in the tree branch with its hand as it bites off the desired parts. In the Mantadia protected area, male and female *Indri* spent similar time feeding on fruit and flowers, yet females spent significantly more time on immature foliage than males. Field observations in the lowland moist evergreen forests of Betampona also revealed a preference for leaves but, unlike those in Mantadia, showed a higher percentage of mature foliage in the diet (Britt et al. 2002). This diet is supported by a gut morphology typical of folivores, with a suite of anatomical specializations, including hypertrophied salivary glands, voluminous stomach, sacculated caecum, and looped colon, which facilitate efficient fermentation of leaf matter. *Indri* molars have high crowns, large crushing surfaces, and long shearing blades (Kay and Hylander 1978) to facilitate the complete mastication of leaf blades and seeds alike. No seeds are passed whole through the gut, which indicates that *Indri* is not a seed disperser but a seed predator.

The feeding behavior of *Indri* revealed a strong preference for tree foliage, reaching a percentage of 94.9% in the Maromizaha Forest (among six groups studied by R. M. Randrianarison [2019]). In Betampona, this percentage drops to 70%, possibly underlying differences in forest quality across sites, resulting in shifts in the diet of local *Indri* populations. In Maromizaha, Indris are reported to feed on 86 tree species (belonging to 53 genera and 35 families) in the more pristine area and on 80 species in the more visited ecotouristic area (R. M. Randrianarison 2019).

In the Maromizaha Forest, the consumption of flowers varies between August–September and November–April. Fruit consumption is more common from November to February. Soil consumption takes place year-round. Other food categories, such as leaf buds of *Dalbergia* (Fabaceae), as well as different types of bark, were consumed from January to November. *Indri* is also reported to spend time feeding on nontree plants such as mosses, lianas, ferns, parasitic plants, and herbs (Powzyk 1997). In Anjozorobe, this species has been observed to feed on mushrooms (V. Sorrentino, unpublished data).

Based on time spent feeding, the 10 most preferred plant parts for *Indri* are all immature leaves of different species. The most popular plant family observed as a food source is the Lauraceae (see Eppley et al., pp. 1839–59, for details on the plants consumed). *Indri* consumes soil on a regular basis (22% of the days monitored), and this rate was half that of the more seed-consuming *Propithecus diadema* (Powzyk 1997), but more than that of the bamboo-eating *Hapalemur* species (C. L. Tan 1999; see Tan et al., pp. 1947–52).

When *Indri* did consume fruit, the majority of its time was spent feeding on just the seeds (Powzyk 1997). Consequently, the consumption of soil may be a means to combat the chemical deterrents often found in fruit seeds (Gillardi et al. 1999). At Maromizaha, *Indri* consumes *Uapaca thouarsii* (Phyllanthaceae; see Ralimanana and Challen, pp. 649–54) throughout the year, as well as several species of Lauraceae (R. M. Randrianarison 2019).

Phytochemical analyses have shown that all leaves and fruits consumed by this species have polyphenols, and three plant species—*Ravensara* sp. (Lauraceae), *Tina striata* (Sapindaceae), and *Xylopia lemurica* (Annonaceae)—have alkaloids, condensed tannins, and hydrolyzable tannins (R. M. Randrianarison 2019). The digestive process of regurgitation-reingestion (R/R) was observed in November (R. M. Randrianarison 2019) in association with the consumption of those three plant species. R/R is an atypical behavior consisting in voluntarily bringing up partially digested food and then reingesting it (Morgan et al. 1993). It has been observed in captive nonhuman primates, particularly gorillas and chimpanzees (Struck et al. 2007), but rarely observed in wild primates. R/R may play a role in reducing certain side effects of feeding, especially digestion associated with, for example, a low-fiber diet (Lukas 1999). Additional research is needed to understand the role and origin of this behavior in *Indri*.

When a nutritional analysis of the most preferred foods was undertaken, the diet of *Indri* showed a significantly lower level of water-soluble carbohydrates and fats compared to the preferred foods of the sympatric *P. diadema*. These low levels of energy-rich carbohydrates can be attributed to the lack of fruit seeds and whole fruits within the top 10 preferred foods for *Indri* (Powzyk and Mowry 2006). The main energy source for this species is derived from the fermentation of complex carbohydrates in the form of plant fiber from immature leaves. *Indri* cannot fully digest plant fiber without the assistance of symbiotic microorganisms that inhabit its gastrointestinal tract. These microorganisms break down the fiber into fatty acids that can then be readily absorbed into the bloodstream. The dependence on energy derived from such a lengthy process may serve to constrain the consumer's energetic budget. This is supported by the physiological mechanism in which movement by an animal shunts blood away from the gut to the limb muscles, which slows digestion (Cartmill et al. 1987), while resting or sleeping serves to increase the rate of digestion (J. D. Smith 1977). The activity pattern of *Indri* reflects these constraints; the mean time this lemur spent resting was eight hours per day during the 12-hour daylight period (Powzyk 1997). This species is the most diurnal of the lemurs; movement at night apparently occurs only during inclement weather (i.e., cyclones, heavy rainfall) or acts of predation.

SOCIAL SYSTEM

Indri lives in socially monogamous family groups (Bonadonna et al. 2019) composed of one adult pair and their offspring (Pollock 1979). Group size varies from two to six individuals (Torti et al. 2013; Gamba et al. 2016). The limited number of adult individuals in a group suggests that intrasexual dominance is age-related (Pollock 1977). Females give birth every two years. Reproduction is highly seasonal, with the birth of a single offspring occurring in May or June. Reproductive maturity is reached between seven and nine years of age (Pollock 1977), but individuals may disperse earlier (V. Torti, unpublished data). Both males and females disperse (Torti et al. 2018; C. Giacoma, unpublished data), and the sex ratio at birth is approximately one to one (Kappeler 1997b). *Indri* has been considered monogamous, forming pairs for life (Pollock 1975a), but recent observations indicate female and male takeovers and extra-pair copulation (Bonadonna et al. 2014), and the mating system of this species may need a reassessment. Despite the recent observation of extra-pair copulation, genetic monogamy is the norm and supports the hypothesis that pair-living social organization is associated with low extra-pair paternity rates.

VOCAL REPERTOIRE

Indri indri has a rich vocal repertoire (Maretti et al. 2010; Sorrentino et al. 2013) and is the only lemur that communicates using songs (Figure 14.53f). Groups emit roars as a warning signal when aerial predators or predators above the group are detected (see Goodman and Ganzhorn, pp. 1829–38, for more details on predation). In contrast, a loud honk call is uttered when ground-dwelling predators or other disturbances on the ground are detected (Maretti et al. 2010). Several vocalizations mediate intragroup dynamics, such as "grunt," "kiss," "wheeze," short- and long-tonal calls, and "hum," which mostly precedes a progression or movement.

The songs of *Indri* are long sequences of vocal units that are organized in phrases (Thalmann et al. 1993; Gamba et al. 2011). They have the form of a chorus in which all the adults and subadults of a group utter their contribution in a precise and coordinated manner (Gamba et al. 2016). Songs have various functions depending on the context in which they are emitted, and they are used for both inter- and intragroup communication (Baker-Médard et al. 2013; Torti et al. 2013, 2018). Furthermore, songs are likely to provide information about the group composition and mediate the formation of new groups (Pollock 1986b; Giacoma et al. 2010; Gamba et al. 2016; Torti et al. 2017; Zanoli et al. 2020). In this species' song, the sexes show some differences, with males holding their notes longer, although the overall investment in singing does not differ between males and females (Giacoma et al. 2010), but the tendency to display nonvocal territorial behaviors is more pronounced in adult males (Pollock 1975b, 1979). Except for very young individuals, all group members seemingly contribute to the chorus. The notes produced during the song are highly variable, but a general pattern can be recognized.

The song starts with a series of roars uttered simultaneously by several members of a group. Long notes, mainly emitted by males, follow the roars, and then there is a long sequence of frequency-modulated units organized in descending phrases (Pollock 1986b; Sorrentino et al. 2013). The descending phrases usually begin with a unit showing a high fundamental frequency, followed by one or several others (up to five) of progressively lower starting frequency. Regularly, two or more individuals coordinate the timing of their descending phrases to achieve a stable duet pattern. The song is dominated by the adult pair, whereas younger individuals may contribute only partially. Both dominant males and females influenced the onset timing of the chorus sequence; the dominant

male and the dominant female in a group overlap with one another more frequently than they do with the nondominants (Gamba et al. 2016).

Although groups may sing simultaneously, group songs are typically contagious and emitted sequentially. It has been suggested that the emission of songs may also follow disturbances such as thunder, birds, or airplanes, as well as the calls of other lemurs (Pollock 1975b). Songs are uttered mainly between 0600 h and 1300 h, with peaks between 0700 h and 1100 h (Powzyk 1997). Throughout the year, the number of daily songs increases around September and peaks during November–December, when calls can also be heard during the night. The number of daily songs decreases in February–March (Pollock 1975b; Powzyk 1997). The *Indri* song plays a role in territorial defense during intergroup encounters, advertising the presence of the group in a particular area of its territory, the definition of territorial boundaries between neighboring groups, group cohesion, communication of environmental conditions, and the reproductive potential of certain individuals (Pollock 1975b; Torti et al. 2013).

HABITAT USE

Groups in fragmented habitat tend to be larger than those in more extensive undisturbed areas (Pollock 1979; Powzyk 1997; Bonadonna et al. 2017). *Indri* groups occupy relatively small territories that have been found to vary among study areas: extreme values recorded were 17.6 and 25.9 ha at Analamazaotra (Pollock 1975a, 1975b; Bonadonna et al. 2017), and 5 and 17.5 ha in Maromizaha (Bonadonna et al. 2017). Powzyk (1997) described territories of 34 ha (group 2) and 40 ha (group 3) in Mantadia, while an average territory size of 27 ha was observed in Betampona (Glessner and Britt 2005). *Indri* movements within the territory are evenly distributed. Daily path lengths average 243 m in Maromizaha (V. Torti, unpublished data) and 774 m in Mantadia (Powzyk 1997). Differences between study sites may be attributed to differences in habitat quality. The Mantadia site is pristine and situated in a larger expanse of forest within the protected area, where there is much more space for animals to disperse out of their natal group and form new groups. Furthermore, the array of potential food species has not been significantly altered by human activity in Mantadia or Maromizaha. In contrast, Analamazaotra underwent considerable selective logging some decades ago and is surrounded by roads and agricultural fields that inhibit dispersal. These conditions may result in a "hyperconcentration" of *Indri* at Analamazaotra (J.-J. Petter and Peyriéras 1974).

As with its indriid congeners, *Avahi* and *Propithecus*, *Indri* moves through its forested habitats with an erect torso by vertical clinging (Figure 14.53e) and leaping (Figure 14.53d) (Oxnard et al. 1990). As groups of this species displace within their territories, individuals scent mark with anogenital and/or cheek glands. Anogenital marking is characterized by the rubbing of the genitals and anal region against a substrate (e.g., tree branch) and is performed by both sexes. This type of scent marking includes glandular secretions from specialized tissue located around the anus (J.-J. Petter et al. 1977). Cheek marking is done by a male or female first rubbing a substrate with one side of its muzzle and then with the other. Saliva from unspecialized salivary glands has been shown to be a viable scent mark in this species (V. Torti, unpublished data), as in *Microcebus* (Glaston 1983; see Kappeler et al., pp. 1927–32).

Indri territories are generally stable in terms of size and location, with core areas usually concentrated in the area that remains stable over the years, and little overlap between adjacent territories (Bonadonna et al. 2020). Thus, it is not surprising that intergroup encounters are rare in this species, although they can occur. Bonadonna et al. (2017) observed only 30 such encounters in 36 months of fieldwork, associated with 16 different groups. However, when two groups meet, they defend their territory ownership by using prolonged vocal interactions, also indicated as territorial songs (Maretti et al. 2010; Torti et al. 2013). During an intergroup encounter, the reproductive males approach and face one another, sometimes engaging in physical fights (Pollock 1975b, 1979; Powzyk and Mowry 2006), while the other members of their family groups remain in a less prominent position and frequently sing or vocalize. After a dispute resolution, the adult males rejoin their respective females and resume their normal ranging and feeding activities (Bonadonna et al. 2020).

DISTRIBUTION

Today, *Indri indri* occurs in moist evergreen forest habitat of eastern Madagascar from the Mangoro River in the south to Anjanaharibe-Sud in the north and to Andapa in the west (Tattersall 1982; Thalmann et al. 1993). In the north it has a patchwork distribution and is absent from the protected areas of Marojejy Massif, approximately 20 km northeast of Anjanaharibe-Sud, as well as Masoala, farther to the southeast. However, it is found in Makira, located between Masoala and Marojejy.

Subfossil remains provide evidence for a much wider distribution of *Indri* in the Late Pleistocene and Holocene. Remains have been unearthed in the Central Highlands as far west as the sites of Ampasambazimba and Antsirabe (Lamberton 1939; Godfrey et al. 1999), and Ankarana in the far north. Further, there is evidence of this genus in the Ankazoabo-Atsimo region, based on subfossil remains recovered from Ampoza (Godfrey et al. 1999). In the Ankarana, *Indri* remains have been found just below a skeleton of the extinct lemur *Babakotia*, which yielded a radiocarbon date of about 4400 years before present (Jungers et al. 1995). *Indri* subfossil specimens are a bit more robust than today's animals (Albrecht et al. 1990; Jungers et al. 1995; Godfrey et al. 1999).

POPULATION DYNAMICS

Few studies on *Indri* population densities are available (Table 14.30). Population densities are presumably low, typically ranging from 5.2 ind/km^2 (individuals per square kilometer) in Mantadia to 22.9 ind/km^2 in Analamazaotra (Powzyk and Thalmann 2003) to 6.9–13.2 ind/km^2 in Betampona (Glessner and Britt 2005). A reasonable estimate, based on few studies (Glessner and Britt 2005; Junge et al. 2011; Brenneman et al. 2016; Nunziata et al. 2016; Bonadonna et al. 2017), would be a total overall population of 1000–10,000 individuals. Herrera et al. (2018), however,

TABLE 14.30. ***Indri indri* population densities across sites**

SITE	DIMENSION (ha)	NUMBER OF INDIVIDUALS	REFERENCES
Betampona	2228	77–147	Glessner and Britt (2005)
Analamazaotra Forestry Station (Mitsinjo)	700	21–32	Junge et al. (2011)
Maromizaha	–	82.32/km^2	Ratsimbazafy et al. (2017)

by combining species-distribution modeling of abiotic and biotic niches with population-size modeling in Makira, estimated an *Indri* abundance of about 38,140 individuals in the whole area of occupancy (4197 km^2). However, in any case, population figures are in decline owing to habitat destruction and hunting. The fragmented nature of *Indri* subpopulations, as well as the lack of a captive population, presents serious conservation challenges for this species (Britt et al. 2002).

CONSERVATION

The principal threat to *Indri indri* is habitat destruction associated with swidden agriculture, logging, and fuelwood gathering, all of which take place even within protected areas. Increasing levels of illegal hunting are also a major problem (R. K. B. Jenkins et al. 2011). Hunting of this species has risen dramatically since the 2009 political crisis and poses a severe threat. Taboos (*fady*) that traditionally protected the species by members of certain ethnic groups are becoming less respected.

Indri indri is listed on Appendix I of CITES. It occurs in 15 protected areas, from north to south: Anjanaharibe-Sud, Makira, Mananara-Nord, Marotandrano, Ambatovaky, Zahamena, Ankeniheny-Zahamena, Betampona, Mangerivola, Sahafina, Mantadia, Torotorofotsy, Analamazaotra, Maromizaha, and Mangabe-Ranomena-Sahasarotra (Goodman et al. 2018b). The forested zones running from Ankeniheny-Zahamena and Maromizaha north to Zahamena are critical for the future of this species, and extensive conservation-education and capacity-building actions have been put in place there. These programs need to continue, strengthening the role of *Indri* as a flagship species. This species has never successfully been kept in captivity, and thus the possibility of captive-breeding programs is highly doubtful.

CONCLUSION

In the next years, in terms of *Indri indri*, it will be of great importance to support local forest management by improving the existing community-based approach (R. Randrianarison et al. 2015). Actions should include the expansion of protected habitats to increase population connectivity (e.g., the Ankeniheny-Zahamena protected area) and to decrease lemur disturbance by rural communities. Without external support, the last remaining forest habitats will be devastated within a few years, resulting in the local extinction of most lemur populations (Schüßler et al. 2018).

Subject editors: Jörg U. Ganzhorn and Steven M. Goodman

INDRIIDAE: *PROPITHECUS*, SIFAKAS, *SIFAKA*

R. R. Lawler and A. F. Richard

The genus *Propithecus* (family Indriidae) comprises diurnal, mostly folivorous, group-living lemurs that inhabit a variety of forest types throughout Madagascar. *Sifaka*, the ubiquitous Malagasy name for members of this genus, comes from their explosive, clicking alarm call. *Propithecus* species have a characteristic leaping mode of locomotion, using their relatively long legs to propel them between tree trunks; their body proportions, similar to those of humans, give rise to a "dancing" form of movement when they are on the ground and moving across open areas (Figure 14.54). Suspensory behaviors, particularly while foraging, are also part of their locomotor repertoire. *Propithecus* species are found in many remaining forests. The overall distribution of the genus is like a ring, with one small gap in the far northwest, although the presence of these animals today is reduced and fragmented as a consequence of habitat destruction and hunting.

TAXONOMY

The taxonomy of *Propithecus*, like that of most lemurs, has undergone several upward revisions in species number in recent years, leading to claims of taxonomic inflation (e.g., Tattersall 2007; Tattersall and Cuozzo 2018). The substance of the debate is beyond the scope of this review, however, and we use the new taxonomy here, which recognizes nine species, elevating previous subspecies

FIGURE 14.54 **A female *Propithecus verreauxi* with dependent offspring moves bipedally across an open space at Bezà-Mahafaly.** (PHOTO by C. Chen-Kraus.)

to species status (Groves and Helgen 2007; Mittermeier et al. 2010; Rowe and Myers 2016). We note that it creates uneven levels of information among species, with some newly elevated species far less studied than the three formerly recognized: *P. diadema*, *P. verreauxi*, and *P. tattersalli*. The new taxonomic scheme includes two species groups: the larger-bodied (~5–8 kg) *P. diadema* group (*P. diadema*, *P. edwardsi*, and *P. candidus*) along the eastern flank of the island, and the smaller-bodied (~3–4.5 kg) *P. verreauxi* group (*P. verreauxi*, *P. deckeni*, *P. coronatus*, and *P. coquereli*) in the west. Two species found in the far northeast—*P. tattersalli* and *P. perrieri*—are considered "outliers" of the *P. verreauxi* and *P. diadema* groups, respectively (Mittermeier et al. 2010). Recent detailed information on the distributions of these species are summarized by the IUCN Red List of Threatened Species (IUCN 2020).

ABUNDANCE

Propithecus species occur at hugely different densities. In general, eastern populations live in smaller social groups occupying larger home ranges at lower densities than populations in the west and the south. In Ranomafana National Park, *P. edwardsi* groups occupy home ranges of 100–200 ha, with a population density of only about eight ind/km^2 (individuals per square kilometer) (P. C. Wright et al. 1987). *Propithecus tattersalli* resides in home ranges of 9–12 ha, with an estimated population density of 10–23 ind/km^2 in the Loky Manambato area (Vargas et al. 2002). Salmona et al. (2014b) reported densities of *P. coronatus* ranging from 49 to 309 ind/km^2 in the northwest coastal region of the Mahavavy and Betsiboka Rivers. Local densities of *P. verreauxi* in small patches of riparian forest in the south and west ranged from 211 ind/km^2 at Berenty (O'Connor 1987) to 400–500 ind/km^2 at Antseranamby (Sussman 1974). These exceptionally high densities plummet over short distances, however, reflecting steep ecological gradients as well as the effects of different human pressures. At Ifotaka, for example, a relatively intact dry spiny thicket a few kilometers from Berenty, a density of just 37 ind/km^2 has been recorded (B. Ferguson, unpublished data). Bealoka, also nearby, is a riverine forest. Unlike Berenty, however, it has been heavily grazed and browsed and supports a much less dense population, with only 47 ind/km^2 (O'Connor 1987). It should be mentioned that in several cases these density estimates are from several decades ago, and at most sites, it is almost certain the numbers are now reduced.

SOCIAL SYSTEM AND REPRODUCTION

The largest social groups reported for the genus, up to 14 individuals, are those of *P. verreauxi*. Both *P. verreauxi* and *P. edwardsi* exhibit large variation in group size, of two to 13 individuals (at Bezà-Mahafaly) and two to 10 individuals, respectively (Richard et al. 1993; Morelli et al. 2009), and a median size of four or five in both species. At a different locale, Kirindy Forest CNFEREF, *P. verreauxi* shows less variation in group size, and the average group size is about four animals (Kappeler et al. 2009). Group sizes are generally small in *P. candidus* and *P. perrieri*, with about three animals per group (Lehman and Mayor 2004; Patel 2009). Average group size in *P. coronatus* is five (Curtis et al. 1998). In *P. diadema*

group size ranges from two to eight animals (Powzyk 1997), in *P. tattersalli* three to 10 (Vargas et al. 2002), and in *P. coquereli* two to eight (Kun-Rodrigues et al. 2014).

Data regarding sociality and social relationships are patchy. Groups contain as few as one adult male and one adult female, or as many as four or five adult males with one or several adult females. Groups have occasionally been observed containing up to four adult females in *P. verreauxi* (Richard 1985) and up to three females in *P. edwardsi* (Pochron and Wright 2003). A striking and presumably shared feature of *Propithecus* social groups is that at least one and often all adult females are socially dominant to males. Dominant females regularly displace males, particularly at feeding sites but also in other contexts. Typically, a male will quickly get out of the way of an approaching dominant female or wait for her to leave a section of a tree before moving there to feed himself. If he fails to notice her or does not move off fast enough, she is likely to lunge, smack at or even bite him, and the male usually exhibits some sort of appeasement or submission behavior.

In a recent study of *P. edwardsi*, each of three social groups contained one female, who received no aggressive signals from, and gave no submissive signals to, others in the group. In all three groups, however, the second female was not only subordinate to the other female, but she also lost in some conflicts with males. Both the recent history of the group and the developmental stages of the males and females present may contribute to shaping the relationships between them (Hemingway 1995). Males of *P. verreauxi* and *P. candidus* have been reported to form dominance hierarchies (Lewis and van Schaik 2007; Patel 2009).

Males of all *Propithecus* species have scent glands, and both males and females have anogenital glands, which they use to deposit scent marks on branches and vertical supports in a wide range of contexts. The information conveyed by these marks is unknown, but the frequency of scent-marking behavior by both sexes suggests that it is a crucial dimension of social communication (Lewis 2005). All species use an array of vocalizations in a variety of contexts, such as responding to the presence of a predator, maintaining contact with or relocating other group members, and initiating travel. There is likely lots of variation in both the acoustic properties and meaning of the various calls found throughout species within the genus; discussions of vocalizations in *Propithecus* can be found in Patel and Owren (2012) and Fichtel and Kappeler (2011).

In *Propithecus* species for which there are reliable data, mating occurs between January and March each year. There is some variation in mating patterns within *P. verreauxi*. At Kirindy Forest CNFEREF, most mating and siring of offspring is done by the dominant male within each group (Kappeler and Schäffler 2008), whereas at Bezà-Mahafaly, extra-group mating by males and females is common (Lawler 2007), coinciding with a breakdown of group boundaries, social instability, and increased intergroup aggression. In *P. edwardsi*, mating takes place within groups, and extra-group mating has not been observed (Morelli et al. 2009).

LIFE HISTORY AND POPULATION DYNAMICS

Population turnover is generally slow in *Propithecus*, although growth and development rates vary widely between populations and perhaps between species as well. Males and females do not differ significantly in size, and their growth rates are similar. Infants are born during a two- to three-month birth season, between June and August each year. Mothers carry their newborns ventrally, but after the first few weeks, infants travel clinging to their mothers' backs (Figure 14.54). Mothers wean their infants during the wet season when they are six to 12 months old and during this time can be seen pushing offspring away from the nipple and shrugging them off when they try to "climb aboard."

At Bezà-Mahafaly in the southwest, *P. verreauxi* youngsters take up to five years to reach full size, and animals continue to gain weight for a further five years. A few females in these forests give birth for the first time when they are three years old, but fewer than half have reproduced by the age of six years (Richard et al. 2002). Under more favorable conditions, animals mature faster. At Berenty, for example, three-year-old females are quite commonly observed with newborns (Jolly 1966). At Ranomafana, in the eastern moist evergreen forest, a female *P. diadema* known to be four years old gave birth, and this was also the age at first birth reported for *P. candidus* (Patel 2009). For many of the more recently recognized species, age at first birth and/or sexual maturity are not known. Life span is unknown for most species but, when reported, usually falls between 25 and 35 years. For example, estimated life span for *P. candidus* is 25–30 years (Patel 2009), for *P. edwardsi* 32 years (P. C. Wright et al. 2012), and for *P. verreauxi* 34 years (Bronikowski et al. 2016).

Infant mortality is high in *Propithecus*. Over a ten-year period at Ranomafana, 43% of all *P. edwardsi* infants died before they were a year old, and data from *P. verreauxi* in the Bezà-Mahafaly yield similar results. Predation appears to be an important cause of mortality in all age groups wherever relatively intact populations of predators are present (see Goodman and Ganzhorn, pp. 1829–38). *Cryptoprocta ferox* preys on all species in the *P. diadema* group, as well as *P. tattersalli* (Irwin 2006). Up to a third of infants born annually in the *P. verreauxi* population in the dry deciduous Kirindy Forest CNFEREF may be lost to predation by *C. ferox* (Rasoloarison et al. 1995). Evidence from nest sites shows that *Polyboroides radiatus* (Madagascar Harrier-hawk) consumes *P. verreauxi* individuals of all sizes (Karpanty and Goodman 1999); several researchers have witnessed attempted predation, and the dramatic response of these lemurs to the presence of raptors overhead suggests that harrier-hawks take individuals alive. At Ranomafana, *P. edwardsi* infants were killed by infanticidal males (Morelli et al. 2009), and episodes of infanticide in *P. verreauxi* have been witnessed at Bezà-Mahafaly and Kirindy Forest CNFEREF (Lewis et al. 2003; Littlefield 2010), but the frequency and demographic impact of these events are unknown. Other causes of death among infants include lactational failure, falls, and possibly hypothermia during the winter.

FORAGING BEHAVIOR AND DIET

Propithecus species resemble other members of the family Indriidae in possessing specializations for a diet with a high leaf content. Their teeth are well suited to slicing and grinding up fibrous materials, and their capacious stomach and intestines facilitate digestion. Observations of feeding behavior both confirm and elaborate

the picture provided by morphology alone. At certain times, leaves dominate the diet of *Propithecus*, but their importance varies widely from month to month and from year to year, apparently depending on what other foods are available. For example, members of a group of *P. edwardsi* at Ranomafana spent 78% of their feeding time on leaves in June and 42% in July 1992. The year before, however, the equivalent percentages were 17% and 11% (Hemingway 1995, 1996). Similarly wide swings have been reported for *P. verreauxi* (Richard 1978). All members of the genus derive much of their diet from a quite narrow spectrum of plant species. Indeed, it is curious that despite huge ecological differences between the forests in which they live and little or no overlap in the identity of plant species eaten, lemurs of the genus *Propithecus* everywhere seem to feed from a total of 75–100 plant species and to spend 60–80% of their time feeding on about 10% of these species.

Similarities notwithstanding, the dietary habits of members of the genus do show some variations, particularly with respect to the kinds of food eaten in addition to leaves. *Propithecus diadema* and *P. tattersalli* feed heavily on seeds, discarding the flesh of the fruits as they do so. Indeed, seed predation accounts for over 50% of feeding time in *P. tattersalli* and 30–35% of feeding time in *P. diadema* (Meyers 1993; Hemingway 1995). *Propithecus verreauxi* likewise destroys most of the seeds it consumes (Ralisoamalala 1996), but compared to its congeners spends more time eating whole fruits, and it is uncommon to see it discarding the flesh (Ranarivelo 1993). Dietary differences have also been documented within a species based on the degree of habitat disturbance. For example, Arrigo-Nelson (2006) found that groups of *P. edwardsi* in logged forests ate more leaves, as well as food items less rich in nutrients and calories, compared to groups in undisturbed forests.

MOLECULAR ECOLOGY

Since the early 2000s, genetic studies have contributed to our understanding of the biology and conservation of *Propithecus*. Several studies characterizing nuclear microsatellite markers and mtDNA variation in *Propithecus* species have been conducted. These data have subsequently been used in several contexts, including the clarification of alpha taxonomy (Mayor et al. 2004) and phylogenetic relationships of species/subspecies within the genus (Pastorini et al. 2001b). Markers isolated by these studies have also been used to explore population structure, kinship, and paternity (e.g., concerning *P. verreauxi*, see Lawler et al. 2003; Kappeler and Schäffler 2008), and for questions related to social behavior and dispersal (e.g., concerning *P. edwardsi*, see Morelli et al. 2009).

Genetic studies have also been used for conservation purposes, such as characterizing levels of genetic diversity across sample sites to assess population fragmentation and gene flow (Quéméré et al. 2010a; Salmona et al. 2015). For example, a major river rather than a national road has been found to impede gene flow among groups of *P. tattersalli* (Quéméré et al. 2010a); these authors also found that geographic proximity (isolation by distance) was a major driver of genetic structure among groups/subpopulations and that individuals were likely able to disperse across a fragmented landscape.

Documenting the historical dynamics of imperiled populations, via genetics, is important for both taxonomic and conservation purposes. Past population bottlenecks may shape current levels of genetic diversity, which in turn provides a basis for diagnosing new species or elevating subspecies to specific status (Lawler 2018), and on the conservation front, historical demography illuminates whether and how a particular population has rebounded from past perturbations. Lawler (2011) used genetic data to examine past changes in the size of a population of *P. verreauxi* in the southwest, finding that the population was larger in the past than today. For another example, Salmona et al. (2017) employed a variety of models to examine the historical factors influencing population size in *P. tattersalli* and *P. perrieri*; these authors found that both climatic and anthropogenic factors played a role in shaping historical population dynamics of these two species.

The scope and influence of genetic studies continue to grow. For example, nuclear sequence variation has recently been used to explore the role of color-vision polymorphism in foraging, with the discovery of novel alleles in the X-linked opsin gene in *P. edwardsi*, *P. diadema*, and *P. candidus* (R. L. Jacobs et al. 2017). Genomic studies are replacing multi-locus genetic approaches that use microsatellites and/or mtDNA, and future studies will undoubtedly focus on whole-genome or whole-exome (coding regions) analyses of all individuals. This will improve the statistical power and resolution of "traditional" molecular analyses as well as open up new avenues of investigation including genotype-phenotype relationships, epigenetics, microbiome studies, and whole-genome comparisons across lemurs and other primates.

CONSERVATION

With populations of all *Propithecus* species showing downward trends in numbers, the latest IUCN Red List assessment (IUCN 2020) lists all species as Critically Endangered, with the exception of *P. edwardsi*, which is considered Endangered. Across the genus, the major threat is habitat destruction, which occurs in many contexts, notably mining, charcoal production, agriculture, logging, and burning to improve pasture. Many species are also hunted (cf. Dunham et al. 2008). On a more sanguine note, some successful translocation/reintroduction programs are underway. Day et al. (2009) successfully translocated *P. diadema* from sites with significant habitat degradation to the Analamazaotra Special Reserve. King et al. (2011–2012) outlined a plan to translocate *P. coronatus* as part of the larger Projet Tsibahaka conservation initiative.

CONCLUSION

Modern research on *Propithecus* began in the early 1960s (J.-J. Petter 1962), and the members of this genus are among the most intensively studied of all lemurs today. Yet, much remains to be learned, not only to advance our understanding of their biology and behavior but also, and most critically, to enhance efforts to conserve them.

Subject editors: Jörg U. Ganzhorn and Steven M. Goodman

DAUBENTONIIDAE: *DAUBENTONIA MADAGASCARIENSIS*, AYE-AYE, *AYE-AYE*

E. J. Sterling, T. Sefczek, G. Perry, J. N. Rakotondrazandry, F. Ravelomandrato, and E. E. Louis Jr.

A curious constellation of morphological and behavioral traits marks *Daubentonia madagascariensis*, also known as the Aye-aye, one of Madagascar's most remarkable mammals. Comparatively little is known about this species, however. Prior to the 1980s, no sustained, long-term research had been undertaken on wild populations of *Daubentonia*, although a team of researchers had observed individuals during short field stays in the 1950s and 1960s (J.-J. Petter and Petter 1967; J.-J. Petter and Peyriéras 1970b; J.-J. Petter 1977; J.-J. Petter et al. 1977). During the 1980s, several researchers undertook field studies of a few days to two years in duration, which enhanced our knowledge of the animal's distribution, diet, habitat preference, locomotor style, and social behavior (reviewed by Sterling 2003). Since the publication of the *D. madagascariensis* contribution in the precursor of this book (Sterling 2003), important advances have been made in the natural history of this species. In particular, the Madagascar Biodiversity Partnership started a long-term monitoring program on *Daubentonia* in the moist evergreen forests of Torotorofotsy and Kianjavato, in 2008 and 2010, respectively. These studies have further elucidated information on diet, home range, and activity budget of this species in eastern moist evergreen forests (Sefczek et al. 2017, 2020a; Randimbiharinirina et al. 2018).

MORPHOLOGY AND TAXONOMY

The large body size, relative to other nocturnal primates; rodent-like, continuously growing anterior dentition; clawed digits; inguinal mammary glands; and nictitating membrane set *Daubentonia* apart from all other primates. Its dexterous, filiform middle finger, which rotates 360 degrees around the metacarpal joint, resembles that of no other living animal except *Dactylopsila trivirgata*, an Australian marsupial. Other characteristic features of the morphology of *Daubentonia* include a two-layer pelage consisting of a thick, short, cream-colored underlayer and an overlayer of long, coarse blackish-brown guard hairs; long naked ears; a short, large head; robust musculature in the neck, shoulders, and arms; longer hind limbs than forelimbs; specialized intrinsic hand musculature; and an unusual wrist bone and cartilaginous protuberance, deemed a "pseudothumb," with three distinct muscles that move it (J.-J. Petter 1977; Soligo 2005; Hartstone-Rose et al. 2019). On average, adults weigh close to 2.5 kg (Feistner and Sterling 1995), making *D. madagascariensis* the largest nocturnal lemur.

Although subfossil remains of a larger species, *D. robusta*, about five times the size of *D. madagascariensis*, have been found in southwestern Madagascar (Jungers et al. 2008; see Godfrey and Jungers, pp. 1824–28), *D. madagascariensis* is the only living member of its family, Daubentoniidae. The taxonomic position of *Daubentonia* was long disputed (Sterling 1994b), but genetic and recent genomic and morphological analyses have strongly confirmed that this taxon, while distantly related to all other extant lemurs, is a member of Lemuroidea to the exclusion of Lorisoidea (A. D. Yoder et al. 1996b; Perry et al. 2012a; Gunnell et al. 2018). Recent genomic studies of this species indicate that nuclear-genome genetic diversity is relatively low compared to that of other lemurs (Perry et al. 2012a, 2012b). Genetic divergence among northern, eastern, and western populations of *D. madagascariensis* is not sufficiently distinct to warrant subspecies classification (Perry et al. 2013; Aylward et al. 2018).

DISTRIBUTION

A common and recurring misconception in the early literature was that *Daubentonia* populations are restricted to eastern coastal forests below 200 m elevation (e.g., J.-J. Petter and Peyriéras 1970b; Poorman-Allen and Izard 1990). This would constitute one of the most restricted ranges among extant lemur species. However, this overlooks historical records that noted Aye-aye populations on the west and east coasts and in the Central Highlands (Sonnerat 1782; Lamberton 1910). Additional confirmed sightings of Aye-ayes show that they exist in the moist evergreen forests from Ampanefana in the north to Andohahela in the south and in the west from Montagne d'Ambre to Bemaraha (Sterling 2003). In the end, *D. madagascariensis* may be one of the most widely distributed primate species on Madagascar, but its population density appears to be low in any one place (E. Sterling and E. E. Louis Jr., unpublished data).

HABITAT USE

Daubentonia seems to be able to adapt to a number of different habitat types, from moist evergreen forests (Ganzhorn and Rabesoa 1986a, 1986b) to dry deciduous forests (Iwano et al. 1991), from largely intact forest (Sterling 1993; Andriamasimanana 1994; Sefczek et al. 2017) to degraded patchy forests and plantations (J.-J. Petter 1977; Ancrenaz et al. 1994; Andriamasimanana 1994; Randimbiharinirina et al. 2018). To date, there is no record of *D. madagascariensis* in the dry spiny thickets, where *D. robusta* subfossil remains have been found. It has been suggested that the distribution—or at least population density—of *D. madagascariensis* is tied to the distribution of one of its resources, seeds of *Canarium* spp. (Burseraceae) (Iwano et al. 1991); however, Aye-ayes have been reported in areas where this tree genus does not grow (Sterling 1998).

The positional repertoire of *Daubentonia* is particularly diverse. Along with typical arboreal and terrestrial quadrupedal movements of most primates (climbing, walking, running, leaping, etc.), it is capable of quadrumanous suspension, descending vertically headfirst (Figure 14.55), tailfirst, or sideways, and vertical clinging and

leaping (Ancrenaz et al. 1994; Curtis and Feistner 1994). In fact, this species is the largest primate known to employ headfirst vertical descent, a positional behavior achievable because of the musculoskeletal adaptations of its neck, shoulders, and arms (Soligo 2005). This array of positional behaviors likely evolved because *Daubentonia* is an exploratory feeder (Teichroeb and Vining 2019). Given that saproxylic larvae, a primary resource in this animal's diet, can occur in almost every forest stratum, these positional behaviors likely help *Daubentonia* maximize encounters with wood-boring larvae. However, these positional behaviors may also help *Daubentonia* access a variety of other resources as well (Ancrenaz et al. 1994), enabling a variable and flexible diet.

DIET

Recent studies of *Daubentonia* have identified invertebrates, particularly saproxylic larvae, as the most frequently consumed resource, often comprising over 65% of the diet (Randimbiharinirina et al. 2018; Sefczek et al. 2020a). Though invertebrates may constitute the majority of its diet, *Daubentonia* can have a varied and flexible diet, including the seeds of indigenous fruits such as those of *Canarium* spp. (A. F. A. Hawkins et al. 1990; Iwano et al. 1991; Goodman and Sterling 1996), *Orania trispatha* (Arecaceae) (D. Halleux and H. Morland, unpublished data), and *Terminalia catappa* (Combretaceae) (Sterling et al. 1994); beetle and moth larvae embedded in trees and bamboo, including those of the families Cerambicidae (Lamiinae, Prioninae), Scarabidae (Dynastinae), Passalidae, and Pyralidae (Phycitinae; Sterling 1993, 1994a); a cankerous growth on *Intsia bijuga* (Fabaceae); nectar from *Ravenala* (Strelitziaceae); and various cultivated crops such as coconuts, lychees, and mangoes (J.-J. Petter 1977).

FIGURE 14.55 A young male *Daubentonia madagascariensis* in Kianjavato travels down bamboo in a headfirst descent. (PHOTO by R. L. Randrianasolo.)

Aye-aye is one of the few primates that defies expectations related to diet and body-size predictions. It is widely accepted that, among primates, body size of insectivorous animals should not exceed 350 g (Kay 1975, 1984; Kay and Covert 1984). However, weighing 2.5 kg on average, *Daubentonia* relied on invertebrates for over 65% of its diet at Kianjavato (Randimbiharinirina et al. 2018) and almost 90% of its diet at Torotorofotsy (Sefczek et al. 2020a). It is likely that the species of larvae consumed by *D. madagascariensis* have high fat and crude protein content (Sterling et al. 1994; McGrew 2014; Rothman et al. 2014), thus helping it to maintain a larger body size on a primarily insectivorous diet.

Daubentonia may specialize on structurally defended resources (e.g., embedded within trees, as with wood-boring larvae, or within a hard coat, as some seeds) that are unavailable to most other vertebrates (Sterling 1994a). It uses its continuously growing anterior teeth and spindly middle finger, separately or in combination, to exploit food resources. Individuals gnaw on the endocarp of *Canarium* and *T. catappa* seeds with their anterior teeth and then extract the cotyledon with their slender middle finger. Insect larvae are removed from fallen deadwood, standing trees (Figure 14.56), intact dead branches, beneath the bark of living trees, bamboo, dead and living lianas, and inside parasitized seeds. Individual animals use their middle digit to tap along the surface of a tree to help locate insect larvae. They then use their anterior teeth to pry open the surface and their middle finger to hook and pull out the larvae (Erickson 1991, 1998). This foraging behavior is known as percussive foraging or tap-scanning (Erickson 1991; Erickson et al. 1998). Aye-ayes have been known to spend 5–41% of their foraging time on percussive foraging (Sterling and McCreless 2006).

Daubentonia is relatively encephalized and reported to have high levels of sensorimotor intelligence (Sterling and Povinelli 1999); its morphology also points to exceptional hearing abilities (Ramsier and Dominy 2012). Due to the morphology of the third digit, the majority of the intrinsic hand muscles (30–32%) are contained within the fourth digit, which it uses, along with its claws, to grip substrates when positioned vertically (Soligo 2005). *Daubentonia* uses its anterior teeth to scrape off and consume a waxy substance—either a gall or a fungus—from the trunks and limbs of *Intsia bijuga*. Nectar from *Ravenala* is scooped out from the flower with rapid back-and-forth movements of the thin middle finger.

NESTS

Daubentonia sleeps during the day in oval-shaped nests located 7–20 m from the ground in a tree fork or in a liana tangle (J.-J. Petter

FIGURE 14.56 **A tree with signs of *Daubentonia madagascariensis* extractive foraging for wood-boring insect larvae in the Loky Manambato protected area near the village of Daraina in northern Madagascar.** (PHOTO by G. Perry.)

1977; J.-J. Petter and Petter 1967). Constructed of branches and lianas from contiguous vegetation, nests are frequently refreshed with new vegetation. Sometimes this species will occupy a nest for a few days at a time (or more than a month for females after parturition; J. N. Rakotondrazandry, unpublished data), while at other times it will change nests every night, not reusing a nest for an extended period. Multiple individuals may use the same nest at different times.

HOME RANGE

Home-range size of *Daubentonia* varies, depending on habitat. For example, on Nosy Mangabe, an island of 520 ha, females ranged over 30–40 ha and males 125–215 ha, with nightly range lengths from 819 to 4392 m (Sterling 1993). These animals were also observed traveling and foraging on the ground more often than any other lemur except *Lemur catta* (Richard and Dewar 1991; Sterling 1993). In the disturbed moist evergreen forest of Kianjavato, a female home range was approximately 98 ha and those of males were 821–973 ha (Randimbiharinirina et al. 2018), while in the undisturbed moist evergreen forest of Torotorofotsy, a female home range was estimated at 756 ha and a male home range was estimated at 2586 ha (Sefczek et al. 2020b). Furthermore, at Torotorofotsy, Aye-ayes rarely traveled on the ground, spending most of their time in the canopy and exploring the vertical space between the understory and the canopy (Sefczek 2018).

SOCIAL SYSTEM

Social organization of *Daubentonia* appears to be more complex than often thought, given that it is frequently portrayed as a "solitary" species. There is evidence of sustained tandem foraging sessions and differing relations between individuals of the same sex (Sterling and Richard 1995). When mating, female Aye-ayes exhibit a repetitive pattern of traveling swiftly over 500–1000 m and then sitting for an hour emitting a characteristic loud call that males respond to by running toward the female. Males chase and fight one another, and females repel some mating attempts while accepting others. A single female is in estrus for only a few days. Data from the wild and captivity indicate that *Daubentonia* may not exhibit the highly seasonal breeding pattern seen in other Malagasy primates. Although it appears that individual females may come into estrus only once per year—perhaps at the same time each year—not all females cycle or become pregnant at the same time. Populations may have either two birth peaks per year or no seasonality to breeding and births across individuals (Sterling 1994c). Little data are available regarding number of young and interbirth interval, but it appears that one young is born at a time. Researchers have identified at least nine different vocalizations for *Daubentonia*, though one of these vocalizations, the "screech" or "cree" call, encompasses considerable acoustic variation and seems to function in several disparate contexts (J.-J. Petter and Petter 1967; J.-J. Petter 1977; Stanger and Macedonia 1994).

CONSERVATION

Because of this species' nocturnal, cryptic habits and researchers' inability to assess density from secondary signs such as feeding remains or nests, there is a paucity of accurate records on the abundance and distribution of *Daubentonia* in the wild. Indeed, a population estimate for this species has never been determined, in large part because of its dispersed polygynous sociality and enormous home ranges. Additionally, the degree of adaptability it has demonstrated, especially in the variability of its home-range size in fragmentary forests, precludes an accurate estimation of population density for the species across its range.

Never thought to exist at high population densities, the species was presumed extinct in the 1930s (J.-J. Petter and Peyriéras 1970b). In 1957, researchers "rediscovered" Aye-ayes in the Ambato Mahambo Forest on the east coast, where a reserve was subsequently created to protect what were then considered the last remaining Aye-ayes in the world (J.-J. Petter and Petter 1967). Six years later the researchers returned to find a road built through the middle of the reserve and no signs of *Daubentonia* (J.-J. Petter and Peyriéras 1970b).

Concerned that the species was facing extinction, the government of Madagascar in 1965 set aside Nosy Mangabe in the Antongil Bay to serve as a *D. madagascariensis* refugium. Nine Aye-ayes (four males and five females) were trapped from coastal forests between Toamasina and Maroantsetra and released onto Nosy Mangabe in 1966–1967. No information is available regarding whether the species existed on the island at that time. The first reports of the success of this conservation effort emerged in the 1970s, when both adults and juveniles were seen on the island (Bomford 1976, 1981). In the mid-1980s, UNESCO began working with the Malagasy government and the Parc Zoologique de Vincennes in Paris to set up an Aye-aye reserve in the Manana-Nord region. In 1989, a 140,000 ha reserve was established there by presidential decree (Albignac 1992).

Habitat destruction and killing by humans are the primary threats to *Daubentonia* populations (Sterling and Feistner 2000). Animals are occasionally killed when raiding crops from gardens, but the greatest threat appears to be local taboos, or *fady*. These *fady* vary from village to village, even within the same geographic region; when an Aye-aye is sighted, the villagers may be obliged to kill the animal, burn down the village, and move, or they may believe that Aye-ayes are embodiments of ancestral spirits, accorded all the rites of a grand chieftain at death (Sterling and Feistner 2000; E. L. Simons and Meyers 2001; Koenig 2005). Given our inability to track the densities of these animals, it is difficult to estimate the effects that these threats have at the level of populations.

Despite this species' wide distribution and location in a number of protected areas (Goodman et al. 2018b), its taxonomic uniqueness combined with the assumption of critically low wild population sizes and restricted ranges, prompted conservationists to rank *Daubentonia* among the highest primate conservation priorities in the world (C. Schwitzer et al. 2019). A number of legal and other measures, both within Madagascar and internationally, accord *Daubentonia* the highest level of protection available to a species. The Malagasy government declared all lemurs "protected" in 1927. *Daubentonia* is listed under Class A of the Africa Convention (Organization of African Unity 1968), is on Appendix I of the CITES convention, is listed as Endangered on the IUCN Red List (IUCN 2020), is classified as "critical" by the Prosimian Taxon Advisory Group, and is identified as a top 25 most endangered primate by the IUCN Species Survival Commission Primate Specialist Group, the International Primatological Society, and Conservation International (C. Schwitzer et al. 2019). These classifications remain highly contentious, as population estimates are still unattainable.

CONCLUSION

Although we have increased our knowledge of behavioral ecology and conservation of *Daubentonia* considerably since the 1990s, we still need more detailed information on the species' on social and reproductive behavior, its resource use in the drier habitats of the west, and a clearer understanding of its distribution—where it is found and why. Much remains to be done before we can develop appropriate conservation efforts for this species.

ACKNOWLEDGMENTS

The work on Nosy Mangabe would not have been possible without the collaboration of V. Baba, B. Damary, F. Toto, and B. Carlson. A special thanks to the Madagascar Biodiversity Partnership aye-aye monitoring local team members at Torotorofotsy Vohitsara (H. Razafimahaleo, M. Ravelojanahary, D. Faralahy, D. Janson, H. Randrianjatovo, F. Randriatsimialona, O. Randrianarison, H. Randriamaronirina, J. Randriamarohova, T. Randrianantenaina, J. Randrianarison, and E. Rajonatana) and Kianjavato (H. Fanoharanomenjanahary, S. Rakotomalala, W. Randriamihaja, S. Randrianirina, E. Razafindrazefa, Y. Razafimandimby, R. Randrianasolo, P. Ratsimbazafy, M. Tsamboto, L. Arnel, S. Randriambololona, J. Randrianasolo, N. Randrianajafy, A. Levola, H. Randriamampionona, and V. Donné) field sites, and the immobilization technical team based at Ranomafana (R. Randriamampionona, F. Razafimanjato, J. R. Rakotonomenjanahary, J. C. Randriamanana, F. Randrianasolo, R. Randrianasolo, G. Nalanirina, J. L. Razafindravelo, J. Andriamadison, J. C. Rakotoniaina, J. Miandrisoa, H. Razafimahatratra, J. Razafindramanana, and J. A. Andriamihaja), who helped to make this research possible.

Subject editors: Jörg U. Ganzhorn and Steven M. Goodman

EUPLERIDAE: *CRYPTOPROCTA FEROX*, FOSA, *FOSA*

B. D. Gerber and C. E. Hawkins

Cryptoprocta ferox (Fosa) is a semiarboreal, euplerid carnivoran and Madagascar's largest extant terrestrial predator. Somewhat resembling a small, slender Puma or Cougar (*Puma concolor*, Felidae), it possesses distinctive characteristics including transient juvenile female masculinization and an unusual, "super-polyandrous" mating system. The female is solitary, but males may form dyadic associations that benefit their hunting and mating success. The species is hypercarnivorous, predating mainly on lemurs and secondarily on other vertebrates and occasionally invertebrates, but within these bounds the diet is highly diverse and considered to relate to prey abundance.

Cryptoprocta ferox is endemic to Madagascar, throughout which it may be found in minimally disturbed forest areas and, to a lesser extent, thicket vegetation. It is generally absent where these native vegetation types are significantly modified or fragmented. The species is listed as Vulnerable by the IUCN (2020), with an estimated global population of between 2635 and 8626 adults. A wide range of threats means that it is likely to be declining in abundance and distribution. Its primary threat is forest habitat loss and degradation, which is typically associated with a subsequent increase in additional threats, such as persecution (for poultry predation), consumption for bushmeat, and competition from introduced carnivorans.

TAXONOMY

The phylogeny of *Cryptoprocta* and all native euplerids has been the subject of numerous studies, with differing conclusions about their family and the structure of their genera and species. Both the genus and species of *C. ferox* were originally described by E. T. Bennett (1833, 1835), who classified the animal as a viverrid. Currently, the agreed phylogeny is based on a multi-gene phylogenetic analysis that places all native Malagasy carnivorans in the monophyletic family Eupleridae, which separated 18–24 Mya from Herpestidae in a single event colonization of Madagascar (A. D. Yoder et al. 2003; also see Veron et al., pp. 1863–65). The name *Cryptoprocta*, derived from the Greek *krypto* (to hide or conceal) and *proktos* (anus), refers to the anus being surrounded by, and thereby somewhat hidden within, a pouch; *ferox* means to be wild, bold, fierce, defiant, or arrogant, befitting the character of this top predator.

Earlier in the Holocene epoch, *C. ferox* coexisted with the larger-bodied *C. spelea*, which is now extinct. The exact timing of this extinction is unknown—though it occurred sometime in the past 2000 years, coinciding generally with Madagascar's large-animal mass extinction (see Godfrey and Douglass, pp. 191–97). *Cryptoprocta spelea* is believed to have occurred throughout most ecoregions (Central Highlands, dry deciduous forests, dry spiny thickets, and presumably moist evergreen forests) (Meador et al. 2019). Paleontological studies have estimated the body mass of *C. spelea*, at 10–15 kg, to be notably greater than that of *C. ferox*, at 5.5–11.5 kg (Meador et al. 2019). Further, *C. spelea* had more robust teeth and long bones and a longer skull length than its living counterpart (Muldoon et al. 2009; Meador et al. 2019). Its relatively large size and congruent anatomy with felid ambush predators of large prey suggest that *C. spelea* would have been able to predate on large-bodied primates weighing up to ~85 kg, but it more often consumed primates of smaller size (Meador et al. 2019).

MORPHOLOGY AND FIELD SIGNS

Cryptoprocta ferox is the largest extant native carnivoran on Madagascar, contending with the Indri (*Indri indri*; average 6.5 kg; see Gamba et al., pp. 1967–71) as the largest extant terrestrial native mammal on Madagascar. In adulthood, it measures on average 1.4 m in total length, with a head-and-body length of 60–80 cm and a similar tail length, 65–75 cm (Albignac 1975; Köhncke and Leonhardt 1986). While slightly smaller than the extinct *C. spelea*, it is still several times larger than the second-largest euplerid carnivoran, *Fossa fossana* (1.3–1.9 kg; see Kerridge et al., pp. 1986–89). Most body-size measurements of wild individuals of *C. ferox* come from the dry deciduous forests, in which there is evidence of sexual dimorphism (C. E. Hawkins 1998). Adult males are recorded as averaging 7.4 ± 1.20 kg (n = 17) (Kirindy Forest CNFEREF; C. E. Hawkins 1998) and 7.4 ± 2.02 kg (n = 23) (Ankarafantsika and Kirindy Mité National Parks; Dollar 2006), and adult females 6.1 ± 0.6 kg (n = 11) (Kirindy Forest CNFEREF; C. E. Hawkins 1998) and 6.4 ± 1.1 kg (n = 10) (Ankarafantsika and Kirindy Mité; Dollar 2006). There is also evidence in this region of two male morphotypes, in which associated males were heavier (9.6 ± 0.8 kg, n = 9) than solitary males (7.3 ± 0.7 kg, n = 8), which were more similar in body mass to females (7.2 ± 0.8 kg, n = 7) (Lührs et al. 2013). An adult male *C. ferox* captured in the moist evergreen forest had a body mass of 8.1 kg (Dollar 1999).

This quadrupedal, semiarboreal species has a long, slender, muscular body and a tail of similar length. The tail is not prehensile but instead acts to counterbalance the body during the complex arboreal locomotion (Laborde 1986a, 1986b) required for a specialist in lemur predation. When running, *C. ferox* uses only its toes, via digitigrade locomotion, but when walking or moving arboreally, the heels also become involved, in plantigrade locomotion (Albignac 1973). The semi-retractile claws are used for grasping prey and climbing trees (Köhncke and Leonhardt 1986); claws are not sheathed completely, as in felids, but do not necessarily contact the ground when the animal is walking or running. Its hairless paw pads, which extend almost to the heels, together with its mobile or "reversible" ankles, enable *C. ferox* to securely grasp both sides of a tree trunk when ascending, descending (headfirst), or jumping to an adjacent trunk. In captivity, a young *C. ferox* is capable of swinging upside down from a knotted rope, gripping the knot with the hind feet alone. It is also capable of moving suspended underneath a tree branch, grasping with the fore- and hind limbs. Large trees are scaled by jumping from the hind legs and grasping the trunk with the forelimbs. Jumping from branch to branch often starts in a crouch, with the hind feet just behind the forefeet; the forefeet land first, and the tail acts to balance the body through the air.

Cryptoprocta ferox is commonly said to resemble a small Puma. The head is relatively small, with prominent round ears, and large, rich mid-brown eyes with slit pupils; the muzzle is short and broad, with long facial vibrissae (whiskers) and a prominent nose. The dentition and jaw structure are typical of a mammalian hypercarnivore, with a shortened braincase, enlarged carnassial teeth, and only a single upper molar. Reflected in torchlight or car headlights, the eyes appear as two orange circles spaced relatively widely apart. This orange color distinguishes *C. ferox* from dogs, the eyes of which are commonly reflected as cyan. Its dorsal pelage is generally uniform sepia brown, with no spot patterns, while the ventral pelage is light brown to cream-colored. The ventral pelage, especially the areas between the forelimbs and hind limbs, can be stained with varying amounts of an orange secretion, turning it orange to dark brown in males of all ages and in subadult females (Vosseler 1929; C. E. Hawkins et al. 2002). The secretion is produced by sternal glands, likely as a means for scent marking. Other scent glands can be found near the penis or vulva and on the neck. The existence of individuals with black dorsal pelage has been speculated (Köhncke and Leonhardt 1986); however, no evidence based on field observations or

specimens is available, and such observations may be misidentified feral domestic cats or introduced wildcats (Borgerson 2013; Farris et al. 2016). The body hairs are dorsally relatively short, straight, and dense, with thinning near the armpits, inner leg areas, and the groin.

The juvenile female *C. ferox* exhibits a period of transient masculinization between one and two years of age, such that it shares several hormonal and morphological features with the male that the adult female lacks (C. E. Hawkins et al. 2002). As first noted in two museum specimens, the clitoris of the juvenile female is partly covered with spines and supported by a small bone. It is proportionately much larger than that of the adult female. Juvenile female masculinization does not appear to be dependent on androgen hormones (C. E. Hawkins et al. 2002). It appears to correspond to age at independence (about one year of age) from the mother and is hypothesized to reduce adult aggression by males and/or females. In females, the uterus is paired, each with its own cervix (Köhncke and Leonhardt 1986), and there are three pairs of functional nipples.

In males, the testes are prominent (the ratio of testes volume to body size exceeds that of many other carnivorans; Lührs and Kappeler 2014), and the penis has a sheath that covers hard spines along the basal two-thirds of its length (see Goodman 2012: Figure 45), supported by a bone that has a mean length of 73 mm (n = 17; C. E. Hawkins et al. 2002).

Tracks may be recognized as five evenly spaced hairless pads around a large central pad. A dog's paw mark may be the same size, but only four outer pads are evident, and the middle two of these pads are relatively close together, often with the visible claws. The scats of *C. ferox* are distinctive gray cylinders with twisted ends, typically 10–14 cm long and 1.5–2.5 cm wide. They are most commonly composed of hair and bone fragments, although they may also entirely comprise tenrec (Tenrecinae) spines. Fresh scats have a strong, musky smell. While the domestic dog occasionally produces scats similar to those of *C. ferox*, these tend to be broader, with rounded ends, contain little or no hair, and when fresh, have a much stronger odor. In dry areas, *C. ferox* scats are easily found, but in wet environments (e.g., moist evergreen forests) they can disintegrate quickly with rainfall or be dismantled or buried by invertebrates.

MATING AND REPRODUCTION

The vast majority of information on mating behavior in *C. ferox* comes from dry deciduous forests, where mating appears to be seasonal, occurring between September and November (C. E. Hawkins and Racey 2009; Lührs and Kappeler 2014). Females sequentially or simultaneously use traditional mating trees, and in an unusual "super-polyandrous" mating system, they actively solicit copulations from multiple males (Lührs and Kappeler 2014), for varying lengths of time, which may reflect the female optimizing the number of males mated, enabling sperm competition and cryptic mate choice (C. E. Hawkins and Racey 2009). Copulations occur high in the mating tree and often on precarious tree limbs, allowing females to choose mates and avoid harassment. Males face both scramble and contest competition; heavier males are preferred by females. In one study, each female mated with an average of 10 males, with single copulations averaging 39 minutes, total number of copulation events averaging 41, and the total time spent mating averaging 27.5 hours (Lührs and Kappeler 2014). During copulation, the male often rests his forepaws on the female's shoulders and is very delicately balanced; if the female stands quickly, it is difficult for the male to continue mating. As in dogs, there is a tie between copulating *C. ferox* pairs, although they can pull apart with a struggle. Female solicitation often involves a characteristic vocalization: a long, plaintive meowing, reminiscent of the call of *Leptosomus discolor* (Cuckoo-roller) (Albignac 1970). Males also vocalize, giving a haunting, loud, trembling sigh when locating a female, as well as other vocalizations postcopulation and when fighting. The mating system may vary with ecoregion. Mating trees are reported to be associated with a riverbed and reliable sources of water (C. E. Hawkins and Racey 2009), which in dry deciduous forests become scarce over the dry season, thereby attracting multiple individuals.

In captivity, gestation is six to eight weeks, physical maturity is reached at two to three years of age, and sexual maturity is reached at three to four years (Albignac 1975; Vogler et al. 2009b). Two to four offspring are typically born in a litter (Albignac 1973), although six are known (A. Winkler, unpublished data). The young are raised by the mother alone, weaned at four months, and believed to gain independence at about one year of age (C. E. Hawkins et al. 2002). Independence from the mother may vary by region, as camera-trap photos from the dry deciduous forests have captured images of a female *C. ferox* traveling with two very young individuals in late June, while in moist evergreen forest areas, young *C. ferox* individuals have been captured traveling alone in June (Z. Farris, unpublished data). Females use dens or hollows during and post-birth.

All growth and development information comes from captive observations. At birth, individuals weigh approximately 100 g, are covered in light and almost white fur, lack teeth, and have closed eyes (Albignac 1969a, 1975; Köhncke and Leonhardt 1986). The eyes open at about one and a half to three weeks and are blue until six weeks of age. The juvenile incisors erupt at about a month, premolars at seven weeks, upper molars at 10 weeks, and second upper molars at 12 weeks (Mueller et al. 2007). Permanent dentition is in place at about one and a half years (Albignac 1973). Young will play with the mother frequently, mounting "attacks," in response to which she will bite back (Albignac 1975). Well-fed young gain weight linearly, reaching 2 kg in six and a half months (Mueller et al. 2007).

DIET AND PREDATION BEHAVIOR

Cryptoprocta ferox has a highly diverse diet that is likely to depend on prey abundance (C. E. Hawkins and Racey 2008; see Goodman and Ganzhorn pp. 1829–38). While it specializes in the difficult task of predating on lemurs, its prey ranges from insects (~7 g) to large-bodied lemurs (8 kg). No other nonprimate mammal includes such a high proportion of primate items in its diet.

Two concerted diet studies of wild *C. ferox* in dry deciduous forests (Dollar et al. 2007; C. E. Hawkins and Racey 2008) found a high proportion of vertebrates in the diet (approximately 90%), of which more than half were lemurs. The main prey items in one study consisted of six lemur species (particularly medium-size nocturnal lemurs: *Lepilemur*, *Phaner*, and *Mirza*), two or three spiny tenrec species, and a variety of other small mammals (C. E. Hawkins and Racey 2008). The diversity of consumed taxa also includes insects,

birds, reptiles (snakes, lizards, and tortoises), and amphibians. Dry- and wet-season diets differed markedly; *Tenrec ecaudatus* (Tailless Tenrec) makes up a much higher proportion of the diet in the wet season, and several lemur species are also eaten much more frequently in the wet season. Small numbers of seeds have been found in scats, suggesting that *Cryptoprocta* eats fruit, possibly as a water source, or obtains this material via the digestive tracts of consumed lemurs (C. E. Hawkins and Racey 2008). One systematic diet study has been carried out in medium-altitude moist evergreen forest: Rasolonandrasana (1994) analyzed scats collected in Montagne d'Ambre almost exclusively during the dry season. Lemurs were the predominant prey based on biomass, but introduced rodents (*Rattus rattus*) were more frequent in terms of the minimum number of individuals detected.

From these studies, together with analyses of smaller scat samples and observed predation events elsewhere, it is clear that *C. ferox* predates upon all small- and large-bodied lemurs (Karpanty and Wright 2007; Irwin et al. 2009), including *Indri indri* and *Propithecus edwardsi*, which are almost of equivalent size. It appears to target the most abundant prey species (C. E. Hawkins and Racey 2008). However, its predation of any one species can be clumped in time, such that it can exert a significant impact on a small population, for example, isolated by habitat fragmentation (Irwin et al. 2009). Smaller-bodied animals, including birds and insects, make up more of its diet at high-elevation montane ericoid thicket (Goodman et al. 1997c). Hunting occurs both on the ground and in trees (Dollar et al. 2007). The powerful forelimbs are used to pin the prey down as a lethal bite is administered to the back of the head or neck. One strategy is to ambush sleeping primates, biting the face, cranium, or neck.

SOCIAL BEHAVIOR AND ACTIVITY RHYTHMS

Females of *C. ferox* are generally solitary (except when caring for young) and territorial with respect to unrelated females (Köhncke and Leonhardt 1986; Lührs and Kappeler 2013). Males are mostly observed to be solitary outside of the breeding season, but in the Kirindy Forest CNFEREF, high levels of dyadic association were recorded between certain, often related, males (Lührs and Kappeler 2013). A benefit of these associations is cooperative hunting (Lührs and Dammhahn 2010) and a correspondingly greater body mass, which facilitates access to mates (Lührs and Kappeler 2014). Cooperative hunting has been also observed on one occasion at Mantadia National Park (J. Powzyk and N. Garbutt, unpublished data). Throughout moist evergreen forests, camera-trap photos have revealed male pairs traveling together during each seasonal period (Figure 14.57).

The time apportioned between the trees and the ground is likely to depend on the forest type and structure; *C. ferox* is observed more frequently in the trees in moist evergreen forests than in dry deciduous forests (J. Powzyk, unpublished data; C. E. Hawkins 1998). This may be a consequence of the lack of shade afforded to resting animals by the canopy of the latter forest type; additionally, *C. ferox* appears to find it difficult to travel through dry deciduous forest canopy.

To scent mark, animals rub the anal region on flat surfaces, including the ground, the neck region on a variety of surfaces, and the genital region (of males) on vertical surfaces such as tree trunks (Albignac 1973). Anogenital scent marking outside the mating season has been observed in captive males and juveniles but not adult females (Klockenkämper 1988). Widespread camera-trapping surveys (>20) across moist evergreen forests have recorded this scent-marking behavior, which primarily occurs from August to October.

FIGURE 14.57 Two males of *Cryptoprocta ferox* photographed by a camera trap set up by E. Wampole in Mantadia National Park.

Nonmating vocalizations include purring, meowing, growling, hissing, yelps, and a distinctive *ugk-ugk-ugk-ugk* or "muckern" call made when the animal is excited (Klockenkämper 1988).

The species' activity rhythms have been described variously as nocturnal, crepuscular, and cathemeral. Most empirical studies have shown it to be cathemeral: *C. ferox* is active throughout the diel cycle but is more frequently active during nighttime hours, and particularly dawn and dusk, than during daylight hours (Gerber et al. 2012a; Farris et al. 2015a; Merson et al. 2019a). Like many mammals, *C. ferox* tends to be more nocturnal in areas where humans and dogs are present and active (Farris et al. 2015a; Merson et al. 2019a). It is particularly active around dusk during the mating season.

SPECIES DISTRIBUTION AND POPULATION ECOLOGY

Cryptoprocta ferox is the most widely distributed endemic carnivoran on Madagascar, found throughout all forest types (western dry deciduous forests and succulent woodlands, dry spiny thickets, and moist evergreen forests). It can also be found in montane ericoid thickets above the tree line (Goodman et al. 1997c). An empirical island-wide distribution model for *C. ferox* (Goodman 2013) found a generally moderate to high probability of occurrence in the eastern moist evergreen forests, including those on the northern tip of the island, and the western dry deciduous forests. The probability of its occurrence is very low to moderate in southern dry spiny thickets, as it is in the Central Highlands, from the

south to the north of the entire island, where forests are few and agriculture and human activity dominant.

While *C. ferox* is observed most commonly in intact and protected forests (Gerber et al. 2012b), it can tolerate a small amount of habitat and anthropogenic disturbance and fragmentation. *Cryptoprocta ferox* has been observed in moist evergreen forest fragments that are near to intact forest areas (<5 km), but it may often be absent from human-dominated open landscapes and more isolated fragments (Gerber et al. 2012b; Kotschwar Logan et al. 2015). Observations of *C. ferox* in seemingly isolated fragments, such as at the Farankaraina Forest, which is approximately 15 km from the large, contiguous Masoala-Makira protected area complex (Z. Farris, unpublished data), may relate to adequate prey availability and low human persecution.

Forest structure, fragmentation, and presence of introduced carnivorans, as described below, are the features most likely to relate to *C. ferox* occurrence; however, several studies found no such associations (e.g., Farris et al. 2015b; Rasambainarivo et al. 2017). This highly mobile species can traverse large areas of contiguous forests as well as degraded and nonforested areas (C. E. Hawkins 1998; Irwin et al. 2009). Published landscape occurrence or habitat-use studies that account for sampling biases (e.g., detection probability) are confined to a select few areas: moist evergreen forests of Ranomafana National Park (Gerber et al. 2010, 2012a, 2012b; Farris et al. 2017a) and the Masoala-Makira protected area complex (e.g., Farris et al. 2015b), and dry deciduous forests of Ankarafantsika National Park and Andranomena Special Reserve (Merson 2017; Merson et al. 2020). These studies have limited spatial coverage relative to the size of the island, and sample points are close together (approximately 500 m). Thus, each of these studies may be at a scale too local to appropriately assess landscape-level factors affecting the habitat use of this highly mobile animal.

Farris et al. (2015b) did find an association between occurrence and topography, with local occurrence highest along ridges, lower in valleys, and lowest in areas along slopes. Increasing forest activity of humans and dogs was suggested as the cause of a recent dramatic decline from 2010 to 2015 in Ranomafana (Farris et al. 2017a). In the dry deciduous forests of Ankarafantsika and Andranomena, local occurrence was negatively associated with *Felis silvestris* (cat) activity (Merson et al. 2020).

On the basis of population density estimates, only the largest and truly protected forest areas are likely to host long-term viable *C. ferox* populations, as in small or unprotected forest blocks, immigration of this species may be constrained by human persecution and introduced carnivorans. Population density estimates (0.09–0.20 adults/km^2) are surprisingly low for a tropical carnivoran of this size. In dry deciduous forests, densities were estimated to be 0.18 adults/km^2 and 0.26 ind/km^2 in Kirindy Forest CNFEREF (C. E. Hawkins and Racey 2005) and 0.20 ind/km^2 in Ankarafantsika (Rahajanirina 2003). Moist evergreen forest density estimates from Ranomafana were a little lower, at 0.17 ± 0.4 ind/km^2 across a mixture of intact forest (Gerber et al. 2010) and, more specifically, 0.12 ± 0.05 adults/km^2 in intact forest and 0.09 ± 0.04 adults/km^2 in selectively logged forest (Gerber et al. 2012b). Landscape-level density estimates across varied intact and degraded areas of the Masoala-Makira protected area complex were estimated to average 0.20 adults/km^2 (Murphy et al. 2018). Annual density estimates from this area showed some variability and suggested a possible decline.

The island-wide population is estimated to comprise between 2635 and 8626 adults, from a simplistic model that accounts for forest cover (as of year 2000), fragmentation, and protected area coverage but not local-scale habitat and anthropogenic variability (Gerber et al. 2012b). About half of the population lives in two moist evergreen forest complexes in the northeast, while the other half is in 38 isolated populations in dry deciduous forests. Gerber et al. (2012b) identified the protected areas with moist evergreen forest of Masoala-Makira and Zahamena-Mantadia-Ankeniheny as the only areas to potentially hold >300 adults of *C. ferox*. The largest population of *C. ferox* is likely to be in the Masoala-Makira region, with an estimated 1061 ± 212 adults (Gerber et al. 2012b; Murphy et al. 2018). While an estimate based exclusively on protected areas may be overly conservative, since the species is known to occur in nonprotected forests, the island-wide estimate is likely much too liberal, as the model does not incorporate local-scale threats.

The genetic structure of wild populations is poorly known. The most comprehensive results indicate an overall low level of genetic polymorphism; this is likely to reflect the high mobility of *C. ferox* through forest and nonforested areas, giving it the capacity to disperse over long distances (Veron et al. 2018). Some genetic structure was found, which may be due to possible population separation by large rivers in the dry deciduous forests.

Home ranges have been exclusively studied in the dry deciduous forests, where ranges vary by sex and social organization (C. E. Hawkins 1998; Lührs and Kappeler 2013). Female and male home-range sizes in Kirindy Forest CNFEREF outside of the October–November mating season have been estimated to average approximately 20 and 37 km^2, respectively (Lührs and Kappeler 2013). Female and male home-range sizes during the mating season have been estimated to average approximately 19 and 54 km^2, respectively (Lührs and Kappeler 2013). The increase in male range size during mating season is likely to reflect the need for males to monitor multiple mating trees for the presence of receptive females. Constraints on food and water availability near the end of the dry season may also lead individuals to travel particularly long distances; in the same forest, one adult male was observed at this time to move a minimum straight-line distance of 7.3 km in 16 hours (C. E. Hawkins, unpublished data).

Female home ranges appear not to overlap with those of unrelated individuals of the same sex, while male ranges overlap with those of both males and females (C. E. Hawkins 1998; Lührs and Kappeler 2013). This species regularly uses trails, in both the dry deciduous and moist evergreen forests (C. E. Hawkins 1998; Dollar 2006); it most often uses the widest trails in the moist evergreen forest (Farris et al. 2015b). Sleep sites have been found in a variety of locations but mostly in trees.

PEOPLE AND *CRYPTOPROCTA*

Perceptions of *C. ferox* vary across regions and ethnic cultures, villages, and people within a village, but persecution of *C. ferox* is widespread (e.g., Golden et al. 2013; Merson et al. 2019b). This is primarily owing to its perceived or actual role in poultry predation (Borgerson et al. 2019a; Merson et al. 2019b). However, some people welcome the presence of *C. ferox* as a native species and predator of introduced rats (*Rattus*) (Kotschwar Logan et al. 2015).

The most comprehensive study across Madagascar found that *C. ferox* predation was the third-largest cause of annual poultry loss at the village level (Merson et al. 2019b). Poultry predation was found to be more common in areas close to dry deciduous forest during the dry season and often occurred at night. People who experienced poultry predation by *C. ferox* disliked it more and purported to kill it in retaliation. However, despite low reported predation of poultry in many villages found in close proximity to moist evergreen forest areas, the majority of interviewees still viewed *C. ferox* as harmful, primarily because of its taste for poultry (Kotschwar Logan et al. 2015). One-third of interviewees and two-thirds of communities reported hunting *C. ferox*. Many *C. ferox* individuals have been recorded on remote cameras carrying nooses from makeshift traps and with numerous scars and missing body parts (ears, lips, tails), thought to be machete wounds from locals trying to kill them for raiding livestock (F. Hawkins 2016a). Some people regard the consumption of carnivorans such as *C. ferox* as *fady* or taboo. In the former Fianarantsoa Province, this relates to the belief that *C. ferox* scavenges on the bodies of dead ancestors buried in the forest (J. P. G. Jones et al. 2008). These may be local or regional beliefs, as the prevalence of this taboo occurred among only 7.7% of interviewed households near the Makira protected area (Golden and Comaroff 2015). The consumption of *C. ferox* has nonetheless generally been found to be widespread (Golden et al. 2013; Farris et al. 2015b; Merson 2017; Borgerson et al. 2019a, 2019b). Because the species is not abundant, the rate of consumption is unlikely to be sustainable (Golden 2009).

The hunting of *C. ferox* is both targeted and opportunistic (Borgerson 2016) and may be attributable to a mixture of retaliation for livestock predation and food insecurity (Golden et al. 2014; Borgerson 2016). Notably, Malagasy have consistently ranked carnivorans, including *Cryptoprocta*, among their least preferred sources of meat, particularly when compared to fish and domestic animals (Merson 2017). At least on the Masoala Peninsula, targeted hunting of this carnivoran (in retaliation for poultry predation) occurs in the austral summer (September–February), which includes the mating season; at this time, many individuals congregate and are perhaps less wary and also more noticeable to people (Borgerson 2016). Hunting of this species is particularly frequent in Ankarafantsika and Masoala, where 3% of households hunted one or more individuals during the prior year. Across all households, a mean of 0.03 and 0.06 *Cryptoprocta* individuals were eaten per household per year in Ankarafantsika and the Masoala Peninsula, respectively (Borgerson et al. 2019a, 2019b).

DISEASE

Domestic dogs and cats may be sources of infections in native carnivorans by several pathogens (Pomerantz et al. 2016). Antibodies for *Toxoplasma* have been found in >93% of captured *C. ferox* individuals in Ankarafantsika and Kirindy Mité (Pomerantz et al. 2016). As there are no native felids on Madagascar, this suggests that there has been parasite spillover from introduced *Felis silvestris* (Rasambainarivo 2018). In *C. ferox* in captivity, encephalomyelitis caused by *T. gondii* has been found in at least one individual (Corpa et al. 2013). Low prevalence of Canine Adenovirus, Canine Distemper Virus, Canine Parvovirus, and Feline Calicivirus has also been found in the wild (Dollar 2006; Pomerantz et al. 2016).

THREATS AND CONSERVATION ACTIONS

Cryptoprocta ferox is listed as Vulnerable by the IUCN (F. Hawkins 2016a) and on Appendix II of CITES. As a highly mobile species that is widely distributed across Madagascar, it encounters a wide range of threats. Coupled with its low density, this suggests it is likely to be declining in abundance and distribution. The most significant threat is the loss and degradation of forests, which is a primary driver of endangerment for many of Madagascar's endemic flora and fauna and continues to increase in rate. For example, in the Menabe Region, where historically *C. ferox* has been considered relatively common, Zinner et al. (2014) found that annual deforestation rates more than doubled from 2003–2006 to 2008–2010 (to 2.55%) and were continuing to increase. Similarly within another stronghold, the Masoala National Park, Allnutt et al. (2013) estimated deforestation rates to have increased to 1.27% per year in 2011. Such activities, combined with illegal settlement in protected areas linked to mining and logging (F. Hawkins 2016a), tend to increase other threats in turn, such as the above-described human conflicts, road mortalities, and direct killing by domestic dogs. Other threats identified as potentially significant include competition with and predation by introduced predators including feral dogs.

The species has legal protected status on Madagascar as per Decree 2006-400 under category I, class II. This does not provide blanket protection of either the species or its habitat; hunting is allowed under authorization, commercial, sport, or regulatory conditions. It appears that many people have poor knowledge of Madagascar's species protection laws (Keane et al. 2011). Oftentimes, it is automatically believed that hunting is allowed where there is a threat to livelihood and livestock (Golden 2009).

Captive-breeding programs have been successful, first starting in France in 1874 and the United States in 1989 (Veron et al. 2018). *Cryptoprocta ferox* has been held in zoos at least since 1874 (Paris; Grzimek 1975). As of 2014, 113 individuals were held in 57 zoos (Veron et al. 2018). Well-cared-for zoo animals have been observed to live beyond 20 years (Köhncke and Leonhardt 1986).

FUTURE RESEARCH NEEDS

Madagascar's carnivorans (Eupleridae) constitute, globally, one of the most threatened and least studied families of Carnivora in the world (Brooke et al. 2014). Research priorities for *C. ferox* are to gain a better understanding of how its ecology and threats vary across this large island, to guide conservation planning and management. Survival and fecundity rates, and the impact of introduced species and direct killing on these rates, are poorly known in general, let alone their plasticity across ecoregions. Most notably, it remains to be confirmed whether dry spiny thickets support a viable population of *C. ferox*. Last, the design, trial, and promotion of an effective method to protect poultry and other livestock from *C. ferox* could be expected to reduce retaliatory killings.

Subject editor: Steven M. Goodman

EUPLERIDAE: *EUPLERES GOUDOTII*, FALANOUC, *FALANOUC*

K. Rivera, B. D. Gerber, and Z. J. Farris

Eupleres goudotii, a member of the endemic family Eupleridae, is commonly known in English as the Falanouc, Eastern Falanouc, Malagasy Mongoose, Slender Fanalouc, or Small-toothed Mongoose, and in Malagasy as the *falanouc*, *fanaloka*, *ridarida*, or *amboa laolo* (Goodman 2012). *Eupleres goudotii* is a primarily nocturnal and terrestrial carnivoran occurring in the moist evergreen forests of Madagascar (Goodman and Helgen 2010), as well as some other vegetation types (see below).

TAXONOMY

The taxonomy of *Eupleres* has been a long-term point of scientific discussion, which continues today. The most recent morphological data suggested there are two distinct, closely related species (*E. goudotii* and *E. major* or Western Falanouc), based on distinct paw structure and coat coloring as well as cranial and dental characteristics (Goodman and Helgen 2010). However, molecular analysis contradicts this conclusion, finding that samples referred to as *E. goudotii* and *E. major* fall within the range of intraspecific variation; using the principal of taxonomic priority, the clade takes the name *E. goudotii* (Veron and Goodman 2018). Limited specimens and in some cases limited genetic data may contribute to the uncertainty in this taxonomic conclusion and indicate a need for additional genetic and/or morphological sampling of wild individuals for further specificity in analysis. Herein, we follow the one-species conclusion.

FIGURE 14.58 ***Eupleres goudotii* adult in the Anjanaharibe conservation site within Makira Natural Park on 25 August 2011. The distinctive pointed rostrum, thick tail, and long, curved, nonretractile claws are visible in the image. The animal was captured on camera at 6:02 a.m., which shows that it is not an exclusively nocturnal species.** (PHOTO by Z. J. Farris.)

MORPHOLOGY

Eupleres goudotii has a stocky appearance, a long narrow snout, large ears, and a tapered cylindrical tail (Figure 14.58). Its pelage is soft and dense, its color varying from red-brown dorsally to light brown ventrally, with a more grayish head and tail. Body mass can vary dramatically by season, fluctuating between 1.5 and 4.6 kg; this is largely due to the accumulation of fat reserves in its tail, which can become rather thick (Albignac 1972a, 1972b). The increase of body fat occurs before the cold, dry season (June–August), when food resources are lacking (Albignac 1974). The head and body measure 46–50 cm in length, and the tail length adds another 22–24 cm (Goodman and Helgen 2010). The hind paw measures 80–83 mm, and the ears 40–44 mm. The teeth are small and conical, which is indicative of the species' vermivorous or other soft-invertebrate diet. The long, curved, nonretractile claws are capable of digging (Albignac 1972a, 1972b). The external morphology of eastern *E. goudotii* is said to differ from that of western *E.* "*major*" by its lighter pelage, smaller overall size (head-and-body length 610–740 cm), and footpad formation. In eastern *Eupleres goudotii*, the digital pads on the palmar surface of the forelimb are moderately developed, while the interdigital and metacarpal pads are largely fused. This is said to vary from *E.* "*major*," in which the digital pads are larger and the hypothenar and thenar pads are separated from the interdigital pads. *Eupleres* "*major*" is also noted to have a more robust skull with a longer cranium, zygomatic-arch breadth, and mandible. Additionally, *E.* "*major*" has a longer palate, shorter anterior palatal foramen, and more expansive auditory bullae. In addition, this form has a significantly larger maxillary tooth row and greater distance across the rostrum and palate (Goodman and Helgen 2010).

MATING AND REPRODUCTION

Direct observations of the reproductive activity of *Eupleres goudotii* are lacking. Albignac (1972b) proposed that copulation takes place between August and September, based on observations of birthing in November. Yet, Borgerson (2016) stated that the mating season is between October and December, and births occur in March. Camera-trap photos from Makira Natural Park have revealed mother and young (small enough to still be carried) traveling together in mid-January, suggesting a November birthing period to be most likely. Additional surveys from Mantadia National Park

showed two individuals (assumed to be female and juvenile) traveling together in late June (E. Wampole, unpublished data). Females have one pair of mammae, and litters normally consist of one pup, which is weaned at two months (Albignac 1972a). Pups are born with their eyes open, at an estimated weight of 150 g; they have a darker-color pelage than adults and begin to walk at one or two days. Around one month of age, juveniles can begin climbing trees and are able to reach higher resting locations (Ravoahangy et al. 2011). Although juveniles have been observed sleeping in trees, this behavior is unknown in adults. Females communicate with young through audible "hiccup" vocalizations. Males and females use secretions from anal and neck glands to mark territory and/or reproductive status and to convey other important communication signals among individuals (Albignac 1973).

DIET AND PREDATION

The small conical and flattened cusps in the dentition of *Eupleres* is a clear indication of a diet composed of invertebrates and other soft-bodied prey. Its long claws are well adapted to scraping food from the ground or rotting wood (Albignac 1974). Camera-trap images have captured *Eupleres* carrying and consuming large earthworms, its main food source. It also consumes insects as well as slugs, frogs, and chameleons (Albignac 1974). Villagers have also reported that *Eupleres* feeds on the fruits of *Aframomum* (Zingiberaceae).

BEHAVIOR

Numerous (n ≥ 20) and widespread camera-trapping surveys (see Farris et al., pp. 1806–11) across eastern Madagascar have confirmed that both males and females are solitary, except when females are caring for offspring; on rare occasions a mother and juvenile have been photographed traveling together. Although limited vocalizations have been observed in the wild, "coughing" and "hiccupping" have been observed in captivity. Olfactory communication is important, and individuals use prominent rocks and low vegetation to scent mark, which has been confirmed via camera-trap photos. *Eupleres* uses dens, though its thin, long claws are not suggestive of the capacity for intensive digging, and it is most likely that it occupies already existing burrows and holes. It is known to use holes or highly vegetated areas at the bases of trees for sleeping (Albignac 1973). This species appears to be highly nocturnal, using and preferring nighttime periods, with activity in crepuscular hours in proportion to available hours, while avoiding the daytime (Gerber et al. 2012a; Farris et al. 2015a; Merson et al. 2017). The use of crepuscular hours may be seasonally driven, with high use of these hours during the cool, wet season but not the hot, dry season (Farris et al. 2015a).

Eupleres is sensitive to environmental shifts. Its site-level occurrence is largely influenced by the percentage of nonforest and the distance to the nearest village (Farris et al. 2015b). Introduced free-ranging *Canis lupus* (dog) and *Viverricula indica* (Small Indian Civet) also have a negative impact on the distribution of *Eupleres*, as this endemic does not occur in sympatry with the two introduced carnivorans (Farris et al. 2015c). In fact, the probability of site-level occurrence of *Eupleres* is considerably higher at sites without free-ranging *C. lupus* present. Negative interactions with *C. lupus* are more likely to occur in patchy forest habitats (Farris et al. 2015c). *Eupleres* can co-occur at sites also used by free-ranging non-native *Felis silvestris* (cat), with unknown consequences (Farris et al. 2015c).

SPECIES DISTRIBUTION AND POPULATION ECOLOGY

Eupleres is most often associated with wetlands within dense moist evergreen forest at elevations between 50 and 600 m containing *Raphia* (Arecaceae) and *Aframomum* (Goodman 2012). However, it has also been observed along the Mandrare River in habitat described as "a mixture of spiny bush and gallery forest that receives less than 500 mm of annual precipitation" (Goodman and Helgen 2010). Throughout its range *Eupleres* is considered rare, but it can be locally common (Albignac 1972a, 1972b), as has been shown by a recent camera-trapping survey (n = 80 camera stations) within Mantadia National Park, in which *Eupleres* was captured at >50% of the surveyed sites (E. Wampole, unpublished data). Farris et al. (2015b) found the probability of site-level occurrence across Makira Natural Park to be relatively low, at 0.31. The species' occurrence was highest in areas where birds and introduced *Viverricula indica* were active. Limited trapping success in the Betampona protected area provided a site-level occupancy of only 0.03. Indirect interactions between introduced and endemic carnivorans were high at Betampona, with distance to village or research center predicting their interactions (Rasambainarivo et al. 2017). In Ranomafana National Park, Gerber et al. (2012b) found *Eupleres* to be absent from fragmented forests and to have a site-level occurrence of 0.07 in intact and 0.31 in selectively logged forested areas.

PEOPLE AND *EUPLERES*

Eupleres is poorly known and little observed across its range; village interviews conducted at Ranomafana and at Ialatsara Forestry Station showed that only 2.2% of interviewees and 17.6% of communities had observed this native carnivoran. The average distance between community centers and *Eupleres* observations was 6.3 km. Interviewee observations were limited even at villages near to continuous forest. This may be owing to the animal's rarity or its nocturnal activity (Kotschwar Logan et al. 2015). It is known to be hunted and consumed in different protected areas (Golden 2009; Farris et al. 2015b; Borgerson 2016). Borgerson (2016) found that 50% of hunters across the Masoala Peninsula targeted and incidentally hunted this carnivoran, particularly during gestation (Borgerson 2016). Farris et al. (2015b) found that 10 animals had been consumed by people across four sites in the Makira protected area between 2005 and 2011.

DISEASE

To our knowledge, there have been no formal studies investigating the disease ecology of *Eupleres*. It is assumed that *Eupleres* is likely experiencing pressures and threats from free-ranging and

introduced carnivorans—*Canis lupus*, *Felis silvestris*, and *Viverricula indica*—via disease transmission similar to those of other euplerid carnivorans (see Rasambainarivo and Zohdy, pp. 298–302).

CONSERVATION

The main threat for this species, which has an IUCN Red List status of Vulnerable, is deforestation caused by itinerant agricultural activity, logging, and charcoal production (Vieilledent et al. 2018). Over a six-year period (2008–2013) in the Makira, the site-level occurrence of *Eupleres* decreased from 0.79 to 0.20, indicating a site-level extirpation probability of 0.31 per year (Farris et al. 2015b). These drastic declines were not observed in Ranomafana, where occupancy changed from 0.09 in 2010 to 0.11 in 2015. This resulted in a colonization probability of 0.07 per year and extirpation probability of 0.59. The species' occupancy never exceeded 0.20 across this six-year period (Farris et al. 2017a, 2017b). The introduction of non-native species, including the free-ranging carnivorans *Canis lupus*, *Felis silvestris*, and *Viverricula indica*, and *Duttaphrynus melanostictus* (Black-spined Toad; see Freeman et al., pp. 1404–10), may also threaten *E. goudotii*. Brown et al. (2016) recently showed that *E. goudotii* shares several niche axes with this introduced and invasive toad, such that if the toad expands its distribution into forests occupied by *Eupleres*, it poses a novel threat owing to its toxicity, which could cause illness or death. Farris et al. (2016) found that *Eupleres* avoided areas where *C. lupus* was present. *Eupleres* also shares a similar temporal activity profile with *V. indica*, although these two species' niche requirements differ. Data on distribution of *E. goudotii* and conflict with humans are lacking, which should prompt further investigations (Kotshwar et al. 2015).

Subject editors: Jörg U. Ganzhorn and Steven M. Goodman

EUPLERIDAE: *FOSSA FOSSANA*, SPOTTED FANALOKA, *FANALOKA*

F. J. Kerridge, S. M. Goodman, and Z. J. Farris

Fossa fossana, a member of the endemic family Eupleridae, is the second-largest of Madagascar's endemic carnivorans after *Cryptoprocta ferox* (see Gerber and Hawkins, pp. 1978–83). The only recognized species in its genus, it is known from scattered localities throughout the moist evergreen forests, including the Sambirano Region (Goodman 2013), occurring at a range of elevations across this zone, from lowland to medium altitude, as well as in littoral forest, at least near Tolagnaro. While detailed population estimates (density and survival) are available for *Fossa*, important details are still lacking, including how various anthropogenic pressures (forest loss, encroachment, hunting, and introduced species) are affecting populations throughout its range.

TAXONOMY

The specific binomial of this animal has varied somewhat in the literature, and the names *Fossa fossa*, *F. daubentoni*, and *F. majori* are synonyms of *F. fossana*. There has been some previous disagreement over which subfamily or family this species should be placed in, although almost universally it had been considered a member of the family Viverridae. Albignac (1973) and G. Petter (1974) transferred this species and *Eupleres goudotii* (see Veron et al., pp. 1863–65) to the Fossinae, but the subfamily name Euplerinae has priority (Wozencraft 1993). More recent work based on molecular data indicates that the Malagasy Carnivora are monophyletic (A. D. Yoder et al. 2003; Veron et al., pp. 1863–65).

MORPHOLOGY

The pelage of this species is tan to light brown with two largely complete blackish middorsal lines, each bordered laterally by two slightly broken stripes, two rows of spots on the upper flanks, and scattered spots on the thighs. Individual animals show unique spot patterns, which allows for individual identification based on camera-trap images. The ventrum color varies from cream to light orange. The cylindrical tail is light to medium brown in ground color with a series of concentric faint dark bands or spots. The tail rings and back markings in young *Fossa* are more distinct than in adults. *Fossa* is digitigrade and relatively large bodied, with slender legs and dainty paws. Individuals have a strong, distinctive musky smell. Albignac (1973) described an anal gland, particularly well developed during the breeding season, which is presumably used in general olfactory communication and in particular to mark territories. He also suggested that these animals possess glands on the neck and cheeks that are used for similar functions. Camera-trap photos and videos have confirmed this scent-marking behavior, with *Fossa* regularly rubbing its chest and anal glands, as well as urinating, on vegetation or downed logs (Figure 14.59a).

As part of a long-term study of this species (F. J. Kerridge, unpublished data), 22 individuals were captured in the Vevembe Forest, near Vondrozo, during a two-week period at the end of July 1999. Adult males (n = 10) weighed 1.5–1.9 kg, and adult females (n = 10) weighed 1.3–1.8 kg. These weights are likely to be at the

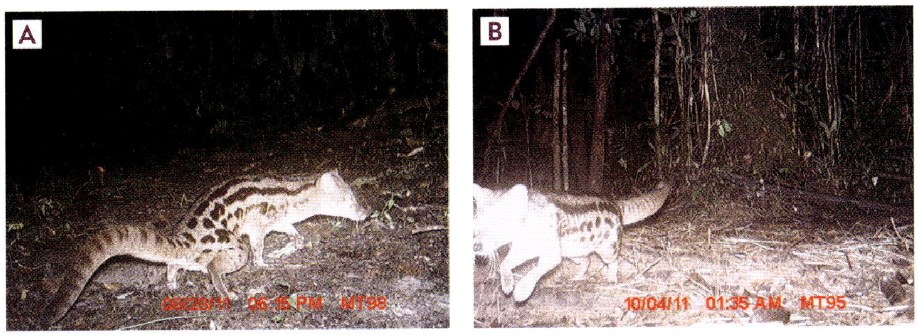

FIGURE 14.59 **Camera-trap photos of *Fossa fossana* from Makira Natural Park. A) *Fossa* scent marking via urination: *Fossa* is captured with camera traps using a wide range of scent-marking behaviors, including using chest and anal glands to mark downed logs or vegetation. B) *Fossa* pouncing on prey item just out of view: *Fossa* is often captured on camera hunting, stalking, or chasing small mammals and other prey.** (PHOTOS by Z. J. Farris.)

lower end of the normal range for adults, as trapping occurred during the winter period, when food may have been in short supply. *Fossa* prepares for food scarcity by storing body fat, especially in the tail, which can reach up to a quarter of its body weight (Albignac 1972a). Three males trapped in the Ranomafana protected area in October 1999 were slightly heavier (1.8–2.1 kg), presumably because they had started to replenish body fat. Two lactating females captured at the same site and during the same period weighed 1.5 and 1.6 kg. Three adults from the southern portion of the moist evergreen forest in Andohahela (parcel 1) had an average total length of 675 ± 39 mm, tail length of 238 ± 23 mm, hind-foot length (excluding claw) of 89.7 ± 4.9 mm, and ear length of 45.7 ± 2.1 mm (Goodman and Pidgeon 1999). As might be expected from a monogamous species, there was no significant body size dimorphism between the sexes, although males at Vevembe had significantly longer canines with significantly greater distance between canine tips than did females.

MATING AND REPRODUCTION

Mating apparently takes place during the months of August and September, and the gestation period is 82–89 days (Albignac 1971, 1984). Females give birth to a single young that is at an advanced stage of development, with open eyes, and notably precocious (Albignac 1971; Wemmer 1971). In captivity, the incisors and premolars commenced to erupt within 3 and 5 days of birth respectively, and within 33 days the young are capable of eating solid food. Camera-trap photos from Mantadia taken during mid-November show female *Fossa* carrying very young infants, presumably moving them to new nesting or den sites. Additional photo data from Makira have shown a juvenile *Fossa* traveling with an adult female *Fossa* in late March (Z. Farris and E. Wampole, unpublished data).

DIET AND PREDATION

Previous accounts (Albignac 1972a, 1984) have described the diet of *Fossa* as somewhat eclectic, including eels and other fish, crustaceans, insects, small birds, rodents, tenrecs, and amphibians. Of 18 individuals captured by Albignac (1971), only three were not captured next to streams, and the propensity for aquatic organisms is therefore fitting. Scats collected sporadically at Vevembe between June and October included remains of two species of rodent (one introduced); perhaps up to six species of tenrecs; remnants of crabs, snakes, frogs, millipedes, carabids and other beetles, and orthopterans; as well as other unidentified mammals and insects (Goodman et al. 2003b). The only evidence of birds in these scats were chicken feathers; their occurrence and the lack of associated bones perhaps indicates that the *Fossa* scavenged the remains of this bird rather than predating upon it. No eel or other fish remains were found in the Vevembe scats. The stomach contents of three individuals dissected by Rand (1935) were composed of insects; one also contained a lizard about 10 cm long. Specimens collected in 1948 near Bemangidy, about 72 km north of Tolagnaro, have written on their data tags, "trapped with meat bait at edge of original forest" and "was trapped with fruit bait beside stream at edge of original forest" (Goodman and Pidgeon 1999). At Makira, Murphy et al. (2017b) found that *Fossa* had a positive spatial co-occurrence (attraction) with *Eliurus* species, *Nesomys* species, and *Setifer setosus*, suggesting, in areas where overlap occurs, these small mammals may be considered important prey for this carnivoran. *Fossa* individuals are often captured by camera traps hunting, stalking, or chasing small mammals and other prey (Figure 14.59b).

BEHAVIOR

Fossa is shy, active during the night, and rarely seen. While nocturnal across its range, *Fossa* has been shown to alter its peak activity period across seasons and in the presence of humans and *Canis lupus* (dog) (Farris et al. 2015a; Gerber et al. 2012b). Evidence from footprints, together with spool-and-line tracking of five individuals, has confirmed its preference for streams and marshy areas near Vevembe. To date, widespread camera trapping has been carried out across at least 20 sites in moist evergreen forests, and no survey or modeling results have revealed any preference for a specific type of habitat (Farris et al. 2015b; Gerber et al. 2012a). Unlike *Galidia elegans*, which often lives in burrows in the ground, *Fossa* in captivity did not dig ground burrows but rather occupied hollows in tree trunks or rock shelters (Albignac 1971, 1984).

At Vevembe, as well as several other sites, *Fossa* is sympatric with the largely diurnal *Galidia elegans*, which was frequently trapped, and the nocturnal *Galidictis fasciata*, which may be distinctly less common. Studies of niche separation, particularly with respect to

diet, could produce some interesting results. At least two, possibly three, *Fossa* were preyed on by *Cryptoprocta ferox* during the course of the Vevembe study, and another four radio-collared animals disappeared from the area during the 1998 and 1999 field seasons; these data and other inferences imply relatively high mortality in this species. Recent research has shown that *Fossa* avoids the introduced *Viverricula indica* (Small Indian Civet) where the two species overlap (Farris et al. 2015c).

SPECIES DISTRIBUTION AND POPULATION ECOLOGY

Recent density estimates from Ranomafana (3.19 ind/km^2) and Makira (2.71 ind/km^2) demonstrate a relatively high population density for *Fossa*; however, density was twice as low in degraded, fragmented forest areas (Farris and Kelly 2011; Gerber et al. 2012a, 2012c). At Vevembe density was also high; 22 animals were trapped in an area of about 2 km^2 during the latter two weeks of July 1999. Rand (1935), who visited the Vondrozo region, presumably within or in close distance of Vevembe, had already noted that this species was locally common. Some of the animals captured in 1999 may not have been resident in the capture area and were possibly dispersing through the area to find food during this lean period—however, 10 individuals were recaptured during the two-week period. Estimates of spatial habitat use (occupancy) also reveal *Fossa* to be widespread, occupying almost the entire landscape at locations such as Ranomafana, Makira, and Anjanaharibe-Sud (Gerber et al. 2012a; Farris et al. 2015b; Beaudrot et al. 2018; P. H. Ross et al. 2020). However, each of these studies revealed considerably lower estimates of occupancy in degraded, disturbed forests and a complete absence of this euplerid in fragmented forests (>5 km from intact forest). These estimates of habitat use across the species' geographic distribution also reveal a wide range of factors influencing its distribution, including elevation, presence of introduced carnivorans, canopy height, and human activity.

Preliminary analyses of data from Vevembe of four individuals that were radio-tracked from mid-July to the end of September 1999 reveal estimated home ranges for males and females of 0.073–0.52 km^2. These individuals were tracked during the breeding season, when males may stay close to females in small core areas of their established territory in order to guard mates from unpaired males. Numerous (n = 20) robust camera-trapping surveys across eastern Madagascar in moist evergreen forests have estimated this species' home range to be no greater than 0.25 km^2 (based on camera spacing and tracking of individual animals). A. Murphy and Z. Farris (unpublished data) recently used a six-year data set from Makira and found estimated home-range movement to range from 0.10 to 0.20 km^2, with an average of 0.16 km^2. This analysis has provided the first survival estimates and found that the average individual *Fossa* was detected for 2.7 years across the six-year study, and probability of survival at a single 10 km^2 site inside Makira was 0.74 per year.

Fossa is known from numerous protected areas on the island, from north to south: Montagne d'Ambre, Loky Manambato, Ankarana, Ampasindava, Manongarivo, Marojejy, Anjanaharibe-Sud, Makira, Masoala, Mananara-Nord, Ambatovaky, Zahamena, Ankeniheny-Zahamena, Betampona, Mangerivola, Mantadia, Torotorofotsy, Analamazaotra, Maromizaha, Ambositra-Vondrozo, Ranomafana, Andringitra, Manombo, Befotaka–Midongy du Sud, Tsitongambarika, Andohahela, and Mandena (Goodman et al. 2018b). Information on population densities is available from only two of these sites: Ranomafana (1.38 and 3.19 ind/km^2) and Makira (1.21 ind/km^2).

PEOPLE AND *FOSSA*

In 1998, people from two villages near the Manombo protected area were questioned about *Fossa fossana*. They regard it and indeed most members of Carnivora as pests, owing to their purported tendency to prey on chickens. These villagers kill carnivorans caught raiding fowl and also set traps in the forest baited with rats or mice. At least at this locality, people eat captured euplerids. At Ranomafana, *Fossa* is rarely observed, due to its nocturnal behavior, and therefore local knowledge of the species is lacking (Kotschwar Logan et al. 2015). Across the Makira region, people hunt and consume *Fossa* and other euplerids; this is particularly prevalent in households of lower socioeconomic levels (Golden 2009; Golden et al. 2014). Borgerson (2016) found 63% of hunters target this euplerid, primarily from September to December, and found a total of 13 individuals were caught in the focal village of her study. The author also reports that villagers primarily caught *Fossa* by using snare traps during early austral summer. The presence and activity of people does negatively influence space use and activity patterns in *Fossa*. Additionally, domestic and free-ranging dogs (*Canis lupus*) have also been shown to cause decreases in *Fossa* distribution and activity (Farris et al. 2015c). The public image of *Fossa* and other euplerids could be improved in rural Madagascar by environmental education that stresses their role as predators of locusts and introduced rodents, which cause havoc to rice crops and food stocks.

DISEASE

To our knowledge, there has been no investigation of disease ecology in wild *Fossa*, which is directly related to the lack of available samples. It is assumed that *Fossa* is likely experiencing the same or similar pressures and threats as other euplerids from introduced carnivorans, specifically free-ranging dogs, *Felis silvestris* (cat), and *Viverricula indica*, via disease transmission (Rasambainarivo et al. 2018; see Rasambainarivo and Zohdy, pp. 298–302).

CONSERVATION

Fossa is currently listed on the IUCN Red List as Vulnerable across its range, and as habitat degradation and human persecution of this species continue, its status is unlikely to improve (F. Hawkins 2015). Along the east coast, ecological niche models show that *Fossa* may overlap extensively in the future with the introduced, invasive, and toxic *Duttaphrynus melanostictus* (Black-spined Toad; see Freeman et al., pp. 1404–10), as the toad expands its distribution and becomes a potential novel prey species (Brown

et al. 2016). Genetic studies show *Fossa* may be sensitive to the toad's poison (Marshall et al. 2018). However, after several years since the introduction and invasion of this toad, there is no evidence to date that it is entering native moist evergreen forest formations. *Fossa* faces threats from the introduced carnivorans mentioned in the previous section. Long-term studies of *Fossa* population parameters are rare; however, multiyear estimates of occupancy at Makira (Farris et al. 2017a) and Ranomafana (Farris et al. 2017b) have shown little to no change in spatial distribution (occupancy) over a six-year period, and colonization rates appear to be higher than extirpation and initial survival estimates for this carnivoran. However, Beaudrot et al. (2018) showed over a six-year period at Ranomafana, *Fossa* occupancy was reduced by 50% at low to medium elevations (690–1010 m), while increasing at higher elevations (1125–1260 m), where these anthropogenic pressures are lower. To improve our understanding and management approaches, population estimates are needed throughout the range of *Fossa fossana*, particularly for degraded, fragmented forests where introduced carnivorans and hunting by people are likely causing measurable decreases.

Subject editors: Jörg U. Ganzhorn and Steven M. Goodman

EUPLERIDAE: *GALIDIA ELEGANS*, RING-TAILED VONTSIRA, *VONTSIRA MENA*

Z. J. Farris and S. M. Goodman

The genus *Galidia*, a member of the endemic family Eupleridae, currently contains one species, *G. elegans*, represented by several geographic forms. This species, the most conspicuous native member of Carnivora on the island, occurs in most types of natural forest formations with the exception of the southern portion of the dry deciduous forest and the dry spiny thicket. Given its largely diurnal habits, distinctive coloration and long ringed tail, and reputation for being an unrelenting camp robber, this species is known to almost anyone who has visited the moist evergreen forests of Madagascar. Recent research has highlighted the threat posed to *Galidia* by human encroachment and domestic, free-ranging introduced carnivorans, namely *Canis lupus* (dog) and *Felis silvestris* (cat). However, the generalist nature of *Galidia* and its ability to persist in slightly disturbed forests make it less of a conservation priority than other euplerid carnivorans.

TAXONOMY

Three subspecies of *Galidia elegans* are currently recognized: *G. e. elegans*, known from most of the length of the moist evergreen forest, from the Tolagnaro region in the south to the mountains ringing the Andapa Basin in the north (type locality restricted to Toamasina by Tate and Rand 1941) (Figure 14.60); *G. e. occidentalis*, occurring in the central west, particularly in dry deciduous forests growing on limestone, from Bemaraha in the south to Soalala and Namoroka in the north; and *G. e. dambrensis*, found in the medium-altitude moist evergreen forests of Montagne d'Ambre, in the dry deciduous forests of Ankarana, and between Ambanja and Ambilobe (Albignac 1973). It is not clear which form occurs in the Sambirano Region. Details on the higher-level relationships of this genus and the phylogeny of Malagasy carnivorans in general are discussed elsewhere (see Veron et al., pp. 1863–65).

FIGURE 14.60 **Camera-trap photo of *Galidia elegans* from a selectively logged trail system within Ranomafana National Park. The single *Galidia* in this photo demonstrates the dark pelage coloration found particularly in animals across the southeastern portion of the species' range.** (PHOTO by B. Gerber.)

TABLE 14.31. External and cranial measurements and weight of different subspecies of *Galidia elegans*

MEASUREMENT	*G. E. ELEGANS*	*G. E. OCCIDENTALIS*	*G. E. DAMBRENSIS*
Head-and-body length (mm)	300–380	315–390	300–390
Tail length (mm)	260–290	260–280	250–280
Hind-foot length (mm)	60–70	65–70	60–70
Ear length (mm)	28–30	21–28	29–30
Skull length (mm)	68–70	65	72
Weight (g)	655–960	680–920	720–990

Source: Based on Albignac (1973).
Note: Sample sizes not indicated.

These subspecies are distinguished largely on the basis of pelage coloration, and they do not appear notably different in external or cranial measurements (Table 14.31). The nominate form is the darkest, with a dark reddish-chestnut body and nearly black venter, feet, and flanks. There is considerable variation in the pelage coloration of this subspecies, however, particularly with regard to the belly color (Albignac 1973; Goodman and Pidgeon 1999). The dorsal portion of the body fur is distinctly paler in the other two subspecies than in the nominate form and approaches a light reddish brown. In *G. e. dambrensis*, the ventrum, feet, and flanks are close to the same color as the dorsum, and in *G. e. occidentalis*, the underside is largely black. Recent molecular research on intraspecific genetic variation has found animals referable to *G. e. dambrensis* to be divergent from *G. e. elegans* from the central east (Veron et al. 2017); *G. e. occidentalis* populations also show notable levels of divergence (C. E. Bennett et al. 2009).

MORPHOLOGY

Galidia cannot be confused with any other mammal species on Madagascar. The body form is typically mongoose-like (although any similarity to members of the family Herpestidae is convergent), with relatively short feet and a plumose furred tail that is slightly more than two-thirds of the body length. The tail is marked with five or six alternating reddish-brown and nearly black bands. Depending on the geographic region, which is associated with the subspecies designation, the general pelage color varies from deep chestnut red to a dull reddish brown (see above). The ears are noticeable, but not really prominent, and are edged with a distinct, light-colored border.

Members of this genus have relatively large feet, with well-developed and naked footpads. There is also a small membrane attaching the bases of the toes. The hind feet are more elongated than the forefeet, and the claws are nonretractile. Detailed descriptions of the foot structure can be found in Pocock (1915c). The various adaptations allow this species to walk and run on the ground, climb in trees, and swim in water (see below).

MATING AND REPRODUCTION

On the basis of observations in captivity, the following details can be presented about mating and reproduction in *Galidia elegans* (Albignac 1969b, 1973; Larkin and Roberts 1979). Before copulating, there is a sequence of chases by the male of the female, and both individuals mark a variety of prominent objects in the territory with their musk glands. The male also frequently sniffs the female's anogenitial area. The female solicits copulation from the male by approaching him with the anterior portion of the body lowered and the raised, quivering tail to one side. The male then mounts the female for between 10 and 30 seconds by grasping her around the abdomen. This sequence terminates when the female rolls to her side, moves quickly away, or turns around and attacks the male. This sequence is repeated between seven and 12 times, and the complete mating bout may last 30–80 minutes. Neck biting has not been observed in this species. There are varied reports of a gestation time of 74–90 days (Albignac 1969b) and 52–77 days (Larkin and Roberts 1979).

Birthing in the moist evergreen forests generally takes place during the months of November and December. *Galidia* bears one young that is born fully furred. The young weigh between 40 and 50 g at birth and grow relatively slowly with respect to other Malagasy carnivorans (Larkin and Roberts 1979). By the fourth day, the eyes are open; by the 14th or 15th day, the youngster starts to move about, play, scent mark, and groom itself; and by the 44th day, it is eating solid food. The deciduous dentition is replaced sometime after the age of seven months, and sexual maturity is reached at about two years.

DIET AND PREDATION

Little quantitative information is available on the diet of *Galidia elegans* in the wild. Rand (1935) reported that the stomach contents of four collected individuals included grasshoppers, beetles, and other types of insects, and reptiles. Albignac (1973) remarked that, based on scat analysis, this species also consumes rodents, tenrecs, and frogs. This same author also noted the remains of crayfish at the stream edge that he considered prey remains of this carnivoran. Further, on the basis of scat analysis and direct observation, it is now known that *Galidia* feeds on *Cheirogaleus major* and *Microcebus rufus* (Goodman et al. 1993a; P. C. Wright and Martin 1995; see Goodman and Ganzhorn, pp. 1829–38). Farris et al. (2014) found that *Microcebus* sp. tended to avoid areas where *Galidia* was present. This may provide further evidence of a predator-prey relationship,

as members of the genus *Microcebus* are arboreal, occurring a few meters off the ground, heights that *Galidia* is able to climb. A scat collected in Andringitra contained chitin of beetles and bones of frogs (S. M. Goodman, unpublished data).

There are also reports of *Galidia* eating snakes and a variety of rodents. In one case, a 2 m–long boa with a maximum body diameter of 10 cm was dispatched by a single *Galidia*, which was subsequently joined by two other individuals to consume the snake (Albignac 1973). Among researchers living in forest camps, this bold, inquisitive, and sometimes pugnacious species has a remarkable reputation. It may persistently raid camp food reserves, creating general havoc, whether by puncturing condensed-milk cans and consuming the contents or by entering tents, seemingly by opening the zipper or simply tearing a hole in the side, to feast on well-guarded biscuits or chocolate. In captivity, it feeds on a wide variety of foods but seems to have a preference for frogs, birds, eggs, and small mammals (Albignac 1973).

Galidia elegans uses a number of hunting techniques. It can be notably arboreal and is able to climb nearly vertical tree trunks. For example, in the medium-altitude moist evergreen forests of Montagne d'Ambre, it is not uncommon to see this species climbing in trees up to 12–15 m off the ground. These animals inspect and tear open clumps of epiphytic vegetation as they move about or jump between tree limbs. Upon encountering animals, presumably relatively small vertebrates and invertebrates alike, they immediately consume the prey. Perhaps while pilfering these epiphytes, they dismantle cavities that are sleeping places of small arboreal nocturnal primates. *Galidia* has also been observed in small rivers in Andohahela feeding on aquatic animals (Goodman and Pidgeon 1999). In one case, the animal directly entered the water, submerged to the lower portion of its venter, and used a sit-and-wait technique to hunt frogs. In another case, it was observed diving into the water from the riverbank to successfully pursue and capture a frog. Finally, *Galidia* has been noted in Ranomafana in an all-out dash after *Nesomys*, a relatively large, diurnal nesomyine rodent (see Carleton et al., pp. 2033–35), which in some areas probably constitutes an important portion of the diet.

BEHAVIOR

Galidia lives largely in excavated ground burrows and may occasionally take up residence in standing or fallen hollow trees or in shelters under large downed trunks. Little is published about the social organization of this species in the wild, but based on field studies, it appears to live, at least seasonally, solitarily or in small groups. In the latter case, these groups are presumably composed of the mated pair and the most recent young (Albignac 1969b, 1973, 1974). Widespread camera trapping across the eastern moist evergreen forest has revealed that *Galidia* occurs almost exclusively in pairs year-round. Multiple photo captures of larger euplerids (*Cryptoprocta ferox*, *Fossa fossana*, and *Eupleres goudotii*) have documented females with young or juveniles; however, to date, no such images have been captured of the genera *Galidia*, *Galidictis*, or *Salanoia* in groups or of mothers with infants or juveniles. On the basis of field studies by Albignac in several different forest types, the home-range area of *Galidia* has been consistently estimated to be between 20 and 25 ha. Adults regularly scent mark within this zone, using urine and a form of musk produced by their perineal, cheek, and submandibular glands.

This species is rather vocal, and its auditory signals have been grouped by Albignac (1973) into the following classes: 1) contact calls between family members, often while moving through the forest; 2) a call given while capturing prey; 3) an intimidation, attack, or defense call; and 4) a copulation call. The first of these vocalizations can be heard regularly in the forest and often draws one's attention to the presence of this species in the immediate vicinity.

Galidia is highly diurnal across its range and overlaps in temporal activity patterns with the sympatric *Salanoia concolor* and introduced *Canis lupus*. Other factors appear to influence *Galidia* activity patterns, including the level of forest habitat degradation and the presence of introduced carnivoran species, namely *Viverricula indica* (Small Indian Civet) and free-ranging *Felis silvestris*, which appear to negatively influence *Galidia* activity patterns and local distribution. Free-ranging *C. lupus* and *F. silvestris* negatively influenced *Galidia* detection as well, further highlighting the impact that introduced carnivorans have on this endemic species (Gerber et al. 2012b; Farris et al. 2015a).

SPECIES DISTRIBUTION AND POPULATION ECOLOGY

Galidia elegans ranges as far north as Montagne d'Ambre and as far south as Andohahela (Goodman et al. 2018b). There is a recent confirmed record of this species in the riparian forests of Berenty in the far south (Schnoell 2012), and given the introduction of different mammals in this area, it is not certain whether this is a natural occurrence. *Galidia e. elegans* is a forest-dwelling animal that is widely distributed across eastern Madagascar from near sea level to the forest line, at about 1950 m (e.g., the Andringitra Massif). In some zones, it can reach noticeably high densities. On Montagne d'Ambre, at 1000 m in the vicinity of the Jardin Botanique and Station Forestière des Roussettes, the local subspecies, *G. e. dambrensis*, is very common. During the course of seven days of trapping at this locality, with 20 National traps set each day, over 28 individuals were captured in a relatively limited area, and animals could be seen moving about on the ground or in trees during the day. This forest is filled with introduced *Rattus*, and the local *Galidia* population feeds on these animals (S. M. Goodman and B. Rasolonandrasana, unpublished data). In Andohahela (parcel 1) and Pic d'Ivohibe, densities of this species appeared to be higher near small streams than away from water (Goodman and Pidgeon 1999; Rasolonandrasana and Goodman 1999). *Galidia* will also frequent the forest edge, particularly the ecotone between moist evergreen forest and *tavy*. In such zones, it may enter into the vicinity of small hamlets (Kotschwar Logan et al. 2015).

In contrast, recent photographic surveys across the Andasibe-Mantadia protected area complex (>100 camera stations surveyed for five months) revealed very low capture rates across Mantadia and an absence of *Galidia* from smaller, fragmented sites, such as the moist evergreen forests of Analamazaotra and Mitsinjo (E. Wampole and Z. Farris, unpublished data). Camera-trapping surveys in other areas of the island have found *Galidia* to

demonstrate high probability of occupancy (habitat use) across both contiguous and degraded forests. For example, in the Makira landscape, *Galidia* occupied almost 50% but showed a strong decrease in occupancy in nonforest matrix. Bird activity and understory cover were the two strongest predictors of *Galidia* presence across Makira. At Ranomafana, *Galidia* had higher occupancy within contiguous, moist evergreen forests and selectively logged forests compared to fragmented and nonforest matrix, and *F. silvestris* had the greatest influence on its distribution (Gerber et al. 2012a; Farris et al. 2015b).

In the moist evergreen forests, *Galidia* occurs in sympatry with other relatively small carnivorans, particularly *Galidictis fasciata*, which is the same general body size, and the slightly larger *Fossa fossana*. In this case, there is presumably niche separation through temporal differences in activity: *Galidia* is diurnal and *Galidictis* and *Fossa* are nocturnal. However, in the northeast, *Galidia* also overlaps with the similar-size, diurnal *Salanoia concolor*. Few details are available on dietary differences among these three vontsira species, and further investigation is needed. Little is known about the carnivoran communities in western dry deciduous forests. The two diurnal euplerids of this region, *Galidia* and *Mungotictis decemlineata* (see Kappeler et al., pp. 1996–98), interestingly, are approximately the same size and have mutually exclusive geographic ranges.

PEOPLE AND *GALIDIA*

Surveyed human families living near Ranomafana stated that *Galidia* was the most commonly observed euplerid, including near villages, research facilities, trash sites, and regular campsites (Kotschwar Logan et al. 2015). Several cultural groups believe that parts of *Galidia* have medicinal properties. Perhaps most important in this regard is a potion made from the tail that is reputed to act as an aphrodisiac. Furthermore, in the south and southeast, the Antaisaka, Antanosy, and Antandroy cultural groups fabricate a type of pendant out of the tail that is worn exclusively by women (Decary 1950). As mentioned earlier, in the east this species occurs at the ecotone between forest and *tavy*, and in such places it has contact with people. In such settings *Galidia* is considered a poultry raider and, as such, is hunted and persecuted (e.g., Goodman 1996b; Kotschwar Logan et al. 2015). Whether this reputation is correct or not is unclear, but it may be partially unjustified, owing to acts of predation by endemic and introduced nocturnal carnivorans that are mistakenly pinned on *Galidia*.

Hunting and poaching of *Galidia* is poorly studied across its range. The species is known to be hunted and consumed widely across Makira, particularly among households of lower socioeconomic levels (Golden 2009; Golden et al. 2014). There are reports that it has been killed and consumed near Ranomafana in retaliation for poultry predation (Kotschwar Logan et al. 2015). Farris et al. (2015b) reported that 58 individuals were consumed at four villages bordering Makira over a three-year period. Borgerson (2016) reported that hunters do not target this species, though these authors recorded seven individuals captured via opportunistic approaches within the focal village. This last author also reported that *Galidia* was captured, killed, and consumed as retribution for predation of livestock. More detailed information on hunting and consumption is needed across the species' range to enable better understanding of the associated impacts on local populations. Domestic or free-ranging introduced carnivorans, namely *C. lupus* and *F. silvestris*, appear to pose an additional strong threat to *Galidia*. *Felis silvestris* may have the biggest negative influence on *Galidia* occupancy (Gerber et al. 2012a; Farris et al. 2017a).

DISEASE

The prevalence and effects of various diseases and/or pathogens on *Galidia* populations have not been investigated across most of this carnivoran's range. In the Betampona protected area, Rasambainarivo et al. (2018) found that 8% of sampled *Galidia* carried antibodies for Canine Parvovirus, while 48% tested positive for toxoplasmosis. Additionally, these same authors showed that indirect interactions between *Galidia* and *Canis lupus* and *Felis silvestris* presented a strong threat of disease transmission, particularly near villages and the local research center at the edge of the protected area.

CONSERVATION

Multiyear surveys from the protected areas of Makira (Farris et al. 2017a) and Ranomafana (Farris et al. 2017b) have shown populations of *Galidia elegans* declining in occupancy by 50%, with a probability of local extirpation of 0.60. Additional analysis showed that elevation best explained changes in occupancy at Ranomafana, as *Galidia* "retracted" from higher elevations (1125–1260 m), while remaining constant at low to mid-elevations (690–1010 m) (Beaudrot et al. 2018). We propose that this change from high to mid-elevation is in response to shifts in populations of a forest-dwelling nesomyine rodent, *Nesomys rufus*, an important prey animal that has exhibited the same change in elevation use. Along the east coast, ecological niche models show that *G. elegans* may overlap extensively with the introduced, toxic *Duttaphrynus melanostictus* (Black-spined Toad; see Freeman et al., pp. 1404–10), a potential novel and deadly prey species (Brown et al. 2016). However, after several years since the introduction and invasion of this toad, there is no evidence to date that it is entering native moist evergreen forests. In a general manner, given the wide distribution of *Galidia* on Madagascar and its relatively high densities in certain areas, it faces little threat to its continued existence. It is known to persist in forest fragments and is able to cross open areas between forest parcels. Thus, this species should not be considered a conservation priority and is currently listed on the IUCN Red List as Least Concern.

Subject editors: Jörg U. Ganzhorn and Steven M. Goodman

EUPLERIDAE: *GALIDICTIS FASCIATA*, BROAD-STRIPED VONTSIRA, *VONTSIRA FOTSY*, *VOTSOTSOKE*

Z. J. Farris and S. M. Goodman

The genus *Galidictis*, a member of the endemic family Eupleridae, has been considered to contain two species, *G. fasciata*, known locally as *vontsira fotsy*, and *G. grandidieri*, known locally as *votsotsoke*. A recent molecular study (see Taxonomy, below) has found low levels of genetic differentiation between these two forms, and the latter is now considered a subspecies of *G. fasciata* (Veron et al. 2017). *Galidictis f. fasciata* is restricted to the moist evergreen forests, and *G. f. grandidieri* to the dry spiny thickets in the vicinity of the Mahafaly Plateau and Lake Tsimanampesotse. These strictly nocturnal members of Carnivora, with distinct black-and-white longitudinal striping on the back and long whitish, bushy tails, are poorly known with regard to their distribution and natural history; they are perhaps the rarest of Madagascar's native carnivorans. Based on its low densities, the subspecies *G. f. grandidieri* is one of the most threatened of all of Madagascar's euplerids.

TAXONOMY

Details on the higher-level relationships of this genus and the phylogeny of Malagasy carnivorans (family Eupleridae) are discussed elsewhere (see Veron et al., pp. 1863–65). As mentioned above, a recent molecular study of *Galidictis* conducted by Veron et al. (2017) found a small amount of genetic differentiation, based on mitochondrial and nuclear markers, between populations allocated to *G. fasciata* and *G. grandidieri*. They concluded that two subspecies should be recognized, *G. f. fasciata* and *G. f. grandidieri*; we follow this suggestion herein.

I. Geoffroy Saint-Hilaire named the genus *Galidictis* in 1839. Pocock (1915b) revised the genus and recognized two species in the form now known as *G. f. fasciata*: "*G. eximius*" and "*G. ornatus*"; the former occurs in the southern portion of the moist evergreen forest, and the latter in the northern portion of this same zone. Albignac (1973), in his assessment of *Galidictis*, reduced Pocock's two *Galidictis* species to one, with two subspecies. On the basis of a complicated series of nomenclature arguments (also see Wozencraft 1986; A. F. A. Hawkins et al. 2000), Albignac (1973) recognized "*G. eximius*" as *G. f. fasciata*, known from the southern half of the moist evergreen forest (at least as far north as the Kianjavato region), and "*G. ornatus*" as *G. f. striata*, occurring in the northern half of the moist evergreen forest from near Brickaville north to the Sihanaka Forest east of Lake Alaotra. The differences between these forms are not clear (Wozencraft 1986), and they are no longer recognized as valid taxa. A recent molecular analysis of *G. f. fasciata* from the southern one-third of the east found no prominent genetic differentiation (Veron et al. 2017).

The original species name proposed for the form previously known as *G. grandidieri* was *G. grandidiensis*, which was subsequently amended by Wozencraft (1987). The holotype of this taxon comes from the dry spiny thicket of the Lake Tsimanampesotse region. Subsequently, this form has been found in different areas of the extreme southwest (Mahazotahy et al. 2006; Marquard et al. 2011; Goodman 2013), and subfossil remains, presumably dating from the Holocene or Late Pleistocene, were identified among material excavated in the Ankazoabo Cave, north of Itampolo, ~50 km south of Lake Tsimanampesotse (Goodman 1996b). Lamberton (1936: 18), who excavated the material, noted, "Mes récoltes comprennent aussi d'autres Carnivores, j'ai notamment un crâne et divers os d'un *Galidictis*, voisin des espèces actuelles" (My collections include other Carnivora, I have notably a skull and miscellaneous bones of a *Galidictis*, close to the living species). It is important to keep in mind that Lamberton was in the area seven years after the passage of Rand, who collected the paratype of *G. f. grandidieri*, and half a century before this taxon was described by Wozencraft (1986). The Ankazoabo Cave is within a few kilometers of the Hatokaliotsy Forest and falls within the modern range of this subspecies. Subfossils from the Ankilitelo Cave, north of the Onilahy River and outside of the modern range of members of this genus, have been identified as *G. f. grandidieri* (Muldoon et al. 2009), indicating that in the recent geological past this genus had a broader geographic distribution.

MORPHOLOGY

Galidictis fasciata has a distinctive pelage coloration that is difficult to confuse with that of any other native species of Malagasy Carnivora. Its body form is typically mongoose-like (although any similarity to members of the family Herpestidae is convergent), and it has relatively short feet and a furred tail, without rings, that is a little less than one-half the total length (Table 14.32). The dorsal pelage of both subspecies is overall grayish beige, which extends to the feet and the proximal portion of the tail; the venter is distinctly whiter. The distal two-thirds of the tail are a distinctive creamy-white color. The head of both forms is a grizzled grayish brown, and the dorsum is distinctly marked with a series of dark brown longitudinal bands that generally run from the nape to the base of the tail. In *G. f. fasciata*, these dark stripes are wider or equal in width to the grayish-beige interlines (Figure 14.61a), and in *G. f. grandidieri*, the dark stripes are narrower than the grayish-beige interlines (Figure 14.61b). The distal portion of the ears in *G. f. fasciata* apparently lacks fur, while in *G. f. grandidieri* the ears are covered with a fine layer of short fur. In both subspecies, the foot structure is largely similar to that of *Galidia elegans* (see Farris and Goodman, pp. 1989–92), except *Galidictis* does not have the slight webbing between the toes found in *Galidia* (Wozencraft 1986).

TABLE 14.32. **External measurements and weight of adult *Galidictis fasciata fasciata* and *G. f. grandidieri***

MEASUREMENT	*G. F. FASCIATA*	*G. F. GRANDIDIERI*
Total length (mm)	590.5 ± 30.6	715.7 ± 19.4
	559–632	703–738
	(n = 4)	(n = 3)
Tail length (mm)	266.5 ± 19.8	313.7 ± 12.0
	249–293	302–326
	(n = 4)	(n = 3)
Hind-foot length (mm)	71.5 ± 2.4	93
	69–74	
	(n = 4)	
Ear length (mm)	31.0 ± 0.8	39
	30–32	
	(n = 4)	
Weight (g)	640.0 ± 105.4	♂♂ 1650 ± 213.2
	520–745	1450–2350
	(n = 4)	(n = 20)
		♀♀ 1400.0 ± 118.4
		1225–1625
		(n = 10)

Source: Based on recently collected specimens and body-weight data of *G. f. grandidieri* from Marquard et al. (2011); further external measurements can be found in that publication.
Note: Data presented as mean ± standard deviation; minimum–maximum range, and number (n) of specimens.

MATING AND REPRODUCTION

Little is known about the reproductive activities and seasonality of *Galidictis f. fasciata*. A female captured in the Andohahela National Park (parcel 1) during November 1995 did not show signs of reproductive activity (Goodman and Pidgeon 1999); the following day, at the same site, a subadult was trapped. Males captured between late October and late November had scrotal testes. During a rapid survey at Tsimanampesotse in November 1989, Wozencraft (1990) caught a number of *G. f. grandidieri* females that were in various stages of reproduction, including lactation, pregnancy, and estrus; at the same time, he also captured subadults of different ages. Thus, it would appear that the different forms of this genus breed throughout the year, rather than during a limited season, as in *Galidia*.

DIET AND PREDATION

No quantitative information is available on the diet of *G. f. fasciata*. Albignac (1973) surmised that this subspecies feeds largely on rodents and small lemurs, and perhaps also on reptiles and amphibians. We are unaware of any evidence of this subspecies feeding on lemurs (Goodman et al. 1993c; see Goodman and Ganzhorn, pp. 1829–38). Camera-trap photos have shown what is believed to be cooperative hunting behavior, with pairs of *G. f. fasciata* digging in the soil to unearth prey; however, no information was obtained of this animal holding or carrying a prey item. Considerably more information is available on the food habits of *G. f. grandidieri*. Rand (1935: 94), who visited Tsimanampesotse, noted, "Shortly after dark it [*G. f. grandidieri*] was heard rattling the stones of the sterile soil as it dug up the bodies of skinned birds buried near camp." A dietary study of scats was conducted over the course of a year at Tsimanampesotse, based on 256 fecal samples collected in the dry season and 86 samples in the wet season (Andriatsimietry et al. 2009). Invertebrates, mostly large cockroaches of the genus *Gromphadorhina*, were the principal prey taken by this animal. Vertebrates composed 8% and 17% of prey individuals taken during the dry and wet seasons, respectively; these figures contributed 58% and 80% of prey biomass in each season, respectively. The different identified vertebrates included reptiles, birds, tenrecs, bats, mouse lemurs, and introduced rodents; 90% of all prey items consumed had a body mass of less than 10 g—rather extraordinary for an animal of this size.

BEHAVIOR

A considerable portion of current information on the natural history of Malagasy euplerids is based on the study of wild-captured animals raised and bred in captivity (e.g., Albignac 1973). The exception, to our knowledge, is *Galidictis*, which apparently has not been studied in captivity.

Galidictis f. fasciata appears to be nocturnal but occasionally is crepuscular (Gerber et al. 2012a; Farris et al. 2015a). This form is largely terrestrial, but individuals have been trapped off the ground climbing on large downed logs; in one case, an individual was observed climbing up a tree about 1.5 m off the ground (Barden et al. 1991). Camera-trap photos confirm this climbing behavior as well. Nothing is known about the types of shelters occupied by *G. f. fasciata*. It is known to raid forest-camp food reserves on occasion (e.g., Goodman 1996a). Almost all camera-trap photo captures of *G. f. fasciata* show it traveling in pairs, and to our knowledge, no image has been taken of more than two individuals. This form in the Makira area avoids areas with free-ranging *Canis lupus* (dog), and its occupancy in forests without this introduced carnivoran is considerably higher than in sites where dogs are present; furthermore, distance to nearby villages influenced this relationship (Farris et al. 2015c). *Galidictis f. fasciata* also does not occur in sympatry with another introduced carnivoran, *Viverricula indica* (Small Indian Civet), and showed avoidance of *V. indica*, which occupies only degraded and fragmented forest areas (Farris et al. 2015c). At Betampona, *G. f. fasciata* demonstrated similar indirect interactions with introduced carnivores, primarily widespread *C. lupus*. *Galidictis f. fasciata* was captured at the same camera stations as *C. lupus* and *Felis silvestris* (cat) within a timeframe allowing for possible disease transmission; furthermore, the distance to a village or research center influenced these spatial interactions (Rasambainarivo et al. 2017).

FIGURE 14.61 Images of *Galidictis fasciata*. A) Camera-trap photo of a pair of *G. f. fasciata* from selectively logged forest within Ranomafana National Park, and B) *G. f. grandidieri* in the Tsimanampesotse protected area along the limestone Mahafaly Plateau.
(PHOTO A by B. D. Gerber and B by H. Schütz.)

Until recently, even less was known regarding the behavior and activity of *G. f. grandidieri*. Wozencraft (1990) noted that *G. f. grandidieri* lives in natural cavities in the karstic limestone Mahafaly Plateau and may not excavate its own burrows. Subsequently, in the 1990s, twice while Goodman was camping near the Mitoho Cave, to the east of the lake and at the edge of the plateau, *G. f. grandidieri* was observed poking around the camp, presumably attracted to food reserves. It was not particularly shy and approached to within 2 m. On the basis of recent studies, some further details are available (Marquard et al. 2011): *G. f. grandidieri* is strictly nocturnal. As the Mahafaly Plateau, where this form occurs, is largely exposed limestone with an abundance of holes and crevices, these cavities are used for den sites, generally in areas without vegetation. In one case, a den was found in a hole about 3 m off the ground in the hollow of an *Albizia* tree. A latrine site was located near each den site, with scats of different ages. In this area, *G. f. grandidieri* occurs in sympatry with the introduced carnivorans *F. silvestris*, *C. lupus*, and *V. indica*.

SPECIES DISTRIBUTION AND POPULATION ECOLOGY

Areas, including official protected areas (PA), with documented records of *G. f. fasciata* include, from north to south: Loky Manambato (PA), Corridor Marojejy–Anjanaharibe-Sud–Tsaratanàna (COMATSA) Nord (PA), Marojejy (PA), Anjanaharibe-Sud (PA), Makira (PA), Farankaraina, Masoala (PA), Mananara-Nord (PA), Ambatovaky (PA), Zahamena (PA) including the Sihanaka Forest, Betampona (PA), Andevoranto, Brickaville region, Mantadia (PA), Maromizaha (PA), Ambositra-Vondrozo (PA), Ranomafana (PA), Ambinanindrano (Ifanadiana), Andringitra (PA), Pic d'Ivohibe (PA), Befotaka–Midongy du Sud (PA), Tsitongambarika (PA), and Andohahela (PA) (Ravoahangy et al. 2011; Farris et al. 2015b; Goodman et al. 2018b; N. Rakotoarison, P. Ross, B. Semel, E. Wampole, unpublished data).

Galidictis f. fasciata is a forest-dwelling animal. It is broadly distributed in eastern Madagascar at elevations from lowland to medium-altitude moist evergreen forests up to about 1500 m. This subspecies is unknown from littoral forest zones, and appears to be limited to forests resting on lateritic soils. It has not been found in high densities, and it is poorly known among people living along the forest edge. This might be associated with its nocturnal activity and the fact that it seldom ventures outside of the forest. Recent studies using noninvasive camera traps have shown that *G. f. fasciata* is rarer than other euplerid carnivorans. These recent surveys have also revealed that the spatial distribution of *G. f. fasciata* was considerably lower in, or this form was completely absent from, more degraded or fragmented forests. Multiple factors affect the spatial distribution of *G. f. fasciata*, including small-mammal activity and distance to nearby villages, as well as forest basal area and fragment size (Gerber et al. 2012b; Farris et al. 2015b).

Galidictis f. grandidieri is known mostly from the western portion of the Mahafaly Plateau and the adjacent zone to the east of Lake Tsimanampesotse. In this area, it occurs both in dry spiny thicket resting on limestone and at the foot of the plateau in a form of dry deciduous forest that has considerable habitat perturbation associated with cattle grazing. Recent work on *G. f. grandidieri* from Tsimanampesotse National Park resulted in captures of 24 unique individuals (12 adult males, five adult females, and seven juveniles) across 640 trap nights (Marquard et al. 2011). Using capture-recapture methods, the authors estimated a population density of 6.24 individuals/km^2 for the 3.13 km^2 sampling grid. Combining live captures with noninvasive transect sampling methods across high- and low-density areas, they estimated the subspecies' total occurrence or range to be 1500 km^2 (excluding small pockets of isolated suitable habitat to maintain viable populations) and the extrapolated estimate of the total number of animals to be between ~3000 and ~5000 individuals.

PEOPLE AND *GALIDICTIS*

Galidictis appears to be poorly known by local people across its range, primarily due to the species' nocturnal behavior, preference for intact habitat, and overall rarity across the landscape. At Ranomafana, only 1% of human respondents, including general members of the population and individuals, not necessarily hunters, who rarely venture into the forest at night, were familiar with or had observed *G. f. fasciata*, even at villages located near continuous forest (Kotschwar et al. 2015). At other sites in southeastern Madagascar, local informants said they were familiar with *G. f. fasciata*, but with further questioning, it was clear that they had confused this native carnivoran with the introduced civet *Viverricula indica*, which has somewhat similar pelage coloration and occurs in open areas and at the forest edge. The introduction of dogs, whether pets, hunting animals, or ferals, may also be a strong contributor to the decreasing populations of *G. f. fasciata* across its range; it shows strong avoidance of dogs roaming in relatively intact moist evergreen forests.

Galidictis fasciata and other native carnivorans are hunted and consumed across the Makira region, particularly within poor households, with an estimated 40% of hunters targeting carnivorans (Golden 2009; Golden et al. 2014). Borgerson (2016) reported that 100% of interviewed hunters in a focal village near the Masoala protected area hunt this euplerid throughout the year, with peak hunting in March, and that it is rarely a targeted species, with most captures incidental.

In the case of *G. f. grandidieri*, there are presumably few direct interactions between people and this animal, as it is nocturnal, and residents in nearby villages seldom venture into the forest at night. However, at the immediate foot of the Mahafaly Plateau, these carnivorans visit the edges of certain villages, such as Tongaenoro, at night and are known to local people. Although not measured, there is presumably a measurable negative impact of grazing domestic animals (zebu, goats, and sheep) on the vegetation, which in turn might be correlated with shifts in prey density. Furthermore, as the forest at the foot of the Mahafaly Plateau is largely open, *V. indica* occurs in this zone in sympatry with *G. f. grandidieri*, in contrast to the closed understory formations of the moist evergreen forests where *G. f. fasciata* is found.

DISEASE

Disease ecology and transmission is little studied for this genus and other euplerid carnivorans. For *G. f. fasciata* at Betampona, Rasambainarivo et al. (2018) found all tested individuals to be negative for Canine Adenovirus, Distemper Virus, and Parvovirus, as well as Feline Calcivirus (see also Rasambainarivo and Zohdy, pp. 298–302). However, of the 28 animals tested, 18% were positive for Canine Herpesvirus, 19% for toxoplasmosis, and 38% for *Leptospira*. These findings further highlight the threat posed to this and other euplerids by introduced carnivorans. *Galidictis f. grandidieri* shares introduced flea species with introduced animals (cats, dogs, chickens, mice, and rats), including mice and rats (Ehlers et al. 2019). The fleas harbored *Rickettsia* bacteria but not *Borrelia* or *Bartonella* (Ehlers et al. 2020). To our knowledge, no virological studies have been conducted on *G. f. grandidieri*.

CONSERVATION

Insufficient information is available on the distribution and population density of the two subspecies of *G. fasciata* to have a real sense of their conservation status. *Galidictis f. fasciata* appears to be broadly distributed across moist evergreen forests and occurs at relatively low density. Further, it occurs in lowland formations that continue to be cleared for swidden agriculture. Multiyear assessments of *G. f. fasciata* populations are rare but have shown very strong decreases in occupancy at one site in Makira since 2008. However, at Ranomafana, occupancy over a six-year period had changed little since 2010, but the probability of extirpation remains high (Farris et al. 2017a, 2017b). The IUCN Red List assessment for *G. f. fasciata* is Vulnerable; and *Galidictis f. grandidieri*, when considered a distinct species, is ranked as Endangered (IUCN 2020).

Galidictis f. grandidieri is considered the most threatened of Madagascar's native carnivorans due to its highly restricted range (Cartagena-Matos et al. 2017). Based on current information, this form is mostly limited to the western portion of the Mahafaly Plateau and the immediate area to the east of Lake Tsimanampesotse; hence, it has a very limited geographic distribution, although locally it is rather common (Marquard et al. 2011). A good portion of the known distribution of this subspecies falls within the Tsimanampesotse protected area. Furthermore, this rather inhospitable zone, with its near lack of fresh water, impenetrable dry spiny thicket, and razor-sharp limestone outcrops, provides another level of protection from severe human encroachment.

Subject editors: Jörg U. Ganzhorn and Steven M. Goodman

EUPLERIDAE: *MUNGOTICTIS DECEMLINEATA*, BOKYBOKY, *BOKY-BOKY*

P. M. Kappeler, L. Razafimanantsoa, and S. M. Goodman

The genus *Mungotictis*, a member of the endemic Eupleridae, contains one species, *M. decemlineata*. Recent molecular work has shown that the native carnivorans of Madagascar represent a unique radiation and remarkable examples of convergence with other families of carnivorans, including the mongooses (family Herpestidae) (see Veron et al., pp. 1863–65). Hence, the formerly used vernacular name for this species, "Narrow-striped Mongoose," is a misnomer, and now the English common name is Bokyboky, derived from the Malagasy name.

DISTRIBUTION AND TAXONOMY

Mungotictis decemlineata is a diurnal carnivoran species confined to areas of dry deciduous forest in western Madagascar between the Tsiribihina and Mangoky Rivers. Recent genetic analyses (Veron et al. 2017) confirmed the existence of two subspecies: *M. d. decemlineata*, which inhabits areas of the central west of Madagascar (central Menabe region); and *M. d. lineata*, which is found in the

southwestern portion of the island (region north of Toliara), including the southern Mikea Forest and the upper Manombo River valley (Goodman et al. 2005c).

MORPHOLOGY

Mungotictis is of relatively small size; in the nominate form, it has a mean body length of 224 mm (n = 18), tail length of 225 mm (n = 18), and mean body mass of 555.4 ± 94.3 g (n = 33) (T. C. Schneider and P. Kappeler, unpublished data). No sexual differences have been noted in coloration or size. The dorsum of the animal is a grizzled gray mixed with light brown or beige and is characterized by a series of eight to 10 broadly spaced, thin longitudinal stripes on the dorsum running from the base of the neck to the base of the tail. The fur on the underside lacks the bicolor appearance of the upperside and approaches pale brownish beige. The muzzle is relatively short and tapers to a point. The ears are somewhat short and rounded. The animal has a low bearing while walking. Its feet have pronounced webbing between the footpads, and the claws are long (Albignac 1976).

MATING AND REPRODUCTION

Reproduction in *Mungotictis decemlineata* is seasonal, with mating peaking in August in the Kirindy Forest CNFEREF. Two females that lost their pup within a month after birth mated again, in December and February, respectively, indicating pronounced flexibility of reproductive schedules. One female of known age began reproducing when she was just under three years old. Gestation length is two to three months, after which females give birth to a single offspring. Only 28% of infants (n = 21) survived their first year of life. Despite a female-biased sex ratio among juveniles, the adult sex ratio was consistently biased in favor of males across a three-year study, indicating high female mortality during the transition into adulthood. The few documented predation events involved *Cryptoprocta ferox* (Fosa), *Canis lupus* (dog), and *Acrantophis madagascariensis* (Madagascar Ground Boa).

DIET AND PREDATION

Mungotictis decemlineata consumes a wide variety of food items, including invertebrates and vertebrates. Rabeantoandro (1997) and Rasolofoniaina et al. (2019) studied the food habits of *Mungotictis* based on fecal analysis and found that it feeds mainly on insects (especially cockroaches, beetles, and spiders), which were represented in virtually all samples examined. Further, remains of a variety of small vertebrates, including lizards, frogs, birds, and small mammals (*Microgale* sp., *Echinops telfairi*, *Eliurus myoxinus*, *Microcebus murinus*, *Cheirogaleus medius*, *Mirza coquereli*, *Lepilemur*, and *Hypogeomys antimena*), were found in about 40% of fecal samples (also see Goodman and Ganzhorn, pp. 1829–38, for more details on lemur predation). *Mungotictis* generally forages by searching through ground litter and by digging into the topsoil. It also sometimes forages on fallen trees or fallen rotten wood. It has an interesting technique to dispatch snails—after finding a snail, this carnivoran either places the animal in the sun to force it to come out of its shell or smashes it against a tree trunk. A systematic experimental investigation of its cognitive abilities revealed that *Mungotictis* acquires foraging techniques via social learning and that it has capacity for causal understanding, innovative problem-solving, and other forms of behavioral flexibility (Rasolofoniaina 2020).

BEHAVIOR AND ECOLOGY

The initial behavioral research on *Mungotictis* were conducted by Albignac (1976) in the central western dry deciduous forests, and more recently this species has been studied in depth in the Kirindy Forest CNFEREF (Rabeantoandro 2020; see Kappeler et al., pp. 127–33) and surrounding areas at the northern end of its range, a zone often referred to as the central Menabe region. *Mungotictis* is forest-dwelling and most often found in areas with relatively dense understory vegetation. Its local abundance is correlated with neither forest structure nor food abundance (Woolaver et al. 2006). It is largely diurnal but can be active at night. The animal is both terrestrial and arboreal; it mainly moves on the ground but can climb trees if necessary. Ranging data and information on behavioral ecology obtained from 63 individuals revealed that *M. decemlineata* in the Kirindy Forest CNFEREF occurs at densities of 20 individuals/km^2 (T. C. Schneider and Kappeler 2016). Radio-collared females formed year-round stable units consisting of adults, juveniles, and infants. Dens of unit members occur in different contexts: 1) partially collapsed burrows in abandoned ant nests, during the dry, cold season; 2) in holes in fallen dead trees, at the beginning of the rainy season; or 3) in holes of still-standing dead or living trees up to 10 m off the ground, during the rainy season. On average, social units comprised 3.7 ± 0.4 individuals, including two adult females (Figure 14.62). The maximum recorded unit size was six individuals. Adult males formed less stable associations of two to four individuals. The composition of this species' social units was variable across years, and their cohesion changed seasonally. During the nonmating season (November–June), males were sighted in association with other males in 58% of daily scans, alone in 36%, and with female units in 6%; whereas during the mating season, males were most often sighted alone, in 61% of daily scans, but also associated with females, in 21%, or other males, in 17%.

POPULATION ECOLOGY AND GENETIC STRUCTURE

Mean home-range size of male *Mungotictis* is two to three times larger than that of females, irrespective of whether 100% or 95% minimum convex polygons (MCP) or kernels are compared (T. C. Schneider and Kappeler 2016). Males used on average an impressive 81.2 ha of forest as their home range (100% MCP), whereas females ranged over 35.5 ha. Female units occupied exclusive territories, whereas male ranges overlapped with those of several

FIGURE 14.62 **A social group of *Mungotictis decemlineata* in the dry deciduous forest of Kirindy Forest CNFEREF. The image was taken in the early morning after the group emerged from its den, the entrance of which is located next to the baobab stump. The individuals in the left and right foreground are juveniles, and the two animals toward the back of the stump are adult females.** (PHOTO by B. Rasolofoniaina.)

other males (associates and nonassociates) and up to four female ranges. Female territorial behavior was expressed by regular scent marking along home-range borders and aggression during occasional direct encounters.

A population-genetics analysis revealed a matrilinear population structure, with several neighboring female units sharing identical haplotypes (T. C. Schneider et al. 2016). Within-group female relatedness was significantly higher than expected by chance in the majority of units, whereas haplotype diversity of males was significantly higher than in females, indicating predominant female philopatry and male-biased dispersal. Nonetheless, female dispersal—in addition to more common male dispersal—was also documented among radio-collared individuals (T. C. Schneider and Kappeler 2016). Moreover, genetic paternity analyses of emergent young revealed indications for a promiscuous mating system and low levels of reproductive skew in both sexes.

A broad-scale analysis of two mitochondrial markers and a nuclear fragment from close to 50 individuals captured at four principal localities in the northern portion of the central Menabe found low sequence divergence across a 130 km–long zone, and the variation was best explained by isolation by distance (van Vuuren et al. 2012). Given that it is presumed that this species is strictly forest dwelling, this pattern is best explained by regular dispersal during periods of more continuous forest cover in the area, and given the relatively recent fragmentation of the regional dry deciduous forests, the genetic signal rests in place.

PEOPLE AND *MUNGOTICTIS*

Local people of the Sakalava cultural group do not hunt or kill this species. However, the high level of ongoing deforestation throughout the geographic range of *Mungotictis decemlineata* is likely having a strong negative effect on this species. Further, dogs used for searching out honey and hunting *Tenrec* in the forest may also have an impact on *Mungotictis* populations.

DISEASE

To our knowledge, there has been no investigation of disease ecology for *Mungotictis*. It is assumed that members of this genus are experiencing similar pressures and threats via disease transmission from introduced carnivorans, specifically free-ranging *Canis lupus* and *Felis silvestris* (cat), as other euplerids in eastern Madagascar (Rasambainarivo et al. 2018; see Rasambainarivo and Zohdy, pp. 298–302).

CONSERVATION

As a result of the threats mentioned in the previous sections, this species is categorized as Endangered on the IUCN Red List of Threatened Species (IUCN 2020) and continues to be threatened by ongoing rapid loss of habitat through deforestation.

Subject editors: Jörg U. Ganzhorn and Steven M. Goodman

EUPLERIDAE: *SALANOIA CONCOLOR*, BROWN-TAILED VONTSIRA, *SALANO*, *VONTSIRA BOKO*

Z. J. Farris and A. Murphy

The genus *Salanoia*, a member of the endemic family Eupleridae, contains a single species, *S. concolor* (for information on a recently proposed second species, *S. durrelli*, see below). *Salanoia concolor*, with its limited range across northeastern Madagascar, is perhaps the rarest and least-known species of this family. On the basis of current information, it occurs within a few protected areas from the Makira in the northeast to Tampolo in the northern central east. *Salanoia* remains little studied, and much information on its reproduction, behavior, diet, and population ecology is lacking.

TAXONOMY

Eupleridae classification and taxonomy are covered in more detail elsewhere in this chapter (see Veron et al., pp. 1863–65). Durbin et al. (2010) proposed a new species of *Salanoia*, *S. durrelli*, from Lake Alaotra, based on morphological differences, namely craniodental morphometrics. However, a recent genetic study suggests that *S. durrelli* is best considered a junior synonym of *S. concolor* (Veron et al. 2017).

MORPHOLOGY

A dark brown dorsal coat and a ventral coat of reddish brown to whitish gray around the chin and throat distinguish *Salanoia concolor* (Figure 14.63b) from its sympatric euplerid cousin *Galidia elegans* (see Farris and Goodman, pp. 1989–92). *Salanoia* lacks rings on the tail and a faint cream color on the distal portions of the ear (both features of *Galidia*) and has considerably less dense hair on the tail. The head-and-body length of *Salanoia* is 350–380 mm. The uniformly colored, dark brown tail measures 160–200 mm in length (Goodman 2012). No differences between males and females have been observed with respect to pelage color or body size. Albignac (1972a) described this species' unique dental formula—incisors 3/3, canines 1/1, premolars 4/3, and molars 2/1—which differs from that of other euplerids.

MATING AND REPRODUCTION

Salanoia may be observed as a single individual or in pairs. Camera-trap photographs from throughout the year show the species almost exclusively in pairs, as has been confirmed by direct observations at Betampona (Britt and Virkaitis 2003). Goodman (2012) reports that groups of up to five individuals have been observed; however, such observations are believed to be exceedingly rare. There is no information on this species' mating habits, but Albignac (1972a) suggests that the gestation period is about three months and the litter size is a single young. It has been proposed that *Salanoia* likely gives birth between the months of November and January, which is similar to the birthing period of the sympatrically occurring *Galidia*. However, camera-trap images from mid-October in the Makira show a female *Salanoia* carrying a nonmobile young (Figure 14.63a). It may be that *Salanoia*, much like *Galidictis* (see Farris and Goodman, pp. 1993–96), has considerable plasticity in its mating season. Additional data on wild *Salanoia* populations throughout their range are needed to fill the major gaps existing in our knowledge of the reproductive habits of this euplerid.

FIGURE 14.63 **A) *Salanoia concolor* female with infant, at the Anjanaharibe conservation site within the Makira protected area. The image was taken in October 2008 and provides important insight on the breeding and birthing season of this poorly known carnivoran. B) Adult *S. concolor* captured in degraded, fragmented forest bordering the Makira protected area. This photo shows this species' unique pelage coloration, which distinguishes it from the sympatrically occurring *Galidia elegans*.** (PHOTO A by Z. J. Farris and M. J. Kelly, and B by Z. J. Farris and A. Murphy.)

DIET AND PREDATION

Albignac (1972a) suggested that the diet of *Salanoia* consists of small rodents, birds, and amphibians; however, no data were available to our knowledge to support these suggestions. The unique dental formula of *Salanoia*, as well as its distinctly pointed rostrum, may indicate some divergence in diet from that of the sympatric vontsira species *Galidia*. Britt and Virkaitis (2003) observed *Salanoia* feeding on beetle larvae extracted from rotten wood and foraging in dead leaves at Betampona. Farris et al. (2015b) found that *Salanoia* occupancy (spatial distribution) was positively associated with bird activity, which could indicate a habitat-mediated or a predator-prey relationship. Further investigation on *Salanoia* diet is needed to better our understanding of these relationships.

BEHAVIOR

There is very little information on basic ecology or behavior of *Salanoia*. Albignac (1972a) believed that this exclusively diurnal species shelters in tree trunks or burrows during the night. In the Makira, *Salanoia* activity seems to peak in the mid-morning hours, before noon, coinciding with that of the sympatric *Galidia*, and these two species overlap in temporal activity 91% of their time (Farris et al. 2015a). *Salanoia* also overlapped considerably in temporal activity with introduced and at least partially feral *Canis lupus* (dog), increasing the likelihood of interactions (Farris et al. 2015c). *Salanoia* appear to strongly avoid areas where free-ranging *C. lupus* and *Felis silvestris* (cat) are active (Farris et al. 2015c), and a multiyear assessment in Makira provided further evidence of this negative interaction, as *Salanoia* declined in occupancy by 60% at a site after it was colonized by these two introduced carnivorans (Farris et al. 2017a). *Salanoia* had the lowest probability of detection across the Makira of all native and introduced carnivorans, and its detection had a strong negative response to human activity (Farris et al. 2015b).

Salanoia emits grunts and guttural squeaks when searching for food and when in danger or a different loud grunt noise when threatened, at the same time erecting its tail and associated fur (Goodman 2012). Britt (1999) states that based on information from local people, *Salanoia* uses this posture to determine if another animal is potential prey and whether to attack or flee. No information is currently available on the home range of this species, though Albignac (1973) estimates it may be larger than that of *Galidia*. *Salanoia* has been observed climbing trees 5–10 m off the ground, likely in search of invertebrates. There are also reports that this species hunts poultry, but based on its known diet and dental structure, these reports, if true, are presumably of misidentified *Galidia*.

SPECIES DISTRIBUTION AND ECOLOGY

Salanoia is an exclusive forest dweller occurring at elevational ranges from 200 to 1020 m, though reports from Tampolo suggest it also occurs near sea level. This genus has one of the most limited geographic ranges among euplerids, second only to that of *Galidictis fasciata grandidieri* (see Farris and Goodman, pp. 1993–96). It occurs in the northeast to the northern central east, in the moist evergreen forests of Makira, Masoala, Mananara-Nord, Tampolo, Lake Alaotra, Zahamena, Ankeniheny-Zahamena, and Betampona (F. Hawkins 2016b). Appropriate habitat exists in the protected areas of Marotandrano and Ambatovaky, two areas falling within the known distribution of this species, but little is known about the locally occurring euplerids at these sites.

No reliable estimates of population density are available; however, *Salanoia* had the lowest occupancy probability (defined as the probability that a species occupies a site while taking into account the probability of detecting a species should it be there) of any native carnivoran across Makira, occurring at only two of seven study sites (Farris et al. 2015b). At Betampona, *Salanoia* occupancy was much higher, and direct observations of the species are much more common (Rasambainarivo et al. 2017). Britt (1999) reported that *Salanoia* was observed frequently by researchers at Betampona, and the population was reproducing successfully in the protected area. The Lake Alaotra population is believed to number only a few hundred individuals (Durbin et al. 2010).

Salanoia seems to be limited to contiguous forest, having not been seen in any forest fragments isolated by 5 km or more from intact forest. In slight contrast, Britt and Virkaitis (2003) and Farris et al. (2015b) obtained multiple observations of *Salanoia* within disturbed and/or degraded forests at Betampona and Makira, respectively. The latter authors believe *Salanoia* is associated with forested sites adjacent or with access to large wetland habitat. The two Makira sites where *Salanoia* was detected border existing or recently degraded wetland areas, as does the Lake Alaotra population. Much information on *Salanoia* distribution and ecology is still lacking and is desperately needed to allow researchers to develop effective, targeted conservation and management plans for this endemic carnivoran.

PEOPLE AND *SALANOIA*

Borgerson (2016) reported that across the Masoala Peninsula, people hunt *Salanoia* throughout the year, though this is considered opportunistic and incidental. Only five individuals were reported to have been captured/consumed during the two-year study period. It is believed that *Salanoia* is hunted and consumed across its range, similar to other endemic carnivorans. However, its overall rarity and apparent low population density likely leads to *Salanoia* being consumed less often than other native species. Farris et al. (2015a) found that *Salanoia* overlaps considerably in temporal activity with free-ranging *C. lupus* and avoids sites where *C. lupus* and *F. silvestris* activity are high. Additionally, the probability of *Salanoia* detection via camera traps had a strong negative relationship with human activity. These findings point to the fact that *Salanoia* is responding negatively to anthropogenic encroachment and disturbance across its range.

DISEASE

The only study of *Salanoia* disease ecology was conducted in Betampona (Rasambainarivo et al. 2017, 2018), where two individuals were tested and found to be free of evidence of Canine Adenovirus,

Distemper Virus, Herpesvirus, or Parvovirus; Feline Calicivirus; or toxoplasmosis. However, one of the two individuals tested positive for *Leptospira* bacteria (see also Rasambainarivo and Zohdy, pp. 298–302).

CONSERVATION

The greatest threat to *Salanoia concolor* populations across its range is the loss of suitable habitat and the subsequent encroachment of anthropogenic pressures (e.g., hunting, invasive species, disease transmission). Farris et al. (2017a) showed that *Salanoia* occupancy (spatial distribution) at one study site in Makira declined by >60% from 2008 to 2013, resulting in a high probability of local extirpation. Additional long-term studies and surveys are needed to allow us to better understand the population dynamics of this species across its limited geographic range. Although the IUCN status of *S. concolor* has been assessed as Vulnerable, we suggest that it is likely one of the most threatened native carnivorans, second to *Galidictis fasciata grandidieri*, given its limited range, reliance upon intact, undisturbed forest, and overall rarity or low density across its range. Additional studies of this native carnivoran are desperately needed to ensure its protection and persistence.

Subject editor: Steven M. Goodman

VIVERRIDAE: *VIVERRICULA INDICA*, SMALL INDIAN CIVET, *JABOADY*

A. Murphy and Z. J. Farris

Viverricula indica, a member of the family Viverridae, is introduced to Madagascar. A habitat generalist, it is widespread across the island, typically occurring outside native forests, in formations including anthropogenic grasslands and the vicinity of villages, or in degraded and fragmented forests. Exclusively nocturnal, it might be mistaken for the endemic *Fossa fossana* (Spotted Fanaloka) (see Kerridge et al., pp. 1986–89), a member of the family Eupleridae that is similar in size and color. *Viverricula indica* feeds on endemic small mammals and birds, and therefore poses an indirect threat to Madagascar's endemic carnivorans via interference competition.

TAXONOMY

Recent genetic analyses identified four subspecies of *Viverricula indica* (Gaubert et al. 2017), one of which has been introduced to Madagascar, *V. i. indica*. Its arrival on the island probably dates to sometime after the ninth century, via western Indian Ocean traders, and its introduction is presumed to be related to "wild farming" of the animal for the collection of its perineal gland, the oil of which was used in Arab and southern Asian perfumery (Jennings and Veron 2009; Choudhury et al. 2015; Gaubert et al. 2017). Its Malagasy vernacular name, *jaboady*, is probably derived from Kiswahili. Skeletal remains of a viverrid, almost certainly *V. indica*, were identified from archaeological remains recovered at Mahilaka, an entrepôt of Islamic traders in the northwest, and dated to 1030 BP (years before present) (Rakotozafy 1996). *Viverricula* remains have been found at various additional paleontological and archaeological sites. The exact source population(s) of this species' introduction to Madagascar is unclear (Gaubert et al. 2017).

MORPHOLOGY

Viverricula indica resembles the endemic euplerid *Fossa fossana*, sharing a somewhat similar pelage coloration. Both species range from tan to light brown, are spotted, and are digitigrade (walk on their digits). However, *Viverricula* has markings on the neck and head (Figure 14.64), whereas *Fossa* has a uniform light tan coloration on the head. In addition, the feet of *Viverricula* are typically darker in color than those of *Fossa*. Both species have a ringed tail, but in *Viverricula* the rings are wider, dark, and more prominent than in *Fossa*, which has less prominent and distinctly fainter markings. In addition, the ears of *Viverricula* are smaller than those of *Fossa*. Finally, *Viverricula* shows some sexual dimorphism and, with a body weight of 2–4 kg, is larger than *Fossa* (Nowak et al. 2005).

MATING AND REPRODUCTION

There is little information on mating and reproduction of *Viverricula* in the wild, and virtually nothing is known about these aspects of the introduced Madagascar population. It is thought that the species can enter estrus at any time of the year, and in Madagascar the breeding season is believed to be from September to October. Based on observations of Asian animals in captivity, it seems that *Viverricula* might have two estrus periods, one from February to April, and another from August to September (Xu et al. 1995). *Viverricula* appears to be polygynandrous, with males mating with multiple females and females mating with multiple males during a given breeding season. During periods of estrus, both sexes mark objects within their environment, including other *Viverricula*

FIGURE 14.64 ***Viverricula indica*, a carnivoran species introduced to Madagascar. This camera-trap image was taken in the Lohan'sanjinja Forest, bordering the Makira protected area.** (PHOTO by Z. J. Farris.)

individuals, with glandular secretions. Copulation is preceded by the male chasing the female, emitting a *da-da-da* sound, and sniffing the anogenital area of the female (Hayssen et al. 1993; Xu et al. 1995). Gestation in captivity is approximately two months, with females giving birth to two to five young in a ground hollow or burrow (Lekagul and McNeely 1977). Young are weaned by the age of four and a half months.

DIET AND PREDATION

There is very little quantitative information on the food types of *Viverricula indica* in the wild. Across the species' broad native geographic range the diet is variable. P. C. Wang et al. (1976), in northern China, found that mammals, particularly rodents, and plants were important in this carnivoran's diet; and Chuang and Lee (1997), in Taiwan, found that insects had the highest relative importance, followed by earthworms, plants, and mammals. H. Wang and Fuller (2003), examining *Viverricula* scat recovered in southeastern China, identified nine food types, with rodents the most frequent, followed by insects and birds. Petersen et al. (2019) found that rodent biomass influenced *Viverricula* distribution during annual periods of rodent scarcity in Thailand. However, this species seems to be a generalist, capable of changing its diet depending on seasonal availability and scarcity (Chuang and Lee 1997). This generalist nature makes it a possible threat to native carnivorans living on islands where *Viverricula* has been introduced (Choudhury et al. 2015). There is no information on the diet of *Viverricula* on Madagascar, although based on its native dietary breadth, it is certainly likely that it is preying on Madagascar's endemic rodents and birds as well as lemurs (see Goodman and Ganzhorn, pp. 1829–38).

BEHAVIOR

Viverricula rests primarily in burrows or hollow logs, including abandoned burrows dug by other species (Nowak et al. 2005). It is terrestrial, although it is able to climb. *Viverricula* is generally thought to be solitary outside of the breeding season. Scent marking via urine and feces may pass along information to other individuals, in addition to marking out territorial boundaries (Xu et al. 1995). One radio-tracked male in Thailand had a home range of 3.1 km^2 (Rabinowitz 1991).

In its native geographic range, *Viverricula* is nocturnal, and this pattern holds on Madagascar. Gerber et al. (2012a) found the species in southeastern Madagascar to be active between 1800 and 600 h, with an activity peak after midnight. This same pattern was found by Farris et al. (2015a) in northeastern moist evergreen forest, with activity peaks from 1800 to 2200 h, at midnight, and then before 600 h. In the western dry deciduous forests of Ankarafantsika, *Viverricula* was primarily active at dusk and during the evenings (Merson et al. 2019a). All these different studies on Madagascar found *V. indica* to overlap temporally in activity periods with *F. fossana*. More specifically, in the study of Farris et al. (2015a), out of three introduced carnivorans—*V. indica*, *Canis lupus* (dog), and *Felis silvestris* (cat)—*V. indica* had the greatest number of temporal overlapping relationships with native carnivorans, specifically *Galidictis fasciata* (0.83 temporal overlap estimate), *Cryptoprocta ferox* (0.82), *Fossa fossana* (0.80), and *Eupleres goudotti* (0.74; Farris et al. 2015a). These relatively high rates of temporal overlap might explain the spatial avoidance relationships that Farris et al. (2015c) found at the same sites, with *V. indica* co-occurring at the same survey locations as *E. goudotti* and *G. fasciata* less often than would be expected at random.

SPECIES DISTRIBUTION AND POPULATION ECOLOGY

In its native geographic range, and based on ecological niche modeling, *Viverricula* occurs mainly at lower elevations, with no preference for forest types, found equally in humid and deciduous forests and ranging from mostly low elevations (below 600 m) up to 1500 m (Jennings and Veron 2011). Despite being predicted to occur in degraded forests at lower rates than in more intact forests, *Viverricula* is believed to be quite tolerant of habitat degradation and fragmentation, occurring in humid forest fragments, tea and coffee plantations, bushland, grassland, marshes, inactive plantations, and towns and villages (Mudappa et al. 2007; M. Chen et al. 2009; Holden and Neang 2009; Choudhury 2013; Choudhury et al. 2015).

On Madagascar, *Viverricula* is widely distributed across much of the island, including southwestern dry spiny thickets (Goodman et al. 2018b). It has been found from sea level up to 1500–2000 m (P. D. Jenkins and Carleton 2005). In southeastern Madagascar, Gerber et al. (2012b) detected *Viverricula* only in forest fragments. Kotschwar Logan et al. (2015) interviewed local people in that same area about carnivorans. These interviews indicated that *Viverricula* was found everywhere, with approximately 88% of communities having at least one observation of the species, in varied habitats

including forest fragments, pine plantations, and along major roads. This species has been observed in open anthropogenic grasslands in the Central Highlands, many tens of kilometers from any native habitat (S. M. Goodman, unpublished data). In the northeast, Farris et al. (2015b) found *Viverricula* to be notably uncommon, having the lowest landscape occupancy estimate of any introduced carnivoran. The only factor that seemed to influence *Viverricula* occupancy was distance to nearby villages, where it had higher occupancy estimates when not so distant (Farris et al. 2015b).

PEOPLE AND *VIVERRICULA*

Viverricula indica has been used for a variety of reasons across its geographic range. The use of its perineal gland secretion in perfume and medicine might be the reason it was released during the Islamic period on islands in the western Indian Ocean, including Madagascar. It is hunted for meat across a large part of its range, including Madagascar, where it is captured mostly by nontargeted snaring (Choudhury et al. 2015). Farris et al. (2015b) found that *Viverricula* was the most widely consumed carnivoran in the northeast of the island, taken at a rate of 90 individuals per year. A researcher noticed dried *Viverricula* and *Galidia* tails hanging from the rear-view mirror of a taxi-brousse on the road from Sambava to Iharana (Vohémar) (Goodman 2012), a practice presumably associated with some magical-medicinal aspect. Retaliatory killings of *V. indica* by local people also occur; 40% of locals interviewed in southeastern Madagascar, despite attributing less than 1% of livestock/poultry predation to *Viverricula*, saw the species as harmful, owing to its potential for killing domestic livestock (Kotschwar Logan et al. 2015).

DISEASE

Wild *Viverricula* outside of Madagascar is known to be affected by a number of external and internal parasites and diseases (Nowak et al. 2005; Sreedevi and Balakrishnan 2006), but no comprehensive study has been conducted on the island to quantify these aspects or their role in transmitting diseases to other species. It is likely that these animals are a reservoir of different pathogens and on Madagascar transmit diseases to endemic euplerid carnivorans and other mammals.

CONSERVATION

Because *Viverricula indica* is introduced to Madagascar, the local population is not a conservation priority. Instead, this introduced carnivoran presents an important threat to a number of native mammals. Multiple studies, referenced throughout this contribution, have highlighted the impact of *V. indica* on the spatial and temporal patterns of native carnivorans. Additional research is needed, particularly on disease transmission, to enable researchers to better understand the full impact of this introduced species on threatened wildlife across Madagascar.

Subject editor: Steven M. Goodman

ARTIODACTYLA, SUIDAE: *POTAMOCHOERUS LARVATUS*, AFRICAN BUSH PIG, *LAMBO*, *LAMBODIA*, *LAMBOALA*, *ANTSANGA*

S. M. Goodman and V. Andrianjakarivelo

Two species of bush pigs are classically recognized to occur in the Afrotropical region: *Potamochoerus porcus*, living in the equatorial regions of western and central Africa; and *P. larvatus*, found in eastern and southern Africa and Madagascar (Grubb 1993). On Madagascar, *P. larvatus* occurs only in a wild state and is common in intact and degraded forested zones and agricultural areas in close proximity to forest. It is considered to be a harmful species.

For decades, there has been some debate about whether the occurrence of *P. larvatus* on Madagascar was the result of natural colonization in recent geological history or introduction by Bantu people sailing from Africa to the island an estimated 1000–500 BP (years before present) (Pierron et al. 2017). Recent molecular studies of African and Malagasy populations of *P. larvatus* point toward human intervention. Other than naturalized deer species known from the island, of which wild populations have disappeared in the past decades (see Goodman and Soarimalala, pp. 1737–69), *P. larvatus* is the only living wild ungulate on Madagascar. Genetic studies by Lee et al. (2020), based on both mitochondrial and nuclear markers, indicate that the species is introduced to the island and similar to populations from central southern Africa (Zimbabwe). However, in this study, genetic samples from coastal southeastern Africa (Mozambique) were lacking, which might be a more likely candidate for the introduction source. In any case, it is presumed that the founder animals physically brought to Madagascar were at least partially domesticated (to have survived the considerable boat ride), their ancestors subsequently became naturalized, and today *P. larvatus* is known on the island only as a feral species.

Two subspecies of *P. larvatus* have been classically recognized on Madagascar (Lönnberg 1910): *P. l. hova*, localized on the east side of the island and characterized by russet fur and larger size than the nominate form; and *P. l. larvatus*, found on the western side of Madagascar and diagnosed by dark fur and smaller size. Several taxonomists, however, have previously noted that the reputed Malagasy forms of *P. larvatus* are indistinguishable from African populations (e.g., Major 1897b; Grubb 1993). The genetic work of Lee et al. (2020) found shared haplotypes and no genetic difference between Malagasy animals from the two regions of the island, and in a conclusive manner showed that the bush pigs on Madagascar form a metapopulation and most likely represent a single introduction to the island.

DESCRIPTION

Potamochoerus is recognizable by its distinctive porcine aspect, including a big head with an elongate snout that is hard and very mobile for digging in the soil (Figure 14.65). In males the canines are developed, serving as defensive weapons. Males have several furred tufts or crests adorned with longer hair: one below the eyes, another on the jowls and upper throat, and the last on the midline from the nape to middle back. In older males the throat "beards" are very pronounced, but they are less developed in young males (Figure 14.65a). The ears, long and pointed, end with hair tufts of variable hue. The coat has long and stiff gray hairs, which are not very dense and are longer and more bristly on the back, running from the nape to the lower back. The body fur is a reddish brown but becomes darker with age, and as mentioned above, there is some variation on Madagascar between eastern and western animals. Young individuals have yellowish and blackish longitudinal streaks that later disappear and, when they reach subadult age, are replaced by grayish fur (Figure 14.65b). *Potamochoerus larvatus* is the largest wild, albeit feral, living terrestrial mammal on Madagascar. Adults vary in total body length from 90 to 120 cm, with tails from 30 to 40 cm long. At the shoulder they measure from 60 to 80 cm. The average weight of females is 55 kg, and males can reach 70 kg (Paulian 1984).

GEOGRAPHIC AND ELEVATIONAL DISTRIBUTION

The occurrence of *P. larvatus* has been noted in all regions of Madagascar, although with a few exceptions the animal is never locally common. It has a considerable capacity to adapt to different ecological settings (Vercammen et al. 1993), including such widely variable habitats as intact and disturbed moist evergreen forests, deciduous dry forests, and dry spiny thickets. Its presence in an area is partially dependent on water, on abundance of food, and to a lesser extent on the vegetation cover; hence, it is notably rare in the dry spiny thickets of the southwest, where it is found only near permanent water sources. It also occurs in open areas, such as agricultural zones or secondary forests, as well as different types of grasslands, generally in close proximity to forested areas and where human hunting pressure is not too strong. The density of these animals seems notably higher in protected forested areas, where they are safe from their main predator, people (Goutard 1999). They are unknown to occur in the vicinity of urban areas but also can be found near isolated hamlets, particularly during the period of crop planting and harvesting. They occur across an elevational gradient from sea level to above forest line, at 2000 m on massifs such as Andringitra (S. M. Goodman, unpublished data).

ECOLOGY, BEHAVIOR, AND REPRODUCTION

Potamochoerus is omnivorous but its diet varies according to the season and availability of food. It generally consumes roots, tubers, and rhizomes but also leaves, fruits, and grasses. Animal prey, such as earthworms, insects, mollusks, crabs, reptiles, small birds, and small mammals, is also taken, as well as bird eggs and carrion. It will

FIGURE 14.65 **Camera traps placed in forest settings have provided a remarkable window into the lives of secretive and nocturnal forest-dwelling animals (see Farris et al., pp. 1806–11, for details on this technique), such as *Potamochoerus larvatus*. The images presented here were taken in the Anjanaharibe site within the Makira protected area. A) A presumed young adult male *P. larvatus* with a somewhat distinct "beard" and notably massive body, 8 October 2012. B) Family group including the adult, based on context a female, in the middle front; a subadult behind her; and four young individuals with yellowish longitudinal streaks, under the adult and in the foreground. One of the paired camera traps can be seen just off the ground behind the female's muzzle.** (PHOTOS by Z. J. Farris.)

often forage within forested areas, but as discussed below (see Impacts), often leaves such areas to feed in agricultural zones and other types of open areas. For example, around Ankarafantsika, it will visit grasslands and consume the fruits of *Strychnos spinosa* (Loganiaceae) during the period of highest abundance, from mid-May to mid-August (Rouillé et al. 2014).

These animals are massive and powerful. They are difficult to observe because of their timid character, nocturnal habits, and sensitivity to the proximity of humans, particularly in areas where they are hunted. During the day, they hide in bushes, under rocks, in holes, or in caves and become active only toward sunset. However, their presence in an area is easily recognizable by a variety of spoor, including droppings, distinct signs of digging, and foot tracks. In regions of the island where hunting pressure is not too heavy, they are partially crepuscular. Shifts in this animal's activities are associated with season and food availability. On Nosy Mangabe, for example, this species is less shy in winter when food resources are rare; it is easy to observe during the day and does not hesitate to approach human habitations near the forest edge in search of food (Andrianjakarivelo 2000).

Little is known about the ecology of Malagasy populations of *P. larvatus*, and most of the information presented below is based on African populations (Vercammen et al. 1993). These animals are notably gregarious and generally live in troops, which on Madagascar can number 10–15 individuals (Decary 1950). Each group is composed of a dominant male, a dominant female, subadult females, and immatures (Figure 14.65b). Troops can be very mobile within an area, with home ranges of between 4 and 10 km^2 that contain water, plant cover, food, and sometimes mud pools for bathing.

The reproductive cycle of *Potamochoerus* is seasonal. Factors such as food availability, photoperiod, and temperature play important roles in triggering the start of breeding. Birth normally takes place at the beginning of the rainy season (October–December) in the eastern and northern portions of Madagascar (Decary 1950). Sexual maturity is reached at 17–22 months of age (Kimmel 1998). Within a group, only the dominant couple reproduces. The female gives birth to a maximum of six to eight young per litter after a 110- to 120-day gestation period (Mauget 1991; Seydack 1991; Vercammen et al. 1993). The male and the female raise the young, and they can be very aggressive during this period. Starting at the age of about eight months, the young start to disperse from the family group (Goutard 1999). Bad weather, food scarcity, and predation pressure are the most important causes of juvenile mortality (Seydack 1990, 1991). On Madagascar, the carnivoran *Cryptoprocta ferox* (see Gerber and Hawkins, pp. 1978–83) is often considered the main wild predator of young *P. larvatus*, and around Ranomafana National Park hunting dogs are reported to kill these animals at night (Valenta et al. 2016).

There are cases of hybridization between *Potamochoerus* and domestic pigs (*Sus scrofa*) in several countries in western and central Africa (Simoons 1953; Vercammen et al. 1993). This phenomenon has also been reported in zones of Madagascar where domestic pigs are free-ranging, such as near Katsepy, Mahajamba, and Soalala in the west (Goutard 1999). *Sus* possesses 34 pairs of chromosomes, and *Potamochoerus* 38 pairs (Melander and Melander 1980). It is not known whether these hybrids are fertile, but there is recent confirmation that hybrids exist on Madagascar (Jori 2000).

On the African continent, *Potamochoerus* is a known host for ticks that are the vectors of African swine fever; in recent years, this subject has been examined in detail on Madagascar and in particular the role this member of Suidae and its associated ticks play in the transmission of this disease to domestic pigs (Roger et al. 2001; Ravaomanana et al. 2011; Jori et al. 2013; Rouillé et al. 2014). Although *P. larvatus* can be infected by African swine fever, it apparently does not show physical manifestations of the disease, and there is little evidence that it spreads it to domestic pigs. However, it is plausible that *Potamochoerus* × *Sus* hybrids are more sensitive to the virus (Jori 2000). The confirmation of the existence of such cross-genera hybrids on Madagascar is important, insofar as it enables the identification of their potential role in the transmission of African swine fever in Madagascar.

IMPACTS

In general, *Potamochoerus* is considered a harmful animal by the Malagasy. According to the Malagasy Government Decret no. 2006–400 of 13 June 2006, *P. larvatus* is classified as "nuisible" and is listed in the appendix to the decree as category II, which includes species that can be hunted, captured, and consumed without authorization throughout the calendar year. The devastation these animals cause is evident on occasion in farming areas: they often leave forested zones after dusk to raid fields of cassava, sweet potatoes, corn, and even rice and sugarcane. During the course of a night, a farmer's subsistence agricultural plot can be completely or largely destroyed. *Potamochoerus* predation on several endemic Malagasy animal species has been cited as a possible reason for those animals' decline. For example, on the Soalala Peninsula, *P. larvatus* has been considered an important factor in the population reduction of *Astrochelys yniphora*, an endemic species of tortoise (see Pedrono et al., pp. 1463–68). About 2% of this tortoise's nests are predated on by *P. larvatus* (Pedrono et al. 2000).

There are few quantitative data on the impact of *P. larvatus* on the Malagasy flora, although bush pigs' constant digging in the ground and often over considerable areas of forest understory is presumed to have a negative effect on the establishment of young trees. These animals have both harmful and beneficial effects on plants. For example, in the Nosy Mangabe Special Reserve they are important dispersers of the seeds of certain plants, most notably *Uapaca ferruginea* (Phyllanthaceae), while their destructive consumption of seeds of *Canarium boivinii* (Burseraceae) impacts the regeneration of this tree (Andrianjakarivelo 2000). In certain areas of the island they feed extensively on the fruits of introduced and invasive tree species, such as *Psidium cattleyanum* (Myrtaceae), and readily disperse their seeds.

Across many areas of Madagascar, *Potamochoerus* is hunted with traps, dogs, or rarely firearms, for their meat or because of agricultural damage (see Golden et al., pp. 204–17, for a detailed account on hunting and consumption of this animal in the northeast and Rakotoarivony 2017 for the west). In zones of the island with elevated populations of *P. larvatus*, these animals constitute not only an important meat source but also the means for extra income for rural populations. For example, near Marovoay (Mahajanga), revenues from meat sales represent significant income

for hunters, who catch on average 10 bush pigs per month (Jori 2000). However, this trading decreases considerably during the hot months, when hunting is less efficient, and in other areas of the island there is considerable seasonal variation in the principal hunting period (Rakotoarivony 2017).

As mentioned above, this animal is classified by Malagasy law as an agricultural pest and is subject to year-round hunting; as such, it could conceivably provide a constant meat source for certain rural human populations and at the same time decrease bushmeat hunting pressure on native mammals, particularly lemurs. Such hunting pressure on *P. larvatus* would also reduce levels of crop destruction. For some peoples, such as the Sakalava and the Antakarana, or religious groups, most notably Muslims, meat of this animal is traditionally considered unclean and taboo for consumption. These taboos provide protection for this species, and populations abound in certain regions. Commercial or sport hunting of these animals requires special permits issued by government authorities, as does hunting with a rifle.

Subject editors: Jörg U. Ganzhorn and Steven M. Goodman

MURIDAE: *RATTUS*—ECOLOGY, INVASIVENESS, AND IMPACTS

T. M. Randriamoria, B. Ramasindrazana, V. Soarimalala, and S. M. Goodman

Rodents of the family Muridae and specifically of the genus *Rattus* are an excellent example of a group of invasive animals that have colonized most of the world through human transport. This is at least in part associated with their generalist "jack-of-all-trades" habits in a range of different ecosystems and their high reproductive output. The ability of these animals to live adjacent to humans has facilitated their transport (Alderton 1996). *Rattus rattus* (Black Rat) and *R. norvegicus* (Brown Rat) are established in many different ecological settings across the world and are among the most widespread and problematic invasive animals (Towns et al. 2006; Angel et al. 2009). Both *R. rattus* (see Figure 14.30a) and *R. norvegicus* (see Figure 14.30b) have been introduced to Madagascar.

On the basis of a comparison of the records of zoological expeditions by Major (1896b) and Webb (1954), and recent investigations, it would appear that the spread of *Rattus* into native forest habitats on the island occurred only within the 20th century. Webb (1954) noted *Rattus* in eastern forests and in remote areas away from villages and hamlets. Further, he made the important observation that *Rattus* species are highly adaptable to living in new environmental conditions and breed more quickly than native rodents of the subfamily Nesomyinae. In this contribution we review the biology, ecology, and invasive aspects of these two species of *Rattus* on Madagascar. For more historical information and aspects on their zoonotic disease potential see Ramasindrazana et al. (pp. 1872–80).

RATTUS RATTUS, BLACK RAT, ALSO KNOWN AS SHIP RAT, ROOF RAT, HOUSE RAT, *VOALAVO*

Populations of *Rattus rattus* on Madagascar are from two successful introduction events, one in the extreme north of the island and the other farther south (Brouat et al. 2014). The latter was the source of a large spatial expansion, which may have initially started from an original area located on the southern coast. Seafarers from the Arabian Peninsula with entrepôts in eastern Africa and on Indian Ocean islands probably brought the species to Madagascar during the Middle Ages, when there was an increase in the movements of humans and trade goods across the Indian Ocean (Tollenaere et al. 2010; Brouat et al. 2014).

Ecology

Today, *Rattus rattus* is widespread across Madagascar and occurs in virtually all natural and anthropogenic habitats on the island, including homes, fields, and natural vegetation formations from sea level up to 2500 m (Goodman 1995; Duplantier and Duchemin 2003b; Andrianjakarivelo et al. 2005; Duplantier et al. 2005; Maminirina et al. 2008). This species is often commensal with humans in rural and urban areas but also can be found in remote forest areas tens of kilometers from the nearest human installation. It is more common in areas with water or at least moist soil conditions and digs burrows and galleries around buildings and water evacuation systems. *Rattus rattus* is also found in undisturbed or degraded natural vegetation formations, including moist evergreen forests, dry deciduous forests, and dry spiny thickets. Its ability to colonize forest areas may be related at least in part to the presence of water sources, which might explain its relative scarcity in dry vegetation formations (Soarimalala and Goodman 2011). In moist evergreen forests, this species is more abundant along streams, which are presumed to act as important dispersion corridors between low-elevation agricultural fields and upland forest areas.

Within favorable environmental conditions, *R. rattus* can breed throughout the year (Duplantier and Rakotondravony 1999), and females give birth three to nine times per year, to up to 10 young rats per birth (A. D. S. Rakotondravony 1992; M. Rasamoelina and Andriamalala 1999). This high population growth potential is also accentuated by young of this species reaching sexual maturity in 68 days and a gestation period of between 20 and 22 days. So, theoretically, a pair can have hundreds of descendants in a year and millions

in three years. However, in general, the average annual litters of a given female do not exceed 25 young. There is evidence that females can also regulate birth rates (A. D. S. Rakotondravony 1992), and in forests and agricultural fields breeding is discontinuous and rather favored during the rainy season, when food resources are more abundant.

Rattus rattus is mainly nocturnal and has an omnivorous diet. In forested and adjacent anthropogenic sites in the central east (Moramanga District), based on stable carbon and nitrogen isotope values, it has been found that *R. rattus* has an extremely wide foraging niche, including food sources from several trophic levels and encompassing the isotopic space covered by the complete local endemic forest-dwelling Malagasy small-mammal community (Dammhahn et al. 2017). This study also found that the stable isotope signature of this species showed a tendency to seasonal variation and differences between natural forests and anthropogenic habitats, further indicating plasticity in feeding niches. Moreover, evidence has been found of frequent dispersal movements for this species between natural forest and anthropogenic habitats.

On Madagascar, movements of *R. rattus* between different types of anthropogenic habitats have also been shown. For example, based on trapping studies at two east coast sites, this species shifted seasonally to villages, particularly around houses, during the period of rice harvest or food scarcity in secondary forested habitat (Rasolozaka 1998). Using rhodamine B as a marker, S. Rahelinirina et al. (2010a) demonstrated that in eastern Madagascar, individuals of this species move regularly between houses, adjacent sisal plantations, and irrigated rice fields, and up to 350 m over a three-month period, associated with food availability.

Invasive Aspects

Rattus rattus is considered among the top 100 of the world's worst invasive organisms (Lowe et al. 2000). In Madagascar, it is known as a crop pest (G. Rasamoelina et al. 1997; FAO and PAM 2013; Soarimalala et al. 2019), causing significant damage to rice and other crops, mainly cassava, sweet potatoes, and tomatoes (Duplantier and Rakotondravony 1999), and corn and beans (FAO and PAM 2013). Until recently, there were few published data on the level of destruction it causes (Swanepoel et al. 2017). *Rattus rattus* invasions have been reported in several regions of Madagascar, including Boeny, Atsimo Atsinanana, Vatovavy Fitovinany, Atsinanana, Analanijirofo, and Haute Matsiatra (FAO and PAM 2013). Each year damage caused by rats increases, and it can reach 15–20% of the rice harvest in certain localities. In the Boeny Region, for example, the evaluation of the damage caused by rats on irrigated rice plots is estimated at around 1.2%, which corresponds at the national level to the equivalent of the harvest of 10,000 ha of rice fields (G. Rasamoelina et al. 1997). In the Lake Alaotra region, the average value of preharvest damage was less than 100 kg of rice per hectare of paddy field (Salvioni 1991). In a study conducted in anthropogenic habitats in central and eastern regions of the island, it has been found that this species was involved in damaging crops (rice, cassava, pineapple, banana, sugarcane), destroying and consuming food stocks, gnawing holes into clothes, and damaging different types of household utensils (Soarimalala et al. 2019).

In certain natural forests, agricultural fields, and village settings, *R. rattus* represents more than 95% of rodents among the small mammals captured during site inventories (Goodman et al. 1997a; Duplantier and Rakotondravony 1999). In areas where *R. rattus* has colonized natural habitats, which range from degraded to intact forests, there is an apparent concordant decline, based on trap captures, of endemic rodents (subfamily Nesomyinae), which for the most part are strictly forest dwelling. However, direct impact of *R. rattus* on the endemic Malagasy mammalian fauna has been difficult to assess to date (Ganzhorn 2003; Miljutin and Lehtonen 2008), partly owing to a lack of information on its diet. Inference on dietary overlap (Goodman and Sterling 1996), as well as external and craniodental morphological characteristics (Miljutin and Lehtonen 2008), suggest interference and exploitation competition for the same resources between rats and indigenous rodents (Dammhahn et al. 2017).

Rattus rattus is known as the host of different ectoparasites (see Ramasindrazana et al., pp. 1872–80; Duchemin et al., pp. 1074–80; Klompen and Apanaskevich, pp. 894–99), and a number of zoonotic diseases can be transmitted to endemic taxa and negatively affect them (see contributions in chapter 6), resulting in an increase of the invasion success of rats. For example, at a forested site in the Central Highlands, *Yersinia pestis* (the bubonic plague bacterium) was isolated from the endemic tenrec *Hemicentetes nigriceps* (Highland Streaked Tenrec) even though the role of this mammal as a reservoir is not yet confirmed (Duplantier et al. 2005). Movement of *Rattus rattus* between different habitats might also increase the probability of disease transmission. In some areas of Madagascar, this rat and its associated fleas are a reservoir for bubonic plague (Duchemin 2003), and it is considered the principal rodent involved in the rural plague cycle, and two fleas, *Xenopsylla cheopis* (introduced) and *Synopsyllus fonquerniei* (endemic), are known as the primary vectors (Duplantier et al. 2005).

RATTUS NORVEGICUS, BROWN RAT, ALSO KNOWN AS COMMON RAT, STREET RAT, SEWER RAT, NORWAY RAT, *VOALAVO*, *VOALAVO SIEDOA*

The source population of this *Rattus* species is in Asia, specifically southeastern Siberia and northern China (Musser and Carleton 1993, 2005). Its colonization history in Madagascar remains unclear. Brygoo (1966) noted that *R. norvegicus* had already arrived at some ports by the 1930s, whereas Petit (1934) concluded that there was no evidence of the species on Madagascar during that period. In 1941, Robic captured four individuals of *R. norvegicus* in the customs stores of the Toamasina port, and in the *Archives de l'Institut Pasteur de Madagascar* there are reports of this species being captured in 1950, 1951, 1952, and 1953 (Blanchy 1995). The definitive year of arrival of this species in towns of the Central Highlands is unknown. Up to the end of the 1970s, only *R. rattus* is mentioned in the daily captures made by the Bureau Municipal d'Hygiène in the capital of Antananarivo. In 1982, *R. norvegicus* was identified in Antananarivo, and reports thereafter increased dramatically. In 1983, of the captured *Rattus*, 502 were *R. norvegicus* and eight *R. rattus*, and in 1987, these numbers were 1334 *R. norvegicus* and 309

R. rattus (Blanchy 1995). In line with these figures, starting in the early 1980s, it was noted that *R. norvegicus* represented more than 80% of the rodent captures in the capital (A. D. S. Rakotondravony 1992; also see Rahalison et al. 2003).

Ecology

Nowadays, *Rattus norvegicus* occurs on Madagascar from sea level up to 1500 m (Soarimalala and Goodman 2011). The species is synanthropic and is commonly found in rural and urban areas in the Central Highlands and in coastal cities. It is particularly abundant in houses, near human settlements mainly near mesic habitats, and in anthropogenic and agricultural areas, and rare in natural forests. When food resources are sufficient, *R. norvegicus* can breed throughout the year. Females give birth three to nine times per year, with up to 10 young rats per litter (M. Rasamoelina and Andriamalala 1999). Sexual maturity is reached at 50–60 days, and the gestation period is 20–22 days. The species is omnivorous and opportunistic.

Invasive Aspects

Due to its scarcity in natural forests of Madagascar, invasive impacts of *Rattus norvegicus* on endemic biodiversity are not well documented and are presumed to be distinctly less important than those of *R. rattus*. Available information is mainly from rural and anthropogenic areas. *Rattus norvegicus* is also recognized on the island as a crop pest (FAO and PAM 2013) and known to be responsible for transmission of zoonotic diseases. In the central east, attacks on young poultry have been reported (Soarimalala et al. 2019). Based on stable isotope analyses, it was found that *R. norvegicus* consumes more animal protein than *R. rattus* in the same region (Dammhahn et al. 2017). *Rattus norvegicus* is also known to have negative impacts on different household goods, including clothes and various utensils. Despite the lack of published data on the impacts caused by this species, it is an important invasive species on the island, as in other countries. For example, on a worldwide basis, *R. norvegicus* costs primary industry hundreds of millions of dollars per year (CABI 2019). It has caused or contributed to the extinction or range reduction of native mammals, birds, reptiles, and invertebrates through predation and competition. It restricts the regeneration of many plant species by eating seeds and seedlings, consumes crops, and spoils human food stores by urinating and defecating in them. Additional economic damage is caused by chewing through power cables and spreading diseases.

CONCLUSION

On Madagascar, *Rattus* species are among the most widespread introduced mammals. They are commonly known to have negative socioeconomic impacts, mainly on agriculture and in household settings, and are known to be reservoirs of different infectious diseases. There is a lack of study and published data on the ecology of *R. norvegicus* on the island, and detailed studies are needed to investigate its impact on human and native mammal ecology.

Subject editor: Steven M. Goodman

NESOMYIDAE: *BRACHYTARSOMYS*, TREE RATS, *ANGATRA*, *ANTSANGY*

M. D. Carleton and S. M. Goodman

Among Madagascar's native rodents, species of *Brachytarsomys* are unmistakable, owing to their large size and clearly arboreal adaptations. From the time of Günther's (1875) original description, *B. albicauda* was the only form known until 1962, when F. Petter named *villosa* as a distinctive subspecies. Carleton and Schmidt (1990) considered the two taxa to represent valid species, a conviction supported by documentation of both forms on opposite slopes of the Anjanaharibe-Sud Massif (Goodman et al. 2003c). Both species require formal fixation of their type localities (see Carleton and Goodman 2003). A subfossil form of *Brachytarsomys*, *B. mahajambaensis* (Mein et al. 2010), has been described from Holocene cave deposits in northwestern Madagascar (see Goodman and Soarimalala, pp. 1737–69).

Ellerman (1941) formally affiliated *Brachytarsomys* with Microtinae (= Cricetidae: Arvicolinae) as the monotypic tribe Brachytarsomyes, an improbable relationship refuted by gene-sequence information. Recent genetic analyses not surprisingly ally *Brachytarsomys* with other members of the Nesomyinae, typically as a basal member to the clade also containing *Gymnuromys* and *Eliurus-Voalavo* (Jansa et al. 2009; Steppan and Schenk 2017; see Jansa and Carleton, pp. 1865–71).

DESCRIPTION

Species of *Brachytarsomys* are large in body size and mass, adults of *B. albicauda* typically weighing over 200 g and those of *B. villosa* closer to 300 g (Table 14.33). Their thick, soft fur has a woolly texture. Brownish-gray to dark gray upperparts distinctly contrast with the lighter venter, which varies from pure white to buffy white or grayish white (Figure 14.66). Dorsal surfaces of the fore- and hind feet, including the proximal phalanges, are similarly darkly furred. For the size of the rodent, the pinnae (ears) appear tiny and

TABLE 14.33. **External and craniodental measurements for species of *Brachytarsomys***

SPECIES	HBL (mm)	TL (mm)	HFL (mm)	WT (g)	ONL (mm)	LM1–3 (mm)
B. albicauda[1] (n = 5)	213.2 ± 17.6	235.8 ± 18.7	38.2 ± 0.8	223.2 ± 46.7	44.4 ± 2.5	8.5 ± 0.2
	198–242	210–258	37–39	172–286	41.1–47.1	8.2–8.7
B. villosa[2] (n = 2)	228, 245	260, 272	40, 41	236, 350	47.4, 50.3	8.6, 8.6

Note: HBL, head-and-body length; TL, tail length; HFL, hind-foot length; WT, weight; ONL, occipitonasal length; LM1–3, coronal length of upper molar row.

[1] Sample statistics for *B. albicauda* include the mean ± one standard deviation, and the minimum–maximum range. Locality: Ambodiamontana, Ranomafana National Park.

[2] Localities: Anjanaharibe-Sud, western slope, 1200 m and 1600 m.

tightly rounded, protruding little above the body fur. The tail length (TL) moderately exceeds head-and-body length (HBL) (TL ~112% of HBL). The tail is bicolored, its proximal portion invested with dark brown or black hairs, and the distal one-third to one-half clothed with white hairs. This anterior-posterior contrast involves both caudal-hair color and epidermal pigmentation. When a live animal of either species is handled, the distal one-quarter of the tail can be wrapped around thin objects and appears partially capable of prehensile action, an adaptation presumably useful as a fifth appendage when climbing. The hind feet are exceptionally short and broad, even more so than observed in *Eliurus* (see Carleton et al., pp. 2014–22), and the elongate fifth digit approximates the second through fourth digits in length; the naked plantar surface bears six large, fleshy pads. Manual and pedal claws are noteworthy for their narrowness and sharpness.

The stout cranium possesses a short, broad rostrum and narrow, hourglass-shaped interorbital constriction. The zygomatic arches project widely from the cranial midline and are parallel-sided over their midsections. Supraorbital shelves and ridges are lacking, but in older animals the low temporal ridges usually meet dorsally and form a weak midsagittal crest. The anterior border of the zygomatic plate does not extend forward to form even a rudimentary zygomatic notch, a condition unique among nesomyine rodents and one resembling arvicolines (Cricetidae) in construction. The incisive foramina are medium long (about 60–65% of the diastema) and wide across their midsection. A single pair of large posterior palatine foramina perforates the broad hard palate; the long mesopterygoid fossa extends well between the upper third molars; and the auditory bullae are small. The wide and heavy upper incisors lack grooves; the planar molars are low crowned and rooted, retaining positional cusp definition. No secondary sexual dimorphism in size is suggested by cranial measurements of *B. albicauda*.

The species *B. villosa* and *B. albicauda* are reliably identifiable based on size, the former being larger than the latter (Table 14.33). Other traits are equally helpful for specific discrimination. A key feature is the relative hairiness of the tail (F. Petter 1962): caudal hairs in *B. albicauda* are extremely short (1–2 mm), the tail appearing naked and scaly; in *B. villosa*, the longer caudal hairs (6–8 mm) impart a bushy appearance to the tail and obscure its scalar pattern (Figure 14.66b). The dorsal pelage of *B. villosa* is dark gray in contrast to the soft brown overtones that mark the dorsum of *B. albicauda* (Figure 14.66a). The face and crown are buffy brown to pale tawny in *B. albicauda*, distinct from the darker brownish gray of the nape, back, and rump; by contrast, the blackish-gray dorsal ground color of *B. villosa* continues onto its head.

The incisive foramina are relatively longer in *B. albicauda*, extending to the level of the anterior root of the first molars; they terminate short of this plane in the few specimens of *B. villosa* examined. In addition, the interorbital constriction appears relatively narrower and the maxillary tooth rows relatively longer in *B. albicauda*. A larger sampling of *B. villosa* should be examined to confirm the reliability of such differences in cranial proportion.

GEOGRAPHIC AND ELEVATIONAL DISTRIBUTION

Brachytarsomys albicauda is broadly distributed, albeit patchily recorded, across moist evergreen forests over a broad elevational range, 455–1875 m (see map in Goodman et al. 2013: 245), from the southern Northern Highlands (Soarimalala and Goodman 2003a), along the eastern portion of the Central Highlands (Carleton and Schmidt 1990; Soarimalala and Goodman 2006; Soarimalala and Raheriarisena 2010), into the Southern Highlands (Ramanana 2010). The larger species, *B. villosa*, is known only from the Northern Highlands (see map in Goodman et al. 2013: 246), centered on the Tsaratanàna Massif, as currently known, and occurring in contiguous mountains, at elevations of 1200–2050 m (Goodman et al. 2003c; Soarimalala and Goodman 2003a; Maminirina et al. 2008). Small-mammal surveys indicate that the Anjanaharibe-Sud Massif forms the divide between the two species, *B. albicauda* occurring on the eastern slopes and *B. villosa* on the western slopes (Goodman et al. 2003c). Many new records of *Brachytarsomys* have become available from areas where it was previously unknown, often based on images taken by naturalists and ecotourists during night walks. The geographic limits of both species require elaboration, because their arboreal habits and nocturnal secrecy apparently thwart standard trapping techniques.

ECOLOGY, BEHAVIOR, AND REPRODUCTION

The broad hind feet with elongate fifth digit and the long, flexible tail of *Brachytarsomys* presuppose an arboreal ecological niche.

FIGURE 14.66 The two extant species of *Brachytarsomys*: A) An individual of *B. albicauda* in the Anjozorobe-Angavo protected area; and B) an adult male (enlarged scrotal testicles visible at the base of the tail) of *B. villosa* clambering up thin branches in the Bemanevika protected area.
(PHOTO A by V. Soarimalala and B by L.-A. Rene de Roland.)

Indeed, all museum specimens of both species with trustworthy ecological provenance issue from lowland or medium-altitude moist evergreen forests (Carleton and Schmidt 1990; Maminirina et al. 2008; Ramamana 2010). Successful trap placements also convey arboreal settings, the animals having been captured while moving across substrate diameters that range from tree trunks to narrower branches and lianas. Individuals have been also observed at night climbing about branches and lianas high above the forest floor (Figure 14.66b). Their bodily proportions and locomotory posture appear lemur-like, as attested by ecotourists who, while walking in the forest at night, often mistake this arboreal rodent as "an odd form of lemur." Across its range, *B. albicauda* have been found to inhabit hollowed portions of standing tree trunks (Stephenson 1993; Soarimalala and Raheriarisena 2010), commonly with the entrance holes positioned 2.5–7 m above the ground and with lianas or branches accessible nearby. In the Analamazaotra protected area, *B. albicauda* and *Allocebus trichotis* (Hairy-eared Dwarf Lemur) have been occasionally found to share the same tree-hole nesting site and even the same nest within the trunk cavity (Biebouw 2009). Such cavities provide protected nesting sites where this rodent raises its young and can access arboreal foraging areas without ever descending to the ground. Presumably, the nesting habits of *B. villosa* are similar to those of its congener.

F. Petter (1972) assumed that members of *Brachytarsomys* feed mainly on fruits, a trophic preference suggested by the response of *B. albicauda* to different live-trap baits utilized in surveys of medium-altitude moist evergreen forest. In the Anjozorobe-Angavo, not a single *B. albicauda* was captured in traps baited with peanut butter during 4200 trap nights, with approximately 20% of traps placed in arboreal positions (about 840 total trap nights) (Soarimalala et al. 2007); whereas, over a total of 1260 trap nights at the same site and the same period, with all stations in arboreal settings, two *B. albicauda* individuals were captured in traps baited with fresh banana (Ralison 2007). In the nearby forest of Ambatovy-Analamay, 4500 trap nights of inventory effort failed to capture any *B. albicauda* in live traps all baited with peanut butter, although the species was visually observed in the area (Soarimalala and Raheriarisena 2010). In captivity, *B. albicauda* readily consumed a variety of fruits (D. Halleux, unpublished data). Two *B. villosa* individuals captured in traps baited with peanut butter had a distinctly sweet smell and highly developed caecum, characteristics often associated with folivory; while held in captivity for a few hours, these two individuals refused to eat leaves of several different forest plants presented to them (S. M. Goodman, unpublished data).

Reproductive parameters of *Brachytarsomys* are poorly known. One *B. albicauda* captured in late October contained six well-formed embryos (Goodman and Carleton 1998), and in captivity litters of up to six young were produced (D. Halleux, unpublished data). Reproductively mature males with large scrotal testes were captured in mid-December, mid- to late January, and mid-June, a long time span that intimates that adult males produce sperm throughout the year. A female collected at Befotaka–Midongy du Sud in mid-February was lactating and had four placental scars. Two captured females had a mammary gland count of four, one pair axial and one pair inguinal. Two males of *B. villosa* obtained in November had scrotal testicles and were in reproductive condition.

Field workers have observed a curious behavior exhibited by fully adult males of both species when temporarily maintained in National live traps after capture. Males have been seen to rub their scrotal testicles with their forepaws for minutes at a time in an intense manner. Whatever the behavioral or physiological significance of this peculiar action, it recalls Malagasy folktales of a large arboreal rodent that may be seen at night furiously rubbing its testicles. Any human passerby who witnesses and dares to laugh, or even smile, at the act will become lost in the forest. The Malagasy vernacular name *angatra* means "phantom," a term that perhaps

evokes the mysterious manner people go astray should they find the peculiar action amusing. Substantiation of this behavior in the field, coupled with the Malagasy vernacular name, leaves little doubt that the central figure in this folklore is *Brachytarsomys*.

Species of *Brachytarsomys* have not been the subject of dedicated epidemiological studies. An unverified report implicated *B. albicauda* in a 1932 bout of bubonic plague in the Moramanga area (Leger 1934; Brygoo 1966). Tick ectoparasites (Ixodida) are known from *Brachytarsomys* (see Klompen and Apanaskevich, pp. 894–99).

CONSERVATION

The IUCN Red List classifies *B. villosa* as Vulnerable and *B. albicauda* as Least Concern (IUCN 2020). The generic distribution, albeit patchy as known to date, directly corresponds to undisturbed and intact moist evergreen forest. The continued decline in the extent and quality of this forest type (Vieilledent et al. 2018) obviously raises concern about population decline of these obligate arboreal species. Given the extensive latitudinal distribution of *Brachytarsomys*, the two species are known from many designated protected areas, *B. villosa* from four (COMATSA Nord, Tsaratanàna, Bemanevika, and Anjanaharibe-Sud) and *B. albicauda* from 13 (Marojejy, Anjanaharibe-Sud, Makira, Masoala, Zahamena, Anjozorobe-Angavo, Ankeniheny-Zahamena, Analamazaotra, Ambositra-Vondrozo, Ranomafana, Befotaka–Midongy du Sud, Tsitongambarika, and Andohahela) (Goodman et al. 2018b).

Subject editor: Steven M. Goodman

NESOMYIDAE: *BRACHYUROMYS*, SHORT-TAILED RATS, MALAGASY VOLES, *VOALAVO*, *VOALAVONDRANO*

S. A. Jansa, V. Soarimalala, and M. D. Carleton

Major (1896c) erected the genus *Brachyuromys* to encompass his type species *B. ramirohitra*, and allocated Bartlett's (1879 [1880]) *Nesomys betsileoensis* to his new genus as a second species. Major (1897a) subsequently provided formal descriptions of both species and discussed their possible affinity with the African mole rats, *Tachyoryctes* (Spalacidae: Tachyoryctinae). Ellerman (1941) seconded Major's interpretation and formally placed *Brachyuromys* within a new tribe, Brachyuromyes, under Tachyoryctinae. Ellerman's classification is untenable, based on morphological traits (e.g., Carleton and Musser 1984), nor is it corroborated by any molecular studies (Jansa and Weksler 2004; Jansa et al. 2009; Steppan and Schenk 2017). The genetic evidence instead relates *Brachyuromys* most closely to *Nesomys* among Madagascar's other endemic genera (see Jansa and Carleton, pp. 1865–71). The physical appearance of *Brachyuromys* (Figure 14.67), particularly the small pinnae (ears) and short tail, has also prompted comparisons to voles of the Holarctic subfamily Arvicolinae (Cricetidae), but their superficial similarity is clearly an example of evolutionary convergence, not phyletic affinity.

FIGURE 14.67 **Adult *Brachyuromys betsileoensis* in the montane grassland zone below the Andringitra summit.** (PHOTO by V. Soarimalala.)

DESCRIPTION

Both species of *Brachyuromys* are medium to large (86–144 g), compactly built rodents with a blunt muzzle, relatively short tail (about 60–70% of head-and-body length), and short legs (Table 14.34). Their pelage is soft and fine, appearing rich and lustrous, overall reddish brown or yellowish brown overlaying a dark undercoat. Long black guard hairs are densely concentrated along the middle dorsum and rump. Dorsal-ventral countershading is very subtle, without an obvious lateral line, the venter only slightly brighter. The short tail is wholly dark brown to black and appears naked to the unaided eye. The fore- and hind feet are small and slender, with short toes, unlike the elongate pedal phalanges of its close kin, *Nesomys* (see Carleton et al.,

TABLE 14.34. External measurements for adult *Brachyuromys betsileoensis* from the Central Highlands at Vohiparara (Ranomafana) and adult *B. ramirohitra* from Andringitra and *Anjanaharibe-Sud*

SPECIES	TOTL (mm)	HBL (mm)	TL (mm)	HFL (mm)	EL (mm)	WT (g)
B. betsileoensis[1] (n = 13)	241.9 ± 9.6	152.8 ± 8.1	88.2 ± 3.9	32.7 ± 1.7	21.1 ± 1.8	120.8 ± 15.8
	223–258	140–163	83–97	30–36	18–23	86–144
B. ramirohitra (n = 2)	282, 293	165, 169	110, 117	33, 34	24, 25	117, 129

Note: TOTL, total length including tail; HBL, head-and-body length, TL, tail length; HFL, hind-foot length; EL, ear length; WT, weight.
[1] Sample statistics for *B. betsileoensis* include the mean ± one standard deviation, and the observed minimum–maximum range.

TABLE 14.35. Craniodental measurements for adult *Brachyuromys betsileoensis* and *B. ramirohitra* from Ampitambe, Moramanga District

SPECIES	ONL (mm)	LR (mm)	IOB (mm)	ZB (mm)	BBC (mm)	LM1–3 (mm)	WM1 (mm)
B. betsileoensis (n = 10)	33.6 ± 1.5	10.2 ± 0.5	5.0 ± 0.2	20.1 ± 1.0	13.9 ± 0.5	6.9 ± 0.2	2.3 ± 0.2
	31.5–36.2	9.6–11.0	4.7–5.3	18.5–21.4	13.3–14.7	6.6–7.2	2.0–2.6
B. ramirohitra (n = 27)	39.1 ± 1.3	13.0 ±0.6	5.1 ± 0.2	22.9 ± 0.9	14.8 ± 0.4	8.7 ± 0.2	2.7 ± 0.1
	36.0–41.5	11.6–13.9	4.5–5.5	20.5–24.4	14.1–15.7	8.1–9.1	2.4–3.0

Source: Goodman and Carleton (1996).
Notes: ONL, occipitonasal length; LR, length of rostrum; IOB, interorbital breadth; ZB, zygomatic breadth; BBC, braincase breadth; LM1–3, coronal length of upper molar tooth row; WM1, width of first upper molar. Sample statistics include the mean ± one standard deviation, and the minimum–maximum range.

pp. 2033–35). The eyes are small, and the pinnae are short (18–25 mm), rounded, and relatively inconspicuous amid the long pelage. Such external proportions easily distinguish the genus from Madagascar's other native rodents, and it may be confused only with immature *Nesomys*.

A short rostrum, squarish braincase, and posteriorly flaring zygomatic arches with deep zygomatic notches characterize the crania of both *Brachyuromys* species. The tightly constricted interorbit is hourglass-shaped, its borders squared but lacking supraorbital ridges. Temporal and lambdoid ridges are weakly expressed except in old adults. Relatively broad and long incisive foramina span most of the diastema and extend to or slightly between the first upper molars. The molars are moderately hypsodont (high-crowned), with planar occlusal surfaces, but are not continuously growing. The upper tooth rows converge anteriorly, their cusps becoming obliquely confluent with wear but retaining positional identity (unlike *Eliurus*, in which lamination is transversely oriented and cusp identity indeterminate).

Species of *Brachyuromys* are easily distinguishable from one another based on size and dental differences, the larger *B. ramirohitra* overlapping minimally with *B. betsileoensis* in most measurements (Tables 14.34 and 14.35). Molar size and enamel configuration provide reliable diagnostic traits: the molars of *B. ramirohitra* are more robust, the length of the upper molar toothrow always >8.0 mm, while those in *B. betsileoensis* range from 6.6 to 7.2 mm. Adult of *B. ramirohitra* generally possesses a longer and more reddish coat than *B. betsileoensis*; this brighter hue is particularly well expressed on the ventral surface.

GEOGRAPHIC AND ELEVATIONAL DISTRIBUTION

Both species are restricted to high elevations, usually above 1000 m, in the eastern portions of Madagascar's uplands (see maps in Goodman et al. 2013: 247–248). To date, *B. betsileoensis* is known from the Central Highlands, from the Lake Alaotra region south to Andringitra National Park (Carleton and Schmidt 1990; Goodman and Carleton 1996; Pidgeon 1996; Soarimalala et al. 2001; Randriamoria 2017). *Brachyuromys ramirohitra* has been documented from vastly separated localities in the Northern Highlands (Soarimalala and Goodman 2003a), Central Highlands (Carleton and Schmidt 1990; Goodman and Carleton 1996; Goodman and Rasolonandrasana 2001), and Southern Highlands (Ramanana 2010—erroneously reported as *B. betsileoensis*; Goodman et al. 2013). In the Central Highlands, both species have been trapped in the region around Ampitambe, Moramanga District, and in overlapping elevational zones in Andringitra National Park. Although both species have been collected at one locality on the Andringitra Massif (Goodman and Carleton 1996), the zone of sympatry appears to be rather limited. Discoveries of *B. ramirohitra* on the western slope of the Anjanaharibe-Sud Massif, Northern Highlands (Soarimalala and Goodman 2003a), and in Andohahela National Park, Southern Highlands (Ramanana 2010; Goodman et al. 2013), signal both the need for additional collecting efforts and for genetic studies to assay the level of differentiation among the isolated populations of each species.

ECOLOGY, BEHAVIOR, AND REPRODUCTION

In Ranomafana National Park, James Ryan found that specimens of *B. betsileoensis* were typically captured in areas with "lots of grass clippings and tunnels—just like *Microtus*!" (United States National Museum field catalogs). Ryan's field notes and skin tags on *B. betsileoensis* specimens refer to habitat settings as "grassy meadow," "grass and brush at edge of pond," "dense cover in meadow, soil moist," and "abandoned rice fields, large marshy wet meadow with some floating vegetation." In the Moramanga District, an individual *B. betsileoensis* was captured in the vicinity of a rice paddy, near human habitation but over 11 km from natural forest (Randriamoria et al. 2015). Within Andringitra National Park, *B. betsileoensis* occurs near the upper limit of medium-altitude moist evergreen forest and adjoining montane ericoid thicket (1960–1990 m) and in open montane grassland above the forest line (2050–2450 m), whereas *B. ramirohitra* is known only from intact medium-altitude moist evergreen forest (1210–1960 m) (Goodman and Carleton 1996; Goodman and Rasolonandrasana 2001). Little is known about the specific habitat preferences of *B. ramirohitra*, but one specimen from Andringitra was trapped "at the opening of a natural tunnel system associated with a massive root entanglement covered by soil and matted litter" (Goodman and Carleton 1996: 264).

Resurgence of field surveys in the 1990s substantively expanded our knowledge of *Brachyuromys* natural history. *Brachyuromys betsileoensis* is apparently active both day and night. In the Ranomafana, J. Ryan (United States National Museum field catalogs) recovered animals in traps checked both in early morning and in late afternoon. In open montane grassland of Andringitra, 70% of animals were trapped during the day (V. Soarimalala and S. M. Goodman, unpublished data). Both species are presumed to be largely or exclusively herbivorous, a diet consistent with their moderately hypsodont molars and preferred habitats. Little reproductive information is available for either species. Records from the Central Highlands near Ranomafana indicate that *B. betsileoensis* is reproductively active during July, which is the dry and cold season; most males collected at this time were scrotal, and several females were pregnant or lactating. In montane grassland of Andringitra, females captured during September had embryos, and the majority of males had enlarged testes and convoluted epididymides. For *B. ramirohitra* collected during October in the Marolambo and Ambositra-Vondrozo protected areas, the majority of males had enlarged testes and convoluted epididymides. Litter size, as currently known based on embryo counts, is two for both species. Skull remains of both species have been recovered from scats of *Cryptoprocta ferox* (Carnivora: Eupleridae) in the montane grassland zone (2000–2100 m) of Andringitra (Goodman et al. 1997a); based on the known distribution of *Brachyuromys*, one can infer that this carnivoran hunts broadly in vegetational zones from at least the upper limit of moist evergreen forest into open montane grasslands.

Species of *Brachyuromys* are hosts to various gastrointestinal parasites, including eight species of Nematoda and two species of Platyhelminthes (Quentin and Durette-Desset 1974; Tenora et al. 1980). Four nematode species recovered from *Brachyuromys* are also found in *Rattus rattus* (*Mastophorus muris*, *Nippostrongylus brasiliensis*, *Heterakis spumosa*, and *Trichuris* sp.), probably signifying recent interspecific transfer after the introduction of the commensal murine to Madagascar. However, other nematodes (*Syphacia* spp.) are unique to *Brachyuromys* and considered paleoendemics (Quentin and Durette-Desset 1974), perhaps dating to the Oligocene, an interpretation consistent with a much earlier origin of nesomyines (see Jansa and Carleton, pp. 1865–71).

CONSERVATION

The IUCN Red List has assessed the conservation status of both species of *Brachyuromys* as Least Concern (IUCN 2020). *Brachyuromys* may represent an exceptional instance in which human-induced habitat change has partially benefited an endemic rodent, such as the abandoned rice fields surveyed around Moramanga and Ranomafana where *B. betsileoensis* was relatively abundant. Limited trapping results have provided anecdotal evidence that *Rattus rattus* can displace *Brachyuromys* even in such marshy habitats: specimens of *B. betsileoensis* were trapped only in the center of abandoned rice fields, while *Rattus* dominated captures around the edges (J. Ryan, United States National Museum field catalogs). In landscapes of the Andringitra Massif above forest line (2050 m), three rodent species were captured (percentage of captures in parentheses): *B. betsileoensis* (55%), *Rattus rattus* (42%), and *Mus musculus* (3%); however, in the higher, 2450 m zone, where nighttime temperatures may annually drop below freezing for several months, *B. betsileoensis* accounted for 80% of the rodents captured (Langrand and Goodman 1997). Indices of morphological similarity, as evaluated by Miljutin and Lehtonen (2008), suggested that ecological competition between populations of *Brachyuromys* and commensal *Rattus* was unlikely. As with all of Madagascar's native rodents, long-term field studies of *Brachyuromys* are necessary to permit researchers to understand their biology, assess their vulnerability to the introduced murine rodents, and ensure their conservation.

Subject editor: Steven M. Goodman

NESOMYINAE: *ELIURUS*, TUFTED-TAIL RATS, *VOALAVO ALA*, *SOKITRALINA*

M. D. Carleton, V. Soarimalala, and S. M. Goodman

Among Madagascar's endemic rodents, the genus *Eliurus* is the most diverse, with 13 currently recognized species (Goodman and Soarimalala 2018; see Goodman and Soarimalala, pp. 1737–69). The genus is nearly ubiquitous throughout the island wherever appreciable stands of wet or dry forest occur, and its constituent species typically constitute an important component of the small-mammal fauna in any such forested community. Webb (1954: 256) appropriately dubbed these rodents "Tufted-tailed Rats" to acknowledge their most visually striking external trait (Figure 14.68).

Ellerman (1949) established the precedent for recognizing only two species of *Eliurus*, a large-bodied species with several geographic forms (*E. myoxinus*) and a small, monotypic form (*E. minor*), a misjudgment of specific diversity that prevailed through the latter 1900s (F. Petter 1972, 1975; Honacki et al. 1982; Corbet and Hill 1991). The current recognition of 13 valid species has stemmed both from resurrection of four of Ellerman's subspecies to species (Carleton 1994) and from descriptions of seven new forms (Carleton 1994; Carleton and Goodman 1998, 2007; Carleton et al. 2001; Goodman et al. 2009a; Jansa et al. 2019). Many newly named species have been uncovered since initiation of directed biological inventory in the middle 1990s (see Jansa et al. 2019: Figure 1). Genetic data, wherever considered in biogeographic or systematic studies, have strongly supported the revised view of *Eliurus* diversity (Jansa et al. 1999, 2019; Goodman et al. 2009a; J.-E. Rakotoarisoa et al. 2010, 2013a, 2013b; Shi et al. 2013; Steppan and Schenk 2017; see Jansa and Carleton, pp. 1865–71).

With advancement in understanding of their relationships, *Eliurus* species have been provisionally sorted into five species groups (Carleton and Goodman 2007; Jansa et al. 2019): *E. antsingy* group (*E. antsingy* and *E. carletoni*); *E. majori* group (*E. danieli*, *E. majori*, and *E. penicillatus*); *E. myoxinus* group (*E. minor* and *E. myoxinus*); *E. petteri* group (*E. grandidieri* and *E. petteri*); and

FIGURE 14.68 **Compared with other members of Nesomyinae and introduced Muridae, rodents of the genus *Eliurus* are immediately recognizable by their short, broad hind feet and a relatively long tail that bears a conspicuous pencil or tuft of long hairs over the distal portion. The vernacular name tufted-tail rat is derived from the latter character. A selection of *Eliurus* species (those preceded by an asterisk were described since the 1990s): A) **E. grandidieri*, Anjanaharibe-Sud; B) *E. minor*, Andringitra; C) **E. ellermani*, Anjanaharibe-Sud; D) *E. webbi*, Montagne d'Ambre; E) **E. tsingimbato*, Bemaraha; and F) **E. danieli*, Isalo.** (PHOTOS by H. Schütz.)

E. tanala group (*E. ellermani*, *E. tanala*, *E. tsingimbato*, and *E. webbi incertae sedis*). Although these groupings are generally consistent with patterns of morphological similarity and phylogeographic structure, insofar as known, deep phylogenesis within *Eliurus* and additional confirmatory evidence for the monophyly of the species groups offer fertile areas for future research (see Jansa and Carleton, pp. 1865–71).

Uncertainty still surrounds the validity of certain species and the morphological boundary of the genus. The distinctiveness of *E. penicillatus* from *E. majori* has been questioned (see Carleton and Goodman 1998, 2000). Further, as better museum series have become available, the pronounced morphological and/or genetic heterogeneity exhibited by certain species—such as *E. grandidieri*, *E. myoxinus*, and *E. webbi*—suggests their composite nature as currently defined (Shi et al. 2013; Everson et al. 2020b). Gene-sequence data derived from cytochrome b support the inclusion of *Voalavo gymnocaudus* (see Jansa and Carleton, pp. 1865–71) within the genus *Eliurus* (Jansa et al. 1999), a finding that invites further corroboration and perhaps amendment of the generic diagnosis (see Jansa and Carleton, pp. 1865–71).

Ellerman (1941) mistakenly interpreted the laminate molar pattern of *Eliurus* as homologous to the murine triserial cusp arrangement. Accordingly, he classified the genus as the sole member of his new group Eliuri, subfamily Murinae (Muridae), a family-level kinship unsupported by any gene-sequence analyses with ample taxonomic representation (Jansa et al. 1999, 2009; Steppan and Schenk 2017). Such studies phyletically relate *Eliurus* most closely to *Voalavo* within the nesomyine radiation (see Jansa and Carleton, pp. 1865–71).

DESCRIPTION

Species of *Eliurus* are small to medium in head-and-body length (HBL ~100–175 mm) and range in mean adult weight from about 35 to 100 g (Table 14.36). Their pelage is soft and fine in texture, the cover hairs moderately long and typically dense. The dorsal pelage in most species is some shade of brown to brownish gray, but it is darker gray in some. The ventral pelage appears light to medium gray in most forms, but it may be uniformly creamy to bright white in certain populations or species. Dorsal-ventral countershading is obvious in most species, although without a pronounced lateral line, except in *E. petteri*. Blackish hairs around the eyes give a more or less well-defined impression of dark eye-rings. With larger locality series and improved geographic representation, intraspecific variation in pelage color has been encountered: for example, Randrianjafy (2003) discerned five morphotypes of *E. myoxinus* from the Ankarafantsika area, differences among which may confuse age-class determination; and Jansa et al. (2019) demonstrated incidental chromatic variation of the ventral pelage and caudal tuft that departs from typical traits of species within the *E. tanala* group.

Members of the genus possess a conspicuous pencil or tuft of long hairs over the distal portion of the tail. The proximal segment appears naked to the unaided eye, the epidermal scales readily visible. Length, width, and color of the tail's penicillate segment aid in specific determination. In all species, tail length (TL) noticeably surpasses the head-and-body length (TL ~115–130% of HBL). The hind foot is relatively short and broad, its plantar surface naked and the fifth digit elongate and semi-opposable; plantar pads total six, all large and fleshy with the medial metatarsal pad (thenar) prominent. The mammae number six, distributed as postaxial, abdominal, and inguinal pairs.

Key traits of an *Eliurus* skull include the hourglass-shaped interorbit that lacks a supraorbital shelf or bead, a smooth and rounded braincase devoid of temporal ridges, and small auditory bullae. The incisive foramina are narrow and short (~40–55% of diastemal length), with a clear gap between their posterior ends and the first molars. The upper incisors are smooth-faced and opisthodont, the enamel surface colored pale yellow to deep orange. The moderately high-crowned (hypsodont) molars are rooted and possess a trilaminate occlusal configuration that is unique among the nesomyine genera. No consistent pattern of sexual dimorphism in cranial size has been detected in any *Eliurus* species for which robust sample sizes are available (Carleton 1994; Goodman and Carleton 1996; Jansa et al. 2019).

Possession of a relatively long tail with conspicuous terminal tuft (Figure 14.68) and a short, broad hind foot typically serve to separate species of *Eliurus* from other nesomyines wherever they co-occur in Malagasy forests.

Morphological identification of many *Eliurus* species is often difficult because specific traits can be subtle to appreciate and apply critically, because standard mensural variables typically overlap (Table 14.36), and because several species may occur in sympatry or elevational allopatry, commonly four or as many as six in some moist evergreen forests (see tabulations for protected areas in Goodman et al. 2018b). Furthermore, subtle intraspecific and nongeographic variation may complicate identification of juveniles and subadults. Those characteristics that are most useful include interspecific size differences—especially linear measurements of the tail, hind foot, skull, and molar row—fur texture, extent of pilosity along the tail length, color of the terminal tail tuft, shape and configuration of caudal scales, fenestration of the bony palate, projection of the lower incisor capsule, and relative length of the upper third molar. Such characteristics are described and/or illustrated in Carleton (1994), Carleton and Goodman (1998), and Jansa et al. (2019), and are regularly highlighted in the identification key to *Eliurus* species presented herein (Table 14.37).

GEOGRAPHIC AND ELEVATIONAL DISTRIBUTION

Species richness of *Eliurus* is concentrated along Madagascar's eastern versant, in moist evergreen forests, where eight of the 13 recognized species occur. In medium-altitude moist evergreen forests, three or four species are commonly recorded in the same trap-line transect. However, the long-held view of only a single species inhabiting the island's dryer western biomes has been overturned by recent studies (Carleton et al. 2001; Carleton and Goodman 2007; Goodman et al. 2009a; Jansa et al. 2019). In addition to the widely distributed *E. myoxinus*, found in dry deciduous forests and dry spiny thickets, three forms have been described from dry deciduous forests often associated with karst landscapes (*E. antsingy*, *E. carletoni*, and *E. tsingimbato*) and one in a sclerophyllous woodland formation (*E. danieli*). Although some of the east–west disparity in

TABLE 14.36. **External measurements for representative series of *Eliurus* species, arranged approximately from smallest to largest by overall size and weight**

SPECIES	HBL (mm)	TL (mm)	HFL (mm)	EL (mm)	WT (g)
E. minor[1] (n = 25)	112.8 ± 6.1	128.9 ± 5.1	21.4 ± 1.0	17.6 ± 0.7	35.1 ± 5.8
	101–124	119–137	20–23	17–19	22–50
E. grandidieri[2] (n = 42–60)	124.8 ± 6.6	161.5 ± 8.7	28.3 ± 1.0	20.1 ± 0.9	50.6 ± 4.0
	111–164	144–176	26–31	19–23	42–62
E. myoxinus[3] (n = 9–11)	127.7 ± 6.4	145.4 ± 12.8	25.4 ± 0.8	23.7 ± 0.8	66 ± 8.3
	117–136	125–167	24–26	23–25	51–75
E. petteri[4] (n = 1, 2)	130, 136	178, 185	30, 31	19, 22	74
E. webbi[1] (n = 19)	138.3 ± 13.9	165.7 ± 10.1	28.6 ± 1.1	22.7 ± 0.9	70.1 ± 9.7
	105–161	150–183	27–31	21–24	54–90
E. tsingimbato[5] (n = 10–12)	148.7 ± 5.5	174 ± 15.9	29.9 ± 1.6	24.8 ± 0.9	94.9 ± 22.3
	140–160	140–195	28–34	23–26	46–125
E. antsingy[5] (n = 5)	149.4 ± 7.4	168.4 ± 11.9	29.4 ± 2.4	25.0 ± 0.7	100.4 ± 18.0
	142–160	153–186	26–32	24–26	87–131
E. tanala[6] (n = 19–22)	155.1 ± 9.1	186.4 ± 12.4	33.6 ± 1.0	24.0 ± 1.3	88.7 ± 11.9
	144–175	163–210	31–37	21–26	66–115
E. carletoni[7] (n = 3–4)	147.7 ± 4.0	174.3 ± 9.6	28.8 ± 0.5	24.3 ± 1.0	94.8 ± 4.7
	143–150	164–183	28–29	23–25	88–99
E. danieli[8] (n = 2)	150, 152	179, 195	30, 32	26, 28	91, 100
E. ellermani[9] (n = 11)	157.1 ± 14.3	180.3 ± 21.2	33.3 ± 2.0	22.2 ± 2.7	99.3 ± 22.0
	126–174	150–204	30–38	18–24	55–120
E. majori[1] (n = 23)	157.9 ± 6.6	190.4 ± 10.4	28.8 ± 1.1	19.6 ± 0.7	97.2 ± 12.9
	145–171	170–207	27–31	18–21	77–122

Notes: HBL, head-and-body length; TL, tail length; HFL, hind-foot length; EL, ear length; WT. Sample statistics include the mean ± one standard deviation, and the minimum–maximum range.

[1] Locality: Andringitra National Park (NP) (Goodman and Carleton 1996).
[2] Marojejy NP (Carleton and Goodman 2000).
[3] Alandraza Analavelo protected area (Carleton et al. 2001).
[4] Fanovana and east of Andasibe (Carleton 1994).
[5] West central Madagascar, all localities (Jansa et al. 2019).
[6] Ranomafana NP and vicinity (Jansa et al. 2019).
[7] Ankarana Special Reserve (SR) (Goodman et al. 2009a).
[8] Isalo NP (Carleton and Goodman 2007).
[9] Anjanaharibe-Sud SR and vicinity (Jansa et al. 2019).

rodent species richness undoubtedly represents real biogeographic differences, perhaps associated with environmental complexity (Muldoon and Goodman 2010; Z. Rakotomalala and Goodman 2010), it is also true that moist evergreen forests have been the historical focus of small-mammal field inventories (Carleton and Schmidt 1990; Soarimalala 2008).

With vastly improved voucher collections of specific occurrences, the ranges of certain species have been found to span nearly the north–south limits of the island, coincident with major vegetation types (e.g., *E. majori*, *E. minor*, *E. webbi*). Populations of *E. myoxinus*, as currently defined (but see Shi et al. 2013), constitute an exception to this pattern, known not only from dry deciduous forests but also from dry spiny thickets in the south and transitional dry deciduous–lowland moist evergreen forests in the far north (Goodman et al. 2018b). In contrast, other *Eliurus* species still appear regionally restricted even in light of the renewed field efforts (e.g., *E. antsingy*, *E. danieli*, *E. penicillatus*, *E. petteri*). The following summaries of distribution and sympatry are based on examined specimens, mostly as reported in recent systematic studies and faunal surveys in the following five major geographic regions:

TABLE 14.37. **Key to currently recognized *Eliurus* species, based on size and external and craniodental characters**

1. Molar rows long and robust (LM1–3 >16% of ONL); 2nd and 3rd molars subequal in size; incisive foramina relatively long (LIF >50% of LD) 2

  2. Dorsal pelage gray, bright in tone with dorsal-ventral pelage contrast well delineated; conspicuous bright-white tail tuft; ectotympanic bullae relatively large, obscuring most of periotic; zygomatic notch extends forward to form distinct dorsal notch; restricted to Isalo Massif ..... *E. danieli*

  2a. Dorsal pelage a dull blackish gray, dorsal-ventral countershading not well defined; ectotympanic bullae relatively small, exposing much of periotic; zygomatic plate narrower, dorsal notch weakly incised; distributed in moist evergreen forest 3

    3. Tail tuft generally mono-colored, dark to tip; size larger (ONL usually >36 mm; LM1–3 usually >6.2 mm) ..... *E. majori*[1]

    3a. Tail tuft bicolor, terminal portion white; size smaller (ONL usually <37 mm; LM1–3 usually <6.2 mm) ..... *E. penicillatus*

1a. Molar rows relatively shorter (LM1–3 <15% of ONL); 3rd molars smaller than 2nd; incisive foramina relatively short (LIF <50% of LD) 4

  4. Size small (HFL <23 mm; ONL <32 mm; LM1–3 <4.3 mm); tail tuft dark to tip, penicillation well developed over distal third of tail ..... *E. minor*

  4a. Size larger (HFL >24 mm; ONL >33 mm; LM1–3 >4.3 mm); tail tuft dark or white toward tip, penicillation variably pronounced 5

    5. Tail relatively short (TL ~110–114% of HBL); tail tuft dark to tip, penicillation well developed over distal half of tail; size medium (HFL ~24–26 mm; ONL ~34–38 mm); interorbit relatively broad and auditory bullae relatively large ..... *E. myoxinus*

    5a. Tail relatively long (TL usually >115% of HBL); tuft color variable, penicillation confined to distal third or less of tail; size medium to large; interorbit relatively narrow and auditory bullae relatively small 6

      6. Tail exceptionally long (TL ~125–135% of HBL); pencillation weakly developed, confined to distal quarter of tail; size medium, upper incisors delicate; alveolar track of lower incisor short and not terminating as a capsular process 7

        7. Tail tuft mono-colored, dark to tip; ventral pelage white; cranial size larger (ONL >36 mm) but molar row short (LM1–3 <5.2 mm); alisphenoid strut absent ..... *E. petteri*

        7a. Tail tuft bicolor, with short white tip; ventral pelage gray; cranial size smaller (ONL <36 mm) but molar row long (LM1–3 >5.3 mm); alisphenoid strut usually present ..... *E. grandidieri*

      6a. Tail moderately long (TL ~115–125% of HBL); penicillation moderately developed over distal third to half of tail length; size larger, upper incisors robust, alveolar track of lower incisor long, with or without capsular process 8

        8. Tail tuft relatively long, dark to tip; incisive foramina moderately long and wide, LIF/LD = 50–58%; incisor capsule indistinct; confined to karst landscapes of northern and western Madagascar 9

          9. Tail tuft relatively long, ~55% of TL; distribution limited to western Madagascar ..... *E. antsingy*

          9a. Tail tuft relatively short, ~45% of TL; distribution limited to northern Madagascar ..... *E. carletoni*

        8a. Tail tuft moderately long, with dark or white tip; incisive foramina relatively short and narrow, LIF/LD = 38–46%; incisor capsule protuberant 10

          10. Size smaller (ONL typically <40 mm; LM1–3 ~5.0–5.6 mm); subsquamosal fenestra usually present; palate usually with single pair of posterior palatine foramina; capsular process smaller, ending below sigmoid notch ..... *E. webbi*

          10a. Size larger (ONL typically >39 mm; LM1–3 ~5.5–6.1); subsquamosal fenestra reduced to slit or absent; palate with supernumerary palatine foramina or elongate vacuities; capsular process larger, ending at or below rim of sigmoid notch 11

            11. Interorbital constriction relatively narrow and auditory bullae relatively large; supernumerary palatal vacuities uncommon; confined to dry deciduous forest, west-central Madagascar ..... *E. tsingimbato*

            11a. Interorbital constriction relatively broad and auditory bullae relatively small; supernumerary palatal vacuities typically present; distribution confined to eastern moist evergreen forests 12

              12. Ventral pelage gray or grayish white, weakly delineated from the dorsum; distribution confined to the Central and Southern Highlands ..... *E. tanala*

              12a. Ventral pelage creamy white, dorsal-ventral countershading pronounced; distribution centered in the Northern Highlands ..... *E. ellermani*

Note: HBL, head-and-body length; TL, tail length; HFL, hind-foot length; ONL, occipitonasal length; LIF, length of incisive foramen; LD, length of diastema; LM1–3, coronal length of upper molar row.

[1] On Montagne d'Ambre, *E. majori* is as small as *E. penicillatus* occurring in the Central Highlands and its eastern flank; in proportional features and color of the tail tuft, however, it resembles *E. majori* proper (see Carleton and Goodman 2000).

- Madagascar, general: Carleton and Schmidt 1990; Carleton 1994; Soarimalala and Goodman 2011; Goodman et al. 2013, 2018b
- Northern Highlands and surrounding lower elevations: Goodman et al. 1996b, 2009a, 2018b; Goodman and Carleton 1998; Carleton and Goodman 2000; Goodman and Soarimalala 2002; Soarimalala and Goodman 2003a; Andrianjakarivelo et al. 2005; Raheriarisena and Goodman 2006; Z. Rakotomalala et al. 2007; Maminirina et al. 2008; J.-E. Rakotoarisoa et al. 2010; Jansa et al. 2019

- Central Highlands, including western and eastern escarpments, and adjoining eastern lowlands: Goodman and Carleton 1996; Goodman et al. 1998b, 2007d, 2018b; Langrand and Goodman 1997; D. Rakotondravony et al. 1998a; Goodman and Rasolonandrasana 1999, 2001; Soarimalala et al. 2001, 2007; P. D. Jenkins and Carleton 2005; Soarimalala and Goodman 2006; Ramanana 2008; Soarimalala and Raheriarisena 2010; Radovimiandrinifarany 2013; Randriamoria et al. 2015; Randriamoria 2017; Jansa et al. 2019
- Southern Highlands: Goodman et al. 1999a, 2018b; Ramanana 2010
- Western Madagascar: Goodman and Ganzhorn 1994; Carleton et al. 2001; Soarimalala and Goodman 2004; Carleton and Goodman 2007; Soarimalala 2008; Z. Rakotomalala and Goodman 2010; Shi et al. 2013; Soarimalala et al. 2013; Goodman et al. 2018b; Jansa et al. 2019

Eliurus antsingy. West central Madagascar, in isolated *tsingy* areas including the Namoroka and Bemaraha Massifs (see map in Jansa et al. 2019: Figure 16). Elevational records from 100 and 200 m. Sympatry recorded with *E. myoxinus* and *E. tsingimbato*.

Eliurus carletoni. Northern Madagascar, in dry deciduous forest associated with exposed limestone of the Ankarana formation and sandstone beds of various massifs in the Loky Manambato area (see map in Jansa et al. 2019: Figure 16). Elevational range 50–550 m. Documented in sympatry with *E. ellermani*, *E. minor*, and *E. myoxinus*.

Eliurus danieli (Figure 14.68f). South-central Madagascar, on the Isalo and Makay Massifs formed by exposed sandstone deposits west of the Southern Highlands (see map in Goodman et al. 2013: 251). Elevational occurrences recorded at 650 and 700 m. Not yet documented in strict syntopy with other *Eliurus*, but specimens of *E. myoxinus* also collected on the Isalo Massif.

Eliurus ellermani (Figure 14.68c). Distribution centered in moist evergreen forests of the Northern Highlands, from the northernmost isolate, Montagne d'Ambre, throughout the core Northern Highlands, to southern outliers in mountains of the Masoala Peninsula and in northernmost reaches of the Central Highlands (see map in Jansa et al. 2019: Figure 16). Recorded elevational range between 440 and 1570 m, most collecting sites falling between 800 and 1200 m. Sympatry documented with *E. carletoni*, *E. grandidieri*, *E. majori*, *E. minor*, and *E. webbi*.

Eliurus grandidieri (Figure 14.68a). Middle and upper elevational forests of the Northern Highlands and localities along the eastern portion of the Central Highlands as far south as Marolambo (see map in Goodman et al. 2013: 252). Documented elevational occurrences between 900 and 2050 m; distribution likely discontinuous. Known to occur sympatrically with *E. ellermani*, *E. majori*, *E. minor*, *E. penicillatus*, *E. tanala*, and *E. webbi*.

Eliurus majori. Montagne d'Ambre in the north, along middle to upper slopes of the Northern and Central Highlands, south to Andohahela in the Anosyenne Mountains, Southern Highlands (see map in Goodman et al. 2013: 253). Elevational range documented from 1000 to 2500 m; in view of highland affinity, distribution likely discontinuous. Known to occur with *E. ellermani*, *E. grandidieri*, *E. minor*, *E. penicillatus*, and *E. tanala*; and with *E. webbi* only on Montagne d'Ambre.

Eliurus minor (Figure 14.68b). From Montagne d'Ambre in the north through the Northern Highlands and the eastern Central Highlands and adjoining lowlands to the southern termini of the Anosyenne and Vohimena Mountains (see map in Goodman et al. 2013: 254). Elevational occurrence broad, from near sea level to 2050 m. In view of its wide geographic and elevational distribution, the species has been collected with most other eastern species of *Eliurus* and with *E. myoxinus* in northern transitional dry deciduous–lowland moist evergreen forest.

Eliurus myoxinus. Broadly distributed in western Madagascar, typically in dry deciduous forest or spiny thicket associations, from the Binara Forest, its northernmost occurrence in Loky Manambato, to the island's southeastern tip in the vicinity of Bevilany (see maps in Goodman et al. 2013: 255; Shi et al. 2013: Figure 1). Recorded from sea level to 1250 m. Sympatry documented with *E. carletoni* and *E. minor* in a mosaic region of transitional dry deciduous–lowland moist evergreen forests in northern Madagascar; and with *E. antsingy* and *E. tsingimbato* in western Madagascar; where the distribution of *E. myoxinus* extends to the lowland moist evergreen forest of northern massifs (Marojejy, Tsaratanàna, and Manongarivo), documentation of strict sympatry with additional species warrants review. Subfossil material identified as *E. myoxinus* and dated as late Holocene (~2500–500 BP) has been recovered from Andrahomana Cave, southeastern Madagascar (Goodman et al. 2006a); from Ankilitelo Cave, southwestern Madagascar (Muldoon et al. 2009); and from caves at Beanka, western Madagascar (Nomenjanahary 2019)—all sites within the known range of living *E. myoxinus*.

Eliurus penicillatus. Known only from a few localities within the Marolambo protected area, along the eastern central flank of the Central Highlands, at elevations from ~900 to 1670 m (see map in Goodman et al. 2013: 256). Collected with *E. grandidieri*, *E. majori*, *E. minor*, and *E. tanala*.

Eliurus petteri. Restricted region of east central Madagascar, from foothills to the east of Moramanga and from several sites in lowland moist evergreen forest (see map in Goodman et al. 2013: 256); documented elevational range correspondingly narrow, 450–1200 m. Recorded in strict sympatry with *E. minor*, *E. tanala*, and *E. webbi*.

Eliurus tanala. Moist evergreen forests along eastern sectors of the Central Highlands and Southern Highlands, from the vicinity of Lake Alaotra as far south as the Anosyenne Mountains and outlying foothills (see Jansa et al. 2019: Figure 16). Elevational records documented from 395 to 1630 m, most occurrences falling between 800 and 1300 m. Sympatry recorded with *E. grandidieri*, *E. majori*, *E. minor*, *E. penicillatus*, *E. petteri*, and *E. webbi*.

Eliurus tsingimbato (Figure 14.68e). Dry deciduous forests that overlie karst landscapes of west central Madagascar, from the

Namoroka Massif southward to the vicinity of Bekopaka, Bemaraha Massif (see map in Jansa et al. 2019: Figure 16). Documented elevational range between 100 and 320 m. Sympatry vouchered with *E. antsingy* and *E. myoxinus*.

Eliurus webbi (Figure 14.68d). Montagne d'Ambre in the north, along lower east-facing slopes of the Northern and Central Highlands, to the southern reaches of the Anosyenne and Vohimena Mountains and littoral forests of the central east and extreme southeast (see map in Goodman et al. 2013: 258). Elevational range of most localities from near sea level to 875 m, although sporadically found up to 1300 m at Tsaratanàna, Manongarivo, Anjozorobe-Angavo, and Befotaka–Midongy du Sud; exceptional elevation, 1500 m, recorded on Pic d'Ivohibe. Records of sympatry with *E. ellermani*, *E. grandidieri*, *E. petteri*, and *E. tanala*, species that range into low or middle elevations; and with *E. minor*, another species common in the eastern lowlands. Collected with *E. majori* in medium-altitude moist evergreen forest on Montagne d'Ambre (1000 m).

ECOLOGY, BEHAVIOR, AND REPRODUCTION

Much of the following life-history information on members of the genus is based on classical trapping results, typically accrued from sustained removal transect lines conducted as part of intense biotic inventories of forested areas (see references listed under Geographic and Elevational Distribution). Some recent work, however, has employed camera traps to provide fresh insights into landscape occupancy, such as specific habitat characteristics, habitat degradation, and fine-scale syntopy with other rodent species and their carnivoran predators (Murphy et al. 2017b).

Species of *Eliurus* are nocturnal and almost uniformly associated with arborescent habitats. Those species that are broadly distributed within moist evergreen forests (*E. majori*, *E. tanala*, and *E. webbi*) demonstrate remarkable fidelity to elevational zones and vegetation types throughout their ranges. Most eastern species inhabit portions of medium-altitude moist evergreen forest (*E. ellermani*, *E. grandidieri*, *E. majori*, *E. penicillatus*, *E. petteri*, and *E. tanala*). Although several of these species may occur in forested zones just below tree line on the highest massifs, none has been captured in montane ericoid thicket or montane grassland. The distribution of *E. webbi* is centered in lowland moist evergreen forest, with populations also occurring in littoral forests or extending into the lower limits of medium-altitude moist evergreen forest. Most sites of *E. petteri* also fall into or just above lowland moist evergreen forest. Within transitional zones between lowland and medium-altitude moist forests, *E. webbi* has been recorded together with *E. ellermani*, in Northern Highlands, or with *E. tanala*, in Central and Southern Highlands. The smallest species, *E. minor*, assuming that its taxonomic recognition as a single species is correct, extends throughout lowland and medium-altitude moist evergreen forest associations. *Eliurus myoxinus* is the most broadly distributed western species and appears eurytopic in its environmental adaptability, documented from localities in dry spiny thicket (spiny bush), dry deciduous forest, transitional dry deciduous–lowland moist evergreen forest, and lowland moist evergreen forest on some northern massifs. Other species of the west (*E. antsingy* and *E. tsingimbato*) or extreme north (*E. carletoni*) are more narrowly restricted to dry deciduous forest that overlies karstic geological formations (*tsingy*) or other types of exposed sedimentary rock, in the case of *E. carletoni*.

The characteristic broad hind foot, with its long outer digit and cushiony plantar pads, and a tail longer than head and body, are physiognomic indicators of proficient climbing and suggestive of scansorial, if not arboreal, habits within the genus. Stephenson (1987) observed that, when released, individuals of *E. webbi* scampered toward trees or ascended lianas draped from a cliff. Such behavior and activity sphere are reinforced by the now extensive data on successful trap captures, showing that species of *Eliurus* have been collected as routinely in arboreal settings (up to 2 m above ground, on lianas, horizontal limbs and branches, leaning trunks suspended by subcanopy vines) as in terrestrial ones (among boulders and rock outcrops, along tree buttresses and fallen logs, among root entanglements, in dense herbaceous ground cover and thick leaf litter) (Goodman and Carleton 1996, 1998; Goodman et al. 1999a, 2009a; Carleton and Goodman 2000; Andrianjakarivelo et al. 2005).

This same body of data collectively suggests that certain species are predominantly scansorial (*E. majori*, *E. myoxinus*, and *E. webbi*), others moderately so (*E. minor* and *E. tanala*), and one infrequently so (*E. grandidieri*). Some intraspecific geographic variation is apparent, as exemplified by *E. grandidieri*, individuals of which were mostly captured on the ground on the Anjanaharibe-Sud and Marojejy Massifs (83% and 90%, respectively; Goodman and Carleton 1998; Carleton and Goodman 2000), whereas a majority of trap captures in the Anjozorobe-Angavo Forest were in arboreal settings (about 75%; V. Soarimalala and S. M. Goodman, unpublished data). Further, the apparent arboreal versus terrestrial tendency revealed by trapping is sometimes variable within a species at different elevations of the same massif—for example, *E. webbi* at 440 and 810 m in Andohahela (Goodman et al. 1999a). These incidental contrasts may reflect the adaptability of the *Eliurus* phenotype to accommodate local variations in vegetation structure or to exploit seasonally available nutritional resources. Because live traps are seldom placed more than 1–3 m—a "reachable" height—above the ground, the possibility of canopy utilization by *Eliurus* cannot be critically addressed. Field workers have occasionally witnessed nocturnal canopy activity of *Eliurus* species, the rodents in some instances climbing as high as 15 m in tree crowns.

The scant information on the home range of *Eliurus* species is limited to *E. myoxinus*. Males established mutually exclusive home ranges, as studied in the Ankarafantsika Forest and Kirindy Forest CNFEREF; however, female home ranges overlapped those of males (Ganzhorn 2003; Randrianjafy 2003). Based on a capture-recapture study at Ankarafantsika (Randrianjafy 2003), females were thought to have larger home ranges than males, juveniles maintained home ranges in proximity to that of their mother until they reach sexual maturity, and females became solitary during the breeding period but were gregarious at other times. Although details of mating behavior are unavailable, circumstantial evidence suggests that *E. myoxinus* is polygynous.

Various combinations of species have been successively collected in the same live trap, whether an arboreal or terrestrial placement: for example, *E. grandidieri*–*E. majori*, *E. grandidieri*–*E. ellermani*,

E. majori–E. tanala, *E. minor–E. majori*, *E. minor–E. tanala*, *E. minor–E. webbi* (Goodman and Carleton 1996, 1998). Although these trapping results suggest little interference competition or inconsequential specific differences in substrate usage, foraging sphere, or microhabitat preference, firm answers to such synecological and autecological questions, as well as age-specific mortality and demographic profiles, await extended field study.

The trophic niche of *Eliurus* similarly lacks detailed substantiation. In captivity, both *E. minor* and *E. webbi* relished offerings of coconut (Stephenson 1987), and *E. myoxinus* readily fed on bananas, cassava, and corn (Randrianjafy 2003). A chamber in the burrow system of *E. webbi* contained a seed cache of *Cryptocarya* (Lauraceae), about half of them gnawed opened and partly eaten (Goodman 1994). In Andohahela National Park (parcel 2), a specimen of *E. myoxinus* was captured in a fruiting Apocynaceae tree located next to a palm tree (*Dypsis decaryi*, Arecaceae) whose fruits the species is believed to consume (J. Ratsirarson, cited in Goodman et al. 1999a: 228). In Ankarafantsika, seeds of *Monanthotaxis valida* (Annonaceae), *Rhopalocarpus* sp. (Sphaerosepalaceae), and *Tabernaemontana coffeoides* (Apocynaceae) were cached in burrows of *E. myoxinus* (Randrianjafy 2003). These few observations, albeit anecdotal in nature, imply granivorous and/or frugivorous food habits, an interpretation generally supported by stable isotope ratios of carbon and nitrogen analyzed for *Eliurus* species (*E. grandidieri*, *E. majori*, and *E. minor*) that inhabit the Tsinjoarivo medium-altitude moist evergreen forest (Dammhahn et al. 2013). Their results indicate that the diets of the three species are notably separate in isotopic space, suggesting resource partitioning, and that, of the three, *E. grandidieri* consumes more animal matter. Possible interspecific differences in diet and the indurate nature of foodstuffs consumed also invite investigation with regard to the range of incisor development noted within the genus (Carleton 1994).

Where *Eliurus* species place their nests, in view of their climbing habits, is so far poorly documented. Webb (1954), who collected *Eliurus* in both eastern and western forests, recorded that *E. myoxinus* nests in tree holes and was further impressed that the western species is "more arboreal than those from the eastern forest and rarely descends to the ground." Webb's observations are supported by Randrianjafy's (2003) study of the species at Ankarafantsika, where sleeping sites were located in tree holes up to 6 m high. The only convincingly documented nest location of an eastern species, *E. webbi* in Andringitra (Goodman 1994), was a terrestrial construction, with two burrow openings and a tunnel descending 85 cm belowground to an apparent food chamber. Other information on nest placement consists of circumstantial evidence, such as individuals captured next to ground hollows and tunnel openings that appear to be rodent burrows (e.g., *E. grandidieri*, *E. majori*, *E. minor*, *E. tanala*). The generality of Webb's observation on western versus eastern *Eliurus* species, their arboreal tendencies, and nest location merits confirmation.

Knowledge of neonatal growth and development within the genus is limited to *E. myoxinus*, based on a laboratory rearing of animals captured in Ankarafantsika (Randrianjafy 2003; Randrianjafy et al. 2007). Young have a rapid linear growth phase from birth until 1 month old; their growth rate continues to increase until one and a half to two months of age but then decreases as they approach weaning, around three and a half months of age. Males grew more rapidly than females. Animals attained adult size after four and a half months, when the first signs of reproductive activity were noted. If females lost their litter at parturition, they rapidly entered a postpartum estrus and would give birth to a new litter after a gestation period of 29–32 days. Additional short-term laboratory investigations such as this would do much to illuminate specific differences in gestation, neonatal growth and development, and ages at weaning and sexual maturity. Litter size, as judged by placental scars or embryo counts (n = 144; Table 14.38), is generally small in species of *Eliurus*, usually two or three young and

TABLE 14.38. Ranges and means of litter size for species of *Eliurus*

SPECIES	LITTER SIZE 1	2	3	4	5	R	X
E. antsingy	–	–	2	–	–	2	–
E. carletoni	–	2	1	1	–	2–4	2.8
E. ellermani	1	1	1	–	–	1–3	2.0
E. grandidieri	–	10	3	–	–	2–3	2.2
E. majori	1	16	17	1	1	1–5	2.6
E. minor	1	18	24	5	–	1–4	2.6
E. myoxinus	1	12	4	–	–	1–3	2.6
E. tanala	1	3	10	1	–	1–4	2.7
E. webbi	–	4	2	–	–	2–3	2.3
Generic totals	5	66	64	8	1	1–5	2.5

Sources: Data from Carleton (1994); Goodman and Carleton (1996, 1998); Goodman et al. (1999a, 2009a); Carleton and Goodman (2000); and V. Soarimalala and S. M. Goodman (unpublished data).

Notes: R, range of litter sizes, as recorded by counts of placental scars and/or implanted embryos; X, mean of litter size in cases of at least three counts.

ranging from one to five. The available data do not support interspecific differences in the average litter size.

An understanding of breeding seasons in populations of *Eliurus* must be pieced together from the numerous biological surveys of forested areas that have now been conducted over most of the island and through much of the year. Still, any one site survey is generally conducted for a short period, usually 7–10 days at a given elevation, a temporal bias that tempers broad conclusions about the onset of reproduction, its cyclical regularity (or not), and its relationship to environmental rhythms (ambient temperature, rainfall patterns, fruiting cycles, insect fluctuations, etc.). Moreover, indication of active breeding is usually deduced when handling animals in the field—males with scrotal testes, females with embryos or lactating, a high proportion of juveniles and subadults in the catch.

Although imperfect, compared with year-round, site-intensive investigations, these information sources permit the following observations about *Eliurus* breeding seasons, largely as derived from inventories undertaken in medium-altitude moist evergreen forest. Most populations of *Eliurus* exhibited moderate to high levels of reproduction during the quarter-year period (October–December) of surveys performed in the Northern Highlands (Carleton and Goodman 1998, 2000; Goodman and Carleton 1998), Central Highlands (Goodman and Carleton 1996), and Southern Highlands (Goodman et al. 1999a). In the Anjozorobe-Angavo Forest, Central Highlands, most *Eliurus* species (*E. grandidieri*, *E. majori*, *E. minor*, and *E. tanala*) captured during October, January, and February evidenced ongoing reproduction, females containing well-developed embryos and males possessing convoluted epididymides. However, *Eliurus* specimens captured on Montagne d'Ambre (*E. majori* and *E. webbi*) and Marojejy (*E. minor* and *E. webbi*) in April and May displayed no signs of active breeding. At two other Central Highlands sites, numerous *E. minor* juveniles dominated captures during March in the Ankazomivady Forest and during June, July, and August at Ambohitantely; furthermore, no gravid females were collected at these two sites during these periods, nor did any females possess developed mammae or placental scars. These lines of evidence suggest that *Eliurus* reproduction ceases at the end of the seasonal rains, around the end of February, and recommences in October, when intermittent rains resume (V. Soarimalala and S. M. Goodman, unpublished data).

Departures from this reproductive pattern are nonetheless numerous. In lowland moist evergreen forest at Marotandrano, some females of *E. ellermani* and *E. grandidieri* captured during May had either embryos or fresh placental scars (M. Raheriarisena, unpublished data). Samples of *E. webbi* in the protected areas of Anjanaharibe-Sud and Marojejy exhibited different levels of reproduction, high in the former and low in the latter, although both massifs are geographically close in the Northern Highlands, and surveys were conducted at essentially the same period of the year (Goodman and Carleton 1998; Carleton and Goodman 2000). In Andringitra, the incidence of breeding activity of *E. tanala* seemingly increased from lower (810 m) to higher elevations (1625 m); whereas, samples of *E. minor*, in the same protected area and over the same collecting zones, disclosed no clear trend of increased reproductive activity as a function of elevation (Goodman and Carleton 1996). In dry deciduous forest at Ankarafantsika, *E. myoxinus* apparently breeds throughout the year: juvenile and subadult specimens were captured at every monthly trapping session, as were adults that exhibited traits of active reproduction (Randrianjafy 2003; Randrianjafy et al. 2007). Firm understanding of annual reproductive patterns and breeding systems within *Eliurus*, as well as possible elevational or latitudinal variation within and among species, can be obtained only from longer term, single locality investigations, specifically using other field protocols such as mark-and-recapture trapping.

Species of *Eliurus* compose an important prey item of predatory birds and mammals in forest communities. Skeletal elements of *Eliurus* have been frequently identified in the regurgitated pellets of several moderately large to large owls. Remains of *E. minor*, *E. majori*, and *E. webbi* have been recovered from the pellets of *Asio madagascariensis* (Madagascar Long-eared Owl), in southeastern and northeastern forests (Goodman et al. 1993b; S. M. Goodman, unpublished data). On the Masoala Peninsula, skeletal remains of *E. minor* and *E. webbi* totaled 61%, by minimum number of individuals, of the prey recorded for *Tyto soumagnei* (Red Owl) (Goodman and Thorstrom 1998); in the Bemanevika Forest, Northern Highlands, this same raptor consumes *E. ellermani*, *E. grandidieri*, *E. majori*, and *E. minor*, which collectively represented about 8% of the identified mammal prey based on number of individuals (J. Ramamonjisoa and S. M. Goodman, unpublished data); in the Ankarana protected area, this owl regularly preyed upon *E. carletoni*, remains of which were common in regurgitated pellets and differed seasonally in the percentage of prey items taken (Cardiff and Goodman 2008). At Sept Lacs, a site along the Onilahy River in the southwest, *E. myoxinus* was occasionally consumed by *T. alba* (Barn Owl) (Rasoma and Goodman 2007). In Ankarafantsika, *Polyboroides radiatus* (Madagascar Harrier-hawk), has been observed to seize young of *E. myoxinus*, using its long legs to probe tree holes and crevices. Several species of *Eliurus* have been identified in the scats of *Cryptoprocta ferox* (Fosa), including *E. majori* and *E. minor* on the Andringitra Massif, Central Highlands (Goodman et al. 1997a), and *E. myoxinus* in the Ankarafantsika Forest and Kirindy Forest CNFEREF, western Madagascar (Randrianjafy 2003; C. E. Hawkins and Racey 2008). At least two species of snakes, *Leioheterodon madagascariensis* and *Madagascarophis colubrinus*, are known to feed on *E. myoxinus* in Ankarafantsika (Randrianjafy 2003).

Species of *Eliurus* have now been the subject of dedicated epidemiological and parasitological study. In the Ranomafana National Park, where samples of *Rattus rattus* were infected with typical *Trypanosoma lewisi*, sympatric species of *Eliurus* were instead infected with a morphologically different trypanostomid (Laakkonen et al. 2003). The feces of *E. webbi* were found to contain five forms of nematodes (Strongylidae), allocated to the genera *Ancylostoma*, *Oesophagostomum*, *Strongyloides*, *Trichostrongylus*?, and one unknown genus (Raharivololona and Ganzhorn 2007). In addition, a species of Trichostrongylina, *Heligmonina tanala*, has been named based on nematodes from *E. tanala* captured in Ranomafana (Durette-Desset et al. 2002a).

A new genetic variant of Thailand Orthohantavirus (THAIV), a type of hantavirus with variants known in Southeast Asia, was detected in one of 15 specimens of *E. majori* tested from the Anjozorobe-Angavo Forest and appropriately named the Anjozorobe Virus (Reynes et al. 2014). Paramyxoviruses were also detected in 11% of samples of *E. minor* and a smaller percentage of *E. tanala* in

the Lakato and Ankazomivady Forests, Central Highlands (Wilkinson et al. 2014). Both serological and virological analyses of *Eliurus* samples collected in a nearby forest during an epizootic outbreak of Rift Valley Fever Virus were negative for this virus (Olive et al. 2013). The bacterial pathogen *Leptospira borgpetersenii*, responsible for human cases of the disease leptospirosis, was isolated from *Eliurus* specimens trapped in the Ankazomivady Forest, revealing that 29% of 112 *E. minor* samples and 0% of four *E. tanala* samples tested were positive (Dietrich et al. 2014; see Dietrich et al., pp. 268–77).

Both ticks (Ixodida) and fleas (Siphonaptera) are known among the ectoparasites reported for *Eliurus*. None of the assorted ticks identified from *E. ellermani*, *E. majori*, *E. tanala*, and *E. webbi* are host-specific but also occur on other nesomyine rodents (see Klompen and Apanaskevich, pp. 894–99). Various endemic fleas are known from several species of *Eliurus*, but none of them are restricted to the genus, parasitizing a variety of other endemic Malagasy mammals as well (Duchemin 2003; see Duchemin et al., pp. 1074–80). The endemic flea *Synopsyllus fonquerniei*, a species known to transmit bubonic plague, has been broadly identified on species of *Eliurus*, namely *E. antsingy*, *E. ellermani*, *E. grandidieri*, *E. majori*, *E. myoxinus*, *E. tanala*, and *E. webbi* (Roubaud and Girard 1943; Duchemin 2003).

CONSERVATION

The stability of *Eliurus* populations, like that of other nesomyine genera whose ecological presence is superimposed on the island's forests, is correspondingly dependent upon the continued preservation of those habitats in extent and quality (e.g., Irwin et al. 2010; Vieilledent et al. 2018). Although the distributions of some *Eliurus* species (*E. antsingy*, *E. danieli*, and *E. penicillatus*) intersect with only one or two protected areas, a majority occur in 10 or more such sites (Goodman et al. 2018b). Perhaps this distributional congruence is reflected in the IUCN (2020) classification of Least Concern for eight *Eliurus* species (*E. carletoni*, *E. danieli*, *E. grandidieri*, *E. majori*, *E. minor*, *E. myoxinus*, *E. tanala*, and *E. webbi*); all these taxa except *E. carletoni* and *E. danieli* have extensive north–south geographic ranges. The two species considered Endangered are known only from restricted areas in east central Madagascar: *E. penicillatus*, occurring along the eastern escarpment, Central Highlands, and *E. petteri*, in the same zone, although farther to the north, and adjoining lowland forest. Of the remaining species, the IUCN acknowledges *E. antsingy* and *E. ellermani* as Data Deficient and has yet to assess the status of *E. tsingimbato*, owing to its recent description (Jansa et al. 2019).

Severe disturbances such as swidden agriculture or commercial logging may eliminate the presence of certain species, specifically those that depend upon pristine or mostly intact forests. For example, the moist forests inhabited by *E. petteri*, an endangered species with a limited geographic range, have experienced considerable reduction and degradation over recent decades (Goodman et al. 2018b; Vieilledent et al. 2018).

Nevertheless, the much expanded surveys of nesomyine distributions since the last portion of the 20th century have revealed that certain species can tolerate some degradation of their natural habitat. For example, *E. webbi* has been recorded in degraded littoral forest associated with introduced tree plantations and in lowland moist evergreen forest invaded by non-native plants; whether such secondary habitats will sustain viable populations of *E. webbi* into the medium- to long-term future remains to be determined (D. Rakotondravony et al. 1998a; Ramanamanjato and Ganzhorn 2001; S. M. Goodman and V. Soarimalala, unpublished data). Forest fragmentation is known to negatively affect capture rates and population density of *E. webbi* (Ramanamanjato and Ganzhorn 2001). Randriamoria (2017) documented the presence of *E. majori*, *E. tanala*, and *E. webbi* in various types of regenerating humid forest habitat (*savoka*) and in a forest near a village, all sites that bordered relatively intact forest. In the remaining large forest block at Ambohitantely, Central Highlands, repeated surveys conducted over two decades and across several seasons indicate that populations of *E. minor* and *E. majori* have remained stable in spite of the invasive ubiquity of *Rattus rattus* (V. Soarimalala and S. M. Goodman, unpublished data).

Ecomorphological similarity of *R. rattus* and larger *Eliurus* species, especially *E. tanala* and *E. webbi*, suggests that their trophic and spatial niches overlap, which may lead to a high probability of interspecific competition with the introduced commensal (Miljutin and Lehtonen 2008; see Ramasindrazana et al., pp. 1872–80). Dietary overlap and possible ecological competition are borne out by stable isotope analyses of rodent hairs, which disclosed an extremely broad trophic profile of *R. rattus* collected in forested areas of the Moramanga District, compared with much narrower trophic habits inferred for the endemic rodent community, which included three *Eliurus* species (Dammhahn et al. 2017).

Subject editor: Steven M. Goodman

NESOMYIDAE: *GYMNUROMYS ROBERTI*, ROBERT'S FOREST RAT, *VOALAVOANALA*

M. D. Carleton and S. M. Goodman

Gymnuromys is a morphologically distinctive genus containing only *G. roberti*, a species discovered by Major and named after his intrepid field assistant, Alphonse Robert (Major 1896b). Major's original type series, collected in 1896 from Ampitambe, represented the best series of museum specimens available until directed small-mammal inventories commenced in the 1990s. These inventories have considerably amplified details about the distribution and life history of *Gymnuromys*. Mitochondrial gene sequences from samples covering much of the species' geographic distribution have disclosed deep genetic divergence of populations inhabiting the Northern Highlands, a finding that recommends further study of *G. roberti* and its possible composite nature (Everson et al. 2020b).

The taxon's unique combination of complex occlusal configuration and intermolar proportions prompted Ellerman (1941) to create the monotypic subfamily Gymnuromyinae within a broadly defined Muridae. Molecular data fail to support this independent status and instead relate the genus to other nesomyines, usually within a clade also including *Eliurus–Voalavo* (Jansa et al. 2009; Steppan and Schenk 2017; see Jansa and Carleton, pp. 1865–71).

FIGURE 14.69 **Adult *Gymnuromys roberti* in Befotaka–Midongy du Sud.** (PHOTO by V. Soarimalala.)

TABLE 14.39. **External measurements for *Gymnuromys roberti* at Pic d'Ivohibe**

HBL (mm)	TL (mm)	HFL (mm)	EL (mm)	WT (g)
165.4 ± 7.1	187.1 ± 7.2	37.1 ± 1.9	22.1 ± 0.8	127.1 ± 14.4
149–175	176–197	33–40	21–24	103–153

Notes: Sample size: n = 13. HBL, head-and-body length; TL, tail length; HFL, hind-foot length; EL, ear length; WT, weight in grams. Sample statistics include the mean ± one standard deviation, and the minimum–maximum range.

DESCRIPTION

Examples of *G. roberti* appear fairly homogeneous in size, pelage color and texture, and craniodental morphology throughout its range. This sleek-furred, dark gray rodent is medium-size (103–153 g), with a tail appreciably longer than its stout body (Figure 14.69) and comparatively long and wide hind feet (Table 14.39). In body proportions and head shape, *G. roberti* superficially resembles a member of *Rattus*. The upperparts are nearly slate over the middle dorsum and slightly paler toward the flanks; individual dorsal hairs are somewhat stiff, imparting a coarser texture than the soft coat of *Eliurus* (see Carleton et al., pp. 2014–22). Cream- to white-tipped, slate-based hairs, or sometimes wholly white hairs, give the ventral fur a brightly contrasting silvery or frosted effect. The pinnae (ears) are moderately large, ovoid, and very finely haired. The tail is scantily haired, appearing naked to the unaided eye (Figure 14.69), and relatively long (about 110–115% of head-and-body length). Tops of the metapodials and phalanges, both front and rear, are covered with fine whitish to hyaline hairs. The hind foot is long but relatively broad, with the outer toes (first and fifth) somewhat shorter than the central three, and bears six plantar pads. Females possess three pairs of mammae, distributed as one axial, one abdominal, and one inguinal pair.

The cranium of *Gymnuromys* is characterized by a smoothly contoured braincase, narrow hourglass-shaped interorbit, very short incisive foramina, and tiny auditory bullae, features that recall the morphology of *Eliurus*. Specimens of *Gymnuromys*, however, lack a subsquamosal foramen (a trait typical of most *Eliurus* species), and their moderately high-crowned molars with convoluted enamel loops and compressed laminae are singularly distinctive. Size and proportions of the individual molars that form each tooth row are unique within Nesomyinae, if not within Muroidea. The third molars, both uppers and lowers, are markedly longer and wider than the second molars, which in turn are slightly longer and wider than the first; this gradient in molar size is the reverse of the typical muroid proportions, in which the first molars are conspicuously the largest in the tooth row, the second and third molars notably smaller. No secondary sexual dimorphism in size is suggested by craniodental measurements nor in body mass (Kappeler et al. 2019).

Examples of *Gymnuromys* resemble those of *E. majori* in size and their grayish-black dorsum. The fur of *E. majori* lacks the fine lustrous sheen characteristic of *G. roberti* and is distinctly woollier; furthermore, the tail of *E. majori* is appreciably longer than the head-and-body length (TL about 120% of HBL) and covered with long caudal hairs that terminate as a bushy tuft, and its hind feet are short and broad with a long fifth digit.

GEOGRAPHIC AND ELEVATIONAL DISTRIBUTION

The distribution of *G. roberti* tightly adheres to moist evergreen forests of eastern Madagascar (see map in Goodman et al. 2013: 259). The species is documented from the southern mountains of the Northern Highlands (Soarimalala and Goodman 2003a), along the eastern flank of the Central Highlands (Soarimalala and Goodman 2006; Soarimalala et al. 2007; Soarimalala and Raheriarisena 2010; Randriamoria 2017), to the southern limits of the Anosyenne Mountains, Southern Highlands (Ramanana 2010). Recorded elevations of collecting localities cover a belt 500 to 1625 m. Given its extensive latitudinal occurrence, *Gymnuromys* has been recorded in sympatry with most other moist forest-dwelling nesomyines, commonly with species of *Eliurus* and *Nesomys*. Populations of the latter genera do occur in the moist evergreen forests that extend into the western Northern Highlands (e.g., Tsaratanàna and Manongarivo), an area where *Gymnuromys* has yet to be recorded despite extensive small-mammal surveys (e.g., Maminirina et al. 2008).

ECOLOGY, BEHAVIOR, AND REPRODUCTION

Populations of *G. roberti* principally inhabit medium-altitude moist evergreen forests but have also been documented from the upper limits of lowland moist evergreen forest on the Andringitra Massif (720 m; Goodman and Carleton 1996) and on foothills west of Vondrozo (500 m—Carleton and Schmidt 1990). To our knowledge, it has never been trapped in montane ericoid thickets. Most captures have been in forest areas with sparse understory vegetation, the traps placed in leaf litter, near deadwood, or by roots and fallen trunks. Although the majority of *G. roberti* specimens have been obtained in standard live traps (Shermans and Nationals), individuals also have been captured in large (15 L) pitfall buckets (Goodman and Carleton 1998; Soarimalala and Raheriarisena 2010). Such pitfall captures mainly comprise subadults, but occasionally adults are trapped, particularly after heavy rains. Virtually without exception, specimens of *Gymnuromys* are never as abundantly captured as the genera *Nesomys*, *Eliurus*, and introduced *Rattus* during small-mammal surveys of moist evergreen forests.

Within its moist-forest environment, *G. roberti* is terrestrial in its habits and nocturnal in its activity rhythm (Ryan et al. 1993; Goodman and Carleton 1996, 1998). Ground burrows have been discovered in the Marojejy and Andringitra protected areas. At the former site, the entrance opened into a fallen log covered with epiphytes and mosses (Carleton and Goodman 2000). At the latter site, the entrance opened under a fallen log and continued as a meter-long, straight tunnel, sloping downward at 15–20° into a small chamber (Goodman and Carleton 1996). *Canarium* (Burseraceae) fruits were cached in the interior chamber, most of which had been gnawed open and the contents eaten; an indurate endocarp encases these seeds, which are rich in fat and crude protein (Bollen et al. 2004b).

Little is known about the reproductive habits of *G. roberti*. Numerous males with scrotal testes, as well as subadults, have been trapped during October–December at a number of sites. Two counts of placental scars and one of embryos disclosed a small litter size of only two young in each instance (Goodman and Carleton 1996; Goodman et al. 1999a; Carleton and Goodman 2000).

Recent epidemiological studies have isolated various zoonotic diseases and their parasitic vectors from *Gymnuromys*. Pathogenic bacteria (*Leptospira*) responsible for the disease leptospirosis have been found in *G. roberti* (Dietrich et al. 2014; see Dietrich et al., pp. 268–77). A variety of ectoparasites are known from *Gymnuromys* including ticks (see Klompen and Apanaskevich, pp. 894–99) and fleas (see Duchemin et al., pp. 1074–80). An endemic genus of nematode (Trichostrongylidae) described from *Gymnuromys* is considered a relict form distantly related to a trichostrongylid group found in the Ethiopian region (Durette-Desset and Chabaud 1992).

CONSERVATION

The preservation of *G. roberti*, like other forest-dwelling Malagasy rodents, is linked to the continued existence of intact forest blocks. The IUCN lists the conservation status of *Gymnuromys* as Least Concern (IUCN 2020), an assessment consistent with the broad distribution of the species and its documentation in many protected areas (Goodman et al. 2018b). Although the species has typically been collected in pristine or nearly intact forests, some records exist for partially degraded, secondary forests (e.g., Stephenson 1993; Randriamoria 2017). For example, several *Gymnuromys* were captured in the Station Forestière de La Mandraka, Central Highlands (F. Rakotondraparany, unpublished data), in secondary forest intermixed with introduced tree species. This instance reinforces the ability of *Gymnuromys* populations to tolerate limited degradation of their forest environment. Coupled with the issue of habitat loss or despoliation is the potential for competition with the introduced commensal rodents, especially *Rattus rattus*. For example, Miljutin and Lehtonen (2008) regarded *G. roberti* as the most vulnerable among Madagascar's endemic rodents to ecological competition with introduced *R. rattus*, based on their estimation of ecomorphological similarity.

Subject editor: Steven M. Goodman

NESOMYIDAE: *HYPOGEOMYS ANTIMENA*, MALAGASY GIANT JUMPING RAT, *VOSITSE*, *VOTSOTSA*

S. Sommer and M. D. Carleton

The French explorer and naturalist Alfred Grandidier encountered a large saltatorial rodent during his 1869 voyage along Madagascar's western coast and soon afterward named it *Hypogeomys antimena*, the first Malagasy native rodent known to western scientists (A. Grandidier 1869; Figure 14.70). This spectacular rodent is as iconic of the island's unique biota as are the majestic baobabs (*Adansonia* spp.; see Karimi et al., pp. 706–10). After Grandidier's publication, systematic awareness of *H. antimena* faded to obscurity for some 70 years, prompting the British Museum (Natural History) to engage Cecil S. Webb, a resourceful natural history collector, to visit Madagascar in 1939 and assess whether the species and some other poorly known vertebrates still survived (Webb 1954). The unflagging Webb finally managed to locate viable populations of *H. antimena*, collecting a small series while driving at night over the road leading south from Beroboka and through dry deciduous forest that struck him as "so different in its aspect from the rain-forest of the east" (Webb 1954: 247).

In molecular studies including both mitochondrial and nuclear genes, *H. antimena* phylogenetically nestles within Nesomyinae, forming the basal member in a clade that also includes *Brachyuromys-Nesomys* (Jansa et al. 2009; Steppan and Schenk 2017; see Jansa and Carleton, pp. 1865–71). Although *H. antimena* remains the only extant member of the genus, Grandidier's son, Guillaume, described a second species, *H. australis*, based on Holocene subfossils from cave deposits in extreme southeastern Madagascar (G. Grandidier 1903). Goodman and Rakotondravony (1996) retained *H. australis* as a species, which may have survived until 1550 BP based on radiocarbon dating of the subfossil material (Burney et al. 2004).

DESCRIPTION

Hypogeomys antimena is the largest species of living rodent on Madagascar, adults attaining a head-and-body length of 284–323 mm and weighing ~975–1315 g (Table 14.40). The body fur is short and dense. The dorsal pelage is commonly grayish brown to dark brown along the middle back, grading to pale brown on the flanks; the ventral pelage varies from cream-colored to buffy white or dull white. Juveniles have notably grayer backs and whiter venters than individuals in fully adult pelage. Descriptions of *Hypogeomys* as "rabbit-like" have been prompted by the animal's rotund body with broad head and somewhat blunt snout, conspicuously long ears (50–73 mm), and elongate hind feet (69–78 mm) (Figures 14.70b and d). The dark thick tail, although covered with short stiff hairs, appears naked macroscopically and is notably shorter in length (TL) than head-and-body length (HBL) (TL ~75% of HBL). The hind feet, albeit robust consonant with the rodent's size and girth, are actually shorter in proportion (hind-foot length [HFL] ~22–24% of HBL) than those of *Macrotarsomys* (HFL ~26–28% of HBL), species of which regularly progress in a bipedal manner (see Carleton et al., pp. 2028–30). The normal locomotion of *H. antimena* is an ambling, quadrupedal gait, although an individual will break into saltatorial, kangaroo-like

FIGURE 14.70 **Active burrow and individuals of *Hypogeomys antimena*, all photographed in the Kirindy Forest CNFEREF, a forest tract within the Menabe Antimena protected area: A) active burrow with two entrances situated at edge of dry deciduous forest; B) adult nursing female in burrow entrance; C) adult female and young in juvenile pelage, the latter about six to eight weeks old and recently emergent from the natal burrow; and D) adult in typical resting posture.** (PHOTO A by S. Sommer, and B, C, and D by H. Schütz.)

TABLE 14.40. **External measurements for adult *Hypogeomys antimena* in Menabe Antimena protected area**

HBL (mm)	TL (mm)	HFL (mm)	EL (mm)	WT (g)
305.8 ± 12.2	231.1 ± 14.4	73.4 ± 2.0	60.6 ± 4.0	1140 ± 90
284–323	197–255	69–78	50–73	975–1315

Notes: Measured on anesthetized live animals by S. Sommer (unpublished data) in 1992. Sample size: n = 42. HBL, head-and-body length; TL, tail length; HFL, hind-foot length, without claw; EL, ear length; WT, weight. Sample statistics include the mean ± one standard deviation, and the minimum–maximum range.

hopping when startled (Cook et al. 1991; Sommer 1996, 1997). Adults exhibit no sexual dimorphism in external characters or coloration, nor do male and female offspring differ by age in body measurements. Subadults normally weigh less than 1000 g in the first year of life and reach adult weight in the second year (Sommer 1996, 2000).

The size and distinctive features of *Hypogeomys* permit no confusion with other members of Nesomyinae, notably the two species, *Eliurus myoxinus* and *Macrotarsomys bastardi*, that may occur in sympatry. The extinct *H. australis* was a larger species than *H. antimena*, as judged from measurements of the molar dentition and limb bones (Goodman and Rakotondravony 1996).

GEOGRAPHIC AND ELEVATIONAL DISTRIBUTION

Populations of *H. antimena* are presently restricted to dry deciduous forest north of Morondava, bounded on the north by the Tsiribihina River and on the south by the Tomitsy River, west central Madagascar (elevational range 40–100 m; see map in Goodman et al. 2013: 260). The geographic ranges of nearly all extant Malagasy mammals dwarf the exceptionally limited distribution of *H. antimena*, which in modern times occurred over an area less than 20 × 40 km, mostly within what is now designated as the Menabe Antimena protected area (see below).

Holocene records, however, document a larger geographic range for *H. antimena* as recently as 1400 BP, extending across southwestern and west central Madagascar, as well as the Central Highlands, where it has been found in subfossil deposits (Goodman and Rakotondravony 1996; Muldoon et al. 2009). The geologically recent contraction of its range is perhaps best explained as result of Holocene aridification and accompanying floristic shifts, changes that may have caused the local disappearance or extinction of other vertebrates adapted to more mesic conditions.

ECOLOGY, BEHAVIOR, AND REPRODUCTION

Hypogeomys antimena inhabits coastal dry deciduous forest mixed with baobabs and growing on sandy soils (Cook et al. 1991). Toward the east, its distribution is limited by a change in soil type, consisting of alluvium or exposed bedrock, and toward the west by mangrove swamps. By the latter half of the 20th century, the distribution of the species into what would become the Menabe Antimena protected area was already subdivided into northern and southern subpopulations, the northern one centered in the Ambadira Forest, and the southern one in the Kirindy Forest CNFEREF (see Kappeler et al., pp. 127–33), two forest blocks separated by the Mandrotra River and a sisal plantation near Beroboka (Sommer and Tichy 1999). Since then, the already limited distribution has been further reduced, owing to continuing anthropogenic pressures (see below). Like the majority of nesomyine rodents, individuals of *H. antimena* appear to avoid secondary forest formations.

These strictly nocturnal rodents, breeding pairs and their offspring alike, spend the day in a spacious underground burrow about 5 m long, usually with one to three, infrequently up to seven, entrance holes (Figure 14.70a). On the tag of a museum specimen he had obtained, C. S. Webb recorded his impression that the species "makes long deep burrow like those of rabbits." Such roomy burrows provide security for raising offspring, protection against predation, and avoidance of diurnal high temperatures. After returning to the burrow from their nocturnal foraging, the occupants seal the entrance with a soil plug, which must be removed before the next night's activity. Burrows may be occupied by new immigrants after the death or disappearance of the residents, but constructing wholly new burrows is rare (Sommer 2000; Sommer and Hommen 2000). In fact, burrows may be occupied across many generations; regular monitoring has revealed that burrows occupied from 1992 to 2005 were still used 28 years later, in 2020. Unoccupied burrows are readily evidenced by the partially collapsed entrance or by leaf litter or spiderwebs spanning the entrance hole.

Reproductively mature individuals of *H. antimena* associate as monogamous pairs, remaining together until one mate dies, after which the surviving adult finds a new mate, usually within a few days or weeks (Cook et al. 1991; Sommer 1997, 2001; Sommer and Tichy 1999). Obligate monogamy like this is a rare breeding system among the 2300 recognized rodent species and is known in fewer than 5% of all mammals (L. L. Carter and Getz 1993; Sommer 2003a). Both sexes of adult *Hypogeomys* are territorial, defending their exclusive territories against conspecifics from neighboring burrows throughout the year, irrespective of food abundance or reproductive state. Only burrow mates have overlapping, similar-size home ranges, averaging about 3.5 ha (Cook et al. 1991). After resuming activity in early evening, the mated male and female typically announce their burrow ownership by stomping the bare ground, using their large hind feet in tandem and in a drum-roll fashion, for as long as two minutes while uttering a *brrr* vocalization, near their burrow entrances. They may also mark their territorial domain with urine, feces, and scent-gland deposits at latrines, reusable sites typically located within 50 m of burrow entrances. Although such behaviors are also performed at home-range borders, overtly aggressive interactions with conspecifics have never been observed (Sommer 1996, 1997; S. Sommer, unpublished data). During the rainy season (December–March), each pair produces only one or two offspring, an inordinately low annual breeding rate for a rodent. Confidence of paternity seems to be very high, as evidenced by the absence of any copulations genetically detected outside of the mated pair (Sommer and Tichy 1999; Sommer 2003b).

Neonatal development of *Hypogeomys* is protracted (Sommer 2001). Offspring spend the first four to six weeks in the natal burrow, not emerging regularly until four to eight weeks of age (Figure 14.70c). Male offspring leave the parental territory around one year old, in

November–December, before the next breeding period, and can reproduce immediately. However, young females delay their dispersal, remaining in the parental territory for two reproductive seasons and probably attaining sexual maturity at about two years old. When female offspring disperse from the parental territory, they establish their own territory, probably remaining there during their lifetime. After the death of her mate, the female in all documented cases kept the burrow and territory until bonding with a new male. When a breeding female dies or disappears, the male companion also normally maintains the burrow and territory. However, in a few documented occasions a widowed male moved into the territory of a recently widowed female. Capture-recapture and radio-tracking of offspring yielded mortality rates of 50–57% until full maturity (Sommer 2000).

The species forages on the forest floor for fallen fruits, seeds, and succulent leaves, occasionally digging for roots and tubers or stripping bark from saplings (Sommer 2003c). Based on his 1939 field observations, as recorded on specimen tags, C. S. Webb noted that the species "feeds mainly on fallen fruits." The animal sits semi-upright (like a rabbit), while holding a food item in its forepaws and manipulating it to take chewable mouthfuls.

Predation is the principal factor that affects offspring and adult mortality (Sommer 2000, 2003c). Based on scat analyses of *Cryptoprocta ferox* (Fosa, Eupleridae), the largest extant carnivoran on Madagascar (see Gerber and Hawkins, pp. 1978–83), *Hypogeomys* remains constituted 3% of prey items identified, a much lower prevalence than all lemurs (50%) collectively consumed by this euplerid (C. E. Hawkins and Racey 2008). Other predators that consume *Hypogeomys* include *Acrantophis madagascariensis* (Madagascar Ground Boa) and perhaps *Asio madagascariensis* (Madagascar Long-eared Owl), a species large enough to take juveniles and subadults. In addition to natural predators, *H. antimena* individuals are vulnerable to roaming dogs of hunters who illegally poach lemurs and spiny tenrecs for bushmeat. Infanticide apparently does not occur, as evidenced, for example, when a new male acquires an established breeding territory and tolerates the offspring sired by the previous male (Sommer and Tichy 1999; Sommer 2000).

To our knowledge, recent epidemiological studies of Malagasy small mammals have yet to sample *Hypogeomys*. Such studies should be conducted, because the immune gene diversity (MHC, or major histocompatibility complex) known to play a central role in pathogen resistance is very low in *H. antimena* compared with other mammalian species (Sommer et al. 2002a; Sommer 2005); genetic variability in noncoding markers is also depleted in the extant population (Sommer 2003a). Whether zoonotic diseases have contributed to the dramatic reduction in distribution and population numbers of *H. antimena* urgently needs study, particularly to allow researchers to gain an understanding of the impact of pathogens introduced by non-native mammals (see Rasambainarivo and Zohdy, pp. 298–302). Ectoparasites known only from *Hypogeomys* include the tick *Ornithodoros grenieri* (see Klompen and Apanaskevich, pp. 894–99) and the flea *Xenopsylla petteri* (see Duchemin et al., pp. 1074–80).

CONSERVATION

When A. Grandidier first encountered populations of *H. antimena* in 1869, the specific geographic range was probably already extremely limited owing to late Holocene (500 BP) climatic change (Goodman and Rakotondravony 1996; Muldoon et al. 2009). Moreover, the arrival of humans on the island, perhaps dating to 10,000 BP (see Wright and Rakotoarisoa, pp. 181–90), undoubtedly wrought further modification or reduction of the critical forest habitat required by *H. antimena*. Today, the remaining natural forest critical to the survival of *H. antimena* is simultaneously threatened by itinerant agriculture, charcoal production, and commercial logging.

Between 1963 and 1993, intact dry deciduous forest between the Tsiribihina and Tomitsy Rivers declined from 162,000 to 133,000 ha and between the Tomitsy and Morondava Rivers from 54,000 to 36,000 ha, forest losses of 18% and 33%, respectively (Genini 1996; Tidd et al. 2001). At the beginning of the present millennium, Sommer et al. (2002b) anticipated the extinction of *H. antimena* within 24 years under the deforestation conditions they observed at the time. Another estimate of population size and geographic range suggested a stable population of the species distributed among the northern and southern subpopulations (R. P. Young et al. 2008). Since the dates of both studies, however, as referenced below, considerable deforestation has subsequently occurred in the areas of these two subpopulations' distribution.

Between 1996 and 2016, an additional 26% of intact dry deciduous forest was lost to similar anthropogenic pressures in Menabe Antimena, which encompasses most of the modern distribution of this species (Goodman et al. 2018b; Durrell Wildlife Conservation Trust, unpublished data). Accelerated anthropogenic destruction continues, rendering forest that recently was suitable for *Hypogeomys* burned or irretrievably degraded. Such losses also include protected areas, such as: 1) the Andranomena Special Reserve (7180 ha), where more than 44% of intact dry deciduous forest has been lost since its dedication in 1955 (A. P. Smith 1997), and where the species has been extirpated; and 2) the Analabe Private Reserve (14,876 ha), near Beroboka, which includes 6000 ha of abandoned sisal plantations (Genini 1996; A. P. Smith 1997) and also now lacks *H. antimena*. Between October 2017 and 2018, large portions of the forest north of the Mandrotra River, inhabited by the northern subpopulation, were burned (NASA 2021). As of 2020, the remaining southern subpopulation of *Hypogeomys* is largely restricted to the Kirindy Forest CNFEREF, now included in the Menabe Antimena protected area. The original 10,000 ha of forest within the Kirindy Forest CNFEREF has declined and continues to decline significantly due to logging for illegal corn cultivation, reducing the preferred habitat for *H. antimena* to perhaps less than 7000 ha. In addition to loss of critical habitat, another lethal pressure upon *Hypogeomys* populations stems from the increased presence of hunters and their dogs; although *Hypogeomys* is not sought as bushmeat by these hunters, their dogs roam the forest and opportunistically kill available prey, including *Hypogeomys* young and adults (Sommer and Hommen 2000). The presence of these dogs coincides with a substantive reduction in *Hypogeomys* population size since about 2000.

The compounding threats of limited geographic range, unabated habitat loss, low reproductive output, and declining breeding population account for the IUCN (2020) classification of *H. antimena* as Endangered, an assessment that seems to underestimate the multiplicity and enormity of pressures upon the species' survival.

Subject editor: Steven M. Goodman

NESOMYIDAE: *MACROTARSOMYS*, BIG-FOOTED MICE, *KELIBOTRA*, *KELOBOTRA*

M. D. Carleton, V. Soarimalala, and S. M. Goodman

In 1939, the British Museum (Natural History) contracted Cecil S. Webb, a professional collector for zoos and natural history museums, to make an expedition to Madagascar and rediscover the "Madagascar Gerbil" (Webb 1954: 244). At the time, this "rare" species was known only from the single specimen used by Milne Edwards and G. Grandidier (1898) to name *Macrotarsomys bastardi*, the last nesomyine genus described until the description of *Monticolomys* in 1996, nearly a century later (see Carleton et al., pp. 2031–32). The specimen had been collected by the French explorer Emile Bastard somewhere in interior Madagascar during his trek from the southwest coast to Antananarivo. After several attempts to retrace Bastard's route, Webb finally located and collected a fine series of *Macrotarsomys bastardi* specimens for the British Museum.

Subsequent small-mammal surveys have not only expanded the known distribution of *M. bastardi* (e.g., Soarimalala 2008) but also led to the description of two larger species, *M. ingens* (F. Petter 1959) and *M. petteri* (Goodman and Soarimalala 2005). A fourth epithet, *occidentalis*, was assigned to a form described as a subspecies of *M. bastardi* (Ellerman 1949) and has been nominally retained at that rank (Carleton and Goodman 1996). A morphometric and genetic study, however, judged the differentiation of specimens falling within the geographic range of *occidentalis* insufficient to retain it as a definable subspecies (Jansa et al. 2008); their molecular data instead highlighted the need for additional evaluation of the status of populations found north of the Betsiboka River in the northwest.

The morphological similarities between the Kenyan Miocene fossil *Protarsomys* and extant *Macrotarsomys* persuaded Lavocat (1973, 1978) to postulate the origin of *Macrotarsomys* and other nesomyines from such an ancestral afrocricetodontine form. Some precipitously extended Lavocat's remarks as a basis for synonymizing *Protarsomys* under *Macrotarsomys* (Chaline et al. 1977; F. Petter 1990), a generic synonymy disputed by others (see Carleton and Goodman 1996: 246–249). Among living nesomyines, the closest generic relative of *Macrotarsomys* is *Monticolomys*, a high-mountain form of the east and far north (Carleton and Goodman 1996; Jansa et al. 2009; Steppan and Schenk 2017; see Jansa and Carleton, pp. 1865–71). Webb's (1954) adoption of the vernacular name "Madagascar Gerbil" for *Macrotarsomys* underscores the remarkable morphological convergence of this nesomyine endemic (Nesomyidae: Nesomyinae) with another group of Old World rodents, the true gerbils (Muridae: Gerbillinae).

DESCRIPTION

As captured by Webb's (1954) vernacular name, "Madagascar Gerbil," the external form of *Macrotarsomys* is strikingly gerbilline, in particular recalling members of *Gerbillus*, which occur in Africa, the Middle East, and western Asia. The species range in size from small (*M. bastardi*), to medium (*M. ingens*), to large (*M. petteri*) (Table 14.41; Figure 14.71). Pelage texture is soft and fine. The dorsal pelage is light sandy to clay brown, and the venter wholly white, such that the dorsal-ventral pelage border is sharply delineated. The pinnae (ears) of *Macrotarsomys* are prominent and appear almost naked and very pliant. Tail length (TL) in all species is much longer than head-and-body length (HBL), the caudal proportions of *M. bastardi* moderately so (TL 133–138% of HBL) and those of *M. ingens* and *M. petteri* exceptionally so (TL ~160% of HBL). Caudal hairs covering the proximal two-thirds of the tail are short and

TABLE 14.41. **External measurements for species of *Macrotarsomys***

SPECIES	HBL (mm)	TL (mm)	HFL (mm)	EL (mm)	WT (g)
M. bastardi[1] (n = 14)	84.7 ± 2.8	114.7 ± 5.5	23.3 ± 0.6	21.4 ± 1.2	24.5 ± 2.7
	78–88	104–123	22–24	20–23	21–28
M. ingens[2] (n = 4–6)	127.0 ± 15.7	209.5 ± 21.7	35.3 ± 2.5	24.3 ± 1.5	64.4 ± 3.3
	115–150	193–240	32–38	23–26	54–73
M. petteri[3] (n = 1)	150	238	37	32	105

Notes: HBL, head-and-body length; TL, tail length; HFL, hind-foot length; EL, ear length; WT, weight. Sample statistics include the mean ± one standard deviation, and the minimum–maximum range.

[1] Data from Jansa et al. (2008); WT from Carleton and Goodman (1996).

[2] Data from Carleton and Goodman (1996); WT from D. Rakotondravony, V. Randrianjafy, and S. M. Goodman (unpublished data).

[3] Data from Goodman and Soarimalala (2005).

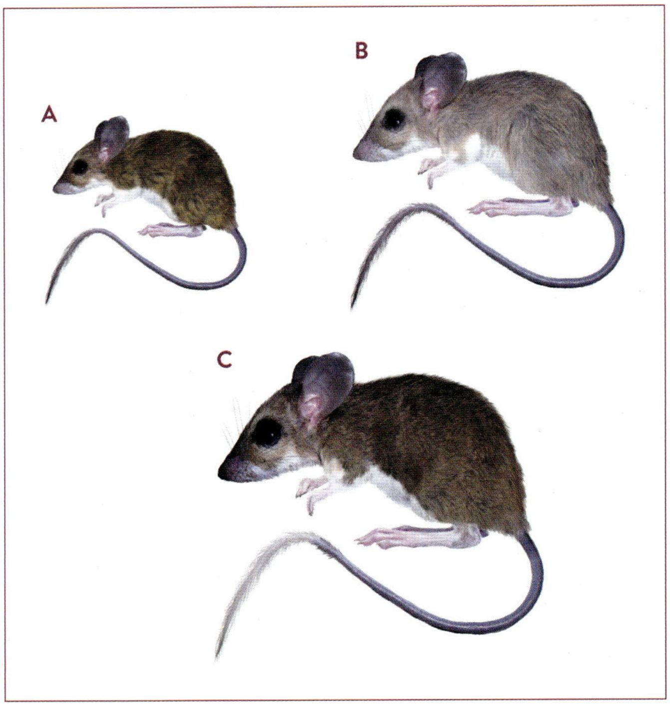

FIGURE 14.71 The three species of *Macrotarsomys*, illustrated in proportion to their relative sizes, allowing comparison of external morphological traits: A) *M. bastardi*, B) *M. ingens*, and C) *M. petteri*. (ARTWORK by V. Simeonovski.)

sparse but lengthen abruptly over the distal one-third to form a penicillate tip (never so pronounced as the terminal tuft seen in *Eliurus*; see Carleton et al., pp. 2014–22). The hind foot is narrow and comparatively long (hind-foot length [HFL] about 26–28% of HBL), particularly as seen in the elongation of the tarsus-metatarsus relative to the phalanges. The hallux and fifth digit are greatly reduced compared with the three central digits. Six plantar pads are retained, but the posterior three have only half the diameter and protuberance of the anterior pads.

The skull of *Macrotarsomys* is lightly built, characterized by a smoothly contoured braincase and pronounced development of the auditory bullae. Bullar inflation is the greatest observed among nesomyines, although it is not as well developed as that found in certain members of true gerbils. The palatal region of *Macrotarsomys* exhibits moderate-size incisive foramina (about 62–68% of diastemal length), a flat and wide bony palate, and broad, shallow parapterygoid fossae that flank a narrow mesopterygoid fossa. Alisphenoid struts are absent. The molars are extremely low-crowned and cuspidate, with definition of a low median mure (-id) in unworn teeth; upper incisors lack enamel grooves and are strongly recurved.

Although the three species can be distinguished based on size alone (Table 14.41; Figure 14.71), certain qualitative and proportional traits also serve to separate them. The development of a terminal caudal brush is strongest in the single known skin specimen of *M. petteri*, weakest in *M. bastardi*. The interorbital region in *M. bastardi* is wider and marked by slight supraorbital shelves along the frontal edges; in contrast, the interorbital constriction in *M. ingens* and *M. petteri* is proportionally narrower and lacks supraorbital shelves.

GEOGRAPHIC AND ELEVATIONAL DISTRIBUTION

Macrotarsomys is one of the two nesomyine genera, along with *Hypogeomys* (see Sommer and Carleton, pp. 2025–27), wholly endemic to western Madagascar and its drier forested landscapes. The smallest species, *M. bastardi*, has the broadest distribution, occurring around Belambo and Ankarafantsika, to the northeast of the Betsiboka River, and widely documented south of the Tsiribihina River, including inland sites, as far as Cap Sainte Marie and eastward to Andohahela and the Petriky Forest (Jansa et al. 2008; Soarimalala 2008; see map in Goodman et al. 2013: 261); vouchered elevational records extend from near sea level to 915 m. Notwithstanding the renewed fieldwork undertaken in western Madagascar (Soarimalala 2008), no records of *M. bastardi*, or any *Macrotarsomys*, yet exist for the vast region between the Betsiboka and Tsiribihina Rivers in west central Madagascar. Although small-mammal surveys conducted in this zone have documented various nesomyine rodents, the majority of inventories have sampled areas with exposed surface sedimentary deposits or alluvium (Soarimalala 2008; Z. Rakotomalala and Goodman 2010; S. M. Goodman and V. Soarmalala, unpublished data), not those with sandy soils, the preferred habitat of *M. bastardi*. Forested areas that rest on sandy soils in this zone have yet to be adequately surveyed, including protected areas such as Antrema, Bombetoka Beloboka, Bemarivo, and Mandrozo (Goodman et al. 2018c). Thus, whether the distribution of *M. bastardi* includes the region between the Betsiboka and Tsiribihina Rivers must await the findings of future surveys.

The two larger species, *M. ingens* and *M. petteri*, are geographically localized: *M. ingens* is known only from the Ankarafantsika Plateau (150–250 m) in the northwest of the island (see map in Goodman et al. 2013: 262); and *M. petteri* has been collected at a single locality, the Mikea Forest (80 m) in the southwest (Goodman and Soarimalala 2005; see map in Goodman et al. 2013: 262). *Macrotarsomys bastardi* and *M. ingens* co-occur with one another and with *Eliurus myoxinus* in the Ankarafantsika Forest. To the south of the Tsiribihina River, *M. bastardi* commonly co-occurs with *E. myoxinus* and locally with *Hypogeomys antimena* in the central Menabe region (Goodman et al. 2018b). Late Holocene subfossils document that the geographic range of *M. petteri* was once broader, extending to the transitional dry region of the southeast, and has contracted only recently, probably due to increased aridification of the region (Goodman et al. 2006a; Muldoon et al. 2009).

ECOLOGY, BEHAVIOR, AND REPRODUCTION

Members of *Macrotarsomys* are principally forest dwelling. The broadly distributed *M. bastardi* inhabits much of the western dry deciduous forests and extends into the dry spiny thickets of the south. Populations of *M. ingens* co-occur with *M. bastardi* in dry deciduous forests of Ankarafantsika National Park. The largest species, *M. petteri*, is so far known from a unique forest setting, transitional between dry deciduous and spiny thicket vegetation. *Macrotarsomys bastardi* appears to be exclusively terrestrial, while *M. ingens* is scansorial. Observations of *M. bastardi* confirm this

small species' gerbil-like locomotion as it moves on the ground, often in pairs, its posture slightly erect, with forelimbs off the ground and the long tail used as a stabilizer, particularly when bounding by bipedal leaps (Randrianjafy 2003). By contrast, solitary individuals of *M. ingens* have been seen moving along narrow tree limbs up to 3 cm in diameter and along vines up to 1.2 m above ground, often resting in tree forks between activity bouts. The single known captured individual of *M. petteri* was taken in a trap placed on the ground.

Little is known about the autecology of species of *Macrotarsomys*. They are nocturnal and utilize ground burrows. In fact, the first specimen of *M. bastardi* Webb collected in his quest to rediscover the "Madagascar Gerbil" was from "a small hole under a rock which was found to contain a single *Macrotarsomys*" (Webb 1954: 255). The species is thought to live in pairs, spending the day in shallow burrows up to 1.5 m in length; these are excavated in sandy soils under large rocks or tree stumps (Ganzhorn 2003), and exits are plugged daily by the resting animals (S. M. Goodman, unpublished data). Burrows of *M. ingens* are easier to locate, with conspicuous spoil and closed entrance holes (F. Petter 1972). The underground burrows of this species studied by Lobban et al. (2014) exceeded a soil depth of >25 cm. According to these authors, captive individuals of *M. ingens* became notably hypothermic at ambient temperatures below 18°C but did not enter daily torpor in a laboratory setting. The burrow system appears to provide a needed thermoregulatory buffer, maintaining an ambient temperature above 22°C during the austral winter.

Individuals of *M. bastardi* are known to consume seeds and fruits; precise information is unavailable for the two larger species, but their diet is presumably similar. Moreover, Ganzhorn (2003) reported that *M. bastardi* feeds also on berries, roots, and some plant stems. Based on his trapping experiences, Webb (1954: 261) observed that "in the plains they [*M. bastardi*] live almost exclusively on the stems of grasses and their seeds." In captivity, an individual of *M. ingens* accepted ripe banana (F. Petter 1959). In a laboratory colony, captive individuals of this species relished a variety of fresh fruits (banana, guava, grapes, apple, and papaya) and rolled oats, mixed grains, nuts, and seeds (Lobban et al. 2014).

The few embryo counts available for *M. bastardi* indicate that litter size is small, only two or three young (Ellerman 1949). Litter size of *M. ingens* is also small, up to two young, based on several embryo counts (Randrianjafy 2003; V. Soarimalala, unpublished data). In the Ankarafantsika area, populations of *M. ingens* probably reproduce throughout the year, and those of *M. bastardi* from March to June (Randrianjafy 2003).

Trapping success for *M. bastardi* may be highly variable from site to site and even in different seasons at the same site. The variable rates may be related to cyclical variation in population levels or food availability, soil substrates, and the corresponding willingness of animals to enter traps (Goodman et al. 1999a). In the Bezà-Mahafaly protected area, an intense inventory of one site, with nearly 33,000 accrued trap nights over a year, produced only three specimens of *M. bastardi*, all captured during May and June (Youssouf Jacky and Rasoazanabary 2008). At two nearby sites within the same protected area, a comparable level of trapping effort yielded not a single individual of the species.

Several predators are known to feed upon these rodents. The first known specimen of *M. ingens*, destined to become the holotype, was recovered alive by Jean-Jacques Petter when the rodent fell to the ground after being released from the talons of a diurnal bird of prey (F. Petter 1959; F. Petter, unpublished data). Randrianjafy (2003) reported that *Tyto alba* (Barn Owl) is among the predators of *M. ingens*. In the Ankarafantsika region, scats collected throughout the year of the endemic *Cryptoprocta ferox* (Eupleridae), the largest living Malagasy carnivoran, yielded remains of both *M. bastardi* and *M. ingens* only during the dry season (Dollar et al. 2007); in the Kirindy Forest CNFEREF, *M. bastardi* is also occasionally consumed by *Cryptoprocta* (C. E. Hawkins and Racey 2008). Regurgitated pellets of *Tyto alba* collected at Ankarafantsika, the Kirindy Forest CNFEREF, and the Sept Lacs region along the Onilahy River contained remains of *M. bastardi* (Rasoma and Goodman 2007; S. M. Goodman, unpublished data). Moreover, one species of boa (*Acrantophis madagascariensis*) is a known predator of *M. ingens* (Randrianjafy 2003) in the Ankarafantsika protected area and presumably would also prey upon *M. bastardi*.

Species of *Macrotarsomys* have yet to receive dedicated epidemiological study. In the Tsimanampesotse area, a tick identified as *Amblyomma chabaudi* was collected from *M. bastardi* and tested positive for *Rickettsia* (Ehlers et al. 2019); this tick is also known from endemic land tortoises but not as yet from other Malagasy mammals. A variety of other ectoparasites are known from this rodent genus, including two species of ticks from *M. bastardi* (see Klompen and Apanaskevich, pp. 894–99), several species of fleas from *M. bastardi*, and another flea known only from *M. ingens* (Duchemin 2003; see Duchemin et al., pp. 1074–80).

CONSERVATION

The IUCN (2020) weighs the conservation status of *M. bastardi* as Least Concern, *and M. ingens* and *M. petteri* as Endangered. Some substantial stands of dry forest still remain in western Madagascar, and the distribution of *M. bastardi* fortuitously overlaps with many protected areas within that forest zone (Goodman et al. 2018b); however, evaluation of the impact of forest fragmentation found that the species is absent in forest blocks smaller than 600 ha (Ganzhorn 2003). Since its description in 1959, the occurrence of *M. ingens* is still known only from the Ankarafantsika protected area, where dramatic declines in forest cover associated with nearly annual large-scale forest fires (Goodman et al. 2018b), coupled with the species' small geographic footprint, have impelled continuing population decline and endangered its survivorship. Based only on a single specimen, Endangered is a sound IUCN rating for *M. petteri*. The only known modern specimen of this species (holotype) was captured during a small-mammal survey of the Mikea Forest, where a single animal was trapped during 3100 trap nights apportioned among six different sites (Soarimalala and Goodman 2004). Subsequently, the Mikea Forest has been severely degraded, having lost more than 10% of its forest cover (Goodman et al. 2018b), and the current fate of this species is uncertain.

Subject editor: Steven M. Goodman

NESOMYIDAE: *MONTICOLOMYS KOOPMANI*, MOUNTAIN-DWELLING MOUSE

M. D. Carleton, S. M. Goodman, and V. Soarimalala

In 1996, Carleton and Goodman named *Monticolomys koopmani* based on a specimen from the Ankaratra Massif, Central Highlands, a specimen whose uniqueness was first appreciated by the late Karl Koopman, curator at the American Museum of Natural History. Coordinated field surveys of small mammals instituted since the mid-1990s have subsequently revealed the wider distribution of this mountain-dwelling mouse in all of Madagascar's major highlands with moist evergreen forest (see below). The extreme distances between the isolated montane occurrences of *Monticolomys* invite careful evaluation of the genetic integrity of this purported single species. The recent identification of *Monticolomys* sp. based on a single molar from Belobaka Cave (Gommery et al. 2018), a Late Pleistocene site east of Mahajanga and far outside the known distribution and habitat of *M. koopmani*, requires confirmation with better samples.

Based on cladistic interpretation of morphological traits, Carleton and Goodman (1996) hypothesized that *Monticolomys* is most closely related to *Macrotarsomys*, a genus represented by three species restricted to the arid and subarid environments of the west (see Carleton et al., pp. 2028–30). To date, gene-sequence studies that have broadly sampled nesomyine and muroid rodents have corroborated this relationship, securing the *Macrotarsomys-Monticolomys* sister group within the radiation of a monophyletic Nesomyinae (Jansa and Weksler 2004; Jansa et al. 2009; Steppan and Schenk 2017; see Jansa and Carleton, pp. 1865–71).

FIGURE 14.72 **Adult *Monticolomys koopmani* in Andringitra. Note that the ears are infested with mites.** (PHOTO by H. Schütz.)

DESCRIPTION

Examples of *M. koopmani* are immediately identifiable by their small size (Table 14.42); short, densely furred pinnae; and a tail length (TL) appreciably greater than head-and-body length (HBL) (TL ~135–140% of HBL). Unlike the tail of species of *Macrotarsomys*, the tail of *Monticolomys* lacks noticeable elongation of caudal hairs toward its tip (Figure 14.72). Dorsal pelage is a somber dark brown, and the venter is dark gray, rendering the dorsal-ventral pelage contrast indistinct. The moderately broad hind foot possesses comparatively long outer digits (one and five), less elongate than observed in *Eliurus* species but more so than in its generic kin *Macrotarsomys*; the naked plantar surface bears six fleshy pads, with the thenar and hypothenar as large as the four interdigital pads. Six mammae are present, one pair each distributed in the postaxial, abdominal, and inguinal regions.

TABLE 14.42. **External measurements for *Monticolomys koopmani***

HBL (mm)	TL (mm)	HFL (mm)	EL (mm)	WT (g)
86.2 ± 1.9	134.4 ± 5.9	23.6 ± 0.6	18.8 ± 0.8	22.6 ± 3.8
84–89	127–142	23–24	18–20	18.5–27.5

Source: Goodman et al. (1999a).

Notes: Series from Andohahela National Park; sample size: n = 5. HBL, head-and-body length; TL, tail length; HFL, hind-foot length; EL, ear length; WT, weight. Sample statistics include the mean ± one standard deviation, and the minimum–maximum range.

Consonant with its small body, the cranium of *Monticolomys koopmani* is delicately built, having a narrow rostrum, an hourglass-shaped interorbital constriction, and slender, gently bowed zygomatic arches. The evenly contoured braincase is devoid of crests and ridges, and the ectotympanic bullae are moderately inflated, albeit much smaller than those characteristic of *Macrotarsomys*. The short upper molar rows (3.4–3.7 mm) diverge anteriorly, and the molars are very brachyodont, cuspidate, and without mesolophs (-ids); the upper and lower third molars are notably smaller than the second molars. The upper incisors have a smooth enamel face, and their shape is strongly recurved.

The size and bodily conformation of *Monticolomys* appear the most mouselike among the nine genera of Nesomyinae. Size and external proportions thus serve to readily separate *Monticolomys* from other nesomyines that may occur sympatrically—*Brachytarsomys villosa*, both species of *Brachyuromys*, certain species of *Eliurus*, *Gymnuromys roberti*, and *Nesomys rufus*—all usually overlapping with *Monticolomys* at or near their upper elevational limits. Among those species of *Eliurus* that may co-occur with *Monticolomys*,

specimens of *E. minor* are most similar in body size, in particular young individuals without a fully developed caudal tuft (see Carleton et al., pp. 2014–22).

GEOGRAPHIC AND ELEVATIONAL DISTRIBUTION

The latitudinal occurrence of *M. koopmani* brackets nearly the full length of the island, but the species' geographic presence is highly discontinuous, occurring mostly in Madagascar's uppermost elevations (see map in Goodman et al. 2013: 263). The taxon has been documented from the Tsaratanàna Massif, Northern Highlands (Maminirina et al. 2008); through isolated massifs and escarpment ridges in the Central Highlands, including (from north to south) Ankaratra, Marolambo, Ranomafana, Andringitra, Ivohibe, and Befotaka–Midongy du Sud (Carleton and Goodman 1996; Goodman and Rasolonandrasana 1999; Soarimalala et al. 2001; S. M. Goodman and V. Soarimalala, unpublished data); to the Andohahela Massif, Southern Highlands (Goodman et al. 1999a; Ramanana 2010). These localities span an elevational range of 900–2050 m. Although known from the Tsaratanàna Massif (Maminirina et al. 2008), the species has yet to be documented in other high mountains of the Northern Highlands, such as the thoroughly surveyed Anjanaharibe-Sud and Marojejy protected areas, where the equally diminutive *Voalavo gymnocaudus* is found (Soarimalala and Goodman 2003a).

ECOLOGY, BEHAVIOR, AND REPRODUCTION

Although the geographic occurrence of *M. koopmani* has been reasonably established, aspects of its natural history remain poorly known. On the Andringitra Massif, specimens of *M. koopmani* were encountered in the upper reaches of medium-altitude moist evergreen forest, along a ridgetop shrouded in mist and clouds, the low-canopy trees laden with mosses, lichens, and epiphytes (Goodman and Carleton 1996). The species also occurs from uppermost medium-altitude moist evergreen forest into montane ericoid thicket (Goodman and Rasolonandrasana 2001), and similar ecological settings are recorded where populations of *M. koopmani* occur on the Andohahela and Tsaratanàna Massifs (Goodman et al. 1999a; Maminirina et al. 2008). The holotype from Ankaratra was collected on a "grass slope with scattered bushes" (Carleton and Goodman 1996: 239); the upper elevations of Ankaratra are now largely grass-covered, interspersed with heath and bracken, and its native forest habitat is severely degraded (Goodman et al. 1996a, 2018b).

Trapping results indicate a nocturnal activity pattern and predominantly terrestrial habits. Most specimens of *M. koopmani* have been captured in live traps placed on the ground in open understory and in pitfalls (Goodman et al. 1999a; Maminirina et al. 2008). In the Andringitra National Park, however, several individuals entered live traps positioned on lianas and on thin, nearly horizontal branches up to 2 m above the ground. Thus, the extent to which the species regularly accesses the lower forest strata is unknown, but the relatively long tail and the hind-foot shape suggest highly developed climbing ability. Animals captured in the montane ericoid thicket of Andringitra were found to readily consume the fruits and seeds of the following plants that survived an intensive fire: *Agauria*, *Vaccinium emirnense*, and *V. secondiflorum* (Ericaceae); *Vachellia farnesiana*, *Mimosa* sp., and *Indigofera lyallii* (Fabaceae); and *Buddleja fusca* (Scrophulariaceae) (Rasolonandrasana and Goodman 2006). Simultaneous trapping regimens that tracked rodent populations in burned habitats versus unburned thicket recovered nearly equal numbers of *Monticolomys koopmani*, suggesting that the species can withstand this form of environmental perturbation.

The birthing period is extrapolated to occur during the rainy season, from late November to about March. Toward the end of this period, several females were recorded as lactating, and a majority of males collected from November to April were noted to have scrotal testicles with convoluted epididymides. A single embryo count disclosed a litter size of three. Details about parental care, nest size and placement, range of litter sizes, neonatal growth, and development of *M. koopmani* are unknown.

Little information is available about predators of *Monticolomys*. In a rock shelter on Mount Papango (1300 m), Befotaka–Midongy du Sud, crania of this species were found in the pellets of an individual *Tyto soumagnei* (Red Owl) that used the site as a day shelter (S. M. Goodman and L. E. Olson, unpublished data). Given the size and nocturnal activity of *M. koopmani*, a variety of avian, reptilian, and mammalian predators potentially feed on this rodent.

Monticolomys koopmani has yet to receive any research attention associated with zoonotic diseases and ectoparasites. To our knowledge, even ticks (see Klompen and Apanaskevich, pp. 894–99) and fleas (see Duchemin et al., pp. 1074–80) have yet to be identified from this species, although mites are known (OConnor 1996).

CONSERVATION

All localities where *M. koopmani* has been documented fall within Madagascar's designated protected areas (Goodman et al. 2018b). The species' conservation status is classified as Least Concern (IUCN 2020). The presence of *Monticolomys* in the upper limits of medium-altitude moist evergreen forest, a zone infrequently occupied by humans, perhaps lessens anthropogenic pressures and affords cautious optimism for the species' near-term survival. Further, populations of *M. koopmani* may be resilient to the passage of fire through montane ericoid thicket, as noted above in the Andringitra Massif (Rasolonandrasana and Goodman 2006). However, habitat regeneration at this site after the fire also witnessed a notable increase of the introduced rodents *Rattus rattus* and *Mus musculus*, both species with larger litter sizes and higher breeding outputs than *Monticolomys*. Among the three murine commensals that occur on Madagascar (see Ramasindrazana et al., pp. 1872–80), Miljutin and Lehtonen (2008) speculated that *Mus musculus* is a potential ecological competitor of *Monticolomys koopmani*, given the latter's mouselike resemblance.

Subject editor: Steven M. Goodman

NESOMYIDAE: *NESOMYS*, RED FOREST RATS, *VOALAVO MENA*, *TSANGIALA*

M. D. Carleton, V. Soarimalala, and J. M. Ryan

Three species of *Nesomys* are currently recognized, as each was originally described, and as was appreciated by Ellerman (1941, 1949): *N. audeberti*, *N. lambertoni*, and *N. rufus* (Figure 14.73). In keeping with the taxonomic habit of the 1900s, however, the more recently named taxa, *audeberti* and *lambertoni*, were for a time uncritically considered junior synonyms of the first-named *N. rufus*, whether as definable subspecies (F. Petter 1972, 1975) or as full synonyms (Honacki et al. 1982; Musser and Carleton 1993). Distributional, morphological, and genetic evidence, however, confirms all three taxa as valid biological species (Carleton and Schmidt 1990; Ryan et al. 1993; Goodman and Carleton 1996; Jansa et al. 1999; Goodman and Schütz 2003). The subfossil form *N. narindaensis* (Mein et al. 2010), described from Holocene cave deposits in northwestern Madagascar, is unquestionably distinct from the living species. Carleton et al. (2014) consolidated the nomenclatural foundation of the genus, including the designation of lectotypes and restriction of type localities. Molecular data uniformly place *Nesomys* as sister genus to *Brachyuromys* (see Jansa et al., pp. 2011–13) within the radiation of Nesomyinae (Jansa et al. 1999, 2009; Steppan and Schenk 2017; see Jansa and Carleton, pp. 1865–71).

DESCRIPTION

Species of *Nesomys* are comparatively large, thickset rats with long, somewhat narrow hind feet and large, pliant pinnae (Table 14.43). Their soft, lax fur is reddish brown on the dorsum, typically darker along the middle dorsum, grading to a brighter rufous along the cheeks, flanks, and rump. Ventral pelage varies from a uniform rufous to pure white or many intermediate shades. The tail length (TL) is not quite as long as the combined head-and-body length (HBL) (TL ~90% of HBL). The elongate hind foot connotes a cursorial conformation, possessing much shorter lateral digits (one and five) relative to the central three; six widely spaced plantar pads are present. The mammary glands typically number four, one pair abdominal and one pair inguinal. Adult males of *N. rufus* average about 3% larger than females in standard external measurements, including weight (series from the Ranomafana region: Ryan et al. 1993; M. D. Carleton, unpublished data), although the weight disparity is not statistically significant (Kappeler et al. 2019).

The cranium and dentition of *Nesomys* are larger and more notably robust compared with those of most other nesomyine taxa—only the giant rat *Hypogeomys* is larger (see Sommer and Carleton, pp. 2025–27). The skull of *Nesomys* possesses a long rostrum, stout and laterally bowed zygomatic arches that frame a relatively wide, hourglass-shaped interorbit. The interorbital region lacks a projecting shelf or raised edges (beading). Zygomatic plates are moderately wide, defining a conspicuous dorsal notch. The smoothly contoured braincase is devoid of temporal and lambdoid ridging, even in old adults. Incisive foramina are spacious and moderately long, spanning about 70% of the diastema. An alisphenoid strut, squamosal-alisphenoid groove, and sphenofrontal and stapedial foramina are consistently present. Upper incisors are stout, with a smooth enamel face; the molars are moderately high-crowned yet retain a cuspidate topography with distinct mesolophs and mesolophids.

The combination of large size and reddish-brown pelage readily serves to separate species of *Nesomys* from other nesomyines that inhabit Malagasy forests and open montane grasslands. Aside from its entirely allopatric western occurrence, *N. lambertoni* is easily distinguished from the two eastern species by its longer pinnae (Table 14.43) and densely dark-furred tail, the bushy caudal hairs wholly obscuring the epidermal scales (Figure 14.73c). Tail fur in both eastern species of *Nesomys* is only moderately developed, not fully concealing the epidermal scalation (Figures 14.73a and b). Where *N. audeberti* and *N. rufus* may be expected in sympatry in eastern moist evergreen forests, the former can be discriminated based on its larger size, especially the hind foot (typically ≥52 mm in *N. audeberti*) and wider interorbit (typically ≥8.5 mm in *N. audeberti*). In addition, the ventral pelage in most specimens of *N. audeberti* exhibits large swaths of fully white hairs, accenting the dorsal-ventral pelage contrast; whereas, in specimens of *N. rufus*, the ventral pelage strongly resembles the dorsum, with patches of white usually limited to the chin and groin, and dorsal-ventral countershading is weakly defined.

GEOGRAPHIC AND ELEVATIONAL DISTRIBUTION

The species *N. audeberti* and *N. rufus* are denizens of the moist evergreen forests of the east and north, but *N. lambertoni* is wholly allopatric to its congeners and known only from dry deciduous forests of the Tsingy de Bemaraha in the central west (see maps in Goodman et al. 2013: 265, and Carleton et al. 2014: Figure 6). The distributions of *N. audeberti* and *N. rufus* span nearly the whole length of the moist evergreen forests of the east (see maps in Goodman et al. 2013: 264, 266). Populations of *N. audeberti* are broadly distributed among localities around Antongil Bay, including the Masoala Peninsula (Andrianjakarivelo et al. 2005; Z. Rakotomalala et al. 2007), southward along the lowlands and lower eastern escarpment of the Central Highlands (Carleton and Schmidt 1990; Soarimalala et al. 2001; Soarimalala and Goodman 2006), to the region of Tsitongambarika, in the Vohimena Mountains (Goodman et al. 2013). These sites embrace an elevational belt from sea level to 1015 m, most of them below 800 m. The geographic occurrence of *N. rufus* somewhat parallels that of *N. audeberti* but over higher elevations, 700–2300 m, from Manongarivo and Tsaratanàna east to the mountains ringing the Andapa Basin, Northern Highlands (Goodman and Soarimalala 2002; Soarimalala and Goodman 2003a; Maminirina et al.

FIGURE 14.73 **The three extant species of *Nesomys*: A) *N. audeberti*, Ranomafana National Park; B) *N. rufus*, Andringitra National Park; and C) *N. lambertoni*, Tsingy de Bemaraha National Park.** (PHOTOS A and B by H. Schütz, and C by T. Dixon.)

2008); portions of the Masoala Peninsula (Andrianajakaivelo et al. 2005); southward through the Central Highlands (Goodman and Rasolonandrasana 1999, 2001; Soarimalala and Goodman 2006; Soarimalala et al. 2007; Soarimalala and Raheriarisena 2010; Randriamoria 2017); to Andohahela National Park, Southern Highlands (Ramanana 2010). Carleton et al. (2014: 446–448) discussed the improbable low-elevation location of the type locality ("Vohima") of *N. rufus* as conventionally interpreted. Sympatric records of *N. audeberti* and *N. rufus* have been documented within a 600–1000 m band, on the Masoala Peninsula (Andrianjakarivelo et al. 2005) and Central Highlands (Ryan et al. 1993; Soarimalala et al. 2001).

ECOLOGY, BEHAVIOR, AND REPRODUCTION

Although tolerant of minor disturbance (e.g., Irwin et al. 2010), all three species of *Nesomys* are strictly forest dwelling, typically found in pristine or nearly intact habitat with a closed or mostly closed canopy. The few vouchered specimens of *N. lambertoni* originate from dry deciduous forest associated with eroded karstic limestone (*tsingy*), areas that experience a well-defined dry season (Goodman and Schütz 2003; Soarimalala 2008). Both eastern species inhabit moist evergreen forest associations, typically floristically rich, with a multilayered canopy. Populations of *N. audeberti* are documented from lowland moist evergreen forest, littoral forest, and the lower reaches of medium-altitude moist evergreen forest (Carleton and Schmidt 1990; Andrianjakarivelo et al. 2005; Z. Rakotomalala et al. 2007). The distribution of *N. rufus* principally adheres to medium-altitude moist evergreen forest, less commonly extending higher into montane ericoid thicket or lower into the upper margins of lowland moist evergreen forest (Goodman et al. 1999a; Goodman and Rasolonandrasana 2001; Soarimalala et al. 2001; Soarimalala and Goodman 2003a; Andrianjakarivelo et al. 2005; Maminirina et al. 2008). Collecting sites where both *N. audeberti* and *N. rufus* have been captured occur within the zone of floristic transition from lowland to medium-altitude evergreen moist forest.

Species of *Nesomys* are exclusively terrestrial, preferring forests with an open understory and relatively thick mat of leaf litter (Goodman and Carleton 1996, 1998; Andrianjakarivelo et al. 2005). The animals are mainly diurnal, occasionally crepuscular (Ryan et al. 1993; Goodman and Schütz 2003), an activity pattern that conveniently enables biologists to visually document *Nesomys* within a forest, although discrimination between the two eastern species by observation alone is unreliable (e.g., Goodman et al. 1999a; Andrianjakarivelo et al. 2005). Radiotelemetry and spool-and-line tracking reveal that *N. rufus* and *N. audeberti* leave their burrows just before sunrise, forage during most of the morning, and reduce their activity during midday; activity resumes around mid- to late afternoon and declines toward dusk, when animals return to their burrows (Ryan et al. 1993). Animals establish their burrow systems under brush piles, shrubbery thickets, fallen logs, or among extensive root entanglements of large trees. Dens and burrow systems excavated by Ryan et al. (1993) included several entrances spaced 2–3 m apart, these leading via 1–2 m long tunnels to one or more interior chambers located on multiple levels; burrows may be lined with freshly clipped plant material, and innermost chambers, presumably sleeping areas, contained dried bedding made of finely shredded palm fronds. On average, *Nesomys* adults travel 400 m per day, moving in an erratic, zigzag pattern punctuated by straight dashes up to 10 m long. Based on radiotelemetric monitoring, home ranges of *N. rufus* and *N. audeberti* cover 0.4–1.4 ha, apparently undefended, and are shared by a male and several females.

Nesomys species occupy a frugivorous and granivorous trophic niche within their forest environments, as understood from the better known food habits of *N. rufus*. Based on direct observations of feeding or burrow excavations of *N. rufus* on the Andringitra

TABLE 14.43. **External measurements for representative series of *Nesomys* species**

SPECIES	HBL (mm)	TL (mm)	HFL (mm)	EL (mm)	WT (g)
N. audeberti[1] (n = 12–15)	197.4 ± 8.4	181.7 ± 13.7	54.6 ± 2.1	26.6 ± 1.4	201.7 ± 26.4
	178–213	167–210	51–58	24–28	155–235
N. lambertoni[2] (n = 2–3)	203.7 ± 20.5	178 ± 16.1	48.7 ± 3.2	30, 31	225, 243
	189–227	160–191	45–51		
N. rufus[1] (n = 22–26)	182.3 ± 9.4	162.9 ± 9.3	48.4 ± 2.2	26.7 ± 1.1	163.7 ± 20.7
	163–198	139–180	43–52	25–29	122–205

Notes: HBL, head-and-body length; TL, tail length; HFL, hind-foot length; EL, ear length; WT, weight. Sample statistics include the mean ± one standard deviation, and the minimum–maximum range.

[1] Locality: Ranomafana National Park and vicinity.

[2] Tsingy de Bemaraha, near Bekopaka.

Massif (Goodman and Carleton 1996), the diet included fallen fruits and nuts from plants such as *Cryptocarya* (Lauraceae), *Canarium* (Burseraceae), *Artabotrys* (Annonaceae), and *Sloanea* (Elaeocarpaceae). The rodents preferentially cache the large, fat-rich seeds of *Canarium* in their burrows (Goodman and Sterling 1996). Near Anjozorobe-Angavo, *N. rufus* individuals were observed to venture beyond the forest into swidden agricultural areas to feed on crops (S. M. Goodman, unpublished data). Based on indices of "ecomorphological similarity," Miljutin and Lehtonen (2008) inferred a high probability of competition between introduced *Rattus rattus* (see Ramasindrazana et al., pp. 1872–80) and species of *Nesomys*, in spite of the predominantly terrestrial habits of the latter. The diurnal activity of *Nesomys* species versus the nocturnal pattern of *R. rattus* is a relevant factor that would hypothetically tamper the level of direct interference competition between them.

Knowledge of breeding cycles and reproductive parameters is principally limited to *N. rufus*, based on field studies conducted from July through mid-December in various forested areas (Ryan et al. 1993; Goodman and Carleton 1996, 1998; Goodman et al. 1999a). Signs of ongoing reproduction—males with scrotal testes; females with enlarged mammae, active lactation, or embryos in utero—have been reported over this period, which largely coincides with the brief dry season and the start of the rainy season in moist evergreen forests. During field surveys conducted in March at Anjozorobe-Angavo, Central Highlands, females of *N. rufus* had recently given birth, as evidenced by their large mammae and the presence of placental scars. Reproductive data are unavailable for the remainder of the year. Litter size in *N. rufus*, as derived from counts of placental scars and implanted embryos (n = 10), averages 2.3 young and varies from one to four. In the Ranomafana region, breeding activity was evident in both *N. audeberti* and *N. rufus* for July and August (Ryan et al. 1993).

Recent epidemiological studies have isolated various zoonotic diseases and their parasitic vectors from *Nesomys*. Pathogenic bacteria (*Leptospira*) responsible for the disease leptospirosis have been found in *N. rufus*, including infections of multiple *Leptospira* species (Dietrich et al. 2014; Moseley et al. 2018; see Dietrich et al., pp. 268–77). Among six species of native rodents studied, only *N. rufus* was found to be infected by the blood parasite *Trypanosoma*, the species indeterminate but morphologically different from *T. lewisi* isolated from locally occurring, introduced *R. rattus* (Laakkonen et al. 2003). A variety of ectoparasites are known from *Nesomys*, including ticks (see Klompen and Apanaskevich, pp. 894–99) and fleas (see Duchemin et al., pp. 1074–80). The first known species of gastrointestinal nematodes (Heligmonellidae) that parasitize *Nesomys* were described from specimens of both *N. audeberti* and *N. rufus* collected in Ranomafana National Park (Durette-Desset et al. 2002b).

The daylight activity of *Nesomys*, coupled with its animated foraging through the leaf litter, potentially attracts the attention of a diverse array of diurnal predators, including large snakes (Boidae), birds of prey (Accipitriformes), and carnivorous mammals (Eupleridae). *Galidia elegans* (Ring-tailed Vontsira; see Farris and Goodman, pp. 1989–92), probably its main predator in moist evergreen forests, has been observed to actively pursue *Nesomys* in Ranomafana National Park. Other likely predators include *Cryptoprocta ferox* (Fosa; see Gerber and Hawkins, pp. 1978–83) and large boids (see Raxworthy and Glaw, pp. 1522–25), although detailed dietary analyses have yet to be performed where populations of *Nesomys* occur. A study of radio-tagged diurnal raptors in Ranomafana National Park identified *N. rufus* as regular prey of *Accipiter henstii* (Henst's Goshawk), *Polyboroides radiata* (Madagascar Harrier-hawk), and *Buteo brachypterus* (Madagascar Buzzard), suggesting the importance of *Nesomys* as a supplementary food source during the nesting and fledgling phase of these birds' reproductive cycles (Karpanty 2003).

CONSERVATION

The IUCN (2020) conservation status of *N. lambertoni* is Endangered and that of *N. audeberti* and *N. rufus* is Least Concern. The moist evergreen forests inhabited by *N. audeberti* and *N. rufus* have long experienced forest degradation from human agency (Vieilledent et al. 2018); in view of the broad geographic occurrence of moist forest associations, populations of these two species overlap numerous protected areas (Goodman et al. 2018b). Furthermore, *N. rufus* seems to tolerate some level of perturbation of its forest habitat. In contrast, the western species, *N. lambertoni*, is known from only one forested area within the Tsingy de Bemaraha protected area; the species' limited geographic distribution makes it highly susceptible to sudden population declines based on multiple factors.

Subject editor: Steven M. Goodman

NESOMYIDAE: *VOALAVO*, WHITE-TAILED MOUNTAIN MICE

V. Soarimalala, M. D. Carleton, and S. M. Goodman

Voalavo represents the last novel genus of native rodents to be recognized, discovered to science during the first thorough biotic inventory of a large massif, Anjanaharibe-Sud, in the Northern Highlands (Goodman 1998). The genus *Voalavo* takes its name from the Malagasy common term for rodents, *voalavo* (Carleton and Goodman 1998). The taxon now comprises two species, *V. gymnocaudus* and *V. antsahabensis*, the former known only from two massifs in the Northern Highlands (Soarimalala and Goodman 2003a), and the latter from one site in the Central Highlands (Goodman et al. 2005d). Genetic divergence between the two species, as assessed from cytochome b sequences, averages a substantial 10%.

In a comparison of *Voalavo* with other genera of Nesomyinae, Carleton and Goodman (1998) hypothesized that *Voalavo* is most closely related to *Eliurus*, based on a variety of external, cranial, and dental features. Although subsequent molecular analyses have supported close kinship between the two taxa, this same body of data has questioned whether recognition of *Voalavo* renders *Eliurus* as a paraphyletic construct (Jansa et al. 1999; Steppan and Schenk 2017). This apparent genealogical contradiction between the gene trees and generic definitions needs resolution (see Jansa and Carleton, pp. 1865–71).

DESCRIPTION

Species of *Voalavo* measure among the smallest of Madagascar's endemic rodents, in body size and weight (Table 14.44). Their pelage is soft and short (6–7 mm), relatively thick, and finely textured (Figure 14.74). The dorsal pelage appears medium to dusky gray, with pale brown admixed on the sides and nape; the underparts are off-white intermixed with pale gray. The tail length (TL) is moderately long relative to the head-and-body length (HBL) (TL ~130% of HBL); it appears nearly bare, but careful inspection reveals fine, short hairs (1–2 mm); and the distal one-third or more is fully white (Figure 14.74) or sometimes bicolored, gray on the dorsum and white below. Pinnae are short and rounded. The relatively broad and short hind foot possesses a long outer (fifth) digit, approximating the length of the middle three digits, and its plantar surface is naked, with six fleshy pads. Mammae number six in total, located in pairs in the postaxial, abdominal, and inguinal regions.

The small, delicate skull (Table 14.45) of *Voalavo* specimens has an hourglass-shaped interorbital constriction, devoid of supraorbital ridges, and a smooth, gently contoured braincase (Carleton and Goodman 1998; Goodman et al. 2005d). Zygomatic arches are thin and outwardly bowed, the plates narrow, and their dorsal notch indistinct. Spacious, medium-long incisive foramina perforate the upper diastema, spanning about 55% of the diastemal length. The moderately high-crowned molars possess transverse laminae that lack any cusp definition; upper and lower third molars are noticeably smaller than the contiguous second molars. The upper incisors are relatively narrow, lack anterior grooves, and recurve only slightly (orthodont).

Examples of *Voalavo* are readily identified by their small size relative to those nesomyines that have been captured in sympatry, namely *Brachytarsomys albicauda*, *B. villosa*, *Brachyuromys betsileoensis*, several species of *Eliurus*, *Gymnuromys roberti*, and *Nesomys rufus*. In addition to diminutive size, *Voalavo* males possess a pair of glands on the chest, a cutaneous specialization unknown in any other nesomyine (Goodman et al. 2005d; S. M. Goodman and V. Soarimalala, unpublished data). Of those *Eliurus* that cohabit the same forest as *Voalavo* species, even the smallest species, *E. minor*, is still larger in external and craniodental variables (Carleton and Goodman 1998: Table 11-7). Many qualitative traits are equally useful for generic discrimination (e.g., Carleton and Goodman 1998: Figure 11-18), but the absence of a tail tuft in *Voalavo* easily contrasts the genus with species of *Eliurus*, all of which exhibit a conspicuous terminal tail tuft (see Carleton et al., pp. 2014–22).

Recognition of the two species of *Voalavo* rests on subtle morphological differences (Tables 14.44 and 14.45), including the length of tail relative to head-and-body size, rostral size, and robustness of the molar dentition. White coloration tends to cover a

TABLE 14.44. **External measurements for adult specimens of *Voalavo gymnocaudus* and *V. antsahabensis***

SPECIES	HBL (mm)	TL (mm)	HFL (mm)	EL (mm)	WT (g)
V. gymnocaudus[1] (n = 11)	86.3 ± 4.0	117.5 ± 4.8	19.5 ± 0.9	14.7 ± 0.5	21.8 ± 2.5
	80–90	107–126	18–21	14–15	17–25.5
V. antsahabensis[2] (n = 23)	92.9 ± 4.0	113.2 ± 5.2	18.3 ± 0.9	15.1 ± 0.8	18.5 ± 1.7
	85–100	102–127	16–20	14–16	18.5–26

Notes: HBL, head-and-body length; TL, tail length; HFL, hind-foot length; EL, ear length; WT, weight. Sample statistics include the mean ± one standard deviation, and the minimum–maximum range.

[1] Locality: Anjanaharibe-Sud and Marojejy.

[2] Anjozorobe-Angavo.

FIGURE 14.74 **Adult *Voalavo antsahabensis* in the Antsahabe Forest, Anjozorobe-Angavo, the type locality of this species.** (PHOTO by V. Soarimalala.)

longer portion of the distal tail in *V. antsahabensis* than in observed examples of *V. gymnocaudus*.

GEOGRAPHIC AND ELEVATIONAL DISTRIBUTION

Species of *Voalavo* are currently documented from elevations above 1200 m in two highland settings (see map in Goodman et al. 2013: 267), *V. gymnocaudus* (1250–1950 m) on the Anjanaharibe-Sud and Marojejy Massifs flanking the Andapa Basin, Northern Highlands (Soarimalala and Goodman 2003a); and *V. antsahabensis* (1250–1425 m) in the Anjozorobe-Angavo region, Central Highlands (Soarimalala et al. 2007). The two taxa are interpreted as vicariant species, their differentiation impelled by isolation in montane forests on either side of the Mandritsara lowlands (Goodman et al. 2005d).

To date, the many small-mammal inventories performed in the Northern and Central Highlands have yet to document both *Voalavo* and *Monticolomys*, another diminutive nesomyine (see Carleton et al., pp. 2031–32), from the same locality in medium-altitude moist evergreen forest, although both genera are known to inhabit different mountain systems within those highlands (Soarimalala and Goodman 2003a; Soarimalala et al. 2007; Maminirina et al. 2008; Goodman et al. 2018b).

ECOLOGY, BEHAVIOR, AND REPRODUCTION

Both species of *Voalavo* inhabit medium-altitude moist evergreen forest over an elevational belt of 1250–1950 m (Soarimalala and Goodman 2003a; Goodman et al. 2005d). Populations have been recorded mostly toward the upper limits of this forest zone, where the canopy tends to be lower, lianas are abundant, and mosses, lichens, and epiphytes heavily carpet the ground and tree surfaces. Such local forest communities are sometimes described as elfin or mossy forest.

Within these forest habitats, *Voalavo* is nocturnal and exhibits both terrestrial and scansorial proclivities, as indicated by capture data. A substantial portion of individuals have been captured after falling into pitfall traps intended for amphibians, reptiles, or small tenrecs (Goodman and Carleton 1998; Carleton and Goodman 2000; Soarimalala et al. 2007). Nevertheless, appreciable numbers of both *V. antsahabensis* and *V. gymnocaudus* have been also captured in live traps placed 1–2 m above the ground on moss-covered limbs of large trees (Goodman and Carleton 1998; V. Soarimalala and S. M. Goodman, unpublished data). The capability of *Voalavo* species to utilize terrestrial and some arborescent resources is presupposed by the animal's long tail and relatively broad hind feet.

Aspects of *Voalavo* life history are sketchy. Detailed dietary information is unavailable, but the possibility of frugivorous preferences is suggested by the significant proportion (30%) of *V. antsahabensis* individuals caught in live traps that had been baited with bananas for small lemurs (Soarimalala et al. 2007). Anecdotal data suggest that nests are located on the ground, as successful traps for this species have been placed by a hole at the base of a tree or under tree roots (Goodman and Carleton 1998). Based on various indicators of ongoing reproduction (males with scrotal testes, females with perforated vaginas or distended mammae, tallies of placental scars), *Voalavo* populations are known to breed from October to February (Goodman and Carleton 1998; Carleton and Goodman 2000; V. Soarimalala, unpublished data). The number of young at birth is apparently small, only two or three per litter based on counts of placental scars (mean 2.1, n = 7) (Goodman and Carleton 1998; Carleton and Goodman 2000; V. Soarimalala, unpublished data).

TABLE 14.45. **Selected craniodental measurements for adult specimens of *Voalavo gymnocaudus* and *V. antsahabensis***

SPECIES	ONL (mm)	BOC (mm)	IOB (mm)	LR (mm)	LD (mm)	LM1–3 (mm)
V. gymnocaudus[1] (n = 12)	26.2 ± 0.5	6.5 ± 0.2	4.5 ± 0.1	8.6 ± 0.2	6.6 ± 0.2	3.8 ± 0.1
	25.4–26.9	6.1–6.6	4.4–4.8	8.3–9.0	6.2–6.9	3.6–3.9
V. antsahabensis[2] (n = 19)	25.8 ± 0.4	6.2 ± 0.2	4.4 ± 0.2	8.2 ± 0.4	6.6 ± 0.3	3.4 ± 0.1
	25–26.5	5.9–6.6	4.1–4.6	7.4–8.7	6.1–7.2	3.2–3.6

Notes: ONL, occipitonasal length; BOC, breadth across occipital condyles; IOB, interorbital breadth; LR, length of rostrum; LD, length of diastema; LM1–3, coronal length of upper molar tooth row. Sample statistics include the mean ± one standard deviation, and the minimum–maximum range.

[1] Locality: Anjanaharibe-Sud and Marojejy.

[2] Anjozorobe-Angavo.

The paired cutaneous chest glands of the breeding male *Voalavo* are distinctly more developed, producing a distinctive musky odor that may function in scent marking trails or home territories (S. M. Goodman and V. Soarimalala, unpublished data).

The slim documentation of predation consists of cranial fragments of *V. gymnocaudus* found in the pellets of *Asio madagascariensis* (Madagascar Long-eared Owl) on the Marojejy Massif (S. M. Goodman, unpublished data). Given the small size of *Voalavo*, other raptors, euplerid carnivorans, and medium-size nocturnal snakes may feed on this genus.

Voalavo has not yet been the subject of epidemiological studies. A new species of mite, *Andreacarus voalavo* (Acari), is known only from *V. gymnocaudus* (Dowling et al. 2007), although this genus of mites has been also recovered from some other members of Nesomyinae, Tenrecinae, and endemic Carnivora.

CONSERVATION

All localities so far documented for *Voalavo* occur within designated protected areas (Goodman et al. 2018b), *V. antsahabensis* within one (Anjozorobe-Angavo) and *V. gymnocaudus* within two (Anjanaharibe-Sud and Marojejy). The conservation status of *V. antsahabensis* is presently evaluated as Endangered and *V. gymnocaudus* as Least Concern (IUCN 2020). As with other nesomyines that inhabit moist evergreen forests, stability of *Voalavo* populations is dependent upon the extent and quality of those forests, which regretfully have long experienced degradation through human activities (Vieilledent et al. 2018).

Subject editor: Steven M. Goodman

REFERENCES

Acharya, K. K., Roy, A., and Krishna, A. 1998. Relative role of olfactory cues and certain nonolfactory factors in foraging of fruit-eating bats. *Behavioral Processes* 44: 59–64.

Ade, M. 1996. Examination of the digestive tract contents of *Tenrec ecaudatus* Schreber 1777 (Tenrecidae, Insectivore) from western Madagascar. In Ecology and economy of a tropical dry forest in Madagascar, eds. J. U. Ganzhorn and J.-P. Sorg. *Primate Report*, special issue, 46(1): 233–249.

Agha, M., Batter, T., Bolas, E. C., Collins, A. C., Gomes da Rocha, D., Monteza-Moreno, C. M., Preckler-Quisquater, S., and Sollmann, R. 2018. A review of wildlife camera trapping trends across Africa. *African Journal of Ecology* 56: 694–701.

Agnarsson, I., Zambrana-Torrelio, C. M., Flores-Saldana, N. P., and May-Collado, L. J. 2011. A time-calibrated species-level phylogeny of bats (Chiroptera, Mammalia). *PLoS Currents Tree of Life* 3 (3): RRN1212. https://doi.org/10.1371/currents.RRN1212.

Al-Asadi, H., Petkova, D., Stephens, M., and Novembre, J. 2019. Estimating recent migration and population-size surfaces. *PLoS Genetics* 15: e1007908. https://doi.org/10.1371/journal.pgen.1007908.

Albignac, R. 1969a. Naissance et élevage en captivité de jeunes *Cryptoprocta ferox*, viverridés malgaches. *Mammalia* 33: 93.

———. 1969b. Notes éthologiques sur quelques Carnivores malgaches: *Galidia elegans* I. Geoffroy. *La Terre et la Vie* 23: 202–215.

———. 1970. Notes éthologiques sur quelques carnivores malgaches: Le *Cryptoprocta ferox* (Bennett). *La Terre et la Vie* 24: 395–402.

———. 1971. Notes éthologiques sur quelques carnivores malgaches: Le *Fossa fossa* (Schreber). *Revue d'Ecologie Appliquée* 24: 383–394.

———. 1972a. The Carnivora of Madagascar. In *Biogeography and Ecology in Madagascar*, eds. R. Battistini and G. Richard-Vindard, pp. 667–682. Dordrecht: Springer Netherlands.

———. 1972b. Premières observations éco-éthologiques d'un carnivore malgache du genre *Eupleres*. *Bulletin de l'Académie Malgache* 50: 115–120.

———. 1973. Mammifères Carnivores. *Faune de Madagascar* 36: 1–210.

———. 1974. Observations éco-éthologiques sur le genre *Eupleres*, viverridé de Madagascar. *La Terre et la Vie* 28: 321–351.

———. 1975. Breeding the fossa (*Cryptoprocta ferox*) at Montpellier Zoo. *International Zoo Yearbook* 15: 147–150.

———. 1976. L'écologie du *Mungotictis decemlineata* dans les forêts décidues de l'ouest de Madagascar. *La Terre et la Vie* 30: 347–376.

———. 1984. The carnivores. In *Key Environments: Madagascar*, eds. A. Jolly, P. Oberlé, and R. Albignac, pp. 167–181. Oxford: Pergamon Press.

———. 1992. *Eco-développement des communautés rurales pour la conservation de la biodiversité*. Paris: UNESCO/PNUD.

Albrecht, G. H., Jenkins, P. D., and Godfrey, L. R. 1990. Ecogeographic size variation among the living and subfossil prosimians of Madagascar. *American Journal of Primatology* 22: 1–50.

Alderton, D. 1996. *Rodents of the World*. New York: Facts on File.

Aleixo-Pais, I., Salmona, J., Sgarlata, G. M., Rakotonanahary, A., Sousa, A. P., et al. 2019. The genetic structure of a mouse lemur living in a fragmented habitat in northern Madagascar. *Conservation Genetics* 20: 229–243. https://doi.org/10.1007/s10592-018-1126-z.

Ali, J. R., and Huber, M. 2010. Mammalian biodiversity on Madagascar controlled by ocean currents. *Nature* 463: 653–680.

Allendorf, F. W. 2017. Genetics and the conservation of natural populations: Allozymes to genomes. *Molecular Ecology* 26: 420–430. https://doi.org/10.1111/mec.13948.

Allibert, C. 1989. Le site de Dembeni (Mayotte, Archipel des Comores). Mission 1984. *Etudes Océan Indien* 11: 63–172.

Allibert, C., and Vérin, P. 1996. The early pre-Islamic history of the Comoros Islands: Links with Madagascar and Africa. In *The Indian Ocean in Antiquity*, ed. J. Reade, pp. 461–470. London: Kegan Paul International.

Allnutt, T. F., Asner, G. P., Golden, C. D., and Powell, G.V.N. 2013. Mapping recent deforestation and disturbance in northeastern Madagascar. *Tropical Conservation Science* 6: 1–15.

Almeida, F. C., Giannini, N. P., Simmons, N. B., and Helgen, K. M. 2014. Each flying fox on its own branch: A phylogenetic tree for *Pteropus* and related genera (Chiroptera: Pteropodidae). *Molecular Phylogenetics and Evolution* 77: 83–95. http://dx. https://doi.org/10.1016/j.ympev.2014.03.009.

Almeida, F. C., Giannini, N. P., and Simmons, N. B. 2016. The evolutionary history of the African fruit bats (Chiroptera: Pteropodidae). *Acta Chiropterologica* 18: 73–90.

Almeida-Rocha, J. M. de, Peres, C. A., and Oliveira, L. C. 2017. Primate responses to anthropogenic habitat disturbance: A pantropical meta-analysis. *Biological Conservation* 215: 30–38.

Alston, E. R. 1876. On the classification of the order Glires. *Proceedings of the Zoological Society of London* 1876: 61–98.

Alumbaugh, J. 2019. Morphometric analysis of subfossil *Macronycteris* spp. (Chiroptera: Hipposideridae) from Madagascar. MS thesis, Northern Illinois University.

Ammerman, L. K., Lee, D. N., and Tipps, T. M. 2012. First molecular phylogenetic insights into the evolution of free-tailed bats in the subfamily Molossinae (Molossidae, Chiroptera). *Journal of Mammalogy* 93: 12–28.

Anantharaman, R., Hall, K., Shah, V. B., and Edelman, A. 2020. Circuitscape in Julia: High performance connectivity modelling to support conservation decisions. *Proceedings of the Julia Conferences* 1: 58. arXiv:1906.03542.

Ancrenaz, M., Lackman-Ancrenaz, I., and Mundy, N. 1994. Field observations of aye-ayes (*Daubentonia madagascariensis*) in Madagascar. *Folia Primatologica* 62: 22–36.

Anderson, A., Clark, G., Haberle, S., Higham, T., Nowak-Kemp, M., et al. 2018. New evidence of megafaunal bone damage indicates late colonization of Madagascar. *PLoS One* 13(10): e0204368. https://doi.org/10.1371/ journal.pone.0204368.

Andrews, C. A., Rambeloarivony, H., Génin, F., and Masters, J. C. 2016. Why cheirogaleids are bad models for primate ancestors: A phylogenetic reconstruction. In *The Dwarf and Mouse Lemurs of Madagascar*, eds. S. M. Lehman, U. Radespiel, and E. Zimmermann, pp. 94–112. Cambridge: Cambridge University Press.

Andrews, K. R., Good, J. M., Miller, M. R., Luikart, G., and Hohenlohe, P. A. 2016. Harnessing the power of RADseq for ecological and evolutionary genomics. *Nature Reviews Genetics* 17: 81–92. https://doi.org/10.1038/nrg.2015.28.

Andrews, J. R., and Birkinshaw, C. R. 1998. A comparison between the daytime and night time diet, activity and feeding height of the black lemur, *Eulemur macaco* (Primates: Lemuridae), in Lokobe Forest, Madagascar. *Folia Primatologica* 69: 175–182.

Andriafidison, D. 2016. Ecologie et conservation de *Pteropus rufus* E. Geoffroy, 1803 (Pteropodidae) dans les régions sèche et humides de Madagascar. PhD thesis, Université d'Antananarivo.

Andriafidison, D., Andrianaivoarivelo, R. A., Ramilijaona, O. R., Razanahoera, M. R., MacKinnon, J., Jenkins, R.K.B., and Racey, P. A. 2006a. Nectarivory by endemic Malagasy fruit bats during the dry season. *Biotropica* 38: 85–90.

Andriafidison, D., Andrianaivoarivelo, R. A., and Jenkins, R.K.B. 2006b. Records of tree roosting bats from western Madagascar. *African Bat Conservation News* 8: 5–6.

Andriafidison, D., Kofoky, A., Mbohoahy, T., Racey, P. A., and Jenkins, R.K.B. 2007. Diet, reproduction and roosting habits of the Madagascar free-tailed bat, *Otomops madagascariensis* Dorst, 1953 (Chiroptera: Molossidae). *Acta Chiropterologica* 9: 445–450.

Andriaholinirina, V. N., Fausser, J.-L., and Rabarivola, J. C. 2003. Etude comparative de *Hapalemur simus* (Gray, 1870) de deux sites de la province autonome de Fianarantsoa, Madagascar: Forêt dégradée d'Ambolomavo et forêt secondaire du Parc National de Ranomafana. *Lemur News* 8: 9–13.

Andriaholinirina, V. N., Rabarivola, C., Hauwy, M., and Rumpler, Y. 2005. Cytogenetic study of *Lepilemur microdon*. *Folia Primatologica* 76: 238–241.

Andriaholinirina, V. N., Fausser, J.-L., Roos, C., Zinner, D., Thalmann, U., et al. 2006. Molecular phylogeny and taxonomic revision of the sportive lemurs (*Lepilemur*, Primates). *BMC Evolutionary Biology* 6: 17. https://doi.org/10.1186/1471-2148-6-17.

Andriamaharoa, H., Birkinshaw, C., and Reza, L. 2010. Day-time feeding ecology of *Eulemur cinereiceps* in the Agnalazaha Forest, Mahabo-Mananivo, Madagascar. *Madagascar Conservation and Development* 5: 55–63.

Andriamandimbiarisoa, L., Blanthorn, T. S., Ernest, R., Ramanamanjato, J.-B., Randriatafika, F., Ganzhorn, J. U., and Donati, G. 2015. Habitat corridor utilisation by the gray mouse lemur, *Microcebus murinus*, in the littoral forest fragments of south eastern Madagascar. *Madagascar Conservation and Development* 10: 144–150.

Andriamasimanana, M. 1994. Ecoethological study of free-ranging aye-ayes (*Daubentonia madagascariensis*) in Madagascar. *Folia Primatologica* 62: 37–45.

Andrianaivoarimanana, V., Kreppel, K., Elissa, N., Duplantier, J.-M., Carniel, E., Rajerison, M., and Jambou, R. 2013. Understanding the persistence of plague foci in Madagascar. *PLoS Neglected Tropical Diseases* 7(11): e2382. https://doi.org/10.1371/journal.pntd.0002382.

Andrianaivoarivelo, R. A. 2012. Ecologie et population de *Rousettus madagascariensis* G. Grandidier, 1928 (Pteropodidae). PhD thesis, Biodiversité et Ecologie, Université Rennes 1.

Andrianaivoarivelo, R. A., Ranaivoson, N., Racey, P. A., and Jenkins, R.K.B. 2006. The diet of three synanthropic bats (Chiroptera: Molossidae) from eastern Madagascar. *Acta Chiropterologica* 8: 439–444.

Andrianaivoarivelo, R. A., Ramilijaona, O. R., and Andriafidison, D. 2007. *Rousettus madagascariensis* Grandidier 1929 feeding on *Dimnocarpus longan* in Madagascar. *African Bat Conservation News* 11: 3–4.

Andrianaivoarivelo, R. A., Shore, G. D., McGuire, S. M., Jenkins, R.K.B., Ramilijaona, O., Louis, E. E., Jr., and Brenneman, R. A. 2009. Characterization of 22 microsatellite marker loci in the Madagascar rousette (*Rousettus madagascariensis*). *Conservation Genetics* 10: 1025–1028. https://doi.org/10.1007/s10592-008-9679-x.

Andrianaivoarivelo, R. A., Andriafidison, D., Rahaingonirina, C., Raharimbola, S., Rakotoarivelo, A. A., Ramilijaona, O. R., Racey, P. A., and Jenkins, R.K.B. 2011a. A conservation assessment of *Rousettus madagascariensis* (Grandidier, 1928, Pteropodidae) roosts in eastern Madagascar. *Madagascar Conservation and Development* 6(2): 78–82.

Andrianaivoarivelo, R. A., Ramilijaona, O. R., Racey, P. A., Razafindrakoto, N., and Jenkins, R.K.B. 2011b. Feeding ecology, habitat use and reproduction of *Rousettus madagascariensis* Grandidier, 1928 (Chiroptera: Pteropodidae) in eastern Madagascar. *Mammalia* 75: 69–78.

Andrianaivoarivelo, A. R., Petit, E. J., Razafindrakoto, N., and Racey P. A. 2012a. Alimentation et dispersion de graines chez *Rousettus madagascariensis* Grandidier 1928, dans le Nord-ouest de Madagascar. *Revue d'Ecologie (La Terre et la Vie)* 67: 179–191.

Andrianaivoarivelo, A. R., Jenkins, R.K.B., Petit, E. J., Ramilijaona, O., Razafindrakoto, N., and Racey, P. A. 2012b. *Rousettus madagascariensis* (Chiroptera: Pteropodidae) shows a preference for native and commercially unimportant fruits. *Endangered Species Research* 19: 19–27.

Andrianandrasana, Z. A. 2019. Bioécologie de *Hapalemur griseus griseus* (Link, 1795) dans la forêt tropicale humide de Maromizaha (Andasibe). PhD thesis, Université d'Antananarivo.

Andrianandrasana, Z. A., Rasolofoharivelo, T., Chamberlan, C., Ratsimbazafy, J., and King, T. 2013. Etude préliminaire de *Prolemur simus* (Ramaimbangy) dans la forêt de basse altitude de Vohibe, bassin versant Nosivolo, Madagascar, et implications pour sa conservation. *Lemur News* 17: 43–49.

Andrianandrasana, [Z.] A., Andrianarimisa, A., Randrianarison, R. M., and Randrianasy, J. 2018. *Buteo brachypterus*: Aerial predator of *Hapalemur g. griseus* in Maromizaha rainforest. *Lemur News* 21: 7.

Andrianarisata, M. 1994. Inventaire des plantes consommées par les *Varecia variegata variegata* dans la Réserve Naturelle de Betampona et étude de leurs abondances. Antananarivo: Missouri Botanical Garden. Available from chris.birkinshaw@mobot.mg..

Andrianarivo, A. 1981. Etude comparée de l'organisation sociale chez *Microcebus coquereli*. Mémoire de DEA, Sciences Biologiques, Université d'Antananarivo.

Andrianjakarivelo, V. 2000. Densité, écologie et rôle écologique des potamochères (*Potamochoerus larvatus*) et leur impact sur la végétation dans la Réserve Spéciale de Nosy Mangabe. Rapport de Mission. Antananarivo: Wildlife Conservation Society.

Andrianjakarivelo, V., Razafimahatratra, E., Razafindrakoto, Y., and Goodman, S. M. 2005. The terrestrial small mammals of the Parc National de Masoala, northeastern Madagascar. *Acta Theriologica* 50: 537–549.

Andriantompohavana, R., Zaonarivelo, J. R., Endberg, S. E., Randriamampionona, R., McGuire, S. M., Shore, G. D., Rakotonomenjanahary, R., Brenneman, R. A., and Louis, E. E., Jr. 2006. Mouse lemurs of northwestern Madagascar with a description of a new species at Lokobe Special Reserve. *Occasional Papers, Museum of Texas Tech University* 259: 1–24.

Andriantompohavana, R., Lei, R., Zaonarivelo, J. R., Engberg, S. E., Nalanirina, G., et al. 2007. Molecular phylogeny and taxonomic revision of the woolly lemurs, genus *Avahi* (Primates: Lemuriformes). *Special Publications, Museum of Texas Tech University* 51: 1–59.

Andriantsiferana, R., and Rahandraha, T. 1974. Effets du séjour au froid sur le microcèbe (*Microcebus murinus* Miller 1777). *Comptes Rendus de l'Académie Sciences*, Paris, 278: 3099–3102.

Andriatsarafara, R. 1988. Note sur les rythmes d'activité et sur le régime alimentaire de *Lemur mongoz* Linnaeus, 1766 à Ampijoroa. In *L'Equilibre des écosystèmes forestiers à Madagascar*, eds. L. Rakotovao, V. Barre, and J. Sayer, pp. 103–106. Gland, Switzerland, and Cambridge, UK: IUCN.

Andriatsimietry, R., Goodman, S. M., Razafimahatratra, R., Jeglinski, J.W.E., Marquard, M., and Ganzhorn, J. U. 2009. Seasonal variation in the diet of *Galidictis grandidieri* Wozencraft, 1986 (Carnivora: Eupleridae) in a sub-arid zone of extreme south-western Madagascar. *Journal of Zoology* 279: 410–415.

Andriatsitohaina, B., Ramsay, M. S., Kiene, F., Lehman, S. M., Rasoloharijaona, S., Rakotondravony, R., and Radespiel, U. 2019. Ecological fragmentation effects in mouse lemurs and small mammals in northwestern Madagascar. *American Journal of Primatology*: e23059. https://doi.org/10.1002/ajp.23059.

Angel, A., Wanless, R. M., and Cooper, J. 2009. Review of impacts of the introduced house mouse on islands in the Southern Ocean: Are mice equivalent to rats? *Biological Invasions* 11: 1743–1754.

Annapragada, A., Brook, C. E., Luskin, M. S., Rahariniaina, R. P., Helin, M., Razafinarivo, O., Ambinintsoa Ralaiarison, R., Randriamady, H. J., Olson, L. E., Goodman, S. M., and Golden, C. D. 2021. Evaluation of tenrec population viability and potential sustainable management under hunting pressure in northeastern Madagascar. *Animal Conservation* 24(6): 1059–1070. https://doi.org/10.1111/acv.12714.

Anthony, R., and Coupin, P. 1931. Tableau résumé d'une classification générique des Primates fossiles et actuels. *Bulletin du Muséum d'Histoire Naturelle*, Paris, 2–3: 566–569.

Apanaskevich, D. A., and Goodman S. M. 2020a. Description of a new species of *Haemaphysalis* Koch, 1844 (Acari: Ixodidae) from the *H.* (*Rhipistoma*) *asiatica* subgroup, parasite of an endemic Malagasy carnivoran (Carnivora: Eupleridae). *Systematic Parasitology* 97: 591–599.

Apanaskevich, D. A., and Goodman, S. M. 2020b. Description of three new species of *Ixodes* Latreille, 1795 (Acari: Ixodidae), parasites of tenrecs (Afrotheria: Tenrecidae) on Madagascar. *Systematic Parasitology* 97: 623–637. https://doi.org/10.1007/s11230-020-09944-2.

Apanaskevich, D. A., Soarimalala, V., and Goodman S. M. 2013. A new *Ixodes* species (Acari: Ixodidae), parasite of shrew tenrecs (Afrosoricida: Tenrecidae) in Madagascar. *Journal of Parasitology* 99: 970–972.

Aplin, K. P., Chesser, T., and ten Have, J. 2003. Evolutionary biology of the genus *Rattus*: Profile of an archetypal rodent pest. In *Rats, Mice and People: Rodent Biology and Management*, eds. G. R. Singleton, L. A. Hinds, C. J. Krebs, and D. M. Spratt, pp. 487–498. Canberra: Australian Centre for International Agricultural Research.

Aplin, K. P., Suzuki, H., Chinen, A. A., Chesser, R. T., ten Have, J., et al. 2011. Multiple geographic origins of commensalism and complex dispersal history of black rats. *PLoS One* 6(11): e26357. https://doi.org/10.1371/journal.pone.0026357.

Archer, M., Arena, D. A., Bassarova, M., Beck, R.M.D., Black, K., et al. 2006. Current status of species-level representation in faunas from selected fossil localities in the Riversleigh World Heritage Area, northwestern Queensland. *Alcheringa*, special issue 1: 1–17.

Ardalan, A., Oskarsson, M. C., van Asch, B., Rabakonandriania, E., and Savolainen, P. 2015. African origin for Madagascan dogs revealed by mtDNA analysis. *Royal Society Open Science* 2(5): 140552. https://doi.org/10.1098/rsos.140552.

Arnaud, J., Meier, B., Dugoujon, J. M., and Rumpler, Y. 1992. Study of the variability of erythrocyte enzymes in captive and wild populations of the black lemur (*Eulemur macaco macaco*). An indispensable preliminary in captive breeding programmes. *Primates* 33: 139–146. https://doi.org/10.1007/BF02382771.

Arrigo-Nelson, S. J. 2006. The impact of habitat disturbance on the feeding ecology of the Milne-Edwards' sifaka (*Propithecus edwardsi*) in Ranomafana National Park, Madagascar. PhD thesis, State University of New York, Stony Brook.

Asher, R. J. 1999. A morphological basis for assessing the phylogeny of the "Tenrecoidea" (Mammalia, Lipotyphla). *Cladistics* 15: 231–252.

———. 2010. Tenrecoidea. In *Cenozoic Mammals of Africa*, eds. L. Werdelin and W. J. Sanders, pp. 99–105. Berkeley: University of California Press.

Asher, R. J., and Hofreiter, M. 2006. Tenrec phylogeny and the noninvasive extraction of nuclear DNA. *Systematic Biology* 55(2): 181–194.

Atsalis, S. 1999a. Diet of the brown mouse lemur (*Microcebus rufus*) in Ranomafana National Park, Madagascar. *International Journal of Primatology* 20: 193–229.

———. 1999b. Seasonal fluctuations in body fat and activity levels in a rain-forest species of mouse lemur, *Microcebus rufus*. *International Journal of Primatology* 20: 883–910.

———. 2000. Spatial distribution and population composition of the brown mouse lemur (*Microcebus rufus*) in Ranomafana National Park, Madagascar, and its implications for social organization. *American Journal of Primatology* 51: 61–78.

Aujard, F., Perret, M., and Vannier, G. 1998. Thermoregulatory responses to variations of photoperiod and ambient temperature in the male lesser mouse lemur: A primitive or an advanced adaptive character? *Journal of Comparative Physiology B: Biochemical, Systemic, and Environmental Physiology* 168: 540–548.

Avise, J. C. 2000. *Phylogeography: The History and Formation of Species*. Cambridge, MA: Harvard University Press.

Aylward, M., Sullivan, A., Perry, G., Johnson, S., and Louis, E. E., Jr. 2018. An environmental DNA sampling method for aye-ayes from their feeding traces. *Ecology and Evolution* 8: 9229–9240.

Bachmann, L., Rumpler, Y., Ganzhorn, J. U., and Tomiuk, J. 2000. Genetic differentiation among natural populations of *Lepilemur ruficaudatus*. *International Journal of Primatology* 21: 853–864. https://doi.org/10.1023/A:1005546709911.

Baden, A. L. 2011. Communal infant care in black-and-white ruffed lemurs (*Varecia variegata*). PhD thesis, State University of New York, Stony Brook.

———. 2019. A description of nesting behaviors, including factors impacting nest site selection, in black-and-white ruffed lemurs (*Varecia variegata*). *Ecology and Evolution* 9: 1010–1028.

Baden, A. L., Brenneman, R. A., and Louis, E. E., Jr. 2008. Morphometrics of wild black-and-white ruffed lemurs [*Varecia variegata*, Kerr 1972]. *American Journal of Primatology* 70: 913–926.

Baden, A. L., Wright, P. C., Louis, E. E., Jr., and Bradley, B. J. 2013. Communal nesting, kinship, and maternal success in a social primate. *Behavioral Ecology and Sociobiology* 67: 1939–1950.

Baden, A. L., Holmes, S. M., Johnson, S. E., Engberg, S. E., Louis, E. E., Jr., and Bradley, B. J. 2014. Species-level view of population structure and gene flow for a Critically Endangered primate (*Varecia variegata*). *Ecology and Evolution* 4: 2675–2692.

Baden, A. L., Webster, T., and Kamilar, J. M. 2016. Resource seasonality and reproduction predict fission-fusion dynamics in a Malagasy strepsirrhine, *Varecia variegata*. *American Journal of Primatology* 78: 256–279.

Baden, A. L., Mancini, A. N., Federman, S., Holmes, S. M., Johnson, S. E., Kamilar, J., Louis, E. E., Jr., and Bradley, B. J. 2019. Anthropogenic pressures drive population genetic structuring across a Critically Endangered lemur species range. *Scientific Reports* 9: 16276. https://doi.org/10.1038/s41598-019-52689-2.

Baden, A. L., Webster, T. H., and Bradley, B. J. 2020. Genetic relatedness cannot explain social preferences in black-and-white ruffed lemurs, *Varecia variegata*. *Animal Behaviour* 164: 73–82. https://doi.org/10.1016/j.anbehav.2020.04.003.

Baden, A. L., Oliveras, J., and Gerber, B. D. 2021. Sex-segregated range use by black-and-white ruffed lemurs (*Varecia variegata*) in Ranomafana National Park, Madagascar. *Folia Primatologia* 92: 12–32. https://doi.org/10.1159/000510965.

Bailey, C. A., McLain, A. T., Paquette, S. R., McGuire, S. M., Shore, G. D., et al. 2016. Evaluating the genetic diversity of three Endangered lemur species (genus: *Propithecus*) from northern Madagascar. *Journal of Primatology* 5(1): 132. https://doi.org/10.4172/2167-6801.1000132.

Baker-Médard, M.S.A., Baker, M. C., and Logue, D. M. 2013. Chorus song of the indri (*Indri indri*: Primates, Lemuridae): Group differences and analysis of within-group vocal interactions. *International Journal of Comparative Psychology* 26: 241–255.

Balestri, M. 2018. Ecology and conservation of the southern woolly lemur (*Avahi meridionalis*) in the Tsitongambarika Protected Area, south-eastern Madagascar. PhD thesis, Oxford Brookes University.

Balestri, M., Barresi, M., Campera, M., Serra, V., Ramanamanjato, J.-B., Heistermann, M., and Donati, G. 2014. Habitat degradation and seasonality affect physiological stress levels of *Eulemur collaris* in littoral forest fragments. *PLoS One* 9:e107698.

Balko, E. A. 1992. A survey of black and white ruffed lemurs (*Varecia variegata variegata*) inhabiting five separate forest communities within the eastern rain forests of Madagascar. Report to the World Conservation Monitoring Centre/IUCN, Gland, Switzerland, and Cambridge, UK.

———. 1998. A behaviorally plastic response to forest composition and logging disturbance by *Varecia variegata variegata* in Ranomafana National Park, Madagascar. PhD thesis, State University of New York, College of Environmental Science and Forestry, Syracuse.

Balko, E. A., and Underwood, H. B. 2005. Effects of forest structure and composition on food availability for *Varecia variegata* at Ranomafana National Park, Madagascar. *American Journal of Primatology* 66: 45–70.

Ballhorn, D. J., Kautz, S., and Rakotoarivelo, F. P., 2009. Quantitative variability of cyanogenesis in *Cathariostachys madagascariensis*. *American Journal of Primatology* 71: 305–315.

Ballhorn, D. J., Rakotoarivelo, F. P., and Kautz, S. 2016. Coevolution of cyanogenic bamboos and bamboo lemurs on Madagascar. *PLoS One* 11(8): e0158935. https://doi.org/10.1371/journal.pone.0158935.

Bambini, L., Kofoky, A. F., Mbohoahy, T., Ralisata, M., Manjoazy, T., Hosken, D. J., and Jenkins, R.K.B. 2011. Do bats need trees? Habitat use of two Malagasy hipposiderid bats *Triaenops furculus* and *T. menamena* in the dry southwest. *Hystrix*, new ser., 22(1): 81–92.

Barden, T. L., Evans, M. I., Raxworthy, C. J., Razafimahaimodison, J.-C., and Wilson, A. 1991. The mammals of Ambatovaky Special Reserve. In *A Survey of Ambatovaky Special Reserve, Madagascar*, eds. P. M. Thompson and M. I. Evans, pp. 5-1–5-22. London: Madagascar Environmental Research Group.

Barre, V., Lebec, A., Petter, J.-J., and Albignac, R. 1988. Etude du Microcèbe par radiotracking dans la forêt de l'Ankarafantsika. In *L'Equilibre des Ecosystèmes Forestiers à Madagascar: Actes d'un Séminaire International*, eds. L. Rakotovato, V. Barre, and J. Sayer, pp. 61–71. Gland, Switzerland, and Cambridge, UK: IUCN.

Bartlett, E. [1880]. Second list of mammals and birds collected by Mr. Thomas Waters in Madagascar. *Proceedings of the Zoological Society*, London 1879: 767–773.

Bastos, A. D., Nair, D., Taylor, P. J., Brettschneider, H., Kirsten, F., et al. 2011. Genetic monitoring detects an overlooked cryptic species and reveals the diversity and distribution of three invasive *Rattus* congeners in South Africa. *BMC Genetics* 12: 26.

Bates, P.J.J., Ratrimomanarivo, F. H., Harrison, D. L., and Goodman, S. M. 2006. A description of a new species of *Pipistrellus* (Chiroptera: Vespertilionidae) from Madagascar with a review of related Vespertilioninae from the island. *Acta Chiropterologica* 8: 299–324.

Battistini, R. 1965. Problèmes géomorphologiques de l'Extrême Nord de Madagascar. *Madagascar, Revue de Géographie* 7: 1–61.

Baum, D. A. 1995. The comparative pollination and floral biology of baobabs (*Adansonia*-Bombacaceae). *Annals of the Missouri Botanical Garden* 82: 322–348.

———. 1996. The ecology and conservation of the baobabs of Madagascar. In Ecology and economy of a tropical dry forest in Madagascar, eds. J. U. Ganzhorn and J.-P. Sorg. *Primate Report,* special issue, 46(1): 311–328.

Baverstock, P. R., Adams, M., Maxson, L. R., and Yosida, T. H. 1983. Genetic differentiation among karyotypic forms of the black rat, *Rattus rattus*. *Genetics* 105: 969–983.

Bearder, S. K., Ambrose, L., Harcourt, C., Honess, P., Perkin, A., Pimley, E., Pullen, S., and Svoboda, N. 2003. Species-typical patterns of infant contact, sleeping site use and social cohesion among nocturnal primates in Africa. *Folia Primatologica* 74: 337–354.

Beaucournu, J.-C., and Goodman, S. M. 2014. Une nouvelle espèce de Puce du genre *Paractenopsyllus*, endémique de Madagascar (Siphonaptera, Ceratophyllidae, Leptopsyllinae). *Bulletin de la Société Entomologique de France* 119(4): 427–431.

Beaucournu, J.-C., and Houin, R. 1967. A propos de la présence à Madagascar de *Polyplax reclinata* (Nitzsch, 1864) *sensu* Johnson 1960 (Insecta, Anoplura), parasite des musaraignes. *Archives de l'Institut Pasteur de Madagascar* 36: 67–81.

Beaucournu, J.-C., and Laudisoit, A. 2014. Une nouvelle espèce malgache de Puce du genre *Tsaractenus* (Siphonaptera, Ceratophyllidae, Leptopsyllinae). *Bulletin de la Société Entomologique de France* 119(3): 299–305.

Beaucournu, J.-C., Prié, V., Ramasindrazana, B., Goodman, S. M., and Laudisoit, A. 2015. Les puces de chauve-souris à Madagascar: Nouvelles données et clé d'identification illustrée actualisée (Siphonaptera, Ischnopsyllidae). *Bulletin de la Société Entomologique de France* 120(3): 323–334.

Beaudrot, L., Acevedo, M., Lessard, J.-P., Sheil, D., Larney, E., Wright, P., and Ahumada, J. 2018. Distributional shifts in a biodiversity hotspot. *Biological Conservation* 228: 252–258.

Beaujard, P. 2012. *Les Mondes de l'Océan Indien*. Vol. 2, *L'Océan Indien, au Cœur des Globalisations de l'Ancien Monde (7th–15th Siècle)*. Paris: Armand Colin.

Beaumont, M. A. 1999. Detecting population expansion and decline using microsatellites. *Genetics* 153: 2013–2029.

———. 2004. Recent developments in genetic data analysis: What can they tell us about human demographic history? *Heredity* 92: 365–379. https://doi.org/10.1038/sj.hdy.6800447.

———. 2010. Approximate Bayesian computation in evolution and ecology. *Annual Review of Ecology, Evolution, and Systematics* 41: 379–406. https://doi.org/10.1146/annurev-ecolsys-102209-144621.

Beaumont, M. A., and Nichols, R. A. 1996. Evaluating loci for use in the genetic analysis of population structure. *Proceedings of the Royal Society of London B: Biological Sciences* 263: 1619–1626. https://doi.org/10.1098/rspb.1996.0237.

Beaumont, M. A., Zhang, W., and Balding, D. J. 2002. Approximate Bayesian computation in population genetics. *Genetics* 162: 2025–2035.

Beddard, P. E. 1884. On some points in the structure of *Hapalemur griseus*. *Proceedings of the Zoological Society of London* 1884: 391–399.

Beeby, N., and Baden, A. L. 2021. Seasonal variability in the diet and feeding ecology of black-and-white ruffed lemurs (*Varecia variegata*) in Ranomafana National Park, southeastern Madagascar. *American Journal of Physical Anthropology* 174(4): 763–775.

Benda, P., and Vallo, P. 2009. Taxonomic revision of the genus *Triaenops* (Chiroptera: Hipposideridae) with description of a new species from southern Arabia and definitions of a new genus and tribe. *Folia Zoologica* 58: 1–45.

Bennett, C. E., Pastorini, J., Dollar, L., and Hahn, W. J. 2009. Phylogeography of the Malagasy ring-tailed mongoose, *Galidia elegans*, from mtDNA sequence analysis. *Mitochondrial DNA* 20: 7–14.

Bennett, E. T. 1833. Notice of a new genus of *Viverridous Mammalia* from Madagascar. *Proceedings of the Zoological Society of London* 1833: 46.

———. 1835. Notice of a mammiferous animal from Madagascar, constituting a new form among the *Viverridous Carnivora*. *Transactions of the Zoological Society of London* 1: 137–140.

Bennett, G., Malone, M., Sauther, M. L., Cuozzo, F. P., White, B., Nelson, K. E., Stumpf, R. M., Knight, R., Leigh, S., and Amato, K. R. 2016. Host age, social group and habitat type influence the gut microbiota of wild, ring-tailed lemurs (*Lemur catta*). *American Journal of Primatology* 78: 883–892. https://doi.org/10.1002/ajp.22555.

Benstead, J. P., and Olson, L. E. 2003. *Limnogale mergulus*. In *The Natural History of Madagascar*, eds. S. M. Goodman and J. P. Benstead, pp. 1267–1273. Chicago: University of Chicago Press.

Benstead, J. P., Barnes, K. H., and Pringle, C. M. 2001. Diet, activity patterns, foraging movement and responses to deforestation of the aquatic tenrec *Limnogale mergulus* (Lipotyphla: Tenrecidae) in eastern Madagascar. *Journal of Zoology* 254: 119–129.

Berkelman, J. 1994. The ecology of the Madagascar buzzard *Buteo brachypterus*. In *Raptor Conservation Today*, eds. B.-U. Meyburg and R. D. Chancellor, pp. 255–256. East Sussex: Pica Press.

Bertoncini, S., D'Ercole, J., Brisighelli, F., Ramanamanjato, J.-B., Capelli, C., Tofanelli, S., and Donati, G. 2017. Stuck in fragments: Population genetics of the Endangered collared brown lemur *Eulemur collaris* in the Malagasy littoral forest. *American Journal of Physical Anthropology* 163: 542–552. https://doi.org/10.1002/ajpa.23230.

Bethge, J., Wist, B., Stalenberg, E., and Dausmann, K. 2017. Seasonal adaptation in energy budgeting in the primate *Lepilemur leucopus*. *Journal of Comparative Physiology B: Biochemical, Systemic, and Environmental Physiology* 187: 827–834.

Biebouw, K. 2009. Revealing the behavioural ecology of the elusive hairy-eared dwarf lemur (*Allocebus trichotis*). PhD thesis, Oxford Brookes University.

Bininda-Emonds, O.R.P., Cardillo, M., Jones, K. E., MacPhee, R.D.E., Beck, R.M.D., Grenyer, R., Price, S. A., Vos, R. A., Gittleman, J. L., and Purvis, A. 2007. The delayed rise of present-day mammals. *Nature* 446: 507–512.

Birkinshaw, C. R. 1999. The importance of the black lemur (*Eulemur macaco*) for seed dispersal in Lokobe Forest, Nosy Be. In *New Directions in Lemur Studies*, eds. B. Rakotosamimanana, H. Rasamimanana, J. U. Ganzhorn, and S. M. Goodman, pp. 189–199. Boston: Springer.

———. 2001. Fruit characteristics of species dispersed by the black lemur (*Eulemur macaco*) in the Lokobe Forest, Madagascar. *Biotropica* 33: 478–486.

Birkinshaw, C. R., and Colquhoun, I. 1998. Pollination of *Ravenala madagascariensis* and *Parkia madagascariensis* by *Eulemur macaco* in Madagascar. *Folia Primatologica* 69: 252–259.

Birkinshaw, C. R., and Colquhoun, I. C. 2003. Lemur food plants. In *The Natural History of Madagascar*, eds. S. M. Goodman and J. P. Benstead, pp. 1207–1220. Chicago: University of Chicago Press.

Blair, C., Heckman, K. L., Russell, A. L., and Yoder, A. D. 2014. Multilocus coalescent analyses reveal the demographic history and speciation patterns of mouse lemur sister species. *BMC Evolutionary Biology* 14: 57. https://doi.org/10.1186/1471-2148-14-57.

Blanchard, M. L., Furnell, S., Sellers, W. I., and Crompton, R. H. 2015. Locomotor flexibility in *Lepilemur* explained by habitat and biomechanics. *American Journal of Physical Anthropology* 156: 58–66.

Blanchy, S. 1995. Contribution de l'histoire à la compréhension de l'épidémiologie de la peste à Madagascar. *Histoire des Sciences Médicales* 24(4): 355–363.

Blanco, M. B. 2010. Reproductive biology of mouse and dwarf lemurs of eastern Madagascar, with an emphasis on brown mouse lemurs (*Microcebus rufus*) at Ranomafana National Park, a southeastern rainforest. PhD thesis, University of Massachusetts, Amherst.

Blanco, M. B., and Godfrey, L. R. 2014. Hibernation patterns of dwarf lemurs in the high altitude forest of eastern Madagascar. In *High Altitude Primates*, eds. S. Gursky, A. Krzton, and N. Grow, pp. 23–42. New York: Springer.

Blanco, M. B., and Klopfer, P. H. 2013. Timing of hibernation bouts in eastern dwarf lemurs. *American Journal of Physical Anthropology* 150, supplement 56: 82.

Blanco, M. B., and Rahalinarivo, V. 2010. First direct evidence of hibernation in an eastern dwarf lemur species (*Cheirogaleus crossleyi*) from the high-altitude forest of Tsinjoarivo, central-eastern Madagascar. *Naturwissenschaften* 97: 945–950.

Blanco, M. B., and Zehr, S. M. 2015. Striking longevity in a hibernating primate. *Journal of Zoology* 296: 177–188.

Blanco, M. B., Godfrey, L. R., Rakotondratsima, M., Rahalinarivo, V., Samonds, K. E., Raharison, J.-L., and Irwin, M. T. 2009. Discovery of sympatric dwarf lemur species in the high altitude forest of Tsinjoarivo, eastern Madagascar: Implications for biogeography and conservation. *Folia Primatologica* 80: 1–17.

Blanco, M. B., Elfawal, M. A., Durden, L. A., Beati, L., Xu, G., Godfrey, L. R., and Rich, S. M. 2013a. Genetic diversity of ixodid ticks parasitizing eastern mouse and dwarf lemurs in Madagascar, with descriptions of the larva, nymph, and male of *Ixodes lemuris* (Acari: Ixodidae). *Journal of Parasitology* 99: 11–18. https://doi.org/10.1645/GE-3183.1.

Blanco, M. B., Dausmann, K. H., Ranaivoarisoa, J. F., and Yoder, A. D. 2013b. Underground hibernation in a primate. *Scientific Reports* 3: 1768.

Blanco, M. B., Andriantsalohimisantatra, A. A., Rivoharison, T. V., and Andriambeloson, J. B. 2017. Evidence of prolonged torpor in Goodman's mouse lemurs at Ankafobe forest, central Madagascar. *Primates* 58: 31–37.

Blanco, M. B., Dausmann, K. H., Faherty, S. L., and Yoder, A. D. 2018. Tropical heterothermy is "cool": The expression of daily torpor and hibernation in primates. *Evolutionary Anthropology* 27: 147–161.

Blanco, M. B., Greene, L. K., Rasambainarivo, F., Toomey, E., Williams, R. C., Andrianandrasana, L., Larsen, P. A., and Yoder, A. D. 2020. Next-generation

technologies applied to age-old challenges in Madagascar. *Conservation Genetics* 21: 785–793. https://doi.org/10.1007/s10592-020-01296-0.
Bloesch, U. 1999. Fire as a tool in the management of a savanna/dry forest reserve in Madagascar. *Applied Vegetation Science* 2(1): 117–124.
Boettger, C. R. 1958. *Die Haustiere Afrikas*. Jena: Gustav Fischer Verlag.
Böhning-Gaese, K., Gaese, B. H., and Rabemanantsoa, S. B. 1995. Seed dispersal by frugivorous tree visitors in the Malagasy tree species *Commiphora guillaumini*. *Ecotropica* 1: 41–50.
Bohr, Y. E.-M. B., Giertz, P., Ratovonamana, Y. R., and Ganzhorn, J. U. 2011. Gray-brown mouse lemurs (*Microcebus griseorufus*) as an example of distributional constraints through increasing desertification. *International Journal of Primatology* 32: 901–913.
Bollen, A. 2003. Fruit-frugivore interactions in a Malagasy littoral forest: A community-wide approach of seed dispersal. PhD thesis, Antwerp University.
Bollen, A., and Donati, G. 2006. Conservation status of the littoral forest of south-eastern Madagascar: A review. *Oryx* 40: 57–66.
Bollen, A., and Van Elsacker, L. 2002. Feeding ecology of *Pteropus rufus* (Pteropodidae) in the littoral forest of Sainte Luce, SE Madagascar. *Acta Chiropterologica* 4: 33–47.
Bollen, A. [L.], Van Elsacker, L., and Ganzhorn, J. U. 2004a. Relations between fruits and disperser assemblages in a Malagasy littoral forest: A community-level approach. *Journal of Tropical Ecology* 20: 599–612.
Bollen, A. L., Van Elsacker, L., and Ganzhorn, J. U. 2004b. Tree dispersal strategies in the littoral forest of Sainte Luce (SE Madagascar). *Oecologia* 139: 604–616.
Bolnick, D. I., and Otto, S. P. 2013. The magnitude of local adaptation under genotype-dependent dispersal. *Ecology and Evolution* 3: 4722–4735. https://doi.org/10.1002/ece3.850.
Bolt, M., and Tennenhouse, E. 2017. Contact calling behavior in the male ring-tailed lemur (*Lemur catta*). *Ethology* 123: 614–616.
Bomford, E. 1976. In search of the aye-aye. *Wildlife* 18: 258–263.
———. 1981. On the road to Nosy Mangabe. *International Wildlife* 11: 20–24.
Bonadonna, G., Torti, V., Randrianarison, R. M., Gamba, M., Martinet, N., and Giacoma, C. 2014. Behavioral correlates of an extra-pair copulation in *Indri indri*. *Primates* 55: 119–123. https://doi.org/10.1007/s10329-013-0376-0.
Bonadonna, G., Torti, V., Sorrentino, V., Randrianarison, R. M., Zaccagno, M., Gamba, M., Tan, C. L., and Giacoma, C. 2017. Territory exclusivity and intergroup encounters in *Indri indri* upon methodological tuning. *European Zoological Journal* 84: 238–251. https://doi.org/10.1080/24750263.2017.1318184.
Bonadonna, G., Torti, V., De Gregorio, C., Valente, D., Randrianarison, R. M., Pozzi, L., Gamba, M., and Giacoma, C. 2019. Evidence of genetic monogamy in the lemur Indri (*Indri indri*). *American Journal of Primatology* 81(6): e2299. https://doi.org/10.1002/ajp.22993.
Bonadonna, G., Zaccagno, M., Torti, V., Valente, D., De Gregorio, C., Randrianarison, R. M., Tan, C. L., Gamba, M., and Giacoma, C. 2020. Intra- and intergroup spatial dynamics of a pair-living singing primate, *Indri indri*: A multiannual study of three *Indri* groups in Maromizaha Forest, Madagascar. *International Journal of Primatology* 41: 224–245. https://doi.org/10.1007/s10764-019-00127-5.
Bondarenco, A., Körtner, G., and Geiser, F. 2013. Some like it cold: Summer torpor by freetail bats in the Australian arid zone. *Journal of Comparative Physiology B: Biochemical, Systemic, and Environmental Physiology* 183: 1113–1122.
Bonner, T. I., Heinemann, R., and Todaro, G. J. 1980. Evolution of DNA sequences has been retarded in Malagasy primates. *Nature* 286: 420–423. https://doi.org/10.1038/286420a0.
Borgerson, C. 2013. The fitoaty: An unidentified carnivoran species from the Masoala Peninsula of Madagascar. *Madagascar Conservation and Development* 8: 81–85.
———. 2015. The effects of illegal hunting and habitat on two sympatric endangered species. *International Journal of Primatology* 36(7): 4–93.
———. 2016. Optimizing conservation policy: The importance of seasonal variation in hunting and meat consumption on the Masoala Peninsula of Madagascar. *Oryx* 50: 405–418.
Borgerson, C., Randrianasolo, J., Andraina, T., Anjaranirina, E., Randriamady, H., Merson, S., Dollar, L., and Golden, C. 2019a. Wildlife hunting in complex human-environmental systems: How understanding natural resource use and human welfare can improve conservation in the Ankarafantsika National Park, Madagascar. *Madagascar Conservation and Development* 14: 37–45.
Borgerson, C., Razafindrapaoly, B., Rajaona, D., Rasolofoniaina, B.J.R., and Golden, C. D. 2019b. Food insecurity and the unsustainable hunting of wildlife in a UNESCO World Heritage Site. *Frontiers in Sustainable Food Systems* 3: 99.
Bourhy, P., Collet, L., Brisse, S., and Picardeau, M. 2014. *Leptospira mayottensis* sp. nov., a pathogenic *Leptospira* species isolated from humans. *International Journal of Systematic and Evolutionary Microbiology* 64: 4061–4067.
Bourlière, F., and Petter-Rousseaux, A. 1966. Existence probable d'un rythme métabolique saisonnier chez les Cheirogaleinae (Lemuroidea). *Folia Primatologica* 4: 249–256.
Boursot, P., Din, W., Anand, R., Darviche, D., Dod, B., et al. 1996. Origin and radiation of the house mouse: Mitochondrial DNA phylogeny. *Journal of Evolutionary Biology* 9: 391–415.
Bradburd, G. S., Ralph, P. L., and Coop, G. M. 2013. Disentangling the effects of geographic and ecological isolation on genetic differentiation. *Evolution* 67: 3258–3273. https://doi.org/10.1111/evo.12193.
Bradburd, G. S., Ralph, P. L., and Coop, G. M. 2016. A spatial framework for understanding population structure and admixture. *PLoS Genetics* 12: e1005703. https://doi.org/10.1371/journal.pgen.1005703.
Brenneman, R. A., Johnson, S. E., Bailey, C. A., Ingraldi, C., Delmore, K. E., Wyman, T. M., Andriamaharoa, H. E., Ralainasolo, F. B., Ratsimbazafy, J. H., and Louis, E. E., Jr. 2011. Population genetics and abundance of the endangered grey-headed lemur *Eulemur cinereiceps* in south-east Madagascar: Assessing risks for fragmented and continuous populations. *Oryx* 46: 298–307. https://doi.org/10.1017/S0030605311000159.
Brenneman, R. [A.], Johnson, S., Bailey, C., Ingraldi, C., Delmore, K., et al. 2012. Population genetics and abundance of the endangered grey-headed lemur *Eulemur cinereiceps* in south-east Madagascar: Assessing risks for fragmented and continuous populations. *Oryx* 46(2): 298–307.
Brenneman, R. A., McLain, A. T., Taylor, J. M., Zaonarivelo, J. R., Lei, R., McGuire, S. M., Andriantompohavana, R., Rylands, A. B., and Louis, E. E., Jr. 2016. Genetic analysis of the *Indri* reveals no evidence of distinct subspecies. *International Journal of Primatology* 37: 460–477. https://doi.org/10.1007/s10764-016-9911-3.
Bridges, A. S., and Noss, A. J. 2011. Behavior and activity patterns. In *Camera Traps in Animal Ecology: Methods and Analyses*, eds. A. F. O'Connell, J. D. Nichols, and K. U. Karanth, pp. 57–69. Berlin: Springer.
Britt, A. 1997. Environmental influences on the behavioural ecology of the black-and-white ruffed lemur (*Varecia variegata variegata*, Kerr 1792). PhD thesis, University of Liverpool.
———. 1999. Observations on two sympatric, diurnal herpestids in the Betampona NR, eastern Madagascar. *Small Carnivore Conservation* 20: 14.
———. 2000. Diet and feeding behavior of the black-and-white ruffed lemur (*Varecia variegata variegata*) in the Betampona Reserve, Madagascar. *Folia Primatologica* 71: 133–141.
Britt, A., and Virkaitis, V. 2003. Brown-tailed mongoose *Salanoia concolor* in the Betampona Reserve, eastern Madagascar: Photographs and an ecological comparison with ring-tailed mongoose *Galidia elegans*. *Small Carnivore Conservation* 28: 1–3.
Britt, A., Axel, A., and Young, R. 1999. Brief surveys of two classified forests in Toamasina Province, eastern Madagascar. *Lemur News* 4: 25–27.
Britt, A., Welch, C., and Katz, A. 2000. Ruffed lemur re-stocking and conservation program update. *Lemur News* 5: 36–38.
Britt, A., Randriamandratonirina, N. J., Glasscock, K. D., and Iambana, B. R. 2002. Diet and feeding behaviour of *Indri indri* in a low-altitude rain forest. *Folia Primatologica* 73: 225–239.
Britt, A., Welch, C., Katz, A., Iambana, B., Porton, I., Junge, R., Crawford, G., Williams, C., and Haring, D. 2004. The re-stocking of captive-bred ruffed lemurs (*Varecia variegata variegata*) into the Betampona Reserve, Madagascar: Methodology and recommendations. *Biodiversity and Conservation* 13: 635–657.
Brockman, D. K. 2003. *Polyboroides radiatus* predation attempts on *Propithecus verreauxi*. *Folia Primatologica* 74: 71–74.
Brockman, D. K., Willis, M. S., and Karesh, W. B. 1987. Management and husbandry of ruffed lemurs, *Varecia variegata*, at the San Diego Zoo. II. Reproduction, pregnancy, parturition, litter size, infant care, and reintroduction of hand-raised infants. *Zoo Biology* 6: 349–363.
Brockman, D. K., Godfrey, L. R., Dollar, L. J, and Ratsirarson, J. 2008. Evidence of invasive *Felis silvestris* predation on *Propithecus verreauxi* at Beza Mahafaly Special Reserve, Madagascar. *International Journal of Primatology* 29: 135–152.
Bronikowski, A. M., Cords, M., Alberts, S. C., Altmann, J., Brockman, D. K., Fedigan, L. M., Pusey, A., Stoinski, T., Strier, K. B., and Morris, W. F. 2016. Female and male life tables for seven wild primate species. *Scientific Data* 3: 160006.
Brook, C. E., Bai, Y., Yu, E. O., Ranaivoson, H. C., Shin, H., Dobson, A. P., Metcalf, C.J.E., Kosoy, M. Y., and Dittmar, K. 2017. Elucidating transmission dynamics and

host-parasite-vector relationships for rodent-borne *Bartonella* spp. in Madagascar. *Epidemics* 20: 56–66.
Brook, C. E., Herrera, J. P., Borgerson, C., Fuller, E. C., Andriamahazoarivosoa, P., et al. 2018. Population viability and harvest sustainability for Madagascar lemurs. *Conservation Biology* 33: 99–111.
Brook, C. E., Ranaivoson, H. C., Andriafidison, D., Ralisata, M., Razafimanahaka, J. H., Héraud, J.-M., Dobson, A. P., and Metcalf, C. J. 2019. Population trends for two Malagasy fruit bats. *Biological Conservation* 234: 165–171.
Brooke, Z. M., Bielby, J., Nambiar, K., and Carbone, C. 2014. Correlates of research effort in carnivores: Body size, range size and diet matter. *PLoS One* 9: e93195.
Brouat, C., Rahelinirina, S., Loiseau, A., Rahalison, L., Rajerison, M., Laffly, D., Handschumacher, P., and Duplantier, J.-M. 2013. Plague circulation and population genetics of the reservoir *Rattus rattus*: The influence of topographic relief on the distribution of the disease within the Madagascan focus. *PLoS Neglected Tropical Diseases* 7: e2266. https://doi.org/10.1371/journal.pntd.0002266.
Brouat, C., Tollenaere, C., Estoup, A., Loiseau, A., Sommer, S., Soanandrasana, R., Rahalison, L., Rajerison, M., Piry, S., and Goodman, S. M. 2014. Invasion genetics of a human commensal rodent: The black rat *Rattus rattus* in Madagascar. *Molecular Ecology* 23: 4153–4167. https://doi.org/10.1111/mec.12848.
Brown, K. A., Farris, Z. J., Yesuf, G., Gerber, B. D., Rasambainarivo, F., et al. 2016. Modeling co-occurrence between toxic prey and naïve predators in an incipient invasion. *Biodiversity and Conservation* 25: 2723–2741.
Brucato, N., Fernandes, V., Mazières, S., Kusuma, P., Cox M., et al. 2018. The Comoros show the earliest Austronesian gene flow into the Swahili corridor. *American Journal of Human Genetics* 102(1): 58–68.
Brygoo, E. R. 1966. Epidémiologie de la peste à Madagascar. *Archives de l'Institut Pasteur de Madagascar* 35: 9–147.
Bublitz, D. C., Wright, P. C., Rasambainarivo, F. T., Arrigo-Nelson, S. J., Bodager, J. R., and Gillespie, T. R. 2015. Pathogenic enterobacteria in lemurs associated with anthropogenic disturbance. *American Journal of Primatology* 77(3): 330–337. https://doi.org/10.1002/ajp.22348.
Buck, C. L., and Barnes, B. M. 2000. Effects of ambient temperature on metabolic rate, respiratory quotient, and torpor in an arctic hibernator. *American Journal of Physiology* 279: 255–262.
Buckley, L. B., Khaliq, I., Swanson, D. L., and Hof, C. 2018. Does metabolism constrain bird and mammal ranges and predict shifts in response to climate change? *Ecology and Evolution* 8: 12375–12385.
Buckley, M. 2013. A molecular phylogeny of *Plesiorycteropus* reassigns the extinct mammalian order "Bibymalagasia." *PLoS One* 8(3): e59614. https://doi.org/10.1371/journal.pone.0059614.
Budnitz, N., and Dainis, K. 1975. *Lemur catta*: Ecology and behavior. In *Lemur Biology*, eds. I. Tattersall and R. W. Sussman, pp. 219–236. New York: Plenum Press.
Buesching, C., Heistermann, M., Hodges, J., and Zimmermann, E. 1998. Multimodal oestrus advertisement in a small nocturnal prosimian, *Microcebus murinus*. *Folia Primatologica* 69: 295–308.
Buettner-Janusch, J., and Tattersall, I. 1985. An annotated catalogue of Malagasy primates (Families Lemuridae, Indriidae, Daubentoniidae, Megaladapidae, Cheirogaleidae) in the collections of the American Museum of Natural History. *American Museum Novitates* 2834: 1–45.
Buffon, G.-L.L. 1789. *Histoire Naturelle, Générale et Particuliére.* Supplément, Tome 7. Paris: L'Imprimerie Royale.
Burke, R. J., and Lehman, S. M. 2013. Edge effects on body mass and habitat use in two sympatric species of mouse lemurs in a Madagascan tropical dry forest. *American Journal of Physical Anthropology* 150: 90.
Burney, D. A. 1999. Rates, patterns, and processes of landscape transformation and extinction in Madagascar. In *Extinction in Near Time*, ed. R.D.E. MacPhee, pp. 145–164. New York: Kluwer Academic/Plenum Press.
———. 2002. Sifaka predation by a large boa. *Folia Primatologica* 73: 144–145.
Burney, D. A., James, H. F., Grady, F. V., Rafamantanantsoa, J.-G., Ramilisonina, Wright, H. T., and Cowart, J. B. 1997. Environmental change, extinction and human activity: Evidence from caves in NW Madagascar. *Journal of Biogeography* 24: 755–767.
Burney, D. A., and Ramilisonina. 1999. The *kilopilopitsofy*, *kidoky*, and *bokyboky*: Accounts of strange animals from Belo-sur-Mer, Madagascar, and the megafaunal "extinction window." *American Anthropologist* 100: 957–966.
Burney, D. A., Burney, L. P., Godfrey, L. R., Jungers, W. L., Goodman, S. M., Wright, H. T., and Jull, A.J.T. 2004. A chronology for late prehistoric Madagascar. *Journal of Human Evolution* 47: 25–63.
Burney, D. A., Vasey, N., Godfrey, L. R., Ramilisonina, Jungers, W. L., Ramarolahy, M., and Raharivony, L. 2008. New findings at Andrahomana Cave, southeastern Madagascar. *Journal of Cave and Karst Studies* 70: 13–24.
Burney, D. [A.], Andriamialison, H., Andrianaivoarivelo, R., Bourne, S., Crowley, B., et al. 2020a. Subfossil lemur discoveries from the Beanka Protected Area in western Madagascar. *Quaternary Research* 93: 187–203. https://doi.org/10.1017/qua.2019.54.
Burney, D. [A.], Hume, J. P., Randalana, R., Andrianarivoarivelo, R. A., Griffiths, O. L., Middleton, G., Rasolondrainy, T., Ramilisonina, and Radimilahy, C. 2020b. Rock art from Andriamamelo Cave in the Beanka Protected Area of western Madagascar. *Journal of Island and Coastal Archaeology*. https://doi.org/10.1080/15564894.2020.1749735.
Burnham, D., Bearder, S. K., Cheyne, S. M., Dunbar, R.I.M., and Macdonald, D. W. 2012. Predation by mammalian carnivores on nocturnal primates: Is the lack of evidence support for the effectiveness of nocturnality as an antipredator strategy? *Folia Primatologica* 83: 236–251.
Burns, S. J., Godfrey, L. R., Faina, P., McGee, D., Hardt, B., Ranivoharimanana, L., and Randrianasy, T. 2016. Rapid human-induced landscape transformation in Madagascar at the end of the first millennium of the Common Era. *Quaternary Science Reviews* 134: 92–99.
Butler, P. M. 1978. Insectivora and Chiroptera. In *Evolution of African Mammals*, eds. V. J. Maglio and H.B.S. Cooke, pp. 56–68. Cambridge, MA: Harvard University Press.
CABI. 2019. *Rattus norvegicus*. Invasive Species Compendium. CAB International. www.cabi.org/isc.
Callmander, M. W., Phillipson, P. B., Schatz, G. E., Andriambololonera, S., Rabarimanarivo, M., Rakotonirina, N., Raharimampionona, J., Chatelain, C., Gautier, L., and Lowry, P. P. 2011. The endemic and non-endemic vascular flora of Madagascar updated. *Plant Ecology and Evolution* 144: 121–125.
Campbell, G. 2020. Commercialisation of cattle in Imperial Madagascar, 1795–1895. In *Animal Trade Histories in the Indian Ocean World*, eds. M. Chaiklin, P. Gooding, and G. Campbell, pp. 181–215. Cham: Palgrave Macmillan. https://doi.org/10.1007/978-3-030-42595-1_7.
Campbell, J. L., Eisemann, J. H., Williams, C. V., and Glenn, K. M. 2000. Description of the gastrointestinal tract of five lemur species: *Propithecus tattersalli*, *Propithecus verreauxi coquereli*, *Varecia variegata*, *Hapalemur griseus*, and *Lemur catta*. *American Journal of Primatology* 52: 133–142.
Campbell, J. L., Williams, C. V., and Eisemann, J. H. 2004. Use of total dietary fiber across four lemur species (*Propithecus verreauxi coquereli*, *Hapalemur griseus griseus*, *Varecia variegata*, and *Eulemur fulvus*): Does fiber type affect digestive efficiency? *American Journal of Primatology* 64: 323–335.
Campera, M. 2012. Eco-ethology of the red collared brown lemur (*Eulemur collaris*): Comparison between groups living in well preserved and degraded littoral forest fragments, in south-eastern Madagascar. Master's thesis, University of Pisa.
———. 2018. Ecological flexibility and conservation of Fleurette's sportive lemur, *Lepilemur fleuretae*, in the lowland rainforest of Ampasy, Tsitongambarika Protected Area. PhD thesis, Oxford Brookes University.
Campera, M., Serra, V., Balestri, M., Barresi, M., Ravaolahy, M., Randriatafika, F., and Donati, G. 2014. Effects of habitat quality and seasonality on ranging patterns of collared brown lemur (*Eulemur collaris*) in littoral forest fragments. *International Journal of Primatology* 35: 957–975.
Campera, M., Balestri, M., Chimienti, M., Nijman, V., Nekaris, K.A.I., and Donati, G. 2019. Temporal niche separation between the two ecologically similar nocturnal primates *Avahi meridionalis* and *Lepilemur fleuretae*. *Behavioral Ecology and Sociobiology* 73: 55. https://doi.org/10.1007/s00265-019-2664-1.
Campera, M., Santini, L., Balestri, M., Nekaris, K.A.I., and Donati, G. 2020. Elevation gradients of lemur abundance emphasise the importance of Madagascar's lowland rainforest for the conservation of endemic taxa. *Mammal Review* 50: 25–37.
Canale, C. I., Perret, M., Théry, M., and Henry, P. Y. 2011. Physiological flexibility and acclimation to food shortage in a heterothermic primate. *Journal of Experimental Biology* 214: 551–560.
Canale, C. I., Perret, M., and Henry, P. Y. 2012. Torpor use during gestation and lactation in a primate. *Naturwissenschaften* 99: 159–163.
Capanna, E., and Civitelli, M. V. 1971. Karyological analysis of four African populations of *Rattus rattus* (L.): A statement of the problem of chromosomal polymorphism in the black rat. *Bolletino di Zoologia* 38: 151–157.

Cardiff, S. G. 2006. Bat cave selection and conservation in Ankarana, northern Madagascar. MA thesis in Conservation Biology, Columbia University.

Cardiff, S. G., and Goodman, S. M. 2008. Natural history of the red owl (*Tyto soumagnei*) in dry deciduous tropical forest in Madagascar. *Wilson Journal of Ornithology* 120(4): 891–897.

Cardiff, S. G., and Jenkins, R.K.B. 2016. The bats of Madagascar: A conservation challenge. *Lessons in Conservation* 6: 80–108.

Cardiff, S. G., Ratrimomanarivo, F. H., Rembert, G., and Goodman, S. M. 2009. Hunting, roost disturbance, and roost persistence of bats at Ankarana, northern Madagascar. *African Journal of Ecology* 47(4): 640–649.

Cardinale, E., Bernard, C., Lecollinet, S., Rakotoharinome, V. M., Ravaomanana, J., et al. 2017. West Nile virus infection in horses, Indian Ocean. *Comparative Immunology, Microbiology and Infectious Diseases* 53: 45–49. https://doi.org/10.1016/j.cimid.2017.06.006.

Carleton, M. D. 1994. Systematic studies of Madagascar's endemic rodents (Muroidea: Nesomyinae): Revision of the genus *Eliurus*. *American Museum Novitates* 3087: 1–55.

Carleton, M. D., and Goodman, S. M. 1996. Systematic studies of Madagascar's endemic rodents (Muroidea: Nesomyinae): A new genus and species from the Central Highlands. In A floral and faunal inventory of the eastern slopes of the Réserve Naturelle Intégrale d'Andringitra, Madagascar: With reference to elevational variation, ed. S. M. Goodman. *Fieldiana: Zoology*, new ser., 85: 231–256.

Carleton, M. D., and Goodman, S. M. 1998. New taxa of nesomyine rodents (Muroidea: Muridae) from Madagascar's northern highlands, with taxonomic comments on previously described forms. In A floral and faunal inventory of the Réserve Spéciale d'Anjanaharibe-Sud, Madagascar: With reference to elevational variation, ed. S. M. Goodman. *Fieldiana: Zoology*, new ser., 90: 163–200.

Carleton, M. D., and Goodman, S. M. 2000. The rodents of the Parc National de Marojejy, Madagascar. In A floral and faunal inventory of the Parc National de Marojejy, Madagascar: With reference to elevational variation, ed. S. M. Goodman. *Fieldiana: Zoology*, new ser., 97: 231–263.

Carleton, M. D., and Goodman, S. M. 2003. Rodentia: *Brachytarsomys*, white-tailed tree rats, *antsangy*. In *The Natural History of Madagascar*, eds. S. M. Goodman and J. P. Benstead, pp. 1368–1370. Chicago: University of Chicago Press.

Carleton, M. D., and Goodman, S. M. 2007. A new species of the *Eliurus majori* complex (Rodentia: Muroidea: Nesomyidae) from south-central Madagascar, with remarks on emergent species groupings in the genus *Eliurus*. *American Museum Novitates* 3547: 1–21.

Carleton, M. D., and Musser, G. G. 1984. Muroid rodents. In *Orders and Families of Recent Mammals of the World*, eds. S. Anderson and J. K. Jones, Jr., pp. 289–379. New York: Wiley.

Carleton, M. D., and Schmidt, D. F. 1990. Systematic studies of Madagascar's endemic rodents (Muroidea: Nesomyinae): An annotated gazetteer of collecting localities of known forms. *American Museum Novitates* 2987: 1–36.

Carleton, M. D., Goodman, S. M., and Rakotondravony, D. 2001. A new species of tufted-tailed rat, genus *Eliurus* (Muridae: Nesomyinae), from western Madagascar, with notes on the distribution of *E. myoxinus*. *Proceedings of the Biological Society of Washington* 114: 972–987.

Carleton, M. D., Smeenk, C., Angermann, R., and Goodman, S. M. 2014. Taxonomy of nesomyine rodents (Muroidea: Nesomyidae: Nesomyinae): Designation of lectotypes and restriction of type localities for species-group taxa in the genus *Nesomys* Peters. *Proceedings of the Biological Society of Washington* 126: 414–455.

Carrai, V., Borgognini-Tarli, S. M., Huffman, M. A., and Bardi, M. 2003. Increase in tannin consumption by sifaka (*Propithecus verreauxi verreauxi*) females during the birth season: A case for self-medication in prosimians? *Primates* 44: 61–66.

Cartagena-Matos, B., Gregório, I., Morais, M., and Ferreira, E. 2017. Trends in the extinction of carnivores in Madagascar. *Animal Biodiversity and Conservation* 40: 103–114.

Carter, A. M., Goodman, S. M., and Enders, A. C. 2008. Female reproductive tract and placentation in sucker-footed bats (Chiroptera: Myzopodidae) endemic to Madagascar. *Placenta* 29: 484–491.

Carter, C. S., and Getz, L. L. 1993. Monogamie bei der Präriewühlmaus. *Spektrum der Wissenschaft* 8: 62–67.

Cartmill, M. 1975. Strepsirhine basicranial structures and the affinities of the Cheirogaleidae. In *Phylogeny of the Primates: A Multidisciplinary Approach*, eds W. P. Luckett and F. Szalay, pp. 313–354. New York: Plenum Press.

Cartmill, M., Hylander, W. L., and Shafland, J. 1987. *Human Structure*. Cambridge, MA: Harvard University Press.

Cavalli-Sforza, L. L. 1966. Population structure and human evolution. *Proceedings of the Royal Society of London B: Biological Sciences*, 164: 362–379. https://doi.org/10.1098/rspb.1966.0038.

Chaline, J., Mein, P., and Petter, F. 1977. Les grandes lignes d'une classification évolutive des Muroidea. *Mammalia* 41: 245–252.

Chan, L. M., Goodman, S. M., Nowak, M. D., Weisrock, D. W., and Yoder, A. D. 2011. Increased population sampling confirms low genetic divergence among *Pteropus* (Chiroptera: Pteropodidae) fruit bats of Madagascar and other western Indian Ocean islands. *PLoS Currents* 3: RRN1226. https://doi.org/10.1371/currents.RRN1226.

Chanteau, S. (coord. scientific). 2006. *Atlas de la peste à Madagascar*. Paris: Editions IRD-Institut Pasteur-AUF.

Chapman, N. G., and Chapman, D. I. 1980. The distribution of fallow deer: A worldwide review. *Mammal Review* 10: 61–138.

Charles-Dominique, P., and Hladik, C. M. 1971. Le lépilemur du sud de Madagascar: Ecologie, alimentation, et vie sociale. *La Terre et la Vie* 25: 3–66.

Charles-Dominique, P., and Petter, J.-J. 1980. Ecology and social life of *Phaner furcifer*. In *Nocturnal Malagasy Primates: Ecology, Physiology, and Behavior*, eds. P. Charles-Dominique, H. M. Cooper, A. Hladik, C. M. Hladik, E. Pagès, G. F. Pariente, A. Petter-Rousseaux, J.-J. Petter, and A. Schilling, pp. 75–96. New York: Academic Press.

Charpentier, M.J.E., and Drea, C. M. 2013. Victims of infanticide and conspecific bite wounding in a female-dominant primate: A long-term study. *PLoS One* 8: e82830. https://doi.org/10.1371/journal.pone.0082830, 2013.

Charpentier, M.J.E., Boulet, M., and Drea, C. M. 2008. Smelling right: The scent of male lemurs advertises genetic quality and relatedness. *Molecular Ecology* 17: 3225–3233. https://doi.org/10.1111/j.1365-294X.2008.03831.x.

Charrier, A., Hladik, A., and Simmen, B. 2007. Stratégie alimentaire et dominance des femelles propithèque de verreaux (*Propithecus v. verreauxi*) dans la forêt à Didiereaceae du sud de Madagascar. *Revue d'Ecologie* (*La Terre et la Vie*) 62: 257–263.

Chatterjee, H. J., Ho, S.Y.W., Barnes, I., and Groves, C. 2009. Estimating the phylogeny and divergence times of primates using a supermatrix approach. *BMC Evolutionary Biology* 9: 259. https://doi.org/10.1186/1471-2148-9-259.

Cheke, A. 2010. The timing of arrival of humans and their commensal animals on western Indian Ocean oceanic islands. *Phelsuma* 18: 38–69.

Chen, K. S., Li, J. Q., Rasoarahona, J., Fousseni, F., and Manjaribe, C. 2015. Diet and seed dispersal by *Eulemur coronatus* (Gray, Primates and Lemuridae) in the Amber Mountain National Park, Madagascar. *International Journal of Biology* 7: 20–31.

Chen, K. S., Li, J. Q., Rasoarahona, J., and Folega, F. 2016. Diet and effects of Sanford's brown lemur (*Eulemur sanfordi*, Archbold 1932) gut-passage on the germination of plant species in Amber forest, Madagascar. *Zoological Studies* 55: 1–13.

Chen, M., Tewes, M. E., Pei, K. J., and Grassman, L. I., Jr. 2009. Activity patterns and habitat use of sympatric small carnivores in southern Taiwan. *Mammalia* 73: 20–26.

Chen, S., Lin, B.-Z., Baig, M., Mitra, B., Lopes, R. J., et al. 2009. Zebu cattle are an exclusive legacy of the South Asia Neolithic. *Molecular Biology and Evolution* 27(1): 1–6.

Chesser, R. K. 1991. Gene diversity and female philopatry. *Genetics* 127: 437–447.

Chikhi, L., and Beaumont, M. A. 2005. Modelling human genetic history. In *The Encyclopedia of Genetics, Genomics, Proteomics and Bioinformatics*, eds. M. J. Dunn, L. B. Jorde, P.F.R. Little, and S. Subramaniam. New York: John Wiley.

Chikhi, L., Sousa, V. C., Luisi, P., Goossens, B., and Beaumont, M. A. 2010. The confounding effects of population structure, genetic diversity and the sampling scheme on the detection and quantification of population size changes. *Genetics* 186: 983–995. https://doi.org/10.1534/genetics.110.118661.

Chikhi, L., Rodríguez, W., Grusea, S., Santos, P., Boitard, S., and Mazet, O. 2018. The IICR (inverse instantaneous coalescence rate) as a summary of genomic diversity: Insights into demographic inference and model choice. *Heredity* 120: 13–24. https://doi.org/10.1038/s41437-017-0005-6.

Choudhury, A. 2013. *The Mammals of North East India*. Guwahati: Gibbon Books and the Rhino Foundation.

Choudhury, A., Duckworth, J. W., Timmins, R., Chutipong, W., Willcox, D.H.A., Rahman, H., Ghimirey, Y., and Mudappa, D. 2015. *Viverricula indica*. The IUCN Red List of Threatened Species 2015: e.T41710A45220632.

Christidis, L., Goodman, S. M., Naughton, K., and Appleton, B. 2014. Insights into the evolution of a cryptic radiation of bats: Dispersal and ecological radiation of Malagasy *Miniopterus* (Chiroptera: Miniopteridae). *PLoS One* 9(3): e92440. https://doi.org/10.1371/journal.pone.0092440.

Chuang, S., and Lee, L. 1997. Food habits of three carnivore species (*Viverricula indica*, *Herpestes uva*, and *Melogale moschata*) in Fushan Forest, northern Taiwan. *Journal of Zoology* 243: 71–79.

Clarke, T. A., Gray, O., Gould, L., and Burrell, A. S. 2015 Genetic diversity of the ring-tailed lemur (*Lemur catta*) in south-central Madagascar. *Folia Primatologica* 86: 76–84. https://doi.org/10.1159/000369386.

Colquhoun, I. C. 1993. The socioecology of *Eulemur macaco*: A preliminary report. In *Lemur Social Systems and Their Ecological Basis*, eds. P. M. Kappeler and J. U. Ganzhorn, pp. 11–23. New York: Plenum Press.

———. 1998. Cathemeral behavior of *Eulemur macaco macaco* at Ambato Massif, Madagascar. *Folia Primatologica* 69: 22–34.

———. 2005. Primates in the forest: Sakalava ethnoprimatology and synecological relations with black lemurs at Ambato Massif, Madagascar. In *Commensalism and Conflict: The Human–Primate Interface*, eds. J. D. Paterson, and J. Wallis, pp. 90–117. Norman: American Society of Primatologists.

Comeron, J. M. 2017. Background selection as null hypothesis in population genomics: insights and challenges from *Drosophila* studies. *Philosophical Transactions of the Royal Society B: Biological Sciences* 372: 20160471. https://doi.org/10.1098/rstb.2016.0471.

Cook, J. M., Trevelyan, R., Walls, S. S., Hatcher, M., and Rakotondraparany, F. 1991. The ecology of *Hypogeomys antimena*, an endemic Madagascan rodent. *Journal of Zoology* 224: 191–200.

Cooper, Z. A. 2017. Sleeping site selection in two sympatric species of lemur: *Avahi meridionalis* and *Lepilemur fleuretae*. MS thesis, Oxford Brookes University.

Corbet, G. B., and Hill, J. E. 1991. *A World List of Mammalian Species*. 3rd ed. London: British Museum (Natural History) Publications.

Corbin, G., and Schmid, J. 1995. Insect secretions determine habitat use patterns by a female lesser mouse lemur (*Microcebus murinus*). *American Journal of Primatology* 37: 317–324.

Cornelis, G., Vernochet, C., Malicorne, S., Souquere, S., Tzika, A. C., et al. 2014. Retroviral envelope syncytin capture in an ancestrally diverged mammalian clade for placentation in the primitive Afrotherian tenrecs. *Proceedings of the National Academy of Sciences of the USA* 111: E4332-E4341. https://doi.org/10.1073/pnas.1412268111.

Cornuet, J. M., and Luikart, G. 1996. Description and power analysis of two tests for detecting recent population bottlenecks from allele frequency data. *Genetics* 144: 2001–2014.

Corpa, J., García-Quirós, A., Casares, M., Gerique, A., Carbonell, M., Gómez-Muñoz, M., Uzal, F. A., and Ortega, J. 2013. Encephalomyelitis by *Toxoplasma gondii* in a captive fossa (*Cryptoprocta ferox*). *Veterinary Parasitology* 193: 281–283.

Couch, L., Laakkonen, J., Goodman, S. M., and Duszynski, D. W. 2011. Two new eimerians (Apicomplexa) from insectivorous mammals in Madagascar. *Journal of Parasitology* 97(2): 293–296.

Cracraft, J. 1989. Speciation and its ontology: The empirical consequences of alternative species concepts for understanding patterns and processes of differentiation. In *Speciation and Its Consequences*, eds. D. Otte and J. A. Endler, pp. 27–59. Sunderland: Sinauer.

Craul, M., Zimmermann, E., Rasoloharijaona, S., Randrianambinina, B., and Radespiel, U. 2007. Unexpected species diversity of Malagasy primates (*Lepilemur* spp.) in the same biogeographical zone: A morphological and molecular approach with the description of two new species. *BMC Evolutionary Biology* 7: 83. https://doi.org/10.1186/1471-2148-7-83.

Craul, M., Radespiel, U., Rasolofoson, D. W., Rakotondratsimba, G., Rakotonirainy, O., et al. 2008. Large rivers do not always act as species barriers for *Lepilemur* sp. *Primates* 49: 211–218.

Craul, M., Chikhi, L., Sousa, V., Olivieri, G. L., Rabesandratana, A., Zimmermann, E., and Radespiel, U. 2009. Influence of forest fragmentation on an endangered large-bodied lemur in northwestern Madagascar. *Biological Conservation* 142: 2862–2871. https://doi.org/10.1016/j.biocon.2009.05.026.

Crawford, G., Puschner, B., Affolter, V., Stalis, I., Davidson, A., Baker, T., Tahara, J., Jolly, A., and Ostapak, S. 2015. Systemic effects of *Leucaena leucocephala* ingestion on ringtailed lemurs (*Lemur catta*) at Berenty Reserve, Madagascar. *American Journal of Primatology* 77: 633–641.

Crofoot, M. C. 2012. Why mob? Reassessing the costs and benefits of primate predator harassment. *Folia Primatologica* 83: 252–272.

Crottini, A., Madsen, O., Poux, C., Strauss, A., Vieites, D. R., and Vences, M. 2012. Vertebrate time-tree elucidates the biogeographic pattern of a major biotic change around the K-T boundary in Madagascar. *Proceedings of the National Academy of Sciences of the USA* 109: 5358–5363.

Crovella, S., and Rumpler, Y. 1992. Confirmation of the specific status of *Hapalemur aureus* (Primates, Strepsirhini) by restriction genomic DNA banding patterns. *Human Evolution* 7: 63–67. https://doi.org/10.1007/BF02437454.

Crovella, S., Montagnon, D., and Rumpler, Y. 1993. Highly repeated DNA analysis and systematics of the Lemuridae, a family of Malagasy prosimians. *Primates* 34: 61–69.

Crovella, S., Montagnon, D., Rakotosamimanana, B., and Rumpler, Y. 1994. Molecular biology and systematics of an extinct lemur: *Pachylemur insignis*. *Primates* 35: 519–522. https://doi.org/10.1007/BF02381961.

Crowley, B. E. 2010. A refined chronology of prehistoric Madagascar and the demise of the megafauna. *Quaternary Science Reviews* 29(19–20): 2591–2603. https://doi.org/10.1016/j.quascirev.2010.06.030.

Crowley, B. E., and Godfrey, L. R. 2013. Why all those spines? Anachronistic defences in the Didiereoideae against now extinct lemurs. *South African Journal of Science* 109(1/2): 1346.

Crowley, B. E., and Godfrey, L. R. 2019. Strontium isotopes support small home ranges for extinct lemurs. *Frontiers in Ecology and Evolution* 7: 490.

Crowley, B. E., and Samonds, K. E. 2013. Stable carbon isotope values confirm a recent increase in grasslands in northwestern Madagascar. *Holocene* 23(7): 1066–1073. https://doi.org/10.1177/0959683613484675.

Crowley, B. E., Godfrey, L. R. and Irwin, M. T. 2011. A glance to the past: Subfossils, stable isotopes, seed dispersal, and lemur species loss in southern Madagascar. *American Journal of Primatology* 73(1): 25–37. https://doi.org/10.1002/ajp.20817.

Crowley, B. E., Godfrey, L. R., Bankoff, R. J., Perry, G. H., Culleton, B. J., Kennett, D. J., Sutherland, M. R., Samonds, K. E., and Burney, D. A. 2017. Island-wide aridity did not trigger recent megafaunal extinctions in Madagascar. *Ecography* 40: 901–912.

Crowley, B. E., Castro, I., Soarimalala, V., and Goodman, S. M. 2018. Isotopic evidence for niche partitioning and the influence of anthropogenic disturbance on endemic and introduced rodents in central Madagascar. *Science of Nature* 105(7–8): 44.

Cuozzo, F. P., and Sauther, M. L. 2006. Severe wear and tooth loss in wild ring-tailed lemurs (*Lemur catta*): A function of dental structure, feeding ecology, and life history. *Journal of Human Evolution* 51: 490–505. https://doi.org/10.1016/j.jhevol.2006.07.001.

Cuozzo, F. P., Sauther, M. L., Gould, L., Sussman, R. W., Villers, L. M., and Lent, C. 2010. Variation in dental wear and tooth loss in known-aged, older ring-tailed lemurs (*Lemur catta*): A comparison between wild and captive individuals. *American Journal of Primatology* 72: 1026–1037. https://doi.org/10.1002/ajp.20846.

Cuozzo, F. P., Head, B. R, Sauther, M. L., Ungar, P. S., and O'Mara T. S. 2014. Sources of tooth wear variation in life among known-aged wild ring-tailed lemurs (*Lemur catta*) at the Bezà Mahafaly Special Reserve, Madagascar. *American Journal of Primatology* 76: 1037–1048. https://doi.org/10.1002/ajp.22291.

Currat, M., Ray, N., and Excoffier, L. 2004. SPLATCHE: A program to simulate genetic diversity taking into account environmental heterogeneity. *Molecular Ecology Notes* 4: 139–142. https://doi.org/10.1046/j.1471-8286.2003.00582.x.

Currat, M., Arenas, M., Quilodràn, C. S., Excoffier, L., and Ray, N. 2019. SPLATCHE3: Simulation of serial genetic data under spatially explicit evolutionary scenarios including long-distance dispersal. *Bioinformatics* 35: 4480–4483. https://doi.org/10.1093/bioinformatics/btz311.

Curtis, D. J. 1997. The mongoose lemur (*Eulemur mongoz*): A study in behaviour and ecology. PhD thesis, University of Zürich.

———. 2007. Cathemerality in lemurs. In *Lemurs: Ecology and Adaptation*, eds. L. Gould and M. L. Sauther, pp. 133–157. Boston: Springer US.

Curtis, D. J., and Donati, G. 2012. Is temporal plasticity in lemurs a strategy for dealing with unpredictable or predictable, seasonal environments? In *Leaping Ahead*, eds. J. Masters, M. Gamba, and F. Génin, pp. 41–48. New York: Springer.

Curtis, D. J., and Feistner, A.T.C. 1994. Positional behaviour in captive aye-ayes (*Daubentonia madagascariensis*). *Folia Primatologica* 62: 155–159.

Curtis, D. J., and Rasmussen, M. A. 2006. The evolution of cathemerality in primates and other mammals: A comparative and chronoecological approach. *Folia Primatologica* 77: 178–193.

Curtis, D. J., and Zaramody, A. 1998. Group size, home range use, and seasonal variation in the ecology of *Eulemur mongoz*. *International Journal of Primatology* 19: 811–835.

Curtis, D. J., and Zaramody, A. 1999. Social structure and seasonal variation in the behaviour of *Eulemur mongoz*. *Folia Primatologica* 70: 79–96.

Curtis, D. J., Velo, A., Raheliarisoa, E. O., Zaramody, A., and Müller, P. 1998. Surveys on *Propithecus verreauxi deckeni*, a melanistic variant, and *P. v. coronatus* in north-west Madagascar. *Oryx* 32: 157–164.

Curtis, D. J., Zaramody, A., and Martin, R. D. 1999. Cathemerality in the mongoose lemur, *Eulemur mongoz*. *American Journal of Primatology* 47: 279–298.
Curtis, D. J., Zaramody, A., Green, D. I., and Pickard, A. R. 2000. Non-invasive monitoring of reproductive status in wild mongoose lemurs (*Eulemur mongoz*). *Reproduction, Fertility and Development* 12: 21–29.
Cushman, S. A. 2006. Effects of habitat loss and fragmentation on amphibians: A review and prospectus. *Biological Conservation* 128: 231–240. https://doi.org/10.1016/j.biocon.2005.09.031.
Cuvier, F. 1822. Du Sanglier à masque et des Phacochoeres. *Mémoires du Muséum d'Histoire Naturelle* 8: 447–455.
Dague, C., and Petter, J.-J. 1988. Observations sur le *Lemur rubriventer* dans son milieu naturel. In *L'Equilibre des écosystèmes forestiers à Madagascar*, eds. L. Rakotovao, V. Barre, and J. Sayer, pp. 78–89. Gland, Switzerland, and Cambridge, UK: IUCN.
Dammhahn, M., and Goodman, S. M. 2013. Trophic niche differentiation and microhabitat utilization revealed by stable isotope analyses in a Malagasy dry forest bat community. *Journal of Tropical Ecology* 30: 97–109.
Dammhahn, M., and Kappeler, P. M. 2005. Social system of *Microcebus berthae*, the world's smallest primate. *International Journal of Primatology* 26: 407–435.
Dammhahn, M., and Kappeler, P. M. 2008a. Comparative feeding ecology of sympatric *Microcebus berthae* and *M. murinus*. *International Journal of Primatology* 29: 1567–1589.
Dammhahn, M., and Kappeler, P. M. 2008b. Small-scale coexistence of two mouse lemur species (*Microcebus berthae* and *M. murinus*) within a homogeneous competitive environment. *Oecologia* 157: 473–483.
Dammhahn, M., and Kappeler, P. M. 2009. Females go where the food is: Does the socio-ecological model explain variation in social organisation of solitary foragers? *Behavioral Ecology and Sociobiology* 63: 939–952.
Dammhahn, M., and Kappeler, P. M. 2010. Scramble or contest competition over food in solitarily foraging mouse lemurs (*Microcebus* spp.): New insights from stable isotopes. *American Journal of Physical Anthropology* 141: 181–189.
Dammhahn, M., Schäffler, L., Fichtel, C., and Kappeler, P. M. 2009. Rapid lemur survey in northern Menabe. *Lemur News* 14: 13–16.
Dammhahn, M., Soarimalala, V., and Goodman, S. M. 2013. Trophic niche differentiation and microhabitat utilization in a species-rich montane forest small mammal community of eastern Madagascar. *Biotropica* 45: 111–118.
Dammhahn, M., Rakotondramanana, C. F., and Goodman, S. M. 2015. Coexistence of morphologically similar bats (family Vespertilionidae) on Madagascar: Stable isotopes reveal fine-grained niche differentiation among cryptic species. *Journal of Tropical Biology* 31: 153–164.
Dammhahn, M., Randriamoria, T. M., and Goodman, S. M. 2017. Broad and flexible stable isotope niches in invasive non-native *Rattus* spp. in anthropogenic and natural habitats of central eastern Madagascar. *BMC Ecology* 17(1):16. https://doi.org/10.1186/s12898-017-0125-0.
Daniels, H. L. 1984. Oxygen consumption in *Lemur fulvus*: Deviation from the ideal model. *Journal of Mammalogy* 65: 584–592.
Dausmann, K. H. 2010. Effective predation defence in *Cheirogaleus medius*. *Lemur News* 15: 19–20.
———. 2014. Flexible patterns in energy savings: Heterothermy in primates. *Journal of Zoology* 292: 101–111.
Dausmann, K. H., and Blanco, M. B. 2016. Possible causes and consequences of different hibernation patterns in *Cheirogaleus* species. In *Dwarf and Mouse Lemurs of Madagascar: Biology, Behavior, and Conservation Biogeography of the Cheirogaleidae*, eds. S. Lehman, U. Radespiel, and E. Zimmermann, pp. 335–349. Cambridge: Cambridge University Press.
Dausmann, K. H., and Glos, J. 2015. No energetic benefits from sociality in tropical hibernation. *Functional Ecology* 29: 498–505.
Dausmann, K. H., Glos, J., Ganzhorn, J. U., and Heldmaier, G. 2004. Hibernation in a tropical primate. *Nature* 429: 825–826.
Dausmann, K. H., Glos, J., Ganzhorn, J. U., and Heldmaier, G. 2005. Hibernation in the tropics: Lessons from a primate. *Journal of Comparative Physiology B: Biochemical, Systemic, and Environmental Physiology* 175: 147–155.
Dausmann, K. H., Glos, J., and Heldmaier, G. 2009. Energetics of tropical hibernation. *Journal of Comparative Physiology B: Biochemical, Systemic, and Environmental Physiology* 179: 345–357.
Dausmann, K. H., Nowack, J., Kobbe, S., and Mzilikazi, N. 2012. Afrotropical heterothermy: A continuum of possibilities. In *Living in a Seasonal World*, eds. T. Ruf, C. Bieber, W. Arnold, and E. Millesi, pp. 13–27. Berlin, Heidelberg, and New York: Springer.
Dausmann, K. H., Levesque, D. L., Wein, J., and Nowack, J. 2020. Ambient temperature cycles affect daily torpor and hibernation patterns in Malagasy tenrecs. *Frontiers in Physiology* 11: 522.
Davis, J. M., and Stamps, J. A. 2004. The effect of natal experience on habitat preferences. *Trends in Ecology and Evolution* 19: 411–416. https://doi.org/10.1016/j.tree.2004.04.006.
Day, S. R., Ramarokoto, R.E.A.F., Sitzmann, B. D., Radriamboahanginjatovo, R., Ramanankirija, H., Randrianindrina, V.R.A., Ravololonarivo, G., and Louis, E. E., Jr. 2009. Re-introduction of diademed sifaka (*Propithecus diadema*) and black and white ruffed lemurs (*Varecia variegata editorum*) at Analamazaotra Special Reserve, eastern Madagascar. *Lemur News* 14: 32–37.
Dearing, M. D. 2013. Temperature-dependent toxicity in mammals with implications for herbivores: A review. *Journal of Comparative Physiology B: Biochemical, Systemic, and Environmental Physiology* 183: 43–50.
Decary, R. 1950. *La faune malgache, son rôle dans les croyances et les usages indigènes*. Paris: Payot.
Dechambre, E. 1935. Observations sur les makis de la ménagerie du Jardin des Plantes. *Bulletin du Muséum National d'Histoire Naturelle*, Paris, série 2, 7(6): 315–319.
———. 1951. Origine des animaux domestiques de Madagascar. *La Terre et la Vie* 4: 187–196.
Decher, J., Hoffmann, A., Schaer, J., Norris, R. W., Kadjo, B., Astrin, J., Monadjem, A., and Hutterer, R. 2015. Bat diversity in the Simandou Mountain range of Guinea, with the description of a new white-winged vespertilionid. *Acta Chiropterologica* 17: 255–282.
Dehgan, A. O. 2003. The behavior of extinction: Predicting the incidence and local extinction of lemurs in fragmented habitats of southeastern Madagascar. PhD thesis, University of Chicago.
Delmore, K. E., Brenneman, R. A., Lei, R., Bailey, C. A., Brelsford, A., Louis, E. E., Jr., and Johnson, S. E. 2013. Clinal variation in a brown lemur (*Eulemur* spp.) hybrid zone: Combining morphological, genetic and climatic data to examine stability. *Journal of Evolutionary Biology* 26: 1677–1690.
DelPero, M., Crovella, S., Cervella, P., Ardito, G., and Rumpler, Y. 1995. Phylogenetic relationships among Malagasy lemurs as revealed by mitochondrial DNA sequence analysis. *Primates* 36: 431–440. https://doi.org/10.1007/BF02382865.
DelPero, M., Pozzi, L., and Masters, J. C. 2006. A composite molecular phylogeny of living lemuroid primates. *Folia Primatologica* 77: 434–445.
Demos, T. C., Webala, P. W., Bartonjo, M., and Patterson, B. D. 2018. Hidden diversity of African yellow house bats (Vespertilionidae, *Scotophilus*): Insights from multilocus phylogenetics and lineage delimitation. *Frontiers in Ecology and Evolution* 6: 86.
Demos, T. C., Webala, P. W., Kerbis Peterhans, J. C., Goodman, S. M., Bartonjo, M., and Patterson, B. D. 2019. Molecular phylogenetics of slit-faced bats (Chiroptera: Nycteridae) reveal deeply divergent African lineages. *Journal of Zoological Systematics and Evolutionary Research*. https://doi.org/10.1111/jzs.12313.
Demos, T. C., Webala, P. W., Lutz, H. L., Kerbis Peterhans, J. C., Goodman, S. M., Cortes-Delgado, N., Bartonjo, M., and Patterson, B. P. 2020. Multilocus phylogeny of a cryptic radiation of Afrotropical longfingered bats (Chiroptera, Miniopteridae). *Zoologica Scripta* 49(1): 1–13.
Demos, T. C., Goodman, S. M., and Patterson, B. D. 2021. The status of *Nycteris madagascariensis* G. Grandidier, 1937, a reputed endemic to Madagascar. *Acta Chiropterologica* 23(1): 21–32.
Dene, H., Goodman, M., Prychodko, W., and Moore, G. W. 1976. Immunodiffusion systematics of the primates. III. The strepsirhini. *Folia Primatologica* 25: 35–61. https://doi.org/10.1159/000155706.
Dene, H., Goodman, M., and Prychodko, W. 1980. Immunodiffusion systematics of the Primates. IV: Lemuriformes. *Mammalia* 44: 211–224. https://doi.org/10.1515/mamm.1980.44.2.211.
Deppe, A. M., Randriamiarisoa, M., Schutte, K., and Wright, P. C. 2007. A brief lemur survey of the Ranomafana Andringitra corridor region in Tolongoina, southeast Madagascar. *Lemur News* 12: 43–46.
Deppe, A. M., Randriamiarisoa, M., Kasparak, A. H., and Wright, P. C. 2008. Predation on the brown mouse lemur (*Microcebus rufus*) by a diurnal carnivore, the ring-tailed mongoose (*Galidia elegans*). *Lemur News* 13: 17–18.
Deschamps, H. 1960. *L'Histoire de Madagascar*. Paris: Berger-Levrault.
DeSisto, C., Park, D. S., Davis, C. C., Ramananjato, V., Tonos, J. M., and Razafindratsima, O. H. 2020. An invasive species spread by endangered lemurs impacts rainforest structure in Madagascar. *Biological Invasions* 22: 2845–2858.
Dew, J. L., and Wright, P. 1998. Frugivory and seed dispersal by four species of primates in Madagascar's eastern rain forest. *Biotropica* 30: 425–437.

Dewar, R. E. 1984. Extinctions in Madagascar: The loss of the subfossil fauna. In *Quaternary Extinctions*, eds. P. S. Martin and R. G. Klein, pp. 574–593. Tucson: University of Arizona Press.

Dewar, R. E., and Rakotovololona, S. 1992. La chasse aux subfossiles: Les preuves du onzième siècle au treizième siècle. *Taloha* 11: 4–15.

Dewar, R. E., and Richard, A. F. 2007. Evolution in the hypervariable environment of Madagascar. *Proceedings of the National Academy of Sciences of the USA* 104: 13723–13727.

Dewar, R. E., and Wright, H. T. 1993. The culture history of Madagascar. *Journal of World Prehistory* 7: 417–466.

Dewar, R. E., Radimilahy, C., Wright, H. T., Jacobs, Z., Kelly, G. O., and Berna, F. 2013. Stone tools and foraging in northern Madagascar challenge Holocene extinction models. *Proceedings of the National Academy of Sciences of the USA* 110(31): 12583–12588. https://doi.org/10.1073/pnas.1306100110.

de Winter, I. I., Gollner, A., and Akom, E. 2013. Diet overlap of *Propithecus verreauxi* and *Eulemur rufifrons* during the late dry season in Kirindy Forest. *Lemur News* 17: 18–21.

de Winter, I. I., van der Hoek, S., Schütt, J., Heitkönig, I.M.A., van Hooft, P., Gort, G., Prins, H.H.T., and Sterck, F. 2018. Anthropogenic disturbance effects remain visible in forest structure, but not in lemur abundances. *Biological Conservation* 225: 106–116.

de Winter, I. I., Qurkhuli, T., de Groot, N., de Vos-Rouweler, A.J.M., van Hooft, P., Heitkönig, I.M.A., Prins, H.H.T., Bontrop, R. E., and Doxiadis, G.G.M. 2019. Determining Mhc-DRB profiles in wild populations of three congeneric true lemur species by noninvasive methods. *Immunogenetics* 71: 97–107. https://doi.org/10.1007/s00251-018-1085-z.

Di Fiore, A. 2003. Molecular genetic approaches to the study of primate behavior, social organization, and reproduction. *American Journal of Physical Anthropology* 122: 62–99. https://doi.org/10.1002/ajpa.10382.

Di Fiore, A., and Valencia, L. M. 2014. The interplay of landscape features and social system on the genetic structure of a primate population: An agent-based simulation study using "tamarins." *International Journal of Primatology* 35: 226–257. https://doi.org/10.1007/s10764-013-9726-4.

Diallo, B. O., Joly, H. I., McKey, D., Hossaert-McKey, M., and Chevallier, M. H. 2007. Genetic diversity of *Tamarindus indica* populations: Any clues on the origin from its current distribution? *African Journal of Biotechnology* 6: 853–860.

Dietrich, M., Wilkinson, D. A., Soarimalala, V., Goodman, S. M., Dellagi, K., and Tortosa, P. 2014. Diversification of an emerging pathogen in a biodiversity hotspot: *Leptospira* in endemic small mammals of Madagascar. *Molecular Ecology* 23(11): 2783–2796.

Dietrich, M., Gomard, Y., Lagadec, E., Ramasindrazana, B., Le Minter, G., et al. 2018. Biogeography of *Leptospira* in wild animal communities inhabiting the insular ecosystem of the western Indian Ocean islands and neighboring Africa. *Emerging Microbes and Infections* 7: 57. doi.10.1038/s41426-018-0059-4.

Din, W., Anand, R., Boursot, P., Darviche, D., Dod, B., et al. 1996. Origin and radiation of the house mouse: Clues from nuclear genes. *Journal of Evolutionary Biology* 9: 519–539.

Dinsmore, M. P., Louis, E. E., Jr., Randriamahazomanana, D., Hachim, A., Zaonarivelo, J. R., and Strier, K. B. 2016. Variation in habitat and behavior of the northern sportive lemur (*Lepilemur septentrionalis*) at Montagne des Français, Madagascar. *Primate Conservation* 30: 73–88.

Djelati, R., Brun, B., and Rumpler, Y. 1997. Meiotic study of hybrids in the genus *Eulemur* and taxonomic considerations. *American Journal of Primatology* 42: 235–245.

Dobson, G. E. 1876. On peculiar structures in the feet of certain species of mammals which enable them to walk on smooth perpendicular surfaces. *Proceedings of the Zoological Society of London* 1876: 526–35.

———. 1878. Notes on *Myxopoda aurita*, Miln.-Edw. *Proceedings of the Zoological Society of London* 1878: 871–873.

Dolch, R., Fiely, J. L., Ndriamiary, J. N., Rafalimandimby, J., Randriampionona, R., Engberg, S. E., and Louis, E. E., Jr. 2008. Confirmation of the greater bamboo lemur, *Prolemur simus*, north of the Torotorofotsy wetlands, eastern Madagascar. *Lemur News* 13: 14–17.

Dollar, L. [J.] 1999. Preliminary report on the status, activity cycle, and ranging of *Cryptoprocta ferox* in the Malagasy rainforest, with implications for conservation. *Small Carnivore Conservation* 20: 7–10.

———. 2006. Morphometrics, diet, and conservation of *Cryptoprocta ferox*. PhD thesis, Duke University.

Dollar, L. [J.], Ganzhorn, J., and Goodman, S. M. 2007. Primates and other prey in the seasonally variable diet of *Cryptoprocta ferox* in the dry deciduous forest of western Madagascar. In *Primate Anti-Predator Strategies*, eds. S. L. Gursky and K.A.I. Nekaris, pp. 63–76. New York: Springer Science.

Dominy, N. J., and Lucas, P. W. 2001. Ecological importance of trichromatic vision to primates. *Nature* 410: 363–366.

Domoinaharivelo, N. 2014. Ecologie alimentaire des deux espèces de Cheirogales, *Cheirogaleus sibreei* (Major, 1896) et *Cheirogaleus crossleyi* (Grandidier, 1870) de Tsinjoarivo Ambatolampy: Application aux études pre et post-hibernation. Mémoire de DEA, Université d'Antananarivo.

Donati, G., and Borgognini-Tarli, S. M. 2006. From darkness to daylight: Cathemeral activity in primates. *Journal of Anthropological Sciences* 84: 7–32.

Donati, G., Lunardini, A., and Kappeler, P. M. 1999. Cathemeral activity of red-fronted brown lemurs (*Eulemur fulvus rufus*) in the Kirindy forest/CFPF. In *New Directions in Lemur Studies*, eds. B. Rakotosamimanana, H. Rasamimanana, J. U. Ganzhorn, and S. M. Goodman, pp. 119–137. Boston: Springer.

Donati, G., Ramanamanjato, J.-B., Ravoahangy, A. M., and Vincelette, M. 2007a. Translocation as a conservation measure for an endangered species in the littoral forest of southeastern Madagascar: The case of *Eulemur collaris*. In *Biodiversity, Ecology and Conservation of Littoral Forest Ecosystems in Southeastern Madagascar, Tolagnaro (Fort Dauphin)*, eds. J. U. Ganzhorn, S. M. Goodman, and M. Vincelette, pp. 237–245. Washington, DC: Smithsonian Institution Press.

Donati, G., Bollen, A., Borgognini-Tarli, S. M., and Ganzhorn, J. U. 2007b. Feeding over the 24-h cycle: Dietary flexibility of cathemeral collared lemurs (*Eulemur collaris*). *Behavioral Ecology and Sociobiology* 61: 1237–1251.

Donati, G., Baldi, N., Morelli, V., Ganzhorn, J. U., and Borgognini-Tarli, S. M. 2009. Proximate and ultimate determinants of cathemeral activity in brown lemurs. *Animal Behaviour* 77: 317–325.

Donati, G., Kesch, K., Ndremifidy, K., Schmidt, S. L., Ramanamanjato, J.-B., Borgognini-Tarli, S. M., and Ganzhorn, J. U. 2011. Better few than hungry: Flexible feeding ecology of collared lemurs *Eulemur collaris* in littoral forest fragments. *PLoS One* 6(5): e19807.

Donati, G., Santini, L., Razafindramanana, J., Boitani, L., and Borgognini-Tarli, S. 2013. (Un-)expected nocturnal activity in "diurnal" *Lemur catta* supports cathemerality as one of the key adaptations of the lemurid radiation. *American Journal of Primatology* 150: 99–106.

Donati, G., Campera, M., Balestri, M., Serra, V., Barresi, M., Schwitzer, C., Curtis, D. J., and Santini, L. 2016. Ecological and anthropogenic correlates of activity patterns in *Eulemur*. *International Journal of Primatology* 37: 29–46.

Donati, G., Santini, L., Eppley, T. M., Arrigo-Nelson, S. J., Balestri, M., et al. 2017. Low levels of fruit nitrogen as drivers for the evolution of Madagascar's primate communities. *Scientific Reports* 7: 14406.

Donati, G., Eppley, T. M., Ralison, J., Youssouf, J., and Ganzhorn, J. U. 2019. Lemurs in mangroves and other flooded habitats. In *Primates in Flooded Habitats: Ecology and Conservation*, eds. K. Nowak, A. A. Barnett, and I. Matsuda, pp. 29–32. Cambridge: Cambridge University Press.

Donati, G., Campera, M., Balestri, M., Barresi, M., Kesch, K., et al. 2020. Life in a fragment: Evolution of foraging strategies of translocated collared brown lemurs, *Eulemur collaris*, over an 18-year period. *American Journal of Primatology* 82(4): e23106.

Donque, P. 1972. The climatology of Madagascar. In *Biogeography and Ecology of Madagascar*, eds. R. Battistini, and G. Richard-Vindard, pp. 87–144. Berlin: Springer.

Dorst, J. 1947. Les chauves-souris de la faune Malgache. *Bulletin du Muséum National d'Histoire Naturelle*, Paris, série 2, 19: 306–313.

dos Reis, M., Gunnell, G. F., Barba-Montoya, J., Wilkins, A., Yang, Z., and Yoder, A. D. 2018. Using phylogenomic data to explore the effects of relaxed clocks and calibration strategies on divergence time estimation: Primates as a test case. *Systematic Biology* 67: 594–615.

Douady, C. J., Catzeflis, F., Kao, D. J., Springer, M. S., and Stanhope, M. J. 2002. Molecular evidence for the monophyly of Tenrecidae (Mammalia) and the timing of the colonization of Madagascar by Malagasy tenrecs. *Molecular Phylogenetics and Evolution* 22: 357–363. https://doi.org/10.1006/mpev.2001.1055.

Douglass, K., Hixon, S., Wright, H. T., Godfrey, L. R., Crowley, B. E., Manjakahery, B., Rasolondrainy, R., Crossland, Z., and Radimilahy, C. 2019. A critical review of radiocarbon dates clarifies the human settlement of Madagascar. *Quaternary Science Reviews* 221: 105878.

Dowling, A.P.G., Bochkov, A. V., and OConnor, B. M. 2007. Revision of the genus *Andreacarus* (Acari: Laelapidae) with description of seven new species and a new genus for Australian species formerly placed in *Andreacarus*. *Journal of Medical Entomology* 44(3): 405–421.

Doyère, M. 1835. Notice sur un mammifère de Madagascar, formant le type d'un nouveau genre de la famille des carnassiers insectivores de M. Cuvier. *Annales des Sciences Naturelles*, Paris, série *Zoologie* 4: 270–283.

Drea, C. M., and Scordato, E. S. 2008. Olfactory communication in the ringtailed lemur (*Lemur catta*): Form and function of multimodal signals. In *Chemical Signals in Vertebrates*, vol. 11, eds. J. L. Hurst, R. J. Beynon, S. C. Roberts, and T. D. Wyatt, pp. 91–102. New York: Springer.

Driscoll, C. A., Menotti-Raymond, M., Roca, A. L., Hupe, K., Johnson, W. E., et al. 2007. The Near Eastern origin of cat domestication. *Science* 317: 519–523. https://doi.org/10.1126/science.1139518.

Dröscher, I., and Kappeler, P. M. 2013. Defining the low end of primate social complexity: The social organization of the nocturnal white-footed sportive lemur (*Lepilemur leucopus*). *International Journal of Primatology* 34: 1225–1243.

Dröscher, I., and Kappeler, P. M. 2014a. Competition for food in a solitarily foraging folivorous primate (*Lepilemur leucopus*)? *American Journal of Primatology* 76: 842–854.

Dröscher, I., and Kappeler, P. M. 2014b. Maintenance of familiarity and social bonding via communal latrine use in a solitary primate (*Lepilemur leucopus*). *Behavioral Ecology and Sociobiology* 68: 2043–2058.

Drummond, A. J., Rambaut, A., Shapiro, B., and Pybus, O. G. 2005. Bayesian coalescent inference of past population dynamics from molecular sequences. *Molecular Biology and Evolution* 22: 1185–1192. https://doi.org/10.1093/molbev/msi103.

Drummond, A. J., Ho, S.Y.W., Phillips, M. J., and Rambaut, A. 2006. Relaxed phylogenetics and dating with confidence. *PLoS Biology* 4: e88.

DuBois, J.-Y., Rakotondravony, D., Hänni, C., Sourouille, P., and Catzeflis, F. M. 1996. Molecular evolutionary relationships of three genera of Nesomyinae, endemic rodent taxa from Madagascar. *Journal of Mammalian Evolution* 3: 239–259.

DuBour, A. 2018. Dietary constraints and strategies in the red-bellied lemur (*Eulemur rubriventer*) and their implications for conservation. MA thesis, Northern Illinois University.

Duchemin, J.-B. 2003. Biogéographie des puces de Madagascar. PhD thesis, Université de Paris 12, Créteil, Val de Marne.

Duckworth, J. W., Evans, M. I., Hawkins, A.F.A., Safford, R. J., and Wilkinson, R. J. 1995. The lemurs of Marojejy Strict Nature Reserve, Madagascar: A status overview with notes on ecology and threats. *International Journal of Primatology* 16: 545–559.

Duckworth, J. W., Hawkins, A.F.A., Randrianasolo, H., Andrianarimisa, A., and Goodman, S. M. 2014. Suggested English names for Madagascar's species of Carnivora. *Small Carnivore Conservation* 50: 54–60.

Dunham, A. E., Erhart, E. M., Overdorff, D. J., and Wright, P. C. 2008. Evaluating effects of deforestation, hunting, and El Niño events on a threatened lemur. *Biological Conservation* 141: 287–297.

Duplantier, J.-M. 2013. *Suncus murinus*, Asian House Shrew. In *Mammals of Africa*. Vol. 4, *Hedgehogs, Shrews and Bats,* eds. M. Happold, and D.C.D. Happold, pp. 179–180. London: Bloomsbury Publishing.

Duplantier, J.-M., and Duchemin, J.-B. 2003a. Human diseases and introduced small mammals. In *The Natural History of Madagascar*, eds. S. M. Goodman and J. P. Benstead, pp. 158–161. Chicago: University of Chicago Press.

Duplantier, J.-M., and Duchemin, J.-B. 2003b. Introduced small mammals and their ectoparasites: A description of their colonization and its consequences. In *The Natural History of Madagascar*, eds. S. M. Goodman and J. P. Benstead, pp. 1191–1194. Chicago: University of Chicago Press.

Duplantier, J.-M., and Rakotondravony, D. 1999. The rodent problem in Madagascar: Agricultural pest and threat to human health. In *Ecologically-Based Rodent Management*, eds. G. R. Singleton, L. A. Hinds, H. Leirs, and Z. Zhang, pp. 441–459. Canberra: Australian Centre for International Agricultural Research.

Duplantier, J.-M., Orth, A., Catalan, J., and Bonhomme, F. 2002. Evidence for a mitochondrial lineage originating from the Arabian Peninsula in the Madagascar house mouse (*Mus musculus*). *Heredity* 89: 154–158.

Duplantier, J.-M., Catalan, J., Orth, A., Grolleau, B., and Britton-Davidian, J. 2003. Systematics of the black rat in Madagascar: Consequences for the transmission and distribution of plague. *Biological Journal of the Linnean Society* 78: 335–341.

Duplantier, J.-M., Duchemin, J.-B., Chanteau, S., and Carniel, E. 2005. From the recent lessons of the Malagasy foci towards a global understanding of the factors involved in plague re-emergence. *Veterinary Research* 36: 437–453.

Durbin, J. 2007. New legislation for the protection of Malagasy species. *Lemur News* 11: 4–6.

Durbin, J., Funk, S. M., Hawkins, F., Hills, D. M., Jenkins, P. D., Moncrieff, C. B., and Ralainasolo, F. B. 2010. Investigations into the status of a new taxon of *Salanoia* (Mammalia: Carnivora: Eupleridae) from the marshes of Lac Alaotra, Madagascar. *Systematics and Biodiversity* 8: 341–355. https://doi.org/10.1080/14772001003756751.

Durette-Desset, M.-C., and Chabaud, A. G. 1992. *Laurostrongylus hoineffae* n. gen., n. sp., a relict trichostrongylid from an endemic Madagascan rodent. *Memórias do Instituto Oswaldo Cruz, Rio de Janeiro* 87: 91–94.

Durette-Desset, M.-C., Lehtonen, J. T., and Haukisalmi, V. 2002a. Trichostrongylina (Nematoda) from Malagasy Muridae. II. Description of two new species of *Heligmonina* (Heligmonellidae) in *Nesomys rufus* and *Eliurus tanala*. *Parasite* 9(2): 127–133.

Durette-Desset, M.-C., Lehtonen, J. T., and Haukisalmi, V. 2002b. Trichostrongylina (Nematoda) from Malagasy Muridae. I. Description of two new species of Heligmonellidae in *Nesomys* spp. *Parasite* 9(1): 29–35.

Dutrillaux, B. 1979. Chromosomal evolution in primates: Tentative phylogeny from *Microcebus murinus* (Prosimian) to man. *Human Genetics* 48: 251–314. https://doi.org/10.1007/BF00272830.

Dutton, C. J., Junge, R. E., and Louis, E. E., Jr. 2003. Biomedical evaluation of free-ranging ring-tailed lemurs (*Lemur catta*) in Tsimanampetsotsa Strict Nature Reserve, Madagascar. *Journal of Zoo and Wildlife Medicine* 34: 16–24.

Dutton, C. J., Junge, R. E., and Louis, E. E., Jr. 2008. Biomedical evaluation of free-ranging red ruffed lemurs (*Varecia rubra*) within the Masoala National Park, Madagascar. *Journal of Zoo and Wildlife Medicine* 39: 76–85.

Eberle, M., and Kappeler, P. M. 2002. Mouse lemurs in space and time: A test of the socioecological model. *Behavioral Ecology and Sociobiology* 51: 131–139.

Eberle, M., and Kappeler, P. M. 2004a. Sex in the dark: Determinants and consequences of mixed male mating tactics in *Microcebus murinus*, a small solitary nocturnal primate. *Behavioral Ecology and Sociobiology* 57: 77–90.

Eberle, M., and Kappeler, P. M. 2004b. Selected polyandry: Female choice and inter-sexual conflict in a small nocturnal solitary primate (*Microcebus murinus*). *Behavioral Ecology and Sociobiology* 57: 91–100.

Eberle, M., and Kappeler, P. M. 2006. Family insurance: Kin selection and cooperative breeding in a solitary primate (*Microcebus murinus*). *Behavioral Ecology and Sociobiology* 60: 582–588.

Eberle, M., and Kappeler, P. M. 2008. Mutualism, reciprocity, or kin selection? Cooperative rescue of a conspecific from a boa in a nocturnal solitary forager the gray mouse lemur. *American Journal of Primatology* 70: 410–414.

Eberle, M., Perret, M., and Kappeler, P. M. 2007. Sperm competition and optimal timing of matings in *Microcebus murinus*. *International Journal of Primatology* 28: 1267–1278.

Eger, J. L., and Mitchell, L. 2003. Chiroptera, bats. In *The Natural History of Madagascar*, eds. S. M. Goodman and J. P. Benstead, pp. 1287–1298. Chicago: University of Chicago Press.

Ehlers, J., Poppert, S., Ratovonamana, R. Y., Ganzhorn, J. U., Tappe, D., and Kruger, A. 2019. Ectoparasites of endemic and domestic animals in southwest Madagascar. *Acta Tropica* 196: 83–92.

Ehlers, J., Krüger, A., Rakotondranary, S. J., Ratovonamana, R. Y., Poppert, S., Ganzhorn, J. U., and Tappe, D., 2020. Molecular detection of *Rickettsia* spp., *Borrelia* spp., *Bartonella* spp. and *Yersinia pestis* in ectoparasites of endemic and domestic animals in southwest Madagascar. *Acta Tropica* 205: 105339.

Ehresmann, P. 2000. Ökologische Differenzierung von zwei sympatrischen Mausmaki-Arten (*Microcebus murinus* und *M. ravelobensis*) im Trockenwald Nordwest-Madagaskars. PhD thesis, University of Hannover.

Eisenberg, J. F., and Gould, E. 1970. The tenrecs: A study in mammalian behavior and evolution. *Smithsonian Contributions to Zoology* 27: 1–137.

Eisfeldt, J., Pettersson, M., Vezzi, F., Wincent, J., Käller, M., Gruselius, J., Nilsson, D., Syk Lundberg, E., Carvalho, C.M.B., and Lindstrand, A. 2019. Comprehensive structural variation genome map of individuals carrying complex chromosomal rearrangements. *PLoS Genetics* 15. https://doi.org/10.1371/journal.pgen.1007858.

Eizirik, E., Murphy, W. J., Koepfli, K.-P., Johnson, W. E., Dragoo, J. W., Wayne, R. K., and O'Brien, S. J. 2010. Pattern and timing of diversification of the mammalian order Carnivora inferred from multiple nuclear gene sequences. *Molecular Phylogenetics and Evolution* 56: 49–63.

Ellerman, J. R. 1941. *The Families and Genera of Living Rodents*. Vol. 2, *Family Muridae*. London: British Museum (Natural History).

———. 1949. *The Families and Genera of Living Rodents*. Vol. 3, Appendix 2, Notes on the rodents from Madagascar in the British Museum, and on a collection from the island obtained by Mr. C. S. Webb. London: British Museum (Natural History).

Ellwanger, N., and Gould, L. 2011. Variations in behavioural patterns between *Lemur catta* groups living in different forest types: Implications for conservation. *Endangered Species Research* 14: 259–270.

Enders, A. C., Blankenship, T. N., Goodman S. M., Soarimalala, V., and Carter, A. M. 2007. Placental diversity in Malagasy tenrecs: Placentation in shrew tenrecs (*Microgale* spp.), the mole-like rice tenrec (*Oryzorictes hova*) and the web-footed tenrec (*Limnogale mergulus*). *Placenta* 28: 748–759.

Engqvist, A., and Richard, A. 1991. Diet as a possible determinant of cathemeral activity patterns in primates. *Folia Primatologica* 57: 169–172.

Eppley, T. M. 2015. Ecological flexibility of the southern bamboo lemur (*Hapalemur meridionalis*) in southeast Madagascar. PhD thesis, University of Hamburg.

Eppley, T. M., and Ravelomanantsoa, R. 2015. Predation of an adult southern bamboo lemur *Hapalemur meridionalis* by a Dumeril's boa *Acrantophis dumerili*. *Lemur News* 19: 2–3.

Eppley, T. M., Verjans, E., and Donati, G. 2011. Coping with low-quality diets: A first account of the feeding ecology of the southern gentle lemur, *Hapalemur meridionalis*, in the Mandena littoral forest, southeast Madagascar. *Primates* 52: 7–13.

Eppley, T. M., Donati, G., Ramanamanjato, J.-B., Randriatafika, F., Andriamandimbiarisoa, L. N., Rabehevitra, D., Ravelomanantsoa, R., and Ganzhorn, J. U. 2015a. The use of an invasive species habitat by a small folivorous primate: Implications for lemur conservation in Madagascar. *PLoS One* 10(11): e0140981. https://doi.org/10.1371/journal.pone.0140981.

Eppley, T. M., Ganzhorn, J. U., and Donati, G. 2015b. Cathemerality in a small, folivorous primate: Proximate control of diel activity in *Hapalemur meridionalis*. *Behavioral Ecology and Sociobiology* 69: 991–1002. https://doi.org/10.1007/s00265-015-1911-3.

Eppley, T. M., Donati, G., and Ganzhorn, J. U. 2016a. Determinants of terrestrial feeding in an arboreal primate: The case of the southern bamboo lemur (*Hapalemur meridionalis*). *American Journal of Physical Anthropology* 161: 328–342.

Eppley, T. M., Ganzhorn, J. U., and Donati, G. 2016b. Latrine behaviour as a multimodal communicatory signal station in wild lemurs: The case of *Hapalemur meridionalis*. *Animal Behaviour* 111: 57–67.

Eppley, T. M., Watzek, J., Dausmann, K. H., Ganzhorn, J. U., and Donati, G. 2017a. Huddling is more important than rest site selection for thermoregulation in southern bamboo lemurs. *Animal Behaviour* 127: 153–161.

Eppley, T. M., Balestri, M., Campera, M., Rabenantoandro, J., Ramanamanjato, J.-B., Randriatafika, F., Ganzhorn, J. U., and Donati, G. 2017b. Ecological flexibility as measured by the use of pioneer and exotic plants by two lemurids: *Eulemur collaris* and *Hapalemur meridionalis*. *International Journal of Primatology* 38: 338–357.

Eppley, T. M., Tan, C. L., Arrigo-Nelson, S. J., Donati, G., Ballhorn, D. J., and Ganzhorn, J. U. 2017c. High energy or protein concentrations in food as possible offsets for cyanide consumption by specialized bamboo lemurs in Madagascar. *International Journal of Primatology* 38: 881–899.

Eppley, T. M., Santini, L., Tinsman, J. C., and Donati, G. 2020. Do functional traits offset the effects of fragmentation? The case of large-bodied diurnal lemur species. *American Journal of Primatology* 82(4): e23104.

Erhart, E. M., and Overdorff, D. J. 1999. Female coordination of group travel in wild *Propithecus* and *Eulemur*. *International Journal of Primatology* 20: 927–940.

Erhart, E. M., and Overdorff, D. J. 2008a. Rates of agonism by diurnal lemuroids: Implications for female social relationships. *International Journal of Primatology* 29: 1227–1247.

Erhart, E. M., and Overdorff, D. J. 2008b. Population demography and social structure changes in *Eulemur fulvus rufus* from 1988 to 2003. *American Journal of Physical Anthropology* 136: 183–193.

Erhart, E. M., Tecot, S. R., and Grassi, C. 2018. Interannual variation in diet, dietary diversity, and dietary overlap in three sympatric strepsirrhine species in southeastern Madagascar. *International Journal of Primatology* 39: 289–311.

Erickson, C. J. 1991. Percussive foraging in the aye-aye, *Daubentonia madagascariensis*. *Animal Behaviour* 41:793–801.

———. 1998. Cues for prey location by aye-ayes (*Daubentonia madagascariensis*). *Folia Primatologica*, supplement 1, 69: 35–40.

Erickson, C. J., Nowicki, S., Dollar, L., and Goehring, N. 1998. Percussive foraging: Stimuli for prey location by aye-ayes (*Daubentonia madagascariensis*). *International Journal of Primatology* 19:111–22.

Evans, B., Rakotondraparany, F., Cole, L., Graham, S., Long, P., and Gandola, R. 2013. The carnivores of Mariarano forest, Madagascar: First insights. *Small Carnivore Conservation* 49: 15–19.

Evasoa, M. R., Radespiel, U., Hasiniaina, A. F., Rasoloharijaona, S., Randrianambinina, B., Rakotondravony, R., and Zimmermann, E. 2018. Variation in reproduction of the smallest-bodied primate radiation, the mouse lemurs (*Microcebus* spp.): A synopsis. *American Journal of Primatology* 80(7): e22874. https://doi.org/10.1002/ajp.22874.

Evasoa, M. R., Zimmermann, E., Hasiniaina, A. F., Rasoloharijaona, S., Randrianambinina, B., and Radespiel, U. 2019. Sources of variation in social tolerance in mouse lemurs (*Microcebus* spp.). *BMC Ecology* 19: 20.

Everson, K. M., Soarimalala, V., Goodman, S. M., and Olson, L. E. 2016. Multiple loci and complete taxonomic sampling resolve the phylogeny and biogeographic history of tenrecs (Mammalia: Tenrecidae) and reveal higher speciation rates in Madagascar's humid forests. *Systematic Biology* 65: 890–909. https://doi.org/10.1093/sysbio/syw034.

Everson, K. M., Hildebrandt, K.B.P., Goodman, S. M., and Olson, L. E. 2018. Caught in the act: Incipient speciation across a latitudinal gradient in a semifossorial mammal from Madagascar, the mole tenrec *Oryzorictes hova* (Tenrecidae). *Molecular Phylogenetics and Evolution* 126: 74–84. https://doi.org/10.1016/j.ympev.2018.02.024.

Everson, K. M., Goodman, S. M., and Olson, L. E. 2020a. Speciation and gene flow in two sympatric small mammals from Madagascar, *Microgale fotsifotsy* and *M. soricoides* (Mammalia: Tenrecidae). *Molecular Ecology* 29(9): 1717–1729. https://doi.org/10.1111/mec.15433.

Everson, K. M., Jansa, S. A., Goodman, S. M., and Olson, L. E. 2020b. Montane regions shape patterns of diversification in small mammals and reptiles from Madagascar's moist evergreen forest. *Journal of Biogeography* 47: 2059–2072. https://doi.org/10.1111/jbi.13945.

Ewens, W. J. 1972. The sampling theory of selectively neutral alleles. *Theoretical Population Biology* 3: 87–112. https://doi.org/10.1016/0040-5809(72)90035-4.

Excoffier, L., Dupanloup, I., Huerta-Sánchez, E., Sousa, V. C., and Foll, M. 2013. Robust demographic inference from genomic and SNP data. *PLoS Genetics* 9: e1003905. https://doi.org/10.1371/journal.pgen.1003905.

Fabre, P.-H., Rodrigues, A., and Douzery, E.J.P. 2009. Patterns of macroevolution among primates inferred from a supermatrix of mitochondrial and nuclear DNA. *Molecular Phylogenetics and Evolution* 53: 808–825.

Fabre, P.-H., Hautier, L., Dimitrov, D., and Douzery, E.J.P. 2012. A glimpse on the pattern of rodent diversification: A phylogenetic approach. *BMC Evolutionary Biology* 12: 88.

Faherty, S. L., Villanueva-Cañas, J. L., Klopfer, P. H., Albà, M. M., and Yoder, A. D. 2016. Gene expression profiling in the hibernating primate, *Cheirogaleus medius*. *Genome Biology and Evolution* 8: 2413–2426. https://doi.org/10.1093/gbe/evw163.

Faherty, S. L., Campbell, C. R., Hilbig, S., and Yoder, A. D. 2017. The effect of body mass and diet composition on torpor patterns in a Malagasy primate (*Microcebus murinus*). *Journal of Comparative Physiology B: Biochemical, Systemic, and Environmental Physiology* 187: 677–688.

Faherty, S. L., Villanueva-Cañas, J. L., Blanco, M. B., Albà, M. M., and Yoder, A. D. 2018. Transcriptomics in the wild: Hibernation physiology in free-ranging dwarf lemurs. *Molecular Ecology* 27: 709–722. https://doi.org/10.1111/mec.14483.

Fahrig, L. 2003. Effects of habitat fragmentation on biodiversity. *Annual Review of Ecology, Evolution, and Systematics* 34(1): 487–515.

Fain, A. 1994. Adaptation, specificity and host-parasite coevolution in mites (Acari). *International Journal for Parasitology* 24(8): 1273–1283.

FAO and PAM. 2013. Mission FAO/PAM d'évaluation de la sécurité alimentaire à Madagascar. http://www.fao.org/3/CA2856FR/ca2856fr.pdf.

Fardi, S., Sauther, M. L., Cuozzo, F. P., Youssouf Jacky, I. A., and Bernstein, R. 2018. The effect of extreme weather events on hair cortisol and body weight in a wild ring-tailed lemur population (*Lemur catta*) in southwestern Madagascar. *American Journal of Primatology* 80 (2): e22731. http://onlinelibrary.wiley.com/doi/10.1002/ajp.22731/full.

Farris, Z. J., and Kelly, M. J. 2011. Assessing carnivore populations across the Makira Protected Area, Madagascar: WCS pilot camera trapping study. [Antananarivo]: Wildlife Conservation Society Madagascar Program.

Farris, Z. J., Kelly, M. J., Karpanty, S. M., Ratelolahy, F., Andrianjakarivelo, V., and Holmes, C. 2012. Brown-tailed Vontsira *Salanoia concolor* (Eupleridae) documented in Makira Natural Park, Madagascar: New insights on distribution and camera-trap success. *Small Carnivore Conservation* 47: 82–86.

Farris, Z. J., Karpanty, S. M., Ratelolahy, F., and Kelly, M. J. 2014. Predator–primate distribution, activity, and co-occurrence in relation to habitat and human activity across fragmented and contiguous forests in northeastern Madagascar. *International Journal of Primatology* 35: 859–880.

Farris, Z. J., Gerber, B., Karpanty, S. M., Murphy, A., Ratelolahy, F., and Kelly, M. J. 2015a. When carnivores roam: Temporal patterns and partitioning among Madagascar's native and exotic carnivores. *Journal of Zoology* 296: 45–57.

Farris, Z. J., Golden, C. D., Karpanty, S., Murphy, A., Stauffer, D., Ratelolahy, F., Andrianjakarivelo, V., Holmes, C. M., and Kelly, M. J. 2015b. Hunting, exotic carnivores, and habitat loss: Anthropogenic effects on a native carnivore community, Madagascar. *PLoS One* 10: e0136456.

Farris, Z. J., Kelly, M. J., Karpanty, S. M., and Ratelolahy, F. 2015c. Patterns of spatial co-occurrence among native and exotic carnivores in NE Madagascar. *Animal Conservation* 19: 189–198.

Farris, Z. J., Boone, H. M., Karpanty, S., Murphy, A., Ratelolahy, F., Andrianjakarivelo, V., and Kelly, M. J. 2016. Feral cats and the fitoaty: First population assessment of the black forest cat in Madagascar's rainforests. *Journal of Mammalogy* 97: 518–525.

Farris, Z. J., Kelly, M. J., Karpanty, S. M., Murphy, A., Ratelolahy, F., Andrianjakarivelo, V., and Holmes, C. 2017a. The times they are a changin': Multi-year surveys reveal exotics replace native carnivores at a Madagascar rainforest site. *Biological Conservation* 206: 320–328.

Farris, Z. J., Gerber, B. D., Valenta, K., Rafaliarison, R., Razafimahaimodison, J.-C., Larney, E., Rajaonarivelo, T., Randriana, Z., Wright, P., and Chapman, C. 2017b. Threats to a rainforest carnivore community: A multi-year assessment of occupancy and co-occurrence in Madagascar. *Biological Conservation* 210: 116–124.

Farris, Z. J., Chan, S., Rafaliarison, R., and Valenta, K. 2019. Occupancy modeling reveals interspecific variation in habitat use and negative effects of dogs on lemur populations. *International Journal of Primatology* 40(6): 706–720.

Farris, Z. J., Gerber, B. D., Karpanty, S., Murphy, A., Wampole, E., Ratelolahy, F., and Kelly, M. J. 2020. Exploring and interpreting spatiotemporal interactions between native and invasive carnivores across a gradient of rainforest degradation. *Biological Invasions* 22: 2033–2046.

Faulkner, A. L., and Lehman, S. M. 2006. Feeding patterns in a small-bodied nocturnal folivore (*Avahi laniger*) and the influence of leaf chemistry: A preliminary study. *Folia Primatologica* 77: 218–227.

Faure, M., and Guérin, C. 1990. *Hippopotamus laloumena* nov. sp., la troisème espèce d'hippopotame holocène de Madagascar. *Comptes Rendus de l'Académie des Sciences, Paris*, série 2, 310: 1299–1305.

Fauroux, E. 1989. La boeuf et le riz dans la vie économique et sociale Sakalava de la vallée de la Maharivo. *Aombe* 2: 1–295.

Fausser, J. L., Rabarivola, C., Meier, B., Hahn, T., and Rumpler, Y. 2000. Genetic comparison between different populations of *Eulemur macaco flavifrons* in northwest Madagascar using RAPD markers. *American Journal of Primatology* 51: 249–255. https://doi.org/10.1002/1098-2345.

Fayenuwo, J. O., and Halstead, L. B. 1974. Breeding cycle of straw-colored fruit bat, *Eidolon helvum*, at Ile Ife Nigeria. *Journal of Mammalogy* 55: 453–454.

Feistner, A.T.C., and Schmid, J. 1999. Lemurs of the Réserve Naturelle Intégrale d'Andohahela, Madagascar. In A floral and faunal inventory of the Réserve Naturelle Intégrale d'Andohahela, Madagascar: With reference to elevational variation, ed. S. M. Goodman. *Fieldiana: Zoology*, new ser., 94: 269–283.

Feistner, A.T.C., and Sterling, E. J. 1995. Body mass and sexual dimorphism in the aye-aye. *Dodo* 31: 73–76.

Felsenstein, J. 1992. Estimating effective population size from samples of sequences: Inefficiency of pairwise and segregating sites as compared to phylogenetic estimates. *Genetics Research* 59: 139–147. https://doi.org/10.1017/S0016672300030354.

Fenton, M. B. 1990. The foraging ecology of animal-eating bats. *Canadian Journal of Zoology* 68: 411–422

Fernández-Llamazares, A, López-Baucells, A., Rocha, R., Andriamitandrina, S., Andriatafika, Z., Burgas, D., Temba, E. M., Torrent, L., and Cabeza, M. 2018. Are sacred caves still safe havens for the endemic bats of Madagascar? *Oryx* 52(2): 271–275.

Fichtel, C. 2007. Avoiding predators at night: Antipredator strategies in red-tailed sportive lemurs (*Lepilemur ruficaudatus*). *American Journal of Primatology* 69: 611–624.

Fichtel, C., and Kappeler, P. M. 2002. Anti-predator behavior of group-living Malagasy primates: Mixed evidence for a referential alarm call system. *Behavioral Ecology and Sociobiology* 51: 262–275

Fichtel, C., and Kappeler, P. M. 2011. Variation in the meaning of alarm calls in Verreaux's and Coquerel's Sifakas (*Propithecus verreauxi*, *P. coquereli*). *International Journal of Primatology* 32: 346–361.

Fichtel, C., Zucchini, W., and Hilgartner, R. 2011. Out of sight but not out of mind? Behavioral coordination in red-tailed sportive lemurs (*Lepilemur ruficaudatus*). *International Journal of Primatology* 32: 1383–1396.

Fietz, J. 1998. Body mass in wild *Microcebus murinus* over the dry season. *Folia Primatologica* 69: 183–190.

———. 1999. Demography and floating males in a population of *Cheirogaleus medius*. In *New Directions in Lemur Studies*, eds. B. Rakotosamimanana, H. Rasamimanana, J. U. Ganzhorn, and S. M. Goodman, pp. 159–172. New York: Kluwer Academic/Plenum Press.

———. 2003. *Cheirogaleus*, dwarf lemurs or fat-tailed lemurs. In *The Natural History of Madagascar*, eds. S. M. Goodman and J. P. Benstead, pp. 1307–1309. Chicago: University of Chicago Press.

Fietz, J., and Dausmann, K. H. 2003. Costs and potential benefits of parental care in the nocturnal fat-tailed dwarf lemur (*Cheirogaleus medius*). *Folia Primatologica* 74(5–6): 246–258.

Fietz, J., and Dausmann, K. H. 2006. Big is beautiful: Fat storage and hibernation as a strategy to cope with marked seasonality in the fat-tailed dwarf lemur (*Cheirogaleus medius*). In *Lemurs: Ecology and Adaptation*, eds. L. Gould and M. L. Sauther, pp. 97–110. New York: Springer.

Fietz, J., and Ganzhorn, J. U. 1999. Feeding ecology of the hibernating primate *Cheirogaleus medius*: How does it get so fat? *Oecologia* 121: 157–164.

Fietz, J., Zischler, H., Schwiegk, C., Tomiuk, J., Dausmann, K. H., and Ganzhorn, J. U. 2000. High rates of extra-pair young in the pair-living fat-tailed dwarf lemur *Cheirogaleus medius*. *Behavioral Ecology and Sociobiology* 49: 8–17. https://doi.org/10.1007/s002650000269.

Fietz, J., Tataruch, F., Dausmann, K. H., and Ganzhorn, J. U. 2003. White adipose tissue composition in the free-ranging fat-tailed dwarf lemur (*Cheirogaleus medius*; Primates), a tropical hibernator. *Journal of Comparative Physiology B: Biochemical, Systemic, and Environmental Physiology* 173: 1–10.

Findley, J. S., and Wilson, D. E. 1974. Observations on the Neotropical disk-winged bat, *Thyroptera tricolor* Spix. *Journal of Mammalogy* 55: 562–671.

Finstermeier, K., Zinner, D., Brameier, M., Meyer, M., Kreuz, E., Hofreiter, M., and Roos, C. 2013. A mitogenomic phylogeny of living primates. *PLoS One* 8(7): e69504. https://doi.org/10.1371/journal.pone.0069504.

Fish, K. 2010. Response of two nocturnal lemurs (*Microcebus murinus* and *Lepilemur leucopus*) to a potential boiidae (*Sanzinia madagascariensis*) predator. *Lemur News* 15: 16–18.

Flacourt, E. de. 1658 (repr. 1995). *Histoire de la Grande Isle Madagascar*. Edition présentée et annotée par Claude Allibert. Paris: INALCO-Karthala.

Flannery, T. 1995. *Mammals of New Guinea*. Cornell: Comstock.

Fleagle, J. G., and Reed, K. E. 1996. Comparing primate communities: A multivariate approach. *Journal of Human Evolution* 30: 489–510.

Flouris, T., Jiao, X., Rannala, B., and Yang, Z. 2019. A Bayesian implementation of the multispecies coalescent model with introgression for comparative genomic analysis. *Molecular Biology and Evolution* 37(4): 1211–1223. https://doi.org/10.1101/766741.

Flower, W. H. 1869. On the value of the characters of the base of the cranium in the classification of the order Carnivora and the systematic position of *Bassaris* and other disputed forms. *Proceedings of the Zoological Society of London* 1869: 4–37.

Foerg, R. 1982. Reproductive behavior in *Varecia variegata*. *Folia Primatologica* 38: 108–121.

Foley, N. M., Thong, V. D., Soisook, P., Goodman, S. M., Armstrong, K. N., Jacobs, D. S., Puechmaille, S. J., and Teeling, E. C. 2015. How and why overcome the impediments to resolution: Lessons from rhinolophid and hipposiderid bats. *Molecular Biology and Evolution* 32: 313–333.

Foley, N. M., Goodman, S. M., Whelan, C. V., Puechmaille, S. J., and Teeling, E. 2017. Towards navigating the minotaur's labyrinth: Cryptic diversity and taxonomic revision within the speciose genus *Hipposideros* (Hipposideridae). *Acta Chiropterologica* 19(1): 1-18.

Fons, R. 1975. Contribution à la connaissance de la Musaraigne étrusque *Suncus etruscus* (Savi, 1822) (Mammifère—Insectivora—Soricidae). PhD thesis, Université de Paris 6.

Fovet, W., Faure, M., and Guérin, C. 2011. *Hippopotamus guldbergi* n. sp.: Révision du statut d'*Hippopotamus madagascariensis* Guldberg, 1883, après plus d'un siècle de malentendus et de confusions taxonomiques. *Zoosystema* 33: 61–82.

Franklin, D. C., Prior, L. D., Hogarth, N. J., and McMahon, C. R. 2010. Bamboo, fire and flood: Consequences of disturbance for the vegetative growth of a clumping, clonal plant. *Plant Ecology* 208: 319–332.

Frasier, C. L., Rakotonirina, J. N., Razanajatovo, L. G., Nasolonjanahary, T. S., Mamiaritiana, S. B., Ramarolahy, J. F., and Louis, E. E., Jr. 2015. Expanding knowledge on life history traits and infant development in the greater bamboo lemur (*Prolemur simus*): Contributions from Kianjavato, Madagascar. *Primate Conservation* 29: 75–86.

Frasier, C. L., Lei, R., McLain, A. T., Taylor, J. M., Bailey, C. A., et al. 2016. A new species of dwarf lemur (Cheirogaleidae: *Cheirogaleus medius* group) from the Ankarana and Andrafiamena-Andavakoera massifs, Madagascar. *Primate Conservation* 30(1): 59–72.

Fredsted, T., Pertoldi, C., Olesen, J. M., Eberle, M., and Kappeler, P. M. 2004. Microgeographic heterogeneity in spatial distribution and mtDNA variability of gray mouse lemurs (*Microcebus murinus*, Primates: Cheirogaleidae). *Behavioral Ecology and Sociobiology* 56: 393–403. https://doi.org/10.1007/s00265-004-0790-9.

Fredsted, T., Pertoldi, C., Schierup, M. H., and Kappeler, P. M. 2005. Microsatellite analyses reveal fine-scale genetic structure in grey mouse lemurs (*Microcebus murinus*). *Molecular Ecology* 14: 2363–2372. https://doi.org/10.1111/j.1365-294X.2005.02596.x.

Freed, B. Z. 1996. Co-occurrence among crowned lemurs (*Lemur coronatus*) and Sanford's lemurs (*Lemur fulvus sanfordi*) of Madagascar. PhD thesis, Department of Anthropology, Washington University, Saint Louis.

Fu, Y. X. 1997. Statistical tests of neutrality of mutations against population growth, hitchhiking and background selection. *Genetics* 147: 915–925.

Fuller, D. Q., and Boivin, N. 2009. Crops, cattle and commensals across the Indian Ocean: Current and potential archaeobiological evidence. In Plantes et Sociétés, ed. G. Lefèvre. *Etudes Océan Indien* 42–43: 13–46.

Gabriel, D. N., Gould, L., and Cook S. 2018. Crowding as a primary source of stress in an endangered fragment-dwelling strepsirrhine primate. *Animal Conservation* 21: 76–85. https://doi.org/10.1111/acv.12375.

Gachot-Neveu, H., Petit, M., and Roeder, J. J. 1999. Paternity determination in two groups of *Eulemur fulvus mayottensis*: Implications for understanding mating strategies. *International Journal of Primatology* 20: 107–119. https://doi.org/10.1023/A:1020588301716.

Gamba, M., Favaro, L., Torti, V., Sorrentino, V., and Giacoma, C. 2011. Vocal tract flexibility and variation in the vocal output in wild indris. *Bioacoustics* 20: 251–266.

Gamba, M., Torti, V., Estienne, V., Randrianarison, R. M., Valente, D., Rovara, P., Bonadonna, G., Friard O., and Giacoma, C. 2016. The indris have got rhythm! Timing and pitch variation of a primate song examined between sexes and age classes. *Frontiers in Neuroscience* 10: 249.

Ganzhorn, J. U. 1985. Utilization of *Eucalyptus* and pine plantations by brown lemurs in the eastern rainforest of Madagascar. *Primate Conservation* 6: 34–35.

———. 1987. A possible role of plantations for primate conservation in Madagascar. *American Journal of Primatology* 12: 205–215.

———. 1988. Food partitioning among Malagasy primates. *Oecologia* 75: 436–450.

———. 1989a. Niche separation of seven lemur species in the eastern rainforest of Madagascar. *Oecologia* 79: 279–286.

———. 1989b. Primate species separation in relation to secondary plant chemicals. *Human Evolution* 4: 125–132.

———. 1993. Flexibility and constraints of *Lepilemur* ecology. In *Lemur Social Systems and Their Ecological Basis*, eds. P. M. Kappeler and J. U. Ganzhorn, pp. 153–165. New York: Plenum Press.

———. 1994. Les lémuriens. In Inventaire biologique forêt de Zombitse, eds. S. M. Goodman and O. Langrand. *Recherches pour le Développement*, série *Sciences Biologiques*, no. spécial: 70–72.

———. 1995. Low-level forest disturbance effects on primary production, leaf chemistry, and lemur population. *Ecology* 76: 2084–2096.

———. 2002. Distribution of a folivorous lemur in relation to seasonally varying food resources: Integrating quantitative and qualitative aspects of food characteristics. *Oecologia* 131: 427–435.

———. 2003. Effects of introduced *Rattus rattus* on endemic small mammals in dry deciduous forest fragments of western Madagascar. *Animal Conservation* 6(2): 147–157.

Ganzhorn, J. U., and Abraham, J.-P. 1991. Possible role of plantations for lemur conservation in Madagascar: Food for folivorous species. *Folia Primatologica* 56: 171–176.

Ganzhorn, J. U., and Kappeler, P. M. 1996. Lemurs of the Kirindy Forest. In Ecology and economy of a tropical dry forest in Madagascar, eds. J. U. Ganzhorn and J.-P. Sorg. *Primate Report*, special issue, 46(1): 257–274.

Ganzhorn, J. U., and Rabesoa, J. 1986a. The aye-aye (*Daubentonia madagascariensis*) found in eastern rain forest of Madagascar. *Folia Primatologica* 46: 125–126.

Ganzhorn, J. U., and Rabesoa, J. 1986b. Sightings of aye-aye in the eastern rainforest of Madagascar. *Primate Conservation* 7: 45.

Ganzhorn, J. U., and Schmid, J. 1998. Different population dynamics of *Microcebus murinus* in primary and secondary deciduous dry forest of Madagascar. *International Journal of Primatology* 19: 785–796.

Ganzhorn, J. U., Abraham, J. P., and Razanahoera-Rakotomalala, M. 1985. Some aspects of the natural history and food selection of *Avahi laniger*. *Primates* 26: 452–463.

Ganzhorn, J. U., Ganzhorn, A. W., Abraham, J. P., Andriamanarivo, and Ramananjatovo, A. 1990. The impact of selective logging on forest structure and tenrec populations in western Madagascar. *Oecologia* 84: 126–133.

Ganzhorn, J. U., Sommer, S., Abraham, J.-P., Ade, M., Raharivololona, B. M., Rakotovao, E. R., Rakotondrasoa, C., and Randriamarosoa, R. 1996. Mammals of the Kirindy Forest with special emphasis on *Hypogeomys antimena* and the effects of logging on the small mammal fauna. In Ecology and economy of a tropical dry forest in Madagascar, eds. J. U. Ganzhorn and J.-P. Sorg. *Primate Report*, special issue, 46(1): 215–232.

Ganzhorn, J. U., Malcomber, S., Andrianantoanina, O., and Goodman, S, M. 1997. Habitat characteristics and lemur species richness in Madagascar. *Biotropica* 29: 331–343.

Ganzhorn, J. U., Fietz, J., Rakotovao, E., Schwab, D., and Zinner, D. 1999a. Lemurs and the regeneration of dry deciduous forest in Madagascar. *Conservation Biology* 13: 794–804.

Ganzhorn, J. U., Wright, P. C., and Ratsimbazafy, J. 1999b. Primate communities: Madagascar. In *Primate Communities*, eds. J. G. Fleagle, C. Janson, and K. E. Reed, pp. 75–89. Cambridge: Cambridge University Press.

Ganzhorn, J. U., Goodman, S. M., and Dehgan, A. 2003. Effects of forest fragmentation on small mammals and lemurs. In *The Natural History of Madagascar*, eds. S. M. Goodman and J. P. Benstead, pp. 1228–1234. Chicago: University of Chicago Press.

Ganzhorn, J. U., Goodman, S. M., Nash, S., and Thalmann, U. 2006. Lemur biogeography. In *Primate Biogeography: Progress and Prospects*, eds. J. Fleagle and S. M. Lehman, pp. 229–254. New York: Kluwer Academic.

Ganzhorn, J. U., Andrianasolo, T., Andrianjazalahatra, T., Donati, G., Fietz, J., et al. 2007. Lemurs in evergreen littoral forest fragments of different size and degrees of degradation. In *Biodiversity, Ecology and Conservation of the Littoral Ecosystems of South-eastern Madagascar*, eds. J. U. Ganzhorn, S. M. Goodman, and M. Vincelette, pp. 223–236. Washington, DC: Smithsonian Institution Press.

Ganzhorn, J. U., Arrigo-Nelson, S. J., Carrai, V., Chalise, M. K., Donati, G., et al. 2017. The importance of protein in leaf selection of folivorous primates. *American Journal of Primatology* 79: e22550.

Gardner, C. J. 2009. A review of the impacts of anthropogenic habitat change on terrestrial biodiversity in Madagascar: Implications for the design and management of new protected areas. *Malagasy Nature* 2: 2–29.

———. 2016. Use of mangroves by lemurs. *International Journal of Primatology* 37: 317–332.

Gardner, C. J., and Jasper, L. 2009. Possible new *Mirza* taxon from the Fiherenana River valley, Atsimo-Andrefana Region. *Lemur News* 14: 46–49.

Gardner, C. J., Radolalaina, P., Rajerison, M., and Greene, H. W. 2015. Cooperative rescue and predator fatality involving a group-living strepsirrhine, Coquerel's sifaka (*Propithecus coquereli*), and a Madagascar ground boa (*Acrantophis madagascariensis*). *Primates* 56: 127–129.

Garza, J. C., and Williamson, E. G. 2001. Detection of reduction in population size using data from microsatellite loci. *Molecular Ecology* 10: 305–318. https://doi.org/10.1046/j.1365-294x.2001.01190.x.

Gascon, C., Williamson, G. B., and da Fonseca, G.A.B. 2000. Receding forest edges and vanishing reserves. *Science* 288(5470): 1356–1358.

Gaubert, P., Wozencraft, W. C., Cordeiro-Estrela, P., and Veron, G. 2005. Mosaic of convergences, noise and misleading morphological phylogenies: What's in a viverrid-like carnivoran? *Systematic Biology* 54: 865–894.

Gaubert, P., Patel, R. P., Veron, G., Goodman, S. M., Willsch, M., et al. 2017. Phylogeography of the Small Indian Civet and origin of introductions to western Indian Ocean islands. *Journal of Heredity* 108(3): 270–279. https://doi.org/10.1093/jhered/esw085.

Gautier, L., Tahinarivony, J. A., Ranirison, P., and Wohlhauser, S. 2018. Végetation/Vegetation. In *Les aires protégées terrestres de Madagascar: Leur histoire, description et biote/The Terrestrial Protected Areas of Madagascar: Their History, Description,*

and Biota, eds. S. M. Goodman, M. J. Raherilalao, and S. Wohlhauser, pp. 207–242. Antananarivo: Association Vahatra.

Geiser, F. 2004. Metabolic rate and body temperature reduction during hibernation and daily torpor. *Annual Review of Physiology* 66: 239–274.

Geiser, F., and Drury, R. L. 2003. Radiant heat affects thermoregulation and energy expenditure during rewarming from torpor. *Journal of Comparative Physiology B: Biochemical, Systemic, and Environmental Physiology* 173: 55–60.

Geiser, F., and Turbill, C. 2009. Hibernation and daily torpor minimize mammalian extinctions. *Naturwissenschaften* 96: 1235–1240.

Gemmill, A., and Gould, L. 2008. Microhabitat variation and its effects on dietary composition and intragroup feeding interactions between adult female *Lemur catta* during the dry season at Beza Mahafaly Special Reserve, southwestern Madagascar. *International Journal of Primatology* 29: 1511–1533.

Genest, H., and Petter, F. 1975. Family Tenrecidae. Part 1.1. In *The Mammals of Africa: An Identification Manual*, eds. J. Meester and H. W. Setzer, pp. 1–7. Washington, DC: Smithsonian Institution Press.

Génin, F. 2003. Female dominance in competition for gum trees in the grey mouse lemur *Microcebus murinus*. *Revue d'Ecologie* (*La Terre et la Vie*) 58: 397–410.

———. 2008. Life in unpredictable environments: First investigation of the natural history of *Microcebus griseorufus*. *International Journal of Primatology* 29: 303–321.

———. 2010. Who sleeps with whom? Sleeping association and socio-territoriality in *Microcebus griseorufus*. *Journal of Mammalogy* 91: 942–951.

Génin, F., and Rambeloarivony, H. 2018. Mouse lemurs (Primates: Cheirogaleidae) cultivate green fruit gardens. *Biological Journal of the Linnean Society* 124: 607–620.

Génin, F., Masters, J. C., and Ganzhorn, J. U. 2010. Gummivory in cheirogaleids: Primitive retention or adaptation to hypervariable environments? In *The Evolution of Exudativory in Primates*, eds. L. T. Nash and A. M. Burrows, pp. 123–140. New York: Springer.

Genini, M. 1996. Deforestation. In Ecology and economy of a tropical dry forest in Madagascar, eds. J. U. Ganzhorn and J.-P. Sorg. *Primate Report*, special issue, 46(1): 49–55.

Geoffroy Saint-Hilaire, I. 1851. Première partie. Mammifères. Catalogue des primates. In *Catalogue méthodique de la collection des mammifères de la collection des oiseaux et des collections annexés, Muséum d'Histoire Naturelle de Paris*. Paris: Gide et Baudry.

Gérard, A., Ganzhorn, J. U., Kull, C. A., and Carrière, S. M. 2015. Possible roles of introduced plants for native vertebrate conservation: The case of Madagascar. *Restoration Ecology* 23: 768–775.

Gerber, B. D. 2010. Comparing density analyses and carnivore ecology in Madagascar's southeastern rainforest. PhD thesis, Virginia Tech.

Gerber, B.[D.], Karpanty, S. M., Crawford, C., Kotschwar, M., and Randrianantenaina, J. 2010. An assessment of carnivore relative abundance and density in the eastern rainforests of Madagascar using remotely-triggered camera traps. *Oryx* 44(02): 219–222.

Gerber, B. D., Karpanty, S. M., and Randrianantenaina, J. 2012a. The impact of forest logging and fragmentation on carnivore species composition, density and occupancy in Madagascar's rainforests. *Oryx* 46: 414–422.

Gerber, B. D., Karpanty, S. M., and Randrianantenaina, J. 2012b. Activity patterns of carnivores in the rain forests of Madagascar: Implications for species coexistence. *Journal of Mammalogy* 93: 667–676.

Gerber, B. D., Karpanty, S. M., and Kelly, M. J. 2012c. Evaluating the potential biases in carnivore capture–recapture studies associated with the use of lure and varying density estimation techniques using photographic-sampling data of the Malagasy civet. *Population Ecology* 54: 43–54.

GERP (Groupe d'Etude et de Recherche sur les Primates de Madagascar). 2016. Red ruffed lemur project: Study on the feasibility of the *Varecia rubra* reintroduction programme in the tropical reserve of Fanankaraina (District of Maroantsetra, Analanjirofo). Executive Summary: Compilation of mission reports in Fanankaraina (2014–2016). Antananarivo: GERP.

Giacoma, C., Sorrentino, V., Rabarivola, C., and Gamba, M. 2010. Sex differences in the song of *Indri indri*. *International Journal of Primatology* 31(4): 539–551. https://doi.org/10.1007/s10764-010-9412-8.

Gilabert, A., Loiseau, A., Duplantier, J.-M., Rahelinirina, S., Rahalison, L., Chanteau, S., and Brouat, C. 2007. Genetic structure of black rat populations in a rural plague focus in Madagascar. *Canadian Journal of Zoology* 85: 965–972. https://doi.org/10.1139/Z07-083.

Gilbert, C., Goodman, S. M., Soarimalala, V., Olson, L. E., O'Brien, P.C.M., Elder, F.F.B., Yang, F., Ferguson-Smith, M. A., and Robinson, T. J. 2007. Chromosomal evolution in tenrecs (*Microgale* and *Oryzorictes*, Tenrecidae) from the Central Highlands of Madagascar. *Chromosome Research* 15: 1075–1091.

Gilbert, M., and Tingay, R. E. 2001. Predation of a fat-tailed dwarf lemur *Cheirogaleus medius* by a Madagascar harrier-hawk *Polyboroides radiatus*: An incidental observation. *Lemur News* 6: 6.

Giroud, S., Blanc, S., Aujard, F., Bertrand, F., Gilbert, C., and Perret, M. 2008. Chronic food shortage and seasonal modulations of daily torpor and locomotor activity in the grey mouse lemur (*Microcebus murinus*). *American Journal of Regulatory and Integrative Comparative Physiology* 294: R1958-R1967.

Glander, K. E., and Powzyk, J. A. 1998. Morphometrics of wild *Indri indri* and *Propithecus diadema diadema*. *Folia Primatologica* 69, supplement 1: 399.

Glander, K. E., Wright, P. C., Seigler, D. S., Randrianasolo, V., and Randrianasolo, B. 1989. Consumption of cyanogenic bamboo by a newly discovered species of bamboo lemur. *American Journal of Primatology* 19: 119–124.

Glaston, A. R. 1983. Olfactory communication in the lesser mouse lemur (*Microcebus murinus*). In *Perspectives in Primate Biology*, ed. P. K. Smith, pp. 63–73. New Delhi: Today and Tomorrow's Printers and Publishers.

Glenn, T. C. 2011. Field guide to next-generation DNA sequencers. *Molecular Ecology Resources* 11: 759–769. https://doi.org/10.1111/j.1755-0998.2011.03024.x.

Glessner, K.D.G., and Britt, A. 2005. Population density and home range size of *Indri indri* in a protected low altitude rain forest. *International Journal of Primatology* 26(4): 855–872. https://doi.org/10.1007/s10764-005-5326-2.

Gligor, M., Ganzhorn, J. U., Rakotondravony, D., Ramilijaona, O. R., Razafimahatratra, E., Zischler, H., and Hapke, A. 2009. Hybridization between mouse lemurs in an ecological transition zone in southern Madagascar. *Molecular Ecology* 18: 520–533. https://doi.org/10.1111/j.1365-294X.2008.04040.x.

Godfrey, L. R. 1986. The tale of the tsy-aomby-aomby. *Sciences* (Jan.–Feb.): 49–51.

Godfrey, L. R., and Jungers, W. L. 2003. The extinct sloth lemurs. *Evolutionary Anthropology* 12: 252–263.

Godfrey, L. R., Lyon, S. K., and Sutherland, M. R. 1993. Sexual dimorphism in large-bodied primates: The case of the subfossil lemurs. *American Journal of Physical Anthropology* 90: 315–334.

Godfrey, L. R., Jungers, W. L., Reed, K. E., Simons, E. L., and Chatrath, P. S. 1997. Subfossil lemurs: Inferences about past and present primate communities in Madagascar. In *Natural Change and Human Impact in Madagascar*, eds. S. M. Goodman and B. D. Patterson, pp. 218–256. Washington, DC: Smithsonian Institution Press.

Godfrey, L. R., Jungers, W. L., Simons, E. L., Chatrath, P. S., and Rakotosamimanana, B. 1999. Past and present distributions of lemurs in Madagascar. In *New Directions in Lemur Studies*, eds. B. Rakotosamimanana, H. Rasamimanana, J. U. Ganzhorn, and S. M. Goodman, pp. 19–53. New York: Kluwer Academic/Plenum Press.

Godfrey, L. R., Samonds, K. E., Jungers, W. L., Sutherland, M. R., and Irwin, M. T. 2004. Ontogenetic correlates of diet in Malagasy lemurs. *American Journal of Physical Anthropology* 123: 250–276.

Godfrey, L. R., Crowley, B. E., Perez, V. R., Burney, D. A., Jungers, W. L., and Ramarolahy M. 2011. A time frame for butchery of giant lemurs and sifakas at Taolambiby, SW Madagascar. *American Journal of Physical Anthropology* 144(S52): 144.

Godfrey, L. R., Crowley, B. E., Muldoon, K. M., Kelley, E. A., King, S. J., Best, A. W., and Berthaume, M. A. 2016. What did *Hadropithecus* eat, and why should paleoanthropologists care? *American Journal of Primatology* 78: 1098–1112.

Godfrey, L. R., Scroxton, N., Crowley, B. E., Burns, S. J., Sutherland, M. R., Pérez, V. R., Faina, P., McGee, D., and Ranivoharimanana, L. 2019. A new interpretation of Madagascar's megafaunal decline: The "subsistence shift hypothesis." *Journal of Human Evolution* 130: 126–140.

Godinot, M. 2006. Lemuriform origins as viewed from the fossil record. *Folia Primatologica* 77: 446–464.

Golden, C. D. 2009. Bushmeat hunting and use in the Makira Forest, north-eastern Madagascar: A conservation and livelihoods issue. *Oryx* 43: 386–392.

Golden, C. D., and Comaroff, J. 2015. Effects of social change on wildlife consumption taboos in northeastern Madagascar. *Ecology and Society* 20(2): 41.

Golden, C. D., Wrangham, R. W., and Brashares, J. S. 2013. Assessing the accuracy of interviewed recall for rare, highly seasonal events: The case of wildlife consumption in Madagascar. *Animal Conservation* 16: 597–603.

Golden, C. D., Bonds, M. H., Brashares, J. S., Rasolofoniaina, B.J.R., and Kremen, C. 2014. Economic valuation of subsistence harvest of wildlife in Madagascar. *Conservation Biology* 28: 234–243.

Goldstein, D. B., and Chikhi, L. 2002. Human migrations and population structure: What we know and why it matters. *Annual Review of Genomics and Human Genetics* 3: 129–152. https://doi.org/10.1146/annurev.genom.3.022502.103200.

Gomard, Y., Dietrich, M., Wieseke, N., Ramasindrazana, B., Lagadec, E., Goodman, S. M., Dellagi, K., and Tortosa, P. 2016. Malagasy bats shelter a considerable genetic diversity of pathogenic *Leptospira* suggesting notable host-specificity patterns. *FEMS Microbiology Ecology* 92. https://doi.org/10.1093/femsec/fiw037.

Gommery, D., Ziegle, P., Ramanivosoa, B., and Cauvin, J. 1998. Découverte d'un nouveau site a lémuriens subfossiles dan les karsts malgaches. *Comptes Rendus de l'Académie des Sciences*, séries IIA, 326: 823–826.

Gommery, D., Senegas, F., Mein, P., Tombomiadana, S., Ramanivosoa, B., Cauvin, J., and Cauvin, C. 2003. Résultats préliminaires des sites subfossiles d'Antsingiavo (Madagascar). *Comptes Rendus Palevol* 2: 639–648.

Gommery, D., Ramanivosoa, B., Faure, M., Guérin, C., Kerloc'h, P., Sénégas, F., and Randrianantenaina, H. 2011. Les plus anciennes traces d'activités anthropiques de Madagascar sur des ossements d'hippopotames subfossiles d'Anjohibe. *Comptes Rendus Palevol* 10: 271–278.

Gommery, D., Ramanivosoa, B., Mein, P., Sénégas, F., Faure, M., and Guérin, C. 2018. Les recherches franco-malgaches à Belobaka de 2003 à 2012 (Province de Mahajanga, nord-ouest de Madagascar). *Revue de Paléobiologie* 37(2): 469–481.

Goodman, M., Baileym, W. J., Hayasaka, K., Stanhope, M. J., Slightom, J., and Czelusniak, J. 1994. Molecular evidence on primate phylogeny from DNA sequences. *American Journal of Physical Anthropology* 94: 3–24. https://doi.org/10.1002/ajpa.1330940103.

Goodman, S. M. 1994. A description of the ground burrow of *Eliurus webbi* (Nesomyinae) and case of cohabitation with an endemic bird (Brachypteraciidae, *Brachypteracias*). *Mammalia* 58: 670–672.

———. 1995. *Rattus* on Madagascar and the dilemma of protecting the endemic rodent fauna. *Conservation Biology* 9: 450–453.

———. 1996a. A subfossil record of *Galidictis grandidieri* (Herpestidae: Galidiinae) from southwestern Madagascar. *Mammalia* 60: 150–151.

———. 1996b. The carnivores of the Réserve Naturelle Intégrale d'Andringitra, Madagascar. In A floral and faunal inventory of the eastern slopes of the Réserve Naturelle Intégrale d'Andringitra, Madagascar: With reference to elevational variation, ed. S. M. Goodman. *Fieldiana: Zoology*, new ser., 85: 289–292.

———, ed. 1998. A floral and faunal inventory of the Réserve Spéciale d'Anjanaharibe-Sud, Madagascar: With reference to elevational variation. *Fieldiana: Zoology*, new ser., 90: 1–246.

———. 2003a. *Oryzorictes*, mole tenrec or rice tenrec. In *The Natural History of Madagascar*, eds. S. M. Goodman and J. P. Benstead, pp. 1278–1281. Chicago: University of Chicago Press.

———. 2003b. Predation on lemurs. In *The Natural History of Madagascar*, eds. S. M. Goodman and J. P. Benstead, pp. 1221–1228. Chicago: University of Chicago Press.

———. 2006. Hunting of Microchiroptera in southwestern Madagascar. *Oryx* 40: 225–228.

———. 2009. Family Eupleridae (Madagascar carnivores). In *Handbook of the Mammals of the World*. Vol. 1, *Carnivores*, eds. D. E. Wilson and R. A. Mittermeier, pp. 330–351. Barcelona: Lynx Edicions.

———. 2011. *Les chauves-souris de Madagascar*. Antananarivo: Association Vahatra.

———. 2012. *Les Carnivora de Madagascar*. Antananarivo: Association Vahatra.

———. 2013. Carnivorans ou ordre des Carnivora/Carnivorans or the Order Carnivora. In *Atlas d'une sélection de vertébrés terrestres de Madagascar/Atlas of Selected Land Vertebrates of Madagascar*, eds. S. M. Goodman and M. J. Raherilalao, pp. 271–285. Antananarivo: Association Vahatra.

Goodman, S. M., and Benstead J. P. 2003. *The Natural History of Madagascar*. Chicago: University of Chicago Press.

Goodman, S. M., and Cardiff, S. G. 2004. A new species of *Chaerephon* (Molossidae) from Madagascar with notes on other members of the family. *Acta Chiropterologica* 6: 227–248.

Goodman, S. M., and Carleton, M. D. 1996. The rodents of the Réserve Naturelle Intégrale d'Andringitra. In A floral and faunal inventory of the eastern slopes of the Réserve Naturelle Intégrale d'Andringitra, Madagascar: With reference to elevational variation, ed. S. M. Goodman. *Fieldiana: Zoology*, new ser., 85: 257–283.

Goodman, S. M., and Carleton, M. D. 1998. The rodents of the Réserve Spéciale d'Anjanaharibe-Sud, Madagascar. In A floral and faunal inventory of the Réserve Spéciale d'Anjanaharibe-Sud, Madagascar: With reference to elevational variation, ed. S. M. Goodman. *Fieldiana: Zoology*, new ser., 90: 201–221.

Goodman, S. M., and Ganzhorn, J. U. 1994. Les petits mammifères. In Inventaire biologique forêt de Zombitse, eds. S. M. Goodman and O. Langrand. *Recherches pour le Développement*, série *Sciences Biologiques*, no. spécial: 58–63.

Goodman, S. M., and Griffiths, O. 2006. A case of exceptionally high predation levels of *Rousettus madagascariensis* by *Tyto alba* (Aves: Tytonidae) in western Madagascar. *Acta Chiropterologica* 8(3): 553–556.

Goodman, S. M., and Griffiths, O. 2009. Notes on the diet of the Barn Owl (Aves: Tytonidae: *Tyto alba*) from Zohin'Andavaka, Beahitse, extreme southwestern Madagascar. *Malagasy Nature* 2: 163–166.

Goodman, S. M., and Helgen, K. M. 2010. Species limits and distribution of the Malagasy carnivoran genus *Eupleres* (family Eupleridae). *Mammalia* 74: 177–185. https://doi.org/10.1515/mamm.2010.018.

Goodman, S. M., and Jenkins, P. D. 1998. The insectivores of the Réserve Spéciale d'Anjanaharibe-Sud, Madagascar. In A floral and faunal inventory of the Réserve Spéciale d'Anjanaharibe-Sud, Madagascar: With reference to elevational variation, ed. S. M. Goodman. *Fieldiana: Zoology*, new ser., 90: 139–161.

Goodman, S. M., and Jenkins, P. D. 2000. Tenrecs (Lipotyphla: Tenrecidae) of the Parc National de Marojejy, Madagascar. In A floral and faunal inventory of the Parc National de Marojejy, Madagascar: With reference to elevational variation, ed. S. M. Goodman. *Fieldiana: Zoology*, new ser., 97: 201–229.

Goodman, S. M., and Jungers, W. L. 2014. *Extinct Madagascar. Picturing the Island's Past*. Chicago: University of Chicago Press.

Goodman, S. M., and Langrand, O. 1996a. Food remains found in a nest of the Madagascar Buzzard (*Buteo brachypterus*) in the Vohibasia Forest. *Newsletter of the Working Group on Birds in the Madagascar Region* 6(2): 13–14.

Goodman, S. M., and Langrand, O. 1996b. A high mountain population of the ring-tailed lemur *Lemur catta* on the Andringitra Massif, Madagascar. *Oryx* 30(4): 259–268.

Goodman, S. M., and Maminirina, C. P. 2007. Specimen records referred to *Miniopterus majori* Thomas, 1906 (Chiroptera) from the Comoros islands. *Mammalia* 2007: 151–156.

Goodman, S. M., and Pidgeon, M. 1992. Madagascar Harrier Hawk (*Polyboroides radiatus*) preying on flying fox (*Pteropus rufus*). *Ostrich* 62: 215–216.

Goodman, S. M., and Pidgeon, M. 1999. Carnivora of the Réserve Naturelle Intégrale d'Andohahela, Madagascar. In A floral and faunal inventory of the Réserve Naturelle Intégrale d'Andohahela, Madagascar: With reference to elevational variation, ed. S. M. Goodman. *Fieldiana, Zoology*, new ser., 94: 256–268.

Goodman, S. M., and Rakotondravony, D. 1996. The Holocene distribution of *Hypogeomys* (Rodentia: Muridae: Nesomyinae) on Madagascar: In *Biogéographie de Madagascar*, ed. W. R. Lourenço, pp. 283–293. Paris: Editions de l'ORSTOM.

Goodman, S. M., and Rakotondravony, D. 2000. The effects of forest fragmentation and isolation on insectivorous small mammals (Lipotyphla) on the Central High Plateau of Madagascar. *Journal of Zoology* 250: 193–200.

Goodman, S. M., and Ramasindrazana, B. 2013. Chauves-souris ou ordre des Chiroptera/Bats or the Order Chiroptera. In *Atlas d'une sélection de vertébrés terrestres de Madagascar/Atlas of Selected Land Vertebrates of Madagascar*, eds. S. M. Goodman and M. J. Raherilalao, pp. 169–209. Antananarivo: Association Vahatra.

Goodman, S. M., and Ranivo, J. 2009. The geographical origin of the type specimens of *Triaenops humbloti* and *T. rufus* (Chiroptera: Hipposideridae) reputed to be from Madagascar and the description of a replacement species name. *Mammalia* 73: 47–55.

Goodman, S. M., and Rasolonandrasana, B.P.N., eds. 1999. Inventaire biologique de la Réserve Spéciale de Pic d'Ivohibe et du couloir forestier qui la relie au Parc National d'Andringitra. *Recherches pour le Développement*, série *Sciences Biologiques*, 15: 1–180.

Goodman, S. M., and Rasolonandrasana, B.P.N. 2001. Elevational zonation of birds, insectivores, rodents and primates on the slopes of the Andringitra Massif, Madagascar. *Journal of Natural History* 35: 285–305.

Goodman, S. M., and Schütz, H. 2003. Specimen evidence of the continued existence of the Malagasy rodent *Nesomys lambertoni* (Muridae: Nesomyinae). *Mammalia* 67: 445–449.

Goodman, S. M., and Soarimalala, V. 2002. Les petits mammifères de la Réserve Spéciale de Manongarivo, Madagascar. In Inventaire floristique et faunistique de la Réserve Spéciale de Manongarivo (NW Madagascar), eds. L. Gautier and S. M. Goodman. *Boissiera* 59: 383–401.

Goodman, S. M., and Soarimalala, V. 2004. A new species of *Microgale* (Lipotyphla: Tenrecidae: Oryzorictinae) from the Forêt des Mikea of southwestern Madagascar. *Proceedings of the Biological Society of Washington* 117(3): 251–265.

Goodman, S. M., and Soarimalala, V. 2005. A new species of *Macrotarsomys* (Rodentia: Muridae: Nesomyinae) from southwestern Madagascar. *Proceedings of the Biological Society of Washington* 118: 450–464.

Goodman, S. M., and Soarimalala, V. 2018. Systématique des rongeurs endémiques malgaches (famille des Nesomyidae: sous-famille des Nesomyinae)/Systematics of endemic Malagasy rodents (family Nesomyidae: subfamily Nesomyinae). In *Les aires protégées terrestres de Madagascar: Leur histoire, description et biote/The Terrestrial Protected Areas of Madagascar: Their History, Description, and Biota*, eds. S. M. Goodman, M. J. Raherilalao, and S. Wohlhauser, pp. 373–381. Antananarivo: Association Vahatra.

Goodman, S. M., and Sterling, E. J. 1996. The utilization of *Canarium* (Burseraceae) seeds by vertebrates in the Réserve Naturelle Intégrale d'Andringitra, Madagascar. In A floral and faunal inventory of the eastern slopes of the Réserve Naturelle Intégrale d'Andringitra, Madagascar: With reference to elevational variation, ed. S. M. Goodman. *Fieldiana: Zoology*, new ser., 85: 83–89.

Goodman, S. M., and Thorstrom, R. 1998. The diet of the Madagascar red owl (*Tyto soumagnei*) on the Masoala Peninsula, Madagascar. *Wilson Bulletin* 110: 417–421.

Goodman, S. M., and Wilmé, L., eds. 2008. Les forêts sèches de Madagascar. *Malagasy Nature* 1: 1–189.

Goodman, S. M., Creighton, G. K., and Raxworthy, C. 1991. The food habits of the Madagascar long-eared owl *Asio madagascariensis* in southeastern Madagascar. *Bonner Zoologische Beiträge* 42: 21–26.

Goodman, S. M., O'Connor, S., and Langrand, O. 1993a. A review of predation on lemurs: Implications for the evolution of social behavior in small, nocturnal primates. In *Lemur Social Systems and Their Ecological Basis*, eds. P. M. Kappeler and J. U. Ganzhorn, pp. 51–66. New York: Plenum Press.

Goodman, S. M., Langrand, O., and Raxworthy, C. 1993b. Food habits of the Madagascar long-eared owl *Asio madagascariensis* in two habitats in southern Madagascar. *Ostrich* 64: 79–85.

Goodman, S. M., Langrand, O., and Raxworthy, C. J. 1993c. The food habits of the barn owl *Tyto alba* at three sites on Madagascar. *Ostrich* 64: 160–171.

Goodman, S. M., Rakotondravony, D., Schatz, G., and Wilmé, L. 1996a. Species richness of forest-dwelling birds, rodents and insectivores in a planted forest of native trees: A test case from the Ankaratra, Madagascar. *Ecotropica* 2: 109–120.

Goodman, S. M., Andrianarimisa, A., Olson, L. E., and Soarimalala, V. 1996b. Patterns of elevational distribution of birds and small mammals in the humid forests of Montagne d'Ambre, Madagascar. *Ecotropica* 2: 87–98.

Goodman, S. M., Lewis, B. A., Phillipson, P. B., and Raharilala, J. 1996c. Appendix 4-2. Vertebrate food plants on the eastern slopes of the RNI d'Andringitra. In A floral and faunal inventory of the eastern slopes of the Réserve Naturelle Intégrale d'Andringitra, Madagascar: With reference to elevational variation, ed. S. M. Goodman. *Fieldiana: Zoology*, new ser., 85: 72–75.

Goodman, S. M., Raxworthy, C. J., and Jenkins, P. D. 1996d. Insectivore ecology in the Réserve Naturelle Intégrale d'Andringitra, Madagascar. In A floral and faunal inventory of the eastern slopes of the Réserve Naturelle Intégrale d'Andringitra, Madagascar: With reference to elevational variation, ed. S. M. Goodman. *Fieldiana: Zoology*, new ser., 85: 218–230.

Goodman, S. M, Ganzhorn, J. U., Olson, L. E., Pidgeon, M., and Soarimalala, V. 1997a. Annual variation in species diversity and relative density of rodents and insectivores in the Parc National de la Montagne d'Ambre, Madagascar. *Ecotropica* 3: 109–118.

Goodman, S. M., Jenkins, P. D., and Langrand, O. 1997b. Exceptional records of *Microgale* species (Insectivora: Tenrecidae) in vertebrate food remains. *Bonner Zoologische Beiträge* 47: 135–138.

Goodman, S. M., Langrand, O., and Rasolonandrasana, B.P.N. 1997c. The food habits of *Cryptoprocta ferox* in the high mountain zone of the Andringitra Massif, Madagascar (Carnivora, Viverridae). *Mammalia* 61: 185–192.

Goodman, S. M., Ganzhorn, J. U., and Wilmé, L. 1997d. Observations at a *Ficus* tree in Malagasy humid forest. *Biotropica* 29: 480–488.

Goodman, S. M., Langrand, O., and Rasoloarison, R. 1997e. Les lémuriens. In Inventaire biologique forêt de Vohibasia et d'Isoky-Vohimena, eds. O. Langrand and S. M. Goodman. *Recherches pour le Développement*, série *Sciences Biologiques*, 12: 156–161.

Goodman, S., Rene de Roland, L.-A., and Thorstrom, R. 1998a. Predation on the eastern woolly lemur (*Avahi laniger*) and other vertebrates by Henst's goshawk (*Accipiter henstii*). *Lemur News* 3: 14–15.

Goodman, S. M., Rakotondravony, D., Olson, L. E., Razafimahatratra, E., and Soarimalala, V. 1998b. Les insectivores et les rongeurs. In Inventaire biologique, Forêt d'Andranomay, Anjozorobe, eds. D. Rakotondravony and S. M. Goodman. *Recherches pour le Développement*, série *Sciences Biologiques*, 13: 80–93.

Goodman, S. M., Carleton, M. D., and Pidgeon, M. 1999a. Rodents of the Réserve Naturelle Intégrale d'Andohahela, Madagascar. In A floral and faunal inventory of the Réserve Naturelle Intégrale d'Andohahela, Madagascar: With reference to elevational variation, ed. S. M. Goodman. *Fieldiana: Zoology*, new ser. 94: 217–249.

Goodman, S. M., Jenkins, P. D., and Pidgeon, M. 1999b. The Lipotyphla (Tenrecidae and Soricidae) of the Réserve Naturelle Intégrale d'Andohahela, Madagascar. In A floral and faunal inventory of the Réserve Naturelle Intégrale d'Andohahela, Madagascar: With reference to elevational variation, ed. S. M. Goodman. *Fieldiana: Zoology*, new ser., 94: 187–216.

Goodman, S. M., Rakotondravony, D., Raherilalao, M. J., Rakotomalala, D., Raselimanana, A. P., Soarimalala, V., Duplantier, J.-M., Duchemin, J.-B., and Rafanomezantsoa, J. 2000. Inventaire biologique de la forêt de Tsinjoarivo, Ambatolampy. *Akon'ny Ala* 27: 18–35.

Goodman, S. M., Raherilalao, M. J., Rakotomalala, D., Rakotondravony, D., Raselimanana, A. P., Razakarivony, V., and Soarimalala, V. 2002. Inventaire des vertébrés dans la forêt du Parc National de Tsimanampetsotsa. *Akon'ny Ala* 28: 1–36.

Goodman, S. M., Ganzhorn, J. U., and Rakotondravony, D. 2003a. Introduction to the mammals. In *The Natural History of Madagascar*, eds. S. M. Goodman and J. P. Benstead, pp. 1159–1186. Chicago: University of Chicago Press.

Goodman, S. M., Kerridge, F. J., and Ralisoamalala, R. C. 2003b. A note on the diet of *Fossa fossana* (Carnivora) in the central eastern humid forests of Madagascar. *Mammalia* 67: 595–598.

Goodman, S. M., Soarimalala, V., and Rakotondravony, D. 2003c. The rediscovery of *Brachytarsomys villosa* F. Petter, 1962 (Rodentia, Nesomyinae) in the northern highlands of Madagascar. *Mammalia* 65: 83–86.

Goodman, S. M., Rasoloarison, R. M., and Ganzhorn, J. U. 2004a. On the specific identification of subfossil *Cryptoprocta* (Mammalia, Carnivora) from Madagascar. *Zoosystema* 26(1): 129–143.

Goodman, S. M., Soarimalala, V., and Ganzhorn, J. U. 2004b. La chasse aux animaux sauvages dans la forêt de Mikea. In Inventaire floristique et faunistique de la forêt de Mikea: Paysage écologique et diversité biologique d'une préoccupation majeure pour la conservation, eds. A. P. Raselimanana, and S. M. Goodman. *Recherches pour le Développement*, série *Sciences Biologiques*, 2: 95–100.

Goodman, S. M., Andriafidison, D., Andrianaivoarivelo, R., Cardiff, S. G., Ifticene, E., et al. 2005a. The distribution and conservation of bats in the dry regions of Madagascar. *Animal Conservation* 8: 153–165.

Goodman, S. M., Jenkins, R.K.B., and Ratrimomanarivo, F. H. 2005b. A review of the genus *Scotophilus* (Chiroptera: Vespertilionidae) on Madagascar, with the description of a new species. *Zoosystema* 27: 867–882.

Goodman, S. M., Thomas, H., and Kidney, D. 2005c. The rediscovery of *Mungotictis decemlineata lineata* Pocock, 1915 (Carnivora: Eupleridae) in southwestern Madagascar: Insights into its taxonomic status and distribution. *Small Carnivore Conservation* 33: 1–5.

Goodman, S. M., Rakotondravony, D., Randriamanantsoa, H. N., and Rakotomalala-Razanahoera, M. 2005d. A new species of rodent from the montane forest of central eastern Madagascar (Muridae: Nesomyinae: *Voalavo*). *Proceedings of the Biological Society of Washington* 118(4): 863–873.

Goodman, S. M., Vasey, N., and Burney, D. A. 2006a. The subfossil occurrence and paleoecological implications of *Macrotarsomys petteri* (Rodentia: Nesomyidae) in extreme southeastern Madagascar. *Comptes Rendus Paleovol* 5: 953–962.

Goodman, S. M., Cardiff, S. G., Ranivo, J., Russell, A. L., and Yoder, A. D. 2006b. A new species of *Emballonura* (Chiroptera: Emballonuridae) from the dry regions of Madagascar. *American Museum Novitates* 3538: 1–24.

Goodman, S. M., Raxworthy, C. J., Maminirina, C. P., and Olson, L. E. 2006c. A new species of shrew tenrec (*Microgale jobihely*) from northern Madagascar. *Journal of Zoology* 270: 384–398.

Goodman, S. M., Ratrimomanarivo, F. H., and Randrianandrianina, F. H. 2006d. A new species of *Scotophilus* (Chiroptera: Vespertilionidae) from western Madagascar. *Acta Chiropterologica* 8: 21–37.

Goodman, S. M., Rakotoarisoa, S. V., and Wilmé, L. 2006e. The distribution and biogeography of the ringtailed lemur (*Lemur catta*). In *Ringtailed Lemur Biology:* Lemur catta *in Madagascar*, eds., A. Jolly, R. W. Sussman, N. Koyama, and H. Rasamimanana, pp. 3–15. New York: Springer.

Goodman, S. M., Vasey, N., and Burney, D. A. 2007a. Description of a new species of subfossil shrew tenrec (Afrosoricida: Tenrecidae: *Microgale*) from cave deposits in southeastern Madagascar. *Proceedings of the Biological Society of Washington* 120: 367–376.

Goodman, S. M., Rakotondraparany, F., and Kofoky, A. 2007b. The description of a new species of *Myzopoda* (Myzopodidae: Chiroptera) from western Madagascar. *Mammalian Biology* 72: 65–81.

Goodman, S. M., Ryan, K. E., Maminirina, C. P., Fahr, J., Christidis, L., and Appleton, B. 2007c. The specific status of populations on Madagascar referred to *Miniopterus fraterculus* (Chiroptera: Vespertilionidae). *Journal of Mammalogy* 88: 1216–1229.

Goodman, S. M., Raselimanana, A. P., and Wilmé, L., eds. 2007d. Inventaires de la faune et de la flore d'Anjozorobe-Angavo. *Recherches pour le Développement*, série *Sciences Biologiques*, 24: 1–217.

Goodman, S. M., Cardiff, S. G., and Ratrimomanarivo, F. 2008a. First record of *Coleura* (Chiroptera: Emballonuridae) on Madagascar and identification and diagnosis of members of the genus. *Systematics and Biodiversity* 6: 283–292.

Goodman, S. M., van Vuuren, B. J., Ratrimomanarivo, F., Probst, J. M., and Bowie, R.C.K. 2008b. Specific status of populations in the Mascarene Islands referred to *Mormopterus acetabulosus* (Chiroptera: Molossidae), with description of a new species. *Journal of Mammalogy* 89: 1316–1327.

Goodman, S. M., Bradman, H. M., Maminirina, C. P., Ryan, K. E., Christidis, L., and Appleton, B. 2008c. A new species of *Miniopterus* (Chiroptera: Vespertilionidae) from lowland southeastern Madagascar. *Mammalian Biology* 73: 199–213.

Goodman, S. M., Raheriarisena, M., and Jansa, S. A. 2009a. A new species of *Eliurus* Milne Edwards, 1885 (Rodentia: Nesomyinae) from the Réserve Spéciale d'Ankarana, northern Madagascar. *Bonner Zoologische Beiträge* 56: 133–149.

Goodman, S. M., Maminirina, C. P., Bradman, H. M., Christidis, L., and Appleton, B. 2009b. The use of molecular phylogenetic and morphological tools to identify cryptic and paraphyletic species: Examples from the diminutive long-fingered bats (*Miniopterus*: Miniopteridae: Chiroptera) on Madagascar. *American Museum Novitates* 3669: 1–33.

Goodman, S. M., Maminirina, C. P., Weyeneth, N., Bradman, H. M., Christidis, L., Ruedi, M., and Appleton, B. 2009c. The use of molecular and morphological characters to resolve the taxonomic identity of cryptic species: The case of *Miniopterus manavi* (Chiroptera: Miniopteridae). *Zoologica Scripta* 38: 339–363.

Goodman, S. M., Chan, L. M., Nowak, M. D., and Yoder, A. D. 2010a. Phylogeny and biogeography of western Indian Ocean *Rousettus* (Chiroptera: Pteropodidae). *Journal of Mammalogy* 91(3): 593–606. https://doi.org/10.1644/09-MAMM-A-283.1.

Goodman, S. M., Buccas, W., Naidoo, T., Taylor, P. J., and Lamb, J. 2010b. Patterns of morphological and genetic variation in the western Indian Ocean members of the *Chaerephon "pumilus"* complex (Chiroptera: Molossidae) with the description of a new species from Madagascar. *Zootaxa* 2551: 1–36.

Goodman, S. M., Maminirina, C. P., Bradman, H. M., Christidis, L., and Appleton, B. 2010c. Patterns of morphological and genetic variation in the endemic Malagasy bat *Miniopterus gleni* (Chiroptera: Miniopteridae), with the description of a new species, *M. griffithsi*. *Journal of Zoological Systematics and Evolutionary Research* 48: 75–86.

Goodman, S. M., Weyeneth, N., Ibrahim, Y., Saïd, I., and Ruedi, M. 2010d. A review of the bat fauna of the Comoro archipelago. *Acta Chiropterologica* 12: 117–141.

Goodman, S. M., Ramasindrazana, B., Maminirina, C. P., Schoeman, M. C., and Appleton, B. 2011. Morphological, bioacoustical, and genetic variation in *Miniopterus* bats from eastern Madagascar, with the description of a new species. *Zootaxa* 2880: 1–19.

Goodman, S. M., Puechmaille, S. J., Weyeneth, N. F., Gerlach, J., Ruedi, M., Schoeman, M. C., Stanley, W. T., and Teeling, E. C. 2012a. Phylogeny of the Emballonurini (Emballonuridae) with descriptions of a new genus and species from Madagascar. *Journal of Mammalogy* 93: 1440–1455.

Goodman, S. M., Taylor, P. J., Ratrimomanarivo, F., and Hoofer, S. 2012b. The genus *Neoromicia* (Family Vespertilionidae) in Madagascar, with the description of a new species. *Zootaxa* 3250: 1–25.

Goodman, S. M., Soarimalala, V., Raheriarisena, M., and Rakotondravony, D. 2013. Petit mammifères ou tenrecs (Tenrecidae) et rongeurs (Nesomyidae)/Small mammals or tenrecs (Tenrecidae) and rodents (Nesomyidae). In *Atlas d'une sélection de vertébrés terrestres de Madagascar/Atlas of Selected Land Vertebrates of Madagascar*, eds. S. M. Goodman and M. J. Raherilalao, pp. 211–269. Antananarivo: Association Vahatra.

Goodman, S. M., Mittermeier, J. C., Ramamonjisoa, J., and Rene de Roland, L.-A. 2014a. The dietary habits of barn owls (*Tyto alba*) in the spiny bush of southwestern Madagascar. *Malagasy Nature* 8: 67–72.

Goodman, S. M., Rakotondratsima, M.P.H., and Rene de Roland, L.-A. 2014b. Further evidence of raptor predation on nocturnal lemurs: Remains collected from a nest of the Madagascar goshawk (*Accipiter henstii*). *Lemur News* 18: 5–7.

Goodman, S. M., Rasoanoro, M., Ralisata, M., and Ramasindrazana, B. 2014c. The bats of the Kianjavato-Vatovavy region, lowland eastern central Madagascar. *Malagasy Nature* 8: 89–102.

Goodman, S. M., Randrenjarison, R. A., Soarimalala, V., and Beaucournu, J.-C. 2015a. The fleas of endemic and introduced small mammals in Central Highland forests of Madagascar: Faunistics, species diversity, and absence of host specificity. *Journal of Medical Entomology* 52: 1135–1143.

Goodman, S. M., Rakotondramanana, C. F., Ramasindrazana, B., Kearney, T., Monadjem, A., Schoeman, M. C., Taylor, P. J., Naughton, K., and Appleton, B. 2015b. An integrative approach to characterize Malagasy bats of the subfamily Vespertilioninae Gray, 1821, with the description of a new species of *Hypsugo*. *Zoological Journal of the Linnean Society* 173: 988–1018.

Goodman, S. M., Ramasindrazana, B., Naughton, K. M., and Appleton, B. 2015c. Description of a new species of the *Miniopterus aelleni* group (Chiroptera: Miniopteridae) from upland areas of central and northern Madagascar. *Zootaxa* 3936: 536–558.

Goodman, S. M., Schoeman, M. C., Rakotoarivelo, A., and Willows-Munro, S. 2016a. How many species of *Hipposideros* have occurred on Madagascar since the late Pleistocene? *Zoological Journal of the Linnean Society* 177: 428–449.

Goodman, S. M., Razakaratrimo, S.V.J., and Rene de Roland, L.-A. 2016b. An analysis of Bat Hawk *Macheiramphus alcinus* diet in the Melaky Region of lowland western Madagascar. *Ostrich* 87(1): 77–80.

Goodman, S. M., Kearney, T., Ratsimbazafy, M. M., and Hassanin, A. 2017a. Description of a new species of *Neoromicia* (Chiroptera: Vespertilionidae) from southern Africa: A name for "*N.* cf. *melckorum*." *Zootaxa* 4236: 351–374.

Goodman, S. M., Rajemison, F. I., and Noroalintseheno Lalarivoniaina, O. S. 2017b. Morphometric patterns of secondary sexual dimorphism and seasonal differences in *Rousettus madagascariensis* from northern Madagascar. *Acta Chiropterologica* 19(1): 71–75.

Goodman, S. M., Soarimalala, V., and Olson, L. E. 2018a. Systématique des tenrecs endémiques malgaches (famille des Tenrecidae)/Systematics of endemic Malagasy tenrecs (family Tenrecidae). In *Les aires protégées terrestres de Madagascar: Leur histoire, description, et biote/The Terrestrial Protected Areas of Madagascar: Their History, Description, and Biota*, eds. S. M. Goodman, M. J. Raherilalao, and S. Wohlhauser, pp. 363–372. Antananarivo: Association Vahatra.

Goodman, S. M., Raherilalao, M. J., and Wohlhauser S., eds. 2018b. *Les aires protégées terrestres de Madagascar: Leur histoire, description et biote/The Terrestrial Protected Areas of Madagascar: Their History, Description, and Biota*. Antananarivo: Association Vahatra.

Goodman, S. M., Raherilalao, M. J., Raselimanana, A. P., and Soarimalala, V. 2018c. Advances over the past 30 years on the land vertebrates occurring in the terrestrial protected areas of Madagascar. In *Les aires protégées terrestres de Madagascar: Leur histoire, description et biote/The Terrestrial Protected Areas of Madagascar: Their History, Description, and Biota*, eds. S. M. Goodman, M. J. Raherilalao, and S. Wohlhauser, pp. 1679–1692. Antananarivo: Association Vahatra.

Goodman, S. M., Fratpietro, S., and Tortosa, P. 2020. Insight into the identity and origin of *Scotophilus borbonicus* (E. Geoffroy, 1803). *Acta Chiropterologica* 22(1): 41–47.

Goossens, B., Chikhi, L., Utami, S., de Ruiter, J., and Bruford, M. 2000. A multi-samples, multi-extracts approach for microsatellite analysis of faecal samples in an arboreal ape. *Conservation Genetics* 1: 157–162.

Goossens, B., Chikhi, L., Ancrenaz, M., Lackman-Ancrenaz, I., Andau, P., and Bruford, M. W. 2006. Genetic signature of anthropogenic population collapse in orangutans. *PLoS Biology* 4: e25. https://doi.org/10.1371/journal.pbio.0040025.

Goossens, B., Anthony, N., Jeffery, K., Johnson-Bawe, M., and Bruford, M. W. 2011. Collection, storage and analysis of non-invasive genetic material in primate biology. In *Field and Laboratory Methods in Primatology: A Practical Guide*, eds. J. M. Setchell and D. J. Curtis, pp. 371–386. Cambridge: Cambridge University Press.

Göpfert, M. C., and Wasserthal, L. T. 1995. Notes on echolocation calls, food and roosting behaviour of the Old World sucker-footed bat *Myzopoda aurita* (Chiroptera, Myzopodidae). *Zeitschrift für Säugetierkunde* 60: 1–8

Gordon, A. D., Johnson, S. E., and Louis, E. E., Jr. 2016. Environmental correlates of body mass in true lemurs (*Eulemur* spp.). *International Journal of Primatology* 37: 89–108.

Gould, E. 1965. Evidence for echolocation in the Tenrecidae of Madagascar. *Proceedings of the American Philosophical Society* 109: 352–360.

Gould, E., and Eisenberg, J. F. 1966. Notes on the biology of the Tenrecidae. *Journal of Mammalogy* 47: 660–686.

Gould, L. 1990. The social development of free-ranging infant *Lemur catta* at Berenty Reserve, Madagascar. *International Journal of Primatology* 11(4): 297–318.

———. 1992. Alloparental care in free-ranging *Lemur catta* at Berenty Reserve, Madagascar. *Folia Primatologica* 58(2): 72–83.

Gould, L., and Andrianomena, P. 2015. Ring-tailed lemurs (*Lemur catta*), forest fragments, and community level conservation in south-central Madagascar. *Primate Conservation* 29: 67–73.

Gould, L., and Cowen, L. E. 2020. *Lemur catta* in small forest fragments: Which variables best predict population viability? *American Journal of Primatology* 82(4): e23095. https://doi.org/10.1002/ajp.23095.

Gould, L., and Gabriel, D. N. 2014. Wet and dry season diets of the Endangered *Lemur catta* (ring-tailed lemur) in two mountainous rocky outcrop forest fragments in south-central Madagascar. *African Journal of Ecology* 53: 320–330.

Gould, L., and Sauther, M. L. 2007. Anti-predator strategies in a diurnal prosimian, the ring-tailed lemur (*Lemur catta*), at the Beza Mahafaly Special Reserve, Madagascar. In *Primate Anti-Predator Strategies*, eds. S. L. Gursky and K.A.I. Nekaris, pp. 275–288. New York: Springer Science.

Gould, L., and Sauther, M. L. 2016. Going, going, gone ... Is the iconic ring-tailed lemur (*Lemur catta*) headed for imminent extirpation? *Primate Conservation* 30: 89–101.

Gould, L., Sussman, R. W., and Sauther, M. L. 1999. Natural disasters and primate populations: The effects of a 2-year drought on a naturally occurring population of ring-tailed lemurs (*Lemur catta*) in southwestern Madagascar. *International Journal of Primatology* 20: 69–84.

Gould, L., Sussman, R. W., and Sauther, M. L. 2003. Demographic and life-history patterns in a population of ring-tailed lemurs (*Lemur catta*) at Beza Mahafaly Reserve, Madagascar: A 15-year perspective. *American Journal of Physical Anthropology* 120(2): 182–194.

Gould, L., Constabel, P., Mellway, R., and Rambeloarivony, H. 2009. Condensed tannin intake in spiny-forest-dwelling *Lemur catta* at Berenty Reserve, Madagascar, during reproductive periods. *Folia Primatologica* 80: 249–263.

Gould, L., Power, M. L., Ellwanger, N., and Rambeloarivony, H. 2011. Feeding behavior and nutrient intake in spiny forest-dwelling ring-tailed lemurs (*Lemur catta*) during early gestation and early to mid-lactation periods: Compensating in a harsh environment. *American Journal of Physical Anthropology* 145: 469–479.

Gould, L., Kelley, E. A., and LaFleur, M. 2015. Reproductive female feeding strategies in spiny forest-dwelling *Lemur catta* in southern and southwestern Madagascar: How do females meet the challenges of reproduction in this harsh habitat? *Folia Primatologica* 86: 16–24. https://doi.org/10.1159/000369580.

Goutard, F. 1999. Investigations épidémiologiques sur le potamochère et son rôle dans le maintien de la PPA à l'état enzootique à Madagascar. Montpellier: CEAV Pathologie Tropicale.

Grandidier, A. 1869. Description de quelques animaux nouveaux, découverts à Madagascar, en Novembre 1869, sur la cote ouest de Madagascar. *Revue et Magasin de Zoologie Pure et Appliquée*, série 2, 21: 337–342.

———. 1870. Description de quelques animaux nouveaux, découverts à Madagascar, en Novembre 1869. *Revue et Magasin de Zoologie Pure et Appliquée*, série 2, 22: 49–50.

Grandidier, G. 1900. Note sur des ossements d'animaux disparus, provenant d'Ambolisatra, sur la côte Sud-Est de Madagascar. *Bulletin du Muséum National d'Histoire Naturelle*, Paris, 6: 214–218.

———. 1901. Un nouvel édenté subfossile de Madagascar. *Bulletin du Muséum National d'Histoire Naturelle*, Paris, 7: 54–56.

———. 1902. Observations sur les lémuriens disparus de Madagascar: Collections Alluaud, Gaubert, Grandidier. *Bulletin du Muséum National d'Histoire Naturelle*, Paris 8: 497–505, 587–592.

———. 1903. Description de l'*Hypogeomys australis*, une nouvelle espèce de rongeur subfossile de Madagascar. *Bulletin du Muséum National d'Histoire Naturelle*, Paris, 9: 13–15.

———. 1905a. Recherches sur les lémuriens disparus et en particulier sur ceux qui vivaient à Madagascar. *Nouvelles Archives du Muséum*, Paris, série 4, 7: 1–142.

———. 1905b. Les animaux disparus de Madagascar: Gisements, époques et causes de leur disparition. *Revue de Madagascar* 7: 111–128.

———. 1912. Une nouvelle espèce subfossile d'*Hypogeomys*, l'*H. Boueli* G. G. *Bulletin du Muséum National d'Histoire Naturelle*, Paris 18: 10–11.

———. 1928. Description de deux nouveux mammifères insectivores de Madagascar. *Bulletin du Muséum National d'Histoire Naturelle*, Paris 34: 63–70.

———. 1937. Mammifères nouveaux de la Région de Diego-Suarez (Madagascar). *Bulletin du Muséum National d'Histoire Naturelle*, série 2, 9: 347–353.

Grandidier, G., and Petit, G. 1930. Description d'une espèce nouvelle d'Insectivore Malgache, suivie de remarques critiques sur le genre *Oryzorictes*. *Bulletin du Muséum National d'Histoire Naturelle*, Paris, série 2, 2: 498–505.

Grassi, C. 2002. Sex differences in feeding, height, and space use in *Hapalemur griseus*. *International Journal of Primatology* 23: 677–693.

———. 2006. Variability in habitat, diet, and social structure of *Hapalemur griseus* in Ranomafana National Park, Madagascar. *American Journal of Physical Anthropology* 131: 50–63.

Gray, J. E. 1863. Revision of the species of lemuroid animals, with the description of some new species. *Proceedings of the Zoological Society of London* 1863: 129–153.

———. 1864. A revision of the genera and species of viverrine animals (Viverridae), founded on the collection in the British Museum. *Proceedings of the Zoological Society of London* 1864: 502–579.

———. 1870. Notes on *Hapalemur simus*, a new species lately living in the gardens of the society. *Proceedings of the Zoological Society of London* 1870: 828–831.

Greene, L. K., Clayton, J. B., Rothman, R. S., Semel, B. P., Semel, M. A., Gillespie, T. R., Wright, P. C., and Drea, C. M. 2019. Local habitat, not phylogenetic relatedness, predicts gut microbiota better within folivorous than frugivorous lemur lineages. *Biology Letters* 15: 20190028. https://doi.org/10.1098/rsbl.2019.0028.

Greenwood, P. J. 1980. Mating systems, philopatry and dispersal in birds and mammals. *Animal Behaviour* 28: 1140–1162. https://doi.org/10.1016/S0003-3472(80)80103-5.

Gregory, W. K., and Hellman, H. 1939. On the evolution and major classification of the civets (Viverridae) and allied fossil and recent Carnivora; a phylogenetic study of the skull and dentition. *Proceedings of the American Philosophical Society* 81: 309–392.

Grigg, G. C., Beard, L. A., and Augee, M. L. 2004. The evolution of endothermy and its diversity in mammals and birds. *Physiological and Biochemical Zoology* 77: 982–997.

Groeneveld, L. F., Weisrock, D. W., Rasoloarison, R. M., Yoder, A. D., and Kappeler, P. M. 2009. Species delimitation in lemurs: Multiple genetic loci reveal low levels of species diversity in the genus *Cheirogaleus*. *BMC Evolutionary Biology* 9: 30.

Groeneveld, L. F., Blanco, M. B., Raharison, J.-L., Rahalinarivo V., Rasoloarison, R. M., Kappeler, P. M., Godfrey, L. R., and Irwin, M. T. 2010. mtDNA and nDNA corroborate existence of sympatric dwarf lemur species at Tsinjoarivo, eastern Madagascar. *Molecular Phylogenetics and Evolution* 55: 833–845.

Grogan, K. E., Sauther, M. L., Cuozzo, F. P., and Drea, C. M. 2017. Genetic wealth, population health: Major histocompatibility complex variation in captive and wild ring-tailed (*Lemur catta*). *Ecology and Evolution* 7: 7638–7649. https://doi.org/10.1002/ece3.3317.

Gronau, I., Hubisz, M. J., Gulko, B., Danko, C. G., and Siepel, A. 2011. Bayesian inference of ancient human demography from individual genome sequences. *Nature Genetics* 43: 1031–1034. https://doi.org/10.1038/ng.937.

Groves, C. P. 1989. *A Theory of Human and Primate Evolution*. London: Oxford University Press.

Groves, C. P. 2000. The genus *Cheirogaleus*: Unrecognized biodiversity in dwarf lemurs. *International Journal of Primatology* 21: 943–962.

———. 2001. *Primate Taxonomy*. Washington, DC: Smithsonian Institution Press.

Groves, C. P., and Helgen, K. M. 2007. Craniodental characters in the taxonomy of *Propithecus*. *International Journal of Primatology* 28: 1363–1383.

Grubb, P. 1993. The Afrotropical suids, *Phacochoerus*, *Hylochoerus* and *Potamochoerus*: Taxonomy and description. In *Pigs, Peccaries, and Hippos*, ed. W.L.R. Olivier, pp. 66–75. Gland: IUCN.

Grzimek, B. 1975. *Animal Life Encyclopedia*. Vol. 12, *Mammals*, bk. 3. New York: Von Nostrand Reinhold.

Guernier, V., Lagadec, E., LeMinter, G., Licciardi, S., Balleydier, E., et al. 2014. Fleas of small mammals on Reunion Island: Diversity, distribution and epidemiological consequences. *PLoS Neglected Tropical Diseases* 8(9): e3129.

Guevara, E. E., Frankel, D. C., Ranaivonasy, J., Richard, A. F., Ratsirarson, J., Lawler, R. R., and Bradley, B. J. 2018. A simple, economical protocol for DNA extraction and amplification where there is no lab. *Conservation Genetics Resources* 10: 119–125. https://doi.org/10.1007/s12686-017-0758-5.

Guillera-Arroita, G., Lahoz-Monfort, J. J., Milner-Gulland, E. J., Young, R. P., and Nicholson, E. 2010. Monitoring and conservation of the critically endangered Alaotran gentle lemur *Hapalemur alaotrensis*. *Madagascar Conservation and Development* 5: 103–109.

Gunnell, G. F. 2010. Chiroptera. In *Cenozoic Mammals of Africa*, eds. L. Werdelin and W. J. Sanders, pp. 581–597. Berkeley: University of California Press.

Gunnell, G. F., and Simmons, N. 2005. Fossil evidence and the origin of bats. *Journal of Mammalian Evolution* 12: 209–246.

Gunnell, G. F., Simmons, N. B., and Seiffert, E. R. 2014. Myzopodidae (Chiroptera) from the Late Paleogene of Egypt: Emended family diagnosis and biogeographic origins of Noctilionoidea. *PLoS One* 9(2): e86712. https://doi.org/10.1371/journal.pone.0086712.

Gunnell, G. F., Butler, P. M., Greenwood, M., and Simmons, N. 2015. Bats (Chiroptera) from Olduvai Gorge, Early Pleistocene, Bed 1 (Tanzania). *American Museum Novitates* 3846: 1–35.

Gunnell, G. F., Boyer, D. M., Friscia, A. R., Heritage, S., Manthi, F. K., Miller, E. R., Sallam, H. M., Simmons, N. B., Stevens, N. J., and Seiffert, E. R. 2018. Fossil lemurs from Egypt and Kenya suggest an African origin for Madagascar's aye-aye. *Nature Communications* 9: 3193.

Günther, A. 1875. Notes on some mammals from Madagascar. *Proceedings of the Zoological Society of London* 1875: 78–80.

Gursky, S. L., and Nekaris, K.A.I. 2007. *Primate Anti-Predator Strategies*. New York: Springer Science.

Gutenkunst, R. N., Hernandez, R. D., Williamson, S. H., and Bustamante, C. D. 2009. Inferring the joint demographic history of multiple populations from multidimensional SNP frequency data. *PLoS Genetics* 5: e1000695. https://doi.org/10.1371/journal.pgen.1000695.

Hafen, T., Neveu, H., Rumpler, Y., Wilden, I., and Zimmermann, E. 1998. Acoustically dimorphic advertisement calls separate morphologically and genetically homogenous populations of the grey mouse lemur (*Microcebus murinus*). *Folia Primatologica* 69(supplement 1): 342–356. https://doi.org/10.1159/000052723.

Hagenah, N. 2001. Ökologie und intrasexuelle Konkurrenz Goldbrauner Mausmaki-Männchen (*Microcebus ravelobensis*) in Nordwest-Madagaskar während der Trockenzeit. Diploma thesis, University of Hannover.

Hale, R., and Swearer, S. E. 2016. Ecological traps: Current evidence and future directions. *Proceedings of the Royal Society of London B: Biological Sciences* 283(1824): 20152647.

Hämäläinen, A., Dammhahn, M., Aujard, F., Eberle, M., Hardy, I., Kappeler, P. M., Perret, M., Schliehe-Diecks, S., and Kraus, C. 2014. Senescence or selective disappearance? Age trajectories of body mass in wild and captive populations of a small-bodied primate. *Proceedings of the Royal Society of London B: Biological Sciences* 281: 20140830.

Han, G.-Z., and Worobey, M. 2012. An endogenous foamy virus in the aye-aye (*Daubentonia madagascariensis*). *Journal of Virology* 86: 7696–7698. https://doi.org/10.1128/JVI.00650-12.

Hand, S., and Archer, M. 2005. A new hipposiderid genus (Microchiroptera) from an early Miocene bat community in Australia. *Paleontology* 48: 371–383.

Hannah, L., Dave, R., Lowry, P. P., Andelman, S., Andrianarisata, M., et al. 2008. Climate change adaptation for conservation in Madagascar. *Biology Letters* 4: 590–594.

Hansford, J., and Turvey, S. 2018. Unexpected diversity within the extinct elephant birds (Aves: Aepyornithidae) and a new identity for the world's largest bird. *Royal Society Open Science* 5: 181295.

Hanski, I. 1994. A practical model of metapopulation dynamics. *Journal of Animal Ecology* 63(1): 151–162.

Hapke, A., Fietz, J., Nash, S. D., Rakotondravony, D., Rakotosamimanana, B., Ramanamanjato, J.-B., Randria, G.F.N., and Zischler, H. 2005. Biogeography of dwarf lemurs: Genetic evidence for unexpected patterns in southeastern Madagascar. *International Journal of Primatology* 26: 873–901.

Hapke, A., Gligor, M., Rakotondranary, S. J., Rosenkranz, D., and Zupke, O. 2011. Hybridization of mouse lemurs: Different patterns under different ecological conditions. *BMC Evolutionary Biology* 11: 297. https://doi.org/10.1186/1471-2148-11-297.

Harcourt, A. H., and Doherty, D. A. 2005. Species-area relationships of primates in tropical forest fragments: A global analysis. *Journal of Applied Ecology* 42(4): 630–637.

Harcourt, C. 1991. Diet and behaviour of a nocturnal lemur, *Avahi laniger*, in the wild. *Journal of Zoology* 223: 667–674.

Hardouin, E. A., Orth, A., Teschke, M., Darvish, J., Tautz, D., and Bonhomme, F. 2015. Eurasian house mouse (*Mus musculus* L.) differentiation at microsatellite loci identifies the Iranian Plateau as a phylogeographic hotspot. *BMC Evolutionary Biology* 15: 26.

Hardy, O. J., and Vekemans, X. 2002. Spagedi: A versatile computer program to analyse spatial genetic structure at the individual or population levels. *Molecular Ecology Notes* 2: 618–620. https://doi.org/10.1046/j.1471-8286.2002.00305.x.

Harimalala, M., Miarinjara, A., Duchemin, J.-B., Ramihangihajason, T., and Boyer, S. 2018. Species diversity and phylogeny of fleas of small terrestrial mammals in the forests of the Central Highlands of Madagascar. *Zootaxa* 4399(2): 181–196.

Harper, G. J., Steininger, M. K., Tucker, C. J., Juhn, D., and Hawkins, F. 2007. Fifty years of deforestation and forest fragmentation in Madagascar. *Environmental Conservation* 34(4): 325–333.

Harris, J. M. 1991. Family Hippopotamidae. In *Koobi Fora Research Project*, ed. J. M. Harris, vol. 3, pp. 31–85. Oxford: Clarendon Press.

Harris, R. L., Boulet, M., Grogan, K. E., and Drea, C. M. 2018. Costs of injury for scent signalling in a strepsirrhine primate. *Scientific Reports* 8: 9882. https://doi.org/10.1038/s41598-018-27322-3.

Hartstone-Rose, A., Dickinson, E., Boettcher, M., and Herrel, A. 2019. A primate with a Panda's thumb: The anatomy of the pseudothumb of *Daubentonia madagascariensis*. *American Journal of Physical Anthropology* 171: 8–16.

Hasegawa, M., Kishino, H., Hayasaka, K., and Horai, S. 1990. Mitochondrial DNA evolution in primates: Transition rate has been extremely low in the lemur. *Journal of Molecular Evolution* 31: 113–121. https://doi.org/10.1007/BF02109480.

Hastriter, M. W. 2016. Description of two new species of bat fleas of the genus *Araeopsylla* (Siphonaptera) from Kenya and Madagascar with notes on miscellaneous bat fleas. *ZooKeys* 572: 7–21. https://doi.org/10.3897/zookeys.572.7823.

Hawkins, A.F.A., Chapman, P. Ganzhorn, J. U., Bloxam, Q.M.C., Barlow, S. C., and Tonge, S. J. 1990. Vertebrate conservation in Ankarana Special Reserve, northern Madagascar. *Biological Conservation* 54: 83–110.

Hawkins, A.F.A., Hawkins, C. E., and Jenkins, P. D. 2000. *Mungotictis decemlineata lineata* (Carnivora: Herpestidae), a mysterious Malagasy mongoose. *Journal of Natural History* 34: 305–310.

Hawkins, C. E. 1998. The behaviour and ecology of the fossa, *Cryptoprocta ferox* (Carnivora: Viverridae) in a dry deciduous forest in western Madagascar. PhD thesis, University of Aberdeen.

Hawkins, C. E., and Racey, P. A. 2005. Low population density of a tropical forest carnivore, *Cryptoprocta ferox*: Implications for protected area management. *Oryx* 39(1): 35–43.

Hawkins, C. E., and Racey, P. A. 2008. Food habits of an endangered carnivore, *Cryptoprocta ferox*, in the dry deciduous forests of western Madagascar. *Journal of Mammalogy* 89(1): 64–74.

Hawkins, C. E., and Racey, P. A. 2009. A novel mating system in a solitary carnivore: The fossa. *Journal of Zoology* 277: 196–204.

Hawkins, C. E., Dallas, J. F., Fowler, P. A., Woodroffe, R., and Racey, P. A. 2002. Transient masculinization in the fossa, *Cryptoprocta ferox* (Carnivora, Viverridae). *Biology of Reproduction* 66: 610–615.

Hawkins, F. 2015. *Fossa fossana*. IUCN Red List of Threatened Species 2015: e. T8668A45197868. Accessed 30 Dec. 2019. http://dx. https://doi.org/10.2305/IUCN.UK.2015-4.RLTS.T8668A45197868.en.

———. 2016a. Fosa, *Cryptoprocta ferox*. IUCN Red List of Threatened Species 2016: e.T5760A45197189. Accessed 8 Jan. 2020. http://dx. https://doi.org/10.2305/IUCN.UK.2016-1.RLTS.T5760A45197189.en.

———. 2016b. *Salanoia concolor*. IUCN Red List of Threatened Species 2016: e. T19852A45202205. https://dx. https://doi.org/10.2305/IUCN.UK.2016-1.RLTS.T19852A45202205.en.

Hawkins, M.T.R., Culligan, R. R., Frasier, C. L., Dikow, R. B., Hagenson, R., Lei, R., and Louis, E. E., Jr. 2018. Genome sequence and population declines in the critically endangered greater bamboo lemur (*Prolemur simus*) and implications for conservation. *BMC Genomics* 19: 445. https://doi.org/10.1186/s12864-018-4841-4.

Hayman, R. W., and Hill, J. E. 1971. Order Chiroptera. In *The Mammals of Africa: An Identification Manual*, eds. J. Meester and H. W. Setzer, pp. 1–73. Washington, DC: Smithsonian Institution Press.

Hayssen, V., Van Tienhoven, A., Van Tienhoven, A., and Asdell, S. 1993. *Asdell's Patterns of Mammalian Reproduction: A Compendium of Species-Specific Data*. Ithaca: Cornell University Press.

Hedges, S. B., Marin, J., Suleski, M., Paymer, M., and Kumar, S. 2015. Tree of life reveals clock-like speciation and diversification. *Molecular Biology and Evolution* 32: 835–845.

Heim de Balsac, H. 1972. Insectivores. In *Biogeography and Ecology in Madagascar*, eds. R. Battisitini and G. Richard-Vindard, pp. 629–660. The Hague: W. Junk.

Hekkala, E. R., Rakotondratsima, M., and Vasey, N. 2007. Habitat and distribution of the ruffed lemur *Varecia*, north of the Bay of Antongil in northeastern Madagascar. *Primate Conservation* 22: 89–95.

Heldmaier, G., Ortmann, S., and Elvert, R. 2004. Natural hypometabolism during hibernation and daily torpor in mammals. *Respiratory Physiology and Neurobiology* 141: 317–329.

Heled, J., and Drummond, A. J. 2008. Bayesian inference of population size history from multiple loci. *BMC Evolutionary Biology* 8: 289. https://doi.org/10.1186/1471-2148-8-289.

Heller, R., Chikhi, L., and Siegismund, H. R. 2013. The confounding effect of population structure on Bayesian skyline plot inferences of demographic history. *PLoS One* 8: e62992. https://doi.org/10.1371/journal.pone.0062992.

Hemingway, C. A. 1995. Feeding and reproductive strategies of the Milne-Edwards' sifaka, *Propithecus diadema edwardsi*. PhD thesis, Duke University.

———. 1996. Morphology and phenology of seeds and whole fruit eaten by Milne-Edwards' sifaka, *Propithecus diadema edwardsi*, in Ranomafana National Park, Madagascar. *International Journal of Primatology* 17: 637–659.

———. 1998. Selectivity and variability in the diet of Milne-Edwards' sifakas (*Propithecus diadema edwardsi*): Implications for folivory and seed-eating. *International Journal of Primatology* 19: 355–377.

———. 1999. Time budgets and foraging in a Malagasy primate: Do sex differences reflect reproductive condition and female dominance? *Behavioral Ecology and Sociobiology* 45: 311–322.

Hemingway, C. A., and Bynum, N. 2005. The influence of seasonality on primate diet and ranging. In *Seasonality in Primates: Studies of Living and Extinct Human and Non-Human Primates*, eds. D. K. Brockman and C. P. van Schaik, pp. 57–104. Cambridge: Cambridge University Press.

Hending, D., McCabe, G., and Holderied, M. 2017. Sleeping and ranging behavior of the Sambirano mouse lemur, *Microcebus sambiranensis*. *International Journal of Primatology* 38: 1072–1089.

Hending, D., Andrianiaina, A., Rakotomalala, Z., and Cotton, S. 2018. The use of vanilla plantations by lemurs: Encouraging findings for both lemur conservation and sustainable agroforestry in the Sava Region, northeast Madagascar. *International Journal of Primatology* 39: 141–153.

Hendry, A. P. 2004. Selection against migrants contributes to the rapid evolution of ecologically dependent reproductive isolation. *Evolutionary Ecology Research* 6: 1219–1236.

Herbots, H.M.J.D. 1994. Stochastic models in population genetics: Genealogy and genetic differentiation in structured populations. PhD thesis, University of London.

Herrera, J. P., and Dávalos, L. M. 2016. Phylogeny and divergence times of lemurs inferred with recent and ancient fossils in the tree. *Systematic Biology* 65: 772–791.

Herrera, J. P., Wright, P. C., Lauterbur, E., Ratovonjanahary, L., and Taylor, L. L. 2011. The effects of habitat disturbance on lemurs at Ranomafana National Park, Madagascar. *International Journal of Primatology* 32: 1091–1108.

Herrera, J. P., Borgerson, C., Tongasoa, L., Andriamahazoarivosoa, P., Rasolofoniaina, B.J.R., et al. 2018. Estimating the population size of lemurs based on their mutualistic food trees. *Journal of Biogeography* 45: 2546–2563.

Hilgartner, R. D. 2005. Some ecological and behavioural notes on the shrew tenrec *Microgale* cf. *longicaudata* in the dry deciduous forest of western Madagascar. *Afrotherian Conservation* 3: 3–5.

Hilgartner, R. [D.], Zinner, D., and Kappeler, P. M. 2008. Life history traits and parental care in *Lepilemur ruficaudatus*. *American Journal of Primatology* 70: 2–11.

Hilgartner, R. [D.], Fichtel, C., Kappeler, P. M., and Zinner, D. 2012. Determinants of pair-living in red-tailed sportive lemurs (*Lepilemur ruficaudatus*). *Ethology* 118: 466–479.

Hill, W.C.O. 1953. *Comparative Anatomy and Taxonomy*. I. *Strepsirrhini*. Edinburgh: University Press.

Hingston, M., Goodman, S. M., Ganzhorn, J. U., and Sommer, S. 2005. Reconstruction of the colonization of southern Madagascar by introduced *Rattus rattus*. *Journal of Biogeography* 32: 1549–1559. https://doi.org/10.1111/j.1365-2699.2005.01311.x.

Hixon, S. W., Smith, E.A.E., Crowley, B. E., Perry, G. H., Randrianasy, J., Ranaivoarisoa, J. F., Kennett, D. J., and Newsome, S. D. 2018. Nitrogen isotope (dN-15) patterns for amino acids in lemur bones are inconsistent with aridity driving megafaunal extinction in south-western Madagascar. *Journal of Quaternary Science* 33: 958–968.

Hladik, C. M., and Charles-Dominique, P. 1974. The behaviour and ecology of the sportive lemur (*Lepilemur mustelinus*) in relation to its dietary peculiarities. In *Prosimian Biology*, eds. R. D. Martin, G. A. Doyle, and A. C. Walker, pp. 23–37. London: Gerald Duckworth.

Hladik, C. M., Charles-Dominique, P., and Petter, J.-J. 1980. Feeding strategies of five nocturnal prosimians in the dry forest of the west coast of Madagascar. In *Nocturnal Malagasy Primates: Ecology, Physiology, and Behavior*, eds. P. Charles-Dominique, H. M. Cooper, A. Hladik, C. M. Hladik, E. Pagès, G. F. Pariente, A. Petter-Rousseaux, J.-J. Petter, and A. Schilling, pp. 41–73. New York: Academic Press.

Hladik, C. M., Pinte, M., and Simmen, B. 1998. Do south Malagasy nocturnal prosimian population densities vary in the long term in public-frequented forest reserves? *Revue d'Ecologie (La Terre et la Vie)* 53: 181–185.

Hogg, R. T., Godfrey, L. R., Schwartz, G. T., Dirks, W., and Bromage, T. G. 2015. Lemur biorhythms and life history evolution. *PLoS One* 10: e0134210.

Hohenbrink, P., Mundy, N. I., and Radespiel, U. 2017. Population genetics of mouse lemur vomeronasal receptors: Current versus past selection and demographic inference. *BMC Evolutionary Biology* 17: 28. https://doi.org/10.1186/s12862-017-0874-6.

Hohenlohe, P. A., Bassham, S., Etter, P. D., Stiffler, N., Johnson, E. A., and Cresko, W. A. 2010. Population genomics of parallel adaptation in threespine stickleback using sequenced RAD tags. *PLoS Genetics* 6(2): e1000862.

Hokan, M., Strube, C., Radespiel, U., and Zimmermann, E. 2017. Sleeping site ecology, but not sex, affect ecto- and hemoparasite risk, in sympatric, arboreal primates (*Avahi occidentalis* and *Lepilemur edwardsi*). *Frontiers in Zoology* 14: 44. https://doi.org/10.1186/s12983-017-0228-7.

Hokan, M., Zimmermann, E., Radespiel, U., Andriatsitohaina, B., Rasoloharijaona, S., and Strube, C. 2018. Are sleeping site ecology and season linked to intestinal helminth prevalence and diversity in two sympatric, nocturnal and arboreal primate hosts (*Lepilemur edwardsi* and *Avahi occidentalis*)? *BMC Ecology* 18: 22. https://doi.org/10.1186/s12898-018-0178-8.

Holden, J., and Neang, T. 2009. Small carnivore records from the Cardamom Mountains, southwestern Cambodia. *Small Carnivore Conservation* 40: 16–21.

Holland, R. A., Waters, D. A., and Rayner, J.M.V. 2004. Echolocation signal structure in the megachiropteran bat *Rousettus aegyptiacus* Geoffroy 1810. *Journal of Experimental Biology* 207: 4361–4369.

Holmes, S. M., Baden, A. L., Brenneman, R. A., Engberg, S. E., Louis, E. E., Jr., and Johnson, S. E. 2013. Patch size and isolation influence genetic patterns in black-and-white ruffed lemur (*Varecia variegata*) populations. *Conservation Genetics* 14: 615–624.

Holmes, S. M., Gordon, A. D., Louis, E. E., Jr., and Johnson, S. E. 2016. Fission-fusion dynamics in black-and-white ruffed lemurs may facilitate both feeding strategies and communal care of infants in a spatially and temporally variable environment. *Behavioral Ecology and Sociobiology* 70: 1949–1960.

Holmes, S. M., Louis, E. E., Jr., and Johnson, S. E. 2019. Range overlap and spatiotemporal relationships of frugivorous lemurs at Kianjavato, Madagascar. *Animal Behaviour* 155: 53–65.

Honacki, J. H., Kinman, K. E., and Koeppl, J. W. 1982. *Mammalian Species of the World: A Taxonomic and Geographic Reference*. Lawrence: Association for Systematic Collections.

Horvath, J. E., Weisrock, D. W., Embry, S. L., Fiorentino, I., Balhoff, J. P., Kappeler, P., Wray, G. A., Willard, H. F., and Yoder, A. D. 2008. Development and application of a phylogenomic toolkit: Resolving the evolutionary history of Madagascar's lemurs. *Genome Research* 18: 489–499.

Hosey, G. R., and Jacques, M. 1994. Interactions between infant ring-tailed lemurs (*Lemur catta*) and their parents and older siblings. In Social development and learning, eds. J. J. Roeder, B. Thierry, J. R. Anderson, and N. Herrenschmidt. *Current Primatology* 2: 315–319.

Hostetler, J. A., Kneip, E., Van Vuren, D. H., and Oli, M. K. 2012. Stochastic population dynamics of a montane ground-dwelling squirrel. *PLoS One* 7: e34379.

Hotaling, S., Foley, M. E., Lawrence, N. M., Bocanegra, J., Blanco, M. B., Rasoloarison, R., Kappeler, P. M., Barrett, M. A., Yoder, A. D., and Weisrock, D. W. 2016. Species discovery and validation in a cryptic radiation of endangered primates: Coalescent-based species delimitation in Madagascar's mouse lemurs. *Molecular Ecology* 25: 2029–2045. https://doi.org/10.1111/mec.13604.

Hsu, T. C., and Benirschke, K. 1970. *An Atlas of Mammalian Chromosomes*. Vol. 4. New York: Springer-Verlag.

Hua, P. Y., Chen, J. P., Sun, M., Liang, B., Zhang, S. Y., and Wu, D. H. 2006. Characterization of microsatellite loci in fulvous fruit bat *Rousettus leschenaulti*. *Molecular Ecology Notes* 6: 939–941. https://doi.org/10.1111/j.1471-8286.2006.01407.x.

Hubby, J. L., and Lewontin, R. C. 1966. A molecular approach to the study of genic heterozygosity in natural populations. I. The number of alleles at different loci in *Drosophila pseudoobscura*. *Genetics* 54: 577–594.

Huchard, E., Canale, C. I., Le Gros, C., Perret, M., Henry, P.-Y., and Kappeler, P. M. 2012. Convenience polyandry or convenience polygyny? Costly sex under female control in a promiscuous primate. *Proceedings of the Royal Society of London B: Biological Sciences* 279: 1371–1379.

Huchard, E., Baniel, A., Schliehe-Diecks, S., and Kappeler, P. M. 2013. MHC-disassortative mate choice and inbreeding avoidance in a solitary primate. *Molecular Ecology* 22: 4071–4086.

Huchard, E., Schliehe-Diecks, S., Kappeler, P. M., and Kraus, C. 2017. The inbreeding strategy of a solitary primate, *Microcebus murinus*. *Journal of Evolutionary Biology* 30: 128–140.

Hudson, R. R. 1990. Gene genealogies and the coalescent process. In *Oxford Surveys in Evolutionary Biology*, eds. D. Futuyma and J. Antonovics, pp. 1–44. Oxford: Oxford University Press.

———. 2002. Generating samples under a Wright-Fisher neutral model of genetic variation. *Bioinformatics* 18: 337–338.

Huffman, M. A. 2003. Animal self-medication and ethno-medicine: Exploration and exploitation of the medicinal properties of plants. *Proceedings of the Nutrition Society* 62: 371–381.

Humphries, M. M., Kramer, D. L., and Thomas, D. W. 2003. The role of energy availability in mammalian hibernation: An experimental test in free-ranging eastern chipmunks. *Physiological and Biochemical Zoology* 76: 180–186.

Hunnicutt, K. E., Tiley, G. P., Williams, R. C., Larsen, P. A., Blanco, M. B., et al. 2020. Comparative genomic analysis of the pheromone receptor class 1 family (V1R) reveals extreme complexity in mouse lemurs (genus, *Microcebus*) and a chromosomal hotspot across mammals. *Genome Biology and Evolution* 12: 3562–3579. https://doi.org/10.1093/gbe/evz200.

Hunt, R. M. 1974. Auditory bullae in Carnivora: An anatomical basis for reappraisal of carnivore evolution. *Journal of Morphology* 134: 21–76.

———. 1987. Evolution of Aeluroidea Carnivora: Significance of auditory structure in the Nimravid Cat *Dinictis*. *American Museum Novitates* 2886: 1–74.

———. 1989. Evolution of the aeluroid Carnivora: Significance of the ventral promontorial process of the petrosal, and the origin of basicranial patterns in the living families. *American Museum Novitates* 2930: 1–32.

Hutterer, R., and Tranier, M. 1990. The immigration of the Asian house shrew (*Suncus murinus*) into Africa and Madagascar. In *Vertebrates in the Tropics*, eds. G. Peters and R. Hutterer, pp. 309–319. Bonn: Museum Alexander Koenig.

Hutterer, R., Decher, J., Monadjem, A., and Astrin, J. J. 2019. A new genus and species of vesper bat from West Africa, with notes on *Hypsugo*, *Neoromicia*, and *Pipistrellus* (Chiroptera: Vespertilionidae). *Acta Chiropterologica* 21: 1–22.

Ichino, S. 2011. New cases of vertebrate predation by the ring-tailed lemur (*Lemur catta*), with references to differences from *Eulemur* species and other primates. *African Study Monographs* 32: 69–80.

Ichino, S., and Koyama, N. 2006. Social changes in a wild population of ringtailed lemurs (*Lemur catta*) at Berenty, Madagascar. In *Ringtailed Lemur Biology:* Lemur catta *in Madagascar*, eds., A. Jolly, R. W. Sussman, N. Koyama, H. Rasamimanana, pp. 233–244. New York: Springer.

Irwin, M. T. 2006. Ecologically enigmatic lemurs: The sifakas of the eastern forests (*Propithecus candidus*, *P. diadema*, *P. edwardsi*, *P. perrieri*, and *P. tattersalli*). In *Lemurs: Ecology and Adaptation*, eds. L. Gould and M. L. Sauther, pp. 305–326. Boston: Springer.

———. 2008. Feeding ecology of *Propithecus diadema* in forest fragments and continuous forest. *International Journal of Primatology* 29(1): 95–115.

Irwin, M. T., and Ravelomanantsoa, H. V. 2004. Illegal rum production threatens health of lemur populations at Tsinjoarivo, eastern central Madagascar: Brief report and request for information. *Lemur News* 9: 16–17.

Irwin, M. T., Samonds, K. E., Raharison, J. L., and Wright, P. C. 2004. Lemur latrines: Observations of latrine behavior in wild primates and possible ecological significance. *Journal of Mammalogy* 85: 420–427.

Irwin, M. T., Johnson, S. E., and Wright, P. C. 2005. The state of lemur conservation in south-eastern Madagascar: Population and habitat assessments for diurnal and cathemeral lemurs using surveys, satellite imagery and GIS. *Oryx* 39: 204–218.

Irwin, M. T., Raharison, F.J.-L., Rakotoarimanana, H., Razanadrakoto, E., Ranaivoson, E., Rakotofanala, J., and Randrianarimanana, C. 2007. Diademed sifakas (*Propithecus diadema*) use olfaction to forage for the inflorescences of subterranean parasitic plants (Balanophoraceae: *Langsdorffia* sp., and Cytinaceae: *Cytinus* sp.). *American Journal of Primatology* 69: 471–476.

Irwin, M. T., Raharison, J. L., and Wright, P. C. 2009. Spatial and temporal variability in predation on rainforest primates: Do forest fragmentation and predation act synergistically? *Animal Conservation* 12: 220–230.

Irwin, M. T., Wright, P. C., Birkinshaw, C., Fisher, B. L., Gardner, C. J., et al. 2010. Patterns of species change in anthropogenically disturbed forests of Madagascar. *Biological Conservation* 143: 2351–2362.

Irwin, M. T., Raharison, J.-L., Raubenheimer, D., Chapman, C. A., and Rothman, J. M. 2014. Nutritional correlates of the "lean season": Effects of seasonality and frugivory on the nutritional ecology of diademed sifakas. *American Journal of Physical Anthropology* 153: 78–91.

Ishak, B., Warter, S., Butrillaux, B., and Rumpler, Y. 1992. Chromosomal rearrangements and speciation of sportive lemurs (*Lepilemur* species). *Folia Primatologica* 58: 121–130.

Ito, R., Rakotondraparany, F., and Sato, H. 2013. Non-flying mammalian fauna of Ampijoroa, Ankarafantsika National Park. *Madagascar Conservation and Development* 8(1): 45–48.

IUCN. 2020. IUCN Red List of threatened species. Accessed 23 Feb. 2020. www.iucnredlist.org.

Iwano, T. 1991. An ecological and behavioral study of the aye-aye (*Daubentonia madagascariensis*). *African Study Monographs* 12: 19–42.

Iwano, T., and Iwakawa, C. 1988. Feeding behaviour of the aye-aye (*Daubentonia madagascariensis*) on nuts of ramy (*Canarium madagascariensis*). *Folia Primatologica* 50: 136–142.

Iwano, T., Randalana, R., and Rakotoarisoa, G. 1991. Ecology of the aye-aye (*Daubentonia madagascariensis*), I. Distribution. In *Primatology Today*, eds. A. Ehara and T. Kimura, pp. 41–42. Amsterdam: Elsevier.

Jacobs, G. H., and Deegan, J. F., II. 1993. Photopigments underlying color vision in ringtail lemurs (*Lemur catta*) and brown lemurs (*Eulemur fulvus*). *American Journal of Primatology* 30: 234–256.

Jacobs, G. H., and Deegan, J. F., II. 2003. Photopigment polymorphism in prosimians and the origins of primate trichromacy. In *Normal and Defective Colour Vision*, eds. J. D. Mollon, J. Pokorny, and K. Knoblauch, pp. 14–20. Oxford: Oxford University Press.

Jacobs, R. L., MacFie, T. S., Spriggs, A. N., Baden, A. L., Morelli, T. L., et al. 2017. Novel opsin gene variation in large-bodied, diurnal lemurs. *Biology Letters* 13: 20170050.

Jacobs, R. L., Frankel, D. C., Rice, R. J., Kiefer, V. J., and Bradley, B. J. 2018. Parentage complexity in socially monogamous lemurs (*Eulemur rubriventer*): Integrating genetic and observational data. *American Journal of Primatology* 80: e22738. https://doi.org/10.1002/ajp.22738.

Jansa, S. A., and Carleton, M. D. 2003a. *Brachyuromys*. In *The Natural History of Madagascar*, eds. S. M. Goodman and J. P. Benstead, pp. 1370–1373. Chicago: University of Chicago Press.

Jansa, S. A., and Carleton, M. D. 2003b. Systematics and phylogenetics of Madagascar's native rodents. In *The Natural History of Madagascar*, eds. S. M Goodman and J. P. Benstead, pp. 1257–1265. Chicago: University of Chicago Press.

Jansa, S. A., and Weksler, M. 2004. Phylogeny of muroid rodents: Relationships within and among major lineages as determined by IRBP gene sequences. *Molecular Phylogenetics and Evolution* 31: 256–276. https://doi.org/10.1016/j.ympev.2003.07.002.

Jansa, S. A., Goodman, S. M., and Tucker, P. K. 1999. Molecular phylogeny and biogeography of the native rodents of Madagascar (Muridae: Nesomyinae): A test of the single-origin hypothesis. *Cladistics* 15: 253–270. https://doi.org/10.1111/j.1096-0031.1999.tb00267.x.

Jansa, S. A., Soarimalala, V., Goodman, S. M., and Barker, F. K. 2008. Morphometric variation and phylogeographic structure in *Macrotarsomys bastardi* (Rodentia: Nesomyidae), an endemic Malagasy dry forest rodent. *Journal of Mammalogy* 89: 316–324.

Jansa, S. A., Giarla, T. C., and Lim, B. K. 2009. The phylogenetic position of the rodent genus *Typhlomys* and the geographic origin of Muroidea. *Journal of Mammalogy* 90: 1083–1094.

Jansa, S. A., Carleton, M. D., Soarimalala, V., Rakotomalala, Z., and Goodman, S. M. 2019. A review of the *Eliurus tanala* complex (Rodentia, Muroidea, Nesomyidae), with description of a new species from dry forests of western Madagascar. *Bulletin of the American Museum of Natural History* 430: 1–67.

Jansky, K., Schubert, B. W., and Wallace, S. C. 2016. Geometric morphometrics of dentaries in *Myotis*: Species identification and its implications for conservation and the fossil record. *Northeastern Naturalist* 23: 184–194.

Jenkins, P. D. 1992. Description of a new species of *Microgale* (Insectivora: Tenrecidae) from eastern Madagascar. *Bulletin of the Natural History Museum*, London, *Zoology* 58(1): 53–59.

———. 1993. A new species of *Microgale* (Insectivora: Tenrecidae) from eastern Madagascar with an unusual dentition. *American Museum Novitates* 3067: 1–11.

———. 2003. *Microgale*, shrew tenrecs. In *The Natural History of Madagascar*, eds. S. M. Goodman and J. P. Benstead, pp. 1273–1278. Chicago: University of Chicago Press.

———. 2018. Family Tenrecidae (tenrecs and shrew tenrecs). In *Handbook of the Mammals of the World*. Vol. 8, *Insectivores, Sloths and Colugos*, eds. D. E. Wilson and R. A. Mittermeier, pp. 134–172. Barcelona: Lynx Edicions.

Jenkins, P. D., and Carleton, M. D. 2005. Charles Immanuel Forsyth Major's expedition to Madagascar, 1894 to 1896: Beginnings of modern systematic study of the island's mammalian fauna. *Journal of Natural History* 39: 1779–1818.

Jenkins, P. D., and Goodman, S. M. 1999. A new species of *Microgale* (Lipotyphla, Tenrecidae) from isolated forest in southwestern Madagascar. *Bulletin of the Natural History Museum*, London, *Zoology* 65: 155–164.

Jenkins, P. D., Goodman, S. M., and Raxworthy, C. J. 1996. The shrew tenrecs (*Microgale*) (Insectivora: Tenrecidae) of the Réserve Naturelle Intégrale d'Andringitra, Madagascar. In A floral and faunal inventory of the eastern slopes of the Réserve Naturelle Intégrale d'Andringitra, Madagascar: With reference to elevational variation, ed. S. M. Goodman. *Fieldiana: Zoology*, new ser., 85: 191–217.

Jenkins, P. D., Raxworthy, C. J., and Nussbaum, R. A. 1997. A new species of *Microgale* (Insectivora, Tenrecidae), with comments on the status of four other taxa of shrew tenrecs. *Bulletin of the Natural History Museum*, London, *Zoology* 63: 1–12.

Jenkins, R.K.B., and Racey, P. A. 2008. Bats as bushmeat in Madagascar. *Madagascar Conservation and Development* 3(1): 22–30.

Jenkins, R.K.B., Andriafidison, D., Razafimanahaka, H. J., Rabearivelo, A., Razafindrakoto, N., Andrianandrasana, R. H., Razafimahatratra, E., and Racey, P. A. 2007. Not rare, but threatened: The endemic Madagascar Flying Fox *Pteropus rufus* in a fragmented landscape. *Oryx* 41: 263–271.

Jenkins, R.K.B., Keane, A., Rakotoarivelo, A. R., Rakotomboavonjy, V., Randrianandrianina, F. H., Razafimanahaka, H. J., Ralaiarimalala, H. R., and Jones, J.P.G. 2011. Analysis of patterns of bushmeat consumption reveals extensive exploitation of protected species in eastern Madagascar. *PLoS One* 6(12): e27570.

Jennings, A. P., and Veron, G. 2009. Family Viverridae. In *Handbook of the Mammals of the World.* Vol. 1, *Carnivores*, eds. D. E. Wilson and R. A. Mittermeier, pp. 174–232. Barcelona: Lynx Edicions.

Jennings, A. P., and Veron, G. 2011. Predicted distributions and ecological niches of 8 civet and mongoose species in southeast Asia. *Journal of Mammalogy* 92: 316–327.

Jentink, F. A. 1879. On a new genus and species of *Mus* from Madagascar. *Notes from the Leyden Museum* 1879: 107–109.

Jernvall, J., Wright, P. C., Ravoavy, F. L., and Simons, E. L. 2003. Report on findings of subfossils at Ampoza and Ampanihy in southwestern Madagascar. *Madagascar Conservation and Development* 8: 21–23.

Johnson, S. E. 2002. Ecology and speciation in brown lemurs: White-collared lemurs (*Eulemur albocollaris*) and hybrids (*Eulemur albocollaris* × *Eulemur fulvus rufus*) in southeastern Madagascar. PhD thesis, University of Texas, Austin.

———. 2007. Evolutionary divergence in the brown lemur species complex. In *Lemurs: Ecology and Adaptation*, eds. L. Gould and M. L. Sauther, pp. 187–210. New York: Springer.

Johnson, S. E., and Overdorff, D. J. 1999. A census of brown lemurs (*Eulemur fulvus* sspp.) in southeastern Madagascar: Methods-testing and conservation implications. *American Journal of Primatology* 47: 51–60.

Johnson, S. E., Lei, R., Martin, S. K., Irwin, M. T., and Louis, E. E., Jr. 2008. Does *Eulemur cinereiceps* exist? Preliminary evidence from genetics and ground surveys in southeastern Madagascar. *American Journal of Primatology* 70: 372–385.

Jolly, A. 1966. *Lemur Behavior*. Chicago: University of Chicago Press.

———. 1998. Pair-bonding, female aggression and the evolution of lemur societies. *Folia Primatologica* 69(supplement 1): 1–13.

———. 2003. *Lemur catta*, ring-tailed lemur. In *The Natural History of Madagascar*, eds. S. M. Goodman and J. P. Benstead, pp. 1329–1331. Chicago: University of Chicago Press.

———. 2012. Berenty Reserve, Madagascar: A long time in a small space. In *Long-Term Field Studies of Primates*, eds. P. M. Kappeler and D. P. Watts, pp. 21–44. Berlin and Heidelberg: Springer.

Jolly, A., and Pride, E. 1999. Troop histories and range inertia of *Lemur catta* at Berenty, Madagascar: A 33-year perspective. *International Journal of Primatology* 20: 359–373.

Jolly, A., Rasamimanana, H. R., Kinnaird, M. F., O'Brien, T. G., Crowley, H. M., Harcourt, C. S., Gardner, S., and Davidson, J. 1993. Territoriality in *Lemur catta* groups during the birth season at Berenty, Madagascar. In *Lemur Social Systems and Their Ecological Basis*, eds. P. M. Kappeler and J. U. Ganzhorn, pp. 85–109. New York: Plenum Press.

Jolly, A., Caless, S., Cavigelli, S., Gould, L., Pereira, M. E., Pitts, A., Pride, R. E., Rabenandrasana, H. D., Walker, J. D., and Zafison, T. 2000. Infant killing, wounding and predation in *Eulemur* and *Lemur*. *International Journal of Primatology* 21: 21–40.

Jolly, A., Dobson, A., Rasamimanana, H. M., Walker, J., O'Connor, S., Solberg, M., and Perel, V. 2002. Demography of *Lemur catta* at Berenty Reserve, Madagascar: Effects of troop size, habitat and rainfall. *International Journal of Primatology* 23(2): 327–355.

Jolly, A., Sussman, R. W., Koyama, N., and Rasamimanana, H., eds. 2006. *Ringtailed Lemur Biology:* Lemur catta *in Madagascar*. New York: Springer

Joly, M., and Zimmermann, E. 2011. Do solitary foraging nocturnal mammals plan their routes? *Biological Letters* 7: 638–640.

Joly-Radko, M., and Zimmermann, E. 2010. Seasonality in gum and honeydew feeding in gray mouse lemurs. In *The Evolution of Exudativory in Primates*, eds. L. T. Nash and A. M. Burrows, pp. 141–154. New York: Springer.

Jones, G., and Teeling, E. C. 2006. The evolution of echolocation in bats. *Trends in Ecology and Evolution* 21(3): 149–156.

Jones, J.P.G., Andriamarovololona, M. M., and Hockley, N. 2008. The importance of taboos and social norms to conservation in Madagascar. *Conservation Biology* 22: 976–986.

Jones, J.P.G., Ratsimbazafy, J., Ratsifandrihamanana, A. N., Watson, J. E., Andrianandrasana, H. T., Cabeza, M., Cinner, J. E., Goodman, S. M., Hawkins, F., and Mittermeier, R. A. 2019. Madagascar: Crime threatens biodiversity. *Science* 363(6429): 825.

Jones, K. D. 1983. Inter-troop transfer of *Lemur catta* males at Berenty, Madagascar. *Folia Primatologica* 40: 145–160.

Jori, F. 2000. Contrôle et éradication d'une épizootie de peste porcine africaine, Madagascar. Rapport de mission. Accra: FAO.

Jori, F., Vial, L., Penrith, M. L., Pérez-Sánchez, R., Etter, E., Albina, E., Michaud, V., and Roger, F. 2013. Review of the sylvatic cycle of African swine fever in sub-Saharan Africa and the Indian Ocean. *Virus Research* 173(1): 212–227.

Jully, A. 1898. Les tourbières d'Antsirabe et les animaux disparus de Madagascar. *Notes, Reconnaissances et Explorations* 1898: 1175–1183.

Jung, K. Y., Crovella, S., and Rumpler, Y. 1992. Phylogenetic relationships among lemuriform species determined from restriction genomic DNA banding patterns. *Folia Primatologica* 58: 224–229. https://doi.org/10.1159/000156634.

Junge, R. E., Barrett, M. A., and Yoder, A. D. 2011. Effects of anthropogenic disturbance on indri (*Indri indri*) health in Madagascar. *American Journal of Primatology* 73: 632–642. https://doi.org/10.1002/ajp.20938.

Junge, R. E., Williams, C. V., Rakotondrainibe, H., Mahefarisoa, K. L., Rajaonarivelo, T., Faulkner, C., and Mass, V. 2017. Baseline health and nutrition evaluation of two sympatric nocturnal lemur species (*Avahi laniger* and *Lepilemur mustelinus*) residing near an active mine site at Ambatovy, Madagascar. *Journal of Zoo and Wildlife Medicine* 48: 794–803.

Jungers, W. L. 1980. Adaptive diversity in subfossil Malagasy prosimians. *Zeitschrift für Morphologie und Anthropologie* 71: 177–186.

———. 1999. Brain size and body size in subfossil Malagasy lemurs. *American Journal of Physical Anthropology* 28(supplement): 163.

Jungers, W. L., Godfrey, L. R., Simons, E. L., Chatrath, P. S., and Rakotosamimanana, B. 1991. Phylogenetic and functional affinities of *Babakotia radofilai*, a new fossil lemur from Madagascar. *Proceedings of the National Academy of Sciences of the USA* 88: 9082–9086.

Jungers, W. L., Godfrey, L. R., Simons, E. L., and Chatrath, P. S. 1995. Subfossil *Indri indri* from the Ankarana Massif of northern Madagascar. *American Journal of Physical Anthropology* 97: 357–366.

Jungers, W. L., Godfrey, L. R., Simons, E. L., Wunderlich, R. E., Richmond, B. G., and Chatrath, P. S. 2002. Ecomorphology and behavior of giant extinct lemurs from Madagascar. In *Reconstructing Behavior in the Primate Fossil Record*, eds. J. M. Plavcan, R. F. Kay, W. L. Jungers, and C. P. van Schaik, pp. 371–411. New York: Kluwer Academic/Plenum Press.

Jungers, W. L., Demes, B., and Godfrey, L. R. 2008. How big were the "giant" extinct lemurs of Madagascar? In *Elwyn Simons: A Search for Origins*, eds. J. G. Fleagle and C. C. Gilbert, pp. 343–360. New York: Springer.

Kamilar, J. M., and Tecot, S. R. 2016. Anthropogenic and climatic effects on the distribution of *Eulemur* species: An ecological niche modeling approach. *International Journal of Primatology* 37: 47–68.

Kappel, P., Hohenbrink, S., and Radespiel, U. 2011. Experimental evidence for olfactory predator recognition in wild mouse lemurs. *American Journal of Primatology* 73: 928–938.

Kappeler, P. M. 1996. Causes and consequences of life-history variation among strepsirhine primates. *American Naturalist* 148: 868–891.

———. 1997a. Intrasexual selection in *Mirza coquereli*: Evidence for scramble competition polygyny in a solitary primate. *Behavioral Ecology and Sociobiology* 45: 115–127.

———. 1997b. Determinants of primate social organization: Comparative evidence and new insights from Malagasy lemurs. *Biological Reviews* 71: 111–151.

———. 1998a. The transmission and function of chemical signals in *Lemur catta*. *Behavioral Ecology and Sociobiology* 42: 411–421.

———. 1998b. Nests, tree holes, and the evolution of primate life histories. *American Journal of Primatology* 46: 7–33.

———. 2000a. Lemur origins: Rafting by groups of hibernators? *Folia Primatologica* 71: 422–425.

———. 2000b. Causes and consequences of unusual sex ratios among lemurs. In *Primate Males: Causes and Consequences of Variation in Group Composition*, ed. P. M. Kappeler, pp. 55–63. Cambridge: Cambridge University Press.

———. 2003. *Mirza coquereli*, Coquerel's dwarf lemur. In *The Natural History of Madagascar*, eds. S. M. Goodman, and J. P. Benstead, pp. 1316–1318. Chicago: University of Chicago Press.

Kappeler, P. M., and Erkert, H. G. 2003. On the move around the clock: Correlates and determinants of cathemeral activity in wild redfronted lemurs (*Eulemur fulvus rufus*). *Behavioral Ecology and Sociobiology* 54: 359–369.

Kappeler, P. M., and Fichtel, C. 2012. A 15-year perspective on the social organization and life history of sifaka in Kirindy Forest. In *Long-Term Field Studies of Primates*, eds. P. M. Kappeler and D. P. Watts, pp. 101–121. Berlin: Springer Verlag.

Kappeler, P. M., and Fichtel, C. 2016. The evolution of *Eulemur* social organization. *International Journal of Primatology* 37: 10–28.

Kappeler, P. M., and Heymann, E. W. 1996. Nonconvergence in the evolution of primate life history and socio-ecology. *Biological Journal of the Linnean Society* 59: 297–326.

Kappeler, P. M., and Schäffler, L. 2008. The lemur syndrome unresolved: Extreme male reproductive skew in sifakas (*Propithecus verreauxi*), a sexually monomorphic primate with female dominance. *Behavioral Ecology and Sociobiology* 62: 1007–1015. https://doi.org/10.1007/s00265-007-0528-6.

Kappeler, P. M., Wimmer, B., Zinner, D., and Tautz, D. 2002. The hidden matrilineal structure of a solitary lemur: Implications for primate social evolution. *Proceedings of the Royal Society of London B: Biological Sciences*, 269: 1755–1763. https://doi.org/10.1098/rspb.2002.2066.

Kappeler, P. M., Rasoloarison, R. M., Razafimanantsoa, L., Walter, L., and Roos, C. 2005. Morphology, behaviour and molecular evolution of giant mouse lemurs (*Mirza* spp.) Gray, 1870, with description of a new species. *Primate Report* 71: 3–26.

Kappeler, P. M., Mass, M., and Port, M. 2009. Even adult sex ratios in lemurs: Potential costs and benefits of subordinate males in Verreaux's sifaka (*Propithecus verreauxi*) in the Kirindy Forest CFPF, Madagascar. *American Journal of Physical Anthropology* 140: 487–497.

Kappeler, P. M., Nunn, C. L., Vining, A. Q., and Goodman, S. M. 2019. Evolutionary dynamics of sexual size dimorphism in non-volant mammals following their independent colonization of Madagascar. *Scientific Reports* 9: 1454. https://doi.org/10.1038/s41598-018-36246-x.

Karanewsky, C. J., and Wright, P. C. 2015. A preliminary investigation of sleeping site selection and sharing by the brown mouse lemur *Microcebus rufus* during the dry season. *Journal of Mammalogy* 96: 1344–1351.

Karanewsky, C. J., Bauert, M. R., and Wright, P. C. 2015. Effects of sex and age on heterothermy in Goodman's mouse lemur (*Microcebus lehilahytsara*). *International Journal of Primatology* 36: 987–998.

Karanth, K. P., Delefosse, T., Rakotosamimanana, B., Parsons, T. J., and Yoder, A. D. 2005. Ancient DNA from giant extinct lemurs confirms single origin of Malagasy primates. *Proceedings of the National Academy of Sciences of the USA* 102: 5090–5095. https://doi.org/10.1073/pnas.0408354102.

Karanth, K. U., Nichols, J. D., Kumar, N. S., and Hines, J. E. 2006. Assessing tiger population dynamics using photographic capture-recapture sampling. *Ecology* 87: 2925–2937.

Karpanty, S. M. 2003. Behavioral and ecological interactions of raptors and lemurs in southeastern Madagascar: A multiple predator approach. PhD thesis, State University of New York, Stony Brook.

———. 2006. Direct and indirect impacts of raptor predation on lemurs in southeastern Madagascar. *International Journal of Primatology* 27: 239–261.

Karpanty, S. M., and Goodman, S. M. 1999. Diet of the Madagascar harrier-hawk, *Polyboroides radiatus*, in southeastern Madagascar. *Journal of Raptor Research* 33: 313–316.

Karpanty, S. M., and Wright, P. C. 2007. Predation on lemurs in the rainforest of Madagascar by multiple predator species: Observations and experiments. In *Primate Anti-Predator Strategies*, eds. S. L. Gursky and K.A.I. Nekaris, pp. 77–99. New York: Springer Science.

Kasangaki, A., Kityo, R., and Kerbis, J. 2003. Diversity of rodents and shrews along an elevational gradient in Bwindi Impenetrable National Park, south-western Uganda. *African Journal of Ecology* 41(2): 115–123.

Kasola, C., Atrefony, F., Louis, F., Odilon, G. N., Ralahinirina, R. G., Menjanahary, T., and Ratovonamana, Y. R. 2020. Population dynamics of *Lemur catta* at selected sleeping sites of Tsimanampesotse National Park. *Malagasy Nature* 14: 69–80.

Katzourakis, A., Aiewsakun, P., Jia, H., Wolfe, N. D., LeBreton, M., Yoder, A. D., and Switzer, W. M. 2014. Discovery of prosimian and afrotherian foamy viruses and potential cross species transmissions amidst stable and ancient mammalian co-evolution. *Retrovirology* 11: 61. https://doi.org/10.1186/1742-4690-11-61.

Kaudern, W. 1915. Saugethiere aus Madagaskar. *Arkiv för Zoologi*, Stockholm, 18: 1–101.

———. 1918. Quartäre Fossilien aus Madagascar. *Zoologische Jahrbücher, Abteilung für Systematik, Geographie und Biologie der Tiere* 41: 521–533.

Kay, R. F. 1975. The functional adaptations of primate molar teeth. *American Journal of Physical Anthropology* 43: 195–216.

———. 1984. On the use of anatomical features to infer foraging behavior in extinct primates. In *Adaptations for Foraging in Nonhuman Primates*, eds. P. S. Rodman and J.G.H. Cant, pp. 21–53. New York: Columbia University Press.

Kay, R. F., and Covert, H. H. 1984. Anatomy and behaviour of extinct primates. In *Food Acquisition and Processing in Primates*, eds. D. J. Chivers, B. A. Wood, and A. Bilsborough, pp. 467–508. Boston: Springer.

Kay, R. F., and Hylander, W. L. 1978. The dental structure of mammalian folivores with special reference to primates and phalangeroids (Marsupiala). In *The Ecology of Arboreal Folivores*, eds. G. G. Montgomery, pp. 173–192. Washington, DC: Smithsonian Institution Press.

Kay, R. F., and Kirk, E. C. 2000. Osteological evidence for the evolution of activity pattern and visual acuity in primates. *American Journal of Physical Anthropology* 113: 235–262.

Kayser, C. 1961. *The Physiology of Natural Hibernation*. Oxford: Pergamon Press.

Keane, A., Ramarolahy, A. A., Jones, J.P.G., and Milner-Gulland, E. J. 2011. Evidence for the effects of environmental engagement and education on knowledge of wildlife laws in Madagascar. *Conservation Letters* 4: 55–63.

Kearney, T. C. 2005. Systematic revision of southern African species in the genera *Eptesicus*, *Neoromicia*, *Hypsugo* and *Pipistrellus* (Chiroptera: Vespertilionidae). PhD thesis, University of KwaZulu-Natal, Durban.

Kelley, E. A. 2011. *Lemur catta* in the region of Cap Sainte-Marie, Madagascar: Introduced cacti, xerophytic Didiereaceae-Euphorbia bush, and tombs. PhD thesis, Washington University, Saint Louis.

———. 2013. The ranging behavior of *Lemur catta* in the region of Cap Sainte-Marie, Madagascar. *American Journal of Physical Anthropology* 150: 122–132.

Kelley, E. A., Sussman, R., and Muldoon, K. 2007. The status of lemur species at Antserananomby: An update. *Primate Conservation* 11: 71–77.

Kemp, J., López-Baucells, A., Rocha, R., Wangensteen, O. S., Andriatafika, Z., Nair, A., and Cabeza, M. 2019. Bats as potential suppressors of multiple agricultural pests: A case study from Madagascar. *Agriculture, Ecosystems and Environment* 269: 88–96. https://doi.org/10.1016/j.agee.2018.09.027.

Kerr, R. 1792. *The Animal Kingdom, or Zoological System of the Celebrated Sir Charles Linnaeus*. London: John Murray.

Kesch, K. 2009. Allomothering and allonursing behavior in collared lemurs (*Eulemur collaris*). *Lemur News* 14: 54–55.

Kiene, F., Andriatsitohaina, B., Ramsay, M. S., Rakotondramanana, H., Rakotondravony, R., Radespiel, U., and Strube, C. 2020. Forest edges affect ectoparasite infestation patterns of small mammalian hosts in fragmented forests in Madagascar. *International Journal for Parasitology* 50(4): 299–313. https://doi.org/10.1016/j.ijpara.2020.01.008.

Kimmel, L. 1998. *Le Potamochère et Ses Possibilités d'Élevage en Afrique*. Montpellier: CIRAD.

King, T., Rodotonirina, L.H.F., Rakotoarisoa, A. H., Ravaloharimanitra, M., and Chamberlan, C. 2011–2012. Projet Tsibahaka: Conserving the crowned sifaka *Propithecus coronatus*. *Lemur News* 16: 32–34.

King, T., Randrianarimanana, H. L., Rakotonirina, L. H., Mihaminekena, T. H., Andrianandrasana, Z. A., et al. 2013. Large-culmed bamboos in Madagascar: Distribution and field identification of the primary food sources of the critically endangered greater bamboo lemur *Prolemur simus*. *Primate Conservation* 27: 33–53.

Kingdon, J. 1974. *East African Mammals: An Atlas of Evolution in Africa*. Vol. 2, pt. A, *Insectivores and Bats*. London: Academic Press.

Kingman, J.F.C. 1982. The coalescent. *Stochastic Processes and Their Applications* 13: 235–248. https://doi.org/10.1016/0304-4149(82)90011-4.

Kirk, E. C. 2006. Eye morphology in cathemeral lemurids and other mammals. *Folia Primatologica* 77: 27–49.

Kistler, L., Ratan, A., Godfrey, L. R., Crowley, B. E., Hughes, C. E., et al. 2015. Comparative and population mitogenomic analyses of Madagascar's extinct, giant "subfossil" lemurs. *Journal of Human Evolution* 79, special issue: 45–54. https://doi.org/10.1016/j.jhevol.2014.06.016.

Kittler, K., and Dietzel, S. 2016. Female infanticide and female-directed lethal targeted aggression in a group of ring-tailed lemurs (*Lemur catta*). *Primate Biology* 3: 41–44. https://doi.org/10.5194/pb-3-41-2016.

Klein, A., Zimmermann, E., Radespiel, U., Schaarschmidt, F., Springer, A., and Strube, C. 2018. Ectoparasite communities of small-bodied Malagasy primates: Seasonal and socioecological influences on tick, mite and lice infestation of *Microcebus murinus* and *M. ravelobensis* in northwestern Madagascar. *Parasites Vectors* 11: 459. https://doi.org/10.1186/s13071-018-3034-y.

Klein, J.-M., and Uilenberg, G. 1966. Données faunistiques et écologiques sur les puces de Madagascar (Siphonaptera). *Cahiers de l'ORSTOM*, série *Entomologie Médicale* 4: 31–60.

Kling, K. J., Yaeger, K., and Wright, P. C. 2020. Trends in forest fragment research in Madagascar: Documented responses by lemurs and other taxa. *American Journal of Primatology* 82(4): e23092.

Klockenkämper, M. 1988. Verhaltensbeobachtungen an der Fossa (*Cryptoprocta ferox* Bennett, 1833). Diploma thesis, Rhenish Friedrich-Wilhelm University of Bonn.

Knoop, S., Chikhi, L., and Salmona, J. 2018. Mouse lemurs' use of degraded habitat. *Lemur News* 21: 20–31.

Kobbe, S., and Dausmann, K. H. 2009. Hibernation in Malagasy mouse lemurs as a strategy to counter environmental challenge. *Naturwissenschaften* 96: 1221–1227.

Kobbe, S., Ganzhorn, J. U., and Dausmann, K. H. 2011. Extreme individual flexibility of heterothermy in free-ranging Malagasy mouse lemurs (*Microcebus griseorufus*). *Journal of Comparative Physiology B: Biochemical, Systemic, and Environmental Physiology* 181: 165–173.

Kobbe, S., Ganzhorn, J. U., and Dausmann, K. H. 2014. Torpor is not the only option: Seasonal variations of the thermoneutral zone in a small primate. *Journal of Comparative Physiology B: Biochemical, Systemic, and Environmental Physiology* 184: 789–797.

Koenig, P. 2005. Découverte d'une dépouille d'aye-aye (*Daubentonia madagascariensis*) dans le nord-ouest de Madagascar. *Lemur News* 10: 6–7.

Kofoky, A. [F.], Andriafidison, D., Razafimanahaka, H. T., Rampilimanana, R. L., and Jenkins, R.K.B. 2006. The first observation of *Myzopoda* sp. (Myzopodidae) roosting in western Madagascar. *African Bat Conservation News* 9: 5–6.

Kofoky, A. [F.], Andriafidison, D., Ratrimomanarivo, F., Razafimanahaka, H. J., Rakotondravony, D., Racey, P. A., and Jenkins, R.K.B. 2007. Habitat use, roost selection and conservation of bats in Tsingy de Bemaraha National Park, Madagascar. *Biodiversity and Conservation* 16: 1039–1053.

Kofoky, A. F., Randrianandrianina, F., Russ, J., Raharinantenaina, I., Cardiff, S. G., Jenkins, R.K.B., and Racey, P. A. 2009. Acoustic description of some insectivorous bats (Microchiroptera) from Madagascar. *Acta Chiropterologica* 11: 375–392.

Köhncke, M., and Leonhardt, K. 1986. Cryptoprocta ferox. *Mammalian Species* 254: 1–5.

Koop, B. F., Tagle, D. A., Goodman, M., and Slightom, J. L. 1989. A molecular view of primate phylogeny and important systematic and evolutionary questions. *Molecular Biology and Evolution* 6: 580–612. https://doi.org/10.1093/oxfordjournals.molbev.a040574.

Kotschwar Logan, M., Gerber, B. D., Karpanty, S. M., Justin, S., and Rabenahy, F.N. 2015. Assessing carnivore distribution from local knowledge across a human-dominated landscape in central-southeastern Madagascar. *Animal Conservation* 18(1): 82–91.

Koubínová, D., Irwin, N., Hulva, P., Koubek, P., and Zima, J. 2013. Hidden diversity in Senegalese bats and associated findings in the systematics of the family Vespertilionidae. *Frontiers in Zoology* 10: 48.

Koyama, N. 1992. Some demographic data of ring-tailed lemurs (*Lemur catta*) at Berenty, Madagascar. In *Social Structure of Madagascar Higher Vertebrates in Relation to Their Adaptive Radiation*, ed. S. Yamagishi, pp. 10–12. Osaka: Osaka University Press.

Koyama, N., Nakamichi, M., Oda, R., Miyamoto, N., Ichino, S., and Takahata, Y. 2001. A ten-year summary of reproductive parameters for ring-tailed lemurs at Berenty, Madagascar. *Primates* 42(1): 1–14.

Koyama, N., Nakamichi, M., Ichino, S., and Takahata, Y. 2002. Population and social dynamics changes in ring-tailed lemur troops at Berenty, Madagascar between 1989–1999. *Primates* 43: 291–314.

Kraus, C., Eberle, M., and Kappeler, P. M. 2008. The costs of risky male behaviour: Sex differences in seasonal survival in a small sexually monomorphic primate. *Proceedings of the Royal Society of London B: Biological Sciences*, 275: 1635–1644.

Krause, D. W., Hartman, J. H., and Wells, N. A. 1997. Late Cretaceous vertebrates from Madagascar: Implications for biotic change in deep time. In *Natural Change and Human Impact in Madagascar*, eds. S. M. Goodman and B. D. Patterson, pp. 3–43. Washington, DC: Smithsonian Institution Press.

Kress, W. J. 1993. Coevolution of plants and animals: Pollination of flowers by primates in Madagascar. *Current Science* 65: 253–257.

Kress, W. J., Schatz, G. E., Andrianifahanana, M., and Morland, H. S. 1994. Pollination of *Ravenala madagascariensis* (Strelitziaceae) by lemurs in Madagascar: Evidence for an archaic coevolutionary system? *American Journal of Botany* 81: 542–551.

Kuhn, H. J. 1972. Die Geschichte des Säugetiere Madagaskars. *Zeitschrift Kölner Zoo* 15: 28–42.

Kulahci. G., Rubenstein, I., and Ghazanfar, A. A. 2015. Lemurs groom-at-a-distance through vocal networks. *Animal Behaviour* 110: 179–186. https://doi.org/10.1016/j.anbehav.2015.09.016.

Kull, C. A., Tassin, J., Moreau, S., Rakoto Ramiarantsoa, H., Blanc-Pamard, C., and Carrière, S. M. 2012. The introduced flora of Madagascar. *Biological Invasions* 14: 875–888.

Kull, C. A., Carrière, S. M., Moreau, S., Ramiarantsoa, H. R., Blanc-Pamard, C., and Tassin, J. 2013. Melting pots of biodiversity: Tropical smallholder farm landscapes as guarantors of sustainability. *Environment: Science and Policy for Sustainable Development* 55: 6–16.

Kull, C. A., Tassin, J., and Carrière, S. M. 2014. Approaching invasive species in Madagascar. *Madagascar Conservation and Development* 9: 60–70.

Kun-Rodrigues, C., Salmona, J., Besolo, A., Rasolondraibe, E., Rabarivola, C., Marques, T. A., and Chikhi, L. 2014. New density estimates of a threatened sifaka species (*Propithecus coquereli*) in Ankarafantsika National Park. *American Journal of Primatology* 76: 515–528.

Laakkonen, J., Goodman, S. M., Duchemin, J.-B., and Duplantier, J.-M. 2003. Trypomastigotes and potential flea vectors of the endemic rodents and the introduced *Rattus rattus* in the rainforests of Madagascar. *Biodiversity and Conservation* 12: 1775–1783.

Laborde, C. 1986a. Caractères d'adaptation des membres au mode de vie arboricole chez *Cryptoprocta ferox* par comparaison avec d'autres Carnivores Viverridés. *Annales des Sciences Naturelles*, Paris, série *Zoologie* 13: 25–39.

———. 1986b. Description de la locomotion arboricole de *Cryptoprocta ferox* (Carnivore Viverridé malgache). *Mammalia* 50: 369–378.

LaFleur, M. 2012. Ecology of ring-tailed lemurs (*Lemur catta*) at the Tsimanampetsotsa National Park, Madagascar: Implications for female dominance and the evolution of lemur traits. PhD thesis, University of Colorado, Boulder.

LaFleur, M., and Gould, L. 2009. Feeding outside the forest: The importance of crop raiding and an invasive weed in the diet of gallery forest ring-tailed lemurs (*Lemur catta*) following a cyclone at the Beza Mahafaly Special Reserve, Madagascar. *Folia Primatologica* 80: 233–246.

LaFleur, M., and Sauther, M. L. 2015. Seasonal feeding ecology of ring-tailed lemurs: A comparison of spiny and gallery forest habitats. In Ring-tailed lemurs: A species reimagined, eds. M. L. Sauther, L. Gould, F. P. Cuozzo, and M. T. O'Mara. *Folia Primatologica* 86: 25–34.

LaFleur, M., Sauther, M. L, Cuozzo, F. P., Yamashita, N., Youssouf Jacky, I. A., and Bender, R. 2014. Cathemerality in wild ring-tailed lemurs (*Lemur catta*) in the spiny forest of Tsimanampetsotsa National Park: Camera trap data and preliminary behavioral observations. *Primates* 55: 207–217.

LaFleur, M., Clarke, T., Reuter, K., and Schaefer, T. 2017a. Rapid decrease in populations of wild ring-tailed lemurs (*Lemur catta*) in Madagascar. *Folia Primatologica* 87: 320–330.

LaFleur, M., Clarke, T., Reuter, K., and Ratsimabazafy, J. 2017b. *Lemur catta* (Linnaeus, 1758). In *Primates in Peril: The World's 25 Most Endangered Primates*, eds. C. Schwitzer, R. A. Mittermeier, A. B. Rylands, F. Chiozza, E. A. Williamson, et al., pp. 35–37. Washington, DC: IUCN SSC Primate Specialist Group, International Primatological Society, Conservation International, and Bristol Zoological Society.

LaFleur, M., Gould, L., Sauther, M. L., Clarke, T., and Reuter, K. 2018. Restating the case for a sharp population decline in *Lemur catta*. *Folia Primatologica* 89: 295–304. https://doi.org/10.1159/000489676.

LaFleur, M., Clarke, T. A., Reuter, K. E., Schaefer, M. S., and Horst C. 2019. Illegal trade of wild-captured *Lemur catta* within Madagascar. *Folia Primatologica* 90: 199–214. https://doi.org/10.1159/000496970.

Lagadec, E., Gomard, Y., Le Minter, G., Cordonin, C., Cardinale, E., Ramasindrazana, B., Dietrich, M., Goodman, S. M., Tortosa, P., and Dellagi, K. 2016. Identification of *Tenrec ecaudatus*, a wild mammal introduced to Mayotte Island, as a reservoir of the newly identified human pathogenic *Leptospira mayottensis*. *PLoS Neglected Tropical Diseases* 10(8): e0004933.

Lahann, P. 2007a. Biology of *Cheirogaleus major* in a littoral rainforest in southeast Madagascar. *International Journal of Primatology* 28: 895–905.

———. 2007b. Feeding ecology and seed dispersal of sympatric cheirogaleid lemurs (*Microcebus murinus*, *Cheirogaleus medius*, *Cheirogaleus major*) in the littoral rainforest of south-east Madagascar. *Journal of Zoology* 271: 88–98.

———. 2008. Habitat utilization of three sympatric cheirogaleid lemur species in a littoral rain forest of southeastern Madagascar. *International Journal of Primatology* 29: 117–134.

Lahann, P., and Dausmann, K. H. 2011. Live fast, die young: Flexibility of life history traits in the fat-tailed dwarf lemur (*Cheirogaleus medius*). *Behavioral Ecology and Sociobiology* 65: 381–390.

Lahann, P., Schmid, J., and Ganzhorn, J. U. 2006. Geographic variation in populations of *Microcebus murinus* in Madagascar: Resource seasonality or Bergmann's rule? *International Journal of Primatology* 27(4): 983–999.

Lamb, J. M., Ralph, T.M.C., Goodman, S. M., Bogdanowicz, W., Fahr, J., Gajewska, M., Bates, P.J.J., Eger, J., Benda, P., and Taylor, P. J. 2008. Phylogeography and predicted distribution of African-Arabian and Malagasy populations of giant mastiff bats, *Otomops* spp. (Chiroptera: Molossidae). *Acta Chiropterologica* 10: 21–40.

Lamb, J. M., Ralph, T.M.C., Naidoo, T., Taylor, P. J., Ratrimomanarivo, F., Stanley, W. T., and Goodman, S. M. 2011. Toward a molecular phylogeny for the Molossidae (Chiroptera) of the Afro-Malagasy region. *Acta Chiropterologica* 13: 1–16.

Lamb, J. M., Naidoo, T., Taylor, P. J., Napier, M., Ratrimomanarivo, F., and Goodman, S. M. 2012. Genetically and geographically isolated lineages of a tropical bat (Chiroptera: Molossidae) show demographic stability over the late Pleistocene. *Biological Journal of the Linnean Society* 106: 18–40. https://doi.org/10.1111/j.1095-8312.2011.01853.x.

Lamberton, C. 1910. Contributions à l'étude des mœurs du aye-aye. *Bulletin de l'Académie Malgache* 8: 129–140.

———. 1936. Fouilles paléontologiques faites en 1936. *Bulletin de l'Académie Malgache*, nouvelle série, 19: 1–19.

———. 1939. Contribution à la connaissance de la faune subfossile de Madagascar: Lémuriens et cryptoproctes. *Mémoire de l'Académie Malgache* 27: 1–193.

———. 1946. Contribution à la connaissance de la faune subfossile de Madagascar. Note 15: Le *Plesiorycteropus madagascariensis* Filhol. *Bulletin de l'Académie Malgache*, nouvelle série, 25: 25–53.

Landguth, E. L., Cushman, S. A., Schwartz, M. K., McKelvey, K. S., Murphy, M., and Luikart, G. 2010. Quantifying the lag time to detect barriers in landscape genetics. *Molecular Ecology* 19: 4179–4191. https://doi.org/10.1111/j.1365-294X.2010.04808.x.

Langrand, O. 1990. *Guide to the Birds of Madagascar.* New Haven: Yale University Press.

Langrand, O., and Goodman, S. M. 1996. Note on the diet of the Madagascar Long-eared Owl (*Asio madagascariensis*) in the Special Reserve of Ambohitantely. *Newsletter of the Working Group on Birds in the Madagascar Region* 6(2): 9–11.

Langrand, O., and Goodman, S. M. 1997. Inventaire des oiseaux et des micro-mammifères des zones sommitales de la Réserve Naturelle Intégrale d'Andringitra. *Akon'ny Ala* 20: 39–54.

Larkin, P., and Roberts, M. 1979. Reproduction in the ring-tailed mongoose *Galidia elegans* at the National Zoological Park, Washington. *International Zoo Yearbook* 19: 188–193.

Larsen, P. A., Campbell, C. R., and Yoder, A. D. 2014. Next-generation approaches to advancing eco-immunogenomic research in critically endangered primates. *Molecular Ecology Resources* 14: 1198–1209. https://doi.org/10.1111/1755-0998.12274.

Larsen, P. A., Hayes, C. E., Williams, C. V., Junge, R. E., Razafindramanana, J., Mass, V., Rakotondrainibe, H., and Yoder, A. D. 2016. Blood transcriptomes reveal novel parasitic zoonoses circulating in Madagascar's lemurs. *Biology Letters* 12: 20150829.

Laudisoit, A., Prié, V., and Beaucournu J.-C. 2012. Une nouvelle espèce de *Lagaropsylla* Jordan & Rothschild, 1921 de Madagascar (Insecta, Siphonaptera, Ischnopsyllidae). *Zoosystema* 34: 737–744.

Laurance, W. F. 2000. Do edge effects occur over large spatial scales? *Trends in Ecology and Evolution* 15: 134–135.

Lavocat, R. 1973. Les rongeurs du Miocène d'Afrique Oriéntale. I. Miocène inferieur. *Mémoires et Travaux de l'Institut de Montpellier de l'Ecole Pratique des Hautes Etudes* 1: 1–284.

———. 1978. Rodentia and Lagomorpha. In *Evolution of African Mammals*, eds. V. J. Maglio and H.B.S. Cooke, pp. 69–89. Cambridge, MA: Harvard University Press.

Lawler, R. R. 2007. Fitness and extra-group reproduction in male Verreaux's sifaka: An analysis of reproductive success from 1989–1999. *American Journal of Physical Anthropology* 132: 267–277. https://doi.org/10.1002/ajpa.20507.

———. 2011. Historical demography of a wild lemur population (*Propithecus verreauxi*) in southwest Madagascar. *Population Ecology* 53: 229–240.

———. 2018. Emerging and enduring issues in primate conservation genetics. *Annual Review of Anthropology* 47: 395–415. https://doi.org/10.1146/annurev-anthro-102317-050006.

Lawler, R. R., Richard, A. F., and Riley, M. A. 2003. Genetic population structure of the white sifaka (*Propithecus verreauxi verreauxi*) at Beza Mahafaly Special Reserve, southwest Madagascar (1992–2001). *Molecular Ecology* 12: 2307–2317. https://doi.org/10.1046/j.1365-294x.2003.01909.x

Lawson, D. J., Hellenthal, G., Myers, S., and Falush, D. 2012. Inference of population structure using dense haplotype data. *PLoS Genetics* 8: e1002453. https://doi.org/10.1371/journal.pgen.1002453.

Leache, A. D., Zhu, T., Rannala, B., and Yang, Z. 2019. The spectre of too many species. *Systematic Biology* 68: 168–181.

Lee, C., Day, J. Goodman, S. M., Pedrono, M., Besnard, G., Frantz, L., Taylor, P. J., Herrera, M. J., and Gongora, J. 2020. Genetic origins and diversity of bushpigs from Madagascar (*Potamochoerus larvatus*, family Suidae). *Scientific Reports* 10: 20629. https://doi.org/10.1038/s41598-020-77279-5.

Leger, J.-P. 1934. Epizootie de rongeurs en Imerina. *Bulletin de la Société de Pathologie Exotique* 27: 534–535.

Lehman, S. M. 2007. Spatial variations in *Eulemur fulvus rufus* and *Lepilemur mustelinus* densities in Madagascar. *Folia Primatologica* 78: 46–55.

Lehman, S. M., and Mayor, M. 2004. Dietary patterns in Perrier's sifakas (*Propithecus diadema perrieri*): A preliminary study. *American Journal of Primatology* 62: 115–122.

Lehman, S. M., and Wright, P. 2000. Preliminary study of the conservation status of lemur communities in the Betsakafandrika region of eastern Madagascar. *Lemur News* 5: 23–25.

Lehman, S. M., Rajaonson, A., and Day, S. 2006a. Edge effects and their influence on lemur density and distribution in southeast Madagascar. *American Journal of Physical Anthropology* 129(2): 232–241.

Lehman, S. M., Rajaonson, A., and Day, S. 2006b. Lemur responses to edge effects in the Vohibola III classified forest, Madagascar. *American Journal of Primatology* 68: 293–299.

Lehman, S. M., Ratsimbazafy, J., Rajaonson, A., and Day, S. 2006c. Decline of *Propithecus diadema edwardsi* and *Varecia variegata variegata* (Primates: Lemuridae) in south-east Madagascar. *Oryx* 40: 108–111.

Lehtonen, J. T., Mustonen, O., Ramiarinjanahary, H., Niemelä, J., and Rita, H. 2001. Habitat use by endemic and introduced rodents along a gradient of forest disturbance in Madagascar. *Biodiversity and Conservation* 10(7): 1185–1202.

Lei, R., Engberg, S. E., Andriantompohavana, R., McGuire, S. M., Mittermeier, R. A., Zaonarivelo, J. R., Brenneman, R. A., and Louis, E. E., Jr. 2008. Nocturnal lemur diversity at Masoala National Park. *Occasional Papers, Museum of Texas Tech University* 53: 1–41.

Lei, R., Frasier, C. L., McLain, A. T., Taylor, J. M., Bailey, C. A., et al. 2014. Revision of Madagascar's dwarf lemurs (Cheirogaleidae: *Cheirogaleus*): Designation of species, candidate species status and geographic boundaries based on molecular and morphological data. *Primate Conservation* 28: 9–35.

Lei, R., Frasier, C. L., Hawkins, M.T.R., Engberg, S. E., Bailey, C. A., et al. 2017. Phylogenomic reconstruction of sportive lemurs (genus *Lepilemur*) recovered from mitogenomes with inferences for Madagascar biogeography. *Journal of Heredity* 108: 107–119. https://doi.org/10.1093/jhered/esw072.

Leipoldt, M., Schlitz, A., Ganzhorn, J. U., and Tomiuk, J. 1996. Genetic analysis of *Lepilemur mustelinus ruficaudatus* populations using RAPD markers. In *Biogéographie de Madagascar*, ed. W. R. Lourenço, pp. 267–274. Paris: Editions de l'ORSTOM.

Leitwein, M., Duranton, M., Rougemont, Q., Gagnaire, P.-A., and Bernatchez, L. 2020. Using haplotype information for conservation genomics. *Trends in Ecology and Evolution* 35: 245–258. https://doi.org/10.1016/j.tree.2019.10.012.

Lekagul, B., and McNeely, J. A. 1977. *Mammals of Thailand*. Bangkok: Association for the Conservation of Wildlife.

Lemelin, P., Hamrick, M. W., Richmond, B. G., Godfrey, L. R., Jungers, W. L., and Burney, D. A. 2008. New hand bones of *Hadropithecus stenognathus*: Implications for the paleobiology of the Archaeolemuridae. *Journal of Human Evolution* 54: 405–413.

Lever, C. 1985. *Naturalized Mammals of the World*. London: Longman.

Levesque, D. L., and Lovegrove, B. G. 2014. Increased homeothermy during reproduction in a basal placental mammal. *Journal of Experimental Biology* 217: 1535–1542.

Levesque, D. L., Lovasoa, O.M.A., Rakotoharimalala, S. N., and Lovegrove, B. G. 2013. High mortality and annual fecundity in a free-ranging basal placental mammal, *Setifer setosus* (Tenrecidae: Afrosoricida). *Journal of Zoology* 291: 205–212.

Levesque, D. L., Lobban, K. D., and Lovegrove, B. G. 2014. Effects of reproductive status and high ambient temperatures on the body temperature of a free-ranging

basoendotherm. *Journal of Comparative Physiology B: Biochemical, Systemic, and Environmental Physiology* 184: 1041–1053.

Levin, E., Plotnik, B., Amichai, E., Braulke, L. J., Landau, S., Yom-Tov, Y., and Kronfeld-Schor, N. 2015. Subtropical mouse-tailed bats use geothermally heated caves for winter hibernation. *Proceedings of the Royal Society of London B: Biological Sciences* 282: 20142781.

Lewis, R. J. 2005. Sex differences in scent-marking in sifaka: Mating conflict or male services? *American Journal of Physical Anthropology* 128: 389–398.

———. 2020. Female power: A new framework for understanding "female dominance" in lemurs. *Folia Primatologica* 91: 48–68.

Lewis, R. J., and Van Schaik, C. P. 2007. Bimorphism in male Verreaux's sifaka in the Kirindy Forest of Madagascar. *International Journal of Primatology* 28: 159–182.

Lewis, R. J., Razafindrasamba, S. M., and Tolojanahary, J. P. 2003. Observed infanticide in a seasonal breeding prosimian (*Propithecus verreauxi verreauxi*) in Kirindy Forest, Madagascar. *Folia Primatologica* 74: 101–103.

Lhota, S., Jůnek, T., Bartos, L., and Kuběna, A. A. 2008. Specialized use of two fingers in free-ranging aye-ayes (*Daubentonia madagascariensis*). *American Journal of Primatology* 70: 786–795.

Li, H., and Durbin, R. 2011. Inference of human population history from individual whole-genome sequences. *Nature* 475: 493–496. https://doi.org/10.1038/nature10231.

Lim, E. S., Deem, S. L., Porton, I. J., Cao, S., and Wang, D. 2015. Species-specific transmission of novel picornaviruses in lemurs. *Journal of Virology* 89: 4002–4010. https://doi.org/10.1128/JVI.03342-14.

Lindblad-Toh, K., Garber, M., Zuk, O., Lin, M. F., Parker, B. J., et al. 2011. A high-resolution map of human evolutionary constraint using 29 mammals. *Nature* 478: 476–482.

Lindsay, N.B.D., and Simons, H. J. 1986. Notes on *Varecia* in the northern limits of its range. *Dodo* 23: 29–24.

Link, H. F. 1795. *Beyträge zur Naturgeschichte*. Rostock and Leipzig: Karl Christoph Stiller.

Linkie, M., Guillera-Arroita, G., Smith, J., Ario, A., Bertagnolio, G., Cheong, F., Clements, G. R., Dinata, Y., Duangchantrasiri, S., and Fredriksson, G. 2013. Cryptic mammals caught on camera: Assessing the utility of range wide camera trap data for conserving the endangered Asian tapir. *Biological Conservation* 162: 107–115.

Liow, L. H., Fortelius, M., Lintulaakso, K., Mannila, H., and Stenseth, N. C. 2009. Lower extinction risk in sleep-or-hide mammals. *American Naturalist* 173: 264–272.

Littlefield, B. L. 2010. Infanticide following male takeover event in Verreaux's sifaka (*Propithecus verreauxi verreauxi*). *Primates* 51: 83–86.

Liu, L., Zhang, J., Rheindt, F. E., Lei, F., Qu, Y., et al. 2017. Genomic evidence reveals a radiation of placental mammals uninterrupted by the KPg boundary. *Proceedings of the National Academy of Sciences of the USA* 114: E7282-E7290.

Liu, X., and Fu, Y.-X. 2015. Exploring population size changes using SNP frequency spectra. *Nature Genetics* 47: 555–559. https://doi.org/10.1038/ng.3254.

Lobban, K. D., Lovegrove, B. G., and Rakotondravony, D. 2014. The energetics of a Malagasy rodent, *Macrotarsomys ingens* (Nesomyinae): A test of island and zoogeographical effects on metabolism. *Journal of Comparative Physiology B: Biochemical, Systemic, and Environmental Physiology* 184(8): 1077–1089.

Loiseau, A., Rahelinirina, S., Rahalison, L., Konečný, A., Duplantier, J.-M., and Brouat, C. 2008. Isolation and characterization of microsatellites in *Rattus rattus*. *Molecular Ecology Resources* 8: 916–918. https://doi.org/10.1111/j.1755-0998.2008.02115.x.

Long, E. 2001. The role of *Pteropus rufus* in pollination and seed dispersal in Madagascar. PhD thesis, University of Aberdeen.

Long, E., and Racey, P. A. 2007. An exotic plantation crop as a keystone resource for an endemic megachiropteran, *Pteropus rufus*, in Madagascar. *Journal of Tropical Ecology* 23: 397–407.

Lönnberg, E. 1910. Contributions to the knowledge of the genus *Potamochoerus*. *Arkiv för Zoologi* 7(6): 1–40.

López-Baucells, A., Rocha, R., Andriatafika, Z., Tojosoa, T., Kemp, J., Forbes, K. M., and Cabeza, M. 2017. Roost site selection by synanthropic bats in rural Madagascar: What makes non-traditional structures so tempting? *Hystrix* 28(1): 28–35.

Louis, E. E., Jr., and Lei, R. 2016. Mitogenomics of the family Cheirogaleidae and relationships to taxonomy and biogeography in Madagascar. In *The Dwarf and Mouse Lemurs of Madagascar: Biology, Behavior and Conservation Biogeography of the Cheirogaleidae*, eds. S. M. Lehman, U. Radespiel, and E. Zimmermann, pp. 54–93. Cambridge: Cambridge University Press. https://doi.org/10.1017/CBO9781139871822.004.

Louis, E. E., Jr., Ratsimbazafy, J. H., Razakamaharavo, V. R., Pierson, D. J., Barber, R. C., and Brenneman, R. A. 2005. Conservation genetics of black and white ruffed lemurs, *Varecia variegata*, from southeastern Madagascar. *Animal Conservation* 8: 105–111. https://doi.org/10.1017/S1367943004001891.

Louis, E. E., Jr., Engberg, S. E., Lei, R., Geng, H., Sommer, J. A., et al. 2006a. Molecular and morphological analyses of the sportive lemurs (family Megaladapidae: genus *Lepilemur*) reveals 11 previously unrecognized species. *Special Publications, Museum of Texas Tech University* 49: 1–47. https://doi.org/10.5962/bhl.title.142646.

Louis, E. E., Jr., Coles, M. S., Andriantompohavana, R., Sommer, J. A., Engberg, S. E., Zaonarivelo, J. R., Mayor, M. I., and Brenneman, R. A. 2006b. Revision of the mouse lemurs (*Microcebus*) of eastern Madagascar. *International Journal of Primatology* 27: 347–389.

Louis, E. E., Jr., Engberg, S. E., McGuire, S. M., McCormick, M. J., Randriamampionona, R., Ranaivoarisoa, J. F., Bailey, C. A., Mittermeier, R. A., and Lei, R. 2008. Revision of the mouse lemurs, *Microcebus* (Primates, Lemuriformes), of northern and northwestern Madagascar with descriptions of two new species at Montagne d'Ambre National Park and Antafondro Classified Forest. *Primate Conservation* 23: 19–38. https://doi.org/10.1896/052.023.0103.

Lovegrove, B. G. 2003. The influence of climate on the basal metabolic rate of small mammals: A slow-fast metabolic continuum. *Journal of Comparative Physiology B: Biochemical, Systemic, and Environmental Physiology* 173: 87–112.

———. 2019. *Fires of Life: Endothermy in Birds and Mammals*. New Haven: Yale University Press.

Lovegrove, B. G., and Génin, F. 2008. Torpor and hibernation in a basal placental mammal, the lesser hedgehog tenrec *Echinops telfairi*. *Journal of Comparative Physiology B: Biochemical, Systemic, and Environmental Physiology* 178: 691–698.

Lovegrove, B. G., Lobban, K. D., and Levesque, D. L. 2014a. Mammal survival at the Cretaceous-Palaeogene boundary: Metabolic homeostasis in prolonged tropical hibernation in tenrecs. *Proceedings of the Royal Society of London B: Biological Sciences* 281: 20141304.

Lovegrove, B. G., Canale, C. I., Levesque, D. L., Fluch, G., Reháková-Petrů, M., and Ruf, T. 2014b. Are tropical small mammals physiologically vulnerable to Arrhenius effects and climate change? *Physiological and Biochemical Zoology* 87: 30–45.

Lowe, S., Browne, M., Boudjelas, S., and De Poorter M. 2000. 100 of the World's Worst Invasive Alien Species: A Selection from the Global Invasive Species Database. Auckland: Invasive Species Specialist Group (ISSG) a specialist group of the Species Survival Commission (SSC) of the World Conservation Union (IUCN). http://www.issg.org/pdf/publications/worst_100/english_100_worst.pdf.

Lowin, A. J. 2010. *Lepilemur* feeding observations from northern Madagascar. *Lemur News* 15: 20–21.

Luft, S., Curio, E., and Tacud, B. 2003. The use of olfaction in the foraging behaviour of the golden-mantled flying fox, *Pteropus pumilus*, and the greater musky fruit bat, *Ptenochirus jagori* (Megachiroptera: Pteropodidae). *Naturwissenschaften* 90: 84–87.

Lührs, M.-L., and Dammhahn, M. 2010. An unusual case of cooperative hunting in a solitary carnivore. *Journal of Ethology* 28: 379–383.

Lührs, M.-L., and Kappeler, P. M. 2013. Simultaneous GPS tracking reveals male associations in a solitary carnivore. *Behavioral Ecology and Sociobiology* 67: 1731–1743.

Lührs, M.-L., and Kappeler, P. M. 2014. Polyandrous mating in treetops: How male competition and female choice interact to determine an unusual carnivore mating system. *Behavioral Ecology and Sociobiology* 68: 879–889.

Lührs, M.-L., Dammhahn, M., and Kappeler, P. 2013. Strength in numbers: Males in a carnivore grow bigger when they associate and hunt cooperatively. *Behavioral Ecology* 24: 21–28. https://doi.org/10.1093/beheco/ars150.

Lukas, K. E. 1999. A review of nutritional and motivational factors contributing to the performance of regurgitation and reingestion in captive lowland gorillas (*Gorilla gorilla gorilla*). *Applied Animal Behaviour Science* 63: 237–249.

Lutermann, H. 2001. Weibchenassoziationen und Fortpflanzungsstrategien beim Grauen Mausmaki (*Microcebus murinus*) in Nordwest-Madagaskar. PhD thesis, University of Hannover.

Lutermann, H., Schmelting, B., Radespiel, U., Ehresmann, P., and Zimmermann, E. 2006. The role of survival for the evolution of female philopatry in a solitary forager, the grey mouse lemur (*Microcebus murinus*). *Proceedings of the Royal Society of London B: Biological Sciences* 273: 2527–2533.

Lutermann, H., Verburgt, L., and Rendigs, A. 2010. Resting and nesting in a small mammal: Sleeping sites as a limiting resource for female grey mouse lemurs. *Animal Behaviour* 79: 1211–1219.

Lyman, C. P., Willis, J. S., Malan, A., and Wang, L.C.H. 1982. *Hibernation and Torpor in Mammals and Birds*. New York: Academic Press.

Lynch, M., Bürger, R., Butcher, D., and Gabriel, W. 1990. The mutational meltdown in asexual populations. *Journal of Heredity* 84: 339–344.

MacArthur, R. H., and Wilson, E. O. 1967. *The Theory of Island Biogeography*. Princeton: Princeton University Press.

Macedonia, J. M. 1986. Individuality in a contact call of the ring-tailed lemur (*Lemur catta*). *American Journal of Primatology* 11: 163–179.

———. 1990. What is communicated in the antipredator calls of lemurs: Evidence from playback experiments with ringtailed and ruffed lemurs. *Ethology* 86: 177–190.

———. 1993a. Adaptation and phylogenetic constraints in the antipredator behavior of ringtailed and ruffed lemurs. In *Lemur Social Systems and Their Ecological Basis*, eds. P. M. Kappeler and J. U. Ganzhorn, pp. 67–84. New York: Plenum Press.

———. 1993b. The vocal repertoire of the ringtailed lemur (*Lemur catta*). *Folia Primatologica* 61: 186–217.

Macedonia, J. M., and Polak, J. F. 1989. Visual assessment of avian threat in semi-captive ringtailed lemurs (*Lemur catta*). *Behaviour* 111: 291–304.

Macedonia, J. M., and Stanger, K. F. 1994. Phylogeny of the Lemuridae revisited: Evidence from communication signals. *Folia Primatologica* 63: 1–43.

Macedonia, J. M., and Yount, P. L. 1991. Auditory assessment of avian threat in semi-captive ringtailed lemurs (*Lemur catta*). *Primates* 32: 169–182.

MacKinnon, J. L., Hawkins, C. E., and Racey, P. A. 2003. Pteropodidae, fruit bats. In *The Natural History of Madagascar*, eds. S. M. Goodman and J. P. Benstead, pp. 1299–1302. Chicago: University of Chicago Press.

MacPhee, R.D.E. 1986. Environment, extinction, and Holocene vertebrate localities in southern Madagascar. *National Geographic Research* 2: 441–455.

———. 1987. The shrew tenrecs of Madagascar: Systematic revision and Holocene distribution of *Microgale* (Tenrecidae, Insectivora). *American Museum Novitates* 2889: 1–45.

———. 1994. Morphology, adaptations, and relationships of *Plesiorycteropus*, and a diagnosis of a new order of eutherian mammals. *Bulletin of the American Museum of Natural History* 220: 1–214.

MacPhee, R.D.E., and Burney, D. A. 1991. Dating of modified femora of extinct dwarf *Hippopotamus* from southern Madagascar: Implications for constraining human colonization and vertebrate extinction events. *Journal of Archaeological Science* 18: 695–706.

MacPhee, R.D.E., Burney, D. A., and Wells, N. A. 1985. Early Holocene chronology and environment of Ampasambazimba, a Malagasy subfossil lemur site. *International Journal of Primatology* 6: 463–489.

Madagascar Catalogue. 2020. Catalogue of the Plants of Madagascar. Missouri Botanical Garden, St. Louis, U.S.A., and Antananarivo, Madagascar. http://legacy.tropicos.org/Project/Madagascar.

Madagascar Lemurs Portal. 2017. Madagascar lemurs portal. www.lemursportal.org.

Madsen, T., Shine, R., Olsson, M., and Wittzell, H. 1999. Restoration of an inbred adder population. *Nature* 402: 34–35.

Magdziak, R. 2017. Energy budgets at the edge: Thermoregulatory adaptations in *Lepilemur leucopus*. MS thesis, University of Hamburg.

Mahaboubi, S., Randrianambinina, B., Rakotondravony, R., Scheumann, M., Zimmermann, E., and Rasoloharijaona, S. 2015. First characterization of the vocal acoustics of Otto's sportive lemur *Lepilemur otto* (Craul et al., 2007) with remarks on its abundance. *Lemur News* 19: 16–21.

Mahazotahy, S., Goodman, S. M., and Andriamanalina, A. 2006. Notes on the distribution and habitat preferences of *Galidictis grandidieri* Wozencraft, 1986 (Carnivora: Eupleridae), a poorly known endemic species of south-western Madagascar. *Mammalia* 70: 328–330.

Mahé, J. 1965. *Les subfossiles Malgaches*. Antananarivo: Imprimerie Nationales.

Mahé, J., and Sourdat, M. 1972. Sur l'extinction des vertébrés subfossiles et l'aridification du climat dans le sud-ouest de Madagascar. *Bulletin de la Société Géologique de France* 14: 295–309.

Major, C.I.F. 1896a. Diagnoses of new mammals from Madagascar. *Annals and Magazine of Natural History*, ser. 6, 18: 319–325.

———. 1896b. On the general results of a zoological expedition to Madagascar in 1894–96. *Proceedings of the Zoological Society of London* 1896: 971–981.

———. 1896c. Descriptions of four additional new mammals from Madagascar. *Annals and Magazine of Natural History*, ser. 6, 18: 461–463.

———. 1897a. On the Malagasy rodent genus *Brachyuromys*; and on the mutual relations of some groups of the Muridae (Hesperomyinae, Microtinae, Murinae, and "Spalacidae") with each other and with the Malagasy Nesomyinae. *Proceedings of the Zoological Society of London* 1897: 695–720.

———. 1897b. On the species of *Potamochoerus*, the bush-pigs of the Ethiopian Region. *Proceedings of the Zoological Society of London* 1897: 359–370.

———. 1908. A giant sub-fossil rat from Madagascar, *Myoryctes rapeto*. *Geological Magazine*, ser. 5, 5: 97–98.

Malcolm, J. R., Valenta, K., and Lehman, S. 2017. Edge effects in tropical dry forests of Madagascar: Additivity or synergy? *Landscape Ecology* 32(2): 327–341.

Malia, M. J., Jr., Adkins, R. M., and Allard, M. W. 2002. Molecular support for Afrotheria and the polyphyly of Lipotyphla based on analyses of the growth hormone receptor gene. *Molecular Phylogenetics and Evolution* 24: 91–101.

Malzy, P. 1964. Zoologie malgache: Sur deux rongeurs importés à Madagascar. *Bulletin de Madagascar* 14(219): 619–623.

———. 1965. Un mammifère aquatique de Madagascar: Le limnogale. *Mammalia* 29(3): 400–411.

Maminirina, C. P., Goodman, S. M., and Raxworthy, C. J. 2008. Les micro-mammifères (Mammalia, Rodentia, Afrosoricida et Soricomorpha) du massif du Tsaratanana et biogéographie des forêts de montagne de Madagascar. *Zoosystema* 30: 695–721.

Mandl, I., Rabemananjara, N. R., Rakotomalala, A.N.A., Sorlin, M., Holderied, M., and Schwitzer, C. 2017. A case of mobbing observed in two species of nocturnal lemur, *Mirza zaza* and *Lepilemur sahamalazensis* in north-west Madagascar. *Lemur News* 20: 6–7.

Mandl, I., Holderied, M., and Schwitzer, C. 2018. The effects of climate seasonality on behavior and sleeping site choice in Sahamalaza sportive lemurs, *Lepilemur sahamalaza*. *International Journal of Primatology* 39: 1039–1067.

Mandl, I., Holderied, M., and Schwitzer, C. 2019a. Spatiotemporal distribution of individuals as an indicator for the social system of *Lepilemur sahamalaza*. *American Journal of Primatology* 81: e22984. https://doi.org/10.1002/ajp.22984.

Mandl, I., Schwitzer, C., and Holderied, M. 2019b. Sahamalaza sportive lemur, *Lepilemur sahamalaza*, vocal communication: Call use, context and gradation. *Folia Primatologica* 90: 336–360.

Manjoazy, T. 2018. Ecomorphologie, bioacoustique et conservation des chiroptères dans les régions sèches de Madagascar. PhD thesis, Biologie Animale, Ecole Doctorale de Biodiversité et Environnement Tropicaux, Université de Toliara.

Mann, G., Rakotondraparany, F., Theseing, S., and Gandola, R. 2016. First record of fossa *Cryptoprocta ferox* in Mariarano forest, Madagascar. *Small Carnivore Conservation* 52: 45–55.

Marciniak, S., Mughal, H. R., Godfrey, L. R., Bergey, C. M., Bankoff, R. J., et al. 2020. Evolutionary and phylogenetic insights from a nuclear genome of the extinct giant koala lemur *Megaladapis edwardsi*. *American Journal of Physical Anthropology* 171(supplement 69): 173–174.

Maretti, G., Sorrentino, V., Finomana, A., Gamba, M., and Giacoma, C. 2010. Not just a pretty song: An overview of the vocal repertoire of *Indri indri*. *Journal of Anthropological Science* 88: 151–165.

Markham, K. 2014. Diet and behavior of adult *Propithecus verreauxi* in southern Madagascar during the birth season. MA thesis, University of Victoria.

Markham, K., and Gould, L. 2018. Diet and behaviour of adult *Propithecus verreauxi* (Verreaux's sifaka) in southern Madagascar during the birth season. *Lemur News* 21: 12–16.

Markolf, M., and Kappeler, P. M. 2013. Phylogeographic analysis of the true lemurs (genus *Eulemur*) underlines the role of river catchments for the evolution of micro-endemism in Madagascar. *Frontiers in Zoology* 10: 70. https://doi.org/10.1186/1742-9994-10-70.

Markolf, M., and Kappeler, P. M. 2020. Observations on the mating behavior of *Mirza coquereli* in Kirindy Forest, western Madagascar. *Lemur News* 22: 19–22.

Markolf, M., Kappeler, P. M., and Rasoloarison, R. 2008. Distribution and conservation status of *Mirza zaza*. *Lemur News* 13: 37–40.

Markolf, M., Brameier, M., and Kappeler, P. M. 2011. On species delimitation: Yet another lemur species or just genetic variation? *BMC Evolutionary Biology* 11: 216.

Markolf, M., Rakotonirina, H., Fichtel, C., von Grumbkow, P., Brameier, M., and Kappeler, P. M. 2013. True lemurs ... true species: Species delimitation using multiple data sources in the brown lemur complex. *BMC Evolutionary Biology* 13: 233. https://doi.org/10.1186/1471-2148-13-233.

Marquard, M. J., Jeglinski, J. W., Razafimahatratra, E., Ratovonamana, Y. R., and Ganzhorn, J. U. 2011. Distribution, population size and morphometrics of the giant-striped mongoose *Galidictis grandidieri* Wozencraft 1986 in the sub-arid zone of south-western Madagascar. *Mammalia* 75: 353–361.

Marrocoli, S., Hamann, M., and Allison, J. 2013. Lemur distributions in a fragmented landscape, northern Madagascar. *Lemur News* 17: 37–39.

Marshall, B. M., Casewell, N. R., Vences, M., Glaw, F., Andreone, F., Rakotoarison, A., Zancolli, G., Woog, F., and Wüster, W. 2018. Widespread vulnerability of Malagasy predators to the toxins of an introduced toad. *Current Biology* 28: R654-R655.

Martin, P. S. 1984. Prehistoric overkill: The global model. In *Quaternary Extinctions: A Prehistoric Revolution*, eds. P. S. Martin and R. G. Klein, pp. 354–403. Tucson: University of Arizona Press.

Martin, R. D. 1972a. A preliminary field-study of the lesser mouse lemur (*Microcebus murinus* J. F. Miller, 1777). *Zeitschrift fur Tierpychologie* 9(supplement): 43–89.

———. 1972b. Adaptive radiation and behaviour of Malagasy lemurs. *Philosophical Transactions of the Royal Society of London B: Biological Sciences*, 264: 295–352.

———. 1973. A review of the behaviour and ecology of the lesser mouse lemur (*Microcebus murinus* J. F. Miller 1777). In *Comparative Ecology and Behaviour of Primates*, eds. R. P. Michael and J. H. Crook, pp. 1–68. London: Academic Press.

———. 1990. *Primate Origins and Evolution: A Phylogenetic Reconstruction*. London: Chapman and Hall.

———. 1995. Prosimians: From obscurity to extinction? In *Creatures of the Dark: The Nocturnal Prosimians*, eds. L. Alterman, G. A. Doyle, and M. K. Izard, pp. 535–563. New York: Plenum Press.

Martinez, B. [T.]. 2008. Occurrence of bamboo lemurs, *Hapalemur griseus occidentalis*, in an agricultural landscape on the Masoala Peninsula. *Lemur News* 13: 11–14.

———. 2010. Forest restoration in Masoala National Park, Madagascar: The contribution of the red-ruffed lemur (*Varecia rubra*) and the livelihoods of subsistence farmers at Ambatoladama. PhD thesis, University of Minnesota, Saint Paul.

Martinez, B. T., and Razafindratsima, O. H. 2014. Frugivory and seed dispersal patterns of the red-ruffed lemur, *Varecia rubra*, at a forest restoration site in Masoala National Park, Madagascar. *Folia Primatologica* 85: 228–243.

Masters, J. C., de Wit, M. J., and Asher, R. J. 2006. Reconciling the origins of Africa, India and Madagascar with vertebrate dispersal scenarios. *Folia Primatologica* 77: 399–418.

Masters, J. C., Silvestro, D., Génin, F., and DelPero, M. 2013. Seeing the wood through the trees: The current state of higher systematics in the Strepsirhini. *Folia Primatologica* 84: 201–219.

Matsui, A., Rakotondraparany, F., Munechika, I., Hasegawa, M., and Horai, S. 2009. Molecular phylogeny and evolution of prosimians based on complete sequences of mitochondrial DNAs. *Gene* 441: 53–66.

Matthews, T. J., Triantis, K. A., Rigal, F., Borregaard, M. K., Guilhaumon, F., and Whittaker, R. J. 2016. Island species–area relationships and species accumulation curves are not equivalent: An analysis of habitat island datasets. *Global Ecology and Biogeography* 25(5): 607–618.

Mauget, R. 1991. Reproductive biology of the wild Suidae. In *Biology of Suidae*, eds. R. H. Barret and F. Spitz, pp. 49–64. Toulouse: Institut de recherche sur les grands mammifères.

May, L. W. 1978. The economic uses and associated folklore of ferns and fern allies. *The Botanical Review* 44: 491–528.

Mayor, M. I., Sommer, J. A., Huebinger, R. M., Barber, R. C., and Louis, E. E., Jr. 2002. Characterization of seven microsatellite marker loci in a genus of Malagasy lemurs (*Propithecus*). *Molecular Ecology Notes* 2: 385–388. https://doi.org/10.1046/j.1471-8286.2002.00177.x.

Mayor, M. I., Sommer, J. A., Houck, M. L., Zaonarivelo, J. R., Wright, P. C., Ingram, C., Engel, S. R., and Louis, E. E., Jr. 2004. Specific status of *Propithecus* spp. *International Journal of Primatology* 25: 875–900.

Mazet, O., Rodríguez, W., Grusea, S., Boitard, S., and Chikhi, L. 2016. On the importance of being structured: Instantaneous coalescence rates and human evolution; Lessons for ancestral population size inference? *Heredity* 116: 362–371. https://doi.org/10.1038/hdy.2015.104.

McGrew, W. C. 2014. The "other faunivory" revisited: Insectivory in human and non-human primates and the evolution of human diet. *Journal of Human Evolution* 71: 4–11.

McKechnie, A. E., and Mzilikazi, N. 2011. Heterothermy in Afrotropical mammals and birds: A review. *Integrative and Comparative Biology* 51: 349–363.

McLain, A. T., Meyer, T. J., Faulk, C., Herke, S. W., Oldenburg, J. M., Bourgeois, M. G., Abshire, C. F., Roos, C., and Batzer, M. A. 2012. An alu-based phylogeny of lemurs (infraorder: Lemuriformes). *PLoS One* 7(8): e44035. https://doi.org/10.1371/journal.pone.0044035.

McLain, A. T., Lei, R., Frasier, C. L., Taylor, J. M., Bailey, C. A., Robertson, B.A.D., Nash, S. D., Randriamanana, J. C., Mittermeier, R. A., and Louis, E. E., Jr. 2017. A new *Cheirogaleus* (Cheirogaleidae: *Cheirogaleus crossleyi* group) species from southeastern Madagascar. *Primate Conservation* 31: 27–36.

McRae, B. H. 2006. Isolation by resistance. *Evolution* 60: 1551–1561. https://doi.org/10.1111/j.0014-3820.2006.tb00500.x.

Meador, L. R., Godfrey, L. R., Rakotondramavo, J. C., Ranivoharimanana, L., Zamora, A., Sutherland, M. R., and Irwin, M. T. 2019. *Cryptoprocta spelea* (Carnivora: Eupleridae): What did it eat and how do we know? *Journal of Mammalian Evolution* 26(2): 237–251.

Meegaskumbura, S., Meegaskumbura, M., and Schneider, C. J. 2012. Phylogenetic position of *Suncus fellowesgordoni* with pigmy shrews from Madagascar and Southeast Asia inferred from cytochrome b. *Ceylon Journal of Science, Biological Sciences*, 41(1): 83–87.

Meier, B., and Albignac, R. 1991. Rediscovery of *Allocebus trichotis* (Primates) in northeast Madagascar. *Folia Primatologica* 56: 57–63.

Meier, B., and Rumpler, Y. 1987. Preliminary survey of *Hapalemur simus* and of a new species of *Hapalemur* in eastern Betsileo, Madagascar. *Primate Conservation* 8: 40–43.

Meier, B., Albignac, R., Peyriéras, A., Rumpler, Y., and Wright, P. 1987. A new species of *Hapalemur* (Primates) from south east Madagascar. *Folia Primatologica* 48: 211–215.

Mein, P., Senegas, F., Gommery, D., Ramanivosoa, B., and Randrianantenaina, H. 2010. Nouvelles espèces subfossiles de rongeurs du Nord-Ouest de Madagascar. *Compte Rendus Palevol* 9(3): 101–112.

Melander, Y., and Melander, H. E. 1980. Chromosome studies in African wild pigs (Suidae, Mammalia). *Hereditas* 92(2): 283–289.

Méndez-Cárdenas, M. G., and Zimmermann, E. 2009. Duetting: A mechanism to strengthen pair bonds in a dispersed pair-living primate (*Lepilemur edwardsi*)? *American Journal of Physical Anthropology* 139: 523–532.

Méndez-Cárdenas, M. [G.], Randrianambinina, B., Rabesandratana, A., Rasoloharijaona, S., and Zimmermann, E. 2008. Geographic variation in loud calls of sportive lemurs (*Lepilemur* ssp.) and their implications for conservation. *American Journal of Primatology* 70: 828–838.

Meredith, R. W., Janečka, J. E., Gatesy, J., Ryder, O. A., Fisher, C. A., et al. 2011. Impacts of the Cretaceous terrestrial revolution and KPg extinction on mammal diversification. *Science* 334: 521–524. https://doi.org/10.1126/science.1211028.

Merenlender, A. 1993. The effects of sociality on the demography and genetic structure of the *Lemur fulvus rufus* (polygamous) and *Lemur rubriventer* (monogamous) and the conservation implications. PhD thesis, University of Rochester.

Merson, S. D. 2017. Bushmeat hunting, retaliatory killing, habitat degradation and exotic species as threats to fosa (*Cryptoprocta ferox*) conservation. PhD thesis, University of Oxford.

Merson, S. D., Macdonald, D. W., and Dollar, L. J. 2017. Novel photographic and morphometric records of the Western Falanouc *Eupleres major* in Ankarafantsika National Park, Madagascar. *Small Carnivore Conservation* 54: 60–67.

Merson, S. D., Dollar, L. J., Tan, C.K.W., and Macdonald, D. W. 2019a. Activity patterns of sympatric living exotic and endemic carnivores (the fosa) in western Madagascar's deciduous forests. *Journal of Zoology* 307: 186–194.

Merson, S. D., Dollar, L. J., Johnson, P. J., and Macdonald, D. W. 2019b. Retaliatory killing and human perceptions of Madagascar's largest carnivore and livestock predator, the fosa (*Cryptoprocta ferox*). *PLoS One* 14: e0213341.

Merson, S. D., Dollar, L. J., Tan, C.K.W., and Macdonald, D. W. 2020. Effects of habitat alteration and disturbance by humans and exotic species on fosa *Cryptoprocta ferox* occupancy in Madagascar's deciduous forests. *Oryx* 54(6): 828–836. https://doi.org/10.1017/S003060531800100X.

Mertl-Millhollen, A. S. 2000. Tradition in *Lemur catta* behavior at Berenty Reserve, Madagascar. *International Journal of Primatology* 21: 287–297.

———. 2006. Scent marking as resource defense by female *Lemur catta*. *American Journal of Primatology* 68: 605–621.

Mertl-Millhollen, A. S., Moret, E. S., Felantsoa, D., Rasamimanana, H., Blumenfeld-Jones, K. C., and Jolly, A. 2003. Ring-tailed lemur home ranges correlate with food abundance and nutritional content at a time of environmental stress. *International Journal of Primatology* 24: 969–985.

Mertl-Millhollen, A. S., Blumenfeld-Jones, K., Raharison, S. M., Tsaramanana, D. R., and Rasamimanana, H. 2011. Tamarind tree seed dispersal by ring-tailed lemurs. *Primates* 52: 391–396.

Meyer, W. K., Venkat, A., Kermany, A. R., van de Geijn, B., Zhang, S., and Przeworski, M. 2015. Evolutionary history inferred from the de novo assembly of a nonmodel organism, the blue-eyed black lemur. *Molecular Ecology* 24: 4392–4405. https://doi.org/10.1111/mec.13327.

Meyers, D. M. 1993. The effects of resource seasonality on behavior and reproduction in the golden-crowned sifaka (*Propithecus tattersalli*, Simons, 1988) in three Malagasy forests. PhD thesis, Duke University.

Meyler, S. V., Salmona, J., Ibouroi, M. T., Besolo, A., Rasolondraibe, E., Radespiel, U., Rabarivola, C., and Chikhi, L. 2012. Density estimates of two endangered

nocturnal lemur species from northern Madagascar: New results and a comparison of commonly used methods. *American Journal of Primatology* 74: 414–422.

Miarinjara, A., Rogier, C., Harimalala, M., Ramihangihajason, T. R., and Boyer, S. 2016. *Xenopsylla brasiliensis* fleas in plague focus areas, Madagascar. *Emerging Infectious Diseases* 22(12): 2207–2208.

Michaud, M. 2019. Impact of ecological strategies on the morphological rate, diversity and integration in Carnivora. PhD thesis, Muséum National d'Histoire Naturelle, Paris.

Mihaminekena, T. H., Ravaloharimanitra, M., Ratsimbazafy, J., and King, T. 2018. Terrestrialité et domaine vital chez *Prolemur simus* d'Ambalafary. *Lemur News* 21: 47–51.

Miljutin, A., and Lehtonen, J. T. 2008. Probability of competition between introduced and native rodents in Madagascar: An estimation based on morphological traits. *Estonian Journal of Ecology* 51(2): 133–152.

Miller, A., Mills, H., Ralantoharijaona, T., Volasoa, N. A., Misandeau, C., Chikhi, L., Bencini, R., and Salmona, J. 2018. Forest type influences population densities of nocturnal lemurs in Manompana, northeastern Madagascar. *International Journal of Primatology* 39: 646–669.

Miller, D. S., Sauther, M. L., Hunter-Ishikawa. M., Fish, K., Culbertson, H., et al. 2007. Biomedical evaluation of free-ranging ring-tailed lemurs (*Lemur catta*) in three habitats at the Beza Mahafaly Special Reserve, Madagascar. *Journal of Zoo and Wildlife Medicine* 38: 201–216.

Miller, G. S. 1907. The families and genera of bats. *United States National Museum Bulletin* 57: 1–282.

Milne Edwards, A., and Grandidier, A. 1867. On the organisation of *Cryptoprocta ferox*. *Annals of Natural History* 20: 382–384.

Milne Edwards, A., and Grandidier, A. 1875. Histoire Naturelle des Mammifères, Tome I, Texte I. In *Histoire Physique, Naturelle et Politique de Madagascar*. Vol. 6, *Les Indrisinés*, ed. A. Grandidier. Paris: Imprimerie Nationale.

Milne Edwards, A., and Grandidier, A. 1878. Note sur un nouveau genre de chiroptères. *Bulletin de la Société Philomathique de Paris,* série 7(1): 220–221.

Milne Edwards, A., and Grandidier, G. 1898. Description d'une espèce nouvelle de Muridé provenant de Madagascar. *Bulletin du Muséum National d'Histoire Naturelle*, Paris, série 1, 4: 179–181.

Mittermeier, R. A., Konstant, W. R., Nicoll, M. E., and Langrand, O. 1992. *Lemurs of Madagascar: An Action Plan for Their Conservation*, 1993–1999. Gland: IUCN/SSC Primate Specialist Group.

Mittermeier, R. A., Tattersall, I., Konstant, W. R., Meyers, D. M., and Mast, R. B. 1994. *Lemurs of Madagascar.* Washington, DC: Conservation International.

Mittermeier, R. A., Konstant, W., Hawkins, F., Louis, E. E., Jr., Langrand, O., et al. 2006. *Lemurs of Madagascar*, 2nd ed. Washington, DC: Conservation International.

Mittermeier, R. A., Ganzhorn, J. U., Konstant, W. R., Glander, K., Tattersall, I., et al. 2008. Lemur diversity in Madagascar. *International Journal of Primatology* 29: 1607–1656.

Mittermeier, R. A., Louis, E. E., Jr., Richardson, M., Schwitzer, C., Langrand, O., et al. 2010. *Lemurs of Madagascar*, 3rd ed. Arlington, Virginia: Conservation International.

Mittermeier, R. A, Louis, E. E., Jr., Langrand, O., Schwitzer, C., Gauthier, C.-A., et al. 2014. *Lémuriens de Madagascar*. Paris: Muséum National d'Histoire Naturelle.

Mivart, St.-G. 1882. On the classification and distribution of the Ailuroidea. *Proceedings of the Zoological Society of London* 1882: 135–208.

Mogilewsky, M. S. 2020. Before and after the storm: Interactions between tree-fall canopy gaps, plant phenology, and frugivorous lemurs in Masoala National Park, Madagascar. PhD thesis, Portland State University, Oregon.

Moizo, B. 1997. Des esprits, des tombeaux, du miel et des boeufs: Perception et utilisation de la fôret en pays Bara Imamono. In Milieux et Sociétés dans le Sud-Ouest de Madagascar, ed. J.-M. Lebigre. *Iles et Archipels* 23: 43–66.

Monadjem, A., Taylor, P. J., Cotterill, F.P.D., and Schoeman, M. C. 2010. *Bats of Southern Africa: A Biogeographic and Taxonomic Synthesis*. Johannesburg: Wits University Press.

Monadjem, A., Taylor, P. J., Cotterill, F.P.D., and Schoeman, M. C. 2020a. *Bats of Central and Southern Africa: A Biogeographic and Taxonomic Synthesis*, 2nd ed. Johannesburg: Wits University Press.

Monadjem, A., Demos, T. C., Dalton, D. L., Webala, P. W., Musila, S., Kerbis Peterhans, J. C., and Patterson, B. D. 2020b. A revision of pipistrelle-like bats (Mammalia: Chiroptera: Vespertilionidae) in East Africa with the description of new genera and species. *Zoological Journal of the Linnean Society* 190:1–33.

Monnier, le, Dr., and Lamberton, C. 1922. Note sur des ossements subfossiles de la Région de Mananjary. *Bulletin de l'Académie Malgache*, nouvelle série 3: 211–213.

Montagnon, D., Crovella, S., and Rumpler, Y. 1993. Comparison of highly repeated DNA sequences in some Lemuridae and taxonomic implications. *Cytogenetic and Genomic Research* 63: 131–134. https://doi.org/10.1159/000133518.

Montero, B. K., Refaly, E., Ramanamanjato, J.-B., Randriatafika, F., Rakotondranary, S. J., Wilhelm, K., Ganzhorn, J. U., and Sommer, S. 2019. Challenges of next-generation sequencing in conservation management: Insights from long-term monitoring of corridor effects on the genetic diversity of mouse lemurs in a fragmented landscape. *Evolutionary Applications* 12(3): 425–442.

Morelli, T. L., King, S., Pochron, S. T., and Wright, P. C. 2009. The rules of disengagement: Takeovers, infanticide, and dispersal in a rainforest lemur, *Propithecus edwardsi*. *Behaviour* 146: 499–523.

Morelli, T. L., Smith, A. B., Mancini, A. N., Balko, E. A., Borgerson, C., et al. 2020. The fate of Madagascar's rainforest habitat. *Nature Climate Change* 10(1): 89–96.

Morgan, L., Howell, S. M., and Fritz, J. 1993. Regurgitation and reingestion in a captive chimpanzee (*Pan troglodytes*). *Laboratory Animals* 22: 42–45.

Morland, H. S. 1990. Parental behavior and infant development in ruffed lemurs (*Varecia variegata variegata*). *American Journal of Primatology* 20: 253–265.

———. 1991a. Social organization and ecology of black and white ruffed lemurs (*Varecia variegata variegata*) in lowland rain forest, Nosy Mangabe, Madagascar. PhD thesis, Yale University.

———. 1991b. Preliminary report on the social organization of ruffed lemurs (*Varecia variegata variegata*) in a northeast Madagascar rain forest. *Folia Primatologica* 56: 157–161.

Moseley, M., Rahelinirina, S., Rajerison, M., Garin, B., Piertney, S., and Telfer, S. 2018. Mixed *Leptospira* infections in a diverse reservoir host community, Madagascar, 2013–2015. *Emerging Infectious Diseases* 24: 1138–1140.

Moses, K. L., and Semple, S. 2011. Primary seed dispersal by the black-and-white ruffed lemur (*Varecia variegata*) in the Manombo forest, south-east Madagascar. *Journal of Tropical Ecology* 27: 529–538.

Motokawa, M. 2018. Asian house shrew, *Suncus murinus*. In *Handbook of the Mammals of the World*. Vol. 8, *Insectivores, Sloths and Colugos*, eds. D. E. Wilson and R. A. Mittermeier, p. 462. Barcelona: Lynx Edicions.

Mouchaty, S. K., Gullberg, A., Janke, A., and Arnason, U. 2000. Phylogenetic position of the tenrecs (Mammalia: Tenrecidae) of Madagascar based on analysis of the complete mitochondrial genome sequence of *Echinops telfairi*. *Zoologica Scripta* 29: 307–317. https://doi.org/10.1046/j.1463-6409.2000.00045.x.

Mudappa, D., Noon, B. R., Kumar, A., and Chellam, R. 2007. Responses of small carnivores to rainforest fragmentation in the southern Western Ghats, India. *Small Carnivore Conservation* 36: 18–26.

Mueller, J., Sironen, A., and Lukas, K. E. 2007. Infant development and behaviour in the fossa *Cryptoprocta ferox*. *Small Carnivore Conservation* 37: 11–17.

Muldoon, K. M., and Goodman, S. M. 2010. Ecological biogeography of Malagasy non-volant mammals: Community structure is correlated with habitat. *Journal of Biogeography* 37(6): 1144–1159.

Muldoon, K. M., de Blieux, D. D., Simons, E. L., and Chatrath, P. S. 2009. The subfossil occurrence and paleoecological significance of small mammals at Ankilitelo Cave, southwestern Madagascar. *Journal of Mammalogy* 90(5): 1111–1131.

Muldoon, K. M., Crowley, B. E., Godfrey, L. R., Rasoamiaramanana, A., Aronson, A., Jernvall, J., Wright, P. C., and Simons, E. L. 2012. Early Holocene fauna from a new subfossil site: A first assessment from Christmas River, south central Madagascar. *Madagascar Conservation and Development* 7: 23–29.

Muldoon, K. M., Godfrey, L. R., Crowley, B. E., and Simons, E. L. 2017. Predation on subfossil *Prolemur simus* by multiple predator species at Ankarana Massif, northern Madagascar. *International Journal of Primatology* 38: 58–79.

Müller, A. E. 1998. A preliminary report on the social organisation of *Cheirogaleus medius* (Cheirogaleidae; Primates) in north-west Madagascar. *Folia Primatologica* 69: 160–166.

———. 1999. Aspects of social life in the fat-tailed dwarf lemur (*Cheirogaleus medius*): Inferences from body weights and trapping data. *American Journal of Primatology* 49: 265–280.

Müller, A. E., and Thalmann, U. 2000. Origin and evolution of primate social organisation: A reconstruction. *Biological Reviews* 75: 405–435.

Müller, A. E., and Thalmann, U. 2002. Biology of the fat-tailed dwarf lemur (*Cheirogaleus medius* E. Geoffroy 1812): New results from the field. *Evolutionary Anthropology* 11: 79–82.

Müller, B., Goodman, S. M., and Peichl, L. 2007. Cone photoreceptor diversity in the retinas of fruit bats (Megachiroptera). *Brain, Behavior and Evolution* 70: 90–104.

Müller, P. 1997. Okologie und Ernahrungsstrategie des Kronensifakas (*Propithecus verreauxi coronatus*). Diploma thesis, University of Zürich.

Munson, L., Brown, J. L., Bush, M., Packer, C., Janssen, D., Reiziss, S. M., and Wildt, D. E. 1996. Genetic diversity affects testicular morphology in free-ranging lions (*Panthera leo*) of the Serengeti Plains and Ngorongoro Crater. *Journal of Reproduction and Fertility* 108: 11–15.

Murcia, C. 1995. Edge effects in fragmented forests: Implications for conservation. *Trends in Ecology and Evolution* 10(2): 58–62.

Murphy, A. J., Farris, Z. J., Karpanty, S., Ratelolahy, F., and Kelly, M. J. 2016. Estimating encounter rates and densities of three lemur species in northeastern Madagascar. *International Journal of Primatology* 37(3): 371–389.

Murphy, A. [J.], Farris, Z. J., Karpanty, S., Kelly, M. J., Miles, K., Ratelolahy, F., Rahariniaina, R., and Golden, C. D. 2017a. Using camera traps to examine distribution and occupancy trends of ground-dwelling rainforest birds in north-eastern Madagascar. *Bird Conservation International* 28(4): 567–580.

Murphy, A. [J.], Goodman, S. M., Farris, Z. J., Karpanty, S. M., Andrianjakarivelo, V., and Kelly, M. J. 2017b. Landscape trends in small mammal occupancy in the Makira–Masoala protected areas, northeastern Madagascar. *Journal of Mammalogy* 98: 272–282.

Murphy, A. J., Ferguson, B., and Gardner, C. J. 2017c. Recent estimates of ring-tailed lemur (*Lemur catta*) population declines are methodologically flawed and misleading. *International Journal of Primatology* 38: 623–628.

Murphy, A. [J.], Gerber, B. D., Farris, Z. J., Karpanty, S., Ratelolahy, F., and Kelly, M. J. 2018. Making the most of sparse data to estimate density of a rare and threatened species: A case study with the fosa, a little-studied Malagasy carnivore. *Animal Conservation* 21(6): 496–504.

Murphy, A. [J.], Kelly, M., Karpanty, S., Andrianjakarivelo, V., and Farris, Z. 2019. Using camera traps to investigate spatial co-occurrence between exotic predators and native prey species: A case study from northeastern Madagascar. *Journal of Zoology* 307: 264–273.

Musser, G. G., and Carleton, M. D. 1993. Family Muridae. In *Mammal Species of the World: A Taxonomic and Geographic Reference*, 2nd ed., eds. D. E. Wilson and D. M. Reeder, pp. 501–755. Washington, DC: Smithsonian Institution Press.

Musser, G. G., and Carleton, M. D. 2005. Superfamily Muroidea. In *Mammal Species of the World: A Taxonomic and Geographic Reference*, 3rd ed., eds. D. E. Wilson and D. M. Reeder, pp. 894–1531. Baltimore: Johns Hopkins University Press.

Mutere, F. A. 1967. The breeding biology of equatorial vertebrates: Reproduction in the fruit bat *Eidolon helvum*, at latitude 0°20′N. *Journal of Zoology* 153: 153–161.

Mutschler, T. 1999. Folivory in a small-bodied lemur: The nutrition of the Alaotran gentle lemur (*Hapalemur griseus alaotrensis*). In *New Directions in Lemur Studies*, eds. B. Rakotosamimanana, H. Rasamimanana, J. U. Ganzhorn, and S. M. Goodman, pp. 221–239. New York: Kluwer Academic/Plenum Press.

———. 2000. Taxonomic distinctiveness of *Hapalemur* and phylogenetic relationships within the genus: Evidence from vocal communication. Unpublished report. Saint Louis: Washington University.

Mutschler, T., and Feistner, A.T.C. 1995. Conservation status and distribution of the Alaotran gentle lemur *Hapalemur griseus alaotrensis*. *Oryx* 29: 267–274.

Mutschler, T., Nievergelt, C., and Feistner, A.T.C. 1995. Human induced loss of habitat at Lac Alaotra and its effect on the Alaotran gentle lemur. In *Environmental Change in Madagascar*, eds. B. D. Patterson, S. M. Goodman, and J. L. Sedlock, pp. 35–36. Chicago: Field Museum.

Mutschler, T., Feistner, A.T.C., and Nievergelt, C. M. 1998. Preliminary field data on group size, diet and activity in the Alaotran gentle lemur, *Hapalemur griseus alaotrensis*. *Folia Primatologica* 69: 325–330.

Mutschler, T., Nievergelt, C. M., and Feistner, A.T.C. 2000. Social organization of the Alaotran gentle lemur (*Hapalemur griseus alaotrensis*). *American Journal of Primatology* 50: 9–24.

Nadhurou, B., Righini, R., Gamba, M., Laiolo, P., Ouledi, A., and Giacoma, C. 2017. Effects of human disturbance on the mongoose lemur *Eulemur mongoz* in Comoros: Implications and potential for the conservation of a critically endangered species. *Oryx* 51: 60–67.

Naidoo, T., Goodman, S. M., Schoeman, M. C., Taylor, P. J., and Lamb, J. M. 2016. Partial support for the classical ring species hypothesis in the *Chaerephon pumilus* species complex (Chiroptera: Molossidae) from southeastern Africa and western Indian Ocean islands. *Mammalia* 80: 627–643.

Nakamichi, M., and Koyama, N. 2000. Intra-troop affiliative relationships of females with newborn infants in wild ring-tailed lemurs (*Lemur catta*). *American Journal of Primatology* 50(3): 187–203.

Narváez-Torres, P. R. 2018. Effects of disturbance and forest structure on the functional diversity and abundance of lemur communities in a fragmented landscape. MA thesis, University of Calgary.

NASA. 2021. Fire Information for Resource Management System (FIRMS). https://firms.modaps.eosdis.nasa.gov.

Nash, L. T. 1998. Vertical clingers and sleepers: Seasonal influences on the activities and substrate use of *Lepilemur leucopus* at Beza Mahafaly Special Reserve, Madagascar. *Folia Primatologica* 69: 204–217.

Nei, M., Maruyama, T., and Chakraborty, R. 1975. The bottleneck effect and genetic variability in populations. *Evolution* 29: 1–10. https://doi.org/10.2307/2407137.

Neveu, H., Hafen, T., Zimmermann, E., and Rumpler, Y. 1998. Comparison of the genetic diversity of wild and captive groups of *Microcebus murinus* using the random amplified polymorphic DNA method. *Folia Primatologica* 69(supplement 1): 127–135. https://doi.org/10.1159/000052706.

Nicoll, M. E. 1982. Reproductive ecology of *Tenrec ecaudatus* (Insectivora: Tenrecidae) in the Seychelles. PhD thesis, University of Aberdeen.

———. 1983. Mechanisms and consequences of large litter production in *Tenrec ecaudatus*. *Annales de la Musée Royale de l'Afrique Centrale, Sciences Zoologiques*, 237: 219–226.

———. 1985. Responses to Seychelles tropical forest seasons by a litter-foraging mammalian insectivore, *Tenrec ecaudatus*, native to Madagascar. *Journal of Animal Ecology* 54: 71–88.

———. 2003. *Tenrec ecaudatus*, tenrec. In *The Natural History of Madagascar*, eds. S. M. Goodman and J. P. Benstead, pp. 1283–1287. Chicago: University of Chicago Press.

Nicoll, M. E., and Racey, P. A. 1985. Follicular development, ovulation, fertilization and fetal development in tenrecs (*Tenrec ecaudatus*). *Journal of Reproduction and Fertility* 74: 47–55.

Nievergelt, C. M., Mutschler, T., and Feistner, A.T.C. 1998. Group encounters and territoriality in wild Alaotran gentle lemurs (*Hapalemur griseus alaotrensis*). *American Journal of Primatology* 46: 251–258.

Nievergelt, C. M., Mutschler, T., Feistner, A.T.C., and Woodruff, D. S. 2002. Social system of the Alaotran gentle lemur (*Hapalemur griseus alaotrensis*): Genetic characterization of group composition and mating system. *American Journal of Primatology* 57: 157–176. https://doi.org/10.1002/ajp.10046.

Nixon, S. W., Elliot Smith, A. A., Crowley, B. E., Perry, G. E., Randrianasy, J., Ranaivoarisoa, J. F., Kennett, D. J., and Newsome, S. E., 2018. Nitrogen isotope ($\delta^{15}N$) patterns for amino acids in lemur bones are inconsistent with aridity driving megafaunal extinction in south-western Madagascar. *Journal of Quarterly Science* 33(8): 958–996.

Nomenjanahary, E. S. 2019. Diversité des vestiges d'animaux de l'Holocène et actuels de deux grottes au sein de l'aire protégée de Beanka (Région Melaky). Mémoire de Master II, Université d'Antananarivo.

Noroalintseheno Lalarivoniaina, O. S., Rajemison, F. I., Andrianarimisa, A., and Goodman, S. M. 2018. Variation saisonnière de la structure d'âge et de la sex-ratio de la population de *Rousettus madagascariensis* (Yinpterochiroptera: Pteropodidae) à Ankarana, nord de Madagascar. *Revue d'Ecologie* (*La Terre et la Vie*) 73: 23–30.

Noroalintseheno Lalarivoniaina, O. S., Rajemison, F. I., Ramanantsalama R. V., Andrianarimisa, A., and Goodman, S. M. 2019. Population size and survival of the Malagasy fruit bat *Rousettus madagascariensis* (Pteropodidae) in Ankarana, northern Madagascar. *Acta Chiropterologica* 21: 103–113.

Noromalala, E. 2016. Aperçu sur les ossements dans les Grottes d'Anjohingidrobe et d'Anjohimaletsy, Forêt de Beanka, Région Melaky, Ouest de Madagascar. Mémoire de Master II, Université d'Antananarivo.

Norscia, I. 2006. Adaptation strategies of a nocturnal lemur (*Avahi laniger*) in a pluvial littoral forest of southeastern Madagascar: Implications for conservation. PhD thesis, University of Pisa.

———. 2008. Pilot survey of avahi population (woolly lemurs) in littoral forest fragments of southeast Madagascar. *Primates* 49: 85–88.

Norscia, I., and Borgognini-Tarli, S. M. 2008. Ranging behavior and possible correlates of pair-living in southeastern avahis (Madagascar). *International Journal of Primatology* 29: 153–171.

Norscia, I., and Palagi, E. 2016. *The Missing Lemur Link: An Ancestral Step in the Evolution of Human Behaviour*. Cambridge: Cambridge University Press.

Norscia, I., Carrai, V., and Borgognini-Tarli, S. 2006. Influence of dry season and food quality and quantity on behavior and feeding strategy of *Propithecus verreauxi* in Kirindy, Madagascar. *International Journal of Primatology* 27: 1001–1022.

Norscia, I., Ramanamanjato, J.-B., and Ganzhorn, J. U. 2012. Feeding patterns and dietary profile of nocturnal southern woolly lemurs (*Avahi meridionalis*) in southeast Madagascar. *International Journal of Primatology* 33: 150–167.

Nosil, P., Egan, S. P., and Funk, D. J. 2008. Heterogeneous genomic differentiation between walking-stick ecotypes: "Isolation by adaptation" and multiple roles for divergent selection. *Evolution* 62: 316–336. https://doi.org/10.1111/j.1558-5646.2007.00299.x.

Nowack, J., Levesque, D. L., Reher, S., and Dausmann, K. H. 2020. Variable climates lead to varying phenotypes: "Weird" mammalian torpor and lessons from non-Holarctic species. *Frontiers in Ecology and Evolution* 8: 60.

Nowak, R., Walker, E., MacDonald, D., and Kays, R. 2005. *Walker's Carnivores of the World*. Baltimore: Johns Hopkins University Press.

Nunziata, S. O., Wallenhorst, P., Barrett, M. A., Junge, R. E., Yoder, A. D., and Weisrock, D. W. 2016. Population and conservation genetics in an endangered lemur, *Indri indri*, across three forest reserves in Madagascar. *International Journal of Primatology* 3: 688–702. https://doi.org/10.1007/s10764-016-9932-y.

Nyakatura, K., and Bininda-Emonds, O.R.P. 2012. Updating the evolutionary history of Carnivora (Mammalia): A new species-level supertree complete with divergence time estimates. *BMC Biology* 10: 12. https://doi.org/10.1186/1741-7007-10-12.

O'Brien, J., Mariani, C., Olson, L., Russell, A. L., Say, L., Yoder, A. D., and Hayden, T. J. 2009. Multiple colonisations of the western Indian Ocean by *Pteropus* fruit bats (Megachiroptera: Pteropodidae): The furthest islands were colonised first. *Molecular Phylogenetics and Evolution* 51: 294–303.

O'Brien, T. G., Kinnaird, M. F., and Wibisono, H. T. 2003. Crouching tigers, hidden prey: Sumatran tiger and prey populations in a tropical forest landscape. *Animal Conservation* 6(2): 131–139.

O'Connell, A. F., Nichols, J. D., and Karanth, K. U. 2010. *Camera Traps in Animal Ecology: Methods and Analyses*. London: Springer Science and Business Media.

O'Connor, S. M. 1987. The effect of human impact on vegetation and the consequences to primates in two riverine forests, southern Madagascar. PhD thesis, University of Cambridge.

OConnor, B. M. 1996. Parasitic and commensal arthropods of some birds and mammals of the Réserve Naturelle Intégrale d'Andringitra, Madagascar. In A floral and faunal inventory of the eastern slopes of the Réserve Naturelle Intégrale d'Andringitra, Madagascar: With reference to elevational variation, ed. S. M. Goodman. *Fieldiana: Zoology*, new ser., 85: 136–141.

———. 1998. Parasitic and commensal arthropods of some birds and mammals of the Réserve Spéciale d'Anjanaharibe-Sud, Madagascar. In A floral and faunal inventory of the Réserve Spéciale d'Anjanaharibe-Sud, Madagascar: With reference to elevational variation, ed. S. M. Goodman. *Fieldiana: Zoology*, new ser., 90: 73–78.

———. 2000. Parasitic and commensal arthropods of some birds and mammals of Parc National de Marojejy, Madagascar. In A floral and faunal inventory of the Parc National de Marojejy, Madagascar: With reference to elevational variation, ed. S. M. Goodman. *Fieldiana: Zoology*, new ser., 97: 137–141.

———. 2003. Acariformes: Parasitic and commensal mites of vertebrates. In *The Natural History of Madagascar*, eds. S. M. Goodman and J. P. Benstead, pp. 593–602. Chicago: University of Chicago Press.

Odo, R. 1996. Effects of contextual and social variables on contact call production in free-ranging ringtailed lemurs (*Lemur catta*). *International Journal of Primatology* 17: 191–205.

Oelkrug, R., Goetze, N., Exner, C., Lee, Y., Ganjam, G. K., et al. 2013. Brown fat in a protoendothermic mammal fuels eutherian evolution. *Nature Communications* 4: 1–8.

Ohdachi, S. D., Kinoshita, G., Oda, S.-I., Motokawa, M., Jogahara, T., et al. 2016. Intraspecific phylogeny of the house shrew, *Suncus murinus-S. montanus* species complex, based on mitochondrial cytochrome b gene. *Mammal Study* 41: 229–238.

Oleksy, R. Z. 2014. The contribution of fruit bats (*Pteropus rufus*) to seed dispersal and forest regeneration in Madagascar. PhD thesis, University of Bristol.

Oleksy, R. [Z.], Randrianandrianina, F., and Jenkins, R.K.B. 2015a. Commercial hunting of foraging fruit bats in western Madagascar. *African Bat Conservation News* 37: 3–5.

Oleksy, R. [Z.], Racey, P. A., and Jones, G. 2015b. High-resolution GPS tracking reveals habitat selection and the potential for long-distance seed dispersal by Madagascan flying foxes *Pteropus rufus*. *Global Ecology and Conservation* 3: 678–692.

Oleksy, R. [Z.], Giuggioli, L., McKetterick, T. J., Racey, P. A., and Jones, G. 2017. Fruit bats create extensive seed shadows and enhance germination success of pioneer plant species in deforested Madagascan landscapes. *PLoS One* 12(9): e0184023.

Olive, M.-M., Razafindralambo, N., Barivelo, T. A., Rafisandratantsoa, J.-T., Soarimalala, V., Goodman, S. M., Rollin, P. E., Heraud, J.-M., and Reynes, J.-M. 2013. Absence of Rift Valley fever virus in wild small mammals, Madagascar. *Emerging Infectious Diseases* 19: 1025–1027.

Olivieri, G. [L.], Zimmermann, E., Randrianambinina, B., Rasoloharijaona, S., Rakotondravony, D., Guschanski, K., and Radespiel, U. 2007. The ever-increasing diversity in mouse lemurs: Three new species in north and northwestern Madagascar. *Molecular Phylogenetics and Evolution* 43: 309–327.

Olivieri, G. L., Sousa, V., Chikhi, L., and Radespiel, U. 2008. From genetic diversity and structure to conservation: Genetic signature of recent population declines in three mouse lemur species (*Microcebus* spp.). *Biological Conservation* 141: 1257–1271. https://doi.org/10.1016/j.biocon.2008.02.025.

Olson, E. R., Marsh, R. A., Bovard, B. N., Randrianarimanana, H. L., Ravaloharimanitra, M., Ratsimbazafy, J. H., and King, T. 2012. Arboreal camera trapping for the critically endangered greater bamboo lemur *Prolemur simus*. *Oryx* 46: 593–597.

Olson, L. E. 2013. Tenrecs. *Current Biology* 23: R5–R8.

Olson, L. E., and Goodman, S. M. 2003. Phylogeny and biogeography of tenrecs. In *The Natural History of Madagascar*, eds. S. M. Goodman and J. P. Benstead, pp. 1235–1242. Chicago: University of Chicago Press.

Olson, L. E., Goodman, S. M., and Yoder, A. D. 2004. Illumination of cryptic species boundaries in long-tailed shrew tenrecs (Mammalia: Tenrecidae: *Microgale*), with new insights into geographic variation and distributional constraints. *Biological Journal of the Linnean Society* 83: 1–22.

Olson, L. E., Rakotomalala, Z., Hildebrandt, K.B.P., Lanier, H. C., Raxworthy, C. J., and Goodman, S. M. 2009. Phylogeography of *Microgale brevicaudata* (Tenrecidae) and description of a new species from western Madagascar. *Journal of Mammalogy* 90: 1095–1110. https://doi.org/10.1644/08-MAMM-A-305.1.

Olsson, A., Emmett, D., Henson, D., and Fanning, E. 2006. Activity patterns and abundance of microchiropteran bats at a cave roost in south-west Madagascar. *African Journal of Ecology* 44: 401–403.

Omar, H., Adamson, E.A.S., Bhassu, S., Goodman, S. M., Soarimalala, V., Hashim, R., and Ruedi, M. 2011. Phylogenetic relationships of Malayan and Malagasy pygmy shrews of the genus *Suncus* (Soricomorpha: Soricidae) inferred from mitochondrial cytochrome *B* gene sequences. *The Raffles Bulletin of Zoology* 59(2): 237–243.

O'Mara, M. T. 2012. Development of feeding in ring-tailed lemurs. PhD thesis, Arizona State University, Tempe.

Ortmann, S., Schmid, J., Ganzhorn, J. U., and Heldmaier, G. 1996. Body temperature and torpor in a Malagasy small primate, the mouse lemur. In *Adaptations to the Cold: Tenth International Hibernation Symposium*, eds. F. Geiser, A. Hulbert, and S. Nicol, pp. 55–61. Armidale: University of New England Press.

Ortmann, S., Heldmaier, G., Schmid, J., and Ganzhorn, J. U. 1997. Spontaneous daily torpor in Malagasy mouse lemurs. *Naturwissenschaften* 84: 28–32.

Ostner, J., and Kappeler, P. M. 1999. Central males instead of multiple pairs of redfronted lemurs, *Eulemur fulvus rufus* (Primates, Lemuridae)? *Animal Behaviour* 58: 1069–1078.

Ostner, J., and Kappeler, P. M. 2004. Male life history and the unusual adult sex ratios of redfronted lemur, *Eulemur fulvus rufus*, groups. *Animal Behaviour* 67: 249–259.

Overdorff, D. J. 1988. Preliminary report on the activity cycle and diet of the red-bellied lemur (*Lemur rubriventer*) in Madagascar. *American Journal of Primatology* 16: 143–153.

———. 1992. Differential patterns in flower feeding by *Eulemur fulvus rufus* and *Eulemur rubriventer* in Madagascar. *American Journal of Primatology* 28: 191–203.

———. 1993. Similarities, differences, and seasonal patterns in the diets of *Eulemur rubriventer* and *Eulemur fulvus rufus* in the Ranomafana National Park, Madagascar. *International Journal of Primatology* 14: 721–753.

———. 1998. Are *Eulemur* species pair-bonded? Social organization and mating strategies in *Eulemur fulvus rufus* from 1988–1995 in southeast Madagascar. *American Journal of Physical Anthropology* 105: 153–166.

Overdorff, D. J., and Rasmussen, M. A. 1995. Determinants of nighttime activity in "diurnal" lemurid primates. In *Creatures of the Dark: The Nocturnal Prosimians*, eds. L. Alterman, G. A. Doyle, and M. K. Izard, pp. 61–74. New York: Plenum Press.

Overdorff, D. J., and Strait, S. G. 1995. Life-history and predation in *Eulemur rubriventer* in Madagascar. *American Journal of Physical Anthropology* 20(supplement): 164–165.

Overdorff, D. J., and Strait, S. G. 1998. Seed handling by three prosimian primates in southeastern Madagascar: Implications for seed dispersal. *American Journal of Primatology* 45: 69–82.

Overdorff, D. J., and Tecot, S. R. 2007. Social pair-bonding and resource defense in wild red-bellied lemurs (*Eulemur rubriventer*). In *Lemurs: Ecology and Adaptation*, eds. L. Gould and M. L. Sauther, pp. 235–254. Boston: Springer US.

Overdorff, D. J., Strait, S. G., and Telo, A. 1997. Seasonal variation in activity and diet in a small-bodied folivorous primate, *Hapalemur griseus*, in southeastern Madagascar. *American Journal of Primatology* 43: 211–223.

Overdorff, D. J., Merenlender, A. M., Talata, P., Telo, A., and Forward, Z. A. 1999. Life history of *Eulemur fulvus rufus* from 1988–1998 in southeastern Madagascar. *American Journal of Physical Anthropology* 108: 295–310.

Overdorff, D. J., Strait, S. G., and Seltzer, R. G. 2002. Species differences in feeding in Milne Edwards' sifakas (*Propithecus diadema edwardsi*), rufus lemurs (*Eulemur fulvus rufus*), and red-bellied lemurs (*Eulemur rubriventer*) in southeastern Madagascar: Implications for predator avoidance. In *Eat or Be Eaten: Predator Sensitive Foraging among Primates*, ed. L. E. Miller, pp. 126–137. Cambridge: Cambridge University Press.

Oxnard, C. E., Crompton, R. H., and Lieberman, S. S. 1990. *Animal Lifestyles and Anatomies*. Seattle: University of Washington Press.

Pagès, E. 1978. Home range, behaviour and tactile communication in a nocturnal Malagasy lemur *Microcebus coquereli*. In *Recent Advances in Primatology*, vol. 3, eds. D. A. Chivers and K. A. Joysey, pp. 171–177. London: Academic Press.

———. 1980. Ethoecology of *Microcebus coquereli* during the dry season. In *Nocturnal Malagasy Primates: Ecology, Physiology and Behavior*, eds. P. Charles-Dominique, H. M. Cooper, A. Hladik, C. M. Hladik, E. Pagès, G. F. Pariente, A. Petter-Rousseaux, J.-J. Petter, and A. Schilling, pp. 97–116. New York: Academic Press.

———. 1983. Identification, characterisation et rôle du jeu social chez un prosimien nocturne, *Microcebus coquereli*. *Biology of Behavior* 8: 319–343.

Pagès-Feuillade, E. 1988. Modalités de l'occupation de l'éspace et rélations interindividuelles chez un prosimien nocturne Malgache (*Microcebus murinus*). *Folia Primatologica* 50: 204–220.

Palagi, E., and Dapporto, L. 2006. Beyond odor discrimination: Demonstrating individual recognition by scent in *Lemur catta*. *Chemical Senses* 31: 437–443. https://doi.org/10.1093/chemse/bjj048.

Parga, J. A., Sauther, M. L., Cuozzo, F. P., Youssouf Jacky, I. A., and Lawler, R. R. 2012. Evaluating ring-tailed lemurs (*Lemur catta*) from southwestern Madagascar for a genetic population bottleneck. *American Journal of Physical Anthropology* 147: 21–29. https://doi.org/10.1002/ajpa.21603

Parga, J. A., Sauther, M. L., Cuozzo, F. P., Youssouf Jacky, I. A., Sussman, R. W., Gould, L., Lawler, R. R., and Pastorini, J. 2015. Molecular evidence for male and female dispersal in wild *Lemur catta*. *Folia Primatologica* 86: 66–75. https://doi.org/10.1159/000369386.

Parga, J. A., Sauther, M. L., Cuozzo, F. P., Youssouf Jacky, I. A., Lawler, R. R., Sussman, R. W., Gould, L., and Pastorini, J. 2016. Paternity in wild ring-tailed lemurs (*Lemur catta*): Implications for male mating strategies. *American Journal of Primatology*. 78: 1316–1325. https://doi.org/10.1002/ajp.22584.

Pariente, G. F. 1979. The role of vision in prosimian behavior. In *The Study of Prosimian Behavior*, eds. G. Doyle and R. D. Martin, pp. 411–459. New York: Academic Press.

Parreira, B. R., and Chikhi, L. 2015. On some genetic consequences of social structure, mating systems, dispersal, and sampling. *Proceedings of the National Academy of Sciences of the USA* 112: E3318-E3326. https://doi.org/10.1073/pnas.1414463112.

Parreira, B. R., Quéméré, E., Vanpé, C., Carvalho, I., and Chikhi, L. 2020. Genetic consequences of social structure in the golden-crowned sifaka. *Heredity* 125: 328–339. https://doi.org/10.1038/s41437-020-0345-5.

Pastorini, J., Forstner, M.R.J., and Martin, R. D. 1999. Molecular phylogenetics of Lemuridae. In *Primatology and Anthropology into the Third Millenium. Centenary Congress of the Anthropological Institute and Museum in Zürich*, p. 40. Irchel: University of Zürich.

Pastorini, J., Zaramody, A., Curtis, D. J., Martin, R. D., and Forstner, M.R.J. 2001a. Sympatric hybridisation between *Eulemur fulvus* and *E. mongoz*. *Folia Primatologica* 72: 176.

Pastorini, J., Forstner, M.R.J., and Martin, R. D. 2001b. Phylogenetic history of sifakas (*Propithecus*: Lemuriformes) derived from mtDNA sequences. *American Journal of Primatology* 53: 1–18.

Pastorini, J., Forstner, M.R.J., and Martin, R. D. 2002. Phylogenetic relationships among Lemuridae (Primates): Evidence from mtDNA. *Journal of Human Evolution* 43: 463–478.

Pastorini, J., Thalmann, U., and Martin, R. D. 2003. A molecular approach to comparative phylogeography of extant Malagasy lemurs. *Proceedings of the National Academy of Sciences of the USA* 100: 5879–5884.

Pastorini, J., Fernando, P., Forstner, M.R.J., and Melnick, D. J. 2005. Characterization of new microsatellite loci for the ring-tailed lemur (*Lemur catta*). *Molecular Ecology Notes* 5: 149–151.

Pastorini, J., Zaramody, A., Curtis, D. J., Nievergelt, C. M., and Mundy, N. I. 2009. Genetic analysis of hybridization and introgression between wild mongoose and brown lemurs. *BMC Evolutionary Biology* 9: 32. https://doi.org/10.1186/1471-2148-9-32.

Pastorini, J., Sauther, M. L., Sussman, R. W., Gould, L., Cuozzo, F. P., Fernando., P., Nievergelt, C. M., and Mundy, N. I. 2015. Comparison of the genetic variation of captive ring-tailed lemurs with a wild population in Madagascar. *Zoo Biology* 34: 463–472. https://doi.org/10.1002/zoo.21225.

Patel, E. R. 2005. Silky sfaka predation (*Propithecus candidus*) by a fossa (*Cryptoprocta ferox*). *Lemur News* 10: 25–27.

———. 2009. Silky sifaka (*Propithecus candidus*). In Primates in peril, eds. R. A. Mittermeier, J. Wallis, A. B. Rylands, J. U. Ganzhorn, J. F. Oates, et al. *Primate Conservation* 20: 23–26.

———. 2012. Acoustic and olfactory communication in eastern sifakas (*Propithecus* sp.) and rhesus macaques (*Macaca mulatta*). PhD thesis, Cornell University.

Patel, E. R., and Owren, M. J. 2012. Silky sifaka (*Propithecus candidus*) "zzuss" vocalizations: Sexual dimorphism, individuality, and function in the alarm call of a monomorphic lemur. *Journal of the Acoustical Society of America* 132(3): 1799–1810.

Patel, E. R., Rabary, D., and Tonkasina, J. H. 2014. Remarkable dependence on non-native bamboo. *SAVA Conservation Newsletter* 3: 6–9.

Patterson, B. D., Webala, P. W., Kerbis Peterhans, J. C., Goodman, S. M., Bartonjo, M., and Demos, T. C. 2019. Genetic variation and relationships among Afrotropical species of *Myotis* (Chiroptera: Vespertilionidae). *Journal of Mammalogy* 100(4): 1130–1143.

Paulian, R. 1961. La zoogéographie de Madagascar et des iles voisines. *Faune de Madagascar* 13: 1–481

———. 1984. Introduction to the mammals. In *Key Environments: Madagascar*, eds. A. Jolly, P. Oberlé, and R. Albignac, pp. 151–154. Oxford: Pergammon Press.

Payne, J., and Francis, C. M. 1998. *A Field Guide to the Mammals of Borneo*. Kota Kinabalu: Sabah Society.

Pearson, R. G., and Raxworthy, C. J. 2009. The evolution of local endemism in Madagascar: Watershed versus climatic gradient hypotheses evaluated by null biogeographic models. *Evolution* 63: 959–967.

Pedrono, M., Sarovy, A, Smith, L. L., and Bour, R. 2000. The status and conservation of endemic Malagasy chelonians: An historic perspective. In *Diversité et endémisme à Madagascar*, eds. W. R. Lourenço and S. M. Goodman, pp. 249–260. Paris: Société de Biogéographie.

Pereira, M. E. 1991. Asynchrony within estrous synchrony among ringtailed lemurs (Primates: Lemuridae). *Physiology and Behavior* 49: 47–52.

Pereira, M. E., and McGlynn, C. A. 1997. Special relationships instead of female dominance for redfronted lemurs, *Eulemur fulvus rufus*. *American Journal of Primatology* 43: 239–258.

Pereira, M. E., and Weiss, M. L. 1991. Female mate choice, male migration, and the threat of infanticide in ringtailed lemurs. *Behavioral Ecology and Sociobiology* 28: 141–152. https://doi.org/10.1007/BF00180991.

Pereira, M. E., Klepper, A., and Simons E. L. 1987. Tactics of care for young infants by forest-living ruffed lemurs *Varecia variegata variegata*: Ground nests, parking and biparental guarding. *American Journal of Primatology* 13: 129–144.

Pereira, M. E., Kaufman, R., Kappeler, P. M., and Overdorff, D. J. 1990. Female dominance does not characterize all of the Lemuridae. *Folia Primatologica* 55: 96–103.

Pereira, M. E., Strohecker, R. A., Cavigelli, S. A., Hughs, C. L., and Pearson, D. D. 1999. Metabolic strategy and social behavior in Lemuridae. In *New Directions in Lemur Studies*, eds. B. Rakotosamimanana, H. Rasamimanana, J. U. Ganzhorn, and S. M. Goodman, pp. 93–118. New York: Plenum Press.

Perelman, P., Johnson, W. E., Roos, C., Seuánez, H. N., Horvath, J. E., et al. 2011. A molecular phylogeny of living primates. *PLoS Genetics* 7: e1001342. https://doi.org/10.1371/journal.pgen.1001342.

Perez, V. R., Godfrey, L. R., Nowak-Kemp, M., Burney, D. A., Ratsimbazafy, J., and Vasey, N. 2005. Evidence of early butchery of giant lemurs in Madagascar. *Journal of Human Evolution* 49(6): 722–742. https://doi.org/10.1016/j.jhevol.2005.08.004.

Perofsky, A. C., Lewis, R. J., Abondano, L. A., Di Fiore, A., and Meyers, L. A. 2017. Hierarchical social networks shape gut microbial composition in wild Verreaux's sifaka. *Proceedings of the Royal Society of London B: Biological Sciences*, 284: 20172274. https://doi.org/10.1098/rspb.2017.2274.

Perofsky, A. C., Lewis, R. J., and Meyers, L. A. 2019. Terrestriality and bacterial transfer: A comparative study of gut microbiomes in sympatric Malagasy mammals. *The ISME Journal* 13: 50–63. https://doi.org/10.1038/s41396-018-0251-5.

Perret, M. 1998. Energetic advantage of nest-sharing in a solitary primate, the lesser mouse lemur (*Microcebus murinus*). *Journal of Mammalogy* 79: 1093–1102.

Perret, M., and Aujard, F. 2001a. Daily hypothermia and torpor in a tropical primate: Synchronization by 24-h light-dark cycle. *American Journal of Physiology* 281: 1925–1933.

Perret, M., and Aujard, F. 2001b. Regulation by photoperiod of seasonal changes in body mass and reproductive function in gray mouse lemurs (*Microcebus murinus*): Differential responses by sex. *International Journal of Primatology* 22: 5–24.

Perry, G., Reeves, D., Melsted, P., Ratan, A., Miller, W., Michelini, K., Louis, E. E., Jr., Pritchard, J., Mason, C., and Gilad, Y. 2012a. A genome sequence resource for the aye-aye (*Daubentonia madagascariensis*), a nocturnal lemur from Madagascar. *Genome Biology and Evolution* 4: 126–135. https://doi.org/10.1093/gbe/evr132.

Perry, G., Melsted, P., Marioni, J., Wang, Y., Bainer, R., et al. 2012b. Comparative RNA sequencing reveals substantial genetic variation in endangered primates. *Genome Research* 22: 602–610.

Perry, G., Louis, E. E., Jr., Ratan, A., Bedoya-Reina, O., Burhans, R., Lei, R., Johnson, S., Schuster, S., and Miller, W. 2013. Aye-aye population genomic analyses highlight an important center of endemism in northern Madagascar. *Proceedings of the National Academy of Sciences of the USA* 110: 5823–5828.

Peters, W.H.C. 1872. Über eine neue Art von Indris, *Lichanotus mitratus*, aus Madagaskar. *Mitteilungsberichte der Königlichen Preussischen Akademie der Wissenschaften* 1871: 360–362.

Petersen, W. J., Savini, T., Steinmetz, R., and Ngoprasert, D. 2019. Periodic resource scarcity and potential for interspecific competition influences distribution of small carnivores in a seasonally dry tropical forest fragment. *Mammalian Biology* 95: 112–122.

Peterson, R. L., Eger, J. L., and Mitchell, L. 1995. Chiroptères. *Faune de Madagascar* 84: 1–204.

Petit, G. 1933. Remarques suggérées par la découverte d'un crâne de chat dans les dépôts subfossiles de Madagascar. *Comptes Rendus des Séances de l'Académie des Sciences,* Paris, 197: 1349–1351.

———. 1934. Contribution à l'étude des rats importés par l'homme à Madagascar. *Bulletin de la Société de Pathologie Exotique* 27: 273–280.

Petter, F. 1959. Un nouveau rongeur de Madagascar (Nesomyinae): *Macrotarsomys ingens* nov. sp. *Mammalia* 23: 139–148.

———. 1961. Affinités des genres *Spalax* et *Brachyuromys* (Rongeurs, Cricetidae). *Mammalia* 25: 485–498.

———. 1962. Un nouveau rongeur Malgache: *Brachytarsomys albicauda villosa*. *Mammalia* 26: 570–572.

———. 1972. The rodents of Madagascar: The seven genera of Malagasy rodents. In *Biogeography and Ecology in Madagascar*, eds. R. Battistini and G. Richard-Vinard, pp. 661–665. The Hague: W. Junk.

———. 1975. Family Cricetidae: Subfamily Nesomyinae. In *The Mammals of Africa: An Identification Manual*, eds. J. Meester and H. W. Setzer. Washington, DC: Smithsonian Institution Press, Part 6.2: 1–4.

———. 1990. Relations de parenté des rongeurs de Madagascar. *Accademie Nazionale des Lincei, Atti dei Convegni Lincei* 85: 829–837.

———. 1974. Rapports phylétiques des viverridés (Carnivores Fissipedes). Les formes de Madagascar. *Mammalia* 38: 605–636.

Petter, J.-J. 1962. Recherches sur l'écologie et l'éthologie des lémuriens Malgaches. *Mémoires du Muséum National d'Histoire Naturelle*, série A, Zoologie, 27(1): 1–146.

———. 1977. The aye-aye. In *Primate Conservation*, eds. Prince Rainer III and G. H. Bourne, pp. 37–57. New York: Academic Press.

Petter, J.-J., and Petter, A. 1967. The aye-aye of Madagascar. In *Social Communication among Primates*, ed. S. A. Altmann, pp. 195–205. Chicago: University of Chicago Press.

Petter, J.-J., and Petter-Rousseaux, A. 1958. Les Lémuriens malgaches et leur protection. *La Terre et la Vie* 1: 45–68.

Petter, J.-J., and Petter-Rousseaux, A. 1960. Remarques sur la systématique du genre *Lepilemur*. *Mammalia* 24: 76–86.

Petter, J.-J., and Peyriéras, A. 1970a. Observations eco-éthologiques sur les lémuriens malgaches du genre *Hapalemur*. *La Terre et la Vie* 24: 356–382.

Petter, J.-J., and Peyriéras, A. 1970b. Nouvelle contribution à l'étude d'un lémurien Malgache, l'aye-aye (*Daubentonia madagascariensis* E Geoffroy). *Mammalia* 34: 167–193.

Petter, J.-J., and Peyriéras, A. 1974. A study of population and density and home ranges of *Indri indri* in Madagascar. In *Prosimian Biology*, eds. R. D. Martin, G. A. Doyle, and A. C. Walker, pp. 39–48. Pittsburgh: University of Pittsburgh Press.

Petter, J.-J., and van der Sloot, J.-H. 2000. *Lemurs of Madagascar and the Comoros*. (CD-ROM). Amsterdam: Expert Center for Taxonomic Identification.

Petter, J.-J., Schilling, A., and Pariente, G. 1971. Observations éco-éthologiques sur deux lémuriens malgaches nocturnes: *Phaner furcifer* et *Microcebus coquereli*. *Terre et Vie* 25: 287–327.

Petter, J.-J., Albignac, R., and Rumpler Y. 1977. Mammifères Lémuriens (Primates Prosimiens). *Faune de Madagascar* 44: 1–513.

Petter-Rousseaux, A. 1980. Seasonal activity rhythms, reproduction, and body weight variations in five sympatric nocturnal prosimians in simulated light and climatic conditions. In *Nocturnal Malagasy Primates: Ecology, Physiology and Behavior*, eds. P. Charles-Dominique, H. M. Cooper, A. Hladik, C. M. Hladik, E. Pagès, G. F. Pariente, A. Petter-Rousseaux, J.-J. Petter, and A. Schilling, pp. 137–152. New York: Academic Press.

Petty, J. A., and Drea, C. M. 2015. Female rule in lemurs is ancestral and hormonally mediated. *Scientific Reports* 5: 9631. https://doi.org/10.1038/srep09631.

Philippe, H., Brinkmann, H., Lavrov, D. V., Littlewood, D.T.J, Manuel, M., Wörheide, G., and Baurain, D. 2011. Resolving difficult phylogenetic questions: Why more sequences are not enough. *PLoS Biology* 9(3): e1000602. https://doi.org/10.1371/journal.pbio.1000602.

Pichon, C., Ramanamisata, R., Tarnaud, L., Bayart, F., Hladik, A., Hladik, C. M., and Simmen, B. 2010. Feeding ecology of the crowned sifaka (*Propithecus coronatus*) in a coastal dry forest in northwest Madagascar (SFUM, Antrema). *Lemur News* 15: 42–46.

Picone, B., and Sineo, L. 2012. The phylogenetic position of *Daubentonia madagascariensis* (Gmelin, 1788: primates, Strepsirhini) as revealed by chromosomal analysis. *Caryologia* 65(3): 223–228.

Picot, M. M., Jenkins, R.K.B., Ramilijaona, O. R., Racey, P. A., and Carrière, S. M. 2007. The feeding ecology of *Eidolon dupreanum* (Pteropodidae) in eastern Madagascar. *African Journal of Ecology* 45: 645–650.

Pidgeon, M. 1996. *An Ecological Survey of Lake Alaotra and Selected Wetlands of Central and Western Madagascar in Analyzing the Demise of the Madagascar Pochard* Aythya innotata*.* Antananarivo: WWF and Missouri Botanical Garden.

Pierron, D., Heiske, M., Razafindrazaka, H., Rakoto, I., Rabetokotany, N., et al. 2017. Genomic landscape of Madagascar. *Proceedings of the National Academy of Science of the USA* 114(32): E6498–E6506.

Pinkus, S., Smith, J.N.M., and Jolly, A. 2006. Feeding competition between introduced *Eulemur fulvus* and native *Lemur catta* during the birth season at Berenty Reserve, southern Madagascar. In *Ringtailed Lemur Biology:* Lemur catta *in Madagascar*, eds. A. Jolly, R. W. Sussman, N. Koyama, and H. Rasamimanana, pp. 119–140. New York: Springer.

Piry, S., Luikart, G., and Cornuet, J.-M. 1999. Computer note. BOTTLENECK: A computer program for detecting recent reductions in the effective size using allele frequency data. *Journal of Heredity* 90: 502–503. https://doi.org/10.1093/jhered/90.4.502.

Pitts, A. 1995. Predation by *Eulemur fulvus rufus* on an infant *Lemur catta* at Berenty, Madagascar. *Folia Primatologica* 65: 169–171.

Pochron, S. T., and Wright, P. C. 2003. Variability in adult group compositions of a prosimian primate. *Behavioral Ecology and Sociobiology* 54: 285–293.

Pocock, R. I. 1915a. On some of the external characters of the genus *Linsang*, with notes upon the genera *Poiana* and *Eupleres*. *The Annals and Magazine of Natural History* 16: 341–351.

———. 1915b. On some external characters of *Galidia*, *Galidictis* and related genera. *The Annals and Magazine of Natural History* 16: 351–356.

———. 1915c. On the species of the Mascarene viverrid *Galidcitis*, with the description of a new genus and a note on *Galidia elegans*. *Annals and Magazine of Natural History*, ser. 8, 16: 113–124.

———. 1916. On some of the external characters of *Cryptoprocta*. *The Annals and Magazine of Natural History* 27: 413–425.

———. 1917. The lemurs of the *Hapalemur* group. *Annals and Magazine of Natural History* 8: 343–352.

Poelstra, J., Salmona, J., Tiley, G. P., Schüßler, D., Blanco, M. B., et al. 2021. Cryptic patterns of speciation in cryptic primates: Microendemic mouse lemurs and the multispecies coalescent. *Systematic Biology* 70(2):203–218. https://doi.org/10.1093/sysbio/syaa053.

Poirotte, C., and Kappeler P. M. 2019. Hygienic personalities in wild grey mouse lemurs vary adaptively with sex. *Proceedings of the Royal Society of London B: Biological Sciences* 286: 20190863.

Poisson, H. 1935. Les animaux domestiques à Madagascar. *Revue de Madagascar* 11–12.

Pollen, F.P.L. 1868. Notices sur quelques autres mammifères habitant Madagascar et les îles voisines. In *Recherches sur la faune de Madagascar et de ses dépendances.* Pt. 2, *H. Schlegel and F.P L. Pollen: Mammifères et oiseaux*, eds. F.P.L. Pollen and D. C. Van Dam, pp. 19–29. Leiden: J. K. Steenhoff.

Pollock, J. I. 1975a. Field observations on *Indri indri*: A preliminary report. In *Lemur Biology*, eds. I. Tattersall, and R. W. Sussman, pp. 287–311. New York: Plenum Press.
———. 1975b. The social behaviour and ecology of *Indri indri*. PhD thesis, University of London.
———. 1977. The ecology and sociology of feeding in *Indri indri*. In *Primate Ecology: Studies of Feeding and Ranging Behaviour in Lemurs, Monkeys and Apes*, ed. T. H. Clutton-Brock, pp. 37–69. London: Academic Press.
———. 1979. Spatial distribution and ranging behavior in lemurs. In *The Study of Prosimian Behavior*, eds. G. A. Doyle and R. D. Martin, pp. 359–409. New York: Academic Press.
———. 1986a. A note on the ecology and behaviour of *Hapalemur griseus. Primate Conservation* 7: 97–100.
———. 1986b. The song of the indris (*Indri indri*; Primates: Lemuroidea): Natural history, form, and function. *International Journal of Primatology* 7: 225–264.
Pollock, J. I., Constable, I. D., Mittermeier, R. A., Ratsirarson, J., and Simons, H. 1985. A note on the diet and feeding behavior of the aye-aye *Daubentonia madagascariensis*. *International Journal of Primatology* 6: 435–447.
Pomerantz, J., Rasambainarivo, F. T., Dollar, L., Rahajanirina, L. P., Andrianaivoarivelo, R., Parker, P., and Dubovi, E. 2016. Prevalence of antibodies to selected viruses and parasites in introduced and endemic carnivores in western Madagascar. *Journal of Wildlife Diseases* 52: 544–552.
Poorman-Allen, P., and Izard, K. 1990. Chromosomes banding patterns of the aye-aye, *Daubentonia madagascariensis* (Primates, Daubentoniidae). *International Journal of Primatology* 11: 401–410.
Porter, C. A., Sampaio, I., Schneider, H., Schneider, M. P. C., Czelusniak, J., and Goodman, M. 1995. Evidence on primate phylogeny from epsilon-globin gene-sequences and flanking regions. *Journal of Molecular Evolution* 40: 30–55.
Poux, C., Madsen, O., Marquard, E., Vieites, D. R., de Jong, W. W., and Vences, M. 2005. Asynchronous colonization of Madagascar by the four endemic clades of primates, tenrecs, carnivores, and rodents as inferred from nuclear genes. *Systematic Biology* 54: 719–730. https://doi.org/10.1080/10635150500234534.
Poux, C., Madsen, O., Glos, J., Jong, W. W. de, and Vences, M. 2008. Molecular phylogeny and divergence times of Malagasy tenrecs: Influence of data partitioning and taxon sampling on dating analyses. *BMC Evolutionary Biology* 8: 102. https://doi.org/10.1186/1471-2148-8-102.
Pouyet, F., Aeschbacher, S., Thiéry, A., and Excoffier, L. 2018. Background selection and biased gene conversion affect more than 95% of the human genome and bias demographic inferences. *eLife* 7: e36317. https://doi.org/10.7554/eLife.36317.
Powzyk, J. A. 1997. The socio-ecology of two sympatric indriids: *Propithecus diadema diadema* and *Indri indri*, a comparison of feeding strategies and their possible repercussions on species-specific behaviors. PhD thesis, Duke University.
Powzyk, J. A., and Mowry, C. B. 2003. Dietary and feeding differences between sympatric *Propithecus diadema diadema* and *Indri indri*. *International Journal of Primatology* 24: 1143–1162.
Powzyk, J. A., and Mowry, C. B. 2006. The feeding ecology and related adaptations of *Indri indri*. In *Lemurs: Ecology and Adaptation*, eds. L. Gould, and M. L. Sauther, pp. 353–368. New York: Springer.
Powzyk, J. [A.], and Thalmann, U. 2003. *Indri indri*, Indri. In *The Natural History of Madagascar*, eds. S. M. Goodman, and J. P. Benstead, pp. 1342–1345. Chicago: University of Chicago Press.
Prager, E. M., Orrego, C., and Sage, R. D. 1998. Genetic variation and phylogeography of Central Asian and other house mice, including a major new mitochondrial lineage in Yemen. *Genetics* 150: 835–861.
Pride, E. 2005. Optimal group size and seasonal stress in ring-tailed lemurs (*Lemur catta*). *Behavioral Ecology* 16: 550–560. https://doi.org/10.1093/beheco/ari025.
Pritchard, J. K., Stephens, M., and Donnelly, P. 2000. Inference of population structure using multilocus genotype data. *Genetics* 155: 945–959.
Prout, T. 1981. A note on the island model with sex dependent migration. *Theoretical and Applied Genetics* 59: 327–332.
Pyritz, L., and Andrianjanahary, T. 2010. Collective mobbing of a boa by a group of red-fronted lemurs (*Eulemur fulvus rufus*). *Lemur News* 15: 14–16.
Quéméré, E., Crouau-Roy, B., Rabarivola, C., Louis, E. E., Jr., and Chikhi, L. 2010a. Landscape genetics of an endangered lemur (*Propithecus tattersalli*) within its entire fragmented range. *Molecular Ecology* 19: 1606–1621. https://doi.org/10.1111/j.1365-294X.2010.04581.x.
Quéméré, E., Louis, E. E., Jr., Ribéron, A., Chikhi, L., and Crouau-Roy, B. 2010b. Non-invasive conservation genetics of the critically endangered golden-crowned sifaka (*Propithecus tattersalli*): High diversity and significant genetic differentiation over a small range. *Conservation Genetics* 11: 675–687. https://doi.org/10.1007/s10592-009-9837-9.
Quéméré, E., Amelot, X., Pierson, J., Crouau-Roy, B., and Chikhi, L. 2012. Genetic data suggest a natural prehuman origin of open habitats in northern Madagascar and question the deforestation narrative in this region. *Proceedings of the National Academy of Sciences of the USA* 109: 13028–13033. https://doi.org/10.1073/pnas.1200153109.
Quéméré, E., Hibert, F., Miquel, C., Lhuillier, E., Rasolondraibe, E., et al. 2013. A DNA metabarcoding study of a primate dietary diversity and plasticity across its entire fragmented range. *PLoS One* 8: e58971.
Quentin, J.-C., and Durette-Desset, M.-C. 1974. Helminthofaune des rongeurs cricétidés malgaches du genre *Brachyuromys*. *Bulletin du Muséum National d'Histoire Naturelle*, Paris, 135: 89–111.
Rabarison, H. 2016. Aperçu de la bioécologie et régime alimentaire des chauves-souris dans la Réserve Naturelle Intégrale de Betampona, Région Antsiranana. Master's memoir, Mention Zoologie et Biodiversité Animale, Université d'Antananarivo.
Rabarivola, C., Meyers, D. M., and Rumpler, Y. 1991. Distribution and morphological characters of intermediate forms between the black lemur (*Eulemur macaco macaco*) and the Sclater's lemur (*E. m. flavifrons*). *Primates* 32: 269–273. https://doi.org/10.1007/BF02381186.
Rabarivola, C., Meier, B., Langer, C., Scheffrahn, W., and Rumpler, Y. 1996. Population genetics of *Eulemur macaco macaco* (Primates: Lemuridae) on the islands of Nosy-Be and Nosy-Komba and the Peninsula of Ambato (Madagascar). *Primates* 37: 215–225. https://doi.org/10.1007/BF02381409.
Rabarivola, C., Zaramody, A., Fausser, J.-L., Andriaholinirina, N., Roos, C., Zinner, D., Marcel, H., and Rumpler, Y. 2006. Cytogenetic and molecular characteristics of a new species of sportive lemur from northern Madagascar. *Lemur News* 11: 45–49.
Rabarivola, C., Prosper, P., Zaramody, A., Andriaholinirina, N., and Hauwy, M. 2007. Cytogenetics and taxonomy of the genus *Hapalemur*. *Lemur News* 12: 46–49.
Rabeantoandro, Z. S. 1997. Contribution à l'étude du *Mungotictis decemlineata* (Grandidier 1867) de la forêt de Kirindy, Morondava. Mémoire de DEA, Université d'Antananarivo.
———. 2020. Cognition in narrow-striped mongooses, *Mungotictis decemlineata*, a Malagasy carnivore species. PhD thesis, University of Göttingen.
Rabinowitz, A. R. 1991. Behaviour and movements of sympatric civet species in Huai Kha Khaeng Wildlife Sanctuary, Thailand. *Journal of Zoology* 223(2): 281–298.
Racey, P. A. 2016. *Pteropus rufus*. The IUCN Red List of Threatened Species 2016: e.T18756A22087230. https://doi.org/10.2305/IUCN.UK.2016-1.RLTS.T18756A22087230.en. Accessed 5 Jan. 2020.
Racey, P. A., and Nicoll, M. E. 1984. Mammals of the Seychelles. In *The Biogeography and Ecology of the Seychelles Islands*, ed. D. Stoddart, pp. 607–626. The Hague: Junk.
Racey, P. A., Goodman, S. M., and Jenkins, R.K.B. 2010. The ecology and conservation of Malagasy bats. In *Island Bats: Evolution, Ecology, and Conservation*, eds. T. H. Fleming and P. A. Racey, pp. 369–404. Chicago: University of Chicago Press.
Radespiel, U. 1998. Die soziale Organisation des grauen Mausmakis (*Microcebus murinus*, J. F. Miller 1777) Eine freilandökologische und laborexperimentelle Studie. PhD thesis, University of Hannover.
———. 2000. Sociality in the gray mouse lemur (*Microcebus murinus*) in northwestern Madagascar. *American Journal of Primatology* 51: 21–40.
———. 2006. Ecological diversity and seasonal adaptations of mouse lemurs (*Microcebus* spp.). In *Lemurs: Ecology and Adaptation*, eds. L. Gould and M. L. Sauther, pp. 211–233. New York: Springer.
———. 2016. Can behavioral ecology help to understand the divergent geographic range sizes of mouse lemurs? In *Dwarf and Mouse Lemurs of Madagascar: Biology, Behavior, and Conservation Biogeography of the Cheirogaleidae*, eds. S. Lehman, U. Radespiel, and E. Zimmermann, pp. 498–519. Cambridge: Cambridge University Press.
Radespiel, U., Cepok, S., Zietemann, V., and Zimmermann, E. 1998. Sex-specific usage patterns of sleeping sites in gray mouse lemurs (*Microcebus murinus*) in northwestern Madagascar. *American Journal of Primatology* 46: 77–84.
Radespiel, U., Sarikaya, Z., Zimmermann, E., and Bruford, M. W. 2001. Sociogenetic structure in a free-living nocturnal primate population: Sex-specific differences in the grey mouse lemur (*Microcebus murinus*). *Behavioral Ecology and Sociobiology* 50: 493–502. https://doi.org/10.1007/s002650100402.
Radespiel, U., Dal Secco, V., Drögemüller, C., Braune, P., Labes, E., and Zimmermann, E. 2002. Sexual selection, multiple mating and paternity in grey mouse lemurs, *Microcebus murinus*. *Animal Behaviour* 63: 259–268.

Radespiel, U., Lutermann, H., Schmelting, B., Bruford, M. W., and Zimmermann, E. 2003. Patterns and dynamics of sex-biased dispersal in a nocturnal primate, the grey mouse lemur, *Microcebus murinus*. *Animal Behaviour* 65: 709–719. https://doi.org/10.1006/anbe.2003.2121.

Radespiel, U., Reimann, W., Rahelinirina, M., and Zimmermann, E. 2006. Feeding ecology of sympatric mouse lemur species in northwestern Madagascar. *International Journal of Primatology* 27: 311–321.

Radespiel, U., Olivieri, G., Rasolofoson, D. W., Rakotondratsimba, G., Rakotonirainy, O., et al. 2008. Exceptional diversity of mouse lemurs (*Microcebus* spp.) in the Makira region with the description of one new species. *American Journal of Primatology* 70: 1033–1046.

Radespiel, U., Jurić, M., and Zimmermann, E. 2009. Sociogenetic structures, dispersal and the risk of inbreeding in a small nocturnal lemur, the golden-brown mouse lemur (*Microcebus ravelobensis*). *Behaviour* 146: 607–628.

Radespiel, U., Ratsimbazafy, J. H., Rasoloharijaona, S., Raveloson, H., Andriaholinirina, N., Rakotondravony, R., Randrianarison, R. M., and Randrianambinina, B. 2012. First indications of a highland specialist among mouse lemurs (*Microcebus* spp.) and evidence for a new mouse lemur species from eastern Madagascar. *Primates* 53: 157–170.

Radespiel, U., Lutermann, H., Schmelting, B., and Zimmermann, E. 2019a. An empirical estimate of the generation time of mouse lemurs. *American Journal of Primatology* 81: e23062. https://doi.org/10.1002/ajp.23062.

Radespiel, U., Schulte, J., Burke, R., and Lehman, S. 2019b. Molecular edge effects in the Endangered golden-brown mouse lemur *Microcebus ravelobensis*. *Oryx* 53(4): 716–726.

Radimilahy, C. 1998. *Mahilaka: An Archaeological Investigation of an Early Town in Northwestern Madagascar*. Studies in African Archaeology 15. Uppsala: Department of Archaeology and Ancient History.

Radimilahy, C., Andrianaivoarivony, R., Rasoarifetra, B., Rakotozafy, L.M.A., and Goodman, S. M. 2013. Rapport sur une mission archéologique à Beanka, Région Melaky, ouest de Madagascar; Dans la forêt de Beanka, Région Melaky, ouest de Madagascar, eds. S. M. Goodman, L. Gautier, and M. J. Raherilalao. *Malagasy Nature* 7: 49–84.

Radovimiandrinifarany, H.T.R. 2013. Diversité des petits mammifères non-volants autres que les primates du massif forestier d'Ankerana, Madagascar. Mémoire de DEA, Université d'Antananarivo.

Rafalinirina, H. A., Aivelo, T., Wright, P. C., and Randrianasy, J. 2015. Comparison of parasitic infections and body condition in rufous mouse lemurs (*Microcebus rufus*) at Ranomafana National Park, southeast Madagascar. *Madagascar Conservation and Development* 10: 60–66.

Rahaingondrahety, V. N., Andriafidison, D., Ratsimbazafy, J., Racey, P. A., and Jenkins, R.K.B. 2008. Three flying fox (Pteropodidae: *Pteropus rufus*) roosts, three conservation challenges in south-eastern Madagascar. *Madagascar Conservation and Development* 3: 17–21.

Rahajanirina, L. P. 2003. Contribution à l'étude biologique, écologique et éthologique de *Cryptoprocta ferox* (Bennett 1883) dans la région du lac Tsimaloto, Parc National d'Ankarafantsika, Madagascar. Mémoire de DEA, Département de Biologie Animale, Université d'Antananarivo.

Rahalison, L., Ranjalahy, M., Duplantier, J.-M., Duchemin, J.-B., Ravelosaona, J., Ratsifasoamanana, L., and Chanteau, S. 2003. Susceptibility to plague of the rodents in Antananarivo, Madagascar. In *The Genus* Yersinia, eds. M. Skurnik, J. A. Bengoechea, and K. Granfors, pp. 439–442. New York: Kluwer Academic/Plenum Press.

Raharimihaja, T.E.A., Rakotoarison, J.L.M., Racey, P. A., and Andrianaivoarivelo, R. A. 2016. A comparison of the effectiveness of deterring pteropodid bats from feeding on commercial fruit in Madagascar. *Journal of Threatened Taxa* 8(13): 9512–9524.

Raharinantenaina, I.M.O., Kofoky, A. F., Mbohoahy, T., Andriafidison, D., Randrianandrianina, F., Ramilijaona, O. R., and Jenkins, R.K.B. 2008. *Hipposideros commersoni* (E. Geoffroy, 1831, Hipposideridae) roosting in trees in littoral forest, south-western Madagascar. *African Bat Conservation News* 15: 2–3.

Raharinjatovo Ny, O. 2012. Role des chauves-souris insectivores dans le contrôle des insectes vecteurs de maladies transmissibles à la homme: Cas des Molossidae. Mémoire de DEA, Département de Biologie Animale, Université d'Antananarivo.

Raharinosy, V., Olive, M.-M., Andriamiarimanana, F. M., Andriamandimby, S. F., Ravalohery, J.-P., Andriamamonjy, S., Filippone, C., Rakoto, D.A.D., Telfer, S., and Heraud, J.-M. 2018. Geographical distribution and relative risk of Anjozorobe virus (Thailand orthohantavirus) infection in black rats (*Rattus rattus*) in Madagascar. *Virology Journal* 15: 83. https://doi.org/10.1186/s12985-018-0992-9.

Raharivololona, B. M. 1996. Impact de l'exploitation sélective de la forêt et la variation saisonnière sur la composition de la population de rongeurs and insectivores dans une forêt seche de l'Ouest de Madagascar. Mémoire de DEA, Université d'Antananarivo.

Raharivololona, B. M., and Ganzhorn, J. U. 2007. Gastrointestinal parasites of small mammals in the littoral forest of Mandena. In *Biodiversity, Ecology, and Conservation of Littoral Ecosystems in Southeastern Madagascar, Tolagnaro (Fort-Dauphin)*, eds. J. U. Ganzhorn, S. M. Goodman, and M. Vincelette, pp. 247–258. Washington, DC: Smithsonian Institution Press.

Raharivololona, B. M., and Ganzhorn, J. U. 2009. Gastrointestinal parasite infection of the gray mouse lemur (*Microcebus murinus*) in the littoral forest of Mandena, Madagascar: Effects of forest fragmentation and degradation. *Madagascar Conservation and Development* 4: 103–112.

Rahelinirina, M. 2002. Contribution à l'étude du rythme d'activités et de l'alimentation de deux femelles de microcèbes sympatriques (*Microcebus murinus* J. F. Miller 1777 et *Microcebus ravelobensis*, Zimmermann et col., 1998) au Jardin Botanique A de la station forestière d'Ampijoroa Ankarafantsika, Mahajanga Madagascar. Mémoire de DEA, Université d'Antananarivo.

Rahelinirina, S. 2009. Le risque pesteux dans les foyers ruraux du moyen-ouest malgache: Déplacements et structuration des populations de rats noirs de l'échelle de l'habitat à celle du paysage. PhD thesis, Université d'Antananarivo.

Rahelinirina, S., Duplantier, J.-M., Ratovonjato, J., Ramilijaona, O., Ratsimba, M., and Rahalison, L. 2010a. Study on the movement of *Rattus rattus* and evaluation of the plague dispersion in Madagascar. *Vector-Borne and Zoonotic Diseases* 10: 77–84.

Rahelinirina, S., Léon, A., Harstskeerl, R. A., Sertour, N., Ahmed, A., et al. 2010b. First isolation and direct evidence for the existence of large small-mammal reservoirs of *Leptospira* sp. in Madagascar. *PLoS One* 5: e14111.

Rahelinirina, S., Rajerison, M., Telfer, S., Savin, C., Carniel, E., and Duplantier, J.-M. 2017. The Asian house shrew *Suncus murinus* as a reservoir and source of human outbreaks of plague in Madagascar. *PLoS Neglected Tropical Diseases* 11(11): e0006072.

Rahelinirina, S., Bourhy, P., Andriamiaramanana, F., Garin, B., and Rajerison, M. 2019. High prevalence of *Leptospira* spp. in rodents in an urban setting in Madagascar. *American Journal of Tropical Medicine and Hygiene* 100: 1079–1081.

Raheriarsena, M. 2005. Régime alimentaire de *Pteropus rufus* (Chiroptera: Pteropodidae) dans la région sub-aride du sud de Madagascar. *Revue d'Ecologie* (*La Terre et la Vie*) 60: 255–264.

Raheriarisena, M., and Goodman, S. M. 2006. Les petits mammifères non-volants dan l'extrême nord de Madagascar (Loky-Manambato, Analamerana et Andavakoera). In Inventaires de la faune et de la flore du nord de Madagascar dans la région Loky-Manambato, Analamerana et Andavakoera, eds. S. M. Goodman and L. Wilmé. *Recherches pour le Développement*, série *Sciences Biologiques*, 23: 175–230.

Rahlfs, M., and Fichtel, C. 2010. Anti-predator behaviour in a nocturnal primate, the grey mouse lemur (*Microcebus murinus*). *Ethology* 116: 429–439.

Railsback, L. B., Dupont, L. A., Liang, F., Brook, G. A., Burney, D. A., Cheng, H., and Edwards, R. L. 2020. Relationships between climate change, human environmental impact, and megafaunal extinction inferred from a 4000-year multi-proxy record from a stalagmite from northwestern Madagascar. *Quaternary Science Reviews* 234: 106244.

Raison, J.-P., and Vérin, P. 1967. Le site de subfossiles de Taolambiby (sud-ouest de Madagascar): Doit-il eˆtre attribué à une intervention humaine? *Annales de l'Université de Madagascar, Série lettres et sciences humaines*, 7: 133–142.

Rajemison, B., and Goodman, S. M. 2007. The diet of *Myzopoda schliemanni*, a recently described Malagasy endemic, based on scat analysis. *Acta Chiropterologica* 9: 311–313.

Rajemison, F. I., Noroalintseheno Lalarivoniaina, O. S., and Goodman, S. M. 2017a. Bat flies (Diptera: Nycteribiidae, Streblidae) of *Rousettus madagascariensis* (Chiroptera: Pteropodidae) in the Parc National d'Ankarana, Madagascar: Species diversity, rates of parasitism and sex ratio. *African Entomology* 25: 72–85.

Rajemison, F. I., Noroalintseheno Lalarivoniaina, O. S., and Goodman, S. M. 2017b. Parasitism by Nycteribiidae and Streblidae flies (Diptera) of a Malagasy fruit bat (Pteropodidae): Effects of body size and throat gland development on parasite abundance. *Journal of Medical Entomology* 54: 805–811.

Rakotoarinivo, T. H., Ravelojaona, R., Razafindramanana, J., and Ratsimbazafy, J. 2017. Etude préliminaire du rythme d'activité et de l'écologie de deux groupes de *Prolemur simus* dans la forêt dégradée de Vohitrarivo, District d'Ifanadiana. *Lemur News* 20: 19–24.

Rakotoarisoa, G., Shore, G., Mcguire, S., Engberg, S., Louis, E., and Brenneman, R. 2006. Characterization of 20 microsatellite marker loci in Coquerel's sifaka

(*Propithecus coquereli*). *Molecular Ecology Notes* 6: 1119–1121. https://doi.org/10.1111/j.1471-8286.2006.01457.x.

Rakotoarisoa, J.-E., and Be, B. 2004. Breeding and foraging behaviour and habitat characteristics of the scaly ground-roller *Geobiastes squamigerus* in Madagascar. *Ostrich* 75(1 and 2): 25–31.

Rakotoarisoa, J.-E., Raheriarisena, M., and Goodman, S. M. 2010. Phylogeny and species boundaries of the endemic species complex, *Eliurus antsingy* and *E. carletoni* (Rodentia: Muroidea: Nesomyidae), in Madagascar using mitochondrial and nuclear DNA sequence data. *Molecular Phylogenetics and Evolution* 57: 11–22.

Rakotoarisoa, J.-E., Raheriarisena, M., and Goodman, S. M. 2013a. Late Quaternary climatic vegetational shifts in an ecological transition zone of northern Madagascar: Insights from genetic analyses of two endemic rodent species. *Journal of Evolutionary Biology* 26: 1019–1034. https://doi.org/10.1111/jeb.12116.

Rakotoarisoa, J.-E., Raheriarisena, M., and Goodman, S. M. 2013b. A phylogeographic study of the endemic rodent *Eliurus carletoni* (Rodentia: Nesomyinae) in an ecological transition zone of northern Madagascar. *Journal of Heredity* 104(1): 23–35. https://doi.org/10.1093/jhered/ess083.

Rakotoarisoa, S. V. 1999. Contribution à l'étude de l'adaptation de *Lemur catta* Linnaeus, 1758, aux zones sommitales de la Réserve Naturelle d'Andringitra. Mémoire de DEA, Faculté des Sciences, Université d'Antananarivo.

Rakotoarisoa, T. F., Richter, T., Rakotondramanana, H., and Mantilla-Contreras, J. 2016. Turning a problem into profit: Using water hyacinth (*Eichhornia crassipes*) for making handicrafts at Lake Alaotra, Madagascar. *Economic Botany* 70: 365–379.

Rakotoarison, N., Zimmermann, H., and Zimmermann, E. 1997. First discovery of the hairy-eared dwarf lemur (*Allocebus trichotis*) in a highland rain forest of eastern Madagascar. *Folia Primatologica* 68: 86–94.

Rakotoarivelo, A. R., and Randrianandrianina, F. H. 2007. A chiropteran survey of the Lac Kinkony-Mahavavy area in western Madagascar. *African Bat Conservation News* 12: 2–5.

Rakotoarivelo, A. R., Ranaivoson, N., Ramilijaona, O. R., Kofoky, A. F., Racey, P. A., and Jenkins, R.K.B. 2007. Seasonal food habits of five sympatric forest microchiropterans in western Madagascar. *Journal of Mammalogy* 88: 959–966.

Rakotoarivelo, A. R., Ralisata, M., Ramilijaona, O. R., Rakotomalala, M. R., Racey, P. A., and Jenkins, R.K.B. 2009. The food habits of a Malagasy giant: *Hipposideros commersoni* (E. Geoffroy, 1813). *African Journal of Ecology* 47: 283–288.

Rakotoarivelo, A. R., Razafimanahaka, H. J., Rabesihanaka, S., Jones, J.P.G., and Jenkins, R.K.B. 2011. Lois et règlements sur la chasse à Madagascar: Progrès accomplis et besoins du futur. *Madagascar Conservation and Development* 6: 37–43.

Rakotoarivelo, A. R., Willows-Munro, S., Schoeman, M. C., Lamb, J. M., and Goodman, S. M. 2015. Cryptic diversity in *Hipposideros commersoni sensu stricto* (Chiroptera: Hipposideridae) in western Madagascar. *BMC Evolutionary Biology* 15: 235.

Rakotoarivelo, A. R., Goodman, S. M., Schoeman, M. C., and Willows-Munro, S. 2019. Phylogeography and population genetics of the endemic Malagasy bat, *Macronycteris commersoni s.s.* (Chiroptera: Hipposideridae). *PeerJ* 7: e5866. https://doi.org/10.7717/peerj.5866.

Rakotoarivony, R.T.N.A. 2017. Enjeux socio-épidémiologiques de la filière viande de brousse: Cas du potamochère (*Potamochoerus larvatus*). Docteur en Médecine Vétérinaire, Université d'Antananarivo.

Rakotomalala, E. J., Rakotondraparany, F., Perofsky, A. C., and Lewis, R. J. 2017. Characterization of the tree holes used by *Lepilemur ruficaudatus* in the dry, deciduous forest of Kirindy Mitea National Park. *Folia Primatologica* 88: 28–41.

Rakotomalala, Z., and Goodman, S. M. 2010. Diversité et remplacement longitudinal des espèces de petits mammifères dans les forêts des bassins versants des fleuves de l'ouest de Madagascar. *Revue d'Ecologie* (*La Terre et la Vie*) 65(4): 343–358.

Rakotomalala, Z., Andrianjakarivelo, V., Rasataharilala, V., and Goodman, S. M. 2007. Les petits mammifères non volant de la forêt de Makira, Madagascar. *Bulletin de la Société Zoologique de France* 13: 117–134.

Rakotomanana, H. 2009. Etude préliminaire de la prédation par *Cryptoprocta ferox* (Bennet, 1833) sur les populations proies dans le Parc National d'Ankarafantsika. Mémoire de DEA, Université d'Antananarivo.

Rakotomanga, M. N., Goodman, S. M., Soarimalala, V., Boyer, S., and Apanaskevich, D. 2017. Les tiques dures (Acari: Ixodidae) ectoparasites de micromammifères non-volants dans la forêt d'Ambohitantely, Madagascar. *Malagasy Nature* 12: 59–67.

Rakotonanahary, R., Harrison, A., Maina, A., Jiang, J., Richards, A., Rajerison, M., and Telfer, S. 2018. Molecular and serological evidence of flea-associated typhus group and spotted fever group rickettsial infections in Madagascar. *Parasites and Vectors* 10: 125.

Rakotonandrasana, E. N., and Goodman, S. M. 2007. Bat inventories of the Madagascar offshore islands of Nosy Be, Nosy Komba and Ile Sainte- Marie. *African Bat Conservation News* 12: 6–10.

Rakotondramanana, C. F. 2011. Des Molossidae dans un arbre gîte de la région de Menabe central: Description et biologie. *Malagasy Nature* 5: 132–135.

Rakotondramanana, C. F., and Goodman, S. M. 2011. Inventaire de chauves-souris dans la concession forestière de Kirindy CNFEREF, Morondava, Madagascar. *Malagasy Nature* 5: 109–120.

Rakotondramanana, C. F., and Goodman, S. M. 2017. A review of the bacular morphology of Malagasy bats. *Acta Chiropterologica* 19: 51–70.

Rakotondramanana, C. F., Rajemison, B., and Goodman, S. M. 2015. Comportement alimentaire des communautés de chauves-souris animalivores de Kirindy (CNFEREF) et d'Antsahabe, Madagascar: Répartition, partage et disponibilité de niche alimentaire. *Malagasy Nature* 9: 68–87.

Rakotondramanana, C. F., Rakotomalala, Z., and Ramasindrazana, B. 2017. Occurrence of *Taphozous mauritianus* (Emballonuridae) in Maintirano, western Madagascar. *Malagasy Nature* 12: 112–113.

Rakotondranary, S. J., and Ganzhorn, J. U. 2011. Habitat separation of sympatric *Microcebus* spp. in the dry spiny forest of south-eastern Madagascar. *Folia Primatologica* 82: 212–223.

Rakotondravony, A.D.S. 1992. Etude comparée de trois rongeurs des milieux malgaches: *Rattus norvegicus* Berkenhout (1769), *Rattus rattus* Linné (1757) et *Eliurus* sp., biologie et dynamique des populations. Thèse de Doctorat de 3ème Cycle, Université d'Antananarivo.

Rakotondravony, D. 1986. La dératisation efficace des cultures sur les Hautes Terres de Madagascar. *Recherches pour le Développement*, série *Sciences Biologiques*, 4: 187–213.

Rakotondravony, D., Goodman, S. M., Duplantier, J.-M., and Soarimalala, V. 1998a. Les petits mammifères. In Inventaire biologique de la forêt littorale de Tampolo (Fenoarivo Atsinanana), eds. J. Ratsirarson and S. M. Goodman. *Recherches pour le Développement*, série *Sciences Biologiques*, 14: 197–212.

Rakotondravony, D., Goodman, S. M., and Soarimalala, V. 1998b. Predation on *Hapalemur griseus griseus* by *Boa manditra* (Boidae) in the littoral forest of eastern Madagascar. *Folia Primatologica* 69: 405–408.

Rakotondravony, D., Randrianjafy, V., and Goodman, S. M. 2002. Evaluation rapide de la diversité des micromammifères de la Réserve Naturelle Intégrale d'Ankarafantsika. In A biological assessment of the Réserve Naturelle Intégrale d'Ankarafantsika, Madagascar, eds., L. E. Alonso, T. S. Schulenberg, S. Radilofe, and O. Missa. *RAP Bulletin of Biological Assessment* 23: 83–87.

Rakotondravony, R., and Radespiel, U. 2009. Varying patterns of coexistence of two mouse lemur species (*Microcebus ravelobensis* and *M. murinus*) in a heterogeneous landscape. *American Journal of Primatology* 71(11): 928–938.

Rakotoniaina, J. H., Kappeler, P. M., Ravoniarimbinina, P., Pechouskova, E., Hämäläinen, A. M., Grass, J., Kirschbaum, C., and Kraus, C. 2016. Does habitat disturbance affect stress, body condition and parasitism in two sympatric lemurs? *Conservation Physiology* 4: cow034.

Rakotoniaina, J. H., Kappeler, P. M., Kaesler, E., Hämäläinen, A. M., Kirschbaum, C., and Kraus, C. 2017. Hair cortisol concentrations correlate negatively with survival in a wild primate population. *BMC Ecology* 17: 30.

Rakotonirina, L.H.[F.], Spiral, G. J., Ratsimbazafy, J. H., Ravelonjanahary, S., Ralaiarison, R., Tecot, S., Hall, A., Calhoon, T., and Randria, G. R. 2010. Effet de la dégradation de l'habitat sur la consommation alimentaire d'*Eulemur rubriventer* dans deux sites: Talatakely et Vatoharanana, du Parc National de Ranomafana. *Lemur News* 15: 47–51.

Rakotonirina, L.H.F., Rajaonson, A., Ratolojanahary, J. H., Missirli, J. M., Fara, L. R., Raholijaona, Andriamanajaranirina, M., and King, T. 2013. Southern range extensions for the critically endangered black-and-white ruffed lemur *Varecia variegata* and greater bamboo lemur *Prolemur simus*. *Primate Conservation* 26: 49–55.

Rakotonirina, L.H.F., Randriantsara, F., Rakotoarisoa, A. H., Rakotondrabe, R., Razafindramanana, J., Ratsimbazafy, J., and King, T. 2014. A preliminary assessment of sifaka (*Propithecus*) distribution, chromatic variation and conservation in western central Madagascar. *Primate Conservation* 28: 43–53. https://doi.org/10.1896/052.028.0116.

Rakotovao, M., Lignereux, Y., Orliac, M. J., Duranthon, F., and Antoine P.-O. 2014. *Hippopotamus lemerlei* Grandidier, 1868 et *Hippopotamus madagascariensis* Guldberg, 1883 (Mammalia, Hippopotamidae): Anatomie crânio-dentaire et révision systématique. *Geodiversitas* 36(1): 117–161. https://doi.org/10.5252/g2014n1a3.

Rakotozafy, L.M.A. 1996. Etude de la constitution du régime alimentaire des habitants du site de Mahilaka du XIè au XIVè siècle à partir des produits de fouilles archéologiques. Doctorat de Troisième Cycle, Université d'Antananarivo.

Rakotozafy, L.M.A., and Goodman, S. M. 2005. Contribution à l'étude zooarchéologique de la région du Sud-ouest et extrême Sud de Madagascar sur la base des collections de l'ICMAA de l'Université d'Antananarivo. *Taloha* 14–15. http://www.taloha.info/document.php?id=137.

Ralainasolo, F. B., Ratsimbazafy, J. H., and Stevens, N. J. 2008. Behavior and diet of the critically endangered *Eulemur cinereiceps* in Manombo forest, southeast Madagascar. *Madagascar Conservation and Development* 3: 38–43.

Ralisata, M. 2005. Contribution à l'étude du comportement alimentaire de la chauve-souris à nez feuillu: *Hipposideros commersoni* (Hill et Bull, 1963) (Chiroptères; Hipposideridae dans le Parc National Ankarafantsika. Mémoire de DEA, Département de Biologie Animale, Université d'Antananarivo.

———. 2018. Ecologie de la chauve-souris a ventouse de Madagascar (*Myzopoda aurita*, Milne-Edwards et Grandidier, 1878) dans la forêt de Kianjavato. PhD thesis, Département de Biologie Animale, Université d'Antananarivo.

Ralisata, M., Andriamboavonjy, F. R., Rakotondravony, D., Ravoahangimalala, O. R., Randrianandrianina, F. H., and Racey, P. A. 2010. Monastic *Myzopoda*: The foraging and roosting ecology of a sexually segregated Malagasy endemic bat. *Journal of Zoology* 282: 130–139.

Ralisata, M., Rakotondravony, D., and Racey, P. A. 2015. The relationship between male sucker-footed bats *Myzopoda aurita* and the traveller's tree *Ravenala madagascariensis* in south-eastern Madagascar. *Acta Chiropterologica* 17(1): 95–103.

Ralisoamalala, R. C. 1996. Rôle de [sic] *Eulemur fulvus rufus* (Audebert, 1799) et de *Propithecus verreauxi verreauxi* (A. Grandidier, 1867) dans la dissémination des graines. In Ecology and economy of a tropical dry forest in Madagascar, eds. J. U. Ganzhorn and J.-P. Sorg. *Primate Report*, special issue, 46(1): 285–293.

Ralison, J. M. 2007. Les lémuriens du couloir forestier d'Anjozorobe-Angavo. In Inventaires de la faune et de la flore du couloir forestier d'Anjozorobe-Angavo, eds. S. M. Goodman, A. P. Raselimanana, and L. Wilmé. *Recherches pour le Développement*, série *Sciences Biologiques*, 24: 183–202.

Ramamonjisoa, J. C. 2014. Etude de la biologie et de l'écologie d'effraie de soumagne *Tyto soumagnei* (Grandidier, 1878) dans la nouvelle aire protégée de Bemanevika, Bealanana. PhD thesis, Université d'Antananarivo.

Ramanamahefa, R., McGuire, S. M., Louis, E. E., Jr., and Brenneman, R. A. 2009a. Population genetic parameter estimates for six populations of crowned lemurs, *Eulemur coronatus* (Gray, 1842), from northern Madagascar. *Lemur News* 14: 21–26.

Ramanamahefa, R., McGuire, S. M., Louis, E. E., Jr., and Brenneman, R. A. 2009b. Population genetic parameter estimates for five populations of Sanford's lemur, *Eulemur sanfordi* (Archbold, 1932), from northern Madagascar. *Lemur News* 14: 26–31.

Ramanamanjato, J.-B., and Ganzhorn, J. U. 2001. Effects of forest fragmentation, introduced *Rattus rattus* and the role of exotic tree plantations and secondary vegetation for the conservation of an endemic rodent and a small lemur in littoral forests of southeastern Madagascar. *Animal Conservation* 4(2): 175–183.

Ramanana, L. T. 2008. Etude de la distribution des petits mammifères non-volants du couloir forestier d'Anjozorobe-Angavo. Mémoire de DEA, Université d'Antananarivo.

———. 2010. Petits mammifères (Afrosoricida et Rodentia) nouvellement recensés dans le Parc National d'Andohahela (parcelle 1), Madagascar. *Malagasy Nature* 4: 66–72.

Ramananjato, V., Rakotomalala, Z., Park, D. S., DeSisto, C.M.M., Raoelinjanakolona, N. N., Guthrie, N. K., Fenosoa, Z.E.S., Johnson, S. E., and Razafindratsima, O. H. 2020. The role of nocturnal omnivorous lemurs as seed dispersers in Malagasy rain forests. *Biotropica* 52: 758–765.

Ramanankirahina, R., Joly, M., and Zimmermann, E. 2012. Seasonal effects on sleeping site ecology in a nocturnal pair-living lemur (*Avahi occidentalis*). *International Journal of Primatology* 33: 428–439.

Ramanankirahina, R., Joly, M., Scheumann, M., and Zimmermann, E. 2016. The role of acoustic signaling for spacing and group coordination in a nocturnal, pair-living primate, the western woolly lemur (*Avahi occidentalis*). *American Journal of Physical Anthropology* 159: 466–477.

Ramanantsalama, R. V., Andrianarimisa, A., Raselimanana, A. P., and Goodman, S. M. 2018. Rates of hematophagous ectoparasite consumption during grooming by an endemic Madagascar fruit bat. *Parasites and Vectors* 11(1): 330. https://doi.org/10.1186/s13071-018-2918-1.

Ramanantsalama, R. V., Noroalintseheno Lalarivoniaina, O. S., Raselimanana, A. P., and Goodman, S. M. 2019. Seasonal variation in diurnal cave-roosting behavior of a Malagasy fruit bat (*Rousettus madagascariensis*, Chiroptera: Pteropodidae). *Acta Chiropterologica* 21: 115–127.

Ramaromilanto, B., Lei, R., Engberg, S. E., Johnson, S. E., Sitzmann, B. D., and Louis, E. E., Jr. 2009. Sportive lemur diversity at Mananara-Nord Biosphere Reserve, Madagascar. *Occasional Papers, Museum of Texas Tech University* 286: 1–22.

Ramasindrazana, B., Rajemison, B., and Goodman, S. M. 2009. The diet of the endemic bat *Myzopoda aurita* (Myzopodidae) based on fecal analysis. *Malagasy Nature* 2: 159–163.

Ramasindrazana, B., Goodman, S. M., Schoeman, M. C., and Appleton, B. 2011. Identification of cryptic species of *Miniopterus* bats (Chiroptera: Miniopteridae) from Madagascar and the Comoros using bioacoustics overlaid on molecular genetic and morphological characters. *Biological Journal of the Linnean Society* 104: 284–302.

Ramasindrazana, B., Rajemison, B., and Goodman, S. M. 2012. Bio-écologie des chauves-souris du Parc National de Tsimanampetsotsa. 2. Variation interspécifique et saisonnière du régime alimentaire. *Malagasy Nature* 6: 117–124.

Ramasindrazana, B., Goodman, S. M., Rakotondramanana, F., and Schoeman, M. C. 2013. Morphological and echolocation call variation in Malagasy trident bats, *Triaenops* Dobson, 1871 (Chiroptera: Hipposideridae). *Acta Chiropterologica* 15: 431–439.

Ramasindrazana, B., Rakotondramanana, C. F., Schoeman, M. C., and Goodman, S. M. 2015. Evidence of echolocation call divergence in *Hipposideros commersoni sensu stricto* (E. Geoffroy, 1803) from Madagascar and correlation with body size. *Acta Chiropterologica* 17(1): 85–94.

Ramasindrazana, B., Andrianaivoarimanana, V., Rakotondramanga, J. M., Birdsell, D. N., Ratsitorahina, M., and Rajerison, M. 2017a. Pneumonic plague transmission, Moramanga, Madagascar, 2015. *Emerging Infectious Diseases* 23(3): 521–524.

Ramasindrazana, B., Goodman, S. M., Gomard, Y., Dick, C., and Tortosa, P. 2017b. Hidden diversity of Nycteribiidae (Diptera) bat flies from the Malagasy Region and insights on host-parasite interactions. *Parasites and Vectors* 10: 630.

Ramsay, M. S., Razafindrakoto, A., and Lehman, S. M. 2019. The effects of a national highway on the endangered golden-brown mouse lemur *Microcebus ravelobensis* in Ankarafantsika National Park, Madagascar. *Oryx* 53(4): 727–731.

Ramsier, M. A., and Dominy, N. J. 2012. Receiver bias and the acoustic ecology of aye-ayes (*Daubentonia madagascariensis*). *Communicative and Integrative Biology* 5(6): 637–640.

Ranaivoarisoa, J. F., Brenneman, L., McGuire, S. M., Lei, R., Ravelonjanahary, S. S., et al. 2010. Population genetic study of the red-collared brown lemur (*Eulemur collaris* É. Geoffroy) in southeastern Madagascar. *The Open Conservation Biology Journal* 4: 1–8.

Ranarivelo, N. A. 1993. Etude de la variation locale et saisonnière du comportement, alimentation et du régime alimentaire de *Propithecus verreauxi verreauxi* dans la première parcelle de la réserve spéciale de Beza Mahafaly. Mémoire de fin d'etudes, Ecole Supérieure des Sciences Agronomiques, Université d'Antananarivo.

Rand, A. L. 1935. On the habits of some Madagascar mammals. *Journal of Mammalogy* 16: 89–104.

Randimbiharinirina, D. R., Raharivololona, B. M., Hawkins, M.T.R., Frasier, C. L., Culligan, R. R., Sefczek, T. M., Randriamampionona, R., and Louis, E. E., Jr. 2018. Behaviour and ecology of male aye-ayes (*Daubentonia madagascariensis*) in the Kianjavato Classified Forest, south-eastern Madagascar. *Folia Primatologica* 89: 123–137.

Randriahaingo, H.N.T., Ravaloharimanitra, M., Randrianarimanana, H.L.L., Chamberlan, C., Ratsimbazafy, J., and King, T. 2014. Etude et conservation du grand hapalémur (*Prolemur simus*) aux alentours de la forêt d'Andriantantely. *Lemur News* 18: 67–72.

Randriamahady, A.N.J.E. 2012. Etude comparative des communautés micromammaliennes (Afrosoricida et Rodentia) de la bordure et de l'intérieur de la forêt sèche de Kirindy CNFEREF, Madagascar et détermination du domaine vital de *Tenrec ecaudatus* (Schreber, 1777). Mémoire de DEA, Université d'Antananarivo.

Randriamanalina, M. H., Rafararano, L., Babary, L., and Laha, R., 2000. Rapport des enquêtes sur les chasses dans les Fotontany d'Ivondro, d'Erara et d'Etsilesy. *Lemur News* 5: 11–14.

Randriamoria, T. M. 2016. Etude éco-biologique des petits mammifères du District de Moramanga et de leurs tiques (Ordre des Ixodida) dans les habitats forestiers et anthropogéniques. PhD thesis, Université d'Antananarivo.

———. 2017. Diversité et écologie des petits mammifères dans les habitats forestiers et anthropiques du District de Moramanga, centre-est de Madagascar. *Malagasy Nature* 12: 78–94.

Randriamoria, T. M., Soarimalala, V., and Goodman, S. M. 2015. Terrestrial "forest-dwelling" endemic small mammals captured outside of natural habitats in the Moramanga District, central eastern Madagascar. *Malagasy Nature* 9: 97–106.

Randrianambinina, B. 2001. Contribution à l'étude comparative de l'écoéthologie de deux microcèbes rouges de Madagascar *Microcebus ravelobensis* (Zimmermann et al., 1998), *Microcebus rufus* (Lesson, 1840). PhD thesis, Université d'Antananarivo.

Randrianambinina, B., Rakotondravony, D., Radespiel, U., and Zimmermann, E. 2003. Seasonal changes in general activity, body mass and reproduction of two small nocturnal primates: A comparison of the golden brown mouse lemur (*Microcebus ravelobensis*) in northwestern Madagascar and the brown mouse lemur (*Microcebus rufus*) in eastern Madagascar. *Primates* 44: 321–331.

Randrianambinina, B., Mbotizafy, S., Rasoloharijaona, S., Ravoahangimalala, R. O., and Zimmermann, E. 2007. Seasonality in reproduction of *Lepilemur edwardsi*. *International Journal of Primatology* 28: 783–790.

Randrianambinina, B., Rasoloharijaona, S., Rakotondravony, R., Zimmermann, E., and Radespiel, U. 2010. Abundance and conservation status of two newly described lemur species in northwestern Madagascar (*Microcebus danfossi*, *Lepilemur grewcockorum*). *Madagascar Conservation and Development* 5: 95–102.

Randrianandrianina, F.[H.], Andriafidison, D., Kofoky, A. F., Ramilijaona, O., Ratrimomanarivo, F., Racey, P. A., and Jenkins, R.K.B. 2006. Habitat use and conservation of bats in rainforest and adjacent human-modified habitats in eastern Madagascar. *Acta Chiropterologica* 8: 429–437.

Randrianandrianina, F. H., Racey, P. A., and Jenkins, R.K.B. 2010. Hunting and consumption of mammals and birds by people in urban areas of western Madagascar. *Oryx* 44(3): 411–415.

Randrianarimalalasoa, V. 2008. Etude de la morphométrie, du comportement et de l'habitat de *Microcebus griseorufus* de la forêt galerie et de la forêt sèche de la Réserve Spéciale de Bezà Mahafaly. Mémoire de DEA, Université d'Antananarivo.

Randrianarison, R., Rajaonson, A., Ralison, J., Rabemananjara, Z., Andrianantenaina, T., Rabearison, J., and Ratsimbazafy, J. 2015. Local socio-economic effects of protected area conservation: The case of Maromizaha forest, Madagascar. *Madagascar Conservation and Development* 10: 93–97. https://doi.org/10.4314/mcd.v10i2.8.

Randrianarison, R. M. 2019. Eco-biologie et complexe régurgitation-réingestion de la population d'*Indri indri* (Gmelin, 1788), forêt pluviale de Maromizaha, est de Madagascar. PhD thesis, Université d'Antananarivo.

Randrianarivo, R. 1979. Essai d'inventaire des lémuriens de la future réserve de Beza Mahafaly. Mémoire de fin d'études, Etablissement d'Enseignement Supérieur des Sciences Agronomiques, Université d'Antananarivo.

Randrianjafy, R. V. 2003. Contribution à l'étude de biologie de conservation de la communauté micromammalienne d'Ankarafantsika. PhD thesis, Université d'Antananarivo.

Randrianjafy, R. V., Ramilijaona, O., and Rakotondravony, D. 2007. Growth of the tufted-tailed rat. *Integrative Zoology* 2(4): 205–211.

Randriatahina, G. H., and Volampeno, S. M. 2012. Predation on two lemur species in Sahamalaza Peninsula, north-western Madagascar. In *Leaping Ahead*, eds. J. Masters, M. Gamba, and F. Génin, pp. 105–110. New York: Springer.

Ranivo, J. C. 2001. Contribution à l'étude de la biologie et de l'effet de la prédation humaine sur la roussette: *Eidolon dupreanum* (Pollen, 1866). Mémoire de DEA, Département de Biologie Animale, Université d'Antananarivo.

Ranivo, J. [C.], and Goodman, S. M. 2007a. Patterns of ecomorphological variation in the Microchiroptera of western Madagascar: Comparisons within and between communities along a latitudinal gradient. *Mammalian Biology* 72: 1–13.

Ranivo, J. [C.], and Goodman, S. M. 2007b. Variation géographique de *Hipposideros commersoni* de la zone sèche de Madagascar (Mammalia, Chiroptera, Hipposideridae). *Verhandlungen des Naturwissenschaftlichen Vereins in Hamburg* 43: 35–56.

Ranorovelohanta, R. 1996. Evaluation du rôle du corridor forestier de Besariaka à partir d'une analyse de sa diversité biologique. Mémoires de fin d'études, Université d'Antananarivo.

Rasambainarivo, F. [T.]. 2018. Interactions and pathogen transmission between carnivores in Madagascar. PhD thesis, University of Missouri–Saint Louis.

Rasambainarivo, F. T., and Goodman, S. M. 2019. Disease risks from introduced species to Malagasy wildlife. In *Fowler's Zoo and Wild Animal Medicine*, eds. R. E. Miller, P. Calle, and N. Lamberski, 9th ed., pp. 292–297. Saint Louis: Elsevier.

Rasambainarivo, F. T., Gillespie, T. R., Wright, P. C., Arsenault, J., Villeneuve, A., and Lair. S. 2013. Survey of *Giardia* and *Cryptosporidium* in lemurs from the Ranomafana National Park, Madagascar. *Journal of Wildlife Diseases* 49(3): 741–743.

Rasambainarivo, F. [T.], Farris, Z. J., Andrianalizah, H., and Parker, P. G. 2017. Interactions between carnivores in Madagascar and the risk of disease transmission. *Ecohealth* 14: 691–703.

Rasambainarivo, F. [T.], Andriamihajarivo, M. N., Dubovi, E., and Parker, P. G. 2018. Patterns of exposure of carnivores to selected pathogens in the Betampona Natural Reserve landscape, Madagascar. *Journal of Wildlife Diseases* 54(2): 386–391.

Rasamimanana, H. [R.]. 1999. Influence of social organization patterns on food intake of *Lemur catta* in the Berenty Reserve. In *New Directions in Lemur Studies*, eds. B. Rakotosamimanana, H. Rasamimanana, J. U. Ganzhorn, and S. M. Goodman, pp. 173–188. Boston: Springer.

Rasamimanana, H. R., and Rafidinarivo, E. 1993. Feeding behavior of *Lemur catta* females in relation to their physiological state. In *Lemur Social Systems and Their Ecological Basis*, eds. P. M. Kappeler and J. U. Ganzhorn, pp. 123–133. New York: Plenum Press.

Rasamison, A. A. 1997. Contribution à l'étude biologique, ecologique et ethologique de *Cryptoprocta ferox* (Bennett, 1833) dans la forêt de Kirindy à Madagascar. Mémoire de DEA, Faculté des Sciences, Université d'Antananarivo.

Rasamoelina, G., Rasamoel, M. Rakotovao, J.-M., and Rafanomezana, S. 1997. Résultats d'une évaluation des dégâts de rats sur le riz irrigué de Madagascar pendant la saison 1996–1997. In *Actes du Symposium National sur les Rongeurs et la Lutte Antimurine*, eds. W. Zehrer and S. Rafanomezana, pp. 119–125. Antananarivo: Département de la Protection des Végétaux and Deutsche Gesellschaft für Technische Zusammenarbeit-German Technical Cooperation.

Rasamoelina, M., and Andriamalala, A. 1999. *Manuel de lutte contre les rats*. Antananarivo: Projet DPV/GTZ Promotion de la Protection Intégrée des Cultures et des Denrées Stockées à Madagascar.

Rasmussen, D. T. 1985. A comparative study of breeding seasonality and litter size in eleven taxa of captive lemurs (*Lemur* and *Varecia*). *International Journal of Primatology* 6: 501–517.

Rasmussen, M. A. 1999. Ecological influences on activity cycle in two cathemeral primates, the mongoose lemur (*Eulemur mongoz*) and the common brown lemur (*Eulemur fulvus fulvus*). PhD thesis, Duke University.

Rasoanindrainy, J. M. 1985a. [Population dynamics of *Propithecus verreauxi*]. *Nauchnye Doklady Vysshei Shkoly Biologicheskie Nauki* 4: 43 (in Russian).

Rasoanindrainy, J. M. 1985b. [Comparative biology of *Propithecus verreauxi verreauxi* and *Lemur catta*, and perspectives for their protection.] PhD thesis, Lomonosov Moscow State University (in Russian).

Rasoanoro, M., Ramasindrazana, B., Rajemison, B., Razafimahatratra, E., and Goodman, S. M. 2015. Préférence alimentaire des chauves-souris de Kianjavato, région de Vatovavy-Fitovinany, Madagascar. *Malagasy Nature* 9: 58–67.

Rasoazanabary, E. 2006. Male and female activity patterns in *Microcebus murinus* during the dry season at Kirindy Forest, western Madagascar. *International Journal of Primatology* 27: 437–464.

———. 2011. The human factor in mouse lemur (*Microcebus griseorufus*) conservation: Local resource utilization and habitat disturbance at Beza Mahafaly, SW Madagascar. PhD thesis, University of Massachusetts, Amherst.

Rasoazanabary, E., and Godfrey, L. 2016. Living in riverine and xeric forests: *Microcebus griseorufus* at Beza Mahafaly, southwestern Madagascar. In *The Dwarf and Mouse Lemurs of Madagascar: Biology, Behavior and Conservation Biogeography of the Cheirogaleidae*, eds. S. M. Lehman, U. Radespiel, and E. Zimmermann, pp. 255–280. Cambridge: Cambridge University Press.

Rasoloarison, R. M., Rasolonandrasana, B.P.N., Ganzhorn, J. U., and Goodman, S. M. 1995. Predation on vertebrates in the Kirindy Forest, western Madagascar. *Ecotropica* 1: 59–65.

Rasoloarison, R. M., Goodman, S. M., and Ganzhorn, J. U. 2000. Taxonomic revision of mouse lemurs (*Microcebus*) in the western portions of Madagascar. *International Journal of Primatology* 21: 963–1019.

Rasoloarison, R. M., Weisrock, D. W., Yoder, A. D., Rakotondravony, D., and Kappeler, P. M. 2013. Two new species of mouse lemurs (Cheirogaleidae: *Microcebus*) from eastern Madagascar. *International Journal of Primatology* 34: 455–469.

Rasolofoniaina, B. N. 2020. Cognition in narrow-striped mongooses, *Mungotictis decemlineata*, a Malagasy carnivore species. PhD thesis, University of Göttingen.

Rasolofoniaina, B. N., Razafy, P., Andrianarimisa, A., Razafimahatratra, E., and Kappeler, P. M. 2019. Feeding ecology of the bokiboky, *Mungotictis decemlineata* (Eupleridae). *Malagasy Nature* 13: 152–161.

Rasoloharijaona, S., Rakotosamimanana, B., and Zimmermann, E. 2000. Infanticide by a male Milne-Edwards' sportive lemur (*Lepilemur edwardsi*) in Ampijoroa, NW-Madagascar. *International Journal of Primatology* 21: 41–45.

Rasoloharijaona, S., Rakotosamimanana, B., Randrianambinina, B., and Zimmermann, E. 2003. Pair-specific usage of sleeping sites and their implications for social organization in a nocturnal Malagasy primate, the Milne Edwards' sportive lemur (*Lepilemur edwardsi*). *American Journal of Physical Anthropology* 122: 251–258.

Rasoloharijaona, S., Randrianambinina, B., Braune, P., and Zimmermann, E. 2006. Loud calling, spacing, and cohesiveness in a nocturnal primate, the Milne Edwards' sportive lemur (*Lepilemur edwardsi*). *American Journal of Physical Anthropology* 129: 591–600.

Rasoloharijaona, S., Randrianambinina, B., and Zimmermann, E. 2008. Sleeping site ecology in a rain-forest dwelling nocturnal lemur (*Lepilemur mustelinus*): Implications for sociality and conservation. *American Journal of Primatology* 70: 247–253.

Rasoloharijaona, S., Randrianambinina, B., and Joly-Radko, M. 2010. Does nonnutritive tree gouging in a rainforest-dwelling lemur convey resource ownership as does loud calling in a dry forest-dwelling lemur? *American Journal of Primatology* 72: 1062–1072.

Rasolonandrasana, B.P.N. 1994. Contribution à l'étude de l'alimentation de *Cryptoprocta ferox* Bennett (1833) dans son milieu naturel. Mémoire de DEA, Service de Paléontologie, Université d'Antananarivo.

Rasolonandrasana, B.P.N., and Goodman, S. M. 1999. Les mammifères carnivores. In Inventaire biologique de la Réserve Spéciale du Pic d'Ivohibe et du couloir forestier qui la relie au Parc National d'Andringitra, eds. S. M. Goodman and B.P.N. Rasolonandrasana. *Recherches pour le Développement*, série *Sciences Biologiques*, 15: 149–156.

Rasolonandrasana, B.P.N., and Goodman, S. M. 2006. The influence of fire on mountain sclerophyllous forests and their small-mammal communities in Madagascar. In *Land Use Change and Mountain Biodiversity*, eds. E. M. Spehn, M. Liberman, and C. Körner, pp. 77–87. Boca Raton: Taylor and Francis.

Rasolozaka, I. N. 1998. Biologie et migration des rats dans les polycultures de la côte est. In *Rongeurs et lutte antimurine à Madagascar: Promotion de la protection intégrée des cultures et des denrées stockées à Madagascar*, eds. W. Zehrer and S. Rafanomezana, pp. 59–67. Antananarivo: Département de la Protection des Végétaux and Deutsche Gesellschaft für Technische Zusammenarbeit–German Technical Cooperation.

Rasoma, J., and Goodman, S. M. 2007. Food habits of the barn owl (*Tyto alba*) in spiny bush habitat of arid southwestern Madagascar. *Journal of Arid Environments* 69: 537–543.

Ratrimomanarivo, F. H. 2007. Etude du régime alimentaire d'*Eidolon dupreanum* (Chiroptera: Pteropodidae) dans la région anthropisée des hautes terres du centre de Madagascar. *Revue d'Ecologie* (*La Terre et la Vie*) 62: 229–244.

Ratrimomanarivo, F. H., and Goodman, S. M. 2005. First records of the synanthropic occurrence of *Scotophilus* spp. on Madagascar. *African Bat Conservation News* 6: 3–5.

Ratrimomanarivo, F. H., Vivian, J., Goodman, S. M., and Lamb, J. 2007. Morphological and molecular assessment of the specific status of *Mops midas* (Chiroptera: Molossidae) from Madagascar and Africa. *African Zoology* 42: 237–253.

Ratrimomanarivo, F. H., Goodman, S. M., Hoosen, N., Taylor, P. J., and Lamb, J. 2008. Morphological and molecular variation in *Mops leucostigma* (Chiroptera: Molossidae) of Madagascar and the Comoros: Phylogeny, phylogeography, and geographic variation. *Mitteilungen aus dem Hamburgischen Zoologischen Museum* 105: 57–101.

Ratrimomanarivo, F. H., Goodman, S. M., Taylor, P. J., Melson, B., and Lamb, J. 2009a. Morphological and genetic variation in *Mormopterus jugularis* (Chiroptera: Molossidae) in different bioclimatic regions of Madagascar with natural history notes. *Mammalia* 73: 110–129. https://doi.org/10.1515/MAMM.2009.032.

Ratrimomanarivo, F. H., Goodman, S. M., Stanley, W. T., Naidoo, T., Taylor, P. J., and Lamb, J. 2009b. Geographic and phylogeographic variation in *Chaerephon leucogaster* (Chiroptera: Molossidae) of Madagascar and the western Indian Ocean islands of Mayotte and Pemba. *Acta Chiropterologica* 11(1): 25–52.

Ratsimbazafy, J. [H.]. 2002. On the brink of extinction and the process of recovery: Responses of black-and-white ruffed lemurs (*Varecia variegata variegata*) to disturbance in Manombo forest Madagascar. PhD thesis, State University of New York, Stony Brook.

———. 2006. Diet composition, foraging, and feeding behavior in relation to habitat disturbance: Implications for the adaptability of ruffed lemurs (*Varecia variegata*) in Manombo Forest. In *Lemurs: Ecology and Adaptation*, eds. L. Gould and M. L. Sauther, pp. 403–422. New York: Springer/Kluwer.

Ratsimbazafy, J. H., Ramarosandratana, H. V., and Zaonarivelo, R. J. 2002. How do black-and-white ruffed lemurs still survive in a highly disturbed habitat? *Lemur News* 7: 7–10.

Ratsimbazafy, J. H., Rajaonson, A., Surrans, R., Rasolofoson, D., Ralison, A., Andrianantoandro, D., and Rabearison, J. B. 2017. Rapport annuel de gestion de la Réserve de Ressorces Naturelles de Maromizaha. Antananarivo: GERP.

Ratsirarson, J. 1986. Contribution à l'étude comparée de l'éco-éthologie de deux espèces de lémuriens: *Lepilemur mustelinus* (I. Geoffroy 1850) et *Lepilemur septentrionalis* (Rumpler et Albignac 1975). Thèse Doctorate d'Etat, Université Louis Pasteur, Strasbourg.

———. 1987. Contribution à l'étude comparative de l'éco-éthologie de *Lemur catta* dans deux habitats différents de la Réserve Spéciale de Bezà-Mahafaly. Mémoire de fin d'étude, Etablissement d'Enseignement Supérieur des Sciences Agronomiques, Université d'Antananarivo.

Ratsirarson, J., and Emady, R. J. 1999. Prédation de *Lepilemur leucopus* par *Buteo brachypterus* dans la forêt galerie de Beza Mahafaly. *Newsletter of the Working Group on Birds in the Madagascar Region* 9: 14–15.

Ratsirarson, J., and Ranaivonasy, J. 2002. Ecologie des lémuriens dans la forêt littorale de Tampolo. *Lemur News* 7: 26–30.

Ratsirarson, J., Randrianarisoa, J., Ellis, E., Emady, R. J., Ranaivonasy, J. R., Razanajaonarivalona, and Richard, A. F. 2001. Bezà Mahafaly: Ecologie et réalités socio-économiques. *Recherches pour le Développement*, série *Sciences Biologiques*, 18: 1–104.

Ravaloharimanitra, M., Ratolojanahary, T., Rafalimandimby, J., Rajaonson, A., Rakotonirina, L., et al. 2011. Gathering local knowledge in Madagascar results in a major increase in the known range and number of sites for critically endangered greater bamboo lemurs (*Prolemur simus*). *International Journal of Primatology* 32: 776–792.

Ravaomanana, J., Jori, F., Vial, L., Pérez-Sánchez, R., Blanco, E., Michaud, V., and Roger, F. 2011. Assessment of interactions between African swine fever virus, bushpigs (*Potamochoerus larvatus*), *Ornithodoros* ticks and domestic pigs in north-western Madagascar. *Transboundary and Emerging Diseases* 58: 247–254.

Ravelojaona, R. N. 2017. Bio-écologie de la communauté chiroptérologique de l'aire protégée de Mandrozo, ouest de Madagascar. Master's memoir, Mention Zoologie et Biodiversité Animale, Université d'Antananarivo.

Ravelomalala, L. S. 2015. Biologie, écologie, et multiplication de cinq espèces végétales consommées par *Eulemur coronatus* (Lemurideae) dans la Montagne des Français (Antsiranana II). Mémoire de DEA, Université d'Antananarivo.

Ravelomanantsoa, N.A.F., Razafimalala, F., Rakotomalala, Z., Ranivo, J., Razafimanjato, G., Rene de Roland, L.-A., Ramasindrazana, B., Rakotondramanana, C. F., and Goodman, S. M. 2019. Les chauves-souris du Paysage Harmonieux Protégé du Complexe Tsimembo Manambolomaty, Région Melaky, Madagascar: Diversité et biogéographie. *Malagasy Nature* 13: 105–116.

Ravoahangy, A., Raveloson, B. A., Raminoarisoa, V. M., and Safford, R. 2011. Notes on the carnivores of Tsitongambarika Forest, Madagascar, including the behaviour of a juvenile eastern falanouc *Eupleres goudotii*. *Small Carnivore Conservation* 45: 2–4.

Ravoavy, F. 1986. Identification et mise en catalogue des vertèbres non-primates subfossiles et actuels des grottes d'Anjohibe (Majunga). Mémoire de DEA, Département de Paleontologie, Université d'Antanananarivo.

Raxworthy, C. J., and Nussbaum, R. A. 1994. A rainforest survey of amphibians, reptiles and small mammals at Montagne d'Ambre, Madagascar. *Biological Conservation* 69: 65–73.

Razafimalala, F. 2017. Bioécologie et ectoparasites de *Taphozous mauritianus* (Emballonuridae) dans l'Aire Protégée Complexe Tsimembo Manambolomaty, Région Melaky, Madagascar. Diplôme de Master, Mention Zoologie et Biodiversité Animale, Université d'Antananarivo.

Razafimanahaka, J. H., Ralisata, M., Randrianandrianina, F., Jenkins, R.K.B., Ratsirarson, J., and Racey, P. A. 2016. Habitat use by the endemic Malagasy bat *Hipposideros commersoni* in a littoral forest. *Acta Chiropterologica* 18(2): 423–431.

Razafindratsima, O. H. 2009. Etude du rôle écologique de *Varecia rubra* (Geoffroy, 1812) et de *Eulemur* [sic] *albifrons* (Geoffroy, 1796) dans le corridor Ambatolaidama du Parc National Masoala. Mémoire de DEA, Université d'Antananarivo.

———. 2017. Post-dispersal seed removal by rodents in Ranomafana rain forest, Madagascar. *Journal of Tropical Ecology* 33: 232–236.

Razafindratsima, O. H., and Razafimahatratra, E. 2010. Effect of red ruffed lemur gut passage on the germination of native rainforest plant species. *Lemur News* 15: 39–42.

Razafindratsima, O. H., Mehtani, S., and Dunham, A. E. 2013. Extinctions, traits and phylogenetic community structure: Insights from primate assemblages in Madagascar. *Ecography* 36: 47–58.

Razafindratsima, O. H., Jones, T. A., and Dunham, A. E. 2014. Patterns of movement and seed dispersal by three lemur species. *American Journal of Primatology* 76: 84–96.

Razakamaharavo, V. R., McGuire, S. M., Vasey, N., Louis, E. E., Jr., and Brenneman, R. A. 2010. Genetic architecture of two red ruffed lemur (*Varecia rubra*) populations of Masoala National Park. *Primates* 51: 53–61. https://doi.org/10.1007/s10329-009-0171-0.

Razakaratrimo, S., Goodman, S. M., Rene de Roland, L.-A., and Andrianarimisa, A. 2019. Caractéristiques du régime alimentaire du Milan des chauves-souris *Macheiramphus alcinus* (Gurney, 1866) dans l'aire protégée de Mandrozo (ouest de Madagascar). *Bulletin de la Société Zoologique de France* 144(3): 107–119.

Razakarivony, V., Rajemison, B., and Goodman, S. M. 2005. The diet of Malagasy Microchiroptera based on stomach contents. *Mammalian Biology* 70(5): 312–316.

Razanahoera, M. R. 1988. Comportement alimentaire de deux espèces sympatriques dans la forêt d'Ankarafantsika (nord-ouest de Madagascar): *Lepilemur edwardsi* et *Avahi laniger* (lémuriens nocturnes). In *L'Equilibre des écosystèmes forestiers à Madagascar*, eds. L. Rakotovao, V. Barre, and J. Sayer, pp. 96–99. Gland, Switzerland and Cambridge, UK: IUCN.

Reardon, T. B., McKenzie, N. L., Cooper, S.J.B., Appleton B., Carthew, D. S., and Adams, M. 2014. A molecular and morphological investigation of species boundaries and phylogenetic relationships in Australian free-tailed bats *Mormopterus* (Chiroptera: Molossidae). *Australian Journal of Zoology* 62: 109–136.

Reher, S., and Dausmann, K. H. 2021. Tropical bats counter heat by combining torpor with adaptive hyperthermia. *Proceedings of the Royal Society of London B: Biological Sciences*. https://doi.org/10.1098/rspb.2020.2059.

Reher, S., Ehlers, J., Rabarison, H., and Dausmann, K. H. 2018. Short and hyperthermic torpor responses in the Malagasy bat *Macronycteris commersoni* reveal a broader hypometabolic scope in heterotherms. *Journal of Comparative Physiology B: Biochemical, Systemic, and Environmental Physiology* 188: 1015–1027. https://doi.org/10.1007/s00360-018-1171-4.

Reher, S., Rabarison, H., Schoroth, M., and Dausmann, K. 2019. Seasonal movements of insectivorous bat species in southwestern Madagascar. *Malagasy Nature* 13: 117–124.

Reimann, W. E. 2002. Koexistenz und Nahrungsökologie von Weibchen des grauen und goldbraunen Mausmakis (*Microcebus murinus* und *M. ravelobensis*) in Nordwest-Madagaskar. PhD thesis, Tierärztliche Hochschule Hannover.

Remmers, S. 2020. Ready for climate change? The importance of adaptive thermoregulatory flexibility for the Malagasy bat species *Triaenops menamena*. MS thesis, University of Hamburg.

Rendigs, A., Radespiel, U., Wrogemann, D., and Zimmermann, E. 2003. Relationship between microhabitat structure and distribution of mouse lemurs (*Microcebus* spp.) in northwestern Madagascar. *International Journal of Primatology* 24: 47–64.

Rendigs, A., Reibelt, L. M., Ralainasolo, F. B., Ratsimbazafy, J. H., and Waeber, P. O. 2015. Ten years into the marshes: *Hapalemur alaotrensis* conservation, one step forward and two steps back? *Madagascar Conservation and Development* 10: 13–20.

Rene de Roland, L.-A. 2000. Contribution à l'étude biologique, écologique et éthologique de trois espèces d'*Accipiter* dans la Presqu'Isle de Masoala. Thèse de doctorat. Université d'Antananarivo.

Reuter, K. E., and Sewall, B. J. 2016. Taboos and sustainability of tenrec hunting in Madagascar. *Afrotherian Conservation* 12: 11–15.

Reuter, K. E., Randell, H., Wills, A. R., Totozafy, E. J., Belahay, T. R., and Sewell, B. J. 2016. Capture, movement, trade, and consumption of mammals in Madagascar. *PLoS One* 11: e0150305. https://doi.org/10.1371/journal.pone.0150305.

Reuter, K. E., Clarke, T. A., LaFleur, M., Ratsimbazafy, J., Holiniaina Kjeldgaard, F., Rodriguez, L., Schaeffer, T., and Schaefer, M. S. 2018. Exploring the role of wealth and religion on the ownership of captive lemurs in Madagascar using qualitative and quantitative data. *Folia Primatologica* 89: 81–96.

Reuter, K. E., LaFleur, M., Clarke, T. A., Kjeldgaard, F. H., Ramanantenasoa, I., Ratolojanahary, T., Ratsimbazafy, J., Rodriguez, L., Schaeffer, T., and Schaefer, M. S. 2019. A national survey of household pet lemur ownership in Madagascar. *PLoS One* 14: e0216593.

Reynes, J.-M., Razafindralambo, N. K., Lacoste, V., Olive, M.-M., Barivelo, T. A., Soarimalala, V., Heraud, J.-M., and Lavergne, A. 2014. Anjozorobe Hantavirus, a new genetic variant of Thailand virus, detected in rodents from Madagascar. *Vector-Borne and Zoonotic Diseases* 14: 212–219. https://doi.org/10.1089/vbz.2013.1359.

Richard, A. [F.] 1974. Intra-specific variation in the social organization and ecology of *Propithecus verreauxi*. *Folia Primatologica* 22: 178–207.

———. 1977. The feeding behaviour of *Propithecus verreauxi*. In *Primate Ecology: Studies of Feeding and Ranging Behaviour in Lemurs, Monkeys and Apes*, ed. T. H. Clutton-Brock, pp. 71–96. London: Academic Press.

———. 1978. *Behavioral Variation: Case Study of a Malagasy Lemur*. Lewisburg, Pennsylvania: Bucknell University Press.

———. 1985. Social boundaries in a Malagasy prosimian, the sifaka (*Propithecus verreauxi*). *International Journal of Primatology* 6: 553–568.

Richard, A. F., and Dewar, R. E. 1991. Lemur ecology. *Annual Review of Ecology and Systematics* 22: 145–175.

Richard, A. F., and Nicoll, M. E. 1987. Female social dominance and basal metabolism in a Malagasy primate, *Propithecus verreauxi*. *American Journal of Primatology* 12: 309–314.

Richard, A. F., Rakotomanga, P., and Schwartz, M. 1991. Demography of *Propithecus verreauxi* at Beza Mahafaly, Madagascar: Sex ratio, survival, and fertility 1984–1988. *American Journal of Physical Anthropology* 84: 307–322.

Richard, A. F., Rakotomanga, P., and Schwartz, M. 1993. Dispersal by *Propithecus verreauxi* at Beza Mahafaly, Madagascar: 1984–1991. *American Journal of Primatology* 30: 1–20.

Richard, A. F., Dewar, R. E., Schwartz, M., and Ratsirarson, J. 2002. Life in the slow lane? Demography and life histories of male and female sifaka (*Propithecus verreauxi verreauxi*). *Journal of Zoology* 256: 421–436.

Richard, A., [F.] Ratsirarson, J., Jaonarisoa, E., Mahereza, S., Youssouf Jacky, I. A., Sauther, M., and Fiorentino, I. 2016a. Diurnal lemurs at Bezà Mahafaly: Resilience and risk. In Suivi écologique et socio-économique dans la Réserve Spéciale de Bezà Mahafaly (Sud-ouest de Madagascar), eds. J. Ranaivonasy, J. Ratsirarson, and A. F. Richard. *Malagasy Nature* 10: 37–49.

Richard, A. [F.], Ratsirarson, J., Jaonarisoa, E., Youssouf Jacky, I. A., Fiorentino, I., and Ranaivonasy, J. 2016b. Mammalian biodiversity at Bezà Mahafaly: An update, eds. J. Ranaivonasy, J. Ratsirarson, and A. F. Richard. *Malagasy Nature* 10: 25–35.

Richards, L. R., Rambau, R. V., Lamb, J. M., Taylor, P. J., Yang, F., Schoeman, M. C., and Goodman, S. M. 2010. Cross-species chromosome painting in bats from Madagascar: The contribution of Myzopodidae to revealing ancestral syntenies in Chiroptera. *Chromosome Research* 18: 635–653.

Richards, L. R., Rambau, R. V., Goodman, S. M., Taylor, P. J., Schoeman, M. C., Yang, F., and Lamb, J. M. 2016. Karyotypic evolution in Malagasy flying foxes (Pteropodidae, Chiroptera) and their hipposiderid relatives as determined by comparative chromosome painting. *Cytogenetics and Genome Research* 148(2–3): 185–198.

Ries, L., Murphy, S. M., Wimp, G. M., and Fletcher, R. J. 2017. Closing persistent gaps in knowledge about edge ecology. *Current Landscape Ecology Reports* 2(1): 30–41.

Rigamonti, M. M. 1993. Home range and diet in red ruffed lemurs (*Varecia variegata rubra*) on the Masoala Peninsula, Madagascar. In *Lemur Social Systems and Their Ecological Basis*, eds. P. M. Kappeler and J. U. Ganzhorn, pp. 25–39. New York: Plenum Press.

———. 1996. Red ruffed lemur (*Varecia variegata rubra*): A rare species from the Masoala rain forests. *Lemur News* 2: 9–11.

Ringbauer, H., Coop, G., and Barton, N. H. 2017. Inferring recent demography from isolation by distance of long shared sequence blocks. *Genetics* 205: 1335–1351. https://doi.org/10.1534/genetics.116.196220.

Riskin, D. K., and Racey, P. A. 2010. How do sucker-footed bats hold on, and why do they roost head-up? *Biological Journal of the Linnean Society* 99(2): 223–240.

Robbins, C., De Vree, F., and Van Cakenberghe, V. 1985. A systematic revision of the African bat genus *Scotophilus* (Vespertilionidae). *Musée Royal de l'Afrique Centrale, Tervuren, Belgique, Sciences Zoologiques* 246: 51–84.

Rocamora, G., and Henriette, E. 2015. *Invasive Alien Species in Seychelles*. Mahé: Island Biodiversity and Conservation Centre.

Rode, E. J., Nekaris, K.E.I., Markolf, M., Schliehe-Diecks, S., Seiler, M., Radespiel, U., and Schwitzer, C. 2013. Social organisation of the northern giant mouse lemur *Mirza zaza* in Sahamalaza, north western Madagascar, inferred from nest group composition and genetic relatedness. *Contributions to Zoology* 82: 71–83.

Rode-Margono, E. J., Nekaris, K.A.I., Kappeler, P. M., and Schwitzer, C. 2015. The largest relative testis size among primates and aseasonal reproduction in a nocturnal lemur, *Mirza zaza*. *American Journal of Physical Anthropology* 158: 165–169.

Rode-Margono, E. J., Schwitzer, C., and Nekaris, K.A.I. 2016. Morphology, behavior, ranging patterns and habitat use of the northern giant mouse lemur *Mirza zaza* in Sahamalaza, northwestern Madagascar. In *Dwarf and Mouse Lemurs of Madagascar: Biology, Behavior and Conservation Biogeography of the Cheirogaleidae*,

eds. S. Lehman, U. Radespiel, and E. Zimmermann, pp. 235–254. Cambridge: Cambridge University Press.

Roelke, M. E., Martenson, J. S., and O'Brien, S. J. 1993. The consequences of demographic reduction and genetic depletion in the endangered Florida panther. *Current Biology* 3: 340–350.

Roger, F., Ratovonjato, J., Vola, P., and Uilenberg, G. 2001. *Ornithodoros porcinus* ticks, bushpigs, and African swine fever in Madagascar. *Experimental and Applied Acarology* 25: 263–269.

Rogers, A. R., and Harpending, H. 1992. Population growth makes waves in the distribution of pairwise genetic differences. *Molecular Biology and Evolution* 9: 552–569. https://doi.org/10.1093/oxfordjournals.molbev.a040727.

Rollin, P. E., Mathiot, C., Nawrocka, E., Ravaoalimalala, V. E., Coulanges, P., Sureau, P., and McCormick, J. B. 1986. La fièvre hémorragique avec syndrome rénal à Madagascar. Première enquête séro-épidémiologique sur les populations de rats. *Archives de l'Institut Pasteur de Madagascar* 52: 181–186.

Roos, C., Schmitz, J., and Zischler, H. 2004. Primate jumping genes elucidate strepsirrhine phylogeny. *Proceedings of the National Academy of Sciences of the USA* 101: 10650–10654.

Rösch, V., Tscharntke, T., Scherber, C., and Batáry, P. 2015. Biodiversity conservation across taxa and landscapes requires many small as well as single large habitat fragments. *Oecologia* 179(1): 209–222.

Rosenberger, A. L., Godfrey, L. R., Muldoon, K. M., Gunnell, G. F., Haingoson, H., et al. 2015. Giant subfossil lemur graveyard discovered, submerged, in Madagascar. *Journal of Human Evolution* 81: 83–87.

Ross, C. F. 2000. Into the light: The origin of the Anthropoidea. *Annual Reviews of Anthropology* 29: 147–194.

Ross, P. H., Patel, E., Ferguson, B., Ravelijaona, R. H., Raoloniana, G. I., Wampole, E., Gerber, B. D., and Farris, Z. J. 2020. Assessment of the threatened carnivore community in the recently expanded rainforest protected area Anjanaharibe-Sud Special Reserve, Madagascar. *Endangered Species Research* 43: 89–98.

Roth, O. 1996. Ecology and social behaviour of the woolly lemur (*Avahi laniger*), a nocturnal Malagasy prosimian. Master's thesis, University of Basel.

Rothman, J. M., Raubenheimer, D., Bryer, M.A.H., Takahashi, M., and Gilbert, C. C. 2014. Nutritional contributions of insects to primate diets: Implications for primate evolution. *Journal of Human Evolution* 71: 59–69.

Roubaud, E., and Girard, G. 1943. Observations sur deux pulicidés de la faune de Madagascar (*P. kerguisteli* et *S. fonquerniei*). *Bulletin de la Société de Pathologie Exotique* 36: 279–281.

Rouillé, A., Pedrono, M., Rakotomalala, E., Grosbois, V., Ramy-Ratiarison, R., and Roger, F. 2014. Abondance du potamochère, *Potamochoerus larvatus*, dans les savanes du Nord-Ouest de Madagascar et risques épidémiologiques associés. *Bois et Forêts des Tropiques* 320(2): 75–82.

Rousset, F. 1997. Genetic differentiation and estimation of gene flow from F-statistics under isolation by distance. *Genetics* 145: 1219–1228.

Rowe, N., and Myers, M. 2016. *All the World's primates*. Charlestown: Pogonias Press.

Ruedi, M., Friedli-Weyeneth, N., Teeling, E. C., Puechmaille, S. J., and Goodman, S. M. 2012. Biogeography of Old World emballonurine bats (Chiroptera: Emballonuridae) inferred with mitochondrial and nuclear DNA. *Molecular Phylogenetics and Evolution* 64: 204–211.

Ruf, T., and Geiser, F. 2015. Daily torpor and hibernation in birds and mammals. *Biological Reviews* 90: 891–926.

Rumpler, Y., and Albignac, R. 1975. Intraspecific chromosome variability in a lemur from the north of Madagascar: *Lepilemur septentrionalis*, species nova. *American Journal of Physical Anthropology* 42: 425–429.

Rumpler, Y., and Albignac, R. 1978. Chromosome studies of the lepilemur, an endemic Malagasy genus of lemurs: Contribution of the cytogenetics to their taxonomy. *Journal of Human Evolution* 7: 191–196. https://doi.org/10.1016/S0047-2484(78)80110-9.

Rumpler, Y., and Dutrillaux, B. 1976. Chromosomal evolution in Malagasy lemurs. *Cytogenetic and Genome Research* 17: 268–281. https://doi.org/10.1159/000130722.

Rumpler, Y., and Dutrillaux, B. 1978. Chromosomal evolution in Malagasy lemurs. III. Chromosome banding studies in the genus *Hapalemur* and the species *Lemur catta*. *Cytogenetics and Cellular Genetics* 21: 201–211.

Rumpler, Y., Ishak, B., Warter, S., and Dutrillaux, B. 1985. Chromosomal evolution in Malagasy lemurs. VIII. Chromosome banding studies of *Lepilemur ruficaudatus*, *L. leucopus*, and *L. septentrionalis*. *Cytogenetic and Genomic Research* 39: 194–199.

Rumpler, Y., Warter, S., Rabarivola, C., Petter, J.-J., and Dutrillaux, B. 1990. Chromosomal evolution in Malagasy lemurs: XII. Chromosomal banding study of *Avahi laniger occidentalis* (Syn: *Lichanotus laniger occidentalis*) and cytogenetic data in favour of its classification in a species apart—*Avahi occidentalis*. *American Journal of Primatology* 21: 307–316.

Rumpler, Y., Prosper, P., Hauwy, M., Rabarivola, C., Rakotoarisoa, G., and Dutrillaux, B. 2002. Chromosomal evolution of the *Hapalemur griseus* subspecies (Malagasy Prosimian), including a new chromosomal polymorphic cytotype. *Chromosome Research* 10: 145–153.

Rumpler, Y., Warter, S., Hauwy, M., Fausser, J. L., Roos, C., and Zinner, D. 2008. Comparing chromosomal and mitochondrial phylogenies of sportive lemurs (Genus *Lepilemur*, Primates). *Chromosome Research* 16: 1143–1158.

Rumpler, Y., Hauwy, M., Fausser, J. L., Roos, C., Zaramody, A., Andriaholinirina, N., and Zinner, D. 2011. Comparing chromosomal and mitochondrial phylogenies of the Indriidae (Primates, Lemuriformes). *Chromosome Research* 19: 209–224.

Russ, J. [M.], and Bennett, D. 1999. *The Bats of Masoala Peninsular, Madagascar and the Use of Time Expansion Ultrasound Detectors in Surveying Microchiropteran Communities*. Final report of Queen's University Belfast Masoala Bat Project. Glossop: Viper.

Russ, J. [M.], Bennett, D., Ross, K., and Kofoky, A. 2003. *The Bats of Madagascar: A Field Guide with Descriptions of Echolocation Calls*. Glossop: Viper Press.

Russ, J. M., Jones, G., Mackie J., and Racey, P. A. 2004. Interspecific responses to distress calls in bats (Chiroptera: Vespertilionidae): A function for convergence in call design? *Animal Behaviour* 67: 1005–1014.

Russell, A. L., Ranivo, J., Palkovacs, E. P., Goodman, S. M., and Yoder, A. D. 2007. Working at the interface of phylogenetics and population genetics: A biogeographical analysis of *Triaenops* spp. (Chiroptera: Hipposideridae). *Molecular Ecology* 16(4): 839–851. https://doi.org/10.1111/j.1365-294X.2007.03192.x.

Russell, A. L., Goodman, S. M., and Cox, M. P. 2008a. Coalescent analyses support multiple mainland-to-island dispersals in the evolution of Malagasy *Triaenops* bats (Chiroptera: Hipposideridae). *Journal of Biogeography* 35(6): 995–1003.

Russell, A. L., Goodman, S. M., Fiorentino, I., and Yoder, A. D. 2008b. Population genetic analysis of *Myzopoda* (Chiroptera: Myzopodidae) in Madagascar. *Journal of Mammalogy* 89(1): 209–221.

Russell, R. J. 1977. The behavior, ecology, and environmental physiology of a nocturnal primate, *Lepilemur mustelinus*. PhD thesis, Duke University.

Ryan, J. M., Creighton, G. K., and Emmons, L. H. 1993. Activity patterns of two species of *Nesomys* (Muridae: Nesomyinae) in a Madagascar rain forest. *Journal of Tropical Ecology* 9: 101–107.

Sabatier, M., and Legendre, S. 1985. Une faune à rongeurs et chiroptères Plio-Pléistocènes de Madagascar. *Actes du 110ème Congrès National des Sociétés Savantes, Montpellier, Section des Sciences*, 6: 21–28.

Sakuma, Y., Ranorosoa, M. C., Kinoshita, G., Shimoji, H., Tsuchiya, K., Ohdachi, S. D., Arai, S., Tanaka, C., Ramino, H., and Suzuki, H. 2016. Variation in the coat-color-controlling genes, Mc1r and Asip, in the house mouse *Mus musculus* from Madagascar. *Mammal Study* 41(3): 131–140. https://doi.org/10.3106/041.041.0303.

Salmona, J., Rakotonanahary, A., Ibouroi, M. T., Zaranaina, R., Ralantoharijaona, T., et al. 2014a. Estimation des densités et tailles de population du Microcèbe Roux du Nord de (*Microcebus tavaratra*) dans la région Loky-Manambato (Daraina). *Lemur News* 18: 73–75.

Salmona, J., Rasolondraibe, E., Jan, F., Besolo, A., Rakotoarisoa, H., Meyler, S. V. Wohlhauser, S., Rabarivola, C., and Chikhi, L. 2014b. Abundance in its northern area of occupancy and conservation status update of a threatened sifaka species (*Propithecus coronatus*). *Primate Conservation* 28: 73–83.

Salmona, J., Teixeira, H., Rasolondraibe, E., Aleixo-Pais, I., Kun-Rodrigues, C., et al. 2015. Genetic diversity, population size, and conservation of the critically endangered Perrier's sifaka (*Propithecus perrieri*). *International Journal of Primatology* 36: 1132–1153. https://doi.org/10.1007/s10764-015-9881-x.

Salmona, J., Heller, R., Quéméré, E., and Chikhi, L. 2017. Climate change and human colonization triggered habitat loss and fragmentation in Madagascar. *Molecular Ecology* 26: 5203–5222. https://doi.org/10.1111/mec.14173.

Salton, J. A., and Sargis, E. J. 2008. Evolution of the Tenrecoidea (Mammalia) forelimb skeleton. In *Mammalian Evolutionary Morphology: A Tribute to Frederick S. Szalay*, eds. E. J. Sargis and M. Dagosto, pp. 51–71. Dordrecht: Springer.

Salton, J. A., and Sargis, E. J. 2009. Evolutionary morphology of the Tenrecoidea (Mammalia) hindlimb skeleton. *Journal of Morphology* 270: 367–387.

Salton, J. A., and Szalay, F. S. 2004. The tarsal complex of Afro-Malagasy Tenrecoidea: A search for phylogenetically meaningful characters. *Journal of Mammalian Evolution* 11(2): 73–104.

Salvioni, M. 1991. Evaluation of rat (*Rattus rattus*) damage in ricefields in Madagascar. *Tropical Pest Management* 37: 175–178.

Samonds, K. E. 2007. Late Pleistocene bat fossils from Anjohibe Cave, northwestern Madagascar. *Acta Chiropterologica* 9(1): 39–65.
Samonds, K. E., and Fordyce, R. E. 2019. The first pre-Pleistocene cetacean from Madagascar, western Indian Ocean. *Journal of African Earth Sciences* 151: 184–188.
Samonds, K. E., Parent, S. N., Muldoon, K. M., Crowley, B. E., and Godfrey, L. R. 2010. Rock matrix surrounding subfossil lemur skull yields diverse collection of mammalian subfossils: Implications for reconstructing Madagascar's paleoenvironments. *Malagasy Nature* 4: 1–16.
Samonds, K. E., Godfrey, L. R., Ali, J. R., Goodman, S. M., Vences, M., Sutherland, M. R., Irwin, M. T., and Krause, D. W. 2012. Spatial and temporal arrival patterns of Madagascar's vertebrate fauna explained by distance, ocean currents, and ancestor type. *Proceedings of the National Academy of Sciences of the USA* 109: 5352–5357.
Samonds, K. E., Crowley, B. E., Rasolofomanana, T.R.N., Andriambelomanana, M. C., Andrianavalona, H. T., et al. 2019. A new late Pleistocene subfossil site, (Tsaramody, Sambaina basin, central Madagascar) with implications for the chronology of habitat and megafaunal community change on Madagascar's Central Highlands. *Journal of Quaternary Science* 34(6): 379–392.
Santini, L., Rojas, D., and Donati, G. 2015. Evolving through day and night: Origin and diversification of activity pattern in modern primates. *Behavioral Ecology* 26: 789–796.
Sarikaya, Z., and Kappeler, P. M. 1997. Nest building behavior of Coquerel's dwarf lemur (*Mirza coquereli*). *Primate Report* 47: 3–9.
Sato, H. 2012. Frugivory and seed dispersal by brown lemurs in a Malagasy tropical dry forest. *Biotropica* 44: 479–488.
———. 2013a. Habitat shifting by the common brown lemur (*Eulemur fulvus fulvus*): A response to food scarcity. *Primates* 54: 229–235.
———. 2013b. Seasonal fruiting and seed dispersal by the brown lemur in a tropical dry forest, north-western Madagascar. *Journal of Tropical Ecology* 29: 61–69.
———. 2018. Predictions of seed shadows generated by common brown lemurs (*Eulemur fulvus*) and their relationship to seasonal behavioral strategies. *International Journal of Primatology* 39: 377–396.
Sato, H., Ichino, S., and Hanya, G. 2014. Dietary modification by common brown lemurs (*Eulemur fulvus*) during seasonal drought conditions in western Madagascar. *Primates* 55: 219–230.
Sato, H., Santini, L., Patel, E. R., Campera, M., Yamashita, N., Colquhoun, I. C., and Donati, G. 2016. Dietary flexibility and feeding strategies of *Eulemur*: A comparison with *Propithecus*. *International Journal of Primatology* 37: 109–129.
Sauther, M. L. 1989. Antipredator behavior in troops of free-ranging *Lemur catta* at Beza Mahafaly Special Reserve, Madagascar. *International Journal of Primatology* 10: 595–606.
———. 1991. Reproductive behavior of free-ranging *Lemur catta* at Beza Mahafaly Special Reserve, Madagascar. *American Journal of Physical Anthropology* 84: 463–477.
———. 1992. The effect of reproductive state, social rank and group size on resource use among free-ranging ringtailed lemurs (*Lemur catta*) of Madagascar. PhD thesis, Washington University, Saint Louis.
———. 1993. Resource competition in wild populations of ringtailed lemurs (*Lemur catta*): Implications for female dominance. In *Lemur Social Systems and Their Ecological Basis*, eds. P. M. Kappeler and J. U. Ganzhorn, pp. 135–152. New York: Plenum Press.
———. 1998. Interplay of phenology and reproduction in ring-tailed lemurs: Implications for ring-tailed lemur conservation. *Folia Primatologica* 69(supplement 1): 309–320.
———. 2002. Group size effects on predation sensitive foraging in wild *Lemur catta*. In *Eat or Be Eaten: Predation Sensitive Foraging*, ed. L. Miller, pp. 107–125. Cambridge: Cambridge University Press.
Sauther, M. L., and Cuozzo, F. P. 2008. Ontogeny and canine dimorphism in wild ring-tailed lemurs (*Lemur catta*). In *Proceedings of the XXIInd Congress of the International Primatological Society*, eds. N. G. Caine, E. Visalberghi, S. J. Schapiro, and K. A. Leighty, p. 131. New York: Springer.
Sauther, M. L, and Cuozzo, F. P. 2009. The impact of fallback foods on wild ring-tailed lemur biology: A comparison of intact and anthropogenically disturbed habitats. *American Journal of Physical Anthropology*, special issue, 140: 671–686. https://doi.org/10.1002/ajpa.21128.
Sauther, M. L., and Sussman, R. W. 1993. A new interpretation of the organization and mating systems of the ringtailed lemur (*Lemur catta*). In *Lemur Social Systems and Their Ecological Basis*, eds. P. M. Kappeler, and J. U. Ganzhorn, pp. 11–121. New York: Plenum Press.
Sauther, M. L., Sussman, R. W., and Gould, L. 1999. The socioecology of the ringtailed lemur: Thirty-five years of research. *Evolutionary Anthropology* 8: 120–132.
Sauther, M. L., Cuozzo, F. P., Youssouf Jacky, I. A., LaFleur, M. L., Fish, K. D., Ravelohasindrazana, L.A.L., and Ravoavy, J. F. 2013. Limestone cliff-face and cave use by wild ring-tailed lemurs (*Lemur catta*) in southwestern Madagascar. *Madagascar Conservation and Development* 82: 73–80. http://dx. https://doi.org/10.4314/mcd.v8i2.5.
Sauther, M. L., Gould, L., Cuozzo, F. P., and O'Mara, M. T., eds. 2015. Ring-tailed lemurs: A species reimagined. *Folia Primatologica* 86(1–2): 1–151. https://doi.org/10.1159/000370321.
Sauther, M. L., Bertolini, F., Dollar, L. J., Pomerantz, J., Alves, P. C., et al. 2020. Taxonomic identification of Madagascar's free-ranging "forest cats." *Conservation Genetics* 21: 443–451. https://doi.org/10.1007/s10592-020-01261-x.
Savage, R.J.G. 1978. Carnivora. In *Evolution of African Mammals*, eds. V. J. Maglio and H.B.S. Cooke, pp. 249–267. Cambridge, MA: Harvard University Press.
Sawyer, R. M., Fenosoa, Z.S.E., Andrianarimisa, A., and Donati, G. 2017. The effect of habitat disturbance on the abundance of nocturnal lemur species on the Masoala Peninsula, northeastern Madagascar. *Primates* 58: 187–197.
Schad, J., Ganzhorn, J. U., and Sommer, S. 2005. Parasite burden and constitution of major histocompatibility complex in the Malagasy mouse lemur, *Microcebus murinus*. *Evolution* 59: 439–450. https://doi.org/10.1111/j.0014-3820.2005.tb01002.x.
Schäffler, L., and Kappeler, P. M. 2014. Distribution and abundance of the world's smallest primate, *Microcebus berthae*, in central western Madagascar. *International Journal of Primatology* 35: 557–572.
Schäffler, L., Saborowski, J., and Kappeler, P. M. 2015. Agent-mediated spatial storage effect in heterogeneous habitat stabilizes competitive mouse lemur coexistence in Menabe Central, western Madagascar. *BMC Ecology* 15: 7.
Scharfe, F., and Schlund, W. 1996. Seed removal by lemurs in a dry deciduous forest of western Madagascar. In Ecology and economy of a tropical dry forest in Madagascar, eds. J. U. Ganzhorn and J.-P. Sorg. *Primate Report*, special issue, 46(1): 295–304.
Schatz, G. E. 2001. *Generic Tree Flora of Madagascar*. Kew: Missouri Botanical Gardens and Royal Botanic Gardens.
Scheel, B. M., Henke-von der Malsburg, J., Giertz, P., Rakotondranary, S. J., Hausdorf, B., and Ganzhorn, J. U. 2015. Testing the influence of habitat structure and geographic distance on the genetic differentiation of mouse lemurs (*Microcebus*) in Madagascar. *International Journal of Primatology* 36: 823–838. https://doi.org/10.1007/s10764-015-9855-z.
Scheumann, M., Rabesandratana, A., and Zimmermann, E. 2007. Predation, communication, and cognition in lemurs. In *Primate Anti-Predator Strategies*, eds. by S. L. Gursky and K.A.I. Nekaris, pp. 100–126. Oxford: Springer.
Schlegel, H. 1866. Contributions á la faune de Madagascar et des îles avoisinantes, d'après les découvertes et observations de Mm. François Pollen et M.D.C. Van Dam. *Nederlandsch Tijdschrift voor de Dierkunde* 3: 73–89.
Schliehe-Diecks, S., Marklof, M., and Huchard, E. 2010. When big lemurs swallow up small ones: Coquerel's dwarf lemur as a predator of grey mouse lemurs and endemic rodents. *Lemur News* 15: 13–14.
Schliehe-Diecks, S., Eberle, M., and Kappeler, P. M. 2012. Walk the line: Dispersal movements of gray mouse lemurs (*Microcebus murinus*). *Behavioral Ecology and Sociobiology* 66: 1175–1185.
Schliemann, H. 1970. Bau und Funktion der Haftorgane von *Thyroptera* und *Myzopoda* (Vespertilionoidea, Microchiroptera, Mammalia). *Zeitschrift für Wissenschaftliche Zoologie* 181: 353–400.
———. 1971. Die Haftorgane von *Thyroptera* und *Myzopoda* (Microchiroptera, Mammalia): Gedanken zu ihrer Entstehung als Parallelbildungen. *Zeitschrift für Zoologische Systematik und Evolutionsforschung* 9: 61–80.
———. 1997. The secondary shoulder joint of the Vespertilionoidea. *Zeitschrift für Saugetierkunde* 62(6): 321–329.
Schliemann, H., and Goodman, S. M. 2003. *Myzopoda aurita*, Old World sucker-footed bat. In *The Natural History of Madagascar*, eds. S. M. Goodman and J. P. Benstead, pp. 1303–1306. Chicago: University of Chicago Press.
Schliemann, H., and Goodman, S. M. 2011. A new study on the structure and function of the adhesive organs of the Old World sucker-footed bat (*Myzopoda*: Myzopodidae) of Madagascar. *Verhandlungen des Naturwissenschaftlichen Vereins in Hamburg* 46: 313–330.
Schliemann, H., and Maas, B. 1978. Myzopoda aurita. *Mammalian Species* 116: 1–2.
Schliemann, H., and Schlosser-Sturm, E. 1999. The shoulder joint of the Chiroptera: Morphological features and functional significance. *Zoologischer Anzeiger* 238(1): 75–86.

Schmelting, B. 2000. Saisonale Aktivität und Reproduktionsbiologie von Grauen Mausmaki-Männchen (*Microcebus murinus*, J. F. Miller 1777) in Nordwest-Madagaskar. PhD thesis, Tierärztliche Hochschule Hannover.

Schmelting, B., Ehresmann, P., Lutermann, H., Randrianambinina, B., and Zimmermann, E. 2000. Reproduction of two sympatric mouse lemur species (*Microcebus murinus* and *M. ravelobensis*) in north-west Madagascar: First results of a long term study. In *Diversité et endémisme à Madagascar*, eds. W. R. Lourenço and S. M. Goodman, pp. 165–175. Paris: Société de Biogéographie.

Schmelting, B., Zimmermann, E., Berke, O., Bruford, M. W., and Radespiel, U. 2007. Experience-dependent recapture rates and reproductive success in male grey mouse lemurs (*Microcebus murinus*). *American Journal of Physical Anthropology* 133: 743–752.

Schmid, J. 1998. Tree holes used for resting by gray mouse lemurs (*Microcebus murinus*) in Madagascar: Insulation capacities and energetic consequences. *International Journal of Primatology* 19: 797–809.

———. 1999. Sex-specific differences in activity patterns and fattening in the grey mouse lemur (*Microcebus murinus*) in Madagascar. *Journal of Mammalogy* 80: 749–757.

———. 2000. Daily torpor in the gray mouse lemur (*Microcebus murinus*) in Madagascar: Energetic consequences and biological significance. *Oecologia* (Berlin) 123: 175–183.

Schmid, J., and Ganzhorn, J. U. 1996. Resting metabolic rates of *Lepilemur ruficaudatus*. *American Journal of Primatology* 38: 169–174.

Schmid, J., and Kappeler, P. M. 1994. Sympatric mouse lemurs (*Microcebus* ssp.) in western Madagascar. *Folia Primatologica* 63: 162–170.

Schmid, J., and Kappeler, P. M. 1998. Fluctuating sexual dimorphism and differential hibernation by sex in a primate, the gray mouse lemur (*Microcebus murinus*). *Behavioral Ecology and Sociobiology* 43: 125–132.

Schmid, J., and Speakman, J. R. 2000. Daily energy expenditure of the grey mouse lemur (*Microcebus murinus*): A small primate that uses torpor. *Journal of Comparative Physiology B: Biochemical, Systemic, and Environmental Physiology* 170: 633–641.

Schmid, J., and Stephenson, P. J. 2003. Physiological adaptations of Malagasy mammals: Lemurs and tenrecs compared. In *The Natural History of Madagascar*, eds. S. M. Goodman and J. P. Benstead, pp. 1198–1203. Chicago: University of Chicago Press.

Schmid, J., Ruf, T., and Heldmaier, G. 2000. Metabolism and temperature regulation during daily torpor in the smallest primate, the pygmy mouse lemur (*Microcebus myoxinus*) in Madagascar. *Journal of Comparative Physiology B: Biochemical, Systemic, and Environmental Physiology* 170: 59–68.

Schmidt, D. A., Iambana, R. B., Britt, A., Junge, R. E., Welch, C. R., Porton, I. J., and Kerley, M. S. 2010. Nutrient composition of plants consumed by black and white ruffed lemurs, *Varecia variegata*, in the Betampona Natural Reserve, Madagascar. *Zoo Biology* 29: 375–396.

Schmidt-Nielsen, K., Schmidt-Nielsen, B., Jarnum, S. A., and Houpt, T. R. 1956. Body temperature of the camel and its relation to water economy. *American Journal of Physiology* 188: 103–112.

Schneider, N., Chikhi, L., Currat, M., and Radespiel, U. 2010. Signals of recent spatial expansions in the grey mouse lemur (*Microcebus murinus*). *BMC Evolutionary Biology* 10: 105. https://doi.org/10.1186/1471-2148-10-105.

Schneider, T. C., and Kappeler, P. M. 2014. Social systems and life-history characteristics of mongooses. *Biological Reviews* 89: 173–198. https://doi.org/10.1111/brv.12050.

Schneider, T. C., and Kappeler, P. M. 2016. Gregarious sexual segregation: The unusual social organization of the Malagasy narrow-striped mongoose (*Mungotictis decemlineata*). *Behavioral Ecology and Sociobiology* 70: 913–926. https://doi.org/10.1007/s00265-016-2113-3.

Schneider, T. C., Kappeler, P. M., and Pozzi, L. 2016. Genetic population structure and relatedness in the narrow-striped mongoose (*Mungotictis decemlineata*), a social Malagasy carnivore with sexual segregation. *Ecology and Evolution* 6: 3734–3749. https://doi.org/10.1002/ece3.2123.

Schnoell, A. V. 2012. Sighting of a ring-tailed vontsira (*Galidia elegans*) in the gallery forest of Berenty Private Reserve, southeastern Madagascar. *Malagasy Nature* 6: 125–126.

Schnoell, A. V., and Fichtel, C. 2011–2012. Predation on redfronted lemurs (*Eulemur rufifrons*) by fossas (*Cryptoprocta ferox*). *Lemur News* 16: 30–32.

Schoeman, M. C., and Goodman, S. M. 2012. Vocalizations in the Malagasy cave-dwelling fruit bat, *Eidolon dupreanum*: Possible evidence of incipient echolocation? *Acta Chiropterologica* 14(2): 409–416.

Schoeman, M. C., Goodman, S. M., Ramasindrazana, B., and Koubínová, D. 2015. Species interactions during diversification and community assembly in Malagasy *Miniopterus* bats. *Evolutionary Ecology* 29(1): 17–47.

Scholl, P. 1974. Temperature regulation in small Madagascar "hedgehog," *Echinops telfairi* (Martin, 1838). *Journal of Comparative Physiology* 89: 175–195.

Scholz, F., and Kappeler, P. M. 2004. Effects of seasonal water scarcity on the ranging behavior of *Eulemur fulvus rufus*. *International Journal of Primatology* 25: 599–613.

Schülke, O. 2001. Social anti-predator behavior in a nocturnal lemur. *Folia Primatologica* 72: 332–334.

———. 2003. To breed or not to breed: Food competition and other factors involved in female breeding decisions in the pair-living nocturnal fork-marked lemur (*Phaner furcifer*). *Behavioural Ecology and Sociobiology* 55: 11–21.

Schülke, O., and Ostner, J. 2001. Predation on *Lepilemur* by the harrier hawk and implications for sleeping site quality. *Lemur News* 6: 50.

Schülke, O., Kappeler, P. M., and Zischler, H. 2004. Small testes size despite high extra-pair paternity in the pair-living nocturnal primate *Phaner furcifer*. *Behavioral Ecology and Sociobiology* 55: 293–301. https://doi.org/10.1007/s00265-003-0709-x.

Schüßler, D., Radespiel, U., Ratsimbazafy, J. H., and Mantilla-Contreras, J. 2018. Lemurs in a dying forest: Factors influencing lemur diversity and distribution in forest remnants of north-eastern Madagascar. *Biological Conservation* 228: 17–26. https://doi.org/10.1016/J.BIOCON.2018.10.008.

Schüßler, D., Blanco, M. B., Salmona, J., Poelstra, J., Andriambeloson, J. B., et al. 2020. Ecology and morphology of mouse lemurs (*Microcebus* spp.) in a hotspot of microendemism in northeastern Madagascar, with the description of a new species. *American Journal of Primatology* 32: e23180. https://doi.org/10.1002/ajp.23180.

Schwab, D. 1999. Predation on *Eulemur fulvus* by *Accipiter henstii* (Henst's goshawk). *Lemur News* 4: 34.

———. 2000. A preliminary study of spatial distribution and mating system of pygmy mouse lemurs (*Microcebus myoxinus*). *American Journal of Primatology* 51: 41–60.

Schwartz, G. T., Samonds, K. E., Godfrey, L. R., Jungers, W. L., and Simons, E. L. 2002. Dental microstructure and life history in subfossil Malagasy lemurs. *Proceedings of the National Academy of Sciences of the USA* 99: 6124–6129.

Schwartz, G. T., Mahoney, P., Godfrey, L. R., Cuozzo, F. P., Jungers, W. L., and Randria, G.F.N. 2005. Dental development in *Megaladapis edwardsi* (Primates, Lemuriformes): Implications for understanding life history variation in subfossil lemurs. *Journal of Human Evolution* 49: 702–721.

Schwartz, J. H., and Tattersall, I. 1985. Evolutionary relationships of living lemurs and lorises (Mammalia, Primates) and their potential affinities with European Eocene Adapidae. *Anthropological Papers of the American Museum of Natural History* 60: 1–100.

Schwarz, E. 1931. A revision of the genera and species of Madagascar Lemuridae. *Proceedings of the Zoological Society of London* 101(2): 399–428.

Schwensow, N., Fietz, J., Dausmann, K. H., and Sommer, S. 2007. Neutral versus adaptive genetic variation in parasite resistance: Importance of major histocompatibility complex supertypes in a free-ranging primate. *Heredity* 99: 265–277. https://doi.org/10.1038/sj.hdy.6800993.

Schwensow, N., Dausmann, K., Eberle, M., Fietz, J., and Sommer, S. 2010a. Functional associations of similar MHC alleles and shared parasite species in two sympatric lemurs. *Infection, Genetics and Evolution* 10: 662–668. https://doi.org/10.1016/j.meegid.2010.03.012.

Schwensow, N., Eberle, M., and Sommer, S. 2010b. Are there ubiquitous parasite-driven major histocompatibility complex selection mechanisms in gray mouse lemurs? *International Journal of Primatology* 31: 519–537. https://doi.org/10.1007/s10764-010-9411-9.

Schwitzer, C., Mittermeier, R. A., Davies, N., Johnson, S., Ratsimabazafy, J., Razafindramanana, J., Louis, E. E., Jr., and Rajaobelina, S., eds. 2013. *Lemurs of Madagascar: A Strategy for Their Conservation, 2013–2016.* Bristol, UK: IUCN SSC Primate Specialist Group, Bristol Conservation and Science Foundation, and Conservation International.

Schwitzer, C., Mittermeier R. A., Johnson, S. E., Donati, G., Irwin, M., et al. 2014. Averting lemur extinctions amid Madagascar's political crisis. *Science* 343: 842–843.

Schwitzer, C., Mittermeier, R. A., Rylands, A. B., Chiozza, F., Williamson, E. A., et al., eds. 2019. *Primates in Peril: The World's 25 Most Endangered Primates 2018–2020.* Washington, DC: IUCN SSC Primate Specialist Group, International Primatological Society, Global Wildlife Conservation, and Bristol Zoological Society.

Schwitzer, N., Kaumanns, W., Seitz, P. C., and Schwitzer, C. 2007. Cathemeral activity patterns of the blue-eyed black lemur *Eulemur macaco flavifrons* in intact and degraded forest fragments. *Endangered Species Research* 3: 239–247.
Scobie, K., Schwitzer, C., and Holderied, M. 2017. Observations of *Avahi meridionalis* in *Eucalyptus* plantations. *Lemur News* 20: 9.
Scordato, E. S, and Drea, C. M. 2007. Scents and sensibility: Information content of olfactory signals in the ringtailed lemur, *Lemur catta*. *Animal Behaviour* 73: 301–314. https://doi.org/10.1016/j.anbehav.2006.08.006.
Scroxton, N., Burns, S. J., McGee, D., Hardt, B., Godfrey, L. R., Ranivoharimanana, L., and Faina, P. 2017. Hemispherically in-phase precipitation variability over the last 1700 years in a Madagascar speleothem record. *Quaternary Science Reviews* 164: 25–36.
Scroxton, N., Burns, S. J., McGee, D., Hardt, B., Godfrey, L. R., Ranivoharimanana, L., and Faina, P. 2019. Competing temperature and atmospheric circulation effects on southwest Madagascan rainfall during the last deglaciation. *Paleoceanography and Paleoclimatology* 34: 275–286.
Seaman, D., Randriahaingo, H.N.T., Randrianarimanana, H. L. Lucien, Ravaloharimanitra, M., Humle, T., and King, T. 2018. Edge effects on indri and black-and-white ruffed lemur distribution in the Andriantantely lowland rainforest, eastern Madagascar. *Lemur News* 21: 51–56.
Sefczek, T. M. 2018. Examining the morphological and behavioral paradox of aye-ayes (*Daubentonia madagascariensis*) in Torotorofotsy, Madagascar. PhD thesis, Ohio State University.
Sefczek, T. M., Randimbiharinirina, D., Raharivololona, B. M., Rabekianja, J. D., Louis, E. E., Jr. 2017. Comparing the use of live trees and deadwood for larval foraging by aye-ayes (*Daubentonia madagascariensis*) at Kianjavato and Torotorofotsy, Madagascar. *Primates* 58: 535–546.
Sefczek, T. M., Rakotomanana, J., Randriamaronirina, H., and Louis, E. E., Jr. 2018. Unsuccessful predation event of an aye-aye (*Daubentonia madagascariensis*) by a fosa (*Cryptoprocta ferox*). *Lemur News* 21: 8–10.
Sefczek, T. M., Randimbiharinirina, D. R., Raharivololona, B. M., Razafimahaleo, H., Randrianarison, O., and Louis, E. E., Jr. 2020a. Re-assessing the applicability of the Jarman/Bell model and Kay's threshold to the insectivorous aye-ayes (*Daubentonia madagascariensis*). *American Journal of Physical Anthropology* 171: 336–341.
Sefczek, T. M., Hagenson, R. A., Randimbiharinirina, D. R., Rakotondrazandry, J. N., and Louis, E. E., Jr. 2020b. Home range size and seasonal variation in habitat use of aye-ayes (*Daubentonia madagascariensis*) in Torotorofotsy, Madagascar. *Folia Primatologica* 91: 558–574. https://doi.org/10.1159/000508620.
Seiffert, E. R., Simons, E. L., and Attia, Y. 2003. Fossil evidence for an ancient divergence of lorises and galagos. *Nature* 422: 421–424.
Seiler, M. 2012. The impact of habitat degradation and fragmentation on ecology and behaviour of the Sahamalaza sportive lemur, *Lepilemur sahamalazensis*, in northwest-Madagascar. PhD thesis, University of Bristol.
Seiler, M., Holderied, M., and Schwitzer, C. 2013a. Effects of habitat degradation on sleeping site choice and use in Sahamalaza sportive lemurs (*Lepilemur sahamalazensis*). *International Journal of Primatology* 34: 260–280.
Seiler, M., Schwitzer, C., Gamba, M., and Holderied, M. W. 2013b. Interspecific semantic alarm call recognition in the solitary Sahamalaza sportive lemur, *Lepilemur sahamalazensis*. *PLoS One* 8: e67397. https://doi.org/10.1371/journal.pone.0067397.
Seiler, M., Holderied, M., and Schwitzer, C. 2014. Habitat selection and use in the critically endangered Sahamalaza sportive lemur *Lepilemur sahamalazensis* in altered habitat. *Endangered Species Research* 24: 273–286.
Seiler, M., Schwitzer, C., and Holderied, M. 2015. Call repertoire of the Sahamalaza sportive lemur, *Lepilemur sahamalazensis*. *International Journal of Primatology* 36: 647–665.
Seiler, M., Hending, D., and Stanger-Hall, K. F. 2019. Spacing and mate attraction: Sex-specific function of advertisement calls in the northern giant mouse lemur (*Mirza zaza*). *Folia Primatologica* 90: 361–378.
Semel, B. 2015. A multi-species approach to elucidating the ecological function of primate geophagy. MA thesis, Northern Illinois University.
Serra, V. 2011. Behavioural ecology of the red collared brown lemur (*Eulemur collaris*): Comparison between groups living in well preserved and degraded littoral forest fragments, in south-eastern Madagascar. Master's thesis, University of Pisa.
Setash, C. M., Zohdy, S., Gerber, B. D., and Karanewsky, C. J. 2017. A biogeographical perspective on the variation in mouse lemur density throughout Madagascar. *Mammal Review* 47: 212–229.
Sexton, J. P., Hangartner, S. B., and Hoffmann, A. A. 2014. Genetic isolation by environment or distance: Which pattern of gene flow is most common? *Evolution* 68: 1–15. https://doi.org/10.1111/evo.12258.
Seydack, A.H.W. 1990. Ecology of the bushpig *Potamochoerus porcus* Linn. 1758 in the Cape Province, South Africa. PhD thesis, Department of Forestry, University of Stellenbosch, Knysna.
———. 1991. Monographie des buschschweines (*Potamochoerus porcus*). *Bongo*, Berlin 18: 85–102.
Sgarlata, G. M., Salmona, J., Razanaparany, T. P., Rabarivola, C., Jan, F., et al. 2016. Mitochondrial genetic diversity in the crowned sifaka (*Propithecus coronatus*) in a fragmented landscape. *Primate Conservation* 30: 39–57.
Sgarlata, G. M., Salmona, J., Aleixo-Pais, I., Rakotonanahary, A., Sousa, A. P., et al. 2018. Genetic differentiation and demographic history of the northern rufous mouse lemur (*Microcebus tavaratra*) across a fragmented landscape in northern Madagascar. *International Journal of Primatology* 39: 65–89. https://doi.org/10.1007/s10764-018-0015-0.
Sgarlata, G. M., Salmona, J., Le Pors, B., Rasolondraibe, E., Jan, F., et al. 2019. Genetic and morphological diversity of mouse lemurs (*Microcebus* spp.) in northern Madagascar: The discovery of a putative new species? *American Journal of Primatology* e23070.
Shafer, A.B.A., and Wolf, J.B.W. 2013. Widespread evidence for incipient ecological speciation: A meta-analysis of isolation-by-ecology. *Ecology Letters* 16: 940–950. https://doi.org/10.1111/ele.12120.
Shapiro, L. J., Seiffert, C.V.M., Godfrey, L. R., Jungers, W. L., Simons, E. L., and Randria, G.F.N. 2005. Morphometric analysis of lumbar vertebrae in extinct Malagasy strepsirrhines. *American Journal of Physical Anthropology* 128: 823–839.
Sheftel, B. I. 2018. Etruscan shrew, *Suncus etruscus*. In *Handbook of the Mammals of the World*. Vol 8, *Insectivores, Sloths and Colugos*, eds. D. E. Wilson, and R. A. Mittermeier, p. 460. Barcelona: Lynx.
Shi, J. J., and Rabosky, D. L. 2015. Speciation dynamics during the global radiation of extant bats. *Evolution* 69(6): 1528–1545.
Shi, J. J., Chan, L. M., Rakotomalala, Z., Heilman, A. M., Goodman, S. M., and Yoder, A. D. 2013. Latitude drives diversification in Madagascar's endemic dry forest rodent, *Eliurus myoxinus* (subfamily Nesomyinae). *Biological Journal of the Linnean Society* 110: 500–517. https://doi.org/10.1111/bij.12143
Shi, J. J., Chan, L. M., Peel, A. J., Lai, R., Yoder, A. D., and Goodman, S. M. 2014. A deep divergence time between sister species of *Eidolon* (family Pteropodidae), with evidence for widespread panmixia. *Acta Chiropterologica* 16(2): 279–292.
Siemers, B. M., Goerlitz, H. R., Robsomanitrandrasana, E., Piep, M., Ramanamanjato, J.-B., Rakotondravony, D., Ramilijaona, O., and Ganzhorn, J. U. 2007. Sensory basis of food detection in wild *Microcebus murinus*. *International Journal of Primatology* 28: 291–304.
Sigaud, M., Caceres, S., Picard. M., Desvars, A., and Michault, A. 2009. Le tanrec (*Tenrec ecaudatus*): Réservoir animal de leptospires ? *Bulletin de la Société de Pathologie Exotique* 102(1): 19–20.
Simmen, B., Hladik, A., Ramasiarisoa, P. L., Iaconelli, S., and Hladik, C. M. 1999. Taste discrimination in lemurs and other primates, and the relationships to distribution of plant allelochemicals in different habitats of Madagascar. In *New Directions in Lemur Studies*, eds. B. Rakotosamimanana, H. Rasamimanana, J. U. Ganzhorn, and S. M. Goodman, pp. 201–219. Boston: Springer.
Simmen, B., Hladik, A., and Ramasiarisoa, P. 2003. Food intake and dietary overlap in native *Lemur catta* and *Propithecus verreauxi* and introduced *Eulemur fulvus* at Berenty, southern Madagascar. *International Journal of Primatology* 24: 949–968.
Simmen, B., Sauther, M. L., Soma, T., Rasamimanana, H., Sussman, R. W., Jolly, A., Tarnaud, L., and Hladik, A. 2006. Plant species fed on by *Lemur catta* in gallery forests of the southern domain of Madagascar. In *Ringtailed Lemur Biology:* Lemur catta *in Madagascar*, eds., A. Jolly, R. W. Sussman, N. Koyama, H. Rasamimanana,, pp. 50–63. New York: Springer.
Simmen, B., Bayart, F., Marez, A., and Hladik, A. 2007. Diet, nutritional ecology, and birth season of *Eulemur macaco* in an anthropogenic forest in Madagascar. *International Journal of Primatology* 28: 1253–1266.
Simmen, B., Bayart, F., Rasamimanana, H., Zahariev, A., Blanc, S., and Pasquet, P. 2010. Total energy expenditure and body composition in two free-living sympatric lemurs. *PLoS One* 5: e9860.
Simmons, N. B. 1998. A reappraisal of interfamilial relationships of bats. In *Bat Biology and Conservation*, eds. T. H. Kunz and P. A. Racey, pp. 3–26. Washington, DC: Smithsonian Institution Press.
Simons, E. L. 1988. A new species of *Propithecus* (Primates) from northeast Madagascar. *Folia Primatologica* 50: 143–151.
———. 1994. The giant aye-aye *Daubentonia robusta*. *Folia Primatologica* 62: 14–21.
Simons, E. L., and Meyers, D. 2001. Folklore and beliefs about the aye aye (*Daubentonia madagascariensis*). *Lemur News* 6: 11–16.

Simons, E. L., and Rumpler, Y. 1988. *Eulemur*: New generic name for species of *Lemur* other than *Lemur catta*. *Comptes Rendus de l'Académie des Sciences*, Paris, 307: 547–551.

Simons, E. L., Godfrey, L. R., Vuillaume-Randriamanantena, M., Chatrath, P. S., and Gagnon, M. 1990. Discovery of new giant subfossil lemurs in the Ankarana Mountains of northern Madagascar. *Journal of Human Evolution* 19: 311–319.

Simons, E. L., Godfrey, L. R., Jungers, W. L., Chatrath, P. S., and Ravaoarisoa, J. 1995. A new species of *Mesopropithecus* (Primates, Palaeopropithecidae) from northern Madagascar. *International Journal of Primatology* 16: 653–682.

Simons, H. J., and Lindsay, N.B.D. 1987. Survey work on ruffed lemurs (*Varecia variegata*) and other primates in the northeastern rain forests of Madagascar. *Primate Conservation* 8: 88–91.

Simoons, F. J. 1953. Notes on the bushpig (*Potamochoerus*). *Uganda Journal* 17: 80–81.

Simpson, G. G. 1940. Mammals and land bridges. *Journal of the Washington Academy of Sciences* 30: 137–163.

———. 1945. The principles of classification and a classification of mammals. *Bulletin of the American Museum of Natural History* 85: 1–350.

———. 1952. Probabilities of dispersal in geologic time. *Bulletin of the American Museum of Natural History* 99: 163–176.

Singleton, C. L., Norris, A. M., Sauther, M. L., Cuozzo, F. P., and Youssouf Jacky, I. A. 2015. Ring-tailed lemur (*Lemur catta*) health parameters across two habitats with varied levels of human disturbance at the Bezà Mahafaly Special Reserve, Madagascar. *Folia Primatologica* 86: 56–65. https://doi.org/10.1159/000369554.

Singleton, C. L., Sauther, M. L., Cuozzo, F. P., and Youssouf Jacky, I. A. 2018. Age-related changes in hematology and blood biochemistry values in endangered, wild ring-tailed lemurs (*Lemur catta*) at the Bezà Mahafaly Special Reserve, Madagascar. *Journal of Zoo and Wildlife Medicine* 49: 30–47. https://doi.org/10.1638/2017-0008R1.1.

Slater, G. J., and Friscia, A. R. 2019. Hierarchy in adaptive radiation: A case study using the Carnivora (Mammalia). *Evolution* 73: 524–539.

Slatkin, M., and Hudson, R. R. 1991. Pairwise comparisons of mitochondrial DNA sequences in stable and exponentially growing populations. *Genetics* 129: 555–562.

Smith, A. C. 2010. Exudativory in primates: Interspecific patterns. In *The Evolution of Exudativory in Primates*, eds. L. T. Nash and A. M. Burrows, pp. 45–88. New York: Springer.

Smith, A. P. 1997. Deforestation, fragmentation, and reserve design in western Madagascar. In *Tropical Forest Remnants*, eds. W. F. Laurance and R. O. Bierregaard, pp. 415–441. Chicago: University of Chicago Press.

Smith, A. P., and Ganzhorn, J. U. 1996. Convergence in community structure and dietary adaptation in Australian possums and gliders and Malagasy lemurs. *Australian Journal of Ecology* 21: 31–46.

Smith, J. D. 1977. Feeding behaviour and social organization in howling monkeys. In *Primate Ecology: Studies of Feeding and Ranging Behaviour in Lemurs, Monkeys and Apes*. ed. T. H. Clutton-Brock, pp. 97–126. London: Academic Press.

Smith, M., and Nelson, B. W. 2011. Fire favours expansion of bamboo-dominated forests in the south-west Amazon. *Journal of Tropical Ecology* 27: 59–64.

Smith, R. J., and Jungers, W. L. 1997. Body mass in comparative primatology. *Journal of Human Evolution* 32: 523–559.

Snow, N. 2011. Studies of Malagasy *Eugenia* (Myrtaceae)—II: Four new species, including one eaten by black lemurs on Nosy Be. *Systematic Botany* 36: 677–689.

Soarimalala, V. 2008. Les petits mammifères non-volants des forêts sèches malgaches. In Les forêts sèches de Madagascar, eds. S. M. Goodman and L. Wilmé. *Malagasy Nature* 1: 106–134.

Soarimalala, V., and Goodman, S. M. 2003a. Diversité biologique des micromammifères non volants (Lipotyphla et Rodentia) dans le complexe Marojejy-Anjanaharibe-Sud. In Nouveaux résultats d'inventaires biologiques faisant référence à l'altitude dans la région des massifs montagneux de Marojejy et d'Anjanaharibe-Sud, eds. S. M. Goodman and L. Wilmé. *Recherches pour le Développement*, série *Sciences Biologiques*, 19: 231–278.

Soarimalala, V., and Goodman, S. M. 2003b. The food habits of Lipotyphla. In *The Natural History of Madagascar*, eds. S. M. Goodman and J. P. Benstead, pp. 1203–1205. Chicago: University of Chicago Press.

Soarimalala, V., and Goodman, S. M. 2004. Les Rodentia, Lipotyphla et Carnivora de la forêt de Mikea. In Inventaire floristique et faunistique de la forêt de Mikea: Paysage écologique et diversité biologique d'une préoccupation majeure pour la conservation, eds. A. P. Raselimanana and S. M. Goodman. *Recherches pour le Développement*, série *Sciences Biologiques*, 21: 69–80.

Soarimalala, V., and Goodman, S. M. 2006. Diversité et distribution des micromammifères dans les zones de forêts humides reliant le complexe Andringitra-Ranomafana au Centre-est de Madagascar. *Bulletin Société Zoologique de France* 131: 117–134.

Soarimalala, V., and Goodman, S. M. 2008. New distributional records of the recently described and endangered shrew tenrec *Microgale nasoloi* (Tenrecidae: Afrosoricida) from central western Madagascar. *Mammalian Biology* 73: 468–471.

Soarimalala, V., and Goodman, S. M. 2011. *Les Petits Mammifères de Madagascar*. Antananarivo: Association Vahatra.

Soarimalala, V., and Raheriarisena, M. 2010. The non-volant and non-primate mammals of the Ambatovy-Analamay forest. In Biodiversity, exploration, and conservation of the natural habitats associated with the Ambatovy project, eds. S. M. Goodman and V. Mass. *Malagasy Nature* 3: 153–177.

Soarimalala, V., Goodman, S. M., Ramiarinjanahary, H., Fenohery, L. L., and Rakotonirina, W. 2001. Les micro-mammifères non-volants du Parc National de Ranomafana et du couloir forestier qui relie au Parc National d'Andringitra. In Inventaire biologique du Parc National de Ranomafana et du couloir forestier qui la relie au Parc National d'Andringitra, eds. S. M. Goodman and V. R. Razafindratsita. *Recherches pour le Développement*, série *Sciences Biologiques*, 17: 197–229.

Soarimalala, V., Ramanana, L. T., Ralison, J. M., and Goodman, S. M. 2007. Les petits mammifères non-volants du "Couloir forestier d'Anjozorobe-Angavo." In Inventaires de la faune et de la flore du couloir forestier d'Anjozorobe-Angavo, eds. S. M. Goodman, A. P. Raselimanana, and L. Wilmé. *Recherches pour le Développement*, série *Sciences Biologiques*, 24: 141–182.

Soarimalala, V., Raheriarisena, M., and Goodman, S. M. 2010. New distributional records from central-eastern Madagascar and patterns of morphological variation in the endangered shrew tenrec *Microgale jobihely* (Afrosoricida: Tenrecidae). *Mammalia* 74: 187–198.

Soarimalala, V., Zafindranoro, H. H., and Goodman, S. M. 2013. Diversité des petits mammifères sur une formation de tsingy: Cas de la forêt de Beanka, Région Melaky, Ouest de Madagascar. In La forêt de Beanka, Région Melaky, Ouest de Madagascar, eds. S. M. Goodman, L. Gautier, and M. J. Raherilalao. *Malagasy Nature* 7: 245–258.

Soarimalala, V., Randriamanana, J. P., Razafindramasy, O. G., Oninjatovo, R. H., Razakafamantanantsoa, A., et al. 2019. Les rats dans le monde rural du Centre-est et du Centre-sud de Madagascar: Dommages causés et systèmes de contrôle. *Malagasy Nature* 13: 125–151.

Soligo, C. 2005. Anatomy of the hand and arm in *Daubentonia madagascariensis*: A functional and phylogenetic outlook. *Folia Primatologica* 76: 262–300.

Sollmann, R., Mohamed, A., Samejima, H., and Wilting, A. 2013. Risky business or simple solution–relative abundance indices from camera-trapping. *Biological Conservation* 159: 405–412.

Soma, T. 2006. Tradition and novelty: *Lemur catta* feeding strategy on introduced tree species at Berenty Reserve. In *Ringtailed Lemur Biology:* Lemur catta *in Madagascar*, eds. A. Jolly, R. W. Sussman, N. Koyama, and H. Rasamimanana, pp. 141–159. New York: Springer.

Sommer, S. 1996. Ecology and social structure of *Hypogeomys antimena*, an endemic rodent of the dry deciduous forest in western Madagascar. In *Biogéographie de Madagascar*, ed. W. R. Lourenço, pp. 295–302. Paris: Editions de l'ORSTOM.

———. 1997. Monogamy in *Hypogeomys antimena*, an endemic rodent of the deciduous dry forest in western Madagascar. *Journal of Zoology* 241: 301–314.

———. 2000. Sex specific predation rates on a monogamous rat (*Hypogeomys antimena*, Nesomyinae) by top predators in the tropical dry forest of Madagascar. *Animal Behaviour* 56: 1087–1094.

———. 2001. Reproductive ecology of the endangered monogamous Malagasy giant jumping rat, *Hypogeomys antimena*. *Mammalian Biology* 66: 111–115.

———. 2003a. Effects of habitat fragmentation and changes of dispersal behaviour after a recent population decline on the genetic variability of non-coding and coding DNA of a monogamous rodent. *Molecular Ecology* 12: 2845–2851.

———. 2003b. Social and reproductive monogamy in rodents: The case of the Malagasy giant jumping rat (*Hypogeomys antimena*). In *Monogamy: Partnerships in Birds, Humans and Other Mammals*, eds. U. Reichard and C. Boesch, pp. 109–124. London: Cambridge University Press.

———. 2003c. *Hypogeomys*, Malagasy giant jumping rat. In *The Natural History of Madagascar*, eds. S. M. Goodman and J. P. Benstead, pp. 1383–1385. Chicago: University of Chicago Press.

———. 2005. MHC-dependent mate choice in a monogamous rodent. *Behavioural Ecology and Sociobiology* 58: 181–189.

Sommer, S., and Hommen, U. 2000. An individual based model to explore the effects of changing ecological parameters on the population dynamics and persistence of

the endangered monogamous Malagasy giant jumping rat (*Hypogeomys antimena*). *Animal Conservation* 4: 333–343.

Sommer, S., and Tichy, H. 1999. MHC-Class II polymorphism and paternity in the monogamous *Hypogeomys antimena*, the endangered, largest endemic Malagasy rodent. *Molecular Ecology* 8: 1259–1272.

Sommer, S., Schwab, D., and Ganzhorn, J. U. 2002a. MHC diversity of endemic Malagasy rodents in relation to geographic range and social system. *Behavioural Ecology and Sociobiology* 51: 214–221. https://doi.org/10.1007/s00265-001-0432-4.

Sommer, S., Toto Volahy, A., and Seal, U. S. 2002b. A population and habitat viability assessment for the highly endangered giant jumping rat (*Hypogeomys antimena*), the largest extant endemic rodent of Madagascar. *Animal Conservation* 5: 263–273.

Sondgeroth, K., Blitvich, B., Blair, C., Terwee, J., Junge, R., Sauther, M., and VandeWoude, S. 2007. Assessing Flavivirus, Lentivirus, and Herpesvirus exposure in free-ranging ring-tailed lemurs in southwestern Madagascar. *Journal of Wildlife Diseases* 43(1): 40–47.

Sonnerat, M. 1782. *Voyage aux Indes Orientales et à la Chine*. Paris: Froulé.

Sorrentino, V., Gamba, M., and Giacoma, C. 2013. A quantitative description of the vocal types emitted in the indri's song. In *Leaping Ahead: Advances in Prosimian Biology*, eds. J. C. Masters, M. Gamba, and F. Génin, pp. 315–322. New York: Springer Science + Business Media.

Souvenir Zafindrajaona, P., and Lauvergne, J. J. 1993. Comparaison de populations de zébu malgache à l'aide des distances génétiques. *Genetics, Selection, and Evolution* (Paris) 25: 373–395.

Spehn, S. E., and Ganzhorn, J. U. 2000. Influence of seed dispersal by brown lemurs on removal rates of three *Grewia* species (Tiliaceae) in the dry deciduous forest of Madagascar. *Ecotropica* 6: 13–21.

Sperber, A. L., Kappeler, P. M., and Fichtel, C. 2019. Should I stay or should I go? Individual movement decisions during group departures in red-fronted lemurs. *Royal Society Open Science* 6: 180991.

Spoor, F., Garland, T., Krovitz, G., Ryan, T., Silcox, M. T., and Walker, A. 2007. The primate semicircular canal system and locomotion. *Proceedings of the National Academy of Sciences of the USA* 104: 10808–10812.

Spriggs, A. N. 2017. *Evolution of Lemur Pelage Color Variation*. PhD thesis, State University of New York, Albany.

Springer, A., Mellmann, A., Fichtel, C., and Kappeler, P. M. 2016. Social structure and *Escherichia coli* sharing in a group-living wild primate, Verreaux's sifaka. *BMC Ecology* 16: 6. https://doi.org/10.1186/s12898-016-0059-y.

Springer, M. S., Cleven, G. C., Madsen, O., de Jong, W. W., Waddell, V. G., Amrine, H. M., and Stanhope, M. J. 1997. Endemic African mammals shake the phylogenetic tree. *Nature* 388: 61–64. https://doi.org/10.1038/40386.

Springer, M. S., Teeling, E. C., Madsen, O., Stanhope, M. J., and de Jong, W. W. 2001. Integrated fossil and molecular data reconstruct bat echolocation. *Proceedings of the National Academy of Sciences of the USA* 98(11): 6241–6246.

Springer, M. S., Meredith, R. W., Gatesy, J., Emerling, C. A., Park, J., et al. 2012. Macroevolutionary dynamics and historical biogeography of primate diversification inferred from a species supermatrix. *PLoS One* 7: e49521. https://doi.org/10.1371/journal.pone.0049521.

Sreedevi, M. B., and Balakrishnan, M. 2006. Intestinal parasites and diseases among the small Indian civet *Viverricula indica* (E. Geoffroy St Hilaire). *Small Carnivore Conservation* 34–35: 26–28.

Standing, H.-F. 1906 (for the year 1905). Rapport sur les ossements subfossiles provenant d'Ampasambazimba. *Bullétin de l'Académie Malgache* 4: 95–100.

———. 1909. Subfossiles provenant des fouilles d'Ampasambazimba. Les lémuriens. *Bulletin de l'Académie Malgache* 6: 9–11.

———. 1910. Note sur les ossements subfossiles provenant des fouilles d'Ampasambazimba. *Bulletin de l'Académie Malgache* 7: 61–64.

Stanger, K. F. 1993. Structure and function of the vocalizations of nocturnal prosimians (Cheirogaleidae). PhD thesis, University of Tübingen.

———. 1995. Vocalizations of some cheirogaleid prosimians evaluated in a phylogenetic context. In *Creatures of the Dark*, eds. L. Alterman, G. Doyle, and M. Izard, pp. 353–376. New York: Plenum Press.

Stanger, K. F., Coffman, B., and Izard, M. 1995. Reproduction in Coquerel's dwarf lemur (*Mirza coquereli*). *American Journal of Primatology* 36: 223–237.

Stanger, K. F., and Macedonia, J. M. 1994. Vocalizations of aye-ayes (*Daubentonia madagascariensis*) in captivity. *Folia Primatologica* 62: 160–169.

Stanger-Hall, K. F. 1997. Phylogenetic affinities among the extant Malagasy lemurs (Lemuriformes) based on morphology and behavior. *Journal of Mammalian Evolution* 4: 163–194.

Stanhope, M. J., Waddell, V. G., Madsen, O., de Jong, W., Hedges, S. B., Cleven, G. C., Kao, D., and Springer, M. S. 1998. Molecular evidence for multiple origins of Insectivora and for a new order of endemic African insectivore mammals. *Proceedings of the National Academy of Sciences of the USA* 95: 9967–9972. https://doi.org/10.1073/pnas.95.17.9967.

Stankiewicz, J., Thiart, C., Masters, J. C., and de Wit, M.J. 2006. Did lemurs have sweepstake tickets? An exploration of Simpson's model for the colonisation of Madagascar by mammals. *Journal of Biogeography* 33: 221–235.

Stankowich, T., and Stensrud, C. 2019. Small but spiny: The evolution of antipredator defenses in Madagascar tenrecs. *Journal of Mammalogy* 100(1): 13–20.

Steffens, K.J.E. 2020. Lemur food plants as options for forest restoration in Madagascar. *Restoration Ecology* 28: 1517–1527.

Steffens, K.J.E., Rakotondranary, S. M., Ratovonamana, Y. R., and Ganzhorn, J. U. 2017. Vegetation thresholds for the occurrence and dispersal of *Microcebus griseorufus* in southwestern Madagascar. *International Journal of Primatology* 38: 1138–1153.

Steffens, T. S., and Lehman, S. M. 2018. Lemur species-specific metapopulation responses to habitat loss and fragmentation. *PLoS One* 13(5): e0195791.

Steffens, T. S., and Lehman, S. M. 2019. Species-area relationships of lemurs in a fragmented landscape in Madagascar. *American Journal of Primatology* 81(4): e22972.

Steffens, T. S., Lehman, S. M., Radespiel, U., and Zimmermann, E. 2016. Factors determining *Microcebus* abundance in a fragmented landscape in Ankarafantsika National Park, Madagascar. In *The Dwarf and Mouse Lemurs of Madagascar: Biology, Behavior and Conservation Biogeography of the Cheirogaleidae*, eds. S. M. Lehman, U. Radespiel, and E. Zimmermann, pp. 477–497. Cambridge: Cambridge University Press.

Steiner, C. C., Putnam, A. S., Hoeck, P.E.A., and Ryder, O. A. 2013. Conservation genomics of threatened animal species. *Annual Review of Animal Biosciences* 1: 261–281. https://doi.org/10.1146/annurev-animal-031412-103636.

Stephenson, P. J. 1987. The ecology and microhabitat segregation of small mammals within lowland tropical rainforest of north-east Madagascar. Independent Project, University of London.

———. 1993. The small mammal fauna of Réserve Spéciale d'Analamazaotra, Madagascar: The effects of human disturbance on endemic species diversity. *Biodiversity and Conservation* 69: 603–615.

———. 1994a. Notes on the biology of the fossorial tenrec, *Oryzorictes hova* (Insectivora: Tenrecidae). *Mammalia* 58: 312–315.

———. 1994b. Resting metabolic rate and body temperature in the aquatic tenrec *Limnogale mergulus* (Insectivora: Tenrecidae). *Acta Theriologica* 39(1): 89–92.

———. 2003. *Geogale aurita*: Large-eared tenrec. In *The Natural History of Madagascar*, eds. S. M. Goodman and J. P. Benstead, pp. 1265–1267. Chicago: University of Chicago Press.

Stephenson, P. J., and Racey, P. A. 1993. Reproductive energetics of the Tenrecidae (Mammalia: Insectivora). II. The shrew-tenrecs, *Microgale* spp. *Physiological Zoology* 66: 644–685.

Stephenson, P. J., and Racey, P. A. 1995. Resting metabolic rate and reproduction in the Insectivora. *Comparative Biochemistry and Physiology A* 112: 215–223.

Stephenson, P. J., Racey, P. A., and Rakotondraparany, F. 1994. Maintenance and reproduction of tenrecs (Tenrecidae) at Parc Tsimbazaza, Madagascar. *International Zoo Yearbook* 33: 194–201.

Stephenson, P. J., Soarimalala, V., and Goodman, S. 2016. *Oryzorictes tetradactylus*. IUCN Red List of Threatened Species 2016: e.T40589A97203050.

Stephenson, P. J., Soarimalala, V., Goodman, S. M., Nicoll, M. E., Andrianjakarivelo, V., et al. 2021. Review of the status and conservation of tenrecs (Mammalia: Afrotheria: Tenrecidae). *Oryx* 55: 13–22. https://doi.org/10.1017/S0030605318001205.

Steppan, S. J., and Schenk, J. J. 2017. Muroid rodent phylogenetics: 900-species tree reveals increasing diversification rates. *PLoS One* 17: e3000494.

Steppan, S. J., Adkins, R. M., and Anderson, J. 2004. Phylogeny and divergence-date estimates of rapid radiations in muroid rodents based on multiple nuclear genes. *Systematic Biology* 53: 533–553.

Sterling, E. J. 1993. Patterns of range use and social organization in aye-aye (*Daubentonia madagascariensis*) on Nosy Mangabe, Madagascar. In *Lemur Social Systems and Their Ecological Basis*, eds. P. M. Kappeler and J. U. Ganzhorn, pp. 1–10. New York: Plenum Press.

———. 1994a. Taxonomy and distribution of *Daubentonia*: A historical perspective. *Folia Primatologica* 62: 8–13.

———. 1994b. Aye-ayes: Specialists on structurally defended resources. *Folia Primatologica* 62: 142–154.
———. 1994c. Evidence for non-seasonal reproduction in aye-ayes (*Daubentonia madagascariensis*) in the wild. *Folia Primatologica* 62: 46–53.
———. 1998. Preliminary report on a survey for *Daubentonia madagascariensis* and other primate species in the west of Madagascar, June–August 1994. *Lemur News* 3: 7–8.
———. 2003. *Daubentonia madagascariensis*, aye-aye. In *The Natural History of Madagascar*, eds. S. M. Goodman and J. P. Benstead, pp. 1348–1351. Chicago: University of Chicago Press.
Sterling, E. J., and Feistner, A.T.C. 2000. Aye-aye (*Daubentonia madagascariensis*). In *Endangered Animals: A Reference Guide to Conflicting Issues*, eds. R. Reading and B. Miller, pp. 45–48. Westport: Greenwood Press.
Sterling, E. J., and McCreless, E. E. 2006. Adaptations in the aye- aye: A review. In *Lemurs: Ecology and Adaptation*, eds. L. Gould and M. L. Sauther, pp. 159–184. New York: Springer.
Sterling, E. J., and McFadden, K. 2000. Rapid census of lemur populations in the Parc National de Marojejy, Madagascar. In A floral and faunal survey of the Parc National de Marojejy, Madagascar: With reference to elevational variation, ed. S. M. Goodman. *Fieldiana: Zoology*, new ser., 97: 265–274.
Sterling, E. J., and Povinelli, D. J. 1999. Tool use, aye-ayes, and sensorimotor intelligence. *Folia Primatologica* 70: 8–16.
Sterling, E. J., and Ramaroson, M. G. 1996. Rapid assessment of the primate fauna of the eastern slopes of the Réserve Naturelle Intégrale d'Andringitra, Madagascar. In A floral and faunal inventory of the eastern slopes of the Réserve Naturelle Intégrale d'Andringitra, Madagascar: With reference to elevational variation, ed. S. M. Goodman. *Fieldiana: Zoology*, new series, 85: 293–305.
Sterling, E. J., and Richard, A. F. 1995. Social organization in the aye-aye (*Daubentonia madagascariensis*) and the perceived distinctiveness of nocturnal primates. In *Creatures of the Dark: The Nocturnal Prosimians*, eds. L. Alterman, G. A. Doyle, and M. K. Izard, pp. 439–451. New York: Plenum Press.
Sterling, E. J., Dierenfeld, E. S., Ashbourne, C. J., and Feistner, A.T.C. 1994. Dietary intake, food composition and nutrient intake in wild and captive populations of *Daubentonia madagascariensis*. *Folia Primatologica* 62: 115–124.
Stocker, M., Razafimanantsoa, H., Nantenaina, F., Desponts, C., and Lalaina, M. 2019. Madagascar economic update: A new start? Washington, DC: World Bank Group. http://documents.worldbank.org/curated/en/535501571854255186/Madagascar-Economic-Update-A-New-Start.
Storey, M., Mahoney, J. J., Saunders, A. D., Duncan, R. A., Kelley, S. P., and Coffin, M. F. 1995. Timing of hot spot-related volcanism and the breakup of Madagascar and India. *Science* 267: 852–855.
Storz, J. F. 1999. Genetic consequences of mammalian social structure. *Journal of Mammalogy* 80: 553–569. https://doi.org/10.2307/1383301.
Storz, J. F., and Beaumont, M. A. 2002. Testing for genetic evidence of population expansion and contraction: An empirical analysis of microsatellite DNA variation using a hierarchical Bayesian model. *Evolution* 56: 154–166. https://doi.org/10.1111/j.0014-3820.2002.tb00857.x.
Stribna, T., Romportl, D., Demjanovič, J., Vogeler, A., Tschapka, M., Benda, P., Horáček, I., Juste, J., Goodman, S. M., and Hulva, P. 2019. Pan African phylogeography and palaeodistribution of rousettine fruit bats: Ecogeographic correlation with Pleistocene climate vegetation cycles. *Journal of Biogeography* 46(10): 2336–2349.
Struck, K., Videan, E., Fritz, J., and Murphy, J. 2007. Attempting to reduce regurgitation and reingestion in a captive chimpanzee through increased feeding opportunities: A case study. *Laboratory Animals* 36: 35–38.
Stuenes, S. 1989. Taxonomy, habits, and relationships of the subfossil Madagascan hippopotami *Hippopotamus lemerlei* and *H. madagascariensis*. *Journal of Vertebrate Paleontology* 9: 241–268.
———. 1991. Taxonomy and palaeobiology of the Madagascan subfossil pygmy hippopotami. *Acta Universitatis Upsaliensis* no. 349.
Sugg, D. W., Chesser, R. K., Stephen Dobson, F., Hoogland, J. L. 1996. Population genetics meets behavioral ecology. *Trends in Ecology and Evolution* 11: 338–342. https://doi.org/10.1016/0169-5347(96)20050-3.
Sündermann, D., Scheumann, M., and Zimmermann, E. 2008. Olfactory predator recognition in predator-naïve gray mouse lemurs (*Microcebus murinus*). *Journal of Comparative Psychology* 122(2):146–155.
Sussman, R. W. 1974. Ecological distinctions in sympatric species of *Lemur*. In *Prosimian Biology*, eds. R. D. Martin, G. A. Doyle, and A. C. Walker, pp. 74–108. Pittsburgh: University of Pittsburgh Press.
———. 1975. A preliminary study of the behavior and ecology of *Lemur fulvus rufus* Audebert 1800. In *Lemur Biology*, eds. I. Tattersall and R. W. Sussman, pp. 237–258. New York: Plenum Press.
———. 1977a. Feeding behaviour of *Lemur catta* and *Lemur fulvus*. In *Primate Ecology: Studies of Feeding and Ranging Behaviour in Lemurs, Monkeys and Apes*, ed. T. H. Clutton-Brock, pp. 1–36. London: Academic Press.
———. 1977b. Socialization, social structure, and ecology of two sympatric species of *Lemur*. In *Primate Bio-Social Development: Biological, Social, and Ecological Determinants*, eds. S. Chevalier-Skolnikoff and F. E. Poirier, pp. 515–528. New York: Garland.
———. 1978. Nectar-feeding by prosimians and its evolutionary and ecological implications. In *Recent Advances in Primatology*, eds. D. J. Chivers and K. A. Joyse, pp. 119–125. London: Academic Press.
———. 1991. Demography and social organization of free-ranging *Lemur catta* in the Beza Mahafaly Reserve, Madagascar. *American Journal of Physical Anthropology* 84: 43–58.
———. 1992. Male life history and intergroup mobility among ringtailed lemurs (*Lemur catta*). *International Journal of Primatology* 13: 395–413.
Sussman, R. W., and Tattersall, I. 1976. Cycles of activity, group composition, and diet of *Lemur mongoz mongoz* Linnaeus 1766 in Madagascar. *Folia Primatologica* 26: 270–283.
Sussman, R. W., Sweeney, S., Green, G. M., Porton, I., Andrianasolondraibe, O. L., and Ratsirarson, J. 2006. A preliminary estimate of *Lemur catta* population density using satellite imagery. In *Ringtailed Lemur Biology:* Lemur catta *in Madagascar*, eds. A. Jolly, R. W. Sussman, N. Koyama, and H. Rasamimanana, pp. 16–31. New York: Springer.
Sussman, R. W., Richard, A. F., Ratsirarson, J., Sauther, M. L., Brockman, D. K., Gould, L., Lawler, R., and Cuozzo, F. P. 2012. Beza Mahafaly Special Reserve: Long-term research on lemurs in southwestern Madagascar. In *Long-term Field Studies of Primates*, eds. P. M. Kappeler and D. P. Watts, pp. 45–66. Berlin and Heidelberg: Springer.
Swanepoel, L. H., Swanepoel, C. M., Brown, P. R., Eiseb, S. J., Goodman, S. M., et al. 2017. A systematic review of rodent pest research in Afro-Malagasy small-holder farming systems: Are we asking the right questions? *PLoS One* 12(4): e0176621.
Swanson, D. L., McKechnie, A. E., and Vezina, F. 2017. How low can you go? An adaptive energetic framework for interpreting basal metabolic rate variation in endotherms. *Journal of Comparative Physiology B: Biochemical, Systemic, and Environmental Physiology* 187: 1039–1056.
Szalay, F. S., and Delson, E. 1979. *Evolutionary History of the Primates*. New York: Academic Press.
Szalay, F. S., and Katz, C. C. 1973. Phylogeny of lemurs, galagos and lorises. *Folia Primatologica* 19: 88–103.
Szulkin, M., Stopher, K. V., Pemberton, J. M., and Reid, J. M. 2013. Inbreeding avoidance, tolerance, or preference in animals? *Trends in Ecology and Evolution* 28: 205–211. https://doi.org/10.1016/j.tree.2012.10.016.
Taberlet, P., Griffin, S., Goossens, B., Questiau, S., Manceau, V., Escaravage, N., Waits, L. P., and Bouvet, J. 1996. Reliable genotyping of samples with very low DNA quantities using PCR. *Nucleic Acids Research* 24: 3189–3194.
Tajima, F. 1989a. Statistical method for testing the neutral mutation hypothesis by DNA polymorphism. *Genetics* 123: 585–595.
———. 1989b. The effect of change in population size on DNA polymorphism. *Genetics* 123: 597–601.
Tan, C. L. 1999. Group composition, home range size, and diet of three sympatric bamboo lemur species (genus *Hapalemur*) in Ranomafana National Park, Madagascar. *International Journal of Primatology* 20(4): 547–566.
———. 2000. Behavior and ecology of three sympatric bamboo lemur species (genus *Hapalemur*) in Ranomafana National Park, Madagascar. PhD thesis, State University of New York, Stony Brook.
———. 2006. Behavior and ecology of gentle lemurs (genus *Hapalemur*). In *Lemurs: Ecology and Adaptation*, eds. L. Gould and M. L. Sauther, pp. 369–381. New York: Springer.
Tan, Y., and Li, W-H. 1999. Trichromatic vision in prosimians. *Nature* 402: 36.
Tang, Q., Fung, T., and Rheindt, F. E. 2020. ResDisMapper: An *r* package for fine-scale mapping of resistance to dispersal. *Molecular Ecology Resources* 20(3): 819–831. https://doi.org/10.1111/1755-0998.13127.
Tate, G.H H., and Rand, A. L. 1941. A new *Galidia* (Viverridae) from Madagascar. *American Museum Novitates* 1112: 1.
Tattersall, I. 1977. Distribution of lemurs. Pt. 1: The lemurs of northern Madagascar. *Annals of the New York Academy of Sciences* 293: 160–169.
———. 1982. *The Primates of Madagascar*. New York: Columbia University Press.

———. 2007. Madagascar's lemurs: Cryptic diversity or taxonomic inflation? *Evolutionary Anthropology* 16: 12–23. https://doi.org/10.1002/evan.20126.

Tattersall, I., and Cuozzo, F. 2018. Systématique des lémuriens malgaches actuels (order des Primates)/Systematics of the extant Malagasy lemurs (order Primates). In *Les aires protégées terrestres de Madagascar: Leur histoire, description et biote/The Terrestrial Protected Areas of Madagascar: Their History, Description, and Biota*,, eds. S. M. Goodman, M. J. Raherilalao, and S. Wohlhauser, pp. 403–424. Antananarivo: Association Vahatra.

Tattersall, I., and Sussman, R. 1998. "Little brown lemurs" of northern Madagascar. *Folia Primatologica* 69(supplement 1): 379–388.

Taylor, L. A., and Schwitzer, C. 2012. Body masses of wild lemurs. *Lemur News* 16: 34–40.

Taylor, P. J., Goodman, S. M., Ratrimomanarivo, F. H., Lamb, J., and Schoeman, M. C. 2012. Wing loading correlates negatively with genetic structuring of eight Afro-Malagasy bat species (Molossidae). *Acta Chiropterologica* 14: 53–62.

Tecot, S. R. 2008. Seasonality and predictability: The hormonal and behavioral responses of the red-bellied lemur, *Eulemur rubriventer*, in southeastern Madagascar. PhD thesis, University of Texas, Austin.

———. 2010. It's all in the timing: Birth seasonality and infant survival in *Eulemur rubriventer*. *International Journal of Primatology* 31: 715–735.

———. 2013. Variable energetic strategies in disturbed and undisturbed rain forest habitats: Fecal cortisol levels in southeastern Madagascar. In *Leaping Ahead: Advances in Prosimian Biology*, eds. J. Masters, M. Gamba, F. Génin, and R. Tuttle, pp. 185–196. New York: Springer.

Tecot, S. R., and Baden, A. L. 2018. Profiling caregivers: Hormonal variation underlying allomaternal care in wild red-bellied lemurs, *Eulemur rubriventer*. *Physiology and Behavior* 193: 135–148.

Tecot, S. R., and Romine, N. K. 2012. Leading ladies: Leadership of group movements in a pair-living, co-dominant, monomorphic primate across reproductive stages and fruit availability seasons. *American Journal of Primatology* 74: 591–601.

Tecot, S. R., Baden, A. L., Romine, N. K., and Kamilar, J. M. 2012. Infant parking and nesting, not allomaternal care, influence Malagasy primate life histories. *Behavioral Ecology and Sociobiology* 66: 1375–1386.

Tecot, S. R., Baden, A. L., Romine, N., and Kamilar, J. M. 2013. Reproductive strategies and infant care in the Malagasy primates. In *Building Babies*, eds. K.B.H. Clancy, K. Hinde, and J. N. Rutherford, pp. 321–359. New York: Springer.

Tecot, S. R., Singletary, B., and Eadie, E. 2016. Why "monogamy" isn't good enough. *American Journal of Primatology* 78: 340–354.

Teeling. E. C., Springer. M. S., Madsen. O., Bates. P., O'Brien. S. J., and Murphy. W. J. 2005. A molecular phylogeny for bats illuminates biogeography and the fossil record. *Science* 307(5709): 580–584.

Teeling, E. C., Dool, S., and Springer, M. S. 2012. Phylogenies, fossils and functional genes: The evolution of echolocation in bats. In *Evolutionary History of Bats: Fossils, Molecules and Morphology,* eds. G. F. Gunnell and N. B. Simmons, pp. 1–22. Cambridge: Cambridge University Press.

Teichroeb, J. A., and Vining, A. Q. 2019. Navigation strategies in three nocturnal lemur species: Diet predicts heuristic use and degree of exploratory behavior. *Animal Cognition* 22: 343–354.

Tenora, F., Mas-Coma, S., Murai, E., and Feliu, C. 1980. The system of cestodes of the suborder Catenotaeniata Spassky, 1963. *Parasitologia Hungarica* 13: 39–57.

Thalmann, U. 2001. Food resource characteristics in two nocturnal lemurs with different social behavior: *Avahi occidentalis* and *Lepilemur edwardsi*. *International Journal of Primatology* 22: 287–324.

———. 2003. *Avahi*, woolly lemurs. In *The Natural History of Madagascar*, eds. S. M. Goodman and J. P. Benstead, pp. 1336–1340. Chicago: University of Chicago Press.

———. 2006. Behavioral and ecological adaptations in two small folivorous lemurs with different social organization: *Avahi* and *Lepilemur*. In *Lemurs: Ecology and Adaptation*, eds. L. Gould and M. L. Sauther, pp. 327–352. Boston: Springer.

Thalmann, U., and Geissmann, T. 2000. Distribution and geographic variation in the western woolly lemur (*Avahi occidentalis*) with description of a new species (*Avahi unicolor*). *International Journal of Primatology* 21: 915–941.

Thalmann, U., and Geissmann, T. 2005. New species of woolly lemur *Avahi* (Primates: Lemuriformes) in Bemaraha (central western Madagascar). *American Journal of Primatology* 67: 371–376.

Thalmann, U., Geissmann, T., Simona, A., and Mutschler, T. 1993. The indris of Anjanaharibe-Sud, northeastern Madagascar. *International Journal of Primatology* 14: 357–381.

Thalmann, U., Kümmerli, R., and Zaramody, A. 2002. Why *Propithecus verreauxi deckeni* and *P. v. coronatus* are valid taxa: Quantitative and qualitative arguments. *Lemur News* 7: 11–16.

Thewissen, J.G.M., and Etnier, S. A. 1995. Adhesive devices on the thumb of vespertilionoid bats (Chiroptera). *Journal of Mammalogy* 76: 925–936.

Thiele, D., Razafimahatratra, E., and Hapke, A. 2013. Discrepant partitioning of genetic diversity in mouse lemurs and dwarf lemurs: Biological reality or taxonomic bias? *Molecular Phylogenetics and Evolution* 69: 593–609.

Thomas, O. 1904. On the osteology and systematic position of the rare Malagasy bat *Myzopoda aurita*. *Proceedings of the Zoological Society of London* 1904(2): 2–6.

———. 1912. Two new genera and a new species of viverrine Carnivora. *Proceedings of the Zoological Society of London* 1912: 498–503.

———. 1915. Notes on the Asiatic bamboo-rats (*Rhizomys*, etc.). *Annals and Magazine of Natural History*, ser. 8, 16: 56–61.

———. 1918. On the arrangement of the small Tenrecidae hitherto referred to *Oryzorictes* and *Microgale*. *Annals and Magazine of Natural History*, ser. 9, 1: 302–307.

Thompson, S. D., and Nicoll, M. E. 1986. Basal metabolic rate and energetics of reproduction in therian mammals. *Nature* 321: 690–693.

Thorén, S., Quietzsch, F., Schwochow, D., Sehen, L., Meusel, C., Meares, K., and Radespiel, U. 2011. Seasonal changes in feeding ecology and activity patterns of two sympatric mouse lemur species, the gray mouse lemur (*Microcebus murinus*) and the golden-brown mouse lemur (*M. ravelobensis*), in northwestern Madagascar. *International Journal of Primatology* 32: 566–586.

Thorne, J. L., Kishino, H., and Painter, I. S. 1998. Estimating the rate of evolution of the rate of molecular evolution. *Molecular Biology and Evolution* 15: 1647–1657.

Thorstrom, R., and La Marca, G. 2000. Nesting biology and behavior of the Madagascar harrier-hawk (*Polyboroides radiatus*) in northeastern Madagascar. *Journal of Raptor Research* 34: 120–125.

Thorstrom, R., and Rene de Roland, L.-A. 2000. First nest description, breeding behaviour and distribution of the Madagascar serpent-eagle *Eutriorchis astur*. *Ibis* 142: 217–224.

Tidd, S. T., Pinder, J. E., and Ferguson, G. W. 2001. Deforestation and habitat loss for the Malagasy flat-tailed tortoise from 1963 through 1993. *Chelonian Conservation and Biology* 4: 59–65.

Tilden, C. D., and Oftedal, O. T. 1995. The bioenergetics of reproduction in prosimian primates: Is it related to female dominance? In *Creatures of the Night: The Nocturnal Prosimians*, eds. M. K. Izard, L. Alterman, and G. A. Doyle, pp. 119–131. New York: Plenum Press.

Tilden, C. T., and Oftedal, O. T. 1997. Milk composition reflects pattern of maternal care in prosimian primates. *American Journal of Primatology* 41: 195–211.

Tingle, C.C.D., McWilliam, A. N., Rafanomezana, S., Rakotondravelo, M. L., and Rakotondrasoa, H. 2003. The fauna of savanna grasslands in the locust outbreak area in southwestern Madagascar. In *The Natural History of Madagascar*, eds. S. M. Goodman and J. P. Benstead, pp. 520–528. Chicago: University of Chicago Press.

Tøien, Ø., Blake, J., Edgar, D. M., Grahn, D. A., Heller, H. C., and Barnes, B. M. 2011. Independence of metabolic suppression from body temperature. *Science* 331: 906–909.

Tokiniaina, H., Bailey, C. A., Shore, G. D., Delmore, K. E., Johnson, S. E., Louis, E. E., Jr., and Brenneman, R. A. 2009. Characterization of 18 microsatellite marker loci in the white-collared lemur (*Eulemur cinereiceps*). *Conservation Genetics* 10: 1459. https://doi.org/10.1007/s10592-008-9760-5.

Tollenaere, C., Brouat, C., Duplantier, J.-M., Rahalison, L., Rahelinirina, S., Pascal, M., Moné, H., Mouahid, G., Leirs, H., and Cosson, J.-F. 2010. Phylogeography of the introduced species *Rattus rattus* in the western Indian Ocean, with special emphasis on the colonization history of Madagascar. *Journal of Biogeography* 37: 398–410. https://doi.org/10.1111/j.1365-2699.2009.02228.x.

Tomiuk, J., Bachmann, L., Leipoldt, M., Ganzhorn, J. U., Ries, R., Weis, M., and Loeschcke, V. 1997. Genetic diversity of *Lepilemur mustelinus ruficaudatus*, a nocturnal lemur of Madagascar. *Conservation Biology* 11: 491–497.

Tomiuk, J., Bachmann, L., Leipoldt, M., Atsalis, S., Kappeler, P. M., Schmid, J., and Ganzhorn, J. U. 1998. The impact of genetics on the conservation of Malagasy lemur species. *Folia Primatologica* 69: 121–126. https://doi.org/10.1159/000052705.

Toomey, R. S., III, Coburn, M. L., and Olson, R. A. 2002. Paleontological evaluation of past use of eaves by the Indiana bat: A significant tool for restoration of hibernacula. In *The Indiana Bat: Biology and Management of an Endangered Species*, eds. A. Kurta and J. Kennedy, pp. 79–85. Austin: Bat Conservation International.

Torti, V., Gamba, M., Rabemananjara, Z. H., and Giacoma, C. 2013. The song of the indris: Contextual variation in the long distance calls of a lemur. *Italian Journal of Zoology* 80: 596–607.

Torti, V., Bonadonna, G., De Gregorio, C., Valente, D., Randrianarison, R. M., Friard, O., Pozzi, L., Gamba, M., and Giacoma, C. 2017. An intra-population analysis of the indris' song dissimilarity in the light of genetic distance. *Scientific Reports* 7: 10140.

Torti, V., Valente, D., De Gregorio, C., Comazzi, C., Miaretsoa, L., Ratsimbazafy, J., Giacoma, C., and Gamba, M. 2018. Call and be counted! Can we reliably estimate the number of callers in the indri's (*Indri indri*) song? *PLoS One* 13: 8.

Tortosa, P., Dsouli, N., Gomard, Y., Ramasindrazana, B., Dick, C. W., and Goodman, S. M. 2013. Evolutionary history of Indian Ocean nycteribiid bat flies mirroring the ecology of their hosts. *PLoS One* 8(9): e75215.

Towns, D. R., Atkinson, I.A.E., and Daugherty, C. H. 2006. Have the harmful effects of introduced rats on islands been exaggerated? *Biological Invasions* 8: 863–891.

Trailcampro. 2020. Trailcampro.com. https://www.trailcampro.com/.

Treat, M. D., Scholer, L., Barrett, B., Khachatryan, A., McKenna, A. J., et al. 2018. Extreme physiological plasticity in a hibernating basoendothermic mammal, *Tenrec ecaudatus*. *Journal of Experimental Biology* 221: jeb185900.

Trochet, A., Courtois, E. A., Stevens, V. M., Baguette, M., Chaine, A., Schmeller, D. S., Clobert, J., and Wiens, J. J. 2016. Evolution of sex-biased dispersal. *Quarterly Review of Biology* 91: 297–320. https://doi.org/10.1086/688097.

Truijillo, R. G. 2005. Phylogenetics of the genus *Scotophilus* (Chiroptera: Vespertilionidae): Perspectives from paternally and maternally inherited genomes with an emphasis on African species. PhD thesis, Texas A&M University.

Trujillo, R. G., Patton, J. C., Schlitter, D. A., and Bickham, J. W. 2009. Molecular phylogenetics of the bat genus *Scotophilus* (Chiroptera: Vespertilionidae): Perspectives from paternally and maternally inherited genomes. *Journal of Mammalogy* 90: 548–560.

Tsagkogeorga, G., Parker, J., Stupka, E., Cotton, J. A., and Rossiter, S. J. 2013. Phylogenomic analyses elucidate the evolutionary relationships of bats. *Current Biology* 23(22): 2262–2267.

Tsibara, M. 2011. Bio-écologie de *Triaenops furculus* (Hipposideridae) et d'*Otomops madagascariensis* (Molossidae) dans la région de Saint Augustin et dans le Parc National Tsingy de Bemaraha. Thèse de Doctorat de Troisième Cycle, Université de Toliara.

Turner, I. M. 1996. Species loss in fragments of tropical rain forest: A review of the evidence. *Journal of Applied Ecology* 33(2): 200–209.

Uilenberg, G., Hoogstraal, H., and Klein, J.-M. 1979. Les tiques (Ixodoidea) de Madagascar et leur rôle vecteur. *Archives de l'Institut Pasteur de Madagasacar*, Numéro Spécial: 1–153.

Upham, N. S., Esselstyn, J. A., and Jetz, W. 2019. Inferring the mammal tree: Species-level sets of phylogenies for questions in ecology, evolution, and conservation. *PLoS Biology* 17: e3000494.

Valenta, K. 2014. Primate-plant interactions in the tropical dry forests of northwestern Madagascar: Seed dispersal and sensory ecology of *Eulemur fulvus*. PhD thesis, University of Toronto.

Valenta, K., and Nevo, O. 2020. The dispersal syndrome hypothesis: How animals shaped fruit traits, and how they did not. *Functional Ecology* 34: 1158–1169.

Valenta, K., Gettinger-Larson, J. A., Chapman, C. A., and Farris, Z. J. 2016. Barking up the right tree: Understanding local attitudes towards dogs in villages surrounding Ranomafana National Park, Madagascar, can benefit applied conservation. *Madagascar Conservation and Development* 11(2): 87–90.

Van Horn, R., and Resko, J. A. 1977. The reproductive cycle of the ring-tailed lemur (*Lemur catta*): Sex steroid levels and sexual receptivity under controlled photoperiods. *Endocrinology* 101: 1579–1586.

van Schaik, C. P., and van Hooff, J.A.R.A.M. 1983. On the ultimate causes of primate social systems. *Behaviour* 85: 91–117.

van Vuuren, B. J., Woolaver, L., and Goodman, S. M. 2012. Genetic population structure in the boky-boky (Carnivora: Eupleridae), a conservation flagship species in the dry deciduous forests of central western Madagascar. *Animal Conservation* 15: 164–173.

Vargas, A., Jiménez, I., Palomares, F., and Palacios, M. J. 2002. Distribution, status, and conservation needs of the golden-crowned sifaka (*Propithecus tattersalli*). *Biological Conservation* 108: 325–334.

Vasey, N. 1996. Clinging to life: *Varecia variegata rubra* and the Masoala coastal forests. *Lemur News* 1(2): 7–9.

———. 1997a. How many red ruffed lemurs are left? *International Journal of Primatology* 18: 207–216.

———. 1997b. Community ecology and behavior of *Varecia variegata rubra* and *Lemur fulvus albifrons*, on the Masoala Peninsula, Madagascar. PhD thesis, Washington University, Saint Louis.

———. 2000a. Plant species composition of diet in two sympatric lemurs: *Varecia variegata rubra* and *Eulemur fulvus albifrons*. *American Journal of Physical Anthropology* 30(supplement): 309–310.

———. 2000b. Niche separation in *Varecia variegata rubra* and *Eulemur fulvus albifrons*: I. Interspecific patterns. *American Journal of Physical Anthropology* 112: 411–431.

———. 2002. Niche separation in *Varecia variegata rubra* and *Eulemur fulvus albifrons*: II. Intraspecific patterns. *American Journal of Physical Anthropology* 118: 169–183.

———. 2003. *Varecia*, ruffed lemurs. In *The Natural history of Madagascar*, eds. S. M. Goodman and J. P. Benstead, pp. 1332–1336. Chicago: University of Chicago Press.

———. 2004. Circadian rhythms in diet and habitat use in red ruffed lemurs (*Varecia rubra*) and white-fronted brown lemurs (*Eulemur fulvus albifrons*). *American Journal of Physical Anthropology* 124: 353–363.

———. 2005a. Activity budgets and activity rhythms in red ruffed lemurs (*Varecia rubra*) on the Masoala Peninsula, Madagascar: Seasonality and reproductive energetics. *American Journal of Primatology* 66: 23–44.

———. 2005b. New developments in the behavioral ecology and conservation of ruffed lemurs (*Varecia*). *American Journal of Primatology* 66: 1–6.

———. 2006. Impact of seasonality and reproduction on social structure, ranging patterns, and fission-fusion social organization in red ruffed lemurs. In *Lemurs: Ecology and Adaptation*, eds. L. Gould and M. L. Sauther, pp. 275–304. New York: Springer/Kluwer.

———. 2007. The breeding system of wild red ruffed lemurs (*Varecia rubra*): A preliminary report. *Primates* 48: 41–54.

Vasey, N., and Borgerson, C. 2009. Social and ecological factors associated with temporary reproductive collapse in red variegated lemurs (*Varecia rubra*) on the Masoala Peninsula, Madagascar. *American Journal of Physical Anthropology* 48(supplement): 261.

Vasey, N., and Godfrey, L. R. Forthcoming. Lemur hunting in Madagascar's present and past: The case of *Pachylemur*. In *World Archeoprimatology: Interconnections of Humans and Nonhuman Primates in the Past*, eds. B. Urbani, D. Youlatos, and A. Antczak. Cambridge: Cambridge University Press.

Vasey, N., and Tattersall, I. 2002. Do ruffed lemurs form a hybrid zone? Distribution and discovery of *Varecia*, with systematic and conservation implications. *American Museum Novitates* 3376: 1–26.

Vasey, N., Mogilewsky, M., and Schatz, G. E. 2018. Infant nest and stash sites of variegated lemurs (*Varecia rubra*): The extended phenotype. *American Journal of Primatology* 80: e22911.

Veilleux, C. C., Louis, E. E., Jr., and Bolnick, D. A. 2013. Nocturnal light environments influence color vision and signatures of selection on the *OPN1SW* Opsin gene in nocturnal lemurs. *Molecular Biology and Evolution* 30: 1420–1437. https://doi.org/10.1093/molbev/mst058.

Veilleux, C. C., Jacobs, R. L., Cummings, M. E., Louis, E. E., Jr., and Bolnick, D. A. 2014. Opsin genes and visual ecology in a nocturnal folivorous lemur. *International Journal of Primatology* 35: 88–107.

Veilleux, C. C., Scarry, C. J., Di Fiore, A., Kirk, E. C., Bolnick, D. A., and Lewis, R. J. 2016. Group benefit associated with polymorphic trichromacy in a Malagasy primate (*Propithecus verreauxi*). *Scientific Reports* 6: 38418.

Vekemans, X., and Hardy, O. J. 2004. New insights from fine-scale spatial genetic structure analyses in plant populations. *Molecular Ecology* 13: 921–935. https://doi.org/10.1046/j.1365-294X.2004.02076.x.

Vercammen, P., Seydack, A.H.W., and Olivier, W.L.R. 1993. The bush pigs (*Potamochoerus porcus* and *P. larvatus*). In *Pigs, Peccaries and Hippos*, ed. W.L.R. Olivier, pp. 93–100. Gland: IUCN.

Veron, G. 1994. Méthodes de recherche en biotaxonomie des mammifères carnivores: Confrontation des méthodes de phylogénie traditionnelle et moléculaire dans la recherche de la position systématique de *Cryptoprocta ferox* (Aeluroidea). PhD thesis, Muséum National d'Histoire Naturelle, Paris.

———. 1995. La position systématique de *Cryptoprocta ferox* (Carnivora): Analyse cladistique des caractères morphologiques de carnivores Aeluroidea actuels et fossiles. *Mammalia* 59: 551–582.

Veron, G., and Catzeflis, F. 1993. Phylogenetic relationships of the endemic Malagasy carnivore *Cryptoprocta ferox* (Aeluroidea): DNA/DNA hybridization experiments. *Journal of Mammalian Evolution* 1: 169–185.

Veron, G., and Goodman, S. M. 2018. One or two species of the rare Malagasy carnivoran *Eupleres* (Eupleridae)? New insights from molecular data. *Mammalia* 82: 107–112.

Veron, G., Colyn, M., Dunham, A., Taylor, P., and Gaubert, P. 2004. Molecular systematics and origin of sociality in mongooses (Herpestidae, Carnivora). *Molecular Phylogenetics and Evolution* 30: 582–598.

Veron, G., Dupré, D., Jennings, A. P., Gardner, C. J., Hassanin, A., and Goodman, S. M. 2017. New insights into the systematics of Malagasy mongoose-like carnivorans (Carnivora, Eupleridae, Galidiinae) based on mitochondrial and nuclear DNA sequences. *Journal of Zoological Systematics and Evolutionary Research* 55: 250–264. https://doi.org/10.1111/jzs.12168.

Veron, G., Dupré, D., Lührs, M.-L., Kappeler, P. M., Dollar, L., Pomerantz, J., and Goodman, S. M. 2018. Genetic polymorphism and structure of wild and zoo populations of the fosa (Eupleridae, Carnivora), the largest living carnivoran of Madagascar. *Mammalian Biology* 92: 68–77. https://doi.org/10.1016/j.mambio.2018.04.007.

Vick, L. G., and Pereira, M. E. 1989. Episodic targeting aggression and the histories of lemur social groups. *Behavioral Ecology and Sociobiology* 25: 3–12.

Vieilledent, G., Grinand, C., Rakotomalala, F. A., Ranaivosoa, R., Rakotoarijaona, J.-R., Allnutt, T. F., and Achard, F. 2018. Combining global tree cover loss data with historical national forest cover maps to look at six decades of deforestation and forest fragmentation in Madagascar. *Biological Conservation* 222: 189–197. https://doi.org/10.1016/j.biocon.2018.04.008.

Vinyard, C. J., Yamashita, N., and Tan, C. 2008. Linking laboratory and field approaches in studying the evolutionary physiology of biting in bamboo lemurs. *International Journal of Primatology* 29: 1421–1439.

Virah-Sawmy, M., Gillson, L., Gardner, C. J., Anderson, A., Clark, G., and Haberle, S. 2016. A landscape vulnerability framework for identifying integrated conservation and adaptation pathways to climate change: The case of Madagascar's spiny forest. *Landscape Ecology* 31: 637–654.

Voarintsoa, N.R.G., Railsback, L. B., Brook, G. A., Wang, L. X., Cheng, H., Li, X. L., Edwards, R. L., Rakotondrazafy, A.F.M., and Razanatseheno, M.O.M. 2017. Three distinct Holocene intervals of stalagmite deposition and nondeposition revealed in NW Madagascar, and their paleoclimate implications. *Climate of the Past* 13: 1771–1790.

Vogler, B. R., Bailey, C. A., Shore, G. D., McGuire, S. M., Engberg, S. E., Fickel, J., Louis, E. E., Jr., and Brenneman, R. A. 2009a. Characterization of 26 microsatellite marker loci in the fossa (*Cryptoprocta ferox*). *Conservation Genetics* 10: 1449. https://doi.org/10.1007/s10592-008-9758-z.

Vogler, B. R., Blevins, B., Goeritz, F., Hildebrandt, T. B., and Dehnhard, M. 2009b. Gonadal activity in male and female captive fossas (*Cryptoprocta ferox*) during the mating season. *Reproduction in Domestic Animals* 44: 98–102.

Volampeno, M.S.N. 2009. Reproductive behaviour and habitat use in the blue-eyed black lemur (*Eulemur flavifrons*, Gray, 1867) at the Sahamalaza-Iles Radama National Park, Madagascar. PhD thesis, University of KwaZulu-Natal, Pietermaritzburg.

Volampeno, M.S.N., Masters, J. C., and Downs, C. T. 2011. Life history traits, maternal behavior and infant development of blue-eyed black lemurs (*Eulemur flavifrons*). *American Journal of Primatology* 73: 474–484.

Vololona, J., Ramavovololona, P., Noroalintseheno Lalarivoniaina, O. S., and Goodman, S. M. 2020. Fleurs visitées par *Rousettus madagascariensis* G. Grandidier (Chiroptera: Pteropodidae) dans la Réserve Spéciale d'Ankarana, Madagascar. *Bulletin de la Société Zoologique de France* 145: 49–67.

Vosseler, J. 1929. Beitrag zur Kenntnis der Fossa (*Cryptoprocta ferox* Benn.) und ihrer Fortpflanzung. *Der Zoologische Garten, Leipzig (Neue Folge)* 2: 1–9.

Vuarin, P., Dammhahn, M., Kappeler, P. M., and Henry, P. Y. 2015. When to initiate torpor use? Food availability times the transition to winter phenotype in a tropical heterotherm. *Oecologia* 179: 43–53.

Vuillaume-Randriamanantena, M., Godfrey, L. R., Jungers, W. L., and Simons, E. L. 1992. Morphology, taxonomy and distribution of *Megaladapis*, giant subfossil lemur from Madagascar. *Comptes Rendus de l'Académie des Sciences*, série II, 315: 1835–1842.

Waeber, P. O., and Hemelrijk, C. K. 2003. Female dominance and social structure in Alaotran gentle lemurs. *Behaviour* 140: 1235–1246.

Waeber, P. O., Ralainasolo, F. B., Ratsimbazafy, J. H., and Nievergelt, C. M. 2019a. Consequences of lakeside living for the diet and social ecology of the lake Alaotran gentle lemur. In *Primates in Flooded Habitats: Ecology and Conservation*, eds. A. Barnett, I. Matsuda, and K. Nowak, pp. 276–278. Cambridge: Cambridge University Press.

Waeber, P. O., Ratsimbazafy, J. H., Andrianandrasana, H., Ralainasolo, F. B., and Nievergelt, C. M. 2019b. *Hapalemur alaotrensis*: A conservation case study from the swamps of Alaotra, Madagascar. In *Primates in Flooded Habitats: Ecology and Conservation*, eds. A. Barnett, I. Matsuda, and K. Nowak, pp. 293–296. Cambridge: Cambridge University Press.

Wakeley, J. 1999. Nonequilibrium migration in human history. *Genetics* 153: 1863–1871.

Walker, A., Ryan, T. M., Silcox, M. T., Simons, E. L., and Spoor, F. 2008. The semicircular canal system and locomotion: The case of extinct lemuroids and lorisoids. *Evolutionary Anthropology* 17: 135–145.

Walker, A. C. 1967. Patterns of extinction among the subfossil Madagascan lemuroids. In *Pleistocene Extinctions: The Search for a Cause*, eds. P. S. Martin and H. E. Wright Jr., pp. 425–432. New Haven: Yale University Press.

Wall, C. 1997. The expanded mandibular condyle of the Megaladapidae. *American Journal of Physical Anthropology* 103: 263–276.

Wang, H., and Fuller, T. K. 2003. Food habits of four sympatric carnivores in southeastern China. *Mammalia* 67: 513–519.

Wang, I. J., and Bradburd, G. S. 2014. Isolation by environment. *Molecular Ecology* 23: 5649–5662. https://doi.org/10.1111/mec.12938.

Wang, I. J., and Summers, K. 2010. Genetic structure is correlated with phenotypic divergence rather than geographic isolation in the highly polymorphic strawberry poison-dart frog. *Molecular Ecology* 19: 447–458. https://doi.org/10.1111/j.1365-294X.2009.04465.x.

Wang, P. C., Sheng, H. L., and Lu, H. J. 1976. The diet analysis and captive care of lesser oriental civet. *Chinese Journal of Zoology* 2: 39–40.

Warren, R. D. 1994. Lazy leapers: A study of the locomotor ecology of two species of saltatory nocturnal lemur in sympatry at Ampijoroa, Madagascar. PhD thesis, University of Liverpool.

Warren, R. D., and Crompton, R. H. 1996. Lazy leapers: Energetics, phylogenetic inertia and the locomotor differentiation of the Malagasy primates. In *Biogéographie de Madagascar*, ed. W. R. Lourenço, pp. 259–266. Paris: OSTROM.

Warren, R. D., and Crompton, R. H. 1997. A comparative study of the ranging behaviour, activity rhythms and sociality of *Lepilemur edwardsi* (Primates, Lepilemuridae) and *Avahi occidentalis* (Primates, Indriidae) at Ampijoroa, Madagascar. *Journal of Zoology* 243: 397–415.

Warter, S., Randrianasolo, G., Dutrillaux, B., and Rumpler, Y. 1987. Cytogenetic study of a new subspecies of *Hapalemur griseus*. *Folia Primatologica* 48: 50–55.

Wasimuddin, Corman, V. M., Ganzhorn, J. U., Rakotondranary, J., Ratovonamana, Y. R., Drosten, C., and Sommer, S. 2019. Adenovirus infection is associated with altered gut microbial communities in a non-human primate. *Scientific Reports* 9: 13410. https://doi.org/10.1038/s41598-019-49829-z.

Waters, D. A., and Vollrath, C. 2003. Echolocation performance and call structure in the megachiropteran fruit-bat *Rousettus aegyptiacus*. *Acta Chiropterologica* 5(2): 209–219.

Watterson, G. A. 1978. The homozygosity test of neutrality. *Genetics* 88: 405–417.

Wearn, O., and Glover-Kapfer, P. 2017. Camera-trapping for conservation: A guide to best-practices. *WWF Conservation Technology Series* 1: 181.

Webb, C. S. 1954. *The Odyssey of an Animal Collector*. London: Longmans, Green.

Webber, A. D., Solofondranohatra, J. S., Razafindramoana, S., Fernández, D., Parker, C. A., Steer, M., Abrahams, M., and Allainguillaume, J. 2020. Lemurs in cacao: Presence and abundance within the shade plantations of northern Madagascar. *Folia Primatologica* 91(2): 96–107.

Weidt, A. 2001. Ökologie und Sozialbiologie von Weibchen des goldbraunen Mausmakis (*Microcebus ravelobensis*) wahrend der Trockenzeit in Nordwest-Madagascar. Diploma thesis, University of Göttingen.

Weidt, A., Hagenah, N., Randrianambinina, B., Radespiel, U., and Zimmermann, E. 2004. Social organization of the golden brown mouse lemur (*Microcebus ravelobensis*). *American Journal of Physical Anthropology* 123: 40–51.

Welch, C., and Katz, A. 1992. Survey and census work on lemurs in the natural reserve of Betampona in eastern Madagascar with a view to restocking. *Dodo* 28: 45–58.

Wemmer, C. 1971. Birth, development and behaviour of a fanaloka *Fossa fossana* at the National Zoological Park, Washington, DC. *International Zoo Yearbook* 11: 113–115.

Weyeneth, N., Goodman, S. M., and Ruedi, M. 2011a. Do diversification models of Madagascar's biota explain the population structure of the endemic bat *Myotis goudoti* (Chiroptera: Vespertilionidae)? *Journal of Biogeography* 38: 44–54. https://doi.org/10.1111/j.1365-2699.2010.02393.x.

Weyeneth, N., Goodman, S. M., Appleton, B., Wood, R., and Ruedi, M. 2011b. Wings or winds: Inferring bat migration in a stepping-stone archipelago. *Journal of Evolutionary Biology* 24: 1298–1306.

White, E. I. 1930. Fossil hunting in Madagascar. *Natural History Magazine* 2(15): 209–235.

White, F. J. 1991. Social organization, feeding ecology, and reproductive strategy of ruffed lemurs, *Varecia variegata variegata*. In *Primatology Today: XII Congress of the International Primatological Society*, eds. T. Kimuya, O. Takenaka, and M. Iwamoto, pp. 81–84. Amsterdam: Elsevier.

White, F. J., Overdorff, D. J., Balko, E. A., and Wright, P. C. 1995. Distribution of ruffed lemurs (*Varecia variegata*) in Ranomafana National Park, Madagascar. *Folia Primatologica* 64: 124–131.

Whitehead, G. K. 1972. *Deer of the World*. London: Constable.

Wilkinson, D. A., Mélade, J., Dietrich, M., Ramasindrazana, B., Soarimalala, V., et al. 2014. Highly diverse morbillivirus-related *Paramyxoviruses* in wild fauna of the southwestern Indian Ocean islands: Evidence of exchange between introduced and endemic small mammals. *Journal of Virology* 88(15): 8268–8277.

Wilkinson, D. A., Duron, O., Cordonin, C., Gomard, Y., Ramasindrazana, B., Mavingui, P., Goodman, S. M., and Tortosa, P. 2016. The bacteriome of bat flies (Nycteribiidae) from the Malagasy region: A community shaped by host-ecology, bacterial transmission mode, and host-vector specificity. *Applied and Environmental Microbiology* 82(6): 1778–1788.

Williams, R. C., Blanco, M. B., Poelstra, J. W., Hunnicutt, K. E., Comeault, A. A., and Yoder, A. D. 2020. Conservation genomic analysis reveals ancient introgression and declining levels of genetic diversity in Madagascar's hibernating dwarf lemurs. *Heredity* 124: 236–251. https://doi.org/10.1038/s41437-019-0260-9.

Wilmé, L., Goodman, S. M., and Ganzhorn, J. U. 2006. Biogeographic evolution of Madagascar's microendemic biota. *Science* 312: 1063–1065.

Wilmet, L., Beudels-Jamar, R. C., Schwitzer, C., Rakotondrainibe, H., Devillers, P., and Vermeulen, C. 2019. Use of space and home range characteristics of *Lepilemur mittermeieri*, an endangered sportive lemur endemic to the Ampasindava Peninsula, north-west Madagascar. *American Journal of Primatology* 81: e23017. https://doi.org/10.1002/ajp.23017.

Wilson, J. M., Stewart, P. D., Ramangason, G.-S., Denning, A. M., and Hutchings, M. S. 1989. Ecology and conservation of the crowned lemur, *Lemur coronatus*, at Ankarana, N. Madagascar. *Folia Primatologica* 52: 1–26.

Wilson, L.A.B., Hand, S. J., López-Aguirre, C., Archer, M., Black, K. H., Beck, R.M.D., Armstrong, K. N., and Wroe, S. 2016. Cranial shape variation and phylogenetic relationships of extinct and extant Old World leaf-nosed bats. *Alcheringa* 40(4): 509–524.

Wimmer, B., and Kappeler, P. M. 2002. The effects of sexual selection and life history on the genetic structure of redfronted lemur, *Eulemur fulvus rufus*, groups. *Animal Behaviour* 64: 557–568. https://doi.org/10.1006/anbe.2002.4003.

Wimmer, B., Tautz, D., and Kappeler, P. M. 2002. The genetic population structure of the gray mouse lemur (*Microcebus murinus*), a basal primate from Madagascar. *Behavioral Ecology and Sociobiology* 52: 166–175. https://doi.org/10.1007/s00265-002-0497-8.

Wimsatt, W. A., and Villa-R., B. 1970. Locomotor adaptations in the Discwinged bat *Thyroptera tricolor*. 1. Functional organization of the adhesive discs. *American Journal of Anatomy* 129: 89–119.

Winge, H. 1923. *Pattedyr Slaegter*. Vol. 2, *Rodentia, Carnivora, Primates*. Copenhagen: H. Hagerups.

Woolaver, L., Nichols, R., Rakotombololona, W. F., Volahy, A. T., and Durbin, J. 2006. Population status, distribution and conservation needs of the narrow-striped mongoose *Mungotictis decemlineata* of Madagascar. *Oryx* 40(1): 67–75.

Wozencraft, W. C. 1986. A new species of striped mongoose from Madagascar. *Journal of Mammalogy* 67: 561–571.

———. 1987. Emendation of species name. *Journal of Mammalogy* 68: 198.

———. 1989. Classification of the recent Carnivora. In *Carnivore Behavior, Ecology, and Evolution*, ed. J. L. Gittleman, pp. 569–593. New York: Cornell University Press.

———. 1990. Alive and well in Tsimanampetsotsa. *Natural History Magazine* 12/90: 28–30.

———. 1993. Order Carnivora. In *Mammal Species of the World: A Taxonomic and Geographic Reference*, 2nd ed., eds. D. E. Wilson and D. M. Reeder, pp. 279–348. Washington, DC: Smithsonian Institution Press.

———. 2005. Order Carnivora. In *Mammal Species of the World: A Taxonomic and Geographic Reference*, 3rd ed., eds. D. E. Wilson and D. M. Reeder, pp. 532–628. Baltimore: Johns Hopkins University Press.

Wright, P. C. 1986. Diet, ranging behavior and activity pattern of the gentle lemur (*Hapalemur griseus*) in Madagascar. *American Journal of Physical Anthropology* 69: 283.

———. 1998. Impact of predation risk on the behaviour of *Propithecus diadema edwardsi* in the rain forest of Madagascar. *Behaviour* 135: 483–512.

———. 1999. Lemur traits and Madagascar ecology: Coping with an island environment. *Yearbook of Physical Anthropology* 42: 31–72.

Wright, P. C., and Martin, L. B. 1995. Predation, pollination and torpor in two nocturnal prosimians: *Cheirogaleus major* and *Microcebus rufus* in the rain forest of Madagascar. In *Creatures of the Dark: The Nocturnal Prosimians*, eds. L. Alterman, G. A. Doyle, and M. K. Izard, pp. 45–60. New York: Plenum Press.

Wright, P. C., Daniels, P. S., Meyers, D. M., Overdorff, D. J., and Rabesoa, J. 1987. A census and study of *Hapalemur* and *Propithecus* in southeastern Madagascar. *Primate Conservation* 8: 84–88.

Wright, P. C., Heckscher, S. K., and Dunham, A. E. 1997. Predation on Milne-Edwards' sikafa (*Propithecus diadema edwardsi*) by the fossa (*Cryptoprocta ferox*) in the rain forest of southeastern Madagascar. *Folia Primatologica* 68: 34–43.

Wright, P. C., Johnson, S. E., Irwin, M. T., Jacobs, R., Schlichting, P., et al. 2008. The crisis of the critically endangered greater bamboo lemur (*Prolemur simus*). *Primate Conservation* 23: 5–17.

Wright, P. C., Tecot, S. R., Erhart, E., King, S. J., Baden, A. L., and Grassi, C. 2011. Frugivory in four sympatric lemurs: Implications for Madagascar's forests. *American Journal of Primatology* 73: 585–602.

Wright, P. C., Erhart, E. M., Tecot, S., Baden, A. L., Arrigo-Nelson, S. J., et al. 2012. Long-term lemur research at Centre ValBio, Ranomafana National Park, Madagascar. In *Long-Term Field Studies of Primates*, eds. P. M. Kappeler and D. P. Watts, pp. 67–100. Berlin: Springer.

Wright, S. 1943. Isolation by distance. *Genetics* 28: 114–138.

Wunderlich, R. E., Simons, E. L., and Jungers, W. L. 1996. New pedal remains of *Megaladapis* and their functional significance. *American Journal of Physical Anthropology* 100: 115–138.

Wyner, Y. [M.], Absher, R., Amato, G., Sterling, E., Stumpf, R., Rumpler, Y., and DeSalle, R. 1999a. Species concepts and the determination of historic gene flow patterns in the *Eulemur fulvus* (brown lemur) complex. *Biological Journal of the Linnean Society* 65: 39–56.

Wyner, Y. M., Amato, G., and DeSalle, R. 1999b. Captive breeding, reintroduction, and the conservation genetics of black and white ruffed lemurs, *Varecia variegata variegata*. *Molecular Ecology* 8: S107–S115.

Wyner, Y. M., Johnson, S. E., Stumpf, R. M., and DeSalle, R. 2002. Genetic assessment of a white-collared × red-fronted lemur hybrid zone at Andringitra, Madagascar. *American Journal of Primatology* 57: 51–66.

Wyza, E., Dollar, L., Rahajanirina, L.P., Popescu, V., and Stevens, N. J. 2020. Spatial dynamics and activity patterns of the fosa *Cryptoprocta ferox* in Ankarafantsika National Park, Madagascar: Carnivores navigating a human-influenced landscape. *Oryx* 54(6): 837–846. https://doi.org/10.1017/S0030605319000498.

Xu, H., Zhu, B., and Sheng, H. 1995. A study of the behavior of small civet (*Viverricula indica*) during the estrus period. *Zoological Research* 16: 359–364.

Yamashita, N. 1996. Seasonally and site specificity of mechanical dietary patterns in two Malagasy lemur families (Lemuridae and Indriidae). *International Journal of Primatology* 17: 355–387.

———. 2002. Diet of two lemur species in different microhabitats in Beza Mahafaly Special Reserve, Madagascar. *International Journal of Primatology* 23: 1025–1051.

———. 2003. Food procurement and tooth use in two sympatric lemur species. *American Journal of Physical Anthropology* 121: 125–133.

———. 2008. Chemical properties of the diets of two lemur species in southwestern Madagascar. *International Journal of Primatology* 29: 339–364.

Yamashita, N., Vinyard, C. J., and Tan, C. L. 2009. Food mechanical properties in three sympatric species of *Hapalemur* in Ranomafana National Park, Madagascar. *American Journal of Physical Anthropology* 139: 368–381.

Yamashita, N., Tan, C. L., Vinyard, C. J., and Williams, C. 2010. Semi-quantitative tests of cyanide in foods and excreta of three *Hapalemur* species in Madagascar. *American Journal of Primatology* 72: 56–61.

Yamashita, N., Sauther, M. L., Cuozzo, F. P., and Youssouf Jacky, I. A. 2015. Beyond the gallery forest: Contrasting habitat and diet in *Lemur catta* troops at Bezà Mahafaly Special Reserve. *Folia Primatologica* 86: 35–43.

Yamashita, N., Cuozzo, F. P., Sauther, M. L., Fitzgerald, E., Riemenschneider, A., and Ungar, P. S. 2016. Mechanical food properties and dental topography differentiate three populations of *Lemur catta* in southwest Madagascar. *Journal of Human Evolution* 98: 66–75. https://doi.org/10.1016/j.jhevol.2015.09.006.

Yoder, A. D. 1994. Relative position of the Cheirogaleidae in strepsirhine phylogeny: A comparison of morphological and molecular methods and results. *American Journal of Physical Anthropology* 94: 25–46.

———. 1997. Back to the future: A synthesis of strepsirrhine systematics. *Evolutionary Anthropology* 6: 11–22.

———. 2003. Phylogeny of the lemurs. In *The Natural History of Madagascar*. eds S. M. Goodman and J. P. Benstead, pp. 1242–1247. Chicago: University of Chicago Press.

———. 2013. The lemur revolution starts now: The genomic coming of age for a non-model organism. *Molecular Phylogenetics and Evolution* 66: 442–452. https://doi.org/10.1016/j.ympev.2012.08.024.

Yoder, A. D., and Nowak, M. D. 2006. Has vicariance or dispersal been the predominant biogeographic force in Madagascar? Only time will tell. *Annual Review of Ecology, Evolution, and Systematics* 37(1): 405–431.

Yoder, A. D., Vilgalys, R., and Ruvolo, M. 1996a. Molecular evolutionary dynamics of cytochrome b in strepsirrhine primates: The phylogenetic significance of third-position transversions. *Molecular Biology and Evolution* 13: 1339–1350. https://doi.org/10.1093/oxfordjournals.molbev.a025580.

Yoder, A. D., Cartmill, M., Ruvolo, M., Smith, K., and Vilgalys, R. 1996b. Ancient single origin for Malagasy primates. *Proceedings of the National Academy of Sciences of the USA* 93: 5122–5126.

Yoder, A. D., Rakotosamimanana, B., and Parsons, T. 1999. Ancient DNA in subfossil lemurs: Methodological challenges and their solutions. In *New Directions in Lemur Studies*, eds. B. Rakotosamimanana, H. Rasamimanana, J. U. Ganzhorn, and S. M. Goodman, pp. 1–17. New York: Kluwer Academic/Plenum Press.

Yoder, A. D., Rasoloarison, R. M., Goodman, S. M., Irwin, J. A., Atsalis, S., Ravosa, M. J., and Ganzhorn, J. U. 2000. Remarkable species diversity in Malagasy mouse lemurs (primates, *Microcebus*). *Proceedings of the National Academy of Sciences of the USA* 97: 11325–11330.

Yoder, A. D., Burns, M. M., Zehr, S., Delefosse, T., Veron, G., Goodman, S. M., and Flynn, J. J. 2003. Single origin of Malagasy Carnivora from an African ancestor. *Nature* 421: 734–737. https://doi.org/10.1038/nature01303.

Yoder, A. D., Campbell, C. R., Blanco, M. B., Reis, M. dos, Ganzhorn, J. U., et al. 2016. Geogenetic patterns in mouse lemurs (genus *Microcebus*) reveal the ghosts of Madagascar's forests past. *Proceedings of the National Academy of Sciences of the USA* 113: 8049–8056. https://doi.org/10.1073/pnas.1601081113.

Yoder, J. B., Clancey, E., Des Roches, S., Eastman, J. M., Gentry, L., et al. 2010. Ecological opportunity and the origin of adaptive radiations. *Journal of Evolutionary Biology* 23: 1581–1596.

Young, A. L., Richard, A. F., and Aiello, L. C. 1990. Female dominance and maternal investment in strepsirrhine primates. *American Naturalist* 135: 473–488.

Young, R. P., Toto Volahy, A., Bourou, R., Lewis, R., Durbin, J., Wright, T. J., Hounsome, T. D., and Fa, J. E. 2008. A baseline estimate of population size for monitoring the endangered Madagascar giant jumping rat *Hypogeomys antimena*. *Oryx* 42: 584–591.

Youssouf Jacky, I. A., and Rasoazanabary, E. 2008. Discovery of *Macrotarsomys bastardi* at Beza Mahafaly Special Reserve, southwest Madagascar, with observations on the dynamics of small mammal interactions. *Madagascar Conservation and Development* 3(1): 31–37.

Yovel, Y., Falk, B., Moss, C. F., and Ulanovsky, N. 2010. Optimal localization by pointing off axis. *Science* 327: 701–704.

Yovel, Y., Geva-Sagiv, M., and Ulanovsky, N. 2011a. Click-based echolocation in bats: Not so primitive after all. *Journal of Comparative Physiology A: Neuroethology, Sensory, Neural, and Behavioral Physiology* 197A: 515–530.

Yovel, Y., Falk, B., Moss, C. F., and Ulanovsky, N. 2011b. Active control of acoustic field-of-view in a biosonar system. *PLoS Biology* 9(9): e1001150. https://doi.org/10.1371/journal.pbio.1001150.

Zanoli, A., De Gregorio, C., Valente, D., Torti, V., Bonadonna, G., Randrianarison, R. M., Giacoma, C., and Gamba, M. 2020. Sexually dimorphic phrase organization in the song of the indris (*Indri indri*). *American Journal of Primatology* 82(6): 1–8.

Zaonarivelo, J. R., Andriantompohavana, R., Engberg, S. E., Kelley, S. G., Randriamanana, J., Louis, E. E., Jr., and Brenneman, R. A. 2007. Morphometric data for indri (*Indri indri*) collected from ten forest fragments in eastern Madagascar. *Lemur News* 12: 17–21.

Zaramody, A., Fausser, J. L., Roos, C., Zinner, D., Andriaholinirina, N., Rabarivola, C., Norscia, I., Tattersall, I., and Rumpler I. 2006. Molecular phylogeny and taxonomic revision of the eastern woolly lemurs (*Avahi laniger*). *Primate Report* 74: 9–23.

Zehr, S. M., Roach, R. G., Haring, D., Taylor, J., Cameron, F. H., and Yoder, A. D. 2014. Life history profiles for 27 strepsirrhine primate taxa generated using captive data from the Duke Lemur Center. *Scientific Data* 1: 140019.

Zeng, L., Ming, C., Li, Y., Su, L.-Y., Su, Y.-H., et al. 2018. Out of southern east Asia of the brown rat revealed by large-scale genome sequencing. *Molecular Biology and Evolution* 35(1): 149–158. https://doi.org/10.1093/molbev/msx276.

Zhou, Y., Wang, S. R., and Ma, J. Z. 2017. Comprehensive species set revealing the phylogeny and biogeography of Feliformia (Mammalia, Carnivora) based on mitochondrial DNA. *PLoS One* 12(3): e0174902.

Zimmermann, E. 1995. Acoustic communication in nocturnal prosimians. In *Creatures of the Dark*, eds. L. Alterman, G. Doyle, and M. Izard, pp. 311–30. New York: Plenum Press.

———. 1998. Waldgeister der Tropen: Die nachtaktiven Lemuren Madagaskars. *Biologie in unserer Zeit* 5: 294–303.

Zimmermann, E., and Radespiel, U. 2014. Species concepts, diversity, and evolution in primates: Lessons to be learned from mouse lemurs. *Evolutionary Anthropology* 23: 11–14.

Zimmermann, E., Cepok, S., Rakotoarison, N., Zietemann, V., and Radespiel, U. 1998. Sympatric mouse lemurs in north-west Madagascar: A new rufous mouse lemur species (*Microcebus ravelobensis*). *Folia Primatologica* 69: 106–114.

Zinner, D., Hilgartner, R. D., Kappeler, P. M., Pietsch, T., and Ganzhorn, J. U. 2003. Social organization of *Lepilemur ruficaudatus*. *International Journal of Primatology* 24: 869–888.

Zinner, D., Roos, C., Fausser, J.-L., Groves, C., and Y. Rumpler. 2007. Disputed taxonomy classification of sportive lemurs (*Lepilemur*) in NW Madagascar. *Lemur News* 12: 53–56.

Zinner, D., Wygoda, C., Razafimanantsoa, L., Rasoloarison, R., Andrianandrasana, H. T., Ganzhorn, J. U., and Torkler, F. 2014. Analysis of deforestation patterns in the central Menabe, Madagascar, between 1973 and 2010. *Regional Environmental Change* 14: 157–166.

Zipkin, E. F., DeWan, A., and Royle, A. 2009. Impacts of forest fragmentation on species richness: A hierarchical approach to community modelling. *Journal of Applied Ecology* 46: 815–822.

Zohdy, S., Grossman, M. K., Fried, I. R., Rasambainarivo, F. T., Wright, P. C., and Gillespie, T. R. 2015. Diversity and prevalence of diarrhea-associated viruses in the lemur community and associated human population of Ranomafana National Park, Madagascar. *International Journal of Primatology* 36: 143–153. https://doi.org/10.1007/s10764-015-9817-5.

CHAPTER 15

CONSERVATION

PROTECTED AREAS

S. M. Goodman, H. M. Rakotondratsimba, and J. C. Ranivo Rakotoson

Much has been written about the protected areas of Madagascar from the perspective of their critical role in conserving the unique natural patrimony of the island (Nicoll and Langrand 1989; Gardner et al. 2018; Goodman et al. 2018), their history (e.g., Langrand and Rene de Roland 2018), their judicial and financial aspects (e.g., Ranivo Rakotoson and Razafimahatratra 2018 for a recent review), and the multifaceted features associated with the system fulfilling its mandate overlaid on the socioeconomic evolution of nearby communities (see Jones et al., pp. 2130–40). The purpose of this contribution as an introduction to this chapter on conservation is not to evaluate or discuss these different aspects, but rather to present a summary of the current protected area system, provide a geographic reference for sites mentioned elsewhere in the book, and therefore set the stage for the contributions that follow.

In the precursor of the current book (Goodman and Benstead 2003), a chapter of slightly more than 170 pages was devoted to "Conservation." Of the 29 different contributions in that chapter, four treated general subjects of existing or potential terrestrial protected areas and forest management and restoration; 16 dealt with site-specific or habitat-specific conservation projects; and nine addressed species-related conservation projects. The site- and habitat-specific contributions focused on official or proposed protected areas of that period, presenting, for example, details on the history, biota, biogeographic importance, management systems, cultural aspects, and positive and challenging aspects of local conservation programs. These contributions were important for various reasons, one being that they provided a summary of the different current and future actions across the notably diverse ecological and cultural landscapes of the island. The critical point was that the idea of using a single methodological approach across Madagascar for effective conservation programs, which at the same time advanced protection of biodiversity and benefited local communities, was simply inapplicable. Instead, each ecological setting and cultural context needed to be considered independently. Further, these contributions provided a broad update to information on the sites, as well as physical (administrative and infrastructural) and technical advancements (rational approaches and strategies to align with community needs) since the previous review of Madagascar's protected area system some 15 years earlier (Nicoll and Langrand 1989).

More recently, a comprehensive review was published of 98 selected terrestrial protected areas on the island (Goodman et al. 2018), updating and filling in many details for sites covered in the conservation chapter contributions in Goodman and Benstead (2003), as well as many sites identified, delineated, and publicly published in the past two decades. Much of the relatively recent expansion of Madagascar's protected area system was associated with the 2003 "Durban Vision," discussed in detail herein in a subsequent contribution (see Jones et al., pp. 2130–40). Hence, it was decided in the current book that a conservation chapter similar to that in the 2003 book would overlap considerably with Goodman et al. (2018) and would be redundant in many aspects. With these points in mind, and to emphasize physical and technical advancements in the conservation of the remaining natural habitats on the island, including many new technologies and methodologies, we have included contributions herein on these developments, as well as a broad overview contribution on the protected area system ranging from the past to the future.

TABLE 15.1. **Official protected areas (PA), arranged alphabetically by short name, as of late November 2020, with site numbers in Figure 15.1**

SITE NUMBER	SHORT NAME OF PA	COMPLETE NAME OF PA	TERRESTRIAL OR MARINE	FORMER PROVINCE(S)	REGION(S)	SURFACE AREA (ha)	SITE MANAGER
60	Agnakatrika	Réserve de Ressources Naturelles d'Agnakatrika	Terrestrial	Fianarantsoa	Atsimo Atsinanana	780	Missouri Botanical Garden (MBG)
56	Agnalazaha	Réserve de Ressources Naturelles d'Agnalazaha	Terrestrial	Fianarantsoa	Atsimo Atsinanana	2745	Missouri Botanical Garden (MBG)
106	Alandraza Analavelo	Monument Naturel de la Forêt Sacrée Alandraza Analavelo	Terrestrial	Toliara	Atsimo Andrefana	4487	Missouri Botanical Garden (MBG)
100	Allée des Baobabs	Monument Naturel de l'Allée des Baobabs	Terrestrial	Toliara	Menabe	320	Fanamby
88	Ambararata Londa	Aire Protégée d'Ambararata Londa	Terrestrial	Toliara	Menabe	10,284	Orphan site
67	Ambatoatsinanana	Paysage Harmonieux Protégé d'Ambatoatsinanana	Predominantly marine with a terrestrial component	Toliara	Anosy	1365	QIT Madagascar Minerals (QMM)
49	Ambatofotsy	Paysage Harmonieux Protégé d'Ambatofotsy	Terrestrial	Toamasina	Alaotra Mangoro	1775	Madagasikara Voakajy (MaVoa)
72	Ambatotsirongorongo	Réserve Spéciale d'Ambatotsirongorongo	Terrestrial	Toliara	Anosy	1033	Orphan site
29	Ambatovaky	Réserve Spéciale d'Ambatovaky	Terrestrial	Toamasina	Analanjirofo	78,139	Madagascar National Parks (MNP)
	Ambodivahibe	Paysage Harmonieux Protégé d'Ambodivahibe	Marine	Antsiranana	DIANA	39,794	Conservation International (CI)
42	Ambohidray	Aire Protégée d'Ambohidray	Terrestrial	Toamasina	Alaotra Mangoro	1241	Département de Biologie et Ecologie Végétale, Université d'Antananarivo (DBEV)
83	Ambohijanahary	Réserve Spéciale d'Ambohijanahary	Terrestrial	Mahajanga, Toliara	Melaky, Menabe	24,750	Sauvegarde de l'Environnement et pour le Développement Intégré de Madagascar (ONG SEDIM)
82	Ambohitantely	Réserve Spéciale d'Ambohitantely	Terrestrial	Antananarivo	Analamanga	5600	Madagascar National Parks (MNP)

SITE NUMBER	SHORT NAME OF PA	COMPLETE NAME OF PA	TERRESTRIAL OR MARINE	FORMER PROVINCE(S)	REGION(S)	SURFACE AREA (ha)	SITE MANAGER
97	Ambondrobe	Paysage Harmonieux Protégé du Complexe Lac-Forêt Ambondrobe	Terrestrial	Toliara	Menabe	6133	Durrell Wildlife Conservation Trust (DWCT)
51	Ambositra-Vondrozo	Paysage Harmonieux Protégé du Corridor Forestier Ambositra-Vondrozo	Terrestrial	Fianarantsoa	Amoron'i Mania, Atsimo Atsinanana, Haute Matsiatra, Ihorombe, Vatovavy Fitovinany	314,186	Conservation International (CI)
108	Amoron'i Onilahy	Paysage Harmonieux Protégé d'Amoron'i Onilahy	Terrestrial	Toliara	Atsimo Andrefana	100,482	World Wide Fund for Nature (WWF)
39	Ampanangandehibe-Behasina	Paysage Harmonieux Protégé d'Ampanangandehibe-Behasina	Terrestrial	Toamasina	Alaotra Mangoro	580	Madagasikara Voakajy (MaVoa)
12	Ampasindava	Paysage Harmonieux Protégé d'Ampasindava	Terrestrial	Antsiranana	DIANA	91,790	Missouri Botanical Garden (MBG)
35	Analabe Betanatanana	Réserve de Ressources Naturelles d'Analabe Betanatanana	Terrestrial	Toamasina	Alaotra Mangoro	435	Madagasikara Voakajy (MaVoa)
36	Analalava–Alaotra Mangoro	Réserve de Ressources Naturelles d'Analalava	Terrestrial	Toamasina	Alaotra Mangoro	472	Madagasikara Voakajy (MaVoa)
34	Analalava-Atsinanana	Réserve Spéciale d'Analalava	Terrestrial	Toamasina	Atsinanana	229	Missouri Botanical Garden (MBG)
78	Analamaitso	Réserve Spéciale de Tampoketsa d'Analamaitso	Terrestrial	Mahajanga, Toamasina	Sofia, Alaotra Mangoro	17,150	Orphan site
46	Analamazaotra	Parc National d'Analamazaotra	Terrestrial	Toamasina	Alaotra Mangoro	874	Madagascar National Parks (MNP)

(continued overleaf)

TABLE 15.1. ***continued***

SITE NUMBER	SHORT NAME OF PA	COMPLETE NAME OF PA	TERRESTRIAL OR MARINE	FORMER PROVINCE(S)	REGION(S)	SURFACE AREA (ha)	SITE MANAGER
5	Analamerana	Réserve Spéciale d'Analamerana	Terrestrial	Antsiranana	DIANA	34,700	Madagascar National Parks (MNP)
63	Andohahela	Parc National d'Andohahela	Terrestrial	Toliara	Anosy	76,140	Madagascar National Parks (MNP)
7	Andrafiamena Andavakoera	Paysage Harmonieux Protégé d'Andrafiamena Andavakoera	Terrestrial	Antsiranana	DIANA	73,319	Fanamby
99	Andranomena	Réserve Spéciale d'Andranomena	Terrestrial	Toliara	Menabe	6420	Madagascar National Parks (MNP)
26	Andreba	Paysage Harmonieux Protégé d'Andreba	Terrestrial	Toamasina	Analanjirofo	39	Wildlife Conservation Society (WCS)
53	Andringitra	Parc National d'Andringitra	Terrestrial	Fianarantsoa	Haute Matsiatra, Ihorombe	31,160	Madagascar National Parks (MNP)
66	Angavo	Aire Protégée d'Angavo	Terrestrial	Toliara	Androy	42,760	Orphan site
22	Anjanaharibe-Sud	Réserve Spéciale d'Anjanaharibe-Sud	Terrestrial	Antsiranana, Mahajanga	SAVA, Sofia	26,903	Madagascar National Parks (MNP)
84	Anjozorobe-Angavo	Paysage Harmonieux Protégé du Complexe Anjozorobe-Angavo	Terrestrial	Antananarivo, Toamasina	Alaotra Mangoro, Analamanga	41,100	Fanamby
59	Ankarabolava	Réserve de Ressources Naturelles d'Ankarabolava	Terrestrial	Fianarantsoa	Atsimo Atsinanana	773	Missouri Botanical Garden (MBG)
79	Ankarafantsika	Parc National d'Ankarafantsika	Terrestrial	Mahajanga	Boeny	136,513	Madagascar National Parks (MNP)
8	Ankarana	Réserve Spéciale d'Ankarana	Terrestrial	Antsiranana	DIANA	18,225	Madagascar National Parks (MNP)
	Ankarea	Paysage Harmonieux Protégé d'Ankarea	Marine	Antsiranana	DIANA	135,556	Wildlife Conservation Society (WCS)
37	Ankeniheny-Zahamena	Réserve de Ressources Naturelles du Corridor Ankeniheny-Zahamena	Terrestrial	Toamasina	Alaotra Mangoro, Atsinanana	369,266	Conservation International (CI)

SITE NUMBER	SHORT NAME OF PA	COMPLETE NAME OF PA	TERRESTRIAL OR MARINE	FORMER PROVINCE(S)	REGION(S)	SURFACE AREA (ha)	SITE MANAGER
	Ankivonjy	Paysage Harmonieux Protégé d'Ankivonjy	Marine	Antsiranana	DIANA	139,410	Wildlife Conservation Society (WCS)
70	Ankodida	Paysage Harmonieux Protégé d'Ankodida	Terrestrial	Toliara	Anosy	11,048	World Wide Fund for Nature (WWF)
50	Ankorabe	Paysage Harmonieux Protégé d'Ampotaka-Ankorabe	Terrestrial	Toamasina	Alaotra Mangoro	97	Madagasikara Voakajy (MaVoa)
74	Antrema	Réserve de Ressources Naturelles du Site Bioculturel d'Antrema	Terrestrial with marine area	Mahajanga	Boeny	20,620	Muséum National d'Histoire Naturelle (Paris)
77	Baie de Baly	Parc National de la Baie de Baly	Terrestrial with marine area	Mahajanga	Boeny	57,418	Madagascar National Parks (MNP)
94	Beanka	Paysage Harmonieux Protégé de Beanka	Terrestrial	Mahajanga	Melaky	17,000	Biodiversity Conservation Madagascar (BCM)
57	Befotaka–Midongy du Sud	Parc National de Befotaka–Midongy du Sud	Terrestrial	Fianarantsoa	Atsimo Atsinanana, Ihorombe	192,198	Madagascar National Parks (MNP)
64	Behara Tranomaro	Aire Protégée de Behara Tranomaro	Terrestrial	Toliara	Anosy	96,588	Orphan site
18	Bemanevika	Paysage Harmonieux Protégé de Bemanevika	Terrestrial	Mahajanga	Sofia	35,605	The Peregrine Fund (TPF)
95	Bemaraha	Parc National de Tsingy de Bemaraha	Terrestrial	Mahajanga	Melaky	157,710	Madagascar National Parks (MNP)
91	Bemarivo	Réserve Spéciale de Bemarivo	Terrestrial	Mahajanga	Melaky	11,575	Orphan site
38	Betampona	Réserve Naturelle Intégrale de Betampona	Terrestrial	Toamasina	Atsinanana	2228	Madagascar National Parks (MNP)
110	Bezà-Mahafaly	Réserve Spéciale de Bezà-Mahafaly	Terrestrial	Toliara	Atsimo Andrefana	4200	Madagascar National Parks (MNP)

(continued overleaf)

TABLE 15.1. ***continued***

SITE NUMBER	SHORT NAME OF PA	COMPLETE NAME OF PA	TERRESTRIAL OR MARINE	FORMER PROVINCE(S)	REGION(S)	SURFACE AREA (ha)	SITE MANAGER
76	Bombetoka Beloboka	Aire Protégée de Bombetoka Beloboka	Terrestrial (delta, mangrove, river)	Mahajanga	Boeny	71,943	Development and Environmental Law Center (DELC)
73	Bongolava	Paysage Harmonieux Protégé du Corridor Forestier Bongolava	Terrestrial	Mahajanga	Sofia	60,589	Fikambanana Bongolava Maitso (FBM)
21	Bora	Réserve Spéciale de Bora	Terrestrial	Mahajanga	Sofia	4841	Orphan site
113	Cap Sainte Marie	Réserve Spéciale de Cap Sainte Marie	Terrestrial with marine area	Toliara	Androy	3610	Madagascar National Parks (MNP)
11	COMATSA Nord	Réserve de Ressources Naturelles du Corridor Marojejy-Anjanaharibe Sud–Tsaratanàna partie Nord	Terrestrial	Antsiranana, Mahajanga	DIANA, SAVA, Sofia	237,883	World Wide Fund for Nature (WWF)
20	COMATSA Sud	Paysage Harmonieux Protégé du Corridor Marojejy-Anjanaharibe Sud–Tsaratanàna partie Sud	Terrestrial	Antsiranana, Mahajanga	SAVA, Sofia	80,204	World Wide Fund for Nature (WWF)
10	Galoko-Kalobinono	Paysage Harmonieux Protégé de Galoko-Kalobinono	Terrestrial	Antsiranana	DIANA	74,205	Missouri Botanical Garden (MBG), currently being transferred to Association Famelona
89	Ibity	Paysage Harmonieux Protégé du Massif d'Ibity	Terrestrial	Antananarivo	Vakinankaratra	6136	Missouri Botanical Garden (MBG)
104	Isalo	Parc National de l'Isalo	Terrestrial	Fianarantsoa	Ihorombe	81,540	Madagascar National Parks (MNP)
90	Itremo	Paysage Harmonieux Protégé du Massif d'Itremo	Terrestrial	Fianarantsoa	Amoron'i Mania	24,788	Royal Botanic Gardens (RBG-Kew)
58	Kalambatritra	Réserve Spéciale de Kalambatritra	Terrestrial	Fianarantsoa, Toliara	Anosy, Ihorombe	28,255	Madagascar National Parks (MNP)

SITE NUMBER	SHORT NAME OF PA	COMPLETE NAME OF PA	TERRESTRIAL OR MARINE	FORMER PROVINCE(S)	REGION(S)	SURFACE AREA (ha)	SITE MANAGER
81	Kasijy	Réserve Spéciale de Kasijy	Terrestrial	Mahajanga	Betsiboka	19,800	Orphan site
101	Kirindy Mité	Parc National de Kirindy Mité	Terrestrial with marine area	Toliara	Menabe	156,350	Madagascar National Parks (MNP)
32	Lake Alaotra	Paysage Harmonieux Protégé du Lac Alaotra	Terrestrial	Toamasina	Alaotra Mangoro	46,432	Durrell Wildlife Conservation Trust (DWCT)
9	Lokobe	Parc National de Lokobe	Terrestrial with marine area	Antsiranana	DIANA	862	Madagascar National Parks (MNP)
6	Loky Manambato	Paysage Harmonieux Protégé de Loky Manambato	Terrestrial with marine area	Antsiranana	SAVA	250,000	Fanamby
75	Mahavavy Kinkony	Paysage Harmonieux Protégé du Complexe Zones Humides Mahavavy Kinkony	Terrestrial with marine area	Mahajanga	Boeny	302,000	Asity Madagascar
40	Mahialambo	Paysage Harmonieux Protégé de Mahialambo	Terrestrial	Toamasina	Alaotra Mangoro	302	Madagasikara Voakajy (MaVoa)
17	Mahimborondro	Réserve de Ressources Naturelles de Mahimborondro	Terrestrial	Antsiranana, Mahajanga	DIANA, Sofia	75,163	The Peregrine Fund (TPF)
23	Makira	Parc Naturel de Makira	Terrestrial	Antsiranana, Mahajanga, Toamasina	Analanjirofo, SAVA, Sofia	372,470	Wildlife Conservation Society (WCS)
16	Makirovana Tsihomanaomby	Réserve de Ressources Naturelles de Makirovana Tsihomanaomby	Terrestrial	Antsiranana	SAVA	3398	Missouri Botanical Garden (MBG)
27	Mananara-Nord	Parc National de Mananara-Nord	Terrestrial with marine area	Toamasina	Analanjirofo	24,000	Madagascar National Parks (MNP)
69	Mandena	Paysage Harmonieux Protégé de Mandena	Terrestrial	Toliara	Anosy	430	QIT Madagascar Minerals (QMM)

(continued overleaf)

TABLE 15.1. ***continued***

SITE NUMBER	SHORT NAME OF PA	COMPLETE NAME OF PA	TERRESTRIAL OR MARINE	FORMER PROVINCE(S)	REGION(S)	SURFACE AREA (ha)	SITE MANAGER
93	Mandrozo	Paysage Harmonieux Protégé de Mandrozo	Terrestrial	Mahajanga	Melaky	15,145	The Peregrine Fund (TPF)
48	Mangabe-Ranomena-Sahasarotra	Réserve de Ressources Naturelles de Mangabe-Ranomena-Sahasarotra	Terrestrial	Toamasina	Alaotra Mangoro	27,346	Madagasikara Voakajy (MaVoa)
41	Mangerivola	Réserve Spéciale de Mangerivola	Terrestrial	Toamasina	Atsinanana	12,475	Madagascar National Parks (MNP)
102	Mangoky Ihotry	Paysage Harmonieux Protégé du Complexe Zones Humides Mangoky Ihotry	Terrestrial	Toliara	Atsimo Andrefana, Menabe	426,146	Asity Madagascar
92	Maningozy	Réserve Spéciale de Maningozy	Terrestrial	Mahajanga	Melaky	7900	Orphan site
85	Manjakatompo Ankaratra	Réserve de Ressources Naturelles de Manjakatompo Ankaratra	Terrestrial	Antananarivo	Vakinankaratra	8130	Vondrona Ivon'ny Fampandrosoana (VIF)
55	Manombo	Réserve Spéciale de Manombo	Terrestrial	Fianarantsoa	Atsimo Atsinanana	5320	Madagascar National Parks (MNP)
14	Manongarivo	Réserve Spéciale de Manongarivo	Terrestrial	Antsiranana, Mahajanga	DIANA, Sofia	51,568	Madagascar National Parks (MNP)
44	Mantadia	Parc National de Mantadia	Terrestrial	Toamasina	Alaotra Mangoro	15,480	Madagascar National Parks (MNP)
19	Marojejy	Parc National de Marojejy	Terrestrial	Antsiranana	SAVA	60,050	Madagascar National Parks (MNP)
86	Marolambo	Parc National de Marolambo	Terrestrial	Antananarivo, Fianarantsoa, Toamasina	Amoron'i Mania, Atsinanana, Vakinankaratra, Vatovavy Fitovinany	95,063	Madagascar National Parks (MNP)
47	Maromizaha	Réserve de Ressources Naturelles de Maromizaha	Terrestrial	Toamasina	Alaotra Mangoro	1880	Groupe d'Etude et de Recherche sur les Primates de Madagascar (GERP)

SITE NUMBER	SHORT NAME OF PA	COMPLETE NAME OF PA	TERRESTRIAL OR MARINE	FORMER PROVINCE(S)	REGION(S)	SURFACE AREA (ha)	SITE MANAGER
28	Marotandrano	Réserve Spéciale de Marotandrano	Terrestrial	Toamasina, Mahajanga	Alaotra Mangoro, Sofia	42,200	Madagascar National Parks (MNP)
24	Masoala	Parc National de Masoala	Terrestrial with marine area	Antsiranana, Toamasina	Analanjirofo, SAVA	230,000	Madagascar National Parks (MNP)
98	Menabe Antimena	Paysage Harmonieux Protégé de Menabe Antimena	Terrestrial with marine area	Toliara	Menabe	210,312	Fanamby
103	Mikea	Parc National de Mikea	Terrestrial	Toliara	Atsimo Andrefana	184,630	Madagascar National Parks (MNP)
4	Montagne d'Ambre	Parc National de Montagne d'Ambre	Terrestrial	Antsiranana	DIANA	30,538	Madagascar National Parks (MNP)
3	Montagne des Français	Paysage Harmonieux Protégé d'Ambohitr'Antsingy Montagne des Français	Terrestrial	Antsiranana	DIANA	6049	Service d'Appui à la Gestion de l'Environnement (SAGE)
80	Namoroka	Parc National de Namoroka	Terrestrial	Mahajanga	Boeny	22,227	Madagascar National Parks (MNP)
65	Nord-Ifotaka	Paysage Harmonieux Protégé de Nord-Ifotaka	Terrestrial	Toliara	Anosy	22,288	World Wide Fund for Nature (WWF)
87	Nosivolo	Paysage Harmonieux Protégé de la Rivière Nosivolo	Terrestrial (river)	Toamasina	Atsinanana	9657	Durrell Wildlife Conservation Trust (DWCT)
	Nosy Antsoha	Paysage Harmonieux Protégé de Nosy Antsoha	Marine	Antsiranana	DIANA	28	Lemuria Land
1	Nosy Hara	Parc National de Nosy Hara	Predominantly marine with a terrestrial component	Antsiranana	DIANA	125,471	Madagascar National Parks (MNP)
25	Nosy Mangabe	Parc National de Nosy Mangabe	Terrestrial with marine area	Toamasina	Analanjirofo	729	Madagascar National Parks (MNP)

(continued overleaf)

TABLE 15.1. ***continued***

SITE NUMBER	SHORT NAME OF PA	COMPLETE NAME OF PA	TERRESTRIAL OR MARINE	FORMER PROVINCE(S)	REGION(S)	SURFACE AREA (ha)	SITE MANAGER
	Nosy Tanikely	Parc National de Nosy Tanikely	Marine	Antsiranana	DIANA	180	Madagascar National Parks (MNP)
	Nosy Ve Androka	Parc National de Nosy Ve Androka	Marine	Toliara	Atsimo Andrefana	91,445	Madagascar National Parks (MNP)
2	Oronjia	Paysage Harmonieux Protégé d'Oronjia	Terrestrial	Antsiranana	DIANA	1648	Missouri Botanical Garden (MBG)
71	Petriky	Paysage Harmonieux Protégé de la Forêt Naturelle de Petriky	Terrestrial	Toliara	Anosy	300	QIT Madagascar Minerals (QMM)
54	Pic d'Ivohibe	Réserve Spéciale du Pic d'Ivohibe	Terrestrial	Fianarantsoa	Ihorombe	3453	Madagascar National Parks (MNP)
30	Pointe à Larrée	Réserve Spéciale de Pointe à Larrée	Terrestrial	Toamasina	Analanjirofo	770	Missouri Botanical Garden (MBG)
	Ranobe Bay	Aire Protégée de Ranobe Bay	Marine	Toliara	Atsimo Andrefana	42,404	Orphan site
107	Ranobe PK32	Aire Protégée de Ranobe PK32	Terrestrial	Toliara	Atsimo Andrefana	168,500	Orphan site
52	Ranomafana	Parc National de Ranomafana	Terrestrial	Fianarantsoa	Haute Matsiatra, Vatovavy Fitovinany	43,550	Madagascar National Parks (MNP)
43	Sahafina	Paysage Harmonieux Protégé de Sahafina	Terrestrial	Toamasina	Atsinanana	2400	Biodiversity Conservation Madagascar (BCM)
15	Sahamalaza-Iles Radama	Parc National de Sahamalaza-Iles Radama	Terrestrial with marine area	Mahajanga	Sofia	26,035	Madagascar National Parks (MNP)
	Soariake	Réserve de Ressources Naturelles de Soariake	Marine	Toliara	Atsimo Andrefana	38,293	Wildlife Conservation Society (WCS)
68	Sud-ouest Ifotaky	Aire Protégée de Sud-Ouest Ifotaky	Terrestrial	Toliara	Androy, Anosy	57,062	Orphan site
31	Tampolo	Paysage Harmonieux Protégé de la Réserve de Tampolo	Terrestrial	Toamasina	Analanjirofo	675	Ecole Supérieure des Sciences Agronomiques-Forêts (ESSA-Forêts), Université d'Antananarivo

SITE NUMBER	SHORT NAME OF PA	COMPLETE NAME OF PA	TERRESTRIAL OR MARINE	FORMER PROVINCE(S)	REGION(S)	SURFACE AREA (ha)	SITE MANAGER
45	Torotorofotsy	Aire Protégée de Torotorofotsy	Terrestrial	Toamasina	Alaotra Mangoro	9764	Asity Madagascar
13	Tsaratanàna	Réserve Naturelle Intégrale de Tsaratanàna	Terrestrial	Antsiranana, Mahajanga	DIANA, SAVA, Sofia	108,610	Madagascar National Parks (MNP)
111	Tsimanampesotse	Parc National de Tsimanampesotse	Terrestrial	Toliara	Atsimo Andrefana	202,525	Madagascar National Parks (MNP)
96	Tsimembo-Manambolomaty	Paysage Harmonieux Protégé du Complexe Tsimembo Manambolomaty	Terrestrial with marine area	Mahajanga	Melaky	62,745	The Peregrine Fund (TPF)
109	Tsinjoriake	Paysage Harmonieux Protégé de Tsinjoriake	Terrestrial	Toliara	Atsimo Andrefana	5484	Tahosoa Alandriake Mitambatse Ianantsono Andatabo (TAMIA)
62	Tsitongambarika	Réserve de Ressources Naturelles de la Forêt Naturelle de Tsitongambarika	Terrestrial	Toliara	Anosy	58,597	Asity Madagascar
	Velondriake	Paysage Harmonieux Protégé de Velondriake	Marine	Toliara	Atsimo Andrefana	63,985	Blue Ventures
61	Vohidava-Betsimalaho	Réserve de Ressources Naturelles de Vohidava-Betsimalaho	Terrestrial	Toliara	Anosy	18,169	Missouri Botanical Garden (MBG)
112	Vohidefo	Aire Protégée de Vohidefo	Terrestrial	Toliara	Atsimo Andrefana	5056	Orphan site
33	Zahamena	Parc National de Zahamena	Terrestrial	Toamasina	Alaotra Mangoro, Analanjirofo, Atsinanana	64,935	Madagascar National Parks (MNP)
105	Zombitse-Vohibasia	Parc National de Zombitse-Vohibasia	Terrestrial	Toliara	Atsimo Andrefana	36,803	Madagascar National Parks (MNP)

Notes: Sites highlighted in color are exclusively marine and are not shown in Figure 15.1; these are discussed in greater detail in Cooke et al. (see pp. 311–58). Information is also given on the administrative aspects of each site including the former provincial system and the current region designations. We have also included details on the site managers, based on Ranivo Rakotoson and Razafimahatratra (2018), with more recent updates. Protected areas designated as orphan sites have been abandoned by the former manager and are under the direction of the Ministère de l'Environnement et du Développement Durable (MEDD).

NATURAL HISTORY AND CONSERVATION

We maintain that in order to advance conservation programs in the context of Madagascar, including prioritization of activities and program advancement, detailed information on the natural history of the organisms concerned is of primary importance. Further and equally important is understanding and considering the positive and negative impacts of these programs on people who live close by and use the natural resources of these sites. As can be seen in the vast majority of contributions in chapters 7 to 14, the theme of the critical need to advance conservation programs at the ecosystem or species level is recurrent, and the word "conservation" should perhaps have been included in the title or subtitle of this book. The considerable growth in knowledge of the island's ecosystems, the constituent organisms, and the local socioeconomic aspects have been very important in a range of different actions to advance the protected area system and conservation programs. Further, a more profound understanding in the context of how these programs must interface with local community needs and development has been an

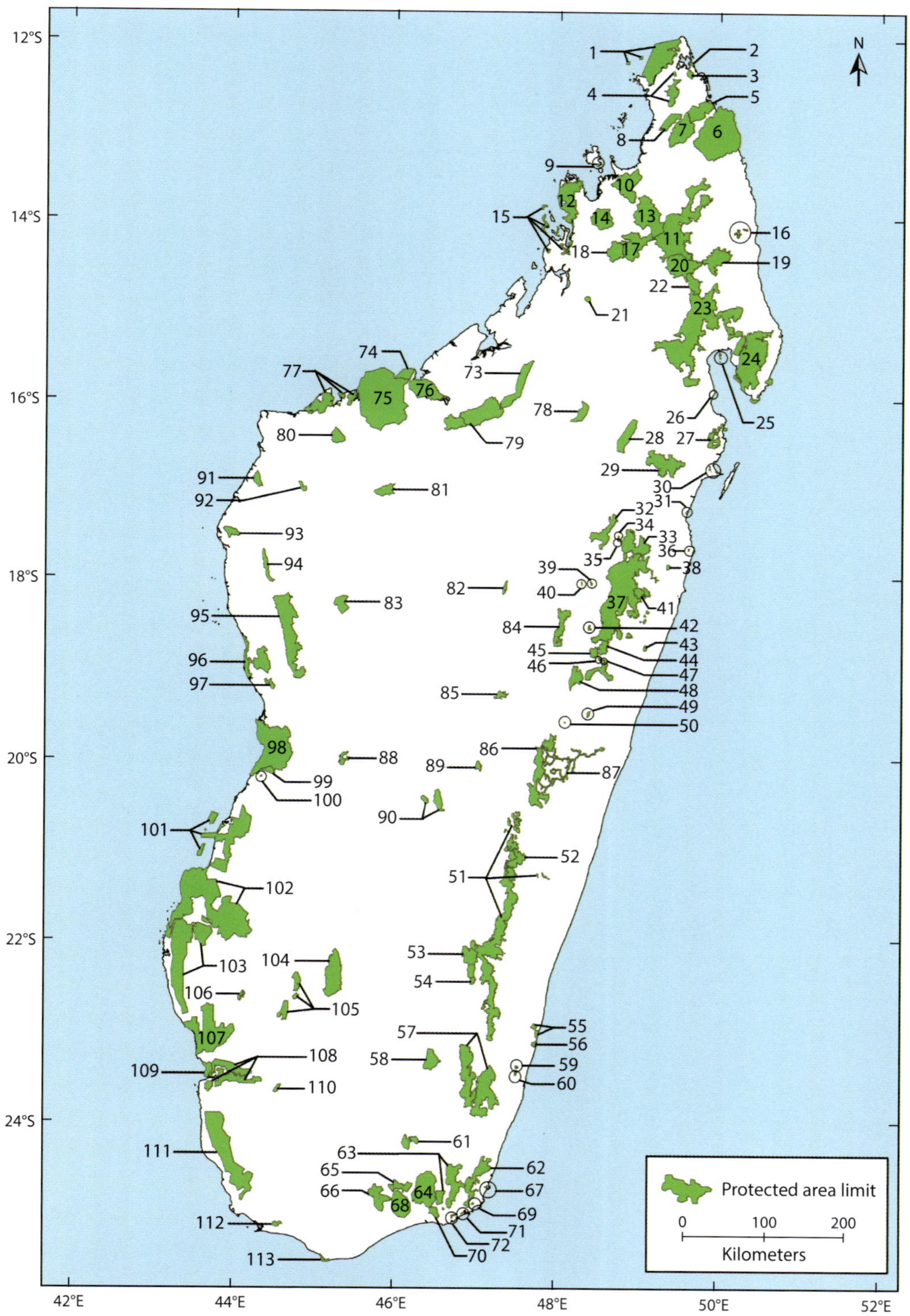

FIGURE 15.1 Map showing the terrestrial and mixed terrestrial-marine official protected areas of Madagascar. To locate sites by protected area name, see Table 15.1; to locate sites by site number, see Table 15.2. For further details on the marine protected area system, see Cooke et al. (pp. 311–58), and for a locator map of marine sites, see Figure 7.10.

TABLE 15.2. **Official protected areas by site number**

SITE NUMBER	SHORT NAME OF PROTECTED AREA
1	Nosy Hara
2	Oronjia
3	Montagne des Français
4	Montagne d'Ambre
5	Analamerana
6	Loky Manambato
7	Andrafiamena Andavakoera
8	Ankarana
9	Lokobe
10	Galoko-Kalobinono
11	COMATSA Nord
12	Ampasindava
13	Tsaratanàna
14	Manongarivo
15	Sahamalaza-Iles Radama
16	Makirovana Tsihomanaomby
17	Mahimborondro
18	Bemanevika
19	Marojejy
20	COMATSA Sud
21	Bora
22	Anjanaharibe-Sud
23	Makira
24	Masoala
25	Nosy Mangabe
26	Andreba
27	Mananara-Nord
28	Marotandrano
29	Ambatovaky
30	Pointe à Larrée
31	Tampolo
32	Lake Alaotra
33	Zahamena
34	Analalava-Atsinanana
35	Analabe Betanatanana
36	Analalava–Alaotra Mangoro
37	Ankeniheny-Zahamena
38	Betampona
39	Ampanangandehibe-Behasina
40	Mahialambo
41	Mangerivola
42	Ambohidray
43	Sahafina
44	Mantadia
45	Torotorofotsy
46	Analamazaotra
47	Maromizaha
48	Mangabe-Ranomena-Sahasarotra
49	Ambatofotsy
50	Ankorabe
51	Ambositra-Vondrozo
52	Ranomafana
53	Andringitra
54	Pic d'Ivohibe
55	Manombo
56	Agnalazaha
57	Befotaka–Midongy du Sud
58	Kalambatritra
59	Ankarabolava
60	Agnakatrika
61	Vohidava-Betsimalaho
62	Tsitongambarika
63	Andohahela
64	Behara Tranomaro
65	Nord-Ifotaka
66	Angavo
67	Ambatoatsinanana
68	Sud-ouest Ifotaky
69	Mandena
70	Ankodida

(continued overleaf)

TABLE 15.2. ***continued***

SITE NUMBER	SHORT NAME OF PROTECTED AREA
71	Petriky
72	Ambatotsirongorongo
73	Bongolava
74	Antrema
75	Mahavavy Kinkony
76	Bombetoka Beloboka
77	Baie de Baly
78	Analamaitso
79	Ankarafantsika
80	Namoroka
81	Kasijy
82	Ambohitantely
83	Ambohijanahary
84	Anjozorobe-Angavo
85	Manjakatompo Ankaratra
86	Marolambo
87	Nosivolo
88	Ambararata Londa
89	Ibity
90	Itremo
91	Bemarivo
92	Maningozy

SITE NUMBER	SHORT NAME OF PROTECTED AREA
93	Mandrozo
94	Beanka
95	Bemaraha
96	Tsimembo-Manambolomaty
97	Ambondrobe
98	Menabe Antimena
99	Andranomena
100	Allée des Baobabs
101	Kirindy Mité
102	Mangoky Ihotry
103	Mikea
104	Isalo
105	Zombitse-Vohibasia
106	Alandraza Analavelo
107	Ranobe PK32
108	Amoron'i Onilahy
109	Tsinjoriake
110	Bezà-Mahafaly
111	Tsimanampesotse
112	Vohidefo
113	Cap Sainte Marie

Note: For a site placement map, see Figure 15.1.

important focus of recent work and the key to long-term successful conservation programs.

MADAGASCAR'S PROTECTED AREA SYSTEM

The island's protected areas cover different ecosystems either from exclusively marine or terrestrial zones, or as a mixture. Table 15.1 lists the protected area sites as of late November 2020; these are official based on their definitive statute following governmental decrees. The exclusively terrestrial and mixed terrestrial-marine sites are presented with unique numeration (following a north–south system across three different longitudinal bands of the island) in Figure 15.1. To help readers navigate the considerable number of protected areas and to provide a "site finder," we present a table by site number (Table 15.2), which can be used as a cross-reference between Table 15.1 and Figure 15.1. Further details on the marine protected areas are presented in Cooke et al. (pp. 311–58), along with a locator map of the marine sites (Figure 7.10).

IUCN PROTECTED AREA CLASSIFICATION

In 2005, the first steps were taken to define different types of management and governmental approaches for a series of future protected areas and what would be called Nouvelles Aires Protégées (NAP). In this context and on the basis of a visit to Madagascar by conservation policy specialists from the International Union for Conservation of Nature (IUCN), a wider range of conservation categories was suggested for these NAPs (Borrini-Feyerabend and Dudley 2005), with IUCN protected area categories ranging from I to VI instead of the previous classification of only I, II, and IV. Each of these six categories has different intended goals, access, and use (Table 15.3). This revised system led to an increase in the diversity of stakeholders involved in the management of protected areas, specifically the NAPs, which included different combinations of shared management between the government and other actors, decentralized governance at the regional and local community levels, and involvement of the private sector, civil society, and local communities.

TABLE 15.3. **Categories of protected areas currently in use on Madagascar after IUCN statutes**

IUCN CATEGORY	STATUS	INTENDED PURPOSE	ACCESS	NATURAL RESOURCE USE
I	Réserve Naturelle Intégrale or Strict Nature Reserve	Strict protection of ecosystems.	Only by special permit from national authority and protected area manager.	Forbidden except for scientific research and based on special permits or very specific ritual purposes approved in the protected area's development and management plan. No human settlements within the site.
II	Parc National or National Park	To protect and conserve natural and/or cultural heritage at something approaching an ecosystem level.	By permit from national authority and protected area manager or paying ticket fees for tourists.	The following are prohibited: the slaughter, hunting, and capture of animals and the destruction or collection of plants, except for scientific reasons and under the control and direction of the protected area manager. Access by local communities for the collection of natural resources (e.g., utilitarian plants) is allowed. Areas occupied by humans to be excluded during delimitation.
III	Monument Naturel or Natural Monument	To protect and preserve elements of remarkable natural or cultural value associated with their natural importance or their spiritual connotation. To conserve biodiversity and associated cultural aspects, such as the last vestiges of natural forests, sacred sites or forests, and archaeological sites or sites of particular aesthetic value.	By permit from national authority and protected area manager or paying ticket fees for tourists.	Any intervention likely to transform the local ecosystem or landscape and any harvesting of natural resources for commercial purposes, except that provided for in the protected area development and management plan, are prohibited throughout.
IV	Réserve Spéciale or Special Reserve	To preserve and conserve specific habitats or species. To guarantee and maintain the habitat conditions necessary for the preservation of species and biological communities or important physical elements of the natural environment. Human interventions can be conducted to optimize management.	By permit from national authority and protected area manager or paying ticket fees for tourists.	Access by local communities for the collection of natural resources (e.g., utilitarian plants) is allowed. Regulated forms of animal exploitation (fishing and hunting), collection of coral and shells, and forest product exploitation are possible, but regulated.

(continued overleaf)

TABLE 15.3. ***continued***

IUCN CATEGORY	STATUS	INTENDED PURPOSE	ACCESS	NATURAL RESOURCE USE
V	Paysage Harmonieux Protégé or Protected Harmonious Landscape	To preserve and conserve ecosystems or species based on harmonious interactions between nature and human culture, including natural services, and to protect terrestrial and marine landscapes. Further, to ensure the maintenance of traditional forms of natural occupation as well as the expression of local sociocultural existence, and to promote sustainable lifestyles and economic activities in harmony with nature and the interests of local communities.	By permit from national authority and protected area manager or arrangements with local authorities for different forms of tourism.	Regulated access by local communities for the utilization of renewable and nonrenewable natural resources (e.g., utilitarian plants), including traditional and artisanal fishing, can take place based on a zoning system allowing exploitation by site rotation.
VI	Réserve de Ressources Naturelles or Managed Resource Protected Area	To ensure the protection and long-term maintenance of the site's biological diversity and other natural values. Further, to protect natural resources against all forms of use likely to harm biological diversity and to use renewable natural resources for the benefit of the local population.	Visiting individuals, whether for tourism or scientific research, are subject to the payment of entrance fees, research rights, and filming rights.	Exploitation of natural resources is regulated according to the development and management plan of the site, which includes traditional rules of management and those of sustainable management. Access by local communities to natural resources (e.g., utilitarian plants) is allowed. Regulated forms of animal exploitation (fishing and hunting) and forest product exploitation are possible. All uses of fire and all clearing, except that decided on and authorized in accordance with the management objectives and legal provisions in force, are prohibited. In the portion of the site falling under controlled occupation zones, local communities are allowed and these areas can be transferred to local communities for management.

Source: Extracted in part from Ranivo Rakotoson and Razafimahatratra (2018).
Note: According to the Code des Aires Protégées (COAP), entrance fees to protected areas (for researchers, tourists, and filming rights) are to be jointly set by the manager of the protected area and the ministry responsible for protected areas.

THE FUTURE

The future of Madagascar with reference to the well-being of the Malagasy people and the conservation of the island's unique biodiversity rests with preserving its natural ecosystems. Amelioration of the current protected area system and advances to resolve various social, economic, and legal problems is paramount for the future. Over the past few decades major progress has been made in better understanding the natural history of different ecosystems and a range of plant and animal species. Of critical importance is national scientists and conservationists finding their rightful places and roles in the governmental and nongovernmental sectors to advance programs and to ensure the future of their island nation. Further, it is important for the private sector to minimize its impacts on biodiversity through effective offset programs and large international institutions to give clear guidance on investment strategies and integrating biodiversity in different programs. Given the current rates of deforestation and the problems created by forest loss, including habitat fragmentation and the isolation of plant and animal populations, large-scale ecological restoration approaching an industrial level with the appropriate vegetation needs to be further advanced, and in certain areas with surrounding fire breaks. Such programs could be a major source of employment for local communities and financial aspects associated with ecosystem services funding. As underlined and emphasized in different contributions in this book, time is short and major advances are critical in the next years to safeguard the natural patrimony and the associated human cultures of Madagascar.

ACKNOWLEDGMENTS

We are grateful to colleagues at Madagascar National Parks, specifically O. D. Andrianambinina and Mamy Rakotoarijaona, for updates on the protected area system of Madagascar.

Subject editor: Olivier Langrand

CONSERVATION TECHNOLOGY

A. Andrianarimisa and M. Andrianarimisa

Technology has touched the overall facets of human society. Along with other major challenges worldwide, biodiversity conservation has made spectacular progress in recent decades as a result of the integration of innovative techniques. It is widely recognized that to be effective, conservation should be evidence based (Sutherland et al. 2004; Pressey et al. 2017). Conservation also needs to be able to respond quickly to changing pressures. The emergence of new technologies is rapidly changing both the science and practice of conservation, providing new sources of data and forms of accessibility. Such conservation technology encompasses a wide range of tools that can provide more data of greater reliability (on finer spatial and temporal scales) than was previously possible. Globally, technology-based conservation has brought new conservation practices to the island, mainly regarding data quality and availability, and movement toward near real-time monitoring to reduce and deter illegal activities (Table 15.4). Below we provide a broad review of some of these new technologies.

DATA PORTALS

Technology-based conservation tools are gaining a significant role in protected area management. This started with the implementation of the Malagasy government's commitment, announced at the World Parks Congress in 2003, to triple the land surface of the protected area network (Norris 2006). The same exercise was conducted more recently for marine protected areas (Allnutt et al. 2012). With the help of many researchers and institutions, the Wildlife Conservation Society set up the REBIOMA data portal (REBIOMA 2021) to gather key species occurrence data and spatial analysis tools for use in designing near-optimal reserve networks (Kremen et al. 2008; Rasoavahiny et al. 2008).

Data portals have also become relevant as part of advancing conservation decisions. These initiatives aim to overcome difficulties in communicating existing data, addressing gaps, and facilitating exchanges between stakeholders with the aim of rapid decision-making. For that, international conservation approaches such as Key Biodiversity Areas (KBAs), Important Bird and Biodiversity Areas (IBAs), and Alliance for Zero Extinction (AZE) (Neugarten et al. 2016) have helped identify sites of global significance for biodiversity conservation on Madagascar. Because of advances in computer science, researchers are able to use different data sources to identify important areas for conserving rare species through niche modeling, such as MaxEnt (Phillips et al. 2006). Examples of such studies include groups such as lemurs (J. Brown and Yoder 2015; Kamilar et al. 2016; Herrera 2017) and birds (Andrianarimisa and Razafimanjato 2010; Razafindrajao et al. 2017; Rabarisoa 2019), as well as subjects related to climate change (Vieilledent et al. 2013) and identification of the Madagascar terrestrial protected area network (Kremen et al. 2008).

TABLE 15.4. **Technology used to improve conservation on Madagascar**

TECHNOLOGY TOOLS	METHODS	MAIN RESULTS	CONSERVATION IMPROVEMENT	EXAMPLES
Data portal	Conservation planning	Priority maps for terrestrial Madagascar Protected Areas System (SAPM)	Maximize the conservation of biodiversity using different analyses	www.rebioma.net; Kremen et al. (2008); Rasoavahiny et al. (2008)
		Priority maps for marine protected areas (MPAs)	Optimal expansion of marine protected areas	www.rebioma.net; Allnutt et al. (2012)
	Species distribution models	Key Biodiversity Areas (KBAs) Important Bird and Biodiversity Areas (IBAs) Alliance Zero Extinction	Determine strongholds for rare and endangered species	www.rebioma.net; Andrianarimisa and Razafimanjato (2010); Rogers et al. (2010); K. Brown et al. (2015); Neugarten et al. (2016)
Remote-sensing tools	Firecast	Free access to forest fire data points and maps	Near real-time forest monitoring and alert system to quicken responses to threats	Musinsky et al. (2018); forestwatcher.globalforestwatch.org/
	Satellite imagery, drones, aerial photography	Land cover classification Climate change resilience	Implementation of market-based incentives for conserving services such as REDD+	www.rebioma.net; Busch et al. (2012); Rabetrano (2018)
Tracking technologies	GPS, bio-logging and bio-telemetry, sensor camera traps, sound landscapes	Occurrence data for rare and elusive species	Increase knowledge of elusive species like carnivores	Farris et al. (2012)
Mobile and digital technologies	SMART, drones, oblique photography	Help identify offenders and dissuade illegal activities	Help reduce illegal activity	Gardner et al. (2015)
	Open Data Kit (ODK)	Natural resource use and socioeconomic survey (e.g., NRGT and BNS)	Help identify key drivers of local community governance and natural resource use	discover.blueventures.org/mobile-monitoring; madagascar.co.uk/application/files/7515/8684/3984/Baseline_Socioeconomic_Assessment.pdf
Data logger technology	Bioacoustic Index	Soundscape survey as indicator of forest disturbance	Improve spatial and temporal surveys of vocal but elusive animal- and human-induced sounds, such as machetes	Rankin and Axel (2017)

REMOTE-SENSING TOOLS

Remote sensing, whether through satellites, aerial photography, or drones, is being increasingly applied to land cover classification (Grinand et al. 2013), biodiversity monitoring, and mitigation of swidden agricultural practices on Madagascar (Gardner et al. 2015). The use of the annual deforestation rate as a key indicator of forest conservation has become more common. Currently, the major uses of remote-sensing tools have contributed particularly to monitoring the status of protected areas by providing information on areas of

human disturbance, the configuration of potential protected areas, and the condition of vegetation. The latter has permitted the implementation of market-based incentives for conserving services such as Reducing Emissions from Deforestation and Forest Degradation (REDD+) (see Grinand and Nourtier, pp. 105–13). In addition, satellite web-based remote-sensing tools have allowed the tracking of ecosystem disturbances such as fires, deforestation, and protected area encroachment, and they can deliver time-sensitive information to decision-makers through e-mail alerts, maps, and reports. There is also the free web-based Forest Watcher, which can be installed on a smartphone to monitor areas of interest and to view deforestation and fire alerts (Forest Watcher 2021). Another near real-time fire alert system is Firecast, which gives decision-makers e-mail information on fire alerts, fire risk conditions, deforestation, and protected area encroachment (Firecast 2021). All of these remote-sensing tools have boosted the responses of protected area managers and decision-makers by identifying large-scale areas with frequent forest fires where personnel and plan surveillance can be deployed within protected areas. These tools are now employed on Madagascar.

TRACKING TECHNOLOGIES

Most people are familiar with the Global Positioning System (GPS), widely used to collect geographic coordinates. In addition, radio and GPS collar tracking are becoming increasingly powerful tools for researching and monitoring animals. They allow the determination of home ranges, daily activity patterns, and habitat use (Parga 2011). On Madagascar, lemurs, birds, and carnivorans have been studied using such tracking techniques. Other electronically tagged sensor devices record audio, speed, orientation, body temperature, and even water depth in the case of marine mammals (Saloma et al. 2018). Tagged sensors allow the identification of different behaviors, interactions, and individual states of an organism in correlation with environmental parameters, patterns of movement and acceleration, and many more variables that can provide crucial knowledge about the biology of species that are difficult to study through direct observation. Similarly, technology like camera traps has enabled the detection and study of elusive animals. Combined with radio or GPS collars, some research has contributed to understanding the natural history of different lemur species (e.g., Wright 1995). These different tracking technologies have helped improve research on species that would otherwise be difficult to follow, such as carnivorans (Farris et al. 2012; see Farris et al., pp. 1806–11) and marine mammals (Cerchio et al. 2015). The growing information on these elusive species provides the means for them to be integrated into conservation recommendations (e.g., Cartagena-Matos et al. 2017).

MOBILE AND DIGITAL TECHNOLOGIES

Madagascar has also benefited from the global development of mobile and digital technologies in the form of handheld devices such as smartphones and tablets. These boost data collection for various conservation purposes (Jeffers et al. 2019) such as biodiversity and law enforcement monitoring. The rosewood crisis that started in 2009 in the northeast (Randriamalala and Liu 2010) illustrated the need for more effective ways to fight illegal activities. Experiences in Africa and Asia with user-friendly technologies that allow data collection in the field without requiring high skill but producing valuable information in a timely manner to combat illegal wildlife activities have motivated the choice of digital and handheld technologies.

One innovative advancement has been free software such as the Spatial Monitoring and Reporting Tool (SMART 2021), which can be integrated with a cyber tracker to produce spatial patterns of different activities and real-time data for rapid decisions. In this case, the idea is to enhance law enforcement monitoring systems to protect wildlife and improve protected area management. Other user-friendly data collection tools, such as the free Open Data Kit (ODK), make data available faster and are easy to operate, particularly for data collection on socioeconomic aspects, including basic necessity surveys (BNS), natural resource governance tools (NRGT), and local village small-scale fisheries monitoring. The ODK Android application allows users to create custom mobile data collection forms with limited prior technical knowledge. Instead of data being collected via paper-based information, data are directly recorded into a smartphone and submitted to a linked cloud server in real time or saved on the smartphone until a mobile network signal is reached.

The use of mobile and digital technologies for conservation projects on Madagascar has contributed to improved information availability and has empowered local communities, which can take part in data collection because no great technical knowledge is required. In addition, these technologies have led to movement toward near real-time monitoring that allows more effective adaptive management within protected areas. In addition, because digital technology is software based, other data sources can be integrated to help broaden the scope of the application in conservation, as with web-based remote-sensing tools such as Firecast, mentioned above.

DATA LOGGER TECHNOLOGY

Data loggers are another next-generation technology used on Madagascar; these electronic devices are designed to record measurements at specific intervals, including environmental variables (e.g., air temperature, humidity, light intensity, rainfall, carbon dioxide, etc.). These devices function as a real-time data recording system. Temperature data loggers are the main devices used on the island, for monitoring microclimate variation (Wollenberg et al. 2008), temperature fluctuations of bird nests (Mizuta 2007), and lemur activity (Kappeler and Erkert 2003).

More recently, AudioMoth, an autonomous full-spectrum miniaturized acoustic recorder device, has been used in various Malagasy forests. It captures the soundscape (frequency and amplitude of sound over time) of insects, birds, forest mammals (mainly bats and lemurs), rain, thunder, and even human activity (Rankin and Axel 2017). AudioMoth is a low-cost, full-spectrum acoustic logger that allows the calculation of various acoustic indices (Eldridge et al. 2016). Soundscape technology provides the means for spatial and temporal survey coverage for vocal but cryptic animal species, bioacoustic study, biodiversity monitoring, and human-induced sounds related to threats (gunshots, logging, etc.). Such technology can be used to study many aspects of wildlife in a nonintrusive way.

SUMMARY

The above examples and many more demonstrate that technology-based applications are becoming central to the efficiency of contemporary conservation practices on Madagascar. The critical question is whether using such advanced technology for conservation on the island has improved protected area management. The response to this question is addressed in some of the following contributions in this chapter. Local villagers, national and international nongovernmental organizations (NGOs), and governmental administrators are all enlisted to manage the island's biodiversity using modern techniques that provide global rationality for conservation science. There should be no illusion that new technologies can help resolve some of the deeply rooted problems of governance, law enforcement, and sometimes even the impunity of certain offenders. However, technology provides important tools that can contribute to successful conservation when deployed in conjunction with traditional approaches.

Subject editors: Steven M. Goodman and Julia P. G. Jones

SMART: TECHNOLOGY-BASED LAW ENFORCEMENT MONITORING IN MADAGASCAR'S PROTECTED AREAS

A. Andrianarimisa, F. O. D. Andrianambinina, and A. R. Mandimbihasina

Law enforcement is defined as the "set of instruments"—punishment for offenses and the apparatus to detect and investigate crimes, convict criminals, and hand out punitive judgments—that makes the prohibitions established by law, and hence by the state, a reality (Foucault 2008). It is simply the action taken by legally qualified authorities to determine noncompliance with rules and norms and to prosecute offenders. For protected areas, "law enforcement monitoring" comprises repeated and regular surveillance and patrols to deter illegal activities and aid in the apprehension and prosecution of offenders. It has been shown to improve the successful management of protected areas and species in a broad range of contexts (Massé 2020). This is especially true where it involves ground patrols with rangers from the local community (Anagnostou et al. 2020).

On Madagascar, protected areas face many pressures (Jones et al. 2019a). With the expansion of terrestrial (e.g., "Durban Vision"; Norris 2006) and marine protected areas (e.g., "Promise of Sydney"; IUCN 2014), combating these threats while improving local communities' livelihood by reducing their high dependency on natural resources is not a simple matter. Strict enforcement of conservation rules in the local communities surrounding protected areas should consider their dependence on natural resources and alternatives for achieving environmental justice (Boillat et al. 2018). However, conservation managers need high-quality information on rule infringements to tackle pressures, and law enforcement monitoring is an important tool. Herein we discuss the ways in which technology associated with this form of monitoring can improve the management of Malagasy protected areas. We first summarize the surveillance and patrol systems that were in use before the employment of technology-based conservation and then explore the major improvements and disadvantages of these new techniques.

PROTECTED AREA MONITORING AND SURVEILLANCE BEFORE SMART

On Madagascar, before the use of technology-based law enforcement monitoring tools, patrol and monitoring data were recorded with paper-based systems and usually stored, analyzed, and visualized in spreadsheets. The quality of this work depended on the skill of the personnel of a particular protected area. There was little or no standardization across protected areas, making comparisons difficult. In addition, paper-based systems require appropriate archives to avoid deterioration from humidity, temperature, and other destructive agents (insects and mildew), which are not evident in the offices associated with many protected areas. The paper approach also requires additional funds to engage enough trained staff to help managers analyze data and produce reports. For instance, Kremen et al. (1998) noted that the monitoring system of the Wildlife Conservation Society (WCS) on the Masoala Peninsula required three person-months per year of a university-trained national field biologist for supervision, data entry, and analysis, as well as an additional six person-months of trained conservation agents for data collection. There were also significant time lags between the collection of data and its collation, analysis, and subsequent availability to resource managers.

For rapid reaction to "near real-time" monitoring (Gross 2014; Henson et al. 2016), data collection and associated analyses should produce reports in short order. Madagascar National Parks (MNP), the organization mandated to manage most of the protected areas of IUCN categories I and II (Langrand and Rene de Roland 2018), has had difficulties obtaining quick results from patrols and ecological monitoring units with the paper-based system. Even with a dedicated unit to assist each protected area (Système d'Informations sur les Aires Protégées Unit), the time required to produce maps and statistics with this type of system is too long for efficient management

(Association Nationale pour la Gestion des Aires Protégées 2002). For this reason, MNP has adopted a simple and suitable solution, which requires neither special knowledge nor sophisticated equipment for ecological monitoring to provide protected area managers information in near real time (Schweter 2012). This new system, as discussed in the next section, has since been integrated into the MNP monitoring manual (Madagascar National Parks 2013).

UTILIZATION OF SMART ON MADAGASCAR IN PROTECTED AREAS

Developed in 2011 by a partnership of nine leading international conservation organizations, including WCS and World Wide Fund for Nature (WWF), SMART (2021) is currently considered the world's foremost tool for law enforcement monitoring and protected area management (Kretser et al. 2017). This free, open-source software combines GPS technology with geographic information system (GIS) automated mapping and can be programmed to provide statistics on, for example, patrol effort, threats, and target species. This technology helps fulfill two fundamental needs of protected area managers: 1) the need for up-to-date, standardized, cost-effective information on threats in protected areas; and 2) the need to track, evaluate, and guide performance of protection staff such as patrol rangers in responding to those threats.

SMART requires geo-referencing data, so in some cases paper-based data collection with a GPS device is necessary, specifically for observations. However, SMART can also run on a smartphone or other GPS-enabled handheld mobile device, in which the cyber tracker "open street map" or OSMTracker data collection applications can be integrated. Because the cyber tracker was originally developed to enable illiterate trackers to record wildlife data on handheld devices (Liebenberg 1990), data collection is rather straightforward for field staff. For instance, icons displayed on the device instead of or alongside text (even in a local language) help illiterate field staff understand instructions or work better with images. Perhaps even more significant with this system, data can be quickly transferred into SMART software. Therefore, the time required to obtain patrol results is significantly reduced, allowing near real-time monitoring and quick decisions on actions to deter threats or for other management purposes. For these reasons, the IUCN recommended SMART during the World Conservation Congress in Honolulu in 2016 (IUCN 2016a), and it has now been adopted in more than 850 protected areas across 65 countries, with 17 adopting it as a national tool; these include seven in Africa, including Madagascar (Henson et al. 2016; SMART Partnership 2018).

WCS introduced SMART to Madagascar in 2013 to improve law enforcement monitoring and illegal wildlife trafficking related to the "rosewood crisis" (Randriamalala and Liu 2010). Since December 2018, it has become the national standard tool for law enforcement monitoring, according to the "Note de Service no. 1258/MEEF/SG" from what is now known as Ministère de l'Environnement et du Développement Durable (MEDD). Now, 66.7% of the current 123 existing protected areas, covering 74% of the entire 7,609,855 ha, use SMART with common standardizations of patrol protocols for threat denomination and target species.

Experiences with SMART implementation reveal three main conditions for law enforcement monitoring to work well. First, without an accepted management authority involved in leading and endorsing the system and using the information generated for adaptive management, it becomes a waste of effort and resources. Second, there must be a commitment to put resources into protection and monitoring activities, and to collect observational field data. Finally, legally qualified authorities should be ready to use the information for prosecution purposes. To ensure effective implementation at the site level, SMART also requires regular feedback meetings between managers and frontline staff such as rangers to fully improve conservation strategy and target rapidly emerging threats.

The full rollout of SMART on Madagascar resulted in increased patrol effort, better patrol planning, and ultimately fewer human-induced threats. SMART allows rangers to instantly capture data in the field and provides managers with near real-time monitoring to better identify hotspots of illegal activities. This in turn allows the more efficient establishment of a patrol plan to deter offenders and apprehend them. This system contributed to reducing the illegal extraction of precious wood in the Makira protected area from 2011 to 2019, in combination with other efforts and initiatives at the local to national level (Figure 15.2). This was also the case for the Masoala protected area, where the number of fresh rosewood stumps dropped from 4136 in 2010 to 328 in 2014 (Ratsimbazafy et al. 2016). The evidence from photos and GPS points recorded and stored easily on SMART has improved the legal documents presented for the prosecution of offenders as well as the legal system at the court level (Table 15.5).

The most important benefit of SMART technology on Madagascar has been the ability to standardize and centrally manage patrol data, facilitate information sharing, and prioritize patrol programs, which together help deter offenders. For instance, the current nationally standardized patrol data structure allows the comparison of patrol efforts and threat levels across the entire protected area network. MNP holds a monthly session to discuss SMART-based law enforcement and prioritize urgent actions on the ground. This has accelerated the efficiency of interventions.

The SMART partnership continues to develop applications to meet the emerging needs of the conservation community. SMART

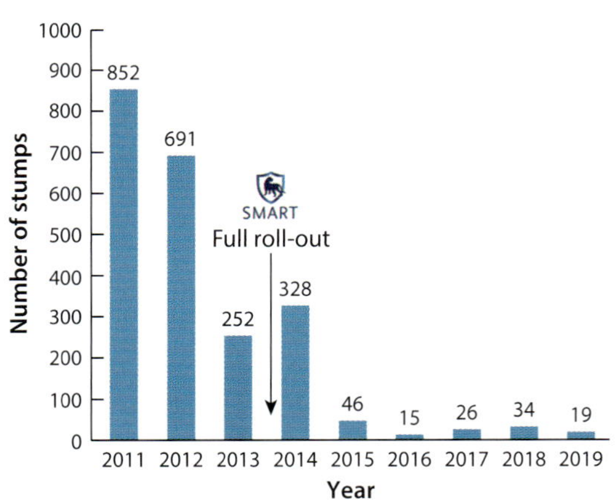

FIGURE 15.2 Number of stumps resulting from illegal logging of precious woods (rosewood, palisander, and ebony) recorded in the Makira protected area from 2011 to 2019.

TABLE 15.5. **Law enforcement percentage before and after full SMART rollout in Makira protected area**

BEFORE FULL SMART ROLLOUT (2007–2012)					
	HUNTING (n = 0)	ILLEGAL INSTALLATION (n = 0)	ILLEGAL LOGGING (n = 15)	MINING (n = 353)	SWIDDEN AGRICULTURE (n = 20)
Offenders apprehended by OPJ				95%	5%
Prosecution documents rejected by the court			73%	1%	85%
Offenders sentenced by the court			27%	5%	10%
AFTER FULL SMART ROLLOUT (2013–2019)					
SANCTIONS	HUNTING (n = 2)	ILLEGAL INSTALLATION (n = 11)	ILLEGAL LOGGING (n = 10)	MINING (n = 23)	SWIDDEN AGRICULTURE (n = 115)
Court summons		36%	60%	25%	10%
Offenders apprehended by OPJ		64%			
Offenders not found					10%
Prosecution documents rejected by the court				27%	7%
Offenders sentenced by the court	100%		40%	13%	69%
Offenders verbally reprimanded by OPJ					4%

Source: Based on prosecution of offenders sent to the court from 2007 to 2019.
Note: OPJ: Officier de Police Judiciaire, or Judicial Police Officer.

Connect is a cloud-based platform that allows the central management of SMART data from different sites and integrates notifications from Global Forest Watch. MNP, WCS, and WWF now use this function to allow near real-time response to forest fires. Where rangers have access to the Internet from smartphones in the field, they can send patrol data recorded from the cyber tracker application directly to SMART Connect. This has been tested and implemented in some protected areas covered by mobile networks, and the results are encouraging.

It is also important to remember that mobile data collection always depends on the accuracy of the data collection and the capacity of the collectors. With additional experience, SMART users learn that quality control conducted by a qualified technician, known as SMART Focal Point, is needed. Regular training updates are required to maintain the commitment of data collectors and to address problems as they arise. A permanent on-site SMART Focal Point technician among the protected area staff is another requirement for a full rollout.

CHALLENGES OF USING SMART ON MADAGASCAR

Despite its many advantages, SMART is not appropriate for use everywhere on the island, as it requires minimal computer skills and preferably someone with a basic knowledge of GIS. This may be problematic in some protected areas under local community management alone, in which computer costs and technical capacity for data handling could become an important constraint. Further, limited access to electricity in many remote areas for computer use and device charging can be problematic, but the recent deployment of solar power capacity could resolve this issue, as in the Baie de Baly protected area.

CONCLUSION

Surveillance and control of illegal activities are key components of protected area management. In developing countries like Madagascar, it is difficult to achieve significant conservation success in protected areas, where there are many severely threatened endemic species and an increasingly well-organized illegal network that exploits a range of these organisms for international contraband markets. Law enforcement on Madagascar suffers from serious deficiencies, including insufficient staff and resourcing, and weak legal governance. A transparent and accountable monitoring system such as SMART is part of the solution with which protected area managers and law enforcement agencies can directly address a range of

problems. SMART's rollout on Madagascar has contributed at the local level to reducing intense illegal extraction of rosewood in the northeast, including in protected areas, through revitalizing and empowering local members of civil society to take the lead in lobbying for effective enforcement by the local court. Real-time recognition of suspicious activity can reduce the impacts of human pressures on the biota of protected areas and create a different form of interaction with surrounding communities.

Subject editors: Steven M. Goodman and Julia P. G. Jones

OBLIQUE AERIAL PHOTOGRAPHY: A SIMPLE AND POWERFUL TOOL TO ADDRESS DEFORESTATION

S. Rafanomezantsoa, T. M. Rasolozaka, and X. Vincke

The principal tool to stem biodiversity loss resulting from anthropogenic processes is the establishment and management of protected areas. Habitat loss, mainly by deforestation, is among the primary threats to biodiversity in tropical developing countries (Giam 2017). This is a particular concern because tropical forests are the richest ecosystems on earth (Poker and MacDicken 2016) and provide a range of ecosystem services. In many tropical developing countries like Madagascar, small-scale farmers practicing shifting cultivation techniques for either subsistence or export-oriented cash cropping remain the principal agents of deforestation (Gardner et al. 2015). Shifting cultivation is particularly difficult for protected area managers to detect, monitor, and manage because, being illegal in most countries, it takes place largely in remote areas. Madagascar's forests are among the most plentiful places on earth in terms of biodiversity and are an important source of livelihood and income for local communities.

On Madagascar, 100,000–300,000 ha of forests are burned each year for swidden agriculture (Leprun et al. 2009). Within the dry deciduous forests of the west and the dry spiny thickets of the south, this practice is regarded as almost irreversible, as these forests have poor regenerative power (Zinner et al. 2014). Herein we use the example of a landscape-based project known as Paysage Mahafaly to illustrate the role that oblique photography can play in addressing deforestation. In the southwest, the dry spiny thickets are cleared for only one year of cultivation. After that short period, the low fertility of the rocky soil forces farmers to clear new patches. Subsequently, swidden agriculture is an important cause of erosion and sedimentation, with drastic impacts not only on terrestrial habitats but also in surrounding coral reefs (Maina et al. 2013). To monitor forest cover loss and develop participative monitoring involving local communities, oblique aerial photography has been used since 2010 in Paysage Mahafaly. Other surveys outside this landscape were also conducted to estimate forest loss, but these data are slightly limited.

BRIEF DESCRIPTION OF METHODS

The technique of oblique aerial photography consists of flying over the targeted protected area and following the same exact routes, programmed into GPS units, each year to monitor changes in forest cover. During an aerial surveillance flight, two photographers take oblique pictures with a focal length zoom of 28 mm at an angle of 45° and geo-reference each photo. Based on experience in the dry spiny thickets of the Paysage Mahafaly, parallel transects 3 km apart (Figure 15.3) permit 100% detection of new clearings >0.5 ha (Gardner et al. 2015). Cleared areas are then drawn in Google Earth if the corresponding period of satellite images is available to estimate their size. If not, photos are processed using recent Landsat images overlaid in Google Earth.

Oblique aerial photography (also known as oblique photography or oblique air photography) is done from a high point at an angle to the subject rather than directly overhead. The ideal angle is between 35° and 65° (Prandi et al. 2008). Such a system produces images of the location in perspective (with relief), which are easier for nonexpert users to interpret because they are more similar to what is seen from the ground. The interpretation of oblique photographs can provide insights into the condition of landscapes, land use, and spatial trends of targeted features; all are well suited for participative monitoring, which includes periodic analysis of information with local community involvement (e.g., comparing maps, number of clearings, etc.). In the Paysage Mahafaly, aerial surveillance with oblique photography was developed specifically to identify remote clearings in large landscapes for rapid reaction, promote community awareness, and reduce swidden agriculture practices.

OBLIQUE AERIAL PHOTOGRAPHY AS A TECHNIQUE FOR PROTECTED AREA MANAGEMENT

Aerial surveillance was developed by Aviation Sans Frontières Belgium in 2006, in collaboration with the Système des Aires Protégées de Madagascar, WWF Madagascar, and Madagascar National Parks. Oblique photographs are useful for covering large areas in a single image, and for depicting terrain relief and scale better than vertical photos. For instance, during two days of aerial surveillance,

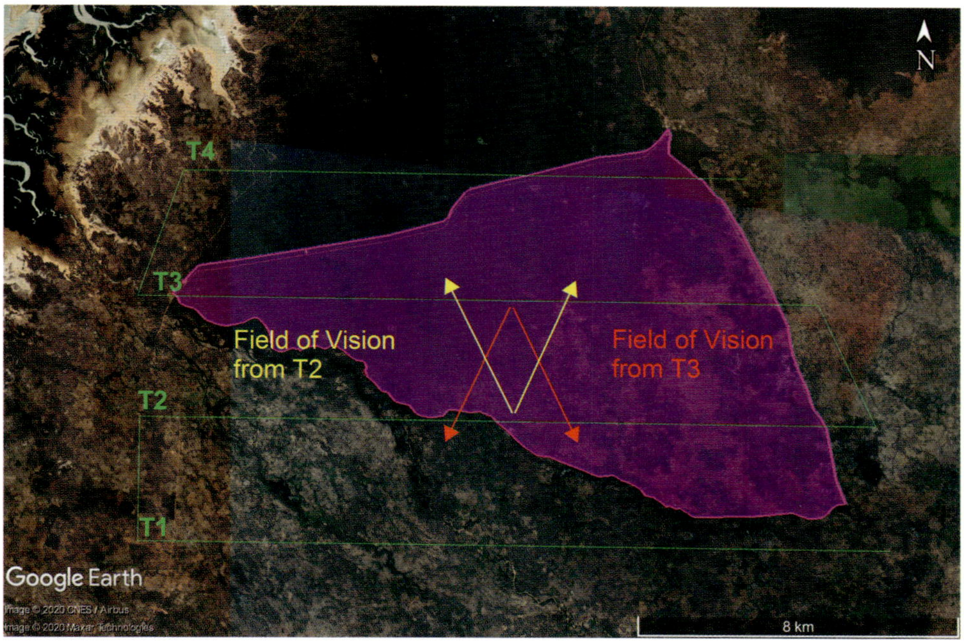

FIGURE 15.3 **Parallel transects of oblique photography sampling routes placed 3 km apart on the Mahafaly Plateau.**

the entire Bemaraha National Park (157,586 ha) and Menabe Antimena protected area (about 107,688 ha) were covered. The maps produced help protected area managers quantify deforestation, guide rapid field intervention to deter threats, and communicate with local communities. Storing the data in SMART software further facilitates analysis and comparison with foot patrol data from rangers. We did this in the Paysage Mahafaly and found that swidden agriculture burns captured with oblique photography could be superimposed on those spotted from ground patrols or from Global Land Analysis and Discovery alerts (GLAD). Since aerial surveillance takes place about once a year, overall ground patrol routes can be compared to the aerial surveys to determine whether any key areas were missed. This helps target ground actions to deter offenses and improves protected area interventions by sharing direct observations from the photos of the extent of forest clearing with local communities.

During community meetings, images from consecutive years provide clear evidence of the evolution of forest cover. Direct observation of superimposed oblique photos allows comparison between successive years (Figure 15.4). The surface area of the clearing, which can be directly calculated using Google Earth Pro or a GIS software such as ArcGIS, is presented at these meetings. Local community members in attendance are able to visualize the impact swidden agriculture can cause on the natural vegetation. Previous research has shown that this approach is correlated with a reduction of clearing for swidden agriculture (Gardner et al. 2015). This approach needs to be combined with various conservation actions on the ground to succeed. In forested zones, repeated aerial

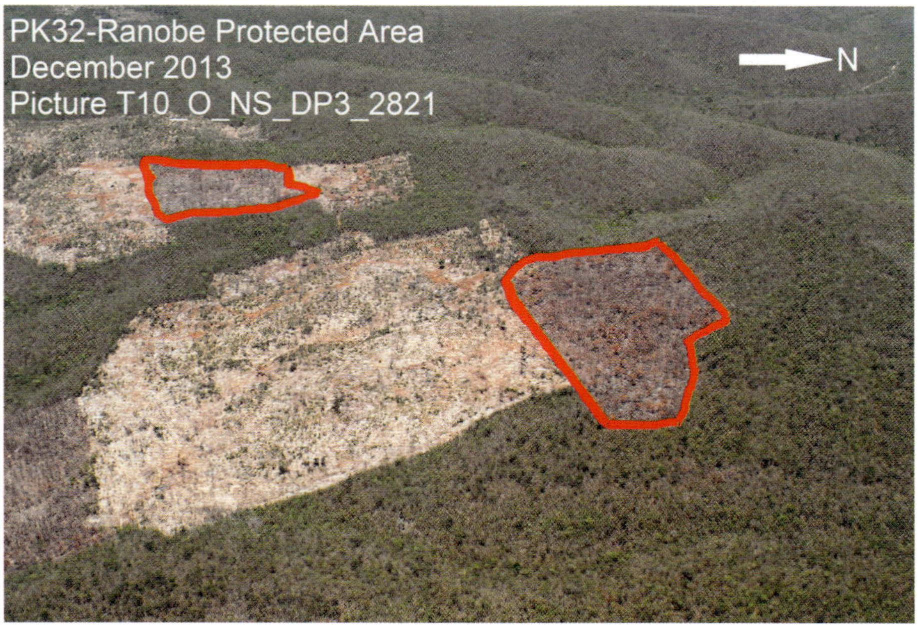

FIGURE 15.4 **Pictures of two successive years from the Ranobe PK32 protected area, which allow new clearings (delineated by red borders) to be located; in this case these are quite obvious because of the ash-gray color.**

TABLE 15.6. **Forest loss estimated by oblique aerial photography from 2010 to 2018**

LANDSCAPE	SITE	SIZE OF SITE (ha)	FOREST LOSS (ha)								
			2010	2011	2012	2013	2014	2015	2016	2017	2018
Paysage Mahafaly	Tsimanampesotse	263,060	20.3	37.4	46.3	23.5	5.9	54.8	8.5	16.3	–
	Amoron'i Onilahy	102,107	–	–	69.3	–	–	201.6	41.0	15.1	20.6
	Zamasy	38,283	–	–	61.8	–	–	370.5	–	487.0	78.8
	Marofototse	43,086	–	–	39.0	–	–	86.6	–	47.6	25.0
	Ilovo	28,648	–	–	–	–	–	65.7	–	–	–
	Angavo	42,743	–	–	–	–	16.0	51.8	–	–	–
	Ranobe PK32	168,500	4121.3	1327.6	2020.5	–	–	–	–	–	–
	Mikea	184,669	58.0	26.0	123.0	–	–	–	–	–	–
	Behara Tranomaro	96,591	–	–	–	63.5	–	–	–	–	–
	Ankitikitike	31,943	–	–	–	–	–	–	–	15.2	5.6
	Beomby	23,325	–	–	–	–	–	–	–	–	19.0
	Tsinjoriake	5475	–	–	–	–	–	–	–	–	0.2
	Voroja	4717	–	–	–	–	–	–	–	–	0.5

Note: A dash (–) indicates no flight surveillance conducted.

surveillance and accompanying field patrols appear to be more effective in raising public awareness about the inappropriateness of swidden agriculture (Table 15.6).

Oblique aerial photography techniques provide a powerful visual communication tool to engage local communities and stakeholders in protected area adaptive management. After priority cleared areas are identified, foot patrols visit the *fokontany* (group of villages) nearest each target area to engage with farmers practicing illegal shifting cultivation to allow them to better understand the ecological and legal impacts of these activities and provide the protected area manager with insight into the drivers of the activities. Representatives of local authorities (the mayor of the commune, head of the *fokontany*, village or traditional leaders, and agents of the Forestry Service) are welcomed, and their presence helps improve awareness and, if needed, secure the possible prosecution of offenders. During awareness sessions, it is important to let local community members compare these pictures and observe the differences. Sometimes these sessions become a special event in which everyone, including kids, can see a real-world view of vegetation burning, which in turn clearly presents a conservation message.

Compared to satellite images, which are only available two months after being taken, aerial oblique photos allow nearly immediate access to images. This allows forest clearing spatial patterns and other threats to be spotted quickly. Such rapidity allows protected area managers to take needed actions. Further, satellite images at the required resolution are often expensive and need highly specialized technical expertise that is beyond the capacity of most protected area personnel. Compared to GLAD images, which are free, oblique photos have the advantage of being at a finer scale. As a result, the number of fires or clearings detected with the oblique images and the associated calculations of forest loss are more accurate. For simple annual deforestation rate estimation, satellite images, which can cover large areas, might be the easiest solution (Jensen 2007), but for near real-time monitoring of swidden agriculture that aims to immediately control threats, aerial photos are more useful.

CHALLENGES OF USING OBLIQUE AERIAL PHOTOGRAPHY

Among the main constraints of oblique aerial photography are aircraft availability, flight costs, and weather (Gardner et al. 2015). One solution to reduce costs is the surveillance of neighboring protected areas to divide associated expenses. Aircraft flights need specific weather conditions, for example winds of less than 10 knots (Ministry of Environment 1998), which excludes oblique aerial photography during windy and wetter periods and in areas of the island with regular rains, such as the Masoala Peninsula, making it challenging to obtain images.

Technically, one important criticism of oblique photography is related to the decisions that need to be made before taking photographs, which might impact the quality of the results. Substantial technical expertise is required to ensure that the camera settings, direction, altitude, and so forth are standardized to produce correct images. The success of the approach depends on the experience and attentiveness of the photographers and pilot. Oblique aerial photography is thus a sampling procedure that can vary between teams and requires professional expertise.

Another technical challenge is scaling the photos. In a high-angle oblique photo, the horizon is evident, while in a low-angle oblique image the horizon is not shown. Hence, to obtain an accurate scale of the photo, which decreases from the foreground to the background, additional work is needed, including trigonometric calculations (Twining and Toro 1955). Further, in some cases, to obtain automated geo-referencing points for the photos, complex procedures need to be conducted (Verykokou and Ioannidis 2018). The analysis of imagery can be time consuming because a single surveillance flight generates many photographs that require treatment. For instance, an experienced analyst can treat about 15 forest clearances in a standard workday for a site such as Tsimanampesotse National Park; to complete the analysis takes about six days (Gardner et al. 2015).

Meetings to report the results of the oblique photos can sometimes turn into disputes between potential offenders and the rest of the local community. This occurs for several reasons, probably the most important being that local perception of law enforcement is often based on respecting the *dina* (local community regulations) rather than national regulations in pursuing offenders. Intense public awareness of such issues is required to improve the understanding of local communities of how national law enforcement should be applied in the case of an offense. Further, within communities there are often a few dominant groups that may direct the debate toward their own interests.

The weak traditional involvement of women can be problematic, although community-based conservation programs have been shown to have better outcomes when women are involved, both on Madagascar (Razafindratsima and Dunham 2015) and elsewhere in the Old World (Soe and Sato 2012). Women have considerable ecological knowledge because of their daily use of natural resources for family needs, which is essential to strengthening natural resource management. Further research is needed to provide important contributions to discussions on the social impacts of conservation areas, the relative effectiveness of strict versus multiple-use protected area models, and the role of different techniques in documenting the evolution of local land use.

CONCLUSION

The use of aerial photography to assess and map landscape change is becoming an important element of ecosystem management. Aerial photographs are ideal for mapping ecosystems and fine-scale landscape features, such as habitat loss associated with swidden agriculture. Since 2010, oblique photography has been employed in the Paysage Mahafaly to explore the extent of deforestation. It has helped to situate clearings and guide ground patrols in controlling and deterring offenses. Since the images produced are easy for the local community to understand because of recognizable landmarks, it has helped improve dialogue with shifting cultivators and other stakeholders, thus contributing to more effective co-management. Oblique photography is one of several robust participatory tools that can complement existing field practices and enhance protected area effectiveness.

Subject editors: Julia P. G. Jones, Aristide Andrianarimisa, and Steven M. Goodman

DRONES AS A PATROL METHOD IN EASTERN FOREST CORRIDORS

J. C. N. Rabenandrasana, M. G. Fitahiantsoa, R. R. Ramanankavana, and M. Andrianarimisa

Drone is a broad term that designates any unmanned aerial vehicle (UAV). It includes miniature pilotless aircraft and flying mini-robots that come in a range of sizes. Many drones have cameras that allow photos and videos to be obtained in places that are often difficult to reach in a timely and efficient manner. Drones of different sorts are rapidly growing in popularity for different forms of surveillance. In fact, drone-based remote sensing allows user-controlled image acquisition and bridges the gap in scale and resolution between ground observations and imagery acquired from conventional piloted aircraft and satellite sensors. Drones can rapidly collect high-resolution imagery that is easily archived for future analyses, and flight paths are highly repeatable over areas of interest, allowing repeat surveys with minimal variation (Barnas et al. 2019). This technique is also cost effective and allows the adaptation of image characteristics to the size of the observed objects, to the aspects that need to be monitored, and to the speed of change within a landscape. Such remote sensing yields excellent spatial and temporal resolutions for research questions or applications (Thamm and Judex 2006; Laliberte et al. 2011).

The earliest scientific publications on environmental data gathered with small drones were studies carried out by Tomlins and Lee (1983) using a hobby-grade model aircraft, and later a custom-designed small drone. Forty-six different environmental applications in which small drones could be useful were identified (Tomlins 1983; Tomlins and Lee 1983). A recent search of the literature on drones in conservation-related applications provided a total of 256 studies, of which 99 were in terrestrial and marine protected areas (Jiménez López and Mulero-Pázmány 2019). Drones are increasingly being used by ecologists to address questions involving vegetation communities and habitat assessments (Cruzan et al. 2016).

In developing countries, where wildlife crime has increased in extent as well as sophistication, protected area managers need a

mechanism to respond in a strategic way to overcome these offenses. Near real-time monitoring is one key component in overcoming such problems (Gross 2014). Drones have been used for monitoring environmental crime, such as poaching and illegal logging, since the 2010s in Africa, Asia, and South America (Henson et al. 2016). On Madagascar, other than its use for entertainment (photos and filming of events), drone technology has been tested to map forest clearing (Williams 2019), to census whale populations (Saloma et al. 2018), and even to deliver medicines to remote villages during the campaign against tuberculosis (Institut Pasteur de Madagascar 2018). The information presented herein was gathered in the context of the Sustainable Landscapes in Eastern Madagascar Project, funded by Green Climate Fund. It focused on the Corridor Ankeniheny-Zahamena (CAZ) and the Corridor Forestier Fandriana-Ambositra-Vondrozo (COFAV), totaling more than 683,452 ha of natural forest. The project used drones for different purposes, including monitoring and assessment of deforestation but also restoration, reforestation, and agroforestry development.

METHODOLOGICAL CONSIDERATIONS

Here we focus on the use of drones to support patrol activities—specifically, their employment to identify the presence of swidden agricultural parcels within large forest tracts and to guide foot patrol agents to these sites to deter illegal activities. A rotary-wing drone (helicopters and autogiros) able to perform vertical takeoff and landing was employed in the Green Climate Fund project. The principal model was the Phantom 4 Pro V2.0, weighing about 1.4 kg with battery and propellers and with a flight duration of about 30 min. The drone was equipped with a 1-inch 20-megapixel sensor capable of recording quality video (4K at 60 frames per second) and rapid images (14 frames per second). The drone was launched from high ground and was generally flown to a position 120 m off the ground to scan surrounding areas and detect clearings. When such areas were found, the drone was piloted to inspect the area and send photos and videos to a smartphone or iPad. The pilot was able to share the videos and images with the foot patrol leader in real time and decide on the actions to be taken. Foot patrollers with handheld GPS units containing the coordinates of the site then identified the shortest route based on their knowledge of the local topography.

ADVANTAGES OF DRONES AS PATROLLING TOOLS

In Madagascar's forested protected areas, patrols are, at least in theory, conducted by rangers on foot. Patrolling in this context can include routine surveillance by both park agents and sometimes law enforcement officers, locally known as Officiers de Police Judiciaire (OPJ), to apprehend offenders. However, the extensive size and difficult access of the forested areas in the study area require a method to guide patrols efficiently. Drones can overcome this issue, as they can rapidly cover large areas, including zones not easily accessible by foot. On a clear day, a drone session at COFAV scanned 2700 ha of forest. This technique reduces the problem of difficult-to-reach areas going unpatrolled for long periods and helps assess changes in forest cover. For instance, Keane et al. (2011) reported that in Masoala National Park, foot patrols between 2005 and 2007 were concentrated around the periphery, with few penetrating the center because of access problems.

Globally, commercial satellite data tend to be either expensive or low resolution. For instance, a typical archived multispectral scene will cost at least US\$20 per km^2, with a minimum purchase of 25 km^2 (Marvin et al. 2016). Other commercially operated traditional large satellite platforms typically offer data of much higher spatial resolution (1–5 m), but at high cost. Those at lower cost are limited in their spectral resolution, often composed of four to eight band images, and do not provide the needed spatial resolution. While free satellite images are available, the resolution is insufficient, for example greater than 10 m for Sentinel images and 30 m for Landsat (Congalton 1991; Tabor and Hewson 2018). Remote-sensing research on Madagascar has shown that the Landsat resolution does not allow visual discrimination between a regenerating forest and an uncultivated area or between a degraded forest and an intact forest (Grinand et al. 2013).

Drone images can be taken with previously unavailable resolution (≤5 cm), allowing increasingly fine-grained analyses for ecological questions (Anderson and Gaston 2013). Drones facilitate the acquisition of imagery with extremely high spatial resolution, with pixels on the order of a few centimeters rather than a few meters (Paneque-Gálvez et al. 2014). During this project we were able to detect specific trees and canopy gaps, enabling unambiguous identification of patches of swidden agriculture (Figure 15.5). By processing images taken during flight with the program Pix4D, we could obtain a map showing the encroachment configuration and

FIGURE 15.5 **Recent swidden agriculture activities in a remote portion of the Corridor Ankeniheny-Zahamena (CAZ) protected area, photographed during a drone mission.**

FIGURE 15.6 Image of forest cover near Ioramaro in the Corridor Forestier Fandriana-Ambositra-Vondrozo (COFAV), using Pix4D to show the evolution of deforestation through time.

its size, making it distinctly more efficient for foot patrols to reach target areas of high threat (Figure 15.6).

Drones attract the attention of the local community. People understand that when they see a drone, they might be in the process of being photographed. Local villagers have been shown photos of forest clearings and other habitat perturbations directly on the iPad of a pilot or the head of a foot patrol, attesting to the efficiency of the tool. Thus, the approach acts as a deterrent, increases the range of action, and prevents potential offenders from trying to evade control. This provides an opportunity to raise awareness about human-induced threats and illegal activities.

CHALLENGES OF USING DRONES AS FOREST PATROLLING TOOLS

Although drones can usually fly low enough that they are not affected by cloud cover, other atmospheric conditions can hinder their operation (Hardin and Jensen 2011). Most drones should not be flown during rain because they are not water resistant, and even landing in wet grass can damage them. Throughout the eastern moist evergreen forests, rainfall is generally over 2000 mm per year, and in some areas such as the Masoala Peninsula, it can be as high as 6000 mm per year (Kremen 2003). During a mission in COFAV in September 2019, for instance, a drone was grounded for three days because of rain. Clear guidelines associated with wind speed allow drone pilots to decide when not to fly, and for best imaging, wind speed should not be higher than 15.25 km per hour (Paneque-Gálvez et al. 2014).

There is a growing awareness of the potential impact of drones on wildlife. Data from 36 published studies and 17 unpublished field campaigns outside Madagascar have revealed that drones elicit a reaction from wild animals (Mulero-Pázmány et al. 2017), including birds (Weissensteiner et al. 2015), reptiles (Bevan et al. 2018), and mammals (Ditmer et al. 2015). Growing awareness has resulted in a set of best-practice guidelines to minimize drone impacts on wildlife (Hodgson and Koh 2016; Mulero-Pázmány et al. 2017). During our study, we believe impacts on wildlife were minimal because the drone was flown at altitudes of about 120 m. However, fixed-wing drones that either approach subjects directly or rapidly change altitude or direction are seen as particularly disturbing to animals (McEvoy et al. 2016).

Current regulations for drones on Madagascar limit their use in protected area surveillance. According to the national civilian aviation authority, Aviation Civile de Madagascar, the highest flight altitude allowed for a drone is 125 m off the ground (Instruction n°01 ACM/DRG/17 relative aux conditions d'exploitation des aéronefs télépilotés, 21 September 2017). Moreover, unless they have special authorization, pilots must keep the drone in direct vision during an overflight, which greatly limits area coverage, particularly in rugged landscapes.

Along with the above challenges, drones are directly implicated in the violation of individual privacy. Questions have been raised about whether it is ethically acceptable to take pictures or recordings of people without their consent (Sandbrook 2015). Further, drones applied to wildlife conservation are indeed used to determine human-induced threats and identify those responsible in the case of law enforcement. During the current study, drones made members of local communities afraid to enter the patrolled protected area zone. In turn, the drones acted as a deterrent for illegal activities but might be considered as violating privacy ethics. This would be true if no prior information were given to the local community about the purposes of the drones, but since local communities were informed before each flight and they benefited from the program through their employment as patrol rangers, they may not have felt victimized. In another case, restricted zones of protected areas were patrolled, where surveillance was part of a legal obligation to conserve these sites. Therefore, we consider it acceptable for protected area managers to collect data with drones to prevent illegal swidden agriculture and other activities.

CONCLUSION

Drones can access difficult places and provide important information with different sensors and devices. Their use in biological field research is increasing, as they provide an economical tool for ecological researchers and environmental managers. They are particularly used for surveying forested zones at previously unprecedented detail for fine-scale habitat assessment. Similarly, monitoring habitat degradation with drones in protected areas and borderlands helps assess the performance of conservation actions and deter offenses. They also constitute a technological advance that can allow better targeting of limited staff and resources. However, these applications are subject to technological, moral, and legal constraints as well as important ethical issues.

Subject editors: Julia P. G. Jones, Aristide Andrianarimisa, and Steven M. Goodman

ASSESSING THE RISK OF ECOSYSTEM COLLAPSE ON MADAGASCAR USING THE IUCN RED LIST OF ECOSYSTEMS

A. Carré, H. Razafindrainibe, H. Rabarison, H. Randrianasolo, V. Ruiz, and Zarasoa

The IUCN Red List of Ecosystems (RLE) represents a new global reference framework for assessing the vulnerability of ecosystems. It integrates a functional dimension of biodiversity as well as links between species and between them and their environment. The use of these parameters allows the identification and assessment of ecosystems with the highest probability of collapse. The objective of this tool is to bring an ecosystem dimension to conservation strategies and knowledge relating to the state of biodiversity, based on easily understandable but scientifically rigorous assessments. The Red List of Ecosystems is also designed to support decision-making regarding nature conservation policies, use of natural resources, and land-use planning, based on the knowledge about ecosystems gathered for this purpose.

The information assembled according to the Red List of Ecosystems methodology and its results, whether at global, regional, national, or local levels, can contribute to the development and implementation of mitigation and adaptation measures for climate change, while helping to preserve the most vulnerable ecosystems. Likewise, these analyses can aid in the quantification of ecosystem services and the potential losses of these services according to the state of the ecosystems concerned; for example, they can develop nature-based solutions that are commensurate with identified societal challenges and ensure human well-being, while contributing to the protection or restoration of ecosystems (Cohen-Shacham et al. 2016).

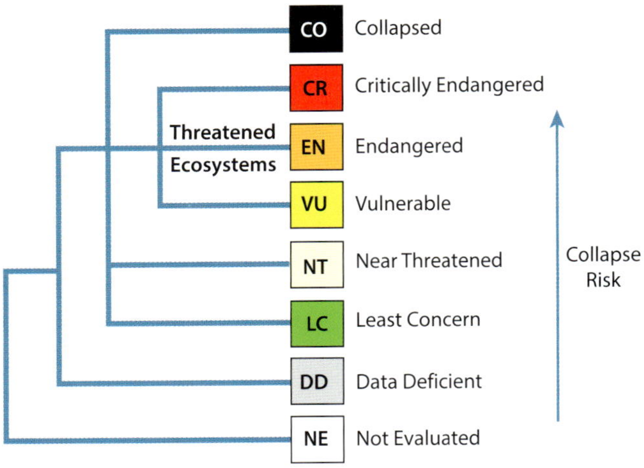

FIGURE 15.7 **Structure of the IUCN Red List of Ecosystems categories.**

CATEGORIES AND CRITERIA

The Red List of Ecosystems offers a standardized methodology that introduces the concept of "risk of collapse," which is similar to the "risk of extinction" of a species, and determines the criteria and quantitative thresholds characteristic of this risk (Bland et al. 2017). A collapsed ecosystem will 1) regress spatially; 2) evolve into another functional entity whose species composition and/or relationships are different; or 3) retain the same assemblages of species, but only in the short term because of changes in the physical environment. The IUCN Red List of Ecosystems includes eight categories: Collapsed (CO), Critically Endangered (CR), Endangered (EN), Vulnerable (VU), Near Threatened (NT), Least Concern (LC), Data Deficient (DD), and Not Evaluated (NE). The first six categories are ordered by decreasing risk of collapse. The Data Deficient and Not Evaluated categories do not indicate a level of risk (Figure 15.7).

The methodology consists of five criteria, with different sub-criteria and quantitative thresholds according to which the threat categories are assigned. Two of these criteria assess the spatial symptoms of ecosystem collapse: reduction of the spatial distribution (criterion A) and the effect of a restricted spatial distribution (criterion B). Two criteria assess the functional symptoms of ecosystem collapse: degradation of the physical environment (abiotic variables, criterion C) and disruption of biological processes and interactions (biotic variables, criterion D). The fifth criterion (criterion E) facilitates the integration of multiple threats and symptoms of collapse using a quantitative model.

The assessment of an ecosystem according to the IUCN methodology does not require the use of all five criteria; the final category of threat assigned corresponds to the highest threat category identified by one of the criteria. However, it is necessary to use the maximum number of criteria depending on the data available.

COMPLEMENTARITY OF THE IUCN RED LISTS

Madagascar's biodiversity conservation and restoration efforts need to focus not only on threatened species (those with IUCN designations of Critically Endangered, Endangered, or Vulnerable) and their habitats, but also on ecosystems that are threatened as a whole, considering the condition of their functionality, their dynamics, and the links that may exist between their different biotic and abiotic components. Thus, the IUCN Red List of Threatened Species and the IUCN Red List of Ecosystems provide the means to synthesize and enhance many existing data. They also provide a robust basis for the development of other tools, such as the identification of Key Biodiversity Areas (IUCN 2016b) or the Alliance for Zero Extinction (2018–2021), as well as mapping tools used in land planning.

Ecosystem vulnerability and trends make it possible to identify the potential for ecosystem restoration and provide important information for the conservation of already threatened species, as well as to identify in advance pressures and threats for species not

assessed or still not considered threatened. In addition, such data should contribute to ecosystem service assessments, in particular using ecosystem condition to map zones where these services are threatened. Finally, it is necessary to underline that in a context like Madagascar, where the threats are as intense as the biodiversity is rich and unique, identifying threatened species and ecosystems remains an important way to prioritize conservation actions, especially when financial resources are limited.

APPLYING THE RED LIST OF ECOSYSTEMS TO MADAGASCAR, A NATIONAL CHALLENGE

Madagascar is well known for its rich and widely endemic biodiversity, but also as a place where human activities have drastically affected the unique ecosystems. Scientists have listed Madagascar as one of the 17 "megadiverse" countries harboring the majority of earth's species and high numbers of endemic species, but also as one of the 34 "biodiversity hotspots," earth's biologically richest but most endangered terrestrial ecoregions (Mittermeier et al. 1997; Myers et al. 2000). Strong demographic growth, intense exploitation of forests for logging and extensive agricultural activities, and continuous exploitation of mineral resources are among the main threats to its biodiversity. Indeed, according to the IUCN Red List of Threatened Species, 1865 species out of the 5477 Malagasy species assessed in 2018 are threatened (Critically Endangered, Endangered, or Vulnerable) based on the above-mentioned human pressures.

Biodiversity conservation is in addition very complex in such a country, given the fragile political context, widespread poverty, and continuing national and international pressure to exploit natural resources. Also, most of the nationwide conservation measures (e.g., 46 protected areas created before 2003 and managed by Madagascar National Parks) have been developed based on the richness and distribution of the main threatened species. It is therefore essential for local communities to support biodiversity conservation at the ecosystem level, as well as for threatened ecosystems to also be represented within the national system of protected areas, as initiated with the numerous new protected areas created since 2003 (see Jones et al., pp. 2130–40)

This first attempt to assess Madagascar's ecosystems according to the IUCN Red List of Ecosystems criteria was initiated in agreement with the IUCN's will to strengthen the implementation at the national level of its "knowledge products," for both public decision-makers and the private sector. The Red List of Ecosystems of Madagascar was indeed designed as a coherent basis for supporting decision-making by contributing to the general objective of more efficient spatial planning for biodiversity conservation, considering ecological functioning and dynamics while enabling identification of gaps in biodiversity knowledge.

Originally designed as a "preliminary" Red List, the Red List of Ecosystems of Madagascar was implemented mostly through the application of criteria A and B only (see above). The threat categories assigned are therefore based mostly on ecosystem spatial dynamics and should be considered provisional or partial, as more in-depth work on the application of criteria C, D, and E is required for a more robust Red List of Ecosystems. However, information was sufficient for some ecosystems to be assessed using all five criteria, especially when they were relevant, particularly in ecosystems whose degradation would result more in internal modifications than in spatial changes, such as marine ecosystems.

Complete assessment sheets were produced for each ecosystem assessed, employing available bibliographic resources and expert knowledge from a wide panel of local experts (see acknowledgments). An IUCN synthetic report has recently been published (Carré et al. 2020), and all ecosystem assessment sheets are available on the global IUCN Red List of Ecosystems website (IUCN 2021). These assessment sheets provide contextual information on the classification and describe the four elements that define an ecosystem (characteristic native biota, abiotic environment, key processes and interactions, and spatial distribution), as well as the main threats and their effects on ecosystem functioning and integrity.

DEFINING A TYPOLOGY FOR ECOSYSTEM ASSESSMENT ON MADAGASCAR

Systematic assessments using the IUCN Red List of Ecosystems methodology require a classification system for habitat/vegetation units that ensures consistency and comparability of ecosystem risk assessments across the area under consideration. These systems can simply outline units on a particular thematic scale, or describe their relationships using hierarchies and nested structures that include a range of thematic scales. On Madagascar, numerous vegetation classification studies have been carried out and revised over the last century (Humbert and Cours Darne 1965; White 1983; Faramalala 1995; Gautier and Goodman 2003; Gautier et al. 2018). However, most of these studies focused on vegetation typology rather than mapping vegetation units on the ground. As a result, most maps produced for the different vegetation types were based on revisions from the 1960s (Humbert and Cours Darne 1965) and the early 20th century (Faramalala 1995; Gautier and Goodman 2003).

In 2007, Conservation International's Center for Applied Biodiversity Science produced a deforestation map using satellite images from 1970, 1990, and 2000 (G. Harper et al. 2007). This map is limited to measuring the extent of forest cover loss, regardless of vegetation type. The Madagascar Vegetation Mapping Project (2003–2006) set itself the objective of producing a new map of Madagascar's vegetation types using the most recent satellite images and remote-sensing techniques in order to determine their actual extent (Moat and Smith 2007).

Here we based our terrestrial ecosystem classification scheme on the *Atlas of the Vegetation of Madagascar* (Moat and Smith 2007), updated with additional data (species distribution, species conservation status, etc.) and new approaches (expert knowledge, substrate type, etc.). On the other hand, there was no detailed and nationally recognized classification for the coastal and marine habitats and ecosystems of Madagascar other than the delimitation of major ecosystem types, despite their environmental, social, or even economic importance at a global and national scale. Indeed, the 5600 km coastline of Madagascar is one of the richest and most diverse natural environments in the western Indian Ocean (Obura et al. 2011). The literature distinguishes eight types of marine and coastal ecosystems on the island, in particular mangroves, seagrass beds, estuaries, coastal marshes, and coral reefs. Information about these large units

is very scarce and, when available, is often inconsistent because of the different ecosystem definitions and methodologies adopted by various authors, particularly in terms of area estimation.

Classification of Terrestrial and Wetland Ecosystems

As part of the implementation of the Red List of Ecosystems on Madagascar, the vegetation typology had to be updated by a panel of local experts to match the purpose of the study, reach consensus between the various experts, and be consistent with the protected area management policies of the country. This classification considers the literature related to characteristics of landscapes, tropical ecosystems, and plant formations on the island (e.g., Baron 1889; Perrier de la Bâthie 1921; Yangambi 1956; Humbert and Cours Darne 1965; Koechlin et al. 1974; White 1983; Faramalala 1995; Gautier and Goodman 2003; Gautier et al. 2018). It is also based mostly on the vegetation typology of Moat and Smith (2007), as well as new data compiled by J. Moat, N. Murray, and D. Keith remodeling the vegetation units of Moat and Smith (2007) with abiotic parameters, specifically the nature of the substrate and altitude. The revised typology, which constitutes a hierarchical classification system, is thus based on a series of modifications at the biogeographic scale (e.g., water bodies and rivers, karst systems, natural and secondary grasslands, etc.), as well as observations by various national and foreign researchers.

The terrestrial ecosystem classification includes six main types: 1) humid forest (see Table 15.7); 2) dry forest, thicket, and bush; 3) high-elevation vegetation; 4) natural and secondary grassland; 5) wetland; and 6) underground environments and geologic complexes. Each of these types is broken down into major ecosystem types, themselves refined into sub-ecosystems according to the four different biomes of Madagascar (east, Central Highlands, west, and south and southwest) and considering elevation, dominant species, and vegetation structure. The four biomes of Madagascar are defined based on climate, phytogeography, relief, geomorphology, and the effect of the main winds (trade winds and monsoons). There are also azonal ecosystems, which are considered an additional biome in the classification.

The sub-ecosystem units were the basis for defining the ecosystem units to be assessed for the Red List of Ecosystems on Madagascar, with possible small adjustments depending on the data available. Specific ecosystems that were not identified in Moat and Smith (2007), sheltering certain populations of native and endemic species that are sometimes threatened and have geographically restricted distributions, have been added: gallery and riverine forests, forests on ferruginous crust, Central Highland saxicolous vegetation of exposed rocky massifs, underground waters, and inselbergs. *Tsingy* limestone karstic systems (see Bardot-Vaucoulon and Gautier, pp. 492–99) are also considered a separate ecosystem for the Red List of Ecosystems, based on their geologic originality; however, they are defined on a different physical scale from the other ecosystems evaluated, as certain forests and thicket formations can be present within these karstic systems, which extend over a large part of western Madagascar. In the end, 23 primary and modified "terrestrial and wetland ecosystems" were assessed within the framework of the Red List of Ecosystems assessment.

Classification of Marine and Coastal Ecosystems

Defining and clearly describing ecosystems is an essential first step for ecosystem assessment. Based on existing data and information, the IUCN Habitat Classification Scheme (version 3.1) provides a useful frame of reference for the assessment of Malagasy marine and coastal ecosystems within the following classes: 9.8 Coral reefs;

TABLE 15.7. **Updated ecosystem classification for the humid forests of Madagascar**

MAIN TYPE	ECOSYSTEM TYPE	BIOME	SUB-ECOSYSTEM	ECOSYSTEM ASSESSED
Humid forests	Coastal forests	East	Coastal forests of the east	Eastern coastal forests
	Dense rainforests	East and Central Highlands	Eastern lowland rainforests (0–800 m)	Eastern lowland moist forests
			Eastern medium-altitude rainforests (800–1200 m)	Eastern medium-altitude moist forests
			Eastern and highland high-altitude rainforests (1200–1800 m)	High-altitude moist forests
		Azonal	Azonal forests on ultrabasic to ultramafic "ferruginous" substrate	Forests on ferruginous crust
	Humid forests	West and Central Highlands	Western and Central Highland humid forests	Western humid forests
	Subhumid forests	West	Western subhumid forests	Western subhumid forests
	Alluvial and riparian forests	Azonal	Gallery or riverine forests	Riparian forests

9.9 Seagrass beds; 9.10 Estuaries; 12.7 Mangrove submerged roots; and 13.4 Coastal brackish/saline lagoons/Marine lakes. These ecosystem types for Madagascar were first assessed on a national scale.

However, the general trends of the results on this scale were too coarse to reflect expert knowledge about disparity in threat levels and the ecological diversity of these ecosystems. Coral reefs, for example, include 86 geomorphologic units and represent 24.4% of the coral reefs inventoried for the Indian Ocean (Cauvin et al. 2010). The assessments for mangroves, coral reefs, and seagrass beds were therefore partitioned according to the five marine biogeographic subregions identified in the western Indian Ocean islands marine ecoregion for coral reefs: northeast bioregion, east bioregion, northwest bioregion, southwest bioregion, and south bioregion (De Mazières and Olson 2012).

The Red List of Ecosystems methodology was applied to 13 marine and coastal ecosystem units: estuaries and deltas in the west; coastal lagoons in the east; mangroves in the northwest and mangroves in the west; five coral reef units (one by marine biogeographic bioregion); and four seagrass bed units (in all subregions except the south bioregion, where seagrass beds are absent).

CONSIDERING HUMAN INFLUENCES ON ECOSYSTEM DYNAMICS

Abiotic factors are the main drivers of ecosystem dynamics, which tend to reach a balance between plant successional dynamics and the specific local abiotic conditions. However, anthropogenic factors have greatly contributed to changes in the physiognomic, structural (flora and fauna), and ecological aspects of ecosystems because of the different socioeconomic activities that take place in the country: agriculture, livestock farming, forestry, mining, and so on. These anthropogenic influences are also responsible for the gradual establishment of invasive or ruderal species, resulting in homogenized ecosystems dominated by secondary vegetation.

The Red List of Ecosystems aims to assess changes in ecosystem condition (distribution, abiotic, and biotic variables) over different periods (around 1750, the last 50 years, and the next 50 years), compared to its current condition on the date of assessment. Therefore, to consider largely intact ecosystems whose current state is degraded, or conversely secondary ecosystems established for a long time in a state of "degraded equilibrium," is one of the main difficulties in ecosystem assessment. This makes typological characterization challenging, especially in contexts where human influence has been exercised for several millennia.

However, in the case of Madagascar, certain ecosystem degradation has taken place over the last centuries, and almost all the ecosystems assessed correspond more or less to largely intact ecosystems (i.e., minimally influenced by human activities and under natural regeneration processes). The main forms of pressure and threats to ecosystems on the island are all linked to human activities. Some of these anthropogenic threats have localized but immediate impacts, while other disturbances implying global changes can affect all environments in the long term. The interdependent nature of ecosystems means that what disturbs one ecosystem can have repercussions or significant consequences for others, particularly when we look at the relationships between terrestrial and marine environments.

Logging and Mining

The humid forests of Madagascar are prone to timber cutting, charcoal production, and mining. Indeed, Madagascar hosts artisanal and industrial mining operations, legal and illegal, which generally involve the total removal of vegetation cover near the mine. These practices are responsible for both the destruction of the forest at the plot level, and the change in its global structure by creating gaps in the forest cover. Coupled with the warm climate and high precipitation regimes, these degradations make regeneration difficult, as the dense humid forest generally grows on uneven terrain, protecting the unstable soils on which it grows. They also cause the reduction or disappearance of key plant and animal species that play an important role in ecosystem functioning. Rehabilitation to an original state is almost impossible, and a new vegetation type can thus replace the intact forest, with the remaining soils largely subjected to erosion.

The local human populations who live around forests also depend to an important extent on natural resources in their everyday life. These include forest products for construction, medicinal plants, and edible wild fruits and tubers. Selective logging also creates marked canopy openings and causes noticeable changes in ecosystem functioning, including colonization of invasive species. Indeed, such species can become pervasive after habitat disturbance. They are of two types according to their mode of installation: 1) plants native to Madagascar that are rapidly installed after disturbance, such as *Psiadia altissima* (Asteraceae), and 2) introduced plants that are rapidly installed and become dominant, such as *Lantana camara* (Verbenaceae). These different plants often cause the disappearance of indigenous species, fragmentation, and changes in forest structure.

Swidden Agricultural Practices

Swidden agriculture, locally known as *tavy*, is particularly used in eastern Madagascar. It consists of cutting the vegetation (mostly forest), letting it dry, setting it on fire, and then planting crops, mostly hill rice, for a few seasonal cycles. In addition to a gradual decline of forests, which are unable to regenerate, these practices have led to an increase in the frequency and intensity of fires, to which these ecosystems are no longer adapted. The intensity and frequency of *tavy* practices also promote soil erosion and cause the silting of marsh areas, greatly reducing their productivity for rice cultivation. The water that feeds these marshes is also increasingly diverted before its arrival, following the construction of upstream irrigation canals and dams (Chaperon et al. 1993; Missouri Botanical Garden 2014). In addition, the transported alluvium is often sandy and poor in nutrients, impoverishing the soil of these marshes. This phenomenon encourages farmers to abandon their old rice fields and clear other swampy areas (Elouard and Gibon 2001). The use of chemical fertilizers in rice cultivation, which is on the increase according to the Food and Agriculture Organization (FAO), can also generate excess nutrients, promote eutrophication, and lead to the colonization of open water by invasive plant species, such as *Eichhornia crassipes* (Pontederiaceae), *Azolla* spp. (Salviniaceae), *Pistia stratiotes* (Araceae), and *Salvinia molesta* (Salviniaceae).

In the western parts of the island, a similar classical agricultural technique, called *hatsake*, is employed, which consists of a similar

form of shifting cultivation, generally planting corn for no more than two or three seasonal cycles. Practiced mostly in ecosystems naturally tolerant to recurring fire, such as dry deciduous forests and dry spiny thickets, *hatsake* increases the frequency of fires and leads to degraded grassy vegetation where the most tolerant species become dominant.

Soil Erosion, Sedimentation, and Water Pollution

Sedimentation in marine and coastal ecosystems results from watershed deforestation and upstream agriculture (Obura et al. 2011; Pierre 2012; Hantanirina and Benbow 2013). The sediments washed out by descending moving waters settle and affect estuaries, deltas, mangroves, seagrass beds, and, in particular, coral reefs. They induce degradation of reefs by suffocation, increased turbidity, and decreased light and are one of the major causes of the deterioration of coral reefs in certain regions of Madagascar (Gabrié et al. 2000).

Sands, silts, and clays constitute the main sediment loads carried by rivers. Calculations by Salomon (2009) for Madagascar indicate that the rates of soil erosion are huge: between 3000 and 5000 t/km^2/year. The total quantities of sediment transported by the main rivers range from 20 to 140 million t/year. The largest amount is certainly from the Betsiboka River, where losses from its watershed are estimated at 35 km^3/year (Vörösmarty et al. 1998). The quantities of eroded soil thus represent between 250 and 400 t/ha/year, which constitutes one of the world records for erosion.

Domestic, agricultural, and industrial pollution constitute various types of nuisances to marine ecosystems, especially in areas of urban concentration and near ports, as the artificial enrichment of coastal waters with nutrients induces eutrophication unfavorable to the native marine and coastal biodiversity. The proliferation of small illegal mining operations along rivers also exposes the marine and coastal ecosystems downstream to intense disturbances. Pollution, in particular the accidental discharge of hydrocarbons, is also not negligible in certain coastal parts of Madagascar, specifically the east, south, and southeast.

Coastal Development and Exploitation of Marine Biological Resources

Mangroves and coral reefs often pay the cost of human settlement and development in coastal areas (acquisition of space for domestic, subsistence, and economic uses, etc.). This is a major threat that continues to augment and lead to a strong degradation of ecosystems and their ecological functions. Coastal urbanization and coastal development (e.g., ports, airports, roads, embankments reclaimed from the sea) often occur to the detriment of coral reefs and mangroves, also generating significant sediment discharges that suffocate the surrounding environment.

Strong exploitation pressures are also exerted on marine and coastal ecosystems for economic purposes (e.g., wood, crustaceans, fish, etc.), bearing primarily on the products in high demand. For example, mangrove crab (*Scylla serrata*) exploitation has more than quadrupled since 1985, and even if the species is probably not overexploited at the national level, the most easily accessible areas show clear signs of overexploitation and important population declines (Zbigniew 2012). In addition, efforts to protect terrestrial forest ecosystems sometimes increase pressure on marine and coastal resources (e.g., fishery resources, mangroves, and even protected species such as black coral).

Climate Change

The current perceived expressions of climate change in the western Indian Ocean, and specifically on Madagascar, are rainfall patterns deviating from the historic seasonal phenology, an increase in both the number and severity of extreme phenomena (cyclones and winds), and sea level rise (Tadross et al. 2008). Cyclones and other extreme phenomena are natural events in the region and, at a natural frequency, play a key role in building the coral islands. However, the observed increase in the frequency and intensity of swells and the strong terrigenous sedimentation at the mouths of rivers, combined with augmented terrestrial erosion, are responsible for massive destruction of coral reefs. The effect of sedimentation is indeed demonstrated clearly on the submerged reef flat of Antrema: sedimentation was particularly important in 2004–2005 when Madagascar experienced many strong cyclones, contributing to the decline of reefs that year (Obura et al. 2017). The increase in the average temperature of the oceans is also damaging coral reefs. Live coral cover has indeed shown a gradual decrease from 1998 to the present, on average a 50% to 30% reduction after each major bleaching event of 1998, 2002, 2012, and especially 2016, one of the most intense events.

OVERVIEW OF THE RED LIST OF ECOSYSTEMS APPLICATION

Out of the 36 ecosystems assessed during this application of the IUCN Red List of Ecosystems of Madagascar, 16 ecosystems are threatened (Vulnerable, Endangered, or Critically Endangered). One is Near Threatened, and only two ecosystems appears to be Least Concern. Because of the lack of relevant information and the significant doubts about their level of threat, 16 ecosystems were assigned to the Data Deficient category (Table 15.8).

Forest Ecosystems

These assessments reveal that almost all of Madagascar's forest ecosystems have regressed sharply in the past and are still under strong pressure, as confirmed by recent work by Vieilledent et al. (2018). In eastern Madagascar (Figure 15.8), the "coastal forests" and "lowland moist dense forests" were respectively assessed as Endangered and Vulnerable based on their strong decline over the last 50 years (>50% and >30%). "High altitude moist forests" were also assessed as Endangered based on their historical (>80%) and recent decline (>50%). Medium-altitude moist evergreen forests were assessed as Near Threatened based on their current decline, but this decline is quite possibly even more significant on the scale of recent decades. The main threats to these eastern moist forests are agricultural land clearing, illegal logging, and mining. In addition, moist forests cannot return to an initial "primary" state and will forever lose a portion of their ecological functions. These forests when heavily disturbed evolve toward secondary forests, grassy formations, or plantations, where soils are largely subjected to erosion (Sussman et al. 1994).

TABLE 15.8. **Ecosystem assessments on Madagascar using IUCN Red List of Ecosystems criteria**

NUMBER	ECOSYSTEM	MAIN THREAT AND OBSERVATIONS	IUCN STATUS	DOWNGRADING CRITERION (MAINLY WITH APPLICATION OF CRITERIA A AND B)
1	Humid western forests	Very restricted distribution and continuous decline caused by repetitive fires.	CR	B1a
2	Eastern coastal forests	Very strong decline in geographic distribution over the past 50 years.	EN	A1
3	Eastern and highland high-altitude dense moist forests	Very strong historical and recent decline in geographic distribution.	EN	A1
4	Azonal eastern forests on ferruginous crust	Very restricted distribution and continuous decline of abiotic environment caused by mining activities.	EN	B1b
5	Tapia forests	Very strong historical decline in geographic distribution.	EN	A3
6	Western dry forests	Very strong observed and estimated decline in geographic distribution (1975–2025).	EN	A2b
7	Southern and southwestern thickets and dry bushes on red sands and limestones	Very strong observed and estimated decline in geographic distribution (1975–2025).	EN	A2b
8	Southwestern coastal bushes	Very restricted distribution and continuous decline of biotic processes and interactions caused by anthropogenic cultivation and exploitation activities.	EN	B1a
9	Coral reefs of the east region	Very restricted distribution and continuous decline of both abiotic environment and biotic processes and interactions, marine heat waves causing significant bleaching episodes on already stressed reefs.	EN	B1
10	Coral reefs of the southwest and west region	Very strong observed and estimated disruption of biotic processes and interactions (increase in algal recovery rate and decrease in vitality of corals).	EN	D2b
11	Mangroves of the west region	Strong to very strong observed and estimated decline in geographic distribution (40–65% loss over 1990–2040 and 2000–2050).	VU/EN	A2b
12	Eastern lowland dense moist forests	Strong decline in geographic distribution over last 50 years (historical decline may be even greater but not documented).	VU	A1
13	Karst system *tsingy*	Strong observed and estimated environmental degradation and disruption of biotic processes and interactions.	VU	C2b/D2b
14	Coral reefs of the northwest region	Restricted distribution and continuous decline of abiotic environment because of massive soil erosion and sedimentation rates.	VU	B1
15	Seagrass beds of the northwest region	Restricted distribution and continuous decline of biotic processes and interactions.	VU	B1

NUMBER	ECOSYSTEM	MAIN THREAT AND OBSERVATIONS	IUCN STATUS	DOWNGRADING CRITERION (MAINLY WITH APPLICATION OF CRITERIA A AND B)
16	Mangroves of the northwest region	Strong observed and estimated decline in geographic distribution (35–50% loss over 1990–2040 and 2000–2050).	VU	A2b
17	Eastern medium-altitude dense moist forests	Observed and estimated decline in geographic distribution over 2005–2055 (historical decline or decline over the last 50 years might be even greater but not documented).	NT	A2b
18	Ericoid bushes and thickets	Little studied but does not seem to face significant threats.	LC	
19	Coral reefs of the northeast region	Not considered to be in continuous decline or likely to collapse in the short term.	LC	
20	Subhumid western forests	Probably threatened but no data to assess the risk of collapse.	DD	
21	Riparian and gallery forests	Undoubtedly very threatened according to experts but no quantified data to assess the risk.	DD	
22	Southern and southwestern xerophytic thickets	Threatened by intensification of swidden agricultural practices, but data remain insufficient regarding impacts.	DD	
23	*Roranga* or eastern secondary grasslands	Uncertainties about the rate of degradation of this ecosystem (already resulting from a degradation of the natural forest environment in the east of the island) do not allow assessment of its vulnerability.	DD	
24	Western and highland grasslands	Uncertainties about the risk of collapse toward "pseudo-steppes" and/or bare and desert areas do not allow risk assessment.	DD	
25	Saxicolous vegetation	Despite increased anthropogenic pressure over the past 25 years, there are no data to assess this ecosystem.	DD	
26	Coral reefs of the south region	Probably threatened by maritime pollution, intensive industrial fishing, or illegal collection of marine resources, but not considered to be facing continuous decline.	DD	
27	Seagrass beds of the northeast region	Few data but seems to be less threatened than the seagrass beds of the other coastal regions.	DD	
28	Seagrass beds of the southwest region	Distribution and decline are insufficiently documented and it is not possible to assess the risk. However, sediment loads in coastal waters certainly determine the vulnerability of the ecosystem.	DD	
29	Seagrass beds of the east region	Despite little coverage on the east coast, distribution and decline are too insufficiently documented. Localized anthropogenic pressures (runoff, fishing, trawling, infrastructure, and pollution) and climate change would still have led to a decline.	DD	

(continued overleaf)

TABLE 15.8. ***continued***

NUMBER	ECOSYSTEM	MAIN THREAT AND OBSERVATIONS	IUCN STATUS	DOWNGRADING CRITERION (MAINLY WITH APPLICATION OF CRITERIA A AND B)
30	Western deltas and estuaries	Cannot be assessed according to spatial characteristics, not enough data to assess environmental degradation or the disturbance of biotic interactions.	DD	
31	Lagoon system of the east coast	Not enough data regarding historical decline in geographic distribution, or to assess environmental degradation or the disturbance of biotic interactions.	DD	
32	Underground waters	Various threats exist such as pollution, deforestation (erosion and siltation), climate change (drying of water pockets, increasing temperature), mining, or even the rambling of cattle, but not enough specific data about this still little-studied ecosystem.	DD	
33	Watercourses (rivers and streams)	Threatened mainly by modification of the abiotic environment (high levels of clay-sandy particles of lateritic origin from the erosion of streambeds and watersheds), but no quantitative data at national level.	DD	
34	Lakes and ponds	Threatened mainly by the effects of invasive species on the characteristic native biota, no quantitative data at national level.	DD	
35	Freshwater marshes	Threatened mainly with filling (surface loss and reduction in depth) from anthropogenic actions (deforestation, clearing of vegetation, silting, and bushfires) and natural phenomena (climatic variation, high concentration of precipitation), no quantitative data at national level	DD	
36	Inselbergs		NE	

Notes: CR, Critically Endangered; DD, Data Deficient; EN, Endangered; LC, Least Concern; NE, Not Evaluated; NT, Near Threatened; VU, Vulnerable.

"Dry forests," "spiny forests," and "coastal bushes" of the south and southwest regions, all assessed as Endangered, are currently under the strong assault of swidden agriculture (>50% regression over a 50-year period including past, present, and future). "Xerophytic thickets" were assessed as Data Deficient because of the lack of data concerning the impacts of intensified swidden farming practices, but they probably face the same threats.

The most threatened forest ecosystem on Madagascar appears to be a very restricted formation near Sakaraha known as the Analavelona Forest (ecosystem 1, Table 15.8, Figure 15.9), assessed as Critically Endangered. This formation occupies about 5000 ha, is within a protected area (Alandraza Analavelo), and is surrounded mostly by dry grassland, but the forest habitat is supported by a local reverse foehn effect, which causes significant precipitation in the upper reaches of the massif. The forest block in question is the subject of nearly annual human-linked grassland fires, which erode the forest edge and cause continual decline in both distribution and ecological functioning.

Experts also agree on the probable very high threat to the "gallery and riparian forests"; however, this has not been sufficiently documented to be scientifically assessed. Under different human influences, such as land clearing linked to swidden agriculture, selective cutting of wood, collection of firewood, and artisanal mining, these formations are gradually replaced by a mosaic of bush formations and grasslands. The presence of gallery forests in protected areas has not been calculated to date, and hence no quantified information is available to assess their vulnerability.

Natural and Secondary Grassland Ecosystems

Grasslands are "fire climax" formations with grasses, shrubs, or dispersed trees whose existence is conditioned by the recurrence of natural fires. They are observed in the western and Central Highland areas of Madagascar, with a tropical climate and a marked dry season in association with "dry forests" and "xerophytic thickets." This type of vegetation has steadily increased over the

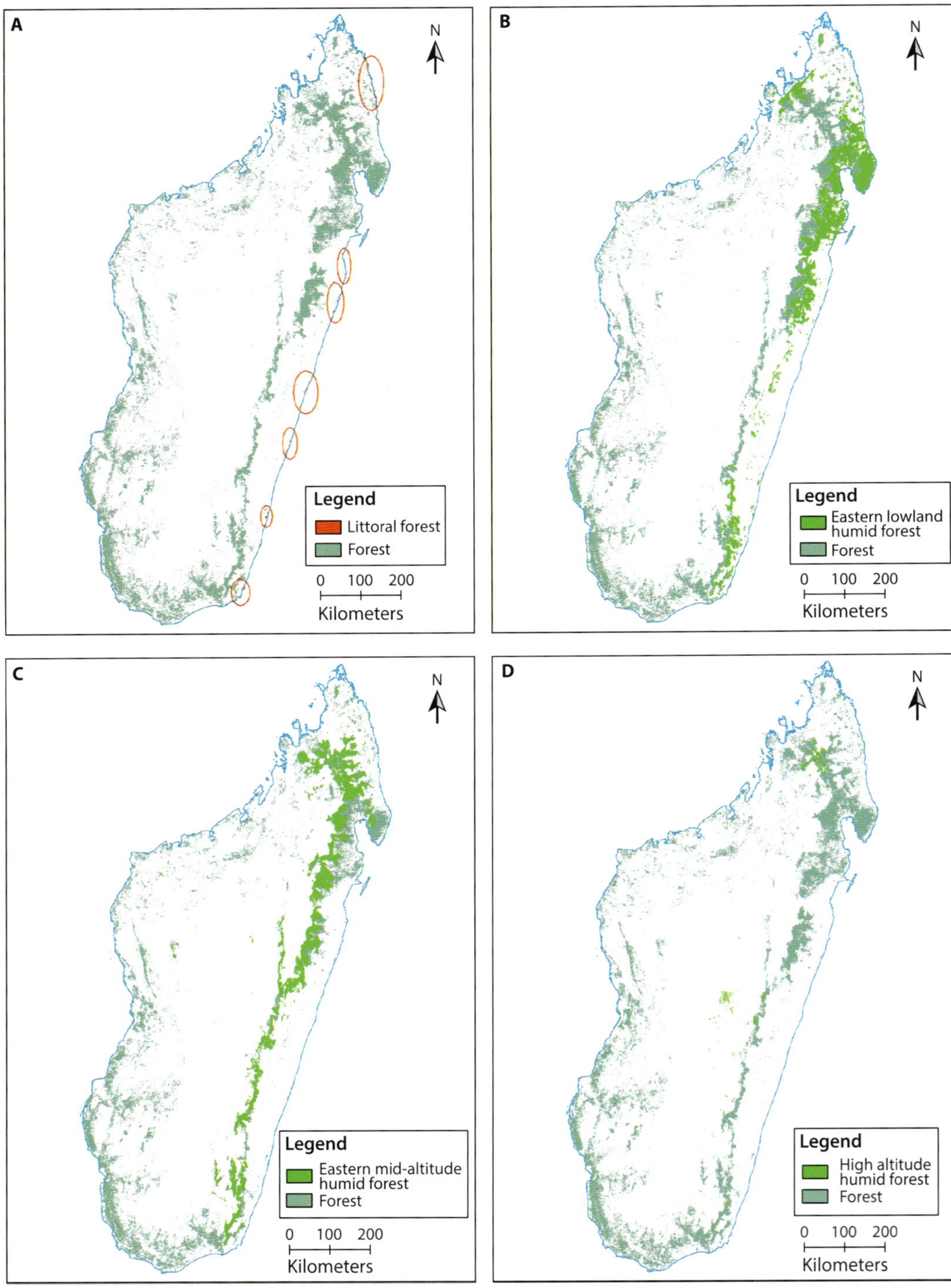

FIGURE 15.8 **Distribution maps of the eastern moist forests of Madagascar, assessed under the Red List of Ecosystems (RLE) methodology. A) littoral forest, B) eastern lowland humid forest, C) eastern medium-altitude humid forest, and D) high-altitude humid forest. (Maps created by R. Andriambolantsoa.)**

past decades following the very marked reduction of dry forest ecosystems under anthropogenic factors. Indeed, increased grazing and swidden agriculture pressure has led to an augmentation in the frequency of fires and the degradation of dry forest into grasslands. But these repetitive and intensive bushfires are followed by soil erosion and runoff, accentuated by steep topography, and the recent transformation of what were formerly natural grasslands into pseudo-steppes has been observed in different areas (Blanc Pamard 2002).

The same situation is observed in eastern Madagascar with *roranga*, a mixed woody vegetation/grass formation whose existence is conditioned by the burning of vegetation linked to shifting agriculture. *Roranga* is indeed especially developed in areas with a humid tropical climate and practically no dry season, and it occurs only as secondary vegetation. This ecosystem has also grown steadily in size since the 1970s and is now sometimes degraded as well because of human activities (cash crops, grazing and agriculture, mining, collection of useful and medicinal plants, etc.). Significant changes are thus currently observed concerning the gradual transformation of *roranga* into more "degraded" vegetation forms. Both grasslands and *roranga* are assessed as Data Deficient.

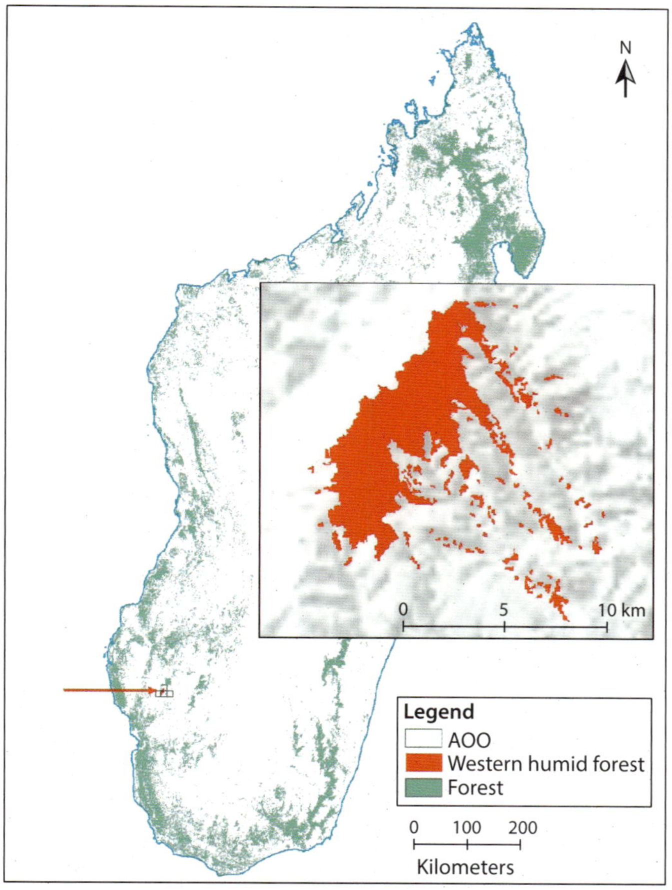

FIGURE 15.9 **Western humid forest ecosystem type classified as Critically Endangered in the Red List of Ecosystems (RLE) evaluation on Madagascar. The area of occupancy (AOO) is indicated on the map. (Map created by R. Andriambolantsoa.)**

Wetland, Lake, and River Ecosystems

No wetland ecosystems could be assessed under the Red List of Ecosystems criteria because of the lack of quantitative data regarding their ecological changes and identified threats. Moreover, these ecosystems are more subject to functional changes than to spatial changes. Indeed, deterioration in the quality of surface water is probably very high and is observed mainly on the physical level. It is characterized by significant levels of clay and sandy particles resulting from massive watershed erosion, and it is responsible for the particular red color of most of the country's major rivers. The drying up of high mountain water sources because of deforestation and the degradation of watersheds is also increasingly common, even in protected areas (Elouard and Gibon 2001).

Rivers descending in the east and entering the Indian Ocean are likely the most disturbed and degraded freshwater habitats on the island because of widespread development and deforestation throughout the ecoregion, even if several of these rivers remain relatively pristine at their headwaters. The eastward-oriented hydrographic network is made up of permanent torrential streams, and the narrow eastern coastal plain causes rivers to form a large network of lagoons parallel to the sandy coast. Over 175 species of freshwater fishes, about 70% of which are endemic, are known to inhabit the rivers and streams of this ecoregion. Two families of fishes, Bedotiidae (rainbowfish) and Anchariidae (catfish), are endemic to Madagascar and are represented in this ecoregion (see Sparks and Stiassny, pp. 1245–60). On the western side, the Central Highlands descend gradually, presenting sedimentary plains with a complex hydrographic network. The northwest basin ecoregion is the richest in freshwater fishes, with 90 species.

Swamps and marshes are also filling and decreasing in depth because of anthropogenic actions (deforestation, clearing of vegetation, sedimentation, and bushfires), accompanied by natural phenomena (climatic variation and highly concentrated precipitation). Little studied, marshes have a remarkable ecological importance on Madagascar, and their disappearance will cause a consequent loss of biodiversity. Even though the two marsh sites of Torotorofotsy and Lake Alaotra are already part of the network of protected areas, this is still insufficient in relation to their total extent and probable level of threat. Permanent lake and pond ecosystems have high levels of threatened endemic species, according to the IUCN Red List. Moreover, most freshwater fish lake communities (e.g., Alaotra, Ihotry, and Itasy) are now dominated by invasive fish species.

Coral Reefs and Mangroves

The coral reefs of Madagascar extend over some 3450 km (McMahon and Webster 2002), including the reefs and offshore shoals, for an estimated area of 5076 km^2 (Andréfouët et al. 2013). Of the five coral reef ecosystems assessed, only the northeast coral reefs appear not to be threatened (Least Concern). Fringing coral reefs on the east coast are assessed as Endangered because of their decline linked to climate change and warming temperatures, which lead to coral bleaching. Western and southwestern coral reefs are also Endangered, threatened by the significant increase in coastal water turbidity over recent decades because of the massive soil erosion driven by deforestation (Obura et al. 2017). Northwestern coral reefs are assessed as Vulnerable, considering the continual decline of their physical environment from massive soil erosion and sedimentation rates observed on the west and northwest coasts of Madagascar. The areas most affected by sedimentation are, for example, the bays of Mahajamba, Baly, and Narinda (southwest, west, and northwest subregions). However, if fringing reefs are experiencing certain levels of degradation and threat, offshore coral reefs seem more or less preserved. Southern coral reefs are threatened by marine pollution, oil spills, intensive industrial fishing, illegal collection of marine resources (black corals and mollusks), and erosion by sea level rise, but these threats are too diffuse and too little quantified to allow assessment.

Mangroves on Madagascar are structured around eight species, according to the characteristic mangrove flora in coastal regions of East Africa (Spalding et al. 2010). Nurseries for peneid shrimp and habitat for the mangrove crab (*Scylla serrata*), these mangroves also harbor many commercial species, some of which are becoming increasingly rare. The threats to mangrove ecosystems consist mainly of excessive sedimentation, in particular on the west coast, prolonged flooding, droughts and abnormal precipitation, cyclones, and strong winds. The most worrying anthropogenic pressure is deforestation for multiple reasons, notably for coal mining, firewood, and nearby urbanization. Ninety-eight percent of the mangrove

ecosystems on Madagascar are located along the west coast, 48% in the northwest region, and 53% in the west region. Mangroves in the west are among the most threatened ecosystems on the island and are assessed as Endangered because of projections of their regression from 2000 to 2050. Despite the large continental alluvial layer that is supposed to promote the growth of deltas and related ecosystems, degradation prevails in most cases over mangrove recovery.

Estuaries, Deltas, and Lagoons

Among these ecosystems, lagoons are nurseries for many aquatic species, such as brackish, marine, and freshwater fishes (Lasserre 1979). They are also important bird sanctuaries. The intensification of anthropogenic activities combined with the growing human population weakens and threatens the lagoons on the east coast of Madagascar. However, it is not possible to quantify the magnitude of abiotic or biotic changes within this ecosystem, based on the Red List of Ecosystems assessment criteria.

CONTRIBUTION OF ECOSYSTEM ASSESSMENT TO NATIONAL STRATEGIES

Among the terrestrial ecosystems of Madagascar, those that have suffered the greatest historical decline in terms of surface losses correspond to the forests of the east, in particular the littoral forests (classified as Endangered), low-altitude moist forests (classified as Vulnerable), and high-altitude moist forests (classified as Endangered). However, the ecosystems that are currently under the greatest pressure and that are the most threatened according to their current regression tendencies are the dry forests, spiny forests, and coastal bushes (all classified as Endangered) in the west, southwest, and south.

Marine and coastal ecosystems are more likely to undergo a modification of their functioning (modification of physical parameters and/or relations between species), rather than losses of area by direct transformation, this latter factor being the long-term result of their modification. Marine and coastal ecosystems of the west and southwest are threatened mainly by the significant increase in coastal water turbidity because of massive soil erosion, while climate change and the growing impact of extreme climatic events also threaten ecosystems of the east coast. Moreover, marine and coastal environments in general remain poorly known on the island, and as a result, consideration of the factors driving their decline is insufficient in both national and local decision-making.

These first ecosystem assessments, according to the IUCN methodology proposed by a team of local experts and the associated IUCN publication (Carré et al. 2020), are particularly timely for Madagascar and are currently at the heart of the implementation of its National Biodiversity Strategy (2018–2025). This strategy indeed raises many expectations, in particular regarding environmental information and communication, with a view to sustainable development and exploitation of Madagascar's natural resources. It announces the country's will to curb the regression of natural ecosystems and assess their quality by 2025. It is important to underline that measuring progress requires reliable and appropriate information on the state and current trends of biodiversity on the island, which a robust Red List of Ecosystems assessment could help provide.

The Malagasy government, in collaboration with IUCN institutions, therefore considers that extending the data provided by the IUCN Red List of Threatened Species to ecosystems, including terrestrial, freshwater, coastal, and marine ecosystems, provides an effective technical and scientific framework to assess the current situation and future prospects, as well as a notable mechanism to support a list of habitats requiring conservation measures on Madagascar. In addition, the lack of data highlighted by the number of ecosystems not assessed should allow better orientation of environmental scientific research, whether national or international.

The objectives of the National Biodiversity Strategy can be achieved based only on an in-depth knowledge of ecosystems and their dynamics, if only to confirm the relevance of the network of protected areas and improve the standards and guarantees for the effective spatial planning of terrestrial and marine spaces. The combination of approaches proposed by the IUCN could then serve as the basis for the development of national plans for the protection of biodiversity and natural resources, as well as for adaptation to climate change. Likewise, this combined approach could play an indispensable role in prioritizing economic investment and defining economic priorities linked to the island's environmental programs. The Red List of Ecosystems of Madagascar thus presents several possible applications:

- Improve understanding of the dynamics and vulnerability of Malagasy ecosystems;
- Guide the ecological restoration of critical ecosystems;
- Identify and assess ecosystem services through environmental programs;
- Improve and update the Biodiversity Strategy and the natural resource management action plan;
- Enrich the biodiversity database through research programs and activities;
- Improve and perfect the application of the Red List of Ecosystems methodology in relation to complex tropical ecological situations;
- Promote scientific publications including Malagasy experts involved in the assessments.

ACKNOWLEDGMENTS

The results presented in this contribution are the fruits of a collegial collaboration. This work brought together numerous Malagasy and international experts for the collection of data and different forms of information, the assessment and assignment of IUCN threat categories, and finally the drafting of the assessment sheets for all ecosystems. This work was coordinated by the IUCN Secretariat and the Ministère de l'Environnement et du Développement Durable, while the technical work was the responsibility of two expert groups: one for terrestrial ecosystems and the other for coastal and marine ecosystems. The experts who carried out this work include the following: Ando Rabearisoa, Andoniaina Bodonarivo Rondroarisoa, Andriambolantsoa Rasolohery, Andry Laurent Razafimahefa, Claire Léa Tojonirina Rasoarimalala,

Daudet Andriafidison, Fano Rajaonary, Fanomezana Mihaja Ratsoavina, Fidy Ratovoson, Franck Rakotonasolo, Guy Arthur Rabarison Andriamirado, Hiarinirina Randrianizana, Jean Charles Lope, Jean Michel Rabary Andriantsilavo, Jean Rasoloariniaina, Luciano Andriamaro, Nadiah Manjato, Njakatiana Ephrem Randrianjafy, Rokiman Letsara, Romer Rabarijaona, Sahoby Ivy Randriamahaleo, Solofo Eric Rakotoarisoa, Tantely Fanomezantsoa Tianarisoa, Tefy Harison Andriamihajarivo, Tsiky Rabetrano, and Yvette Razafindrakoto. David Keith, Justin Moat, and Nicholas Murray also gave specific assistance in providing cartographic data associated with Moat and Smith (2007).

Subject editor: Steven M. Goodman

FOREST CONSERVATION ON MADAGASCAR: PAST, PRESENT, AND FUTURE

J. P. G. Jones, O. S. Rakotonarivo, and J. H. Razafimanahaka

Ny lasa tsy anenenana fa ahombiazana ny ho avy. (The past is not to be regretted but to inform the future.)

—Malagasy proverb

Almost every article about Madagascar's biodiversity starts with a list of superlatives reflecting the country's status as one of the world's "hottest" biodiversity hotspots (Ganzhorn et al. 2001). However, in the conservation of that biodiversity, many other extremes are also relevant. Madagascar is one of the poorest countries in the world (World Bank 2019), with a higher proportion of people living in extreme poverty than almost anywhere else on the planet (Roser and Ortiz-Ospina 2019), as well as widespread food insecurity (Rakotomanana et al. 2017). This affects all aspects of conservation on the island. Madagascar is also one of the highest recipients of biodiversity-related aid (Miller et al. 2013; Waeber et al. 2016). It was one of the first Southern Hemisphere countries to introduce laws facilitating community-based natural resource management (Rasolofoson et al. 2017), and it has undergone one of the most comprehensive recent expansions of a protected area network in the world (Goodman et al. 2018). So many challenges and so many opportunities.

At this critical time for the future of Madagascar's biodiversity (Jones et al. 2019a), we first review the past, touching on conservation from the pre- to postcolonial periods before focusing on the period that most dramatically shaped the country's current conservation-related institutions and policies (1984–2009). Next we examine evidence for the effectiveness (or lack thereof) of the current main approaches to forest conservation on the island. We look in detail at how conservation has conceptualized the link between the environment and development on Madagascar, the impact of measures by conservationists to transform rural livelihoods, and the effectiveness of protected areas, community-based natural resource management, and environmental impact assessment legislation. Finally, we look to the future and consider how pressures on Madagascar's biodiversity, and the conservation community's responses, are evolving and need to evolve.

This is, of course, hugely ambitious. We are attempting to cover a significant chunk of history for a diverse mini-continent. We bring in literature from anthropology, political ecology, economics, and conservation science. We can hope to do this only incompletely. We focus on forest conservation partly because such a high proportion of Madagascar's biodiversity is found in forests (Goodman and Benstead 2005), but also because other contributions in this book cover conservation issues faced by specific taxonomic groups.

CONSERVATION PAST

The Precolonial Context of Conservation on Madagascar

The livelihoods of Malagasy people have always been varied; for example, livestock herding is dominant in the dry south and west, and fishing in coastal areas (Dewar 2014). Where there is forest, people use shifting or swidden agriculture (known as *tavy* in the Central Highlands and the east, *jinja* in the north, and *hatsake* in the south and west; hereafter *tavy*) (Figure 15.10a) to meet their subsistence needs. The ancestors of the current Malagasy ethnic groups developed institutions to manage the natural resources on which they depended (Ostrom 1990). Perhaps we can see vestiges of how these institutions may have looked in some aspects of the *fady* (Malagasy taboos and social norms; Jones et al. 2008) and *dina* (locally imposed regulations; Rakotoson and Tanner 2006; Andriamalala and Gardner 2010), which contribute to traditional natural resource management today. However, these institutions would have been highly variable across the island and are poorly documented (Kull 2014). Like others, we therefore skip over the first millennia of natural resource management on Madagascar to consider the beginning of top-down rules, which emerged during the Merina royal dynasty.

At the end of the 18th century, the first king who attempted to unite Madagascar (Andrianampoinimerina, 1745–1810) introduced

FIGURE 15.10 **A)** ***Tavy*** **on the edge of Zahamena National Park. B) and C) Malagasy people have always used products collected from the forest (including building and roofing materials and food such as freshwater crayfish). D) Payment for Ecosystem Services Schemes, where users of hydroelectricity or operators of dams pay upstream farmers to maintain forest and reduce siltation, may contribute to future funding of forest conservation on Madagascar. E) Micro-development interventions such as improved bean cultivation can be popular and bring benefits but have tended not to result in significant transformation of farming systems. F) Functioning ecosystems can provide benefits;** ***Mormopterus jugularis*** **(Peters' Goblin Bat) predates pests of rice fields. G) Communities in western Madagascar are exploring the potential of working with international cosmetics companies interested in baobab fruits, a potentially high-value product allowing them to benefit from the endemic trees.** (PHOTOS A, C, and D by J. P. G. Jones; B and G by Madagasikara Voakajy; E by M. Poudyal; and F by Adrià López-Baucells.)

some of the earliest documented rules concerning the conservation of natural resources in the Afro-Malagasy region (Scales 2014a). Presented using the magnificent Malagasy oral tradition of *kabary*, these were written down by missionaries, such as the French Jesuit priest Callet, in the 1860s and 1870s (Langrand and Rene de Roland 2018). Andrianampoinimerina clearly considered the forest a public good whose products could be used by the poor. "Here is the forest, a patrimony not susceptible of division among the subjects. It is there that the orphans, the widows and all the unfortunate will come and seek their means of existence, as without the forest they would have no resources to sell." He expressly banned forest clearance except for making charcoal to support metalwork, and this exploitation was to be conducted only at forest edges (Langrand and Rene de Roland 2018). Subsequent Malagasy royals (particularly King Radama II, 1829–1863; and Queen Ranavalona II, 1829–1883) further developed and formalized laws controlling the clearance of forest land and introduced the state ownership of forests that remains the default to this day (Raik 2007; Pollini 2011). The focus of these rules was retaining access to precious hardwoods for royal and state-approved uses. While these rules purported to apply to the whole island, in reality the Merina dynasty had limited control outside the lands of the Imerina and Betsileo ethnic groups (Central Highlands), certainly until the mid-19th century (M. Brown 2000; Randrianja and Ellis 2009). Other leaders outside the Imerina presumably had their own systems of natural resource management that are less well known.

The Colonial and Immediate Postcolonial Periods

France formally annexed Madagascar in 1896. With growing awareness of the economic value of forests in French colonies, Madagascar's forest service, the Département des Eaux et Forêts (DEF), grew rapidly in the early part of the 20th century (Langrand and Rene de Roland 2018). A major focus of the authorities was on limiting traditional shifting agriculture and the use of fire, while extracting valuable timber and promoting cash crops for export (Jarosz 1993; Kull 2004; Scales 2014b). The DEF was also responsible for planting and managing large tracts of eucalyptus and pine plantations to provide timber and fuelwood to support building projects and the energy needs of the two French-built railways (Olson 1984).

Colonial scientists and naturalists believed that Madagascar had been entirely forested before the arrival of humans (McConnell and Kull 2014). Paleoecological studies of pollen records and analysis of the species in Madagascar's grassland communities have now shown beyond doubt that grasslands of the Central Highlands pre-dated human settlement (Dewar 2014; Vorontsova et al. 2016). They are therefore not entirely anthropocentric. Such misunderstanding of how much forest existed "originally," and the relatively limited attention given to the role of logging and commercial plantations during the colonial period, have resulted in overemphasis on the role of *tavy* in the narrative of Madagascar's deforestation (Jarosz 1993; Scales 2011; McConnell and Kull 2014).

French botanists stationed on Madagascar noted the unusual flora and started arguing for protection of the various phytogeographic domains from the early 20th century (Saboureau 1946; Langrand and Rene de Roland 2018). The Parc Botanique et Zoologique de Tsimbazaza was created in 1925 for the scientific study of Madagascar's flora, and the country's first 10 nature reserves followed soon afterward. More widely, the colonial administration perpetuated and expanded state control of Madagascar's forests with a strong focus on ensuring access to valuable natural resources (Montagne and Ramamonjisoa 2006). The early protected areas were put under the management of the DEF. For a time, the department was well resourced and included highly trained professional foresters; rural people with memories of life in the 1950s indicate that the *ben'ny ala* (forest guards) were generally well respected. However, in the postcolonial period the DEF was progressively starved of funds (Corson 2016), and its capacity to manage forest resources collapsed.

In 1961, the year after it became an independent nation, Madagascar joined the World Conservation Union, which is now known as the International Union for Conservation of Nature (IUCN). In 1972 it sent a high-level delegation to the United Nations environment conference where the vice president of Madagascar made a forward-looking speech highlighting the need to reconcile conservation and sustainable use of natural resources (Repoblika Malagasy 1972). In 1975 Didier Ratsiraka's socialist government, with its policy of "nonalignment" with western powers and emphatic rejection of French neocolonialism (M. Brown 2000), took power and actively encouraged rural people to clear forest to create farmland. A favorite slogan, repeated by the president in his own version of Mao Zedong's *Little Red Book* (Ratsiraka 1975), was "Mamokatra, mamokatra, mamokatra hatrany" (Produce, produce, produce continually). There was little progress in terms of environmental institutions or policy development until the mid-1980s.

The Beginning of Modern Conservation on Madagascar (1984–2009)

At the start of the 1980s, Madagascar's economy was in a very poor state and Ratsiraka's government was forced to turn to the International Monetary Fund for urgent debt relief (M. Brown 2000). At the time, lack of capacity in the DEF had created a de facto open-access situation in much of Madagascar's forests (Raik 2007), although it is important to note that customary management persisted in certain areas of the island (Rabesahala Horning 2005). Forests (both those inside and outside the very limited protected areas of that period) were being lost rapidly (Eklund et al. 2016; Vieilledent et al. 2018). As the country underwent economic reform (forced by the terms of the International Monetary Fund deal), there was growing donor interest in Madagascar (Rabesahala Horning 2008; Kull 2014; Corson 2016). The United States Agency for International Development (USAID), for example, set up its mission in 1984. Particularly influential in galvanizing the donors was an international conference attended by Prince Philip (then president of WWF), which was held on Madagascar in 1985 (Jolly 2015). The next 25 years saw rapid change in Madagascar's environmental institutions and policies, strongly influenced by donor requirements (Corson 2016).

The National Environmental Action Plan: In the mid-1980s, the World Bank started encouraging African nations to adopt formal environmental action plans in recognition of the importance of both the environment and economic policies to sustainable

development (Mercier 2009). Madagascar's National Environmental Action Plan (NEAP), one of the first in Africa (Greve et al. 1995), was agreed on in 1988 and signed into law in 1990 (Figure 15.11). This ambitious, multi-donor program of support was planned to last 15 years and bring in hundreds of millions of dollars (US) to transform environmental management on the island (Corson 2016).

The NEAP had three major phases. The first (1991–1996) established key national institutions for environmental management, such as the Office National pour l'Environnement (ONE), and developed the newly formed Association National pour la Gestion des Aires Protégées (ANGAP, now called Madagascar National Parks). ANGAP was created as a parastatal organization, outside the direct control of the government, to take over the management of protected areas from the DEF (Kull 2014). The first phase of the NEAP also set up and supported new protected areas through integrated conservation and development programs (ICDPs). Reviews of these ICDP projects suggested that development approaches had been poorly targeted and delivered limited conservation benefit. There was also growing awareness of how much of Madagascar's biodiversity remained outside protected areas and that protected areas alone might be too small to ensure the survival of key species (K. Freudenberger 2010). This resulted in a shift in focus to wider landscapes, the "ecoregional" approach. The second and third

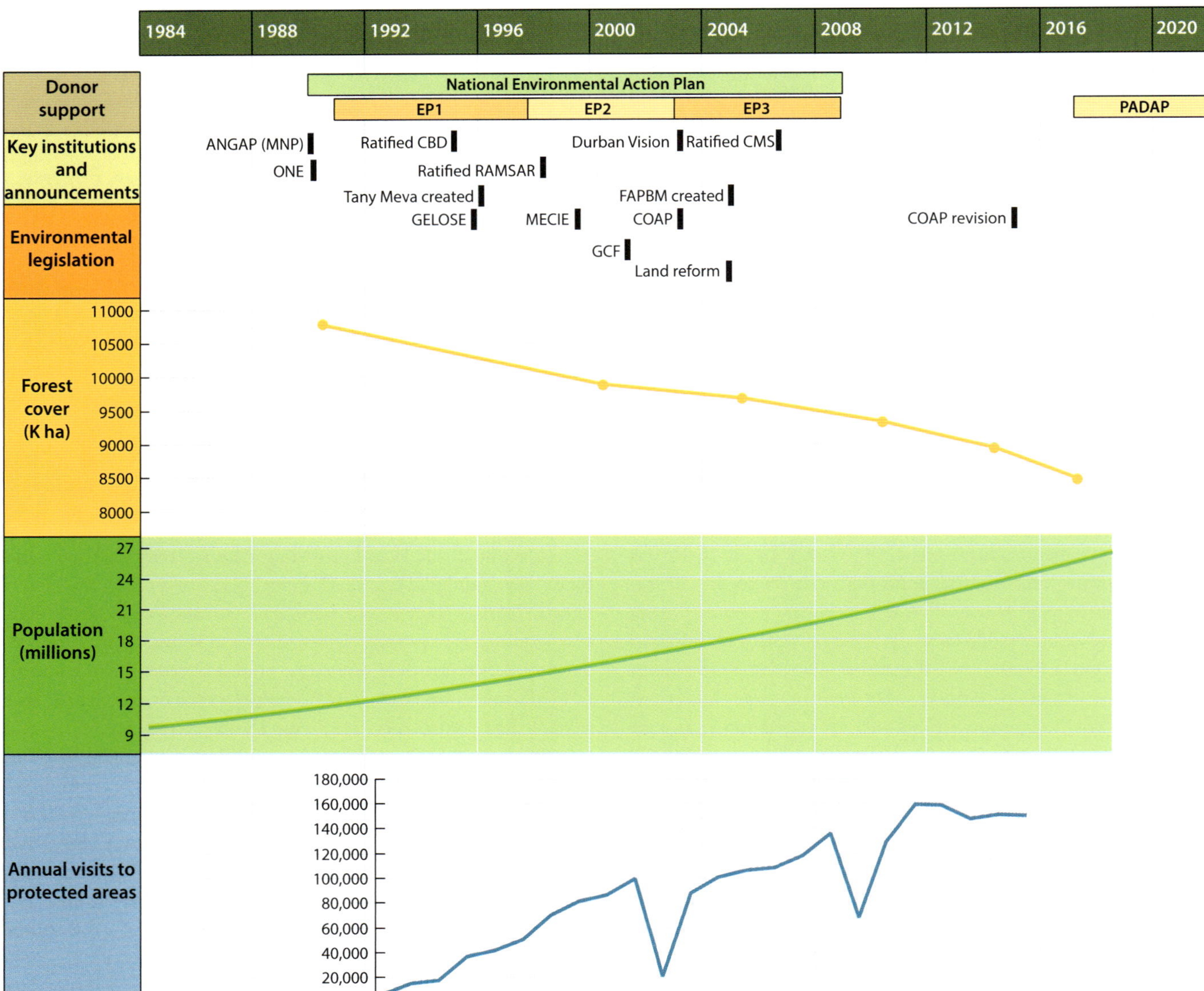

FIGURE 15.11 **A timeline showing key events related to conservation on Madagascar over a span of ~35 years. Data on forest cover come from Vieilledent et al. (2018); data on population come from World Bank (2019); data on annual visits to protected areas come from Goodman et al. (2018). ANGAP: Association Nationale pour la Gestion des Aires Protégées (MNP: Madagascar National Parks); CBD: Convention on Biological Diversity; CMS: Convention on Migratory Species; COAP: Codes des Aires Protégées de Madagascar; EP1, 2, 3: the first, second, and third phases of the National Environmental Action Plan; GCF: Gestion Contractualisée des Forêts; GELOSE: Gestion Locale Sécurisée; MECIE: Mise en Compatibilité des Investissements avec l'Environnement; PADAP: Projet Agriculture Durable par une Approche Paysage.**

phases of the NEAP (1997–2003 and 2003–2008) supported the development of legal frameworks allowing co-management of natural resources with local communities, and the national law requiring environmental impact assessment and impact mitigation for new developments (Figure 15.11).

The Durban Vision and Rapid Expansion of Madagascar's Protected Area Network: Madagascar's protected area system, with a particular emphasis on terrestrial sites, gradually increased during the first two phases of the NEAP. However, in 2003, the former president Marc Ravalomanana dramatically announced at the World Parks Congress in Durban that the national government would more than triple the country's terrestrial protected area network, from approximately 3% of the territory to approximately 10% (Figure 15.11). The announcement mobilized substantial additional international donor support (Corson 2016). Malagasy and international conservation scientists pulled together the best available biodiversity data to inform the design of this new protected area network (Kremen et al. 2008). By 2008, a substantial proportion of the planned sites had received temporary protected status, although it took another seven years for this status for be formalized (Ranivo Rakotoson and Razafimahatratra 2018). Protected areas established before 2003 were state managed through the parastatal ANGAP (now Madagascar National Parks). However, the years following the Durban Vision saw a rewriting of the protected area code to permit different organizations, ranging from NGOs to universities and even mining companies, to act as the legal managers of new protected areas (Gardner et al. 2018).

The Introduction of Community-Based Natural Resource Management: A string of Malagasy legislation was established that started in precolonial times and remained unbroken until the late 1990s, enforcing the state as the only legitimate manager of forests (Raik 2007). However, during the 1980s and 1990s there was growing realization around the world that state ownership of forests, especially in the context of weak and poorly resourced forest services, could result in a de facto open-access situation and rapid overexploitation (Ostrom 1990; Rabesahala Horning 2005). Community-Based Natural Resource Management (also known as co-management) was proposed as a way for communities to take greater responsibility for their natural resources (Montagne and Ramamonjisoa 2006). Two procedures for co-management were put in place on the island to transfer some degree of management authority to local groups: Gestion Locale Sécurisée (known as GELOSE) in 1996, and Gestion Contractualisée des Forêts (GCF) in 2001 (Figure 15.11). These legal structures, some of the first in the Afro-Malagasy region, were intended to deliver environmental benefits while supporting local livelihoods (Ramiarantsoa et al. 2012; Ferguson et al. 2014).

CONSERVATION PRESENT

In 2009, Madagascar underwent a major political crisis because of an undemocratic change of government. Many donors left the country. USAID took this opportunity to conduct a retrospective, exploring what had or had not been achieved since it set up its mission on the island in 1984. This fascinating document (K. Freudenberger 2010), has a subdued tone: "As we step back after 25 years, honesty compels us to conclude that the environmental crisis in Madagascar is far more acute now than it was at the outset of [the first phase of NEAP]."

If we simply compare before and after, we might conclude that conservation on the island over the last few decades has failed. At the start of the NEAP, Madagascar had 11 million ha of forest. This has since been reduced substantially, and by 2014 nearly 50% of the remaining forest was within 100 m of the forest edge (Vieilledent et al. 2018). However, the appropriate comparison is with what might have occurred without any conservation efforts. This is of course inherently unknowable (Baylis et al. 2016), but there are a growing number of robust evaluations of the impact of Malagasy conservation efforts (Rasolofoson et al. 2015, 2018a; Eklund et al. 2016) that formally attempt to estimate the counterfactual. In this section we consider different (overlapping) aspects of Madagascar's current conservation approaches and use the best available evidence to evaluate the impacts.

Assumptions about the Relationship between Poverty and Conservation

It has long been accepted that biodiversity loss and poverty are linked problems, but the nature of the relationship between these policy realms is complex and uncertain (Adams et al. 2004; Roe et al. 2019). Madagascar's biodiversity is a priceless national heritage. It also plays a key role in attracting international and national tourists and donor support (Corson 2016) and provides important national ecosystem services (Wendland et al. 2010). In these ways, conservation can contribute to poverty alleviation at the national scale (Jones et al. 2019a). There are also clear local benefits from conservation. For example, communities recognize the role of forests in hazard mitigation such as reducing sediment flow after heavy rain (Dave et al. 2017) and providing valued products such as wild foods during times of famine (Figures 15.10b and c; Noromiarilanto et al. 2016). There is also empirical evidence that children with access to forests have more diverse diets and suffer less from micronutrient deficiency than otherwise similar children (Golden et al. 2011; Rasolofoson et al. 2018b). Healthy ecosystems can provide valuable pest control services (Figure 15.10f; Kemp et al. 2019) and contribute to water availability for consumption, agriculture, and hydropower (Neugarten et al. 2016).

However, while it is true that forest conservation brings local benefits, this does not mean that conservation will inevitably contribute to poverty alleviation at the local scale. Unfortunately, "win-wins" (happy alignments of the interests of forest-edge communities and the national and international conservation communities) have not generally been borne out in practice (Serpantié et al. 2007; K. Freudenberger 2010; Pollini 2011). For example, conservationists tend to see *tavy* as an unsustainable and therefore inherently irrational agricultural practice, meaning that both farmers and the environment would benefit from a change. But this flexible, low-input system is well adapted to the conditions faced by forest-edge farmers (M. Freudenberger and Freudenberger 2002; Scales 2014b), and it is often their only real option to ensure food security. By preventing local people from expanding their agricultural lands through *tavy*, or prohibiting charcoal burning and hunting, forest conservation can

bring genuine local costs (Ramamonjisoa and Rabemananjara 2012; Poudyal et al. 2018), as well as benefits. These costs are often disproportionately borne by some of the poorest. As a man from the eastern moist evergreen forests put it in an interview with one of us (Rakotonarivo 2016): "Land [accessed through forest clearance] is the most valuable inheritance you can leave to your children ... I am grieving that people are put in jail because they are making a living from the forestlands which are Zanahary's [God's] creation, not the government's property." This quote captures the hardship caused by enforcing severe penalties for land clearance without providing alternatives. Recognition that there is a moral obligation for conservation to avoid making poor people poorer was formalized in the revision of the protected area code in 2015, but implementation of these social safeguards is lacking (Poudyal et al. 2018).

Some see poverty as a critical constraint on conservation, meaning that conservation must consider poverty alleviation, if only for pragmatic reasons (Adams et al. 2004). There is a clear rationale for this on Madagascar, where a significant proportion of land clearance is driven by poor people's need to achieve food security. However, it does not necessarily follow that conservation will inevitably be achieved if poverty is reduced. Among poor rural farmers, a small increase in available resources may result in an increase, not a decrease, in their ability to clear land (M. Freudenberger and Freudenberger 2002; Llopis et al. 2019). Also, it is often not the poorest who hunt wildlife (Jenkins et al. 2011; see Golden et al., pp. 204–17) or illegally exploit precious wood (Randriamalala and Liu 2010; Wilmé et al. 2020). Together, these observations all mean that interventions that successfully raise incomes, while desperately needed, cannot be relied on to reduce pressure on the environment.

Efforts by Conservationists to Transform Rural Livelihoods

The evocative descriptions of *tavy* written in 1661 by the French governor Etienne de Flacourt (quoted in Jarosz 1993) are perfectly familiar to anyone who spends time in the villages of Madagascar's eastern forests. This illustrates just how little agricultural practices at the forest frontier have changed in centuries, despite the long antipathy toward this agricultural system by the authorities (Kull 2004). Throughout the last 35 years, conservationists (and projects funded with conservation as the ultimate objective) have implemented a range of interventions aimed at encouraging a shift away from *tavy* toward more intensive production systems.

Initial efforts focused on increasing productivity in irrigated rice fields in the belief that this would reduce forest clearance for *tavy*. This was based on rather simplistic assumptions. For example, the much promoted System of Rice Intensification (SRI) could increase yields on small plots (Stoop et al. 2002), but because it required high labor inputs and close control of water levels, take-up was disappointing (Moser and Barrett 2003). Another issue was that many of the farmers clearing forest did not have access to irrigated land; they needed technologies to maintain fertility and increase production on their *tavy* fields. A range of approaches were taken to address this, including promoting soil fertility through composting, planting cover crops, and using perennial grasses such as vetiver (*Vetiveria*, Poaceae) to support irrigated terraces on steep slopes (M. Freudenberger and Freudenberger 2002).

Throughout the years of the NEAP and in the decade after it ended, conservation projects also widely promoted alternative livelihoods such as fish farming, honey production, or essential oil production. While these alternative livelihood approaches brought some successes (Bidaud et al. 2017; Harvey et al. 2018; Poudyal et al. 2018), and they may have been important to legitimize the presence of conservation organizations working in an area, large-scale agricultural transformation did not generally occur, and their results were often disappointing (Laney and Turner 2015; Rakotonarivo et al. 2017).

There are many explanations for the lack of widespread success of these conservation-funded investments intended to transform local farming systems (Figure 15.10e). First, land tenure issues are an important constraint on farmers' ability to invest in the land they farm. Many farmers borrow or rent land, and even those who do enjoy customary ownership may hesitate to invest because of uncertainties in tenure (Aubert et al. 2013; Burnod et al. 2014). Second, labor constraints (Tucker 2007) and the inability of poor Malagasy farmers to risk investing in new approaches (Rakotonarivo et al. 2018) may have been underestimated. Third, the poor state of rural infrastructure (especially for transport and irrigation) has consistently limited the potential of micro-development projects to lead to large-scale change (K. Freudenberger 2010). Finally, and perhaps most important, while many projects have been large in absolute dollar terms, the amount available for interventions at the forest frontier, where thousands of widely dispersed households needed to be reached (Jolly 2015; Poudyal et al. 2016), was actually quite small. Perhaps it is not surprising that many schemes did not deliver what was hoped for.

The US$100 million Projet Agriculture Durable par une Approche Paysage (co-funded by the World Bank, the Agence Française de Développement, and the Global Environment Facility) aims to increase agricultural productivity in connection with sustainable management of natural resources (Agence Française de Développement 2017; World Bank 2017). The project documents suggest that replacing unsustainable *tavy* with agroforestry will provide a "win-win in the sense that they will benefit both the landholders themselves and environmental service users." This positive wording rather glosses over the failures stretching back to colonial time of attempts to prevent this practice, and it ignores the reasons that this remains such a popular agricultural system in rural Madagascar. However, the project does directly address some of the limitations of earlier interventions, for example by investing in irrigation infrastructure and working on land tenure issues. There seems to be increasing recognition that sustainable transformation of agriculture on Madagascar is likely to require investment and collaboration across a range of sectors. This is very positive and greatly needed. Successful conservation on Madagascar will be impossible without sustainable agricultural development.

The State of Madagascar's Protected Area Network

Madagascar's current protected area system, remarkably representative of the nation's world-renowned biodiversity (Goodman et al. 2018), is a priceless national treasure (Randrianandianina et al. 2003; Ramangason 2018). The 144 protected areas (as of 2020; Vyawahare 2020), including sites representing principally terrestrial or marine ecosystems, represent the full spectrum of management from IUCN category I to VI (Gardner et al. 2018; Goodman et al. 2018).

Madagascar's protected areas face many pressures (Jones et al. 2019b). Some suffer from sporadic exploitation of precious hardwoods (Wilmé et al. 2020), hunting of wildlife for bushmeat (Razafimanahaka et al. 2012; Brook et al. 2019), or gold and gem mining (Cabeza et al. 2019). Large-scale land clearance to produce cash crops (Filou 2019), charcoal production (Gardner et al. 2016), and continued degradation driven by small-scale subsistence agriculture (Desbureaux and Damania 2018) are also important threats.

Despite these pressures, protected areas on Madagascar have tended to effectively slow forest loss. Protected areas tend to be located in areas subject to lower deforestation pressures than unprotected forests; this bias needs to be accounted for when evaluating the impact of protected areas. Such robust analysis has shown that in all three major forest biomes of Madagascar (humid, dry deciduous, and spiny), protected areas have slowed deforestation, at least up to 2010 (Eklund et al. 2016). A different analysis using a similar approach has suggested that post-2010 protected areas have also slowed deforestation, but only in dry years when pressures on forests are highest (Desbureaux and Damania 2018).

Since the early days of the NEAP, tourism has been at the heart of plans for funding protected areas on Madagascar (Méral et al. 2011). Tourism can play an important role in generating jobs and support for conservation (Ormsby and Mannle 2006), although this is far from universal (Cameron 2017). However, although visits to protected areas have increased (Figure 15.11), and park entrance fees were substantially raised in 2015, park receipts still contribute relatively little to the running costs of Madagascar National Parks (Goodman et al. 2018). Tourism revenue can also be extremely fickle. Past political crises have crashed tourist numbers, and international press coverage of a violent incident involving a tourist rapidly resulted in cancellations. The Fondation pour les Aires Protégées et la Biodiversité de Madagascar (FAPBM) was established in 2005 as a national foundation to provide sustainable financing for Madagascar's protected areas. It is endowed with more than US$70 million (as of 2018), but available funding has not kept pace with protected area expansion (Gardner et al. 2018), and FAPBM's annual income now provides less than 10% of the current management costs of the network (Jones et al. 2019a).

Since the mid-1990s, there has been criticism that protected areas on Madagascar have brought local costs without providing adequate support to impoverished local communities (Peters 1998; J. Harper 2002; Jolly 2015). While there are examples of Madagascar National Parks and other conservation actors working well with communities to develop small-scale development projects (Ormsby and Mannle 2006; Aymoz et al. 2013), this problem remains today. The new protected areas created under the Durban Vision were subject to stringent rules driven by the World Bank social safeguards, supposedly guaranteeing compensation to anyone suffering from economic displacement. However, detailed research in the Ankeniheny-Zahamena Corridor (eastern moist evergreen forests) revealed that such compensation tended to benefit the better off and those less affected by conservation rules (Poudyal et al. 2016). While benefits from conservation may of course come in the future, this work shows that overall none of the 6000-odd affected households were fully compensated according to the World Bank rules (Poudyal et al. 2018). Studies in other new protected areas on Madagascar have drawn similar conclusions (Brimont et al. 2015; Ward et al. 2018).

These findings pose difficult challenges for those concerned with the future of Madagascar's protected areas. The network is vital to biodiversity conservation in the country. However, despite their immeasurable national and global value, mechanisms do not yet appear to have been found to fully ensure their effective, and critically their equitable, conservation (Hockley et al. 2018).

Success and Failure of Community-Based Natural Resource Management

By 2014, 15% of Madagascar's natural forests were under co-management (Rasolofoson et al. 2017), and the vast majority of the post–Durban Vision protected areas involve some degree of co-management with local communities over at least part of their area (Toillier et al. 2011a; Gardner et al. 2018). The rationale behind co-management is that devolution of rights to make management decisions and capture benefits from natural resources will result in more sustainable management. However, the extent to which co-management has resulted in any substantial devolution of rights to rural people on Madagascar has been debated (Kull 2004). Some have suggested that instead of devolving real power, co-management aimed simply to co-opt community efforts to further the agenda of the conservation organizations (Pollini et al. 2014). This argument suggests that despite the justification for the approach being framed in terms of the now familiar concept of "win-wins" (i.e., benefits for both the environment and local people), the rules tended to result in limited benefit for local communities.

There has been extensive debate in the literature about the extent to which the community groups to which management authority is devolved (usually called VOI, Vondron Olona Ifotony) do indeed represent local community interests and what the most effective and appropriate structure should be. The relevant laws, somewhat surprisingly, do not require that the VOI be representative (Pollini et al. 2014; Rabemananjara et al. 2016). In this way, co-management can in practice support the privatization of natural resource management, rather than its decentralization (Pollini et al. 2014). There are many examples of VOI being controlled by local elites for their own private benefit (Hockley and Andriamarovololona 2007; Pollini and Lassoie 2011).

An important question of course is whether co-management has delivered its objectives in terms of providing environmental and welfare benefits. Qualitative evaluation at seven sites in the eastern moist evergreen forests (Hockley and Andriamarovololona 2007) suggested that all VOIs had made efforts to exclude others but had often struggled, as the backup they needed from state authorities was not forthcoming. A robust counterfactual impact evaluation (comparing deforestation rates in pixels under co-management with statistically matched pixels without any form of management) suggested that between 2000 and 2010, co-management did not, on average, slow deforestation on the island (Rasolofoson et al. 2015). This result was unchanged even when the analysis was restricted to include only those sites where there was evidence of implementation on the ground (many co-management agreements, especially those using GCF legislation, were made in a rush with little local engagement and very limited training or capacity transfer). However, there was some evidence that co-managed forests where commercial logging was prohibited did have some impact in terms of reducing

deforestation compared to co-management where such use was allowed, and compared to forests without co-management. A similar national-scale analysis of the impacts of community forest management on economic well-being (Rasolofoson et al. 2017) also showed no positive impacts on average, but it was at least able to reject the hypothesis of substantial negative impacts.

Such national-scale analyses give a useful overview, but because they inevitably lump together co-management implemented with varying degrees of investment and care, they say little about the potential of the approach. What is certain is that many communities agreed in good faith to set up these new institutions, which they often believed would solidify their rights over their land (Rasolofoson et al. 2018a). However, in many cases they were then given little support as donor funding ended and NGO partners moved on.

Dealing with the Environmental Impacts of Development

The legal framework for requiring environmental impact assessment on Madagascar (Mise en Compatibilité des Investissements avec l'Environnement, commonly known as the MECIE decree) is considered by some to be one of the big successes of the NEAP (K. Freudenberger 2010). It requires large forestry or agricultural operations (Ratsialonana et al. 2011), extractive industries (Nwapi and Nliam 2018), and infrastructure projects to undergo a scoping process overseen by the national regulator (Office National pour l'Environnement, or ONE), and it lays out when in-depth social and environmental impact assessment and remediation measures are needed (Huff 2016). These assessments should, in theory, provide the government with the tools to balance the need for development investment with its commitment to protect the environment. However, implementation has been mixed. One challenge has been that the regulator is increasingly dependent on fees paid by developers, potentially undermining its ability to independently regulate the sector (Nwapi and Nliam 2018; Gerety 2019). Monitoring of the environmental impact assessment (EIA) agreements has often been lacking (Huff 2016; Bidaud et al. 2018). There is also concern that the legislation itself is not fit for tackling new and evolving industries on Madagascar. For example, the criteria that would be used under MECIE to determine whether an oil sands mining development required an EIA are not clearly linked to the likely extent of environmental impact from the proposed extraction (Nwapi and Nliam 2018; Gerety 2019). Our own observations (J. H. Razafimanahaka, unpublished data) suggest similar issues for both the extraction of essential oils and the harvest of bat guano from cave deposits. There are efforts to revise the decree to more explicitly incorporate the mitigation hierarchy and require strategic environmental assessment (Jones et al. 2019a).

CONSERVATION FUTURE

The pressures on Madagascar's natural resources continue to grow. Just since the year 2000, the human population has nearly doubled. Some urbanization has occurred, but a significant majority of Malagasy still live in rural areas (World Bank 2019). This means that the number of farmers seeking to make a living at the forest frontier has rapidly increased. While tree cover (mostly fruit trees and non-natives) is increasing in pockets of the Central Highlands (McConnell et al. 2015), a forest transition (where land-use trends change from a period of net loss to a period of net gain) is not expected at the national scale anytime soon (Kull et al. 2007; Jones et al. 2018). At the same time, climate change is shifting the distribution of some forest species (Vieilledent et al. 2013) and will make life even more difficult and precarious for many rural people (Harvey et al. 2014). In this section, we highlight some of the most important areas where progress is needed if current trends in forest and biodiversity loss are to be reversed.

Without Effective Governance and Government, Conservation on Madagascar Is Impossible

In Madagascar's recent history, governance issues have significantly hampered conservation efforts (Gerety 2017a; Jones et al. 2019b). Madagascar appears 105th out of 128 countries in the Rule of Law Index and performs particularly poorly on measures of corruption and criminal justice (World Justice Project 2020). Corruption involving Madagascar's elites has been implicated in a number of important conservation issues, including illegal rosewood trafficking (Anonymous 2018) and the trade of threatened animal species (Mandimbihasina et al. 2020). Saying that improving the rule of law is vital to effective conservation on Madagascar should not be interpreted as a call for an increase in enforcement-heavy conservation strategies (Neimark 2019). Given the issues faced by the judiciary and prison system (Amnesty International 2018), a clampdown on poor farmers who break environmental laws is not what is needed. However, broader accountability, just laws, open government, and accessible justice (the four universal principles of the rule of law; World Justice Project 2020) are vital for both Madagascar's development prospects and effective conservation (Jones et al. 2019b).

Political crises associated with transfers of power have been a regular feature of Madagascar's postcolonial history (Ratsimbaharison 2017; Razafindrakoto et al. 2020). Each crisis tends to impact the stability of conservation programs. For example, both the 2003 and 2008 crises saw dramatic reductions in the number of visits to protected areas (Figure 15.11), affecting the resources available to Madagascar National Parks for management activities and local development projects. The political crises have also been associated with increases in illegal lemur hunting (Schwitzer et al. 2014) and precious wood extraction (Randriamalala and Liu 2010). Madagascar, and indirectly its biodiversity, would greatly benefit from stable transitions of power.

An uncomfortable question concerns the extent to which the international community has been complicit in allowing the poor state of governance on the island to develop. By being quick to announce problematic elections as free and fair, and continuing aid programs despite failures of governance, donor governments and NGOs can undermine democracy (Klaas 2016).

Support from Civil Society Is Vital to the Future of Conservation on Madagascar

While Madagascar's biodiversity has global value, it is first and foremost Madagascar's natural heritage—something that was too often

forgotten by foreign conservationists in the early days (Jolly 1980). The influence of foreign-driven conservation programs on Madagascar during the late 1980s and 1990s has been criticized (K. Freudenberger 2010). Ordinary Malagasy, especially rural people most affected by conservation policies, tended to have little or no voice in and very limited influence on the government's decision-making. This is in contrast to countries such as Brazil where grassroots activists have had significant political weight (Kull 2014). In their keenness to conserve Madagascar's precious biodiversity, donor governments and NGOs may have unhelpfully contributed to the idea that biodiversity is something only foreigners care about or have a say in (Kaufmann 2014; Ramiarantsoa et al. 2015; Corson 2016).

This is problematic, as conservation on Madagascar cannot succeed without support to people at all levels of society. There is progress, however. Civil society groups and the independent media have become more active in environmental discourse on the island, holding the government to account over issues such as illegal rosewood exploitation (Rakotovao and Raymond 2019) and advocating for the rights and interests of local communities (Razafindrakoto et al. 2020). There has been rapid growth of Malagasy NGOs working on conservation issues. Associations and NGOs such as Fanamby, Madagasikara Voakajy, Groupe d'Etude et de Recherche sur les Primates de Madagascar (GERP), and Asity manage some of Madagascar's new protected areas, while Tafo Mihavo works to give local communities a strong voice. Many have come together in the Alliance Voahary Gasy, a platform for civil society groups pushing for transparent governance of natural resources. The Critical Ecosystem Partnership Fund, which gives grants only to civil society organizations, has been a vital funder, allowing the growth of this homegrown conservation sector.

A related issue has been the dominance of foreign researchers in biodiversity and conservation-related research on Madagascar (Waeber et al. 2016). This matters because research by foreigners is less likely to result in sustained impact on the ground (Gerety 2017b). Again, there is progress in this area. The high-profile Association for Tropical Biology and Conservation conference was held on Madagascar in 2019 (only the second time it has been held in the African region in its 55-year history). More than 30% of the presentations were by Malagasy students and researchers. Over 29% of contributors to this book are Malagasy, a great improvement over previous edited volumes on Malagasy biodiversity and conservation. Conservation on Madagascar urgently needs the leadership and advocacy that these people can provide.

Conservation on Madagascar Needs to Draw on More Diverse Funding

As well as needing public support, conservation needs money. Funds are required to cover the management costs of Madagascar's expanding protected area network (paying staff, monitoring, and enforcing laws, for example). Because conservation can bring significant local costs, substantial (and sustained) financial resources will also often be needed to compensate for these costs (Poudyal et al. 2018), or to help establish schemes that ensure conservation is a viable option locally (Brimont and Bidaud 2014). Madagascar's tax base is largely insufficient to cover even a portion of these costs, and donor support is therefore likely to be required for some time to come, but all donors are looking for an exit strategy.

Carbon finance, in particular the idea of Reducing Emissions from Deforestation and Forest Degradation (REDD+) (see Grinand and Nourtier, pp. 105–13), has been the big hope for providing sustainable funding for tropical forest conservation for the last 15 years (Seymour and Busch 2016). There have been a number of high-profile REDD+ pilot projects on Madagascar (Ferguson 2009). In line with global recognition that project-level forest carbon projects allow leakage (carbon emissions are displaced rather than avoided), the Malagasy government has been moving away from scattered individual projects and toward jurisdictional REDD+. The Malagasy government is currently seeking funds to fully implement the first of five land-scale programs covering each forest type (Repoblikan'i Madagasikara 2018). The first covers the moist evergreen forests of the northeast and central east, incorporating the protected areas of Makira and the Ankeniheny-Zahamena Corridor (two prominent REDD+ pilots). While REDD+ can produce substantial revenue, which at least in theory should be sufficient to compensate for local opportunity costs (Poudyal et al. 2018), research suggests that programs have often not succeeded in ensuring that benefits reach remote forest-edge communities (Brimont et al. 2015; Poudyal et al. 2016). International scrutiny of the implementation of the social safeguards associated with carbon payments is increasing. For example, public concern about a major funding proposal to the Green Climate Fund for a project involving Madagascar, the Democratic Republic of Congo, and Peru (known as FP123) resulted in it being withdrawn before member governments had a chance to vote on it in 2019 (Green Climate Fund 2020). Therefore, for pragmatic reasons (as well as the moral obligation that conservation should not exacerbate poverty), those involved in designing these large programs must take the issue of social safeguards seriously.

There is also interest from the Malagasy government in other forms of payment for ecosystem services as a way to fund conservation (Figure 15.10d). One idea, explored sporadically over the past decade, is that those operating or benefiting from hydroelectric dams should pay upstream farmers to retain forest and thus reduce siltation (Toillier et al. 2011b). While some success has been demonstrated with small, donor-funded schemes (Cerqueira 2016), lack of willingness from the state-owned water and electricity company JIRAMA has so far prevented the development of schemes to help fund the conservation of the watersheds of major dams. As a number of new hydroelectric dams are currently in the planning stage on Madagascar (Praene et al. 2017), such a funding mechanism might be worth exploring further.

There has long been the hope that Madagascar's biodiversity holds undiscovered products with medicinal or cosmetic use, and that this value could be captured for the sake of conservation. The development of cancer drugs from the rosy periwinkle (*Catharanthus roseus*, family Apocynaceae; see Liede-Schumann, pp. 774–83), which was known locally as a medicinal plant, has become a textbook example of the potential of bioprospecting for delivering useful products. However, although the drug company Eli Lilly netted hundreds of millions of dollars (US) from its commercialization of this discovery, Madagascar has not received a penny (Stone 1992). Since then, both international law and what is considered

best practice by industry have changed (Neimark 2012). In 2014 the Nagoya Protocol "on access to genetic resources and the fair and equitable sharing of benefits arising from their utilization" entered into force as part of the Convention on Biological Diversity (to which Madagascar is a signature country). This should put Madagascar in a better position to defend and benefit from the value of its genetic resources. However, procedures to deliver access and benefit sharing have proven difficult to implement in many countries (Hinsley and Roberts 2018), and Madagascar is no exception. Although there is interest from commercial companies in using the protocol to deliver benefits to local communities from their extraction of, for example, baobab fruits or essential oils (Figure 15.10g), the legal frameworks are not yet in place to make this work as a significant source of funding for conservation.

NGOs and associations also have an important role to play in raising funds for forest conservation on Madagascar. International conservation organizations (particularly WWF, Conservation International, and the Wildlife Conservation Society) have often been able to sustain support for their conservation programs during political crises when donor governments withdraw (Corson 2016). Their ability to do this is a result of their diverse funding base, including private donations from members (especially in the case of WWF) or private foundations, or working with companies that donate as part of corporate responsibility. While most such funding still comes from outside Madagascar, residents of Antananarivo are willing to pay for forest conservation (Randrianarison and Wätzold 2017). As Madagascar develops, NGOs and associations (particularly Malagasy ones) could raise a higher proportion of conservation funding from within Madagascar.

The Mining Boom Poses Difficult Questions for Conservationists on Madagascar

Madagascar has exceptional mineral wealth. Gold deposits are found across the island, some of the most highly valued sapphires and rubies in the world are concentrated in fluvial deposits especially in the east and south, and certain soils are rich in nickel, titanium oxide, and even rare earth metals (Cardiff and Andriamanalina 2009; Cook and Healy 2012). Large operations, such as the US$8 billion Ambatovy nickel and cobalt mine in the moist evergreen forests of the central east and the US$1 billion QMM titanium oxide mine in the littoral forests of the extreme southeast, together make a very significant contribution to Madagascar's tax base. Artisanal mining, though unquantified and poorly taxed, provides much-needed income in rural areas, especially during times of drought (Lawson 2018), and employs around 500,000 people (Fritz et al. 2017). Given Madagascar's urgent need for development, it is clear the country will exploit this mineral wealth (Canavesio 2014). Many analysts agree that if trust in government were to increase (giving investors confidence), mining could rapidly increase on Madagascar. This poses challenges for conservation, as many key resources are found in areas of high biodiversity (Cardiff and Andriamanalina 2009).

Ambatovy and QMM, the two most significant international mining operations on Madagascar, both made very ambitious public commitments to address their environmental impacts (Temple et al. 2012; von Hase et al. 2014). International best practice and the demands of many lenders such as the International Finance Corporation (2012) require such developments to follow the mitigation hierarchy. This means they must avoid, minimize, and remediate biodiversity impacts as much as possible and then offset any residual impacts to achieve at least no net loss of biodiversity (Business and Biodiversity Offsets Partnership 2012). In 2004, Rio Tinto (which partially owns QMM with the Malagasy government) declared it would go beyond its regulatory requirements and achieve a net positive impact on biodiversity in all its operations including QMM. Ambatovy has publicly committed to at least no net loss and preferably net gain (von Hase et al. 2014). QMM, and to a lesser extent Ambatovy, have faced some criticism for the environmental and social impacts of their mines and the limitations on their biodiversity mitigation measures (Seagle 2012; Ferguson et al. 2014; Virah-Sawmy et al. 2014; Bidaud et al. 2017). However, conservationists putting pressure on firms such as Ambatovy and QMM face a delicate balance. Given the importance of mining to the Malagasy economy, the alternative is unlikely to be no mining—it may instead be mining by firms less open to scrutiny and potentially with much lower commitment to environmental performance.

Madagascar has been receiving increasing investment from China over the past decade (Chen and Landry 2016). This will increase because Madagascar joined the Chinese government's massive infrastructure project known as the Belt and Road Initiative in 2017. This investment is much needed, and China is also increasingly contributing development aid to Madagascar (Liu 2019). However, there has already been concern over the lack of transparency associated with a deal involving access to Madagascar's marine resources (Environmental Justice Atlas 2018), and a Chinese company was given a 40-year lease to operate a gold mine in Soamahamanina (Razafindrakoto et al. 2020). Some conservationists are worried that if Madagascar's large mines were to be taken over by Chinese companies (which are less likely to be subject to environmental and social performance standards, for example), exploitation would be more environmentally damaging.

CONCLUSIONS

Writing this sweeping, bird's-eye view of conservation on Madagascar has been a sobering experience. One thing that has emerged is that on the island, as elsewhere, donors have tended to become frustrated with an approach if the desired outcomes are not fully delivered over a short timescale. There is a constant search for the silver bullet for conserving biodiversity while tackling poverty. Unfortunately, such a silver bullet does not exist. If conservation is to be successful on Madagascar, it will need diverse approaches, sustainable funding, a clear voice for forest-edge communities, and much greater support from the top to the bottom of Malagasy society.

Numerous studies have criticized conservation efforts on Madagascar over the past few decades. They have pointed out that biodiversity objectives have not always been met (K. Freudenberger 2010; Waeber et al. 2016), that processes have often fallen short of their own stated standards of effective local participation (Jolly 2015; Hockley et al. 2018), and, most seriously, that conservation measures have sometimes made life worse for rural communities (J. Harper 2002; Poudyal et al. 2018). However, criticism is easy.

Conservation, especially in the Malagasy context of extreme poverty and food insecurity, weak governance, and a large rural population heavily dependent on natural resources, is truly difficult. Most rich countries struggle to do the right thing by their biodiversity. Expecting effective conservation that also contributes to the enormous challenge of poverty alleviation on Madagascar is asking a lot.

We are writing this during the global lockdowns that happened during the Covid-19 virus. This unprecedented global crisis will put extra pressure on Madagascar's biodiversity and make the difficult work of conservation harder (Vyawahare 2020). International tourism is on hold and unlikely to recover anytime soon. This will slash the available budget for Madagascar National Parks. There are already signs of increased pressures on protected areas (J. Eklund, unpublished data) as local incomes are reduced and people turn to the forest for resources, as they have always done in times of need. Lethargy in international markets will negatively impact the interest income from FAPBM investments, and donor support for conservation on Madagascar may be at risk if governments prioritize domestic concerns in a global recession. This is an extra set of difficulties for conservation.

Despite the challenges, the experiences of the past few decades offer much to improve the chance of a positive future for conservation on Madagascar. Malagasy conservation has always had some excellent leaders (Jolly 2015), and capacity is increasing fast among a new generation (Gerety 2017b). The legal frameworks for conservation are mostly well established. New technology, such as near real-time data on forest fires, provides invaluable information that would have been unimaginable a few years back. There is growing global recognition of the importance of nature-based solutions to the global existential threat of climate change (Seddon et al. 2020), which should result in continued international support for forest conservation on Madagascar. There is also much better understanding that conservation is a hugely challenging social endeavor, and that to be successful it has to make sense (economically and socially) to the local population. Finally, a huge body of research can, if accessible to the right people (Rafidimanantsoa et al. 2018), inform future decisions. The very existence of innumerable unique species and habitats depends on this.

> *Tsy misy mafy tsy laitry ny zoto.* (There are no difficulties that cannot be overcome by the determined.)
>
> —Malagasy proverb

ACKNOWLEDGMENTS

Karen Freudenberger was an important mentor to JPGJ during her first five years working on Madagascar. Her insightful review of USAID's interventions was a key source. Katie Devenish produced the timeline. The Bangor University conservation science group (especially Neal Hockley and Jorge Llopis), Mark Freudenberger, Barry Ferguson, Christian Kull, Ranaivo Rasolofoson, and Rachel Neugarten provided helpful comments. We thank the Forest4Climate&People project funded by the UK government's Foreign and Commonwealth Office for support.

Subject editors: Steven M. Goodman and Aristide Andrianarimisa

REFERENCES

Adams, W. M., Aveling, R., Brockington, D., Dickson, B., Elliott, J., Hutton, J., Roe, D., Vira, B., and Wolmer, W. 2004. Biodiversity conservation and the eradication of poverty. *Science* 306(5699): 1146–1149.

Agence Française de Développement. 2017. Promouvoir une agriculture durable par l'approche paysage (PADAP). Accessed 31 Mar. 2020. https://www.afd.fr/fr/carte-des-projets/promouvoir-une-agriculture-durable-par-lapproche-paysage-padap.

Alliance for Zero Extinction. 2018–2019. Conserving the world's most threatened species. https://www.zeroextinction.org.

Allnutt, T. F., McClanahan, T. R., Andréfouët, S., Baker, M., Lagabrielle, E., McClennen, C., Rakotomanjaka, A.J.M., Tianarisoa, T. F., Watson, R., and Kremen, C. 2012. Comparison of marine spatial planning methods in Madagascar demonstrates value of alternative approaches. *PLoS One* 7(2): e28969.

Amnesty International. 2018. *Punished for Being Poor: Unjustified, Excessive and Prolonged Pre-trial Detention in Madagascar*. London: Amnesty International.

Anagnostou, M., Mwedde, G., Roe, D., Smith, R. J., Travers, H., and Baker, J. 2020. Ranger perceptions of the role of local communities in providing actionable information on wildlife crime. *Conservation Science and Practice* 2(6): 1–13.

Anderson, K., and Gaston, K. J. 2013. Lightweight unmanned aerial vehicles will revolutionize spatial ecology. *Frontiers in Ecology and the Environment* 11(3): 138–146.

Andréfouët, S., Guillaume, M.M.M., Delval, A., Rasoamanendrika, F.M.A., Blanchot, J., and Bruggemann, J. H. 2013. Fifty years of changes in reef flat habitats of the Grand Récif of Toliara (SW Madagascar) and the impact of gleaning. *Coral Reefs* 32: 757–768. https://doi.org/10.1007/s00338-013-1026-0.

Andriamalala, G., and Gardner, C. J. 2010. L'utilisation du dina comme outil de gouvernance des ressources naturelles: Leçons tirés de Velondriake, sud-ouest de Madagascar. *Tropical Conservation Science* 3(4): 447–472.

Andrianarimisa, A., and Razafimanjato, G. 2010. Madagascar sacred ibis *Threskiornis bernieri*: Current population status, distribution, and implications for conservation. In *Proceedings of the 12th Pan-African Ornithological Congress, Cape Town, South Africa, 2008*, eds. D. M. Harebottle, A.J.F.K. Craig, M. D. Anderson, H. Rakotomanana, and M. Muchai, pp. 120–130. Cape Town: Animal Demography Unit.

Anonymous. 2018. Rosewood democracy in the political forests of Madagascar. *Political Geography* 62: 170–183.

Association Nationale pour la Gestion des Aires Protégées (ANGAP). 2002. *Conservation Management and Ecological Monitoring in Madagascar's Protected Areas: Status Report*. Antananarivo: Madagascar National Parks.

Aubert, S., Rambintsaotra, S., and Razafiarijaona, J. 2013. L'insécurité foncière dans et autour des Aires Protégées de Madagascar: Un obstacle à surmonter pour la conservation de la biodiversité et le développement rural. *Développement Durable et Territoires* 4(1): 9661. https://doi.org/10.4000/DEVELOPPEMENTDURABLE.9661.

Aymoz, B.G.P., Randrianjafy, V. R., Randrianjafy, Z.J.N., and Khasa, D. P. 2013. Community management of natural resources: A case study from Ankarafantsika National Park, Madagascar. *Ambio* 42(6): 767–775.

Barnas, A. F., Darby, B. J., Vandeberg, G. S., Rockwell, R. F., and Ellis-Felege, S. N. 2019. A comparison of drone imagery and ground-based methods for estimating the extent of habitat destruction by lesser snow geese (*Anser caerulescens caerulescens*) in La Pérouse Bay. *PLoS One* 14(8): 1–19.

Baron, R. 1889. The flora of Madagascar. *Journal of the Linnean Society, Botany*, 42: 246–294.

Baylis, K., Honey-Rosés, J., Börner, J., Corbera, E., Ezzine-de-Blas, D., Ferraro, P. J., Lapeyre, R., Persson, U. M., Pfaff, A., and Wunder, S. 2016. Mainstreaming impact evaluation in nature conservation. *Conservation Letters* 9(1): 58–64.

Bevan, E., Whiting, S., Tucker, T., Guinea, M., Raith, A., and Douglas, R. 2018. Measuring behavioral responses of sea turtles, saltwater crocodiles, and crested terns to drone disturbance to define ethical operating thresholds. *PLoS One* 13(3): 1–17.

Bidaud, C., Schreckenberg, K., Rabeharison, M., Ranjatson, P., Gibbons, J., and Jones, J.P.G. 2017. The sweet and the bitter: Intertwined positive and negative social impacts of a biodiversity offset. *Conservation and Society* 15(1): 1.

Bidaud, C., Schreckenberg, K., and Jones, J.P.G. 2018. The local costs of biodiversity offsets: Comparing standards, policy and practice. *Land Use Policy* 77: 43–50.

Blanc Pamard, C. 2002. La forêt et l'arbre en pays Masikoro (Madagascar). *Bois et Forêts des Tropiques* 271: 5–21.

Bland, L. M., Keith, D. A., Miller, R. M., Murray, N. J., and Rodríguez, J. P., eds. 2017. *Guidelines for the Application of IUCN Red List of Ecosystems Categories and Criteria*. Version 1.1. Gland: IUCN.

Boillat, S., Gerber, J.-D., Oberlack, C., Zaehringer, J., Ifejika Speranza, C., and Rist, S. 2018. Distant interactions, power, and environmental justice in protected area governance: A telecoupling perspective. *Sustainability* 10(11): 3954.

Borrini-Feyerabend, G., and Dudley, N. 2005. *Elan Durban: Nouvelles perspectives pour les Aires Protégées à Madagascar*. Gland: IUCN.

Brimont, L., and Bidaud, C. 2014. Incentivising forest conservation: Payments for environmental services and reducing carbon emissions from deforestation. In *Conservation and Environmental Management in Madagascar*, ed. I. R. Scales, pp. 299–319. London: Routledge.

Brimont, L., Ezzine-de-Blas, D., Karsenty, A., and Toulon, A. 2015. Achieving conservation and equity amidst extreme poverty and climate risk: The Makira REDD+ Project in Madagascar. *Forests* 6(12): 748–768.

Brook, C. E., Herrera, J. P., Borgerson, C., Fuller, E. C., Andriamahazoarivosoa, P., et al. 2019. Population viability and harvest sustainability for Madagascar lemurs. *Conservation Biology* 33(1): 99–111.

Brown, J. L., and Yoder, A. D. 2015. Shifting ranges and conservation challenges for lemurs in the face of climate change. *Ecology and Evolution* 5(6): 1131–1142.

Brown, K. A., Parks, K. E., Bethell, C. A., Johnson, S. E., and Mulligan, M. 2015. Predicting plant diversity patterns in Madagascar: Understanding the effects of climate and land cover change in a biodiversity hotspot. *PLoS One* 10(4): e0122721.

Brown, M. 2000. *A History of Madagascar*. Cambridge, UK: Damien Tunnacliffe.

Burnod, P., Andrianirina-Ratsialonana, R., and Ravelomanantsoa, Z. 2014. Land certification in Madagascar: Formalizing (f)or securing? 2014 World Bank Conference on Land and Poverty, Washington, DC, 15. https://agritrop.cirad.fr/574062/1/document_574062.pdf.

Busch, J., Dave, R., Hannah, L., Cameron, A., Rasolohery, A., Roehrdanz, P., and Schatz, G. 2012. Climate change and the cost of conserving species in Madagascar. *Conservation Biology* 26(3): 408–419.

Business and Biodiversity Offsets Partnership. 2012. *Standard on Biodiversity Offsets*. Washington, DC: Business and Biodiversity Offsets Partnership.

Cabeza, M., Terraube, J., Burgas, D., Temba, E. M., and Rakoarijaoana, M. 2019. Gold is not green: Artisanal gold mining threatens Ranomafana National Park's biodiversity. *Animal Conservation* 22(5): 417–419.

Cameron, S. E. 2017. Ecotourism's dirty laundry? Exploring the relationship between participation, equity and conservation around protected areas in Madagascar. MS thesis, University of Kent.

Canavesio, R. 2014. Formal mining investments and artisanal mining in southern Madagascar: Effects of spontaneous reactions and adjustment policies on poverty alleviation. *Land Use Policy* 36: 145–154.

Cardiff, S., and Andriamanalina, A. 2009. Contested spatial coincidence of conservation and mining efforts in Madagascar. *Madagascar Conservation and Development* 2(1): 28–34.

Carré, A., Rabarison, H., Randrianasolo, H., Razafindrainibe, H., Ruiz, V., and Zarasoa. 2020. *Dynamiques spatiales des écosystèmes terrestres, côtiers et marin de Madagascar: Une première application des critères de la Liste rouge des écosystèmes de l'UICN*. Gland: IUCN.

Cartagena-Matos, B., Gregório, I., Morais, M., and Ferreira, E. 2017. Trends in the extinction of carnivores in Madagascar. *Animal Biodiversity and Conservation* 40(1): 103–114.

Cauvin, B., Koonjul, M., Quatre, R., Ahamed, S., Gough, C., Desiré, S., and Quod, J. P. 2010. Suivi de l'état de santé des récifs coralliens des îles—Sud Ouest de l'Océan Indien: Réseau COI/GCRMN synthèse régionale 2010. Quatre Borne: Commission de l'Océan Indien.

Cerchio, S., Andrianarivelo, N., and Andrianantenaina, B. 2015. Ecology and conservation status of Indian Ocean humpback dolphins (*Sousa plumbea*) in Madagascar. In *Advances in Marine Biology*, vol. 72, eds. T. A. Jefferson and B. E. Curry, pp. 163–199. Oxford: Academic Press.

Cerqueira, J. 2016. What coalitions of stakeholders to electrify Madagascar? *Journal of Field Actions* 15: 34–45.

Chaperon, P., Danloux, J., and Ferry, L. 1993. *Fleuves et rivières de Madagascar*. Paris: ORSTOM Editions.

Chen, Y., and Landry, D. 2016. *Where Africa Meets Asia: Chinese Agricultural and Manufacturing Investment in Madagascar*. Washington, DC: Department for International Development.

Cohen-Shacham, E., Walters, G., Janzen, C., and Maginnis, S., eds. 2016. *Nature-Based Solutions to Address Global Societal Challenges*. Gland: IUCN.

Congalton, R. G. 1991. A review of assessing the accuracy of classifications of remotely sensed data. *Remote Sensing of Environment* 37(1): 35–46.

Cook, R., and Healy, T. 2012. *Artisanal and Small-Scale Mining in and around Protected Areas and Critical Ecosystems Project: Madagascar Case Study*. Nairobi: WWF.

Corson, C. 2016. *Corridors of Power: The Politics of Environmental Aid to Madagascar*. New Haven: Yale University Press.

Cruzan, M. B., Weinstein, B. G., Grasty, M. R., Kohrn, B. F., Hendrickson, E. C., Arredondo, T. M., and Thompson, P. G. 2016. Small unmanned aerial vehicles (micro-UAVs, drones) in plant ecology. *Applications in Plant Sciences* 4(9): 1–11.

Dave, R., Tompkins, E. L., and Schreckenberg, K. 2017. Forest ecosystem services derived by smallholder farmers in northwestern Madagascar: Storm hazard mitigation and participation in forest management. *Forest Policy and Economics* 84: 72–82.

De Mazières, J., and Olson, D. 2012. L'écorégion marine des îles de l'Océan Indien occidental. Quatre Borne: Commission de l'Océan Indien.

Desbureaux, S., and Damania, R. 2018. Rain, forests and farmers: Evidence of drought induced deforestation in Madagascar and its consequences for biodiversity conservation. *Biological Conservation* 221: 357–364.

Dewar, R. E. 2014. Early human settlers and their impact on Madagascar's landscapes. In *Conservation and Environmental Management in Madagascar*, ed. I. R. Scales, pp. 44–65. London: Routledge.

Ditmer, M. A., Vincent, J. B., Werden, L. K., Tanner, J. C., Laske, T. G., Iaizzo, P. A., Garshelis, D. L., and Fieberg, J. R. 2015. Bears show a physiological but limited behavioral response to unmanned aerial vehicles. *Current Biology* 25(17): 2278–2283.

Eklund, J., Guillaume Blanchet, F., Nyman, J., Rocha, R., Virtanen, T., and Cabeza, M. 2016. Contrasting spatial and temporal trends of protected area effectiveness in mitigating deforestation in Madagascar. *Biological Conservation* 203: 290–297.

Eldridge, A., Casey, M., Moscoso, P., and Peck, M. 2016. A new method for ecoacoustics? Toward the extraction and evaluation of ecologically-meaningful soundscape components using sparse coding methods. *PeerJ* 4(6): e2108.

Elouard, J.-M., and Gibon, F. M. 2001. *Biodiversité et biotypologie des eaux continentales de Madagascar*. Antananarivo: Laboratoire de Recherche sur les Systèmes Aquatiques et Leur Environnement.

Environmental Justice Atlas. 2018. The impacts of fishing agreements with Chinese investors in Madagascar. https://ejatlas.org/conflict/the-impacts-of-fishing-agreements-with-chinese-investors-and-fishing-fleet.

Faramalala, M. H. 1995. *Formations végétales et domaine forestier national de Madagascar*. 1:1,000,000 color map. Antananarivo: Conservation International (CI), Département des Eaux et Forêts (DEF), Centre National de Recherches sur l'Environnement (CNRE), and Foiben-Taosarintanin'i Madagasikara (FTM).

Farris, Z., Kelly, M., Karpanty, S., Ratelolahy, F., Andrianjakarivelo, V., and Holmes, C. 2012. Brown-tailed vontsira *Salanoia concolor* (Eupleridae) documented in Makira Natural Park, Madagascar: New insights on distribution and camera-trap success. *Small Carnivore Conservation* 47: 82–86.

Ferguson, B. 2009. REDD comes into fashion in Madagascar. *Madagascar Conservation and Development* 4(2): 132–137. https://doi.org/10.4314/mcd.v4i2.48654.

Ferguson, B., Gardner, C. J., Andriamarovolonona, M. M., Healy, T., Muttenzer, F., Smith, S. M., Hockley, N., and Gingembre, M. 2014. Governing ancestral land in Madagascar. In *Governance for Justice and Environmental Sustainability*, eds. M. Sowman and R. Wynberg, pp. 63–93. London: Routledge.

Filou, E. 2019. Illegal corn farming menaces a Madagascar protected area. Mongabay. https://news.mongabay.com/2019/02/illegal-corn-farming-menaces-a-madagascar-protected-area/.

Firecast. 2021. https://firecast.conservation.org/.

Forest Watcher. 2021. https://forestwatcher.globalforestwatch.org/.

Foucault, M. 2008. *The Birth of Biopolitics: Lectures at the College de France, 1978–1979*. New York: Picador.

Freudenberger, K. S. 2010. *Paradise Lost? Lessons from 25 Years of Environmental Programs in Madagascar*. Washington, DC: USAID.

Freudenberger, M., and Freudenberger, K. S. 2002. Contradictions in agricultural intensification and improved natural resource management: Issues in the Fianarantsoa forest corridor of Madagascar. In *Natural Resources Management in African Agriculture: Understanding and Improving Current Practices*, eds. C. B. Barrett, F. Place, and A. A. Aboud, pp. 181–192. Wallingford: CABI.

Fritz, M., McQuilken, J., Collins, N., and Weldegiorgis, F. 2017. *Global Trends in Artisanal and Small-Scale Mining (ASM): A Review of Key Numbers and Issues.* Winnipeg: International Institute for Sustainable Development.

Gabrié, C., Vasseur, P., Randriamiarana, H., Maharavo, J., and Mara, E. 2000. The coral reefs of Madagascar. In *Coral Reefs of the Indian Ocean: Their Ecology and Conservation*, eds. T. McClanahan, C.R.C. Sheppard, and D. Obura, pp. 441–444. Oxford: Oxford University Press.

Ganzhorn, J. U., Lowry, P. P., Schatz, G. E., and Sommer, S. 2001. The biodiversity of Madagascar: One of the world's hottest hotspots on its way out. *Oryx* 35(4): 346–348.

Gardner, C. J., Vincke, X., Rafanomezantsoa, S., and Virah-Sawmy, M. 2015. Oblique aerial photography: A novel tool for the monitoring and participatory management of protected areas. *Parks* 21(1): 13–28.

Gardner, C. J., Gabriel, F.U.L., St. John, F.A.V., and Davies, Z. G. 2016. Changing livelihoods and protected area management: A case study of charcoal production in south-west Madagascar. *Oryx* 50(3): 495–505.

Gardner, C. J., Nicoll, M. E., Birkinshaw, C., Harris, A., Lewis, R. E., Rakotomalala, D., and Ratsifandrihamanana, A. N. 2018. The rapid expansion of Madagascar's protected area system. *Biological Conservation* 220: 29–36.

Gautier, L., and Goodman, S. M. 2003. Introduction to the flora of Madagascar. In *The Natural History of Madagascar*, eds. S. M. Goodman and J. P. Benstead, pp. 229–250. Chicago: University of Chicago Press.

Gautier, L., Tahinarivony, J. A., Ranirison, P., and Wohlhauser, S. 2018. Végétation / Vegetation. In *Les aires protégées terrestres de Madagascar: Leur histoire, description et biote / The Terrestrial Protected Areas of Madagascar: Their History, Description, and Biota*, eds. S. M. Goodman, M. J. Raherilalao, and S. Wohlhauser, pp. 207–242. Antananarivo: Association Vahatra.

Gerety, R. M. 2017a. Conservation in a weak state: Madagascar struggles with enforcement. Mongabay. https://news.mongabay.com/2017/10/conservation-in-a-weak-state-madagascar-struggles-with-enforcement/.

———. 2017b. Building conservation's brain trust in Madagascar. Mongabay. https://news.mongabay.com/2017/10/building-conservations-brain-trust-in-madagascar/.

———. 2019. The ecologists and the mine. *Scientific American*. https://www.scientificamerican.com/article/the-ecologists-and-the-mine/.

Giam, X. 2017. Global biodiversity loss from tropical deforestation. *Proceedings of the National Academy of Sciences of the USA* 114(23): 5775–5777.

Golden, C. D., Fernald, L.C.H., Brashares, J. S., Rasolofoniaina, B.J.R., and Kremen, C. 2011. Benefits of wildlife consumption to child nutrition in a biodiversity hotspot. *Proceedings of the National Academy of Sciences of the USA* 108(49): 19653–19656.

Goodman, S. M., and Benstead, J. P., eds. 2003. *The Natural History of Madagascar*. Chicago: University of Chicago Press.

———. 2005. Updated estimates of biotic diversity and endemism for Madagascar. *Oryx* 39(1): 73–77.

Goodman, S. M., Raherilalao, M. J., and Wohlhauser, S., eds. 2018. *The Terrestrial Protected Areas of Madagascar: Their History, Description, and Biota*. Antananarivo: Association Vahatra.

Green Climate Fund. 2020. Report of the twenty-fourth meeting of the board, 12–14 November 2019, Songdo, Korea.

Greve, A. M., Lampietti, J., and Falloux, F. 1995. National environmental action plans in sub-Saharan Africa. *World Bank Working Paper Series*, 20973, 1.

Grinand, C., Rakotomalala, F., Gond, V., Vaudry, R., Bernoux, M., and Vieilledent, G. 2013. Remote sensing of environment estimating deforestation in tropical humid and dry forests in Madagascar from 2000 to 2010 using multi-date Landsat satellite images and the random forests classifier. *Remote Sensing of Environment* 139: 68–80.

Gross, M. 2014. Connecting with the natural world. *Current Biology* 24(14): 629–632.

Hantanirina, J.M.O., and Benbow, S. 2013. Diversity and coverage of seagrass ecosystems in the south-west. *African Journal of Marine Species* 35: 291–297.

Hardin, P. J., and Jensen, R. R. 2011. Small-scale unmanned aerial vehicles in environmental remote sensing: Challenges and opportunities. *GIScience and Remote Sensing* 48(1): 99–111.

Harper, G. J., Steininger, M. K., Tucker, C. J., Juhn, D., and Hawkins, F. 2007. Fifty years of deforestation and forest fragmentation in Madagascar. *Environmental Conservation* 34(4): 1–9.

Harper, J. 2002. *Endangered Species: Health, Illness, and Death among Madagascar's People of the Forest*. Durham: Carolina Academic Press.

Harvey, C. A., Rakotobe, Z. L., Rao, N. S., Dave, R., Razafimahatratra, H., Rabarijohn, R. H., Rajaofara, H., and MacKinnon, J. L. 2014. Extreme vulnerability of smallholder farmers to agricultural risks and climate change in Madagascar. *Philosophical Transactions of the Royal Society of London B: Biological Sciences* 369(1639): 20130089.

Harvey, C. A., Rambeloson, A. M., Andrianjohaninarivo, T., Andriamaro, L., Rasolohery, A., et al. 2018. Local perceptions of the livelihood and conservation benefits of small-scale livelihood projects in rural Madagascar. *Society and Natural Resources* 31(9): 1045–1063.

Henson, D. W., Malpas, R. C., and D'Udine, F.A.C. 2016. Wildlife law enforcement in sub-Saharan African protected areas: A review of best practices. *Occasional Paper of the IUCN Species Survival Commission* 58: 1–65.

Herrera, J. P. 2017. Prioritizing protected areas in Madagascar for lemur diversity using a multidimensional perspective. *Biological Conservation* 207: 1–8.

Hinsley, A., and Roberts, D. L. 2018. Assessing the extent of access and benefit sharing in the wildlife trade: Lessons from horticultural orchids in Southeast Asia. *Environmental Conservation* 45(3): 261–268.

Hockley, N., and Andriamarovololona, M. M. 2007. *The Economics of Community Forest Management in Madagascar: Is There a Free Lunch? An Analysis of Transfert de Gestion*. Washington, DC: USAID.

Hockley, N., Mandimbiniaina, R. H., and Rakotonarivo, O. S. 2018. Fair and equitable conservation: Do we really want it, and if so, do we know how to achieve it? *Madagascar Conservation and Development* 13: 1–5.

Hodgson, J. C., and Koh, L. P. 2016. Best practice for minimising unmanned aerial vehicle disturbance to wildlife in biological field research. *Current Biology* 26(10): 404–405.

Huff, A. 2016. *Black Sands, Green Plans and Conflict: Structural Adjustment, Sectoral Reforms and the Mining-Conservation-Conflict Nexus in Southern Madagascar.* Brighton: Institute of Development Studies.

Humbert, H., and Cours Darne, G. 1965. Carte internationale du tapis végétal et des conditions écologiques. 3 coupures à 1/1.000.000 de Madagascar. *Travaux de la Section Scientifique et de l'Institut Français de Pondichéry*, hors série, 6.

Institut Pasteur de Madagascar. 2018. Amélioration de l'accès aux soins par les drones. http://www.pasteur.mg/amelioration-de-lacces-aux-soins-par-les-drones/.

International Finance Corporation. 2012. *Performance Standards on Environmental and Social Sustainability*. Washington, DC: International Finance Corporation.

IUCN. 2014. IUCN World Parks Congress 2014 Report. *IUCN Bulletin* 89(16): 1–43.

———. 2016a. *IUCN Resolutions, Recommendations and Other Decisions*. Gland: IUCN.

———. 2016b. *A Global Standard for the Identification of Key Biodiversity Areas*. Version 1.0. 1st ed. Gland: IUCN.

———. 2021. Red List of Ecosystems. https://www.iucnrle.org/.

Jarosz, L. 1993. Defining and explaining tropical deforestation: Shifting cultivation and population growth in colonial Madagascar (1896–1940). *Economic Geography* 69(4): 366–379.

Jeffers, V. F., Humber, F., Nohasiarivelo, T., Botosoamananto, R., and Anderson, L. G. 2019. Trialling the use of smartphones as a tool to address gaps in small-scale fisheries catch data in southwest Madagascar. *Marine Policy* 99: 267–274.

Jenkins, R.K.B., Keane, A., Rakotoarivelo, A. R., Rakotomboavonjy, V., Randrianandrianina, F. H., Razafimanahaka, H. J., Ralaiarimalala, S. R., and Jones, J.P.G. 2011. Analysis of patterns of bushmeat consumption reveals extensive exploitation of protected species in eastern Madagascar. *PLoS One* 6(12): e27570.

Jensen, J. R. 2007. *Remote Sensing of the Environment: An Earth Resource Perspective*. 2nd ed. Upper Saddle River: Prentice-Hall.

Jiménez López, J., and Mulero-Pázmány, M. 2019. Drones for conservation in protected areas: Present and future. *Drones* 3(1): 1–23.

Jolly, A. 1980. *A World like Our Own: Man and Nature in Madagascar*. New Haven: Yale University Press.

———. 2015. *Thank You Madagascar: The Conservation Diaries of Alison Jolly*. London: Zed Books.

Jones, J.P.G., Andriamarovololona, M. M., and Hockley, N. 2008. The importance of taboos and social norms to conservation in Madagascar. *Conservation Biology* 22(4): 976–986.
Jones, J.P.G., Mandimbiniaina, R., Kelly, R., Ranjatson, P., Rakotojoelina, B., Schreckenberg, K., and Poudyal, M. 2018. Human migration to the forest frontier: Implications for land use change and conservation management. *Geo: Geography and Environment* 5(1). https://doi.org/10.1002/geo2.50.
Jones, J.P.G., Ratsimbazafy, J., Ratsifandrihamanana, A. N., Watson, J.E.M., Andrianandrasana, H. T., et al. 2019a. Last chance for Madagascar's biodiversity. *Nature Sustainability* 2(5). https://doi.org/10.1038/s41893-019-0288-0.
———. 2019b. Madagascar: Crime threatens biodiversity. *Science* 363: 6429.
Kamilar, J. M., Blanco, M. B., and Muldoon, K. 2016. Ecological niche modeling of mouse lemurs (*Microcebus* spp.) and its implications for their species diversity and biogeography. In *The Dwarf and Mouse Lemurs of Madagascar: Biology, Behavior and Conservation Biogeography of the Cheirogaleidae*, eds. S. Lehman, U. Radespiel, and E. Zimmermann, pp. 449–461. Cambridge: Cambridge University Press.
Kappeler, P. M., and Erkert, H. G. 2003. On the move around the clock: Correlates and determinants of cathemeral activity in wild redfronted lemurs (*Eulemur fulvus rufus*). *Behavioral Ecology and Sociobiology* 54(4): 359–369.
Kaufmann, J. C. 2014. Contrasting visions of nature and landscapes. In *Conservation and Environmental Management in Madagascar*, ed. I. R. Scales, pp. 320–342. London: Routledge.
Keane, A., Jones, J.P.G., and Milner-Gulland, E. J. 2011. Encounter data in resource management and ecology: Pitfalls and possibilities. *Journal of Applied Ecology* 48(5): 1164–1173.
Kemp, J., López-Baucells, A., Rocha, R., Wangensteen, O. S., Andriatafika, Z., Nair, A., and Cabeza, M. 2019. Bats as potential suppressors of multiple agricultural pests: A case study from Madagascar. *Agriculture, Ecosystems and Environment* 269: 88–96.
Klaas, B. P. 2016. *The Despot's Accomplice: How the West Is Aiding and Abetting the Decline of Democracy*. London: Hurst.
Koechlin, J., Guillaumet, J.-L., and Morat, P. 1974. *Flore et végétation de Madagascar*. Vanduz: Cramer.
Kremen, C. 2003. The Masoala Peninsula. In *The Natural History of Madagascar*, eds. S. M. Goodman and J. P. Benstead, pp. 1459–1466. Chicago: University of Chicago Press.
Kremen, C., Raymond, I., and Lance, K. 1998. An interdisciplinary tool for monitoring conservation impacts in Madagascar. *Conservation Biology* 12(3): 549–563.
Kremen, C., Cameron, A., Moilanen, A., Phillips, S. J., Thomas, C. D., et al. 2008. Aligning conservation priorities across taxa in Madagascar with high-resolution planning tools. *Science* 320: 222–226.
Kretser, H., Stokes, E., Wich, S., Foran, D., and Montefiore, A. 2017. Technological innovations supporting wildlife crime detection, deterrence, and enforcement. In *Conservation Criminology*, ed. M. L. Gore, pp. 155–177. Chichester: John Wiley and Sons.
Kull, C. A. 2004. *Isle of Fire: The Political Ecology of Landscape Burning in Madagascar*. Chicago: University of Chicago Press.
———. 2014. The roots, persistence, and character of Madagascar's conservation boom. In *Conservation and Environmental Management in Madagascar*, ed. I. R. Scales, pp. 146–172. London: Routledge.
Kull, C. A., Ibrahim, C. K., and Meredith, T. C. 2007. Tropical forest transitions and globalization: Neo-liberalism, migration, tourism, and international conservation agendas. *Society and Natural Resources* 20(8): 723–737.
Laliberte, A. S., Winters, C., and Rango, A. 2011. UAS remote sensing missions for rangeland applications. *Geocarto International* 26(2): 141–156.
Laney, R., and Turner, B. L. 2015. The persistence of self-provisioning among smallholder farmers in northeast Madagascar. *Human Ecology* 43(6): 811–826.
Langrand, O., and Rene de Roland, L.-A. 2018. Histoire des aires protégées de Madagascar / History of Madagascar's protected areas. In *Les aires protégées terrestres de Madagascar: Leur histoire, description et biote / The Terrestrial Protected Areas of Madagascar: Their History, Description, and Biota*, eds. S. M. Goodman, M. J. Raherilalao, and S. Wohlhauser, pp. 79–104. Antananarivo: Association Vahatra.
Lasserre, G. 1979. Bilan de la situation des pêches aux Pangalanes-Est (Zone Tamatave-Andevorante) au Lac Anony (région Fort-Dauphin): Perspective et aménagement. Antananarivo: Projet PNUD/FAO MAG/76/002.
Lawson, L. 2018. Rice, sapphires and cattle: Work lives of women artisanal and small-scale miners in Madagascar. In *Between the Plough and the Pick: Informal, Artisanal and Small-Scale Mining in the Contemporary World*, ed. K. Lahiri-Dutt, pp. 171–192. Canberra: ANU Press.
Leprun, J. C., Grouzis, M., and Randriambanona, H. 2009. Post-cropping change and dynamics in soil and vegetation properties after forest clearing: Example of the semi-arid Mikea region (southwestern Madagascar). *Comptes Rendus—Geoscience* 341(7): 526–537.
Liebenberg, L. W. 1990. *The Art of Tracking: The Origin of Science*. Cape Town: David Philip.
Liu, X. 2019. From microanalysis to macroperspective of China's foreign aid: Madagascar's General Hospital Project. In *South-South Cooperation and Chinese Foreign Aid*, eds. M. Huang, X. Xu, and X. Mao, pp. 49–59. Singapore: Palgrave Macmillan.
Llopis, J. C., Harimalala, P. C., Bär, R., Heinimann, A., Rabemananjara, Z. H., and Zaehringer, J. 2019. Effects of protected area establishment and cash crop price dynamics on land use transitions 1990–2017 in north-eastern Madagascar. *Journal of Land Use Science* 14(1): 52–80.
Madagascar National Parks. 2013. *Référentiel technique Septembre 2013*. Antananarivo: Madagascar National Parks.
Maina, J., De Moel, H., Zinke, J., Madin, J., McClanahan, T., and Vermaat, J. E. 2013. Human deforestation outweighs future climate change impacts of sedimentation on coral reefs. *Nature Communications* 4: 1986.
Mandimbihasina, A. R., Woolaver, L. G., Concannon, L. E., Milner-Gulland, E. J., Lewis, R., Terry, A.M.R., Filazaha, N., Rabetafika, L. L., and Young, R. P. 2020. The illegal pet trade is driving Madagascar's ploughshare tortoise to extinction. *Oryx* 54: 188–196.
Marvin, D. C., Koh, L. P., Lynam, A. J., Wich, S., Davies, A. B., Krishnamurthy, R., Stokes, E., Starkey, R., and Asner, G. P. 2016. Integrating technologies for scalable ecology and conservation. *Global Ecology and Conservation* 7: 262–275.
Massé, F. 2020. Conservation law enforcement: Policing protected areas. *Annals of the American Association of Geographers* 110 (3): 758–773.
McConnell, W. J., and Kull, C. A. 2014. Deforestation in Madagascar debates over the island's forest cover and challenges of measuring forest change. In *Conservation and Environmental Management in Madagascar*, ed. I. R. Scales, pp. 67–105. London: Routledge.
McConnell, W. J., Viña, A., Kull, C., and Batko, C. 2015. Forest transition in Madagascar's highlands: Initial evidence and implications. *Land* 4(4): 1155–1181.
McEvoy, J. F., Hall, G. P., and McDonald, P. G. 2016. Evaluation of unmanned aerial vehicle shape, flight path and camera type for waterfowl surveys: Disturbance effects and species recognition. *PeerJ* 4(3): e1831.
McMahon, K., and Webster, F. J. 2002. *An Assessment of Coral Reefs in North West Madagascar*. Stockholm: Cordio.
Méral, P., Froger, G., Andriamahefazafy, F., and Rabearisoa, A. 2011. Financing protected areas in Madagascar: New methods. In *Protected Areas, Sustainable Land?*, eds. C. Aubertin and E. Rodary, pp. 105–120. Paris: IRD.
Mercier, J.-R. 2009. The preparation of the National Environmental Action Plan (NEAP): Was it a false start? *Madagascar Conservation and Development* 1(1): 50–54. doi:10.4314/mcd.v1i1.44122.
Miller, D. C., Agrawal, A., and Roberts, J. T. 2013. Biodiversity, governance, and the allocation of international aid for conservation. *Conservation Letters* 6(1): 12–20.
Ministry of Environment. 1998. *Inventory Methods for Riverine Birds: Harlequin Duck, Belted Kingfisher and American Dipper; Standards for Components for British Columbia's Biodiversity*. No. 12. British Columbia: Resource Inventory Committee.
Missouri Botanical Garden. 2014. Inventaires de références des sites du projet MRPA—lot n°1: Ampasindava-Galoka—DP N°01—13 /DP/UCPE/MRPA. Rapport final. London: Missouri Botanical Garden.
Mittermeier, R. A., Robles Gil, P., and Mittermeier, C. G., eds. 1997. *Megadiversity: Earth's Biologically Wealthiest Nations*. Mexico City: CEMEX.
Mizuta, T. 2007. Identification of nest predator and time of predation on the Madagascar paradise flycatcher by use of temperature data loggers. *Bird Research* 3: 21–28.
Moat, J., and Smith, P. 2007. *Atlas of the Vegetation of Madagascar*. Kew: Royal Botanic Gardens.
Montagne, P., and Ramamonjisoa, B. S. 2006. Politiques forestières à Madagascar entre répression et autonomie des acteurs. *Economie Rural* 294: 9–26.
Moser, C. M., and Barrett, C. B. 2003. The disappointing adoption dynamics of a yield-increasing, low external-input technology: The case of SRI in Madagascar. *Agricultural Systems* 76(3): 1085–1100.
Mulero-Pázmány, M., Jenni-Eiermann, S., Strebel, N., Sattler, T., Negro, J. J., and Tablado, Z. 2017. Unmanned aircraft systems as a new source of disturbance for wildlife: A systematic review. *PLoS One* 12(6): 1–14.

Musinsky, J., Tabor, K., Cano, C. A., Ledezma, J. C., Mendoza, E., Rasolohery, A., and Sajudin, E. R. 2018. Conservation impacts of a near real-time forest monitoring and alert system for the tropics. *Remote Sensing in Ecology and Conservation* 4(3): 189–196.

Myers, N., Mittermeier, R. A., Mittermeier, C. G., Da Fonseca, G.A.B., and Kent, J. 2000. Biodiversity hotspots for conservation priorities. *Nature* 403: 853–858.

Neimark, B. 2012. Industrializing nature, knowledge, and labour: The political economy of bioprospecting in Madagascar. *Geoforum* 43(5): 980–990.

———. 2019. Address the roots of environmental crime. *Science* 364 (6436): 139.

Neugarten, R. A., Honzák, M., Carret, P., Koenig, K., Andriamaro, L., et al. 2016. Rapid assessment of ecosystem service co-benefits of biodiversity priority areas in Madagascar. *PLoS One* 11(12): e0168575.

Nicoll, M., and Langrand, O. 1989. *Madagascar: Revue de la conservation et des aires protégées.* Gland: WWF.

Noromiarilanto, F., Brinkmann, K., Faramalala, M. H., and Buerkert, A. 2016. Assessment of food self-sufficiency in smallholder farming systems of south-western Madagascar using survey and remote sensing data. *Agricultural Systems* 149: 139–149.

Norris, S. 2006. Madagascar defiant. *BioScience* 56(12): 960–965.

Nwapi, C., and Nliam, O. 2018. EIA legislation and sustainable development of oil sands projects in Madagascar: A critical assessment. *Journal of Energy and Natural Resources Law* 36(1): 103–129.

Obura, D., Di Carlo, G., Rabearisoa, A., and Oliver, T., eds. 2011. A rapid marine biodiversity assessment of the coral reefs of northeast Madagascar. *RAP Bulletin of Biological Assessment* 61: 1–100.

Obura, D., Gudka, M., Rabi, F. A., Gian, S. B., Bijoux, J., et al. 2017. Coral reef status report for the western Indian Ocean. Global Coral Reef Monitoring Network (GCRMN) / International Coral Reef Initiative (ICRI).

Olson, S. H. 1984. The robe of the ancestors: Forests in the history of Madagascar. *Forest and Conservation History* 28(4): 174–186.

Ormsby, A., and Mannle, K. 2006. Ecotourism benefits and the role of local guides at Masoala National Park, Madagascar. *Journal of Sustainable Tourism* 14(3): 271–287.

Ostrom, E. 1990. *Governing the Commons: The Evolution of Institutions for Collective Action.* Cambridge: Cambridge University Press.

Paneque-Gálvez, J., McCall, M. K., Napoletano, B. M., Wich, S. A., and Koh, L. P. 2014. Small drones for community-based forest monitoring: An assessment of their feasibility and potential in tropical areas. *Forests* 5(6): 1481–1507.

Parga, J. A. 2011. Nocturnal ranging by a diurnal primate: Are ring-tailed lemurs (*Lemur catta*) cathemeral? *Primates* 52(3): 201–205.

Perrier de la Bâthie, H. 1921. La végétation malgache. *Annales du Musée Colonial de Marseille*, série 3, 9: 1–268.

Peters, J. 1998. Transforming the integrated conservation and development project (ICDP) approach: Observations from the Ranomafana National Park project, Madagascar. *Journal of Agricultural and Environmental Ethics* 11(1): 17–47.

Phillips, S. J., Anderson, R. P., and Schapire, R. E. 2006. Maximum entropy modeling of species geographic distributions. *Ecological Modelling* 190(3–4): 231–259.

Pierre, S. 2012. Point study of human impacts on vegetal covers and species diversity of seagrass in southwest Madagascar. SIT Madagascar Biodiversity and Natural Resource Management, New York University. http://www.reefdoctor.org/wp-content/uploads/SIT-Seagrass-report.pdf.

Poker, J., and MacDicken, K. 2016. Tropical forest resources: Facts and tables. In *Tropical Forestry Handbook*, eds. L. Pancel and M. Köhl, pp. 3–45. Berlin: Springer.

Pollini, J. 2011. The difficult reconciliation of conservation and development objectives: The case of the Malagasy Environmental Action Plan. *Human Organization* 70(1): 74–87.

Pollini, J., and Lassoie, J. P. 2011. Trapping farmer communities within global environmental regimes: The case of the GELOSE legislation in Madagascar. *Society and Natural Resources* 24(8): 814–830.

Pollini, J., Hockley, N., and Muttenzer, F. D. 2014. The transfer of natural resource management rights to local communities. In *Conservation and Environmental Management in Madagascar*, ed. I. R. Scales, pp. 196–216. London: Routledge.

Poudyal, M., Ramamonjisoa, B. S., Hockley, N., Rakotonarivo, O. S., Gibbons, J. M., Mandimbiniaina, R., Rasoamanana, A., and Jones, J.P.G. 2016. Can REDD+ social safeguards reach the "right" people? Lessons from Madagascar. *Global Environmental Change* 37: 31–42.

Poudyal, M., Jones, J.P.G., Rakotonarivo, O. S., Hockley, N., Gibbons, J. M., Mandimbiniaina, R., Rasoamanana, A., Andrianantenaina, N. S., and Ramamonjisoa, B. S. 2018. Who bears the cost of forest conservation? *PeerJ* 6: e5106.

Praene, J. P., Radanielina, M. H., Rakotoson, V. R., Andriamamonjy, A. L., Sinama, F., Morau, D., and Rakotondramiarana, H. 2017. Electricity generation from renewables in Madagascar: Opportunities and projections. *Renewable and Sustainable Energy Reviews* 76: 1066–1079.

Prandi, F., Achille, C., Brumana, R., Fassi, S., and Fregonese, L. 2008. LiDAR and pictometry images integrated use for 3D model generation. *International Archives of the Photogrammetry, Remote Sensing and Spatial Information Sciences* 37(B2): 763–769.

Pressey, R. L., Weeks, R., and Gurney, G. G. 2017. From displacement activities to evidence-informed decisions in conservation. *Biological Conservation* 212: 337–348.

Rabarisoa, R. 2019. Status assessment and population trends of the glossy ibis *Plegadis falcinellus* in Madagascar between 1993 and 2016. In Glossy Ibis Ecology and Conservation, eds. S. Santoro, K.S.G. Sundar, and L. S. Cano Alonso. *Stork, Ibis and Spoonbill Conservation*, special issue 1: 60–64.

Rabemananjara, Z. H., Andriamanankasinarihaja, R., Aubert, S., and Ramamonjisoa, B. S. 2016. Vu d'ailleurs: Les limites juridiques et institutionnelles de 25 ans de gestion communautaire des ressources forestières (GCRF) à Madagascar. In *La gestion inclusive des forêts d'Afrique centrale*, eds. G. Buttoud and J.-C. Nguinguiri, pp. 93–107. Bogor: CIFOR.

Rabesahala Horning, N. 2005. The cost of ignoring rules: Forest conservation and rural livelihood outcomes in Madagascar. *Forests, Trees and Livelihoods* 15(2): 149–166.

———. 2008. Madagascar's biodiversity conservation challenge: From local- to national-level dynamics. *Environmental Sciences* 5(2): 109–128.

Rabetrano, T. 2018. REBIOMA data portal: Tool for conservation planning in Madagascar. *Biodiversity Information Science and Standards* 2: e25864.

Rafidimanantsoa, H. P., Poudyal, M., Ramamonjisoa, B. S., and Jones, J.P.G. 2018. Mind the gap: The use of research in protected area management in Madagascar. *Madagascar Conservation and Development* 13(1): 15–25.

Raik, D. 2007. Forest management in Madagascar: An historical overview. *Madagascar Conservation and Development* 2(1): 5–10.

Rakotomanana, H., Gates, G. E., Hildebrand, D., and Stoecker, B. J. 2017. Determinants of stunting in children under 5 years in Madagascar. *Maternal and Child Nutrition* 13(4): e12409.

Rakotonarivo, O. S. 2016. Improving the estimation of local welfare costs of conservation in low income countries using choice experiments: Empirical evidence from Madagascar. PhD thesis, Bangor University.

Rakotonarivo, O. S., Jacobsen, J. B., Larsen, H. O., Jones, J.P.G., Nielsen, M. R., Ramamonjisoa, B. S., Mandimbiniaina, R. H., and Hockley, N. 2017. Qualitative and quantitative evidence on the true local welfare costs of forest conservation in Madagascar: Are discrete choice experiments a valid ex ante tool? *World Development* 94: 478–491.

Rakotonarivo, O. S., Bredahl Jacobsen, J., Poudyal, M., Rasoamanana, A., and Hockley, N. 2018. Estimating welfare impacts where property rights are contested: Methodological and policy implications. *Land Use Policy* 70: 71–83.

Rakotoson, L. R., and Tanner, K. 2006. Community-based governance of coastal zone and marine resources in Madagascar. *Ocean and Coastal Management* 49(11): 855–872.

Rakotovao, J., and Raymond, R. 2019. Rosewood smuggling: A female economic operator from Antalaha is reported to be at the head of Operation "Flying." Malina. https://www.malina.mg/en/article/rosewood-smuggling--a-female-economic-operator-from-antalaha-is-reported-to-be-at-the-head-of-operation--flying.

Ramamonjisoa, B. S., and Rabemananjara, Z. H. 2012. Une évaluation économique de la foresterie communautaire. *Les Cahiers des Outres Mer* 257: 125–155.

Ramangason, G. S. 2018. Preface. In *Les aires protégées terrestres de Madagascar: Leur histoire, description et biote / The Terrestrial Protected Areas of Madagascar: Their History, Description, and Biota*, eds. S. M. Goodman, M. J. Raherilalao, and S. Wohlhauser, pp. 11–15. Antananarivo: Association Vahatra.

Ramiarantsoa, R. H., Ramamonjisoa, B. S., Fara, L. R., and Ranaivoson, S. 2012. Echec ou succès? La foresterie paysanne contractualisée dans ses paradoxes. *Les Cahiers des Outres Mer* 258: 301–310.

Ramiarantsoa, R. H., Mellac, M., André-Lamat, V., and Amelot, X. 2015. Les discours sur la nature à Madagascar, dans le sillage du *teny baiko*. *Autrepart* 73(1): 73.

Randriamalala, H., and Liu, Z. 2010. Rosewood of Madagascar: Between democracy and conservation. *Madagascar Conservation and Development* 5(1): 11–22.

Randrianandianina, B. N., Andriamahaly, L. R., Harisoa, F. M., and Nicoll, M. E. 2003. The role of protected areas in the management of the island's biodiversity. In

The Natural History of Madagascar, eds. S. M. Goodman and J. P. Benstead, pp. 1423–1432. Chicago: University of Chicago Press.

Randrianarison, H., and Wätzold, F. 2017. Are buyers of forest ecosystem services willing to consider distributional impacts of payments to local suppliers? Results from a choice experiment in Antananarivo, Madagascar. *Environmental Conservation* 44(1): 74–81.

Randrianja, S., and Ellis, S. 2009. *Madagascar: A Short History*. Chicago: University of Chicago Press.

Ranivo Rakotoson, J., and Razafimahatratra, P. 2018. Aspects légaux, juridiques et financiers des aires protégées à Madagascar: Passé, present et future / Legal, judiciary, and financial aspects of Madagascar protected areas: Past, present, and future. In *Les aires protégées terrestres de Madagascar: Leur histoire, description et biote / The Terrestrial Protected Areas of Madagascar: Their History, Description, and Biota*, eds. S. M. Goodman, M. J. Raherilalao, and S. Wohlhauser, pp. 105–168. Antananarivo: Association Vahatra.

Rankin, L., and Axel, A. C. 2017. Biodiversity assessment in tropical biomes using ecoacoustics: Linking soundscape to forest structure in a human-dominated tropical dry forest in southern Madagascar. In *Ecoacoustics: The Ecological Role of Sounds*, eds. A. Farina and S. H. Gage, pp. 129–144. Hoboken: John Wiley and Sons.

Rasoavahiny, L., Andrianarisata, M., Razafimpahanana, A., and Ratsifandrihamanana, A. N. 2008. Conducting an ecological gap analysis for the new Madagascar protected area system. *Parks* 17: 12–21.

Rasolofoson, R. A., Ferraro, P. J., Jenkins, C. N., and Jones, J.P.G. 2015. Effectiveness of community forest management at reducing deforestation in Madagascar. *Biological Conservation* 184: 271–277.

Rasolofoson, R. A., Ferraro, P. J., Ruta, G., Rasamoelina, M. S., Randriankolona, P. L., Larsen, H. O., and Jones, J.P.G. 2017. Impacts of community forest management on human economic well-being across Madagascar. *Conservation Letters* 10(3): 346–353.

Rasolofoson, R. A., Nielsen, M. R., and Jones, J.P.G. 2018a. The potential of the Global Person Generated Index for evaluating the perceived impacts of conservation interventions on subjective well-being. *World Development* 105: 107–118.

Rasolofoson, R. A., Hanauer, M. M., Pappinen, A., Fisher, B., and Ricketts, T. H. 2018b. Impacts of forests on children's diet in rural areas across 27 developing countries. *Science Advances* 4(8): eaat2853.

Ratsialonana, A. R., Burnod, P., Ramarojohn, L., and Teyssier, A. 2011. *After Daewoo? Current Status and Perspectives of Large-Scale Land Acquisition in Madagascar*. Rome: International Land Coalition.

Ratsimbaharison, A. M. 2017. *The Political Crisis of March 2009 in Madagascar: A Case Study of Conflict and Conflict Mediation*. London: Rowman and Littlefield.

Ratsimbazafy, C., Newton, D. J., and Ringuet, S. 2016. Timber island: The rosewood and ebony trade of Madagascar. TRAFFIC report. USAID Madagascar.

Ratsiraka, D. 1975. *Boky Mena: The Charter of the Malagasy Socialist Revolution*. Antananarivo: Repoblika Malagasy.

Razafimanahaka, J. H., Jenkins, R.K.B., Andriafidison, D., Randrianandrianina, F., Rakotomboavonjy, V., Keane, A., and Jones, J.P.G. 2012. Novel approach for quantifying illegal bushmeat consumption reveals high consumption of protected species in Madagascar. *Oryx* 46(4): 584–592.

Razafindrajao, F., Bamford, A. J., Young, H. G., Andrianarimisa, A., Iahia, A., Aboudou, B.I.N., and Lewis, R. E. 2017. Reassessing the conservation outlook for Madagascar's endemic Anatidae following the creation of new protected areas. *Wildfowl* 67: 72–86.

Razafindrakoto, M., Roubaud, F., and Wachsberger, J.-M. 2020. *Puzzle and Paradox: A Political Economy of Madagascar*. Cambridge: Cambridge University Press.

Razafindratsima, O., and Dunham, A. 2015. Increasing women's participation in community-based conservation: Key to success? *Madagascar Conservation and Development* 10(2): 45–47.

REBIOMA. 2021. REBIOMA data portal. http://data.rebioma.net/.

Repoblika Malagasy. 1972. *Rapport national de la République Malgache pour la Conférence des Nations Unies sur l'Environnement*. Antananarivo: Repoblika Malagasy.

Repoblikan'i Madagasikara. 2018. *Stratégie national REDD+ Madagascar*. Antananarivo: Repoblikan'i Madagasikara.

Roe, D., Seddon, N., and Elliott, J. 2019. *Biodiversity Loss Is a Development Issue: A Rapid Review of the Evidence*. London: International Institute for Environment and Development.

Rogers, H. M., Glew, L., Honzák, M., and Hudson, M. D. 2010. Prioritizing key biodiversity areas in Madagascar by including data on human pressure and ecosystem services. *Landscape and Urban Planning* 96(1): 48–56.

Roser, M., and Ortiz-Ospina, E. 2019. Global extreme poverty. Our World in Data. https://ourworldindata.org/extreme-poverty.

Saboureau, P. 1946. Le Service des Eaux et Forêts à Madagascar. *Revue Internationale de Botanique Appliquée et d'Agriculture Tropicale* 26(286 bis): 475–490.

Saloma, A., Marchesseau, S., Charrier, I., Andrianarimisa, A., Antogiorgi, E., and Adam, O. 2018. Do the newborn calves of humpback whales (*Megaptera novaeangliae*) have a preference to position themselves at the side of their mother? *Western Indian Ocean Journal of Marine Science*, special issue 1: 1–9.

Salomon, J.-N. 2009. L'accrétion littorale sur la côte ouest de Madagascar. *Physio-Géo, Géographie Physique et Environnement* 3: 35–59.

Sandbrook, C. 2015. The social implications of using drones for biodiversity conservation. *Ambio* 44(4): 636–647.

Scales, I. R. 2011. Farming at the forest frontier: Land use and landscape change in western Madagascar, 1896–2005. *Environment and History* 17(4): 499–524.

———. 2014a. A brief history of the state and politics of natural resource use in Madagascar. In *Conservation and Environmental Management in Madagascar*, ed. I. R. Scales, pp. 129–146. London: Routledge.

———. 2014b. The drivers of deforestation and the complexity of land use in Madagascar. In *Conservation and Environmental Management in Madagascar*, ed. I. R. Scales, pp. 105–125. London: Routledge.

Schweter, M. 2012. *Développement d'un protocole de suivi écologique standard pour le réseau de parcs et réserves gérés par MNP*. Rapport de mission de courte durée en mars 2012. Antananarivo: Madagascar National Parks.

Schwitzer, C., Mittermeier, R. A., Johnson, S. E., Donati, G., Irwin, M., et al. 2014. Averting lemur extinctions amid Madagascar's political crisis. *Science* 343(6173): 842–843.

Seagle, C. 2012. Inverting the impacts: Mining, conservation and sustainability claims near the Rio Tinto/QMM ilmenite mine in southeast Madagascar. *Journal of Peasant Studies* 39(2): 447–477.

Seddon, N., Chausson, A., Berry, P., Girardin, C.A.J., Smith, A., and Turner, B. 2020. Understanding the value and limits of nature-based solutions to climate change and other global challenges. *Philosophical Transactions of the Royal Society of London B: Biological Sciences* 375(1794): 1–20.

Serpantié, G., Rasolofoharinoro, and Carrière, S. 2007. *Transitions agraires, dynamiques écologiques et conservation: Le "corridor" Ranomafana-Andringitra (Madagascar)*. Paris: IRD.

Seymour, F., and Busch, J. 2016. *Why Forests? Why Now? The Science, Economics and Politics of Tropical Forests and Climate Change*. Washington, DC: Center for Global Development.

SMART. 2021. Spatial Monitoring and Reporting Tool. https://smartconservationtools.org.

SMART Partnership. 2018. Annual report. https://smartconservationtools.org.

Soe, A. K., and Sato, N. 2012. Local people's attitudes towards the community forestry: The case studies in the central dry zone of Myanmar. *Journal of the Faculty of Agriculture, Kyushu University* 57(1): 273–280.

Spalding, M., Kainuma, M., and Collins, L. 2010. *World Atlas of Mangroves*. London: Earthscan.

Stone, R. 1992. The biodiversity treaty: Pandora's box or fair deal? *Science* 256(5064): 1624.

Stoop, W. A., Uphoff, N., and Kassam, A. 2002. A review of agricultural research issues raised by the system of rice intensification (SRI) from Madagascar: Opportunities for improving farming systems for resource-poor farmers. *Agricultural Systems* 71(3): 249–274.

Sussman, R. W., Green, G. M., and Sussman, L. K. 1994. Satellite imagery, human ecology, anthropology, and deforestation in Madagascar. *Human Ecology* 22(3): 333–354.

Sutherland, W. J., Pullin, A. S., Dolman, P. M., and Knight, T. M. 2004. The need for evidence-based conservation. *Trends in Ecology and Evolution* 19(6): 305–308.

Tabor, K., and Hewson, J. 2018. The evolution of remote sensing applications vital to effective biodiversity conservation and sustainable development. In *Satellite Remote Sensing for Conservation Action: Case Studies from Aquatic and Terrestrial Ecosystems*, eds. A. K. Leidner and G. M. Buchanan, pp. 274–300. Cambridge: Cambridge University Press.

Tadross, M., Randriamarolaza, L., Rabefitia, Z., and Zheng, K. Y. 2008. *Climate Change in Madagascar: Recent Past and Future*. Washington, DC: World Bank.

Temple, H. J., Anstee, S., Ekstrom, J., Pilgrim, J. D., Rabenantoandro, J., Ramanamanjato, J.-B., Randriatafika, F., and Vincelette, M. 2012. *Forecasting the Path towards a Net Positive Impact on Biodiversity for Rio Tinto QMM*. Gland: IUCN.

Thamm, H. P., and Judex, M. 2006. The "low cost drone": An interesting tool for process monitoring in a high spatial and temporal resolution. In *Proceedings of the*

ISPRS Commission VII Mid-term Symposium "Remote Sensing from Pixels to Processes," pp. 140–144. Enschede: International Society for Photogrammetry and Remote Sensing.

Toillier, A., Serpantié, G., Hervé, D., and Lardon, S. 2011a. Livelihood strategies and land use changes in response to conservation: Pitfalls of community-based forest management in Madagascar. *Journal of Sustainable Forestry* 30(1): 20–56.

Toillier, A., Andriamahefazafy, F., Cahen-Fourot, L., Serpantié, G., and Méral, P. 2011b. Les PSE-eau à Madagascar: Une gouvernance à deux vitesses. Montpellier: Programme SERENA.

Tomlins, G. F. 1983. Some considerations in the design of low cost remotely-piloted aircraft for civil remote sensing applications. *Canadian Surveyor* 37(3): 157–167.

Tomlins, G. F., and Lee, Y. J. 1983. Remotely piloted aircraft: An inexpensive option for large-scale aerial photography in forestry applications. *Canadian Journal of Remote Sensing* 9(2): 76–85.

Tucker, B. 2007. Applying behavioral ecology and behavioral economics to conservation and development planning: An example from the Mikea Forest, Madagascar. *Human Nature* 18(3): 190–208.

Twining, N. F., and Toro, E. E. 1955. *Aerial Photographic Reconnaissance.* Washington, DC: Department of the Air Force.

Verykokou, S., and Ioannidis, C. 2018. Oblique aerial images: A review focusing on georeferencing procedures. *International Journal of Remote Sensing* 39(11): 3452–3496.

Vieilledent, G., Cornu, C., Cuní Sanchez, A., Leong Pock-Tsy, J. M., and Danthu, P. 2013. Vulnerability of baobab species to climate change and effectiveness of the protected area network in Madagascar: Towards new conservation priorities. *Biological Conservation* 166: 11–22.

Vieilledent, G., Grinand, C., Rakotomalala, F. A., Ranaivosoa, R., Rakotoarijaona, J.-R., Allnutt, T. F., and Achard, F. 2018. Combining global tree cover loss data with historical national forest cover maps to look at six decades of deforestation and forest fragmentation in Madagascar. *Biological Conservation* 222: 189–197.

Virah-Sawmy, M., Ebeling, J., and Taplin, R. 2014. Mining and biodiversity offsets: A transparent and science-based approach to measure "no-net-loss." *Journal of Environmental Management* 143: 61–70.

von Hase, A., Cooke, A., Andrianarimisa, A., Andriamparany, R., Mass, V., Mitchell, R., and Ten Kate, K. 2014. Working towards NNL of biodiversity and beyond: Ambatovy, Madagascar; A case study. https://www.forest-trends.org/wp-content/uploads/imported/ambatovy-bbop-nnl-2014-final-pdf.pdf.

Vorontsova, M. S., Besnard, G., Forest, F., Malakasi, P., Moat, J., et al. 2016. Madagascar's grasses and grasslands: Anthropogenic or natural? *Proceedings of the Royal Society of London B: Biological Sciences* 283 (1823): 20152262.

Vörösmarty, C. J., Fekete, B. M., and Tucker, B. A. 1998. Global river discharge, 1807–1991. Version 1.1 (RivDIS). Oak Ridge: Oak Ridge National Laboratory. http://dx.doi.org/10.3334/ORNLDAAC/199.

Vyawahare, M. 2020. Q&A with Minister Vahinala Raharinirina. Mongabay. https://news.mongabay.com/2020/04/covid-19-will-hurt-madagascars-conservation-funding-qa-with-minister-vahinala-raharinirina/.

Waeber, P. O., Wilmé, L., Mercier, J. R., Camara, C., and Lowry, P. P. 2016. How effective have thirty years of internationally driven conservation and development efforts been in Madagascar? *PLoS One* 11(8): e0161115.

Ward, C., Stringer, L. C., and Holmes, G. 2018. Protected area co-management and perceived livelihood impacts. *Journal of Environmental Management* 228: 1–12.

Weissensteiner, M. H., Poelstra, J. W., and Wolf, J.B.W. 2015. Low-budget ready-to-fly unmanned aerial vehicles: An effective tool for evaluating the nesting status of canopy-breeding bird species. *Journal of Avian Biology* 46(4): 425–430.

Wendland, K. J., Honzák, M., Portela, R., Vitale, B., Rubinoff, S., and Randrianarisoa, J. 2010. Targeting and implementing payments for ecosystem services: Opportunities for bundling biodiversity conservation with carbon and water services in Madagascar. *Ecological Economics* 69(11): 2093–2107.

White, F. 1983. *The Vegetation of Africa: A Descriptive Memoir to Accompany the UNESCO/AETFAT/UNSO Vegetation Map of Africa.* Paris: UNESCO.

Williams, J. 2019. We can see beyond the trees. Royal Botanic Gardens Kew. https://www.kew.org/read-and-watch/see-beyond-the-trees.

Wilmé, L., Innes, J. L., Schuurman, D., Ramamonjisoa, B., Langrand, M., et al. 2020. The elephant in the room: Madagascar's rosewood stocks and stockpiles. *Conservation Letters* 13(4). doi:10.1111/conl.12714.

Wollenberg, K. C., Vieites, D. R., and Vences, M. 2008. Annual temperature data for two Malagasy sites of high anuran diversity. *Monografie di Museo Regionale di Scienze Naturali, Torino* 45(Jan.): 85–94.

World Bank. 2017. Sustainable landscape management project. http://documents.worldbank.org/curated/en/275181490493719670/pdf/Madagascar-PAD-03062017.pdf.

———. 2019. Madagascar country overview. https://www.worldbank.org/en/country/madagascar.

World Justice Project. 2020. Rule of Law Index 2020. Washington, DC. https://worldjusticeproject.org/our-work/research-and-data/wjp-rule-law-index-2020.

Wright, P. C. 1995. Demography and life history of free-ranging *Propithecus diadema edwardsi* in Ranomafana National Park, Madagascar. *International Journal of Primatology* 16(5): 835–854.

Yangambi. 1956. Classification phytogéographique de Yangambi. *Adansonia*, série 2, 18(2): 243–256.

Zbigniew, K. 2012. Une analyse globale de la chaîne d'approvisionnement de la pêcherie du crabe de mangrove (*Scylla serrata*) à Madagascar. Programme pour la mise en œuvre d'une stratégie de pêche pour la région Afrique orientale-australe et Océan Indien. Rapport SF/2012/24. Commission de l'Océan Indien. http://www.fao.org/3/a-az394f.pdf.

Zinner, D., Wygoda, C., Razafimanantsoa, L., Rasoloarison, R., Andrianandrasana, H. T., Ganzhorn, J. U., and Torkler, F. 2014. Analysis of deforestation patterns in the central Menabe, Madagascar, between 1973 and 2010. *Regional Environmental Change* 14: 157–166.

CONTRIBUTORS

Abdallah Iahia Bin Aboudou
Durrell Wildlife Conservation Trust, BP 8511, Antananarivo 101, Madagascar; email: kassidi@durrell.org

Claudine Ah-Peng
Université de La Réunion, UMR PVBMT, 7 Chemin de l'IRAT, 97410 Saint-Pierre, La Réunion, France; email: claudine.ahpeng@univ-reunion.fr

Lalao Aigrette
Blue Ventures, Villa Huguette, Lot II U 86, Cité Planton, Ampahibe, Antananarivo 101, Madagascar; email: lalao@blueventures.org

Jason R. Ali
Department of Earth Sciences, University of Hong Kong, Pokfulam Road, Hong Kong; email: jrali@hku.hk

Frank Almeda
California Academy of Sciences, Institute for Biodiversity Science and Sustainability, Department of Botany, 55 Music Concourse Drive, Golden Gate Park, San Francisco, California 94118-4599, USA; email: falmeda@calacademy.org

Jamie L. Alumbaugh
Department of Biological Sciences, Northern Illinois University, DeKalb, Illinois 60115, USA; and Department of Geography, University of Tennessee, Knoxville, Tennessee 37996, USA; email: jalumbau@vols.utk.edu

Franco Andreone
Museo Regionale di Scienze Naturali, Via Giovanni Giolitti 36, 10123 Turin, Italy; email: franco.andreone@gmail.com

Daudet Andriafidison
Madagasikara Voakajy, BP 5181, Antananarivo 101, Madagascar; email: andriafidison@voakajy.mg

Fifaliana Andriamaharavo
Madagasikara Voakajy, BP 5181, Antananarivo 101, Madagascar; email: fifalianaandriamiravo@gmail.com

Lalao Andriamahefarivo
Missouri Botanical Garden, 4344 Shaw Boulevard, Saint Louis, Missouri 63110, USA; and Institut de Systématique, Evolution et Biodiversité (ISYEB), Muséum National d'Histoire Naturelle, Centre National de la Recherche Scientifique, Sorbonne Université, Ecole Pratique des Hautes Etudes, Université des Antilles, C.P. 39, 57 rue Cuvier, 75005 Paris: email: Lalao.Andriamahefarivo@mobot.mg

Lantoniaina Andriamampianina
Wildlife Conservation Society, BP 8500, Antananarivo 101, Madagascar; email: lanto@wcs.org

Soa Fy Andriamandimby
Institut Pasteur de Madagascar, BP 1274, Antananarivo 101, Madagascar; email: soafy@pasteur.mg

Mahefa N. N. Andriamavosoloarisoa
Mention Zoologie et Biodiversité Animale, Université d'Antananarivo, BP 906, Antananarivo 101, Madagascar; email: abalouda@yahoo.com

Sylvie Andriambololonera
Missouri Botanical Garden, Madagascar Research and Conservation Program, BP 3391, Antananarivo 101, Madagascar; email: sylvie.andriambololonera@mobot.mg

Fanja Andriamialisoa
11816 Riders Lane, Reston, Virginia 20191, USA; email: FAndriamialisoa@aol.com

Radosoa Andrianaivoarivelo
Biodiversity Conservation Madagascar, Villa No. 3, Residence Fanambinantsoa, Tanjambato, Antananarivo 101, Madagascar; email: aniainodna@yahoo.fr

F. Ollier D. Andrianambinina
Madagascar National Parks, Lot AI 10C Ambatobe, Antananarivo 103, Madagascar; email: ollier_adsi@mnparks.mg

Boris Andrianantenaina
Conservation International, Avenue Lally Tollendal, Antsiranana 201, Madagascar; email: bandrianantenaina@conservation.org

Aristide Andrianarimisa
Wildlife Conservation Society, Madagascar, Villa Ifanomezantsoa, Soavimbahoaka BP 8500, Antananarivo 101, Madagascar; email: aristide@wcs.org

Mahandry Andrianarimisa
Mention Zoologie et Biodiversité Animale, Université d'Antananarivo, BP 906, Antananarivo 101, Madagascar; email: andrianarimisamahandry@gmail.com

Norbert Andrianarivelo
Institut Halieutique et des Sciences Marines de l'Université de Toliara, Rue Dr. Rabesandratana, Toliara 601, Madagascar; email: a.norbert@ihsm.mg

Vonjy Andrianjakarivelo
Wildlife Conservation Society, BP 8500, Antananarivo 101, Madagascar; email: vandrianjakarivelo@wcs.org

Raphali R. Andriantsimanarilafy
Madagasikara Voakajy, BP 5181, Antananarivo 101, Madagascar; email: arraphali@voakajy.mg

Luca Andriatahina
Institut Halieutique et des Sciences Marines, Université de Toliara, Rue Dr. Rabesandratana, BP 141, Toliara 601, Madagascar; email: andriiluca@gmail.com

Dmitry A. Apanaskevich
United States National Tick Collection, James H. Oliver Jr. Institute for Coastal Plain Science, Georgia Southern University, Statesboro, Georgia 30460-8042, USA; email: dapanaskevich@georgiasouthern.edu

Wendy L. Applequist
Missouri Botanical Garden, 4344 Shaw Boulevard, Saint Louis, Missouri 63110, USA; email: wendy.applequist@mobot.org

André Aptroot
Laboratório de Botânica / Liquenologia, Instituto de Biociências, Universidade Federal de Mato Grosso do Sul, Avenida Costa e Silva s/n, Bairro Universitário, CEP 79070-900, Campo Grande, Mato Grosso do Sul, Brazil; email: andreaptroot@gmail.com

Amanda H. Armstrong
GESTAR, NASA Goddard Space Flight Center, Universities Space Research Association, 7178 Columbia Gateway Drive, Columbia, Maryland 21046, USA; and University of Virginia, Department of Environmental Sciences, Clark Hall 288, 290 McCormick Road, Charlottesville, Virginia 22902, USA; email: amanda.h.armstrong@nasa.gov

Daniel Aslanian
Laboratoire de Géodynamique et d'Enregistrements Sédimentaires, REM/GM/LGS, Institut Français de Recherche pour l'Exploration de la Mer (IFREMER), Plouzané, France; email: Daniel.aslanian@ifremer.fr

Yildiz Aumeeruddy-Thomas
Centre d'Ecologie Fonctionnelle et Evolutive (CEFE), UMR 5175, CNRS, Université de Montpellier, Université Paul-Valéry Montpellier, EPHE, 1919 Route de Mende, 34293 Montpellier Cedex 05, France; email: Yildiz.AUMEERUDDY-THOMAS@cefe.cnrs.fr

Andrea L. Baden
Hunter College of the City University of New York, Department of Anthropology, 695 Park Avenue, New York, New York 10065, USA; The Graduate Center of the City University of New York, Departments of Anthropology and Biology, New York, New York 10065, USA; and The New York Consortium in Evolutionary Primatology, New York, New York 10016, USA; email: andrea.baden@hunter.cuny.edu

Michela Balestri
Department of Social Sciences, Oxford Brookes University, Headington Campus, Oxford OX3 0BP, United Kingdom; email: michela.balestri@gmail.com

Martine Bardot-Vaucoulon
Institut de Systématique, Evolution et Biodiversité (UMR 7205-CNRS, MNHN, UPMC, EPHE), Muséum National d'Histoire Naturelle, Sorbonne Universités, Case Postale 39, 57, rue Cuvier, 75213 Paris Cedex 05, France; email: martine.bardot-vaucoulon@mnhn.fr, martine.bardot@gmail.com

Aaron M. Bauer
Department of Biology, Villanova University, 800 Lancaster Avenue, Villanova, Pennsylvania 19085, USA; email: aaron.bauer@villanova.edu

David A. Baum
University of Wisconsin–Madison, Department of Botany, 430 Lincoln Drive, Madison, Wisconsin 53706, USA; email: dbaum@wisc.edu

Henk Beentje
Herbarium, Royal Botanic Gardens, Kew, Richmond, Surrey TW9 3AE, United Kingdom; email: h.beentje@kew.org

Olivier Behra
Man and The Environment, Lot 102 B Ampandrana, Antananarivo 101, Madagascar; email: olivierbehraperso@gmail.com

Etienne Bemanaja
Bureau de la Représentation du Centre National de Recherches Océanographiques, 21 rue Fernand Kassanga, Tsimbazaza

Andoharano, Antananarivo 101, Madagascar; email: bemanaja@yahoo.fr

Armand Benjara
The Peregrine Fund, BP 4113, Antananarivo 101, Madagascar; email: benjara204@gmail.com

Ben Bennett
Natural Resources Institute, University of Greenwich, Central Avenue, Chatham Maritime, Kent ME4 4TB, United Kingdom; email: Ben.Bennett@greenwich.ac.uk

Johannes Bergsten
Department of Zoology, Swedish Museum of Natural History, Box 50007, 104 05 Stockholm, Sweden; email: johannes.bergsten@nrm.se

Paul E. Berry
University of Michigan Herbarium and Department of Ecology and Evolutionary Biology, 3600 Varsity Drive, Ann Arbor, Michigan 48108, USA; email: peberry@umich.edu

Guillaume Besnard
CNRS, Université Paul Sabatier, IRD, UMR 5174 EDB (Laboratoire Evolution and Diversité Biologique), 118 route de Narbonne, F-31062 Toulouse, France; email: guillaume.besnard@univ-tlse3.fr

Janina Bethge
Institute of Zoology, Universität Hamburg, Martin-Luther-King-Platz 3, 20146 Hamburg, Germany; email: janina.bethge@gmail.com

†Jean-Marie Betsch
Muséum National d'Histoire Naturelle, Département Ecologie et Gestion de la Biodiversité, USM 306, 4 avenue du Petit-Château, F-91800 Brunoy, France

Brigitte A. Bezandry
Institut Supérieur de Sciences, Environnement and Développement Durable, Université de Toamasina, BP 591, Toamasina 501, Madagascar; email: bezandrybrigitteannie@gmail.com

Chris R. Birkinshaw
Missouri Botanical Garden, Madagascar Research and Conservation Program, BP 3391, Antananarivo 101, Madagascar; email: chris.birkinshaw@mobot.mg

Marina B. Blanco
Duke Lemur Center, 3705 Erwin Road, Durham, North Carolina 27705, USA; email: marina.blanco@duke.edu

Molly Bletz
Department of Biology, University of Massachusetts Boston, 100 Morrissey Boulevard, Boston, Massachusetts 02125, USA; email: molly.bletz@gmail.com

Nicholas L. Block
Biology Department, Stonehill College, 320 Washington Street, Easton, Massachusetts 02357, USA; email: nblock@stonehill.edu

Carlos G. Boluda
Conservatoire et Jardin botaniques de la Ville de Genève and Laboratoire de Systématique Végétale et Biodiversité de l'Université de Genève, Case Postale 71, 1292 Chambésy/Genève, Switzerland; email: carlos.boluda@ville-ge.ch

Cortni Borgerson
Department of Anthropology, Montclair State University, Montclair, New Jersey 07043, USA; and Madagascar Health and Environmental Research (MAHERY), Maroantsetra 512, Madagascar; email: borgersonc@montclair.edu

Art Borkent
Research Associate of the American Museum of Natural History, 691-8th Avenue SE, Salmon Arm, British Columbia V1E 2C2, Canada; email: artborkent@telus.net

Philippe Bouchet
Muséum National d'Histoire Naturelle, 55 rue Buffon, 75005 Paris, France; email: philippe.bouchet@mnhn.fr

Philippe Boussès
MIVEGEC Unit, Université de Montpellier, IRD, CNRS, 34394 Montpellier, France; email: philippe.bousses@ird.fr

Sven Bradler
Department of Animal Evolution and Biodiversity, Johann-Friedrich-Blumenbach Institute for Zoology and Anthropology, University of Göttingen, 37073 Göttingen, Germany; email: sbradle@gwdg.de

Lee D. Brady
Calumma Ecological Services, 13 Woodside, Dunkirk-Faversham, Kent ME13 9NY, United Kingdom; email: l.brady@calummaecologicalservices.co.uk

Cara E. Brook
Department of Integrative Biology, University of California, Berkeley, 2200 University Avenue, Berkeley, California 94720, USA; Current address: Department of Ecology and Evolution, The University of Chicago, 1101 East 57th Street, Chicago, Illinois 60637, USA; email: cbrook@uchicago.edu

Jason L. Brown
Department of Zoology, Southern Illinois University, Carbondale, Illinois 62901, USA; email: jasonleebrown@gmail.com

Kerry A. Brown
Department of Geography, Geology and the Environment, Kingston University London, Penrhyn Road, Kingston upon Thames, KT1 2EE, United Kingdom; email: k.brown@kingston.ac.uk

Mike Bruton
Mike Bruton Imagineering, 22 Forth Road, Rondebosch 7700, Cape Town, South Africa; email: mikefishesbruton@gmail.com

Sven Buerki
Department of Biological Sciences, Boise State University, 1910 University Drive, Boise, Idaho 83725, USA; email: svenbuerki@boisestate.edu

Frank T. Burbrink
Department of Herpetology, American Museum of Natural History, 200 Central Park West, New York, New York 10024, USA; email: fburbrink@amnh.org

James W. Byng
Naturalis Biodiversity Center, Botany, PO Box 9517, 2300 RA, Leiden, The Netherlands; email: james.byng@naturalis.nl

Michelle E. Byrnes
Louisiana State University, Museum of Natural Science, 119 Foster Hall, Baton Rouge, Louisiana 70803-3216, USA; email: mbyrne8@lsu.edu

John E. Cadle
East Georgia State College, Department of Biology, 131 College Circle, Swainsboro, Georgia 30401, USA; email: jecadle@ega.edu

Martin W. Callmander
Conservatoire et Jardin botaniques de la Ville de Genève and Laboratoire de Systématique Végétale et Biodiversité de l'Université de Genève, Case Postale 71, 1292 Chambésy/Genève, Switzerland; email: Martin.Callmander@ville-ge.ch

Sam Cameron
Feedback Madagascar-Ny Tanintsika, BP 1345, Fianarantsoa 301, Madagascar; email: sam@feedbackmadagascar.org

Michael D. Carleton
Department of Vertebrate Zoology, National Museum of Natural History, Smithsonian Institution, Washington, DC, 20560-0108, USA; email: mike.carleton@comcast.net

Angus I. Carpenter
School of Animal Rural and Environmental Sciences, Nottingham Trent University, Brackenhurst Campus, Southwell, Nottingham NG25 0QF, United Kingdom; email: carpenter.angus@gmail.com, angus.carpenter@ntu.ac.uk

Aurélien Carré
European Topic Centre on Biological Diversity, Muséum National d'Histoire Naturelle, 36 rue Geoffroy Saint-Hilaire, 75005 Paris, France; email: aurelien.carre@mnhn.fr

Stéphanie M. Carrière
UMR SENS (Savoirs, ENvironnement et Sociétés)–IRD, CIRAD, UPVM–Université Paul-Valéry, Site St Charles, Route de Mende, 34199 Montpellier Cedex 05, France; email: stephanie.carriere@ird.fr

Fabio Carvalho
Lancaster Environment Centre, Lancaster University, Lancaster LA1 4YQ, United Kingdom; email: f.carvalho@lancaster.ac.uk

Salvatore Cerchio
African Aquatic Conservation Fund, PO Box 366, Chilmark, Massachusetts 02535, USA; email: scerchio@africanaquaticconservation.org

Prosanta Chakrabarty
Louisiana State University, Museum of Natural Science, 119 Foster Hall, Baton Rouge, Louisiana 70803-3216, USA; email: prosanta@lsu.edu

Gill Challen
Royal Botanic Gardens, Kew, Richmond, Surrey TW9 3AE, United Kingdom; email: g.challen@kew.org

Lauren Chan
Department of Biology, Pacific University, 2043 College Way, Forest Grove, Oregon 97116, USA; email: lchan@pacificu.edu

Lounès Chikhi
Laboratoire Evolution et Diversité Biologique (EDB UMR 5174), CNRS, IRD, UPS, Université de Toulouse Midi-Pyrénées, 31000 Toulouse, France; and Instituto Gulbenkian de Ciência, Rua da Quinta Grande, 6, 2780-156 Oeiras, Portugal; email: lounes.chikhi@univ-tlse3.fr, chikhi@igc.gulbenkian.pt

Emily Chou
Wildlife Conservation Society, 2300 Southern Boulevard, Bronx, New York 10460, USA; email: echou@wcs.org

Stéphane Ciccione
Kelonia, 46 rue du Gral de Gaulle, 97436 Saint-Leu, La Réunion, France; email: stephane.ciccione@museesreunion.re

Nikolas Gioia Cipola
Instituto Nacional de Pesquisas da Amazônia–INPA, Laboratório de Sistemática e Ecologia de Invertebrados do Solo, Av. André Araujo, N°2936, campus II, Aleixo, Manaus, Amazonas, 69067-375, Brazil; email: nikolasgc@gmai.com

Nicolas Cliquennois
Collège Français Jules-Verne, BP 141, Antsirabe 101, Madagascar; email: nicolascliquennois@yahoo.fr

Alan S. Collins
Tectonics and Earth Systems (TES) Group, Department of Earth Sciences, University of Adelaide, Adelaide, SA 5005, Australia; email: Alan.Collins@adelaide.edu.au

Ian C. Colquhoun
Department of Anthropology and Centre for Environment and Sustainability, University of Western Ontario, London, Ontario N6A 5C2, Canada; email: colquhou@uwo.ca

Jérôme Constant
Royal Belgian Institute of Natural Sciences, Department of Entomology, Vautier Street 29, B-1000 Brussels, Belgium; email: jerome.constant@naturalsciences.be

Andrew Cooke
Resolve sarl, Ivandry Business Center, Antananarivo 101, Madagascar; email: andrew@resolve.mg

Colette Cordonin
Unité Mixte de Recherche Processus Infectieux en Milieu Insulaire Tropical (UMR PIMIT), Université de La Réunion, CNRS 9192, INSERM 1187, IRD 249, 97490 Sainte-Clotilde, La Réunion, France; email: cdn.colette@gmail.com

Márcia S. Couri
Museu Nacional, Universidade Federal do Rio de Janeiro, Quinta da Boa Vista, Rio de Janeiro, 20940-040, Brazil; email: courimarcia@gmail.com

Adrian J. K. Craig
Department of Zoology and Entomology, Rhodes University, Grahamstown, 6140, South Africa; email: A.Craig@ru.ac.za

Keith A. Crandall
Computational Biology Institute, George Washington University, 800 22nd Street, NW, Suite 7000D, Washington, DC, 20052, USA; email: kcrandall@gwu.edu

Angelica Crottini
CIBIO, Research Centre in Biodiversity, Genetics and Evolution, InBIO, Universidade do Porto, Campus Agrário de Vairão, Rua Padre Armando Quintas, 7, 4485-661 Vairão, Portugal; email: acrottini@cibio.up.pt; tiliquait@yahoo.it

Astrid Cruaud
Centre de Biologie pour la Gestion des Populations (CBGP), INRAE, CIRAD, IRD, Montpellier SupAgro, Université de Montpellier, Montpellier, France; email: astrid.cruaud@inrae.fr

Neil Cumberlidge
Department of Biology, Northern Michigan University, Marquette, Michigan 49855, USA; email: ncumberl@nmu.edu

Frank P. Cuozzo
Lajuma Research Centre, PO Box 522, Louis Trichardt (Makhado) 0920, South Africa; and Mammal Research Institute, Department of Zoology and Entomology, University of Pretoria, Private Bag 20, Pretoria, South Africa; email: makiteeth@hotmail.com

Kristina Curry Rogers
Biology and Geology Departments, Macalester College, 1600 Grand Avenue, Saint Paul, Minnesota 55105, USA; email: rogersk@macalester.edu

Douglas C. Daly
Institute of Systematic Botany, New York Botanical Garden, 2900 Southern Boulevard, Bronx, New York 10458-5126, USA; email: ddaly@nybg.org

Thomas F. Daniel
Department of Botany, California Academy of Sciences, 55 Music Concourse Drive, Golden Gate Park, San Francisco, California 94118, USA; email: tdaniel@calacademy.org

Pascal Danthu
CIRAD, UPR HortSys, Université de Montpellier, Campus de Baillarguet, 34392 Montpellier, France; email: pascal.danthu@cirad.fr

Iain Darbyshire
Royal Botanic Gardens, Kew, Richmond, Surrey TW9 3AE, United Kingdom; email: I.Darbyshire@kew.org

Kathrin H. Dausmann
Institute of Zoology, Universität Hamburg, Martin-Luther-King-Platz 3, 20146 Hamburg, Germany; email: kathrin.dausmann@uni-hamburg.de

Tammy E. Davies
BirdLife International, David Attenborough Building, Pembroke Street, Cambridge CB2 3QZ, United Kingdom; email: tammy.davies@birdlife.org

Patricia Z. R. Davis
Community Centered Conservation, 29 Old Gloucester Street, London WC1N 3AX, United Kingdom; email: patricia@c-3.org.uk

Petra De Block
Botanic Garden Meise, Nieuwelaan 38, B-1860 Meise, Belgium; email: petra.deblock@plantentuinmeise.be

Neil D'Cruze
Wildlife Conservation Research Unit, Department of Zoology, University of Oxford, Recanati-Kaplan Centre, Abingdon Road, Tubney House, Tubney OX13 5QL, United Kingdom; email: neil.dcruze@zoo.ox.ac.uk

Hélène Delatte
CIRAD, UMR, PVBMT, 97410 Saint-Pierre, La Réunion, France; email: helene.delatte@cirad.fr

Marc De Meyer
Royal Museum for Central Africa, Leuvensesteenweg 13, B-3080 Tervuren, Belgium; email: marc.de.meyer@africamuseum.be

Jérôme Depaquit
Université de Reims Champagne-Ardenne, ANSES, SFR Cap Santé, EA7510 ESCAPE–USC VECPAR, 51096 Reims, France; and Laboratoire de Parasitologie-Mycologie, Pôle de Biologie Territoriale, CHU de Reims, rue Cognacq-Jay, 51100 Reims, France; email: jerome.depaquit@univ-reims.fr

Patrick de Rham
26, chemin de Montolivet, CH 10106 Lausanne, Switzerland; email: pderham@bluewin.ch

Camille DeSisto
Department of Organismic and Evolutionary Biology, Harvard University, 26 Oxford Street, Cambridge, Massachusetts 02138, USA; email: cdesisto97@gmail.com

Stella Diamant
Madagascar Whale Shark Project, Baleines Rand'eau Office, Madirokely Beach, Nosy Be 207, Madagascar; and Avenue Circulaire 70, B-1180 Brussels, Belgium; email: stelladiamant@gmail.com

Christopher H. Dietrich
Illinois Natural History Survey, Prairie Research Institute, University of Illinois, Champaign, Illinois 61820, USA; email: chdietri@illinois.edu

Muriel Dietrich
Unité Mixte de Recherche Processus Infectieux en Milieu Insulaire Tropical (UMR PIMIT), Université de La Réunion, CNRS 9192, INSERM 1187, IRD 249, 97490 Sainte-Clotilde, La Réunion, France; email: muriel.dietrich@ird.fr

Carl W. Dick
Department of Biology, Western Kentucky University, Bowling Green, Kentucky 42101, USA; and Integrative Research Center, Field Museum of Natural History, 1400 South DuSable Lake Shore Drive, Chicago, Illinois 60605, USA; email: carl.dick@wku.edu

Klaas-Douwe B. Dijkstra
Naturalis Biodiversity Center, PO Box 9517, 2300 RA Leiden, The Netherlands; email: african.dragonflies@gmail.com

Dmitry A. Dmitriev
Illinois Natural History Survey, Prairie Research Institute, University of Illinois, Champaign, Illinois 61820, USA; email: proceps@illinois.edu

Rainer Dolch
Association Mitsinjo, Andasibe 514, Madagascar; email: rdolch@gmx.de

Giuseppe Donati
Department of Social Sciences, Oxford Brookes University, Headington Campus, Oxford OX3 0BP, United Kingdom; email: gdonati@brookes.ac.uk

Kristina G. Douglass
Department of Anthropology, 321 Carpenter Building, Pennsylvania State University, University Park, Pennsylvania 16802, USA; email: kdouglass@psu.edu

John Dransfield
Herbarium, Royal Botanic Gardens, Kew, Richmond, Surrey TW9 3AE, United Kingdom; email: j.dransfield@kew.org

Soejatmi Dransfield
Comparative Plant and Fungal Biology, Royal Botanic Gardens, Kew, Richmond, Surrey TW9 3AE, United Kingdom; email: s.dransfield@kew.org

Jean-Bernard Duchemin
Institut Pasteur of the French Guiana, Amazonian Vectopole, Medical Entomology Laboratory, BP 6010, Cayenne Cedex 97306, French Guiana; email: jbduchemin@pasteur-cayenne.fr

Amy E. Dunham
1600 Main Street, Department of BioSciences, Rice University, Houston, Texas 77005, USA; email: aed4@rice.edu

Jean-Marc Duplantier
2 Impasse Arioucap, 65400 Gaillagos, France; email: jean-marc.duplantier0137@orange.fr

Louis Du Preez
School of Environmental Sciences and Development, North-West University, Potchefstroom Campus, Private Bag X6001, Potchefstroom 2520, South Africa; email: Louis.DuPreez@nwu.ac.za

Josephine D'Urban Jackson
Sir Martin Evans Building, School of Biosciences, Cardiff University, CF10 3AX, United Kingdom; email: josiedjackson@gmail.com

Lance A. Durden
Department of Biology, Georgia Southern University, 4324 Old Register Road, Statesboro, Georgia 30458, USA; email: ldurden@georgiasouthern.edu

Devin Edmonds
Illinois Natural History Survey, Prairie Research Institute, University of Illinois Urbana-Champaign, Champaign, Illinois 61821, USA; email: devin@amphibiancare.com

Paul Eggleton
Life Sciences Department, The Natural History Museum, Cromwell Road, South Kensington, London SW7 5BD, United Kingdom; email: p.eggleton@nhm.ac.uk

Jonathan Ekstrom
The Biodiversity Consultancy Ltd., 3E King's Parade, Cambridge CB2 1SJ, United Kingdom; email: jonathan@thebiodiversityconsultancy.com

Jean-Marc Elouard
Chemin de la Devèze, F-34270 Lauret, France; email: jmelouard@yahoo.fr

Henrik Enghoff
Natural History Museum of Denmark, University of Copenhagen, Universitetsparken 15, DK-2100 Koebenhavn OE, Denmark; email: henghoff@snm.ku.dk

Timothy M. Eppley
Conservation Science and Wildlife Health, San Diego Zoo Wildlife Alliance, PO Box 120551, San Diego, California 92112, USA; and Department of Anthropology, Portland State University, PO Box 751, Portland, Oregon 97297, USA; email: teppley@sdzwa.org

Marcial Escudero
Departamento de Biología Vegetal y Ecología, Universidad de Sevilla, 41012, Seville, Spain; email: amesclir@gmail.com

Kathryn M. Everson
University of Kentucky, Department of Biology, 101 T. H. Morgan Building, 675 Rose Street, Lexington, Kentucky 40508, USA; email: kathryn.everson@uky.edu

Diego A. Fachin
Laboratório de Evolução e Morfologia de Diptera, Departamento de Biologia, Faculdade de Filosofia, Ciências e Letras de Ribeirão Preto, Universidade de São Paulo, Avenida Bandeirantes 3900, Monte Alegre, Ribeirão Preto, São Paulo, 14040–901, Brazil; email: diegoafachin@gmail.com

Mai Fahmy
35 Landview Drive, Dix Hills, New York 11746, USA; email: mfahmy@amnh.org

Manoa L. Faliarivola
Mention Zoologie et Biodiversité Animale, Université d'Antananarivo, BP 906, Antananarivo 101, Madagascar; and Association Vahatra, BP 3972, Antananarivo 101, Madagascar; email: manoalahatriniavo@gmail.com

Zach J. Farris
Appalachian State University, Department of Health and Exercise Science, Boone, North Carolina 28608, USA; email: farriszj@appstate.edu

Cobi Feijen
Naturalis Biodiversity Centre, Postbus 9517, 2300 RA Leiden, The Netherlands; email: cobi.feijen@naturalis.nl

Hans R. Feijen
Naturalis Biodiversity Centre, Postbus 9517, 2300 RA Leiden, The Netherlands; email: hans.feijen@naturalis.nl

Claudia Fichtel
Behavioral Ecology and Sociobiology Unit, German Primate Center (DPZ) Kellnerweg 4, 37077 Göttingen, Germany; email: claudia.fichtel@gwdg.de

Claudia Filippone
Institut Pasteur de Madagascar, BP 1274, Antananarivo 101, Madagascar; email: cfilippone@pasteur.mg

Brian L Fisher
Entomology, California Academy of Sciences, Golden Gate Park, 55 Music Concourse Drive, San Francisco, California 94118, USA; email: bfisher@calacademy.org

Matthew Fisher
Faculty of Medicine, School of Public Health, Imperial College London, Norfolk Place, London W2 1PG, United Kingdom; email: matthew.fisher@imperial.ac.uk

Matana Gabriel Fitahiantsoa
Conservation International, 2ème Etage immeuble NEAMAT, Boulevard Ratsimilaho, Toamasina 501, Madagascar; email: mfitahiantsoa@conservation.org

John J. Flynn
Division of Paleontology, American Museum of Natural History, 200 Central Park West, New York, New York 10024, USA; email: jflynn@amnh.org

Cynthia Frasier
Omaha's Henry Doorly Zoo and Aquarium, Department of Conservation Genetics, 3701 South 10th Street, Omaha, Nebraska 68107, USA; email: cynthiaf@omahazoo.com

Karen L. M. Freeman
Madagascar Fauna and Flora Group, BP 442, Toamasina 501, Madagascar; email: karenlmfreeman@hotmail.com

Marco Gamba
Department of Life Sciences and Systems Biology, University of Turin, Via Accademia Albertina 13, 10123 Turin, Italy; email: marco.gamba@unito.it

Jörg U. Ganzhorn
Tierökologie und Naturschutz, Universität Hamburg, Martin-Luther-King-Platz 3, 20146 Hamburg, Germany; email: ganzhorn@uni-hamburg.de

Gerardo García
Chester Zoo, Cedar House, Upton by Chester, Chester CH2 1LH, United Kingdom; email: g.garcia@chesterzoo.org

Charlie J. Gardner
Durrell Institute of Conservation and Ecology, School of Anthropology and Conservation, University of Kent, Canterbury, Kent CT2 7NR, United Kingdom; email: cjamgardner@yahoo.co.uk

Jean-Luc Gattolliat
Museum of Zoology, Palais de Rumine, Place Riponne 6, CH-1005 Lausanne, Switzerland; and Department of Ecology and Evolution, Biophore, University of Lausanne, CH-1015 Lausanne, Switzerland; email: jean-luc.gattolliat@vd.ch

Laurent Gautier
Conservatoire et Jardin botaniques de la Ville de Genève and Laboratoire de Systématique Végétale et Biodiversité de l'Université de Genève, Case Postale 71, 1292 Chambésy/Genève, Switzerland; email: laurent.gautier@ville-ge.ch

Philip-Sebastian Gehring
Faculty of Biology/Biologiedidaktik, University of Bielefeld, Universitätsstraße 25, 33615 Bielefeld, Germany; email: sebastiangehring@web.de

Fabien Génin
AEON, Earth Stewardship Science Research Institute, Nelson Mandela University, Port Elizabeth 6001, South Africa; email: fsgenin@gmail.com

Brian D. Gerber
University of Rhode Island, Department of Natural Resources Science, Kingston, Rhode Island 02881-2018, USA; email: bgerber@uri.edu

Cristina Giacoma
Department of Life Sciences and Systems Biology, University of Turin, Via Accademia Albertina 13, 10123 Turin, Italy; email: cristina.giacoma@unito.it

François-Marie Gibon
CBGP, IRD, CIRAD, INRA, Montpellier SupAgro, Université de Montpellier, Montpellier, France; and Cassagnettes, 12510 Olemps, France; email: fmgibon@laposte.net

Hannah Gilchrist
Blue Ventures Conservation, The Old Library, Trinity Road, Bristol BS2 0NW, United Kingdom; email: hannahgilchrist92@gmail.com

Jessica P. Gillung
Lyman Entomological Museum, McGill University, 21111 Lakeshore Drive, Sainte-Anne-de-Bellevue, Quebec H9X 3V9, Canada; email: jessica.gillung@mcgill.ca

Frank Glaw
Sektion Herpetologie, Zoologische Staatssammlung München, Münchhausenstr. 21, 81247 Munich, Germany; email: glaw@snsb.de

Julian Glos
Animal Ecology and Conservation, Universität Hamburg, Martin-Luther-King-Platz 3, 20146 Hamburg, Germany; email: julian.glos@uni-hamburg.de

Vladimir M. Gnezdilov
Zoological Institute, Russian Academy of Sciences, 1 Universitetskaya Emb., Saint Petersburg 199034, Russia; email: vmgnezdilov@mail.ru, vgnezdilov@zin.ru

Laurie R. Godfrey
Department of Anthropology, 240 Hicks Way, University of Massachusetts, Amherst, Massachusetts 01003, USA; email: lgodfrey@umass.edu

Christopher D. Golden
Department of Nutrition, Harvard T. H. Chan School of Public Health, 665 Huntington Avenue, Building 2, 3rd Floor, Boston, Massachusetts 02115, USA; and Madagascar Health and Environmental Research (MAHERY), Maroantsetra 512, Madagascar; email: golden@hsph.harvard.edu

Yann Gomard
Unité Mixte de Recherche Processus Infectieux en Milieu Insulaire Tropical (UMR PIMIT), Université de La Réunion, CNRS 9192, INSERM 1187, IRD 249, 97490 Sainte-Clotilde, La Réunion, France; email: yann.gomard@gmail.com

Steven M. Goodman
Field Museum of Natural History, 1400 South DuSable Shore Drive, Chicago, Illinois 60605, USA; and Association Vahatra, BP 3972, Antananarivo 101, Madagascar; email: sgoodman@fieldmuseum.org

Morgan Gostel
Botanical Research Institute of Texas, 1700 University Drive, Fort Worth, Texas 76107-3400, USA; email: mgostel@brit.org

Charlotte L. A. Gough
Centre for Ecology and Conservation, College of Life and Environmental Sciences, University of Exeter, Cornwall Campus, Penryn TR10 9EZ, United Kingdom; email: charlie@blueventures.org

Owen Griffiths
BCM Ltd, Senneville, Riviere des Anguilles, 60601, Mauritius; email: owen@bcm.intnet.mu

Richard A. Griffiths
Durrell Institute of Conservation and Ecology, School of Anthropology and Conservation, Marlowe Building, University of Kent, Canterbury CT2 7NR, United Kingdom; email: R.A.Griffiths@kent.ac.uk

Clovis Grinand
Nitidæ, 29 rue Imbert Colomès, 69001 Lyon, France; email: c.grinand@nitidae.org

Charles E. Griswold
Arachnology (Emeritus), California Academy of Sciences, 55 Music Concourse Drive, San Francisco, California 94118, USA; email: cgriswold@calacademy.org

Hélène Guis
Institut Pasteur de Madagascar, BP 1274, Antananarivo 101, Madagascar; email: helene.guis@cirad.fr

Grey T. Gustafson
Department of Ecology and Evolutionary Biology, 1200 Sunnyside Avenue, University of Kansas, Lawrence, Kansas 66045, USA; email: gtgustafson@gmail.com

Jan Hackel
Comparative Plant and Fungal Biology, Royal Botanic Gardens, Kew, Richmond, Surrey TW9 3AE, United Kingdom; email: j.hackel@kew.org

Thomas Haevermans
Institut de Systématique Evolution Biodiversité, Muséum National d'Histoire Naturelle, CNRS, EPHE, UA, SU, 45 rue Buffon, CP 50, 75005 Paris, France; email: thomas.haevermans@mnhn.fr

Jiří Hájek
Department of Entomology, National Museum, Cirkusová 1740, 193 00 Praha 9 - Horní Počernice, Prague, Czech Republic; email: jiri_hajek@nm.cz

Margaret Hanes
Department of Biology, Eastern Michigan University, 401M Mark Jefferson, Ypsilanti, Michigan 48197, USA; email: mkoopma2@emich.edu

Mireille Harimalala
Institut Pasteur of Madagascar, Medical Entomology Unit, BP 1274, Ambatofotsikely, Avaradoha, Antananarivo 101, Madagascar; email: hmireille@pasteur.mg

Martin Hauser
California Department of Food and Agriculture, Plant Pest Diagnostics Branch, 3294 Meadowview Road, Sacramento, California 95832-1448, USA; email: phycus@gmail.com

A.F.A. Hawkins
IUCN, 1630 Connecticut Ave, NW, Suite 300, Washington, DC, 20009, USA; email: afahawkins@gmail.com

Clare E. Hawkins
School of Natural Sciences, University of Tasmania, Hobart, Tasmania 7001, Australia; email: clare.hawkins@utas.edu.au

Terry A. J. Hedderson
Bolus Herbarium, University of Cape Town, Private Bag X3, 7701 Rondebosch, South Africa; email: terry.hedderson@uct.ac.za

Jean-Michel Héraud
Institut Pasteur de Madagascar, BP 1274, Antananarivo 101, Madagascar; email: jean-michel.heraud@pasteur.fr

David G. Herbert
National Museum of Wales, Cathays Park, Cardiff CF10 3NP, United Kingdom; email: phasianella@gmail.com

Johan Hermans
Herbarium, Royal Botanic Gardens, Kew, Richmond, Surrey TW9 3AE, United Kingdom; and Core Facility, Botanical Garden, University of Vienna, Rennweg 14, 1030 Vienna, Austria; email: j.hermans@kew.org

Dominique Hervé
UMR SENS (Savoirs, ENvironnement et Sociétés)–IRD, CIRAD, UPVM–Université Paul-Valéry, Site St-Charles, Route de Mende, 34199 Montpellier Cedex 05, France; email: dominique.herve@ird.fr

Wilbert L. A. Hetterscheid
National Tree Museum Gimborn, Velperengh 13, 3941 BZ Doorn, The Netherlands; email: hetter@xs4all.nl

Axel O. G. Hoarau
Unité Mixte de Recherche Processus Infectieux en Milieu Insulaire Tropical (UMR PIMIT), Université de La Réunion, CNRS 9192, INSERM 1187, IRD 249, 97490 Sainte-Clotilde, La Réunion, France; email: axel.hoarau@univ-reunion.fr

Cynthia Hong-Wa
Claude E. Phillips Herbarium, Delaware State University, Dover, Delaware 19901, USA; email: chwa@desu.edu

Martine Hossaert-McKey
Centre d'Ecologie Fonctionnelle et Evolutive (CEFE), UMR 5175, CNRS, Université Paul-Valéry Montpellier, EPHE, 1919 Route de Mende, 34293 Montpellier Cedex 05, France; email: Martine.HOSSAERT@cnrs-dir.fr

Melanie-Jayne Howes
Royal Botanic Gardens, Kew, Richmond, Surrey TW9 3AE, United Kingdom; and Institute of Pharmaceutical Science, Faculty of Life Sciences and Medicine, King's College, London SE1 9NH, United Kingdon; email: M.Howes@kew.org

Matthew Huber
Department of Earth, Atmospheric, and Planetary Sciences, Purdue University, West Lafayette, Indiana 47907, USA; email: huberm@purdue.edu

Thierry Huck
UnivBrest, CNRS, IFREMER, IRD, Laboratoire d'Océanographie Physique et Spatiale (LOPS), UMR 6523, IUEM, 29280 Plouzané, France; email: thierry.huck@univ-brest.fr

Sylvain Hugel
Institut des Neurosciences Cellulaires et Intégratives, CNRS, Université de Strasbourg, 8, allée du Général Rouvillois, F-67000 Strasbourg, France; email: hugels@inci-cnrs.unistra.fr

Carl R. Hutter
Museum of Natural Sciences and Department of Biological Sciences, Louisiana State University, Baton Rouge, Louisiana 70803, USA; email: carl.hutter@gmail.com

Audrey Jaeger
UMR ENTROPIE, UR CNRS IRD IFREMER UNC, Faculté des Sciences et Technologies, Université de la Réunion, 15, avenue René Cassin - CS 92003, 97744 Saint Denis Cedex 9, La Réunion, France; email: audrey.jaeger@univ-reunion.fr

Sharon A. Jansa
Department of Ecology, Evolution, and Behavior, and Bell Museum, University of Minnesota, 1479 Gortner Avenue, Saint Paul, Minnesota 55108, USA; email: jansa003@umn.edu

Vololoniaina Jeannoda
Mention Biologie et Ecologie Végétales, Université d'Antananarivo, BP 906, Antananarivo 101, Madagascar; email: vololoniaina.jeannoda@gmail.com

Paula D. Jenkins
Vertebrates Division, Department of Life Sciences, The Natural History Museum, Cromwell Road, London SW7 5BD, United Kingdom; email: P.Jenkins@nhm.ac.uk

Richard K. B. Jenkins
IUCN Global Species Programme, 219c Huntingdon Road, Cambridge CB3 0DL, United Kingdom; email: rkbjenkins@gmail.com

Pedro Jiménez-Mejías
Departamento de Biología (Botánica), Facultad de Ciencias Biológicas, Universidad Autónoma de Madrid, C. Darwin, 2, 28049 Madrid, Spain; and Centro de Investigación en Biodiversidad y Cambio Global (CIBC-UAM), Universidad Autónoma de Madrid, 28049 Madrid, Spain; email: pedro.jimenez@uam.es

Léa Joffrin
Unité Mixte de Recherche Processus Infectieux en Milieu Insulaire Tropical (UMR PIMIT), Université de La Réunion, CNRS 9192, INSERM 1187, IRD 249, 97490 Sainte-Clotilde, La Réunion, France; email: lea.joffrin@univ-reunion.fr

Kevin Johnson
Amphibian Ark, 12101 Johnny Cake Ridge Road, Apple Valley, Minnesota 55124-8151, USA; email: kevinj@amphibianark.org

Steig E. Johnson
Department of Anthropology and Archaeology, University of Calgary, 2500 University Drive NW, Calgary, Alberta T2N 1N4, Canada; email: steig.johnson@ucalgary.ca

Julia P. G. Jones
School of Natural Sciences, Thoday Building, Deniol Road, Bangor University, Gwynedd LL57 2UW, United Kingdom; email: julia.jones@bangor.ac.uk

Trevor Gareth Jones
Department of Forest Resources Management, Faculty of Forestry, 2424 Main Mall, Vancouver, British Columbia V6T 1Z4, Canada; email: trevor@blueventures.org

William L. Jungers
Association Vahatra, BP 3972, Antananarivo 101, Madagascar; email: williamjungers@gmail.com

Mark R. Jury
Geography Department, University of Zululand, KwaDlangezwa, 3886, South Africa; and Physics Department, University of Puerto Rico, Mayaguez, Puerto Rico 00681, USA; email: mark.jury@upr.edu

Kent Kainulainen
Gothenburg Botanical Garden, Carl Skottbergs Gata 22A, SE-41319 Gothenburg, Sweden; email: kent.kainulainen@vgregion.se

Peter M. Kappeler
Behavioral Ecology and Sociobiology Unit, German Primate Center (DPZ) Kellnerweg 4, 37077 Göttingen, Germany; email: pkappel@gwdg.de

Nisa Karimi
University of Wisconsin–Madison, Department of Botany, 430 Lincoln Drive, Madison, Wisconsin 53706, USA; email: nkarimi@wisc.edu

Kristopher B. Karsten
California Lutheran University, 60 West Olsen Road #3700, Thousand Oaks, California 91360, USA; email: karsten@callutheran.edu

Frankie J. Kerridge
School of Sport and Biological Sciences, University of Bolton, Queen Street, Farnworth, Greater Manchester BL4 7DX, United Kingdom; email: F.Kerridge@bolton.ac.uk

Carrie A. Kiel
California Botanic Garden, 1500 North College Avenue, Claremont, California 91711, USA; email: ckiel@rsabg.org

Jeremy J. Kiszka
Department of Biological Sciences, Coastlines and Oceans Division, Institute of Environment, Florida International University, 3000 NE 151st Street, North Miami, Florida 33181, USA; email: jkiszka@fiu.edu

Finn Kjellberg
Centre d'Ecologie Fonctionnelle et Evolutive (CEFE), UMR 5175, CNRS, Université de Montpellier, Université Paul-Valéry Montpellier, EPHE, 1919 Route de Mende, 34293 Montpellier Cedex 05, France; email: Finn.KJELLBERG@cefe.cnrs.fr

Hans Klompen
Acarology Laboratory, Ohio State University, 1315 Kinnear Road, Columbus, Ohio 43212, USA; email: klompen.1@osu.edu

Amyot F. Kofoky
Association Vahatra, BP 3972, Antananarivo 101, Madagascar; Current address: DREDD Haute Matsiatra, Isaha, Fianarantsoa 301, Madagascar; email: amyotkof@gmail.com

Jörn Köhler
Hessisches Landesmuseum Darmstadt, Friedensplatz 1, 64283 Darmstadt, Germany; email: joern.koehler@hlmd.de

Randall A. Kramer
Nicholas School of the Environment, 9 Circuit Drive, Duke Box 90328, Duke University, Durham, North Carolina 27708, USA; and Duke Global Health Institute, Duke University, Trent Hall, Trent Drive, Durham, North Carolina 27708, USA; email: kramer@duke.edu

David W. Krause
Department of Earth Sciences, Denver Museum of Nature and Science, 2001 Colorado Boulevard, Denver, Colorado 80205; and Department of Anatomical Sciences, Stony Brook University, Stony Brook, New York 11794, USA; email: David.Krause@dmns.org

Sindu M. Krishnankutty
Invaio Sciences, 75 Moulton Street, Cambridge, Massachusetts 02138, USA; email: oriolealis@gmail.com

Gerald Kuchling
School of Biological Sciences, University of Western Australia, 35 Stirling Highway, Crawley, Western Australia 6009, Australia; email: gerald.kuchling@uwa.edu.au

Christian A. Kull
Institut de Géographie et Durabilité, Université de Lausanne, 1015 Lausanne, Switzerland; email: christian.kull@unil.ch

Vanesse Labeyrie
UMR SENS (Savoirs, ENvironnement et Sociétés)–CIRAD, IRD, UPVM–CIRAD, F-34398, Montpellier, France; email: vanesse.labeyrie@cirad.fr

Marc Lacroix
4c rue Danièle Casanova, F26100 Romans sur Isère, France; email: hannetons@orange.fr

Michel Omer Laivao
Ministère de l'Environnement, de l'Ecologie et des Forêts, BP 571, Antananarivo 101, Madagascar; email: laivao2002@yahoo.fr

Olivier Langrand
Critical Ecosystem Partnership Fund (CEPF), 2011 Crystal Drive, Suite 600, Arlington, Virginia 22202, USA; email: olangrand@cepf.net

Sophie Laran
Observatoire Pelagis, UMS 3462–La Rochelle Université, CNRS, 5 allée de l'Océan, 17000, La Rochelle, France; email: slaran@univ-lr.fr

Isabel Larridon
Royal Botanic Gardens, Kew, Richmond, Surrey TW9 3AE, United Kingdom; and Systematic and Evolutionary Botany Lab, Department of Biology, Ghent University, K. L. Ledeganckstraat 35, 9000 Ghent, Belgium; email: i.larridon@kew.org

Richard R. Lawler
71 Alumnae Drive, MSC 7501, Harrisonburg, Virginia 22807, USA; email: lawler.jmu@gmail.com

Abigail Leadbeater
Blue Ventures Conservation, The Old Library, Trinity Road, Bristol BS2 0NW, United Kingdom; email: abigail@blueventures.org

Camille Lebarbenchon
Unité Mixte de Recherche Processus Infectieux en Milieu Insulaire Tropical (UMR PIMIT), Université de La Réunion, CNRS 9192, INSERM 1187, IRD 249, 97490 Sainte-Clotilde, La Réunion, France; email: camille.lebarbenchon@univ-reunion.fr

Matthieu Le Corre
UMR ENTROPIE, UR CNRS IRD IFREMER UNC, Faculté des Sciences et Technologies, Université de la Réunion, 15, avenue René Cassin–CS 92003, 97744 Saint Denis Cedex 9, La Réunion, France; email: lecorre@univ-reunion.fr

Ruth H. Leeney
Kilrane, Rosslare Harbour, County Wexford, Ireland; email: ruth.leeney@gmail.com

David C. Lees
Department of Life Sciences, The Natural History Museum, Cromwell Road, London SW7 5BD, United Kingdom; email: davil@nhm.ac.uk, dclees@gmail.com

Gilbert Le Goff
MIVEGEC Unit, Université de Montpellier, IRD, CNRS, 34394 Montpellier, France; email: gilbert.legoff@ird.fr

Shawn M. Lehman
Department of Anthropology, University of Toronto, Toronto, Ontario M5S 2S2, Canada; email: shawn.lehman@utoronto.ca

Caroline E. R. Lehmann
Tropical Diversity, Royal Botanic Garden Edinburgh, 20a Inverleith Row, Edinburgh EH3 5LR, United Kingdom; and School of GeoSciences, University of Edinburgh, Drummond Street, Edinburgh EH8 9XP, United Kingdom; email: clehmann@rbge.org.uk

Richard M. Lehtinen
Department of Biology, College of Wooster, 931 College Mall, Wooster, Ohio 44691, USA; email: rlehtinen@wooster.edu

Jean-Michel Leong Pock Tsy
Centre National des Recherche Appliquée au Développement Rural (FOFIFA), Département de Recherche Forestière et Gestion des Ressources Naturelles, BP 904, Antananarivo 101, Madagascar; email: iharana_jm@yahoo.fr

Rokiman Letsara
Flora Department, Parc Botanique et Zoologique de Tsimbazaza, BP 4096, Antananarivo 101, Madagascar; email: letsararo@yahoo.com

Gwilym P. Lewis
Comparative Plant and Fungal Biology Department, Royal Botanic Gardens, Kew, Richmond, Surrey TW9 3AE, United Kingdom; email: g.lewis@kew.org

Richard E. Lewis
Durrell Wildlife Conservation Trust, BP 8511, Antananarivo 101, Madagascar; email: richard.lewis@durrell.org

Sigrid Liede-Schumann
Department of Plant Systematics, University of Bayreuth, Universitätsstrasse 30, 95440 Bayreuth, Germany; email: sigrid.Liede@uni-bayreuth.de

Christine Lippai
CL Consulting, 10 Tomfields, Wood Lane, Stoke-on-Trent ST7 8PJ, United Kingdom; email: christine.lippai@gmail.com

Stefan D. Löfstrand
Department of Botany and Biodiversity Research, University of Vienna, Rennweg 14, AT-1030 Vienna, Austria; email: stefan.loefstrand@univie.ac.at

Paul V. Loiselle
374 Raleigh Road, Rahway, New Jersey 78065, USA; email: pvl2413@aol.com

Edward E. Louis Jr.
Omaha's Henry Doorly Zoo and Aquarium, Conservation Genetics Department, 3701 South 10th Street, Omaha, Nebraska 68107, USA; email: edlo@omahazoo.com, kelynews1@yahoo.com

Wilson R. Lourenço
Muséum National d'Histoire Naturelle, Sorbonne Universités, Institut de Systématique, Evolution et Biodiversité (ISYEB), UMR7205-CNRS, MNHN, UPMC, EPHE, CP 53, 57 rue Cuvier, 75005 Paris, France; email: wilson.lourenco@mnhn.fr

Porter P. Lowry II
Missouri Botanical Garden, 4344 Shaw Boulevard, Saint Louis, Missouri 63110, USA; and Institut de Systématique, Evolution et Biodiversité (ISYEB), Muséum National d'Histoire Naturelle, Centre National de la Recherche Scientifique, Sorbonne Université, Ecole Pratique des Hautes Etudes, Université des Antilles, C.P. 39, 57 rue Cuvier, 75005 Paris, France; email: Pete.Lowry@mobot.org

Cyrille Maharombaka
Ecole Doctorale Ecosystèmes Naturels, Université de Mahajanga, Mahajanga 401, Madagascar; email: maharocyrille@gmail.com.

Fernando Mercado Malabet
Department of Anthropology, University of Toronto, Toronto, Ontario M5S 2S2, Canada; email: fernando.mercadomalabet@mail.utoronto.ca

Nadiah V. Manjato
Missouri Botanical Garden, Madagascar Research and Conservation Program, BP 3391, Antananarivo 101, Madagascar; email: nadiah.manjato@mobot.mg

Michaël Manuel
Institut de Systématique, Evolution et Biodiversité (ISYEB), UMR 7205, Sorbonne Université, MNHN, CNRS, EPHE, UA, Case 05, 7 quai St Bernard, 75005 Paris, France; email: michael.manuel@upmc.fr

Juliette Mariel
UMR SENS (Savoirs, ENvironnement et Sociétés)–CIRAD, IRD, UPVM–CIRAD, F-34398, Montpellier, France; email: juliette.mariel@cirad.fr

Matthias Markolf
Department Sociobiology/Anthropology, University of Göttingen, Kellnerweg 6, 37077 Göttingen, Germany; email: matthias.markolf@uni-goettingen.de

Lovanomenjanahary Marline
Department of Biological Sciences, University of Cape Town, Private Bag X3, 7701 Rondebosch, South Africa; Current address: Association Vahatra, BP 3972, Antananarivo 101, Madagascar; Kew Madagascar Conservation Centre, Lot II J 131 B, Ambodivoanjo Ivandry, Antananarivo 101, Madagascar; and Gothenburg Global Biodiversity Center, University of Gothenburg, 413 19 Gothenburg, Sweden; email: marlinelova@gmail.com

José Ignacio Márquez-Corro
Departamento de Biología Molecular e Ingeniería Bioquímica, Universidad Pablo de Olavide, Carretera de Utrera km 1, ES-41013 Seville, Spain; email: jimarcorr@gmail.com

Santiago Martín-Bravo
Departamento de Biología Molecular e Ingeniería Bioquímica, Universidad Pablo de Olavide, Carretera de Utrera km 1, ES-41013 Seville, Spain; email: smarbra@upo.es

Judith C. Masters
Department of Zoology and Entomology, University of Fort Hare, Alice 5700, South Africa; and Department of Botany and Zoology, Stellenbosch University, Matieland 7602, South Africa; email: jdthmasters@gmail.com

Guido Mathieu
Zwemdoklei 64, 2390 Brasschaat, Belgium; email: guido.mathieu@taxa.be

Patrick Mavingui
Unité Mixte de Recherche Processus Infectieux en Milieu Insulaire Tropical (UMR PIMIT), Université de La Réunion, CNRS 9192, INSERM 1187, IRD 249, 97490 Sainte-Clotilde, La Réunion, France; email: patrick.mavingui@cnrs.fr

Paul P. A. Mazza
Department of Earth Sciences, University of Florence, Via La Pira 4, 50121, Florence, Italy; email: paul.mazza@unifi.it

Anasvaler Mbelomanana
Institut Halieutique et des Sciences Marines, Université de Toliara, Rue Dr. Rabesandratana, BP 141, Toliara 601, Madagascar; and Faculté des Sciences, Université d'Antsiranana, Lazaret Sud, Antsiranana 201, Madagascar; email: mb2anasvaler@gmail.com

Lucinda McDade
California Botanic Garden, 1500 North College Avenue, Claremont, California 91711, USA; email: lmcdade@rsabg.org

Doyle McKey
Centre d'Ecologie Fonctionnelle et Evolutive (CEFE), UMR 5175, CNRS, Université de Montpellier, Université Paul-Valéry Montpellier, EPHE, 1919 Route de Mende, 34293 Montpellier Cedex 05, France; email: Doyle.MCKEY@cefe.cnrs.fr

Guntram G. Meier
InGrip-Consulting and Animal Control, Hausburgstrasse 24, 10249 Berlin, Germany; email: ggm@ingrip.com

Emily Mertz
Leadership and Integrative Studies, Arizona State University, Tempe, Arizona 85281, USA; email: emmertz@asu.edu

Longondraza Miaretsoa
Department of Life Sciences and Systems Biology, University of Turin, Via Accademia Albertina 13, 10123 Turin, Italy; email: longondraza.miaretsoa@unito.it

Margot Michaud
Institut de Systématique, Evolution et Biodiversité (ISYEB), Muséum National d'Histoire Naturelle, CNRS, SU, EPHE, UA; CP 51, 57 rue Cuvier, 75231 Paris Cedex 05, France; email: m.mar33@hotmail.fr

James S. Miller
Missouri Botanical Garden, 4434 Shaw Boulevard, Saint Louis, Missouri 63110, USA; email: james.miller@mobot.org

Joël Minet
Institut de Systématique, Evolution et Biodiversité (ISYEB), Muséum National d'Histoire Naturelle, 57 rue Cuvier, CP 50 (Entomologie) 75005 Paris, France; email: joel.minet@mnhn.fr

Aurélien Miralles
Institut de Systématique, Evolution et Biodiversité (ISYEB), Muséum National d'Histoire Naturelle, 25 rue Cuvier, 75005 Paris, France; email: miralles.skink@gmail.com

Jiří Moravec
Sadová 336/21, 679 04 Czech Republic; email: jirmor@quick.cz

Joseph A. Morton
Comparative Plant and Fungal Biology, Royal Botanic Gardens, Kew, Richmond, Surrey TW9 3AE, United Kingdom; and Queen Mary University of London, Mile End Road, London E1 4NS, United Kingdom; email: j.morton@kew.org

A. Muthama Muasya
Bolus Herbarium, University of Cape Town, Private Bag X3, Rondebosch, 7701 Cape Town, South Africa; email: Muthama.muasya@uct.ac.za

Raoul A. Mulder
School of BioSciences, University of Melbourne, Victoria 3010, Australia; email: r.mulder@unimelb.edu.au

Asia Murphy
Department of Ecosystem Science and Management, Huck Institutes of the Life Sciences, Pennsylvania State University, University Park, Pennsylvania 16802, USA; email: aum432@psu.edu

Thomas Mutschler
Panoramaweg 16, 9533 Kirchberg SG, Switzerland; email: t.mutschler@bluewin.ch

Yamama Naciri
Conservatoire et Jardin botaniques de la Ville de Genève and Laboratoire de Systématique Végétale et Biodiversité de

l'Université de Genève, Case Postale 71, 1292 Chambésy/Genève, Switzerland; email: yamama.naciri@ville-ge.ch

Serge H. Ndriantsoa
Amphibian Survival Alliance, c/o Durrell Wildlife Conservation Trust–Madagascar Programme, BP 8511, Antananarivo 101, Madagascar; email: sndriantsoa@amphibians.org

Heok Hee Ng
c/o Lee Kong Chian Natural History Museum, National University of Singapore, 2 Conservatory Drive, Singapore 117377, Malaysia; email: heokhee.ng@gmail.com

Daniel L. Nickrent
Plant Biology Program, School of Biological Sciences, Southern Illinois University, Carbondale, Illinois 62901, USA; email: nickrent@plant.siu.edu

†Martin E. Nicoll
WWF Madagascar Country Office, BP 738, Antananarivo 101, Madagascar

Jeanne Aimée Norosoarinaivo
LVDI International, 941 Camino del Arroyo Drive, San Marcos, California 92078, USA; and Mention Zoologie et Biodiversité Animale, Université d'Antananarivo, BP 906, Antananarivo 101, Madagascar; email: norosoa@lvdiinternational.org

Ivan Norscia
Department of Life Sciences and Systems Biology, University of Turin, Via Accademia Albertina 13, 10123, Turin, Italy; email: ivan.norscia@unito.it

Marie Nourtier
Nitidæ, 29 rue Imbert Colomès, 69001 Lyon, France; email: m.nourtier@nitidae.org

Charles L. Nunn
Department of Evolutionary Anthropology, Duke University, Biological Sciences Building, Science Drive, Durham, North Carolina 27708, USA; and Duke Global Health Institute, Duke University, Trent Hall, Trent Drive, Durham, North Carolina 27708, USA; email: clnunn@duke.edu

Jenny Oates
Blue Ventures Conservation, The Old Library, Trinity Road, Bristol BS2 0NW, United Kingdom; email: jenny.oates@blueventures.org

Patrick M. O'Connor
Department of Biomedical Sciences, Ohio University Heritage College of Osteopathic Medicine, Ohio University, Athens, Ohio 45701; and Ohio Center for Ecology and Evolutionary Studies, Irvine Hall, Ohio University, Athens, Ohio 45701, USA; email: oconnorp@ohio.edu

Ryszard Z. Oleksy
Ecosystem Restoration Alliance, Indian Ocean, No. 7 Site and Services, Circonstance, Saint-Pierre, 81402, Mauritius; email: roleksy@eraindianocean.org

Marie-Marie Olive
Unité Mixte de Recherche Maladies Infectieuses et Vecteurs: Ecologie, Génétique, Evolution et Contrôle (UMR MIVEGEC), Université de Montpellier, IRD 224, CNRS 5290, 911 Avenue Agropolis, 34394 Montpellier, France; email: marie-marie.olive@cirad.fr

Link E. Olson
University of Alaska Museum, 1962 Yukon Drive, Fairbanks, Alaska 99775, USA; email: link.olson@alaska.edu

Deborah J. Overdorff
Saint Francis School, 300 East Huntland Drive, Austin, Texas 78752, USA; email: djoverdorff@gmail.com

Maciej Pabijan
Department of Comparative Anatomy, Institute of Zoology and Biomedical Research, Jagiellonian University, ul Gronostajowa 9, 30-387 Kraków, Poland; email: maciej.pabijan@uj.edu.pl

Miguel Pedrono
CIRAD, Campus International de Baillarguet, 34398 Montpellier, France; email: miguel.pedrono@cirad.fr

Romain Pellen
AEON, Earth Stewardship Science Research Institute, Nelson Mandela University, Port Elizabeth 6001, South Africa; email: romin.pellen@gmail.com

George Perry
Departments of Anthropology and Biology, Huck Institutes of the Life Sciences, Pennsylvania State University, Carpenter Building, University Park, Pennsylvania 16802, USA; email: ghp3@psu.edu

Leanne N. Phelps
Tropical Diversity, Royal Botanic Garden Edinburgh, 20a Inverleith Row, Edinburgh EH3 5LR, United Kingdom; and School of GeoSciences, University of Edinburgh, Drummond Street, Edinburgh EH8 9XP, United Kingdom; email: LeanneNPhelps@gmail.com

Peter B. Phillipson
Missouri Botanical Garden, 4344 Shaw Boulevard, Saint Louis, Missouri 63110, USA; and Institut de Systématique, Evolution et Biodiversité (ISYEB), Muséum National d'Histoire Naturelle, Centre National de la Recherche Scientifique, Sorbonne Université, Ecole Pratique des Hautes Etudes, Université des Antilles, C.P. 39, 57 rue Cuvier, 75005 Paris, France; email: Peter.Phillipson@mobot.org

Simon J. Pierce
Marine Megafauna Foundation, 11260 Donner Pass Road, Truckee, California 96161, USA; email: simon@marinemegafauna.org

Gregory M. Plunkett
New York Botanical Garden, 2900 Southern Boulevard, Bronx, New York 10458-5126, USA; email: gplunkett@nybg.org

Adrian C. Pont
Oxford University Museum of Natural History, Parks Road, Oxford OX1 3PW, United Kingdom; email: muscidman2@gmail.com

Joyce Powzyk
Wesleyan University, Biology Department, 52 Lawn Avenue, Middletown, Connecticut 06459, USA; email: jpowzyk@wesleyan.edu

David Prötzel
Sektion Herpetologie, Zoologische Staatssammlung München, Münchhausenstr. 21, 81247 Munich, Germany; email: david.proetzel@mail.de

Richard O. Prum
Department of Ecology and Evolutionary Biology, and Peabody Museum of Natural History, Yale University, New Haven, Connecticut 06511, USA; email: richard.prum@yale.edu

Gabriel Costa Queiroz
Museu Nacional, Department of Entomology, Quinta da Boa Vista s/no., São Cristóvão, Rio de Janeiro, Brazil, 20940-040; email: gabriel_cq@yahoo.com.br

Jérôme Queste
Centre de Coopération Internationale en Recherche Agronomique pour le Développement, Ampandrianomby, BP 853, Antananarivo 101, Madagascar; email: jerome.queste@cirad.fr

Marina Rabarimanarivo
Missouri Botanical Garden, Research and Conservation Program Madagascar, BP 3391, Antananarivo 101, Madagascar; email: marina.rabarimanarivo@mobot.mg

Rivo Rabarisoa
Asity Madagascar, BP 1074, Antananarivo 101, Madagascar; email: rivo.rabarisoa@birdlife-mada.org

Harison Rabarison
Mention Biologie et Ecologie Végétale, Université d'Antananarivo, BP 906, Antananarivo 101, Madagascar; email: rabarisonrh@yahoo.fr

Jeanneney Rabearivony
Faculté des Sciences, Université d'Antsiranana, Antsiranana 201, Madagascar; email: r.jeanneney@gmail.com

David Rabehevitra
Kew Madagascar Conservation Centre, Lot II J 131 B, Ambodivoanjo Ivandry, Antananarivo 101, Madagascar; email: d.rabehevitra@kew.org

H. Aina Rabemananjara
Institut Pasteur de Madagascar, BP 1274, Antananarivo 101, Madagascar; email: harinirina@pasteur.mg

Falitiana C. E. Rabemananjara
Mention Zoologie et Biodiversité Animale, Université d'Antananarivo, BP 906, Antananarivo 101, Madagascar; email: frabemnjr@gmail.com

Jean Clarck Neloni Rabenandrasana
Conservation International, BP 5178, II W 27 D rue Vittori Francois, Ankorahotra, Antananarivo 101, Madagascar; email: crabenandrasana@conservation.org

Nirhy H. C. Rabibisoa
Technologies et de l'Environnement, Université de Mahajanga, Faculté des Sciences, Mahajanga 401, Madagascar; email: nhcrabibisoa@gmail.com

Marina Rabineau
CNRS, UnivBrest, Université Bretagne-Sud, Laboratoire Géosciences Océan (LGO), UMR 6538, IUEM, F-29280 Plouzané, France; email: marina.rabineau@univ-brest.fr

Paul A. Racey
Centre for Ecology and Conservation, University of Exeter, Penryn, Cornwall TR10 9FE, United Kingdom; email: p.a.racey@exeter.ac.uk

Christinah J. H. Radafiarimanana
Mention Zoologie et Biodiversité Animale, Université d'Antananarivo, BP 906, Antananarivo 101, Madagascar; email: tinah.ninie@yahoo.fr

Ute Radespiel
Institute of Zoology, University of Veterinary Medicine Hannover, Buenteweg 17, 30559 Hannover, Germany; email: ute.radespiel@tiho-hannover.de

Simon Rafanomezantsoa
WWF Madagascar Country Office, BP 738, Antananarivo 101, Madagascar; email: srafanomezantsoa@wwf.mg

Verohanitra M. Rafidison
Mention Biologie et Ecologie Végétales, Université d'Antananarivo, BP 906, Antananarivo 101, Madagascar; email: verohani@yahoo.fr

Jeannie Raharimampionona
Missouri Botanical Garden, Madagascar Research and Conservation Program, BP 3391, Antananarivo 101, Madagascar; email: jeannie.raharimampionona@mobot.mg

Soanandrasana Rahelinirina
Institut Pasteur de Madagascar, BP 1274 Ambatofotsikely, Antananarivo 101, Madagascar; email: rahelinirina@pasteur.mg

Marie Jeanne Raherilalao
Mention Zoologie et Biodiversité Animale, Université d'Antananarivo, BP 906, Antananarivo 101, Madagascar; and Association Vahatra, BP 3972, Antananarivo 101, Madagascar; email: jraherilalao@gmail.com

Mihanta A. F. Raholdina
Mention Zoologie et Biodiversité Animale, Université d'Antananarivo, BP 906, Antananarivo 101, Madagascar; email: poushy25@yahoo.fr

Mamy Tiana Rajaonah
Royal Botanic Gardens, Kew, Richmond, Surrey TW9 3AE, United Kingdom; and Kew Madagascar Conservation Centre, Lot II J 131 B, Ambodivoanjo Ivandry, Antananarivo 101, Madagascar; email: mrajaonah.rbgkew@moov.mg

Landy Rajaovelona
Kew Madagascar Conservation Centre, Lot II J 131 B, Ambodivoanjo Ivandry, Antananarivo 101, Madagascar; email: lrajaovelona.rbgkew@moov.mg

Vonjison Rakotoarimanana
Laboratoire de Botanique, Mention Biologie et Ecologie Végétales, Université d'Antananarivo, BP 906, Antananarivo 101, Madagascar; email: vonjison@yahoo.fr

Mijoro Rakotoarinivo
Mention Biologie et Ecologie Végétales, Université d'Antananarivo, BP 906, Antananarivo 101, Madagascar; email: rakotoarinivo@outlook.com

Jean-Aimé Rakotoarisoa
Cité des Professeurs, Résidence 11, Manakambahiny, Antananarivo 101, Madagascar; and 8 Place Rosa Parks, 44000 Nantes, France; email: jarakoto@gmail.com

Justin Claude Rakotoarisoa
Association Mitsinjo, Andasibe 514, Madagascar; email: babakotokely@gmail.com

Solofo Rakotoarisoa
Kew Madagascar Conservation Centre, Lot II J 131 B, Ambodivoanjo Ivandry, Antananarivo 101, Madagascar; email: s.rakotoarisoa@kew.org

Andolalao Rakotoarison
Mention Zoologie et Biodiversité Animale, Université d'Antananarivo, BP 906, Antananarivo 101, Madagascar; email: andomailaka@gmail.com

Feno Rakotoarison
Royal Botanic Gardens, Kew, Richmond, Surrey TW9 3AE, United Kingdom; and Kew Madagascar Conservation Centre, Tanambao Mission, Ambanja 203, Madagascar; email: frakotoarison.rbgkew@moov.mg

Nivo H. Rakotoarivelo
Missouri Botanical Garden, Madagascar Research and Conservation Program, BP 3391, Antananarivo 101, Madagascar; email: nivo.rakotoarivelo@mobot.mg

Fortunat Rakotoarivony
Missouri Botanical Garden, Madagascar Research and Conservation Program, BP 3391, Antananarivo 101, Madagascar; email: fortunat.rakotoarivony@mobot.mg

Domoina Rakotomalala
WWF Madagascar Country Office, BP 738, Antananarivo 101, Madagascar; email: drakotomalala@wwf.mg

Nantenaina H. Rakotomalala
Kew Madagascar Conservation Centre, Lot II J 131 B, Ambodivoanjo Ivandry, Antananarivo 101, Madagascar; email: n.rakotomalala@kew.org

Tsanta F. Rakotonanahary
Amphibian Survival Alliance, c/o Durrell Wildlife Conservation Trust–Madagascar Programme, BP 8511, Antananarivo 101, Madagascar; email: trakotonanahary@amphibians.org

O. Sarobidy Rakotonarivo
Ecole Supérieure des Sciences Agronomiques, Université d'Antananarivo, BP 175, Antananarivo 101, Madagascar; email: sarobidy.rakotonarivo@gmail.com

Rivontsoa A. Rakotonasolo
Kunming Institute of Botany, Chinese Academy of Sciences, Kunming, Yunnan 650201, China; and Kew Madagascar Conservation Centre, Lot II J 131 B, Ambodivoanjo Ivandry, Antananarivo 101, Madagascar; email: andry_bol6@yahoo.fr

Eddie F. Rakotondrasoa
Madagasikara Voakajy, BP 5181, Antananarivo 101, Madagascar; email: rakotoedds1@gmail.com

Herivololona M. Rakotondratsimba
Association Vahatra, BP 3972, Antananarivo 101, Madagascar; email: rakobola@yahoo.fr

Jeannin Nicolas Rakotondrazandry
Ecole Doctorale des Ecosystèmes Naturels, Université de Mahajanga, 5 rue Georges V, Immeuble KAKAL, BP 652, Mahajanga 401, Madagascar; email: jeannin.n@yahoo.com

Alain J. V. Rakotondrina
Madagasikara Voakajy, BP 5181, Antananarivo 101, Madagascar; email: alainrakoto@mvoakajy.mg

Nivohenintsoa Rakotonirina
Missouri Botanical Garden, Research and Conservation Program Madagascar, BP 3391, Antananarivo 101, Madagascar; email: nivo.rakotonirina@mobot.mg

Bakoliarisoa Rakotozafy
Domaine des Sciences et Technologies, Mention Bassins Sédimentaires, Evolution, Conservation, Université d'Antananarivo, BP 906, Antananarivo 101, Madagascar; email: koli12bako@gmail.com

Fidimala B. Ralainasolo
Durrell Wildlife Conservation Trust, BP 8511, Antananarivo 101, Madagascar; email: fidy.ralainasolo@durrell.org

Hélène Ralimanana
Kew Madagascar Conservation Centre, Lot II J 131 B, Ambodivoanjo Ivandry, Antananarivo 101, Madagascar; email: h.ralimanana@kew.org, hralimanana.rbgkew@moov.mg

Mahefatiana Ralisata
Madagasikara Voakajy, BP 5181, Antananarivo 101, Madagascar; Current address: Ny Tanintsika, Près Lot 089/3606-02 Ivory, Fianarantsoa 301, Madagascar; email: mahefatiana@gmail.com

Andriamirado Tahina Ramahandrison
Mention Biologie et Ecologie Végétales, Université d'Antananarivo, BP 906, Antananarivo 101, Madagascar; email: mirad.95@gmail.com

Veronarindra Ramananjato
Mention Zoologie et Biodiversité Animale, Université d'Antananarivo, BP 906, Antananarivo 101, Madagascar; email: vero.narindra@gmail.com

Ralph Ranoasy Ramanankavana
Conservation International, Bâtiment MNP, Rez de chaussée Antsororokavo, Fianarantsoa 301, Madagascar; email: rranoasy@conservation.org

Beza Ramasindrazana
Institut Pasteur de Madagascar, BP 1274 Ambatofotsikely, Antananarivo 101; and Domaine Sciences et Technologie, Université d'Antananarivo, BP 906, Antananarivo 101, Madagascar; email: ramasindrazana@gmail.com, rbeza@pasteur.mg

Robert Ramiarison
30 Ewing Drive, Romsey, Victoria 3010, Australia; email: yalymg@yahoo.com.au

Malcolm S. Ramsay
Department of Anthropology, University of Toronto, Toronto, Ontario M5S 2S2, Canada; email: malcolm.ramsay@mail.utoronto.ca

Angelo Ramy
Durrell Wildlife Conservation Trust, BP 8511, Antananarivo 101, Madagascar; email: angelo.ramy@durrell.org

Hafaliana C. Ranaivoson
Institut Pasteur de Madagascar, BP 1274, Antananarivo 101, Madagascar; email: gammarinema@gmail.com

Ny Sanda Ranaivoson
Time+Tide Foundation, Miavana, 25 rue Colbert, Place Kabary, BP 310, Antsiranana 201, Madagascar; email: nysanda@miavana.com

Hery Lisy Ranarijaona
Ecole Doctorale Ecosystèmes Naturels, Université de Mahajanga, Mahajanga 401, Madagascar; email: hranarijaona@gmail.com

Tolotra Ranarilalatiana
Département d'Entomologie, Université d'Antananarivo, BP 906, Antananarivo 101, Madagascar; email: t.ranarilalatiana@gmail.com

Heritiana Ranarivelo
California Academy of Sciences, Institute for Biodiversity Science and Sustainability, Department of Botany, 55 Music Concourse Drive, Golden Gate Park, San Francisco, California 94118-4599, USA; email: hranarivelo@calacademy.org

Hervet J. Randriamady
Madagascar Health and Environmental Research (MAHERY), Maroantsetra 512, Madagascar; email: hervetjoseph@gmail.com

Josoa R. Randriamalala
Département des Eaux et Forêts, Ecole Supérieure des Sciences Agronomiques, BP 175, Université d'Antananarivo, Antananarivo 101, Madagascar; email: ramarolanonana@gmail.com

Herizo Randriambanona
Centre National de Recherches sur l'Environnement (CNRE), BP 1739, Antananarivo 101, Madagascar; and Institut Supérieur de Sciences, Environnement et Développement Durable, Université de Toamasina, BP 591, Toamasina 501, Madagascar; email: zombanona@yahoo.fr

Randriamialisoa
Madagasikara Voakajy, BP 5181, Antananarivo 101, Madagascar; email: randriamialisoa29@gmail.com

Botovao Auguste Randriamiarisoa
Ecole Doctorale Ecosystèmes Naturels, Université de Mahajanga, Mahajanga 401, Madagascar; email: botovaoauguste@gmail.com.

Toky M. Randriamoria
Mention Zoologie et Biodiversité Animale, Université d'Antananarivo, BP 906, Antananarivo 101, Madagascar; and Association Vahatra, BP 3972, Antananarivo 101, Madagascar; email: tokilaci@yahoo.fr

Richard Randrianaivo
Missouri Botanical Garden, Madagascar Research and Conservation Program, BP 3391, Antananarivo 101, Madagascar; email: randrianaivo.richard@mobot.mg

Fano J. Randrianambinintsoa
Université de Reims Champagne-Ardenne, ANSES, SFR Cap Santé, EA7510 ESCAPE–USC VECPAR, 51096 Reims, France; email: fanoujo@yahoo.fr

Christian Randrianantoandro
Mention Zoologie et Biodiversité Animale, Université d'Antananarivo, BP 906, Antananarivo, 101, Madagascar; email: crandrianantoandro@gmail.com

Rose Marie Randrianarison
LVDI International, 941 Camino del Arroyo Drive, San Marcos, California 92078, USA; Mention d'Anthropobiologie de Développement Durable, Université d'Antananarivo, Antananarivo 101, Madagascar; and Multipurpose Research Center of Maromizaha, Andasibe 514, Madagascar; email: sissie@lvdiinternational.org, rosemarie.randrianarison@unito.it

Milijaona Randrianarivelojosia
Institut Pasteur de Madagascar, BP 1274, Antananarivo 101, Madagascar; email: milijaon@pasteur.mg

Tabita N. Randrianarivony
Missouri Botanical Garden, Madagascar Research and Conservation Program, BP 3391, Antananarivo 101, Madagascar; email: tabita.randrianarivony@mobot.mg

Armand Randrianasolo
Missouri Botanical Garden, 4344 Shaw Boulevard, Saint Louis, Missouri 63110, USA; email: armand.randrianasolo@mobot.org

Harison Randrianasolo
Conservation International Madagascar, BP 5178, Antananarivo 101, Madagascar; email: hrandrianasolo@conservation.org

†Hiary Randrianizahana
Ministère de l'Environnement et du Développement Durable, Nanisana, Antananarivo 101, Madagascar; email: zahana_hi@yahoo.fr

Tahiry Randrianjafimanana
Blue Ventures, Villa Huguette, Lot II U 86, Cité Planton, Ampahibe, Antananarivo 101, Madagascar; email: tahiry@blueventures.org

Aina Randriarisoa
Conservatoire et Jardin botaniques de la Ville de Genève and Laboratoire de Systématique Végétale et Biodiversité de l'Université de Genève, Case Postale 71, 1292 Chambésy/Genève, Switzerland; email: aina.randriarisoa@ville-ge.ch

Julie C. Ranivo Rakotoson
Lot VN 82 D Antsahabe, Antananarivo 101, Madagascar; email: ranivojc@gmail.com

Lova Ranivoharimanana
Laboratoire de Paléontologie des Vertébrés, Mention Bassins Sédimentaires, Evolution, Conservation, Faculté des Sciences, Université d'Antananarivo, BP 906, Antananarivo 101, Madagascar; email: ranivolova@gmail.com

Estelle Raobson
Mention Zoologie et Biodiversité Animale, Université d'Antananarivo, BP 906, Antananarivo 101, Madagascar; and Association Vahatra, BP 3972, Antananarivo 101, Madagascar; email: estelleraobson@gmail.com

Fidisoa Rasambainarivo
Mahaliana Labs, Lot II B 55 Amboditsiry, Antananarivo 101, Madagascar; email: f.rasambainarivo@gmail.com

Voahangielisoa Miatrana Rasamoelina
Institut Pasteur de Madagascar, Unité d'Epidémiologie et de Recherche Clinique, Ambatofotsikely, BP 1274, Antananarivo 101, Madagascar; email: r.miatrana@gmail.com

Jeanne Rasamy Razanabolana
Mention Zoologie et Biodiversité Animale, Université d'Antananarivo, BP 906, Antananarivo 101, Madagascar; email: jr.rasamy@gmail.com

Achille P. Raselimanana
Association Vahatra, BP 3972, Antananarivo 101, Madagascar; and Mention Zoologie et Biodiversité Animale, Université d'Antananarivo, BP 906, Antananarivo 101, Madagascar; email: raselimananaachille@gmail.com

Miary Raselimanana
Mention Zoologie et Biodiversité Animale, Université d'Antananarivo, BP 906, Antananarivo 101, Madagascar; and Association Vahatra, BP 3972, Antananarivo 101, Madagascar; email: miaryras@gmail.com

Mercia Rasoanoro
Institut Pasteur de Madagascar, BP 1274, Antananarivo 101, Madagascar; email: rasoumercia@gmail.com

Tahina Rasoloarijao
African Aquatic Conservation Fund, Antaravay, Toliara 601, Madagascar; email: tmagics@gmail.com

Rodin M. Rasoloarison
Behavioral Ecology and Sociobiology Unit, German Primate Center (DPZ), Kellnerweg 4, 37077 Göttingen, Germany; and German Primate Center (DPZ), Morondava 619, Madagascar; email: rmrasoloarison@yahoo.fr

Henriette Rasolofoarivao
Département d'Entomologie, Faculté des Sciences, Université d'Antananarivo, BP 906, Antananarivo 101, Madagascar; email: henriette_72@yahoo.fr

Solofonirina Rasoloharijaona
Faculté des Sciences, Université de Mahajanga, BP 652, Campus Ambondrona, Mahajanga 401, Madagascar; and Ecole Doctorale EDEN, Université de Mahajanga, Immeuble DRAMSY, Ampasika, Mahajanga 401, Madagascar; email: rasoloharijaona@gmail.com

Rindra Rasoloniriana
Blue Ventures, Villa Huguette, Lot II U 86, Cité Planton, Ampahibe, Antananarivo 101, Madagascar; email: rindra@blueventures.org

Tojo Michaël Rasolozaka
WWF Madagascar Country Office, BP 738, Antananarivo 101, Madagascar; email: trasolozaka@wwf.mg

Jean-Yves Rasplus
Centre de Biologie pour la Gestion des Populations (CBGP), INRAE, CIRAD, IRD, Montpellier SupAgro, Université de Montpellier, Montpellier, France; email: jean-yves.rasplus@inrae.fr

Ismaël Ratefinjanahary
Blue Ventures, Villa Huguette, Lot II U 86, Cité Planton, Ampahibe, Antananarivo 101, Madagascar; email: ismael@blueventures.org

Jonah H. Ratsimbazafy
Groupe d'Etude et de Recherche sur les Primates de Madagascar, Fort Duchesne Logement 34, Cité des Professeurs, BP 779, Antananarivo 101, Madagascar; email: jonah@gerp-mg.org

Fanomezana M. Ratsoavina
Mention Zoologie et Biodiversité Animale, Université d'Antananarivo, BP 906, Antananarivo, 101, Madagascar; email: fanomezanarts@gmail.com

Clemence Ravelo
Institut Halieutique et des Sciences Marines, Université de Toliara, Rue Dr. Rabesandratana, BP 141, Toliara 601, Madagascar; email: clemence.ravelo@ihsm.mg

Tsilavina Ravelomanana
Mention Zoologie et Biodiversité Animale, Université d'Antananarivo, BP 906, Antananarivo 101, Madagascar; email: tsil21@hotmail.com

Faranky Ravelomandrato
Mention Zoologie et Biodiversité Animale, Université d'Antananarivo, BP 906, Antananarivo 101, Madagascar; email: rfaranky@yahoo.com

Jaona Ravelonjatovo
Blue Ventures, Villa Huguette, Lot II U 86, Cité Planton, Ampahibe, Antananarivo 101, Madagascar; email: jaona@blueventures.org

Minosoa Ravoloharinjara
Resolve sarl, Ivandry Business Center, Antananarivo 101, Madagascar; email: mino@resolve.mg

Christopher J. Raxworthy
Department of Herpetology, American Museum of Natural History, 200 Central Park West, New York, New York 10024, USA; email: rax@amnh.org

Julie Hanta Razafimanahaka
Madagasikara Voakajy, BP 5181, Antananarivo 101, Madagascar; email: hantajulie@voakajy.mg

Léonard Razafimanantsoa
Behavioral Ecology and Sociobiology Unit, German Primate Center (DPZ), Kellnerweg 4, 37077 Göttingen, Germany; German Primate Center (DPZ), Morondava 619, Madagascar; email: leonrazafy@yahoo.com

Sylvain G. Razafimandimbison
Department of Botany, Swedish Museum of Natural History, Box 50007, SE-10405 Stockholm, Sweden; email: sylvain.razafimandimbison@nrm.se

Harizoly Razafimandimby
Centre National des Recherche Appliquée au Développement Rural (FOFIFA), Département de Recherche Forestière et Gestion des Ressources Naturelles, BP 904, Antananarivo 101, Madagascar; email: mandimbizo@yahoo.fr

Hajanirina Razafindrainibe
Centre National de Recherches Océanographiques, Nosy Be 207, Madagascar; email: hajaniry@gmail.com

Felix Razafindrajao
Durrell Wildlife Conservation Trust, BP 8511, Antananarivo 101, Madagascar; email: felix.razafindrajao@durrell.org

Noromampiandra Razafindrakoto
Wildlife Conservation Society, Maroantsetra 502, Madagagascar; email: noromampiandra@gmail.com

Onja H. Razafindratsima
Department of Natural Resource Management, South Dakota State University, 1390 College Avenue, Brookings, South Dakota 57007, USA; Current address: Department of Integrative Biology, University of California, 3040 Valley Life Sciences Building, Berkeley, California 94720-3140, USA; email: onja@berkeley.edu

Vololontiana R. Razafindratsita
Madagascar Institut pour la Conservation des Ecosystèmes Tropicaux (MICET), Lot VU 283 D Manakambahiny, BP 3715, Antananarivo 101, Madagascar; email: tianamicet@gmail.com

Théodore Razakamanana
Département des Sciences de la Terre, Université de Toliara, Toliara 601, Madagascar; email: razakamananat@yahoo.fr

Henintsoa Razanajatovo
Kew Madagascar Conservation Centre, Lot II J 131 B, Ambodivoanjo Ivandry, Antananarivo 101, Madagascar; email: h.razanajatovo@kew.org

Samuel Razanaka
Centre National de Recherches sur l'Environnement, BP 1739, Antananarivo 101, Madagascar; email: samuel.razanaka@gmail.com

Onja Hariveloniaina Razanamaro
Mention Biologie et Ecologie Végétales, Université d'Antananarivo, BP 906, Antananarivo 101, Madagascar; email: onjarh@gmail.com

Louisette Razanamparany
Laboratoire de Biochimie Appliqué aux Sciences de l'Alimentation, Université d'Antananarivo, BP 906, Antananarivo 101, Madagascar; email: razanamparany.louisette@yahoo.fr

Jacqueline Razanatsoa
Herbier, Département Flore, Parc Botanique et Zoologique de Tsimbazaza, Antananarivo 101, Madagascar; email: jrazanatsoa@gmail.com

Sushma Reddy
Bell Museum of Natural History and Department of Fisheries, Wildlife, Conservation Biology, University of Minnesota–Twin Cities, 2003 Upper Buford Circle, Saint Paul, Minnesota 55108, USA; email: sreddy@umn.edu

Stephanie Reher
Institute of Zoology, Universität Hamburg, Martin-Luther-King-Platz 3, 20146 Hamburg, Germany; email: stephanie.reher@uni-hamburg.de

Lily-Arison Rene de Roland
The Peregrine Fund, BP 4113, Antananarivo 101, Madagascar; email: lilyarison@yahoo.fr

Angelinah René de Rolland
The Peregrine Fund, BP 4113, Antananarivo 101, Madagascar; and Ecole Doctorale Biodiversité et Environnements Tropicaux, Université de Toliara, BP 304, Toliara 601, Madagascar; email: linahange@gmail.com

Alison F. Richard
10 Sachem Street, New Haven, Connecticut 06511, USA; email: alisonfrichard@gmail.com

Jana C. Riemann
Animal Ecology and Conservation, Universität Hamburg, Martin-Luther-King-Platz 3, 20146 Hamburg, Germany; email: riemann@pollichia.de

Kimberly Rivera
Department of Natural Resources Science, University of Rhode Island, 1 Greenhouse Road, Kingston, Rhode Island 02881, USA; email: karivera@uri.edu

Vincent Robert
MIVEGEC Unit, Université de Montpellier, IRD, CNRS, 34394 Montpellier, France; email: vincent.robert@ird.fr

Eric Robsomanitrandrasana
Ministère de l'Environnement et du Développement Durable, Nanisana, Antananarivo 101, Madagascar; email: robsomanitrandrasana@gmail.com

Mark-Oliver Rödel
Museum für Naturkunde Berlin, Leibniz Institute for Evolution and Biodiversity Science, Invalidenstr. 43, 10115 Berlin, Germany; email: Mark-Oliver.Roedel@mfn-berlin.de

Raymond R. Rogers
Geology Department, Macalester College, 1600 Grand Avenue, Saint Paul, Minnesota 55105, USA; email: rogers@macalester.edu

Gonçalo M. Rosa
Centre for Ecology, Evolution and Environmental Changes (CE3C), Faculdade de Ciências, Universidade de Lisboa, 1749-016 Lisboa, Portugal; email: goncalo.m.rosa@gmail.com

Howard C. Rosenbaum
Wildlife Conservation Society, 2300 Southern Boulevard, Bronx, New York 10460, USA; email: hrosenbaum@wcs.org

Sara Ruane
Department of Biological Sciences, Rutgers University–Newark, 195 University Avenue, Newark, New Jersey 07102, USA; Current address: Field Museum of Natural History, 1400 South DuSable Shore Drive, Chicago, Illinois 60605, USA; email: sruane@fieldmuseum.org

Veronica Ruiz
International Union for Conservation of Nature, 28 rue Mauverney, CH-1196 Gland, Switzerland; email: veronica.ruiz@iucn.org

James M. Ryan
Department of Biology, Hobart and William Smith Colleges, Geneva, New York 14456, USA; email: ryan@hws.edu

Roger J. Safford
BirdLife International, David Attenborough Building, Pembroke Street, Cambridge CB2 3QZ, United Kingdom; email: Roger.Safford@birdlife.org

Jordi Salmona
CNRS, Université Paul Sabatier, IRD, UMR 5174 EDB (Laboratoire Evolution et Diversité Biologique), 118 route de Narbonne, F-31062 Toulouse, France; email: jordi.salmona@gmail.com

Anjara Saloma
Cétamada, Ambodiforaha, Ile Sainte Marie 515, Madagascar; email: anjara@cetamada.org

Karen E. Samonds
Department of Biological Sciences, Northern Illinois University, DeKalb, Illinois 60115, USA; email: ksamonds@niu.edu

Michel Sartori
Museum of Zoology, Palais de Rumine, Place Riponne 6, CH-1005 Lausanne, Switzerland; and Department of Ecology and Evolution, Biophore, University of Lausanne, CH-1015 Lausanne, Switzerland; email: michel.sartori@vd.ch

Michelle L. Sauther
Department of Anthropology, 1350 Pleasant Street 233, University of Colorado, Boulder, Colorado 80309, USA; email: sauther@colorado.edu

George E. Schatz
Missouri Botanical Garden, 4344 Shaw Boulevard, Saint Louis, Missouri 63110, USA; email: george.schatz@mobot.org

Mark D. Scherz
Department of Biology, Universität Konstanz, Universitätstr. 10, 78464 Konstanz, Germany; Sektion Herpetologie, Zoologische Staatssammlung München, Münchhausenstr. 21, 81247 Munich, Germany; and Zoological Institute, Technische Universität Braunschweig, Mendelssohnstr. 4, 38106 Braunschweig, Germany; Current address: Natural History Museum of Denmark, University of Copenhagen, Universitetsparken 15, DK-2100 Koebenhavn OE, Denmark; email: mark.scherz@gmail.com

Harald Schliemann
Center of Natural History, Zoological Museum, Universität Hamburg, Martin-Luther-King-Platz-3, 20146 Hamburg, Germany; email: Schliemann@uni-hamburg.de

†Evert I. Schlinger
c/o Jane and Brad Omick, 3428 Woodview, Lafayette, California 94549, USA; email: janeomick@gmail.com

M. Corrie Schoeman
School of Life Sciences, Westville Campus, University of KwaZulu-Natal, Private Bag X54001, Durban, 4000, South Africa; email: m.corrie.schoeman@gmail.com

Thomas S. Schulenberg
Cornell Lab of Ornithology, 159 Sapsucker Woods Road, Ithaca, New York 14850, USA; email: tss62@cornell.edu

Felix Schumm
Mozartstrasse 9, D-73117 Wangen, Germany; email: fschumm@online.de

Nathalie Seddon
Department of Zoology, University of Oxford, 11a Mansfield Road, Oxford OX1 3SZ, United Kingdom; email: nathalie.seddon@zoo.ox.ac.uk

Timothy Sefczek
Omaha's Henry Doorly Zoo and Aquarium, Conservation Genetics Department, 3701 South 10th Street, Omaha, Nebraska 68107, USA; email: timothy.sefczek@omahazoo.com

Bernard Séret
Ichtyo-Consult, 6 bis rue du Centre, 91430 Igny, France; email: seret.bernard@orange.fr

Joseph J. W. Sertich
Department of Earth Sciences, Denver Museum of Nature and Science, 2001 Colorado Boulevard, Denver, Colorado 80205, USA; email: Joe.Sertich@dmns.org

Gabriele Maria Sgarlata
Instituto Gulbenkian de Ciência, Rua da Quinta Grande, 6, 2780-156 Oeiras, Portugal; email: gabriele.sgarlata@gmail.com

John W. Short
BioAccess Australia, PO Box 662, Burpengary, Queensland 4505, Australia; email: J.Short@bioaccess.com.au

Mark E. Siddall
Invertebrate Zoology, American Museum of Natural History, 200 Central Park West, New York, New York 10024, USA; email: mark@marksiddall.net

Nancy B. Simmons
Department of Mammalogy, Division of Vertebrate Zoology, American Museum of Natural History, 200 Central Park West, New York, New York 10024, USA; email: simmons@amnh.org

Cindy Skema
Morris Arboretum of University of Pennsylvania, 100 East Northwestern Avenue, Philadelphia, Pennsylvania 19119, USA; email: cskema@upenn.edu

Lora L. Smith
Joseph W. Jones Ecological Research Center, 3988 Jones Center Road, Newton, Georgia 39870, USA; email: lora.smith@jonesctr.org

William L. Smith
Biodiversity Institute, Dyche Hall, 1345 Jayhawk Boulevard, University of Kansas, Lawrence, Kansas 66045, USA; email: leosmith@ku.edu

Neil Snow
Department of Biology, Pittsburg State University, Pittsburg, Kansas 66762, USA; email: nsnow@pittstate.edu

Voahangy Soarimalala
Association Vahatra, BP 3972, Antananarivo 101, Madagascar; and Institut des Sciences et Techniques de l'Environnement, Université de Fianarantsoa, BP 1264, Fianarantsoa 301, Madagascar; email: voahangysoarimalala@gmail.com

Mathilde Soazandry
Direction Régionale de l'Environnement et du Développement Durable, Analanjirofo, Fenerive-Est 509, Madagascar; email: soathilde@gmail.com

Alma Solis
Department of Evolutionary Anthropology, Duke University, Biological Sciences Building, Science Drive, Durham, North Carolina 27708, USA; and Duke Global Health Institute, Duke University, Trent Hall, Trent Drive, Durham, North Carolina 27708, USA; email: alma.solis@duke.edu

Cédrique L. Solofondranohatra
Laboratoire de Botanique, Université d'Antananarivo, Université d'Antananarivo, BP 566, Antananarivo 101, Madagascar; and Kew Madagascar Conservation Centre, Lot II J 131 B, Ambodivoanjo Ivandry, Antananarivo 101, Madagascar; email: lovacedrique@gmail.com

Simone Sommer
University of Ulm, Evolutionary Ecology and Conservation Genomics, Albert-Einstein-Allee 11, 89081 Ulm, Germany; email: simone.sommer@uni-ulm.de

Daniel Spalink
Department of Ecosystem Science and Management, Texas A&M University, College Station, Texas 77843, USA; email: dspalink@tamu.edu

John S. Sparks
Department of Ichthyology, American Museum of Natural History, 200 Central Park West, New York, New York 10024-5102, USA; email: jsparks@amnh.org

Kim J. E. Steffens
Department of Biology, Institute of Zoology, Universität Hamburg, 20146 Hamburg, Germany; email: kimsteffens1@gmail.com

Travis S. Steffens
Department of Sociology and Anthropology, University of Guelph, Guelph, Ontario, N1G 2W1 Canada; and Planet Madagascar, Guelph, Ontario, N1H 7N2 Canada; email: tsteffen@uoguelph.ca

Eleanor J. Sterling
Center for Biodiversity and Conservation, American Museum of Natural History, 200 Central Park West, New York, New York 10024, USA; email: eleanor7@hawaii.edu

Melanie L. J. Stiassny
Department of Ichthyology, American Museum of Natural History, 200 Central Park West, New York, New York 10024-5102, USA; email: mljs@amnh.org

R. Douglas Stone
School of Life Sciences and Bews Herbarium, University of KwaZulu-Natal, Private Bag X01, Pietermaritzburg 3209, South Africa; email: r.douglas.stone@gmail.com

Axel Strauß
University of Tübingen, Faculty of Medecine, Geissweg 5/1, 72076 Tübingen, Germany; email: Axel@tsiboboka.de

Adam Stroiński
Museum and Institute of Zoology, Polish Academy of Sciences, Wilcza 64, 00-679 Warszawa, Poland; email: adam@miiz.waw.pl

Jens-Hermann Stuke
Roter Weg 22, 26789 Leer, Germany; email: jstuke@zfn.uni-bremen.de

Dariusz Świerczewski
Faculty of Science and Technology, Jan Długosz University, Armii Krajowej 13/15, 42-202 Częstochowa, Poland; email: dswier@ujd.edu.pl

Tamás Székely
Milner Centre for Evolution, Department of Biology and Biochemistry, University of Bath, 12, Bath BA2 7AY, United Kingdom; email: T.Szekely@bath.ac.uk

Daniela M. Takiya
Laboratório de Entomologia, Departamento de Zoologia, Universidade Federal do Rio de Janeiro, Caixa Postal 68044, Rio de Janeiro, 21941-971, Brazil; email: takiya@gmail.com

Chia L. Tan
LVDI International, 941 Camino del Arroyo Drive, San Marcos, California 92078, USA; email: chia@lvdiinternational.org

Luciano Tantely
Laboratoire d'Entomologie Médicale, Institut Pasteur de Madagascar, BP 1274, Antananarivo 101, Madagascar; email: lucinambi@pasteur.mg

Charlotte M. Taylor
Missouri Botanical Garden, PO Box 299, Saint Louis, Missouri 62166-299, USA; email: charlotte.taylor@mobot.org

Stacey R. Tecot
School of Anthropology, University of Arizona, 1009 East South Campus Drive, Tucson, Arizona 85721, USA; email: stecot@arizona.edu

Urs Thalmann
Department of Penal Law and Philosophy of Law, University Fribourg, Avenue Beauregard 13, CH-1700 Fribourg, Switzerland; email: uthal@bt-biofor.ch

Russell Thorstrom
5668 West Flying Hawk Lane, The Peregrine Fund, Boise, Idaho 83709, USA; email: rthorstrom@peregrinefund.org

Mats Thulin
Systematic Biology, Department of Organismal Biology, Uppsala University, Norbyvägen 18D, SE-752 36 Uppsala, Sweden; email: mats.thulin@ebc.uu.se

George P. Tiley
Department of Biology, Duke University, Durham, North Carolina 27708, USA; email: george.tiley@duke.edu

Toany
Institut Halieutique et des Sciences Marines, Université de Toliara, Rue Dr. Rabesandratana, BP 141, Toliara 601, Madagascar; email: toanydp@yahoo.fr

Joseph A. Tobias
Department of Life Sciences, Imperial College London, Silwood Park, Buckhurst Road, Ascot, Berkshire SL5 7PY, United Kingdom; email: j.tobias@imperial.ac.uk

Jadelys Tonos
1600 Main Street, Department of BioSciences, Rice University, Houston, Texas 77005, USA; email: jtm11@rice.edu

Valeria Torti
Department of Life Sciences and Systems Biology, University of Turin, Via Accademia Albertina 13, 10123 Turin, Italy; email: valeria.torti@unito.it

Pablo Tortosa
Unité Mixte de Recherche Processus Infectieux en Milieu Insulaire Tropical (UMR PIMIT), Université de La Réunion, CNRS 9192, INSERM 1187, IRD 249, 97490 Sainte-Clotilde, La Réunion, France; email: pablo.tortosa@univ-reunion.fr

Erin Tripp
Museum of Natural History, University of Colorado, Boulder, Colorado 80309, USA; email: erin.tripp@colorado.edu

Miloš Trýzna
Czech University of Life Sciences, Faculty of Forestry and Wood Sciences, Department of Forest Protection and Entomology, Kamýcká 1176, CZ–165 21 Praha 6–Suchdol, Czech Republic; and Municipal Museum of Ústí nad Labem, Natural History Department, Masarykova 1000/3, CZ–400 01 Ústí nad Labem, Czech Republic; email: anthribidae@gmail.com

Ginah A. Tsiorisoa
Mention Zoologie et Biodiversité Animale, Université d'Antananarivo, BP 906, Antananarivo 101, Madagascar; email: fentsiur@gmail.com

Denis Vallan
Naturama Aargau, Feerstrasse 17, 5000 Aara, Switzerland; email: denis.vallan@bluewin.ch

Olivier Van Canneyt
Observatoire Pelagis, UMS 3462, La Rochelle Université CNRS, 5 allée de l'Océan, 17000, La Rochelle, France; email: olivier.van-canneyt@univ-lr.fr

Benjamin W. van Ee
Departamento de Biología, Universidad de Puerto Rico, Recinto Universitario de Mayagüez, Mayagüez, Puerto Rico 00680, USA; email: bvanee@uwalumni.com

Natalie Vasey
Department of Anthropology, Portland State University, Portland, Oregon 97207 USA; and Doctoral Program in Earth, Environment and Society, Portland State University, Portland, Oregon 97207, USA; email: nvasey@pdx.edu

Juliette Velosoa
Durrell Wildlife Conservation Trust–Madagascar Programme, BP 8511, Antananarivo 101, Madagascar; email: juliette.velosoa@durrell.org

Miguel Vences
Department of Evolutionary Biology, Zoological Institute, Technische Universität Braunschweig, Mendelssohnstr. 4, 38106 Braunschweig, Germany; email: m.vences@tu-braunschweig.de

Géraldine Veron
Institut de Systématique, Evolution et Biodiversité (ISYEB), Muséum National d'Histoire Naturelle, CNRS, SU, EPHE, UA; CP 51, 57 rue Cuvier, 75231 Paris Cedex 05, France; email: geraldine.veron@mnhn.fr

David R. Vieites
Museo Nacional de Ciencias Naturales, Consejo Superior de Investigaciones Científicas (CSIC), C/José Gutierrez Abascal 2, Madrid 28006, Spain; email: vieites@gmail.com

Xavier Vincke
Aviation sans Frontières Belgique, La maison des Ailes, rue Montoyer 1–Box 36, B-1000 Bruxelles, Belgium; email: xavier.vincke@asfbelgium.org

Juan Viruel
Royal Botanic Gardens, Kew, Richmond, Surrey TW9 3AE, United Kingdom; email: J.Viruel@kew.org

Maria S. Vorontsova
Comparative Plant and Fungal Biology, Royal Botanic Gardens, Kew, Richmond, Surrey TW9 3AE, United Kingdom; email: m.vorontsova@kew.org

Patrick O. Waeber
ETH Zurich, Institute of Terrestrial Ecosystems, Forest Management and Development (ForDev) Group, Universitätstrasse 16, 8092 Zurich, Switzerland; email: patrick.waeber@usys.ethz.ch

Gregory A. Wahlert
Cheadle Center for Biodiversity and Ecological Restoration, University of California, Santa Barbara, California 93106, USA; email: rinorea@gmail.com

Ryan C. J. Walker
The Ecology Co-op, Unit 4 Langham Stables, Langham Lane, Lodsworth, West Sussex GU28 9BU, United Kingdom; email: ryan@nautilusecology.org

Erin M. Wampole
Department of Natural Resources Science, University of Rhode Island, Kingston, Rhode Island 02881, USA; email: emwampole@uri.edu

Christiane Weirauch
Department of Entomology, University of California, Riverside, 900 University Avenue, Riverside, California 92521, USA; email: christiane.weirauch@ucr.edu

Ché Weldon
Unit for Environmental Science and Management, North-West University, Private Bag X6001, Potchefstroom 2520, South Africa; email: Che.Weldon@nwu.ac.za

Sue Wells
95 Burnside, Cambridge CB1 3PA, United Kingdom; email: suewells1212@gmail.com

Thomas Wesener
Zoologisches Forschungsmuseum Alexander Koenig (ZFMK), Leibniz Institute for Animal Biodiversity, ZTE, Section Myriapoda, Adenauerallee 160, D-53113 Bonn, Germany; email: t.wesener@leibniz-zfmk.de

Nicholas Wilding
Missouri Botanical Garden, 4344 Shaw Boulevard, Saint Louis, Missouri 63110, USA; email: nwilding@mobot.org

Paul Wilkin
Royal Botanic Gardens, Kew, Richmond, Surrey TW9 3AE, United Kingdom; email: P.Wilkin@kew.org

David Wilkinson
Unité Mixte de Recherche Processus Infectieux en Milieu Insulaire Tropical (UMR PIMIT), Université de La Réunion, CNRS 9192, INSERM 1187, IRD 249, 97490 Sainte-Clotilde, La Réunion, France; email: david.wilkinson@univ-reunion.fr

Lucienne Wilmé
Missouri Botanical Garden, Madagascar Research and Conservation Program, BP 3391, Antananarivo 101, Madagascar; and World Resources Institute, Madagascar Program, Hôtel Colbert, Business Center Area, BP 3884, Antananarivo 101, Madagascar; email: lucienne.wilme@wri.org, lucienne.wilme@mobot-mg.org

John M. A. Wojahn
Department of Biological Sciences, Boise State University, 1910 University Drive, Boise, Idaho 83725, USA; email: mikewojahn@boisestate.edu

Katharina C. Wollenberg Valero
Department of Biological and Marine Sciences, University of Hull, Cottingham Road, Hull HU6 7RX, United Kingdom; email: kc.wollenberg@gmail.com

Hannah M. Wood
Department of Entomology, MRC105, National Museum of Natural History, Smithsonian Institution, 10th Street and Constitution Avenue, NW, Washington, DC, 20560-0188, USA; email: woodh@si.edu

Norman E. Woodley
Research Associate, Department of Entomology, Smithsonian Institution, c/o 8920 South Bryerly Court, Hereford, Arizona 85615-8412, USA; email: normwoodley@gmail.com

Henry T. Wright
Museum of Anthropology, University of Michigan, 101 West Hall, 1085 South University Avenue, Ann Arbor, Michigan 48109-1107, USA; email: hwright@umich.edu

Kenneth J. Wurdack
Department of Botany, National Museum of Natural History, Smithsonian Institution, MRC-166, PO Box 37012, Washington, DC, 20013-7012, USA; email: wurdackk@si.edu

André R. Wyss
Department of Earth Science, 1112 Webb Hall, University of California, Santa Barbara, California 93106, USA; email: wyss@geol.ucsb.edu

Gabriel Yesuf
Lancaster Environment Centre, Lancaster University, Lancaster LA1 4YQ, United Kingdom; email: Gabriel.Yesuf@kingston.ac.uk

Anne D. Yoder
Department of Biology, Duke University, Durham, North Carolina 27708, USA; email: anne.yoder@duke.edu

H. Glyn Young
Durrell Wildlife Conservation Trust, Les Augrès Manor, Trinity, Jersey JE3 5BP; email: glyn.young@durrell.org

Alphonse Zaramody
Département de Biologie Animale, Faculté des Sciences, de Technologies et de l'Environnement, Université de Mahajanga, Mahajanga 401, Madagascar; email: zaramodyalphonse401@yahoo.fr

Zarasoa
Ministère de l'Environnement et du Développement Durable, BP 243, Antananarivo 101, Madagascar; email: zarasoa.zara20@gmail.com

Theo Zeegers
Eikenlaan 24, 3768 EV Soest, The Netherlands; email: th.zeegers@xs4all.nl

Sama Zefania
Institut d'Enseignement Supérieur de Menabe, C/O Port, Morondava 619, Madagascar; email: samazefania@gmail.com

Yurui Zhang
Université de Bretagne Occidentale, CNRS, IFREMER, IRD, Laboratoire d'Océanographie Physique et Spatiale (LOPS), UMR 6523, IUEM, 29280 Plouzané, France; email: yuruizhang@xmu.edu.cn

Sarah Zohdy
School of Forestry and Wildlife Sciences and College of Veterinary Medicine, 3231 SFWS Building, Auburn University, Auburn, Alabama 36849, USA; email: sarahzohdy@gmail.com

INDEX OF SCIENTIFIC NAMES

D

H

I

N

Q

R

INDEX OF MALAGASY LOCALITIES

This listing does not cover geological formations, administrative localities (including regions), biogeographical domains or geographical regions.